AHA Guide® to the Health Care Field

2019 Edition

W9-BKQ-796

AHA Members $285.00
Nonmembers $425.00
AHA Item Number 010019
Telephone ORDERS 1–800–AHA–2626

ISSN 0094–8969
ISBN–13: 978–0–87258–987–2

Contents

Section

 Indexes

Acknowledgements and Advisements

Acknowledgements

The AHA Guide® to the Health Care Field is published annually by Health Forum LLC, an affiliate of the American Hospital Association. Contributions are made by Information Systems and Technology, Member Relations, Office of the President, Office of the Secretary, Printing Services Group, AHA Resource Center and the following participants:

Grant Denten	Peter Kralovec
Dianna Doyle	Mary Krzywicki
DeAnn Ellis	Andrea Liebig
Joan Finn	Denise Loggins
Deanna Frazier	Rob Merrell
Jennifer Gillespie	Bethany Parnell
Tan Harris	Kathy Poole
Stella Hines	Susan Sheffey
Clisby Jackson	Elaine Singh
Danny Jackson	Jill Syftestad
Kimberly Jackson	Marty Weitzel

Health Forum LLC acknowledges the cooperation given by many professional groups and government agencies in the health care field, particularly the following: American College of Surgeons; American Medical Association; Council of Teaching Hospitals of the Association of American Medical Colleges; The Joint Commission; DNV Healthcare Inc.; Center for Improvement in Healthcare Quality; Commission on Accreditation of Rehabilitation Facilities; American Osteopathic Association, Centers for Medicare & Medicaid Services; and various offices within the U.S. Department of Health and Human Services.

Advisements

The data published here should be used with the following advisements: The data is based on replies to an annual survey that seeks a variety of information, not all of which is published in this book. The information gathered by the survey includes specific services, but not all of each hospital's services. Therefore, the data does not reflect an exhaustive list of all services offered by all hospitals. For information on the availability of additional data and products, please contact Health Forum LLC at 800/821–2039, or visit our web site.

Health Forum LLC does not assume responsibility for the accuracy of information voluntarily reported by the individual institutions surveyed. **The purpose of this publication is to provide basic data reflecting the delivery of health care in the United States and associated areas, and is not to serve as an official and all inclusive list of services offered by individual hospitals. The information reflected is based on data collected as of September 12, 2017.**

An Introduction to AHA Guide

Welcome, and thank you for purchasing the 2019 edition of *AHA Guide®*. This section is designed to aid you in using the book. While the primary focus of *AHA Guide* is on hospitals, it also contains information on other areas of the health care field, divided across its two major sections:

- **A.** Hospitals
- **B.** Health care systems, networks, and alliances

The information contained within this publication was compiled using AHA membership, and the AHA Annual Survey of Hospitals. *AHA Guide* is the leading hospital directory and represents hospitals with or without AHA membership.

Additional information contained in the front of AHA Guide includes:

- A section by section table of contents
- Recognition of the source of data in the *Acknowledgements and Advisements* section
- Information on AHA's history as well as a listing of our awards in *AHA Offices, Officers, Historical Data, and Awards*

Open the front cover and *AHA Guide* begins with the *2019 AHA Guide Code Chart*. This two page section (front and back) explains how to find and understand the most important elements of each hospital's listing.

The *Code Chart* is a very useful tool to have when reading. It allows new users to become familiar with the data, and it aids returning users in understanding the new design and layout of *AHA Guide*. At the top of the chart, there is a sample listing. If you have used this publication before, you will notice the new columnar listing of all hospital entries by city. The city and county names are highlighted in gray, and all hospitals within the city follow. After the hospital name, you will find the address, telephone number, approval, facility and service codes, and health care systems to which the hospital belongs. Following this are the chief administrators and classifications for the hospital.

Utilization data for the hospital is found in the box at the bottom of each hospital's entry in *AHA Guide*.

The chart further demonstrates how to understand these important elements:

1. **Approval codes** refer to certifications held by a hospital; they represent information supplied by various national approving and reporting bodies. For example, code A–3 indicates accreditation under one of the programs of the Accreditation Council for Graduate Medical Education, evidence that the hospital has been approved for participation in residency training.
2. **Physician codes** represent the different types of arrangements the hospital participates in with its physicians. In this section, code P-1 signifies a closed physician-hospital organization.
3. **Health Care System names** reference specific health care system headquarters to which the hospital belongs. The presence of a system name indicates that the hospital is a member. If no names are listed, the hospital does not belong to a system.
4. **Titles of Chief Administrators** including the Chief Executive Officer and, when available, other C-Suite officers such as the Chief Financial Officer, Chief Information Officer, Chief Medical Officer, Chief Operating Officer, Chief Human Resources Officer, and Chief Nursing Officer.
5. **Classification** refers to two items in *AHA Guide*. **Control** classification indicates the organization that operates the hospital, and **Service** classification refers to the type of service the hospital offers. Previously, this section utilized numerical codes corresponding with a literal value, but the new

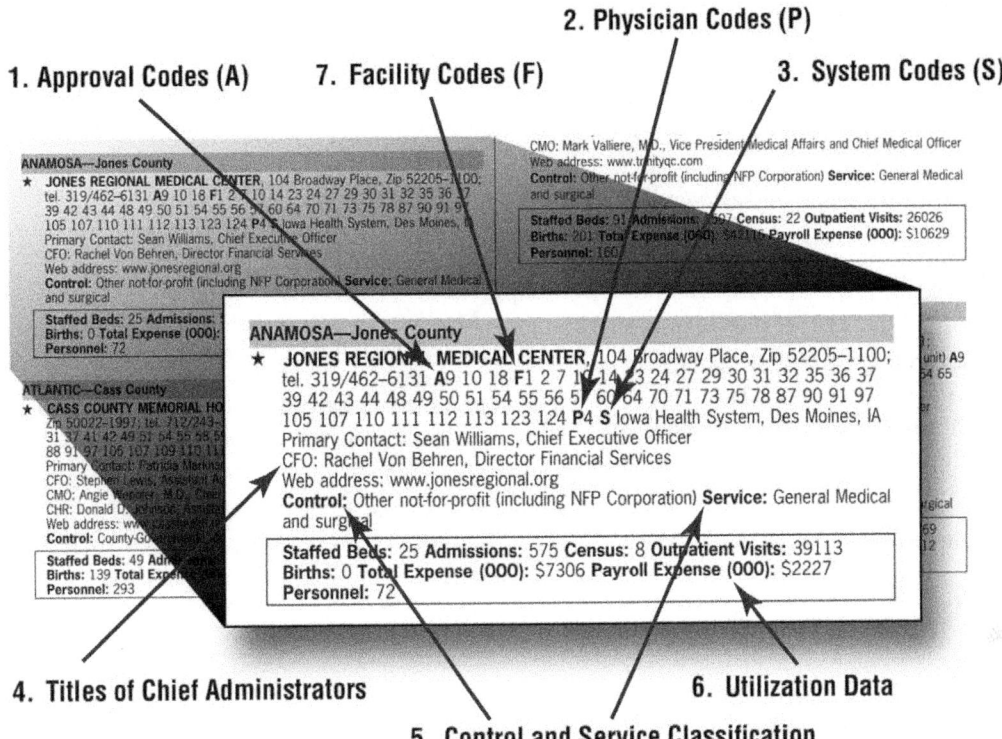

1. Approval Codes (A)
2. Physician Codes (P)
3. System Codes (S)
4. Titles of Chief Administrators
5. Control and Service Classification
6. Utilization Data
7. Facility Codes (F)

design of *AHA Guide* bypasses the codes and instead displays the literal classifications for control and service.

- **Control:** In this section, organizations are divided among nonfederal government hospitals, nongovernment not-for-profit hospitals, investor owned for-profit hospitals, and federal government hospitals.
- **Service:** This section displays the primary type of service that a hospital offers. The most common value is general hospital. Among the other services listed in this section are specialties such as psychiatric hospitals or children's hospitals.

6. **Utilization Data** contains the statistics related to the day-to-day and cumulative operation of the hospital. The information included in this section consists of:

- **Beds:** Number of beds regularly maintained.
- **Admissions:** Amount of patients accepted for inpatient services over a 12-month period.
- **Census:** Average number of patients receiving care each day.
- **Outpatient Visits:** Amount of visits by patients not lodged in the hospital while receiving care.

- **Births:** Number of infants born in the hospital and accepted for service in a newborn infant bassinet.
- **Expense:** Includes all expenses (including payroll) that the hospital had over the 12- month period.
- **Personnel:** Represents personnel situations as they existed at the end of the reporting period. In this area, full time equivalency is calculated on the basis that two part-time persons equal one full-time person.

7. **Facility codes** provide a description of the specific services offered by a hospital. Code F-14, for instance, indicates that the hospital contains a Blood Donor Center.

How To Use This Book

Section A begins with the *AHA Guide Hospital Listing Requirements*. This explains the requisite accreditations or characteristics a hospital must meet to be included in *AHA Guide*.

After this there is *An Explanation of the Hospital Listings*. These two pages review the information included in the Code Chart and are a vital resource in identifying the information, symbols, and codes for each hospital's listing.

Next up are the *Annual Survey* definitions, which go into even greater detail in explaining the facility and physician codes. Please note that these are arranged alphabetically and numerically to correspond with the code chart. Also included here are the definitions of the terms for Control and Service found in the Classification section. The listings of *Hospitals in the United States, by State* follow the definitions.

Finding Hospitals & Health Care Professionals in Section A

There are two ways to locate hospitals in the print version of *AHA Guide*. One is by the hospital's geographic classification. In Section A, hospitals are arranged alphabetically by state and then by city. The second method is through the *Hospital Index* that appears directly after the listings.

There is also an *Index of Health Care Professionals* which begins after the first index that lists key people from hospitals and health systems.

AHA Membership Organizations

Section A ends with a description of the AHA Membership categories along with a listing of various AHA Membership organizations.

For more information on Systems, Networks, and Alliances, please read the introduction to Section B.

AHA Offices, Officers, and Historical Data

Chicago: 155 N. Wacker Drive, Chicago, IL 60606; tel. 312/422–3000

Chairman of the Board of Trustees: Brian Gragnolati, Atlantic Health System, 475 South Street, PO Box 1905, Morristown, NJ 07962

Chair-Elect of the Board of Trustees: Melinda L. Estes, M.D., Saint Luke's Health System, 901 East 104th Street, Kansas City, MO 64131

Washington: 800 10th Street, N.W., Two CityCenter, Suite 400, Washington, DC 20001; tel. 202/638–1100

Immediate Past Chair of the Board of Trustees: Nancy Howell Agee, Carilion Clinic, 1906 Belleview Avenue, Roanoke, VA 24014

President & CEO: Richard J. Pollack, 800 10th Street, NW, Two CityCenter, Suite 400, Washington, DC 20001

Senior Vice President and Secretary: Gail Lovinger Goldblatt, 155 N. Wacker Drive, Chicago, IL 60606

Senior Vice President, Association Services and Chief Financial Officer: Christina Fisher, 155 N. Wacker Drive, Chicago, IL 60606

Executive Vice President and Chief Operating Officer: Maryjane Wurth, 155 N. Wacker Drive, Chicago, IL 60606

Past Presidents/Chairs†

1899	★James S. Knowles	1940	★Fred G. Carter, M.D.	1981	★Bernard J. Lachner
1900	★James S. Knowles	1941	★B. W. Black, M.D.	1982	★Stanley R. Nelson
1901	★Charles S. Howell	1942	★Basil C. MacLean, M.D.	1983	★Elbert E. Gilbertson
1902	★J. T. Duryea	1943	★James A. Hamilton	1984	Thomas R. Matherlee
1903	★John Fehrenbatch	1944	★Frank J. Walter	1985	★Jack A. Skarupa
1904	★Daniel D. Test	1945	★Donald C. Smelzer, M.D.	1986	Scott S. Parker
1905	★George H. M. Rowe, M.D.	1946	★Peter D. Ward, M.D.	1987	Donald C. Wegmiller
1906	★George P. Ludlam	1947	★John H. Hayes	1988	★Eugene W. Arnett
1907	★Renwick R. Ross, M.D.	1948	★Graham L. Davis	1989	★Edward J. Connors
1908	★Sigismund S. Goldwater, M.D.	1949	★Joseph G. Norby	1990	David A. Reed
1909	★John M. Peters, M.D.	1950	★John N. Hatfield	1991	C. Thomas Smith
1910	★H. B. Howard, M.D.	1951	★Charles F. Wilinsky, M.D.	1992	D. Kirk Oglesby, Jr.
1911	★W. L. Babcock, M.D.	1952	★Anthony J. J. Rourke, M.D.	1993	Larry L. Mathis
1912	★Henry M. Hurd, M.D.	1953	★Edwin L. Crosby, M.D.	1994	Carolyn C. Roberts
1913	★F. A. Washburn, M.D.	1954	★Ritz E. Heerman	1995	Gail L. Warden
1914	★Thomas Howell, M.D.	1955	★Frank R. Bradley	1996	Gordon M. Sprenger
1915	★William O. Mann, M.D.	1956	★Ray E. Brown	1997	Reginald M. Ballantyne III
1916	★Winford H. Smith, M.D.	1957	★Albert W. Snoke, M.D.	1998	John G. King
1917	★Robert J. Wilson, M.D.	1958	★Tol Terrell	1999	Fred L. Brown
1918	★A. B. Ancker, M.D.	1959	★Ray Amberg	2000	★Carolyn Boone Lewis
1919	★A. R. Warner, M.D.	1960	Russell A. Nelson, M.D.	2001	Gary A. Mecklenburg
1920	★Joseph B. Howland, M.D.	1961	★Frank S. Groner	2002	Sr. Mary Roch Rocklage, RSM
1921	★Louis B. Baldwin, M.D.	1962	★Jack Masur, M.D.	2003	Dennis R. Barry
1922	★George O'Hanlon, M.D.	1963	★T. Stewart Hamilton, M.D.	2004	David L. Bernd
1923	★Asa S. Bacon	1964	★Stanley A. Ferguson	2005	George F. Lynn
1924	★Malcolm T. MacEachern, M.D.	1965	★Clarence E. Wonnacott	**January–April 2006**	Richard J. Umbdenstock
1925	★E. S. Gilmore	1966	★Philip D. Bonnet, M.D.	**April–December 2006**	George F. Lynn
1926	★Arthur C. Bachmeyer, M.D.	1967	★George E. Cartmill	2007	Kevin E. Lofton
1927	★R. G. Brodrick, M.D.	1968	★David B. Wilson, M.D.	2008	William D. Petasnick
1928	★Joseph C. Doane, M.D.	1969	★George William Graham, M.D.	2009	Thomas M. Priselac
1929	★Louis H. Burlingham, M.D.	1970	★Mark Berke	2010	Richard P. de Filippi
1930	★Christopher G. Parnall, M.D.	1971	★Jack A. L. Hahn	2011	John W. Bluford
1931	★Lewis A. Sexton, M.D.	1972	★Stephen M. Morris	2012	Teri G. Fontenot
1932	★Paul H. Fesler	1973	★John W. Kauffman	2013	Benjamin K. Chu, MD
1933	★George F. Stephens, M.D.	1974	★Horace M. Cardwell	2014	James H. Hinton
1934	★Nathaniel W. Faxon, M.D.	1975	Wade Mountz	2015	Jonathan B. Perlin, MD, PhD
1935	★Robert Jolly	1976	★H. Robert Cathcart	2016	Jim Skogsbergh
1936	★Robin C. Buerki, M.D.	1977	★John M. Stagl	2017	Eugene A. Woods
1937	★Claude W. Munger, M.D.	1978	★Samuel J. Tibbitts	2018	Nancy Howell Agee
1938	★Robert E. Neff	1979	W. Daniel Barker		
1939	★G. Harvey Agnew, M.D.	1980	★Sister Irene Kraus		

Chief Executive Officers

1917–18	★William H. Walsh, M.D.	1954–72	★Edwin L. Crosby, M.D.	1991–2007	★Richard J. Davidson
1919–24	★Andrew Robert Warner, M.D.	1972	★Madison B. Brown, M.D. (acting)	2007–2015	Richard J. Umbdenstock
1925–27	★William H. Walsh, M.D.	1972–86	★J. Alexander McMahon	2015	Richard J. Pollack (current)
1928–42	★Bert W. Caldwell, M.D.	1986–91	Carol M. McCarthy, Ph.D., J.D.		
1943–54	★George Bugbee	1991	★Jack W. Owen (acting)		

★Deceased

Distinguished Service Award

The award recognizes significant lifetime contributions and service to health care institutions and associations.

1934	Matthew O. Foley	1966	Frank S. Groner		Jack W. Owen
1939	Malcolm T. MacEachern, M.D.	1967	Rev. John J. Flanagan, S.J.	1994	George Adams
1940	Sigismund S. Goldwater, M.D.	1968	Stanley W. Martin	1995	Scott S. Parker
1941	Frederic A. Washburn, M.D.	1969	T. Stewart Hamilton, M.D.	1996	John A. Russell
1942	Winford H. Smith, M.D.	1970	Charles Patteson Cardwell, Jr.	1997	D. Kirk Oglesby, Jr.
1943	Arthur C. Bachmeyer, M.D.	1971	Mark Berke	1998	Henry B. Betts, M.D.
1944	Rt. Rev. Msgr. Maurice F. Griffin, LL.D.	1972	Stanley A. Ferguson	1999	Mitchell T. Rabkin, M.D.
1945	Asa S. Bacon	1973	Jack A. L. Hahn	2000	Gail L. Warden
1946	George F. Stephens, M.D.	1974	George William Graham, M.D.	2001	Gordon M. Sprenger
1947	Robin C. Buerki, M.D.	1975	George E. Cartmill	2002	Carolyn Boone Lewis
1948	James A. Hamilton	1976	D. O. McClusky, Jr.	2003	C. Thomas Smith
1949	Claude W. Munger, M.D.	1977	Boone Powell	2004	Michael C. Waters
1950	Nathaniel W. Faxon, M.D.	1978	Richard J. Stull	2005	John G. King
1951	Bert W. Caldwell, M.D.	1979	Horace M. Cardwell	2006	Gary A. Mecklenburg
1952	Fred G. Carter, M.D.	1980	Donald W. Cordes		Sr. Mary Roch Rocklage, RSM
1953	Basil C. MacLean, M.D.	1981	Sister Mary Brigh Cassidy	2007	Richard J. Davidson
1954	George Bugbee	1982	R. Zach Thomas, Jr.	2008	Fred L. Brown
1955	Joseph G. Norby	1983	H. Robert Cathcart	2009	George F. Lynn
1956	Charles F. Wilinsky, M.D.	1984	Matthew F. McNulty, Jr., Sc.D.	2010	James J. Mongan, M.D.
1957	John H. Hayes	1985	J. Alexander McMahon	2011	Thomas C. Royer, M.D.
1958	John N. Hatfield	1986	Sister Irene Kraus	2012	Karen Davis, Ph.D.
1959	Edwin L. Crosby, M.D.	1987	W. Daniel Barker	2013	Thomas C. Dolan, Ph.D., FACHE
1960	Oliver G. Pratt	1988	Elbert E. Gilbertson	2014	Thomas M. Priselac
1961	E. M. Bluestone, M.D.	1989	Donald G. Shropshire	2015	Richard P. de Filippi
1962	Mother Loretto Bernard, S.C., R.N.	1990	John W. Colloton	2016	William Petasnick
1963	Ray E. Brown	1991	Carol M. McCarthy, Ph.D., J.D.	2017	Richard J. Umbdenstock
1964	Russell A. Nelson, M.D.	1992	David H. Hitt	2018	C. Duane Dauner
1965	Albert W. Snoke, M.D.	1993	Edward J. Connors		

†On June 3, 1972, the House of Delegates changed the title of the chief elected officer to chairman of the Board of Trustees, and the title of president was conferred on the chief executive officer of the Association.

Award of Honor

Awarded to individuals, organizations, or groups to recognize an exemplary contribution to the health and well being of the people through leadership on a major health policy or social initiative.

1966	Senator Lister Hill		Habitat for Humanity International	2008	Regina M. Benjamin, MD, MBA Alfred G. Stubblefield
1967	Emory W. Morris, D.D.S.	1998	John E. Curley, Jr.	2009	The Center to Advance Palliative Care Paul B.
1971	Special Committee on Provision of Health Services		National Civic League		Hofmann, Dr.PH
	(staff also)	1999	Joseph Cardinal Bernardin, Literacy Volunteers of	2010	Jack Bovender
1982	Walter J. McNerney		America	2011	Cary Medical Center, Caribou, ME
1989	Ruth M. Rothstein	2000	Institute for Safe Medication Practices	2012	Ronald McDonald House Charities
1990	Joyce C. Clifford, R.N.	2001	Dennis R. Barry		The Schwartz Center for Compassionate Healthcare
1991	Haynes Rice	2002	Donald M. Berwick, M.D.	2013	George C. Halvorson
1992	Donald W. Dunn	2003	Steven A. Schroeder, M.D.		Reach Out and Read
	Ira M. Lane, Jr.		Dan S. Wilford	2014	Rhonda Anderson, RN
1993	Elliott C. Roberts, Sr.	2004	Ron J. Anderson, M.D.		Ohio Hospital Association
	William A. Spencer, M.D.		Johnson & Johnson	2015	Spencer C. Johnson
1994	Robert A. Derzon	2005	Sr. Mary Jean Ryan		Robert Wood Johnson Foundation
1995	Russell G. Mawby, Ph.D. John K. Springer	2006	Jordan J. Cohen, M.D.	2016	Henry J. Kaiser Family Foundation
1996	Stephen J. Hegarty		James W. Varnum	2017	Joel T. Allison
	Mothers Against Drunk Driving (MADD)	2007	Edward A. Eckenhoff		Doug Leonard
1997	Paul B. Batalden, M.D.		Stanley F. Hupfeld	2018	Ronald R. Peterson
					Sister Carol Keehan

Justin Ford Kimball Innovators Award

Recognition to individuals or organizations that have made outstanding, innovative contributions to health care financing and/or delivery that improves access or coordination of care.

1958	E. A. van Steenwyk	1975	Earl H. Kammer	1997	Harvey Pettry
1959	George A. Newbury	1976	J. Ed McConnell		D. David Sniff
1960	C. Rufus Rorem, Ph.D.	1978	Edwin R. Werner	1998	Montana Health Research and Education Foundation
1961	James E. Stuart	1979	Robert M. Cunningham, Jr.	1999	Kenneth W. Kizer, M.D.
1962	Frank Van Dyk	1981	Maurice J. Norby	2002	David M. Lawrence, M.D.
1963	William S. McNary	1982	Robert E. Rinehimer	2003	Lowell C. Kruse
1964	Frank S. Groner	1983	John B. Morgan, Jr.	2006	Spencer Foreman, M.D.
1965	J. Douglas Colman	1984	Joseph F. Duplinsky	2009	On Lok
1967	Walter J. McNemey	1985	David W. Stewart	2012	Thomas S. Nesbitt, M.D.
1968	John W. Paynter	1988	Ernest W. Saward, M.D.	2015	Glenn D. Steele, Jr., MD
1970	Edwin L. Crosby, M.D.	1990	James A. Vohs	2016	Dan Wolterman
1971	H. Charles Abbott	1993	John C. Lewin, M.D.	2017	James N. Weinstein, DO
1972	John R. Mannix	1994	Donald A. Brennan	2018	Nicholas Wolter, M.D.
1973	Herman M. Somers	1995	E. George Middleton, Jr.		
1974	William H. Ford, Ph.D.		Glenn R. Mitchell		

Board of Trustees Award

Individuals or groups who have made substantial and noteworthy contributions to the work of the American Hospital Association.

1959	Joseph V. Friel	1982	John Bigelow	2002	Victor L. Campbell
	John H. Hayes		Robert W. O'Leary		Joseph A. Parker
1960	Duncan D. Sutphen, Jr.		Jack W. Owen	2003	J. Richard Gaintner, M.D.
1963	Eleanor C. Lambertsen, R.N., Ed.D.	1984	Howard J. Berman		Donald A. Wilson
1964	John R. Mannix		O. Ray Hurst	2004	Richard L. Clarke
1965	Albert G. Hahn		James R. Neely		Thelma Traut
	Maurice J. Norby	1985	James E. Ferguson	2005	Merrill Gappmayer
1966	Madison B. Brown, M.D.		Cleveland Rodgers		Leo Greenawalt
	Kenneth Williamson	1986	Rex N. Olsen	2006	Robert L. Harman
1967	Alanson W. Wilcox	1987	Michael Lesparre		Kenneth G. Stella
1968	E. Dwight Barnett, M.D.	1988	Barbara A. Donaho, R.N.	2007	Deborah Freund, Ph.D.
1969	Vane M. Hoge, M.D.	1989	Walter H. MacDonald		Michael D. Stephens
	Joseph H. McNinch, M.D.		Donald R. Newkirk	2008	James R. Castle
1972	David F. Drake, Ph.D.	1990	William T. Robinson	2009	Richard M. Knapp, Ph.D.
	Paul W. Earle	1992	Jack C. Bills	2010	Fred Hessler
	Michael Lesparre		Anne Hall Davis		John G. O'Brien
	Andrew Pattullo	1993	Theodore C. Eickhoff, M.D.	2011	Carolyn F. Scanlan
1973	Tilden Cummings		Stephen W. Gamble		Charlotte S. Yeh, MD
	Edmond J. Lanigan		Yoshi Honkawa	2012	Larry S. Gage
1974	James E. Hague	1994	Roger M. Busfield, Jr., Ph.D.		Larry McAndrews
	Sister Marybelle	1995	Stephen L. Dorn	2013	Jeffrey D. Selberg
1975	Helen T. Yast		William L. Yates	2014	Russell D. Harrington, Jr.
1976	Boynton P. Livingston	1996	Leigh E. Morris		Daniel Sisto
	James Ludlam		John Quigley	2015	Todd C. Linden
	Helen McGuire	1998	John D. Leech		R. Timothy Rice
1979	Newton J. Jacobson	1999	Sister Carol Keehan	2016	Sandra Bennett Bruce
	Edward W. Weimer		C. Edward McCauley		Michael G. Rock, M.D.
1980	Robert B. Hunter, M.D.		Stephen Rogness	2017	Kris A. Doody, RN
	Samuel J. Tibbitts	2000	Dennis May		Daniel L. Gross, RN
1981	Vernon A. Knutson	2001	Spencer C. Johnson	2018	Ian Morrison
	John E. Sullivan		Michael M. Mitchel		

Citation for Meritorious Service

1968	F. R. Knautz		Gordon McLachlan	1983	David M. Kinzer
	Sister Conrad Mary, R.N.	1977	Theodore Cooper, M.D.	1984	Donald L. Custis, M.D.
1971	Hospital Council of Southern California	1979	Norman D. Burkett	1985	John A. D. Cooper, M.D.
1972	College of Misericordia, Dallas, PA		John L. Quigley		Imperial Council of the Ancient Arabic Order of the
1973	Madison B. Brown, M.D.		William M. Whelan		Nobles of the Mystic Shrine for North America
	Samuel J. Tibbitts	1980	Sister Grace Marie Hiltz	1986	Howard F. Cook
1975	Kenneth B. Babcock, M.D.		Leo J. Gehrig, M.D.	1987	David H. Hitt
	Sister Mary Maurita Sengelaube	1981	Richard Davi		Lucile Packard
1976	Chaiker Abbis		Pearl S. Fryar		
	Susan Jenkins	1982	Jorge Brull Nater		

This citation is no longer awarded

AHA NOVA Awards

This award honors effective, collaborative programs focused on improving community health status.

1994

Health Partners of Philadelphi (PA): Albert Einstein Medical Center, Episcopal Hospital, Frankford Hospital, Medical College of Pennsylvania Hospital, St. Christopher's Hospital for Children, Temple University Hospital

Decker Family Development Center: Children's Hospital Medical Center of Akron (OH)
Denver (CO) School–Based Clinics: The Children's Hospital

Basic Health Plan: Dominican Network; Mount Carmel Hospital, Colville, WA; St. Joseph's Hospital, Chewelah, WA; and Holy Family Hospital, Spokane, WA
HealthLink: Lakes Region General Hospital, Laconia, NH

1995

Bladen Community Care Network: Bladen County Hospital, Elizabethtown, NC
Building a Healthier Community: Community– Kimball Health Care System, Toms River, NJ '

Injury Prevention Program: Harlem Hospital Center, New York City, NY
The Community Ministries & Outreach Program: Reaching Out to Our Vickery/Meadow Neighborhood: Presbyterian Healthcare System, Dallas, TX

"CHOICES": Shriners Hospitals for Crippled Children, Tampa, FL

1996

Lincoln and Sunnyslope: John C. Lincoln Hospital and Health Center, Sunnyslope, AZ
Growing into Life Task Force: Aiken (SC) Regional Medical Centers

People Caring for People: Beatrice (NE) Community Hospital and Health Center
Injury Prevention Center of the Greater Dayton (OH) Area: The Children's Medical Center, Good Samaritan Hospital and Health Center, Grandview Hospital, Kettering Memorial

Hospital, Miami Valley Hospital, and St. Elizabeth Medical Center
Family Road: Hutzel Hospital, Detroit, MI

1997

Health Promotion Schools of Excellence Program: Alliant Health System and Kosair Children's Hospital, Louisville, KY
Health, Outreach, Prevention, and Education (HOPE): Health First Holmes Regional Medical Center, Melbourne, FL

Healthy Community Initiative: Roper Care Alliance, Charleston, SC
Obstetrical Care and Prenatal Counseling Program: St. Alexius Medical Center, Bismarck, ND

HIV/AIDS Neighborhood Service Program: Yale–New Haven Hospital, New Haven, CT

1998

Partners for a Healthier Community: Evergreen Community Health Care, Group Health Cooperative of Puget Sound, Overlake Hospital Medical Center, Providence Health System/Medalia HealthCare, Seattle, WA
Glenwood–Lyndale Community Clinic: Hennepin County Medical Center, Minneapolis, MN

Greater Dallas (TX) Injury Prevention Center: Parkland Health & Hospital System, Children's Medical Center of Dallas, Baylor Health Care System, Methodist Hospitals of Dallas, and Presbyterian Healthcare System
Network of Trust: Phoebe Putney Memorial Hospital, Albany, GA

The Lauderdale Court: A Community Partnership:St. Joseph Hospital and Health Centers, Memphis, TN

1999

Making a Case for Community Health: Middletown (OH) Regional Hospital
The Family Resource Center: Mount Carmel Medical Center, Pittsburgh, KS

The Health Neighborhood Project: St. Patrick Hospital, Missoula, MT
Kids for Health: Washington Regional Medical Center, Fayetteville, AR

Children's Village: Yakima Memorial Hospital, Yakima, WA

2000

Community Healthcare Network: Columbus (GA) Regional Healthcare System
Pasadena County Asthma Project: Huntington Memorial Hospital, Pasadena, CA

Ashe County Health Council "Health Carolinias Task Force": Ashe Memorial Hospital, Jefferson, NC
Caritas–Connection Project: St. Mary's Hospital, Passaic, NJ

Correctional Health Care Program: Baystate Health System, Springfield, MA

2001

J.C. Lewis Health Center: Memorial Health and St. Joseph's Candler Health System, Savannah, GA
Project C.A.R.E.: Mercy Medical Center, Canton, OH

TeenHealthFX.com: Atlantic Health System, Florham Park, NJ
Vista ElderCARE: Vista Health, Waukegan, IL

Western Village Enterprise School: INTEGRIS Health, Oklahoma City, OK

2002

Chester Community Connections: Crozer– Keystone Health System, Springfield, PA
The Hope Street Family Center: California Hospital Medical Center, Los Angeles, CA

Mobile Health Outreach Ministry: St. Vincent's Health System, Jacksonville, FL
Operation Access: Kaiser Foundation Hospitals, Oakland; Sutter Health, Sacramento; San Francisco General Hospital,

San Francisco; St. Rose Hospital, Hayward; and Santa Rosa Memorial Hospital, Santa Rosa, CA
Wilmington Health Access for Teens: New Hanover Health Network, Wilmington, NC

2003

C.O.A.C.H. for Kids: Cedars–Sinai Medical Center, Los Angeles, CA
Community Action Network: Trinity Regional Medical Center, Fort Dodge, IA

Hearts N' Health: Glendale Adventist Medical Center, Glendale, CA
Saint Joseph Health Center: Saint Joseph Regional Medical Center, South Bend, IN

St. Mary Medical Center Bensalem Ministries: St. Mary Medical Center, Langhorne, PA

2004

Better Beginnings: Brockton Hospital, Brockton, MA
Buffalo County Community Health Partners: Good Samaritan Health Systems, Kearney, NE

Quad City Health Initiative: Genesis Health System, Davenport, IA and Trinity Regional Health System, Rock Island, IL
Quality of Life in the Truckee Meadows: Washoe Health System, Reno, NV

Solano Coalition for Better Health, Inc.: NorthBay Healthcare Group, Fairfield, CA; Sutter Solano Medical Center, Vallejo, CA; and Kaiser Permanente, Martinez, CA

2005

Children's Health Connection: McKay-Dee Hospital Center, Ogden, UT
Palmetto Health's Vision Health Initiative: Palmetto Health, Columbia, SC

Project Dulce, Whittier Institute for Diabetes: Scripps Health, San Diego, CA
Toledo/Lucas County CareNet: Mercy Health Partners, ProMedica Health System, and Medical University of Ohio, all of Toledo, OH and St. Luke's Hospital, Maumee, O

Volunteer Health Advisor (VHA) Program: Cambridge Health Alliance, Cambridge, MA

2006

Healthy Learners, Columbia, SC: Allendale County Hospital, Fairfax, SC; McLeod Medical Center–Dillon, Dillon, SC; Sisters of Charity Providence Hospitals, Columbia, SC; and Self Regional Healthcare, Greenwood, SC

Primary Care Access Network (PCAN): Health Central, Ocoee, FL; Florida Hospital, Winter Park, FL; and Orlando Regional Healthcare, Orlando, FL **ProHealth Care Community Health Outreach Initiative:** ProHealth Care, Waukesha, WI

St. Joseph Mobile Health Services: Saint Joseph HealthCare Inc., Lexington, KY
Yonkers Childhood Health Initiative: St. John's Riverside, Yonkers, NY

2007
Medical-Legal Partnership for Children: Boston Medical Center, Boston, MA
NOW (Nutritional Options for Wellness) Program: Spectrum Health, Grand Rapids, MI
Richland Care: Palmetto Health, Columbia, SC

Trauma Nurses Talk Tough: Legacy Health System, Portland, OR
UMass Memorial Medical Center Healthy Youth Development Initiative: UMass Memorial Health Care, Worcester, MA

Youth Health Partnership-Patee Market Youth Dental Clinic: Heartland Health, St. Joseph, MO

2008
Partnership for Community Health: California Pacific Medical Center, San Francisco, CA
Every Child Succeeds: Cincinnati Children's Hospital Medical Center, Cincinnati, OH

Memorial Hermann Health Centers for Schools: Memorial Hermann, Houston, TX
Nutrition Center of Maine: Saint Mary's Health System, Lewiston, ME

ENERGIZE! **Pediatric Diabetes Intervention Program:** WakeMed Health & Hospitals, Raleigh, NC

2009
Lighten Up 4 Life: Mission Health System, Asheville, NC
Project BRIEF: Jacobi Medical Center and North Central Bronx Hospital, Bronx, NY

Really Awesome Health (RAH) and Wholesome Routines: Duke Raleigh Hospital, Raleigh, NC

Student Success Jobs Program: Brigham and Women's Hospital, Boston, MA
Taos First Steps Program: Holy Cross Hospital, Taos, NM

2010
Community-Based Alternatives to the Emergency Room: Lee Memorial Health System, Fort Meyers, FL
Health-e-Access Telemedicine: University of Rochester Medical Center, Rochester, NY

Healthy Futures: Munson Healthcare System, Traverse City, MI
Healthy San Francisco: San Francisco General Hospital, University of California Medical Center, Chinese Hospital, California Pacific Medical Center, Saint Francis Memorial

Hospital, St. Mary's Medical Center, and Kaiser Permanente, San Francisco, CA
Pediatric Asthma Program: Sinai Health System, Chicago, IL

2011
Emergency Department Consistent Care Program: Providence St. Peter Hospital, Olympia, WA
Integrated Community Nursing Program at Parkview Health: Parkview Health, Fort Wayne, IN

Milwaukee Health Care Partnership: Aurora Health Care, Children's Hospital & Health System, Inc., Columbia St. Mary's, and Froedtert Health, all of Milwaukee, WI, and Wheaton Franciscan Healthcare, Glendale, WI

The Diabetes Collaborative: Northwestern Memorial Hospital, Chicago, IL
Rochester Youth Violence Partnership: University of Rochester Medical Center and Rochester General Health System, Rochester, NY

2012
The Beth Embraces Wellness: An Integrated Approach to Prevention in the Community: Newark Beth Israel Medical Center and Children's Hospital of New Jersey, Newark, NJ

CARE Network: St. Joseph Health Queen of the Valley Medical Center, Napa, CA
Fitness in the City: Boston Children's Hospital, Boston, MA
Puff City: Henry Ford Health System, Detroit, MI

Rural Health Initiative: Shawano Medical Center of ThedaCare, Shawano, WI

2013
Bangor Beacon Community: EMHS, Brewer, ME and St. Joseph Healthcare, Bangor, ME
Chippewa Health Improvement Partnership (CHIP): St. Joseph's Hospital, Chippewa Falls, WI

Core Health Program of Healthier Communities: Spectrum Health, Grand Rapids, MI
Free Preventive Screenings Program: Good Samaritan Hospital, Vincennes, IN

Hope Clinic and Pharmacy: Ephraim McDowell Health, Danville, KY

2014
FirstReach: FirstHealth of the Carolinas, Pinehurst, NC
Children's Hospital Center for Pediatric Medicine Asthma Action Team: Greenville Health System, Greenville, SC

Let's Go!: The Barbara Bush Children's Hospital at Maine Medical Center, Portland, ME
Hearts Beat Back: The Heart of New Ulm (HONU) Project: New Ulm Medical Center, part of Allina Health, New Ulm, MN

Finney County Community Health Coalition: St. Catherine Hospital, Garden City, KS

2015
Activate Whittier: PIH Health, Whittier, Calif. And Kaiser Permanente Downey Medical Center, Downey, CA
Bithlo Transformation Effort: Florida Hospital, Orlando, FL

Blood Pressure Advocate Program: University of Rochester Medical Center, Rochester, NY
Community Health: Healthy Eating: Presbyterian Healthcare Services, Albuquerque, NM

Mayor's Healthy City Initiative (Healthy BR): Baton Rouge General Medical Center, Ochsner Medical Center-Baton Rouge, Our Lady of the Lake Regional Medical Center and Woman's Hospital, Baton Rouge, LA

2016
Baylor Scott & White Health's Diabetes Health and Wellness Institute at the Juanita J. Craft Recreation Center: Baylor Scott & White Health, Dallas, TX

Building a Healthy Community Initiative, East Ocean View: Bon Secours Hampton Roads Health System, Norfolk, VA
Memorial Hermann Mobile Dental Program: Memorial Hermann Health System, Houston, TX

Spectrum Health Healthier Communities – Strong Beginnings: Spectrum Health, Grand Rapids, MI
Get Healthy, Live Well: Tanner Health System, Carrollton, GA

2017
Morrison County Community-Based Care Coordination: CHI St. Gabriel's Health, Little Falls, MN
The Health and Wellness Alliance Asthma Collaboration: Children's Health, Dallas, TX

Healthy Youth Transitions: Memorial Healthcare System, Hollywood, FL
Pediatric Care-A-Van: Norwegian American Hospital, Chicago, IL

Palmetto Health Dental Health Initiative: Palmetto Health, Columbia, SC

2018
Unity Center for Behavioral Health: Adventist Health, Kaiser Permanente, Legacy Health, Oregon Health & Science University, Portland, OR
Annapolis Community Health Partnership: Anne Arundel Medical Center, Annapolis, MD

Enos Park Access to Care Collaborative: HSHS St. John's Hospital and Memorial Medical Center, Springfield, IL
Kids Teaching Kids: Medical City Healthcare, Dallas, TX

Healthy Kids Express: St. Louis Children's Hospital, St. Louis, MO

The Carolyn Boone Lewis Living the Vision Award

Organizations and individuals living AHA's vision of a society of healthy communities where all individuals reach their highest potential for health.

1998	Memorial Healthcare System, Hollywood, FL Baptist Health System, Montgomery, AL	**2004**	Jamaica Hospital Medical Center, Jamaica, NY	**2014**	TPR Collaborative, MD
1999	Robert A. DeVries, Battle Creek, MI Memorial Health System, South Bend, IN	**2005**	Fairbanks Memorial Hospital, Fairbanks, AK Boston Medical Center, Boston, MA	**2016**	Saint Elizabeth's Medical Center, Wabasha, MN
2000	Rockingham Memorial Hospital, Harrisonburg, VA	**2010**	Lehigh Valley Health Network, Allentown, PA		
2001	Salina Regional Health Center, Salina, KS	**2011**	Alaska Native Tribal Health Consortium, Anchorage, AK		
2002	Health Improvement Collaborative of Greater Cincinnati, Cincinnati, OH	**2013**	St. Joseph's Hospital Health Center, Syracuse, NY Cheshire Medical Center/Dartmouth–Hitchcock Keene, Keene, NH		
2003	Franklin Memorial Hospital, Farmington, ME				

Circle of Life Award

This award celebrates innovation in palliative and end-of-life care.

2000

Improving Care through the End of Life, Franciscan Health System, Gig Harbor, WA

The Hospice of The Florida Suncoast, Largo, FL

Louisiana State Penitentiary Hospice Program, Angola, LA

2001

Department of Pain Medicine and Palliative Care, Beth Israel Medical Center, New York, NY

Palliative CareCenter & Hospice of the North Shore, Evanston , IL

St. Joseph's Manor, Trumbull, CT

2002

Children's Program of San Diego Hospice and Children's Hospital and Health Center of San Diego, San Diego, CA
Hospice of the Bluegrass, Lexington, KY

Project Safe Conduct, Hospice of the Western Reserve and Ireland Cancer Center, Cleveland, OH

Special Circle of Life Award Population–based Palliative Care Research Network (PoPCRN), Denver, CO

2003

Hospice & Palliative CareCenter, Winston–Salem, NC

Providence Health System, Portland, OR

University of California Davis Health System, Sacramento, CA

2004

Hope Hospice and Palliative Care, Fort Myers, FL
St. Mary's Healthcare System for Children, Bayside, NY

University of Texas M.D. Anderson Cancer Center Palliative Care, Houston, TX

2005

High Point Regional Health System, High Point, NC

Palliative and End-of-life Care Program, Hoag Memorial Hospital Presbyterian, Newport Beach, CA

Thomas Palliative Care Unit, VCU Massey Cancer Center, Richmond, VA

2006

Continuum Hospice Care, New York, NY

Mercy Supportive Care, St. Joseph Mercy Oakland, Pontiac, MI

Transitions and Life Choices, Fairview Health Services, Minneapolis, MN

2007

UCSF Palliative Care Program, San Francisco, CA
Covenant Hospice, Pensacola, FL

Woodwell: A Program of Presbyterian SeniorCare and Family Hospice and Palliative Care, Oakmont, PA

2008

Children's Hospitals and Clinics of Minnesota, Pain and Palliative Care Program, Minneapolis, MN

Haven Hospice, Gainesville, FL

The Pediatric Advanced Care Team, The Children's Hospital of Philadelphia, Philadelphia, PA

2009

Four Seasons, Flat Rock, NC

Oregon Health and Science University Palliative Medicine & Comfort Care Program, Portland, OR

Wishard Health Services Palliative Care Program, Indianapolis, IN

2010

Department of Veteran Affairs, VA New York/New Jersey Healthcare Network, Brooklyn, NY

Kansas City Hospice & Palliative Care, Kansas City, MO
Snohomish Palliative Partnership, Everett, WA

2011

The Center for Hospice & Palliative Care, Cheektowaga, NY

Gilchrist Hospice Care, Hunt Valley, MD

St. John Providence Health System, Detroit, MI

2012

Haslinger Family Pediatric Palliative Care Center, Akron Children's Hospital, Akron, OH

Calvary Hospital, Bronx, NY
Sharp HealthCare, San Diego, CA

2013

The Denver Hospice and Optio Health Services, Denver, CO

Hertzberg Palliative Care Institute at the Mount Sinai Medical Center, New York, NY

UnityPoint Health, Iowa and Illinois

2014

OACIS/Palliative Medicine, Lehigh Valley Health Network, Allentown, PA

Supportive & Palliative Care, Baylor Health Care System, Dallas, TX

Yakima Valley Memorial Hospital, Yakima, WA

2015

Care Dimensions, Danvers, MA

2016

Bon Secours Palliative Medicine, Richmond, VA

Cambia Palliative Care Center of Excellence at UW Medicine, Seattle, WA

Susquehanna Health Hospice and Palliative Care, Williamsport, PA

2017

Bluegrass Care Navigators, formerly Hospice of the Bluegrass, Lexington, KY

Providence TrinityCare Hospice, Providence Little Company of Mary Medical Center Torrance and Providence Institute for Human Caring, Torrance, CA

2018

Hospice of the Valley, Phoenix, AZ

Western Connecticut Health Network, Danbury, CT

Penn Wissahickon Hospice and Caring Way, Philadelphia, PA

The American Hospital Association Quest for Quality Prize*

Honoring Leadership and Innovation in Patient Care Quality, Safety, and Commitment

2002

Missouri Baptist Medical Center, St. Louis, MO

Finalist: Fairview Hospital, Greater, Barrington, MA

Finalist: Minnesota Children's Hospital and Clinics, Minneapolis, MN

(*This award was sponsored from 2001-2016 by McKesson. RL Solutions is the current sponsor.)

2003		
Abington Memorial Hospital, Abington, PA	**Finalist:** Beaumont Hospitals, Royal Oak, MI	**Finalist:** University of Wisconsin Hospital and Clinics, Madison, WI

2004		
Sentara Norfolk General Hospital, Norfolk, VA	**Finalist:** The Johns Hopkins Hospital, Baltimore, MD	**Finalist:** Mary Lanning Memorial Hospital, Hastings, NE

2005		
North Mississippi Medical Center, Tupelo, MS	**Finalist:** El Camino Hospital, Mountain View, CA	**Finalist:** NewYork-Presbyterian Hospital, New York, NY

2006	
Cincinnati Children's Hospital Medical Center, Cincinnati, OH	

2007		
Columbus Regional Hospital, Columbus, IN	**Finalist:** Cedars-Sinai Medical Center, Los Angeles, CA	**Finalist:** INTEGRIS Baptist Medical Center, Oklahoma City, OK

2008	
Munson Medical Center, Traverse City, MI	**Finalist:** University of Michigan Hospitals & Health Centers, Ann Arbor, MI

2009	
Bronson Methodist Hospital, Kalamazoo, MI	**Finalist:** Beth Israel Deaconess Medical Center, Boston, MA

2010	
McLeod Regional Medical Center, Florence, SC	**Finalist:** Henry Ford Hospital, Detroit, MI

2011		
Memorial Regional Hospital, Hollywood, FL	**Finalist:** AtlantiCare Regional Medical Center, Atlantic City, NJ	**Finalist:** Northwestern Memorial Hospital, Chicago, IL

2012		
University Hospitals Case Medical Center, Cleveland, OH	**Finalist:** Lincoln Medical and Mental Health Center, Bronx, NY	**Finalist:** University of North Carolina Hospitals, Chapel Hill, NC and Life Choices, Fairview Health Services, Minneapolis, MN

2013	
Beth Israel Deaconess Medical Center, Boston, MA	**Finalist:** Franklin Woods Community Hospital, Johnson City, TN

2014	
VCU Medical Center, Richmond, VA	**Finalist:** Carolinas Medical Center-Northeast, Concord, NC

2015	
Children's Hospital Colorado in Aurora, CO	**Finalist:** Duke University Hospital, Durham, NC

2016	
Memorial Medical Center, Springfield, IL	**Finalist:** Memorial Hermann Greater Heights, Houston, TX

2018		
Northwell Health, New Hyde Park, NY	**Finalist:** Anne Arundel Medical Center, Annapolis, MD	**Finalist:** Aurora Health Care, Milwaukee, WI

Foster G. McGaw Prize

Honors health delivery organizations that have demonstrated exceptional commitment to community service.

1986	Lutheran Medical Center, Brooklyn, NY	1995	Our Lady of Lourdes Medical Center, Camden, NJ	2006	Memorial Healthcare System, Hollywood, FL
1987	Copley Hospital, Morrisville, VT Mount Sinai Hospital, Hartford, CT	1996	St. Mary's Hospital, Rochester, NY	2007	Harborview Medical Center, Seattle, WA
		1997	Bladen County Hospital Rural Health Network,	2008	St. Mary's Health System, Lewiston, ME
1988	MetroHealth System, Cleveland, OH		Elizabethtown, NC	2009	Heartland Health, St. Joseph, MO
1989	Greater Southeast Healthcare System, Washington, DC	1998	Allina Health System, Minneapolis, MN	2010	Allegiance Health, Jackson, MI
1990	Mount Zion Medical Center of The University of	1999	LAC+USC Healthcare Network, Los Angeles, CA	2011	Mt. Ascutney Hospital and Health Center, Windsor, VT
	California-San Francisco, San Francisco, CA	2000	Kaweah Delta Health Care District, Visalia, CA	2012	St. Joseph's/Candler Health System, Savannah, GA
1991	Franklin Regional Hospital, Franklin, NH	2001	Memorial Hospital of South Bend, South Bend, IN	2013	Crozer–Keystone Health System, Delaware County, PA
1992	Mount Sinai Hospital Medical Center of Chicago,	2002	John C. Lincoln Health Network, Phoenix, AZ	2014	Palmetto Health, Columbia, SC
	Chicago, IL	2003	Phoebe Putney Memorial Hospital, Albany, GA	2015	Massachusetts General Hospital, Boston
1993	The Cambridge Hospital, Cambridge, MA	2004	Henry Ford Health System, Detroit, MI	2016	Spectrum Health, Grand Rapids, MI
1994	Parkland Memorial Hospital, Dallas, TX	2005	Venice Family Clinic, Venice, CA	2017	Yale New Haven Hospital, New Haven, CT

Dick Davidson Quality Milestone Award for Allied Association Leadership

The award recognizes state, regional or metropolitan hospital association leadership in improving health care quality.

2011	Michigan Health & Hospital Association	2013	Florida Hospital Association	2015	Minnesota Hospital Association
	South Carolina Hospital Association		Tennessee Hospital Association	2016	Maryland Hospital Association
2012	Iowa Hospital Association	2014	Connecticut Hospital Association	2017	California's Hospital Quality Institute
	Washington State Hospital Association		Wisconsin Hospital Association	2018	Missouri Hospital Association

AHA Equity of Care Award

The award is presented to hospitals or care systems that are noteworthy leaders and examples to the field in the area of equitable care.

2014	Massachusetts General Hospital, Boston, MA
2015	Henry Ford Health System, Detroit, MI
	Robert Wood Johnson University Hospital, New Brunswick, NJ
2016	Cleveland Clinic, Cleveland, OH
2017	Kaiser Permanente, Oakland, CA
2018	Navicent Health, Macon, GA

A

**Hospitals,
Institutional and
Associate Members**

AHA Guide
Hospital Listing Requirements

An institution is considered a hospital by the American Hospital Association if it is licensed as general or specialty hospital by the appropriate state agency, and accredited as a hospital by one of the following organizations: The Joint Commission; Healthcare Facilities Accreditation Program (HFAP); DNV Healthcare accreditation; Center for Improvement in Healthcare Quality accreditation; or Medicare certified as a provider of acute service under Title 18 of the Social Security Act.

Types of Hospitals

Hospitals are listed as one of four types of hospitals: general, special, rehabilitation and chronic disease, or psychiatric. The following definitions of function by type of hospital and special requirements are:

General

The primary function of the institution is to provide patient services, diagnostic and therapeutic, for a variety of medical conditions. A general hospital also shall provide:

- diagnostic x–ray services with facilities and staff for a variety of procedures
- clinical laboratory service with facilities and staff for a variety of procedures and with anatomical pathology services regularly and conveniently available
- operating room service with facilities and staff.

Special

The primary function of the institution is to provide diagnostic and treatment services for patients who have specified medical conditions, both surgical and nonsurgical. A special hospital also shall provide:

- such diagnostic and treatment services as may be determined by the Executive Committee of the Board of Trustees of the American Hospital Association to be appropriate for the specified medical conditions for which medical services are provided shall be maintained in the institution with suitable facilities and staff. If such conditions do not normally require diagnostic x–ray service, laboratory service, or operating room service, and if any such services are therefore not maintained in the institution, there shall be written arrangements to make them available to patients requiring them.
- clinical laboratory services capable of providing tissue diagnosis when offering pregancy termination services.

Rehabilitation and Chronic Disease

The primary function of the institution is to provide diagnostic and treatment services to handicapped or disabled individuals requiring restorative and adjustive services. A rehabilitation and chronic disease hospital also shall provide:

- arrangements for diagnostic x–ray services, as required, on a regular and conveniently available basis
- arrangements for clinical laboratory service, as required on a regular and conveniently available basis
- arrangements for operating room service, as required, on a regular and conveniently available basis
- a physical therapy service with suitable facilities and staff in the institution

- an occupational therapy service with suitable facilities and staff in the institution
- arrangements for psychological and social work services on a regular and conveniently available basis
- arrangements for educational and vocational services on a regular and conveniently available basis
- written arrangements with a general hospital for the transfer of patients who require medical, obstetrical, or surgical services not available in the institution.

Psychiatric

The primary function of the institution is to provide diagnostic and treatment services for patients who have psychiatric–related illnesses. A psychiatric hospital also shall provide:

- arrangements for clinical laboratory service, as required, on a regular and conveniently available basis
- arrangements for diagnostic x–ray services, as required on a regular and conveniently available basis
- psychiatric, psychological, and social work service with facilities and staff in the institution
- arrangements for electroencephalograph services, as required, on a regular and conveniently available basis
- written arrangements with a general hospital for the transfer of patients who require medical, obstetrical, or surgical services not available in the institution

The American Hospital Association may, at the sole discretion of the Executive Committee of the Board of Trustees, grant, deny, or withdraw the listing of an institution.

---

* Physician–Term used to describe an individual with an M.D. or D.O. degree who is fully licensed to practice medicine in all its phases.
‡ The completed records in general shall contain at least the following: the patient's identifying data and consent forms, medical history, record of physical examination, physicians' progress notes, operative notes, nurses' notes, routine x–ray and laboratory reports, doctors' orders, and final diagnosis.

Sample Hospital Listing:

ANYTOWN, Universal County

✠ **ANYTOWN HOSPITAL & CLINICS (777777)**, (Formerly Anytown Area Community Hospital and Clinic), 100 South Main Street, Zip 12345–6789; tel. 123/456–7890 **A**9 10] ①
F10 12 23 24 29 30 31 37 39 49 51 55 57 64 65 66 68 70 71 72 77 78 83 87 88 91 96 97 106 107 110 111 113 124 **P**1 2 3 **S** Universal ⑦
County Health System ② ③
Primary Contact: Ann M. Generic, Chief Executive Officer
COO: Ann M. Generic
CFO: Michael M. Generic
CMO: Peterl Van Generic, President Medical Staff ④
CHR: Jerry Generic, Human Resources Director
CNO: Danielle Generic, R.N., Chief Nursing Officer
Web address: www.website.org
Control: Other not–for–profit (including NFP Corporation) **Service:** General Medical and Surgical ⑤

Staffed Beds: 25 **Admissions:** 892 **Census:** 9 **Outpatient Visits:** 44014
Births: 51 **Total Expense ($000):** 19210 **Payroll Expense ($000):** 5864
Personnel: 182

ANYTOWN, Universal County

✠ **ANYTOWN HOSPITAL & CLINICS (777777)**, (Formerly Anytown Area Community Hospital and Clinic), 100 South Main Street, Zip 12345–6789; tel. 123/456–7890 **A**9 10

① = **Approval Codes**
② = **Physician Codes**
③ = **Health Care System Name**
④ = **Titles of Chief Administrators**
⑤ = **Control and Service Classifications**
⑥ = **Utilization Data**
⑦ = **Facility Codes**

⑥

Hospital, Medicare Provider Number, Address, Telephone, Approval, Facility, and Physician Codes, Health Care System

★ American Hospital Association (AHA) membership   ○ Healthcare Facilities Accreditation Program   ⇑ Center for Improvement in Healthcare Quality Accreditation
□ The Joint Commission accreditation   ◇ DNV Healthcare Inc. accreditation   △ Commission on Accreditation of Rehabilitation Facilities (CARF) accreditation

---

① Approval Codes

Reported by the approving bodies specified, as of the dates noted.

1 Accreditation under the hospital program of The Joint Commission (February 2018).
2 Cancer program approved by American College of Surgeons (January 2017).
3 Participating site recognized for one or more Accreditation Council for Graduate Medical Education accredited programs (March 2018).
5 Medical school affiliation, reported to the American Medical Association (March 2018).
6 Accreditation by Commission on Accreditation of Rehabilitation Facilities (March 2018).

7 Member of Council of Teaching Hospitals of the Association of American Medical Colleges (January 2018).
10 Certified for participation in the Health Insurance for the Aged (Medicare) Program by the Centers for Medicare and Medicaid Services (January 2018).
11 Healthcare Facilities Accreditation Program (January 2018).
12 Internship approved by American Osteopathic Association (February 2018).

13 Residency or fellowship approved by American Osteopathic Association (February 2018).
18 Critical Access Hospitals (January 2018).
19 Rural Referral Center (January 2018).
20 Sole Community Provider (January 2018).
21 Accreditation by DNV Healthcare Inc. (January 2018).
22 Accreditation by Center for Improvement in Healthcare Quality (January 2018)

Nonreporting indicates that the 2017 Annual Survey questionnaire for the hospital was not received prior to publication.

---

② Physician Codes

Actually available within, and reported by the institution; for definitions, see page A12.

(Alphabetical/Numerical Order)

1 Closed physician–hospital organization (PHO)
2 Equity model
3 Foundation

4 Group practice without walls
5 Independent practice association (IPA)
6 Integrated salary model

7 Management service organization (MSO)
8 Open physician–hospital organization (PHO)

---

③ Healthcare System Name

The inclusion of the letter "S" (1) indicates that the hospital belongs to a health care system and (2) identifies the specific system to which the hospital belongs.

---

④ Titles of Chief Administrators

⑤ Control and Service Classification

For a list of control and service classifications, see page A13.

Control–The type of organization that is responsible for establishing policy for overall operation of the hospital.

Service–The type of service the hospital provides to the majority of admissions.

---

⑥ Utilization Data

Definitions are based on the American Hospital Association's Hospital Administration Terminology. In completing the survey, hospitals were requested to report data for a full year, in accord with their fiscal year, ending in 2017.

Beds–Number of beds regularly maintained (set up and staffed for use) for inpatients as of the close of the reporting period. Excludes newborn bassinets.

Admissions–Number of patients accepted for inpatient service during a 12–month period; does not include newborn.

Census–Average number of inpatients receiving care each day during the 12–month reporting period; does not include newborn.

Outpatient Visits–A visit by a patient who is not lodged in the hospital while receiving medical, dental, or other services. Each appearance of an outpatient in each unit constitutes one visit regardless of the number of diagnostic and/or therapeutic treatments that a patient receives.

Births–Number of infants born in the hospital and accepted for service in a newborn infant bassinet during a 12–month period; excludes stillbirths.

Expense: Expense for a 12–month period; both total expense and payroll components are shown. Payroll expenses include all salaries and wages.

Personnel: Represents personnel situations as they existed at the end of the reporting period; includes full-time equivalents of part–time personnel. Full–time equivalents were calculated on the basis that two part–time persons equal one full–time person.

Sample Hospital Listing:

ANYTOWN, Universal County

✠ **ANYTOWN HOSPITAL & CLINICS (777777)**, (Formerly Anytown Area
Community Hospital and Clinic), 100 South Main Street, Zip 12345–6789;
tel. 123/456–7890 **A**9 10] ①

F10 12 23 24 29 30 31 37 39 49 51 55 57 64 65 66 68 70 71 72 77
78 83 87 88 91 96 97 106 107 110 111 113 124 **P**1 2 3 **S** Universal — ⑦

County Health System ② ③
Primary Contact: Ann M. Generic, Chief Executive Officer
COO: Ann M. Generic
CFO: Michael M. Generic ④
CMO: Peterl Van Generic, President Medical Staff
CHR: Jerry Generic, Human Resources Director
CNO: Danielle Generic, R.N., Chief Nursing Officer
Web address: www.website.org
Control: Other not–for–profit (including NFP Corporation) **Service:** General
Medical and Surgical ⑤

Staffed Beds: 25 **Admissions:** 892 **Census:** 9 **Outpatient Visits:** 44014
Births: 51 **Total Expense ($000):** 19210 **Payroll Expense ($000):** 5864
Personnel: 182

ANYTOWN, Universal County

✠ **ANYTOWN HOSPITAL & CLINICS (777777)**, (Formerly Anytown Area
Community Hospital and Clinic), 100 South Main Street, Zip 12345–6789;
tel. 123/456–7890 **A**9 10

① = Approval Codes
② = Physician Codes
③ = Health Care System Name
④ = Titles of Chief Administrators
⑤ = Control and Service Classifications
⑥ = Utilization Data
⑦ = Facility Codes

Hospital, Medicare Provider Number, Address, Telephone, Approval, Facility, and Physician Codes, Health Care System

★ American Hospital Association (AHA) membership   ○ Healthcare Facilities Accreditation Program   ⇑ Center for Improvement in Healthcare Quality Accreditation
□ The Joint Commission accreditation   ◇ DNV Healthcare Inc. accreditation   △ Commission on Accreditation of Rehabilitation Facilities (CARF) accreditation

---

⑦ Facility Codes

Provided directly by the hospital; for definitions, see page A6.

(Numerical Order)

1 Acute long-term care	53 Fitness center	108 Diagnostic radioisotope facility
2 Adult day care program	54 Freestanding outpatient care center	109 Electron beam computed tomography (EBCT)
3 Airborne infection isolation room	55 Genetic testing/counseling	110 Full–field digital mammography (FFDM)
4 Alcoholism-drug abuse or dependency inpatient services	56 Geriatric services	111 Magnetic resonance imaging (MRI)
5 Alcoholism-drug abuse or dependency outpatient services	57 Health fair	112 Intraoperative magnetic resonance imaging
6 Alzheimer center	58 Health research	113 Magnetoencephalography (MEG)
7 Ambulance services	59 Health screenings	114 Multi–slice spiral computed tomography (MSCT) (<64 slice CT)
8 Ambulatory surgery center	60 Hemodialysis	115 Multi–slice spiral computed tomography (64 + slice CT)
9 Arthritis treatment center	61 HIV–AIDS services	
10 Assisted living	62 Home health services	116 Positron emission tomography (PET)
11 Auxiliary	63 Hospice program	117 Positron emission tomography/CT (PET/ CT)
12 Bariatric/weight control services	64 Hospital–based outpatient care center services	118 Single photon emission computerized tomography (SPECT)
13 Birthing room-LDR room-LDRP room	65 Immunization program	119 Ultrasound
14 Blood donor center	66 Indigent care clinic	120 Image–guided radiation therapy (IGRT)
15 Breast cancer screening/mammograms	67 Intermediate nursing care	121 Intensity–modulated radiation therapy (IMRT)
16 Burn care services	68 Linguistic/translation services	
17 Cardiac intensive care	69 Meals on wheels	122 Proton beam therapy
18 Adult cardiology services	70 Medical surgical intensive care services	123 Shaped beam radiation therapy
19 Pediatric cardiology services	71 Mobile health services	124 Stereotactic radiosurgery
20 Adult diagnostic catheterization	72 Neonatal intensive care	125 Retirement housing
21 Pediatric diagnostic catheterization	73 Neonatal intermediate care	126 Robotic surgery
22 Adult interventional cardiac catheterization	74 Neurological services	127 Rural health clinic
23 Pediatric interventional cardiac catheterization	75 Nutrition programs	128 Skilled nursing care
24 Adult cardiac surgery	76 Obstetrics	129 Sleep center
25 Pediatric cardiac surgery	77 Occupational health services	130 Social work services
26 Adult cardiac electrophysiology	78 Oncology services	131 Sports medicine
27 Pediatric cardiac electrophysiology	79 Orthopedic services	132 Support groups
28 Cardiac rehabilitation	80 Other special care	133 Swing bed services
29 Case management	81 Outpatient surgery	134 Teen outreach services
30 Chaplaincy/pastoral care services	82 Pain management program	135 Tobacco treatment/cessation program
31 Chemotherapy	83 Inpatient palliative care unit	136 Bone marrow transplant services
32 Children's wellness program	84 Palliative care program	137 Heart transplant
33 Chiropractic services	85 Patient controlled analgesia (PCA)	138 Kidney transplant
34 Community health education	86 Patient education center	139 Liver transplant
35 Community outreach	87 Patient representative services	140 Lung transplant
36 Complementary and alternative medicine services	88 Pediatric intensive care services	141 Tissue transplant
37 Computer assisted orthopedic surgery (CAOS)	89 Pediatric medical–surgical care	142 Other transplant
38 Crisis prevention	90 Physical rehabilitation inpatient services	143 Transportation to health services
39 Dental services	91 Assistive technology center	144 Urgent care center
40 Emergency department	92 Electrodiagnostic services	145 Virtual colonoscopy
41 Pediatric emergency department	93 Physical rehabilitation outpatient services	146 Volunteer services department
43 Trauma center (certified)	94 Prosthetic and orthotic services	147 Women's health center/services
44 Enabling services	95 Robot-assisted walking therapy	148 Wound management services
45 Optical colonoscopy	96 Simulated rehabilitation environment	149 Violence prevention programs for the workplace
46 Endoscopic ultrasound	97 Primary care department	150 Violence prevention programs for the community
47 Ablation of Barrett's esophagus	98 Psychiatric care	
48 Esophageal impedance study	99 Psychiatric pediatric care	151 Alcoholism-chemical dependency pediatric services
49 Endoscopic retrograde cholangiopancreatography (ERCP)	100 Psychiatric consultation–liaison services	152 Alcoholism-chemical dependency partial hospitalization services
50 Enrollment assistance services	101 Psychiatric education services	
51 Extracorporeal shock wave lithotripter (ESWL)	102 Psychiatric emergency services	153 Psychiatric intensive outpatient services
52 Fertility clinic	103 Psychiatric geriatric services	154 Telehealth
	104 Psychiatric outpatient services	
	105 Psychiatric partial hospitalization services	
	106 Psychiatric residential treatment	
	107 CT scanner	

Each year, an annual survey of hospitals is conducted by the American Hospital Association through its Health Forum affiliate.

The facilities and services found below are provided by the hospital. For data products reflecting the services provided by a hospital through its health care system, or network or through a formal arrangement with another provider contact Health Forum at 800/821–2039, or visit www.healthforum.com.

The AHA Guide to the Health Care Field does not include all data collected from the 2015 Annual Survey. Requests for purchasing other Annual Survey data should be directed to Health Forum LLC, an affiliate of the American Hospital Association, 155 N. Wacker Drive, Chicago, IL 60606, 800/821–2039.

Definitions of Facility Codes

1. **Acute long–term care.** Provides specialized acute hospital care to medically complex patients who are critically ill, have multisystem complications and/or failure, and require hospitalization averaging 25 days, in a facility offering specialized treatment programs and therapeutic intervention on a 24–hour/7 day a week basis.

2. **Adult day care program.** Program providing supervision, medical and psychological care, and social activities for older adults who live at home or in another family setting, but cannot be alone or prefer to be with others during the day. May include intake assessment, health monitoring, occupational therapy, personal care, noon meal, and transportation services.

3. **Airborne infection isolation room.** A single–occupancy room for patient care where environmental factors are controlled in an effort to minimize the transmission of those infectious agents, usually spread person to person by droplet nuclei associated with coughing and inhalation. Such rooms typically have specific ventilation requirements for controlled ventilation, air pressure and filtration.

4. **Alcoholism–drug abuse or dependency inpatient unit.** Provides diagnosis and therapeutic services to patients with alcoholism or other drug dependencies. Includes care for inpatient/residential treatment for patients whose course of treatment involves more intensive care than provided in an outpatient setting or where patient requires supervised withdrawal.

5. **Alcoholism–drug abuse or dependency outpatient unit.** Organized hospital services that provide medical care and/or rehabilitative treatment services to outpatients for whom the primary diagnosis is alcoholism or other chemical dependency.

6. **Alzheimer center.** Facility that offers care to persons with Alzheimer's disease and their families through an integrated program of clinical services, research, and education.

7. **Ambulance services.** Provision of ambulance services to the ill and injured who require medical attention on a scheduled or unscheduled basis.

8. **Ambulatory surgery center.** Facility that provides care to patients requiring surgery who are admitted and discharged on the same day. Ambulatory surgery centers are distinct from same day surgical units within the hospital outpatient departments for purposes of Medicare payments.

9. **Arthritis treatment center.** Specifically equipped and staffed center for the diagnosis and treatment of arthritis and other joint disorders.

10. **Assisted living.** A special combination of housing, supportive services, personalized assistance and health care designed to respond to the individual needs of those who need help in activities of daily living and instrumental activities of daily living. Supportive services are available, 24 hours a day, to meet scheduled and unscheduled needs, in a way that promotes maximum independence and dignity for each resident and encourages the involvement of a resident's family, neighbor and friends.

11. **Auxiliary.** A volunteer community organization formed to assist the hospital in carrying out its purpose and to serve as a link between the institution and the community.

12. **Bariatric/weight control services.** Bariatrics is the medical practice of weight reduction.

13. **Birthing room–LDR room– LDRP room.** A single room–type of maternity care with a more homelike setting for families than the traditional three–room unit (labor/delivery/recovery) with a separate postpartum area. A birthing room combines labor and delivery in one room. An LDR room accommodates three stages in the birthing process— labor, delivery, and recovery. An LDRP room accommodates all four stages of the birth process—labor, delivery, recovery and postpartum.

14. **Blood donor center.** A facility that performs, or is responsible for the collection, processing, testing or distribution of blood and components.

15. **Breast cancer screening/ mammograms.** Mammography screening–the use of breast x–ray to detect unsuspected breast cancer in asymptomatic women. Diagnostic mammography–the x–ray imaging of breast tissue in symptomatic women who are considered to have a substantial likelihood of having breast cancer already.

16. **Burn care services.** Provides care to severely burned patients. Severely burned patients are those with any of the following: 1. Second–degree burns of more than 25% total body surface area for adults or 20% total body surface area for children; 2. Third–degree burns of more than 10% total body surface area; 3. Any severe burns of the hands, face, eyes, ears or feet or; 4. All inhalation injuries, electrical burns, complicated burn injuries involving fractures and other major traumas, and all other poor risk factors.

17. **Cardiac intensive care.** Provides patient care of a more specialized nature than the usual medical and surgical care, on the basis of

physicians' orders and approved nursing care plans. The unit is staffed with specially trained nursing personnel and contains monitoring and specialized support or treatment equipment for patients who, because of heart seizure, one-heart surgery, or other life-threatening conditions, require intensified, comprehensive observation and care. May include myocardial infarction, pulmonary care, and heart transplant units.

18. **Adult cardiology services.** An organized clinical service offering diagnostic and interventional procedures to manage the full range of adult heart conditions.

19. **Pediatric cardiology services.**

20. **Adult diagnostic catheterization.** (also called coronary angiography or coronary arteriography) is used to assist in diagnosing complex heart conditions. Cardiac angiography involves the insertion of a tiny catheter up into the artery in the groin then carefully threading the catheter up into the aorta where the coronary arteries originate. Once the catheter is in place, a dye is injected which allows the cardiologist to see the size, shape and distribution of the coronary arteries. These images are used to diagnose heart disease and to determine, among other things, whether or not surgery is indicated.

21. **Pediatric diagnostic catheterization.** (also called coronary angiography or coronary arteriography) is used to assist in diagnosing complex heart conditions. Cardiac angiography involves the insertion of a tiny catheter up into the artery in the groin then carefully threading the catheter up into the aorta where the coronary arteries originate. Once the catheter is in place, a dye is injected which allows the cardiologist to see the size, shape and distribution of the coronary arteries. These images are used to diagnose heart disease and to determine, among other things, whether or not surgery is indicated.

22. **Adult interventional cardiac catheterization.** Nonsurgical procedure that utilizes the same basic principles as diagnostic cathetereization and then uses advanced the techniques to improve the heart's function. It can be less invasive alternative to heart surgery.

23. **Pediatric diagnostic catheterization.** Nonsurgical procedure that utilizes the same basic principles as diagnostic cathetereization and then uses advanced the techniques to improve the heart's function. It can be less invasive alternative to heart surgery.

24. **Adult cardiac surgery.** Includes minimally invasive procedures that include surgery done with only a small incision or no incision at all, such as through a laparoscope or an endoscope and more invasive major surgical procedures that include open chest and open heart surgery.

25. **Pediatric cardiac surgery.** Includes minimally invasive procedures that include surgery done with only a small incision or no incision at all, such as through a laparoscope or an endoscope and more invasive major surgical procedures that include open chest and open heart surgery defibrillator implantation and follow- up.

26. **Adult cardiac electrophysiology.** Evaluation and management of patients with complex rhythm or conduction abnormalities, including diagnostic testing, treatment of arrhythmias by catheter ablation or drug therapy, and pacemaker/ defibrillator implantation and follow- up.

27. **Pediatric cardiac electrophysiology.**

28. **Cardiac rehabilitation.** A medically supervised program to help heart patients recover quickly and improve their overall physical and mental functioning. The goal is to reduce risk of another cardiac event or to keep an already present heart condition from getting worse. Cardiac rehabilitation programs include: counseling to patients, an exercise program, helping patients modify risk factors such as smoking and high blood pressure, providing vocational guidance to enable the patient to return to work, supplying information on physical limitations and lending emotional support.

29. **Case management.** A system of assessment, treatment planning, referral and follow–up that ensures the provision of comprehensive and continuous services and the coordination of payment and reimbursement for care.

30. **Chaplaincy/pastoral care services.** A service ministering religious activities and providing pastoral counseling to patients, their families, and staff of a health care organization.

31. **Chemotherapy.** An organized program for the treatment of cancer by the use of drugs or chemicals.

32. **Children's wellness program.** A program that encourages improved health status and a healthful lifestyle of children through health education, exercise, nutrition and health promotion.

33. **Chiropractic services.** An organized clinical service including spinal manipulation or adjustment and related diagnostic and therapeutic services.

34. **Community health education.** Education that provides health information to individuals and populations as well as support for personal, family and community health decisions with the objective of improving health status.

35. **Community outreach.** A program that systematically interacts with the community to identify those in need of services, alerting persons and their families to the availability of services, locating needed services, and enabling persons to enter the service delivery system.

36. **Complementary and alternative medicine services.** Organized hospital services or formal arrangements to providers that provide care or treatment not based solely on traditional western allopathic medical teachings as instructed in most U.S. medical schools. Includes any of the following; acupuncture, chiropractic, homeopathy, osteopathy, diet and lifestyle changes, herbal medicine, massage therapy, etc.

37. **Computer assisted orthopedic surgery (CAOS).** Orthopedic surgery using computer technology, enabling three–dimensional graphic models to visualize a patient's anatomy.

38. **Crisis prevention.** Services provided in order to promote physical and mental well being and the early identification of disease and ill health prior to the onset and recognition of symptoms so as to permit early treatment.

39. **Dental services.** An organized dental service, not necessarily involving special facilities, that provides dental or oral services to inpatients or outpatients.

40. **Emergency department.** Hospital facilities for the provision of unscheduled outpatient services to patients whose conditions require immediate care. Must be staffed 24 hours a day.

41. Pediatric emergency department. Hospital facilities for the provision of unscheduled outpatient services to patients whose conditions require immediate care.

43. Trauma center (certified). A facility certified to provide emergency and specialized intensive care to critically ill and injured patients.

44. Enabling services. A program that is designed to help the patient access health care services by offering any of the following linguistic services, transportation services, and/or referrals to local social services agencies.

45. Optical colonoscopy. An examination of the interior of the colon using a long, flexible, lighted tube with a small built-in camera.

46. Endoscopic ultrasound. Specially designed endoscope that incorporates an ultrasound transducer used to obtain detailed images of organs in the chest and abdomen. The endoscope can be passed through the mouth or the anus. When combined with needle biopsy the procedure can assist in diagnosis and staging of cancer.

47. Ablation of Barrett's esophagus. Premalignant condition that can lead to adenocarcinoma of the esophagus. The non surgical ablation of the premalignant tissue in Barrett's esophagus by the application of thermal energy or light through an endoscope passed from the mouth into the esophagus.

48. Esophageal impedance study. A test in which a catheter is placed through the nose into the esophagus to measure whether gas or liquids are passing from the stomach into the esophagus and causing symptoms.

49. Endoscopic retrograde cholangiopancreatography (ERCP). A procedure in which a catheter is introduced through an endoscope into the bile ducts and pancreatic ducts. Injection of contrast materials permits detailed x–ray of these structures. The procedure is used diagnostically as well as therapeutically to relieve obstruction or remove stones

50. Enrollment assistance services. A program that provides enrollment assistance for patients who are potentially eligible for public health insurance programs such as Medicaid, State Children's Health Insurance, or local/state indigent care programs. The specific services offered could include explanation of benefits, assist applicants in completing the application and locating all relevant documents, conduct eligibilty interviews, and/or forward applications and documentation to state/local social service or health agency.

51. Extracorporeal shock wave lithotripter (ESWL). A medical device used for treating stones in the kidney or urethra. The device disintegrates kidney stones noninvasively through the transmission of acoustic shock waves directed at the stones.

52. Fertility clinic. A specialized program set in an infertility center that provides counseling and education   as well as advanced reproductive techniques such as: injectable therapy, reproductive surgeries, treatment for endometriosis, male factor infertility, tubal reversals, in vitro fertilization (IVF), donor eggs, and other such services to help patients achieve successful pregnancies.

53. Fitness center. Provides exercise, testing, or evaluation programs and fitness activities to the community and hospital employees.

54. Freestanding outpatient care center. A facility owned and operated by the hospital, but physically separate from the hospital, that provides various medical treatments on an outpatient basis only. In addition to treating minor illnesses or injuries, the center will stabilize seriously ill or injured patients before transporting them to a hospital. Laboratory and radiology services are usually available.

55. Genetic testing/counseling. A service equipped with adequate laboratory facilities and directed by a qualified physician to advise parents and prospective parents on potential problems in cases of genetic defects. A genetic test is the analysis of human DNA, RNA, chromosomes, proteins, and certain metabolites in order to detect heritable disease– related genotypes, mutations, phenotypes, or karyotypes for clinical purposes. Genetic tests can have diverse purposes, including the diagnosis of genetic diseases in newborns, children, and adults; the identification of future health risks; the prediction of drug responses; and the assessment of risks to future children.

56. Geriatric services. The branch of medicine dealing with the physiology of aging and the diagnosis and treatment of disease affecting the aged. Services could include: Adult day care program; Alzheimer's diagnostic–assessment services; Comprehensive geriatric assessment; Emergency response system; Geriatric acute care unit; and/or Geriatric clinics.

57. Health fair. Community health education events that focus on the prevention of disease and promotion of health through such activities as audiovisual exhibits and free diagnostic services.

58. Health research. Organized hospital research program in any of the following areas: basic research, clinical research, community health research, and/or research on innovative health care delivery.

59. Health screenings. A preliminary procedure, such as a test or examination to detect the most characteristic sign or signs of a disorder that may require further investigation.

60. Hemodialysis. Provision of equipment and personnel for the treatment of renal insufficiency on an inpatient or outpatient basis.

61. HIV–AIDS services. Services may include one or more of the following: HIV–AIDS unit (special unit or team designated and equipped specifically for diagnosis, treatment, continuing care planning, and counseling services for HIV–AIDS patients and their families.) General inpatient care for HIV–AIDS (inpatient diagnosis and treatment for human immunodeficiency virus and acquired immunodeficiency syndrome patients, but dedicated unit is not available.) Specialized outpatient program for HIV–AIDS (special outpatient program providing diagnostic, treatment, continuing care planning, and counseling for HIV–AIDS patients and their families.)

62. Home health services. Service providing nursing, therapy, and health–related homemaker or social services in the patient's home.

63. Hospice program. A program providing palliative care, chiefly medical relief of pain and supportive services, addressing the emotional, social, financial, and legal needs of terminally ill patients and their families. Care can be provided in a variety of settings, both inpatient and at home.

64. Hospital–based outpatient care center services. Organized hospital health care services offered by appointment on an ambulatory basis. Services may include outpatient surgery, examination, diagnosis, and treatment of a variety of medical conditions on a nonemergency basis, and laboratory and other diagnostic testing as ordered by staff or outside physician referral.

65. Immunization program. Program that plans, coordinates and conducts immunization services in the community.

66. Indigent care clinic. Health care services for uninsured and underinsured persons where care is free of charge or charged on a sliding scale. This would include "free clinics" staffed by volunteer practitioners, but could also be staffed by employees with sponsoring health care organizations subsidizing the cost of service.

67. Intermediate nursing care. Provides health–related services (skilled nursing care and social services) to residents with a variety of physical conditions or functional disabilities. These residents do not require the care provided by a hospital or skilled nursing facility, but do need supervision and support services.

68. Linguistic/translation services. Services provided by the hospital designed to make health care more accessible to non–English speaking patients and their physicians.

69. Meals on wheels. A hospital sponsored program which delivers meals to people, usually the elderly, who are unable to prepare their own meals. Low cost, nutritional meals are delivered to individuals' homes on a regular basis.

70. Medical surgical intensive care services. Provides patient care of a more intensive nature than the usual medical and surgical care, on the basis of physicians' orders and approved nursing care plans. These units are staffed with specially trained nursing personnel and contain monitoring and specialized support equipment of patients who, because of shock, trauma, or other life–threatening conditions,

require intensified, comprehensive observation and care. Includes mixed intensive care units.

71. Mobile health services. Vans and other vehicles used to deliver primary care services.

72. Neonatal intensive care. A unit that must be separate from the newborn nursery providing intensive care to all sick infants including those with the very lowest birth weights (less that 1500 grams). NICU has potential for providing mechanical ventilation, neonatal surgery, and special care for the sickest infants born in the hospital or transferred from another institution. A full–time neonatologist serves   as director of the NICU.

73. Neonatal intermediate care. A unit that must be separate from the normal newborn nursery and that provides intermediate and/or recovery care and some specialized services, including immediate resuscitation, intravenous therapy, and capacity for prolonged oxygen therapy and monitoring.

74. Neurological services. Services provided by the hospital dealing with the operative and nonoperative management of disorders of the central, peripheral, and autonomic nervous system.

75. Nutrition programs. Those services within a health care facility which are designed to provide inexpensive, nutritionally sound meals to patients.

76. Obstetrics. Levels should be designated: (1) unit provides services for uncomplicated maternity and newborn cases; (2) unit provides services for uncomplicated cases, the majority of complicated problems, and special neonatal services; and (3) unit provides services for all serious illnesses and abnormalities and is supervised by a full–time maternal/ fetal specialist.

77. Occupational health services. Includes services designed to protect the safety of employees from hazards in the work environment.

78. Oncology services. Inpatient and outpatient services for patients with cancer, including comprehensive care, support and guidance in addition to patient education and preventiion, chemotherapy, counseling, and other treatment methods.

79. Orthopedic services. Services provided for the prevention or correction of injuries or disorders of the skeletal system and associated muscles, joints, and ligaments.

80. Other special care. Provides care to patients requiring care more intensive than that provided in the acute area, yet not sufficiently intensive to require admission to an intensive care unit. Patients admitted to the area are usually transferred here from an intensive care unit once their condition has improved. These units are sometimes referred to as definitive observation, step–down, or progressive care units.

81. Outpatient surgery. Scheduled surgical services provided to patients who do not remain in the hospital overnight. The surgery may be performed in operating suites also used for inpatient surgery, specially designated surgical suites for outpatient surgery, or procedure rooms within an outpatient care facility.

82. Pain management program. A hospital wide formalized program that includes staff education for the management of chronic and acute pain based on guidelines and protocols like those developed by the agency for Health Care Policy Research, etc.

83. Inpatient palliative care unit. An inpatient palliative care ward is a physically discreet, inpatient nursing unit where the focus is palliative care. The patient care focus is on symptom relief for complex patients who may be continuing to undergo primary treatment. Care is delivered by palliative medicine specialists.

84. Palliative care program. An organized program providing specialized medical care, drugs or therapies for the management of acute or chronic pain and/or the control of symptoms adminstered by specially trained physicians and other clinicians; and supportive care services, such as counseling on advanced directives, spiritual care, and social services, to patients with advanced disease and their families.

85. Patient controlled analgesia (PCA). Patient Controlled Analgesia (PCA) is intravenously administered pain medicine under the patient's control. The patient has a button on the end of a cord than can be pushed at will, whenever more pain medicine is desired. This button will only deliver more pain medicine at pre-determined intervals, as programmed by the doctor's order.

86. **Patient education center.** Written goals and objectives for the patient and/or family related to therapeutic regimens, medical procedures, and self care.

87. **Patient representative services.** Organized hospital services providing personnel through whom patients and staff can seek solutions to institutional problems affecting the delivery of high–quality care and services.

88. **Pediatric intensive care services.** Provides care to pediatric patients that is of a more intensive nature than that usually provided to pediatric patients. The unit is staffed with specially trained personnel and contains monitoring and specialized support equipment for treatment of patients who, because of shock, trauma, or other life–threatening conditions, require intensified, comprehensive observation and care.

89. **Pediatric medical–surgical care.** Provides acute care to pediatric settings) or in a traditional setting (gymnasium) using motor learning principles.

90. **Physical rehabilitation inpatient services.** Provides care encompassing a comprehensive array of restoration services for the disabled and all support services necessary to help patients attain their maximum functional capacity.

91. **Assistive technology center.** A program providing access to specialized hardware and software with adaptations allowing individuals greater independence with mobility, dexterity, or increased communication options.

92. **Electrodiagnostic services.** Diagnostic testing services for nerve and muscle function including services such as nerve conduction studies and needle electromyography.

93. **Physical rehabilitation outpatient services.** Outpatient program providing medical, health–related, therapy, social, and/or vocational services to help disabled persons attain or retain their maximum functional capacity.

94. **Prosthetic and orthotic services.** Services providing comprehensive prosthetic and orthotic evaluation, fitting, and training.

95. **Robot-assisted walking therapy.** A form of physical therapy that uses a courts, public health nurses, welfare agencies, clergy and so forth. The purpose is to expand the mental health knowledge and competence of personnel not working in the mental health field and to promote good mental health through improved understanding, attitudes, and behavioral patterns.

96. **Simulated rehabilitation environment.** Rehabilitation focused on retraining functional skills in a contextually appropriate environment (simulated home and community settings) or in a traditional setting (gymnasium) using motor learning principles.

97. **Primary care department.** A unit or clinic within the hospital that provides primary care services (e.g. general pediatric care, general internal medicine, family practice and gynecology) through hospital–salaried medical and or nursing staff, focusing on evaluating and diagnosing medical problems and providing medical treatment on an outpatient basis.

98. **Psychiatric care.** Provides acute or long–term care to emotionally disturbed patients, including patients admitted for diagnosis and those admitted for treatment of psychiatric problems, on the basis of physicians' orders and approved nursing care plans. Long–term care may include intervention, and assistance to persons suffering acute emotional or mental distress.

99. **Psychiatric pediatric care.** The branch of medicine focused on the diagnosis, treatment, and prevention of mental, emotional, and behavioral disorders in pediatric patients.

100. **Psychiatric consultation–liaison services.** Provides organized psychiatric consultation/liaison services to nonpsychiatric hospital staff and/or department on psychological aspects of medical care that may be generic or specific to individual patients.

101. **Psychiatric education services.** Provides psychiatric educational services to community agencies and workers such as schools, police, courts, public health nurses, welfare agencies, clergy and so forth. The purpose is to expand the mental health knowledge and competence of personnel not working in the mental health field and to promote good mental health through improved understanding, attitudes, and behavioral patterns.

102. **Psychiatric emergency services.** Services or facilities available on a 24–hour basis to provide immediate unscheduled outpatient care, diagnosis, evaluation, crisis intervention, and assistance to persons suffering acute emotional or mental distress.

103. **Psychiatric geriatric services.** Provides care to emotionally disturbed elderly patients, including those admitted for diagnosis and those admitted for treatment.

104. **Psychiatric outpatient services.** Provides medical care, including diagnosis and treatment of psychiatric outpatients.

105. **Psychiatric partial hospitalization services.** Organized hospital services of intensive day/evening outpatient services of three hours or more duration, distinguished from other outpatient visits of one hour.

106. **Psychiatric residential treatment.**

107. **CT scanner.** Computed tomographic scanner for head and whole body scans.

108. **Diagnostic radioisotope facility.** The use of radioactive isotopes (Radiopharmaceutical) as tracers or indicators to detect an abnormal condition or disease.

109. **Electron beam computed tomography (EBCT).** A high tech computed tomography scan used to detect coronary artery disease by measuring coronary calcifications. This imaging procedure uses electron beams which are magnetically steered to produce a visual of the coronary artery and the images are produced faster than conventional CT scans.

110. **Full–field digital mammography (FFDM).** Combines the x–ray generators and tubes used in analog screen–film mammography (SFM) with a detector plate that converts the x–rays into a digital signal.

111. **Magnetic resonance imaging (MRI).** The use of a uniform magnetic field and radio frequencies to study tissue and structure of the body. This procedure enables the

visualization of biochemical activity of the cell in vivo without the use of ionizing radiation, radioisotopic substances, or high–frequency sound.

112. **Intraoperative magnetic resonance imaging.** An integrated surgery system which provides an MRI system in an operating room. The system allows for immediate evaluation of the degree to tumor resection while the patient is undergoing a surgical resection. Intraoperative MRI exists when a MRI (low–field or high–field) is placed in the operating theater and is used during surgical resection without moving the patient from the operating room to the diagnostic imaging suite.

113. **Magnetoencephalography (MEG).** A noninvasive neurophysiological measurement tool used to study magnetic fields generated by neuronal activity of the brain. MEG provides direct information about the dynamics of evoked and spontaneous neural activity and the location of their sources in the brain. The primary uses of MEG include assisting surgeons in localizing the source of epilepsy, sensory mapping and the study of brain function. When it is combined with structural imaging, it is known as magnetic source imaging (MSI).

114. **Multi–slice spiral computed tomography (MSCT) (<64 slice CT).** A specialized computed tomography cycles per second to visualize internal body structures.

115. **Multi–slice spiral computed tomography (64 + slice CT).** Involves the acquisition of volumetric tomographic x–ray absorption data expressed in Hounsfield units using multiple rows of detectors. 64+ systems reconstruct the equivalent of 64 or greater slices to cover the imaged volume.

116. **Positron emission tomography (PET).** A nuclear medicine imaging technology which uses radioactive (positron emitting) isotopes created in a cyclotron or generator and computers to produce composite pictures of the brain and heart at work. PET scanning produces sectional images depicting metabolic activity or blood flow rather than anatomy.

117. **Positron emission tomography/CT (PET/CT).** Provides metabolic functional information for the monitoring of chemotherapy, radiotherapy and surgical planning.

118. **Single photon emission computerized tomography (SPECT).** A nuclear medicine imaging technology that combines existing technology of gamma camera imaging with computed tomographic imaging technology to provide a more precise and clear image.

119. **Ultrasound.** The use of acoustic waves above the range of 20,000 cycles per second to visualize internal body structures.

120. **Image–guided radiation therapy (IGRT).** Automated system for image– guided radiation therapy that enables clinicians to obtain high–resolution x– ray images to pinpoint tumor sites, adjust patient positioning when necessary, and complete a treatment, all within the standard treatment time slot, allowing for more effective cancer treatments.

121. **Intensity–modulated radiation Therapy (IMRT).** A type of three–dimensional radiation therapy, which improves the targeting of treatment delivery in a way that is likely to decrease damage to normal tissues and allows varying intensities diagnosis of genetic diseases in newborns, children, and adults; the identification of future health risks; arrange for acute and long term care through affiliated institutions.

122. **Proton beam therapy.** A form of radiation therapy which administers proton beams. While producing the same biologic effects as x–ray beams, the energy distribution of protons differs from conventional x–ray beams in that they can be more precisely focused in tissue volumes in a three–dimensional pattern resulting in less surrounding tissue damage than conventional radiation therapy permitting administration of higher doses.

123. **Shaped beam radiation therapy.** A precise, non–invasive treatment that involves targeting beams of radiation that mirror the exact size and shape of a tumor at a specific area of a tumor to shrink or destroy cancerous cells. This procedure delivers a therapeutic dose of radiation that conforms precisely to the shape of the tumor, thus minimizing the risk to nearby tissues.

124. Stereotactic radiosurgery. Stereotactic radiosurgery (SRS) is a radiotherapy modality that delivers a high dosage of radiation to a discrete treatment area in as few as one treatment session. Includes gamma knife, cyberknife, etc.

125. **Retirement housing.** A facility which provides social activities to senior citizens, usually retired persons, who do not require health care but some short–term skilled nursing care may be provided. A retirement center may furnish housing and may also have acute hospital and long–term care facilities, or it may arrange for acute and long term care through affiliated institutions.

126. **Robotic surgery.** The use of mechanical guidance devices to remotely manipulate surgical instrumentation.

127. **Rural health clinic.** A clinic located in a rural, medically under-served area in the United States that has a separate reimbursement structure from the standard medical office under the Medicare and Medicaid programs.

128. **Skilled nursing care.** Provides non–acute medical and skilled nursing care services, therapy, and social services under the supervision of a licensed registered nurse on a 24–hour basis.

129. **Sleep center.** Specially equipped and staffed center for the diagnosis and treatment of sleep disorders.

130. **Social work services.** Services may include one or more of the following: Organized social work services (services that are properly directed and sufficiently staffed by qualified individuals who provide assistance and counseling to patients and their families in dealing with social, emotional, and environmental problems associated with illness or disability, often in the context of financial or discharge planning coordination.) Outpatient social work services (social work services provided in ambulatory care areas.) Emergency department social work services (social work services provided to emergency department patients by social workers dedicated to the emergency department or on call.)

131. **Sports medicine.** Provision of diagnostic screening and assessment and clinical and rehabilitation services for the prevention and treatment of sports–related injuries.

132. **Support groups.** A hospital sponsored program which allows a

group of individuals with the same or similar problems who meet periodically to share experiences, problems, and solutions, in order to support each other.

133. Swing bed services. A hospital bed that can be used to provide either acute or long–term care depending on community or patients needs. To be eligible a hospital must have a Medicare provider agreement in place, have fewer than 100 beds, be located in a rural area, not have a 24 hour nursing service waiver in effect, have not been terminated from the program in the prior two years, and meet various service conditions.

134. Teen outreach services. A program focusing on the teenager which encourages an improved health status and a healthful lifestyle including physical, emotional, mental, social, spiritual and economic health through education, exercise, nutrition and health promotion.

135. Tobacco treatment/cessation program. Organized hospital services with the purpose of ending tobacco–use habits of patients addicted to tobacco/nicotine.

136.–142. Transplant services. The branch of medicine that transfers an organ or tissue from one person to another or from one body part to another to replace a diseased structure or to restore function or to change appearance. Services could include: Bone marrow transplant program (136. Bone marrow); heart (137. Heart transplant), kidney (138. Kidney transplant), liver (139. Liver transplant) lung (140. Lung transplant), tissue (141. Tissue transplant). Please include heart/lung or other multi- transplant surgeries inn other (142. Other Transplant).

143. Transportation to health services. A long–term care support service designed to assist the mobility of the elderly. Some programs offer improved financial access by offering reduced rates and barrier–free buses or vans with ramps and lifts to assist the elderly or handicapped; others offer subsidies for public transport systems or operate mini–bus services

144. Urgent care center. A facility that provides care and treatment for problems that are not life–threatening but require attention over the short term. These units function like emergency rooms but are separate from hospitals with which they may have backup affiliation arrangements.

145. Virtual colonoscopy. Noninvasive screening procedure used to visualize, analyze and detect cancerous or potentially cancerous polyps in the colon.

146. Volunteer services department. An organized hospital department responsible for coordinating the services of volunteers working within the institution.

147. Women's center. An area set aside for coordinated education and treatment services specifically for and promoted by women as provided by this special unit. Services may or may not include obstetrics but include a range of services other than OB.

148. Wound management services. Services for patients with chronic wounds and non–healing wounds often resulting from diabetes, poor circulation, improper seating and immunocompromising conditions. The goals are to progress chronic wounds through stages of healing, reduce and eliminate infections, increase physical function to minimize complications from current wounds and prevent future chronic wounds. Wound management services are provided on an inpatient or outpatient basis, depending on the intensity of service needed.

149. Violence prevention programs for the workplace. A violence prevention program with goals and objectives for preventing workplace violence against staff and patients.

150. Violence prevention programs for the community. An organized program that attempts to make a positive impact on the type(s) of violence a community is experiencing.

For example, it can assist victims of violent crimes, e.g., rape, or incidents, e.g., bullying, to hospital or to community services to prevent further victimization or retaliation. A program that targets the underlying circumstances that contribute to violence such as poor housing, insufficient job training, and/or substance abuse through means such as direct involvement and support, education, mentoring, anger management, crisis intervention and training programs would also qualify.

151. Alcoholism-chemical dependency pediatric services. Provides diagnosis and therapeutic services to pediatric patients with alcoholism or other drug dependencies. Includes care for inpatient/ residential treatment for patients whose course of treatment involves more intensive care than provided in an outpatient setting or where patient requires supervised withdrawal.

152. Alcoholism-chemical dependency partial hospitalization services. Organized hospital services providing intensive day/evening outpatient services of three hour or more duration, distinguished from other outpatient visits of one hour.

153. Psychiatric intensive outpatient services. A prescribed course of treatment in which the patient receives outpatient care no less than three times a week (which might include more than one service/day).

154. Telehealth. A broad variety of technologies and tactics to deliver virtual medical, public health, health education delivery, and support services using telecommunications technologies. Telehealth is used more commonly as it describes the wide range of diagnosis and management, education, and other related fields of health care. This includes, but are not limited to: dentistry, counseling, physical and occupational therapy, home health, chronic disease monitoring and management, disaster management, and consumer and professional education.

Definitions of Physician Codes

1. Closed physician–hospital organization (PHO). A PHO that restricts physician membership to those practitioners who meet criteria for cost effectiveness and/or high quality.

2. Equity model. Allows established practitioners to become shareholders in a professional corporation in exchange for tangible and intangible assets of their existing practices.

3. Foundation. A corporation, organized either as a hospital affiliate or subsidiary, which purchases both the tangible and intangible assets of one or more medical group practices. Physicians remain in a separate corporate entity but sign a professional services agreement with the foundation.

4. Group practice without walls. Hospital sponsors the formation of, or provides capital to physicians to establish, a 'quasi' group to share administrative expenses while remaining independent practitioners.

5. **Independent practice association (IPA).** A legal entity that hold managed care contracts. The IPA then contracts with physicians, usually in solo practice, to provide care either on a fee–for–services or capitated basis. The purpose of an IPA is to assist solo physicians in obtaining managed care contracts.

6. **Integrated salary model.** Physicians are salaried by the hospital or another entity of a health system to provide medical services for primary care and specialty care.

7. **Management services organization (MSO).** A corporation, owned by the hospital or a physician/hospital joint venture, that provides management services to one or more medical group practices. The MSO purchases the tangible assets of the practices and leases them back as part of a full–service management agreement, under which the MSO employs all non–physician staff and provides all supplies/administrative systems for a fee.

8. **Open physician–hospital organization (PHO).** A joint venture between the hospital and all members of the medical staff who wish to participate. The PHO can act as a unified agent in managed care contracting, own a managed care plan, own and operate ambulatory care centers or ancillary services projects, or provide administrative services to physician members.

Control and Service Classifications

Control

Government, nonfederal
State
County
City
City–county
Hospital district or authority

Nongovernment not-for-profit
Church operated
Other

Investor–owned (for–profit)
Individual
Partnership
Corporation

Government, federal
Air
Force
Army
Navy

Public Health Service other than 47
Veterans Affairs

Osteopathic
Church operated Other not–for–profit
Other
Individual for–profit
Partnership for–profit
Corporation for–profit

Service

General medical and surgical
Hospital unit of an institution (prison hospital, college infirmary, etc.)
Hospital unit within a facility for persons with intellectual disabilities
Surgical
Psychiatric
Tuberculosis and other respiratory diseases
Cancer
Heart
Obstetrics and gynecology

Eye, ear, nose, and throat
Rehabilitation
Orthopedic
Chronic disease
Other specialty
Children's general
Children's hospital unit of an institution
Children's psychiatric
Children's tuberculosis and other respiratory diseases
Children's eye, ear, nose, and throat

Children's rehabilitation
Children's orthopedic
Children's chronic disease
Children's other specialty
Intellectual disabilities
Long–Term Acute Care
Alcoholism and other chemical dependency
Children's Long–Term Acute Care
Children's Cancer
Children's Heart

ALABAMA

ALABASTER—Shelby County

☐ **NOLAND HOSPITAL SHELBY (012013)**, 1000 First Street North, 3rd Floor, Zip 35007–8703; tel. 205/620–8641, (Nonreporting) **A**1 10 **S** Noland Health Services, Inc., Birmingham, AL
Primary Contact: Laura S. Wills, Administrator
Web address: www.nolandhospitals.com
Control: Other not–for–profit (including NFP Corporation) **Service:** Acute long–term care hospital

Staffed Beds: 15

✠ **SHELBY BAPTIST MEDICAL CENTER (010016)**, 1000 First Street North, Zip 35007–8703; tel. 205/620–8100, **A**1 3 10 **F**3 8 11 12 13 15 17 18 20 22 24 26 28 29 30 31 34 35 40 43 45 47 48 49 50 57 59 64 70 72 74 75 76 77 79 81 82 84 85 87 93 98 103 107 108 110 111 114 115 118 119 124 126 127 129 130 131 135 146 147 148 149 **S** TENET Healthcare Corporation, Dallas, TX
Primary Contact: Daniel Listi, Chief Executive Officer
CFO: Jennifer Pittman, Chief Financial Officer
CMO: Mark Scofield, M.D., Chief Medical Officer
CIO: Mike Nighman, Facility Coordinator Information Systems
CHR: Cindy Nicholson, Director Human Resources
CNO: Ed Price, Chief Nurse Officer
Web address: www.brookwoodbaptisthealth.com
Control: Corporation, Investor–owned (for–profit) **Service:** General medical and surgical

Staffed Beds: 231 Admissions: 11789 Census: 164 Outpatient Visits: 97910 Births: 962 Total Expense ($000): 151290 Payroll Expense ($000): 50774 Personnel: 898

ALEXANDER CITY—Tallapoosa County

☐ **RUSSELL MEDICAL (010065)**, 3316 Highway 280, Zip 35010–3369, Mailing Address: P.O. Box 939, Zip 35011–0939; tel. 256/329–7100, **A**1 3 10 19 **F**3 11 13 15 18 20 22 28 29 30 31 34 35 40 43 45 46 47 50 53 57 58 59 60 64 67 68 74 75 76 77 78 79 80 81 82 85 87 89 93 102 107 108 110 111 115 116 119 121 123 126 129 131 132 143 146 148 149
Primary Contact: Lother E. Peace III, President and Chief Executive Officer
CFO: J. Matthew Fisher, Chief Financial Officer
CMO: Michele Goldhagen, M.D., Chief Medical Officer
CIO: Donna Carter, Chief Information Officer and Security Officer
CHR: Mary Shockley, Human Resources Director
Web address: www.russellmedcenter.com
Control: Other not–for–profit (including NFP Corporation) **Service:** General medical and surgical

Staffed Beds: 69 Admissions: 2810 Census: 26 Outpatient Visits: 93401 Births: 378 Total Expense ($000): 76662 Payroll Expense ($000): 25007 Personnel: 530

ANDALUSIA—Covington County

✠ **ANDALUSIA HEALTH (010036)**, 849 South Three Notch Street, Zip 36420–5325, Mailing Address: P.O. Box 760, Zip 36420–1214; tel. 334/222–8466, (Nonreporting) **A**1 10 **S** LifePoint Health, Brentwood, TN
Primary Contact: John C. Yanes, Chief Executive Officer
CFO: Shirley M Smith, Chief Financial Officer
CIO: Matthew Perry, Director Information Systems
CHR: Brian Woods, Human Resources Director
CNO: Pam Aud, Chief Clinical Officer
Web address: www.andalusiahealth.com
Control: Corporation, Investor–owned (for–profit) **Service:** General medical and surgical

Staffed Beds: 88

ANNISTON—Calhoun County

☐ **NOLAND HOSPITAL ANNISTON (012011)**, 400 East 10th Street, 4th Fl, Zip 36207–4716; tel. 256/741–6141, (Nonreporting) **A**1 10 **S** Noland Health Services, Inc., Birmingham, AL
Primary Contact: Trina Woods, Administrator
Web address: www.nolandhealth.com
Control: Other not–for–profit (including NFP Corporation) **Service:** Acute long–term care hospital

Staffed Beds: 38

✠ **RMC ANNISTON (010078)**, 400 East Tenth Street, Zip 36207–4716, Mailing Address: P.O. Box 2208, Zip 36202–2208; tel. 256/235–5121, (Nonreporting) **A**1 2 10 **S** Regional Medical Center, Anniston, AL
Primary Contact: Louis A. Bass, Chief Executive Officer
CMO: David Zinn, M.D., Vice President Medical Affairs
CIO: Pete Furlow, Director Information Technology Services
CHR: Doug Scott, Corporate Director Human Resources
CNO: Elaine Davis, Chief Nursing Officer and Vice President Patient Services
Web address: www.rmccares.org
Control: Hospital district or authority, Government, nonfederal **Service:** General medical and surgical

Staffed Beds: 276

✠ **RMC–STRINGFELLOW MEMORIAL HOSPITAL (010038)**, 301 East 18th Street, Zip 36207–3952; tel. 256/235–8900, (Nonreporting) **A**1 10 **S** Regional Medical Center, Anniston, AL
Primary Contact: Joe Weaver, Chief Executive Officer
CIO: Peggy Henderson, Director Health Information
CHR: Tamatha Johnson, Director Human Resources
Web address: www.stringfellowmemorial.com
Control: Corporation, Investor–owned (for–profit) **Service:** General medical and surgical

Staffed Beds: 29

ASHLAND—Clay County

CLAY COUNTY HOSPITAL (010073), 83825 Highway 9, Zip 36251–7981, Mailing Address: P.O. Box 1270, Zip 36251–1270; tel. 256/354–2131, (Nonreporting) **A**10
Primary Contact: Joel W. Tate, FACHE, Chief Executive Officer
CFO: Kerry W Tomlin, Associate Administrator
CMO: David Hensleigh, Director Medical Staff
CIO: Patrick Smith, Director Information Technology
CHR: Linda T Smith, Director Human Resources
CNO: Charles Griffin, Director of Nursing
Web address: www.claycountyhospital.com
Control: County, Government, nonfederal **Service:** General medical and surgical

Staffed Beds: 129

ATHENS—Limestone County

☐ **ATHENS–LIMESTONE HOSPITAL (010079)**, 700 West Market Street, Zip 35611–2457, Mailing Address: P.O. Box 999, Zip 35612–0999; tel. 256/233–9292, **A**1 5 10 **F**3 7 8 11 13 15 18 28 29 34 35 40 43 46 48 50 51 53 54 56 57 58 59 64 68 70 73 75 76 77 79 81 82 85 86 87 89 93 98 107 108 109 110 111 114 115 118 119 129 130 131 132 143 144 146 147 148 149 **P**6 **S** Huntsville Hospital Health System, Huntsville, AL
Primary Contact: David Pryor, President
COO: Randy Comer, Chief Operating Officer
CFO: Randy Comer, Chief Financial Officer
CMO: Jon Bignault, M.D., Chief of Staff
CIO: Kim Hoback, Supervisor Information Systems
CHR: Rachel Frey, Director Human Resources
CNO: Jan Lenz, Chief Nursing Officer
Web address: www.athenslimestonehospital.com
Control: Hospital district or authority, Government, nonfederal **Service:** General medical and surgical

Staffed Beds: 71 Admissions: 3855 Census: 40 Outpatient Visits: 103716 Births: 456 Total Expense ($000): 77591 Payroll Expense ($000): 33319 Personnel: 729

NORTH ALABAMA SPECIALTY HOSPITAL (012014), 700 West Market Street, 2 South, Zip 35611–2457; tel. 256/262–6767, (Nonreporting) **A**10
Primary Contact: Gene Smith, Chief Executive Officer
Web address: www.amgnash.com
Control: Corporation, Investor–owned (for–profit) **Service:** Acute long–term care hospital

Staffed Beds: 31

Hospital, Medicare Provider Number, Address, Telephone, Approval, Facility, and Physician Codes, Health Care System

★ American Hospital Association (AHA) membership   ○ Healthcare Facilities Accreditation Program   ⇑ Center for Improvement in Healthcare Quality Accreditation
☐ The Joint Commission accreditation   ◇ DNV Healthcare Inc. accreditation   △ Commission on Accreditation of Rehabilitation Facilities (CARF) accreditation

ATMORE—Escambia County

ATMORE COMMUNITY HOSPITAL (010169), 401 Medical Park Drive, Zip 36502–3091; tel. 251/368–2500, (Nonreporting) **A**10 **S** Infirmary Health System, Mobile, AL
Primary Contact: Douglas Tanner, President
CFO: Keith Strickling, Chief Financial Officer
CHR: Linda Lowrey, Human Resources Officer
CNO: Ashley Chunn, Director of Nursing
Web address: www.ebaptisthealthcare.org/AtmoreCommunityHospital/
Control: Other not–for–profit (including NFP Corporation) **Service**: General medical and surgical

Staffed Beds: 33

BAY MINETTE—Baldwin County

NORTH BALDWIN INFIRMARY (010129), 1815 Hand Avenue, Zip 36507–4110, Mailing Address: P.O. Box 1409, Zip 36507–1409; tel. 251/937–5521, (Nonreporting) **A**10 **S** Infirmary Health System, Mobile, AL
Primary Contact: Benjamin K. Hansert, Administrator
CFO: J Patrick Murphy, Chief Financial Officer
Web address: www.mobileinfirmary.org
Control: Other not–for–profit (including NFP Corporation) **Service**: General medical and surgical

Staffed Beds: 50

BESSEMER—Jefferson County

☐ **MEDICAL WEST (010114)**, 995 Ninth Avenue SW, Zip 35022–4527; tel. 205/481–7000, (Data for 273 days) **A**1 3 10 **F**3 11 13 15 18 20 29 30 31 34 40 43 45 49 50 53 54 57 59 60 64 68 70 74 75 76 77 78 79 81 82 85 86 90 92 93 94 96 98 100 101 102 103 104 107 108 110 111 114 115 118 119 129 130 132 143 146 147 148 149 **P**6 **S** UAB Health System, Birmingham, AL
Primary Contact: Brian Keith. Pennington, President and Chief Executive Officer
COO: Sean Tinney, FACHE, Chief Operating Officer
CFO: Brandon H Slocum, Senior Vice President and Chief Financial Officer
CMO: Conrad De Los Santos, President Medical Staff
CIO: Bob Duckworth, Director Information Systems
CHR: Gannon Davis, Director Human Resources
CNO: Pamela Spencer Autrey, R.N., Ph.D., MSN, Chief Nursing Officer
Web address: www.medicalwesthospital.org
Control: Hospital district or authority, Government, nonfederal **Service**: General medical and surgical

Staffed Beds: 231 Admissions: 5264 Census: 114 Outpatient Visits: 169144 Births: 274 Total Expense ($000): 90523 Payroll Expense ($000): 36642 Personnel: 1117

BIRMINGHAM—Jefferson County

⊞ **BIRMINGHAM VETERANS AFFAIRS MEDICAL CENTER**, 700 South 19th Street, Zip 35233–1927; tel. 205/933–8101, (Nonreporting) **A**1 2 3 5 8 **S** Department of Veterans Affairs, Perry Point, MD
Primary Contact: Thomas C. Smith III, FACHE, Director
COO: Phyllis J. Smith, Associate Director
CFO: Mary S Mitchell, Chief Resource Management Services
CMO: William F Harper, M.D., Chief of Staff
CIO: Antonia Mohamed, Acting Chief Information Officer
CHR: Jacqueline Caron, Chief Human Resources
CNO: Cynthia Cleveland, Ph.D., R.N., Associate Director for Patient Care Services and Nurse Executive
Web address: www.birmingham.va.gov/
Control: Veterans Affairs, Government, federal **Service**: General medical and surgical

Staffed Beds: 151

⊞ **BROOKWOOD BAPTIST MEDICAL CENTER (010139)**, 2010 Brookwood Medical Center Drive, Zip 35209–6875; tel. 205/877–1000, **A**1 2 3 5 10 **F**3 11 12 13 15 17 18 20 22 24 26 29 30 31 34 35 38 40 43 45 46 47 48 49 50 56 57 58 59 64 70 72 74 75 76 78 79 81 82 85 86 87 90 98 100 101 102 103 104 107 108 109 110 111 114 115 116 117 118 119 120 121 123 124 126 129 130 132 135 145 146 147 148 **S** TENET Healthcare Corporation, Dallas, TX
Primary Contact: Keith Parrott FACHE, Chief Executive Officer
COO: Kathy Healy–Collier, Chief Operating Officer
CFO: Jay M. Pennisson, Chief Financial Officer
CMO: Vish Sachdev, M.D., Chief Medical Officer
CIO: Manuel Price, Director Information Systems
CHR: Ronnelle Stewart, Chief Human Resources Officer
CNO: Marye Elliott, Chief Nursing Officer
Web address: www.brookwoodbaptisthealth.com/
Control: Corporation, Investor–owned (for–profit) **Service**: General medical and surgical

Staffed Beds: 607 Admissions: 22745 Census: 361 Outpatient Visits: 108861 Births: 3322 Total Expense ($000): 358436 Payroll Expense ($000): 114251 Personnel: 2035

⊞ **CHILDREN'S OF ALABAMA (013300)**, 1600 Seventh Avenue South, Zip 35233–1785; tel. 205/638–9100, **A**1 3 5 10 **F**3 7 8 9 11 12 16 17 19 20 21 22 23 25 27 28 29 30 31 32 34 35 36 37 38 39 40 41 43 44 46 48 50 54 55 57 58 59 60 61 64 65 68 72 74 75 77 78 79 80 81 82 84 85 86 87 88 89 91 92 93 94 96 97 98 99 100 101 102 104 107 108 109 111 114 115 116 117 118 119 126 129 130 131 132 134 135 136 137 138 139 142 143 146 148 149 154
Primary Contact: Wm. Michael. Warren Jr, President and Chief Executive Officer
COO: Tom Shufflebarger, Chief Operating Officer
CFO: Dawn Walton, Chief Financial Officer
CMO: Crayton A Fargason, M.D., Medical Director
CIO: Robert Sarnecki, Interim Chief Information Officer
CHR: Douglas B Dean, Chief Human Resources Officer
CNO: Deb Wesley, MSN, Chief Nursing Officer
Web address: www.childrensal.org
Control: Other not–for–profit (including NFP Corporation) **Service**: Children's general medical and surgical

Staffed Beds: 339 Admissions: 15561 Census: 253 Outpatient Visits: 677549 Births: 0 Total Expense ($000): 693052 Payroll Expense ($000): 268843 Personnel: 4231

⊞ **ENCOMPASS HEALTH LAKESHORE REHABILITATION HOSPITAL (013025)**, 3800 Ridgeway Drive, Zip 35209–5599; tel. 205/868–2000, **A**1 10 **F**3 29 75 86 87 90 91 93 95 96 130 132 135 148 **S** Encompass Health Corporation, Birmingham, AL
Primary Contact: Michael Bartell, Chief Executive Officer
CFO: Kimberly Thrasher, Controller
CMO: Michael Rosemore, M.D., Medical Director
CHR: Julie Smith, Director Human Resources
CNO: April Cobb, Chief Nursing Officer
Web address: www.encompasshealth.com/lakeshorerehab
Control: Corporation, Investor–owned (for–profit) **Service**: Rehabilitation

Staffed Beds: 100 Admissions: 2706 Census: 87 Outpatient Visits: 11080 Births: 0 Total Expense ($000): 34960 Payroll Expense ($000): 18102 Personnel: 344

⊞ **GRANDVIEW MEDICAL CENTER (010104)**, 3690 Grandview Parkway, Zip 35243–3326; tel. 205/971–1000, **A**1 2 3 5 10 13 **F**3 11 12 13 15 17 18 20 22 24 26 28 29 30 31 34 35 40 43 45 46 47 48 49 50 51 54 57 58 59 64 70 72 74 75 76 77 78 79 81 82 84 85 90 93 96 98 99 100 101 102 103 107 108 110 111 115 119 126 129 130 131 132 135 146 147 148 149 154 **S** Community Health Systems, Inc., Franklin, TN
Primary Contact: Drew Mason, Chief Executive Officer
COO: Justin O. Bryant, Chief Operating Officer
CFO: Julie Soekoro, Chief Financial Officer
CMO: Rebecca Byrd, President Medical Staff
CIO: Tim Townes, Director Information Systems
CHR: Jeri Wink, Director Human Resources
CNO: James Epperson, Interim Chief Nursing Officer
Web address: www.grandviewhealth.com
Control: Corporation, Investor–owned (for–profit) **Service**: General medical and surgical

Staffed Beds: 379 Admissions: 19613 Census: 279 Outpatient Visits: 281711 Births: 1226 Total Expense ($000): 369682 Payroll Expense ($000): 124507 Personnel: 1961

☐ **HILL CREST BEHAVIORAL HEALTH SERVICES (014000)**, 6869 Fifth Avenue South, Zip 35212–1866; tel. 205/833–9000, (Nonreporting) **A**1 10 **S** Universal Health Services, Inc., King of Prussia, PA
Primary Contact: Steve McCabe, Chief Executive Officer
CFO: Mark Teske, Chief Financial Officer
Web address: www.hillcrestbhs.com
Control: Corporation, Investor–owned (for–profit) **Service**: Psychiatric

Staffed Beds: 94

☐ **NOLAND HOSPITAL BIRMINGHAM (012009)**, 50 Medical Park East Drive, 8th Floor, Zip 35235; tel. 205/808–5100, (Nonreporting) **A**1 10 **S** Noland Health Services, Inc., Birmingham, AL
Primary Contact: Laura S. Wills, Administrator
COO: Sharon Engle, Director Clinical Services
CMO: Mark Middlebrooks, M.D., Medical Director
CHR: Ashley Clark, Coordinator Human Resources
CNO: Rachel Chapman, Nurse Manager
Web address: www.nolandhealth.com
Control: Other not–for–profit (including NFP Corporation) **Service**: Acute long–term care hospital

Staffed Beds: 45

✠ **PRINCETON BAPTIST MEDICAL CENTER (010103)**, 701 Princeton Avenue SW, Zip 35211–1303; tel. 205/783–3000, **A**1 2 3 5 10 **F**3 11 12 13 15 17 18 20 22 24 26 28 29 30 31 34 35 40 43 45 46 47 48 49 50 55 56 57 58 59 64 67 70 72 74 75 76 78 79 81 82 83 84 85 87 91 92 93 94 98 103 107 108 110 111 114 115 117 118 119 120 121 123 124 126 129 130 131 132 146 147 148 149 154 **S** TENET Healthcare Corporation, Dallas, TX
Primary Contact: Michael Neuendorf, Chief Executive Officer
COO: Sarah Nunnelly, Chief Operating Officer
CFO: Amanda Dyle, Chief Financial Officer
CMO: Alan Craig, M.D., Chief Medical Officer
CHR: Jason Hatter, Chief Human Resource Officer
CNO: Paula Davenport, Chief Nursing Officer
Web address: www.bhsala.com
Control: Partnership, Investor–owned (for–profit) **Service:** General medical and surgical

Staffed Beds: 315 Admissions: 14251 Census: 222 Outpatient Visits: 108789 **Births: 364 Total Expense ($000): 235641 Payroll Expense ($000): 73392 Personnel: 1463**

✠ **SELECT SPECIALTY HOSPITAL–BIRMINGHAM (012008)**, 2010 Brookwood Medical Center Drive, 3rd Floor, Zip 35209–6804; tel. 205/599–4600, (Nonreporting) **A**1 10 **S** Select Medical Corporation, Mechanicsburg, PA
Primary Contact: Clifton Quinn, Chief Executive Officer
CMO: Allan Goldstein, M.D., Medical Director and Chief of Staff
Web address: www.birmingham.selectspecialtyhospitals.com
Control: Corporation, Investor–owned (for–profit) **Service:** Acute long–term care hospital

Staffed Beds: 38

✠ **ST. VINCENT'S BIRMINGHAM (010056)**, 810 St Vincent's Drive, Zip 35205–1695, Mailing Address: P.O. Box 12407, Zip 35202–2407; tel. 205/939–7000, **A**1 2 3 5 10 **F**3 11 13 15 17 18 20 22 24 26 28 29 30 31 34 35 37 40 43 45 53 57 58 59 60 62 68 70 72 74 76 77 78 79 81 82 84 85 86 87 91 93 94 107 110 111 114 119 120 121 123 124 126 131 132 135 146 147 149 **S** Ascension Healthcare, Saint Louis, MO
Primary Contact: Evan Ray, FACHE, Chief Executive Officer
COO: Andy Davis, Chief Operating Officer
CFO: Wilma Newton, Executive Vice President and Chief Financial Officer
CMO: Gregory L James, D.O., Chief Medical Officer
CIO: Timothy Stettheimer, Vice President and Chief Information Officer
CHR: Michelle Galipeau, Director Human Resources
Web address: www.stvhs.com
Control: Other not–for–profit (including NFP Corporation) **Service:** General medical and surgical

Staffed Beds: 409 Admissions: 20207 Census: 261 Outpatient Visits: 189794 **Births: 3246 Total Expense ($000): 402666 Payroll Expense ($000): 103662 Personnel: 1699**

✠ **ST. VINCENT'S EAST (010011)**, 50 Medical Park East Drive, Zip 35235–9987; tel. 205/838–3000, **A**1 2 3 5 10 **F**3 11 12 13 15 17 18 20 22 24 26 28 29 30 31 35 40 43 44 45 46 47 49 50 51 53 57 59 70 72 74 76 77 78 79 81 85 86 87 90 93 98 100 102 103 107 108 111 114 118 119 120 121 123 124 129 130 132 135 146 147 149 **S** Ascension Healthcare, Saint Louis, MO
Primary Contact: Andrew Gnann, Vice President Operations
COO: Andrew Gnann, Vice President Operations
CFO: Jan DiCesare, Vice President Financial Operations
CMO: Frank Malensek, M.D., Chief Medical Officer
CIO: Beverly Golightly, Director Information Technology
CHR: Carol Maietta, Vice President Human Resources and Chief Learning Officer
CNO: Amy Shelton, Chief Nursing Officer
Web address: www.stvhs.com
Control: Other not–for–profit (including NFP Corporation) **Service:** General medical and surgical

Staffed Beds: 362 Admissions: 16091 Census: 259 Outpatient Visits: 130907 **Births: 918 Total Expense ($000): 213977 Payroll Expense ($000): 67676 Personnel: 1107**

UAB HIGHLANDS See University of Alabama Hospital, Birmingham

✠ **UNIVERSITY OF ALABAMA HOSPITAL (010033)**, 619 19th Street South, Zip 35249–1900; tel. 205/934–4011, (Includes UAB HIGHLANDS, 1201 11th Avenue South, Birmingham, AL, Zip 35205–5299; tel. 205/930–7000; Anthony Patterson, FACHE, Chief Operating Officer) **A**1 2 3 5 8 10 **F**1 3 4 5 7 8 9 11 12 13 15 16 17 18 20 22 24 26 27 28 29 30 31 33 34 35 37 38 39 40 43 44 45 46 47 48 49 50 52 53 54 55 56 57 58 59 60 61 62 64 65 66 67 68 70 71 72 73 74 75 76 77 78 79 80 81 82 83 84 85 86 87 88 89 90 91 92 93 94 95 96 97 98 100 101 102 103 104 107 108 110 111 113 114 115 116 117 118 119 120 121 123 124 126 128 129 130 131 132 135 136 137 138 139 140 141 142 143 144 145 146 147 148 149 152 154 **P**3 **S** UAB Health System, Birmingham, AL
Primary Contact: Reid F. Jones, Chief Executive Officer
CMO: Loring Rue, M.D., Senior Vice President, Quality Patient Safety and Clinical Effectiveness
CIO: Joan Hicks, Chief Information Officer
CHR: Alesia Jones, Chief Human Resources Officer
CNO: Terri Lyn Poe, Interim Chief Nursing Officer
Web address: www.uabmedicine.org
Control: State, Government, nonfederal **Service:** General medical and surgical

Staffed Beds: 1191 Admissions: 50532 Census: 975 Outpatient Visits: 723185 **Births: 4476 Total Expense ($000): 1589583 Payroll Expense ($000): 579954 Personnel: 9193**

VETERANS AFFAIRS MEDICAL CENTER See Birmingham Veterans Affairs Medical Center, Perry Point

BOAZ—Marshall County

☐ **MARSHALL MEDICAL CENTER SOUTH (010005)**, US Highway 431 North, Zip 35957–0999, Mailing Address: P.O. Box 758, Zip 35957–0758; tel. 256/593–8310, **A**1 10 19 **F**3 7 8 9 11 12 13 15 18 20 22 26 28 29 31 32 34 35 37 40 43 45 46 50 51 53 54 57 59 64 68 70 74 75 76 78 79 81 84 85 86 87 89 92 93 100 107 108 110 111 114 115 117 119 121 123 129 130 131 132 135 141 146 147 148 149 154 **P**6 **S** Marshall Health System, Guntersville, AL
Primary Contact: John D. Anderson, FACHE, Administrator
CFO: Kathy Nelson, Chief Financial Officer
Web address: www.mmcenters.com//index.php/facilities/marshall_south
Control: Hospital district or authority, Government, nonfederal **Service:** General medical and surgical

Staffed Beds: 114 Admissions: 4695 Census: 55 Outpatient Visits: 322201 **Births: 681 Total Expense ($000): 99304 Payroll Expense ($000): 36806 Personnel: 677**

BREWTON—Escambia County

☐ **D. W. MCMILLAN MEMORIAL HOSPITAL (010099)**, 1301 Belleville Avenue, Zip 36426–1306, Mailing Address: P.O. Box 908, Zip 36427–0908; tel. 251/867–8061, **A**1 10 **F**3 7 11 15 29 30 31 34 35 40 43 45 57 59 62 64 70 75 76 78 81 85 86 89 93 107 108 111 114 119 127 129 130 131 132 135 143 144 146 149 154 **P**6
Primary Contact: Christopher B. Griffin, Chief Executive Officer
CFO: Rick Owens, Chief Financial Officer
CIO: Ian Vickery, Director Information Technology
CHR: Autherine Davis, Director Human Resources
CNO: Bob Ellis, Director of Nursing
Web address: www.dwmmh.org
Control: Hospital district or authority, Government, nonfederal **Service:** General medical and surgical

Staffed Beds: 49 Admissions: 1490 Census: 14 Outpatient Visits: 56601 **Births: 256 Total Expense ($000): 25117 Payroll Expense ($000): 10097 Personnel: 227**

BUTLER—Choctaw County

CHOCTAW GENERAL HOSPITAL (011304), 401 Vanity Fair Avenue, Zip 36904–3032; tel. 205/459–9100, (Nonreporting) **A**10 18 **S** Rush Health Systems, Meridian, MS
Primary Contact: J W. Cowan, Administrator
Web address: www.choctawgeneral.com/cgh/
Control: Corporation, Investor–owned (for–profit) **Service:** General medical and surgical

Staffed Beds: 25

Hospital, Medicare Provider Number, Address, Telephone, Approval, Facility, and Physician Codes, Health Care System

★ American Hospital Association (AHA) membership
☐ The Joint Commission accreditation
○ Healthcare Facilities Accreditation Program
◇ DNV Healthcare Inc. accreditation
⇑ Center for Improvement in Healthcare Quality Accreditation
△ Commission on Accreditation of Rehabilitation Facilities (CARF) accreditation

CARROLLTON—Pickens County

PICKENS COUNTY MEDICAL CENTER (010109), 241 Robert K Wilson Drive, Zip 35447, Mailing Address: P.O. Box 478, Zip 35447–0478; tel. 205/367–8111, (Nonreporting) **A**10 20
Primary Contact: John O'Neil, Chief Executive Officer
CFO: Janice Winters, Controller
CMO: William R Brooke, M.D., President Medical Staff
CHR: Dottie D Wilson, Director Human Resources
Web address: www.pcmc.care/
Control: County, Government, nonfederal **Service**: General medical and surgical

Staffed Beds: 52

CENTRE—Cherokee County

✠ **FLOYD CHEROKEE MEDICAL CENTER (010022)**, 400 Northwood Drive, Zip 35960–1023; tel. 256/927–5531, (Nonreporting) **A**1 10 **S** Floyd Healthcare Management, Rome, GA
Primary Contact: Brandon Reece, Chief Executive Officer
CFO: Zac Allen, CPA, Chief Financial Officer
CHR: Marlene Benefield, Director Human Resources
Web address: www.cherokeemedicalcenter.com
Control: Corporation, Investor–owned (for–profit) **Service**: General medical and surgical

Staffed Beds: 45

CENTREVILLE—Bibb County

BIBB MEDICAL CENTER (010058), 208 Pierson Avenue, Zip 35042–2918; tel. 205/926–4881, (Total facility includes 131 beds in nursing home–type unit) **A**3 10 13 **F**3 11 13 15 29 31 34 35 40 45 50 53 56 57 59 64 66 75 76 77 80 81 86 87 93 97 107 114 119 125 127 128 130 133 135 143 144 146 148 149 150 **P**6
Primary Contact: Joseph Marchant, Administrator
CFO: Heather Desmond, Chief Financial Officer
CMO: John Meigs, M.D., Jr. Chief of Staff
CHR: Karen Daniel, Director Human Resources
Web address: www.bibbmedicalcenter.com
Control: Hospital district or authority, Government, nonfederal **Service**: General medical and surgical

Staffed Beds: 180 Admissions: 999 Census: 131 Outpatient Visits: 53345 Births: 59 Total Expense ($000): 18465 Payroll Expense ($000): 10003 Personnel: 237

CHATOM—Washington County

★ **WASHINGTON COUNTY HOSPITAL (011300)**, 14600 St Stephens Avenue, Zip 36518–9998, Mailing Address: P.O. Box 1299, Zip 36518–1299; tel. 251/847–2223, (Nonreporting) **A**10 18
Primary Contact: Teresa G. Grimes, Chief Executive Officer
CFO: Alyson Overstreet, Chief Financial Officer
CMO: Steve Donald, M.D., Chief of Staff
CIO: Brady Wright, Information Technology Network Administrator
CHR: Linda Randolph, Director Personnel Services
CNO: Michelle Alford, R.N., MSN, Director of Nursing
Web address: www.wchnh.org
Control: County, Government, nonfederal **Service**: General medical and surgical

Staffed Beds: 25

CLANTON—Chilton County

★ **ST. VINCENT'S CHILTON HOSPITAL (010173)**, 2030 Lay Dam Road, Zip 35045; tel. 205/258–4400, (Data for 273 days) **A**10 **F**3 11 15 29 30 35 40 43 45 46 50 59 60 64 68 70 79 81 82 85 87 93 107 108 110 111 119 130 135 146 148 149 **S** Ascension Healthcare, Saint Louis, MO
Primary Contact: Suzannah Campbell, Administrator
Web address: www.stvhs.com/chilton/
Control: Other not–for–profit (including NFP Corporation) **Service**: General medical and surgical

Staffed Beds: 36 Admissions: 737 Census: 10 Outpatient Visits: 20827 Births: 0 Total Expense ($000): 20569 Payroll Expense ($000): 6400 Personnel: 124

CULLMAN—Cullman County

☐ **CULLMAN REGIONAL MEDICAL CENTER (010035)**, 1912 Alabama Highway 157, Zip 35055, Mailing Address: P.O. Box 1108, Zip 35056–1108; tel. 256/737–2000, **A**1 3 10 **F**3 7 12 13 15 18 20 22 26 28 29 30 34 35 37 40 41 43 45 46 49 50 51 53 57 59 62 63 68 70 71 74 75 76 79 81 82 84 85 86 87 89 93 97 107 108 110 111 114 118 119 120 129 130 131 132 133 134 135 146 147 148 149 154
Primary Contact: James Clements, Chief Executive Officer
CFO: Nesha Donaldson, Chief Financial Officer
CMO: William E. Smith, M.D., Chief of Staff
CIO: Nancy Zavatchen, Director Information Technology
CHR: Toni Geddings, Director Human Resources
CNO: Cheryl Bailey, R.N., Chief Nursing Officer Vice President Patient Care Services
Web address: www.crmchospital.com
Control: Other not–for–profit (including NFP Corporation) **Service**: General medical and surgical

Staffed Beds: 115 Admissions: 7810 Census: 79 Outpatient Visits: 96452 Births: 599 Total Expense ($000): 103635 Payroll Expense ($000): 41558 Personnel: 939

DADEVILLE—Tallapoosa County

LAKE MARTIN COMMUNITY HOSPITAL (010052), 201 Mariarden Road, Zip 36853–6251, Mailing Address: P.O. Box 629, Zip 36853–0629; tel. 256/825–7821, (Nonreporting) **A**10
Primary Contact: Michael D. Bruce, Chief Executive Officer
CHR: Karen Treadwell, Director Human Resources
Web address: www.lakemartincommunityhospital.com
Control: Partnership, Investor–owned (for–profit) **Service**: General medical and surgical

Staffed Beds: 25

DAPHNE—Baldwin County

✠ **EASTPOINTE HOSPITAL (014017)**, 7400 Roper Lane, Zip 36526–5274; tel. 251/378–6500, **A**1 10 **F**29 98 106 130 143 **S** AltaPointe Health Systems, Mobile, AL
Primary Contact: Philip L. Cusa, Hospital Director
CFO: Kevin Markham, Chief Financial Officer
CMO: Sandra K Parker, M.D., Chief Medical Officer
CIO: Steve Dolan, Chief Information Officer
CHR: Alicia Donoghue, Director Human Resources
Web address: www.altapointe.org/eastpointe.php
Control: Other not–for–profit (including NFP Corporation) **Service**: Psychiatric

Staffed Beds: 50 Admissions: 1418 Census: 43 Outpatient Visits: 0 Births: 0 Total Expense ($000): 10354 Payroll Expense ($000): 6417 Personnel: 170

DECATUR—Morgan County

☐ **DECATUR MORGAN HOSPITAL (010085)**, 1201 Seventh Street SE, Zip 35601–3303, Mailing Address: P.O. Box 2239, Zip 35609–2239; tel. 256/341–2000, (Includes DECATUR MORGAN HOSPITAL PARKWAY CAMPUS, 1874 Beltline Road SW, Decatur, AL, Zip 35601–5509, Mailing Address: P.O. Box 2239, Zip 35609–2239, tel. 256/350–2211; DECATUR MORGAN HOSPITAL–WEST, 2205 Beltline Road SW, Decatur, AL, Zip 35601–3687, Mailing Address: P.O. Box 2240, Zip 35609–2240, tel. 256/306–4000) (Nonreporting) **A**1 5 10 **S** Huntsville Hospital Health System, Huntsville, AL
Primary Contact: Nathaniel Richardson Jr, President
CFO: Kim Shrewsbury, Vice President and Chief Financial Officer
CMO: Allen J Schmidt, M.D., Medical Staff
CIO: Mark Megehee, Vice President and Chief Information Officer
CNO: Anita Walden, Vice President and Chief Nursing Officer
Web address: www.decaturgeneral.org
Control: Hospital district or authority, Government, nonfederal **Service**: General medical and surgical

Staffed Beds: 127

PARKWAY MEDICAL CENTER See Decatur Morgan Hospital Parkway Campus

DEMOPOLIS—Marengo County

BRYAN W. WHITFIELD MEMORIAL HOSPITAL (010112), 105 US Highway 80 East, Zip 36732–3616, Mailing Address: P.O. Box 890, Zip 36732–0890; tel. 334/289–4000, (Nonreporting) **A**3 10 20 **S** UAB Health System, Birmingham, AL
Primary Contact: Douglas L. Brewer, Chief Executive Officer
COO: Dereck Morrison, Assistant Administrator
CFO: Doug A. Brooker, Chief Financial Officer
CMO: John G. Kahler, M.D., Radiologist
Web address: www.bwwmh.com
Control: Hospital district or authority, Government, nonfederal **Service**: General medical and surgical

Staffed Beds: 82

DOTHAN—Houston County

✠ **ENCOMPASS HEALTH REHABILITATION HOSPITAL OF DOTHAN (013030)**, 1736 East Main Street, Zip 36301–3040, Mailing Address: P.O. Box 6708, Zip 36302–6708; tel. 334/712–6333, (Nonreporting) **A**1 10 **S** Encompass Health Corporation, Birmingham, AL
Primary Contact: Margaret A. Futch, Chief Executive Officer
CFO: Heath Watson, Controller
CHR: Lydia Christion, Director Human Resources
Web address: www.encompasshealth.com/dothanrehab
Control: Corporation, Investor–owned (for–profit) **Service**: Rehabilitation

Staffed Beds: 51

✠ **FLOWERS HOSPITAL (010055)**, 4370 West Main Street, Zip 36305–4000, Mailing Address: P.O. Box 6907, Zip 36302–6907; tel. 334/793–5000, **A**1 2 3 10 19 **F**3 4 12 13 15 17 18 19 20 22 24 26 28 29 30 31 34 35 40 43 46 48 49 50 51 56 57 59 60 61 64 67 68 70 72 74 75 76 77 78 79 81 82 85 86 87 89 90 92 97 98 100 107 108 110 111 114 115 116 117 118 119 126 128 129 130 131 132 134 135 146 147 148 154 **S** Community Health Systems, Inc., Franklin, TN
Primary Contact: Heath Phillips, Chief Executive Officer
CFO: Talana Bell, Chief Financial Officer
CIO: Matthew Garrett, Director Information Systems
CHR: Jennifer Odom, Interim Director Human Resources
CNO: Dan L Cumbie, Chief Nursing Officer
COO: Matthew H. Blevins, Chief Operating Officer
Web address: www.flowershospital.com
Control: Corporation, Investor–owned (for–profit) **Service**: General medical and surgical

Staffed Beds: 147 **Admissions:** 11782 **Census:** 138 **Outpatient Visits:** 223078 **Births:** 1309 **Total Expense ($000):** 185027 **Payroll Expense ($000):** 54305 **Personnel:** 1280

☐ **LAUREL OAKS BEHAVIORAL HEALTH CENTER (014013)**, 700 East Cottonwood Road, Zip 36301–3644; tel. 334/794–7373, **A**1 10 **F**29 98 99 106 **S** Universal Health Services, Inc., King of Prussia, PA
Primary Contact: Derek Johnson, Chief Executive Officer
CMO: Nelson Handol, M.D., Medical Director
CHR: Lorrie Evans, Director Human Resources
Web address: www.laureloaksbhc.com
Control: Corporation, Investor–owned (for–profit) **Service**: Children's hospital psychiatric

Staffed Beds: 38 **Admissions:** 891 **Census:** 36 **Outpatient Visits:** 0 **Births:** 0 **Total Expense ($000):** 12952 **Payroll Expense ($000):** 8040 **Personnel:** 233

☐ **NOLAND HOSPITAL DOTHAN (012010)**, 1108 Ross Clark Circle, 4th Floor, Zip 36301–3022; tel. 334/699–4300, (Nonreporting) **A**1 10 **S** Noland Health Services, Inc., Birmingham, AL
Primary Contact: Kaye Burk, Administrator
Web address: www.nolandhealth.com
Control: Other not–for–profit (including NFP Corporation) **Service**: Acute long–term care hospital

Staffed Beds: 38

✠ ⇧ **SOUTHEAST ALABAMA MEDICAL CENTER (010001)**, 1108 Ross Clark Circle, Zip 36301–3024, Mailing Address: P.O. Box 6987, Zip 36302–6987; tel. 334/793–8111, (Nonreporting) **A**1 2 3 10 13 21
Primary Contact: Richard O. Sutton, FACHE, Chief Executive Officer
COO: Charles C Brannen, Senior Vice President and Chief Operating Officer
CFO: Derek Miller, Senior Vice President and Chief Financial Officer
CMO: Charles Harkness, D.O., Vice President Medical Affairs
CIO: Eric Allen Daffron, Division Director, Information Systems
CHR: Tony Welch, Vice President Human Resources
CNO: Diane Buntyn, MSN, R.N., Vice President Patient Care Services
Web address: www.samc.com
Control: Hospital district or authority, Government, nonfederal **Service**: General medical and surgical

Staffed Beds: 420

ENTERPRISE—Coffee County

✠ **MEDICAL CENTER ENTERPRISE (010049)**, 400 North Edwards Street, Zip 36330–2510; tel. 334/347–0584, (Nonreporting) **A**1 10 **S** Community Health Systems, Inc., Franklin, TN
Primary Contact: Suzanne Woods, Chief Executive Officer
CFO: Greg McGilvray, Chief Financial Officer
CMO: Rick Harrelson, M.D., President Medical Staff
CIO: Stephen Smothers, Director Information Systems
CHR: Toni Kaminski, Director Human Resources
CNO: Bobby Phillips, Chief Nursing Officer
Web address: www.mcehospital.com
Control: Corporation, Investor–owned (for–profit) **Service**: General medical and surgical

Staffed Beds: 117

EUFAULA—Barbour County

MEDICAL CENTER BARBOUR (010069), 820 West Washington Street, Zip 36027–1899; tel. 334/688–7000, (Nonreporting) **A**10 20
Primary Contact: Christy Moore, Interim Chief Executive Officer
CFO: Debbie Norton, Chief Financial Officer
CHR: Cindy Griffin, Director Human Resources
CNO: Christy Moore, Chief Nursing Officer
Web address: www.medctrbarbour.org
Control: Hospital district or authority, Government, nonfederal **Service**: General medical and surgical

Staffed Beds: 47

EUTAW—Greene County

★ **GREENE COUNTY HEALTH SYSTEM (010051)**, 509 Wilson Avenue, Zip 35462–1099; tel. 205/372–3388, (Total facility includes 72 beds in nursing home–type unit) **A**10 **F**11 15 29 34 40 54 56 59 64 65 77 86 87 90 93 97 107 110 119 127 128 130 133 143 146
Primary Contact: Marcia Pugh, Chief Executive Officer
Web address: www.gcheutaw.com
Control: County, Government, nonfederal **Service**: General medical and surgical

Staffed Beds: 92 **Admissions:** 255 **Census:** 55 **Outpatient Visits:** 3300 **Births:** 0 **Personnel:** 111

EVERGREEN—Conecuh County

EVERGREEN MEDICAL CENTER (010148), 101 Crestview Avenue, Zip 36401–3333, Mailing Address: P.O. Box 706, Zip 36401–0706; tel. 251/578–2480, (Nonreporting) **A**10 **S** Gilliard Health Services, Montgomery, AL
Primary Contact: Tom McLendon, Administrator
CFO: Sharon Jones, Chief Financial Officer
CMO: William Farmer, M.D., Chief of Staff
CHR: Tracey Rhodes, Coordinator Human Resources
CNO: Angie Hendrix, Director of Nursing
Web address: www.evergreenmedical.org
Control: Partnership, Investor–owned (for–profit) **Service**: General medical and surgical

Staffed Beds: 39

FAIRHOPE—Baldwin County

☐ **THOMAS HOSPITAL (010100)**, 750 Morphy Avenue, Zip 36532–1812, Mailing Address: P.O. Box 929, Zip 36533–0929; tel. 251/928–2375, (Nonreporting) **A**1 3 10 19 **S** Infirmary Health System, Mobile, AL
Primary Contact: Ormand P. Thompson, President
COO: Douglas Garner, Vice President
CMO: Michael McBrearty, M.D., Vice President Medical Affairs
CNO: Julie Rowell, R.N., Chief Nursing Officer
Web address: www.thomashospital.com
Control: Other not–for–profit (including NFP Corporation) **Service**: General medical and surgical

Staffed Beds: 136

Hospital, Medicare Provider Number, Address, Telephone, Approval, Facility, and Physician Codes, Health Care System

★ American Hospital Association (AHA) membership
☐ The Joint Commission accreditation
◯ Healthcare Facilities Accreditation Program
◇ DNV Healthcare Inc. accreditation
⇧ Center for Improvement in Healthcare Quality Accreditation
△ Commission on Accreditation of Rehabilitation Facilities (CARF) accreditation

FAYETTE—Fayette County

☐ **FAYETTE MEDICAL CENTER (010045)**, 1653 Temple Avenue North,
Zip 35555–1314, Mailing Address: P O Drawer 710, Zip 35555–0710;
tel. 205/932–5966, (Total facility includes 122 beds in nursing home–type unit) **A**1
10 **F**11 15 28 29 30 40 70 81 107 110 111 114 119 127 128 130 133 146 **S**
DCH Health System, Tuscaloosa, AL
Primary Contact: Donald J. Jones, FACHE, Administrator
CFO: Jeff Huff, Assistant Administrator Finance
CHR: Felicia Solomon–Owens, Director Human Resources
Web address: www.dchsystem.com
Control: Hospital district or authority, Government, nonfederal **Service**: General
medical and surgical

Staffed Beds: 167	Admissions: 1002	Census: 123	Births: 0	Total Expense
($000): 25881	Payroll Expense ($000): 11177	Personnel: 272		

FLORENCE—Lauderdale County

☐ **ELIZA COFFEE MEMORIAL HOSPITAL (010006)**, 205 Marengo Street,
Zip 35630–6033, Mailing Address: P.O. Box 818, Zip 35631–0818;
tel. 256/768–9191, (Nonreporting) **A**1 10 **S** RCCH HealthCare Partners,
Brentwood, TN
Primary Contact: Russell Pigg, Chief Executive Officer
COO: Mike Howard, Chief Operating Officer
CFO: Steve E. Hobbs, Chief Financial Officer
CMO: Oliver Matthews, M.D., Chief Medical Officer
CIO: Raul Velez, Information Technology Director
CHR: Cheryl Lee, Human Resources Director
CNO: Gilbert Glenn Humbert Jr Interim Chief Nursing Officer
Web address: www.chgroup.org
Control: Hospital district or authority, Government, nonfederal **Service**: General
medical and surgical

Staffed Beds: 278

FOLEY—Baldwin County

✠ **SOUTH BALDWIN REGIONAL MEDICAL CENTER (010083)**, 1613 North
McKenzie Street, Zip 36535–2299; tel. 251/949–3400, (Nonreporting) **A**1 3 10
19 **S** Community Health Systems, Inc., Franklin, TN
Primary Contact: Daniel McKinney, Chief Executive Officer
CFO: Brad Hardcastle, Chief Financial Officer
CMO: Lee Eslava, Chief Medical Officer
CHR: Pamela J Brunson, Director Human Resources
CNO: Margaret Roley, Chief Nursing Officer
Web address: www.southbaldwinrmc.com
Control: Corporation, Investor–owned (for–profit) **Service**: General medical and
surgical

Staffed Beds: 112

FORT PAYNE—Dekalb County

✠ **DEKALB REGIONAL MEDICAL CENTER (010012)**, 200 Medical Center
Drive, Zip 35968–3458, Mailing Address: P.O. Box 680778, Zip 35968–1608;
tel. 256/845–3150, (Nonreporting) **A**1 10 20 **S** Quorum Health, Brentwood, TN
Primary Contact: Patrick Trammell, Chief Executive Officer
CFO: Chris Benson, Chief Financial Officer
CMO: Anthony Sims, M.D., Chief of Staff
CIO: Joseph Helms, Director Information Systems
CHR: Diane McMichen, Director Human Resources
CNO: Marquita Bailey, Chief Nursing Officer
Web address: www.dekalbregional.com
Control: Corporation, Investor–owned (for–profit) **Service**: General medical and
surgical

Staffed Beds: 115

GADSDEN—Etowah County

✠ **ENCOMPASS HEALTH REHABILITATION HOSPITAL OF GADSDEN (013032)**,
801 Goodyear Avenue, Zip 35903–1133; tel. 256/439–5000, **A**1 10 **F**28 29 30
90 91 94 95 96 148 **S** Encompass Health Corporation, Birmingham, AL
Primary Contact: Kayla Feazell, Chief Executive Officer
COO: Kayla Feazell, Chief Executive Officer
CFO: Lori Norman, Chief Financial Officer
CMO: Vladimir Slutsker, Medical Director
CIO: Lori Norman, Chief Financial Officer
CHR: Rhonda Young, Human Resource Director
CNO: Barry Eads, Chief Nursing Officer
Web address: www.encompasshealth.com/gadsdenrehab
Control: Corporation, Investor–owned (for–profit) **Service**: Rehabilitation

Staffed Beds: 44	Admissions: 1150	Census: 39	Outpatient Visits: 0
Births: 0	Total Expense ($000): 15125	Payroll Expense ($000): 7796	
Personnel: 135			

✠ **GADSDEN REGIONAL MEDICAL CENTER (010040)**, 1007 Goodyear Avenue,
Zip 35903–1195; tel. 256/494–4000, **A**1 2 10 **F**3 13 15 18 20 22 24 29 30 31
34 35 40 43 45 49 50 56 57 59 64 68 70 74 77 78 79 80 81 85 93 98 102
103 107 108 110 111 114 115 119 120 121 124 126 129 130 131 146 147
148 149 **S** Community Health Systems, Inc., Franklin, TN
Primary Contact: Corey Ewing, Chief Executive Officer
COO: Josh Hester, Chief Operating Officer
CFO: Michael Cotton, Chief Financial Officer
CMO: Arthur Boykin, M.D., Chief of Staff
CIO: Glenn Phillips, Director Information Systems
CHR: Gale H Sanders, Director
CNO: Martha Seahorn, Chief Nursing Officer
Web address: www.gadsdenregional.com
Control: Corporation, Investor–owned (for–profit) **Service**: General medical and
surgical

Staffed Beds: 279	Admissions: 13726	Census: 187	Outpatient Visits:
80052	Births: 901	Total Expense ($000): 182758	Payroll Expense
($000): 57184	Personnel: 985		

☐ **MOUNTAIN VIEW HOSPITAL (014006)**, 3001 Scenic Highway,
Zip 35904–3047, Mailing Address: P.O. Box 8406, Zip 35902–8406;
tel. 256/546–9265, (Nonreporting) **A**1 10
Primary Contact: G Michael. Shehi, M.D., Chief Executive Officer
COO: Sara Romano, R.N., Vice President
CFO: Mary Jensen, Controller
CMO: G Michael Shehi, M.D., Medical Director
CHR: Dave Jensen, Director Human Resources, Performance Improvement and
Risk Management
Web address: www.mtnviewhospital.com
Control: Corporation, Investor–owned (for–profit) **Service**: Psychiatric

Staffed Beds: 68

✠ **RIVERVIEW REGIONAL MEDICAL CENTER (010046)**, 600 South Third Street,
Zip 35901–5399; tel. 256/543–5200, (Nonreporting) **A**1 10 **S** Prime Healthcare,
Ontario, CA
Primary Contact: John Langlois, Chief Executive Officer
CIO: Jay Terrell, Manager Management Information Systems
CHR: Leslie Morton, Manager Human Resources
CNO: Tammy Harlow, Chief Nurse Executive
Web address: www.riverviewregional.com
Control: Corporation, Investor–owned (for–profit) **Service**: General medical and
surgical

Staffed Beds: 280

GENEVA—Geneva County

WIREGRASS MEDICAL CENTER (010062), 1200 West Maple Avenue,
Zip 36340–1694; tel. 334/684–3655, (Total facility includes 96 beds in nursing
home–type unit) **A**10 **F**1 3 4 11 15 17 18 29 30 40 41 43 45 47 48 50 59 64
65 70 81 90 98 103 107 108 110 114 119 128 130 **P**5
Primary Contact: Jeffrey M. Brannon, Chief Executive Officer
CHR: Tim Tidwell, Human Resources Director
CNO: Ashley Tanner, Director of Nursing
Web address: www.alaweb.com/~tgarske
Control: Hospital district or authority, Government, nonfederal **Service**: General
medical and surgical

Staffed Beds: 147	Admissions: 1497	Census: 128	Outpatient Visits:
22356	Births: 0		

GEORGIANA—Butler County

GEORGIANA HOSPITAL (010047), 515 Miranda Street, Zip 36033–4519,
Mailing Address: P.O. Box 548, Zip 36033–0548; tel. 334/376–2205,
(Nonreporting) **A**10
Primary Contact: Harry Cole Jr, Administrator
Web address: www.georgianahospital.com/
Control: Partnership, Investor–owned (for–profit) **Service**: General medical and
surgical

Staffed Beds: 22

GREENSBORO—Hale County

HALE COUNTY HOSPITAL (010095), 508 Green Street, Zip 36744–2316;
tel. 334/624–3024, (Nonreporting) **A**10
Primary Contact: Shay Fondren, Administrator
Web address: www.halecountyhospital.com
Control: Hospital district or authority, Government, nonfederal **Service**: General
medical and surgical

Staffed Beds: 20

GREENVILLE—Butler County

✠ **L. V. STABLER MEMORIAL HOSPITAL (010150)**, 29 L V Stabler Drive,
Zip 36037–3800; tel. 334/382–2671, (Nonreporting) **A**1 5 10
Primary Contact: Donald R. Rentfro, Chief Executive Officer
CFO: David Wilcox, Chief Financial Officer
CMO: Norman F McGowin, M.D., III Chief of Staff
CIO: Doug Burkett, Manager Information Technology
CHR: Robert Foster, Director Human Resources
CNO: Kimberli Weaver, Chief Nursing Officer
Web address: www.lvstabler.com
Control: City, Government, nonfederal **Service**: General medical and surgical

Staffed Beds: 15

GROVE HILL—Clarke County

★ **GROVE HILL MEMORIAL HOSPITAL (010091)**, 295 South Jackson
Street, Zip 36451–3231, Mailing Address: P.O. Box 935, Zip 36451–0935;
tel. 251/275–3191, (Nonreporting) **A**10
Primary Contact: Emily Steadham, Administrator
CFO: Elaine Averett, Chief Financial Officer
CMO: Eniola Fagbongbe, M.D., Chief Medical Staff
CIO: Aaron Harrell, Director
CHR: Aubrey Sheffield, Administrative Assistant Human Resources and Public
Relations
CNO: Karen Coleman, Director of Nursing
Web address: www.grovehillmemorial.org
Control: City, Government, nonfederal **Service**: General medical and surgical

Staffed Beds: 34

GUNTERSVILLE—Marshall County

MARSHALL MEDICAL CENTER NORTH (010010), 8000 Alabama Highway 69,
Zip 35976; tel. 256/753–8000, **A**5 10 **F**3 11 12 13 15 26 28 29 32 34 35 37
38 40 43 45 49 50 51 53 54 57 59 64 68 70 74 75 76 79 81 82 85 86 87 89
92 93 98 100 102 104 107 108 110 111 114 115 119 130 131 132 135 141
146 147 149 154 **P**6 **S** Marshall Health System, Guntersville, AL
Primary Contact: Cheryl M. Hays, FACHE, Administrator and Chief Operating Officer
COO: Cheryl M Hays, FACHE, Administrator and Chief Operating Officer
CFO: Kathy Nelson, Chief Financial Officer
CMO: Don Jones, M.D., Chief Medical Officer
CIO: Kim Bunch, Director Information Technology
CHR: Sabrina Weaver, Director of Human Resources
CNO: Kathy Woodruff, R.N., MSN, Chief Nursing Officer
Web address: www.mmcenters.com
Control: Hospital district or authority, Government, nonfederal **Service**: General
medical and surgical

Staffed Beds: 90 **Admissions**: 3850 **Census**: 49 **Outpatient Visits**: 179007
Births: 430 **Total Expense ($000)**: 59979 **Payroll Expense ($000)**: 24328
Personnel: 357

HALEYVILLE—Winston County

☐ **LAKELAND COMMUNITY HOSPITAL (010125)**, Highway 195 East,
Zip 35565–9536, Mailing Address: P.O. Box 780, Zip 35565–0780;
tel. 205/486–5213, (Nonreporting) **A**1 10
Primary Contact: Cynthia Nichols, R.N., MSN, Chief Executive Officer
CFO: Penny Westmoreland, Chief Financial Officer
Web address: www.lakelandcommunityhospital.com/
Control: Hospital district or authority, Government, nonfederal **Service**: General
medical and surgical

Staffed Beds: 56

HAMILTON—Marion County

✠ **NORTH MISSISSIPPI MEDICAL CENTER–HAMILTON (010044)**, 1256 Military
Street South, Zip 35570–5003; tel. 205/921–6200, (Nonreporting) **A**1 10 **S**
North Mississippi Health Services, Inc., Tupelo, MS
Primary Contact: Robert Trimm, Administrator
CMO: Jarred Sartain, M.D., President Medical Staff
CHR: Anne Lawler, Director Human Resources
CNO: Jennifer Cagle, Director of Nursing
Web address: www.nmhs.net
Control: Other not–for–profit (including NFP Corporation) **Service**: General
medical and surgical

Staffed Beds: 15

HUNTSVILLE—Madison County

✠ **CRESTWOOD MEDICAL CENTER (010131)**, One Hospital Drive,
Zip 35801–3403; tel. 256/429–4000, (Nonreporting) **A**1 5 10 **S** Community
Health Systems, Inc., Franklin, TN
Primary Contact: Pamela Hudson, M.D., Chief Executive Officer
COO: Bobby Ginn, Chief Operating Officer
CFO: Sherry J Jones, Chief Financial Officer
CHR: Elyria Sinclair, Director Human Resources
CNO: Martha Delaney Walls, R.N., MSN, Chief Nursing Officer
Web address: www.crestwoodmedcenter.com
Control: Corporation, Investor–owned (for–profit) **Service**: General medical and
surgical

Staffed Beds: 147

✠ **ENCOMPASS REHABILITATION HOSPITAL OF NORTH ALABAMA (013029)**,
107 Governors Drive SW, Zip 35801–4326; tel. 256/535–2300, (Nonreporting)
A1 10 **S** Encompass Health Corporation, Birmingham, AL
Primary Contact: Douglas H. Beverly, Chief Executive Officer
Web address: www.encompasshealth.com/huntsvillerehab
Control: Corporation, Investor–owned (for–profit) **Service**: Rehabilitation

Staffed Beds: 70

☐ **HUNTSVILLE HOSPITAL (010039)**, 101 Sivley Road SW, Zip 35801–4470;
tel. 256/265–1000, (Includes HUNTSVILLE HOSPITAL FOR WOMEN AND
CHILDREN, 911 Big Cove Road SE, Huntsville, AL, Zip 35801–3784;
tel. 256/265–1000; MADISON HOSPITAL, 8375 Highway 72 West, Madison, AL,
Zip 35758–9573; tel. 256/265–2012; Mary Lynne Wright, R.N., President) **A**1 2 3
5 10 **F**5 7 8 12 13 14 15 17 18 19 20 21 22 23 24 25 26 28 29 30 31 35 37
38 40 41 43 46 49 50 51 53 54 56 57 59 66 70 71 72 73 76 78 79
80 81 82 84 85 86 87 88 89 93 98 100 101 102 103 107 108 109 110 111
114 115 116 117 118 119 126 129 130 131 142 145 146 147 148 154 **P**6 **S**
Huntsville Hospital Health System, Huntsville, AL
Primary Contact: David S. Spillers, Chief Executive Officer
COO: Jeff Samz, Chief Operating Officer
CFO: Kelli Powers, Chief Financial Officer
CMO: Robert Chappell, M.D., Chief Medical Officer and Chief Quality Officer
CIO: Rick Corn, Chief Information Officer
CHR: Andrea P Rosler, Vice President Human Resources
CNO: Karol Jones, Chief Nursing Officer
Web address: www.huntsvillehospital.org
Control: Hospital district or authority, Government, nonfederal **Service**: General
medical and surgical

Staffed Beds: 927 **Admissions**: 47744 **Census**: 652 **Outpatient Visits**:
832170 **Births**: 5174 **Total Expense ($000)**: 900076 **Payroll Expense
($000)**: 345867 **Personnel**: 7433

UNITY PSYCHIATRIC CARE–HUNTSVILLE (014018), 5315 Millennium Drive
NW, Zip 35806–2458; tel. 256/964–6700, **A**10 **F**6 29 34 35 38 56 59 65 75 77
86 87 98 101 103 130 135 148 **S** Tennessee Health Management, Parsons, TN
Primary Contact: Bradley Moss, Administrator
Web address: www.thmgt.com/locations/behavioral–healthcare–center–at–
huntsville
Control: Corporation, Investor–owned (for–profit) **Service**: Psychiatric

Staffed Beds: 20 **Admissions**: 242 **Census**: 10 **Outpatient Visits**: 0
Births: 0

JACKSON—Clarke County

JACKSON MEDICAL CENTER (010128), 220 Hospital Drive, Zip 36545–2459,
Mailing Address: P.O. Box 428, Zip 36545–0428; tel. 251/246–9021,
(Nonreporting) **A**10 **S** Gilliard Health Services, Montgomery, AL
Primary Contact: Jennifer M. Ryland, R.N., Chief Executive Officer
COO: Jennifer M Ryland, R.N., Chief Administrative Officer
CHR: Kathy Jones, Director Human Resources
Web address: www.jacksonmedicalcenter.org
Control: Partnership, Investor–owned (for–profit) **Service**: General medical and
surgical

Staffed Beds: 26

Hospital, Medicare Provider Number, Address, Telephone, Approval, Facility, and Physician Codes, Health Care System

★ American Hospital Association (AHA) membership   ○ Healthcare Facilities Accreditation Program   ⇑ Center for Improvement in Healthcare Quality Accreditation
☐ The Joint Commission accreditation   ◇ DNV Healthcare Inc. accreditation   △ Commission on Accreditation of Rehabilitation Facilities (CARF) accreditation

JASPER—Walker County

✠ **WALKER BAPTIST MEDICAL CENTER (010089)**, 3400 Highway 78
East, Zip 35501–8907, Mailing Address: P.O. Box 3547, Zip 35502–3547;
tel. 205/387–4000, **A**1 10 20 **F**4 8 11 13 15 18 20 24 29 30 34 38 39 40 45
46 48 50 51 56 57 59 60 65 66 68 70 74 75 76 77 79 81 82 84 86 87 89
91 92 93 97 98 100 101 102 103 104 107 110 111 114 115 119 124 126
127 130 131 132 146 147 148 151 153 154 **S** TENET Healthcare Corporation,
Dallas, TX
Primary Contact: Robert A. Phillips, Chief Executive Officer
CFO: Amanda Dyle, Chief Financial Officer
CIO: Kenny Horton, Director Information Systems
CHR: Pat Morrow, Director Human Resources
CNO: Robbie Hindman, Vice President Patient Care Services and Chief Nursing
Officer
Web address: www.bhsala.com
Control: Corporation, Investor–owned (for–profit) **Service**: General medical and
surgical

Staffed Beds: 158 **Admissions**: 7773 **Census**: 97 **Outpatient Visits**: 75407
Births: 779 **Total Expense ($000)**: 85846 **Payroll Expense ($000)**: 27863
Personnel: 626

LUVERNE—Crenshaw County

☐ **BEACON CHILDREN'S HOSPITAL (014015)**, 150 Hospital Drive, Zip 36049;
tel. 334/335–5040, **A**1 10 **F**68 98 99
Primary Contact: Bradley Eisemann, Administrator
Web address: www.beaconchildrenshospital.com
Control: Partnership, Investor–owned (for–profit) **Service**: Children's hospital
psychiatric

Staffed Beds: 28 **Admissions**: 473 **Census**: 17 **Outpatient Visits**: 0
Births: 0 **Total Expense ($000)**: 3558 **Payroll Expense ($000)**: 2480
Personnel: 72

CRENSHAW COMMUNITY HOSPITAL (010008), 101 Hospital Circle,
Zip 36049–7344; tel. 334/335–3374, (Nonreporting) **A**10
Primary Contact: David L. Hughes, Adminstrator
COO: Victoria Lawrenson, Chief Operating Officer
CMO: Charles Tompkins, M.D., Chief of Staff
CHR: Patricia Jarry, Manager Human Resources
Web address: www.crenshawcommunityhospital.com
Control: Corporation, Investor–owned (for–profit) **Service**: General medical and
surgical

Staffed Beds: 65

MADISON—Madison County

BRADFORD HEALTH SERVICES AT HUNTSVILLE, 1600 Browns Ferry
Road, Zip 35758–9601, Mailing Address: P.O. Box 1488, Zip 35758–0176;
tel. 256/461–7272, (Nonreporting) **S** Bradford Health Services, Birmingham, AL
Primary Contact: Bob Hinds, Executive Director
Web address: www.bradfordhealth.com
Control: Corporation, Investor–owned (for–profit) **Service**: Alcoholism and other
chemical dependency

Staffed Beds: 84

MOBILE—Mobile County

★ **BAYPOINTE BEHAVIORAL HEALTH (014014)**, 5800 Southland Drive,
Zip 36693–3313; tel. 251/661–0153, **A**3 10 **F**38 98 99 100 101 106 130 132
154 **S** AltaPointe Health Systems, Mobile, AL
Primary Contact: Jarett Crum, Hospital Director
Web address: www.altapointe.org
Control: Other not–for–profit (including NFP Corporation) **Service**: Children's
hospital psychiatric

Staffed Beds: 60 **Admissions**: 1306 **Census**: 36 **Outpatient Visits**: 0
Births: 0 **Total Expense ($000)**: 7103 **Payroll Expense ($000)**: 4621
Personnel: 196

☐ **INFIRMARY LONG TERM ACUTE CARE HOSPITAL (012006)**, 5
Mobile Infirmary Circle, Zip 36607–3513, Mailing Address: P.O. Box 2226,
Zip 36652–2226; tel. 251/660–5239, (Nonreporting) **A**1 10 **S** Infirmary Health
System, Mobile, AL
Primary Contact: Susanne Marmande, Administrator
Web address: www.theinfirmary.com/
Control: Other not–for–profit (including NFP Corporation) **Service**: Acute long–
term care hospital

Staffed Beds: 38

☐ △ **MOBILE INFIRMARY MEDICAL CENTER (010113)**, 5 Mobile Infirmary
Drive North, Zip 36607–3513, Mailing Address: P.O. Box 2144, Zip 36652–2144;
tel. 251/435–2400, (Includes ROTARY REHABILITATION HOSPITAL, 5 Mobile
Infirmary Circle, Mobile, AL, Zip 36607, Mailing Address: P.O. Box 2144,
Zip 36652, tel. 251/435–3400) (Nonreporting) **A**1 2 3 5 7 10 **S** Infirmary Health
System, Mobile, AL
Primary Contact: Joe Stough, Interim President
CFO: Joe Denton, Executive Vice President and Chief Financial Officer
CMO: John Dixon, Chief Medical Officer
CIO: Eddy Stephens, Vice President Information Technology
CHR: Sheila Young, Vice President Human Resources
Web address: www.infirmaryhealth.org
Control: Other not–for–profit (including NFP Corporation) **Service**: General
medical and surgical

Staffed Beds: 526

✠ **PROVIDENCE HOSPITAL (010090)**, 6801 Airport Boulevard, Zip 36608–3785,
Mailing Address: P.O. Box 850429, Zip 36685–0429; tel. 251/633–1000, **A**1 2
3 5 10 **F**3 11 13 15 17 18 20 22 24 26 28 29 30 31 34 35 40 44 45 49 50 51
53 54 55 57 58 59 60 61 64 65 68 70 73 74 75 76 77 78 79 80 81 82 83 84
85 86 87 89 92 93 96 102 107 108 110 111 114 115 117 119 120 121 124
126 129 130 131 132 135 146 148 149 **P**5 6 **S** Ascension Healthcare, Saint
Louis, MO
Primary Contact: Todd S. Kennedy, President and Chief Executive Officer
COO: C Susan Cornejo, Chief Operating Officer
CMO: William M Lightfoot, M.D., Vice President Medical Services
CHR: Christopher Cockrell, Executive Director Human Resources
CNO: Peter Lindquist, Vice President and Chief Nursing Officer
Web address: www.providencehospital.org
Control: Church operated, Nongovernment, not–for–profit **Service**: General
medical and surgical

Staffed Beds: 305 **Admissions**: 14867 **Census**: 207 **Outpatient
Visits**: 144875 **Births**: 1632 **Total Expense ($000)**: 213142 **Payroll
Expense ($000)**: 64699 **Personnel**: 1446

ROTARY REHABILITATION HOSPITAL See Mobile Infirmary Medical Center,
Mobile

☐ **SPRINGHILL MEMORIAL HOSPITAL (010144)**, 3719 Dauphin Street,
Zip 36608–1798, Mailing Address: P.O. Box 8246, Zip 36689–0246;
tel. 251/344–9630, **A**1 10 **F**11 13 15 17 18 20 22 24 26 28 29 30 31 34 40
45 46 47 49 50 51 57 60 70 74 75 76 77 78 79 81 82 84 86 87 88 89 90 93
107 110 111 115 118 119 126 127 129 130 132 146 147 148 149
Primary Contact: Jeffery M. St Clair, President and Chief Executive Officer
COO: Rene Areaux, Vice President and Chief Operating Officer
CFO: Jan Grigsby, Vice President and Chief Financial Officer
CMO: Liston Jones, M.D., Medical Director
CIO: Mark Kilborn, Director Information Systems
CHR: Daniela Batchelor, Director Human Resources
CNO: Paul Read, R.N., MSN, Vice President and Chief Nursing Officer
Web address: www.springhillmedicalcenter.com
Control: Corporation, Investor–owned (for–profit) **Service**: General medical and
surgical

Staffed Beds: 219 **Admissions**: 11537 **Census**: 163 **Outpatient
Visits**: 177291 **Births**: 981 **Total Expense ($000)**: 171558 **Payroll Expense
($000)**: 51215 **Personnel**: 1165

✠ **UNIVERSITY OF SOUTH ALABAMA CHILDREN'S AND WOMEN'S HOSPITAL
(013301)**, 1700 Center Street, Zip 36604–3301; tel. 251/415–1000, **A**1 3 5 10
F7 11 13 15 21 27 29 31 40 41 48 49 52 55 58 59 64 72 73 74 75 76 77 78
79 81 85 86 87 88 89 93 107 111 114 126 130 146 147 **S** University of South
Alabama Health System, Mobile, AL
Primary Contact: Chris Jett, Administrator
CFO: Traci Jones, Chief Financial Officer
CIO: Garry Adkins, Chief Information Officer
CHR: Janice Rehm, Manager Human Resources
CNO: Scotty Roberson, Assistant Administrator and Chief Nursing Officer
Web address: www.usahealthsystem.com/usacwh
Control: State, Government, nonfederal **Service**: Other specialty treatment

Staffed Beds: 172 **Admissions**: 8717 **Census**: 158 **Outpatient Visits**:
67699 **Births**: 2595 **Total Expense ($000)**: 142389 **Payroll Expense
($000)**: 57943 **Personnel**: 1084

⊞ **USA HEALTH UNIVERSITY HOSPITAL (010087)**, 2451 USA Medical Center Drive, Zip 36617–2293; tel. 251/471–7000, **A**1 2 3 5 8 10 **F**3 7 11 13 15 16 17 21 27 29 31 34 40 43 45 46 47 48 49 57 58 59 61 64 65 68 70 74 78 79 80 81 85 87 107 108 111 114 115 119 120 121 124 126 130 131 132 145 146 148 149 **S** University of South Alabama Health System, Mobile, AL
Primary Contact: Sam Dean, Administrator
CFO: Traci Jones, Chief Financial Officer
CIO: Mark Lauteren, Chief Information Officer
CHR: Anita Shirah, Director Human Resources
CNO: Lisa Mestas, Associate Administrator and System Chief Nursing Officer
Web address: www.usahealthsystem.com/usamc
Control: State, Government, nonfederal **Service**: General medical and surgical

Staffed Beds: 142 Admissions: 7816 Census: 127 Outpatient Visits: 74321 Births: 0 Total Expense ($000): 205473 Payroll Expense ($000): 91452 Personnel: 1473	

MONROEVILLE—Monroe County

☐ **MONROE COUNTY HOSPITAL (010120)**, 2016 South Alabama Avenue, Zip 36460–3044, Mailing Address: P.O. Box 886, Zip 36461–0886; tel. 251/575–3111, (Nonreporting) **A**1 10 20
Primary Contact: Wes Nall, Interim Chief Executive Officer
CFO: Wes Nall, Chief Financial Officer
CMO: David Stallworth, M.D., Chief of Staff
CIO: Jody Falkenberry, Director Information Systems
CHR: Tara Nowling, Director Human Resources
CNO: Barbara Harned, R.N., MSN, Chief Nursing Officer
Web address: www.mchcare.com
Control: Hospital district or authority, Government, nonfederal **Service**: General medical and surgical

Staffed Beds: 44	

MONTGOMERY—Montgomery County

☐ **BAPTIST MEDICAL CENTER EAST (010149)**, 400 Taylor Road, Zip 36117–3512, Mailing Address: P.O. Box 241267, Zip 36124–1267; tel. 334/277–8330, **A**1 3 10 **F**3 11 12 13 15 29 30 34 35 40 44 45 47 49 50 56 57 63 64 68 70 72 73 75 76 77 79 81 82 85 86 89 90 93 94 107 108 111 114 115 119 126 129 130 132 135 146 147 **S** Baptist Health, Montgomery, AL
Primary Contact: Jeff G. Rains, Chief Executive Officer
CFO: Katrina Belt, Chief Financial Officer
CHR: Kay R Bennett, Vice President Human Resources
CNO: Kathy Gaston, Chief Nursing Officer
Web address: www.baptistfirst.org
Control: Hospital district or authority, Government, nonfederal **Service**: General medical and surgical

Staffed Beds: 164 Admissions: 9786 Census: 123 Outpatient Visits: 111005 Births: 3472 Total Expense ($000): 108197 Payroll Expense ($000): 48919 Personnel: 897	

☐ **BAPTIST MEDICAL CENTER SOUTH (010023)**, 2105 East South Boulevard, Zip 36116–2409, Mailing Address: Box 11010, Zip 36111–0010; tel. 334/288–2100, **A**1 3 5 10 **F**3 5 11 12 13 15 17 18 20 22 24 26 28 29 30 31 34 35 40 43 44 45 46 47 49 50 56 57 58 59 60 61 63 64 68 70 72 74 75 76 78 79 81 82 84 85 86 87 89 90 93 94 98 100 101 102 103 104 107 108 110 111 114 115 116 117 118 119 126 129 130 131 132 135 146 147 148 **S** Baptist Health, Montgomery, AL
Primary Contact: J Peter. Selman, FACHE, Chief Executive Officer
CFO: Melissa Johnson, Chief Financial Officer
CMO: Donovan Kendrick, M.D., Chief Medical Officer
CIO: Steve Miller, Director Information Systems
CHR: Kay R Bennett, System Director Human Resources
CNO: Karen McCaa, R.N., Vice President Patient Care Services and Chief Nursing Officer
Web address: www.baptistfirst.org
Control: Hospital district or authority, Government, nonfederal **Service**: General medical and surgical

Staffed Beds: 389 Admissions: 18455 Census: 272 Outpatient Visits: 237441 Births: 757 Total Expense ($000): 406180 Payroll Expense ($000): 119036 Personnel: 2049	

⊞ **CENTRAL ALABAMA VETERANS HEALTH CARE SYSTEM**, 215 Perry Hill Road, Zip 36109–3798; tel. 334/272–4670, (Includes MONTGOMERY DIVISION, 215 Perry Hill Road, Montgomery, AL, Zip 36109–3798; tel. 334/272–4670; TUSKEGEE DIVISION, 2400 Hospital Road, Tuskegee, AL, Zip 36083–5001; tel. 334/727–0550) (Nonreporting) **A**1 3 **S** Department of Veterans Affairs, Perry Point, MD
Primary Contact: Linda Lake. Boyle, R.N., MSN, Director
CFO: Debra Nicholson, Manager Finance
CMO: Cliff Robinson, M.D., Chief of Staff
CIO: Rhoda Tyson, Chief Information Officer
CHR: Janice Hardy, Chief Human Resource Management Service
Web address: www.centralalabama.va.gov/
Control: Veterans Affairs, Government, federal **Service**: General medical and surgical

Staffed Beds: 245	

⊞ **ENCOMPASS HEALTH REHABILITATION HOSPITAL OF MONTGOMERY (013028)**, 4465 Narrow Lane Road, Zip 36116–2900; tel. 334/284–7700, **A**1 10 **F**3 9 28 29 34 35 54 56 57 59 64 74 75 77 86 90 93 95 130 131 132 143 146 148 **P**5 **S** Encompass Health Corporation, Birmingham, AL
Primary Contact: Randy Thompson, Chief Executive Officer
CFO: Heath Watson, Controller
CMO: Jeffrey Eng, M.D., Medical Director
CIO: Anidra Billingslea, Health Insurance Management
CHR: Kim McDaniel, Director Human Resources
CNO: Gretchen Vercher, Chief Nursing Officer
Web address: www.encompasshealth.com/montgomeryrehab
Control: Corporation, Investor–owned (for–profit) **Service**: Rehabilitation

Staffed Beds: 70 Admissions: 1893 Census: 63 Outpatient Visits: 3941 Births: 0 Total Expense ($000): 26090 Payroll Expense ($000): 12827 Personnel: 148	

⊞ **JACKSON HOSPITAL AND CLINIC (010024)**, 1725 Pine Street, Zip 36106–1117; tel. 334/293–8000, **A**1 3 10 **F**13 15 17 18 20 22 24 26 29 30 31 34 40 45 46 48 49 57 59 64 68 70 74 76 77 78 79 81 82 84 85 86 87 89 107 108 110 111 115 116 117 118 119 126 129 130 131 135 144 146 147 148 154 **P**6
Primary Contact: Joe B. Riley, FACHE, President and Chief Executive Officer
COO: Michael James, Chief Operations Officer
CFO: Paul Peiffer, Chief Financial Officer and Vice President
CHR: Gilbert Darrington, Director Human Resources
Web address: www.jackson.org
Control: Other not–for–profit (including NFP Corporation) **Service**: General medical and surgical

Staffed Beds: 262 Admissions: 14695 Census: 196 Outpatient Visits: 167959 Births: 1367 Total Expense ($000): 216260 Payroll Expense ($000): 92355 Personnel: 1440	

LONG TERM CARE HOSPITAL See Noland Hospital Montgomery

MONTGOMERY DIVISION See Central Alabama Veterans Health Care System, Montgomery

☐ **NOLAND HOSPITAL MONTGOMERY (012007)**, 1725 Pine Street, 5 North, Zip 36106–1109; tel. 334/240–0532, (Nonreporting) **A**1 10 **S** Noland Health Services, Inc., Birmingham, AL
Primary Contact: Dale Jones, Administrator
Web address: www.nolandhealth.com
Control: Other not–for–profit (including NFP Corporation) **Service**: Acute long–term care hospital

Staffed Beds: 65	

MOULTON—Lawrence County

☐ **LAWRENCE MEDICAL CENTER (010059)**, 202 Hospital Street, Zip 35650–1218, Mailing Address: P.O. Box 39, Zip 35650–0039; tel. 256/974–2200, **A**1 10 **F**15 28 29 30 34 35 40 45 46 47 50 54 56 57 59 64 65 66 68 75 81 85 86 87 93 107 108 111 114 118 119 127 130 132 133 135 144 146 147 **P**5 **S** Huntsville Hospital Health System, Huntsville, AL
Primary Contact: Dean A. Griffin, Chief Executive Officer
CFO: Jim Crawford, Chief Financial Officer
CIO: Jeremy Duncan, Director Information Systems
CHR: Diane K Secor, Director Human Resources
Web address: www.lawrencemedicalcenter.com
Control: County, Government, nonfederal **Service**: General medical and surgical

Staffed Beds: 43 Admissions: 645 Census: 8 Outpatient Visits: 66459 Births: 0	

Hospital, Medicare Provider Number, Address, Telephone, Approval, Facility, and Physician Codes, Health Care System		
★ American Hospital Association (AHA) membership	○ Healthcare Facilities Accreditation Program	⇑ Center for Improvement in Healthcare Quality Accreditation
☐ The Joint Commission accreditation	◇ DNV Healthcare Inc. accreditation	△ Commission on Accreditation of Rehabilitation Facilities (CARF) accreditation

MUSCLE SHOALS—Colbert County

☐ **SHOALS HOSPITAL (010157)**, 201 Avalon Avenue, Zip 35661–2805, Mailing Address: P.O. Box 3359, Zip 35662–3359; tel. 256/386–1600, (Nonreporting) **A1** 10 **S** RCCH HealthCare Partners, Brentwood, TN
Primary Contact: Kidada Hawkins, Chief Executive Officer
CFO: Steve E. Hobbs, Chief Financial Officer
CMO: Terry true, M.D., Chief of Staff
CIO: William Johnson, Director Information Systems
CHR: Nancy Bowling, Director Human Resources
Web address: www.shoalshospital.com
Control: Hospital district or authority, Government, nonfederal **Service**: General medical and surgical

Staffed Beds: 137

ONEONTA—Blount County

☒ **ST. VINCENT'S BLOUNT (011305)**, 150 Gilbreath, Zip 35121–2827, Mailing Address: P.O. Box 1000, Zip 35121–0013; tel. 205/274–3000, **A1** 10 18 **F3** 11 15 18 29 30 35 40 45 46 50 57 59 60 64 70 81 85 87 93 97 107 108 110 111 119 127 133 135 146 149 **S** Ascension Healthcare, Saint Louis, MO
Primary Contact: Greg Brown, Administrator
CFO: Jennifer Kingry, Chief Financial Officer
CMO: David R Wilson, M.D., Chief of Staff
CIO: John Laliberte, Chief Information Officer
CHR: Kristin L. Costanzo, Direct–In–Market Lead Human Relations Partner
CNO: Kira Schnittker, Director of Nursing
Web address: www.stvhs.com
Control: Other not–for–profit (including NFP Corporation) **Service**: General medical and surgical

Staffed Beds: 25 **Admissions:** 837 **Census:** 13 **Outpatient Visits:** 34367 **Births:** 0 **Total Expense ($000):** 21274 **Payroll Expense ($000):** 7106 **Personnel:** 103

OPELIKA—Lee County

☒ **EAST ALABAMA MEDICAL CENTER (010029)**, 2000 Pepperell Parkway, Zip 36801–5452; tel. 334/749–3411, (Includes EAST ALABAMA MEDICAL CENTER–LANIER, 4800 48th Street, Valley, AL, Zip 36854–3666; tel. 334/756–9180; Greg Nichols, Chief Executive Officer) (Total facility includes 216 beds in nursing home–type unit) **A**1 2 10 19 **F3** 7 11 13 15 17 18 20 22 24 26 28 29 30 31 33 34 35 37 40 43 45 47 48 50 51 53 54 57 59 61 64 67 68 70 74 75 76 77 78 79 81 82 84 85 86 89 90 98 99 100 101 102 104 107 108 110 111 114 117 119 120 121 123 124 125 126 128 129 130 131 132 135 146 147 148 149 154
Primary Contact: Laura D. Grill, Chief Executive Officer
COO: Laura D Grill, R.N., Executive Vice President and Administrator
CFO: Sam Price, Executive Vice President Finance/Chief Financial Officer
CMO: William Golden, M.D., Chief Medical Officer
CIO: Sarah Gray, Vice President Information Services
CHR: Susan Johnston, Vice President Human Resources
CNO: Jane Fullum, Vice President Patient Care Services
Web address: www.eamc.org
Control: Hospital district or authority, Government, nonfederal **Service**: General medical and surgical

Staffed Beds: 560 **Admissions:** 15067 **Census:** 390 **Outpatient Visits:** 175793 **Births:** 2108 **Total Expense ($000):** 352139 **Payroll Expense ($000):** 143297 **Personnel:** 3027

OPP—Covington County

☐ **MIZELL MEMORIAL HOSPITAL (010007)**, 702 Main Street, Zip 36467–1626, Mailing Address: P.O. Box 1010, Zip 36467–1010; tel. 334/493–3541, (Nonreporting) **A**10
Primary Contact: Jana Wyatt, Chief Executive Officer
CFO: Amy Bess, Chief Financial Officer
CIO: Elizabeth Cook, Chief Information Officer
CHR: Dianne Morrison, Director Human Resources
CNO: Steven Skeen, R.N., Chief Nursing Officer
Web address: www.mizellmh.com
Control: Other not–for–profit (including NFP Corporation) **Service**: General medical and surgical

Staffed Beds: 59

OZARK—Dale County

☐ **DALE MEDICAL CENTER (010021)**, 126 Hospital Avenue, Zip 36360–2080; tel. 334/774–2601, (Nonreporting) **A**10
Primary Contact: Vernon Johnson, Administrator
CFO: Brad Hull, Chief Financial Officer
CMO: Steve Brandt, M.D., Chief of Staff
CHR: Sheila Dunn, Assistant Administrator Human Resources
Web address: www.dalemedical.org
Control: Corporation, Investor–owned (for–profit) **Service**: General medical and surgical

Staffed Beds: 75

PELHAM—Shelby County

☐ **ENCOMPASS HEALTH REHABILITATION HOSPITAL OF SHELBY COUNTY**, 900 Oak Mountain Commons Lane, Zip 35124; tel. 205/216–7600, (Nonreporting) **A**1 **S** Encompass Health Corporation, Birmingham, AL
Primary Contact: Robert Russell, Chief Executive Officer
Web address: www.encompasshealth.com/shelbycountyrehab
Control: Corporation, Investor–owned (for–profit) **Service**: Rehabilitation

Staffed Beds: 35

PELL CITY—St. Clair County

☒ **ST. VINCENT'S ST. CLAIR (010130)**, 7063 Veterans Parkway, Zip 35125–1499; tel. 205/814–2105, **A**1 10 **F3** 11 15 29 30 35 40 43 45 46 50 59 60 64 68 70 79 81 82 85 87 93 107 108 110 111 119 130 135 146 148 149 **S** Ascension Healthcare, Saint Louis, MO
Primary Contact: Lisa Nichols, R.N., Administrator
CFO: Jason Lynn, Director Finance
Web address: www.stvhs.com
Control: Other not–for–profit (including NFP Corporation) **Service**: General medical and surgical

Staffed Beds: 40 **Admissions:** 1898 **Census:** 20 **Outpatient Visits:** 48703 **Births:** 0 **Total Expense ($000):** 26012 **Payroll Expense ($000):** 8928 **Personnel:** 143

PHENIX CITY—Russell County

☐ **JACK HUGHSTON MEMORIAL HOSPITAL (010168)**, 4401 Riverchase Drive, Zip 36867–7483; tel. 334/732–3000, **A**1 3 10 13 **F3** 29 40 45 70 79 81 89 107 111 115 119 130 131
Primary Contact: Mark A. Baker, Chief Executive Officer
COO: Rachel H. Crenshaw, Chief Operating Officer
CFO: Angela Shelton, Chief Financial Officer
CMO: James F. Zumstein, M.D., Chief of Medicine
CHR: Lana Thomas–Folds, System Director Human Resources
CNO: Sylvia Thomas, Chief Nursing Officer
Web address: www.hughston.com
Control: Corporation, Investor–owned (for–profit) **Service**: General medical and surgical

Staffed Beds: 35 **Admissions:** 2513 **Census:** 17 **Outpatient Visits:** 17003 **Births:** 0 **Total Expense ($000):** 45694 **Payroll Expense ($000):** 13750 **Personnel:** 285

☒ **REGIONAL REHABILITATION HOSPITAL (013033)**, 3715 Highway 280/431 North, Zip 36867; tel. 334/732–2200, (Nonreporting) **A**1 10 **S** Encompass Health Corporation, Birmingham, AL
Primary Contact: Lora Davis, FACHE, Chief Executive Officer
CFO: Bobby Edmondson, Controller
CMO: Nitin Desei, M.D., Medical Director
CIO: Jacki Cuevas, Director Health Information Services
CHR: Cindy Glynn, Director Human Resources
CNO: Wendy Lee, Chief Nursing Officer
Web address: www.regionalrehabhospital.com
Control: Partnership, Investor–owned (for–profit) **Service**: Rehabilitation

Staffed Beds: 48

PRATTVILLE—Autauga County

☐ **PRATTVILLE BAPTIST HOSPITAL (010108)**, 124 South Memorial Drive, Zip 36067–3619, Mailing Address: P.O. Box 681630, Zip 36068–1638; tel. 334/365–0651, **A**1 3 10 **F3** 11 12 15 18 29 30 34 35 40 44 45 50 56 57 59 60 63 64 68 70 74 75 81 82 84 85 86 87 93 107 111 114 119 129 132 146 154 **S** Baptist Health, Montgomery, AL
Primary Contact: Eric Morgan, Chief Executive Officer
CFO: LaDonna McDaniel, Financial Manager
CIO: B Blaine Brown, Vice President and General Counsel
CHR: Kymberli Skipper, Manager Human Resources
Web address: www.baptistfirst.org/facilities/prattville–baptist–hospital/default.aspx
Control: Hospital district or authority, Government, nonfederal **Service**: General medical and surgical

Staffed Beds: 55 **Admissions:** 3428 **Census:** 39 **Outpatient Visits:** 80912 **Births:** 0 **Total Expense ($000):** 42262 **Payroll Expense ($000):** 17650 **Personnel:** 325

Many Facility Codes have changed. Please refer to the AHA Guide Code Chart. © 2018 AHA Guide

RED BAY—Franklin County

★ **RED BAY HOSPITAL (011302)**, 211 Hospital Road, Zip 35582–3858, Mailing Address: P.O. Box 490, Zip 35582–0490; tel. 256/356–9532, **A**10 18 **F**7 11 15 29 34 35 40 53 57 59 68 77 85 87 93 97 107 110 114 119 127 130 131 133 135 **S** Huntsville Hospital Health System, Huntsville, AL
Primary Contact: Sherry Jolley, Director of Operations and Nursing
CFO: Penny Westmoreland, Chief Financial Officer
CMO: Kristy Crandell, M.D., Medical Staff President
CHR: Amy Leigh Bishop, Director Human Resources
CNO: Margaret Thorn, Interim Director of Nursing
Web address: www.redbayhospital.com
Control: Hospital district or authority, Government, nonfederal **Service**: General medical and surgical

Staffed Beds: 25 Admissions: 400 Census: 9 Outpatient Visits: 9649 Births: 0 Total Expense ($000): 9310 Payroll Expense ($000): 3950 Personnel: 109

RUSSELLVILLE—Franklin County

☐ **RUSSELLVILLE HOSPITAL (010158)**, 15155 Highway 43, Zip 35653–1975, Mailing Address: P.O. Box 1089, Zip 35653–1089; tel. 256/332–1611, (Nonreporting) **A**1 10 **S** Curae Health, Clinton, TN
Primary Contact: Christine R. Stewart, FACHE, Chief Executive Officer
CFO: Penny Westmoreland, Chief Financial Officer
CHR: Stephen Proctor, Director of Human Resources/Risk
CNO: Belinda Johnson, R.N., Chief Nursing Officer/Chief Clinical Officer
Web address: www.russellvillehospital.com
Control: Partnership, Investor–owned (for–profit) **Service**: General medical and surgical

Staffed Beds: 92

SCOTTSBORO—Jackson County

☐ **HIGHLANDS MEDICAL CENTER (010061)**, 380 Woods Cove Road, Zip 35768–2428, Mailing Address: P.O. Box 1050, Zip 35768–1050; tel. 256/259–4444, (Nonreporting) **A**1 5 10 20
Primary Contact: Lonnie Albin, M.D., Interim Chief Executive Officer
CFO: Dan Newell, Chief Financial Officer
CIO: Doug Newby, Chief Information Officer
CHR: Susanna S Sivley, Chief Personnel Officer
Web address: www.highlandsmedcenter.com
Control: Hospital district or authority, Government, nonfederal **Service**: General medical and surgical

Staffed Beds: 92

SELMA—Dallas County

✠ **VAUGHAN REGIONAL MEDICAL CENTER (010118)**, 1015 Medical Center Parkway, Zip 36701–6352; tel. 334/418–4100, **A**1 3 5 10 **F**8 11 13 15 17 18 20 22 29 30 34 40 45 50 57 59 70 74 76 79 81 85 89 93 107 108 110 111 114 115 118 119 120 127 129 130 131 146 **S** LifePoint Health, Brentwood, TN
Primary Contact: J. David. McCormack, Chief Executive Officer
CFO: Tyler Adkins, Chief Financial Officer
CMO: Walid Freij, M.D., Chief of Staff
CIO: Matthew McHugh, Director Information Services
CHR: Dionne Williams, Director Human Resources
CNO: Patricia Hannon, Chief Nursing Officer
Web address: www.vaughanregional.com
Control: Corporation, Investor–owned (for–profit) **Service**: General medical and surgical

Staffed Beds: 149 Admissions: 5208 Census: 47 Outpatient Visits: 38322 Births: 623

SHEFFIELD—Colbert County

☐ **HELEN KELLER HOSPITAL (010019)**, 1300 South Montgomery Avenue, Zip 35660–6334, Mailing Address: P.O. Box 610, Zip 35660–0610; tel. 256/386–4196, **A**1 10 **F**3 7 8 11 13 15 18 20 21 28 29 30 31 34 35 40 45 47 49 50 51 53 57 59 60 64 65 68 70 74 75 76 77 78 79 80 81 82 83 84 85 86 87 89 91 92 93 94 107 108 110 111 114 115 117 118 119 126 129 130 131 132 135 145 146 147 148 149 **S** Huntsville Hospital Health System, Huntsville, AL
Primary Contact: Paul Storey, FACHE, President and Chief Executive Officer
CFO: Morris S Strickland, Chief Financial Officer
CHR: Pam Bryant, Director Human Resources
Web address: www.helenkeller.com
Control: Hospital district or authority, Government, nonfederal **Service**: General medical and surgical

Staffed Beds: 145 Admissions: 6729 Census: 68 Outpatient Visits: 93045 Births: 818 Total Expense ($000): 94624 Payroll Expense ($000): 37686 Personnel: 827

SYLACAUGA—Talladega County

☐ **COOSA VALLEY MEDICAL CENTER (010164)**, 315 West Hickory Street, Zip 35150–2996; tel. 256/401–4000, (Nonreporting) **A**1 10
Primary Contact: Glenn C. Sisk, President
CFO: Janice Brown, Chief Financial Officer
CIO: Sandra Murchison, Director Medical Records
CHR: Christy Knowles, Chief Human Resources Officer
Web address: www.cvhealth.net
Control: Other not–for–profit (including NFP Corporation) **Service**: General medical and surgical

Staffed Beds: 101

TALLADEGA—Talladega County

✠ **CITIZENS BAPTIST MEDICAL CENTER (010101)**, 604 Stone Avenue, Zip 35160–2217, Mailing Address: P.O. Box 978, Zip 35161–0978; tel. 256/362–8111, (Nonreporting) **A**1 10 19 **S** TENET Healthcare Corporation, Dallas, TX
Primary Contact: Frank D. Thomas, Chief Executive Officer
CFO: Zach Abercrombie, Chief Financial Officer
CHR: Sandra Willis, Director of Human Resources
CNO: Ann McEntire, MSN, R.N., Chief Nursing Officer
Web address: www.brookwoodbaptisthealth.org
Control: Church operated, Nongovernment, not–for–profit **Service**: General medical and surgical

Staffed Beds: 72

TALLASSEE—Elmore County

COMMUNITY HOSPITAL (010034), 805 Friendship Road, Zip 36078–1234; tel. 334/283–6541, (Nonreporting) **A**10
Primary Contact: Jennie R. Rhinehart, Administrator and Chief Executive Officer
Web address: www.chal.org
Control: Other not–for–profit (including NFP Corporation) **Service**: General medical and surgical

Staffed Beds: 47

TROY—Pike County

☐ **TROY REGIONAL MEDICAL CENTER (010126)**, 1330 Highway 231 South, Zip 36081–3058; tel. 334/670–5000, (Nonreporting) **A**1 10
Primary Contact: Ronald Dean, Chief Executive Officer
CFO: Janet Smith, Chief Financial Officer
CMO: Paul Dulaney, M.D., Chief of Staff
CIO: Michael Moore, Director Information Systems
CHR: Beth Nissen, Director Human Resources
CNO: Amy Minor, Chief Nursing Officer
Web address: www.troymedicalcenter.com
Control: Corporation, Investor–owned (for–profit) **Service**: General medical and surgical

Staffed Beds: 45

TUSCALOOSA—Tuscaloosa County

☐ **BRYCE HOSPITAL (014007)**, 200 University Boulevard, Zip 35401–1294; tel. 205/507–8299, (Nonreporting) **A**1 5 10
Primary Contact: Shelia Penn, Facility Director
CFO: Wendell Summerville, Chief Financial Officer
CMO: Cynthia Moore Sledge, M.D., Medical Director
CIO: Ronene Howell, Director Health Information Management
CHR: Jim Elliott, Director Human Resources
Web address: www.mh.alabama.gov/
Control: State, Government, nonfederal **Service**: Psychiatric

Staffed Beds: 820

Hospitals, U.S. / ALABAMA

☐ **DCH REGIONAL MEDICAL CENTER (010092)**, 809 University Boulevard East, Zip 35401–2029; tel. 205/759–7111, (Includes NORTHPORT MEDICAL CENTER, 2700 Hospital Drive, Northport, AL, Zip 35476–3360; tel. 205/333–4500; Luke Standeffer, Administrator) **A**1 2 3 5 10 20 **F**3 11 12 13 15 18 20 22 24 26 28 29 30 31 34 35 38 40 43 45 46 48 49 50 51 58 59 60 61 62 64 68 70 71 72 74 75 76 77 78 79 81 82 84 86 87 89 90 93 94 98 100 101 102 103 107 108 110 111 114 115 117 118 119 120 121 124 126 129 130 131 132 146 147 148 **S** DCH Health System, Tuscaloosa, AL
Primary Contact: Paul Betz, FACHE, Administrator
CFO: Nina Dusang, Vice President Finance and Chief Financial Officer
CMO: Kenneth Aldridge, M.D., Vice President Medical Affairs
CIO: Kim Ligon, Director Information Services
CHR: Peggy Sease, Vice President Human Resources
CNO: Lorraine Yehlen, R.N., Vice President Patient Care Services
Web address: www.dchsystem.com
Control: Hospital district or authority, Government, nonfederal **Service**: General medical and surgical

Staffed Beds: 583 **Admissions**: 32127 **Census**: 467 **Outpatient Visits**: 580367 **Births**: 3420 **Total Expense ($000)**: 486314 **Payroll Expense ($000)**: 210740 **Personnel**: 3823

☐ **MARY S HARPER GERIATRIC PSYCHIATRY CENTER (014012)**, 200 University Boulevard, Zip 35401–1250; tel. 205/759–0900, (Nonreporting) **A**1 10
Primary Contact: Beverly White, MS, Facility Director
CFO: Sarah Mitchell, Director Finance
CMO: Robin Barton Lariscy, M.D., Medical Director
CIO: Sarah Mitchell, Director Finance
CHR: Jim Elliott, Director Human Resources
Web address: www.mh.alabama.gov
Control: Corporation, Investor–owned (for–profit) **Service**: Psychiatric

Staffed Beds: 96

☐ **NOLAND HOSPITAL TUSCALOOSA (012012)**, 809 University Blvd E, 4th Fl, Zip 35401–2029; tel. 205/759–7241, (Nonreporting) **A**1 10 **S** Noland Health Services, Inc., Birmingham, AL
Primary Contact: Jack Gibson, Administrator
Web address: www.nolandhealth.com
Control: Other not–for–profit (including NFP Corporation) **Service**: Acute long–term care hospital

Staffed Beds: 32

☐ **TAYLOR HARDIN SECURE MEDICAL FACILITY (014011)**, 1301 Jack Warner Parkway, Zip 35404–1060; tel. 205/556–7060, (Nonreporting) **A**1 10
Primary Contact: Barbara Jackson, Ed.D., Acting Facility Director
Web address: www.mh.alabama.gov/
Control: Corporation, Investor–owned (for–profit) **Service**: Psychiatric

Staffed Beds: 114

☒ **TUSCALOOSA VETERANS AFFAIRS MEDICAL CENTER**, 3701 Loop Road East, Zip 35404–5015; tel. 205/554–2000, (Total facility includes 114 beds in nursing home–type unit) **A**1 5 **F**29 30 34 35 36 38 39 56 57 58 59 61 63 65 71 74 75 77 82 83 84 86 87 90 93 94 97 98 100 101 104 106 107 119 127 128 130 132 135 143 146 147 148 149 153 154 **S** Department of Veterans Affairs, Perry Point, MD
Primary Contact: John F. Merkle, Medical Center Director
COO: Gary D Trende, FACHE, Associate Director
CFO: Angelia Stevenson, Manager Finance
CMO: Carlos E. Berry, M.D., Acting Chief of Staff
Web address: www.tuscaloosa.va.gov
Control: Veterans Affairs, Government, federal **Service**: Psychiatric

Staffed Beds: 305 **Admissions**: 1695 **Census**: 252 **Outpatient Visits**: 247122 **Births**: 0 **Personnel**: 1084

TUSKEGEE—Macon County

TUSKEGEE DIVISION See Central Alabama Veterans Health Care System, Montgomery

UNION SPRINGS—Bullock County

BULLOCK COUNTY HOSPITAL (010110), 102 West Conecuh Avenue, Zip 36089–1303; tel. 334/738–2140, (Nonreporting) **A**10 20
Primary Contact: Jacques Jarry, Administrator
COO: Victoria Lawrenson, Chief Operating Officer
CMO: Maria Bernardo, M.D., Chief of Staff
Web address: www.unionspringsalabama.com/
Control: Corporation, Investor–owned (for–profit) **Service**: General medical and surgical

Staffed Beds: 44

WARRIOR—Jefferson County

☐ **BRADFORD HEALTH SERVICES AT WARRIOR LODGE**, 1189 Allbritt Road, Zip 35180, Mailing Address: P.O. Box 129, Zip 35180–0129; tel. 205/647–1945, (Nonreporting) **A**1 **S** Bradford Health Services, Birmingham, AL
Primary Contact: Roy M. Ramsey, Executive Director
Web address: www.bradfordhealth.com
Control: Corporation, Investor–owned (for–profit) **Service**: Alcoholism and other chemical dependency

Staffed Beds: 100

WEDOWEE—Randolph County

TANNER MEDICAL CENTER/EAST ALABAMA (010032), 1032 South Main Street, Zip 36278–7428; tel. 256/357–2111, (Nonreporting) **A**10 **S** Tanner Health System, Carrollton, GA
Primary Contact: Jerry Morris, Administrator
Web address: www.tanner.org/eastalabama
Control: County, Government, nonfederal **Service**: General medical and surgical

Staffed Beds: 26

WETUMPKA—Elmore County

ELMORE COMMUNITY HOSPITAL (010097), 500 Hospital Drive, Zip 36092–1625, Mailing Address: P.O. Box 130, Zip 36092–0003; tel. 334/567–4311, (Nonreporting) **A**10
Primary Contact: Michael Ritzus, Chief Executive Officer
CFO: Mike Bruce, Chief Financial Officer
CHR: Cindy Futral, Director Human Resources
Web address: www.elmorehospital.com/
Control: Partnership, Investor–owned (for–profit) **Service**: General medical and surgical

Staffed Beds: 49

WINFIELD—Marion County

☐ **NORTHWEST MEDICAL CENTER (010086)**, 1530 US Highway 43, Zip 35594–5056; tel. 205/487–7000, (Nonreporting) **A**1 10 **S** Curae Health, Clinton, TN
Primary Contact: Michael D. Windham, Chief Executive Officer
CFO: Glenda Reyes, Chief Financial Officer
CMO: David Corbett, M.D., Chief of Staff
Web address: www.northwestmedcenter.com
Control: Corporation, Investor–owned (for–profit) **Service**: General medical and surgical

Staffed Beds: 43

YORK—Sumter County

HILL HOSPITAL OF SUMTER COUNTY (010138), 751 Derby Drive, Zip 36925–2121; tel. 205/392–5263, (Nonreporting) **A**10
Primary Contact: Loretta Wilson, Administrator
CFO: Joyce Wedgeworth, Financial Clerk
CMO: Gary Walton, M.D., Chief Medical Officer
CNO: Cynthia Brown, Director of Nursing
Control: Other not–for–profit (including NFP Corporation) **Service**: General medical and surgical

Staffed Beds: 33

Many Facility Codes have changed. Please refer to the AHA Guide Code Chart.

ALASKA

ANCHORAGE—Anchorage County

☒ **ALASKA NATIVE MEDICAL CENTER (020026)**, 4315 Diplomacy Drive,
Zip 99508–5926; tel. 907/563–2662, **A**1 3 5 10 **F**1 3 4 8 11 13 15 16 18 20
22 29 30 31 32 34 35 38 39 40 41 43 44 45 47 48 49 50 51 54 55 56 57 58
59 61 63 64 65 66 67 68 70 72 73 74 75 76 77 78 79 81 82 84 85 86 87 88
89 92 93 94 107 110 111 114 115 119 127 130 135 141 142 143 144 146
147 148 149 154 **P**6
Primary Contact: Roald Helgesen, Chief Executive Officer
CMO: Paul Franke, M.D., Chief Medical Officer
CHR: Sonya Conant, Senior Director Human Resources
Web address: www.dhss.alaska.gov/dbh/Pages/api/default.aspx
Control: Other not–for–profit (including NFP Corporation) **Service**: General
medical and surgical

> **Staffed Beds:** 172 **Admissions:** 7847 **Census:** 128 **Outpatient Visits:**
> 411877 **Births:** 1626 **Total Expense ($000):** 495648 **Payroll Expense**
> **($000):** 189237 **Personnel:** 1840

☐ **ALASKA PSYCHIATRIC INSTITUTE (024002)**, 3700 Piper Street,
Zip 99508–4677; tel. 907/269–7100, (Nonreporting) **A**1 10
Primary Contact: Ron B. Hale, Chief Executive Officer
COO: Gavin H Carmichael, FACHE, Chief Operating Officer
CFO: Gavin H Carmichael, FACHE, Chief Operating Officer
CMO: Claudette A. Zarema, M.D., Medical Officer
CIO: Stephen Schneider, Manager Information Services
CHR: Katie E. Gratrix, Administrative Assistant III
CNO: Sharon Bergstedt, Director of Nursing
Web address: www.hss.state.ak.us/dbh/API/
Control: State, Government, nonfederal **Service**: Psychiatric

> **Staffed Beds:** 80

☒ **ALASKA REGIONAL HOSPITAL (020017)**, 2801 Debarr Road,
Zip 99508–2997; tel. 907/264–1754, (Nonreporting) **A**1 2 10 **S** HCA Healthcare,
Nashville, TN
Primary Contact: Julie Taylor, FACHE, Chief Executive Officer
COO: Victor Rosenbaum, Chief Operating Officer
CFO: Lynn Kennington, Chief Financial Officer
CMO: David Cadogan, Chief Medical Officer
CIO: Gene Kaplanis, Director Information Technology
CHR: Tammy Kaminski, Director Human Resources
CNO: Linda Doughty, Chief Nursing Officer
Web address: www.alaskaregional.com
Control: Corporation, Investor–owned (for–profit) **Service**: General medical and
surgical

> **Staffed Beds:** 132

☒ **NORTH STAR BEHAVIORAL HEALTH SYSTEM (024001)**, 2530 DeBarr
Circle, Zip 99508–2948; tel. 907/258–7575, (Includes NORTH STAR
BEHAVIORAL HEALTH, 1650 South Bragaw, Anchorage, AK, Zip 99508–3467;
tel. 907/258–7575) (Nonreporting) **A**1 5 10 **S** Universal Health Services, Inc., King
of Prussia, PA
Primary Contact: Andrew Mayo, Ph.D., Chief Executive Officer and Managing
Director
CFO: Alan Barnes, Chief Financial Officer
CMO: Ruth Dukoff, M.D., Medical Director
CIO: Brian O'Connell, Director Information Services
CHR: Sabrina Ben, Director Human Resources
CNO: Brandy Proctor, Director of Nursing
Web address: www.northstarbehavioral.com
Control: Corporation, Investor–owned (for–profit) **Service**: Psychiatric

> **Staffed Beds:** 200

☒ **PROVIDENCE ALASKA MEDICAL CENTER (020001)**, 3200 Providence
Drive, Zip 99508–4615; Mailing Address: P.O. Box 196604, Zip 99519–6604;
tel. 907/562–2211, (Includes CHILDREN'S HOSPITAL AT PROVIDENCE, 3200
Providence Drive, Anchorage, AK, Zip 99508; tel. 907/212–3130) **A**1 2 3 5 10
13 **F**3 8 11 12 13 17 18 19 20 21 22 24 25 26 28 29 30 31 34 35 38 39 40
41 43 45 46 47 49 50 53 55 56 57 58 59 60 62 63 65 67 68 70 72 74 75 77
78 79 81 82 83 84 85 86 87 88 90 92 93 94 97 98 100 101 102 104 105 107
108 111 115 118 119 120 121 123 124 126 130 131 132 146 148 149 154 **S**
Providence St. Joseph Health, Renton, WA
Primary Contact: Ella M. Goss, MSN, R.N., Chief Executive Officer
CFO: Anthony Dorsch, Chief Financial Officer
CMO: Roy Davis, M.D., Chief Medical Officer
CIO: Stephanie Morton, Chief Information Officer
CHR: Scott Jungwirth, Chief Human Resources Officer
Web address: www.alaska.providence.org/locations/p/pamc
Control: Church operated, Nongovernment, not–for–profit **Service**: General
medical and surgical

> **Staffed Beds:** 401 **Admissions:** 16625 **Census:** 298 **Outpatient Visits:**
> 401297 **Births:** 2417 **Total Expense ($000):** 455907 **Payroll Expense**
> **($000):** 220336 **Personnel:** 2648

☒ **ST. ELIAS SPECIALTY HOSPITAL (022001)**, 4800 Cordova Street,
Zip 99503–7218; tel. 907/561–3333, **A**1 10 **F**1 3 18 28 29 30 60 65 68 75 77
86 107 114 119 129
Primary Contact: Sharon H. Kurz, Ph.D., Chief Executive Officer
CFO: Andrew Fitch, Chief Financial Officer
Web address: www.st-eliashospital.com
Control: Partnership, Investor–owned (for–profit) **Service**: Acute long–term care
hospital

> **Staffed Beds:** 59 **Admissions:** 324 **Census:** 35 **Outpatient Visits:** 0
> **Births:** 0 **Total Expense ($000):** 37250 **Personnel:** 195

BARROW—North Slope County

☒ **SAMUEL SIMMONDS MEMORIAL HOSPITAL (021312)**, 7000 Uulu Street,
Zip 99723, Mailing Address: P.O. Box 29, Zip 99723–0029; tel. 907/852–4611,
(Nonreporting) **A**1 10 18
Primary Contact: Richard Hall, Chief Executive Officer
CMO: Devon Allen, M.D., Chief of Medical Staff
Web address: www.arcticslope.org
Control: Other not–for–profit (including NFP Corporation) **Service**: General
medical and surgical

> **Staffed Beds:** 14

BETHEL—Bethel County

☒ **YUKON–KUSKOKWIM DELTA REGIONAL HOSPITAL (020018)**, 700 Chief
Eddie Hoffman Highway, Zip 99559–3000, Mailing Address: P.O. Box 528,
Zip 99559–0528; tel. 907/543–6300, **A**1 3 5 10 **F**3 5 13 15 29 34 35 38 39 40
45 50 53 54 57 58 59 64 65 66 68 71 75 76 81 82 84 85 87 89 91 93 97 99
100 101 102 103 104 106 107 110 127 130 134 135 144 147 148 151 152
153 154 **P**6
Primary Contact: Dan Winkelman, President and Chief Executive Officer
CFO: Tommy Tompkins, Vice President, Finance and Chief Financial Officer
CIO: William Pearch, Chief Information Officer
Web address: www.ykhc.org
Control: Other not–for–profit (including NFP Corporation) **Service**: General
medical and surgical

> **Staffed Beds:** 37 **Admissions:** 2060 **Census:** 21 **Outpatient Visits:** 205049
> **Births:** 336 **Total Expense ($000):** 172392 **Payroll Expense ($000):** 82839
> **Personnel:** 218

Hospital, Medicare Provider Number, Address, Telephone, Approval, Facility, and Physician Codes, Health Care System

★ American Hospital Association (AHA) membership   ○ Healthcare Facilities Accreditation Program   ⇑ Center for Improvement in Healthcare Quality Accreditation
☐ The Joint Commission accreditation   ◇ DNV Healthcare Inc. accreditation   △ Commission on Accreditation of Rehabilitation Facilities (CARF) accreditation

AK

CORDOVA—Valdez–Cordova County

★ **CORDOVA COMMUNITY MEDICAL CENTER (021307)**, 602 Chase Avenue, Zip 99574, Mailing Address: P.O. Box 160, Zip 99574–0160; tel. 907/424–8000, (Total facility includes 10 beds in nursing home–type unit) **A**10 18 **F**29 34 35 40 57 59 65 69 75 93 97 100 101 102 104 107 114 119 128 130 133 146 153 154 **P**6
Primary Contact: Scot Mitchell, FACHE, Chief Executive Officer and Administrator
CFO: Lee W Bennett, Interim Chief Financial Officer
CMO: Sam Blackadar, M.D., Medical Director
CHR: Kim Wilson, Human Resources Coordinator
CNO: Mary Rios, R.N., Interim Director of Nursing
Web address: www.cdvcmc.com
Control: City, Government, nonfederal **Service**: General medical and surgical

Staffed Beds: 23 **Admissions:** 88 **Census:** 15 **Outpatient Visits:** 1744 **Births:** 0 **Total Expense ($000):** 10766 **Payroll Expense ($000):** 4105 **Personnel:** 66

DILLINGHAM—Dillingham County

⊞ **BRISTOL BAY AREA HEALTH CORPORATION (021309)**, 6000 Kanakanak Road, Zip 99576, Mailing Address: P.O. Box 130, Zip 99576–0130; tel. 907/842–5201, (Nonreporting) **A**1 3 10 18
Primary Contact: Robert J. Clark, President and Chief Executive Officer
COO: Lucrecia Scotford, Executive Vice President and Chief Operations Officer
CFO: David Morgan, Vice President and Chief Financial Officer
CMO: Arnold Loera, M.D., Clinical Director
CIO: Bill Wilcox, Chief Information Technology Officer
CHR: John Davis, Chief Human Resources Officer
CNO: Starla Fox, Director of Nursing
Web address: www.bbahc.org
Control: Other not–for–profit (including NFP Corporation) **Service**: General medical and surgical

Staffed Beds: 16

ELMENDORF AFB—Anchorage County

⊞ **U.S. AIR FORCE REGIONAL HOSPITAL**, 5955 Zeamer Avenue, Zip 99506–3702; tel. 907/580–3006, (Nonreporting) **A**1 **S** Department of the Air Force, Washington, DC
Primary Contact: Major Mark Lamey, Commander
COO: Colonel Rebecca Seese, Chief Operating Officer
CFO: Major Felicia Burks, Chief Financial Officer
CMO: Colonel Marriner Oldham, M.D., Chief Medical Officer
CIO: Major Phillip Oliphant, Chief Information Officer
CHR: Mark Clark, Human Resources Liaison
Web address: www.elmendorf.af.mil/
Control: Air Force, Government, federal **Service**: General medical and surgical

Staffed Beds: 64

FAIRBANKS—Fairbanks North Star County

⊞ **FAIRBANKS MEMORIAL HOSPITAL (020012)**, 1650 Cowles Street, Zip 99701–5998; tel. 907/452–8181, (Nonreporting) **A**1 2 3 5 10
Primary Contact: Jim Lynch, Chief Executive Officer
CFO: Steve Leslie, Chief Financial Officer
CIO: Carl J Kegley, System Director Information Technology
CHR: Nicole Welch, Chief Human Resources Officer
CNO: Karen Justin–Tanner, R.N., Chief Nursing Officer
Web address: www.foundationhealth.org/fmh
Control: Other not–for–profit (including NFP Corporation) **Service**: General medical and surgical

Staffed Beds: 307

FORT WAINWRIGHT—Fairbanks North Star County

⊞ **BASSETT ARMY COMMUNITY HOSPITAL**, 1060 Gaffney Road, Box 7400, Zip 99703–5001, Mailing Address: 1060 Gaffney Road, Box 7440, Zip 99703–5001; tel. 907/361–4000, **A**1 **F**3 7 8 13 15 29 30 32 33 34 35 36 38 39 40 45 50 52 53 54 56 57 59 64 65 68 75 76 77 79 81 85 86 87 89 97 100 101 102 104 107 110 111 114 119 130 131 132 135 144 145 146 147 148 149 150 154 **S** Department of the Army, Office of the Surgeon General, Falls Church, VA
Primary Contact: Timothy Bergeron, Deputy Commander, Administration
CMO: Colonel Leo Bennett, M.D., Deputy Commander Clinical Services
CHR: Terri Morefield, Deputy Chief Human Resources Division
Web address: www.alaska.amedd.army.mil
Control: Army, Government, federal **Service**: General medical and surgical

Staffed Beds: 21 **Admissions:** 311 **Census:** 6 **Outpatient Visits:** 295886 **Births:** 564

HOMER—Kenai Peninsula County

★ **SOUTH PENINSULA HOSPITAL (021313)**, 4300 Bartlett Street, Zip 99603–7000; tel. 907/235–8101, (Nonreporting) **A**10 18
Primary Contact: Joseph L. Woodin, Chief Executive Officer
CMO: Sarah Spencer, M.D., Chief of Staff
CIO: Jim Bartilson, Manager Information Systems
CNO: Von Kilpatrick, Chief Nursing Officer
Web address: www.sphosp.org
Control: Hospital district or authority, Government, nonfederal **Service**: General medical and surgical

Staffed Beds: 50

JUNEAU—Juneau County

⊞ **BARTLETT REGIONAL HOSPITAL (020008)**, 3260 Hospital Drive, Zip 99801–7808; tel. 907/796–8900, **A**1 5 10 20 **F**3 4 5 13 15 28 29 31 34 35 36 40 43 45 50 51 57 59 64 70 75 76 77 81 82 85 86 93 98 100 101 102 104 105 107 108 110 111 114 115 119 120 129 130 132 148 149 150 152 153 154 **P**6 7
Primary Contact: Charles E. Bill, Chief Executive Officer
CFO: Alan Ulrich, Chief Financial Officer
CMO: Sharon Fisher, M.D., Chief of Staff
CIO: Martha Palicka, Director Information Systems
CHR: Dallas Hargrave, Human Resources Director
CNO: William Gardner, Chief Clinical Officer
Web address: www.bartletthospital.org
Control: City, Government, nonfederal **Service**: General medical and surgical

Staffed Beds: 73 **Admissions:** 2275 **Census:** 10 **Outpatient Visits:** 33003 **Births:** 347 **Total Expense ($000):** 95282 **Payroll Expense ($000):** 43459 **Personnel:** 509

KETCHIKAN—Ketchikan Gateway County

★ ⇧ **PEACEHEALTH KETCHIKAN MEDICAL CENTER (021311)**, 3100 Tongass Avenue, Zip 99901–5746; tel. 907/225–5171, (Nonreporting) **A**5 10 18 21 **S** PeaceHealth, Vancouver, WA
Primary Contact: Edward E. Freysinger, Chief Administrative Officer
CFO: Ken Tonjes, Chief Financial Officer
CMO: Peter Rice, M.D., Medical Director
CIO: Tim Walker, Manager Information Services
CHR: Lanetta Lundberg, Vice President Culture and People
Web address: www.peacehealth.org
Control: Other not–for–profit (including NFP Corporation) **Service**: General medical and surgical

Staffed Beds: 50

KODIAK—Kodiak Island County

⊞ **PROVIDENCE KODIAK ISLAND MEDICAL CENTER (021306)**, 1915 East Rezanof Drive, Zip 99615–6602; tel. 907/486–3281, (Nonreporting) **A**1 10 18 **S** Providence St. Joseph Health, Renton, WA
Primary Contact: Regina L. Bishop, Administrator
COO: Brenda Zawacki, Chief Operating Manager
CFO: Timothy Hocum, Chief Financial Officer
CMO: Steve Smith, M.D., Chief of Staff
CIO: David Johnson, Manager Information Services
CNO: LeeAnn Horn, Chief Nurse Executive
Web address: www.providence.org
Control: Other not–for–profit (including NFP Corporation) **Service**: General medical and surgical

Staffed Beds: 6

KOTZEBUE—Northwest Arctic County

☐ **MANIILAQ HEALTH CENTER (021310)**, 436 5th Avenue, Zip 99752–0043, Mailing Address: P.O. Box 43, Zip 99752–0043; tel. 907/442–7344, (Nonreporting) **A**1 10 18
Primary Contact: Paul Hansen, Administrator
COO: Timothy Schuerch, President and Chief Executive Officer
CFO: Lucy Nelson, Director Finance, Vice President
CMO: Patricia Clancy, M.D., Director Medical Services
CIO: Eugene Smith, Chief Information Officer
CHR: Gerty Gallahom, Director Human Resources
CNO: Commander Donna K Biagioni, R.N., MSN, Director of Nursing
Web address: www.maniilaq.org
Control: Other not–for–profit (including NFP Corporation) **Service**: General medical and surgical

Staffed Beds: 17

Many Facility Codes have changed. Please refer to the AHA Guide Code Chart. © 2018 AHA Guide

NOME—Nome County

⊞ **NORTON SOUND REGIONAL HOSPITAL (021308)**, Bering Straits, Zip 99762, Mailing Address: P.O. Box 966, Zip 99762–0966; tel. 907/443–3311, (Nonreporting) **A**1 10 18
Primary Contact: Angela Gorn, Vice President
COO: Roy Agloinga, Chief Administrative Officer
CMO: David Head, M.D., Chief Medical Staff
CIO: Dan Bailey, Director Information Systems
CHR: Tiffany Martinson, Director Human Resources
Web address: www.nortonsoundhealth.org
Control: Other not–for–profit (including NFP Corporation) **Service:** General medical and surgical

Staffed Beds: 36

PALMER—Matanuska–Susitna County

⊞ **MAT–SU REGIONAL MEDICAL CENTER (020006)**, 2500 South Woodworth Loop, Zip 99645–8984, Mailing Address: P.O. Box 1687, Zip 99645–1687; tel. 907/861–6000, (Nonreporting) **A**1 3 10 20 **S** Community Health Systems, Inc., Franklin, TN
Primary Contact: David Wallace, Chief Executive Officer
CMO: Christopher Sahlstrom, M.D., Chief of Staff
CIO: Bryan Meurer, Director Information Systems
CHR: Cathy Babuscio, Director Human Resources
CNO: Emily Stevens, Chief Nursing Officer
Web address: www.matsuregional.com
Control: Partnership, Investor–owned (for–profit) **Service:** General medical and surgical

Staffed Beds: 74

PETERSBURG—Petersburg County

★ **PETERSBURG MEDICAL CENTER (021304)**, 103 Fram Street, Zip 99833, Mailing Address: Box 589, Zip 99833–0589; tel. 907/772–4291, (Total facility includes 15 beds in nursing home–type unit) **A**10 18 **F**15 31 34 40 45 56 57 59 62 64 67 77 79 81 84 85 93 97 107 110 114 119 133 146 148 149 **P**6
Primary Contact: Peter A. Hofstetter, Chief Executive Officer
CFO: Doran Hammett, Chief Financial Officer
CHR: Cynthia Newman, Manager Human Resources
CNO: Jennifer Bryner, Director Nursing
Web address: www.pmcak.org
Control: City–county, Government, nonfederal **Service:** General medical and surgical

Staffed Beds: 27 **Admissions:** 124 **Census:** 17 **Outpatient Visits:** 10193 **Births:** 0 **Total Expense ($000):** 17600 **Payroll Expense ($000):** 10044 **Personnel:** 101

SEWARD—Kenai Peninsula County

★ **PROVIDENCE SEWARD MEDICAL CENTER (021302)**, 417 First Avenue, Zip 99664, Mailing Address: P.O. Box 365, Zip 99664–0365; tel. 907/224–5205, (Total facility includes 40 beds in nursing home–type unit) **A**10 18 **F**3 29 30 40 43 67 68 75 77 85 86 93 94 107 108 119 130 132 133 146 148 149 154 **P**6 **S** Providence St. Joseph Health, Renton, WA
Primary Contact: Joseph Fong, Administrator
Web address: www.providence.org
Control: City, Government, nonfederal **Service:** General medical and surgical

Staffed Beds: 46 **Admissions:** 91 **Census:** 46 **Outpatient Visits:** 10745 **Births:** 0 **Total Expense ($000):** 18791 **Payroll Expense ($000):** 11001 **Personnel:** 119

SITKA—Sitka County

⊞ **SEARHC MT. EDGECUMBE HOSPITAL (021314)**, 222 Tongass Drive, Zip 99835–9416; tel. 907/966–2411, **A**1 5 10 18 **F**3 5 13 15 29 30 34 35 36 38 39 40 43 44 45 48 50 53 54 59 62 68 70 75 77 79 81 82 85 86 87 92 93 94 96 97 100 102 104 107 108 110 111 115 119 130 131 132 133 134 135 143 144 147 148 149 153 154 **P**6
Primary Contact: Charles Clement, Chief Executive Officer
COO: Daniel P Neumeister, Senior Vice President and Chief Operating Officer
CFO: Barbara Searls, Chief Financial Officer
CMO: David Vastola, Medical Director
CIO: Bob Cita, Chief Information Officer
CHR: Peggy Bernhardt–Kadlec, Chief Human Resources Officer
CNO: Patricia L Giampa, Chief Nursing Officer
Web address: www.searhc.org
Control: Other not–for–profit (including NFP Corporation) **Service:** General medical and surgical

Staffed Beds: 25 **Admissions:** 383 **Census:** 4 **Outpatient Visits:** 172016 **Births:** 38 **Total Expense ($000):** 159347 **Payroll Expense ($000):** 70298 **Personnel:** 660

★ **SITKA COMMUNITY HOSPITAL (021303)**, 209 Moller Avenue, Zip 99835–7142; tel. 907/747–3241, (Nonreporting) **A**10 18
Primary Contact: Rob Allen, Chief Executive Officer
CFO: Lee W Bennett, Chief Financial Officer
CHR: Shannon Callahan, Director Human Resources
Web address: www.sitkahospital.org
Control: City, Government, nonfederal **Service:** General medical and surgical

Staffed Beds: 27

SOLDOTNA—Kenai Peninsula County

⊞ **CENTRAL PENINSULA HOSPITAL (020024)**, 250 Hospital Place, Zip 99669–6999; tel. 907/714–4404, (Total facility includes 60 beds in nursing home–type unit) **A**1 3 10 20 **F**3 4 5 11 13 15 28 29 30 31 34 35 36 38 40 45 46 47 48 49 51 57 59 65 68 70 74 75 76 77 78 79 81 82 84 85 86 87 93 97 105 106 107 108 110 111 115 119 128 129 130 131 132 133 134 135 145 146 147 148 149 152 153 154
Primary Contact: Richard Davis, Chief Executive Officer
COO: Matt Dammeyer, Ph.D., Chief Operating Officer
CMO: Gregg Motonaga, M.D., Chief of Staff
CIO: Bryan Downs, Director Information Systems
CHR: John Dodd, Vice President Human Resources
Web address: www.cpgh.org
Control: Other not–for–profit (including NFP Corporation) **Service:** General medical and surgical

Staffed Beds: 119 **Admissions:** 2570 **Census:** 81 **Outpatient Visits:** 127720 **Births:** 366 **Total Expense ($000):** 147950 **Payroll Expense ($000):** 63600 **Personnel:** 731

VALDEZ—Valdez–Cordova County

★ **PROVIDENCE VALDEZ MEDICAL CENTER (021301)**, 911 Meals Avenue, Zip 99686–0550, Mailing Address: P.O. Box 550, Zip 99686–0550; tel. 907/835–2249, (Nonreporting) **A**10 18 **S** Providence St. Joseph Health, Renton, WA
Primary Contact: Jeremy O'Neil, Administrator
CMO: John Cullen, M.D., Chief of Staff and Medical Director Long Term Care
CHR: Maureen Radotich, Director Human Resources
Web address: www.providence.org/alaska
Control: City, Government, nonfederal **Service:** General medical and surgical

Staffed Beds: 21

WRANGELL—Wrangell County

★ **WRANGELL MEDICAL CENTER (021305)**, First Avenue & Bennett Street, Zip 99929, Mailing Address: P.O. Box 1081, Zip 99929–1081; tel. 907/874–7000, (Total facility includes 14 beds in nursing home–type unit) **A**10 18 **F**3 15 29 31 34 35 40 45 50 57 59 65 66 67 77 81 85 86 93 107 110 114 119 130 148 149
Primary Contact: Robert A. Rang, R.N., Chief Executive Officer
CIO: Cathy Gross, Director Health Information Management Systems
CNO: Sherri Austin, MSN, R.N., Chief Nursing Officer
Web address: www.wrangellmedicalcenter.org/
Control: City, Government, nonfederal **Service:** General medical and surgical

Staffed Beds: 22 **Admissions:** 140 **Census:** 16 **Outpatient Visits:** 7129 **Births:** 0 **Total Expense ($000):** 11720 **Payroll Expense ($000):** 4821 **Personnel:** 65

Hospital, Medicare Provider Number, Address, Telephone, Approval, Facility, and Physician Codes, Health Care System

★ American Hospital Association (AHA) membership
□ The Joint Commission accreditation
○ Healthcare Facilities Accreditation Program
◇ DNV Healthcare Inc. accreditation
⇑ Center for Improvement in Healthcare Quality Accreditation
△ Commission on Accreditation of Rehabilitation Facilities (CARF) accreditation

ARIZONA

APACHE JUNCTION—Pinal County

✠ **BANNER GOLDFIELD MEDICAL CENTER (030134)**, 2050 West Southern Avenue, Zip 85120–7305; tel. 480/733–3300, **A**1 10 **F**3 11 29 40 41 45 68 75 77 81 87 107 130 135 146 147 149 154 **S** Banner Health, Gilbert, AZ
Primary Contact: Sharon Lind, MSN, FACHE, Chief Executive Officer
CFO: Tracy French, Chief Financial Officer
CMO: Jason Brown, M.D., Chief Medical Officer
CHR: Rebecca McLaughlin, Chief Human Resource Officer
CNO: Terresa Ann Paulus, Chief Nursing Officer
Web address: www.bannerhealth.com/Locations/Arizona/
Banner+Goldfield+Medical+Center/_Welcome+to+Banner+Goldfield.htm
Control: Other not–for–profit (including NFP Corporation) **Service**: General medical and surgical

Staffed Beds: 20 Admissions: 556 Census: 4 Total Expense ($000): 20412 Payroll Expense ($000): 7174 Personnel: 89

AVONDALE—Maricopa County

COPPER SPRINGS HOSPITAL (034032), 10550 West Mcdowell Road, Zip 85392–4864; tel. 602/314–7800, (Nonreporting)
Primary Contact: Jessica Black, Chief Executive Officer
Web address: www.coppersspringshealth.com
Control: Corporation, Investor–owned (for–profit) **Service**: Psychiatric

Staffed Beds: 72

BENSON—Cochise County

★ **BENSON HOSPITAL (031301)**, 450 South Ocotillo Street, Zip 85602–6403, Mailing Address: P.O. Box 2290, Zip 85602–2290; tel. 520/586–2261, **A**10 18 **F**3 11 29 30 34 35 40 43 50 54 57 59 64 75 77 86 87 93 107 111 114 119 132 133 146 148
Primary Contact: Richard Polheber, Chief Executive Officer
COO: Teresa Vincifora, Chief Operating Officer
CFO: Ken Goranson, Chief Financial Officer
CMO: Barbara Hartley, Chief Medical Officer
CIO: Rob Roberts, Director Information Technology
CHR: Ashley Dickey, Director Human Resources
Web address: www.bensonhospital.org
Control: Other not–for–profit (including NFP Corporation) **Service**: General medical and surgical

Staffed Beds: 22 Admissions: 357 Census: 5 Outpatient Visits: 14939 Births: 0 Total Expense ($000): 15802 Payroll Expense ($000): 7494 Personnel: 131

BISBEE—Cochise County

★ **COPPER QUEEN COMMUNITY HOSPITAL (031312)**, 101 Cole Avenue, Zip 85603–1399; tel. 520/432–5383, **A**10 18 **F**1 3 8 11 15 18 29 30 34 40 45 46 61 62 74 75 77 81 85 93 97 107 110 111 114 119 127 130 135 147 154
Primary Contact: Robert L. Seamon, Chief Executive Officer
COO: Daniel Roe, M.D., Chief Operating Officer
CFO: James Ehasz, Chief Financial Officer
CIO: David Chmura, Chief Information Officer
CHR: Virginia Martinez, Director Human Resources
CNO: Sadie Maestas, Interim Chief Nursing Officer
Web address: www.cqch.org
Control: Other not–for–profit (including NFP Corporation) **Service**: General medical and surgical

Staffed Beds: 14 Admissions: 271 Census: 3 Outpatient Visits: 54163 Births: 0 Total Expense ($000): 30965 Payroll Expense ($000): 15243 Personnel: 250

BULLHEAD CITY—Mohave County

✠ **WESTERN ARIZONA REGIONAL MEDICAL CENTER (030101)**, 2735 Silver Creek Road, Zip 86442–8303; tel. 928/763–2273, (Nonreporting) **A**1 10 19 **S** Community Health Systems, Inc., Franklin, TN
Primary Contact: Mike Stenger, Interim Chief Executive Officer
CFO: Kenneth Pannell, Chief Financial Officer
CNO: Tara Barth, Chief Nursing Officer
Web address: www.warmc.com
Control: Corporation, Investor–owned (for–profit) **Service**: General medical and surgical

Staffed Beds: 139

CASA GRANDE—Pinal County

✠ **BANNER CASA GRANDE MEDICAL CENTER (030016)**, 1800 East Florence Boulevard, Zip 85122–5399; tel. 520/381–6300, **A**1 10 **F**3 13 15 18 20 22 29 30 34 35 40 41 49 57 64 68 70 73 75 76 77 79 81 85 87 91 92 93 107 111 114 115 117 119 126 129 130 131 135 145 146 147 148 149 154 **S** Banner Health, Gilbert, AZ
Primary Contact: Rona Curphy, President and Chief Executive Officer
CFO: Robert Bender, Chief Financial Officer
CMO: Devin Minior, M.D., Chief Medical Officer
CHR: Carol D'Souza, Chief Human Resources Officer
CNO: Dan Lingle, Chief Nursing Officer
Web address: www.bannerhealth.com/Locations/Arizona/
Banner+Casa+Grande+Medical+Center/_Banner+Casa+Grande+Medical+Center.htm
Control: Other not–for–profit (including NFP Corporation) **Service**: General medical and surgical

Staffed Beds: 84 Admissions: 5477 Census: 59 Births: 707 Total Expense ($000): 118706 Payroll Expense ($000): 44213 Personnel: 616

CHANDLER—Maricopa County

☐ **ARIZONA ORTHOPEDIC SURGICAL HOSPITAL (030112)**, 2905 West Warner Road, Suite 1, Zip 85224–1674; tel. 480/603–9000, (Nonreporting) **A**1 10 **S** United Surgical Partners International, Addison, TX
Primary Contact: Patricia K. Alice, Chief Executive Officer
CFO: Shalen Young, Chief Financial Officer
CMO: Randall Hardison, M.D., Chief Medical Officer
CIO: John Langenfeld, Medical Records Coordinator
CNO: Caroline Herpfer, Chief Nursing Officer
Web address: www.azosh.com
Control: Corporation, Investor–owned (for–profit) **Service**: Surgical

Staffed Beds: 24

✠ **CHANDLER REGIONAL MEDICAL CENTER (030036)**, 1955 West Frye Road, Zip 85224–6282; tel. 480/728–3000, **A**1 3 10 **F**3 8 11 12 13 15 17 18 20 22 24 26 28 29 30 31 32 34 35 37 40 41 43 44 45 46 47 48 49 50 51 54 57 58 59 60 64 65 66 68 70 71 72 73 74 75 76 77 78 79 81 82 83 84 85 86 87 93 96 107 108 110 111 114 115 119 126 130 131 132 135 143 144 146 147 148 **P**6 **S** Dignity Health, San Francisco, CA
Primary Contact: Jane E. Hanson, R.N., Interim Chief Executive Officer
COO: Jane E Hanson, R.N., Chief Operating Officer
CFO: Mark Kem, Vice President Finance and Chief Financial Officer
CMO: Terry J Happel, M.D., Vice President and Chief Medical Officer
CHR: Renea Brunke, Vice President Human Resources
CNO: Peg Smith, Vice President and Chief Nursing Officer
Web address: www.chandlerregional.com
Control: Other not–for–profit (including NFP Corporation) **Service**: General medical and surgical

Staffed Beds: 338 Admissions: 26332 Census: 278 Outpatient Visits: 196671 Births: 3954 Total Expense ($000): 488079 Payroll Expense ($000): 164628 Personnel: 2584

OASIS BEHAVIORAL HEALTH – CHANDLER (034029), 2190 North Grace Boulevard, Zip 85225–3416; tel. 480/917–9301, **F**98 106 153 **S** Acadia Healthcare Company, Inc., Franklin, TN
Primary Contact: James Gallagher, Chief Executive Officer
CFO: Dino Quarante, CPA, Chief Financial Officer
CHR: Barbara Mitchell, Director Human Resources
CNO: Charissa Davis, Chief Nursing Officer and Director of Nursing
Web address: www.obhhospital.com/about/location
Control: Corporation, Investor–owned (for–profit) **Service**: Psychiatric

Staffed Beds: 146 Admissions: 2854 Census: 116 Births: 0 Total Expense ($000): 15106

CHINLE—Apache County

✠ **CHINLE COMPREHENSIVE HEALTH CARE FACILITY (030084)**, Highway 191, Zip 86503, Mailing Address: P O Drawer PH, Zip 86503–8000; tel. 928/674–7001, (Nonreporting) **A**1 10 **S** U.S. Indian Health Service, Rockville, MD
Primary Contact: Ron Tso, Chief Executive Officer
CFO: Philene Tyler, Chief Finance Officer
CMO: Eric Ritchie, M.D., Clinical Director
CIO: Perry Francis, Supervisory Information Technology Specialist
CHR: Lorraine Begaye, Supervisory Human Resource Specialist
Web address: www.ihs.gov
Control: PHS, Indian Service, Government, federal **Service**: General medical and surgical

Staffed Beds: 60

COTTONWOOD—Yavapai County

★ ⇧ **VERDE VALLEY MEDICAL CENTER (030007)**, 269 South Candy Lane, Zip 86326–4170; tel. 928/639–6000, **A**10 13 20 21 **F**3 8 11 13 15 18 20 22 28 29 30 31 32 34 35 40 44 45 46 47 48 49 50 53 54 57 58 59 60 64 65 68 70 75 76 77 78 79 81 82 85 86 87 91 92 93 94 96 97 98 100 101 102 103 105 107 108 110 111 114 115 118 119 120 121 123 124 129 130 131 132 135 143 145 146 147 148 149 154 **P**1 **S** Northern Arizona Healthcare, Flagstaff, AZ
Primary Contact: Barbara Firminger, Chief Administrative Officer
CFO: Jeffrey Treasure, Chief Financial Officer, Northern Arizona Healthcare
CMO: Amy Gottschalk, M.D., Chief Medical Officer, Verde Valley Medical Center; Vice President Quality, Northern Arizona Healthcare
CIO: Marilyn Black, Chief Information Officer, Northern Arizona Healthcare
CHR: Ronald Haase, Chief Human Resources Officer, Northern Arizona Healthcare
CNO: Lori A Stevens, MSN, R.N., Interim Chief Nursing Officer
Web address: www.nahealth.com
Control: Other not–for–profit (including NFP Corporation) **Service:** General medical and surgical

Staffed Beds: 98 **Admissions:** 4394 **Census:** 50 **Births:** 550 **Total Expense ($000):** 130473 **Payroll Expense ($000):** 49825 **Personnel:** 950

FLAGSTAFF—Coconino County

★ ⇧ **FLAGSTAFF MEDICAL CENTER (030023)**, 1200 North Beaver Street, Zip 86001–3118; tel. 928/779–3366, **A**3 5 10 21 **F**3 5 7 8 11 13 15 17 18 20 22 24 26 28 29 30 31 32 34 35 37 40 43 44 45 46 49 50 53 54 57 58 59 60 61 65 66 68 70 72 74 75 76 77 78 79 81 82 84 85 86 87 88 89 93 94 98 99 101 102 103 104 105 107 108 110 111 114 115 116 117 118 119 120 121 123 124 126 130 131 132 144 145 146 147 148 149 154 **P**1 **S** Northern Arizona Healthcare, Flagstaff, AZ
Primary Contact: Florence (Flo). Spyrow, Chief Administrative Officer
CFO: Jeffrey Treasure, Chief Financial Officer, Northern Arizona Healthcare
CMO: Richard Neff, M.D., Interim Chief Medical Officer
CIO: Marilynn Black, Chief Information Officer, Northern Arizona Healthcare
CHR: Ronald Haase, Chief Human Resources Officer, Northern Arizona Healthcare
CNO: Katy Wilkens, Chief Nursing Officer and Vice President, Northern Arizona Healthcare
Web address: www.nahealth.com
Control: Other not–for–profit (including NFP Corporation) **Service:** General medical and surgical

Staffed Beds: 264 **Admissions:** 12599 **Census:** 163 **Outpatient Visits:** 72744 **Births:** 1171 **Total Expense ($000):** 378806 **Payroll Expense ($000):** 127609 **Personnel:** 2078

☐ **GUIDANCE CENTER (034023)**, 2187 North Vickey Street, Zip 86004–6121; tel. 928/527–1899, (Nonreporting) **A**1 10
CFO: Steve Finch, Chief Financial Officer
CMO: Chris Linskey, M.D., Acting Chief Medical Officer
CIO: John Crockett, Chief Information Officer
Web address: www.tgcaz.org
Control: Other not–for–profit (including NFP Corporation) **Service:** Psychiatric

Staffed Beds: 10

FORT DEFIANCE—Apache County

★ **TSEHOOTSOOI MEDICAL CENTER (030071)**, Highway 12 & Bonito Drive, Zip 86504, Mailing Address: P.O. Box 649, Zip 86504–0649; tel. 928/729–8000, (Nonreporting) **A**3 10
Primary Contact: Sandi Aretino, M.D., Chief Executive Officer
COO: Valonia Hardy, Chief Healthy Living Officer
CFO: Rachel Sorrell, Chief Financial Officer
CMO: Michael Tutt, M.D., Chief Medical Officer
CIO: Virgil Chavez, Director Information Technology
CHR: Vivian Santistevan, Chief Human Resources
CNO: Tori Davidson, R.N., Chief Nursing Officer
Web address: www.fdihb.org
Control: Public Health Service other than 47, Government, federal **Service:** General medical and surgical

Staffed Beds: 39

FORT MOHAVE—Mohave County

⊞ **VALLEY VIEW MEDICAL CENTER (030117)**, 5330 South Highway 95, Zip 86426–9225; tel. 928/788–2273, **A**1 10 **F**3 8 11 13 15 18 20 22 29 45 50 51 56 59 64 70 76 77 81 85 87 90 93 107 108 111 114 115 116 117 119 135 144 149 154 **S** LifePoint Health, Brentwood, TN
Primary Contact: Feliciano Jiron, Chief Executive Officer
CFO: Emma Canlas, Chief Financial Officer
CIO: Monique Murphy–Mijares, Chief Information Officer
CHR: Bonnie Guerrero, Director Human Resources
CNO: Lesa Lock, Chief Nursing Officer
Web address: www.valleyviewmedicalcenter.net
Control: Corporation, Investor–owned (for–profit) **Service:** General medical and surgical

Staffed Beds: 84 **Admissions:** 2167 **Census:** 22 **Births:** 374

GANADO—Apache County

⊞ **SAGE MEMORIAL HOSPITAL (031309)**, Highway 264, Zip 86505, Mailing Address: P.O. Box 457, Zip 86505–0457; tel. 928/755–4500, **A**1 10 18 **F**3 5 34 35 39 40 50 53 57 59 65 68 93 107 115 119 127 128 130 133 144 149 150 152 154
Primary Contact: Christi J. El–Meligi, R.N., Chief Executive Officer
COO: Netrisha Dalgai, Director of Operations
CHR: Gary Pahe, Manager Human Resources
CNO: Ernasha McIntosh, Interim Director of Nursing
Web address: www.sagememorial.com
Control: State, Government, nonfederal **Service:** General medical and surgical

Staffed Beds: 24 **Admissions:** 364 **Census:** 3 **Outpatient Visits:** 24000

GILBERT—Maricopa County

⊞ **BANNER GATEWAY MEDICAL CENTER (030122)**, 1900 North Higley Road, Zip 85234–1604; tel. 480/543–2000, **A**1 3 10 **F**3 8 12 13 15 18 29 30 31 34 35 36 40 44 45 46 47 49 50 51 55 57 59 60 63 68 70 72 74 75 76 77 78 79 81 84 85 87 93 107 108 110 111 114 116 117 118 119 120 121 124 126 130 132 134 136 141 142 146 147 148 149 154 **S** Banner Health, Gilbert, AZ
Primary Contact: Lamont M. Yoder, R.N., MSN, FACHE, Chief Executive Officer
COO: James R Powell, Associate Administrator
CFO: Thomas M Matenaer, Chief Financial Officer
CMO: Nikunj Doshi, D.O., Chief Medical Officer
CHR: Michele Mustacchia, Chief Human Resources Officer
CNO: Debra Adornetto–Garcia, MSN, R.N., Chief Nursing Officer
Web address: www.bannerhealth.com/Locations/Arizona/Banner+Gateway+Medical+Center/
Control: Other not–for–profit (including NFP Corporation) **Service:** General medical and surgical

Staffed Beds: 177 **Admissions:** 12337 **Census:** 132 **Births:** 4066 **Total Expense ($000):** 315739 **Payroll Expense ($000):** 94631 **Personnel:** 1514

⊞ **MERCY GILBERT MEDICAL CENTER (030119)**, 3555 South Val Vista Road, Zip 85297–7323; tel. 480/728–8000, **A**1 10 **F**3 8 11 13 15 18 20 22 26 28 29 30 31 32 34 35 37 38 40 41 44 46 47 49 50 51 57 58 59 60 64 65 66 68 70 73 74 75 76 77 78 79 81 82 83 84 85 86 87 96 100 101 102 103 107 108 110 111 114 115 119 126 129 130 131 132 135 144 145 146 147 148 **P**6 **S** Dignity Health, San Francisco, CA
Primary Contact: Jane E. Hanson, R.N., Interim President and Chief Executive Officer
COO: Jane E Hanson, R.N., Chief Operating Officer
CFO: Chuck Sowers, Vice President Finance and Chief Financial Officer
CMO: Phil Fracica, M.D., Vice President and Chief Medical Officer
CIO: Larissa Spraker, Vice President Business Development and Chief Strategy Officer
CHR: Anita Harger, Director Human Resources
Web address: www.mercygilbert.org
Control: Other not–for–profit (including NFP Corporation) **Service:** General medical and surgical

Staffed Beds: 198 **Admissions:** 15917 **Census:** 149 **Outpatient Visits:** 86906 **Births:** 3543 **Total Expense ($000):** 262329 **Payroll Expense ($000):** 87976 **Personnel:** 1711

AZ

Hospital, Medicare Provider Number, Address, Telephone, Approval, Facility, and Physician Codes, Health Care System

★ American Hospital Association (AHA) membership
☐ The Joint Commission accreditation
○ Healthcare Facilities Accreditation Program
◇ DNV Healthcare Inc. accreditation
⇧ Center for Improvement in Healthcare Quality Accreditation
△ Commission on Accreditation of Rehabilitation Facilities (CARF) accreditation

GLENDALE—Maricopa County

✉ **ABRAZO ARROWHEAD CAMPUS (030094)**, 18701 North 67th Avenue, Zip 85308–7100; tel. 623/561–1000, (Includes ABRAZO ARIZONA HEART HOSPITAL, 1930 East Thomas Road, Phoenix, AZ, Zip 85016; tel. 602/532–1000; Jeff Patterson, Chief Executive Officer) (Nonreporting) **A**1 3 10 **S** TENET Healthcare Corporation, Dallas, TX
Primary Contact: Jeff Patterson, Chief Executive Officer
CMO: Patrick Smith, M.D., Chief Medical Officer
CHR: Sharon M Chadwick, Director Human Resources
Web address: www.arrowheadhospital.com
Control: Corporation, Investor–owned (for–profit) **Service**: General medical and surgical

Staffed Beds: 234

☐ **AURORA BEHAVIORAL HEALTH SYSTEM WEST (034024)**, 6015 West Peoria Avenue, Zip 85302–1213; tel. 623/344–4400, (Nonreporting) **A**1 10 **S** Signature Healthcare Services, Corona, CA
Primary Contact: Bruce Waldo, Chief Executive Officer
CFO: Rebekah Francis, JD, Chief Financial Officer
CHR: Vicki Thomsen, Director Human Resources
CNO: Lori Milus, R.N., MSN, Director of Nursing
Web address: www.aurorabehavioral.com
Control: Corporation, Investor–owned (for–profit) **Service**: Psychiatric

Staffed Beds: 80

✉ **BANNER THUNDERBIRD MEDICAL CENTER (030089)**, 5555 West Thunderbird Road, Zip 85306–4696; tel. 602/865–5555, (Includes BANNER BEHAVIORAL HEALTH CENTER–THUNDERBIRD CAMPUS, 5555 West Thunderbird Road, Glendale, AZ, Zip 85306; tel. 602/588–5555) **A**1 3 10 **F**3 5 14 17 18 19 20 21 22 23 24 26 27 28 29 30 31 32 34 40 41 43 45 46 49 50 51 59 60 61 64 65 67 68 70 72 74 75 76 77 78 79 81 84 85 87 88 89 92 96 98 100 101 102 104 107 108 109 111 112 114 115 116 117 118 119 120 121 122 123 124 126 129 130 132 135 146 147 148 149 153 154 **S** Banner Health, Gilbert, AZ
Primary Contact: Debra J. Krmpotic, R.N., Chief Executive Officer
CFO: Richard Miller, Administrator Finance
CMO: Kathryn Perkins, M.D., Chief Medical Officer
CHR: Laura Witt, Administrator Human Resources
Web address: www.bannerhealth.com/Locations/Arizona/Banner+Thunderbird+Medical+Center/
Control: Other not–for–profit (including NFP Corporation) **Service**: General medical and surgical

Staffed Beds: 458 **Admissions:** 25694 **Census:** 347 **Births:** 5352 **Total Expense ($000):** 446927 **Payroll Expense ($000):** 160618 **Personnel:** 2635

✉ **ENCOMPASS HEALTH VALLEY OF THE SUN REHABILITATION HOSPITAL (033032)**, 13460 North 67th Avenue, Zip 85304–1042; tel. 623/878–8800, (Nonreporting) **A**1 10 **S** Encompass Health Corporation, Birmingham, AL
Primary Contact: Beth Bacher, Chief Executive Officer
CFO: Kathryn Haney, Controller
CMO: Michael Kravetz, M.D., Medical Director
CHR: Danette Garcia, Director Human Resources
CNO: Stephanie Palmer, Chief Nursing Officer
Web address: www.encompasshealth.com/valleyofthesunrehab
Control: Corporation, Investor–owned (for–profit) **Service**: Rehabilitation

Staffed Beds: 75

GLOBE—Gila County

COBRE VALLEY COMMUNITY HOSPITAL See Cobre Valley Regional Medical Center

★ **COBRE VALLEY REGIONAL MEDICAL CENTER (031314)**, 5880 South Hospital Drive, Zip 85501–9454; tel. 928/425–3261, **A**10 18 **F**3 11 12 13 15 18 20 22 28 29 30 34 35 40 41 43 45 46 49 51 55 57 59 64 70 74 75 76 78 79 81 82 87 92 93 96 97 107 108 110 111 115 117 118 119 127 129 130 133 135 146 147 148 149 154 **P**5 **S** HealthTech Management Services, Brentwood, TN
Primary Contact: Neal Jensen, Chief Executive Officer
CFO: Frank Napier, Interim Chief Financial Officer
CIO: Sharon Bennett, Manager Information Systems
CHR: Rita Murphy, Director Human Resources
Web address: www.cvrmc.org
Control: Other not–for–profit (including NFP Corporation) **Service**: General medical and surgical

Staffed Beds: 25 **Admissions:** 1520 **Census:** 13 **Outpatient Visits:** 46388 **Births:** 306 **Total Expense ($000):** 50631 **Payroll Expense ($000):** 19490 **Personnel:** 239

GOODYEAR—Maricopa County

✉ **ABRAZO WEST CAMPUS (030110)**, 13677 West McDowell Road, Zip 85395–2635; tel. 623/882–1500, (Nonreporting) **A**1 10 **S** TENET Healthcare Corporation, Dallas, TX
Primary Contact: Stan Holm, Chief Executive Officer
COO: Jeffrey Dossett, Chief Operating Officer
CFO: Asja DiMuria, Chief Financial Officer
CNO: Scott David Morey, Chief Nursing Officer
Web address: www.abrazohealth.com
Control: Corporation, Investor–owned (for–profit) **Service**: General medical and surgical

Staffed Beds: 106

✉ **WESTERN REGIONAL MEDICAL CENTER (030127)**, 14200 West Celebrate Life way, Zip 85338–3005; tel. 623/207–3000, **A**1 2 10 **F**3 15 29 30 31 33 34 35 36 44 45 46 47 48 49 55 57 58 59 68 70 75 77 78 79 81 82 84 85 86 87 93 100 101 107 108 109 110 111 112 113 116 117 118 119 120 121 123 124 126 130 132 135 143 146 148 149 **S** Cancer Treatment Centers of America, Schaumburg, IL
Primary Contact: Robert Gould, President and Chief Executive Officer
Web address: www.cancercenter.com/western-hospital.cfm
Control: Corporation, Investor–owned (for–profit) **Service**: Cancer

Staffed Beds: 12 **Admissions:** 444 **Census:** 6 **Outpatient Visits:** 26303 **Births:** 0 **Personnel:** 368

GREEN VALLEY—Cochise County

⇑ **SANTA CRUZ VALLEY REGIONAL HOSPITAL (030137)**, 4455 South I–19 Frontage Road, Zip 85614; tel. 520/393–4700, (Nonreporting) **A**21
Primary Contact: Kelly Adams, Chief Executive Officer
CFO: Sara Ghali, Chief Financial Officer
CNO: Mona R. Smith, Chief Nursing Officer
Web address: www.greenvalleyhospital.com
Control: Corporation, Investor–owned (for–profit) **Service**: General medical and surgical

Staffed Beds: 98

KEAMS CANYON—Navajo County

✉ **HOPI HEALTH CARE CENTER (031305)**, Highway 264 Mile Marker 388, Zip 86042, Mailing Address: P.O. Box 4000, Polacca, Zip 86042–4000; tel. 928/737–6000, (Nonreporting) **A**1 3 10 18 **S** U.S. Indian Health Service, Rockville, MD
Primary Contact: Mose Herne, Chief Executive Officer
COO: Leonard H Lopez, Chief Operating Officer
CFO: Dorothy Sulu, Budget Analyst
CMO: Darren Vicenti, M.D., Clinical Director
CHR: Trudy Begay, Human Resources Specialist
Web address: www.ihs.gov/index.asp
Control: PHS, Indian Service, Government, federal **Service**: General medical and surgical

Staffed Beds: 15

KINGMAN—Mohave County

★ ⇑ **KINGMAN REGIONAL MEDICAL CENTER (030055)**, 3269 North Stockton Hill Road, Zip 86409–3691; tel. 928/757–2101, (Nonreporting) **A**3 10 13 21
Primary Contact: Brian Turney, Chief Executive Officer
COO: Ryan Kennedy, Chief Operating Officer
CFO: Timothy D Blanchard, Chief Financial Officer
CMO: Thomas Gaughan, M.D., Chief Medical Officer
CIO: Cheryl Martin, Chief Information Officer
CHR: Anita Harger, Chief Human Resource Officer
CNO: Kimberly Miyauchi, R.N., Chief Nursing Officer
Web address: www.azkrmc.com
Control: Hospital district or authority, Government, nonfederal **Service**: General medical and surgical

Staffed Beds: 180

LAKE HAVASU CITY—Mohave County

✉ **HAVASU REGIONAL MEDICAL CENTER (030069)**, 101 Civic Center Lane, Zip 86403–5683; tel. 928/855–8185, (Nonreporting) **A**1 10 **S** LifePoint Health, Brentwood, TN
Primary Contact: Michael N. Patterson, Chief Executive Officer
COO: Wes Taylor, Chief Operating Officer
CFO: Christina DiMambro, Chief Financial Officer
CMO: Michael Rosen, M.D., Chief Medical Officer
CIO: Linda Toy, Director Information Systems
Web address: www.havasuregional.com
Control: Corporation, Investor–owned (for–profit) **Service**: General medical and surgical

Staffed Beds: 162

LAKESIDE—Navajo County

CCC AT PINEVIEW HOSPITAL (034027), 1920 West Commerce Drive,
Zip 85929; tel. 928/368–4110, **A**10 **F**4 98 102 154 **P**6
Primary Contact: Rosemary Anderson, Administrator
Web address: www.ccc–az.org
Control: Other not–for–profit (including NFP Corporation) **Service**: Psychiatric

Staffed Beds: 16 **Admissions**: 659 **Census**: 10

LAVEEN—Maricopa County

☐ **DIGNITY HEALTH ARIZONA GENERAL HOSPITAL (030136)**, 7171 South 51st
Avenue, Zip 85339–2923; tel. 623/584–5100, (Nonreporting) **A**1
Primary Contact: Mark F. Slyter, FACHE, President and Chief Executive Officer, East
Valley
CFO: Anthony Cirocco, Chief Financial Officer
CMO: Fred Johnson, M.D., Chief Medical Officer
CNO: Victoria Nugent, Chief Nursing Officer
Web address: www.dignityhealth.org/arizonageneral/
Control: Other not–for–profit (including NFP Corporation) **Service**: Acute long–
term care hospital

Staffed Beds: 16

MESA—Maricopa County

☐ **ARIZONA SPINE AND JOINT HOSPITAL (030107)**, 4620 East Baseline Road,
Zip 85206–4624; tel. 480/832–4770, (Nonreporting) **A**1 10 **S** National Surgical
Healthcare, Chicago, IL
Primary Contact: Todd Greene, Chief Executive Officer
CHR: Diane Hearne, Director Human Resources
CNO: Stacy Hayes, R.N., Chief Nursing Officer
Web address: www.azspineandjoint.com
Control: Corporation, Investor–owned (for–profit) **Service**: Orthopedic

Staffed Beds: 23

⊞ **BANNER BAYWOOD MEDICAL CENTER (030088)**, 6644 East Baywood Avenue,
Zip 85206–1797; tel. 480/321–2000, **A**1 10 **F**3 15 18 29 30 31 34 35 36 37 40
41 43 44 45 46 47 48 49 50 51 56 57 58 59 60 61 63 64 65 70 74 75 77 78
79 81 82 84 85 86 87 90 91 92 94 96 100 102 107 108 110 111 115 118 119
126 129 130 135 141 146 147 148 149 154 **S** Banner Health, Gilbert, AZ
Primary Contact: Lamont M. Yoder, R.N., MSN, FACHE, Chief Executive Officer
CFO: Derek Lythgoe, Chief Financial Officer
CMO: Michael P. O'Connor, M.D., Chief Medical Officer
CIO: Lori Matthews, Vice President Information Technology System
CHR: Tiffany Werner, Senior Human Resource Business Partner
CNO: Kelley Kieffer, Chief Nursing Officer
Web address: www.bannerhealth.com/locations/Arizona/
banner+baywood+medical+center
Control: Other not–for–profit (including NFP Corporation) **Service**: General
medical and surgical

Staffed Beds: 359 **Admissions**: 17046 **Census**: 221 **Births**: 457 **Total
Expense ($000)**: 253861 **Payroll Expense ($000)**: 95446 **Personnel**: 1496

BANNER CHILDREN'S HOSPITAL See Cardon Children's Medical Center

⊞ **BANNER DESERT MEDICAL CENTER (030065)**, 1400 South Dobson
Road, Zip 85202–4707; tel. 480/412–3000, (Includes CARDON CHILDREN'S
MEDICAL CENTER, 1400 South Dobson Road, Mesa, AZ, Zip 85202–4707;
tel. 480/412–3000; Justin Bradshaw, Chief Executive Officer; SAMARITAN
BEHAVIORAL HEALTH CENTER–DESERT SAMARITAN MEDICAL CENTER, 2225 West
Southern Avenue, Mesa, AZ, Zip 85202; tel. 602/464–4000) **A**1 3 5 10 **F**3 11 12
13 17 18 19 20 21 22 23 24 25 26 27 28 29 30 31 32 34 35 36 40 41 43 45
46 47 48 49 50 51 56 58 59 60 61 63 64 68 70 71 72 74 75 76 77 78 79 81
84 85 86 87 88 89 91 92 93 96 107 108 110 111 114 115 118 119 120 121 123
124 126 129 130 132 135 146 147 148 149 154 **S** Banner Health, Gilbert, AZ
Primary Contact: Laura Robertson, R.N., Chief Executive Officer
COO: Cristal Mackay, Chief Operating Officer
CFO: Scott Leckey, Chief Financial Officer
CMO: Tanya Kne, M.D., Chief Medical Officer
CIO: Stacey Hinkle, Director Information Technology
CHR: Kevin McVeigh, Chief Human Resources Officer
Web address: www.bannerhealth.com/Locations/Arizona/
Banner+Desert+Medical+Center
Control: Other not–for–profit (including NFP Corporation) **Service**: General
medical and surgical

Staffed Beds: 595 **Admissions**: 32068 **Census**: 424 **Births**: 3870 **Total
Expense ($000)**: 605881 **Payroll Expense ($000)**: 205346 **Personnel**: 3296

⊞ **BANNER HEART HOSPITAL (030105)**, 6750 East Baywood Avenue,
Zip 85206–1749; tel. 480/854–5000, **A**1 3 10 **F**3 8 12 13 15 18 29 30 31 34
35 36 40 44 45 46 47 49 50 51 55 57 59 60 63 68 70 72 74 75 76 77 78 79
81 84 85 87 93 102 107 108 110 111 114 116 117 118 119 120 121 124
126 130 134 136 141 142 146 147 148 149 154 **S** Banner Health, Gilbert, AZ
Primary Contact: Lamont M. Yoder, R.N., MSN, FACHE, Chief Executive Officer
CFO: Derek Lythgoe, Chief Financial Officer
CMO: Paul Hurst, M.D., Chief Medical Officer
CIO: Lori Matthews, Vice President, Information Technology System
CHR: Tiffany Werner, Senior Human Resource Business Partner
CNO: Kelley Kieffer, Chief Nursing Officer
Web address: www.bannerhealth.com/Locations/Arizona/Banner+Heart+Hospital/
Control: Other not–for–profit (including NFP Corporation) **Service**: Heart

Staffed Beds: 111 **Admissions**: 4682 **Census**: 57 **Births**: 0 **Total Expense
($000)**: 111429 **Payroll Expense ($000)**: 29156 **Personnel**: 1514

CARDON CHILDREN'S MEDICAL CENTER See Banner Desert Medical Center,
Mesa

⊞ **EMCOMPASS HEALTH REHABILITATION HOSPITAL OF EAST (033037)**, 5652
East Baseline Road, Zip 85206–4713; tel. 480/567–0350, (Nonreporting) **A**1 10
S Encompass Health Corporation, Birmingham, AL
Primary Contact: Jeffrey Roberts, Chief Executive Officer
CMO: Martin Yee, M.D., Medical Director
CHR: Nancy Pickler, Director of Human Resources
CNO: Hope Dunn, Chief Nursing Officer
Web address: www.healthsoutheastvalley.com
Control: Corporation, Investor–owned (for–profit) **Service**: Rehabilitation

Staffed Beds: 60

HACIENDA CHILDREN'S HOSPITAL (033303), 610 West Jerome Avenue,
Zip 85210; tel. 480/579–2400, (Nonreporting) **A**10 22
Primary Contact: William Timmons, President and Chief Executive Officer
Web address: www.haciendahealthcare.org/careproviders/hacienda–childrens–
hospital/
Control: Other not–for–profit (including NFP Corporation) **Service**: Children's
general medical and surgical

Staffed Beds: 24

★ ⇑ **MOUNTAIN VISTA MEDICAL CENTER (030121)**, 1301 South Crismon
Road, Zip 85209–3767; tel. 480/358–6100, **A**3 10 13 21 **F**6 7 8 9 10 11 12 13
14 15 18 20 22 24 26 29 30 31 34 35 37 38 40 43 45 50 51 56 57 59 68 70
72 74 79 81 82 87 93 94 96 98 100 102 103 107 108 110 111 114 119 126
130 131 143 146 147 148 **P**7 **S** Steward Health Care System, LLC, Dallas, TX
Primary Contact: Jacob Golich, Chief Executive Officer
CFO: Marty Bakos, Chief Financial Officer
CNO: Elizabeth Kearney, R.N., Chief Nursing Officer
Web address: www.mvmedicalcenter.com
Control: Corporation, Investor–owned (for–profit) **Service**: General medical and
surgical

Staffed Beds: 178 **Admissions**: 7644 **Census**: 94 **Outpatient Visits**: 44419
Births: 711 **Total Expense ($000)**: 154361 **Payroll Expense ($000)**: 48000
Personnel: 767

PROMISE HOSPITAL OF PHOENIX (032006), 433 East 6th Street,
Zip 85203–7104; tel. 480/427–3000, (Nonreporting) **A**10 **S** Promise Healthcare,
Boca Raton, FL
Primary Contact: Wayne Kinsey, Chief Executive Officer
COO: Wendy Larson, Chief Clinical Officer
CFO: Theo Clark, Director Financial Services
CMO: Syed Shahryar, M.D., Medical Director
CHR: Christie Brea, Manager Human Resources
Web address: www.promise–phoenix.com
Control: Corporation, Investor–owned (for–profit) **Service**: Acute long–term care
hospital

Staffed Beds: 40

**SAMARITAN BEHAVIORAL HEALTH CENTER–DESERT SAMARITAN MEDICAL
CENTER** See Banner Desert Medical Center, Mesa

Hospital, Medicare Provider Number, Address, Telephone, Approval, Facility, and Physician Codes, Health Care System

★ American Hospital Association (AHA) membership ○ Healthcare Facilities Accreditation Program ⇑ Center for Improvement in Healthcare Quality Accreditation
☐ The Joint Commission accreditation ◇ DNV Healthcare Inc. accreditation △ Commission on Accreditation of Rehabilitation Facilities (CARF) accreditation

---

AZ

NOGALES—Santa Cruz County

✠ **CARONDELET HOLY CROSS HOSPITAL (031313)**, 1171 West Target Range Road, Zip 85621–2415; tel. 520/285–3000, **A**1 3 10 18 **F**3 13 29 30 31 32 34 35 40 50 51 56 57 59 64 65 68 70 75 76 77 79 81 85 86 87 89 93 107 111 119 130 132 133 134 135 146 149 **S** TENET Healthcare Corporation, Dallas, TX
Primary Contact: Debbie Knapheide, MSN, Site Administrator, Chief Nursing Officer and Chief Operating Officer
COO: Debbie Knapheide, MSN, Site Administrator, Chief Nursing Officer and Chief Operating Officer
CFO: Alan Strauss, Chief Financial Officer
CMO: Roy Farrell, M.D., Chief Medical Officer
CNO: Debbie Knapheide, MSN, Site Administrator, Chief Nursing Officer and Chief Operating Officer
Web address: www.carondelet.org
Control: Corporation, Investor–owned (for–profit) **Service**: General medical and surgical

Staffed Beds: 25 **Admissions**: 1082 **Census**: 7 **Outpatient Visits**: 47080 **Births**: 670 **Total Expense ($000)**: 23965 **Payroll Expense ($000)**: 12479 **Personnel**: 146

ORO VALLEY—Pima County

✠ **ORO VALLEY HOSPITAL (030114)**, 1551 East Tangerine Road, Zip 85755–6213; tel. 520/901–3500, (Nonreporting) **A**1 10 **S** Community Health Systems, Inc., Franklin, TN
Primary Contact: Jae Dale, Chief Executive Officer
CFO: Maurene Polashek, Chief Financial Officer
CNO: Julie Hunt, R.N., MS, Chief Nursing Officer
Web address: www.orovalleyhospital.com
Control: Corporation, Investor–owned (for–profit) **Service**: General medical and surgical

Staffed Beds: 144

PAGE—Coconino County

✠ **PAGE HOSPITAL (031304)**, 501 North Navajo Drive, Zip 86040, Mailing Address: P.O. Box 1447, Zip 86040–1447; tel. 928/645–2424, **A**1 10 18 **F**3 13 15 18 29 34 35 40 43 45 47 49 50 59 68 70 71 75 76 81 82 85 91 93 94 107 110 111 114 119 133 146 148 154 **S** Banner Health, Gilbert, AZ
Primary Contact: Brian Kellar, Chief Executive Officer
CFO: Darcy Robertson, Chief Financial Officer
CMO: Thomas Wood, M.D., Chief Medical Officer
CIO: Paul Caldwell, Facility Coordinator Information Technology Customer Relations
CHR: Ed Franklin, Chief Human Resources Officer
CNO: Susan Eubanks, Chief Nursing Officer
Web address: www.bannerhealth.com/Locations/Arizona/Page+Hospital
Control: Other not–for–profit (including NFP Corporation) **Service**: General medical and surgical

Staffed Beds: 25 **Admissions**: 386 **Census**: 3 **Births**: 129 **Total Expense ($000)**: 15635 **Payroll Expense ($000)**: 7164 **Personnel**: 99

PARKER—La Paz County

LA PAZ REGIONAL HOSPITAL (031317), 1200 West Mohave Road, Zip 85344–6349; tel. 928/669–9201, (Nonreporting) **A**10 18
Primary Contact: Kevin Brown, Chief Executive Officer
CFO: Carl J. Flanagan, Chief Financial Officer
CMO: Jack Dunn, M.D., Chief of Staff
CHR: Regina M Martinez, Director Human Resources
CNO: Maria Martinez, Chief Nursing Officer
Web address: www.lapazhospital.org
Control: Other not–for–profit (including NFP Corporation) **Service**: General medical and surgical

Staffed Beds: 25

✠ **U.S. PUBLIC HEALTH SERVICE INDIAN HOSPITAL (031307)**, 12033 Agency Road, Zip 85344–7718; tel. 928/669–2137, (Nonreporting) **A**1 10 18 **S** U.S. Indian Health Service, Rockville, MD
Primary Contact: Elizabeth Helsel, Chief Executive Officer
CFO: Robin Tahbo, Financial Management Officer
CMO: Laurence Norick, M.D., Clinical Director
CIO: JayLynn Saavedra, Chief Information Officer
Web address: www.ihs.gov
Control: PHS, Indian Service, Government, federal **Service**: General medical and surgical

Staffed Beds: 20

PAYSON—Gila County

✠ **BANNER PAYSON MEDICAL CENTER (030033)**, 807 South Ponderosa Street, Zip 85541–5599; tel. 928/474–3222, **A**1 3 10 20 **F**3 11 13 15 18 26 29 30 31 34 35 38 40 44 45 46 50 51 57 59 68 70 75 76 77 79 81 85 87 89 93 100 107 108 110 111 119 127 130 132 135 145 146 147 148 149 154 **S** Banner Health, Gilbert, AZ
Primary Contact: Lance Porter, Chief Executive Officer
CFO: Peter Finelli, Chief Financial Officer
CMO: John Vandruff, M.D., Chief of Staff
CIO: Nick Vandermeer, Director Information Systems
CHR: Shawn M. Thomas, Director Human Resources
CNO: Hart Hintze, Chief Nursing Officer
Web address: www.paysonhospital.com
Control: Corporation, Investor–owned (for–profit) **Service**: General medical and surgical

Staffed Beds: 25 **Admissions**: 1573 **Census**: 11 **Outpatient Visits**: 30036 **Births**: 164 **Total Expense ($000)**: 42791 **Payroll Expense ($000)**: 13700 **Personnel**: 232

PEORIA—Maricopa County

CURAHEALTH PHOENIX See Curahealth Phoenix, Phoenix

PERIDOT—Gila County

✠ **SAN CARLOS APACHE HEALTHCARE CORPORATION (030077)**, 103 Medicine Way Road, Zip 85542; tel. 928/475–1400, (Nonreporting) **A**1 10 **S** U.S. Indian Health Service, Rockville, MD
Primary Contact: Victoria D. Began, R.N., MS, President and Chief Executive Officer
CFO: Vivie Hosteenez, Chief Financial Officer
CMO: Douglas Brinkerhoff, M.D., Clinical Director
CIO: Nimmy Mathews, Acting Director Quality Management
CHR: Shirley M Boni, Administrative Officer
Web address: www.ihs.gov
Control: PHS, Indian Service, Government, federal **Service**: General medical and surgical

Staffed Beds: 8

PHOENIX—Maricopa County

✠ **ABRAZO CENTRAL CAMPUS (030030)**, 2000 West Bethany Home Road, Zip 85015–2443; tel. 602/249–0212, (Nonreporting) **A**1 3 5 10 **S** TENET Healthcare Corporation, Dallas, TX
Primary Contact: Frank L. Molinaro, Chief Executive Officer
COO: Jayleen Casano, Ph.D., FACHE, Chief Operations and Nursing Officer
CFO: Paul Hymel, Chief Financial Officer
CHR: Dana George, Chief Human Resources Officer
Web address: www.abrazohealth.com
Control: Corporation, Investor–owned (for–profit) **Service**: General medical and surgical

Staffed Beds: 215

✠ **ABRAZO SCOTTSDALE CAMPUS (030083)**, 3929 East Bell Road, Zip 85032–2196; tel. 602/923–5000, (Nonreporting) **A**1 10 **S** TENET Healthcare Corporation, Dallas, TX
Primary Contact: Frank L. Molinaro, Chief Executive Officer
CFO: Jeffrey Zyla, Chief Financial Officer
CHR: Kendrick Russell, Chief Human Resources Officer
CNO: Vicki Lynn Huber, R.N., MSN, Chief Nursing Officer
Web address: www.abrazoscottsdale.com
Control: Corporation, Investor–owned (for–profit) **Service**: General medical and surgical

Staffed Beds: 142

☐ **ARIZONA STATE HOSPITAL (034021)**, 2500 East Van Buren Street, Zip 85008–6079; tel. 602/244–1331, (Nonreporting) **A**1 10
Primary Contact: Aaron Bowen, Chief Executive Officer
CMO: Steve Dingle, M.D., Chief Medical Officer
CHR: Jeanine Decker, Manager Human Resources
Web address: www.hs.state.az.us
Control: State, Government, nonfederal **Service**: Psychiatric

Staffed Beds: 299

Many Facility Codes have changed. Please refer to the AHA Guide Code Chart. © 2018 AHA Guide

AZ

⊞ △ **BANNER – UNIVERSITY MEDICAL CENTER PHOENIX (030002)**, 1111 East McDowell Road, Zip 85006–2666, Mailing Address: P.O. Box 2989, Zip 85062–2989; tel. 602/239–2000, **A**1 3 5 7 8 10 **F**1 3 8 9 11 12 13 15 17 18 19 21 22 24 26 28 29 30 31 33 34 35 36 37 38 39 40 41 43 44 45 46 47 48 49 50 51 53 54 55 56 57 58 59 60 61 64 65 66 68 70 72 74 75 76 77 78 79 80 81 82 84 85 86 87 90 91 92 93 94 96 97 98 100 101 102 103 104 107 108 110 111 114 115 116 117 118 119 123 124 126 129 130 131 132 135 138 139 141 142 143 145 146 147 148 149 150 **S** Banner Health, Gilbert, AZ
Primary Contact: Steve Narang, M.D., Chief Executive Officer
CFO: Kathy Kotin, Chief Financial Officer
CMO: Paul Stander, M.D., Chief Medical Officer
CIO: Michael S Warden, Senior Vice President Information Technology
CHR: Michael Fleming, Chief People Officer
Web address: www.bannerhealth.com/Locations/Arizona/Banner+Good+Samaritan+Medical+Center
Control: Other not–for–profit (including NFP Corporation) **Service:** General medical and surgical

Staffed Beds: 685 **Admissions:** 31547 **Census:** 482 **Births:** 5462 **Total Expense ($000):** 808394 **Payroll Expense ($000):** 243654 **Personnel:** 4006

⊞ **BANNER ESTRELLA MEDICAL CENTER (030115)**, 9201 West Thomas Road, Zip 85037–3332; tel. 623/327–4000, **A**1 3 10 **F**3 11 12 13 18 20 22 29 30 31 34 35 36 37 38 40 41 43 44 45 46 49 50 51 57 58 59 60 61 64 68 73 74 75 76 77 78 79 81 82 84 85 86 87 96 102 107 108 111 114 115 118 119 126 130 131 132 135 144 145 146 147 148 149 151 154 **S** Banner Health, Gilbert, AZ
Primary Contact: Courtney Ophaug, FACHE, Chief Executive Officer
COO: Gary Foster, R.N., Associate Administrator
CFO: Dean Shepardson, Chief Financial Officer
CHR: Wendy Labadie, Chief Human Resource Officer
CNO: Sheri Dahlstrom, R.N., Chief Nursing Officer
Web address: www.bannerhealth.com/Locations/Arizona/Banner+Estrella+Medical+Center/
Control: Other not–for–profit (including NFP Corporation) **Service:** General medical and surgical

Staffed Beds: 278 **Admissions:** 16443 **Census:** 179 **Births:** 4600 **Total Expense ($000):** 256132 **Payroll Expense ($000):** 92154 **Personnel:** 1396

⊞ **CURAHEALTH PHOENIX (032000)**, 40 East Indianola Avenue, Zip 85012–2059; tel. 602/280–7000, (Includes CURAHEALTH PHOENIX, 13216 North Plaza Del Rio Boulevard, Peoria, AZ, Zip 85381–4907; tel. 623/974–5463; Karen Shammas, Chief Executive Officer) (Nonreporting) **A**1 10 **S** Curahealth Hospitals, Garland, TX
Primary Contact: Karen Cawley, Chief Executive Officer
Web address: www.curahealth.com
Control: Corporation, Investor–owned (for–profit) **Service:** Acute long–term care hospital

Staffed Beds: 58

HAVEN SENIOR HORIZONS (034020), 1201 South 7th Avenue, Suite 200, Zip 85007–4076; tel. 623/236–2000, **A**10 **F**56 68 98 100 101 102 103 **S** Haven Behavioral Healthcare, Nashville, TN
Primary Contact: Ashley Ellis, Chief Executive Officer
CHR: Erin McEldowney, Manager Human Resources
CNO: Char Ralstin, Director of Nursing
Web address: www.havenbehavioral.com
Control: Corporation, Investor–owned (for–profit) **Service:** Psychiatric

Staffed Beds: 45 **Admissions:** 1157 **Census:** 39 **Outpatient Visits:** 0 **Births:** 0

★ ⇑ **HONORHEALTH DEER VALLEY MEDICAL CENTER (030092)**, 19829 North 27th Avenue, Zip 85027–4002; tel. 623/879–6100, (Nonreporting) **A**10 21 **S** HonorHealth, Scottsdale, AZ
Primary Contact: David Price, Chief Executive Officer
CMO: Mary Ann Turley, D.O., Medical Director
CHR: Frank L Cummins, Vice President Human Resources
Web address: www.jcl.com
Control: Other not–for–profit (including NFP Corporation) **Service:** General medical and surgical

Staffed Beds: 204

★ ⇑ **HONORHEALTH JOHN C. LINCOLN MEDICAL CENTER (030014)**, 250 East Dunlap Avenue, Zip 85020–2825; tel. 602/943–2381, (Nonreporting) **A**3 10 13 21 **S** HonorHealth, Scottsdale, AZ
Primary Contact: Margaret Elizabeth. Griffin, Chief Executive Officer
CMO: Christopher Shearer, M.D., Chief Medical Officer
CNO: Jelden Arcilla, R.N., Vice President and Chief Nursing Officer
Web address: www.jcl.com
Control: Other not–for–profit (including NFP Corporation) **Service:** General medical and surgical

Staffed Beds: 262

LOS NINOS HOSPITAL (033301), 2303 East Thomas Road, Zip 85016–7827; tel. 602/954–7311, (Nonreporting) **A**10
Primary Contact: William Timmons, Chief Executive Officer
Web address: www.losninoshospital.com
Control: Other not–for–profit (including NFP Corporation) **Service:** Children's other specialty

Staffed Beds: 15

★ ⇑ **MARICOPA INTEGRATED HEALTH SYSTEM (030022)**, 2601 East Roosevelt Street, Zip 85008–4956; tel. 602/344–5011, (Includes ARIZONA CHILDREN'S CENTER, 2601 East Roosevelt Street, Phoenix, AZ, Zip 85008–4973; tel. 602/344–5051) **A**3 5 8 10 21 **F**3 13 15 16 18 20 22 29 30 31 34 39 40 41 43 45 46 47 48 49 50 51 54 57 58 59 60 61 64 65 68 70 72 74 75 76 77 78 79 81 85 86 87 88 89 93 97 98 100 101 103 104 107 108 110 111 114 115 118 119 126 130 132 135 146 147 148 149 150 153 154 **P**1
Primary Contact: Stephen A. Purves, FACHE, President and Chief Executive Officer
COO: Kris Gaw, Executive Vice President and Chief Operating Officer
CFO: Kathleen Benaquista, Executive Vice President and Chief Financial Officer
CMO: John Hitt, M.D., Executive Vice President and Chief Medical Officer
CIO: Kelly Summers, Chief Information Officer
CHR: Marshall Jones, Senior Vice President Human Resources
CNO: Sherry Stotler, R.N., MSN, Chief Nursing Officer
Web address: www.mihs.org
Control: Hospital district or authority, Government, nonfederal **Service:** General medical and surgical

Staffed Beds: 544 **Admissions:** 14411 **Census:** 367 **Outpatient Visits:** 470546 **Births:** 2332 **Total Expense ($000):** 485192 **Payroll Expense ($000):** 220742 **Personnel:** 2892

⊞ **MAYO CLINIC HOSPITAL (030103)**, 5777 East Mayo Boulevard, Zip 85054–4502; tel. 480/342–2000, **A**1 2 3 5 8 10 **F**3 6 8 9 11 12 14 15 17 18 20 22 24 26 28 29 30 31 34 35 36 37 39 40 44 45 46 47 48 49 50 51 54 55 56 57 58 59 60 61 64 65 67 68 70 74 75 77 78 79 80 81 82 83 84 85 86 87 90 92 93 96 97 100 104 107 108 110 111 112 114 115 116 117 118 119 120 121 122 123 124 126 129 130 131 132 135 136 137 138 139 140 141 142 145 146 147 148 149 154 **P**6 **S** Mayo Clinic, Rochester, MN
Primary Contact: Wyatt Decker, Chief Executive Officer, Mayo Clinic in Arizona
CFO: Jeffrey R Froisland, Chief Financial Officer
CMO: Alyssa B Chapital, M.D., Medical Director, Mayo Clinic Hospital
CIO: Paul Lenko, Section Head Information Technology
CHR: Nichelle A Baker, Chair Human Resources
CNO: Teresa Connolly, R.N., Chief Nursing Officer
Web address: www.mayoclinic.org/arizona/
Control: Other not–for–profit (including NFP Corporation) **Service:** General medical and surgical

Staffed Beds: 280 **Admissions:** 15789 **Census:** 202 **Outpatient Visits:** 75311 **Births:** 0 **Personnel:** 3395

☐ **OASIS HOSPITAL (030131)**, 750 North 40th Street, Zip 85008–6486; tel. 602/797–7700, (Nonreporting) **A**1 3 10
Primary Contact: Tim Bogardus, Chief Executive Officer
Web address: www.oasishospital.com
Control: Partnership, Investor–owned (for–profit) **Service:** Orthopedic

Staffed Beds: 64

⊞ **PHOENIX CHILDREN'S HOSPITAL (033302)**, 1919 East Thomas Road, Zip 85016–7710; tel. 602/933–1000, **A**1 3 5 10 **F**3 8 11 15 17 19 21 23 25 27 29 30 31 32 34 35 37 38 39 40 41 43 44 46 48 49 50 54 55 57 58 59 60 61 64 65 66 68 71 72 73 74 75 77 78 79 81 82 84 85 86 87 88 89 91 92 93 94 96 97 98 99 100 101 102 104 105 107 108 111 113 114 115 116 117 118 119 129 130 131 132 134 136 137 138 139 144 146 148 153 **P**6
Primary Contact: Robert L. Meyer, President and Chief Executive Officer
COO: Betsy Kuzas, Executive Vice President and Chief Operating Officer
CFO: Douglas Myers, Executive Vice President and Chief Financial Officer
CMO: H. Stacy Nicholson, M.D., M.P.H., Physician in Chief
CIO: David Higginson, Executive Vice President and Chief Administrative Officer
CHR: Lisa Phelps, Senior Vice President, Human Resources
CNO: Julie Bowman, Senior Vice President, Patient Care and Chief Nursing Officer
Web address: www.phoenixchildrens.com
Control: Other not–for–profit (including NFP Corporation) **Service:** Children's general medical and surgical

Staffed Beds: 381 **Admissions:** 13757 **Census:** 212 **Outpatient Visits:** 310731 **Births:** 0 **Total Expense ($000):** 816111 **Payroll Expense ($000):** 357693 **Personnel:** 3740

Hospital, Medicare Provider Number, Address, Telephone, Approval, Facility, and Physician Codes, Health Care System

★ American Hospital Association (AHA) membership   ○ Healthcare Facilities Accreditation Program   ⇑ Center for Improvement in Healthcare Quality Accreditation
☐ The Joint Commission accreditation   ◇ DNV Healthcare Inc. accreditation   △ Commission on Accreditation of Rehabilitation Facilities (CARF) accreditation

---

AZ

✠ **PHOENIX VETERANS AFFAIRS HEALTH CARE SYSTEM**, 650 East Indian School Road, Zip 85012–1892; tel. 602/277–5551, (Nonreporting) **A**1 3 5 **S** Department of Veterans Affairs, Perry Point, MD
Primary Contact: RimaAnn O. Nelson, R.N., Director
CFO: Christine Hollingsworth, Chief Financial Officer
CMO: Maureen McCarthy, M.D., Chief of Staff
Web address: www.phoenix.va.gov/
Control: Veterans Affairs, Government, federal **Service:** General medical and surgical

Staffed Beds: 197

★ **QUAIL RUN BEHAVIORAL HEALTH (034031)**, 2545 West Quail Avenue, Zip 85027–2418; tel. 602/455–5700, (Nonreporting)
Primary Contact: David Carnahan, Chief Executive Officer
Web address: www.quailrunbehavioral.com/
Control: Other not–for–profit (including NFP Corporation) **Service:** Psychiatric

Staffed Beds: 102

✠ **SELECT SPECIALTY HOSPITAL–PHOENIX (032001)**, 350 West Thomas Road, 3rd Floor Main, Zip 85013–4409; tel. 602/406–6810, **A**1 10 **F**1 29 75 77 87 148 **S** Select Medical Corporation, Mechanicsburg, PA
Primary Contact: Karen Crowley, Chief Executive Officer
Web address: www.https://phoenix.selectspecialtyhospitals.com
Control: Corporation, Investor–owned (for–profit) **Service:** Acute long–term care hospital

Staffed Beds: 48 Admissions: 522 Census: 39 Outpatient Visits: 0 Births: 0 Total Expense ($000): 24778 Payroll Expense ($000): 10182

✠ **SELECT SPECIALTY HOSPITAL–PHOENIX DOWNTOWN (032005)**, 1012 East Wiletta Street, 4th Floor, Zip 85006; tel. 602/839–6550, (Nonreporting) **A**1 **S** Select Medical Corporation, Mechanicsburg, PA
Primary Contact: David Selman, Chief Executive Officer
Web address: www.selectmedicalcorp.com
Control: Corporation, Investor–owned (for–profit) **Service:** Acute long–term care hospital

Staffed Beds: 33

✠ △ **ST. JOSEPH'S HOSPITAL AND MEDICAL CENTER (030024)**, 350 West Thomas Road, Zip 85013–4496, Mailing Address: P.O. Box 2071, Zip 85001–2071; tel. 602/406–3000, (Includes CHILDREN'S HEALTH CENTER, 350 West Thomas Road, Phoenix, AZ, Zip 85013–4409; tel. 602/344–5051; ST. JOSEPH'S WESTGATE MEDICAL CENTER, 7300 North 99th Avenue, Glendale, AZ, Zip 85307–3003; tel. 602/406–0000) **A**1 2 3 5 7 8 10 **F**2 3 6 10 11 12 13 15 17 18 20 22 24 26 29 30 31 32 34 35 36 38 39 40 41 43 44 45 46 47 48 49 50 51 53 54 55 56 57 58 59 60 61 64 66 68 70 71 72 74 75 76 77 78 79 80 81 82 84 85 86 87 90 91 92 93 95 96 97 100 101 102 104 107 108 110 111 112 114 115 117 118 119 120 121 123 124 126 127 130 131 132 134 135 138 139 140 141 144 145 146 147 148 149 150 153 154 **P**6 **S** Dignity Health, San Francisco, CA
Primary Contact: Patty White, R.N., MS, President
CMO: Edward Donahue, M.D., Chief Medical Officer
CHR: Maureen Sterbach, Vice President Human Resources
CNO: Julie Ward, MSN, R.N., Chief Nursing Officer
Web address: www.stjosephs–phx.org
Control: Other not–for–profit (including NFP Corporation) **Service:** General medical and surgical

Staffed Beds: 577 Admissions: 31362 Census: 434 Outpatient Visits: 607395 Births: 5173 Total Expense ($000): 1155269 Payroll Expense ($000): 441055 Personnel: 5094

☐ **ST. LUKE'S BEHAVIORAL HEALTH CENTER (034013)**, 1800 East Van Buren, Zip 85006–3742; tel. 602/251–8546, (Nonreporting) **A**1 10 **S** Steward Health Care System, LLC, Dallas, TX
Primary Contact: Gregory L. Jahn, R.N., Chief Executive Officer
CFO: Ruby Majhail, Chief Financial Officer
CMO: Mario Tafur, M.D., Chief of Staff
CIO: Chris Ulrey, Director Management Information Systems
CHR: Amy M Howell, Director Human Resources
Web address: www.iasishealthcare.com
Control: Corporation, Investor–owned (for–profit) **Service:** Psychiatric

Staffed Beds: 85

★ ⇑ **ST. LUKE'S MEDICAL CENTER (030037)**, 1800 East Van Buren Street, Zip 85006–3742; tel. 602/251–8100, (Includes TEMPE ST. LUKE'S HOSPITAL, 1500 South Mill Avenue, Tempe, AZ, Zip 85281–6699; tel. 480/784–5510; James Flinn, JD, FACHE, Chief Executive Officer) (Nonreporting) **A**3 10 21 **S** Steward Health Care System, LLC, Dallas, TX
Primary Contact: James Flinn, JD, FACHE, Chief Executive Officer
CFO: Ken Walsh, Chief Financial Officer
CHR: Trinise Thompson, Director Human Resources
Web address: www.stlukesmedcenter.com
Control: Corporation, Investor–owned (for–profit) **Service:** General medical and surgical

Staffed Beds: 284

☐ **THE CORE INSTITUTE SPECIALTY HOSPITAL (030108)**, 6501 North 19th Avenue, Zip 85015–1646; tel. 602/795–6020, (Nonreporting) **A**1 10
Primary Contact: Kurt Loveless, Chief Executive Officer
CFO: Barbara Chacon, Chief Financial Officer
CMO: Christopher A. Yeung, M.D., Chief of Staff
CHR: Sherrie A Wagner, Manager Human Resources
CNO: Deborah Roberts, R.N., Chief Nursing Officer
Web address: www.thecoreinstitutehospital.com/
Control: Corporation, Investor–owned (for–profit) **Service:** Surgical

Staffed Beds: 33

✠ **U.S. PUBLIC HEALTH SERVICE PHOENIX INDIAN MEDICAL CENTER (030078)**, 4212 North 16th Street, Zip 85016–5389; tel. 602/263–1200, (Nonreporting) **A**1 3 5 10 **S** U.S. Indian Health Service, Rockville, MD
Primary Contact: Rear Admiral Michael Weahkee, Chief Executive Officer
CFO: Geraldine Harney, Chief Financial Officer
CMO: Dave Civic, M.D., Associate Director Clinical Services
CIO: Vina Montour, Director Information Technology
CHR: Betty Weston, Chief Human Resources Officer
Web address: www.ihs.gov
Control: PHS, Indian Service, Government, federal **Service:** General medical and surgical

Staffed Beds: 127

☐ **VALLEY HOSPITAL PHOENIX (034026)**, 3550 East Pinchot Avenue, Zip 85018–7434; tel. 602/957–4000, (Nonreporting) **A**1 10 **S** Universal Health Services, Inc., King of Prussia, PA
Primary Contact: Michelle David, Chief Executive Officer
Web address: www.valleyhospital–phoenix.com
Control: Corporation, Investor–owned (for–profit) **Service:** Psychiatric

Staffed Beds: 122

PRESCOTT—Yavapai County

✠ **NORTHERN ARIZONA VETERANS AFFAIRS HEALTH CARE SYSTEM**, 500 Highway 89 North, Zip 86313–5000; tel. 928/445–4860, (Nonreporting) **A**1 **S** Department of Veterans Affairs, Perry Point, MD
Primary Contact: Malcolm Keith. Piatt, M.D., Interim Director
COO: James Belmont, Associate Director
CFO: Ame Callahan, Acting Manager Resource Management Service
CMO: A Panneer Selvam, M.D., Chief of Staff
CIO: Scott McCrimmon, Manager Information Technology
CHR: Jane Lewerke, Manager Human Resources
Web address: www.prescott.va.gov/
Control: Veterans Affairs, Government, federal **Service:** General medical and surgical

Staffed Beds: 147

★ **YAVAPAI REGIONAL MEDICAL CENTER (030012)**, 1003 Willow Creek Road, Zip 86301–1668; tel. 928/445–2700, (Includes YAVAPAI REGIONAL MEDICAL CENTER – EAST, 7700 East Florentine Road, Prescott Valley, AZ, Zip 86314–2245; tel. 928/445–2700; John R. Amos, Chief Executive Officer) **A**10 20 **F**3 11 13 15 17 18 20 22 24 26 28 29 30 31 32 34 35 40 45 46 50 53 54 57 59 60 64 68 70 71 72 74 75 76 77 78 79 81 82 84 85 86 87 89 91 93 107 108 111 114 116 117 118 119 130 131 132 135 146 147 148 154 **P**6
Primary Contact: John R. Amos, President and Chief Executive Officer
COO: Larry P Burns Jr Chief Operating Officer
CFO: Lee Livin, Chief Financial Officer
CMO: Anthony Torres, M.D., Chief Medical Officer
CHR: Mark Timm, Executive Director Human Resources
CNO: Diane Drexler, R.N., Chief Nursing Officer
Web address: www.yrmc.org
Control: Other not–for–profit (including NFP Corporation) **Service:** General medical and surgical

Staffed Beds: 206 Admissions: 11430 Census: 100 Outpatient Visits: 138241 Births: 956 Total Expense ($000): 313543 Payroll Expense ($000): 120362 Personnel: 1354

PRESCOTT VALLEY—Yavapai County

☐ **MOUNTAIN VALLEY REGIONAL REHABILITATION HOSPITAL (033036)**, 3700 North Windsong Drive, Zip 86314–1253; tel. 928/759–8800, (Nonreporting) **A**1 10 **S** Ernest Health, Inc., Albuquerque, NM
Primary Contact: Judy Baum, Chief Executive Officer
CFO: Mark A. Roth, Chief Financial Officer
CMO: Alan S. Berman, M.D., Medical Director
CHR: Troy Eagar, Director Human Resources
CNO: Leah Walters, R.N., Director of Nursing
Web address: www.mvrrh.ernesthealth.com
Control: Corporation, Investor–owned (for–profit) **Service:** Rehabilitation

Staffed Beds: 16

WINDHAVEN PSYCHIATRIC HOSPITAL (034025), 3347 North Windsong Drive, Zip 86314-2283, Mailing Address: 3343 North Windsong Drive, Zip 86314-1213; tel. 928/445-5211, (Nonreporting) **A**10
Primary Contact: Larry D. Green Jr, Chief Executive Officer
COO: Pamela Pierce, Deputy Chief Executive Officer
CFO: Doug Oliver, Chief Financial Officer
CMO: Shane Russell-Jenkins, M.D., Medical Director
CIO: Laura Norman, Chief Development and Information Officer
CHR: Pamela Pierce, Deputy Chief Executive Officer
CNO: Esther Grear, Director Hospital Social Work and Assistant Hospital Administrator
Web address: www.wygc.org
Control: Other not-for-profit (including NFP Corporation) **Service**: Psychiatric

Staffed Beds: 16

SACATON—Pinal County

☐ **HUHUKAM MEMORIAL HOSPITAL (031308)**, 483 West Seed Farm Road, Zip 85147, Mailing Address: P.O. Box 38, Zip 85147-0001; tel. 602/528-1200, (Nonreporting) **A**1 3 10 18
Primary Contact: Lorrie Henderson, Ph.D., Chief Executive Officer
COO: Pamela Thompson, Chief Operations Officer
CMO: Noel Habib, M.D., Chief Medical Officer
CHR: Michael Freeman, Director Human Resources
Web address: www.grhc.org
Control: Other not-for-profit (including NFP Corporation) **Service**: General medical and surgical

Staffed Beds: 15

SAFFORD—Graham County

★ **MT. GRAHAM REGIONAL MEDICAL CENTER (030068)**, 1600 South 20th Avenue, Zip 85546-4097; tel. 928/348-4000, **A**3 10 20 **F**3 11 13 15 18 29 30 31 34 35 40 43 45 46 47 48 49 50 57 59 63 64 66 70 75 76 77 78 79 81 84 85 97 107 108 110 111 114 119 127 129 130 132 133 135 146 147 148 154 **P**6
Primary Contact: Mark E. Marchetti, President and Chief Executive Officer
CFO: Keith Bryce, Vice President Finance and Chief Financial Officer
CIO: Anthon Ellsworth, Director Information Technology
CHR: Irvan Wick"" Lewis, Vice President Human Resources
CNO: Lori Burress, Vice President Patient Services and Chief Nursing Officer
Web address: www.mtgraham.org
Control: Hospital district or authority, Government, nonfederal **Service**: General medical and surgical

Staffed Beds: 49 Admissions: 1351 Census: 11 Outpatient Visits: 71253 Births: 564 Total Expense ($000): 56669 Payroll Expense ($000): 24038 Personnel: 364

SAN TAN VALLEY—Pinal County

⊞ **BANNER IRONWOOD MEDICAL CENTER (030130)**, 37000 North Gantzel Road, Zip 85140-7303; tel. 480/394-4000, **A**1 10 **F**3 13 30 39 40 41 43 49 64 68 70 75 76 77 79 81 85 87 107 111 115 119 126 130 131 135 146 147 149 154 **S** Banner Health, Gilbert, AZ
Primary Contact: Sharon Lind, MSN, FACHE, Chief Executive Officer
CFO: Tracy French, Chief Financial Officer
CMO: Darren West, M.D., Interim Chief Medical Officer
CHR: Janine Polito, Chief Human Resources Officer
CNO: Terresa Ann Paulus, Chief Nursing Officer
Web address: www.bannerhealth.com/Locations/Arizona/Banner+Ironwood/
Control: Other not-for-profit (including NFP Corporation) **Service**: General medical and surgical

Staffed Beds: 53 Admissions: 2866 Census: 24 Births: 873 Total Expense ($000): 65415 Payroll Expense ($000): 21234 Personnel: 347

SCOTTSDALE—Maricopa County

⊞ **BANNER BEHAVIORAL HEALTH HOSPITAL – SCOTTSDALE (034004)**, 7575 East Earll Drive, Zip 85251-6915; tel. 480/941-7500, **A**1 3 10 **F**4 5 29 30 34 35 38 44 50 57 68 75 86 87 98 99 101 102 104 130 134 135 146 149 153 **S** Banner Health, Gilbert, AZ
Primary Contact: William Southwick, R.N., Chief Executive Officer
CFO: Michael A. Cimino Jr Chief Financial Officer
CMO: Gagandeep Singh, M.D., Chief Medical Officer Behavioral Health
CHR: Zsaber Gere, Chief Human Resource Officer
CNO: Cherri Anderson, Chief Nursing Officer
Web address: www.bannerhealth.com/locations/scottsdale/banner-behavioral-health-hospital
Control: Other not-for-profit (including NFP Corporation) **Service**: Psychiatric

Staffed Beds: 104 Admissions: 3696 Census: 68 Births: 0 Total Expense ($000): 36845 Payroll Expense ($000): 16922 Personnel: 344

⊞ **ENCOMPASS HEALTH REHABILITATION HOSPITAL OF SCOTTSDALE (033025)**, 9630 East Shea Boulevard, Zip 85260-6267; tel. 480/551-5400, (Nonreporting) **A**1 10 **S** Encompass Health Corporation, Birmingham, AL
Primary Contact: Kenneth Bell, Chief Executive Officer
CFO: Lisa Barrick, Controller
CMO: Keith W Cunningham, M.D., Medical Director
CHR: Mary Beth Giczi, Director Human Resources
CNO: Diane M Caruso, MSN, Chief Nursing Officer
Web address: www.encompasshealth.com/locations/scottsdalerehab
Control: Corporation, Investor-owned (for-profit) **Service**: Rehabilitation

Staffed Beds: 60

⊞ **HONORHEALTH REHABILITATION HOSPITAL (033038)**, 8850 East Pima Center Parkway, Zip 85258-4619; tel. 480/800-3900, (Nonreporting) **A**1 10 **S** Select Medical Corporation, Mechanicsburg, PA
Primary Contact: Scott R. Keen, Chief Executive Officer
Web address: www.scottsdale-rehab.com/
Control: Partnership, Investor-owned (for-profit) **Service**: Rehabilitation

Staffed Beds: 50

★ ⇧ **HONORHEALTH SCOTTSDALE OSBORN MEDICAL CENTER (030038)**, 7400 East Osborn Road, Zip 85251-6403; tel. 480/882-4000, (Nonreporting) **A**2 3 5 8 10 21 **S** HonorHealth, Scottsdale, AZ
Primary Contact: Kimberly Post, Senior Vice President and Chief Executive Officer
CMO: James Burke, M.D., Senior Vice President and Chief Medical Officer
CIO: James R Cramer, Vice President and Chief Information Officer
Web address: www.shc.org
Control: Other not-for-profit (including NFP Corporation) **Service**: General medical and surgical

Staffed Beds: 347

★ ⇧ **HONORHEALTH SCOTTSDALE SHEA MEDICAL CENTER (030087)**, 9003 East Shea Boulevard, Zip 85260-6771; tel. 480/323-3000, (Nonreporting) **A**2 3 5 10 21 **S** HonorHealth, Scottsdale, AZ
Primary Contact: Gary E. Baker, Senior Vice President and Chief Executive Officer
CMO: James Burke, M.D., Senior Vice President and Chief Medical Officer
CIO: James R Cramer, Vice President and Chief Information Officer
Web address: www.shc.org
Control: Other not-for-profit (including NFP Corporation) **Service**: General medical and surgical

Staffed Beds: 409

★ ⇧ **HONORHEALTH SCOTTSDALE THOMPSON PEAK MEDICAL CENTER (030123)**, 7400 East Thompson Peak Parkway, Zip 85255-4109; tel. 480/324-7000, **A**3 10 21 **F**3 5 20 22 24 26 29 30 31 34 35 37 40 45 46 49 50 51 57 58 59 70 77 78 79 81 82 107 110 111 112 119 126 130 131 132 133 134 135 143 144 145 146 147 148 149 150 **S** HonorHealth, Scottsdale, AZ
Primary Contact: David Price, Chief Executive Officer
COO: Bruce Pearson, Senior Vice President and Chief Operating Officer
CFO: Alice H Pope, Chief Financial Officer
CMO: Stephanie Jackson, M.D., Vice President and Chief Medical Officer
CIO: Charles Scully, Chief Information Officer
CHR: Wendy Crawford, Chief Human Resource Officer
CNO: Kimberly Post, Senior Vice President and Chief Clinical Officer
Web address: www.shc.org
Control: Other not-for-profit (including NFP Corporation) **Service**: General medical and surgical

Staffed Beds: 92 Admissions: 6642 Census: 59 Births: 0

⇧ **SCOTTSDALE LIBERTY HOSPITAL**, 17500 North Perimeter Drive, Zip 85255-7808; tel. 480/586-2300, (Nonreporting) **A**21 **S** Nobilis Health Corporation, Houston, TX
Primary Contact: Steven M. Siwek, M.D., President and Chief Executive Officer
COO: Michael Adams, Chief Operating Officer
CFO: Douglas B Kell, Chief Financial Officer
CMO: Natalie Shand, M.D., Vice President Integrative Medicine and Chief Medical Officer
CIO: Milad Najjar, Information Technology
CHR: Samantha Mendez, Human Resources
CNO: Jani Manseau, Vice President Operations and Chief Nursing Officer
Web address: www.freedompainhospital.com
Control: Corporation, Investor-owned (for-profit) **Service**: Other specialty treatment

Staffed Beds: 12

Hospital, Medicare Provider Number, Address, Telephone, Approval, Facility, and Physician Codes, Health Care System

★ American Hospital Association (AHA) membership   ○ Healthcare Facilities Accreditation Program   ⇧ Center for Improvement in Healthcare Quality Accreditation
☐ The Joint Commission accreditation   ◇ DNV Healthcare Inc. accreditation   △ Commission on Accreditation of Rehabilitation Facilities (CARF) accreditation

AZ

SELLS—Pima County

✠ **U.S. PUBLIC HEALTH SERVICE INDIAN HOSPITAL–SELLS (030074)**, Highway 86 & Topawa Road, Zip 85634, Mailing Address: P.O. Box 548, Zip 85634–0548; tel. 520/383–7251, (Nonreporting) **A**1 10 **S** U.S. Indian Health Service, Rockville, MD
Primary Contact: Angela Fallon, Acting Chief Executive Officer
COO: Diane Shanley, Deputy Service Unit Director
CFO: Vivian Draper, Chief Financial Officer
CNO: Donna Hobbs, Nurse Executive
Web address: www.ihs.gov
Control: PHS, Indian Service, Government, federal **Service**: General medical and surgical

> **Staffed Beds**: 12

SHOW LOW—Navajo County

★ **SUMMIT HEALTHCARE REGIONAL MEDICAL CENTER (030062)**, 2200 East Show Low Lake Road, Zip 85901–7800; tel. 928/537–4375, **A**3 10 20 **F**11 13 15 18 20 22 28 29 30 31 32 34 35 36 38 40 41 43 45 46 47 53 54 55 57 59 62 64 65 68 70 71 73 75 77 78 79 81 82 84 91 92 93 97 107 108 110 111 114 115 118 119 121 127 129 130 131 132 133 135 146 147 148 149 154 **P**4 6
Primary Contact: Ronald L. McArthur, Chief Executive Officer
COO: Doug Gilchrist, Chief Operating Officer
CFO: David Rothenberger, Chief Financial Officer
CMO: Alan Neil DeWitt, Chief Medical Officer
CIO: Aaron Young, Chief Information Officer
CHR: Connie Kakavas, Chief Human Resources Officer
CNO: Cynthia Ebert–Loomis, R.N., Chief Nursing Officer
Web address: www.summithealthcare.net
Control: Other not–for–profit (including NFP Corporation) **Service**: General medical and surgical

> **Staffed Beds**: 89 **Admissions**: 4824 **Census**: 37 **Outpatient Visits**: 68804 **Births**: 929 **Total Expense ($000)**: 138487 **Payroll Expense ($000)**: 73820

SIERRA VISTA—Cochise County

☐ **CANYON VISTA MEDICAL CENTER (030043)**, 5700 East Highway 90, Zip 85635–9110; tel. 520/263–2000, **A**1 10 13 20 **F**3 13 15 18 20 22 24 26 28 29 30 31 34 35 40 43 44 45 51 57 59 60 61 63 64 70 72 74 75 76 77 79 80 81 85 93 94 96 98 100 103 107 108 109 111 114 115 118 119 120 122 123 130 131 145 146 147 148 **S** RCCH HealthCare Partners, Brentwood, TN
Primary Contact: Bob Gomes, FACHE, President and Chief Executive Officer
COO: Ashley L. Johnson, Chief Operations Officer
CIO: Jorge Moreno, Director Information Technology Operations
CHR: Traci Meyer, Director Human Resources
Web address: www.canyonvistamedicalcenter.com/
Control: Corporation, Investor–owned (for–profit) **Service**: General medical and surgical

> **Staffed Beds**: 100 **Admissions**: 5332 **Census**: 53 **Births**: 831

SPRINGERVILLE—Apache County

WHITE MOUNTAIN REGIONAL MEDICAL CENTER (031315), 118 South Mountain Avenue, Zip 85938–5104; tel. 928/333–4368, (Nonreporting) **A**10 18
Primary Contact: Gregory J. Was, CPA, Chief Executive Officer
CFO: James Hamblin, Chief Financial Officer
CMO: Scott Hamblin, M.D., President Medical Staff
Web address: www.wmrmc.com
Control: Other not–for–profit (including NFP Corporation) **Service**: General medical and surgical

> **Staffed Beds**: 20

SUN CITY—Maricopa County

✠ **BANNER BOSWELL MEDICAL CENTER (030061)**, 10401 West Thunderbird Blvd, Zip 85351–3004, Mailing Address: P.O. Box 1690, Zip 85372–1690; tel. 623/832–4000, (Total facility includes 78 beds in nursing home–type unit) **A**1 2 3 10 **F**3 9 11 15 17 18 20 22 24 26 28 29 30 31 34 35 36 37 40 43 44 45 46 47 48 49 50 51 53 56 57 58 59 60 61 63 64 65 69 70 74 75 78 79 81 84 85 86 87 90 91 92 93 94 96 107 108 110 111 114 115 117 119 120 121 124 126 128 130 131 132 135 141 145 146 147 148 149 154 **S** Banner Health, Gilbert, AZ
Primary Contact: Debbie Flores, Interim Chief Executive Officer
CFO: Jeremy Williams, Chief Financial Officer
CMO: Kathryn Perkins, M.D., Chief Medical Officer
CHR: Brenda Dietrich, Chief Human Resources Officer
Web address: www.bannerhealth.com/locations/sun–city/banner–boswell–medical–center
Control: Other not–for–profit (including NFP Corporation) **Service**: General medical and surgical

> **Staffed Beds**: 429 **Admissions**: 15869 **Census**: 247 **Births**: 0 **Total Expense ($000)**: 317588 **Payroll Expense ($000)**: 106205 **Personnel**: 1777

SUN CITY WEST—Maricopa County

✠ **BANNER DEL E. WEBB MEDICAL CENTER (030093)**, 14502 West Meeker Boulevard, Zip 85375–5299; tel. 623/524–4000, **A**1 3 10 **F**3 4 5 9 11 13 15 18 20 22 28 29 30 31 34 36 37 38 40 43 44 45 46 47 49 50 51 53 56 57 58 59 60 61 63 64 65 70 74 75 76 78 79 80 81 85 86 87 90 91 92 93 94 96 98 100 102 103 104 107 108 110 111 114 115 118 119 126 130 131 132 135 141 145 146 147 148 149 153 154 **S** Banner Health, Gilbert, AZ
Primary Contact: Debbie Flores, Chief Executive Officer
COO: Nathan Shinagawa, Chief Operating Officer
CFO: Dan Stimpson, Chief Financial Officer
CMO: Scott Anderson, Chief Medical Officer
CHR: Carole Smith, Senior Human Resource Business Partner
CNO: Nancy Adamson, Chief Nursing Officer
Web address: www.bannerhealth.com/Locations/Arizona/Banner+Del+Webb+Medical+Center/
Control: Other not–for–profit (including NFP Corporation) **Service**: General medical and surgical

> **Staffed Beds**: 390 **Admissions**: 17767 **Census**: 225 **Births**: 1861 **Total Expense ($000)**: 269435 **Payroll Expense ($000)**: 96040 **Personnel**: 1544

SURPRISE—Maricopa County

COBALT REHABILITATION HOSPITAL (033039), 13060 West Bell Road, Zip 85378–1200; tel. 623/499–9100, **A**10 22 **F**28 29 54 65 75 77 90 91 95 96 100 145 154 **P**5
Primary Contact: Sharon Noe, Chief Executive Officer
Web address: www.colbaltrehab.com
Control: Corporation, Investor–owned (for–profit) **Service**: Rehabilitation

> **Staffed Beds**: 40 **Admissions**: 715 **Census**: 24 **Outpatient Visits**: 2300 **Births**: 0 **Total Expense ($000)**: 13830 **Payroll Expense ($000)**: 5070 **Personnel**: 120

TEMPE—Maricopa County

☐ **AURORA BEHAVIORAL HEALTH SYSTEM EAST (034028)**, 6350 South Maple Street, Zip 85283–2857; tel. 480/345–5400, (Nonreporting) **A**1 10 **S** Signature Healthcare Services, Corona, CA
Primary Contact: Bruce Waldo, Chief Executive Officer
CFO: Rebekah Francis, JD, Chief Financial Officer
CMO: Jason Friday, M.D., Medical Director
CHR: Vicki Thomsen, Director Human Resources
Web address: www.auroraarizona.com
Control: Partnership, Investor–owned (for–profit) **Service**: Psychiatric

> **Staffed Beds**: 70

TUBA CITY—Coconino County

✠ **TUBA CITY REGIONAL HEALTH CARE CORPORATION (030073)**, 167 Main Street, Zip 86045–0611, Mailing Address: P.O. Box 600, Zip 86045–0600; tel. 928/283–2501, (Nonreporting) **A**1 3 5 10
Primary Contact: Lynette Bonar, FACHE, R.N., Chief Executive Officer
CFO: Christine Keyonnie, CPA, Chief Financial Officer
CMO: Holly Van Dyk, M.D., Interim Chief Medical Officer
CIO: Shawn Davis, Chief Information Officer
CHR: George Hunter, Interim Chief Human Resources Officer
CNO: Alvina Rosales, R.N., Chief Nursing Officer
Web address: www.tchealth.org
Control: Other not–for–profit (including NFP Corporation) **Service**: General medical and surgical

> **Staffed Beds**: 53

TUCSON—Pima County

✠ **BANNER – UNIVERSITY MEDICAL CENTER SOUTH (030111)**, 2800 East Ajo Way, Zip 85713–6289; tel. 520/874–2000, **A**1 3 5 10 **F**3 11 18 20 22 29 30 34 40 41 43 45 47 48 51 54 56 58 59 60 61 64 65 66 67 68 70 71 74 75 77 79 81 82 84 85 86 87 93 97 98 99 100 101 102 103 104 107 108 111 114 115 119 130 131 132 135 146 148 149 154 **S** Banner Health, Gilbert, AZ
Primary Contact: Sarah Frost, Chief Executive Officer
COO: Sarah Frost, Administrator and Chief Operating Officer
CFO: Jeff Buehrle, Chief Financial Officer
CMO: David Sheinbein, Chief Medical Officer
CIO: Ryan K Smith, Senior Vice President Information Technology
CHR: Jennifer L Sherwood, Division, Human Resource Business Partner
CNO: Cathy Townsend, Chief Nursing Officer
Web address: www.bannerhealth.com
Control: Other not–for–profit (including NFP Corporation) **Service**: General medical and surgical

> **Staffed Beds**: 167 **Admissions**: 7673 **Census**: 103 **Births**: 0 **Total Expense ($000)**: 183023 **Payroll Expense ($000)**: 53465 **Personnel**: 876

BANNER – UNIVERSITY MEDICAL CENTER TUCSON (030064), 1501 North Campbell Avenue, Zip 85724–5128; tel. 520/694–0111, (Includes DIAMOND CHILDREN'S HOSPITAL, 1501 North Campbell Avenue, Tucson, AZ, Zip 85724–0001; tel. 520/694–0111) **A**1 2 3 5 8 10 **F**3 11 12 13 15 16 19 20 21 22 23 25 26 27 28 29 30 31 34 35 40 41 43 45 46 47 49 50 51 53 54 55 56 57 58 59 60 61 64 65 67 68 70 71 72 74 75 76 77 78 79 80 81 82 84 85 86 87 88 89 92 93 97 100 104 107 108 110 111 114 115 116 117 118 119 120 121 123 124 126 129 130 131 132 135 136 137 138 139 140 141 142 145 146 147 148 149 154 **S** Banner Health, Gilbert, AZ
Primary Contact: Sarah Frost, Chief Executive Officer
COO: Sarah Frost, Chief Operating Officer and Administrator, University of Arizona Medical Center – South Campus
CFO: Misty Hansen, Chief Financial Officer
CMO: Andreas Theodorou, Chief Medical Officer
CIO: Dan Critchley, Chief Information Officer
CHR: John Marques, Vice President Human Resources
Web address: www.bannerhealth.com/locations/tucson/banner–university–medical–center–tucson
Control: Other not–for–profit (including NFP Corporation) **Service:** General medical and surgical

Staffed Beds: 439 **Admissions:** 21839 **Census:** 352 **Births:** 1554
Total Expense ($000): 822227 **Payroll Expense ($000):** 208458
Personnel: 3110

CARONDELET ST. JOSEPH'S HOSPITAL (030011), 350 North Wilmot Road, Zip 85711–2678; tel. 520/873–3000, **A**1 5 10 **F**3 5 12 13 18 20 22 24 28 29 30 31 34 35 38 40 44 45 46 47 49 50 57 59 60 64 68 69 70 72 74 75 76 77 78 79 81 82 83 84 85 86 87 90 92 93 98 100 101 102 104 107 108 114 115 118 119 126 129 130 132 135 145 146 147 148 **S** TENET Healthcare Corporation, Dallas, TX
Primary Contact: Mark A. Benz, President and Chief Executive Officer
CFO: Alan Strauss, Chief Financial Officer
CMO: Donald Denmark, M.D., Chief Medical Officer
CIO: Sally Zambrello, Chief Information Officer
CHR: Igor Shegolev, Vice President Human Resources
CNO: Robin Conklin, R.N., Chief Nursing Officer
Web address: www.carondelet.org
Control: Corporation, Investor–owned (for–profit) **Service:** General medical and surgical

Staffed Beds: 486 **Admissions:** 15832 **Census:** 188 **Outpatient Visits:** 110658 **Births:** 2405 **Total Expense ($000):** 235853 **Payroll Expense ($000):** 99600 **Personnel:** 1167

CARONDELET ST. MARY'S HOSPITAL (030010), 1601 West St Mary's Road, Zip 85745–2682; tel. 520/872–3000, **A**1 5 10 **F**3 12 15 17 18 20 22 24 26 28 29 30 31 34 38 40 44 45 46 47 49 50 51 53 56 57 58 59 60 64 68 70 74 77 78 79 81 82 84 85 86 87 90 92 93 96 98 100 101 102 103 107 108 110 111 114 115 118 119 126 129 130 131 132 146 148 149 **S** TENET Healthcare Corporation, Dallas, TX
Primary Contact: Mark A. Benz, President and Chief Executive Officer
CMO: Donald Denmark, M.D., Chief Medical Officer
Web address: www.carondelet.org
Control: Corporation, Investor–owned (for–profit) **Service:** General medical and surgical

Staffed Beds: 300 **Admissions:** 11300 **Census:** 166 **Outpatient Visits:** 112925 **Births:** 0 **Total Expense ($000):** 194450 **Payroll Expense ($000):** 85114 **Personnel:** 1047

CHG HOSPITAL TUCSON, LLC (032004), 7220 East Rosewood Drive, Zip 85710–1350; tel. 520/546–4595, (Nonreporting) **A**1 10 **S** Cornerstone Healthcare Group, Dallas, TX
Primary Contact: Vanessa Acevedo, Interim Chief Executive Officer
CFO: Kurt Schultz, Group Chief Financial Officer
CMO: Haroon Haque, M.D., Medical Director
CIO: Adam Davis, Director Information Technology
CHR: Deborah Darcy, Human Resources
CNO: Jose' Sanchez, Chief Nursing Officer
Web address: www.chghospitals.com
Control: Corporation, Investor–owned (for–profit) **Service:** Acute long–term care hospital

Staffed Beds: 34

CURAHEALTH TUCSON (032002), 355 North Wilmot Road, Zip 85711–2601; tel. 520/584–4500, (Nonreporting) **A**1 10 **S** Curahealth Hospitals, Garland, TX
Primary Contact: Camie Overton, Chief Executive Officer
CMO: Sunil Natrajan, M.D., Medical Director
CNO: Globert Empedrad, Chief Clinical Officer
Web address: www.curahealth.com
Control: Corporation, Investor–owned (for–profit) **Service:** Acute long–term care hospital

Staffed Beds: 51

ENCOMPASS HEALTH REHABILITATION HOSPITAL OF NORTHWEST TUCSON (033029), 1921 West Hospital Drive, Zip 85704–7806; tel. 520/742–2800, (Nonreporting) **A**1 10 **S** Encompass Health Corporation, Birmingham, AL
Primary Contact: Timothy T. Poore, Chief Executive Officer
CFO: Kaleigh Hotchkiss, Controller
CMO: Susan R. Bulen, M.D., Medical Director
CHR: Neil Cullen, Director Human Resources
CNO: Virginia Ragonese–Green, Chief Nursing Officer
Web address: www.encompasshealth.com/northwesttucsonrehab
Control: Corporation, Investor–owned (for–profit) **Service:** Rehabilitation

Staffed Beds: 60

ENCOMPASS HEALTH REHABILITATION INSTITUTE OF TUCSON (033028), 2650 North Wyatt Drive, Zip 85712–6108; tel. 520/325–1300, **A**1 3 5 10 **F**29 34 35 62 90 93 96 130 132 **S** Encompass Health Corporation, Birmingham, AL
Primary Contact: Jeffrey Christensen, Chief Executive Officer
CFO: Mary Donovan, Controller
CMO: Jon Larson, M.D., Medical Director
CHR: Dawn Mosier, Director Human Resources
Web address: www.encompasshealth.com/rehabinstituteoftucson
Control: Corporation, Investor–owned (for–profit) **Service:** Rehabilitation

Staffed Beds: 80 **Admissions:** 1507 **Census:** 54 **Outpatient Visits:** 0 **Births:** 0 **Total Expense ($000):** 20636 **Payroll Expense ($000):** 11619 **Personnel:** 185

NORTHWEST MEDICAL CENTER (030085), 6200 North La Cholla Boulevard, Zip 85741–3599; tel. 520/742–9000, (Nonreporting) **A**1 5 10 **S** Community Health Systems, Inc., Franklin, TN
Primary Contact: Kevin Stockton, Chief Executive Officer
CFO: Ronald Patrick, Chief Financial Officer
CIO: David Bullock, Director Information Services
CNO: Kay Stubbs, Chief Nursing Officer
Web address: www.northwestmedicalcenter.com
Control: Corporation, Investor–owned (for–profit) **Service:** General medical and surgical

Staffed Beds: 270

PALO VERDE BEHAVIORAL HEALTH (034030), 2695 North Craycroft Road, Zip 85712–2244; tel. 520/322–2888, (Nonreporting) **A**3 5 10 **S** Universal Health Services, Inc., King of Prussia, PA
Primary Contact: Melissa Eckstein, Chief Executive Officer
CFO: Richard N England, Chief Financial Officer
CHR: Michelle Carrasco, Director Human Resources
Web address: www.paloverdebh.com/
Control: Other not–for–profit (including NFP Corporation) **Service:** Psychiatric

Staffed Beds: 48

TUCSON—Pinal County

SIERRA TUCSON, 39580 South Lago Del Oro Parkway, Zip 85739–1091; tel. 520/624–4000, (Nonreporting) **A**1 3 **S** CRC Health Group, Inc., Cupertino, CA
Primary Contact: Stephen P. Fahey, Executive Director
COO: Stephen P Fahey, Executive Director
CFO: Amy Fritton, Controller
CMO: Jerome Lerner, M.D., Medical Director
CHR: Betty Dickens, Director Human Resources
CNO: Sue Menzie, R.N., Director Patient Care
Web address: www.sierratucson.com
Control: Corporation, Investor–owned (for–profit) **Service:** Alcoholism and other chemical dependency

Staffed Beds: 139

Hospital, Medicare Provider Number, Address, Telephone, Approval, Facility, and Physician Codes, Health Care System

★ American Hospital Association (AHA) membership ○ Healthcare Facilities Accreditation Program ⇑ Center for Improvement in Healthcare Quality Accreditation
☐ The Joint Commission accreditation ◇ DNV Healthcare Inc. accreditation △ Commission on Accreditation of Rehabilitation Facilities (CARF) accreditation

AZ

TUCSON—Pima County

☐ **SONORA BEHAVIORAL HEALTH HOSPITAL (034022)**, 6050 North Corona Road, #3, Zip 85704–1096; tel. 520/469–8700, **A**1 10 **F**5 29 50 98 99 100 102 104 105 130 132 153 **S** Acadia Healthcare Company, Inc., Franklin, TN
Primary Contact: Edeli Kinsala, Chief Executive Officer
CMO: Steven Bupp, M.D., Medical Director
CHR: Ciria Soto, Director Human Resources
CNO: Angel Payne, Clinical Director, Director of Nursing
Control: Corporation, Investor–owned (for–profit) **Service:** Psychiatric

Staffed Beds: 106 Admissions: 3817 Census: 77 Births: 0

⊞ △ **SOUTHERN ARIZONA VETERANS AFFAIRS HEALTH CARE SYSTEM**, 3601 Sout 6th Avenue, Zip 85723–0002, Mailing Address: 3601 South 6th Avenue, Zip 85723–0002; tel. 520/792–1450, **A**1 3 5 7 8 **F**3 4 5 15 18 20 22 24 26 28 29 30 31 33 34 35 36 38 39 40 44 45 46 49 52 53 54 56 57 58 59 60 61 63 64 65 66 70 71 74 75 77 78 79 80 81 82 83 84 85 86 87 90 91 92 93 94 96 97 98 100 101 102 103 104 105 106 107 108 111 114 116 117 118 119 126 127 128 129 130 132 135 143 146 147 148 149 150 152 153 154 **P**6 **S** Department of Veterans Affairs, Perry Point, MD
Primary Contact: William J. Caron, Director
CMO: Jayendra H Shah, M.D., Chief Medical Officer
CIO: John Walston, Chief Information Officer
CHR: Patrice Craig, Manager Human Resources
Web address: www.tucson.va.gov
Control: Veterans Affairs, Government, federal **Service:** General medical and surgical

Staffed Beds: 328 Admissions: 8795 Census: 217 Outpatient Visits: 377212 Births: 0 Personnel: 2513

TMC FOR CHILDREN See TMC Healthcare, Tucson

★ **TMC HEALTHCARE (030006)**, 5301 East Grant Road, Zip 85712–2874; tel. 520/324–5461, (Includes TMC FOR CHILDREN, 5301 East Grant Road, Tucson, AZ, Zip 85712–2805; tel. 520/327–5461; Judy F. Rich, MSN, R.N., President and Chief Executive Officer) **A**3 5 10 **F**3 8 11 12 13 14 15 17 18 20 22 24 25 26 27 28 29 30 31 32 34 35 37 40 41 45 46 47 48 49 50 51 53 54 56 57 58 59 60 63 64 65 66 68 72 74 75 76 77 78 79 81 82 83 85 87 88 89 93 94 98 102 103 107 110 111 114 115 118 119 124 126 129 130 132 135 146 147 148 149 154 **P**6
Primary Contact: Judy F. Rich, MSN, R.N., President and Chief Executive Officer
COO: Karen Mlawsky, Senior Vice President and Chief Operations Officer
CFO: Stephen Bush, Chief Financial Officer
CMO: Rick Anderson, M.D., Senior Vice President and Chief Medical Officer
CIO: Frank Marini, Senior Vice President and Chief Information Officer
CHR: Alex Horvath, Vice President and Chief Human Resources Officer
CNO: Mimi Coomler, R.N., Vice President and Chief Nursing Officer
Web address: www.tmcaz.com
Control: Other not–for–profit (including NFP Corporation) **Service:** General medical and surgical

Staffed Beds: 586 Admissions: 33727 Census: 392 Outpatient Visits: 167160 Births: 5224 Total Expense ($000): 519125 Payroll Expense ($000): 205911 Personnel: 3645

WHITERIVER—Navajo County

☐ **U.S. PUBLIC HEALTH SERVICE INDIAN HOSPITAL-WHITERIVER (030113)**, 200 West Hospital Drive, Zip 85941–0860, Mailing Address: State Route 73, Box 860, Zip 85941–0860; tel. 928/338–4911, **A**1 3 10 **F**3 8 13 29 31 32 34 35 36 38 39 40 41 44 45 46 50 53 54 56 57 59 61 64 65 66 68 75 76 78 79 81 82 84 85 86 87 89 91 93 94 97 100 101 104 107 115 119 130 131 132 135 144 146 147 148 149 **S** U.S. Indian Health Service, Rockville, MD
Primary Contact: Michelle Martinez, Chief Executive Officer
COO: Brian Campbell, Director Professional Services
CFO: Desdemona Leslie, Finance Officer
CMO: John Umhau, M.D., Clinical Director
CIO: Russell Barker, Information Officer
CHR: Lena Fasthorse, Supervisor Human Resource
CNO: Jana Towne, Nurse Executive
Web address: www.ihs.gov
Control: PHS, Indian Service, Government, federal **Service:** General medical and surgical

Staffed Beds: 35 Admissions: 861 Census: 9 Outpatient Visits: 232051 Births: 47 Personnel: 586

WICKENBURG—Maricopa County

★ **WICKENBURG COMMUNITY HOSPITAL (031300)**, 520 Rose Lane, Zip 85390–1447; tel. 928/684–5421, (Nonreporting) **A**10 18
Primary Contact: James Tavary, Chief Executive Officer
CFO: Jackie Lundblad, Chief Financial Officer
CMO: Todd Kravetz, Chief of Staff
CIO: Michael McKay, Chief Information Officer
CNO: Linda Brockwell, Director of Nursing, Administrative
Web address: www.wickhosp.com
Control: Other not–for–profit (including NFP Corporation) **Service:** General medical and surgical

Staffed Beds: 19

WILLCOX—Cochise County

★ **NORTHERN COCHISE COMMUNITY HOSPITAL (031302)**, 901 West Rex Allen Drive, Zip 85643–1009; tel. 520/384–3541, **A**10 18 **F**11 15 29 34 35 40 41 43 57 59 65 75 77 87 90 93 107 110 111 115 119 127 128 133 146 149
Primary Contact: Roland Knox, Chief Executive Officer
CFO: Kim Aguirre, Director Finance
CMO: Hisham Hamam, M.D., Chief of Staff
CIO: Dennis Drury, Director Information Technology
CNO: Pam Noland, Director of Nursing
Web address: www.ncch.com
Control: Hospital district or authority, Government, nonfederal **Service:** General medical and surgical

Staffed Beds: 24 Admissions: 447 Census: 5 Outpatient Visits: 16857 Births: 0 Total Expense ($000): 16898 Payroll Expense ($000): 7015 Personnel: 154

WINSLOW—Navajo County

LITTLE COLORADO MEDICAL CENTER (031311), 1501 Williamson Avenue, Zip 86047–2797; tel. 928/289–4691, **A**3 10 18 **F**29 34 40 50 65 79 81 107 127 130 133
Primary Contact: John J. Dempsey, Chief Executive Officer
CFO: Gina Reffner, Chief Financial Officer
CMO: Perry Mitchell, M.D., Chief of Staff
CIO: Jacob Garcia, Chief Information Officer
CHR: Nina L Ferguson, Director Human Resources
Web address: www.lcmcwmh.com
Control: Other not–for–profit (including NFP Corporation) **Service:** General medical and surgical

Staffed Beds: 25 Admissions: 1138 Census: 10 Births: 171 Total Expense ($000): 29643 Payroll Expense ($000): 12698

YUMA—Yuma County

★ ○ **YUMA REGIONAL MEDICAL CENTER (030013)**, 2400 South Avenue 'A', Zip 85364–7170; tel. 928/344–2000, **A**3 5 10 11 **F**3 8 12 13 15 18 20 22 24 26 28 29 30 31 32 34 35 39 40 41 45 46 47 48 49 50 54 57 58 59 64 68 70 72 74 75 76 77 78 79 81 82 83 84 85 86 87 89 97 104 107 108 109 110 111 112 114 115 116 117 118 119 120 121 122 123 124 126 130 132 141 146 147 148 149 154 **P**6
Primary Contact: Robert Trenschel, D.O., FACHE, M.P.H., President and Chief Executive Officer
CFO: David Willie, Chief Financial Officer
CMO: Bharat Magu, M.D., Chief Medical Officer
CIO: Fred Peet, Chief Information Officer
CHR: Randal M. Etzler, Chief Human Resources Officer
CNO: Deb Aders, MS, R.N., Interim Chief Nursing Officer
Web address: www.yumaregional.org
Control: Other not–for–profit (including NFP Corporation) **Service:** General medical and surgical

Staffed Beds: 406 Admissions: 17461 Census: 181 Outpatient Visits: 291308 Births: 3278 Total Expense ($000): 423873 Payroll Expense ($000): 168462 Personnel: 2074

⊞ **YUMA REHABILITATION HOSPITAL, A PARTNERSHIP OF ENCOMPASS HEALTH AND YRMC (033034)**, 901 West 24th Street, Zip 85364–6384; tel. 928/726–5000, (Nonreporting) **A**1 10 **S** Encompass Health Corporation, Birmingham, AL
Primary Contact: Ian Hodge, Chief Executive Officer
CMO: Bapu Aluri, M.D., Chief Medical Officer
CHR: Linda Woen, Director Human Resources
CNO: Kristin Parra, Chief Nursing Officer
Web address: www.encompasshealth.com/yumarehab
Control: Corporation, Investor–owned (for–profit) **Service:** Rehabilitation

Staffed Beds: 41

Many Facility Codes have changed. Please refer to the AHA Guide Code Chart. © 2018 AHA Guide

ARKANSAS

ARKADELPHIA—Clark County

✠ **BAPTIST HEALTH MEDICAL CENTER-ARKADELPHIA (041321)**, 3050 Twin Rivers Drive, Zip 71923-4299; tel. 870/245-2622, **A**1 10 18 **F**3 11 13 15 29 30 34 35 40 41 43 45 46 50 57 59 64 65 68 69 70 75 76 79 81 85 87 93 96 97 102 107 110 111 114 119 127 129 130 131 133 135 146 148 154 **S** Baptist Health, Little Rock, AR
Primary Contact: Tony Hardage, Assistant Vice President and Administrator
CFO: Robert C Roberts, Vice President and Chief Financial Officer
CMO: Eddie Phillips, M.D., Chief Medical Officer
CIO: David House, Vice President and Chief Information Officer
CHR: Anthony Kendall, Vice President Human Resources
Web address: www.baptist-health.com/locations/accesspoint. aspx?accessPointID=187
Control: Other not-for-profit (including NFP Corporation) **Service:** General medical and surgical

Staffed Beds: 25 **Admissions:** 1220 **Census:** 11 **Outpatient Visits:** 36694 **Births:** 475 **Total Expense ($000):** 24479 **Payroll Expense ($000):** 10489 **Personnel:** 233

ASHDOWN—Little River County

★ **LITTLE RIVER MEMORIAL HOSPITAL (041320)**, 451 West Locke Street, Zip 71822-3325; tel. 870/898-5011, **A**10 18 **F**3 40 56 59 62 65 77 93 97 107 110 115 119 129 133
Primary Contact: James Dowell, Administrator and Chief Executive Officer
CFO: Jackie Rainey, Chief Financial Officer
CIO: Mitchell Jones, Director Information Technology
CHR: Vicki Keener, Administrative Assistant and Director Human Resources
CNO: Cynthia Metzger, Chief Nursing and Operations Officer
Web address: www.little-river-memorial-hospital.placestars.com/
Control: Other not-for-profit (including NFP Corporation) **Service:** General medical and surgical

Staffed Beds: 25 **Admissions:** 149 **Census:** 1 **Outpatient Visits:** 13652 **Births:** 0 **Total Expense ($000):** 9445 **Payroll Expense ($000):** 5626 **Personnel:** 128

BARLING—Sebastian County

☐ **VALLEY BEHAVIORAL HEALTH SYSTEM (044006)**, 10301 Mayo Drive, Zip 72923-1660; tel. 479/494-5700, **A**1 10 **F**29 34 35 75 87 98 99 100 101 102 105 130 135 153 **P**6 **S** Acadia Healthcare Company, Inc., Franklin, TN
Primary Contact: Andrea Norman, Chief Executive Officer
CFO: Paul D Ervin, Chief Financial Officer
CMO: Richard Livingston, M.D., Medical Director
CHR: Patricia J Moore, Director Human Resource
CNO: Landon Horton, Director of Nursing
Web address: www.valleybehavioral.com
Control: State, Government, nonfederal **Service:** Psychiatric

Staffed Beds: 114 **Admissions:** 2351 **Census:** 75 **Outpatient Visits:** 84611 **Births:** 0 **Total Expense ($000):** 18484 **Payroll Expense ($000):** 10173 **Personnel:** 177

BATESVILLE—Independence County

★ **WHITE RIVER MEDICAL CENTER (040119)**, 1710 Harrison Street, Zip 72501-7303, Mailing Address: P.O. Box 2197, Zip 72503-2197; tel. 870/262-1200, (Total facility includes 11 beds in nursing home-type unit) **A**3 10 **F**3 8 11 12 13 15 17 20 22 26 28 29 30 31 34 35 38 40 43 44 45 48 50 51 56 57 59 60 64 68 70 74 75 76 77 78 79 81 82 84 85 86 87 90 92 93 98 100 101 102 103 107 108 110 111 114 115 119 121 126 127 128 129 130 131 132 135 144 146 147 148 154 **P**6 **S** White River Health System, Batesville, AR
Primary Contact: Gary Bebow, FACHE, Administrator and Chief Executive Officer
CFO: Phillip Hacker, Chief Financial Officer
CMO: Doug Bernard, M.D., Chief Medical Officer
CIO: Gary Paxson, Chief Information Officer
CHR: Gary McDonald, Chief Facilities and Personnel Officer
CNO: Terri Bunch, MSN, R.N., MSN, Chief Nursing Officer
Web address: www.whiteriverhealthsystem.com
Control: Other not-for-profit (including NFP Corporation) **Service:** General medical and surgical

Staffed Beds: 210 **Admissions:** 8681 **Census:** 107 **Outpatient Visits:** 459587 **Births:** 722 **Total Expense ($000):** 210809 **Payroll Expense ($000):** 88148 **Personnel:** 1419

BENTON—Saline County

☐ **RIVENDELL BEHAVIORAL HEALTH SERVICES OF ARKANSAS (044007)**, 100 Rivendell Drive, Zip 72019-9100; tel. 501/316-1255, (Nonreporting) **A**1 10 **S** Universal Health Services, Inc., King of Prussia, PA
Primary Contact: Ballard Sheppard, Chief Executive Officer
CFO: Mike Rainbolt, Chief Financial Officer
Web address: www.rivendellofarkansas.com
Control: Corporation, Investor-owned (for-profit) **Service:** Children's hospital psychiatric

Staffed Beds: 77

★ **SALINE MEMORIAL HOSPITAL (040084)**, 1 Medical Park Drive, Zip 72015-3354; tel. 501/776-6000, **A**10 **F**3 7 11 12 13 15 18 20 22 26 29 30 34 35 39 40 41 49 50 57 59 62 63 70 74 75 76 77 79 81 85 87 89 90 98 103 107 108 110 111 114 115 118 119 129 130 132 135 146 148 **P**8
Primary Contact: Bob Trautman, Chief Executive Officer
COO: Carla Robertson, Chief Operating Officer and Chief Financial Officer
CFO: Carla Robertson, Chief Operating Officer and Chief Financial Officer
CIO: Andy Dick, Director Information Services
CHR: Carol Matthews, Director Human Resources
CNO: Debbie Burrow, R.N., Chief Nursing Officer
Web address: www.salinememorial.org
Control: Corporation, Investor-owned (for-profit) **Service:** General medical and surgical

Staffed Beds: 125 **Admissions:** 6084 **Census:** 76 **Outpatient Visits:** 84171 **Births:** 528 **Total Expense ($000):** 103923 **Payroll Expense ($000):** 49115 **Personnel:** 627

BERRYVILLE—Carroll County

✠ **MERCY HOSPITAL BERRYVILLE (041329)**, 214 Carter Street, Zip 72616-4303; tel. 870/423-3355, **A**1 10 18 **F**3 11 15 28 29 30 31 34 35 40 41 45 46 48 50 57 59 61 64 75 78 81 82 85 86 87 93 96 107 108 110 111 114 119 129 130 131 132 133 146 148 **S** Mercy, Chesterfield, MO
Primary Contact: VonDa Moore, Administrator
CFO: Sherry Clouse Day, Vice President Finance
CHR: Taya James, Director
CNO: Michele Gann, Vice President Patient Services
Web address: www.mercy.net/berryvillear
Control: Church operated, Nongovernment, not-for-profit **Service:** General medical and surgical

Staffed Beds: 25 **Admissions:** 417 **Census:** 4 **Outpatient Visits:** 28180 **Births:** 0 **Total Expense ($000):** 15825 **Payroll Expense ($000):** 7882 **Personnel:** 121

BLYTHEVILLE—Mississippi County

✠ **GREAT RIVER MEDICAL CENTER (040069)**, 1520 North Division Street, Zip 72315-1448, Mailing Address: P.O. Box 108, Zip 72316-0108; tel. 870/838-7300, **A**1 10 **F**13 15 28 29 34 43 46 53 57 59 64 68 70 75 76 79 81 82 89 93 97 107 108 110 111 114 119 120 135 147 148 154 **P**7 **S** QHR, Brentwood, TN
Primary Contact: Chris Lee. Raymer, R.N., MSN, Chief Executive Officer
COO: Paul Pieffer, Chief Operating Officer
CFO: Randy Nichols, Chief Financial Officer
CIO: Tammy Bratcher, Director System Information Technology
CHR: Cheri Blurton, Director Human Resources, HIPAA Privacy Officer
CNO: Felicia Pierce, R.N., Chief Nursing Officer
Web address: www.mchsys.org
Control: County, Government, nonfederal **Service:** General medical and surgical

Staffed Beds: 73 **Admissions:** 1688 **Census:** 11 **Outpatient Visits:** 30398 **Births:** 378 **Total Expense ($000):** 21986 **Payroll Expense ($000):** 9833 **Personnel:** 278

Hospital, Medicare Provider Number, Address, Telephone, Approval, Facility, and Physician Codes, Health Care System

★ American Hospital Association (AHA) membership	○ Healthcare Facilities Accreditation Program	⇑ Center for Improvement in Healthcare Quality Accreditation
☐ The Joint Commission accreditation	◇ DNV Healthcare Inc. accreditation	△ Commission on Accreditation of Rehabilitation Facilities (CARF) accreditation

BOONEVILLE–Logan County

★ **MERCY HOSPITAL BOONEVILLE (041318)**, 880 West Main Street, Zip 72927–3443; tel. 479/675–2800, **A**10 18 **F**3 11 15 35 40 43 45 57 59 62 64 65 68 81 85 107 119 127 133 148 149 **P**6 8 **S** Mercy, Chesterfield, MO
Primary Contact: Teresa Williams, R.N., Regional Administrator
CMO: Michael Miranda, Chief of Staff
CHR: Doris Whitaker, Vice President and Manager
CNO: Kimberly Russell, Chief Nursing Officer
Web address: www.mercy.net
Control: Church operated, Nongovernment, not–for–profit **Service**: General medical and surgical

Staffed Beds: 25 Admissions: 327 Census: 4 Outpatient Visits: 16481 Births: 0 Total Expense ($000): 14794 Payroll Expense ($000): 5590 Personnel: 70

CALICO ROCK–Logan County

IZARD COUNTY MEDICAL CENTER (041306), 61 Grasse Street, Zip 72519, Mailing Address: P.O. Box 438, Zip 72519–0438; tel. 870/297–3726, (Nonreporting) **A**10 18
Primary Contact: Kim Skidmore, Chief Executive Officer
COO: Cathy Franks RN Chief Operating Officer
CMO: Bethany Knight, M.D., Chief of Staff
CIO: Quentin Wildhagen, Systems Administrator
CHR: Crystal R Moody, Director Human Resources
CNO: Dana Hicks, Director of Nursing
Web address: www.cmcofic.org
Control: Other not–for–profit (including NFP Corporation) **Service**: General medical and surgical

Staffed Beds: 25

CAMDEN–Ouachita County

★ **OUACHITA COUNTY MEDICAL CENTER (040050)**, 638 California Avenue SW, Zip 71701–4699, Mailing Address: P.O. Box 797, Zip 71711–0797; tel. 870/836–1000, **A**10 20 **F**3 4 5 7 11 13 15 29 31 34 35 40 41 43 45 50 57 59 62 63 64 69 70 75 76 79 81 85 87 89 93 100 102 107 108 110 111 114 115 119 127 129 130 132 133 135 145 146 147 148 149 150 152 154
Primary Contact: Peggy L. Abbott, President and Chief Executive Officer
CFO: Robert Anders, Chief Financial Officer
CIO: Kenny Frachiseur, Chief Information Officer
CHR: Mary Bridges, Director Human Resources
CNO: Diane Isaacs, Director of Nursing
Web address: www.ouachitamedcenter.com
Control: Other not–for–profit (including NFP Corporation) **Service**: General medical and surgical

Staffed Beds: 45 Admissions: 1703 Census: 16 Outpatient Visits: 48661 Births: 231 Total Expense ($000): 34465 Payroll Expense ($000): 15040 Personnel: 393

OUACHITA MEDICAL CENTER See Ouachita County Medical Center

CLARKSVILLE–Johnson County

★ **JOHNSON REGIONAL MEDICAL CENTER (040002)**, 1100 East Poplar Street, Zip 72830–4419, Mailing Address: P.O. Box 738, Zip 72031–0738; tel. 479/754–5454, **A**10 **F**3 7 11 13 15 29 34 35 40 45 50 51 57 62 64 68 70 75 76 77 79 81 85 90 91 93 96 98 103 104 107 108 110 111 115 119 129 130 131 132 133 147 148 153 154
Primary Contact: Michael A. Dorsey, FACHE, Chief Executive Officer
CFO: Joe Jeans, CPA, Chief Financial Officer
CIO: Scott Cook, Chief Information Officer
CHR: Betty Collier, Chief Human Resources Officer
CNO: Nancy Hill, R.N., Chief Nursing Officer
Web address: www.jrmc.com
Control: Other not–for–profit (including NFP Corporation) **Service**: General medical and surgical

Staffed Beds: 90 Admissions: 2318 Census: 34 Outpatient Visits: 45154 Births: 330 Total Expense ($000): 40600 Payroll Expense ($000): 18604 Personnel: 328

CLINTON–Van Buren County

OZARK HEALTH MEDICAL CENTER (041313), Highway 65 South, Zip 72031–9045, Mailing Address: P.O. Box 206, Zip 72031–0206; tel. 501/745–7000, (Total facility includes 118 beds in nursing home–type unit) **A**10 18 **F**11 15 28 29 34 35 40 43 45 57 59 62 64 65 75 79 81 93 107 110 111 114 119 128 132 133 146
Primary Contact: David Deaton, Chief Executive Officer
CFO: Mike Deaton, Chief Financial Officer
CMO: Steve Schoettle, M.D., Chief Medical Staff
CHR: Sally D Cassell, Manager Human Resources
CNO: Edna Prosser, Chief Nursing Officer
Web address: www.ozarkhealthinc.com
Control: Other not–for–profit (including NFP Corporation) **Service**: General medical and surgical

Staffed Beds: 143 Admissions: 830 Census: 93 Outpatient Visits: 32861 Births: 2 Total Expense ($000): 26140 Payroll Expense ($000): 13199 Personnel: 289

CONWAY–Faulkner County

★ **BAPTIST HEALTH MEDICAL CENTER – CONWAY (040154)**, 1555 Exchange Avenue, Zip 72032–7824; tel. 501/585–2000, **A**10 **F**3 13 15 18 20 22 28 29 30 35 40 45 46 51 59 60 64 68 70 74 76 79 81 85 87 107 108 110 111 115 118 119 130 133 135 141 146 148 **S** Baptist Health, Little Rock, AR
Primary Contact: Tim Bowen, Vice President and Administrator
CNO: Stephana Loyd, Vice President, Chief Nursing Officer
Web address: www.baptist–health.com/location/baptist–health–medical–center–conway–conway
Control: Other not–for–profit (including NFP Corporation) **Service**: General medical and surgical

Staffed Beds: 111 Admissions: 2146 Census: 18 Outpatient Visits: 34340 Births: 91 Total Expense ($000): 74055 Payroll Expense ($000): 19709 Personnel: 388

☐ **CONWAY BEHAVIORAL HEALTH HOSPITAL**, 2255 Sturgis Road, Zip 72034–8029; tel. 501/858–3048, (Nonreporting) **A**1 **S** Acadia Healthcare Company, Inc., Franklin, TN
Primary Contact: Doris Singleton, Chief Executive Officer
CFO: Andrea Lane, Chief Financial Officer
CMO: Thomas Stinnett, M.D., Chief Medical Officer
CHR: Levi J. King, Director Human Resources
CNO: Beth Williams, R.N., Chief Nursing Officer
Web address: www.conwaybh.com
Control: Corporation, Investor–owned (for–profit) **Service**: Psychiatric

Staffed Beds: 80

⊠ **CONWAY REGIONAL MEDICAL CENTER (040029)**, 2302 College Avenue, Zip 72034–6297; tel. 501/329–3831, **A**1 10 **F**3 8 11 13 15 17 18 20 22 24 28 29 30 31 35 40 43 45 49 50 51 53 56 57 59 60 62 64 70 74 75 76 77 78 79 81 84 85 87 89 93 103 107 108 110 111 115 117 119 120 127 130 131 132 146 147 148 **P**8
Primary Contact: Matthew Troup, President and Chief Executive Officer
COO: Alan Finley, Chief Operating Officer
CFO: Dallas Gosa, Interim Chief Financial Officer
CMO: James France, M.D., Chief of Staff
CHR: Richard Tyler, Corporate Director Human Resources
CNO: Jacquelyn Wilkerson, R.N., Chief Nursing Officer
Web address: www.conwayregional.org
Control: Other not–for–profit (including NFP Corporation) **Service**: General medical and surgical

Staffed Beds: 150 Admissions: 7667 Census: 84 Outpatient Visits: 100554 Births: 1826 Total Expense ($000): 155270 Payroll Expense ($000): 56738 Personnel: 1024

CONWAY REGIONAL REHABILITATION HOSPITAL (043033), 2210 Robinson Avenue, Zip 72034–4943; tel. 501/932–3500, **A**10 **F**3 29 90 91 96 130 132 143 154 **P**8
Primary Contact: Alicia Kunert, MS, Executive Director
COO: Christy Scroggin, Chief Operating Officer
CMO: Roy Denton, M.D., Chief Medical Officer
CNO: Darrallyn Webb, R.N., Chief Nursing Officer
Web address: www.conwayregional.org
Control: Partnership, Investor–owned (for–profit) **Service**: Rehabilitation

Staffed Beds: 26 Admissions: 397 Census: 14 Outpatient Visits: 0 Births: 0 Total Expense ($000): 2756 Payroll Expense ($000): 1626 Personnel: 39

CROSSETT–Ashley County

★ **ASHLEY COUNTY MEDICAL CENTER (041323)**, 1015 Unity Road, Zip 71635–9443, Mailing Address: P.O. Box 400, Zip 71635–0400; tel. 870/364–4111, **A**10 18 **F**3 11 13 15 18 29 31 34 35 40 45 50 53 56 57 59 62 64 68 70 75 76 77 78 79 81 85 93 98 100 103 104 107 108 110 111 115 119 127 129 130 132 133 148 153 154
Primary Contact: Phillip K. Gilmore, FACHE, Chief Executive Officer
CFO: Bill Couch, Chief Financial Officer
CMO: Brad Walsh, M.D., Chief of Staff
CIO: Dan Austin, Manager Data Processing
CHR: Shirley White, Director Human Resources
CNO: Emily Bendinelli, Director of Nurses
Web address: www.acmconline.org
Control: Other not–for–profit (including NFP Corporation) **Service**: General medical and surgical

Staffed Beds: 33 Admissions: 1015 Census: 17 Outpatient Visits: 79006 Births: 112 Total Expense ($000): 33360 Payroll Expense ($000): 15600 Personnel: 305

Many Facility Codes have changed. Please refer to the AHA Guide Code Chart. © 2018 AHA Guide

DANVILLE–Yell County

★ **CHAMBERS MEMORIAL HOSPITAL (040011)**, 719 Detroit Avenue,
Zip 72833–9607, Mailing Address: P.O. Box 639, Zip 72833–0639;
tel. 479/495–2241, **A**10 20 **F**3 11 15 29 34 35 40 43 45 57 59 62 68 75 77
81 87 93 96 97 107 110 114 119 128 130 133 154 **P**6
Primary Contact: Mike McCoy, Chief Executive Officer
CMO: Thomas Tinnesz, M.D., Chief Medical Officer
CIO: Ken Masters, Director Information Technology
CNO: Joeann Bowerman, Director of Nursing
Web address: www.chambershospital.com
Control: Other not-for-profit (including NFP Corporation) **Service**: General
medical and surgical

Staffed Beds: 41 **Admissions**: 1696 **Census**: 15 **Outpatient Visits**: 37329 **Births**: 0 **Total Expense ($000)**: 19146 **Payroll Expense ($000)**: 9325 **Personnel**: 205	

DARDANELLE–Yell County

RIVER VALLEY MEDICAL CENTER (041302), 200 North Third Street,
Zip 72834–3802, Mailing Address: P.O. Box 578, Zip 72834–0578;
tel. 479/229–4677, (Nonreporting) **A**10 18 **S** Allegiance Health Management,
Shreveport, LA
Primary Contact: Vicki Andert, Chief Executive Officer
CMO: William P Scott, M.D., Chief of Staff
CHR: Kathy Hastin, Administrative Assistant Human Resources
Web address: www.rivervalleymedicalcenter.com/
Control: Corporation, Investor–owned (for–profit) **Service**: General medical and surgical

Staffed Beds: 35	

DE QUEEN–Sevier County

DE QUEEN MEDICAL CENTER (041319), 1306 Collin Raye Drive,
Zip 71832–2502; tel. 870/584–4111, **A**10 18 **F**3 11 29 30 34 35 40 57 59 62
64 65 68 75 77 87 90 91 93 94 96 97 107 108 109 114 119 133 146 148
Primary Contact: Ryan Capshew, Chief Executive Officer
CFO: Vicky Kelly, Chief Financial Officer
CMO: Jason Lofton, M.D., Medical Director
CIO: David Harris, Director Information Systems
CHR: Ramona Driver, Director Human Resources
CNO: Kristy Richardson, Director of Nursing
Web address: www.dequeenhospital.com
Control: Corporation, Investor–owned (for–profit) **Service**: General medical and surgical

Staffed Beds: 35 **Admissions**: 543 **Census**: 12 **Outpatient Visits**: 56840 **Births**: 2 **Personnel**: 143	

DEWITT–Arkansas County

★ **DEWITT HOSPITAL (041314)**, 1641 South Whitehead Drive, Zip 72042–9481,
Mailing Address: P.O. Box 32, Zip 72042–0032; tel. 870/946–3571, (Total facility
includes 45 beds in nursing home–type unit) **A**10 18 **F**3 11 29 30 34 35 40 50
57 59 64 65 67 87 107 111 119 127 128 129 130 132 133 143 145 149 **P**6
Primary Contact: Jason McKewan, Interim Chief Executive Officer
CFO: Brandon Cotten, Chief Financial Officer
CMO: Stan Burleson, M.D., Chief Medical Staff
CIO: Brian Brooks, Information Manager
CHR: Alisa Brown, Administrative Assistant
CNO: Jerrilyn Horton, R.N., Chief Nursing Officer
Web address: www.dhnh.org
Control: Other not-for-profit (including NFP Corporation) **Service**: General
medical and surgical

Staffed Beds: 70 **Admissions**: 801 **Census**: 45 **Outpatient Visits**: 11332 **Births**: 0 **Total Expense ($000)**: 12590 **Payroll Expense ($000)**: 7222 **Personnel**: 155	

DUMAS–Desha County

DELTA MEMORIAL HOSPITAL (041326), 811 South Highway 65,
Zip 71639–3006, Mailing Address: P.O. Box 887, Zip 71639–0887;
tel. 870/382–4303, (Nonreporting) **A**10 18
Primary Contact: Ashley Anthony, R.N., Chief Executive Officer
CMO: Thomas Lewellen, D.O., Chief of Staff
CIO: Chris McTigrit, Manager Information Technology
CHR: Doris Fortenberry, Coordinator Human Resources
CNO: Dana Miles, Chief Nursing Officer and Chief Clinical Officer
Web address: www.deltamem.org
Control: Other not-for-profit (including NFP Corporation) **Service**: General
medical and surgical

Staffed Beds: 25	

EL DORADO–Union County

✠ **MEDICAL CENTER OF SOUTH ARKANSAS (040088)**, 700 West Grove Street,
Zip 71730–4416; tel. 870/863–2000, **A**1 10 **F**3 11 13 15 17 18 20 22 24 28
29 31 34 40 41 43 45 46 50 56 57 59 64 65 70 71 73 76 78 79 80 81 82 85
89 90 93 96 107 108 110 111 115 118 119 130 146 147 149 154 **P**7 8 **S**
Community Health Systems, Inc., Franklin, TN
Primary Contact: Scott Street, Chief Executive Officer
CFO: Dale Maddox, Chief Financial Officer
CMO: Misty Kneeland, Chief Medical Staff
CIO: Rob Robison, Director Information Technology
CHR: LaKeitha Davis, Director Human Resources
CNO: Kathy Degenstein Gartman, Chief Nursing Officer
Web address: www.themedcenter.net
Control: Corporation, Investor–owned (for–profit) **Service**: General medical and
surgical

Staffed Beds: 117 **Admissions**: 3525 **Census**: 38 **Outpatient Visits**: 53217 **Births**: 615 **Total Expense ($000)**: 58025 **Payroll Expense ($000)**: 21177 **Personnel**: 400	

EUREKA SPRINGS–Carroll County

EUREKA SPRINGS HOSPITAL (041304), 24 Norris Street, Zip 72632–3541;
tel. 479/253–7400, (Nonreporting) **A**10 18 **S** Allegiance Health Management,
Shreveport, LA
Primary Contact: Vicki Andert, Chief Executive Officer
CFO: Taylor Smith, Chief Financial Officer
CMO: John House, M.D., Chief of Staff
CIO: Drew Wood, Director Information Technology
CHR: Jodi Smith, Administrative Assistant Human Resources
Web address: www.eurekaspringshospital.com
Control: Corporation, Investor–owned (for–profit) **Service**: General medical and
surgical

Staffed Beds: 15	

FAYETTEVILLE–Washington County

✠ **HEALTHSOUTH REHABILITATION HOSPITAL (043032)**, 153 East Monte Painter
Drive, Zip 72703–4002; tel. 479/444–2200, **A**1 10 **F**3 29 34 57 59 75 77 79
90 91 92 94 95 96 149 **P**8 **S** Encompass Health Corporation, Birmingham, AL
Primary Contact: Jack C. Mitchell, FACHE, Chief Executive Officer
CMO: Marty Hurlbut, M.D., Medical Director
CHR: Missy Cole, Director Human Resources
CNO: Miriam Irvin, CNO
Web address: www.healthsouthfayetteville.com
Control: Corporation, Investor–owned (for–profit) **Service**: Rehabilitation

Staffed Beds: 80 **Admissions**: 1716 **Census**: 55 **Outpatient Visits**: 0 **Births**: 0 **Total Expense ($000)**: 17777 **Payroll Expense ($000)**: 10185 **Personnel**: 206	

★ ○ **PHYSICIANS' SPECIALTY HOSPITAL (040152)**, 3873 North Parkview
Drive, Zip 72703–6286; tel. 479/571–7070, (Nonreporting) **A**3 10 11 **S**
Community Health Systems, Inc., Franklin, TN
Primary Contact: Denten Park, Chief Executive Officer
CFO: Joshua Harmond, Assistant Chief Financial Officer
CNO: Tim Kimball, Chief Nursing Officer
Web address: www.pshfay.com
Control: Partnership, Investor–owned (for–profit) **Service**: Surgical

Staffed Beds: 21	

✠ **SPRINGWOODS BEHAVIORAL HEALTH HOSPITAL (044019)**, 1955 West
Truckers Drive, Zip 72704–5637; tel. 479/973–6000, **A**1 10 **F**3 29 56 98
99 100 103 105 130 152 153 **P**6 **S** Universal Health Services, Inc., King of
Prussia, PA
Primary Contact: Jordon Babcock, Interim Chief Executive Officer
Web address: www.springwoodsbehavioral.com
Control: Corporation, Investor–owned (for–profit) **Service**: Psychiatric

Staffed Beds: 80 **Admissions**: 2307 **Census**: 47 **Outpatient Visits**: 2241 **Births**: 0 **Total Expense ($000)**: 15355 **Payroll Expense ($000)**: 6385 **Personnel**: 175	

AR

Hospital, Medicare Provider Number, Address, Telephone, Approval, Facility, and Physician Codes, Health Care System

★ American Hospital Association (AHA) membership ○ Healthcare Facilities Accreditation Program ⇑ Center for Improvement in Healthcare Quality Accreditation
☐ The Joint Commission accreditation ◇ DNV Healthcare Inc. accreditation △ Commission on Accreditation of Rehabilitation Facilities (CARF) accreditation

AR

☐ **VANTAGE POINT OF NORTHWEST ARKANSAS (044004)**, 4253 North Crossover Road, Zip 72703–4596; tel. 479/521–5731, **A**1 10 **F**30 56 87 98 99 100 101 102 103 130 132 153 **P**6 **S** Acadia Healthcare Company, Inc., Franklin, TN
Primary Contact: Connie Borengasser, Chief Executive Officer
CFO: Ben Winbery, Chief Financial Officer
CMO: Norman Snyder, M.D., Medical Director
CIO: Margaret Brown, Director Medical Records
CHR: Kathy Vickers, Director Human Resources
CNO: Suzette Branscum, Director of Nursing
Web address: www.vantagepointnwa.com
Control: Corporation, Investor–owned (for–profit) **Service**: Psychiatric

Staffed Beds: 114 Admissions: 2439 Census: 98 Outpatient Visits: 130189 Births: 0 Total Expense ($000): 27686 Payroll Expense ($000): 16696 Personnel: 217

⊞ **VETERANS HEALTH CARE SYSTEM OF THE OZARKS**, 1100 North College Avenue, Zip 72703–1944; tel. 479/443–4301, (Nonreporting) **A**1 2 3 **S** Department of Veterans Affairs, Perry Point, MD
Primary Contact: Kelvin L. Parks, Interim Director
CMO: Bonnie Baker, M.D., Chief Medical Services
CIO: Michael Gracie, Chief Information Officer
CHR: Kathryn L Barker, Chief Human Resources Management
Web address: www.fayettevillear.va.gov
Control: Veterans Affairs, Government, federal **Service**: General medical and surgical

Staffed Beds: 72

⊞ **WASHINGTON REGIONAL MEDICAL CENTER (040004)**, 3215 North Hills Boulevard, Zip 72703–4424; tel. 479/463–1000, **A**1 3 10 **F**3 11 13 17 18 20 22 24 26 28 29 30 31 34 35 40 41 43 45 46 47 48 49 50 56 57 58 59 60 62 63 64 68 70 71 72 74 75 76 77 78 79 80 81 84 85 86 87 89 92 100 102 107 108 111 115 118 119 126 129 130 132 135 141 146 147 148 149 154 **P**1 6
Primary Contact: J. Larry. Shackelford, President and Chief Executive Officer
CFO: Dan Eckels, Chief Financial Officer
CMO: David Ratcliff, M.D., Chief Medical Affairs
CIO: Becky Magee, Chief Information Officer
CHR: Laurie Morrow, Executive Director Human Resources
CNO: Meredith Green, Senior Vice President and Chief Nursing Officer
Web address: www.wregional.com
Control: Other not–for–profit (including NFP Corporation) **Service**: General medical and surgical

Staffed Beds: 363 Admissions: 16781 Census: 178 Outpatient Visits: 162251 Births: 2747 Total Expense ($000): 266876 Payroll Expense ($000): 102047 Personnel: 2477

FORDYCE–Dallas County

★ **DALLAS COUNTY MEDICAL CENTER (041317)**, 201 Clifton Street, Zip 71742–3099; tel. 870/352–6300, **A**10 18 **F**3 11 29 30 32 34 35 40 43 45 53 57 59 68 75 77 81 86 87 90 91 93 97 107 119 127 128 130 133 146 149
Primary Contact: Kenneth Sanders, Administrator and Chief Executive Officer
CFO: Billie Launius, Director Business Finance
CMO: Michael Payne, M.D., Chief of Staff
CHR: Audrey Allen, Coordinator Benefits
CNO: Hollie Raney, Director of Nursing
Web address: www.dallascountymedicalcenter.com
Control: County, Government, nonfederal **Service**: General medical and surgical

Staffed Beds: 25 Admissions: 169 Census: 1 Outpatient Visits: 47850 Births: 0 Total Expense ($000): 10331 Payroll Expense ($000): 3875 Personnel: 107

FORREST CITY–St. Francis County

⊞ **FORREST CITY MEDICAL CENTER (040019)**, 1601 Newcastle Road, Zip 72335–2218; tel. 870/261–0000, **A**1 10 20 **F**3 7 13 15 21 29 30 34 40 43 45 56 57 68 70 76 81 85 87 91 92 93 98 100 102 103 107 108 109 110 111 112 114 119 129 130 133 145 146 147 148 **P**6 **S** Quorum Health, Brentwood, TN
Primary Contact: Kevin Decker, Chief Executive Officer
CFO: Misty Gates, Chief Financial Officer
CMO: James DeRossitt, M.D., Chief of Staff
CIO: David Shaw, Director Information Technology
CHR: Sherry McLaughlin, Director Human Resources
CNO: Leslie Harris, Chief Nursing Officer
Web address: www.forrestcitymedicalcenter.com
Control: Corporation, Investor–owned (for–profit) **Service**: General medical and surgical

Staffed Beds: 55 Admissions: 2181 Census: 18 Outpatient Visits: 38328 Births: 876 Total Expense ($000): 29119 Payroll Expense ($000): 10088 Personnel: 227

FORT SMITH–Sebastian County

⊞ **CHRISTUS DUBUIS HOSPITAL OF FORT SMITH (042008)**, 7301 Rogers Avenue, 4th Floor, Zip 72903–4100; tel. 479/314–4900, **A**1 10 **F**1 3 29 85 130 148 **S** LHC Group, Lafayette, LA
Primary Contact: Julie Cormack, Administrator
CFO: Paul Veillon, CPA, Chief Financial Officer
Web address: www.christusdubuis.org/fortsmith
Control: Partnership, Investor–owned (for–profit) **Service**: Acute long–term care hospital

Staffed Beds: 25 Admissions: 201 Census: 8 Outpatient Visits: 0 Births: 0 Total Expense ($000): 2186 Payroll Expense ($000): 1156 Personnel: 55

⊞ **HEALTHSOUTH REHABILITATION HOSPITAL OF FORT SMITH (043028)**, 1401 South 'J' Street, Zip 72901–5155; tel. 479/785–3300, **A**1 10 **F**29 30 34 77 90 91 94 95 96 130 132 149 **S** Encompass Health Corporation, Birmingham, AL
Primary Contact: Dawn Watts, Chief Executive Officer
CFO: Brenda Forbes, Controller
CMO: Cygnet Schroeder, D.O., Medical Director
CHR: S Janette Daniels, Director Human Resources
Web address: www.healthsouthfortsmith.com
Control: Corporation, Investor–owned (for–profit) **Service**: Rehabilitation

Staffed Beds: 60 Admissions: 1458 Census: 46 Outpatient Visits: 0 Births: 0 Total Expense ($000): 16025 Payroll Expense ($000): 9319

⊞ **MERCY HOSPITAL FORT SMITH (040062)**, 7301 Rogers Avenue, Zip 72903–4189, Mailing Address: P.O. Box 17000, Zip 72917–7000; tel. 479/314–6000, (Includes MERCY ORTHOPEDIC HOSPITAL FORT SMITH, 3601 South 79th Street, Fort Smith, AR, Zip 72903–6255; tel. 479/709–8500; Ryan Gehrig, President) **A**1 2 10 13 **F**3 12 13 15 17 18 20 22 24 26 28 29 30 31 32 34 35 36 38 40 43 44 45 48 49 50 53 56 57 58 59 60 61 62 63 64 65 68 70 71 72 73 74 75 76 77 78 79 81 82 83 84 85 86 87 89 90 91 93 95 96 102 107 108 109 110 111 114 115 116 117 119 120 121 123 124 129 130 134 135 143 146 147 148 149 154 **P**8 **S** Mercy, Chesterfield, MO
Primary Contact: Ryan Gehrig, President
COO: Julianne Stec, Chief Operating Officer
CFO: Greta Wilcher, Senior Vice President and Chief Financial Officer
CMO: David Hunton, M.D., Chief Medical Officer
CHR: Bryan Brown, Executive Director
CNO: Marianne Rataj, R.N., MS, Chief Nursing Officer
Web address: www.mercy.net/fortsmithar
Control: Church operated, Nongovernment, not–for–profit **Service**: General medical and surgical

Staffed Beds: 352 Admissions: 15797 Census: 193 Outpatient Visits: 219144 Births: 2334 Total Expense ($000): 289399 Payroll Expense ($000): 104255 Personnel: 1688

⊞ **SELECT SPECIALTY HOSPITAL–FORT SMITH (042006)**, 1001 Towson Avenue, 6 Central, Zip 72901–4921; tel. 479/441–3960, **A**1 10 **F**1 3 29 34 45 46 57 74 75 78 79 94 148 **S** Select Medical Corporation, Mechanicsburg, PA
Primary Contact: Shannon Grams, Chief Executive Officer
Web address: www.https://fortsmith.selectspecialtyhospitals.com/
Control: Corporation, Investor–owned (for–profit) **Service**: Acute long–term care hospital

Staffed Beds: 34 Admissions: 330 Census: 22 Outpatient Visits: 0 Births: 0 Total Expense ($000): 11502 Payroll Expense ($000): 5038 Personnel: 83

⊞ **SPARKS REGIONAL MEDICAL CENTER (040055)**, 1001 Towson Avenue, Zip 72901–4921, Mailing Address: P.O. Box 2406, Zip 72917–7006; tel. 479/441–4000, **A**1 3 10 **F**3 8 12 13 14 15 17 18 20 21 22 24 26 28 29 30 31 34 35 40 43 45 46 47 48 49 50 51 53 54 56 58 59 60 64 67 70 72 74 75 76 77 78 79 81 82 85 86 87 89 93 97 98 103 107 108 109 110 111 112 113 114 115 116 117 119 120 121 122 124 126 129 130 144 146 147 148 154 **P**8 **S** Community Health Systems, Inc., Franklin, TN
Primary Contact: Brandon Bullard, Interim Chief Executive Officer
COO: Aimee Arzoumanian, Chief Operating Officer
CFO: Brandon Bullard, Chief Financial Officer
CMO: Katherine Irish–Clardy, M.D., Chief Medical Officer
CIO: Tom Sallis, Director Information Systems
CHR: Robert Freeman, Director Human Resources
CNO: Stephanie Whitaker, Chief Nursing Officer
Web address: www.sparkshealth.com/
Control: Corporation, Investor–owned (for–profit) **Service**: General medical and surgical

Staffed Beds: 303 Admissions: 15315 Census: 200 Outpatient Visits: 215362 Births: 1133 Total Expense ($000): 236083 Payroll Expense ($000): 64487 Personnel: 1447

GRAVETTE–Benton County

OZARKS COMMUNITY HOSPITAL (041331), 1101 Jackson Street Sw, Zip 72736–9121; tel. 479/787–5291, **A**10 18 **F**3 29 34 35 40 44 45 50 56 57 59 64 65 74 75 77 79 81 82 85 87 89 91 93 96 97 100 104 107 111 115 119 127 128 129 130 131 133 143 148 153 154 **P**6
Primary Contact: Paul Taylor, Administrator
Web address: www.ochonline.com/
Control: Corporation, Investor–owned (for–profit) **Service:** General medical and surgical

Staffed Beds: 25 **Admissions:** 625 **Census:** 19 **Outpatient Visits:** 68549
Births: 0 **Total Expense ($000):** 35575 **Payroll Expense ($000):** 14990
Personnel: 316

HARRISON–Boone County

★ **NORTH ARKANSAS REGIONAL MEDICAL CENTER (040017)**, 620 North Main Street, Zip 72601–2911; tel. 870/414–4000, **A**10 **F**3 7 8 11 13 15 17 18 28 29 30 31 32 34 35 39 40 41 43 45 50 53 56 57 59 62 63 64 65 68 70 73 75 76 77 78 79 81 82 85 86 87 89 93 97 98 102 103 104 107 108 110 111 114 115 118 119 120 121 123 127 128 131 132 135 144 146 147 148 149 154 **P**8
Primary Contact: Vincent Leist, President and Chief Executive Officer
CFO: Deana Thomas, Vice President Finance and Chief Financial Officer
CIO: William J Bogle, Director Information Systems
CNO: Sammie Cribbs, Vice President Clinical Services and Chief Nursing Officer
Web address: www.narmc.com
Control: Other not–for–profit (including NFP Corporation) **Service:** General medical and surgical

Staffed Beds: 113 **Admissions:** 3399 **Census:** 23 **Outpatient Visits:** 200180 **Births:** 734 **Total Expense ($000):** 86919 **Payroll Expense ($000):** 37827 **Personnel:** 816

HEBER SPRINGS–Cleburne County

⊞ **BAPTIST HEALTH MEDICAL CENTER–HEBER SPRINGS (041312)**, 1800 Bypass Road, Zip 72543–9135; tel. 501/887–3000, **A**1 10 18 **F**3 8 11 14 15 18 28 29 30 31 34 35 36 40 43 45 48 50 51 57 59 64 68 74 75 77 78 79 81 82 85 93 102 107 110 111 115 116 117 118 119 127 129 131 132 133 143 146 149 154 **S** Baptist Health, Little Rock, AR
Primary Contact: Edward L. Lacy, FACHE, Vice President and Administrator
Web address: www.baptist-health.com/maps–directions/bhmc–heber–springs
Control: Other not–for–profit (including NFP Corporation) **Service:** General medical and surgical

Staffed Beds: 25 **Admissions:** 836 **Census:** 9 **Outpatient Visits:** 31278
Births: 0 **Total Expense ($000):** 21156 **Payroll Expense ($000):** 7713
Personnel: 156

HELENA–Phillips County

⊞ **HELENA REGIONAL MEDICAL CENTER (040085)**, 1801 Martin Luther King Drive, Zip 72342, Mailing Address: P.O. Box 788, Zip 72342–0788; tel. 870/338–5800, **A**1 10 20 **F**3 11 13 15 29 34 40 50 59 62 70 74 76 79 81 82 86 87 89 91 93 97 107 108 111 113 114 119 130 132 133 135 145 146 147 148 **S** Quorum Health, Brentwood, TN
Primary Contact: Leah Osbahr, M.P.H., Chief Executive Officer
CFO: Amy Rice, Chief Financial Officer
CIO: Christopher Hunt, Director, Information Technologies, FISO
CHR: Juril Fonzie, Director Human Resources
CNO: Judith LeAnn Gerlach, Chief Nursing Officer
Web address: www.helenarmc.com
Control: Corporation, Investor–owned (for–profit) **Service:** General medical and surgical

Staffed Beds: 105 **Admissions:** 1547 **Census:** 12 **Outpatient Visits:** 29987
Births: 226 **Total Expense ($000):** 23590 **Payroll Expense ($000):** 7254
Personnel: 149

HOPE–Hempstead County

⇑ **WADLEY REGIONAL MEDICAL CENTER AT HOPE (040153)**, 2001 South Main Street, Zip 71801–8194; tel. 870/722–3800, **A**10 21 **F**3 11 15 18 29 34 35 40 50 56 57 59 64 70 86 93 98 103 107 110 111 114 119 127 130 **S** Steward Health Care System, LLC, Dallas, TX
Primary Contact: Thomas D. Gilbert, FACHE, Chief Executive Officer
CFO: Bonny Sorensen, Chief Financial Officer
CIO: Matt Kesterson, Director Information Services
CHR: Debby Butler, Director Human Resources
CNO: Shelly Strayhorn, R.N., Chief Nursing Officer
Web address: www.wadleyhealthathope.com
Control: Corporation, Investor–owned (for–profit) **Service:** General medical and surgical

Staffed Beds: 79 **Admissions:** 966 **Census:** 15 **Outpatient Visits:** 27802
Births: 0 **Total Expense ($000):** 13191 **Payroll Expense ($000):** 6199
Personnel: 139

HOT SPRINGS–Garland County

⊞ **CHI ST. VINCENT HOT SPRINGS (040026)**, 300 Werner Street, Zip 71913–6406; tel. 501/622–1000, **A**1 2 10 19 **F**3 11 12 13 15 17 18 20 22 24 26 28 29 30 31 34 35 37 38 40 43 45 47 49 50 56 57 59 62 64 65 66 68 69 70 71 74 75 76 77 78 79 81 85 86 87 89 93 107 108 110 111 112 114 115 116 117 118 119 120 121 123 124 130 132 135 146 147 148 149 150 154 **P**6 **S** Catholic Health Initiatives, Englewood, CO
Primary Contact: Anthony Houston, FACHE, President
CFO: Shawn Barnett, Senior Vice President and Chief Financial Officer
CIO: Tracy Kirby, Assistant Vice President Business Relationship Management
CHR: Aaron Austin, Market Vice President Human Resources
CNO: Bryan Williams, R.N., Vice President Patient Care Services
Web address: www.chistvincent.com/Hospitals/st-vincent-hot-springs
Control: Church operated, Nongovernment, not–for–profit **Service:** General medical and surgical

Staffed Beds: 241 **Admissions:** 13774 **Census:** 173 **Outpatient Visits:** 172980 **Births:** 1000 **Total Expense ($000):** 205179 **Payroll Expense ($000):** 67277 **Personnel:** 1036

□ △ **NATIONAL PARK MEDICAL CENTER (040078)**, 1910 Malvern Avenue, Zip 71901–7799; tel. 501/321–1000, **A**1 7 10 19 **F**3 8 11 12 13 15 17 18 20 22 24 28 29 30 31 34 35 40 45 46 47 48 49 56 57 59 64 70 73 74 75 78 79 81 85 87 90 92 93 98 103 107 110 111 115 119 124 130 131 132 146 148 **P**1 **S** RCCH HealthCare Partners, Brentwood, TN
Primary Contact: Jerry D. Mabry, FACHE, Chief Executive Officer
COO: Brian Bell, Associate Administrator and Chief Operating Officer
CFO: Robbie Pettey, Chief Financial Officer
CMO: Robert Breving, M.D., Chief of Staff
CIO: Brian Coffman, Director Information System
CHR: Tina Albright, Director Human Resources
CNO: Patsy Sue Crumpton, R.N., Chief Nursing Officer
Web address: www.nationalparkmedical.com
Control: Corporation, Investor–owned (for–profit) **Service:** General medical and surgical

Staffed Beds: 208 **Admissions:** 6045 **Census:** 93 **Outpatient Visits:** 57604
Births: 360 **Total Expense ($000):** 76957 **Payroll Expense ($000):** 29060
Personnel: 527

HOT SPRINGS NATIONAL PARK–Garland County

⊞ **CHRISTUS DUBIS HOSPITAL OF HOT SPRINGS (042004)**, 300 Werner Street, 3rd Floor East, Zip 71913–6406; tel. 501/609–4300, (Data for 273 days) **A**1 **F**1 3 29 130 135 **S** LHC Group, Lafayette, LA
Primary Contact: Kenneth Costello, Administrator
CFO: Paul Veillon, CPA, Chief Financial Officer
CIO: David Cook, Manager Information Systems
Web address: www.christusdubis.org/hotsprings
Control: Partnership, Investor–owned (for–profit) **Service:** Acute long–term care hospital

Staffed Beds: 26 **Admissions:** 108 **Census:** 9 **Outpatient Visits:** 0 **Births:** 0
Total Expense ($000): 1612 **Payroll Expense ($000):** 932

★ **LEVI HOSPITAL (040132)**, 300 Prospect Avenue, Zip 71901–4097; tel. 501/624–1281, **A**10 **F**3 40 57 59 64 93 98 102 103 104 107 130 131 132 153
Primary Contact: Patrick G. McCabe Jr, FACHE, President and Chief Executive Officer
CFO: Stuart Lisko, Vice President, Chief Financial Officer and Compliance Officer
CMO: P Ross Bandy, M.D., Chief Medical Officer and Chief of Staff
CIO: Stuart Lisko, Vice President, Chief Financial Officer and Compliance Officer
CHR: Susan Kramer, Director of Human Resources
CNO: Steven Boyd, R.N., Nurse Executive
Web address: www.levihospital.com
Control: Other not–for–profit (including NFP Corporation) **Service:** Psychiatric

Staffed Beds: 35 **Admissions:** 1427 **Census:** 16 **Outpatient Visits:** 15015
Births: 0 **Total Expense ($000):** 7978 **Payroll Expense ($000):** 4342
Personnel: 96

Hospital, Medicare Provider Number, Address, Telephone, Approval, Facility, and Physician Codes, Health Care System

★ American Hospital Association (AHA) membership   ○ Healthcare Facilities Accreditation Program   ⇑ Center for Improvement in Healthcare Quality Accreditation
□ The Joint Commission accreditation   ◇ DNV Healthcare Inc. accreditation   △ Commission on Accreditation of Rehabilitation Facilities (CARF) accreditation

---

JACKSONVILLE–Pulaski County

NORTH METRO MEDICAL CENTER (040074), 1400 West Braden Street, Zip 72076–3788; tel. 501/985–7000, **A**10 **F**2 3 5 6 7 8 9 10 11 12 14 15 18 20 22 29 34 35 38 40 41 43 45 50 56 57 59 62 64 65 68 70 77 81 82 83 84 85 86 87 97 98 100 103 106 107 108 110 115 119 130 145 146 147 148 149 150 151 152 154 **S** Allegiance Health Management, Shreveport, LA
Primary Contact: Dale Anderson, RN, Chief Executive Officer
CFO: Lynn Muller, Chief Financial Officer
CMO: Ann Layton, M.D., Chief of Staff
CHR: Jane Rockwell, Director Support Services
Web address: www.northmetromed.com
Control: Corporation, Investor–owned (for–profit) **Service**: Psychiatric

Staffed Beds: 113 **Admissions**: 1753 **Census**: 36 **Outpatient Visits**: 27182 **Births**: 0 **Total Expense ($000)**: 34017 **Payroll Expense ($000)**: 14492 **Personnel**: 318

JONESBORO–Craighead County

✠ **HEALTHSOUTH REHABILITATION HOSPITAL OF JONESBORO (043029)**, 1201 Fleming Avenue, Zip 72401–4311, Mailing Address: P.O. Box 1680, Zip 72403–1680; tel. 870/932–0440, (Nonreporting) **A**1 10 **S** Encompass Health Corporation, Birmingham, AL
Primary Contact: Donna Harris, Chief Executive Officer
CFO: Allan Jones, Controller
CMO: Virendar Verma, M.D., Medical Director
CHR: Tammy Barley, Director, Human Resources
CNO: Becky Kimble, R.N., Chief Nursing Officer
Web address: www.healthsouthjonesboro.com
Control: Corporation, Investor–owned (for–profit) **Service**: Rehabilitation

Staffed Beds: 67

✠ **NEA BAPTIST MEMORIAL HOSPITAL (040118)**, 4800 East Johnson Avenue, Zip 72401–8413; tel. 870/936–1000, **A**1 3 10 13 **F**3 11 12 13 15 17 18 20 22 24 26 28 29 30 31 34 39 40 41 43 45 46 48 49 57 58 59 60 74 75 76 77 78 79 81 82 84 85 86 87 90 93 96 107 108 110 111 115 118 119 120 121 123 124 126 130 132 135 146 148 **P**8 **S** Baptist Memorial Health Care Corporation, Memphis, TN
Primary Contact: Brad Parsons, FACHE, Administrator and Chief Executive Officer
CFO: Kyle Sanders, Chief Financial Officer
CMO: Stephen Woodruff, M.D., Chief Medical Officer
CIO: Terry Crider, Information Technology Site Manager
CHR: James Keller, Director Human Resources
CNO: Paula Grimes, R.N., MSN, Chief Nursing Officer
Web address: www.neabaptist.com
Control: Other not–for–profit (including NFP Corporation) **Service**: General medical and surgical

Staffed Beds: 228 **Admissions**: 10264 **Census**: 134 **Outpatient Visits**: 95375 **Births**: 695 **Total Expense ($000)**: 172500 **Payroll Expense ($000)**: 53668 **Personnel**: 993

✠ **ST. BERNARDS MEDICAL CENTER (040020)**, 225 East Jackson Avenue, Zip 72401–3119; tel. 870/207–4100, **A**1 2 3 10 13 19 **F**3 5 11 12 13 15 17 18 19 20 22 24 26 27 28 29 30 31 32 34 35 38 39 40 41 43 45 53 54 55 56 57 58 59 60 62 63 64 66 68 70 71 72 74 75 76 77 78 79 81 82 83 84 85 86 87 89 91 92 93 97 98 100 101 102 103 104 107 108 109 110 111 114 115 116 117 118 119 120 121 123 124 126 129 130 131 132 134 135 141 145 146 147 148 149 154 **P**6 8
Primary Contact: Chris B. Barber, FACHE, President and Chief Executive Officer
COO: Michael K Givens, FACHE, Administrator
CFO: Harry Hutchison, Vice President Fiscal Services
CMO: Kasey Holder, M.D., Vice President Medical Affairs
CIO: Josh Melton, Chief Information Officer
CHR: Lori J. Smith, Vice President Human Resources
CNO: Susan Greenwood, R.N., Vice President and Chief Nursing Officer
Web address: www.stbernards.info
Control: Church operated, Nongovernment, not–for–profit **Service**: General medical and surgical

Staffed Beds: 386 **Admissions**: 17752 **Census**: 219 **Outpatient Visits**: 289088 **Births**: 1425 **Total Expense ($000)**: 302816

LAKE VILLAGE–Chicot County

★ **CHICOT MEMORIAL MEDICAL CENTER (041328)**, 2729 Highway 65 and 82 South, Zip 71653; tel. 870/265–5351, **A**10 18 **F**3 7 11 15 16 29 34 35 39 40 43 49 53 57 59 62 64 66 68 75 77 81 82 85 86 87 89 93 97 107 110 111 119 127 129 130 132 133 146 147 148 154 **P**6
Primary Contact: David Mantz, Chief Executive Officer
CFO: Vicki Allen, Chief Financial Officer
CMO: Michael Bradley Mayfield, M.D., Chief of Staff
CIO: David Andrews, Manager Information Systems
CNO: Eric Selby, R.N., Chief Nursing Officer
Web address: www.chicotmemorial.com
Control: Other not–for–profit (including NFP Corporation) **Service**: General medical and surgical

Staffed Beds: 25 **Admissions**: 823 **Census**: 10 **Outpatient Visits**: 18498 **Births**: 0 **Total Expense ($000)**: 17204 **Payroll Expense ($000)**: 7284 **Personnel**: 156

SOUTHEAST REHABILITATION HOSPITAL (043034), 2729–A Highway 65 and 82 South, Zip 71653; tel. 870/265–4333, **A**10 **F**90 91 94 **P**5
Primary Contact: Catherine M. Waldrop, Administrator
CNO: Michael Vaughn, Director of Nursing
Web address: www.southeastrehab.com
Control: Partnership, Investor–owned (for–profit) **Service**: Rehabilitation

Staffed Beds: 10 **Admissions**: 211 **Census**: 7 **Outpatient Visits**: 0 **Births**: 0 **Total Expense ($000)**: 3282 **Payroll Expense ($000)**: 2322 **Personnel**: 55

LITTLE ROCK–Pulaski County

ALLEGIANCE SPECIALTY HOSPITAL OF LITTLE ROCK See Cornerstone Hospital of Little Rock

✠ **ARKANSAS CHILDREN'S HOSPITAL (043300)**, 1 Children's Way, Zip 72202–3500; tel. 501/364–1100, **A**1 3 5 8 10 **F**3 7 11 12 16 17 19 21 23 25 27 28 29 30 31 32 34 35 38 39 40 41 43 45 46 48 50 53 55 57 58 59 60 64 68 71 72 74 75 77 78 79 80 81 82 84 85 86 87 88 89 90 91 93 94 97 102 107 108 111 115 118 119 126 129 130 131 132 135 136 137 138 143 146 149 150 154 **P**8
Primary Contact: Marcella Doderer, FACHE, President and Chief Executive Officer
COO: Chanda Cashen Chacon, Executive Vice President and Chief Operating Officer
CFO: Gena Wingfield, Senior Vice President and Chief Financial Officer
CMO: Robert Williams, M.D., Chief Medical Officer
CIO: Jonathan Goldberg, Senior Vice President and Chief Information Officer
CHR: Andree Trosclair, Vice President Human Resources
CNO: Lee Anne Eddy, Senior Vice President and Chief Nursing Officer
Web address: www.archildrens.org
Control: Other not–for–profit (including NFP Corporation) **Service**: Children's general medical and surgical

Staffed Beds: 336 **Admissions**: 15308 **Census**: 231 **Outpatient Visits**: 364483 **Births**: 0 **Total Expense ($000)**: 514396 **Payroll Expense ($000)**: 210466 **Personnel**: 3510

✠ **ARKANSAS HEART HOSPITAL (040134)**, 1701 South Shackleford Road, Zip 72211–4335; tel. 501/219–7000, (Nonreporting) **A**1 3 5 10
Primary Contact: Bruce Murphy, M.D., President and Chief Executive Officer
Web address: www.arheart.com
Control: Partnership, Investor–owned (for–profit) **Service**: Heart

Staffed Beds: 112

☐ **ARKANSAS STATE HOSPITAL (044011)**, 305 South Palm Street, Zip 72205–5432; tel. 501/686–9000, **A**1 3 5 10 **F**11 29 30 50 53 57 58 59 61 64 65 68 75 86 87 97 98 99 100 101 102 103 106 130 132 133 135 143 146 148 154 **P**6
Primary Contact: H. Jay Battle, M.D., Chief Executive Officer
CFO: Gary W Hollis, Comptroller
CMO: Steven Domon, M.D., Medical Director
CIO: Tina Grissom, Chief Information Technology Officer
CHR: Donna Sadler, Director Human Resources
CNO: James Scoggins, Director of Nursing
Web address: www.state.ar.us/dhs/dmhs
Control: State, Government, nonfederal **Service**: Psychiatric

Staffed Beds: 222 **Admissions**: 507 **Census**: 208 **Outpatient Visits**: 0 **Births**: 0 **Total Expense ($000)**: 48379 **Payroll Expense ($000)**: 23642 **Personnel**: 659

★ **BAPTIST HEALTH EXTENDED CARE HOSPITAL (042012)**, 9601 Baptist Health Drive, Zip 72205–7202; tel. 501/202–1070, **A**10 **F**1 3 29 31 77 87 130 148 **S** Baptist Health, Little Rock, AR
Primary Contact: Lee Gentry, FACHE, Vice President and Administrator
CFO: Robert C Roberts, Vice President
CMO: Gail McCracken, M.D., Medical Director
CIO: David House, Vice President
CHR: Anthony Kendall, Vice President Human Resources
CNO: Christopher Cox, Chief Nursing Officer
Web address: www.baptist–health.com/maps–directions/bh_extended_care/default.aspx
Control: Other not–for–profit (including NFP Corporation) **Service**: Acute long–term care hospital

Staffed Beds: 55 **Admissions**: 352 **Census**: 30 **Outpatient Visits**: 0 **Births**: 0 **Total Expense ($000)**: 16237 **Payroll Expense ($000)**: 6571 **Personnel**: 113

Many Facility Codes have changed. Please refer to the AHA Guide Code Chart. © 2018 AHA Guide

⊞ △ **BAPTIST HEALTH MEDICAL CENTER–LITTLE ROCK (040114)**, 9601 Baptist Health Drive, Zip 72205–7299; tel. 501/202–2000, **A**1 3 5 7 10 **F**3 4 5 7 8 11 12 13 15 17 18 20 22 24 26 28 29 30 31 32 34 35 36 37 38 40 43 44 45 46 47 48 49 50 54 55 57 58 59 60 61 62 64 65 67 68 70 72 73 74 75 76 77 78 79 81 82 84 85 86 87 89 93 98 100 101 102 103 104 107 108 110 111 114 115 119 126 128 129 130 131 132 134 135 137 143 144 146 147 148 154 **S** Baptist Health, Little Rock, AR
Primary Contact: Greg Crain, FACHE, Senior Vice President and Administrator
CFO: Robert C Roberts, Senior Vice President Financial Services
CMO: Anthony Bennett, M.D., Chief Clinical Affairs
CIO: David House, Vice President and Chief Information Officer
CHR: Anthony Kendall, Vice President Human Resources
CNO: Michele Diedrich, R.N., Chief Nursing Officer, Vice President Patient Care
Web address: www.baptist-health.org/maps-directions/bhmc-lr
Control: Other not–for–profit (including NFP Corporation) **Service**: General medical and surgical

Staffed Beds: 682 **Admissions**: 29690 **Census**: 448 **Outpatient Visits**: 141097 **Births**: 2870 **Total Expense ($000)**: 500129 **Payroll Expense ($000)**: 158864 **Personnel**: 2599

⊞ △ **BAPTIST HEALTH REHABILITATION INSTITUTE (043026)**, 9501 Baptist Health Drive, Zip 72205–6225; tel. 501/202–7000, **A**1 3 5 7 10 **F**29 30 34 35 50 53 64 75 86 87 90 91 93 95 96 130 132 143 **S** Baptist Health, Little Rock, AR
Primary Contact: Julie Nix, Vice President and Administrator
CFO: Robert C Roberts, Senior Vice President
CIO: David House, Vice President and Chief Information Officer
CHR: Anthony Kendall, Vice President Human Resources
Web address: www.baptist-health.com/locations/accesspoint.aspx?accessPointID=202
Control: Other not–for–profit (including NFP Corporation) **Service**: Rehabilitation

Staffed Beds: 120 **Admissions**: 1455 **Census**: 48 **Outpatient Visits**: 83128 **Births**: 0 **Total Expense ($000)**: 31183 **Payroll Expense ($000)**: 15636 **Personnel**: 212

⊞ △ **CENTRAL ARKANSAS VETERANS HEALTHCARE SYSTEM**, 4300 West Seventh Street, Zip 72205–5446; tel. 501/257–1000, (Includes NORTH LITTLE ROCK DIVISION, 2200 Fort Roots Drive, North Little Rock, AR, Zip 72114–1706; tel. 501/661–1202) (Nonreporting) **A**1 2 3 5 7 8 **S** Department of Veterans Affairs, Perry Point, MD
Primary Contact: Margie A. Scott, M.D., Director
CFO: Colonel Nate Todd, Chief Financial Officer
CIO: Jim Hall, Acting Chief Information Officer
CHR: Richard Nelson, Chief of Human Resources Management Services
Web address: www.littlerock.va.gov/
Control: Veterans Affairs, Government, federal **Service**: General medical and surgical

Staffed Beds: 637

⊞ **CHI ST. VINCENT INFIRMARY MEDICAL CENTER (040007)**, Two St Vincent Circle, Zip 72205–5499; tel. 501/552–3000, **A**1 3 5 10 **F**3 11 13 17 18 20 22 24 26 28 29 30 31 34 35 37 40 43 44 45 46 48 49 50 51 53 54 56 57 58 59 60 61 64 68 70 72 74 75 76 77 78 79 80 81 82 84 85 86 87 91 92 93 96 97 98 100 101 102 107 108 109 110 111 112 114 115 116 117 118 119 124 126 129 130 132 135 143 146 147 148 149 150 **P**6 7 **S** Catholic Health Initiatives, Englewood, CO
Primary Contact: Polly J. Davenport, FACHE, R.N., President
CFO: Shawn Barnett, Senior Vice President and Chief Financial Officer
CIO: Tracy Kirby, Assistant Vice President Business Relationship Management
CHR: Aaron Austin, Market Vice President Human Resources
CNO: Kathy E. Neely, R.N., Interim Vice President Patient Care Services
Web address: www.chistvincent.com/
Control: Church operated, Nongovernment, not–for–profit **Service**: General medical and surgical

Staffed Beds: 423 **Admissions**: 21343 **Census**: 316 **Outpatient Visits**: 162093 **Births**: 952 **Total Expense ($000)**: 413810 **Payroll Expense ($000)**: 162109 **Personnel**: 1856

CORNERSTONE HOSPITAL OF LITTLE ROCK (042010), 2 Saint Vincent Circle, 6th Floor, Zip 72205–5423; tel. 501/265–0600, **A**10 22 **F**1 3 29 85 **S** Cornerstone Healthcare Group, Dallas, TX
Primary Contact: James H. Rogers, FACHE, Chief Executive Officer
CNO: Joy Miller, Chief Nursing Officer
Web address: www.chghospitals.com/littlerock/
Control: Corporation, Investor–owned (for–profit) **Service**: Acute long–term care hospital

Staffed Beds: 30 **Admissions**: 342 **Census**: 27 **Outpatient Visits**: 0 **Births**: 0 **Total Expense ($000)**: 11739 **Payroll Expense ($000)**: 5822 **Personnel**: 92

☐ **PINNACLE POINTE HOSPITAL (044013)**, 11501 Financial Center Parkway, Zip 72211–3715; tel. 501/223–3322, **A**1 10 **F**5 29 34 35 38 50 75 87 98 99 101 102 104 105 130 134 143 **S** Universal Health Services, Inc., King of Prussia, PA
Primary Contact: Shane Frazier, Chief Executive Officer
CFO: Gina Dailey, Chief Financial Officer
CMO: Ben Nimmo, M.D., Medical Director
CIO: James L Howe, Director Human Resources
CHR: James L Howe, Director Human Resources
CNO: Bobby Alexander, R.N., Chief Nursing Officer
Web address: www.pinnaclepointehospital.com
Control: Corporation, Investor–owned (for–profit) **Service**: Children's hospital psychiatric

Staffed Beds: 127 **Admissions**: 3016 **Census**: 110 **Outpatient Visits**: 0 **Births**: 0 **Total Expense ($000)**: 18184 **Payroll Expense ($000)**: 11152 **Personnel**: 238

⊞ **UAMS MEDICAL CENTER (040016)**, 4301 West Markham Street, Zip 72205–7101; tel. 501/686–7000, **A**1 3 5 8 10 **F**3 5 11 12 13 15 17 18 20 22 24 26 29 30 31 34 40 43 44 45 46 47 48 49 50 52 53 54 55 56 57 58 59 60 61 64 68 70 71 72 73 74 75 76 77 78 79 80 81 82 84 85 86 87 91 92 93 94 96 97 98 99 100 101 102 104 105 106 107 108 110 111 114 115 116 117 118 119 120 121 123 124 126 127 129 130 131 132 136 138 139 141 142 145 146 147 148 152 153 154 **P**6
Primary Contact: Richard Turnage, M.D., Chief Executive Officer
COO: Timothy Hill, Chief Operating Officer
CFO: William Bowes, Chief Financial Officer
CMO: Nicholas P Lang, M.D., Chief Medical Officer
CHR: Jeff Risinger, Director Human Resources
CNO: Mary Helen Forrest, R.N., Chief Nursing Officer
Web address: www.uams.edu/medcenter
Control: State, Government, nonfederal **Service**: General medical and surgical

Staffed Beds: 522 **Admissions**: 25274 **Census**: 417 **Outpatient Visits**: 552590 **Births**: 3640 **Total Expense ($000)**: 1009624 **Payroll Expense ($000)**: 407366 **Personnel**: 5982

MAGNOLIA–Columbia County

★ **MAGNOLIA REGIONAL MEDICAL CENTER (040067)**, 101 Hospital Drive, Zip 71753–2415, Mailing Address: P.O. Box 629, Zip 71754–0629; tel. 870/235–3000, **A**3 10 20 **F**3 11 13 15 29 31 34 35 40 43 45 50 59 62 64 70 76 81 87 93 107 108 110 111 115 119 129 130 132 133 146 147 148 149
Primary Contact: Rex Jones, Chief Executive Officer
CFO: Roxane Stewart, Chief Financial Officer
CMO: James W Chambliss, Chief of Staff
CHR: Shawnee Cooper, Director Human Resources
CNO: Joycelyn Watkins, R.N., Chief Nursing Officer
Web address: www.magnoliarmc.org
Control: City, Government, nonfederal **Service**: General medical and surgical

Staffed Beds: 37 **Admissions**: 1295 **Census**: 12 **Outpatient Visits**: 27573 **Births**: 216 **Total Expense ($000)**: 23808 **Payroll Expense ($000)**: 11062 **Personnel**: 212

MALVERN–Hot Spring County

★ **BAPTIST HEALTH MEDICAL CENTER–HOT SPRING COUNTY (040076)**, 1001 Schneider Drive, Zip 72104–4811; tel. 501/332–1000, **A**10 **F**3 11 12 15 17 29 30 34 35 40 43 45 57 59 64 70 75 81 93 98 102 106 107 110 111 115 119 129 130 132 146 152 154 **S** Baptist Health, Little Rock, AR
Primary Contact: Sheila Williams, Vice President and Administrator
CMO: Allen Gerber, M.D., Chief of Staff
CHR: Kelli Hopkins, Director Human Resources
CNO: Dee Schall, R.N., Chief Nursing Officer
Web address: www.baptist-health.com/location/baptist-health-medical-center-hot-spring-county-hot-spring-county
Control: Other not–for–profit (including NFP Corporation) **Service**: General medical and surgical

Staffed Beds: 72 **Admissions**: 2236 **Census**: 25 **Outpatient Visits**: 23453 **Births**: 0 **Total Expense ($000)**: 20893 **Payroll Expense ($000)**: 9001 **Personnel**: 183

AR

MAUMELLE–Pulaski County

☐ **METHODIST BEHAVIORAL HOSPITAL OF ARKANSAS (044017)**, 1601 Murphy Drive, Zip 72113–6187; tel. 501/803–3388, **A**1 10 **F**98 99 104 153 154
Primary Contact: Andy Altom, President and Chief Executive Officer
Web address: www.umch.org
Control: Other not–for–profit (including NFP Corporation) **Service**: Children's hospital psychiatric

Staffed Beds: 60 **Admissions**: 1865 **Census**: 55 **Outpatient Visits**: 88533
Births: 0 **Total Expense ($000)**: 18596 **Payroll Expense ($000)**: 8572
Personnel: 110

MCGEHEE–Desha County

★ **MCGEHEE HOSPITAL (041308)**, 900 South Third, Zip 71654–2562, Mailing Address: P.O. Box 351, Zip 71654–0351; tel. 870/222–5600, **A**10 18 **F**3 11 29 40 57 59 62 64 68 107 114 119 132 133 135 146 148 154
Primary Contact: John E. Heard, Chief Executive Officer
CFO: Teresa Morgan, Chief Financial Officer
CMO: James Young, M.D., Chief of Staff
CIO: Shaun Perry, Chief Information Officer
CNO: Sarah Calvert, Chief Nursing Officer
Control: Other not–for–profit (including NFP Corporation) **Service**: General medical and surgical

Staffed Beds: 25 **Admissions**: 283 **Census**: 3 **Outpatient Visits**: 27564
Births: 0 **Total Expense ($000)**: 12272 **Payroll Expense ($000)**: 5703
Personnel: 146

MENA–Polk County

★ **MENA REGIONAL HEALTH SYSTEM (040015)**, 311 North Morrow Street, Zip 71953–2516; tel. 479/394–6100, **A**10 20 **F**3 4 11 13 15 29 30 34 35 40 43 45 56 57 59 64 68 70 75 76 77 79 81 86 87 90 91 93 96 98 100 101 103 104 107 108 110 111 115 119 129 130 144 146 147 149 **P**8
Primary Contact: Jay Quebedeaux, Chief Executive Officer
CFO: Mark Henke, Chief Financial Officer
CMO: Richard Lochala, Chief of Staff
CIO: Nicholas Dunn, Director Information Systems
CHR: Chandler Cox, Director Human Resources
CNO: Teresa Wise, R.N., Chief Nursing Officer
Web address: www.menaregional.com
Control: City, Government, nonfederal **Service**: General medical and surgical

Staffed Beds: 65 **Admissions**: 1475 **Census**: 20 **Outpatient Visits**: 33208
Births: 303 **Total Expense ($000)**: 29735 **Payroll Expense ($000)**: 14424
Personnel: 283

MONTICELLO–Drew County

★ **DREW MEMORIAL HEALTH SYSTEM (040051)**, 778 Scogin Drive, Zip 71655–5729; tel. 870/367–2411, (Nonreporting) **A**10 20
Primary Contact: Scott G. Barrilleaux, FACHE, Chief Executive Officer
COO: Wade Smith, Chief Operating Officer
CFO: Melodie Colwell, Chief Financial Officer
CMO: Julia Nichoson, M.D., Chief Medical Officer
CIO: Rusty Bryant, Director Information Technology
CHR: Seth Givens, Chief Human Resource Officer
CNO: Jonathan Schell, Chief Nursing Officer
Web address: www.drewmemorial.org
Control: County, Government, nonfederal **Service**: General medical and surgical

Staffed Beds: 49

MORRILTON–Conway County

★ **CHI ST. VINCENT MORRILTON (041324)**, 4 Hospital Drive, Zip 72110–4510; tel. 501/977–2300, **A**10 18 **F**3 11 15 18 28 29 30 34 35 40 43 44 45 48 50 57 59 62 63 64 77 79 80 81 85 87 93 97 107 108 110 111 119 127 129 130 132 133 143 145 146 148 **P**6 **S** Catholic Health Initiatives, Englewood, CO
Primary Contact: Leslie Arnold, Chief Executive Officer and Administrator
CFO: Shawn Barnett, Senior Vice President and Chief Financial Officer
CIO: Tracy Kirby, Assistant Vice President Business Relationship Management
CHR: Aaron Austin, Market Vice President Human Resources
CNO: Kathy E. Neely, R.N., Interim Vice President Patient Care Services
Web address: www.chistvincent.com/Hospitals/st–vincent–morrilton
Control: Church operated, Nongovernment, not–for–profit **Service**: General medical and surgical

Staffed Beds: 25 **Admissions**: 813 **Census**: 8 **Outpatient Visits**: 36825
Births: 0 **Total Expense ($000)**: 21236 **Payroll Expense ($000)**: 9048
Personnel: 123

ST. ANTHONY'S MEDICAL CENTER See Chi St. Vincent Morrilton

MOUNTAIN HOME–Baxter County

★ **BAXTER REGIONAL MEDICAL CENTER (040027)**, 624 Hospital Drive, Zip 72653–2955; tel. 870/508–1000, **A**10 **F**7 11 13 15 17 18 20 22 24 28 29 30 31 36 40 41 43 45 46 47 49 53 56 57 59 62 63 64 70 71 74 76 77 78 79 81 82 85 86 87 89 90 93 98 103 104 107 108 111 114 115 116 117 119 124 126 127 129 130 132 135 146 147 148 149 154 **P**6 8
Primary Contact: Ron Peterson, FACHE, President and Chief Executive Officer
COO: David R. Fox, Vice President and Chief Operating Officer
CFO: Debbie Henry, Vice President and Chief Financial Officer
CHR: Karen Adams, Vice President Human Resources
Web address: www.baxterregional.org
Control: Other not–for–profit (including NFP Corporation) **Service**: General medical and surgical

Staffed Beds: 209 **Admissions**: 8991 **Census**: 75 **Outpatient Visits**: 120839 **Births**: 667 **Total Expense ($000)**: 194954 **Payroll Expense ($000)**: 78616 **Personnel**: 1498

MOUNTAIN VIEW–Stone County

★ **STONE COUNTY MEDICAL CENTER (041310)**, 2106 East Main Street, Zip 72560–6439, Mailing Address: P.O. Box 510, Zip 72560–0510; tel. 870/269–4361, **A**10 18 **F**3 11 15 28 29 34 40 43 45 57 59 64 79 81 85 93 107 110 111 114 119 128 133 146 147 148 154 **S** White River Health System, Batesville, AR
Primary Contact: Kevin Spears, Chief Executive Officer
CFO: Phillip Hacker, Chief Financial Officer
CIO: Gary Paxson, Associate Administrator Information Systems
CHR: Gary McDonald, Associate Administrator Human Resources
CNO: Diana Shelden, Chief Nursing Officer
Web address: www.whiteriverhealthsystem.com/doctors/facilities/stone–county–medical–center
Control: Other not–for–profit (including NFP Corporation) **Service**: General medical and surgical

Staffed Beds: 25 **Admissions**: 686 **Census**: 6 **Outpatient Visits**: 26522
Births: 0 **Total Expense ($000)**: 13792 **Payroll Expense ($000)**: 5607
Personnel: 116

NASHVILLE–Howard County

★ **HOWARD MEMORIAL HOSPITAL (041311)**, 130 Medical Circle, Zip 71852–8606; tel. 870/845–4400, **A**10 18 **F**3 11 15 28 29 30 34 35 40 43 45 50 53 57 64 65 70 77 81 85 87 93 102 107 108 110 115 119 133 146 **P**6
Primary Contact: Debra J. Wright, R.N., Chief Executive Officer
CFO: William J Craig, CPA, Chief Financial Officer
CMO: John Hearnsberger, M.D., Chief of Staff
CHR: Gayla Lacefield, Director Human Resources
CNO: Alesha Danielle Collins, MSN, R.N., Chief Nursing Officer
Web address: www.howardmemorial.com
Control: Other not–for–profit (including NFP Corporation) **Service**: General medical and surgical

Staffed Beds: 20 **Admissions**: 586 **Census**: 5 **Outpatient Visits**: 36748
Births: 0 **Total Expense ($000)**: 22035 **Payroll Expense ($000)**: 9470
Personnel: 194

NORTH LITTLE ROCK–Pulaski County

☐ **ARKANSAS SURGICAL HOSPITAL (040147)**, 5201 North Shore Drive, Zip 72118–5312; tel. 501/748–8000, **A**1 10 **F**3 29 30 35 40 64 74 75 78 79 81 82 85 86 87 107 111 114 119 126 130 131 146 148 149
Primary Contact: Carrie Helm, Chief Executive Officer
CFO: Charles Powell, Chief Financial Officer
CMO: Kenneth A Martin, M.D., Chief of Staff
CIO: Scott Davis, Manager Information Technology
CNO: Judy Jones, Chief Clinical Officer
Web address: www.ArkSurgicalHospital.com
Control: Corporation, Investor–owned (for–profit) **Service**: General medical and surgical

Staffed Beds: 49 **Admissions**: 3559 **Census**: 19 **Outpatient Visits**: 17120
Births: 0 **Total Expense ($000)**: 55186 **Payroll Expense ($000)**: 14033
Personnel: 226

Many Facility Codes have changed. Please refer to the AHA Guide Code Chart.
© 2018 AHA Guide

⊞ △ **BAPTIST HEALTH MEDICAL CENTER – NORTH LITTLE ROCK (040036)**, 3333 Springhill Drive, Zip 72117–2922; tel. 501/202–3000, **A**1 7 10 **F**3 8 11 13 15 17 18 20 22 24 26 28 29 30 31 38 40 43 45 46 47 48 49 50 53 54 56 59 60 64 65 70 72 74 75 76 77 78 79 81 85 86 87 89 90 93 94 107 108 110 111 114 115 118 119 124 126 128 129 130 135 144 146 147 148 **S** Baptist Health, Little Rock, AR
Primary Contact: Mike Perkins, Vice President and Administrator
COO: Doug Weeks, Executive Vice President and Chief Operations Officer
CFO: Robert C Roberts, Senior Vice President Financial Services
CMO: Eddie Phillips, M.D., Chief Medical Affairs
CIO: David House, Vice President and Chief Information Officer
CHR: Cathy C Dickinson, Vice President Human Resources
CNO: Kelley Hamby, Vice President Patient Care
Web address: www.baptist-health.com/location/baptist-health-medical-center–north–little–rock–north–little–rock
Control: Other not-for-profit (including NFP Corporation) **Service:** General medical and surgical

Staffed Beds: 177 **Admissions:** 11059 **Census:** 136 **Outpatient Visits:** 100625 **Births:** 1206 **Total Expense ($000):** 176078 **Payroll Expense ($000):** 59599 **Personnel:** 987

NORTH LITTLE ROCK DIVISION See Central Arkansas Veterans Healthcare System, Little Rock

☐ **THE BRIDGEWAY (044005)**, 21 Bridgeway Road, Zip 72113–9516; tel. 501/771–1500, **A**1 10 **F**4 5 34 56 98 99 101 102 103 104 105 106 149 151 152 153 154 **P**5 6 **S** Universal Health Services, Inc., King of Prussia, PA
Primary Contact: Jonathon Gammon, Interim Chief Executive Officer
CFO: Fred Woods, Chief Financial Officer
CMO: Philip L Mizell, M.D., Medical Director
CHR: Neely Robison, Director Human Resources
Web address: www.thebridgeway.com
Control: Corporation, Investor-owned (for-profit) **Service:** Psychiatric

Staffed Beds: 127 **Admissions:** 4597 **Census:** 92 **Outpatient Visits:** 25579 **Births:** 0 **Total Expense ($000):** 24707 **Payroll Expense ($000):** 10467 **Personnel:** 196

OSCEOLA–Mississippi County

⊞ **SOUTH MISSISSIPPI COUNTY REGIONAL MEDICAL CENTER (041316)**, 611 West Lee Avenue, Zip 72370–3001, Mailing Address: P.O. Box 108, Blytheville, Zip 72316–0108; tel. 870/563–7000, **A**1 10 18 **F**29 40 43 57 59 68 75 81 93 107 114 119 130 133 146 154 **S** QHR, Brentwood, TN
Primary Contact: Chris Lee. Raymer, R.N., MSN, Chief Executive Officer
COO: Paul Pieffer, Chief Operating Officer
CFO: Randy Nichols, Chief Financial Officer
CMO: Pratapji Thakor, M.D., Chief of Staff
CIO: Tammy Bratcher, Director Information Technology
CHR: Cheri Blurton, Director Human Resources
CNO: Felicia Pierce, R.N., Chief Nursing Officer
Web address: www.mchsys.org
Control: County, Government, nonfederal **Service:** General medical and surgical

Staffed Beds: 25 **Admissions:** 438 **Census:** 5 **Outpatient Visits:** 13038 **Births:** 0 **Total Expense ($000):** 9982 **Payroll Expense ($000):** 3923 **Personnel:** 62

OZARK–Franklin County

★ **MERCY HOSPITAL OZARK (041303)**, 801 West River Street, Zip 72949–3023; tel. 479/667–4138, **A**10 18 **F**3 15 35 40 43 45 57 59 64 65 68 81 85 107 119 129 133 148 149 **P**6 8 **S** Mercy, Chesterfield, MO
Primary Contact: Teresa Williams, BSN, R.N., Regional Administrator
COO: Brent Hubbard, Chief Operating Officer
CMO: John Lachowsky, M.D., Chief Medical Officer
CIO: Tiana Bolduc, Chief Information Officer
Web address: www.mercy.net/practice/mercy–hospital–ozark/
Control: Church operated, Nongovernment, not-for-profit **Service:** General medical and surgical

Staffed Beds: 25 **Admissions:** 248 **Census:** 3 **Outpatient Visits:** 14034 **Births:** 0 **Total Expense ($000):** 10637 **Payroll Expense ($000):** 4147 **Personnel:** 55

PARAGOULD–Greene County

⊞ △ **ARKANSAS METHODIST MEDICAL CENTER (040039)**, 900 West Kingshighway, Zip 72450–5942, Mailing Address: P.O. Box 339, Zip 72451–0339; tel. 870/239–7000, **A**1 7 10 13 19 **F**3 7 10 11 13 15 18 20 22 28 29 32 34 35 39 40 43 45 49 50 51 53 54 57 59 62 64 68 70 75 76 78 79 81 85 86 87 89 90 93 97 107 108 110 111 114 115 119 125 129 130 131 132 133 135 146 147 148 154 **P**6 8
Primary Contact: Barry L. Davis, FACHE, President and Chief Executive Officer
CFO: Brad Bloemer, Vice President Finance and Chief Financial Officer
CMO: Aaron Thompson, M.D., Chief of Staff
CIO: Dan Austin, Director Information Technology
CHR: Kevin Thielemier, Director Human Resources
CNO: Lana R Williams, Chief Nursing Officer
Web address: www.arkansasmethodist.org
Control: Other not-for-profit (including NFP Corporation) **Service:** General medical and surgical

Staffed Beds: 125 **Admissions:** 4119 **Census:** 51 **Outpatient Visits:** 134705 **Births:** 594 **Total Expense ($000):** 62245 **Payroll Expense ($000):** 28297 **Personnel:** 631

PARIS–Logan County

★ **MERCY HOSPITAL PARIS (041300)**, 500 East Academy, Zip 72855–4040; tel. 479/963–6101, **A**10 18 **F**3 15 35 40 43 45 57 59 64 65 68 81 85 107 119 127 129 133 148 149 **P**6 8 **S** Mercy, Chesterfield, MO
Primary Contact: Teresa Williams, BSN, RN, Regional Administrator
COO: Brent Hubbard, Chief Operating Officer
Web address: www.mercy.net/fortsmithar
Control: Church operated, Nongovernment, not-for-profit **Service:** General medical and surgical

Staffed Beds: 16 **Admissions:** 134 **Census:** 1 **Outpatient Visits:** 15046 **Births:** 0 **Total Expense ($000):** 9669 **Payroll Expense ($000):** 3845 **Personnel:** 57

PIGGOTT–Clay County

★ **PIGGOTT COMMUNITY HOSPITAL (041330)**, 1206 Gordon Duckworth Drive, Zip 72454–1911; tel. 870/598–3881, **A**10 18 **F**3 7 8 11 18 29 30 34 35 40 43 45 46 57 59 62 64 65 71 77 81 86 87 93 107 111 114 119 127 129 130 132 133 135 143 146 148 154 **P**6
Primary Contact: James L. Magee, Executive Director
CFO: Linda Ort, Chief Financial Officer
Web address: www.piggottcommunityhospital.com
Control: City, Government, nonfederal **Service:** General medical and surgical

Staffed Beds: 25 **Admissions:** 833 **Census:** 12 **Outpatient Visits:** 15999 **Births:** 0 **Total Expense ($000):** 16463 **Payroll Expense ($000):** 7734 **Personnel:** 200

PINE BLUFF–Jefferson County

★ △ **JEFFERSON REGIONAL MEDICAL CENTER (040071)**, 1600 West 40th Avenue, Zip 71603–6301; tel. 870/541–7100, **A**3 7 10 20 **F**3 8 11 13 15 17 18 20 22 28 29 30 31 34 35 38 40 43 45 46 48 49 50 51 53 54 56 57 59 60 61 64 65 70 72 73 74 75 76 77 78 79 81 82 85 86 87 89 90 96 97 98 100 101 102 103 105 107 108 110 111 114 115 116 117 118 119 124 130 131 132 135 143 144 145 146 147 148 149 154 **P**6 7
Primary Contact: Brian N. Thomas, President and Chief Executive Officer
CFO: Bryan G Jackson, Vice President and Chief Financial Officer
CMO: Reid Pierce, M.D., Chief Medical Officer
CIO: Patrick Neece, Chief Information Officer
CHR: M Daryl Scott, Assistant Vice President
CNO: Louise Hickman, R.N., Vice President of Patient Care Services
Web address: www.jrmc.org
Control: Other not-for-profit (including NFP Corporation) **Service:** General medical and surgical

Staffed Beds: 286 **Admissions:** 9207 **Census:** 146 **Outpatient Visits:** 224674 **Births:** 749 **Total Expense ($000):** 186046 **Payroll Expense ($000):** 76984 **Personnel:** 1364

AR

POCAHONTAS–Randolph County

FIVE RIVERS MEDICAL CENTER (040047), 2801 Medical Center Drive, Zip 72455–9436; tel. 870/892–6000, **A**10 20 **F**3 11 29 40 43 45 50 57 59 62 68 70 77 79 81 85 87 93 97 98 103 107 111 115 119 127 129 130 131 133 146 154
Primary Contact: Luther J. Lewis, FACHE, Chief Executive Officer
CFO: Joey Radcliff, Chief Financial Officer
CHR: Anita Dickson, Director Human Resources
CNO: Paula Lewis, Interim Chief Nursing Officer
Web address: www.fiveriversmc.com
Control: Other not–for–profit (including NFP Corporation) **Service**: General medical and surgical

Staffed Beds: 36 **Admissions**: 817 **Census**: 13 **Outpatient Visits**: 26954 **Births**: 0 **Total Expense ($000)**: 18841 **Payroll Expense ($000)**: 9739 **Personnel**: 178

ROGERS–Benton County

✠ **MERCY HOSPITAL ROGERS (040010)**, 2710 Rife Medical Lane, Zip 72758–1452; tel. 479/338–8000, **A**1 3 10 **F**3 11 12 13 15 17 18 20 22 24 26 28 29 30 34 35 40 43 45 46 48 49 54 57 59 62 64 68 70 71 72 74 75 76 77 79 81 82 84 85 86 87 89 93 104 107 108 110 111 114 115 118 119 129 130 131 135 146 147 148 153 154 **S** Mercy, Chesterfield, MO
Primary Contact: Eric Pianalto, Chief Executive Officer
COO: Charlotte Rankin, R.N., Chief Operating Officer
CFO: Benny Stover, Vice President Finance
CMO: Chris Johnson, M.D., Chief of Staff
CHR: Rick Barclay, Vice President Support Services
Web address: www.mercy.net/practice/mercy–hospital–northwest–arkansas/
Control: Church operated, Nongovernment, not–for–profit **Service**: General medical and surgical

Staffed Beds: 191 **Admissions**: 11378 **Census**: 111 **Outpatient Visits**: 279867 **Births**: 1635 **Total Expense ($000)**: 208614 **Payroll Expense ($000)**: 72612 **Personnel**: 1346

RUSSELLVILLE–Pope County

☐ **SAINT MARY'S REGIONAL MEDICAL CENTER (040041)**, 1808 West Main Street, Zip 72801–2724; tel. 479/968–2841, (Nonreporting) **A**1 10 19 **S** RCCH HealthCare Partners, Brentwood, TN
Primary Contact: James Davidson, Chief Executive Officer
COO: Scott Bailey, Chief Operating Officer
CFO: Wendell VanEs, Chief Financial Officer
CMO: Vickie Henderson, M.D., Chief Medical Officer
CHR: Connie Gragg, Director Human Resources
CNO: Carol Gore, MSN, R.N., Chief Nursing Officer
Web address: www.saintmarysregional.com
Control: Corporation, Investor–owned (for–profit) **Service**: General medical and surgical

Staffed Beds: 141

SALEM–Fulton County

FULTON COUNTY HOSPITAL (041322), 679 North Main Street, Zip 72576–9451, Mailing Address: P.O. Box 517, Zip 72576–0517; tel. 870/895–2691, **A**10 18 **F**3 7 11 28 29 30 34 40 43 45 57 59 64 87 107 114 119 133 146 148 154
Primary Contact: Curren Everett, Chief Executive Officer
Web address: www.fultoncountyhospital.org
Control: County, Government, nonfederal **Service**: General medical and surgical

Staffed Beds: 25 **Admissions**: 1294 **Census**: 5 **Outpatient Visits**: 7819 **Births**: 0 **Total Expense ($000)**: 9767 **Payroll Expense ($000)**: 4644 **Personnel**: 162

SEARCY–White County

ADVANCED CARE HOSPITAL OF WHITE COUNTY (042011), 1200 South Main Street, Zip 72143–7321; tel. 501/278–3155, **A**10 **F**1 3 29 68 **P**5
Primary Contact: Terri L. Parsons, Administrator
CMO: Miguel Aguinaga, M.D., FACS, Medical Director
CNO: Mistie Vannatter, Chief Nursing Officer
Web address: www.https://unity–health.org/advanced–care
Control: Other not–for–profit (including NFP Corporation) **Service**: Acute long–term care hospital

Staffed Beds: 27 **Admissions**: 177 **Census**: 13 **Outpatient Visits**: 0 **Births**: 0 **Total Expense ($000)**: 6720 **Payroll Expense ($000)**: 3102 **Personnel**: 61

★ **UNITY HEALTH WHITE COUNTY MEDICAL CENTER (040014)**, 3214 East Race Avenue, Zip 72143–4810; tel. 501/268–6121, (Includes UNITY HEALTH HARRIS MEDICAL CENTER, 1205 McLain Street, Newport, AR, Zip 72112–3533; tel. 870/523–8911; Darren Caldwell, Vice President and Administrator; UNITY HEALTH SPECIALTY CARE, 1200 South Main Street, Searcy, AR, Zip 72143–7397; tel. 501/278–3100; Steven B. Webb, FACHE, President and Chief Executive Officer) **A**3 10 13 **F**1 3 11 13 15 17 18 20 22 24 28 29 30 31 34 35 38 39 40 43 45 50 51 57 58 59 62 64 65 68 69 70 74 75 76 77 78 79 81 84 85 86 87 89 90 93 98 100 102 103 104 105 107 108 110 111 114 115 119 126 129 130 132 134 135 144 146 147 148 152 154 **P**2 6
Primary Contact: Steven B. Webb, FACHE, President and Chief Executive Officer
CFO: Stuart Hill, Vice President and Treasurer
CMO: John Henderson, M.D., Chief Medical Officer
CIO: Phil Miller, Chief Information Officer
CHR: Pamela G Williams, Director Human Resources
CNO: Peggy Turner, Assistant Vice President and Director of Nursing
Web address: www.unity–health.org
Control: Other not–for–profit (including NFP Corporation) **Service**: General medical and surgical

Staffed Beds: 373 **Admissions**: 12861 **Census**: 156 **Outpatient Visits**: 112272 **Births**: 1473 **Total Expense ($000)**: 240350 **Payroll Expense ($000)**: 116309 **Personnel**: 1773

SHERWOOD–Pulaski County

★ **CHI ST. VINCENT MEDICAL CENTER–NORTH (040137)**, 2215 Wildwood Avenue, Zip 72120–5089; tel. 501/552–7100, **A**10 **F**3 11 15 18 20 22 26 29 30 35 40 44 45 50 64 68 70 74 79 81 85 87 107 110 111 115 118 119 129 130 146 149 150 **P**6 **S** Catholic Health Initiatives, Englewood, CO
Primary Contact: Polly J. Davenport, BSN, DSC, FACHE, President
CFO: Shawn Barnett, Senior Vice President and Chief Financial Officer
Web address: www.stvincenthealth.com
Control: Church operated, Nongovernment, not–for–profit **Service**: General medical and surgical

Staffed Beds: 69 **Admissions**: 1917 **Census**: 19 **Outpatient Visits**: 32996 **Births**: 0 **Total Expense ($000)**: 29967 **Payroll Expense ($000)**: 12041 **Personnel**: 180

✠ **ST. VINCENT REHABILITATION HOSPITAL (043031)**, 2201 Wildwood Avenue, Zip 72120–5074; tel. 501/834–1800, (Nonreporting) **A**1 10 **S** Encompass Health Corporation, Birmingham, AL
Primary Contact: Lisa Watson, Chief Executive Officer
CFO: Stacy Shilling, Controller
CMO: Kevin J. Collins, M.D., Medical Director
CNO: Carolynn Whitley, Chief Nursing Officer
Web address: www.stvincentrehabhospital.com/
Control: Partnership, Investor–owned (for–profit) **Service**: Rehabilitation

Staffed Beds: 80

SILOAM SPRINGS–Benton County

✠ **SILOAM SPRINGS REGIONAL HOSPITAL (040001)**, 603 North Progress Avenue, Zip 72761–4352; tel. 479/215–3000, **A**1 10 **F**3 11 13 15 28 29 30 34 40 45 50 57 59 64 68 70 75 76 77 79 81 85 91 93 107 108 110 111 115 118 119 129 130 144 146 147 154 **P**6 **S** Community Health Systems, Inc., Franklin, TN
Primary Contact: Patrick Kerrwood, Chief Executive Officer
CFO: Todd Williams, Chief Financial Officer
CMO: Ashish Mathur, M.D., Chief of Staff
CHR: Cindy Ruffing, Director Human Resources
CNO: Maria Wleklinski, Chief Nursing Officer
Web address: www.ssrh.net
Control: Corporation, Investor–owned (for–profit) **Service**: General medical and surgical

Staffed Beds: 44 **Admissions**: 1606 **Census**: 10 **Outpatient Visits**: 57157 **Births**: 602 **Total Expense ($000)**: 32593 **Payroll Expense ($000)**: 13701 **Personnel**: 212

SPRINGDALE–Washington County

★ **ARKANSAS CHILDREN'S NORTHWEST (043301)**, 2601 Gene George Boulevard, Zip 72762; tel. 479/725–6800, (Nonreporting)
Primary Contact: Marcella Doderer, FACHE, President and Chief Executive Officer
Control: Other not–for–profit (including NFP Corporation) **Service**: Children's general medical and surgical

Staffed Beds: 24

Many Facility Codes have changed. Please refer to the AHA Guide Code Chart.

✠ **NORTHWEST MEDICAL CENTER – SPRINGDALE (040022)**, 609 West Maple Avenue, Zip 72764–5394, Mailing Address: P.O. Box 47, Zip 72765–0047; tel. 479/751–5711, (Includes NORTHWEST MEDICAL CENTER – BENTONVILLE, 3000 Medical Center Parkway, Bentonville, AR, Zip 72712; tel. 479/553–1000; Denten Park, Chief Executive Officer; WILLOW CREEK WOMEN'S HOSPITAL, 4301 Greathouse Springs Road, Johnson, AR, Zip 72741–0544, Mailing Address: P.O. Box 544, Zip 72741–0544, tel. 479/684–3000; Denten Park, Chief Executive Officer) **A**1 3 10 **F**3 7 8 11 12 13 15 17 18 20 22 24 26 28 29 30 37 40 43 45 46 47 48 49 50 51 56 60 61 70 72 74 76 77 79 81 82 85 86 87 90 91 92 93 96 98 102 107 108 110 111 114 115 118 119 124 126 129 130 131 135 146 147 148 **P**5 8 **S** Community Health Systems, Inc., Franklin, TN
Primary Contact: Denten Park, Chief Executive Officer
COO: Tom Sledge, Chief Operating Officer
CMO: James Tanner, M.D., Chief Medical Officer
CIO: Mark Bokon, Chief Information Officer
CNO: Karen Y Labonte, Chief Nursing Officer
Web address: www.northwesthealth.com
Control: Corporation, Investor–owned (for–profit) **Service:** General medical and surgical

Staffed Beds: 323 **Admissions:** 13708 **Census:** 142 **Outpatient Visits:** 148298 **Births:** 2362 **Total Expense ($000):** 208560 **Payroll Expense ($000):** 70397

✠ **REGENCY HOSPITAL OF NORTHWEST ARKANSAS – SPRINGDALE (042009)**, 609 West Maple Avenue, 6th Fl, Zip 72764; tel. 479/757–2600, **A**1 10 **F**1 3 29 84 130 148 **S** Select Medical Corporation, Mechanicsburg, PA
Primary Contact: Robert Poole, Chief Executive Officer
COO: Ruth Jones, Chief Clinical Officer
CMO: Gary Templeton, M.D., Medical Director
CHR: Melissa Ross–Cole, Director Human Resources
Web address: www.regencyhospital.com
Control: Corporation, Investor–owned (for–profit) **Service:** Acute long–term care hospital

Staffed Beds: 25 **Admissions:** 255 **Census:** 17 **Outpatient Visits:** 0 **Births:** 0 **Total Expense ($000):** 9516 **Payroll Expense ($000):** 4305 **Personnel:** 74

STUTTGART–Arkansas County

★ **BAPTIST HEALTH MEDICAL CENTER–STUTTGART (040072)**, 1703 North Buerkle Road, Zip 72160–1905, Mailing Address: P.O. Box 1905, Zip 72160–1905; tel. 870/673–3511, **A**1 10 **F**3 11 13 15 18 29 30 34 35 39 40 43 45 53 56 57 59 64 68 75 76 78 79 81 85 87 93 97 98 107 110 111 114 119 127 129 130 132 133 135 146 148 154 **S** Baptist Health, Little Rock, AR
Primary Contact: Kevin L. Storey, Vice President and Administrator
CMO: Seth M. Kleinbeck, M.D., Chief of Staff
CIO: Warren Horton, Information Technologist
CNO: Susan Williams, R.N., Chief Nursing Officer
Web address: www.baptist–health.com/location/baptist–health–medical–center–stuttgart–stuttgart
Control: Church operated, Nongovernment, not–for–profit **Service:** General medical and surgical

Staffed Beds: 49 **Admissions:** 1296 **Census:** 13 **Outpatient Visits:** 22461 **Births:** 185 **Total Expense ($000):** 29216 **Payroll Expense ($000):** 10651 **Personnel:** 198

TEXARKANA–Miller County

☐ **RIVERVIEW BEHAVIORAL HEALTH (044020)**, 701 Arkansas Boulevard, Zip 71854–2105; tel. 870/772–5028, (Nonreporting) **A**1 10 **S** Acadia Healthcare Company, Inc., Franklin, TN
Primary Contact: Sherrie James, R.N., Chief Executive Officer
CFO: Kimberly Hibschman, Chief Financial Officer
CIO: Jim Cruson, Chief Information Officer
CHR: Roberta Bachman, Director Human Resources
CNO: Carrie Gray, Director of Nursing
Web address: www.riverviewbehavioralhealth.com
Control: Corporation, Investor–owned (for–profit) **Service:** Psychiatric

Staffed Beds: 62

VAN BUREN–Crawford County

✠ **SPARKS MEDICAL CENTER – VAN BUREN (040018)**, East Main and South 20th Streets, Zip 72956–5715, Mailing Address: P.O. Box 409, Zip 72957–0409; tel. 479/474–3401, **A**1 10 **F**12 29 40 43 68 70 79 81 107 108 111 116 117 151 152 **S** Community Health Systems, Inc., Franklin, TN
Primary Contact: Brandon Bullard, Interim Chief Executive Officer
CHR: James Ford, Director Human Resources
Web address: www.sparkshealth.com/
Control: Corporation, Investor–owned (for–profit) **Service:** General medical and surgical

Staffed Beds: 33 **Admissions:** 1016 **Census:** 8 **Outpatient Visits:** 30643 **Births:** 0 **Total Expense ($000):** 17591 **Payroll Expense ($000):** 5803 **Personnel:** 101

WALDRON–Scott County

★ **MERCY HOSPITAL WALDRON (041305)**, 1341 West 6th Street, Zip 72958–7642; tel. 479/637–4135, **A**10 18 **F**3 15 35 40 43 45 57 59 64 65 68 81 85 107 119 127 133 148 **P**6 8 **S** Mercy, Chesterfield, MO
Primary Contact: Teresa Williams, R.N., Regional Administrator
COO: Brent Hubbard, Chief Operating Officer
CFO: Greta Wilcher, Senior Vice President and Chief Financial Officer
CNO: Nick Hunt, Interim Director of Nursing
Web address: www.mercy.net/practice/mercy–hospital–waldron/
Control: Church operated, Nongovernment, not–for–profit **Service:** General medical and surgical

Staffed Beds: 24 **Admissions:** 201 **Census:** 2 **Outpatient Visits:** 14357 **Births:** 0 **Total Expense ($000):** 10981 **Payroll Expense ($000):** 4376 **Personnel:** 59

WALNUT RIDGE–Lawrence County

✠ **LAWRENCE MEMORIAL HOSPITAL (041309)**, 1309 West Main, Zip 72476–1430, Mailing Address: P.O. Box 839, Zip 72476–0839; tel. 870/886–1200, (Total facility includes 179 beds in nursing home–type unit) **A**1 10 18 **F**3 4 11 15 28 29 32 34 35 40 45 46 47 57 59 84 85 97 107 111 114 119 127 128 129 130 133 135 146
Primary Contact: Gary R. Sparks, Interim President
COO: Junior Briner, Chief Operating Officer
CFO: Vanessa Wagner, Chief Financial Officer
CMO: Kevin M. Diamond, M.D., Chief Medical Officer
CIO: Josh Wise, Director Information Technology
CHR: Brigett Montgomery, Director Human Resource
CNO: Rosalind C Casillas, Chief Nursing Officer
Web address: www.lawrencehealth.net
Control: County, Government, nonfederal **Service:** General medical and surgical

Staffed Beds: 204 **Admissions:** 1043 **Census:** 146 **Outpatient Visits:** 26392 **Births:** 1 **Total Expense ($000):** 24066 **Payroll Expense ($000):** 11584 **Personnel:** 302

WARREN–Bradley County

★ **BRADLEY COUNTY MEDICAL CENTER (041327)**, 404 South Bradley Street, Zip 71671–3493; tel. 870/226–3731, **A**10 18 **F**3 11 13 15 29 30 34 35 40 45 49 50 56 57 59 62 68 76 81 87 98 103 104 107 108 110 111 115 118 119 130 132 133 146 147 153 154 **P**6
Primary Contact: Steve Henson, Chief Executive Officer
CFO: Brandon Gorman, Chief Financial Officer
CMO: Joe H Wharton, M.D., Chief of Staff
CHR: Brooke Hatch, Director Human Resource
CNO: Sarah Tucker, Chief Nursing Officer
Web address: www.bradleycountymedicalcenter.com
Control: Other not–for–profit (including NFP Corporation) **Service:** General medical and surgical

Staffed Beds: 33 **Admissions:** 867 **Census:** 12 **Outpatient Visits:** 59437 **Births:** 109 **Total Expense ($000):** 21127 **Payroll Expense ($000):** 8837 **Personnel:** 198

WYNNE–Cross County

✠ **CROSSRIDGE COMMUNITY HOSPITAL (041307)**, 310 South Falls Boulevard, Zip 72396–3013, Mailing Address: P.O. Box 590, Zip 72396–0590; tel. 870/238–3300, **A**1 10 18 **F**3 11 15 28 34 35 40 50 57 59 62 64 68 69 81 93 107 110 111 114 119 130 133 146 148
Primary Contact: Gary R. Sparks, Administrator
COO: Bryan Mattes, Associate Administrator
CFO: Janice Morris, Accountant
CIO: Gail Copeland, Director Management Information Systems
CHR: Bertha Ragle, Director Personnel
CNO: Amelia Davis, Director of Nursing
Web address: www.stbernards.info
Control: Church operated, Nongovernment, not–for–profit **Service:** General medical and surgical

Staffed Beds: 15 **Admissions:** 736 **Census:** 9 **Outpatient Visits:** 20688 **Births:** 0 **Total Expense ($000):** 15413 **Payroll Expense ($000):** 6295 **Personnel:** 139

Hospital, Medicare Provider Number, Address, Telephone, Approval, Facility, and Physician Codes, Health Care System

★ American Hospital Association (AHA) membership
☐ The Joint Commission accreditation
◯ Healthcare Facilities Accreditation Program
◇ DNV Healthcare Inc. accreditation
⇑ Center for Improvement in Healthcare Quality Accreditation
△ Commission on Accreditation of Rehabilitation Facilities (CARF) accreditation

CALIFORNIA

ALAMEDA—Alameda County

★ **ALAMEDA HOSPITAL (050211)**, 2070 Clinton Avenue, Zip 94501–4397; tel. 510/522–3700, (Total facility includes 181 beds in nursing home–type unit) **A**10 **F**3 11 15 17 18 29 31 34 35 36 39 40 43 46 50 57 58 59 70 77 78 79 81 82 85 93 97 107 108 110 114 118 119 128 130 131 132 146 147 148 **S** Alameda Health System, San Leandro, CA
Primary Contact: John Chapman, Chief Administrative Officer
CFO: Robert C Anderson, Interim Chief Financial Officer
CMO: Aika Sharma, M.D., President Medical Staff
CIO: Robert Lundy–Paine, Director Information Systems
CHR: Phyllis Weiss, Director Human Resources
Web address: www.alamedahealthsystem.org
Control: Hospital district or authority, Government, nonfederal **Service:** General medical and surgical

> **Staffed Beds:** 247 **Admissions:** 2505 **Census:** 204 **Outpatient Visits:** 29466 **Births:** 0 **Total Expense ($000):** 102092 **Payroll Expense ($000):** 49948 **Personnel:** 537

ALHAMBRA—Los Angeles County

☐ **ALHAMBRA HOSPITAL MEDICAL CENTER (050281)**, 100 South Raymond Avenue, Zip 91801–3199, Mailing Address: P.O. Box 510, Zip 91802–2510; tel. 626/570–1606, (Nonreporting) **A**1 10 **S** AHMC & Healthcare, Inc., Alhambra, CA
Primary Contact: Iris Lai, Chief Executive Officer
CFO: Linda Marsh, Vice President Financial Services and Chief Financial Officer
CMO: Stephen Chen, M.D., Chief Medicare
CIO: Johnson Legaspi, Director Information Systems
CHR: Elizabeth Sabandit, Director Human Resources
CNO: Eleanor Martinez, Chief Nursing Officer
Web address: www.alhambrahospital.com
Control: Partnership, Investor–owned (for–profit) **Service:** General medical and surgical

> **Staffed Beds:** 144

ALTURAS—Modoc County

MODOC MEDICAL CENTER (051330), 228 West McDowell Avenue, Zip 96101–3934; tel. 530/233–5131, (Nonreporting) **A**10 18
Primary Contact: Kevin Kramer, Chief Executive Officer
CMO: Ed Richert, M.D., Chief of Staff
CHR: Diane Hagelthorn, Human Resources Generalist
Web address: www.modocmedicalcenter.org
Control: County, Government, nonfederal **Service:** General medical and surgical

> **Staffed Beds:** 87

ANAHEIM—Orange County

☐ **AHMC ANAHEIM REGIONAL MEDICAL CENTER (050226)**, 1111 West La Palma Avenue, Zip 92801–2881; tel. 714/774–1450, (Nonreporting) **A**1 10 **S** AHMC & Healthcare, Inc., Alhambra, CA
Primary Contact: Richard Castro, Chief Executive Officer
COO: Mary Anne Monje, Chief Operations Officer
CFO: Mary Anne Monje, Chief Financial Officer
CMO: Amitabh Prakash, M.D., Chief Medical Officer
CIO: Jeff DesRoches, Director Information Systems
CHR: Jason Jaquez, Human Resource Director
CNO: Lisa Hahn, R.N., Chief Nursing Officer
Web address: www.anaheimregionalmc.com
Control: Other not–for–profit (including NFP Corporation) **Service:** General medical and surgical

> **Staffed Beds:** 223

☐ **ANAHEIM GLOBAL MEDICAL CENTER (050744)**, 1025 South Anaheim Boulevard, Zip 92805–5806; tel. 714/533–6220, (Nonreporting) **A**1 10 **S** KPC Healthcare, Inc., Santa Ana, CA
Primary Contact: Scott Rifkin, Chief Executive Officer
CFO: John Collins, Chief Financial Officer
CMO: Beena Shah, M.D., Chief of Staff and Chief Medical Officer
CNO: Bonita Wells Veal, Chief Nursing Officer
Web address: www.anaheim–gmc.com
Control: Corporation, Investor–owned (for–profit) **Service:** General medical and surgical

> **Staffed Beds:** 188

ANAHEIM MEDICAL CENTER See Kaiser Permanente Orange County Anaheim Medical Center

✠ **KAISER PERMANENTE ORANGE COUNTY ANAHEIM MEDICAL CENTER (050609)**, 3440 East La Palma Avenue, Zip 92806–2020; tel. 714/644–2000, (Includes ORANGE COUNTY IRVINE MEDICAL CENTER, 6640 Alton Parkway, Irvine, CA, Zip 92618; tel. 949/932–5000; Mark E Costa, Executive Director) **A**1 3 5 10 **F**3 13 14 15 18 19 20 29 30 31 35 37 40 44 45 46 47 48 49 50 53 56 59 60 61 62 63 65 66 68 70 72 74 75 76 78 79 81 82 84 85 87 89 92 93 100 107 108 110 111 114 115 117 119 130 135 143 146 148 149 150 154 **S** Kaiser Foundation Hospitals, Oakland, CA
Primary Contact: Mark E. Costa, Executive Director
COO: Margie Harrier, MSN, R.N., Medical Center Chief Operations Officer
CFO: Marcus Hoffman, Area Chief Financial Officer
CMO: Nancy Gin, M.D., Area Associate Medical Director
CIO: James Brady, Area Information Officer
CHR: Jocelyn A. Herrera, Director Human Resources
CNO: Martha Dispoto, R.N., I Chief Nurse Executive, Anaheim Medical Center
Web address: www.kp.org
Control: Other not–for–profit (including NFP Corporation) **Service:** General medical and surgical

> **Staffed Beds:** 436 **Admissions:** 26011 **Census:** 279 **Outpatient Visits:** 395165 **Births:** 6487 **Personnel:** 2750

✠ **WEST ANAHEIM MEDICAL CENTER (050426)**, 3033 West Orange Avenue, Zip 92804–3183; tel. 714/827–3000, (Nonreporting) **A**1 10 13 **S** Prime Healthcare, Ontario, CA
Primary Contact: Edward Mirzabegian, Chief Executive Officer
CFO: Kora Guoyavatin, Chief Financial Officer
CMO: Hassan Alkhouli, M.D., Chief Medical Officer
CIO: Vic Mahan, Director Information Technology
CHR: Stephanie Sioson, Director Human Resources
Web address: www.westanaheimmedctr.com
Control: Partnership, Investor–owned (for–profit) **Service:** General medical and surgical

> **Staffed Beds:** 219

ANTIOCH—Contra Costa County

✠ **KAISER PERMANENTE ANTIOCH MEDICAL CENTER (050760)**, 4501 Sand Creek Road, Zip 94531–8687; tel. 925/813–6500, **A**1 2 5 10 **F**3 13 15 18 29 30 34 35 39 40 45 46 47 48 49 50 51 53 57 60 62 63 68 70 73 74 75 76 77 78 79 81 82 84 85 86 87 107 108 110 111 112 114 115 116 117 118 119 126 130 146 147 148 149 154 **S** Kaiser Foundation Hospitals, Oakland, CA
Primary Contact: Colleen McKeown, Senior Vice President and Area Manager
CFO: Kerry Easthope, Area Finance Officer
CMO: Dale Poppert, M.D., Chief of Staff
CIO: Mical Cayton, Area Information Officer
CHR: Davida Lindsay–Bell, Area Human Resources Leader
CNO: Janet Jule, Chief Nurse Executive
Web address: www.https://health.kaiserpermanente.org/wps/portal/facility/100382
Control: Other not–for–profit (including NFP Corporation) **Service:** General medical and surgical

> **Staffed Beds:** 150 **Admissions:** 7904 **Census:** 63 **Births:** 2448

✠ **SUTTER DELTA MEDICAL CENTER (050523)**, 3901 Lone Tree Way, Zip 94509–6253; tel. 925/779–7200, **A**1 10 **F**3 8 11 13 15 18 20 22 26 29 30 31 34 35 40 41 45 47 49 50 51 60 64 65 66 68 70 72 74 75 76 77 78 79 81 82 85 86 93 94 96 107 108 110 111 114 115 119 127 130 132 135 146 147 148 149 154 **P**3 5 **S** Sutter Health, Sacramento, CA
Primary Contact: Dori Stevens, Chief Executive Officer
CFO: Julie Peterson, Chief Financial Officer
CMO: Anupam Mapara, M.D., Chief of Staff
CIO: Kathy Frederickson, Information Systems Site Lead
CHR: Noemi Whitehead, Administrative Director Human Resources
CNO: James Christopher Reedy, Chief Nursing Officer
Web address: www.sutterdelta.org
Control: Other not–for–profit (including NFP Corporation) **Service:** General medical and surgical

> **Staffed Beds:** 132 **Admissions:** 7482 **Census:** 81 **Outpatient Visits:** 74121 **Births:** 847 **Total Expense ($000):** 204468 **Payroll Expense ($000):** 71059 **Personnel:** 830

Many Facility Codes have changed. Please refer to the AHA Guide Code Chart.

CA

APPLE VALLEY—San Bernardino County

✠ **ST. MARY MEDICAL CENTER (050300)**, 18300 Highway 18, Zip 92307–2206, Mailing Address: P.O. Box 7025, Zip 92307–0725; tel. 760/242–2311, **A**1 3 10 **F**8 11 13 15 18 20 22 24 26 28 29 30 34 35 40 45 46 49 50 57 59 60 64 65 66 68 70 71 72 74 75 76 77 78 79 81 84 85 86 87 89 91 93 100 107 108 111 114 115 119 120 121 126 127 130 132 135 146 147 148 149 154 **P**5 **S** Providence St. Joseph Health, Renton, WA
Primary Contact: Alan H. Garrett, President and Chief Executive Officer
CFO: Tracey Fernandez, Chief Financial Officer
CMO: Riad Z. Abdelkarim, M.D., Vice President and Chief Medical Officer
CIO: Doug Kleine, IT Director
CHR: Jean Holtman, Vice President, Human Resources
CNO: Marilyn Drone, R.N., MSN, Vice President, CNO
Web address: www.stmaryapplevalley.com/
Control: Church operated, Nongovernment, not–for–profit **Service**: General medical and surgical

Staffed Beds: 212 **Admissions:** 14919 **Census:** 179 **Outpatient Visits:** 141138 **Births:** 2255 **Total Expense ($000):** 293260 **Payroll Expense ($000):** 106943 **Personnel:** 1524

ARCADIA—Los Angeles County

✠ **METHODIST HOSPITAL OF SOUTHERN CALIFORNIA (050238)**, 300 West Huntington Drive, Zip 91007–3473, Mailing Address: P.O. Box 60016, Zip 91066–6016; tel. 626/898–8000, **A**1 2 3 10 **F**3 12 13 14 15 17 18 20 22 24 26 28 29 30 34 35 37 38 40 45 46 48 49 50 51 55 56 57 58 59 60 64 65 68 70 72 73 74 75 76 77 78 79 81 82 84 85 86 87 90 92 94 96 107 108 110 111 114 115 119 130 132 135 146 147 148
Primary Contact: Dan F. Ausman, President and Chief Executive Officer
COO: Steven A. Sisto, Senior Vice President and Chief Operating Officer
CFO: William E. Grigg, Senior Vice President and Chief Financial Officer
CHR: Gwen Chambers, Executive Director Human Resources
CNO: Roberta A McCaffrey, R.N., Vice President and Chief Nursing Officer
Web address: www.methodisthospital.org
Control: Other not–for–profit (including NFP Corporation) **Service**: General medical and surgical

Staffed Beds: 272 **Admissions:** 15645 **Census:** 199 **Outpatient Visits:** 77642 **Births:** 1597 **Total Expense ($000):** 262078 **Payroll Expense ($000):** 127976 **Personnel:** 1455

ARCATA—Humboldt County

○ **MAD RIVER COMMUNITY HOSPITAL (050028)**, 3800 Janes Road, Zip 95521–4788, Mailing Address: P.O. Box 1115, Zip 95518–1115; tel. 707/822–3621, (Nonreporting) **A**10 11
Primary Contact: Douglas A. Shaw, Chief Executive Officer
CFO: Michael Young, Chief Financial Officer
CMO: Bonnie MacEvoy, Chief of Staff
CIO: Jedd Rudd, Director of Ancillary Services and Safety
CNO: Sara Isaacson, Chief Nursing Officer
Web address: www.madriverhospital.com
Control: Corporation, Investor–owned (for–profit) **Service**: General medical and surgical

Staffed Beds: 42

ARROYO GRANDE—San Luis Obispo County

★ **ARROYO GRANDE COMMUNITY HOSPITAL (050016)**, 345 South Halcyon Road, Zip 93420–3896; tel. 805/489–4261, (Nonreporting) **A**10
Primary Contact: Kenneth Dalebout, Site Administrator
CHR: Ami Padilla, Director Human Resources
Web address: www.arroyograndehospital.org
Control: Other not–for–profit (including NFP Corporation) **Service**: General medical and surgical

Staffed Beds: 67

ATASCADERO—San Luis Obispo County

□ **ATASCADERO STATE HOSPITAL**, 10333 El Camino Real, Zip 93422–5808, Mailing Address: P.O. Box 7001, Zip 93423–7001; tel. 805/468–2000, (Nonreporting) **A**1
Primary Contact: Bob Hushing–Kline, Hospital Administrator
COO: David Landrum, Chief Police Services
CFO: Janie Pagnini, Administrator Accounting
CMO: David Fennell, M.D., Acting Medical Director
CIO: James Grover, Manager Data Processing
CHR: Elizabeth Andres, Director Human Resources
CNO: Liz Souza, Coordinator Nursing Services
Web address: www.dmh.ca.gov/statehospitals/atascadero
Control: State, Government, nonfederal **Service**: Psychiatric

Staffed Beds: 1184

AUBURN—Placer County

✠ **SUTTER AUBURN FAITH HOSPITAL (050498)**, 11815 Education Street, Zip 95602–2410; tel. 530/888–4500, **A**1 2 10 **F**3 8 11 12 15 17 18 20 28 29 30 31 34 35 37 39 44 45 47 49 50 57 58 59 62 63 64 68 70 74 75 78 79 81 85 86 87 90 92 93 107 108 110 111 114 115 117 119 130 132 135 145 146 147 148 **P**3 5 **S** Sutter Health, Sacramento, CA
Primary Contact: Mitchell J. Hanna, Chief Executive Officer
CFO: Gary Hubschman, Administrative Director Finance
CMO: John Mesic, M.D., Chief Medical Officer
CIO: Tom Ream, Regional Chief Information Officer
CHR: Yvette Martinez, Director Human Resources
CNO: Gina Temple, Chief Nurse Executive
Web address: www.sutterhealth.org
Control: Other not–for–profit (including NFP Corporation) **Service**: General medical and surgical

Staffed Beds: 72 **Admissions:** 3036 **Census:** 29 **Outpatient Visits:** 72982 **Births:** 0 **Total Expense ($000):** 137529 **Payroll Expense ($000):** 41145 **Personnel:** 412

AVALON—Los Angeles County

★ **CATALINA ISLAND MEDICAL CENTER (051307)**, 100 Falls Canyon Road, Zip 90704, Mailing Address: P.O. Box 1563, Zip 90704–1563; tel. 310/510–0700, **A**10 18 **F**3 11 28 34 36 40 50 57 64 65 75 93 96 107 113 119 121 130 134 146 154
Primary Contact: Jason Paret, Chief Executive Officer
COO: Stacie Amarantos, Chief Operating Officer
CFO: John Lovrich, Chief Financial Officer
CMO: Laura Ulibarri, M.D., Chief of Staff
CIO: Leah Keeline, Clinical Infirmatics Specialist
CHR: Lilly Hernandez, Human Resources Director
CNO: Stacie Amarantos, Chief Operating Officer
Web address: www.catalinaislandmedicalcenter.org
Control: Other not–for–profit (including NFP Corporation) **Service**: General medical and surgical

Staffed Beds: 12 **Admissions:** 12 **Census:** 8 **Outpatient Visits:** 22104 **Births:** 0 **Total Expense ($000):** 10395 **Payroll Expense ($000):** 3705 **Personnel:** 99

BAKERSFIELD—Kern County

✠ **ADVENTIST HEALTH BAKERSFIELD (050455)**, 2615 Chester Avenue, Zip 93301–2014, Mailing Address: P.O. Box 2615, Zip 93303–2615; tel. 661/395–3000, **A**1 3 10 **F**3 8 11 12 13 15 18 20 22 24 26 28 29 30 31 34 35 36 40 45 46 47 48 49 50 51 54 55 56 57 59 64 65 68 70 71 72 74 75 76 77 78 79 81 82 84 85 86 87 91 107 108 110 111 114 115 116 117 118 119 120 121 123 124 126 130 132 135 146 147 148 149 **S** Adventist Health, Roseville, CA
Primary Contact: Sharlet Briggs, Ph.D., Market Chief Executive Officer and President
COO: Sharlet Briggs, Ph.D., Chief Operating Officer
CFO: Brent Soper, Chief Financial Officer
CHR: Marlene Kreidler, Executive Director Human Resources
Web address: www.sanjoaquinhospital.org
Control: Church operated, Nongovernment, not–for–profit **Service**: General medical and surgical

Staffed Beds: 254 **Admissions:** 17972 **Census:** 192 **Outpatient Visits:** 132770 **Births:** 3140 **Total Expense ($000):** 394592 **Payroll Expense ($000):** 115380 **Personnel:** 1928

□ **BAKERSFIELD HEART HOSPITAL (050724)**, 3001 Sillect Avenue, Zip 93308–6337; tel. 661/316–6000, (Nonreporting) **A**1 10
Primary Contact: Michelle Oxford, Chief Operating Officer, Acting Chief Executive Officer
COO: Michelle Oxford, Chief Operating Officer, Acting Chief Executive Officer
CFO: Vickie Scharr, Chief Financial Officer
CMO: Brijesh Bhambi, M.D., Chief Medical Officer
CIO: Peter Mayer, Director Information Systems
CHR: Linda Hansen, Director Human Resources
Web address: www.bakersfieldhearthospital.com
Control: Partnership, Investor–owned (for–profit) **Service**: Heart

Staffed Beds: 47

Hospital, Medicare Provider Number, Address, Telephone, Approval, Facility, and Physician Codes, Health Care System

★ American Hospital Association (AHA) membership
□ The Joint Commission accreditation
○ Healthcare Facilities Accreditation Program
◇ DNV Healthcare Inc. accreditation
⇧ Center for Improvement in Healthcare Quality Accreditation
△ Commission on Accreditation of Rehabilitation Facilities (CARF) accreditation

CA

⊞ **BAKERSFIELD MEMORIAL HOSPITAL (050036)**, 420 34th Street, Zip 93301–2237; tel. 661/327–1792, **A**1 3 5 10 13 **F**3 11 13 15 16 17 18 20 22 24 26 28 29 30 31 37 40 45 50 58 60 68 70 72 74 75 76 77 78 79 81 84 85 86 88 89 93 107 108 109 111 114 115 119 120 124 126 130 146 147 148 149 **S** Dignity Health, San Francisco, CA
Primary Contact: Jon Van Boening, President and Chief Executive Officer
COO: Bruce Peters, Vice President and Chief Operating Officer
CFO: Jesica Hanson, Vice President and Chief Financial Officer
CMO: Rodney Mark Root, D.O., Vice President Medical Affairs
CHR: Sheri Comaianni, Vice President Human Resources
Web address: www.bakersfieldmemorial.org
Control: Other not–for–profit (including NFP Corporation) **Service**: General medical and surgical

Staffed Beds: 401 **Admissions:** 15832 **Census:** 170 **Outpatient Visits:** 149515 **Births:** 3034 **Total Expense ($000):** 410511 **Payroll Expense ($000):** 152334 **Personnel:** 1551

☐ **GOOD SAMARITAN HOSPITAL (050257)**, 901 Olive Drive, Zip 93308–4144, Mailing Address: P.O. Box 85002, Zip 93380–5002; tel. 661/215–7500, (Nonreporting) **A**1 10
Primary Contact: Ganesh Acharya, Chief Executive Officer
COO: Anand Manohara, Chief Operating Officer
CFO: Rogelio Monzon, Chief Financial Officer
CMO: Gurmant Singh, Chief of Staff
CHR: Anand Manohara, Chief Operating Officer
CNO: Toby Davis, Chief Nursing Officer
Web address: www.goodsamhospital.com
Control: Partnership, Investor–owned (for–profit) **Service**: General medical and surgical

Staffed Beds: 154

⊞ **HEALTHSOUTH BAKERSFIELD REHABILITATION HOSPITAL (053031)**, 5001 Commerce Drive, Zip 93309–0689; tel. 661/323–5500, (Nonreporting) **A**1 10 **S** Encompass Health Corporation, Birmingham, AL
Primary Contact: Martha Samora, R.N., FACHE, Chief Executive Officer
CFO: Robert Mosesian, Controller
CMO: Chris Yoon, M.D., Medical Director
CHR: Lori Brackett, Director Human Resources
CNO: Kathleen Szura, R.N., Chief Nursing Officer
Web address: www.healthsouthbakersfield.com
Control: Corporation, Investor–owned (for–profit) **Service**: Rehabilitation

Staffed Beds: 66

☐ **KERN MEDICAL CENTER (050315)**, 1700 Mount Vernon Avenue, Zip 93306–4018; tel. 661/326–2000, (Nonreporting) **A**1 2 3 5 10
Primary Contact: Russell V. Judd, Chief Executive Officer
COO: Jared Leavitt, Chief Operating Officer
CFO: Andrew Cantu, Chief Financial Officer
CMO: Glenn Goldis, Chief Medical Officer
CHR: Lisa K. Hockersmith, Vice President Human Resources
CNO: Toni Smith, Chief Nursing Officer
Web address: www.kernmedical.com
Control: County, Government, nonfederal **Service**: General medical and surgical

Staffed Beds: 188

⊞ **MERCY HOSPITALS OF BAKERSFIELD (050295)**, 2215 Truxtun Avenue, Zip 93301–3698, Mailing Address: P.O. Box 119, Zip 93302–0119; tel. 661/632–5000, (Includes MERCY SOUTHWEST HOSPITAL, 400 Old River Road, Bakersfield, CA, Zip 93311; tel. 661/663–6000) **A**1 2 3 10 **F**11 12 13 15 26 29 30 31 34 35 36 40 43 44 45 46 47 48 49 51 54 57 59 62 64 65 68 69 70 71 72 74 75 76 77 78 79 81 84 85 86 87 92 97 100 101 102 107 108 110 111 112 113 114 115 116 117 118 119 120 121 122 124 126 130 131 132 135 143 146 147 148 149 154 **P**3 **S** Dignity Health, San Francisco, CA
Primary Contact: Bruce Peters, Chief Executive Officer
CFO: Rodney Winegarner, Chief Financial Officer
CIO: Jeff Vague, Regional Manager Information Systems
CHR: Jay King, Vice President Human Resources
Web address: www.mercybakersfield.org
Control: Other not–for–profit (including NFP Corporation) **Service**: General medical and surgical

Staffed Beds: 200 **Admissions:** 12398 **Census:** 122 **Outpatient Visits:** 127325 **Births:** 2798 **Total Expense ($000):** 304162 **Payroll Expense ($000):** 124193 **Personnel:** 1141

BALDWIN PARK—Los Angeles County

BALDWIN PARK MEDICAL CENTER See Kaiser Permanente Baldwin Park Medical Center

⊞ **KAISER PERMANENTE BALDWIN PARK MEDICAL CENTER (050723)**, 1011 Baldwin Park Boulevard, Zip 91706–5806; tel. 626/851–1011, **A**1 3 10 **F**3 8 13 15 29 30 31 32 34 35 38 40 41 46 50 53 56 57 59 60 61 62 63 64 65 66 68 70 72 74 75 76 77 78 79 81 82 83 84 85 86 87 92 93 94 97 107 108 110 111 112 114 115 116 117 118 119 130 131 132 135 146 147 148 149 154 **P**6 **S** Kaiser Foundation Hospitals, Oakland, CA
Primary Contact: Margaret H. Pierce, Executive Director
COO: Payman Roshan, Chief Operating Officer
CFO: Rebecca Wheeler, Director Finance
CMO: John Bigley, M.D., Medical Director
CIO: Linda C Salazar, Information Technology Leader
CNO: Michelle Nowicki, R.N., MSN, Chief Nurse Executive
Web address: www.kp.org
Control: Other not–for–profit (including NFP Corporation) **Service**: General medical and surgical

Staffed Beds: 257 **Admissions:** 13017 **Census:** 98 **Outpatient Visits:** 382007 **Births:** 3049 **Personnel:** 1618

⊞ **KINDRED HOSPITAL–BALDWIN PARK (052045)**, 14148 Francisquito Avenue, Zip 91706–6120; tel. 626/388–2700, (Nonreporting) **A**1 10 **S** Kindred Healthcare, Louisville, KY
Primary Contact: Fiona Basa–Reyes, Chief Executive Officer
COO: Dina Garrow, Chief Nursing Officer and Chief Operating Officer
CFO: Christine Saltonstall, Chief Financial Officer
CMO: Anil Gupta, M.D., Chief of Staff
CHR: Antoinette Bibal, Director Human Resources
CNO: Dina Garrow, Chief Nursing Officer and Chief Operating Officer
Web address: www.khbaldwinpark.com
Control: Corporation, Investor–owned (for–profit) **Service**: Acute long–term care hospital

Staffed Beds: 91

VISTA SPECIALTY HOSPITAL OF SAN GABRIEL VALLEY See Kindred Hospital–Baldwin Park

BANNING—Riverside County

⊞ **SAN GORGONIO MEMORIAL HOSPITAL (050054)**, 600 North Highland Springs Avenue, Zip 92220–3046; tel. 951/845–1121, **A**1 10 22 **F**3 8 11 13 15 18 28 29 30 34 35 40 45 49 50 56 57 68 70 76 79 81 82 85 87 104 107 108 110 115 119 130 146 147 148 149
Primary Contact: Steven R. Barron, Interim Chief Executive Officer
CFO: David Recupero, Chief Financial Officer
CIO: Dan Howard, Director, Information Services
CHR: Annah Karam, Director Human Resources
CNO: Pat Brown, R.N., Chief Nursing Officer
Web address: www.sgmh.org
Control: Hospital district or authority, Government, nonfederal **Service**: General medical and surgical

Staffed Beds: 79 **Admissions:** 3401 **Census:** 38 **Outpatient Visits:** 52549 **Births:** 288 **Total Expense ($000):** 83739 **Payroll Expense ($000):** 37510 **Personnel:** 599

BARSTOW—San Bernardino County

⊞ **BARSTOW COMMUNITY HOSPITAL (050298)**, 820 East Mountain View Street, Zip 92311–3004; tel. 760/256–1761, (Nonreporting) **A**1 10 20 **S** Quorum Health, Brentwood, TN
Primary Contact: Matthew H. Blevins, Chief Executive Officer
CFO: Carrie Howell, Chief Financial Officer
CIO: Scott Bullock, Director Information Systems
CNO: Donna M Smith, Chief Nursing Officer
Web address: www.barstowhospital.com
Control: Corporation, Investor–owned (for–profit) **Service**: General medical and surgical

Staffed Beds: 30

BERKELEY—Alameda County

⊞ **ALTA BATES SUMMIT MEDICAL CENTER (050305)**, 2450 Ashby Avenue, Zip 94705–2067; tel. 510/204–4444, (Includes ALTA BATES MEDICAL CENTER–HERRICK CAMPUS, 2001 Dwight Way, Berkeley, CA, Zip 94704; tel. 510/204–4444) **A**1 3 5 10 **F**3 5 8 11 13 17 26 28 29 30 34 35 36 37 40 45 46 47 49 51 55 56 57 58 59 60 61 64 68 70 72 74 75 76 77 78 79 81 82 84 85 86 87 90 93 98 99 100 103 104 105 106 107 108 110 111 114 116 117 118 119 120 121 123 124 130 132 135 136 141 146 147 148 149 **P**3 5 **S** Sutter Health, Sacramento, CA
Primary Contact: Julie A. Petrini, Chief Executive Officer
CFO: Robert Petrina, Chief Financial Officer
CMO: John Gentile, M.D., Vice President Medical Affairs
Web address: www.altabatessummit.org/
Control: Other not–for–profit (including NFP Corporation) **Service**: General medical and surgical

Staffed Beds: 416 **Admissions:** 16445 **Census:** 416 **Outpatient Visits:** 167365 **Births:** 5323 **Total Expense ($000):** 705319 **Payroll Expense ($000):** 191635 **Personnel:** 1234

Many Facility Codes have changed. Please refer to the AHA Guide Code Chart. © 2018 AHA Guide

BIG BEAR LAKE—San Bernardino County

★ **BEAR VALLEY COMMUNITY HOSPITAL (051335)**, 41870 Garstin Drive, Zip 92315, Mailing Address: P.O. Box 1649, Zip 92315–1649; tel. 909/866–6501, (Total facility includes 21 beds in nursing home–type unit) **A**10 18 **F**3 15 29 34 35 40 50 57 59 81 85 93 97 104 107 110 114 119 127 128 133 146 149 150 154 **S** Quorum Health, Brentwood, TN
Primary Contact: John P. Friel, Chief Executive Officer
CFO: Garth Hamblin, Chief Financial Officer
CMO: Steven Knapik, M.D., Chief of Staff
CHR: Erin Wilson, Human Resource Director
CNO: Kerri Jex, R.N., Chief Nursing Officer
Web address: www.bvchd.com
Control: Hospital district or authority, Government, nonfederal **Service**: General medical and surgical

Staffed Beds: 30 **Admissions**: 181 **Census**: 21 **Outpatient Visits**: 52586 **Births**: 0 **Total Expense ($000)**: 22722 **Payroll Expense ($000)**: 9169 **Personnel**: 149

BISHOP—Inyo County

☒ **NORTHERN INYO HOSPITAL (051324)**, 150 Pioneer Lane, Zip 93514–2599; tel. 760/873–5811, (Nonreporting) **A**1 10 18
Primary Contact: Kevin Flanigan, M.D., Chief Executive Officer
COO: Kelli Huntsinger, Chief Operating Officer
CMO: Thomas Boo, M.D., Chief of Staff
CIO: Adam Taylor, Manager Information Technology
CHR: Georgan L. Stottlemyre, Chief Human Relations Officer
CNO: Tracy Aspel, Chief Nursing Officer
Web address: www.nih.org
Control: Hospital district or authority, Government, nonfederal **Service**: General medical and surgical

Staffed Beds: 25

BLYTHE—Riverside County

⇑ **PALO VERDE HOSPITAL (050423)**, 250 North First Street, Zip 92225–1702; tel. 760/922–4115, **A**10 20 21 **F**3 13 29 30 34 35 40 45 46 50 64 70 76 81 107 119 149
Primary Contact: Sandra J. Anaya, R.N., Chief Executive Officer
CFO: Christa Ronde, Assistant Chief Financial Officer
CMO: Hossain Sahlolbei, M.D., Chief of Staff
CIO: Jerome Learson, Manager Information Technology and Chief Security Officer
CHR: Myrna Davis, Manager Human Resources
CNO: Nena Foreman, Chief Nursing Officer
Web address: www.paloverdehospital.org
Control: Hospital district or authority, Government, nonfederal **Service**: General medical and surgical

Staffed Beds: 42 **Admissions**: 871 **Census**: 6 **Outpatient Visits**: 10443 **Births**: 150 **Total Expense ($000)**: 21400 **Payroll Expense ($000)**: 8685 **Personnel**: 133

BRAWLEY—Imperial County

★ ⇑ **PIONEERS MEMORIAL HEALTHCARE DISTRICT (050342)**, 207 West Legion Road, Zip 92227–7780; tel. 760/351–3333, **A**3 10 21 **F**13 15 18 29 30 31 34 40 45 46 49 50 51 54 57 60 64 68 70 72 74 76 78 79 80 81 82 85 89 93 107 110 111 115 117 119 127 130 144 146 147 148
Primary Contact: Lawrence E. Lewis, Chief Executive Officer
COO: Stephen J Campbell, Chief Operating Officer
CFO: Roger Armstrong, Interim Chief Financial Officer
CMO: Kestutis V Kuraitis, M.D., Chief of Staff
CIO: Kathleen S. McKernan, Director Information Systems
CHR: Julie Cunningham, Associate Administrator and Chief Human Resources Officer
CNO: Robyn Atadero, R.N., Chief Nursing Officer
Web address: www.pmhd.org
Control: Hospital district or authority, Government, nonfederal **Service**: General medical and surgical

Staffed Beds: 107 **Admissions**: 5834 **Census**: 54 **Outpatient Visits**: 148327 **Births**: 1835 **Total Expense ($000)**: 121531 **Payroll Expense ($000)**: 50255 **Personnel**: 756

BREA—Orange County

☒ **KINDRED HOSPITAL–BREA (052039)**, 875 North Brea Boulevard, Zip 92821–2699; tel. 714/529–6842, (Nonreporting) **A**1 10 **S** Kindred Healthcare, Louisville, KY
Primary Contact: Rafael Pena, Chief Executive Officer
COO: Denise Jenkins, Chief Clinical Officer
CFO: John Browne, Assistant Administrator Finance
CMO: Jyotika Wali, M.D., Chief of Staff
Web address: www.kindredhospitalbrea.com/
Control: Corporation, Investor–owned (for–profit) **Service**: Acute long–term care hospital

Staffed Beds: 48

BURBANK—Los Angeles County

☒ △ **PROVIDENCE SAINT JOSEPH MEDICAL CENTER (050235)**, 501 South Buena Vista Street, Zip 91505–4866; tel. 818/843–5111, **A**1 2 3 7 10 **F**3 11 12 13 15 17 18 20 22 24 26 29 30 31 34 35 36 40 41 45 46 47 48 49 50 51 53 55 56 57 58 59 62 63 64 65 70 72 74 75 76 77 78 79 81 82 83 84 85 86 87 90 92 93 97 100 101 107 108 110 111 114 115 116 117 119 120 121 122 123 124 126 130 131 132 143 145 146 147 148 149 151 154 **P**5 **S** Providence St. Joseph Health, Renton, WA
Primary Contact: Kelly Linden, Chief Executive Officer
CFO: Glenn Bales, Chief Financial Officer
CMO: Nick Testa, M.D., Chief Medical Officer
CIO: Anne Marie Brody, Director Information Systems Customer Service
CHR: LaDonna Najieb, Service Area Director Human Resources
CNO: Elizabeth Hart, R.N., MSN, Chief Nursing Officer
Web address: www.providence.org
Control: Church operated, Nongovernment, not–for–profit **Service**: General medical and surgical

Staffed Beds: 383 **Admissions**: 16049 **Census**: 198 **Outpatient Visits**: 306901 **Births**: 2490 **Total Expense ($000)**: 321428 **Payroll Expense ($000)**: 155309 **Personnel**: 2251

BURLINGAME—San Mateo County

☒ **MILLS–PENINSULA HEALTH SERVICES (050007)**, 1501 Trousdale Drive, Zip 94010–3282; tel. 650/696–5400, (Includes MILLS HEALTH CENTER, 100 South San Mateo Drive, San Mateo, CA, Zip 94401; tel. 650/696–4400; Janet Wagner, R.N., Chief Executive Officer; MILLS–PENINSULA MEDICAL CENTER, 1501 Trousdale Drive, Burlingame, CA, Zip 94010–3205; tel. 650/696–5400; Janet Wagner, R.N., Chief Executive Officer) **A**1 10 **F**2 3 4 5 6 11 12 13 15 18 20 22 24 26 28 29 30 31 34 35 36 37 40 41 44 45 46 47 48 49 50 51 53 54 55 56 57 58 59 61 64 65 68 69 70 73 74 75 76 77 78 79 81 84 85 87 90 93 98 99 100 101 102 103 104 105 106 107 108 110 111 115 116 117 118 119 120 121 123 124 126 130 132 135 146 147 148 149 154 **P**3 5 **S** Sutter Health, Sacramento, CA
Primary Contact: Janet Wagner, R.N., Chief Executive Officer
COO: Dolores S. Gomez, R.N., Chief Operating Officer
CFO: Catherine Messman, Chief Financial Officer
CMO: Ranjit Hundal, M.D., Chief Medical Officer
CIO: Michael Reandeau, Chief Information Officer
CHR: Claudia Christensen, Director, Human Resources
CNO: Vicki White, R.N., MS, Chief Nurse Executive
Web address: www.mills–peninsula.org
Control: Other not–for–profit (including NFP Corporation) **Service**: General medical and surgical

Staffed Beds: 266 **Admissions**: 13391 **Census**: 161 **Outpatient Visits**: 401046 **Births**: 2033 **Total Expense ($000)**: 607138 **Payroll Expense ($000)**: 160786 **Personnel**: 1476

CAMARILLO—Ventura County

★ **ST. JOHN'S PLEASANT VALLEY HOSPITAL (050616)**, 2309 Antonio Avenue, Zip 93010–1414; tel. 805/389–5800, (Nonreporting) **A**10 **S** Dignity Health, San Francisco, CA
Primary Contact: Darren W. Lee, President and Chief Executive Officer
COO: Richard Montmeny, Vice President Professional Services, On–Site Administrator
CFO: Donald P Bernard, Chief Financial Officer
CMO: Sahin Yanik, M.D., Vice President Medical Associate
CIO: Jeff Perry, Director Information Technology
CHR: Ed Gonzales, Vice President Human Resources
CNO: Dana Littlepage, Interim Chief Nursing Officer
Web address: www.dignityhealth.org/pleasantvalley
Control: Other not–for–profit (including NFP Corporation) **Service**: General medical and surgical

Staffed Beds: 127

CA

Hospital, Medicare Provider Number, Address, Telephone, Approval, Facility, and Physician Codes, Health Care System

★ American Hospital Association (AHA) membership
□ The Joint Commission accreditation
○ Healthcare Facilities Accreditation Program
◇ DNV Healthcare Inc. accreditation
⇑ Center for Improvement in Healthcare Quality Accreditation
△ Commission on Accreditation of Rehabilitation Facilities (CARF) accreditation

CAMP PENDLETON—San Diego County

✠ **NAVAL HOSPITAL CAMP PENDLETON**, 200 Mercy Circle, Zip 92055–5191, Mailing Address: P.O. Box 555191, Zip 92055–5191; tel. 760/725–1304, (Nonreporting) **A**1 3 5 **S** Bureau of Medicine and Surgery, Department of the Navy, Falls Church, VA
Primary Contact: Captain Frank P. Pearson, Commanding Officer
CFO: Commander Gordon Blighton, Director Resource Management
CIO: Gabe Vallido, Chief Information Officer
CHR: Lieutenant Jet Ramos, Head Staff Administration
Web address: www.cpen.med.navy.mil/
Control: Navy, Government, federal **Service:** General medical and surgical

Staffed Beds: 72

CARMICHAEL—Sacramento County

✠ **MERCY SAN JUAN MEDICAL CENTER (050516)**, 6501 Coyle Avenue, Zip 95608–0306; tel. 916/537–5000, (Nonreporting) **A**1 2 3 5 10 **S** Dignity Health, San Francisco, CA
Primary Contact: Michael Korpiel, FACHE, Chief Executive Officer
COO: Paul R Luehrs, Chief Operating Officer
CFO: Robert Pascuzzi, Chief Financial Officer
CMO: Mark Owens, M.D., Vice President Medical Affairs
CHR: Donna Utley, Vice President Human Resources
Web address: www.mercysanjuan.org
Control: Church operated, Nongovernment, not–for–profit **Service:** General medical and surgical

Staffed Beds: 340

CASTRO VALLEY—Alameda County

✠ **EDEN MEDICAL CENTER (050488)**, 20103 Lake Chabot Road, Zip 94546–5305; tel. 510/537–1234, **A**1 2 3 10 **F**3 11 13 15 18 29 30 31 34 35 38 40 43 46 47 49 50 51 53 54 56 57 58 59 60 65 68 70 73 74 75 76 77 78 79 81 84 85 87 93 100 101 102 107 108 110 111 115 117 118 119 120 121 123 130 132 135 144 146 147 148 154 **P**3 5 **S** Sutter Health, Sacramento, CA
Primary Contact: Stephen Gray, Chief Executive Officer
Web address: www.edenmedcenter.org
Control: Other not–for–profit (including NFP Corporation) **Service:** General medical and surgical

Staffed Beds: 130 **Admissions:** 8773 **Census:** 105 **Outpatient Visits:** 91840 **Births:** 1012 **Total Expense ($000):** 337732 **Payroll Expense ($000):** 111386 **Personnel:** 948

CEDARVILLE—Modoc County

SURPRISE VALLEY HEALTH CARE DISTRICT (051308), 741 North Main Street, Zip 96104, Mailing Address: P.O. Box 246, Zip 96104–0246; tel. 530/279–6111, (Nonreporting) **A**10 18
Primary Contact: Richard Cornwell, Chief Executive Officer
CFO: Renae Sweet, Chief Financial Officer
CMO: Chuck Colas, M.D., Medical Director
CHR: William Bostic, Administrative Assistant Human Resources
Web address: www.svhospital.org/
Control: Hospital district or authority, Government, nonfederal **Service:** General medical and surgical

Staffed Beds: 4

CERRITOS—Los Angeles County

☐ **COLLEGE HOSPITAL CERRITOS (054055)**, 10802 College Place, Zip 90703–1579; tel. 562/924–9581, **A**1 10 **F**3 29 98 103 105 149 153 **S** College Health Enterprises, Santa Fe Springs, CA
Primary Contact: Stephen Witt, President and Chief Executive Officer
CFO: Roderick Bell, Chief Financial Officer
CHR: Holly Risha, Administrative Director Human Resources
Web address: www.collegehospitals.com
Control: Corporation, Investor–owned (for–profit) **Service:** Psychiatric

Staffed Beds: 187 **Admissions:** 5734 **Census:** 173 **Outpatient Visits:** 0 **Births:** 0

CHESTER—Plumas County

SENECA HEALTHCARE DISTRICT (051327), 130 Brentwood Drive, Zip 96020–0737, Mailing Address: P.O. Box 737, Zip 96020–0737; tel. 530/258–2151, (Nonreporting) **A**5 10 18
Primary Contact: Linda S. Wagner, R.N., MSN, FACHE, Chief Executive Officer
CFO: Carlene Slusher, Director Finance
CMO: Dana Ware, M.D., Chief of Staff
CIO: Elizabeth Steffen, Director Information Technology
CHR: James Kooyman, Human Resources Manager
CNO: Karen Turner, Chief Nursing Officer
Web address: www.senecahospital.org
Control: Hospital district or authority, Government, nonfederal **Service:** General medical and surgical

Staffed Beds: 26

CHICO—Butte County

✠ **ENLOE MEDICAL CENTER (050039)**, 1531 Esplanade, Zip 95926–3386; tel. 530/332–7300, (Includes ENLOE MEDICAL CENTER–COHASSET, 560 Cohasset Road, Chico, CA, Zip 95926; tel. 530/332–7300) **A**1 10 **F**3 7 8 11 12 13 17 18 19 20 22 24 26 28 29 30 31 34 35 36 38 39 40 43 44 45 46 49 50 51 54 57 59 61 62 63 64 65 68 69 70 73 74 75 76 77 78 79 81 84 85 87 89 90 91 92 93 94 96 98 100 102 107 108 109 111 114 115 116 117 118 119 120 121 123 124 130 132 143 144 146 147 148 149
Primary Contact: Michael C. Wiltermood, President and Chief Executive Officer
CMO: Forrest Olson, M.D., Chief Medical Officer
CHR: Carol Linscheid, Vice President Human Resources
Web address: www.enloe.org
Control: Other not–for–profit (including NFP Corporation) **Service:** General medical and surgical

Staffed Beds: 298 **Admissions:** 17165 **Census:** 221 **Outpatient Visits:** 357863 **Births:** 1703 **Total Expense ($000):** 541841 **Payroll Expense ($000):** 196202 **Personnel:** 3030

CHINO—San Bernardino County

☐ **CANYON RIDGE HOSPITAL (054111)**, 5353 'G' Street, Zip 91710–5250; tel. 909/590–3700, (Nonreporting) **A**1 3 10 **S** Universal Health Services, Inc., King of Prussia, PA
Primary Contact: Burt Harris, Acting Chief Executive Officer
CFO: Burt Harris, Chief Financial Officer
CMO: Mir Ali–Khan, M.D., Medical Director
CIO: Maria Patterson, Manager Health Information Management
CHR: Ericca Lopez, Director Human Resources
Web address: www.canyonridgehospital.com
Control: Corporation, Investor–owned (for–profit) **Service:** Psychiatric

Staffed Beds: 106

★ ○ **CHINO VALLEY MEDICAL CENTER (050586)**, 5451 Walnut Avenue, Zip 91710–2672; tel. 909/464–8600, **A**10 11 12 13 **F**3 15 70 **S** Prime Healthcare, Ontario, CA
Primary Contact: James M. Lally, D.O., President and Chief Medical Officer
CIO: Vic Mahan, Chief Information Officer
Web address: www.cvmc.com
Control: State, Government, nonfederal **Service:** General medical and surgical

Staffed Beds: 112 **Admissions:** 5478 **Census:** 44 **Outpatient Visits:** 49080 **Births:** 0 **Personnel:** 4610

CHULA VISTA—San Diego County

SCRIPPS MERCY HOSPITAL CHULA VISTA See Scripps Mercy Hospital, San Diego

✠ **SHARP CHULA VISTA MEDICAL CENTER (050222)**, 751 Medical Center Court, Zip 91911–6699; tel. 619/502–5800, (Total facility includes 100 beds in nursing home–type unit) **A**1 2 10 **F**8 11 12 13 15 17 18 20 22 24 26 28 29 30 31 34 35 40 45 46 47 49 51 53 54 57 59 60 63 64 65 70 72 75 76 77 78 79 81 82 84 85 86 87 93 107 108 114 115 118 119 120 121 123 124 126 128 130 132 143 146 147 148 **P**5 **S** Sharp HealthCare, San Diego, CA
Primary Contact: Pablo Velez, R.N., Ph.D., Chief Executive Officer
CMO: Lynn Welling, M.D., Chief Medical Officer
CHR: Zoe Gardner, Manager Human Resources
Web address: www.sharp.com
Control: Other not–for–profit (including NFP Corporation) **Service:** General medical and surgical

Staffed Beds: 339 **Admissions:** 16141 **Census:** 283 **Outpatient Visits:** 175994 **Births:** 2731 **Total Expense ($000):** 376112 **Payroll Expense ($000):** 158699 **Personnel:** 1801

CLEARLAKE—Lake County

✠ **ADVENTIST HEALTH CLEAR LAKE (051317)**, 15630 18th Avenue, Zip 95422–9336, Mailing Address: P.O. Box 6710, Zip 95422; tel. 707/994–6486, (Nonreporting) **A**1 10 18 **S** Adventist Health, Roseville, CA
Primary Contact: David Santos, President and Chief Executive Officer
COO: David Santos, President Chief Executive Officer
CFO: Carlton Jacobson, Vice President of Finance
CMO: Marc Shapiro, M.D., Chief Medical Officer
CIO: Cambria Wheeler, Communications and Marketing
CHR: Audrey Barrall, Director Human Resources
CNO: Colleen Assavapisitkul, Chief Nursing Officer
Web address: www.adventisthealth.org
Control: Church operated, Nongovernment, not–for–profit **Service:** General medical and surgical

Staffed Beds: 25

CA

Many Facility Codes have changed. Please refer to the AHA Guide Code Chart. © 2018 AHA Guide

CLOVIS—Fresno County

CLOVIS COMMUNITY MEDICAL CENTER (050492), 2755 Herndon Avenue, Zip 93611–6801; tel. 559/324–4000, (Nonreporting) **A**10 **S** Community Medical Centers, Fresno, CA
Primary Contact: Craig Castro, Chief Executive Officer
CFO: Tracy Kiritani, Vice President and Chief Financial Officer
CIO: George Vasquez, Chief Technology Officer
CHR: Ginny Burdick, Senior Vice President and Chief Human Resources Officer
Web address: www.communitymedical.org
Control: Other not–for–profit (including NFP Corporation) **Service:** General medical and surgical

Staffed Beds: 109

COLTON—San Bernardino County

★ **ARROWHEAD REGIONAL MEDICAL CENTER (050245)**, 400 North Pepper Avenue, Zip 92324–1819; tel. 909/580–1000, **A**3 5 10 12 13 **F**3 8 13 15 16 18 20 22 28 29 30 31 32 34 35 36 39 40 43 45 47 49 50 51 52 54 55 56 57 60 64 66 68 70 71 72 74 75 76 77 78 79 81 82 84 85 86 87 89 91 92 93 97 98 100 101 102 107 108 110 111 114 115 116 118 119 120 121 130 132 135 146 147 148 149 150 **P**5
Primary Contact: William L. Gilbert, Hospital Director
CFO: Arvind Oswal, Interim Chief Financial Officer
CMO: Richard Pitts, D.O., Ph.D., Medical Director
CIO: Felix Ekpo, Manager, Information Systems
CHR: Kevin Saunders, Human Resources Officer III
CNO: Jerome Dayao, MSN, Chief Nursing Officer
Web address: www.arrowheadmedcenter.org
Control: County, Government, nonfederal **Service:** General medical and surgical

Staffed Beds: 456 **Admissions:** 21430 **Census:** 312 **Outpatient Visits:** 397924 **Births:** 3746 **Total Expense ($000):** 652938 **Payroll Expense ($000):** 197587 **Personnel:** 3075

CONCORD—Contra Costa County

✠ **JOHN MUIR BEHAVIORAL HEALTH CENTER (054131)**, 2740 Grant Street, Zip 94520–2265; tel. 925/674–4100, (Nonreporting) **A**1 10 **S** John Muir Health, Walnut Creek, CA
Primary Contact: Cindy Bolter, Chief Nursing and Operations Officer
COO: Arman Danielyan, M.D., Chief of Staff
CFO: Christian Pass, Senior Vice President and Chief Financial Officer
CMO: O B Towery, M.D., Chief of Staff
CIO: Jim Wesley, Senior Vice President and Chief Information Officer
CHR: Lisa Foust, Senior Vice President Human Resources
CNO: Cindy Bolter, Chief Nursing and Operations Officer
Web address: www.johnmuirhealth.com
Control: Other not–for–profit (including NFP Corporation) **Service:** Psychiatric

Staffed Beds: 73

✠ **JOHN MUIR MEDICAL CENTER, CONCORD (050496)**, 2540 East Street, Zip 94520–1906; tel. 925/682–8200, **A**1 2 3 10 **F**3 12 15 17 18 20 22 24 26 28 29 30 31 34 37 39 40 41 44 45 46 47 48 49 50 55 56 57 58 59 61 64 68 70 74 75 77 78 79 80 81 82 83 84 85 86 87 93 100 102 107 108 110 115 118 119 120 121 123 126 130 132 141 145 146 148 149 **P**5 7 **S** John Muir Health, Walnut Creek, CA
Primary Contact: Michael S. Thomas, President and Chief Administrative Officer
COO: Michael S Thomas, President and Chief Administrative Officer
CFO: Christian Pass, Interim Chief Financial Officer
CMO: John Merson, M.D., Chief of Staff
CIO: Jon Russell, Senior Vice President and Chief Information Officer
CHR: Lisa Foust, Senior Vice President Human Resources
CNO: Donna Brackley, R.N., MSN, Senior Vice President Patient Care Services
Web address: www.johnmuirhealth.com
Control: Other not–for–profit (including NFP Corporation) **Service:** General medical and surgical

Staffed Beds: 207 **Admissions:** 11299 **Census:** 143 **Outpatient Visits:** 173707 **Births:** 0 **Total Expense ($000):** 473921 **Payroll Expense ($000):** 175082 **Personnel:** 1052

CORONA—Riverside County

☐ **CORONA REGIONAL MEDICAL CENTER (050329)**, 800 South Main Street, Zip 92882–3400; tel. 951/737–4343, (Includes CORONA REGIONAL MEDICAL CENTER–REHABILITATION, 730 Magnolia Avenue, Corona, CA, Zip 92879; tel. 951/736–7200) (Nonreporting) **A**1 10 **S** Universal Health Services, Inc., King of Prussia, PA
Primary Contact: Mark H. Uffer, Chief Executive Officer
COO: Mitchell Winnik, Chief Operating Officer
CFO: Kanner Tillman, Chief Financial Officer
CMO: Alaa Y Afifi, M.D., Chief of Staff
CIO: De'Niro Pankey, Director Information Systems
CHR: Dale Cole, Director, Human Resources
CNO: Kim Colonnelli, Chief Nursing Officer
Web address: www.coronaregional.com
Control: Corporation, Investor–owned (for–profit) **Service:** General medical and surgical

Staffed Beds: 238

CORONADO—San Diego County

✠ **SHARP CORONADO HOSPITAL AND HEALTHCARE CENTER (050234)**, 250 Prospect Place, Zip 92118–1999; tel. 619/522–3600, (Total facility includes 122 beds in nursing home–type unit) **A**1 10 **F**3 8 11 15 29 30 34 35 36 37 40 41 45 46 47 49 53 57 58 59 60 64 65 68 70 74 75 77 79 81 82 84 85 86 87 91 93 107 111 114 119 126 128 130 132 135 146 148 149 154 **S** Sharp HealthCare, San Diego, CA
Primary Contact: Susan Stone, R.N., Ph.D., Senior Vice President and Chief Executive Officer
CFO: Victoria Day, Chief Financial Officer and Vice President of Ancillary Services
CHR: Rachel Davis, Director
CNO: Christopher Walker, Chief Nursing Officer and Operating Officer
Web address: www.sharp.com
Control: Other not–for–profit (including NFP Corporation) **Service:** General medical and surgical

Staffed Beds: 181 **Admissions:** 2258 **Census:** 118 **Outpatient Visits:** 89857 **Births:** 0 **Total Expense ($000):** 98270 **Payroll Expense ($000):** 42570 **Personnel:** 438

COSTA MESA—Orange County

☐ **COLLEGE HOSPITAL COSTA MESA (050543)**, 301 Victoria Street, Zip 92627–7131; tel. 949/642–2734, (Nonreporting) **A**1 10 **S** College Health Enterprises, Santa Fe Springs, CA
Primary Contact: Susan L. Taylor, JD, Chief Executive Officer
CFO: Dale Bracy, Chief Financial Officer
CMO: Michael Schwartz, M.D., Chief of Staff
CIO: Eladio Aldana, Manager Information Systems
CHR: Sharon DuBruyne, Director Human Resources
Web address: www.collegehospitals.com/cosHome
Control: Corporation, Investor–owned (for–profit) **Service:** Psychiatric

Staffed Beds: 122

FAIRVIEW DEVELOPMENTAL CENTER (050548), 2501 Harbor Boulevard, Zip 92626; tel. 714/957–5000, (Nonreporting) **A**10
Primary Contact: Cheryl Bright, Executive Director
Web address: www.dds.ca.gov/fairview/index.cfm
Control: State, Government, nonfederal **Service:** Intellectual disabilities

Staffed Beds: 237

COVINA—Los Angeles County

☐ **AURORA CHARTER OAK HOSPITAL (054069)**, 1161 East Covina Boulevard, Zip 91724–1599; tel. 626/966–1632, (Nonreporting) **A**1 10 **S** Signature Healthcare Services, Corona, CA
Primary Contact: Todd A. Smith, Chief Executive Officer
COO: Sheila Cordova, Director Clinical Services and Chief Operating Officer
CMO: Adib Bitar, M.D., Medical Director
CHR: Christine de la Paz, Director Human Resources
CNO: Sheila Cordova, Chief Operating Officer and Chief Nursing Officer
Web address: www.charteroakhospital.com
Control: Corporation, Investor–owned (for–profit) **Service:** Psychiatric

Staffed Beds: 146

CA

Hospital, Medicare Provider Number, Address, Telephone, Approval, Facility, and Physician Codes, Health Care System

★ American Hospital Association (AHA) membership   ○ Healthcare Facilities Accreditation Program   ⇑ Center for Improvement in Healthcare Quality Accreditation
☐ The Joint Commission accreditation   ◇ DNV Healthcare Inc. accreditation   △ Commission on Accreditation of Rehabilitation Facilities (CARF) accreditation

© 2018 AHA Guide   *Many Facility Codes have changed. Please refer to the AHA Guide Code Chart.*   Hospitals **A55**

★ **CITRUS VALLEY MEDICAL CENTER–INTER COMMUNITY CAMPUS (050382)**, 210 West San Bernadino Road, Zip 91723–1515, Mailing Address: P.O. Box 6108, Zip 91722–5108; tel. 626/331–7331, (Includes CITRUS VALLEY MEDICAL CENTER–INTER–COMMUNITY CAMPUS, 210 West San Bernardino Road, Covina, CA, Zip 91723–1515, Mailing Address: P.O. Box 6108, Zip 91722–5108, tel. 626/331–7331; Robert H Curry, President and Chief Executive Officer; CITRUS VALLEY MEDICAL CENTER–QUEEN OF THE VALLEY CAMPUS, 1115 South Sunset Avenue, West Covina, CA, Zip 91790–3940, Mailing Address: P.O. Box 1980, Zip 91793–1980, tel. 626/962–4011; Robert H Curry, President and Chief Executive Officer) **A**3 10 **F**3 11 15 17 18 20 22 24 26 28 29 30 31 34 35 40 49 50 53 56 57 59 60 61 62 63 68 69 70 72 74 75 76 77 78 79 80 81 84 85 87 89 90 98 100 107 108 110 111 114 115 119 120 121 124 128 130 131 132 143 146 148 149 154 **P**5 **S** Citrus Valley Health Partners, Covina, CA
Primary Contact: Robert H. Curry, President and Chief Executive Officer
CFO: Roger Sharma, Executive Vice President/Chief Financial Officer
CIO: Daniel J Nash, Chief Information Officer
CHR: Ryan Burke Esq Vice President, Human Resources
CNO: Melissa Howard, Chief Nurse Executive, ICH & FPH
Web address: www.cvhp.org
Control: Other not–for–profit (including NFP Corporation) **Service:** General medical and surgical

Staffed Beds: 320 **Admissions:** 24387 **Census:** 298 **Outpatient Visits:** 197653 **Births:** 4072 **Total Expense ($000):** 441108 **Payroll Expense ($000):** 147999 **Personnel:** 1948

CRESCENT CITY—Del Norte County

✠ **SUTTER COAST HOSPITAL (050417)**, 800 East Washington Boulevard, Zip 95531–8359; tel. 707/464–8511, **A**1 10 20 **F**3 11 13 15 18 24 29 31 34 35 40 43 44 45 46 47 48 50 54 57 59 62 64 65 68 70 75 76 77 78 79 81 85 87 90 93 97 100 102 107 108 110 111 115 119 127 130 132 144 146 147 148 149 154 **P**3 **S** Sutter Health, Sacramento, CA
Primary Contact: Mitchell J. Hanna, Chief Executive Officer
CNO: Rose Corcoran, R.N., Chief Nursing Executive
Web address: www.sutterhealth.org
Control: Other not–for–profit (including NFP Corporation) **Service:** General medical and surgical

Staffed Beds: 49 **Admissions:** 2613 **Census:** 26 **Outpatient Visits:** 66690 **Births:** 286 **Total Expense ($000):** 79894 **Payroll Expense ($000):** 24069 **Personnel:** 342

CULVER CITY—Los Angeles County

SOUTHERN CALIFORNIA HOSPITAL AT CULVER CITY (050752), 3828 Delmas Terrace, Zip 90232–6806; tel. 310/836–7000, (Nonreporting) **S** Prospect Medical Holdings, Los Angeles, CA
Primary Contact: Sean Fowler, Chief Executive Officer
CFO: Vincent Rubin, Chief Financial Officer
CMO: Martha Sonnenberg, M.D., Chief of Staff
CIO: Carrie Bonar, Chief Information Officer
CHR: Betty J Harris, Director Human Resources
Web address: www.sch–culvercity.com
Control: Corporation, Investor–owned (for–profit) **Service:** General medical and surgical

Staffed Beds: 239

DALY CITY—San Mateo County

☐ **SETON MEDICAL CENTER (050289)**, 1900 Sullivan Avenue, Zip 94015–2229; tel. 650/992–4000, (Total facility includes 116 beds in nursing home–type unit) **A**1 2 3 10 **F**3 8 15 18 20 22 24 26 29 30 31 34 35 37 39 40 44 45 46 48 49 50 51 56 57 58 59 60 64 66 68 70 74 75 77 78 79 81 82 84 85 87 92 93 96 98 100 102 103 107 108 110 111 114 116 117 118 119 120 121 123 124 126 128 130 132 135 141 143 146 148 149 154 **P**3 **S** Verity Health System, Los Angeles, CA
Primary Contact: Mark Fratzke, R.N., President and Chief Executive Officer
COO: Stephanie Mearns, Vice President Patient Care Services and Chief Nurse Executive
CFO: Richard Wood, Chief Financial Officer
CMO: Timothy Ranney, M.D., Chief Medical Officer
CHR: Patricia White, Vice President Human Resources
CNO: Mark R Brown, Chief Nursing Officer
Web address: www.setonmedicalcenter.org
Control: Other not–for–profit (including NFP Corporation) **Service:** General medical and surgical

Staffed Beds: 393 **Admissions:** 5664 **Census:** 206 **Outpatient Visits:** 31131 **Births:** 0 **Total Expense ($000):** 265333 **Payroll Expense ($000):** 97130 **Personnel:** 939

DAVIS—Yolo County

✠ **SUTTER DAVIS HOSPITAL (050537)**, 2000 Sutter Place, Zip 95616–6201, Mailing Address: P.O. Box 1617, Zip 95617–1617; tel. 530/756–6440, **A**1 3 5 10 **F**3 8 11 13 15 18 28 29 30 31 34 39 40 45 57 60 65 68 70 74 75 76 78 79 81 85 86 87 92 93 102 107 108 111 115 119 124 130 131 141 142 146 147 149 154 **P**3 5 **S** Sutter Health, Sacramento, CA
Primary Contact: Rachael McKinney, FACHE, Chief Executive Officer
CFO: Patti Pilgrim, Chief Financial Officer
CMO: Deven Merchant, M.D., Chief Medical Executive
CHR: Don Hartman, Director Human Resources
CNO: Myrna Chang, Chief Nursing Executive
Web address: www.sutterhealth.org
Control: Other not–for–profit (including NFP Corporation) **Service:** General medical and surgical

Staffed Beds: 48 **Admissions:** 3849 **Census:** 30 **Outpatient Visits:** 52667 **Births:** 1401 **Total Expense ($000):** 116672 **Payroll Expense ($000):** 36808 **Personnel:** 406

DELANO—Kern County

○ **DELANO REGIONAL MEDICAL CENTER (050608)**, 1401 Garces Highway, Zip 93215–3690, Mailing Address: P.O. Box 460, Zip 93216–0460; tel. 661/725–4800, (Nonreporting) **A**10 11
Primary Contact: Bahram Ghaffari, President
CFO: Bahram Ghaffari, President
CIO: Sandy Bakich, Director Information Management
CHR: Del Garbanzos, Director Human Resources
CNO: Amy Scroggs, Chief Nursing Officer
Web address: www.drmc.com
Control: Other not–for–profit (including NFP Corporation) **Service:** General medical and surgical

Staffed Beds: 100

DOWNEY—Los Angeles County

✠ **KAISER PERMANENTE DOWNEY MEDICAL CENTER (050139)**, 9333 Imperial Highway, Zip 90242–2812; tel. 562/657–9000, **A**1 3 10 **F**3 8 11 12 13 15 18 19 29 30 31 32 34 35 38 39 40 41 44 45 46 47 48 49 50 51 52 53 54 55 56 57 58 59 60 61 62 63 64 65 66 68 70 71 72 73 74 75 76 77 78 79 81 82 83 84 85 86 87 88 89 93 94 96 97 100 102 104 107 108 110 111 114 115 119 126 129 130 132 134 135 141 144 146 147 148 149 153 154 **S** Kaiser Foundation Hospitals, Oakland, CA
Primary Contact: James Branchick, R.N., MS, Senior Vice President and Area Manager
CNO: Patricia J Clausen, R.N., Chief Nurse Executive
Web address: www.kaiserpermanente.org
Control: Other not–for–profit (including NFP Corporation) **Service:** General medical and surgical

Staffed Beds: 409 **Admissions:** 16533 **Census:** 190 **Outpatient Visits:** 220862 **Births:** 4279 **Personnel:** 3300

★ **PIH HEALTH HOSPITAL – DOWNEY (050393)**, 11500 Brookshire Avenue, Zip 90241–4917; tel. 562/904–5000, **A**3 10 12 13 22 **F**3 11 13 15 18 20 22 24 29 30 31 40 41 45 46 49 50 56 60 64 68 70 72 74 75 76 77 79 81 85 89 93 107 108 110 111 115 118 119 130 146 148 149 **P**3 5 **S** PIH Health, Whittier, CA
Primary Contact: James R. West, President and Chief Executive Officer
COO: Ramona Pratt, Chief Operating Officer
CFO: Greg Williams, Chief Financial Officer
CIO: Jason Fischer, Chief Information Officer
CHR: Sherri Hollingsworth, Chief Human Resources Officer
CNO: Judy Pugach, Chief Nursing Officer
Web address: www.PIHHealth.org
Control: Other not–for–profit (including NFP Corporation) **Service:** General medical and surgical

Staffed Beds: 181 **Admissions:** 7920 **Census:** 82 **Outpatient Visits:** 80283 **Births:** 1000 **Total Expense ($000):** 154491 **Payroll Expense ($000):** 67011 **Personnel:** 968

☐ △ **RANCHO LOS AMIGOS NATIONAL REHABILITATION CENTER (050717)**, 7601 East Imperial Highway, Zip 90242–3496; tel. 562/401–7111, (Nonreporting) **A**1 3 5 7 10 **S** Los Angeles County–Department of Health Services, Los Angeles, CA
Primary Contact: Jorge Orozco, Chief Executive Officer
COO: Benjamin Ovando, Chief Operations Officer
CFO: Robin Bayus, Chief Financial Officer
CMO: Mindy Aisen, M.D., Chief Medical Officer
CIO: Francis Tang, Chief Information Officer
CHR: Elizabeth Jacobi, Associate Director Human Resources
CNO: Aries Limbaga, R.N., Chief Nursing Officer
Web address: www.rancho.org
Control: County, Government, nonfederal **Service:** Rehabilitation

Staffed Beds: 207

CA

DUARTE—Los Angeles County

☒ **CITY OF HOPE'S HELFORD CLINICAL RESEARCH HOSPITAL (050146)**, 1500 East Duarte Road, Zip 91010–3012; tel. 626/256–4673, **A**1 2 3 5 8 10 **F**3 8 11 14 15 18 29 30 31 34 35 36 38 44 45 46 47 49 50 55 56 57 58 59 61 64 68 70 74 75 77 78 79 80 81 82 84 85 86 87 88 89 91 92 93 94 96 100 101 104 107 108 110 111 115 117 118 119 120 121 123 124 126 130 132 135 136 144 145 146 147 148 149 154 **P**3
Primary Contact: Robert Stone, President and Chief Executive Officer
COO: Jeff E. Walker, Chief Operating Officer
CFO: Jennifer Parkhurst, Chief Financial Officer
CMO: William D. Boswell, M.D., Jr Chief Medical Officer
CIO: Mark Hulse, MSN, Chief Digital Officer
CHR: Stephanie Neuvirth, Chief Human Resource and Diversity Officer
Web address: www.cityofhope.org
Control: Other not-for-profit (including NFP Corporation) **Service**: Cancer

Staffed Beds: 215 **Admissions**: 6714 **Census**: 195 **Outpatient Visits**: 243200 **Births**: 0 **Total Expense ($000)**: 1071405 **Payroll Expense ($000)**: 321415 **Personnel**: 3855

EL CENTRO—Imperial County

☒ **EL CENTRO REGIONAL MEDICAL CENTER (050045)**, 1415 Ross Avenue, Zip 92243–4398; tel. 760/339–7100, (Nonreporting) **A**1 3 10
Primary Contact: Adolphe Edward, Chief Executive Officer
COO: Tomas Virgen, R.N., MSN, Chief Operating Officer
CFO: Kathleen Farmer, Assistant Administrator Finance and Chief Financial Officer
CIO: John Gaede, Director Information Systems
CHR: Bill Moore, Chief Human Resources
Web address: www.ecrmc.org
Control: City, Government, nonfederal **Service**: General medical and surgical

Staffed Beds: 161

ELDRIDGE—Sonoma County

SONOMA DEVELOPMENTAL CENTER (050547), 15000 Arnold Drive, Zip 95431–8900, Mailing Address: P.O. Box 1493, Zip 95431–1493; tel. 707/938–6000, (Nonreporting) **A**10
Primary Contact: Aleana Carreon, Executive Director
COO: Karen Clark, Director Administrative Services
CMO: Carol Castillo, Medical Director
CHR: Brenda Dukes, Director Human Resources
Web address: www.dds.ca.gov/sonoma
Control: State, Government, nonfederal **Service**: Intellectual disabilities

Staffed Beds: 546

ENCINITAS—San Diego County

☒ △ **SCRIPPS MEMORIAL HOSPITAL–ENCINITAS (050503)**, 354 Santa Fe Drive, Zip 92024–5182, Mailing Address: P.O. Box 230817, Zip 92023–0817; tel. 760/633–6501, **A**1 3 7 10 **F**3 8 11 13 14 15 18 20 22 26 29 30 31 34 35 40 44 49 54 57 58 59 64 65 68 70 74 75 76 77 78 79 81 82 84 85 86 87 90 91 92 93 95 96 107 108 110 111 114 115 118 119 126 130 132 141 146 148 **P**3 5 **S** Scripps Health, San Diego, CA
Primary Contact: Carl J. Etter, Chief Executive and Senior Vice President
COO: Jan Zachry, R.N., Vice President Administrator and Chief Operations Executive
CFO: Sharon Creal, Vice President Financial Operations
CHR: Steve Rust, Director, Human Resources
CNO: Jan Zachry, R.N., Vice President Administrator and Chief Operations Executive
Web address: www.scripps.org
Control: Other not-for-profit (including NFP Corporation) **Service**: General medical and surgical

Staffed Beds: 155 **Admissions**: 11943 **Census**: 142 **Outpatient Visits**: 81291 **Births**: 1912 **Total Expense ($000)**: 268445 **Payroll Expense ($000)**: 107799 **Personnel**: 1376

ENCINO—Los Angeles County; See Los Angeles

ESCONDIDO—San Diego County

☒ △ **PALOMAR MEDICAL CENTER (050115)**, 2185 West Citracado Parkway, Zip 92029–4159; tel. 760/739–3000, **A**1 3 5 7 10 **F**3 12 13 15 17 18 20 22 24 26 28 29 30 31 40 43 45 46 49 50 51 62 64 68 70 74 75 76 77 78 79 81 82 84 85 87 90 93 96 98 100 102 103 104 106 107 108 111 112 114 115 119 120 121 123 124 126 129 130 146 147 148 149 153 **P**3 **S** Palomar Health, Escondido, CA
Primary Contact: Mariellena Sudak, R.N., MSN, Vice President and Chief Nursing Officer
CMO: Duane Buringrud, M.D., Chief Medical and Quality Officer
CIO: Prudence August, Chief Information Officer
CHR: Brenda C Turner, Chief Human Resources Officer
CNO: Mariellena Sudak, R.N., MSN, Vice President and Chief Nursing Officer
Web address: www.palomarhealth.org
Control: Hospital district or authority, Government, nonfederal **Service**: General medical and surgical

Staffed Beds: 344 **Admissions**: 24709 **Census**: 265 **Outpatient Visits**: 198371 **Births**: 3194 **Total Expense ($000)**: 550644 **Payroll Expense ($000)**: 202029 **Personnel**: 1852

EUREKA—Humboldt County

HUMBOLDT COUNTY MENTAL HEALTH (054124), 720 Wood Street, Zip 95501–4413; tel. 707/268–2900, (Nonreporting) **A**10
Primary Contact: Jet L. DeKruse, Administrator
CMO: Harpreet Duggal, M.D., Medical Director, Department of Health and Human Services
CNO: Sherry Gallagher, Director Nursing, Department of Health and Human Services
Web address: www.https://co.humboldt.ca.us/hhs/mhb/
Control: County, Government, nonfederal **Service**: Psychiatric

Staffed Beds: 16

☒ **ST. JOSEPH HOSPITAL (050006)**, 2700 Dolbeer Street, Zip 95501–4799; tel. 707/445–8121, (Includes GENERAL HOSPITAL, 2200 Harrison Avenue, Eureka, CA, Zip 95501–3299; tel. 707/445–5111) **A**1 2 10 19 **F**3 8 11 12 13 15 17 18 20 22 24 26 28 29 30 31 35 39 40 43 45 46 47 48 49 53 54 62 63 64 68 70 72 74 75 76 78 79 81 82 84 85 86 87 90 93 96 107 108 110 111 114 115 118 119 120 121 123 124 129 130 131 146 148 152 154 **P**5 **S** Providence St. Joseph Health, Renton, WA
Primary Contact: Roberta Luskin–Hawk, M.D., Chief Executive
CFO: Michel Riccioni, Chief Financial Officer
CMO: Mathew Miller, M.D., Vice President and Chief Medical Officer
CIO: Wendy Thorpe, Area Director Information Systems
CHR: Linda Cook, Vice President Human Resources
CNO: Carol Reeder, R.N., Chief Nursing Officer
Web address: www.stjosepheureka.org
Control: Church operated, Nongovernment, not-for-profit **Service**: General medical and surgical

Staffed Beds: 153 **Admissions**: 7694 **Census**: 99 **Outpatient Visits**: 168433 **Births**: 522 **Total Expense ($000)**: 243774 **Payroll Expense ($000)**: 91358 **Personnel**: 1171

FAIRFIELD—Solano County

☒ **NORTHBAY MEDICAL CENTER (050367)**, 1200 B. Gale Wilson Boulevard, Zip 94533–3587; tel. 707/646–5000, (Includes NORTHBAY VACAVALLEY HOSPITAL, 1000 Nut Tree Road, Vacaville, CA, Zip 95687–4100; tel. 707/624–7000; Aimee Brewer, President, NorthBay Healthcare Group) **A**1 2 5 10 **F**2 3 6 8 11 13 17 18 19 20 22 24 26 28 29 30 31 32 34 35 36 40 41 43 44 45 46 49 50 51 54 55 56 57 59 62 63 64 65 70 72 73 74 75 76 77 78 79 80 81 82 84 85 87 89 92 93 94 96 97 100 102 106 107 114 115 118 119 120 121 124 130 131 132 144 146 147 148 154 **P**3
Primary Contact: Aimee Brewer, President, NorthBay Healthcare Group
CFO: Arthur E DeNio, Vice President and Chief Financial Officer
CMO: Seth Kaufman, M.D., Chief Medical Officer
CIO: Christopher Timbers, Vice President and Chief Information Officer
CNO: Traci A Duncan, Vice President, Chief Nursing Officer
Web address: www.northbay.org
Control: Other not-for-profit (including NFP Corporation) **Service**: General medical and surgical

Staffed Beds: 176 **Admissions**: 41691 **Census**: 114 **Outpatient Visits**: 342681 **Births**: 1239 **Total Expense ($000)**: 574173 **Payroll Expense ($000)**: 253752 **Personnel**: 1660

CA

CA

FALL RIVER MILLS—Shasta County

★ **MAYERS MEMORIAL HOSPITAL DISTRICT (051305)**, 43563 Highway 299 East, Zip 96028–0459, Mailing Address: P.O. Box 459, Zip 96028–0459; tel. 530/336–5511, (Total facility includes 87 beds in nursing home–type unit) **A**10 18 **F**3 6 7 11 13 18 28 34 40 41 45 50 53 56 57 59 63 64 65 75 79 81 85 86 89 90 93 107 114 119 128 132 133 135 146 148 149 154
Primary Contact: Louis James. Ward, Interim Chief Executive Officer
COO: Louis James Ward, Chief Operating Officer
CFO: Travis Lakey, Chief Financial Officer
CMO: Thomas Watson, M.D., Chief of Staff
CIO: Chris Broadway, Manager Information Technology
CHR: Julie Thompson, Manager Personnel and Payroll
CNO: Sherry Wilson, R.N., Chief Nursing Officer
Web address: www.mayersmemorial.com
Control: Hospital district or authority, Government, nonfederal **Service**: General medical and surgical

Staffed Beds: 97 **Admissions**: 457 **Census**: 77 **Outpatient Visits**: 22864 **Births**: 0

FOLSOM—Sacramento County

✚ **MERCY HOSPITAL OF FOLSOM (050414)**, 1650 Creekside Drive, Zip 95630–3400; tel. 916/983–7400, **A**1 5 10 **F**3 8 11 12 13 29 30 34 35 36 37 39 40 49 57 59 60 64 66 68 70 74 75 76 77 79 81 82 84 85 86 93 107 108 114 115 118 119 130 132 146 147 148 154 **P**3 4 5 **S** Dignity Health, San Francisco, CA
Primary Contact: Randall W. Ross, FACHE, President and Chief Executive Officer
CMO: Robert Allen, M.D., Chief Medical Officer
CHR: Anthony Robinson, Manager, Human Resources
CNO: Josh Freilich, Vice President and Chief Nurse Executive
Web address: www.mercyfolsom.org
Control: Church operated, Nongovernment, not–for–profit **Service**: General medical and surgical

Staffed Beds: 106 **Admissions**: 6870 **Census**: 65 **Outpatient Visits**: 60230 **Births**: 880 **Total Expense ($000)**: 198266 **Payroll Expense ($000)**: 75891 **Personnel**: 602

✚ **VIBRA HOSPITAL OF SACRAMENTO (052033)**, 330 Montrose Drive, Zip 95630–2720; tel. 916/351–9151, **A**1 10 **F**1 3 29 30 34 46 49 68 70 75 77 84 85 91 119 130 148 149 **S** Vibra Healthcare, Mechanicsburg, PA
Primary Contact: Kimberly Horton, R.N., MSN, Chief Executive Officer
CFO: Todd Scott, Chief Financial Officer
CMO: S. Kwon Lee, M.D., Chief of Staff
CHR: Glenda Franco, Director, Human Resources
Web address: www.vhsacramento.com
Control: Individual, Investor–owned (for–profit) **Service**: Acute long–term care hospital

Staffed Beds: 58 **Admissions**: 388 **Census**: 43 **Outpatient Visits**: 0 **Births**: 0

FONTANA—San Bernardino County

✚ **KAISER PERMANENTE FONTANA MEDICAL CENTER (050140)**, 9961 Sierra Avenue, Zip 92335–6794; tel. 909/427–5000, (Includes KAISER PERMANENTE ONTARIO MEDICAL CENTER, 2295 South Vineyard Avenue, Ontario, CA, Zip 91761–7925; tel. 909/724–5000; Greg Christian, Sr Vice President, Area Manager – San Bernardino County Area) **A**1 3 5 10 **F**3 8 11 12 13 29 30 31 34 40 41 44 45 46 48 49 50 51 53 57 58 59 60 61 62 63 64 65 68 70 72 73 74 75 76 77 78 79 81 82 84 85 86 87 88 89 100 102 107 108 110 111 114 115 117 118 119 126 130 131 132 135 141 143 144 145 146 148 149 154 **P**6 **S** Kaiser Foundation Hospitals, Oakland, CA
Primary Contact: Greg Christian, Senior Vice President, Area Manager – San Bernardino County Area
COO: Ken Rivers, Chief Operating Officer, Fontana Medical Center
CFO: Trish Lopez, Area Chief Financial Officer
CMO: Timothy Jenkins, M.D., Area Medical Director and Chief of Staff
CIO: Heather Raymond, Area Public Relations Director
CHR: Irene Ruiz, Area Human Resources Director
CNO: Raye Burkhardt, Chief Nurse Executive, Fontana Medical Center
Web address: www.kaiserpermanente.org
Control: Other not–for–profit (including NFP Corporation) **Service**: General medical and surgical

Staffed Beds: 490 **Admissions**: 31084 **Census**: 357 **Outpatient Visits**: 187242 **Births**: 6735 **Personnel**: 3892

FORT BRAGG—Mendocino County

✚ **MENDOCINO COAST DISTRICT HOSPITAL (051325)**, 700 River Drive, Zip 95437–5495; tel. 707/961–1234, **A**1 10 18 **F**7 8 11 13 15 18 29 30 31 34 36 40 57 59 62 63 70 75 76 77 78 79 81 82 85 86 87 93 94 96 97 107 108 110 111 114 115 119 127 130 132 133 148 149
Primary Contact: Bob S. Edwards Jr, FACHE, Chief Executive Officer
CFO: Mike Ellis, Chief Financial Officer
CMO: John Kermen, D.O., Chief Medical Staff
CIO: Jeff Edwards, Manager Information Services
CNO: Bonnie Kittner, R.N., Chief Nursing Officer
Web address: www.mcdh.org
Control: Hospital district or authority, Government, nonfederal **Service**: General medical and surgical

Staffed Beds: 25 **Admissions**: 1017 **Census**: 12 **Outpatient Visits**: 58224 **Births**: 106 **Total Expense ($000)**: 53631 **Payroll Expense ($000)**: 17000 **Personnel**: 281

FORT IRWIN—San Bernardino County

✚ **WEED ARMY COMMUNITY HOSPITAL**, Inner Loop Road and 4th Street, Building 166, Zip 92310–5065, Mailing Address: P.O. Box 105109, Zip 92310–5109; tel. 760/380–3108, (Nonreporting) **A**1 **S** Department of the Army, Office of the Surgeon General, Falls Church, VA
Primary Contact: Colonel Martin Doperak, Commander
CIO: Michael Haenelt, Chief Information Management
Web address: www.irwin.amedd.army.mil
Control: Army, Government, federal **Service**: General medical and surgical

Staffed Beds: 27

FORTUNA—Humboldt County

★ **REDWOOD MEMORIAL HOSPITAL (051318)**, 3300 Renner Drive, Zip 95540–3198; tel. 707/725–3361, **A**10 18 **F**3 11 13 15 18 29 30 34 35 39 40 45 50 53 56 57 59 63 64 68 70 75 77 79 81 82 84 85 86 93 107 110 114 119 130 131 132 133 146 **S** Providence St. Joseph Health, Renton, WA
Primary Contact: Roberta Luskin–Hawk, M.D., Chief Executive
COO: Joseph J Rogers, Vice President and Chief Operating Officer
CHR: Bob Sampson, Vice President Human Resources
Web address: www.redwoodmemorial.org/
Control: Church operated, Nongovernment, not–for–profit **Service**: General medical and surgical

Staffed Beds: 25 **Admissions**: 1272 **Census**: 13 **Outpatient Visits**: 46694 **Births**: 317 **Total Expense ($000)**: 42506 **Payroll Expense ($000)**: 14303 **Personnel**: 164

FOUNTAIN VALLEY—Orange County

✚ **FOUNTAIN VALLEY REGIONAL HOSPITAL AND MEDICAL CENTER (050570)**, 17100 Euclid Street, Zip 92708–4043; tel. 714/966–7200, **A**1 2 5 10 **F**3 12 13 17 18 20 22 24 26 29 30 31 34 40 45 49 56 57 60 68 70 72 73 74 75 76 77 78 79 81 82 84 85 87 88 89 100 107 111 114 115 119 126 130 146 148 149 154 **S** TENET Healthcare Corporation, Dallas, TX
Primary Contact: Kenneth D. McFarland, Chief Executive Officer
COO: Edward Littlejohn, Chief Operating Officer
CFO: Ken Jordan, Chief Financial Officer
CMO: Daniel Hilton, M.D., Chief of Staff
CIO: Freddie Sanchez, Director Information Systems
CHR: Ricky Russell, Chief Human Resources Officer
CNO: Kristin Christophersen, Chief Nursing Officer
Web address: www.fountainvalleyhospital.com
Control: Corporation, Investor–owned (for–profit) **Service**: General medical and surgical

Staffed Beds: 243 **Admissions**: 19192 **Census**: 243 **Outpatient Visits**: 73713 **Births**: 3277 **Personnel**: 1575

✚ **MEMORIALCARE, ORANGE COAST MEMORIAL MEDICAL CENTER (050678)**, 9920 Talbert Avenue, Zip 92708–5115; tel. 714/378–7000, **A**1 2 10 **F**3 8 11 12 13 15 18 20 22 24 26 28 29 30 31 34 35 38 40 44 45 46 47 48 49 50 51 53 55 56 57 58 59 64 65 68 70 72 74 75 76 77 78 79 81 82 84 85 86 87 93 107 108 110 111 114 115 116 117 118 119 124 126 130 131 132 135 143 145 146 147 149 154 **S** MemorialCare, Fountain Valley, CA
Primary Contact: Marcia Manker, Chief Executive Officer
COO: Emily Randle, Vice President Operations
CFO: Steve McNamara, Chief Financial Officer
CIO: Scott Raymond, Director Information Systems
CHR: Michelle Gutierrez, Executive Director Human Resources
CNO: Dale Vital, Chief Nursing Officer
Web address: www.memorialcare.org
Control: Other not–for–profit (including NFP Corporation) **Service**: General medical and surgical

Staffed Beds: 218 **Admissions**: 11470 **Census**: 110 **Outpatient Visits**: 107631 **Births**: 1538 **Total Expense ($000)**: 305094 **Payroll Expense ($000)**: 79689 **Personnel**: 1143

Many Facility Codes have changed. Please refer to the AHA Guide Code Chart. © 2018 AHA Guide

FREMONT—Alameda County

⊠ **FREMONT HOSPITAL (054110)**, 39001 Sundale Drive, Zip 94538–2005;
tel. 510/796–1100, (Nonreporting) **A**1 10 **S** Universal Health Services, Inc., King
of Prussia, PA
Primary Contact: Marlon Rollins, Ph.D., Chief Executive Officer
CMO: Vikas Duvvuri, M.D., Medical Director
CHR: Tom Piz, Director Human Resources
Web address: www.fremonthospital.com
Control: Corporation, Investor–owned (for–profit) **Service:** Psychiatric

Staffed Beds: 148

⊠ **KAISER PERMANENTE FREMONT MEDICAL CENTER (050512)**, 39400
Paseo Padre Parkway, Zip 94538–2310; tel. 510/248–3000, **A**1 10 **F**3 8 12
29 30 31 35 40 41 45 70 74 75 77 78 79 81 82 85 130 146 148 149 154 **S**
Kaiser Foundation Hospitals, Oakland, CA
Primary Contact: Victoria O'Gorman, Administrator
Web address: www.kp.org
Control: Other not–for–profit (including NFP Corporation) **Service:** General
medical and surgical

Staffed Beds: 76 **Admissions:** 6620 **Census:** 34

⊠ **WASHINGTON HOSPITAL HEALTHCARE SYSTEM (050195)**, 2000 Mowry
Avenue, Zip 94538–1746; tel. 510/797–1111, (Nonreporting) **A**1 2 10
Primary Contact: Nancy D. Farber, Chief Executive Officer
COO: Edward J Fayen, Associate Administrator Operations and Support
CFO: Chris Henry, Associate Administrator and Chief Financial Officer
CMO: Albert Brooks, M.D., Chief Medical Staff Services
CIO: Robert Thorwald, Chief Information Officer
CHR: Bryant Welch, Chief Human Resources
CNO: Stephanie Williams, R.N., Chief Nursing Officer
Web address: www.whhs.com
Control: Hospital district or authority, Government, nonfederal **Service:** General
medical and surgical

Staffed Beds: 269

FRENCH CAMP—San Joaquin County

☐ **SAN JOAQUIN GENERAL HOSPITAL (050167)**, 500 West Hospital Road,
Zip 95231–9693, Mailing Address: P.O. Box 1020, Stockton, Zip 95201–3120;
tel. 209/468–6000, (Nonreporting) **A**1 3 5 10
Primary Contact: David K. Culberson, Chief Executive Officer
CFO: Ron Kreutner, Chief Financial Officer
CMO: Sheela Kapre, M.D., Chief Medical Officer
CIO: Don Johnston, Chief Information Officer
CHR: Lisa M Lopez, Director Human Resources
CNO: Erlinda Bolor, R.N., Chief Nursing Officer
Web address: www.sjgeneral.org/
Control: County, Government, nonfederal **Service:** General medical and surgical

Staffed Beds: 110

FRESNO—Fresno County

COMMUNITY BEHAVIORAL HEALTH CENTER, 7171 North Cedar Avenue,
Zip 93720–3311; tel. 559/449–8000, (Nonreporting) **S** Community Medical
Centers, Fresno, CA
Primary Contact: Craig Wagoner, Chief Executive Officer
CFO: Stephen Walter, Senior Vice President and Chief Financial Officer
CMO: Tom Utecht, M.D., Senior Vice President and Chief Quality Officer
CIO: George Vasquez, Vice President Information Services
CHR: Ginny Burdick, Vice President Human Resources
CNO: Karen L Buckley, R.N., Chief Nursing Officer
Web address: www.communitymedical.org
Control: Corporation, Investor–owned (for–profit) **Service:** Psychiatric

Staffed Beds: 61

☐ **COMMUNITY REGIONAL MEDICAL CENTER (050060)**, 2823 Fresno
Street, Zip 93721–1324, Mailing Address: P.O. Box 1232, Zip 93715–1232;
tel. 559/459–6000, (Nonreporting) **A**1 2 3 5 8 10 **S** Community Medical Centers,
Fresno, CA
Primary Contact: Craig Wagoner, Chief Executive Officer
COO: Patrick W Rafferty, Executive Vice President and Chief Operating Officer
CFO: Stephen Walter, Senior Vice President and Chief Financial Officer
CMO: Tom Utecht, M.D., Chief Medical and Quality Officer
CIO: Craig Castro, Chief Information Officer
CHR: Ginny Burdick, Vice President Human Resources
Web address: www.communitymedical.org
Control: Other not–for–profit (including NFP Corporation) **Service:** General
medical and surgical

Staffed Beds: 808

☐ **FRESNO HEART AND SURGICAL HOSPITAL (050732)**, 15 East Audubon Drive,
Zip 93720–1542; tel. 559/433–8000, (Nonreporting) **A**1 3 10 **S** Community
Medical Centers, Fresno, CA
Primary Contact: Ben Armfield, Associate Administrator
CFO: Ben Armfield, Chief Financial Officer
CMO: Tom Utecht, M.D., Corporate Chief Quality Officer
CIO: George Vasquez, Corporate Chief Information Officer
CHR: Julie Adair, Interim Corporate Chief Human Resources Officer
CNO: Heather Rodriguez, Chief Nursing Officer
Web address: www.fresnoheartandsurgical.org
Control: Corporation, Investor–owned (for–profit) **Service:** Heart

Staffed Beds: 60

FRESNO MEDICAL CENTER See Kaiser Permanente Fresno Medical Center

☐ **FRESNO SURGICAL HOSPITAL (050708)**, 6125 North Fresno Street,
Zip 93710–5207; tel. 559/431–8000, (Nonreporting) **A**1 10
Primary Contact: Kristine Kassahn, Chief Executive Officer
CFO: Bruce Cecil, Chief Financial Officer
CMO: Bruce Witmer, M.D., Medical Director
CHR: Laura Patillo, Manager Human Resources
Web address: www.fresnosurgicalhospital.com
Control: Partnership, Investor–owned (for–profit) **Service:** Surgical

Staffed Beds: 16

⊠ **KAISER PERMANENTE FRESNO MEDICAL CENTER (050710)**, 7300 North
Fresno Street, Zip 93720–2942; tel. 559/448–4500, **A**1 3 5 10 **F**3 12 13 29 30
31 35 40 45 46 50 68 70 72 73 74 75 76 77 78 79 81 82 84 85 87 130 146
148 149 **S** Kaiser Foundation Hospitals, Oakland, CA
Primary Contact: Debbie Hemker, Senior Vice President and Area Manager
CFO: Paula Armstrong, Chief Financial Officer
CMO: Smita Rouillard, M.D., Physician in Chief
CIO: Patty Thompson, Area Compliance Officer
CHR: Mike Silveira Suffix Human Resources Leader
CNO: Karen S Strauman, R.N., Chief Nurse Executive
Web address: www.kaiserpermanente.org
Control: Other not–for–profit (including NFP Corporation) **Service:** General
medical and surgical

Staffed Beds: 169 **Admissions:** 8671 **Census:** 75 **Births:** 1513

⊠ **SAINT AGNES MEDICAL CENTER (050093)**, 1303 East Herndon Avenue,
Zip 93720–3397; tel. 559/450–3000, **A**1 2 3 10 **F**3 8 11 13 15 17 18 20 22 24
26 28 29 30 31 34 35 37 40 44 45 46 47 49 50 51 55 56 57 58 59 61 64 66
70 74 75 76 77 78 79 81 82 84 85 86 87 91 92 93 94 95 96 97 102 107 108
110 111 112 113 114 115 116 117 118 119 120 121 123 124 126 130 132
135 146 147 148 149 154 **P**1 2 3 5 **S** Trinity Health, Livonia, MI
Primary Contact: Nancy Hollingsworth, R.N., MSN, President and Chief Executive
Officer
COO: Mark T Bateman, Interim Chief Operating Officer
CFO: Phil Robinson, Chief Financial Officer
CMO: Stephen Soldo, M.D., Chief Medical Officer
CIO: Irfan Ali, Director Information Services
CHR: Stacy Vaillancourt, Vice President Marketing, Communications, Advocacy and
Human Resources
Web address: www.samc.com
Control: Church operated, Nongovernment, not–for–profit **Service:** General
medical and surgical

Staffed Beds: 436 **Admissions:** 25282 **Census:** 267 **Outpatient
Visits:** 190447 **Births:** 3092 **Total Expense ($000):** 450225 **Payroll
Expense ($000):** 158841 **Personnel:** 1806

⊠ △ **SAN JOAQUIN VALLEY REHABILITATION HOSPITAL (053032)**, 7173
North Sharon Avenue, Zip 93720–3329; tel. 559/436–3600, (Nonreporting) **A**1 7
10 **S** Vibra Healthcare, Mechanicsburg, PA
Primary Contact: Mary Jo Jacobson, Chief Executive Officer
CFO: Margaret Casarez, Chief Financial Officer
CMO: Michael Azevedo, M.D., Medical Director
CIO: Christi Rolff, Director Business Development
CHR: Jennifer Morrow, Director Human Resources
Web address: www.sanjoaquinrehab.com
Control: Corporation, Investor–owned (for–profit) **Service:** Rehabilitation

Staffed Beds: 62

CA

Hospital, Medicare Provider Number, Address, Telephone, Approval, Facility, and Physician Codes, Health Care System

★ American Hospital Association (AHA) membership
☐ The Joint Commission accreditation
○ Healthcare Facilities Accreditation Program
◇ DNV Healthcare Inc. accreditation
⇧ Center for Improvement in Healthcare Quality Accreditation
△ Commission on Accreditation of Rehabilitation Facilities (CARF) accreditation

✉ **VETERANS AFFAIRS CENTRAL CALIFORNIA HEALTH CARE SYSTEM**, 2615 East Clinton Avenue, Zip 93703–2223; tel. 559/225–6100, (Nonreporting) **A**1 3 5 **S** Department of Veterans Affairs, Perry Point, MD
Primary Contact: Stephen R. Bauman, Medical Center Director
CMO: Wessel H. Meyer, M.D., Chief of Staff
CHR: Sandra Stein, Chief Human Resources Management
Web address: www.fresno.va.gov/
Control: Veterans Affairs, Government, federal **Service**: General medical and surgical

Staffed Beds: 117

FULLERTON—Orange County

✉ △ **ST. JUDE MEDICAL CENTER (050168)**, 101 East Valencia Mesa Drive, Zip 92835–3875; tel. 714/992–3000, **A**1 2 3 5 7 10 **F**2 3 8 9 11 12 13 15 18 20 22 24 26 28 29 30 31 32 34 35 36 39 40 43 44 45 46 47 48 49 50 51 53 54 55 56 57 58 59 60 61 62 63 64 65 66 68 70 71 72 74 75 76 77 78 79 81 82 83 84 85 86 87 90 91 92 93 95 96 97 100 107 108 109 110 111 112 114 115 116 117 118 119 120 121 123 124 126 129 130 131 132 134 135 143 145 146 147 148 149 154 **P**3 5 **S** Providence St. Joseph Health, Renton, WA
Primary Contact: Brian Helleland, Chief Executive Officer
CFO: Ed Salvador, Chief Financial Officer
CMO: Eugene P. Kim, M.D., Chief Medical Officer
CHR: Mark Jablonski, Vice President Mission Integration
CNO: Linda Jenkins, R.N., Vice President Patient Care Services
Web address: www.stjudemedicalcenter.org
Control: Church operated, Nongovernment, not–for–profit **Service**: General medical and surgical

Staffed Beds: 320 **Admissions:** 15326 **Census:** 192 **Outpatient Visits:** 488168 **Births:** 2318 **Total Expense ($000):** 543218 **Payroll Expense ($000):** 171946 **Personnel:** 2300

GARBERVILLE—Humboldt County

★ **JEROLD PHELPS COMMUNITY HOSPITAL (051309)**, 733 Cedar Street, Zip 95542–3292; tel. 707/923–3921, (Total facility includes 8 beds in nursing home–type unit) **A**10 18 **F**34 35 40 50 57 59 65 66 68 77 91 97 110 127 128 133 143 149 154 **P**5
Primary Contact: Matthew Rees, Administrator
COO: Kent Scown, Director Operations and Information Services
CFO: Harry Jasper, Chief Financial Officer
CMO: Marcin Matuszkiewicz, M.D., Chief of Staff and Medical Director
CIO: Kent Scown, Director Operations and Information Services
CHR: Dee Way, Director Human Resources
CNO: Sarah Beach, Director of Nursing
Web address: www.shchd.org
Control: Hospital district or authority, Government, nonfederal **Service**: General medical and surgical

Staffed Beds: 17 **Admissions:** 56 **Census:** 8 **Outpatient Visits:** 14804 **Births:** 2 **Total Expense ($000):** 11166 **Payroll Expense ($000):** 4757 **Personnel:** 70

GARDEN GROVE—Orange County

✉ **GARDEN GROVE HOSPITAL AND MEDICAL CENTER (050230)**, 12601 Garden Grove Boulevard, Zip 92843–1959; tel. 714/537–5160, (Nonreporting) **A**1 3 10 **S** Prime Healthcare, Ontario, CA
Primary Contact: Richard M. Rowe, PharmD, Chief Executive Officer
CFO: Kora Guoyavatin, Chief Financial Officer
CMO: Hassan Alkhouli, M.D., Chief Medical Officer
CIO: Vic Mahan, Director Information Systems
CHR: Stephanie Sioson, Director Human Resources
CNO: Wanda Ruben, R.N., Chief Nursing Officer
Web address: www.gardengrovehospital.com
Control: Corporation, Investor–owned (for–profit) **Service**: General medical and surgical

Staffed Beds: 167

GARDENA—Los Angeles County

✉ **KINDRED HOSPITAL SOUTH BAY (052050)**, 1246 West 155th Street, Zip 90247–4062; tel. 310/323–5330, (Nonreporting) **A**1 10 **S** Kindred Healthcare, Louisville, KY
Primary Contact: Michael D. Kerr, Chief Executive Officer
CHR: Michelle Parra, Director Human Resources
Web address: www.khsouthbay.com/
Control: Corporation, Investor–owned (for–profit) **Service**: Acute long–term care hospital

Staffed Beds: 84

✉ **MEMORIAL HOSPITAL OF GARDENA (050468)**, 1145 West Redondo Beach Boulevard, Zip 90247–3528; tel. 310/532–4200, (Nonreporting) **A**1 10 **S** Avanti Hospitals, El Segundo, CA
Primary Contact: Kathy Wojno, R.N., MSN, Administrator
CFO: Daniel R Heckathorne, Chief Financial Officer
CMO: Nosratian Farshao, M.D., Chief Medical Staff
CHR: Matthew Kempiak, Director Human Resources and Administrative Services
CNO: Glenda Luce, Chief Nursing Officer
Web address: www.mhglax.com/
Control: Corporation, Investor–owned (for–profit) **Service**: General medical and surgical

Staffed Beds: 172

VISTA HOSPITAL OF SOUTH BAY See Kindred Hospital South Bay

GILROY—Santa Clara County

☐ **SAINT LOUISE REGIONAL HOSPITAL (050688)**, 9400 No Name Uno, Zip 95020–3528; tel. 408/848–2000, (Nonreporting) **A**1 10 **S** Verity Health System, Los Angeles, CA
Primary Contact: John Hennelly, Chief Executive Officer
COO: Carol Furgurson, Chief Operating Officer
CFO: Nicole Thomson, Chief Financial Officer
CMO: Arthur Douville, M.D., Chief Medical Officer
CIO: Dick Hutsell, Vice President Information Technology Services
CHR: Lin Velasquez, Vice President Human Resources
CNO: Marilyn Gerrior, R.N., MSN, Chief Nursing Executive
Web address: www.verity.org
Control: Church operated, Nongovernment, not–for–profit **Service**: General medical and surgical

Staffed Beds: 93

GLENDALE—Los Angeles County

✉ **GLENDALE MEMORIAL HOSPITAL AND HEALTH CENTER (050058)**, 1420 South Central Avenue, Zip 91204–2594; tel. 818/502–1900, (Nonreporting) **A**1 10 **S** Dignity Health, San Francisco, CA
Primary Contact: Jill Welton, President and Chief Executive Officer
COO: Ann Lee, Vice President and Chief Operating Officer
CFO: Rebecca Cheng, Chief Financial Officer
CIO: Brian Gregor, Manager Information Technology Operations
CHR: Nga Nguyen, Manager Human Resources and Organizational Development
CNO: Jason Black Esq Vice President and Chief Nursing Officer
Web address: www.glendalememorial.com
Control: Other not–for–profit (including NFP Corporation) **Service**: General medical and surgical

Staffed Beds: 334

★ ⇑ **USC VERDUGO HILLS HOSPITAL (050124)**, 1812 Verdugo Boulevard, Zip 91208–1409; tel. 818/790–7100, **A**3 10 21 **F**3 6 11 12 13 14 15 17 18 28 29 30 34 35 37 38 40 41 44 45 46 47 48 49 50 51 53 56 57 59 60 64 65 68 70 74 75 76 77 78 79 81 83 84 85 86 87 91 93 94 96 98 100 101 102 103 104 107 108 110 111 115 119 126 128 130 131 132 135 145 146 147 148 149 153 **P**6 8 **S** Keck Medicine of USC, Los Angeles, CA
Primary Contact: Keith Hobbs, Chief Executive Officer
COO: Kenny Pawlek, Chief Operating Officer
CMO: Stephanie Hall, M.D., Chief Medical Officer
CHR: Eva Herberger, Administrator Human Resources
CNO: Theresa Murphy, Chief Nursing Officer
Web address: www.uscvhh.org
Control: Other not–for–profit (including NFP Corporation) **Service**: General medical and surgical

Staffed Beds: 156 **Admissions:** 6635 **Census:** 90 **Outpatient Visits:** 62400 **Births:** 388 **Total Expense ($000):** 111923 **Payroll Expense ($000):** 48970 **Personnel:** 608

GLENDORA—Los Angeles County

✉ **FOOTHILL PRESBYTERIAN HOSPITAL (050597)**, 250 South Grand Avenue, Zip 91741–4218; tel. 626/963–8411, **A**1 10 **F**3 7 11 13 15 17 18 29 30 31 34 35 40 41 44 45 49 50 51 60 64 68 70 74 75 76 77 78 79 81 85 86 87 98 107 108 114 119 130 131 143 146 154 **S** Citrus Valley Health Partners, Covina, CA
Primary Contact: Robert H. Curry, President and Chief Executive Officer
COO: Elvia Foulke, Executive Vice President and Chief Operating Officer
CMO: John DiMare, M.D., Medical Director
CIO: David McCobb, Chief Information Officer
Web address: www.cvhp.org/Our_Facilities/Foothill_Presbyterian.aspx
Control: Other not–for–profit (including NFP Corporation) **Service**: General medical and surgical

Staffed Beds: 72 **Admissions:** 5945 **Census:** 60 **Outpatient Visits:** 64785 **Births:** 985 **Total Expense ($000):** 99596 **Payroll Expense ($000):** 38379 **Personnel:** 470

Many Facility Codes have changed. Please refer to the AHA Guide Code Chart. © 2018 AHA Guide

★ ○ **GLENDORA COMMUNITY HOSPITAL (050205)**, 150 West Route 66, Zip 91740–6207; tel. 626/852–5000, (Nonreporting) **A**10 11 **S** Prime Healthcare, Ontario, CA
Primary Contact: Sofia Abrina, R.N., Chief Executive Officer
CFO: Robert Bonner, Chief Financial Officer
CMO: Oliver Solomon, M.D., Chief Medical Officer
CIO: Jeffrey Cox, Chief Information Officer
CHR: Diana Cancel, Director Human Resources
CNO: Mary Ann Bennett, Chief Nursing Officer
Web address: www.evhmc.com
Control: Other not–for–profit (including NFP Corporation) **Service**: General medical and surgical

Staffed Beds: 128

GRASS VALLEY—Nevada County

⊞ **SIERRA NEVADA MEMORIAL HOSPITAL (050150)**, 155 Glasson Way, Zip 95945–5723, Mailing Address: P.O. Box 1029, Zip 95945–1029; tel. 530/274–6000, (Nonreporting) **A**1 2 10 19 **S** Dignity Health, San Francisco, CA
Primary Contact: Katherine A. Medeiros, President and Chief Executive Officer
CFO: Carolyn Canady, Chief Financial Officer
CMO: Jeffrey M. Rosenburg, Chief Medical Officer
CHR: Terri Labriola, Human Resources Officer
CNO: Jill McWilliams, Chief Nursing Officer
Web address: www.snmh.org
Control: Other not–for–profit (including NFP Corporation) **Service**: General medical and surgical

Staffed Beds: 104

GREENBRAE—Marin County

⊞ **MARIN GENERAL HOSPITAL (050360)**, 250 Bon Air Road, Zip 94904–1784, Mailing Address: P.O. Box 8010, San Rafael, Zip 94912–8010; tel. 415/925–7000, **A**1 2 10 **F**3 8 13 15 18 20 22 24 26 29 30 31 34 35 36 37 40 43 45 46 47 48 49 50 51 57 58 60 64 68 70 73 74 75 76 77 78 79 81 84 85 87 89 98 105 107 108 110 112 114 115 118 119 120 121 122 123 124 126 130 132 141 146 148 149 153 154
Primary Contact: Lee Domanico, Chief Executive Officer
CFO: David W Cox, Chief Financial Officer
CMO: Joel Sklar, M.D., Chief Medical Officer
CIO: Mark Zielazinski, Chief Information and Technology Integration Officer
CHR: Linda Lang, Chief Human Resources Officer
Web address: www.maringeneral.org
Control: Hospital district or authority, Government, nonfederal **Service**: General medical and surgical

Staffed Beds: 164 Admissions: 9274 Census: 114 Outpatient Visits: 197450 Births: 1272 Total Expense ($000): 385586 Payroll Expense ($000): 167755 Personnel: 1421

GRIDLEY—Butte County

★ ⇑ **ORCHARD HOSPITAL (051311)**, 240 Spruce Street, Zip 95948–2216, Mailing Address: P.O. Box 97, Zip 95948–0097; tel. 530/846–5671, (Nonreporting) **A**10 18 21
Primary Contact: Steve Stark, Chief Executive Officer
COO: Tracy Atkins, Chief Operating and Nursing Officer
CFO: Kristina Sanke, Chief Financial Officer
CMO: Henry Starkes, M.D., Medical Director
CIO: John Helvey, Chief Information Officer
CNO: Tracy Atkins, Chief Operating and Nursing Officer
Web address: www.orchardhospital.com
Control: Other not–for–profit (including NFP Corporation) **Service**: General medical and surgical

Staffed Beds: 45

HANFORD—Kings County

⊞ **ADVENTIST MEDICAL CENTER – HANFORD (050121)**, 115 Mall Drive, Zip 93230–3513; tel. 559/582–9000, (Includes ADVENTIST MEDICAL CENTER–SELMA, 1141 Rose Avenue, Selma, CA, Zip 93662–3241; tel. 559/891–1000; Richard L Rawson, President and Chief Executive Officer) (Nonreporting) **A**1 3 5 10 **S** Adventist Health, Roseville, CA
Primary Contact: Wayne Ferch, President and Chief Executive Officer
CIO: Michael Aubry, Director Information Systems
Web address: www.adventisthealthcv.com/hospital_newhanfordhospital.aspx
Control: Church operated, Nongovernment, not–for–profit **Service**: General medical and surgical

Staffed Beds: 199

⊞ **CENTRAL VALLEY GENERAL HOSPITAL (050196)**, 1025 North Douty Street, Zip 93230–3722, Mailing Address: P.O. Box 480, Zip 93232–2113; tel. 559/583–2100, (Nonreporting) **A**1 10 **S** Adventist Health, Roseville, CA
Primary Contact: Wayne Ferch, President and Chief Executive Officer
Web address: www.hanfordhealth.com
Control: Corporation, Investor–owned (for–profit) **Service**: General medical and surgical

Staffed Beds: 49

HARBOR CITY—Los Angeles County; See Los Angeles

HAYWARD—Alameda County

☐ **ST. ROSE HOSPITAL (050002)**, 27200 Calaroga Avenue, Zip 94545–4383; tel. 510/264–4000, (Nonreporting) **A**1 10 **S** Alecto Healthcare, Irvine, CA
Primary Contact: Aman Dhuper, President and Chief Executive Officer
CFO: Michael Taylor, Vice President Financial Services and Chief Financial Officer
CMO: Charles S Feldstein, M.D., Vice President Medical Affairs
CHR: John Davini, Vice President
Web address: www.srhca.org
Control: Church operated, Nongovernment, not–for–profit **Service**: General medical and surgical

Staffed Beds: 150

HEALDSBURG—Sonoma County

☐ **HEALDSBURG DISTRICT HOSPITAL (051321)**, 1375 University Avenue, Zip 95448–3382; tel. 707/431–6500, **A**1 10 18 **F**3 8 15 18 29 30 34 35 40 45 46 48 50 51 54 57 59 64 65 68 70 74 75 77 79 81 82 85 87 93 97 104 107 110 111 115 119 128 130 133 146 147 148 149 153 154
Primary Contact: Joseph P. Harrington, Interim Chief Executive Officer
COO: Regina Novello, R.N., Chief Operating Officer
CFO: John S Parigi II Interim Chief Financial Officer
CMO: Judy Widger, M.D., Chief of Staff
CIO: Steven Hansen, Director Information Technology
CHR: Kristina Holloway, Chief Human Resources Officer
CNO: Susan G Spoelma, MSN, R.N., Chief Nursing Officer
Web address: www.nschd.org
Control: Hospital district or authority, Government, nonfederal **Service**: General medical and surgical

Staffed Beds: 38 Admissions: 749 Census: 21 Outpatient Visits: 44689 Births: 0 Total Expense ($000): 49056 Payroll Expense ($000): 19244 Personnel: 171

HEMET—Riverside County

☐ **HEMET VALLEY MEDICAL CENTER (050390)**, 1117 East Devonshire Avenue, Zip 92543–3083; tel. 951/652–2811, (Nonreporting) **A**1 3 10 12 13 **S** Physicians for Healthy Hospitals, Hemet, CA
Primary Contact: Dan C. McLaughlin, Chief Hospital Executive Officer
CFO: John R Collins, Chief Financial Officer
CHR: Michele Bird, Chief Human Resources Officer
CNO: Kathryn McLaughlin, Chief Nursing Officer
Web address: www.physiciansforhealthyhospitals.com
Control: Hospital district or authority, Government, nonfederal **Service**: General medical and surgical

Staffed Beds: 238

HOLLISTER—San Benito County

⊞ **HAZEL HAWKINS MEMORIAL HOSPITAL (050296)**, 911 Sunset Drive, Zip 95023–5695; tel. 831/637–5711, (Includes WILLIAM AND INEZ MABIE SKILLED NURSING FACILITY, 911 Sunset Drive, Hollister, CA, Zip 95023; tel. 408/637–5711) (Nonreporting) **A**1 10
Primary Contact: Ken Underwood, Chief Executive Officer
CFO: Mark Robinson, Associate Administrator and Chief Financial Officer
CIO: Julio Gil, Manager Information Services
CHR: Ysidro Gallardo, Associate Administrator Human Resources
Web address: www.hazelhawkins.com
Control: Hospital district or authority, Government, nonfederal **Service**: General medical and surgical

Staffed Beds: 181

Hospital, Medicare Provider Number, Address, Telephone, Approval, Facility, and Physician Codes, Health Care System

★ American Hospital Association (AHA) membership ○ Healthcare Facilities Accreditation Program ⇑ Center for Improvement in Healthcare Quality Accreditation
☐ The Joint Commission accreditation ◇ DNV Healthcare Inc. accreditation △ Commission on Accreditation of Rehabilitation Facilities (CARF) accreditation

CA

HUNTINGTON BEACH—Orange County

✠ **HUNTINGTON BEACH HOSPITAL (050526)**, 17772 Beach Boulevard, Zip 92647–6896; tel. 714/843–5000, (Nonreporting) **A**1 10 **S** Prime Healthcare, Ontario, CA
Primary Contact: Richard M. Rowe, PharmD, Chief Executive Officer
CFO: Alan H Smith, Chief Financial Officer
CMO: Hassan Alkhouli, M.D., Medical Director
CIO: Adam Morquecho, Director Information Technology
CHR: Stephanie Sioson, Director Human Resources
Web address: www.hbhospital.com
Control: Other not–for–profit (including NFP Corporation) **Service**: General medical and surgical

Staffed Beds: 102

HUNTINGTON PARK—Los Angeles County

COMMUNITY AND MISSION HOSPITALS OF HUNTINGTON PARK See Community Hospital of Huntington Park

★ ○ **COMMUNITY HOSPITAL OF HUNTINGTON PARK (050091)**, 2623 East Slauson Avenue, Zip 90255–2926; tel. 323/583–1931, (Nonreporting) **A**10 11 **S** Avanti Hospitals, El Segundo, CA
Primary Contact: Patricia Rives, R.N., MSN, Chief Executive Officer
CFO: Cheryl Tong, Corporate Chief Financial Officer
CMO: Jose Rivas, M.D., Chief of Staff
CIO: Jason Cervantes, Corporate Chief Information Officer
CHR: Paul Celuch, Corporate Human Resources Director
CNO: Lisa Jacobson, Director of Nursing
Web address: www.avantihospitals.com/community–hospital–of–huntington–park
Control: Corporation, Investor–owned (for–profit) **Service**: General medical and surgical

Staffed Beds: 81

INDIO—Riverside County

✠ **JOHN F. KENNEDY MEMORIAL HOSPITAL (050534)**, 47111 Monroe Street, Zip 92201–6799; tel. 760/347–6191, **A**1 10 **F**3 8 18 20 29 30 34 35 37 40 46 47 48 49 50 54 56 57 59 68 70 74 76 78 79 81 85 87 89 90 97 107 108 111 118 119 126 130 146 148 154 **S** TENET Healthcare Corporation, Dallas, TX
Primary Contact: Gary Honts, Chief Executive Officer
COO: Philip Fitzgerald, Chief Operating Officer
CFO: Lorna Curtis, Chief Financial Officer
CHR: Raymond Konieczek, Chief Human Resources Officer
CNO: Heather Adams, Chief Nursing Officer
Web address: www.jfkmemorialhosp.com
Control: Corporation, Investor–owned (for–profit) **Service**: General medical and surgical

Staffed Beds: 145 Admissions: 6550 Census: 50 Outpatient Visits: 53425 Births: 2017 Total Expense ($000): 113548 Payroll Expense ($000): 50604 Personnel: 594

INGLEWOOD—Los Angeles County

✠ **CENTINELA HOSPITAL MEDICAL CENTER (050739)**, 555 East Hardy Street, Zip 90301–4011, Mailing Address: P.O. Box 720, Zip 90312–6720; tel. 310/673–4660, (Nonreporting) **A**1 10 **S** Prime Healthcare, Ontario, CA
Primary Contact: Linda Bradley, Chief Executive Officer
CFO: Paul Sennett, Chief Financial Officer
CMO: Paryus Patel, M.D., Chief Medical Officer
CIO: Martin Cordova, Director Information Services
CHR: George Akopyan, Director Human Resources
CNO: Mohammad Abdelnaser, Chief Nursing Officer
Web address: www.centinelamed.com
Control: Corporation, Investor–owned (for–profit) **Service**: General medical and surgical

Staffed Beds: 369

IRVINE—Orange County

⇑ **HOAG ORTHOPEDIC INSTITUTE (050769)**, 16250 Sand Canyon Avenue, Zip 92618–3714; tel. 949/517–3149, **A**3 21 **F**3 8 29 34 37 65 68 77 79 81 85 130 131 134 146 149 **P**2
Primary Contact: Carlos Prietto, President and Chief Executive Officer
CMO: Robert Gorab, M.D., Chief Medical Officer
Web address: www.orthopedichospital.com/
Control: Partnership, Investor–owned (for–profit) **Service**: Orthopedic

Staffed Beds: 70 Admissions: 4641 Census: 26 Outpatient Visits: 914 Births: 0 Total Expense ($000): 92737 Payroll Expense ($000): 24417 Personnel: 269

ORANGE COUNTY IRVINE MEDICAL CENTER See Kaiser Permanente Orange County Anaheim Medical Center, Anaheim

JACKSON—Amador County

✠ **SUTTER AMADOR HOSPITAL (050014)**, 200 Mission Boulevard, Zip 95642–2564; tel. 209/223–7500, **A**1 5 10 20 **F**29 34 35 40 46 47 49 54 59 64 65 70 75 76 77 78 79 81 84 85 87 93 102 107 108 110 111 115 119 129 130 132 146 148 149 **P**3 5 **S** Sutter Health, Sacramento, CA
Primary Contact: Anne Platt, Chief Executive Officer
CFO: Brett Moore, CPA, Assistant Administrator Finance
CMO: Ron Hood, M.D., Chief of Staff
CIO: Joy Bailey, Director Information Technology
CHR: Beverly Revels, Director Human Resources
CNO: Nikki Allen, Patient Care Executive
Web address: www.sutteramador.org
Control: Other not–for–profit (including NFP Corporation) **Service**: General medical and surgical

Staffed Beds: 52 Admissions: 2412 Census: 24 Outpatient Visits: 55513 Births: 292 Total Expense ($000): 80488 Payroll Expense ($000): 27983 Personnel: 310

JOSHUA TREE—San Bernardino County

✠ **HI-DESERT MEDICAL CENTER (050279)**, 6601 White Feather Road, Zip 92284; tel. 760/366–3711, (Total facility includes 120 beds in nursing home– type unit) **A**1 10 20 **F**3 8 13 15 18 29 30 34 40 45 50 54 62 63 64 68 70 75 76 77 79 81 82 85 87 92 93 104 107 108 110 111 115 119 128 130 135 146 148 149 **S** TENET Healthcare Corporation, Dallas, TX
Primary Contact: Karen Faulis, Chief Executive Officer
COO: David Cooke, R.N., Chief Operating Officer
CMO: Jeffrey Seip, M.D., Chief Medical Staff
CIO: Darrell Goodman, Chief Information Officer
CHR: Nicole Smith, Director Human Resources
CNO: David Cooke, R.N., Chief Operating Officer
Web address: www.hdmc.org
Control: Corporation, Investor–owned (for–profit) **Service**: General medical and surgical

Staffed Beds: 179 Admissions: 2488 Census: 108 Outpatient Visits: 62059 Births: 386 Total Expense ($000): 62077 Payroll Expense ($000): 26509 Personnel: 476

KENTFIELD—Marin County

✠ **KENTFIELD REHABILITATION AND SPECIALTY HOSPITAL (052043)**, 1125 Sir Francis Drake Boulevard, Zip 94904–1455; tel. 415/456–9680, (Nonreporting) **A**1 10 **S** Vibra Healthcare, Mechanicsburg, PA
Primary Contact: Lauren Suarez, Chief Executive Officer
CFO: Stephanie Lawrence, Chief Financial Officer
CMO: Curtis Roebken, M.D., Chief Medical Staff
CHR: Julene English, Director Human Resources
Web address: www.kentfieldrehab.com
Control: Corporation, Investor–owned (for–profit) **Service**: Acute long–term care hospital

Staffed Beds: 60

KING CITY—Monterey County

☐ **MEE MEMORIAL HOSPITAL (050189)**, 300 Canal Street, Zip 93930–3431; tel. 831/385–6000, (Nonreporting) **A**1 10 20
Primary Contact: Susan M. Childers, CPA, Chief Executive Officer
CFO: Gary L Wangsmo, Chief Financial Officer
CMO: Schindelheim Roy, M.D., Chief of Staff
CIO: Mike McNamara, Chief Information Officer
CHR: Karen Wong, Chief Human Resources Officer
Web address: www.meememorial.com
Control: Other not–for–profit (including NFP Corporation) **Service**: General medical and surgical

Staffed Beds: 119

LA JOLLA—San Diego County

✠ **SCRIPPS GREEN HOSPITAL (050424)**, 10666 North Torrey Pines Road, Zip 92037–1093; tel. 858/455–9100, **A**1 3 5 8 10 **F**3 8 11 12 14 15 17 18 20 22 24 26 29 30 31 34 35 36 37 44 45 46 47 49 50 51 54 57 58 59 61 64 68 70 74 75 77 78 79 80 81 82 84 85 86 87 93 107 108 110 111 115 118 119 120 121 123 124 126 130 131 132 136 138 139 141 142 146 148 **P**3 **S** Scripps Health, San Diego, CA
Primary Contact: Carl J. Etter, Chief Executive Officer
CFO: Richard Rothberger, Corporate Executive Vice President and Chief Financial Officer
CMO: James LaBelle, M.D., Chief Medical Officer
CIO: Andy Crowder, Chief Information Officer and Corporate Senior Vice President
CHR: Victor Buzachero, Corporate Senior Vice President for Innovation, Human Resources and Performance Management
Web address: www.scrippshealth.org
Control: Other not–for–profit (including NFP Corporation) **Service**: General medical and surgical

Staffed Beds: 173 Admissions: 8191 Census: 84 Outpatient Visits: 82097 Births: 0 Total Expense ($000): 279948 Payroll Expense ($000): 89640 Personnel: 1163

CA

☒ **SCRIPPS MEMORIAL HOSPITAL–LA JOLLA (050324)**, 9888 Genesee Avenue, Zip 92037–1200, Mailing Address: P.O. Box 28, Zip 92038–0028; tel. 858/626–4123, **A**1 3 5 10 **F**3 8 11 12 13 14 15 17 18 20 22 24 26 28 29 30 31 34 35 40 43 44 45 46 48 49 51 53 54 55 57 58 59 64 65 68 70 74 75 76 77 78 79 81 82 84 85 86 87 91 92 94 100 101 102 107 108 110 111 114 115 116 117 118 119 124 126 130 132 141 145 146 147 148 **S** Scripps Health, San Diego, CA
Primary Contact: Carl J. Etter, Chief Executive Officer
COO: Cindy Steckel, Ph.D., R.N., Vice President Chief Nurse and Operations Executive
CFO: Alan Mandal, Vice President Financial Operations
CMO: James LaBelle, M.D., Chief Medical Officer
CHR: Shelly Blazakis, Director Human Resources Services
CNO: Cindy Steckel, Ph.D., R.N., Vice President Chief Nurse and Operations Executive
Web address: www.scripps.org/locations/hospitals__scripps–memorial–hospital–la–jolla
Control: Other not–for–profit (including NFP Corporation) **Service**: General medical and surgical

Staffed Beds: 302 Admissions: 18084 Census: 228 Outpatient Visits: 99021 Births: 3276 Total Expense ($000): 569595 Payroll Expense ($000): 198015 Personnel: 2461

LA MESA—San Diego County

☐ **ALVARADO PARKWAY INSTITUTE BEHAVIORAL HEALTH SYSTEM (054075)**, 7050 Parkway Drive, Zip 91942–1535; tel. 619/465–4411, **A**1 10 **F**4 5 29 30 34 35 64 68 87 98 100 101 102 103 104 105 130 132 143 149 152 153
Primary Contact: Patrick C. Ziemer, Chief Executive Officer
CFO: Chad Engbrecht, Chief Financial Officer
CMO: R. Bradley Sanders, D.O., Executive Medical Director
CNO: Bonnie Asada, Chief Nursing Officer
Web address: www.apibhs.com
Control: Partnership, Investor–owned (for–profit) **Service**: Psychiatric

Staffed Beds: 66 Admissions: 2246 Census: 61 Outpatient Visits: 137141 Births: 0 Total Expense ($000): 26254 Payroll Expense ($000): 14203 Personnel: 329

☒ **SHARP GROSSMONT HOSPITAL (050026)**, 5555 Grossmont Center Drive, Zip 91942–3019, Mailing Address: PO Box 158, Zip 91944–0158; tel. 619/740–6000, (Total facility includes 6 beds in nursing home–type unit) **A**1 2 3 10 **F**3 8 11 13 15 17 18 20 22 24 26 28 29 30 31 34 35 43 45 46 47 48 49 50 51 54 55 56 57 58 59 61 62 63 64 65 66 68 70 72 73 74 75 76 77 78 79 80 81 82 83 84 85 86 87 90 91 92 93 94 96 98 100 101 102 104 107 108 109 110 111 114 115 116 117 118 119 120 121 123 124 126 128 129 130 132 135 141 143 145 146 147 148 149 154 **P**5 **S** Sharp HealthCare, San Diego, CA
Primary Contact: Scott Evans, PharmD, FACHE, Senior Vice President and Chief Executive Officer
COO: Maryann Cone, Chief Operating Officer
CFO: Kari Cornicelli, Chief Financial Officer
CMO: Michael Murphy, M.D., JD, Chief Medical Officer
CIO: Kenneth Lawonn, Senior Vice President and Chief Information Officer
CHR: George Holtz, Director Human Resources
Web address: www.sharp.com
Control: Other not–for–profit (including NFP Corporation) **Service**: General medical and surgical

Staffed Beds: 509 Admissions: 27193 Census: 357 Outpatient Visits: 383699 Births: 3473 Total Expense ($000): 668213 Payroll Expense ($000): 278414 Personnel: 2706

LA MIRADA—Los Angeles County

☒ **KINDRED HOSPITAL–LA MIRADA (052038)**, 14900 East Imperial Highway, Zip 90638–2172; tel. 562/944–1900, (Includes KINDRED HOSPITAL SAN GABRIEL VALLEY, 845 North Lark Ellen Avenue, West Covina, CA, Zip 91791–1069; tel. 626/339–5451; Julie Myers, Chief Executive Officer; KINDRED HOSPITAL SANTA ANA, 1901 North College Avenue, Santa Ana, CA, Zip 92706–2334; tel. 714/564–7800) (Nonreporting) **A**1 10 **S** Kindred Healthcare, Louisville, KY
Primary Contact: David Kowalski, Chief Executive Officer
CFO: Rishab Punjabi, Chief Financial Officer
CMO: Prakash Chandra Patel, M.D., Chief of Staff
CHR: Susan Bergquist, Human Resources Generalist
CNO: Esperanza Sanchez, Chief Clinical Officer
Web address: www.kindredlamirada.com/
Control: Corporation, Investor–owned (for–profit) **Service**: Acute long–term care hospital

Staffed Beds: 216

LA PALMA—Orange County

☒ **LA PALMA INTERCOMMUNITY HOSPITAL (050580)**, 7901 Walker Street, Zip 90623–1764; tel. 714/670–7400, (Nonreporting) **A**1 10 **S** Prime Healthcare, Ontario, CA
Primary Contact: Edward Mirzabegian, Chief Executive Officer
CFO: Alan H Smith, Chief Financial Officer
CMO: Sami Shoukair, M.D., Chief Medical Officer
CIO: Vic Mahan, Director Information Technology
CHR: Stephanie Sioson, Director Human Resources
CNO: Hilda Manzo–Luna, Chief Nursing Officer
Web address: www.lapalmaintercommunityhospital.com
Control: Other not–for–profit (including NFP Corporation) **Service**: General medical and surgical

Staffed Beds: 140

LAGUNA HILLS—Orange County

☒ **MEMORIALCARE, SADDLEBACK MEMORIAL MEDICAL CENTER (050603)**, 24451 Health Center Drive, Zip 92653–3689; tel. 949/837–4500, **A**1 10 **F**3 11 13 14 15 18 20 22 24 26 28 29 30 31 34 35 36 38 40 44 45 46 47 48 49 50 51 53 54 55 56 57 58 59 62 63 64 65 68 70 72 74 75 76 77 78 79 81 82 84 85 86 87 93 94 100 107 108 110 111 115 116 117 118 119 120 121 123 124 126 130 132 135 141 142 143 145 146 147 148 149 154 **S** MemorialCare, Fountain Valley, CA
Primary Contact: Marcia Manker, Chief Executive Officer
COO: Ryan Olsen, Chief Operating Officer
CFO: Aaron Coley, Chief Financial Officer, Orange County
CMO: Kathleen Sullivan, M.D., Chief of Staff
CIO: J Scott Joslyn, Senior Vice President and Chief Information Officer
CHR: Michelle Gutierrez, Executive Director Human Resources, Orange County
CNO: Brandi Cassingham, Chief Nursing Officer
Web address: www.memorialcare.org
Control: Other not–for–profit (including NFP Corporation) **Service**: General medical and surgical

Staffed Beds: 313 Admissions: 12880 Census: 128 Outpatient Visits: 193695 Births: 2634 Total Expense ($000): 293797 Payroll Expense ($000): 92737 Personnel: 1303

LAKE ARROWHEAD—San Bernardino County

☒ **SAN BERNARDINO MOUNTAINS COMMUNITY HOSPITAL DISTRICT (051312)**, 29101 Hospital Road, Zip 92352–9706, Mailing Address: P.O. Box 70, Zip 92352–0070; tel. 909/336–3651, (Nonreporting) **A**1 10 18
Primary Contact: Charles Harrison, Chief Executive Officer
COO: Terry Pena, Chief Operating Officer and Chief Nursing Officer
CFO: Yvonne Waggener, Chief Financial Officer
CMO: Walter M. Maier, Chief of Staff
CIO: Patrick Miller, Technology Coordinator
CHR: Julie Atwood, Director Human Resources
CNO: Terry Pena, Chief Operating Officer and Chief Nursing Officer
Web address: www.mchcares.com
Control: Hospital district or authority, Government, nonfederal **Service**: General medical and surgical

Staffed Beds: 37

LAKE ISABELLA—Kern County

KERN VALLEY HEALTHCARE DISTRICT (051314), 6412 Laurel Avenue, Zip 93240–9529, Mailing Address: P.O. Box 1628, Zip 93240–1628; tel. 760/379–2681, (Nonreporting) **A**10 18
Primary Contact: Timothy McGlew, Chief Executive Officer
CFO: Chester Beedle, Chief Financial Officer
CMO: Gary A Finstad, M.D., Chief of Staff
CIO: Paul Quinn, Information Systems Manager
CHR: Debra Hoffman, Human Resources Manager
CNO: Mark Gordon, Chief Nursing Officer
Web address: www.kvhd.org
Control: Hospital district or authority, Government, nonfederal **Service**: General medical and surgical

Staffed Beds: 99

CA

LAKEPORT—Lake County

✠ **SUTTER LAKESIDE HOSPITAL (051329)**, 5176 Hill Road East,
Zip 95453–6300; tel. 707/262–5000, **A**1 10 18 **F**3 8 11 13 15 18 29 30 34 35
36 40 41 43 45 46 51 53 54 56 57 59 61 64 65 66 68 70 74 75 76 77 79 81
82 85 86 87 91 93 96 97 107 108 110 111 114 115 118 119 127 130 131
133 135 146 147 148 149 154 **P**3 5 **S** Sutter Health, Sacramento, CA
Primary Contact: Dan Peterson, Chief Administrative Officer
CFO: Linnea Humble, Director of Finance
CMO: Diane Pege, M.D., Vice President Medical Affairs
CIO: Jack Buell, Director Information Services
CHR: Brenda DeRamus, Manager Human Resources
CNO: Teresa Campbell, R.N., Chief Nursing Executive
Web address: www.sutterlakeside.org
Control: Other not–for–profit (including NFP Corporation) **Service**: General
medical and surgical

Staffed Beds: 25 **Admissions**: 1858 **Census**: 18 **Outpatient Visits**: 61990
Births: 308 **Total Expense ($000)**: 86977 **Payroll Expense ($000)**: 26293
Personnel: 310

LAKEWOOD—Los Angeles County

✠ **LAKEWOOD REGIONAL MEDICAL CENTER (050581)**, 3700 East South
Street, Zip 90712–1498, Mailing Address: P.O. Box 6070, Zip 90712;
tel. 562/531–2550, **A**1 10 **F**3 11 15 17 18 20 22 24 26 29 30 34 35 38 40 45
49 50 51 57 59 64 68 70 74 75 77 79 81 85 87 93 107 108 109 111 115 118
119 120 126 130 132 143 146 148 149 154 **S** TENET Healthcare Corporation,
Dallas, TX
Primary Contact: John A. Grah, FACHE, Chief Executive Officer
COO: Robert Shappley, Chief Operating Officer
CFO: Eric Delgado, Chief Financial Officer
CIO: Pat Pierce, Director Information Systems
CHR: Mary Okuhara, Chief Human Resource Officer
CNO: Terri Newton, Chief Nursing Officer
Web address: www.lakewoodregional.com
Control: Corporation, Investor–owned (for–profit) **Service**: General medical and
surgical

Staffed Beds: 153 **Admissions**: 8697 **Census**: 111 **Outpatient
Visits**: 55893 **Births**: 0 **Total Expense ($000)**: 161575 **Payroll Expense
($000)**: 76278 **Personnel**: 773

LANCASTER—Los Angeles County

✠ **ANTELOPE VALLEY HOSPITAL (050056)**, 1600 West Avenue 'J',
Zip 93534–2894; tel. 661/949–5000, (Nonreporting) **A**1 2 3 5 10
Primary Contact: Michael L. Wall, FACHE, President and Chief Executive Officer
COO: Colette Menzel, Ph.D., Chief Operating Officer and Chief Financial Officer
CFO: Colette Menzel, Ph.D., Chief Operating Officer and Chief Financial Officer
CMO: Radha Krishnan, M.D., Chief Medical Officer
CIO: Dale Lepper, Chief Information Officer
CHR: George Leisher Jr Chief Human Resources Officer
CNO: Jack J Burke, MS, R.N., Chief Operating Officer and Chief Nursing Officer
Web address: www.avhospital.org
Control: Hospital district or authority, Government, nonfederal **Service**: General
medical and surgical

Staffed Beds: 368

LEMOORE—Kings County

★ **NAVAL HOSPITAL LEMOORE**, 937 Franklin Avenue, Zip 93246–0001;
tel. 559/998–4481, (Nonreporting) **S** Bureau of Medicine and Surgery, Department
of the Navy, Falls Church, VA
Primary Contact: Captain Kristen Attenbury, Commanding Officer
CFO: Thomas M Brui, Director Resource Management
CMO: Scott Cota, M.D., Director Medical Services
CIO: Victor Dela Torre, Command Legal Officer
CHR: Billy Newman, Department Head
Web address: www.med.navy.mil/sites/nhlem/Pages/index.aspx
Control: Navy, Government, federal **Service**: General medical and surgical

Staffed Beds: 16

LIVERMORE—Alameda County

VALLEY MEMORIAL See Stanford Health Care – Valleycare, Pleasanton

**VETERANS AFFAIRS PALO ALTO HEALTH CARE SYSTEM, LIVERMORE
DIVISION** See Va Palo Alto Health Care System, Palo Alto

LODI—San Joaquin County

✠ **ADVENTIST HEALTH LODI MEMORIAL (050336)**, 975 South Fairmont
Avenue, Zip 95240–5118, Mailing Address: P.O. Box 3004, Zip 95241–1908;
tel. 209/334–3411, (Includes LODI MEMORIAL HOSPITAL WEST, 800 South Lower
Sacramento Road, Lodi, CA, Zip 95242; tel. 209/333–0211) (Nonreporting) **A**1
10 **S** Adventist Health, Roseville, CA
Primary Contact: Daniel Wolcott, President and Chief Executive Officer
CFO: Terry Deak, Chief Financial Officer
CHR: Mark T Wallace, Director Human Resources
CNO: Debbie Moreno, R.N., Chief Nursing Officer
Web address: www.lodihealth.org
Control: Other not–for–profit (including NFP Corporation) **Service**: General
medical and surgical

Staffed Beds: 190

LOMA LINDA—San Bernardino County

LOMA LINDA UNIVERSITY CHILDREN'S HOSPITAL (050778), 11234
Anderson Street, Zip 92354–2804; tel. 909/558–8000, (Data for 181 days) **A**3
5 **F**3 11 13 19 21 23 25 27 29 31 34 39 44 50 54 55 57 58 59 60 61 64 65
66 68 71 72 74 75 76 77 78 79 80 81 82 84 85 86 87 88 89 97 119 130
132 134 135 136 137 138 141 146 147 149 154 **P**3 **S** Loma Linda University
Adventist Health Sciences Center, Loma Linda, CA
Primary Contact: Kerry Heinrich, JD, Chief Executive Officer
COO: Trevor Wright, Chief Operating Officer
CFO: Angela Lalas, Senior Vice President, Finance
CMO: Richard Chinnock, Chief Medical Officer, LLUCH
CIO: Mark Zirkelbach, Chief Information Officer
CHR: Lizette O Norton, Vice President, Human Resources
CNO: Helen Staples–Evans, Chief Nursing Officer, LLUCH
Web address: www.llu.edu/lluch
Control: Other not–for–profit (including NFP Corporation) **Service**: Children's
general medical and surgical

Staffed Beds: 337 **Admissions**: 6887 **Census**: 214 **Outpatient
Visits**: 33899 **Births**: 1401 **Total Expense ($000)**: 197197 **Payroll Expense
($000)**: 71575 **Personnel**: 1302

LOMA LINDA UNIVERSITY HEART & SURGICAL HOSPITAL See Loma Linda
University Medical Center, Loma Linda

✠ △ **LOMA LINDA UNIVERSITY MEDICAL CENTER (050327)**, 11234
Anderson Street, Zip 92354–2804, Mailing Address: P.O. Box 2000,
Zip 92354–0200; tel. 909/558–4000, (Includes LOMA LINDA UNIVERSITY EAST
CAMPUS HOSPITAL, 25333 Barton Road, Loma Linda, CA, Zip 92354–3053;
tel. 909/558–6000; LOMA LINDA UNIVERSITY HEART & SURGICAL HOSPITAL,
26780 Barton Road, Loma Linda, CA, Zip 92354; tel. 909/583–2900) (Data for
181 days) **A**1 2 3 5 7 8 10 **F**2 3 8 11 12 15 17 18 20 22 24 26 28 29 30 31 34
35 37 40 41 43 44 45 46 47 48 49 50 54 57 58 59 60 62 64 65 68 70 74 75
77 78 79 81 82 84 85 86 87 90 91 92 93 94 96 102 107 108 110 111 114
115 117 118 119 120 121 122 123 124 126 129 130 132 137 138 139 141
142 143 144 146 147 148 149 154 **P**3 **S** Loma Linda University Adventist Health
Sciences Center, Loma Linda, CA
Primary Contact: Kerry Heinrich, JD, Chief Executive Officer
COO: Trevor Wright, Chief Operating Officer
CFO: Steve Mohr, Senior Vice President Finance and Chief Financial Officer
CMO: H Roger Hadley, M.D., Vice President, Medical Affairs
CIO: Mark Zirkelbach, Chief Information Officer
CNO: Judith Storfjell, Ph.D., R.N., Senior Vice President and Chief Nursing Officer
Web address: www.llumc.edu
Control: Other not–for–profit (including NFP Corporation) **Service**: General
medical and surgical

Staffed Beds: 538 **Admissions**: 11001 **Census**: 358 **Outpatient
Visits**: 308810 **Births**: 0 **Total Expense ($000)**: 532785 **Payroll Expense
($000)**: 163302 **Personnel**: 4592

✠ △ **VETERANS AFFAIRS LOMA LINDA HEALTHCARE SYSTEM**, 11201
Benton Street, Zip 92357–1000; tel. 909/825–7084, (Nonreporting) **A**1 2 3 5 7 8
S Department of Veterans Affairs, Perry Point, MD
Primary Contact: Andrew Welch, Interim Director
COO: Shane Elliott, Associate Director Administration
CFO: Eric C Sorenson, Chief Financial Officer
CMO: Dwight Evans, M.D., Chief of Staff
CIO: Doug Wirthgen, Facility Chief Information Officer
CHR: Eugene Wylie, Chief Human Resources Officer
CNO: Anne Gillespie, R.N., Associate Director Patient Care and Nursing Services
Web address: www.lomalinda.va.gov
Control: Veterans Affairs, Government, federal **Service**: General medical and
surgical

Staffed Beds: 268

LOMPOC—Santa Barbara County

★ **LOMPOC VALLEY MEDICAL CENTER (050110)**, 1515 East Ocean Avenue, Zip 93436–7092, Mailing Address: P.O. Box 1058, Zip 93438–1058; tel. 805/737–3300, (Nonreporting) **A**10 22
Primary Contact: James J. Raggio, Chief Executive Officer
COO: Naishadh Buch, Chief Operating Officer
CFO: Robert M Baden, Chief Financial Officer
CMO: Randall Michel, M.D., Chief of Staff
CIO: Jim White, Chief Information Officer
CHR: Edwin R Braxton, Director Human Resources
CNO: Yvette Renee Cope, Chief Nurse Executive
Web address: www.lompocvmc.com
Control: Hospital district or authority, Government, nonfederal **Service**: General medical and surgical

Staffed Beds: 170

LONE PINE—Inyo County

SOUTHERN INYO HEALTHCARE DISTRICT (051302), 501 East Locust Street, Zip 93545–1009, Mailing Address: P.O. Box 1009, Zip 93545–1009; tel. 760/876–5501, (Nonreporting) **A**10 18
Primary Contact: Alan Germany, Chief Executive Officer and Chief Restructuring Officer
CFO: Marise Andrade, Controller
CIO: Phyllis Gregory, Registered Health Information Administrator
CHR: Nancy Erickson, Human Resource Director
CNO: Colleen Wilson, Chief Nursing Officer
Web address: www.sihd.org
Control: Hospital district or authority, Government, nonfederal **Service**: General medical and surgical

Staffed Beds: 4

LONG BEACH—Los Angeles County

⇑ **COLLEGE MEDICAL CENTER (050776)**, 2776 Pacific Avenue, Zip 90806–2613; tel. 562/595–1911, **A**3 10 12 13 21 **F**2 3 17 19 29 34 35 40 45 49 50 57 59 60 64 68 70 74 75 77 79 81 82 85 86 87 93 98 100 101 102 103 104 105 107 108 111 119 130 143 149 153 **P**1 5
Primary Contact: Joseph Avelino, Chief Executive Officer
COO: Jennifer Ensminger, Chief Operating Officer
CFO: Jim Canedo, Chief Financial Officer
CMO: Luke Watson, M.D., Chief of Staff
CIO: Rohan Corea, Director Healthcare Information Technology
CHR: Ann Mattia Schiller, Vice President Human Resources
Web address: www.collegemedicalcenter.com/
Control: Individual, Investor–owned (for–profit) **Service**: Psychiatric

Staffed Beds: 137 Admissions: 9166 Census: 167 Outpatient Visits: 76179 Births: 0 Total Expense ($000): 88787 Payroll Expense ($000): 41295 Personnel: 786

⊞ △ **MEMORIALCARE, LONG BEACH MEMORIAL MEDICAL CENTER (050485)**, 2801 Atlantic Avenue, Zip 90806–1701, Mailing Address: P.O. Box 1428, Zip 90801–1428; tel. 562/933–2000, **A**1 2 3 5 7 8 10 **F**3 8 9 11 12 14 15 17 18 20 22 24 26 28 29 31 34 35 36 37 38 39 40 43 44 45 47 48 49 50 52 53 55 56 57 58 59 61 63 64 65 68 70 74 75 77 78 79 81 82 84 85 86 87 90 93 96 97 107 108 110 111 114 115 116 117 118 119 120 121 123 124 126 128 129 130 131 132 135 141 142 143 144 146 147 148 149 150 154 **S** MemorialCare, Fountain Valley, CA
Primary Contact: John Bishop, Chief Executive Officer
COO: Ikenna Mmeje, Chief Operating Officer
CFO: Yair Katz, Chief Financial Officer
CMO: Susan Melvin, D.O., Chief Medical Officer
CIO: Danny Asaoka, Executive Director Information Systems
CHR: Marcie Atchison, Vice President Human Resources
CNO: Judith A Fix, R.N., MSN, Senior Vice President and Chief Nursing Officer
Web address: www.memorialcare.org/LongBeach
Control: Other not–for–profit (including NFP Corporation) **Service**: General medical and surgical

Staffed Beds: 458 Admissions: 20428 Census: 283 Outpatient Visits: 203211 Births: 0 Total Expense ($000): 580068 Payroll Expense ($000): 191198 Personnel: 2997

☐ **MEMORIALCARE, MILLER CHILDREN'S & WOMEN'S HOSPITAL LONG BEACH (053309)**, 2801 Atlantic Avenue, Zip 90806–1701; tel. 562/933–5437, **A**1 2 3 5 10 **F**3 11 12 13 14 15 19 21 23 25 27 29 30 31 32 34 35 36 37 38 40 41 43 44 45 47 48 49 50 52 53 54 55 57 58 59 61 64 65 66 68 72 74 75 76 77 78 79 81 82 84 85 86 87 88 89 93 96 97 99 100 101 102 104 107 108 111 114 115 116 117 118 119 120 121 123 124 126 129 130 132 134 135 141 142 143 144 146 147 148 149 154 **S** MemorialCare, Fountain Valley, CA
Primary Contact: John Bishop, Chief Executive Officer
COO: Tamra Kaplan, PharmD, Chief Operating Officer
CFO: Yair Katz, Chief Financial Officer
CMO: Graham Tse, M.D., Chief Medical Officer
CIO: Danny Asaoka, Executive Director Information Systems
CHR: Marcie Atchison, Vice President Human Resources
Web address: www.memorialcare.org
Control: Other not–for–profit (including NFP Corporation) **Service**: Children's general medical and surgical

Staffed Beds: 371 Admissions: 15603 Census: 198 Outpatient Visits: 105653 Births: 4212 Total Expense ($000): 402542 Payroll Expense ($000): 138570 Personnel: 1244

⊞ **ST. MARY MEDICAL CENTER (050191)**, 1050 Linden Avenue, Zip 90813–3321, Mailing Address: P.O. Box 887, Zip 90801–0887; tel. 562/491–9000, **A**1 3 5 10 **F**3 8 12 13 15 18 19 20 22 24 26 28 29 30 31 32 34 35 38 39 40 41 43 45 46 47 48 49 50 54 55 56 57 59 64 65 66 68 70 71 72 74 75 76 77 78 79 80 81 82 84 85 86 87 89 90 92 93 96 97 100 104 107 108 110 111 114 115 118 119 120 121 122 123 130 143 145 146 147 148 153 **P**5 **S** Dignity Health, San Francisco, CA
Primary Contact: Carolyn P. Caldwell, FACHE, President and Chief Executive Officer
COO: Bonnie Panlasigui, Chief Operating Officer
CFO: Leon Choiniere, Vice President, Chief Financial Officer
CIO: David Ung, Site Director
CHR: Denise Livingston, Director Human Resources
CNO: Nancy Valla, R.N., Chief Nursing Officer
Web address: www.stmarymedicalcenter.org
Control: Other not–for–profit (including NFP Corporation) **Service**: General medical and surgical

Staffed Beds: 302 Admissions: 11253 Census: 150 Outpatient Visits: 141309 Births: 2489 Total Expense ($000): 316352 Payroll Expense ($000): 120392 Personnel: 1111

⊞ △ **VA LONG BEACH HEALTHCARE SYSTEM**, 5901 East 7th Street, Zip 90822–5201; tel. 562/826–8000, **A**1 2 3 5 7 8 **F**1 3 5 8 9 12 14 15 17 18 20 22 25 28 29 30 31 34 35 36 38 39 40 44 45 46 47 48 49 50 51 52 53 54 56 57 58 59 60 61 63 64 65 67 68 70 71 74 75 77 78 79 80 81 82 84 85 86 87 90 91 92 93 94 97 98 100 101 102 103 104 107 108 110 111 114 115 116 117 118 119 120 121 123 124 126 127 128 129 130 131 132 133 135 143 145 146 147 148 150 151 153 154 **P**1 **S** Department of Veterans Affairs, Perry Point, MD
Primary Contact: Walt Dannenberg, Director
COO: Anthony DeFrancesco, Associate Director
CFO: Michael J Rupert, Chief Financial Officer
CMO: Sandor Szabo, M.D., Ph.D., M.P.H., Chief of Staff
CIO: Rodney Sagmit, Chief Information Management
CHR: Mary E McCartan, Manager Human Resources
Web address: www.longbeach.va.gov/
Control: Veterans Affairs, Government, federal **Service**: General medical and surgical

Staffed Beds: 358 Admissions: 8025 Census: 314 Outpatient Visits: 832569 Births: 0 Total Expense ($000): 562600 Payroll Expense ($000): 270000 Personnel: 2804

LOS ALAMITOS—Orange County

⊞ **LOS ALAMITOS MEDICAL CENTER (050551)**, 3751 Katella Avenue, Zip 90720–3164; tel. 562/598–1311, (Nonreporting) **A**1 10 13 **S** TENET Healthcare Corporation, Dallas, TX
Primary Contact: Kent G. Clayton, Chief Executive Officer
COO: Clay Farell, Chief Operation Officer
CFO: Dave Vickers, Chief Financial Officer
CMO: Nirav Patel, M.D., Chief of Staff
CIO: Sally Andrada, Chief Information Officer
CHR: Mark Fisher, Chief Human Resources Officer
CNO: Judy Chabot, Chief Nursing Officer
Web address: www.losalamitosmedctr.com
Control: Corporation, Investor–owned (for–profit) **Service**: General medical and surgical

Staffed Beds: 167

CA

Hospital, Medicare Provider Number, Address, Telephone, Approval, Facility, and Physician Codes, Health Care System

★ American Hospital Association (AHA) membership   ○ Healthcare Facilities Accreditation Program   ⇑ Center for Improvement in Healthcare Quality Accreditation
☐ The Joint Commission accreditation   ◇ DNV Healthcare Inc. accreditation   △ Commission on Accreditation of Rehabilitation Facilities (CARF) accreditation

LOS ANGELES—Los Angeles County

(Mailing Addresses—Canoga Park, Encino, Granada Hills, Harbor City, Hollywood, Mission Hills, North Hollywood, Northridge, Panorama City, San Pedro, Sepulveda, Sherman Oaks, Sun Valley, Sylmar, Tarzana, Van Nuys, West Hills, West Los Angeles, Woodland Hills)

☒ ⇑ **ADVENTIST HEALTH GLENDALE (050239)**, 8700 Beverly Blvd, NT–3138, Zip 90048, Mailing Address: 1509 Wilson Terrace, Glendale, Zip 91206–4098; tel. 818/409–8000, **A**1 2 3 5 10 21 **F**3 4 5 8 12 13 15 17 18 20 22 24 26 28 29 30 31 32 34 35 36 37 39 40 44 45 46 47 48 49 51 53 54 56 57 58 59 63 64 65 68 70 71 72 74 75 76 77 78 79 81 82 83 84 85 86 87 90 91 92 93 96 98 100 101 102 103 104 105 107 108 109 110 111 114 115 118 119 120 121 124 126 128 129 130 131 132 135 145 146 147 148 149 152 **P**3 **S** Adventist Health, Roseville, CA
Primary Contact: Alice H. Issai, President
COO: Warren Tetz, Senior Vice President and Chief Operating Officer
CFO: Kelly Turner, Senior Vice President Finance and Chief Financial Officer
CMO: Arby Nahapetian, M.D., Vice President Medical Affairs and Quality
CIO: Sharon Correa, Vice President and Chief Information Officer
CNO: Judy Blair, Senior Vice President Clinical Services and Chief Nursing Officer
Web address: www.glendaleadventist.com
Control: Church operated, Nongovernment, not–for–profit **Service**: General medical and surgical

Staffed Beds: 462 **Admissions**: 20986 **Census**: 267 **Outpatient Visits**: 276521 **Births**: 2128 **Total Expense ($000)**: 477377 **Payroll Expense ($000)**: 146412 **Personnel**: 2230

☒ **ADVENTIST HEALTH WHITE MEMORIAL (050103)**, 1720 Cesar Chavez Avenue, Zip 90033–2414; tel. 323/268–5000, (Total facility includes 27 beds in nursing home–type unit) **A**1 2 3 5 8 10 **F**3 11 13 15 17 18 19 20 22 24 26 27 28 29 30 31 34 35 40 41 45 46 47 48 49 50 51 53 57 58 59 64 68 70 72 74 75 76 78 79 81 82 84 85 86 87 88 89 90 91 92 93 96 98 102 103 107 108 109 110 111 114 115 116 117 118 119 120 121 123 126 128 130 131 132 146 147 148 149 154 **P**3 5 **S** Adventist Health, Roseville, CA
Primary Contact: John Raffoul, Chief Executive Officer
CIO: Ralf Weissenberger, Director Information Systems
CHR: Natasha Milatovich, Association Vice President Human Resources
CNO: Patricia Stone, R.N., MSN, Senior Vice President Operations and Chief Nursing Officer
Web address: www.whitememorial.com
Control: Church operated, Nongovernment, not–for–profit **Service**: General medical and surgical

Staffed Beds: 353 **Admissions**: 19381 **Census**: 238 **Outpatient Visits**: 73152 **Births**: 3751 **Total Expense ($000)**: 435707 **Payroll Expense ($000)**: 124551 **Personnel**: 1632

☒ **BARLOW RESPIRATORY HOSPITAL (052031)**, 2000 Stadium Way, Zip 90026–2696; tel. 213/250–4200, **A**1 10 **F**1 3 14 29 30 35 45 46 60 68 84 107 111 119 130 148
Primary Contact: Amit Mohan, President and Chief Executive Officer
CFO: Edward Engesser, Chief Financial Officer and Chief Information Officer
CMO: David Nelson, M.D., Medical Director
CIO: Edward Engesser, Chief Financial Officer and Chief Information Officer
CHR: Rashawn Woods, Vice President Human Resources
CNO: Gladys D'Souza, Chief Nursing Officer
Web address: www.barlow2000.org
Control: Other not–for–profit (including NFP Corporation) **Service**: Acute long–term care hospital

Staffed Beds: 105 **Admissions**: 1015 **Census**: 72 **Outpatient Visits**: 0 **Births**: 0 **Total Expense ($000)**: 58268 **Payroll Expense ($000)**: 26986 **Personnel**: 382

☒ **CALIFORNIA HOSPITAL MEDICAL CENTER (050149)**, 1401 South Grand Avenue, Zip 90015–3010; tel. 213/748–2411, (Total facility includes 31 beds in nursing home–type unit) **A**1 3 5 10 **F**13 17 18 20 22 24 26 29 30 31 32 34 35 40 41 43 45 49 50 51 57 58 59 60 64 68 70 72 74 75 76 77 78 79 81 83 85 87 89 97 107 108 110 111 114 119 130 132 133 134 135 136 146 147 148 149 154 **S** Dignity Health, San Francisco, CA
Primary Contact: Margaret R. Peterson, Ph.D., R.N., President
CFO: Rebecca Cheng, Chief Financial Officer
CMO: Joseph Nussbaum, M.D., Chief of Staff
CIO: David Ung, Director, Information Technology
CHR: Kristin Anderson, Director, Human Resources
CNO: Valarie McPherson, MSN, Chief Nursing Executive
Web address: www.chmcla.org
Control: Other not–for–profit (including NFP Corporation) **Service**: General medical and surgical

Staffed Beds: 318 **Admissions**: 17780 **Census**: 196 **Outpatient Visits**: 102751 **Births**: 3657 **Total Expense ($000)**: 416895 **Payroll Expense ($000)**: 152866 **Personnel**: 1672

★ **CALIFORNIA REHABILITATION INSTITUTE (053039)**, 2070 Century Park East, Zip 90067–1907; tel. 424/363–1000, (Nonreporting) **A**3 10 **S** Select Medical Corporation, Mechanicsburg, PA
Primary Contact: Scott T. Rotsted, Chief Executive Officer
Web address: www.californiarehabinstitute.com/
Control: Corporation, Investor–owned (for–profit) **Service**: Rehabilitation

Staffed Beds: 138

☒ △ **CEDARS–SINAI MEDICAL CENTER (050625)**, 8700 Beverly Boulevard, Zip 90048–1865; tel. 310/423–5000, **A**1 2 3 5 7 8 10 **F**3 5 6 8 9 11 12 13 14 15 17 18 19 20 21 22 23 24 25 26 27 28 29 30 31 32 33 34 35 36 37 38 39 40 41 43 44 45 46 47 48 49 50 51 52 53 54 55 56 57 58 59 60 61 64 65 66 68 69 70 71 72 74 75 76 77 78 79 81 82 83 84 85 86 87 88 89 91 92 93 96 97 100 102 107 108 109 110 111 112 113 114 115 116 117 118 119 120 121 123 124 126 130 131 132 133 134 135 136 137 138 139 140 141 142 144 145 146 147 148 149 150 154 **P**3 5 6 **S** Cedars–Sinai Health System, West Hollywood, CA
Primary Contact: Thomas M. Priselac, President and Chief Executive Officer
COO: Jeffrey A. Smith, M.D., Executive Vice President Hospital Operations and Chief Operating Officer
CFO: Edward M Prunchunas, Executive Vice President and Chief Financial Officer
CMO: Michael L Langberg, M.D., Senior Vice President Medical Affairs and Chief Medical Officer
CIO: Darren Dworkin, Senior Vice President Enterprise Information Systems and Chief Information Officer
CHR: Andrew Ortiz, Senior Vice President, Human Resources and Organization Development
CNO: Linda Burnes Bolton, Dr.PH, R.N., Vice President and Chief Nurse Executive
Web address: www.cedars–sinai.edu
Control: Other not–for–profit (including NFP Corporation) **Service**: General medical and surgical

Staffed Beds: 885 **Admissions**: 50082 **Census**: 714 **Outpatient Visits**: 857567 **Births**: 6603 **Total Expense ($000)**: 2979597 **Payroll Expense ($000)**: 1133469 **Personnel**: 13488

☒ **CHILDREN'S HOSPITAL LOS ANGELES (053302)**, 4650 West Sunset Boulevard, Zip 90027–6062, Mailing Address: 4650 West Sunset Boulevard, MS #1, Zip 90027–6062; tel. 323/660–2450, **A**1 3 5 8 10 **F**3 5 7 8 9 11 12 14 17 19 21 23 25 27 29 30 31 32 34 35 36 39 40 41 43 44 45 46 49 50 51 55 56 58 60 61 64 65 68 71 72 74 75 77 78 79 81 82 84 85 86 87 88 89 90 92 93 95 96 97 100 107 108 111 115 116 117 118 119 120 121 123 124 126 129 130 131 132 134 135 136 137 138 139 141 146 148 149 154
Primary Contact: Paul S. Viviano, President and Chief Executive Officer
CFO: Lannie Tonnu, Senior Vice President and Chief Financial Officer
CMO: Brent Polk, M.D., Chair Department of Pediatrics and Vice President Academic Affairs
CIO: TJ Malseed, Vice President and Chief Information Officer
CHR: Myra Gregorian, Vice President and Chief Human Resources Officer
CNO: Mary Dee Hacker, R.N., Vice President, Patient Care Services and Chief Nursing Officer
Web address: www.chla.org
Control: Other not–for–profit (including NFP Corporation) **Service**: Children's general medical and surgical

Staffed Beds: 374 **Admissions**: 16917 **Census**: 296 **Outpatient Visits**: 377733 **Births**: 0 **Total Expense ($000)**: 1046243 **Payroll Expense ($000)**: 387586 **Personnel**: 5222

☐ **EAST LOS ANGELES DOCTORS HOSPITAL (050641)**, 4060 Whittier Boulevard, Zip 90023–2526; tel. 323/268–5514, (Nonreporting) **A**1 10 **S** Avanti Hospitals, El Segundo, CA
Primary Contact: Gerald B. Clute, Chief Executive Officer
CFO: Steven Blake, Corporate Chief Financial Officer
CMO: Janine King, M.D., Chief of Staff
CIO: Jason Cervantes, Chief Information Officer
CHR: Paul Celuch, Chief Human Resource Officer
CNO: Kimberly Frazier, R.N., Chief Nursing Officer
Web address: www.avantihospitals.com
Control: Corporation, Investor–owned (for–profit) **Service**: General medical and surgical

Staffed Beds: 127

☒ **ENCINO HOSPITAL MEDICAL CENTER (050158)**, 16237 Ventura Boulevard, Zip 91436–2272; tel. 818/995–5000, (Nonreporting) **A**1 10 **S** Prime Healthcare, Ontario, CA
Primary Contact: Bockhi Park, Chief Executive Officer
CFO: Kanner Tillman, Chief Financial Officer
CMO: Muhammad Anwar, M.D., Chief Medical Officer
CIO: Edward Barrera, Director Communications
CHR: Barbara Back, Manager Human Resources
CNO: Vilma L Dinham, R.N., Chief Nursing Officer
Web address: www.encinomed.com
Control: Other not–for–profit (including NFP Corporation) **Service**: General medical and surgical

Staffed Beds: 80

○ **GATEWAYS HOSPITAL AND MENTAL HEALTH CENTER (054028)**, 1891 Effie Street, Zip 90026–1793; tel. 323/644–2000, (Nonreporting) **A**10 11
Primary Contact: Philip Wong, PsyD, Chief Executive Officer
COO: Philip Wong, PsyD, Chief Operating Officer
CMO: Imani Walker, M.D., Medical Director
CIO: Rozelle DeVera, Director of Information Systems
CHR: Vahan Demlakian, Director of Human Resources
Web address: www.gatewayshospital.org
Control: Other not–for–profit (including NFP Corporation) **Service:** Psychiatric

Staffed Beds: 55

□ ⇑ **GOOD SAMARITAN HOSPITAL (050471)**, 1225 Wilshire Boulevard, Zip 90017–2395; tel. 213/977–2121, **A**1 2 3 5 10 21 **F**3 7 8 11 13 14 15 17 18 20 22 24 26 28 29 30 31 34 35 37 40 43 45 46 47 48 49 50 51 53 57 58 59 60 64 65 68 70 72 74 75 76 77 78 79 81 84 85 86 87 93 107 108 110 111 114 115 117 118 119 120 121 123 124 126 129 130 132 145 146 148 149 **P**5
Primary Contact: Andrew B. Leeka, President and Chief Executive Officer
COO: Phillip Wolfe, Vice President of Professional Operations
CFO: Alan Ino, Chief Financial Officer
CMO: Margaret Bates, Chief of Staff
CIO: Dean Campbell, Vice President Information Services and Chief Information Officer
CHR: Lexie Schuster, Vice President Human Resources
CNO: Margaret Pfeiffer, R.N., MSN, Vice President Patient Care Services
Web address: www.goodsam.org
Control: Other not–for–profit (including NFP Corporation) **Service:** General medical and surgical

Staffed Beds: 374 **Admissions:** 11778 **Census:** 154 **Outpatient Visits:** 76273 **Births:** 2669 **Total Expense ($000):** 308149 **Payroll Expense ($000):** 151826 **Personnel:** 1158

⊠ **HOLLYWOOD PRESBYTERIAN MEDICAL CENTER (050063)**, 1300 North Vermont Avenue, Zip 90027–6306; tel. 213/413–3000, **A**1 3 5 10 **F**3 8 13 15 17 18 20 22 24 26 29 30 31 34 40 41 45 46 49 50 51 56 57 59 60 61 64 68 70 72 74 75 76 77 78 79 80 81 85 87 89 90 92 96 97 107 108 110 111 115 119 130 146 147 148 149 154 **P**5
Primary Contact: Robert Allen, President and Chief Executive Officer
COO: Wontae Cha, Chief Operating Officer
CFO: John Keefe, Chief Financial Officer
CIO: Steve Giles, Chief Information Officer
CHR: George Leisher Jr Vice President Human Resources
CNO: Farideh Ara, Interim Chief Nursing Officer
Web address: www.hollywoodpresbyterian.com
Control: Partnership, Investor–owned (for–profit) **Service:** General medical and surgical

Staffed Beds: 434 **Admissions:** 13071 **Census:** 238 **Outpatient Visits:** 51856 **Births:** 3714 **Total Expense ($000):** 249716 **Payroll Expense ($000):** 121455 **Personnel:** 1231

KAISER FOUNDATION MENTAL HEALTH CENTER See Kaiser Permanente Los Angeles Medical Center, Los Angeles

⊠ **KAISER PERMANENTE LOS ANGELES MEDICAL CENTER (050138)**, 4867 Sunset Boulevard, Zip 90027–5961; tel. 323/783–4011, (Includes KAISER FOUNDATION MENTAL HEALTH CENTER, 765 West College Street, Los Angeles, CA, Zip 90012; tel. 213/580–7200) **A**1 3 5 10 **F**3 8 13 15 17 18 19 20 21 22 23 24 26 29 30 31 34 35 36 38 40 44 45 46 47 49 50 51 54 55 56 57 58 59 60 61 62 63 64 65 66 68 70 72 74 75 76 77 78 79 81 82 83 84 85 86 87 88 89 92 93 97 98 99 101 102 103 104 105 107 108 109 110 111 113 114 115 118 119 120 121 122 123 124 126 129 130 131 132 135 144 146 147 148 149 150 154 **P**6 **S** Kaiser Foundation Hospitals, Oakland, CA
Primary Contact: William N. Grice, Executive Director
COO: Derek Berz, Chief Operating Officer
CFO: Brad Malsed, Area Chief Financial Officer
CMO: Michael Tome, M.D., Medical Director
CIO: David Strickland, Area Information Officer
CHR: Paul J Martin, Director Human Resources
Web address: www.kaiserpermanente.org
Control: Other not–for–profit (including NFP Corporation) **Service:** General medical and surgical

Staffed Beds: 528 **Admissions:** 27065 **Census:** 377 **Outpatient Visits:** 111663 **Births:** 2684 **Personnel:** 6315

⊠ **KAISER PERMANENTE PANORAMA CITY MEDICAL CENTER (050137)**, 13652 Cantara Street, Zip 91402–5497; tel. 818/375–2000, **A**1 3 5 10 **F**3 8 11 13 15 18 29 30 31 32 34 35 38 40 41 44 45 49 50 51 53 54 55 56 57 58 59 60 61 62 63 64 65 66 68 70 71 72 74 75 76 77 78 79 81 82 84 85 86 87 93 94 97 100 101 102 104 107 108 111 114 116 117 118 119 126 129 130 131 132 134 135 141 143 144 146 147 148 149 154 **P**6 **S** Kaiser Foundation Hospitals, Oakland, CA
Primary Contact: Payman Roshan, Senior Vice President and Area Manager
COO: Murtaza Sanwari, Chief Operating Officer
CFO: Karla Valle, Area Chief Financial Officer
CMO: James Lau, M.D., Area Medical Director
CIO: Earle Johnson, Area Information Officer
CHR: Carole L Erken, Human Resources Leader
CNO: Celeste Farugia, R.N., MSN, Chief Nurse Executive
Web address: www.kaiserpermanente.org
Control: Other not–for–profit (including NFP Corporation) **Service:** General medical and surgical

Staffed Beds: 115 **Admissions:** 8768 **Census:** 82 **Outpatient Visits:** 80034 **Births:** 2410

⊠ **KAISER PERMANENTE SOUTH BAY MEDICAL CENTER (050411)**, 25825 Vermont Avenue, Zip 90710–3599; tel. 310/325–5111, **A**1 3 10 **F**2 3 5 6 9 11 12 13 15 17 28 29 30 31 32 34 35 36 38 39 40 44 45 46 47 48 49 50 51 53 54 55 56 57 58 59 60 61 64 65 66 68 70 72 74 75 76 77 78 79 80 81 82 84 85 86 87 91 92 93 94 96 97 100 107 108 110 111 114 115 116 117 118 119 130 131 132 134 135 144 146 147 148 149 150 154 **P**6 **S** Kaiser Foundation Hospitals, Oakland, CA
Primary Contact: Lesley A. Wille, Executive Director
Web address: www.kaiserpermanente.org
Control: Other not–for–profit (including NFP Corporation) **Service:** General medical and surgical

Staffed Beds: 172 **Admissions:** 10236 **Census:** 98 **Outpatient Visits:** 75002 **Births:** 2530 **Personnel:** 2483

⊠ **KAISER PERMANENTE WEST LOS ANGELES MEDICAL CENTER (050561)**, 6041 Cadillac Avenue, Zip 90034–1700; tel. 323/857–2201, **A**1 3 5 10 **F**3 12 13 15 29 30 31 32 34 35 37 40 45 46 47 48 49 50 55 56 57 58 59 60 61 64 65 68 70 72 73 74 75 76 78 79 80 81 82 84 85 87 100 107 108 110 111 114 115 116 117 119 126 130 132 135 146 147 148 149 154 **P**6 **S** Kaiser Foundation Hospitals, Oakland, CA
Primary Contact: Georgina R. Garcia, R.N., Executive Director
CMO: Fred Alexander, M.D., Medical Director
CIO: Gregory M Sincock, Information Technology Leader
Web address: www.kaiserpermanente.org
Control: Other not–for–profit (including NFP Corporation) **Service:** General medical and surgical

Staffed Beds: 118 **Admissions:** 15337 **Census:** 216 **Outpatient Visits:** 83423 **Births:** 1842 **Personnel:** 1371

⊠ **KAISER PERMANENTE WOODLAND HILLS MEDICAL CENTER (050677)**, 5601 DeSoto Avenue, Zip 91367–6798; tel. 818/719–2000, **A**1 3 5 10 **F**3 6 8 13 15 18 29 30 31 34 35 38 40 41 44 45 46 48 49 50 51 53 54 55 56 57 58 59 60 61 64 65 68 70 73 74 75 76 77 78 79 80 81 82 84 85 86 87 89 92 93 97 100 101 102 104 107 108 110 111 114 115 117 119 124 130 132 141 144 146 147 148 149 150 154 **P**6 **S** Kaiser Foundation Hospitals, Oakland, CA
Primary Contact: Dennis C. Benton, Senior Vice President and Area Manager
COO: Richard Trogman, FACHE, Chief Operating Officer
CFO: Marilou Cheung, Assistant Administrator Finance
CMO: Gregory Kelman, M.D., Area Medical Director
CIO: Earle Johnson, Area Information Officer
CHR: Cathy Cousineau, Director Human Resources
CNO: Nancy Tankel, R.N., Chief Nurse Executive
Web address: www.kaiserpermanente.org
Control: Other not–for–profit (including NFP Corporation) **Service:** General medical and surgical

Staffed Beds: 138 **Admissions:** 9011 **Census:** 88 **Outpatient Visits:** 92929 **Births:** 1952 **Personnel:** 1091

CA

✠ **KECK HOSPITAL OF USC (050696)**, 1500 San Pablo Street, Zip 90033–5313; tel. 323/442–8500, **A**1 3 5 8 10 **F**3 6 8 9 11 12 14 15 17 18 20 22 24 26 29 30 31 34 35 36 37 38 39 43 44 45 46 47 48 49 50 51 52 53 54 55 56 57 58 59 60 61 64 65 68 70 71 74 75 77 78 79 81 82 84 85 86 87 90 92 93 94 95 96 97 100 101 104 107 108 109 110 111 112 113 114 115 116 117 118 119 120 121 123 124 126 129 130 131 132 135 137 138 139 140 141 142 143 145 146 147 148 149 150 154 **P**6 **S** Keck Medicine of USC, Los Angeles, CA
Primary Contact: Rodney B. Hanners, Chief Executive Officer
CMO: Stephanie Hall, M.D., Chief Medical Officer
CIO: Timothy James Malseed, Chief Information Officer
CHR: Matthew McElrath, Chief Human Resources Officer
CNO: Annette Sy, Chief Nursing Officer
Web address: www.keckhospitalofusc.org
Control: Other not–for–profit (including NFP Corporation) **Service**: General medical and surgical

Staffed Beds: 401 Admissions: 12303 Census: 226 Outpatient Visits: 315875 Births: 0 Total Expense ($000): 927036 Payroll Expense ($000): 318359 Personnel: 2900

KEDREN COMMUNITY MENTAL HEALTH CENTER (054083), 4211 South Avalon Boulevard, Zip 90011–5699; tel. 323/233–0425, (Nonreporting) **A**10
Primary Contact: John H. Griffith, Ph.D., President and Chief Executive Officer
COO: Madeline Valencerina, Chief Operating Officer
CFO: Rizwan A. Uraizee, Chief Financial Officer
CMO: Frank L. Williams, Executive Vice President/ Medical Director
CNO: Essie Adams, Director of Nursing
Web address: www.kedrenmentalhealth.com
Control: Other not–for–profit (including NFP Corporation) **Service**: Psychiatric

Staffed Beds: 72

✠ **KINDRED HOSPITAL–LOS ANGELES (052032)**, 5525 West Slauson Avenue, Zip 90056–1067; tel. 310/642–0325, (Nonreporting) **A**1 10 **S** Kindred Healthcare, Louisville, KY
Primary Contact: Phillip R. Wolfe, Chief Executive Officer
CFO: Charles Natcher, Chief Financial Officer
Web address: www.kindredhospitalla.com/
Control: Corporation, Investor–owned (for–profit) **Service**: Acute long–term care hospital

Staffed Beds: 81

☐ **LAC–OLIVE VIEW–UCLA MEDICAL CENTER (050040)**, 14445 Olive View Drive, Zip 91342–1438; tel. 818/364–1555, **A**1 3 5 10 **F**3 13 15 18 19 20 22 24 26 29 30 31 34 40 41 44 45 46 48 49 50 51 58 59 60 61 62 63 64 65 66 68 70 72 74 75 76 78 79 80 81 82 84 85 87 89 93 94 97 98 100 102 104 107 108 110 111 114 115 116 117 118 119 129 130 143 144 146 147 148 149 **S** Los Angeles County–Department of Health Services, Los Angeles, CA
Primary Contact: Carolyn F. Rhee, Chief Executive Officer
COO: Niloo Shahi, Chief Operating Officer
CFO: Anthony Gray, Chief Financial Officer
CMO: Shannon Thyne, Chief Medical Officer
CIO: Susan Aintablian, Chief Information Officer
CHR: Thomas Beggane, Manager Human Resources
CNO: Dellone Pascascio, Chief Nursing Officer
Web address: www.ladhs.org
Control: County, Government, nonfederal **Service**: General medical and surgical

Staffed Beds: 198 Admissions: 11287 Census: 186 Outpatient Visits: 245836 Births: 631 Total Expense ($000): 536593 Payroll Expense ($000): 220968 Personnel: 2562

☐ **LAC+USC MEDICAL CENTER (050373)**, 2051 Marengo Street, Zip 90033–1352; tel. 323/409–1000, (Includes GENERAL HOSPITAL, 1200 North State Street, Los Angeles, CA, Zip 90033; tel. 213/580–7200; WOMEN'S AND CHILDREN'S HOSPITAL, 1240 North Mission Road, Los Angeles, CA, Zip 90033; tel. 213/580–7200) **A**1 2 3 5 10 **F**3 12 13 15 16 17 18 19 20 21 22 23 24 25 26 29 30 31 32 34 35 38 39 40 41 43 45 46 47 48 49 50 51 52 54 55 56 57 58 59 60 61 64 65 66 68 70 71 72 74 75 76 77 78 79 81 82 84 85 86 87 88 89 92 93 94 97 98 99 100 101 102 104 107 108 110 111 114 115 116 117 119 120 121 126 129 130 131 132 135 141 144 146 147 148 149 150 153 154 **P**6 **S** Los Angeles County–Department of Health Services, Los Angeles, CA
Primary Contact: Dan A. Castillo, FACHE, Chief Executive Officer
COO: Henry Ornelas, Chief Operating Officer
CFO: Mark Corbet, Interim Chief Financial Officer
CMO: Brad Spellberg, M.D., Chief Medical Officer
CIO: Oscar Autelli, Chief Information Officer
CHR: Elizabeth Jacobi, Human Resources Director
CNO: Isabel Milan, R.N., Chief Nursing Officer
Web address: www.lacusc.org
Control: County, Government, nonfederal **Service**: General medical and surgical

Staffed Beds: 538 Admissions: 29135 Census: 539 Outpatient Visits: 641661 Births: 1016 Total Expense ($000): 1387746 Payroll Expense ($000): 546738 Personnel: 7887

☐ **LOS ANGELES COMMUNITY HOSPITAL AT LOS ANGELES (050663)**, 4081 East Olympic Boulevard, Zip 90023–3330; tel. 323/267–0477, (Includes LOS ANGELES COMMUNITY HOSPITAL OF NORWALK, 13222 Bloomfield Avenue, Norwalk, CA, Zip 90650; tel. 562/863–4763) (Nonreporting) **A**1 10 **S** Prospect Medical Holdings, Los Angeles, CA
Primary Contact: Omar Ramirez, Chief Executive Officer
CFO: Johnnette Chong, Chief Financial Officer
Web address: www.altacorp.com/altacorp/our–hospitals/lach–menu.html
Control: Corporation, Investor–owned (for–profit) **Service**: General medical and surgical

Staffed Beds: 180

LOS ANGELES COUNTY CENTRAL JAIL HOSPITAL, 441 Bauchet Street, Zip 90012–2906; tel. 213/473–6100, (Nonreporting)
Primary Contact: Tom Flaherty, Assistant Administrator
Control: County, Government, nonfederal **Service**: Hospital unit of an institution (prison hospital, college infirmary, etc.)

Staffed Beds: 190

LOS ANGELES MEDICAL CENTER See Kaiser Permanente Los Angeles Medical Center

MARTIN LUTHER KING, JR. COMMUNITY HOSPITAL (050779), 1680 East 120th Street, Zip 90059–3026; tel. 424/338–8000, (Nonreporting)
Primary Contact: Elaine Batchlor, M.D., M.P.H., Chief Executive Officer
COO: Myrna Allen, R.N., MS, Chief Operating and Nursing Officer
CMO: John Fisher, M.D., Chief Medical Officer
CIO: Sajid Ahmed, Chief Information and Innovation Officer
CHR: Susan M Burrows, Vice President Human Resources
CNO: Myrna Allen, R.N., MS, Chief Operating and Nursing Officer
Web address: www.mlkcommunityhospital.org/
Control: Other not–for–profit (including NFP Corporation) **Service**: General medical and surgical

Staffed Beds: 46

☐ **MIRACLE MILE MEDICAL CENTER (050751)**, 6000 San Vicente Boulevard, Zip 90036–4404; tel. 323/930–1040, (Nonreporting) **A**1 10
Primary Contact: Gil Tepper, M.D., Chief Executive Officer
COO: Liz Cheever, Administrator
CFO: Bert Roberts, Controller
CMO: Gil Tepper, M.D., Chief of Staff
CIO: Jonathan Lindell, Director Information Technology
CHR: Liz Cheever, Administrator
CNO: Melody Bradley, Chief Nursing Officer
Web address: www.miraclemilemedicalcenter.com
Control: Individual, Investor–owned (for–profit) **Service**: General medical and surgical

Staffed Beds: 17

☐ **MISSION COMMUNITY HOSPITAL (050704)**, 14850 Roscoe Boulevard, Zip 91402–4677; tel. 818/787–2222, (Nonreporting) **A**1 5 10
Primary Contact: James Theiring, Chief Executive Officer
CMO: Glenn Marshak, M.D., Chief of Staff
CIO: Eric Rivers, Chief Information Officer
CHR: Carolyn Fish, Director Human Resources
CNO: Gwendolyn Dianne Wagner, R.N., MSN, Chief Nursing Officer
Web address: www.mchonline.org
Control: Other not–for–profit (including NFP Corporation) **Service**: General medical and surgical

Staffed Beds: 145

MOTION PICTURE AND TELEVISION FUND HOSPITAL AND RESIDENTIAL SERVICES (050552), 23388 Mulholland Drive, Zip 91364–2792; tel. 818/876–1888, (Nonreporting) **A**10
Primary Contact: Bob Beitcher, Chief Executive Officer
COO: David Asplund, Chief Operating Officer
CFO: Frank Guarrera, Executive Vice President and Chief Financial Officer
CHR: Nancy Rubin, Vice President Human Resources
Web address: www.mptvfund.org
Control: Other not–for–profit (including NFP Corporation) **Service**: General medical and surgical

Staffed Beds: 20

Many Facility Codes have changed. Please refer to the AHA Guide Code Chart. © 2018 AHA Guide

CA

☒ △ **NORTHRIDGE HOSPITAL MEDICAL CENTER (050116)**, 18300 Roscoe Boulevard, Zip 91328–4167; tel. 818/885–8500, **A**1 2 3 5 7 10 **F**1 2 3 5 8 11 13 14 15 17 18 20 22 24 26 28 29 30 31 34 35 38 40 41 43 48 49 56 57 58 59 60 61 64 68 70 72 73 74 75 76 77 78 79 81 82 84 85 86 87 88 89 90 93 97 98 100 101 102 103 104 105 106 107 108 110 111 114 117 118 119 121 124 126 129 130 132 134 146 147 148 152 153 **S** Dignity Health, San Francisco, CA
Primary Contact: Saliba Salo, President
CFO: Michael Taylor, Vice President Finance
CHR: Susan Paulsen, Director Human Resources
CNO: Mary Jane Jones, R.N., MSN, Vice President Nursing Operations
Web address: www.northridgehospital.org
Control: Other not–for–profit (including NFP Corporation) **Service**: General medical and surgical

Staffed Beds: 371 **Admissions:** 13907 **Census:** 177 **Outpatient Visits:** 68933 **Births:** 954 **Total Expense ($000):** 415499 **Payroll Expense ($000):** 153429 **Personnel:** 1671

⇑ **OLYMPIA MEDICAL CENTER (050742)**, 5900 West Olympic Boulevard, Zip 90036–4671; tel. 310/657–5900, (Nonreporting) **A**3 10 21 **S** Alecto Healthcare, Irvine, CA
Primary Contact: Matthew Williams, R.N., Chief Executive Officer
CFO: Matthew Williams, R.N., Chief Financial Officer
CMO: Panch Jeyakumar, M.D., Chief of Staff
CIO: Jason Williams, Director Information Systems
CHR: Joseph Ambrosini, Director Human Resources
CNO: Sylvia A Ventura, R.N., MS, Chief Nursing Officer
Web address: www.olympiamc.com
Control: Partnership, Investor–owned (for–profit) **Service**: General medical and surgical

Staffed Beds: 204

☐ **PACIFICA HOSPITAL OF THE VALLEY (050378)**, 9449 San Fernando Road, Zip 91352–1489; tel. 818/767–3310, (Nonreporting) **A**1 10 **S** Southwest Healthcare System, Scottsdale, AZ
Primary Contact: Ayman Mousa, R.N., Ph.D., Chief Executive Officer
COO: Daniel Santos, Director Ancillary Services
CFO: Eileen Fisler, Chief Financial Officer
CMO: Joseph Eipe, M.D., Chief Medical Officer
CIO: Mubashir Hashmi, Chief Information Officer
CHR: Patti Alonzo, Manager Human Resources
CNO: Janet B. Latto, Chief Nursing Officer and Disaster Officer
Web address: www.pacificahospital.com
Control: Corporation, Investor–owned (for–profit) **Service**: General medical and surgical

Staffed Beds: 231

PANORAMA CITY MEDICAL CENTER See Kaiser Permanente Panorama City Medical Center

☐ **PROMISE HOSPITAL OF EAST LOS ANGELES (052046)**, 443 South Soto Street, Zip 90033–4398; tel. 323/261–1181, (Includes PROMISE HOSPITAL OF EAST LOS ANGELES, SUBURBAN MEDICAL CENTER CAMPUS, 16453 South Colorado Avenue, Paramount, CA, Zip 90723–5011; tel. 562/531–3110; Michael D Kerr, Chief Executive Officer) **A**1 10 **F**3 29 35 45 48 49 56 57 59 65 68 70 74 75 77 78 79 81 82 84 85 86 87 100 101 107 108 119 130 148 149 154 **S** Promise Healthcare, Boca Raton, FL
Primary Contact: Michael D. Kerr, Chief Executive Officer
Web address: www.promiseeastla.com
Control: Corporation, Investor–owned (for–profit) **Service**: Acute long–term care hospital

Staffed Beds: 177 **Admissions:** 1050 **Census:** 105 **Outpatient Visits:** 315 **Births:** 0 **Total Expense ($000):** 72546 **Payroll Expense ($000):** 38697 **Personnel:** 591

☒ △ **PROVIDENCE LITTLE COMPANY OF MARY MEDICAL CENTER SAN PEDRO (050078)**, 1300 West Seventh Street, Zip 90732–3505; tel. 310/832–3311, (Total facility includes 125 beds in nursing home–type unit) **A**1 7 10 **F**2 3 4 5 11 13 14 15 18 29 30 32 34 35 40 41 44 45 49 50 51 56 57 59 60 63 64 65 66 68 70 71 74 75 76 77 78 79 81 82 84 85 86 87 90 92 93 94 95 96 98 100 101 102 103 104 107 108 110 111 114 119 120 123 128 130 131 132 135 145 146 147 149 150 153 154 **S** Providence St. Joseph Health, Renton, WA
Primary Contact: Garry M. Olney, Chief Executive Officer
CFO: Elizabeth Zuanich, Chief Financial Officer
CMO: Richard Glimp, M.D., Chief Medical Officer
CIO: Kim Brant–Lucich, Director, Information Systems
CHR: Melissa Baker, Director, Human Resources
Web address: www.https://california.providence.org/san-pedro
Control: Church operated, Nongovernment, not–for–profit **Service**: General medical and surgical

Staffed Beds: 318 **Admissions:** 6838 **Census:** 201 **Outpatient Visits:** 50703 **Births:** 512 **Total Expense ($000):** 123999 **Payroll Expense ($000):** 76583 **Personnel:** 1000

☒ **PROVIDENCE TARZANA MEDICAL CENTER (050761)**, 18321 Clark Street, Zip 91356–3521; tel. 818/881–0800, **A**1 10 **F**3 7 13 15 17 18 19 20 22 24 26 28 29 30 31 34 35 37 40 41 44 45 46 49 50 51 54 56 57 59 63 64 70 72 74 75 76 77 78 79 81 82 83 84 85 86 87 88 89 91 92 93 107 108 110 111 114 115 116 119 126 133 143 146 147 148 149 154 **P**3 5 **S** Providence St. Joseph Health, Renton, WA
Primary Contact: Dale Surowitz, Chief Executive
COO: Phyllis Bushart, R.N., Chief Operating Officer
CMO: Howard Z Davis, M.D., Chief Medical Officer
CIO: Alex Nury, Chief Information Officer
CHR: Beverly Murray, Director of Human Resources
CNO: Deborah Carver, Chief Nursing Officer
Web address: www.providence.org/tarzana
Control: Church operated, Nongovernment, not–for–profit **Service**: General medical and surgical

Staffed Beds: 249 **Admissions:** 13532 **Census:** 143 **Outpatient Visits:** 157089 **Births:** 2566 **Total Expense ($000):** 217817 **Payroll Expense ($000):** 112088 **Personnel:** 1124

☒ **RONALD REAGAN UCLA MEDICAL CENTER (050262)**, 757 Westwood Plaza, Zip 90095–8358; tel. 310/825–9111, (Includes MATTEL CHILDREN'S HOSPITAL, 757 Westwood Plaza, Los Angeles, CA, Zip 90095; tel. 310/825–9111) **A**1 3 5 8 10 **F**3 6 7 8 9 11 12 13 14 15 17 18 19 20 21 22 23 24 25 26 27 28 29 30 31 32 33 35 36 37 39 40 41 43 44 45 46 47 48 49 50 51 52 54 55 56 57 58 59 61 62 64 65 66 68 70 71 72 74 75 76 77 78 79 81 82 84 85 86 87 88 89 92 93 94 96 97 102 107 108 110 111 112 113 114 115 116 117 118 119 120 121 123 124 126 129 130 131 132 135 136 137 138 139 140 141 142 143 145 146 147 148 149 154 **P**6 **S** University of California Systemwide Administration, Oakland, CA
Primary Contact: Johnese Spisso, Chief Executive Officer
COO: J. Shannon O'Kelley, Chief Operating Officer
CFO: Paul Staton, Chief Financial Officer
CMO: Robert Cherry, M.D., Chief Medical and Quality Officer
CIO: Michael Pfeffer, M.D., Chief Information Officer
CHR: Susi Takeuchi, Chief Human Resources and Organization Development Officer
CNO: Karen A Grimley, Chief Nursing Executive
Web address: www.uclahealth.org
Control: State, Government, nonfederal **Service**: General medical and surgical

Staffed Beds: 445 **Admissions:** 23172 **Census:** 455 **Outpatient Visits:** 574507 **Births:** 1943 **Total Expense ($000):** 1886000 **Payroll Expense ($000):** 708570 **Personnel:** 7949

☒ **SHERMAN OAKS HOSPITAL (050755)**, 4929 Van Nuys Boulevard, Zip 91403–1777; tel. 818/981–7111, (Nonreporting) **A**1 5 10 **S** Prime Healthcare, Ontario, CA
Primary Contact: Bockhi Park, Chief Executive Officer
CFO: Daniel Leon, Chief Financial Officer
CMO: Michael Malamed, M.D., Chief of Staff
Web address: www.shermanoakshospital.com
Control: Other not–for–profit (including NFP Corporation) **Service**: General medical and surgical

Staffed Beds: 90

☐ **SILVER LAKE MEDICAL CENTER (050763)**, 1711 West Temple Street, Zip 90026–5421; tel. 213/989–6100, (Includes SILVER LAKE MEDICAL CENTER–INGLESIDE HOSPITAL, 7500 East Hellman Avenue, Rosemead, CA, Zip 91770; tel. 626/288–1160) **A**1 10 **F**3 29 34 35 38 44 45 46 49 56 57 59 60 64 65 68 70 74 75 79 81 85 86 87 96 98 100 101 102 103 104 105 107 108 114 119 120 130 131 143 144 148 149 153 **S** Success Healthcare, Boca Raton, FL
Primary Contact: Brent A. Cope, Chief Executive Officer
CFO: John Cowles, Chief Financial Officer
CMO: Louis Acosta, M.D., Chief of Staff
CIO: Scott Musack, Chief Information Officer
CHR: Sylvia Cloud, Director Human Resources
Web address: www.silverlakemc.com
Control: Partnership, Investor–owned (for–profit) **Service**: General medical and surgical

Staffed Beds: 175 **Admissions:** 6453 **Census:** 142 **Outpatient Visits:** 23828 **Births:** 0

SOUTHERN CALIFORNIA HOSPITAL AT VAN NUYS See Southern California Hospital At Hollywood, Los Angeles

☐ **SOUTHERN CALIFORNIA HOSPITAL AT HOLLYWOOD (050135)**, 6245 De Longpre Avenue, Zip 90028–9001; tel. 323/462–2271, (Includes SOUTHERN CALIFORNIA HOSPITAL AT VAN NUYS, 14433 Emelita Street, Van Nuys, CA, Zip 91401; tel. 818/787–1511) (Nonreporting) **A**1 10 **S** Prospect Medical Holdings, Los Angeles, CA
Primary Contact: Bruce P. Grimshaw, FACHE, Chief Executive Officer
Web address: www.hollywoodcommunityhospital.org/
Control: Corporation, Investor–owned (for–profit) **Service:** General medical and surgical

Staffed Beds: 45

☐ **ST. VINCENT MEDICAL CENTER (050502)**, 2131 West Third Street, Zip 90057–1901, Mailing Address: P.O. Box 57992, Zip 90057–0992; tel. 213/484–7111, (Total facility includes 27 beds in nursing home–type unit) **A**1 3 10 **F**3 15 18 20 22 24 26 29 30 31 34 35 36 40 45 47 49 50 54 57 58 59 60 63 64 65 68 70 71 74 75 77 78 79 81 82 85 87 90 91 96 107 108 110 111 116 118 119 120 121 128 130 136 138 142 143 146 148 149 154 **S** Verity Health System, Los Angeles, CA
Primary Contact: Frank J. Cracolici, President and Chief Executive Officer
CFO: Michael Garko, Chief Financial Officer
CMO: Brian Itagaki, M.D., Chief of Staff
CIO: Dan Robbins, Information Technology and Account Executive
CHR: Gail Watts, Director
CNO: Judy McCurdy, R.N., Vice President and Chief Nursing Officer
Web address: www.stvincentmedicalcenter.com
Control: Other not–for–profit (including NFP Corporation) **Service:** General medical and surgical

Staffed Beds: 271 Admissions: 11099 Census: 177 Outpatient Visits: 75106 Births: 0 Total Expense ($000): 273709 Payroll Expense ($000): 83407 Personnel: 926

☒ **STEWART & LYNDA RESNICK NEUROPSYCHIATRIC HOSPITAL AT UCLA (054009)**, 150 UCLA Medical Plaza, Zip 90095–8353; tel. 310/825–9989, **A**1 3 5 10 **F**3 5 6 29 30 35 40 43 55 56 64 68 77 86 87 98 99 100 101 102 103 104 105 130 132 134 147 149 153 154 **P**1 **S** University of California Systemwide Administration, Oakland, CA
Primary Contact: Peter Whybrow, M.D., Chief Executive Officer
COO: Ruth Irwin, Associate Director Clinical Operations
CFO: Ronald Anthony Davis, Chief Financial Officer – UCLA Hospital System
CMO: Thomas Strouse, M.D., Medical Director and Professor of Clinical Psych
CIO: Michael Pfeffer, M.D., Chief Medical Informatics Officer, UCLA Health
CHR: Monica Rodriquez, Director of Human Resources
CNO: Patricia Matos, Chief Nursing Officer
Web address: www.semel.ucla.edu/resnick
Control: State, Government, nonfederal **Service:** Psychiatric

Staffed Beds: 74 Admissions: 1751 Census: 68 Outpatient Visits: 17820 Births: 0 Total Expense ($000): 73288 Payroll Expense ($000): 37087 Personnel: 389

☒ **USC NORRIS COMPREHENSIVE CANCER CENTER (050660)**, 1441 Eastlake Avenue, Zip 90089–0112; tel. 323/865–3000, **A**1 2 3 5 8 10 **F**3 8 9 11 15 18 29 30 31 34 35 36 38 39 44 45 46 47 48 49 50 51 54 55 56 57 58 59 60 61 64 65 68 70 74 75 77 78 79 81 82 84 85 86 87 92 93 94 97 100 101 104 107 108 109 110 111 114 115 118 119 120 121 123 124 126 130 132 134 135 136 143 145 146 147 148 149 150 154 **P**6 **S** Keck Medicine of USC, Los Angeles, CA
Primary Contact: Rodney B. Hanners, Chief Executive Officer
COO: Tarek Salaway, R.N., Chief Operating Officer
CMO: Stephanie Hall, M.D., Medical Director
CHR: Matthew McElrath, Chief Human Resources Officer
CNO: Annette Sy, Chief Nursing Officer
Web address: www.uscnorriscancerhospital.org
Control: Other not–for–profit (including NFP Corporation) **Service:** Cancer

Staffed Beds: 60 Admissions: 1637 Census: 36 Outpatient Visits: 115024 Births: 0 Total Expense ($000): 190644 Payroll Expense ($000): 56294 Personnel: 428

USC UNIVERSITY HOSPITAL See Keck Hospital of USC

☒ △ **VA GREATER LOS ANGELES HEALTHCARE SYSTEM**, 11301 Wilshire Boulevard, Zip 90073–1003; tel. 310/478–3711, (Nonreporting) **A**1 3 5 7 8 **S** Department of Veterans Affairs, Perry Point, MD
Primary Contact: Ann R. Brown, M.D., Director
COO: Susan Shyshka, Associate Director
CFO: Joseph Schmitt, Chief Financial Officer
CIO: Eugene Archey, Chief Information Technology
CHR: Brenda Cabunoc, Chief Human Resources
CNO: James Doelling, Chief Nurse Executive
Web address: www.losangeles.va.gov/
Control: Veterans Affairs, Government, federal **Service:** General medical and surgical

Staffed Beds: 1087

★ ⇑ **VALLEY PRESBYTERIAN HOSPITAL (050126)**, 15107 Vanowen Street, Zip 91405–4597; tel. 818/782–6600, **A**5 10 21 **F**3 13 18 20 22 24 28 29 30 31 34 35 40 41 44 45 46 49 50 53 55 57 59 64 65 70 72 74 75 76 77 78 79 81 85 86 88 89 90 96 107 108 114 115 118 119 130 145 146 148 149 154 **P**5
Primary Contact: Gustavo A. Valdespino, President and Chief Executive Officer
COO: Lori Cardle, Senior Vice President, Chief Operating Officer
CFO: Janice Klostermeier, Senior Vice President and Chief Financial Officer
CMO: Clyde Wesp, M.D., Chief Medical Officer
CIO: Jeff Allport, Vice President, Chief Information Officer
CHR: Deborah Gac, Vice President Human Resources
CNO: Lori Burnell, R.N., Ph.D., Senior Vice President and Chief Nursing Officer
Web address: www.valleypres.org
Control: Other not–for–profit (including NFP Corporation) **Service:** General medical and surgical

Staffed Beds: 333 Admissions: 13556 Census: 196 Outpatient Visits: 116329 Births: 3395

☒ **WEST HILLS HOSPITAL AND MEDICAL CENTER (050481)**, 7300 Medical Center Drive, Zip 91307–1900; tel. 818/676–4000, (Nonreporting) **A**1 10 **S** HCA Healthcare, Nashville, TN
Primary Contact: Douglas Long, President and Chief Executive Officer
COO: John Neidenbach, Vice President and Chief Operating Officer
CFO: David Cantrell, CPA, Vice President and Chief Financial Officer
CMO: Yale D. Podnos, M.D., Chief Medical Officer
CHR: Diana Steel, Vice President Human Resources
CNO: Stephanie Mearns, R.N., Vice President and Chief Nursing Officer
Web address: www.westhillshospital.com
Control: Corporation, Investor–owned (for–profit) **Service:** General medical and surgical

Staffed Beds: 225

WEST LOS ANGELES MEDICAL CENTER See Kaiser Permanente West Los Angeles Medical Center

WOODLAND HILLS MEDICAL CENTER See Kaiser Permanente Woodland Hills Medical Center

LOS BANOS—Merced County

☒ **MEMORIAL HOSPITAL LOS BANOS (050528)**, 520 West 'I' Street, Zip 93635–3498; tel. 209/826–0591, **A**1 10 20 **F**2 3 8 11 13 15 18 29 30 34 35 39 40 44 45 46 49 50 54 57 59 60 64 65 68 70 74 75 76 81 82 85 86 87 107 110 111 115 119 127 130 132 135 146 149 154 **P**5 **S** Sutter Health, Sacramento, CA
Primary Contact: Doug Archer, Administrator
CFO: Timothy J Noakes, Chief Financial Officer
CHR: Shawn Garcia, Manager Human Resources
CNO: Kristie Marion, Chief Nurse Executive
Web address: www.memoriallosbanos.org/
Control: Other not–for–profit (including NFP Corporation) **Service:** General medical and surgical

Staffed Beds: 44 Admissions: 1885 Census: 11 Outpatient Visits: 74879 Births: 742 Total Expense ($000): 59674 Payroll Expense ($000): 18567 Personnel: 246

LYNWOOD—Los Angeles County

☐ **ST. FRANCIS MEDICAL CENTER (050104)**, 3630 East Imperial Highway, Zip 90262–2636; tel. 310/900–8900, (Nonreporting) **A**1 3 10 **S** Verity Health System, Los Angeles, CA
Primary Contact: Gerald T. Kozai, PharmD, President and Chief Executive Officer
COO: Jeffrey Stout, MSN, R.N., Chief Operating Officer
CFO: Anil Jain, Chief Financial Officer
CMO: Rahul Dhawan, M.D., Chief Medical Officer
CIO: Judi Binderman, Chief Information Technology Officer and Chief Medical Informatics Officer
CHR: Laura Kato, Vice President Human Resources
CNO: Derek Scott Drake, Chief Nursing Officer
Web address: www.dochs.org
Control: Church operated, Nongovernment, not–for–profit **Service:** General medical and surgical

Staffed Beds: 323

Many Facility Codes have changed. Please refer to the AHA Guide Code Chart.
© 2018 AHA Guide

MADERA—Madera County

○ **MADERA COMMUNITY HOSPITAL (050568)**, 1250 East Almond Avenue, Zip 93637–5696, Mailing Address: P.O. Box 1328, Zip 93639–1328; tel. 559/675–5501, **A**10 11 19 **F**3 13 15 29 34 35 40 45 54 60 64 65 70 76 79 81 82 89 107 110 111 119 127 146 **P**5
Primary Contact: Karen Paolinelli, Chief Executive Officer
CFO: Mark Foote, Chief Financial Officer
CIO: Jerry Kovalski, Director Information Systems
CHR: Christine M Watts–Johnson, Assistant Vice President
CNO: Meri Combs, R.N., Vice President and Chief Nursing Officer
Web address: www.maderahospital.org
Control: Other not-for-profit (including NFP Corporation) **Service:** General medical and surgical

Staffed Beds: 106 **Admissions:** 3779 **Census:** 38 **Outpatient Visits:** 144248 **Births:** 1016 **Total Expense ($000):** 84979 **Payroll Expense ($000):** 31028 **Personnel:** 645

☒ △ **VALLEY CHILDREN'S HEALTHCARE (053300)**, 9300 Valley Children's Place, Zip 93636–8761; tel. 559/353–3000, **A**1 3 5 7 8 10 **F**3 8 9 11 19 21 23 25 27 28 29 30 31 32 34 35 38 41 43 44 46 48 49 50 55 57 58 59 60 61 62 64 65 68 72 73 74 75 77 78 79 81 82 84 85 86 87 88 89 90 93 94 107 108 111 114 115 119 127 129 130 131 132 134 143 146 147 148 149 **P**3
Primary Contact: Todd A. Suntrapak, President and Chief Executive Officer
COO: Debra A Flores, R.N., MS, President and Chief Operating Officer
CFO: Michele Waldron, Senior Vice President and Chief Financial Officer
CMO: David Christensen, M.D., Senior Vice President and Chief Medical Officer
CIO: Kevin Shimamoto, Vice President and Chief Informational Officer
CHR: Nat Ponticello, Vice President Human Resources
CNO: Beverly P. Hayden–Pugh, R.N., Senior Vice President and Chief Nursing Officer
Web address: www.valleychildrens.org
Control: Other not-for-profit (including NFP Corporation) **Service:** Children's general medical and surgical

Staffed Beds: 358 **Admissions:** 12378 **Census:** 209 **Outpatient Visits:** 284952 **Births:** 0 **Total Expense ($000):** 552418 **Payroll Expense ($000):** 203178 **Personnel:** 2349

MAMMOTH LAKES—Mono County

⇑ **MAMMOTH HOSPITAL (051303)**, 85 Sierra Park Road, Zip 93546–2073, Mailing Address: P.O. Box 660, Zip 93546–0660; tel. 760/934–3311, (Nonreporting) **A**10 18 21
Primary Contact: Gary Myers, Chief Executive Officer
CFO: Melanie Van Winkle, Chief Financial Officer
CMO: Yuri Parisky, M.D., Chief of Staff
CIO: Mark Lind, Chief Information Officer
CHR: Sarah Vigilante, Manager Human Resources
CNO: Kathleen Alo, Chief Nursing Officer
Web address: www.mammothhospital.com
Control: Hospital district or authority, Government, nonfederal **Service:** General medical and surgical

Staffed Beds: 17

MANTECA—San Joaquin County

☒ **DOCTORS HOSPITAL OF MANTECA (050118)**, 1205 East North Street, Zip 95336–4900; tel. 209/823–3111, **A**1 10 **F**3 11 12 13 15 29 31 34 35 40 45 49 50 51 64 75 76 78 79 81 85 102 107 108 110 111 115 116 117 118 119 130 132 146 147 148 149 154 **S** TENET Healthcare Corporation, Dallas, TX
Primary Contact: Brandon May, Chief Executive Officer
COO: Carmen Silva, R.N., Chief Operating Officer
CFO: Michael Szymanski, Chief Financial Officer
CHR: Traci Holzer, Chief Human Resources Officer
CNO: Beverly Fick, Chief Nursing Officer
Web address: www.doctorsmanteca.com
Control: Corporation, Investor–owned (for-profit) **Service:** General medical and surgical

Staffed Beds: 56 **Admissions:** 3858 **Census:** 38 **Outpatient Visits:** 69400 **Births:** 628 **Total Expense ($000):** 90163 **Payroll Expense ($000):** 40488 **Personnel:** 402

☒ **KAISER PERMANENTE MANTECA MEDICAL CENTER (050748)**, 1777 West Yosemite Avenue, Zip 95337–5187; tel. 209/825–3700, (Includes MODESTO MEDICAL CENTER, 4601 Dale Road, Modesto, CA, Zip 95356–9718; tel. 209/735–5000; Corwin N Harper, Administrator) (Total facility includes 38 beds in nursing home–type unit) **A**1 10 **F**3 8 13 18 20 22 26 29 30 31 35 40 41 44 45 46 47 48 49 50 51 53 55 57 65 68 70 72 74 75 76 78 79 81 82 84 85 87 92 93 100 101 107 111 114 115 119 128 130 141 146 148 149 154 **S** Kaiser Foundation Hospitals, Oakland, CA
Primary Contact: Corwin N. Harper, Senior Vice President and Area Manager
COO: Corwin N Harper, Senior Vice President and Area Manager
CFO: Debra L Brown, Area Financial Officer
CMO: Moses D Elam, M.D., Physician–in–Chief
CIO: Tom J Osteen, Director Area Technology
CHR: Pat McKeldin, Human Resource Business Partner
Web address: www.kaiserpermanente.org
Control: Other not-for-profit (including NFP Corporation) **Service:** General medical and surgical

Staffed Beds: 251 **Admissions:** 11933 **Census:** 111 **Outpatient Visits:** 93328 **Births:** 3110

MARINA DEL REY—Los Angeles County

☒ **MARINA DEL REY HOSPITAL (050740)**, 4650 Lincoln Boulevard, Zip 90292–6306; tel. 310/823–8911, (Nonreporting) **A**1 10 **S** Cedars–Sinai Health System, West Hollywood, CA
Primary Contact: Paulette Heitmeyer, Administrator and Chief Operating Officer
COO: Phyllis Buchart, Chief Operating Officer
CFO: Stephen A Hargett, Senior Vice President and Chief Financial Officer
Web address: www.marinahospital.com
Control: Corporation, Investor–owned (for-profit) **Service:** General medical and surgical

Staffed Beds: 145

MARIPOSA—Mariposa County

★ **JOHN C. FREMONT HEALTHCARE DISTRICT (051304)**, 5189 Hospital Road, Zip 95338–9524, Mailing Address: P.O. Box 216, Zip 95338–0216; tel. 209/966–3631, (Nonreporting) **A**10 18
Primary Contact: Matthew Matthiessen, Interim Chief Executive Officer
CFO: Matthew Matthiessen, Chief Financial Officer
CMO: Kenneth P Smith, Chief of Staff
CHR: Martha Robichaux, Chief Human Resources Officer
CNO: Theresa Loya, R.N., Chief Nursing Officer
Web address: www.jcf–hospital.com
Control: Hospital district or authority, Government, nonfederal **Service:** General medical and surgical

Staffed Beds: 34

MARTINEZ—Contra Costa County

☒ **CONTRA COSTA REGIONAL MEDICAL CENTER (050276)**, 2500 Alhambra Avenue, Zip 94553–3156; tel. 925/370–5000, **A**1 2 3 10 **F**3 11 13 15 18 30 31 35 36 39 40 45 49 50 54 56 59 61 62 64 65 66 68 70 71 72 73 74 75 76 77 78 79 81 82 84 85 86 87 93 97 98 100 102 104 107 108 111 115 119 130 132 143 146 147 148 149 **P**6
Primary Contact: Anna M. Roth, R.N., MS, M.P.H., Chief Executive Officer
COO: Timothy Thompson–Cook, Chief Operating Officer
CFO: Patrick Godley, Chief Financial Officer
CMO: David Goldstein, M.D., Chief Medical Officer
CNO: Jaspreet Benepal, Chief Nursing Officer
Web address: www.cchealth.org/medical_center/
Control: County, Government, nonfederal **Service:** General medical and surgical

Staffed Beds: 113 **Admissions:** 7930 **Census:** 119 **Outpatient Visits:** 501904 **Births:** 2070 **Total Expense ($000):** 559119 **Payroll Expense ($000):** 193082 **Personnel:** 2015

KAISER FOUNDATION HOSPITAL See Kaiser Permanente Walnut Creek Medical Center, Walnut Creek

CA

Hospital, Medicare Provider Number, Address, Telephone, Approval, Facility, and Physician Codes, Health Care System

★ American Hospital Association (AHA) membership   ○ Healthcare Facilities Accreditation Program   ⇑ Center for Improvement in Healthcare Quality Accreditation
□ The Joint Commission accreditation   ◇ DNV Healthcare Inc. accreditation   △ Commission on Accreditation of Rehabilitation Facilities (CARF) accreditation

MARYSVILLE—Yuba County

★ **RIDEOUT MEMORIAL HOSPITAL (050133)**, 726 Fourth Street,
Zip 95901–5600; tel. 530/749–4300, (Includes FREMONT MEDICAL CENTER,
970 Plumas Street, Yuba City, CA, Zip 95991–4087; tel. 530/751–4000)
(Nonreporting) **A**2 10 20
Primary Contact: Richard Rawson, Chief Executive Officer
COO: Cyndy Gordon, Chief Operating Officer
CFO: Diane Moon, Chief Financial Officer
CMO: Azad Sheikh, Chief Medical Officer
CIO: Daniel Chibaya, Chief Information Officer
CHR: Bart R Minsky, Interim Vice President Human Resources
CNO: Inna Makievsky, Interim Chief Nursing Officer
Web address: www.frhg.org
Control: Other not-for-profit (including NFP Corporation) **Service:** General
medical and surgical

Staffed Beds: 233

MENLO PARK—San Mateo County

✠ **MENLO PARK SURGICAL HOSPITAL (050754)**, 570 Willow Road,
Zip 94025–2617; tel. 650/324–8500, **A**1 10 **F**18 29 35 64 68 79 81 82 85 119
149 **P**3 5 **S** Sutter Health, Sacramento, CA
Primary Contact: Jeanette Engle–Ramirez, Chief Executive Officer
CMO: Andrew Gutow, M.D., Medical Director
CNO: Marjorie Eckford, Chief Nursing Officer
Web address: www.pamf.org/mpsh
Control: Other not-for-profit (including NFP Corporation) **Service:** General
medical and surgical

Staffed Beds: 16 Admissions: 230 Census: 1 Outpatient Visits: 3886
Births: 0 Total Expense ($000): 14047 Payroll Expense ($000): 4469
Personnel: 41

MERCED—Merced County

✠ **MERCY MEDICAL CENTER MERCED (050444)**, 333 Mercy Avenue,
Zip 95340–8319; tel. 209/564–5000, (Includes MERCY MEDICAL CENTER
MERCED–DOMINICAN CAMPUS, 2740 'M' Street, Merced, CA, Zip 95340–2880;
tel. 209/384–6444; Charles Kassis, President) **A**1 3 5 10 19 **F**3 8 13 15 18 20
26 28 29 30 32 34 35 40 41 45 46 49 50 54 57 59 62 64 65 66 68 69 70 74
75 77 79 81 83 84 85 86 87 88 90 92 93 96 97 107 108 110 111 115 118
119 127 130 132 135 146 148 149 154 **P**3 **S** Dignity Health, San Francisco, CA
Primary Contact: Charles Kassis, President
CFO: Michael Strasser, Vice President and Chief Financial Officer
CMO: Robert Streeter, M.D., Vice President Medical Affairs
CIO: Daniel Andresen, Chief information Officer
CHR: Julie Rocha, Vice President Human Resources
CNO: Greg Rouleau, Vice President Nursing
Web address: www.mercymercedcares.org
Control: Other not-for-profit (including NFP Corporation) **Service:** General
medical and surgical

Staffed Beds: 186 Admissions: 12732 Census: 133 Outpatient
Visits: 170575 Births: 2786 Total Expense ($000): 297543 Payroll
Expense ($000): 110455 Personnel: 1165

MISSION HILLS—Los Angeles County

✠ △ **PROVIDENCE HOLY CROSS MEDICAL CENTER (050278)**, 15031 Rinaldi
Street, Zip 91345–1207; tel. 818/365–8051, (Total facility includes 48 beds in
nursing home–type unit) **A**1 2 7 10 **F**3 8 11 13 15 17 18 20 22 24 26 28 29 30
31 34 35 36 40 41 43 44 46 49 50 54 55 56 57 58 59 60 61 64 65 68 70
71 72 74 75 77 78 79 81 82 83 84 85 87 90 93 94 97 105 107 108 110 111
114 115 116 117 119 120 121 123 124 126 128 130 131 132 133 143 146
147 148 149 150 153 154 **S** Providence St. Joseph Health, Renton, WA
Primary Contact: Bernard Klein, M.D., Chief Executive
CFO: Paul Steinke, Chief Financial Officer
CMO: Bob Raggi, M.D., Chief Medical Officer
CHR: Pam Stahl, Regional Chief Human Resources Officer
CNO: Jodi Hein, R.N., Chief Nursing Officer
Web address: www.https://california.providence.org/holy–cross/Pages/default.
aspx
Control: Church operated, Nongovernment, not-for-profit **Service:** General
medical and surgical

Staffed Beds: 377 Admissions: 17807 Census: 260 Outpatient
Visits: 328403 Births: 3307 Total Expense ($000): 331708 Payroll
Expense ($000): 166470 Personnel: 2084

MISSION VIEJO—Orange County

☐ **CHOC CHILDREN'S AT MISSION HOSPITAL (053306)**, 27700 Medical Center
Road, Zip 92691–6426; tel. 949/347–8400, **A**1 5 10 **F**3 11 36 72 74 79 81 85
88 89 92 129 154
Primary Contact: Kimberly C. Cripe, President and Chief Executive Officer
COO: Matthew S Gerlach, Chief Operating Officer
CFO: Kerri Ruppert Schiller, Senior Vice President and Chief Financial Officer
CMO: Maria Minon, M.D., Vice President Medical Affairs and Chief Medical Officer
CIO: John Henderson, Chief Information Officer
CHR: Thomas Capizzi, Vice President Human Resources
Web address: www.choc.org
Control: Other not-for-profit (including NFP Corporation) **Service:** Children's
general medical and surgical

Staffed Beds: 54 Admissions: 2002 Census: 22 Outpatient Visits: 22676
Births: 0 Total Expense ($000): 54487 Payroll Expense ($000): 9739
Personnel: 103

✠ △ **MISSION HOSPITAL (050567)**, 27700 Medical Center Road,
Zip 92691–6474; tel. 949/364–1400, (Includes MISSION HOSPITAL LAGUNA
BEACH, 31872 Coast Highway, Laguna Beach, CA, Zip 92651–6775;
tel. 949/499–1311; Tarek Salaway, R.N., Chief Executive) **A**1 2 3 7 10 **F**3 4 5 11
13 14 15 17 18 20 22 24 26 28 29 30 31 32 34 35 36 37 38 39 40 41 43 44
45 46 47 48 49 50 53 54 55 56 57 58 59 60 64 65 68 70 74 75 76 77 78 79
80 81 82 84 85 86 87 90 93 96 98 100 102 105 107 108 110 111 114 115
116 117 118 119 120 121 123 126 130 131 132 134 135 141 142 146 147
148 149 150 152 153 154 **P**3 5 **S** Providence St. Joseph Health, Renton, WA
Primary Contact: Tarek Salaway, R.N., Chief Executive
COO: Terrence Wooten, Vice President of Operations, Support Services
CFO: Eileen Haubl, Senior Vice President and Chief Financial Officer
CMO: Linda Sieglen, M.D., Chief Medical Officer
CIO: Bill Russell, Senior Chief Information Officer
CHR: Terri Covert, Vice President Human Resources
CNO: Jennifer Cord, R.N., Chief Nursing Officer
Web address: www.mission4health.com
Control: Church operated, Nongovernment, not-for-profit **Service:** General
medical and surgical

Staffed Beds: 257 Admissions: 20367 Census: 233 Outpatient
Visits: 222393 Births: 2545 Total Expense ($000): 573850 Payroll
Expense ($000): 167054 Personnel: 2309

MODESTO—Stanislaus County

⇑ **CENTRAL VALLEY SPECIALTY HOSPITAL (052055)**, 730 17th Street,
Zip 95354–1209; tel. 209/248–7700, (Nonreporting) **A**21
Primary Contact: Gia Smith, Chief Executive Officer
Web address: www.centralvalleyspecialty.org/CVSH/
Control: Partnership, Investor–owned (for-profit) **Service:** Acute long–term care
hospital

Staffed Beds: 36

✠ **DOCTORS MEDICAL CENTER OF MODESTO (050464)**, 1441 Florida
Avenue, Zip 95350–4418, Mailing Address: P.O. Box 4138, Zip 95352–4138;
tel. 209/578–1211, **A**1 2 3 10 **F**3 5 12 13 15 17 18 20 22 24 26 28 29 30 31
34 35 40 43 45 46 47 48 49 50 51 55 58 59 60 61 63 64 65 70 72 73
74 75 76 77 78 79 80 81 82 84 85 87 89 98 100 101 102 103 104 105 107
108 109 110 111 113 114 115 119 126 130 135 146 147 148 149 152 **S**
TENET Healthcare Corporation, Dallas, TX
Primary Contact: Warren J. Kirk, Chief Executive Officer
CFO: Greg Berry, Chief Financial Officer
CMO: Gabrielle Gaspar, M.D., Chief Medical Officer
CIO: Debbie Fuller, Director Health Information Systems and Chief Information
Officer
CHR: Michele Bava, Director Human Resources
CNO: Cheryl Harless, Chief Nursing Officer
Web address: www.dmc–modesto.com
Control: Corporation, Investor–owned (for-profit) **Service:** General medical and
surgical

Staffed Beds: 461 Admissions: 26416 Census: 358 Outpatient
Visits: 158226 Births: 3534 Total Expense ($000): 515006 Payroll
Expense ($000): 228639 Personnel: 2257

HEALTHSOUTH REHABILITATION HOSPITAL OF MODESTO (053040), 1303
Mable Avenue, Zip 95355; tel. 209/857–3400, (Nonreporting) **A**10
Primary Contact: Kay E. Peck, Ph.D., Chief Executive Officer
CFO: Seth Rogers, Controller
CMO: Greg A. Vigna, M.D., Medical Director
CHR: Tina Reed, Director of Human Resources
CNO: Mark Dinardo, Chief Nursing Officer
Web address: www.healthsouthmodesto.com/
Control: Corporation, Investor–owned (for-profit) **Service:** Rehabilitation

Staffed Beds: 50

Many Facility Codes have changed. Please refer to the AHA Guide Code Chart.

☒ **MEMORIAL MEDICAL CENTER (050557)**, 1700 Coffee Road, Zip 95355–2869, Mailing Address: P.O. Box 942, Zip 95353–0942; tel. 209/526–4500, (Includes MEMORIAL MEDICAL CENTER, 1700 Coffee Road, Modesto, CA, Zip 95355, Mailing Address: Box 942, Zip 95353, tel. 209/526–4500) **A**1 2 10 **F**3 5 8 11 12 13 15 18 20 22 24 26 28 29 30 31 34 35 36 37 39 40 43 44 45 46 47 48 49 50 51 57 58 59 60 64 68 70 72 74 75 76 77 78 79 81 82 84 85 86 87 89 107 108 111 114 115 119 120 121 123 124 126 129 130 132 146 147 148 154 **P**3 5 **S** Sutter Health, Sacramento, CA
Primary Contact: Eugene Patrizio, Chief Executive Officer
COO: Steve Mitchell, Chief Operating Officer
CFO: Eric Dalton, Chief Financial Officer
CIO: Patrick Anderson, Chief Information Officer
CHR: Paula Rafala, Director, Human Resources
CNO: Sandra Proctor, R.N., MS, Chief Nurse Executive
Web address: www.memorialmedicalcenter.org
Control: Other not–for–profit (including NFP Corporation) **Service**: General medical and surgical

Staffed Beds: 220 **Admissions**: 17406 **Census**: 209 **Outpatient Visits**: 144994 **Births**: 1833 **Total Expense ($000)**: 579257 **Payroll Expense ($000)**: 165158 **Personnel**: 1967

MODESTO MEDICAL CENTER See Kaiser Permanente Manteca Medical Center, Manteca

★ **STANISLAUS SURGICAL HOSPITAL (050726)**, 1421 Oakdale Road, Zip 95355–3356; tel. 209/572–2700, (Nonreporting) **A**5 10 **S** Sutter Health, Sacramento, CA
Primary Contact: Douglas V. Johnson, Chief Executive Officer
CFO: Richard Hart, Chief Financial Officer
CMO: Wesley Kinzie, M.D., Chief of Staff
CIO: Richard Hart, Chief Financial Officer
CHR: Tyson Hubbard, Director Human Resources
CNO: Susan Gonzalez, Director of Clinical Services
Web address: www.stanislaussurgical.com
Control: Individual, Investor–owned (for–profit) **Service**: General medical and surgical

Staffed Beds: 23

MONROVIA—Los Angeles County

○ **MONROVIA MEMORIAL HOSPITAL (052054)**, 323 South Heliotrope Avenue, Zip 91016–2914; tel. 626/408–9800, (Nonreporting) **A**10 11
Primary Contact: Ron Kupferstein, Chief Executive Officer
Web address: www.monroviamemorial.com
Control: Partnership, Investor–owned (for–profit) **Service**: Acute long–term care hospital

Staffed Beds: 49

MONTCLAIR—San Bernardino County

☒ **MONTCLAIR HOSPITAL MEDICAL CENTER (050758)**, 5000 San Bernardino Street, Zip 91763–2326; tel. 909/625–5411, (Nonreporting) **A**1 3 10 **S** Prime Healthcare, Ontario, CA
Primary Contact: Sofia Abrina, R.N., Administrator
CFO: Robert Bonner, Chief Financial Officer
CMO: Joseph Hourany, Chief Medical Officer
CNO: Gail Aviado, Chief Nursing Officer
Web address: www.montclair–hospital.com
Control: Other not–for–profit (including NFP Corporation) **Service**: General medical and surgical

Staffed Beds: 102

MONTEBELLO—Los Angeles County

⇑ **BEVERLY HOSPITAL (050350)**, 309 West Beverly Boulevard, Zip 90640–4308; tel. 323/726–1222, **A**10 21 **F**3 13 15 17 18 20 22 24 29 30 31 34 35 40 41 45 49 50 51 57 59 60 65 68 70 72 74 75 76 77 78 79 81 86 89 107 108 110 111 115 118 119 130 132 143 145 146 147 148 149 **P**5
Primary Contact: Alice Cheng, President and Chief Executive Officer
CFO: Larry Pugh, Vice President and Chief Financial Officer
CIO: Mark Turner, Director Information Systems
CHR: John Barnes, Administrative Director Human Resources
CNO: Kathy Wojno, R.N., MSN, Vice President Nursing Services and Chief Nursing Officer
Web address: www.beverly.org
Control: Other not–for–profit (including NFP Corporation) **Service**: General medical and surgical

Staffed Beds: 224 **Admissions**: 9206 **Census**: 106 **Outpatient Visits**: 59057 **Births**: 753 **Total Expense ($000)**: 192025 **Payroll Expense ($000)**: 52374 **Personnel**: 809

MONTEREY—Monterey County

☒ **COMMUNITY HOSPITAL OF THE MONTEREY PENINSULA (050145)**, 23625 Holman Highway, Zip 93940–5902, Mailing Address: Box 'HH', Zip 93942–6032; tel. 831/624–5311, (Total facility includes 28 beds in nursing home–type unit) **A**1 2 10 **F**3 5 11 12 13 15 17 18 20 22 24 26 28 29 30 31 32 34 35 37 40 44 45 46 47 48 49 50 51 53 54 57 58 59 60 61 62 63 64 66 68 70 71 73 74 75 76 77 78 79 81 82 83 84 85 86 87 89 90 91 92 93 94 96 98 99 100 101 102 103 104 105 107 110 111 114 115 116 117 118 119 120 121 123 124 128 129 130 132 134 135 145 146 148 149 150 151 153 154
Primary Contact: Steven J. Packer, M.D., President and Chief Executive Officer
CFO: Laura Zehm, Vice President and Chief Financial Officer
CMO: Anthony D Chavis, M.D., Vice President Enterprise Medical Officer, Community Hospital Foundation
Web address: www.chomp.org
Control: Other not–for–profit (including NFP Corporation) **Service**: General medical and surgical

Staffed Beds: 248 **Admissions**: 12040 **Census**: 166 **Outpatient Visits**: 340264 **Births**: 1167 **Total Expense ($000)**: 487471 **Payroll Expense ($000)**: 193453 **Personnel**: 1919

MONTEREY PARK—Los Angeles County

☐ **GARFIELD MEDICAL CENTER (050737)**, 525 North Garfield Avenue, Zip 91754–1205; tel. 626/573–2222, (Nonreporting) **A**1 10 **S** AHMC & Healthcare, Inc., Alhambra, CA
Primary Contact: Patrick A. Petre, Chief Executive Officer
COO: Herbert Villafuerte, Chief Operating Officer/Chief Nursing Officer
CFO: Steve Maekawa, Chief Financial Officer
CMO: Thomas Lam, Chief Medical Officer
CIO: Angelica Ching, Director Information Systems
CHR: Darcy Castro, Director Human Resources
CNO: Herbert Villafuerte, Chief Operating Officer and Chief Nursing Officer
Web address: www.garfieldmedicalcenter.com
Control: Partnership, Investor–owned (for–profit) **Service**: General medical and surgical

Staffed Beds: 195

☐ **MONTEREY PARK HOSPITAL (050736)**, 900 South Atlantic Boulevard, Zip 91754–4780; tel. 626/570–9000, (Nonreporting) **A**1 10 **S** AHMC & Healthcare, Inc., Alhambra, CA
Primary Contact: Philip A. Cohen, Chief Executive Officer
COO: Ericka Smith, Chief Operating Officer
CFO: Daniel Song, Chief Financial Officer
CMO: Ruben Ramirez, M.D., Chief of Staff
CIO: Angelica Ching, Director Information Systems
CHR: Gretchen Lindeman, Director of Human Resources
CNO: Shirley Tang, R.N., Chief Nursing Officer
Web address: www.montereyparkhosp.com
Control: Partnership, Investor–owned (for–profit) **Service**: General medical and surgical

Staffed Beds: 101

MORENO VALLEY—Riverside County

☒ **KAISER PERMANENTE MORENO VALLEY MEDICAL CENTER (050765)**, 27300 Iris Avenue, Zip 92555–4800; tel. 951/243–0811, **A**1 3 10 **F**3 13 15 17 29 30 35 40 44 45 46 49 50 59 60 64 65 68 70 71 74 75 76 77 78 79 81 82 84 85 87 97 100 101 102 104 107 108 109 110 111 115 117 119 130 135 144 146 148 149 154 **S** Kaiser Foundation Hospitals, Oakland, CA
Primary Contact: Vita M. Willett, Senior Vice President, Area Manager
COO: Corey A Seale, Chief Operating Officer
CFO: JiJi Abraham, Area Chief Financial Officer
CMO: Frank M. Flowers, M.D., Area Medical Director
CIO: Alfred T Velasquez, Area Information Officer
CHR: Cheryl M Witt, Human Resources Director
CNO: Sonia A. Bravo, Chief Nurse Executive
Control: Other not–for–profit (including NFP Corporation) **Service**: General medical and surgical

Staffed Beds: 94 **Admissions**: 3908 **Census**: 33 **Outpatient Visits**: 49115 **Births**: 1349 **Personnel**: 367

CA

Hospital, Medicare Provider Number, Address, Telephone, Approval, Facility, and Physician Codes, Health Care System

★ American Hospital Association (AHA) membership ☐ The Joint Commission accreditation
○ Healthcare Facilities Accreditation Program ◇ DNV Healthcare Inc. accreditation
⇑ Center for Improvement in Healthcare Quality Accreditation △ Commission on Accreditation of Rehabilitation Facilities (CARF) accreditation

CA

☒ **RIVERSIDE UNIVERSITY HEALTH SYSTEM–MEDICAL CENTER (050292)**, 26520 Cactus Avenue, Zip 92555–3911; tel. 951/486–4000, **A**1 3 5 10 12 13 **F**3 11 13 15 18 19 26 29 30 31 34 35 40 43 45 46 47 49 50 55 57 58 59 64 68 70 72 74 75 76 77 78 79 80 81 84 85 87 88 89 92 93 98 100 102 107 108 110 111 114 115 119 126 131 132 135 143 146 147 148 149 154 **P**8
Primary Contact: Jennifer Cruikshank, R.N., Chief Executive Officer
CFO: Christopher Hans, Chief Financial Officer
CMO: Arnold Tabuenca, M.D., Medical Director
CNO: Judi Nightingale, R.N., Dr.PH, Chief Nursing Officer
Web address: www.rcrmc.org
Control: County, Government, nonfederal **Service**: General medical and surgical

Staffed Beds: 439 **Admissions**: 17480 **Census**: 281 **Outpatient Visits**: 206036 **Births**: 1598 **Total Expense ($000)**: 570609 **Payroll Expense ($000)**: 232534 **Personnel**: 2625

MOUNT SHASTA—Siskiyou County

☒ **MERCY MEDICAL CENTER MOUNT SHASTA (051319)**, 914 Pine Street, Zip 96067–2143; tel. 530/926–6111, **A**1 10 18 **F**3 11 13 15 29 30 35 40 43 50 53 56 57 59 62 63 64 68 70 75 76 77 79 81 82 84 89 93 107 108 110 111 114 118 119 121 127 130 131 132 133 143 146 148 149 **S** Dignity Health, San Francisco, CA
Primary Contact: Kenneth E S. Platou, President
CFO: Kimberly Miranda, Chief Financial Officer
CMO: Todd Guthrie, Chief of Staff
CHR: Michelle Michl, Director Human Resources
CNO: Lisa Hubbard, Vice President and Chief Nursing Executive
Web address: www.mercymtshasta.org
Control: Other not–for–profit (including NFP Corporation) **Service**: General medical and surgical

Staffed Beds: 33 **Admissions**: 1132 **Census**: 9 **Outpatient Visits**: 62157 **Births**: 137 **Total Expense ($000)**: 56728 **Payroll Expense ($000)**: 21865 **Personnel**: 231

MOUNTAIN VIEW—Santa Clara County

☒ **EL CAMINO HOSPITAL (050308)**, 2500 Grant Road, Zip 94040–4302, Mailing Address: P.O. Box 7025, Zip 94039–7025; tel. 650/940–7000, (Includes EL CAMINO HOSPITAL LOS GATOS, 815 Pollard Road, Los Gatos, CA, Zip 95032–1438; tel. 408/378–6131) (Nonreporting) **A**1 2 3 10
Primary Contact: Dan Woods, Chief Executive Officer
CFO: Iftikhar Hussain, Chief Financial Officer
CMO: Mark C. Adams, M.D., Chief Medical Officer
CIO: Deborah Muro, Chief Information Officer
CHR: Kathryn M Fisk, Chief Human Resources Officer
CNO: Cheryl Reinking, R.N., MS, Chief Nursing Officer
Web address: www.elcaminohospital.org
Control: Hospital district or authority, Government, nonfederal **Service**: General medical and surgical

Staffed Beds: 420

MURRIETA—Riverside County

☐ **LOMA LINDA UNIVERSITY MEDICAL CENTER–MURRIETA (050770)**, 28062 Baxter Road, Zip 92563–1401; tel. 951/290–4000, (Data for 188 days) **A**1 10 **F**3 11 13 15 17 18 20 22 24 26 28 29 30 31 34 35 40 44 45 46 47 48 49 50 54 57 58 59 60 64 65 68 70 72 74 75 76 77 78 79 81 82 85 86 87 89 91 92 93 96 107 108 110 111 114 115 117 118 119 120 121 123 124 126 130 132 143 146 147 148 149 154 **S** Loma Linda University Adventist Health Sciences Center, Loma Linda, CA
Primary Contact: Peter Baker, Senior Vice President and Administrator
COO: Richard M Tibbits, Vice President and Chief Operating Officer
CFO: James Uli, Chief Financial Officer
CMO: Jeff Conner, M.D., Chief Medical Staff
Web address: www.llumcmurrieta.org
Control: Other not–for–profit (including NFP Corporation) **Service**: General medical and surgical

Staffed Beds: 106 **Admissions**: 4234 **Census**: 81 **Outpatient Visits**: 37797 **Births**: 444 **Total Expense ($000)**: 95694 **Payroll Expense ($000)**: 27805 **Personnel**: 741

☒ **SOUTHWEST HEALTHCARE SYSTEM (050701)**, 25500 Medical Center Drive, Zip 92562–5965; tel. 951/696–6000, (Includes INLAND VALLEY MEDICAL CENTER, 36485 Inland Valley Drive, Wildomar, CA, Zip 92595–9700; tel. 951/677–1111; Bradley D Neet, FACHE, Chief Executive Officer; RANCHO SPRINGS MEDICAL CENTER, 25500 Medical Center Drive, Murrieta, CA, Zip 92562–5965; tel. 951/696–6000) **A**1 10 **F**3 8 11 12 13 15 29 30 34 35 37 40 43 45 48 49 50 51 57 59 67 68 70 72 74 76 77 79 81 84 85 87 93 96 100 102 107 108 110 111 114 115 118 119 126 130 132 134 146 147 149 154 **S** Universal Health Services, Inc., King of Prussia, PA
Primary Contact: Bradley D. Neet, FACHE, Chief Executive Officer
COO: Jared Giles, Chief Operating Officer
CFO: Jon Zilkow, Chief Financial Officer
CMO: Reza Vaezazizi, M.D., Chief of Staff
CIO: Jeffrey Upcraft, Director Information Services
CHR: Della G Stange, Director Human Resources
CNO: Kristen Johnson, Chief Nursing Officer
Web address: www.swhealthcaresystem.com/
Control: Corporation, Investor–owned (for–profit) **Service**: General medical and surgical

Staffed Beds: 240 **Admissions**: 16305 **Census**: 158 **Outpatient Visits**: 113091 **Births**: 3509 **Total Expense ($000)**: 234971 **Payroll Expense ($000)**: 100854 **Personnel**: 1226

NAPA—Napa County

☐ **NAPA STATE HOSPITAL (054122)**, 2100 Napa–Vallejo Highway, Zip 94558–6293; tel. 707/253–5000, **A**1 3 5 10 **F**30 39 53 56 59 61 67 68 77 86 98 103 128 130 132 135 146 149 **P**6
Primary Contact: Dolly Matteucci, Executive Director
COO: Dolly Matteucci, Executive Director
Web address: www.dmh.ca.gov
Control: State, Government, nonfederal **Service**: Psychiatric

Staffed Beds: 1284 **Admissions**: 789 **Census**: 1219 **Outpatient Visits**: 0 **Births**: 0 **Total Expense ($000)**: 316063 **Payroll Expense ($000)**: 184894 **Personnel**: 2239

☒ **QUEEN OF THE VALLEY MEDICAL CENTER (050009)**, 1000 Trancas Street, Zip 94558–2906, Mailing Address: P.O. Box 2340, Zip 94558–0688; tel. 707/252–4411, **A**1 2 10 **F**3 11 13 15 18 20 22 24 26 29 30 31 34 35 37 39 40 41 43 44 45 46 47 48 49 50 51 53 54 56 57 59 68 70 71 72 74 75 76 77 78 79 81 82 84 85 86 87 90 91 92 93 96 107 108 110 111 114 115 117 118 119 120 121 123 124 126 130 132 135 144 146 149 154 **P**3 **S** Providence St. Joseph Health, Renton, WA
Primary Contact: Larry Coomes, Chief Executive Officer
COO: Vincent Morgese, M.D., Executive Vice President, Chief Operating Officer and Chief Medical Officer
CFO: Michel Riccioni, Vice President and Chief Financial Officer, Northern California Region
CMO: Vincent Morgese, M.D., Executive Vice President, Chief Operating Officer and Chief Medical Officer
CHR: Robert A Eisen, Vice President Human Resources, Northern California Region
Web address: www.thequeen.org
Control: Other not–for–profit (including NFP Corporation) **Service**: General medical and surgical

Staffed Beds: 120 **Admissions**: 6735 **Census**: 91 **Outpatient Visits**: 143035 **Births**: 655 **Total Expense ($000)**: 272503 **Payroll Expense ($000)**: 81798 **Personnel**: 1209

NATIONAL CITY—San Diego County

☒ △ **PARADISE VALLEY HOSPITAL (050024)**, 2400 East Fourth Street, Zip 91950–2099; tel. 619/470–4321, (Includes BAYVIEW BEHAVIORAL HEALTH CAMPUS, 330 Moss Street, Chula Vista, CA, Zip 91911–2005; tel. 619/470–4321; Neerav Jadeja, Administrator) (Nonreporting) **A**1 3 7 10 **S** Prime Healthcare, Ontario, CA
Primary Contact: Neerav Jadeja, Administrator
CFO: Becky Levy, Chief Financial Officer
CMO: Rosemarie Lim, M.D., Chief Medical Officer
CIO: Allan Tojino, Director, Information Systems
CHR: Lorraine Villegas, Manager Human Resources
CNO: Gemma Rama–Banaag, R.N., MSN, Chief Nursing Officer
Web address: www.paradisevalleyhospital.org
Control: Corporation, Investor–owned (for–profit) **Service**: General medical and surgical

Staffed Beds: 256

Many Facility Codes have changed. Please refer to the AHA Guide Code Chart. © 2018 AHA Guide

NEEDLES—San Bernardino County

COLORADO RIVER MEDICAL CENTER (051323), 1401 Bailey Avenue,
Zip 92363–3198; tel. 760/326–7100, **A**10 18 **F**3 29 30 34 35 40 41 44 45 46
47 48 49 50 53 57 59 64 65 68 79 81 86 87 89 91 92 93 107 111 114 119
130 143 145 146 148 149 154
Primary Contact: Steve Kelley. Lopez, Chief Executive Officer
COO: Knaya Tabora, Chief Operating Officer and Chief Nursing Officer
CFO: Steve Kelley Lopez, Chief Financial Officer
CMO: Robert Strecker, M.D., Chief of Staff
CIO: Ron Chieffo, Chief Information Officer
CHR: Pam Barrett, Human Resources Director
CNO: Knaya Tabora, Chief Operating Officer and Chief Nursing Officer
Web address: www.crmccares.com
Control: Other not–for–profit (including NFP Corporation) **Service:** General
medical and surgical

**Staffed Beds: 25 Admissions: 530 Census: 4 Outpatient Visits: 9658
Births: 0 Total Expense ($000): 9674 Payroll Expense ($000): 4053
Personnel: 82**

NEWPORT BEACH—Orange County

★ ⇑ **HOAG MEMORIAL HOSPITAL PRESBYTERIAN (050224)**, One Hoag
Drive, Zip 92663–4120, Mailing Address: P.O. Box 6100, Zip 92658–6100;
tel. 949/764–4624, (Includes HOAG HOSPITAL IRVINE, 16200 Sand Canyon
Avenue, Irvine, CA, Zip 92618–3714; tel. 949/764–8240) **A**3 5 10 21 **F**3 4 5
8 11 13 14 15 17 18 20 22 24 26 28 29 30 31 34 35 36 37 40 44 45 46 47
48 49 50 51 52 53 54 55 57 58 59 64 68 70 72 74 75 76 77 78 79 81 82 84
85 86 87 92 93 94 96 97 100 101 102 104 107 108 110 111 113 114 115
116 117 118 119 120 121 123 124 126 129 130 131 132 134 135 141 143
144 145 146 147 148 149 150 152 154 **P**3 **S** Providence St. Joseph Health,
Renton, WA
Primary Contact: Robert Braithwaite, President and Chief Executive Officer
COO: Michael Ricks, Chief Operating Officer
CFO: Andrew Guarni, Chief Financial Officer
CIO: Patrick Anderson, Chief Information Officer and Senior Vice President
CHR: Jan L Blue, Vice President Human Resources
CNO: Richard A Martin, MSN, R.N., Senior Vice President and Chief Nursing Officer
Web address: www.hoaghospital.org
Control: Other not–for–profit (including NFP Corporation) **Service:** General
medical and surgical

**Staffed Beds: 470 Admissions: 29682 Census: 317 Outpatient
Visits: 425859 Births: 6770 Total Expense ($000): 917999 Payroll
Expense ($000): 329654 Personnel: 4817**

NEWPORT BAY HOSPITAL (054135), 1501 East 16th Street, Zip 92663–5924;
tel. 949/650–9750, (Nonreporting) **A**10
Primary Contact: James E. Parkhurst, President and Chief Executive Officer
COO: Garry Hardwick, R.N., Chief Operating Officer
CFO: Rocky Gentner, Chief Financial Officer
CMO: Jason Kellogg, M.D., Chief of Staff
CIO: Nina Swenson, Director Business Services
CHR: Phyllis Parkhurst, Vice President Support Services
CNO: Diana Hakenson, Director of Patient Care Services
Web address: www.newportbayhospital.com
Control: Corporation, Investor–owned (for–profit) **Service:** Psychiatric

Staffed Beds: 34

NORTHRIDGE—Los Angeles County; See Los Angeles

NORWALK—Los Angeles County

COAST PLAZA DOCTORS HOSPITAL See Coast Plaza Hospital

☐ **COAST PLAZA HOSPITAL (050771)**, 13100 Studebaker Road,
Zip 90650–2500; tel. 562/868–3751, (Nonreporting) **A**1 10 **S** Avanti Hospitals, El
Segundo, CA
Primary Contact: Gregory Padilla, Administrator
CFO: Mihi Lee, Chief Financial Officer
CMO: Galal S Gough, M.D., Chief of Staff
CIO: Linda K Roman, Administrator
Web address: www.avantihospitals.com/coast-plaza-hospital
Control: Corporation, Investor–owned (for–profit) **Service:** General medical and
surgical

Staffed Beds: 123

LOS ANGELES COMMUNITY HOSPITAL OF NORWALK See Los Angeles
Community Hospital At Los Angeles, Los Angeles

☐ **METROPOLITAN STATE HOSPITAL (054133)**, 11401 Bloomfield Avenue,
Zip 90650–2015; tel. 562/863–7011, (Nonreporting) **A**1 10
Primary Contact: Michael Barsom, M.D., Executive Director
CFO: Maybelle Manlagnit, Senior Accounting Officer
CIO: Paul Mello, Manager Data Processing
CHR: Jorge Banuedos, Director Human Resources
Web address: www.dmh.ca.gov
Control: State, Government, nonfederal **Service:** Psychiatric

Staffed Beds: 657

NOVATO—Marin County

☒ **NOVATO COMMUNITY HOSPITAL (050131)**, 180 Rowland Way,
Zip 94945–5009, Mailing Address: P.O. Box 1108, Zip 94948–1108;
tel. 415/209–1300, **A**1 10 **F**3 15 18 29 30 34 36 40 45 50 51 54 56 59 60 64
68 70 75 77 79 81 84 85 87 93 107 108 111 115 119 130 131 132 143 144
146 148 149 **P**3 5 **S** Sutter Health, Sacramento, CA
Primary Contact: Michael L. Purvis, Chief Executive Officer
CMO: Barbara Nylund, M.D., Chief of Staff
CIO: Kathryn Graham, Director Communications and Community Relations
CHR: Diana G Johnson, Acting Chief Human Resources Officer
Web address: www.novatocommunity.sutterhealth.org
Control: Other not–for–profit (including NFP Corporation) **Service:** General
medical and surgical

**Staffed Beds: 40 Admissions: 1831 Census: 17 Outpatient Visits: 90432
Births: 0 Total Expense ($000): 82850 Payroll Expense ($000): 24524
Personnel: 233**

OAKDALE—Stanislaus County

☒ **OAK VALLEY HOSPITAL DISTRICT (050067)**, 350 South Oak Avenue,
Zip 95361–3581; tel. 209/847–3011, (Nonreporting) **A**1 10
Primary Contact: John McCormick, President and Chief Executive Officer
CMO: Chaitanya Mahida, M.D., Chief of Staff
CIO: Sherry Peral, Manager Information Systems
CHR: Brian Beck,PHR,MHROD, Vice President Human Resources
CNO: Joann L. Saporito, R.N., Vice President Nursing Services
Web address: www.oakvalleycares.org
Control: Hospital district or authority, Government, nonfederal **Service:** General
medical and surgical

Staffed Beds: 150

OAKLAND—Alameda County

☒ △ **ALTA BATES SUMMIT MEDICAL CENTER – SUMMIT CAMPUS (050043)**,
350 Hawthorne Avenue, Zip 94609–3100; tel. 510/655–4000, **A**1 2 5 7 10 **F**3 4
5 8 11 12 15 17 18 20 22 24 26 29 30 31 34 35 36 40 45 46 47 49 51 56 57
58 59 60 61 64 68 70 74 75 77 78 79 81 82 84 85 86 87 90 97 107 108 111
114 115 116 117 118 119 120 121 123 124 126 130 132 135 146 148 149
P3 5 **S** Sutter Health, Sacramento, CA
Primary Contact: Charles Prosper, Chief Executive Officer
CMO: John Gentile, M.D., Vice President Medical Affairs
CHR: Mark Beiting, Vice President Human Resources
Web address: www.altabatessummit.org
Control: Other not–for–profit (including NFP Corporation) **Service:** General
medical and surgical

**Staffed Beds: 427 Admissions: 12982 Census: 478 Outpatient
Visits: 128048 Births: 0 Total Expense ($000): 614406 Payroll Expense
($000): 155631 Personnel: 1470**

☒ **HIGHLAND HOSPITAL (050320)**, 1411 East 31st Street, Zip 94602–1018;
tel. 510/437–4800, (Includes FAIRMONT HOSPITAL, 15400 Foothill Boulevard,
San Leandro, CA, Zip 94578–1009; tel. 510/895–4200; Richard Espinoza, Chief
Administrative Officer; JOHN GEORGE PSYCHIATRIC HOSPITAL, 2060 Fairmont
Drive, San Leandro, CA, Zip 94578–1001; tel. 510/346–1300; Guy C Qvistgaard,
Chief Executive Officer) (Total facility includes 109 beds in nursing home–type unit)
A1 3 5 10 **F**3 5 11 13 15 18 20 22 28 29 30 31 32 34 35 36 38 39 40 43 44
45 46 49 50 54 56 57 58 59 60 61 64 65 66 68 70 71 73 74 75 77 78 79 81
82 84 85 86 87 90 92 93 94 96 97 98 100 101 102 104 105 107 111 112
114 115 119 128 130 132 134 135 142 143 144 146 147 148 152 153 154
P6 **S** Alameda Health System, San Leandro, CA
Primary Contact: Delvecchio Finley, Chief Executive Officer
CFO: Marion Schales, Chief Financial Officer
CMO: Sang–ick Chang, M.D., M.P.H., Chief Medical Officer
CHR: Jeanette L Louden Corbett, Chief Human Resources Officer
Web address: www.alamedahealthsystem.org
Control: Hospital district or authority, Government, nonfederal **Service:** General
medical and surgical

**Staffed Beds: 382 Admissions: 15340 Census: 333 Outpatient
Visits: 414920 Births: 1396 Total Expense ($000): 793178 Payroll
Expense ($000): 344973 Personnel: 3032**

KAISER PERMANENTE OAKLAND MEDICAL CENTER (050075), 3600 Broadway, Zip 94611-5693; tel. 510/752-1000, (Includes KAISER PERMANENTE RICHMOND MEDICAL CENTER, 901 Nevin Avenue, Richmond, CA, Zip 94801-2555; tel. 510/307-1500; Jeffrey A Collins, M.D., Chief Executive Officer) **A**1 2 3 5 8 10 **F**3 8 12 13 20 22 29 30 31 39 40 49 51 62 63 64 68 70 72 74 75 76 77 78 79 81 82 83 85 86 87 88 89 100 107 108 111 112 114 116 117 119 130 131 135 146 149 154 **S** Kaiser Foundation Hospitals, Oakland, CA
Primary Contact: Jeffrey A. Collins, M.D., Senior Vice President and Area Manager
CFO: Dennis Morris, Area Finance Officer
CMO: John Loftus, M.D., Chief of Staff
CIO: Johnny Law, Area Information Officer
CHR: Rick Mead, Human Resources Leader
CNO: Charlene Boyer, Chief Nursing Officer
Web address: www.kaiserpermanente.org
Control: Other not-for-profit (including NFP Corporation) **Service**: General medical and surgical

Staffed Beds: 297 **Admissions:** 27209 **Census:** 251 **Outpatient Visits:** 143268 **Births:** 3012

OAKLAND MEDICAL CENTER See Kaiser Permanente Oakland Medical Center

☐ **TELECARE HERITAGE PSYCHIATRIC HEALTH CENTER (054146)**, 2633 East 27th Street, Zip 94601-1912; tel. 510/535-5115, (Nonreporting) **A**1 10
Primary Contact: Anne L. Bakar, President and Chief Executive Officer
Web address: www.tbhcare.com/
Control: Partnership, Investor-owned (for-profit) **Service**: Psychiatric

Staffed Beds: 26

UCSF BENIOFF CHILDREN'S HOSPITAL OAKLAND (053301), 747 52nd Street, Zip 94609-1859; tel. 510/428-3000, (Nonreporting) **A**1 3 5 10
Primary Contact: Bertram Lubin, M.D., President and Chief Executive Officer
CIO: Don Livsey, Vice President and Chief Information Officer
Web address: www.childrenshospitaloakland.org
Control: Other not-for-profit (including NFP Corporation) **Service**: Children's general medical and surgical

Staffed Beds: 190

OCEANSIDE—San Diego County

TRI-CITY MEDICAL CENTER (050128), 4002 Vista Way, Zip 92056-4593; tel. 760/724-8411, (Nonreporting) **A**1 2 3 5 10
Primary Contact: Steve Dietlin, Chief Executive Officer
CMO: Scott Worman, Chief of Staff
CIO: Kim Cook, Interim Clinical Applications Services Manager
CHR: Esther Beverly, Vice President Human Resources
CNO: Sharon A Schultz, MSN, R.N., M.P.H., Chief Nurse Executive and Vice President
Web address: www.tricitymed.org
Control: Hospital district or authority, Government, nonfederal **Service**: General medical and surgical

Staffed Beds: 330

OJAI—Ventura County

⇑ **OJAI VALLEY COMMUNITY HOSPITAL (051334)**, 1306 Maricopa Highway, Zip 93023-3163; tel. 805/646-1401, (Nonreporting) **A**18 21 **S** Community Memorial Health System, Ventura, CA
Primary Contact: Haady Lashkari, Chief Administrative Officer
CFO: David Glyer, Vice President Finance
CIO: Mark Turner, Manager Information Technology
CHR: Deborah Gallagher, Manager Human Resources
Web address: www.cmhshealth.org/locations/ojai-valley-community-hospital/
Control: Other not-for-profit (including NFP Corporation) **Service**: General medical and surgical

Staffed Beds: 96

ONTARIO—San Bernardino County

KINDRED HOSPITAL–ONTARIO (052037), 550 North Monterey Avenue, Zip 91764-3399; tel. 909/391-0333, (Nonreporting) **A**1 10 **S** Kindred Healthcare, Louisville, KY
Primary Contact: Vincent Trac, Chief Executive Officer
CFO: Omar Oregel, Controller
CMO: Marc Lynch, D.O., Chief of Staff
CHR: Laurel Scharber, Administrative Assistant and Coordinator Human Resources
CNO: Holly Ramos, R.N., Chief Clinical Officer
Web address: www.khontario.com/
Control: Corporation, Investor-owned (for-profit) **Service**: Acute long-term care hospital

Staffed Beds: 81

ORANGE—Orange County

☐ **CHAPMAN GLOBAL MEDICAL CENTER (050745)**, 2601 East Chapman Avenue, Zip 92869-3296; tel. 714/633-0011, (Nonreporting) **A**1 10 **S** KPC Healthcare, Inc., Santa Ana, CA
Primary Contact: Ada Yeh, Chief Executive Officer
CFO: John Collins, Corporate Chief Financial Officer
CMO: Gary Bennett, M.D., Chief of Medical Staff
CHR: JoAnne Suehs, Manager Human Resources
CNO: Ada Yeh, Chief Operating Officer and Chief Nursing Officer
Web address: www.Chapman-GMC.com
Control: Corporation, Investor-owned (for-profit) **Service**: General medical and surgical

Staffed Beds: 100

☐ **CHILDREN'S HOSPITAL OF ORANGE COUNTY (053304)**, 1201 West La Veta Avenue, Zip 92868-4203, Mailing Address: PO Box 5700, Zip 92863-5700; tel. 714/997-3000, **A**1 3 5 10 **F**3 14 17 19 21 23 25 27 29 30 31 32 34 35 40 41 43 50 55 57 58 59 60 61 64 65 66 68 71 72 74 75 77 78 79 81 82 84 85 86 87 88 89 91 92 93 97 100 101 104 107 111 113 114 115 118 119 121 123 126 129 130 131 132 134 136 146 149 153 154 **P**3 5
Primary Contact: Kimberly C. Cripe, President and Chief Executive Officer
COO: Matthew S Gerlach, Chief Operating Officer
CFO: Kerri Ruppert Schiller, Senior Vice President and Chief Financial Officer
CMO: Maria Minon, M.D., Vice President Medical Affairs and Chief Medical Officer
CIO: John Henderson, Vice President and Chief Information Officer
CHR: Mamoon Syed, Vice President Human Resources
CNO: Melanie Patterson, R.N., Vice President Patient Care Services and Chief Nursing Officer
Web address: www.choc.org
Control: Other not-for-profit (including NFP Corporation) **Service**: Children's general medical and surgical

Staffed Beds: 260 **Admissions:** 12898 **Census:** 169 **Outpatient Visits:** 562280 **Births:** 0 **Total Expense ($000):** 675398 **Payroll Expense ($000):** 195547 **Personnel:** 3067

⇑ **HEALTHBRIDGE CHILDREN'S HOSPITAL (053308)**, 393 South Tustin Street, Zip 92866-2501; tel. 714/289-2400, (Nonreporting) **A**10 21 **S** Nexus Health Systems, Houston, TX
Primary Contact: Alex Villarruz, Chief Executive Officer
CIO: Roberta Consolver, Chief Information Officer
Web address: www.HealthBridgeOrange.com
Control: Partnership, Investor-owned (for-profit) **Service**: Rehabilitation

Staffed Beds: 27

ST. JOSEPH HOSPITAL (050069), 1100 West Stewart Drive, Zip 92868-3849, Mailing Address: P.O. Box 5600, Zip 92863-5600; tel. 714/633-9111, **A**1 2 3 5 10 **F**3 5 8 12 13 15 17 18 19 20 22 24 26 28 29 30 31 34 35 37 40 41 45 46 47 49 50 51 53 54 55 57 58 59 60 64 65 68 69 70 74 75 76 77 78 79 80 81 82 84 85 86 87 91 92 93 98 100 101 102 104 105 107 108 109 110 111 113 114 115 116 117 118 119 120 121 123 124 126 129 130 131 132 135 138 141 146 147 148 149 152 153 154 **P**3 5 **S** Providence St. Joseph Health, Renton, WA
Primary Contact: Jeremy Zoch, Chief Executive
COO: Jeremy Zoch, Executive Vice President and Chief Operating Officer
CFO: Kristi Liberatore, Vice President and Chief Financial Officer
CMO: Scott Rusk, M.D., Chief Medical Officer
CIO: Jeremy Zoch, Executive Vice President and Chief Operating Officer
CHR: Mary P Leahy, Regional Vice Presiden, Chief Human Resources Officer
CNO: Katie Skelton, MSN, R.N., Vice President Nursing and Chief Nursing Officer
Web address: www.sjo.org
Control: Other not-for-profit (including NFP Corporation) **Service**: General medical and surgical

Staffed Beds: 379 **Admissions:** 21175 **Census:** 225 **Outpatient Visits:** 336728 **Births:** 4783 **Total Expense ($000):** 621531 **Payroll Expense ($000):** 187938 **Personnel:** 2489

UC IRVINE MEDICAL CENTER (050348), 101 The City Drive South, Zip 92868-3298; tel. 714/456-6011, **A**1 2 3 5 8 10 **F**3 6 8 9 11 12 13 14 15 16 17 18 19 20 21 22 24 26 27 28 29 30 31 32 34 35 36 37 39 40 41 43 44 45 46 47 48 49 50 51 53 54 55 56 57 58 59 60 61 64 65 66 68 70 71 72 73 74 75 76 77 78 79 80 81 82 84 85 86 87 88 89 90 91 92 93 96 97 98 99 100 101 102 104 105 107 108 110 111 114 115 116 117 118 119 120 121 123 124 126 130 131 132 134 135 138 141 142 144 145 148 149 150 153 154 **P**4 6 **S** University of California Systemwide Administration, Oakland, CA
Primary Contact: Richard Gannotta, Chief Executive Officer
COO: Richard Gannotta, Chief Operating Officer
CFO: Ajay Sial, Chief Financial Officer, UC Irvine Health
CMO: William Wilson, M.D., Chief Medical Officer
CIO: Charles H Podesta, Chief Information Officer
CHR: Ramona Agrela, Associate Chancellor & Chief Human Resources Executive
CNO: Sonia Lane, Interim Chief Nursing Officer
Web address: www.ucirvinehealth.org
Control: State, Government, nonfederal **Service**: General medical and surgical

Staffed Beds: 417 **Admissions:** 21173 **Census:** 338 **Outpatient Visits:** 786917 **Births:** 1802 **Total Expense ($000):** 1077291 **Payroll Expense ($000):** 407671 **Personnel:** 4365

OROVILLE—Butte County

★ **OROVILLE HOSPITAL (050030)**, 2767 Olive Highway, Zip 95966–6118;
tel. 530/533–8500, **A**10 **F**3 5 8 11 13 15 18 19 26 27 28 29 30 31 32 33 34
35 36 38 39 40 41 44 45 46 47 48 49 50 51 52 54 56 57 59 60 61 62 63 64
65 66 68 70 74 75 76 77 78 79 81 82 83 84 85 86 87 91 93 94 96 97 107
108 110 111 114 115 116 117 118 119 120 121 123 124 126 127 129 130
131 132 134 135 144 145 146 147 148 149
Primary Contact: Robert J. Wentz, President and Chief Executive Officer
COO: Scott Chapple, Chief Operating Officer
CFO: Ashok Khanchandani, Chief Financial Officer
CMO: Mathew N. Fine, M.D., Chief Medical Officer
CIO: Denise LeFevre, Chief Information Officer
CHR: Scott Chapple, Chief Operating Officer
CNO: Carol Speer–Smith, R.N., Chief Nursing Officer
Web address: www.orovillehospital.com
Control: Other not–for–profit (including NFP Corporation) **Service**: General
medical and surgical

Staffed Beds: 133 **Admissions:** 12769 **Census:** 120 **Outpatient
Visits:** 460566 **Births:** 395 **Total Expense ($000):** 257987 **Payroll Expense
($000):** 101280 **Personnel:** 1372

OXNARD—Ventura County

⊞ **ST. JOHN'S REGIONAL MEDICAL CENTER (050082)**, 1600 North Rose
Avenue, Zip 93030–3723; tel. 805/988–2500, (Nonreporting) **A**1 2 10 **S** Dignity
Health, San Francisco, CA
Primary Contact: Darren W. Lee, President and Chief Executive Officer
CFO: Donald P Bernard, Chief Financial Officer
CMO: Sahin Yanik, M.D., Vice President Medical Administration
CIO: Jeff Perry, Director Information Technology
CHR: Ed Gonzales, Vice President Human Resources
Web address: www.stjohnshealth.org
Control: Other not–for–profit (including NFP Corporation) **Service**: General
medical and surgical

Staffed Beds: 139

PALM SPRINGS—Riverside County

⊞ ⇑ **DESERT REGIONAL MEDICAL CENTER (050243)**, 1150 North Indian
Canyon Drive, Zip 92262–4872; tel. 760/323–6511, (Total facility includes 30
beds in nursing home–type unit) **A**1 2 3 10 13 21 **F**3 12 13 15 17 18 20 22 24
26 28 29 30 31 34 35 40 43 46 47 48 49 50 51 52 54 55 56 57 58 59
60 61 62 64 65 68 70 72 74 75 77 78 79 81 82 85 86 87 89 90 92 93 94 100
102 107 108 109 110 111 114 115 116 117 119 120 124 126 128 130 131
132 144 146 147 148 **S** TENET Healthcare Corporation, Dallas, TX
Primary Contact: Michele Finney, Chief Executive Officer
COO: James Santucci, Chief Operating Officer
CFO: Judi Stimson, Chief Financial Officer
CMO: Charles Anderson, M.D., Chief Medical Officer
CIO: Robert Klingseis, Director Information Systems
CHR: James Kelley, Chief Human Resources Officer
CNO: Beverly Fick, Chief Nursing Officer
Web address: www.desertregional.com
Control: Individual, Investor–owned (for–profit) **Service**: General medical and
surgical

Staffed Beds: 382 **Admissions:** 19661 **Census:** 288 **Outpatient
Visits:** 168102 **Births:** 3015 **Total Expense ($000):** 461071 **Payroll
Expense ($000):** 187196 **Personnel:** 1991

PALMDALE—Los Angeles County

☐ **PALMDALE REGIONAL MEDICAL CENTER (050204)**, 38600 Medical Center
Drive, Zip 93551–4483; tel. 661/382–5000, **A**1 10 **F**3 11 12 18 20 22 24 26
29 31 34 35 40 41 45 46 47 48 49 50 56 57 60 63 64 68 70 74 78 79 81 85
87 90 93 96 102 107 108 111 114 115 119 126 130 132 135 146 148 149
154 **S** Universal Health Services, Inc., King of Prussia, PA
Primary Contact: Richard Allen, Chief Executive Officer
CFO: Kurt Broten, Chief Financial Officer
CIO: Roy Singleton, Director Computer Information Systems
CHR: Karen Hickling, Director Human Resources
Web address: www.palmdaleregional.com
Control: Corporation, Investor–owned (for–profit) **Service**: General medical and
surgical

Staffed Beds: 184 **Admissions:** 9178 **Census:** 110 **Outpatient
Visits:** 78208 **Births:** 0 **Total Expense ($000):** 161229 **Payroll Expense
($000):** 64254 **Personnel:** 682

PALO ALTO—Santa Clara County

⊞ **LUCILE SALTER PACKARD CHILDREN'S HOSPITAL STANFORD (053305)**,
725 Welch Road, Zip 94304–1614; tel. 650/497–8000, **A**1 3 5 10 **F**3 7 8 11 12
13 17 19 25 27 28 29 30 31 32 34 35 36 38 39 44 45 46 47 48 49 50 52 54
55 57 58 59 60 61 64 65 66 68 71 72 73 74 75 76 77 78 79 80 81 82 84 85
86 87 88 89 91 92 93 96 97 99 100 101 104 107 111 115 119 124 126 129
130 131 132 134 136 137 138 139 140 141 142 144 145 146 148 149 154
P3
Primary Contact: Dennis Lund, M.D., Interim Chief Executive Officer
CMO: Dennis Lund, M.D., Chief Medical Officer
CIO: Kim Roberts, Chief Strategy Officer
CHR: Greg Souza, Vice President Human Resources
CNO: Kelly M Johnson, Chief Nursing Officer
Web address: www.stanfordchildrens.org
Control: Other not–for–profit (including NFP Corporation) **Service**: Children's
general medical and surgical

Staffed Beds: 251 **Admissions:** 12528 **Census:** 228 **Outpatient
Visits:** 92924 **Births:** 4329 **Total Expense ($000):** 1136731 **Payroll
Expense ($000):** 394211 **Personnel:** 3862

⊞ **STANFORD HEALTH CARE (050441)**, 300 Pasteur Drive, Suite H3200,
Zip 94304–2203; tel. 650/723–4000, **A**1 3 5 8 10 **F**3 5 6 8 9 11 12 14 15 17
18 20 22 24 26 28 29 30 31 33 34 35 36 37 38 40 41 43 45 46 47 48 49 50
51 54 55 56 57 58 59 60 61 64 65 68 70 74 75 77 78 79 80 81 82 84 85
86 87 92 93 95 96 97 98 100 102 104 107 108 110 111 114 115 117
118 119 120 121 123 124 126 129 130 131 132 135 136 137 138 139 140
141 142 145 146 147 148 149 150 154 **P**3 5 6 **S** Stanford Health Care, Palo
Alto, CA
Primary Contact: David Entwistle, President and Chief Executive Officer
COO: Quinn McKenna, Chief Operating Officer
CFO: Daniel Morrissette, Chief Financial Officer
CMO: Norman Rizk, M.D., Chief Medical Officer
CIO: Pravene Nath, Chief Information Officer
CHR: Kety Duron, Vice President Human Resources
CNO: Nancy Lee, R.N., MSN, Vice President Patient Care Services and Chief
Nursing Officer
Web address: www.stanfordhealthcare.org
Control: Other not–for–profit (including NFP Corporation) **Service**: General
medical and surgical

Staffed Beds: 477 **Admissions:** 26177 **Census:** 426 **Outpatient
Visits:** 1646161 **Births:** 0 **Total Expense ($000):** 3545136 **Payroll Expense
($000):** 1122339 **Personnel:** 10094

⊞ △ **VA PALO ALTO HEALTH CARE SYSTEM**, 3801 Miranda Avenue,
Zip 94304–1207; tel. 650/493–5000, (Includes PALO ALTO DIVISION, 3801
Miranda Avenue, Palo Alto, CA, Zip 94304–1207; tel. 650/493–5000; VETERANS
AFFAIRS PALO ALTO HEALTH CARE SYSTEM, LIVERMORE DIVISION, 4951 Arroyo
Road, Livermore, CA, Zip 94550; tel. 510/447–2560) (Nonreporting) **A**1 2 3 5 7
S Department of Veterans Affairs, Perry Point, MD
Primary Contact: Thomas J. Fitzgerald III, Interim Director
CFO: Mel Niese, Chief Fiscal Service
CMO: Lawrence Leung, M.D., Chief of Staff
CIO: Doug Wirthgen, Chief Information Officer
CHR: Lori Peery, Chief Human Resource Management Services
Web address: www.paloalto.va.gov/
Control: Veterans Affairs, Government, federal **Service**: General medical and
surgical

Staffed Beds: 808

PANORAMA CITY—Los Angeles County; See Los Angeles

PARADISE—Butte County

⊞ **ADVENTIST HEALTH FEATHER RIVER (050225)**, 5974 Pentz Road,
Zip 95969–5593; tel. 530/877–9361, (Nonreporting) **A**1 2 10 **S** Adventist Health,
Roseville, CA
Primary Contact: Monty E. Knittel, Chief Executive Officer
CFO: Dan Gordon, Chief Financial Officer
CMO: Anthony Nasr, M.D., Chief Medical Staff
CIO: Dan Gordon, Chief Financial Officer
CHR: Denton Gruzensky, Director Human Resources
Web address: www.frhosp.org
Control: Church operated, Nongovernment, not–for–profit **Service**: General
medical and surgical

Staffed Beds: 54

CA

Hospital, Medicare Provider Number, Address, Telephone, Approval, Facility, and Physician Codes, Health Care System

★ American Hospital Association (AHA) membership ○ Healthcare Facilities Accreditation Program ⇑ Center for Improvement in Healthcare Quality Accreditation
☐ The Joint Commission accreditation ◇ DNV Healthcare Inc. accreditation △ Commission on Accreditation of Rehabilitation Facilities (CARF) accreditation

---

CA

PASADENA—Los Angeles County

✠ **HUNTINGTON MEMORIAL HOSPITAL (050438)**, 100 West California Boulevard, Zip 91105–3097, Mailing Address: P.O. Box 7013, Zip 91109–7013; tel. 626/397–5000, (Nonreporting) **A**1 2 3 5 10
Primary Contact: Lori J. Morgan, M.D., President and Chief Executive Officer
CFO: James S Noble, Chief Financial Officer
CMO: Paula Verrette, M.D., Senior Vice President Quality and Physician Services and Chief Medical Officer
CIO: Debbie Tafoya, Vice President and Chief Information Officer
CHR: Debbie Ortega, Chief Human Resource Officer and Vice President Administrative Services
CNO: Gloria Sanchez–Rico, Chief Nursing Officer and Vice President
Web address: www.huntingtonhospital.com
Control: Other not–for–profit (including NFP Corporation) **Service**: General medical and surgical

Staffed Beds: 625

☐ **LAS ENCINAS HOSPITAL (054078)**, 2900 East Del Mar Boulevard, Zip 91107–4399; tel. 626/795–9901, (Nonreporting) **A**1 10 **S** Signature Healthcare Services, Corona, CA
Primary Contact: Thomas J. Mahle, Chief Executive Officer
CMO: Daniel Suzuki, M.D., Medical Director
CIO: Eric Kim, Chief Information Officer
CHR: Veronica Herrera, Director Human Resources
Web address: www.lasencinashospital.com
Control: Corporation, Investor–owned (for–profit) **Service**: Psychiatric

Staffed Beds: 138

PATTON—San Bernardino County

☐ **PATTON STATE HOSPITAL**, 3102 East Highland Avenue, Zip 92369–7813; tel. 909/425–7000, **A**1 3 **F**3 29 30 39 53 57 58 59 61 65 74 75 77 86 87 98 100 101 103 130 132 135 143 146 149 **P**1
Primary Contact: Harry Oreol, Acting Chief Executive Officer
CFO: Kathleen Gamble, Fiscal Officer
CMO: George Christison, M.D., Medical Director
CIO: Cindy Barrett, Administrative Assistant
CHR: Nancy Varela, Director Human Resources
Web address: www.dmh.cahwnet.gov/statehospitals/patton
Control: State, Government, nonfederal **Service**: Psychiatric

Staffed Beds: 1527 **Admissions:** 1487 **Census:** 1481 **Outpatient Visits:** 0 **Births:** 0 **Total Expense ($000):** 333291 **Payroll Expense ($000):** 210554 **Personnel:** 2329

PERRIS—Riverside County

★ **KINDRED HOSPITAL RIVERSIDE (052052)**, 2224 Medical Center Drive, Zip 92571–2638; tel. 951/436–3535, (Nonreporting) **A**10 **S** Kindred Healthcare, Louisville, KY
Primary Contact: William Mitchell, Chief Executive Officer and Administrator
COO: Guay Khim Fugate, Chief Operations Officer
CFO: John Browne, Senior Chief Financial Officer
CHR: Tom Wright, Director Human Resources
Web address: www.khriverside.com
Control: Corporation, Investor–owned (for–profit) **Service**: Acute long–term care hospital

Staffed Beds: 40

PETALUMA—Sonoma County

✠ **PETALUMA VALLEY HOSPITAL (050136)**, 400 North McDowell Boulevard, Zip 94954–2366; tel. 707/778–1111, **A**1 10 **F**3 11 13 15 29 30 31 35 40 44 45 46 49 50 51 57 60 63 64 68 70 74 75 76 77 78 79 81 84 85 87 91 92 93 100 107 108 110 111 115 119 130 146 148 149 150 154
Primary Contact: Todd Salnas, President
CFO: Michel Riccioni, Chief Financial Officer
CIO: Patrick Wylie, Director Information Systems
Web address: www.stjosephhealth.org/About–Us/Facilities/Petaluma–Valley–Hospital.aspx
Control: Other not–for–profit (including NFP Corporation) **Service**: General medical and surgical

Staffed Beds: 51 **Admissions:** 2421 **Census:** 28 **Outpatient Visits:** 59749 **Births:** 404 **Total Expense ($000):** 96551 **Payroll Expense ($000):** 32962 **Personnel:** 324

PLACENTIA—Orange County

✠ **PLACENTIA–LINDA HOSPITAL (050589)**, 1301 North Rose Drive, Zip 92870–3899; tel. 714/993–2000, (Nonreporting) **A**1 10 **S** TENET Healthcare Corporation, Dallas, TX
Primary Contact: Christina E. Oh, Chief Executive Officer
COO: Dwayne Richardson, Chief Operating Officer
CFO: Eric Delgado, Chief Financial Officer
CIO: Eleanor Laneaux, Director Information Systems
CHR: Michelle Miller, Chief Human Resources
CNO: Nancy Lee, Chief Nursing Officer
Web address: www.placentialinda.com
Control: Corporation, Investor–owned (for–profit) **Service**: General medical and surgical

Staffed Beds: 114

PLACERVILLE—El Dorado County

✠ **MARSHALL MEDICAL CENTER (050254)**, 1100 Marshall Way, Zip 95667–5722; tel. 530/622–1441, (Total facility includes 14 beds in nursing home–type unit) **A**1 2 10 **F**3 8 11 13 15 18 20 22 28 29 31 34 35 40 41 43 46 49 50 51 56 57 59 62 65 66 70 74 75 76 77 78 79 81 84 85 86 87 89 93 107 108 110 111 115 116 117 119 126 127 128 130 131 135 143 146 147 148 149 150 154 **P**3
Primary Contact: James Whipple, Chief Executive Officer
COO: Shannon Truesdell, Chief Operating Officer
CFO: Laurie Eldridge, Chief Financial Officer
CMO: Rajiv Pathak, Chief of Staff
CIO: Mike Jones, Executive Director
CHR: Scott M Comer, Vice President Human Resources
CNO: Kathy Blair Krejci, Chief Nursing Officer
Web address: www.marshallmedical.org
Control: Other not–for–profit (including NFP Corporation) **Service**: General medical and surgical

Staffed Beds: 119 **Admissions:** 5535 **Census:** 68 **Outpatient Visits:** 508906 **Births:** 492 **Total Expense ($000):** 249428 **Payroll Expense ($000):** 92447 **Personnel:** 1094

PLEASANTON—Alameda County

✠ **STANFORD HEALTH CARE – VALLEYCARE (050283)**, 5555 West Las Positas Boulevard, Zip 94588–4000; tel. 925/847–3000, (Includes VALLEY MEMORIAL, 1111 East Stanley Boulevard, Livermore, CA, Zip 94550–4115; tel. 925/447–7000) (Total facility includes 22 beds in nursing home–type unit) **A**1 2 10 **F**3 8 10 11 12 13 15 17 18 20 22 24 26 28 29 30 31 34 35 39 40 41 45 47 49 50 53 56 57 59 60 69 70 72 74 75 76 77 78 79 81 84 85 89 93 107 111 116 119 126 128 129 130 131 132 144 146 147 **S** Stanford Health Care, Palo Alto, CA
Primary Contact: Scott Gregerson, President and Chief Executive Officer
COO: Tracey Lewis–Taylor, Chief Operating Officer
CMO: David Svec, M.D., Chief Medical Officer
CIO: Bob Woods, Chief Information Officer
CHR: Chris Faber, Human Resources Analyst
Web address: www.valleycare.com
Control: Other not–for–profit (including NFP Corporation) **Service**: General medical and surgical

Staffed Beds: 193 **Admissions:** 7621 **Census:** 100 **Outpatient Visits:** 201092 **Births:** 1423 **Total Expense ($000):** 276257 **Payroll Expense ($000):** 121652 **Personnel:** 1123

POMONA—Los Angeles County

✠ △ **CASA COLINA HOSPITAL AND HEALTH SYSTEMS (053027)**, 255 East Bonita Avenue, Zip 91767–1923, Mailing Address: P.O. Box 6001, Zip 91769–6001; tel. 909/596–7733, **A**1 3 7 10 13 **F**2 3 15 18 28 29 30 34 35 37 44 45 46 48 49 50 53 54 56 57 58 59 64 65 68 70 74 75 79 81 85 86 87 90 91 92 93 95 96 97 104 107 108 110 111 115 118 119 126 130 131 132 134 145 146 147 148
Primary Contact: Felice L. Loverso, Ph.D., President and Chief Executive Officer
CFO: David Morony, Chief Financial Officer
CMO: Christopher Chalian, M.D., Medical Director
CIO: Ross Lesins, Chief Information Officer
CHR: Karen Du Pont, Chief Human Resource Officer
CNO: Kathryn Johnson, Chief Nursing Officer
Web address: www.casacolina.org
Control: Other not–for–profit (including NFP Corporation) **Service**: Rehabilitation

Staffed Beds: 99 **Admissions:** 2789 **Census:** 74 **Outpatient Visits:** 105223 **Births:** 0 **Total Expense ($000):** 82964 **Payroll Expense ($000):** 38474 **Personnel:** 490

⊞ **POMONA VALLEY HOSPITAL MEDICAL CENTER (050231)**, 1798 North Garey Avenue, Zip 91767–2918; tel. 909/865–9500, **A**1 2 3 5 10 **F**3 11 13 15 17 18 20 22 24 26 28 29 30 31 34 35 40 41 43 45 46 47 49 50 51 53 54 55 57 58 59 60 61 63 64 68 69 70 72 74 75 76 77 78 79 81 84 85 87 89 92 93 107 108 110 111 114 115 116 117 118 119 120 121 123 124 126 129 130 131 132 135 144 145 146 147 148 149 154 **P**5 7
Primary Contact: Richard E. Yochum, FACHE, President and Chief Executive Officer
CFO: Michael Nelson, Executive Vice President and Chief Financial Officer
CMO: Kenneth Nakamoto, M.D., Vice President Medical Affairs
CIO: Kent Hoyos, Chief Information Officer
CHR: Ray Inge, Vice President Human Resources
CNO: Darlene Scafiddi, R.N., MSN, Vice President Nursing and Patient Care Services
Web address: www.pvhmc.org
Control: Other not–for–profit (including NFP Corporation) **Service**: General medical and surgical

Staffed Beds: 399 **Admissions**: 22251 **Census**: 245 **Outpatient Visits**: 558026 **Births**: 6392 **Total Expense ($000)**: 605581 **Payroll Expense ($000)**: 259498 **Personnel**: 2700

PORTERVILLE—Tulare County

PORTERVILLE DEVELOPMENTAL CENTER (050546), 26501 Avenue 140, Zip 93257–9109, Mailing Address: P.O. Box 2000, Zip 93258–2000; tel. 559/782–2222, (Nonreporting) **A**10
Primary Contact: Theresa Billeci, Executive Director
COO: Betty Davis, Director Administrative Services
CFO: Karen Warren, Fiscal Officer
CMO: Joseph Mendoza, M.D., Medical Director
CIO: Vincent Chandler, Director Information Services
CHR: Shawna Gregg, Director Human Resources
CNO: Tom Shelton, Coordinator of Nursing Services
Web address: www.pdc.dds.ca.gov
Control: State, Government, nonfederal **Service**: Intellectual disabilities

Staffed Beds: 484

☐ **SIERRA VIEW MEDICAL CENTER (050261)**, 465 West Putnam Avenue, Zip 93257–3320; tel. 559/784–1110, (Total facility includes 35 beds in nursing home–type unit) **A**1 10 **F**3 8 13 15 20 22 29 30 31 34 35 40 45 49 54 57 59 60 65 68 70 72 75 76 78 79 81 84 85 87 89 93 107 108 110 111 114 115 119 120 121 123 124 130 132 135 144 146 147 148 149
Primary Contact: Donna J. Hefner, R.N., President and Chief Executive Officer
CFO: John Chivers, Senior Vice President Finance
CIO: Traci Follett, Director Clinical Infomatics
CHR: Sharon Brown, Vice President Human Resources
Web address: www.sierra–view.com
Control: Hospital district or authority, Government, nonfederal **Service**: General medical and surgical

Staffed Beds: 158 **Admissions**: 5536 **Census**: 91 **Outpatient Visits**: 177893 **Births**: 1454 **Total Expense ($000)**: 140880 **Payroll Expense ($000)**: 51022 **Personnel**: 819

PORTOLA—Plumas County

EASTERN PLUMAS HEALTH CARE (051300), 500 First Avenue, Zip 96122–9406; tel. 530/832–6500, (Nonreporting) **A**10 18
Primary Contact: Thomas P. Hayes, Chief Executive Officer
CFO: Katherine Pairish, Chief Financial Officer
CMO: Eric Bugna, M.D., Chief of Staff
CHR: Cathy Conant, Chief Human Resources and Personnel
Web address: www.ephc.org
Control: Hospital district or authority, Government, nonfederal **Service**: General medical and surgical

Staffed Beds: 66

POWAY—San Diego County

⊞ **POMERADO HOSPITAL (050636)**, 15615 Pomerado Road, Zip 92064–2460; tel. 858/613–4000, (Total facility includes 125 beds in nursing home–type unit) **A**1 10 **F**3 11 12 13 15 29 30 34 35 36 38 40 45 46 47 49 50 51 54 55 56 57 58 59 64 65 67 68 70 72 74 75 76 77 79 81 82 84 85 87 91 94 97 98 100 101 102 103 107 108 110 111 119 120 128 130 132 143 144 146 147 148 149 **P**3 **S** Palomar Health, Escondido, CA
Primary Contact: Cheryl Olson, Vice President
CIO: Steven Tanaka, Chief Information Officer
CHR: Brenda C Turner, Chief Human Resources Officer
Web address: www.pph.org
Control: Hospital district or authority, Government, nonfederal **Service**: General medical and surgical

Staffed Beds: 201 **Admissions**: 6378 **Census**: 165 **Outpatient Visits**: 89596 **Births**: 1079 **Total Expense ($000)**: 165116 **Payroll Expense ($000)**: 66135 **Personnel**: 722

QUINCY—Plumas County

☐ **PLUMAS DISTRICT HOSPITAL (051326)**, 1065 Bucks Lake Road, Zip 95971–9599; tel. 530/283–2121, (Nonreporting) **A**1 5 10 18
Primary Contact: Jeffrey Kepple, M.D., Chief Executive Officer
CMO: Vincent Frantz, M.D., Chief of Staff
CIO: Brenda Compton, Manager Information Technology
CHR: Denise Harding, Director Human Resources
Web address: www.pdh.org
Control: Hospital district or authority, Government, nonfederal **Service**: General medical and surgical

Staffed Beds: 25

RANCHO CUCAMONGA—San Bernardino County

⊞ **KINDRED HOSPITAL RANCHO (052049)**, 10841 White Oak Avenue, Zip 91730–3811; tel. 909/581–6400, (Nonreporting) **A**1 10 **S** Kindred Healthcare, Louisville, KY
Primary Contact: Victor Carrasco, Chief Executive Officer
COO: Jody Knox, Chief Operating Officer
Web address: www.khrancho.com
Control: Corporation, Investor–owned (for–profit) **Service**: Acute long–term care hospital

Staffed Beds: 55

RANCHO MIRAGE—Riverside County

⊞ △ **EISENHOWER MEDICAL CENTER (050573)**, 39000 Bob Hope Drive, Zip 92270–3221; tel. 760/340–3911, **A**1 2 3 7 10 **F**2 3 9 11 12 15 17 18 20 22 24 26 28 29 30 31 34 35 37 40 41 45 47 49 50 53 54 56 57 58 59 60 61 64 65 68 70 74 75 77 78 79 81 82 84 85 86 87 90 93 96 97 100 101 102 104 107 108 109 110 111 112 114 115 118 119 120 121 123 124 126 129 130 131 132 135 143 144 145 146 147 148 149 **P**3
Primary Contact: G Aubrey. Serfling, President and Chief Executive Officer
COO: Martin Massiello, Executive Vice President and Chief Operating Officer
CFO: Ken Wheat, Senior Vice President and Chief Financial Officer
CMO: Alan Williamson, M.D., Chief Medical Officer
CIO: David Perez, Vice President and Chief Information Officer
CHR: Liz Guignier, Vice President Human Resources
CNO: Ann R Mostofi, MSN, R.N., Vice President Patient Care and Chief Nursing Officer
Web address: www.emc.org
Control: Other not–for–profit (including NFP Corporation) **Service**: General medical and surgical

Staffed Beds: 410 **Admissions**: 19925 **Census**: 218 **Outpatient Visits**: 875987 **Births**: 0 **Total Expense ($000)**: 720375 **Payroll Expense ($000)**: 248481 **Personnel**: 3212

RED BLUFF—Tehama County

⊞ **ST. ELIZABETH COMMUNITY HOSPITAL (050042)**, 2550 Sister Mary Columba Drive, Zip 96080–4397; tel. 530/529–8000, (Nonreporting) **A**1 10 20 **S** Dignity Health, San Francisco, CA
Primary Contact: Jordan Wright, Chief Executive Officer
CFO: Kim Miranda, Chief Financial Officer
CMO: James DeSoto, M.D., Vice President Medical Affairs
CIO: Henry Niessink, Senior Manager Information Technology Systems
CHR: Denise Little, Director Human Resources
Web address: www.mercy.org
Control: Church operated, Nongovernment, not–for–profit **Service**: General medical and surgical

Staffed Beds: 65

REDDING—Shasta County

⊞ **MERCY MEDICAL CENTER REDDING (050280)**, 2175 Rosaline Avenue, Zip 96001–2549, Mailing Address: P.O. Box 496009, Zip 96049–6009; tel. 530/225–6000, (Nonreporting) **A**1 2 3 5 10 **S** Dignity Health, San Francisco, CA
Primary Contact: G. Todd. Smith, Chief Executive Officer
COO: Patrick Varga, Chief Operating Officer
CFO: Kimberly Miranda, Regional Vice President Finance and Chief Financial Officer
CMO: James DeSoto, M.D., Vice President Medical Affairs
CIO: Henry Niessink, Regional Director Information Technology Services
CNO: Kimberly Shaw, Vice President Patient Care and Chief Nursing Executive
Web address: www.mercy.org
Control: Church operated, Nongovernment, not–for–profit **Service**: General medical and surgical

Staffed Beds: 267

Hospital, Medicare Provider Number, Address, Telephone, Approval, Facility, and Physician Codes, Health Care System

★ American Hospital Association (AHA) membership
☐ The Joint Commission accreditation
○ Healthcare Facilities Accreditation Program
◇ DNV Healthcare Inc. accreditation
⇑ Center for Improvement in Healthcare Quality Accreditation
△ Commission on Accreditation of Rehabilitation Facilities (CARF) accreditation

NORTHERN CALIFORNIA REHABILITATION HOSPITAL See Vibra Hospital of Northern California

PATIENTS' HOSPITAL OF REDDING (050697), 2900 Eureka Way, Zip 96001–0220; tel. 530/225–8700, (Nonreporting) **A**10
Primary Contact: Shari Lejsek, Administrator
CFO: Kim Needles, Manager Business Office
CMO: James Tate, M.D., Chief of Staff
CIO: Kim Cameron, Manager Health Information Services
CHR: Brenda Meline, Manager Human Resources
CNO: Diane Rieke, Director Patient Care Services
Web address: www.patientshospital.com
Control: Individual, Investor–owned (for–profit) **Service:** Surgical

Staffed Beds: 10

SHASTA REGIONAL MEDICAL CENTER (050764), 1100 Butte Street, Zip 96001–0853, Mailing Address: P.O. Box 496072, Zip 96049–6072; tel. 530/244–5400, (Nonreporting) **A**1 5 10 **S** Prime Healthcare, Ontario, CA
Primary Contact: Casey Fatch, Chief Executive Officer
COO: Becky Levy, Chief Operating Officer
CFO: Becky Levy, Chief Financial Officer
CMO: Marcia McCampbell, M.D., Chief Medical Officer
CIO: Tony VanBoekel, Director Information Systems
CHR: Andrew Torge, Director Human Resources
Web address: www.shastaregional.com
Control: Corporation, Investor–owned (for–profit) **Service:** General medical and surgical

Staffed Beds: 113

VIBRA HOSPITAL OF NORTHERN CALIFORNIA (052047), 2801 Eureka Way, Zip 96001–0222; tel. 530/246–9000, (Nonreporting) **A**1 10 **S** Vibra Healthcare, Mechanicsburg, PA
Primary Contact: Chris Jones, Chief Executive Officer
COO: Lisa Stevens, Chief Clinical Officer and Chief Operating Officer
CFO: Rebecca Andrews, Chief Financial Officer
CMO: Nanda Kumar, M.D., Chief of Staff
CIO: Mark Cardenas, Director Plant Operations
CHR: Wendy Tempest, Director Human Resources
Web address: www.norcalrehab.com
Control: Corporation, Investor–owned (for–profit) **Service:** Acute long–term care hospital

Staffed Beds: 88

REDLANDS—San Bernardino County

LOMA LINDA UNIVERSITY BEHAVIORAL MEDICINE CENTER (054093), 1710 Barton Road, Zip 92373–5304; tel. 909/558–9200, (Data for 181 days) **A**1 3 5 10 **F**4 5 29 30 34 44 50 57 87 98 99 100 101 103 104 105 130 132 134 135 152 153 154 **P**3 **S** Loma Linda University Adventist Health Sciences Center, Loma Linda, CA
Primary Contact: Edward Field, Administrator
COO: Ruthita J Fike, Chief Executive Officer
CFO: Steve Mohr, Senior Vice President Finance and Chief Financial Officer
CMO: William Murdoch, M.D., Medical Director
CIO: Mark Zirkelback, Chief Information Officer
CHR: Mark Hubbard, Vice President Risk Management
CNO: Norie Lee Reyes Bencito Acaac, R.N., MS, Executive Director
Web address: www.llu.edu
Control: Other not–for–profit (including NFP Corporation) **Service:** Psychiatric

Staffed Beds: 89 Admissions: 2432 Census: 76 Outpatient Visits: 21910 Births: 0 Total Expense ($000): 19506 Payroll Expense ($000): 9407 Personnel: 258

REDLANDS COMMUNITY HOSPITAL (050272), 350 Terracina Boulevard, Zip 92373–0742, Mailing Address: P.O. Box 3391, Zip 92373–0742; tel. 909/335–5500, (Total facility includes 16 beds in nursing home–type unit) **A**1 10 **F**3 11 13 15 20 28 29 30 31 34 35 40 45 46 47 49 54 57 59 62 63 64 65 66 68 69 70 72 74 75 76 77 78 79 81 82 84 85 87 93 96 97 98 102 104 105 107 108 110 111 115 117 119 121 126 128 130 132 143 146 147 148 **P**5
Primary Contact: James R. Holmes, President and Chief Executive Officer
CFO: Michelle Mok, Chief Financial Officer
CHR: Lisa Guzman, Human Resource Vice President
CNO: Lauren Spilsbury, R.N., MSN, Vice President for Patient Care Services
Web address: www.redlandshospital.org
Control: Other not–for–profit (including NFP Corporation) **Service:** General medical and surgical

Staffed Beds: 197 Admissions: 11473 Census: 120 Outpatient Visits: 173016 Births: 2344 Total Expense ($000): 302976 Payroll Expense ($000): 101650 Personnel: 1420

REDWOOD CITY—San Mateo County

KAISER PERMANENTE REDWOOD CITY MEDICAL CENTER (050541), 1100 Veterans Boulevard, Zip 94063–2087; tel. 650/299–2000, **A**1 3 5 10 **F**3 8 11 13 18 20 22 26 29 30 31 34 35 40 44 49 50 51 57 58 60 62 63 68 70 73 74 75 76 77 78 79 81 82 84 85 87 100 107 108 110 111 114 115 119 130 146 149 154 **S** Kaiser Foundation Hospitals, Oakland, CA
Primary Contact: Michelle Gaskill–Hames, R.N., Senior Vice President & Area Manager
COO: Sheila Gilson, R.N., Chief Operating Officer
CFO: Doug Reynolds, Area Finance Officer
CMO: William Firtch, M.D., Physician In Chief
CHR: Kimberly A Seitz, Area Human Resources Leader
CNO: Jodi B. Galli, R.N., Chief Nursing Officer
Web address: www.kaiserpermanente.org
Control: Other not–for–profit (including NFP Corporation) **Service:** General medical and surgical

Staffed Beds: 145 Admissions: 8352 Census: 78 Outpatient Visits: 59018 Births: 1983

SEQUOIA HOSPITAL (050197), 170 Alameda De Las Pulgas, Zip 94062–2799; tel. 650/369–5811, **A**1 10 **F**11 12 13 15 18 20 22 24 26 28 29 30 31 32 34 35 37 40 45 46 49 50 53 57 59 60 64 68 70 74 75 76 77 78 79 81 84 86 87 92 93 94 107 108 110 111 115 118 119 120 121 123 124 126 130 132 135 146 147 149 154 **P**3 5 **S** Dignity Health, San Francisco, CA
Primary Contact: Bill Graham, President
CFO: Kim Osborn, Chief Financial Officer
CMO: Anita Chandrasena, M.D., Vice President Medical Affairs
CIO: Ian Vallely, Information Technology Site Leader
CHR: Linde Cheema, Vice President Human Resources
CNO: Sherie Ambrose, Chief Nurse Executive
Web address: www.sequoiahospital.org
Control: Other not–for–profit (including NFP Corporation) **Service:** General medical and surgical

Staffed Beds: 131 Admissions: 5506 Census: 54 Outpatient Visits: 79645 Births: 1450 Total Expense ($000): 281397 Payroll Expense ($000): 89698 Personnel: 698

REEDLEY—Fresno County

ADVENTIST MEDICAL CENTER–REEDLEY (050192), 372 West Cypress Avenue, Zip 93654–2199; tel. 559/638–8155, (Nonreporting) **A**1 3 10 **S** Adventist Health, Roseville, CA
Primary Contact: Wayne Ferch, President and Chief Executive Officer
CFO: Teresa Jacques, Interim Chief Financial Officer
CMO: Todd Spencer, M.D., Chief Medical Staff
CIO: Valerie Alvarez, Executive Assistant
CHR: Ramona Alvarado, Interim Manager Human Resources
Web address: www.skdh.org
Control: Hospital district or authority, Government, nonfederal **Service:** General medical and surgical

Staffed Beds: 49

RESEDA—Los Angeles County

JOYCE EISENBERG–KEEFER MEDICAL CENTER (054147), 7150 Tampa Avenue, Zip 91335–3700; tel. 818/774–3000, (Total facility includes 239 beds in nursing home–type unit) **A**1 10 **F**29 30 34 35 39 50 53 56 62 63 65 68 74 75 77 82 84 90 98 103 128 130 132 143 146 148 149 154
Primary Contact: Molly Forrest, President and Chief Executive Officer
CNO: Haya Berci, Executive Director of Nursing
Web address: www.jha.org
Control: Other not–for–profit (including NFP Corporation) **Service:** Psychiatric

Staffed Beds: 249 Admissions: 526 Census: 242 Outpatient Visits: 0 Births: 0 Total Expense ($000): 42431 Payroll Expense ($000): 18276 Personnel: 413

RICHMOND—Contra Costa County

KAISER PERMANENTE RICHMOND MEDICAL CENTER See Kaiser Permanente Oakland Medical Center, Oakland

RIDGECREST—Kern County

★ ⇑ **RIDGECREST REGIONAL HOSPITAL (051333)**, 1081 North China Lake Boulevard, Zip 93555–3130; tel. 760/446–3551, (Total facility includes 125 beds in nursing home–type unit) **A**10 18 21 **F**8 15 18 28 29 30 31 32 33 34 35 39 40 43 45 46 50 57 59 62 63 64 65 68 69 70 71 75 76 77 78 79 81 84 85 86 87 89 93 94 97 107 108 109 110 111 112 113 114 115 116 117 118 119 127 128 129 130 132 133 135 143 144 146 147 148 149 154
Primary Contact: James A. Suver, FACHE, Chief Executive Officer
CFO: John Chivers, Chief Financial Officer
CHR: Michelle Lemke, Administrator Human Resources and Support Services
Web address: www.rrh.org
Control: Other not–for–profit (including NFP Corporation) **Service:** General medical and surgical

Staffed Beds: 197 Admissions: 1848 Census: 92 Outpatient Visits: 231375 Births: 429 Total Expense ($000): 116382 Payroll Expense ($000): 41124 Personnel: 754

CA

RIVERSIDE—Riverside County

⊠ **KAISER PERMANENTE RIVERSIDE MEDICAL CENTER (050686)**, 10800 Magnolia Avenue, Zip 92505–3000; tel. 951/353–2000, **A**1 3 5 10 **F**3 13 15 17 28 29 30 31 34 35 40 44 45 46 48 49 50 51 59 60 62 63 64 65 68 70 71 72 74 75 76 77 78 79 81 82 84 85 86 87 89 92 93 97 100 102 107 108 109 110 111 114 115 116 117 118 119 130 131 132 135 143 144 146 147 148 149 150 154 **S** Kaiser Foundation Hospitals, Oakland, CA
Primary Contact: Vita M. Willett, Executive Director
COO: Robin D. Mackenroth, Chief Operating Officer
CFO: JiJi Abraham, Chief Financial Officer
CMO: Frank M. Flowers, M.D., Area Medical Director
CIO: Alfred T Velasquez, Area Information Officer
CHR: Michelle Skipper, Director Human Resources
CNO: Rosemary M Butler, R.N., MSN, Chief Nurse Executive
Web address: www.kaiserpermanente.org
Control: Other not-for-profit (including NFP Corporation) **Service:** General medical and surgical

Staffed Beds: 226 **Admissions:** 9750 **Census:** 117 **Outpatient Visits:** 62162 **Births:** 3326 **Personnel:** 1437

☐ **PACIFIC GROVE HOSPITAL (054130)**, 5900 Brockton Avenue, Zip 92506–1862; tel. 951/275–8400, (Nonreporting) **A**1 10 **S** Acadia Healthcare Company, Inc., Franklin, TN
Primary Contact: Nichol Sheffield, Chief Executive Officer
Web address: www.pacificgrovehospital.com
Control: Corporation, Investor-owned (for-profit) **Service:** Psychiatric

Staffed Beds: 68

☐ **PARKVIEW COMMUNITY HOSPITAL MEDICAL CENTER (050102)**, 3865 Jackson Street, Zip 92503–3998; tel. 951/688–2211, **A**1 10 **F**3 4 8 11 12 13 15 16 17 18 29 34 35 40 45 46 49 50 56 57 59 60 62 65 68 70 72 73 74 75 76 77 79 80 81 84 85 86 87 88 89 99 90 98 100 107 110 111 114 115 119 130 132 135 143 145 146 147 148 149 154
Primary Contact: Steven Popkin, Chief Executive Officer
COO: Robert Brown, Chief Operating Officer
CFO: Nancy Wilson, Chief Financial Officer
CMO: Serafin Salazar, M.D., Chief of Staff
CIO: John Ciccarelli, Director Information Technology
CHR: Ilyssa DeCasperis, Director of Human Resources
CNO: Karen T. Descent, Chief Nursing Officer
Web address: www.pchmc.org
Control: Other not-for-profit (including NFP Corporation) **Service:** General medical and surgical

Staffed Beds: 193 **Admissions:** 8392 **Census:** 94 **Outpatient Visits:** 67227 **Births:** 2068 **Total Expense ($000):** 152698 **Payroll Expense ($000):** 58460 **Personnel:** 921

RIVERSIDE CENTER FOR BEHAVIORAL MEDICINE See Pacific Grove Hospital

⊠ **RIVERSIDE COMMUNITY HOSPITAL (050022)**, 4445 Magnolia Avenue, Zip 92501–4199; tel. 951/788–3000, (Nonreporting) **A**1 2 3 5 10 **S** HCA Healthcare, Nashville, TN
Primary Contact: Patrick D. Brilliant, President and Chief Executive Officer
COO: Daniel Bowers, Chief Operating Officer
CFO: Todd LaCaze, Chief Financial Officer
CMO: David Tito, M.D., President Medical Staff
CIO: Cae Swanger, Chief Information Officer
CHR: Tammy Kaminski, Vice President Human Relations
CNO: Annette June Greenwood, Chief Nursing Officer
Web address: www.riversidecommunityhospital.com
Control: Corporation, Investor-owned (for-profit) **Service:** General medical and surgical

Staffed Beds: 373

RIVERSIDE MEDICAL CENTER See Kaiser Permanente Riverside Medical Center

ROSEMEAD—Los Angeles County

☐ **BHC ALHAMBRA HOSPITAL (054032)**, 4619 North Rosemead Boulevard, Zip 91770–1478, Mailing Address: P.O. Box 369, Zip 91770–0369; tel. 626/286–1191, (Nonreporting) **A**1 3 10 **S** Universal Health Services, Inc., King of Prussia, PA
Primary Contact: Peggy Minnick, R.N., Chief Executive Officer
CFO: Michelle Jackson, Chief Financial Officer
CMO: Wakelin McNeel, M.D., Medical Director
CIO: Debbie Irvin, Director Health Information Management
CHR: Venus Taylor, Director Human Resources
Web address: www.bhcalhambra.com
Control: Corporation, Investor-owned (for-profit) **Service:** Psychiatric

Staffed Beds: 97

ROSEVILLE—Placer County

⊠ **KAISER PERMANENTE ROSEVILLE MEDICAL CENTER (050772)**, 1600 Eureka Road, Zip 95661–3027; tel. 916/784–4000, **A**1 2 5 10 **F**3 8 13 18 20 22 24 29 30 31 32 35 39 40 45 46 47 49 50 51 61 64 68 70 72 73 75 76 78 79 81 84 86 87 88 89 107 108 109 110 111 112 114 115 116 117 118 119 122 130 146 148 149 154 **S** Kaiser Foundation Hospitals, Oakland, CA
Primary Contact: Jordan Herget, Senior Vice President and Manager
Web address: www.kp.org
Control: Other not-for-profit (including NFP Corporation) **Service:** General medical and surgical

Staffed Beds: 340 **Admissions:** 23362 **Census:** 242

⊠ **SUTTER ROSEVILLE MEDICAL CENTER (050309)**, One Medical Plaza Drive, Zip 95661–3037; tel. 916/781–1000, **A**1 2 5 10 **F**3 5 8 12 13 15 18 20 22 28 29 30 31 34 35 40 43 45 46 49 50 55 56 58 59 60 63 64 65 68 70 72 74 75 76 78 79 81 82 84 85 89 90 93 94 96 107 108 109 111 114 116 119 126 130 131 132 141 146 147 148 154 **P**3 5 **S** Sutter Health, Sacramento, CA
Primary Contact: Brian Alexander, Chief Executive Officer
COO: Dionne Miller, Chief Operating Officer
CFO: Gary Hubschman, Administrative Director Finance
CMO: Stuart Bostrom, M.D., Director Medical Affairs
CIO: Nancy Turner, Director Communications
CHR: Lynda Dasaro, Director Human Resources
CNO: Barbara J Nelson, Ph.D., R.N., Chief Nursing Executive
Web address: www.sutterroseville.org
Control: Other not-for-profit (including NFP Corporation) **Service:** General medical and surgical

Staffed Beds: 328 **Admissions:** 19625 **Census:** 247 **Outpatient Visits:** 162065 **Births:** 2479 **Total Expense ($000):** 551055 **Payroll Expense ($000):** 173830 **Personnel:** 1688

SACRAMENTO—Sacramento County

☐ **HERITAGE OAKS HOSPITAL (054104)**, 4250 Auburn Boulevard, Zip 95841–4164; tel. 916/489–3336, (Nonreporting) **A**1 3 5 10 **S** Universal Health Services, Inc., King of Prussia, PA
Primary Contact: Shawn Silva, Chief Executive Officer
CFO: Art Wong, Chief Financial Officer
CMO: Joseph Sison, M.D., Medical Director
CHR: Lisa Myers, Director Human Resources
Web address: www.heritageoakshospital.com
Control: Corporation, Investor-owned (for-profit) **Service:** Psychiatric

Staffed Beds: 120

⊠ **KAISER PERMANENTE SACRAMENTO MEDICAL CENTER (050425)**, 2025 Morse Avenue, Zip 95825–2100; tel. 916/973–5000, **A**1 2 3 5 10 **F**3 8 17 18 20 22 29 30 31 34 35 40 41 44 45 46 48 49 50 51 56 57 60 64 68 70 74 75 77 78 79 81 82 84 85 102 107 108 111 114 115 118 119 120 129 130 146 148 149 154 **S** Kaiser Foundation Hospitals, Oakland, CA
Primary Contact: Sandy Sharon, Senior Vice President and Area Manager
CFO: Jim Eldridge, Area Financial Officer
CMO: Chris Palkowski, M.D., Physician in Chief
CIO: Philip Fasano, Chief Information Officer
CHR: Gay Westfall, Senior Vice President Human Resources
Web address: www.kp.org
Control: Other not-for-profit (including NFP Corporation) **Service:** General medical and surgical

Staffed Beds: 200 **Admissions:** 11766 **Census:** 126 **Births:** 0

CA

Hospital, Medicare Provider Number, Address, Telephone, Approval, Facility, and Physician Codes, Health Care System

★ American Hospital Association (AHA) membership   ○ Healthcare Facilities Accreditation Program   ⇑ Center for Improvement in Healthcare Quality Accreditation
☐ The Joint Commission accreditation   ◇ DNV Healthcare Inc. accreditation   △ Commission on Accreditation of Rehabilitation Facilities (CARF) accreditation

CA

✠ **KAISER PERMANENTE SOUTH SACRAMENTO MEDICAL CENTER (050674)**,
6600 Bruceville Road, Zip 95823–4691; tel. 916/688–2430, **A**1 3 5 10 **F**3 12
13 15 18 20 22 29 30 31 34 35 40 43 44 45 47 49 50 51 58 59 60 61 62 63
64 65 68 70 73 74 75 76 77 78 79 81 82 84 85 86 87 89 93 96 97 100 104
107 108 110 111 114 115 119 120 126 129 130 131 135 144 146 147 148
149 150 154 **S** Kaiser Foundation Hospitals, Oakland, CA
Primary Contact: Patricia M. Rodriguez, Senior Vice President and Area Manager
CFO: Kevin L Smith, Area Finance Officer
CIO: Michelle Odell, Director of Public Affairs
CHR: James Kevin Peterson, Human Resources Leader
CNO: Terri Owensby, R.N., Chief Nursing Executive
Web address: www.kp.org
Control: Other not–for–profit (including NFP Corporation) **Service**: General
medical and surgical

Staffed Beds: 217 **Admissions:** 18342 **Census:** 158 **Births:** 2633

✠ △ **MERCY GENERAL HOSPITAL (050017)**, 4001 'J' Street,
Zip 95819–3600; tel. 916/453–4545, **A**1 2 3 5 7 10 **F**3 8 11 13 15 17 18 20
22 24 26 28 29 30 31 34 35 36 37 38 39 40 44 45 46 47 48 49 50 51 53 56
57 58 59 63 64 66 68 70 74 75 76 77 78 79 81 82 85 86 87 90 91 93 94
96 100 107 108 109 111 114 115 119 124 126 130 131 132 135 143 145
146 149 154 **P**3 5 **S** Dignity Health, San Francisco, CA
Primary Contact: Edmundo Castaneda, President
COO: Clare Lee, Chief Operating Officer
CFO: Bonnie Jenkins, Chief Financial Officer
CMO: Brian Evans, M.D., Esq Chief Medical Officer
CHR: Cyndi Kirch, Vice President Human Resources
CNO: Allison Cotterill, Chief Nursing Officer
Web address: www.mercygeneral.org
Control: Other not–for–profit (including NFP Corporation) **Service**: General
medical and surgical

Staffed Beds: 305 **Admissions:** 14682 **Census:** 166 **Outpatient
Visits:** 101049 **Births:** 1088 **Total Expense ($000):** 556526 **Payroll
Expense ($000):** 188910 **Personnel:** 1725

✠ **METHODIST HOSPITAL OF SACRAMENTO (050590)**, 7500 Hospital Drive,
Zip 95823–5477; tel. 916/423–3000, (Nonreporting) **A**1 3 5 10 **S** Dignity Health,
San Francisco, CA
Primary Contact: Phyllis Baltz, Chief Executive Officer
COO: Anita J Kennedy, Vice President Operations
CFO: Bonnie Jenkins, Chief Financial Officer
CMO: Amir Sweha, M.D., Vice President Medical Administration
CHR: Cyndi Kirch, Vice President Human Resources
CNO: Martina Evans–Harrison, R.N., MSN, Chief Nurse Executive
Web address: www.methodistsacramento.org
Control: Other not–for–profit (including NFP Corporation) **Service**: General
medical and surgical

Staffed Beds: 281

☐ **SHRINERS HOSPITALS FOR CHILDREN–NORTHERN CALIFORNIA (053311)**,
2425 Stockton Boulevard, Zip 95817–2215; tel. 916/453–2000, (Nonreporting)
A1 3 5 10 **S** Shriners Hospitals for Children, Tampa, FL
Primary Contact: Margaret Bryan, Administrator
COO: Margaret Bryan, Administrator
CFO: William Dalby, Director Fiscal Services
CIO: John Bevel, Manager Information Systems
CHR: Deborah Rubens, Director Human Resources
Web address: www.shrinershospitalsforchildren.org/Hospitals/Locations/
NorthernCalifornia.aspx
Control: Other not–for–profit (including NFP Corporation) **Service**: Children's
general medical and surgical

Staffed Beds: 70

☐ **SIERRA VISTA HOSPITAL (054087)**, 8001 Bruceville Road, Zip 95823–2329;
tel. 916/288–0300, (Nonreporting) **A**1 10 **S** Universal Health Services, Inc., King
of Prussia, PA
Primary Contact: Mike Zauner, Chief Executive Officer
COO: Ixel Morell, Chief Operating Officer
CFO: Nicole Samuel, Chief Financial Officer
CMO: Alok Banga, M.D., Medical Director
CNO: Gwen Hubbard, Chief Nursing Officer
Web address: www.sierravistahospital.com
Control: Corporation, Investor–owned (for–profit) **Service**: Psychiatric

Staffed Beds: 120

SOUTH SACRAMENTO MEDICAL CENTER See Kaiser Permanente South
Sacramento Medical Center

✠ **SUTTER CENTER FOR PSYCHIATRY (054096)**, 7700 Folsom Boulevard,
Zip 95826–2608; tel. 916/386–3000, **A**1 10 **F**4 29 30 34 35 44 68 98 99 100
101 104 105 130 132 134 143 149 153 **S** Sutter Health, Sacramento, CA
Primary Contact: John W. Boyd, PsyD, Chief Executive Officer
CFO: Pamela Ansley, Director Finance
CMO: Cindy Thygeson, M.D., Director Medical Affairs
CHR: Kristin Daniels, Manager Human Resources
Web address: www.sutterpsychiatry.org
Control: Other not–for–profit (including NFP Corporation) **Service**: Psychiatric

Staffed Beds: 71 **Admissions:** 2836 **Census:** 56 **Outpatient Visits:** 4345
Births: 0 **Total Expense ($000):** 36256 **Payroll Expense ($000):** 15545
Personnel: 230

✠ **SUTTER MEDICAL CENTER, SACRAMENTO (050108)**, 2801 'L' Street,
Zip 95816–5680; tel. 916/454–3333, (Includes SUTTER CHILDREN'S CENTER,
5151 F Street, Sacramento, CA, Zip 95819–3223; tel. 800/478–8837;
SUTTER GENERAL HOSPITAL, 2801 'L' Street, Sacramento, CA, Zip 95816;
tel. 916/454–2222) **A**1 2 3 5 10 **F**3 11 12 15 17 18 19 20 21 22 23 24 25 26
27 28 29 30 31 34 35 36 37 39 40 41 45 46 48 49 55 56 58 59 61 63 64 68
70 72 74 75 76 77 78 79 81 84 85 86 87 88 89 93 102 107 108 111 114 115
118 119 124 126 129 130 132 134 136 137 146 147 148 149 154 **P**3 5 **S**
Sutter Health, Sacramento, CA
Primary Contact: David Cheney, Chief Executive Officer
CFO: Richard SooHoo, Chief Financial Officer
CMO: Muhammed Afzal, M.D., Chief of Staff
CIO: Jim Mills, Regional Director Information Technology
CHR: Colleen Peschel, Director Human Resources
CNO: Marchelle M McGriff, Chief Nursing Executive
Web address: www.sutterhealth.org
Control: Other not–for–profit (including NFP Corporation) **Service**: General
medical and surgical

Staffed Beds: 523 **Admissions:** 29651 **Census:** 378 **Outpatient
Visits:** 251351 **Births:** 6720 **Total Expense ($000):** 1090013 **Payroll
Expense ($000):** 309832 **Personnel:** 3166

✠ **UNIVERSITY OF CALIFORNIA, DAVIS MEDICAL CENTER (050599)**, 2315
Stockton Boulevard, Zip 95817–2282; tel. 916/734–2011, (Includes UNIVERSITY
OF CALIFORNIA DAVIS CHILDREN'S HOSPITAL, 2315 Stockton Boulevard,
Sacramento, CA, Zip 95817–2201; tel. 800/282–3284; Ann Madden Rice, Chief
Executive Officer) **A**1 2 3 5 8 10 **F**3 5 6 8 9 11 12 13 15 16 17 18 19 20 21 22
23 24 25 26 27 28 29 30 31 32 34 35 36 37 38 39 40 41 43 44 45 46 47 48
49 50 51 53 54 55 56 57 58 59 60 61 62 63 64 65 66 68 70 72 73 74 75 76
77 78 79 81 82 83 84 85 86 87 88 89 90 91 92 93 94 95 96 97 99 100 101
102 103 104 107 108 110 111 114 115 116 117 118 119 120 121 123 124
126 129 130 131 132 134 135 136 138 141 142 145 146 147 148 149 150
153 154 **P**6 **S** University of California Systemwide Administration, Oakland, CA
Primary Contact: Ann Madden. Rice, Chief Executive Officer
COO: Brad Simmons, Chief Operating Officer
CFO: Timothy Maurice, Chief Financial Officer
CMO: J. Douglas Kirk, M.D., Chief Medical Officer
CIO: John Cook, Interim Chief Information Officer
CHR: Stephen Chilcott, Associate Director Human Resources
CNO: Toby Marsh, MSN, R.N., Interim Chief Patient Care Services Officer
Web address: www.ucdmc.ucdavis.edu
Control: Other not–for–profit (including NFP Corporation) **Service**: General
medical and surgical

Staffed Beds: 601 **Admissions:** 34698 **Census:** 532 **Outpatient
Visits:** 1117191 **Births:** 1602 **Total Expense ($000):** 1983664 **Payroll
Expense ($000):** 844408 **Personnel:** 8459

SAINT HELENA—Napa County

✠ **ADVENTIST HEALTH ST. HELENA (050013)**, 10 Woodland Road,
Zip 94574–9554; tel. 707/963–3611, **A**1 10 **F**3 8 15 17 18 20 22 24 26 28
29 30 31 34 35 36 37 40 45 47 50 51 53 56 57 58 59 60 62 64 65 70 74 75
76 77 78 79 81 82 84 85 86 87 92 97 98 100 101 102 103 104 105 107 108
110 111 115 117 119 120 121 126 130 131 135 146 147 148 153 154 **P**3 **S**
Adventist Health, Roseville, CA
Primary Contact: Steven Herber, M.D., FACS, President and Chief Executive Officer
COO: Hal Chilton, Senior Vice President and Chief Operating Officer
CMO: Timothy Lyons, M.D., Chief Medical Officer
CIO: David Noll, Director
CHR: Audrey Barrall, Director Human Resources
CNO: Nia Lendaris, Regional Vice President Patient Care
Web address: www.sthelenahospital.org
Control: Church operated, Nongovernment, not–for–profit **Service**: General
medical and surgical

Staffed Beds: 116 **Admissions:** 4502 **Census:** 49 **Outpatient Visits:** 45227
Births: 207

Many Facility Codes have changed. Please refer to the AHA Guide Code Chart.   © 2018 AHA Guide

CA

SALINAS—Monterey County

☒ **NATIVIDAD MEDICAL CENTER (050248)**, 1441 Constitution Boulevard, Zip 93906–3100, Mailing Address: P.O. Box 81611, Zip 93912–1611; tel. 831/647–7611, (Nonreporting) **A**1 3 5 10
Primary Contact: Gary Gray, D.O., Chief Executive Officer
CMO: Craig Walls, M.D., Ph.D., Chief Medical Officer
CIO: Ari Entin, Chief Information Officer
CHR: Lawanda Janine Bouyea, Director Human Resources
Web address: www.natividad.com
Control: County, Government, nonfederal **Service**: General medical and surgical

Staffed Beds: 166

☒ **SALINAS VALLEY MEMORIAL HEALTHCARE SYSTEM (050334)**, 450 East Romie Lane, Zip 93901–4098; tel. 831/757–4333, **A**1 2 10 **F**3 13 15 17 18 19 20 22 24 26 28 29 30 31 34 35 37 40 45 46 49 50 57 58 59 64 66 68 70 72 74 75 76 77 78 79 81 84 85 87 89 107 108 110 111 115 118 119 127 129 130 131 132 144 146 147 148 149
Primary Contact: Pete Delgado, President and Chief Executive Officer
COO: Henry Ornelas, Chief Operating Officer
CFO: Augustine Lopez, Chief Financial Officer
CMO: Allen Radner, M.D., Chief Medical Officer
CIO: Audrey Parks, Chief Information Officer
CHR: Michelle Childs, Chief Human Resources Officer
CNO: Christie Gonder, R.N., Chief Nursing Officer
Web address: www.svmh.com
Control: Hospital district or authority, Government, nonfederal **Service**: General medical and surgical

Staffed Beds: 214 Admissions: 10056 Census: 124 Outpatient Visits: 115982 Births: 1728 Total Expense ($000): 418357 Payroll Expense ($000): 219444 Personnel: 1473

SAN ANDREAS—Calaveras County

☒ **MARK TWAIN MEDICAL CENTER (051332)**, 768 Mountain Ranch Road, Zip 95249–9998; tel. 209/754–3521, **A**1 10 18 **F**3 15 28 29 30 31 34 35 40 45 50 57 59 65 68 70 75 77 78 79 81 87 93 100 101 107 110 111 115 119 127 130 131 132 133 135 146 147 148 149 **P**6 **S** Dignity Health, San Francisco, CA
Primary Contact: Robert Diehl, President
CFO: Jacob Lewis, Chief Financial Officer
CHR: Nancy Vargas, Director Human Resources
Web address: www.marktwainhospital.com
Control: Church operated, Nongovernment, not–for–profit **Service**: General medical and surgical

Staffed Beds: 25 Admissions: 917 Census: 10 Outpatient Visits: 72486 Births: 0 Total Expense ($000): 69438 Payroll Expense ($000): 24918

SAN BERNARDINO—San Bernardino County

☒ △ **BALLARD REHABILITATION HOSPITAL (053037)**, 1760 West 16th Street, Zip 92411–1160; tel. 909/473–1200, (Nonreporting) **A**1 7 10 **S** Vibra Healthcare, Mechanicsburg, PA
Primary Contact: Mary Miles. Hunt, Chief Executive Officer
CMO: Van Chen, M.D., Medical Director
CNO: Chris Bauman, Director of Nursing
Web address: www.ballardrehab.com
Control: Corporation, Investor–owned (for–profit) **Service**: Rehabilitation

Staffed Beds: 55

☒ **COMMUNITY HOSPITAL OF SAN BERNARDINO (050089)**, 1805 Medical Center Drive, Zip 92411–1214; tel. 909/887–6333, (Nonreporting) **A**1 10 **S** Dignity Health, San Francisco, CA
Primary Contact: June Collison, President
COO: Victoria Selby MHA, BSN, Vice President, Ancillary and Support Services
CFO: Dave Evans, Chief Financial Officer
CMO: Andrew Fragen, M.D., Chief Medical Officer
CIO: James Borrenpohl, Market Site Director
CHR: Deena Marano, Human Resources Director
CNO: Roz Nolan, Interim Chief Nursing Officer
Web address: www.dignityhealth.org/san–bernardino
Control: Other not–for–profit (including NFP Corporation) **Service**: General medical and surgical

Staffed Beds: 379

☒ **ST. BERNARDINE MEDICAL CENTER (050129)**, 2101 North Waterman Avenue, Zip 92404–4855; tel. 909/883–8711, **A**1 3 10 **F**3 8 11 12 13 15 17 18 20 22 24 26 28 29 30 31 34 35 40 44 45 46 47 49 50 54 57 58 59 60 64 65 66 68 70 72 74 75 76 77 78 79 81 84 85 86 87 92 93 102 107 108 110 111 114 119 120 121 126 130 131 132 134 144 146 147 148 149 154 **P**8 **S** Dignity Health, San Francisco, CA
Primary Contact: Douglas V. Kleam, President
CMO: Betty Daniels, M.D., Chief of Staff
CIO: James Croker, Director Information Systems
CHR: Dee Webb, Vice President Human Resources
Web address: www.stbernardinemedicalcenter.com
Control: Other not–for–profit (including NFP Corporation) **Service**: General medical and surgical

Staffed Beds: 342 Admissions: 14481 Census: 174 Outpatient Visits: 171944 Births: 1304 Total Expense ($000): 388187 Payroll Expense ($000): 137562 Personnel: 1452

SAN DIEGO—San Diego County

☒ **ALVARADO HOSPITAL MEDICAL CENTER (050757)**, 6655 Alvarado Road, Zip 92120–5208; tel. 619/287–3270, (Nonreporting) **A**1 3 10 **S** Prime Healthcare, Ontario, CA
Primary Contact: Robin Gomez, R.N., MSN, Administrator
CMO: Larry Emdur, D.O., Chief Medical Officer
CIO: Wayne Bartlett, Director Information Systems
CHR: Sara Turner, Director Human Resources
CNO: Peggy Jezsu, Chief Nursing Officer
Web address: www.alvaradohospital.com
Control: Corporation, Investor–owned (for–profit) **Service**: General medical and surgical

Staffed Beds: 306

☐ **AURORA BEHAVIORAL HEALTHCARE SAN DIEGO (054095)**, 11878 Avenue of Industry, Zip 92128–3490; tel. 858/487–3200, (Nonreporting) **A**1 10 **S** Signature Healthcare Services, Corona, CA
Primary Contact: Alain Azcona, Chief Executive Officer
COO: Barbara Kennison, Director Clinical Services
CFO: Gene Fantano, Chief Financial Officer
CMO: Thomas Flanagan, M.D., Medical Director
CIO: Alain Azcona, Director Business Development
CHR: Susan Haas, Director Human Resources
Web address: www.sandiego.aurorabehavioral.com/
Control: Corporation, Investor–owned (for–profit) **Service**: Psychiatric

Staffed Beds: 80

☒ **KAISER PERMANENTE SAN DIEGO MEDICAL CENTER (050515)**, 4647 Zion Avenue, Zip 92120–2507; tel. 619/528–5000, (Includes KAISER PERMANENTE SAN DIEGO MEDICAL CENTER, 9455 Clairemont Mesa Boulevard, San Diego, CA, Zip 92123–1297; tel. 800/282–3284; Jane Finley, Senior Vice President and Area Manager) **A**1 3 5 10 **F**3 8 13 15 18 19 26 28 29 30 31 33 34 35 38 40 41 45 46 47 48 49 50 51 54 56 57 60 61 64 65 68 70 72 74 75 76 77 78 79 81 82 84 85 86 87 89 94 97 100 102 104 107 108 110 111 114 115 117 118 119 126 130 131 146 148 149 154 **S** Kaiser Foundation Hospitals, Oakland, CA
Primary Contact: Jane Finley, Senior Vice President & Area Manager
COO: Sam Totah, Chief Operating Officer
CFO: Lynette Seid, Area Chief Financial Officer
CMO: Paul E Bernstein, M.D., Area Medical Director
CIO: Laura Sullivant, Area Chief Information Officer
CHR: Jocelyn A. Herrera, Human Resources Director
CNO: Anne Marie Watkins, Chief Nurse Executive
Web address: www.kaiserpermanente.org
Control: Other not–for–profit (including NFP Corporation) **Service**: General medical and surgical

Staffed Beds: 541 Admissions: 34589 Census: 606 Outpatient Visits: 161676 Births: 4660 Personnel: 4495

☒ **KINDRED HOSPITAL–SAN DIEGO (052036)**, 1940 El Cajon Boulevard, Zip 92104–1096; tel. 619/543–4500, **A**1 10 **F**1 3 29 107 119 130 148 **S** Kindred Healthcare, Louisville, KY
Primary Contact: Kerry Ashment, Chief Executive Officer
CMO: Davies Wong, M.D., Medical Director
CHR: Jody Dewen Moore, District Director Human Resources
CNO: Maureen Bodine, Chief Clinical Officer
Web address: www.kindredsandiego.com
Control: Corporation, Investor–owned (for–profit) **Service**: Acute long–term care hospital

Staffed Beds: 58 Admissions: 569 Census: 52 Outpatient Visits: 0 Births: 0 Total Expense ($000): 36182 Payroll Expense ($000): 16775 Personnel: 162

Hospital, Medicare Provider Number, Address, Telephone, Approval, Facility, and Physician Codes, Health Care System

★ American Hospital Association (AHA) membership ○ Healthcare Facilities Accreditation Program ⇑ Center for Improvement in Healthcare Quality Accreditation
☐ The Joint Commission accreditation ◇ DNV Healthcare Inc. accreditation △ Commission on Accreditation of Rehabilitation Facilities (CARF) accreditation

CA

NAVAL MEDICAL CENTER SAN DIEGO, 34800 Bob Wilson Drive, Zip 92134–5000; tel. 619/532–6400, (Nonreporting) **A**1 2 3 5 **S** Bureau of Medicine and Surgery, Department of the Navy, Falls Church, VA
Primary Contact: Captain Joel A. Roos, Commanding Officer
CFO: Commander Thomas J. Piner, Director for Resources Management
CIO: Lieutenant Commander Ryan Jarmer, Chief Information Officer
Web address: www.med.navy.mil/sites/nmcsd/Pages/default.aspx
Control: Navy, Government, federal **Service**: General medical and surgical

Staffed Beds: 285

PROMISE HOSPITAL OF SAN DIEGO (052051), 5550 University Avenue, Zip 92105–2307; tel. 619/582–3800, (Nonreporting) **A**1 10 **S** Promise Healthcare, Boca Raton, FL
CFO: Kevin Ohler, Director of Finance
CMO: Larry Emdur, D.O., Chief of Staff
CIO: Jim Wilson, Vice President Information Technology
CHR: Kathleen Greene, Director Human Resources
CNO: Kevin Wood, Interim Chief Clinical Officer
Web address: www.promisesandiego.com
Control: Corporation, Investor–owned (for–profit) **Service**: Acute long–term care hospital

Staffed Beds: 100

RADY CHILDREN'S HOSPITAL – SAN DIEGO (053303), 3020 Childrens Way, Zip 92123–4223; tel. 858/576–1700, (Total facility includes 43 beds in nursing home–type unit) **A**1 3 5 10 **F**1 3 4 7 8 9 10 11 16 17 19 20 21 22 23 24 25 26 27 28 29 30 31 32 34 35 36 38 39 40 41 43 45 46 47 48 50 51 54 55 57 58 59 60 61 62 63 64 65 66 67 68 70 71 72 73 74 75 77 78 79 80 81 82 83 84 85 86 87 88 89 90 91 92 93 94 98 99 100 101 102 104 107 108 111 114 115 118 119 122 124 128 129 130 131 132 134 135 136 137 138 141 143 144 145 146 148 149 150 153 154 **P**3 5
Primary Contact: Patricio A. Frias, M.D., President and Chief Executive Officer
COO: Meg Norton, Executive Vice President and Chief Administrative Officer
CFO: Roger Roux, Chief Financial Officer
CMO: Irvin A Kaufman, M.D., Chief Medical Officer
CIO: Albert Oriol, Vice President Information Management and Chief Information Officer
CHR: Mamoon Syed, Vice President Human Resources
CNO: Mary Fagan, MSN, R.N., Chief Nursing Officer
Web address: www.rchsd.org
Control: Other not–for–profit (including NFP Corporation) **Service**: Children's general medical and surgical

Staffed Beds: 432 Admissions: 20658 Census: 307 Outpatient Visits: 533184 Births: 0 Total Expense ($000): 1058963 Payroll Expense ($000): 356364 Personnel: 4499

RADY CHILDREN'S HOSPITAL AND HEALTH CENTER See Rady Children's Hospital – San Diego

SAN DIEGO COUNTY PSYCHIATRIC HOSPITAL (054114), 3853 Rosecrans Street, Zip 92110–3115, Mailing Address: P.O. Box 85524, Zip 92186–5524; tel. 619/692–8211, (Nonreporting) **A**1 10
Primary Contact: Izabela Karmach, R.N., Administrator
COO: Izabela Karmach, R.N., Administrator
CFO: Raul J Loyo–Rodriguez, Administrative Analyst III
CMO: Michael Krelstein, M.D., Medical Director
CIO: Linda Cannon, Chief Medical Records Services
CHR: Francisco Puentes, Human Resource Officer
Web address: www.sdcounty.ca.gov
Control: County, Government, nonfederal **Service**: Psychiatric

Staffed Beds: 357

SAN DIEGO MEDICAL CENTER See Kaiser Permanente San Diego Medical Center

SCRIPPS MERCY HOSPITAL (050077), 4077 Fifth Avenue, Zip 92103–2105; tel. 619/294–8111, (Includes SCRIPPS MERCY HOSPITAL CHULA VISTA, 435 'H' Street, Chula Vista, CA, Zip 91912–6617, Mailing Address: P.O. Box 1537, Zip 91910–1537, tel. 619/691–7000; Thomas A Gammiere, Chief Executive Officer) **A**1 2 3 5 10 **F**3 8 11 12 13 14 15 17 18 20 22 24 26 28 29 30 31 32 34 35 39 40 43 44 45 46 49 50 51 54 56 58 59 61 64 65 66 68 70 73 74 75 76 77 78 79 81 82 84 85 86 87 92 93 97 98 100 101 102 103 107 108 110 111 114 115 119 126 130 132 134 135 141 146 147 148 154 **S** Scripps Health, San Diego, CA
Primary Contact: Thomas A. Gammiere, Chief Executive, Senior Vice President
CFO: Edward Turk, Vice President Finance
CMO: Davis Cracroft, M.D., Senior Director Medical Affairs
CIO: Drexel DeFord, Chief Information Officer
Web address: www.scrippshealth.org
Control: Other not–for–profit (including NFP Corporation) **Service**: General medical and surgical

Staffed Beds: 392 Admissions: 30091 Census: 392 Outpatient Visits: 173033 Births: 3737 Total Expense ($000): 684998 Payroll Expense ($000): 271065 Personnel: 3337

SHARP MEMORIAL HOSPITAL (050100), 7901 Frost Street, Zip 92123–2701; tel. 858/939–3400, **A**1 2 3 10 **F**3 8 11 12 15 17 18 20 22 24 26 28 29 30 31 33 34 35 36 40 43 44 45 46 49 50 56 57 58 59 60 62 64 65 68 70 74 75 77 78 79 80 81 82 84 85 86 87 90 92 93 107 108 109 110 114 115 117 118 119 120 121 123 124 126 129 130 131 132 135 137 138 142 143 145 146 148 149 150 **P**5 **S** Sharp HealthCare, San Diego, CA
Primary Contact: Tim Smith, Senior Vice President and Chief Executive Officer
COO: Janie Kramer, Chief Operating Officer
CFO: Kari Cornicelli, Chief Financial Officer
CMO: Geoffrey Stiles, M.D., Chief Medical Officer
CIO: Kenneth Lawonn, Senior Vice President and Chief Information Officer
CHR: Connie Duquette, Director Human Resources
CNO: Pamela Wells, R.N., MSN, Chief Nursing Officer
Web address: www.sharp.com
Control: Other not–for–profit (including NFP Corporation) **Service**: General medical and surgical

Staffed Beds: 450 Admissions: 20424 Census: 283 Outpatient Visits: 460913 Births: 0 Total Expense ($000): 744499 Payroll Expense ($000): 287057 Personnel: 3586

SHARP MESA VISTA HOSPITAL (054145), 7850 Vista Hill Avenue, Zip 92123–2717; tel. 858/278–4110, (Includes SHARP MCDONALD CENTER, 7989 Linda Vista Road, San Diego, CA, Zip 92111–5106; tel. 858/637–6920; Trisha Khaleghi, Chief Executive Officer) **A**1 10 **F**4 5 11 29 30 31 34 35 40 49 56 57 58 59 64 68 87 98 99 100 101 102 103 104 105 106 130 132 135 143 146 149 150 152 153 **P**5 **S** Sharp HealthCare, San Diego, CA
Primary Contact: Trisha Khaleghi, Senior Vice President and Chief Executive Officer
CFO: Kari Cornicelli, Chief Financial Officer
CMO: Michael Plopper, M.D., Chief Medical Officer
CIO: Kenneth Lawonn, Senior Vice President Information Systems
CHR: Carlisle Lewis III Senior Vice President Legal and Human Resources
CNO: Cheryl Odell, R.N., Chief Nursing Officer
Web address: www.sharp.com
Control: Other not–for–profit (including NFP Corporation) **Service**: Psychiatric

Staffed Beds: 168 Admissions: 5220 Census: 136 Outpatient Visits: 85125 Births: 0 Total Expense ($000): 84076 Payroll Expense ($000): 46773 Personnel: 574

UC SAN DIEGO HEALTH (050025), 200 West Arbor Drive, Zip 92103–9000; tel. 619/543–6222, (Includes THORNTON HOSPITAL, 9300 Campus Point Drive, La Jolla, CA, Zip 92037–1300; tel. 858/657–7000; UC SAN DIEGO SHILEY EYE INSTITUTE, 9415 Campus Point Drive, Room 2411 Dept Of, Department of Ophthalmology, Mail Code 0946, La Jolla, CA, Zip 92093–0946, Mailing Address: 9415 Campus Point Drive, Zip 92093–0946, tel. 858/534–6290; Karen Anisko Ryan, Director Business Development and Communications) **A**1 2 3 5 8 10 **F**3 6 9 11 12 13 15 16 17 18 20 22 23 25 27 30 31 33 34 36 37 40 43 44 45 46 47 48 49 50 51 54 55 56 57 58 59 60 61 63 64 65 66 68 70 72 73 74 75 76 77 78 79 80 81 82 83 84 85 86 87 91 92 93 94 96 97 98 100 101 102 103 104 107 108 109 110 111 113 114 115 117 118 119 120 121 123 124 126 129 130 131 132 133 137 138 139 140 143 144 145 146 147 148 149 153 154 **P**8 **S** University of California Systemwide Administration, Oakland, CA
Primary Contact: Patty Maysent, Chief Executive Officer
COO: Margarita Baggett, MSN, R.N., Interim Chief Operating Officer
CFO: Lori Donaldson, Chief Financial Officer
CMO: Angela Scioscia, M.D., Chief Medical Officer
CIO: Ed Babakanian, Chief Information Officer
CHR: William J Murin, Chief Human Resources Officer
CNO: Margarita Baggett, MSN, R.N., Chief Nursing Officer
Web address: www.health.ucsd.edu
Control: State, Government, nonfederal **Service**: General medical and surgical

Staffed Beds: 664 Admissions: 29264 Census: 504 Outpatient Visits: 854929 Births: 2934 Total Expense ($000): 1690080 Payroll Expense ($000): 577044 Personnel: 6937

UNIVERSITY OF CALIFORNIA SAN DIEGO MEDICAL CENTER See UC San Diego Health

△ **VA SAN DIEGO HEALTHCARE SYSTEM**, 3350 LaJolla Village Drive, Zip 92161–0002; tel. 858/552–8585, (Nonreporting) **A**1 3 5 7 8 **S** Department of Veterans Affairs, Perry Point, MD
Primary Contact: Robert M. Smith, M.D., Director
COO: Cynthia Abair, Associate Director
CFO: Ronald Larson, Chief Financial Officer
CIO: Ruey Keller, Acting Chief Information Officer
CHR: Stephanie Wright, Director Human Resources Management
Web address: www.sandiego.va.gov
Control: Veterans Affairs, Government, federal **Service**: General medical and surgical

Staffed Beds: 248

Many Facility Codes have changed. Please refer to the AHA Guide Code Chart. © 2018 AHA Guide

VIBRA HOSPITAL OF SAN DIEGO (052044), 555 Washington Street, Zip 92103–2294; tel. 619/260–8300, (Nonreporting) **A**1 10 **S** Vibra Healthcare, Mechanicsburg, PA
Primary Contact: Yameeka Jones, Chief Executive Officer
CFO: Mike Gonzales, Chief Financial Officer
CMO: John Fox, M.D., Medical Director
CHR: Tania Khalique, Director Human Resources
Web address: www.vhsandiego.com/
Control: Corporation, Investor–owned (for–profit) **Service**: Acute long–term care hospital

Staffed Beds: 110

SAN DIMAS—Los Angeles County

SAN DIMAS COMMUNITY HOSPITAL (050588), 1350 West Covina Boulevard, Zip 91773–3219; tel. 909/599–6811, (Nonreporting) **A**1 10 **S** Prime Healthcare, Ontario, CA
Primary Contact: Parrish Scarboro, Chief Executive Officer
CFO: Edward Matthews, Chief Financial Officer
CMO: Rajnish Jandial, M.D., Chief Medical Officer
CIO: Jeffrey Cox, Director Information Technology
CHR: Kristina Mack, Manager, Human Resources
CNO: Holly Nagatoshi, R.N., Chief Nursing Officer
Web address: www.sandimashospital.com/
Control: Corporation, Investor–owned (for–profit) **Service**: General medical and surgical

Staffed Beds: 101

SAN FRANCISCO—San Francisco County

△ **CALIFORNIA PACIFIC MEDICAL CENTER (050047)**, 2333 Buchanan Street, Zip 94115–1925, Mailing Address: P.O. Box 7999, Zip 94120–7999; tel. 415/600–6000, (Total facility includes 38 beds in nursing home–type unit) **A**1 2 3 5 7 8 10 **F**2 3 6 7 8 12 13 15 17 18 19 20 22 24 26 28 29 30 31 32 34 35 36 37 38 39 40 41 45 46 47 48 49 50 51 52 55 56 57 58 59 60 61 63 64 65 68 70 72 74 75 76 77 78 79 81 82 83 84 85 86 87 88 89 90 91 92 93 96 97 98 100 101 102 104 107 108 110 111 114 115 116 117 118 119 120 121 123 124 126 128 130 132 133 135 137 138 139 141 142 143 144 145 146 147 148 149 154 **P**3 5 **S** Sutter Health, Sacramento, CA
Primary Contact: Warren S. Browner, M.D., M.P.H., Chief Executive Officer
COO: Hamila Kownacki, Chief Operating Officer
CFO: Henry Yu, Vice President Finance and Chief Financial Officer
CMO: Vernon Giang, M.D., Chief Medical Executive
CIO: Ann Barr, Chief Information Officer – Bay Area
CHR: Edward Battista, Vice President Human Resources
CNO: Diana M. Karner, R.N., MSN, Chief Nursing Officer
Web address: www.cpmc.org
Control: Other not–for–profit (including NFP Corporation) **Service**: General medical and surgical

Staffed Beds: 640 **Admissions:** 23825 **Census:** 406 **Outpatient Visits:** 504308 **Births:** 4172 **Total Expense ($000):** 1156673 **Payroll Expense ($000):** 368054 **Personnel:** 3525

★ **CALIFORNIA PACIFIC MEDICAL CENTER–DAVIES CAMPUS (050008)**, Castro and Duboce Streets, Zip 94114; tel. 415/600–6000, (Nonreporting) **A**3 5 **S** Sutter Health, Sacramento, CA
Primary Contact: Mary Lanier, Vice President, Post Acute Services and Site Administrator
Web address: www.cpmc.org
Control: Other not–for–profit (including NFP Corporation) **Service**: General medical and surgical

Staffed Beds: 154

CALIFORNIA PACIFIC MEDICAL CENTER–ST. LUKE'S CAMPUS (050055), 3555 Cesar Chavez Street, Zip 94110–4403; tel. 415/600–6000, (Total facility includes 79 beds in nursing home–type unit) **A**1 3 5 10 **F**3 8 13 15 18 29 30 34 35 40 50 55 59 60 63 64 65 66 67 68 70 72 75 76 77 78 79 81 82 84 85 87 89 93 97 100 107 108 110 111 114 118 119 128 130 143 146 147 148 149 154 **S** Sutter Health, Sacramento, CA
Primary Contact: Warren S. Browner, M.D., M.P.H., Chief Executive Officer
COO: Hamila Kownacki, Chief Operating Officer
CFO: Henry Yu, Vice President Finance and Chief Financial Officer
CMO: Vernon Giang, M.D., Chief Medical Executive
CIO: Ann Barr, Chief Information Officer – Bay Area
CHR: Edward Battista, Vice President Human Resources
CNO: Diana M. Karner, R.N., MSN, Chief Nursing Executive
Web address: www.stlukes-sf.org
Control: Other not–for–profit (including NFP Corporation) **Service**: General medical and surgical

Staffed Beds: 165 **Admissions:** 3594 **Census:** 85 **Outpatient Visits:** 69651 **Births:** 749 **Total Expense ($000):** 165086 **Payroll Expense ($000):** 52495 **Personnel:** 428

CHINESE HOSPITAL (050407), 845 Jackson Street, Zip 94133–4899; tel. 415/982–2400, **A**1 10 **F**3 11 15 18 29 30 31 34 35 36 40 45 47 49 50 57 59 64 65 70 75 77 78 79 81 86 87 97 107 110 111 115 118 119 130 132 135 145 146 147
Primary Contact: Jian Q. Zhang, MSN, Chief Executive Officer
COO: Jian Q Zhang, MSN, Chief Operating Officer
CFO: Scott Goodin, Chief Financial Officer
CMO: William Chung, M.D., Chief of Staff
CIO: Keith Minard, Chief Information Officer
CHR: Lydia Mahr–Chan, Director of Human Resources
CNO: Peggy Cmiel, R.N., Chief Nursing Officer
Web address: www.chinesehospital-sf.org
Control: Other not–for–profit (including NFP Corporation) **Service**: General medical and surgical

Staffed Beds: 30 **Admissions:** 1293 **Census:** 18 **Outpatient Visits:** 73614 **Births:** 0 **Total Expense ($000):** 121878 **Payroll Expense ($000):** 40616 **Personnel:** 323

JEWISH HOME OF SAN FRANCISCO (054089), 302 Silver Avenue, Zip 94112–1510; tel. 415/334–2500, (Nonreporting) **A**3 10
Primary Contact: Daniel R. Ruth, President and Chief Executive Officer
COO: Kevin Ward, Chief Operating Officer
CFO: Victor E Meinke, Chief Financial Officer
CNO: Edwin Cabigao, Chief Nursing Officer
Web address: www.jhsf.org
Control: Other not–for–profit (including NFP Corporation) **Service**: Psychiatric

Staffed Beds: 374

KAISER PERMANENTE SAN FRANCISCO MEDICAL CENTER (050076), 2425 Geary Boulevard, Zip 94115–3358; tel. 415/833–2000, **A**1 2 3 5 10 **F**3 11 13 15 17 18 20 22 24 26 28 29 30 31 32 34 35 36 38 40 44 45 46 47 48 49 50 53 56 57 58 59 60 61 62 63 64 65 66 68 70 72 73 75 76 77 78 79 81 82 84 85 86 87 89 91 92 94 96 100 107 108 109 111 114 115 119 126 130 132 135 146 147 148 149 150 154 **S** Kaiser Foundation Hospitals, Oakland, CA
Primary Contact: Ronald Groepper, Senior Vice President and Area Manager
COO: Helen Archer–Duste, Chief Operating Officer
CFO: Alex Khoo, Interim Area Finance Officer
CMO: Robert Mithun, M.D., Physician in Chief
CIO: Peti Arunamata, Interim Area Director Information Technology
CHR: Diane J Easterwood, Human Resources Business Partner
Web address: www.kaiserpermanente.org
Control: Other not–for–profit (including NFP Corporation) **Service**: General medical and surgical

Staffed Beds: 239 **Admissions:** 11758 **Census:** 161 **Births:** 3016

★ **LAGUNA HONDA HOSPITAL AND REHABILITATION CENTER (050668)**, 375 Laguna Honda Boulevard, Zip 94116–1499; tel. 415/759–2300, (Nonreporting) **A**10
Primary Contact: Mivic Hirose, Executive Administrator
COO: Michael R Llewellyn, Chief Operating Officer
CFO: Tess Navarro, Chief Financial Officer
CMO: Colleen Riley, M.D., Medical Director
CIO: Pat Skala, Chief Information Officer
CHR: Willie Ramirez, Manager Labor Relations
Web address: www.lagunahonda.org/
Control: City–county, Government, nonfederal **Service**: Rehabilitation

Staffed Beds: 780

△ **SAINT FRANCIS MEMORIAL HOSPITAL (050152)**, 900 Hyde Street, Zip 94109–4899, Mailing Address: P.O. Box 7726, Zip 94120–7726; tel. 415/353–6000, (Nonreporting) **A**1 2 3 7 10 **S** Dignity Health, San Francisco, CA
Primary Contact: David G. Klein, M.D., President
CFO: Alan Fox, Chief Financial Officer
CHR: Richard Mead, Senior Director Human Resources
Web address: www.saintfrancismemorial.org
Control: Other not–for–profit (including NFP Corporation) **Service**: General medical and surgical

Staffed Beds: 239

SAN FRANCISCO MEDICAL CENTER See Kaiser Permanente San Francisco Medical Center

CA

CA

⊞ **SAN FRANCISCO VA MEDICAL CENTER**, 4150 Clement Street, Zip 94121–1545; tel. 415/221–4810, (Total facility includes 120 beds in nursing home–type unit) **A**1 3 5 **F**1 3 4 5 9 10 11 12 15 16 17 18 20 22 24 26 28 29 30 31 33 37 38 39 40 44 45 46 47 48 49 50 56 58 59 60 61 62 63 64 65 67 68 70 72 73 74 75 76 77 78 79 80 81 82 83 84 85 86 87 88 89 90 91 92 93 94 96 97 98 100 101 102 104 107 111 112 114 115 116 117 118 119 120 121 122 123 126 127 128 129 130 132 135 143 144 145 146 147 148 149 153 154 **S** Department of Veterans Affairs, Perry Point, MD
Primary Contact: Bonnie S. Graham, Director
CFO: Brian Kelly, Acting Chief Fiscal Service
CMO: C. Diana Nicoll, M.D., Ph.D., Chief of Staff
CIO: Ryan Chun, Information Resources Management
CHR: Jerry Mills, Chief Human Resources Management Services
CNO: Shirley Pikula, MSN, Associate Director Patient Center Care
Web address: www.sanfrancisco.va.gov/
Control: Veterans Affairs, Government, federal **Service**: General medical and surgical

Staffed Beds: 241 **Admissions**: 5235 **Census**: 180 **Outpatient Visits**: 665706 **Births**: 0 **Total Expense ($000)**: 679531 **Payroll Expense ($000)**: 287040 **Personnel**: 2642

⊞ △ **ST. MARY'S MEDICAL CENTER (050457)**, 450 Stanyan Street, Zip 94117–1079; tel. 415/668–1000, (Nonreporting) **A**1 2 3 5 7 10 **S** Dignity Health, San Francisco, CA
Primary Contact: John P. Allen, President
COO: Deborah Kolhede, Vice President and Chief Operating Officer
CMO: Francis Charlton, M.D., Jr Chief Medical Staff
CHR: Barbara Morrissett, Vice President Human Resources
CNO: Barbara Eusebio, R.N., JD, Vice President, Chief Nurse Executive
Web address: www.stmarysmedicalcenter.com
Control: Other not–for–profit (including NFP Corporation) **Service**: General medical and surgical

Staffed Beds: 232

⊞ **UCSF MEDICAL CENTER (050454)**, 500 Parnassus Avenue, Zip 94143–0296, Mailing Address: 500 Parnassus Avenue, Box 0296, Zip 94143–0296; tel. 415/476–1000, (Includes UCSF BENIOFF CHILDREN'S HOSPITAL, 500 Parnassus Avenue, San Francisco, CA, Zip 94143–2203, Mailing Address: 505 Parnassus Avenue, Zip 94143–2203, tel. 888/689–8273; Michael Anderson, M.D., President; UCSF MEDICAL CENTER MISSION BAY, 1975 4th Street, San Francisco, CA, Zip 94158–2351; tel. 415/353–3000) **A**1 2 3 5 8 10 **F**3 6 7 8 9 11 12 13 14 15 17 18 19 20 21 22 23 24 25 26 27 29 30 31 32 33 34 35 36 37 38 39 40 41 43 44 45 46 47 48 49 50 51 52 53 54 55 56 57 58 59 60 63 64 65 66 68 70 72 73 74 75 76 77 78 79 81 82 83 84 85 86 87 88 89 90 91 92 93 94 96 97 98 99 100 101 102 103 104 105 106 107 108 110 111 112 113 114 115 116 117 118 119 120 121 123 124 126 129 130 131 132 134 135 136 137 138 139 140 141 142 144 145 146 147 148 149 150 153 154 **P**3 6 7 **S** University of California Systemwide Administration, Oakland, CA
Primary Contact: Mark R. Laret, Chief Executive Officer
COO: Ken M Jones, Chief Operating Officer
CFO: Barrie Strickland, Chief Financial Officer
CMO: Josh Adler, M.D., Chief Medical Officer
CIO: Joe Bergfort, Chief Information Officer
CHR: David Odato, Chief Administrative and Chief Human Resources Officer
CNO: Sheila Antrum, R.N., President
Web address: www.ucsfhealth.org
Control: Other not–for–profit (including NFP Corporation) **Service**: General medical and surgical

Staffed Beds: 978 **Admissions**: 44894 **Census**: 735 **Outpatient Visits**: 1480545 **Births**: 3249 **Total Expense ($000)**: 4051507 **Payroll Expense ($000)**: 1505406 **Personnel**: 16580

VETERANS AFFAIRS MEDICAL CENTER See San Francisco Va Medical Center

⊞ **ZUCKERBERG SAN FRANCISCO GENERAL HOSPITAL AND TRAUMA CENTER (050228)**, 1001 Potrero Avenue, Zip 94110–3518; tel. 415/206–8000, (Total facility includes 26 beds in nursing home–type unit) **A**1 2 3 5 8 10 **F**3 13 15 18 20 22 29 30 31 34 35 36 38 39 40 41 43 44 45 46 47 48 49 50 57 58 59 60 61 64 65 68 70 71 72 73 74 75 76 77 78 79 81 82 83 84 85 86 87 89 92 93 94 97 98 100 102 105 107 108 110 111 115 119 128 129 130 131 132 135 144 146 147 148 149 150 154
Primary Contact: Susan P. Ehrlich, M.D., Chief Executive Officer
COO: Tosan O. Boyo, Chief Operating Officer
CFO: Valerie Inouye, Chief Financial Officer
CMO: Todd May, M.D., Chief Medical Officer
CIO: Winona Windolovich, Associate Chief Information Officer
CHR: Karen Hill, Departmental Personnel Officer
CNO: Terry Dentoni, Chief Nursing Officer
Web address: www.zuckerbergsanfranciscogeneral.org/
Control: City–county, Government, nonfederal **Service**: General medical and surgical

Staffed Beds: 285 **Admissions**: 17181 **Census**: 279 **Outpatient Visits**: 553370 **Births**: 1181 **Total Expense ($000)**: 1081556 **Payroll Expense ($000)**: 354455 **Personnel**: 2150

SAN GABRIEL—San Francisco County

☐ **SAN GABRIEL VALLEY MEDICAL CENTER (050132)**, 438 West Las Tunas Drive, Zip 91776–1216, Mailing Address: P.O. Box 1507, Zip 91778–1507; tel. 626/289–5454, **A**1 10 **F**3 13 29 31 34 35 36 40 45 49 50 51 56 57 59 64 65 68 70 72 73 74 75 76 78 79 81 85 87 98 102 103 107 115 119 128 130 146 147 148 149 154 **S** AHMC & Healthcare, Inc., Alhambra, CA
Primary Contact: Jonathon F. Aquino, Chief Executive Officer
CFO: Andrew Grim, Chief Financial Officer
CIO: Bernie Sauer, Director Information Technology
CHR: Victor Voisard, Director Human Resources
CNO: Gail Freeman, Chief Nursing Officer
Web address: www.sgvmc.org
Control: Partnership, Investor–owned (for–profit) **Service**: General medical and surgical

Staffed Beds: 273 **Admissions**: 9589 **Census**: 163 **Outpatient Visits**: 29666 **Births**: 2150 **Total Expense ($000)**: 174493 **Payroll Expense ($000)**: 70260 **Personnel**: 795

SAN JOSE—Santa Clara County

⊞ **GOOD SAMARITAN HOSPITAL (050380)**, 2425 Samaritan Drive, Zip 95124–3997, Mailing Address: P.O. Box 240002, Zip 95154–2402; tel. 408/559–2011, (Nonreporting) **A**1 2 10 **S** HCA Healthcare, Nashville, TN
Primary Contact: Joseph DeSchryver, Chief Executive Officer
COO: Jordan Herget, Chief Operating Officer
CFO: Lana Arad, Chief Financial Officer
CMO: Bruce Wilbur, M.D., Chief Medical Officer
CIO: Darrell O'Dell, Director Information Services
CHR: Edward Battista, Vice President Human Resources
CNO: Darina Kavanagh, R.N., MSN, Chief Nursing Officer
Web address: www.goodsamsanjose.com
Control: Corporation, Investor–owned (for–profit) **Service**: General medical and surgical

Staffed Beds: 349

⊞ **KAISER PERMANENTE SAN JOSE MEDICAL CENTER (050604)**, 250 Hospital Parkway, Zip 95119–1199; tel. 408/972–7000, (Nonreporting) **A**1 2 3 5 10 **S** Kaiser Foundation Hospitals, Oakland, CA
Primary Contact: Irene Chavez, Senior Vice President and Area Manager
COO: Irene Chavez, Senior Vice President and Area Manager
CFO: Stephen L Kalsman, Area Finance Officer
CMO: Raj Bhandari, M.D., Physician–in–Chief
CIO: Greg Tuck, Area Information Officer
CHR: Susan Franzella, Human Resource Business Partner
CNO: Theresa R Nero, R.N., MS, Chief Nursing Officer
Web address: www.kaiserpermanente.org
Control: Other not–for–profit (including NFP Corporation) **Service**: General medical and surgical

Staffed Beds: 222

☐ **O'CONNOR HOSPITAL (050153)**, 2105 Forest Avenue, Zip 95128–1471; tel. 408/947–2500, (Nonreporting) **A**1 2 3 5 10 **S** Verity Health System, Los Angeles, CA
Primary Contact: Jordan Herget, President and Chief Executive Officer
CMO: Arthur Douville, M.D., Chief Medical Officer
CIO: Richard Hutsell, Vice President and Chief Information Officer, Daughters of Charity Health System
CHR: Julie Hatcher, Vice President Human Resources
CNO: Dawn Marie Goeringer, Chief Clinical Care Officer
Web address: www.oconnorhospital.org
Control: Other not–for–profit (including NFP Corporation) **Service**: General medical and surgical

Staffed Beds: 202

⊞ **REGIONAL MEDICAL CENTER OF SAN JOSE (050125)**, 225 North Jackson Avenue, Zip 95116–1603; tel. 408/259–5000, (Nonreporting) **A**1 2 10 **S** HCA Healthcare, Nashville, TN
Primary Contact: Michael T. Johnson, FACHE, President and Chief Executive Officer
COO: Brian J Knecht, Chief Operating Officer
CFO: Fred Ashworth, Chief Financial Officer
CMO: William Scott, M.D., Vice President Medical Affairs
CIO: Shirley Joyal, Director Information Systems
CHR: Nancy Clark, Vice President Human Resources
Web address: www.regionalmedicalsanjose.com
Control: Partnership, Investor–owned (for–profit) **Service**: General medical and surgical

Staffed Beds: 247

SAN JOSE BEHAVORIAL HEALTH (054154), 455 Silicon Valley Boulevard, Zip 95138–1858; tel. 888/210–2484, **A**10 **F**3 29 34 35 38 57 68 75 86 87 98 99 100 101 103 130 149 154 **S** Acadia Healthcare Company, Inc., Franklin, TN
Primary Contact: Rob Marsh, Chief Executive Officer
Web address: www.sanjosebh.com
Control: Corporation, Investor–owned (for–profit) **Service**: Psychiatric

Staffed Beds: 80 Admissions: 2113 Census: 61 Outpatient Visits: 761 Births: 0 Total Expense ($000): 24297 Payroll Expense ($000): 9245 Personnel: 172

SAN JOSE MEDICAL CENTER See Kaiser Permanente San Jose Medical Center

☐ △ **SANTA CLARA VALLEY MEDICAL CENTER (050038)**, 751 South Bascom Avenue, Zip 95128–2699; tel. 408/885–5000, **A**1 3 5 7 10 **F**3 5 9 11 12 15 16 17 18 19 20 22 24 26 28 29 30 31 32 34 35 36 39 40 41 43 44 45 46 49 50 51 54 55 56 58 59 60 61 64 65 66 68 70 71 72 74 75 76 77 78 79 80 81 82 84 85 86 87 88 89 90 91 92 93 95 96 97 98 100 101 102 104 107 108 110 111 114 115 117 118 119 120 121 123 124 129 130 131 132 134 135 144 146 147 148 149 **P**6
Primary Contact: Paul E. Lorenz, Chief Executive Officer
COO: Benita McLarin, Chief Operating Officer
CMO: Jeffrey Arnold, M.D., Chief Medical Officer
CIO: Lee Herrmann, Chief Healthcare Technology Officer
CHR: David Manson, Manager Human Resources
CNO: Trudy Johnson, R.N., RN Chief Nursing Officer
Web address: www.scvmed.org
Control: County, Government, nonfederal **Service**: General medical and surgical

Staffed Beds: 481 Admissions: 22188 Census: 337 Outpatient Visits: 802145 Births: 3254 Total Expense ($000): 1646512 Payroll Expense ($000): 717033 Personnel: 5954

SAN LEANDRO—Alameda County

FAIRMONT HOSPITAL See Highland Hospital, Oakland

⊞ **KAISER PERMANENTE SAN LEANDRO MEDICAL CENTER (050777)**, 2500 Merced Street, Zip 94577–4201; tel. 510/454–1000, **A**1 3 10 **F**3 13 29 30 31 35 40 41 70 72 73 74 75 76 77 78 79 81 82 85 130 146 148 149 154 **S** Kaiser Foundation Hospitals, Oakland, CA
Primary Contact: Thomas S. Hanenburg, Senior Vice President and Area Manager
Web address: www.kaiserpermanente.org
Control: Other not–for–profit (including NFP Corporation) **Service**: General medical and surgical

Staffed Beds: 184 Admissions: 20398 Census: 127

⊞ **KINDRED HOSPITAL–SAN FRANCISCO BAY AREA (052034)**, 2800 Benedict Drive, Zip 94577–6840; tel. 510/357–8300, (Nonreporting) **A**1 10 **S** Kindred Healthcare, Louisville, KY
Primary Contact: Jacob M. McCarty, Chief Executive Officer
CFO: Ziba Aflak, Chief Financial Officer
CHR: Erin Greene, Coordinator Human Resources
CNO: Emily Gard, Chief Clinical Officer
Web address: www.kindredhospitalsfba.com
Control: Corporation, Investor–owned (for–profit) **Service**: Acute long–term care hospital

Staffed Beds: 99

☐ **SAN LEANDRO HOSPITAL (050773)**, 13855 East 14th Street, Zip 94578–2600; tel. 510/357–6500, **A**1 10 **F**3 15 18 29 30 31 34 35 40 43 44 45 50 51 57 59 60 68 70 77 79 81 87 107 108 110 111 114 119 130 146 **S** Alameda Health System, San Leandro, CA
Primary Contact: James E T. Jackson, M.P.H., Chief Administrative Officer
Web address: www.sanleandrohospital.org
Control: Hospital district or authority, Government, nonfederal **Service**: General medical and surgical

Staffed Beds: 45 Admissions: 3307 Census: 36 Outpatient Visits: 36288 Births: 0 Total Expense ($000): 80783 Payroll Expense ($000): 44847 Personnel: 341

☐ **WILLOW ROCK CENTER (054149)**, 2050 Fairmont Drive, Zip 94578–1001; tel. 510/895–5502, (Nonreporting) **A**1 10
Primary Contact: Anne L. Bakar, President and Chief Executive Officer
Web address: www.tbhcare.com
Control: County, Government, nonfederal **Service**: Psychiatric

Staffed Beds: 16

SAN LUIS OBISPO—San Luis Obispo County

CALIFORNIA MENS COLONY CORRECTIONAL TREATMENT CENTER, Highway 1, Zip 93409–8101, Mailing Address: P.O. Box 8101, Zip 93403–8101; tel. 805/547–7913, (Nonreporting)
Primary Contact: Martha Wallace, Administrator
CFO: William Cook, Associate Warden Business Service
CIO: Terry Knight, Public Information Officer and Administrative Assistant
Web address: www.yaca.ca.gov/visitors/fac_prison_cmc.html
Control: State, Government, nonfederal **Service**: Hospital unit of an institution (prison hospital, college infirmary, etc.)

Staffed Beds: 39

⊞ **FRENCH HOSPITAL MEDICAL CENTER (050232)**, 1911 Johnson Avenue, Zip 93401–4197; tel. 805/543–5353, (Nonreporting) **A**1 2 10 **S** Dignity Health, San Francisco, CA
Primary Contact: Alan Iftiniuk, Chief Executive Officer
COO: Julia Fogelson, R.N., Chief Operating Officer and Chief Nursing Executive
CFO: Sue Andersen, Chief Financial Officer
CMO: Chris Voge, Chief of Staff
CIO: Cyndi Lang, Director Information Services
CHR: Barry Nateman, Manager Human Resources
CNO: Julia Fogelson, R.N., Chief Operating Officer and Chief Nursing Executive
Web address: www.frenchmedicalcenter.org
Control: Other not–for–profit (including NFP Corporation) **Service**: General medical and surgical

Staffed Beds: 72

⊞ **SIERRA VISTA REGIONAL MEDICAL CENTER (050506)**, 1010 Murray Avenue, Zip 93405–1806, Mailing Address: P.O. Box 1367, Zip 93405; tel. 805/546–7600, (Nonreporting) **A**1 2 10 19 **S** TENET Healthcare Corporation, Dallas, TX
Primary Contact: Mark P. Lisa, FACHE, Chief Executive Officer
COO: Eleze Armstrong, Chief Operating Officer
CFO: Rollie Pirkl, Chief Financial Officer
CIO: Robert Leonard, Director Information Services
CHR: Kristin Flynn, Chief Human Resources Officer
CNO: Nicki E Edwards, Ph.D., R.N., Interim Chief Nursing Officer
Web address: www.sierravistaregional.com
Control: Corporation, Investor–owned (for–profit) **Service**: General medical and surgical

Staffed Beds: 164

SAN MATEO—San Mateo County

MILLS HEALTH CENTER See Mills–Peninsula Health Services, Burlingame

☐ **SAN MATEO MEDICAL CENTER (050113)**, 222 West 39th Avenue, Zip 94403–4398; tel. 650/573–2222, (Nonreporting) **A**1 3 5 10
Primary Contact: Chester Kunnappilly, M.D., Interim Chief Executive Officer
COO: John Thomas, Chief Operating Officer
CFO: David S McGrew, Chief Financial Officer
CMO: Susan Fernyak, M.D., Interim Chief Medical Officer & Chief Quality Officer
CIO: Michael Aratow, M.D., Chief Information Officer
CHR: Angela Gonzales, Manager Human Resources
CNO: Joan G Spicer, R.N., Chief Nursing Officer
Web address: www.sanmateomedicalcenter.org
Control: County, Government, nonfederal **Service**: General medical and surgical

Staffed Beds: 90

SAN PEDRO—Los Angeles County; See Los Angeles

SAN RAFAEL—Marin County

⊞ **KAISER PERMANENTE SAN RAFAEL MEDICAL CENTER (050510)**, 99 Montecillo Road, Zip 94903–3397; tel. 415/444–2000, **A**1 5 10 **F**3 5 11 12 15 18 19 20 22 26 29 30 31 32 34 35 36 38 40 41 44 49 50 54 56 57 58 59 61 62 64 65 68 70 74 75 77 78 79 81 82 84 85 86 87 92 93 94 97 100 101 102 104 107 108 110 111 114 115 119 130 131 132 134 135 144 146 147 148 149 150 153 154 **S** Kaiser Foundation Hospitals, Oakland, CA
Primary Contact: Judy Coffey, R.N., Senior Vice President and Area Manager
CFO: Diane Hernandez, Area Finance Officer
CMO: Gary Mizono, M.D., Physician–in–Chief
CIO: Stanley Dobrawa, Area Information Officer
Web address: www.kaiserpermanente.org
Control: Other not–for–profit (including NFP Corporation) **Service**: General medical and surgical

Staffed Beds: 116 Admissions: 4845 Census: 43 Outpatient Visits: 34078

SAN RAMON—Contra Costa County

☒ **SAN RAMON REGIONAL MEDICAL CENTER (050689)**, 6001 Norris Canyon Road, Zip 94583–5400; tel. 925/275–9200, **A**1 10 **F**3 8 11 13 15 18 20 22 24 26 28 29 30 31 34 35 37 40 45 46 47 48 49 53 57 59 64 70 72 75 76 77 78 79 81 85 86 87 93 107 108 110 118 119 126 130 131 132 146 147 148 149 **P**3 5 **S** TENET Healthcare Corporation, Dallas, TX
Primary Contact: Ann Lucena, Chief Executive Officer
CFO: Beenu Chadha, Chief Financial Officer
CMO: Raymond Cheung, M.D., Chief of Staff
CIO: Anthony Abbate, Director of Information Services
CHR: Dennis Mills, Chief Human Resources Officer
Web address: www.sanramonmedctr.com
Control: Partnership, Investor–owned (for–profit) **Service**: General medical and surgical

Staffed Beds: 123 **Admissions**: 4888 **Census**: 51 **Outpatient Visits**: 67238 **Births**: 676 **Total Expense ($000)**: 148609 **Payroll Expense ($000)**: 71136 **Personnel**: 466

SANTA ANA—Orange County

☐ **ORANGE COUNTY GLOBAL MEDICAL CENTER, INC. (050746)**, 1001 North Tustin Avenue, Zip 92705–3577; tel. 714/953–3500, (Nonreporting) **A**1 3 5 10 **S** KPC Healthcare, Inc., Santa Ana, CA
Primary Contact: Ann Abe, Interim Chief Executive Officer
COO: Ann Abe, Administrator and Chief Operating Officer
CFO: John Collins, Chief Financial Officer
CMO: Steven Bui, M.D., Chief of Staff
CIO: Charles Flack, Interim Chief Information Officer
CHR: Terry Bohn, Director, Human Resources
CNO: Sandra Moreno, Chief Nursing Officer
Web address: www.orangecounty–gmc.com
Control: Corporation, Investor–owned (for–profit) **Service**: General medical and surgical

Staffed Beds: 282

☐ **SOUTH COAST GLOBAL MEDICAL CENTER (050747)**, 2701 South Bristol Street, Zip 92704–6278; tel. 714/754–5454, (Nonreporting) **A**1 10 **S** KPC Healthcare, Inc., Santa Ana, CA
Primary Contact: Ada Yeh, Chief Executive Officer
CFO: John Collins, Chief Financial Officer
CHR: Cynthia Garren–Oster, Human Resource Manager
Web address: www.SouthCoast–GMC.com
Control: Corporation, Investor–owned (for–profit) **Service**: General medical and surgical

Staffed Beds: 178

SANTA BARBARA—Santa Barbara County

COTTAGE REHABILITATION HOSPITAL See Santa Barbara Cottage Hospital, Santa Barbara

☒ **GOLETA VALLEY COTTAGE HOSPITAL (050357)**, 351 South Patterson Avenue, Zip 93111–2496, Mailing Address: Box 6306, Zip 93160–6306; tel. 805/967–3411, **A**1 10 **F**8 11 12 15 29 40 65 68 70 79 81 107 110 114 119 124 130 148 149 **S** Cottage Health, Santa Barbara, CA
Primary Contact: Ronald C. Werft, President and Chief Executive Officer
COO: Steven A Fellows, Executive Vice President and Chief Operating Officer
CFO: Joan Bricher, Senior Vice President Finance and Chief Financial Officer
CMO: Edmund Wroblewski, M.D., Vice President Medical Affairs and Chief Medical Officer
CIO: Alberto Kywi, Chief Information Officer
CHR: Patrice Ryan, Vice President Human Resources
Web address: www.sbch.org
Control: Other not–for–profit (including NFP Corporation) **Service**: General medical and surgical

Staffed Beds: 28 **Admissions**: 1644 **Census**: 10 **Outpatient Visits**: 48046 **Births**: 0 **Total Expense ($000)**: 71702 **Payroll Expense ($000)**: 28015 **Personnel**: 279

☒ △ **SANTA BARBARA COTTAGE HOSPITAL (050396)**, 400 West Pueblo Street, Zip 93105–4390, Mailing Address: P.O. Box 689, Zip 93102–0689; tel. 805/682–7111, (Includes COTTAGE CHILDREN'S HOSPITAL, 400 West Pueblo Street, Santa Barbara, CA, Zip 93105–4353; tel. 877/247–3260; COTTAGE REHABILITATION HOSPITAL, 2415 De la Vina Street, Santa Barbara, CA, Zip 93105–3819; tel. 805/687–7444; Melinda Staveley, President and Chief Executive Officer) **A**1 2 3 5 7 10 **F**3 4 5 8 11 12 13 15 17 18 20 22 24 26 28 29 30 31 34 35 40 43 46 50 53 54 57 58 59 60 64 65 68 70 72 74 75 76 78 79 81 84 86 88 89 90 91 92 93 96 98 100 102 103 104 106 107 110 111 114 115 117 119 126 130 132 135 146 148 149 151 152 153 **S** Cottage Health, Santa Barbara, CA
Primary Contact: Ronald C. Werft, President and Chief Executive Officer
COO: Steven A Fellows, Executive Vice President and Chief Operating Officer
CFO: Joan Bricher, Senior Vice President Finance and Chief Financial Officer
CMO: Edmund Wroblewski, M.D., Vice President Medical Affairs and Chief Medical Officer
CIO: Alberto Kywi, Chief Information Officer
CHR: Patrice Ryan, Vice President Human Resources
CNO: Herb J Geary, Vice President Patient Care Services and Chief Nursing Officer
Web address: www.cottagehealthsystem.org
Control: Other not–for–profit (including NFP Corporation) **Service**: General medical and surgical

Staffed Beds: 363 **Admissions**: 17739 **Census**: 242 **Outpatient Visits**: 118452 **Births**: 2217 **Total Expense ($000)**: 634408 **Payroll Expense ($000)**: 248542 **Personnel**: 2437

SANTA BARBARA COUNTY PSYCHIATRIC HEALTH FACILITY (054125), 315 Camino Del Remedio, Zip 93110–1332; tel. 805/681–5244, (Nonreporting) **A**10
Primary Contact: Ole Behrendtsen, M.D., Interim Director
CFO: Michael C. Evans, Chief Executive Officer and Deputy Director of Finance and Administration
CMO: Ole Behrendtsen, M.D., Medical Director
CIO: Dana Fahey, Manager Management Information Systems
CHR: Elena Molelus, Manager Human Resources
Web address: www.countyofsb.org
Control: County, Government, nonfederal **Service**: Psychiatric

Staffed Beds: 16

SANTA CLARA—Santa Clara County

☒ **KAISER PERMANENTE SANTA CLARA MEDICAL CENTER (050071)**, 700 Lawrence Expressway, Zip 95051–5173; tel. 408/851–1000, **A**1 2 3 5 10 **F**3 5 8 11 12 13 15 17 18 20 22 24 26 27 28 29 31 32 34 35 36 38 40 41 44 45 48 49 50 51 52 53 54 55 56 57 58 59 60 61 62 63 64 65 68 70 71 72 74 75 77 78 79 81 82 83 84 85 86 87 88 91 92 93 94 97 99 100 101 102 104 107 108 109 110 111 114 115 116 117 118 119 120 121 123 124 126 129 130 131 132 134 135 144 146 147 148 149 150 152 153 154 **P**1 2 3 4 5 6 7 **S** Kaiser Foundation Hospitals, Oakland, CA
Primary Contact: Christopher L. Boyd, Senior Vice President and Area Manager
CFO: Tim O'Connor, Area Finance Officer
CMO: Susan Smarr, M.D., Physician–in–Chief
CIO: Scott May, Area Director Technology
CHR: Robert Hyde, Human Resources Business Partner
CNO: Lori Armstrong, R.N., MSN, Chief Nursing Officer
Web address: www.kaiserpermanente.org
Control: Other not–for–profit (including NFP Corporation) **Service**: General medical and surgical

Staffed Beds: 327 **Admissions**: 20007 **Census**: 217 **Births**: 4775

SANTA CRUZ—Santa Cruz County

☒ **DOMINICAN HOSPITAL (050242)**, 1555 Soquel Drive, Zip 95065–1794; tel. 831/462–7700, (Nonreporting) **A**1 2 10 **S** Dignity Health, San Francisco, CA
Primary Contact: Nanette Mickiewicz, M.D., President
COO: Chris Wernke, Chief Operating Officer
CFO: Rick Harron, Chief Financial Officer
CMO: Freddie Weinstein, M.D., Chief Medical Officer
CIO: Lee Vanderpool, Vice President
CHR: Vicki Miranda, Vice President Human Resources
Web address: www.dominicanhospital.org
Control: Church operated, Nongovernment, not–for–profit **Service**: General medical and surgical

Staffed Beds: 223

CA

Many Facility Codes have changed. Please refer to the AHA Guide Code Chart. © 2018 AHA Guide

⊞ SUTTER MATERNITY AND SURGERY CENTER OF SANTA CRUZ (050714), 2900 Chanticleer Avenue, Zip 95065–1816; tel. 831/477–2200, **A**1 10 **F**3 13 29 34 36 45 51 57 68 76 77 79 81 83 85 100 119 126 130 132 135 141 146 147 149 **P**3 5 **S** Sutter Health, Sacramento, CA
Primary Contact: Trina White, President and Chief Executive Officer
CFO: Bonnie Liang, Divisional Finance Officer
CMO: Joseph Fabry, D.O., Chief of Staff
CIO: Ann Barr, Chief Information Officer, Sutter Health Bay Area
CHR: Maynard Jenkins, Regional Vice President Human Resources
CNO: Sherri Stout–Torres, R.N., Chief Nursing Executive
Web address: www.suttersantacruz.org
Control: Other not–for–profit (including NFP Corporation) **Service:** Other specialty treatment

Staffed Beds: 30 **Admissions:** 1535 **Census:** 11 **Outpatient Visits:** 16364 **Births:** 1007 **Total Expense ($000):** 70094 **Payroll Expense ($000):** 22808 **Personnel:** 198

SANTA MARIA—Santa Barbara County

⊞ MARIAN REGIONAL MEDICAL CENTER (050107), 1400 East Church Street, Zip 93454–5906; tel. 805/739–3000, (Nonreporting) **A**1 2 3 10 13 **S** Dignity Health, San Francisco, CA
Primary Contact: Kerin A. Mase, President and Chief Executive Officer
COO: Mark Allen, Chief Operating Officer
CFO: Sue Andersen, Vice President and Service Area and Chief Financial Officer
CMO: Chuck Merrill, M.D., Vice President Medical Affairs
CIO: Patricia Haase, Director Information Technology and Communications
CHR: Ed Gonzales, Vice President Human Resources
CNO: Candice Monge, R.N., Chief Nurse Executive Officer
Web address: www.marianmedicalcenter.org
Control: Church operated, Nongovernment, not–for–profit **Service:** General medical and surgical

Staffed Beds: 286

SANTA MONICA—Los Angeles County

⊞ PROVIDENCE SAINT JOHN'S HEALTH CENTER (050290), 2121 Santa Monica Boulevard, Zip 90404–2091; tel. 310/829–5511, **A**1 2 10 **F**3 8 14 15 18 20 22 24 26 29 30 31 34 35 37 40 43 45 46 47 48 49 50 55 58 59 60 64 70 72 74 76 78 79 81 84 85 93 107 108 110 111 118 119 120 121 123 124 126 130 131 132 146 147 **P**2 3 5 **S** Providence St. Joseph Health, Renton, WA
Primary Contact: Marcel C. Loh, FACHE, Chief Executive Officer
COO: David A Tam, M.D., FACHE, Chief Operating Officer
CFO: James Uli, Chief Financial Officer
CMO: Donald Larsen, M.D., Chief Medical Officer
CIO: Martha Ponce, Director Information Technologies and Telecommunications
CHR: Laura Morton Rowe, Director of Human Resources
CNO: Dawna Hendel, R.N., Chief Nursing Officer and Vice President Patient Care Services
Web address: www.providence.org/saintjohns
Control: Church operated, Nongovernment, not–for–profit **Service:** General medical and surgical

Staffed Beds: 228 **Admissions:** 12378 **Census:** 151 **Outpatient Visits:** 184635 **Births:** 1879 **Total Expense ($000):** 284648 **Payroll Expense ($000):** 132637 **Personnel:** 1339

⊞ UCLA MEDICAL CENTER–SANTA MONICA (050112), 1250 16th Street, Zip 90404–1249; tel. 310/319–4000, **A**1 3 5 10 **F**3 8 9 11 12 13 15 18 20 22 24 26 29 30 31 34 35 37 39 40 41 45 46 47 48 49 50 51 52 54 55 56 57 58 59 62 64 65 68 70 72 74 75 76 78 79 81 82 83 84 85 86 87 89 93 96 97 102 107 108 110 111 114 115 116 117 118 119 130 131 143 145 146 147 149 154 **P**6 **S** University of California Systemwide Administration, Oakland, CA
Primary Contact: Paul Watkins, JD, Chief Administrative Officer
COO: Posie Carpenter, R.N., MSN, Chief Administrative Officer
CFO: Paul Staton, Chief Financial Officer
CMO: James Atkinson, M.D., Medical Director
CIO: Virginia McFerran, Chief Information Officer
CHR: Mark Speare, Senior Associate Director Patient Relations and Human Resources
Web address: www.healthcare.ucla.edu
Control: State, Government, nonfederal **Service:** General medical and surgical

Staffed Beds: 265 **Admissions:** 16054 **Census:** 218 **Outpatient Visits:** 184008 **Births:** 1484 **Total Expense ($000):** 571260 **Payroll Expense ($000):** 198880 **Personnel:** 1961

SANTA ROSA—Sonoma County

AURORA SANTA ROSA HOSPITAL (054151), 1287 Fulton Road, Zip 95401–4923; tel. 707/800–7700, (Nonreporting)
Primary Contact: Kay E. Seim, Chief Executive Officer
Web address: www.aurorasantarosa.com
Control: Corporation, Investor–owned (for–profit) **Service:** Rehabilitation

Staffed Beds: 95

⊞ KAISER PERMANENTE SANTA ROSA MEDICAL CENTER (050690), 401 Bicentennial Way, Zip 95403–2192; tel. 707/393–4000, **A**1 3 5 10 **F**3 8 13 26 29 30 31 40 41 44 45 49 50 51 53 56 60 62 64 68 70 73 74 75 76 77 78 79 81 82 84 85 87 89 100 102 107 108 110 111 115 119 130 132 146 148 149 154 **S** Kaiser Foundation Hospitals, Oakland, CA
Primary Contact: Judy Coffey, R.N., Senior Vice President and Area Manager
COO: Vicky Locey, R.N., MSN, Chief Operating Officer and Chief Nursing Executive
CFO: Diane Hernandez, Area Finance Officer
CMO: Kirk Pappas, M.D., Physician–in–Chief
CIO: Stanley Dobrawa, Area Information Officer
CNO: Vicky Locey, R.N., MSN, Chief Operating Officer and Chief Nursing Executive
Web address: www.kaiserpermanente.org
Control: Other not–for–profit (including NFP Corporation) **Service:** General medical and surgical

Staffed Beds: 173 **Admissions:** 9874 **Census:** 95 **Outpatient Visits:** 66924 **Births:** 1778

⊞ SANTA ROSA MEMORIAL HOSPITAL (050174), 1165 Montgomery Drive, Zip 95405–4897, Mailing Address: P.O. Box 522, Zip 95402–0522; tel. 707/546–3210, (Nonreporting) **A**1 2 10 **S** Providence St. Joseph Health, Renton, WA
Primary Contact: Todd Salnas, President
COO: Tyler Hedden, Chief Operating Officer
CFO: Robert Petrina, Interim Chief Financial Officer
CMO: Chad Krilich, M.D., Chief Medical Officer
CIO: Les Brooks, System Director Information Technology
CHR: John Bibby, Regional Vice President, Human Resources
CNO: Vicki White, Chief Nursing Officer
Web address: www.stjosephhealth.org
Control: Other not–for–profit (including NFP Corporation) **Service:** General medical and surgical

Staffed Beds: 278

⊞ SUTTER SANTA ROSA REGIONAL HOSPITAL (050291), 30 Mark West Springs Road, Zip 95403; tel. 707/576–4000, (Includes WARRACK CAMPUS, 2449 Summerfield Road, Santa Rosa, CA, Zip 95405–7815; tel. 707/576–4200) **A**1 3 5 10 **F**3 11 12 13 18 20 22 24 26 29 30 31 34 35 36 40 45 49 50 51 56 59 60 61 64 65 68 70 72 75 76 77 78 79 81 84 85 87 107 108 111 119 126 130 146 148 149 **P**3 5 **S** Sutter Health, Sacramento, CA
Primary Contact: Mike Purvis, Chief Administrative Officer
CMO: William Carroll, M.D., Chief Medical Executive
Web address: www.sutterhealth.org
Control: Other not–for–profit (including NFP Corporation) **Service:** General medical and surgical

Staffed Beds: 84 **Admissions:** 6551 **Census:** 70 **Outpatient Visits:** 59414 **Births:** 1596 **Total Expense ($000):** 263815 **Payroll Expense ($000):** 75193 **Personnel:** 676

SEBASTOPOL—Sonoma County

⇑ SONOMA WEST MEDICAL CENTER (050781), 501 Petaluma Avenue, Zip 95472–4215; **A**10 21 **F**3 8 11 15 29 34 35 40 45 57 70 79 81 91 92 107 110 119 130 132 146 148 154
Primary Contact: John Peleuses, Interim Chief Executive Officer
CFO: Robert Heinemeier, Interim Chief Financial Officer
Web address: www.sonomawesthealth.org/
Control: Hospital district or authority, Government, nonfederal **Service:** General medical and surgical

Staffed Beds: 20 **Admissions:** 189 **Census:** 9 **Outpatient Visits:** 9952 **Births:** 0 **Total Expense ($000):** 28965 **Payroll Expense ($000):** 5619

CA

Hospital, Medicare Provider Number, Address, Telephone, Approval, Facility, and Physician Codes, Health Care System

★ American Hospital Association (AHA) membership
□ The Joint Commission accreditation
○ Healthcare Facilities Accreditation Program
◇ DNV Healthcare Inc. accreditation
⇑ Center for Improvement in Healthcare Quality Accreditation
△ Commission on Accreditation of Rehabilitation Facilities (CARF) accreditation

SHERMAN OAKS—Los Angeles County; See Los Angeles

SIMI VALLEY—Ventura County

☒ **SIMI VALLEY HOSPITAL (050236)**, 2975 North Sycamore Drive, Zip 93065–1277; tel. 805/955–6000, **A**1 2 10 **F**3 8 11 13 15 18 20 22 24 26 29 30 31 32 34 35 36 40 41 44 45 46 49 50 51 54 56 57 58 59 62 63 64 65 68 70 72 74 75 76 77 78 79 81 82 84 85 86 87 93 96 97 100 101 102 107 108 110 111 114 115 116 117 118 119 120 121 123 130 131 132 134 141 144 146 147 148 149 150 154 **P**3 4 **S** Adventist Health, Roseville, CA
Primary Contact: Jennifer Swenson, President and Chief Executive Officer
COO: Caroline Esparza, Sr. VP, COO & CNO
CFO: Brian Anderson, Chief Financial Officer
CMO: John Dingilian, M.D., Chief Medical Officer
CIO: Bridget Nakamura, Director Information Systems
CHR: Susan Crabtree, Director Human Resources
CNO: Caroline Esparza, Senior Vice President, Chief Operating Officer and Chief Nurse Officer
Web address: www.simivalleyhospital.com
Control: Other not–for–profit (including NFP Corporation) **Service**: General medical and surgical

Staffed Beds: 144 **Admissions**: 8347 **Census**: 73 **Outpatient Visits**: 72820 **Births**: 597 **Total Expense ($000)**: 153098 **Payroll Expense ($000)**: 51573 **Personnel**: 705

SOLVANG—Santa Barbara County

☒ **SANTA YNEZ VALLEY COTTAGE HOSPITAL (051331)**, 2050 Viborg Road, Zip 93463–2295; tel. 805/688–6431, **A**1 10 18 **F**15 28 40 57 68 81 85 107 111 114 119 143 146 149 **S** Cottage Health, Santa Barbara, CA
Primary Contact: Ronald C. Werft, President and Chief Executive Officer
COO: Steven A Fellows, Executive Vice President and Chief Operating Officer
CFO: Brett Tande, Chief Financial Officer
CMO: Edmund Wroblewski, M.D., Vice President Medical Affairs and Chief Medical Officer
CHR: Patrice Ryan, Vice President Human Resources
CNO: Herb J Geary, Chief Nursing Officer
Web address: www.cottagehealthsystem.org
Control: Other not–for–profit (including NFP Corporation) **Service**: General medical and surgical

Staffed Beds: 11 **Admissions**: 265 **Census**: 2 **Outpatient Visits**: 20317 **Births**: 0 **Total Expense ($000)**: 16374 **Payroll Expense ($000)**: 7940 **Personnel**: 75

SONOMA—Sonoma County

SONOMA VALLEY HOSPITAL (050090), 347 Andrieux Street, Zip 95476–6811, Mailing Address: P.O. Box 600, Zip 95476–0600; tel. 707/935–5000, (Nonreporting) **A**10 22
Primary Contact: Kelly Mather, Chief Executive Officer
CFO: Jeanette Tarver, Director of Finance
CMO: Sabrina Kidd, M.D., Chief Medical Officer
CIO: Fe Sendaydiego, Director Information Systems
CHR: Paula M Davis, Chief Human Resources Officer
CNO: Leslie Lovejoy, R.N., Ph.D., Chief Nursing and Quality Officer
Web address: www.svh.com
Control: Hospital district or authority, Government, nonfederal **Service**: General medical and surgical

Staffed Beds: 75

SONORA—Tuolumne County

☒ **ADVENTIST HEALTH SONORA (050335)**, 1000 Greenley Road, Zip 95370–4819; tel. 209/536–5000, (Total facility includes 68 beds in nursing home–type unit) **A**1 10 **F**3 8 11 13 15 17 18 20 28 29 30 31 34 35 37 39 40 45 49 53 54 56 57 59 62 63 64 70 71 75 76 77 78 79 81 84 85 86 87 93 94 96 97 104 107 108 110 111 114 115 117 118 119 120 121 123 127 128 129 130 131 132 133 143 144 145 146 148 149 **P**6 **S** Adventist Health, Roseville, CA
Primary Contact: Michelle Fuentes, President
CFO: Greg McCulloch, CPA, Vice President of Finance and Chief Financial Officer
CMO: Ed Clinite, D.O., Chief of Staff
CIO: Manty Drews, Chief Information Officer
CNO: Julie Kline, Senior Vice President Patient Services
Web address: www.sonoramedicalcenter.org/
Control: Church operated, Nongovernment, not–for–profit **Service**: General medical and surgical

Staffed Beds: 152 **Admissions**: 4725 **Census**: 115 **Outpatient Visits**: 438966 **Births**: 575 **Total Expense ($000)**: 239973 **Payroll Expense ($000)**: 75380 **Personnel**: 1205

SOUTH EL MONTE—Los Angeles County

☐ **GREATER EL MONTE COMMUNITY HOSPITAL (050738)**, 1701 Santa Anita Avenue, Zip 91733–3411; tel. 626/579–7777, **A**1 10 **F**3 13 14 17 18 29 34 35 40 41 45 49 50 57 59 64 68 70 75 76 77 78 79 81 82 85 87 89 92 93 107 108 119 128 130 146 **S** AHMC & Healthcare, Inc., Alhambra, CA
Primary Contact: Stanley Toy Jr, M.D., Chief Executive Officer
COO: Jose Ortega, Chief Operating Officer
CFO: Michael Chung, Chief Financial Officer
CMO: Dilip Patel, M.D., Chief of Staff
CIO: Jay Geldhof, Director Information Systems
CHR: Jason Jaquez, Director Human Resources
CNO: Evelyn Calubaquib, Chief Nursing Officer
Web address: www.greaterelmonte.com
Control: Hospital district or authority, Government, nonfederal **Service**: General medical and surgical

Staffed Beds: 117 **Admissions**: 3467 **Census**: 51 **Outpatient Visits**: 23613 **Births**: 275 **Total Expense ($000)**: 65687 **Payroll Expense ($000)**: 23328 **Personnel**: 319

SOUTH LAKE TAHOE—El Dorado County

☒ **BARTON MEMORIAL HOSPITAL (050352)**, 2170 South Avenue, Zip 96150–7026, Mailing Address: P.O. Box 9578, Zip 96158–9578; tel. 530/541–3420, (Total facility includes 48 beds in nursing home–type unit) **A**1 3 5 10 20 **F**3 8 11 13 15 18 29 30 32 34 35 38 40 43 45 46 47 48 50 54 57 59 62 63 64 65 66 68 70 75 76 77 79 81 82 83 84 85 86 87 89 90 92 93 94 96 97 99 100 103 104 107 109 110 111 112 113 114 115 116 117 118 119 121 122 123 124 126 127 128 129 130 131 132 135 143 144 146 147 148 149 154
Primary Contact: Clint Purvance, M.D., President and Chief Executive Officer
CFO: Richard P Derby, Vice President Finance
CMO: Rhonda Sneeringer, M.D., Chief Medical Officer
CIO: Jason Roberts, Director of Information Services
CNO: Susan Fairley, Chief Nursing Officer
Web address: www.bartonhealth.org
Control: Other not–for–profit (including NFP Corporation) **Service**: General medical and surgical

Staffed Beds: 111 **Admissions**: 2226 **Census**: 61 **Outpatient Visits**: 180131 **Births**: 324 **Total Expense ($000)**: 110084 **Payroll Expense ($000)**: 48438 **Personnel**: 851

SOUTH SAN FRANCISCO—San Mateo County

☒ **KAISER PERMANENTE SOUTH SAN FRANCISCO (050070)**, 1200 El Camino Real, Zip 94080–3208; tel. 650/742–2000, **A**1 3 5 10 **F**3 11 12 15 18 28 29 30 31 34 35 36 38 40 44 45 46 47 48 49 50 53 55 56 57 58 59 60 61 62 63 64 65 66 68 70 74 75 77 78 79 82 84 85 86 87 91 92 96 100 107 108 110 111 114 115 119 130 132 135 146 148 149 150 154 **S** Kaiser Foundation Hospitals, Oakland, CA
Primary Contact: Ronald Groepper, Senior Vice President and Area Manager
CMO: Michelle Caughey, M.D., Physician In Chief
CIO: Angel Shew, Director Area Technology
CHR: Sharon Barncord, Human Resource Business Partner
Web address: www.kaiserpermanente.org
Control: Other not–for–profit (including NFP Corporation) **Service**: General medical and surgical

Staffed Beds: 120 **Admissions**: 6604 **Census**: 58 **Births**: 0

STOCKTON—San Joaquin County

☐ **DAMERON HOSPITAL (050122)**, 525 West Acacia Street, Zip 95203–2484; tel. 209/944–5550, (Nonreporting) **A**1 10
Primary Contact: Lorraine P. Auerbach, FACHE, President and Chief Executive Officer
COO: Michael Glasberg, Senior Vice President, Chief Operating Officer
CFO: Elizabeth R Propp, Vice President Finance and Chief Financial Officer
CMO: Bradley Reinke, M.D., Vice President Medical Affairs and Chief Medical Officer
CIO: David Kerrins, Vice President Information Services and Chief Information Officer
CHR: Tresha Moreland, MS, Regional Vice President Human Resources
CNO: Denise J. Hair, Vice President of Nursing Services and Chief Nursing Officer
Web address: www.dameronhospital.org
Control: Other not–for–profit (including NFP Corporation) **Service**: General medical and surgical

Staffed Beds: 202

CA

⊞ **ST. JOSEPH'S BEHAVIORAL HEALTH CENTER (054123)**, 2510 North
California Street, Zip 95204–5568; tel. 209/461–2000, **A**1 10 **F**5 29 38
68 98 100 101 103 104 105 130 132 143 146 153 **S** Dignity Health, San
Francisco, CA
Primary Contact: Paul Rains, R.N., MSN, President
CFO: Doreen Hartmann, Chief Financial Officer
CMO: David Robinson, D.O., Medical Director
CHR: Nancy Vargas, Chief Human Resources
CNO: Benny Lee Lucas Jr Chief Nursing Executive
Web address: www.stjosephscanhelp.org
Control: Other not-for-profit (including NFP Corporation) **Service:** Psychiatric

Staffed Beds: 35 **Admissions:** 1744 **Census:** 32 **Outpatient Visits:** 10697
Births: 0 **Total Expense ($000):** 17810 **Payroll Expense ($000):** 9906
Personnel: 113

⊞ **ST. JOSEPH'S MEDICAL CENTER (050084)**, 1800 North California Street,
Zip 95204–6019, Mailing Address: P.O. Box 213008, Zip 95213–9008;
tel. 209/943–2000, (Nonreporting) **A**1 2 3 10 **S** Dignity Health, San Francisco, CA
Primary Contact: Donald J. Wiley, President and Chief Executive Officer
COO: Michaell Rose, Chief Operating Officer
CFO: Nikki Ochoa, Interim Chief Financial Officer
CIO: Randall Gamino, Director Perot Site
CHR: Nancy Vargas, Vice President Human Resources
Web address: www.stjosephsCARES.org
Control: Church operated, Nongovernment, not-for-profit **Service:** General
medical and surgical

Staffed Beds: 273

SUN CITY—Riverside County

☐ **MENIFEE VALLEY MEDICAL CENTER (050684)**, 28400 McCall Boulevard,
Zip 92585–9537; tel. 951/679–8888, (Nonreporting) **A**1 3 10 **S** Physicians for
Healthy Hospitals, Hemet, CA
Primary Contact: Dan C. McLaughlin, Chief Executive Officer
CHR: Michele Bird, Chief Human Resources Officer
Web address: www.valleyhealthsystem.com
Control: Hospital district or authority, Government, nonfederal **Service:** General
medical and surgical

Staffed Beds: 74

SUN VALLEY—Los Angeles County; See Los Angeles

SUSANVILLE—Lassen County

⊞ **BANNER LASSEN MEDICAL CENTER (051320)**, 1800 Spring Ridge Drive,
Zip 96130–6100; tel. 530/252–2000, **A**1 10 18 **F**3 13 15 29 30 31 34 38 39
40 43 45 59 76 79 81 85 87 89 93 107 110 111 114 119 129 130 146 148
149 **P**5 **S** Banner Health, Gilbert, AZ
Primary Contact: Catherine S. Harshbarger, R.N., Chief Executive Officer
CFO: Jon R McMillan, Chief Financial Officer
CMO: Hal Meadows, M.D., Chief Medical Officer
CIO: Randy Moore, Chief Information Officer
CHR: Ruth Smith, Division Human Resources Business Partner
CNO: Claudia Helmes, R.N., Chief Nursing Officer
Web address: www.bannerhealth.com/locations/susanville/banner-lassen-
medical-center
Control: Other not-for-profit (including NFP Corporation) **Service:** General
medical and surgical

Staffed Beds: 25 **Admissions:** 985 **Census:** 9 **Outpatient Visits:** 32779
Births: 249 **Total Expense ($000):** 33232 **Payroll Expense ($000):** 15614
Personnel: 166

SYLMAR—Los Angeles County; See Los Angeles

TARZANA—Los Angeles County; See Los Angeles

TEHACHAPI—Kern County

★ ⇑ **ADVENTIST HEALTH MEDICAL CENTER – TEHACHAPI VALLEY (051301)**,
115 West 'E' Street, Zip 93561–1607, Mailing Address: P.O. Box 1900,
Zip 93581–1900; tel. 661/823–3000, (Nonreporting) **A**10 18 21 **S** Adventist
Health, Roseville, CA
Primary Contact: Eugene Suksi, Chief Executive Officer
CFO: Chester Beedle, Interim Chief Financial Officer
CMO: Susan Cribbs, D.O., Chief of Staff
CIO: Dusty Colvard, Manager Information Technology
CHR: Susan Nelson-Jones, Director Human Resources
CNO: Juliana Kay Kirby, R.N., MSN, Chief Nursing Officer
Web address: www.tvhd.org
Control: Hospital district or authority, Government, nonfederal **Service:** General
medical and surgical

Staffed Beds: 24

TEMECULA—Riverside County

⊞ **TEMECULA VALLEY HOSPITAL (050775)**, 31700 Temecula Parkway,
Zip 92592–5896; tel. 951/331–2216, (Nonreporting) **A**1 10 **S** Universal Health
Services, Inc., King of Prussia, PA
Primary Contact: Darlene Wetton, R.N., Chief Executive Officer
Web address: www.temeculavalleyhospital.com
Control: Corporation, Investor-owned (for-profit) **Service:** General medical and
surgical

Staffed Beds: 140

TEMPLETON—San Luis Obispo County

⊞ **TWIN CITIES COMMUNITY HOSPITAL (050633)**, 1100 Las Tablas Road,
Zip 93465–9796; tel. 805/434–3500, **A**1 10 **F**3 13 29 30 34 39 40 45 49 50
55 56 57 59 60 64 67 68 70 74 75 76 77 79 81 84 85 87 107 108 111 115
119 130 146 148 149 154 **S** TENET Healthcare Corporation, Dallas, TX
Primary Contact: Mark P. Lisa, FACHE, Chief Executive Officer
COO: Mike Lane, Chief Operating Officer
CFO: Lois Johnson, Chief Financial Officer
CHR: Diane D McCluskey, Chief Human Resources Officer
CNO: William Gamba, Chief Nursing Officer
Web address: www.twincitieshospital.com
Control: Corporation, Investor-owned (for-profit) **Service:** General medical and
surgical

Staffed Beds: 89 **Admissions:** 4390 **Census:** 41 **Outpatient Visits:** 46740
Births: 597 **Total Expense ($000):** 89711 **Payroll Expense ($000):** 40895
Personnel: 461

THOUSAND OAKS—Ventura County

⊞ ⇑ **LOS ROBLES HOSPITAL AND MEDICAL CENTER (050549)**, 215 West
Janss Road, Zip 91360–1899; tel. 805/370–4421, (Includes THOUSAND
OAKS SURGICAL HOSPITAL, 401 Rolling Oaks Drive, Thousand Oaks, CA,
Zip 91361–1050; tel. 805/497–2727; Natalie Mussi, President and Chief
Executive Officer) (Nonreporting) **A**1 2 10 21 **S** HCA Healthcare, Nashville, TN
Primary Contact: Natalie Mussi, President and Chief Executive Officer
COO: Austin Lane Manning, Chief Operating Officer
CMO: Hannah Grossman, M.D., Chief Medical Officer
CIO: Alex Bryer, Director Information Management
CHR: Geoff Washburn, Vice President Human Resources
CNO: Cynthia J Johnson, R.N., Chief Nursing Officer
Web address: www.losrobleshospital.com
Control: Corporation, Investor-owned (for-profit) **Service:** General medical and
surgical

Staffed Beds: 325

TORRANCE—Los Angeles County

☐ **DEL AMO HOSPITAL (054053)**, 23700 Camino Del Sol, Zip 90505–5000;
tel. 310/530–1151, (Nonreporting) **A**1 10 **S** Universal Health Services, Inc., King
of Prussia, PA
Primary Contact: Steven Oppenheimer, Chief Executive Officer
Web address: www.delamohospital.com
Control: Corporation, Investor-owned (for-profit) **Service:** Psychiatric

Staffed Beds: 70

☐ **HARBOR-UCLA MEDICAL CENTER (050376)**, 1000 West Carson Street,
Zip 90502–2059; tel. 310/222–2345, (Nonreporting) **A**1 2 3 5 8 10 **S** Los
Angeles County–Department of Health Services, Los Angeles, CA
Primary Contact: Kimberly McKenzie, R.N., MSN, Interim Chief Executive Officer
COO: Kimberly McKenzie, R.N., MSN, Chief Nursing Officer and Chief Operations
Officer
CFO: Jody Nakasuji, Chief Financial Officer
CMO: Timothy Van Natta, M.D., Chief Medical Officer
CIO: Sandy Mungovan, Chief Information Officer
CHR: Karyl Smith, Director Human Resources
CNO: Kimberly McKenzie, R.N., MSN, Chief Nursing Officer and Chief Operations
Officer
Web address: www.harbor-ucla.org
Control: County, Government, nonfederal **Service:** General medical and surgical

Staffed Beds: 397

CA

Hospital, Medicare Provider Number, Address, Telephone, Approval, Facility, and Physician Codes, Health Care System

★ American Hospital Association (AHA) membership
☐ The Joint Commission accreditation
◯ Healthcare Facilities Accreditation Program
◇ DNV Healthcare Inc. accreditation
⇑ Center for Improvement in Healthcare Quality Accreditation
△ Commission on Accreditation of Rehabilitation Facilities (CARF) accreditation

© 2018 AHA Guide   *Many Facility Codes have changed. Please refer to the AHA Guide Code Chart.*   Hospitals **A91**

✠ **PROVIDENCE LITTLE COMPANY OF MARY MEDICAL CENTER – TORRANCE (050353)**, 4101 Torrance Boulevard, Zip 90503–4664; tel. 310/540–7676, (Total facility includes 85 beds in nursing home–type unit) **A**1 2 10 **F**3 7 8 11 12 13 14 15 18 19 20 22 24 26 28 29 30 31 34 35 37 39 40 45 46 49 50 51 54 55 57 58 59 60 62 63 64 68 70 72 74 75 76 77 78 79 81 82 84 85 86 87 89 91 92 93 94 100 107 108 110 111 114 115 116 117 118 119 120 121 123 126 128 130 131 132 143 145 146 147 148 149 150 154 **S** Providence St. Joseph Health, Renton, WA
Primary Contact: Garry M. Olney, Chief Executive Officer
CFO: Elizabeth Zuanich, Chief Financial Officer
CMO: Richard Glimp, M.D., Chief Medical Officer
CIO: Andrea Flores, Director, Information Systems
CHR: Melissa Baker, Director, Human Resources
CNO: Michael Jongsma, R.N., Chief Nursing Officer
Web address: www.providence.org
Control: Church operated, Nongovernment, not–for–profit **Service**: General medical and surgical

Staffed Beds: 386 Admissions: 19681 Census: 247 Outpatient Visits: 279105 Births: 2422 Total Expense ($000): 314250 Payroll Expense ($000): 161362 Personnel: 2326

✠ **TORRANCE MEMORIAL MEDICAL CENTER (050351)**, 3330 Lomita Boulevard, Zip 90505–5073; tel. 310/325–9110, (Total facility includes 40 beds in nursing home–type unit) **A**1 2 10 **F**3 5 8 9 11 12 13 14 15 16 17 18 19 20 22 24 26 28 29 30 31 32 34 35 36 37 39 40 41 44 45 46 47 48 49 50 51 55 56 57 58 59 60 61 62 63 64 68 70 72 74 75 76 77 78 79 81 82 83 84 85 86 87 89 91 92 93 96 107 108 109 110 111 114 115 116 117 118 119 120 121 123 124 126 128 129 130 132 134 135 137 141 143 145 146 147 148 149 154 **P**2 3 5 7 **S** Cedars–Sinai Health System, West Hollywood, CA
Primary Contact: Craig Leach, President and Chief Executive Officer
CFO: Bill Larson, Vice President Finance and Chief Financial Officer
CMO: John McNamara, M.D., Senior Vice President, Chief Medical Officer
CIO: Bernadette Reid, Vice President, Information Technology and Chief Information Officer
CHR: Linda Dobie, R.N., JD, Vice President, Legal Affairs
CNO: Margaret Berwald, R.N., MSN, Senior Vice President Patient Services
Web address: www.torrancememorial.org
Control: Other not–for–profit (including NFP Corporation) **Service**: General medical and surgical

Staffed Beds: 444 Admissions: 26408 Census: 304 Outpatient Visits: 425719 Births: 2790 Total Expense ($000): 640281 Payroll Expense ($000): 241624 Personnel: 3227

TRACY—San Joaquin County

✠ **SUTTER TRACY COMMUNITY HOSPITAL (050313)**, 1420 North Tracy Boulevard, Zip 95376–3497; tel. 209/835–1500, **A**1 10 **F**3 11 13 15 18 29 30 31 34 35 39 40 44 45 46 49 50 54 57 59 60 64 65 68 70 74 75 76 77 78 79 81 82 84 85 86 87 93 107 108 110 111 115 117 119 124 130 132 135 146 148 149 154 **P**3 5 **S** Sutter Health, Sacramento, CA
Primary Contact: David M. Thompson, Chief Executive Officer
CFO: Eric Dalton, Chief Financial Officer
CIO: Catherine M Larsen, Director Marketing
CHR: Melanie Wallace, Manager Human Resources
Web address: www.suttertracy.org
Control: Other not–for–profit (including NFP Corporation) **Service**: General medical and surgical

Staffed Beds: 33 Admissions: 3828 Census: 34 Outpatient Visits: 79276 Births: 600 Total Expense ($000): 116444 Payroll Expense ($000): 41003 Personnel: 475

TRAVIS AFB—Solano County

✠ **DAVID GRANT USAF MEDICAL CENTER**, 101 Bodin Circle, Zip 94535–1809; tel. 707/423–7300, (Nonreporting) **A**1 3 5 **S** Department of the Air Force, Washington, DC
Primary Contact: Lieutenant Michael Higgins, Commander
CFO: Major Jonathan Richards, Chief Financial Officer
CMO: Colonel Chris Scharenbrock, M.D., Chief Medical Staff
Web address: www.travis.af.mil/units/dgmc/index.asp
Control: Air Force, Government, federal **Service**: General medical and surgical

Staffed Beds: 116

TRUCKEE—Nevada County

★ **TAHOE FOREST HOSPITAL DISTRICT (051328)**, 10121 Pine Avenue, Zip 96161–4856, Mailing Address: P.O. Box 759, Zip 96160–0759; tel. 530/587–6011, (Total facility includes 36 beds in nursing home–type unit) **A**2 3 5 10 18 **F**3 8 11 13 28 29 30 31 32 34 35 40 45 49 53 59 62 63 64 65 66 70 75 76 77 78 79 81 82 84 85 86 87 97 107 108 110 115 116 117 119 121 122 123 128 130 131 133 135 146 147 148 149 **P**7 **S** Tahoe Forest Health System, Truckee, CA
Primary Contact: Harry Weis, Chief Executive Officer
COO: Judy Newland, R.N., Chief Operating Officer
CFO: Crystal Betts, Chief Financial Officer
CMO: Shawni Coll, D.O., Chief Medical Officer
CIO: Jake Dorst, Chief Information Officer
CHR: Alex MacLennan, Chief Human Resources Officer
CNO: Karen Baffone, R.N., Chief Nursing Officer
Web address: www.tfhd.com
Control: Hospital district or authority, Government, nonfederal **Service**: General medical and surgical

Staffed Beds: 62 Admissions: 1845 Census: 30 Outpatient Visits: 96667 Births: 398 Total Expense ($000): 142447 Payroll Expense ($000): 47747

TURLOCK—Stanislaus County

✠ **EMANUEL MEDICAL CENTER (050179)**, 825 Delbon Avenue, Zip 95382–2016, Mailing Address: P.O. Box 819005, Zip 95382; tel. 209/667–4200, **A**1 10 **F**3 8 11 15 18 20 22 23 26 29 30 31 34 35 40 47 48 49 54 59 60 64 68 70 73 75 76 77 78 79 81 89 93 97 107 108 110 111 114 115 118 119 120 121 123 130 132 146 147 **S** TENET Healthcare Corporation, Dallas, TX
Primary Contact: Lani Dickinson, Chief Executive Officer
CFO: David Neapolitan, Chief Financial Officer
CIO: Beth Walker, Chief Information Officer
CHR: Terry Gray, Vice President Human Resources
CNO: Antonio M. Garcia, Chief Nursing Officer
Web address: www.emanuelmedicalcenter.org
Control: Corporation, Investor–owned (for–profit) **Service**: General medical and surgical

Staffed Beds: 104 Admissions: 9060 Census: 93 Outpatient Visits: 129549 Births: 1367 Total Expense ($000): 184560 Personnel: 971

TUSTIN—Orange County

○ **FOOTHILL REGIONAL MEDICAL CENTER (050780)**, 14662 Newport Avenue, Zip 92780–6064; tel. 714/838–9600, **A**10 11 **F**3 8 12 26 29 34 40 45 49 57 68 70 74 77 79 81 82 85 87 92 93 100 107 108 111 115 119 130 132 135 149 **S** Prospect Medical Holdings, Los Angeles, CA
Primary Contact: Barbara Schneider, R.N., Chief Executive Officer
COO: Kara Bourne, R.N., MSN, Chief Nursing Officer and Chief Operating Officer
CIO: Darla Kennedy, Chief Information Officer
CHR: Aprille Major, Director Human Resources
Web address: www.hfcis.cdph.ca.gov/longtermcare/Facility.aspx?fac=060000013
Control: Corporation, Investor–owned (for–profit) **Service**: General medical and surgical

Staffed Beds: 80 Admissions: 2506 Census: 26 Outpatient Visits: 3569 Births: 0

✠ **HEALTHSOUTH TUSTIN REHABILITATION HOSPITAL (053034)**, 14851 Yorba Street, Zip 92780–2925; tel. 714/832–9200, (Nonreporting) **A**1 10 **S** Encompass Health Corporation, Birmingham, AL
Primary Contact: Diana Hanyak, Chief Executive Officer
CFO: Paula Redmond, Controller
CMO: Ann Vasile, M.D., Medical Director
CHR: JoAnn Roiz, Director Human Resources
CNO: LaDonna Butler Esq Chief Nursing Officer
Web address: www.tustinrehab.com
Control: Corporation, Investor–owned (for–profit) **Service**: Rehabilitation

Staffed Beds: 48

TWENTYNINE PALMS—San Bernardino County

✠ **ROBERT E. BUSH NAVAL HOSPITAL**, 1145 Sturgis Road, Zip 92278, Mailing Address: Box 788250, MCAGCC, Zip 92278–8250; tel. 760/830–2190, (Nonreporting) **A**1 3 **S** Bureau of Medicine and Surgery, Department of the Navy, Falls Church, VA
Primary Contact: Captain Jay C. Sourbeer, Commanding Officer
CHR: Virginia Ward, Human Resources Officer
CNO: Captain Sandra Mason, MSN, R.N., Director Nursing Services and Senior Nurse Executive
Web address: www.med.navy.mil/sites/nhtp/Pages/default.aspx
Control: Navy, Government, federal **Service**: General medical and surgical

Staffed Beds: 29

Many Facility Codes have changed. Please refer to the AHA Guide Code Chart.

CA

UKIAH—Mendocino County

⊞ **UKIAH VALLEY MEDICAL CENTER (050301)**, 275 Hospital Drive, Zip 95482–4531; tel. 707/462–3111, **A**1 5 10 **F**3 8 11 12 13 15 18 29 30 31 32 34 35 36 38 40 44 45 46 48 49 50 51 54 57 59 60 64 65 68 70 72 75 76 77 78 79 81 82 84 85 86 87 93 94 97 107 108 110 111 114 115 116 117 118 119 127 130 131 132 135 144 146 147 148 **P**3 **S** Adventist Health, Roseville, CA
Primary Contact: Gwen Matthews, R.N., MSN, Chief Executive Officer
CIO: David Eastman, Site Director
CHR: Rebecca Ryan, Interim Director Human Resources and Employee Health
Web address: www.adventisthealth.org
Control: Church operated, Nongovernment, not–for–profit **Service:** General medical and surgical

Staffed Beds: 50 **Admissions:** 3475 **Census:** 31 **Outpatient Visits:** 131251 **Births:** 764 **Total Expense ($000):** 154224 **Payroll Expense ($000):** 41817 **Personnel:** 566

UPLAND—San Bernardino County

⊞ **SAN ANTONIO REGIONAL HOSPITAL (050099)**, 999 San Bernardino Road, Zip 91786–4920, Mailing Address: Box 5001, Zip 91785–5001; tel. 909/985–2811, **A**1 2 3 10 **F**3 8 11 13 15 17 18 20 22 24 26 28 29 31 35 38 40 45 46 49 50 54 57 59 60 61 64 65 69 70 72 74 75 76 77 78 79 80 81 82 83 84 85 86 87 89 91 92 93 94 107 108 110 111 114 115 118 119 121 123 124 130 132 146 147 148
Primary Contact: Harris F. Koenig, President and Chief Executive Officer
CFO: Wah Chung Hsu, Senior Vice President Finance
CMO: Rohinder Sandhu, M.D., President of the Medical Staff
CIO: Kamel Pandya, Director Information Services
CHR: Laura Kato, Vice President of Human Resources
CNO: Gudrun Moll, R.N., MSN, Chief Nursing Officer
Web address: www.sarh.org
Control: Other not–for–profit (including NFP Corporation) **Service:** General medical and surgical

Staffed Beds: 363 **Admissions:** 17228 **Census:** 179 **Outpatient Visits:** 245506 **Births:** 2335 **Total Expense ($000):** 374652 **Payroll Expense ($000):** 147935 **Personnel:** 1900

VACAVILLE—Solano County

CALIFORNIA MEDICAL FACILITY, 1600 California Drive, Zip 95687; tel. 707/448–6841, (Nonreporting)
Primary Contact: David Horch, Chief Executive
CMO: Raymond Andreasen, M.D., Chief Medical Officer–Inpatient
Web address: www.cya.ca.gov/visitors/fac_prison_cmf.html
Control: State, Government, nonfederal **Service:** Hospital unit of an institution (prison hospital, college infirmary, etc.)

Staffed Beds: 215

⊞ **KAISER PERMANENTE VACAVILLE MEDICAL CENTER (050767)**, 1 Quality Drive, Zip 95688–9494; tel. 707/624–4000, **A**1 2 3 10 **F**3 5 8 13 15 18 29 30 34 35 36 40 43 44 45 46 47 48 49 50 51 52 57 58 59 61 64 65 68 70 74 75 76 77 78 79 81 82 84 85 86 87 92 93 97 99 100 101 102 103 104 107 108 110 111 114 115 119 130 131 132 135 141 144 146 147 148 149 153 154 **S** Kaiser Foundation Hospitals, Oakland, CA
Primary Contact: Norair Jemjemian, Senior Vice President and Area Manager
Web address: www.kp.org
Control: Other not–for–profit (including NFP Corporation) **Service:** General medical and surgical

Staffed Beds: 140 **Admissions:** 9439 **Census:** 67 **Outpatient Visits:** 601051 **Births:** 1291

NORTHBAY VACAVALLEY HOSPITAL See Northbay Medical Center, Fairfield

VALENCIA—Los Angeles County

⊞ **HENRY MAYO NEWHALL HOSPITAL (050624)**, 23845 McBean Parkway, Zip 91355–2083; tel. 661/200–2000, **A**1 2 10 **F**3 8 11 13 15 17 18 20 22 24 26 28 29 30 31 34 35 38 40 41 43 45 49 50 55 57 59 60 64 70 72 74 76 77 78 79 81 82 84 85 86 87 90 93 98 100 102 107 108 110 115 119 126 130 132 135 146 147 148 **P**7
Primary Contact: Roger E. Seaver, President and Chief Executive Officer
COO: John V Schleif, Senior Vice President and Chief Operating Officer
CFO: Ted Sirotta, Senior Vice President and Chief Financial Officer
CMO: Richard Frankenstein, M.D., Vice President and Chief Medical Officer
CIO: Ray Moss, Vice President and Chief Information Officer
CHR: Mark Puleo, Vice President and Chief Human Resources Officer
CNO: Jennifer Castaldo, R.N., Vice President, Patient Care and Chief Nursing Officer
Web address: www.henrymayo.com
Control: Other not–for–profit (including NFP Corporation) **Service:** General medical and surgical

Staffed Beds: 238 **Admissions:** 12571 **Census:** 161 **Outpatient Visits:** 116764 **Births:** 1362 **Total Expense ($000):** 319762 **Payroll Expense ($000):** 107183 **Personnel:** 1732

VALLEJO—Solano County

⊞ **ADVENTIST HEALTH ST. HELENA (054074)**, 525 Oregon Street, Zip 94590–3201; tel. 707/648–2200, **A**1 10 **F**29 30 50 64 65 68 98 104 105 130 146 153 154 **S** Adventist Health, Roseville, CA
Primary Contact: Steven Herber, M.D., FACS, President and Chief Executive Officer
CFO: Edward A McDonald, Chief Financial Officer
Web address: www.sthelenahospitals.org/location/center–for–behavioral–health
Control: Other not–for–profit (including NFP Corporation) **Service:** Psychiatric

Staffed Beds: 61 **Admissions:** 3267 **Census:** 83 **Outpatient Visits:** 18743 **Births:** 0

⊞ △ **KAISER PERMANENTE VALLEJO MEDICAL CENTER (050073)**, 975 Sereno Drive, Zip 94589–2441; tel. 707/651–1000, **A**1 2 3 5 7 10 **F**3 5 13 15 18 20 22 28 29 30 31 34 35 36 40 44 45 46 47 48 49 50 51 57 58 59 61 62 63 64 65 68 70 73 74 75 76 77 78 79 81 82 84 85 86 87 90 91 92 93 94 97 99 100 101 102 103 104 107 108 110 111 114 115 118 119 129 130 132 135 141 142 144 146 147 148 149 153 154 **S** Kaiser Foundation Hospitals, Oakland, CA
Primary Contact: Corwin N. Harper, Senior Vice President and Area Manager
COO: Karen Grisnak, R.N., Chief Operating Officer and Assistant Administrator Quality Services
CFO: Joseph D'Angina, Area Finance Officer
CMO: Steven Stricker, M.D., Physician in Chief
CIO: Gale Austin–Moore, Director Area Technology
CHR: Sherri Stegge, Director Human Resources
Web address: www.kaiserpermanente.org
Control: Other not–for–profit (including NFP Corporation) **Service:** General medical and surgical

Staffed Beds: 248 **Admissions:** 13454 **Census:** 145 **Outpatient Visits:** 828937 **Births:** 1590

⊞ **SUTTER SOLANO MEDICAL CENTER (050101)**, 300 Hospital Drive, Zip 94589–2574, Mailing Address: P.O. Box 3189, Zip 94590–0669; tel. 707/554–4444, **A**1 2 10 **F**3 8 11 13 15 18 29 30 31 34 35 40 41 45 46 49 50 51 55 57 58 59 60 64 68 70 74 75 76 77 78 79 81 84 85 86 87 100 107 108 110 111 114 118 119 120 121 123 124 130 132 146 149 154 **P**3 5 **S** Sutter Health, Sacramento, CA
Primary Contact: Abhishek Dosi, Chief Executive Officer
CHR: Jean Willhite, Director Human Resources
Web address: www.suttersolano.org
Control: Other not–for–profit (including NFP Corporation) **Service:** General medical and surgical

Staffed Beds: 108 **Admissions:** 4329 **Census:** 51 **Outpatient Visits:** 60922 **Births:** 505 **Total Expense ($000):** 158225 **Payroll Expense ($000):** 52605 **Personnel:** 476

CA

Hospital, Medicare Provider Number, Address, Telephone, Approval, Facility, and Physician Codes, Health Care System

★ American Hospital Association (AHA) membership
□ The Joint Commission accreditation
○ Healthcare Facilities Accreditation Program
◇ DNV Healthcare Inc. accreditation
⇑ Center for Improvement in Healthcare Quality Accreditation
△ Commission on Accreditation of Rehabilitation Facilities (CARF) accreditation

CA

VAN NUYS—Los Angeles County; See Los Angeles

VENTURA—Ventura County

★ ⇧ **COMMUNITY MEMORIAL HOSPITAL (050394)**, 147 North Brent Street, Zip 93003–2809; tel. 805/652–5011, (Includes COMMUNITY MEMORIAL HOSPITAL, 147 North Brent Street, Ventura, CA, Zip 93003–2854; tel. 805/652–5011) (Total facility includes 67 beds in nursing home–type unit) **A**2 3 5 10 13 21 **F**3 8 11 12 13 15 17 18 19 20 22 24 26 28 29 30 31 32 34 35 40 45 46 47 48 49 53 54 57 59 64 65 66 68 70 71 72 74 75 76 77 78 79 81 82 83 84 85 86 89 91 93 97 104 107 108 110 111 114 115 118 119 126 127 128 130 131 132 141 144 145 146 147 148 **P**4 5 7 **S** Community Memorial Health System, Ventura, CA
Primary Contact: Gary Wilde, President and Chief Executive Officer
COO: Adam Thunell, Chief Operating Officer and Vice President Operations
CFO: David Glyer, Vice President Finance
CMO: Stanley Frochtzwajg, M.D., Chief Medical Officer
CIO: Ron Sandifer, Chief Information Officer
CHR: Diany Klein, Vice President Human Resources
Web address: www.cmhshealth.org
Control: Other not–for–profit (including NFP Corporation) **Service**: General medical and surgical

Staffed Beds: 284 **Admissions**: 12620 **Census**: 199 **Outpatient Visits**: 496607 **Births**: 2656 **Total Expense ($000)**: 395215 **Payroll Expense ($000)**: 140642 **Personnel**: 1991

⊞ **VENTURA COUNTY MEDICAL CENTER (050159)**, 3291 Loma Vista Road, Zip 93003–3099; tel. 805/652–6000, (Nonreporting) **A**1 3 10
Primary Contact: Kim S. Milstien, Chief Executive Officer
CMO: Bryan Wong, M.D., Medical Director
CIO: Terry Theobald, Chief Information Officer
CHR: Tim Rhyne, Personnel Officer
CNO: Susan Scott, Chief Nurse Executive
Web address: www.vchca.org
Control: County, Government, nonfederal **Service**: General medical and surgical

Staffed Beds: 160

☐ **VISTA DEL MAR HOSPITAL (054077)**, 801 Seneca Street, Zip 93001–1411; tel. 805/653–6434, (Nonreporting) **A**1 10 **S** Signature Healthcare Services, Corona, CA
Primary Contact: Mayla Krebsbach, Chief Executive Officer
CFO: Kurt Broten, Chief Financial Officer
CMO: Steve Ruths, M.D., Chief Medical Officer
Web address: www.vistadelmarhospital.com
Control: Corporation, Investor–owned (for–profit) **Service**: Psychiatric

Staffed Beds: 87

VICTORVILLE—San Bernardino County

★ ○ **DESERT VALLEY HOSPITAL (050709)**, 16850 Bear Valley Road, Zip 92395–5795; tel. 760/241–8000, (Nonreporting) **A**10 11 **S** Prime Healthcare, Ontario, CA
Primary Contact: Fred Hunter, R.N., Chief Executive Officer
COO: Luis Leon, Chief Operating Officer
CFO: Martin Mansukhani, Chief Financial Officer
CIO: Sreekant Gotti, Director Information Systems
Web address: www.dvmc.com
Control: Corporation, Investor–owned (for–profit) **Service**: General medical and surgical

Staffed Beds: 110

☐ **VICTOR VALLEY GLOBAL MEDICAL CENTER (050517)**, 15248 Eleventh Street, Zip 92395–3704; tel. 760/245–8691, (Nonreporting) **A**1 10
Primary Contact: Suzanne Richards, R.N., M.P.H., FACHE, Chief Executive Officer
COO: Doreen Dann, R.N., Chief Operating Officer
CIO: Joe Archer, Chief Information Officer
CHR: Cesar Lugo, Director Human Resources
Web address: www.vvgmc.com
Control: Other not–for–profit (including NFP Corporation) **Service**: General medical and surgical

Staffed Beds: 101

VISALIA—Tulare County

⊞ △ **KAWEAH DELTA MEDICAL CENTER (050057)**, 400 West Mineral King Boulevard, Zip 93291–6263; tel. 559/624–2000, (Includes SOUTH CAMPUS, 1633 South Court Street, Visalia, CA, Zip 93277; tel. 559/624–6090) **A**1 3 5 7 10 **F**3 13 15 17 18 20 22 24 26 28 29 30 31 34 35 40 41 43 45 49 50 51 53 54 56 57 59 60 62 63 64 65 68 70 73 74 75 76 77 78 79 81 82 84 85 86 87 89 90 93 97 98 100 101 102 103 104 107 108 110 111 114 116 117 118 119 123 124 126 127 128 129 130 131 132 134 135 144 146 147 148 149
Primary Contact: Gary Herbst, Chief Executive Officer
COO: Thomas J Rayner, Senior Vice President and Chief Operating Officer
CMO: Edward Hirsch, M.D., Vice President Chief Medical and Quality Officer
CIO: Doug Leeper, Chief Information Officer
CHR: Dianne E Cox, Vice President of Human Resources
CNO: Regina Sawyer, Vice President Chief Nursing Officer
Web address: www.kaweahdelta.org
Control: Hospital district or authority, Government, nonfederal **Service**: General medical and surgical

Staffed Beds: 441 **Admissions**: 26630 **Census**: 401 **Outpatient Visits**: 761387 **Births**: 4665 **Total Expense ($000)**: 629730 **Payroll Expense ($000)**: 246481 **Personnel**: 4670

WALNUT CREEK—Contra Costa County

⊞ △ **JOHN MUIR MEDICAL CENTER, WALNUT CREEK (050180)**, 1601 Ygnacio Valley Road, Zip 94598–3194; tel. 925/939–3000, **A**1 2 3 7 10 **F**3 11 13 15 17 18 19 20 22 24 26 28 29 30 31 32 34 35 37 39 40 41 43 44 45 46 47 48 49 50 54 55 56 57 58 59 61 62 64 65 68 70 72 74 75 76 77 78 79 80 81 82 83 84 85 86 87 88 89 90 91 93 95 96 100 102 108 110 118 119 120 121 123 124 126 130 131 132 141 145 146 147 148 149 150 154 **P**5 7 **S** John Muir Health, Walnut Creek, CA
Primary Contact: Jane Willemsen, President and Chief Administrative Officer
COO: Raymond Nassief, Senior Vice President, Hospital Operations and Support Services
CFO: Christian Pass, Senior Vice President & Chief Financial Officer
CMO: Irving Pike, M.D., Senior Vice President and Chief Medical Officer
CIO: Jon Russell, Senior Vice President & Chief Information Officer
CHR: Lisa Foust, Senior Vice President, Human Resources
CNO: Michelle Anne Lopes, MSN, R.N., Senior Vice President, Patient Care Services & Chief Nursing Officer
Web address: www.johnmuirhealth.com/
Control: Other not–for–profit (including NFP Corporation) **Service**: General medical and surgical

Staffed Beds: 425 **Admissions**: 20480 **Census**: 281 **Outpatient Visits**: 329707 **Births**: 2678 **Total Expense ($000)**: 822332 **Payroll Expense ($000)**: 289643 **Personnel**: 1957

⊞ **KAISER PERMANENTE WALNUT CREEK MEDICAL CENTER (050072)**, 1425 South Main Street, Zip 94596–5300; tel. 925/295–4000, (Includes KAISER FOUNDATION HOSPITAL, 200 Muir Road, Martinez, CA, Zip 94553–4696; tel. 510/372–1000) **A**1 2 3 5 10 **F**3 12 15 18 20 29 30 31 34 35 40 45 46 47 48 49 50 51 53 57 60 62 63 68 70 73 74 75 76 77 78 79 81 82 84 85 86 87 89 107 108 110 111 114 115 116 117 118 119 126 130 146 147 148 149 154 **S** Kaiser Foundation Hospitals, Oakland, CA
Primary Contact: Colleen McKeown, Senior Vice President and Area Manager
CFO: Yakesun Wing, Business Strategy and Finance Leader
Web address: www.kaiserpermanente.org
Control: Other not–for–profit (including NFP Corporation) **Service**: General medical and surgical

Staffed Beds: 233 **Admissions**: 11967 **Census**: 132 **Births**: 3346

WATSONVILLE—Santa Cruz County

⊞ **WATSONVILLE COMMUNITY HOSPITAL (050194)**, 75 Nielson Street, Zip 95076–2468; tel. 831/724–4741, **A**1 10 **F**3 11 13 15 18 20 29 34 35 40 45 49 50 51 53 57 60 64 68 70 72 74 76 77 79 81 87 89 93 97 107 111 115 119 126 130 146 148 149 **S** Quorum Health, Brentwood, TN
Primary Contact: Audra Earle, FACHE, Chief Executive Officer
CFO: Rachel Jones, Chief Financial Officer
CIO: Sergio Nell, Director Information Systems
CNO: Donna Salvi, Chief Nursing Officer
Web address: www.watsonvillehospital.com
Control: Corporation, Investor–owned (for–profit) **Service**: General medical and surgical

Staffed Beds: 106 **Admissions**: 3783 **Census**: 40 **Outpatient Visits**: 65990 **Births**: 986 **Total Expense ($000)**: 111399 **Payroll Expense ($000)**: 51895 **Personnel**: 591

WEAVERVILLE—Trinity County

TRINITY HOSPITAL (051315), 60 Easter Avenue, Zip 96093, Mailing Address: P.O. Box 1229, Zip 96093–1229; tel. 530/623–5541, (Nonreporting) **A**10 18
Primary Contact: Aaron Rogers, Chief Executive Officer
CFO: Kathy Walker, Chief Financial Officer
CMO: Donald Krouse, M.D., Chief of Staff
CIO: Jake Odom, Chief Information Officer
CHR: Heidi Corrigan, Manager Human Resources
CNO: Judy Nordlund, R.N., Chief Nursing Officer
Web address: www.mcmedical.org
Control: Hospital district or authority, Government, nonfederal **Service**: General medical and surgical

Staffed Beds: 47

WEST COVINA—Los Angeles County

☐ **WEST COVINA MEDICAL CENTER (050096)**, 725 South Orange Avenue, Zip 91790–2614; tel. 626/338–8481, (Nonreporting) **A**1 10
Primary Contact: Gerald H. Wallman, Administrator
CFO: Kami Horvat, Chief Financial Officer
CMO: Erich Pollak, M.D., Chief of Staff
CHR: Lourdes Meza, Coordinator Human Resources
CNO: Guadalupe Ojeda, R.N., Chief Nursing Officer
Control: Corporation, Investor–owned (for–profit) **Service**: General medical and surgical

Staffed Beds: 46

WEST HILLS—Los Angeles County; See Los Angeles

WESTMINSTER—Orange County

⊞ **KINDRED HOSPITAL–WESTMINSTER (052035)**, 200 Hospital Circle, Zip 92683–3910; tel. 714/893–4541, (Nonreporting) **A**1 10 **S** Kindred Healthcare, Louisville, KY
Primary Contact: Julie Myers, Chief Executive Officer
CFO: Dale Wagner, Chief Financial Officer
Web address: www.khwestminster.com/
Control: Corporation, Investor–owned (for–profit) **Service**: Acute long–term care hospital

Staffed Beds: 109

WHITTIER—Los Angeles County

⊞ **PIH HEALTH HOSPITAL – WHITTIER (050169)**, 12401 Washington Boulevard, Zip 90602–1099; tel. 562/698–0811, (Total facility includes 18 beds in nursing home–type unit) **A**1 2 3 5 10 **F**1 3 11 12 13 15 18 20 22 24 26 28 29 30 31 34 35 36 37 40 41 44 45 46 49 50 51 54 55 56 57 58 59 60 61 62 63 64 65 68 70 74 75 76 77 78 79 81 84 85 86 87 90 92 93 96 107 108 110 111 114 115 116 117 118 119 120 121 122 123 124 128 130 131 132 135 143 145 146 147 148 149 **P**3 5 **S** PIH Health, Whittier, CA
Primary Contact: James R. West, President and Chief Executive Officer
COO: Reanna Thompson, R.N., Chief Operating Officer and Chief Nursing Officer
CFO: Greg Williams, Chief Financial Officer
CMO: Rosalio J Lopez, M.D., Senior Vice President and Chief Medical Officer
CIO: Jason Fischer, Chief Information Officer
CNO: Reanna Thompson, R.N., Chief Operating Officer and Chief Nursing Officer
Web address: www.PIHHealth.org
Control: Other not–for–profit (including NFP Corporation) **Service**: General medical and surgical

Staffed Beds: 212 **Admissions:** 16843 **Census:** 189 **Outpatient Visits:** 340292 **Births:** 1742 **Total Expense ($000):** 523602 **Payroll Expense ($000):** 183162 **Personnel:** 2875

☐ **WHITTIER HOSPITAL MEDICAL CENTER (050735)**, 9080 Colima Road, Zip 90605–1600; tel. 562/945–3561, (Nonreporting) **A**1 10 **S** AHMC & Healthcare, Inc., Alhambra, CA
Primary Contact: Richard Castro, Chief Executive Officer
COO: Mary Anne Monje, Chief Financial Officer and Chief Operating Officer
CFO: Mary Anne Monje, Chief Financial Officer and Chief Operating Officer
CIO: Jay Geldhof, Director Information Systems
CHR: Martha Salcedo, Interim Director Human Resources
CNO: Sarkis Vartanian, Chief Nursing Officer
Web address: www.whittierhospital.com
Control: Corporation, Investor–owned (for–profit) **Service**: General medical and surgical

Staffed Beds: 100

WILLITS—Mendocino County

⊞ **ADVENTIST HEALTH HOWARD MEMORIAL (051310)**, One Marcela Drive, Zip 95490–4298; tel. 707/459–6801, **A**1 10 18 **F**11 15 29 30 34 35 40 57 59 68 70 75 79 81 93 97 107 110 111 115 119 127 131 132 133 135 146 147 148 **P**7 **S** Adventist Health, Roseville, CA
Primary Contact: Jason Wells, President and Chief Executive Officer
CFO: Judson Howe, Chief Financial Officer
CMO: Kimberly Faucher, M.D., Chief Medical Officer
CIO: Cecilia Winiger, Community Outreach and Communication Manager
CHR: Darcy De Leon, Executive Director, Human Resources
CNO: Karen M Scott, Vice President Patient Care
Web address: www.howardhospital.com
Control: Church operated, Nongovernment, not–for–profit **Service**: General medical and surgical

Staffed Beds: 25 **Admissions:** 1632 **Census:** 18 **Outpatient Visits:** 45047 **Births:** 0 **Total Expense ($000):** 62051 **Payroll Expense ($000):** 20177 **Personnel:** 235

WILLOWS—Glenn County

GLENN MEDICAL CENTER (051306), 1133 West Sycamore Street, Zip 95988–2745; tel. 530/934–1800, (Nonreporting) **A**10 18
Primary Contact: Timothy M. Moran, Chief Executive Officer
CFO: John Lovrich, Chief Financial Officer
CHR: Deborah McMillan, Director Human Resources
CNO: Timothy Speek I Director of Nursing
Web address: www.glennmed.org
Control: Other not–for–profit (including NFP Corporation) **Service**: General medical and surgical

Staffed Beds: 15

WOODLAND—Yolo County

⊞ **WOODLAND HEALTHCARE (050127)**, 1325 Cottonwood Street, Zip 95695–5199; tel. 530/662–3961, (Nonreporting) **A**1 5 10 **S** Dignity Health, San Francisco, CA
Primary Contact: H Kevin. Vaziri, President
CMO: Sarada Mylavarapu, M.D., Chief Medical Officer
Web address: www.woodlandhealthcare.org
Control: Other not–for–profit (including NFP Corporation) **Service**: General medical and surgical

Staffed Beds: 108

WOODLAND HILLS—Los Angeles County; See Los Angeles

YREKA—Siskiyou County

☐ **FAIRCHILD MEDICAL CENTER (051316)**, 444 Bruce Street, Zip 96097–3450; tel. 530/842–4121, (Nonreporting) **A**1 10 18
Primary Contact: Jonathon Andrus, Chief Executive Officer
CFO: Kelly Martin, Chief Financial Officer
CMO: Moudy Youssef, M.D., Chief Medical Officer
CIO: Randy Ferguson, Information Systems Manager
CHR: Joann Sarmento, Manager Human Resources
CNO: Susan Westphal, Assistant Administrator, Patient Care Services
Web address: www.fairchildmed.org
Control: Other not–for–profit (including NFP Corporation) **Service**: General medical and surgical

Staffed Beds: 25

YUBA CITY—Sutter County

FREMONT MEDICAL CENTER See Rideout Memorial Hospital, Marysville

☐ **SUTTER SURGICAL HOSPITAL – NORTH VALLEY (050766)**, 455 Plumas Boulevard, Zip 95991–5074; tel. 530/749–5700, **A**1 10 **F**3 26 29 30 34 46 57 64 68 74 79 81 85 86 111 146 149 **S** Sutter Health, Sacramento, CA
Primary Contact: Shawndra Simpson, Interim Chief Executive Officer
CHR: Michelle Guina, Manager Human Resources
CNO: David Cooke, R.N., Chief Nursing Officer
Web address: www.sshnv.org
Control: Corporation, Investor–owned (for–profit) **Service**: Surgical

Staffed Beds: 14 **Admissions:** 506 **Census:** 3 **Outpatient Visits:** 5157 **Births:** 0 **Total Expense ($000):** 24675 **Personnel:** 78

Hospital, Medicare Provider Number, Address, Telephone, Approval, Facility, and Physician Codes, Health Care System

★ American Hospital Association (AHA) membership ○ Healthcare Facilities Accreditation Program ⇑ Center for Improvement in Healthcare Quality Accreditation
☐ The Joint Commission accreditation ◇ DNV Healthcare Inc. accreditation △ Commission on Accreditation of Rehabilitation Facilities (CARF) accreditation

COLORADO

CO

ALAMOSA—Alamosa County

★ **SAN LUIS VALLEY HEALTH (060008)**, 106 Blanca Avenue, Zip 81101–2393; tel. 719/589–2511, **A**3 10 20 **F**3 7 11 13 15 18 28 29 30 31 33 34 40 43 45 53 57 59 70 74 75 77 78 79 81 82 85 93 97 107 108 110 111 115 119 129 130 131 146 147 148 154 **P**6 **S** San Luis Valley Health, Alamosa, CO
Primary Contact: Konnie Martin, Chief Executive Officer
COO: Patti Thompson, Chief Operating Officer
CFO: Shane Mortensen, Chief Financial Officer
CMO: Gregory McAuliffe, M.D., Chief Medical Officer
CIO: Chuck Laufle, Director of Information Services
CHR: Mandy Lee Crockett, Director Human Resources
Web address: www.sanluisvalleyhealth.org
Control: Other not-for-profit (including NFP Corporation) **Service**: General medical and surgical

Staffed Beds: 44 **Admissions**: 1960 **Census**: 16 **Outpatient Visits**: 137712 **Births**: 437 **Total Expense ($000)**: 84651 **Payroll Expense ($000)**: 38999 **Personnel**: 603

ASPEN—Pitkin County

✠ **ASPEN VALLEY HOSPITAL (061324)**, 0401 Castle Creek Road, Zip 81611–1159; tel. 970/925–1120, **A**1 10 18 **F**3 7 8 10 11 13 15 18 28 29 31 34 35 36 37 40 43 50 53 54 57 59 64 68 70 75 76 77 78 79 81 82 85 86 87 89 91 93 107 108 110 111 115 118 119 126 129 130 131 132 133 135 144 146 147 148 149
Primary Contact: David Ressler, Chief Executive Officer
CFO: Ginette Sebenaler, Associate Chief Financial Officer
CMO: J Christopher Beck, D.O., President Medical Staff
CIO: Ginny Dyche, Director Community Relations
CHR: Alicia Miller, Director Human Resources
CNO: Elaine Gerson, Chief Clinical Officer and General Counsel
Web address: www.avhaspen.org
Control: Hospital district or authority, Government, nonfederal **Service**: General medical and surgical

Staffed Beds: 25 **Admissions**: 893 **Census**: 7 **Births**: 182 **Personnel**: 415

AURORA—Adams County

✠ **CHILDREN'S HOSPITAL COLORADO (063301)**, 13123 East 16th Avenue, Zip 80045–7106; tel. 720/777–1234, (Includes CHILDREN'S HOSPITAL OF COLORADO AT MEMORIAL, 1400 East Boulder Street, Colorado Springs, CO, Zip 80909–5533; tel. 719/365–5000; Greg Raymond, Regional Vice President, Southern Colorado) **A**1 3 5 10 **F**3 11 12 13 14 17 19 21 23 25 27 28 29 30 31 32 34 35 36 38 39 40 41 43 44 45 46 48 49 50 51 53 54 55 58 59 60 61 64 65 66 68 71 72 74 75 76 77 78 79 80 81 82 84 85 86 87 88 89 91 92 93 95 96 97 98 99 100 101 102 104 107 108 111 114 115 116 117 119 126 129 130 131 132 134 136 137 138 139 141 144 146 147 148
Primary Contact: Jena Hausman, President and Chief Executive Officer
COO: David Biggerstaff, Chief Operating Officer
CFO: Jeff Harrington, Chief Financial Officer
CMO: Joan Bothner, M.D., Chief Medical Officer
CIO: Dana Moore, Chief Information Officer
CNO: Patricia Givens, R.N., Chief Nursing Officer
Web address: www.thechildrenshospital.org
Control: Other not-for-profit (including NFP Corporation) **Service**: Children's general medical and surgical

Staffed Beds: 486 **Admissions**: 15415 **Census**: 267

AURORA—Arapahoe County

✠ **KINDRED HOSPITAL–AURORA (062013)**, 700 Potomac Street 2nd Floor, Zip 80011–6844; tel. 720/857–8333, (Nonreporting) **A**1 10 **S** Kindred Healthcare, Louisville, KY
Primary Contact: Jeanette Williams, Chief Executive Officer
CMO: Eric Yaeger, M.D., Chief Medical Officer
CHR: Becky Small, Chief Human Resources Officer
CNO: Paul Green, Chief Clinical Officer
Web address: www.khaurora.com/
Control: Corporation, Investor–owned (for–profit) **Service**: Acute long–term care hospital

Staffed Beds: 37

✠ **MEDICAL CENTER OF AURORA (060100)**, 1501 South Potomac Street, Zip 80012–5411; tel. 303/695–2600, (Includes MEDICAL CENTER OF AURORA NORTH, 700 Potomac Street, Aurora, CO, Zip 80011–6792; tel. 303/363–7200; MEDICAL CENTER OF AURORA, 700 Potomac Street, Aurora, CO, Zip 80011; tel. 303/360–3030; Daniel Miller, FACHE, President and Chief Executive Officer; SOUTH CAMPUS, 1501 South Potomac, Aurora, CO, Zip 80012; tel. 303/695–2600) (Nonreporting) **A**1 2 3 10 **S** HCA Healthcare, Nashville, TN
Primary Contact: Daniel Miller, FACHE, President and Chief Executive Officer
COO: Mark S Deno, Chief Operating Officer
CFO: Bryce DeHaven, Chief Financial Officer
CMO: Dianne McCallister, M.D., Chief Medical Officer
CNO: Stacy Black, MSN, R.N., Associate Chief Nursing Officer
Web address: www.auroramed.com
Control: Corporation, Investor–owned (for–profit) **Service**: General medical and surgical

Staffed Beds: 340

AURORA—Adams County

✠ **SPALDING REHABILITATION HOSPITAL (063027)**, 900 Potomac Steet, Zip 80011–6716; tel. 303/367–1166, (Nonreporting) **A**1 10 **S** HCA Healthcare, Nashville, TN
Primary Contact: Daniel Miller, FACHE, President and Chief Executive Officer
COO: Debbie Petersen, R.N., Chief Operating Officer and Chief Nursing Officer
CFO: Joyce Webber, Chief Financial Officer
CHR: Donna Greeley, Director Human Resources
CNO: Stacy Black, MSN, R.N., Chief Nursing Officer
Web address: www.spaldingrehab.com
Control: Partnership, Investor–owned (for–profit) **Service**: Rehabilitation

Staffed Beds: 40

✠ **UNIVERSITY OF COLORADO HOSPITAL (060024)**, 12401 East 17th Avenue, MS F417, Zip 80045–2545; tel. 720/848–0000, **A**1 2 3 5 8 10 **F**3 4 5 6 8 9 11 12 13 15 16 17 18 20 22 24 26 28 29 30 31 33 34 35 36 37 38 40 43 44 45 46 47 48 49 50 52 53 54 55 56 57 58 59 60 61 63 64 65 68 70 71 72 74 75 76 77 78 79 80 81 82 83 84 85 86 87 90 91 92 93 96 97 98 100 101 102 104 107 108 109 110 111 112 113 114 115 117 118 119 120 121 123 124 126 129 130 131 132 134 135 136 137 138 139 140 141 142 146 147 148 149 150 152 154 **S** UCHealth, Fort Collins, CO
Primary Contact: William Cook, President and Chief Executive Officer
COO: Thomas Gronow, Chief Operating Officer
CFO: Barbara Carveth, Chief Financial Officer
CMO: Jean Kutner, M.D., Chief Medical Officer
CIO: Steve Hess, Vice President Information Services and Chief Information Officer
CNO: Carolyn Lucey Sanders, Senior Vice President Patient Services and Chief Nursing Officer
Web address: www.uchealth.org
Control: Hospital district or authority, Government, nonfederal **Service**: General medical and surgical

Staffed Beds: 673 **Admissions**: 30125 **Census**: 547 **Outpatient Visits**: 1212290 **Births**: 3861 **Total Expense ($000)**: 1426546 **Payroll Expense ($000)**: 424156 **Personnel**: 5975

BOULDER—Boulder County

✠ △ **BOULDER COMMUNITY HEALTH (060027)**, 4747 Arapahoe Ave, Zip 80303–1133, Mailing Address: P.O. Box 9019, Zip 80301–9019; tel. 303/415–7000, (Includes BOULDER COMMUNITY FOOTHILLS HOSPITAL, 4747 Arapahoe Avenue, Boulder, CO, Zip 80303–1133, Mailing Address: P.O. Box 9047, Zip 80301–9047, tel. 720/854–7000; Robert Vissers, M.D., President and Chief Executive Officer) **A**1 2 3 5 7 10 **F**3 5 7 8 13 15 18 20 22 24 26 28 29 30 31 34 35 36 37 40 43 45 46 49 50 54 56 59 60 61 62 64 65 68 70 72 74 75 76 77 78 79 81 84 85 87 90 93 94 96 97 98 100 101 102 104 107 109 110 111 112 114 115 118 119 126 130 132 144 146 147 148 149 153 **P**4 5 6
Primary Contact: Robert Vissers, M.D., President and Chief Executive Officer
CFO: Bill Munson, Vice President and Chief Financial Officer
CMO: Paul Lewis, M.D., Chief Medical Officer, Vice President
CNO: Jacqueline M Attlesey–Pries, MS, R.N., Chief Nursing Officer, Vice President
Web address: www.bch.org
Control: Other not-for-profit (including NFP Corporation) **Service**: General medical and surgical

Staffed Beds: 178 **Admissions**: 7985 **Census**: 93 **Outpatient Visits**: 420719 **Births**: 736 **Total Expense ($000)**: 349717 **Payroll Expense ($000)**: 157915 **Personnel**: 2047

Many Facility Codes have changed. Please refer to the AHA Guide Code Chart.   © 2018 AHA Guide

BRIGHTON—Adams County

⊞ **PLATTE VALLEY MEDICAL CENTER (060004)**, 1600 Prairie Center Parkway,
Zip 80601–4006; tel. 303/498–1600, **A**1 5 10 **F**3 7 13 15 18 20 22 26 28 29 30 31
34 35 40 43 45 49 57 68 70 72 74 75 76 77 78 79 81 85 87 90 92 93 107 108
110 111 115 119 130 132 135 146 147 148 149 154 **S** SCL Health, Broomfield, CO
Primary Contact: John R. Hicks, President and Chief Executive Officer
COO: Kurt G Gensert, FACHE, R.N., Vice President Operations
CFO: Harold Dupper, Chief Financial Officer
CMO: Kirk Quackenbush, M.D., Chief of Staff
CIO: Timothy Brannigan, Director Information Services
CHR: Jackie J. Dunkin, Director Human Resources
Web address: www.pvmc.org
Control: Other not–for–profit (including NFP Corporation) **Service**: General
medical and surgical

Staffed Beds: 70 **Admissions:** 3445 **Census:** 32 **Outpatient Visits:** 79470
Births: 806 **Total Expense ($000):** 119230 **Payroll Expense ($000):** 41979
Personnel: 622

BROOMFIELD—Denver County

☐ **UCHEALTH BROOMFIELD HOSPITAL**, 11820 Destination Drive, Zip 80021;
tel. 303/460–6000, (Nonreporting) **A**1 **S** UCHealth, Fort Collins, CO
Primary Contact: Derek Rushing, Chief Executive Officer
Web address: www.uchealth.org/pages/OHAM/OrgUnitDetails.aspx?
Control: Other not–for–profit (including NFP Corporation) **Service**: General
medical and surgical

Staffed Beds: 22

BRUSH—Morgan County

★ **EAST MORGAN COUNTY HOSPITAL (061303)**, 2400 West Edison Street,
Zip 80723–1640; tel. 970/842–6200, **A**10 18 **F**3 13 15 28 29 34 35 36 40
43 45 50 53 57 59 61 65 68 75 76 77 79 81 85 86 87 89 93 96 107 108
110 115 119 127 130 131 132 133 135 141 146 147 148 149 154 **S** Banner
Health, Gilbert, AZ
Primary Contact: Linda Thorpe, Chief Executive Officer
CFO: Edith Pemberton, Chief Financial Officer
CHR: Cynthia Wentworth, Chief Human Resource Officer
CNO: Linda Lyn Roan, Chief Nursing Officer
Web address: www.emchbrush.com
Control: Other not–for–profit (including NFP Corporation) **Service**: General
medical and surgical

Staffed Beds: 19 **Admissions:** 423 **Census:** 4 **Outpatient Visits:** 26826
Births: 65 **Total Expense ($000):** 28378 **Payroll Expense ($000):** 12942
Personnel: 185

BURLINGTON—Kit Carson County

★ **KIT CARSON COUNTY HEALTH SERVICE DISTRICT (061313)**, 286 16th
Street, Zip 80807–1697; tel. 719/346–5311, (Nonreporting) **A**10 18
Primary Contact: Corey J. Fedie, Chief Operating Officer
COO: Corey J Fedie, Chief Operating Officer
CMO: Bong Pham, Chief Medical Officer
CIO: Paul Velasco, IT Manager
CHR: Robin Konecne, Manager Human Resources
CNO: Kandi Kuper, Chief Nursing Officer
Web address: www.kcchsd.org
Control: Hospital district or authority, Government, nonfederal **Service**: General
medical and surgical

Staffed Beds: 19

CANON CITY—Fremont County

⊞ **ST. THOMAS MORE HOSPITAL (060016)**, 1338 Phay Avenue, Zip 81212–2302;
tel. 719/285–2000, **A**1 10 20 **F**3 8 11 12 13 15 29 30 34 35 40 43 51 53 57 59
64 66 69 70 75 77 79 81 82 85 86 87 93 97 107 108 110 111 119 127 129 131
132 133 135 146 147 148 151 154 **S** Catholic Health Initiatives, Englewood, CO
Primary Contact: Sheri Trahern, CPA, FACHE, Chief Executive Officer
COO: Dennis Bruens, Vice President Operations
CFO: Gwenyth Howard, Vice President Finance
CMO: Kern Low, M.D., Chief Medical Officer
CIO: Jillian Maes, Director Marketing and Public Relations
CHR: Janet Reedy, Manager Human Resources
CNO: James Woodard, Chief Nursing Officer
Web address: www.stmhospital.org
Control: Church operated, Nongovernment, not–for–profit **Service**: General
medical and surgical

Staffed Beds: 25 **Admissions:** 1821 **Census:** 16 **Outpatient Visits:** 43563
Births: 224 **Total Expense ($000):** 47420 **Payroll Expense ($000):** 18744
Personnel: 496

CASTLE ROCK—Douglas County

⊞ **CASTLE ROCK ADVENTIST HOSPITAL (060125)**, 2350 Meadows Boulevard,
Zip 80109–8405; tel. 720/455–5000, **A**1 10 **F**3 11 13 15 18 20 22 29 30 32
34 35 37 38 40 41 43 44 45 48 49 50 53 57 59 60 62 64 65 67 68 70 72 74
75 76 77 79 81 85 86 87 89 91 93 101 102 107 108 110 111 114 115 118
119 129 130 131 135 146 147 148 154 **P**6 **S** Adventist Health System Sunbelt
Health Care Corporation, Altamonte Springs, FL
Primary Contact: Todd Folkenberg, Chief Executive Officer
CFO: Jeremy Pittman, Chief Financial Officer
Web address: www.castlerockhospital.org
Control: Church operated, Nongovernment, not–for–profit **Service**: General
medical and surgical

Staffed Beds: 53 **Admissions:** 2899 **Census:** 25 **Outpatient Visits:** 36105
Births: 812 **Total Expense ($000):** 74783 **Payroll Expense ($000):** 26111
Personnel: 501

CHEYENNE WELLS—Cheyenne County

★ **KEEFE MEMORIAL HOSPITAL (060043)**, 602 North 6th Street West,
Zip 80810, Mailing Address: P.O. Box 578, Zip 80810–0578; tel. 719/767–5661,
(Nonreporting) **A**10 18 20
Primary Contact: Stella Worley, Interim Chief Executive Officer
CFO: Stella Worley, Director of Finance
CMO: Christine Connolly, M.D., Chief of Staff
CIO: Jeanne Moffat, Manager Information Technology
CHR: Carrie Rico, Chief Human Resource Officer
CNO: Jesse Smith, Director of Nursing
Web address: www.keefememorial.com
Control: County, Government, nonfederal **Service**: General medical and surgical

Staffed Beds: 11

COLORADO SPRINGS—El Paso County

☐ **CEDAR SPRINGS HOSPITAL (064009)**, 2135 Southgate Road,
Zip 80906–2693; tel. 719/633–4114, (Nonreporting) **A**1 10 **S** Universal Health
Services, Inc., King of Prussia, PA
Primary Contact: Christopher D. Burke, Ph.D., Chief Executive Officer
CFO: Cynthia D Deboer, Chief Financial Officer
CMO: Larry Shores, M.D., Executive Medical Director
CHR: Jessica McCoy, Director Human Resources
CNO: Jodi Mattson, Director of Nursing
Web address: www.cedarspringsbhs.com
Control: Corporation, Investor–owned (for–profit) **Service**: Psychiatric

Staffed Beds: 110

⊞ **HEALTHSOUTH REHABILITATION HOSPITAL OF COLORADO SPRINGS
(063030)**, 325 Parkside Drive, Zip 80910–3134; tel. 719/630–8000,
(Nonreporting) **A**1 10 **S** Encompass Health Corporation, Birmingham, AL
Primary Contact: Stephen Schaefer, Chief Executive Officer
CFO: Stephanie Davis, Controller
CHR: Diana Crepeau, Director Human Resources
CNO: Cindy Nordell, Chief Nursing Officer
Web address: www.healthsouthcoloradosprings.com
Control: Corporation, Investor–owned (for–profit) **Service**: Rehabilitation

Staffed Beds: 60

☐ **PEAK VIEW BEHAVIORAL HEALTH (064026)**, 7353 Sisters Grove,
Zip 80923–2615; tel. 719/444–8484, **A**1 3 10 13 **F**29 35 38 54 56 98 99 100
101 103 104 105 153 **S** Strategic Behavioral Health, LLC, Memphis, TN
Primary Contact: Dan Zarecky, Chief Executive Officer
Web address: www.strategicbh.com/peakview.html
Control: Corporation, Investor–owned (for–profit) **Service**: Psychiatric

Staffed Beds: 112 **Admissions:** 3632 **Census:** 80 **Outpatient Visits:** 1141
Births: 0 **Total Expense ($000):** 15291 **Payroll Expense ($000):** 9794
Personnel: 309

Hospital, Medicare Provider Number, Address, Telephone, Approval, Facility, and Physician Codes, Health Care System

★ American Hospital Association (AHA) membership	○ Healthcare Facilities Accreditation Program	⇑ Center for Improvement in Healthcare Quality Accreditation
☐ The Joint Commission accreditation	◇ DNV Healthcare Inc. accreditation	△ Commission on Accreditation of Rehabilitation Facilities (CARF) accreditation

✠ △ **PENROSE–ST. FRANCIS HEALTH SERVICES (060031)**, 2222 North Nevada Avenue, Zip 80907–6799; tel. 719/776–5000, (Includes PENROSE HOSPITAL, 2222 North Nevada Avenue, Colorado Springs, CO, Zip 80907; tel. 719/776–5000; Brian Erling, Interim Chief Executive Officer; ST. FRANCIS MEDICAL CENTER, 6001 East Woodmen Road, Colorado Springs, CO, Zip 80923–2601; tel. 719/776–5000; Brian Erling, Interim Chief Executive Officer) **A**1 2 3 7 10 **F**3 5 11 12 13 14 15 17 18 20 22 24 26 28 29 30 31 34 35 36 37 38 39 40 41 43 44 45 46 47 48 49 50 52 53 54 55 56 57 58 59 61 62 64 65 68 70 71 72 74 75 76 77 78 79 81 82 84 85 86 87 89 90 91 92 93 94 96 97 100 101 102 107 108 110 114 115 118 119 120 121 123 124 126 127 129 130 131 132 135 144 146 147 148 149 150 154 **P**5 **S** Catholic Health Initiatives, Englewood, CO
Primary Contact: Brian Erling, Interim Chief Executive Officer
COO: Lonnie Cramer, Chief Operating Officer
CFO: Danny Reeves, Chief Financial Officer
CMO: David Dull, M.D., Chief Medical Officer
CHR: James Humphrey, Vice President Talent Resources and Human Resources for South Side Operating Group
CNO: Cynthia Latney, Chief Nursing Officer
Web address: www.penrosestfrancis.org
Control: Church operated, Nongovernment, not–for–profit **Service**: General medical and surgical

Staffed Beds: 444 **Admissions**: 24343 **Census**: 263 **Outpatient Visits**: 188037 **Births**: 3218 **Total Expense ($000)**: 500458 **Payroll Expense ($000)**: 160087 **Personnel**: 2754

☐ **UCHEALTH GRANDVIEW HOSPITAL**, 5623 Pulpit Peak View, Zip 80918; tel. 719/272–3600, (Nonreporting) **A**1 **S** UCHealth, Fort Collins, CO
Primary Contact: Derek Rushing, Chief Executive Officer
Web address: www.uchealth.org/Pages/OHAM/OrgUnitDetails.aspx?OrganizationalUnitId=514
Control: Other not–for–profit (including NFP Corporation) **Service**: General medical and surgical

Staffed Beds: 22

✠ **UCHEALTH MEMORIAL HOSPITAL (060022)**, 1400 East Boulder Street, Zip 80909–5599; tel. 719/365–5000, (Includes UCHEALTH MEMORIAL HOSPITAL NORTH, 4050 Briargate Parkway, Colorado Springs, CO, Zip 80909, Mailing Address: 1400 East Boulder Street, Zip 80909, tel. 719/365–5000; Joel P. Yuhas, FACHE, President and Chief Executive Officer) **A**1 2 3 10 **F**3 8 12 13 15 17 18 19 20 21 22 23 24 26 27 28 29 30 31 34 35 36 37 39 40 41 43 44 45 46 47 48 49 54 55 57 58 59 61 64 68 70 72 74 76 77 78 79 81 82 84 85 86 87 88 89 90 92 93 96 97 107 108 109 110 111 114 115 116 117 118 119 120 121 123 124 126 129 130 131 132 135 141 144 146 148 149 154 **P**6 **S** UCHealth, Fort Collins, CO
Primary Contact: Joel P. Yuhas, FACHE, President and Chief Executive Officer
COO: Cherie Gorby, Chief Operations Officer
CFO: Dan Rieber, Chief Financial Officer
CMO: Jose Melendez, M.D., Chief Medical Officer
CHR: Jeffrey Johnson, Vice President
CNO: Kay J Miller, R.N., MSN, Chief Nursing Officer
Web address: www.uchealth.org/southerncolorado
Control: Other not–for–profit (including NFP Corporation) **Service**: General medical and surgical

Staffed Beds: 509 **Admissions**: 27497 **Census**: 306 **Outpatient Visits**: 354170 **Births**: 3882 **Personnel**: 2636

CORTEZ—Montezuma County

★ ⇑ **SOUTHWEST HEALTH SYSTEM (061327)**, 1311 North Mildred Road, Zip 81321–2299; tel. 970/565–6666, (Nonreporting) **A**10 18 21
Primary Contact: Anthony G. Sudduth, CPA, Interim Chief Executive Officer
CHR: Travis Parker, Director Human Resources
Web address: www.swhealth.org
Control: Other not–for–profit (including NFP Corporation) **Service**: General medical and surgical

Staffed Beds: 25

CRAIG—Moffat County

✠ ⇑ **MEMORIAL REGIONAL HEALTH (061314)**, 750 Hospital Loop, Zip 81625–8750; tel. 970/824–9411, **A**1 10 18 21 **F**3 11 13 15 18 29 31 32 34 35 40 43 45 49 50 51 57 59 68 70 75 76 77 78 79 81 85 86 87 91 93 97 102 107 108 110 111 112 114 119 129 130 131 132 133 135 146 147 148
Primary Contact: Andrew J. Daniels, Chief Executive Officer
COO: Jennifer Riley, Vice President Operations
CFO: Kelsea Henry, Chief Financial Offical
CMO: Scott Ellis, D.O., Chief Medical Officer
CIO: Bryan Curtis, Chief Information Officer
CNO: Amy Peck, R.N., Chief Nursing Officer
Web address: www.thememorialhospital.com
Control: County, Government, nonfederal **Service**: General medical and surgical

Staffed Beds: 25 **Admissions**: 1084 **Census**: 8 **Births**: 159

DEL NORTE—Rio Grande County

★ **RIO GRANDE HOSPITAL (061301)**, 310 County Road 14, Zip 81132–8719; tel. 719/657–2510, **A**10 18 **F**34 40 43 57 65 81 93 107 111 115 119 127 129 133
Primary Contact: Arlene Harms, Chief Executive Officer
CFO: Greg Porter, Chief Financial Officer
CMO: Heidi E Helgeson, M.D., Chief Medical Officer
CIO: Denise Fietek, Information Technology
CHR: Paula Warner–Pacheco, Chief Human Resources
CNO: Candice Allen, Director of Nursing
Web address: www.rio-grande-hospital.org/
Control: Other not–for–profit (including NFP Corporation) **Service**: General medical and surgical

Staffed Beds: 17 **Admissions**: 561 **Census**: 6 **Outpatient Visits**: 51055 **Births**: 0

DELTA—Delta County

★ ⇑ **DELTA COUNTY MEMORIAL HOSPITAL (060071)**, 1501 East 3rd Street, Zip 81416–2815, Mailing Address: P.O. Box 10100, Zip 81416–0008; tel. 970/874–7681, **A**10 21 **F**3 8 9 13 15 28 29 30 31 34 40 43 45 50 57 59 62 70 75 76 77 78 79 81 85 87 90 93 107 108 110 111 115 119 129 135 141 144 146 147 148
Primary Contact: Jason Cleckler, Chief Executive Officer
CFO: Bev Carlson, Chief Financial Officer
CMO: John P Knutson, M.D., Chief Medical Staff
CIO: Mitch Van Scoyk, Manager Information Systems
CHR: Larry Vincent, Director Human Resources
Web address: www.deltahospital.org
Control: Hospital district or authority, Government, nonfederal **Service**: General medical and surgical

Staffed Beds: 49 **Admissions**: 1649 **Census**: 13 **Outpatient Visits**: 115013 **Births**: 195

DENVER—Denver, Adams and Arapaho Coun County

✠ **COLORADO ACUTE LONG TERM HOSPITAL (062012)**, 1690 North Meade Street, Zip 80204–1552; tel. 303/264–6900, (Nonreporting) **A**1 10 **S** LifeCare Management Services, Plano, TX
Primary Contact: Craig Bailey, MS, Chief Executive Officer and Administrator
Web address: www.lifecare-hospitals.com/hospital/colorado
Control: Corporation, Investor–owned (for–profit) **Service**: Acute long–term care hospital

Staffed Beds: 63

☐ **COLORADO MENTAL HEALTH INSTITUTE AT FORT LOGAN (064003)**, 3520 West Oxford Avenue, Zip 80236–3197; tel. 303/866–7066, (Nonreporting) **A**1 3 5 10
Primary Contact: David M. Polunas, Director
CFO: Sabina Genesio, Finance Officer for Institutes
CMO: Bruce Leonard, M.D., Medical Director and Chief of Psychiatry
CNO: Nancy Kehiayan, Director of Nursing
Web address: www.cdhs.state.co.us/cmhifl
Control: State, Government, nonfederal **Service**: Psychiatric

Staffed Beds: 297

✠ **DENVER HEALTH (060011)**, 777 Bannock Street, Zip 80204–4507, Mailing Address: 777 Bannock Street, MC0278, Zip 80204–4507; tel. 303/436–6000, **A**1 5 10 **F**3 5 7 8 11 12 13 15 18 19 20 22 26 28 29 30 31 32 34 35 36 37 38 39 40 41 43 44 45 46 49 50 52 53 54 55 56 57 58 59 60 61 64 65 66 68 70 71 72 74 75 76 77 78 79 80 81 82 84 85 86 87 88 89 90 92 93 94 96 97 98 99 100 101 102 103 104 107 108 110 111 114 115 118 119 127 129 130 131 132 134 135 143 144 146 147 148 149 153 **P**6
Primary Contact: Robin D. Wittenstein, Ed.D., Chief Executive Officer
COO: Tim Harlin, M.D., Chief Operations Officer
CFO: Peg Burnette, Chief Financial Officer
CMO: Connie Price, M.D., Chief Medical Officer
CIO: Jeff Pelot, Interim Chief Information Officer
CHR: Tim Hansen, Interim Chief Human Resource Officer
CNO: Kathy Boyle, R.N., Ph.D., Chief Nursing Officer
Web address: www.denverhealth.org
Control: Hospital district or authority, Government, nonfederal **Service**: General medical and surgical

Staffed Beds: 457 **Admissions**: 21728 **Census**: 304 **Outpatient Visits**: 906796 **Births**: 3320 **Total Expense ($000)**: 1072548 **Payroll Expense ($000)**: 502249 **Personnel**: 6531

Many Facility Codes have changed. Please refer to the AHA Guide Code Chart.

CO

CO

★ **KINDRED HOSPITAL DENVER SOUTH (062015)**, 2525 South Downing Street, 3 South, Zip 80210–5817; tel. 303/715–7373, (Nonreporting) **S** Kindred Healthcare, Louisville, KY
Primary Contact: Marc Lemon, Chief Executive Officer
Web address: www.kindreddenversouth.com/
Control: Corporation, Investor–owned (for–profit) **Service**: Acute long–term care hospital

Staffed Beds: 28

✠ **KINDRED HOSPITAL–DENVER (062009)**, 1920 High Street, Zip 80218–1213; tel. 303/320–5871, (Nonreporting) **A**1 10 **S** Kindred Healthcare, Louisville, KY
Primary Contact: Janelle Kircher, R.N., MSN, Chief Executive Officer
CFO: Tim Stecker, Chief Financial Officer
CMO: Eric Yaeger, M.D., Medical Director
Web address: www.kh–denver.com
Control: Corporation, Investor–owned (for–profit) **Service**: Acute long–term care hospital

Staffed Beds: 68

✠ **NATIONAL JEWISH HEALTH (060107)**, 1400 Jackson Street, Zip 80206–2762; tel. 303/388–4461, **A**1 3 5 10 **F**1 3 9 11 12 18 20 28 29 30 31 32 34 35 36 44 45 46 48 50 53 54 55 57 58 59 61 62 64 65 66 68 70 74 75 77 78 84 86 87 89 90 93 96 97 98 99 100 101 104 107 108 111 114 115 116 117 118 119 127 129 130 132 134 135 143 145 146 147 149 154 **P**6
Primary Contact: Michael Salem, M.D., President and Chief Executive Officer
COO: Ron Berge, Executive Vice President and Chief Operating Officer
CFO: Christine Forkner, Executive Vice President and Chief Financial Officer
CMO: Gary Cott, M.D., Executive Vice President Medical and Clinical Services
CIO: Lots Pook, Chief Information Officer
CHR: Sarah Taylor, Chief Human Resources
CNO: Jeff Downing, R.N., MS, Chief Nursing Officer
Web address: www.njhealth.org
Control: Other not–for–profit (including NFP Corporation) **Service**: Tuberculosis and other respiratory diseases

Staffed Beds: 76 Admissions: 45 Census: 1 Outpatient Visits: 114167 Births: 0 Total Expense ($000): 252416 Payroll Expense ($000): 128234 Personnel: 1625

✠ **PORTER ADVENTIST HOSPITAL (060064)**, 2525 South Downing Street, Zip 80210–5876; tel. 303/778–1955, **A**1 2 3 10 **F**3 4 5 6 8 11 15 17 18 20 22 24 26 28 29 30 31 34 35 36 37 40 43 44 45 46 47 48 49 50 52 53 54 56 57 58 59 60 63 64 65 68 70 74 75 77 78 79 81 82 83 84 85 86 87 90 91 92 93 94 96 97 98 100 101 102 103 104 107 108 109 110 111 112 114 115 116 117 118 119 120 121 122 123 124 125 126 129 130 131 132 135 138 139 141 142 146 147 148 153 **P**6 **S** Adventist Health System Sunbelt Health Care Corporation, Altamonte Springs, FL
Primary Contact: Morre Dean, Chief Executive Officer
COO: David Dookeeram, Chief Operating Officer
CFO: Andrew Gaasch, Chief Financial Officer
CHR: Oz Muller, Director Human Resources
Web address: www.porterhospital.org/poh/home/
Control: Church operated, Nongovernment, not–for–profit **Service**: General medical and surgical

Staffed Beds: 250 Admissions: 9929 Census: 130 Outpatient Visits: 61698 Births: 0 Total Expense ($000): 267637 Payroll Expense ($000): 92206 Personnel: 1758

✠ **PRESBYTERIAN–ST. LUKE'S MEDICAL CENTER (060014)**, 1719 East 19th Avenue, Zip 80218–1281; tel. 303/839–6000, (Includes ROCKY MOUNTAIN HOSPITAL FOR CHILDREN, 1719 East 19th Avenue, Denver, CO, Zip 80218–1235; tel. 720/754–1000; Maureen Tarrant, President and Chief Executive Officer) **A**1 2 3 5 10 **F**3 11 12 13 14 18 19 20 21 22 23 24 25 26 27 28 29 30 31 34 35 36 37 40 41 45 46 47 48 49 50 52 53 54 56 58 59 60 61 64 65 68 70 72 73 74 75 76 77 78 79 80 81 82 84 85 86 87 88 89 91 92 93 94 95 96 97 102 107 108 111 114 115 116 117 118 119 120 121 123 126 129 130 131 132 136 138 139 146 147 148 **P**2 4 6 **S** HCA Healthcare, Nashville, TN
Primary Contact: Maureen Tarrant, President and Chief Executive Officer
CFO: Shari Collier, Chief Financial Officer
CMO: Stephen Cobb, M.D., Chief Medical Officer
CIO: Jason Brakenhoff, Director Information Services
CHR: Keri Moore, Vice President Human Resources and Support Services
CNO: Amanda Veit, R.N., Chief Nursing Officer
Web address: www.pslmc.com
Control: Corporation, Investor–owned (for–profit) **Service**: General medical and surgical

Staffed Beds: 374 Admissions: 10916 Census: 212 Outpatient Visits: 57967 Births: 1315 Personnel: 1610

✠ **ROSE MEDICAL CENTER (060032)**, 4567 East Ninth Avenue, Zip 80220–3941; tel. 303/320–2121, **A**1 2 3 5 10 **F**3 8 11 12 13 15 17 18 20 22 24 26 28 29 30 31 34 35 40 44 45 46 49 50 52 53 54 58 59 60 61 63 64 65 68 70 72 74 75 76 77 78 79 81 82 84 85 86 87 91 92 93 94 96 97 100 101 102 107 108 110 111 112 114 115 116 117 118 119 120 121 122 123 126 129 130 131 132 135 144 146 147 148 149 154 **P**8 **S** HCA Healthcare, Nashville, TN
Primary Contact: Ryan Tobin, President and Chief Executive Officer
CFO: Jac Connelly, Chief Financial Officer
CMO: Andrew Ziller, M.D., Chief Medical Officer
CIO: Dave Trevathan, Director Information Systems
CHR: Clarence McDavid, Vice President Human Resources
CNO: Lynne Wagner, R.N., Chief Nursing Officer
Web address: www.rosebabies.com
Control: Corporation, Investor–owned (for–profit) **Service**: General medical and surgical

Staffed Beds: 282 Admissions: 11323 Census: 112

✠ **SAINT JOSEPH HOSPITAL (060028)**, 1375 East 19th Avenue, Zip 80218–1126; tel. 303/837–7111, **A**1 2 3 5 10 **F**3 8 11 12 13 15 18 20 22 24 26 28 29 30 31 34 35 37 40 43 45 46 49 50 53 55 58 60 63 64 66 68 70 71 72 74 75 76 77 78 79 81 82 84 85 87 93 107 108 110 111 115 116 117 119 120 121 123 124 126 130 145 146 149 154 **P**6 7 **S** SCL Health, Broomfield, CO
Primary Contact: Jameson Smith, President
COO: Barbara A. Jahn, Chief Operating Officer
CFO: Alice W. Rigdon, Vice President Finance
CMO: Shawn Dufford, M.D., Vice President Medical Affairs and Chief Medical Officer
CHR: William R Gould, Vice President Human Resources
CNO: Mary Shepler, R.N., Vice President and Chief Nursing Officer
Web address: www.saintjosephdenver.org/
Control: Other not–for–profit (including NFP Corporation) **Service**: General medical and surgical

Staffed Beds: 379 Admissions: 20095 Census: 256 Outpatient Visits: 132343 Births: 4444 Total Expense ($000): 504771 Payroll Expense ($000): 159637 Personnel: 2192

✠ **VETERANS AFFAIRS EASTERN COLORADO HEALTH CARE SYSTEM**, 1055 Clermont Street, Zip 80220–3877; tel. 303/399–8020, (Nonreporting) **A**1 3 5 **S** Department of Veterans Affairs, Perry Point, MD
Primary Contact: Sallie Houser–Hanfelder, FACHE, Director
CFO: Eliott R Vanderstek, Chief Fiscal Service
CMO: Ellen Mangione, M.D., Chief of Staff
CIO: Don Huckaby, Chief Information Management Service
CHR: Lorene Connel, Chief Human Resources Management Service
Web address: www.denver.va.gov/
Control: Veterans Affairs, Government, federal **Service**: General medical and surgical

Staffed Beds: 271

DURANGO—La Plata County

✠ **ANIMAS SURGICAL HOSPITAL (060117)**, 575 Rivergate Lane, Zip 81301–7487; tel. 970/247–3537, (Nonreporting) **A**10
Primary Contact: Brett Gosney, Chief Executive Officer
Web address: www.animassurgical.com/
Control: Corporation, Investor–owned (for–profit) **Service**: Surgical

Staffed Beds: 12

✠ **MERCY REGIONAL MEDICAL CENTER (060013)**, 1010 Three Springs Boulevard, Zip 81301–8296; tel. 970/247–4311, **A**1 2 10 20 **F**3 11 13 15 18 20 22 24 26 27 28 29 30 31 35 36 40 43 45 49 50 59 60 61 70 74 75 76 78 79 81 83 84 85 87 93 94 96 97 107 108 111 115 119 120 126 127 129 130 131 132 133 135 144 146 147 148 149 150 154 **P**6 **S** Catholic Health Initiatives, Englewood, CO
Primary Contact: William McConnell, Ph.D., President and Chief Executive Officer
CFO: Jane Strobel, Vice President and Chief Financial Officer
CMO: William Plauth, M.D., Vice President Operations and Chief Medical Officer
CIO: Neil Stock, Director Technology and Facilities
CHR: Cathy Roberts, Vice President Mission Integration and Human Resources
CNO: Nancy Gerilyn Hoyt, R.N., Vice President Operations/Clinical and Chief Nursing Officer
Web address: www.mercydurango.org
Control: Church operated, Nongovernment, not–for–profit **Service**: General medical and surgical

Staffed Beds: 82 Admissions: 4274 Census: 38 Outpatient Visits: 130296 Births: 896 Total Expense ($000): 142487 Payroll Expense ($000): 46319 Personnel: 785

Hospital, Medicare Provider Number, Address, Telephone, Approval, Facility, and Physician Codes, Health Care System

★ American Hospital Association (AHA) membership
☐ The Joint Commission accreditation
○ Healthcare Facilities Accreditation Program
◇ DNV Healthcare Inc. accreditation
⇧ Center for Improvement in Healthcare Quality Accreditation
△ Commission on Accreditation of Rehabilitation Facilities (CARF) accreditation

CO

EADS—Kiowa County

★ **WEISBROD MEMORIAL COUNTY HOSPITAL (061300)**, 1208 Luther Street, Zip 81036, Mailing Address: P.O. Box 817, Zip 81036–0817; tel. 719/438–5401, **A**10 18 **F**7 29 30 34 40 57 59 64 75 82 84 87 93 96 97 107 119 127 133 135 143 148
Primary Contact: Charlene Korrell, Interim Chief Executive Officer
CFO: Shannon Dixon, Manager Business Office
CMO: Jeff Waggoner, M.D., Chief of Staff
CHR: Shannon Dixon, Manager Business Office
CNO: Wendy McDowell, R.N., Director of Nursing
Web address: www.kchd.org
Control: Hospital district or authority, Government, nonfederal **Service**: General medical and surgical

Staffed Beds: 25 **Admissions**: 33 **Census**: 1 **Outpatient Visits**: 2522 **Births**: 0 **Total Expense ($000)**: 6579 **Payroll Expense ($000)**: 2992 **Personnel**: 84

ENGLEWOOD—Arapahoe County

⊞ **CRAIG HOSPITAL (062011)**, 3425 South Clarkson Street, Zip 80113–2899; tel. 303/789–8000, **A**1 3 5 10 **F**29 30 34 35 36 44 50 53 58 64 68 74 75 77 81 86 87 90 91 93 95 96 97 100 104 130 132 146 148 149
Primary Contact: Michael L. Fordyce, President and Chief Executive Officer
CFO: Julie Keegan, Vice President Finance
CMO: Thomas E Balazy, M.D., Medical Director
CIO: Chris Watkins, Director of Information Technology
CHR: Stacy L Abel, Director Human Resources
CNO: Diane Reinhard, R.N., Vice President of Patient Care Services
Web address: www.craighospital.org
Control: Other not–for–profit (including NFP Corporation) **Service**: Rehabilitation

Staffed Beds: 93 **Admissions**: 473 **Census**: 79 **Outpatient Visits**: 15786 **Births**: 0 **Total Expense ($000)**: 101944 **Payroll Expense ($000)**: 49260 **Personnel**: 786

DENVER SPRINGS (064028), 8835 American Way, Zip 80112–7056; tel. 720/643–4300, (Data for 341 days) **A**10 **F**4 5 38 40 53 64 68 75 77 87 98 100 101 102 104 105 130 132 133 135 143 151 152 153 154 **P**5 **S** Springstone, Louisville, KY
Primary Contact: David Morris, Chief Executive Officer
Web address: www.denversprings.com/
Control: State, Government, nonfederal **Service**: Psychiatric

Staffed Beds: 96 **Admissions**: 591 **Census**: 10 **Births**: 0

⊞ **SWEDISH MEDICAL CENTER (060034)**, 501 East Hampden Avenue, Zip 80113–2702; tel. 303/788–5000, (Nonreporting) **A**1 2 3 10 13 **S** HCA Healthcare, Nashville, TN
Primary Contact: Richard A. Hammett, President and Chief Executive Officer
CFO: Kathy Ashenfelter, Vice President Finance
CMO: Monique Butler, MD, Chief Medical Officer
CIO: Jeff Schnoor, Director Information Systems
CHR: Lisa Morris, Vice President Human Resources
CNO: Shari Chavez, Chief Nursing Officer
Web address: www.swedishhospital.com
Control: Partnership, Investor–owned (for–profit) **Service**: General medical and surgical

Staffed Beds: 361

ESTES PARK—Larimer County

ESTES PARK MEDICAL CENTER (061312), 555 Prospect Avenue, Zip 80517–6312, Mailing Address: P.O. Box 2740, Zip 80517–2740; tel. 970/586–2317, (Nonreporting) **A**10 18
Primary Contact: Larry E. Leaming, Ph.D., FACHE, Chief Executive Officer
CFO: Tim Cashman, Chief Financial Officer
CMO: Paul Fonken, M.D., Chief of Staff
CIO: Gary Hall, Vice President of Information Technology
CHR: Randy Brigham, Chief Human Resource Officer
CNO: Cynthia Standlee, R.N., Chief Nursing Officer
Web address: www.epmedcenter.com
Control: Hospital district or authority, Government, nonfederal **Service**: General medical and surgical

Staffed Beds: 85

FORT CARSON—El Paso County

⊞ **EVANS U.S. ARMY COMMUNITY HOSPITAL**, 1650 Cochrane Circle, Building 7500, Zip 80913–4613; tel. 719/526–7200, (Nonreporting) **A**1 3 **S** Department of the Army, Office of the Surgeon General, Falls Church, VA
Primary Contact: Colonel Patrick M. Garman, Commander
CFO: Major Bradley Robinson, Chief Financial Officer
CHR: Lieutenant Colonel Lory Gurr, Chief Human Resources Division
Web address: www.evans.amedd.army.mil
Control: Army, Government, federal **Service**: General medical and surgical

Staffed Beds: 69

FORT COLLINS—Larimer County

★ **BANNER FORT COLLINS MEDICAL CENTER (060126)**, 4700 Lady Moon Drive, Zip 80528–4426; tel. 970/821–4000, **F**3 13 15 18 29 30 34 35 36 38 40 43 47 57 59 60 68 70 74 76 77 79 81 84 85 86 87 89 107 108 111 114 115 119 130 135 146 149 154 **S** Banner Health, Gilbert, AZ
Primary Contact: Margo Karsten, Ph.D., MSN, Chief Executive Officer
COO: Marilyn Fain, R.N., MSN, Chief Operating Officer
CFO: Lori Sehrt, Associate Chief Financial Officer Northern Colorado
CMO: Bert Honea, M.D., Associate Chief Medical Officer Northern Colorado
CHR: Kelly Hurt, Chief Human Resources Officer Northern Colorado and Western Region
CNO: Roberta Bean, R.N., Associate Chief Nursing Officer
Web address: www.bannerhealth.com/Locations/Colorado/Banner+Fort+Collins+Medical+Center
Control: Other not–for–profit (including NFP Corporation) **Service**: General medical and surgical

Staffed Beds: 23 **Admissions**: 1080 **Census**: 7 **Outpatient Visits**: 15466 **Births**: 357 **Total Expense ($000)**: 46858 **Payroll Expense ($000)**: 11982 **Personnel**: 186

⊞ **UCHEALTH POUDRE VALLEY HOSPITAL (060010)**, 1024 South Lemay Avenue, Zip 80524–3998, Mailing Address: 2315 East Harmony Road, Suite 200, Zip 80528; tel. 970/495–7000, (Includes MOUNTAIN CREST HOSPITAL, 4601 Corbett Drive, Fort Collins, CO, Zip 80525; tel. 970/270–4800) **A**1 2 3 5 10 19 **F**3 5 7 11 12 13 14 15 18 20 22 28 29 30 31 32 34 35 38 39 40 43 44 45 46 47 48 49 50 53 54 55 57 58 59 60 61 64 65 66 68 69 70 72 73 74 75 76 77 78 79 80 81 82 83 84 85 86 87 89 92 93 98 99 100 101 102 103 104 105 106 107 108 110 111 114 115 118 119 120 121 123 124 126 129 130 131 132 134 135 143 146 147 148 149 150 153 154 **P**5 6 **S** UCHealth, Fort Collins, CO
Primary Contact: Kevin L. Unger, Ph.D., FACHE, President and Chief Executive Officer
COO: Ryan Rohman, MSN, R.N., Chief Operating Officer
CFO: Stephanie Doughty, Chief Financial Officer
CMO: Thomas Downes, M.D., Chief Medical Officer
CIO: Fernando Pedroza, Vice President Information Technology
CNO: Donna D Poduska, MS, R.N., Chief Nursing Officer
Web address: www.uchealth.org
Control: Other not–for–profit (including NFP Corporation) **Service**: General medical and surgical

Staffed Beds: 275 **Admissions**: 15744 **Census**: 156 **Outpatient Visits**: 345659 **Births**: 2098 **Total Expense ($000)**: 472303 **Payroll Expense ($000)**: 167446

FORT MORGAN—Morgan County

⊞ **COLORADO PLAINS MEDICAL CENTER (060044)**, 1000 Lincoln Street, Zip 80701–3298; tel. 970/867–3391, **A**1 3 10 20 **F**3 11 13 15 29 31 34 35 40 43 44 45 46 48 50 51 53 56 57 59 64 65 70 75 76 77 79 81 85 86 87 89 93 94 97 98 100 101 103 104 107 108 110 111 115 119 129 130 133 146 147 148 153 154 **P**6 **S** LifePoint Health, Brentwood, TN
Primary Contact: Gene L. O'Hara, Chief Executive Officer
CFO: Christina Patton, Chief Financial Officer
CHR: Janet Brinkman, Director Human Resources
CNO: Sonya Bass, MS, Chief Nursing Officer
Web address: www.coloradoplainsmedicalcenter.com
Control: Corporation, Investor–owned (for–profit) **Service**: General medical and surgical

Staffed Beds: 50 **Admissions**: 1269 **Census**: 19 **Outpatient Visits**: 45466 **Births**: 322 **Total Expense ($000)**: 35094 **Payroll Expense ($000)**: 13230 **Personnel**: 227

FRISCO—Summit County

⊞ **ST. ANTHONY SUMMIT MEDICAL CENTER (060118)**, 340 Peak One Drive, Zip 80443, Mailing Address: P.O. Box 738, Zip 80443–0738; tel. 970/668–3300, **A**1 10 **F**3 15 29 30 34 35 40 43 45 57 59 66 68 70 75 76 77 79 81 82 84 85 97 107 110 111 119 129 130 132 146 147 **S** Catholic Health Initiatives, Englewood, CO
Primary Contact: Marshall Denkinger, M.D., Interim Chief Executive Officer
CNO: Trixie VanderSchaaff, Chief Nursing Officer
Web address: www.summitmedicalcenter.org
Control: Church operated, Nongovernment, not–for–profit **Service**: General medical and surgical

Staffed Beds: 34 **Admissions**: 1313 **Census**: 9 **Outpatient Visits**: 23730 **Births**: 330 **Total Expense ($000)**: 47748 **Payroll Expense ($000)**: 17157 **Personnel**: 353

Many Facility Codes have changed. Please refer to the AHA Guide Code Chart. © 2018 AHA Guide

FRUITA—Mesa County

★ **COLORADO CANYONS HOSPITAL AND MEDICAL CENTER (061302)**, 300 West Ottley Avenue, Zip 81521–2118, Mailing Address: P.O. Box 130, Zip 81521–0130; tel. 970/858–9871, **A**10 18 **F**3 9 15 29 30 34 35 36 40 41 43 45 50 54 56 57 59 64 65 68 74 75 77 79 81 82 85 86 87 90 93 107 110 111 115 119 128 130 131 132 133 143 144 146 148 149 **P**6
Primary Contact: Mark J. Francis, President and Chief Executive Officer
CFO: Mark J Francis, President and Chief Executive Officer
CMO: Christopher Wibblesman, M.D., Chief of Staff
CIO: Derrick Diddle, Chief Information Officer
CHR: Kelly Murphy, Vice President Human Resources
CNO: Lori Henderson, Chief Nursing Officer, Vice President Clinical
Web address: www.fhw.org
Control: Other not–for–profit (including NFP Corporation) **Service**: General medical and surgical

Staffed Beds: 16 **Admissions**: 405 **Census**: 12 **Outpatient Visits**: 58955 **Births**: 0 **Total Expense ($000)**: 35218 **Payroll Expense ($000)**: 11875 **Personnel**: 264

GLENWOOD SPRINGS—Garfield County

✠ **VALLEY VIEW HOSPITAL (060075)**, 1906 Blake Avenue, Zip 81601–4259; tel. 970/945–6535, **A**1 2 10 20 **F**3 4 11 13 14 15 18 20 22 26 28 29 30 31 32 34 35 36 37 40 43 45 46 49 50 51 54 57 58 59 64 68 69 70 74 75 76 77 78 79 81 82 84 85 86 87 92 93 94 97 100 104 107 108 110 111 114 115 116 117 118 119 120 121 123 124 126 129 130 131 132 135 145 146 147 148 151 154 **P**6
Primary Contact: Gary L. Brewer, Chief Executive Officer
CFO: Charles Crevling, Chief Financial Officer
CMO: David Brooks, M.D., Chief Medical Officer
CHR: Daniel Biggs, Director Human Resources
CNO: Sandra Hurley, MS, R.N., Chief Nursing Officer
Web address: www.vvh.org
Control: Other not–for–profit (including NFP Corporation) **Service**: General medical and surgical

Staffed Beds: 49 **Admissions**: 3038 **Census**: 33 **Outpatient Visits**: 127229 **Births**: 684 **Total Expense ($000)**: 209988 **Payroll Expense ($000)**: 88057 **Personnel**: 951

GRAND JUNCTION—Mesa County

✠ **COMMUNITY HOSPITAL (060054)**, 2351 G Road, Zip 81505; tel. 970/242–0920, (Nonreporting) **A**1 10 **S** QHR, Brentwood, TN
Primary Contact: Chris Thomas, FACHE, President and Chief Executive Officer
CMO: Donald Nicolay, M.D., Chief Medical Officer
CIO: Bart Butzine, Director Information Technology
CNO: Kristin Gundt, Chief Nursing Officer
Web address: www.yourcommunityhospital.com
Control: Other not–for–profit (including NFP Corporation) **Service**: General medical and surgical

Staffed Beds: 78

✠ **GRAND JUNCTION VETERANS HEALTH CARE SYSTEM**, 2121 North Avenue, Zip 81501–6428; tel. 970/242–0731, (Nonreporting) **A**1 **S** Department of Veterans Affairs, Perry Point, MD
Primary Contact: Michael T. Kilmer, Director
COO: Patricia A Hitt, Associate Director
CFO: Laquita Gruver, Fiscal Officer
CMO: William R Berryman, M.D., Chief of Staff
CIO: Craig Frerichs, Chief Information Technology Service
CHR: William Chester, Manager Human Resources
Web address: www.grandjunction.va.gov/
Control: Veterans Affairs, Government, federal **Service**: General medical and surgical

Staffed Beds: 23

✠ **ST. MARY'S HOSPITAL AND MEDICAL CENTER (060023)**, 2635 North 7th Street, Zip 81501–8209, Mailing Address: P.O. Box 1628, Zip 81502–1628; tel. 970/298–2273, **A**1 2 3 10 **F**3 7 13 14 15 17 18 20 22 24 26 28 29 30 31 34 35 37 40 43 45 49 50 51 54 55 57 58 59 60 61 64 65 68 69 70 71 72 74 75 76 77 78 79 81 82 84 85 86 87 89 90 91 92 93 96 97 102 107 108 109 110 111 113 114 115 116 117 119 120 121 122 123 124 126 129 130 131 132 135 143 145 146 147 148 149 154 **P**6 **S** SCL Health, Broomfield, CO
Primary Contact: Brian Davidson, M.D., President and Chief Medical Officer
COO: Reza Kaleel, Executive Vice President and Chief Operating Officer
CFO: Terri Chinn, Vice President Finance
CIO: John Bullard, Director Information Technology
CHR: Judy White House, Vice President Human Resources
CNO: Shelley Peterson, R.N., Vice President Patient Services and Chief Nursing Officer
Web address: www.stmarygj.com
Control: Church operated, Nongovernment, not–for–profit **Service**: General medical and surgical

Staffed Beds: 315 **Admissions**: 12980 **Census**: 176 **Outpatient Visits**: 190099 **Births**: 1473 **Total Expense ($000)**: 385352 **Payroll Expense ($000)**: 111922 **Personnel**: 1954

VETERANS AFFAIRS MEDICAL CENTER See Grand Junction Veterans Health Care System

WEST SPRINGS HOSPITAL (064023), 515 28 3/4 Road, Zip 81501–5016; tel. 970/263–4918, (Nonreporting) **A**10
Primary Contact: Sharon Raggio, President and Chief Executive Officer
COO: Brandi Kroese, Director Operations
CFO: John Rattle, Chief Financial Officer
CMO: Jules Rosen, M.D., Chief Medical Officer
CIO: Charles Andrews, Director Information Technology
CHR: Karen Birmingham, Director Human Resources
CNO: Deborah Sharpe, R.N., Director of Nursing
Web address: www.WestSpringsHospital.org
Control: Other not–for–profit (including NFP Corporation) **Service**: Psychiatric

Staffed Beds: 32

GREELEY—Weld County

✠ **NORTH COLORADO MEDICAL CENTER (060001)**, 1801 16th Street, Zip 80631–5154; tel. 970/352–4121, **A**1 2 3 10 **F**3 7 11 13 14 15 16 18 20 22 24 26 28 29 30 31 34 35 36 38 40 43 44 46 49 50 51 53 54 55 57 58 59 60 61 64 65 68 70 73 75 76 77 78 79 80 81 82 84 85 86 87 89 93 96 100 102 107 108 110 111 114 115 116 117 118 119 120 121 123 126 129 130 131 132 133 135 141 146 148 149 154 **S** Banner Health, Gilbert, AZ
Primary Contact: Margo Karsten, Ph.D., MSN, Chief Executive Officer
COO: Wendy Sparks, Chief Operating Officer
CFO: Mary McCabe, Chief Financial Officer
CHR: Jeannie Gallagher, Chief Human Resource Officer
CNO: Tiffany Erin Hettinger, Associate Chief Nursing Officer
Web address: www.ncmcgreeley.com
Control: Other not–for–profit (including NFP Corporation) **Service**: General medical and surgical

Staffed Beds: 236 **Admissions**: 10726 **Census**: 124 **Births**: 1590 **Total Expense ($000)**: 347702 **Payroll Expense ($000)**: 102335 **Personnel**: 1891

GUNNISON—Gunnison County

✠ **GUNNISON VALLEY HOSPITAL (061320)**, 711 North Taylor Street, Zip 81230–2296; tel. 970/641–1456, **A**1 10 18 **F**3 7 11 13 15 29 30 31 32 34 35 40 43 44 45 56 57 59 64 68 76 77 78 85 87 93 97 107 110 111 114 119 129 132 133 135 146 147 148
Primary Contact: Robert J. Santilli, Chief Executive Officer
CFO: James P Barbuat, Chief Financial Officer
CIO: Trevor Smith, Chief Management Information Services
CHR: Christina Lovelace, Director Human Resources
CNO: Lisa Loughran, Chief Nursing Officer
Web address: www.gvh–colorado.org
Control: County, Government, nonfederal **Service**: General medical and surgical

Staffed Beds: 24 **Admissions**: 527 **Census**: 4 **Births**: 101

CO

Hospital, Medicare Provider Number, Address, Telephone, Approval, Facility, and Physician Codes, Health Care System

★ American Hospital Association (AHA) membership ◯ Healthcare Facilities Accreditation Program ⇑ Center for Improvement in Healthcare Quality Accreditation
☐ The Joint Commission accreditation ◇ DNV Healthcare Inc. accreditation △ Commission on Accreditation of Rehabilitation Facilities (CARF) accreditation

HAXTUN—Phillips County

★ **HAXTUN HOSPITAL DISTRICT (061304)**, 235 West Fletcher Street, Zip 80731–2737; tel. 970/774–6123, **A**10 18 **F**3 7 40 43 54 56 59 64 65 75 77 87 93 97 107 114 119 129 133 146
Primary Contact: Dewane Pace, President and Chief Executive Officer
CFO: Rick Lee Nader, Chief Financial Officer
CMO: Colby Jolley, D.O., Acting Chief of Staff
CIO: Andrea Evers, Director Information Technology
CNO: Gail Phelps, R.N., Chief Nursing Officer
Web address: www.haxtunhealth.org
Control: Hospital district or authority, Government, nonfederal **Service**: General medical and surgical

Staffed Beds: 25 **Admissions**: 124 **Census**: 19 **Outpatient Visits**: 30225
Births: 0 **Total Expense ($000)**: 9761 **Payroll Expense ($000)**: 5143

HOLYOKE—Phillips County

★ **MELISSA MEMORIAL HOSPITAL (061305)**, 1001 East Johnson Street, Zip 80734–1854; tel. 970/854–2241, **A**10 18 **F**3 7 8 15 18 28 29 34 40 41 43 53 57 64 66 68 82 87 90 97 107 108 109 110 112 114 115 116 119 127 128 133 144 146 147 148 150 **P**3
Primary Contact: Trampas Hutches, Chief Executive Officer
CFO: Jason McCormick, Interim Chief Financial Officer
CMO: Dennis Jelden, M.D., Chief of Staff
CIO: David Bickford, Chief Information Officer
CHR: Sharon Greenman, Director Human Resources
CNO: Pat Notter, R.N., Chief Nursing Officer and Director Quality
Web address: www.melissamemorial.org
Control: Hospital district or authority, Government, nonfederal **Service**: General medical and surgical

Staffed Beds: 13 **Admissions**: 168 **Census**: 3 **Births**: 0

HUGO—Lincoln County

★ **LINCOLN COMMUNITY HOSPITAL AND NURSING HOME (061306)**, 111 6th Street, Zip 80821–0248, Mailing Address: P.O. Box 248, Zip 80821–0248; tel. 719/743–2421, (Total facility includes 35 beds in nursing home–type unit) **A**10 18 **F**7 10 15 29 34 35 40 43 45 56 59 62 63 64 77 81 82 90 93 97 100 102 104 107 108 110 111 114 119 128 130 133 143 148 **P**6
Primary Contact: Kevin M. Stansbury, Chief Executive Officer
CMO: Mark Olson, M.D., Chief of Staff
CIO: Michael Gaskins, Director Information Technology
CHR: Susan Petersen, Human Resources
CNO: Dan Walker, Chief Nursing Officer
Web address: www.lincolncommunityhospital.com
Control: County, Government, nonfederal **Service**: General medical and surgical

Staffed Beds: 50 **Admissions**: 211 **Census**: 28 **Outpatient Visits**: 27245
Births: 0 **Total Expense ($000)**: 17783 **Payroll Expense ($000)**: 8671

JOHNSTOWN—Larimer County

☐ **NORTHERN COLORADO LONG TERM ACUTE HOSPITAL (062017)**, 4401 Union Street, Zip 80534; tel. 970/619–3663, (Nonreporting) **A**1 10 **S** Ernest Health, Inc., Albuquerque, NM
Primary Contact: Lamar McBride, Chief Executive Officer
Web address: www.ncltah.ernesthealth.com/
Control: Partnership, Investor–owned (for–profit) **Service**: Acute long–term care hospital

Staffed Beds: 40

☐ **NORTHERN COLORADO REHABILITATION HOSPITAL (063033)**, 4401 Union Street, Zip 80534–2800; tel. 970/619–3400, (Nonreporting) **A**1 10 **S** Ernest Health, Inc., Albuquerque, NM
Primary Contact: Elizabeth Bullard, Chief Executive Officer
CFO: Bonnie Cushman, Chief Financial Officer
CMO: Revelyn Arrogante, M.D., Medical Director
CHR: Amy Lauridsen, Director Human Resources
CNO: Mark Smith, Director Nursing Operations
Web address: www.ncrh.ernesthealth.com
Control: Corporation, Investor–owned (for–profit) **Service**: Rehabilitation

Staffed Beds: 40

JULESBURG—Sedgwick County

SEDGWICK COUNTY HEALTH CENTER (061310), 900 Cedar Street, Zip 80737–1199; tel. 970/474–3323, (Total facility includes 52 beds in nursing home–type unit) **A**10 13 15 32 40 43 45 53 56 57 59 64 65 66 67 68 76 77 81 89 107 110 111 114 119 127 128 133 145 148 **P**6
Primary Contact: Robert Thorn, FACHE, Interim Chief Executive Officer
CFO: Karla Dunker, Director Finance
CMO: Donald Regier, M.D., Chief Medical Officer
CHR: Sonja Bell, Coordinator Human Resources
Web address: www.schealth.org/
Control: County, Government, nonfederal **Service**: General medical and surgical

Staffed Beds: 67 **Admissions**: 151 **Census**: 47 **Outpatient Visits**: 15245
Births: 18 **Total Expense ($000)**: 9976 **Payroll Expense ($000)**: 4898
Personnel: 97

KREMMLING—Grand County

★ **MIDDLE PARK MEDICAL CENTER–KREMMLING (061318)**, 214 South Fourth Street, Zip 80459, Mailing Address: P.O. Box 399, Zip 80459–0399; tel. 970/724–3442, (Includes MIDDLE PARK MEDICAL CENTER – GRANBY, 1000 Granby Park Drive South, Granby, CO, Zip 80446, Mailing Address: P.O. Box 399, Kremmling, Zip 80446, tel. 970/887–5800; Robert Flake, Chief Executive Officer) (Nonreporting) **A**10 18
Primary Contact: Robert Flake, Chief Executive Officer
CFO: Robert Flake, Chief Financial Officer
CMO: Thomas C. Coburn, M.D., Chief Medical Officer
CHR: Jason Bryan, Director Human Resources
CNO: Debra Plemmons, Chief Nursing Officer
Web address: www.mpmc.org
Control: Hospital district or authority, Government, nonfederal **Service**: General medical and surgical

Staffed Beds: 10

LA JARA—Conejos County

★ **SAN LUIS VALLEY HEALTH CONEJOS COUNTY HOSPITAL (061308)**, 19021 US Highway 285, Zip 81140–0639, Mailing Address: P.O. Box 639, Zip 81140–0639; tel. 719/274–5121, **A**10 18 **F**3 40 43 54 56 59 64 70 76 87 89 93 97 107 114 119 127 128 133 **S** San Luis Valley Health, Alamosa, CO
Primary Contact: Kelly Gallegos, Administrator
CFO: Shane Mortensen, Chief Financial Officer
CMO: Gregory McAuliffe, M.D., Chief Medical Officer
CIO: Kathy Rogers, Vice President Marketing
CHR: Mandy Lee Crockett, Director Human Resources
CNO: Tandra Dunn, Director of Nursing
Web address: www.sanluisvalleyhealth.org/locations/conejos–county–hospital
Control: Other not–for–profit (including NFP Corporation) **Service**: General medical and surgical

Staffed Beds: 17 **Admissions**: 137 **Census**: 2 **Births**: 0

LA JUNTA—Otero County

⊞ **ARKANSAS VALLEY REGIONAL MEDICAL CENTER (060036)**, 1100 Carson Avenue, Zip 81050–2799; tel. 719/383–6000, (Nonreporting) **A**1 10 18 **S** Quorum Health, Brentwood, TN
Primary Contact: Lynn Crowell, Chief Executive Officer
CMO: Kent E. Gay, M.D., Chief of Medical Staff
CIO: Heidi Gearhart, Director Information Systems
CHR: Kelsey B. Brundage, Director Human Resources
CNO: Carrie Cutrell, Chief Nursing Officer
Web address: www.avrmc.org
Control: Other not–for–profit (including NFP Corporation) **Service**: General medical and surgical

Staffed Beds: 106

LAFAYETTE—Boulder County

⊞ **GOOD SAMARITAN MEDICAL CENTER (060116)**, 200 Exempla Circle, Zip 80026–3370; tel. 303/689–4000, **A**1 2 10 **F**3 11 12 13 15 18 20 22 26 28 29 30 31 32 34 35 36 40 41 43 45 46 47 49 50 51 60 64 68 70 72 74 75 76 77 78 79 80 81 84 85 86 87 91 92 93 100 102 107 108 110 111 114 115 117 119 120 121 123 126 130 132 135 143 145 146 147 148 149 150 154 **P**1 4 6 **S** SCL Health, Broomfield, CO
Primary Contact: Jennifer Alderfer, President
COO: Beth Forsyth, Chief Operating Officer
CFO: John Higgins, Vice President and Chief Financial Officer
CMO: Todd Mydler, M.D., Vice President and Chief Medical Officer
CHR: Amy Pacey, Vice President Human Resources
CNO: Susan Kerschen, MS, R.N., Vice President and Chief Nursing Officer
Web address: www.goodsamaritancolorado.org/
Control: Other not–for–profit (including NFP Corporation) **Service**: General medical and surgical

Staffed Beds: 185 **Admissions**: 13041 **Census**: 144 **Outpatient Visits**: 94176 **Births**: 2080 **Total Expense ($000)**: 283170 **Payroll Expense ($000)**: 91578 **Personnel**: 1261

LAKEWOOD—Jefferson County

⊞ **ORTHOCOLORADO HOSPITAL (060124)**, 11650 West 2nd Place, Zip 80228–1527; tel. 720/321–5000, (Nonreporting) **A**1 10 **S** Catholic Health Initiatives, Englewood, CO
Primary Contact: Jude Torchia, Chief Executive Officer
Web address: www.orthocolorado.org
Control: Partnership, Investor–owned (for–profit) **Service**: Orthopedic

Staffed Beds: 48

CO

☒ **ST. ANTHONY HOSPITAL (060015)**, 11600 West Second Place,
Zip 80228–1527; tel. 720/321–0000, **A**1 2 3 5 10 **F**3 7 8 11 15 17 18 20
22 24 26 28 29 30 31 34 35 36 38 40 43 45 46 47 48 49 50 53 56 57 59 64
65 66 69 70 74 75 77 78 79 81 82 89 90 92 93 96 97 102 107 108
111 114 115 116 117 118 119 120 121 123 124 126 129 130 131 132 133
134 135 146 147 148 149 154 **S** Catholic Health Initiatives, Englewood, CO
Primary Contact: Edward H. Sim, Chief Executive Officer
CMO: Brian Erling, Group Chief Medical Officer
CHR: Michelle Fornier–Johnson, Group Vice President Human Resources
Web address: www.stanthonyhosp.org
Control: Church operated, Nongovernment, not–for–profit **Service:** General
medical and surgical

> **Staffed Beds:** 219 **Admissions:** 11749 **Census:** 164 **Outpatient Visits:**
> 92126 **Births:** 0 **Total Expense ($000):** 318164 **Payroll Expense**
> **($000):** 102760 **Personnel:** 2081

LAMAR—Prowers County

★ **PROWERS MEDICAL CENTER (061323)**, 401 Kendall Drive, Zip 81052–3993;
tel. 719/336–4343, **A**10 18 **F**3 11 13 15 18 20 28 29 31 34 35 40 44 45 50
56 57 59 62 64 65 66 68 75 76 77 78 81 85 86 93 96 97 107 111 115 119 127
130 131 132 133 135 146 147 148 154 **P**6 **S** QHR, Brentwood, TN
Primary Contact: Craig Loveless, Chief Executive Officer
COO: Karen Bryant, Chief Support Services Officer
CFO: Audrey Kane, Interim Chief Financial Officer
CMO: Barry Portner, M.D., Chief of Staff
CIO: Jason Spano, Director of Information Technology
CHR: Karen Bryant, Chief Support Services Officer
Web address: www.prowersmedical.com
Control: Hospital district or authority, Government, nonfederal **Service:** General
medical and surgical

> **Staffed Beds:** 25 **Admissions:** 1012 **Census:** 8 **Outpatient Visits:** 29933
> **Births:** 171

LEADVILLE—Lake County

ST. VINCENT GENERAL HOSPITAL DISTRICT (061319), 822 West 4th Street,
Zip 80461–3897; tel. 719/486–0230, (Nonreporting) **A**10 18
Primary Contact: Gary Campbell, Chief Executive Officer
CMO: Gary Petry, M.D., Chief of Staff
CHR: Cheryl Snider, Director Human Resources
CNO: Von Kilpatrick, Chief Nursing Officer
Web address: www.svghd.org
Control: Hospital district or authority, Government, nonfederal **Service:** General
medical and surgical

> **Staffed Beds:** 2

LITTLETON—Jefferson County

FEDERAL CORRECTIONAL INSTITUTE HOSPITAL, 9595 West Quincy Street,
Zip 80123–1159; tel. 303/985–1566, (Nonreporting)
Primary Contact: Mike Hudson, Administrator
Control: Department of Justice, Government, federal **Service:** Hospital unit of an
institution (prison hospital, college infirmary, etc.)

> **Staffed Beds:** 6

LITTLETON—Arapahoe County

☒ **HEALTHSOUTH REHABILITATION HOSPITAL OF LITTLETON (063034)**, 1001
West Mineral Avenue, Zip 80120–4507; tel. 303/334–1100, (Nonreporting) **A**1 10
S Encompass Health Corporation, Birmingham, AL
Primary Contact: David H. Shefte, Chief Executive Officer
CFO: Liz Freudenberg, Chief Financial Officer
CMO: Jill Castro, M.D., Medical Director
CHR: Sarah Thomas, Director of Human Resources
Web address: www.healthsouthdenver.com
Control: Corporation, Investor–owned (for–profit) **Service:** Rehabilitation

> **Staffed Beds:** 28

LITTLETON—Douglas County

☐ **HIGHLANDS BEHAVIORAL HEALTH SYSTEM (064024)**, 8565 South Poplar
Way, Zip 80130–3602; tel. 720/348–2800, (Nonreporting) **A**1 10 **S** Universal
Health Services, Inc., King of Prussia, PA
Primary Contact: Elicia Bunch, Chief Executive Officer
Web address: www.highlandsbhs.com
Control: Corporation, Investor–owned (for–profit) **Service:** Psychiatric

> **Staffed Beds:** 86

LITTLETON—Arapahoe County

☒ **LITTLETON ADVENTIST HOSPITAL (060113)**, 7700 South Broadway Street,
Zip 80122–2628; tel. 303/730–8900, **A**1 2 5 10 **F**3 11 13 15 17 18 20 22 26
29 30 31 34 35 36 37 39 40 41 43 44 45 46 47 48 49 50 53 54 55 57 58 59
64 68 70 72 74 75 76 77 78 79 81 82 83 84 85 86 87 89 90 91 92 93 97
107 108 110 111 114 115 116 117 118 119 120 121 126 130 131 132 135
146 147 148 **P**6 **S** Adventist Health System Sunbelt Health Care Corporation,
Altamonte Springs, FL
Primary Contact: Brett Spenst, Chief Executive Officer
COO: Geoff Lawton, Vice President Operations
CFO: Cheryl Curry, Chief Financial Officer
CMO: Lawrence Wood, M.D., Chief Medical Officer
CHR: Rita K Arthur, Director Human Resources
CNO: Rhonda Ward, R.N., MSN, Chief Nursing Officer
Web address: www.centura.org
Control: Church operated, Nongovernment, not–for–profit **Service:** General
medical and surgical

> **Staffed Beds:** 176 **Admissions:** 9202 **Census:** 114 **Outpatient Visits:**
> 56986 **Births:** 1589 **Total Expense ($000):** 199273 **Payroll Expense**
> **($000):** 72170 **Personnel:** 1325

LONE TREE—Douglas County

☒ **SKY RIDGE MEDICAL CENTER (060112)**, 10101 Ridge Gate Parkway,
Zip 80124–5522; tel. 720/225–1000, **A**1 2 3 5 10 12 13 **F**3 8 12 13 15 17 18
20 22 26 28 29 30 31 34 35 36 37 40 41 43 44 45 46 47 48 49 50 54 57 58
59 64 70 72 73 74 75 76 77 78 79 81 82 84 85 86 87 89 93 97 107 108 111
114 115 116 120 121 123 126 129 130 131 132 135 146 147 149 **S**
HCA Healthcare, Nashville, TN
Primary Contact: Susan Hicks, Chief Executive Officer
CFO: Craig Sammons, Chief Financial Officer
CMO: David Markenson, M.D., Chief Medical Officer
CIO: Evan Tice, Director Information Technology and Systems
CHR: Jim Ritchey, Director Human Resources
CNO: Marian Savitsky, R.N., Chief Nursing Officer
Web address: www.skyridgemedcenter.com
Control: Corporation, Investor–owned (for–profit) **Service:** General medical and
surgical

> **Staffed Beds:** 274 **Admissions:** 17050 **Census:** 153 **Outpatient Visits:**
> 100570 **Births:** 3419 **Personnel:** 1084

LONGMONT—Boulder County

☒ **LONGMONT UNITED HOSPITAL (060003)**, 1950 West Mountain View
Avenue, Zip 80501–3162, Mailing Address: P.O. Box 1659, Zip 80502–1659;
tel. 303/651–5111, (Total facility includes 15 beds in nursing home–type unit) **A**1
2 10 **F**2 3 11 13 15 18 20 22 28 29 30 31 34 35 36 37 38 40 43 44 45 47 48
49 50 53 54 56 57 59 61 64 68 70 73 74 75 76 77 78 79 81 82 84 85 86 87
89 92 93 107 108 110 111 114 115 118 119 121 123 126 128 129 130 131
132 135 146 148 149 150 154 **P**6 **S** Catholic Health Initiatives, Englewood, CO
Primary Contact: Christina Johnson, M.D., Chief Executive Officer
CFO: Daniel Frank, Chief Financial Officer
CMO: Wyatt Hall, M.D., Chief Medical Officer
CHR: Warren Laughlin, Vice President Human Resources
CNO: Nancy Driscoll, Chief Nursing Officer
Web address: www.luhcares.org
Control: Other not–for–profit (including NFP Corporation) **Service:** General
medical and surgical

> **Staffed Beds:** 146 **Admissions:** 6616 **Census:** 75 **Outpatient Visits:** 90627
> **Births:** 846 **Total Expense ($000):** 168028 **Payroll Expense ($000):** 61290
> **Personnel:** 736

LOUISVILLE—Boulder County

☒ **AVISTA ADVENTIST HOSPITAL (060103)**, 100 Health Park Drive,
Zip 80027–9583; tel. 303/673–1000, **A**1 3 10 **F**3 8 11 13 15 17 18 20 22 28 29
30 31 34 40 43 44 45 47 48 49 50 56 59 60 62 63 64 68 70 72 74 75 76 77
79 81 82 84 85 86 87 90 93 107 108 111 114 115 119 129 130 131 132 135
146 147 **P**6 **S** Adventist Health System Sunbelt Health Care Corporation, Altamonte
Springs, FL
Primary Contact: Jillyan McKinney, Chief Executive Officer
CMO: David Ehrenberger, M.D., Chief Medical Officer
CHR: Becky Ortega, Manager Human Resources
CNO: Lavah Boyers Lowe, Chief Nursing Officer
Web address: www.avistahospital.org
Control: Church operated, Nongovernment, not–for–profit **Service:** General
medical and surgical

> **Staffed Beds:** 108 **Admissions:** 4271 **Census:** 34 **Outpatient Visits:** 50608
> **Births:** 2243 **Total Expense ($000):** 95105 **Payroll Expense ($000):** 35071
> **Personnel:** 654

CO

Hospital, Medicare Provider Number, Address, Telephone, Approval, Facility, and Physician Codes, Health Care System

★ American Hospital Association (AHA) membership	○ Healthcare Facilities Accreditation Program	⇑ Center for Improvement in Healthcare Quality Accreditation
☐ The Joint Commission accreditation	◇ DNV Healthcare Inc. accreditation	△ Commission on Accreditation of Rehabilitation Facilities (CARF) accreditation

☐ **CENTENNIAL PEAKS HOSPITAL (064007)**, 2255 South 88th Street, Zip 80027–9716; tel. 303/673–9990, **A**1 10 **F**5 98 104 105 152 153 **S** Universal Health Services, Inc., King of Prussia, PA
Primary Contact: Elicia Bunch, Chief Executive Officer
COO: Lisa Strub, Chief Operating Officer
CFO: Tim Ryan, Chief Financial Officer
CMO: Konoy Mandal, M.D., Medical Director
CHR: Suzanne Martinez, Director Human Resources
CNO: Donia L Andersen, Director of Nursing
Web address: www.centennialpeaks.com
Control: Partnership, Investor–owned (for–profit) **Service**: Psychiatric

Staffed Beds: 104 **Admissions**: 3429 **Census**: 70 **Outpatient Visits**: 4515
Total Expense ($000): 21877 **Payroll Expense ($000)**: 10815

LOVELAND—Larimer County

⊞ **MCKEE MEDICAL CENTER (060030)**, 2000 Boise Avenue, Zip 80538–4281; tel. 970/669–4640, **A**1 2 10 **F**2 3 8 11 13 14 15 18 20 22 26 28 29 30 31 34 35 36 40 43 44 50 54 56 59 60 62 64 65 68 70 74 75 76 77 78 79 81 84 85 87 89 92 93 97 107 108 110 111 114 115 119 120 121 122 123 124 126 129 130 135 144 146 147 148 149 154 **S** Banner Health, Gilbert, AZ
Primary Contact: Margo Karsten, Ph.D., MSN, Chief Executive Officer
COO: Julie Klein, Chief Operating Officer
CFO: Lori Sehrt, Chief Financial Officer
CMO: Bert Honea, M.D., Medical Director
CIO: Steve Rains, Director Information Services
CHR: Jeannie Gallagher, jeannie.gallagher@bannerhealth.com
CNO: Kelly Sturler, Chief Nursing Officer
Web address: www.mckeeloveland.com
Control: Other not–for–profit (including NFP Corporation) **Service**: General medical and surgical

Staffed Beds: 96 **Admissions**: 3323 **Census**: 28 **Births**: 650 **Total Expense ($000)**: 125140 **Payroll Expense ($000)**: 36557 **Personnel**: 635

⊞ **UCHEALTH MEDICAL CENTER OF THE ROCKIES (060119)**, 2500 Rocky Mountain Avenue, Zip 80538–9004; tel. 970/624–2500, **A**1 3 5 10 **F**3 11 13 14 15 17 18 20 22 24 26 28 29 30 31 32 34 35 38 39 40 43 44 45 47 49 50 54 55 57 58 59 60 61 64 65 68 70 74 75 76 77 78 79 80 81 82 83 84 85 86 87 89 90 92 93 96 100 102 107 108 110 111 114 115 118 119 126 129 130 131 132 134 135 146 147 148 149 150 154 **S** UCHealth, Fort Collins, CO
Primary Contact: Kevin L. Unger, Ph.D., FACHE, President and Chief Executive Officer
COO: Ryan Rohman, MSN, R.N., Chief Operating Officer
CFO: Stephanie Doughty, Chief Financial Officer
CMO: William Neff, M.D., Chief Medical Officer
CIO: Steve Hess, Vice President & Chief Information Officer
Web address: www.medctrrockies.org
Control: Other not–for–profit (including NFP Corporation) **Service**: General medical and surgical

Staffed Beds: 187 **Admissions**: 11989 **Census**: 130 **Outpatient Visits**: 86784 **Births**: 1379 **Total Expense ($000)**: 374217 **Payroll Expense ($000)**: 109042

MEEKER—Rio Blanco County

★ **PIONEERS MEDICAL CENTER (061325)**, 100 Pioneers Medical Center Drive, Zip 81641–3181; tel. 970/878–5047, (Total facility includes 30 beds in nursing home–type unit) **A**10 18 **F**15 18 34 40 45 50 59 62 64 65 77 79 81 93 107 108 111 119 127 128 129 133 143 146 **S** QHR, Brentwood, TN
Primary Contact: Kenneth Harman, Chief Executive Officer
COO: Karen Iacuone, Chief Nursing Officer and Chief Operating Officer
CFO: James W Worrell, Chief Financial Officer
CMO: Christopher Williams, M.D., Chief of Staff
CIO: Curtis Cooper, Manager Information Systems
CHR: Twyla Jensen, Director Human Resources
CNO: Karen Iacuone, Chief Nursing Officer
Web address: www.pioneershospital.org
Control: Hospital district or authority, Government, nonfederal **Service**: General medical and surgical

Staffed Beds: 40 **Admissions**: 274 **Census**: 29 **Outpatient Visits**: 9358 **Births**: 0 **Total Expense ($000)**: 23549 **Payroll Expense ($000)**: 8541 **Personnel**: 108

MONTROSE—Montrose County

⊞ **MONTROSE MEMORIAL HOSPITAL (060006)**, 800 South Third Street, Zip 81401–4212; tel. 970/249–2211, **A**1 10 20 **F**3 13 15 18 20 22 28 29 30 31 34 35 40 43 44 45 46 50 51 57 59 64 68 70 74 75 77 78 79 81 82 85 90 92 93 96 107 108 110 111 115 118 119 126 129 130 132 135 146 147 148 154 **P**1 5 **S** QHR, Brentwood, TN
Primary Contact: James R. Kiser II, Chief Executive Officer
COO: Mary E Snyder, Chief Operations Officer
CFO: Stephan A Wilson, Chief Financial Officer
CMO: Richard Shannon, M.D., Chief of Staff
CIO: Carlos Lovera, Director Information Systems
CHR: Kathy McKie, Director Human Resources
Web address: www.montrosehospital.com
Control: Other not–for–profit (including NFP Corporation) **Service**: General medical and surgical

Staffed Beds: 60 **Admissions**: 3074 **Census**: 27 **Births**: 431 **Total Expense ($000)**: 107755 **Payroll Expense ($000)**: 39093 **Personnel**: 598

PAGOSA SPRINGS—Archuleta County

PAGOSA SPRINGS MEDICAL CENTER (061328), 95 South Pagosa Boulevard, Zip 81147–8329; tel. 970/731–3700, **A**10 18 **F**3 7 15 18 29 31 34 40 43 45 59 64 74 77 78 79 81 82 85 87 89 93 97 102 104 107 110 111 115 119 127 131 133 146 147 154 **P**6
Primary Contact: Rhonda Webb, M.D., Chief Executive Officer
Web address: www.pagosaspringsmedicalcenter.org/
Control: Hospital district or authority, Government, nonfederal **Service**: General medical and surgical

Staffed Beds: 11 **Admissions**: 426 **Census**: 3 **Outpatient Visits**: 63005 **Births**: 0 **Total Expense ($000)**: 31396 **Payroll Expense ($000)**: 16688 **Personnel**: 223

PARKER—Douglas County

⊞ **PARKER ADVENTIST HOSPITAL (060114)**, 9395 Crown Crest Boulevard, Zip 80138–8573; tel. 303/269–4000, **A**1 2 10 **F**3 11 12 13 15 20 22 29 30 31 34 35 36 37 38 40 43 45 46 47 48 49 50 54 55 57 59 64 70 72 73 74 75 76 77 78 79 81 82 83 84 85 87 93 96 97 107 110 111 114 115 116 117 118 119 120 121 123 126 129 130 131 132 146 147 148 **P**6 **S** Adventist Health System Sunbelt Health Care Corporation, Altamonte Springs, FL
Primary Contact: Michael Goebel, Chief Executive Officer
CFO: Andrew Gaasch, Chief Financial Officer
Web address: www.parkerhospital.org
Control: Church operated, Nongovernment, not–for–profit **Service**: General medical and surgical

Staffed Beds: 167 **Admissions**: 7634 **Census**: 79 **Outpatient Visits**: 76924 **Births**: 1281 **Total Expense ($000)**: 197945 **Payroll Expense ($000)**: 67816 **Personnel**: 1292

PUEBLO—Pueblo County

☐ **COLORADO MENTAL HEALTH INSTITUTE AT PUEBLO (064001)**, 1600 West 24th Street, Zip 81003–1499; tel. 719/546–4000, (Nonreporting) **A**1 3 5 10
Primary Contact: Ron Hale, Superintendent
CFO: Jim Duff, Chief Financial Officer
CMO: Al Singleton, M.D., Chief Psychiatry and Chief Medical Staff
CIO: Eunice Wolther, Public Information Officer
CHR: Mary Young, Director Human Resources
Web address: www.cdhs.state.co.us/cmhip
Control: State, Government, nonfederal **Service**: Psychiatric

Staffed Beds: 514

⊞ △ **PARKVIEW MEDICAL CENTER (060020)**, 400 West 16th Street, Zip 81003–2781; tel. 719/584–4000, (Total facility includes 20 beds in nursing home–type unit) **A**1 3 7 10 13 **F**2 3 4 5 8 11 13 15 18 20 22 24 26 28 29 30 31 34 35 37 38 40 43 45 46 49 50 51 53 54 56 57 58 59 62 64 70 72 74 75 76 78 79 81 82 84 85 86 87 89 90 92 93 94 95 96 97 98 99 100 101 102 103 104 107 108 110 111 114 115 119 126 128 129 130 131 132 135 141 146 147 148 **P**6 8
Primary Contact: Michael T. Baxter, President and Chief Executive Officer
CFO: Leslie Barnes, Chief Financial Officer
CMO: Steve Nafziger, M.D., Vice President Medical Affairs
CIO: Steve Shirley, Chief Information Officer
CHR: Darrin Smith, Vice President Human Resources
CNO: Linda Flores, R.N., MSN, Vice President Nursing Services
Web address: www.parkviewmc.org
Control: Other not–for–profit (including NFP Corporation) **Service**: General medical and surgical

Staffed Beds: 370 **Admissions**: 15440 **Census**: 225 **Outpatient Visits**: 232084 **Births**: 1502 **Total Expense ($000)**: 322597 **Payroll Expense ($000)**: 129415 **Personnel**: 2659

CO

ST. MARY–CORWIN MEDICAL CENTER (060012), 1008 Minnequa Avenue, Zip 81004–3798; tel. 719/557–4000, **A**1 2 3 10 13 **F**3 13 15 18 20 22 26 28 29 30 31 34 35 40 43 45 47 48 49 50 53 55 57 59 64 68 70 72 73 75 76 78 79 81 82 84 85 86 87 89 90 107 108 109 110 111 114 115 117 119 120 121 123 124 126 129 130 131 132 135 146 147 148 149 154 **P**6 **S** Catholic Health Initiatives, Englewood, CO
Primary Contact: Michael Cafasso, Chief Executive Officer
COO: Michael Cafasso, Chief Operating Officer
CFO: Janiece McNichols, Chief Financial Officer
CMO: Kern Low, M.D., Chief Medical Officer
CHR: Timea Kennedy, Director Human Resources
CNO: Constance Schmidt, FACHE, R.N., Vice President Patient Care Services and Chief Nursing Officer
Web address: www.stmarycorwin.org
Control: Church operated, Nongovernment, not–for–profit **Service:** General medical and surgical

Staffed Beds: 125 **Admissions:** 6381 **Census:** 78 **Outpatient Visits:** 91799 **Births:** 532 **Total Expense ($000):** 154053 **Payroll Expense ($000):** 55743 **Personnel:** 822

RANGELY—Rio Blanco County

★ **RANGELY DISTRICT HOSPITAL (061307)**, 225 Eagle Crest Drive, Zip 81648–2104; tel. 970/675–5011, **A**10 18 **F**1 3 7 10 15 29 32 34 35 40 43 45 50 54 57 59 62 64 65 67 68 90 91 93 97 107 110 115 116 127 128 129 131 133 144 148 149
Primary Contact: Nick Goshe, Chief Executive Officer
COO: Bernard Rice, Chief Compliance Officer
CFO: Jim Dillon, Chief Financial Officer
CMO: Abigail R. Urish, M.D., Chief of Staff
CHR: Cynthia S. Stults, Executive Assistant and Human Resources Director
CNO: Sharma Vaughn Esq Chief Nursing Officer
Web address: www.rangelyhospital.com
Control: Hospital district or authority, Government, nonfederal **Service:** General medical and surgical

Staffed Beds: 18 **Admissions:** 55 **Census:** 10 **Outpatient Visits:** 15287 **Births:** 0 **Total Expense ($000):** 19536 **Payroll Expense ($000):** 7951 **Personnel:** 120

RIFLE—Garfield County

★ **GRAND RIVER HOSPITAL DISTRICT (061317)**, 501 Airport Road, Zip 81650–8510, Mailing Address: P.O. Box 912, Zip 81650–0912; tel. 970/625–1510, (Total facility includes 57 beds in nursing home–type unit) **A**10 18 **F**3 11 12 15 29 31 32 34 35 36 38 39 40 41 43 45 50 55 57 59 64 68 69 75 77 79 81 85 87 93 96 97 107 108 110 111 115 119 127 128 129 130 131 132 133 144 146 147 148 149 **P**6
Primary Contact: James Coombs, Chief Executive Officer
COO: Bill Noel, Chief Operating Officer
CFO: Cris Bolin, Chief Financial Officer
CMO: Kevin Coleman, M.D., Chief Medical Officer
CIO: Diana Murray, Director Information Systems
CHR: Dawn Hodges, Director Human Resources
CNO: Stacy Pemberton, Chief Nursing Officer
Web address: www.grhd.org
Control: Hospital district or authority, Government, nonfederal **Service:** General medical and surgical

Staffed Beds: 69 **Admissions:** 679 **Census:** 49 **Outpatient Visits:** 117609 **Births:** 0 **Total Expense ($000):** 77764 **Payroll Expense ($000):** 37251 **Personnel:** 465

SALIDA—Chaffee County

★ **HEART OF THE ROCKIES REGIONAL MEDICAL CENTER (061322)**, 1000 Rush Drive, Zip 81201–9627, Mailing Address: P.O. Box 429, Zip 81201–0429; tel. 719/530–2200, **A**10 18 **F**3 5 11 13 15 28 29 31 34 35 40 43 45 50 54 57 59 64 68 70 74 75 76 77 78 79 81 82 85 91 93 97 102 104 107 110 111 115 119 127 129 130 131 132 133 135 146 147 148
Primary Contact: Robert A. Morasko, Chief Executive Officer
CFO: Lesley Fagerberg, Vice President Fiscal Services
CMO: Daniel Wardrop, M.D., Medical Director
CIO: Andy Waldbart, Department Manager
CHR: Barbara Lutz, Vice President Human Resources
CNO: Linda Johnson, R.N., Vice President, Patient Services Risk Management and Chief Nursing Officer
Web address: www.hrrmc.com
Control: Hospital district or authority, Government, nonfederal **Service:** General medical and surgical

Staffed Beds: 25 **Admissions:** 1071 **Census:** 10 **Outpatient Visits:** 86642 **Births:** 109 **Total Expense ($000):** 60124 **Payroll Expense ($000):** 26915 **Personnel:** 386

SPRINGFIELD—Baca County

★ **SOUTHEAST COLORADO HOSPITAL DISTRICT (061311)**, 373 East Tenth Avenue, Zip 81073–1699; tel. 719/523–4501, (Total facility includes 56 beds in nursing home–type unit) **A**10 18 **F**6 7 11 29 40 45 50 57 62 63 66 68 81 91 114 119 127 130 133 148 **P**6
Primary Contact: David Engel, Chief Executive Officer and Administrator
CFO: Dorothy Burke, Chief Financial Officer
CMO: Andrea Wismann, M.D., Chief of Staff
CIO: Chris Westphal, Chief Information Technology Officer
CHR: Sherrilyn Turner, Director Human Resources
CNO: Cecelia Deen Esq Chief Nursing Officer
Web address: www.sechosp.org
Control: Hospital district or authority, Government, nonfederal **Service:** General medical and surgical

Staffed Beds: 79 **Admissions:** 200 **Census:** 48 **Outpatient Visits:** 34010 **Births:** 0 **Total Expense ($000):** 11573 **Payroll Expense ($000):** 5394 **Personnel:** 140

STEAMBOAT SPRINGS—Routt County

UCHEALTH YAMPA VALLEY MEDICAL CENTER (060049), 1024 Central Park Drive, Zip 80487–8813; tel. 970/879–1322, **A**1 2 10 20 **F**3 13 15 18 28 29 30 31 34 35 36 40 43 45 46 48 49 50 51 57 64 68 70 73 75 76 77 78 79 81 82 84 85 86 87 93 97 107 110 111 115 119 126 129 130 131 132 133 135 143 146 147 149 **S** UCHealth, Fort Collins, CO
Primary Contact: Frank May, Chief Executive Officer
CMO: Lisa Kettering, Chief Medical Officer
CIO: Mark Clark, Chief Information Officer
CHR: Soniya Fidler, MS, Chief Human Resources and Compliance Officer
CNO: Marie Timlin, R.N., Chief Nursing Officer
Web address: www.yvmc.org
Control: Other not–for–profit (including NFP Corporation) **Service:** General medical and surgical

Staffed Beds: 39 **Admissions:** 1335 **Census:** 10 **Outpatient Visits:** 63727 **Births:** 282 **Total Expense ($000):** 94650 **Payroll Expense ($000):** 28949 **Personnel:** 366

STERLING—Logan County

STERLING REGIONAL MEDCENTER (060076), 615 Fairhurst Street, Zip 80751–4523; tel. 970/522–0122, **A**1 3 10 20 **F**3 13 15 18 28 29 31 34 35 38 40 41 43 57 59 64 70 76 77 78 79 81 85 87 91 93 96 97 107 108 111 115 119 120 121 127 129 130 131 146 147 148 154 **S** Banner Health, Gilbert, AZ
Primary Contact: Hoyt Skabelund, Chief Executive Officer
CFO: Tiffany Weber, Chief Financial Officer
CMO: Jeff Bacon, D.O., Chief Medical Officer
CNO: Wade Alan Tyrrell RN Chief Nursing Officer
Web address: www.bannerhealth.com/Locations/Colorado/Sterling+Regional+MedCenter
Control: Other not–for–profit (including NFP Corporation) **Service:** General medical and surgical

Staffed Beds: 25 **Admissions:** 1028 **Census:** 8 **Births:** 209 **Total Expense ($000):** 45594 **Payroll Expense ($000):** 16507 **Personnel:** 260

THORNTON—Adams County

NORTH SUBURBAN MEDICAL CENTER (060065), 9191 Grant Street, Zip 80229–4341; tel. 303/451–7800, **A**1 3 10 **F**3 8 11 12 13 15 20 22 29 30 31 34 35 40 41 43 45 48 50 51 54 59 64 70 72 74 75 76 77 78 79 80 81 82 85 87 89 107 108 110 111 114 115 119 126 130 132 135 146 147 148 149 154 **S** HCA Healthcare, Nashville, TN
Primary Contact: Daphne G. David, President and Chief Executive Officer
CIO: Marty Hoesch, Director Information Systems
CHR: Dena Schmaedecke, Vice President Human Resources
CNO: Linnet Jung, Chief Nursing Officer
Web address: www.northsuburban.com
Control: Corporation, Investor–owned (for–profit) **Service:** General medical and surgical

Staffed Beds: 139 **Admissions:** 7669 **Census:** 74 **Outpatient Visits:** 72413 **Births:** 1087

CO

Hospital, Medicare Provider Number, Address, Telephone, Approval, Facility, and Physician Codes, Health Care System

★ American Hospital Association (AHA) membership ○ Healthcare Facilities Accreditation Program ⇑ Center for Improvement in Healthcare Quality Accreditation
☐ The Joint Commission accreditation ◇ DNV Healthcare Inc. accreditation △ Commission on Accreditation of Rehabilitation Facilities (CARF) accreditation

✠ **VIBRA HOSPITAL OF DENVER (062014)**, 8451 Pearl Street, Zip 80229–4804; tel. 303/288–3000, (Nonreporting) **A**1 10 **S** Vibra Healthcare, Mechanicsburg, PA
Primary Contact: Linda Tautz, Chief Executive Officer
CMO: John Buckley, M.D., President Medical Staff
CHR: Lorna Fulton, Director Human Resources
Web address: www.vhdenver.com
Control: Corporation, Investor–owned (for–profit) **Service:** Acute long–term care hospital

Staffed Beds: 71

TRINIDAD—Las Animas County

★ **MT. SAN RAFAEL HOSPITAL (061321)**, 410 Benedicta Avenue, Zip 81082–2093; tel. 719/846–9213, **A**10 18 **F**3 15 28 29 32 34 35 40 43 45 46 47 48 50 59 64 65 66 75 79 81 82 87 90 93 97 107 110 111 115 116 117 119 127 128 129 133 146 147 148 154
Primary Contact: John Tucker, Chief Executive Officer
CFO: David W Rollins, Chief Financial Officer
CIO: Michael Archuleta, Chief Information Technology Officer
CHR: Tammy Rogers, Director Human Resources
CNO: Mandy Shaiffer, Chief Nursing Officer
Web address: www.msrhc.org
Control: Other not–for–profit (including NFP Corporation) **Service:** General medical and surgical

Staffed Beds: 18 **Admissions:** 668 **Census:** 8 **Outpatient Visits:** 40497 **Births:** 0 **Total Expense ($000):** 29310 **Payroll Expense ($000):** 14245 **Personnel:** 213

VAIL—Eagle County

✠ **VAIL HEALTH (060096)**, 181 West Meadow Drive, Zip 81657–5242, Mailing Address: P.O. Box 40000, Zip 81658–7520; tel. 970/476–2451, **A**1 3 10 20 **F**3 11 13 15 18 28 29 31 34 35 36 37 40 43 50 51 54 57 59 64 68 70 72 75 76 77 78 79 81 82 85 86 87 93 107 108 110 111 115 116 117 119 120 121 123 129 130 131 135 141 142 144 146 147 148 149 150
Primary Contact: Doris Kirchner, President and Chief Executive Officer
CFO: Ted Sirotta, Chief Financial Officer
CMO: Barry Hammaker, M.D., Chief Medical Officer and Chief Clinical Officer
CIO: Brian Foster, Chief Information Officer
CHR: Rick Smith, Senior Vice President Human Resources and Chief Administrative Officer
CNO: Sheila Sherman, Vice President Patient Care Services
Web address: www.vvmc.com
Control: Other not–for–profit (including NFP Corporation) **Service:** General medical and surgical

Staffed Beds: 58 **Admissions:** 2165 **Census:** 16 **Outpatient Visits:** 124026 **Births:** 391

WALSENBURG—Huerfano County

★ **SPANISH PEAKS REGIONAL HEALTH CENTER (061316)**, 23500 US Highway 160, Zip 81089–9524; tel. 719/738–5100, (Total facility includes 120 beds in nursing home–type unit) **A**10 18 **F**6 7 15 18 26 27 28 29 32 34 35 40 43 45 50 57 59 64 65 66 67 69 79 81 82 83 93 96 97 107 110 115 119 127 132 133 134 135 143 146 147 148
Primary Contact: Kay L. Whitley, President and Chief Executive Officer
CFO: Lionel J. Montoya, Chief Financial Officer
CMO: Michael A. Moll, M.D., Chief Medical Officer and Chief of Staff
CHR: Tony Marostica, Chief Compliance and Human Resource Officer
CNO: Mary Cope, R.N., Chief Clinical Officer
Web address: www.sprhc.org
Control: Hospital district or authority, Government, nonfederal **Service:** General medical and surgical

Staffed Beds: 140 **Admissions:** 197 **Census:** 95 **Births:** 0 **Total Expense ($000):** 29027 **Payroll Expense ($000):** 15223 **Personnel:** 217

WESTMINSTER—Adams County

✠ **ST. ANTHONY NORTH HEALTH CAMPUS (060104)**, 14300 Orchard Parkway, Zip 80023–9206; tel. 720/627–0000, **A**1 2 3 10 **F**3 11 13 15 18 20 22 26 28 29 30 31 34 35 36 38 40 43 45 46 49 54 55 57 59 60 63 64 65 68 70 72 74 75 76 77 78 79 81 82 84 85 87 91 92 93 97 102 103 107 108 110 111 114 115 119 130 131 132 142 146 147 148 **S** Catholic Health Initiatives, Englewood, CO
Primary Contact: Kevin Jenkins, President and Chief Executive Officer
CFO: Alison Mizer, Chief Financial Officer
CHR: Robert Archibold, Director, Human Resources
CNO: Carol A Butler, R.N., MSN, VP Patient Care Services & Operations
Web address: www.stanthonynorth.org
Control: Church operated, Nongovernment, not–for–profit **Service:** General medical and surgical

Staffed Beds: 97 **Admissions:** 5584 **Census:** 50 **Outpatient Visits:** 76856 **Births:** 1177 **Total Expense ($000):** 138808 **Payroll Expense ($000):** 48439 **Personnel:** 932

WHEAT RIDGE—Jefferson County

✠ **LUTHERAN MEDICAL CENTER (060009)**, 8300 West 38th Avenue, Zip 80033–6005; tel. 303/425–4500, (Includes EXEMPLA WEST PINES, 3400 Lutheran Parkway, Wheat Ridge, CO, Zip 80033; tel. 303/467–4000) (Total facility includes 118 beds in nursing home–type unit) **A**1 2 3 10 **F**3 4 5 11 12 13 15 18 20 22 24 26 28 29 30 31 33 35 36 40 43 45 47 48 49 50 55 56 58 59 60 61 63 64 67 68 70 71 72 74 75 76 77 78 79 81 83 84 85 86 87 94 98 100 101 102 103 104 105 106 107 108 110 111 114 115 119 120 121 123 124 126 128 129 130 132 146 147 148 149 152 153 154 **P**6 **S** SCL Health, Broomfield, CO
Primary Contact: Grant Wicklund, President and Chief Executive Officer
CFO: Karen Scremin, Vice President Finance
CMO: Christina Johnson, M.D., Vice President and Chief Clinical and Quality Officer
CHR: Scott Day, Vice President Human Resources
CNO: Geraldine Towndrow, R.N., Senior Vice President Nursing
Web address: www.sclhealth.org/locations/lutheran–medical–center/
Control: Other not–for–profit (including NFP Corporation) **Service:** General medical and surgical

Staffed Beds: 518 **Admissions:** 15816 **Census:** 201 **Outpatient Visits:** 183104 **Births:** 2295 **Total Expense ($000):** 356706 **Payroll Expense ($000):** 127258 **Personnel:** 1684

WOODLAND PARK—Teller County

⇑ **PIKES PEAK REGIONAL HOSPITAL (061326)**, 16420 West Highway 24, Zip 80863; tel. 719/687–9999, **A**10 18 21 **F**3 15 29 30 34 40 41 43 45 50 57 59 64 65 68 75 77 79 80 81 85 87 93 97 107 110 111 114 119 129 131 133 146 148 **S** Steward Health Care System, LLC, Dallas, TX
Primary Contact: Kimberly Monjesky, Chief Executive Officer
CFO: Robin Ruff, Chief Financial Officer
CMO: Richard Malyszek, M.D., Chief of Staff
CHR: Arianne Randolph, Director Human Resources
CNO: Marsha Sensat, R.N., Chief Nursing Officer
Web address: www.pprmc.org
Control: Corporation, Investor–owned (for–profit) **Service:** General medical and surgical

Staffed Beds: 15 **Admissions:** 492 **Census:** 6 **Births:** 0

WRAY—Yuma County

★ **WRAY COMMUNITY DISTRICT HOSPITAL (061309)**, 1017 West 7th Street, Zip 80758–1420; tel. 970/332–4811, (Nonreporting) **A**3 10 18
Primary Contact: Jennie Sullivan, Chief Executive Officer
CMO: Monte Uyemura, M.D., Chief of Staff
Web address: www.wraycommunitydistricthospital.com/
Control: Hospital district or authority, Government, nonfederal **Service:** General medical and surgical

Staffed Beds: 15

YUMA—Yuma County

★ **YUMA DISTRICT HOSPITAL (061315)**, 1000 West 8th Avenue, Zip 80759–2641; tel. 970/848–5405, **A**10 18 **F**3 11 13 15 28 29 30 31 34 35 36 40 43 44 50 53 57 59 62 64 65 68 74 75 76 77 78 79 81 82 87 93 97 99 101 102 103 104 107 111 115 119 127 130 133 148
Primary Contact: Beth Saxton, R.N., Chief Executive Officer
CFO: Rick Korf, Chief Financial Officer
CMO: John Wolz, M.D., Chief Medical Staff
CIO: Jason Hawley, Director of Information Services and Security
CHR: Gini Adams, Director Employee and Public Relations
Web address: www.yumahospital.org
Control: Hospital district or authority, Government, nonfederal **Service:** General medical and surgical

Staffed Beds: 12 **Admissions:** 160 **Census:** 1

CO

CONNECTICUT

BRANFORD—New Haven County

☐ **THE CONNECTICUT HOSPICE (070038)**, 100 Double Beach Road, Zip 06405–4909; tel. 203/315–7500, (Nonreporting) **A**1 5 10
Primary Contact: Ronny Knight, President and Chief Executive Officer
Web address: www.hospice.com
Control: Other not–for–profit (including NFP Corporation) **Service:** Other specialty treatment

Staffed Beds: 52

BRIDGEPORT—Fairfield County

⊞ **BRIDGEPORT HOSPITAL (070010)**, 267 Grant Street, Zip 06610–2805, Mailing Address: P.O. Box 5000, Zip 06610–0120; tel. 203/384–3000, **A**1 2 3 5 8 10 **F**3 5 6 8 11 12 13 14 15 16 17 18 20 22 24 26 28 29 30 31 32 34 35 36 37 38 39 40 41 43 44 45 46 47 48 49 50 51 52 54 55 56 57 58 59 61 64 65 66 68 70 74 75 76 78 79 80 81 82 84 85 86 87 93 96 97 98 101 102 103 104 107 108 110 111 114 115 116 117 118 119 120 121 123 124 126 129 130 131 132 134 144 145 146 147 148 149 153 154 **P**3 5 **S** Yale New Haven Health, New Haven, CT
Primary Contact: Michael Ivy, MD, Interim Chief Executive Officer
CFO: Patrick McCabe, Senior Vice President Finance and Chief Financial Officer
CMO: Michael Ivy, M.D., Senior Vice President for Medical Affairs and Chief Medical Officer
CIO: Daniel Barchi, Senior Vice President, Technical Services and Chief Information Officer
CHR: Melissa Turner, Senior Vice President Human Resources
CNO: MaryEllen Kosturko, R.N., Senior Vice President Patient Care Operations and Chief Nursing Officer
Web address: www.bridgeporthospital.org
Control: Other not–for–profit (including NFP Corporation) **Service:** General medical and surgical

Staffed Beds: 358 **Admissions:** 19119 **Census:** 281 **Outpatient Visits:** 314565 **Births:** 2205 **Total Expense ($000):** 511566 **Payroll Expense ($000):** 166862 **Personnel:** 2532

☐ **SOUTHWEST CONNECTICUT MENTAL HEALTH SYSTEM (074012)**, 1635 Central Avenue, Zip 06610–2717; tel. 203/551–7400, (Nonreporting) **A**1 10 **S** Connecticut Department of Mental Health and Addiction Services, Hartford, CT
Primary Contact: Alicia Feller, Chief Executive Officer
COO: Cindy Perjon, Associate Director
CFO: Linda Woznikaitis, Chief Financial Officer
CMO: Sandra Gomez–Luna, Medical Director
CIO: Bernetta Witcher–Boateng, Ph.D., Director Quality Improvement Services and Compliance
CHR: Nancy Derman, Director Human Resources
Web address: www.ct.gov/dmhas/cwp/view.asp?a=2946&q=378936
Control: State, Government, nonfederal **Service:** Psychiatric

Staffed Beds: 62

⊞ **ST. VINCENT'S MEDICAL CENTER (070028)**, 2800 Main Street, Zip 06606–4292; tel. 203/576–6000, (Includes ST. VINCENT'S BEHAVIORAL HEALTH, 47 Long Lots Road, Westport, CT, Zip 06880–3800; tel. 203/221–8813) **A**1 2 3 5 10 **F**3 4 5 8 11 12 13 15 17 18 20 22 24 26 28 29 30 31 34 35 36 38 40 43 44 45 46 47 48 49 50 51 54 55 56 57 58 59 61 63 64 65 68 70 71 72 73 74 75 76 77 78 79 80 81 82 84 85 86 87 90 93 96 97 98 99 100 101 102 104 105 107 108 110 111 114 115 116 117 118 119 120 121 122 123 124 126 130 132 134 135 143 144 145 146 147 148 149 150 153 154 **P**3 8 **S** Ascension Healthcare, Saint Louis, MO
Primary Contact: Dawn Rudolph, President and Chief Executive Officer
CFO: Stephen Franko, Senior Vice President and Chief Financial Officer
CMO: Dan Gottschall, Senior Vice President and Chief Clinical Officer
CIO: Rick McCarthy, Chief Information Officer
CNO: Dale G Danowski, R.N., Senior Vice President, Chief Nursing Officer
Web address: www.stvincents.org
Control: Other not–for–profit (including NFP Corporation) **Service:** General medical and surgical

Staffed Beds: 343 **Admissions:** 14769 **Census:** 231 **Outpatient Visits:** 259529 **Births:** 873 **Total Expense ($000):** 519431 **Payroll Expense ($000):** 184489 **Personnel:** 2508

BRISTOL—Hartford County

⊞ **BRISTOL HOSPITAL (070029)**, 41 Brewster Road, Zip 06010–5161, Mailing Address: P.O. Box 977, Zip 06011–0977; tel. 860/585–3000, (Nonreporting) **A**1 2 5 10
Primary Contact: Kurt A. Barwis, FACHE, President and Chief Executive Officer
COO: Marc D Edelman, Vice President Operations
CFO: Peter Freytag, Senior Vice President Finance and Chief Financial Officer
CMO: Leonard Banco, M.D., Senior Vice President and Chief Medical Officer
CIO: David Rackliffe, Assistant Vice President Information Services
CHR: Jeanine Reckdenwald, Vice President Human Resources and Support Services
Web address: www.bristolhospital.org
Control: Other not–for–profit (including NFP Corporation) **Service:** General medical and surgical

Staffed Beds: 110

DANBURY—Fairfield County

⊞ **DANBURY HOSPITAL (070033)**, 24 Hospital Avenue, Zip 06810–6099; tel. 203/739–7000, (Includes NEW MILFORD HOSPITAL, 21 Elm Street, New Milford, CT, Zip 06776–2993; tel. 860/355–2611; John M Murphy, M.D., President and Chief Executive Officer, Western Connecticut Health Network) **A**1 2 3 5 8 10 **F**3 5 8 9 12 13 14 15 17 18 20 22 24 26 28 29 30 31 32 34 35 36 37 38 39 40 43 44 45 46 47 49 50 51 54 55 56 57 58 59 61 64 65 66 68 70 72 74 75 76 77 78 79 81 82 83 84 85 86 87 89 90 93 96 97 98 100 101 102 104 105 106 107 108 110 111 115 117 119 120 121 123 124 126 129 130 131 132 134 135 144 145 146 147 148 149 152 153 154 **P**3 8 **S** Western Connecticut Health Network, Danbury, CT
Primary Contact: John M. Murphy, M.D., President
COO: Sharon Adams, Chief Operating Officer
CFO: Steven Rosenberg, Chief Financial Officer
CMO: Patricia Tietjen, M.D., Vice President, Medical Affairs
CIO: Kathleen DeMatteo, Chief Information Officer
CHR: Cathy Frierson, Chief Human Resource Officer
CNO: Sharon Adams, Chief Nursing Officer
Web address: www.danburyhospital.org
Control: Other not–for–profit (including NFP Corporation) **Service:** General medical and surgical

Staffed Beds: 265 **Admissions:** 18656 **Census:** 251 **Outpatient Visits:** 422254 **Births:** 2041 **Total Expense ($000):** 618698 **Payroll Expense ($000):** 216860 **Personnel:** 2508

DERBY—New Haven County

⊞ **GRIFFIN HOSPITAL (070031)**, 130 Division Street, Zip 06418–1326; tel. 203/735–7421, **A**1 2 3 5 10 **F**3 5 12 13 15 18 28 29 30 34 35 36 38 40 45 49 50 51 53 56 57 58 59 64 65 66 68 70 71 74 75 76 77 78 79 81 82 84 85 86 87 92 93 94 96 97 98 100 101 102 104 107 108 110 111 115 117 118 119 120 121 123 124 126 129 130 132 134 135 144 146 147 148 149 152 153 154 **P**8
Primary Contact: Patrick Charmel, President and Chief Executive Officer
CMO: Kenneth V Schwartz, M.D., Medical Director
CIO: George Tomas, Director Information Services
CHR: Steve Mordecai, Director Human Resources
CNO: Barbara J Stumpo, R.N., Vice President Patient Care Services
Web address: www.griffinhealth.org
Control: Other not–for–profit (including NFP Corporation) **Service:** General medical and surgical

Staffed Beds: 111 **Admissions:** 6724 **Census:** 81 **Outpatient Visits:** 187795 **Births:** 504 **Total Expense ($000):** 162390 **Payroll Expense ($000):** 68812 **Personnel:** 983

CT

Hospital, Medicare Provider Number, Address, Telephone, Approval, Facility, and Physician Codes, Health Care System

★ American Hospital Association (AHA) membership ○ Healthcare Facilities Accreditation Program ⇑ Center for Improvement in Healthcare Quality Accreditation
☐ The Joint Commission accreditation ◇ DNV Healthcare Inc. accreditation △ Commission on Accreditation of Rehabilitation Facilities (CARF) accreditation

FARMINGTON—Hartford County

☒ **UCONN, JOHN DEMPSEY HOSPITAL (070036)**, 263 Farmington Avenue, Zip 06032–1941; tel. 860/679–2000, **A**1 2 3 5 8 10 12 13 19 **F**3 5 6 7 8 9 11 12 13 15 18 20 22 24 26 29 30 31 34 35 36 37 38 39 40 44 45 46 47 48 49 50 51 52 53 54 55 56 57 58 59 60 61 63 64 65 66 68 70 74 75 76 77 78 79 81 82 83 84 85 86 87 91 92 93 94 97 98 100 101 102 103 104 105 107 108 110 111 114 115 117 118 119 120 121 123 124 126 127 129 130 131 132 134 135 143 144 145 146 147 148 149 152 153 154 **P**6
Primary Contact: Andrew Agwunobi, M.D., Chief Executive Officer
COO: Kevin Larsen, Associate Vice President, Business and Ancillary Services
CFO: Jeffrey Geoghegan, Chief Financial Officer
CMO: Richard Simon, M.D., Chief of Staff
CIO: Jonathan Carroll, Chief Information Officer
CHR: Carolle Andrews, Interim Human Resources Officer
CNO: Ann Marie Capo, R.N., Chief Nursing Officer
Web address: www.uchc.edu
Control: State, Government, nonfederal **Service**: General medical and surgical

Staffed Beds: 176 **Admissions**: 8674 **Census**: 102 **Outpatient Visits**: 317568 **Births**: 571 **Total Expense ($000)**: 426007 **Payroll Expense ($000)**: 117423 **Personnel**: 1198

GREENWICH—Fairfield County

☒ **GREENWICH HOSPITAL (070018)**, 5 Perryridge Road, Zip 06830–4697; tel. 203/863–3000, **A**1 2 3 5 8 10 **F**3 5 11 12 13 14 15 18 20 22 26 28 29 30 31 32 34 35 36 37 38 39 40 41 44 45 46 47 48 49 50 51 52 53 54 55 56 57 58 59 61 63 64 65 66 68 70 72 74 75 76 78 79 80 81 82 84 85 86 87 89 91 93 96 97 100 101 104 107 108 110 111 114 115 116 117 118 119 120 121 123 124 126 129 130 131 132 134 135 146 147 148 149 **P**2 3 5 **S** Yale New Haven Health, New Haven, CT
Primary Contact: Norman G. Roth, President
COO: Diane Kelly, Chief Operating Officer
CFO: Eugene Colucci, Vice President Finance
CMO: A Michael Marino, M.D., Senior Vice President Medical Administration
Web address: www.greenhosp.org
Control: Other not–for–profit (including NFP Corporation) **Service**: General medical and surgical

Staffed Beds: 174 **Admissions**: 10704 **Census**: 139 **Outpatient Visits**: 279551 **Births**: 2682 **Total Expense ($000)**: 363265 **Payroll Expense ($000)**: 123391 **Personnel**: 1727

HARTFORD—Hartford County

☒ **CONNECTICUT CHILDREN'S MEDICAL CENTER (073300)**, 282 Washington Street, Zip 06106–3322; tel. 860/545–9000, **A**1 3 5 10 **F**3 7 8 11 12 19 21 23 27 29 30 31 32 34 35 36 39 40 41 43 48 49 50 51 54 55 57 58 59 60 61 63 64 65 68 72 74 75 78 79 81 82 84 85 86 87 88 89 91 92 93 97 107 111 114 115 119 126 129 130 131 132 134 146 149 150 154
Primary Contact: James E. Shmerling, President and Chief Executive Officer
COO: Gil Peri, President and Chief Operating Officer
CFO: Gerald J Boisvert, Vice President and Chief Financial Officer
CMO: Paul Dworkin, M.D., Physician–in–Chief
CIO: Kelly R Styles, Vice President and Chief Information Officer
CHR: Elizabeth Rudden, Vice President Human Resources
Web address: www.connecticutchildrens.org/
Control: Other not–for–profit (including NFP Corporation) **Service**: Children's general medical and surgical

Staffed Beds: 186 **Admissions**: 6002 **Census**: 116 **Outpatient Visits**: 213526 **Births**: 0 **Total Expense ($000)**: 313992 **Payroll Expense ($000)**: 133195 **Personnel**: 2281

☒ **HARTFORD HOSPITAL (070025)**, 80 Seymour Street, Zip 06102–8000, Mailing Address: P.O. Box 5037, Zip 06102–5037; tel. 860/545–5000, (Includes INSTITUTE OF LIVING, 400 Washington Street, Hartford, CT, Zip 06106–3392; tel. 860/545–7000) (Total facility includes 104 beds in nursing home–type unit) **A**1 2 3 5 10 19 **F**2 5 6 7 8 9 10 11 12 13 15 17 18 20 22 24 26 28 29 30 31 34 35 36 37 38 39 40 43 44 45 46 47 48 49 50 51 52 53 54 55 56 57 58 59 60 61 63 64 65 66 68 70 71 74 75 76 77 78 79 80 81 82 83 84 85 86 87 91 92 93 94 95 96 97 98 99 100 101 102 103 104 105 106 107 108 110 111 114 115 116 117 118 119 120 121 123 124 125 126 128 129 130 131 132 133 134 135 137 138 139 141 143 145 146 147 148 149 150 152 153 154 **P**6 **S** Hartford HealthCare, Hartford, CT
Primary Contact: Bimal Patel, President
CMO: Stuart Markowitz, M.D., Chief Medical Officer
CIO: Stephan O'Neill, Vice President Information Services
CHR: Richard McAloon, Vice President Human Resources
Web address: www.harthosp.org
Control: Other not–for–profit (including NFP Corporation) **Service**: General medical and surgical

Staffed Beds: 900 **Admissions**: 34598 **Census**: 720 **Outpatient Visits**: 454531 **Births**: 3720 **Total Expense ($000)**: 1193729 **Payroll Expense ($000)**: 449112 **Personnel**: 5906

☒ **MOUNT SINAI REHABILITATION HOSPITAL (073025)**, 490 Blue Hills Avenue, Zip 06112–1513; tel. 860/714–3500, **A**1 10 **F**29 30 34 54 58 59 64 68 74 75 82 91 92 93 94 95 96 130 131 132 **S** Trinity Health, Livonia, MI
Primary Contact: Robert J. Krug, M.D., Chief Executive Officer
CFO: David Bittner, Chief Financial Officer
Web address: www.stfranciscare.org
Control: Other not–for–profit (including NFP Corporation) **Service**: Rehabilitation

Staffed Beds: 32 **Admissions**: 815 **Census**: 31 **Outpatient Visits**: 45947 **Births**: 0 **Total Expense ($000)**: 26178 **Payroll Expense ($000)**: 16811 **Personnel**: 217

☒ **SAINT FRANCIS HOSPITAL AND MEDICAL CENTER (070002)**, 114 Woodland Street, Zip 06105–1208; tel. 860/714–4000, **A**1 2 3 5 8 10 19 **F**3 8 11 12 13 15 17 18 20 22 24 26 28 29 30 31 34 35 36 38 39 40 43 45 46 47 48 49 50 53 54 55 56 57 58 59 61 64 65 66 67 68 70 72 74 75 76 77 78 79 81 82 84 85 87 91 92 93 94 95 96 97 98 99 100 101 102 103 104 107 108 110 111 115 117 118 119 120 121 123 124 126 129 130 131 132 135 146 147 148 150 **P**8 **S** Trinity Health, Livonia, MI
Primary Contact: John F. Rodis, M.D., President
CFO: Jennifer S. Schneider, Vice President of Finance
CMO: Michael Grey, M.D., Interim Chief Medical Officer
CIO: Linda L. Shanley, Vice President, Chief Information Officer
CHR: Dennis W. Sparks, Vice President of Human Resources
Web address: www.saintfranciscare.com
Control: Church operated, Nongovernment, not–for–profit **Service**: General medical and surgical

Staffed Beds: 456 **Admissions**: 29739 **Census**: 388 **Outpatient Visits**: 263886 **Births**: 2774 **Total Expense ($000)**: 775070 **Payroll Expense ($000)**: 245405 **Personnel**: 4944

MANCHESTER—Hartford County

☐ **MANCHESTER MEMORIAL HOSPITAL (070027)**, 71 Haynes Street, Zip 06040–4188; tel. 860/646–1222, (Nonreporting) **A**1 2 3 5 10 12 13 **S** Prospect Medical Holdings, Los Angeles, CA
Primary Contact: Michael F. Collins, Chief Executive Officer
CFO: Michael D. Veillette, Senior Vice President and Chief Financial Officer
CMO: Joel R Reich, M.D., Senior Vice President Medical Affairs
CIO: Richard Daigle, Chief Information Officer
CHR: Natalie Cook, Administrative Director of Human Resources
CNO: Mary Powers, R.N., MSN, Senior Vice President and Chief Nursing Officer
Web address: www.echn.org
Control: Other not–for–profit (including NFP Corporation) **Service**: General medical and surgical

Staffed Beds: 156

MANSFIELD CENTER—Tolland County

☒ **NATCHAUG HOSPITAL (074008)**, 189 Storrs Road, Zip 06250–1683; tel. 860/456–1311, **A**1 10 **F**3 4 5 50 53 75 77 98 99 100 101 104 105 130 132 135 149 151 152 153 **S** Hartford HealthCare, Hartford, CT
Primary Contact: Patricia Rehmer, MSN, FACHE, President
COO: David Klein, Ph.D., Vice President Operations, Behavioral Health Network
CFO: Paul V Maloney, Vice President Finance, Behavioral Health Network
CMO: Deborah Weidner, Medical Director
CIO: Mark Olson, Interim Chief Information Officer, Behavioral Health Network
CHR: Janet Keown, Vice President Human Resources, Behavioral Health Network
CNO: Justin Sleeper, Vice President Clinical Operations, Behavioral Health Network
Web address: www.natchaug.org
Control: Other not–for–profit (including NFP Corporation) **Service**: Psychiatric

Staffed Beds: 57 **Admissions**: 2000 **Census**: 54 **Outpatient Visits**: 0 **Births**: 0 **Personnel**: 350

MERIDEN—New Haven County

☒ **MIDSTATE MEDICAL CENTER (070017)**, 435 Lewis Avenue, Zip 06451–2101; tel. 203/694–8200, **A**1 2 10 **F**3 11 12 13 15 18 26 28 29 30 31 34 35 36 38 39 40 44 45 46 47 48 49 50 51 53 54 56 57 59 61 63 64 68 70 74 75 76 78 79 81 82 84 85 86 87 97 102 107 108 110 111 114 115 117 118 119 120 121 123 124 126 129 130 131 132 144 145 146 147 148 149 154 **P**6 **S** Hartford HealthCare, Hartford, CT
Primary Contact: Gary C. Havican, President
CMO: Kenneth R Kurz, M.D., Chief of Staff
CIO: Jennifer Comerford, Manager Information Services
CHR: Ken Cesca, Vice President Human Resources
Web address: www.midstatemedical.org
Control: Other not–for–profit (including NFP Corporation) **Service**: General medical and surgical

Staffed Beds: 85 **Admissions**: 7346 **Census**: 82 **Outpatient Visits**: 151028 **Births**: 816 **Total Expense ($000)**: 219365 **Payroll Expense ($000)**: 64709 **Personnel**: 910

CT

Many Facility Codes have changed. Please refer to the AHA Guide Code Chart.

MIDDLETOWN—Middlesex County

☐ **ALBERT J. SOLNIT PSYCHIATRIC CENTER – SOUTH CAMPUS**, 915 River Road, Zip 06457–3921, Mailing Address: P.O. Box 2792, Zip 06457–9292; tel. 860/704–4000, **A**1 3 5 **F**30 32 38 53 59 65 68 75 77 86 91 98 99 100 106 130 132 146 149 154
Primary Contact: Michelle Sarofin, Superintendent
CFO: Connie Tessarzik, Business Manager
CMO: Lesley Siegel, M.D., Medical Director
CIO: Andrew J A Kass, M.D., Assistant Superintendent
Web address: www.ct.gov/
Control: State, Government, nonfederal **Service**: Children's hospital psychiatric

Staffed Beds: 50 **Admissions:** 122 **Census:** 40 **Outpatient Visits:** 0 **Births:** 0 **Total Expense ($000):** 38440 **Payroll Expense ($000):** 19502 **Personnel:** 281

☐ **CONNECTICUT VALLEY HOSPITAL (074003)**, 1000 Silver Street, Zip 06457–3947; tel. 860/262–5000, (Includes WHITING FORENSIC HOSPITAL, 70 O'Brien Drive, Middletown, CT, Zip 6457, Mailing Address: Box 70, Zip 06457–3942, tel. 860/262–5400; Michael A Norko, M.D., Acting Chief Executive Officer) **A**1 3 5 10 **F**3 4 29 30 34 36 39 50 53 56 57 58 59 60 61 65 68 74 75 77 82 84 86 87 90 91 94 97 98 100 101 103 106 119 130 132 135 146 148 149 **S** Connecticut Department of Mental Health and Addiction Services, Hartford, CT
Primary Contact: Helene M. Vartelas, MSN, Chief Executive Officer
COO: John D'Eramo, Chief Operating Officer
CFO: Cindy Butterfield, Director, Fiscal and Administrative Services
CMO: Thomas Pisano, M.D., Chief Professional Services
CIO: Kathryn Connelly, Manager Information Technology
CHR: Cheryl Thompson, Facility Director Human Resources
CNO: Jerilynn Lamb–Pagone, Nurse Executive
Web address: www.ct.gov/dmhas/cwp/view.asp?a=3519&q=416778
Control: State, Government, nonfederal **Service**: Psychiatric

Staffed Beds: 596 **Admissions:** 3466 **Census:** 564 **Outpatient Visits:** 0 **Births:** 0 **Total Expense ($000):** 288649 **Payroll Expense ($000):** 147789 **Personnel:** 1548

✠ **MIDDLESEX HOSPITAL (070020)**, 28 Crescent Street, Zip 06457–3650; tel. 860/358–6000, **A**1 2 3 5 10 **F**3 5 7 8 12 13 15 18 20 22 24 28 29 30 31 32 34 35 36 38 40 45 46 47 49 50 51 54 55 57 58 59 60 62 63 64 65 68 70 74 75 76 77 78 79 81 83 84 85 86 87 89 92 93 94 97 98 100 101 102 104 105 107 108 110 111 114 115 116 117 118 119 120 121 123 124 126 129 130 131 132 134 135 143 144 145 146 147 148 149 152 153 154 **P**6
Primary Contact: Vincent G. Capece Jr, President and Chief Executive Officer
CFO: Susan Martin, Vice President Finance
CMO: Arthur V McDowell, M.D., III Vice President Clinical Affairs
CIO: Evan Jackson, Vice President Information Technology
CHR: Gregory Nokes, Vice President Human Resources
CNO: Jacquelyn Calamari, MSN, MS, Chief Nursing Officer and Vice President, Patient Care Services
Web address: www.middlesexhospital.org
Control: Other not–for–profit (including NFP Corporation) **Service**: General medical and surgical

Staffed Beds: 233 **Admissions:** 12864 **Census:** 147 **Outpatient Visits:** 597088 **Births:** 1090 **Total Expense ($000):** 375317 **Payroll Expense ($000):** 178691 **Personnel:** 1856

WHITING FORENSIC HOSPITAL See Connecticut Valley Hospital, Middletown

MILFORD—New Haven County

✠ **MILFORD HOSPITAL (070019)**, 300 Seaside Avenue, Zip 06460–4603; tel. 203/876–4000, (Nonreporting) **A**1 10
Primary Contact: Lloyd Friedman, M.D., Interim President and Chief Operating Officer
COO: Lloyd Friedman, M.D., Vice President Medical Affairs and Chief Operating Officer
CFO: Laura Smith, Vice President Finance and Chief Financial Officer
CMO: Lloyd Friedman, M.D., Vice President Medical Affairs and Chief Operating Officer
CIO: Brian Evans, Chief Information Officer
CHR: Jeffrey Komornik, Director Human Resources
CNO: Joan DeMaio, Vice President Nursing
Web address: www.milfordhospital.org
Control: Other not–for–profit (including NFP Corporation) **Service**: General medical and surgical

Staffed Beds: 41

NEW BRITAIN—Hartford County

✠ △ **HOSPITAL FOR SPECIAL CARE (072004)**, 2150 Corbin Avenue, Zip 06053–2298; tel. 860/223–2761, (Nonreporting) **A**1 3 5 7 10
Primary Contact: Lynn Ricci, President and Chief Executive Officer
CFO: Laurie A Whelan, Senior Vice President Finance and Chief Financial Officer
CMO: J. Kevin Shushtari, M.D., Chief Medical Officer
CIO: Stan Jankowski, Vice President and Chief Information Officer
CHR: Judi Trczinski, Vice President and Chief Human Resources Officer
Web address: www.hfsc.org
Control: Other not–for–profit (including NFP Corporation) **Service**: Acute long–term care hospital

Staffed Beds: 228

✠ **THE HOSPITAL OF CENTRAL CONNECTICUT (070035)**, 100 Grand Street, Zip 06052–2017, Mailing Address: P.O. Box 100, Zip 06052–2017; tel. 860/224–5011, (Includes BRADLEY MEMORIAL, 81 Meriden Avenue, Southington, CT, Zip 06489–3297; tel. 860/276–5000; NEW BRITAIN GENERAL, 100 Grand Street, New Britain, CT, Zip 06052–2017, Mailing Address: P.O. Box 100, Zip 06050–0100, tel. 860/224–5011) **A**1 2 3 5 10 **F**3 11 12 13 15 18 20 22 26 28 29 30 31 34 35 38 40 44 45 49 50 51 53 54 57 58 59 60 61 64 65 66 68 70 72 74 75 76 77 78 79 81 84 85 86 87 89 93 97 98 100 101 102 104 107 108 110 111 114 115 117 118 119 120 121 123 124 126 129 130 132 135 144 146 147 148 149 153 154 **P**6 **S** Hartford HealthCare, Hartford, CT
Primary Contact: Gary C. Havican, President
CFO: Brian Rogoz, Vice President Finance and Treasurer
CIO: Frank Pinto, Chief Information Officer
CHR: Elizabeth A Lynch, Vice President Human Resources
Web address: www.thocc.org
Control: Other not–for–profit (including NFP Corporation) **Service**: General medical and surgical

Staffed Beds: 173 **Admissions:** 13597 **Census:** 166 **Outpatient Visits:** 442905 **Births:** 1581 **Total Expense ($000):** 364037 **Payroll Expense ($000):** 137998 **Personnel:** 1683

NEW CANAAN—Fairfield County

✠ **SILVER HILL HOSPITAL (074014)**, 208 Valley Road, Zip 06840–3899; tel. 203/966–3561, (Nonreporting) **A**1 10
Primary Contact: John Santopietro, M.D., President and Medical Director
COO: Elizabeth Moore, Chief Operating Officer
CFO: Ruurd Leegstra, Chief Financial Officer
CMO: John Santopietro, M.D., President and Medical Director
CIO: Maria Klinga, Director Management Information Systems
CHR: Rich Juliana, Director Human Resources
Web address: www.silverhillhospital.org
Control: Other not–for–profit (including NFP Corporation) **Service**: Psychiatric

Staffed Beds: 60

NEW HAVEN—New Haven County

☐ **CONNECTICUT MENTAL HEALTH CENTER (074011)**, 34 Park Street, Zip 06519–1109, Mailing Address: P.O. Box 1842, Zip 06508–1842; tel. 203/974–7144, (Nonreporting) **A**1 3 5 10 **S** Connecticut Department of Mental Health and Addiction Services, Hartford, CT
Primary Contact: Michael Sernyak, M.D., Director
COO: Robert Cole, Chief Operating Officer
CFO: Robert Cole, Chief Operating Officer
CMO: Jeanne Steines, D.O., Medical Director
CIO: Paul Moore, Chief Information Officer
CHR: Carolyn Wallace, Director Human Resources
Web address: www.ct.gov/dmhas/cwp/view.asp?a=2906&q=334596
Control: State, Government, nonfederal **Service**: Psychiatric

Staffed Beds: 32

HOSPITAL OF SAINT RAPHAEL See Yale–New Haven Hospital–Saint Raphael Campus

CT

Hospital, Medicare Provider Number, Address, Telephone, Approval, Facility, and Physician Codes, Health Care System

★ American Hospital Association (AHA) membership
☐ The Joint Commission accreditation
◯ Healthcare Facilities Accreditation Program
◇ DNV Healthcare Inc. accreditation
⇑ Center for Improvement in Healthcare Quality Accreditation
△ Commission on Accreditation of Rehabilitation Facilities (CARF) accreditation

⊞ **YALE–NEW HAVEN HOSPITAL (070022)**, 20 York Street, Zip 06510–3202; tel. 203/688–4242, (Includes YALE–NEW HAVEN CHILDREN'S HOSPITAL, 1 Park Street, New Haven, CT, Zip 06504–8901; tel. 203/688–4242; Cynthia Sparer, Senior Vice President and Executive Director Women's & Children; YALE–NEW HAVEN HOSPITAL–SAINT RAPHAEL CAMPUS, 1450 Chapel Street, New Haven, CT, Zip 06511–4405; tel. 203/789–3000; Richard D'Aquila, President; YALE–NEW HAVEN PSYCHIATRIC HOSPITAL, 184 Liberty Street, New Haven, CT, Zip 06519–1625; tel. 203/688–9704; Mark Sevilla, Executive Director) **A**1 2 3 5 8 10 **F**3 5 6 8 9 10 11 12 13 14 15 17 18 19 20 21 22 23 24 25 26 27 28 29 30 31 32 34 35 36 37 38 39 40 41 43 44 45 46 47 48 49 50 51 52 53 54 55 56 57 58 59 61 64 65 66 70 72 73 74 75 76 77 78 79 80 81 82 84 85 86 87 88 89 90 91 92 93 94 96 97 98 99 100 101 102 103 104 105 107 108 109 110 111 112 114 115 116 117 118 119 120 121 123 124 126 129 130 131 132 134 135 136 137 138 139 141 142 143 144 145 146 147 148 149 150 153 154 **P**2 3 5 6 **S** Yale New Haven Health, New Haven, CT
Primary Contact: Marna P. Borgstrom, Chief Executive Officer
CFO: Vincent Tammaro, Chief Financial Officer
CMO: Thomas Balcezak, M.D., Senior Vice President Medical Affairs and Chief Medical Officer
CIO: Lisa Stump, Interim Chief Information Officer
CHR: Kevin A Myatt, Senior Vice President Human Resources
CNO: Patricia Sue Fitzsimons, R.N., Ph.D., Senior Vice President Patient Services
Web address: www.ynhh.org
Control: Other not–for–profit (including NFP Corporation) **Service**: General medical and surgical

> **Staffed Beds:** 1389 **Admissions:** 75868 **Census:** 1214 **Outpatient Visits:** 1361193 **Births:** 5685 **Total Expense ($000):** 2630582 **Payroll Expense ($000):** 861867 **Personnel:** 12117

NEW LONDON—New London County

⊞ △ **LAWRENCE + MEMORIAL HOSPITAL (070007)**, 365 Montauk Avenue, Zip 06320–4769; tel. 860/442–0711, **A**1 2 3 7 10 **F**3 11 13 15 17 18 19 20 22 26 28 29 30 31 34 35 38 39 40 41 44 46 49 50 51 54 55 57 59 60 63 64 65 68 70 72 74 75 76 77 78 79 81 82 84 85 86 87 89 90 91 92 93 96 98 99 100 101 102 104 107 108 110 111 114 115 116 117 118 119 120 121 123 124 126 129 130 131 132 146 147 148 149 153 **P**3 5 **S** Yale New Haven Health, New Haven, CT
Primary Contact: Patrick Green, FACHE, President and Chief Executive Officer
CFO: Seth Van Essendelft, Vice President and Chief Financial Officer
CMO: Oliver Mayorga, M.D., Chief Medical Officer
CIO: Kimberly Kalajainen, Vice President Operations and Chief Information Officer
CHR: Donna Epps, Vice President and Chief Human Resources Officer
CNO: Caren Lewis, R.N., Chief Nursing Officer
Web address: www.lmhospital.org
Control: Other not–for–profit (including NFP Corporation) **Service**: General medical and surgical

> **Staffed Beds:** 251 **Admissions:** 13379 **Census:** 165 **Outpatient Visits:** 312561 **Births:** 1390 **Total Expense ($000):** 331031 **Payroll Expense ($000):** 129895 **Personnel:** 1370

NORWALK—Fairfield County

⊞ **NORWALK HOSPITAL (070034)**, 34 Maple Street, Zip 06850–3894; tel. 203/852–2000, **A**1 2 3 5 8 10 **F**3 5 7 8 11 12 13 15 17 18 20 22 26 28 29 30 31 34 35 36 39 40 43 44 46 49 50 51 54 55 57 58 59 64 66 68 70 72 74 75 76 77 78 79 80 81 82 84 85 87 89 93 96 97 98 100 101 102 103 104 105 106 107 108 110 111 114 115 117 118 119 120 121 123 124 126 129 130 131 132 135 145 146 148 149 152 153 154 **P**3 8 **S** Western Connecticut Health Network, Danbury, CT
Primary Contact: Michael Daglio, President
CFO: Michael Kruzick, Acting Chief Financial Officer
CMO: Michael Marks, M.D., Chief of Staff
CHR: Anthony Aceto, Vice President Human Resources
Web address: www.norwalkhospital.org
Control: Other not–for–profit (including NFP Corporation) **Service**: General medical and surgical

> **Staffed Beds:** 150 **Admissions:** 11741 **Census:** 135 **Outpatient Visits:** 240153 **Births:** 1504 **Total Expense ($000):** 360762 **Payroll Expense ($000):** 134236 **Personnel:** 1331

NORWICH—New London County

⊞ **THE WILLIAM W. BACKUS HOSPITAL (070024)**, 326 Washington Street, Zip 06360–2740; tel. 860/889–8331, **A**1 2 3 5 10 **F**3 9 11 12 13 15 18 20 26 28 29 30 31 34 35 36 37 40 43 45 46 49 50 51 54 57 58 59 61 63 64 65 70 71 74 75 76 78 79 81 82 84 85 86 87 89 92 93 97 98 100 101 102 104 105 107 108 110 111 114 115 116 117 118 119 120 121 126 130 132 134 135 144 145 146 147 148 149 153 154 **P**6 **S** Hartford HealthCare, Hartford, CT
Primary Contact: Donna Handley, President
COO: Carolyn Trantalis, R.N., MSN, Regional Vice President, Clinical Services and Operations
CFO: Anthony Mastroianni, Regional Vice President Finance
CMO: Robert Sidman, M.D., Regional Vice President, Medical Affairs
CIO: Angie Mathieu, System Director Information Technology and Regional Chief Information Officer
CHR: Karen James, Regional Director, Human Resources
CNO: Carolyn Trantalis, R.N., MSN, Regional Vice President, Clinical Services and Operations
Web address: www.backushospital.org
Control: Other not–for–profit (including NFP Corporation) **Service**: General medical and surgical

> **Staffed Beds:** 184 **Admissions:** 9341 **Census:** 121 **Outpatient Visits:** 506939 **Births:** 945 **Total Expense ($000):** 281671 **Payroll Expense ($000):** 108962 **Personnel:** 1261

PUTNAM—Windham County

☐ **DAY KIMBALL HOSPITAL (070003)**, 320 Pomfret Street, Zip 06260–1836; tel. 860/928–6541, **A**1 2 5 10 **F**3 8 13 15 17 18 28 29 30 31 34 35 36 38 40 45 46 50 54 56 58 59 62 63 64 65 68 70 75 76 77 78 79 81 82 85 87 89 93 98 100 102 103 104 107 108 109 110 115 118 119 124 129 130 132 135 145 146 147 148 149 153 154 **P**3
Primary Contact: Anne Diamond, President and Chief Executive Officer
CFO: Paul Beaudoin, Chief Financial Officer
CMO: John Graham, M.D., Vice President Medical Affairs
CIO: Odile Romanick, Chief information Officer
CHR: Jeffrey T. Corrigan, Vice President Human Resources
CNO: John O'Keefe, Chief Nursing Officer
Web address: www.daykimball.org
Control: Other not–for–profit (including NFP Corporation) **Service**: General medical and surgical

> **Staffed Beds:** 62 **Admissions:** 3946 **Census:** 42 **Outpatient Visits:** 672280 **Births:** 465 **Total Expense ($000):** 102455 **Payroll Expense ($000):** 43298 **Personnel:** 772

ROCKY HILL—Hartford County

CONNECTICUT VETERANS HOME AND HOSPITAL (072006), 287 West Street, Zip 06067–3501; tel. 860/616–3606, (Nonreporting) **A**10
Primary Contact: Seam Connolly, Commissioner
CFO: Michael Clark, Fiscal Administrative Manager
CMO: Vamseedhar Alla, M.D., Director Medical Staff
CIO: Sheri DeVaux, Information Technology Manager
CHR: Noreen Sinclair, Human Resources Administrator
CNO: Jeff Lord, Director of Nursing
Web address: www.ct.gov/ctva
Control: State, Government, nonfederal **Service**: Acute long–term care hospital

> **Staffed Beds:** 125

SHARON—Litchfield County

☐ **SHARON HOSPITAL (070004)**, 50 Hospital Hill Road, Zip 06069–2096, Mailing Address: P.O. Box 789, Zip 06069–0789; tel. 860/364–4000, **A**1 10 20 **F**1 3 13 15 17 18 28 29 34 35 40 41 44 45 46 48 49 50 51 53 56 57 59 67 68 70 72 73 74 75 76 77 79 81 82 83 84 85 87 89 90 93 97 98 100 102 103 107 108 110 111 115 119 120 128 130 132 135 146 147 148 149 154 **P**6 **S** Health Quest Systems, Inc., LaGrangeville, NY
Primary Contact: Peter Cordeau, Chief Executive Officer
CMO: Michael Parker, M.D., Chief of Staff
CHR: Kathleen Berlinghoff, Director Human Resources
Web address: www.sharonhospital.com
Control: Other not–for–profit (including NFP Corporation) **Service**: General medical and surgical

> **Staffed Beds:** 57 **Admissions:** 2000 **Census:** 25 **Outpatient Visits:** 35375 **Births:** 254 **Total Expense ($000):** 21219 **Payroll Expense ($000):** 8387 **Personnel:** 302

CT

Many Facility Codes have changed. Please refer to the AHA Guide Code Chart. © 2018 AHA Guide

SOMERS—Tolland County

CONNECTICUT DEPARTMENT OF CORRECTION'S HOSPITAL, 100 Bilton Road, Zip 06071–1059, Mailing Address: P.O. Box 100, Zip 06071–0100; tel. 860/749–8391, (Nonreporting) **A**5
Primary Contact: Edward A. Blanchette, M.D., Director
Control: State, Government, nonfederal **Service**: Hospital unit of an institution (prison hospital, college infirmary, etc.)

Staffed Beds: 29

SOUTHINGTON—Hartford County

BRADLEY MEMORIAL See The Hospital of Central Connecticut, New Britain

STAFFORD SPRINGS—Tolland County

☒ **JOHNSON MEMORIAL MEDICAL CENTER (070008)**, 201 Chestnut Hill Road, Zip 06076–4005; tel. 860/684–4251, (Nonreporting) **A**1 2 10 **S** Trinity Health, Livonia, MI
Primary Contact: Stuart E. Rosenberg, President
CFO: John Grish, Chief Financial Officer
CMO: Ian Tucker, M.D., Vice President Medical Affairs
CHR: Donna M Megliola, Assistant Vice President
CNO: Patricia Jagoe, Assistant Vice President Patient Care
Web address: www.jmmc.com
Control: Other not–for–profit (including NFP Corporation) **Service**: General medical and surgical

Staffed Beds: 88

STAMFORD—Fairfield County

☒ **STAMFORD HOSPITAL (070006)**, One Hospital Plaza, Zip 6902, Mailing Address: P.O. Box 9317, Zip 06904–9317; tel. 203/276–1000, **A**1 2 3 5 10 **F**3 8 12 13 15 18 19 20 22 24 26 28 29 30 31 32 34 35 36 37 38 40 41 43 44 45 46 47 48 49 50 52 53 54 55 56 57 58 59 60 61 64 66 68 70 72 74 75 76 77 78 79 81 82 84 85 86 87 89 90 91 92 93 95 96 97 98 100 107 108 110 111 114 115 116 117 118 119 120 121 123 124 126 129 130 131 132 135 144 145 146 147 148 149 150 154 **P**6
Primary Contact: Brian G. Grissler, President and Chief Executive Officer
COO: Kathleen A Silard, R.N., MS, FACHE, Executive Vice President Operations and Chief Operating Officer
CFO: Kevin Gage, Chief Financial Officer
CMO: Sharon Kiely, M.D., Senior Vice President Medical Affairs and Chief Medical Officer
CIO: Steven Sakovits, Vice President Information Systems and Chief Information Officer
CHR: Elaine Guglielmo, Vice President Human Resources and Organizational Development
CNO: Ellen M Komar, R.N., Vice President Patient Care Services and Chief Nursing Officer
Web address: www.stamhealth.org
Control: Other not–for–profit (including NFP Corporation) **Service**: General medical and surgical

Staffed Beds: 305 Admissions: 12903 Census: 186 Outpatient Visits: 478184 **Births:** 2140 **Total Expense ($000):** 495287 **Payroll Expense ($000):** 200940 **Personnel:** 2879

TORRINGTON—Litchfield County

☒ **CHARLOTTE HUNGERFORD HOSPITAL (070011)**, 540 Litchfield Street, Zip 06790–6679, Mailing Address: P.O. Box 988, Zip 06790–0988; tel. 860/496–6666, **A**1 2 10 **F**3 5 8 11 13 15 18 28 29 30 31 34 35 38 40 41 44 45 47 48 49 50 51 54 59 64 70 74 75 76 77 78 79 81 82 84 85 87 89 93 97 98 100 102 104 105 107 110 111 115 117 119 120 121 123 129 130 131 132 144 146 148 149 152 153 154 **P**6 **S** Hartford HealthCare, Hartford, CT
Primary Contact: Daniel J. McIntyre, President
CFO: Susan Schapp, Vice President Finance and Treasurer
CMO: Mark Prete, M.D., Vice President Medical Affairs
CHR: R James Elliott, Vice President Human Resources
Web address: www.charlottehungerford.org
Control: Other not–for–profit (including NFP Corporation) **Service**: General medical and surgical

Staffed Beds: 66 Admissions: 5171 Census: 62 Outpatient Visits: 303091 **Births:** 386 **Total Expense ($000):** 124831 **Payroll Expense ($000):** 55973 **Personnel:** 793

VERNON—Tolland County

☐ **ROCKVILLE GENERAL HOSPITAL (070012)**, 31 Union Street, Zip 06066–3160; tel. 860/872–0501, (Nonreporting) **A**1 5 10 **S** Prospect Medical Holdings, Los Angeles, CA
Primary Contact: Michael F. Collins, Chief Executive Officer
CFO: Michael D. Veillette, Senior Vice President and Chief Financial Officer
CMO: Joel R Reich, M.D., Senior Vice President Medical Affairs
CIO: Richard Daigle, Chief Information Officer
CHR: Natalie Cook, Administrative Director, Human Resources
CNO: Mary Powers, R.N., MSN, Senior Vice President and Chief Nursing Officer
Web address: www.echn.org
Control: Other not–for–profit (including NFP Corporation) **Service**: General medical and surgical

Staffed Beds: 47

WALLINGFORD—New Haven County

☐ △ **GAYLORD HOSPITAL (072003)**, 50 Gaylord Farm Road, Zip 06492–7048, Mailing Address: P.O. Box 400, Zip 06492–7048; tel. 203/284–2800, **A**1 3 5 7 10 **F**1 29 30 31 34 35 50 53 54 59 60 64 74 75 82 84 85 86 87 91 93 94 95 96 97 114 119 130 131 132 135 146 148 149 **P**5
Primary Contact: George M. Kyriacou, President and Chief Executive Officer
CFO: Art Tedesco, Interim Chief Financial Officer
CMO: Stephen Holland, M.D., Vice President Chief Medical Officer and Medical Director
CIO: Gerry Maroney, Chief Information Officer and Security Officer
CHR: Wally G Harper, Vice President Human Resources
CNO: Lisa Kalafus, MSN, R.N., Chief Nursing Officer
Web address: www.gaylord.org
Control: Other not–for–profit (including NFP Corporation) **Service**: Acute long–term care hospital

Staffed Beds: 122 Admissions: 1400 Census: 108 Outpatient Visits: 77486 **Births:** 0 **Total Expense ($000):** 75156 **Payroll Expense ($000):** 42419 **Personnel:** 481

★ **MASONICARE HEALTH CENTER (070039)**, 22 Masonic Avenue, Zip 06492–3048, Mailing Address: P.O. Box 70, Zip 06492–7001; tel. 203/679–5900, (Nonreporting) **A**3 5 10
Primary Contact: Jon–Paul Venoit, President and Chief Executive Officer
COO: Jon–Paul Venoit, Chief Operating Officer
CFO: Raymond Scott Thelen, Vice President and Chief Financial Officer
CMO: Ronald Schwartz, M.D., Medical Director
CIO: Michael Nichols, Chief Information Officer
CHR: Edward Dooling, Vice President, Human Resources
CNO: Patti Russell, Vice President Nursing
Web address: www.masonicare.org
Control: Other not–for–profit (including NFP Corporation) **Service**: Other specialty treatment

Staffed Beds: 65

WATERBURY—New Haven County

☒ **SAINT MARY'S HOSPITAL (070016)**, 56 Franklin Street, Zip 06706–1281; tel. 203/709–6000, **A**1 2 3 5 10 **F**3 5 8 11 12 13 14 15 17 18 20 22 24 26 28 29 30 31 34 35 37 38 40 41 43 44 45 46 48 49 50 51 54 55 56 57 59 64 65 66 70 72 74 75 76 77 78 79 80 81 82 83 84 85 86 87 91 92 93 97 98 100 101 102 104 105 106 107 108 110 111 115 118 119 120 126 129 130 131 132 135 144 146 147 148 149 152 153 154 **P**6 8 **S** Trinity Health, Livonia, MI
Primary Contact: Steven E. Schneider, M.D., President
COO: Charles Flinn, Vice President, Chief Operating Officer
CFO: Ralph W Becker, Vice President, Chief Financial Officer
CIO: Michael Novak, Vice President, Operations and Chief Information Officer
CHR: M Clark Kearney, Vice President Human Resources
CNO: Elizabeth Bozzuto, R.N., Chief Nursing Officer and Vice President
Web address: www.stmh.org
Control: Church operated, Nongovernment, not–for–profit **Service**: General medical and surgical

Staffed Beds: 187 Admissions: 11037 Census: 126 Outpatient Visits: 292683 **Births:** 1068 **Total Expense ($000):** 254576 **Payroll Expense ($000):** 98295 **Personnel:** 1958

✠ **WATERBURY HOSPITAL (070005)**, 64 Robbins Street, Zip 06708–2600;
tel. 203/573–6000, (Nonreporting) **A**1 2 3 5 10 **S** Prospect Medical Holdings,
Los Angeles, CA
Primary Contact: Peter J. Adamo, President and Chief Executive Officer
CFO: Colleen M Scott, Vice President Finance
CMO: David Puzzuto, M.D., Vice President Medical Affairs and Chief Medical Officer
CIO: Michael J Cemeno, Chief Information Officer
CHR: Diane Woolley, Vice President Human Resources
CNO: Sandra Ladarola, Chief Nursing Officer
Web address: www.waterburyhospital.org
Control: Other not–for–profit (including NFP Corporation) **Service**: General
medical and surgical

> **Staffed Beds:** 183

WEST HARTFORD—Hartford County

★ **HEBREW SENIOR CARE (070040)**, 1 Abrahms Boulevard, Zip 06117–1525;
tel. 860/523–3800, **A**10 **F**2 10 11 56 98 103 119 130 149 **P**5
Primary Contact: Denise Peterson, R.N., FACHE, President and Chief Executive
Officer
COO: Marcia H Hickey, Senior Vice President Operations
CFO: David Houle, Executive Vice President and Chief Financial Officer
CMO: Ava Pannullo, M.D., Vice President Medical Services and Physician in Chief
CHR: Sam Vogt, Manager Human Resources
Web address: www.hebrewhealthcare.org
Control: Other not–for–profit (including NFP Corporation) **Service**: Chronic
disease

> **Staffed Beds:** 45 **Admissions:** 411 **Census:** 21 **Outpatient Visits:** 0
> **Births:** 0 **Total Expense ($000):** 7089 **Payroll Expense ($000):** 4365
> **Personnel:** 52

WEST HAVEN—New Haven County

✠ **VETERANS AFFAIRS CONNECTICUT HEALTHCARE SYSTEM**, 950 Campbell
Avenue, Zip 06516–2770; tel. 203/932–5711, (Includes WEST HAVEN DIVISION,
950 Campbell Avenue, West Haven, CT, Zip 06516–2700; tel. 203/932–5711)
(Nonreporting) **A**1 2 3 5 8 **S** Department of Veterans Affairs, Perry Point, MD
Primary Contact: Gerald F. Culliton, Medical Center Director
CFO: Joseph LaMadeleine, Chief Financial Officer
CMO: Michael Ebert, M.D., Chief of Staff
CIO: Joseph Erdos, M.D., Chief Information Officer
CHR: Mark Bain, Chief Human Resources
Web address: www.connecticut.va.gov
Control: Veterans Affairs, Government, federal **Service**: General medical and
surgical

> **Staffed Beds:** 197

WESTPORT—Fairfield County

ST. VINCENT'S BEHAVIORAL HEALTH See St. Vincent's Medical Center,
Bridgeport

WILLIMANTIC—Windham County

WINDHAM COMMUNITY MEMORIAL HOSPITAL See Windham Hospital

✠ **WINDHAM HOSPITAL (070021)**, 112 Mansfield Avenue, Zip 06226–2040;
tel. 860/456–9116, **A**1 2 5 10 **F**2 3 6 8 11 13 15 18 28 29 30 31 32 34 35
36 40 45 48 50 51 53 54 56 57 59 60 61 64 65 66 68 75 76 77 90 98 99
100 101 103 105 107 108 110 111 115 116 117 118 119 126 129 130 131
132 134 135 144 146 147 148 149 151 153 154 **P**6 **S** Hartford HealthCare,
Hartford, CT
Primary Contact: Donna Handley, President
COO: Carolyn Trantalis, R.N., MSN, Chief Operating Officer, East Region
CFO: Daniel E Lohr, Regional Vice President Finance
CMO: Nadia Nashid, M.D., Chief of Staff
CHR: Theresa L Buss, Regional Vice President Human Resources
Web address: www.windhamhospital.org
Control: Other not–for–profit (including NFP Corporation) **Service**: General
medical and surgical

> **Staffed Beds:** 99 **Admissions:** 2369 **Census:** 26 **Outpatient Visits:** 78724
> **Births:** 104 **Total Expense ($000):** 83666 **Payroll Expense ($000):** 32202
> **Personnel:** 360

CT

DELAWARE

DOVER—Kent County

✠ **BAYHEALTH MEDICAL CENTER (080004)**, 640 South State Street, Zip 19901–3530; tel. 302/674–4700, (Includes BAYHEALTH MEDICAL CENTER AT KENT GENERAL, 640 South State Street, Dover, DE, Zip 19901–3597; tel. 203/932–5711; BAYHEALTH MEDICAL CENTER, MILFORD MEMORIAL HOSPITAL, 21 West Clarke Avenue, Milford, DE, Zip 19963–1840, Mailing Address: P.O. Box 199, Zip 19963–0199, tel. 302/430–5738; Michael Ashton, Administrator) **A**1 2 3 5 10 **F**3 8 11 12 13 15 17 18 20 22 24 26 28 29 30 31 32 34 35 38 40 41 43 44 45 47 48 49 50 51 53 54 55 57 58 59 60 61 62 64 67 68 70 72 73 74 75 76 77 78 79 81 82 84 85 86 87 88 89 90 93 94 98 99 100 101 102 103 104 107 108 110 111 114 115 117 118 119 120 121 123 124 126 129 130 131 132 134 135 144 146 147 148
Primary Contact: Terry Murphy, President and Chief Executive Officer
COO: Deborah Watson, Senior Vice President and Chief Operating Officer
CFO: Mike Tretina, Senior Vice President and Chief Financial Officer
CMO: Gary M Siegelman, M.D., MSC, Senior Vice President and Chief Medical Officer
CIO: Richard Mohnk, Vice President Corporate Services
CHR: Shana Ross, Vice President Human Resources
CNO: Brenda Blain, MSN, Senior Vice President and Chief Nursing Executive
Web address: www.bayhealth.org
Control: Other not–for–profit (including NFP Corporation) **Service**: General medical and surgical

Staffed Beds: 351 **Admissions**: 18909 **Census**: 263 **Outpatient Visits**: 565654 **Births**: 2212 **Total Expense ($000)**: 545265 **Payroll Expense ($000)**: 249664 **Personnel**: 3210

☐ **DOVER BEHAVIORAL HEALTH SYSTEM (084004)**, 725 Horsepond Road, Zip 19901–7232; tel. 302/741–0140, (Nonreporting) **A**1 10 **S** Universal Health Services, Inc., King of Prussia, PA
Primary Contact: Jean–Charles Constant, Administrator
Web address: www.doverbehavioral.com
Control: Corporation, Investor–owned (for–profit) **Service**: Psychiatric

Staffed Beds: 72

LEWES—Sussex County

✠ **BEEBE HEALTHCARE (080007)**, 424 Savannah Road, Zip 19958–1462; tel. 302/645–3300, **A**1 2 3 10 19 **F**3 11 12 13 15 17 18 20 22 24 28 29 30 31 32 34 40 41 43 45 46 49 51 54 56 57 59 62 64 67 70 74 75 76 77 78 79 81 82 84 85 87 89 93 96 97 107 108 110 111 114 115 117 118 119 120 121 123 124 130 146 147 148 154 **P**4
Primary Contact: Jeffrey M. Fried, FACHE, President and Chief Executive Officer
CFO: Paul Pernice, Vice President Finance
CMO: Jeffrey Hawtof, M.D., Vice President Medical Operations and Informatics
CIO: Michael Maksymow, Vice President Information Systems
CHR: Catherine Halen, Vice President Human Resources
CNO: Steve Rhone, R.N., MS, Vice President Patient Care Services
Web address: www.beebemed.org
Control: Other not–for–profit (including NFP Corporation) **Service**: General medical and surgical

Staffed Beds: 155 **Admissions**: 11082 **Census**: 134 **Outpatient Visits**: 412966 **Births**: 844 **Total Expense ($000)**: 338622 **Payroll Expense ($000)**: 124072 **Personnel**: 2186

MIDDLETOWN—New Castle County

HEALTHSOUTH REHABILITATION HOSPITAL OF MIDDLETOWN (083026), 250 East Hampden Road, Zip 19709–5303; tel. 302/464–3400, **F**3 29 90 95 96 146 148 149 **S** Encompass Health Corporation, Birmingham, AL
Primary Contact: Mathew Gooch, Chief Executive Officer
CFO: Lisa Trimble, Controller
CMO: Ashish Khandelwal, M.D., Medical Director
CHR: Anitra Robinson, Human Resources Director
CNO: Rebecca Boney, R.N., Chief Nursing Officer
Web address: www.healthsouthmiddletown.com
Control: Corporation, Investor–owned (for–profit) **Service**: Rehabilitation

Staffed Beds: 37 **Admissions**: 946 **Census**: 33 **Outpatient Visits**: 0 **Births**: 0 **Total Expense ($000)**: 13385 **Payroll Expense ($000)**: 7077 **Personnel**: 138

MILFORD—Sussex County

BAYHEALTH MEDICAL CENTER, MILFORD MEMORIAL HOSPITAL See Bayhealth Medical Center, Dover

NEW CASTLE—New Castle County

☐ **DELAWARE PSYCHIATRIC CENTER (084001)**, 1901 North Dupont Highway, Zip 19720–1199; tel. 302/255–2700, **A**1 3 5 10 **F**30 34 39 59 65 68 75 86 87 98 100 101 103 106 130 132 135 143 149 **P**1
Primary Contact: Norman Vetter, Chief Executive Officer, Division of Substance Abuse and Mental Health
CIO: James Nau, Manager Computer and Applications Support
Web address: www.dhss.delaware.gov
Control: State, Government, nonfederal **Service**: Psychiatric

Staffed Beds: 166 **Admissions**: 366 **Census**: 113 **Outpatient Visits**: 0 **Births**: 0 **Total Expense ($000)**: 36748 **Payroll Expense ($000)**: 19193 **Personnel**: 258

☐ **MEADOW WOOD BEHAVIORAL HEALTH SYSTEM (084003)**, 575 South Dupont Highway, Zip 19720–4606; tel. 302/328–3330, (Nonreporting) **A**1 10 **S** Acadia Healthcare Company, Inc., Franklin, TN
Primary Contact: Bill A. Mason, Chief Executive Officer
CFO: Maria Valdenegro, Chief Financial Officer
Web address: www.meadowwoodhospital.com
Control: Corporation, Investor–owned (for–profit) **Service**: Psychiatric

Staffed Beds: 53

NEWARK—New Castle County

✠ **CHRISTIANA CARE HEALTH SYSTEM (080001)**, 4755 Ogletown–Stanton Road, Zip 19718–0002, Mailing Address: P.O. Box 6001, Zip 19718; tel. 302/733–1000, **A**1 2 3 5 8 10 12 13 **F**2 3 5 6 7 8 11 12 13 15 17 18 20 22 24 26 28 29 30 31 32 34 35 36 37 38 39 40 41 43 44 45 46 47 48 49 50 53 54 55 56 57 58 59 60 61 62 64 65 66 68 70 72 74 75 76 77 78 79 80 81 82 84 85 86 87 89 90 92 93 94 96 97 98 100 101 102 104 107 108 110 111 114 115 117 118 119 120 121 123 124 126 129 130 131 132 134 135 136 138 143 144 145 146 147 148 149 150 154 **P**6 **S** Christiana Care Health System, Wilmington, DE
Primary Contact: Janice E. Nevin, M.D., M.P.H., Chief Executive Officer
CFO: Rob McMurray, Chief Financial Officer
CMO: Kenneth L Silverstein, M.D., Chief Clinical Officer
CIO: Randall Gaboriault, Chief Information Officer
CHR: Christopher Cowan, Senior Vice President and Chief Human Resources Officer
CNO: Richard Cuming, R.N., MSN, Ed.D., Chief Nurse Executive
Web address: www.christianacare.org
Control: Other not–for–profit (including NFP Corporation) **Service**: General medical and surgical

Staffed Beds: 1080 **Admissions**: 52928 **Census**: 794 **Outpatient Visits**: 602339 **Births**: 6374 **Total Expense ($000)**: 1702370 **Payroll Expense ($000)**: 819199 **Personnel**: 10170

☐ **ROCKFORD CENTER (084002)**, 100 Rockford Drive, Zip 19713–2121; tel. 302/996–5480, **A**1 3 10 **F**5 98 99 103 104 105 154 **P**6 **S** Universal Health Services, Inc., King of Prussia, PA
Primary Contact: John F. McKenna, Chief Executive Officer and Managing Director
CFO: Kumar Purohit, Chief Financial Officer
CMO: Saurabh Gupta, Chief Medical Officer
CHR: Jessi Stewart, Director Human Resources
CNO: Michelle Singletary–Twyman, Chief Nursing Officer
Web address: www.rockfordcenter.com
Control: Corporation, Investor–owned (for–profit) **Service**: Psychiatric

Staffed Beds: 128 **Admissions**: 5003 **Census**: 127 **Outpatient Visits**: 10791 **Births**: 0 **Total Expense ($000)**: 26135 **Payroll Expense ($000)**: 13839 **Personnel**: 294

DE

Hospital, Medicare Provider Number, Address, Telephone, Approval, Facility, and Physician Codes, Health Care System

★ American Hospital Association (AHA) membership
☐ The Joint Commission accreditation
○ Healthcare Facilities Accreditation Program
◇ DNV Healthcare Inc. accreditation
⇑ Center for Improvement in Healthcare Quality Accreditation
△ Commission on Accreditation of Rehabilitation Facilities (CARF) accreditation

SEAFORD—Sussex County

✠ **NANTICOKE MEMORIAL HOSPITAL (080006)**, 801 Middleford Road, Zip 19973–3636; tel. 302/629–6611, **A**1 2 10 19 **F**3 12 13 15 18 20 22 28 29 30 31 32 34 35 37 40 43 45 49 50 51 54 57 59 64 65 70 74 75 76 77 78 79 81 84 85 86 87 89 93 107 108 111 114 115 117 119 120 121 123 129 130 132 135 144 146 147 148 149 154
Primary Contact: Steven A Rose, R.N., President and Chief Executive Officer
COO: Penny Short, R.N., Chief Operating Officer
CFO: Denise Jester, Chief Financial Officer
CMO: Harry C. Anthony, M.D., Chief Medical Officer
CIO: Charles Palmer, Director Information Technology
CNO: Lori L Lee, Vice President Nursing
Web address: www.nanticoke.org
Control: Other not–for–profit (including NFP Corporation) **Service**: General medical and surgical

Staffed Beds: 99 **Admissions**: 5371 **Census**: 52 **Outpatient Visits**: 106581
Births: 854 **Total Expense ($000)**: 126472 **Payroll Expense ($000)**: 44202
Personnel: 963

WILMINGTON—New Castle County

✠ △ **ALFRED I. DUPONT HOSPITAL FOR CHILDREN (083300)**, 1600 Rockland Road, Zip 19803–3616, Mailing Address: Box 269, Zip 19899–0269; tel. 302/651–4000, **A**1 2 3 5 7 10 **F**3 8 11 12 17 18 19 20 21 22 23 24 25 26 27 29 30 31 32 34 35 36 37 39 41 43 44 45 47 48 50 53 54 55 56 57 58 59 60 61 64 65 66 68 72 73 74 75 77 78 79 80 81 82 84 85 86 87 88 89 90 92 93 94 96 97 99 100 101 102 104 107 111 113 114 115 116 118 119 126 127 129 130 131 132 134 136 137 138 139 143 144 146 148 149 154 **S** Nemours, Jacksonville, FL
Primary Contact: Roy Proujansky, M.D., Chief Executive Officer
COO: Paul D Kempinski, Chief Operating Officer
CFO: William N Britton, Associate Administrator Finance
CMO: Brent R King, Chief Medical Officer and Chief Physician
Web address: www.nemours.org
Control: Other not–for–profit (including NFP Corporation) **Service**: Children's general medical and surgical

Staffed Beds: 200 **Admissions**: 9234 **Census**: 140 **Outpatient Visits**: 223210 **Births**: 0 **Total Expense ($000)**: 442250 **Payroll Expense ($000)**: 156251 **Personnel**: 2567

✠ **SELECT SPECIALTY HOSPITAL–WILMINGTON (082000)**, 701 North Clayton Street, 5th Floor, Zip 19805–3948; tel. 302/421–4545, **A**1 10 **F**1 18 29 74 79 130 148 **S** Select Medical Corporation, Mechanicsburg, PA
Primary Contact: Donna Gares, R.N., FACHE, MSN, Chief Executive Officer
CFO: David Huffman, Vice President and Controller
CMO: Hummayun Ismail, M.D., Medical Director
CHR: Barbara A Foster, Regional Human Resources Director
Web address: www.wilmington.selectspecialtyhospitals.com
Control: Corporation, Investor–owned (for–profit) **Service**: Acute long–term care hospital

Staffed Beds: 35 **Admissions**: 359 **Census**: 29 **Outpatient Visits**: 0
Births: 0 **Total Expense ($000)**: 17900 **Payroll Expense ($000)**: 8121
Personnel: 122

✠ **ST. FRANCIS HOSPITAL (080003)**, 701 North Clayton Street, Zip 19805, Mailing Address: P.O. Box 2500, Zip 19805–0500; tel. 302/421–4100, (Nonreporting) **A**1 2 3 5 10 **S** Trinity Health, Livonia, MI
Primary Contact: Daniel J. Sinnott, President and Chief Executive Officer
CIO: Paul W Rowe, Director Information Technology
CHR: Charlene J Wilson, Vice President Human Resources
Web address: www.stfrancishealthcare.org
Control: Other not–for–profit (including NFP Corporation) **Service**: General medical and surgical

Staffed Beds: 214

✠ **WILMINGTON VETERANS AFFAIRS MEDICAL CENTER**, 1601 Kirkwood Highway, Zip 19805–4989; tel. 302/994–2511, (Nonreporting) **A**1 3 5 8 **S** Department of Veterans Affairs, Perry Point, MD
Primary Contact: Robert W. Callahan Jr, Interim Director
CFO: Mary Ann Kozel, Chief Fiscal
CMO: Enrique Guttin, M.D., FACS, Chief of Staff
CIO: Scott Vlars, Chief Information Technology Services
CHR: Louis McCloskey, Chief Human Resources
Web address: www.va.gov/wilmington
Control: Veterans Affairs, Government, federal **Service**: General medical and surgical

Staffed Beds: 60

Many Facility Codes have changed. Please refer to the AHA Guide Code Chart. © 2018 AHA Guide

DE

DISTRICT OF COLUMBIA

WASHINGTON—District Of Columbia County

☐ **BRIDGEPOINT HOSPITAL CAPITOL HILL (092002)**, 700 Constitution Avenue NE, Zip 20002–6058; tel. 202/546–5700, (Nonreporting) **A**1 10 **S** BridgePoint Healthcare, Portsmouth, NH
Primary Contact: James Linhares, Chief Executive Officer
COO: Delores Clair Oliver, Chief Clinical Officer and Chief Operating Officer
CFO: Michael Grubb, Chief Financial Officer
CMO: Gerald Moawad, Chief Medical Officer
CHR: Karen Brown, Senior Director of Human Resources
CNO: Delores Clair Oliver, Chief Clinical Officer and Chief Operating Officer
Web address: www.bridgepointhealthcare.com/
Control: Corporation, Investor–owned (for–profit) **Service:** Acute long–term care hospital

Staffed Beds: 177

BRIDGEPOINT HOSPITAL NATIONAL HARBOR (092003), 4601 Martin Luther King Jr Avenue, SW, Zip 20032–1131; tel. 202/574–5700, (Nonreporting) **A**10 22 **S** BridgePoint Healthcare, Portsmouth, NH
Primary Contact: Swenda Moreh, Interim Chief Executive Officer
COO: Swenda Moreh, Vice President and Chief Operating Officer
CFO: Michael Grubb, Chief Financial Officer
CMO: Khosrow Davachi, Chief Medical Officer
CHR: Antoninette Saldivar, Vice President, Human Resources
CNO: Diane White, Chief Clinical Officer and Chief Nursing Officer
Web address: www.bridgepointhealthcare.com/
Control: Corporation, Investor–owned (for–profit) **Service:** Acute long–term care hospital

Staffed Beds: 82

⊞ **CHILDREN'S NATIONAL HEALTH SYSTEM (093300)**, 111 Michigan Avenue NW, Zip 20010–2916; tel. 202/476–5000, **A**1 3 5 8 10 **F**1 3 4 5 7 8 11 12 14 16 17 18 19 21 23 25 27 29 30 31 32 34 35 36 38 39 40 41 43 44 45 46 48 49 50 51 54 55 57 58 59 60 61 64 65 66 67 68 70 71 72 73 74 75 77 78 79 80 81 82 83 84 85 86 87 88 89 90 91 92 93 94 96 97 98 99 100 102 104 105 106 107 111 112 115 116 117 118 119 126 128 129 130 131 132 134 136 137 138 141 142 146 148 **P**6
Primary Contact: Kurt Newman, M.D., President and Chief Executive Officer
COO: Kathleen Gorman, MSN, R.N., Executive Vice President Patient Care Services and Chief Operating Officer
CMO: Mark L Batshaw, M.D., Physician–in–Chief, Executive Vice President and Chief Academic Officer
CIO: Brian Jacobs, M.D., Vice President Chief Information Officer and Chief Medical Information Officer
CHR: Darryl Varnado, Executive Vice President and Chief People Officer
CNO: Linda Talley, MS, R.N., Vice President and Chief Nursing Officer
Web address: www.childrensnational.org
Control: Other not–for–profit (including NFP Corporation) **Service:** Children's general medical and surgical

Staffed Beds: 313 **Admissions:** 15700 **Census:** 256 **Outpatient Visits:** 523206 **Births:** 0 **Total Expense ($000):** 784955 **Payroll Expense ($000):** 352565 **Personnel:** 5217

⊞ △ **GEORGE WASHINGTON UNIVERSITY HOSPITAL (090001)**, 900 23rd Street NW, Zip 20037–2342; tel. 202/715–4000, **A**1 2 3 5 7 8 10 **F**3 8 11 12 13 15 17 18 20 22 24 26 29 31 34 35 37 38 39 40 43 44 45 46 47 48 49 51 53 54 55 56 57 58 59 60 61 63 64 65 66 70 71 72 74 75 76 77 78 79 80 81 82 84 85 86 87 90 91 92 93 94 96 98 102 107 108 110 111 114 115 116 117 118 119 120 121 123 124 126 129 130 131 132 134 135 136 138 141 146 147 148 149 150 **S** Universal Health Services, Inc., King of Prussia, PA
Primary Contact: Kimberly Russo, Chief Executive Officer
COO: Kimberly Russo, Chief Operating Officer
CFO: Richard Davis, Chief Financial Officer
CMO: Gary Little, M.D., Medical Director
CIO: Louis Duhe, Senior Director Information Technology
CHR: Erin Fagan, Manager Human Resources
Web address: www.gwhospital.com
Control: Partnership, Investor–owned (for–profit) **Service:** General medical and surgical

Staffed Beds: 385 **Admissions:** 19842 **Census:** 292 **Outpatient Visits:** 191039 **Births:** 3469 **Personnel:** 2704

GEORGETOWN UNIVERSITY HOSPITAL See Medstar Georgetown University Hospital

⊞ **HOWARD UNIVERSITY HOSPITAL (090003)**, 2041 Georgia Avenue NW, Zip 20060–0002; tel. 202/865–6100, **A**1 2 3 5 8 10 **F**3 8 12 13 15 17 18 24 26 28 29 30 31 32 34 35 36 38 39 40 41 43 44 45 46 50 53 54 55 56 57 58 59 60 61 64 65 66 68 70 71 72 74 75 76 77 78 79 81 82 85 86 87 93 97 98 99 100 101 102 103 104 107 108 110 111 114 115 118 119 123 124 129 130 132 146 147 148
Primary Contact: James A. Diegel, FACHE, Chief Executive Officer
COO: James A. Diegel, FACHE, Chief Executive Officer
CFO: Ed Gyimah, Chief Financial Officer
CMO: Shelly McDonald–Pinkett, Chief Medical Officer
CIO: Becky Quammen, Chief Information Officer
CHR: Jeronica Goodwin, Senior Director Human Resources
CNO: Shirley Evers–Manly, Chief Nursing Officer
Web address: www.huhealthcare.com
Control: Other not–for–profit (including NFP Corporation) **Service:** General medical and surgical

Staffed Beds: 217 **Admissions:** 8088 **Census:** 91 **Outpatient Visits:** 111448 **Births:** 754 **Total Expense ($000):** 265942 **Payroll Expense ($000):** 95685 **Personnel:** 1383

⊞ **MEDSTAR GEORGETOWN UNIVERSITY HOSPITAL (090004)**, 3800 Reservoir Road NW, Zip 20007–2197; tel. 202/444–2000, **A**1 2 3 5 8 10 **F**3 9 11 13 18 20 26 29 30 31 32 34 35 36 37 39 40 41 44 45 46 47 48 49 50 51 54 55 56 57 58 59 60 61 63 64 65 66 70 71 72 74 75 76 77 78 79 80 81 82 84 85 86 87 88 89 92 93 97 98 100 101 102 104 105 107 108 109 110 111 114 115 116 117 118 119 121 123 124 126 128 129 130 131 132 134 135 136 138 139 141 142 145 146 147 148 149 150 153 **P**6 **S** MedStar Health, Columbia, MD
Primary Contact: Michael Sachtleben, President
CFO: Paul Warda, Chief Financial Officer
CMO: Lisa Boyle, M.D., Vice President Medical Affairs and Medical Director
CIO: John Rasmussen, Vice President for Information Technology
CHR: Mary Jo Schweickhardt, Vice President Human Resources
CNO: Eileen Brennan Ferrell, MS, R.N., Vice President and Chief Nursing Officer
Web address: www.georgetownuniversityhospital.org
Control: Other not–for–profit (including NFP Corporation) **Service:** General medical and surgical

Staffed Beds: 409 **Admissions:** 15853 **Census:** 323 **Outpatient Visits:** 624129 **Births:** 1044 **Total Expense ($000):** 983811 **Payroll Expense ($000):** 443479 **Personnel:** 5743

⊞ △ **MEDSTAR NATIONAL REHABILITATION HOSPITAL (093025)**, 102 Irving Street NW, Zip 20010–2949; tel. 202/877–1000, **A**1 3 5 7 10 **F**9 11 28 29 30 33 34 35 36 44 53 54 56 58 59 60 64 68 74 75 77 78 79 82 86 87 90 91 92 93 94 95 96 119 129 130 131 132 146 148 149 **P**1 6 **S** MedStar Health, Columbia, MD
Primary Contact: John D. Rockwood, President
CFO: Michael Boemmel, Vice President and Chief Financial Officer
CMO: Michael R Yochelson, M.D., Vice President and Medical Director
CHR: Pamela Ashby, Vice President Human Resources
CNO: Rosemary C Welch, R.N., Vice President and Chief Nursing Officer
Web address: www.medstarnrh.org
Control: Other not–for–profit (including NFP Corporation) **Service:** Rehabilitation

Staffed Beds: 137 **Admissions:** 2162 **Census:** 98 **Outpatient Visits:** 401552 **Births:** 0 **Total Expense ($000):** 132933 **Payroll Expense ($000):** 72697 **Personnel:** 1344

DC

Hospital, Medicare Provider Number, Address, Telephone, Approval, Facility, and Physician Codes, Health Care System		
★ American Hospital Association (AHA) membership	◯ Healthcare Facilities Accreditation Program	⇑ Center for Improvement in Healthcare Quality Accreditation
☐ The Joint Commission accreditation	◇ DNV Healthcare Inc. accreditation	△ Commission on Accreditation of Rehabilitation Facilities (CARF) accreditation

✠ **MEDSTAR WASHINGTON HOSPITAL CENTER (090011)**, 110 Irving Street NW, Zip 20010–3017; tel. 202/877–7000, **A**1 2 3 5 8 10 **F**3 4 5 12 13 15 16 17 18 20 22 24 26 28 29 30 31 34 35 36 37 38 39 40 43 44 45 46 47 48 49 50 51 54 55 56 57 58 59 60 61 62 63 64 65 66 68 70 72 73 74 75 76 77 78 79 80 81 82 84 85 86 87 97 98 100 101 102 104 105 107 108 110 111 114 115 116 117 118 119 120 121 123 124 126 130 131 132 134 135 137 146 147 148 149 **P**1 6 **S** MedStar Health, Columbia, MD
Primary Contact: Gregory J. Argyros, M.D., Senior Vice President and President
COO: Robert Ross, Chief Operating Officer
CFO: William Gayne, Chief Financial Officer
CIO: Joe Brothman, Assistant Vice President, Information Systems
CHR: James P Hill, Senior Vice President Administrative Services
CNO: Susan E. Eckert, R.N., MSN, Senior Vice President and Chief Nursing Officer
Web address: www.whcenter.org
Control: Other not–for–profit (including NFP Corporation) **Service:** General medical and surgical

Staffed Beds: 763 **Admissions:** 33773 **Census:** 602 **Outpatient Visits:** 380366 **Births:** 3537 **Total Expense ($000):** 1242810 **Payroll Expense ($000):** 560870 **Personnel:** 5497

NATIONAL REHABILITATION HOSPITAL See Medstar National Rehabilitation Hospital

✠ **PROVIDENCE HOSPITAL (090006)**, 1150 Varnum Street NE, Zip 20017–2104; tel. 202/269–7000, (Total facility includes 252 beds in nursing home–type unit) **A**1 3 5 10 **F**4 7 12 13 15 17 18 20 29 30 31 34 35 38 40 45 46 50 54 56 57 58 59 60 61 64 68 70 72 75 76 77 78 79 81 82 84 85 87 90 93 97 98 100 101 102 104 107 110 111 112 115 116 117 118 119 125 128 129 130 131 132 135 143 146 147 148 149 150 153 154 **S** Ascension Healthcare, Saint Louis, MO
Primary Contact: Darcy Burthay, MSN, R.N., President and Chief Executive Officer
CFO: Rick Talento, Senior Vice President and Chief Financial Officer
CMO: Raymond L. Cox, M.D., Chief Medical Officer
CIO: Alan Wyman, Chief Information Officer
CHR: Matt Lasecki, Interim Vice President Human Resources
CNO: Thedosia Munford, Senior Vice President and Chief Nursing Officer
Web address: www.provhosp.org
Control: Other not–for–profit (including NFP Corporation) **Service:** General medical and surgical

Staffed Beds: 447 **Admissions:** 10865 **Census:** 369 **Outpatient Visits:** 101799 **Births:** 1989 **Total Expense ($000):** 222920 **Payroll Expense ($000):** 86096

☐ **PSYCHIATRIC INSTITUTE OF WASHINGTON (094004)**, 4228 Wisconsin Avenue NW, Zip 20016–2138; tel. 202/885–5600, (Nonreporting) **A**1 5 10
Primary Contact: Dina Levi, Director, Business Development
COO: Carol Desjeunes, Vice President and Chief Operating Officer
CFO: Aarti Subramanian, Vice President and Chief Financial Officer
CMO: Howard Hoffman, M.D., Medical Director
CIO: Ray Santina, Director Information Systems
CHR: Dawn Hatterer–Hoag, Director Human Resources
Web address: www.psychinstitute.com
Control: Corporation, Investor–owned (for–profit) **Service:** Psychiatric

Staffed Beds: 124

★ **SAINT ELIZABETHS HOSPITAL (094001)**, 1100 Alabama Avenue SE, Zip 20032–4540; tel. 202/299–5000, **A**3 5 10 **F**29 30 39 56 59 65 74 75 86 91 98 103 130 135 146 148
Primary Contact: Mark J. Chastang, M.P.H., Chief Executive Officer
COO: K. Singh Taneja, Chief Operating Officer
CFO: James V. Jackson, Budget Director
CMO: Hannah Ong, Director, Medical Affairs
CIO: Brady Birdsong, Chief Information Officer
CHR: Frankie Wheeler, Director, Human Resources
CNO: Clotilde Vidoni–Clark, Ph.D., R.N., Chief Nursing Executive
Web address: www.dbh.dc.gov/
Control: State, Government, nonfederal **Service:** Psychiatric

Staffed Beds: 292 **Admissions:** 440 **Census:** 263 **Outpatient Visits:** 0 **Births:** 0 **Personnel:** 755

✠ **SIBLEY MEMORIAL HOSPITAL (090005)**, 5255 Loughboro Road NW, Zip 20016–2633; tel. 202/537–4000, (Total facility includes 45 beds in nursing home–type unit) **A**1 2 3 5 10 **F**3 6 8 10 12 13 15 20 29 30 31 34 35 36 37 38 44 45 46 47 48 49 50 53 54 55 57 58 59 64 68 70 73 74 75 76 77 78 79 81 82 84 85 86 87 91 92 93 94 97 98 100 101 102 103 104 107 108 109 110 111 113 114 115 116 117 118 119 120 121 123 126 128 130 132 135 146 147 148 **P**6 **S** Johns Hopkins Health System, Baltimore, MD
Primary Contact: Richard O. Davis, Ph.D., President
COO: Sanjay K Saha, Chief Operating Officer
CFO: Marty Basso, Chief Financial Officer
CMO: M. Therese McDonnell, M.D., Interim Vice President Patient Safety, Quality and Medical Affairs
CIO: Christopher T Timbers, Chief Information Officer
CHR: Queenie C Plater, Vice President Human Resources for JHM Community Division
CNO: Lynn Meuer, Interim Chief Nursing Officer
Web address: www.sibley.org
Control: Other not–for–profit (including NFP Corporation) **Service:** General medical and surgical

Staffed Beds: 258 **Admissions:** 11629 **Census:** 151 **Outpatient Visits:** 115701 **Births:** 3542 **Total Expense ($000):** 338338 **Payroll Expense ($000):** 127718 **Personnel:** 1562

✠ **THE HSC PEDIATRIC CENTER**, 1731 Bunker Hill Road NE, Zip 20017–3096; tel. 202/832–4400, **A**1 3 **F**3 12 29 30 31 32 34 35 39 50 54 58 64 65 68 71 75 80 83 84 86 90 91 93 94 96 130 132 143 146 148 **P**6
Primary Contact: Debbie C. Holson, R.N., MSN, Chief Operating Officer
COO: Debbie C Holson, R.N., MSN, Chief Operating Officer
CFO: Ray Vicks, Senior Vice President, Finance and Chief Financial Officer
CMO: Andrew Metinko, M.D., Chief Medical Officer
CIO: Khalil Bouharoun, Chief Information Officer
CHR: Lynne Hostetter, Vice President Human Resources
Web address: www.hscpediatriccenter.org/
Control: Other not–for–profit (including NFP Corporation) **Service:** Children's chronic disease

Staffed Beds: 118 **Admissions:** 250 **Census:** 23 **Outpatient Visits:** 14083 **Births:** 0 **Total Expense ($000):** 30102 **Payroll Expense ($000):** 13625 **Personnel:** 201

✠ **UNITED MEDICAL CENTER (090008)**, 1310 Southern Avenue SE, Zip 20032–4623; tel. 202/574–6000, (Nonreporting) **A**1 10
Primary Contact: Matthew Hamilton, Chief Executive Officer
CFO: Lilian Chukwuma, Chief Financial Officer
CMO: Eric Li, M.D., Chief Medical Officer
CIO: Alan Johnson, Interim Chief Information Officer
CHR: Eric M. Johnson, Director
Web address: www.united–medicalcenter.com
Control: Other not–for–profit (including NFP Corporation) **Service:** General medical and surgical

Staffed Beds: 354

VETERANS AFFAIRS MEDICAL CENTER See Washington DC Veterans Affairs Medical Center

✠ △ **WASHINGTON DC VETERANS AFFAIRS MEDICAL CENTER**, 50 Irving Street NW, Zip 20422–0002; tel. 202/745–8000, (Nonreporting) **A**1 2 3 5 7 **S** Department of Veterans Affairs, Perry Point, MD
Primary Contact: Adam M. Robinson, Acting Director
CFO: Frank Filosa, Fiscal Manager
CIO: Amanda Graves, Chief Information Systems
Web address: www.washingtondc.va.gov/
Control: Veterans Affairs, Government, federal **Service:** General medical and surgical

Staffed Beds: 291

WASHINGTON HOSPITAL CENTER See Medstar Washington Hospital Center

DC

Many Facility Codes have changed. Please refer to the AHA Guide Code Chart. © 2018 AHA Guide

FLORIDA

ALTAMONTE SPRINGS—Seminole County

FLORIDA HOSPITAL–ALTAMONTE See Florida Hospital, Orlando

⊠ **HEALTHSOUTH REHABILITATION HOSPITAL OF ALTAMONTE SPRINGS
(103045)**, 831 South State Road 434, Zip 32714–3502; tel. 407/587–8600,
A1 **F**3 29 68 74 75 77 79 82 86 90 91 96 130 148 149 **S** Encompass Health
Corporation, Birmingham, AL
Primary Contact: George Welton, Chief Executive Officer
Web address: www.healthsouthaltamontesprings.com
Control: Corporation, Investor–owned (for–profit) **Service**: Rehabilitation

> **Staffed Beds: 50 Admissions: 1139 Census: 45 Outpatient Visits: 0
> Births: 0 Total Expense ($000): 16506 Payroll Expense ($000): 8946
> Personnel: 162**

APALACHICOLA—Franklin County

GEORGE E. WEEMS MEMORIAL HOSPITAL (101305), 135 Avenue
G, Zip 32320–1613, Mailing Address: P.O. Box 580, Zip 32329–0580;
tel. 850/653–8853, (Nonreporting) **A**10 18
Primary Contact: H D. Cannington, Interim Chief Executive Officer
CHR: Ginny Griner, Director Human Resources
Web address: www.weemsmemorial.com
Control: Partnership, Investor–owned (for–profit) **Service**: General medical and
surgical

> **Staffed Beds: 25**

APOPKA—Orange County

FLORIDA HOSPITAL–APOPKA See Florida Hospital, Orlando

ARCADIA—Desoto County

☐ **DESOTO MEMORIAL HOSPITAL (100175)**, 900 North Robert Avenue,
Zip 34266–8712, Mailing Address: P.O. Box 2180, Zip 34265–2180;
tel. 863/494–3535, **A**1 10 20 **F**15 18 28 29 31 34 35 40 45 46 54 55 57 62
64 65 68 70 74 75 77 78 79 81 82 85 87 93 104 107 110 111 114 119 120
130 135 146 148 149
Primary Contact: Vincent A. Sica, President and Chief Executive Officer
CFO: Dan Hogan, Chief Financial Officer
CMO: Steven Mishkind, M.D., Chief of Staff
CIO: Kristen Spahr, Director of Marketing
CHR: Lois Hilton, Director Human Resources
CNO: Joseph La Cava, Chief Nursing Officer and Director Of Anesthesia
Web address: www.dmh.org
Control: Hospital district or authority, Government, nonfederal **Service**: General
medical and surgical

> **Staffed Beds: 49 Admissions: 1489 Census: 10 Outpatient Visits: 71549
> Births: 261 Total Expense ($000): 33411 Payroll Expense ($000): 13537
> Personnel: 279**

ATLANTIS—Palm Beach County

⊠ **JFK MEDICAL CENTER (100080)**, 5301 South Congress Avenue,
Zip 33462–1197; tel. 561/965–7300, (Nonreporting) **A**1 2 3 5 10 **S** HCA
Healthcare, Nashville, TN
Primary Contact: Gina Melby, Chief Executive Officer
CFO: Jim Leamon, Chief Financial Officer
CIO: Jane Stewart, Director Information Services
CHR: Trudy Bromley, Vice President Human Resources
Web address: www.jfkmc.com
Control: Corporation, Investor–owned (for–profit) **Service**: General medical and
surgical

> **Staffed Beds: 424**

AVENTURA—Miami–Dade County

⊠ **AVENTURA HOSPITAL AND MEDICAL CENTER (100131)**, 20900 Biscayne
Boulevard, Zip 33180–1407; tel. 305/682–7000, (Nonreporting) **A**1 2 3 10 **S**
HCA Healthcare, Nashville, TN
Primary Contact: Lee B. Chaykin, Chief Executive Officer
COO: Luanne Ansaldo, Chief Operating Officer
CFO: Alisa Bert, Chief Financial Officer
CMO: Martin Grossman, Chief of Staff
CHR: Rosemarie Amberson, Vice President Human Resources
Web address: www.aventurahospital.com
Control: Corporation, Investor–owned (for–profit) **Service**: General medical and
surgical

> **Staffed Beds: 359**

BARTOW—Polk County

⊠ **BARTOW REGIONAL MEDICAL CENTER (100121)**, 2200 Osprey Boulevard,
Zip 33830–3308; tel. 863/533–8111, **A**1 10 **F**3 11 12 15 18 20 22 26 29 30
31 34 35 40 45 46 49 50 51 57 58 59 60 64 68 70 74 75 77 78 79 81 82
84 85 86 87 92 93 94 97 100 101 107 108 110 111 114 115 118 119 123
124 126 129 130 131 132 135 145 146 147 148 149 154 **S** Trinity Health,
Livonia, MI
Primary Contact: Philip Minden, Chief Executive Officer
CFO: Michael Boscia, Chief Financial Officer
CMO: Stuart Patterson, M.D., Chief of Staff
CIO: Vilakon Champavannarath, Director Information Systems
CHR: Marie Horton, Director Associate Relations
Web address: www.bartowregional.com
Control: Other not–for–profit (including NFP Corporation) **Service**: General
medical and surgical

> **Staffed Beds: 72 Admissions: 3111 Census: 30 Outpatient Visits: 40159
> Births: 0 Total Expense ($000): 55136 Payroll Expense ($000): 18963
> Personnel: 321**

BAY PINES—Pinellas County

⊠ △ **BAY PINES VETERANS AFFAIRS HEALTHCARE SYSTEM**, 10000
Bay Pines Boulevard, Zip 33744–8200, Mailing Address: P.O. Box 5005,
Zip 33744–5005; tel. 727/398–6661, **A**1 2 3 5 7 **F**3 4 5 8 12 15 18 20 22 26
28 29 30 31 33 35 36 38 39 40 45 46 47 49 51 53 54 56 57 58 59 60 61 62
63 64 65 66 68 70 71 74 75 77 78 79 81 82 83 84 85 86 87 90 91 92 93 94
97 98 100 101 102 103 104 105 106 107 108 110 111 114 115 116 117 118
119 120 121 123 128 129 130 131 132 133 135 143 144 146 147 148 149 151
152 153 154 **P**6 **S** Department of Veterans Affairs, Perry Point, MD
Primary Contact: Suzanne M. Klinker, Director
COO: Kris Brown, Associate Director
CFO: Jeanine Ergle, Chief Financial Officer
CMO: George F Van Buskirk, M.D., Chief of Staff
CIO: John Williams, Chief Information Officer
CHR: Paula Buchele, Chief Human Resources
Web address: www.baypines.va.gov/
Control: Veterans Affairs, Government, federal **Service**: General medical and surgical

> **Staffed Beds: 396 Admissions: 10199 Census: 301 Outpatient Visits:
> 1445082 Births: 0 Total Expense ($000): 798215 Payroll Expense
> ($000): 334517 Personnel: 4487**

BELLE GLADE—Palm Beach County

GLADES GENERAL HOSPITAL See Lakeside Medical Center

⊠ **LAKESIDE MEDICAL CENTER (100130)**, 39200 Hooker Highway,
Zip 33430–5368; tel. 561/996–6571, (Nonreporting) **A**1 10 13
Primary Contact: Stephanie Dardenello, Administrator
COO: Darcy Davis, Chief Financial Officer
CFO: Darcy Davis, Chief Financial Officer
CMO: Ron Wiewora, M.D., Chief Medical Officer
Web address: www.lakesidemedical.org
Control: Hospital district or authority, Government, nonfederal **Service**: General
medical and surgical

> **Staffed Beds: 70**

FL

Hospital, Medicare Provider Number, Address, Telephone, Approval, Facility, and Physician Codes, Health Care System

★ American Hospital Association (AHA) membership ◯ Healthcare Facilities Accreditation Program ⇧ Center for Improvement in Healthcare Quality Accreditation
☐ The Joint Commission accreditation ◇ DNV Healthcare Inc. accreditation △ Commission on Accreditation of Rehabilitation Facilities (CARF) accreditation

---

BLOUNTSTOWN—Calhoun County

CALHOUN–LIBERTY HOSPITAL (101304), 20370 NE Burns Avenue,
Zip 32424–1045, Mailing Address: P.O. Box 419, Zip 32424–0419;
tel. 850/674–5411, **A**10 18 **F**3 7 29 30 40 59 97 107 114 119 127 133 143
154 **P**5 6 **S** Alliant Management Services, Louisville, KY
Primary Contact: Charles E. Durant Jr, FACHE, Chief Executive Officer
CFO: Nathan Ebersole, Controller
CIO: Michael Flowers, Director Information Management
CHR: Lynn Pitts, Director Human Resources
CNO: Debra Summers, Chief Nursing Officer
Web address: www.calhounlibertyhospital.com
Control: Other not–for–profit (including NFP Corporation) **Service:** General
medical and surgical

Staffed Beds: 25 **Admissions:** 491 **Census:** 11 **Outpatient Visits:** 23996
Births: 0 **Total Expense ($000):** 11826 **Payroll Expense ($000):** 6225
Personnel: 169

BOCA RATON—Palm Beach County

BOCA RATON COMMUNITY HOSPITAL See Boca Raton Regional Hospital

☐ **BOCA RATON REGIONAL HOSPITAL (100168)**, 800 Meadows Road,
Zip 33486–2368; tel. 561/955–7100, **A**1 2 3 5 **F**3 6 8 11 12 13 15 17 18
20 22 24 26 28 29 30 31 34 35 36 37 40 44 45 46 47 48 49 50 51 54 55 56
57 58 59 60 61 62 64 68 70 71 73 74 75 76 78 79 81 82 84 85 86 87 92 93
96 97 101 102 107 108 109 110 111 112 114 115 116 117 118 119 120 121
123 124 126 130 131 132 135 144 145 146 147 148 149 154 **P**6
Primary Contact: Jerry J. Fedele, President and Chief Executive Officer
COO: Mindy Shikiar, MSN, Chief Operating Officer
CFO: Dawn Jauersack, Vice President and Chief Financial Officer
CMO: Charles Posternack, M.D., Vice President
CIO: Robin Hildwein, Chief Information Officer
CHR: Mindy Raymond, Vice President Human Resources
CNO: Melissa Durbin, R.N., MSN, Chief Nursing Officer
Web address: www.brrh.com
Control: Other not–for–profit (including NFP Corporation) **Service:** General
medical and surgical

Staffed Beds: 374 **Admissions:** 19002 **Census:** 232 **Outpatient Visits:**
296264 **Births:** 2486 **Total Expense ($000):** 490368 **Payroll Expense
($000):** 189155 **Personnel:** 2564

☒ **WEST BOCA MEDICAL CENTER (100268)**, 21644 State Road 7,
Zip 33428–1899; tel. 561/488–8000, (Nonreporting) **A**1 3 5 10 **S** TENET
Healthcare Corporation, Dallas, TX
Primary Contact: Mitchell S. Feldman, Chief Executive Officer
COO: Ryan Lee, Chief Operating Officer
CFO: Brook Thomas, Chief Financial Officer
CMO: Jack L Harari, M.D., Chief Medical Officer
CIO: Lauren Spagna, Marketing Director
CHR: Stephanie Sherman, Chief Human Resources Officer
CNO: Ruth Schwarzkopf, R.N., Chief Nursing Officer
Web address: www.westbocamedctr.com
Control: Corporation, Investor–owned (for–profit) **Service:** General medical and
surgical

Staffed Beds: 195

BONIFAY—Holmes County

☐ **DOCTORS MEMORIAL HOSPITAL (101307)**, 2600 Hospital Drive,
Zip 32425–4264, Mailing Address: P.O. Box 188, Zip 32425–0188;
tel. 850/547–8000, (Nonreporting) **A**1 10 18
Primary Contact: Joann Baker, Administrator
CFO: Celia F Ward, Controller and Chief Financial Officer
CMO: Leisa Bailey, M.D., Chief of Staff
CIO: Rohan Anderson, Chief Information Officer
CHR: Christy Booth, Chief Human Resources Officer
CNO: Karla Rockwell, Director of Nursing
Web address: www.doctorsmemorial.org
Control: Hospital district or authority, Government, nonfederal **Service:** General
medical and surgical

Staffed Beds: 20

BOYNTON BEACH—Palm Beach County

☒ **BETHESDA HOSPITAL EAST (100002)**, 2815 South Seacrest Boulevard,
Zip 33435–7995; tel. 561/737–7733, (Includes BETHESDA HOSPITAL WEST,
9655 West Boynton Beach Boulevard, Boynton Beach, FL, Zip 33472–4421;
tel. 561/336–7000; Roger L Kirk, President and Chief Executive Officer) **A**1 3 5
10 **F**3 8 11 12 13 17 18 20 22 24 26 28 29 31 32 37 40 41 45 46 49 50 51
56 58 60 61 64 68 70 72 74 75 76 77 78 79 81 86 87 88 89 90 91 92 93 94
96 107 108 109 110 111 112 113 114 115 116 117 118 119 124 126 129
131 143 145 146 147 148 **P**6 **S** Baptist Health South Florida, Coral Gables, FL
Primary Contact: Roger L. Kirk, President and Chief Executive Officer
COO: Ela C Lena, Administrator and Vice President Operations
CFO: Joanne Aquilina, Vice President Finance and Chief Financial Officer
CMO: Albert Biehl, M.D., Vice President Medical Affairs
CIO: Leslie Albright, Vice President Information Systems
CHR: Regina Bellucy, Vice President Human Resources
CNO: Ela C Lena, Interim System Chief Nursing Officer
Web address: www.bethesdaweb.com
Control: Other not–for–profit (including NFP Corporation) **Service:** General
medical and surgical

Staffed Beds: 481 **Admissions:** 21768 **Census:** 285 **Outpatient Visits:**
265769 **Births:** 2786 **Total Expense ($000):** 342041 **Payroll Expense
($000):** 114024 **Personnel:** 2201

BRADENTON—Manatee County

☒ △ **BLAKE MEDICAL CENTER (100213)**, 2020 59th Street West,
Zip 34209–4669; tel. 941/792–6611, **A**1 2 3 7 10 **F**3 11 15 16 17 18 20 22 24
26 28 29 30 31 34 35 40 43 45 48 49 50 53 57 58 59 64 68 70 74 75 77 78 79
80 81 85 87 90 91 92 93 94 96 100 107 108 110 111 114 115 118 119 126
129 130 131 132 141 146 147 148 149 150 154 **S** HCA Healthcare, Nashville, TN
Primary Contact: Randy Currin, Chief Executive Officer
COO: Ben Brodersen, Vice President of Operations
CFO: Andrew Smith, Chief Financial Officer
CMO: Alan Harmatz, M.D., Chief Medical Officer
CIO: Shannon Piatkowski, Director Information Technology
CHR: Veronica Lequeux, Vice President Human Resources
CNO: Adam Fletcher, Chief Nursing Officer
Web address: www.blakemedicalcenter.com
Control: Corporation, Investor–owned (for–profit) **Service:** General medical and
surgical

Staffed Beds: 383 **Admissions:** 15650 **Census:** 214 **Outpatient Visits:**
94570 **Births:** 0 **Total Expense ($000):** 212975 **Payroll Expense
($000):** 84765 **Personnel:** 1143

CENTERSTONE HOSPITAL (104040), 2020 26th Avenue East,
Zip 34208–7753, Mailing Address: P.O. Box 9478, Zip 34206–9478;
tel. 941/782–4600, (Nonreporting) **A**10 13
Primary Contact: Melissa Larkin–Skinner, Chief Executive Officer
CFO: Sean Gingras, CPA, Chief Financial Officer
CMO: Ranjay Halder, M.D., Chief Medical Director
CIO: Heidi L Blair, Vice President Administration
CHR: Colleen O'Connor, Director Human Resources
Web address: www.manateeglens.org
Control: Individual, Investor–owned (for–profit) **Service:** Other specialty treatment

Staffed Beds: 30

☐ **LAKEWOOD RANCH MEDICAL CENTER (100299)**, 8330 Lakewood Ranch
Boulevard, Zip 34202–5174; tel. 941/782–2100, (Nonreporting) **A**1 10 **S**
Universal Health Services, Inc., King of Prussia, PA
Primary Contact: Andrew Guz, Chief Executive Officer
COO: Linda S Widra, FACHE, Ph.D., R.N., Chief Operating Officer
CFO: Gerald Christine, Chief Financial Officer
CHR: Trish Morales, Director Human Resources
Web address: www.lakewoodranchmedicalcenter.com
Control: Corporation, Investor–owned (for–profit) **Service:** General medical and
surgical

Staffed Beds: 120

☐ **MANATEE MEMORIAL HOSPITAL (100035)**, 206 Second Street East,
Zip 34208–1000; tel. 941/746–5111, (Nonreporting) **A**1 2 3 5 10 12 13 **S**
Universal Health Services, Inc., King of Prussia, PA
Primary Contact: Kevin DiLallo, Chief Executive Officer
COO: Camie Patterson, Chief Operating Officer
CFO: Mark A Tierney, Chief Financial Officer
CMO: Eric Deppert, M.D., Chief Medical Officer
CIO: Troy Beaubien, Director Information Services
CHR: Sheree Threewits, Director Human Resources
CNO: Candace Susan Smith, Chief Nursing Officer
Web address: www.manateememorial.com
Control: Partnership, Investor–owned (for–profit) **Service:** General medical and
surgical

Staffed Beds: 319

Many Facility Codes have changed. Please refer to the AHA Guide Code Chart. © 2018 AHA Guide

☐ **SUNCOAST BEHAVIORAL HEALTH CENTER (104078)**, 4480 51st Street West, Zip 34210–2855; tel. 941/251–5000, (Nonreporting) **A1 S** Universal Health Services, Inc., King of Prussia, PA
Primary Contact: Brandy Hamilton, Chief Executive Officer
CFO: Linda Weymouth, Chief Financial Officer
CMO: Randolph Hemsath, M.D., Medical Director
CNO: Janey Sweeney, Chief Nursing Officer
Web address: www.suncoastbhc.com
Control: Corporation, Investor–owned (for–profit) **Service:** Children's hospital psychiatric

Staffed Beds: 80

BRANDON—Hillsborough County

⊞ **BRANDON REGIONAL HOSPITAL (100243)**, 119 Oakfield Drive, Zip 33511–5779; tel. 813/681–5551, (Nonreporting) **A1 3 5 10 S** HCA Healthcare, Nashville, TN
Primary Contact: Bland Eng, Chief Executive Officer
COO: Liz Durrence, Chief Operating Officer
CFO: Gary Searls, Chief Financial Officer
CMO: Joseph C. Corcoran, D.O., Chief Medical Officer
CIO: Aaron Fountain, Chief Information Officer
CHR: Doug Goodman, Vice President Human Resources
CNO: William Kyle Thrift, Chief Nursing Officer
Web address: www.brandonhospital.com
Control: Corporation, Investor–owned (for–profit) **Service:** General medical and surgical

Staffed Beds: 407

BROOKSVILLE—Hernando County

⊞ **BAYFRONT HEALTH BROOKSVILLE (100071)**, 17240 Cortez Boulevard, Zip 34601–8921, Mailing Address: P.O. Box 37, Zip 34605–0037; tel. 352/796–5111, (Includes BAYFRONT HEALTH SPRING HILL, 10461 Quality Drive, Spring Hill, FL, Zip 34609–9634; tel. 352/688–8200; Michael Irvin, Chief Executive Officer) (Nonreporting) **A1 10 S** Community Health Systems, Inc., Franklin, TN
Primary Contact: Kenneth R. Wicker, Chief Executive Officer
COO: Scott Hartsell, Chief Operating Officer
CFO: Matthew Seagroves, Chief Financial Officer
CMO: Mohammad A Joud, M.D., Chief of Staff
CIO: Lee Burch, Director Management Information Systems
CHR: Claudia L Jack, Director Associate Relations
Web address: www.brooksvilleregionalhospital.org
Control: Corporation, Investor–owned (for–profit) **Service:** General medical and surgical

Staffed Beds: 120

⊞ **HEALTHSOUTH REHABILITATION HOSPITAL OF SPRING HILL (103042)**, 12440 Cortez Boulevard, Zip 34613–2628; tel. 352/592–4250, (Nonreporting) **A1 10 S** Encompass Health Corporation, Birmingham, AL
Primary Contact: Jeffrey Alexander, Chief Executive Officer
CFO: Kimberly Lunt, Controller
CMO: Mira Zelin, D.O., Medical Director
CIO: Myra Merillo, Supervisor Health Information Management
CHR: Mary Salamanca, Director Human Resources
Web address: www.healthsouthspringhill.com
Control: Corporation, Investor–owned (for–profit) **Service:** Rehabilitation

Staffed Beds: 80

⊞ **OAK HILL HOSPITAL (100264)**, 11375 Cortez Boulevard, Zip 34613–5409; tel. 352/596–6632, (Nonreporting) **A1 2 3 10 S** HCA Healthcare, Nashville, TN
Primary Contact: Mickey Smith, Chief Executive Officer
COO: Steve Young, Chief Operating Officer
CFO: Matt Romero, Chief Financial Officer
CMO: Ed Nast, M.D., Chief Medical Officer
CHR: Charles Snider, Vice President Human Resources
CNO: Leanne Salazar, Chief Nursing Officer
Web address: www.oakhillhospital.com
Control: Corporation, Investor–owned (for–profit) **Service:** General medical and surgical

Staffed Beds: 262

☐ **SPRINGBROOK HOSPITAL (104057)**, 7007 Grove Road, Zip 34609–8610; tel. 352/596–4306, (Nonreporting) **A1 10**
Primary Contact: Timothy Cowart, Administrator
Web address: www.springbrookhospital.org/
Control: Other not–for–profit (including NFP Corporation) **Service:** Psychiatric

Staffed Beds: 66

CAPE CORAL—Lee County

★ ⇑ **CAPE CORAL HOSPITAL (100244)**, 636 Del Prado Boulevard, Zip 33990–2695; tel. 239/424–2000, **A2** 10 21 **F3** 11 13 14 18 20 28 29 30 34 35 40 45 46 48 50 51 56 57 59 60 65 66 68 70 74 75 76 77 79 81 82 84 85 86 87 93 94 97 107 108 111 114 119 129 130 132 135 146 147 148 **S** Lee Health, Fort Myers, FL
Primary Contact: Lawrence Antonucci, M.D., President and Chief Executive Officer
CFO: Ben Spence, Chief Financial Officer
CMO: Mark Greenberg, M.D., Chief Medical Officer
CIO: Mike Smith, Chief Information Officer
CHR: Jon C Cecil, Chief Human Resource Officer
CNO: Lisa Sgarlata, MSN, Chief Patient Care Officer
Web address: www.leememorial.org
Control: Hospital district or authority, Government, nonfederal **Service:** General medical and surgical

Staffed Beds: 291 **Admissions:** 16429 **Census:** 183 **Outpatient Visits:** 240532 **Births:** 1416 **Total Expense ($000):** 201369 **Payroll Expense ($000):** 97217 **Personnel:** 1364

CELEBRATION—Osceola County

FLORIDA HOSPITAL CELEBRATION HEALTH See Florida Hospital, Orlando

CHATTAHOOCHEE—Gadsden County

FLORIDA STATE HOSPITAL (104000), US Highway 90 East, Zip 32324–1000, Mailing Address: P.O. Box 1000, Zip 32324–1000; tel. 850/663–7536, (Nonreporting) **A10**
Primary Contact: Marguerite J. Morgan, Administrator
CFO: Bill Jones, Chief Financial Officer
CMO: Josefina Balulga, M.D., Clinical Director
CIO: Wesley Pelham
CHR: Keri Bassett, Human Resources Business Partner
Web address: www.dcf.state.fl.us/institutions/fsh
Control: State, Government, nonfederal **Service:** Psychiatric

Staffed Beds: 987

CHIPLEY—Washington County

☐ **NORTHWEST FLORIDA COMMUNITY HOSPITAL (101308)**, 1360 Brickyard Road, Zip 32428–6303, Mailing Address: P.O. Box 889, Zip 32428–0889; tel. 850/638–1610, (Total facility includes 34 beds in nursing home–type unit) **A1** 10 18 **F**11 15 29 30 34 40 45 56 57 59 65 68 81 82 85 93 97 107 108 110 111 115 119 127 130 131 132 133 146 148 153 154 **S** Alliant Management Services, Louisville, KY
Primary Contact: Michael A. Kozar, Chief Executive Officer
COO: Janet Kinney, Chief Operating Officer
CFO: Marcey Black, Chief Financial Officer
CHR: Shelia Schiefelbein, Coordinator Human Resources
CNO: Joan Beard, Chief Nursing Officer
Web address: www.nfch.org
Control: Corporation, Investor–owned (for–profit) **Service:** General medical and surgical

Staffed Beds: 59 **Admissions:** 845 **Census:** 46 **Outpatient Visits:** 42991 **Births:** 0

CLEARWATER—Pinellas County

⊞ **MORTON PLANT HOSPITAL (100127)**, 300 Pinellas Street, Zip 33756–3804, Mailing Address: P.O. Box 210, Zip 33757–0210; tel. 727/462–7000, (Total facility includes 120 beds in nursing home–type unit) **A1** 2 3 5 10 **F3** 11 13 15 17 18 20 22 24 26 28 29 30 31 34 35 36 37 38 40 44 45 46 47 48 49 50 51 53 54 55 56 57 58 59 60 61 62 64 65 66 68 70 72 74 75 76 77 78 79 80 81 82 84 85 86 87 91 92 93 98 100 101 102 107 108 109 110 111 112 114 115 116 117 118 119 120 121 123 124 126 128 129 130 131 132 135 143 145 146 147 148 149 154 **S** Morton Plant Mease Health Care, Clearwater, FL
Primary Contact: N. Kristopher. Hoce, President
CFO: Carl Tremonti, Chief Financial Officer
CMO: Jeff Jensen, D.O., Vice President, Medical Affairs
CIO: Timothy Thompson, Senior Vice President and Chief Information Officer
CHR: Angel Brown, Director Human Resources
CNO: Thomas Doria, Vice President Patient Services – West
Web address: www.mortonplant.com
Control: Other not–for–profit (including NFP Corporation) **Service:** General medical and surgical

Staffed Beds: 710 **Admissions:** 28159 **Census:** 328 **Outpatient Visits:** 383316 **Births:** 2164 **Total Expense ($000):** 503954 **Payroll Expense ($000):** 151012 **Personnel:** 2848

FL

Hospital, Medicare Provider Number, Address, Telephone, Approval, Facility, and Physician Codes, Health Care System

★ American Hospital Association (AHA) membership   ○ Healthcare Facilities Accreditation Program   ⇑ Center for Improvement in Healthcare Quality Accreditation
☐ The Joint Commission accreditation   ◇ DNV Healthcare Inc. accreditation   △ Commission on Accreditation of Rehabilitation Facilities (CARF) accreditation

☐ **WINDMOOR HEALTHCARE OF CLEARWATER (104017)**, 11300 US 19 North, Zip 33764; tel. 727/541–2646, (Nonreporting) **A**1 10 **S** Universal Health Services, Inc., King of Prussia, PA
Primary Contact: Wendy Merson, Chief Executive Officer
Web address: www.windmoor.com
Control: Corporation, Investor–owned (for–profit) **Service**: Psychiatric

Staffed Beds: 100

CLERMONT—Lake County

☐ **SOUTH LAKE HOSPITAL (100051)**, 1900 Don Wickham Drive, Zip 34711–1979; tel. 352/394–4071, (Total facility includes 30 beds in nursing home–type unit) **A**1 3 10 **F**3 8 11 13 15 18 20 22 26 28 29 30 31 32 34 35 37 40 45 46 47 48 49 50 51 53 54 57 59 60 62 64 65 66 68 70 74 75 76 77 78 79 81 82 85 86 87 89 92 93 107 108 110 111 114 115 116 117 119 120 121 124 126 127 128 130 131 132 135 146 147 148 149 154 **P**6 **S** Orlando Health, Orlando, FL
Primary Contact: John Moore, President
COO: Paul Johns, Chief Operating Officer
CFO: Lance Sewell, Chief Financial Officer
CHR: Joy L. Sylvester, Administrator, People Services
CNO: Bonnie Onofre, Chief Nursing Officer
Web address: www.southlakehospital.com
Control: Hospital district or authority, Government, nonfederal **Service**: General medical and surgical

Staffed Beds: 170 **Admissions**: 10379 **Census**: 136 **Outpatient Visits**: 123328 **Births**: 767 **Total Expense ($000)**: 187423 **Payroll Expense ($000)**: 70328 **Personnel**: 1235

CLEWISTON—Hendry County

☒ **HENDRY REGIONAL MEDICAL CENTER (101309)**, 524 West Sagamore Avenue, Zip 33440–3514; tel. 863/902–3000, **A**1 10 18 **F**3 11 15 29 34 35 40 45 50 57 59 64 65 68 70 75 77 79 80 82 85 91 93 97 107 110 111 114 119 127 133 135 146 **P**6 **S** QHR, Brentwood, TN
Primary Contact: R D Williams, Chief Executive Officer
CFO: John Beltz, Chief Financial Officer
CMO: Leonard Carroll, M.D., Chief of Staff
CIO: Harrington Fuller, Information Technology Director
CHR: Lisa Miller, Director Human Resources
CNO: Rebecca Springer, MSN, R.N., Chief Nursing Officer
Web address: www.hendryregional.org
Control: Hospital district or authority, Government, nonfederal **Service**: General medical and surgical

Staffed Beds: 25 **Admissions**: 461 **Census**: 3 **Outpatient Visits**: 34204 **Births**: 0 **Total Expense ($000)**: 30970 **Payroll Expense ($000)**: 14028 **Personnel**: 238

COCOA BEACH—Brevard County

☒ **HEALTH FIRST CAPE CANAVERAL HOSPITAL (100177)**, 701 West Cocoa Beach Causeway, Zip 32931–5595, Mailing Address: P.O. Box 320069, Zip 32932–0069; tel. 321/799–7111, **A**1 10 **F**3 11 13 15 18 20 22 26 29 30 31 34 40 41 45 46 49 50 54 59 60 64 68 70 74 75 76 77 78 79 80 81 85 86 87 93 102 107 108 109 110 111 114 115 118 119 129 130 132 141 146 147 148 149 154 **S** Health First, Inc., Rockledge, FL
Primary Contact: Aaron Robinson, Chief Executive Officer, Health First Community Hospitals
COO: Deborah Angerami, Chief Operating Officer, Health First Community Hospitals
CFO: Joseph G Felkner, Senior Vice President Finance and Chief Financial Officer
CMO: Lee Scheinbart, M.D., Vice President Medical Affairs, Health First Community Hospitals
CIO: Alex Popowycz, Senior Vice President and Chief Information Officer
CHR: Paula Just, Vice President Human Resources
CNO: Connie Bradley, R.N., MSN, FACHE, Chief Nursing Officer
Web address: www.health–first.org
Control: Other not–for–profit (including NFP Corporation) **Service**: General medical and surgical

Staffed Beds: 144 **Admissions**: 7035 **Census**: 77 **Outpatient Visits**: 112054 **Births**: 715 **Total Expense ($000)**: 126584 **Payroll Expense ($000)**: 58827 **Personnel**: 532

CORAL GABLES—Miami–Dade County

☒ **BAPTIST HEALTH SOUTH FLORIDA, DOCTORS HOSPITAL (100296)**, 5000 University Drive, Zip 33146–2094; tel. 786/308–3000, **A**1 3 5 10 **F**3 11 18 29 30 31 34 35 37 40 45 47 49 63 64 65 67 74 75 76 77 78 79 81 82 84 85 86 87 93 94 102 107 108 111 114 115 119 124 126 130 131 132 140 141 143 146 148 149 150 154 **S** Baptist Health South Florida, Coral Gables, FL
Primary Contact: Nelson Lazo, Chief Executive Officer
CFO: Maria J Yanez, Chief Financial Officer
Web address: www.baptisthealth.net
Control: Other not–for–profit (including NFP Corporation) **Service**: General medical and surgical

Staffed Beds: 126 **Admissions**: 6398 **Census**: 84 **Outpatient Visits**: 61172 **Births**: 0 **Total Expense ($000)**: 181951 **Payroll Expense ($000)**: 59189 **Personnel**: 792

☒ **CORAL GABLES HOSPITAL (100183)**, 3100 Douglas Road, Zip 33134–6914; tel. 305/445–8461, (Nonreporting) **A**1 10 **S** TENET Healthcare Corporation, Dallas, TX
Primary Contact: Cristina Jimenez, Chief Executive Officer
COO: Madison Workman, Chief Operating Officer
CFO: Henry Capote, Interim Chief Financial Officer
CMO: Pedro Friarte, Director of Physician Services
CIO: Mercy Hermosa, Director of Information System
CHR: Ana Paguaga, Director of Human Resources
Web address: www.coralgableshospital.com
Control: Corporation, Investor–owned (for–profit) **Service**: General medical and surgical

Staffed Beds: 256

CORAL SPRINGS—Broward County

☒ **BROWARD HEALTH CORAL SPRINGS (100276)**, 3000 Coral Hills Drive, Zip 33065–4108; tel. 954/344–3000, **A**1 10 **F**3 11 12 13 15 20 29 31 34 35 40 41 48 51 55 57 58 59 61 63 64 66 68 70 72 74 75 76 77 78 79 80 81 82 84 85 86 87 88 89 93 107 108 111 114 115 118 119 126 129 130 131 132 143 146 147 148 154 **P**6 **S** Broward Health, Fort Lauderdale, FL
Primary Contact: Jared M. Smith, Chief Executive Officer
COO: Michael Leopold, Chief Operating Officer
CFO: Onel Rodriguez, Chief Financial Officer
CMO: Kutty Chandran, M.D., Regional Medical Officer
CHR: Janene John, Chief Human Resource Officer
CNO: Carolyn Lizann Carter, Chief Nursing Officer
Web address: www.browardhealth.org
Control: Hospital district or authority, Government, nonfederal **Service**: General medical and surgical

Staffed Beds: 196 **Admissions**: 12596 **Census**: 127 **Outpatient Visits**: 134328 **Births**: 2212 **Total Expense ($000)**: 158462 **Payroll Expense ($000)**: 62882 **Personnel**: 951

CRESTVIEW—Okaloosa County

☒ **NORTH OKALOOSA MEDICAL CENTER (100122)**, 151 Redstone Avenue SE, Zip 32539–6026; tel. 850/689–8100, **A**1 10 **F**3 8 11 13 15 18 20 22 28 29 30 34 35 40 47 49 50 54 59 64 70 75 76 79 81 85 86 87 89 107 108 109 110 111 114 115 116 117 118 119 126 127 129 130 131 146 147 148 149 150 154 **P**6 **S** Community Health Systems, Inc., Franklin, TN
Primary Contact: Ronnie Daves, Chief Executive Officer
CFO: Jim Andrews, Chief Financial Officer
CMO: Michael Foley, M.D., Chief Medical Officer
CIO: Jenny Zeitler, Network Administrator
CHR: Melody M Miller–Collette, Director Human Resources
CNO: Nina Perez, R.N., MSN, Chief Nursing Officer
Web address: www.northokaloosa.com
Control: Corporation, Investor–owned (for–profit) **Service**: General medical and surgical

Staffed Beds: 110 **Admissions**: 5182 **Census**: 55

CRYSTAL RIVER—Citrus County

☒ **SEVEN RIVERS REGIONAL MEDICAL CENTER (100249)**, 6201 North Suncoast Boulevard, Zip 34428–6712; tel. 352/795–6560, (Nonreporting) **A**1 10 19 **S** Community Health Systems, Inc., Franklin, TN
Primary Contact: Linda Stockton, Interim Chief Executive Officer
CFO: Vickie Magurean, Chief Financial Officer
CHR: Joann Mramor, Director Human Resources
CNO: Cynthia Heitzman, R.N., Chief Nursing Officer
Web address: www.srrmc.com
Control: Corporation, Investor–owned (for–profit) **Service**: General medical and surgical

Staffed Beds: 128

CUTLER BAY—Miami–Dade County

HEALTHSOUTH REHABILITATION HOSPITAL See Healthsouth Rehabilitation Hospital of Miami

★ **HEALTHSOUTH REHABILITATION HOSPITAL OF MIAMI (103038)**, 20601 Old Cutler Road, Zip 33189–2400; tel. 305/251–3800, (Nonreporting) **A**10 **S** Encompass Health Corporation, Birmingham, AL
Primary Contact: Enrique A. Vicens–Rivera Jr, JD, Chief Executive Officer
CFO: Reyna Hernandez, Chief Financial Officer
CIO: Miguel Cruz, Medical Staff Credentialing Coordinator
CHR: Susan Riley, Director Human Resources
CNO: Ellen Romanowski, Chief Nursing Officer
Web address: www.healthsouthmiami.com
Control: Corporation, Investor–owned (for–profit) **Service**: Rehabilitation

Staffed Beds: 60

Many Facility Codes have changed. Please refer to the AHA Guide Code Chart. © 2018 AHA Guide

DADE CITY—Pasco County

⊞ **FLORIDA HOSPITAL DADE CITY (100211)**, 13100 Fort King Road, Zip 33525–5294; tel. 352/521–1100, (Nonreporting) **A**1 10 **S** Adventist Health System Sunbelt Health Care Corporation, Altamonte Springs, FL
Primary Contact: Amanda Maggard, Chief Executive Officer
CFO: Ann Barr, Interim Chief Financial Officer
CMO: Petros Tsambiras, M.D., Chief of Staff
CIO: Cheryl Kaufman, Director Health Information Management
CHR: Tabatha Wallace, Director Human Resources
Web address: www.floridahospital.com/dade-city
Control: Corporation, Investor–owned (for–profit) **Service**: General medical and surgical

Staffed Beds: 120

DAVENPORT—Polk County

⊞ **HEART OF FLORIDA REGIONAL MEDICAL CENTER (100137)**, 40100 Highway 27, Zip 33837–5906; tel. 863/422–4971, **A**1 10 **F**3 12 13 15 17 18 20 22 26 28 29 30 34 35 37 40 45 49 50 51 57 59 60 64 68 70 74 75 76 77 79 81 82 85 87 89 92 93 96 100 107 110 111 114 115 116 117 118 119 126 130 132 135 144 146 147 148 149 154 **S** Community Health Systems, Inc., Franklin, TN
Primary Contact: Ann Barnhart, Chief Executive Officer
CFO: Tonja Mosley, Chief Financial Officer
CMO: Claudio Manubens, M.D., Chief of Staff
CIO: Louis Jones, Director Management Information Systems
CHR: Joan Allard, Director Human Resources
CNO: Dottie Mileto, Chief Nursing Officer
Web address: www.heartofflorida.com
Control: Corporation, Investor–owned (for–profit) **Service**: General medical and surgical

Staffed Beds: 193 **Admissions**: 9820 **Census**: 101 **Outpatient Visits**: 78013 **Births**: 893 **Total Expense ($000)**: 140578 **Payroll Expense ($000)**: 52906 **Personnel**: 674

DAYTONA BEACH—Volusia County

⊞ **FLORIDA HOSPITAL MEMORIAL MEDICAL CENTER (100068)**, 301 Memorial Medical Parkway, Zip 32117–5167; tel. 386/676–6000, (Includes FLORIDA HOSPITAL–OCEANSIDE, 264 South Atlantic Avenue, Ormond Beach, FL, Zip 32176–8192; tel. 386/672–4161) **A**1 2 10 **F**3 11 12 13 15 17 18 20 22 24 26 28 29 30 31 32 34 35 40 41 45 46 47 49 50 53 54 57 58 59 65 70 72 74 75 76 77 78 79 81 85 86 87 89 90 91 92 93 96 97 107 108 109 110 111 112 114 115 116 117 119 120 121 123 124 130 131 132 135 146 147 148 149 154 **P**6 **S** Adventist Health System Sunbelt Health Care Corporation, Altamonte Springs, FL
Primary Contact: Ed Noseworthy, Chief Executive Officer
COO: Darlinda Copeland, Chief Operating Officer
CFO: Debora Thomas, Chief Financial Officer
CMO: Kris David Gray, Chief Medical Officer
CHR: Opal R Howard, Executive Director Human Resources
CNO: Michele Goeb–Burkett, R.N., MSN, Chief Nursing Officer
Web address: www.floridahospitalmemorial.org
Control: Church operated, Nongovernment, not–for–profit **Service**: General medical and surgical

Staffed Beds: 326 **Admissions**: 16725 **Census**: 259 **Outpatient Visits**: 333871 **Births**: 1586 **Total Expense ($000)**: 338870 **Payroll Expense ($000)**: 135116 **Personnel**: 2027

☐ **HALIFAX HEALTH MEDICAL CENTER OF DAYTONA BEACH (100017)**, 303 North Clyde Morris Boulevard, Zip 32114–2700; tel. 386/425–4000, (Includes HALIFAX BEHAVIORAL SERVICES, 841 Jimmy Ann Drive, Daytona Beach, FL, Zip 32117–4599; tel. 386/425–3900; HALIFAX HEALTH MEDICAL CENTER OF PORT ORANGE, 1041 Dunlawton Avenue, Port Orange, FL, Zip 32127; tel. 386/425–4700; Ann Martorano, Chief Operating Officer) **A**1 2 3 5 10 **F**3 8 12 13 14 17 18 20 22 24 26 28 29 30 31 32 33 34 35 40 41 43 45 46 47 49 50 53 55 57 59 60 62 64 65 66 70 72 74 75 76 77 78 79 81 82 85 86 87 88 89 90 91 93 94 96 97 98 99 100 101 102 103 105 119 120 121 123 124 126 131 132 135 138 145 146 147 148 149 153
Primary Contact: Jeff Feasel, Chief Executive Officer
COO: Mark Billings, Chief Operating Officer
CFO: Eric Peburn, Chief Financial Officer
CMO: Margaret Crossman, M.D., Chief Medical Officer
CIO: Tom Stafford, Chief Information Officer
CHR: Kimberly Fulcher, Chief Human Resources Officer
CNO: Catherine Luchsinger, MSN, Chief Nursing Officer
Web address: www.halifax.org
Control: Hospital district or authority, Government, nonfederal **Service**: General medical and surgical

Staffed Beds: 668 **Admissions**: 23213 **Census**: 378 **Outpatient Visits**: 263594 **Births**: 1761 **Total Expense ($000)**: 495172 **Payroll Expense ($000)**: 209743 **Personnel**: 2470

★ **SELECT SPECIALTY HOSPITAL DAYTONA BEACH (102030)**, 301 Memorial Medical Parkway, 11th Floor, Zip 32117–5167; tel. 386/231–3436, (Nonreporting) **S** Select Medical Corporation, Mechanicsburg, PA
Primary Contact: Adrianne Lutes, Chief Executive Officer
Web address: www.daytonabeach.selectspecialtyhospitals.com
Control: Corporation, Investor–owned (for–profit) **Service**: Acute long–term care hospital

Staffed Beds: 34

DEERFIELD BEACH—Broward County

★ △ **BROWARD HEALTH NORTH (100086)**, 201 East Sample Road, Zip 33064–3502; tel. 954/941–8300, **A**2 7 10 **F**3 6 11 15 17 18 20 22 29 30 31 34 35 37 40 43 45 46 49 50 51 57 58 59 64 66 68 70 74 75 77 78 79 80 81 82 85 86 87 90 92 93 94 96 100 107 108 110 111 114 115 117 118 119 129 130 131 132 143 145 146 148 154 **S** Broward Health, Fort Lauderdale, FL
Primary Contact: Alice Taylor, R.N., MSN, Chief Executive Officer
COO: Susan Newton, Chief Operating Officer
CFO: Kim Braxl–Cole, Chief Financial Officer
CMO: Narendra Maheshwari, M.D., Chief of Staff
CHR: Carl McDonald, Chief Human Resources Officer
CNO: Bettiann S Ruditz, MS, R.N., Chief Nursing Officer
Web address: www.browardhealth.org
Control: Hospital district or authority, Government, nonfederal **Service**: General medical and surgical

Staffed Beds: 344 **Admissions**: 14378 **Census**: 213 **Outpatient Visits**: 103671 **Births**: 0 **Total Expense ($000)**: 244882 **Payroll Expense ($000)**: 89221 **Personnel**: 1324

DEFUNIAK SPRINGS—Walton County

HEALTHMARK REGIONAL MEDICAL CENTER (100081), 4413 US Highway 331 South, Zip 32435–6307; tel. 850/951–4500, **A**10 **F**3 29 34 35 40 45 46 48 50 55 56 59 62 66 70 75 81 82 86 97 107 111 114 115 119 127 130 133 135 143 146 149 152 **P**5
Primary Contact: James H. Thompson, Ph.D., FACHE, Owner and Chief Executive Officer
COO: Gerald C Beard, Chief Operating Officer
CFO: Jim Brewer, M.P.H., Chief Financial Officer
CMO: Edward Tenewitz, M.D., Chief of Staff
CIO: Ray Downs, Senior Staff Accountant
CHR: Debra Tiller, Director Personnel and Administrative Secretary
Web address: www.healthmarkregional.com
Control: Individual, Investor–owned (for–profit) **Service**: General medical and surgical

Staffed Beds: 50 **Admissions**: 657 **Census**: 7 **Outpatient Visits**: 19829 **Births**: 0 **Total Expense ($000)**: 9820 **Payroll Expense ($000)**: 4335 **Personnel**: 123

DELAND—Volusia County

★ **FLORIDA HOSPITAL DELAND (100045)**, 701 West Plymouth Avenue, Zip 32720–3236; tel. 386/943–4522, (Nonreporting) **A**2 10 **S** Adventist Health System Sunbelt Health Care Corporation, Altamonte Springs, FL
Primary Contact: Lorenzo Brown, Chief Executive Officer
COO: Samuel Aguero, Chief Operating Officer
CFO: Kyle Glass, Chief Financial Officer
CMO: Samuel Edwards, M.D., Chief of Staff
CIO: Kevin Piper, Director Information Systems
CNO: Patricia Ann Stark, R.N., CNO
Web address: www.fhdeland.org
Control: Other not–for–profit (including NFP Corporation) **Service**: General medical and surgical

Staffed Beds: 156

DELRAY BEACH—Palm Beach County

⊞ △ **DELRAY MEDICAL CENTER (100258)**, 5352 Linton Boulevard, Zip 33484–6580; tel. 561/498–4440, (Includes FAIR OAKS PAVILION, 5440 Linton Boulevard, Delray Beach, FL, Zip 33484–6578; tel. 561/495–1000; PINECREST REHABILITATION HOSPITAL, 5360 Linton Boulevard, Delray Beach, FL, Zip 33484–6538; tel. 561/495–0400) **A**1 3 5 7 10 **F**3 4 11 12 15 17 18 20 22 24 26 28 29 30 31 34 35 37 38 40 43 45 46 49 50 51 56 57 58 59 60 64 65 70 74 75 77 78 79 80 81 82 83 84 85 87 90 91 93 94 96 97 98 100 101 102 103 104 107 108 111 115 118 119 126 129 130 132 135 143 146 147 148 **S** TENET Healthcare Corporation, Dallas, TX
Primary Contact: Margaret Gill, Chief Executive Officer
COO: Teresa C. Urquhart, Chief Operating Officer
CMO: Anthony Dardano, M.D., Chief Medical Officer
CIO: Robens Rosena, Director Information Systems
CHR: Shannon Wills, Director Human Resources
Web address: www.delraymedicalctr.com
Control: Corporation, Investor–owned (for–profit) **Service**: General medical and surgical

Staffed Beds: 536 **Admissions**: 18447 **Census**: 284 **Outpatient Visits**: 90908 **Births**: 0 **Personnel**: 1671

Hospital, Medicare Provider Number, Address, Telephone, Approval, Facility, and Physician Codes, Health Care System

★ American Hospital Association (AHA) membership
☐ The Joint Commission accreditation
○ Healthcare Facilities Accreditation Program
◇ DNV Healthcare Inc. accreditation
⇑ Center for Improvement in Healthcare Quality Accreditation
△ Commission on Accreditation of Rehabilitation Facilities (CARF) accreditation

FL

DUNEDIN—Pinellas County

☒ **BAYCARE ALLIANT HOSPITAL (102021)**, 601 Main Street, Zip 34698–5848; tel. 727/736–9991, **A**1 10 **F**1 3 28 29 34 35 36 57 130 148 154 **S** Trinity Health, Livonia, MI
Primary Contact: Jacqueline Arocho, Administrator
CFO: John Proni, CPA, Manager Finance and Operations
CMO: Leonard Dunn, M.D., Chief Medical Officer
CHR: Darlene Shelton, Coordinator Team Resources
Web address: www.baycare.org
Control: Other not–for–profit (including NFP Corporation) **Service:** Acute long–term care hospital

Staffed Beds: 35 **Admissions:** 391 **Census:** 29 **Outpatient Visits:** 0 **Births:** 0 **Total Expense ($000):** 19062 **Payroll Expense ($000):** 6765 **Personnel:** 103

☒ **MEASE DUNEDIN HOSPITAL (100043)**, 601 Main Street, Zip 34698–5891; tel. 727/733–1111, **A**1 10 **F**3 12 15 18 26 29 30 31 34 35 37 38 40 44 45 49 56 57 59 60 62 64 68 70 74 75 78 79 81 84 85 86 87 97 98 99 100 102 103 107 108 110 111 114 118 119 130 132 135 143 145 146 149 154 **S** Trinity Health, Livonia, MI
Primary Contact: Lou Galdieri, R.N., President
CFO: Carl Tremonti, Chief Financial Officer
CMO: Tony Schuster, M.D., Vice President of Physician Services
CIO: Tim Thompson, Senior Vice President, Information Services and Chief Information Officer
CHR: Kyle J Barr, Senior Vice President, Chief Team Resources Officer
CNO: Thomas Doria, Vice President, Patient Services and Chief Nursing Officer
Web address: www.mpmhealth.com
Control: Other not–for–profit (including NFP Corporation) **Service:** General medical and surgical

Staffed Beds: 120 **Admissions:** 7015 **Census:** 85 **Outpatient Visits:** 37178 **Births:** 0 **Total Expense ($000):** 92934 **Payroll Expense ($000):** 36813 **Personnel:** 580

EGLIN AFB—Okaloosa County

☒ **U.S. AIR FORCE REGIONAL HOSPITAL**, 307 Boatner Road, Suite 114, Zip 32542–1282; tel. 850/883–8221, (Nonreporting) **A**1 3 5 **S** Department of the Air Force, Washington, DC
Primary Contact: Colonel Pamela Smith, Commander
Web address: www.eglin.af.mil
Control: Air Force, Government, federal **Service:** General medical and surgical

Staffed Beds: 57

ENGLEWOOD—Sarasota County

☒ **ENGLEWOOD COMMUNITY HOSPITAL (100267)**, 700 Medical Boulevard, Zip 34223–3978; tel. 941/475–6571, (Nonreporting) **A**1 10 **S** HCA Healthcare, Nashville, TN
Primary Contact: Valerie L. Powell–Stafford, Chief Executive Officer
COO: Alex Chang, Chief Operating Officer
CFO: Vickie Magurean, Chief Financial Officer
CMO: L. Craig McAskill, M.D., Chief Medical Officer
CNO: Kathleen Pace, MSN, R.N., Chief Nursing Officer
Web address: www.englewoodcommunityhospital.com
Control: Corporation, Investor–owned (for–profit) **Service:** General medical and surgical

Staffed Beds: 100

FERNANDINA BEACH—Nassau County

☒ **BAPTIST MEDICAL CENTER NASSAU (100140)**, 1250 South 18th Street, Zip 32034–3098; tel. 904/321–3500, **A**1 10 **F**3 11 13 15 18 26 28 29 30 34 35 40 45 49 64 70 74 76 79 81 82 85 91 92 93 102 107 108 110 111 114 115 119 124 129 132 146 148 149 **S** Baptist Health, Jacksonville, FL
Primary Contact: Edward T. Hubel, FACHE, President
CFO: Patricia K Hausauer, Director Finance
CHR: Erin Jackson, Human Resources Specialist
Web address: www.baptistjax.com/locations/baptist–medical–center–nassau
Control: Other not–for–profit (including NFP Corporation) **Service:** General medical and surgical

Staffed Beds: 52 **Admissions:** 3819 **Census:** 34 **Outpatient Visits:** 60641 **Births:** 534 **Total Expense ($000):** 62157 **Payroll Expense ($000):** 19291 **Personnel:** 354

FORT LAUDERDALE—Broward County

☒ **BROWARD HEALTH IMPERIAL POINT (100200)**, 6401 North Federal Highway, Zip 33308–1495; tel. 954/776–8500, **A**1 3 10 **F**3 11 12 15 20 29 34 35 40 45 51 53 55 57 58 59 61 63 64 68 70 74 75 77 78 79 80 81 82 84 85 86 87 93 98 100 102 107 108 110 111 114 115 118 119 126 130 131 132 143 146 147 148 **S** Broward Health, Fort Lauderdale, FL
Primary Contact: Jonathan Watkins, Chief Executive Officer
COO: Netonua Reyes, MSN, Chief Operating Officer and Chief Nursing Officer
CHR: Carl McDonald, Regional Director Human Resources
CNO: Netonua Reyes, MSN, Chief Operating Officer and Chief Nursing Officer
Web address: www.browardhealth.org
Control: Hospital district or authority, Government, nonfederal **Service:** General medical and surgical

Staffed Beds: 180 **Admissions:** 8190 **Census:** 110 **Outpatient Visits:** 83689 **Births:** 0 **Total Expense ($000):** 120702 **Payroll Expense ($000):** 45880 **Personnel:** 746

☒ **BROWARD HEALTH MEDICAL CENTER (100039)**, 1600 South Andrews Avenue, Zip 33316–2510; tel. 954/355–4400, (Includes CHRIS EVERT CHILDRENS HOSPITAL, 1600 South Andrews Avenue, Fort Lauderdale, FL, Zip 33316–2510; tel. 954/355–4400; Calvin E Glidewell Jr, Chief Executive Officer) **A**1 2 3 5 10 12 13 **F**3 11 13 15 17 18 20 22 24 26 28 29 30 31 34 35 40 41 43 45 48 49 50 51 53 57 59 60 61 62 63 64 65 66 68 70 71 72 73 74 75 76 77 78 79 80 81 82 83 84 85 87 88 89 91 93 94 98 100 102 105 107 108 111 114 115 116 117 119 120 121 126 129 130 139 146 147 149 **S** Broward Health, Fort Lauderdale, FL
Primary Contact: Jonathan Turton, FACHE, Chief Executive Officer
COO: Natassia Orr, Chief Operating Officer
CFO: Alexander Fernandez, Chief Financial Officer
CMO: Louis Yogel, M.D., Chief of Staff
CHR: Dionne Wong, Vice President and Chief Human Resources Officer
CNO: Robyn Farrington, Chief Nursing Officer
Web address: www.browardhealth.org
Control: Hospital district or authority, Government, nonfederal **Service:** General medical and surgical

Staffed Beds: 656 **Admissions:** 27064 **Census:** 439 **Outpatient Visits:** 214124 **Births:** 3561 **Total Expense ($000):** 492196 **Payroll Expense ($000):** 185855 **Personnel:** 2916

FLORIDA MEDICAL CENTER See Florida Medical Center – A Campus of North Shore

☐ **FORT LAUDERDALE HOSPITAL (104026)**, 1601 East Las Olas Boulevard, Zip 33301–2393; tel. 954/463–4321, (Nonreporting) **A**1 10 **S** Universal Health Services, Inc., King of Prussia, PA
Primary Contact: Manuel R. Llano, Chief Executive Officer
CFO: Varonica Oehl, Chief Financial Officer
CMO: Sherrie Bieniek, M.D., Medical Director
CHR: Carlos A Gato, Director of Human Resources
CNO: Maria Spingos, Director of Nursing
Web address: www.fortlauderdalehospital.org
Control: Corporation, Investor–owned (for–profit) **Service:** Psychiatric

Staffed Beds: 100

☒ **HOLY CROSS HOSPITAL (100073)**, 4725 North Federal Highway, Zip 33308–4668, Mailing Address: P.O. Box 23460, Zip 33307–3460; tel. 954/771–8000, **A**1 2 3 5 10 **F**3 8 11 12 13 15 17 18 20 22 24 26 28 29 30 31 34 35 36 37 40 44 45 46 47 48 49 50 51 53 54 55 56 57 58 59 61 62 64 65 66 67 70 71 72 74 75 76 77 78 79 81 82 84 85 87 90 91 92 93 96 97 100 107 108 110 111 115 117 118 119 120 121 123 124 126 130 131 132 134 143 144 145 146 147 149 **P**6 **S** Trinity Health, Livonia, MI
Primary Contact: Patrick Taylor, M.D., President and Chief Executive Officer
COO: Luisa Gutman, Senior Vice President and Chief Operating Officer
CFO: Ronald Brandenburg, Vice President and Chief Financial Officer
CMO: Kenneth Homer, M.D., Chief Medical Officer
CIO: Jeff Smith, Chief Information Officer
CNO: Taren Ruggiero, R.N., MSN, Vice President and Chief Nursing Officer
Web address: www.holy–cross.com
Control: Other not–for–profit (including NFP Corporation) **Service:** General medical and surgical

Staffed Beds: 367 **Admissions:** 15898 **Census:** 206 **Outpatient Visits:** 172724 **Births:** 762 **Total Expense ($000):** 327727 **Payroll Expense ($000):** 120414 **Personnel:** 2731

IMPERIAL POINT MEDICAL CENTER See Broward Health Imperial Point

⊠ **KINDRED HOSPITAL SOUTH FLORIDA–FORT LAUDERDALE (102010)**, 1516 East Las Olas Boulevard, Zip 33301–2399; tel. 954/764–8900, (Includes KINDRED HOSPITAL SOUTH FLORIDA–CORAL GABLES, 5190 SW Eighth Street, Coral Gables, FL, Zip 33134–2495; tel. 305/445–1364; Brian Soares, Chief Executive Officer; KINDRED HOSPITAL SOUTH FLORIDA–HOLLYWOOD, 1859 Van Buren Street, Hollywood, FL, Zip 33020–5127; tel. 954/920–9000; David Wagner, South Florida Market Chief Executive Officer) (Nonreporting) **A**1 10 **S** Kindred Healthcare, Louisville, KY
Primary Contact: Michael S. Roffelsen, Chief Executive Officer
CFO: Dean Card, Chief Financial Officer
Web address: www.khfortlauderdale.com/
Control: Corporation, Investor–owned (for–profit) **Service:** Acute long–term care hospital

Staffed Beds: 123

FORT MYERS—Lee County

GOLISANO CHILDREN'S HOSPITAL OF SOUTHWEST FLORIDA See Lee Memorial Hospital, Fort Myers

★ ⇑ **GULF COAST MEDICAL CENTER (100220)**, 13681 Doctor's Way, Zip 33912–4300; tel. 239/343–1000, **A**10 21 **F**3 11 13 14 17 18 20 22 24 26 28 29 30 40 45 46 60 64 70 74 76 77 79 81 84 85 86 87 91 93 102 107 108 111 115 118 119 130 138 146 154 **S** Lee Health, Fort Myers, FL
Primary Contact: Lawrence Antonucci, M.D., President and Chief Executive Officer
CFO: Ben Spence, Chief Financial Officer
CMO: Mark Greenberg, M.D., Medical Director
CIO: Mike Smith, Chief Information Officer
CHR: Jon C Cecil, Chief Human Resource Officer
CNO: Lisa Sgarlata, MSN, Chief Patient Care Officer
Web address: www.leememorial.org
Control: Hospital district or authority, Government, nonfederal **Service:** General medical and surgical

Staffed Beds: 349 **Admissions:** 23018 **Census:** 283 **Outpatient Visits:** 77862 **Births:** 1430 **Total Expense ($000):** 337580 **Payroll Expense ($000):** 142900 **Personnel:** 1945

★ △ ⇑ **LEE MEMORIAL HOSPITAL (100012)**, 2776 Cleveland Avenue, Zip 33901–5855, Mailing Address: P.O. Box 2218, Zip 33902–2218; tel. 239/343–2000, (Includes GOLISANO CHILDREN'S HOSPITAL OF SOUTHWEST FLORIDA, 9981 South HealthPark Drive, Fort Myers, FL, Zip 33908; tel. 239/343–5437; HEALTHPARK MEDICAL CENTER, 9981 South HealthPark Drive, Fort Myers, FL, Zip 33908; tel. 239/433–7799; THE REHABILITATION HOSPITAL, 2776 Cleveland Avenue, Fort Myers, FL, Zip 33901; tel. 239/343–3900) **A**2 3 7 10 21 **F**3 11 12 13 14 15 17 18 19 20 21 22 24 26 28 29 30 31 32 34 35 38 40 41 43 45 48 50 51 53 54 56 57 58 59 61 62 64 65 68 70 72 73 74 75 76 77 78 79 81 82 84 85 86 87 88 89 90 93 94 97 100 102 104 107 108 110 111 113 114 115 116 117 119 126 128 129 130 131 132 134 135 138 146 147 148 154 **S** Lee Health, Fort Myers, FL
Primary Contact: Lawrence Antonucci, M.D., President and Chief Executive Officer
CFO: Ben Spence, Chief Financial Officer
CMO: Alex Daneshmand, D.O., Chief Patient Safety Officer
CIO: Mike Smith, Chief Information Officer
CHR: Jon C Cecil, Chief Human Resource Officer
CNO: Donna Giannuzzi, R.N., Chief Nursing Officer
Web address: www.leememorial.org
Control: Hospital district or authority, Government, nonfederal **Service:** General medical and surgical

Staffed Beds: 812 **Admissions:** 38073 **Census:** 502 **Outpatient Visits:** 172310 **Births:** 3273 **Total Expense ($000):** 633358 **Payroll Expense ($000):** 281581 **Personnel:** 3796

☐ **PARK ROYAL HOSPITAL (104074)**, 9241 Park Royal Drive, Zip 33908–9204; tel. 239/985–2700, (Nonreporting) **A**1 10 **S** Acadia Healthcare Company, Inc., Franklin, TN
Primary Contact: Michael Ham, Chief Executive Officer
CFO: Amy Ciampa, Chief Financial Officer
CHR: Robert Raynor, Human Resources Director
Web address: www.ParkRoyalHospital.com
Control: Corporation, Investor–owned (for–profit) **Service:** Psychiatric

Staffed Beds: 103

PROMISE HOSPITAL OF FORT MYERS (102029), 3050 Champion Ring Road, Zip 33905–5599; tel. 239/313–2900, (Nonreporting) **S** Promise Healthcare, Boca Raton, FL
Primary Contact: Patrick G. Ryan, Chief Executive Officer
Web address: www.promisefortmyers.com
Control: Corporation, Investor–owned (for–profit) **Service:** Acute long–term care hospital

Staffed Beds: 60

FORT PIERCE—St. Lucie County

⊠ △ **LAWNWOOD REGIONAL MEDICAL CENTER & HEART INSTITUTE (100246)**, 1700 South 23rd Street, Zip 34950–4803; tel. 772/461–4000, (Includes LAWNWOOD PAVILION, 1860 North Lawnwood Circle, Fort Pierce, FL, Zip 34950, Mailing Address: P.O. Box 1540, Zip 34954–1540, tel. 361/466–1500) (Nonreporting) **A**1 3 7 10 **S** HCA Healthcare, Nashville, TN
Primary Contact: Eric Goldman, Chief Executive Officer
CFO: Robert Dunwoody, Chief Financial Officer
CIO: Eric Castle, Director Information Services
CHR: Pam Burchell, Director Human Resources
Web address: www.lawnwoodmed.com
Control: Corporation, Investor–owned (for–profit) **Service:** General medical and surgical

Staffed Beds: 331

FORT WALTON BEACH—Okaloosa County

⊠ **FORT WALTON BEACH MEDICAL CENTER (100223)**, 1000 Mar–Walt Drive, Zip 32547–6795; tel. 850/862–1111, (Nonreporting) **A**1 2 10 **S** HCA Healthcare, Nashville, TN
Primary Contact: Mitchell P. Mongell, FACHE, Chief Executive Officer
CFO: Jeffrey Steve Moore, Chief Financial Officer
CMO: Colonel Tama Van Decar, M.D., Chief Medical Officer
CIO: Amy Caldeira, Director Information Technology and Systems
CHR: Julia Truman, Vice President Human Resources
CNO: Holly McGucken, R.N., Chief Nursing Officer
Web address: www.fwbmc.com
Control: Corporation, Investor–owned (for–profit) **Service:** General medical and surgical

Staffed Beds: 257

GAINESVILLE—Alachua County

⊠ **NORTH FLORIDA REGIONAL MEDICAL CENTER (100204)**, 6500 Newberry Road, Zip 32605–4392, Mailing Address: P.O. Box 147006, Zip 32614–7006; tel. 352/333–4000, (Nonreporting) **A**1 2 3 10 **S** HCA Healthcare, Nashville, TN
Primary Contact: Eric Lawson, Chief Executive Officer
CFO: Jay St Pierre, Chief Financial Officer
CMO: Ann Weber, M.D., Chief Medical Officer
CIO: Eric Strand, Director Information Services
CHR: Jane Fuller, Vice President Human Resources
CNO: Natalie Ransom, Chief Nursing Officer
Web address: www.nfrmc.com
Control: Corporation, Investor–owned (for–profit) **Service:** General medical and surgical

Staffed Beds: 432

⊠ **NORTH FLORIDA/SOUTH GEORGIA VETERAN'S HEALTH SYSTEM**, 1601 SW Archer Road, Zip 32608–1135; tel. 352/376–1611, (Includes GAINESVILLE VETERANS AFFAIRS MEDICAL CENTER, 1601 SW Archer Road, Gainesville, FL, Zip 32608–1197; tel. 352/376–1611; LAKE CITY VETERANS AFFAIRS MEDICAL CENTER, 619 South Marion Avenue, Lake City, FL, Zip 32025–5898; tel. 386/755–3016) (Nonreporting) **A**1 3 5 **S** Department of Veterans Affairs, Perry Point, MD
Primary Contact: Thomas Wisnieski, FACHE, Director
COO: Thomas Sutton, Associate Director
CFO: Jim Taylor, Chief Business Office
CMO: Brad Bender, M.D., Chief of Staff
CIO: Deborah Michel–Ogborn, Chief Information Resource Management
CHR: Michelle Manderino, Chief Human Resources
Web address: www.northflorida.va.gov
Control: Veterans Affairs, Government, federal **Service:** General medical and surgical

Staffed Beds: 623

⊠ **SELECT SPECIALTY HOSPITAL–GAINESVILLE (102022)**, 2708 SW Archer Road, Zip 32608–1316; tel. 352/337–3240, (Nonreporting) **A**1 10 **S** Select Medical Corporation, Mechanicsburg, PA
Primary Contact: Ronnie Wagley, Market Chief Executive Officer
Web address: www.gainesville.selectspecialtyhospitals.com/
Control: Corporation, Investor–owned (for–profit) **Service:** Acute long–term care hospital

Staffed Beds: 44

FL

Hospital, Medicare Provider Number, Address, Telephone, Approval, Facility, and Physician Codes, Health Care System

★ American Hospital Association (AHA) membership   ◯ Healthcare Facilities Accreditation Program   ⇑ Center for Improvement in Healthcare Quality Accreditation
☐ The Joint Commission accreditation   ◇ DNV Healthcare Inc. accreditation   △ Commission on Accreditation of Rehabilitation Facilities (CARF) accreditation

✠ △ **UF HEALTH SHANDS HOSPITAL (100113)**, 1600 SW Archer Road, Zip 32610–3003, Mailing Address: PO Box 100326, Zip 32610–0326; tel. 352/265–0111, (Includes UF HEALTH SHANDS CANCER HOSPITAL, 1515 SW Archer Road, Gainesville, FL, Zip 32608–1134, Mailing Address: PO Box 100326, Zip 32610–0326, tel. 352/265–0111; Edward Jimenez, Chief Executive Officer; UF HEALTH SHANDS CHILDREN'S HOSPITAL, 1600 SW Archer Road, Gainesville, FL, Zip 32610–3003, Mailing Address: PO Box 100326, Zip 32610–0326, tel. 352/265–0111; Edward Jimenez, Chief Executive Officer; UF HEALTH SHANDS PSYCHIATRIC HOSPITAL, 4101 NW 89th Boulevard, Gainesville, FL, Zip 32606, tel. 352/265–5481; Roxane Harcourt, Interim Administrator; UF HEALTH SHANDS REHAB HOSPITAL, 4101 NW 89th Boulevard, Gainesville, FL, Zip 32606–3813; tel. 352/265–5499; Marina T. Cecchini, Administrator) **A**1 2 3 5 7 8 10 **F**2 3 4 5 6 7 9 11 12 13 15 16 17 18 19 20 21 22 23 24 25 26 27 28 29 30 31 32 34 35 36 37 38 39 40 41 43 44 45 46 47 48 49 50 51 52 53 54 55 56 57 58 59 60 61 62 63 64 65 66 68 69 70 72 73 74 75 76 77 78 79 80 81 82 84 85 86 87 88 89 90 91 92 93 94 96 97 98 99 100 101 102 103 104 105 107 108 109 110 111 114 115 116 117 118 119 120 121 123 124 126 129 130 131 132 134 135 136 137 138 139 140 141 142 143 144 145 146 147 148 149 150 152 154 **P**6 **S** UF Health Shands, Gainesville, FL
Primary Contact: Edward Jimenez, Chief Executive Officer
CFO: James J. Kelly Jr Senior Vice President and Chief Financial Officer
CMO: Parker Gibbs, M.D., Chief Medical Officer
CIO: Kari Cassel, Senior Vice President and Chief Information Officer
CHR: Janet L. Christie, Senior Vice President Human Resources
CNO: Irene Alexaitis, R.N., Vice President of Nursing and Patient Services and Chief Nursing Officer
Web address: www.https://ufhealth.org/
Control: Other not–for–profit (including NFP Corporation) **Service**: General medical and surgical

Staffed Beds: 986 **Admissions**: 47408 **Census**: 800 **Outpatient Visits**: 1064010 **Births**: 2879 **Total Expense ($000)**: 1288880 **Payroll Expense ($000)**: 467981 **Personnel**: 8272

UF HEALTH SHANDS REHAB HOSPITAL See UF Health Shands Hospital, Gainesville

GREEN COVE SPRINGS—Clay County

✠ **KINDRED HOSPITAL NORTH FLORIDA (102015)**, 801 Oak Street, Zip 32043–4317; tel. 904/284–9230, **A**1 10 **F**1 3 29 62 85 91 107 119 148 **P**5 **S** Kindred Healthcare, Louisville, KY
Primary Contact: Patrick McVey, Chief Executive Officer
CFO: Rickie Simmons, Controller
CMO: Uriel Nazario, M.D., Chief of Medical Staff
CIO: Rick Chapman, Chief Information Officer
CNO: Ashley McRae, Chief Clinical Officer
Web address: www.khnorthflorida.com
Control: Corporation, Investor–owned (for–profit) **Service**: Acute long–term care hospital

Staffed Beds: 80 **Admissions**: 651 **Census**: 50 **Outpatient Visits**: 4 **Births**: 0 **Total Expense ($000)**: 27482 **Payroll Expense ($000)**: 10316 **Personnel**: 229

GULF BREEZE—Santa Rosa County

✠ **GULF BREEZE HOSPITAL (100266)**, 1110 Gulf Breeze Parkway, Zip 32561–4884; tel. 850/934–2000, **A**1 3 10 **F**3 8 11 15 26 29 40 44 45 46 50 54 57 59 64 68 70 74 75 78 79 81 82 84 85 86 91 93 107 110 111 114 119 120 121 123 129 130 131 132 143 146 147 148 **S** Baptist Health Care Corporation, Pensacola, FL
Primary Contact: Scott Raynes, President
CFO: Kerry Vermillion, Senior Vice President Finance and Chief Financial Officer
Web address: www.ebaptisthealthcare.org/GulfBreezeHospital/
Control: Other not–for–profit (including NFP Corporation) **Service**: General medical and surgical

Staffed Beds: 65 **Admissions**: 3871 **Census**: 39 **Outpatient Visits**: 122940 **Births**: 0 **Total Expense ($000)**: 80792 **Payroll Expense ($000)**: 26796 **Personnel**: 478

HIALEAH—Miami–Dade County

✠ **HIALEAH HOSPITAL (100053)**, 651 East 25th Street, Zip 33013–3878; tel. 305/693–6100, (Nonreporting) **A**1 10 **S** TENET Healthcare Corporation, Dallas, TX
Primary Contact: Ben A. Rodriguez, Chief Executive Officer
COO: Lourdes Camps, Chief Operating Officer
CFO: Gary Nymoen, Chief Financial Officer
CMO: Orlando Garcia, M.D., Chief Medical Officer
CHR: Yamila Herrera, Director Human Resources
CNO: Maribel Torres, Chief Nursing Officer
Web address: www.hialeahhosp.com
Control: Corporation, Investor–owned (for–profit) **Service**: General medical and surgical

Staffed Beds: 191

□ **PALM SPRINGS GENERAL HOSPITAL (100050)**, 1475 West 49th Street, Zip 33012–3275, Mailing Address: P.O. Box 2804, Zip 33012–2804; tel. 305/558–2500, (Nonreporting) **A**1 10 12
Primary Contact: Nicholas T. Smith, Chief Executive Officer
CFO: Tony Milian, Chief Financial Officer
CHR: Lourdes Anton, Director Human Resources
Web address: www.psghosp.com
Control: Corporation, Investor–owned (for–profit) **Service**: General medical and surgical

Staffed Beds: 190

✠ **PALMETTO GENERAL HOSPITAL (100187)**, 2001 West 68th Street, Zip 33016–1898; tel. 305/823–5000, (Nonreporting) **A**1 3 5 10 12 13 **S** TENET Healthcare Corporation, Dallas, TX
Primary Contact: Ana J. Mederos, Chief Executive Officer
COO: Georgina Diaz, Chief Operating Officer
CFO: Oscar Vicente, Chief Financial Officer
CMO: Eloy Roman, M.D., Chief of Staff
CHR: Ana Gonzalez–Fajardo, Human Resources Director
CNO: Barbara Vazquez, Chief Nursing Officer
Web address: www.palmettogeneral.com
Control: Corporation, Investor–owned (for–profit) **Service**: General medical and surgical

Staffed Beds: 360

HIALEAH—Dade County

SOUTHERN WINDS HOSPITAL See Westchester General Hospital, Miami

HOLLYWOOD—Broward County

□ **LARKIN COMMUNITY HOSPITAL BEHAVIORAL HEALTH SERVICES (104015)**, 1201 North 37th Avenue, Zip 33021–5498; tel. 954/962–1355, (Nonreporting) **A**1 3
Primary Contact: Iris Berges, Chief Executive Officer
COO: Christopher Gabel, Chief Operating Officer
CFO: Rocky Davidson, Chief Financial Officer
CHR: Len Alpert, Director Human Resources
Web address: www.hollywoodpavilion.com
Control: Corporation, Investor–owned (for–profit) **Service**: Psychiatric

Staffed Beds: 50

✠ △ **MEMORIAL REGIONAL HOSPITAL (100038)**, 3501 Johnson Street, Zip 33021–5421; tel. 954/987–2000, (Includes JOE DIMAGGIO CHILDREN'S HOSPITAL, 1005 Joe DiMaggio Drive, Hollywood, FL, Zip 33021–5426; tel. 954/987–2000; Caitlin Beck Stella, Chief Executive Officer; MEMORIAL REGIONAL HOSPITAL SOUTH, 3600 Washington Street, Hollywood, FL, Zip 33021–8216; tel. 954/966–4500; Douglas Zaren, FACHE, Administrator and CEO) **A**1 2 3 5 7 8 10 **F**3 5 11 12 13 15 17 18 19 20 21 22 23 24 25 26 27 28 29 30 31 32 34 37 38 39 40 41 43 44 45 46 47 49 50 51 53 54 55 56 57 58 59 60 61 64 65 66 67 68 70 71 72 73 74 75 76 77 78 79 81 82 84 85 87 88 89 90 93 95 96 97 98 99 100 101 102 103 104 107 108 110 111 114 115 118 119 120 121 123 126 130 132 134 135 137 145 146 147 148 149 150 153 **P**1 6 **S** Memorial Healthcare System, Hollywood, FL
Primary Contact: Zeff Ross, FACHE, Executive Vice President and Chief Executive Officer
CFO: Walter Bussell, Chief Financial Officer
CMO: Donald Kim, M.D., Chief Medical Officer
CIO: Forest Blanton, Administrator Process Engineering
CHR: Margie Vargas, Chief Human Resources Officer
Web address: www.mhs.net
Control: Hospital district or authority, Government, nonfederal **Service**: General medical and surgical

Staffed Beds: 1064 **Admissions**: 37274 **Census**: 651 **Outpatient Visits**: 454264 **Births**: 5353 **Total Expense ($000)**: 950438 **Payroll Expense ($000)**: 394412 **Personnel**: 5633

□ **SOUTH FLORIDA STATE HOSPITAL (104001)**, 800 East Cypress Drive, Zip 33025–4543; tel. 954/392–3000, (Nonreporting) **A**1 10
Primary Contact: Lee Packer, Administrator
Web address: www.geocarellc.com/Locations/SouthFloridaStateHospital
Control: State, Government, nonfederal **Service**: Psychiatric

Staffed Beds: 355

FL

HOMESTEAD—Miami–Dade County

☒ **BAPTIST HEALTH SOUTH FLORIDA, HOMESTEAD HOSPITAL (100125)**, 975 Baptist Way, Zip 33033–7600; tel. 786/243–8000, **A**1 10 **F**3 11 13 15 18 29 30 31 34 35 40 41 45 47 49 50 51 53 57 58 59 60 61 63 64 68 70 74 75 76 78 79 81 82 84 85 86 87 89 93 102 107 108 110 111 114 115 119 129 130 131 132 134 135 145 146 147 148 149 150 154 **S** Baptist Health South Florida, Coral Gables, FL
Primary Contact: William M. Duquette, Chief Executive Officer
COO: Kenneth R Spell, Vice President Operations
CFO: David Abercrombie, Controller
CMO: George R. Tershakovec, M.D., President Medical Staff
CIO: Mimi Taylor, Corporate Vice President Information Technology
CHR: Adriene McCoy, Corporate Vice President
CNO: Nancy Gail Gordon, R.N., MSN, Chief Nursing Officer and Vice President of Nursing
Web address: www.baptisthealth.net
Control: Other not–for–profit (including NFP Corporation) **Service**: General medical and surgical

Staffed Beds: 142 Admissions: 9751 Census: 96 Outpatient Visits: 115174 **Births:** 1396 **Total Expense ($000):** 223403 **Payroll Expense ($000):** 77316 **Personnel:** 1037

HUDSON—Pasco County

☒ **REGIONAL MEDICAL CENTER BAYONET POINT (100256)**, 14000 Fivay Road, Zip 34667–7199; tel. 727/869–5400, (Nonreporting) **A**1 2 3 10 13 **S** HCA Healthcare, Nashville, TN
Primary Contact: Thomas Lawhorne, Interim Chief Executive Officer
COO: Joe Rudisill, Chief Operating Officer
CFO: Thomas Lawhorne, Chief Financial Officer
CMO: Joseph Pino, M.D., Chief Medical Officer
CIO: Mike Wilms, Director Information Systems
CHR: Geoffrey A. Washburn, Vice President
CNO: Melanie Wetmore, MSN, R.N., Chief Nursing Officer
Web address: www.rmchealth.com
Control: Corporation, Investor–owned (for–profit) **Service**: General medical and surgical

Staffed Beds: 290

INVERNESS—Citrus County

☒ **CITRUS MEMORIAL HEALTH SYSTEM (100023)**, 502 West Highland Boulevard, Zip 34452–4754; tel. 352/726–1551, (Nonreporting) **A**1 10 19 **S** HCA Healthcare, Nashville, TN
Primary Contact: Ralph A. Aleman, President and Chief Executive Officer
COO: George Mavros, Chief Operating Officer
CFO: Glenn Romig, Chief Financial Officer
CMO: Raylene Platel, M.D., Chief Medical Officer
CIO: Nick Brooks, Director of Information Systems
CHR: Lee Glotzback, Director Human Resources
CNO: Caroline Stewart, Chief Nursing Officer
Web address: www.citrusmh.com
Control: Other not–for–profit (including NFP Corporation) **Service**: General medical and surgical

Staffed Beds: 204

JACKSONVILLE—Duval County

☒ **BAPTIST MEDICAL CENTER JACKSONVILLE (100088)**, 800 Prudential Drive, Zip 32207–8202; tel. 904/202–2000, (Includes BAPTIST MEDICAL CENTER SOUTH, 14550 St Augustine Road, Jacksonville, FL, Zip 32258–2160; tel. 904/821–6000; Nicole B. Thomas, President; WOLFSON CHILDREN'S HOSPITAL, 800 Prudential Drive, Jacksonville, FL, Zip 32207; tel. 904/202–8000; Michael D Aubin, President) **A**1 2 3 5 10 **F**3 5 6 8 11 12 13 15 17 18 19 20 21 22 23 24 25 26 27 28 29 30 31 32 34 35 36 37 38 39 40 41 45 46 47 48 49 50 51 53 54 55 56 57 58 59 60 61 62 64 68 70 72 73 74 75 76 77 78 79 81 82 83 85 86 87 88 89 92 93 94 98 99 100 101 102 103 104 105 107 108 109 110 111 112 113 114 115 116 117 118 119 120 121 123 124 126 129 130 132 134 135 136 145 146 147 148 149 153 **P**6 **S** Baptist Health, Jacksonville, FL
Primary Contact: Michael A. Mayo, FACHE, President
COO: John F Wilbanks, FACHE, Chief Operating Officer
CFO: Scott Wooten, Senior Vice President and Chief Financial Officer
CMO: Keith L Stein, M.D., Senior Vice President Medical Affairs and Chief Medical Officer
CIO: Roland Garcia, Senior Vice President and Chief Information Officer
CHR: M. Beth Mehaffey, Senior Vice President Human Resources
Web address: www.e–baptisthealth.com
Control: Other not–for–profit (including NFP Corporation) **Service**: General medical and surgical

Staffed Beds: 941 Admissions: 51271 Census: 688 Outpatient Visits: 610428 **Births:** 4491 **Total Expense ($000):** 1075569 **Payroll Expense ($000):** 308683 **Personnel:** 5732

☒ △ **BROOKS REHABILITATION HOSPITAL (103039)**, 3599 University Boulevard South, Zip 32216–4252; tel. 904/345–7600, **A**1 3 7 10 **F**3 28 29 30 50 90 91 95 96 130 149
Primary Contact: Douglas M. Baer, Chief Executive Officer
COO: Michael Spigel, Executive Vice President & Chief Operating Officer
CMO: Trevor Paris, M.D., Medical Director
CIO: Karen Green, Chief Information Officer
CHR: Karen Gallagher, Vice President Human Resources and Learning
CNO: Joanne Hoertz, Vice President of Nursing
Web address: www.brookshealth.org
Control: Other not–for–profit (including NFP Corporation) **Service**: Rehabilitation

Staffed Beds: 144 Admissions: 3049 Census: 131 Outpatient Visits: 0 Births: 0 Total Expense ($000): 71010 **Payroll Expense ($000):** 26686 **Personnel:** 479

★ **MAYO CLINIC HOSPITAL IN FLORIDA (100151)**, 4500 San Pablo Road South, Zip 32224–1865; tel. 904/953–2000, **A**2 3 5 8 10 **F**3 6 8 9 11 12 14 15 17 18 20 22 24 26 28 29 30 31 34 35 36 37 39 40 44 45 46 47 48 49 50 51 54 55 56 57 58 59 60 61 64 65 68 70 74 75 77 78 79 80 81 82 84 85 86 87 92 93 96 97 100 104 107 108 110 111 112 114 115 116 117 118 119 120 121 123 124 126 129 130 131 132 135 136 137 138 139 140 141 142 145 146 147 148 149 150 153 154 **P**6 **S** Mayo Clinic, Rochester, MN
Primary Contact: Gianrico Farrugia, M.D., Vice President and Chief Executive Officer
CFO: Kevin Lockett, Interim Chief Financial Officer
CMO: David Thiel, M.D., Medical Director
CIO: John Crooks, Chair Information Services
CHR: Rosemary McMullan, Chief Human Resources
CNO: Ryannon Frederick, Chief Nursing Officer
Web address: www.mayoclinic.org/jacksonville/
Control: Other not–for–profit (including NFP Corporation) **Service**: General medical and surgical

Staffed Beds: 263 Admissions: 13471 Census: 184 Outpatient Visits: 54257 **Births:** 0 **Personnel:** 2798

☒ **MEMORIAL HOSPITAL JACKSONVILLE (100179)**, 3625 University Boulevard South, Zip 32216–4207; tel. 904/702–6111, **A**1 2 3 10 **F**3 11 12 13 15 17 18 20 22 24 26 28 29 30 32 34 35 38 40 41 43 45 47 48 49 51 53 54 55 56 57 58 59 64 65 70 72 74 75 76 77 78 79 81 82 84 87 89 97 98 100 101 102 103 104 107 108 110 111 114 115 116 117 118 119 124 126 130 131 146 147 148 149 154 **S** HCA Healthcare, Nashville, TN
Primary Contact: Bradley S. Talbert, FACHE, President and Chief Executive Officer
COO: Cory Darling, Chief Operating Officer
CFO: Andy Miller, Chief Financial Officer
CMO: John Lazenby, M.D., Chief Medical Officer
CIO: Patrick Adesso, Director Information Technology and Systems
CHR: Stuart Thompson, Vice President Human Resources
CNO: Suzanne Woods, Senior Vice President of Nursing
Web address: www.memorialhospitaljax.com
Control: Corporation, Investor–owned (for–profit) **Service**: General medical and surgical

Staffed Beds: 418 Admissions: 23342 Census: 310 Outpatient Visits: 152509 **Births:** 1415

☒ **NAVAL HOSPITAL JACKSONVILLE**, 2080 Child Street, Zip 32214–5000; tel. 904/542–7300, (Nonreporting) **A**1 3 5 **S** Bureau of Medicine and Surgery, Department of the Navy, Falls Church, VA
Primary Contact: Commander Darryl Green, Director Administration
CFO: Lieutenant Commander Michael Gregonis, Comptroller
CMO: Captain Christopher Quarles, M.D., Director Medical Services
CIO: Mike Haytaian, Head Director Information Resources Management
CHR: Captain Ruby Tennyson, Director Administration
Web address: www.med.navy.mil/SITES/NAVALHOSPITALJAX/Pages/default.aspx
Control: Navy, Government, federal **Service**: General medical and surgical

Staffed Beds: 64

☐ **RIVER POINT BEHAVIORAL HEALTH (104016)**, 6300 Beach Boulevard, Zip 32216–2782; tel. 904/724–9202, (Nonreporting) **A**1 10 **S** Universal Health Services, Inc., King of Prussia, PA
Primary Contact: Kevin McGee, Chief Executive Officer
CFO: Jenni Stackhouse, Chief Financial Officer
CIO: Bill Willis, Director Information Technology
CHR: Cathy Calhoun, Director Human Resources
Web address: www.riverpointbehavioral.com
Control: Corporation, Investor–owned (for–profit) **Service**: Psychiatric

Staffed Beds: 92

Hospital, Medicare Provider Number, Address, Telephone, Approval, Facility, and Physician Codes, Health Care System

★ American Hospital Association (AHA) membership
☐ The Joint Commission accreditation
○ Healthcare Facilities Accreditation Program
◇ DNV Healthcare Inc. accreditation
⇑ Center for Improvement in Healthcare Quality Accreditation
△ Commission on Accreditation of Rehabilitation Facilities (CARF) accreditation

FL

⊞ **SPECIALTY HOSPITAL JACKSONVILLE (102012)**, 4901 Richard Street, Zip 32207–7328; tel. 904/737–3120, (Nonreporting) **A**1 10 **S** Curae Health, Clinton, TN
Primary Contact: Barbara McCarthy, Chief Executive Officer
CFO: Joshua Szostek, Chief Financial Officer
CMO: Wendell H Williams, M.D., Jr Medical Director
CIO: Patrick Adesso, Director Information Technology and Systems
CHR: Lisa Ayala, R.N., Director Human Resources
Web address: www.specialtyhospitaljax.com
Control: Corporation, Investor–owned (for–profit) **Service:** Acute long–term care hospital

Staffed Beds: 62

⊞ **ST. VINCENT'S MEDICAL CENTER RIVERSIDE (100040)**, 1 Shircliff Way, Zip 32204–4748, Mailing Address: P.O. Box 2982, Zip 32203–2982; tel. 904/308–7300, **A**1 2 3 10 13 **F**3 12 13 15 17 18 20 22 24 26 28 29 30 31 34 40 44 45 46 47 48 49 53 55 57 58 61 64 65 70 72 74 76 78 79 81 85 86 87 91 93 107 108 110 111 114 115 118 119 120 121 123 124 126 130 131 132 146 147 149 154 **S** Ascension Healthcare, Saint Louis, MO
Primary Contact: Thomas J. VanOsdol, Chief Executive Officer
CIO: Ann Carey, Vice President and Chief Information Officer
CHR: Michelle Adamolekun, Chief Human Resource Officer
CNO: Lorraine Keith, Chief Nursing Officer
Web address: www.jaxhealth.com
Control: Church operated, Nongovernment, not–for–profit **Service:** General medical and surgical

Staffed Beds: 482 Admissions: 24393 Census: 302 Outpatient Visits: 114679 Births: 1634 Total Expense ($000): 433695 Payroll Expense ($000): 126309 Personnel: 1995

⊞ **ST. VINCENT'S MEDICAL CENTER SOUTHSIDE (100307)**, 4201 Belfort Road, Zip 32216–1431; tel. 904/296–3700, **A**1 3 5 10 **F**3 12 13 15 18 20 22 26 29 30 31 34 40 44 47 49 50 57 60 61 64 65 70 72 74 76 78 79 81 85 86 87 93 96 102 107 108 110 111 114 115 119 126 128 129 130 131 132 146 147 149 154 **S** Ascension Healthcare, Saint Louis, MO
Primary Contact: Thomas J. VanOsdol, Chief Executive Officer
CIO: Ann Carey, Chief Information Officer
CHR: Kaye W Lunsford, System Director Human Resources
CNO: Lorraine Keith, Chief Nursing Officer
Web address: www.jaxhealth.com
Control: Church operated, Nongovernment, not–for–profit **Service:** General medical and surgical

Staffed Beds: 289 Admissions: 12038 Census: 134 Outpatient Visits: 43902 Births: 1518 Total Expense ($000): 166460 Payroll Expense ($000): 46313 Personnel: 674

⊞ **UF HEALTH JACKSONVILLE (100001)**, 655 West Eighth Street, Zip 32209–6595; tel. 904/244–0411, (Total facility includes 56 beds in nursing home–type unit) **A**1 3 5 8 10 **F**3 5 8 11 12 13 15 17 18 20 22 24 26 28 29 30 31 32 34 35 36 37 38 40 41 43 44 45 46 47 49 50 51 53 54 55 56 57 58 59 60 61 62 64 65 66 68 70 71 72 74 75 76 77 78 79 81 82 84 85 86 87 88 92 93 94 96 97 98 99 100 101 102 103 104 107 108 109 110 111 114 115 116 117 118 119 120 121 123 124 126 128 129 130 131 132 134 135 141 145 146 147 148 149 150 154 **S** UF Health Shands, Gainesville, FL
Primary Contact: Leon L. Haley Jr, M.D., Chief Executive Officer
COO: Greg Miller, Senior Vice President Operations
CFO: William Ryan, Vice President and Chief Financial Officer
CMO: David Vukich, M.D., Senior Vice President, Chief Medical Officer and Chief Quality Officer
CIO: Kari Cassel, Senior Vice President and Chief Information Officer
CHR: Lesli Ward, Vice President Human Resources
CNO: Patrice I. Jones, R.N., MSN, Vice President and Chief Nursing Officer
Web address: www.ufhealthjax.org/
Control: Other not–for–profit (including NFP Corporation) **Service:** General medical and surgical

Staffed Beds: 585 Admissions: 26829 Census: 443 Outpatient Visits: 578821 Births: 3185 Total Expense ($000): 697695 Payroll Expense ($000): 246029 Personnel: 4078

☐ **WEKIVA SPRINGS (104069)**, 3947 Salisbury Road, Zip 32216–6115; tel. 904/296–3533, (Nonreporting) **A**1 10 **S** Universal Health Services, Inc., King of Prussia, PA
Primary Contact: Sheila Carr, Chief Executive Officer
Web address: www.wekivacenter.com
Control: Other not–for–profit (including NFP Corporation) **Service:** Psychiatric

Staffed Beds: 60

JACKSONVILLE BEACH—Duval County

⊞ **BAPTIST MEDICAL CENTER BEACHES (100117)**, 1350 13th Avenue South, Zip 32250–3205; tel. 904/627–2900, **A**1 10 **F**3 8 11 13 15 18 20 28 29 30 34 35 36 40 43 45 49 50 53 54 56 57 59 61 64 74 75 76 77 78 79 80 81 82 85 86 93 107 108 110 111 114 115 118 119 126 129 130 146 147 148 **S** Baptist Health, Jacksonville, FL
Primary Contact: Joseph M. Mitrick, FACHE, President
COO: John F Wilbanks, FACHE, Chief Operating Officer
CFO: Scott Wooten, Senior Vice President and Chief Financial Officer
CMO: Keith L Stein, M.D., Chief Medical Officer
CIO: Roland Garcia, Senior Vice President and Chief Information Officer
CHR: Dana Voiselle, Director Human Resources and Community Relations
Web address: www.community.e–baptisthealth.com/bmc/beaches/index.html
Control: Other not–for–profit (including NFP Corporation) **Service:** General medical and surgical

Staffed Beds: 135 Admissions: 7376 Census: 75 Outpatient Visits: 79944 Births: 1040 Total Expense ($000): 110255 Payroll Expense ($000): 35251 Personnel: 655

JAY—Santa Rosa County

★ **JAY HOSPITAL (100048)**, 14114 South Alabama Street, Zip 32565–1219; tel. 850/675–8000, **A**10 **F**3 11 15 18 29 30 34 35 40 45 48 50 57 59 64 75 77 81 82 85 93 107 110 114 119 127 130 133 **S** Baptist Health Care Corporation, Pensacola, FL
Primary Contact: Michael T. Hutchins, Administrator
CFO: Keith Strickling, Chief Accountant
CMO: C David Smith, M.D., Chief Medical Officer
CHR: Heather Suggs, Manager Human Resources
CNO: Patsy Jackson, Director of Nursing
Web address: www.bhcpns.org/jayhospital/
Control: Other not–for–profit (including NFP Corporation) **Service:** General medical and surgical

Staffed Beds: 21 Admissions: 583 Census: 8 Outpatient Visits: 17170 Births: 0 Total Expense ($000): 12919 Payroll Expense ($000): 5698 Personnel: 103

JUPITER—Palm Beach County

⊞ **JUPITER MEDICAL CENTER (100253)**, 1210 South Old Dixie Highway, Zip 33458–7299; tel. 561/263–2234, (Nonreporting) **A**1 2 10
Primary Contact: Donald McKenna, President and Chief Executive Officer
COO: Steven Seeley, Vice President, Chief Operating Officer, Chief Nursing Officer
CFO: Dale E Hocking, Chief Financial Officer
CIO: Thomas Schoenig, Chief Information Officer
CHR: Peter Gloggner, Chief Human Resources Officer
CNO: Steven Seeley, Vice President, Chief Operating Officer, Chief Nursing Officer
Web address: www.jupitermed.com
Control: Other not–for–profit (including NFP Corporation) **Service:** General medical and surgical

Staffed Beds: 207

KEY WEST—Monroe County

⊞ **LOWER KEYS MEDICAL CENTER (100150)**, 5900 College Road, Zip 33040–4396, Mailing Address: P.O. Box 9107, Zip 33041–9107; tel. 305/294–5531, (Includes DE POO HOSPITAL, 1200 Kennedy Drive, Key West, FL, Zip 33041; tel. 305/294–4692) (Nonreporting) **A**1 10 **S** Community Health Systems, Inc., Franklin, TN
Primary Contact: David Clay, Chief Executive Officer
CFO: Henrietta Skeens, Cheif Financial Officer
CMO: Jerome Covington, M.D., Chief Medical Officer
Web address: www.lkmc.com
Control: Corporation, Investor–owned (for–profit) **Service:** General medical and surgical

Staffed Beds: 90

KISSIMMEE—Osceola County

FLORIDA HOSPITAL KISSIMMEE See Florida Hospital, Orlando

⊞ **OSCEOLA REGIONAL MEDICAL CENTER (100110)**, 700 West Oak Street, Zip 34741–4996; tel. 407/846–2266, (Nonreporting) **A**1 2 3 5 8 10 13 **S** HCA Healthcare, Nashville, TN
Primary Contact: Davide M. Carbone, FACHE, Chief Executive Officer
COO: Steve Gordon, Chief Operating Officer
CFO: Carrie Biggar, Chief Financial Officer
CMO: Stephens Stoops, M.D., Chief Medical Officer
CIO: Carrie Biggar, Chief Financial Officer
CHR: Sylvia Lollis, Director Human Resources
CNO: Barbara K Watson, Chief Nursing Officer
Web address: www.osceolaregional.com
Control: Corporation, Investor–owned (for–profit) **Service:** General medical and surgical

Staffed Beds: 235

⊞ **POINCIANA MEDICAL CENTER (100320)**, 325 Cypress Parkway, Zip 34758; tel. 407/530–2000, (Nonreporting) **A**1 10 **S** HCA Healthcare, Nashville, TN
Primary Contact: Christopher Cosby, Chief Executive Officer
CFO: Tom Eisel, Chief Financial Officer
CNO: Sharon Dillard, Chief Nursing Officer
Web address: www.poincianamedicalcenter.com
Control: Corporation, Investor–owned (for–profit) **Service:** General medical and surgical

Staffed Beds: 24

LAKE BUTLER—Union County

LAKE BUTLER HOSPITAL HAND SURGERY CENTER (101303), 850 East Main Street, Zip 32054–1353, Mailing Address: P.O. Box 748, Zip 32054–0748; tel. 386/496–2323, (Nonreporting) **A**10 18
Primary Contact: Pamela B. Howard, R.N., Chief Executive Officer, Administrator and Risk Manager
COO: Jennifer Thomas, Chief Operating Officer and Director of Public Relations
CFO: Paula Webb, Chief Financial Officer and Compliance Officer
CMO: Cynthia Larimer, M.D., Chief of Staff
CIO: Diane Cason, Chief Information Officer, Controller and Director Human Resources
CNO: Mandy Dicks, Director of Nursing
Web address: www.lakebutlerhospital.com
Control: Corporation, Investor–owned (for–profit) **Service:** General medical and surgical

Staffed Beds: 25

RECEPTION AND MEDICAL CENTER, State Road 231 South, Zip 32054, Mailing Address: P.O. Box 628, Zip 32054–0628; tel. 386/496–6000, (Nonreporting)
Primary Contact: Maxine Streeter, Administrator
Web address: www.dc.state.fl.us
Control: State, Government, nonfederal **Service:** Hospital unit of an institution (prison hospital, college infirmary, etc.)

Staffed Beds: 120

LAKE CITY—Columbia County

⊞ **LAKE CITY MEDICAL CENTER (100156)**, 340 NW Commerce Drive, Zip 32055–4709; tel. 386/719–9000, (Nonreporting) **A**1 10 **S** HCA Healthcare, Nashville, TN
Primary Contact: Rick Naegler, Chief Executive Officer
COO: Jennifer B Adams, Chief Operating Officer and Chief Financial Officer
CFO: Jennifer B Adams, Chief Operating Officer and Chief Financial Officer
CMO: Miguel Tepedino, M.D., Chief Medicine
CIO: Taylor Dickerson, Chief Information Officer
CHR: Steve Gordon, Director Human Resources
Web address: www.lakecitymedical.com
Control: Corporation, Investor–owned (for–profit) **Service:** General medical and surgical

Staffed Beds: 67

⊞ **SHANDS LAKE SHORE REGIONAL MEDICAL CENTER (100102)**, 368 NE Franklin Street, Zip 32055–3047; tel. 386/292–8000, (Nonreporting) **A**1 3 10 **S** Community Health Systems, Inc., Franklin, TN
Primary Contact: Rhonda Kay. Sherrod, R.N., MSN, Chief Executive Officer
COO: Francis A Pommett Jr Chief Operating Officer
CFO: Steve Davis, Chief Financial Officer
CMO: Mohammad Faisal, President Medical Staff
CHR: Angie Altman, Director Human Resources
CNO: Gary Goelz, R.N., Chief Nursing Officer
Web address: www.shandslakeshore.com
Control: Partnership, Investor–owned (for–profit) **Service:** General medical and surgical

Staffed Beds: 85

VETERANS AFFAIRS MEDICAL CENTER See Lake City Veterans Affairs Medical Center

LAKE WALES—Polk County

⊞ **LAKE WALES MEDICAL CENTER (100099)**, 410 South 11th Street, Zip 33853–4256; tel. 863/676–1433, **A**1 10 **F**3 11 15 18 20 29 30 34 35 40 45 46 49 50 56 57 59 64 70 74 75 79 81 82 85 86 87 89 91 92 93 94 96 98 103 107 108 110 111 114 115 119 124 129 131 132 146 147 148 149 **S** Community Health Systems, Inc., Franklin, TN
Primary Contact: Rebecca Brewer, FACHE, Chief Executive Officer
CFO: Danny Warren, Chief Financial Officer
CMO: Sunil Nihalani, M.D., Chief Medical Staff
CIO: Erwin Jaropillo, Director Information Systems
CHR: Renee Latterner, Director Human Resources
CNO: Jennifer Huston, Chief Nursing Officer
Web address: www.lakewalesmedicalcenter.com
Control: Corporation, Investor–owned (for–profit) **Service:** General medical and surgical

Staffed Beds: 131 **Admissions:** 4312 **Census:** 59 **Outpatient Visits:** 56752 **Births:** 0 **Total Expense ($000):** 56674 **Payroll Expense ($000):** 23497 **Personnel:** 382

LAKE WORTH—Palm Beach County

⊞ **SELECT SPECIALTY HOSPITAL–PALM BEACH (102023)**, 3060 Melaleuca Lane, Zip 33461–5174; tel. 561/357–7200, (Nonreporting) **A**1 10 **S** Select Medical Corporation, Mechanicsburg, PA
Primary Contact: Larry Melby, Chief Executive Officer
Web address: www.selectspecialtyhospitals.com/company/locations/palmbeach.aspx
Control: Corporation, Investor–owned (for–profit) **Service:** Acute long–term care hospital

Staffed Beds: 60

LAKELAND—Polk County

⊞ **LAKELAND REGIONAL HEALTH MEDICAL CENTER (100157)**, 1324 Lakeland Hills Blvd, Zip 33805–4543, Mailing Address: P.O. Box 95448, Zip 33804–5448; tel. 863/687–1100, **A**1 2 3 5 10 **F**3 4 11 13 18 20 22 24 26 28 29 30 31 34 37 38 40 41 43 44 45 46 47 49 51 55 56 57 58 59 60 61 64 65 66 70 71 72 74 75 76 77 78 79 80 81 82 83 84 85 86 87 88 89 93 95 96 98 99 100 101 102 103 104 107 108 109 110 111 114 115 118 119 120 121 123 124 126 130 131 132 135 143 144 146 147 148 154 **P**6 **S** Orlando Health, Orlando, FL
Primary Contact: Timothy Regan, M.D., President and Chief Medical Officer
COO: Sarah Bhagat, Chief Operating Officer and Vice President of Organizational Effectiveness
CFO: Evan Jones, Executive Vice President and Chief Financial Officer
CMO: Timothy Regan, M.D., President and Chief Medical Officer
CIO: Elizabeth Kerns, Senior Vice President and Chief Information Officer
CHR: Scott Dimmick, Senior Vice President and Chief Human Resources Officer
CNO: Janet Fansler, R.N., Executive Vice President and Chief Nurse Executive
Web address: www.mylrh.org
Control: Other not–for–profit (including NFP Corporation) **Service:** General medical and surgical

Staffed Beds: 849 **Admissions:** 40486 **Census:** 523 **Outpatient Visits:** 280618 **Births:** 2929 **Total Expense ($000):** 620970 **Payroll Expense ($000):** 240060 **Personnel:** 4745

LAND O'LAKES—Pasco County

⊞ **FLORIDA HOSPITAL AT CONNERTON LONG TERM ACUTE CARE (102026)**, 9441 Health Center Drive, Zip 34637–5837; tel. 813/903–3701, **A**1 10 **F**1 3 29 30 31 34 91 107 119 146 148 **S** Adventist Health System Sunbelt Health Care Corporation, Altamonte Springs, FL
Primary Contact: Brian Adams, President and Chief Executive Officer
COO: Debora Martoccio, R.N., Chief Operating Officer
CMO: Sharad Patel, M.D., Medical Director
Web address: www.elevatinghealthcare.org
Control: Church operated, Nongovernment, not–for–profit **Service:** Acute long–term care hospital

Staffed Beds: 50 **Admissions:** 705 **Census:** 49 **Outpatient Visits:** 0 **Births:** 0 **Total Expense ($000):** 27576 **Payroll Expense ($000):** 11169 **Personnel:** 224

FL

Hospital, Medicare Provider Number, Address, Telephone, Approval, Facility, and Physician Codes, Health Care System

★ American Hospital Association (AHA) membership ○ Healthcare Facilities Accreditation Program ⇑ Center for Improvement in Healthcare Quality Accreditation
☐ The Joint Commission accreditation ◇ DNV Healthcare Inc. accreditation △ Commission on Accreditation of Rehabilitation Facilities (CARF) accreditation

LARGO—Pinellas County

✠ **HEALTHSOUTH REHABILITATION HOSPITAL OF LARGO (103037)**, 901 North Clearwater–Largo Road, Zip 33770–4126; tel. 727/586–2999, (Nonreporting) **A**1 10 **S** Encompass Health Corporation, Birmingham, AL
Primary Contact: Tripp Smith, Chief Executive Officer
CFO: Judith Johnson, Controller
CMO: Richard A Liles, M.D., Medical Director
CHR: Jackie Chalk, Director Human Resources
CNO: Pattie Brenner, R.N., Chief Nursing Officer
Web address: www.healthsouthlargo.com
Control: Corporation, Investor–owned (for–profit) **Service**: Rehabilitation

| Staffed Beds: 70 |

✠ △ **LARGO MEDICAL CENTER (100248)**, 201 14th Street SW, Zip 33770–3133; tel. 727/588–5200, (Includes LARGO MEDICAL CENTER – INDIAN ROCKS, 2025 Indian Rocks Road, Largo, FL, Zip 33774–1096, Mailing Address: P.O. Box 2025, Zip 33779–2025, tel. 727/581–9474) (Nonreporting) **A**1 2 3 5 7 10 12 13 **S** HCA Healthcare, Nashville, TN
Primary Contact: Anthony M Degina, President and Chief Executive Officer
COO: Stephanie McNulty, Chief Operating Officer
CFO: Robert E Billings, Chief Financial Officer
CMO: David Weiland, M.D., Chief Medical Officer
CIO: David Saly, Director, Information Services
CNO: Brenda Simpson, R.N., Chief Nursing Officer
Web address: www.largomedical.com
Control: Corporation, Investor–owned (for–profit) **Service**: General medical and surgical

| Staffed Beds: 243 |

LAUDERDALE LAKES—Broward County

☐ △ **ST. ANTHONY'S REHABILITATION HOSPITAL (103027)**, 3485 NW 30th Street, Zip 33311–1890; tel. 954/739–6233, **A**1 7 10 **F**28 29 30 34 35 60 64 68 74 75 79 86 90 91 93 94 96 130 131 132 148 149 **S** Catholic Health Services, Lauderdale Lakes, FL
Primary Contact: Joseph M. Catania, Chief Executive Officer
COO: James Ball, Chief Operating Officer, Executive
CFO: David D'Amico
CMO: Mark Reiner, Chief Medical Office, Executive
CIO: Dario Achury, Director of Information Management
CHR: Barbara Griffith, Vice President Human Resources
Web address: www.catholichealthservices.org
Control: Church operated, Nongovernment, not–for–profit **Service**: Rehabilitation

| Staffed Beds: 26 **Admissions:** 471 **Census:** 17 **Outpatient Visits:** 2744 **Births:** 0 **Total Expense ($000):** 7401 **Payroll Expense ($000):** 3439 **Personnel:** 79 |

LEESBURG—Lake County

✠ **LEESBURG REGIONAL MEDICAL CENTER (100084)**, 600 East Dixie Avenue, Zip 34748–5999; tel. 352/323–5762, **A**1 2 10 **F**3 8 11 13 15 17 18 20 22 24 26 28 29 30 31 34 35 40 45 47 48 49 53 54 57 59 64 68 70 74 75 76 77 78 79 81 82 84 85 87 89 93 96 98 103 107 108 110 111 114 115 119 130 132 135 144 146 147 149 **P**1 **S** Central Florida Health, Leesburg, FL
Primary Contact: Donald G. Henderson, FACHE, President and Chief Executive Officer
COO: Saad Ehtisham, R.N., FACHE, Senior Vice President and Chief Operating Officer
CFO: Diane P Harden, Chief Financial Officer
CIO: David Steele, Vice President Chief Information Officer
CHR: Amie A Richason, Vice President Human Resources
CNO: Joshua Fleming, Vice President Chief Clinical Officer
Web address: www.centralfloridahealth.org
Control: Other not–for–profit (including NFP Corporation) **Service**: General medical and surgical

| Staffed Beds: 330 **Admissions:** 13774 **Census:** 228 **Outpatient Visits:** 83319 **Births:** 1308 **Personnel:** 1492 |

LIFESTREAM BEHAVIORAL CENTER (104018), 2020 Tally Road, Zip 34748–3426, Mailing Address: P.O. Box 491000, Zip 34749–1000; tel. 352/315–7500, (Nonreporting) **A**10
Primary Contact: Jonathan M. Cherry, President and Chief Executive Officer
COO: David Braughton, Chief Operating Officer
CFO: Carol Dozier, Chief Financial Officer
CMO: T. J. Valente, M.D., Medical Director
CIO: Chad Heim, Management Information System Director
CHR: Ben Hargrove, Human Resources Director
Web address: www.lsbc.net
Control: Other not–for–profit (including NFP Corporation) **Service**: Psychiatric

| Staffed Beds: 46 |

LEHIGH ACRES—Lee County

✠ **LEHIGH REGIONAL MEDICAL CENTER (100107)**, 1500 Lee Boulevard, Zip 33936–4835; tel. 239/369–2101, (Nonreporting) **A**1 10 **S** Prime Healthcare, Ontario, CA
Primary Contact: Gary C. Bell, LFACHE, Chief Executive Officer
CFO: Osman Gruhonjic, Chief Financial Officer
CMO: Joe Lemmons, D.O., Chief of Staff
CIO: Jeff Hampton, Director Information Systems
CHR: Mary Gray, Director Human Resources
CNO: Julie G Banker, R.N., MSN, Chief Nursing Officer
Web address: www.lehighregional.com
Control: Corporation, Investor–owned (for–profit) **Service**: General medical and surgical

| Staffed Beds: 88 |

LIVE OAK—Suwannee County

✠ **SHANDS LIVE OAK REGIONAL MEDICAL CENTER (101301)**, 1100 SW 11th Street, Zip 32064–3608; tel. 386/362–0800, (Nonreporting) **A**1 10 18 **S** Community Health Systems, Inc., Franklin, TN
Primary Contact: Rhonda Kay. Sherrod, R.N., MSN, Chief Executive Officer
CFO: Jennifer Grafton, Chief Financial Officer
CMO: Andrew C. Bass, M.D., Medical Director
CIO: Justin Marlowe, Information Technology Director
CHR: Dana Abbott, Market Human Resources Director
CNO: Donna Ragan, R.N., Chief Nursing Officer
Web address: www.shandsliveoak.com/
Control: Partnership, Investor–owned (for–profit) **Service**: General medical and surgical

| Staffed Beds: 25 |

LOXAHATCHEE—Palm Beach County

✠ **PALMS WEST HOSPITAL (100269)**, 13001 Southern Boulevard, Zip 33470–9203; tel. 561/798–3300, (Nonreporting) **A**1 3 10 **S** HCA Healthcare, Nashville, TN
Primary Contact: Joshua DeTillio, Chief Executive Officer
COO: Lorna Kernivan, Chief Operating Officer
CFO: Steven Burroughs, Chief Financial Officer
CIO: Martha Stinson, Director of Information Technology
CHR: Marcy Mills–Mathews, Director Human Resources
CNO: Silvia Stradi, Chief Nursing Officer
Web address: www.palmswesthospital.com
Control: Corporation, Investor–owned (for–profit) **Service**: General medical and surgical

| Staffed Beds: 204 |

MACCLENNY—Baker County

ED FRASER MEMORIAL HOSPITAL AND BAKER COMMUNITY HEALTH CENTER (100134), 159 North Third Street, Zip 32063–2103, Mailing Address: P.O. Box 484, Zip 32063–0484; tel. 904/259–3151, (Nonreporting) **A**10 20
Primary Contact: Dennis R. Markos, Chief Executive Officer
CFO: W. Steve Dudley, CPA, Chief Financial Officer
CMO: Mark Hardin, M.D., Medical Director
CIO: Ernie Waller, Director Information Technology
CHR: Stacey Conner, Director Personnel
CNO: Valerie Markos, Chief Nursing Officer
Web address: www.bcmedsvcs.com
Control: Other not–for–profit (including NFP Corporation) **Service**: General medical and surgical

| Staffed Beds: 68 |

MADISON—Madison County

MADISON COUNTY MEMORIAL HOSPITAL (101311), 224 NW Crane Avenue, Zip 32340–2561; tel. 850/973–2271, (Nonreporting) **A**10 18
Primary Contact: Tammy Stevens, Chief Executive Officer
CMO: Brett Perkins, M.D., Chief Medical Staff
CIO: Patrick Stiff, Coordinator Information Technology
CHR: Cindi Burnett, Chief Human Resources Officer
Web address: www.mcmh.us/
Control: Other not–for–profit (including NFP Corporation) **Service**: General medical and surgical

| Staffed Beds: 25 |

Many Facility Codes have changed. Please refer to the AHA Guide Code Chart.   © 2018 AHA Guide

MARGATE—Broward County

☒ **NORTHWEST MEDICAL CENTER (100189)**, 2801 North State Road 7, Zip 33063–5727; tel. 954/974–0400, (Nonreporting) **A**1 10 **S** HCA Healthcare, Nashville, TN
Primary Contact: Erica Gulrich, Chief Executive Officer
CFO: Ananda Rampat, Chief Financial Officer
CMO: Jose Martinez, M.D., Chief Medical Officer
CIO: David Irizarri, Director Information Technology
CHR: Lynda Bryan, Vice President Human Resources
CNO: Sandra Emeott, R.N., Chief Nursing Officer
Web address: www.northwestmed.com
Control: Corporation, Investor–owned (for–profit) **Service:** General medical and surgical

Staffed Beds: 228

MARIANNA—Jackson County

☒ **JACKSON HOSPITAL (100142)**, 4250 Hospital Drive, Zip 32446–1917, Mailing Address: P.O. Box 1608, Zip 32447–5608; tel. 850/526–2200, **A**1 10 20 **F**3 11 13 15 20 28 29 30 31 34 35 40 45 50 53 54 57 59 70 75 76 78 81 85 86 87 97 107 108 110 111 114 119 120 127 130 132 133 135 146 147 148 **S** QHR, Brentwood, TN
Primary Contact: James Platt, Chief Executive Officer
CFO: Kevin Rovito, Chief Financial Officer
CMO: Steven Walter Spence, M.D., Chief Medical Officer
CIO: Jamie Hussey, Chief Information Officer
CHR: Brooke G Donaldson, Assistant Administrator Human Resources
CNO: Robbin K Pumphrey, Chief Nursing Officer
Web address: www.jacksonhosp.com
Control: Hospital district or authority, Government, nonfederal **Service:** General medical and surgical

Staffed Beds: 68 **Admissions:** 2777 **Census:** 35 **Outpatient Visits:** 70527 **Births:** 422 **Total Expense ($000):** 49822 **Payroll Expense ($000):** 23957 **Personnel:** 484

MELBOURNE—Brevard County

☐ **CIRCLES OF CARE (104024)**, 400 East Sheridan Road, Zip 32901–3184; tel. 321/722–5200, (Nonreporting) **A**1 5 10
Primary Contact: David L. Feldman, President and Chief Executive Officer
CFO: David L Feldman, Executive Vice President and Treasurer
CMO: Jose Alvarez, M.D., Chief Medical Staff
CHR: Linda Brannon, Vice President Human Resources
Web address: www.circlesofcare.org
Control: Other not–for–profit (including NFP Corporation) **Service:** Psychiatric

Staffed Beds: 134

DEVEREUX HOSPITAL AND CHILDREN'S CENTER OF FLORIDA, 8000 Devereux Drive, Zip 32940–7907; tel. 321/242–9100, (Nonreporting) **S** Devereux, Villanova, PA
Primary Contact: Steven Murphy, Executive Director
COO: Eva Horner, Assistant Executive Director Operations
CFO: Kelly Messer, Director of Finance
CMO: Manal Durgin, Network Medical Director
CIO: Diana Deitrick, Director Information Services
CHR: Tim Dillion, Vice President of Human Resources
Web address: www.devereux.org
Control: Other not–for–profit (including NFP Corporation) **Service:** Children's hospital psychiatric

Staffed Beds: 100

☒ **HEALTH FIRST HOLMES REGIONAL MEDICAL CENTER (100019)**, 1350 South Hickory Street, Zip 32901–3224; tel. 321/434–7000, **A**1 5 10 **F**3 11 13 17 18 20 22 24 26 28 29 30 31 34 39 40 41 43 45 46 49 50 59 60 64 68 70 72 74 75 76 77 78 79 81 82 84 85 86 87 89 92 93 102 107 108 111 114 115 118 119 126 130 132 141 146 148 149 **S** Health First, Inc., Rockledge, FL
Primary Contact: Brett A. Esrock, FACHE, Chief Executive Officer
CFO: Joseph G Felkner, Executive Vice President/Chief Financial Officer
CMO: Mark Rosenbloom, M.D., Vice President of Medical Affairs
CIO: Dustin Leek, Vice President of Enterprise Technology Services
CHR: Paula Just, Chief Human Resources Officer
CNO: Barbara Seymour, Vice President of Nursing
Web address: www.health-first.org
Control: Other not–for–profit (including NFP Corporation) **Service:** General medical and surgical

Staffed Beds: 514 **Admissions:** 30255 **Census:** 389 **Outpatient Visits:** 219676 **Births:** 3056 **Total Expense ($000):** 470785 **Payroll Expense ($000):** 177888 **Personnel:** 2192

☐ **HEALTH FIRST VIERA HOSPITAL (100315)**, 8745 North Wickham Road, Zip 32940–5997; tel. 321/434–9164, **A**1 5 10 **F**3 12 15 20 29 30 31 34 39 40 41 45 46 47 49 50 54 59 60 64 68 70 75 77 78 79 80 81 85 86 87 93 102 107 108 110 111 114 115 117 118 119 126 129 130 132 141 146 148 149 154 **S** Health First, Inc., Rockledge, FL
Primary Contact: Aaron Robinson, Chief Executive Officer, Health First Community Hospitals
COO: Deborah Angerami, Chief Operating Officer
CFO: Joseph G Felkner, Chief Financial Officer
CMO: Scott Gettings, M.D., Senior Vice President and Chief Medical Officer
CIO: Alex Popowycz, Chief Information Officer
CHR: Paula Just, Chief Human Resources Officer
CNO: Connie Bradley, R.N., MSN, FACHE, Senior Vice President and Chief Nursing Officer
Web address: www.vierahospital.org
Control: Other not–for–profit (including NFP Corporation) **Service:** General medical and surgical

Staffed Beds: 84 **Admissions:** 4977 **Census:** 49 **Outpatient Visits:** 69381 **Births:** 0 **Total Expense ($000):** 90002 **Payroll Expense ($000):** 32373 **Personnel:** 383

☒ **SEA PINES REHABILITATION HOSPITAL (103034)**, 101 East Florida Avenue, Zip 32901–8301; tel. 321/984–4600, (Nonreporting) **A**1 10 **S** Encompass Health Corporation, Birmingham, AL
Primary Contact: Denise B. McGrath, Chief Executive Officer
CFO: Dana Edwards, Chief Financial Officer
CMO: Juan Lebron, M.D., Medical Officer
CHR: James L Henry, Director Human Resources
CNO: Lisa Truman, Chief Nursing Officer
Web address: www.healthsouthseapines.com
Control: Corporation, Investor–owned (for–profit) **Service:** Rehabilitation

Staffed Beds: 90

☒ **KINDRED HOSPITAL MELBOURNE (102027)**, 765 West Nasa Boulevard, Zip 32901–1815; tel. 321/733–5725, (Nonreporting) **A**1 10 **S** Kindred Healthcare, Louisville, KY
Primary Contact: Pamela R. Reed, Chief Executive Officer
Web address: www.khmelbourne.com
Control: Corporation, Investor–owned (for–profit) **Service:** Acute long–term care hospital

Staffed Beds: 60

☒ **MELBOURNE REGIONAL MEDICAL CENTER (100291)**, 250 North Wickham Road, Zip 32935–8625; tel. 321/752–1200, (Nonreporting) **A**1 10 **S** Steward Health Care System, LLC, Dallas, TX
Primary Contact: Ron Gicca, Chief Executive Officer
CFO: Dale Armour, Chief Financial Officer
Web address: www.wuesthoff.com/locations/wuesthoff–medical–center–melbourne
Control: Corporation, Investor–owned (for–profit) **Service:** General medical and surgical

Staffed Beds: 119

MIAMI—Miami–Dade County

☒ △ **BAPTIST HEALTH SOUTH FLORIDA, BAPTIST HOSPITAL OF MIAMI (100008)**, 8900 North Kendall Drive, Zip 33176–2197; tel. 786/596–1960, (Includes BAPTIST CHILDREN'S HOSPITAL, 8900 North Kendall Drive, Miami, FL, Zip 33176–2118; tel. 786/596–1960; Albert Leon Boulenger, R.N., Chief Executive Officer) **A**1 2 5 7 10 **F**3 11 13 15 17 18 19 20 22 24 26 27 28 29 30 31 32 34 35 39 40 41 45 46 47 48 49 50 51 53 54 55 56 57 58 59 60 61 63 64 66 68 70 72 74 75 76 77 78 79 81 82 84 85 86 87 88 89 90 91 92 93 94 96 100 102 107 108 109 110 111 112 114 115 116 117 118 119 120 121 123 124 126 129 130 132 135 141 143 144 145 146 147 148 149 150 154 **S** Baptist Health South Florida, Coral Gables, FL
Primary Contact: Patricia M. Rosello, Chief Executive Officer
CFO: Ralph E Lawson, Executive Vice President and Chief Financial Officer
CMO: Mark J Hauser, M.D., Chief Medical Officer
CIO: Mimi Taylor, Corporate Vice President Information Technology
CHR: Adriene McCoy, Chief Human Resource Officer
CNO: Becky Montesino–King, MS, R.N., MSN, Vice President and Chief Nursing Officer
Web address: www.baptisthealth.net
Control: Other not–for–profit (including NFP Corporation) **Service:** General medical and surgical

Staffed Beds: 720 **Admissions:** 30623 **Census:** 499 **Outpatient Visits:** 485356 **Births:** 3611 **Total Expense ($000):** 943839 **Payroll Expense ($000):** 310478 **Personnel:** 3978

FL

Hospital, Medicare Provider Number, Address, Telephone, Approval, Facility, and Physician Codes, Health Care System

★ American Hospital Association (AHA) membership   ○ Healthcare Facilities Accreditation Program   ⇑ Center for Improvement in Healthcare Quality Accreditation
☐ The Joint Commission accreditation   ◇ DNV Healthcare Inc. accreditation   △ Commission on Accreditation of Rehabilitation Facilities (CARF) accreditation

© 2018 AHA Guide   *Many Facility Codes have changed. Please refer to the AHA Guide Code Chart.*   Hospitals **A129**

⊞ **BAPTIST HEALTH SOUTH FLORIDA, SOUTH MIAMI HOSPITAL (100154)**, 6200 SW 73rd Street, Zip 33143–4679; tel. 786/662–4000, **A**1 2 3 10 **F**3 5 8 11 12 13 15 16 17 18 20 22 24 26 28 29 30 31 34 35 36 40 44 45 46 48 49 50 51 52 53 54 57 58 59 60 61 64 66 68 70 72 74 75 76 77 78 79 81 82 84 85 86 87 91 93 94 96 100 102 107 108 110 111 114 115 116 117 118 119 126 129 130 132 135 141 144 146 147 148 149 150 154 **S** Baptist Health South Florida, Coral Gables, FL
Primary Contact: Lincoln S. Mendez, Chief Executive Officer
COO: Jeanette Stone, Vice President Operations
CFO: Erik Long, Controller
CMO: Jeremy Tabak, M.D., President Medical Staff
CIO: Mimi Taylor, Vice President Information Technology
CHR: Diana Montenegro, Director Human Resources
CNO: Kathy Sparger, R.N., MSN, Chief Nursing Officer
Web address: www.baptisthealth.net
Control: Other not–for–profit (including NFP Corporation) **Service:** General medical and surgical

Staffed Beds: 336 **Admissions:** 15157 **Census:** 205 **Outpatient Visits:** 265841 **Births:** 3718 **Total Expense ($000):** 483387 **Payroll Expense ($000):** 157017 **Personnel:** 1886

⊞ **BAPTIST HEALTH SOUTH FLORIDA, WEST KENDALL BAPTIST HOSPITAL (100314)**, 9555 SW 162nd Avenue, Zip 33196–6408; tel. 786/467–2000, **A**1 3 10 **F**3 11 13 18 19 29 30 31 34 35 40 41 45 49 50 51 53 57 58 59 60 63 64 68 70 74 75 76 78 79 81 82 84 85 86 87 93 100 102 107 108 109 111 114 115 119 126 130 131 132 135 146 147 148 149 150 154 **S** Baptist Health South Florida, Coral Gables, FL
Primary Contact: Javier Hernandez–Lichtl, Chief Executive Officer
CFO: Odalys Remigio, Assistant Vice President, Finance
CMO: Juan–Carlos Verdeja, M.D., President of Medical Staff
CHR: Hilde Zamora de Aguero, Human Resources Site Director
CNO: Denise H. Harris, R.N., MSN, Chief Nursing Officer
Web address: www.baptisthealth.net/en/facilities/West–Kendall–Baptist–Hospital/Pages/default.aspx
Control: Other not–for–profit (including NFP Corporation) **Service:** General medical and surgical

Staffed Beds: 133 **Admissions:** 8504 **Census:** 95 **Outpatient Visits:** 87184 **Births:** 940 **Total Expense ($000):** 202619 **Payroll Expense ($000):** 71212 **Personnel:** 1034

JACKSON BEHAVIORAL HEALTH HOSPITAL See Jackson Health System, Miami

☐ △ **JACKSON HEALTH SYSTEM (100022)**, 1611 NW 12th Avenue, Zip 33136–1005; tel. 305/585–1111, (Includes HOLTZ CHILDREN'S HOSPITAL, 1611 NW 12th Avenue, Miami, FL, Zip 33136–1005; tel. 305/585–5437; Don S Steigman, Chief Executive Officer; JACKSON BEHAVIORAL HEALTH HOSPITAL, 1695 NW Ninth Avenue, Miami, FL, Zip 33136–1409; tel. 305/324–4357; Nicolette B Tessler, Chief Executive Officer of Behavioral Health Hospital; JACKSON MEMORIAL HOSPITAL, 1611 NW 12th Avenue, Miami, FL, Zip 33136; tel. 305/585–1111; David Zambrana, Ph.D., R.N., Senior Vice President and Chief Executive Officer; JACKSON NORTH MEDICAL CENTER, 160 NW 170th Street, North Miami Beach, FL, Zip 33169–5576; tel. 305/651–1100; Roy L. Hawkins Jr, Senior Vice President and Chief Executive Officer; JACKSON SOUTH COMMUNITY HOSPITAL, 9333 SW 152nd Street, Miami, FL, Zip 33157–1780; tel. 305/251–2500; Georgina Diaz, Chief Executive Officer) (Total facility includes 343 beds in nursing home–type unit) **A**1 3 5 7 8 10 **F**1 3 4 5 8 11 12 13 15 16 17 18 19 20 21 22 23 24 25 26 27 29 30 31 34 35 38 39 40 41 43 44 45 46 49 50 54 55 56 57 58 59 60 61 64 65 66 67 68 70 71 72 73 74 75 76 77 78 79 80 81 82 83 84 85 86 87 88 89 90 93 94 96 97 98 99 100 101 102 103 104 107 108 109 110 111 114 115 116 117 118 119 120 121 123 124 126 128 129 130 131 132 135 136 137 138 139 140 141 142 144 146 147 148 149 154
Primary Contact: Carlos A. Migoya, President and Chief Executive Officer
COO: Don S Steigman, Chief Operating Officer
CFO: Mark T Knight, Executive Vice President and Chief Financial Officer
CMO: Peter G Paige, Chief Medical Officer
CIO: Michael A Garcia, Vice President and Chief Information Officer
CHR: Julie Staub, Chief Human Resources Officer
Web address: www.jacksonhealth.org
Control: County, Government, nonfederal **Service:** General medical and surgical

Staffed Beds: 2026 **Admissions:** 65762 **Census:** 1560 **Outpatient Visits:** 483935 **Births:** 6561 **Total Expense ($000):** 1866803 **Payroll Expense ($000):** 881185 **Personnel:** 11619

JACKSON SOUTH COMMUNITY HOSPITAL See Jackson Health System, Miami

⊞ **KENDALL REGIONAL MEDICAL CENTER (100209)**, 11750 Bird Road, Zip 33175–3530; tel. 305/223–3000, (Nonreporting) **A**1 3 10 **S** HCA Healthcare, Nashville, TN
Primary Contact: Brandon Haushalter, Chief Executive Officer
COO: Randy Gross, Chief Operating Officer
CFO: Robert Grace, Chief Financial Officer
CMO: Bradley Shumaker, Chief Medical Officer
CIO: Matt Hernandez, Director of Information Technology and System
CHR: Knicole S White, Vice–President, Human Resources
CNO: Maria Villa, Interim Chief Nursing Officer
Web address: www.kendallmed.com
Control: Partnership, Investor–owned (for–profit) **Service:** General medical and surgical

Staffed Beds: 300

☐ **MIAMI JEWISH HOME AND HOSPITAL FOR AGED (100277)**, 5200 NE Second Avenue, Zip 33137–2706; tel. 305/751–8626, (Nonreporting) **A**1 5 10
Primary Contact: Jeffrey P. Freimark, Chief Executive Officer
CFO: Lisa Jo Desmarteau, Chief Financial Officer
CMO: Brian Kiedrowski, M.D., Chief Medical Director
CHR: Larry McDonald, Director Human Resources
Web address: www.mjhha.org
Control: Other not–for–profit (including NFP Corporation) **Service:** General medical and surgical

Staffed Beds: 32

⊞ △ **MIAMI VETERANS AFFAIRS HEALTHCARE SYSTEM**, 1201 NW 16th Street, Zip 33125–1624; tel. 305/575–7000, (Nonreporting) **A**1 3 5 7 **S** Department of Veterans Affairs, Perry Point, MD
Primary Contact: Paul M. Russo, FACHE, Director
COO: Lance Davis, PharmD, Associate Director
CFO: Albert Tucker, Chief Financial Officer
CMO: Vincent DeGennaro, M.D., Chief of Staff
CIO: Anthony Brooks, Chief Information Officer
CHR: Loyman Marin, Chief Human Resources
CNO: Marcia C Lysaght, R.N., MSN, Associate Director Patient Care Services
Web address: www.miami.va.gov/
Control: Veterans Affairs, Government, federal **Service:** General medical and surgical

Staffed Beds: 401

★ ⇑ **NICKLAUS CHILDREN'S HOSPITAL (103301)**, 3100 SW 62nd Avenue, Zip 33155–3009; tel. 305/666–6511, **A**2 3 5 8 10 12 13 21 **F**3 7 8 9 17 18 19 20 21 22 23 24 25 26 27 29 30 31 32 34 35 36 37 38 39 40 41 43 44 45 46 47 48 49 50 51 53 54 55 57 58 59 60 61 64 65 66 68 71 72 73 74 75 77 78 79 81 82 84 85 86 87 88 89 92 93 94 97 98 99 100 101 102 104 105 107 108 109 111 112 114 115 116 117 118 119 126 129 130 131 132 134 135 136 142 143 144 145 146 148 153 154 **P**6
Primary Contact: M Narendra. Kini, M.D., President and Chief Executive Officer
COO: Martha McGill, Executive Vice President and Chief Operating Officer
CFO: Timothy L Birkenstock, Chief Financial Officer
CMO: Deise Granado–Villar, M.D., Chief Medical Officer and Senior Vice President Medical Affairs
CIO: Edward Martinez, Chief Information Officer
CHR: Michael S. Kushner, Senior Vice President and Chief Talent Officer
CNO: Jacqueline Gonzalez, Senior Vice President and Chief Nursing Officer
Web address: www.mch.com
Control: Other not–for–profit (including NFP Corporation) **Service:** Children's general medical and surgical

Staffed Beds: 281 **Admissions:** 10629 **Census:** 190 **Outpatient Visits:** 515289 **Births:** 0 **Total Expense ($000):** 586862 **Payroll Expense ($000):** 220809 **Personnel:** 3858

⊞ **NORTH SHORE MEDICAL CENTER (100029)**, 1100 NW 95th Street, Zip 33150–2098; tel. 305/835–6000, (Includes FLORIDA MEDICAL CENTER – A CAMPUS OF NORTH SHORE, 5000 West Oakland Park Boulevard, Fort Lauderdale, FL, Zip 33313–1585; tel. 954/735–6000; Trey Abshier, Chief Executive Officer) (Nonreporting) **A**1 3 10 **S** TENET Healthcare Corporation, Dallas, TX
Primary Contact: Mark Racicot, Chief Executive Officer
COO: Shana Crittenden, Chief Operating Officer
CFO: Howard Brown, Chief Financial Officer
CMO: Marcia Bierman, M.D., Chief of Staff
CIO: Luis Estrada, Director Multifacility Information Systems
CHR: Carmen Gomez, Director Human Resources
Web address: www.northshoremedical.com
Control: Corporation, Investor–owned (for–profit) **Service:** General medical and surgical

Staffed Beds: 816

PROMISE HOSPITAL OF MIAMI (100326), 14001 NW 82nd Avenue, Zip 33158; tel. 786/609-9200, (Nonreporting) **S** Promise Healthcare, Boca Raton, FL
Primary Contact: Charles Doten, Chief Executive Officer
Web address: www.promise-miami.com
Control: Corporation, Investor-owned (for-profit) **Service**: Acute long-term care hospital

Staffed Beds: 60

✠ **SELECT SPECIALTY HOSPITAL-MIAMI (102001)**, 955 NW 3rd Street, Zip 33128-1274; tel. 305/416-5700, (Nonreporting) **A**1 10 **S** Select Medical Corporation, Mechanicsburg, PA
Primary Contact: Dionisio Bencomo, Chief Executive Officer
Web address: www.selectspecialtyhospitals.com/company/locations/miami.aspx
Control: Corporation, Investor-owned (for-profit) **Service**: Acute long-term care hospital

Staffed Beds: 47

☐ **SISTER EMMANUEL HOSPITAL (102016)**, 3663 South Miami Avenue, Zip 33133-4253; tel. 305/285-2939, (Nonreporting) **A**1 10
Primary Contact: Miguel Vasquez, Chief Executive Officer
CFO: Miguel Vasquez, Chief Financial Officer
CMO: Hugo Gonzalez, M.D., Chief Medical Officer
CIO: Macarena Restrepo, Manager Business Office
CHR: Kathy Mainieri, Human Resource Specialist
Web address: www.sisteremmanuelhospital.org/
Control: Church operated, Nongovernment, not-for-profit **Service**: Acute long-term care hospital

Staffed Beds: 29

✠ **UNIVERSITY OF MIAMI HOSPITAL AND CLINICS (100079)**, 1475 NW 12th Avenue, Zip 33136-1002; tel. 305/243-4000, (Includes BASCOM PALMER EYE INSTITUTE-ANNE BATES LEACH EYE HOSPITAL, 900 NW 17th Street, Miami, FL, Zip 33136-1199, Mailing Address: Box 016880, Zip 33101-6880, tel. 305/326-6000; Michael B Gittelman, Administrator; UNIVERSITY OF MIAMI HOSPITAL, 1400 NW 12th Avenue, Miami, FL, Zip 33136-1003; tel. 305/325-5511; Michael B Gittelman, Chief Executive Officer) **A**1 2 3 5 10 **F**3 11 15 29 30 31 34 35 36 38 44 45 46 47 48 49 50 54 55 57 58 59 64 68 70 74 75 77 78 79 80 81 82 84 85 86 87 93 100 107 108 110 111 114 115 117 118 119 120 121 123 124 126 130 132 135 136 141 145 146 147 148 149 **P**6
Primary Contact: Michael B. Gittelman, Chief Executive Officer
CFO: Harry Rohrer, Chief Financial Officer
CMO: W Jarrad Goodwin, M.D., Director
Web address: www.uhealthsystem.com
Control: Other not-for-profit (including NFP Corporation) **Service**: Cancer

Staffed Beds: 40 Admissions: 1080 Census: 30 Outpatient Visits: 434367 Births: 0 Total Expense ($000): 600482 Payroll Expense ($000): 96670 Personnel: 1362

VETERANS AFFAIRS MEDICAL CENTER See Miami Veterans Affairs Healthcare System

✠ △ **WEST GABLES REHABILITATION HOSPITAL (103036)**, 2525 SW 75th Avenue, Zip 33155-2800; tel. 305/262-6800, **A**1 7 10 **F**29 34 74 75 87 90 93 96 130 131 148 149 **S** Select Medical Corporation, Mechanicsburg, PA
Primary Contact: Walter Concepcion, Chief Executive Officer
CFO: Sara Reohr, Regional Controller
CMO: Jose L Vargas, M.D., Medical Director
CHR: Barbara Etchason, HR Manager
CNO: Lucia Benjamin, Chief Nursing Officer
Web address: www.westgablesrehabhospital.com/
Control: Corporation, Investor-owned (for-profit) **Service**: Rehabilitation

Staffed Beds: 60 Admissions: 1458 Census: 55 Outpatient Visits: 9498 Births: 0 Total Expense ($000): 22276 Payroll Expense ($000): 12688 Personnel: 190

○ **WESTCHESTER GENERAL HOSPITAL (100284)**, 2500 SW 75th Avenue, Zip 33155-2805; tel. 305/264-5252, (Includes SOUTHERN WINDS HOSPITAL, 4225 West 20th Street, Hialeah, FL, Zip 33012-5835; tel. 305/558-9700) **A**10 11 12 13 **F**3 15 18 29 31 40 45 49 56 65 70 74 75 77 78 79 81 85 87 98 100 102 103 107 108 110 114 115 119 130
Primary Contact: Rudy Garcia, Chief Executive Officer
CFO: Joel Snook, Chief Financial Officer
CMO: Rogelio Zaldivar, M.D., Medical Director
CHR: Jennifer Ricardo, Director of Human Resources
Web address: www.westchestergeneralhospital.com/
Control: Corporation, Investor-owned (for-profit) **Service**: General medical and surgical

Staffed Beds: 125 Admissions: 4121 Census: 68 Outpatient Visits: 25967 Births: 0 Total Expense ($000): 48282 Payroll Expense ($000): 22574 Personnel: 465

MIAMI BEACH—Dade County

MIAMI HEART CAMPUS AT MOUNT SINAI MEDICAL CENTER See Mount Sinai Medical Center, Miami Beach

MIAMI BEACH—Miami-Dade County

☐ △ **MOUNT SINAI MEDICAL CENTER (100034)**, 4300 Alton Road, Zip 33140-2948; tel. 305/674-2121, (Includes MIAMI HEART CAMPUS AT MOUNT SINAI MEDICAL CENTER, 4701 North Meridian Avenue, Miami Beach, FL, Zip 33140-2910; tel. 305/672-1111) **A**1 2 3 5 7 8 10 13 **F**1 3 4 6 8 9 12 13 14 15 16 17 18 19 20 22 24 26 28 29 30 31 34 35 36 37 38 39 40 41 44 45 46 47 48 49 50 51 53 54 55 56 57 58 59 60 61 62 63 64 65 66 67 68 70 71 72 73 74 75 76 77 78 79 80 81 82 83 84 85 86 87 88 89 90 91 92 93 96 97 98 100 101 102 103 104 105 107 108 110 111 114 115 118 119 120 121 123 124 126 128 129 130 131 132 135 141 143 145 146 147 148 149 152 154 **P**6
Primary Contact: Steven D. Sonenreich, President and Chief Executive Officer
COO: Angel Pallin, Senior Vice President of Operations
CFO: Alex A Mendez, Executive Vice President of Operations and Chief Financial Officer
CMO: Robert Goldszer, M.D., Senior Vice President and Chief Medical Officer
CIO: Tom Gillette, Senior Vice President and Chief Information Officer
CHR: Georgia McLean, Director Human Resources
CNO: Karen W Moyer, R.N., Senior Vice President and Chief Nursing Officer
Web address: www.msmc.com
Control: Other not-for-profit (including NFP Corporation) **Service**: General medical and surgical

Staffed Beds: 608 Admissions: 20753 Census: 357 Outpatient Visits: 204237 Births: 2762 Total Expense ($000): 562543 Payroll Expense ($000): 260395 Personnel: 3942

MIDDLEBURG—Clay County

✠ **ST. VINCENT'S MEDICAL CENTER CLAY COUNTY (100321)**, 1670 St. Vincent's Way, Zip 32068-8427, Mailing Address: 1670 St. Vincents Way, Zip 32068-8447; tel. 904/602-1000, **A**1 10 **F**3 13 15 18 20 22 29 30 34 37 40 44 49 57 61 64 65 70 74 76 79 81 84 85 86 87 93 107 108 110 111 114 115 118 119 124 130 131 132 146 147 149 **S** Ascension Healthcare, Saint Louis, MO
Primary Contact: James Machado, President
Web address: www.jaxhealth.com/
Control: Church operated, Nongovernment, not-for-profit **Service**: General medical and surgical

Staffed Beds: 106 Admissions: 6710 Census: 62 Outpatient Visits: 48816 Births: 390 Total Expense ($000): 85109 Payroll Expense ($000): 28069 Personnel: 407

MILTON—Santa Rosa County

✠ **SANTA ROSA MEDICAL CENTER (100124)**, 6002 Berryhill Road, Zip 32570-5062; tel. 850/626-7762, (Nonreporting) **A**1 10 **S** Community Health Systems, Inc., Franklin, TN
Primary Contact: Doug Sills, Chief Executive Officer
CFO: Jared Whipkey, Chief Financial Officer
CIO: Rick Payne, Director Information Systems
CHR: Christopher Foreman, Director Human Resources
CNO: Trish Davis, Chief Nursing Officer
Web address: www.santarosamedicalcenter.org
Control: Corporation, Investor-owned (for-profit) **Service**: General medical and surgical

Staffed Beds: 68

WEST FLORIDA COMMUNITY CARE CENTER (104027), 5500 Stewart Street, Zip 32570-4304; tel. 850/983-5500, (Nonreporting) **A**10
Primary Contact: Joshua Willis, Chief Executive Officer
Web address: www.elakeviewcenter.org/MentalHealth/Adult/Inpatient-WFCCC.aspx
Control: Other not-for-profit (including NFP Corporation) **Service**: Psychiatric

Staffed Beds: 100

FL

Hospital, Medicare Provider Number, Address, Telephone, Approval, Facility, and Physician Codes, Health Care System

★ American Hospital Association (AHA) membership
☐ The Joint Commission accreditation
○ Healthcare Facilities Accreditation Program
◇ DNV Healthcare Inc. accreditation
⇑ Center for Improvement in Healthcare Quality Accreditation
△ Commission on Accreditation of Rehabilitation Facilities (CARF) accreditation

MIRAMAR—Broward County

✈ **MEMORIAL HOSPITAL MIRAMAR (100285)**, 1901 SW 172nd Avenue, Zip 33029–5592; tel. 954/538–5000, **A**1 10 **F**3 13 15 29 30 35 40 41 45 49 50 55 57 59 61 64 68 70 72 74 75 76 78 79 81 82 84 85 87 91 93 107 108 110 111 114 115 119 126 130 131 132 135 145 146 147 **S** Memorial Healthcare System, Hollywood, FL
Primary Contact: Grisel Fernandez–Bravo, R.N., Administrator and Chief Executive Officer
CFO: Judy Sada, Chief Financial Officer
CMO: Stanley Marks, M.D., FACS, Chief Medical Officer
CIO: Forest Blanton, Senior VP and Chief Information Officer
CHR: Ray Kendrick, Chief Human Resources Officer
CNO: Denise Reynolds, Chief Nursing Officer
Web address: www.mhs.net
Control: Hospital district or authority, Government, nonfederal **Service**: General medical and surgical

Staffed Beds: 178 **Admissions**: 9723 **Census**: 95 **Outpatient Visits**: 135224 **Births**: 3675 **Total Expense ($000)**: 149541 **Payroll Expense ($000)**: 74716 **Personnel**: 847

MIRAMAR BEACH—Walton County

✈ **SACRED HEART HOSPITAL ON THE EMERALD COAST (100292)**, 7800 Highway 98 West, Zip 32550; tel. 850/278–3000, (Nonreporting) **A**1 10 **S** Ascension Healthcare, Saint Louis, MO
Primary Contact: Roger L. Hall, President
CMO: Gary M. Pablo, M.D., Chief Medical Officer
Web address: www.sacredheartemerald.org
Control: Other not–for–profit (including NFP Corporation) **Service**: General medical and surgical

Staffed Beds: 58

NAPLES—Collier County

LANDMARK HOSPITAL OF SOUTHWEST FLORIDA, 1285 Creekside Boulevard East, Zip 34108; tel. 239/529–1800, (Nonreporting) **A**22 **S** Landmark Hospitals, Cape Girardeau, MO
Primary Contact: James Whitacre, Chief Executive Officer
Web address: www.landmarkhospitals.com/our–hospitals/southwest–florida/
Control: Partnership, Investor–owned (for–profit) **Service**: Acute long–term care hospital

Staffed Beds: 50

✈ △ **NCH BAKER HOSPITAL (100018)**, 350 Seventh Street North, Zip 34102–5754, Mailing Address: P.O. Box 413029, Zip 34101–3029; tel. 239/624–4000, (Includes NCH NORTH NAPLES HOSPITAL, 11190 Health Park Blvd, Naples, FL, Zip 34110–5729, Mailing Address: 11190 Health Park Boulevard, Zip 34110–5729, tel. 239/552–7000) **A**1 2 3 7 10 **F**3 11 12 13 14 15 17 18 19 20 22 24 26 28 29 30 31 32 34 35 37 40 41 44 45 47 48 49 50 53 56 57 59 64 68 70 72 74 75 76 77 78 79 81 84 85 86 87 88 89 90 91 92 93 95 96 98 100 102 103 107 108 110 111 114 115 116 117 119 126 131 135 145 146 147 148 149 **P**6
Primary Contact: Allen S. Weiss, M.D., President and Chief Executive Officer
COO: Phillip C Dutcher, Chief Operating Officer
CFO: Mike Stephens, Chief Financial Officer
CMO: Doug Ardion, M.D., Chief Medical Officer
CHR: John McGirl, Chief Human Resources Officer
CNO: Michele Thoman, R.N., Chief Nursing Officer
Web address: www.nchmd.org
Control: Other not–for–profit (including NFP Corporation) **Service**: General medical and surgical

Staffed Beds: 713 **Admissions**: 27065 **Census**: 371 **Outpatient Visits**: 340275 **Births**: 3341 **Total Expense ($000)**: 432528 **Payroll Expense ($000)**: 171603 **Personnel**: 2944

✈ **PHYSICIANS REGIONAL – PINE RIDGE (100286)**, 6101 Pine Ridge Road, Zip 34119–3900; tel. 239/348–4000, (Includes PHYSICIANS REGIONAL, 8300 Collier Boulevard, Naples, FL, Zip 34114; tel. 239/354–6000; C Scott Campbell, Market Chief Executive Officer) (Nonreporting) **A**1 10 **S** Community Health Systems, Inc., Franklin, TN
Primary Contact: Scott Lowe, Interim Market Chief Executive Officer
COO: Susan Takacs, Market Chief Operating Officer
CFO: Ken Warriner, Market Chief Financial Officer
CHR: Jill Gaffoli, Director Human Resources
Web address: www.physiciansregional.com
Control: Corporation, Investor–owned (for–profit) **Service**: General medical and surgical

Staffed Beds: 201

☐ **THE WILLOUGH AT NAPLES (104063)**, 9001 Tamiami Trail East, Zip 34113–3304; tel. 239/775–4500, (Nonreporting) **A**1 10
Primary Contact: Kathleen Melo, Administrator
CFO: Steve Baldwin, Vice President Finance
Web address: www.thewilloughatnaples.com/
Control: Corporation, Investor–owned (for–profit) **Service**: Psychiatric

Staffed Beds: 80

NEW PORT RICHEY—Pasco County

✈ △ **MORTON PLANT NORTH BAY HOSPITAL (100063)**, 6600 Madison Street, Zip 34652–1900; tel. 727/842–8468, **A**1 7 10 **F**3 11 18 20 22 28 29 30 31 34 35 40 44 49 50 57 58 59 64 68 70 74 75 78 79 81 84 85 86 87 90 93 94 96 98 99 100 102 107 108 111 114 115 118 119 129 130 131 132 135 143 146 147 149 154 **S** Morton Plant Mease Health Care, Clearwater, FL
Primary Contact: Sarah Naumowich, Interim President
CFO: Carl Tremonti, Chief Financial Officer
CMO: Jeff Jensen, D.O., Vice President, Medical Affairs
CIO: Timothy Thompson, Senior Vice President and Chief Information Officer
CHR: Kyle J Barr, Senior Vice President, Chief Team Resources Officer
CNO: Thomas Doria, Vice President and Patient Services – West
Web address: www.mpmhealth.com
Control: Other not–for–profit (including NFP Corporation) **Service**: General medical and surgical

Staffed Beds: 222 **Admissions**: 12701 **Census**: 169 **Outpatient Visits**: 42999 **Births**: 0 **Total Expense ($000)**: 138348 **Payroll Expense ($000)**: 54752 **Personnel**: 861

NEW SMYRNA BEACH—Volusia County

✈ **FLORIDA HOSPITAL NEW SMYRNA (100014)**, 401 Palmetto Street, Zip 32168–7399; tel. 386/424–5000, (Nonreporting) **A**1 10 **S** Adventist Health System Sunbelt Health Care Corporation, Altamonte Springs, FL
Primary Contact: Kenneth R. Mattison, Chief Executive Officer
COO: Steven W Harrell, FACHE, Chief Operating Officer
CFO: Al W Allred, Chief Financial Officer
CMO: Dennis Hernandez, Chief Medical Officer
CIO: Calvin Patrick II Director Information Services
CHR: Nancy K Evolga, Director Human Resources
CNO: Linda G Breum, R.N., MSN, Chief Nursing Officer
Web address: www.floridahospital.com/new–smyrna
Control: Hospital district or authority, Government, nonfederal **Service**: General medical and surgical

Staffed Beds: 112

NICEVILLE—Okaloosa County

✈ **TWIN CITIES HOSPITAL (100054)**, 2190 Highway 85 North, Zip 32578–1045; tel. 850/678–4131, (Nonreporting) **A**1 10 **S** HCA Healthcare, Nashville, TN
Primary Contact: David Whalen, Chief Executive Officer
CFO: Mark Day, Chief Financial Officer
CHR: Cyndi Ronca, Director Human Resources
Web address: www.tchealthcare.com
Control: Corporation, Investor–owned (for–profit) **Service**: General medical and surgical

Staffed Beds: 65

NORTH MIAMI—Miami–Dade County

☐ △ **ST. CATHERINE'S REHABILITATION HOSPITAL (103026)**, 1050 NE 125th Street, Zip 33161–5881; tel. 305/357–1735, (Nonreporting) **A**1 7 10 **S** Catholic Health Services, Lauderdale Lakes, FL
Primary Contact: Jaime Gonzalez, Administrator
COO: Jim Ball, Chief Operating Officer
CFO: Mary Jo Frick, Director Finance
CMO: Miriam Feliz, M.D., Medical Director
Web address: www.catholichealthservices.org
Control: Other not–for–profit (including NFP Corporation) **Service**: Rehabilitation

Staffed Beds: 60

NORTH MIAMI BEACH—Miami–Dade County

JACKSON NORTH MEDICAL CENTER See Jackson Health System, Miami

OCALA—Marion County

☒ **HEALTHSOUTH REHABILITATION HOSPITAL OF OCALA (103043)**, 2275 SW 22nd Lane, Zip 34471–7710; tel. 352/282–4000, (Nonreporting) **A**1 10 **S** Encompass Health Corporation, Birmingham, AL
Primary Contact: Karthik Muthu, Chief Executive Officer
CFO: Sammy King, Controller
CMO: Amy Clunn, M.D., Medical Director
CHR: Tracy Sapp, Director Human Resources
CNO: Wendy Milam, Chief Nursing Officer
Web address: www.healthsouthocala.com
Control: Corporation, Investor–owned (for–profit) **Service**: Rehabilitation

Staffed Beds: 40

☒ **KINDRED HOSPITAL OCALA (102019)**, 1500 SW 1st Avenue, Zip 34471–6504; tel. 352/369–0513, (Nonreporting) **A**1 10 **S** Kindred Healthcare, Louisville, KY
Primary Contact: Merlene Bhoorasingh, Administrator
CFO: Dean Cocchi, Chief Financial Officer
Web address: www.kindredocala.com/
Control: Corporation, Investor–owned (for–profit) **Service**: Acute long–term care hospital

Staffed Beds: 31

☒ **FLORIDA HOSPITAL OCALA (100062)**, 1500 SW 1st Avenue, Zip 34471–6504, Mailing Address: P.O. Box 6000, Zip 34478–6000; tel. 352/351–7200, (Nonreporting) **A**1 3 5 10 **S** Adventist Health System Sunbelt Health Care Corporation, Altamonte Springs, FL
Primary Contact: James F. O'Loughlin, Chief Executive Officer
COO: Philoron A. Wright, FACHE, II Chief Operating Officer
CFO: Eric LaChance, Chief Financial Officer
CMO: Lon McPherson, M.D., Senior Vice President Medical Affairs and Chief Quality Officer
CIO: Carl Candullo, Chief Information Officer
CNO: Pamela W Michell, R.N., Vice President, Chief Nursing Officer
Web address: www.munroeregional.com
Control: Other not–for–profit (including NFP Corporation) **Service**: General medical and surgical

Staffed Beds: 420

☒ **OCALA REGIONAL MEDICAL CENTER (100212)**, 1431 SW First Avenue, Zip 34471–6500, Mailing Address: P.O. Box 2200, Zip 34478–2200; tel. 352/401–1000, (Includes WEST MARION COMMUNITY HOSPITAL, 4600 SW 46th Court, Ocala, FL, Zip 34474; tel. 352/291–3000) (Nonreporting) **A**1 2 3 10 13 **S** HCA Healthcare, Nashville, TN
Primary Contact: Chad Christianson, Chief Executive Officer
CMO: Art Osberg, M.D., Chief Medical Officer
CIO: Brandon Holbert, Director, Information Services
CHR: Wayne Nielsen, Director Human Resources
Web address: www.ocalaregional.com
Control: Corporation, Investor–owned (for–profit) **Service**: General medical and surgical

Staffed Beds: 270

THE CENTERS (104068), 5664 SW 60th Avenue, Zip 34474–5677; tel. 352/291–5500, **A**3 10 **F**98 101 102 103 104 130
Primary Contact: Donald J. Baracskay II, M.D., Chief Executive Officer
Web address: www.thecenters.us
Control: Other not–for–profit (including NFP Corporation) **Service**: Psychiatric

Staffed Beds: 12 **Admissions:** 763 **Census:** 10 **Outpatient Visits:** 0 **Births:** 0

THE VINES (104071), 3130 SW 27th Avenue, Zip 34471–4306; tel. 352/671–3130, **A**10 **F**4 5 38 40 98 100 101 102 103 104 105 106 132 147 152 153 154 **S** Universal Health Services, Inc., King of Prussia, PA
Primary Contact: Stephen Quintyne, Chief Executive Officer
Web address: www.thevineshospital.com
Control: Corporation, Investor–owned (for–profit) **Service**: Psychiatric

Staffed Beds: 98 **Admissions:** 3323 **Census:** 65 **Outpatient Visits:** 4223 **Births:** 0 **Total Expense ($000):** 18020 **Payroll Expense ($000):** 7285 **Personnel:** 165

OCOEE—Orange County

☒ **HEALTH CENTRAL HOSPITAL (100030)**, 10000 West Colonial Drive, Zip 34761–3499; tel. 407/296–1000, (Total facility includes 228 beds in nursing home–type unit) **A**1 3 10 **F**3 8 11 12 15 17 18 20 22 26 28 29 30 34 35 37 40 45 46 48 49 50 51 57 59 60 64 68 74 75 79 80 81 82 85 86 87 93 97 107 108 110 111 115 118 119 126 128 130 132 135 144 146 148 149 150 154 **P**6 **S** Orlando Health, Orlando, FL
Primary Contact: Mark A. Marsh, President
COO: Rick Smith, Chief Operating Officer
CFO: Michael E Mueller, Chief Financial Officer
CMO: James Barton Rodier, M.D., Chief Quality Officer
CIO: John T Sills, Chief Information Officer
CHR: Nancy Dinon, Vice President Human Resources
CNO: Christina Marie McGuirk, R.N., Chief Nursing Officer
Web address: www.healthcentral.org
Control: Other not–for–profit (including NFP Corporation) **Service**: General medical and surgical

Staffed Beds: 439 **Admissions:** 12222 **Census:** 356 **Outpatient Visits:** 112887 **Births:** 725 **Total Expense ($000):** 205298 **Payroll Expense ($000):** 89079 **Personnel:** 1293

OKEECHOBEE—Okeechobee County

☒ **RAULERSON HOSPITAL (100252)**, 1796 Highway 441 North, Zip 34972–1918, Mailing Address: P.O. Box 1307, Zip 34973–1307; tel. 863/763–2151, (Nonreporting) **A**1 10 20 **S** HCA Healthcare, Nashville, TN
Primary Contact: Brian Melear, Chief Executive Officer
CFO: Terry L Brown, Chief Financial Officer
CMO: Arif Shakoor, Chief of Staff
CIO: Tim Hearing, Associate Information Technology Director
CHR: Cynthia Jackson, Vice President Human Resources
CNO: Adam Kless, Chief Nursing Officer
Web address: www.raulersonhospital.com
Control: Corporation, Investor–owned (for–profit) **Service**: General medical and surgical

Staffed Beds: 100

ORANGE CITY—Volusia County

☒ **FLORIDA HOSPITAL FISH MEMORIAL (100072)**, 1055 Saxon Boulevard, Zip 32763–8468; tel. 386/917–5000, (Nonreporting) **A**1 10 **S** Adventist Health System Sunbelt Health Care Corporation, Altamonte Springs, FL
Primary Contact: Robert Deininger, Chief Executive Officer
COO: Danielle Johnson, Chief Operating Officer
CFO: Eric Osterly, Chief Financial Officer
CMO: Leighton Smith, M.D., Chief Medical Officer
CHR: Jannina Garcia, Director of Human Resources
CNO: Jennifer Shull, R.N., Chief Nursing Officer
Web address: www.fhfishmemorial.org
Control: Church operated, Nongovernment, not–for–profit **Service**: General medical and surgical

Staffed Beds: 175

ORANGE PARK—Clay County

☒ **ORANGE PARK MEDICAL CENTER (100226)**, 2001 Kingsley Avenue, Zip 32073–5156; tel. 904/639–8500, (Nonreporting) **A**1 2 3 10 **S** HCA Healthcare, Nashville, TN
Primary Contact: Chad Patrick, President and Chief Executive Officer
CFO: Heath King, Chief Financial Officer
CMO: Lawrence Coots, M.D., Chief Medical Officer
CHR: Chris Marlin, Director Human Resources
CNO: Kathy Hester, Chief Nursing Officer
Web address: www.opmedical.com
Control: Corporation, Investor–owned (for–profit) **Service**: General medical and surgical

Staffed Beds: 297

ORLANDO—Orange County

ARNOLD PALMER HOSPITAL FOR CHILDREN See Orlando Regional Medical Center, Orlando

FL

Hospital, Medicare Provider Number, Address, Telephone, Approval, Facility, and Physician Codes, Health Care System

★ American Hospital Association (AHA) membership
□ The Joint Commission accreditation
○ Healthcare Facilities Accreditation Program
◇ DNV Healthcare Inc. accreditation
⇧ Center for Improvement in Healthcare Quality Accreditation
△ Commission on Accreditation of Rehabilitation Facilities (CARF) accreditation

ASPIRE HEALTH PARTNERS (104067), 1800 Mercy Drive, Zip 32808–5646; tel. 407/875–3700, **A**10 **F**29 35 38 61 66 98 130 132 134 143 154
Primary Contact: Jerry Kassab, President and Chief Executive Officer
Web address: www.lakesidecares.org
Control: Other not–for–profit (including NFP Corporation) **Service**: Psychiatric

Staffed Beds: 64 **Admissions**: 3955 **Census**: 56 **Outpatient Visits**: 0
Births: 0 **Total Expense ($000)**: 9541 **Payroll Expense ($000)**: 3517
Personnel: 34

☐ **CENTRAL FLORIDA BEHAVIORAL HOSPITAL (104072)**, 6601 Central Florida Parkway, Zip 32821–8064; tel. 407/370–0111, (Nonreporting) **A**1 5 10 **S** Universal Health Services, Inc., King of Prussia, PA
Primary Contact: Vickie Lewis, Chief Executive Officer
CFO: Marsha Burick, Chief Financial Officer
Web address: www.centralfloridabehavioral.com
Control: Other not–for–profit (including NFP Corporation) **Service**: Psychiatric

Staffed Beds: 126

★ △ ⇑ **FLORIDA HOSPITAL (100007)**, 601 East Rollins Street, Zip 32803–1248; tel. 407/303–6611, (Includes FLORIDA HOSPITAL CELEBRATION HEALTH, 400 Celebration Place, Celebration, FL, Zip 34747; tel. 407/303–4000; Douglas Harcombe, Chief Executive Officer; FLORIDA HOSPITAL EAST ORLANDO, 7727 Lake Underhill Drive, Orlando, FL, Zip 32822; tel. 407/277–8110; FLORIDA HOSPITAL FOR CHILDREN–WALT DISNEY PAVILION, 601 East Rollins Street, Orlando, FL, Zip 32803–1248; tel. 407/303–9732; Lars D Houmann, President; FLORIDA HOSPITAL KISSIMMEE, 2450 North Orange Blossom Trai, Kissimmee, FL, Zip 34741; tel. 407/846–4343; William Haupt, Administrator; FLORIDA HOSPITAL–ALTAMONTE, 601 East Altamonte Drive, Altamonte Springs, FL, Zip 32701; tel. 407/830–4321; David Ottati, Regional Chief Executive Officer; FLORIDA HOSPITAL–APOPKA, 201 North Park Avenue, Apopka, FL, Zip 32703; tel. 407/889–1000; Verbelee Neilsen Swanson, Administrator; WINTER PARK MEMORIAL HOSPITAL, 200 North Lakemont Avenue, Winter Park, FL, Zip 32792–3273; tel. 407/646–7000; Douglas Harcombe, Administrator) **A**2 3 5 7 8 10 21 **F**3 6 7 9 11 12 13 15 19 20 21 22 23 24 25 26 27 28 29 30 31 32 34 35 36 37 38 39 40 41 44 45 46 47 48 49 50 51 53 54 56 57 58 59 60 61 62 64 65 66 68 70 71 72 73 74 75 76 77 78 79 80 81 82 83 84 85 86 87 88 89 90 92 93 94 96 97 98 99 100 101 102 103 107 108 109 110 111 112 113 114 115 116 117 118 119 120 121 123 124 126 129 130 131 132 134 135 136 137 138 139 140 141 142 145 146 147 148 149 154 **P**1 5 6 **S** Adventist Health System Sunbelt Health Care Corporation, Altamonte Springs, FL
Primary Contact: Daryl Tol, President and Chief Executive Officer
COO: Brian Paradis, Chief Operating Officer
CFO: Eddie Soler, Chief Financial Officer
CMO: David Moorhead, M.D., Chief Medical Officer
CHR: Sheryl Dodds, Chief Clinical Officer
Web address: www.floridahospital.com/orlando
Control: Other not–for–profit (including NFP Corporation) **Service**: General medical and surgical

Staffed Beds: 2877 **Admissions**: 142006 **Census**: 1881 **Outpatient Visits**: 1224548 **Births**: 12190 **Total Expense ($000)**: 3092734 **Payroll Expense ($000)**: 1084631 **Personnel**: 19289

⊞ **NEMOURS CHILDREN'S HOSPITAL (103304)**, 13535 Nemours Parkway, Zip 32827–7402; tel. 407/567–4000, **A**1 3 5 10 **F**17 19 21 23 25 27 29 30 31 32 34 35 40 41 45 48 50 53 57 58 59 60 64 68 72 73 74 75 77 78 79 80 81 82 84 85 86 87 88 89 90 91 92 93 94 96 97 100 107 108 111 115 118 119 120 121 130 131 146 149 154 **S** Nemours, Jacksonville, FL
Primary Contact: Dana Bledsoe, MS, R.N., President
COO: Randall W Hartley, Chief Operating Officer
CFO: Rodney McKendree, Senior Vice President and Chief Financial Officer
CMO: Andre Hebra, M.D., Chief Medical Officer
CIO: Bernard Rice, Chief Information Officer
CHR: Theresa M Young, Senior Vice President Human Resources
CNO: Helen M Case, Chief Nursing Officer
Web address: www.nemours.org
Control: Other not–for–profit (including NFP Corporation) **Service**: Children's general medical and surgical

Staffed Beds: 92 **Admissions**: 3366 **Census**: 53 **Outpatient Visits**: 82895
Births: 0 **Total Expense ($000)**: 191534 **Payroll Expense ($000)**: 63571
Personnel: 899

⊞ △ **ORLANDO REGIONAL MEDICAL CENTER (100006)**, 52 West Underwood Street, Zip 32806; tel. 407/841–5111, (Includes ARNOLD PALMER HOSPITAL FOR CHILDREN, 92 West Miller Street, Orlando, FL, Zip 32806; tel. 407/649–6960; Cary D'Ortona, President; ORLANDO HEALTH SOUTH SEMINOLE HOSPITAL, 555 West State Road 434, Longwood, FL, Zip 32750–4999; tel. 407/767–1200; Karen Frenier, President; WINNIE PALMER HOSPITAL FOR WOMEN AND BABIES, 83 West Miller Street, Orlando, FL, Zip 32806; tel. 321/843–9792; Kelly Nierstedt, President) **A**1 2 3 5 7 10 **F**3 4 5 8 10 11 13 15 16 17 18 19 20 21 22 23 24 25 26 27 28 29 30 31 34 35 36 37 40 41 43 44 45 46 47 48 49 50 51 54 55 57 58 59 60 61 62 64 68 70 71 72 73 74 75 76 77 78 79 80 81 82 84 85 86 87 88 89 90 91 92 93 94 96 97 98 99 100 101 102 104 107 108 110 111 114 115 116 117 118 119 120 121 122 123 124 126 129 130 131 132 134 135 143 146 147 148 149 152 154 **P**6 **S** Orlando Health, Orlando, FL
Primary Contact: Mark A. Jones, President
COO: Carlos Carrasco, Chief Operating Officer
CFO: Steve Miglietta, Chief Financial Officer
CMO: Charles Heard, M.D., Chief of Staff
CIO: Rick Schooler, Vice President and Chief Information Officer
CHR: Greg Thompson, Corporate Director, Human Resources
CNO: Jayne Willis, Vice President Nursing and Chief Nursing Officer
Web address: www.orlandohealth.com/facilities/orlando–regional–medical–center
Control: Other not–for–profit (including NFP Corporation) **Service**: General medical and surgical

Staffed Beds: 1203 **Admissions**: 77323 **Census**: 1049 **Outpatient Visits**: 900643 **Births**: 13922 **Total Expense ($000)**: 1827455 **Payroll Expense ($000)**: 705819 **Personnel**: 12532

ORLANDO VA MEDICAL CENTER, 13800 Veterans Way, Zip 32827–7403; tel. 407/631–1000, (Nonreporting) **A**3 **S** Department of Veterans Affairs, Perry Point, MD
Primary Contact: Timothy Liezert, Medical Center Director
Web address: www.orlando.va.gov
Control: Veterans Affairs, Government, federal **Service**: General medical and surgical

Staffed Beds: 134

⊞ **SELECT SPECIALTY HOSPITAL–ORLANDO (102003)**, 2250 Bedford Road, Zip 32803–1443; tel. 407/303–7869, (Includes SELECT SPECIALTY HOSPITAL– ORLANDO SOUTH, 5579 South Orange Avenue, Orlando, FL, Zip 32809–3493; tel. 407/241–4800) (Nonreporting) **A**1 10 **S** Select Medical Corporation, Mechanicsburg, PA
Primary Contact: Theodore Mena, Chief Executive Officer
Web address: www.selectspecialtyhospitals.com/company/locations/orlando.aspx
Control: Corporation, Investor–owned (for–profit) **Service**: Acute long–term care hospital

Staffed Beds: 75

WINNIE PALMER HOSPITAL FOR WOMEN AND BABIES See Orlando Regional Medical Center, Orlando

OVIEDO—Seminole County

★ **OVIEDO MEDICAL CENTER (100329)**, 8300 Red Bug Lake Road, Zip 32765–6801; tel. 407/890–2273, (Nonreporting) **A**10 **S** HCA Healthcare, Nashville, TN
Primary Contact: Kenneth C. Donahey, Chief Executive Officer
Web address: www.oviedomedicalcenter.com
Control: Other not–for–profit (including NFP Corporation) **Service**: General medical and surgical

Staffed Beds: 64

OXFORD—Sumter County

PROMISE HOSPITAL OF FLORIDA AT THE VILLAGES (102028), 5050 County Road 472, Zip 34484; tel. 352/689–6400, (Nonreporting) **A**10 **S** Promise Healthcare, Boca Raton, FL
Primary Contact: Hoyt Ross, Chief Executive Officer
CNO: Janice M McCoy, MS, R.N., Chief Clinical Officer
Web address: www.promise–villages.com
Control: Corporation, Investor–owned (for–profit) **Service**: Acute long–term care hospital

Staffed Beds: 40

PALATKA—Putnam County

⊞ **PUTNAM COMMUNITY MEDICAL CENTER (100232)**, 611 Zeagler Drive, Zip 32177–3810; tel. 386/328–5711, (Nonreporting) **A**1 10 **S** HCA Healthcare, Nashville, TN
Primary Contact: Mark J. Dooley, Chief Executive Officer
CFO: Stewart Whitmore, Chief Financial Officer
CIO: Yvette A Jones, Health Information Management Director
CHR: John Schneider, Human Resources Director
CNO: Kari Bolin, Chief Nursing Officer
Web address: www.pcmcfl.com
Control: Corporation, Investor–owned (for–profit) **Service**: General medical and surgical

Staffed Beds: 99

FL

PALM BAY—Brevard County

☐ **HEALTH FIRST PALM BAY HOSPITAL (100316)**, 1425 Malabar Road NE,
Zip 32907–2506; tel. 321/434–8000, **A**1 5 10 **F**3 11 12 15 20 29 30 34 37 39
40 41 45 47 49 50 59 60 64 68 70 74 75 77 79 80 81 84 85 86 87 93 98 102
103 107 108 110 111 114 115 118 119 126 130 132 141 146 148 149 153
154 **S** Health First, Inc., Rockledge, FL
Primary Contact: Aaron Robinson, Chief Executive Officer, Health First Community
Hospitals
COO: Deborah Angerami, Chief Operating Officer, Health First Community Hospitals
CFO: Joseph G Felkner, Executive Vice President and Chief Financial Officer
CMO: Lee Scheinbart, M.D., Vice President Medical Affairs, Health First Community
Hospitals
CIO: Alex Popowycz, Senior Vice President and Chief Information Officer
CHR: Paula Just, Chief Human Resources Officer
CNO: Connie Bradley, R.N., MSN, FACHE, Chief Nursing Officer
Web address: www.health-first.org/hospitals_services/pbch/index.cfm
Control: Other not-for-profit (including NFP Corporation) **Service:** General
medical and surgical

Staffed Beds: 138 **Admissions:** 6484 **Census:** 81 **Outpatient Visits:** 86692
Births: 0 **Total Expense ($000):** 96287 **Payroll Expense ($000):** 42585
Personnel: 510

PALM BEACH GARDENS—Palm Beach County

☒ **PALM BEACH GARDENS MEDICAL CENTER (100176)**, 3360 Burns Road,
Zip 33410–4323; tel. 561/622–1411, (Nonreporting) **A**1 10 **S** TENET Healthcare
Corporation, Dallas, TX
Primary Contact: Trey Abshier, Chief Executive Officer
CFO: Judi Stimson, Chief Financial Officer
CIO: James Vega, Director Information Systems
CHR: Kevin Caracciolo, Chief Human Resources Officer
Web address: www.pbgmc.com
Control: Corporation, Investor–owned (for–profit) **Service:** General medical and surgical

Staffed Beds: 199

PALM COAST—Flagler County

☒ **FLORIDA HOSPITAL FLAGLER (100118)**, 60 Memorial Medical Parkway,
Zip 32164–5980; tel. 386/586–2000, (Nonreporting) **A**1 2 10 **S** Adventist Health
System Sunbelt Health Care Corporation, Altamonte Springs, FL
Primary Contact: Ronald Jimenez, M.D., Chief Executive Officer
COO: JoAnne King, Chief Operating Officer
CFO: Cory Domayer, Chief Financial Officer
CMO: Ron Thomas, M.D., Chief Medical Officer
CHR: Joshua I Champion, Director
CNO: Robert Davis, Chief Nursing Officer
Web address: www.floridahospitalflagler.com/
Control: Church operated, Nongovernment, not–for–profit **Service:** General
medical and surgical

Staffed Beds: 99

PANAMA CITY—Bay County

☒ **BAY MEDICAL SACRED HEART (100026)**, 615 North Bonita Avenue,
Zip 32401–3600, Mailing Address: P.O. Box 59515, Zip 32412–0515;
tel. 850/769–1511, (Nonreporting) **A**1 2 10 **S** Ardent Health Services, Nashville, TN
Primary Contact: Scott Campbell, Chief Executive Officer
COO: Heath Evans, Chief Operating Officer
CHR: Donna Baird, Vice President Corporate Services
CNO: Jan Thornton, Chief Nursing Officer
Web address: www.baymedical.org
Control: Hospital district or authority, Government, nonfederal **Service:** General
medical and surgical

Staffed Beds: 273

☐ **EMERALD COAST BEHAVIORAL HOSPITAL (104073)**, 1940 Harrison Avenue,
Zip 32405–4542; tel. 850/763–0017, (Nonreporting) **A**1 10 **S** Universal Health
Services, Inc., King of Prussia, PA
Primary Contact: Tim Bedford, Chief Executive Officer
CFO: Michael J Zenone, Chief Financial Officer
CMO: Roy Deal, Chief Medical Officer
CNO: Michael B Barbour, Chief Nursing Officer
Web address: www.emeraldcoastbehavioral.com
Control: Corporation, Investor–owned (for–profit) **Service:** Psychiatric

Staffed Beds: 86

☒ **GULF COAST REGIONAL MEDICAL CENTER (100242)**, 449 West 23rd
Street, Zip 32405–4593, Mailing Address: P.O. Box 15309, Zip 32406–5309;
tel. 850/769–8341, (Nonreporting) **A**1 2 10 **S** HCA Healthcare, Nashville, TN
Primary Contact: Brad Griffin, Chief Executive Officer
COO: Holly Jackson, Chief Operating Officer
CFO: Laurie Haynes, Chief Financial Officer
CHR: Tracy McGlon, Director Human Resources
CNO: Brian Pinelle, R.N., Chief Nursing Officer
Web address: www.egulfcoastmedical.com
Control: Corporation, Investor–owned (for–profit) **Service:** General medical and
surgical

Staffed Beds: 176

☒ **HEALTHSOUTH EMERALD COAST REHABILITATION HOSPITAL (103040)**,
1847 Florida Avenue, Zip 32405–4640; tel. 850/914–8600, **A**1 10 **F**3 28 29 34
57 59 68 75 77 85 86 87 90 91 95 96 130 131 132 148 **S** Encompass Health
Corporation, Birmingham, AL
Primary Contact: Tony N. Bennett, Chief Executive Officer
CFO: Bradley Tilghman, Controller
CMO: Michael Hennigan, M.D., Medical Director
CHR: Traci Powell, Director Human Resources
CNO: Sharon Hamilton, Chief Nursing Officer
Web address: www.healthsouthpanamacity.com
Control: Corporation, Investor–owned (for–profit) **Service:** Rehabilitation

Staffed Beds: 75 **Admissions:** 1623 **Census:** 58 **Outpatient Visits:** 0
Births: 0 **Total Expense ($000):** 22478 **Payroll Expense ($000):** 11538
Personnel: 213

☒ **SELECT SPECIALTY HOSPITAL–PANAMA CITY (102017)**, 615 North Bonita
Avenue, 3rd Floor, Zip 32401–3623; tel. 850/767–3180, (Nonreporting) **A**1 10 **S**
Select Medical Corporation, Mechanicsburg, PA
Primary Contact: Randal S. Hamilton, Chief Executive Officer
CMO: Amir Manzoor, M.D., Medical Director
Web address: www.selectspecialtyhospitals.com/company/locations/panamacity.
aspx
Control: Corporation, Investor–owned (for–profit) **Service:** Acute long–term care
hospital

Staffed Beds: 30

PEMBROKE PINES—Broward County

☒ **MEMORIAL HOSPITAL PEMBROKE (100230)**, 7800 Sheridan Street,
Zip 33024–2536; tel. 954/883–8482, **A**1 10 **F**3 12 17 29 30 34 40 44 45
46 47 48 49 50 51 59 64 65 66 70 74 75 79 81 82 85 86 87 107 108 111
114 115 119 126 130 132 144 146 148 154 **S** Memorial Healthcare System,
Hollywood, FL
Primary Contact: Mark Doyle, Administrator and Chief Executive Officer
CFO: Joseph Stuczynski, Assistant Administrator Finance and Support
CMO: Stanley Marks, M.D., FACS, Chief Medical Officer
CIO: Forest Blanton, Chief Information Officer
CNO: Judy Frum, R.N., Chief Nursing Officer
Web address: www.memorialpembroke.com/
Control: Hospital district or authority, Government, nonfederal **Service:** General
medical and surgical

Staffed Beds: 157 **Admissions:** 7621 **Census:** 92 **Outpatient Visits:** 98779
Births: 0 **Total Expense ($000):** 140549 **Payroll Expense ($000):** 59777

☒ **MEMORIAL HOSPITAL WEST (100281)**, 703 North Flamingo Road,
Zip 33028–1014; tel. 954/436–5000, **A**1 2 10 **F**3 12 13 15 17 18 22 26 28 29
30 31 34 35 36 40 41 45 46 47 49 53 55 56 57 58 60 68 70 72 74 75 76 78
79 81 82 84 85 87 91 93 107 108 110 111 114 115 119 120 121 123 124 126
130 131 132 136 145 146 147 **S** Memorial Healthcare System, Hollywood, FL
Primary Contact: Leah A. Carpenter, Administrator and Chief Executive Officer
CFO: Walter Bussell, Chief Financial Officer
CMO: Eric Freling, M.D., Director Medical Staff Affairs
CIO: Forest Blanton, Chief Information Officer
CHR: Maria Naranjo, Director Human Resources
Web address: www.mhs.net
Control: Hospital district or authority, Government, nonfederal **Service:** General
medical and surgical

Staffed Beds: 382 **Admissions:** 21280 **Census:** 285 **Outpatient Visits:**
288957 **Births:** 3841 **Total Expense ($000):** 409649 **Payroll Expense
($000):** 165078 **Personnel:** 2070

FL

Hospital, Medicare Provider Number, Address, Telephone, Approval, Facility, and Physician Codes, Health Care System

★ American Hospital Association (AHA) membership   ○ Healthcare Facilities Accreditation Program   ⇑ Center for Improvement in Healthcare Quality Accreditation
☐ The Joint Commission accreditation   ◇ DNV Healthcare Inc. accreditation   △ Commission on Accreditation of Rehabilitation Facilities (CARF) accreditation

PENSACOLA—Escambia County

⊞ **BAPTIST HOSPITAL (100093)**, 1000 West Moreno Street, Zip 32501–2316, Mailing Address: P.O. Box 17500, Zip 32522–7500; tel. 850/434–4011, **A**1 2 3 10 **F**3 8 11 12 13 15 17 18 20 22 24 26 28 29 30 31 34 35 40 43 45 46 47 48 49 50 51 53 54 55 57 58 59 60 61 63 64 70 71 74 75 76 77 78 79 80 81 82 84 85 86 87 91 92 93 97 98 99 100 101 102 103 104 107 108 110 111 114 115 116 117 118 119 120 121 123 124 126 130 131 132 135 146 147 148 **S** Baptist Health Care Corporation, Pensacola, FL
Primary Contact: Scott Raynes, President
CFO: Sharon Nobles, Interim Chief Financial Officer
CMO: Mike Oleksyk, M.D., Vice President and Chief Medical Officer
CIO: Steven Sarros, Vice President and Chief Information Officer
CHR: Darlene Stone, Vice President Human Resources
CNO: Cynde Gamache, R.N., Vice President and Chief Nursing Officer
Web address: www.ebaptisthealthcare.org
Control: Other not–for–profit (including NFP Corporation) **Service**: General medical and surgical

Staffed Beds: 340 **Admissions**: 18232 **Census**: 240 **Outpatient Visits**: 252856 **Births**: 892 **Total Expense ($000)**: 303392 **Payroll Expense ($000)**: 99107 **Personnel**: 1721

⊞ **NAVAL HOSPITAL PENSACOLA**, 6000 West Highway 98, Zip 32512–0003; tel. 850/505–6601, (Nonreporting) **A**1 3 5 **S** Bureau of Medicine and Surgery, Department of the Navy, Falls Church, VA
Primary Contact: Commander Devin Morrison, Director Administration
COO: Commander Devin Morrison, Director for Administration
CMO: Commander Carolyn Rice, M.D., Director Medical Services
CIO: Lieutenant Commander William Berg, Chief Information Officer
CHR: Commander Devin Morrison, Director for Administration
CNO: Captain Amy Tarbay, Director Nursing Services
Web address: www.med.navy.mil/sites/pcola/Pages/default.aspx
Control: Navy, Government, federal **Service**: General medical and surgical

Staffed Beds: 28

⊞ **SACRED HEART HOSPITAL PENSACOLA (100025)**, 5151 North Ninth Avenue, Zip 32504–8795, Mailing Address: P.O. Box 2700, Zip 32513–2700; tel. 850/416–7000, **A**1 2 3 5 10 13 **F**3 8 11 12 13 15 17 18 19 20 21 22 24 26 28 29 30 31 34 35 40 41 43 45 46 47 48 49 50 54 55 57 58 59 60 61 65 68 70 71 72 73 74 75 76 77 79 81 82 84 85 87 88 89 90 92 93 96 97 107 108 110 111 112 114 116 117 119 120 124 126 130 131 132 135 138 145 146 147 148 149 **S** Ascension Healthcare, Saint Louis, MO
Primary Contact: Henry Stovall, President
COO: Terri Smith, Chief Operating Officer
CFO: C Susan Cornejo, Chief Financial Officer
CMO: Peter Jennings, M.D., Chief Medical Officer
CIO: Donna Roach, Chief Information Officer
CHR: Michelle Adamolekun, Vice President Human Resource Market Lead Florida/Alabama Ministry Market
CNO: Terrie Fontenot, Chief Nursing Officer
Web address: www.sacred–heart.org
Control: Other not–for–profit (including NFP Corporation) **Service**: General medical and surgical

Staffed Beds: 440 **Admissions**: 25624 **Census**: 345 **Outpatient Visits**: 352873 **Births**: 3863 **Total Expense ($000)**: 459044 **Payroll Expense ($000)**: 129144

⊞ **SELECT SPECIALTY HOSPITAL–PENSACOLA (102024)**, 7000 Cobble Creek Drive, Zip 32504–8638; tel. 850/473–4800, (Nonreporting) **A**1 10 **S** Select Medical Corporation, Mechanicsburg, PA
Primary Contact: Adam Principe, Chief Executive Officer
CMO: John Bray, M.D., Medical Director
Web address: www.https://pensacola.selectspecialtyhospitals.com/
Control: Corporation, Investor–owned (for–profit) **Service**: Acute long–term care hospital

Staffed Beds: 75

⊞ △ **WEST FLORIDA HOSPITAL (100231)**, 8383 North Davis Highway, Zip 32514–6088; tel. 850/494–4000, (Includes THE PAVILION, 8383 North Davis Highway, Pensacola, FL, Zip 32523, Mailing Address: P.O. Box 18900, Zip 32523, tel. 904/494–5000; WEST FLORIDA REHABILITATION INSTITUTE, 8383 North Davis Highway, Pensacola, FL, Zip 32514, Mailing Address: P.O. Box 18900, Zip 32523, tel. 850/494–6000) (Nonreporting) **A**1 2 7 10 **S** HCA Healthcare, Nashville, TN
Primary Contact: Carlton Ulmer, President and Chief Executive Officer
COO: Jessica O'Neal, Chief Operating Officer
CFO: Randy Butler, Chief Financial Officer
CMO: Terry Stallings, M.D., Chief Medical Officer
CIO: Jeff Amerson, Director Information System
CHR: Wanda Salley, Vice President Human Resources
CNO: Karen White–Trevino, Chief Nursing Officer
Web address: www.westfloridahospital.com
Control: Corporation, Investor–owned (for–profit) **Service**: General medical and surgical

Staffed Beds: 339

WEST FLORIDA REHABILITATION INSTITUTE See West Florida Hospital, Pensacola

PERRY—Taylor County

DOCTOR'S MEMORIAL HOSPITAL (100106), 333 North Byron Butler Parkway, Zip 32347–2300; tel. 850/584–0800, **A**10 20 **F**3 7 11 15 17 29 30 34 35 40 45 50 57 59 62 70 76 81 85 89 93 107 110 111 114 119 126 127 129 132 133 146
Primary Contact: Thomas J. Stone, FACHE, Chief Executive Officer
CHR: David Dawkins, Director Human Resources
CNO: Mary Lescher, Chief Clinical Officer
Web address: www.doctorsmemorial.com
Control: Other not–for–profit (including NFP Corporation) **Service**: General medical and surgical

Staffed Beds: 24 **Admissions**: 878 **Census**: 7 **Outpatient Visits**: 14521 **Births**: 4 **Total Expense ($000)**: 23853 **Payroll Expense ($000)**: 10497 **Personnel**: 222

PLANT CITY—Hillsborough County

⊞ **SOUTH FLORIDA BAPTIST HOSPITAL (100132)**, 301 North Alexander Street, Zip 33563–4303; tel. 813/757–1200, **A**1 10 **F**3 11 12 13 15 18 20 22 28 29 30 31 34 35 37 40 41 44 45 47 48 49 50 51 57 59 60 64 68 70 71 74 75 76 77 78 79 80 81 85 87 89 93 107 108 110 114 115 118 119 124 126 130 131 132 135 145 146 147 148 154 **S** Trinity Health, Livonia, MI
Primary Contact: Karen Kerr, R.N., President
COO: Beth Tancredo, Director Operations
CFO: Carl Tremonti, Chief Financial Officer
CMO: Mark Vaaler, M.D., Chief Medical Officer
CIO: Tim Thompson, Senior Vice President, Chief Information Officer
CHR: Pat Lipton, Director Team Resources
CNO: Teresa Colletti, Director Patient Services
Web address: www.https://baycare.org/sfbh
Control: Other not–for–profit (including NFP Corporation) **Service**: General medical and surgical

Staffed Beds: 133 **Admissions**: 7753 **Census**: 78 **Outpatient Visits**: 58452 **Births**: 559 **Total Expense ($000)**: 120186 **Payroll Expense ($000)**: 44114 **Personnel**: 682

PLANTATION—Broward County

⊞ **PLANTATION GENERAL HOSPITAL (100167)**, 401 NW 42nd Avenue, Zip 33317–2882; tel. 954/587–5010, (Includes MERCY HOSPITAL – A CAMPUS OF PLANTATION GENERAL HOSPITAL, 3663 South Miami Avenue, Miami, FL, Zip 33133–4237; tel. 305/854–4400; Barbara Simmons, R.N., Chief Executive Officer) (Nonreporting) **A**1 2 3 10 **S** HCA Healthcare, Nashville, TN
Primary Contact: Madeline Nava, Chief Executive Officer
COO: Patrick Rohan, Chief Operating Officer
CFO: Irfan Mirza, Chief Financial Officer
CIO: Mia McGlynn, Director Management Information Systems
CHR: Jennifer Allen, Vice President Human Resources
CNO: Jesse Gabuat, Chief Nursing Officer
Web address: www.plantationgeneral.com/
Control: Corporation, Investor–owned (for–profit) **Service**: General medical and surgical

Staffed Beds: 264

⊞ **WESTSIDE REGIONAL MEDICAL CENTER (100228)**, 8201 West Broward Boulevard, Zip 33324–2701; tel. 954/473–6600, (Nonreporting) **A**1 10 **S** HCA Healthcare, Nashville, TN
Primary Contact: Barbara Simmons, R.N., Chief Executive Officer
COO: Shana Sappington–Crittenden, Chief Operating Officer
CFO: Kevin Corcoran, Chief Financial Officer
CMO: Brian Weinstein, M.D., Chief of Staff
CIO: Andres Blanco, Director Management Information Systems
CHR: Maria Rivera, Director Human Resources
Web address: www.westsideregional.com
Control: Corporation, Investor–owned (for–profit) **Service**: General medical and surgical

Staffed Beds: 215

PORT CHARLOTTE—Charlotte County

✠ **BAYFRONT HEALTH PORT CHARLOTTE (100077)**, 2500 Harbor Boulevard, Zip 33952–5000; tel. 941/766–4122, **A**1 5 10 **F**12 13 15 17 18 20 22 24 26 29 30 34 40 45 46 48 49 50 54 59 64 70 72 74 75 76 77 79 81 85 89 93 107 110 111 114 115 119 126 131 132 135 146 147 148 154 **S** Community Health Systems, Inc., Franklin, TN
Primary Contact: Timothy J. Cerullo, Chief Executive Officer
COO: Brian Cruddas, Chief Operating Officer
CFO: Jeffrey Mullis, Interim Chief Financial Officer
CMO: Thomas Noone, M.D., Chief Medical Officer
CHR: Karen Gardiner, Human Resources Director
CNO: Debra Clark, Chief Nursing Officer
Web address: www.bayfrontcharlotte.com
Control: Corporation, Investor–owned (for–profit) **Service**: General medical and surgical

Staffed Beds: 254 **Admissions**: 10228 **Census**: 126 **Outpatient Visits**: 50026 **Births**: 969 **Total Expense ($000)**: 131036 **Payroll Expense ($000)**: 44726 **Personnel**: 858

✠ △ **FAWCETT MEMORIAL HOSPITAL (100236)**, 21298 Olean Boulevard, Zip 33952–6765; tel. 941/629–1181, (Nonreporting) **A**1 2 7 10 **S** HCA Healthcare, Nashville, TN
Primary Contact: William Hawley, President and Chief Executive Officer
CFO: Vickie Magurean, Chief Financial Officer
CMO: Mark Callman, M.D., Chief Medical Officer
CHR: Linda Bryan, Vice President Human Resources
CNO: Brandy Hershberger, Chief Nursing Officer
Web address: www.fawcetthospital.com
Control: Corporation, Investor–owned (for–profit) **Service**: General medical and surgical

Staffed Beds: 237

PORT ST JOE—Gulf County

✠ **SACRED HEART HOSPITAL ON THE GULF (100313)**, 3801 East Highway 98, Zip 32456–5318; tel. 850/229–5600, (Nonreporting) **A**1 10 **S** Ascension Healthcare, Saint Louis, MO
Primary Contact: Roger L. Hall, President
CNO: Katherine L Chastain, R.N., Chief Nursing Officer
Web address: www.sacred–heart.org/gulf/
Control: Other not–for–profit (including NFP Corporation) **Service**: General medical and surgical

Staffed Beds: 19

PORT ST LUCIE—St. Lucie County

☐ **PORT ST. LUCIE HOSPITAL (104070)**, 2550 SE Walton Road, Zip 34952–7168; tel. 772/335–0400, (Nonreporting) **A**1 10
Primary Contact: Mercy Estevez, Administrator
Web address: www.portstluciehospitalinc.com
Control: Other not–for–profit (including NFP Corporation) **Service**: Psychiatric

Staffed Beds: 75

✠ **ST. LUCIE MEDICAL CENTER (100260)**, 1800 SE Tiffany Avenue, Zip 34952–7521; tel. 772/335–4000, (Nonreporting) **A**1 3 10 13 **S** HCA Healthcare, Nashville, TN
Primary Contact: Jay Finnegan, Chief Executive Officer
COO: Calvin Thomas IV Chief Operating Officer
CFO: Kevin Keeling, Chief Financial Officer
Web address: www.stluciemed.com
Control: Corporation, Investor–owned (for–profit) **Service**: General medical and surgical

Staffed Beds: 194

PUNTA GORDA—Charlotte County

✠ **BAYFRONT HEALTH PUNTA GORDA (100047)**, 809 East Marion Avenue, Zip 33950–3819, Mailing Address: P.O. Box 51–1328, Zip 33951–1328; tel. 941/639–3131, (Nonreporting) **A**1 10 **S** Community Health Systems, Inc., Franklin, TN
Primary Contact: Andrew Emery, Chief Executive Officer
Web address: www.bayfrontcharlotte.com
Control: Corporation, Investor–owned (for–profit) **Service**: General medical and surgical

Staffed Beds: 190

RIVIERA BEACH—Palm Beach County

✠ **KINDRED HOSPITAL THE PALM BEACHES (102025)**, 5555 West Blue Heron Boulevard, Zip 33418–7813; tel. 561/840–0754, (Nonreporting) **A**1 10 **S** Kindred Healthcare, Louisville, KY
Primary Contact: Elayne Lopreato, Chief Executive Officer
CFO: Dean Card, Chief Financial Officer
CNO: Elayne Lopreato, Chief Clinical Officer
Web address: www.khthepalmbeaches.com/
Control: Corporation, Investor–owned (for–profit) **Service**: Acute long–term care hospital

Staffed Beds: 70

ROCKLEDGE—Brevard County

✠ **ROCKLEDGE REGIONAL MEDICAL CENTER (100092)**, 110 Longwood Avenue, Zip 32955–2887, Mailing Address: P.O. Box 565002, Mail Stop 1, Zip 32956–5002; tel. 321/636–2211, (Data for 245 days) **A**1 2 10 **F**3 13 15 17 18 20 22 24 26 28 29 30 31 34 35 40 46 49 50 51 54 59 60 64 68 70 72 74 75 76 78 79 81 82 84 85 87 93 98 102 107 108 111 114 115 117 119 126 130 131 132 135 146 147 148 149 153 154 **S** Steward Health Care System, LLC, Dallas, TX
Primary Contact: Andrew Romine, Chief Executive Officer
CFO: Jonathan R Immordino, Chief Financial Officer
CMO: Vinay Mehindru, M.D., Medical Director
CIO: David Barnhart, Director Information Systems
CHR: Marchita H Marino, Vice President Human Resources
CNO: Mary Sue Zinsmeister, MSN, R.N., Chief Nursing Officer
Web address: www.wuesthoff.org
Control: Corporation, Investor–owned (for–profit) **Service**: General medical and surgical

Staffed Beds: 215 **Admissions**: 8669 **Census**: 168 **Outpatient Visits**: 115078 **Births**: 440 **Total Expense ($000)**: 95623 **Payroll Expense ($000)**: 32088 **Personnel**: 924

SAFETY HARBOR—Pinellas County

✠ **MEASE COUNTRYSIDE HOSPITAL (100265)**, 3231 McMullen Booth Road, Zip 34695–6607; tel. 727/725–6111, **A**1 2 10 **F**3 8 13 15 17 18 20 22 26 28 29 30 32 34 35 37 38 40 41 44 46 49 50 51 55 56 57 59 60 62 64 68 70 72 74 75 76 77 78 79 81 84 85 86 87 89 92 93 107 108 109 111 114 115 116 117 118 119 126 129 130 131 132 135 143 145 146 147 148 149 154 **S** Trinity Health, Livonia, MI
Primary Contact: Lou Galdieri, R.N., President
CFO: Carl Tremonti, Chief Financial Officer
CMO: Tony Schuster, M.D., Vice President of Physician Services
CIO: Tim Thompson, Senior Vice President, Informant Services and Chief Information Officer
CHR: Kyle Barr, Senior Vice President, Chief Team Resources Officer
CNO: Thomas Doria, Vice President, Patient Services and Chief Nursing Officer
Web address: www.mpmhealth.com
Control: Other not–for–profit (including NFP Corporation) **Service**: General medical and surgical

Staffed Beds: 311 **Admissions**: 18049 **Census**: 219 **Outpatient Visits**: 124049 **Births**: 2079 **Total Expense ($000)**: 285767 **Payroll Expense ($000)**: 99664 **Personnel**: 1517

SAINT AUGUSTINE—St. Johns County

☐ **FLAGLER HOSPITAL (100090)**, 400 Health Park Boulevard, Zip 32086–5784; tel. 904/819–5155, **A**1 2 5 10 20 **F**3 5 8 11 12 13 14 15 18 20 22 24 28 29 30 31 34 35 38 40 44 45 49 50 53 56 57 58 59 65 70 72 74 75 76 78 79 81 82 85 86 87 89 98 100 101 102 104 105 107 108 110 111 114 115 119 120 126 129 130 132 135 146 152 153 154 **P**8
Primary Contact: Jason P. Barrett, Chief Executive Officer
CFO: Lynda I Kirker, Chief Financial Officer
CMO: Douglas Dew, M.D., President Medical Staff
CIO: Bill Rieger, Chief Information Officer
CHR: Jeff Hurley, Vice President Human Resources
Web address: www.flaglerhospital.org
Control: Other not–for–profit (including NFP Corporation) **Service**: General medical and surgical

Staffed Beds: 204 **Admissions**: 14371 **Census**: 171 **Outpatient Visits**: 146548 **Births**: 1577 **Total Expense ($000)**: 243195 **Payroll Expense ($000)**: 89222 **Personnel**: 1528

FL

Hospital, Medicare Provider Number, Address, Telephone, Approval, Facility, and Physician Codes, Health Care System

★ American Hospital Association (AHA) membership
☐ The Joint Commission accreditation
○ Healthcare Facilities Accreditation Program
◇ DNV Healthcare Inc. accreditation
⇧ Center for Improvement in Healthcare Quality Accreditation
△ Commission on Accreditation of Rehabilitation Facilities (CARF) accreditation

SAINT CLOUD—Osceola County

☒ **ST. CLOUD REGIONAL MEDICAL CENTER (100302)**, 2906 17th Street, Zip 34769–6099; tel. 407/892–2135, (Nonreporting) **A**1 10 **S** Community Health Systems, Inc., Franklin, TN
Primary Contact: Brent Burish, Chief Executive Officer
COO: Andrea Thomas, Chief Operating Officer
CFO: Carl Caley, Chief Financial Officer
CIO: James Devlin, Director Information Systems
CHR: Jennifer Harmon, Director of Human Resources
CNO: Perry Horne, Chief Nursing Officer
Web address: www.stcloudregional.com
Control: Corporation, Investor–owned (for–profit) **Service**: General medical and surgical

Staffed Beds: 84

SAINT PETERSBURG—Pinellas County

☒ **BAYFRONT HEALTH ST. PETERSBURG (100032)**, 701 Sixth Street South, Zip 33701–4891; tel. 727/823–1234, **A**1 3 5 10 **F**8 13 18 20 22 24 26 28 29 30 34 40 43 45 46 47 49 50 53 54 60 70 74 75 76 77 79 81 83 84 85 90 91 92 93 94 97 107 108 110 111 115 116 117 118 119 126 129 130 131 135 137 144 148 154 **P**8 **S** Community Health Systems, Inc., Franklin, TN
Primary Contact: John R. McLain, President and Chief Executive Officer
COO: Austin Brown, Chief Operating Officer
CFO: Eric Smith, Chief Financial Officer
CIO: Kevin Murphy, Director, Information Technology Services
CHR: Jim Reames, Director Human Resources
CNO: Karen Long, R.N., FACHE, Vice President Nursing
Web address: www.bayfrontstpete.com
Control: Corporation, Investor–owned (for–profit) **Service**: General medical and surgical

Staffed Beds: 480 **Admissions:** 15428 **Census:** 171 **Outpatient Visits:** 120850 **Births:** 4119 **Total Expense ($000):** 259825 **Payroll Expense ($000):** 93108 **Personnel:** 1313

☒ **JOHNS HOPKINS ALL CHILDREN'S HOSPITAL (103300)**, 501 6th Avenue South, Zip 33701–4634; tel. 727/898–7451, **A**1 3 5 8 10 **F**3 11 12 17 18 19 20 21 22 23 24 25 26 27 29 30 31 32 34 35 36 37 39 40 41 43 44 45 46 47 48 49 50 54 55 57 58 59 60 61 62 64 65 68 72 73 74 75 77 78 79 81 82 84 85 86 87 88 89 90 92 93 96 97 99 100 107 111 114 115 116 118 119 126 129 130 131 132 134 135 136 137 141 142 143 144 146 147 148 **S** Johns Hopkins Health System, Baltimore, MD
Primary Contact: Jonathan M. Ellen, M.D., President
CFO: Nancy Templin, Vice President Finance and Chief Financial Officer
CMO: Michael Epstein, M.D., Senior Vice President Medical Affairs
CIO: John McLendon, Vice President and Chief Information Officer
CHR: Jay Kuhns, Vice President Human Resources
CNO: Melissa Macogay, Vice Presiident and Chief Nursing Officer
Web address: www.allkids.org
Control: Other not–for–profit (including NFP Corporation) **Service**: Children's general medical and surgical

Staffed Beds: 259 **Admissions:** 6943 **Census:** 162 **Outpatient Visits:** 343211 **Births:** 0 **Total Expense ($000):** 418233 **Payroll Expense ($000):** 158716 **Personnel:** 2927

☒ ⇑ **NORTHSIDE HOSPITAL (100238)**, 6000 49th Street North, Zip 33709–2145; tel. 727/521–4411, (Nonreporting) **A**1 3 10 12 13 21 **S** HCA Healthcare, Nashville, TN
Primary Contact: Dia Nichols, Chief Executive Officer
COO: Peter Kennedy, Chief Operating Officer
CFO: Peggy Gatliff, Chief Financial Officer
CMO: Ira Siegman, M.D., Chief Medical Officer
CIO: Kirk Hendrick, Director Information Systems
CHR: Maggie Miklos, Director Human Resources
CNO: John Polisknowski, Chief Nursing Officer
Web address: www.northsidehospital.com
Control: Corporation, Investor–owned (for–profit) **Service**: General medical and surgical

Staffed Beds: 217

☒ **PALMS OF PASADENA HOSPITAL (100126)**, 1501 Pasadena Avenue South, Zip 33707–3798; tel. 727/381–1000, (Nonreporting) **A**1 10 **S** HCA Healthcare, Nashville, TN
Primary Contact: Jacob Fisher, Chief Executive Officer
COO: Glenn J. Saldanha, Chief Operating Officer
CFO: Chase Redden, Chief Financial Officer
CMO: Mitchell Rubinstein, M.D., Chief Medical Officer
CIO: Danny Waters, Director, Information Services
CHR: Karen Casteel, Director Human Resources
CNO: Colleen Thielk, MSN, R.N., Chief Nursing Officer
Web address: www.palmspasadena.com
Control: Corporation, Investor–owned (for–profit) **Service**: General medical and surgical

Staffed Beds: 187

☒ **ST. ANTHONY'S HOSPITAL (100067)**, 1200 Seventh Avenue North, Zip 33705–1388, Mailing Address: P.O. Box 12588, Zip 33733–2588; tel. 727/825–1100, **A**1 2 5 10 **F**3 11 12 15 17 18 20 22 26 28 29 30 31 34 35 40 44 45 46 49 51 57 59 60 64 68 70 74 75 77 78 79 81 84 85 87 93 98 100 102 103 107 108 110 111 114 115 117 118 119 121 123 124 126 129 130 131 132 135 146 148 149 154 **S** Trinity Health, Livonia, MI
Primary Contact: M. Scott Smith, President
CFO: Carl Tremonti, Chief Financial Officer
CMO: James McClintic, M.D., Vice President Medical Affairs
CIO: Tim Thompson, Senior Vice President and Chief Informatics Officer
CHR: Kristen A Betts, Director Team Resources
CNO: Thomas Doria, Vice President and Patient Services West
Web address: www.stanthonys.com/
Control: Other not–for–profit (including NFP Corporation) **Service**: General medical and surgical

Staffed Beds: 393 **Admissions:** 21934 **Census:** 285 **Outpatient Visits:** 108403 **Births:** 0 **Total Expense ($000):** 330445 **Payroll Expense ($000):** 117917 **Personnel:** 1967

☒ **ST. PETERSBURG GENERAL HOSPITAL (100180)**, 6500 38th Avenue North, Zip 33710–1629; tel. 727/384–1414, (Nonreporting) **A**1 2 3 10 12 13 **S** HCA Healthcare, Nashville, TN
Primary Contact: Janice Balzano, President and Chief Executive Officer
COO: Stephanie McNulty, Chief Operating Officer
CFO: Shawn Gregory, Chief Financial Officer
CMO: Mitchell Rubinstein, M.D., Chief Medical Officer
CHR: Jennifer B Robinson, Vice President Human Resources
CNO: JoAnne Cattell, Chief Nursing Officer
Web address: www.stpetegeneral.com
Control: Corporation, Investor–owned (for–profit) **Service**: General medical and surgical

Staffed Beds: 219

SANFORD—Seminole County

☒ △ **CENTRAL FLORIDA REGIONAL HOSPITAL (100161)**, 1401 West Seminole Boulevard, Zip 32771–6764; tel. 407/321–4500, (Nonreporting) **A**1 7 10 **S** HCA Healthcare, Nashville, TN
Primary Contact: Wendy H. Brandon, Chief Executive Officer
COO: Glenn Carney, Chief Operating Officer
CFO: Richard Read, Chief Financial Officer
CIO: Jerry Ballard, Director Information Systems
CHR: Linda V Smith, Vice President Human Resources
CNO: Maria Calloway, R.N., MSN, Chief Nursing Officer
Web address: www.centralfloridaregional.com
Control: Corporation, Investor–owned (for–profit) **Service**: General medical and surgical

Staffed Beds: 226

SARASOTA—Sarasota County

☒ **COMPLEX CARE HOSPITAL AT RIDGELAKE (102018)**, 6150 Edgelake Drive, Zip 34240–8803; tel. 941/342–3000, (Nonreporting) **A**1 10 **S** LifeCare Management Services, Plano, TX
Primary Contact: Robert E. Mallicoat, Chief Executive Officer
CFO: Leah Drabant, Director of Finance
CMO: Craig Harcup, M.D., Hospital Medical Director
CHR: Jennifer Sparks, Human Resources Generalist
CNO: Timothy Mitchell, R.N., Chief Nursing Officer
Web address: www.lifecare-hospitals.com/hospital.php?id=23
Control: Corporation, Investor–owned (for–profit) **Service**: Acute long–term care hospital

Staffed Beds: 40

☒ **DOCTORS HOSPITAL OF SARASOTA (100166)**, 5731 Bee Ridge Road, Zip 34233–5056; tel. 941/342–1100, (Nonreporting) **A**1 10 **S** HCA Healthcare, Nashville, TN
Primary Contact: Robert C. Meade, Chief Executive Officer
COO: Wyatt Chocklett, Chief Operating Officer
CFO: Charles Schwaner III Chief Financial Officer
CMO: Thomas Trinchetto, M.D., Chief Medical Officer
CHR: Theresa Levering, Director Human Resources
CNO: Kathy Mitchell, R.N., Chief Nursing Officer
Web address: www.doctorsofsarasota.com
Control: Corporation, Investor–owned (for–profit) **Service**: General medical and surgical

Staffed Beds: 168

FL

▣ △ **HEALTHSOUTH REHABILITATION HOSPITAL OF SARASOTA (103031)**, 6400 Edgelake Drive, Zip 34240–8813; tel. 941/921–8600, **A**1 7 10 **F**28 29 62 75 90 96 132 143 **S** Encompass Health Corporation, Birmingham, AL
Primary Contact: Marcus Braz, Chief Executive Officer
CFO: Barbara Bierut, Chief Financial Officer
CMO: Alexander De Jesus, M.D., Medical Director
CHR: Brenda Benner, Director Human Resources
Web address: www.healthsouthsarasota.com
Control: Corporation, Investor–owned (for–profit) **Service**: Rehabilitation

Staffed Beds: 96 **Admissions**: 2326 **Census**: 85 **Outpatient Visits**: 0
Births: 0 **Total Expense ($000)**: 27374 **Payroll Expense ($000)**: 15658
Personnel: 286

HEALTHSOUTH RIDGELAKE HOSPITAL See Complex Care Hospital at Ridgelake

☐ △ ⇑ **SARASOTA MEMORIAL HEALTH CARE SYSTEM (100087)**, 1700 South Tamiami Trail, Zip 34239–3555; tel. 941/917–9000, **A**1 2 3 5 7 8 10 21 **F**3 6 7 8 11 12 13 15 17 18 19 20 22 24 26 28 29 30 31 32 34 35 36 37 38 39 40 43 44 45 46 47 48 49 50 51 53 54 55 56 57 58 59 60 61 64 66 68 70 72 73 74 75 76 77 78 79 80 81 82 84 85 86 87 89 90 91 92 93 95 96 97 98 99 100 101 102 103 107 108 110 111 114 115 118 119 124 126 129 130 131 132 134 135 143 144 146 147 148 149 150 154 **P**5 8
Primary Contact: David Verinder, President and Chief Executive Officer
COO: David Verinder, President and Chief Executive Officer
CFO: Bill Woeltjen, Chief Financial Officer
CMO: James Fiorica, M.D., Chief Medical Officer
CIO: Denis Baker, Chief Information Officer
CHR: Laurie Bennett, Director Human Resources
CNO: Connie Andersen, R.N., MS, Chief Nursing Officer
Web address: www.smh.com
Control: Hospital district or authority, Government, nonfederal **Service**: General medical and surgical

Staffed Beds: 749 **Admissions**: 33262 **Census**: 437 **Outpatient Visits**: 570246 **Births**: 3519 **Total Expense ($000)**: 649949 **Payroll Expense ($000)**: 257458 **Personnel**: 4518

SEBASTIAN—Indian River County

▣ **SEBASTIAN RIVER MEDICAL CENTER (100217)**, 13695 North US Hwy 1, Zip 32958–3230, Mailing Address: Box 780838, Zip 32978–0838; tel. 772/589–3186, (Nonreporting) **A**1 10 **S** Steward Health Care System, LLC, Dallas, TX
Primary Contact: Kelly Enriquez, Chief Executive Officer
CFO: John McEachern, Controller
CMO: Ralph Geiger, M.D., Chief of Staff
CHR: Kam Storey, Director Human Resources
Web address: www.sebastianrivermedical.com
Control: Corporation, Investor–owned (for–profit) **Service**: General medical and surgical

Staffed Beds: 187

SEBRING—Highlands County

▣ **FLORIDA HOSPITAL HEARTLAND MEDICAL CENTER (100109)**, 4200 Sun'n Lake Boulevard, Zip 33872–1986, Mailing Address: P.O. Box 9400, Zip 33871–9400; tel. 863/314–4466, (Includes FLORIDA HOSPITAL LAKE PLACID, 1210 US 27 North, Lake Placid, FL, Zip 33852–7948; tel. 863/465–3777; Eric Stevens, Chief Executive Officer) **A**1 10 19 **F**11 13 15 18 20 22 24 26 28 29 30 34 35 37 40 44 45 49 50 53 54 57 59 60 62 64 70 75 76 78 79 81 86 87 89 97 98 100 101 103 104 105 107 108 110 111 114 115 116 117 121 123 126 127 129 130 132 135 146 147 148 149 153 154 **P**6 **S** Adventist Health System Sunbelt Health Care Corporation, Altamonte Springs, FL
Primary Contact: Randy Surber, Chief Executive Officer
CFO: Rosalie Oliver, Chief Financial Officer
CMO: Jorge F Gonzalez, M.D., Chief Medical Officer
CHR: Anthony Stahl, Vice President
CNO: Gloria N Santos, R.N., MS, Chief Nursing Officer
Web address: www.floridahospital.com/heartland/our–location
Control: Church operated, Nongovernment, not–for–profit **Service**: General medical and surgical

Staffed Beds: 197 **Admissions**: 11553 **Census**: 145 **Outpatient Visits**: 141782 **Births**: 784 **Total Expense ($000)**: 195595 **Payroll Expense ($000)**: 84043 **Personnel**: 1359

▣ **HIGHLANDS REGIONAL MEDICAL CENTER (100049)**, 3600 South Highlands Avenue, Zip 33870–5495, Mailing Address: Drawer 2066, Zip 33871–2066; tel. 863/385–6101, (Nonreporting) **A**1 10 19 **S** HCA Healthcare, Nashville, TN
Primary Contact: John D. Montois, Interim Chief Executive Officer
CFO: Paul Damron, Chief Financial Officer
CIO: Nate Johnson, Chief Information Officer
CHR: Brenda Dane, Director, Human Resources
CNO: Adam Kless, Chief Nursing Officer
Web address: www.highlandsregional.com
Control: Corporation, Investor–owned (for–profit) **Service**: General medical and surgical

Staffed Beds: 80

SOUTH MIAMI—Miami–Dade County

☐ **LARKIN COMMUNITY HOSPITAL (100181)**, 7031 SW 62nd Avenue, Zip 33143–4781; tel. 305/284–7500, **A**1 3 10 12 13 **F**3 8 10 18 20 22 26 29 30 31 34 40 44 45 46 49 54 56 57 60 62 64 68 70 74 77 78 81 82 87 91 93 98 99 100 101 102 104 105 107 111 115 116 117 118 119 124 126 130 135 148 153
Primary Contact: Sandra Sosa–Guerrero, Chief Executive Officer
COO: George J Michel, Chief Operating Officer
CFO: Edgar Castillo, Chief Financial Officer
CMO: Mario Almeida–Suarez, M.D., Chief of Staff
CIO: Orlando Suarez, Director Information Technology
CHR: Carolina Pena, Assistant Director Administrator
CNO: Mercedes Perez, Vice President Nursing
Web address: www.larkinhospital.com
Control: Individual, Investor–owned (for–profit) **Service**: General medical and surgical

Staffed Beds: 146 **Admissions**: 4979 **Census**: 77 **Outpatient Visits**: 17669
Births: 0 **Total Expense ($000)**: 98207

STARKE—Bradford County

SHANDS STARKE See Shands Starke Regional Medical Center

▣ **SHANDS STARKE REGIONAL MEDICAL CENTER (101310)**, 922 East Call Street, Zip 32091–3699; tel. 904/368–2300, (Nonreporting) **A**1 10 18 **S** Community Health Systems, Inc., Franklin, TN
Primary Contact: John Emery, Chief Executive Officer
CFO: Wendy Martin, Chief Financial Officer
Web address: www.shandsstarke.com
Control: Partnership, Investor–owned (for–profit) **Service**: General medical and surgical

Staffed Beds: 49

STUART—Martin County

▣ **HEALTHSOUTH REHABILITATION HOSPITAL AT MARTIN HEALTH (103044)**, 5850 SE Community Drive, Zip 34997–6420; tel. 772/324–3500, (Nonreporting) **A**1 10 **S** Encompass Health Corporation, Birmingham, AL
Primary Contact: Ivette Miranda, Chief Executive Officer
CFO: Dawn Salas, Controller
CMO: Stephen L Chastain, M.D., Chief Medical Officer
CHR: Donna Holder–Hooper, Chief Human Resource Officer
CNO: Charmaine Blanchard, Chief Nursing Officer
Web address: www.healthsouthmartin.com
Control: Corporation, Investor–owned (for–profit) **Service**: Rehabilitation

Staffed Beds: 54

▣ **MARTIN HEALTH SYSTEM (100044)**, 200 SE Hospital Avenue, Zip 34994–2346, Mailing Address: P.O. Box 9010, Zip 34995–9010; tel. 772/287–5200, (Includes MARTIN MEMORIAL HOSPITAL SOUTH, 2100 SE Salerno Road, Stuart, FL, Zip 34997; tel. 772/223–2300; Mark E Robitaille, FACHE, President and Chief Executive Officer; TRADITION MEDICAL CENTER, 10000 SW Innovation Way, Port St Lucie, FL, Zip 34987–2111; tel. 772/345–8100; Mark E Robitaille, FACHE, President and Chief Executive Officer) **A**1 2 10 **F**3 8 11 12 13 15 17 18 20 22 24 26 28 29 30 31 35 36 37 40 45 46 47 49 50 51 53 55 60 64 68 70 72 74 75 76 77 78 79 81 82 85 86 87 91 93 94 95 107 108 110 111 114 115 116 117 118 119 120 121 123 124 126 129 130 132 143 144 146 149 154 **P**6
Primary Contact: Robert L. Lord, JD, President and Chief Executive Officer
CFO: Chuck Cleaver, Vice President and Chief Financial Officer
CMO: Fernando Petry, M.D., Vice President and Chief Medical Officer
CIO: Edmund Collins, Chief Information Officer
CHR: Angie L Metcalf, Vice President and Chief Human Resource Officer
CNO: Mary Elizabeth Flippo, R.N., MSN, Vice President and Chief Nursing Officer
Web address: www.martinhealth.org
Control: Other not–for–profit (including NFP Corporation) **Service**: General medical and surgical

Staffed Beds: 358 **Admissions**: 26112 **Census**: 325 **Outpatient Visits**: 134704 **Births**: 2352 **Total Expense ($000)**: 464707 **Payroll Expense ($000)**: 197560 **Personnel**: 4031

FL

Hospital, Medicare Provider Number, Address, Telephone, Approval, Facility, and Physician Codes, Health Care System

★ American Hospital Association (AHA) membership
☐ The Joint Commission accreditation
○ Healthcare Facilities Accreditation Program
◇ DNV Healthcare Inc. accreditation
⇑ Center for Improvement in Healthcare Quality Accreditation
△ Commission on Accreditation of Rehabilitation Facilities (CARF) accreditation

SUN CITY CENTER—Hillsborough County

✠ **SOUTH BAY HOSPITAL (100259)**, 4016 Sun City Center Blvd, Zip 33573–5298; tel. 813/634–3301, **A**1 10 **F**3 15 18 20 24 29 30 31 34 35 37 40 45 49 50 57 59 64 68 70 74 75 77 78 79 81 82 85 86 87 93 107 108 110 111 114 118 119 132 146 148 149 **S** HCA Healthcare, Nashville, TN
Primary Contact: Sharon L. Roush, Chief Executive Officer
COO: Daniel Bender, Chief Operating Officer
CFO: Warren Pate, Chief Financial Officer
CMO: Joseph C. Corcoran, D.O., Chief Medical Officer
CIO: Eric Young, Director Information Technology and Systems
CHR: Stacie Novosel, Vice President, Human Resources
CNO: Marcy Frisina, Chief Nursing Officer
Web address: www.southbayhospital.com/
Control: Corporation, Investor–owned (for–profit) **Service**: General medical and surgical

Staffed Beds: 138 **Admissions**: 6485 **Census**: 74 **Outpatient Visits**: 31127 **Births**: 0 **Personnel**: 375

SUNRISE—Broward County

✠ **HEALTHSOUTH SUNRISE REHABILITATION HOSPITAL (103028)**, 4399 North Nob Hill Road, Zip 33351–5899; tel. 954/749–0300, **A**1 3 10 **F**3 18 29 34 35 56 57 59 62 82 90 91 93 95 96 130 132 148 **S** Encompass Health Corporation, Birmingham, AL
Primary Contact: Michael S. Roffelsen, Chief Executive Officer
CFO: Ruth Goodstein, Controller
CMO: Scott Tannenbaum, M.D., Medical Director
CIO: Angela Manning, Director Health Information Services
CHR: Barbara Dunkiel, Director Human Resources
CNO: Omaira D. Riano, Chief Nursing Officer
Web address: www.healthsouthsunrise.com
Control: Corporation, Investor–owned (for–profit) **Service**: Rehabilitation

Staffed Beds: 126 **Admissions**: 2619 **Census**: 97 **Outpatient Visits**: 14981 **Births**: 0 **Total Expense ($000)**: 37871 **Personnel**: 290

TALLAHASSEE—Leon County

✠ **CAPITAL REGIONAL MEDICAL CENTER (100254)**, 2626 Capital Medical Boulevard, Zip 32308–4499; tel. 850/325–5000, (Nonreporting) **A**1 2 10 **S** HCA Healthcare, Nashville, TN
Primary Contact: Alan Seesee, Chief Executive Officer
CMO: Steve West, M.D., Chief Medical Officer
CIO: Robert A Steed, Director Information Systems
CHR: Louise Truitt, Vice President Human Resources
Web address: www.capitalregionalmedicalcenter.com
Control: Individual, Investor–owned (for–profit) **Service**: General medical and surgical

Staffed Beds: 198

EASTSIDE PSYCHIATRIC HOSPITAL (104059), 2634 Capital Circle NE, Zip 32308–4106; tel. 850/523–3333, (Nonreporting) **A**10
Primary Contact: Jay A. Reeve, Ph.D., President and Chief Executive Officer
COO: Sue Conger, Chief Operating Officer
CFO: Virginia Kelly, Chief Financial Officer
CMO: Ludmila de Faria, M.D., Chief Medical Officer
CIO: Thad Moorer, Chief Information Officer
CHR: Candy Landry, Chief Human Resource Officer
CNO: Judy Goreau, R.N., Director of Nursing
Web address: www.apalacheecenter.org
Control: Other not–for–profit (including NFP Corporation) **Service**: Psychiatric

Staffed Beds: 24

✠ **HEALTHSOUTH REHABILITATION HOSPITAL OF TALLAHASSEE (103033)**, 1675 Riggins Road, Zip 32308–5315; tel. 850/656–4800, (Nonreporting) **A**1 10 **S** Encompass Health Corporation, Birmingham, AL
Primary Contact: K. Dale. Neely, FACHE, Chief Executive Officer
CFO: Jennifer Spooner, Controller
CMO: Robert Rowland, M.D., Medical Director
CIO: Michael Spangler, Health Information Management Services Supervisor
CHR: Carol Bugayong, Human Resources Director
CNO: Elizabeth Squires, R.N., Chief Nursing Officer
Web address: www.healthsouthtallahassee.com
Control: Corporation, Investor–owned (for–profit) **Service**: Rehabilitation

Staffed Beds: 76

✠ **SELECT SPECIALTY HOSPITAL–TALLAHASSEE (102020)**, 1554 Surgeons Drive, Zip 32308–4631; tel. 850/219–6950, (Nonreporting) **A**1 10 **S** Select Medical Corporation, Mechanicsburg, PA
Primary Contact: Jay Faherty, Chief Executive Officer
Web address: www.tallahassee.selectspecialtyhospitals.com/
Control: Corporation, Investor–owned (for–profit) **Service**: Acute long–term care hospital

Staffed Beds: 29

✠ **TALLAHASSEE MEMORIAL HEALTHCARE (100135)**, 1300 Miccosukee Road, Zip 32308–5054; tel. 850/431–1155, (Total facility includes 42 beds in nursing home–type unit) **A**1 2 3 5 10 **F**2 3 5 6 8 11 12 13 15 17 18 19 20 22 24 26 28 29 30 31 34 35 37 40 43 46 47 48 49 50 51 53 54 55 56 57 58 59 60 61 62 64 65 68 70 72 73 74 75 76 77 78 79 80 81 82 84 85 86 87 88 89 91 93 96 97 98 99 100 102 103 104 107 108 110 113 114 115 117 118 119 120 121 123 124 126 127 128 129 130 131 132 135 143 144 146 147 148 149 154 **P**6
Primary Contact: G. Mark. O'Bryant, President and Chief Executive Officer
COO: Jason H Moore, Vice President and Chief Operating Officer
CFO: William A Giudice, Vice President and Chief Financial Officer
CMO: Dean Watson, M.D., Chief Medical Officer
CIO: Don Lindsey, Vice President and Chief Information Officer
CHR: Steven W Adriaanse, Vice President and Chief Human Resources Officer
Web address: www.tmh.org
Control: Other not–for–profit (including NFP Corporation) **Service**: General medical and surgical

Staffed Beds: 495 **Admissions**: 28864 **Census**: 395 **Outpatient Visits**: 776075 **Births**: 3876 **Total Expense ($000)**: 643139 **Payroll Expense ($000)**: 267920 **Personnel**: 3910

TAMARAC—Broward County

✠ **UNIVERSITY HOSPITAL AND MEDICAL CENTER (100224)**, 7201 North University Drive, Zip 33321–2996; tel. 954/721–2200, (Includes UNIVERSITY PAVILION, 7425 North University Drive, Tamarac, FL, Zip 33328; tel. 305/722–9933) (Nonreporting) **A**1 3 10 **S** HCA Healthcare, Nashville, TN
Primary Contact: Dana C. Oaks, Chief Executive Officer
CFO: Aurelio Gonzalez, Chief Financial Officer
CMO: Ran Abrahamy, M.D., Chief of Staff
CIO: Tom Scharff, Director Information Services
Web address: www.uhmchealth.com
Control: Corporation, Investor–owned (for–profit) **Service**: General medical and surgical

Staffed Beds: 317

TAMPA—Hillsborough County

✠ **FLORIDA HOSPITAL CARROLLWOOD (100069)**, 7171 North Dale Mabry Highway, Zip 33614–2665; tel. 813/932–2222, (Nonreporting) **A**1 3 10 **S** Adventist Health System Sunbelt Health Care Corporation, Altamonte Springs, FL
Primary Contact: Erika Skula, President and Chief Executive Officer
COO: Mary C Whillock, R.N., MS, Associate Nursing Officer and Chief Operating Officer
CFO: Chris Sauder, Vice President and Chief Financial Officer
CNO: Deborah W Kumar, MSN, Chief Nursing Officer
Web address: www.floridahospital.com/carrollwood
Control: Church operated, Nongovernment, not–for–profit **Service**: General medical and surgical

Staffed Beds: 96

✠ △ **FLORIDA HOSPITAL TAMPA (100173)**, 3100 East Fletcher Avenue, Zip 33613–4688; tel. 813/971–6000, **A**1 3 5 7 10 **F**3 11 12 13 15 16 17 18 19 20 21 22 24 25 26 27 28 29 30 31 34 35 37 40 41 44 45 46 47 48 49 50 54 57 58 59 60 64 65 70 72 74 75 76 77 78 79 80 81 82 84 85 86 87 88 89 90 91 92 93 96 105 107 108 109 110 111 112 114 115 116 117 118 119 120 121 123 124 126 129 130 132 135 143 144 146 147 148 149 152 **P**6 7 **S** Adventist Health System Sunbelt Health Care Corporation, Altamonte Springs, FL
Primary Contact: Brian Adams, President and Chief Executive Officer
COO: Dick Tibbits, Vice President and Chief Operating Officer
CFO: Dima Didenko, Chief Financial Officer
CMO: Brad Bjornstad, M.D., Vice President and Chief Medical Officer
CHR: Dick Tibbits, Vice President and Chief Operating Officer
CNO: Theresa Trivette, R.N., Chief Nursing Officer
Web address: www.floridahospital.com/tampa
Control: Other not–for–profit (including NFP Corporation) **Service**: General medical and surgical

Staffed Beds: 536 **Admissions**: 22997 **Census**: 355 **Outpatient Visits**: 144304 **Births**: 1886 **Total Expense ($000)**: 475811 **Payroll Expense ($000)**: 157392 **Personnel**: 2867

✠ **H. LEE MOFFITT CANCER CENTER AND RESEARCH INSTITUTE (100271)**, 12902 Magnolia Drive, Zip 33612–9497; tel. 813/745–4673, **A**1 2 5 10 **F**3 8 15 26 29 30 31 34 35 36 37 45 46 47 49 50 54 55 56 57 58 59 64 68 70 71 74 75 77 78 79 80 81 82 84 85 86 87 91 92 93 96 97 100 101 103 104 107 108 110 111 114 115 117 118 119 120 121 123 124 126 130 132 135 136 144 145 146 147 148 149 154 **P**6
Primary Contact: Alan F. List, M.D., President and Chief Executive Officer
COO: John A Kolosky, Executive Vice President and Chief Operating Officer
CFO: Yvette Tremonti, Chief Financial Officer
CMO: Bob Keenan, Chief Medical Officer
CIO: Jennifer Greenman, Vice President Chief Information Officer
CHR: Mariana Bugallo-Muros, Vice President Chief Human Resources Officer
CNO: Jane Fusilero, Vice President Chief Nursing Officer
Web address: www.moffitt.org
Control: Other not–for–profit (including NFP Corporation) **Service**: Cancer

Staffed Beds: 206 **Admissions**: 9210 **Census**: 168 **Outpatient Visits**: 384857 **Births**: 0 **Total Expense ($000)**: 1098339 **Payroll Expense ($000)**: 439930 **Personnel**: 6422

Many Facility Codes have changed. Please refer to the AHA Guide Code Chart. © 2018 AHA Guide

FL

⊞ △ **JAMES A. HALEY VETERANS' HOSPITAL–TAMPA**, 13000 Bruce B Downs Boulevard, Zip 33612–4745; tel. 813/972–2000, (Total facility includes 64 beds in nursing home–type unit) **A**1 3 5 7 8 **F**3 5 9 12 15 17 18 20 22 24 26 28 29 30 31 33 34 35 36 38 39 40 45 46 47 48 49 50 51 53 54 55 56 57 58 59 60 61 62 63 64 65 70 71 74 75 77 78 79 80 81 82 83 84 85 86 87 90 91 92 93 94 95 96 97 98 100 101 102 103 104 105 107 108 109 110 111 113 114 115 116 117 118 119 120 121 123 126 127 128 129 130 131 132 135 143 144 146 147 148 149 152 153 154 **P**1 **S** Department of Veterans Affairs, Perry Point, MD
Primary Contact: Joe Battle, Director
CFO: Robert Konkel, Manager Finance
CMO: Edward Cutolo, M.D., Jr Chief of Staff
CIO: Jose Seymour, Chief Information Resource Management
CHR: Andrew Sutton, Chief, Human Resources Management Service
CNO: Laureen Doloresco, R.N., Associate Director for Patient Care and Nursing Services
Web address: www.tampa.va.gov/
Control: Veterans Affairs, Government, federal **Service**: General medical and surgical

Staffed Beds: 499 **Admissions**: 11552 **Census**: 378 **Outpatient Visits**: 1330542 **Births**: 0	

⊞ **KINDRED HOSPITAL BAY AREA–TAMPA (102009)**, 4555 South Manhattan Avenue, Zip 33611–2397; tel. 813/839–6341, (Includes KINDRED HOSPITAL–BAY AREA ST. PETERSBURG, 3030 Sixth Street South, Saint Petersburg, FL, Zip 33705–3720; tel. 727/894–8719; Debra Plummer, Chief Executive Officer) (Nonreporting) **A**1 10 **S** Kindred Healthcare, Louisville, KY
Primary Contact: Suthanthira M. Ratnasamy, R.N., FACHE, Chief Executive Officer
CFO: Frank Billy, Chief Financial Officer
CHR: Deborah Basria, Human Resources Payroll Administrator
Web address: www.khtampa.com/
Control: Corporation, Investor–owned (for–profit) **Service**: Acute long–term care hospital

Staffed Beds: 73

⊞ **KINDRED HOSPITAL CENTRAL TAMPA (102013)**, 4801 North Howard Avenue, Zip 33603–1411; tel. 813/874–7575, (Nonreporting) **A**1 10 **S** Kindred Healthcare, Louisville, KY
Primary Contact: Ralph Selner, Chief Executive Officer
CFO: John Miner, Chief Financial Officer
Web address: www.kindredcentraltampa.com/
Control: Corporation, Investor–owned (for–profit) **Service**: Acute long–term care hospital

Staffed Beds: 102

⊞ **MEMORIAL HOSPITAL OF TAMPA (100206)**, 2901 Swann Avenue, Zip 33609–4057; tel. 813/873–6400, (Nonreporting) **A**1 5 10 **S** HCA Healthcare, Nashville, TN
Primary Contact: Sonia I. Wellman, Chief Executive Officer
COO: Tom Grondin, Chief Operating Officer
CFO: Shelley V Kolseth, Chief Financial Officer
CMO: Christos Politis, M.D., Chief Medical Officer
CIO: John Riton, Director Information Services
CNO: Molly Arau, Chief Nursing Officer
Web address: www.memorialhospitaltampa.com
Control: Corporation, Investor–owned (for–profit) **Service**: General medical and surgical

Staffed Beds: 139

☐ **SHRINERS HOSPITALS FOR CHILDREN–TAMPA (103303)**, 12502 USF Pine Drive, Zip 33612–9499; tel. 813/972–2250, **A**1 3 5 10 **F**3 29 34 35 50 57 64 68 74 77 79 81 85 89 91 93 94 95 96 107 131 146 149 **S** Shriners Hospitals for Children, Tampa, FL
Primary Contact: Fleury Yelvington, Administrator
CFO: Ruth Gregos, Director Finance
CMO: Maureen Maciel, M.D., Chief of Staff
CHR: Amy Schenker, Human Resources Director
Web address: www.shrinershospitalsforchildren.org/Hospitals/Locations/Tampa.aspx
Control: Other not–for–profit (including NFP Corporation) **Service**: Children's orthopedic

Staffed Beds: 60 **Admissions**: 224 **Census**: 1 **Outpatient Visits**: 13506 **Births**: 0 **Total Expense ($000)**: 23760 **Payroll Expense ($000)**: 12379 **Personnel**: 168

⊞ **ST. JOSEPH'S HOSPITAL (100075)**, 3001 West Martin Luther King Jr. Boulevard, Zip 33607–6387; Mailing Address: P.O. Box 4227, Zip 33677–4227; tel. 813/870–4000, (Includes ST. JOSEPH'S CHILDREN'S HOSPITAL, 3001 Dr Martin Luther King Jr Boulevard, Tampa, FL, Zip 33607; tel. 813/554–8500; Kate Reed, President; ST. JOSEPH'S HOSPITAL – NORTH, 4211 Van Dyke Road, Lutz, FL, Zip 33558–8005; tel. 813/443–7000; Paula McGinnis, Chief Executive Officer; ST. JOSEPH'S HOSPITAL BEHAVIORAL HEALTH CENTER, 4918 North Habana Avenue, Tampa, FL, Zip 33614–6815; tel. 813/870–4300; ST. JOSEPH'S HOSPITAL–SOUTH, 6901 Simmons Loop, Riverview, FL, Zip 33578–9498; tel. 813/302–8000; Scott Smith, President; ST. JOSEPH'S WOMEN'S HOSPITAL, 3030 West Dr Martin L King Boulevard, Tampa, FL, Zip 33607–6394; tel. 813/872–2950; Kate Reed, President) **A**1 2 3 5 10 **F**3 7 11 12 13 15 17 18 19 20 21 22 23 24 25 26 27 28 29 30 31 32 34 35 36 37 39 40 41 43 44 45 46 48 49 51 55 57 58 59 60 61 64 65 66 68 70 71 72 73 74 75 76 78 79 81 82 84 85 86 87 88 89 92 93 94 98 99 100 101 102 107 108 110 111 112 114 115 116 117 118 119 120 121 123 124 126 127 129 130 131 132 134 135 143 145 146 147 148 149 150 154 **S** Trinity Health, Livonia, MI
Primary Contact: Kimberly Guy, President
CFO: Cathy Yoder, Chief Financial Officer
CMO: Mark Vaaler, M.D., Vice President Medical Staff Affairs
CIO: Lindsey Jarrell, Vice President Information Services
CHR: Pat Lipton, Director Team Resources
Web address: www.sjbhealth.org
Control: Other not–for–profit (including NFP Corporation) **Service**: General medical and surgical

Staffed Beds: 1049 **Admissions**: 59261 **Census**: 724 **Outpatient Visits**: 571403 **Births**: 8638 **Total Expense ($000)**: 1053851 **Payroll Expense ($000)**: 365544 **Personnel**: 5739

⊞ **TAMPA COMMUNITY HOSPITAL (100255)**, 6001 Webb Road, Zip 33615–3291; tel. 813/888–7060, (Nonreporting) **A**1 5 10 **S** HCA Healthcare, Nashville, TN
COO: Paulina Tam, Vice President of Operations
CMO: Christos Politis, M.D., Chief Medical Officer
CIO: Albert Lacy, Associate Director of Information Technology
CHR: Stephanie Kunkel, Vice President of Human Resources
CNO: Susan Laber, R.N., Chief Nursing Officer
Web address: www.tampacommunityhospital.com/
Control: Partnership, Investor–owned (for–profit) **Service**: General medical and surgical

Staffed Beds: 201

⊞ △ **TAMPA GENERAL HOSPITAL (100128)**, 1 Tampa General Circle, Zip 33606–3571; Mailing Address: P.O. Box 1289, Zip 33601–1289; tel. 813/844–7000, (Includes TAMPA GENERAL HOSPITAL CHILDREN'S MEDICAL CENTER, 1 Tampa General Circle, Tampa, FL, Zip 33606–3571; tel. 813/844–7000) **A**1 3 5 7 8 10 **F**3 7 8 11 12 13 15 16 17 18 19 20 22 24 26 28 29 30 31 32 33 34 35 37 38 39 40 41 43 44 45 46 47 48 49 50 52 53 54 55 56 57 58 59 60 61 62 63 64 66 68 70 72 73 74 75 76 77 78 79 81 82 83 84 85 86 87 88 89 90 91 92 93 94 96 97 99 100 101 102 103 107 108 109 110 111 112 114 115 119 120 121 123 124 126 129 130 132 134 135 137 138 139 140 141 142 143 145 146 147 148 149 154 **P**6
Primary Contact: John D. Couris, Chief Executive Officer
COO: Kelly Cullen, R.N., Executive Vice President and Chief Operating Officer
CFO: Judith M. Ploszek, Chief Financial Officer
CMO: Sally Houston, M.D., Executive Vice President and Chief Medical Officer
CIO: Scott Arnold, Senior Vice President Information Systems
CHR: Chris Roederer, Senior Vice President Human Resources
CNO: Janet Davis, R.N., MS, Senior Vice President and Chief Nursing Officer
Web address: www.tgh.org
Control: Other not–for–profit (including NFP Corporation) **Service**: General medical and surgical

Staffed Beds: 1011 **Admissions**: 46381 **Census**: 801 **Outpatient Visits**: 440056 **Births**: 5952 **Total Expense ($000)**: 1234722 **Payroll Expense ($000)**: 465541 **Personnel**: 8109

FL

TARPON SPRINGS—Pinellas County

☒ **FLORIDA HOSPITAL NORTH PINELLAS (100055)**, 1395 South Pinellas Avenue, Zip 34689–3790; tel. 727/942–5000, **A**1 5 10 **F**3 15 17 18 20 22 26 28 29 30 31 34 35 37 38 40 45 46 49 50 51 54 55 56 57 59 64 65 68 70 71 74 75 76 78 79 81 84 85 87 93 94 96 97 107 108 110 111 114 115 117 119 126 128 129 130 131 132 135 146 148 149 154 **S** Adventist Health System Sunbelt Health Care Corporation, Altamonte Springs, FL
Primary Contact: Jason Dunkel, President and Chief Executive Officer
CFO: Caleb Heinrich, Chief Financial Officer
CMO: Brian Williams, M.D., Chief of Medical Staff
CIO: Brett Peterson, Director of Information Services
CHR: Vernon Elarbee, Director of Human Resources
CNO: Jennifer Segur, Chief Nursing Officer and Chief Clinical Officer
Web address: www.fhnorthpinellas.com/
Control: Church operated, Nongovernment, not–for–profit **Service**: General medical and surgical

Staffed Beds: 187 **Admissions**: 5859 **Census**: 81 **Outpatient Visits**: 45423 **Births**: 209

TAVARES—Lake County

☒ **FLORIDA HOSPITAL WATERMAN (100057)**, 1000 Waterman Way, Zip 32778–5266; tel. 352/253–3333, **A**1 2 10 **F**3 11 13 15 17 18 20 22 24 26 28 29 30 31 32 34 35 36 37 40 45 49 50 53 54 55 56 57 59 62 64 66 70 74 75 76 77 78 79 81 85 86 87 89 91 93 107 108 110 111 114 115 116 117 118 119 120 121 123 124 126 130 132 143 144 146 147 148 149 **P**8 **S** Adventist Health System Sunbelt Health Care Corporation, Altamonte Springs, FL
Primary Contact: Abel Biri, Chief Executive Officer
COO: Anita Young, Chief Operating Officer
CFO: Frances H Crunk, Vice President and Chief Financial Officer
CMO: Vinay Mehindru, M.D., Vice President/Chief Medical Officer
CHR: Madge Springer, Director Human Resources
CNO: Michael Stimson, Chief Nursing Officer
Web address: www.fhwat.org
Control: Church operated, Nongovernment, not–for–profit **Service**: General medical and surgical

Staffed Beds: 269 **Admissions**: 15619 **Census**: 182 **Outpatient Visits**: 116577 **Births**: 530 **Total Expense ($000)**: 221330 **Payroll Expense ($000)**: 82197 **Personnel**: 1378

TAVERNIER—Monroe County

☒ **BAPTIST HEALTH SOUTH FLORIDA, MARINERS HOSPITAL (101313)**, 91500 Overseas Highway, Zip 33070–2547; tel. 305/434–3000, **A**1 10 18 **F**3 11 15 18 28 29 30 31 34 35 40 45 47 50 53 57 59 68 70 74 75 78 79 81 84 85 93 97 102 107 108 110 111 114 115 129 130 131 132 133 145 146 147 148 149 150 154 **P**8 **S** Baptist Health South Florida, Coral Gables, FL
Primary Contact: Rick Freeburg, Chief Executive Officer
CFO: David Abercrombie, Controller
CIO: Mimi Taylor, Vice President Information Technology
CHR: John Williamson, Human Resources Site Manager
Web address: www.baptisthealth.net/en/facilities/mariners–hospital/Pages/default.aspx
Control: Other not–for–profit (including NFP Corporation) **Service**: General medical and surgical

Staffed Beds: 25 **Admissions**: 644 **Census**: 6 **Outpatient Visits**: 35884 **Births**: 0 **Total Expense ($000)**: 49547 **Payroll Expense ($000)**: 15478 **Personnel**: 196

THE VILLAGES—Sumter County

☒ **THE VILLAGES REGIONAL HOSPITAL (100290)**, 1451 El Camino Real, Zip 32159–0041; tel. 352/751–8000, **A**1 2 10 **F**3 8 11 15 18 20 22 24 26 28 29 30 31 34 35 40 45 49 51 57 59 64 68 70 74 75 77 78 79 81 84 85 87 90 92 93 96 97 107 108 111 114 115 119 126 130 132 135 146 147 149 150 **P**1 **S** Central Florida Health, Leesburg, FL
Primary Contact: Donald G. Henderson, FACHE, President and Chief Executive Officer
COO: Saad Ehtisham, R.N., FACHE, Vice President and Chief Operating Officer
CFO: Diane P Harden, Senior Vice President and Chief Financial Officer
CHR: Amie A Richason, Vice President Human Resources
CNO: Mary Jane Curry–Pelyak, R.N., Vice President and Chief Clinical Officer
Web address: www.cfhalliance.org
Control: Other not–for–profit (including NFP Corporation) **Service**: General medical and surgical

Staffed Beds: 297 **Admissions**: 14661 **Census**: 201 **Outpatient Visits**: 65495 **Births**: 0 **Personnel**: 981

THE VILLAGES REGIONAL HOSPITAL See The Villages Regional Hospital

TITUSVILLE—Brevard County

☐ **PARRISH MEDICAL CENTER (100028)**, 951 North Washington Avenue, Zip 32796–2163; tel. 321/268–6111, (Nonreporting) **A**1 2 10
Primary Contact: George Mikitarian Jr, FACHE, President and Chief Executive Officer
CFO: Timothy Skeldon, Senior Vice President and Chief Financial Officer
CMO: Lisa Alexanda, M.D., Vice President Medical Affairs
CIO: William Moore, Chief Information Officer
Web address: www.parrishmed.com
Control: Hospital district or authority, Government, nonfederal **Service**: General medical and surgical

Staffed Beds: 210

TRINITY—Pasco County

COMMUNITY HOSPITAL See Medical Center of Trinity, Trinity

MEDICAL CENTER OF TRINITYA 1 2 3 10
COO: Sally Seymour, Chief Operating Officer
CFO: Michael Wyers, Chief Financial Officer
CMO: Elbert Barnes, M.D., Chief Medical Officer
CIO: Kurt Hornung, Director
CHR: Christena Miano, Human Resources Director
CNO: Nancy Maysilles, R.N., Chief Nursing Officer
Web address: www.medicalcentertrinity.com

☒ **MEDICAL CENTER OF TRINITY (100191)**, 9330 State Road 54, Zip 34655–1808; tel. 727/834–4900, (Nonreporting) **A**1 2 3 10 **S** HCA Healthcare, Nashville, TN
Primary Contact: Leigh Massengill, Chief Executive Officer
COO: Sally Seymour, Chief Operating Officer
CFO: Michael Wyers, Chief Financial Officer
CMO: Elbert Barnes, M.D., Chief Medical Officer
CIO: Kurt Hornung, Director
CHR: Christena Miano, Human Resources Director
CNO: Nancy Maysilles, R.N., Chief Nursing Officer
Web address: www.medicalcentertrinity.com
Control: Corporation, Investor–owned (for–profit) **Service**: General medical and surgical

Staffed Beds: 276

VENICE—Sarasota County

☒ **VENICE REGIONAL BAYFRONT HEALTH (100070)**, 540 The Rialto, Zip 34285–7711, **A**1 10 **F**3 8 11 12 15 17 18 20 22 24 26 28 29 34 35 37 40 45 46 47 49 50 51 54 56 57 59 64 70 74 77 79 81 82 85 87 93 96 107 108 110 111 114 115 118 119 126 129 130 146 148 149 154 **S** Community Health Systems, Inc., Franklin, TN
Primary Contact: Karen Fordham, Chief Executive Officer
COO: Kristen Gentry, Chief Operating Officer
CFO: Maria Caruso, Chief Financial Officer
CIO: Eloy Rivas, Director of Information Systems
CHR: John Ware, Director of Human Resources
CNO: Dawn Beljin, R.N., Chief Nursing Officer
Web address: www.veniceregional.com
Control: Corporation, Investor–owned (for–profit) **Service**: General medical and surgical

Staffed Beds: 221 **Admissions**: 8581 **Census**: 96 **Outpatient Visits**: 93908 **Births**: 0 **Total Expense ($000)**: 147385 **Payroll Expense ($000)**: 49993 **Personnel**: 1000

VERO BEACH—Indian River County

☒ **HEALTHSOUTH TREASURE COAST REHABILITATION HOSPITAL (103032)**, 1600 37th Street, Zip 32960–4863; tel. 772/778–2100, (Nonreporting) **A**1 10 **S** Encompass Health Corporation, Birmingham, AL
Primary Contact: Michael Kissner, Chief Executive Officer
CFO: Kevin Hardy, Chief Financial Officer
CMO: Jimmy Wayne Lockhart, M.D., Medical Director
CHR: Linda Rinehart, Director Human Resources
Web address: www.healthsouthtreasurecoast.com
Control: Corporation, Investor–owned (for–profit) **Service**: Rehabilitation

Staffed Beds: 80

FL

Many Facility Codes have changed. Please refer to the AHA Guide Code Chart. © 2018 AHA Guide

⊞ **INDIAN RIVER MEDICAL CENTER (100105)**, 1000 36th Street, Zip 32960–6592; tel. 772/567–4311, (Includes BEHAVIORAL HEALTH CENTER, 1190 37th Street, Vero Beach, FL, Zip 32960–6507; tel. 772/563–4666; Jeffrey L Susi, President and Chief Executive Officer) **A**1 2 10 **F**3 11 12 13 15 17 18 20 22 24 26 28 29 30 31 34 35 37 40 44 45 46 47 48 49 50 51 57 58 59 60 61 64 70 74 75 76 77 78 79 80 82 84 85 87 89 92 93 96 97 98 99 100 101 102 103 104 107 108 110 111 114 115 116 117 118 119 120 121 124 126 129 130 131 132 135 144 146 147 148 **P**6
Primary Contact: Karen Davis, Interim Chief Executive Officer
CFO: Greg Gardner, Senior Vice President and Chief Financial Officer
CMO: Charles Mackett, M.D., Senior Vice President and Chief Medical Officer
CIO: William Neil, Vice President and Chief Information Officer
CNO: Linda Walton, R.N., MSN, Chief Nursing Officer
Web address: www.irmc.cc
Control: Other not–for–profit (including NFP Corporation) **Service**: General medical and surgical

Staffed Beds: 220 Admissions: 13643 Census: 157 Outpatient Visits: 105539 Births: 1007 Total Expense ($000): 283295 Payroll Expense ($000): 139285 Personnel: 1823

WAUCHULA—Hardee County

⊞ **FLORIDA HOSPITAL WAUCHULA (101300)**, 533 West Carlton Street, Zip 33873–3407; tel. 863/773–3101, **A**1 10 18 **F**29 30 34 40 57 59 107 110 111 119 127 130 133 149 **P**6 **S** Adventist Health System Sunbelt Health Care Corporation, Altamonte Springs, FL
Primary Contact: Denise Grimsley, R.N., Vice President and Administrator
CFO: Rosalie Oliver, Senior Vice President and Chief Financial Officer
CMO: Jorge F Gonzalez, M.D., Vice President and Chief Nursing Officer
CIO: Jeff McDonald, Information Technology Manager
CHR: Michelle F. Myers, Director Human Resources
CNO: Gloria N Santos, R.N., MS, Vice President and Chief Nursing Officer
Web address: www.fh.floridahospital.com/heartland/home.aspx
Control: Church operated, Nongovernment, not–for–profit **Service**: General medical and surgical

Staffed Beds: 25 Admissions: 775 Census: 22 Outpatient Visits: 23786 Births: 0 Total Expense ($000): 20333 Payroll Expense ($000): 8174 Personnel: 128

WELLINGTON—Palm Beach County

☐ **WELLINGTON REGIONAL MEDICAL CENTER (100275)**, 10101 Forest Hill Boulevard, Zip 33414–6199; tel. 561/798–8500, **A**1 10 12 13 **F**3 7 8 11 12 13 15 18 20 22 26 29 30 31 34 35 37 40 44 45 49 50 51 53 54 56 57 58 59 64 70 72 73 74 75 76 77 78 79 81 82 85 86 87 93 96 107 110 111 114 115 119 124 126 130 131 132 135 144 146 147 148 149 **P**2 **S** Universal Health Services, Inc., King of Prussia, PA
Primary Contact: Robbin Lee, Chief Executive Officer
COO: Pamela S Tahan, Chief Operating Officer
CFO: Tonja Mosley, Chief Financial Officer
CMO: Richard Hays, M.D., Chief Medical Officer
CIO: Pierre Bergeron, Information Services Director
CHR: Mary Jo Caracciolo, Human Resource Director
CNO: Asenath Cassel, Chief Nursing Officer
Web address: www.wellingtonregional.com
Control: Individual, Investor–owned (for–profit) **Service**: General medical and surgical

Staffed Beds: 233 Admissions: 11621 Census: 139 Outpatient Visits: 70009 Births: 2313 Personnel: 791

WESLEY CHAPEL—Pasco County

★ ⇑ **FLORIDA HOSPITAL WESLEY CHAPEL (100319)**, 2600 Bruce B Downs Bouelvard, Zip 33544–9207; tel. 813/929–5000, **A**5 10 21 **F**3 11 13 15 18 20 22 26 29 30 34 35 40 45 46 47 49 51 53 57 59 64 70 74 75 77 79 81 85 87 93 107 108 109 110 111 115 117 119 120 126 130 132 145 146 147 149 154 **S** Adventist Health System Sunbelt Health Care Corporation, Altamonte Springs, FL
Primary Contact: Denyse Bales–Chubb, President and Chief Executive Officer
Web address: www.floridahospital.com/wesley-chapel
Control: Other not–for–profit (including NFP Corporation) **Service**: General medical and surgical

Staffed Beds: 145 Admissions: 7110 Census: 60 Outpatient Visits: 58695 Births: 365 Total Expense ($000): 149528 Payroll Expense ($000): 46232 Personnel: 917

☐ **NORTH TAMPA BEHAVIORAL HEALTH (104075)**, 29910 State Road 56, Zip 33543–8800; tel. 813/922–3300, (Nonreporting) **A**1 10 **S** Acadia Healthcare Company, Inc., Franklin, TN
Primary Contact: Tracy Rogers, Chief Executive Officer
Web address: www.northtampabehavioralhealth.com
Control: Corporation, Investor–owned (for–profit) **Service**: Psychiatric

Staffed Beds: 75

WEST PALM BEACH—Palm Beach County

⊞ **GOOD SAMARITAN MEDICAL CENTER (100287)**, 1309 North Flagler Drive, Zip 33401–3499; tel. 561/655–5511, (Nonreporting) **A**1 2 5 10 **S** TENET Healthcare Corporation, Dallas, TX
Primary Contact: Tara McCoy, Chief Executive Officer
CFO: Cynthia McCauley, Chief Financial Officer
CIO: Candace Helms, Director Information Services
Web address: www.goodsamaritanmc.com
Control: Corporation, Investor–owned (for–profit) **Service**: General medical and surgical

Staffed Beds: 174

☐ **JEROME GOLDEN CENTER FOR BEHAVIORAL HEALTH, INC. (104008)**, 1041 45th Street, Zip 33407–2494; tel. 561/383–8000, (Nonreporting) **A**1 10
Primary Contact: Linda De Piano, Ph.D., Chief Executive Officer
CFO: America Cordoves, Controller
CMO: Suresh Rajpara, M.D., Chief Medical Officer
CIO: Iris Garcia, Director, Information Services
CHR: Nadine Wilson, Manager, Human Resources
CNO: Holly Horvath, Director of Nursing
Web address: www.goldenctr.org
Control: Other not–for–profit (including NFP Corporation) **Service**: Psychiatric

Staffed Beds: 44

⊞ **JFK MEDICAL CENTER NORTH CAMPUS (100234)**, 2201 45th Street, Zip 33407–2047; tel. 561/842–6141, (Nonreporting) **A**1 10 **S** HCA Healthcare, Nashville, TN
Primary Contact: Patricia Burns, Chief Executive Officer
COO: Patrick Chapman, Assistant Vice President Operations
CMO: Paul Seltzer, M.D., Chief of Staff
CIO: Kenneth Vasquez, Associate Director
CHR: Donna Boyle, Director
CNO: Geraldine DeStefano, R.N., MS, Chief Nursing Officer
Web address: www.westpalmhospital.com
Control: Corporation, Investor–owned (for–profit) **Service**: General medical and surgical

Staffed Beds: 245

⊞ △ **ST. MARY'S MEDICAL CENTER (100288)**, 901 45th Street, Zip 33407–2495; tel. 561/844–6300, (Includes PALM BEACH CHILDREN'S HOSPITAL, 901 45th Street, West Palm Beach, FL, Zip 33407; tel. 561/844–6300) (Nonreporting) **A**1 3 7 10 **S** TENET Healthcare Corporation, Dallas, TX
Primary Contact: Gabrielle Finley–Hazle, Chief Executive Officer
COO: Joey Bulfin, R.N., Interim Chief Executive Officer
CFO: Michelle Cartwright, Chief Financial Officer
CMO: Jeffrey Davis, D.O., Chief Medical Officer
CIO: Rich Avato, Director
CHR: Thomas J Piszczatoski, Chief Human Resource Officer
CNO: Donna Small, R.N., Chief Nursing Officer
Web address: www.stmarysmc.com
Control: Corporation, Investor–owned (for–profit) **Service**: General medical and surgical

Staffed Beds: 464

VETERANS AFFAIRS MEDICAL CENTER See West Palm Beach Veterans Affairs Medical Center

⊞ **WEST PALM BEACH VETERANS AFFAIRS MEDICAL CENTER**, 7305 North Military Trail, Zip 33410–6400; tel. 561/422–8262, (Nonreporting) **A**1 3 5 **S** Department of Veterans Affairs, Perry Point, MD
Primary Contact: Donna Katen–Bahensky, Director
CFO: Lori Hancock, Chief Business Officer
CMO: Deepak Mandi, M.D., Chief of Staff
CIO: Karen Gabaldon, Chief Management Information Systems
CHR: David Green, Chief Human Resources
Web address: www.westpalmbeach.va.gov/
Control: Veterans Affairs, Government, federal **Service**: General medical and surgical

Staffed Beds: 300

FL

Hospital, Medicare Provider Number, Address, Telephone, Approval, Facility, and Physician Codes, Health Care System

★ American Hospital Association (AHA) membership   ○ Healthcare Facilities Accreditation Program   ⇑ Center for Improvement in Healthcare Quality Accreditation
☐ The Joint Commission accreditation   ◇ DNV Healthcare Inc. accreditation   △ Commission on Accreditation of Rehabilitation Facilities (CARF) accreditation

WESTON—Broward County

✠ **CLEVELAND CLINIC FLORIDA (100289)**, 2950 Cleveland Clinic Boulevard,
Zip 33331–3602; tel. 954/659–5000, **A**1 2 3 5 10 **F**3 7 8 9 11 12 15 17 18
20 22 24 26 28 29 30 31 34 35 36 37 39 40 41 44 45 46 47 48 49 50 51 54
55 56 57 58 59 60 61 63 64 65 68 70 71 74 75 77 78 79 80 81 82 84 85 86
87 91 92 93 96 97 100 107 108 109 110 111 114 115 116 117 119 120 121
123 124 126 129 130 131 132 135 137 138 139 141 145 146 147 148 149
154 **P**6 **S** Cleveland Clinic Health System, Cleveland, OH
Primary Contact: Wael Barsoum, M.D., President
CFO: Keith Nilsson, Chief Financial Officer
CMO: Raul Rosenthal, M.D., Interim Chief of Staff
CIO: John Santangelo, Director Information Technology
CHR: Jackie Puntel, Senior Director Human Resources
CNO: Kerry Major, R.N., MSN, Chief Nursing Officer
Web address: www.clevelandclinic.org/florida
Control: Other not–for–profit (including NFP Corporation) **Service**: General
medical and surgical

Staffed Beds: 155 **Admissions:** 10934 **Census:** 133 **Outpatient Visits:**
51766 **Births:** 0 **Total Expense ($000):** 261113 **Payroll Expense
($000):** 94636 **Personnel:** 2504

WILLISTON—Levy County

NATURE COAST REGIONAL HOSPITAL See Regional General Hospital

REGIONAL GENERAL HOSPITAL (100322), 125 SW Seventh Street,
Zip 32696–2403; tel. 352/528–2801, (Nonreporting) **A**10
Primary Contact: Edith Mears, Chief Executive Officer
CFO: Barbara Miller, Manager Business Office
CMO: Jeremie Young, M.D., Chief of Staff
CHR: Karla Dass, Director Human Resources
Web address: www.regionalgeneral.com/
Control: Partnership, Investor–owned (for–profit) **Service**: General medical and
surgical

Staffed Beds: 20

WINTER HAVEN—Polk County

✠ △ **WINTER HAVEN HOSPITAL (100052)**, 200 Avenue F NE,
Zip 33881–4193; tel. 863/293–1121, **A**1 7 10 **F**3 8 11 13 14 15 17 18 20 22
24 26 28 29 30 31 34 37 40 45 47 49 57 58 59 60 64 68 70 72 73 74 75 76
77 78 79 81 82 84 85 86 87 89 93 94 98 100 101 102 104 107 108 109 110
111 114 115 118 119 120 121 122 123 126 130 132 135 144 146 147 148
P6 7 **S** Trinity Health, Livonia, MI
Primary Contact: Stephen A. Nierman, President
COO: Jacques Vasconcellos, Director, Operations
CFO: Tina Solomon, Executive Director Finance
CMO: Khurram Kamran, M.D., Vice President, Physician Services
CIO: Cal Cole, Director Information Systems
CHR: Rosemary Myers, Manager, Team Resources
CNO: Carol Koeppel–Olsen, Vice President, Patient Care Services
Web address: www.winterhavenhospital.org
Control: Other not–for–profit (including NFP Corporation) **Service**: General
medical and surgical

Staffed Beds: 361 **Admissions:** 19521 **Census:** 230 **Outpatient Visits:**
143848 **Births:** 1625 **Total Expense ($000):** 300356 **Payroll Expense
($000):** 112966 **Personnel:** 1901

WINTER PARK—Orange County

WINTER PARK MEMORIAL HOSPITAL See Florida Hospital, Orlando

ZEPHYRHILLS—Pasco County

✠ **FLORIDA HOSPITAL ZEPHYRHILLS (100046)**, 7050 Gall Boulevard,
Zip 33541–1399; tel. 813/788–0411, (Nonreporting) **A**1 5 10 **S** Adventist Health
System Sunbelt Health Care Corporation, Altamonte Springs, FL
Primary Contact: Amanda Maggard, Chief Executive Officer
COO: Donald E Welch, Chief Operating Officer
CFO: Bill Heinrich, Chief Financial Officer
CMO: Hugar McNamee, D.O., Chief Medical Officer
CIO: Kelley Sasser, Director Information Systems
CHR: Laura Asaftei, Administrative Director
CNO: Gwen Alonso, Chief Nursing Officer
Web address: www.fhzeph.org
Control: Church operated, Nongovernment, not–for–profit **Service**: General
medical and surgical

Staffed Beds: 139

FL

Many Facility Codes have changed. Please refer to the AHA Guide Code Chart. © 2018 AHA Guide

GEORGIA

ADEL—Cook County

☒ **COOK MEDICAL CENTER–A CAMPUS OF TIFT REGIONAL MEDICAL CENTER (110101)**, 706 North Parrish Avenue, Zip 31620–1511; tel. 229/896–8000, (Total facility includes 95 beds in nursing home–type unit) **A**1 10 **F**11 15 29 30 34 35 45 56 57 59 63 64 65 68 75 77 81 84 85 86 87 93 97 98 101 103 104 107 108 110 111 114 119 127 129 130 133 135 146 147 148 149 154 **P**6 **S** Tift Regional Health System, Tifton, GA
Primary Contact: Michael L. Purvis, Chief Executive Officer
COO: Kim Wills, Chief Operating Officer
CIO: Barry Medley, Director Information Systems
CHR: Shirley Padgett, Director Human Resources
Web address: www.cookmedicalcenter.com
Control: Hospital district or authority, Government, nonfederal **Service:** General medical and surgical

Staffed Beds: 155 **Admissions:** 574 **Census:** 100 **Outpatient Visits:** 12827 **Births:** 0 **Total Expense ($000):** 18870 **Payroll Expense ($000):** 8675 **Personnel:** 189

ALBANY—Dougherty County

★ ⇑ **PHOEBE PUTNEY MEMORIAL HOSPITAL (110007)**, 417 West Third Avenue, Zip 31701–1943, Mailing Address: P.O. Box 3770, Zip 31706–3770; tel. 229/312–4100, (Includes PHOEBE NORTH, 2000 Palmyra Road, Albany, GA, Zip 31701–1528, Mailing Address: P.O. Box 1908, Zip 31702–1908, tel. 229/434–2000) **A**2 3 5 10 21 **F**3 5 7 11 12 13 15 17 18 20 22 24 26 28 29 30 31 34 35 40 44 45 46 49 50 51 53 54 56 57 59 60 61 62 63 64 68 70 72 73 74 75 76 77 78 79 81 82 83 84 85 86 87 89 90 91 92 93 94 96 97 98 100 101 102 103 104 105 107 108 110 111 114 115 116 117 118 119 120 121 123 124 126 127 129 130 131 132 134 135 136 144 145 146 147 148 149 153 **P**1 7 **S** Phoebe Putney Health System, Albany, GA
Primary Contact: Joel Wernick, President and Chief Executive Officer
COO: Joe Austin, Executive Vice President and Chief Operating Officer
CFO: Brian Church, Senior Vice President and Chief Financial Officer
CMO: Steven Kitchen, M.D., Chief Medical Officer
CIO: Jesse Diaz, Chief Information Officer
CHR: David J Baranski, Vice President Human Resources
CNO: Laura Shearer, R.N., MSN, Senior Vice President and Chief Nursing Officer
Web address: www.phoebeputney.com
Control: Other not–for–profit (including NFP Corporation) **Service:** General medical and surgical

Staffed Beds: 449 **Admissions:** 18131 **Census:** 281 **Outpatient Visits:** 1051859 **Births:** 2249 **Total Expense ($000):** 517137 **Payroll Expense ($000):** 145086 **Personnel:** 2560

ALMA—Bacon County

☒ **BACON COUNTY HOSPITAL AND HEALTH SYSTEM (111327)**, 302 South Wayne Street, Zip 31510–2922, Mailing Address: P O Drawer 1987, Zip 31510–0987; tel. 912/632–8961, (Nonreporting) **A**1 10 18
Primary Contact: Cindy R. Turner, Chief Executive Officer
COO: Cindy R Turner, Chief Executive Officer
CFO: Kyle Kimmel, Chief Financial Officer
CMO: Lou Ellen Hutcheson, M.D., Chief of Staff
CIO: Neil O'Steen, Director Information Technology
CHR: Kerry Hancock, Director Human Resources
CNO: Deanna Hoff, R.N., Director of Nursing
Web address: www.baconcountyhospital.com
Control: Other not–for–profit (including NFP Corporation) **Service:** General medical and surgical

Staffed Beds: 113

AMERICUS—Sumter County

★ ⇑ **PHOEBE SUMTER MEDICAL CENTER (110044)**, 126 Highway, 280 West, Zip 31719, Mailing Address: 126 Highway 280 West, Zip 31719; tel. 229/924–6011, **A**10 21 **F**3 8 11 12 13 15 29 31 35 40 41 45 46 47 49 50 51 53 56 57 59 60 61 63 64 68 70 75 76 78 79 81 83 85 87 92 97 107 108 111 127 129 130 141 146 **S** Phoebe Putney Health System, Albany, GA
Primary Contact: Brandi Lunneborg, Chief Executive Officer
CHR: Cassandra Haynes Aldridge, Chief Human Resources Officer
CNO: Susan Bruns, Chief Nursing Officer
Web address: www.phoebesumter.org
Control: Other not–for–profit (including NFP Corporation) **Service:** General medical and surgical

Staffed Beds: 44 **Admissions:** 2880 **Census:** 29

ATHENS—Clarke County

☐ **LANDMARK HOSPITAL OF ATHENS (112017)**, 775 Sunset Drive, Zip 30606–2211; tel. 706/425–1500, **A**1 10 22 **F**1 3 29 45 130 **S** Landmark Hospitals, Cape Girardeau, MO
Primary Contact: Vivian Goff, R.N., Chief Executive Officer
Web address: www.landmarkhospitals.com
Control: Individual, Investor–owned (for–profit) **Service:** Acute long–term care hospital

Staffed Beds: 42 **Admissions:** 345 **Census:** 29 **Outpatient Visits:** 0 **Births:** 0 **Personnel:** 113

☒ **PIEDMONT ATHENS REGIONAL MEDICAL CENTER (110074)**, 1199 Prince Avenue, Zip 30606–2797; tel. 706/475–7000, (Data for 273 days) **A**1 2 3 10 **F**3 8 13 15 17 18 20 22 24 26 28 29 30 31 32 34 35 36 40 43 45 46 47 48 49 50 51 54 55 56 57 58 59 60 61 62 64 66 68 70 71 72 73 74 76 77 78 79 80 81 83 84 85 86 87 89 91 92 93 94 96 100 102 107 108 110 111 114 115 116 117 118 119 120 121 123 124 126 129 130 131 132 135 144 145 146 147 148 **S** Piedmont Healthcare, Roswell, GA
Primary Contact: Charles A. Peck, M.D., President and Chief Executive Officer
COO: Jason Smith, Chief Operating Officer
CFO: Wendy J. Cook, Chief Financial Officer
CMO: Robert Sinyard, M.D., Chief Medical Officer
CIO: Louis H. Duhe, Executor Director, Information Services
CHR: Robert D. Finch, Director, Human Resources
CNO: Tamara Jackson, Chief Nursing Officer
Web address: www.piedmont.org/locations/piedmont–athens
Control: Other not–for–profit (including NFP Corporation) **Service:** General medical and surgical

Staffed Beds: 343 **Admissions:** 14791 **Census:** 245 **Outpatient Visits:** 233971 **Births:** 1808 **Personnel:** 2483

☒ △ **ST. MARY'S HEALTH CARE SYSTEM (110006)**, 1230 Baxter Street, Zip 30606–3791; tel. 706/389–3000, **A**1 3 7 10 **F**3 11 12 13 15 18 20 22 26 28 29 30 31 34 35 40 41 45 46 48 49 50 53 54 57 58 59 61 62 63 64 68 70 73 74 75 76 77 79 80 81 83 84 85 87 89 90 93 107 110 111 114 115 118 119 126 129 130 131 132 135 141 145 146 147 148 149 **S** Trinity Health, Livonia, MI
Primary Contact: D. Montez. Carter, Chief Executive Officer
CFO: Marty Hutson, Chief Financial Officer
CMO: Bruce Middendorf, M.D., Chief Medical Officer
CIO: Kerry Vaughn, Chief Information Officer
CHR: Jeff English, Vice President Human Resources
CNO: Titus E. Gambrell, Vice President and Chief Nursing Officer
Web address: www.stmarysathens.com
Control: Church operated, Nongovernment, not–for–profit **Service:** General medical and surgical

Staffed Beds: 174 **Admissions:** 10011 **Census:** 130 **Outpatient Visits:** 207785 **Births:** 1559 **Total Expense ($000):** 182925 **Payroll Expense ($000):** 68745 **Personnel:** 1185

ATLANTA—Fulton and De Kalb County

☐ **ANCHOR HOSPITAL (114032)**, 5454 Yorktowne Drive, Zip 30349–5317; tel. 770/991–6044, **A**1 10 **F**4 5 98 100 102 103 104 105 130 152 153 154 **S** Universal Health Services, Inc., King of Prussia, PA
Primary Contact: Lloyd Noble, Chief Executive Officer
CFO: John Kim, Chief Financial Officer
CMO: Shailesh Patel, M.D., Medical Director
CIO: Chris Hill, Information Technology
CHR: Danna Nordin, Director Human Resources
CNO: Angelica Jackson, Director of Nursing
Web address: www.anchorhospital.com
Control: Corporation, Investor–owned (for–profit) **Service:** Psychiatric

Staffed Beds: 122 **Admissions:** 3952 **Census:** 99 **Births:** 0

GA

☐ △ **CHILDREN'S HEALTHCARE OF ATLANTA (113300)**, 1600 Tullie Circle, NE, Zip 30329–2303; tel. 404/785–7000, (Includes CHILDREN'S HEALTHCARE OF ATLANTA AT EGLESTON, 1600 Tullie Circle, Atlanta, GA, Zip 30329; tel. 404/325–6000; CHILDREN'S HEALTHCARE OF ATLANTA AT HUGHES SPALDING, 35 Jesse Hill Jr Drive, SE, Atlanta, GA, Zip 30303–3032; tel. 404/785–9500; CHILDREN'S HEALTHCARE OF ATLANTA AT SCOTTISH RITE, 1001 Johnson Ferry Road NE, Atlanta, GA, Zip 30342–1600; tel. 404/256–5252) (Nonreporting) **A**1 3 5 7 8 10
Primary Contact: Donna W. Hyland, President and Chief Executive Officer
COO: Carolyn Kenny, Executive Vice President Clinical Care
CFO: Ruth Fowler, Senior Vice President and Chief Financial Officer
CMO: Daniel Salinas, M.D., Senior Vice President and Chief Medical Officer
CIO: Allana Cummings, Chief Information Officer
CHR: Linda Matzigkeit, Senior Vice President Human Resources
Web address: www.choa.org
Control: Other not–for–profit (including NFP Corporation) **Service**: Children's general medical and surgical

Staffed Beds: 496

⊞ **EMORY REHABILITATION HOSPITAL (113031)**, 1441 Clifton Road NE, Zip 30322–1004; tel. 404/712–5512, **A**1 10 **F**11 29 30 34 35 36 50 56 58 64 68 74 75 77 79 82 85 86 87 90 93 94 95 96 130 131 132 135 146 148 149 **P**6 **S** Emory Healthcare, Atlanta, GA
Primary Contact: Michael Eric. Garrard, FACHE, Chief Executive Officer
CMO: S. Byron Milton, M.D., Medical Director
CHR: Janine Diaz, Human Resources Manager
CNO: Deborah Almauhy, R.N., Chief Nursing Officer
Web address: www.emoryhealthcare.org/rehabilitation
Control: Partnership, Investor–owned (for–profit) **Service**: Rehabilitation

Staffed Beds: 46 **Admissions:** 991 **Census:** 39 **Outpatient Visits:** 22841 **Births:** 0 **Total Expense ($000):** 23704 **Payroll Expense ($000):** 13324 **Personnel:** 282

⊞ **EMORY SAINT JOSEPH'S HOSPITAL OF ATLANTA (110082)**, 5665 Peachtree Dunwoody Road NE, Zip 30342–1701; tel. 678/843–7001, **A**1 2 3 10 **F**3 15 17 18 20 22 24 26 28 29 30 31 34 35 37 40 44 45 46 47 49 50 51 53 54 55 57 58 59 60 64 68 70 71 74 75 77 78 79 81 82 84 85 86 87 102 107 108 110 111 115 117 118 119 120 121 123 124 126 130 132 135 145 146 147 148 149 154 **P**6 **S** Emory Healthcare, Atlanta, GA
Primary Contact: Heather Dexter, Chief Executive Officer
CFO: Kevin Brenan, Chief Financial Officer
CMO: Thomas P. McGahan, M.D., Chief Medical Officer
CIO: Dedra Cantrell, Chief Information Officer
CHR: Audra Farish, Vice President Human Resources
Web address: www.emoryhealthcare.org/locations/hospitals/emory–saint–josephs–hospital/
Control: Other not–for–profit (including NFP Corporation) **Service**: General medical and surgical

Staffed Beds: 273 **Admissions:** 15015 **Census:** 187 **Outpatient Visits:** 125343 **Births:** 0 **Total Expense ($000):** 344370 **Payroll Expense ($000):** 108489 **Personnel:** 1559

⊞ **EMORY UNIVERSITY HOSPITAL (110010)**, 1364 Clifton Road NE, Zip 30322; tel. 404/712–2000, (Includes EMORY UNIVERSITY ORTHOPAEDIC AND SPINE HOSPITAL, 1455 Montreal Road, Tucker, GA, Zip 30084; tel. 404/251–3600; June Conner, R.N., Chief Operating Officer; EMORY WESLEY WOODS GERIATRIC HOSPITAL, 1821 Clifton Road NE, Atlanta, GA, Zip 30329–4021; tel. 404/728–6200; Jennifer Schuck, Associate Administrator) **A**1 2 3 5 8 10 **F**3 11 15 17 18 20 22 24 26 29 30 31 34 35 36 38 39 40 44 45 46 47 48 49 50 55 56 57 58 59 60 61 63 64 68 70 74 75 77 78 79 80 81 82 84 85 86 87 92 93 98 100 101 102 103 104 105 107 108 110 111 112 114 115 116 117 118 119 120 121 123 124 126 129 130 131 132 135 136 137 138 139 140 141 142 145 146 147 148 149 153 154 **P**6 **S** Emory Healthcare, Atlanta, GA
Primary Contact: Bryce D. Gartland, M.D., Chief Executive Officer
CFO: Carla Chandler, Vice President and Chief Financial Officer
CMO: Chad W.M. Ritenour, M.D., Chief Medical Officer
CIO: Sheila M Sanders, Chief Information Officer
CHR: Mary Beth Allen, Vice President Human Resources
CNO: Nancye R. Feistritzer, Chief Nursing Officer
Web address: www.emoryhealthcare.org
Control: Other not–for–profit (including NFP Corporation) **Service**: General medical and surgical

Staffed Beds: 563 **Admissions:** 26843 **Census:** 479 **Outpatient Visits:** 185876 **Births:** 0 **Total Expense ($000):** 820237 **Payroll Expense ($000):** 262158 **Personnel:** 3780

⊞ **EMORY UNIVERSITY HOSPITAL MIDTOWN (110078)**, 550 Peachtree Street NE, Zip 30308–2247; tel. 404/686–4411, **A**1 2 3 5 8 10 **F**3 11 12 13 15 17 18 20 22 24 26 29 30 31 34 35 36 38 40 44 45 46 47 48 49 50 51 52 55 57 58 59 60 61 64 68 70 72 73 74 75 76 77 78 79 81 82 84 85 86 87 92 93 100 101 102 107 108 110 111 114 115 116 117 118 119 120 121 123 124 126 130 131 132 135 141 146 147 148 149 **P**6 **S** Emory Healthcare, Atlanta, GA
Primary Contact: Daniel Owens, Chief Executive Officer
CMO: James P Steinberg, M.D., Chief Medical Officer
CIO: Dedra Cantrell, Chief Information Officer
CHR: Dallis Howard–Crow, Chief Human Resources Officer
Web address: www.emoryhealthcare.org
Control: Other not–for–profit (including NFP Corporation) **Service**: General medical and surgical

Staffed Beds: 459 **Admissions:** 22672 **Census:** 368 **Outpatient Visits:** 256495 **Births:** 4721 **Total Expense ($000):** 786388 **Payroll Expense ($000):** 217787 **Personnel:** 2785

⊞ **GRADY MEMORIAL HOSPITAL (110079)**, 80 Jesse Hill Jr Drive SE, Zip 30303–3031, Mailing Address: P.O. Box 26189, Zip 31329–0386; tel. 404/616–1000, (Total facility includes 291 beds in nursing home–type unit) **A**1 2 3 5 8 10 **F**2 3 5 7 8 13 15 16 18 20 22 24 26 29 30 31 34 35 38 39 40 43 45 46 47 49 50 51 52 53 54 55 56 57 58 59 60 61 62 64 65 66 68 70 72 73 74 75 76 77 78 79 81 82 87 88 93 94 97 98 100 101 102 103 104 105 107 108 109 110 111 112 113 114 115 116 117 118 119 120 121 126 128 129 130 132 134 135 143 144 146 147 148 153 154
Primary Contact: John M. Haupert, FACHE, President and Chief Executive Officer
COO: Rhonda A Scott, Ph.D., R.N., Chief Operating Officer
CFO: Mark Meyer, Chief Financial Officer
CMO: Robert Jansen, M.D., Chief Medical Officer
CIO: Ben McKeeby, Senior Vice President and Chief Information Officer
CHR: Larry A. Callahan, Senior Vice President Human Resources
CNO: Jacqueline Herd, R.N., MSN, Chief Nursing Officer
Web address: www.gradyhealthsystem.org
Control: Other not–for–profit (including NFP Corporation) **Service**: General medical and surgical

Staffed Beds: 1019 **Admissions:** 32349 **Census:** 816 **Outpatient Visits:** 691783 **Births:** 2716 **Total Expense ($000):** 1077842 **Payroll Expense ($000):** 394161 **Personnel:** 5392

⊞ **NORTHSIDE HOSPITAL (110161)**, 1000 Johnson Ferry Road NE, Zip 30342–1611; tel. 404/851–8000, **A**1 2 3 10 **F**3 5 8 11 12 13 15 17 18 20 22 26 28 29 30 31 34 35 37 40 44 45 46 47 48 49 50 54 55 57 58 59 60 64 68 70 71 72 73 74 75 76 77 78 79 80 81 82 84 85 86 87 93 100 104 107 108 110 111 114 115 117 118 119 120 121 123 124 126 129 130 132 135 136 144 145 146 147 148 **S** Northside Healthcare System, Atlanta, GA
Primary Contact: Robert Quattrocchi, President and Chief Executive Officer
CFO: Debbie Mitcham, Chief Financial Officer
CIO: Tina Wakim, Vice President Information
Web address: www.northside.com
Control: Other not–for–profit (including NFP Corporation) **Service**: General medical and surgical

Staffed Beds: 603 **Admissions:** 36761 **Census:** 410 **Outpatient Visits:** 1845831 **Births:** 16383 **Total Expense ($000):** 1927319 **Payroll Expense ($000):** 597943 **Personnel:** 9068

☐ **PEACHFORD BEHAVIORAL HEALTH SYSTEM (114010)**, 2151 Peachford Road, Zip 30338–6599; tel. 770/455–3200, (Nonreporting) **A**1 10 **S** Universal Health Services, Inc., King of Prussia, PA
Primary Contact: Matthew Crouch, Chief Executive Officer and Managing Director
COO: Sharon Stackhouse, Assistant Administrator and Director Risk Management
CFO: April Hughes, Chief Financial Officer
CMO: Asaf Aleem, M.D., Medical Director
CHR: Clay Boyles, Director Human Resources
Web address: www.peachfordhospital.com
Control: Corporation, Investor–owned (for–profit) **Service**: Psychiatric

Staffed Beds: 246

⇑ **PIEDMONT HOSPITAL (110083)**, 1968 Peachtree Road NW, Zip 30309–1281; tel. 404/605–5000, **A**2 3 5 10 21 **F**3 8 11 12 13 15 17 18 20 22 24 26 28 29 30 31 34 35 40 44 45 46 47 48 49 50 51 53 54 55 56 57 58 59 60 61 63 64 65 68 70 72 73 74 75 76 77 78 79 81 82 84 85 86 87 92 93 107 108 110 111 114 115 116 117 118 119 120 121 123 124 126 129 130 131 132 135 138 139 141 142 145 146 147 148 154 **P**1 6 **S** Piedmont Healthcare, Roswell, GA
Primary Contact: Patrick M. Battey, FACS, M.D., Chief Executive Officer
COO: Ed Lovern, Chief Operating Officer
CFO: Sheryl Klink, Chief Financial Officer
CMO: Mark Cohen, M.D., Chief Medical Officer
CHR: Vicki A Cansler, Chief Human Resource Officer
CNO: Kelly Hulsey, MSN, R.N., Chief Nursing Officer
Web address: www.piedmont.org
Control: Other not–for–profit (including NFP Corporation) **Service**: General medical and surgical

Staffed Beds: 510 **Admissions:** 28110 **Census:** 407 **Outpatient Visits:** 339650 **Births:** 3691 **Personnel:** 3245

GA

Many Facility Codes have changed. Please refer to the AHA Guide Code Chart.   © 2018 AHA Guide

SAINT JOSEPH'S HOSPITAL OF ATLANTA See Emory Saint Joseph's Hospital of Atlanta

☒ **SELECT SPECIALTY HOSPITAL MIDTOWN ATLANTA (112004)**, 705 Juniper Street NE, Zip 30308–1307; tel. 404/873–2871, (Nonreporting) **A**1 10 **S** Select Medical Corporation, Mechanicsburg, PA
Primary Contact: Adriene Kinnaird, Chief Executive Officer
CFO: Michael Nelson, Chief Financial Officer
CMO: David N. DeRuyter, M.D., President Medical Staff
CHR: Armetria Gibson, Human Resources Generalist
CNO: Annette Harrilson, Chief Clinical Officer
Web address: www.selectspecialtyhospitals.com/
Control: Partnership, Investor–owned (for–profit) **Service**: Acute long–term care hospital

Staffed Beds: 72

☐ △ **SHEPHERD CENTER (112003)**, 2020 Peachtree Road NW, Zip 30309–1465; tel. 404/352–2020, **A**1 3 5 7 10 **F**3 29 30 34 35 36 53 58 59 64 65 70 74 75 77 82 90 91 93 94 95 111 119 130 131 132 143 146 148 **P**6
Primary Contact: Sarah Morrison, President and Chief Executive Officer
CFO: Stephen B Holleman, Chief Financial Officer
CMO: Donald P Leslie, M.D., Medical Director
CIO: Brian Barnette, Chief Information Officer
CHR: Lorie Hutcheson, Vice President of Human Resources
CNO: Tamara King, R.N., MSN, Chief Nurse Executive
Web address: www.shepherd.org
Control: Other not–for–profit (including NFP Corporation) **Service**: Rehabilitation

Staffed Beds: 131 **Admissions**: 886 **Census**: 124 **Outpatient Visits**: 67695 **Births**: 0 **Total Expense ($000)**: 201605 **Payroll Expense ($000)**: 95466 **Personnel**: 1244

☐ **VERITAS COLLABORATIVE**, 6600 Peachtree Dunwoody Road, Embassy Row, Building 400, Suite 150, Zip 30328–6773; tel. 770/871–3730, (Nonreporting) **A**1
Primary Contact: Mederic D. McLaughlin, Executive Director
Web address: www.https://veritascollaborative.com
Control: Partnership, Investor–owned (for–profit) **Service**: Psychiatric

Staffed Beds: 50

☒ **WELLSTAR ATLANTA MEDICAL CENTER (110115)**, 303 Parkway Drive NE, Zip 30312–1212; tel. 404/265–4000, (Includes WELLSTAR ATLANTA MEDICAL CENTER – SOUTH CAMPUS, 1170 Cleveland Avenue, Atlanta, GA, Zip 30344–3665; tel. 404/466–1170; Daniel Jackson, Vice President, Administrator) **A**1 2 3 5 8 10 **F**3 11 12 13 15 17 18 20 22 24 26 28 29 30 31 34 35 36 37 38 40 43 44 45 46 50 53 54 56 57 59 60 61 64 65 66 68 70 72 73 74 75 76 77 78 79 81 84 85 86 87 90 93 96 97 98 101 102 103 106 107 108 111 114 118 119 126 129 130 132 134 144 146 147 148 149 150 154 **P**5 6 **S** WellStar Health System, Marietta, GA
Primary Contact: Kimberly Ryan, President
CFO: Jason K Limbaugh, Vice President and Chief Financial Officer
CMO: Albert Barrocas, M.D., Chief Medical Officer
CIO: Mike Sharp, Interim Director
CHR: Detra Bickerstaff, Vice President, Human Resources
CNO: Stuart D. Downs, Vice President and Chief Operating Officer
Web address: www.atlantamedcenter.com
Control: Other not–for–profit (including NFP Corporation) **Service**: General medical and surgical

Staffed Beds: 494 **Admissions**: 18707 **Census**: 314 **Outpatient Visits**: 194117 **Births**: 2227 **Personnel**: 1827

WESLEY WOODS GERIATRIC HOSPITAL OF EMORY UNIVERSITY See Emory Wesley Woods Geriatric Hospital

AUGUSTA—Richmond County

☒ **AUGUSTA UNIVERSITY MEDICAL CENTER (110034)**, 1120 15th Street, Zip 30912–0004; tel. 706/721–0211, (Includes CHILDREN'S HOSPITAL OF GEORGIA, 1446 Harper Street, Augusta, GA, Zip 30912–0012; tel. 706/721–5437; Lee Ann Liska, Chief Executive Officer) **A**1 2 3 5 8 10 13 **F**3 5 6 9 11 12 13 14 15 17 18 19 20 21 22 23 24 25 26 27 28 29 30 31 32 34 35 36 38 40 41 43 45 46 48 49 50 51 54 55 56 58 59 60 61 64 66 70 72 73 74 75 76 77 78 79 81 82 84 85 86 87 88 89 91 92 93 97 98 99 100 101 102 103 104 107 108 111 113 115 116 117 118 119 120 121 123 124 126 127 129 130 131 132 134 138 141 142 143 146 147 148 151 154
Primary Contact: Lee Ann Liska, Chief Executive Officer
COO: Shawn Vincent, Interim Chief Operating Officer
CFO: Greg Damron, Vice President Finance and Chief Financial Officer
CMO: Kevin Dellsperger, M.D., Chief Medical Officer
CIO: Charles Enicks, Chief Information Officer
CHR: Susan Norton, Vice President Human Resources
CNO: Laura E Brower, R.N., MSN, Chief Nursing Officer
Web address: www.grhealth.org
Control: Other not–for–profit (including NFP Corporation) **Service**: General medical and surgical

Staffed Beds: 499 **Admissions**: 20362 **Census**: 334 **Outpatient Visits**: 438259 **Births**: 1519 **Total Expense ($000)**: 670817 **Payroll Expense ($000)**: 239223 **Personnel**: 3750

☒ △ **CHARLIE NORWOOD VETERANS AFFAIRS MEDICAL CENTER**, 1 Freedom Way, Zip 30904–6285; tel. 706/733–0188, (Nonreporting) **A**1 2 3 5 7 8 **S** Department of Veterans Affairs, Perry Point, MD
Primary Contact: Robin E. Jackson, Ph.D., Interim Acting Director
COO: John D Stenger, Acting Associate Director
CFO: Earline Corder, Chief Fiscal
CIO: Sandy Williford, Chief Health Information Management and Revenue Administration
CHR: Roger W Buterbaugh, Chief Human Resources Officer
Web address: www.augusta.va.gov/
Control: Veterans Affairs, Government, federal **Service**: General medical and surgical

Staffed Beds: 338

☒ **DOCTORS HOSPITAL (110177)**, 3651 Wheeler Road, Zip 30909–6426; tel. 706/651–3232, (Nonreporting) **A**1 2 3 5 10 **S** HCA Healthcare, Nashville, TN
Primary Contact: Douglas Welch, Chief Executive Officer
CIO: Dona Hornung, Director Information and Technology Services
Web address: www.doctors–hospital.net
Control: Corporation, Investor–owned (for–profit) **Service**: General medical and surgical

Staffed Beds: 307

☐ **EAST CENTRAL REGIONAL HOSPITAL (114029)**, 3405 Mike Padgett Highway, Zip 30906–3897; tel. 706/790–2011, (Includes EAST CENTRAL REGIONAL HOSPITAL, 100 Myrtle Boulevard, Gracewood, GA, Zip 30812–1299; tel. 706/790–2011) **A**1 3 5 10 **F**29 34 38 39 59 65 67 75 77 98 101 102 128 130 132 135 **P**6
Primary Contact: Paul Brock, Administrator
CFO: Candace Walker, Chief Financial Officer
Web address: www.dbhdd.ga.gov
Control: State, Government, nonfederal **Service**: Psychiatric

Staffed Beds: 363 **Admissions**: 663 **Census**: 328 **Outpatient Visits**: 0 **Births**: 0 **Total Expense ($000)**: 89671 **Payroll Expense ($000)**: 38077 **Personnel**: 1138

☒ **WALTON REHABILITATION HOSPITAL (113030)**, 1355 Independence Drive, Zip 30901–1037; tel. 706/724–7746, **A**1 5 10 **F**29 62 63 90 96 **S** Encompass Health Corporation, Birmingham, AL
Primary Contact: Eric Crossan, Chief Executive Officer
CMO: Pamela Salazar, M.D., Chief of Staff
CIO: Ann Keller, Supervisor Health Information Management
CHR: Volante Henderson, Director Human Resources
CNO: Lynn Beaulieu, R.N., Chief Nursing Officer
Web address: www.healthsouthwalton.com/
Control: Corporation, Investor–owned (for–profit) **Service**: Rehabilitation

Staffed Beds: 58 **Admissions**: 1333 **Census**: 44 **Outpatient Visits**: 0 **Births**: 0

MEDICAL COLLEGE OF GEORGIA HEALTH See Augusta University Medical Center

☒ **SELECT SPECIALTY HOSPITAL–AUGUSTA (112013)**, 1537 Walton Way, Zip 30904–3764; tel. 706/731–1200, (Nonreporting) **A**1 10 **S** Select Medical Corporation, Mechanicsburg, PA
Primary Contact: E Rick. Lowe, FACHE, Chief Executive Officer
CHR: Terrie Richardson, Coordinator Human Resources
CNO: Kim Pippin, Chief Nursing Officer
Web address: www.augusta.selectspecialtyhospitals.com
Control: Corporation, Investor–owned (for–profit) **Service**: Acute long–term care hospital

Staffed Beds: 80

☒ **UNIVERSITY HOSPITAL (110028)**, 1350 Walton Way, Zip 30901–2629; tel. 706/722–9011, **A**1 2 3 5 10 **F**3 12 13 15 17 18 20 22 24 26 28 29 30 31 34 35 37 38 40 41 44 48 49 50 54 55 56 57 59 60 62 64 68 70 71 72 73 74 75 76 77 78 79 80 81 82 83 84 85 86 87 89 93 96 100 107 108 110 111 114 115 116 117 118 119 126 129 130 132 134 135 146 147 148 149 150 154 **P**8 **S** University Health Care System, Augusta, GA
Primary Contact: James R. Davis, Chief Executive Officer
CFO: David Belkoski, Senior Vice President and Chief Financial Officer
CMO: William L Farr, M.D., Chief Medical Officer
CIO: Shirley Gabriel, Vice President and Chief Information Officer
CHR: Laurie Ott, Vice President Human Resources and President University Health Care Foundation
Web address: www.universityhealth.org
Control: Other not–for–profit (including NFP Corporation) **Service**: General medical and surgical

Staffed Beds: 554 **Admissions**: 25809 **Census**: 339 **Outpatient Visits**: 565053 **Births**: 3152 **Total Expense ($000)**: 479527 **Payroll Expense ($000)**: 169361 **Personnel**: 2540

GA

Hospital, Medicare Provider Number, Address, Telephone, Approval, Facility, and Physician Codes, Health Care System

★ American Hospital Association (AHA) membership ○ Healthcare Facilities Accreditation Program ⇑ Center for Improvement in Healthcare Quality Accreditation
☐ The Joint Commission accreditation ◇ DNV Healthcare Inc. accreditation △ Commission on Accreditation of Rehabilitation Facilities (CARF) accreditation

✠ **UNIVERSITY HOSPITAL SUMMERVILLE (110039)**, 2260 Wrightsboro Road, Zip 30904–4726; tel. 706/481–7000, (Nonreporting) **A**1 10 **S** University Health Care System, Augusta, GA
Primary Contact: James R. Davis, Chief Executive Officer
CFO: Rodney Sisk, Chief Financial Officer
CMO: C. Judson Pickett, Chief of Staff
CIO: Charlotte Choate, Director Information Systems
CHR: Diana Maxson, Director Human Resources
Web address: www.universityhealth.org/summerville/
Control: Corporation, Investor–owned (for–profit) **Service**: General medical and surgical

Staffed Beds: 105

VETERANS AFFAIRS MEDICAL CENTER See Charlie Norwood Veterans Affairs Medical Center

WALTON REHABILITATION HOSPITAL See Healthsouth Walton Rehabilitation Hospital

AUSTELL—Cobb County

✠ △ **WELLSTAR COBB HOSPITAL (110143)**, 3950 Austell Road, Zip 30106–1121; tel. 470/732–4000, **A**1 2 3 7 10 **F**3 4 5 11 13 15 16 17 18 20 22 26 28 29 30 31 38 40 41 44 45 48 49 50 51 53 54 55 58 59 60 61 64 65 66 68 70 72 73 74 75 76 77 78 79 81 82 84 85 86 87 90 93 94 96 97 98 100 101 102 104 105 106 107 108 111 115 119 120 121 123 124 126 130 131 132 135 141 146 147 148 149 153 154 **P**5 6 **S** WellStar Health System, Marietta, GA
Primary Contact: Callie Andrews, President
CFO: Darold Etheridge, Vice President and Chief Financial Officer
CMO: Thomas McNamara, D.O., Vice President Medical Affairs
CIO: Jonathan B Morris, M.D., Senior Vice President and Chief Information Officer
CHR: Danyale Ziglor, Assistant Vice President Human Resources
CNO: Kay Kennedy, Chief Nurse Executive
Web address: www.wellstar.org
Control: Other not–for–profit (including NFP Corporation) **Service**: General medical and surgical

Staffed Beds: 370 **Admissions:** 21629 **Census:** 275 **Outpatient Visits:** 223406 **Births:** 3507 **Personnel:** 2011

BAINBRIDGE—Decatur County

⇑ **MEMORIAL HOSPITAL AND MANOR (110132)**, 1500 East Shotwell Street, Zip 39819–4256; tel. 229/246–3500, (Nonreporting) **A**10 21
Primary Contact: James M. Lambert, FACHE, Chief Executive Officer
COO: Lee Harris, Assistant Administrator Support Services
CFO: Karen Faircloth, Chief Financial Officer
CMO: Shawn Surratt, M.D., Chief of Staff
CIO: Nelda Moore, Director Data Processing
CHR: Angel Sykes, Director Human Resources
CNO: Cynthia Vickers, R.N., Assistant Administrator for Nursing Services
Web address: www.mh–m.org
Control: Hospital district or authority, Government, nonfederal **Service**: General medical and surgical

Staffed Beds: 80

BAXLEY—Appling County

⇑ **APPLING HEALTHCARE SYSTEM (110071)**, 163 East Tollison Street, Zip 31513–0120; tel. 912/367–9841, (Nonreporting) **A**10 20 21
Primary Contact: Raymond J. Leadbetter Jr, Interim Chief Executive Officer
COO: Judy M Long, R.N., MS, Chief Nursing Officer and Chief Operating Officer
CFO: Raymond J. Leadbetter Jr Revenue Cycle Consultant
CMO: Garland Martin, M.D., Chief of Staff
CIO: Gary Gower, Chief Information Officer
CHR: Carla McLendon, Director Human Resources
CNO: Judy M Long, R.N., MS, Chief Nursing Officer and Chief Operating Officer
Web address: www.appling–hospital.org
Control: County, Government, nonfederal **Service**: General medical and surgical

Staffed Beds: 150

BLAIRSVILLE—Union County

★ ⇑ **UNION GENERAL HOSPITAL (110051)**, 35 Hospital Road, Zip 30512–3139; tel. 706/745–2111, (Total facility includes 150 beds in nursing home–type unit) **A**10 20 21 **F**7 11 13 15 18 28 29 30 34 35 40 45 49 51 53 56 57 59 64 65 66 70 75 76 79 81 85 86 87 93 96 97 100 104 107 108 110 111 115 119 127 129 130 132 133 135 143 146 147 148 154 **P**1 **S** Union General Hospital, Inc., Blairsville, GA
Primary Contact: Lewis Kelley, Interim Chief Executive Officer
COO: Lewis Kelley, Chief Operating Officer
CFO: Stephanie L Fletcher, CPA, Chief Financial Officer
CMO: Andre Schaeffer, M.D., Chief of Staff
CIO: Mike Johnston, Director Facilities Operations
CHR: Kathy Hood, Administrative Assistant Human Resources
CNO: Julia Barnett, Chief Nursing Officer
Web address: www.uniongeneralhospital.com
Control: Other not–for–profit (including NFP Corporation) **Service**: General medical and surgical

Staffed Beds: 195 **Admissions:** 2821 **Census:** 165 **Outpatient Visits:** 66118 **Births:** 404 **Total Expense ($000):** 64778 **Payroll Expense ($000):** 27039 **Personnel:** 700

BLAKELY—Early County

★ ⇑ **LIFEBRITE COMMUNITY HOSPITAL OF EARLY (111314)**, 11740 Columbia Street, Zip 39823–2574; tel. 229/723–4241, (Nonreporting) **A**10 18 21
Primary Contact: Ginger Cushing, Chief Executive Officer
Web address: www.pchearly.com
Control: Corporation, Investor–owned (for–profit) **Service**: General medical and surgical

Staffed Beds: 152

BLUE RIDGE—Fannin County

✠ **FANNIN REGIONAL HOSPITAL (110189)**, 2855 Old Highway 5, Zip 30513–6248; tel. 706/632–3711, (Nonreporting) **A**1 10 **S** Quorum Health, Brentwood, TN
Primary Contact: David S. Sanders, Chief Executive Officer
CFO: Phillip Fouts, Chief Financial Officer
CMO: Dillon D Miller, M.D., Chief Medical Officer
CIO: Timothy Snider, Manager Information Systems
CHR: Terrasina Ensley, Director Human Resources
CNO: Jason L. Jones, R.N., Chief Nursing Officer
Web address: www.fanninregionalhospital.com
Control: Corporation, Investor–owned (for–profit) **Service**: General medical and surgical

Staffed Beds: 50

BRASELTON—Hall County

✠ **NORTHEAST GEORGIA MEDICAL CENTER BRASELTON**, 1400 River Place, Zip 30517–5600; tel. 770/219–9000, (Nonreporting) **A**3 **S** Northeast Georgia Health System, Gainesville, GA
Primary Contact: Carol H. Burrell, Chief Executive Officer
CNO: Cynthia Danner, Chief Nursing Officer
Web address: www.nghs.com/locations/braselton
Control: Other not–for–profit (including NFP Corporation) **Service**: General medical and surgical

Staffed Beds: 100

BREMEN—Haralson County

✠ **HIGGINS GENERAL HOSPITAL (111320)**, 200 Allen Memorial Drive, Zip 30110–2012; tel. 770/824–2000, **A**1 10 18 **F**3 11 15 29 31 38 40 45 48 50 51 59 60 68 81 97 107 110 111 114 119 123 124 127 130 133 146 147 154 **P**1 6 **S** Tanner Health System, Carrollton, GA
Primary Contact: Jerry Morris, Administrator
COO: James D Griffith, Chief Operating Officer
CFO: Carol Crews, Chief Financial Officer
CMO: Bill Waters, M.D., Chief Medical Officer
CIO: Terri Lee, Chief Information Officer
CHR: Shari W Gainey, Human Resource Director
CNO: B. J. Brock, Nursing Director
Web address: www.tanner.org/Main/HigginsGeneralHospitalBremen.aspx
Control: Other not–for–profit (including NFP Corporation) **Service**: General medical and surgical

Staffed Beds: 23 **Admissions:** 639 **Census:** 16 **Outpatient Visits:** 86340 **Births:** 0 **Total Expense ($000):** 27855 **Payroll Expense ($000):** 14972 **Personnel:** 229

GA

BRUNSWICK—Glynn County

⊞ **SOUTHEAST GEORGIA HEALTH SYSTEM BRUNSWICK CAMPUS (110025)**, 2415 Parkwood Drive, Zip 31520–4722, Mailing Address: P.O. Box 1518, Zip 31521–1518; tel. 912/466–7000, (Total facility includes 278 beds in nursing home–type unit) **A**1 2 10 **F**3 6 8 11 12 13 15 17 18 20 22 26 28 29 30 31 34 35 37 40 44 45 46 47 48 49 50 51 54 57 59 64 66 68 70 71 74 75 76 77 78 79 81 84 85 86 87 89 91 93 94 96 100 107 108 110 111 114 115 117 119 120 121 124 126 129 131 132 135 144 146 147 148 149 **P**5 **S** Southeast Georgia Health System, Brunswick, GA
Primary Contact: Michael D. Scherneck, President and Chief Executive Officer
CFO: Janice Dunn, Vice President and Chief Financial Officer
CMO: Robert Bernasek, M.D., Vice President and Chief Medical Officer
CIO: Charles Bumgardner
CNO: Judith Henson, Vice President Patient Care Services
Web address: www.sghs.org
Control: Other not–for–profit (including NFP Corporation) **Service**: General medical and surgical

Staffed Beds: 532 **Admissions**: 12124 **Census**: 397 **Outpatient Visits**: 235054 **Births**: 1268 **Total Expense ($000)**: 339075 **Payroll Expense ($000)**: 155112 **Personnel**: 1398

BRYON—Peach County

★ ⇑ **MEDICAL CENTER OF PEACH COUNTY, NAVICENT HEALTH (111310)**, 1960 Highway 247 Connector, Zip 31008; tel. 478/654–2000, (Nonreporting) **A**10 18 21 **S** Navicent Health, Macon, GA
Primary Contact: Darren Pearce, Administrator and Chief Executive Officer
CFO: Lisa Urbistondo, Chief Financial Officer
CMO: Crystal Brown, M.D., Medical Director
CNO: Brenda Goodman, Chief Nursing Officer
Web address: www.navicenthealth.org
Control: Hospital district or authority, Government, nonfederal **Service**: General medical and surgical

Staffed Beds: 25

CAIRO—Grady County

⊞ **GRADY GENERAL HOSPITAL (110121)**, 1155 Fifth Street SE, Zip 39828–3142, Mailing Address: P.O. Box 360, Zip 39828–0360; tel. 229/377–1150, **A**1 10 **F**3 11 13 15 28 29 30 39 40 45 57 59 68 76 77 79 81 85 93 107 111 119 128 133 154 **P**8 **S** Archbold Medical Center, Thomasville, GA
Primary Contact: Crystal Wells, Administrator
COO: Jim Carter, Chief Operating Officer
CFO: Skip Hightower, Chief Financial Officer
CIO: Tracy Gray, Chief Information Officer
CHR: Michelle Pledger, Coordinator Human Resources
CNO: Tammy Harlow, Director of Nursing
Web address: www.archbold.org
Control: Other not–for–profit (including NFP Corporation) **Service**: General medical and surgical

Staffed Beds: 39 **Admissions**: 1343 **Census**: 18 **Outpatient Visits**: 52417 **Births**: 220 **Total Expense ($000)**: 23148 **Payroll Expense ($000)**: 8667 **Personnel**: 131

CALHOUN—Gordon County

⊞ ○ **GORDON HOSPITAL (110023)**, 1035 Red Bud Road, Zip 30701–2082, Mailing Address: P.O. Box 12938, Zip 30703–7013; tel. 706/629–2895, **A**1 2 10 11 19 **F**3 7 11 13 15 18 20 29 30 31 34 35 37 40 46 57 59 62 64 70 75 76 77 78 79 81 82 85 86 87 93 107 108 111 115 119 120 121 123 129 130 135 144 146 147 148 154 **P**1 6 **S** Adventist Health System Sunbelt Health Care Corporation, Altamonte Springs, FL
Primary Contact: Pete M. Weber, President and Chief Executive Officer
COO: Brandon M Nudd, Chief Operating Officer
CFO: Cory Reeves, Chief Financial Officer
CMO: Will Theus, M.D., Chief of Staff
CHR: Jeni Hasselbrack, Director Human Resources
CNO: Amy Jordan, Chief Nursing Officer/Vice President of Nursing
Web address: www.gordonhospital.com
Control: Church operated, Nongovernment, not–for–profit **Service**: General medical and surgical

Staffed Beds: 83 **Admissions**: 4080 **Census**: 44 **Outpatient Visits**: 239456 **Births**: 562 **Total Expense ($000)**: 134569 **Payroll Expense ($000)**: 59500 **Personnel**: 1071

CAMILLA—Mitchell County

⊞ **MITCHELL COUNTY HOSPITAL (111331)**, 90 East Stephens Street, Zip 31730–1836, Mailing Address: P.O. Box 639, Zip 31730–0639; tel. 229/336–5284, (Total facility includes 156 beds in nursing home–type unit) **A**1 10 18 **F**3 15 29 30 35 40 41 50 54 57 58 59 68 93 102 107 110 111 114 119 125 127 128 133 135 154 **P**8 **S** Archbold Medical Center, Thomasville, GA
Primary Contact: James Womack, Administrator
COO: LaDon Toole, Vice President Network Operations
CFO: Skip Hightower, Senior Vice President and Chief Financial Officer
CIO: Tracy Gray, Chief Information Officer
CHR: Vickie County–Teemer, Coordinator Human Resources
CNO: Carla Beasley, Director of Nursing
Web address: www.archbold.org
Control: Other not–for–profit (including NFP Corporation) **Service**: General medical and surgical

Staffed Beds: 181 **Admissions**: 387 **Census**: 162 **Outpatient Visits**: 34379 **Births**: 0 **Total Expense ($000)**: 26416 **Payroll Expense ($000)**: 11424 **Personnel**: 167

CANTON—Cherokee County

⊞ **NORTHSIDE HOSPITAL–CHEROKEE (110008)**, 450 Northside Cherokee Boulevard, Zip 30115–8015, Mailing Address: P.O. Box 906, Zip 30169–0906; tel. 770/720–5100, **A**1 10 **F**3 8 11 12 13 15 18 20 22 26 28 29 30 31 34 35 40 44 45 49 50 54 55 57 59 60 64 68 70 73 74 75 76 79 81 82 85 86 87 93 107 108 110 111 114 118 119 120 121 123 124 126 129 130 131 132 144 145 146 147 148 **S** Northside Healthcare System, Atlanta, GA
Primary Contact: William M. Hayes, Chief Executive Officer
COO: Mike Patterson, Director of Operations
CFO: Brian Jennette, Chief Financial Officer
CMO: Alexander Kessler, M.D., Chief of Staff
CIO: Bill Dunford, Manager
CHR: Roslyn Roberts, Manager
Web address: www.northside.com
Control: Other not–for–profit (including NFP Corporation) **Service**: General medical and surgical

Staffed Beds: 109 **Admissions**: 7402 **Census**: 88 **Outpatient Visits**: 320150 **Births**: 1353 **Total Expense ($000)**: 296525 **Payroll Expense ($000)**: 110162 **Personnel**: 1855

CARROLLTON—Carroll County

⊞ **TANNER MEDICAL CENTER–CARROLLTON (110011)**, 705 Dixie Street, Zip 30117–3818; tel. 770/836–9666, **A**1 2 10 **F**3 11 13 15 18 20 22 26 28 29 30 31 34 35 40 45 47 49 56 57 58 59 62 63 64 68 70 71 73 74 75 76 78 79 81 82 84 85 87 89 107 108 110 111 115 116 117 118 119 120 121 123 124 126 129 130 132 143 146 147 148 149 154 **P**1 6 **S** Tanner Health System, Carrollton, GA
Primary Contact: Loy M. Howard, Chief Operating Officer
COO: James D Griffith, Chief Operating Officer
CFO: Carol Crews, Chief Financial Officer
CMO: William Waters, M.D., IV Chief Medical Officer
CNO: Deborah Matthews, Chief Nursing Officer
Web address: www.tanner.org
Control: Other not–for–profit (including NFP Corporation) **Service**: General medical and surgical

Staffed Beds: 142 **Admissions**: 8442 **Census**: 92 **Outpatient Visits**: 253617 **Births**: 1314 **Total Expense ($000)**: 282519 **Payroll Expense ($000)**: 113100 **Personnel**: 1683

CARTERSVILLE—Bartow County

⊞ **CARTERSVILLE MEDICAL CENTER (110030)**, 960 Joe Frank Harris Parkway, Zip 30120–2129; tel. 770/382–1530, (Nonreporting) **A**1 2 3 10 **S** HCA Healthcare, Nashville, TN
Primary Contact: J. Christopher. Mosley, Chief Executive Officer
COO: Lori Rakes, Chief Operating Officer
CNO: Jan Tidwell, Chief Nursing Officer
Web address: www.cartersvillemedical.com
Control: Corporation, Investor–owned (for–profit) **Service**: General medical and surgical

Staffed Beds: 80

GA

Hospital, Medicare Provider Number, Address, Telephone, Approval, Facility, and Physician Codes, Health Care System

★ American Hospital Association (AHA) membership
□ The Joint Commission accreditation
○ Healthcare Facilities Accreditation Program
◇ DNV Healthcare Inc. accreditation
⇑ Center for Improvement in Healthcare Quality Accreditation
△ Commission on Accreditation of Rehabilitation Facilities (CARF) accreditation

CEDARTOWN—Polk County

⊞ **POLK MEDICAL CENTER (111330)**, 2360 Rockmart Highway,
Zip 30125–6029; tel. 770/748–2500, **A**1 10 18 **F**3 15 28 29 30 34 35 40 50
56 57 59 64 68 75 77 81 93 103 107 108 110 114 119 129 130 132 133 135
143 146 147 148 149 **S** Floyd Healthcare Management, Rome, GA
Primary Contact: Tifani Kinard, Administrator and Chief Nursing Officer
CFO: Rick Sheerin, Chief Financial Officer
CHR: Jeanna Smith, Administrative Assistant and Human Resources Officer
CNO: Tifani Kinard, Administrator and Chief Nursing Officer
Web address: www.polkhospital.org
Control: Hospital district or authority, Government, nonfederal **Service**: General
medical and surgical

Staffed Beds: 25 **Admissions**: 556 **Census**: 21 **Outpatient Visits**: 41370
Births: 0 **Total Expense ($000)**: 24774 **Payroll Expense ($000)**: 9782
Personnel: 143

CHATSWORTH—Murray County

⊞ **MURRAY MEDICAL CENTER (110050)**, 707 Old Dalton Ellijay Road,
Zip 30705–2060, Mailing Address: P.O. Box 1406, Zip 30705–1406;
tel. 706/695–4564, **A**1 10 **F**3 7 15 29 30 34 35 40 57 59 64 79 81 93
107 111 115 119 146 **P**6 8 **S** Adventist Health System Sunbelt Health Care
Corporation, Altamonte Springs, FL
Primary Contact: Karen Steely, Administrator
CMO: Blaine Minor, M.D., Chief of Staff
CIO: Jose C Rios, Director Information Services
CHR: Brandy Rymer, Coordinator Human Resources
CNO: Susan Shook, Interim Chief Executive officer
Web address: www.murraymedical.org/
Control: Church operated, Nongovernment, not–for–profit **Service**: General
medical and surgical

Staffed Beds: 12 **Admissions**: 534 **Census**: 5 **Outpatient Visits**: 58917
Births: 0 **Total Expense ($000)**: 24341 **Payroll Expense ($000)**: 9127
Personnel: 214

CLAXTON—Evans County

☐ **EVANS MEMORIAL HOSPITAL (110142)**, 200 North River Street,
Zip 30417–1659, Mailing Address: P.O. Box 518, Zip 30417–0518;
tel. 912/739–2611, (Nonreporting) **A**1 10
Primary Contact: Nikki NeSmith, Chief Executive Officer and Chief Nursing Officer
CFO: John Wiggins, Chief Financial Officer
CMO: Kyle Parks, M.D., Chief of Staff
CIO: Steve Schmidt, Director Information Systems
CHR: Gina Waters, Director Human Resources
CNO: Nikki NeSmith, Chief Nursing Officer
Web address: www.evansmemorialhospital.org/
Control: Hospital district or authority, Government, nonfederal **Service**: General
medical and surgical

Staffed Beds: 10

CLAYTON—Rabun County

MOUNTAIN LAKES MEDICAL CENTER (111336), 196 Ridgecrest Circle,
Zip 30525–4111; tel. 706/782–4233, (Nonreporting) **A**10 18
Primary Contact: Jeff Dowis, M.D., Interim Chief Executive Officer
CFO: Jimmy Norman, Chief Financial Officer
CHR: Charles Harbaugh, Director Human Resources
Web address: www.mountainlakesmedicalcenter.com
Control: Hospital district or authority, Government, nonfederal **Service**: General
medical and surgical

Staffed Beds: 25

COCHRAN—Bleckley County

⇧ **BLECKLEY MEMORIAL HOSPITAL (111302)**, 145 East Peacock Street,
Zip 31014–7846, Mailing Address: P.O. Box 536, Zip 31014–0536;
tel. 478/934–6211, (Nonreporting) **A**10 18 21
Primary Contact: Jon Green, R.N., Chief Executive Officer
COO: John Roland, R.N., Chief Operating Officer and Chief Nursing Officer
CFO: Sandra Herndon, CPA, Chief Financial Officer
CIO: Scott Wynne, Chief Information Officer Director
CHR: Jean Allen, Human Resources Director
CNO: John Roland, R.N., Chief Operating Officer and Chief Nursing Officer
Web address: www.bleckleymemorial.com
Control: Hospital district or authority, Government, nonfederal **Service**: General
medical and surgical

Staffed Beds: 25

COLQUITT—Miller County

⇧ **MILLER COUNTY HOSPITAL (111305)**, 209 North Cuthbert Street,
Zip 39837–3518, Mailing Address: P.O. Box 7, Zip 39837–0007;
tel. 229/758–3305, (Total facility includes 167 beds in nursing home–type unit)
A10 18 21 **F**15 28 29 32 34 35 40 44 45 50 56 57 59 66 68 75 81 83 84 85
86 87 89 93 97 107 110 119 127 128 129 130 133 135 148 149
Primary Contact: Robin Rau, Chief Executive Officer
CFO: Jill Brown, Chief Financial Officer
CMO: William Swofford, M.D., Chief of Staff
CIO: Keith Lovering, Information Technician
CHR: Karie Spence, Director Human Resources
CNO: Shawn Whittaker, Chief Nursing Officer
Web address: www.millercountyhospital.com
Control: Hospital district or authority, Government, nonfederal **Service**: General
medical and surgical

Staffed Beds: 192 **Admissions**: 918 **Census**: 179 **Outpatient Visits**: 47363
Births: 0 **Total Expense ($000)**: 38809 **Payroll Expense ($000)**: 19661
Personnel: 461

COLUMBUS—Muscogee County

BRADLEY CENTER OF ST. FRANCIS See St. Francis Hospital, Columbus

☐ **COLUMBUS SPECIALTY HOSPITAL (112012)**, 616 19th Street,
Zip 31901–1528, Mailing Address: P.O. Box 910, Zip 31902–0910;
tel. 706/494–4075, (Nonreporting) **A**1 10
Primary Contact: William Eckstein, Chief Executive Officer and Chief Financial
Officer
CFO: William Eckstein, Chief Executive Officer and Chief Financial Officer
CHR: Myra Whitley, Vice President, Human Resources
Web address: www.columbusspecialtyhospital.net
Control: Other not–for–profit (including NFP Corporation) **Service**: Acute long–
term care hospital

Staffed Beds: 33

HUGHSTON HOSPITAL See Piedmont Columbus Regional Northside

☐ **PIEDMONT COLUMBUS REGIONAL MIDTOWN (110064)**, 710 Center
Street, Zip 31901–1527, Mailing Address: P.O. Box 951, Zip 31902–0951;
tel. 706/571–1000, (Includes MIDTOWN MEDICAL CENTER WEST, 616 19th
Street, Columbus, GA, Zip 31901–1528, Mailing Address: P.O. Box 2188,
Zip 31902–2188, tel. 706/494–4262; Ryan Chandler, Chief Executive Officer) **A**1
2 3 5 10 12 13 **F**3 11 12 13 18 20 22 29 30 31 34 35 38 40 41 43 44 45 46
47 48 49 50 51 55 56 57 58 59 60 61 64 65 66 68 70 72 73 74 75 76 77 78
79 81 82 85 86 87 88 89 92 93 94 97 102 107 108 111 114 115 116 117
119 120 121 123 124 126 130 131 132 135 146 147 148 149 **S** Piedmont
Healthcare, Roswell, GA
Primary Contact: M. Scott. Hill, President and Chief Executive Officer
Web address: www.columbusregional.com
Control: Other not–for–profit (including NFP Corporation) **Service**: General
medical and surgical

Staffed Beds: 550 **Admissions**: 14840 **Census**: 220 **Outpatient Visits**:
250482 **Births**: 2691 **Total Expense ($000)**: 305001 **Payroll Expense
($000)**: 101773 **Personnel**: 1971

☐ **PIEDMONT COLUMBUS REGIONAL NORTHSIDE (110200)**, 100 Frist
Court, Zip 31909–3578, Mailing Address: P.O. Box 7188, Zip 31908–7188;
tel. 706/494–2100, **A**1 3 10 **F**3 11 29 30 34 35 38 44 45 50 59 60 61 64 65
68 70 74 75 77 79 81 82 85 86 87 90 92 93 94 96 97 107 108 111 119 129
130 131 132 146 149 **S** Columbus Regional Healthcare System, Columbus, GA
Primary Contact: M. Scott. Hill, President and Chief Executive Officer
COO: Michelle Breitfelder, Chief Operating Officer
CFO: Roland Thacker, Chief Financial Officer
CMO: Lyle Norwood, M.D., Chief of Staff
CIO: Douglas Colburn, Chief Information Officer
CHR: Becky Augustyniak, Director Human Resources
Web address: www.columbusregional.com
Control: Other not–for–profit (including NFP Corporation) **Service**: General
medical and surgical

Staffed Beds: 100 **Admissions**: 2711 **Census**: 39 **Outpatient Visits**: 19478
Births: 0 **Total Expense ($000)**: 66106 **Payroll Expense ($000)**: 16830
Personnel: 376

GA

Many Facility Codes have changed. Please refer to the AHA Guide Code Chart. © 2018 AHA Guide

☒ **ST. FRANCIS HOSPITAL (110129)**, 2122 Manchester Expressway, Zip 31904–6878, Mailing Address: P.O. Box 7000, Zip 31908–7000; tel. 706/596–4000, (Includes BRADLEY CENTER OF ST. FRANCIS, 2000 16th Avenue, Columbus, GA, Zip 31906–0308; tel. 706/320–3700) **A**1 3 10 **F**3 11 13 15 17 18 20 22 24 26 28 29 30 31 34 35 40 45 46 49 50 51 53 54 56 59 60 64 70 74 75 76 77 78 79 81 82 85 86 98 99 100 101 102 103 104 105 106 107 108 110 111 115 119 126 129 130 131 144 145 146 147 148 153 **P**6 **S** LifePoint Health, Brentwood, TN
Primary Contact: Danny L. Jones Jr, FACHE, Chief Executive Officer
COO: Alan E George, Chief Operating Officer
CFO: Greg Hembree, Senior Vice President and Chief Financial Officer
CMO: Bobbi Farber, M.D., Chief Medical Officer
CIO: Jonathon R Jager, Chief Information Officer
CHR: E Rick Lowe, FACHE, Operations Support Risk Management and Compliance
CNO: Charlene Falgout, Chief Nursing Officer
Web address: www.mystfrancis.com
Control: Corporation, Investor–owned (for–profit) **Service:** General medical and surgical

Staffed Beds: 302 **Admissions:** 14320 **Census:** 193 **Outpatient Visits:** 205979 **Births:** 1342 **Total Expense ($000):** 253485 **Payroll Expense ($000):** 78712 **Personnel:** 1768

☐ **WEST CENTRAL GEORGIA REGIONAL HOSPITAL (114013)**, 3000 Schatulga Road, Zip 31907–3117, Mailing Address: P.O. Box 12435, Zip 31917–2435; tel. 706/568–5000, **A**1 10 **F**39 98 130 135 149
Primary Contact: John L. Robertson, Administrator
COO: Marcia Capshaw, Chief Operating Officer
CFO: John Frederick, Chief Financial Officer
CMO: David Morton, M.D., Clinical Director
CIO: Karen Fisher–Ford, Director of Health Information Management
CHR: Peri Johnson, Human Resources Director
CNO: Nicolise Claassens, Nurse Executive
Web address: www.dbhdd.georgia.gov/west–central–georgia–regional–hospital–columbus
Control: State, Government, nonfederal **Service:** Psychiatric

Staffed Beds: 194 **Admissions:** 248 **Census:** 187 **Outpatient Visits:** 0 **Births:** 0 **Personnel:** 566

☒ **NORTHRIDGE MEDICAL CENTER (110040)**, 70 Medical Center Drive, Zip 30529–1078; tel. 706/335–1000, (Total facility includes 167 beds in nursing home–type unit) **A**1 10 **F**3 15 18 29 30 34 40 45 53 56 57 59 68 79 81 85 89 90 98 100 103 107 108 110 111 114 119 128 130 133 **P**6
Primary Contact: Judy Warrner, Chief Operating Officer
CMO: Narasimhulu Neelagaru, M.D., Chief of Staff
Web address: www.northridgemc.com
Control: Other not–for–profit (including NFP Corporation) **Service:** General medical and surgical

Staffed Beds: 207 **Admissions:** 1114 **Census:** 164 **Outpatient Visits:** 28686 **Births:** 0 **Total Expense ($000):** 30190 **Payroll Expense ($000):** 12341 **Personnel:** 370

☒ **PIEDMONT ROCKDALE HOSPITAL (110091)**, 1412 Milstead Avenue NE, Zip 30012–3877; tel. 770/918–3000, (Nonreporting) **A**1 5 10 **S** Piedmont Healthcare, Roswell, GA
Primary Contact: Richard Tanzella, Chief Executive Officer
COO: Blake Watts, Chief Operating Officer
CFO: Diane Roth, Chief Financial Officer
CMO: Lisa Gillespie, M.D., Chief Medical Officer
CIO: Gail Waldo, Director Information Technology
CHR: Marianne Freeman, Vice President Human Resources
CNO: Eleanor Post, R.N., Chief Nursing Officer
Web address: www.rockdalemedicalcenter.org
Control: Corporation, Investor–owned (for–profit) **Service:** General medical and surgical

Staffed Beds: 138

☒ **CRISP REGIONAL HOSPITAL (110104)**, 902 North Seventh Street, Zip 31015–3234; tel. 229/276–3100, (Total facility includes 243 beds in nursing home–type unit) **A**1 3 10 20 **F**3 10 11 13 15 29 30 31 34 35 40 43 44 45 48 49 50 51 54 56 57 58 59 60 61 62 63 64 65 68 70 75 76 77 78 79 81 84 85 86 87 89 90 93 96 97 107 108 110 111 114 115 117 118 125 126 127 128 129 132 133 135 144 146 147 148 149 154 **P**2 8
Primary Contact: Steven Gautney, Chief Executive Officer
COO: Mary Jim Montgomery, R.N., MSN, FACHE, Chief Operating Officer
CFO: Jessica Y Carter, Chief Financial Officer
CMO: David Kavtaradze, M.D., Chief of Staff
CHR: George M Laurin, Interim Director Human Resources
CNO: Marsha L. Mulderig, R.N., MSN, Chief Nursing Officer
Web address: www.crispregional.org
Control: County, Government, nonfederal **Service:** General medical and surgical

Staffed Beds: 316 **Admissions:** 2904 **Census:** 171 **Outpatient Visits:** 104743 **Births:** 274 **Personnel:** 475

☐ **PIEDMONT NEWTON HOSPITAL (110018)**, 5126 Hospital Drive, Zip 30014–2567; tel. 770/786–7053, **A**1 10 **F**3 7 11 13 15 18 20 28 29 30 34 35 39 40 45 47 49 50 51 53 54 57 59 60 68 70 73 75 76 79 81 85 93 107 108 110 111 114 115 119 130 131 143 146 147 148 154 **P**8 **S** Piedmont Healthcare, Roswell, GA
Primary Contact: Eric Bour, M.D., FACS, Chief Executive Officer
CFO: Troy Brooks, Assistant Administrator Fiscal Services
CMO: B. Carter Rogers, Chief of Staff
CIO: Brad Collier, Director
CHR: Greg H Richardson, Assistant Administrator Human Resources
CNO: Jeremiah Bame, R.N., Chief Nursing Officer
Web address: www.newtonmedical.com
Control: Other not–for–profit (including NFP Corporation) **Service:** General medical and surgical

Staffed Beds: 103 **Admissions:** 5417 **Census:** 49 **Outpatient Visits:** 78692 **Births:** 858 **Personnel:** 557

☒ **NORTHSIDE HOSPITAL–FORSYTH (110005)**, 1200 Northside Forsyth Drive, Zip 30041–7659; tel. 770/844–3200, **A**1 10 **F**3 8 11 12 13 15 18 20 22 26 28 29 30 31 34 35 37 40 44 45 48 49 50 54 55 57 59 60 64 68 70 72 73 74 75 76 78 79 81 82 85 86 87 93 107 108 110 111 114 115 117 119 120 121 123 124 126 129 130 132 135 144 145 146 147 148 **S** Northside Healthcare System, Atlanta, GA
Primary Contact: Lynn Jackson, Administrator
CFO: Eric Caldwell, Director Finance
Web address: www.northside.com
Control: Other not–for–profit (including NFP Corporation) **Service:** General medical and surgical

Staffed Beds: 289 **Admissions:** 14976 **Census:** 196 **Outpatient Visits:** 398012 **Births:** 3235 **Total Expense ($000):** 468147 **Payroll Expense ($000):** 176758 **Personnel:** 2678

★ ⇑ **SOUTHWEST GEORGIA REGIONAL MEDICAL CENTER (111300)**, 361 Randolph Street, Zip 39840–6127; tel. 229/732–2181, (Nonreporting) **A**10 18 21 **S** Phoebe Putney Health System, Albany, GA
Primary Contact: Kim Gilman, Chief Executive Officer and Chief Nursing Officer
CFO: Candace Guarnieri, Chief Financial Officer
CNO: Kim Gilman, Chief Executive Officer and Chief Nursing Officer
Web address: www.phoebeputney.com/
Control: Hospital district or authority, Government, nonfederal **Service:** General medical and surgical

Staffed Beds: 25

Hospital, Medicare Provider Number, Address, Telephone, Approval, Facility, and Physician Codes, Health Care System

★ American Hospital Association (AHA) membership
☐ The Joint Commission accreditation
○ Healthcare Facilities Accreditation Program
◇ DNV Healthcare Inc. accreditation
⇑ Center for Improvement in Healthcare Quality Accreditation
△ Commission on Accreditation of Rehabilitation Facilities (CARF) accreditation

GA

DALTON—Whitfield County

✠ **HAMILTON MEDICAL CENTER (110001)**, 1200 Memorial Drive,
Zip 30720–2529, Mailing Address: P.O. Box 1168, Zip 30722–1168;
tel. 706/272–6000, **A**1 2 10 19 **F**3 4 5 8 12 13 15 18 20 22 26 28 29 30 31
34 35 40 43 44 45 46 47 48 49 50 51 53 54 57 59 60 62 63 64 68 70 72 73
74 75 76 77 78 79 81 82 84 85 86 87 89 93 96 97 98 100 101 102 103 104
107 108 110 111 114 115 116 117 118 119 120 121 123 124 126 129 130
131 132 135 144 146 147 148 149
Primary Contact: Jeffrey D. Myers, President and Chief Executive Officer
COO: Sandra D. McKenzie, Executive Vice President and Chief Operating Officer
CFO: Gary L Howard, Senior Vice President and Chief Financial Officer
CMO: Stephen G. Rohn, M.D., Vice President and Chief Medical Officer
CIO: John M Forrester, Director Information Services
CHR: Jason Hopkins, Director, Human Resources
CNO: Cathy Ferguson, R.N., MSN, Vice President and Chief Nursing Officer
Web address: www.hamiltonhealth.com
Control: Other not–for–profit (including NFP Corporation) **Service**: General
medical and surgical

Staffed Beds: 227 **Admissions**: 9928 **Census**: 116 **Outpatient Visits**:
238355 **Births**: 1752 **Personnel**: 1160

DECATUR—Dekalb County

✠ **ATLANTA VETERANS AFFAIRS MEDICAL CENTER**, 1670 Clairmont Road,
Zip 30033–4004; tel. 404/321–6111, (Nonreporting) **A**1 2 3 5 8 **S** Department of
Veterans Affairs, Perry Point, MD
Primary Contact: Annette Walker, Director
CFO: Pamela Watkins, Chief Financial Officer
CMO: David Bower, M.D., Chief of Staff
CIO: William Brock, Chief Information Officer
CHR: Zeta Ferguson, Chief Human Resources
CNO: Sandy Leake, MSN, R.N., Associate Director, Nursing and Patient Care
Services
Web address: www.atlanta.va.gov/
Control: Veterans Affairs, Government, federal **Service**: General medical and
surgical

Staffed Beds: 239

☐ **DEKALB MEDICAL AT DOWNTOWN DECATUR (112006)**, 450 North Candler
Street, Zip 30030–2671; tel. 404/501–6700, (Nonreporting) **A**1 5 10 **S** Emory
Healthcare, Atlanta, GA
Primary Contact: Robert E. Wilson Esq, Chief Executive Officer
CMO: David Snyder, M.D., Chief of Staff
CHR: Tom Crawford, Vice President Human Resources
Web address: www.dekalbmedicalcenter.org
Control: Other not–for–profit (including NFP Corporation) **Service**: Acute long–
term care hospital

Staffed Beds: 44

✠ **DEKALB MEDICAL AT NORTH DECATUR (110076)**, 2701 North Decatur
Road, Zip 30033–5995; tel. 404/501–1000, (Nonreporting) **A**1 2 3 10 **S** Emory
Healthcare, Atlanta, GA
Primary Contact: Robert E. Wilson Esq, Chief Executive Officer
COO: Jim Forstner, Chief Operating Officer
CFO: Robin Nichols, Interim Chief Financial Officer
CIO: Beth Patino, Chief Information Officer
CHR: LeRoy Walker, Vice President Human Resources
CNO: Susan Breslin, R.N., MSN, Vice President Patient Care Services and Chief
Nursing Officer
Web address: www.dekalbmedical.org
Control: Other not–for–profit (including NFP Corporation) **Service**: General
medical and surgical

Staffed Beds: 417

☐ **GEORGIA REGIONAL HOSPITAL AT ATLANTA (114019)**, 3073 Panthersville
Road, Zip 30034–3828; tel. 404/243–2100, (Nonreporting) **A**1 3 5 10
Primary Contact: Susan Trueblood, Chief Executive Officer
COO: Sonny Slate, Chief Operating Officer
CFO: Reginald Jones, Business Manager
CMO: Emile Risby, M.D., Clinical Director
CIO: Elfie Early, Manager Data Services
CHR: Lorraine Farr, Manager Human Resources
Web address: www.atlantareg.dhr.state.ga.us
Control: State, Government, nonfederal **Service**: Psychiatric

Staffed Beds: 319

VETERANS AFFAIRS MEDICAL CENTER See Atlanta Veterans Affairs Medical
Center

DEMOREST—Habersham County

★ ⇧ **HABERSHAM MEDICAL CENTER (110041)**, 541 Historic Highway
441, Zip 30535–3118, Mailing Address: P.O. Box 37, Zip 30535–0037;
tel. 706/754–2161, (Total facility includes 84 beds in nursing home–type unit) **A**10
21 **F**7 8 13 15 28 29 30 34 35 40 45 46 50 53 57 59 64 68 70 75 76 77 79
81 82 87 91 93 97 101 107 111 114 119 128 129 130 133 143 146
Primary Contact: Barbara Duncan, Interim Chief Executive Officer
COO: Michael Gay, Chief Operating Officer
CFO: Barbara Duncan, Chief Financial Officer
CMO: Josh Garrett, Chief of Staff
CHR: Ryan Snow, Director Human Resources
Web address: www.habershammedical.com/
Control: Hospital district or authority, Government, nonfederal **Service**: General
medical and surgical

Staffed Beds: 137 **Admissions**: 2245 **Census**: 103 **Outpatient Visits**:
80086 **Births**: 439 **Total Expense ($000)**: 42463 **Payroll Expense
($000)**: 18420 **Personnel**: 553

DONALSONVILLE—Seminole County

⇧ **DONALSONVILLE HOSPITAL (110194)**, 102 Hospital Circle, Zip 39845–1199;
tel. 229/524–5217, (Total facility includes 75 beds in nursing home–type unit) **A**10
21 **F**13 34 40 45 46 57 59 64 68 76 77 81 87 93 107 111 115 119 128 133
147 148
Primary Contact: Charles H. Orrick, Administrator
CFO: James Moody, Chief Financial Officer
CMO: C O Walker, M.D., Chief of Staff
CHR: Jo Adams, Director Human Resources
Control: Other not–for–profit (including NFP Corporation) **Service**: General
medical and surgical

Staffed Beds: 140 **Admissions**: 853 **Census**: 63 **Outpatient Visits**: 24946
Births: 210 **Total Expense ($000)**: 24501 **Payroll Expense ($000)**: 11187
Personnel: 284

DOUGLAS—Coffee County

☐ **COFFEE REGIONAL MEDICAL CENTER (110089)**, 1101 Ocilla Road,
Zip 31533–2207, Mailing Address: P.O. Box 1287, Zip 31534–1287;
tel. 912/384–1900, **A**1 10 20 **F**3 7 11 13 15 18 20 26 28 29 30 31 34 35 40
41 44 45 47 50 51 53 54 56 57 59 60 61 64 65 68 70 71 74 75 76 77 78 79
81 82 85 86 87 89 92 93 97 107 108 110 111 114 115 119 124 127 130 131
132 135 143 146 147 148 149 154
Primary Contact: Vicki Lewis, R.N., MS, FACHE, President and Chief Executive
Officer
CFO: Lavonda Cravey, Chief Financial Officer
CHR: Laura Bloom, Director Human Resources
Web address: www.coffeeregional.org
Control: Other not–for–profit (including NFP Corporation) **Service**: General
medical and surgical

Staffed Beds: 88 **Admissions**: 3860 **Census**: 40 **Outpatient Visits**: 83683
Births: 566 **Total Expense ($000)**: 83178 **Payroll Expense ($000)**: 31070
Personnel: 562

DOUGLASVILLE—Douglas County

★ **WELLSTAR DOUGLAS HOSPITAL (110184)**, 8954 Hospital Drive,
Zip 30134–2282; tel. 770/949–1500, **A**2 10 **F**3 11 13 15 18 20 22 28 29 30
31 37 38 40 44 45 48 49 50 51 54 58 59 60 61 64 68 70 74 75 76 77 78 79
81 82 84 85 86 87 93 94 102 107 108 110 111 114 115 117 118 119 129
130 132 135 146 147 148 **P**5 6 **S** WellStar Health System, Marietta, GA
Primary Contact: Craig A. Owens, President
CFO: Bradley Greene, Chief Financial Officer
CMO: Noel Holtz, M.D., Chief Medical Officer
CHR: Danyale Ziglor, Assistant Director Human Resources
Web address: www.wellstar.org
Control: Other not–for–profit (including NFP Corporation) **Service**: General
medical and surgical

Staffed Beds: 108 **Admissions**: 6522 **Census**: 69 **Outpatient Visits**:
131349 **Births**: 396 **Personnel**: 735

YOUTH VILLAGES INNER HARBOUR CAMPUS, 4685 Dorsett Shoals Road,
Zip 30135–4999; tel. 770/942–2391, (Nonreporting)
Primary Contact: Patrick Lawler, Chief Executive Officer
CFO: J Steve Lewis, Director Finance
CIO: Laura Sellers, Director Information Systems
CHR: Sherry Kollmeyer, Vice President Human Resources
Web address: www.innerharbour.org
Control: Other not–for–profit (including NFP Corporation) **Service**: Children's
hospital psychiatric

Staffed Beds: 190

GA

Many Facility Codes have changed. Please refer to the AHA Guide Code Chart. © 2018 AHA Guide

DUBLIN—Laurens County

CARL VINSON VETERANS AFFAIRS MEDICAL CENTER, 1826 Veterans Boulevard, Zip 31021–3620; tel. 478/272–1210, (Nonreporting) **A**1 3 **S** Department of Veterans Affairs, Perry Point, MD
Primary Contact: David VanMeter, Interim Director
COO: Gerald M DeWorth, Associate Director
CFO: Kimberly Johnson–Miller, Chief Financial Officer
CMO: Christopher Blasy, D.O., Chief of Staff
CIO: Mark Cowart, Facility Chief Information Officer
CHR: Kurt Oster, Human Resources Officer
CNO: Connie Hampton, R.N., Associate Director for Patient Care Services
Web address: www.dublin.va.gov/
Control: Veterans Affairs, Government, federal **Service:** General medical and surgical

Staffed Beds: 178

FAIRVIEW PARK HOSPITAL (110125), 200 Industrial Boulevard, Zip 31021–2997, Mailing Address: P.O. Box 1408, Zip 31040–1408; tel. 478/275–2000, (Nonreporting) **A**1 10 19 **S** HCA Healthcare, Nashville, TN
Primary Contact: Donald R. Avery, FACHE, President and Chief Executive Officer
CFO: Ted Short, Chief Financial Officer
CMO: George E. Harrison, M.D., Chief Medical Officer
CIO: Marsha Morris, Manager Information Services
CHR: Jeff Bruton, Director Human Resources
CNO: Donna Trickey, R.N., Chief Nursing Officer
Web address: www.fairviewparkhospital.com
Control: Corporation, Investor–owned (for–profit) **Service:** General medical and surgical

Staffed Beds: 168

DULUTH—De Kalb County

GWINNETT MEDICAL CENTER–DULUTH See Gwinnett Hospital System, Lawrenceville

EAST POINT—Fulton County

REGENCY HOSPITAL OF SOUTH ATLANTA (112014), 1170 Cleveland Avenue, 4th Floor, Zip 30344–3615; tel. 404/466–6250, (Nonreporting) **A**1 3 10 **S** Select Medical Corporation, Mechanicsburg, PA
Primary Contact: Michelle Tenhengel–deVille, Chief Executive Officer
Web address: www.regencyhospital.com
Control: Corporation, Investor–owned (for–profit) **Service:** Acute long–term care hospital

Staffed Beds: 40

EASTMAN—Dodge County

DODGE COUNTY HOSPITAL (110092), 901 Griffin Avenue, Zip 31023–6720, Mailing Address: PO BOX 4309, Zip 31023–4309; tel. 478/374–4000, **A**10 21 **F**3 11 13 15 29 30 31 40 45 57 59 64 69 70 75 76 79 81 85 86 98 101 103 107 108 110 111 114 119 146 147
Primary Contact: Kevin Bierschenk, Chief Executive Officer
CFO: Jan Hamrick, Chief Financial Officer
CIO: Victor Woodard, Manager Information Technology
CHR: Wendy Selph, Director Human Resources
CNO: Sandra M. Campbell, R.N., Chief Nursing Officer
Web address: www.dodgecountyhospital.com
Control: Hospital district or authority, Government, nonfederal **Service:** General medical and surgical

Staffed Beds: 35 **Admissions:** 1510 **Census:** 22 **Outpatient Visits:** 32147
Births: 110 **Total Expense ($000):** 19787 **Payroll Expense ($000):** 8818
Personnel: 231

EATONTON—Putnam County

PUTNAM GENERAL HOSPITAL (111313), 101 Lake Oconee Parkway, Zip 31024–6054; tel. 706/485–2711, **A**1 10 18 **F**3 11 15 18 28 29 35 40 45 50 51 57 59 64 67 81 93 107 110 111 114 119 128 129 133 146
Primary Contact: Alan Horton, Administrator
CFO: Judy Ware, Chief Financial Officer
CMO: Omar Akhras, M.D., Chief of Staff
CIO: Marcel Lundy, Chief Information Officer
CHR: Jeanine Martinez, Director Human Resources
CNO: Pam Douglas, Chief Nursing Officer
Web address: www.putnamgeneral.com
Control: Hospital district or authority, Government, nonfederal **Service:** General medical and surgical

Staffed Beds: 25 **Admissions:** 622 **Census:** 10 **Outpatient Visits:** 19087
Births: 0 **Total Expense ($000):** 20422 **Payroll Expense ($000):** 4847
Personnel: 116

ELBERTON—Elbert County

ELBERT MEMORIAL HOSPITAL (110026), 4 Medical Drive, Zip 30635–1897; tel. 706/283–3151, **A**1 10 20 **F**3 11 15 29 40 45 50 53 57 59 70 77 79 81 85 87 102 107 110 119 128 130 133 146 147 **P**6
Primary Contact: Kerry A. Trapnell, Chief Executive Officer
CIO: Greg Fields, Director Information Technology
CHR: Georgian Walton, Director Human Resources
CNO: Sonya Elrod, Chief Nursing Officer
Web address: www.emhcare.net
Control: Hospital district or authority, Government, nonfederal **Service:** General medical and surgical

Staffed Beds: 35 **Admissions:** 720 **Census:** 9 **Outpatient Visits:** 19163
Births: 0 **Total Expense ($000):** 12548 **Payroll Expense ($000):** 5812
Personnel: 126

FAYETTEVILLE—Fayette County

PIEDMONT FAYETTE HOSPITAL (110215), 1255 Highway 54 West, Zip 30214–4526; tel. 770/719–7000, **A**2 3 10 21 **F**11 13 15 18 20 22 26 28 29 30 31 34 35 36 40 44 45 46 47 48 49 50 51 53 55 57 59 64 70 72 73 74 75 76 77 78 79 81 84 85 86 87 93 94 97 107 108 110 111 114 115 118 119 120 121 123 126 129 130 132 146 147 148 **S** Piedmont Healthcare, Roswell, GA
Primary Contact: Michael Burnett, Chief Executive Officer
COO: Nathan Nipper, Chief Operating Officer
CFO: Scott A. Wolfe, Chief Financial Officer
CMO: Angela Swayne, M.D., Chief Medical Officer
CIO: Geoffrey Brown, Chief Information Officer
CHR: Holly Sawyer, Director and Human Resources Business Partner
CNO: Merry Heath, Chief Nursing Officer
Web address: www.piedmont.org
Control: Other not–for–profit (including NFP Corporation) **Service:** General medical and surgical

Staffed Beds: 210 **Admissions:** 14494 **Census:** 179 **Outpatient Visits:** 170492 **Births:** 2453 **Personnel:** 1530

FITZGERALD—Ben Hill County

DORMINY MEDICAL CENTER (110073), 200 Perry House Road, Zip 31750–8857, Mailing Address: P.O. Box 1447, Zip 31750–1447; tel. 229/424–7100, **A**10 21 **F**3 11 13 15 29 31 35 39 40 57 59 60 63 70 75 76 77 78 79 81 84 85 87 90 93 107 108 110 111 114 119 127 129 130 132 133 146 148
Primary Contact: Mel Pyne, Regional Chief Executive Officer
CFO: Paige Wynn, Chief Financial Officer
CMO: Davey Herring, M.D., Chief Medical Officer
CIO: Chris Ward, Director Management Information Systems
CHR: Denise Steverson, Director Human Resources
CNO: Staci Mims, Chief Nursing Officer
Web address: www.dorminymedical.org
Control: Hospital district or authority, Government, nonfederal **Service:** General medical and surgical

Staffed Beds: 58 **Admissions:** 981 **Census:** 10 **Outpatient Visits:** 32913
Births: 108 **Total Expense ($000):** 20873 **Payroll Expense ($000):** 6581
Personnel: 197

FORSYTH—Monroe County

MONROE COUNTY HOSPITAL (111318), 88 Martin Luther King Jr Drive, Zip 31029–1682, Mailing Address: P.O. Box 1068, Zip 31029–1068; tel. 478/994–2521, **A**1 10 18 **F**3 11 15 29 35 40 57 59 68 75 77 81 107 110 114 119 132 133 146 148 **P**1 2 3
Primary Contact: Lorraine Smith, Chief Executive Officer
CFO: Judy King Ware, Chief Financial Officer
CMO: Jeremy Goodwin, M.D., President, Medical Staff
CIO: Tiffany Purmont, Supervisor Medical Records
CHR: Deborah Flowers, Director Human Resources
CNO: Casey Fleckenstein, Nurse Manager
Web address: www.monroehospital.org
Control: Hospital district or authority, Government, nonfederal **Service:** General medical and surgical

Staffed Beds: 25 **Admissions:** 445 **Census:** 9 **Outpatient Visits:** 12522
Births: 0 **Total Expense ($000):** 10242 **Payroll Expense ($000):** 3404
Personnel: 85

GA

Hospital, Medicare Provider Number, Address, Telephone, Approval, Facility, and Physician Codes, Health Care System

★ American Hospital Association (AHA) membership ○ Healthcare Facilities Accreditation Program ⇑ Center for Improvement in Healthcare Quality Accreditation
☐ The Joint Commission accreditation ◇ DNV Healthcare Inc. accreditation △ Commission on Accreditation of Rehabilitation Facilities (CARF) accreditation

FORT BENNING—Muscogee County

✠ **MARTIN ARMY COMMUNITY HOSPITAL**, 7950 Martin Loop, Zip 31905–5648, Mailing Address: 7950 Martin Loop, B9200, Room 010, Zip 31905–5648; tel. 706/544–2516, (Nonreporting) **A**1 3 5 **S** Department of the Army, Office of the Surgeon General, Falls Church, VA
Primary Contact: Colonel Marie Dominguez, Commander
CHR: Major Bernita Hightower, Chief Human Resources
Web address: www.martin.amedd.army.mil
Control: Army, Government, federal **Service:** General medical and surgical

Staffed Beds: 57

FORT GORDON—Richmond County

✠ **DWIGHT DAVID EISENHOWER ARMY MEDICAL CENTER**, 300 West Hospital Road, Zip 30905–5741; tel. 706/787–5811, (Nonreporting) **A**1 2 3 5 **S** Department of the Army, Office of the Surgeon General, Falls Church, VA
Primary Contact: Colonel John P. Lamoureux, Commander
CMO: Colonel James M Baunchalk, Deputy Chief Clinical Services
CIO: Major Joseph A Ponce, Chief Information Management
CHR: Elizabeth Shelt, Civilian Personnel Officer
Web address: www.ddeamc.amedd.army.mil
Control: Army, Government, federal **Service:** General medical and surgical

Staffed Beds: 107

FORT OGLETHORPE—Catoosa County

★ ⇑ **CHI MEMORIAL HOSPITAL – GEORGIA (110236)**, 100 Gross Crescent Circle, Zip 30742–3669; tel. 706/858–2000, (Nonreporting) **A**10 21 **S** Catholic Health Initiatives, Englewood, CO
Primary Contact: Angie Hullander, Administrator and Special Operations
COO: Kevin Hopkins, Vice President of Operations
CFO: Farrell Hayes, Chief Financial Officer
CMO: John Erdman, M.D., Chief of Staff
CIO: Ruth Wright–Whitaker, Director Information Services
CHR: Cathy Hulsey, Manager of Human Resources
CNO: Sandra Siniard, Vice President of Patient Care Services
Web address: www.memorial.org/chi–memorial–hospital–georgia
Control: Hospital district or authority, Government, nonfederal **Service:** General medical and surgical

Staffed Beds: 179

GAINESVILLE—Hall County

★ △ ⇑ **NORTHEAST GEORGIA MEDICAL CENTER (110029)**, 743 Spring Street NE, Zip 30501–3899; tel. 770/219–3553, (Total facility includes 252 beds in nursing home–type unit) **A**2 7 10 19 21 **F**3 4 7 11 12 13 15 17 18 20 22 24 26 28 29 30 31 34 35 38 40 43 44 45 46 47 48 49 50 51 54 56 57 58 59 60 61 63 64 68 70 72 73 74 75 76 77 78 79 81 82 83 84 85 86 87 89 90 93 98 99 100 101 104 105 107 108 110 111 114 115 116 117 119 120 121 123 124 126 128 129 130 131 132 143 144 146 147 148 149 151 152 153 154 **S** Northeast Georgia Health System, Gainesville, GA
Primary Contact: Carol H. Burrell, Chief Executive Officer
CFO: Brian D Steines, Chief Financial Officer
CMO: Sam Johnson, M.D., Chief Medical Officer
CIO: Chris Paravate, Chief Information Officer
CHR: Deborah Weber, Chief Human Resource Officer
CNO: Brenda Simpson, Chief Nursing Officer
Web address: www.nghs.com
Control: Other not–for–profit (including NFP Corporation) **Service:** General medical and surgical

Staffed Beds: 906 Admissions: 38599 Census: 699 Outpatient Visits: 548455 Births: 4505 Personnel: 4890

GRACEWOOD—Richmond County

EAST CENTRAL REGIONAL HOSPITAL See East Central Regional Hospital, Augusta

GREENSBORO—Greene County

✠ **ST. MARY'S GOOD SAMARITAN HOSPITAL (111329)**, 5401 Lake Oconee Parkway, Zip 30642–4232; tel. 706/453–7331, **A**1 10 18 **F**3 11 15 18 26 29 30 34 35 40 45 50 51 57 64 65 68 74 75 77 79 81 85 87 93 107 108 115 119 129 130 133 146 147 **S** Trinity Health, Livonia, MI
Primary Contact: Tanya M. Adcock, President
CMO: Dave Ringer, M.D., Chief of Staff
CNO: Celia Covington, MSN, R.N., Director of Nursing
Web address: www.stmarysgoodsam.org
Control: Church operated, Nongovernment, not–for–profit **Service:** General medical and surgical

Staffed Beds: 25 Admissions: 878 Census: 11 Outpatient Visits: 40461 Births: 0 Total Expense ($000): 23800 Payroll Expense ($000): 8013 Personnel: 154

GRIFFIN—Spalding County

✠ **WELLSTAR SPALDING REGIONAL HOSPITAL (110031)**, 601 South Eighth Street, Zip 30224–4294, Mailing Address: P O Drawer 'V', Zip 30224–1168; tel. 770/228–2721, **A**1 2 10 **F**3 7 11 13 15 18 20 22 29 30 31 34 35 40 45 49 50 53 54 57 59 64 70 73 75 76 77 78 79 80 81 85 87 89 93 107 108 110 111 114 115 119 129 130 131 135 146 147 **P**5 6 **S** WellStar Health System, Marietta, GA
Primary Contact: Tamara Ison, Senior Vice President and President
COO: Tamara Ison, Chief Operating Officer
CMO: Philip Osehobo, M.D., Chief Medical Officer
CIO: Steve Brown, Director Information Systems
CHR: Amanda Remington, Director Human Resources
CNO: Wadra McCullough, Chief Nursing Officer
Web address: www.spaldingregional.com
Control: Other not–for–profit (including NFP Corporation) **Service:** General medical and surgical

Staffed Beds: 160 Admissions: 8460 Census: 97 Outpatient Visits: 104800 Births: 1006 Personnel: 696

HAWKINSVILLE—Pulaski County

⇑ **TAYLOR REGIONAL HOSPITAL (110135)**, Macon Highway, Zip 31036, Mailing Address: P.O. Box 1297, Zip 31036–7297; tel. 478/783–0200, (Nonreporting) **A**3 10 21
Primary Contact: E.R. McDannald, Interim Chief Executive Officer
CFO: Lisa Halliday, Director Accounting Services
CMO: Al Baggett, M.D., Interim Chief of Staff
CIO: Dawn Warnock, Director Medical Records
Web address: www.taylorregional.org
Control: Other not–for–profit (including NFP Corporation) **Service:** General medical and surgical

Staffed Beds: 57

HAZLEHURST—Jeff Davis County

☐ **JEFF DAVIS HOSPITAL (111333)**, 163 South Tallahassee Street, Zip 31539–2921, Mailing Address: P.O. Box 1690, Zip 31539–1690; tel. 912/375–7781, **A**1 10 18 **F**29 30 40 57 59 70 81 104 107 111 119 133
Primary Contact: Tammy Mims, Chief Executive Officer
CFO: Cathy Cason, Chief Financial Officer
CIO: Brian Fowler, Information Technology Director
CHR: Brenda McEachin, Human Resources Director
CNO: Allen Crawford, Chief Nursing Officer
Web address: www.jeffdavishospital.org
Control: Hospital district or authority, Government, nonfederal **Service:** General medical and surgical

Staffed Beds: 25 Admissions: 550 Census: 8 Outpatient Visits: 19789 Births: 0 Total Expense ($000): 10568 Payroll Expense ($000): 4866

HIAWASSEE—Towns County

CHATUGE REGIONAL HOSPITAL AND NURSING HOME (111324), 110 Main Street, Zip 30546–3408, Mailing Address: P.O. Box 509, Zip 30546–0509; tel. 706/896–2222, (Total facility includes 112 beds in nursing home–type unit) **A**10 18 **F**3 11 15 29 34 35 40 45 56 57 59 64 65 70 75 77 81 86 87 93 97 98 100 103 104 107 108 110 111 115 119 127 128 130 132 133 135 146 148 149 **P**1 **S** Union General Hospital, Inc., Blairsville, GA
Primary Contact: Ryan Snow, Administrator
CFO: Tim Henry, Accountant
CMO: Robert F Stahlkuppe, M.D., Chief of Staff
CIO: Walt Stafford, Director Information Technology
CHR: Rita Bradshaw, Director Human Resources
Web address: www.chatugeregionalhospital.org
Control: Hospital district or authority, Government, nonfederal **Service:** General medical and surgical

Staffed Beds: 150 Admissions: 948 Census: 117 Outpatient Visits: 24025 Births: 0 Total Expense ($000): 24085 Payroll Expense ($000): 12185 Personnel: 300

HINESVILLE—Liberty County

☐ **LIBERTY REGIONAL MEDICAL CENTER (111335)**, 462 Elma G Miles Parkway, Zip 31313–4000, Mailing Address: P.O. Box 919, Zip 31310–0919; tel. 912/369–9400, (Nonreporting) **A**1 10 18
Primary Contact: Michael Hester, Chief Executive Officer
CFO: Derek Rozier, Chief Financial Officer
CNO: Donna R. Cochrane, Chief Nursing Officer
Web address: www.libertyregional.org
Control: Hospital district or authority, Government, nonfederal **Service:** General medical and surgical

Staffed Beds: 25

GA

Many Facility Codes have changed. Please refer to the AHA Guide Code Chart.
© 2018 AHA Guide

⊞ **WINN ARMY COMMUNITY HOSPITAL**, 1061 Harmon Avenue, Zip 31314–5641, Mailing Address: 1061 Harmon Avenue, Suite 2311B, Zip 31314–5641; tel. 912/435–6965, (Nonreporting) **A**1 5 **S** Department of the Army, Office of the Surgeon General, Falls Church, VA
Primary Contact: Colonel Kirk W. Eggleston, Commanding Officer
CIO: Arthur N Kirshner, Chief Information Management
CHR: Major Yvette McCrea, Chief Human Resources
CNO: Colonel Sharon Brown, Deputy Commander Nursing
Web address: www.winn.amedd.army.mil/
Control: Army, Government, federal **Service**: General medical and surgical

> **Staffed Beds:** 37

HIRAM—Paulding County

⊞ **WELLSTAR PAULDING HOSPITAL (110042)**, 2518 Jimmy Lee Smith Parkway, Zip 30141; tel. 470/644–7000, (Total facility includes 182 beds in nursing home–type unit) **A**1 2 10 **F**3 11 15 18 20 28 29 30 31 37 38 40 41 44 45 49 50 53 54 55 59 61 64 68 70 75 77 78 79 80 81 82 85 86 87 93 102 107 108 110 111 114 118 119 120 121 123 124 128 129 130 135 146 148 154 **P**5 6 **S** WellStar Health System, Marietta, GA
Primary Contact: John Kueven, Senior Vice President and President
COO: Lindsay Rehn, Executive Director of Financial Operations
CFO: Lindsay Rehn, Executive Director of Financial Operations
CMO: Guillermo Pierluisi, Vice President of Medical Affairs
CHR: Jessica Bedsole, Director, Human Resources
CNO: Vicky Hogue, R.N., Vice President Patient Services and Chief Nursing Officer
Web address: www.wellstar.org
Control: Other not–for–profit (including NFP Corporation) **Service**: General medical and surgical

> **Staffed Beds:** 294 **Admissions:** 6200 **Census:** 224 **Outpatient Visits:** 131174 **Births:** 0 **Personnel:** 795

HOMERVILLE—Clinch County

★ **CLINCH MEMORIAL HOSPITAL (111308)**, 1050 Valdosta Highway, Zip 31634–9701, Mailing Address: P.O. Box 516, Zip 31634–0516; tel. 912/487–5211, **A**10 18 **F**3 7 11 15 29 34 35 40 45 57 59 64 93 107 114 119 129 130 133 135 146 149 154
Primary Contact: Angela Ammons, Administrator
COO: Wallace D Mincey, Chief Executive Officer
CFO: Sandra Hughes, Chief Financial Officer
CMO: Samuel Cobarrubias, M.D., Chief of Staff
CIO: Shelly Studebaker, Director Management Information Systems
CHR: Shelly Studebaker, Manager Human Resources
CNO: Kellie Register, Director of Nursing
Web address: www.clinchmemorialhospital.org
Control: County, Government, nonfederal **Service**: General medical and surgical

> **Staffed Beds:** 25 **Admissions:** 298 **Census:** 3 **Outpatient Visits:** 11432 **Births:** 0 **Total Expense ($000):** 10250 **Payroll Expense ($000):** 3954 **Personnel:** 86

JACKSON—Butts County

★ **WELLSTAR SYLVAN GROVE HOSPITAL (111319)**, 1050 McDonough Road, Zip 30233–1599; tel. 770/775–7861, **A**10 18 **F**15 29 34 35 40 50 57 59 68 77 93 107 119 133 **P**5 6 **S** WellStar Health System, Marietta, GA
Primary Contact: Tamara Ison, Senior Vice President and President
CFO: Tamara Ison, Chief Financial Officer
CIO: Steve Brown, Chief Information Officer
CHR: Amanda Remington, Director Human Resources
Web address: www.sylvangrovehospital.com
Control: Other not–for–profit (including NFP Corporation) **Service**: General medical and surgical

> **Staffed Beds:** 24 **Admissions:** 334 **Census:** 11 **Outpatient Visits:** 20017 **Births:** 0 **Personnel:** 63

JASPER—Pickens County

⇑ **PIEDMONT MOUNTAINSIDE HOSPITAL (110225)**, 1266 Highway 515 South, Zip 30143–4872; tel. 706/692–2441, **A**10 21 **F**3 13 15 20 28 29 34 35 40 41 45 46 49 53 57 59 64 70 75 76 77 79 81 85 107 108 110 111 114 115 119 124 129 130 132 135 146 149 154 **S** Piedmont Healthcare, Roswell, GA
Primary Contact: Denise Ray, Chief Executive Officer
CMO: Moiz Master, M.D., Medical Director of Quality
CIO: Geoffrey Brown, Chief Information Officer
CHR: Frank Leist, Human Resources Manager
CNO: Michelle Breitfelder, Chief Nursing Officer
Web address: www.piedmont.org
Control: Other not–for–profit (including NFP Corporation) **Service**: General medical and surgical

> **Staffed Beds:** 52 **Admissions:** 3324 **Census:** 33 **Outpatient Visits:** 75033 **Births:** 334 **Total Expense ($000):** 59056 **Payroll Expense ($000):** 25500 **Personnel:** 359

JESUP—Wayne County

☐ **WAYNE MEMORIAL HOSPITAL (110124)**, 865 South First Street, Zip 31545–0210, Mailing Address: P.O. Box 410, Zip 31598–0410; tel. 912/427–6811, (Nonreporting) **A**1 10 20
Primary Contact: Joseph P. Ierardi, Chief Executive Officer
CFO: Greg Jones, Chief Financial Officer
CMO: Dan Collipp, M.D., Chief of Staff
CIO: Deborah Six, Coordinator Data Processing
CHR: John McIwain, Director Human Resources
Web address: www.wmhweb.com
Control: County, Government, nonfederal **Service**: General medical and surgical

> **Staffed Beds:** 84

JOHNS CREEK—Fulton County

⊞ **EMORY JOHNS CREEK HOSPITAL (110230)**, 6325 Hospital Parkway, Zip 30097–5775; tel. 678/474–7000, **A**1 2 3 10 **F**3 11 12 13 15 18 20 22 26 29 30 31 34 35 36 40 45 49 50 54 55 57 58 59 60 64 68 70 72 73 74 75 76 77 78 79 81 82 84 85 86 87 93 100 101 102 107 108 110 111 115 116 117 119 126 129 130 131 132 141 146 147 148 149 154 **P**6 **S** Emory Healthcare, Atlanta, GA
Primary Contact: Marilyn Margolis, MSN, Chief Executive Officer
COO: Laurie Hansen, Vice President of Operations
CFO: JoAnn Manning, Chief Financial Officer
CMO: Adedapo Odetoyinbo, M.D., Chief Medical Office
CHR: Hannah Henry, Interim Vice President of Human Resources
CNO: Heather Redrick, Chief Nursing Officer
Web address: www.emoryjohnscreek.com
Control: Other not–for–profit (including NFP Corporation) **Service**: General medical and surgical

> **Staffed Beds:** 113 **Admissions:** 7311 **Census:** 83 **Outpatient Visits:** 74881 **Births:** 1300 **Total Expense ($000):** 140468 **Payroll Expense ($000):** 48920 **Personnel:** 697

KENNESAW—Cobb County

DEVEREUX ADVANCED BEHAVIORAL HEALTH GEORGIA, 1291 Stanley Road NW, Zip 30152–4359; tel. 770/427–0147, **F**98 106 **S** Devereux, Villanova, PA
Primary Contact: Gwendolyn Skinner, Operational Vice President
COO: Mary H Esposito, Assistant Executive Director
CFO: Kathy Goggin, Director of Finance
CMO: Yolanda Graham, M.D., Medical Director
CIO: Sam Maguta, Coordinator Information Systems
CHR: Rudie Delien, Director of Human Resources
CNO: Debra Sharpton, Director of Nursing
Web address: www.devereuxga.org
Control: Other not–for–profit (including NFP Corporation) **Service**: Children's hospital psychiatric

> **Staffed Beds:** 100 **Admissions:** 331 **Census:** 97 **Outpatient Visits:** 99 **Births:** 0 **Total Expense ($000):** 20825 **Payroll Expense ($000):** 11305 **Personnel:** 334

LAGRANGE—Troup County

⊞ **WELLSTAR WEST GEORGIA MEDICAL CENTER (110016)**, 1514 Vernon Road, Zip 30240–4131; tel. 706/882–1411, (Total facility includes 260 beds in nursing home–type unit) **A**1 2 10 19 **F**3 11 12 13 15 18 20 22 26 28 29 30 31 34 35 40 44 47 48 49 50 56 57 58 59 62 63 64 66 68 70 73 74 75 76 77 78 79 80 81 82 84 85 86 87 89 92 93 96 107 108 110 111 114 115 119 120 121 123 124 128 129 130 132 135 146 147 148 149 154 **S** WellStar Health System, Marietta, GA
Primary Contact: Gerald N. Fulks, President
COO: Charis L Acree, Vice President and Chief Operating Officer
CFO: Paul R Perrotti, CPA, Chief Financial Officer
CIO: Alan Whitehouse, Chief Information Officer
CHR: Tommy Britt, Vice President of Human Resources
CNO: Tracy Gynther, R.N., Vice President and Chief Nursing Officer
Web address: www.wghealth.org/
Control: Other not–for–profit (including NFP Corporation) **Service**: General medical and surgical

> **Staffed Beds:** 390 **Admissions:** 7394 **Census:** 294 **Outpatient Visits:** 143833 **Births:** 931 **Personnel:** 1195

GA

Hospital, Medicare Provider Number, Address, Telephone, Approval, Facility, and Physician Codes, Health Care System

★ American Hospital Association (AHA) membership
☐ The Joint Commission accreditation
○ Healthcare Facilities Accreditation Program
◇ DNV Healthcare Inc. accreditation
⇑ Center for Improvement in Healthcare Quality Accreditation
△ Commission on Accreditation of Rehabilitation Facilities (CARF) accreditation

LAKELAND—Lanier County

✠ **SOUTH GEORGIA MEDICAL CENTER LANIER CAMPUS (111326)**, 116 West Thigpen Avenue, Zip 31635–1011; tel. 229/482–3110, (Nonreporting) **A**1 10 18 **S** South Georgia Medical Center, Valdosta, GA
Primary Contact: Richard Huth, Administrator
CFO: Libby Flemming, Controller and Chief Information Officer
CMO: Bruce Herrington, M.D., Chief Medical Officer
CIO: Libby Flemming, Controller and Chief Information Officer
CHR: Vicki Dinkins, Director Human Resources
Web address: www.sgmc.org
Control: Other not–for–profit (including NFP Corporation) **Service**: Other specialty treatment

Staffed Beds: 87

LAVONIA—Franklin County

✠ **ST. MARY'S SACRED HEART HOSPITAL (110027)**, 367 Clear Creek Parkway, Zip 30553–4173; tel. 706/356–7800, **A**1 10 **F**3 11 13 15 18 29 30 34 35 40 49 50 53 57 59 70 74 75 76 79 81 85 87 93 107 108 110 111 115 119 129 130 132 149 154 **S** Trinity Health, Livonia, MI
Primary Contact: Jeff English, President
CIO: Tim Vickery, Chief Information Officer
CHR: Lauren Papka, Chief Administrative Officer
CNO: Evelyn Murphy, R.N., Chief Nursing Officer
Web address: www.stmaryssacredheart.org/
Control: Church operated, Nongovernment, not–for–profit **Service**: General medical and surgical

Staffed Beds: 41 **Admissions:** 1780 **Census:** 17 **Outpatient Visits:** 46317 **Births:** 313 **Total Expense ($000):** 33680 **Payroll Expense ($000):** 11956 **Personnel:** 231

LAWRENCEVILLE—Gwinnett County

✠ **GWINNETT HOSPITAL SYSTEM (110087)**, 1000 Medical Center Boulevard, Zip 30046–7694, Mailing Address: P.O. Box 348, Zip 30046–0348; tel. 678/312–1000, (Includes GWINNETT MEDICAL CENTER–DULUTH, 3620 Howell Ferry Road, Duluth, GA, Zip 30096; tel. 678/312–6800; GWINNETT MEDICAL CENTER, 1000 Medical Center Boulevard, Lawrenceville, GA, Zip 30245, Mailing Address: Box 348, Zip 30246, tel. 678/312–1000; Thomas Shepherd, Executive Vice President and Chief Operating Officer) (Total facility includes 89 beds in nursing home–type unit) **A**1 2 3 8 10 13 **F**3 8 11 12 13 15 17 18 20 22 24 26 28 29 30 31 34 35 36 37 38 40 41 43 44 45 46 47 48 49 50 53 54 55 56 58 59 64 67 68 70 71 72 73 74 75 76 77 78 79 81 82 84 85 86 87 90 93 96 97 107 108 110 111 115 116 117 118 119 126 128 129 130 131 132 134 135 146 147 148 149 **P**6 8
Primary Contact: Philip R. Wolfe, President and Chief Executive Officer
COO: Thomas Shepherd, Executive Vice President and Chief Operating Officer
CFO: Thomas Y McBride III Executive Vice President and Chief Financial Officer
CMO: Alan Bier, M.D., Executive Vice President and Chief Medical Officer
CIO: Patricia A Lavely, FACHE, Senior Vice President and Chief Information Officer
CHR: Stephen Nadeau, Senior Vice President Human Resources
CNO: Carol Danielson, R.N., Senior Vice President and Chief Nursing Officer
Web address: www.gwinnettmedicalcenter.org
Control: Other not–for–profit (including NFP Corporation) **Service**: General medical and surgical

Staffed Beds: 569 **Admissions:** 29709 **Census:** 488 **Outpatient Visits:** 424144 **Births:** 4790 **Total Expense ($000):** 693957 **Payroll Expense ($000):** 274158 **Personnel:** 4109

☐ **SUMMITRIDGE HOSPITAL (114004)**, 250 Scenic Highway, Zip 30046–5675; tel. 678/442–5800, **A**1 10 **F**4 5 98 99 102 103 104 105 152 153 154
Primary Contact: Tim E. Merritt, Chief Executive Officer
Web address: www.summitridgehospital.net
Control: Corporation, Investor–owned (for–profit) **Service**: Psychiatric

Staffed Beds: 96 **Admissions:** 3698 **Census:** 80 **Outpatient Visits:** 7803 **Births:** 0 **Total Expense ($000):** 15965 **Payroll Expense ($000):** 9119 **Personnel:** 170

LITHONIA—Dekalb County

☐ **DEKALB MEDICAL AT HILLANDALE (110226)**, 2801 DeKalb Medical Parkway, Zip 30058–4996; tel. 404/501–8000, **A**1 10 **F**3 11 15 29 30 31 33 34 35 40 45 47 48 49 56 57 59 60 70 74 75 77 78 79 81 85 87 93 102 107 108 111 114 119 120 130 146 **S** Emory Healthcare, Atlanta, GA
Primary Contact: Robert E. Wilson Esq, Chief Executive Officer
CMO: Duane Barclay, D.O., Chief Medical Officer
CIO: Mark Trocino, Chief Information Officer
CHR: Tom Crawford, Vice President Human Resources
Web address: www.dekalbmedical.org
Control: Other not–for–profit (including NFP Corporation) **Service**: General medical and surgical

Staffed Beds: 80 **Admissions:** 4611 **Census:** 55 **Outpatient Visits:** 99516 **Births:** 0 **Total Expense ($000):** 74012 **Payroll Expense ($000):** 29874

LOUISVILLE—Jefferson County

⇑ **JEFFERSON HOSPITAL (110100)**, 1067 Peachtree Street, Zip 30434–1599; tel. 478/625–7000, **A**10 20 21 **F**3 11 15 29 30 34 35 40 43 46 50 57 59 64 65 66 68 75 77 81 86 90 91 93 96 97 102 107 110 115 119 127 129 130 133 146 148 154 **P**4
Primary Contact: Louis Semrad, Chief Executive Officer
CFO: Lieutenant John Graham, Chief Financial Officer
CMO: James Polhill, M.D., Chief Medical Officer
CHR: Catherine Hall, Manager Human Resources
CNO: Stacey Smith, R.N., Director of Nursing
Web address: www.jeffersonhosp.com
Control: County, Government, nonfederal **Service**: General medical and surgical

Staffed Beds: 37 **Admissions:** 388 **Census:** 4 **Outpatient Visits:** 25800 **Births:** 0 **Total Expense ($000):** 11700 **Payroll Expense ($000):** 6211 **Personnel:** 120

MACON—Bibb County

✠ **COLISEUM MEDICAL CENTERS (110164)**, 350 Hospital Drive, Zip 31217–3871; tel. 478/765–7000, (Includes COLISEUM CENTER FOR BEHAVIORAL HEALTH, 340 Hospital Drive, Macon, GA, Zip 31217–3838; tel. 478/741–1355; Stephen J. Daugherty, Interim Chief Executive Officer) (Nonreporting) **A**1 2 3 10 **S** HCA Healthcare, Nashville, TN
Primary Contact: Stephen J. Daugherty, Chief Executive Officer
COO: Kelly Lindsay, Chief Operating Officer
CFO: Scott Anderton, Chief Financial Officer
CIO: Joan Morstad, Director Information Systems
CHR: Laura Booras, Vice President Human Resources
Web address: www.coliseumhealthsystem.com
Control: Corporation, Investor–owned (for–profit) **Service**: General medical and surgical

Staffed Beds: 227

✠ **COLISEUM NORTHSIDE HOSPITAL (110201)**, 400 Charter Boulevard, Zip 31210–4853, Mailing Address: P.O. Box 4627, Zip 31208–4627; tel. 478/757–8200, (Nonreporting) **A**1 10 **S** HCA Healthcare, Nashville, TN
Primary Contact: Greg Caples, Chief Executive Officer
CFO: Elmer Polite, Chief Financial Officer
CHR: Louise Truitt, Human Resource Director
CNO: Patricia Derrico, FACHE, R.N., Chief Nursing Officer
Web address: www.coliseumhealthsystem.com
Control: Corporation, Investor–owned (for–profit) **Service**: General medical and surgical

Staffed Beds: 103

★ ⇑ **MEDICAL CENTER, NAVICENT HEALTH (110107)**, 777 Hemlock Street, Zip 31201–2155; tel. 478/633–1000, (Includes CHILDREN'S HOSPITAL, NAVICENT HEALTH, 888 Pine Street, Macon, GA, Zip 31201–2155; tel. 478/633–1000) **A**2 3 5 8 10 21 **F**3 7 8 11 12 13 14 15 17 18 20 22 24 26 28 29 30 31 32 34 35 36 39 40 43 44 45 46 47 48 49 50 51 53 54 56 57 58 59 60 61 62 63 64 65 66 68 70 72 73 74 75 76 77 78 79 80 81 84 85 86 87 88 89 92 93 94 97 98 100 101 102 104 107 108 110 111 114 115 119 126 130 132 135 143 144 145 146 147 148 149 150 154 **P**1 **S** Navicent Health, Macon, GA
Primary Contact: Ninfa M. Saunders, Chief Executive Officer
COO: Susan Harris, R.N., Chief Operating Officer
CFO: Rhonda S. Perry, Chief Financial Officer
CMO: Christopher Hendry, M.D., Chief Medical Officer
CIO: Ed Brown, Chief Information Officer
CHR: Bernard J Price, Chief Human Resources Officer
CNO: Tracey Blalock, MSN, R.N., Chief Nurse Executive
Web address: www.navicenthealth.org/
Control: Other not–for–profit (including NFP Corporation) **Service**: General medical and surgical

Staffed Beds: 627 **Admissions:** 29191 **Census:** 468 **Outpatient Visits:** 382287 **Births:** 2450 **Total Expense ($000):** 630037 **Payroll Expense ($000):** 206407 **Personnel:** 4350

✠ **REGENCY HOSPITAL OF CENTRAL GEORGIA (112016)**, 535 Coliseum Drive, Zip 31217–0104; tel. 478/803–7300, (Nonreporting) **A**1 10 **S** Select Medical Corporation, Mechanicsburg, PA
Primary Contact: Wayne B. Boutwell, Chief Executive Officer
Web address: www.regencyhospital.com
Control: Corporation, Investor–owned (for–profit) **Service**: Acute long–term care hospital

Staffed Beds: 60

Many Facility Codes have changed. Please refer to the AHA Guide Code Chart. © 2018 AHA Guide

★ ⇑ **REHABILITATION HOSPITAL, NAVICENT HEALTH (113029)**, 3351 Northside Drive, Zip 31210–2587; tel. 478/201–6500, (Nonreporting) **A**3 10 21 **S** Navicent Health, Macon, GA
Primary Contact: Gina Tipton, Director of Operations
COO: Darren Pearce, Executive Director
CFO: Beverly Owens, Controller
CMO: Allison Scheetz, M.D., Medical Director
Web address: www.navicenthealth.org/service–center/rehabilitation–hospital–navicent–health
Control: Other not–for–profit (including NFP Corporation) **Service:** Rehabilitation

Staffed Beds: 58

MADISON—Morgan County

☐ **MORGAN MEMORIAL HOSPITAL (111304)**, 1077 South Main Street, Zip 30650–2073, Mailing Address: P.O. Box 860, Zip 30650–0860; tel. 706/342–1667, (Nonreporting) **A**1 10 18
Primary Contact: Ralph A. Castillo, CPA, Chief Executive Officer
CFO: Kyle Wilkinson, Chief Financial Officer
CMO: Dan Zant, M.D., Chief of Staff
CIO: Patrick Cook, Vice President Support Services
CHR: Sarah Phillips, Manager Human Resources
CNO: Beth O'Neill, Chief Nursing Officer
Web address: www.mmh.org
Control: Hospital district or authority, Government, nonfederal **Service:** General medical and surgical

Staffed Beds: 25

MARIETTA—Cobb County

⊞ △ **WELLSTAR KENNESTONE HOSPITAL (110035)**, 677 Church Street, Zip 30060–1148; tel. 770/793–5000, **A**1 2 3 5 7 10 **F**3 10 11 12 13 15 17 18 20 22 24 26 28 29 30 31 34 36 37 38 40 41 43 44 45 46 47 48 49 50 51 53 54 55 58 59 60 61 64 66 68 70 72 73 74 75 76 77 78 79 80 81 82 84 85 86 87 89 90 93 94 96 97 100 102 107 108 110 111 114 115 116 117 118 119 120 121 123 124 125 126 129 130 132 141 146 147 148 154 **P**5 6 **S** WellStar Health System, Marietta, GA
Primary Contact: Mary Chatman, Ph.D., Chief Executive Officer
CFO: Douglas Arvin, Vice President Finance and Chief Financial Officer
CMO: Robert Lubitz, M.D., Vice President of Medical Affairs
CIO: Jonathan B Morris, M.D., Senior Vice President and Chief Information Officer
CHR: Jimmy Duncan, Vice President Human Resources
CNO: Lynn Meurer, MSN, R.N., Interim Chief Nursing Officer
Web address: www.wellstar.org
Control: Other not–for–profit (including NFP Corporation) **Service:** General medical and surgical

Staffed Beds: 657 **Admissions:** 40613 **Census:** 531 **Outpatient Visits:** 458709 **Births:** 5556 **Personnel:** 4049

⊞ **WELLSTAR WINDY HILL HOSPITAL (112007)**, 2540 Windy Hill Road, Zip 30067–8632; tel. 770/644–1000, **A**1 2 10 **F**1 3 11 15 28 29 30 44 45 50 51 60 61 64 68 75 77 79 81 82 85 86 87 93 100 101 107 108 110 111 114 118 119 129 130 131 135 141 146 147 148 **P**5 6 **S** WellStar Health System, Marietta, GA
Primary Contact: Monte Wilson, President
CFO: Marsha Burke, Senior Vice President and Chief Financial Officer
CMO: Larry Haldeman, M.D., Executive Vice President and Chief Medical Officer
CIO: Leigh Cox, Chief Information Officer
Web address: www.wellstar.org
Control: Other not–for–profit (including NFP Corporation) **Service:** Acute long–term care hospital

Staffed Beds: 55 **Admissions:** 345 **Census:** 27 **Outpatient Visits:** 96880 **Births:** 0 **Personnel:** 326

METTER—Candler County

☐ **CANDLER COUNTY HOSPITAL (111334)**, 400 Cedar Street, Zip 30439–3338, Mailing Address: P.O. Box 597, Zip 30439–0597; tel. 912/685–5741, (Nonreporting) **A**1 10 18
Primary Contact: Mel Pyne, Chief Executive Officer
COO: David Flanders, Chief Operating Officer
CNO: Christy Blackburn, R.N., Chief Nursing Officer
Web address: www.candlercountyhospital.com
Control: Hospital district or authority, Government, nonfederal **Service:** General medical and surgical

Staffed Beds: 25

MILLEDGEVILLE—Baldwin County

☐ **CENTRAL STATE HOSPITAL**, 620 Broad Street, Zip 31062–0001; tel. 478/445–4128, (Nonreporting) **A**1 3
Primary Contact: Susan Trueblood, Regional Hospital Administrator
COO: Terry McGee, Chief Operations Officer
CMO: Scott VanSant, M.D., Chief Medical Officer
CIO: Betsy Bradley, Coordinator Performance Improvement
CHR: Myra Holloway, Director Human Resources Management
Web address: www.centralstatehospital.org
Control: State, Government, nonfederal **Service:** Psychiatric

Staffed Beds: 202

⊞ **NAVICENT HEALTH BALDWIN (110150)**, 821 North Cobb Street, Zip 31061–2351, Mailing Address: P.O. Box 690, Zip 31059–0690; tel. 478/454–3505, (Nonreporting) **A**1 10 19 **S** Navicent Health, Macon, GA
Primary Contact: Todd Dixon, R.N., Chief Executive Officer
CFO: Brenda Qualls, Chief Financial Officer
CNO: Deborah Block, Vice President Nursing and Chief Nursing Officer
Web address: www.navicenthealth.org/nhb/home
Control: Other not–for–profit (including NFP Corporation) **Service:** General medical and surgical

Staffed Beds: 90

MILLEN—Jenkins County

OPTIM MEDICAL CENTER – JENKINS (111311), 931 East Winthrope Avenue, Zip 30442–1839; tel. 478/982–4221, (Nonreporting) **A**10 18 **S** National Surgical Healthcare, Chicago, IL
Primary Contact: Robert R. Sellers, Chief Executive Officer
CFO: Cindy Bierschenk, Director of Financial Services
CIO: Christian Rekowski, Information Technology Director
CHR: Natalie Peterson, Director of Human Resources
CNO: Sharon Lagina Evans, R.N., Assistant Chief Nursing Officer
Web address: www.optimhealth.com
Control: Hospital district or authority, Government, nonfederal **Service:** General medical and surgical

Staffed Beds: 25

MONROE—Walton County

⊞ **PIEDMONT WALTON HOSPITAL (110046)**, 2151 West Spring Street, Zip 30655–3115, Mailing Address: PO BOX 1346, Zip 30655–1346; tel. 770/267–8461, (Nonreporting) **A**1 10 **S** Piedmont Healthcare, Roswell, GA
Primary Contact: Michael Johnson, Chief Executive Officer
CFO: Jeffrey Mullis, Interim Chief Financial Officer
CMO: Robert Sinyard, M.D., Chief Medical Officer
CIO: Cory Crayton, Director of Information Systems
CHR: Michele Monsrud, Director Human Resources
CNO: Sharon H Queen, R.N., Chief Nursing Officer
Web address: www.piedmont.org/locations/piedmont–walton/home
Control: Corporation, Investor–owned (for–profit) **Service:** General medical and surgical

Staffed Beds: 77

MONTEZUMA—Macon County

⇑ **FLINT RIVER COMMUNITY HOSPITAL (110190)**, 509 Sumter Street, Zip 31063–1733, Mailing Address: P.O. Box 770, Zip 31063–2502; tel. 478/472–3100, (Nonreporting) **A**10 21
Primary Contact: Michael C. Patterson, Chief Executive Officer
CMO: Quincy Jordan, M.D., Chief of Staff
CHR: Vicki Stotts, Coordinator Human Resources
CNO: Lee Hughes, R.N., Chief Nursing Officer
Web address: www.flintriverhospital.com/
Control: Corporation, Investor–owned (for–profit) **Service:** General medical and surgical

Staffed Beds: 49

GA

Hospital, Medicare Provider Number, Address, Telephone, Approval, Facility, and Physician Codes, Health Care System

★ American Hospital Association (AHA) membership
☐ The Joint Commission accreditation
○ Healthcare Facilities Accreditation Program
◇ DNV Healthcare Inc. accreditation
⇑ Center for Improvement in Healthcare Quality Accreditation
△ Commission on Accreditation of Rehabilitation Facilities (CARF) accreditation

MONTICELLO—Jasper County

JASPER MEMORIAL HOSPITAL (111303), 898 College Street,
Zip 31064–1258; tel. 706/468–6411, (Total facility includes 55 beds in nursing home–type unit) **A**10 18 **F**11 18 29 34 40 57 59 65 77 93 97 107 119 128 133 146 148 149 **P**6
Primary Contact: Jan Gaston, Administrator
CFO: Stuart Abney, Controller
CHR: Laura E Hudgins, Assistant Administrator
CNO: Robin Carey, Director of Nursing
Web address: www.jaspermemorialhospital.org
Control: Other not–for–profit (including NFP Corporation) **Service:** General medical and surgical

Staffed Beds: 67 **Admissions:** 162 **Census:** 56 **Outpatient Visits:** 8295 **Births:** 0 **Total Expense ($000):** 10825 **Payroll Expense ($000):** 5039 **Personnel:** 135

MOULTRIE—Colquitt County

◻ ○ **COLQUITT REGIONAL MEDICAL CENTER (110105)**, 3131 South Main Street, Zip 31768–6925, Mailing Address: P.O. Box 40, Zip 31776–0040; tel. 229/985–3420, **A**1 3 10 11 **F**3 7 11 12 13 15 17 20 29 30 31 32 34 35 40 45 47 48 49 56 57 59 60 61 62 63 65 68 70 74 75 76 77 78 79 81 82 85 86 87 89 91 93 97 107 108 110 111 115 119 126 127 129 130 131 132 133 135 143 146 147 148
Primary Contact: James L. Matney, President and Chief Executive Officer
COO: Greg K Johnson, Chief Operating Officer
CFO: Shamb Purohit, Chief Financial Officer
CMO: Andy Wills, M.D., Medical Director
CIO: Bill Bishop, Chief Information Officer
CHR: Dawn Johns, Director Human Resources
CNO: Dena Zinker, MSN, R.N., Vice President Patient Services
Web address: www.colquittregional.com
Control: Hospital district or authority, Government, nonfederal **Service:** General medical and surgical

Staffed Beds: 99 **Admissions:** 4567 **Census:** 58 **Outpatient Visits:** 144784 **Births:** 522 **Total Expense ($000):** 109554 **Payroll Expense ($000):** 45105 **Personnel:** 906

TURNING POINT HOSPITAL (110209), 3015 Veterans Parkway South, Zip 31788–6705, Mailing Address: P.O. Box 1177, Zip 31776–1177; tel. 229/985–4815, **A**10 **F**4 5 30 75 87 98 130 135 143 152 **P**6 **S** Universal Health Services, Inc., King of Prussia, PA
Primary Contact: Judy H. Payne, Chief Executive Officer
COO: Mark A Heatley, Associate Administrator
CFO: Edwin Bennett, Controller
CMO: Muhammad M Alam, M.D., Medical Director
CHR: Michelle Hamilton, Human Resource Manager
CNO: Faith Connell, Director of Nursing
Web address: www.turningpointcare.com
Control: Corporation, Investor–owned (for–profit) **Service:** Alcoholism and other chemical dependency

Staffed Beds: 59 **Admissions:** 3784 **Census:** 57 **Outpatient Visits:** 33332 **Births:** 0 **Total Expense ($000):** 25018 **Payroll Expense ($000):** 13495 **Personnel:** 230

NASHVILLE—Berrien County

◻ **SOUTH GEORGIA MEDICAL CENTER BERRIEN CAMPUS (110234)**, 1221 East McPherson Avenue, Zip 31639–2326; tel. 229/433–8600, (Nonreporting) **A**1 10 **S** South Georgia Medical Center, Valdosta, GA
Primary Contact: Richard Huth, Administrator
Web address: www.sgmc.org/
Control: Other not–for–profit (including NFP Corporation) **Service:** General medical and surgical

Staffed Beds: 39

NEWNAN—Coweta County

⇧ **PIEDMONT NEWNAN HOSPITAL (110229)**, 745 Poplar Road, Zip 30265–1618; tel. 770/400–1000, **A**2 10 21 **F**3 11 12 13 15 18 20 26 28 29 30 31 34 35 40 45 46 49 51 53 57 59 60 64 68 70 72 73 74 75 76 77 78 79 81 84 85 86 87 93 107 108 110 111 114 115 116 117 118 119 120 121 123 126 129 130 132 135 146 148 **S** Piedmont Healthcare, Roswell, GA
Primary Contact: Michael Robertson, Chief Executive Officer
COO: Nathan Nipper, Vice President and Chief Operating Officer
CFO: John Miles, Chief Financial Officer
CMO: Jeffrey R Folk, M.D., Vice President Medical Affairs and Chief Medical Officer
CIO: Henry Scott, Executive Director, Technical Services
CHR: Clay Boyles, Executive Director, Human Resources
CNO: Jennifer Key, Chief Nursing Officer
Web address: www.piedmont.org/locations/piedmont–newnan/pnh–home
Control: Other not–for–profit (including NFP Corporation) **Service:** General medical and surgical

Staffed Beds: 146 **Admissions:** 9211 **Census:** 105 **Outpatient Visits:** 126771 **Births:** 1254 **Total Expense ($000):** 139434 **Payroll Expense ($000):** 57034 **Personnel:** 772

◻ **SOUTHEASTERN REGIONAL MEDICAL CENTER (110233)**, 600 Celebrate Life Parkway, Zip 30265–8000; tel. 770/400–6000, **A**1 2 10 **F**3 7 15 29 30 31 33 34 35 36 45 46 47 49 55 64 67 70 75 77 78 81 82 84 85 86 87 93 107 108 109 110 111 114 115 116 117 118 119 120 121 123 124 130 132 135 146 148 **P**6 **S** Cancer Treatment Centers of America, Schaumburg, IL
Primary Contact: Anne Meisner, MSN, President and Chief Executive Officer
COO: David Kent, Chief Operating Officer
CFO: Scott Walker, Chief Financial Officer
CNO: Gloria V. Barnes, MSN, Assistant Vice President Patient Care Services
Web address: www.cancercenter.com/southeastern–hospital.cfm
Control: Corporation, Investor–owned (for–profit) **Service:** Cancer

Staffed Beds: 50 **Admissions:** 1838 **Census:** 27 **Outpatient Visits:** 27583 **Births:** 0 **Personnel:** 887

NORCROSS—Gwinnett County

LAKEVIEW BEHAVIORAL HEALTH, 1 Technology Parkway South, Zip 30092–2928; tel. 678/713–2600, (Nonreporting) **S** Acadia Healthcare Company, Inc., Franklin, TN
Primary Contact: Bill Anderson, Chief Executive Officer
Web address: www.lakeviewbehavioralhealth.com
Control: Corporation, Investor–owned (for–profit) **Service:** Psychiatric

Staffed Beds: 70

OCILLA—Irwin County

⇧ **IRWIN COUNTY HOSPITAL (110130)**, 710 North Irwin Avenue, Zip 31774–5011; tel. 229/468–3800, (Total facility includes 30 beds in nursing home–type unit) **A**10 21 **F**3 13 15 29 40 59 81 107 110 119 123 128 130
Primary Contact: Paige Wynn, Administrator
CFO: Tami Gray, Chief Financial Officer
CMO: Ashfaq Saiyed, M.D., Medical Director
CHR: Becky Edwards, Manager Human Resources
Web address: www.irwincntyhospital.com
Control: Hospital district or authority, Government, nonfederal **Service:** General medical and surgical

Staffed Beds: 64 **Admissions:** 711 **Census:** 35 **Outpatient Visits:** 7057 **Births:** 378 **Total Expense ($000):** 14246 **Payroll Expense ($000):** 6605 **Personnel:** 149

PERRY—Houston County

◻ **PERRY HOSPITAL (110153)**, 1120 Morningside Drive, Zip 31069–2906; tel. 478/987–3600, **A**1 10 **F**3 11 15 18 29 30 34 35 39 40 45 48 50 57 59 61 64 68 70 75 79 81 82 85 86 87 89 93 100 107 110 111 114 115 119 129 130 131 132 133 134 135 146 149 **S** Houston Healthcare System, Warner Robins, GA
Primary Contact: David Campbell, Administrator
COO: Charles G Briscoe, FACHE, Chief Operating Officer
CFO: Sean Whilden, Chief Financial Officer
CMO: Larry D. Stewart Jr Chief Medical Officer and Vice President, Medical Affairs
CHR: Michael O'Hara, Senior Executive Director
CNO: Melinda D. Hartley, R.N., Vice President Patient Care Services
Web address: www.hhc.org
Control: Other not–for–profit (including NFP Corporation) **Service:** General medical and surgical

Staffed Beds: 39 **Admissions:** 1419 **Census:** 17 **Outpatient Visits:** 40542 **Births:** 0 **Total Expense ($000):** 25802 **Payroll Expense ($000):** 10113 **Personnel:** 209

QUITMAN—Brooks County

◻ **BROOKS COUNTY HOSPITAL (111332)**, 903 North Court Street, Zip 31643–1315, Mailing Address: P.O. Box 5000, Zip 31643–5000; tel. 229/263–4171, **A**1 10 18 **F**15 29 30 34 40 87 93 107 110 119 133 146 149 154 **P**8 **S** Archbold Medical Center, Thomasville, GA
Primary Contact: Nancy M. Williams, R.N., Administrator
CFO: Skip Hightower, Chief Financial Officer
CMO: Michael Sopt, M.D., Chief of Staff
CHR: Janet Eldridge, Director Human Resources and Personnel
CNO: June Furney, R.N., Director of Nursing
Web address: www.archbold.org
Control: Other not–for–profit (including NFP Corporation) **Service:** General medical and surgical

Staffed Beds: 25 **Admissions:** 415 **Census:** 14 **Outpatient Visits:** 23339 **Births:** 0 **Total Expense ($000):** 10875 **Payroll Expense ($000):** 4842 **Personnel:** 91

GA

REIDSVILLE—Tattnall County

★ **OPTIM MEDICAL CENTER – TATTNALL (111323)**, 247 South Main Street, Zip 30453–4605; tel. 912/557–1000, (Nonreporting) **A**10 18 **S** National Surgical Healthcare, Chicago, IL
Primary Contact: Rob Snipes, Administrator
Web address: www.optimmedicalcenter.com
Control: Corporation, Investor–owned (for–profit) **Service:** Orthopedic

Staffed Beds: 25

RIVERDALE—Clayton County

☐ **RIVERWOODS BEHAVIORAL HEALTH SYSTEM (114035)**, 233 Medical Center Drive, Zip 30274–2640; tel. 770/991–8500, (Nonreporting) **A**1 5 10 **S** Acadia Healthcare Company, Inc., Franklin, TN
Primary Contact: John B. Warburton, Chief Executive Officer
COO: Jenifer Harcourt, Chief Operating Officer
CFO: Tricia Nelson, Chief Financial Officer
CIO: Hema Patel, Director Medical Records
CHR: Tareka Beasley, Director Human Resources
Web address: www.riverwoodsbehavioral.com
Control: Corporation, Investor–owned (for–profit) **Service:** Psychiatric

Staffed Beds: 75

⊞ **SOUTHERN CRESCENT HOSPITAL FOR SPECIALTY CARE (112015)**, 11 Upper Riverdale Road SW, 6th Floor, Zip 30274–2615; tel. 770/897–7600, (Nonreporting) **A**1 10 **S** LHC Group, Lafayette, LA
Primary Contact: Ulysses Fisher, Administrator
Web address: www.christusdubuis.org/SouthernCrescentHospitalforSpecialtyCare
Control: Church operated, Nongovernment, not–for–profit **Service:** Acute long–term care hospital

Staffed Beds: 30

⊞ **SOUTHERN REGIONAL MEDICAL CENTER (110165)**, 11 Upper Riverdale Road SW, Zip 30274–2615; tel. 770/991–8000, (Nonreporting) **A**1 2 5 10 **S** Prime Healthcare, Ontario, CA
Primary Contact: Charlotte W. Dupre, Chief Executive Officer
COO: Therese O Sucher, Senior Vice President Operations
CFO: Richard G Stovall, Senior Vice President Fiscal Services and Chief Financial Officer
CMO: Willie Cochran, M.D., Jr Chief of Staff
CIO: Karen Moore, Vice President Information Technology and Chief Information Officer
CHR: Norma Adams, Director Human Resources
Web address: www.southernregional.org
Control: Other not–for–profit (including NFP Corporation) **Service:** General medical and surgical

Staffed Beds: 331

ROME—Floyd County

⊞ **FLOYD MEDICAL CENTER (110054)**, 304 Turner McCall Boulevard, Zip 30165–5621; Mailing Address: P.O. Box 233, Zip 30162–0233; tel. 706/509–5000, **A**1 2 3 5 10 13 19 **F**3 4 5 6 7 8 9 11 12 13 15 17 18 20 22 26 28 29 30 31 32 34 35 36 37 38 39 40 43 44 45 46 48 49 50 51 53 54 56 57 58 59 61 63 64 65 66 68 70 71 72 74 75 76 77 78 79 81 82 84 85 86 87 89 90 93 96 97 98 100 101 102 103 104 105 107 108 110 111 114 115 118 119 129 130 131 132 134 135 143 144 146 147 148 149 151 152 154 **S** Floyd Healthcare Management, Rome, GA
Primary Contact: Kurt Stuenkel, FACHE, President and Chief Executive Officer
COO: Warren Alston Rigas, Executive Vice President and Chief Operating Officer
CFO: Rick Sheerin, Vice President Fiscal Services
CMO: Joseph Biuso, M.D., Vice President and Chief of Medical Affairs
CIO: Jeff Buda, Chief Information Officer
CHR: Beth Bradford, Director Human Resources
CNO: Sheila Bennett, R.N., Vice President & Chief Nursing Officer
Web address: www.floyd.org
Control: Other not–for–profit (including NFP Corporation) **Service:** General medical and surgical

Staffed Beds: 327 **Admissions:** 14699 **Census:** 208 **Outpatient Visits:** 277172 **Births:** 2294 **Total Expense ($000):** 402449 **Payroll Expense ($000):** 173688 **Personnel:** 2547

⊞ **KINDRED HOSPITAL ROME (112010)**, 304 Turner McCall Boulevard, Zip 30165–5621; tel. 706/378–6800, (Nonreporting) **A**1 10 **S** Kindred Healthcare, Louisville, KY
Primary Contact: Al Diaz, M.D., Chief Executive Officer
CFO: Julia Smith, Chief Financial Officer
CMO: Brij Singh, Medical Staff Director
CHR: Holly Murdock, Human Resources Coordinator
CNO: Jennifer Johnstone, Chief Clinical Officer
Web address: www.kindredrome.com
Control: Corporation, Investor–owned (for–profit) **Service:** Acute long–term care hospital

Staffed Beds: 45

⊞ **REDMOND REGIONAL MEDICAL CENTER (110168)**, 501 Redmond Road, Zip 30165–1415, Mailing Address: P.O. Box 107001, Zip 30164–7001; tel. 706/291–0291, (Nonreporting) **A**1 2 3 10 19 **S** HCA Healthcare, Nashville, TN
Primary Contact: John Quinlivan, Chief Executive Officer
COO: David Bradley Stockton, Chief Operating Officer
CFO: Kenneth Metteauer, Chief Financial Officer
CMO: Julie Coffman Barnes, M.D., Chief Medical Officer
CIO: Brad Treglown, Director Information Systems
CHR: Patsy Adams, Vice President Human Resources
CNO: Stephanie Jones, R.N., Chief Nursing Officer
Web address: www.redmondregional.com
Control: Corporation, Investor–owned (for–profit) **Service:** General medical and surgical

Staffed Beds: 230

SPECIALTY HOSPITAL See Kindred Hospital Rome

ROSWELL—Fulton County

⊞ **WELLSTAR NORTH FULTON HOSPITAL (110198)**, 3000 Hospital Boulevard, Zip 30076–3899; tel. 770/751–2500, **A**1 2 3 10 13 **F**3 13 15 18 20 22 28 29 31 34 35 37 40 43 45 48 49 55 57 59 67 68 70 73 74 75 76 77 78 79 81 82 85 86 87 90 91 92 107 108 110 111 114 115 118 119 126 130 146 147 148 152 **P**5 6 **S** WellStar Health System, Marietta, GA
Primary Contact: Jon–Paul Croom, President
COO: Lindsey Petrini, Chief Operating Officer
CFO: Felix Sotoizaguirre, Chief Financial Officer
CMO: Karim Godamunne, M.D., Chief Medical Officer
CHR: Susan Brown, Chief Human Resources Officer
CNO: Nancy Melcher, Chief Nursing Officer
Web address: www.nfultonhospital.com
Control: Other not–for–profit (including NFP Corporation) **Service:** General medical and surgical

Staffed Beds: 173 **Admissions:** 6613 **Census:** 102 **Outpatient Visits:** 84241 **Births:** 937 **Personnel:** 738

SAINT MARYS—Camden County

⊞ **SOUTHEAST GEORGIA HEALTH SYSTEM CAMDEN CAMPUS (110146)**, 2000 Dan Proctor Drive, Zip 31558–3810; tel. 912/576–6200, **A**1 10 20 **F**3 11 13 15 18 29 30 31 34 35 40 45 46 47 48 49 50 57 59 64 68 70 71 75 76 77 78 79 81 85 86 87 93 94 107 108 110 111 114 116 117 119 120 129 130 131 132 146 149 **P**5 **S** Southeast Georgia Health System, Brunswick, GA
Primary Contact: Howard W. Sepp Jr, Vice–President and Administrator
CFO: Janice Dunn, Chief Financial Officer
CMO: Robert Bernasek, M.D., Chief Medical Officer
CIO: Charles Bumgardner, Director
CNO: Judith Henson, Vice President, Patient Care Services
Web address: www.sghs.org
Control: City–county, Government, nonfederal **Service:** General medical and surgical

Staffed Beds: 40 **Admissions:** 1966 **Census:** 18 **Outpatient Visits:** 87361 **Births:** 636 **Total Expense ($000):** 41123 **Payroll Expense ($000):** 15775 **Personnel:** 274

SAINT SIMONS ISLAND—Glynn County

☐ **SAINT SIMONS BY–THE–SEA HOSPITAL (114016)**, 2927 Demere Road, Zip 31522–1620; tel. 912/638–1999, **A**1 10 **F**98 102 154 **S** Universal Health Services, Inc., King of Prussia, PA
Primary Contact: Chuck Flavio, Chief Executive Officer
CMO: Kim Masters, M.D., Medical Director
CIO: Chisty Mosely, Director Information Management
Web address: www.ssbythesea.com
Control: Corporation, Investor–owned (for–profit) **Service:** Psychiatric

Staffed Beds: 101 **Admissions:** 2587 **Census:** 45 **Outpatient Visits:** 0 **Births:** 0 **Total Expense ($000):** 12426 **Payroll Expense ($000):** 6474

GA

Hospital, Medicare Provider Number, Address, Telephone, Approval, Facility, and Physician Codes, Health Care System

★ American Hospital Association (AHA) membership
☐ The Joint Commission accreditation
○ Healthcare Facilities Accreditation Program
◇ DNV Healthcare Inc. accreditation
⇑ Center for Improvement in Healthcare Quality Accreditation
△ Commission on Accreditation of Rehabilitation Facilities (CARF) accreditation

SANDERSVILLE—Washington County

☐ **WASHINGTON COUNTY REGIONAL MEDICAL CENTER (110086)**, 610 Sparta Road, Zip 31082–1860, Mailing Address: P.O. Box 636, Zip 31082–0636; tel. 478/240–2000, (Nonreporting) **A**1 10 20
Primary Contact: Antoine Poythress, Interim Chief Executive Officer
CFO: Antoine Poythress, Chief Financial Officer
CMO: Rob Gatliff, Chief of Medical Staff
CHR: Misty Ivey, Human Resources Manager
CNO: Pamela Stewart, Director of Nursing
Web address: www.wcrmc.com
Control: Hospital district or authority, Government, nonfederal **Service**: General medical and surgical

Staffed Beds: 116

SAVANNAH—Chatham County

✠ △ **CANDLER HOSPITAL (110024)**, 5353 Reynolds Street, Zip 31405–6015; tel. 912/819–6000, (Total facility includes 11 beds in nursing home–type unit) **A**1 7 10 **F**2 3 11 13 15 18 20 29 30 31 32 34 35 36 38 39 40 44 45 46 47 48 49 50 53 54 57 58 59 60 61 64 65 68 70 71 73 74 75 76 77 78 80 81 82 84 85 86 87 89 90 93 94 96 107 108 110 111 115 117 118 119 120 121 123 124 126 128 129 130 131 132 135 146 147 148 149
Primary Contact: Paul P. Hinchey, President and Chief Executive Officer
CFO: Gregory J Schaack, CPA, Vice President and Chief Financial Officer
CMO: James Scott, M.D., Vice President Medical Affairs
CIO: George Evans, Vice President and Chief Information Officer
CHR: Don Stubbs, Vice President Human Resources
CNO: Sherry Danello, MSN, R.N., Vice President and Chief Nursing Officer
Web address: www.sjchs.org
Control: Church operated, Nongovernment, not–for–profit **Service**: General medical and surgical

Staffed Beds: 285 **Admissions**: 11393 **Census**: 172 **Outpatient Visits**: 256822 **Births**: 2700 **Total Expense ($000)**: 281669 **Payroll Expense ($000)**: 101134 **Personnel**: 1740

☐ **COASTAL HARBOR TREATMENT CENTER (114008)**, 1150 Cornell Avenue, Zip 31406–2702; tel. 912/354–3911, **A**1 10 **F**5 98 99 102 103 104 105 106 153 **P**6 **S** Universal Health Services, Inc., King of Prussia, PA
Primary Contact: Sally Perry, Chief Executive Officer
COO: Ray Heckerman, Chief Executive Officer and Managing Director
CFO: Brad Lavoie, Chief Financial Officer
CMO: Reemon Bishara, M.D., Medical Director
CHR: Kellie Carlson, Director Human Resources
CNO: Jillisa Thornton, Director of Nursing
Web address: www.coastalharbor.com
Control: Corporation, Investor–owned (for–profit) **Service**: Psychiatric

Staffed Beds: 191 **Admissions**: 3825 **Census**: 150 **Outpatient Visits**: 20720 **Births**: 0 **Total Expense ($000)**: 27375 **Payroll Expense ($000)**: 14143 **Personnel**: 274

GEORGE AND MARIE BACKUS CHILDREN'S HOSPITAL See Memorial Children's Hospital

☐ **GEORGIA REGIONAL HOSPITAL AT SAVANNAH (114028)**, 1915 Eisenhower Drive, Zip 31406–5098; tel. 912/356–2011, (Nonreporting) **A**1 10
Primary Contact: Andy Mannich, Regional Administrator
COO: Thomas F Kurtz Jr Chief Operating Officer
CFO: Janet Edenfield, Director Financial Services
CMO: Donald Manning, M.D., Clinical Director
CHR: Jamekia Powers, Assistant Director Human Resources
Web address: www.dbhdd.georgia.gov/georgia–regional–hospital–savannah
Control: State, Government, nonfederal **Service**: Psychiatric

Staffed Beds: 105

LANDMARK HOSPITAL OF SAVANNAH (112018), 800 East 68th Street, Zip 31405–4710; tel. 912/298–1000, (Nonreporting) **A**22 **S** Landmark Hospitals, Cape Girardeau, MO
Primary Contact: John Salandi, Chief Executive Officer
Web address: www.landmarkhospitals.com/savannah
Control: Partnership, Investor–owned (for–profit) **Service**: Acute long–term care hospital

Staffed Beds: 50

✠ △ **MEMORIAL HEALTH (110036)**, 4700 Waters Avenue, Zip 31404–6283, Mailing Address: P.O. Box 23089, Zip 31403–3089; tel. 912/350–8000, (Includes MEMORIAL CHILDREN'S HOSPITAL, 4700 Waters Avenue, Savannah, GA, Zip 31404–6220, Mailing Address: PO Box 23089, Zip 31403–3089, tel. 912/350–7337) **A**1 2 3 5 7 8 10 **F**3 8 11 12 13 14 15 17 18 19 20 22 24 26 28 29 30 31 32 34 35 36 37 39 40 41 43 44 45 46 49 50 53 54 55 56 57 59 60 61 64 65 66 68 70 71 72 73 74 75 76 77 78 79 80 81 82 83 84 85 86 87 88 89 92 93 96 97 98 100 101 102 104 105 107 110 111 115 117 118 119 120 121 122 123 124 126 129 130 131 132 135 143 144 146 147 148 149 153 **P**6 **S** HCA Healthcare, Nashville, TN
Primary Contact: Shayne George, Chief Executive Officer
COO: Matthew Steven Hasbrouck, Chief Operating Officer
CFO: Laura Dow, Chief Financial Officer
CMO: Ramon V Meguiar, M.D., Chief Medical Officer
CIO: Kathryn McClellan, Chief Information Officer
CHR: Alisa R Griner, Director, Human Resources
CNO: Mary Chatman, Ph.D., Senior Vice President, Chief Operating Officer and Chief Nursing Officer
Web address: www.memorialhealth.com
Control: Other not–for–profit (including NFP Corporation) **Service**: General medical and surgical

Staffed Beds: 523 **Admissions**: 26737 **Census**: 415 **Outpatient Visits**: 245147 **Births**: 2949 **Total Expense ($000)**: 516520 **Payroll Expense ($000)**: 174561 **Personnel**: 2463

★ **REHABILITATION HOSPITAL OF SAVANNAH (113033)**, 6510 Seawright DR, Zip 31406–2752; tel. 800/622–7269, (Nonreporting) **A**10 **S** Encompass Health Corporation, Birmingham, AL
Primary Contact: Kathy Kleinsteuber, Chief Executive Officer
Web address: www.rehabilitationhospitalsavannah.com
Control: Corporation, Investor–owned (for–profit) **Service**: Rehabilitation

Staffed Beds: 50

✠ **SELECT SPECIALTY HOSPITAL–SAVANNAH (112011)**, 5353 Reynolds Street, 4 South, Zip 31405–6015; tel. 912/819–7972, (Nonreporting) **A**1 10 **S** Select Medical Corporation, Mechanicsburg, PA
Primary Contact: Greg Wuchter, R.N., MSN, Chief Executive Officer
Web address: www.savannah.selectspecialtyhospitals.com
Control: Corporation, Investor–owned (for–profit) **Service**: Acute long–term care hospital

Staffed Beds: 40

ST. JOSEPH'S CANDLER HOSPITAL See Candler Hospital

☐ △ **ST. JOSEPH'S HOSPITAL (110043)**, 11705 Mercy Boulevard, Zip 31419–1791; tel. 912/819–4100, (Total facility includes 11 beds in nursing home–type unit) **A**1 2 7 10 **F**2 3 11 15 17 18 20 22 34 35 36 37 38 39 40 41 44 45 49 50 56 57 58 59 60 65 70 74 75 77 79 80 81 82 84 85 86 90 94 96 110 111 114 115 119 126 128 130 131 132 135 146 148 149 150
Primary Contact: Paul P. Hinchey, President and Chief Executive Officer
COO: Kyle McCann, Chief Operating Officer
CFO: Gregory J Schaack, CPA, Vice President and Chief Financial Officer
CMO: James Scott, M.D., Vice President Medical Affairs
CIO: Nolan Henessee, Vice President and Chief Information Officer
CHR: Steve Pound, Vice President Human Resources
CNO: Sherry Danello, MSN, R.N., Vice President and Chief Nursing Officer
Web address: www.sjchs.org
Control: Church operated, Nongovernment, not–for–profit **Service**: General medical and surgical

Staffed Beds: 230 **Admissions**: 11296 **Census**: 171 **Outpatient Visits**: 82827 **Births**: 0 **Total Expense ($000)**: 224145 **Payroll Expense ($000)**: 79388 **Personnel**: 1315

SMYRNA—Cobb County

✠ **RIDGEVIEW INSTITUTE (114012)**, 3995 South Cobb Drive SE, Zip 30080–6397; tel. 770/434–4567, (Nonreporting) **A**1 3 5 10
Primary Contact: Luis Betances, Chief Executive Officer
CFO: Ruth Jenkins, Chief Financial Officer
CMO: Thomas Bradford Johns, M.D., Medical Director
CIO: Lynn Leger, Director Information Systems
CHR: Betty Sonderman, Manager Human Resources
Web address: www.ridgeviewinstitute.com
Control: Other not–for–profit (including NFP Corporation) **Service**: Psychiatric

Staffed Beds: 102

GA

Many Facility Codes have changed. Please refer to the AHA Guide Code Chart. © 2018 AHA Guide

SNELLVILLE—Gwinnett County

✠ **EASTSIDE MEDICAL CENTER (110192)**, 1700 Medical Way, Zip 30078–2195; tel. 770/979–0200, (Nonreporting) **A**1 2 10 **S** HCA Healthcare, Nashville, TN
Primary Contact: Trent Lind, Chief Executive Officer
CMO: Michael O'Neill, M.D., Chief Medical Officer
CIO: Pattie Page, Director Marketing and Public Relations
CNO: Tracey Smithson, MSN, R.N., Chief Nursing Officer
Web address: www.eastsidemedical.com
Control: Corporation, Investor–owned (for–profit) **Service**: General medical and surgical

Staffed Beds: 294

SPRINGFIELD—Effingham County

✠ **EFFINGHAM HOSPITAL (111306)**, 459 Highway 119 South, Zip 31329–3021, Mailing Address: P.O. Box 386, Zip 31329–0386; tel. 912/754–6451, (Total facility includes 105 beds in nursing home–type unit) **A**1 10 18 **F**3 6 11 15 18 29 34 35 40 41 43 45 50 54 59 64 74 77 81 85 97 107 110 111 114 119 127 128 130 133 135 146 147 **P**6
Primary Contact: Francine Baker–Witt, R.N., Chief Executive Officer
CFO: Matthew Moore, Director of Financial Reporting
CMO: Claude Sanks, Chief Medical Staff
CIO: Mary Pizzino, Chief Information Officer
CHR: Marie Murphy, Director Human Resources
CNO: Betsy Smith, Chief Nursing Officer
Web address: www.effinghamhospital.org
Control: Hospital district or authority, Government, nonfederal **Service**: General medical and surgical

Staffed Beds: 130 Admissions: 1021 Census: 108 Outpatient Visits: 42865 Births: 0 Total Expense ($000): 43847 Payroll Expense ($000): 18131 Personnel: 319

STATESBORO—Bulloch County

✠ **EAST GEORGIA REGIONAL MEDICAL CENTER (110075)**, 1499 Fair Road, Zip 30458–1683, Mailing Address: P.O. Box 1048, Zip 30459–1048; tel. 912/486–1000, (Nonreporting) **A**1 10 19 **S** Community Health Systems, Inc., Franklin, TN
Primary Contact: Paul Theriot, Chief Executive Officer
COO: Erin Smith, Chief Operating Officer
CFO: Christine Markowitz, Chief Financial Officer
CMO: Mark McCracken, M.D., Chief of Staff
CIO: Brian Girardeau, Director Information System
CHR: Michael Black, Director Human Resources
CNO: Marie Burdette, Chief Nursing Officer
Web address: www.eastgeorgiaregional.com
Control: Corporation, Investor–owned (for–profit) **Service**: General medical and surgical

Staffed Beds: 149

WILLINGWAY HOSPITAL, 311 Jones Mill Road, Zip 30458–4765; tel. 912/764–6236, (Nonreporting) **A**3
Primary Contact: Cherie Tolley, Chief Executive Officer
CMO: Robert W Mooney, M.D., Medical Director
Web address: www.willingway.com
Control: Corporation, Investor–owned (for–profit) **Service**: Alcoholism and other chemical dependency

Staffed Beds: 40

STOCKBRIDGE—Henry County

⇑ **PIEDMONT HENRY HOSPITAL (110191)**, 1133 Eagle's Landing Parkway, Zip 30281–5099; tel. 678/604–1000, **A**2 10 21 **F**3 8 11 13 15 18 20 22 26 29 30 31 34 35 37 40 45 49 54 57 59 61 64 70 72 73 74 75 76 77 78 79 81 82 84 85 86 87 93 100 107 108 110 111 114 115 118 119 120 121 124 130 132 135 144 146 147 148 **S** Piedmont Healthcare, Roswell, GA
Primary Contact: Deborah Armstrong, Chief Executive Officer
COO: James Atkins, PharmD, Chief Operating Officer
CFO: Wesley James, Chief Financial Officer
CMO: Lily Henson, M.D., Chief Medical Officer
CHR: Jana Warren, Human Resources Business Partner
CNO: Paula Yvonne Butts, Chief Nursing Officer
Web address: www.piedmont.org
Control: Other not–for–profit (including NFP Corporation) **Service**: General medical and surgical

Staffed Beds: 214 Admissions: 14191 Census: 185 Outpatient Visits: 153722 Births: 2130 Total Expense ($000): 204332 Payroll Expense ($000): 82865 Personnel: 1277

SWAINSBORO—Emanuel County

⇑ **EMANUEL MEDICAL CENTER (110109)**, 117 Kite Road, Zip 30401–3231, Mailing Address: P.O. Box 879, Zip 30401–0879; tel. 478/289–1100, (Nonreporting) **A**10 20 21
Primary Contact: Mel Pyne, Chief Executive Officer
CFO: Rhonda Durden, Chief Financial Officer
CMO: Cedric Porter, M.D., President Medical Staff
CIO: Damien Scott, Chief Information Officer
CHR: Ellen Boyd, Director Human Resources
Web address: www.emanuelmedical.org
Control: Hospital district or authority, Government, nonfederal **Service**: General medical and surgical

Staffed Beds: 91

SYLVANIA—Screven County

★ **OPTIM MEDICAL CENTER – SCREVEN (111312)**, 215 Mims Road, Zip 30467–2097; tel. 912/564–7426, (Nonreporting) **A**10 18 **S** National Surgical Healthcare, Chicago, IL
Primary Contact: Robert R. Sellers, Chief Executive Officer
CFO: Cindy Bierschenk, Finance Director
CMO: Sherma Peter, M.D., Chief of Staff
CIO: Christian Rekowski, Information Technology Manager
CHR: Natalie Peterson, Director of Human Resources
CNO: Sharon Lagina Evans, R.N., Assistant Chief Nursing Officer
Web address: www.optimhealth.com
Control: County, Government, nonfederal **Service**: General medical and surgical

Staffed Beds: 25

SYLVESTER—Worth County

★ ⇑ **PHOEBE WORTH MEDICAL CENTER (111328)**, 807 South Isabella Street, Zip 31791–7554, Mailing Address: P.O. Box 545, Zip 31791–0545; tel. 229/776–6961, (Nonreporting) **A**10 18 21 **S** Phoebe Putney Health System, Albany, GA
Primary Contact: Kim Gilman, Chief Executive Officer
CFO: Candace Guarnieri, Chief Financial Officer
CMO: Natu M Patel, M.D., Chief of Staff
CHR: Mandy Gordon, Human Resource Coordinator
CNO: Kim Gilman, Chief Nursing Officer
Web address: www.phoebeputney.com
Control: Other not–for–profit (including NFP Corporation) **Service**: General medical and surgical

Staffed Beds: 18

THOMASTON—Upson County

★ ⇑ **UPSON REGIONAL MEDICAL CENTER (110002)**, 801 West Gordon Street, Zip 30286–3426, Mailing Address: P.O. Box 1059, Zip 30286–0027; tel. 706/647–8111, **A**10 21 **F**11 13 15 20 21 22 23 28 29 30 31 34 35 38 40 45 46 49 50 57 59 61 64 70 76 78 79 80 81 82 85 86 87 89 98 103 107 108 111 114 115 118 119 124 130 131 132 135 148 **P**6 **S** HealthTech Management Services, Brentwood, TN
Primary Contact: Tripp Penn, Chief Executive Officer
CFO: John Williams, Chief Financial Officer
CIO: Douglas Thompson, Chief Information Officer
CHR: Rich Williams, Director Human Resources
CNO: Marilyn Ray, MSN, Chief Nursing Officer
Web address: www.urmc.org
Control: Other not–for–profit (including NFP Corporation) **Service**: General medical and surgical

Staffed Beds: 81 Admissions: 2901 Census: 27 Outpatient Visits: 74610 Births: 362 Total Expense ($000): 68293 Payroll Expense ($000): 25072 Personnel: 596

THOMASVILLE—Thomas County

✠ **JOHN D. ARCHBOLD MEMORIAL HOSPITAL (110038)**, 915 Gordon Avenue, Zip 31792–6614, Mailing Address: P.O. Box 1018, Zip 31799–1018; tel. 229/228–2000, (Total facility includes 64 beds in nursing home–type unit) **A**1 2 10 19 **F**3 8 11 13 15 18 20 22 26 28 29 30 31 32 34 35 38 40 43 45 46 47 48 49 50 51 54 56 57 58 59 60 61 62 63 64 65 66 67 68 70 73 74 75 76 77 78 79 80 81 82 84 85 86 87 90 91 92 93 96 97 98 100 101 102 103 104 107 108 110 111 114 115 116 117 119 120 121 123 124 126 128 129 130 131 135 143 144 146 147 148 149 154 **P**8 **S** Archbold Medical Center, Thomasville, GA
Primary Contact: J Perry. Mustian, President and Chief Executive Officer
CFO: Skip Hightower, Senior Vice President and Chief Financial Officer
CIO: Tracy Gray, Senior Vice President Information Services
CHR: Zachariah P Wheeler, Senior Vice President Human Resources
CNO: Amy Griffin, Vice President Patient Care Services
Web address: www.archbold.org
Control: Other not–for–profit (including NFP Corporation) **Service**: General medical and surgical

Staffed Beds: 306 Admissions: 10273 Census: 224 Outpatient Visits: 267160 Births: 794 Total Expense ($000): 239459 Payroll Expense ($000): 80156 Personnel: 1509

GA

Hospital, Medicare Provider Number, Address, Telephone, Approval, Facility, and Physician Codes, Health Care System

★ American Hospital Association (AHA) membership   ◯ Healthcare Facilities Accreditation Program   ⇑ Center for Improvement in Healthcare Quality Accreditation
☐ The Joint Commission accreditation   ◇ DNV Healthcare Inc. accreditation   △ Commission on Accreditation of Rehabilitation Facilities (CARF) accreditation

THOMSON—McDuffie County

✠ **UNIVERSITY HOSPITAL MCDUFFIE (110111)**, 2460 Washington Road, NE, Zip 30824; tel. 706/595–1411, **A**1 10 **F**3 11 15 29 30 40 45 50 59 64 68 79 81 85 87 107 110 114 119 130 132 133 146 148 149 **S** University Health Care System, Augusta, GA
Primary Contact: Bob Kepshire, R.N., MS, Administrator and Chief Nursing Officer
CFO: Dave Belkoski, Chief Financial Officer
CNO: Bob Kepshire, R.N., MS, Administrator and Chief Nursing Officer
Web address: www.universityhealth.org/mcduffie
Control: Other not–for–profit (including NFP Corporation) **Service**: General medical and surgical

Staffed Beds: 22 **Admissions:** 720 **Census:** 13 **Outpatient Visits:** 33191 **Births:** 0 **Total Expense ($000):** 19125 **Payroll Expense ($000):** 5905 **Personnel:** 94

TIFTON—Tift County

✠ **TIFT REGIONAL MEDICAL CENTER (110095)**, 901 East 18th Street, Zip 31794–3648, Mailing Address: Drawer 747, Zip 31793–0747; tel. 229/382–7120, **A**1 2 10 19 **F**3 8 9 11 12 13 15 18 20 22 26 28 29 30 31 33 34 35 40 45 47 49 50 51 54 57 59 60 63 64 68 70 74 75 76 77 78 79 81 82 84 85 86 87 89 92 93 97 100 104 107 108 110 111 114 115 118 119 120 121 123 126 129 130 131 132 135 143 144 146 147 148 149 154 **P**6 **S** Tift Regional Health System, Tifton, GA
Primary Contact: Christopher Dorman, President and Chief Executive Officer
CFO: Dennis L Crum, Senior Vice President and Chief Financial Officer
CMO: William Guest, M.D., Senior Vice President and Chief Medical Officer
CIO: Guy McAllister, Vice President and Chief Information Officer
CHR: Lori S Folsom, Assistant Vice President Human Resources
CNO: Carol Smith, Vice President Patient Care and Chief Nursing Officer
Web address: www.tiftregional.com
Control: Hospital district or authority, Government, nonfederal **Service**: General medical and surgical

Staffed Beds: 181 **Admissions:** 9620 **Census:** 109 **Outpatient Visits:** 191182 **Births:** 1305 **Total Expense ($000):** 330418 **Payroll Expense ($000):** 141070 **Personnel:** 2017

TOCCOA—Stephens County

✠ **STEPHENS COUNTY HOSPITAL (110032)**, 163 Hospital Drive, Zip 30577–6820; tel. 706/282–4200, (Total facility includes 92 beds in nursing home–type unit) **A**1 10 **F**3 7 11 13 15 28 30 34 35 40 45 51 57 59 60 64 65 68 70 75 76 77 79 81 85 86 89 93 107 108 110 111 115 119 125 129 130 146 148 149
Primary Contact: Lynne Anderson, Chief Executive Officer
CFO: Jeff Laird, Controller
CHR: Diane Hardeman, Director Personnel
CNO: Faye M Taylor, R.N., Director of Nursing
Web address: www.stephenscountyhospital.com
Control: Hospital district or authority, Government, nonfederal **Service**: General medical and surgical

Staffed Beds: 188 **Admissions:** 1757 **Census:** 114 **Outpatient Visits:** 63124 **Births:** 242 **Total Expense ($000):** 55877 **Payroll Expense ($000):** 22332 **Personnel:** 422

VALDOSTA—Lowndes County

☐ **GREENLEAF BEHAVIORAL HEALTH HOSPITAL (114036)**, 2209 Pineview Drive, Zip 31602–7316; tel. 229/247–4357, **A**1 10 **F**5 29 38 53 54 98 99 100 101 103 104 105 106 130 132 134 143 151 152 153 154 **P**5 6 **S** Acadia Healthcare Company, Inc., Franklin, TN
Primary Contact: Stephen Register, Chief Executive Officer
Web address: www.greenleafcounseling.net
Control: Corporation, Investor–owned (for–profit) **Service**: Psychiatric

Staffed Beds: 103 **Admissions:** 2718 **Census:** 70 **Births:** 0

✠ **SOUTH GEORGIA MEDICAL CENTER (110122)**, 2501 North Patterson Street, Zip 31602–1735, Mailing Address: P.O. Box 1727, Zip 31603–1727; tel. 229/333–1000, (Includes SMITH NORTHVIEW HOSPITAL, 4280 North Valdosta Road, Valdosta, GA, Zip 31602, Mailing Address: P.O. Box 10010, Zip 31604, tel. 229/671–2000; Leonard Carter, Campus Administrator) (Nonreporting) **A**1 2 10 19 **S** South Georgia Medical Center, Valdosta, GA
Primary Contact: Bill Forbes, Interim Chief Executive Officer
COO: Andrew Flemer, Chief Operating Officer
CMO: Kimberly Megow, M.D., Chief Medical Officer
CIO: Bob Foster, Chief Information Officer
CHR: Johnny Percy Ball III Assistant Administrator Human Resources
CNO: Denida A. Cox, Chief Nursing Officer
Web address: www.sgmc.org
Control: Other not–for–profit (including NFP Corporation) **Service**: General medical and surgical

Staffed Beds: 302

VIDALIA—Toombs County

✠ **MEADOWS REGIONAL MEDICAL CENTER (110128)**, One Meadows Parkway, Zip 30474–8759, Mailing Address: P.O. Box 1048, Zip 30475–1048; tel. 912/535–5555, **A**1 10 20 **F**11 13 15 18 20 22 29 30 31 34 35 37 40 43 45 46 47 50 51 53 54 57 59 64 68 70 75 76 77 78 79 81 85 86 87 93 97 107 108 110 111 115 118 119 120 121 123 124 127 129 130 131 132 146 147 148 154 **P**6
Primary Contact: Alan Kent, Chief Executive Officer
COO: James Nixon, Chief Operating Officer
CFO: John Cornell, Vice President Finance
CIO: Charles Bondurant, Chief Information Officer
Web address: www.meadowsregional.org
Control: Other not–for–profit (including NFP Corporation) **Service**: General medical and surgical

Staffed Beds: 57 **Admissions:** 4057 **Census:** 38 **Outpatient Visits:** 83146 **Births:** 780 **Total Expense ($000):** 113636 **Payroll Expense ($000):** 42202 **Personnel:** 597

VILLA RICA—Carroll County

✠ **TANNER MEDICAL CENTER–VILLA RICA (110015)**, 601 Dallas Highway, Zip 30180–1202; tel. 770/456–3000, (Includes WILLOWBROOKE AT TANNER, 20 Herrell Road, Villa Rica, GA, Zip 30180–5527; tel. 770/812–3266; Paula Gresham, Vice President, Hospital Administrator) **A**1 10 **F**3 5 11 13 15 18 20 22 29 30 31 34 38 40 49 50 59 60 64 68 70 74 76 78 79 81 85 87 91 98 100 101 102 103 104 105 107 108 110 111 115 118 119 129 135 147 149 152 153 154 **P**1 6 **S** Tanner Health System, Carrollton, GA
Primary Contact: Eric Dalton, Administrator
CFO: Carol Crews, Senior Vice President and Chief Financial Officer
CMO: William Waters, M.D., IV Executive Vice President
CIO: Terri Lee, Chief Information Officer
CHR: Shari W Gainey, Chief Human Resource Officer
CNO: Deborah Matthews, Senior Vice President
Web address: www.tanner.org
Control: Other not–for–profit (including NFP Corporation) **Service**: General medical and surgical

Staffed Beds: 118 **Admissions:** 5137 **Census:** 94 **Outpatient Visits:** 131854 **Births:** 319 **Total Expense ($000):** 82022 **Payroll Expense ($000):** 38351 **Personnel:** 578

WARM SPRINGS—Meriwether County

☐ **ROOSEVELT WARM SPRINGS REHABILITATION AND SPECIALTY HOSPITALS – LTAC (112000)**, 6135 Roosevelt Highway, Zip 31830–2757, Mailing Address: P.O. Box 280, Zip 31830–2757; tel. 706/655–5291, **A**1 10 **F**1 29 30 34 35 57 60 74 75 77 84 86 87 90 91 100 146 148
Primary Contact: David L. Mork Jr, Chief Executive Officer
CFO: Susan Wilder, Director Financial Services
CMO: Carlos Parrado, M.D., Sr Chief Medical Officer
CHR: Laura Stokes, Director Human Resources
CNO: Cathy Harbin, Chief Nursing Officer
Web address: www.augustahealth.org/roosevelt–warm–springs/rwsh
Control: Other not–for–profit (including NFP Corporation) **Service**: Acute long–term care hospital

Staffed Beds: 28 **Admissions:** 148 **Census:** 13 **Outpatient Visits:** 0 **Births:** 0

✠ **ROOSEVELT WARM SPRINGS REHABILITATION HOSPITAL – REHAB (113028)**, 6135 Roosevelt Highway, Zip 31830–2757, Mailing Address: P.O. Box 280, Zip 31830–0280; tel. 706/655–5515, **A**1 10 **F**3 29 30 60 68 74 75 82 85 87 90 91 94 146 148 154
Primary Contact: David L. Mork Jr, Chief Executive Officer
CFO: Susan Wilder, Director Financial Services
CMO: Ara Chitchyan, M.D., Medical Director
CIO: Christen Carter, Director Public Relations
CHR: Laura Stokes, Director Human Resources
CNO: Cathy Harbin, Chief Nursing Officer
Web address: www.augustahealth.org/roosevelt–warm–springs/rwsh
Control: Other not–for–profit (including NFP Corporation) **Service**: Rehabilitation

Staffed Beds: 32 **Admissions:** 390 **Census:** 16 **Outpatient Visits:** 0 **Births:** 0

GA

Many Facility Codes have changed. Please refer to the AHA Guide Code Chart. © 2018 AHA Guide

⊠ **WARM SPRINGS MEDICAL CENTER (111316)**, 5995 Spring Street,
Zip 31830–2149, Mailing Address: P.O. Box 8, Zip 31830–0008;
tel. 706/655–3331, (Total facility includes 79 beds in nursing home–type unit) **A**1
10 18 **F**3 15 29 30 34 35 40 41 45 46 47 48 57 59 60 64 65 68 75 81 93 107
110 114 119 128 130 133 135 143 146 148 149
Primary Contact: Karen Daniel, Chief Executive Officer
CFO: Patrick Flynn, Chief Financial Officer
CMO: Alan Thompson, M.D., President Medical Staff
CIO: Milo Varnadoe, Director Information Systems
CHR: Theresa Passarelli, Human Resources Generalist
CNO: Lynda Ligon, Chief Nursing Officer
Web address: www.warmspringsmc.org
Control: Partnership, Investor–owned (for–profit) **Service**: General medical and
surgical

Staffed Beds: 104 **Admissions**: 375 **Census**: 83 **Outpatient Visits**: 8603
Births: 0 **Total Expense ($000)**: 13260 **Payroll Expense ($000)**: 5922
Personnel: 125

WARNER ROBINS—Houston County

⊠ **HOUSTON MEDICAL CENTER (110069)**, 1601 Watson Boulevard,
Zip 31093–3431, Mailing Address: P.O. Box 2886, Zip 31099–2886;
tel. 478/922–4281, **A**1 3 10 13 **F**3 8 11 13 15 18 20 22 26 28 29 30 31 34
35 38 39 40 45 46 48 49 50 51 57 59 60 61 64 68 70 73 74 75 76 78 79
81 82 85 86 87 89 91 92 93 98 100 102 103 107 108 110 111 114 115 117
118 119 129 130 131 132 134 135 144 146 147 148 149 150 154 **S** Houston
Healthcare System, Warner Robins, GA
Primary Contact: Cary Martin, Chief Executive Officer
COO: Charles G Briscoe, FACHE, Chief Operating Officer
CFO: Sean Whilden, Chief Financial Officer
CIO: George Curtis, Chief Information Officer
CHR: Michael O'Hara, Senior Executive Director Human Resources
Web address: www.hhc.org
Control: Other not–for–profit (including NFP Corporation) **Service**: General
medical and surgical

Staffed Beds: 237 **Admissions**: 13002 **Census**: 163 **Outpatient Visits**:
232187 **Births**: 1882 **Total Expense ($000)**: 216836 **Payroll Expense**
($000): 88048 **Personnel**: 1800

WASHINGTON—Wilkes County

☐ **WILLS MEMORIAL HOSPITAL (111325)**, 120 Gordon Street, Zip 30673–1602,
Mailing Address: P.O. Box 370, Zip 30673–0370; tel. 706/678–2151,
(Nonreporting) **A**1 10 18
Primary Contact: Tracie Haughey, Chief Executive Officer and Chief Financial
Officer
CFO: Tracie Haughey, Chief Executive Officer and Chief Financial Officer
CMO: Robert J. Williams, M.D., Chief Medical Staff
CIO: David Harper, Chief Information Officer
CHR: Susan Pope, Director Human Resources
CNO: Angie Radford, R.N., Director of Nursing
Web address: www.willsmemorialhospital.com
Control: Hospital district or authority, Government, nonfederal **Service**: General
medical and surgical

Staffed Beds: 25

WAYCROSS—Ware County

⊠ **MEMORIAL SATILLA HEALTH (110003)**, 1900 Tebeau Street, Zip 31501–6357,
Mailing Address: P.O. Box 139, Zip 31502–0139; tel. 912/283–3030,
(Nonreporting) **A**1 2 3 5 10 **S** HCA Healthcare, Nashville, TN
Primary Contact: Bobby McCullough, Chief Executive Officer
COO: Mark Roberts, Chief Operaing Officer
CFO: Patrick Sloan, Chief Financial Officer
CIO: Barry Rudd, Chief Information Officer
CHR: Brigitte Churchill, Director of Human Resources
CNO: Holli Sweat, Associate Administrator and Chief Nursing Officer
Web address: www.memorialsatillahealth.com/
Control: Other not–for–profit (including NFP Corporation) **Service**: General
medical and surgical

Staffed Beds: 199

WAYNESBORO—Burke County

☐ **BURKE MEDICAL CENTER (110113)**, 351 Liberty Street, Zip 30830–9686;
tel. 706/554–4435, (Nonreporting) **A**1 10
Primary Contact: Thomas K. Steiner, Interim Chief Executive Officer
CFO: Karen ONeal, Chief Financial Officer
CHR: Kim Anthony, Director Human Resources
CNO: Debra Burch, Chief Nursing Officer
Web address: www.burkemedical.net
Control: Hospital district or authority, Government, nonfederal **Service**: General
medical and surgical

Staffed Beds: 40

WINDER—Barrow County

⊠ **NORTHEAST GEORGIA MEDICAL CENTER BARROW (110045)**, 316 North
Broad Street, Zip 30680–2150, Mailing Address: P.O. Box 688, Zip 30680–0688;
tel. 770/867–3400, **A**1 10 **F**3 11 15 29 30 34 35 38 40 44 45 50 57 59 60
68 70 74 75 77 79 81 82 85 107 108 110 111 114 115 118 119 124 130
131 132 135 143 146 147 148 149 154 **S** Northeast Georgia Health System,
Gainesville, GA
Primary Contact: Chad Hatfield, Chief Executive Officer
CMO: Jon Horn, M.D., Chief of Staff
CIO: Cory Crayton, Director Information Systems
CHR: Carlotta Hannah Newman, Human Resources Manager
CNO: Heather Standard, Chief Nursing Officer
Web address: www.barrowregional.com
Control: Other not–for–profit (including NFP Corporation) **Service**: General
medical and surgical

Staffed Beds: 30 **Admissions**: 947 **Census**: 8 **Outpatient Visits**: 23882
Births: 0 **Personnel**: 184

GA

HAWAII

AIEA—Honolulu County

⊞ **PALI MOMI MEDICAL CENTER (120026)**, 98–1079 Moanalua Road, Zip 96701–4713; tel. 808/486–6000, **A**1 2 3 5 10 **F**3 12 15 18 20 22 26 29 31 32 34 35 40 43 44 45 46 49 50 54 57 59 63 64 65 70 74 75 77 78 79 80 81 84 85 86 87 92 107 108 110 111 114 115 118 119 126 130 132 135 146 147 148 149 **P**8 **S** Hawaii Pacific Health, Honolulu, HI
Primary Contact: Art Gladstone, R.N., Chief Executive Officer
CFO: David Okabe, Executive Vice President, Chief Financial Officer and Treasurer
CMO: James Kakuda, M.D., Chief of Staff
CIO: Steve Robertson, Senior Vice President
CHR: Gail Lerch, R.N., Vice President Human Resources
CNO: Brigitte McKale, MSN, FACHE, Vice President and Chief Nurse Executive
Web address: www.palimomi.org
Control: Other not–for–profit (including NFP Corporation) **Service**: General medical and surgical

Staffed Beds: 118 **Admissions:** 5757 **Census:** 87 **Outpatient Visits:** 219296 **Births:** 0 **Total Expense ($000):** 211198 **Payroll Expense ($000):** 78451 **Personnel:** 965

EWA BEACH—Honolulu County

⊞ **SUTTER HEALTH KAHI MOHALA (124001)**, 91–2301 Old Fort Weaver Road, Zip 96706–3602; tel. 808/671–8511, **A**1 3 10 **F**29 30 35 44 68 98 99 100 101 103 104 105 106 127 130 132 133 143 **S** Sutter Health, Sacramento, CA
Primary Contact: Leonard Licina, Chief Executive Officer
CFO: Quin Ogawa, Chief Financial Officer
CMO: Steven Chaplin, M.D., Medical Director
CHR: Christina Enoka, Director Human Resources and Risk Management
CNO: Charles St. Louis, Director of Patient Care Services
Web address: www.kahimohala.org
Control: Other not–for–profit (including NFP Corporation) **Service**: Psychiatric

Staffed Beds: 76 **Admissions:** 473 **Census:** 71 **Outpatient Visits:** 2114 **Births:** 0 **Total Expense ($000):** 21529 **Payroll Expense ($000):** 11178 **Personnel:** 197

HILO—Hawaii County

⊞ **HILO MEDICAL CENTER (120005)**, 1190 Waianuenue Avenue, Zip 96720–2089; tel. 808/932–3000, (Nonreporting) **A**1 3 5 10 20 **S** Hawaii Health Systems Corporation, Honolulu, HI
Primary Contact: Dan Brinkman, R.N., Chief Executive Officer
COO: Dan Brinkman, R.N., Chief Operating Officer
CMO: Ted Peskin, M.D., Acute Care Medical Director
CIO: Money Atwal, Chief Information Officer
CHR: Holly Ka'akimaka, Director Human Resources
CNO: Arthur Sampaga, Assistant Director Nursing
Web address: www.hilomedicalcenter.org/
Control: State, Government, nonfederal **Service**: General medical and surgical

Staffed Beds: 199

HONOKAA—Hawaii County

★ **HALE HO'OLA HAMAKUA (121307)**, 45–547 Plumeria Street, Zip 96727–6902; tel. 808/932–4100, (Nonreporting) **A**5 10 18 **S** Hawaii Health Systems Corporation, Honolulu, HI
Primary Contact: Denise Mackey, Administrator
CMO: Bruce Graves, M.D., Chief of Staff
CNO: Gayle Green, Director of Nursing
Web address: www.halehoolahamakua.org
Control: State, Government, nonfederal **Service**: General medical and surgical

Staffed Beds: 77

HONOLULU—Honolulu County

⊞ **KAISER PERMANENTE MEDICAL CENTER (120011)**, 3288 Moanalua Road, Zip 96819–1469; tel. 808/432–0000, **A**1 2 3 5 10 **F**3 12 13 15 17 18 19 20 21 22 24 26 29 30 31 32 34 35 36 38 40 41 45 46 47 48 49 50 51 54 55 56 57 58 59 60 61 62 64 65 68 70 72 74 75 76 77 78 79 80 81 82 83 84 85 86 87 88 89 92 93 94 97 100 101 104 107 108 110 111 115 119 129 130 131 134 135 146 148 149 154 **S** Kaiser Foundation Hospitals, Oakland, CA
Primary Contact: James Y. Lee, Hospital Administrator
CFO: Thomas Risse, Chief Financial Officer and Vice President Business Services
CMO: Keith Ogasawara, M.D., Associate Medical Director and Professional Chief of Staff
CIO: Donna Scannell, Vice President Information Technology
CHR: Jean Melnikoff, Vice President Human Resources
CNO: Kecia Kelly, R.N., Chief Nurse Executive
Web address: www.kaiserpermanente.org
Control: Other not–for–profit (including NFP Corporation) **Service**: General medical and surgical

Staffed Beds: 193 **Admissions:** 11557 **Census:** 176 **Outpatient Visits:** 60967 **Births:** 1435 **Personnel:** 1484

☐ **KAPIOLANI MEDICAL CENTER FOR WOMEN & CHILDREN (123300)**, 1319 Punahou Street, Zip 96826–1001; tel. 808/983–6000, **A**1 2 3 5 10 **F**3 13 15 19 25 29 31 32 34 35 36 38 40 41 43 44 45 50 52 53 54 55 57 58 59 64 65 68 70 72 73 74 75 76 77 78 79 81 84 85 86 87 88 89 91 92 93 94 100 102 107 108 110 111 114 115 119 126 130 131 132 134 135 136 146 147 148 149 **S** Hawaii Pacific Health, Honolulu, HI
Primary Contact: Martha Smith, Chief Executive Officer
CFO: David Okabe, Senior Vice President, Chief Financial Officer and Treasurer
CIO: Steve Robertson, Vice President
CHR: Gail Lerch, R.N., Vice President
Web address: www.kapiolani.org
Control: Other not–for–profit (including NFP Corporation) **Service**: Other specialty treatment

Staffed Beds: 185 **Admissions:** 9740 **Census:** 183 **Outpatient Visits:** 204522 **Births:** 6296 **Total Expense ($000):** 329488 **Payroll Expense ($000):** 127783 **Personnel:** 1447

⊞ **KUAKINI MEDICAL CENTER (120007)**, 347 North Kuakini Street, Zip 96817–2381; tel. 808/536–2236, **A**1 2 3 5 10 **F**3 15 17 18 20 22 24 26 28 29 31 34 35 40 45 46 49 57 58 59 60 68 70 74 75 77 78 79 80 81 82 84 85 86 87 107 108 110 111 115 117 118 119 121 129 130 131 132 135 145 146 147 148 149 **P**1
Primary Contact: Gary K. Kajiwara, President and Chief Executive Officer
CFO: Quin Ogawa, Vice President Finance and Chief Financial Officer
CMO: Nobuyuki Miki, M.D., Vice President Medical Services and Chief Medical Officer
CIO: Gary K Kajiwara, President and Chief Executive Officer
CHR: Ann N. Choy, Manager Human Resources and Payroll
CNO: Virginia Walker, Vice President Nursing Services and Chief Nursing Officer
Web address: www.kuakini.org
Control: Other not–for–profit (including NFP Corporation) **Service**: General medical and surgical

Staffed Beds: 100 **Admissions:** 3854 **Census:** 70 **Outpatient Visits:** 53865 **Births:** 0 **Total Expense ($000):** 145649 **Payroll Expense ($000):** 57585 **Personnel:** 795

★ **LEAHI HOSPITAL (122001)**, 3675 Kilauea Avenue, Zip 96816–2398; tel. 808/733–8000, (Nonreporting) **A**10 **S** Hawaii Health Systems Corporation, Honolulu, HI
Primary Contact: Derek Akiyoshi, Chief Executive Officer
CFO: Edward Chu, Chief Financial Officer
CMO: Albert Yazawa, M.D., Regional Medical Director
CHR: Russel Higa, JD, Regional Director Human Resources
CNO: Amy Vasunaga, Chief Nurse Executive
Web address: www.hhsc.org
Control: State, Government, nonfederal **Service**: Acute long–term care hospital

Staffed Beds: 164

HI

✠ **REHABILITATION HOSPITAL OF THE PACIFIC (123025)**, 226 North Kuakini Street, Zip 96817–2488; tel. 808/531–3511, **A**1 10 **F**3 11 28 29 34 36 44 54 57 58 64 68 74 75 77 79 82 90 91 93 94 96 130 131 132 135 143 146 147 148
Primary Contact: Timothy J. Roe, M.D., President and Chief Executive Officer
CFO: Wendy Manuel, Vice President and Chief Financial Officer
CMO: Jason Chang, Chief Medical Officer and Vice President of Medical Affairs
CIO: Colbert Seto, Chief Information Officer
CHR: Faye Miyamoto, Assistant Vice President Human Resources
CNO: Brenda Hiromoto, Director of Nursing
Web address: www.rehabhospital.org
Control: Other not–for–profit (including NFP Corporation) **Service**: Rehabilitation

Staffed Beds: 82 **Admissions**: 1925 **Census**: 61 **Outpatient Visits**: 44420
Births: 0 **Total Expense ($000)**: 48202 **Payroll Expense ($000)**: 25763

☐ **SHRINERS HOSPITALS FOR CHILDREN–HONOLULU (123301)**, 1310 Punahou Street, Zip 96826–1099; tel. 808/941–4466, (Nonreporting) **A**1 3 5 10 **S** Shriners Hospitals for Children, Tampa, FL
Primary Contact: Anton C. Smith, Administrator
CFO: Patricia Miyasawa, CPA, Director Fiscal Service
CMO: Craig Ono, M.D., Chief of Staff
CIO: Gregory A Wolf, Director Information Systems
CHR: Derek Ito, Director Human Resources
CNO: Andrea Kubota, R.N., MSN, Director Patient Care Services and Nurse Executive
Web address: www.shrinershospitalsforchildren.org/honolulu
Control: Other not–for–profit (including NFP Corporation) **Service**: Children's orthopedic

Staffed Beds: 16

☐ **STRAUB MEDICAL CENTER (120022)**, 888 South King Street, Zip 96813–3097; tel. 808/522–4000, **A**1 2 3 5 10 **F**3 9 15 16 18 20 21 22 23 24 26 27 28 29 31 34 35 40 44 45 47 48 49 50 54 56 57 59 63 64 65 68 70 71 74 75 77 78 79 80 81 84 85 86 87 92 93 97 100 104 107 108 110 111 115 119 129 130 131 132 135 144 145 146 147 148 149 154 **P**6 8 **S** Hawaii Pacific Health, Honolulu, HI
Primary Contact: Art Gladstone, R.N., Chief Executive Officer
COO: Maureen Flannery, Vice President Clinic Operations
CFO: David Okabe, Executive Vice President, Chief Financial Officer and Treasurer
CMO: Randy Yates, M.D., Chief Medical Officer
CIO: Steve Robertson, Executive Vice President and Chief Information Officer
CHR: Gail Lerch, R.N., Executive Vice President Human Resources
CNO: Patricia Boeckmann, R.N., Chief Operating Officer and Chief Nursing Officer
Web address: www.straubhealth.org
Control: Other not–for–profit (including NFP Corporation) **Service**: General medical and surgical

Staffed Beds: 118 **Admissions**: 7230 **Census**: 115 **Outpatient Visits**: 875594 **Births**: 0 **Total Expense ($000)**: 450123 **Payroll Expense ($000)**: 197076 **Personnel**: 1757

✠ **THE QUEEN'S MEDICAL CENTER (120001)**, 1301 Punchbowl Street, Zip 96813–2499; tel. 808/691–5100, (Includes QUEEN'S MEDICAL CENTER – WEST OAHU, 91–2141 Fort Weaver Road, Ewa Beach, HI, Zip 96706–1993; tel. 808/691–3000; Susan Murray, FACHE, Chief Operating Officer) **A**1 2 3 5 10 **F**3 5 7 11 12 13 15 17 18 20 22 24 26 28 29 30 31 34 35 37 38 39 40 43 44 45 46 47 48 49 50 51 55 56 57 58 59 60 61 62 63 64 66 68 70 73 74 75 76 77 78 79 81 82 84 85 86 87 93 96 97 98 99 100 101 102 104 105 107 108 110 111 115 117 118 119 120 121 124 126 129 130 131 132 135 138 139 142 143 146 147 148 151 152 154 **S** Queen's Health Systems, Honolulu, HI
Primary Contact: Arthur A. Ushijima, FACHE, President
COO: Jason Chang, Executive Vice President and Chief Operating Officer
CFO: Michel Riccioni, Chief Financial Officer
CMO: Whitney Limm, M.D., Executive Vice President and Chief Physician Executive
CIO: Brian Yoshii, Vice President Information Technology and Chief Information Officer
CHR: Nona Tamanaha, Vice President Human Resources
CNO: Madeline Harris, R.N., Vice President and Chief Nursing Officer
Web address: www.queensmedicalcenter.org
Control: Other not–for–profit (including NFP Corporation) **Service**: General medical and surgical

Staffed Beds: 517 **Admissions**: 27156 **Census**: 519 **Outpatient Visits**: 529695 **Births**: 1665 **Total Expense ($000)**: 1084948 **Payroll Expense ($000)**: 419906 **Personnel**: 4139

✠ **TRIPLER ARMY MEDICAL CENTER**, 1 Jarret White Road, Zip 96859–5001; tel. 808/433–6661, (Nonreporting) **A**1 2 3 5 **S** Department of the Army, Office of the Surgeon General, Falls Church, VA
Primary Contact: Colonel Mary Krueger, Commanding Officer
COO: Major Elias B. Lozano, Executive Officer
CFO: Lieutenant Colonel Christopher A. Wodarz, Chief, Resource Management Division
CMO: Captain Andrew L. Findlay, Deputy Commander Clinical Services
CIO: Lieutenant Colonel Donna E Beed, Chief Information Management Division
CHR: Colonel James N. Davidson, Troop Commander
CNO: Colonel Jennifer L. Bedick, Deputy Commander Nursing
Web address: www.tamc.amedd.army.mil
Control: Army, Government, federal **Service**: General medical and surgical

Staffed Beds: 194

★ **VETERANS AFFAIRS PACIFIC ISLANDS HEALTH CARE SYSTEM**, 459 Patterson Road, Zip 96819–1522; tel. 808/433–0600, (Nonreporting) **A**3 **S** Department of Veterans Affairs, Perry Point, MD
Primary Contact: Jennifer S. Gutowski, FACHE, Director
Web address: www.hawaii.va.gov/
Control: Veterans Affairs, Government, federal **Service**: General medical and surgical

Staffed Beds: 80

KAHUKU—Honolulu County

★ **KAHUKU MEDICAL CENTER (121304)**, 56–117 Pualalea Street, Zip 96731–2052; tel. 808/293–9221, (Nonreporting) **A**10 18
Primary Contact: Alan MacPhee, Chief Executive Officer
COO: Jerome Flores, Chief Financial Officer and Chief Operating Officer
CFO: Jerome Flores, Chief Financial Officer and Chief Operating Officer
CMO: P Douglas Nielson, M.D., Chief of Staff
Web address: www.kahuku.hhsc.org/
Control: Other not–for–profit (including NFP Corporation) **Service**: General medical and surgical

Staffed Beds: 21

KAILUA—Honolulu County

✠ **ADVENTIST HEALTH CASTLE (120006)**, 640 Ulukahiki Street, Zip 96734–4454; tel. 808/263–5500, **A**1 3 10 **F**3 8 12 13 15 18 20 22 24 26 29 30 31 32 34 35 37 40 45 46 49 50 51 54 56 57 59 64 68 69 70 74 75 76 78 79 81 84 85 86 91 92 93 97 98 102 105 107 108 110 111 114 119 120 126 127 130 135 146 147 149 152 **P**6 8 **S** Adventist Health, Roseville, CA
Primary Contact: Kathryn A. Raethel, R.N., M.P.H., President and Chief Executive Officer
COO: Travis Clegg, Vice President, Operations
CFO: Heidar Thordarson, Chief Financial Officer
CMO: Alan Cheung, M.D., Vice President Medical Affairs
CHR: Todd Reese, Director Human Resources
CNO: Laura R. Westphal, R.N., Vice President Patient Care Services
Web address: www.castlemed.org
Control: Church operated, Nongovernment, not–for–profit **Service**: General medical and surgical

Staffed Beds: 160 **Admissions**: 7585 **Census**: 88 **Outpatient Visits**: 101234 **Births**: 1068 **Total Expense ($000)**: 166168 **Payroll Expense ($000)**: 56829 **Personnel**: 903

KAMUELA—Hawaii County

✠ **NORTH HAWAII COMMUNITY HOSPITAL (120028)**, 67–1125 Mamalahoa Highway, Zip 96743–8496; tel. 808/885–4444, **A**1 3 10 20 **F**3 8 13 15 18 26 29 30 31 34 35 36 40 41 43 44 45 46 49 50 53 54 57 59 62 64 68 70 75 77 78 79 81 85 86 87 93 97 102 107 108 110 111 115 119 130 131 132 146 147 148 154 **P**6 **S** Queen's Health Systems, Honolulu, HI
Primary Contact: Cynthia Kamikawa, R.N., MSN, President
CFO: Michel Riccioni, Chief Financial Officer
CMO: Gary Goldberg, M.D., Chief Medical Officer
CNO: Miquel Noelani Simms, R.N., Chief Nursing Officer
Web address: www.nhch.com
Control: Other not–for–profit (including NFP Corporation) **Service**: General medical and surgical

Staffed Beds: 35 **Admissions**: 1784 **Census**: 16 **Outpatient Visits**: 78595 **Births**: 464 **Total Expense ($000)**: 78336 **Payroll Expense ($000)**: 26531 **Personnel**: 310

HI

Hospital, Medicare Provider Number, Address, Telephone, Approval, Facility, and Physician Codes, Health Care System

★ American Hospital Association (AHA) membership
☐ The Joint Commission accreditation
○ Healthcare Facilities Accreditation Program
◇ DNV Healthcare Inc. accreditation
⇑ Center for Improvement in Healthcare Quality Accreditation
△ Commission on Accreditation of Rehabilitation Facilities (CARF) accreditation

KANEOHE—Honolulu County

☐ **HAWAII STATE HOSPITAL**, 45–710 Keaahala Road, Zip 96744–3597;
tel. 808/247–2191, (Nonreporting) **A**1 3 5
Primary Contact: William J. May, Administrator
COO: Anthony Fraiola, Associate Administrator Administrative and Support Services
CFO: Stephen Teeter, Business Manager
CMO: James Westphal, M.D., AMHD Medical Director
CIO: John Jansen, Management Information Specialist
CHR: Karen Hara, Personnel Management Specialist
CNO: Lani Tsuneishi, Nursing Services Manager
Web address: www.hawaii.gov/health/
Control: State, Government, nonfederal **Service:** Psychiatric

Staffed Beds: 178

KAPAA—Kauai County

★ **SAMUEL MAHELONA MEMORIAL HOSPITAL (121306)**, 4800 Kawaihau Road,
Zip 96746–1971; tel. 808/822–4961, (Nonreporting) **A**10 18 **S** Hawaii Health
Systems Corporation, Honolulu, HI
Primary Contact: Lance Segawa, Chief Executive Officer
CFO: Michael Perel, Regional Chief Financial Officer
CMO: Gerald Tomory, M.D., Regional Medical Director
CIO: Sandra McMaster, Regional Chief Information Officer
CHR: Lani Aranio, Regional Director Human Resources
Web address: www.smmh.hhsc.org
Control: State, Government, nonfederal **Service:** General medical and surgical

Staffed Beds: 80

KAUNAKAKAI—Maui County

⊞ **MOLOKAI GENERAL HOSPITAL (121303)**, 280 Home Olu Place, Zip 96748–0408,
Mailing Address: P.O. Box 408, Zip 96748–0408; tel. 808/553–5331, (Nonreporting)
A1 10 18 **S** Queen's Health Systems, Honolulu, HI
Primary Contact: Janice Kalanihuia, President
CFO: Zessica L Apiki, Accountant
CMO: William Thomas, M.D., Jr Medical Director Clinical and Internal Affairs
CIO: Sampson Wescoatt, Manager Information Technology
CHR: Alicia Teves, Coordinator Human Resources
Web address: www.queens.org
Control: Other not–for–profit (including NFP Corporation) **Service:** General
medical and surgical

Staffed Beds: 15

KEALAKEKUA—Hawaii County

⊞ **KONA COMMUNITY HOSPITAL (120019)**, 79–1019 Haukapila Street,
Zip 96750–7920; tel. 808/322–9311, (Nonreporting) **A**1 10 20 **S** Hawaii Health
Systems Corporation, Honolulu, HI
Primary Contact: Jay E. Kreuzer, FACHE, Chief Executive Officer
CFO: Dean Herzog, Chief Financial Officer
CMO: Richard McDowell, M.D., Medical Director
CHR: Kathryn Salomon, Director Human Resources
CNO: Patricia Kalua, Chief Nurse Executive
Web address: www.kch.hhsc.org
Control: Other not–for–profit (including NFP Corporation) **Service:** General
medical and surgical

Staffed Beds: 94

KOHALA—Hawaii County

★ **KOHALA HOSPITAL (121302)**, 54–383 Hospital Road, Zip 96755, Mailing
Address: P.O. Box 10, Kapaau, Zip 96755–0010; tel. 808/889–6211,
(Nonreporting) **A**10 18 **S** Hawaii Health Systems Corporation, Honolulu, HI
Primary Contact: Eugene Amar Jr, Administrator
CMO: Silvia Sonnenschein, M.D., Chief of Staff
Web address: www.koh.hhsc.org
Control: State, Government, nonfederal **Service:** General medical and surgical

Staffed Beds: 28

KULA—Maui County

★ **KULA HOSPITAL (121308)**, 100 Keokea Place, Zip 96790–7450;
tel. 808/878–1221, (Nonreporting) **A**10 18 **S** Kaiser Foundation Hospitals, Oakland, CA
Primary Contact: Paul Harper–O'Connor, Interim Chief Executive Officer
CFO: Nerissa Garrity, Chief Financial Officer
CMO: Nicole Apoliona, M.D., Medical Director
Web address: www.mauihealthsystem.org/kula–hospital/
Control: Other not–for–profit (including NFP Corporation) **Service:** General
medical and surgical

Staffed Beds: 6

LANAI CITY—Maui County

★ **LANAI COMMUNITY HOSPITAL (121305)**, 628 Seventh Street, Zip 96763–0650,
Mailing Address: P.O. Box 630650, Zip 96763–0650; tel. 808/565–8450,
(Nonreporting) **A**10 18 **S** Kaiser Foundation Hospitals, Oakland, CA
Primary Contact: Paul Harper–O'Connor, Interim Administrator
Web address: www.mauihealthsystem.org/lanai–hospital/
Control: Other not–for–profit (including NFP Corporation) **Service:** General
medical and surgical

Staffed Beds: 24

LIHUE—Kauai County

☐ **WILCOX MEDICAL CENTER (120014)**, 3–3420 Kuhio Highway,
Zip 96766–1099; tel. 808/245–1100, **A**1 2 10 20 **F**3 13 15 18 28 29 31 32 34
35 37 39 40 41 43 44 45 49 50 53 55 56 57 59 63 64 65 70 75 76 77 78 79
81 82 84 85 86 87 92 93 107 108 110 111 114 115 119 126 130 131 132
133 135 146 147 148 149 154 **P**8 **S** Hawaii Pacific Health, Honolulu, HI
Primary Contact: Jen Chahanovich, President and Chief Executive Officer
CFO: David Okabe, Executive Vice President, Chief Financial Officer and Treasurer
CMO: Craig Netzer, M.D., President Medical Staff
CIO: Steve Robertson, Executive Vice President Revenue Cycle Management and
Chief Information Officer
CNO: Mary Ann England, Chief Nurse Executive
Web address: www.wilcoxhealth.org
Control: Other not–for–profit (including NFP Corporation) **Service:** General
medical and surgical

Staffed Beds: 65 **Admissions:** 3407 **Census:** 42 **Outpatient Visits:** 96253
Births: 507 **Total Expense ($000):** 112440 **Payroll Expense ($000):** 37086
Personnel: 464

PAHALA—Hawaii County

★ **KA'U HOSPITAL (121301)**, 1 Kamani Street, Zip 96777, Mailing Address: P.O.
Box 40, Zip 96777–0040; tel. 808/932–4200, (Nonreporting) **A**10 18 **S** Hawaii
Health Systems Corporation, Honolulu, HI
Primary Contact: Merilyn Harris, Administrator
CMO: Clifford Field, M.D., Medical Director
Web address: www.hhsc.org
Control: State, Government, nonfederal **Service:** General medical and surgical

Staffed Beds: 21

WAHIAWA—Honolulu County

⊞ **WAHIAWA GENERAL HOSPITAL (120004)**, 128 Lehua Street, Zip 96786–2036;
tel. 808/621–8411, (Nonreporting) **A**1 3 5 10
Primary Contact: Brian Cunningham, Chief Executive Officer
CMO: Manuel Abundo, M.D., Chief of Staff
CIO: Jason Fujinaka, Manager Information System
CHR: Liflor Barrera, Manager Human Resources
CNO: Tammy Kohrer, Director of Nursing–Acute
Web address: www.wahiawageneral.org
Control: Other not–for–profit (including NFP Corporation) **Service:** General
medical and surgical

Staffed Beds: 160

WAILUKU—Maui County

⊞ **MAUI MEMORIAL MEDICAL CENTER (120002)**, 221 Mahalani Street,
Zip 96793–2581; tel. 808/244–9056, (Nonreporting) **A**1 10 20 **S** Kaiser
Foundation Hospitals, Oakland, CA
Primary Contact: Michael A. Rembis, FACHE, Chief Executive Officer
COO: Debbie Walsh, MSN, Chief Operating Officer
CIO: Dana Mendoza, Chief Information Officer
Web address: www.mauihealthsystem.org/maui–memorial/
Control: Other not–for–profit (including NFP Corporation) **Service:** General
medical and surgical

Staffed Beds: 213

WAIMEA—Kauai County

⊞ **KAUAI VETERANS MEMORIAL HOSPITAL (121300)**, 4643 Waimea
Canyon Road, Zip 96796, Mailing Address: P.O. Box 337, Zip 96796–0337;
tel. 808/338–9431, (Nonreporting) **A**1 10 18 **S** Hawaii Health Systems
Corporation, Honolulu, HI
Primary Contact: Lance Segawa, Chief Executive Officer
CFO: Michael Perel, Regional Chief Financial Officer
CMO: Gerald Tomory, M.D., Regional Medical Director
CIO: Sandra McMaster, Regional Chief Information Officer
CHR: Solette Perry, Regional Director Human Resources
Web address: www.kvmh.hhsc.org
Control: State, Government, nonfederal **Service:** General medical and surgical

Staffed Beds: 45

HI

IDAHO

AMERICAN FALLS—Power County

★ **POWER COUNTY HOSPITAL DISTRICT (131304)**, 510 Roosevelt Street, Zip 83211–1362, Mailing Address: P.O. Box 420, Zip 83211–0420; tel. 208/226–3200, (Nonreporting) **A**10 18
Primary Contact: Dallas Clinger, Administrator
COO: Rock Roy, Professional Services Director
CFO: Jeremy Claunch, Chief Financial Officer
CMO: Spencer Garrett Seibold, M.D., Chief of Medical Staff
CIO: Mindy Earl, Health Information Manager
CHR: Kendra Sweat, Director Human Resources
CNO: June Mortenson, R.N., Director of Nursing
Web address: www.pchd.net
Control: Hospital district or authority, Government, nonfederal **Service:** General medical and surgical

Staffed Beds: 10

ARCO—Butte County

LOST RIVERS MEDICAL CENTER (131324), 551 Highland Drive, Zip 83213–9771, Mailing Address: P.O. Box 145, Zip 83213–0145; tel. 208/527–8206, (Nonreporting) **A**10 18
Primary Contact: Brad Huerta, Chief Executive Officer and Administrator
CFO: Jon Smith, Chief Financial Officer
CMO: Jeffrey Haskell, M.D., Chief Medical Staff
CHR: Tina Akins, Director Human Resources
CNO: Geri Cammack, R.N., Director of Nursing
Web address: www.lostriversmedical.com
Control: Hospital district or authority, Government, nonfederal **Service:** General medical and surgical

Staffed Beds: 43

BLACKFOOT—Bingham County

⌧ **BINGHAM MEMORIAL HOSPITAL (131325)**, 98 Poplar Street, Zip 83221–1799; tel. 208/785–4100, (Total facility includes 60 beds in nursing home–type unit) **A**1 3 5 10 18 **F**3 12 13 15 18 20 22 26 29 34 35 36 37 40 44 45 47 48 50 51 52 55 56 57 58 59 64 65 66 68 74 75 76 77 79 81 82 85 86 87 92 93 97 104 107 108 109 110 111 115 119 126 127 128 129 130 131 132 133 134 135 144 146 147 148 **P**6 7
Primary Contact: Jake Erickson, Chief Executive Officer
CFO: John Fullmer, Chief Financial Officer
CIO: Robert Weis, Director Information Systems
CHR: Tara Preston, Director Human Resources
CNO: Carolyn Hansen, Chief Nursing Officer
Web address: www.binghammemorial.org
Control: Other not–for–profit (including NFP Corporation) **Service:** General medical and surgical

Staffed Beds: 85 **Admissions:** 2264 **Census:** 53 **Outpatient Visits:** 175676 **Births:** 352 **Total Expense ($000):** 112392 **Payroll Expense ($000):** 49202 **Personnel:** 742

MOUNTAIN RIVER BIRTHING AND SURGERY CENTER (130067), 350 North Meridian Street, Zip 83221–1625; tel. 208/782–0300, **A**10 **F**3 8 29 68 79 81 85 148
Primary Contact: D. Jeffery. Daniels, Chief Executive Officer
COO: Dan Cochran, Chief Operating Officer
CIO: Robert Weis, Director Information Technology
CHR: Tara Preston, Director Human Resources
CNO: Nathan Buck, R.N., Nursing Manager
Web address: www.binghammemorial.org
Control: Partnership, Investor–owned (for–profit) **Service:** Surgical

Staffed Beds: 8 **Admissions:** 71 **Census:** 1 **Outpatient Visits:** 4765 **Births:** 0 **Total Expense ($000):** 4519 **Payroll Expense ($000):** 799 **Personnel:** 17

□ **STATE HOSPITAL SOUTH (134010)**, 700 East Alice Street, Zip 83221–4925, Mailing Address: P.O. Box 400, Zip 83221–0400; tel. 208/785–1200, (Nonreporting) **A**1 10
Primary Contact: James Price, Hospital Administrator
COO: Greg Horton, Director Support Services
CFO: Angela Loosli, Assistant Administrator, Operations
CMO: Kelly Palmer, D.O., Medical Director
CIO: Julie Sutton, Director Performance Improvement
CHR: Sheryl Donnelly, Human Resources Specialist
CNO: Randy Walker, Director Nursing Services
Web address: www.healthandwelfare.idaho.gov
Control: State, Government, nonfederal **Service:** Psychiatric

Staffed Beds: 135

BOISE—Ada County

BOISE BEHAVIORAL HEALTH HOSPITAL See Safe Haven Hospital of Treasure Valley

⌧ **BOISE VETERANS AFFAIRS MEDICAL CENTER**, 500 West Fort Street, Zip 83702–4598; tel. 208/422–1000, (Total facility includes 28 beds in nursing home–type unit) **A**1 3 5 **F**1 2 3 4 5 8 9 10 12 29 30 31 34 35 38 39 40 43 45 46 47 50 53 54 56 57 58 59 60 61 62 63 64 65 66 67 68 70 71 74 75 77 78 79 81 82 83 84 85 86 87 90 91 92 93 94 96 97 98 100 101 102 104 107 108 111 112 119 120 121 122 123 124 127 128 129 130 132 133 135 143 144 145 146 147 148 149 150 152 154 **S** Department of Veterans Affairs, Perry Point, MD
Primary Contact: David P. Wood, FACHE, Director
CFO: Ron Blanton, Chief Fiscal Services
CMO: Paul Lambert, M.D., Chief of Staff
CHR: Randy Turner, Chief Human Resource Management Services
Web address: www.boise.va.gov/
Control: Veterans Affairs, Government, federal **Service:** General medical and surgical

Staffed Beds: 100 **Admissions:** 3120 **Census:** 66 **Outpatient Visits:** 372150 **Births:** 0 **Total Expense ($000):** 252620 **Payroll Expense ($000):** 150000 **Personnel:** 1226

IDAHO ELKS REHABILITATION HOSPITAL See St. Luke's Rehabilitation Hospital

□ **INTERMOUNTAIN HOSPITAL (134002)**, 303 North Allumbaugh Street, Zip 83704–9208; tel. 208/377–8400, (Nonreporting) **A**1 10 **S** Universal Health Services, Inc., King of Prussia, PA
Primary Contact: Jeffrey F. Morrell, Chief Executive Officer
CFO: JeDonne Hines, Chief Financial Officer
CMO: Charles Novak, M.D., Chief Medical Officer
CHR: Nancy Nelson, Director Human Resources
CNO: Jennifer Beaulieu, Director of Nursing
Web address: www.intermountainhospital.com
Control: Corporation, Investor–owned (for–profit) **Service:** Psychiatric

Staffed Beds: 140

SAFE HAVEN HOSPITAL OF TREASURE VALLEY (134009), 8050 Northview Street, Zip 83704–7126; tel. 208/327–0504, (Nonreporting) **A**10 **S** Safe Haven Health Care, Pocatello, ID
Primary Contact: Scott Proctor, Chief Executive Officer
CMO: David Kent, M.D., Chief Medical Officer
CIO: Debra Alexander, Chief Information Officer
CHR: Kathy Cady, Coordinator Human Resources, Accounts Payable and Payroll
Web address: www.boisepsychhospital.com
Control: Corporation, Investor–owned (for–profit) **Service:** Psychiatric

Staffed Beds: 22

ID

Hospital, Medicare Provider Number, Address, Telephone, Approval, Facility, and Physician Codes, Health Care System

★ American Hospital Association (AHA) membership ○ Healthcare Facilities Accreditation Program ⇑ Center for Improvement in Healthcare Quality Accreditation
□ The Joint Commission accreditation ◇ DNV Healthcare Inc. accreditation △ Commission on Accreditation of Rehabilitation Facilities (CARF) accreditation

✠ △ **SAINT ALPHONSUS REGIONAL MEDICAL CENTER (130007)**, 1055 N Curtis Rd, Zip 83706–1309, Mailing Address: 1055 North Curtis Road, Zip 83706–1309; tel. 208/367–2121, **A**1 2 3 5 7 10 **F**3 9 11 12 13 15 17 18 20 22 24 26 28 29 30 31 32 33 34 35 36 37 38 39 40 43 44 45 49 50 54 55 56 57 58 59 64 65 66 68 70 71 72 74 75 76 77 78 79 81 82 84 85 86 87 89 90 91 93 94 96 97 98 99 100 101 102 103 104 107 108 110 111 114 115 117 118 119 121 124 126 127 128 129 130 131 132 134 135 144 146 147 148 149 150 153 154 **P**6 8 **S** Trinity Health, Livonia, MI
Primary Contact: Odette Bolano, R.N., Chief Executive Officer
CFO: Kenneth Fry, Chief Financial Officer
CMO: Steve Brown, M.D., Chief Quality Officer
CIO: Dwight Pond, TIS Boise
CHR: Teresa Sargent, Vice President Human Resources
CNO: Sherry Parks, R.N., MS, Chief Nursing Officer
Web address: www.saintalphonsus.org
Control: Church operated, Nongovernment, not–for–profit **Service:** General medical and surgical

Staffed Beds: **399** Admissions: **18084** Census: **248** Outpatient Visits: **1029511** Births: **1456** Total Expense ($000): **604380** Payroll Expense ($000): **254951** Personnel: **2924**

✠ **ST. LUKE'S REGIONAL MEDICAL CENTER (130006)**, 190 East Bannock Street, Zip 83712–6241; tel. 208/381–2222, (Includes ST. LUKE'S CHILDREN'S HOSPITAL, 190 East Bannock Street, Boise, ID, Zip 83712–6241; tel. 208/381–2222; ST. LUKE'S MERIDIAN MEDICAL CENTER, 520 South Eagle Road, Meridian, ID, Zip 83642, Mailing Address: 520 S Eagle RD, Zip 83642–6351, tel. 208/706–5000; Dennis Mesaros, Administrator) **A**1 2 3 10 **F**7 8 11 12 13 15 17 18 19 20 21 22 23 24 25 26 27 28 29 30 31 32 34 35 36 37 40 41 46 47 48 49 53 54 56 57 58 59 60 61 62 63 64 68 69 70 71 72 74 75 76 77 78 79 81 82 84 86 87 88 89 90 93 107 108 110 111 114 115 116 117 118 119 120 121 124 126 127 129 130 131 132 134 135 136 144 146 147 154 **P**6 8 **S** St. Luke's Health System, Boise, ID
Primary Contact: David M. McFadyen, Administrator
CFO: Jeff Taylor, Vice President Finance
CMO: Jim Souza, Chief Medical Officer
CIO: Marc Chasin, M.D., Chief Information Officer
CHR: Phillip Johnson, Vice President, Chief Human Resources Officer
CNO: Barbara Hocking, Chief Nursing Officer
Web address: www.stlukesonline.org/boise
Control: Other not–for–profit (including NFP Corporation) **Service:** General medical and surgical

Staffed Beds: **604** Admissions: **32554** Census: **377** Outpatient Visits: **1630158** Births: **5583** Total Expense ($000): **1849809** Payroll Expense ($000): **754083** Personnel: **9253**

★ △ **ST. LUKE'S REHABILITATION HOSPITAL (133025)**, 600 North Robbins Road, Zip 83702–4565, Mailing Address: P.O. Box 1100, Zip 83701–1100; tel. 208/489–4444, (Nonreporting) **A**5 7 10 **S** St. Luke's Health System, Boise, ID
Primary Contact: Nolan Hoffer, Senior Director
COO: Melissa Honsinger, Chief Operating Officer
CFO: Doug Lewis, Chief Financial Officer
CMO: Lee Kornfield, M.D., Medical Director
CIO: Scott Pyrah, Director Information Systems
CHR: Jim Atkins, Director Employee Services
Web address: www.idahoelksrehab.org
Control: Other not–for–profit (including NFP Corporation) **Service:** Rehabilitation

Staffed Beds: **31**

☐ **TREASURE VALLEY HOSPITAL (130063)**, 8800 West Emerald Street, Zip 83704–8205; tel. 208/373–5000, (Nonreporting) **A**1 3 10
Primary Contact: Nick Genna, Administrator
CMO: Jeffrey Hessing, M.D., Medical Director
CHR: Kathleen Phelps, Director Human Resources
Web address: www.treasurevalleyhospital.com
Control: Corporation, Investor–owned (for–profit) **Service:** General medical and surgical

Staffed Beds: **9**

VETERANS AFFAIRS MEDICAL CENTER See Boise Veterans Affairs Medical Center

✠ **VIBRA HOSPITAL OF BOISE (132002)**, 6651 West Franklin Road, Zip 83709–0914; tel. 877/801–2244, (Nonreporting) **A**1 3 10 **S** Vibra Healthcare, Mechanicsburg, PA
Primary Contact: Cynthia Newsom, Chief Executive Officer
Web address: www.vhboise.com
Control: Corporation, Investor–owned (for–profit) **Service:** Acute long–term care hospital

Staffed Beds: **60**

BONNERS FERRY—Boundary County

★ �sh **BOUNDARY COMMUNITY HOSPITAL (131301)**, 6640 Kaniksu Street, Zip 83805–7532; tel. 208/267–3141, (Total facility includes 28 beds in nursing home–type unit) **A**10 18 21 **F**3 11 15 28 29 34 35 40 41 50 57 64 75 77 79 81 85 93 97 107 110 111 115 119 127 128 130 132 133 143 149
Primary Contact: Craig A. Johnson, Chief Executive Officer
CFO: Holly McDonald, Controller
CMO: Chuck Newhouse, M.D., Chief of Staff
CHR: Ann Coughlin, Director Human Resources
CNO: Tari Yourzek, Chief Nursing Officer
Web address: www.boundarycommunityhospital.org
Control: County, Government, nonfederal **Service:** General medical and surgical

Staffed Beds: **48** Admissions: **153** Census: **29** Outpatient Visits: **23112** Births: **0** Total Expense ($000): **13764** Payroll Expense ($000): **8014** Personnel: **169**

BURLEY—Cassia County

✠ **CASSIA REGIONAL HOSPITAL (131326)**, 1501 Hiland Avenue, Zip 83318–2688; tel. 208/678–4444, **A**1 10 18 **F**3 7 13 15 18 28 29 30 31 33 34 35 38 39 40 44 45 46 47 48 50 57 64 68 70 75 76 77 78 79 81 85 86 87 92 93 97 102 107 108 110 111 115 119 127 129 130 132 141 146 147 148 149 **S** Intermountain Healthcare, Inc., Salt Lake City, UT
Primary Contact: Ben Smalley, Administrator
CFO: Mark Christensen, Director, Finance
CMO: Bernard Boehmer, M.D., Medical Director
CIO: Carie Call, Computer Support
CHR: Keri Perrigot, Manager Human Resources
CNO: Michele Pond–Bell, R.N., Nurse Administrator
Web address: www.cassiaregional.org
Control: Other not–for–profit (including NFP Corporation) **Service:** General medical and surgical

Staffed Beds: **25** Admissions: **1448** Census: **10** Outpatient Visits: **111464** Births: **619** Total Expense ($000): **51807** Payroll Expense ($000): **20574** Personnel: **322**

CALDWELL—Canyon County

✠ **WEST VALLEY MEDICAL CENTER (130014)**, 1717 Arlington, Zip 83605–4802; tel. 208/459–4641, **A**1 3 5 10 **F**3 8 11 13 15 18 20 22 26 28 29 30 34 35 40 41 45 50 51 54 57 59 60 64 68 70 72 74 75 76 77 79 81 82 84 85 86 87 89 91 92 93 98 100 101 102 104 105 107 108 110 111 114 115 119 126 130 131 135 146 147 148 149 154 **S** HCA Healthcare, Nashville, TN
Primary Contact: Elizabeth Hunsicker, Chief Executive Officer
COO: Jennifer Opsut, Interim Chief Operating Officer
CFO: Kate Fowler, Chief Financial Officer
CMO: Richard Augustus, M.D., Chief Medical Officer
CIO: Jason Martinez, Director Information Technology
CHR: Senta Cornelius, Director Human Resources
CNO: Edith E Irving, R.N., MS, FACHE, Chief Nursing Officer
Web address: www.westvalleymedctr.com
Control: Corporation, Investor–owned (for–profit) **Service:** General medical and surgical

Staffed Beds: **105** Admissions: **4439** Census: **46**

CASCADE—Valley County

CASCADE MEDICAL CENTER (131308), 402 Lake Cascade Pkwy, Zip 83611–7702, Mailing Address: P.O. Box 1330, Zip 83611–1330; tel. 208/382–4242, **A**10 18 **F**11 29 32 34 40 53 59 64 65 87 89 93 97 102 104 107 111 127 130 133 135 147 154
Primary Contact: Charles Johnston, Chief Executive Officer
CFO: Penny Lancaster, Controller
CMO: Mikael Bedell, M.D., Medical Director
CNO: Teri Coombs, R.N., Director Nursing Services
Web address: www.cascademedicalcenter.net
Control: Hospital district or authority, Government, nonfederal **Service:** General medical and surgical

Staffed Beds: **8** Admissions: **10** Census: **1** Outpatient Visits: **7035**

ID

COEUR D'ALENE—Kootenai County

★ ⇑ **KOOTENAI HEALTH (130049)**, 2003 Kootenai Health Way, Zip 83814–2677; tel. 208/625–4000, (Includes KOOTENAI BEHAVIORAL HEALTH, 2301 North Ironwood Place, Coeur D'Alene, ID, Zip 83814–2650; tel. 208/625–4800) **A**2 3 5 10 19 21 **F**3 4 5 9 11 13 14 15 18 19 20 22 24 26 28 29 30 31 32 33 34 35 37 40 41 43 44 45 46 47 48 49 50 51 53 54 56 57 58 59 60 63 64 65 68 70 71 72 74 75 76 78 79 81 82 83 84 85 86 87 89 91 93 95 96 97 98 99 100 101 102 104 107 108 110 111 114 115 116 117 119 121 124 126 127 129 130 131 132 135 143 145 146 148 149 154 **P**6
Primary Contact: Jon Ness, Chief Executive Officer
COO: Jeremy Evans, Vice President Operations
CFO: Kimberly Webb, Chief Financial Officer
CMO: Walter Fairfax, M.D., Chief Medical Officer
CHR: Daniel Klocko, Vice President Human Resources
CNO: Joan M. Simon, R.N., FACHE, Chief Nursing Officer
Web address: www.kh.org
Control: Hospital district or authority, Government, nonfederal **Service**: General medical and surgical

Staffed Beds: 299 **Admissions**: 14279 **Census**: 192 **Outpatient Visits**: 318908 **Births**: 1830 **Total Expense ($000)**: 483593 **Payroll Expense ($000)**: 217532 **Personnel**: 2630

COTTONWOOD—Idaho County

★ **ST. MARY'S HOSPITAL (131321)**, 701 Lewiston Street, Zip 83522–9750, Mailing Address: P.O. Box 137, Zip 83522–0137; tel. 208/962–3251, (Nonreporting) **A**5 10 18 **S** Essentia Health, Duluth, MN
Primary Contact: Lenne Bonner, President
CFO: Jyl Ruland, Chief Financial Officer
CHR: Debbie Schumacher, Chief Human Resource Officer
Web address: www.smh-cvhc.org/getpage.php?name=index
Control: Other not–for–profit (including NFP Corporation) **Service**: General medical and surgical

Staffed Beds: 28

DRIGGS—Teton County

★ **TETON VALLEY HEALTH CARE (131313)**, 120 East Howard Street, Zip 83422–5112; tel. 208/354–2383, **A**10 18 **F**3 15 18 29 30 31 34 35 38 39 40 41 43 45 50 55 56 57 59 64 65 68 74 75 77 78 79 81 82 84 85 87 93 97 100 102 104 107 110 111 114 119 127 131 133 135 146 147 148 154 **P**6
Primary Contact: Keith Gnagey, Chief Executive Officer
CFO: Wesley D White, Chief Financial Officer
CMO: Nathan Levanger, M.D., Chief of Staff
CHR: Dory Harris, Director Human Resource
CNO: Angela Booker, Director of Nursing Services
Web address: www.tvhcare.org
Control: Other not–for–profit (including NFP Corporation) **Service**: General medical and surgical

Staffed Beds: 13 **Admissions**: 189 **Census**: 2

EMMETT—Gem County

⇑ **VALOR HEALTH (131318)**, 1202 East Locust Street, Zip 83617–2715; tel. 208/365–3561, **A**10 18 21 **F**11 13 29 31 34 35 40 45 48 50 57 59 75 76 78 81 83 85 89 97 107 111 115 119 127 129 133 135 144 146 148
Primary Contact: Brad Turpen, FACHE, Interim Chief Executive Officer
CHR: Susan Vahlberg, Director Employee and Community Relations
Web address: www.wkmh.org
Control: County, Government, nonfederal **Service**: General medical and surgical

Staffed Beds: 12 **Admissions**: 202 **Census**: 2 **Births**: 41 **Total Expense ($000)**: 19783

GOODING—Gooding County

★ **NORTH CANYON MEDICAL CENTER (131302)**, 267 North Canyon Drive, Zip 83330–5500; tel. 208/934–4433, **A**10 18 **F**3 5 11 12 15 29 32 33 34 35 36 37 40 41 44 45 50 56 57 59 63 64 65 68 75 77 79 81 84 85 87 90 93 97 107 110 111 114 119 126 127 130 131 133 135 143 144 148
Primary Contact: Tim Powers, Chief Executive Officer
COO: J'Dee Adams, Chief Operating Officer
CFO: Sara DeMoe, Chief Financial Officer
CMO: Jennifer Olsen, M.D., Chief of Staff
CIO: Margie McLeod, Director Information Technology
CHR: Sara Otto, Chief Compliance Officer
CNO: Lisa Mangum, Chief Nursing Officer
Web address: www.ncm-c.org
Control: Hospital district or authority, Government, nonfederal **Service**: General medical and surgical

Staffed Beds: 18 **Admissions**: 458 **Census**: 6 **Outpatient Visits**: 30342 **Births**: 1 **Total Expense ($000)**: 25107 **Payroll Expense ($000)**: 10045 **Personnel**: 188

GRANGEVILLE—Idaho County

★ **SYRINGA HOSPITAL AND CLINICS (131315)**, 607 West Main Street, Zip 83530–1396; tel. 208/983–1700, **A**10 18 **F**7 13 29 30 40 50 58 76 81 89 93 107 119 127 130 133
Primary Contact: Abner King, Chief Executive Officer
CFO: Betty A Watson, Chief Financial Officer
CMO: Daniel Griffis, M.D., Chief Medical Officer
CIO: Darla Whitley, Manager Health Information Technology
CHR: Katy Eimers, Human Resources Officer
CNO: Cindy Daly, R.N., Director of Nursing
Web address: www.syringahospital.org
Control: Hospital district or authority, Government, nonfederal **Service**: General medical and surgical

Staffed Beds: 14 **Admissions**: 453 **Census**: 3 **Births**: 52 **Total Expense ($000)**: 14895 **Payroll Expense ($000)**: 7923 **Personnel**: 155

IDAHO FALLS—Bonneville County

⊠ **EASTERN IDAHO REGIONAL MEDICAL CENTER (130018)**, 3100 Channing Way, Zip 83404–7533, Mailing Address: P.O. Box 2077, Zip 83403–2077; tel. 208/529–6111, (Nonreporting) **A**1 10 19 **S** HCA Healthcare, Nashville, TN
Primary Contact: Jeff Sollis, Chief Executive Officer
COO: Sandee Moore, Chief Operating Officer
CFO: Judd Taylor, Chief Financial Officer
CMO: R. Lee Biggs, M.D., Chief Medical Officer
CHR: Wendy Andersen, Director Human Resources
CNO: Ann Marie Kjosa, R.N., MSN, Chief Nursing Officer
Web address: www.eirmc.com
Control: Corporation, Investor–owned (for–profit) **Service**: General medical and surgical

Staffed Beds: 293

MOUNTAIN VIEW HOSPITAL (130065), 2325 Coronado Street, Zip 83404–7407; tel. 208/557–2700, (Nonreporting) **A**3 5 10
Primary Contact: James Adamson, Chief Executive Officer
COO: Peter Fabrick, Vice President Clinical Operations
CHR: Eilene Horne, Manager Human Resources
Web address: www.mountainviewhospital.org
Control: Corporation, Investor–owned (for–profit) **Service**: General medical and surgical

Staffed Beds: 22

JEROME—Jerome County

★ **ST. LUKE'S JEROME (131310)**, 709 North Lincoln Street, Zip 83338–1851, Mailing Address: 709 North Lincoln Avenue, Zip 83338–1851; tel. 208/814–9500, **A**3 10 18 **F**7 13 15 29 30 32 34 39 40 56 57 59 64 65 68 76 77 79 81 86 87 97 107 111 119 127 133 146 147 **P**6 **S** St. Luke's Health System, Boise, ID
Primary Contact: Curtis Maier, Administrator
CMO: Elizabeth Sugden, M.D., Chief Medical Officer
CHR: Mark Stevens, Director Human Resources
CNO: Jill Howell, Chief Nursing Officer
Web address: www.stlukesonline.org/jerome/
Control: Other not–for–profit (including NFP Corporation) **Service**: General medical and surgical

Staffed Beds: 25 **Admissions**: 430 **Census**: 6 **Outpatient Visits**: 38229 **Births**: 146 **Total Expense ($000)**: 18663 **Payroll Expense ($000)**: 10505 **Personnel**: 148

KELLOGG—Shoshone County

⇑ **SHOSHONE MEDICAL CENTER (131314)**, 25 Jacobs Gulch, Zip 83837–2023; tel. 208/784–1221, (Nonreporting) **A**10 18 21
Primary Contact: Jerry Brantz, Chief Executive Officer and Chief Financial Officer
CMO: David Lawhorn, M.D., Chief Medical Officer
CIO: John Wohlman, Manager Information Systems
CHR: Dana Hemphill, Manager Human Resources
CNO: Karen Mann, R.N., Chief Nursing Officer
Web address: www.shoshonehealth.com
Control: Hospital district or authority, Government, nonfederal **Service**: General medical and surgical

Staffed Beds: 25

ID

Hospital, Medicare Provider Number, Address, Telephone, Approval, Facility, and Physician Codes, Health Care System

★ American Hospital Association (AHA) membership ○ Healthcare Facilities Accreditation Program ⇑ Center for Improvement in Healthcare Quality Accreditation
□ The Joint Commission accreditation ◇ DNV Healthcare Inc. accreditation △ Commission on Accreditation of Rehabilitation Facilities (CARF) accreditation

KETCHUM—Blaine County

✠ **ST. LUKE'S WOOD RIVER MEDICAL CENTER (131323)**, 100 Hospital Drive, Zip 83340, Mailing Address: P.O. Box 100, Zip 83340–0100; tel. 208/727–8800, **A**1 5 10 18 **F**3 7 11 13 15 29 30 31 32 34 35 36 37 39 40 43 45 50 54 56 57 59 62 64 65 68 74 75 76 77 79 81 82 85 86 87 91 93 97 99 101 103 104 107 108 110 111 114 115 119 126 130 131 132 133 134 135 143 146 147 148 **P**6 8 **S** St. Luke's Health System, Boise, ID
Primary Contact: Cody Langbehn, Administrator
CNO: Suzanne Miller, R.N., MSN, Senior Director Patient Care Services and Nursing
Web address: www.slrmc.org
Control: Other not–for–profit (including NFP Corporation) **Service:** General medical and surgical

Staffed Beds: 25 **Admissions:** 1062 **Census:** 8 **Outpatient Visits:** 94323 **Births:** 179 **Total Expense ($000):** 67233 **Payroll Expense ($000):** 32064 **Personnel:** 364	

LEWISTON—Nez Perce County

✠ **ST. JOSEPH REGIONAL MEDICAL CENTER (130003)**, 415 Sixth Street, Zip 83501–2431; tel. 208/743–2511, **A**1 2 10 **F**8 11 15 18 20 22 26 29 30 31 34 35 40 41 43 44 45 46 47 48 49 50 54 57 59 60 63 64 68 69 70 71 74 75 76 77 78 79 80 81 83 84 86 87 89 91 93 97 98 101 102 104 107 108 109 110 111 114 115 116 117 118 119 120 121 122 123 124 129 130 132 135 146 148 **S** RCCH HealthCare Partners, Brentwood, TN
Primary Contact: Blain Claypool, Chief Executive Officer
CFO: Thomas Safley, Chief Financial Officer
CHR: Susan Dokken, Chief Human Resources
CNO: Joan Agee, Vice President Patient Care Services
Web address: www.sjrmc.org
Control: Church operated, Nongovernment, not–for–profit **Service:** General medical and surgical

Staffed Beds: 123 **Admissions:** 5071 **Census:** 41 **Births:** 740 **Total Expense ($000):** 155227	

MALAD CITY—Oneida County

NELL J. REDFIELD MEMORIAL HOSPITAL (131303), 150 North 200 West, Zip 83252–1239, Mailing Address: Box 126, Zip 83252–0126; tel. 208/766–2231, (Nonreporting) **A**10 18
Primary Contact: John Williams, Administrator and Chief Executive Officer
CFO: Cindy Howard, Director Financial Services
CHR: Kathy Hubbard, Manager Human Resources
Web address: www.oneidahospital.com
Control: County, Government, nonfederal **Service:** General medical and surgical

Staffed Beds: 11	

MCCALL—Valley County

★ **ST. LUKE'S MCCALL (131312)**, 1000 State Street, Zip 83638–3704; tel. 208/634–2221, **A**5 10 18 **F**3 8 9 11 15 30 32 34 35 36 38 40 45 46 50 57 59 64 66 68 79 81 85 86 87 93 97 107 115 119 130 132 133 134 135 146 149 **P**6 8 **S** St. Luke's Health System, Boise, ID
Primary Contact: Sean McCallister, Administrator
CFO: Matt Groenig, Vice President Finance
Web address: www.stlukesonline.org/communities–and–locations/facilities/ hospitals–and–medical–centers/st–lukes–mccall–medical–center
Control: Other not–for–profit (including NFP Corporation) **Service:** General medical and surgical

Staffed Beds: 15 **Admissions:** 564 **Census:** 4 **Outpatient Visits:** 56276 **Births:** 103 **Total Expense ($000):** 37174 **Payroll Expense ($000):** 17871 **Personnel:** 217	

MERIDIAN—Ada County

ST. LUKE'S MERIDIAN MEDICAL CENTER See St. Luke's Regional Medical Center, Boise

MONTPELIER—Bear Lake County

★ **BEAR LAKE MEMORIAL HOSPITAL (131316)**, 164 South Fifth Street, Zip 83254–1597; tel. 208/847–1630, (Total facility includes 36 beds in nursing home–type unit) **A**10 18 **F**1 2 3 5 10 11 12 13 15 18 28 29 31 32 34 35 40 45 50 53 56 57 59 60 62 64 65 66 68 70 75 76 77 79 81 82 85 86 87 90 93 94 97 102 105 107 110 115 119 127 128 129 130 131 132 133 135 144 146 147 148 152 154
Primary Contact: Dennis Carlson, Chief Executive Officer
Web address: www.blmhospital.com
Control: County, Government, nonfederal **Service:** General medical and surgical

Staffed Beds: 57 **Admissions:** 377 **Census:** 37 **Outpatient Visits:** 80058 **Births:** 77 **Total Expense ($000):** 23797 **Payroll Expense ($000):** 11187 **Personnel:** 187	

MOSCOW—Latah County

✠ **GRITMAN MEDICAL CENTER (131327)**, 700 South Main Street, Zip 83843–3056; tel. 208/882–4511, **A**1 10 18 **F**3 8 11 13 15 19 28 29 34 35 36 37 40 45 46 49 51 53 54 56 57 59 64 65 70 75 76 77 79 81 82 85 86 87 89 91 93 96 97 107 108 110 111 115 119 124 127 129 130 131 132 133 135 143 146 147 148 149 **S** QHR, Brentwood, TN
Primary Contact: Kara Besst, President and Chief Executive Officer
CMO: Michael Patmas, M.D., Chief Medical Officer
CIO: Kane Francetich, Chief Information Officer
CHR: Dennis Cockrell, Director Human Resources
Web address: www.gritman.org
Control: Other not–for–profit (including NFP Corporation) **Service:** General medical and surgical

Staffed Beds: 25 **Admissions:** 1326 **Census:** 12	

MOUNTAIN HOME—Elmore County

✠ **ST. LUKE'S ELMORE (131311)**, 895 North Sixth East Street, Zip 83647–2207, Mailing Address: P.O. Box 1270, Zip 83647–1270; tel. 208/587–8401, (Total facility includes 34 beds in nursing home–type unit) **A**1 10 18 **F**3 7 11 13 29 30 34 35 40 45 57 64 75 77 81 107 111 114 119 127 128 129 130 133 146 149 **P**6 **S** St. Luke's Health System, Boise, ID
Primary Contact: Michael Blauer, Administrator
COO: Cody Mangum, Director Operations
CFO: Tricia Senger, Chief Financial Officer
CNO: Lisa Sanford, Chief Nursing Officer
Web address: www.stlukesonline.org/elmore/
Control: Other not–for–profit (including NFP Corporation) **Service:** General medical and surgical

Staffed Beds: 56 **Admissions:** 764 **Census:** 25 **Outpatient Visits:** 56092 **Births:** 144 **Total Expense ($000):** 35297 **Payroll Expense ($000):** 15959 **Personnel:** 223	

NAMPA—Canyon County

MERCY MEDICAL CENTER See Saint Alphonsus Medical Center – Nampa

✠ **SAINT ALPHONSUS MEDICAL CENTER – NAMPA (130013)**, 4300 East Flamingo Avenue, Zip 83686–6008; tel. 208/205–1000, **A**1 3 10 **F**3 8 11 12 13 14 15 18 20 22 28 29 30 31 32 34 35 37 39 40 41 43 44 45 50 51 57 64 65 66 68 69 70 71 72 75 76 77 78 79 81 82 85 86 87 92 107 108 110 111 115 118 119 120 121 123 126 129 130 132 133 134 135 141 143 145 146 147 148 149 **S** Trinity Health, Livonia, MI
Primary Contact: Travis Leach, President
CFO: Lannie Checketts, Chief Financial Officer
CMO: Dustan Hughes, M.D., Vice President Medical Affairs
CIO: Daniel Wright, Director Information Technology
CHR: Stefanie Thiel, Senior Human Resources Business Partner
CNO: Clint L Child, R.N., Chief Nursing Officer
Web address: www.saintalphonsus.org/nampa
Control: Church operated, Nongovernment, not–for–profit **Service:** General medical and surgical

Staffed Beds: 106 **Admissions:** 5897 **Census:** 53 **Outpatient Visits:** 117202 **Births:** 1095 **Total Expense ($000):** 114478 **Payroll Expense ($000):** 39894 **Personnel:** 698	

ST. LUKE'S NAMPA (130071), 9850 West St.Luke's Drive, Zip 83687; tel. 208/505–2000, (Nonreporting) **A**3 10 **S** St. Luke's Health System, Boise, ID
Primary Contact: Ed Castledine, Chief Executive Officer
Control: Other not–for–profit (including NFP Corporation) **Service:** General medical and surgical

Staffed Beds: 87	

OROFINO—Clearwater County

★ **CLEARWATER VALLEY HOSPITAL AND CLINICS (131320)**, 301 Cedar, Zip 83544–9029; tel. 208/476–4555, (Nonreporting) **A**10 18 **S** Essentia Health, Duluth, MN
Primary Contact: Lenne Bonner, President
CFO: Jyl Ruland, Chief Financial Officer
CMO: Kelly McGrath, Chief Medical Officer
CHR: Debbie Schumacher, Chief Human Resource Officer
Web address: www.smh–cvhc.org
Control: Other not–for–profit (including NFP Corporation) **Service:** General medical and surgical

Staffed Beds: 23	

ID

Many Facility Codes have changed. Please refer to the AHA Guide Code Chart.   © 2018 AHA Guide

STATE HOSPITAL NORTH, 300 Hospital Drive, Zip 83544–9034;
tel. 208/476–4511, (Nonreporting)
Primary Contact: Todd Hurt, Administrator
CMO: Karla Eisele, M.D., Clinical Director
CIO: James Sarbacher, Chief Information Officer
CHR: Heather Vandenbark, Human Resources Specialist
Web address: www.healthandwelfare.idaho.gov
Control: State, Government, nonfederal **Service:** Psychiatric

Staffed Beds: 60

POCATELLO—Bannock County

⊞ **PORTNEUF MEDICAL CENTER (130028)**, 777 Hospital Way, Zip 83201–5175;
tel. 208/239–1000, **A**1 3 5 10 20 **F**3 8 11 12 13 15 17 18 19 20 22 24 26 28
29 31 34 35 37 39 40 43 44 45 46 47 48 49 50 56 57 58 59 61 64 65 68 70
71 72 74 75 77 78 79 80 81 82 85 86 87 88 90 93 96 97 98 100 101 102
104 107 108 109 110 111 114 115 118 119 120 121 123 124 126 127 129
130 132 143 146 147 149 154 **P**2 **S** Ardent Health Services, Nashville, TN
Primary Contact: Daniel Ordyna, Chief Executive Officer
COO: Don Wadle, Vice President Clinical and Support Services
CFO: John Abreu, Vice President and Chief Financial Officer
CMO: Dan Snell, Chief Medical Officer
CHR: Don Wadle, Interim Director Human Resources
CNO: Angela Treasure, Chief Nursing Officer
Web address: www.portmed.org
Control: Corporation, Investor–owned (for–profit) **Service:** General medical and
surgical

Staffed Beds: 175 Admissions: 8377 Census: 93 Outpatient Visits:
247180 Births: 1304 Total Expense ($000): 218540 Payroll Expense
($000): 76227 Personnel: 1089

SAFE HAVEN HOSPITAL OF POCATELLO (134011), 1200 Hospital Way,
Zip 83201–2708; tel. 208/232–2570, (Nonreporting) **A**10 **S** Safe Haven Health
Care, Pocatello, ID
Primary Contact: Karen Neilson, Administrator
Web address: www.safehavenhealthcare.org/safehaven_hospital/index.html
Control: Individual, Investor–owned (for–profit) **Service:** Rehabilitation

Staffed Beds: 87

POST FALLS—Kootenai County

☐ **NORTHERN IDAHO ADVANCED CARE HOSPITAL (132001)**, 600 North Cecil
Road, Zip 83854–6200; tel. 208/262–2800, (Nonreporting) **A**1 10 **S** Ernest
Health, Inc., Albuquerque, NM
Primary Contact: Una Alderman, Chief Executive Officer
Web address: www.niach.ernesthealth.com
Control: Corporation, Investor–owned (for–profit) **Service:** Acute long–term care
hospital

Staffed Beds: 40

☐ **NORTHWEST SPECIALTY HOSPITAL (130066)**, 1593 East Polston Avenue,
Zip 83854–5326; tel. 208/262–2300, **A**1 10 **F**3 29 34 35 45 47 48 49 54 59
64 65 75 77 79 81 82 87 107 111 119 129 144 **S** National Surgical Healthcare,
Chicago, IL
Primary Contact: Rick Rasmussen, Chief Executive Officer
CIO: Craig McIntosh, Chief Information Officer
CHR: Gina Schneider, Director Human Resources
CNO: Christi Nance, R.N., MSN, Chief Nursing Officer
Web address: www.northwestspecialtyhospital.com
Control: Corporation, Investor–owned (for–profit) **Service:** Surgical

Staffed Beds: 34 Admissions: 1163 Census: 5 Births: 0

△ **REHABILITATION HOSPITAL OF THE NORTHWEST (133027)**, 3372 East
Jenalan Avenue, Zip 83854–7787; tel. 208/262–8700, (Nonreporting) **A**7 **S**
Ernest Health, Inc., Albuquerque, NM
Primary Contact: Darby Brockette, Chief Executive Officer
Web address: www.ernesthealth.com
Control: Corporation, Investor–owned (for–profit) **Service:** Rehabilitation

Staffed Beds: 25

PRESTON—Franklin County

★ **FRANKLIN COUNTY MEDICAL CENTER (131322)**, 44 North First East Street,
Zip 83263–1399; tel. 208/852–0137, (Total facility includes 35 beds in nursing
home–type unit) **A**10 18 **F**3 8 13 15 29 34 35 39 40 41 45 46 49 50 56 57 59
62 63 64 65 68 76 77 79 81 83 84 85 87 90 91 92 93 96 100 105 107 110
127 129 130 131 132 133 135 143 144 146 147 148 149 154
Primary Contact: Darin Dransfield, Chief Executive Officer
CFO: Paul Smart, CPA, Chief Financial Officer
CHR: Courtney Dursteler, Chief Human Resources Officer
CNO: Patrica Bowles, R.N., Chief Nursing Officer
Web address: www.fcmc.org
Control: County, Government, nonfederal **Service:** General medical and surgical

Staffed Beds: 55 Admissions: 612 Census: 35 Births: 87

REXBURG—Madison County

★ ⇑ **MADISON MEMORIAL HOSPITAL (130025)**, 450 East Main Street,
Zip 83440–2048, Mailing Address: P.O. Box 310, Zip 83440–0310;
tel. 208/359–6900, **A**10 21 **F**3 11 13 28 29 31 34 35 39 40 41 45 54 57 59
60 65 66 68 70 72 75 76 77 78 79 81 82 85 86 87 89 91 93 96 107 108 111
115 118 119 126 129 130 131 146 147 148 149 154 **P**8
Primary Contact: Rachel Ann Gonzales, Chief Executive Officer
COO: Audrey Fletcher, Chief Operating Officer
CFO: Troy Christensen, Chief Financial Officer
CMO: Clay Prince, M.D., Chief Medical Officer
Web address: www.madisonmemorial.org
Control: County, Government, nonfederal **Service:** General medical and surgical

Staffed Beds: 69 Admissions: 2881 Census: 22 Outpatient Visits: 27327
Births: 1532 Total Expense ($000): 59261 Payroll Expense ($000): 23868
Personnel: 423

RUPERT—Minidoka County

★ **MINIDOKA MEMORIAL HOSPITAL (131319)**, 1224 Eighth Street,
Zip 83350–1599; tel. 208/436–0481, (Total facility includes 43 beds in nursing
home–type unit) **A**10 18 **F**3 7 8 11 15 29 30 34 35 37 40 45 50 56 57 59 62
63 64 65 68 70 75 77 79 81 83 84 85 86 87 97 107 108 111 114 119 127
128 130 131 132 133 134 143 146 147 148 149 **P**1 3 5
Primary Contact: Tom Murphy, Chief Executive Officer
CFO: Jason Gibbons, Chief Financial Officer
CMO: Brian Muir, Chief of Staff
CIO: Nick Martin, Chief Information Officer
CHR: Eric Gochnour, Director Human Resources
CNO: Erinn Neilson, Chief Nursing Officer
Web address: www.minidokamemorial.com
Control: County, Government, nonfederal **Service:** General medical and surgical

Staffed Beds: 72 Admissions: 447 Census: 43 Outpatient Visits: 19169
Births: 0 Total Expense ($000): 22621 Payroll Expense ($000): 12801
Personnel: 202

MINIDOKA MEMORIAL HOSPITAL AND EXTENDED CARE FACILITY See
Minidoka Memorial Hospital

SAINT MARIES—Benewah County

⇑ **BENEWAH COMMUNITY HOSPITAL (131317)**, 229 South Seventh Street,
Zip 83861–1803; tel. 208/245–5551, **A**10 18 21 **F**13 15 29 31 34 35 40 56 57
59 64 76 79 81 89 90 93 96 97 107 110 111 114 119 127 129 130 131 133
135 146 147
Primary Contact: Lori Minier, Chief Executive Officer
CFO: Lori Minier, Chief Financial Officer
CMO: William Wheeler, M.D., Chief of Staff
CIO: Joseph Getchius, Director Information Technology
CHR: Marlana Martin, Director Human Resources
CNO: Rhonda Smith, Chief Nursing Officer
Web address: www.bchmed.org
Control: County, Government, nonfederal **Service:** General medical and surgical

Staffed Beds: 19 Admissions: 411 Census: 4 Births: 19 Total Expense
($000): 19884

ID

Hospital, Medicare Provider Number, Address, Telephone, Approval, Facility, and Physician Codes, Health Care System

★ American Hospital Association (AHA) membership
☐ The Joint Commission accreditation
○ Healthcare Facilities Accreditation Program
◇ DNV Healthcare Inc. accreditation
⇑ Center for Improvement in Healthcare Quality Accreditation
△ Commission on Accreditation of Rehabilitation Facilities (CARF) accreditation

SALMON—Lemhi County

★ **STEELE MEMORIAL MEDICAL CENTER (131305)**, 203 South Daisy Street,
Zip 83467–4709; tel. 208/756–5600, **A**10 18 **F**3 11 13 15 18 28 29 31 34 35
40 45 55 57 59 64 65 66 68 75 76 77 78 79 81 82 85 86 87 90 93 97 104
107 110 111 115 119 127 131 132 133 135 146 148 **S** QHR, Brentwood, TN
Primary Contact: Jeanine Gentry, Chief Executive Officer
COO: Abner King, Chief Operating Officer
CFO: Jim Peterson, Chief Financial Officer
CMO: Richard Natelson, M.D., Chief of Staff
CHR: Libby Brittain, Director Human Resources
CNO: Stephanie Orr, Chief Nursing Officer
Web address: www.steelemh.org
Control: County, Government, nonfederal **Service**: General medical and surgical

> **Staffed Beds:** 18 **Admissions:** 364 **Census:** 3 **Births:** 54 **Total Expense
> ($000):** 23631

SANDPOINT—Bonner County

★ ⇑ **BONNER GENERAL HOSPITAL (131328)**, 520 North Third Avenue,
Zip 83864–1507; tel. 208/263–1441, **A**10 18 21 **F**3 11 13 15 17 22 26 28 29
30 34 35 40 43 45 46 47 48 54 57 59 62 63 64 68 75 76 77 79 81 85 86 87
93 102 107 108 110 111 114 118 119 127 130 131 132 144 146 148
Primary Contact: Sheryl Rickard, Chief Executive Officer
CFO: John Hennessy, Chief Financial Officer
CIO: Jeremy Welser, Director Information Systems
CHR: Brad Waterbury, Director Human Resources
CNO: Misty Robertson, R.N., Chief Nursing Officer
Web address: www.bonnergeneral.org
Control: Other not–for–profit (including NFP Corporation) **Service**: General
medical and surgical

> **Staffed Beds:** 25 **Admissions:** 1788 **Census:** 12 **Outpatient Visits:** 77047
> **Births:** 285 **Total Expense ($000):** 54225 **Payroll Expense ($000):** 24021
> **Personnel:** 353

SODA SPRINGS—Caribou County

★ **CARIBOU MEMORIAL HOSPITAL AND LIVING CENTER (131309)**, 300 South
Third West, Zip 83276–1598; tel. 208/547–3341, (Nonreporting) **A**10 18
Primary Contact: Christina Thomas, MHA, RN, FACHE, Chief Executive Officer
CMO: John K Franson, M.D., Chief Medical Staff
CIO: Johnathan Inskeep, Chief Information Officer
CHR: Michael D Peck, Assistant Administrator
CNO: Brenda Bergholm, MSN, R.N., Chief Nursing Officer
Web address: www.cmhlc.org/
Control: County, Government, nonfederal **Service**: General medical and surgical

> **Staffed Beds:** 55

TWIN FALLS—Twin Falls County

⊠ △ **ST. LUKE'S MAGIC VALLEY MEDICAL CENTER (130002)**, 801 Pole Line
Road West, Zip 83301–5810, Mailing Address: P.O. Box 409, Zip 83303–0409;
tel. 208/814–1000, **A**1 2 3 7 10 **F**3 5 7 8 11 13 15 18 20 22 29 30 31 35 40
57 62 63 68 70 72 76 77 78 79 81 85 87 89 90 93 96 98 104 107 110 111
114 119 130 146 **P**6 8 **S** St. Luke's Health System, Boise, ID
Primary Contact: Michael A. Fenello, Administrator and West Region Chief
Executive Officer
CFO: Joshua Custer, Director Finance
CIO: Melissa Capps, Site Leader Information Technology
CHR: Mark Stevens, Senior Director Human Resources
CNO: Amy Bearden, R.N., MSN, Vice President Patient Care Services and Chief
Nursing Officer
Web address: www.stlukesonline.org
Control: Other not–for–profit (including NFP Corporation) **Service**: General
medical and surgical

> **Staffed Beds:** 224 **Admissions:** 12212 **Census:** 120 **Outpatient Visits:**
> 582883 **Births:** 1811 **Total Expense ($000):** 374720 **Payroll Expense
> ($000):** 123068 **Personnel:** 1984

WEISER—Washington County

★ ⇑ **WEISER MEMORIAL HOSPITAL (131307)**, 645 East Fifth Street,
Zip 83672–2202; tel. 208/549–0370, **A**10 18 21 **F**3 11 13 29 34 35 40 43 45
46 56 57 59 65 68 75 76 79 81 82 85 89 91 97 107 114 119 127 129 130
131 133 135 144 146 147 149 154 **S** St. Luke's Health System, Boise, ID
Primary Contact: Steven D. Hale, FACHE, Chief Executive Officer
CFO: Mark Christensen, Chief Financial Officer
CMO: Lore Wooton, M.D., Chief of Medical Staff
CHR: Terri Kautz, Manager Human Resources
Web address: www.weisermemorialhospital.org
Control: Hospital district or authority, Government, nonfederal **Service**: General
medical and surgical

> **Staffed Beds:** 18 **Admissions:** 355 **Census:** 3 **Outpatient Visits:** 14499
> **Births:** 69 **Total Expense ($000):** 16505 **Payroll Expense ($000):** 5811
> **Personnel:** 136

ID

Many Facility Codes have changed. Please refer to the AHA Guide Code Chart. © 2018 AHA Guide

ILLINOIS

ALEDO—Mercer County

★ **GENESIS MEDICAL CENTER–ALEDO (141304)**, 409 NW Ninth Avenue, Zip 61231–1296; tel. 309/582–9100, **A**10 18 **F**3 5 11 15 28 29 34 40 45 50 56 57 59 64 67 75 81 82 87 89 93 94 97 107 108 115 119 127 128 130 131 133 144 146 149 **P**6 **S** Genesis Health System, Davenport, IA
Primary Contact: Ted Rogalski, Administrator
CFO: Mark G Rogers, Vice President, Finance and Chief Financial Officer
CMO: Julio Santiago, M.D., Chief of Staff
CIO: Robert Frieden, Vice President, Information Services and Chief Information Officer
CHR: Tammy Hagedorn, Chief Human Resource Officer
CNO: Heidi Hess, Chief Nursing Officer
Web address: www.genesishealth.com
Control: Other not–for–profit (including NFP Corporation) **Service**: General medical and surgical

Staffed Beds: 22 **Admissions:** 221 **Census:** 3 **Outpatient Visits:** 17330 **Births:** 0 **Total Expense ($000):** 15637 **Payroll Expense ($000):** 6078 **Personnel:** 100

ALTON—Madison County

⊠ **ALTON MEMORIAL HOSPITAL (140002)**, One Memorial Drive, Zip 62002–6722; tel. 618/463–7311, (Total facility includes 120 beds in nursing home–type unit) **A**1 10 **F**3 6 7 11 13 15 18 20 22 29 30 31 34 35 36 38 39 40 45 46 49 50 56 57 59 64 69 70 74 75 76 77 78 79 81 82 85 86 87 89 92 93 96 98 103 104 107 108 110 111 114 115 116 117 118 119 120 121 123 128 129 130 131 132 135 146 148 149 154 **S** BJC HealthCare, Saint Louis, MO
Primary Contact: David A. Braasch, President
COO: Brad Goacher, Vice President Administration
CFO: Susan Koesterer, Vice President, Finance
CMO: Sebastian Rueckert, M.D., Vice President and Chief Medical Officer
CIO: Jerry Fox Jr Chief Information Officer
CHR: Bryan Hartwick, Vice President Human Resources
CNO: Debra Turpin, R.N., MSN, Vice President Patient Care Services and Chief Nursing Officer
Web address: www.altonmemorialhospital.org
Control: Other not–for–profit (including NFP Corporation) **Service**: General medical and surgical

Staffed Beds: 258 **Admissions:** 7795 **Census:** 131 **Outpatient Visits:** 155660 **Births:** 735 **Total Expense ($000):** 145947 **Payroll Expense ($000):** 54134 **Personnel:** 750

☐ **ALTON MENTAL HEALTH CENTER (144016)**, 4500 College Avenue, Zip 62002–5099; tel. 618/474–3800, **A**1 10 **F**98 106 **S** Division of Mental Health, Department of Human Services, Springfield, IL
Primary Contact: Brian E. Thomas, Administrator
CFO: Susan Shobe, Director Administration and Support Services
CMO: Claudia Kachigion, M.D., Medical Director
Control: State, Government, nonfederal **Service**: Psychiatric

Staffed Beds: 125 **Admissions:** 111 **Census:** 102

⊠ **OSF HEALTHCARE SAINT ANTHONY'S HEALTH CENTER (140052)**, 1 Saint Anthony's Way, Zip 62002–4579, Mailing Address: PO Box 340, Zip 62002–0340; tel. 618/465–2571, (Includes OSF HEALTHCARE SAINT CLARE'S HOSPITAL, 915 East Fifth Street, Alton, IL, Zip 62002–6434; tel. 618/463–5151) **A**1 2 10 **F**3 5 10 11 13 15 18 20 22 29 30 31 34 35 37 38 39 40 41 44 45 47 48 49 50 51 53 56 57 58 59 60 61 64 65 68 69 70 74 75 76 77 78 79 81 82 84 85 86 87 89 91 92 93 95 96 99 100 101 102 103 104 107 108 110 111 114 115 116 117 118 119 120 121 123 125 129 130 131 132 134 135 146 147 148 149 **P**6 **S** OSF Healthcare, Peoria, IL
Primary Contact: Ajay Pathak, President
COO: Sister M. Anselma Belongea, Chief Operating Officer
CFO: Mathew Hanley, Chief Financial Officer
CMO: Dennis Sands, Chief Medical Officer
CIO: Georgia Henke, Operational Account Manager
CHR: Robyn Grissom, Director of Human Resources
CNO: Colleen Becker, Chief Nursing Officer
Web address: www.osfsaintanthonys.org
Control: Church operated, Nongovernment, not–for–profit **Service**: General medical and surgical

Staffed Beds: 140 **Admissions:** 2889 **Census:** 42 **Outpatient Visits:** 88418 **Births:** 264 **Total Expense ($000):** 84913 **Payroll Expense ($000):** 27726 **Personnel:** 407

ANNA—Union County

☐ **CHOATE MENTAL HEALTH CENTER (144038)**, 1000 North Main Street, Zip 62906–1699; tel. 618/833–5161, **A**1 10 **F**34 39 59 65 75 86 98 101 102 103 130 143 149 154 **S** Division of Mental Health, Department of Human Services, Springfield, IL
Primary Contact: Elaine Ray, Administrator
COO: Elaine Ray, Administrator
CMO: John Larcas, M.D., Acting Medical Director
CIO: Cindy Flamm, Manager Quality
CHR: Tammy Tellor, Acting Director Human Resources
Control: State, Government, nonfederal **Service**: Psychiatric

Staffed Beds: 79 **Admissions:** 92 **Census:** 42 **Births:** 0 **Total Expense ($000):** 41175 **Payroll Expense ($000):** 33392

⊠ **UNION COUNTY HOSPITAL (141342)**, 517 North Main Street, Zip 62906–1696; tel. 618/833–4511, (Total facility includes 22 beds in nursing home–type unit) **A**1 10 18 **F**3 11 15 28 29 34 35 40 44 49 50 57 59 64 68 75 77 81 85 87 93 97 107 110 111 114 119 127 130 133 146 148 **P**6 **S** Quorum Health, Brentwood, TN
Primary Contact: James R. Farris, FACHE, Chief Executive Officer
CFO: Terry Paligo, Chief Financial Officer
CMO: Christine Lucas, Chief of Staff
CIO: John Hegger, Director Information Systems
CHR: Tammy Davis, Director Human Resources
CNO: Tammy H. Wheaton, Interim Chief Nursing Officer
Web address: www.unioncountyhospital.com
Control: Corporation, Investor–owned (for–profit) **Service**: General medical and surgical

Staffed Beds: 47 **Admissions:** 566 **Census:** 18 **Outpatient Visits:** 35804 **Births:** 0 **Total Expense ($000):** 20867 **Payroll Expense ($000):** 8760 **Personnel:** 159

ARLINGTON HEIGHTS—Cook County

⊠ **NORTHWEST COMMUNITY HOSPITAL (140252)**, 800 West Central Road, Zip 60005–2392; tel. 847/618–1000, **A**1 2 5 10 **F**3 5 8 12 13 15 18 20 22 24 26 28 29 30 31 32 33 34 35 37 38 39 40 41 43 44 45 46 47 48 49 50 53 54 55 56 57 59 61 62 63 64 65 68 70 71 72 73 74 75 76 77 78 79 81 82 85 86 87 89 90 91 92 93 94 96 98 99 100 102 103 104 107 108 110 111 114 115 116 117 118 119 120 121 123 124 126 129 130 131 132 135 144 145 146 147 148 149 152 154 **P**8
Primary Contact: Stephen Scogna, President and Chief Executive Officer
COO: Michael Hartke, Executive Vice President, Chief Operating Officer
CFO: Marsha Liu, Executive Vice President and Chief Financial Officer
CIO: Glen Malan, Vice President Information Technology and Chief Information Officer
CHR: Ann M Patrick, Vice President Human Resources
Web address: www.nch.org
Control: Other not–for–profit (including NFP Corporation) **Service**: General medical and surgical

Staffed Beds: 395 **Admissions:** 20472 **Census:** 260 **Outpatient Visits:** 463652 **Births:** 2527 **Total Expense ($000):** 456753 **Payroll Expense ($000):** 189128 **Personnel:** 3255

AURORA—Du Page and Kane Counties County

⊠ **PRESENCE MERCY MEDICAL CENTER (140174)**, 1325 North Highland Avenue, Zip 60506–1449; tel. 630/859–2222, **A**1 2 10 **F**3 5 12 13 15 18 20 22 24 26 28 29 30 31 34 35 36 38 40 43 45 46 49 56 57 59 61 65 68 70 75 76 77 78 79 81 82 85 86 87 89 93 97 98 99 100 102 103 104 105 107 111 114 115 119 125 126 130 132 135 144 146 147 152 153 **P**5 **S** Ascension Healthcare, Saint Louis, MO
Primary Contact: Michael L. Brown, Regional President and Chief Executive Officer
COO: Roxann E Barber, Regional Ambulatory Care and Ancillary Services Officer
CFO: Kevin Larkin, Regional Chief Financial Officer
CMO: Anil Gopinath, FACHE, M.D., Regional Chief Medical Officer
CHR: Michael O'Rourke, Regional Human Resource Officer
CNO: Grace McBride, Regional Chief Nursing Officer
Web address: www.presencehealth.org/mercy/
Control: Church operated, Nongovernment, not–for–profit **Service**: General medical and surgical

Staffed Beds: 242 **Admissions:** 8219 **Census:** 105 **Outpatient Visits:** 185579 **Births:** 173 **Total Expense ($000):** 183425 **Payroll Expense ($000):** 47274 **Personnel:** 801

IL

Hospital, Medicare Provider Number, Address, Telephone, Approval, Facility, and Physician Codes, Health Care System

★ American Hospital Association (AHA) membership   ○ Healthcare Facilities Accreditation Program   ⇑ Center for Improvement in Healthcare Quality Accreditation
☐ The Joint Commission accreditation   ◇ DNV Healthcare Inc. accreditation   △ Commission on Accreditation of Rehabilitation Facilities (CARF) accreditation

PROVENA MERCY MEDICAL CENTER See Presence Mercy Medical Center

☒ △ **RUSH–COPLEY MEDICAL CENTER (140029)**, 2000 Ogden Avenue, Zip 60504–7222; tel. 630/978–6200, **A**1 2 3 5 7 10 **F**3 7 8 13 15 17 18 19 20 22 24 26 29 30 31 32 35 36 38 39 40 43 44 45 46 47 49 50 51 52 53 54 55 57 58 59 60 61 64 65 66 68 70 72 73 74 75 76 77 78 79 81 82 84 85 86 87 89 90 92 93 94 96 97 107 108 110 111 114 115 117 118 119 120 121 123 124 126 130 131 132 134 135 143 144 145 146 147 148 149 154 **P**6 **S** Rush University Medical Center, Chicago, IL
Primary Contact: Barry C. Finn, President and Chief Executive Officer
COO: John A Diederich, Senior Vice President Operations and Chief Operating Officer
CFO: Brenda VanWyhe, Senior Vice President Finance and Chief Financial Officer
CMO: Steve B Lowenthal, M.D., M.P.H., FACS, Senior Vice President Medical Affairs and Chief Medical Officer
CIO: Dennis DeMasie, Vice President Information Systems and Chief Information Officer
CNO: Mary Shilkaitis, Vice President Patient Care and Chief Nursing Officer
Web address: www.rushcopley.com
Control: Other not–for–profit (including NFP Corporation) **Service:** General medical and surgical

Staffed Beds: 210 **Admissions:** 12828 **Census:** 146 **Outpatient Visits:** 226337 **Births:** 3296 **Total Expense ($000):** 293021 **Payroll Expense ($000):** 123836 **Personnel:** 1768

BARRINGTON—Lake County

★ ⇑ **ADVOCATE GOOD SHEPHERD HOSPITAL (140291)**, 450 West Highway 22, Zip 60010–1919; tel. 847/381–0123, **A**2 10 21 **F**3 11 12 13 15 17 18 19 20 22 24 26 28 29 30 31 34 40 43 45 46 47 48 49 54 57 59 63 64 65 68 70 74 75 76 77 78 79 81 82 84 87 89 91 92 93 94 97 100 107 108 110 111 114 115 116 117 118 119 120 121 123 124 126 129 130 131 132 135 144 146 148 154 **P**8 **S** Advocate Aurora Health, Downers Grove, IL
Primary Contact: Karen A. Lambert, President
COO: Michael Ploszek, Vice President Physician Strategy and Clinical Operations
CFO: George Teufel, Vice President Finance
CMO: Barry Rosen, M.D., Vice President Medical Management
CIO: Chuck Malik, Director Information Systems
CHR: Jason Spigner, Vice President Human Resources
CNO: Marianne D Araujo, R.N., Ph.D., FACHE, Vice President Nursing and Chief Nurse Executive
Web address: www.advocatehealth.com/gshp/
Control: Church operated, Nongovernment, not–for–profit **Service:** General medical and surgical

Staffed Beds: 176 **Admissions:** 9880 **Census:** 106 **Outpatient Visits:** 248185 **Births:** 1208 **Total Expense ($000):** 248249 **Payroll Expense ($000):** 75001 **Personnel:** 1198

BELLEVILLE—St. Clair County

★ ○ **MEMORIAL HOSPITAL (140185)**, 4500 Memorial Drive, Zip 62226–5399; tel. 618/233–7750, (Total facility includes 76 beds in nursing home–type unit) **A**3 10 11 **F**3 11 13 15 18 20 22 24 26 28 29 30 31 34 44 45 47 48 49 53 54 57 59 62 64 67 70 74 76 77 79 81 82 84 85 87 92 93 94 107 108 110 111 114 115 118 119 126 128 129 130 131 132 145 146 147 148 **S** BJC HealthCare, Saint Louis, MO
Primary Contact: Mark J. Turner, FACHE, President
COO: Michael T McManus, Chief Operating Officer
CFO: Jane Gusmano, Interim Vice President Finance
CMO: William Casperson, M.D., Vice President Medical Affairs
CIO: Jennifer Meinkoth, Executive Director, IS
CHR: John C Ziegler, FACHE, Vice President Human Resources
CNO: Teresa Halloran, Ph.D., R.N., Vice President Nursing Services
Web address: www.memhosp.com
Control: Other not–for–profit (including NFP Corporation) **Service:** General medical and surgical

Staffed Beds: 302 **Admissions:** 13092 **Census:** 297 **Outpatient Visits:** 195781 **Births:** 686 **Total Expense ($000):** 243182 **Payroll Expense ($000):** 108225 **Personnel:** 1749

BENTON—Franklin County

FRANKLIN HOSPITAL DISTRICT (141321), 201 Bailey Lane, Zip 62812–1969; tel. 618/439–3161, **A**10 18 **F**11 15 29 30 34 35 40 45 56 57 59 66 75 77 81 93 97 107 115 119 127 132 133 148 154 **P**6
Primary Contact: James Johnson, Chief Executive Officer
COO: Derek Johnson Sr Chief Operating Officer
CFO: Rikki S Bonthron, Chief Financial Officer
CMO: Richard Rethorst, Chief of Medical Staff
CIO: David Williams, Director Information Technology
CNO: Terri Hermann, R.N., Chief Nursing Officer
Web address: www.franklinhospital.net
Control: Hospital district or authority, Government, nonfederal **Service:** General medical and surgical

Staffed Beds: 16 **Admissions:** 273 **Census:** 3 **Outpatient Visits:** 45835 **Births:** 0 **Total Expense ($000):** 19342 **Payroll Expense ($000):** 8899 **Personnel:** 184

BERWYN—Cook County

☒ **MACNEAL HOSPITAL (140054)**, 3249 South Oak Park Avenue, Zip 60402–0715; tel. 708/783–9100, **A**1 2 3 5 8 10 13 **F**3 5 12 13 15 18 19 20 22 24 26 28 29 30 31 34 35 37 38 40 41 43 44 45 46 47 48 49 50 54 56 57 58 59 64 65 68 70 74 75 76 77 78 79 81 82 85 86 87 89 90 91 93 96 97 98 100 101 102 103 104 105 107 108 110 111 114 115 118 119 126 128 130 131 132 144 146 147 148 149 150 152 153 **P**5 6 **S** Trinity Health, Livonia, MI
Primary Contact: Mary Elizabeth. Cleary, President
CMO: Charles Bareis, M.D., Medical Director
CIO: Tom Haslett, Interim Chief Information Officer
Web address: www.macneal.com
Control: Corporation, Investor–owned (for–profit) **Service:** General medical and surgical

Staffed Beds: 358 **Admissions:** 13979 **Census:** 182 **Outpatient Visits:** 226678 **Births:** 1423 **Personnel:** 1911

BLOOMINGTON—Mclean County

☒ **OSF ST. JOSEPH MEDICAL CENTER (140162)**, 2200 East Washington Street, Zip 61701–4323; tel. 309/662–3311, (Total facility includes 12 beds in nursing home–type unit) **A**1 2 10 **F**3 11 12 13 15 18 20 22 24 26 28 30 31 34 35 37 40 43 45 49 50 51 53 54 57 59 60 61 64 65 68 70 74 75 76 77 78 79 81 82 84 85 86 87 89 92 93 96 97 107 108 110 111 114 115 118 119 127 128 129 131 132 135 144 146 147 148 149 150 154 **P**6 **S** OSF Healthcare, Peoria, IL
Primary Contact: Lynn Fulton, President
CFO: John R Zell, Chief Financial Officer
CMO: Paul E Pedersen, M.D., Vice President and Chief Medical Officer
CHR: Misti Tompkins, Employee Relations Director
Web address: www.osfstjoseph.org
Control: Church operated, Nongovernment, not–for–profit **Service:** General medical and surgical

Staffed Beds: 149 **Admissions:** 6522 **Census:** 75 **Outpatient Visits:** 167838 **Births:** 724 **Total Expense ($000):** 138521 **Payroll Expense ($000):** 44658 **Personnel:** 768

BLUE ISLAND—Cook County

☒ **METROSOUTH MEDICAL CENTER (140118)**, 12935 South Gregory Street, Zip 60406–2470; tel. 708/597–2000, (Nonreporting) **A**1 10 **S** Quorum Health, Brentwood, TN
Primary Contact: John D. Baird, Chief Executive Officer
CHR: Alanna Barker, Director Human Resources
CNO: Kathleen Hartman, Chief Nursing Officer
Web address: www.metrosouthmedicalcenter.com
Control: Corporation, Investor–owned (for–profit) **Service:** General medical and surgical

Staffed Beds: 285

BOLINGBROOK—Will County

☒ **AMITA HEALTH ADVENTIST MEDICAL CENTER BOLINGBROOK (140304)**, 500 Remington Boulevard, Zip 60440–4906; tel. 630/312–5000, **A**1 10 **F**3 12 13 15 18 20 22 28 29 30 31 34 35 37 40 41 43 44 45 46 49 50 54 56 57 59 61 64 70 73 74 76 78 79 81 82 85 86 87 98 100 101 102 103 107 108 110 111 114 115 119 130 132 146 147 149 154 **S** Adventist Health System Sunbelt Health Care Corporation, Altamonte Springs, FL
Primary Contact: Bruce C. Christian, Chief Executive Officer
COO: Richard Roehr, Chief Operating Officer
CFO: Rebecca Mathis, Chief Financial Officer
CMO: Richard Carroll, M.D., Chief Medical officer
CIO: John McLendon, Senior Vice President and Chief Information Officer
CHR: Katie Baio, Human Resource Director
CNO: Obed Cruz, Vice President and Chief Nursing Officer
Web address: www.keepingyouwell.com/abh/
Control: Church operated, Nongovernment, not–for–profit **Service:** General medical and surgical

Staffed Beds: 136 **Admissions:** 6266 **Census:** 67 **Outpatient Visits:** 103602 **Births:** 933 **Total Expense ($000):** 125043 **Payroll Expense ($000):** 38397 **Personnel:** 529

BREESE—Clinton County

☒ **HSHS ST. JOSEPH'S HOSPITAL (140145)**, 9515 Holy Cross Lane, Zip 62230–3618, Mailing Address: PO Box 99, Zip 62230–0099; tel. 618/526–4511, **A**1 10 **F**3 11 12 13 15 18 25 28 29 30 31 32 34 35 38 40 43 45 50 53 54 57 59 64 68 70 76 78 79 81 85 87 89 91 93 94 96 97 104 107 108 110 111 115 118 119 127 129 130 131 132 135 146 147 149 154 **P**6 **S** HSHS Hospital Sisters Health System, Springfield, IL
Primary Contact: Chris Klay, President and Chief Executive Officer
CFO: John Jeffries, Director Finance
CHR: Jason T Snow, Director Human Resources
CNO: Helen Essenpreis, MSN, R.N., Chief Nursing Officer
Web address: www.stjoebreese.com
Control: Church operated, Nongovernment, not–for–profit **Service:** General medical and surgical

Staffed Beds: 65 **Admissions:** 1207 **Census:** 9 **Outpatient Visits:** 93267 **Births:** 484 **Total Expense ($000):** 51559 **Payroll Expense ($000):** 16720 **Personnel:** 322

Many Facility Codes have changed. Please refer to the AHA Guide Code Chart.

© 2018 AHA Guide

CANTON—Fulton County

✠ **GRAHAM HOSPITAL ASSOCIATION (140001)**, 210 West Walnut Street, Zip 61520–2497; tel. 309/647–5240, (Total facility includes 38 beds in nursing home–type unit) **A**1 3 10 20 **F**3 11 13 15 26 28 29 30 40 45 50 53 54 57 59 62 63 64 65 67 70 75 76 79 81 82 85 87 89 91 97 107 108 110 111 114 115 119 124 127 128 129 130 131 132 135 143 144 145 146 **P**3
Primary Contact: Robert G. Senneff, FACHE, President and Chief Executive Officer
CFO: Eric Franz, Vice President, Finance and Chief Financial Officer
CIO: Jim Schreiner, Chief Information Officer
CHR: Canise A McComb, Director Human Resources
CNO: Teresa L McConkey, MSN, R.N., Vice President of Nursing and Chief Nursing Officer
Web address: www.grahamhealthsystem.org
Control: Other not–for–profit (including NFP Corporation) **Service**: General medical and surgical

Staffed Beds: 87 **Admissions:** 2360 **Census:** 47 **Outpatient Visits:** 239835 **Births:** 237 **Total Expense ($000):** 82954 **Payroll Expense ($000):** 29853 **Personnel:** 610

CARBONDALE—Jackson County

✠ **MEMORIAL HOSPITAL OF CARBONDALE (140164)**, 405 West Jackson Street, Zip 62901–1467, Mailing Address: P.O. Box 10000, Zip 62902–9000; tel. 618/549–0721, **A**1 2 3 5 10 13 19 **F**3 11 13 18 20 22 24 26 28 29 30 31 34 35 40 45 46 48 49 54 56 57 59 64 68 70 72 74 75 76 77 78 79 81 82 83 84 85 86 87 89 107 108 111 112 114 115 119 120 121 126 130 131 132 135 145 146 147 154 **P**1 **S** Southern Illinois Healthcare, Carbondale, IL
Primary Contact: Al Taylor, Vice President and Administrator
CFO: Michael Kasser, Vice President Chief Financial Officer and Treasurer
CMO: Marci Moore–Connelly, M.D., Vice President Chief Medical Officer
CIO: David Holland, Vice President Chief Innovation Officer
CHR: Pamela S Henderson, Vice President Human Resources
CNO: Julie Firman, R.N., FACHE, Vice President and Chief Nursing Officer
Web address: www.sih.net
Control: Other not–for–profit (including NFP Corporation) **Service**: General medical and surgical

Staffed Beds: 167 **Admissions:** 10538 **Census:** 97 **Outpatient Visits:** 122329 **Births:** 2010 **Total Expense ($000):** 265277 **Payroll Expense ($000):** 64706 **Personnel:** 1214

CARLINVILLE—Macoupin County

★ **CARLINVILLE AREA HOSPITAL (141347)**, 20733 North Broad Street, Zip 62626–1499; tel. 217/854–3141, **A**10 18 **F**11 15 28 29 34 35 40 45 64 77 79 81 91 93 107 110 115 127 129 133 148 149 154 **P**6 **S** HealthTech Management Services, Brentwood, TN
Primary Contact: Kenneth G. Reid, President and Chief Executive Officer
CFO: Mike Brown, Chief Financial Officer
CMO: Therese Polo, Medical Staff President
CIO: Jerod Cottingham, Director Information Systems
CHR: Tracy Koster, Director Human Resources
CNO: Sara McPeak, Chief Nursing Officer
Web address: www.cahcare.com
Control: Other not–for–profit (including NFP Corporation) **Service**: General medical and surgical

Staffed Beds: 25 **Admissions:** 694 **Census:** 9 **Outpatient Visits:** 23958 **Births:** 0 **Total Expense ($000):** 24728 **Payroll Expense ($000):** 9547 **Personnel:** 191

CARROLLTON—Greene County

THOMAS H. BOYD MEMORIAL HOSPITAL (141300), 800 School Street, Zip 62016–1498; tel. 217/942–6946, (Nonreporting) **A**10 18
Primary Contact: Deborah Campbell, Administrator
CHR: Lisa Eldridge, Human Resources Officer
Control: Other not–for–profit (including NFP Corporation) **Service**: General medical and surgical

Staffed Beds: 65

CARTHAGE—Hancock County

☐ **MEMORIAL HOSPITAL (141305)**, 1454 North County Road 2050, Zip 62321–3551, Mailing Address: P.O. Box 160, Zip 62321–0160; tel. 217/357–8500, (Nonreporting) **A**1 10 18 **S** UnityPoint Health, West Des Moines, IA
Primary Contact: Ada Bair, Chief Executive Officer
COO: Florine Dixon, Chief Operating Officer
CFO: Teresa Smith, Chief Financial Officer
CIO: Syndi Horn, Director Information Systems
CHR: Dan Smith, Director Human Resources
Web address: www.mhtlc.org
Control: Other not–for–profit (including NFP Corporation) **Service**: General medical and surgical

Staffed Beds: 18

CENTRALIA—Marion County

✠ **SSM HEALTH ST. MARY'S HOSPITAL CENTRALIA (140034)**, 400 North Pleasant Avenue, Zip 62801–3056; tel. 618/436–8000, **A**1 2 10 **F**3 5 11 12 13 15 18 20 26 28 29 30 31 32 34 35 37 38 40 44 45 46 50 54 56 57 59 60 61 64 68 70 73 74 75 76 77 78 79 80 81 82 84 85 86 87 89 90 91 92 93 94 98 99 100 101 102 103 104 105 107 108 110 111 114 118 119 120 121 129 130 131 132 135 144 146 147 148 149 152 153 **P**6 8 **S** SSM Health, Saint Louis, MO
Primary Contact: Damon R. Harbison, President
COO: Mark A Clark, Vice President Operations
CFO: Deland Evischi, Chief Financial Officer
CMO: Rajendra Shroff, M.D., Administrative Medical Director
CIO: Steve Murphy, Director Information Systems
CHR: Brenda Alexander, System Vice President, Human Resources
CNO: Sherry Dunlay, R.N., MSN, Vice President Patient Care Services and Chief Nursing Officer
Web address: www.ssmhealth.com/locations/st–marys–hospital–centralia
Control: Church operated, Nongovernment, not–for–profit **Service**: General medical and surgical

Staffed Beds: 124 **Admissions:** 5528 **Census:** 56 **Outpatient Visits:** 202693 **Births:** 292 **Total Expense ($000):** 98925 **Payroll Expense ($000):** 34646 **Personnel:** 835

CENTREVILLE—St. Clair County

☐ **TOUCHETTE REGIONAL HOSPITAL (140077)**, 5900 Bond Avenue, Zip 62207–2326; tel. 618/332–3060, **A**1 10 **F**3 11 13 15 18 29 30 39 40 45 47 50 54 55 62 64 68 70 73 75 76 79 81 85 87 92 98 99 101 102 103 104 105 107 108 110 114 119 130 135 143 146 148 149 150 153 **P**6
Primary Contact: Larry W. McCulley, President and Chief Executive Officer
COO: Tom Mikkelson, M.D., Interim Chief Operating Officer
CFO: John Majchrzak, Chief Financial Officer
CMO: Tom Mikkelson, M.D., Vice President Medical Affairs
Web address: www.touchette.org
Control: Other not–for–profit (including NFP Corporation) **Service**: General medical and surgical

Staffed Beds: 121 **Admissions:** 2445 **Census:** 24 **Outpatient Visits:** 57085 **Births:** 121 **Total Expense ($000):** 59125 **Payroll Expense ($000):** 26254 **Personnel:** 469

CHAMPAIGN—Champaign County

☐ **THE PAVILION (144029)**, 809 West Church Street, Zip 61820–3399; tel. 217/373–1700, **A**1 10 **F**98 99 101 102 103 105 106 152 **P**6 **S** Universal Health Services, Inc., King of Prussia, PA
Primary Contact: Mark Littrell, Group Director
CFO: Edith Frasca, Controller and Chief Financial Officer
Web address: www.pavilionhospital.com
Control: Corporation, Investor–owned (for–profit) **Service**: Psychiatric

Staffed Beds: 106 **Admissions:** 2246 **Census:** 91 **Outpatient Visits:** 7472 **Births:** 0

IL

CHESTER—Randolph County

☐ **CHESTER MENTAL HEALTH CENTER**, Chester Road, Zip 62233–0031, Mailing Address: Box 31, Zip 62233–0031; tel. 618/826–4571, (Nonreporting) **A**1 **S** Division of Mental Health, Department of Human Services, Springfield, IL
Primary Contact: Leah Hammel, Acting Administrator
CFO: Sarah Imhoff, Business Administrator
CMO: Maitra Rupa, M.D., Acting Medical Director
CIO: Anthony Young, Information Services Specialist
CHR: Kim Holsapple, Human Resource Specialist
CNO: Jennifer Klingeman, Director of Nursing
Control: State, Government, nonfederal **Service**: Psychiatric

Staffed Beds: 245

☐ **MEMORIAL HOSPITAL (141338)**, 1900 State Street, Zip 62233–1116, Mailing Address: P.O. Box 609, Zip 62233–0609; tel. 618/826–4581, (Nonreporting) **A**1 10 18
Primary Contact: Brett Bollmann, Administrator
CFO: Gail Miesner, Chief Financial Officer
CMO: Alan Liefer, M.D., President Medical Staff
CIO: Becky Bunselmeyer, Director Information Services
CHR: May Rose, Director Human Resources
Web address: www.mhchester.com
Control: Hospital district or authority, Government, nonfederal **Service**: General medical and surgical

Staffed Beds: 25

CHICAGO—Cook County

ADVOCATE BETHANY HOSPITAL See RML Specialty Hospital

★ ⇑ **ADVOCATE ILLINOIS MASONIC MEDICAL CENTER (140182)**, 836 West Wellington Avenue, Zip 60657–5147; tel. 773/975–1600, **A**2 3 5 8 10 13 21 **F**3 5 12 13 15 17 18 19 20 22 24 26 28 29 30 31 34 35 37 38 40 43 44 45 46 47 48 49 50 53 54 55 56 57 58 59 60 64 66 68 70 71 72 73 74 75 76 77 78 79 81 82 84 85 86 87 89 90 92 93 96 97 98 100 101 102 104 107 110 111 115 117 118 119 120 121 123 124 126 129 130 131 132 134 135 141 143 146 147 148 149 153 154 **P**8 **S** Advocate Aurora Health, Downers Grove, IL
Primary Contact: Susan Nordstrom Lopez, President
CFO: Jack Gilbert, Vice President Finance and Facilities
CMO: Clifton Clarke, Vice President Medical Management
CIO: Chuck Malik, Director Information Systems
CHR: Katie Bata, Vice President Human Resources
CNO: Donna King, R.N., FACHE, Vice President Clinical Operations and Chief Nursing Executive
Web address: www.advocatehealth.com/masonic
Control: Other not–for–profit (including NFP Corporation) **Service**: General medical and surgical

Staffed Beds: 334 Admissions: 14046 Census: 177 Outpatient Visits: 193247 Births: 2031 Total Expense ($000): 375074 Payroll Expense ($000): 146916 Personnel: 2101

★ ⇑ **ADVOCATE TRINITY HOSPITAL (140048)**, 2320 East 93rd Street, Zip 60617–3909; tel. 773/967–2000, **A**10 21 **F**3 13 15 18 20 22 24 26 28 29 30 31 34 35 40 45 49 50 55 56 57 58 59 60 61 64 65 68 70 74 75 76 77 78 79 81 82 87 89 92 93 107 110 111 114 115 119 126 130 132 135 146 148 154 **P**8 **S** Advocate Aurora Health, Downers Grove, IL
Primary Contact: Rashard Johnson, President
COO: Dan Doherty, Vice President, Operations
CFO: Maureen Morrison, Vice President, Finance
CMO: James Keller, M.D., Vice President, Medical Management
CIO: Bonita Brown–Roberts, Director Information Systems
CHR: Kristin Landini, Vice President, Human Resources
CNO: Jacquelyn Whitten, MSN, RN, Chief Executive Nurse
Web address: www.advocatehealth.com/trin/
Control: Church operated, Nongovernment, not–for–profit **Service**: General medical and surgical

Staffed Beds: 174 Admissions: 7573 Census: 80 Outpatient Visits: 75332 Births: 713 Total Expense ($000): 155824 Payroll Expense ($000): 54195 Personnel: 806

⊞ **ANN & ROBERT H. LURIE CHILDREN'S HOSPITAL OF CHICAGO (143300)**, 225 East Chicago Avenue, Zip 60611–2991; tel. 312/227–4000, **A**1 3 5 8 10 **F**3 8 9 11 12 17 18 19 21 23 24 25 27 28 29 30 31 32 34 35 36 37 38 39 40 41 43 44 45 46 48 49 50 51 52 54 55 57 58 59 60 61 63 64 65 68 72 74 75 78 79 81 82 84 85 86 87 88 89 91 92 93 94 96 97 98 99 100 101 102 104 105 107 108 111 115 116 117 118 119 124 126 129 130 131 132 134 136 137 138 139 141 142 144 146 148 149 150 154
Primary Contact: Patrick M. Magoon, President and Chief Executive Officer
COO: Michelle Stephenson, R.N., Executive Vice President & Chief Operations Officer
CFO: Ron Blaustein, Chief Financial Officer
CMO: Michael Kelleher, Chief Medical Officer
CIO: Lisa Dykstra, Senior Vice President and Chief Information Officer
CHR: Joani Duncan, Chief Human Resource Officer
CNO: Brian M Stahulak, R.N., Chief Nursing Officer
Web address: www.luriechildrens.org
Control: Other not–for–profit (including NFP Corporation) **Service**: Children's general medical and surgical

Staffed Beds: 240 Admissions: 11049 Census: 219 Outpatient Visits: 621420 Births: 0 Total Expense ($000): 752185 Payroll Expense ($000): 318028 Personnel: 5417

BERNARD MITCHELL HOSPITAL See University of Chicago Medical Center, Chicago

☐ **CHICAGO LAKESHORE HOSPITAL (144005)**, 4840 North Marine Drive, Zip 60640–4296; tel. 773/878–9700, **A**1 3 5 10 **F**4 5 54 56 98 99 102 103 104 105 153 **P**1 **S** Signature Healthcare Services, Corona, CA
Primary Contact: David Fletcher–Janzen, Chief Executive Officer
CFO: Carol Peart, Chief Financial Officer
CMO: Peter Nierman, M.D., Chief Medical Officer
CHR: Michelle Culpepper, Director Human Resources
Web address: www.chicagolakeshorehospital.com
Control: Corporation, Investor–owned (for–profit) **Service**: Psychiatric

Staffed Beds: 161 Admissions: 5274 Census: 121 Outpatient Visits: 8776 Births: 0 Total Expense ($000): 38297 Payroll Expense ($000): 18249 Personnel: 357

CHICAGO LYING–IN (CLI) See University of Chicago Medical Center, Chicago

☐ **CHICAGO–READ MENTAL HEALTH CENTER (144010)**, 4200 North Oak Park Avenue, Zip 60634–1457; tel. 773/794–4000, (Nonreporting) **A**1 10 **S** Division of Mental Health, Department of Human Services, Springfield, IL
Primary Contact: Richard Carmik, Facility Director and Hospital Administrator
Control: State, Government, nonfederal **Service**: Psychiatric

Staffed Beds: 200

CHILDREN'S MEMORIAL HOSPITAL See Ann & Robert H. Lurie Children's Hospital of Chicago

COMER CHILDREN'S HOSPITAL See University of Chicago Medical Center, Chicago

☐ **COMMUNITY FIRST MEDICAL CENTER (140251)**, 5645 West Addison Street, Zip 60634–4403; tel. 773/282–7000, (Nonreporting) **A**1 3 10
Primary Contact: Sheila Senn, PsyD, Chief Clinical and Administrative Officer
COO: Dennis FitzMaurice, Vice President, Professional Services
CFO: Richard Franco, Chief Financial Officer
CMO: David Bordo, M.D., Vice President and Chief Medical Officer
CIO: George Chessum, Senior Vice President and Chief Information Officer
CHR: Ivy McKinley, Regional Human Resources Officer
Web address: www.cfmedicalcenter.com
Control: Church operated, Nongovernment, not–for–profit **Service**: General medical and surgical

Staffed Beds: 279

☐ **GARFIELD PARK HOSPITAL (144039)**, 520 North Ridgeway Avenue, Zip 60624–1232; tel. 773/265–3700, **A**1 10 **F**98 99 101 102 104 105 130 132 135 153 154 **S** Universal Health Services, Inc., King of Prussia, PA
Primary Contact: Steven Airhart, Chief Executive Officer
CMO: Tina Mahera, M.D., Chief Medical Officer
CHR: Janice Clark, Manager Human Resources
Web address: www.garfieldparkhospital.com
Control: Corporation, Investor–owned (for–profit) **Service**: Children's hospital psychiatric

Staffed Beds: 88 Admissions: 967 Census: 33 Births: 0

☐ **HARTGROVE HOSPITAL (144026)**, 5730 West Roosevelt Road, Zip 60644–1580; tel. 773/413–1700, (Nonreporting) **A**1 10 **S** Universal Health Services, Inc., King of Prussia, PA
Primary Contact: Steven Airhart, Chief Executive Officer
CFO: Srbo Nikolic, Chief Financial Officer
CMO: Johnny Williamson, M.D., Chief Medical Officer
CHR: Anthony Rivera, Director Human Resources
CNO: Jody Bhambra, Chief Nursing Officer
Web address: www.hartgrovehospital.com
Control: Corporation, Investor–owned (for–profit) **Service**: Psychiatric

Staffed Beds: 128

★ ◯ **HOLY CROSS HOSPITAL (140133)**, 2701 West 68th Street, Zip 60629–1882; tel. 773/884–9000, **A**3 10 11 **F**3 5 11 12 13 15 17 18 20 22 24 26 28 29 30 31 32 34 35 38 40 44 45 49 50 56 57 59 63 64 65 66 68 70 74 75 76 78 79 81 82 84 85 86 87 90 91 92 93 97 98 100 101 102 103 104 107 108 110 111 114 115 118 119 121 123 130 132 134 135 143 146 147 148 149 150 153 154 **P**8 **S** Sinai Health System, Chicago, IL
Primary Contact: Lori Pacura, MSN, R.N., President
COO: Donnica Austin, Vice President, Operations
CFO: Charles Weis, Executive Vice President and Chief Financial Officer
CMO: James Richardson, Chief Medical Officer
CHR: Ann Hatches, Director, Human Resources
CNO: Deborah Davisson, MSN, Chief Nursing Officer and Vice President, Patient Care Services
Web address: www.holycrosshospital.org
Control: Other not–for–profit (including NFP Corporation) **Service**: General medical and surgical

Staffed Beds: 298 Admissions: 9000 Census: 118 Outpatient Visits: 75575 Births: 319 Total Expense ($000): 119206 Payroll Expense ($000): 57917 Personnel: 731

☐ **JACKSON PARK HOSPITAL AND MEDICAL CENTER (140177)**, 7531 Stony Island Avenue, Zip 60649–3993; tel. 773/947–7500, (Nonreporting) **A**1 3 10
Primary Contact: William Dorsey, M.D., Board Chairman and Chief Executive Officer
COO: Randall Smith, Executive Vice President
CFO: Nelson Vasquez, Vice President Finance
CMO: Bangalore Murthy, M.D., Director Medical Staff
CIO: Thomas Pankow, Chief Information Officer
CHR: Tracey Jones, Director Human Resources
Web address: www.jacksonparkhospital.org
Control: Other not–for–profit (including NFP Corporation) **Service**: General medical and surgical

Staffed Beds: 118

⊞ △ **JESSE BROWN VETERANS AFFAIRS MEDICAL CENTER**, 820 South Damen, Zip 60612–3776; tel. 312/569–8387, (Nonreporting) **A**1 3 5 7 8 **S** Department of Veterans Affairs, Perry Point, MD
Primary Contact: Marc Magill, MS, Medical Center Director
COO: Michelle Blakely, FACHE, Ph.D., Associate Director
CFO: Kalpana Mehta, Chief Fiscal Services
CMO: Wendy W Brown, M.D., M.P.H., Chief of Staff
CIO: Howard Loewenstein, Chief Information Resource Management Services
CHR: Wayne Davis, Manager Human Resources
Web address: www.chicago.va.gov/
Control: Veterans Affairs, Government, federal **Service**: General medical and surgical

Staffed Beds: 207

⊞ **JOHN H. STROGER JR. HOSPITAL OF COOK COUNTY (140124)**, 1969 West Ogden Avenue, Zip 60612–3714; tel. 312/864–6000, **A**1 2 3 5 8 10 13 **F**3 5 11 13 15 16 17 18 19 20 22 24 29 30 31 34 35 36 38 39 40 41 43 44 45 46 47 48 49 50 51 52 54 55 56 57 58 59 60 61 64 65 68 70 72 74 75 76 77 78 79 81 82 84 85 86 87 88 89 91 92 93 94 97 99 100 101 102 103 104 107 108 110 111 114 115 118 119 121 123 129 130 132 134 135 146 147 148 149 154 **P**6 **S** Cook County Health and Hospitals System, Chicago, IL
Primary Contact: John Jay. Shannon, M.D., Chief Executive Officer
CFO: John R Morales, Chief Financial Officer
CMO: Claudia Fegan, M.D., Chief Medical Officer
CIO: Bala Hota, Interim Chief Information Officer
CHR: Paris I Partee, Associate Administrator and Director Human Resources
CNO: Antoinette Williams, Chief Nursing Officer
Web address: www.cookcountyhealth.net
Control: County, Government, nonfederal **Service**: General medical and surgical

Staffed Beds: 450 Admissions: 19047 Census: 255 Outpatient Visits: 938276 Births: 1222 Total Expense ($000): 787679 Payroll Expense ($000): 394177 Personnel: 5149

JOHNSTON R. BOWMAN HEALTH CENTER See Rush University Medical Center, Chicago

KINDRED CHICAGO LAKESHORE See Kindred Chicago–Central Hospital, Chicago

⊞ **KINDRED CHICAGO–CENTRAL HOSPITAL (142009)**, 4058 West Melrose Street, Zip 60641–4797; tel. 773/736–7000, (Includes KINDRED CHICAGO LAKESHORE, 6130 North Sheridan Road, Chicago, IL, Zip 60660; tel. 773/381–1222; Diane Otteman, Chief Executive Officer; KINDRED HOSPITAL CHICAGO NORTH, 2544 West Montrose Avenue, Chicago, IL, Zip 60618–1589; tel. 773/267–2622; Larry Foster, R.N., MSN, Chief Executive Officer) (Nonreporting) **A**1 10 **S** Kindred Healthcare, Louisville, KY
Primary Contact: , R.N., MSN
COO: Joanne Garcia, Chief Operating Officer
CFO: Mary Treacy Shiff, Chief Financial Officer
Web address: www.khchicagocentral.com
Control: Corporation, Investor–owned (for–profit) **Service**: Acute long–term care hospital

Staffed Beds: 187

KINDRED HOSPITAL CHICAGO NORTH See Kindred Chicago–Central Hospital, Chicago

⊞ **LA RABIDA CHILDREN'S HOSPITAL (143301)**, 6501 South Promontory Drive, Zip 60649–1003; tel. 773/363–6700, **A**1 3 5 10 **F**3 12 29 32 34 35 38 40 41 50 57 59 64 65 74 75 77 79 82 84 85 86 87 89 91 93 94 96 97 100 101 104 107 119 130 132 134 143 144 146 148 149 **P**6
Primary Contact: Brenda J. Wolf, President and Chief Executive Officer
CFO: Mark Renfree, Chief Financial Officer
CMO: David Soglin, Chief Medical Officer
CIO: Sheelah Cabrera, Chief Information Officer
CHR: Frances Lefkow, Director Human Resources
CNO: Aden Henry, R.N., Vice President, Patient Care
Web address: www.larabida.org
Control: Other not–for–profit (including NFP Corporation) **Service**: Children's chronic disease

Staffed Beds: 30 Admissions: 340 Census: 25 Outpatient Visits: 29660 Births: 0 Total Expense ($000): 57631 Payroll Expense ($000): 28516 Personnel: 441

☐ **LORETTO HOSPITAL (140083)**, 645 South Central Avenue, Zip 60644–5059; tel. 773/626–4300, (Nonreporting) **A**1 10
Primary Contact: George Miller, President and Chief Executive Officer
CFO: Kenneth Mcghee, Vice President and Chief Financial Officer
CMO: Sonia Mehta, M.D., Chief Medical Officer
CIO: Syed Haque, Vice President and Chief Information Officer
CHR: Tania A White, Director Human Resources
Web address: www.lorettohospital.org
Control: Other not–for–profit (including NFP Corporation) **Service**: General medical and surgical

Staffed Beds: 113

⊞ **LOUIS A. WEISS MEMORIAL HOSPITAL (140082)**, 4646 North Marine Drive, Zip 60640–5759; tel. 773/878–8700, **A**1 2 3 5 10 **F**3 8 9 15 18 20 28 29 30 31 34 35 36 37 40 44 45 49 56 57 58 59 61 64 65 66 68 70 74 75 77 78 79 81 82 85 86 87 90 91 92 93 96 97 98 100 101 102 103 107 108 109 110 111 114 115 119 121 129 130 131 132 135 141 143 146 147 148 149 154 **P**5 6 8 **S** TENET Healthcare Corporation, Dallas, TX
Primary Contact: Mary Shehan, R.N., MSN, Chief Executive Officer
CFO: Jeffrey L Meigs, Chief Financial Officer
CIO: Thomas Crawford, Chicago Market Chief Information Officer
CHR: Keoni Nader, Director Human Resources
Web address: www.weisshospital.com
Control: Corporation, Investor–owned (for–profit) **Service**: General medical and surgical

Staffed Beds: 153 Admissions: 5754 Census: 86 Outpatient Visits: 67832 Births: 0 Total Expense ($000): 108103 Payroll Expense ($000): 47269 Personnel: 735

IL

★ ○ **MERCY HOSPITAL AND MEDICAL CENTER (140158)**, 2525 South Michigan Avenue, Zip 60616–2333; tel. 312/567–2000, **A**2 3 5 10 11 **F**3 5 12 13 15 17 18 20 22 24 26 28 29 30 31 32 33 34 35 36 40 44 45 46 49 50 51 53 54 55 56 57 58 59 61 64 65 66 70 74 76 77 78 79 81 82 84 85 86 87 90 91 92 93 96 97 98 99 100 101 102 103 104 107 108 110 111 114 115 117 118 119 120 121 123 124 126 129 130 131 132 133 143 144 145 146 147 148 149 150 153 154 **P**1 5 **S** Trinity Health, Livonia, MI
Primary Contact: Carol L. Schneider, President and Chief Executive Officer
COO: Richard Cerceo, Executive Vice President and Chief Operating Officer
CFO: Eric Krueger, Chief Financial Officer
CMO: Michael McDonnell, M.D., Chief Medical Officer
CIO: John Romeo, Chief Information Officer
CHR: Nancy L Hill-Davis, Vice President Human Resources
CNO: Carla Campbell, R.N., Chief Nurse Officer
Web address: www.mercy–chicago.org
Control: Other not–for–profit (including NFP Corporation) **Service**: General medical and surgical

Staffed Beds: 354 **Admissions**: 11785 **Census**: 148 **Outpatient Visits**: 316829 **Births**: 1905 **Personnel**: 1711

○ **METHODIST HOSPITAL OF CHICAGO (140197)**, 5025 North Paulina Street, Zip 60640–2772; tel. 773/271–9040, (Nonreporting) **A**10 11
Primary Contact: Joseph Chandy, Administrator
CFO: Jim Gregory, Controller
Web address: www.bethanymethodist.org
Control: Other not–for–profit (including NFP Corporation) **Service**: General medical and surgical

Staffed Beds: 189

✠ **MOUNT SINAI HOSPITAL (140018)**, 1500 South Fairfield Avenue, Zip 60608–1729; tel. 773/542–2000, (Includes SINAI CHILDREN'S HOSPITAL, California Avenue at 15th Street, Chicago, IL, Zip 60608; tel. 773/542–2000; Karen Teitelbaum, President and Chief Executive Officer) **A**1 2 3 5 8 10 **F**3 5 11 12 13 15 17 18 19 20 22 24 25 26 28 29 30 31 32 34 35 38 40 43 44 45 49 50 55 56 57 58 59 60 61 64 65 66 68 70 72 74 75 77 78 79 81 82 84 85 86 87 88 89 97 98 100 101 102 104 107 108 110 111 114 115 118 121 123 130 132 134 135 143 144 146 147 148 149 150 154 **P**8 **S** Sinai Health System, Chicago, IL
Primary Contact: Loren Chandler, President
CFO: Charles Weis, Chief Financial Officer
CMO: Mark Multach, M.D., Chief Medical Officer
CHR: Ann Hatches, Interim Director Human Resources
CNO: Michele A Mazurek, Interim Vice President Patient Care Services and Chief Nursing Officer
Web address: www.sinai.org
Control: Other not–for–profit (including NFP Corporation) **Service**: General medical and surgical

Staffed Beds: 288 **Admissions**: 12057 **Census**: 158 **Outpatient Visits**: 256645 **Births**: 1997 **Total Expense ($000)**: 268241 **Payroll Expense ($000)**: 116283 **Personnel**: 2910

✠ **NORTHWESTERN MEMORIAL HOSPITAL (140281)**, 251 East Huron Street, Zip 60611–2908; tel. 312/926–2000, (Includes PRENTICE WOMEN'S HOSPITAL, 250 East Superior Street, Chicago, IL, Zip 60611; tel. 312/926–2000; STONE INSTITUTE OF PSYCHIATRY, 251 East Huron Street, Chicago, IL, Zip 60611; tel. 312/926–2000) **A**1 2 3 5 8 10 **F**3 4 5 6 9 11 12 13 14 15 17 18 20 22 24 26 28 29 30 31 33 34 35 36 38 39 40 43 44 45 46 47 48 49 50 51 52 54 55 56 57 58 59 60 61 63 64 65 66 68 70 72 73 74 75 76 77 78 79 80 81 82 84 85 86 87 92 93 94 96 97 98 100 101 102 103 104 107 108 110 111 114 115 116 117 118 119 120 121 123 124 126 129 130 131 132 135 136 137 138 139 140 141 142 144 146 147 148 149 150 152 153 154 **P**6 **S** Northwestern Memorial HealthCare, Chicago, IL
Primary Contact: Julie L. Creamer, President, Northwestern Memorial Hospital and Senior Vice President Northwestern Memorial HealthCare
CFO: Francis D Fraher, Vice President, Finance, Northwestern Memorial Hospital
CMO: Gary Noskin, Senior Vice President and Chief Medical Officer, Northwestern Memorial Hospital
CIO: Carl Christensen, Senior Vice President and Chief Information Officer, Northwestern Memorial HealthCare
CHR: Michael Vivoda, Senior Vice President, Administration
CNO: Kristin Ramsey, R.N., Senior Vice President and Chief Nursing Executive, Northwestern Memorial Hospital
Web address: www.nm.org
Control: Other not–for–profit (including NFP Corporation) **Service**: General medical and surgical

Staffed Beds: 894 **Admissions**: 44479 **Census**: 668 **Outpatient Visits**: 1832025 **Births**: 11628 **Total Expense ($000)**: 2438175 **Payroll Expense ($000)**: 822906 **Personnel**: 11357

✠ **NORWEGIAN AMERICAN HOSPITAL (140206)**, 1044 North Francisco Avenue, Zip 60622–2743; tel. 773/292–8200, (Nonreporting) **A**1 3 5 10
Primary Contact: Jose R. Sanchez, President and Chief Executive Officer
COO: Michelle Blakely, FACHE, Ph.D., Chief Operating Officer
CFO: Gary M Krugel, Chief Financial Officer
CIO: Stephen DePooter, Chief Information Officer
CHR: Neil Teatsorth, Vice President Human Resources
CNO: William Duffy, Interim Chief Nursing Officer
Web address: www.nahospital.org
Control: Other not–for–profit (including NFP Corporation) **Service**: General medical and surgical

Staffed Beds: 195

OUR LADY OF THE RESURRECTION MEDICAL CENTER See Community First Medical Center

PRENTICE WOMEN'S HOSPITAL See Northwestern Memorial Hospital, Chicago

✠ △ **PRESENCE RESURRECTION MEDICAL CENTER (140117)**, 7435 West Talcott Avenue, Zip 60631–3746; tel. 773/774–8000, **A**1 2 3 5 7 10 13 **F**3 11 13 15 17 18 19 20 22 24 26 28 29 30 31 34 35 37 38 39 40 41 45 46 47 49 50 53 57 58 59 60 62 64 66 68 70 73 74 75 76 78 79 81 82 83 84 85 86 87 89 90 93 96 97 100 107 108 110 111 113 114 115 117 118 119 120 121 123 124 126 130 131 132 133 135 146 147 148 154 **S** Ascension Healthcare, Saint Louis, MO
Primary Contact: Robert Dahl, President and Chief Executive Officer
CFO: Colleen Koppenhaver, Interim Chief Financial Officer
CMO: David Bordo, M.D., Chief Medical Officer
CHR: Ivy McKinley, Regional Lead Human Resources
CNO: Pam Bell, Vice President Patient Care Services and Chief Nursing Officer
Web address: www.presencehealth.org
Control: Church operated, Nongovernment, not–for–profit **Service**: General medical and surgical

Staffed Beds: 337 **Admissions**: 12715 **Census**: 180 **Outpatient Visits**: 136124 **Births**: 1080 **Total Expense ($000)**: 267322 **Payroll Expense ($000)**: 87012 **Personnel**: 1234

✠ **PRESENCE SAINT JOSEPH HOSPITAL (140224)**, 2900 North Lake Shore Drive, Zip 60657–6274; tel. 773/665–3000, **A**1 2 3 5 10 **F**3 5 8 11 12 13 15 18 19 20 22 24 25 26 28 29 30 31 32 33 34 35 36 38 39 40 41 45 46 47 48 49 50 53 54 55 56 57 58 59 60 61 63 64 65 66 68 70 72 74 75 76 77 78 79 81 82 84 85 86 87 89 90 92 93 96 97 98 100 101 102 103 104 107 108 110 111 114 115 117 118 119 120 121 122 123 124 126 128 129 130 131 132 135 143 145 146 147 148 151 152 154 **P**8 **S** Ascension Healthcare, Saint Louis, MO
Primary Contact: James L. Robinson III, PsyD, President
CFO: Stanley Kazmierczak, Controller
CMO: M Todd Grendon, M.D., President Medical Staff
CIO: George Chessum, Senior Vice President Information Systems and Chief Information Officer
CHR: Denise Brown, Vice President Human Resources
Web address: www.reshealth.org
Control: Church operated, Nongovernment, not–for–profit **Service**: General medical and surgical

Staffed Beds: 361 **Admissions**: 12336 **Census**: 179 **Outpatient Visits**: 79787 **Births**: 1190 **Total Expense ($000)**: 232817 **Payroll Expense ($000)**: 75146 **Personnel**: 1315

✠ **PRESENCE SAINTS MARY & ELIZABETH MEDICAL CENTER (140180)**, 2233 West Division Street, Zip 60622–3086; tel. 312/770–2000, (Includes PRESENCE SAINTS MARY & ELIZABETH MEDICAL CENTER, CLAREMONT AVENUE, 1431 North Claremont Avenue, Chicago, IL, Zip 60622–1791; tel. 773/278–2000; Martin H Judd, Regional President and Chief Executive Officer) **A**1 2 3 5 10 **F**3 4 13 15 18 19 20 22 24 26 28 29 30 31 32 34 35 36 38 40 45 46 47 49 50 52 57 58 59 60 64 65 66 68 70 74 75 76 77 78 79 81 82 84 85 86 87 89 90 91 92 93 94 96 98 99 100 101 102 103 107 108 110 111 114 115 116 117 119 120 121 123 126 128 129 130 132 135 143 146 147 148 149 154 **P**8 **S** Ascension Healthcare, Saint Louis, MO
Primary Contact: Martin H. Judd, Regional President and Chief Executive Officer
CFO: Bob Cech, Regional Finance Officer
CMO: Laura Concannon, M.D., Regional Chief Medical Officer
CIO: Cheryl Rodenfels, System Vice President, IT Operations
CHR: Melanie Saenz, Regional Human Resources Officer
CNO: Suzanne Lambert, R.N., Regional Chief Nursing Officer and Support Services
Web address: www.presencehealth.org/presence–saints–mary–and–elizabeth–medical–center–chicago
Control: Church operated, Nongovernment, not–for–profit **Service**: General medical and surgical

Staffed Beds: 495 **Admissions**: 19175 **Census**: 290 **Outpatient Visits**: 158613 **Births**: 1317 **Total Expense ($000)**: 303732 **Payroll Expense ($000)**: 98565 **Personnel**: 1719

IL

⊞ **PROVIDENT HOSPITAL OF COOK COUNTY (140300)**, 500 East 51st Street, Zip 60615–2494; tel. 312/572–2000, **A**1 3 5 10 **F**3 8 15 18 29 30 34 35 40 45 50 53 57 59 61 64 66 68 78 81 85 87 92 94 104 107 119 130 132 135 143 146 147 149 154 **P**6 **S** Cook County Health and Hospitals System, Chicago, IL
Primary Contact: John Jay. Shannon, M.D., Chief Executive Officer
CFO: Barbara Patterson, Chief Financial Officer
CMO: Aaron Hamb, M.D., Chief Medical Officer
CIO: Donna Hart, Chief Information Officer
Web address: www.ccbhs.org/pages/ProvidentHospitalofCookCounty.htm
Control: County, Government, nonfederal **Service**: General medical and surgical

Staffed Beds: 25 **Admissions**: 610 **Census**: 8 **Outpatient Visits**: 31031
Births: 0 **Total Expense ($000)**: 80458 **Payroll Expense ($000)**: 32592
Personnel: 318

RESURRECTION MEDICAL CENTER See Presence Resurrection Medical Center

○ **ROSELAND COMMUNITY HOSPITAL (140068)**, 45 West 111th Street, Zip 60628–4294; tel. 773/995–3000, (Nonreporting) **A**10 11
Primary Contact: Timothy Egan, President and Chief Executive Officer
CFO: Marlo Kemp, Vice President and Chief Financial Officer
CMO: Alan Jackson, M.D., Medical Director
CIO: Mariusz Mazek, Vice President Information Technology and Chief Information Officer
CHR: Paulette Clark, Chief Human Resource Officer
CNO: Jeraldene Shaffer, MSN, Chief Nursing Officer
Web address: www.roselandhospital.org
Control: Other not–for–profit (including NFP Corporation) **Service**: General medical and surgical

Staffed Beds: 134

⊞ △ **RUSH UNIVERSITY MEDICAL CENTER (140119)**, 1653 West Congress Parkway, Zip 60612–3833; tel. 312/942–5000, (Includes JOHNSTON R. BOWMAN HEALTH CENTER, 700 South Paulina, Chicago, IL, Zip 60612; tel. 312/942–7000; RUSH CHILDREN'S HOSPITAL, 1653 Wes Congress Parkway, Chicago, IL, Zip 60612–3833; tel. 888/352–7874) **A**1 2 3 5 7 8 10 **F**1 2 3 4 6 8 9 11 12 13 14 15 16 17 18 19 20 21 22 23 24 25 26 27 28 29 30 31 32 34 35 36 37 38 39 40 41 43 44 45 46 47 48 49 50 51 52 53 54 55 56 57 58 59 60 61 62 63 64 65 66 67 68 70 72 73 74 75 76 77 78 79 80 81 82 83 84 85 86 87 88 89 90 91 92 93 94 95 96 97 98 100 101 102 104 107 110 111 114 115 117 118 119 120 121 123 124 125 126 128 129 130 131 132 134 135 136 137 138 139 141 142 145 146 147 148 149 154 **P**8 **S** Rush University Medical Center, Chicago, IL
Primary Contact: Larry J. Goodman, M.D., Chief Executive Officer
COO: Michael J Dandorph, President and Chief Operating Officer
CFO: John P Mordach, Senior Vice President and Chief Financial Officer
CMO: David A Ansell, M.D., Senior Vice President Clinical Affairs and Chief Medical Officer
CIO: Lac Tran, Senior Vice President Information Services
CHR: Mary Ellen Schopp, Senior Vice President Human Resources
CNO: Angelique Richard, R.N., Ph.D., Vice President Clinical Nursing, Chief Nursing Officer and Associate Dean for Practice, College of Nursing
Web address: www.rush.edu
Control: Other not–for–profit (including NFP Corporation) **Service**: General medical and surgical

Staffed Beds: 673 **Admissions**: 31480 **Census**: 477 **Outpatient Visits**: 621923 **Births**: 2168 **Personnel**: 7981

⊞ **SAINT ANTHONY HOSPITAL (140095)**, 2875 West 19th Street, Zip 60623–3596; tel. 773/484–1000, **A**1 3 10 **F**3 13 15 18 19 29 30 31 32 34 35 40 41 44 49 50 51 54 56 57 59 60 64 65 68 70 74 75 76 77 78 79 81 82 85 86 87 89 93 96 97 98 100 101 102 107 108 110 111 114 115 118 119 130 131 132 143 144 146 147 148 149 150 **P**8
Primary Contact: Guy A. Medaglia, President and Chief Executive Officer
CFO: Justin Bynum, Chief Financial Officer
CIO: Mark Jennings, Chief Information Officer
CHR: Malinda Yvonne Carter, Vice President Human Resources
Web address: www.sahchicago.org
Control: Church operated, Nongovernment, not–for–profit **Service**: General medical and surgical

Staffed Beds: 151 **Admissions**: 5324 **Census**: 74 **Outpatient Visits**: 114546 **Births**: 1315 **Total Expense ($000)**: 114504 **Payroll Expense ($000)**: 56273 **Personnel**: 836

SAINT JOSEPH HOSPITAL See Presence Saint Joseph Hospital

SAINTS MARY & ELIZABETH MEDICAL CENTER See Presence Saints Mary & Elizabeth Medical Center

⊞ **SCHWAB REHABILITATION HOSPITAL (143025)**, 1401 South California Avenue, Zip 60608–1858; tel. 773/522–2010, **A**1 3 5 10 **F**9 29 30 34 35 44 50 57 58 59 64 66 68 77 86 87 90 91 92 93 96 128 131 143 **S** Sinai Health System, Chicago, IL
Primary Contact: Karen Teitelbaum, Chief Executive Officer
CFO: Charles Weis, Chief Financial Officer
CMO: Michelle Gittler, M.D., Medical Director
CNO: Mary A Gollinger, MS, R.N., Director of Nursing
Web address: www.schwabrehab.org
Control: Other not–for–profit (including NFP Corporation) **Service**: Rehabilitation

Staffed Beds: 83 **Admissions**: 1421 **Census**: 53 **Outpatient Visits**: 10500
Births: 0 **Total Expense ($000)**: 33056 **Payroll Expense ($000)**: 19273
Personnel: 362

⊞ **SHIRLEY RYAN ABILITYLAB (143026)**, 345 East Erie Street, Zip 60611–2654, Mailing Address: 355 East Erie Street, Zip 60611–2654; tel. 312/238–1000, (Nonreporting) **A**1 5 8 10
Primary Contact: Joanne C. Smith, M.D., President and Chief Executive Officer
COO: Peggy Kirk, Senior Vice President Clinical Operations
CFO: Ed Case, Executive Vice President and Chief Financial Officer
CMO: James Sliwa, M.D., Chief Medical Officer
CIO: Tim McKula, Vice President Information Systems and Chief Information Officer
CHR: Lois Huggins, Chief Human Resources Officer and Senior Vice President Human Resources
CNO: Karen M Colby, MS, Chief Nursing Officer
Web address: www.ric.org
Control: Other not–for–profit (including NFP Corporation) **Service**: Rehabilitation

Staffed Beds: 182

☐ **SHRINERS HOSPITALS FOR CHILDREN–CHICAGO (143302)**, 2211 North Oak Park Avenue, Zip 60707–3392; tel. 773/622–5400, (Nonreporting) **A**1 3 5 10 **S** Shriners Hospitals for Children, Tampa, FL
Primary Contact: Mark L. Niederpruem, FACHE, Administrator
CFO: Philip Magid, Director Fiscal Services
CMO: Jeffrey D. Ackman, M.D., Chief of Staff
CHR: James E Pawlowicz, Director Human Resources
CNO: Terry Wheat, R.N., M.P.H., Director of Patient Care Services
Web address: www.shrinershospitalsforchildren.org/Hospitals/Locations/Chicago.aspx
Control: Other not–for–profit (including NFP Corporation) **Service**: Children's orthopedic

Staffed Beds: 36

○ **SOUTH SHORE HOSPITAL (140181)**, 8012 South Crandon Avenue, Zip 60617–1124; tel. 773/768–0810, (Nonreporting) **A**10 11
Primary Contact: Timothy Caveney, President
CFO: Scott Spencer, Chief Financial Officer
CMO: James Bob Achebe, M.D., President Medical Staff
CIO: Jim Ritchie, Director Management Information Systems
CHR: Roger Rak, Director Human Resources
CNO: Laura Gonzalez, Interim Chief Nurse Executive
Web address: www.southshorehospital.com
Control: Other not–for–profit (including NFP Corporation) **Service**: General medical and surgical

Staffed Beds: 137

☐ **ST. BERNARD HOSPITAL AND HEALTH CARE CENTER (140103)**, 326 West 64th Street, Zip 60621–3146; tel. 773/962–3900, (Nonreporting) **A**1 10
Primary Contact: Charles Holland, President and Chief Executive Officer
COO: Roland Abellera, Vice President and Chief Operating Officer
CFO: James P Porter, Chief Financial Officer
CNO: Evelyn Jones, R.N., Vice President Nursing Services
Web address: www.stbernardhospital.com
Control: Church operated, Nongovernment, not–for–profit **Service**: General medical and surgical

Staffed Beds: 100

IL

★ ○ **SWEDISH COVENANT HOSPITAL (140114)**, 5145 North California Avenue, Zip 60625–3661; tel. 773/878–8200, **A**2 3 5 10 11 13 **F**3 13 15 18 19 20 22 24 26 28 29 30 31 32 33 34 35 36 38 39 40 45 46 47 49 50 53 56 57 58 59 60 64 68 70 74 75 76 78 79 81 82 84 85 86 87 89 90 92 93 95 96 97 98 100 101 102 103 107 110 111 114 115 116 117 118 119 120 121 124 126 128 129 130 131 132 134 135 143 144 146 147 148 154 **P**1 5 7
Primary Contact: Anthony Guaccio, President and Chief Executive Officer
COO: Jonathan Lind, Chief Operating Officer
CFO: Thomas J Garvey, Senior Vice President Operations and Chief Financial Officer
CMO: Bruce McNulty, Chief Medical Officer
CIO: Karen Sheehan, Vice President and Chief Information Officer
CNO: Kathryn Donofrio, Chief Nursing Officer
Web address: www.schosp.org
Control: Church operated, Nongovernment, not–for–profit **Service**: General medical and surgical

Staffed Beds: 267 **Admissions**: 12545 **Census**: 168 **Outpatient Visits**: 288891 **Births**: 2238 **Total Expense ($000)**: 252964 **Payroll Expense ($000)**: 100676 **Personnel**: 2026

○ **THOREK MEMORIAL HOSPITAL (140115)**, 850 West Irving Park Road, Zip 60613–3077; tel. 773/525–6780, (Nonreporting) **A**3 10 11
Primary Contact: Edward Budd, President and Chief Executive Officer
COO: Peter N Kamberos, Chief Operating Officer
CMO: Ilona Carlos, M.D., President Medical Staff
CIO: Tony Vavarutsos, Director Information Systems
CHR: Brett Wakefield, Director Human Resources
CNO: Mary McCahill, Chief Nursing Officer
Web address: www.thorek.org
Control: Other not–for–profit (including NFP Corporation) **Service**: General medical and surgical

Staffed Beds: 134

⊞ **UNIVERSITY OF CHICAGO MEDICAL CENTER (140088)**, 5841 South Maryland Avenue, Zip 60637–1443; tel. 773/702–1000, (Includes BERNARD MITCHELL HOSPITAL, 5815 South Maryland Avenue, Chicago, IL, Zip 60637, Mailing Address: 5841 S. Maryland Ave., Zip 60637, tel. 773/702–1000; Sharon L O'Keefe, President, University of Chicago Medical Center; CHICAGO LYING–IN (CLI), 5815 South Maryland Avenue, Chicago, IL, Zip 60637, Mailing Address: 5841 South Maryland Avenue, Zip 60637, tel. 773/702–1000; Sharon L O'Keefe, President, University of Chicago Medical Center; COMER CHILDREN'S HOSPITAL, 5721 South Maryland Avenue, Chicago, IL, Zip 60637, Mailing Address: 5841 South Maryland Avenue, Zip 60637, tel. 773/702–1000; Sharon L O'Keefe, President, University of Chicago Medical Center) **A**1 2 3 5 8 10 **F**3 5 6 9 11 12 13 14 15 16 17 18 19 20 21 22 23 24 25 26 27 28 29 30 31 32 33 34 35 36 37 38 40 41 43 44 45 46 47 48 49 50 51 52 53 54 55 56 57 58 59 60 61 63 64 65 68 70 71 72 73 74 75 76 77 78 79 81 82 83 84 85 86 87 88 89 92 93 97 100 101 102 104 107 108 109 110 111 112 114 115 116 117 118 119 120 121 123 124 126 129 130 131 132 134 135 136 137 138 139 140 141 142 143 144 145 146 147 148 149 150 **P**1 **S** University of Chicago Medicine, Chicago, IL
Primary Contact: Sharon L. O'Keefe, President
COO: Jason Keeler, Executive Vice President and Chief Operating Officer
CFO: Rich Silveria, Executive Vice President and Chief Financial Officer
CMO: Stephen Weber, M.D., Chief Medical Officer
CHR: Bob Hanley, Chief Human Resources Officer
CNO: Debra Albert, MSN, R.N., Senior Vice President Patient Care and Chief Nursing Officer
Web address: www.uchospitals.edu
Control: Other not–for–profit (including NFP Corporation) **Service**: General medical and surgical

Staffed Beds: 650 **Admissions**: 30097 **Census**: 547 **Outpatient Visits**: 728129 **Births**: 2442 **Total Expense ($000)**: 1657078 **Payroll Expense ($000)**: 592290 **Personnel**: 8860

⊞ △ **UNIVERSITY OF ILLINOIS HOSPITAL & HEALTH SCIENCES SYSTEM (140150)**, 1740 West Taylor Street, Zip 60612–7232; tel. 312/996–7000, **A**1 2 3 5 7 8 10 **F**3 9 12 13 15 17 18 19 20 21 22 23 24 25 26 28 29 30 31 32 34 35 37 38 39 40 41 45 47 48 49 50 52 54 55 56 57 58 59 60 61 64 65 66 68 70 72 74 75 76 77 78 79 81 82 84 85 86 87 88 89 91 92 93 96 97 98 99 100 101 102 103 104 107 108 110 111 114 115 116 117 118 119 120 121 123 124 126 129 130 131 132 134 135 136 138 139 141 142 144 145 146 147 148 150 154 **P**4
Primary Contact: Michael B. Zenn, Chief Executive Officer
COO: David Loffing, Chief Operating Officer
CMO: Bernard Pygon, M.D., Chief Medical Officer
CIO: Audrius Polikaitis, Chief Information Officer
CHR: Mary Jo Smith, Chief Human Resources Officer
Web address: www.hospital.uillinois.edu/
Control: State, Government, nonfederal **Service**: General medical and surgical

Staffed Beds: 406 **Admissions**: 18623 **Census**: 310 **Outpatient Visits**: 585703 **Births**: 2341 **Total Expense ($000)**: 1022704 **Payroll Expense ($000)**: 315918 **Personnel**: 3841

CHICAGO HEIGHTS—Cook County

ST. JAMES HOSPITAL AND HEALTH CENTERS – CHICAGO HEIGHTS CAMPUS See Franciscan Health Olympia Fields, Olympia Fields

CLINTON—De Witt County

WARNER HOSPITAL AND HEALTH SERVICES (141303), 422 West White Street, Zip 61727–2272; tel. 217/935–9571, (Nonreporting) **A**10 18
Primary Contact: Paul Skowron, Chief Executive Officer
CFO: Donna Wisner, Chief Financial Officer
CMO: Brit Williams, M.D., President Medical Staff
CIO: Larry Schleicher, Manager Information Services
CHR: Sarah Gerke, Manager Human Resources
CNO: Heidi Cook, Chief Nursing Officer
Web address: www.djwhospital.org
Control: City, Government, nonfederal **Service**: General medical and surgical

Staffed Beds: 25

DANVILLE—Vermilion County

⊞ **OSF SACRED HEART MEDICAL CENTER (140093)**, 812 North Logan, Zip 61832–3788; tel. 217/443–5000, **A**1 2 5 10 19 **F**3 8 12 13 15 18 20 24 26 28 29 30 31 35 40 45 46 47 48 49 59 64 68 70 74 75 76 78 79 81 82 87 89 92 93 94 96 97 102 107 108 110 111 114 115 118 119 120 121 122 123 129 130 132 146 147 148 **S** OSF Healthcare, Peoria, IL
Primary Contact: Jared Rogers, M.D., President and Chief Executive Officer
CFO: Lucas Morton, Regional Chief Financial Officer
CMO: Vincent Kucich, FACHE, FACS, M.D., Chief Medical Officer
CIO: Paula Keele, Manager Information Systems
CHR: Michael Zimmerman, Human Resource Officer
CNO: Molly Nicholson, MS, R.N., Vice President of Patient Care/Chief Nurse Executive
Web address: www.presencehealth.org/usmc
Control: Church operated, Nongovernment, not–for–profit **Service**: General medical and surgical

Staffed Beds: 117 **Admissions**: 5052 **Census**: 47 **Births**: 587 **Total Expense ($000)**: 89442 **Payroll Expense ($000)**: 28659 **Personnel**: 493

⊞ **VETERANS AFFAIRS ILLIANA HEALTH CARE SYSTEM**, 1900 East Main Street, Zip 61832–5198; tel. 217/554–3000, (Nonreporting) **A**1 3 5 **S** Department of Veterans Affairs, Perry Point, MD
Primary Contact: Diana Carranza, Interim Director
COO: Diana Carranza, Associate Director
CFO: Becky Tissier, Chief Fiscal Service
CMO: Khiem Tran, M.D., Acting Chief of Staff
CIO: Frank D. Jackson III Facility Chief Information Officer
CHR: Connie Ohl, Acting Chief Human Resources
Web address: www.danville.va.gov/
Control: Veterans Affairs, Government, federal **Service**: General medical and surgical

Staffed Beds: 221

DECATUR—Macon County

⊞ △ **DECATUR MEMORIAL HOSPITAL (140135)**, 2300 North Edward Street, Zip 62526–4192; tel. 217/876–8121, **A**1 2 3 5 7 10 19 **F**3 8 11 12 13 15 18 19 20 22 24 26 28 29 30 31 34 35 37 40 43 45 46 47 48 49 51 53 54 56 57 58 59 60 61 62 63 64 65 69 70 71 73 74 75 76 77 78 79 81 82 84 85 86 87 89 91 92 93 94 96 97 98 100 102 103 104 107 108 110 111 112 114 115 116 117 118 119 120 121 123 124 126 129 130 131 132 135 141 143 144 145 146 147 148 149 153 154 **P**6 7 8
Primary Contact: Timothy D. Stone Jr, President and Chief Executive Officer
COO: John Ridley, Executive Vice President & Chief Operating Officer
CFO: Deborah L Bragg, Senior Vice President, Finance
CMO: Larry T Hegland, M.D., Chief Medical Officer
CIO: Linda L Fahey, R.N., Chief Information Officer and Senior Vice President Quality Systems
CHR: Kevin Horath, Vice President Human Resources
CNO: Robyn Reising, R.N., Chief Nursing Officer
Web address: www.dmhcares.com
Control: Other not–for–profit (including NFP Corporation) **Service**: General medical and surgical

Staffed Beds: 304 **Admissions**: 9120 **Census**: 100 **Outpatient Visits**: 252650 **Births**: 843 **Total Expense ($000)**: 269807 **Payroll Expense ($000)**: 123201 **Personnel**: 1979

Many Facility Codes have changed. Please refer to the AHA Guide Code Chart. © 2018 AHA Guide

⊠ △ **HSHS ST. MARY'S HOSPITAL (140166)**, 1800 East Lake Shore Drive, Zip 62521–3883; tel. 217/464–2966, **A**1 3 7 10 **F**2 3 5 11 13 15 18 20 22 28 29 30 31 34 35 40 44 45 50 54 56 57 59 64 66 70 74 75 76 77 78 79 81 82 85 86 87 89 90 91 92 93 96 98 99 100 101 102 103 104 105 107 108 110 111 114 117 119 120 121 122 123 124 126 129 130 131 132 141 142 146 148 149 150 **P**7 **S** HSHS Hospital Sisters Health System, Springfield, IL
Primary Contact: Evert J. Kuiper, Interim President and Chief Executive Officer
CMO: Phil Barnell, Chief Medical Officer
CHR: Denise Smith, Director People Services
CNO: Michelle Oliver, Chief Nursing Officer
Web address: www.stmarysdecatur.com
Control: Church operated, Nongovernment, not–for–profit **Service**: General medical and surgical

Staffed Beds: 230 Admissions: 7077 Census: 93 Outpatient Visits: 164800 Births: 573 Total Expense ($000): 144640 Payroll Expense ($000): 43516 Personnel: 670

DEKALB—DeKalb County

⊠ **NORTHWESTERN MEDICINE KISHWAUKEE HOSPITAL (140286)**,
1 Kish Hospital Drive, Zip 60115–9602, Mailing Address: P.O. Box 707, Zip 60115–0707; tel. 815/756–1521, **A**1 2 10 **F**3 5 8 11 13 15 18 20 22 26 28 29 30 31 32 34 35 36 38 43 44 45 46 48 49 50 51 54 57 58 59 60 64 65 66 68 70 71 73 74 75 76 77 78 79 80 81 82 85 86 87 89 93 94 96 97 98 100 101 102 104 107 108 110 111 114 115 116 117 118 119 127 129 130 131 132 133 135 144 145 146 147 148 149 150 152 153 154 **P**6 8 **S** Northwestern Memorial HealthCare, Chicago, IL
Primary Contact: Jay Anderson, President
COO: Brad Copple, Vice President, Operations
CFO: John Orsini, Senior Vice President, Chief Financial Officer
CMO: Michael Kulisz, D.O., Chief Medical Officer
CIO: Carl Christensen, Senior Vice President, Chief Information Officer
CHR: Michael Vivoda, Senior Vice President, Human Resources
CNO: Pamela Duffy, MSN, R.N., Vice President Operations and Chief Nursing Officer
Web address: www.nm.org
Control: Other not–for–profit (including NFP Corporation) **Service**: General medical and surgical

Staffed Beds: 98 Admissions: 5241 Census: 59 Outpatient Visits: 334244 Births: 783 Total Expense ($000): 191363 Payroll Expense ($000): 72480 Personnel: 1136

DES PLAINES—Cook County

HOLY FAMILY MEDICAL CENTER See Presence Holy Family Medical Center

⊠ **PRESENCE HOLY FAMILY MEDICAL CENTER (142011)**, 100 North River Road, Zip 60016–1255; tel. 847/297–1800, **A**1 10 **F**1 3 5 15 18 29 30 34 35 45 46 50 53 57 59 60 63 64 65 66 81 82 84 85 87 92 93 107 110 111 118 119 124 129 130 132 135 141 143 146 147 148 149 150 154 **S** Ascension Healthcare, Saint Louis, MO
Primary Contact: Yolande Wilson–Stubbs, President
CFO: Gene Yakovenko, Director of Finance
CMO: David Bordo, M.D., Chief Medical Officer
CIO: David Lundal, Senior Vice President Information Systems and Chief Information Officer
CHR: Ivy McKinley, Director Human Resources
Web address: www.presencehealth.org
Control: Church operated, Nongovernment, not–for–profit **Service**: Acute long–term care hospital

Staffed Beds: 178 Admissions: 1471 Census: 86 Outpatient Visits: 18747 Births: 0 Total Expense ($000): 72407 Payroll Expense ($000): 29665 Personnel: 510

DIXON—Lee County

★ **KATHERINE SHAW BETHEA HOSPITAL (140012)**, 403 East First Street, Zip 61021–3187; tel. 815/288–5531, **A**3 5 10 **F**3 5 11 13 15 18 20 22 28 29 30 34 35 38 39 40 44 45 46 47 50 54 55 56 57 61 62 64 65 69 70 74 75 76 79 81 82 84 85 86 87 89 91 92 93 94 96 97 98 100 101 102 104 107 108 110 111 112 115 119 127 129 130 131 132 135 145 146 147 148 149 150 **P**6
Primary Contact: David L. Schreiner, FACHE, President and Chief Executive Officer
COO: Julie D Mann, Vice President and Chief Administrative Officer
CFO: Anthony Evers, Chief Financial Officer
CMO: Pratip Nag, Vice President, Chief Medical Officer
CHR: Christy Pierce, Director of Human Resources
CNO: Linda Clemen, R.N., MS, Vice President and Chief Nursing Officer
Web address: www.ksbhospital.com
Control: Other not–for–profit (including NFP Corporation) **Service**: General medical and surgical

Staffed Beds: 64 Admissions: 3153 Census: 29 Outpatient Visits: 258132 Births: 338 Total Expense ($000): 132703 Payroll Expense ($000): 58689 Personnel: 780

DOWNERS GROVE—Dupage County

★ ⇧ **ADVOCATE GOOD SAMARITAN HOSPITAL (140288)**, 3815 Highland Avenue, Zip 60515–1590; tel. 630/275–5900, **A**2 5 10 21 **F**3 5 11 12 13 15 17 18 20 22 24 26 28 29 34 35 36 37 38 40 41 43 44 45 46 47 49 50 53 54 55 56 57 59 60 63 64 68 70 72 74 75 76 77 78 79 81 82 84 85 86 87 89 93 97 98 100 101 102 104 105 107 108 109 110 111 114 115 118 119 120 121 123 124 126 129 130 131 132 135 144 145 146 147 148 149 152 153 154 **P**8 **S** Advocate Aurora Health, Downers Grove, IL
Primary Contact: Nancy M. Tinsley, RN, MBA, FACHE, President
COO: Sandi Churchill, Vice President Business Development and Operations, Professional Services
CFO: Mary Treacy–Shiff, Vice President Finance
CMO: Charles Derus, M.D., Vice President Medical Management
CHR: Elizabeth Calby, Vice President Human Resources
CNO: Susan K Okuno–Jones, Vice President Patient Care Services and Chief Nursing Executive
Web address: www.advocatehealth.com/gsam
Control: Church operated, Nongovernment, not–for–profit **Service**: General medical and surgical

Staffed Beds: 278 Admissions: 15870 Census: 187 Outpatient Visits: 112013 Births: 1679 Total Expense ($000): 361797 Payroll Expense ($000): 122472 Personnel: 1808

DU QUOIN—Perry County

⊠ **MARSHALL BROWNING HOSPITAL (141331)**, 900 North Washington Street, Zip 62832–1233, Mailing Address: P.O. Box 192, Zip 62832–0192; tel. 618/542–2146, **A**1 10 18 **F**3 11 15 28 29 34 35 40 57 59 81 93 97 104 107 114 119 125 127 129 133 144 154
Primary Contact: Dan Eaves, Chief Executive Officer
CFO: Brice Harsy, Chief Financial Officer
CIO: Brian Schandl, Chief Information Officer
CNO: Laurie Kellerman, MSN, Chief Clinical Officer
Web address: www.marshallbrowninghospital.com
Control: Other not–for–profit (including NFP Corporation) **Service**: General medical and surgical

Staffed Beds: 25 Admissions: 613 Census: 8 Outpatient Visits: 38389 Births: 0 Total Expense ($000): 22182 Payroll Expense ($000): 8740 Personnel: 221

EFFINGHAM—Effingham County

⊠ **HSHS ST. ANTHONY'S MEMORIAL HOSPITAL (140032)**, 503 North Maple Street, Zip 62401–2099; tel. 217/342–2121, **A**1 2 3 5 10 19 **F**3 11 13 15 18 20 28 29 30 31 32 34 35 37 40 45 50 57 59 62 63 64 68 70 75 76 79 81 82 84 85 87 89 93 107 108 110 111 114 115 117 118 119 126 129 130 131 132 144 146 147 154 **S** HSHS Hospital Sisters Health System, Springfield, IL
Primary Contact: Theresa Rutherford, R.N., MS, FACHE, President and Chief Executive Officer
CFO: Dave Storm, Director Business Support
CNO: Kelly Sage, Chief Nursing Officer
Web address: www.stanthonyshospital.org
Control: Church operated, Nongovernment, not–for–profit **Service**: General medical and surgical

Staffed Beds: 123 Admissions: 5127 Census: 43 Outpatient Visits: 150866 Births: 802 Total Expense ($000): 125558 Payroll Expense ($000): 42688 Personnel: 712

ELDORADO—Saline County

★ **FERRELL HOSPITAL (141324)**, 1201 Pine Street, Zip 62930–1634; tel. 618/273–3361, **A**10 18 **F**3 11 15 28 29 30 34 35 40 45 57 59 65 81 85 87 101 104 107 110 115 119 127 130 133 146 148 153
Primary Contact: Alisa Coleman, Chief Executive Officer
CFO: Joseph Hohenberger, Chief Financial Officer
CIO: Brent Volkert, Director Information Technology
CHR: Caleigh Bruce, Vice President Human Resources
CNO: Rachael Prather, Chief Nursing Officer
Web address: www.ferrellhosp.org
Control: Other not–for–profit (including NFP Corporation) **Service**: General medical and surgical

Staffed Beds: 25 Admissions: 712 Census: 8 Outpatient Visits: 72577 Births: 0 Total Expense ($000): 18692 Payroll Expense ($000): 8784 Personnel: 196

IL

Hospital, Medicare Provider Number, Address, Telephone, Approval, Facility, and Physician Codes, Health Care System

★ American Hospital Association (AHA) membership   ◯ Healthcare Facilities Accreditation Program   ⇧ Center for Improvement in Healthcare Quality Accreditation
☐ The Joint Commission accreditation   ◇ DNV Healthcare Inc. accreditation   △ Commission on Accreditation of Rehabilitation Facilities (CARF) accreditation

ELGIN—Kane County

★ ⇑ **ADVOCATE SHERMAN HOSPITAL (140030)**, 1425 North Randall Road, Zip 60123–2300; tel. 847/742–9800, **A**2 10 21 **F**3 11 13 15 18 20 22 24 26 28 29 30 31 34 35 38 40 41 43 45 46 47 48 49 50 54 57 59 64 65 68 70 71 73 74 75 76 77 78 79 81 82 85 87 89 92 93 100 102 107 108 110 111 114 115 116 117 118 119 120 121 123 126 129 130 132 135 144 146 147 148 149 154 **P**6 8 **S** Advocate Aurora Health, Downers Grove, IL
Primary Contact: Linda Deering, MSN, R.N., President
CMO: Bruce Hyman, M.D., Vice President Clinical Performance
CHR: Melissa O'Neill, Vice President Human Resources
CNO: Cheri Goll, MSN, R.N., Chief Nursing Executive
Web address: www.advocatehealth.com/sherman
Control: Other not–for–profit (including NFP Corporation) **Service**: General medical and surgical

Staffed Beds: 255 **Admissions:** 14327 **Census:** 160 **Outpatient Visits:** 300813 **Births:** 2382 **Total Expense ($000):** 292851 **Payroll Expense ($000):** 99946 **Personnel:** 1403

☐ **ELGIN MENTAL HEALTH CENTER (144037)**, 750 South State Street, Zip 60123–7692; tel. 847/742–1040, **A**1 3 5 10 **F**29 30 38 39 50 59 65 68 87 98 101 130 132 143 **S** Division of Mental Health, Department of Human Services, Springfield, IL
Primary Contact: Meredith Kiss, Administrator
CFO: Tajudeen Ibrahim, Interim Business Administrator
CMO: Malini Patel, M.D., Medical Director
CIO: Kelly Callahan, Public Information Officer
CHR: Darek Williams, Director Human Resources
Web address: www.dhs.state.il.us
Control: State, Government, nonfederal **Service**: Psychiatric

Staffed Beds: 383 **Admissions:** 753 **Census:** 371 **Outpatient Visits:** 0 **Births:** 0 **Total Expense ($000):** 72052 **Payroll Expense ($000):** 58940 **Personnel:** 675

✠ △ **PRESENCE SAINT JOSEPH HOSPITAL (140217)**, 77 North Airlite Street, Zip 60123–4912; tel. 847/695–3200, **A**1 2 7 10 **F**5 11 12 17 18 20 22 24 26 28 29 30 31 34 35 36 37 38 40 43 44 49 50 53 54 56 57 58 59 60 61 62 63 64 65 68 69 70 74 75 77 78 81 82 84 85 86 87 90 93 94 96 97 98 99 100 101 102 103 104 105 107 108 111 114 115 117 119 120 121 123 124 130 132 134 135 143 145 146 147 148 153 **S** Ascension Healthcare, Saint Louis, MO
Primary Contact: Michael L. Brown, Regional President and Chief Executive Officer
CFO: Kevin Larkin, Regional Chief Financial Officer
CIO: Trevor O'Malley, Site Manager
CHR: Michael O'Rourke, Regional Human Resources Lead
Web address: www.provena.org
Control: Church operated, Nongovernment, not–for–profit **Service**: General medical and surgical

Staffed Beds: 184 **Admissions:** 7027 **Census:** 106 **Outpatient Visits:** 141325 **Births:** 0 **Total Expense ($000):** 142457 **Payroll Expense ($000):** 39469 **Personnel:** 696

PROVENA SAINT JOSEPH HOSPITAL See Presence Saint Joseph Hospital

⇑ **SHERMAN HOSPITAL** See Advocate Sherman Hospital

ELK GROVE VILLAGE—Cook County

✠ **AMITA HEALTH ELK GROVE VILLAGE (140258)**, 800 Biesterfield Road, Zip 60007–3397; tel. 847/437–5500, (Includes AMITA HEALTH REHABILITATION HOSPITAL, 935 Beisner Road, Elk Grove Village, IL, Zip 60007; tel. 847/640–5600; John Dunkin, Executive Director) **A**1 2 3 5 10 **F**3 11 12 13 15 17 18 19 20 22 24 26 28 29 30 34 35 36 37 38 39 40 43 44 45 46 47 48 49 50 54 55 57 59 62 63 64 70 73 74 76 78 79 81 82 84 85 86 87 89 90 91 92 93 95 96 98 103 107 108 110 111 114 115 116 117 118 119 120 121 124 126 129 130 132 135 143 145 146 147 148 149 154 **S** Ascension Healthcare, Saint Louis, MO
Primary Contact: John P. Werrbach, President and Chief Executive Officer
COO: Laurence Dry, Chief Operating Officer, Acute Care Hospitals Northern Region
CFO: Henry Zeisel, Chief Financial Officer, Northern Region
CIO: Sherrie Russell, Senior Vice President & Chief Information Officer
CHR: Donald Russell, Senior Vice President and Chief Human Resources Officer
CNO: Chris Budzinsky, Vice President, Nursing and Chief Nursing Officer
Web address: www.AMITAHealth.org
Control: Church operated, Nongovernment, not–for–profit **Service**: General medical and surgical

Staffed Beds: 380 **Admissions:** 17481 **Census:** 271 **Outpatient Visits:** 422599 **Births:** 1766 **Total Expense ($000):** 445226 **Payroll Expense ($000):** 139443 **Personnel:** 2021

ELMHURST—Dupage County

✠ **ELMHURST HOSPITAL (140200)**, 155 East Brush Hill Road, Zip 60126–5658; tel. 331/221–1000, **A**1 2 5 10 **F**3 7 12 13 15 16 18 19 20 22 24 26 28 29 30 31 32 34 35 36 37 38 39 40 41 43 44 45 46 47 48 49 50 54 55 57 58 59 61 63 64 65 70 73 74 75 76 77 78 79 81 82 84 85 86 87 89 91 92 93 96 97 99 100 101 102 103 107 108 109 110 111 115 117 119 120 121 123 129 130 131 132 135 144 146 147 148 149 154 **P**3 6 8 **S** Edward–Elmhurst Healthcare, Naperville, IL
Primary Contact: Pamela L. Dunley, MS, R.N., Chief Executive Officer
CMO: Daniel Sullivan, D.O., Chief Medical Officer, Vice President Medical Administration
CHR: Robert Blazek, System Director, Human Resources Business Partners
CNO: Jean Lydon, MS, R.N., System Vice President Operations, Chief Nursing Officer
Web address: www.eehealth.org
Control: Other not–for–profit (including NFP Corporation) **Service**: General medical and surgical

Staffed Beds: 267 **Admissions:** 17256 **Census:** 188 **Outpatient Visits:** 610572 **Births:** 2170 **Total Expense ($000):** 431636 **Payroll Expense ($000):** 137838 **Personnel:** 2339

EUREKA—Woodford County

★ ⇑ **ADVOCATE EUREKA HOSPITAL (141309)**, 101 South Major Street, Zip 61530–1246; tel. 309/467–2371, **A**10 18 21 **F**3 15 18 28 29 30 34 35 39 40 44 45 50 56 57 59 64 65 66 67 68 74 75 77 78 79 81 85 86 87 90 93 97 107 108 110 111 114 119 127 128 129 130 132 133 144 146 149 154 **P**8 **S** Advocate Aurora Health, Downers Grove, IL
Primary Contact: Colleen Kannaday, FACHE, President
CFO: Aron Klein, Vice President of Finance
CMO: Steven K Jones, M.D., Medical Director
CIO: David Harper, Director, Site Information Systems
CHR: Antonio Coletta, Vice President Human Resources
CNO: Nancy Allen, R.N., MS, Director, Patient Services and Chief Nursing Executive
Web address: www.advocatehealth.com/eureka/
Control: Church operated, Nongovernment, not–for–profit **Service**: General medical and surgical

Staffed Beds: 11 **Admissions:** 234 **Census:** 4 **Outpatient Visits:** 30327 **Births:** 0 **Total Expense ($000):** 16211 **Payroll Expense ($000):** 6189 **Personnel:** 95

⇑ **EUREKA COMMUNITY HOSPITAL** See Advocate Eureka Hospital

EVANSTON—Cook County

✠ **NORTHSHORE UNIVERSITY HEALTH SYSTEM (140010)**, 2650 Ridge Avenue, Zip 60201–1613; tel. 847/570–2000, (Includes NORTHSHORE EVANSTON HOSPITAL, 2650 Ridge Avenue, Evanston, IL, Zip 60201–1797; tel. 847/570–2000; Douglas M Silverstein, President; NORTHSHORE GLENBROOK HOSPITAL, 2100 Pfingsten Road, Glenview, IL, Zip 60025; tel. 847/657–5800; Jesse Peterson Hall, President; NORTHSHORE HIGHLAND PARK HOSPITAL, 718 Glenview Avenue, Highland Park, IL, Zip 60035–2497; tel. 847/432–8000; Gabrielle Cummings, President; NORTHSHORE SKOKIE HOSPITAL, 9600 Gross Point Road, Skokie, IL, Zip 60076–1257; tel. 847/677–9600; David Rahija, FACHE, President) **A**1 2 3 5 8 10 **F**3 5 8 9 11 12 13 14 15 17 18 19 20 22 24 26 28 29 30 31 32 34 35 36 37 38 39 40 43 44 45 46 47 48 49 50 54 55 56 57 58 59 60 61 62 63 64 66 68 70 72 74 75 76 77 78 79 81 82 84 85 86 87 88 89 90 92 93 96 97 98 99 100 101 102 103 104 105 107 108 110 111 114 115 116 117 118 119 120 123 126 129 130 131 132 134 135 136 144 145 146 147 148 149 153 154 **P**4 5
Primary Contact: J. P. Gallagher, President and Chief Executive Officer
CFO: Gary Weiss, Chief Financial Officer
CIO: Steven Smith, Chief Information Officer
CHR: Bill Luehrs, Chief Human Resources Officer
CNO: Nancy Semerdjian, R.N., Chief Nursing Officer
Web address: www.northshore.org
Control: Other not–for–profit (including NFP Corporation) **Service**: General medical and surgical

Staffed Beds: 663 **Admissions:** 39015 **Census:** 463 **Outpatient Visits:** 2148093 **Births:** 4746 **Total Expense ($000):** 1502351 **Payroll Expense ($000):** 508888 **Personnel:** 6245

✠ **PRESENCE SAINT FRANCIS HOSPITAL (140080)**, 355 Ridge Avenue, Zip 60202–3399; tel. 847/316–4000, **A**1 2 3 5 10 **F**3 11 12 13 15 18 20 22 24 26 28 29 30 31 32 34 35 38 40 41 43 44 45 47 48 49 56 57 58 59 60 61 64 68 70 74 75 76 77 78 79 81 82 84 85 86 87 91 92 93 97 100 107 108 110 111 114 115 118 119 120 121 123 125 126 129 130 131 132 146 147 148 154 **P**8 **S** Ascension Healthcare, Saint Louis, MO
Primary Contact: Kenneth Jones, President
CMO: David DiLoreto, M.D., Executive Vice President and Chief Medical Officer
CIO: George Chessum, Vice President Information Systems
CHR: Paul Skiem, Senior Vice President Human Resources
Web address: www.reshealth.org
Control: Church operated, Nongovernment, not–for–profit **Service**: General medical and surgical

Staffed Beds: 189 **Admissions:** 7481 **Census:** 85 **Outpatient Visits:** 89822 **Births:** 585 **Total Expense ($000):** 177023 **Payroll Expense ($000):** 54485 **Personnel:** 965

IL

SAINT FRANCIS HOSPITAL See Presence Saint Francis Hospital

EVERGREEN PARK—Cook County

☐ **LITTLE COMPANY OF MARY HOSPITAL AND HEALTH CARE CENTERS (140179)**, 2800 West 95th Street, Zip 60805–2795; tel. 708/422–6200, **A**1 2 3 10 **F**3 5 11 12 13 15 17 18 20 22 26 29 30 31 34 35 36 38 40 41 45 46 47 49 50 54 56 57 59 60 62 63 64 65 70 71 73 74 75 76 77 78 79 81 82 83 84 85 86 87 89 92 93 94 98 100 101 102 103 104 105 107 108 110 111 114 115 119 120 121 124 126 129 130 131 132 133 144 146 147 148 149 150 152 153 **P**6 7 8 **S** American Province of Little Company of Mary Sisters, Evergreen Park, IL
Primary Contact: John Hanlon, MD, President and Chief Executive Officer
COO: Mary Freyer, Chief Operating Officer
CFO: Robert Tarola, Chief Financial Officer
CMO: Kent A W Armbruster, M.D., Vice President Medical Affairs
CIO: Darryl Mazzuca, Director Management Information Systems
CHR: Colleen Rohan, Director Human Resources
CNO: Lisa DiMarco, R.N., FACHE, Vice President Patient Care Service and Chief Nursing Officer
Web address: www.lcmh.org
Control: Other not–for–profit (including NFP Corporation) **Service:** General medical and surgical

Staffed Beds: 254 **Admissions:** 11473 **Census:** 145 **Outpatient Visits:** 203403 **Births:** 986 **Total Expense ($000):** 213316 **Payroll Expense ($000):** 91111 **Personnel:** 1697

FAIRFIELD—Wayne County

☒ **FAIRFIELD MEMORIAL HOSPITAL (141311)**, 303 NW 11th Street, Zip 62837–1203; tel. 618/842–2611, (Total facility includes 30 beds in nursing home–type unit) **A**1 10 18 **F**3 11 15 18 28 31 34 35 38 40 41 45 46 50 56 57 59 62 64 65 70 71 75 77 81 85 86 87 93 97 104 107 108 110 115 119 127 128 130 132 135 144 146 149 153 **P**6
Primary Contact: Katherine Bunting Esq, Chief Executive Officer
COO: Dana Shantel Taylor, Director Organizational Development
CFO: Amy Marsh, Chief Financial Officer
CMO: Wesley Thompson, M.D., President Medical Staff
CIO: Brad August, Director Information Systems
CHR: Robert Musoiu, Director Human Resources
CNO: Tracy Taylor, Chief Nurse Executive
Web address: www.fairfieldmemorial.org
Control: Other not–for–profit (including NFP Corporation) **Service:** General medical and surgical

Staffed Beds: 55 **Admissions:** 702 **Census:** 26 **Outpatient Visits:** 43162 **Births:** 0 **Total Expense ($000):** 28803 **Payroll Expense ($000):** 12166 **Personnel:** 287

FLORA—Clay County

☒ **CLAY COUNTY HOSPITAL (141351)**, 911 Stacy Burk Drive, Zip 62839–3241, Mailing Address: P.O. Box 280, Zip 62839–0280; tel. 618/662–2131, (Nonreporting) **A**1 10 18 **S** SSM Health, Saint Louis, MO
Primary Contact: Chris Hunt, President
COO: Jamie Veach, Chief Operating Officer
CFO: Mike Hobbs, Chief Financial Officer
CMO: Colleen Murphy, M.D., Chief of Staff
CIO: Phil Bute, Manager Information Technology
CHR: Chelsea Musgrave, Director of Human Resources
Web address: www.claycountyhospital.org
Control: County, Government, nonfederal **Service:** General medical and surgical

Staffed Beds: 22

FOREST PARK—Cook County

☐ **RIVEREDGE HOSPITAL (144009)**, 8311 West Roosevelt Road, Zip 60130–2500; tel. 708/771–7000, **A**1 10 **F**98 99 100 101 102 104 105 106 153 **S** Universal Health Services, Inc., King of Prussia, PA
Primary Contact: Carey Carlock, Chief Executive Officer
COO: Joseph Baw, Chief Operating Officer
CFO: Mark Hennessy, Chief Financial Officer
CMO: Lucyna M. Puszkarska, M.D., Medical Director
CIO: Kyle Heinze, Coordinator Information Technology
CHR: Joseph Rinke, Director of Human Resources
Web address: www.riveredgehospital.com
Control: Corporation, Investor–owned (for–profit) **Service:** Psychiatric

Staffed Beds: 210 **Admissions:** 4224 **Census:** 123 **Outpatient Visits:** 27791 **Births:** 0 **Total Expense ($000):** 28156 **Payroll Expense ($000):** 14313

FREEPORT—Stephenson County

★ **FHN MEMORIAL HOSPITAL (140160)**, 1045 West Stephenson Street, Zip 61032–4899; tel. 815/599–6000, **A**10 **F**3 11 13 14 15 18 20 22 28 29 30 31 32 34 38 40 46 47 48 49 50 51 53 57 59 61 63 64 65 68 69 74 75 76 77 78 79 81 82 84 85 86 87 93 97 99 100 101 102 103 104 107 108 109 110 111 114 119 129 130 131 132 135 146 149 153 154 **P**6 8
Primary Contact: Mark Gridley, FACHE, President and Chief Executive Officer
CFO: Michael Clark, Executive Vice President and Chief Financial Officer
CMO: Keith Martin, MD, Chief Medical Officer
CIO: Mike Willams, Chief Information Officer
CHR: Leonard M Carter, Chief Human Resources Officer
CNO: Kathryn J Martinez, Chief Nursing Officer
Web address: www.fhn.org
Control: Other not–for–profit (including NFP Corporation) **Service:** General medical and surgical

Staffed Beds: 100 **Admissions:** 3820 **Census:** 38 **Outpatient Visits:** 101647 **Births:** 331 **Total Expense ($000):** 105722 **Payroll Expense ($000):** 33150 **Personnel:** 440

GALENA—Jo Daviess County

★ **MIDWEST MEDICAL CENTER (141302)**, One Medical Center Drive, Zip 61036–1697; tel. 815/777–1340, (Nonreporting) **A**10 18
Primary Contact: Tracy Bauer, Chief Executive Officer
COO: Steve Busch, Chief Operating Officer
CMO: Grant Westenfelder, M.D., Chief Medical Officer
CHR: Melissa Conley, Director Human Resources
Web address: www.midwestmedicalcenter.org
Control: Corporation, Investor–owned (for–profit) **Service:** General medical and surgical

Staffed Beds: 25

GALESBURG—Knox County

☒ **GALESBURG COTTAGE HOSPITAL (140040)**, 695 North Kellogg Street, Zip 61401–2885; tel. 309/343–8131, (Nonreporting) **A**1 10 19 **S** Quorum Health, Brentwood, TN
Primary Contact: James Flynn, Chief Executive Officer
COO: James Stanley, Interim Chief Operating Officer
CFO: Patricia Ellison, Chief Financial Officer
CMO: Parthasarathy Srinivasan, M.D., President Medical Staff
CIO: Richard Tran, Director Information Technology
CHR: Barbara Hendricks, Interim Human Resources Director
CNO: Pam Davis, Chief Nursing Officer
Web address: www.cottagehospital.com
Control: Other not–for–profit (including NFP Corporation) **Service:** General medical and surgical

Staffed Beds: 119

☒ **OSF ST. MARY MEDICAL CENTER (140064)**, 3333 North Seminary Street, Zip 61401–1299; tel. 309/344–3161, **A**1 10 **F**3 11 13 15 18 26 28 29 30 31 32 34 35 40 41 43 44 45 46 49 50 51 53 56 57 59 63 64 65 70 75 76 77 78 79 81 82 84 85 86 87 89 93 96 107 108 110 111 115 118 119 129 130 131 132 135 145 146 147 149 **P**6 **S** OSF Healthcare, Peoria, IL
Primary Contact: Jennifer Junis, MSN, R.N., President
COO: Don Shadensack, Vice President Clinical Services
CFO: Curt Lipe, Vice President, Chief Financial Officer
CMO: Clifford G Martin, M.D., Regional Vice President and Chief Medical Officer
CIO: Becky Lynch, Manager Business Entity Management and Information Systems
CHR: Jenny Jacobs, Director Human Resources
CNO: Alice Snyder, Vice President, Chief Nursing Officer
Web address: www.osfstmary.org
Control: Church operated, Nongovernment, not–for–profit **Service:** General medical and surgical

Staffed Beds: 81 **Admissions:** 3200 **Census:** 32 **Outpatient Visits:** 107322 **Births:** 396 **Total Expense ($000):** 72504 **Payroll Expense ($000):** 27940 **Personnel:** 400

IL

Hospital, Medicare Provider Number, Address, Telephone, Approval, Facility, and Physician Codes, Health Care System

★ American Hospital Association (AHA) membership
☐ The Joint Commission accreditation
○ Healthcare Facilities Accreditation Program
◇ DNV Healthcare Inc. accreditation
⇑ Center for Improvement in Healthcare Quality Accreditation
△ Commission on Accreditation of Rehabilitation Facilities (CARF) accreditation

GENESEO—Henry County

★ ⇧ **HAMMOND–HENRY HOSPITAL (141319)**, 600 North College Avenue, Zip 61254–1099; tel. 309/944–6431, (Total facility includes 38 beds in nursing home–type unit) **A**10 18 21 **F**3 8 11 13 15 28 29 34 35 40 45 49 50 57 59 62 70 75 76 81 87 88 89 93 107 111 114 119 128 129 130 131 132 133 144 146 154 **P**6 **S** HealthTech Management Services, Brentwood, TN
Primary Contact: Mark Kuhn, Chief Executive Officer
CFO: Jodie Criswell, Vice President of Fiscal Services
CIO: Heather Henry, Information Technology Manager
CHR: Hazel Butter, Manager Human Resources
Web address: www.hammondhenry.com
Control: Hospital district or authority, Government, nonfederal **Service**: General medical and surgical

Staffed Beds: 61 **Admissions**: 1273 **Census**: 42 **Outpatient Visits**: 109408 **Births**: 195 **Total Expense ($000)**: 41485 **Payroll Expense ($000)**: 14895 **Personnel**: 303

GENEVA—Kane County

⊞ **NORTHWESTERN MEDICINE DELNOR HOSPITAL (140211)**, 300 Randall Road, Zip 60134–4200; tel. 630/208–3000, **A**1 2 10 **F**3 12 13 15 18 20 22 26 28 29 30 31 33 34 35 36 37 39 40 41 43 44 45 46 47 48 49 50 51 53 55 57 59 60 64 65 68 70 73 74 75 76 77 78 79 81 82 84 85 86 87 89 92 93 94 96 97 100 101 102 104 105 107 108 110 111 114 115 116 117 118 119 120 121 123 126 129 130 131 132 135 146 147 148 149 150 153 154 **P**6 7 **S** Northwestern Memorial HealthCare, Chicago, IL
Primary Contact: Maureen A. Bryant, FACHE, President
CFO: John Orsini, Executive Vice President and Chief Financial Officer
CMO: Mark Daniels, M.D., Vice President Physician Enterprise
CIO: Daniel F Kinsella, Executive Vice President Information Technology
Web address: www.nm.org
Control: Other not–for–profit (including NFP Corporation) **Service**: General medical and surgical

Staffed Beds: 154 **Admissions**: 8070 **Census**: 80 **Outpatient Visits**: 436379 **Births**: 1324 **Total Expense ($000)**: 368107 **Payroll Expense ($000)**: 123855 **Personnel**: 3313

GIBSON CITY—Ford County

⊞ **GIBSON AREA HOSPITAL AND HEALTH SERVICES (141317)**, 1120 North Melvin Street, Zip 60936–1477, Mailing Address: P.O. Box 429, Zip 60936–0429; tel. 217/784–4251, (Total facility includes 42 beds in nursing home–type unit) **A**1 5 10 18 **F**3 7 11 13 15 18 28 29 31 34 35 40 44 45 51 53 56 57 59 64 67 68 69 70 75 76 77 78 79 81 82 84 85 87 89 90 93 97 98 100 101 102 103 104 107 110 111 115 118 119 127 128 129 130 131 132 133 135 141 143 144 146 147 148 149 154 **P**8 **S** Alliant Management Services, Louisville, KY
Primary Contact: Robert C. Schmitt II, CPA, FACHE, Chief Executive Officer
COO: Robin Rose, R.N., Chief Operating and Clinical Officer
CFO: Matthew Ertel, Chief Financial Officer
CMO: Mark Spangler, M.D., Chief Medical Officer
CIO: Julie Bowen, Executive Director of IT
CHR: Ty Royal, Executive Director of Human Resources and Support Services
CNO: Barb Meyer, Executive Director of Nursing
Web address: www.gibsonhospital.org
Control: Other not–for–profit (including NFP Corporation) **Service**: General medical and surgical

Staffed Beds: 67 **Admissions**: 925 **Census**: 41 **Outpatient Visits**: 152823 **Births**: 259 **Total Expense ($000)**: 96132 **Payroll Expense ($000)**: 44357 **Personnel**: 667

GLENDALE HEIGHTS—DuPage County

⊞ **AMITA HEALTH ADVENTIST MEDICAL CENTER GLENOAKS (140292)**, 701 Winthrop Avenue, Zip 60139–1403; tel. 630/545–8000, **A**1 10 **F**3 11 13 15 18 20 22 26 29 30 31 34 35 38 40 41 43 44 45 49 50 56 57 59 61 64 70 73 74 76 78 79 81 82 85 86 87 89 98 100 101 103 107 108 110 111 114 115 119 130 131 132 146 147 148 149 154 **S** Adventist Health System Sunbelt Health Care Corporation, Altamonte Springs, FL
Primary Contact: Bruce C. Christian, President and Chief Executive Officer
COO: Richard Roehr, Vice President and Chief Operating Officer
CFO: Chase Aalborg, Vice President and Chief Financial Officer
CMO: Richard Carroll, M.D., Vice President and Chief Medical Officer
CIO: Sherrie Russell, AMITA Health Senior Vice President and Chief Information Officer
CHR: Donald Russell, AMITA Health Senior Vice President and Chief Human Resources Officer
CNO: Suzette Mahneke, Associate Vice President of Nursing
Web address: www.AMITAHealth.org
Control: Church operated, Nongovernment, not–for–profit **Service**: General medical and surgical

Staffed Beds: 123 **Admissions**: 5724 **Census**: 80 **Outpatient Visits**: 37072 **Births**: 337 **Total Expense ($000)**: 89991 **Payroll Expense ($000)**: 35849 **Personnel**: 460

GLENVIEW—Cook County

NORTHSHORE GLENBROOK HOSPITAL See Northshore University Health System, Evanston

GRANITE CITY—Madison County

⊞ **GATEWAY REGIONAL MEDICAL CENTER (140125)**, 2100 Madison Avenue, Zip 62040–4799; tel. 618/798–3000, (Nonreporting) **A**1 10 **S** Quorum Health, Brentwood, TN
Primary Contact: M Edward. Cunningham, Chief Executive Officer
CMO: Mike Adams, M.D., Chief Medical Officer
CIO: Dennis Kampwerth, Director Management Information Systems
CHR: Reva S Weems, Director Human Resources
CNO: Sam R White, Chief Nursing Officer
Web address: www.gatewayregional.net
Control: Corporation, Investor–owned (for–profit) **Service**: General medical and surgical

Staffed Beds: 268

GREENVILLE—Bond County

★ ○ **HSHS HOLY FAMILY HOSPITAL IN GREENVILLE (140137)**, 200 Healthcare Drive, Zip 62246–1154; tel. 618/664–1230, **A**10 11 **F**3 11 13 15 18 30 31 34 40 41 45 49 50 56 57 59 76 78 79 81 85 89 93 94 97 98 103 104 107 110 111 115 119 125 127 129 130 133 135 154 **P**6 **S** HSHS Hospital Sisters Health System, Springfield, IL
Primary Contact: James F. Dover, FACHE, Interim Chief Executive Officer
CFO: Mark S Ennen, Director of Finance
CHR: Vicki Kloeckner, Director Human Resources
CNO: Lorna Keaster, Interim Chief Nursing Officer
Web address: www.greenvilleregionalhospital.com
Control: Other not–for–profit (including NFP Corporation) **Service**: General medical and surgical

Staffed Beds: 42 **Admissions**: 1130 **Census**: 13 **Outpatient Visits**: 31539 **Births**: 190 **Total Expense ($000)**: 30736 **Payroll Expense ($000)**: 10765 **Personnel**: 219

HARRISBURG—Saline County

⊞ **HARRISBURG MEDICAL CENTER (140210)**, 100 Dr Warren Tuttle Drive, Zip 62946–2718, Mailing Address: P.O. Box 428, Zip 62946–0428; tel. 618/253–7671, **A**1 10 20 **F**3 8 11 15 28 29 30 31 34 40 45 50 56 57 59 61 62 64 75 77 78 79 81 85 87 91 93 94 97 98 100 101 102 103 104 107 108 110 111 118 119 127 129 130 131 133 146 154
Primary Contact: Donald Hutson, President and Chief Executive Officer
COO: Danny Lampley, Chief Operating Officer
CFO: June Hayes, Chief Financial Officer
CIO: Rick Pyle, Director Information Systems
CHR: Dorene L Ewell, Director Human Resources and Education
CNO: Leslie Ferrell, Chief Nursing Officer
Web address: www.harrisburgmc.com
Control: Other not–for–profit (including NFP Corporation) **Service**: General medical and surgical

Staffed Beds: 76 **Admissions**: 3030 **Census**: 39 **Outpatient Visits**: 96160 **Births**: 0 **Total Expense ($000)**: 58735 **Payroll Expense ($000)**: 25633 **Personnel**: 499

HARVARD—Mchenry County

⊞ **MERCYHEALTH HOSPITAL AND MEDICAL CENTER – HARVARD (141335)**, 901 Grant Street, Zip 60033–1898, Mailing Address: P.O. Box 850, Zip 60033–0850; tel. 815/943–5431, (Total facility includes 34 beds in nursing home–type unit) **A**1 10 18 **F**3 11 15 28 29 30 35 40 45 46 57 59 64 69 70 75 77 79 81 82 85 87 93 96 107 108 110 119 128 129 130 131 132 143 146 149 **P**6 **S** Mercy Health System, Janesville, WI
Primary Contact: Javon R. Bea, Chief Executive Officer
COO: Jennifer Hallatt, Chief Operating Officer
CFO: Shannon Dunphy–Alexander, Director
CMO: Douglas Bryan, President, Medical Staff
CHR: Heather Niles, Director Human Resources Operations
CNO: Caryn Lynn Oleston, FACHE, MSN, R.N., Chief Nursing Officer
Web address: www.mercyhealthsystem.org
Control: Other not–for–profit (including NFP Corporation) **Service**: General medical and surgical

Staffed Beds: 50 **Admissions**: 521 **Census**: 27 **Outpatient Visits**: 68250 **Births**: 0 **Total Expense ($000)**: 23055 **Payroll Expense ($000)**: 8677 **Personnel**: 107

IL

Many Facility Codes have changed. Please refer to the AHA Guide Code Chart.   © 2018 AHA Guide

HARVEY—Cook County

★ △ ⇑ **INGALLS MEMORIAL HOSPITAL (140191)**, One Ingalls Drive, Zip 60426–3591; tel. 708/333–2300, **A**2 3 5 7 10 21 **F**3 4 5 7 8 11 12 13 15 18 20 22 24 26 28 29 30 31 34 35 36 37 40 45 46 47 49 50 51 54 56 57 58 59 60 62 63 64 68 70 74 75 76 77 78 79 81 82 84 85 86 87 89 90 92 93 96 97 98 99 101 102 103 104 105 107 108 110 111 113 114 115 116 117 118 119 120 121 123 124 126 129 130 131 132 135 143 144 146 147 148 152 153 **P**8 **S** University of Chicago Medicine, Chicago, IL
Primary Contact: Jonathan R. Goble, FACHE, Interim President
COO: Michael L Hicks, Senior Vice President and Chief Operating Officer
CFO: Michael Lawrence, Chief Financial Officer
CNO: Kathleen A Mikos, R.N., Vice President and Chief Nursing Officer
Web address: www.ingallshealthsystem.org
Control: Other not–for–profit (including NFP Corporation) **Service**: General medical and surgical

Staffed Beds: 199 **Admissions:** 12997 **Census:** 181 **Outpatient Visits:** 358012 **Births:** 895 **Total Expense ($000):** 302245 **Payroll Expense ($000):** 97902 **Personnel:** 1562

HAVANA—Mason County

✉ **MASON DISTRICT HOSPITAL (141313)**, 615 North Promenade Street, Zip 62644–1243, Mailing Address: P.O. Box 530, Zip 62644–0530; tel. 309/543–4431, (Nonreporting) **A**1 10 18
Primary Contact: Douglas D. Kosier, Chief Executive Officer
CMO: Tad A. Yetter, M.D., President Medical Staff
CIO: Aaron Coots, Information Technology Director
CHR: Anne Davis, Director Human Resources
CNO: Rhonda Hine, R.N., Interim Chief Nursing Executive
Web address: www.masondistricthospital.org
Control: Hospital district or authority, Government, nonfederal **Service**: General medical and surgical

Staffed Beds: 20

HAZEL CREST—Cook County

★ ⇑ **ADVOCATE SOUTH SUBURBAN HOSPITAL (140250)**, 17800 South Kedzie Avenue, Zip 60429–0989; tel. 708/799–8000, **A**2 3 10 21 **F**3 11 13 15 18 20 22 24 26 28 29 30 31 34 35 36 40 45 46 47 49 50 51 53 55 57 59 60 63 64 68 70 75 76 78 79 81 82 85 87 89 92 93 100 107 108 110 111 114 115 118 119 126 130 132 145 146 147 148 149 154 **P**8 **S** Advocate Aurora Health, Downers Grove, IL
Primary Contact: Rashard Johnson, President
COO: Karen Clark, MS, R.N., Vice President Operations
CFO: Brian Kelly, Vice President Finance
CMO: Richard Multack, D.O., Vice President Medical Management
CIO: Beth Turek, Site Manager Information Systems
CHR: Kristin Landini, Vice President Human Resources
CNO: Sharon A. Otten, Vice President Nursing
Web address: www.advocatehealth.com/ssub/
Control: Church operated, Nongovernment, not–for–profit **Service**: General medical and surgical

Staffed Beds: 215 **Admissions:** 10997 **Census:** 149 **Outpatient Visits:** 140696 **Births:** 818 **Total Expense ($000):** 218986 **Payroll Expense ($000):** 75507 **Personnel:** 902

HERRIN—Williamson County

☐ **HERRIN HOSPITAL (140011)**, 201 South 14th Street, Zip 62948–3631; tel. 618/942–2171, **A**1 5 10 **F**3 11 12 18 28 29 30 34 35 46 47 49 50 51 54 56 57 59 60 61 64 68 70 74 75 78 79 81 82 84 85 86 87 90 92 93 100 107 108 111 114 115 119 130 131 132 135 143 146 148 154 **P**1 **S** Southern Illinois Healthcare, Carbondale, IL
Primary Contact: Rodney Smith, Vice President and Administrator
CFO: Michael Kasser, Chief Financial Officer
CMO: Michelle Jenkins, M.D., President Medical Staff
CIO: David Holland, Chief Information Officer
CHR: Teresa A Lovellette, Manager Human Resources
Web address: www.sih.net
Control: Other not–for–profit (including NFP Corporation) **Service**: General medical and surgical

Staffed Beds: 114 **Admissions:** 6667 **Census:** 78 **Outpatient Visits:** 170106 **Births:** 0 **Total Expense ($000):** 146286 **Payroll Expense ($000):** 44261 **Personnel:** 876

HIGHLAND—Madison County

✉ **HSHS ST. JOSEPH'S HOSPITAL (141336)**, 12866 Troxler Avenue, Zip 62249–1698; tel. 618/651–2600, **A**1 10 18 **F**3 8 11 15 26 27 28 29 30 34 35 40 41 44 45 47 49 51 53 57 59 64 70 75 79 81 84 86 87 93 97 107 108 110 111 114 119 124 126 129 130 131 132 133 135 143 146 147 154 **S** HSHS Hospital Sisters Health System, Springfield, IL
Primary Contact: John A. Ludwig, President and Chief Operating Officer
COO: Chris Govero, Director of Operations
CFO: David Nosacka, Southern Illinois Division Chief Financial Officer
CHR: Christie Silvey, Director People Services
CNO: Teresa Cornelius, R.N., Interim Chief Nursing Officer
Web address: www.stjosephshighland.com
Control: Church operated, Nongovernment, not–for–profit **Service**: General medical and surgical

Staffed Beds: 25 **Admissions:** 1377 **Census:** 18 **Outpatient Visits:** 61489 **Births:** 0 **Total Expense ($000):** 40527 **Payroll Expense ($000):** 11831 **Personnel:** 217

HIGHLAND PARK—Lake County

NORTHSHORE HIGHLAND PARK HOSPITAL See Northshore University Health System, Evanston

HILLSBORO—Montgomery County

✉ **HILLSBORO AREA HOSPITAL (141332)**, 1200 East Tremont Street, Zip 62049–1900; tel. 217/532–6111, **A**1 10 18 **F**2 3 10 15 28 29 30 34 35 40 56 57 59 64 65 75 77 79 81 85 86 87 89 92 93 94 97 107 110 111 115 125 129 130 131 133 135 146 148 **S** HealthTech Management Services, Brentwood, TN
Primary Contact: Rex H. Brown, President and Chief Executive Officer
CFO: Terri L Carroll, Vice President Financial Services
CHR: Sharon Clark, Director Human Resources
Web address: www.hillsborohealth.org
Control: Other not–for–profit (including NFP Corporation) **Service**: General medical and surgical

Staffed Beds: 25 **Admissions:** 374 **Census:** 5 **Outpatient Visits:** 15290 **Births:** 0 **Total Expense ($000):** 20290 **Payroll Expense ($000):** 7518 **Personnel:** 180

HINES—Cook County

✉ △ **EDWARD HINES, JR. VETERANS AFFAIRS HOSPITAL**, 5000 South Fifth Avenue, Zip 60141–3030, Mailing Address: P.O. Box 5000, Zip 60141–5000; tel. 708/202–8387, (Nonreporting) **A**1 2 3 5 7 **S** Department of Veterans Affairs, Perry Point, MD
Primary Contact: Steven E. Braverman, M.D., Director
CFO: Yolanda Martinez, Chief Fiscal Services
CMO: Jack Bulmash, M.D., Chief of Staff
CIO: Robert Tanjuakio, Chief Information Resources Management
CNO: Marianne Locke, R.N., MSN, Associate Director Patient Care Services
Web address: www.hines.va.gov/
Control: Veterans Affairs, Government, federal **Service**: General medical and surgical

Staffed Beds: 485

☐ **JOHN J. MADDEN MENTAL HEALTH CENTER (144028)**, 1200 South First Avenue, Zip 60141–0800; tel. 708/338–7202, (Nonreporting) **A**1 3 5 10 **S** Division of Mental Health, Department of Human Services, Springfield, IL
Primary Contact: Edith Newman, Interim Administrator
CFO: Janice Evans, Chief Financial Officer
Control: State, Government, nonfederal **Service**: Psychiatric

Staffed Beds: 125

VETERANS AFFAIRS EDWARD HINES, JR. HOSPITAL See Edward Hines, Jr. Veterans Affairs Hospital

IL

HINSDALE—DuPage County

✠ **AMITA HEALTH ADVENTIST MEDICAL CENTER – HINSDALE (140122)**, 120 North Oak Street, Zip 60521–3890; tel. 630/856–6001, **A**1 2 3 5 10 13 **F**3 4 13 15 18 20 22 24 26 28 29 30 31 34 37 38 39 40 41 43 44 45 47 49 54 55 57 58 59 61 64 70 72 73 74 76 78 79 81 82 84 85 86 87 89 92 93 97 98 99 100 107 108 114 115 126 129 130 131 132 135 143 146 147 149 151 154 **S** Adventist Health System Sunbelt Health Care Corporation, Altamonte Springs, FL
Primary Contact: Steven Province, President and Chief Executive Officer
CFO: Rebecca Mathis, Vice President and Chief Financial Officer
CMO: Bonny Chen, M.D., Vice President and Chief Medical Officer
CHR: Mary P Leurck, Human Resources Director
CNO: Mary S Murphy, MSN, Vice President and Chief Nursing Officer
Web address: www.AMITAhealth.org
Control: Church operated, Nongovernment, not–for–profit **Service**: General medical and surgical

Staffed Beds: 261 **Admissions**: 11974 **Census**: 136 **Outpatient Visits**: 274356 **Births**: 2219 **Total Expense ($000)**: 305086 **Payroll Expense ($000)**: 92932 **Personnel**: 1437

✠ **RML SPECIALTY HOSPITAL (142010)**, 5601 South County Line Road, Zip 60521–4875; tel. 630/286–4000, (Includes RML SPECIALTY HOSPITAL, 3435 West Van Buren Street, Chicago, IL, Zip 60624–3312; tel. 773/826–6300; James R Prister, President and Chief Executive Officer) **A**1 3 5 10 **F**1 3 18 29 30 31 45 53 58 74 85 107 114 115 119 130 146 148 149 **P**6
Primary Contact: James R. Prister, President and Chief Executive Officer
COO: Ken Pawola, Chief Operating Officer
CFO: Tom Pater, Chief Financial Officer
CMO: Patrick Fahey, M.D., Chief Medical Officer
CIO: Vincent S Vitali, Chief Information Officer
CHR: John Landstrom, Director Human Resources
CNO: Marti Edwards, MSN, R.N., Chief Nursing Officer
Web address: www.rmlspecialtyhospital.org
Control: Other not–for–profit (including NFP Corporation) **Service**: Acute long–term care hospital

Staffed Beds: 165 **Admissions**: 1365 **Census**: 136 **Outpatient Visits**: 0 **Births**: 0 **Total Expense ($000)**: 93446 **Payroll Expense ($000)**: 46274 **Personnel**: 677

HOFFMAN ESTATES—Cook County

✠ **ALEXIAN BROTHERS BEHAVIORAL HEALTH HOSPITAL (144031)**, 1650 Moon Lake Boulevard, Zip 60169–1010; tel. 847/882–1600, (Nonreporting) **A**1 5 10 **S** Ascension Healthcare, Saint Louis, MO
Primary Contact: Clayton Ciha, President and Chief Executive Officer
COO: Christopher Novak, Chief Operating Officer
CFO: David Jones, Chief Financial Officer
CMO: Gregory Teas, M.D., Chief Medical Officer
CIO: Sherrie Russell, Vice President and Chief Information Officer
CNO: Christine Quinlan, MS, R.N., Chief Nursing Officer
Web address: www.abbhh.org
Control: Church operated, Nongovernment, not–for–profit **Service**: Psychiatric

Staffed Beds: 141

✠ **AMITA HEALTH HOFFMAN ESTATES (140290)**, 1555 Barrington Road, Zip 60169–1019; tel. 847/843–2000, (Includes AMITA HEALTH WOMEN & CHILDREN'S HOSPITAL, 1555 Barrington Road, Hoffman Estates, IL, Zip 60169–1019; tel. 847/843–2000; Kevin Rath, Vice President and Executive Director) **A**1 2 3 5 10 **F**3 8 11 12 13 15 18 19 20 22 26 29 30 31 32 34 35 37 39 40 41 43 44 45 46 47 48 49 50 54 55 57 59 63 64 70 72 73 74 76 77 78 79 81 82 84 85 86 87 88 89 93 107 108 110 111 114 115 118 119 120 121 124 126 130 132 145 146 147 148 149 154 **S** Ascension Healthcare, Saint Louis, MO
Primary Contact: Leonard Wilk, President and Chief Executive Officer
COO: Laurence Dry, Chief Operating Officer, Acute Care Hospitals Northern Region
CFO: Henry Zeisel, Chief Financial Officer, Northern Region
CIO: Sherrie Russell, Senior Vice President and Chief Information Officer
CHR: Donald Russell, Senior Vice President and Chief Human Resources Officer
CNO: Chris Budzinsky, Vice President Nursing and Chief Nursing Officer Alexian Brothers Acute Care Ministries
Web address: www.AMITAHealth.org
Control: Church operated, Nongovernment, not–for–profit **Service**: General medical and surgical

Staffed Beds: 290 **Admissions**: 17067 **Census**: 199 **Outpatient Visits**: 226599 **Births**: 3736 **Total Expense ($000)**: 316373 **Payroll Expense ($000)**: 96987 **Personnel**: 1380

HOOPESTON—Vermilion County

★ ⇑ **CARLE HOOPESTON REGIONAL HEALTH CENTER (141316)**, 701 East Orange Street, Zip 60942–1801; tel. 217/283–5531, **A**3 10 18 21 **F**3 15 29 35 40 45 57 59 65 79 81 85 89 90 93 107 108 110 111 115 119 128 133 **S** Carle Foundation, Urbana, IL
Primary Contact: Harry Brockus, Chief Executive Officer
CHR: Melodee Bowers, Director Human Resources
Web address: www.carle.org
Control: Other not–for–profit (including NFP Corporation) **Service**: General medical and surgical

Staffed Beds: 13 **Admissions**: 350 **Census**: 3 **Outpatient Visits**: 12255 **Births**: 0 **Total Expense ($000)**: 27952 **Payroll Expense ($000)**: 6023 **Personnel**: 101

HOPEDALE—Tazewell County

HOPEDALE MEDICAL COMPLEX (141330), 107 Tremont Street, Zip 61747–7525, Mailing Address: PO Box 267, Zip 61747–7525; tel. 309/449–3321, (Nonreporting) **A**10 18
Primary Contact: Alfred N. Rossi, M.D., Chief Executive Officer
COO: Mark F Rossi, Chief Operating Officer and General Counsel
CFO: Nicholas A. Penn, Chief Financial Officer
CHR: Andrea Halley, Vice President of Non–Clinical Operations/Director Human Resources
CNO: Timothy Sondag, Senior Nursing Officer
Web address: www.hopedalemc.com
Control: Other not–for–profit (including NFP Corporation) **Service**: General medical and surgical

Staffed Beds: 18

JACKSONVILLE—Morgan County

✠ **PASSAVANT AREA HOSPITAL (140058)**, 1600 West Walnut Street, Zip 62650–1136; tel. 217/245–9541, (Total facility includes 15 beds in nursing home–type unit) **A**1 10 **F**3 13 14 15 28 29 30 31 34 35 40 41 45 50 51 57 58 59 64 68 69 70 75 76 78 79 81 82 85 86 87 89 93 97 98 104 107 108 110 111 115 118 119 121 124 127 128 129 130 131 141 146 147 148 **S** Memorial Health System, Springfield, IL
Primary Contact: Harry M. Schmidt, President and Chief Executive Officer
CFO: David Bolen, Vice President and Chief Financial Officer
CMO: Marshall Hale, M.D., Chief Medical Officer
CIO: Janie Cook, Director Information Systems
CHR: Jim Bormann, Director Human Resources
CNO: Karen Daum, R.N., MS, Vice President and Chief Nursing Officer
Web address: www.passavanthospital.com
Control: Church operated, Nongovernment, not–for–profit **Service**: General medical and surgical

Staffed Beds: 118 **Admissions**: 4128 **Census**: 47 **Outpatient Visits**: 93462 **Births**: 395 **Total Expense ($000)**: 98435 **Payroll Expense ($000)**: 41229 **Personnel**: 710

JERSEYVILLE—Jersey County

✠ **JERSEY COMMUNITY HOSPITAL (140059)**, 400 Maple Summit Road, Zip 62052–2028, Mailing Address: P.O. Box 426, Zip 62052–0426; tel. 618/498–6402, **A**1 10 **F**3 7 11 15 18 28 29 31 32 34 35 36 38 40 41 46 51 53 57 59 64 70 79 81 82 84 85 87 94 97 104 107 111 114 115 117 118 119 127 129 130 131 132 133 146 147 148 154 **P**6
Primary Contact: Jonathan O. Wade, Chief Executive Officer
CFO: Beth King, Chief Financial Officer
CMO: Michael McNear, M.D., Chief Medical Officer
CIO: Shane Winters, Chief Information Officer
CHR: Sharon K Sanford, Director Human Resources
CNO: Julie Smith, R.N., MSN, Director of Nursing
Web address: www.jch.com
Control: Hospital district or authority, Government, nonfederal **Service**: General medical and surgical

Staffed Beds: 46 **Admissions**: 913 **Census**: 8 **Outpatient Visits**: 153600 **Births**: 0 **Total Expense ($000)**: 41356 **Payroll Expense ($000)**: 19225 **Personnel**: 368

Many Facility Codes have changed. Please refer to the AHA Guide Code Chart. © 2018 AHA Guide

JOLIET—Will County

⊞ △ **PRESENCE SAINT JOSEPH MEDICAL CENTER (140007)**, 333 North Madison Street, Zip 60435–8200; tel. 815/725–7133, **A**1 2 7 10 **F**3 11 12 13 15 17 18 20 22 24 26 28 29 30 31 32 34 35 36 38 39 40 41 43 44 45 46 47 49 50 53 54 56 57 58 59 60 61 64 65 68 70 72 74 75 76 77 79 80 81 82 84 85 86 87 88 89 90 92 93 96 97 98 99 100 101 102 103 105 107 108 110 111 114 115 118 119 120 121 123 124 126 129 130 131 132 134 135 143 145 146 147 149 154 **P8 S** Ascension Healthcare, Saint Louis, MO
Primary Contact: Robert J. Erickson, President
CFO: Deb Schimerowski, Regional Finance Officer
CMO: Gary Lipinski, M.D., Chief Medical Officer
CHR: Monica Simzyk, Regional Human Resource Officer
CNO: Lynn Watson, Interim Chief Nursing Officer
Web address: www.presencehealth.org/stjoes
Control: Church operated, Nongovernment, not–for–profit **Service:** General medical and surgical

Staffed Beds: 460 **Admissions:** 21052 **Census:** 272 **Births:** 1103
Total Expense ($000): 389252 **Payroll Expense ($000):** 114760
Personnel: 1258

PROVENA SAINT JOSEPH MEDICAL CENTER See Presence Saint Joseph Medical Center

KANKAKEE—Kankakee County

⊞ **PRESENCE ST. MARY'S HOSPITAL (140155)**, 500 West Court Street, Zip 60901–3661; tel. 815/937–2400, **A**1 2 10 **F**3 5 11 12 13 15 18 20 22 26 28 29 30 31 32 34 35 36 38 39 40 43 44 45 46 47 48 49 50 54 56 57 58 59 60 61 64 65 68 70 74 75 76 77 78 79 81 82 84 85 86 87 89 92 93 97 98 100 101 102 103 104 105 107 108 110 111 114 115 119 129 130 131 132 135 143 146 147 149 152 153 154 **S** Ascension Healthcare, Saint Louis, MO
Primary Contact: Chris Shride, President
CFO: Deb Schimerowski, Regional Chief Financial Officer
CMO: Kalisha Hill, M.D., Chief Medical Officer
CIO: Russell Soliman, Director Information Services
CHR: Monica Simzyk, Regional Chief Human Resources Officer
CNO: Karen M Gallagher, MSN, Chief Nursing Office, Vice President Operations
Web address: www.presencehealth.org/presence–st–marys–hospital–kankakee
Control: Church operated, Nongovernment, not–for–profit **Service:** General medical and surgical

Staffed Beds: 156 **Admissions:** 5203 **Census:** 58 **Outpatient Visits:** 82152
Births: 360 **Total Expense ($000):** 123563 **Payroll Expense ($000):** 34229
Personnel: 400

PROVENA ST. MARY'S HOSPITAL See Presence St. Mary's Hospital

★ △ ⇑ **RIVERSIDE MEDICAL CENTER (140186)**, 350 North Wall Street, Zip 60901–2901; tel. 815/933–1671, **A**2 3 5 7 10 13 21 **F**3 4 5 6 7 8 9 12 13 15 17 18 20 22 24 26 28 29 30 34 35 36 38 39 40 41 43 44 45 46 47 49 50 51 54 55 56 57 58 59 61 62 64 65 66 68 70 71 74 75 76 77 78 79 81 82 84 85 86 87 89 90 92 93 96 97 98 99 100 101 102 103 104 105 107 108 110 111 114 115 118 119 120 121 123 124 126 127 129 130 131 132 134 135 141 143 144 146 147 148 149 150 151 152 153
Primary Contact: Phillip M. Kambic, President and Chief Executive Officer
CFO: Bill Douglas, Senior Vice President and Chief Financial Officer
CMO: Keith A Moss, Vice President & Chief Medical Informatics Officers
CIO: Kyle Hansen, Corporate Director Information Systems
CHR: Becky Kay Hinrichs, Vice President Human Resources
CNO: Michael Mutterer, Senior Vice President and Chief Nursing Officer
Web address: www.riversidehealthcare.org
Control: Other not–for–profit (including NFP Corporation) **Service:** General medical and surgical

Staffed Beds: 318 **Admissions:** 11290 **Census:** 156 **Outpatient Visits:** 533543 **Births:** 978 **Total Expense ($000):** 322803 **Payroll Expense ($000):** 140119 **Personnel:** 2150

KEWANEE—Henry County

★ **OSF SAINT LUKE MEDICAL CENTER (141325)**, 1051 West South Street, Zip 61443–8354, Mailing Address: P.O. Box 747, Zip 61443–0747; tel. 309/852–7500, **A**10 18 **F**3 11 15 29 30 32 34 35 36 38 40 45 50 57 59 64 65 66 70 75 77 78 79 81 82 85 86 87 92 93 96 97 108 110 111 115 119 127 129 130 131 132 133 135 146 147 148 149 **P**6 **S** OSF Healthcare, Peoria, IL
Primary Contact: Jacqueline D. Kernan, President
CFO: John Bowser, Vice President, Chief Financial Officer
CMO: Clifford G Martin, M.D., Regional Vice President and Chief Medical Officer
CHR: Renee A Salisbury, Director Human Resources
CNO: Shelley Wiborg, MS, R.N., Chief Nursing Officer
Web address: www.osfsaintluke.org
Control: Other not–for–profit (including NFP Corporation) **Service:** General medical and surgical

Staffed Beds: 25 **Admissions:** 500 **Census:** 3 **Outpatient Visits:** 38786
Births: 0 **Total Expense ($000):** 29494 **Payroll Expense ($000):** 10851
Personnel: 118

LA GRANGE—Cook County

⊞ **AMITA HEALTH ADVENTIST LA GRANGE MEDICAL CENTER (140065)**, 5101 South Willow Spring Road, Zip 60525–2600; tel. 708/245–9000, **A**1 2 3 5 10 13 **F**3 4 13 15 18 20 22 24 28 29 30 31 34 37 40 41 43 44 45 49 54 57 58 59 61 64 70 73 76 77 78 79 81 82 84 85 86 87 90 91 93 96 97 101 107 108 110 111 114 115 119 126 129 130 131 143 146 147 148 149 154 **S** Adventist Health System Sunbelt Health Care Corporation, Altamonte Springs, FL
Primary Contact: Michael Murrill, President and Chief Executive Officer
CFO: Rebecca Mathis, Chief Financial Officer
CIO: Thomas Schoenig, Chief Information Officer
CHR: Garry Giertuga, Site Manager Human Resources
CNO: Mary S Murphy, MSN, Regional Chief Nursing Officer
Web address: www.keepingyouwell.com
Control: Church operated, Nongovernment, not–for–profit **Service:** General medical and surgical

Staffed Beds: 191 **Admissions:** 8481 **Census:** 150 **Outpatient Visits:** 107062 **Births:** 388 **Total Expense ($000):** 165422 **Payroll Expense ($000):** 55948 **Personnel:** 755

LAKE FOREST—Lake County

LAKE FOREST HOSPITAL See Northwestern Medicine Lake Forest Hospital

⊞ **NORTHWESTERN MEDICINE LAKE FOREST HOSPITAL (140130)**, 1000 North Westmoreland Road, Zip 60045–1696, Mailing Address: 660 North Westmoreland Road, Zip 60045–1696; tel. 847/234–5600, **A**1 2 3 5 10 **F**3 8 9 11 13 15 18 20 22 26 28 29 30 31 32 34 35 36 38 40 41 43 44 45 46 48 49 50 51 52 53 54 55 56 59 60 62 64 65 66 73 74 75 76 77 78 79 81 82 84 85 86 87 89 92 93 96 97 100 102 104 107 108 110 111 114 115 116 117 119 120 121 123 126 129 130 131 132 135 144 146 147 148 149 150 154 **P**6 **S** Northwestern Memorial HealthCare, Chicago, IL
Primary Contact: Thomas J. McAfee, President, North Region
CFO: Richard A. Franco, Vice President and Chief Financial Officer
CMO: Jeffrey D. Kopin, Senior Vice President and Chief Medical Officer
CNO: Denise J. Majeski, Vice President Operations and Chief Nurse Executive
Web address: www.nm.org
Control: Other not–for–profit (including NFP Corporation) **Service:** General medical and surgical

Staffed Beds: 123 **Admissions:** 7551 **Census:** 87 **Outpatient Visits:** 502773 **Births:** 1413 **Total Expense ($000):** 392847 **Payroll Expense ($000):** 165449 **Personnel:** 3516

LAWRENCEVILLE—Lawrence County

LAWRENCE COUNTY MEMORIAL HOSPITAL (141344), 2200 West State Street, Zip 62439–1852; tel. 618/943–1000, **A**10 18 **F**3 11 15 28 29 30 35 40 75 77 81 93 107 110 114 127 130 133 **S** QHR, Brentwood, TN
Primary Contact: Donald Robbins, Chief Executive Officer
CFO: Larry Spore, Chief Financial Officer
CIO: Gary Theriac, Director Information Technology
CHR: Kim Alldredge, Director Human Resources
CNO: Rita Garvey, Chief Nursing Officer
Web address: www.lcmhosp.org
Control: Other not–for–profit (including NFP Corporation) **Service:** General medical and surgical

Staffed Beds: 25 **Admissions:** 630 **Census:** 7 **Outpatient Visits:** 47980
Births: 0 **Total Expense ($000):** 16045 **Payroll Expense ($000):** 6742
Personnel: 149

IL

Hospital, Medicare Provider Number, Address, Telephone, Approval, Facility, and Physician Codes, Health Care System

★ American Hospital Association (AHA) membership
□ The Joint Commission accreditation
○ Healthcare Facilities Accreditation Program
◇ DNV Healthcare Inc. accreditation
⇑ Center for Improvement in Healthcare Quality Accreditation
△ Commission on Accreditation of Rehabilitation Facilities (CARF) accreditation

LIBERTYVILLE—Lake County

★ ⇑ **ADVOCATE CONDELL MEDICAL CENTER (140202)**, 801 South Milwaukee Avenue, Zip 60048–3199; tel. 847/362–2900, **A**2 10 21 **F**1 3 4 11 12 13 15 16 17 18 19 20 22 24 26 28 29 30 31 32 34 35 36 37 39 40 41 43 44 45 46 47 48 49 50 51 53 54 55 56 57 59 60 64 65 67 68 70 72 73 74 75 76 77 78 79 80 81 82 85 86 87 88 89 90 92 93 94 96 98 107 108 110 111 114 115 117 118 119 120 121 123 124 126 128 130 132 135 144 145 146 147 148 154 **P**8 **S** Advocate Aurora Health, Downers Grove, IL
Primary Contact: Karen A. Lambert, President
CFO: David A Cartwright, Vice President Finance and Support Services
CMO: Debra Susie–Lattner, M.D., Vice President Medical Management
CIO: Harold Kromer, Director Site Information Systems
CHR: Amy Antani Logue, Ph.D., Vice President Human Resources
CNO: Mary Hillard, R.N., MSN, Vice President Patient Care Services and Clinical Operations, Chief Nursing Executive
Web address: www.advocatehealth.com/condell/
Control: Other not–for–profit (including NFP Corporation) **Service**: General medical and surgical

Staffed Beds: 283 **Admissions**: 16131 **Census**: 187 **Outpatient Visits**: 234637 **Births**: 1765 **Total Expense ($000)**: 305695 **Payroll Expense ($000)**: 103975 **Personnel**: 1553

LINCOLN—Logan County

⊞ **ABRAHAM LINCOLN MEMORIAL HOSPITAL (141322)**, 200 Stahlhut Drive, Zip 62656–5066; tel. 217/732–2161, **A**1 10 18 **F**13 15 28 29 30 34 35 40 57 59 64 75 76 77 79 81 82 87 93 107 108 110 111 119 129 130 131 132 133 144 146 149 **P**5 **S** Memorial Health System, Springfield, IL
Primary Contact: Dolan Dalpoas, President and Chief Executive Officer
CFO: Andrew Costic, Regional Chief Financial Officer
CMO: Amir J. Wahab, M.D., Medical Staff President
CIO: Keenan Leesman, Director Information Systems
CHR: Michelle Long, Human Resources Business Partner
CNO: Roxanne Harling, Chief Nursing Officer
Web address: www.almh.org
Control: Other not–for–profit (including NFP Corporation) **Service**: General medical and surgical

Staffed Beds: 25 **Admissions**: 896 **Census**: 9 **Outpatient Visits**: 48125 **Births**: 189 **Total Expense ($000)**: 42833 **Payroll Expense ($000)**: 15891 **Personnel**: 288

LITCHFIELD—Montgomery County

⊞ **HSHS ST. FRANCIS HOSPITAL (141350)**, 1215 Franciscan Drive, Zip 62056–1799, Mailing Address: P.O. Box 1215, Zip 62056–0999; tel. 217/324–2191, **A**1 10 18 **F**3 8 11 13 15 18 28 29 30 31 34 35 40 44 45 46 50 56 57 59 64 68 70 74 75 76 77 78 79 81 82 85 86 87 92 93 107 111 114 117 118 119 129 131 132 133 134 135 146 147 149 154 **S** HSHS Hospital Sisters Health System, Springfield, IL
Primary Contact: John Peipert, R.N., Interim President and Chief Executive Officer
CFO: Marisa Murray, CPA, Director Finance
CNO: John Peipert, R.N., Chief Nursing Officer
Web address: www.stfrancis–litchfield.org
Control: Church operated, Nongovernment, not–for–profit **Service**: General medical and surgical

Staffed Beds: 25 **Admissions**: 1406 **Census**: 13 **Outpatient Visits**: 68720 **Births**: 252 **Total Expense ($000)**: 34485 **Payroll Expense ($000)**: 11070 **Personnel**: 222

MACOMB—Mcdonough County

⊞ **MCDONOUGH DISTRICT HOSPITAL (140089)**, 525 East Grant Street, Zip 61455–3318; tel. 309/833–4101, **A**1 10 20 **F**3 5 7 11 13 15 28 29 31 34 35 38 40 45 47 48 50 51 54 56 57 59 62 63 64 68 70 75 76 77 78 79 81 82 84 85 86 91 93 94 96 97 98 100 101 102 103 104 107 108 110 115 119 124 127 129 130 131 132 133 135 146 147 148 **P**8
Primary Contact: Brian Dietz, Interim Chief Executive Officer
CFO: Linda Dace, Vice President Finance
CMO: Edwin Card, President Medical Staff
CIO: Harlan T Baker, Department Leader Information Systems
CHR: Sue Dexter, Administrative Department Leader Human Resources
CNO: Wanda Foster, R.N., MS, FACHE, MSN, Vice President Nursing
Web address: www.mdh.org
Control: Hospital district or authority, Government, nonfederal **Service**: General medical and surgical

Staffed Beds: 60 **Admissions**: 1485 **Census**: 16 **Outpatient Visits**: 184415 **Births**: 286 **Total Expense ($000)**: 84387 **Payroll Expense ($000)**: 38614 **Personnel**: 522

MARION—Williamson County

⊞ **HEARTLAND REGIONAL MEDICAL CENTER (140184)**, 3333 West DeYoung, Zip 62959–5884; tel. 618/998–7000, (Nonreporting) **A**1 10 **S** Quorum Health, Brentwood, TN
Primary Contact: Melisa Adkins, Chief Executive Officer
COO: Kolbe Sheridan, Chief Operating Officer
CFO: Jeff Thomas, Chief Financial Officer
CHR: Sam Hood, Director Human Resources
Web address: www.heartlandregional.com
Control: Corporation, Investor–owned (for–profit) **Service**: General medical and surgical

Staffed Beds: 92

⊞ **MARION VETERANS AFFAIRS MEDICAL CENTER**, 2401 West Main Street, Zip 62959–1188; tel. 618/997–5311, (Nonreporting) **A**1 3 5 **S** Department of Veterans Affairs, Perry Point, MD
Primary Contact: Jo–Ann M. Ginsberg, R.N., MSN, Director
COO: Frank Kehus, Associate Director for Operations
CFO: Connie McDonald, Chief Financial Officer
CMO: Michael Ladwig, M.D., Chief of Staff
CIO: Adam Powell, Program Manager
CHR: Tim Hartwell, Chief Human Resources
CNO: Rose Burke, Associate Director Patient Care Services
Web address: www.marion.va.gov
Control: Veterans Affairs, Government, federal **Service**: General medical and surgical

Staffed Beds: 99

MARYVILLE—Madison County

⊞ △ **ANDERSON HOSPITAL (140289)**, 6800 State Route 162, Zip 62062–8500; tel. 618/288–5711, **A**1 7 10 **F**3 11 13 15 18 20 22 28 29 30 31 34 35 40 49 50 54 57 59 62 64 70 74 75 76 78 79 81 85 90 93 107 110 111 115 117 118 119 120 121 123 126 129 130 132 144 146 147 148 149 154
Primary Contact: Keith Allen. Page, President and Chief Executive Officer
CFO: Michael Marshall, Vice President Finance and Chief Financial Officer
CMO: Charles A. Lane, Chief Medical Officer
CIO: Michael Ward, Director Information Services
CHR: Robin Steinmann, Administrative Director Human Resources
CNO: Lisa Klaustermeier, R.N., MSN, Chief Nursing Officer
Web address: www.andersonhospital.org
Control: Other not–for–profit (including NFP Corporation) **Service**: General medical and surgical

Staffed Beds: 154 **Admissions**: 5029 **Census**: 51 **Outpatient Visits**: 170213 **Births**: 1501 **Total Expense ($000)**: 129477 **Payroll Expense ($000)**: 52142 **Personnel**: 1118

MATTOON—Coles County

⊞ **SARAH BUSH LINCOLN HEALTH CENTER (140189)**, 1000 Health Center Drive, Zip 61938–9253; tel. 217/258–2525, **A**1 10 20 **F**3 11 12 13 15 18 20 22 28 29 30 31 32 34 35 36 38 39 40 41 44 45 49 50 53 54 56 57 59 61 62 63 64 65 66 68 69 70 71 74 75 76 77 78 79 81 82 84 85 86 87 89 93 97 98 100 101 102 104 105 107 110 111 115 117 119 120 121 123 127 129 130 131 132 134 135 144 145 146 147 148 154 **P**6
Primary Contact: Jerry Esker, President and Chief Executive Officer
COO: Dennis Pluard, Vice President Finance and Operations
CFO: Dennis Pluard, Vice President Finance and Operations
CMO: James Hildebrandt, D.O., Vice President Medical Affairs
CIO: Maggie Ratliff, Vice President Information Systems
CHR: Eric Benson, Vice President Human Resources & Wellness
CNO: Lisa J. Hernandez, R.N., Vice President, Patient Care Continuum and Chief Nursing Officer
Web address: www.sarahbush.org
Control: Other not–for–profit (including NFP Corporation) **Service**: General medical and surgical

Staffed Beds: 120 **Admissions**: 7317 **Census**: 66 **Outpatient Visits**: 492691 **Births**: 785 **Total Expense ($000)**: 290741 **Payroll Expense ($000)**: 142742 **Personnel**: 2065

IL

MAYWOOD—Cook County

✠ **LOYOLA UNIVERSITY MEDICAL CENTER (140276)**, 2160 South First Avenue, Zip 60153–3328; tel. 708/216–9000, (Includes RONALD MCDONALD CHILDREN'S HOSPITAL, 2160 South 1St Avenue, Maywood, IL, Zip 60153–3328; tel. 888/584–7888) **A**1 2 3 5 8 10 **F**3 4 6 7 8 9 11 12 13 14 15 16 17 18 19 20 21 22 23 24 25 26 27 28 29 30 31 32 33 34 35 36 37 38 39 40 41 43 44 45 46 47 48 49 50 51 54 55 56 57 58 59 60 61 64 65 66 68 70 71 72 73 74 75 76 77 78 79 80 81 82 84 85 86 87 88 89 91 92 93 94 96 97 99 100 101 102 103 104 107 108 110 111 114 115 116 117 118 119 120 121 123 124 126 129 130 131 132 134 135 136 137 138 139 140 141 142 143 144 145 146 147 148 149 150 154 **P**6 **S** Trinity Health, Livonia, MI
Primary Contact: Daniel J. Post, Interim President
CFO: Jay Sial, Chief Financial Officer
CMO: Joshua Lee, M.D., Chief Medical Officer
CIO: Arthur J Krumrey, Chief Information Officer
CHR: Vicky Piper, Vice President Human Resources
Web address: www.loyolamedicine.org/Medical_Services/index.cfm
Control: Other not–for–profit (including NFP Corporation) **Service:** General medical and surgical

Staffed Beds: 524 **Admissions:** 22493 **Census:** 371 **Outpatient Visits:** 940880 **Births:** 1302 **Personnel:** 6840

MCHENRY—Mchenry County

✠ **CENTEGRA HOSPITAL – MCHENRY (140116)**, 4201 Medical Center Drive, Zip 60050–8409; tel. 815/344–5000, (Includes CENTEGRA HOSPITAL–HUNTLEY, 10400 Haligus Road, Huntley, IL, Zip 60142; tel. 224/654–0000; Michael S Eesley, Chief Executive Officer) **A**1 2 3 5 10 **F**3 4 11 12 13 15 18 20 22 24 26 28 29 30 31 34 35 37 38 39 41 44 45 47 49 50 51 54 55 57 58 59 62 64 68 69 70 74 75 76 78 79 81 82 85 86 87 89 90 93 96 97 100 101 102 107 108 110 111 114 115 116 117 118 119 120 121 123 124 126 129 130 131 132 143 146 147 148 154 **P**6 8 **S** Centegra Health System, Crystal Lake, IL
Primary Contact: Michael S. Eesley, Chief Executive Officer
COO: Jason Sciarro, President and Chief Operating Officer
CFO: David Tomlinson, Executive Vice President Chief Financial Officer and Chief Information Officer
CMO: Irfan Hafiz, Vice President Medical Affairs
CIO: David Tomlinson, Executive Vice President Chief Financial Officer and Chief Information Officer
CHR: Bernadette S Szczepanski, Senior Vice President, Human Resources
Web address: www.centegra.com
Control: Other not–for–profit (including NFP Corporation) **Service:** General medical and surgical

Staffed Beds: 296 **Admissions:** 12634 **Census:** 150 **Outpatient Visits:** 311900 **Births:** 1710 **Total Expense ($000):** 395457 **Payroll Expense ($000):** 141312 **Personnel:** 1418

MCLEANSBORO—Hamilton County

HAMILTON MEMORIAL HOSPITAL DISTRICT (141326), 611 South Marshall Avenue, Zip 62859–1213, Mailing Address: P.O. Box 429, Mc Leansboro, Zip 62859–0429; tel. 618/643–2361, **A**10 18 **F**3 11 15 28 29 40 41 43 57 59 65 81 93 107 108 115 119 127 129 133 154
Primary Contact: Victoria Woodrow, Chief Executive Officer
CFO: Kent Mitchell, Chief Financial Officer
CIO: Mark Todd, Senior Systems Administrator
CHR: Sheila Thompson, Director Human Resources
CNO: Patty Blazier, Chief Nursing Officer
Web address: www.hmhospital.org
Control: Hospital district or authority, Government, nonfederal **Service:** General medical and surgical

Staffed Beds: 25 **Admissions:** 714 **Census:** 10 **Births:** 0 **Total Expense ($000):** 19382 **Payroll Expense ($000):** 7947

MELROSE PARK—Cook County

✠ **GOTTLIEB MEMORIAL HOSPITAL (140008)**, 701 West North Avenue, Zip 60160–1612; tel. 708/681–3200, **A**1 3 5 10 **F**2 3 11 12 15 18 20 22 24 26 28 29 30 31 34 35 36 39 40 43 44 45 47 49 50 53 54 56 57 59 60 64 65 68 70 74 75 77 78 79 81 85 86 87 89 90 92 93 96 97 98 103 107 108 110 111 114 116 117 118 119 126 128 129 130 131 132 143 144 145 146 147 148 149 150 **P**8 **S** Trinity Health, Livonia, MI
Primary Contact: Lori Price, President
CFO: Ellyn Chin, Vice President Finance
CMO: Gerald Luger, M.D., President Medical Staff
CIO: Maurita Adler, Director Information Services
CHR: Brett Wakefield, Vice President Human Resources
Web address: www.gottliebhospital.org
Control: Other not–for–profit (including NFP Corporation) **Service:** General medical and surgical

Staffed Beds: 171 **Admissions:** 6669 **Census:** 120 **Outpatient Visits:** 76504 **Births:** 0 **Personnel:** 880

✠ **WESTLAKE HOSPITAL (140240)**, 1225 Lake Street, Zip 60160–4000; tel. 708/681–3000, (Nonreporting) **A**1 5 10 **S** TENET Healthcare Corporation, Dallas, TX
Primary Contact: Joseph Ottolino, Chief Executive Officer
COO: Michael Ditoro, Chief Operating Officer
CFO: Jennifer Lamont, Chief Financial Officer
CMO: Robert Chase, M.D., Chief Medical Officer
CHR: Nancy Gunnell, Chief Human Resource Officer
CNO: Ruth Matthei, R.N., MS, Chief Nursing Officer
Web address: www.westlakehosp.com
Control: Corporation, Investor–owned (for–profit) **Service:** General medical and surgical

Staffed Beds: 181

MENDOTA—Lasalle County

★ **OSF SAINT PAUL MEDICAL CENTER (141310)**, 1401 East 12th Street, Zip 61342–9216; tel. 815/539–7461, **A**10 18 **F**3 11 15 28 29 30 31 34 40 49 57 59 64 69 70 77 78 79 81 82 85 93 107 110 111 115 127 129 130 133 146 **S** OSF Healthcare, Peoria, IL
Primary Contact: Dawn Trompeter, President
CMO: Leonardo Lopez, President Medical Staff
CHR: Kimberly Kennedy, Manager Human Resources
CNO: Heather Bomstad, MSN, R.N., Vice President Patient Care Services and Chief Nursing Officer
Web address: www.osfhealthcare.org/saint–paul
Control: Other not–for–profit (including NFP Corporation) **Service:** General medical and surgical

Staffed Beds: 25 **Admissions:** 486 **Census:** 6 **Outpatient Visits:** 32709 **Births:** 0 **Total Expense ($000):** 33968 **Payroll Expense ($000):** 11918 **Personnel:** 125

METROPOLIS—Massac County

★ **MASSAC MEMORIAL HOSPITAL (141323)**, 28 Chick Street, Zip 62960–2467, Mailing Address: P.O. Box 850, Zip 62960–0850; tel. 618/524–2176, (Nonreporting) **A**10 18
Primary Contact: Rick Goins, Chief Executive Officer
CFO: Randy Rushing, Chief Financial Officer
CHR: Johnna Douglas, Human Resources Manager
Web address: www.massachealth.org
Control: Hospital district or authority, Government, nonfederal **Service:** General medical and surgical

Staffed Beds: 25

MOLINE—Rock Island County

UNITYPOINT HEALTH – TRINITY MOLINE See Unitypoint Health – Trinity Rock Island, Rock Island

MONMOUTH—Warren County

★ **OSF HOLY FAMILY MEDICAL CENTER (141318)**, 1000 West Harlem Avenue, Zip 61462–1007; tel. 309/734–3141, **A**10 18 **F**11 15 28 29 30 34 40 45 46 50 57 59 64 65 68 75 77 81 85 87 93 97 107 110 115 118 119 127 129 130 132 133 143 145 146 **S** OSF Healthcare, Peoria, IL
Primary Contact: Patricia A. Luker, President
CFO: Theresa Springer, Chief Financial Officer
CMO: Clifford G Martin, M.D., Regional Vice President and Chief Medical Officer
CIO: Lew McCann, Director Management Information Systems
CHR: Jenny Jacobs, Director Human Resources
CNO: Shelley Wiborg, MS, R.N., Director of Nursing
Web address: www.osfholyfamily.org
Control: Church operated, Nongovernment, not–for–profit **Service:** General medical and surgical

Staffed Beds: 23 **Admissions:** 316 **Census:** 4 **Outpatient Visits:** 66159 **Births:** 0 **Total Expense ($000):** 27686 **Payroll Expense ($000):** 10382 **Personnel:** 100

IL

MONTICELLO—Piatt County

☒ **KIRBY MEDICAL CENTER (141301)**, 1000 Medical Center Drive,
Zip 61856–2116; tel. 217/762–2115, (Nonreporting) **A**1 5 10 18
Primary Contact: Steven D. Tenhouse, FACHE, Chief Executive Officer
COO: Mark Fred, R.N., Chief Operating Officer
CFO: Alexander Nazarian, CPA, Chief Financial Officer
CMO: Narain Mandhan, M.D., Chief Medical Officer
CIO: Alexander Nazarian, CPA, Director Information Technology
CHR: Andrew Buffenbarger, Chief Compliance Officer
CNO: Jennifer Moss, MS, R.N., Chief Clinical Officer
Web address: www.kirbyhealth.org
Control: Other not–for–profit (including NFP Corporation) **Service**: General medical and surgical

Staffed Beds: 16

MORRIS—Grundy County

★ ○ **MORRIS HOSPITAL & HEALTHCARE CENTERS (140101)**, 150 West High
Street, Zip 60450–1497; tel. 815/942–2932, **A**2 10 11 **F**3 11 13 15 18 19 20
22 26 28 29 34 35 40 43 45 47 49 50 54 57 59 64 65 66 69 70 75 77 78 79
81 82 85 86 87 93 97 102 107 108 110 111 114 115 118 119 120 121 123
130 132 135 143 144 146 149 154 **P**6
Primary Contact: Mark B. Steadham, President and Chief Executive Officer
CFO: Mary Lou Tate, Chief Financial Officer
CHR: Erin Murphy–Frobish, Vice President Human Resources
CNO: Kimberly A. Landers, MS, R.N., Vice President Patient Care Services
Web address: www.morrishospital.org
Control: Other not–for–profit (including NFP Corporation) **Service**: General medical and surgical

Staffed Beds: 89 **Admissions**: 4073 **Census**: 39 **Outpatient Visits**: 344770 **Births**: 509 **Total Expense ($000)**: 163803 **Payroll Expense ($000)**: 74580 **Personnel**: 874

MORRISON—Whiteside County

MORRISON COMMUNITY HOSPITAL (141329), 303 North Jackson Street,
Zip 61270–3042; tel. 815/772–4003, **A**10 18 **F**7 11 15 29 34 35 38 40 45 59
64 81 93 94 97 104 107 114 119 127 130 133 135 143 146 148 154
Primary Contact: Pam Pfister, Chief Executive Officer
COO: Pam Pfister, Chief Executive Officer
CFO: Cami Megli, Controller
CMO: Duncan Dinkha, M.D., Chief of Staff
CIO: Pam Pfister, Chief Executive Officer
CHR: Amber L Temple, Director Human Resources
Web address: www.morrisonhospital.com
Control: Hospital district or authority, Government, nonfederal **Service**: General medical and surgical

Staffed Beds: 25 **Admissions**: 265 **Census**: 8 **Outpatient Visits**: 24244 **Births**: 0 **Total Expense ($000)**: 14314 **Payroll Expense ($000)**: 6969 **Personnel**: 128

MOUNT CARMEL—Wabash County

☒ **WABASH GENERAL HOSPITAL (141327)**, 1418 College Drive,
Zip 62863–2638; tel. 618/262–8621, (Nonreporting) **A**1 10 18 **S** Alliant
Management Services, Louisville, KY
Primary Contact: Jay Purvis, President and Chief Executive Officer
COO: Karissa Turner, Vice President Operations
CFO: Steve McGill, Vice President Finance and Chief Financial Officer
CMO: Lawrence Jennings, Chief of Staff
CIO: Bobby Gage, Director Information Technology
CHR: Bridget Shepard, Vice President Human Resources
CNO: Tamara Gould, R.N., Vice President Clinical Services and Chief Nursing Officer
Web address: www.wabashgeneral.com
Control: County, Government, nonfederal **Service**: General medical and surgical

Staffed Beds: 25

MOUNT VERNON—Jefferson County

☒ **CROSSROADS COMMUNITY HOSPITAL (140294)**, 8 Doctors Park Road,
Zip 62864–6224; tel. 618/244–5500, (Nonreporting) **A**1 10 **S** Quorum Health,
Brentwood, TN
Primary Contact: Amanda J. Basso, Chief Executive Officer
CIO: Bryan Delaney, Director Information Technology
CHR: Jessica Connaway, Director Human Resources
CNO: Stephanie Maines, Chief Nursing Officer
Web address: www.crossroadshospital.com
Control: Corporation, Investor–owned (for–profit) **Service**: General medical and surgical

Staffed Beds: 47

☒ **GOOD SAMARITAN REGIONAL HEALTH CENTER (140046)**, 1 Good Samaritan
Way, Zip 62864–2402; tel. 618/242–4600, **A**1 2 10 19 **F**3 4 8 11 13 15 18 20
22 24 26 28 29 30 31 34 35 38 40 44 45 46 50 51 54 56 57 59 60 61 64 68
70 73 74 75 76 77 78 79 80 81 82 84 85 86 87 89 90 92 93 94 96 102 104
107 108 110 111 114 115 119 124 126 130 131 132 135 144 146 147 148
149 154 **P**6 8 **S** SSM Health, Saint Louis, MO
Primary Contact: Kerry Swanson, Regional President, President Good Samaritan
COO: Mark A Clark, Vice President Operations
CFO: Deland Evischi, Regional Chief Financial Officer, Southern Illinois
CMO: Daniel Hoffman, M.D., Administrative Medical Director
CIO: Steve Murphy, FM–East Region IS
CHR: Thomas W Blythe, System Vice President Human Resources
CNO: Chris Adams, Vice President Patient Care Services
Web address: www.smgsi.com
Control: Church operated, Nongovernment, not–for–profit **Service**: General medical and surgical

Staffed Beds: 134 **Admissions**: 8076 **Census**: 86 **Outpatient Visits**: 232760 **Births**: 1108 **Total Expense ($000)**: 187554 **Payroll Expense ($000)**: 57529 **Personnel**: 1042

MURPHYSBORO—Jackson County

★ **ST. JOSEPH MEMORIAL HOSPITAL (141334)**, 2 South Hospital Drive,
Zip 62966–3333; tel. 618/684–3156, **A**10 18 **F**3 11 18 28 29 30 31 34 35
40 45 49 56 57 59 64 74 75 77 78 79 81 82 84 85 86 87 93 104 107 111
114 119 129 130 132 133 135 146 148 154 **P**1 **S** Southern Illinois Healthcare,
Carbondale, IL
Primary Contact: Susan Odle, Administrator
CMO: Emily Hanson, M.D., President, Medical Staff
CIO: David Holland, Vice President Information Services
CHR: Kelly Stevens, Manager Human Resources
CNO: Julie Firman, R.N., FACHE, Chief Nursing Officer
Web address: www.sih.net
Control: Other not–for–profit (including NFP Corporation) **Service**: General medical and surgical

Staffed Beds: 25 **Admissions**: 684 **Census**: 12 **Outpatient Visits**: 74401 **Births**: 0 **Total Expense ($000)**: 50423 **Payroll Expense ($000)**: 12961 **Personnel**: 235

NAPERVILLE—Dupage County

☒ **EDWARD HOSPITAL (140231)**, 801 South Washington Street, Zip 60540–7499;
tel. 630/527–3000, **A**1 2 10 **F**3 5 7 12 13 15 17 18 19 20 22 24 26 28 29 30
31 32 34 35 37 38 39 40 41 43 44 45 46 47 48 49 50 53 54 55 57 58 59 61
63 64 65 70 72 73 74 75 76 77 78 79 81 82 84 85 86 87 88 89 91 92 93 96
97 99 100 101 102 103 107 108 110 111 114 115 117 118 119 120 121 123
124 126 129 130 131 132 135 144 146 147 148 149 154 **P**6 8 **S** Edward–
Elmhurst Healthcare, Naperville, IL
Primary Contact: Bill Kottmann, President and Chief Executive Officer
CMO: Sanjeeb Khatua, M.D., Chief Medical Officer and Vice President
CHR: Chris Devereux, Human Resources Director, Business Partner
CNO: Lynn Cochran, R.N., System Vice President Operations,Chief Nursing Officer
Web address: www.eehealth.org
Control: Other not–for–profit (including NFP Corporation) **Service**: General medical and surgical

Staffed Beds: 350 **Admissions**: 22847 **Census**: 246 **Outpatient Visits**: 987458 **Births**: 3156 **Total Expense ($000)**: 628990 **Payroll Expense ($000)**: 198259 **Personnel**: 2532

☒ **LINDEN OAKS HOSPITAL (144035)**, 852 South West Street, Zip 60540–6400;
tel. 630/305–5500, **A**1 3 5 10 **F**4 5 29 34 35 38 44 56 57 59 64 75 86 87 98
99 100 101 103 104 105 130 132 134 149 150 151 152 153 **P**6 8 **S** Edward–
Elmhurst Healthcare, Naperville, IL
Primary Contact: Gina Sharp, FACHE, President and Chief Executive Officer
CFO: Kristen Refness, Director, Financial Operations
CMO: Barry Rabin, M.D., Regional Medical Director
CIO: David Pickering, System Director, Applications
CHR: Lisa Dixon, Business Partner and Human Resource Director
CNO: Trish Fairbanks, R.N., Associate Vice President and Chief Nursing Officer
Web address: www.eehealth.org/services/behavioral–health
Control: Other not–for–profit (including NFP Corporation) **Service**: Psychiatric

Staffed Beds: 108 **Admissions**: 4340 **Census**: 85 **Outpatient Visits**: 62903 **Births**: 0 **Total Expense ($000)**: 45814 **Payroll Expense ($000)**: 26633 **Personnel**: 437

NASHVILLE—Washington County

☐ **WASHINGTON COUNTY HOSPITAL (141308)**, 705 South Grand Avenue, Zip 62263–1534; tel. 618/327–8236, (Total facility includes 28 beds in nursing home–type unit) **A**1 10 18 **F**8 11 15 28 29 31 34 40 49 50 75 78 81 85 93 104 107 114 119 127 129 133 145 146 148 154 **P**6
Primary Contact: Nancy M. Newby, FACHE, Ph.D., R.N., President and Chief Executive Officer
CFO: Elaine Matzenbacher, Chief Financial Officer
CMO: Alfonso Urdaneta, M.D., President Medical Staff
CIO: Kim Larkin, Chief Information Officer
CHR: David Davenport, Director Human Resources
CNO: Lisa Little, Chief Nursing Officer
Web address: www.washingtoncountyhospital.org
Control: Hospital district or authority, Government, nonfederal **Service**: General medical and surgical

Staffed Beds: 42 **Admissions**: 197 **Census**: 25 **Outpatient Visits**: 32428 **Births**: 0 **Total Expense ($000)**: 14559 **Payroll Expense ($000)**: 6607 **Personnel**: 134

NEW LENOX—Will County

☒ △ **SILVER CROSS HOSPITAL (140213)**, 1900 Silver Cross Boulevard, Zip 60451–9509; tel. 815/300–1100, **A**1 2 7 10 **F**3 4 5 11 13 15 18 20 22 26 28 29 30 35 37 38 40 43 44 45 46 47 48 49 50 53 56 57 59 60 62 64 65 67 68 70 74 75 76 78 79 81 82 84 85 86 87 89 90 92 93 96 97 98 99 100 101 102 104 105 107 108 110 111 114 115 116 117 118 119 126 128 129 130 131 132 133 135 144 145 146 147 148 149 153 154 **P**8
Primary Contact: Ruth A. Colby, President and Chief Executive Officer
COO: Mary Bakken, Executive Vice President and Chief Operating Officer
CFO: Vincent Pryor, Senior Vice President and Chief Financial Officer
CMO: Christopher Udovich, M.D., Chief of Staff
CIO: Kevin Lane, Vice President Information Systems
CHR: Mark Jepson, Vice President
CNO: Peggy Gricus, R.N., Vice President, Patient Care Services and Chief Nursing Officer
Web address: www.silvercross.org
Control: Other not–for–profit (including NFP Corporation) **Service**: General medical and surgical

Staffed Beds: 302 **Admissions**: 21274 **Census**: 226 **Outpatient Visits**: 259782 **Births**: 2803 **Total Expense ($000)**: 363222 **Payroll Expense ($000)**: 125603 **Personnel**: 1868

NORMAL—Mclean County

★ ⇑ **ADVOCATE BROMENN MEDICAL CENTER (140127)**, 1304 Franklin Avenue, Zip 61761–3558, Mailing Address: P.O. Box 2850, Bloomington, Zip 61702–2850; tel. 309/454–1400, (Includes ADVOCATE BROMENN REGIONAL MEDICAL CENTER, 1304 Franklin Avenue, Normal, IL, Zip 61761–3558, Mailing Address: PO Box 2850, Bloomington, Zip 61702–2850, tel. 309/454–1400; Colleen Kannaday, FACHE, President) **A**2 5 10 13 21 **F**2 3 4 11 12 13 15 18 20 22 24 26 28 29 30 31 32 34 35 37 38 39 40 43 44 45 49 50 51 54 55 57 59 64 65 66 68 70 73 74 75 76 77 78 79 81 82 84 85 86 87 89 90 93 96 97 98 100 101 102 103 107 108 110 111 114 115 118 119 126 129 130 131 132 135 141 146 147 148 149 152 154 **P**8 **S** Advocate Aurora Health, Downers Grove, IL
Primary Contact: Colleen Kannaday, FACHE, President
CFO: Aron Klein, Vice President Finance
CMO: James Nevin, M.D., Vice President Medical Management
CHR: Antonio Coletta, Vice President Human Resources
CNO: Laurie Round, MS, R.N., Chief Nurse Executive
Web address: www.advocatehealth.com
Control: Church operated, Nongovernment, not–for–profit **Service**: General medical and surgical

Staffed Beds: 198 **Admissions**: 8757 **Census**: 92 **Outpatient Visits**: 122696 **Births**: 1635 **Total Expense ($000)**: 166971 **Payroll Expense ($000)**: 58481 **Personnel**: 1032

⇑ **ADVOCATE BROMENN REGIONAL MEDICAL CENTER** See Advocate Bromenn Medical Center

NORTH CHICAGO—Lake County

☒ **CAPTAIN JAMES A. LOVELL FEDERAL HEALTH CARE CENTER**, 3001 Green Bay Road, Zip 60064–3049; tel. 847/688–1900, (Total facility includes 121 beds in nursing home–type unit) **A**1 3 5 8 **F**3 4 8 11 14 15 18 29 30 31 32 34 35 36 38 39 40 44 45 46 48 49 54 56 58 59 61 62 63 64 65 68 70 71 74 75 77 78 79 81 83 84 86 87 90 91 92 94 96 97 98 100 101 102 103 104 107 108 110 111 115 118 119 128 129 130 131 132 133 135 143 146 147 148 149 154 **P**6 **S** Department of Veterans Affairs, Perry Point, MD
Primary Contact: Daniel Zomcheck, Interim Director
CFO: Barbara Meadows, Chief Financial Manager
CMO: Tariq Hassan, M.D., Associate Director of Patient Care
CIO: Jonathan Friedman, Public Affairs Officer
CHR: Amy Sanders, Chief Human Resources
CNO: Sarah Fouse, Associate Director of Patient Services
Web address: www.lovell.fhcc.va.gov
Control: Veterans Affairs, Government, federal **Service**: General medical and surgical

Staffed Beds: 314 **Admissions**: 4985 **Census**: 46 **Outpatient Visits**: 658596 **Births**: 0 **Personnel**: 1749

NORTHLAKE—Cook County

☒ **KINDRED HOSPITAL CHICAGO–NORTHLAKE (142008)**, 365 East North Avenue, Zip 60164–2628; tel. 708/345–8100, (Nonreporting) **A**1 10 **S** Kindred Healthcare, Louisville, KY
Primary Contact: Beverly Foster, Chief Executive Officer
COO: Sandra Buckhoy, Chief Clinical Officer
CFO: Jay Schweikart, Chief Financial Officer
CMO: Maher Najjar, M.D., Medical Director
Web address: www.kindrednorthlake.com/
Control: Corporation, Investor–owned (for–profit) **Service**: Acute long–term care hospital

Staffed Beds: 94

OAK LAWN—Cook County

★ △ ⇑ **ADVOCATE CHRIST MEDICAL CENTER (140208)**, 4440 West 95th Street, Zip 60453–2699; tel. 708/684–8000, (Includes ADVOCATE HOPE CHILDREN'S HOSPITAL, 4440 West 95th Street, Oak Lawn, IL, Zip 60453–2600; tel. 708/684–8000) **A**2 3 5 7 8 10 13 21 **F**3 4 5 8 11 13 15 17 18 19 20 21 22 23 24 25 26 27 28 29 30 31 32 34 35 37 38 39 40 41 43 44 45 46 47 48 49 50 52 54 55 56 57 58 59 60 61 62 63 64 65 66 68 70 71 72 74 75 76 77 78 79 81 82 84 85 86 87 88 89 90 92 93 96 97 98 100 101 102 103 104 105 107 108 109 110 111 114 115 116 117 118 119 120 121 123 124 126 130 131 132 134 135 137 138 140 143 145 146 147 148 149 152 154 **P**1 8 **S** Advocate Aurora Health, Downers Grove, IL
Primary Contact: Matthew Lee Primack, President
COO: Michael Wilkins, Chief Operating Officer
CFO: Robert Pekofske, Vice President Finance
CMO: Robert Stein, M.D., Vice President Medical Management
CIO: Brian Banbury, Director Site Information Systems
Web address: www.advocatehealth.com/christ
Control: Other not–for–profit (including NFP Corporation) **Service**: General medical and surgical

Staffed Beds: 778 **Admissions**: 44279 **Census**: 655 **Outpatient Visits**: 365004 **Births**: 4300 **Total Expense ($000)**: 1126533 **Payroll Expense ($000)**: 368135 **Personnel**: 4963

OAK PARK—Cook County

☒ **RUSH OAK PARK HOSPITAL (140063)**, 520 South Maple Avenue, Zip 60304–1097; tel. 708/383–9300, (Total facility includes 22 beds in nursing home–type unit) **A**1 3 5 10 **F**3 11 15 18 20 22 29 30 34 40 45 47 49 50 56 57 58 59 64 70 74 75 77 79 81 82 85 87 90 91 92 93 94 96 107 108 110 111 114 115 119 128 130 141 145 146 148 149 154 **P**1 8 **S** Rush University Medical Center, Chicago, IL
Primary Contact: Bruce M. Elegant, FACHE, President and Chief Executive Officer
COO: Robert S Spadoni, Vice President of Hospital Operations
CFO: Elvy Yap, Director of Finance
CMO: Michael R. Silver, M.D., Vice President Medical Affairs
CIO: Michael R. Silver, M.D., Chief Information Officer
CHR: Arlene Cruz, Director
CNO: Karen M Mayer, Ph.D., R.N., FACHE, Senior Vice President Patient Care Services
Web address: www.roph.org
Control: Other not–for–profit (including NFP Corporation) **Service**: General medical and surgical

Staffed Beds: 127 **Admissions**: 4585 **Census**: 59 **Outpatient Visits**: 128662 **Births**: 0 **Total Expense ($000)**: 119089 **Payroll Expense ($000)**: 57567 **Personnel**: 863

IL

Hospital, Medicare Provider Number, Address, Telephone, Approval, Facility, and Physician Codes, Health Care System

★ American Hospital Association (AHA) membership
☐ The Joint Commission accreditation
○ Healthcare Facilities Accreditation Program
◇ DNV Healthcare Inc. accreditation
⇑ Center for Improvement in Healthcare Quality Accreditation
△ Commission on Accreditation of Rehabilitation Facilities (CARF) accreditation

✠ **WEST SUBURBAN MEDICAL CENTER (140049)**, 3 Erie Court,
Zip 60302–2599; tel. 708/383–6200, (Nonreporting) **A**1 2 3 5 10 13 **S** TENET
Healthcare Corporation, Dallas, TX
Primary Contact: Joseph Ottolino, Chief Executive Officer
COO: Joseph Ottolino, Chief Operating Officer
CFO: Jennifer Lamont, Chief Financial Officer
CMO: Robert Chase, M.D., Physician Advisor
CHR: Nancy Gunnell, Chief Human Resource Officer
CNO: Roslyn J Lennon, R.N., MS, Chief Nursing Officer
Web address: www.westsuburbanmc.com/Home.aspx
Control: Corporation, Investor–owned (for–profit) **Service:** General medical and surgical

Staffed Beds: 172

O'FALLON—St. Clair County

✠ △　**HSHS ST. ELIZABETH'S HOSPITAL (140187)**, One St. Elizabeth's
Boulevard, Zip 62269; tel. 618/234–2120, (Nonreporting) **A**1 5 7 10 **S** HSHS
Hospital Sisters Health System, Springfield, IL
Primary Contact: Patricia Fischer, FACHE, R.N., President and Chief Executive Officer
CFO: David Nosacka, Chief Financial Officer
CMO: Shelly Harkins, M.D., Chief Medical Officer
CIO: Leslee Martin, Manager Information Technology
CHR: Jason T Snow, Director People Services
Web address: www.steliz.org
Control: Church operated, Nongovernment, not–for–profit **Service:** General medical and surgical

Staffed Beds: 260

OLNEY—Richland County

★ ○　**CARLE RICHLAND MEMORIAL HOSPITAL (140147)**, 800 East Locust
Street, Zip 62450–2553; tel. 618/395–2131, (Total facility includes 34 beds in
nursing home–type unit) **A**10 11 **F**3 7 11 13 15 18 28 29 31 34 35 40 45 47 57 59 61
62 63 64 68 69 70 75 76 78 79 81 85 87 89 93 97 98 107 108 110 111 115 119
127 128 129 130 131 132 133 135 143 146 147 **S** Carle Foundation, Urbana, IL
Primary Contact: Harry Brockus, Chief Executive Officer
COO: Jennifer Emmons, Chief Operating Officer & Director of Physician Services
CFO: Christina Bare, Director of Business Operations
CMO: Robert Nash, M.D., Chief of Staff
CIO: Tim Gillespie, Manager Information Systems
CHR: Jill Van Hyning, Director Human Resources
CNO: Gina Thomas, Chief Nursing Officer & Director of Patient Care Services
Web address: www.richlandmemorial.com
Control: Other not–for–profit (including NFP Corporation) **Service:** General medical and surgical

Staffed Beds: 74 Admissions: 1688 Census: 23 Outpatient Visits: 101485 Births: 224 Total Expense ($000): 52900 Payroll Expense ($000): 24519 Personnel: 448

OLYMPIA FIELDS—Cook County

★ ○　**FRANCISCAN HEALTH OLYMPIA FIELDS (140172)**, 20201 South
Crawford Avenue, Zip 60461–1010; tel. 708/747–4000, (Includes FRANCISCAN
HEALTH OLYMPIA FIELDS, 20201 Crawford Avenue, Olympia Fields, IL,
Zip 60461–1010; tel. 708/747–4000; ST. JAMES HOSPITAL AND HEALTH
CENTERS – CHICAGO HEIGHTS CAMPUS, 1423 Chicago Road, Chicago Heights,
IL, Zip 60411–3483; tel. 708/756–1000; Allan M Spooner, President and
Chief Executive Officer) (Nonreporting) **A**3 10 11 12 13 **S** Franciscan Health,
Mishawaka, IN
Primary Contact: Allan M. Spooner, President and Chief Executive Officer
CIO: Stephen Maes, Director Information Systems
Web address: www.franciscanalliance.org/hospitals/olympiafields/pages/default.aspx
Control: Church operated, Nongovernment, not–for–profit **Service:** General medical and surgical

Staffed Beds: 329

ST. JAMES HOSPITAL AND HEALTH CENTERS See Franciscan Health Olympia
Fields

OTTAWA—Lasalle County

✠ **OSF SAINT ELIZABETH MEDICAL CENTER (140110)**, 1100 East Norris Drive,
Zip 61350–1687; tel. 815/433–3100, **A**1 10 19 **F**3 11 13 15 17 19 22 30 34 35
40 45 48 49 53 56 57 59 68 70 75 76 77 79 81 82 84 85 86 87 93 94 98 99
100 101 102 103 104 105 107 108 110 111 115 116 117 118 119 120 121
129 130 131 132 135 143 144 146 148 149 153 **S** OSF Healthcare, Peoria, IL
Primary Contact: Kenneth Beutke, President
CMO: Brian S Rosborough, M.D., Chief Medical Officer
CHR: Karen M Russell, Director of Employee Relations
CNO: Pat Torrico, Chief Nursing Officer
Web address: www.osfsaintelizabeth.org
Control: Church operated, Nongovernment, not–for–profit **Service:** General medical and surgical

Staffed Beds: 87 Admissions: 4093 Census: 38 Outpatient Visits: 149570 Births: 380 Total Expense ($000): 98921 Payroll Expense ($000): 38655 Personnel: 622

PALOS HEIGHTS—Cook County

☐ **PALOS HEALTH (140062)**, 12251 South 80th Avenue, Zip 60463–0930;
tel. 708/923–4000, (Nonreporting) **A**1 2 10
Primary Contact: Terrence Moisan, M.D., Chief Executive Officer
CFO: Hugh Rose, Vice President Fiscal Management
CIO: Peggy Carroll, Chief Information Officer
CHR: Mary Denisienko, Vice President Human Resources
Web address: www.paloshealth.com/
Control: Other not–for–profit (including NFP Corporation) **Service:** General medical and surgical

Staffed Beds: 362

PANA—Christian County

★ **PANA COMMUNITY HOSPITAL (141341)**, 101 East Ninth Street,
Zip 62557–1785; tel. 217/562–2131, **A**10 18 **F**3 11 15 28 29 30 31 34 35 40
46 49 50 53 55 57 62 63 69 75 77 78 79 81 87 91 93 107 115 124 127 130
131 132 133 143 146 148 149 **P**6
Primary Contact: Trina Casner, President and Chief Executive Officer
CFO: James Moon, Chief Financial Officer
CMO: Alan Frigy, M.D., President Medical Staff
CIO: Dianne Bailey, Chief Information Officer
CHR: Luann A Funk, Administrative Assistant and Manager Human Resources
CNO: Vickie Coen, Chief Clinical Officer and Nurse Executive
Web address: www.panahospital.com
Control: Other not–for–profit (including NFP Corporation) **Service:** General medical and surgical

Staffed Beds: 22 Admissions: 435 Census: 4 Outpatient Visits: 51175 Births: 0 Total Expense ($000): 23312 Payroll Expense ($000): 11128 Personnel: 187

PARIS—Edgar County

✠ **PARIS COMMUNITY HOSPITAL (141320)**, 721 East Court Street,
Zip 61944–2460; tel. 217/465–4141, **A**1 10 18 **F**3 12 15 28 29 30 31 34 35
40 45 47 50 57 59 64 65 69 74 75 77 78 79 81 82 85 86 87 93 107 108
110 111 115 119 127 129 130 131 132 133 135 144 146 148 149 154 **P**6 **S**
Alliant Management Services, Louisville, KY
Primary Contact: Oliver Smith, President and Chief Executive Officer
CFO: Martin D. Adams, CPA, Vice President Finance and Chief Financial Officer
CIO: Ed Weeks, Manager Information Services
CHR: Cathy Thompson, Manager Human Resources
CNO: Tiffany Turner, MSN, R.N., Vice President of Nursing and Chief Nursing Officer
Web address: www.pariscommunityhospital.com
Control: Other not–for–profit (including NFP Corporation) **Service:** General medical and surgical

Staffed Beds: 25 Admissions: 483 Census: 5 Outpatient Visits: 114653 Births: 0 Total Expense ($000): 45542 Payroll Expense ($000): 23990 Personnel: 332

PARK RIDGE—Cook County

★ △ ⇑ **ADVOCATE LUTHERAN GENERAL HOSPITAL (140223)**, 1775
Dempster Street, Zip 60068–1174; tel. 847/723–2210, **A**2 3 5 7 8 10 13 21 **F**2
3 5 6 8 9 11 13 15 17 18 19 20 22 24 25 26 27 28 29 30 31 32 34 35 37 38
39 40 41 43 44 45 46 47 48 49 50 53 55 56 57 58 59 60 61 63 64 65 66 68
69 70 72 74 75 76 78 79 80 81 82 84 85 86 87 88 89 90 92 93 94 96 97 98
99 100 101 102 103 104 105 107 108 110 111 114 115 116 117 118
119 120 121 124 126 129 130 131 132 134 135 136 143 146 147 148 149
150 152 153 154 **P**6 8 **S** Advocate Aurora Health, Downers Grove, IL
Primary Contact: Terika Richardson, MPH, President
COO: Allyson Wyler, Vice President, Operations
CFO: Beth Hickey, Vice President, Finance
CMO: Leo Kelly, Vice President Medical Management
CIO: Mark Beitzel, Director Information Systems
CHR: Katie Bata, Vice President Human Resources
CNO: Jane Denten, MSN, R.N., Chief Nurse Executive
Web address: www.advocatehealth.com/luth/
Control: Other not–for–profit (including NFP Corporation) **Service:** General medical and surgical

Staffed Beds: 623 Admissions: 29154 Census: 434 Outpatient Visits: 343760 Births: 4032 Total Expense ($000): 717273 Payroll Expense ($000): 251653 Personnel: 3472

PEKIN—Tazewell County

☒ **UNITYPOINT HEALTH–PEKIN HOSPITAL (140120)**, 600 South 13th Street, Zip 61554–4936; tel. 309/347–1151, (Nonreporting) **A**1 5 10 **S** UnityPoint Health, West Des Moines, IA
Primary Contact: Deborah R. Simon, RN, Regional Chief Executive Officer
CFO: Steve Hall, Chief Financial Officer
CMO: Kathryn Kramer, M.D., President Medical Staff
CHR: Anne Dierker, Vice President Hospital Services
Web address: www.pekinhospital.org
Control: Other not–for–profit (including NFP Corporation) **Service:** General medical and surgical

Staffed Beds: 107

PEORIA—Peoria County

GREATER PEORIA SPECIALTY HOSPITAL See Kindred Hospital Peoria

☒ **KINDRED HOSPITAL PEORIA (142013)**, 500 West Romeo B Garrett Avenue, Zip 61605–2301; tel. 309/680–1500, (Nonreporting) **A**1 10 **S** Kindred Healthcare, Louisville, KY
Primary Contact: Christopher Curry, Chief Executive Officer
CMO: Michael Peil, M.D., Chief Medical Director
Web address: www.khpeoria.com/
Control: Corporation, Investor–owned (for–profit) **Service:** Acute long–term care hospital

Staffed Beds: 50

METHODIST MEDICAL CENTER OF ILLINOIS See Unitypoint Health – Peoria

☒ △ **OSF SAINT FRANCIS MEDICAL CENTER (140067)**, 530 NE Glen Oak Avenue, Zip 61637–0001; tel. 309/655–2000, (Includes CHILDREN'S HOSPITAL OF ILLINOIS, 530 NE Glen Oak Avenue, Peoria, IL, Zip 61637–0001; tel. 309/655–7171; Kelly Nierstedt, President) **A**1 2 3 5 7 8 10 **F**3 8 9 11 12 13 15 17 18 19 20 21 22 23 24 25 26 27 28 29 30 31 32 34 35 37 38 39 40 41 43 44 45 46 47 48 49 50 51 52 54 56 57 58 59 60 64 65 66 67 69 70 71 72 73 74 75 76 77 78 79 80 81 82 83 84 85 86 87 88 89 90 91 92 93 94 96 97 100 107 108 110 111 112 114 115 116 117 118 119 120 121 123 124 126 127 129 130 132 134 138 145 146 147 148 **P**6 **S** OSF Healthcare, Peoria, IL
Primary Contact: Robert G. Anderson Jr, President
CFO: Ken Harbaugh, Vice President and Chief Financial Officer
CMO: Robert T. Sparrow, M.D., Vice President, Chief Medical Officer
CHR: Jacki L. Fugitt, Director Employee Relations
CNO: Jennifer Hopwood, Vice President, Chief Nursing Officer
Web address: www.osfsaintfrancis.org
Control: Church operated, Nongovernment, not–for–profit **Service:** General medical and surgical

Staffed Beds: 629 **Admissions:** 31456 **Census:** 435 **Outpatient Visits:** 587876 **Births:** 2756 **Total Expense ($000):** 909967 **Payroll Expense ($000):** 317010 **Personnel:** 5040

☒ **UNITYPOINT HEALTH – PEORIA (140209)**, 221 NE Glen Oak Avenue, Zip 61636–4310; tel. 309/672–5522, **A**1 2 5 10 13 **F**3 9 11 12 13 15 17 18 20 22 24 26 29 30 31 32 34 35 36 38 40 43 44 45 46 47 48 49 50 53 54 56 57 58 59 60 62 63 64 68 70 74 75 76 77 78 79 81 82 84 85 86 87 89 90 92 93 96 98 99 100 101 102 104 105 107 108 110 111 114 115 116 117 118 119 120 121 126 127 129 130 131 132 134 135 136 143 144 145 146 147 148 149 150 154 **P**1 8 **S** UnityPoint Health, West Des Moines, IA
Primary Contact: Deborah R. Simon, R.N., Regional Chief Executive Officer
COO: Keith Knepp, M.D., President, UnityPoint Health – Methodist, UnityPoint Health – Proctor, UnityPoint Clinic, ProHealth Medical Group
CFO: Robert Quin, Regional Vice President Finance, and Chief Financial Officer
CMO: Gary Knepp, D.O., Regional Chief Medical Officer and Chief Quality Officer
CHR: Joy Ledbetter, Regional Chief Human Resources Officer
CNO: Jeanine R Spain, R.N., MS, Chief Operating Office, UnityPoint Health – Pekin, Regional Chief Nursing Officer
Web address: www.unitypoint.org/peoria
Control: Other not–for–profit (including NFP Corporation) **Service:** General medical and surgical

Staffed Beds: 262 **Admissions:** 13604 **Census:** 178 **Outpatient Visits:** 584298 **Births:** 1720 **Total Expense ($000):** 404253 **Payroll Expense ($000):** 186319 **Personnel:** 2436

☐ **UNITYPOINT HEALTH – PROCTOR (140013)**, 5409 North Knoxville Avenue, Zip 61614–5069; tel. 309/691–1000, (Total facility includes 24 beds in nursing home–type unit) **A**1 3 5 10 **F**3 4 5 11 15 18 20 22 24 28 29 30 34 40 45 51 53 54 57 59 60 64 70 74 75 79 81 85 86 87 93 98 103 104 107 108 110 111 114 115 118 119 128 129 130 132 135 143 145 146 148 149 150 151 152 154 **P**1 8 **S** UnityPoint Health, West Des Moines, IA
Primary Contact: Deborah R. Simon, R.N., President and Chief Executive Officer
CFO: Roger Armstrong, Vice President Finance and Chief Financial Officer
CHR: Linda K Buck, Vice President Human Resources
Web address: www.proctor.org
Control: Other not–for–profit (including NFP Corporation) **Service:** General medical and surgical

Staffed Beds: 125 **Admissions:** 3947 **Census:** 61 **Outpatient Visits:** 65553 **Births:** 0 **Total Expense ($000):** 98467 **Payroll Expense ($000):** 30286 **Personnel:** 587

PERU—Lasalle County

★ **ILLINOIS VALLEY COMMUNITY HOSPITAL (140234)**, 925 West Street, Zip 61354–2757; tel. 815/223–3300, **A**10 **F**2 3 11 13 15 18 28 29 30 31 34 35 38 40 45 46 47 48 49 50 51 54 57 59 63 64 65 66 68 69 70 74 75 76 77 79 81 82 85 87 93 96 97 104 107 110 111 114 118 119 127 129 130 131 132 133 135 143 144 146 147 148 149 154 **P**8
Primary Contact: Tommy Hobbs, Chief Executive Officer
COO: Bobby Smith, Vice President Physician Services and Quality
CFO: Lisa Lynch, Chief Financial Officer
CMO: Mark Fernandez, M.D., Chief of Staff and President Medical Staff
CIO: Nancy McDonnell, Manager Information Systems
CHR: Mary Beth Herron, Director of Human Resources
CNO: Robert Fortney, MS, R.N., Chief Nursing Officer and Vice President of Patient Care
Web address: www.ivch.org
Control: Other not–for–profit (including NFP Corporation) **Service:** General medical and surgical

Staffed Beds: 49 **Admissions:** 2444 **Census:** 26 **Outpatient Visits:** 206452 **Births:** 446 **Total Expense ($000):** 83975 **Payroll Expense ($000):** 32885 **Personnel:** 532

PINCKNEYVILLE—Perry County

★ **PINCKNEYVILLE COMMUNITY HOSPITAL (141307)**, 5383 State Route 154, Zip 62274–1099, Mailing Address: PO Box 437, Zip 62274–1099; tel. 618/357–2187, **A**10 18 **F**3 11 15 28 29 31 34 40 43 45 50 53 56 57 65 78 81 85 93 107 108 110 119 127 130 132 133 **P**6
Primary Contact: Randall W. Dauby, CPA, Chief Executive Officer
CFO: Kara Jo Carson, Chief Financial Officer
CIO: Jeff Roberts, Director Information Technology
CHR: Christie Gajewski, Director Human Resources
CNO: Eva Hopp, Chief Nurse Executive
Web address: www.pvillehosp.org/
Control: Hospital district or authority, Government, nonfederal **Service:** General medical and surgical

Staffed Beds: 17 **Admissions:** 411 **Census:** 8 **Outpatient Visits:** 46563 **Births:** 0 **Total Expense ($000):** 24853 **Payroll Expense ($000):** 9799 **Personnel:** 185

PITTSFIELD—Pike County

☒ **ILLINI COMMUNITY HOSPITAL (141315)**, 640 West Washington Street, Zip 62363–1350; tel. 217/285–2113, **A**1 10 18 **F**3 15 18 19 28 29 30 31 34 40 46 50 53 59 64 65 68 70 75 77 78 81 85 87 89 97 98 100 101 103 104 107 110 115 119 127 129 130 131 132 133 144 146 149 154 **P**6
Primary Contact: Kathy Hull, President and Chief Executive Officer
CFO: Tim Moore, Vice President Finance
CMO: Bashar Alzein, M.D., President Medical Staff
CHR: Becky Myers, Human Resources Specialist
CNO: Holly A Jones, Administrative Director Nursing Services
Web address: www.illinihospital.org
Control: Other not–for–profit (including NFP Corporation) **Service:** General medical and surgical

Staffed Beds: 25 **Admissions:** 529 **Census:** 8 **Outpatient Visits:** 7446 **Births:** 0 **Total Expense ($000):** 25600 **Payroll Expense ($000):** 9595 **Personnel:** 185

IL

PONTIAC—Livingston County

⊞ **OSF SAINT JAMES – JOHN W. ALBRECHT MEDICAL CENTER (140161)**, 2500 West Reynolds, Zip 61764–9774; tel. 815/842–2828, **A**1 10 20 **F**3 8 11 13 15 18 28 29 30 32 34 35 40 45 50 51 56 57 59 64 68 70 75 76 77 81 82 84 85 86 87 89 90 91 93 96 107 110 111 115 117 118 119 128 129 130 131 132 133 135 144 146 147 154 **S** OSF Healthcare, Peoria, IL
Primary Contact: Bradley V. Solberg, FACHE, President
CFO: Paula Corrigan, Vice President and Chief Financial Officer
CMO: John M. Rinker, Chief Medical Officer
CNO: Elizabeth Davidson, R.N., MSN, Vice President, Patient Care Services
Web address: www.osfsaintjames.org
Control: Church operated, Nongovernment, not–for–profit **Service**: General medical and surgical

> **Staffed Beds:** 42 **Admissions:** 1725 **Census:** 15 **Outpatient Visits:** 72425 **Births:** 195 **Total Expense ($000):** 47675 **Payroll Expense ($000):** 16630 **Personnel:** 263

PRINCETON—Bureau County

PERRY MEMORIAL HOSPITAL (141337), 530 Park Avenue East, Zip 61356–2598; tel. 815/875–2811, **A**10 18 **F**3 11 15 18 28 29 30 31 32 34 35 40 41 45 48 49 50 51 56 57 59 64 65 70 75 77 78 79 81 82 83 85 86 87 93 97 100 104 105 107 108 110 111 115 116 118 119 127 129 130 131 132 133 144 145 146 148 149 153 154 **P**1
Primary Contact: Annette Schnabel, FACHE, President and Chief Executive Officer
COO: Chris J. Williams, FACHE, Vice President Operations
CFO: Mike DeFoe, Chief Financial Officer
CMO: T Doran, M.D., Chief of Staff
CIO: Karen Behrens, Director Technology Services
CHR: James Lewandowski, Vice President Human Resources
Web address: www.perry–memorial.org
Control: City, Government, nonfederal **Service**: General medical and surgical

> **Staffed Beds:** 25 **Admissions:** 910 **Census:** 8 **Births:** 1 **Total Expense ($000):** 41655 **Payroll Expense ($000):** 17720

QUINCY—Adams County

⊞ △ **BLESSING HOSPITAL (140015)**, Broadway at 11th Street, Zip 62305–7005, Mailing Address: P.O. Box 7005, Zip 62305–7005; tel. 217/223–1200, (Includes BLESSING HOSPITAL, Broadway & 14th Street, Quincy, IL, Zip 62301, Mailing Address: P.O. Box 7005, Zip 62305–7005; tel. 217/223–1200) (Total facility includes 20 beds in nursing home–type unit) **A**1 2 3 5 7 10 13 **F**3 5 8 11 12 13 15 17 18 20 22 24 26 28 29 30 31 32 33 34 35 40 43 44 48 49 50 53 56 57 58 59 60 61 62 63 64 66 68 70 73 74 75 76 77 78 79 81 82 84 85 86 87 89 90 94 96 98 99 100 101 102 104 105 107 108 110 111 114 115 118 119 120 121 123 124 126 127 128 129 130 131 132 135 144 146 147 148 149 152 153 154 **P**8
Primary Contact: Maureen A. Kahn, R.N., President and Chief Executive Officer
COO: Tim Moore, Chief Accounting Officer and Vice President Ancillary Services and Finance
CFO: Patrick M Gerveler, Vice President Finance and Chief Financial Officer
CMO: George Liesmann, M.D., Chief Medical Officer
CNO: Jill K Mason, MS, R.N., Chief Nursing Officer
Web address: www.blessinghospital.org
Control: Other not–for–profit (including NFP Corporation) **Service**: General medical and surgical

> **Staffed Beds:** 306 **Admissions:** 15596 **Census:** 185 **Outpatient Visits:** 346186 **Births:** 1108 **Total Expense ($000):** 350827 **Payroll Expense ($000):** 117674 **Personnel:** 2323

RED BUD—Randolph County

⊞ **RED BUD REGIONAL HOSPITAL (141348)**, 325 Spring Street, Zip 62278–1105; tel. 618/282–3831, (Nonreporting) **A**1 10 18 **S** Quorum Health, Brentwood, TN
Primary Contact: Shane Watson, Chief Executive Officer
CFO: Zach Schmitt, Chief Financial Officer
CMO: Julie Kelley, M.D., Chief of Staff
CIO: Nick Behnken, IT Director
CHR: Lori Brooks, Director Human Resources
Web address: www.redbudregional.com
Control: Corporation, Investor–owned (for–profit) **Service**: General medical and surgical

> **Staffed Beds:** 140

ROBINSON—Crawford County

★ **CRAWFORD MEMORIAL HOSPITAL (141343)**, 1000 North Allen Street, Zip 62454–1167; tel. 618/544–3131, (Total facility includes 38 beds in nursing home–type unit) **A**10 18 **F**3 11 12 13 15 28 30 31 40 46 53 59 62 64 76 77 78 79 80 81 82 85 93 107 108 111 119 127 128 129 130 132 133 146 147 **S** QHR, Brentwood, TN
Primary Contact: Douglas Florkowski, Chief Executive Officer
CFO: Richard Carlson, Chief Financial Officer
CMO: Gary Tennison, M.D., Chief of Staff
CIO: Tim Richard, IT Coordinator
CHR: Kristi Zane, Chief Human Resources Officer
CNO: Tammy Fralicker, MS, R.N., Chief Nursing Officer
Web address: www.crawfordmh.net
Control: Hospital district or authority, Government, nonfederal **Service**: General medical and surgical

> **Staffed Beds:** 63 **Admissions:** 800 **Census:** 36 **Outpatient Visits:** 50387 **Births:** 190 **Total Expense ($000):** 48022 **Payroll Expense ($000):** 21520 **Personnel:** 376

ROCHELLE—Ogle County

⊞ **ROCHELLE COMMUNITY HOSPITAL (141312)**, 900 North Second Street, Zip 61068–1764; tel. 815/562–2181, **A**1 10 18 **F**3 15 29 30 31 34 35 40 41 45 50 53 57 59 64 68 70 74 75 77 78 81 82 85 86 87 97 107 110 115 130 132 133 135 144 146 **P**6
Primary Contact: Mark Batty, Chief Executive Officer
CFO: Lori Gutierrez, Chief Financial Officer
CMO: Jason Popp, Chief of Medical Staff
CIO: Scott Stewart, Manager Information Services
CHR: Laura Cirone, Manager Human Resources
CNO: Julie Norem, MSN, Chief Nursing Officer
Web address: www.rcha.net
Control: Other not–for–profit (including NFP Corporation) **Service**: General medical and surgical

> **Staffed Beds:** 17 **Admissions:** 493 **Census:** 4 **Outpatient Visits:** 44510 **Births:** 0 **Total Expense ($000):** 32046 **Payroll Expense ($000):** 12560 **Personnel:** 222

ROCK ISLAND—Rock Island County

⊞ △ **UNITYPOINT HEALTH – TRINITY ROCK ISLAND (140280)**, 2701 17th Street, Zip 61201–5393; tel. 309/779–5000, (Includes UNITYPOINT HEALTH – TRINITY MOLINE, 500 John Deere Road, Moline, IL, Zip 61265; tel. 309/779–5000) (Total facility includes 29 beds in nursing home–type unit) **A**1 3 7 10 **F**3 5 11 12 13 15 18 20 22 24 26 28 29 30 31 34 35 37 38 40 43 44 45 46 47 48 49 50 57 58 59 64 68 70 74 76 78 79 81 82 85 86 87 90 93 96 98 102 104 105 107 108 110 114 115 118 119 120 121 123 126 128 129 130 132 146 147 148 149 150 152 153 154 **P**8 **S** UnityPoint Health, West Des Moines, IA
Primary Contact: Richard A. Seidler, FACHE, President and Chief Executive Officer
CFO: Katie A Marchik, Chief Financial Officer
CMO: Paul McLoone, M.D., Chief Medical Officer
CHR: Cara Fuller, Vice President Human Resources
CNO: Ginger L Renkiewicz, Chief Clinical Officer, Chief Nursing Executive, and Chief Quality Officer
Web address: www.trinityqc.com
Control: Other not–for–profit (including NFP Corporation) **Service**: General medical and surgical

> **Staffed Beds:** 343 **Admissions:** 13814 **Census:** 166 **Outpatient Visits:** 347550 **Births:** 1289 **Total Expense ($000):** 326350 **Payroll Expense ($000):** 109358 **Personnel:** 2000

ROCKFORD—Winnebago County

⊞ **MERCYHEALTH HOSPITAL – ROCKTON AVENUE (140239)**, 2400 North Rockton Avenue, Zip 61103–3655; tel. 815/971–5000, **A**1 2 3 5 10 **F**3 11 12 13 18 19 20 22 24 26 27 28 29 30 31 32 34 35 39 40 41 43 44 45 46 47 48 49 50 51 53 54 55 56 57 59 63 64 65 68 70 71 72 74 75 76 77 78 79 81 82 83 84 85 86 87 88 89 91 93 97 98 100 101 102 103 107 108 111 114 115 118 119 121 122 123 126 129 130 131 132 135 145 146 147 148 149 **P**6 **S** Mercy Health System, Janesville, WI
Primary Contact: Javon R. Bea, President and Chief Executive Officer
COO: Sue Ripsch, Senior Vice President & Chief Operating Officer
CFO: John Cook, Senior Vice President & Chief Financial Officer
CMO: John T Dorsey, M.D., Vice President Physician Services and Chief Medical Officer
CIO: Ruth Yarbrough, Vice President
CHR: Heidi Elsbree, Vice President People and Culture
CNO: Doreen Timm, MSN, Senior Director and Chief Nursing Officer
Web address: www.rhsnet.org
Control: Other not–for–profit (including NFP Corporation) **Service**: General medical and surgical

> **Staffed Beds:** 288 **Admissions:** 12873 **Census:** 178 **Outpatient Visits:** 325135 **Births:** 2304 **Total Expense ($000):** 327717 **Payroll Expense ($000):** 115574 **Personnel:** 2909

Many Facility Codes have changed. Please refer to the AHA Guide Code Chart. © 2018 AHA Guide

⊠ **OSF SAINT ANTHONY MEDICAL CENTER (140233)**, 5666 East State Street, Zip 61108–2425; tel. 815/226–2000, **A**1 2 3 5 10 **F**3 11 12 13 15 16 17 18 19 20 22 24 26 28 29 30 31 32 34 35 36 37 38 40 41 43 44 45 46 49 50 51 53 55 56 57 58 59 63 64 66 70 73 74 75 76 77 78 79 81 82 84 85 86 87 89 92 93 107 108 110 111 114 115 116 117 118 119 120 121 123 124 126 129 130 131 132 135 145 146 147 148 149 150 **P**6 **S** OSF Healthcare, Peoria, IL
Primary Contact: Paula A. Carynski, MS, R.N., President
COO: James Girardy, M.D., Vice President, Chief Surgical Officer
CFO: David Stenerson, Vice President and Chief Financial Officer
CMO: Harneet Bath, M.D., Vice President, Chief Medicine Officer
CIO: Kathy Peterson, Director Information Services
CHR: Karen C Brown, Vice President Chief Operating Officer
Web address: www.osfhealth.com
Control: Church operated, Nongovernment, not–for–profit **Service**: General medical and surgical

Staffed Beds: 235 **Admissions**: 11660 **Census**: 136 **Outpatient Visits**: 230699 **Births**: 521 **Total Expense ($000)**: 330119 **Payroll Expense ($000)**: 102547 **Personnel**: 1376

⊠ **SWEDISHAMERICAN – A DIVISION OF UW HEALTH (140228)**, 1401 East State Street, Zip 61104–2315; tel. 815/968–4400, **A**1 2 3 5 10 **F**3 13 15 17 18 20 22 24 26 28 29 30 31 34 35 36 38 39 40 43 44 45 46 48 49 50 51 56 57 58 59 60 61 63 64 65 68 70 73 74 75 76 77 78 79 81 82 84 85 86 87 89 92 93 98 99 100 101 102 103 104 105 107 108 110 111 115 118 119 126 129 130 132 135 146 147 148 149 154 **P**6
Primary Contact: Michael J. Born, M.D., President and Chief Executive Officer
COO: Don Daniels, Executive Vice President and Chief Operating Officer
CFO: Patti DeWane, Vice President Finance and Treasurer
CMO: Mike Polizzotto, Chief Medical Officer
CIO: Sheryl Johnson, Chief Information Officer
CHR: Gerard Guinane, Vice President Human Resources
CNO: Ann M Gantzer, Ph.D., R.N., Vice President Patient Services and Chief Nursing Officer
Web address: www.swedishamerican.org
Control: Other not–for–profit (including NFP Corporation) **Service**: General medical and surgical

Staffed Beds: 291 **Admissions**: 14833 **Census**: 175 **Outpatient Visits**: 261865 **Births**: 2094 **Total Expense ($000)**: 329398 **Payroll Expense ($000)**: 126478 **Personnel**: 2001

⊠ **VAN MATRE HEALTHSOUTH REHABILITATION HOSPITAL (143028)**, 950 South Mulford Road, Zip 61108–4274; tel. 815/381–8500, (Nonreporting) **A**1 10 **S** Encompass Health Corporation, Birmingham, AL
Primary Contact: Jeffrey Reese, Chief Executive Officer
CFO: Tim Anderson, Controller
CMO: Ricardo Knight, Interim Medical Director
CIO: Angela Bergman, Director of Quality, Risk and Health Information Management
CHR: Dorothy Richardson, Director Human Resources
CNO: Chrisi Karcz, Chief Nursing Officer
Web address: www.healthsouth.com
Control: Corporation, Investor–owned (for–profit) **Service**: Rehabilitation

Staffed Beds: 61

ROSICLARE—Hardin County

★ **HARDIN COUNTY GENERAL HOSPITAL (141328)**, 6 Ferrell Road, Zip 62982, Mailing Address: P.O. Box 2467, Zip 62982–2467; tel. 618/285–6634, **A**10 18 **F**3 11 29 30 40 45 46 47 48 59 64 65 66 87 93 107 114 119 127 129 130 133 148
Primary Contact: Roby D. Williams, Administrator
CFO: Janie Parker, Chief Financial Officer
CMO: Marcos N Sunga, M.D., Chief of Staff
CIO: Brian Casteel, Information Technology Technician
CHR: Joyce Shelby, Manager Human Resources
CNO: Courtney Spivey, Chief Nursing Officer
Web address: www.ilhcgh.org
Control: Other not–for–profit (including NFP Corporation) **Service**: General medical and surgical

Staffed Beds: 25 **Admissions**: 554 **Census**: 8 **Outpatient Visits**: 16434 **Births**: 0 **Total Expense ($000)**: 11210 **Payroll Expense ($000)**: 6230 **Personnel**: 127

RUSHVILLE—Schuyler County

★ **SARAH D. CULBERTSON MEMORIAL HOSPITAL (141333)**, 238 South Congress Street, Zip 62681–1472; tel. 217/322–4321, **A**10 18 **F**15 28 29 31 34 40 56 57 59 65 69 75 77 81 85 93 96 97 104 107 110 114 119 125 127 129 130 132 133 135 146 148 149 **P**6
Primary Contact: Lynn E. Stambaugh, R.N., Chief Executive Officer
CFO: Alan Palo, Chief Financial Officer
CMO: Marguerite Taillefer, M.D., Acting President Medical Staff
CIO: Dan Wise, Manager Information Technology
CNO: Lisa M Downs, R.N., Chief Nursing Officer
Web address: www.cmhospital.com
Control: Hospital district or authority, Government, nonfederal **Service**: General medical and surgical

Staffed Beds: 22 **Admissions**: 228 **Census**: 2 **Outpatient Visits**: 38209 **Births**: 0 **Total Expense ($000)**: 21832 **Payroll Expense ($000)**: 8276 **Personnel**: 174

SALEM—Marion County

★ **SALEM TOWNSHIP HOSPITAL (141345)**, 1201 Ricker Drive, Zip 62881–4263; tel. 618/548–3194, (Nonreporting) **A**10 18
Primary Contact: Kendra Taylor, RN, President and Chief Executive Officer
CFO: Teresa Stroud, Chief Financial Officer
CMO: Seth Hahs, Chief of Staff
CIO: Steve Turner, Director Information Technology
CHR: Diane Boswell, Director Human Resources and Marketing
Web address: www.sthcares.org
Control: City–county, Government, nonfederal **Service**: General medical and surgical

Staffed Beds: 22

SANDWICH—Dekalb County

⊠ **NORTHWESTERN MEDICINE VALLEY WEST HOSPITAL (141340)**, 1302 North Main Street, Zip 60548–2587; tel. 815/786–8484, **A**1 10 18 **F**3 11 13 15 18 28 29 30 31 32 34 35 36 38 40 41 44 45 46 49 50 51 57 58 59 60 64 68 70 71 73 75 76 77 78 79 81 82 85 87 89 93 102 104 107 108 110 111 115 119 129 130 131 132 135 146 147 149 150 153 **S** Northwestern Memorial HealthCare, Chicago, IL
Primary Contact: Jay Anderson, President
COO: Brad Copple, Vice President Operations
CFO: Matthew J Flynn, Chief Financial Officer West Region
CMO: Michael Kulisz, D.O., Vice President, Chief Medical Officer
CIO: Heath Bell, Vice President, Information Services
CHR: Michael Vivoda, Senior Vice President Human Resources
CNO: Pamela Duffy, MSN, R.N., Vice President Operations and Chief Nursing Executive
Web address: www.nm.org
Control: Other not–for–profit (including NFP Corporation) **Service**: General medical and surgical

Staffed Beds: 25 **Admissions**: 849 **Census**: 6 **Outpatient Visits**: 38198 **Births**: 211 **Total Expense ($000)**: 37955 **Payroll Expense ($000)**: 12435 **Personnel**: 185

SHELBYVILLE—Shelby County

★ ⇑ **HSHS GOOD SHEPHERD HOSPITAL (140019)**, 200 South Cedar Street, Zip 62565–1838; tel. 217/774–3961, (Data for 303 days) **A**10 20 21 **F**3 15 28 29 34 35 40 45 57 59 62 64 77 81 93 97 107 108 110 118 119 127 129 131 132 133 146 154 **S** HSHS Hospital Sisters Health System, Springfield, IL
Primary Contact: Aaron Puchbauer, President
CFO: Marilyn Sears, Chief Financial Officer
CMO: David Oligschlaeger, Medical Staff President
CIO: Ian Kuhlman, Manager Information Technology
CHR: Amy Koehler, Director Human Resources
CNO: Michelle Oliver, Chief Nursing Executive
Web address: www.mysmh.org
Control: Church operated, Nongovernment, not–for–profit **Service**: General medical and surgical

Staffed Beds: 30 **Admissions**: 426 **Census**: 4 **Outpatient Visits**: 19599 **Births**: 0 **Total Expense ($000)**: 13165 **Payroll Expense ($000)**: 5301 **Personnel**: 162

IL

Hospital, Medicare Provider Number, Address, Telephone, Approval, Facility, and Physician Codes, Health Care System

★ American Hospital Association (AHA) membership   ○ Healthcare Facilities Accreditation Program   ⇑ Center for Improvement in Healthcare Quality Accreditation
□ The Joint Commission accreditation   ◇ DNV Healthcare Inc. accreditation   △ Commission on Accreditation of Rehabilitation Facilities (CARF) accreditation

SHILOH—St. Clair County

★ ○ **MEMORIAL HOSPITAL EAST (140307)**, 1404 Cross Street,
Zip 62269–2988; tel. 618/607–1000, **A**11 **F**3 11 13 15 18 20 22 29 30 31 34
40 45 49 54 57 59 62 64 70 74 76 77 79 81 82 84 85 87 92 93 94 107 108
111 114 115 119 130 146 147 148 **S** BJC HealthCare, Saint Louis, MO
Primary Contact: Mark J. Turner, FACHE, President
COO: Michael T McManus, Chief Operating Officer
CFO: Jane Gusmano, Interim Vice President Finance
CMO: William Casperson, Vice President Medical Affairs
CIO: Jennifer Meinkoth, Executive Director I.S.
CHR: John C Ziegler, FACHE, Vice President Human Resources
CNO: Teresa Halloran, Ph.D., R.N., Vice President Nursing Services
Web address: www.memhospeast.com
Control: Other not–for–profit (including NFP Corporation) **Service**: General
medical and surgical

Staffed Beds: 68 **Admissions:** 4840 **Census:** 46 **Outpatient Visits:** 54520
Births: 1330 **Total Expense ($000):** 91541 **Payroll Expense ($000):** 32747
Personnel: 499

SILVIS—Rock Island County

⊞ **GENESIS MEDICAL CENTER, SILVIS (140275)**, 801 Illini Drive,
Zip 61282–1893; tel. 309/281–4000, **A**1 10 **F**3 7 13 15 18 20 22 26 28 29 30
31 34 35 40 43 45 46 47 50 51 53 59 60 62 64 65 68 70 75 76 77 79 81 84
85 87 89 107 108 110 111 114 119 129 130 132 135 146 147 149 **S** Genesis
Health System, Davenport, IA
Primary Contact: Theresa Summers–Main, R.N., Interim President
CFO: Mark G Rogers, Interim Vice President Finance and Chief Financial Officer
CMO: Peter Metcalf, M.D., President Medical Staff
CIO: Robert Frieden, Vice President Information Systems
CHR: Heidi Kahly–McMahon, Vice President Human Resources
Web address: www.genesishealth.com
Control: Other not–for–profit (including NFP Corporation) **Service**: General
medical and surgical

Staffed Beds: 135 **Admissions:** 4130 **Census:** 32 **Outpatient Visits:**
114136 **Births:** 426 **Total Expense ($000):** 83218 **Payroll Expense**
($000): 24763 **Personnel:** 391

SPARTA—Randolph County

SPARTA COMMUNITY HOSPITAL (141349), 818 East Broadway Street,
Zip 62286–1820, Mailing Address: P.O. Box 297, Zip 62286–0297;
tel. 618/443–2177, **A**10 18 **F**3 11 15 28 29 34 35 40 41 45 53 57 59 62 64
65 75 77 81 93 97 107 110 111 115 119 127 130 131 132 133 135 143 146
147 149
Primary Contact: Joann Emge, Chief Executive Officer
CFO: Paul Mueller, Chief Financial Officer
CMO: Mark Pruess, M.D., Chief Medical Staff
CIO: Susan Gutjahr, Reimbursement Specialist
CHR: Darla Shawgo, Director Human Resources
CNO: Lori Clinton, Chief Nursing Officer
Web address: www.spartahospital.com
Control: Hospital district or authority, Government, nonfederal **Service**: General
medical and surgical

Staffed Beds: 25 **Admissions:** 651 **Census:** 3 **Outpatient Visits:** 96644
Births: 0 **Total Expense ($000):** 35113 **Payroll Expense ($000):** 13858
Personnel: 253

SPRING VALLEY—Bureau County

ST. MARGARET'S HOSPITAL (140143), 600 East First Street, Zip 61362–1512;
tel. 815/664–5311, **A**10 **F**3 11 13 15 28 29 30 31 32 34 35 38 40 44 45 46
47 49 53 57 58 59 63 70 74 75 76 77 79 81 82 84 85 87 90 93 96 107 108
110 111 115 118 119 129 130 131 132 133 135 143 144 146 147 148 149
P6 8 **S** Sisters of Mary of the Presentation Health System, Fargo, ND
Primary Contact: Tim Muntz, President and Chief Executive Officer
CFO: Kim D Santman, Vice President Finance
CIO: John Sabotta, Director Information Systems
CHR: Lisa R Blackburn, Director Human Resources
CNO: Mary Vega, R.N., MSN, Vice President Nursing
Web address: www.aboutsmh.org
Control: Church operated, Nongovernment, not–for–profit **Service**: General
medical and surgical

Staffed Beds: 41 **Admissions:** 1923 **Census:** 18 **Outpatient Visits:** 293554
Births: 329 **Total Expense ($000):** 81856 **Payroll Expense ($000):** 35573
Personnel: 539

SPRINGFIELD—Sangamon County

☐ **ANDREW MCFARLAND MENTAL HEALTH CENTER (144021)**, 901 East
Southwind Road, Zip 62703–5125; tel. 217/786–6994, (Nonreporting) **A**1 5 10 **S**
Division of Mental Health, Department of Human Services, Springfield, IL
Primary Contact: Karen Schweighart, R.N., MS, Administrator
CFO: Jeff Frey, Business Administrator
CMO: Kasturi Kripakaran, M.D., Medical Director
CIO: Josh Kates, Information Technology Analyst
CNO: Frances Collins, Director of Nursing
Control: State, Government, nonfederal **Service**: Psychiatric

Staffed Beds: 118

⊞ **HSHS ST. JOHN'S HOSPITAL (140053)**, 800 East Carpenter Street,
Zip 62769–0002; tel. 217/544–6464, (Includes ST. JOHN'S CHILDREN'S
HOSPITAL, 800 East Carpenter Street, Springfield, IL, Zip 62769;
tel. 217/544–6464) **A**1 2 3 5 10 **F**3 11 13 15 17 18 20 22 24 26 28 29 30 31
34 35 36 37 39 40 41 43 44 45 46 47 48 49 50 51 53 54 56 57 58 59 60 61
62 63 64 68 70 72 74 75 76 77 78 79 81 82 83 84 85 86 87 88 89 92 93 94
96 98 102 103 105 106 107 110 111 114 115 117 118 119 120 121 122 123
124 126 129 130 131 132 135 146 147 148 149 150 154 **S** HSHS Hospital
Sisters Health System, Springfield, IL
Primary Contact: Charles Lucore, M.D., President and Chief Executive Officer
COO: David R Olejniczak, Chief Operating Officer
CFO: Patty Allen, St. John's Vice President Finance
CIO: Ryan Leach, Chief Information Officer
CHR: Becky Puclik, Division Chief People Officer
CNO: Allison Kay Paul, R.N., Chief Nursing Officer
Web address: www.st–johns.org
Control: Other not–for–profit (including NFP Corporation) **Service**: General
medical and surgical

Staffed Beds: 402 **Admissions:** 18507 **Census:** 264 **Outpatient Visits:**
236546 **Births:** 2030 **Total Expense ($000):** 482943 **Payroll Expense**
($000): 144791 **Personnel:** 2500

KINDRED HOSPITAL SPRINGFIELD See Vibra Hospital of Springfield

☐ **LINCOLN PRAIRIE BEHAVIORAL HEALTH CENTER**, 5230 South Sixth Street,
Zip 62703–5128; tel. 217/585–1180, **A**1 3 5 **F**98 99 100 101 104 105 153
154 **S** Universal Health Services, Inc., King of Prussia, PA
Primary Contact: Mark Littrell, Chief Executive Officer
CFO: Chris Statz, Chief Financial Officer
CMO: Pamela Campbell, M.D., Medical Director
CNO: Renae Hale, Chief Nursing Officer
Web address: www.lincolnprairiebhc.com/
Control: Corporation, Investor–owned (for–profit) **Service**: Children's hospital psychiatric

Staffed Beds: 97 **Admissions:** 1899 **Census:** 74 **Outpatient Visits:** 10996
Births: 0 **Total Expense ($000):** 15127 **Payroll Expense ($000):** 8171
Personnel: 191

⊞ △ **MEMORIAL MEDICAL CENTER (140148)**, 701 North First Street,
Zip 62781–0001; tel. 217/788–3000, **A**1 2 3 5 7 8 10 **F**3 8 11 12 13 14 15 16
17 18 20 22 24 26 28 29 30 31 32 34 35 36 37 40 43 44 45 46 47 48 49 50
51 54 57 58 59 60 61 63 64 68 69 70 74 75 76 77 78 79 81 82 84 85 86 87
89 90 92 93 96 97 98 102 105 107 110 111 114 115 116 117 118 119 120
121 123 124 126 129 130 131 132 134 135 138 141 145 146 147 148 149 **S**
Memorial Health System, Springfield, IL
Primary Contact: Edgar J. Curtis, FACHE, President and Chief Executive Officer
COO: Charles D Callahan, Ph.D., Executive Vice President and Chief Operating Officer
CFO: Robert W Kay, Senior Vice President and Chief Financial Officer
CMO: Rajesh G Govindaiah, M.D., Chief Medical Officer
CIO: David B Graham, M.D., Senior Vice President and Chief Information Officer
CHR: Robert F Scott, Vice President and Chief Human Resources Officer
CNO: Marsha A Prater, Ph.D., R.N., Senior Vice President and Chief Nursing Officer
Web address: www.memorialmedical.com
Control: Other not–for–profit (including NFP Corporation) **Service**: General
medical and surgical

Staffed Beds: 475 **Admissions:** 25738 **Census:** 338 **Outpatient Visits:**
513327 **Births:** 1564 **Total Expense ($000):** 649838 **Payroll Expense**
($000): 212047 **Personnel:** 3741

⊞ **VIBRA HOSPITAL OF SPRINGFIELD (142014)**, 701 North Walnut Street,
Zip 62702–4931; tel. 217/528–1217, **A**1 3 10 **F**1 3 29 60 68 77 82 85 87 96
148 149 **S** Vibra Healthcare, Mechanicsburg, PA
Primary Contact: Jeffrey Paul. Weier, Chief Executive Officer
CHR: Cynthia J. Dodge, Director Human Resources
CNO: Shane Foster, R.N., Chief Nursing Officer
Web address: www.vhspringfield.com
Control: Corporation, Investor–owned (for–profit) **Service**: Acute long–term care hospital

Staffed Beds: 50 **Admissions:** 335 **Census:** 2 **Outpatient Visits:** 0
Births: 0 **Total Expense ($000):** 14698 **Payroll Expense ($000):** 7782
Personnel: 120

IL

STAUNTON—Macoupin County

COMMUNITY HOSPITAL OF STAUNTON (141306), 400 Caldwell Street,
Zip 62088–1499; tel. 618/635–2200, (Nonreporting) **A**10 18
Primary Contact: Susie Campbell, Chief Executive Officer
CFO: Brian Engelke, Chief Financial Officer
CMO: Joshua Poos, M.D., President Medical Staff
CIO: Cheryl Horner, Supervisor Data Processing
CHR: Marilyn Herbeck, Coordinator Human Resources
CNO: Roberta Brown, Chief Nursing Officer
Web address: www.stauntonhospital.org
Control: Other not–for–profit (including NFP Corporation) **Service**: General medical and surgical

Staffed Beds: 25

STERLING—Whiteside County

☒ **CGH MEDICAL CENTER (140043)**, 100 East LeFevre Road, Zip 61081–1279;
tel. 815/625–0400, **A**1 10 **F**3 7 8 11 13 15 18 20 22 28 29 30 31 34 35 40 45
47 49 50 51 57 59 62 64 68 70 74 76 78 79 81 82 85 86 87 89 93 97 107
108 110 111 112 115 116 117 118 119 124 129 130 132 133 135 144 145
146 147 148 **P**6
Primary Contact: Paul Steinke, D.O., President and Chief Executive Officer
CFO: Ben Schaab, Vice President, Chief Financial Officer
CMO: Keith Martin, M.D., Vice President, Chief Medical Officer
CIO: Randy Davis, Vice President and Chief Information Officer
CHR: Paul Steinke, D.O., President and Chief Executive Officer
CNO: Kristie A Geil, Vice President, Chief Nursing Officer
Web address: www.cghmc.com
Control: City, Government, nonfederal **Service**: General medical and surgical

Staffed Beds: 99 **Admissions**: 4101 **Census**: 37 **Outpatient Visits**: 376775
Births: 552 **Total Expense ($000)**: 206354 **Payroll Expense ($000)**: 92026
Personnel: 1012

STREAMWOOD—Cook County

☐ **STREAMWOOD BEHAVIORAL HEALTH CENTER (144034)**, 1400 East Irving
Park Road, Zip 60107–3203; tel. 630/837–9000, **A**1 10 **F**98 99 100 101 104
105 130 153 **P**6 **S** Universal Health Services, Inc., King of Prussia, PA
Primary Contact: Ron Weglarz, Chief Executive Officer and Managing Director
CMO: Joseph McNally, M.D., Medical Director
CHR: Joseph Rinke, Director Human Resources
CNO: Olieth Lightbourne, Chief Nursing Officer
Web address: www.streamwoodhospital.com
Control: Corporation, Investor–owned (for–profit) **Service**: Psychiatric

Staffed Beds: 178 **Admissions**: 3811 **Census**: 113 **Outpatient Visits**:
32164 **Births**: 0 **Total Expense ($000)**: 31828 **Payroll Expense**
($000): 19691 **Personnel**: 370

SYCAMORE—Dekalb County

☒ **KINDRED HOSPITAL–SYCAMORE (142006)**, 225 Edward Street,
Zip 60178–2137; tel. 815/895–2144, (Nonreporting) **A**1 10 **S** Kindred
Healthcare, Louisville, KY
Primary Contact: Jim Cohick, Chief Executive Officer
CFO: Jay Schweikart, Chief Financial Officer
CMO: Manav Salwan, Medical Director
CNO: Beth Ann Navarro, Chief Clinical Officer
Web address: www.kindredhospitalsyc.com/
Control: Corporation, Investor–owned (for–profit) **Service**: Acute long–term care hospital

Staffed Beds: 69

TAYLORVILLE—Christian County

☒ **TAYLORVILLE MEMORIAL HOSPITAL (141339)**, 201 East Pleasant Street,
Zip 62568–1597; tel. 217/824–3331, **A**1 3 5 10 18 **F**8 15 28 29 30 34 35 40
45 46 50 57 59 64 75 77 79 81 87 89 93 103 107 108 110 111 115 119 129
130 131 132 133 144 146 149 **P**5 **S** Memorial Health System, Springfield, IL
Primary Contact: Kimberly L. Bourne, Chief Executive Officer
CFO: Andrew Costic, Regional Chief Financial Officer
CHR: Michelle Long, Regional Human Resource Manager
CNO: Tracy Seaton, Director of Nursing
Web address: www.taylorvillememorial.org
Control: Other not–for–profit (including NFP Corporation) **Service**: General
medical and surgical

Staffed Beds: 25 **Admissions**: 786 **Census**: 8 **Outpatient Visits**: 36894
Births: 0 **Total Expense ($000)**: 38274 **Payroll Expense ($000)**: 14964
Personnel: 269

URBANA—Champaign County

★ △ ⇧ **CARLE FOUNDATION HOSPITAL (140091)**, 611 West Park Street,
Zip 61801–2529; tel. 217/383–3311, **A**2 3 5 7 10 13 21 **F**3 8 12 15 17 18
20 22 24 26 28 29 30 31 34 35 40 43 44 45 46 47 48 49 50 51 53 56 57
58 59 60 61 62 63 64 68 70 72 73 74 75 76 77 78 79 80 81 82 84 85 86
87 89 90 91 92 93 96 97 104 107 108 110 111 114 115 117 118 119 120
121 123 124 126 129 130 131 132 145 146 148 149 154 **S** Carle Foundation,
Urbana, IL
Primary Contact: James C. Leonard, M.D., President and Chief Executive Officer
COO: John Snyder, Executive Vice President and System Chief Operating Officer
CFO: Dennis Hesch, Executive Vice President Finance, System Chief Financial
Officer
CMO: Matthew Gibb, M.D., Executive Vice President and System Chief Medical
Officer
CIO: Rick Rinehart, Vice President, Chief Information Officer
CHR: L J Fallon, JD, Executive Vice President, Chief Legal and Human Resources Officer
CNO: Pamela Bigler, R.N., Senior Vice President, Chief Nursing Officer
Web address: www.carle.org
Control: Other not–for–profit (including NFP Corporation) **Service**: General
medical and surgical

Staffed Beds: 391 **Admissions**: 23714 **Census**: 312 **Outpatient Visits**:
1335217 **Births**: 2659 **Total Expense ($000)**: 723567 **Payroll Expense**
($000): 188498 **Personnel**: 3161

☒ △ **OSF HEART OF MARY MEDICAL CENTER (140113)**, 1400 West Park
Street, Zip 61801–2396, Mailing Address: P.O. Box 6259, Peoria, Zip 61601;
tel. 217/337–2000, **A**1 3 5 7 10 **F**3 8 12 13 15 18 20 22 24 26 28 29 30 35
40 45 46 47 48 49 57 59 64 68 70 72 74 75 76 79 81 82 87 89 90 92 94 96
97 98 100 102 103 107 108 110 111 112 113 114 115 119 126 130 132 146
147 148 **S** OSF Healthcare, Peoria, IL
Primary Contact: Jared Rogers, M.D., President and Chief Executive Officer
CFO: Lucas Morton, Regional Chief Financial Officer
CMO: Vincent Kucich, FACHE, FACS, M.D., Chief Medical Officer
CIO: Paula Keele, Manager Information Systems
CHR: Michael Zimmerman, Human Resource Officer
CNO: Molly Nicholson, MS, R.N., Chief Nurse Executive
Web address: www.presencehealth.org/covenant
Control: Church operated, Nongovernment, not–for–profit **Service**: General
medical and surgical

Staffed Beds: 181 **Admissions**: 6684 **Census**: 73 **Births**: 732 **Total**
Expense ($000): 126161 **Payroll Expense ($000)**: 35824 **Personnel**: 627

VANDALIA—Fayette County

☒ **FAYETTE COUNTY HOSPITAL (141346)**, 650 West Taylor Street,
Zip 62471–1296; tel. 618/283–1231, (Total facility includes 85 beds in nursing
home–type unit) **A**1 10 18 **F**3 7 11 15 28 29 30 34 40 45 49 57 59 77 80 81
86 93 107 110 111 112 114 116 117 119 127 128 130 132 133 144 145 146
P5 **S** Alliant Management Services, Louisville, KY
Primary Contact: Gregory D. Starnes, Chief Executive Officer
CFO: David H Wiesman, Interim Chief Financial Officer
CMO: Joseph Blaser, Chief Medical Officer
CIO: Gary Hood, Chief Information Officer
CHR: Susan Crawford, Manager Human Resources
CNO: Marci Barth, Chief Nursing Officer
Web address: www.fayettecountyhospital.org
Control: Corporation, Investor–owned (for–profit) **Service**: General medical and
surgical

Staffed Beds: 110 **Admissions**: 677 **Census**: 51 **Outpatient Visits**: 45285
Births: 0 **Total Expense ($000)**: 28421 **Payroll Expense ($000)**: 11377
Personnel: 263

WATSEKA—Iroquois County

☐ **IROQUOIS MEMORIAL HOSPITAL AND RESIDENT HOME (140167)**, 200
Fairman Avenue, Zip 60970–1644; tel. 815/432–5841, (Total facility includes 35
beds in nursing home–type unit) **A**1 3 10 20 **F**3 7 11 14 15 18 20 28 29 30 31
34 35 38 40 43 45 46 49 56 57 59 62 63 65 69 70 75 77 81 82 85 86 87
92 93 97 107 108 110 115 119 127 128 129 130 132 133 135 145 146 147
154 **P**4
Primary Contact: Tim Smith, Chief Executive Officer
CFO: Lori Yelenick, Chief Financial Officer
CMO: Aravind Reddy, M.D., Chief of Staff
CHR: Jamie Neumann, Director Human Resources
CNO: Mary Cahoe, Chief Nursing Officer
Web address: www.imhrh.org
Control: Other not–for–profit (including NFP Corporation) **Service**: General
medical and surgical

Staffed Beds: 60 **Admissions**: 782 **Census**: 32 **Outpatient Visits**: 34959
Births: 85 **Total Expense ($000)**: 35372 **Payroll Expense ($000)**: 17498
Personnel: 311

IL

WAUKEGAN—Lake County

☒ **VISTA MEDICAL CENTER EAST (140084)**, 1324 North Sheridan Road, Zip 60085–2161; tel. 847/360–3000, **A**1 2 3 5 10 **F**3 12 13 15 18 20 22 24 26 28 29 30 31 34 35 38 39 40 41 43 45 46 47 48 49 50 57 59 68 70 74 76 78 79 81 82 84 85 87 89 93 100 102 107 108 110 111 114 115 119 126 129 130 132 146 147 148 **S** Quorum Health, Brentwood, TN
Primary Contact: Norman F. Stephens, Interim Chief Executive Officer
COO: Kim Needham, Assistant Chief Executive Officer
CFO: Kerry Hill, Chief Financial Officer
CMO: Daniel Liesen, M.D., Chief Medical Officer
CHR: Michael R Isaacs, Vice President Human Resources
CNO: Trisha E Musich, R.N., Chief Nursing Officer
Web address: www.vistahealth.com
Control: Corporation, Investor–owned (for–profit) **Service**: General medical and surgical

Staffed Beds: 190 **Admissions**: 10159 **Census**: 115 **Outpatient Visits**: 128340 **Births**: 1500 **Total Expense ($000)**: 147839 **Payroll Expense ($000)**: 53072 **Personnel**: 839

☒ △ **VISTA MEDICAL CENTER WEST (140033)**, 2615 Washington Street, Zip 60085–4988; tel. 847/249–3900, **A**1 7 10 **F**29 38 40 43 56 64 68 77 87 96 98 99 101 102 103 104 105 107 119 130 153
Primary Contact: Norman F. Stephens, Interim Chief Executive Officer
COO: Kim Needham, Assistant Chief Executive Officer
CFO: Kerry Hill, Chief Financial Officer
CMO: Daniel Liesen, M.D., Chief Medical Officer
CHR: Michael R Isaacs, Vice President Human Resources
CNO: Trisha E Musich, R.N., Chief Nursing Officer
Web address: www.vistahealth.com
Control: Corporation, Investor–owned (for–profit) **Service**: Psychiatric

Staffed Beds: 42 **Admissions**: 1255 **Census**: 25 **Outpatient Visits**: 11461 **Births**: 0 **Total Expense ($000)**: 19334 **Payroll Expense ($000)**: 6504 **Personnel**: 62

WHEATON—Du Page County

☒ △ **NORTHWESTERN MEDICINE MARIANJOY REHABILITATION HOSPITAL (143027)**, 26 West 171 Roosevelt Road, Zip 60187–0795, Mailing Address: P.O. Box 795, Zip 60187–0795; tel. 630/909–8000, (Total facility includes 27 beds in nursing home–type unit) **A**1 3 7 10 **F**3 11 29 30 34 35 36 44 50 53 54 57 58 64 68 74 75 77 79 82 86 87 90 91 92 93 95 96 119 128 130 131 132 143 146 148 149 **P**6 **S** Northwestern Memorial HealthCare, Chicago, IL
Primary Contact: Brian J. Lemon, President
COO: John Brady, Vice President Physician Services and Organizational Planning
CFO: Michael Hedderman, Senior Vice President Finance and Chief Financial Officer
CMO: Jeffrey Oken, Vice President of Medical Affairs
CIO: Robert Sinickas, Director Information Services
CHR: Teresa Chapman, Vice President Human Resources
Web address: www.marianjoy.org
Control: Other not–for–profit (including NFP Corporation) **Service**: Rehabilitation

Staffed Beds: 127 **Admissions**: 3017 **Census**: 117 **Outpatient Visits**: 59899 **Births**: 0 **Total Expense ($000)**: 95125 **Payroll Expense ($000)**: 55974 **Personnel**: 696

WINFIELD—DuPage County

☒ **NORTHWESTERN MEDICINE CENTRAL DUPAGE HOSPITAL (140242)**, 25 North Winfield Road, Zip 60190; tel. 630/933–1600, (Includes BEHAVIORAL HEALTH CENTER, 27 West 350 High Lake Road, Winfield, IL, Zip 60190; tel. 630/653–4000) **A**1 2 3 5 10 **F**3 4 5 6 8 9 11 12 13 15 17 18 19 20 22 24 26 28 29 30 31 32 34 35 36 37 38 39 40 41 43 44 45 46 47 48 49 50 54 55 57 58 59 60 64 65 68 70 72 73 74 75 76 77 78 79 81 82 84 85 86 87 88 89 91 92 93 94 96 97 98 99 100 101 102 103 104 105 107 108 110 111 112 114 115 116 117 118 119 120 121 122 123 124 126 129 130 131 132 135 144 146 147 148 149 152 153 154 **P**6 **S** Northwestern Memorial HealthCare, Chicago, IL
Primary Contact: Brian J. Lemon, President
CFO: John Orsini, Executive Vice President and Chief Financial Officer
CMO: Kevin Most, D.O., Vice President Medical Affairs
CIO: Daniel F Kinsella, Vice President and Chief Information Officer
Web address: www.nm.org
Control: Other not–for–profit (including NFP Corporation) **Service**: General medical and surgical

Staffed Beds: 413 **Admissions**: 21657 **Census**: 263 **Outpatient Visits**: 1411384 **Births**: 2993 **Total Expense ($000)**: 983874 **Payroll Expense ($000)**: 347129 **Personnel**: 6530

WOODSTOCK—Mchenry County

★ **CENTEGRA HOSPITAL – WOODSTOCK (140176)**, 3701 Doty Road, Zip 60098–7509, Mailing Address: P.O. Box 1990, Zip 60098–1990; tel. 815/338–2500, **A**10 **F**3 4 5 11 12 15 18 28 29 30 31 34 35 37 38 39 40 41 44 45 47 49 50 51 54 57 58 59 64 68 69 70 74 75 78 79 81 82 85 86 87 89 92 93 98 100 101 102 103 105 107 108 110 111 114 118 119 129 130 131 132 143 146 147 148 152 153 **P**6 8 **S** Centegra Health System, Crystal Lake, IL
Primary Contact: Michael S. Eesley, Chief Executive Officer
COO: Jason Sciarro, President and Chief Operating Officer
CFO: David Tomlinson, Executive Vice President Chief Financial Officer and Chief Information Officer
CMO: Irfan Hafiz, Vice President Medical Affairs
CIO: David Tomlinson, Senior Vice President, Chief Information Officer
CHR: Bernadette S Szczepanski, Senior Vice President Human Resources
Web address: www.centegra.org
Control: Other not–for–profit (including NFP Corporation) **Service**: General medical and surgical

Staffed Beds: 104 **Admissions**: 4335 **Census**: 54 **Outpatient Visits**: 59366 **Births**: 0 **Total Expense ($000)**: 104274 **Payroll Expense ($000)**: 40935 **Personnel**: 483

ZION—Lake County

☒ **MIDWESTERN REGIONAL MEDICAL CENTER (140100)**, 2520 Elisha Avenue, Zip 60099–2587; tel. 847/872–4561, **A**1 2 10 **F**3 7 8 15 18 26 28 29 30 31 33 34 36 37 38 40 44 45 46 48 49 50 55 57 58 59 60 64 68 70 74 75 77 78 79 81 82 85 86 87 92 93 94 95 107 108 110 111 115 117 118 119 120 121 123 124 126 129 130 132 133 142 143 144 146 147 148 154 **P**6 **S** Cancer Treatment Centers of America, Schaumburg, IL
Primary Contact: Scott Jones, President and Chief Executive Officer
COO: Pete Govorchin, Senior Vice President Operations
CFO: Cecilia Taylor, Chief Financial Officer
CMO: Bradford Tan, M.D., Chief Medical Officer
CHR: Amy VanStrien, Director Talent Operations
CNO: Jacklynn Lesniak, R.N., MS, Vice President Patient Care Services and Chief Nursing Officer
Web address: www.cancercenter.com
Control: Corporation, Investor–owned (for–profit) **Service**: Cancer

Staffed Beds: 72 **Admissions**: 1679 **Census**: 25 **Outpatient Visits**: 34244 **Births**: 0 **Personnel**: 973

IL

Many Facility Codes have changed. Please refer to the AHA Guide Code Chart.   © 2018 AHA Guide

INDIANA

ANDERSON—Madison County

⊠ **COMMUNITY HOSPITAL OF ANDERSON & MADISON COUNTY (150113)**, 1515 North Madison Avenue, Zip 46011–3453; tel. 765/298–4242, **A**1 2 10 **F**3 10 11 13 15 18 20 22 28 29 30 31 32 34 35 40 43 44 46 49 50 51 54 55 56 57 58 59 60 61 64 68 70 74 75 76 77 78 79 81 82 85 86 87 89 93 107 108 109 110 111 114 115 119 120 121 122 123 126 129 130 132 135 143 144 146 147 148 149 **P**6 **S** Community Health Network, Indianapolis, IN
Primary Contact: Beth S. Tharp, R.N., President and Chief Executive Officer
CFO: John B. Harris, Vice President Finance and Chief Financial Officer
CHR: Michael Harpe, Vice President Human Resources
CNO: Carol Whitesel, MSN, R.N., Vice President Patient Care Services and Chief Nursing Officer
Web address: www.communityanderson.com
Control: Other not–for–profit (including NFP Corporation) **Service:** General medical and surgical

Staffed Beds: 140 **Admissions:** 6200 **Census:** 67 **Outpatient Visits:** 216741 **Births:** 828 **Total Expense ($000):** 153203 **Payroll Expense ($000):** 65892 **Personnel:** 1152

⊠ **ST. VINCENT ANDERSON (150088)**, 2015 Jackson Street, Zip 46016–4339; tel. 765/649–2511, **A**1 2 10 **F**3 4 5 8 11 13 14 15 18 20 22 28 29 30 31 32 34 35 36 38 39 40 43 44 45 46 49 50 51 54 55 56 57 58 59 60 61 64 65 66 68 70 74 75 76 77 78 79 81 82 84 85 86 87 89 90 92 93 94 96 98 99 100 101 102 103 104 105 106 107 108 110 111 114 115 116 117 118 119 120 121 123 124 129 130 132 134 135 145 146 147 148 149 151 153 154 **P**6 **S** Ascension Healthcare, Saint Louis, MO
Primary Contact: Mike K. Schroyer, FACHE, MSN, R.N., President
COO: Nick Theohares, Executive Director, Operations
CFO: Laura L Rose, Chief Financial Officer
CIO: Robert A. Pope, Director I
CHR: Ross Brodhead, Senior Director, Human Resource
Web address: www.stvincent.org/anderson
Control: Church operated, Nongovernment, not–for–profit **Service:** General medical and surgical

Staffed Beds: 141 **Admissions:** 6309 **Census:** 95 **Outpatient Visits:** 181982 **Births:** 413 **Total Expense ($000):** 196440 **Payroll Expense ($000):** 62135 **Personnel:** 703

ANGOLA—Steuben County

★ **CAMERON MEMORIAL COMMUNITY HOSPITAL (151315)**, 416 East Maumee Street, Zip 46703–2015; tel. 260/665–2141, **A**10 18 **F**3 11 13 15 18 28 29 30 34 35 40 44 45 50 53 57 59 62 63 65 68 75 76 77 79 81 85 86 87 90 93 97 103 104 107 108 110 111 114 115 117 119 125 127 129 130 131 132 133 144 146 149 **P**6
Primary Contact: Connie McCahill, R.N., President and Chief Executive Officer
CFO: Douglas Bomba, Chief Financial Officer
CMO: Jon Alley, D.O., President Medical Staff
CIO: Kris Keen, Chief Information Officer
CHR: Nancy Covell, Director Human Resources
CNO: Sharon Springer, Chief Nursing Officer
Web address: www.cameronmch.com
Control: Other not–for–profit (including NFP Corporation) **Service:** General medical and surgical

Staffed Beds: 25 **Admissions:** 1359 **Census:** 10 **Outpatient Visits:** 118695 **Births:** 192 **Total Expense ($000):** 62677 **Payroll Expense ($000):** 22388 **Personnel:** 388

AUBURN—Dekalb County

★ **DEKALB HEALTH (150045)**, 1316 East Seventh Street, Zip 46706–2515, Mailing Address: P.O. Box 542, Zip 46706–0542; tel. 260/925–4600, **A**10 **F**3 7 11 13 15 28 29 32 34 35 36 40 45 53 56 57 59 62 63 64 70 73 75 76 77 79 81 82 84 85 86 87 89 93 97 107 108 110 111 114 115 119 129 130 132 135 144 146 147 148 149 **P**4 6
Primary Contact: Natasha Eicher, President and Chief Executive Officer
CMO: Emilio Vazquez, M.D., Chief Medical Officer
CIO: Ed Hobbs, Director Information Services
CNO: Donna S Wisemore, R.N., Vice President and Chief Nursing Officer
Web address: www.dekalbhealth.com
Control: Other not–for–profit (including NFP Corporation) **Service:** General medical and surgical

Staffed Beds: 56 **Admissions:** 2440 **Census:** 20

NORTHEASTERN CENTER (154050), 1850 Wesley Road, Zip 46706–3653; tel. 260/927–0726, (Nonreporting) **A**10
Primary Contact: Jerry Hollister, Chief Executive Officer
Web address: www.necmh.org
Control: Other not–for–profit (including NFP Corporation) **Service:** Psychiatric

Staffed Beds: 16

AVON—Hendricks County

CLARIAN WEST MEDICAL CENTER See Indiana University Health West Hospital

⊠ **INDIANA UNIVERSITY HEALTH WEST HOSPITAL (150158)**, 1111 North Ronald Reagan Parkway, Zip 46123–7085; tel. 317/217–3000, **A**1 2 3 5 10 **F**3 13 15 18 22 26 28 29 30 34 35 40 41 46 47 48 49 50 51 57 59 64 70 73 74 75 76 77 78 79 81 82 85 86 87 89 93 100 107 110 111 113 114 115 119 120 121 129 130 132 135 146 147 148 **S** Indiana University Health, Indianapolis, IN
Primary Contact: Arthur Vasquez, President
CMO: Andrew Nigh, M.D., Chief of Staff
CHR: Tamarah Brownlee, Vice President, Human Resources
CNO: Lisa Sparks, R.N., Chief Nursing Officer and Vice President Patient Care Services
Web address: www.iuhealth.org
Control: Other not–for–profit (including NFP Corporation) **Service:** General medical and surgical

Staffed Beds: 127 **Admissions:** 7010 **Census:** 82 **Outpatient Visits:** 250645 **Births:** 986 **Total Expense ($000):** 159641 **Payroll Expense ($000):** 48278 **Personnel:** 746

BATESVILLE—Ripley County

⊠ **MARGARET MARY HEALTH (151329)**, 321 Mitchell Avenue, Zip 47006–8909, Mailing Address: P.O. Box 226, Zip 47006–0226; tel. 812/934–6624, **A**1 2 10 18 **F**3 13 15 28 30 31 34 35 36 40 45 46 50 54 56 59 62 63 64 65 70 75 76 77 78 81 85 86 87 93 107 108 110 111 114 115 118 119 121 123 129 130 131 132 135 144 146 148 **P**6
Primary Contact: Timothy L. Putnam, FACHE, President and Chief Executive Officer
CFO: Brian Daeger, Chief Financial Officer and Vice President Financial Services
CMO: Charles McGovern, Chief of Staff
CIO: Trisha Prickel, Information Systems Director
CHR: Kimberly Inscho, Vice President Human Resources and Marketing
CNO: Elizabeth Leising, Chief Nursing Officer and Vice President Patient Services
Web address: www.mmhealth.org
Control: Other not–for–profit (including NFP Corporation) **Service:** General medical and surgical

Staffed Beds: 25 **Admissions:** 1614 **Census:** 12 **Outpatient Visits:** 176366 **Births:** 460 **Total Expense ($000):** 96887 **Payroll Expense ($000):** 42278

BEDFORD—Lawrence County

BEDFORD REGIONAL MEDICAL CENTER See Indiana University Health Bedford Hospital

DUNN MEMORIAL HOSPITAL See St. Vincent Dunn Hospital

⊠ **INDIANA UNIVERSITY HEALTH BEDFORD HOSPITAL (151328)**, 2900 West 16th Street, Zip 47421–3583; tel. 812/275–1200, **A**1 2 10 18 **F**3 7 11 15 18 28 29 30 31 34 35 36 38 40 41 44 45 46 49 50 53 57 59 64 65 68 70 74 75 77 78 79 81 85 86 87 91 92 93 94 97 102 107 108 110 111 115 118 119 129 131 132 133 134 135 146 149 154 **S** Indiana University Health, Indianapolis, IN
Primary Contact: Bradford W. Dykes, President and Chief Executive Officer
CFO: Mike Craig, Vice President, Chief Financial Officer
CMO: Joanne F Smart, M.D., Director Medical Affairs
CHR: Bruce Wade, Vice President Human Resources
CNO: Brenda Davis, Vice President Patient Services
Web address: www.iuhealth.org
Control: Other not–for–profit (including NFP Corporation) **Service:** General medical and surgical

Staffed Beds: 25 **Admissions:** 1003 **Census:** 10 **Outpatient Visits:** 79205 **Births:** 0 **Total Expense ($000):** 51241 **Payroll Expense ($000):** 14593 **Personnel:** 212

Hospital, Medicare Provider Number, Address, Telephone, Approval, Facility, and Physician Codes, Health Care System

★ American Hospital Association (AHA) membership
☐ The Joint Commission accreditation
○ Healthcare Facilities Accreditation Program
◇ DNV Healthcare Inc. accreditation
⇧ Center for Improvement in Healthcare Quality Accreditation
△ Commission on Accreditation of Rehabilitation Facilities (CARF) accreditation

IN

✠ **ST. VINCENT DUNN HOSPITAL (151335)**, 1600 23rd Street, Zip 47421–4704; tel. 812/275–3331, (Nonreporting) **A**1 10 18 **S** Ascension Healthcare, Saint Louis, MO
Primary Contact: Jerry Laue, Administrator
CFO: Crystal Plano, Controller
CMO: Deborah W Craton, M.D., Chief Medical Officer
CIO: Chad Damon, Contractor
CHR: Darci Medlock, Manager Human Resources
CNO: Michelle Dotts–McCool, Chief Nursing Officer
Web address: www.stvincent.org/St–Vincent–Dunn/Default.aspx
Control: Other not–for–profit (including NFP Corporation) **Service:** General medical and surgical

Staffed Beds: 25

BLOOMINGTON—Monroe County

BLOOMINGTON HOSPITAL See Indiana University Health Bloomington Hospital

✠ **BLOOMINGTON MEADOWS HOSPITAL (154041)**, 3600 North Prow Road, Zip 47404–1616; tel. 812/331–8000, **A**1 10 **F**4 5 98 99 101 102 104 105 151 152 153 154 **S** Universal Health Services, Inc., King of Prussia, PA
Primary Contact: Christopher Downers, Chief Executive Officer
CFO: Becky T Nyberg, Chief Financial Officer
CMO: David Gilliam, M.D., Medical Director
CHR: Amanda Shettlesworth, Director Human Resources
CNO: Penny Caswell, Director of Nursing
Web address: www.bloomingtonmeadows.com
Control: Corporation, Investor–owned (for–profit) **Service:** Psychiatric

Staffed Beds: 71 Admissions: 2322 Census: 45 Outpatient Visits: 6036 Births: 0 Total Expense ($000): 11732 Payroll Expense ($000): 7213 Personnel: 143

✠ △ **INDIANA UNIVERSITY HEALTH BLOOMINGTON HOSPITAL (150051)**, 601 West Second Street, Zip 47403–2317, Mailing Address: P.O. Box 1149, Zip 47402–1149; tel. 812/336–6821, **A**1 2 7 10 19 **F**3 7 8 11 12 13 17 18 19 20 22 24 26 28 29 30 31 32 34 35 38 40 43 45 46 47 48 49 50 53 54 55 57 59 61 62 63 64 65 69 70 72 74 75 76 77 78 79 81 82 84 85 86 87 89 90 92 93 94 97 98 100 101 102 104 107 108 111 114 115 119 120 121 124 126 129 130 131 132 135 143 144 146 147 148 149 153 154 **P**6 **S** Indiana University Health, Indianapolis, IN
Primary Contact: Brian T. Shockney, FACHE, Interim President
COO: Brian T Shockney, FACHE, Chief Operating Officer
CFO: Mike Craig, Chief Financial Officer
CMO: Ken Marshall, M.D., Chief Medical Officer
CIO: Mark W McMath, Chief Information Officer
CHR: Steven D Deckard, Vice President Human Resources
Web address: www.iuhealth.org
Control: Other not–for–profit (including NFP Corporation) **Service:** General medical and surgical

Staffed Beds: 274 Admissions: 11864 Census: 150 Outpatient Visits: 226831 Births: 1950 Total Expense ($000): 333818 Payroll Expense ($000): 108665 Personnel: 1696

✠ **MONROE HOSPITAL (150183)**, 4011 South Monroe Medical Park Boulevard, Zip 47424; tel. 812/825–1111, **A**1 10 **F**3 15 18 20 29 34 35 40 41 45 46 47 48 49 50 56 57 59 64 65 68 70 75 79 80 81 85 86 87 91 97 107 108 109 110 111 114 115 119 126 135 144 148 149 154 **S** Prime Healthcare, Ontario, CA
Primary Contact: Nancy Bakewell, Administrator
CFO: Hilary Dolbee, Chief Financial Officer
CMO: Amandeep Singh, Chief Medical Officer
CIO: LaDonna Cagle, HIM Appeals Coordinator III
CHR: Karyn Batdorf, Director of Human Resources
CNO: Nancy Bakewell, Chief Nursing Officer
Web address: www.monroehospital.com
Control: Corporation, Investor–owned (for–profit) **Service:** General medical and surgical

Staffed Beds: 32 Admissions: 1239 Census: 12 Outpatient Visits: 27201 Births: 0 Total Expense ($000): 25291 Payroll Expense ($000): 9706 Personnel: 303

BLUFFTON—Wells County

✠ **BLUFFTON REGIONAL MEDICAL CENTER (150075)**, 303 South Main Street, Zip 46714–2503; tel. 260/824–3210, (Total facility includes 13 beds in nursing home–type unit) **A**1 10 19 **F**3 13 15 18 28 29 30 34 35 40 41 45 49 50 57 59 64 70 74 75 76 79 81 85 86 87 89 91 93 94 96 97 107 108 110 111 114 119 128 129 130 132 135 146 147 148 149 150 154 **S** Community Health Systems, Inc., Franklin, TN
Primary Contact: Brent Parsons, Chief Executive Officer
COO: Julie Thompson, Chief Operating Officer and Chief Nursing Officer
CFO: Larry W DeBolt, Chief Financial Officer
CMO: Harish Ardeshna, Pulmonologist & Chief Medical Officer
CHR: Patricia Sprinkle, Vice President, Human Resources
CNO: Julie Thompson, Chief Operating Officer and Chief Nursing Officer
Web address: www.blufftonregional.com
Control: Corporation, Investor–owned (for–profit) **Service:** General medical and surgical

Staffed Beds: 54 Admissions: 1707 Census: 22 Outpatient Visits: 54956 Births: 206 Total Expense ($000): 34855 Payroll Expense ($000): 13042 Personnel: 222

BOONVILLE—Warrick County

✠ **ST. VINCENT WARRICK HOSPITAL (151325)**, 1116 Millis Avenue, Zip 47601–2204; tel. 812/897–4800, (Nonreporting) **A**1 10 18 **S** Ascension Healthcare, Saint Louis, MO
Primary Contact: Kathy J. Hall, Administrator
CFO: Crystal Heaton, Director of Finance
CNO: Karen Waters, Chief Nursing Officer
Web address: www.stmarys.org/warrick
Control: Other not–for–profit (including NFP Corporation) **Service:** General medical and surgical

Staffed Beds: 35

BRAZIL—Clay County

✠ **ST. VINCENT CLAY HOSPITAL (151309)**, 1206 East National Avenue, Zip 47834–2797, Mailing Address: 1206 East National Ave, Zip 47834–0489; tel. 812/442–2500, **A**1 10 18 **F**3 12 15 18 29 30 34 35 40 45 50 57 59 65 68 75 77 79 81 82 85 86 87 107 108 110 111 115 119 128 130 132 133 135 146 148 154 **S** Ascension Healthcare, Saint Louis, MO
Primary Contact: Jerry Laue, Administrator
CFO: Wayne Knight, Director Finance
CMO: Stephen Tharp, Regional Chief Medical Officer
CHR: Lainie Collins, Human Resources Partner
CNO: Paulette Sue Gaskill, Executive Director of Nursing
Web address: www.stvincent.org
Control: Church operated, Nongovernment, not–for–profit **Service:** General medical and surgical

Staffed Beds: 25 Admissions: 311 Census: 4 Outpatient Visits: 33188 Births: 0 Total Expense ($000): 18330 Payroll Expense ($000): 5739 Personnel: 64

BREMEN—Marshall County

★ **COMMUNITY HOSPITAL OF BREMEN (151300)**, 1020 High Road, Zip 46506–1093, Mailing Address: P.O. Box 8, Zip 46506–0008; tel. 574/546–2211, **A**10 18 **F**3 11 13 15 29 34 35 40 45 50 57 59 64 69 75 76 77 79 81 82 85 93 107 110 111 115 119 129 130 132 133 135 146 149 **P**6
Primary Contact: David Bailey, FACHE, Chief Executive Officer
CFO: Amy Lashbrook, Chief Financial Officer
CMO: Lindy Sergeant, Medical Staff President
CHR: Patricia Board, Vice President Human Resources
CNO: Sue Bettcher, R.N., Vice President of Nursing Services
Web address: www.bremenhospital.com
Control: Other not–for–profit (including NFP Corporation) **Service:** General medical and surgical

Staffed Beds: 24 Admissions: 305 Census: 2 Outpatient Visits: 52511 Births: 129 Total Expense ($000): 20397 Payroll Expense ($000): 9592 Personnel: 141

DOCTORS NEUROPSYCHIATRIC HOSPITAL AND RESEARCH INSTITUTE (154058), 417 South Whitlock Street, Zip 46506–1626; tel. 574/546–0330, (Nonreporting) **A**10 **S** NeuroPsychiatric Hospitals, Mishawaka, IN
Primary Contact: Christy Gilbert, Interim Chief Executive Officer
Control: Corporation, Investor–owned (for–profit) **Service:** Psychiatric

Staffed Beds: 20

IN

CARMEL—Hamilton County

CLARIAN NORTH MEDICAL CENTER See Indiana University Health North Hospital

○ **FRANCISCAN HEALTH CARMEL (150182)**, 12188B North Meridian Street, Zip 46032–4840; tel. 317/705–4500, (Nonreporting) **A**10 11 **S** Franciscan Health, Mishawaka, IN
Primary Contact: Stephen J. Wheatley, Director of Operations
CFO: Keith A. Lauter, Chief Financial Officer
CMO: Christopher Doehring, M.D., Vice President of Medical Affairs
CIO: Rebecca Merkel, Privacy Officer
CHR: Corey Baute, Vice President of Human Resource
CNO: Agnes Therady, MSN, FACHE, Vice President and Chief Nursing Officer
Web address: www.franciscanalliance.org/hospitals/carmel/Pages/default.aspx
Control: Other not–for–profit (including NFP Corporation) **Service:** General medical and surgical

Staffed Beds: 6

⊠ **INDIANA UNIVERSITY HEALTH NORTH HOSPITAL (150161)**, 11700 North Meridian Avenue, Zip 46032–4656; tel. 317/688–2000, **A**1 3 5 10 **F**3 13 15 18 19 20 22 25 29 30 31 34 35 36 37 40 45 47 49 55 57 60 64 68 70 72 74 75 76 78 79 81 85 87 88 89 91 92 93 107 108 110 111 115 119 124 130 132 135 146 147 148 154 **S** Indiana University Health, Indianapolis, IN
Primary Contact: Randall C. Yust, Interim President
COO: Randall C Yust, Chief Operating Officer and Chief Financial Officer
CFO: Randall C Yust, Chief Operating Officer and Chief Financial Officer
CMO: Paul Calkins, M.D., Chief Medical Officer
CIO: Steve Bodenham, Senior Manager Clinical Engineering
CHR: Steven E Kile, Vice President Human Resources
Web address: www.iuhealth.org/north
Control: Other not–for–profit (including NFP Corporation) **Service:** General medical and surgical

Staffed Beds: 161 **Admissions:** 7391 **Census:** 83 **Outpatient Visits:** 210803 **Births:** 2466 **Total Expense ($000):** 197109 **Payroll Expense ($000):** 59995 **Personnel:** 895

⊠ **ST. VINCENT CARMEL HOSPITAL (150157)**, 13500 North Meridian Street, Zip 46032–1456; tel. 317/582–7000, (Nonreporting) **A**1 10 **S** Ascension Healthcare, Saint Louis, MO
Primary Contact: Gary Fammartino, Regional President
COO: Daniel LaReau, Executive Director, Operations and Information
CFO: Robert A. Bates, Chief Financial Officer
CMO: Steven Priddy, M.D., VP of Physician Affairs/Chief Medical Officer
CIO: Daniel LaReau, Executive Director, Operations and Information
CHR: Ross Brodhead, Senior Director, Human Resources
CNO: Ted Eads, Interim Chief Nursing Officer
Web address: www.stvincent.org
Control: Church operated, Nongovernment, not–for–profit **Service:** General medical and surgical

Staffed Beds: 121

CLARKSVILLE—Clark County

○ **KENTUCKIANA MEDICAL CENTER (150176)**, 4601 Medical Plaza Way, Zip 47129–9204; tel. 812/284–6100, (Nonreporting) **A**10 11
Primary Contact: Paul Newsom, Chief Operating Officer
Web address: www.kentuckianamedcen.com/
Control: Corporation, Investor–owned (for–profit) **Service:** General medical and surgical

Staffed Beds: 40

CLINTON—Vermillion County

UNION HOSPITAL CLINTON (151326), 801 South Main Street, Zip 47842–2261; tel. 765/832–1234, **A**10 18 **F**3 11 15 18 29 30 34 35 40 45 50 57 59 64 65 68 70 75 81 85 86 87 91 93 97 107 108 110 115 119 130 132 133 146
Primary Contact: Stephanie Laws, Vice President, Administrator
CFO: Wayne Hutson, Chief Financial Officer
CMO: John Albrecht, Chief of Staff
CIO: Jack Hill, Vice President and Chief Operating Officer
Web address: www.myunionhospital.org/unionhospital/union–hospital–clinton
Control: Other not–for–profit (including NFP Corporation) **Service:** General medical and surgical

Staffed Beds: 21 **Admissions:** 680 **Census:** 5 **Outpatient Visits:** 45978 **Births:** 0 **Total Expense ($000):** 22334 **Payroll Expense ($000):** 7771 **Personnel:** 122

COLUMBIA CITY—Whitley County

⊠ **PARKVIEW WHITLEY HOSPITAL (150101)**, 1260 East State Road 205, Zip 46725–9492; tel. 260/248–9000, **A**1 10 **F**3 7 13 15 28 29 30 34 35 38 40 45 50 54 59 64 70 75 76 79 81 82 85 87 89 91 93 96 102 107 108 110 111 115 119 129 132 135 143 146 148 154 **P**6 **S** Parkview Health, Fort Wayne, IN
Primary Contact: Scott F. Gabriel, President
COO: Scott F Gabriel, President
CFO: Lisa Peppler, Financial Manager
CMO: Jeffrey Brookes, M.D., Medical Director
CHR: Dianne P Potter, Manager Human Resources
CNO: Bridget Dolohanty–Johnson, MSN, R.N., Vice President Patient Care Services
Web address: www.parkview.com
Control: Other not–for–profit (including NFP Corporation) **Service:** General medical and surgical

Staffed Beds: 30 **Admissions:** 1516 **Census:** 12 **Outpatient Visits:** 67526 **Births:** 420 **Total Expense ($000):** 65064 **Payroll Expense ($000):** 17528 **Personnel:** 292

COLUMBUS—Bartholomew County

★ ○ **COLUMBUS REGIONAL HOSPITAL (150112)**, 2400 East 17th Street, Zip 47201–5360; tel. 812/379–4441, **A**2 10 11 19 **F**3 7 11 12 13 15 18 20 22 24 26 28 29 30 31 34 35 38 39 40 45 46 47 49 50 51 53 58 59 68 70 73 74 75 76 77 78 79 81 85 86 87 89 90 93 97 98 100 101 102 103 107 108 110 111 114 115 117 118 119 120 121 123 124 126 129 130 131 132 135 146 147 148 149 **P**6
Primary Contact: Jim Bickel, Chief Executive Officer
CFO: Marlene Weatherwax, Vice President and Chief Financial Officer
CMO: Thomas Sonderman, M.D., Vice President and Chief Medical Officer
CIO: Steve Baker, Vice President and Chief Technology and Information Officer
CHR: John R Loya, Vice President Human Resources and Organizational Development
CNO: Holly Cheek, Vice President and Chief Nursing Officer
Web address: www.crh.org
Control: County, Government, nonfederal **Service:** General medical and surgical

Staffed Beds: 197 **Admissions:** 9221 **Census:** 95 **Outpatient Visits:** 254268 **Births:** 1247 **Total Expense ($000):** 254004 **Payroll Expense ($000):** 80218 **Personnel:** 1577

CONNERSVILLE—Fayette County

○ **FAYETTE REGIONAL HEALTH SYSTEM (150064)**, 1941 Virginia Avenue, Zip 47331–2833; tel. 765/825–5131, (Nonreporting) **A**10 11
Primary Contact: Randall White, Chief Executive Officer
CFO: Debra Michalek, Chief Financial Officer
CMO: Mike Rowe, M.D., Chief of Staff
CIO: Andy Merida, Director Management Information Systems
CHR: Rhonda McPherson, Vice President Human Resources
CNO: Beth A Wampler, R.N., Chief Nursing Officer
Web address: www.fayetteregional.org
Control: Other not–for–profit (including NFP Corporation) **Service:** General medical and surgical

Staffed Beds: 75

CORYDON—Harrison County

★ **HARRISON COUNTY HOSPITAL (151331)**, 1141 Hospital Drive N W, Zip 47112–1774; tel. 812/738–4251, **A**10 18 **F**7 13 15 28 29 31 34 35 40 57 59 64 68 70 76 77 78 79 81 93 97 107 108 110 111 115 116 117 118 119 129 131 132 133 143 144 146 154 **P**6
Primary Contact: Steven L. Taylor, Chief Executive Officer
CFO: Jeff Davis, Chief Financial Officer
CIO: Chuck Wiley, Manager Information Systems
CHR: Loren Haverstock, Manager Human Resources
CNO: Ruth Donahue, R.N., Chief Nursing Officer
Web address: www.hchin.org
Control: County, Government, nonfederal **Service:** General medical and surgical

Staffed Beds: 25 **Admissions:** 1448 **Census:** 13 **Outpatient Visits:** 54084 **Births:** 402 **Total Expense ($000):** 54880 **Payroll Expense ($000):** 25724 **Personnel:** 509

IN

Hospital, Medicare Provider Number, Address, Telephone, Approval, Facility, and Physician Codes, Health Care System		
★ American Hospital Association (AHA) membership	○ Healthcare Facilities Accreditation Program	⇑ Center for Improvement in Healthcare Quality Accreditation
☐ The Joint Commission accreditation	◇ DNV Healthcare Inc. accreditation	△ Commission on Accreditation of Rehabilitation Facilities (CARF) accreditation

CRAWFORDSVILLE—Montgomery County

○ **FRANCISCAN HEALTH CRAWFORDSVILLE (150022)**, 1710 Lafayette Road, Zip 47933–1099; tel. 765/362–2800, **A**10 11 **F**3 11 15 18 19 28 29 30 31 35 36 45 50 54 57 64 69 70 74 75 77 78 79 81 82 85 87 93 98 102 103 104 107 108 110 111 114 115 118 119 120 121 126 129 130 132 135 145 146 148 154 **S** Franciscan Health, Mishawaka, IN
Primary Contact: Terrence Klein, Ph.D., Vice President and Chief Operating Officer
COO: Terrence Klein, Ph.D., Vice President and Chief Operating Officer
CFO: Keith A. Lauter, Vice President Finance
Web address: www.stclaremedical.org
Control: Church operated, Nongovernment, not–for–profit **Service:** General medical and surgical

Staffed Beds: 40 **Admissions:** 1296 **Census:** 15 **Outpatient Visits:** 65015 **Births:** 0 **Total Expense ($000):** 49335 **Payroll Expense ($000):** 10470 **Personnel:** 177

ST. CLARE MEDICAL CENTER See Franciscan Health Crawfordsville

CROWN POINT—Lake County

○ **FRANCISCAN HEALTH CROWN POINT (150126)**, 1201 South Main Street, Zip 46307–8483; tel. 219/738–2100, (Nonreporting) **A**2 10 11 **S** Franciscan Health, Mishawaka, IN
Primary Contact: Daniel McCormick, M.D., President and Chief Executive Officer
CFO: Marc Golan, Chief Financial Officer
CIO: Tim Loosemore, Director
CNO: Carol E Schuster, R.N., Chief Nursing Officer and Vice President Patient Care Services
Web address: www.franciscanalliance.org
Control: Church operated, Nongovernment, not–for–profit **Service:** General medical and surgical

Staffed Beds: 254

○ **PINNACLE HOSPITAL (150166)**, 9301 Connecticut Drive, Zip 46307–7486; tel. 219/756–2100, (Nonreporting) **A**10 11
Primary Contact: Haroon Naz, Chief Executive Officer
Web address: www.pinnaclehealthcare.net
Control: Partnership, Investor–owned (for–profit) **Service:** General medical and surgical

Staffed Beds: 18

ST. ANTHONY MEDICAL CENTER See Franciscan Health Crown Point

⊠ **VIBRA HOSPITAL OF NORTHWESTERN INDIANA (152028)**, 9509 Georgia Street, Zip 46307–6518; tel. 219/472–2200, (Nonreporting) **A**1 10 **S** Vibra Healthcare, Mechanicsburg, PA
Primary Contact: Larry Deal, R.N., Chief Executive Officer
CFO: Douglas Morris, Chief Financial Officer
CMO: Raja Devanathan, M.D., Chief Medical Officer
CNO: Robert Beard, Chief Clinical Officer
Web address: www.vhnwindiana.com/
Control: Corporation, Investor–owned (for–profit) **Service:** Acute long–term care hospital

Staffed Beds: 40

DANVILLE—Hendricks County

★ ○ **HENDRICKS REGIONAL HEALTH (150005)**, 1000 East Main Street, Zip 46122–1948, Mailing Address: P.O. Box 409, Zip 46122–0409; tel. 317/745–4451, **A**2 5 10 11 **F**3 8 9 11 13 15 17 18 20 22 28 29 30 31 32 34 35 38 40 41 43 44 45 47 48 50 53 54 55 56 57 58 59 60 61 64 65 66 69 70 71 73 74 75 76 77 78 79 81 82 83 84 85 86 87 89 90 92 93 94 96 97 107 108 109 110 111 114 115 117 118 119 121 123 127 128 129 130 131 132 133 135 144 146 147 148 150 154 **P**6
Primary Contact: Kevin Speer, Chief Executive Officer
CFO: John Komenda, Chief Financial Officer
CMO: John Sparzo, M.D., Vice President Medical Affairs
CIO: Lowell Nicodemus, Director Information Systems
CHR: Gary Lenard, Director Human Resources
Web address: www.hendrickshospital.org
Control: County, Government, nonfederal **Service:** General medical and surgical

Staffed Beds: 127 **Admissions:** 5699 **Census:** 51 **Outpatient Visits:** 372305 **Births:** 1296 **Total Expense ($000):** 277193 **Payroll Expense ($000):** 114470 **Personnel:** 1631

DECATUR—Adams County

★ **ADAMS MEMORIAL HOSPITAL (151330)**, 1100 Mercer Avenue, Zip 46733–2303, Mailing Address: P.O. Box 151, Zip 46733–0151; tel. 260/724–2145, (Total facility includes 195 beds in nursing home–type unit) **A**10 18 **F**3 5 7 10 13 15 28 29 30 34 35 38 40 47 50 53 56 57 59 64 65 66 67 70 74 75 76 77 79 81 82 85 86 87 93 97 98 101 102 103 104 105 107 108 110 111 115 119 125 127 128 129 130 131 132 133 135 143 144 146 147 148 149 152 153 **P**6
Primary Contact: JoEllen Eidam, FACHE, Chief Executive Officer
CFO: Dane Wheeler, Chief Financial Officer
CMO: Scott Smith, M.D., Chief Medical Officer
CIO: Nick Nelson, Director Support Services
CHR: Alison Kukelhan, Manager Human Resources
CNO: Theresa Bradtmiller, MSN, R.N., Chief Nursing Officer
Web address: www.adamshospital.com
Control: County, Government, nonfederal **Service:** General medical and surgical

Staffed Beds: 234 **Admissions:** 2281 **Census:** 168 **Outpatient Visits:** 143300 **Births:** 199 **Total Expense ($000):** 74623 **Payroll Expense ($000):** 35906 **Personnel:** 615

DYER—Lake County

☐ ○ **FRANCISCAN HEALTH DYER (150090)**, 24 Joliet Street, Zip 46311–1799; tel. 219/865–2141, (Nonreporting) **A**1 3 5 10 11 **S** Franciscan Health, Mishawaka, IN
Primary Contact: Patrick J. Maloney, Chief Executive Officer
Control: Church operated, Nongovernment, not–for–profit **Service:** General medical and surgical

Staffed Beds: 341

SAINT MARGARET MERCY HEALTHCARE CENTERS–SOUTH CAMPUS See Franciscan Health Dyer

EAST CHICAGO—Lake County

⊠ **REGENCY HOSPITAL OF NORTHWEST INDIANA (152024)**, 4321 Fir Street, 4th Floor, Zip 46312–3049; tel. 219/392–7799, (Includes REGENCY HOSPITAL OF PORTER COUNTY, 3630 Willow Creek Road, Portage, IN, Zip 46368; tel. 219/364–3800) (Nonreporting) **A**1 10 **S** Select Medical Corporation, Mechanicsburg, PA
Primary Contact: Eleyce Winn, Chief Executive Officer
Web address: www.regencyhospital.com/company/locations/indiana–northwest–indiana.aspx
Control: Corporation, Investor–owned (for–profit) **Service:** Acute long–term care hospital

Staffed Beds: 61

☐ △ **ST. CATHERINE HOSPITAL (150008)**, 4321 Fir Street, Zip 46312–3097; tel. 219/392–1700, **A**1 7 10 **F**1 3 5 11 13 15 17 18 20 22 24 26 28 29 30 31 34 35 40 46 49 54 57 58 59 61 62 64 68 74 75 76 77 78 79 80 81 82 85 86 87 89 92 93 98 100 101 102 103 104 107 108 110 111 112 115 119 129 130 132 135 146 147 148 149 153 **P**5 8 **S** Community Healthcare System, Hammond, IN
Primary Contact: Leo Correa, Chief Executive Officer and Administrator
COO: Craig Bolda, Chief Operating Officer
CMO: John Griep, M.D., Chief Medical Director
CIO: Gary Weiner, Chief Information Officer
CNO: Paula C Swenson, R.N., Vice President and Chief Nursing Officer
Web address: www.stcatherinehospital.org
Control: Other not–for–profit (including NFP Corporation) **Service:** General medical and surgical

Staffed Beds: 220 **Admissions:** 7404 **Census:** 110 **Outpatient Visits:** 145753 **Births:** 584 **Total Expense ($000):** 220701 **Payroll Expense ($000):** 57876 **Personnel:** 853

ELKHART—Elkhart County

★ ○ △ **ELKHART GENERAL HOSPITAL (150018)**, 600 East Boulevard, Zip 46514–2499, Mailing Address: P.O. Box 1329, Zip 46515–1329; tel. 574/294–2621, **A**2 7 10 11 **F**3 12 13 15 17 18 20 22 24 26 28 29 30 31 34 35 40 45 46 48 49 50 57 59 64 65 68 69 70 72 74 75 76 77 78 79 81 82 84 85 86 87 89 90 91 92 93 98 100 102 104 107 108 110 111 114 115 118 119 120 121 123 126 129 130 131 132 134 135 146 147 148 **P**8 **S** Beacon Health System, South Bend, IN
Primary Contact: Carl W. Risk II, President
CFO: Jeff Costello, Chief Financial Officer
CMO: Gene Grove, M.D., Chief of Staff
CIO: Mark Warlick, Chief Information Officer
CHR: Steven M Eller, Vice President Human Resources
Web address: www.egh.org
Control: Other not–for–profit (including NFP Corporation) **Service:** General medical and surgical

Staffed Beds: 230 **Admissions:** 10340 **Census:** 113 **Outpatient Visits:** 295173 **Births:** 1366 **Total Expense ($000):** 256277 **Payroll Expense ($000):** 78734 **Personnel:** 1462

IN

ELWOOD—Madison County

☒ **ST. VINCENT MERCY HOSPITAL (151308)**, 1331 South 'A' Street, Zip 46036–1942; tel. 765/552–4600, **A**1 2 10 18 **F**3 8 15 28 29 30 31 34 35 40 44 45 50 51 57 59 64 68 74 75 78 79 81 85 86 89 93 107 108 110 111 115 119 129 130 132 133 135 146 148 149 150 154 **S** Ascension Healthcare, Saint Louis, MO
Primary Contact: Ann C. Yates, R.N., MSN, Administrator and Chief Nursing Officer
CFO: John Arthur, Chief Financial Officer
CMO: Gary Brazel, M.D., Chief Medical Officer
CHR: Ross Brodhead, Manager Human Resources
CNO: Ann C Yates, R.N., MSN, Chief Nursing Officer
Web address: www.stvincent.org
Control: Church operated, Nongovernment, not–for–profit **Service:** General medical and surgical

Staffed Beds: 12 **Admissions:** 345 **Census:** 3 **Outpatient Visits:** 34500 **Births:** 0 **Total Expense ($000):** 23384 **Payroll Expense ($000):** 7775 **Personnel:** 76

EVANSVILLE—Vanderburgh County

★ ○ **DEACONESS HOSPITAL (150082)**, 600 Mary Street, Zip 47710–1658; tel. 812/450–5000, (Includes DEACONESS CROSS POINTE CENTER, 7200 East Indiana Street, Evansville, IN, Zip 47715; tel. 812/476–7200; Cheryl Rietman, Chief Administrative Officer) **A**2 3 10 11 **F**2 3 5 9 11 12 15 17 18 19 20 22 24 26 29 30 31 32 34 35 36 38 39 40 43 44 45 46 47 48 49 50 51 53 54 56 57 58 59 60 61 62 63 64 65 66 68 70 71 74 75 77 78 79 81 82 84 85 86 87 88 89 92 93 94 96 97 98 99 100 101 102 104 105 107 108 110 111 114 115 116 117 118 119 120 121 123 124 126 129 130 132 134 135 143 145 146 148 149 150 153 154 **P**6 8 **S** Deaconess Health System, Evansville, IN
Primary Contact: Shawn W. McCoy, Chief Executive Officer
CFO: Cheryl A Wathen, Interim Chief Financial Officer
CHR: Larry Pile, Director Human Resources
Web address: www.deaconess.com
Control: Other not–for–profit (including NFP Corporation) **Service:** General medical and surgical

Staffed Beds: 483 **Admissions:** 27162 **Census:** 337 **Outpatient Visits:** 649034 **Births:** 0 **Total Expense ($000):** 716421 **Payroll Expense ($000):** 258366 **Personnel:** 3803

EVANSVILLE PSYCHIATRIC CHILDREN CENTER (15J200), 3300 East Morgan Avenue, Zip 47715–2232; tel. 812/477–6436, (Nonreporting) **A**10
Primary Contact: Lottie Cook, Superintendent
COO: Melinda Kendle, Manager Business Office
CMO: Shannon Jones, M.D., Medical Director and Attending Psychiatrist
CIO: David Wirtz, Supervisor Information Technology
CHR: Jennifer Sontz, Director Human Resources
CNO: Elizabeth Angermeier, Director of Nursing
Web address: www.ih.gov
Control: State, Government, nonfederal **Service:** Children's hospital psychiatric

Staffed Beds: 28

☐ **EVANSVILLE STATE HOSPITAL (154056)**, 3400 Lincoln Avenue, Zip 47714–0146; tel. 812/469–6800, **A**1 10 **F**30 98 130 132 135 146
Primary Contact: Cathe Fulcher, Superintendent
CFO: Melinda Kendle, Director Fiscal Management
CMO: Melba Briones, M.D., Medical Director
CIO: David Wirtz, Senior LAN Administrator
CHR: Jennifer Sontz, Director Human Resources
Control: State, Government, nonfederal **Service:** Psychiatric

Staffed Beds: 168 **Admissions:** 109 **Census:** 151 **Outpatient Visits:** 0 **Births:** 0

☒ **HEALTHSOUTH DEACONESS REHABILITATION HOSPITAL (153025)**, 4100 Covert Avenue, Zip 47714–5567, Mailing Address: P.O. Box 5349, Zip 47716–5349; tel. 812/476–9983, **A**1 10 **F**28 29 57 64 68 75 87 90 91 93 94 95 96 130 132 143 148 149 **S** Encompass Health Corporation, Birmingham, AL
Primary Contact: Blake Bunner, Chief Executive Officer
CFO: Rhonda Ramsey, Controller
CMO: Mohammed Adeel, Medical Director
CHR: Wendy Gumbel, Director of Human Resources
CNO: Trish Draeger, Chief Nursing Officer
Web address: www.healthsouthdeaconess.com
Control: Corporation, Investor–owned (for–profit) **Service:** Rehabilitation

Staffed Beds: 103 **Admissions:** 2272 **Census:** 80 **Outpatient Visits:** 6874 **Births:** 0 **Total Expense ($000):** 27189 **Payroll Expense ($000):** 13672 **Personnel:** 283

☒ **SELECT SPECIALTY HOSPITAL–EVANSVILLE (152014)**, 400 SE 4th Street, Zip 47713–1206; tel. 812/421–2500, **A**1 10 **F**1 3 29 45 46 48 60 63 75 77 96 107 108 114 119 **S** Select Medical Corporation, Mechanicsburg, PA
Primary Contact: Scott A. Butler, Chief Executive Officer
Web address: www.selectspecialtyhospitals.com/company/locations/evansville.aspx
Control: Corporation, Investor–owned (for–profit) **Service:** Acute long–term care hospital

Staffed Beds: 51 **Admissions:** 547 **Census:** 39 **Outpatient Visits:** 0 **Births:** 0 **Total Expense ($000):** 22757 **Payroll Expense ($000):** 10599

☒ △ **ST. VINCENT EVANSVILLE (150100)**, 3700 Washington Avenue, Zip 47714–0541; tel. 812/485–4000, (Nonreporting) **A**1 2 7 10 **S** Ascension Healthcare, Saint Louis, MO
Primary Contact: Daniel A. Parod, President
COO: Gwynn Perlich, Chief Operating Officer
CFO: Craig Polkow, Vice President, Finance
CMO: Vernon Maas, M.D., Vice President, Medical Affairs
CIO: Jose Diaz, Director Information Systems
CHR: Marty Mattingly, Chief Human Resources Officer
CNO: Darcy Ellison, R.N., MSN, Senior Vice President, Chief Nursing Officer and Inpatient Flow
Web address: www.stmarys.org
Control: Church operated, Nongovernment, not–for–profit **Service:** General medical and surgical

Staffed Beds: 436

FISHERS—Hamilton County

☒ **ST. VINCENT FISHERS HOSPITAL (150181)**, 13861 Olio Road, Zip 46037–3487; tel. 317/415–9000, (Nonreporting) **A**1 10 **S** Ascension Healthcare, Saint Louis, MO
Primary Contact: Gary Fammartino, Regional President
CMO: Craig Wilson, Chief Medical Officer
Web address: www.stvincent.org
Control: Other not–for–profit (including NFP Corporation) **Service:** General medical and surgical

Staffed Beds: 46

FORT WAYNE—Allen County

☒ **DUPONT HOSPITAL (150150)**, 2520 East Dupont Road, Zip 46825–1675; tel. 260/416–3000, **A**1 10 **F**3 8 13 15 18 29 30 34 35 39 40 45 50 56 57 58 59 60 64 65 68 70 72 73 74 75 77 78 79 81 82 83 84 85 86 87 107 110 111 114 115 118 119 126 129 130 131 132 135 141 146 147 148 154 **S** Community Health Systems, Inc., Franklin, TN
Primary Contact: Lorenzo Suter, Chief Executive Officer
COO: Darrick Hoopingarner, Chief Operating Officer
CFO: Brian Schneider, Chief Financial Officer
CIO: Janis Gray, Chief Information Officer
CNO: Kimberly Fulkerson, Chief Nursing Officer
Web address: www.thedupontdifference.com
Control: Partnership, Investor–owned (for–profit) **Service:** General medical and surgical

Staffed Beds: 131 **Admissions:** 4641 **Census:** 51 **Outpatient Visits:** 93618 **Births:** 2393 **Total Expense ($000):** 103683 **Payroll Expense ($000):** 35213 **Personnel:** 586

☒ **LUTHERAN HOSPITAL OF INDIANA (150017)**, 7950 West Jefferson Boulevard, Zip 46804–4140; tel. 260/435–7001, **A**1 2 3 5 10 **F**3 7 11 12 13 15 17 18 20 23 24 26 28 29 30 31 32 34 35 41 43 44 45 46 47 48 49 50 51 54 57 58 59 60 64 65 68 70 72 74 75 76 77 78 79 80 81 84 85 86 87 88 89 91 92 93 94 96 107 108 109 110 111 112 113 114 115 116 117 118 119 120 121 122 123 124 126 129 130 132 137 138 141 144 145 146 147 149 154 **S** Community Health Systems, Inc., Franklin, TN
Primary Contact: Paula R. Autry, FACHE, Chief Executive Officer
CFO: Cully Chapman, Chief Financial Officer
CIO: Keith A. Neuman, Chief Information Officer
CHR: Maria Kurtz, Director Human Resources
CNO: Angela Logan, Chief Nursing Officer
Web address: www.lutheranhospital.com
Control: Corporation, Investor–owned (for–profit) **Service:** General medical and surgical

Staffed Beds: 407 **Admissions:** 19195 **Census:** 268 **Outpatient Visits:** 488688 **Births:** 953 **Total Expense ($000):** 417549 **Payroll Expense ($000):** 122533 **Personnel:** 2380

Hospital, Medicare Provider Number, Address, Telephone, Approval, Facility, and Physician Codes, Health Care System

★ American Hospital Association (AHA) membership
☐ The Joint Commission accreditation
○ Healthcare Facilities Accreditation Program
◇ DNV Healthcare Inc. accreditation
⇑ Center for Improvement in Healthcare Quality Accreditation
△ Commission on Accreditation of Rehabilitation Facilities (CARF) accreditation

IN

ORTHOPAEDIC HOSPITAL OF LUTHERAN HEALTH NETWORK (150168), 7952 West Jefferson Boulevard, Zip 46804–4140; tel. 260/435–2999, **A**1 10 **F**29 30 34 35 37 64 77 79 80 81 82 90 93 94 96 111 131 **P**8 **S** Community Health Systems, Inc., Franklin, TN
Primary Contact: Lorie Ailor, Chief Executive Officer
CFO: Amy Hochstetler, Chief Financial Officer
CMO: Kevin Rahn, President Medical Staff
CIO: Keith A. Neuman, Chief Information Officer
CHR: Maria Kurtz, Director Human Resources
CNO: Marci Hamilton, Chief Nursing Officer
Web address: www.theorthohospital.com
Control: Corporation, Investor–owned (for–profit) **Service**: Orthopedic

Staffed Beds: 43 Admissions: 2432 Census: 15 Outpatient Visits: 53695 Births: 0 Total Expense ($000): 57563 Payroll Expense ($000): 14042 Personnel: 212

PARKVIEW ORTHO HOSPITAL (150167), 11130 Parkview Circle Drive, Zip 46845–1735; tel. 260/672–5000, **A**1 10 **F**3 8 29 30 34 45 50 58 65 68 79 81 82 84 85 86 87 90 91 93 94 96 107 111 119 131 135 141 149 154 **P**6 **S** Parkview Health, Fort Wayne, IN
Primary Contact: Julie Fleck, Chief Operating Officer
Web address: www.parkview.com
Control: Corporation, Investor–owned (for–profit) **Service**: Orthopedic

Staffed Beds: 37 Admissions: 2719 Census: 15 Outpatient Visits: 8369 Births: 0 Total Expense ($000): 70495 Payroll Expense ($000): 14384 Personnel: 195

PARKVIEW REGIONAL MEDICAL CENTER (150021), 11109 Parkview Plaza Drive, Zip 46845–1701; tel. 260/266–1000, (Includes PARKVIEW HOSPITAL RANDALLIA, 2200 Randallia Drive, Fort Wayne, IN, Zip 46805–4699; tel. 260/373–4000; Marlon Wardlow, Chief Operating Officer; PARKVIEW NORTH HOSPITAL, 11115 Parkview Plaza Drive, Fort Wayne, IN, Zip 46845; tel. 260/672–4000) (Total facility includes 31 beds in nursing home–type unit) **A**1 2 10 **F**3 5 7 11 12 13 14 15 17 18 19 20 22 24 26 28 29 30 31 32 34 35 39 40 41 43 44 45 46 47 48 49 50 51 53 54 55 56 57 58 59 60 61 62 63 64 65 67 68 70 72 74 75 76 78 79 80 81 82 83 84 85 86 87 88 89 90 91 92 93 95 96 98 99 100 101 102 103 104 105 107 108 109 111 114 115 118 119 120 121 123 124 126 128 129 130 131 132 135 141 146 147 148 149 152 153 154 **P**6 **S** Parkview Health, Fort Wayne, IN
Primary Contact: Ben Miles, President
CNO: Judy Boerger, MSN, Chief Nursing Executive
Web address: www.parkview.com
Control: Other not–for–profit (including NFP Corporation) **Service**: General medical and surgical

Staffed Beds: 732 Admissions: 37610 Census: 514 Outpatient Visits: 568220 Births: 3395 Total Expense ($000): 935465 Payroll Expense ($000): 246282 Personnel: 3897

REHABILITATION HOSPITAL OF FORT WAYNE (153030), 7970 West Jefferson Boulevard, Zip 46804–4140; tel. 260/435–6100, **A**1 7 10 **F**29 30 60 68 69 90 94 96 130 132 146 148 **P**5 **S** Community Health Systems, Inc., Franklin, TN
Primary Contact: Ryan Cassedy, Chief Administrative Officer
COO: Shelley Boxell, R.N., Interim Chief Operating Officer
CFO: Edward Romero, Chief Financial Officer
CMO: Preeti Dembla, Chief Medical Officer and Medical Director
CIO: Janis Gray, Chief Information Officer
CHR: Deborah Giardina, Director Human Resources and Medical Staff Services
CNO: Shelley Boxell, R.N., Chief Nursing Officer
Web address: www.rehabhospital.com
Control: Corporation, Investor–owned (for–profit) **Service**: Rehabilitation

Staffed Beds: 36 Admissions: 537 Census: 17 Outpatient Visits: 90 Births: 0 Total Expense ($000): 10311 Payroll Expense ($000): 5808 Personnel: 96

ST. JOSEPH HOSPITAL (150047), 700 Broadway, Zip 46802–1493; tel. 260/425–3000, (Nonreporting) **A**1 3 5 10 13 **S** Community Health Systems, Inc., Franklin, TN
Primary Contact: Lisa Dolan, Interim Chief Executive Officer
COO: Vince Green, Chief Operating Officer
CHR: Steve Heggen, Administrative Director Human Resources
Web address: www.stjoehospital.com
Control: Corporation, Investor–owned (for–profit) **Service**: General medical and surgical

Staffed Beds: 182

VETERANS AFFAIRS NORTHERN INDIANA HEALTH CARE SYSTEM, 2121 Lake Avenue, Zip 46805–5100; tel. 260/426–5431, (Includes VETERANS AFFAIRS NORTHERN INDIANA HEALTH CARE SYSTEM–MARION CAMPUS, 1700 East 38th Street, Marion, IN, Zip 46953–4589; tel. 765/674–3321) (Nonreporting) **A**1 **S** Department of Veterans Affairs, Perry Point, MD
Primary Contact: Michael Hershmann, Medical Center Director
COO: Helen Rhodes, R.N., Associate Director Operations
CFO: Jay H Vandermark, Chief Financial Officer
CMO: Ajay Dhawan, M.D., Chief of Staff
CIO: David Troyer, Chief Information Officer
CHR: Brian Flynn, Chief Human Resources Officer
Web address: www.northernindiana.va.gov/
Control: Veterans Affairs, Government, federal **Service**: General medical and surgical

Staffed Beds: 217

VIBRA HOSPITAL OF FORT WAYNE (152027), 2200 Randallia Drive, Zip 46805–4638; tel. 260/399–2900, **A**1 10 **F**1 3 29 75 85 148 149 **S** Vibra Healthcare, Mechanicsburg, PA
Primary Contact: Fred Price, R.N., Chief Executive Officer
Web address: www.vhfortwayne.com
Control: Corporation, Investor–owned (for–profit) **Service**: Acute long–term care hospital

Staffed Beds: 24 Admissions: 327 Census: 19 Outpatient Visits: 0 Births: 0

FRANKFORT—Clinton County

INDIANA UNIVERSITY HEALTH FRANKFORT (151316), 1300 South Jackson Street, Zip 46041–3313; tel. 765/656–3000, (Data for 214 days) **A**1 10 **F**3 11 15 18 28 29 30 34 35 40 45 50 57 59 64 68 75 79 81 82 85 86 89 90 93 107 110 111 114 119 133 146 148 **S** Indiana University Health, Indianapolis, IN
Primary Contact: Kelly Braverman, President
CFO: Wayne Knight, Chief Financial Officer
CMO: Stephen Tharp, Medical Director
CHR: Krista Wright, Director Human Resources
Web address: www.stvincent.org
Control: Other not–for–profit (including NFP Corporation) **Service**: General medical and surgical

Staffed Beds: 25 Admissions: 208 Census: 3 Outpatient Visits: 12337 Births: 0 Total Expense ($000): 13950 Payroll Expense ($000): 4047 Personnel: 85

FRANKLIN—Johnson County

★ ○ **JOHNSON MEMORIAL HOSPITAL (150001)**, 1125 West Jefferson Street, Zip 46131–2140, Mailing Address: P.O. Box 549, Zip 46131–0549; tel. 317/736–3300, **A**5 10 11 **F**12 13 15 18 20 22 28 29 30 31 34 35 36 40 44 45 49 50 54 57 59 62 64 68 70 74 75 76 77 78 79 81 82 85 87 90 93 97 107 108 110 111 113 114 118 119 129 130 131 132 134 135 144 146 147 148 154 **P**8
Primary Contact: Larry Heydon, President and Chief Executive Officer
COO: Steve Wohlford, Chief Operating Officer
CFO: Tim Balasia, Chief Financial Officer
CMO: David Dunkle, Vice President Medical Affairs
CIO: Scott Krodel, Vice President Information Systems
CHR: Judy Ware, Director Human Resources
CNO: Anita M. Keller, R.N., MSN, Chief Nursing Officer
Web address: www.johnsonmemorial.org
Control: County, Government, nonfederal **Service**: General medical and surgical

Staffed Beds: 94 Admissions: 2085 Census: 21 Outpatient Visits: 134998 Births: 356 Total Expense ($000): 80244 Payroll Expense ($000): 39623 Personnel: 671

GARY—Lake County

★ ○ △ **METHODIST HOSPITALS (150002)**, 600 Grant Street, Zip 46402–6099; tel. 219/886–4000, (Includes SOUTHLAKE CAMPUS, 8701 Broadway, Merrillville, IN, Zip 46410; tel. 219/738–5500) **A**2 3 5 7 10 11 **F**3 8 11 12 13 15 18 20 22 24 26 28 29 30 31 32 34 35 37 40 43 45 47 48 49 50 51 54 55 59 62 64 67 70 72 73 74 75 76 77 78 79 81 82 85 86 87 89 90 91 93 96 98 99 100 101 102 103 107 108 110 111 114 115 118 119 120 121 123 124 126 130 132 133 135 146 147 148 **P**6
Primary Contact: Raymond Grady, FACHE, President and Chief Executive Officer
CFO: Matthew Doyle, Chief Financial Officer
CIO: Timothy Diamond, Chief Information Officer
CHR: Alex Horvath, Vice President Human Resources
CNO: James M Renneker, FACHE, MSN, R.N., Vice President and Chief Nursing Officer
Web address: www.methodisthospitals.org
Control: Other not–for–profit (including NFP Corporation) **Service**: General medical and surgical

Staffed Beds: 504 Admissions: 15443 Census: 263 Outpatient Visits: 313026 Births: 1228 Total Expense ($000): 346551 Payroll Expense ($000): 152263 Personnel: 2209

IN

Many Facility Codes have changed. Please refer to the AHA Guide Code Chart. © 2018 AHA Guide

GOSHEN—Elkhart County

GOSHEN GENERAL HOSPITAL See Goshen Health

⊠ **GOSHEN HEALTH (150026)**, 200 High Park Avenue, Zip 46526–4899, Mailing Address: P.O. Box 139, Zip 46527–0139; tel. 574/533–2141, **A**1 2 10 **F**3 8 11 12 13 15 17 18 20 22 24 26 28 29 30 31 34 35 36 40 45 46 47 49 50 54 57 58 59 62 63 64 68 70 71 74 75 77 78 79 80 81 82 83 84 85 86 87 91 92 93 97 107 109 110 111 112 113 114 115 116 117 118 119 120 121 122 123 124 126 130 131 132 135 141 142 144 146 147 154 **P**4 8
Primary Contact: Randal Christophel, President and Chief Executive Officer
COO: Robert T Myers, Chief Operating Officer
CMO: Randall Cammenga, M.D., Vice President Medical Affairs
CHR: Alan Weldy, Vice President Human Resources, Compliance and Legal Services
Web address: www.https://goshenhealth.com/Home
Control: Other not–for–profit (including NFP Corporation) **Service:** General medical and surgical

Staffed Beds: 122 **Admissions:** 5534 **Census:** 57 **Outpatient Visits:** 146936 **Births:** 1315 **Total Expense ($000):** 235451 **Payroll Expense ($000):** 74194

OAKLAWN PSYCHIATRIC CENTER (154031), 330 Lakeview Drive, Zip 46528–9365, Mailing Address: P.O. Box 809, Zip 46527–0809; tel. 574/533–1234, **A**10 **F**5 29 30 35 38 54 98 104 106 130 146 152 153 154 **P**6
Primary Contact: Laurie N. Nafziger, President and Chief Executive Officer
CFO: Joseph Barkman, Vice President Financial Services
CMO: Daniel Kinsey, M.D., Medical Director
CIO: Jennifer Glick, Manager Clinical Informatics
CHR: Jill Seifer, Vice President Human Resources
CNO: Elaine G Miller, Director of Nursing
Web address: www.oaklawn.org
Control: State, Government, nonfederal **Service:** Psychiatric

Staffed Beds: 16 **Admissions:** 593 **Census:** 12 **Outpatient Visits:** 379166 **Births:** 0 **Total Expense ($000):** 50567 **Payroll Expense ($000):** 33202 **Personnel:** 815

GREENCASTLE—Putnam County

PUTNAM COUNTY HOSPITAL (151333), 1542 Bloomington Street, Zip 46135–2297; tel. 765/653–5121, (Nonreporting) **A**2 10 18
Primary Contact: Dennis Weatherford, Chief Executive Officer
CFO: Kevin Fowler, Director Finance
Web address: www.pchosp.org/
Control: County, Government, nonfederal **Service:** General medical and surgical

Staffed Beds: 25

GREENFIELD—Hancock County

★ ○ **HANCOCK REGIONAL HOSPITAL (150037)**, 801 North State Street, Zip 46140–1270, Mailing Address: P.O. Box 827, Zip 46140–0827; tel. 317/462–5544, **A**10 11 **F**3 11 13 15 18 20 22 28 29 30 31 32 34 35 38 40 41 44 45 48 49 51 53 54 55 56 57 59 62 63 64 65 70 74 75 76 78 79 81 82 83 84 85 86 87 89 92 93 98 100 101 102 103 104 107 108 110 111 114 115 119 120 121 123 124 127 129 130 132 134 135 144 146 147 149 154 **P**8
Primary Contact: Steven V. Long, FACHE, President and Chief Executive Officer
COO: Robert Lawrence Matt, Vice President and Chief Operating Officer
CFO: Rick Edwards, Vice President and Chief Financial Officer
CMO: Michael Fletcher, M.D., Vice President and Chief Medical Officer
CIO: Jon Miller, Director Accounting and Information Services
CHR: Laura L Nichols, Director Human Resources
Web address: www.hancockregional.org
Control: County, Government, nonfederal **Service:** General medical and surgical

Staffed Beds: 68 **Admissions:** 3461 **Census:** 35 **Outpatient Visits:** 155439 **Births:** 341 **Total Expense ($000):** 130669 **Payroll Expense ($000):** 44164 **Personnel:** 736

GREENSBURG—Decatur County

★ ⇑ **DECATUR COUNTY MEMORIAL HOSPITAL (151332)**, 720 North Lincoln Street, Zip 47240–1398; tel. 812/663–1171, (Total facility includes 370 beds in nursing home–type unit) **A**2 10 18 21 **F**3 7 11 13 15 18 28 29 30 31 34 35 36 40 44 45 50 51 53 54 57 59 62 64 65 68 74 75 76 77 78 79 80 81 85 87 89 92 93 96 97 104 107 108 110 111 115 118 119 128 129 130 131 132 133 135 143 144 146 147 148 **P**6
Primary Contact: Rex McKinney, President and Chief Executive Officer
COO: Eric Stokes, Vice President of Operations
CFO: Jerry Marks, Vice President Finance
CMO: Jennifer Fletcher, Chief of Staff
CHR: Amy Lynn Wickens, Executive Director Human Resources
CNO: Kathy Stephens, Vice President of Patient Care
Web address: www.dcmh.net
Control: County, Government, nonfederal **Service:** General medical and surgical

Staffed Beds: 395 **Admissions:** 1651 **Census:** 241 **Outpatient Visits:** 93146 **Births:** 221 **Total Expense ($000):** 74779 **Payroll Expense ($000):** 39063 **Personnel:** 755

GREENWOOD—Johnson County

☐ **VALLE VISTA HOSPITAL (154024)**, 898 East Main Street, Zip 46143–1400; tel. 317/887–1348, (Nonreporting) **A**1 10 **S** Universal Health Services, Inc., King of Prussia, PA
Primary Contact: Sherri R. Jewett, Chief Executive Officer
CFO: Tim Sides, Chief Financial Officer
CMO: Jennifer Comer, M.D., Medical Director
CIO: Karen Hayden, Director Health Information Services, Performance Improvement and Risk Management
CHR: Ismael Santos, Director Human Resources
Web address: www.vallevistahospital.com
Control: Corporation, Investor–owned (for–profit) **Service:** Psychiatric

Staffed Beds: 102

HAMMOND—Lake County

★ ○ △ **FRANCISCAN HEALTH HAMMOND (150004)**, 5454 Hohman Avenue, Zip 46320–1999; tel. 219/932–2300, (Includes SAINT MARGARET MERCY HEALTHCARE CENTERS–NORTH CAMPUS, 5454 Hohman Avenue, Hammond, IN, Zip 46320; tel. 219/932–2300) (Nonreporting) **A**2 3 7 10 11 **S** Franciscan Health, Mishawaka, IN
Primary Contact: Patrick J. Maloney, Chief Executive Officer
CFO: Marc Golan, Chief Financial Officer
Web address: www.franciscanhealth.org/healthcare–facilities/franciscan–health–hammond–18
Control: Church operated, Nongovernment, not–for–profit **Service:** General medical and surgical

Staffed Beds: 406

⊠ **KINDRED HOSPITAL NORTHWEST INDIANA (152012)**, 5454 Hohman Avenue, 5th Floor, Zip 46320–1931; tel. 219/937–9900, (Nonreporting) **A**1 10 **S** Kindred Healthcare, Louisville, KY
Primary Contact: Frank A. Solare, Chief Executive Officer
Web address: www.khnwindiana.com
Control: Corporation, Investor–owned (for–profit) **Service:** Acute long–term care hospital

Staffed Beds: 70

SAINT MARGARET MERCY HEALTHCARE CENTERS See Franciscan Health Hammond

TRIUMPH HOSPITAL NORTHWEST INDIANA See Kindred Hospital Northwest Indiana

HARTFORD CITY—Blackford County

BLACKFORD COMMUNITY HOSPITAL See Indiana University Health Blackford Hospital

IN

Hospital, Medicare Provider Number, Address, Telephone, Approval, Facility, and Physician Codes, Health Care System

★ American Hospital Association (AHA) membership
☐ The Joint Commission accreditation
○ Healthcare Facilities Accreditation Program
◇ DNV Healthcare Inc. accreditation
⇑ Center for Improvement in Healthcare Quality Accreditation
△ Commission on Accreditation of Rehabilitation Facilities (CARF) accreditation

© 2018 AHA Guide *Many Facility Codes have changed. Please refer to the AHA Guide Code Chart.* Hospitals **A205**

✠ **INDIANA UNIVERSITY HEALTH BLACKFORD HOSPITAL (151302)**, 410 Pilgrim Boulevard, Zip 47348–1897; tel. 765/348–0300, **A**1 10 18 **F**3 11 15 28 29 34 35 40 44 45 50 57 59 64 75 81 85 87 93 107 110 115 119 130 132 133 **S** Indiana University Health, Indianapolis, IN
Primary Contact: David W. Hyatt, President
CFO: John Vanator, CPA, Chief Financial Officer
CNO: Rodney Stevens, East Central Region Director of Nursing Practice
Web address: www.iuhealth.org/blackford
Control: Other not–for–profit (including NFP Corporation) **Service**: General medical and surgical

Staffed Beds: 15 **Admissions:** 456 **Census:** 6 **Outpatient Visits:** 38813 **Births:** 0 **Total Expense ($000):** 17433 **Payroll Expense ($000):** 6306 **Personnel:** 93	

HOBART—Lake County

☐ △ **ST. MARY MEDICAL CENTER (150034)**, 1500 South Lake Park Avenue, Zip 46342–6699; tel. 219/942–0551, **A**1 2 7 10 **F**3 8 11 12 13 15 18 20 22 24 26 28 29 30 31 34 35 36 38 39 40 45 47 49 50 54 57 58 59 62 64 65 67 70 74 75 76 77 78 79 80 81 82 84 85 86 87 89 90 91 92 93 96 107 108 110 111 114 115 116 117 119 120 121 123 126 129 130 131 132 135 144 146 147 148 **S** Community Healthcare System, Hammond, IN
Primary Contact: Janice L. Ryba, JD, Chief Executive Officer
CFO: Mary Sudicky, Chief Financial Officer
CIO: Gary Weiner, Vice President Information Technology and Chief Information Officer
CHR: Tony Ferracane, Vice President Human Resources
CNO: Tammie R. Jones, R.N., Chief Nursing Officer
Web address: www.comhs.org
Control: Other not–for–profit (including NFP Corporation) **Service**: General medical and surgical

Staffed Beds: 200 **Admissions:** 10386 **Census:** 150 **Outpatient Visits:** 236216 **Births:** 581 **Total Expense ($000):** 235851 **Payroll Expense ($000):** 66677 **Personnel:** 1020	

HUNTINGTON—Huntington County

✠ **PARKVIEW HUNTINGTON HOSPITAL (150091)**, 2001 Stults Road, Zip 46750–1291; tel. 260/355–3000, **A**1 10 **F**3 7 8 13 15 28 29 30 31 32 34 35 36 38 39 40 44 45 50 53 56 57 59 64 68 69 70 75 76 77 78 79 81 85 86 87 93 96 97 107 108 111 119 129 130 131 132 134 135 146 148 154 **P**6 **S** Parkview Health, Fort Wayne, IN
Primary Contact: Juli Johnson, MSN, R.N., President
CMO: Jeffrey Brooks, M.D., Chief Medical Officer
CIO: Ron Double, Chief Information Officer
CHR: Dena M Jacquay, Chief Human Resource Officer
CNO: Doug R Selig, MSN, R.N., Vice President of Patient Services
Web address: www.parkview.com
Control: Other not–for–profit (including NFP Corporation) **Service**: General medical and surgical

Staffed Beds: 36 **Admissions:** 1882 **Census:** 13 **Outpatient Visits:** 47678 **Births:** 358 **Total Expense ($000):** 52166 **Payroll Expense ($000):** 15104 **Personnel:** 243	

INDIANAPOLIS—Marion County

CLARIAN HEALTH PARTNERS See Indiana University Health University Hospital

✠ **COMMUNITY HOSPITAL EAST (150074)**, 1500 North Ritter Avenue, Zip 46219–3095; tel. 317/355–1411, (Includes COMMUNITY HEART AND VASCULAR HOSPITAL, 8075 North Shadeland Avenue, Indianapolis, IN, Zip 46250–2693; tel. 317/621–8000; Kathleen R Krusie, FACHE, President) **A**1 2 3 5 10 **F**3 11 13 17 18 20 22 26 28 29 30 31 34 35 38 40 43 44 45 46 47 48 49 50 51 53 56 57 59 70 74 75 76 77 78 79 80 81 85 87 92 96 98 107 111 114 115 118 119 120 121 123 124 126 129 130 132 146 147 148 149 154 **P**1 8 **S** Community Health Network, Indianapolis, IN
Primary Contact: Scott L. Teffeteller, Senior Vice President and President of East Region
Web address: www.ecommunity.com/east/
Control: Other not–for–profit (including NFP Corporation) **Service**: General medical and surgical

Staffed Beds: 337 **Admissions:** 14819 **Census:** 191	

✠ **COMMUNITY HOSPITAL NORTH (150169)**, 7150 Clearvista Drive, Zip 46256–1695, Mailing Address: 7250 Clearvista Drive, Suite 200, Zip 46256–1695; tel. 317/355–2469, (Nonreporting) **A**1 3 10 **S** Community Health Network, Indianapolis, IN
Primary Contact: Kathleen R. Krusie, FACHE, President
CFO: Amy Campbell, Chief Financial Officer
CMO: Wesley Wong, M.D., Acting Vice President Medical and Academic Affairs
CIO: Ron Thieme, Ph.D., Chief Knowledge and Information Officer
CHR: Steve Pearcy, Director Human Resources
Web address: www.ecommunity.com/north
Control: Other not–for–profit (including NFP Corporation) **Service**: General medical and surgical

Staffed Beds: 308	

✠ **COMMUNITY HOSPITAL SOUTH (150128)**, 1402 East County Line Road South, Zip 46227–0963; tel. 317/887–7000, **A**1 3 10 **F**3 11 12 13 15 18 20 22 28 29 30 31 35 37 40 45 46 47 48 49 54 60 64 69 70 73 74 75 76 77 78 79 81 82 84 85 86 89 107 108 110 111 114 115 119 126 129 130 131 135 145 146 147 148 **P**1 8 **S** Community Health Network, Indianapolis, IN
Primary Contact: David Kiley, M.D., Vice President
COO: Nichole Goddard, Chief Operating Officer, South Region
CFO: Leslie Yoder, Executive Director, Finance
CMO: Randy Lee, M.D., Senior Vice President Medical Affairs
CHR: Edie Garriott, Director Human Resources
CNO: Anita Capps, R.N., Chief Nursing Executive
Web address: www.ecommunity.com
Control: Other not–for–profit (including NFP Corporation) **Service**: General medical and surgical

Staffed Beds: 167 **Admissions:** 9845 **Census:** 99 **Outpatient Visits:** 134552 **Births:** 1659 **Total Expense ($000):** 193625 **Payroll Expense ($000):** 59335	

☐ **ESKENAZI HEALTH (150024)**, 720 Eskenazi Avenue, Zip 46202–5166; tel. 317/880–0000, **A**1 3 5 8 10 **F**3 5 7 10 13 14 15 16 18 20 22 28 29 30 31 32 34 35 36 38 39 40 43 44 47 48 49 50 53 54 55 56 57 59 61 62 64 65 66 68 70 71 72 74 75 77 78 79 81 82 83 84 85 86 87 93 97 98 99 100 101 102 103 104 105 106 107 110 111 115 119 130 132 134 135 143 144 145 146 147 148 150 152 153 154
Primary Contact: Lisa E. Harris, M.D., Chief Executive Officer
COO: Neil Johnson, Chief Operating Officer
CFO: Kathi Johnson, Chief Financial Officer
CMO: David W Crabb, M.D., Chief Medical Officer
CIO: Scott Morris, Vice President Information Systems
CHR: Christia Hicks, Vice President Human Resources
CNO: Lee Ann Blue, MSN, R.N., Chief Nursing Officer and Executive Vice President Patient Care Services
Web address: www.eskenazihealth.edu
Control: County, Government, nonfederal **Service**: General medical and surgical

Staffed Beds: 259 **Admissions:** 16308 **Census:** 227	

☐ **FAIRBANKS (150179)**, 8102 Clearvista Parkway, Zip 46256–4698; tel. 317/849–8222, **A**1 3 10 **F**4 5 30 75 87 100 135 151 152 **P**6
Primary Contact: Barb Elliott, Interim President and Chief Executive Officer
CFO: Barb Elliott, Chief Financial Officer
CMO: Dennis Rhyne, M.D., Acting Medical Director
CIO: Randy Walls, Manager Information Services
CHR: Sharon Baker, Director Support Services
CNO: Jennifer M Horstman, R.N., Chief Nursing Officer and Chief Information Officer
Web address: www.fairbankscd.org
Control: Other not–for–profit (including NFP Corporation) **Service**: Alcoholism and other chemical dependency

Staffed Beds: 86 **Admissions:** 3757 **Census:** 51 **Outpatient Visits:** 22731 **Births:** 0 **Total Expense ($000):** 24537 **Payroll Expense ($000):** 12033 **Personnel:** 259	

○ △ **FRANCISCAN HEALTH INDIANAPOLIS (150162)**, 8111 South Emerson Avenue, Zip 46237–8601; tel. 317/528–5000, (Nonreporting) **A**2 3 5 7 10 11 **S** Franciscan Health, Mishawaka, IN
Primary Contact: James Callaghan III, M.D., President and Chief Executive Officer
CFO: Keith A. Lauter, Regional Chief Financial Officer
CMO: Christopher Doehring, M.D., Vice President Medical Affairs
CIO: Barbara Coulter, Director Information Systems
CHR: Corey Baute, Vice President Human Resources
CNO: Agnes Therady, MSN, FACHE, Vice President and Chief Nursing Officer
Web address: www.stfrancishospitals.org
Control: Church operated, Nongovernment, not–for–profit **Service**: General medical and surgical

Staffed Beds: 485	

INDIANA UNIVERSITY HEALTH METHODIST HOSPITAL See Indiana University Health University Hospital, Indianapolis

Many Facility Codes have changed. Please refer to the AHA Guide Code Chart. © 2018 AHA Guide

IN

☒ **INDIANA UNIVERSITY HEALTH UNIVERSITY HOSPITAL (150056)**, 550 University Boulevard, Zip 46202–5149, Mailing Address: P.O. Box 1367, Zip 46206–1367; tel. 317/944–5000, (Includes INDIANA UNIVERSITY HEALTH METHODIST HOSPITAL, 1701 North Senate Boulevard, Indianapolis, IN, Zip 46202, Mailing Address: 1701 North Senate Boulevard, Zip 46202, tel. 317/962–2000; Ryan Nagy, M.D., Interim President and Chief Medical Officer; INDIANA UNIVERSITY HEALTH SAXONY HOSPITAL, 13000 East 136th Street, Fishers, IN, Zip 46037–9478; tel. 317/678–2000; Alicia Schulhof, President and Chief Executive Officer; INDIANA UNIVERSITY HOSPITAL, 550 North University Boulevard, Indianapolis, IN, Zip 46202–5262; tel. 317/274–5000; RILEY HOSPITAL FOR CHILDREN AT INDIANA UNIVERSITY HEALTH, 702 Barnhill Drive, Indianapolis, IN, Zip 46202–5225, Mailing Address: 705 Riley Hospital Dr, Zip 46202, tel. 317/274–5000) **A**1 2 3 5 8 10 **F**3 5 6 7 8 9 11 12 13 15 16 17 18 19 20 21 22 23 24 25 26 27 28 29 30 31 32 33 34 35 36 37 38 39 40 41 43 44 45 46 47 48 49 50 51 52 53 54 55 56 57 58 59 60 61 62 63 64 65 68 69 70 71 72 73 74 75 76 77 78 79 80 81 82 83 84 85 86 87 88 89 90 91 92 93 94 95 96 97 98 99 100 101 102 103 104 105 106 107 108 109 110 111 112 113 114 115 116 117 118 119 120 121 122 123 124 126 129 130 131 132 134 135 136 137 138 139 140 141 142 144 145 146 147 148 149 150 151 152 153 154 **S** Indiana University Health, Indianapolis, IN
Primary Contact: Ryan Nagy, M.D., Interim President and Chief Medical Officer
Web address: www.iuhealth.org
Control: Other not–for–profit (including NFP Corporation) **Service:** General medical and surgical

Staffed Beds: 1282 **Admissions:** 47709 **Census:** 913 **Outpatient Visits:** 1337055 **Births:** 3206 **Total Expense ($000):** 2862367 **Payroll Expense ($000):** 996490 **Personnel:** 13944

INDIANA UNIVERSITY HOSPITAL See Indiana University Health University Hospital, Indianapolis

☒ **KINDRED HOSPITAL INDIANAPOLIS NORTH (152013)**, 8060 Knue Road, Zip 46250–1976; tel. 317/813–8900, (Nonreporting) **A**1 10 **S** Kindred Healthcare, Louisville, KY
Primary Contact: Nakia Tremble, Chief Executive Officer
CHR: Kelly Becker, Administrative Coordinator Human Resources
Web address: www.kindredindynorth.com/
Control: Corporation, Investor–owned (for–profit) **Service:** Acute long–term care hospital

Staffed Beds: 45

☒ **KINDRED HOSPITAL–INDIANAPOLIS (152007)**, 1700 West 10th Street, Zip 46222–3802; tel. 317/636–4400, (Nonreporting) **A**1 10 **S** Kindred Healthcare, Louisville, KY
Primary Contact: Bryan Chatterton, Chief Executive Officer
COO: Angela Lynne Rotert, Chief Clinical Officer
CFO: William Brenner, Chief Financial Officer
CHR: Joe Housh, District Director Human Resources
Web address: www.kindredhospitalindy.com/
Control: Corporation, Investor–owned (for–profit) **Service:** Acute long–term care hospital

Staffed Beds: 59

☐ **LARUE D. CARTER MEMORIAL HOSPITAL (154008)**, 2601 Cold Spring Road, Zip 46222–2273; tel. 317/941–4000, (Nonreporting) **A**1 5 10
Primary Contact: Robert Clover, Interim Superintendent
CFO: Michael Logar, Assistant Superintendent
CMO: Beth Pfau, M.D., Chief Medical Officer
CIO: Denton Gross, Director Information Services
CHR: Rebecca Dutton, Director Human Resources
CNO: Todd Rittman, Director of Nursing
Control: State, Government, nonfederal **Service:** Psychiatric

Staffed Beds: 148

METHODIST HOSPITAL See Indiana University Health Methodist Hospital

NEUROPSYCHIATRIC HOSPITAL OF INDIANAPOLIS (154063), 6720 Parkdale Place, Zip 46254–4668; tel. 317/744–9200, (Nonreporting) **S** NeuroPsychiatric Hospitals, Mishawaka, IN
Primary Contact: Tracy Davis, Chief Executive Officer
Web address: www.neuropsychiatrichospitals.net
Control: Corporation, Investor–owned (for–profit) **Service:** Psychiatric

Staffed Beds: 50

☐ **OPTIONS BEHAVIORAL HEALTH SYSTEM (154057)**, 5602 Caito Drive, Zip 46226–1346; tel. 317/544–4340, (Nonreporting) **A**1 10 **S** Acadia Healthcare Company, Inc., Franklin, TN
Primary Contact: Chris Rupert, Chief Executive Officer
Web address: www.optionsbehavioralhealthsystem.com/
Control: Corporation, Investor–owned (for–profit) **Service:** Psychiatric

Staffed Beds: 84

○ **ORTHOINDY HOSPITAL (150160)**, 8400 Northwest Boulevard, Zip 46278–1381; tel. 317/956–1000, (Nonreporting) **A**3 10 11
Primary Contact: Stacie Vance, Chief Nursing Officer and Chief Operations Officer
COO: Stacie Vance, Chief Nursing Officer and
CFO: Anthony Gioia, Chief Financial Officer
CMO: Joseph Randolph, M.D., Chairman Medical Executive Committee
CIO: Paul Frey, Director Information Technology Applications
CHR: Kristy Hensley, Director Human Resources
CNO: Stacie Vance, Chief Nursing Officer and Vice President Operations
Web address: www.orthoindy.com
Control: Corporation, Investor–owned (for–profit) **Service:** Orthopedic

Staffed Beds: 37

☐ △ **REHABILITATION HOSPITAL OF INDIANA (153028)**, 4141 Shore Drive, Zip 46254–2607; tel. 317/329–2000, **A**1 3 5 7 10 **F**28 29 30 33 35 54 58 64 75 79 86 87 90 91 92 93 96 130 131 132 146 148 **P**5 **S** Indiana University Health, Indianapolis, IN
Primary Contact: Daniel B. Woloszyn, Chief Executive Officer
COO: Monte Spence, Chief Operating Officer
CFO: Marjorie Basey, Chief Financial Officer
CMO: Flora Hammond, M.D., Chief Medical Affairs
CIO: Gary Skinner, Director Information Technology
CHR: Joni Brown, Director Human Resources
CNO: Debra Cordes, Chief Nursing Officer
Web address: www.rhin.com
Control: Other not–for–profit (including NFP Corporation) **Service:** Rehabilitation

Staffed Beds: 83 **Admissions:** 1278 **Census:** 54 **Outpatient Visits:** 21717 **Births:** 0 **Total Expense ($000):** 39599 **Payroll Expense ($000):** 20134 **Personnel:** 339

☒ △ **RICHARD L. ROUDEBUSH VETERANS AFFAIRS MEDICAL CENTER**, 1481 West Tenth Street, Zip 46202–2884; tel. 317/554–0000, **A**1 2 3 5 7 8 **F**3 5 18 20 22 24 26 28 29 30 31 33 34 35 36 38 39 40 44 45 46 47 49 50 53 54 56 57 58 59 60 61 62 63 64 65 66 67 70 71 74 75 77 78 79 80 81 82 83 84 85 86 87 90 91 92 93 94 96 97 98 100 101 102 103 104 105 106 107 108 111 115 117 118 119 120 121 123 124 126 127 130 132 135 143 144 146 147 148 149 152 153 154 **S** Department of Veterans Affairs, Perry Point, MD
Primary Contact: Brian Hancock, M.D., Director
COO: Ginny L Creasman, Associate Director
CFO: Colin Lennon, Chief Financial Officer
CMO: Imtiaz A Munshi, M.D., Chief of Staff
CIO: Steve Stoner, Chief Information Officer
CHR: Chari Weddle, Chief Human Resource Management Service
CNO: Patricia Mathis, Associate Director Patient Care Service
Web address: www.indianapolis.va.gov
Control: Veterans Affairs, Government, federal **Service:** General medical and surgical

Staffed Beds: 209 **Admissions:** 8267 **Census:** 127 **Outpatient Visits:** 775317 **Births:** 0 **Total Expense ($000):** 553250 **Payroll Expense ($000):** 216603 **Personnel:** 2557

RILEY HOSPITAL FOR CHILDREN See Riley Hospital For Children At Indiana University Health

RILEY HOSPITAL FOR CHILDREN AT INDIANA UNIVERSITY HEALTH See Indiana University Health University Hospital, Indianapolis

ST. FRANCIS HOSPITAL AND HEALTH CENTERS – SOUTH CAMPUS See Franciscan Health Indianapolis

IN

Hospital, Medicare Provider Number, Address, Telephone, Approval, Facility, and Physician Codes, Health Care System

★ American Hospital Association (AHA) membership ☐ The Joint Commission accreditation ○ Healthcare Facilities Accreditation Program ◇ DNV Healthcare Inc. accreditation ⇑ Center for Improvement in Healthcare Quality Accreditation △ Commission on Accreditation of Rehabilitation Facilities (CARF) accreditation

INDIANAPOLIS—Hamilton County

✠ **ST. VINCENT HEART CENTER (150153)**, 10580 North Meridian Street, Zip 46290–1028; tel. 317/583–5000, **A**1 10 **F**3 18 20 22 24 26 28 29 30 34 35 40 43 45 46 58 59 75 81 85 86 87 107 111 115 119 129 130 135 149 154 **P**2 **S** Ascension Healthcare, Saint Louis, MO
Primary Contact: Blake A. Dye, FACHE, President
CFO: Becky Jacobson, Vice President Finance
CMO: Don Stogsdill, Chief Medical Officer
CIO: Jeremy Long, Chief Information Officer
CNO: Lori Shannon, Chief Nursing Officer
Web address: www.bestheartcare.com/
Control: Partnership, Investor–owned (for–profit) **Service:** Heart

Staffed Beds: 80 **Admissions:** 4568 **Census:** 56 **Outpatient Visits:** 11775
Births: 0 **Total Expense ($000):** 108184 **Payroll Expense ($000):** 29131
Personnel: 299

INDIANAPOLIS—Marion County

✠ **ST. VINCENT INDIANAPOLIS HOSPITAL (150084)**, 2001 West 86th Street, Zip 46260–1991, Mailing Address: P.O. Box 40970, Zip 46240–0970; tel. 317/338–2345, (Includes PEYTON MANNING CHILDREN'S HOSPITAL AT ST. VINCENT, 2001 West 86th Street, Indianapolis, IN, Zip 46260, Mailing Address: P.O. Box 40970, Zip 46240–0970, tel. 317/415–8111; Hossain Marandi, M.D., FACHE, President and Chief Executive Officer; PEYTON MANNING CHILDREN'S HOSPITAL, 1707 West 86th Street, Indianapolis, IN, Zip 46240, Mailing Address: P.O. Box 40407, Zip 46240, tel. 317/415–5500; Hossain Marandi, M.D., FACHE, President and Chief Executive Officer; ST. VINCENT STRESS CENTER, 8401 Harcourt Road, Indianapolis, IN, Zip 46260, Mailing Address: P.O. Box 80160, Zip 46280, tel. 317/338–4600; Sheila Mishler, Chief Executive Officer; ST. VINCENT WOMEN'S HOSPITAL, 8111 Township Line Road, Indianapolis, IN, Zip 46260–8043; tel. 317/415–8111; Anne Coleman, Administrator) **A**1 2 3 5 8 10 **F**3 4 5 7 8 9 11 13 15 17 18 19 20 21 22 23 24 25 26 27 28 29 30 31 32 34 35 36 37 38 39 40 41 43 44 45 46 47 48 49 50 51 53 54 55 56 57 58 59 61 62 63 64 65 66 68 70 71 72 73 74 75 76 77 78 79 81 82 83 84 85 86 87 88 89 90 91 92 93 94 95 96 97 98 99 100 101 102 103 104 105 107 108 109 110 111 114 115 117 118 119 120 121 124 126 129 130 131 132 134 135 137 138 141 142 143 144 146 147 148 149 151 152 153 154 **P**6 **S** Ascension Healthcare, Saint Louis, MO
Primary Contact: Joel Feldman, Regional President
COO: Erica Wehrmeister, Chief Operating Officer
CFO: Terry Metzger, Vice President, Finance
CMO: Richard Freeman, Chief Medical Officer
CIO: Randy Cox, Chief Information Officer
CHR: Audra Pratt, Chief Human Resource Officer
CNO: Mary Myers, R.N., MSN, Chief Nursing Officer
Web address: www.stvincent.org
Control: Church operated, Nongovernment, not–for–profit **Service:** General medical and surgical

Staffed Beds: 832 **Admissions:** 33608 **Census:** 564 **Outpatient Visits:** 741741 **Births:** 3034 **Total Expense ($000):** 1046345 **Payroll Expense ($000):** 370565 **Personnel:** 4024

✠ **ST. VINCENT SETON SPECIALTY HOSPITAL (152020)**, 8050 Township Line Road, Zip 46260–2478; tel. 317/415–8500, **A**1 10 **F**1 3 29 30 31 35 44 68 75 85 107 114 119 130 132 148 151 154 **S** Ascension Healthcare, Saint Louis, MO
Primary Contact: Joel Feldman, Regional President
CFO: Terry Metzger, Chief Financial Officer
CMO: Alain Broccard, M.D., Chief Medical Officer
Web address: www.stvincent.org/
Control: Church operated, Nongovernment, not–for–profit **Service:** Acute long–term care hospital

Staffed Beds: 74 **Admissions:** 428 **Census:** 50 **Outpatient Visits:** 0
Births: 0 **Total Expense ($000):** 35137 **Payroll Expense ($000):** 17352
Personnel: 242

JASPER—Dubois County

✠ **MEMORIAL HOSPITAL AND HEALTH CARE CENTER (150115)**, 800 West Ninth Street, Zip 47546–2516; tel. 812/996–2345, (Total facility includes 20 beds in nursing home–type unit) **A**1 2 10 19 **F**3 5 7 8 11 12 13 18 20 22 24 26 28 29 30 31 34 35 36 40 41 45 46 47 48 49 51 54 56 57 59 62 64 66 68 70 74 75 76 77 78 79 81 82 84 85 86 87 89 90 93 97 98 100 101 102 103 104 107 108 110 111 112 113 114 115 116 117 118 119 120 121 126 127 128 129 130 131 132 135 144 146 147 148 149 154 **P**6 **S** American Province of Little Company of Mary Sisters, Evergreen Park, IL
Primary Contact: E Kyle. Bennett, President and Chief Executive Officer
CFO: Ted Miller, Vice President and Chief Financial Officer
CMO: Stan Tretter, M.D., Chief Medical Officer
CIO: Gary Light, Vice President and Chief Information Officer
CHR: Richard Pea, Director Human Resources
CNO: Tonya Heim, R.N., MSN, Vice President Patient Services and Chief Nursing Officer
Web address: www.mhhcc.org
Control: Church operated, Nongovernment, not–for–profit **Service:** General medical and surgical

Staffed Beds: 143 **Admissions:** 5565 **Census:** 64 **Outpatient Visits:** 259497 **Births:** 915 **Total Expense ($000):** 213460 **Payroll Expense ($000):** 97739 **Personnel:** 1367

JEFFERSONVILLE—Clark County

✠ **CLARK MEMORIAL HOSPITAL (150009)**, 1220 Missouri Avenue, Zip 47130–3743, Mailing Address: P.O. Box 69, Zip 47131–0600; tel. 812/282–6631, **A**1 2 3 5 10 **F**3 5 8 15 17 18 20 22 26 28 29 30 31 34 35 38 40 45 46 49 50 54 56 57 59 64 65 70 73 74 75 76 77 78 79 81 82 85 86 87 92 98 101 102 103 104 105 107 108 110 111 114 115 119 129 130 132 135 144 145 146 147 148 149 153 **P**6 **S** LifePoint Health, Brentwood, TN
Primary Contact: Martin Padgett, President and Chief Executive Officer
CFO: Kirk Strack, Vice President and Chief Financial Officer
CMO: William Templeton, M.D., III Medical Director
CIO: Larry Reverman, Director Information Systems
CHR: Scott Hicks, Vice President
CNO: Kathy Neuner, R.N., Chief Nursing Officer
Web address: www.clarkmemorial.org
Control: Corporation, Investor–owned (for–profit) **Service:** General medical and surgical

Staffed Beds: 185 **Admissions:** 9887 **Census:** 102 **Outpatient Visits:** 109749 **Births:** 1372 **Total Expense ($000):** 149156 **Payroll Expense ($000):** 48666 **Personnel:** 992

☐ **WELLSTONE REGIONAL HOSPITAL (154051)**, 2700 Vissing Park Road, Zip 47130–5989; tel. 812/284–8000, **A**1 10 **F**4 5 29 35 38 40 56 65 98 99 100 101 102 103 104 105 130 152 153 **S** Universal Health Services, Inc., King of Prussia, PA
Primary Contact: Greg Stewart, Chief Executive Officer
CFO: Gracia Winsett, Chief Financial Officer
CMO: Asad Ismail, M.D., Medical Director
CIO: Billy Leftwitch, Director, Information Technology
CHR: Tiffany Pierce, Director Human Resources
CNO: Anthony Aemmer, Director of Nursing
Web address: www.wellstonehospital.com
Control: Corporation, Investor–owned (for–profit) **Service:** Psychiatric

Staffed Beds: 100 **Admissions:** 3521 **Census:** 78 **Outpatient Visits:** 9398
Births: 0 **Total Expense ($000):** 15608 **Payroll Expense ($000):** 9771
Personnel: 204

KENDALLVILLE—Noble County

✠ **PARKVIEW NOBLE HOSPITAL (150146)**, 401 Sawyer Road, Zip 46755–2568; tel. 260/347–8700, **A**1 10 **F**3 7 13 15 28 29 34 35 40 45 46 47 50 54 57 59 64 70 74 75 76 79 81 82 85 87 93 94 97 107 108 110 111 114 118 119 129 130 132 135 143 145 146 154 **P**6 **S** Parkview Health, Fort Wayne, IN
Primary Contact: Gary W. Adkins, President
COO: Gary W Adkins, Chief Executive Officer
CFO: Kem Prince, Manager of Finance
CMO: Gerald Warrener, M.D., Chief Medical Officer
CIO: Ron Double, Chief Information Officer
CHR: Bruce Buttermore, Manager Human Resources
CNO: Catherine Byrd, Vice President Patient Services
Web address: www.parkview.com
Control: Other not–for–profit (including NFP Corporation) **Service:** General medical and surgical

Staffed Beds: 31 **Admissions:** 2035 **Census:** 16 **Outpatient Visits:** 62788
Births: 251 **Total Expense ($000):** 55529 **Payroll Expense ($000):** 15441
Personnel: 224

KNOX—St. Joseph County

☐ **MEDICAL BEHAVIORAL HOSPITAL OF MISHAWAKA (154061)**, 5985 E 200 S, Zip 46534, Mailing Address: 1625 East Jefferson Boulevard, Mishawaka, Zip 46545–7103; tel. 574/255–1400, (Nonreporting) **A**1 10 **S** NeuroPsychiatric Hospitals, Mishawaka, IN
Primary Contact: Emily Ryan, Chief Executive Officer
COO: Christy Gilbert, President and Chief Operating Officer
Web address: www.physicianshospitalsystem.net/
Control: Partnership, Investor–owned (for–profit) **Service:** Acute long–term care hospital

Staffed Beds: 30

KNOX—Starke County

✠ **STARKE HOSPITAL (150102)**, 102 East Culver Road, Zip 46534–2216, Mailing Address: P.O. Box 339, Zip 46534–0339; tel. 574/772–6231, **A**1 10 **F**3 15 18 29 30 32 34 35 38 40 45 46 49 50 53 57 59 65 68 74 75 77 79 81 85 87 93 94 107 108 110 111 114 115 116 117 119 130 146 149 **S** Community Health Systems, Inc., Franklin, TN
Primary Contact: Jeff Vice, Chief Operating Officer and Interim Chief Executive Officer
COO: Jeff Vice, Chief Operating Officer
CFO: Drew Keesbury, Chief Financial Officer
CMO: A N Damodaran, M.D., President Medical Staff
CIO: Ashley Norem, Chief Information Systems
CHR: Doug Jesch, Director Human Resources
CNO: Anetra Jones, R.N., M.P.H., Chief Nursing Officer
Web address: www.iuhealth.org/starke/
Control: Other not–for–profit (including NFP Corporation) **Service:** General medical and surgical

Staffed Beds: 15 **Admissions:** 472 **Census:** 4 **Outpatient Visits:** 34244
Births: 0 **Total Expense ($000):** 19616 **Payroll Expense ($000):** 6579
Personnel: 109

Many Facility Codes have changed. Please refer to the AHA Guide Code Chart. © 2018 AHA Guide

IN

STARKE MEMORIAL HOSPITAL See Starke Hospital

KOKOMO—Howard County

⊞ **COMMUNITY HOWARD REGIONAL HEALTH (150007)**, 3500 South Lafountain Street, Zip 46902–3803, Mailing Address: P.O. Box 9011, Zip 46904–9011; tel. 765/453–0702, (Nonreporting) **A**1 2 10 **S** Community Health Network, Indianapolis, IN
Primary Contact: Joseph Hooper, President and Chief Executive Officer
COO: Theodore Brown, Chief Operating Officer
CFO: Theodore Brown, Vice President Financial Services
CIO: Kevin Purvis, Chief Information Officer
CHR: Michael L Williams, FACHE, Vice President Human Resources
CNO: Melodi Greene, R.N., MS, Chief Nursing Officer
Web address: www.howardregional.org
Control: Other not–for–profit (including NFP Corporation) **Service**: General medical and surgical

Staffed Beds: 137

⊞ **COMMUNITY HOWARD SPECIALTY HOSPITAL (153039)**, 829 North Dixon Road, Zip 46901–7709; tel. 765/452–6700, **A**1 10 **F**28 29 30 34 57 77 90 93 129 131 132 154 **P**1 8 **S** Community Health Network, Indianapolis, IN
Primary Contact: Jeffrey Weiss, Interim Director
CFO: Julie Pena, Director Finance
CMO: Brad Vossberg, M.D., Chief Rehabilitation
CNO: Claudia Jean Lowry, R.N., Director of Nursing
Web address: www.ecommunity.com
Control: Partnership, Investor–owned (for–profit) **Service**: Rehabilitation

Staffed Beds: 30 Admissions: 442 Census: 15 Births: 0

HOWARD REGIONAL HEALTH SYSTEM See Community Howard Regional Health

HOWARD REGIONAL HEALTH SYSTEM WEST CAMPUS SPECIALTY HOSPITAL See Community Howard Specialty Hospital

⊞ **ST. VINCENT KOKOMO (150010)**, 1907 West Sycamore Street, Zip 46901–4197; tel. 765/452–5611, **A**1 10 **F**3 4 5 7 8 13 15 18 20 28 29 30 31 34 35 36 40 44 45 49 50 51 53 55 57 59 64 66 68 69 70 73 74 75 77 78 79 81 82 85 86 87 90 93 96 98 100 101 102 104 105 107 108 110 111 115 119 120 121 123 129 130 131 132 135 143 145 146 147 148 149 151 **S** Ascension Healthcare, Saint Louis, MO
Primary Contact: Margaret M. Johnson, President, St. Vincent Northwest Region
CFO: Dennis Ressler, Chief Financial Officer
CMO: David L Williams, M.D., Chief Medical Officer
CIO: Jeffrey Scott, Chief Information Officer
CHR: Cindy Babb, Executive Director Human Resources and Organizational Effectiveness
CNO: Kathleen K Peoples, R.N., MS, Vice President of Nursing
Web address: www.stvincent.org/stjoseph
Control: Church operated, Nongovernment, not–for–profit **Service**: General medical and surgical

Staffed Beds: 129 Admissions: 6105 Census: 61 Outpatient Visits: 188036 Total Expense ($000): 129776 Payroll Expense ($000): 41729 Personnel: 662

LA PORTE—Laporte County

⊞ **LA PORTE HOSPITAL (150006)**, 1007 Lincolnway, Zip 46350–3201, Mailing Address: P.O. Box 250, Zip 46352–0250; tel. 219/326–1234, **A**1 2 10 19 **F**1 3 4 8 11 13 15 16 17 18 20 22 24 26 27 28 29 30 31 32 34 35 36 39 40 45 46 47 48 49 50 51 53 54 56 57 59 60 62 63 64 65 66 67 68 70 71 72 73 74 75 76 77 78 79 81 85 86 87 88 89 91 92 93 94 96 97 98 107 108 110 111 115 118 119 126 128 129 130 131 132 135 144 145 146 147 148 149 154 **S** Community Health Systems, Inc., Franklin, TN
Primary Contact: Ashley Dickinson, Chief Executive Officer
CFO: Drew Keesbury, Chief Financial Officer
CNO: Anetra Jones, R.N., M.P.H., Chief Nursing Officer
Web address: www.iuhealth.org
Control: Corporation, Investor–owned (for–profit) **Service**: General medical and surgical

Staffed Beds: 129 Admissions: 4547 Census: 48 Outpatient Visits: 117242 Births: 656 Total Expense ($000): 135293 Payroll Expense ($000): 42749 Personnel: 996

LA PORTE REGIONAL HEALTH SYSTEM See La Porte Hospital

LAFAYETTE—Tippecanoe County

CLARIAN ARNETT HOSPITAL See Indiana University Health Arnett Hospital

○ **FRANCISCAN HEALTH LAFAYETTE EAST (150109)**, 1701 South Creasy Lane, Zip 47905–4972; tel. 765/502–4000, (Includes FRANCISCAN HEALTH LAFAYETTE CENTRAL, 1501 Hartford Street, Lafayette, IN, Zip 47904–2134; tel. 765/423–6011; Terrance E Wilson, President and Chief Executive Officer) **A**2 5 10 11 **F**3 11 13 15 17 18 19 20 22 24 28 29 30 31 34 35 37 40 43 45 49 50 51 54 55 57 60 62 63 64 68 69 70 72 75 76 77 78 79 81 82 84 85 87 89 90 93 94 96 97 98 102 107 110 111 114 115 118 119 120 121 126 129 130 132 135 145 146 147 148 **S** Franciscan Health, Mishawaka, IN
Primary Contact: Terrance E. Wilson, President and Chief Executive Officer
Web address: www.ste.org
Control: Church operated, Nongovernment, not–for–profit **Service**: General medical and surgical

Staffed Beds: 187 Admissions: 10528 Census: 122 Outpatient Visits: 349456 Births: 1977 Total Expense ($000): 303367 Payroll Expense ($000): 94502 Personnel: 1598

★ ○ **INDIANA UNIVERSITY HEALTH ARNETT HOSPITAL (150173)**, 5165 McCarty Lane, Zip 47905–8764, Mailing Address: P.O. Box 5545, Zip 47903–5545; tel. 765/448–8000, **A**2 3 5 10 11 **F**3 8 11 12 13 15 17 18 20 22 24 26 28 29 30 31 34 35 40 43 45 46 49 50 51 54 56 57 59 61 64 65 68 69 70 72 74 75 76 77 78 79 81 82 84 85 87 89 92 93 97 100 104 107 108 110 111 114 115 116 117 118 119 120 121 126 129 130 131 132 135 144 145 146 147 148 154 **P**6 **S** Indiana University Health, Indianapolis, IN
Primary Contact: Daniel Neufelder, President
CFO: Cara Breidster, Chief Financial Officer
CMO: Jeffrey P Brown, M.D., Chief Medical Officer
CIO: Rusty McGill, System Director Information Technology
CHR: Koreen H Kyhnell, Vice President Human Resources
Web address: www.iuhealth.org
Control: Other not–for–profit (including NFP Corporation) **Service**: General medical and surgical

Staffed Beds: 187 Admissions: 9080 Census: 112 Outpatient Visits: 104835 Births: 1612 Total Expense ($000): 416727 Payroll Expense ($000): 173120 Personnel: 1819

⊞ **LAFAYETTE REGIONAL REHABILITATION HOSPITAL (153042)**, 950 Park East Boulevard, Zip 47905–0792; tel. 765/447–4040, **A**1 10 **F**3 28 29 35 60 64 75 90 93 94 132 143 148 154 **P**5 **S** Ernest Health, Inc., Albuquerque, NM
Primary Contact: Michelle Russell, Chief Executive Officer
Web address: www.lrrh.ernesthealth.com
Control: Corporation, Investor–owned (for–profit) **Service**: Rehabilitation

Staffed Beds: 40 Admissions: 561 Census: 19 Outpatient Visits: 3390 Births: 0 Total Expense ($000): 11398 Payroll Expense ($000): 4924 Personnel: 113

ST. ELIZABETH CENTRAL See Franciscan Health Lafayette Central

☐ **SYCAMORE SPRINGS HOSPITAL (154059)**, 833 Park East Boulevard, Zip 47905–0785; tel. 765/743–4400, (Nonreporting) **A**1 10 **S** Springstone, Louisville, KY
Primary Contact: Zoe Frantz, Chief Executive Officer
CFO: Michael Huth, Chief Financial Officer
CMO: Nizar El Khalili, M.D., Medical Director
CHR: Pam Sichts, Director Human Resources
CNO: Brooke Lavignette, Director of Nursing
Web address: www.sycamorespringshealth.com
Control: Corporation, Investor–owned (for–profit) **Service**: Psychiatric

Staffed Beds: 48

IN

Hospital, Medicare Provider Number, Address, Telephone, Approval, Facility, and Physician Codes, Health Care System

★ American Hospital Association (AHA) membership   ○ Healthcare Facilities Accreditation Program   ⇑ Center for Improvement in Healthcare Quality Accreditation
☐ The Joint Commission accreditation   ◇ DNV Healthcare Inc. accreditation   △ Commission on Accreditation of Rehabilitation Facilities (CARF) accreditation

LAGRANGE—Lagrange County

☒ **PARKVIEW LAGRANGE HOSPITAL (151323)**, 207 North Townline Road, Zip 46761–1325; tel. 260/463–9000, **A**1 10 18 **F**3 7 13 15 17 26 29 30 34 35 40 45 50 51 57 59 63 64 70 75 76 79 81 82 83 84 85 86 87 89 90 93 96 107 108 109 110 111 114 118 119 128 130 132 133 143 146 148 154 **P**6 **S** Parkview Health, Fort Wayne, IN
Primary Contact: Jordi K. Disler, President
CFO: Vickie Stanski, Financial Manager
CMO: Jeffrey Brookes, M.D., Chief Medical Officer
CIO: Ron Double, Chief Information Technology Officer
CHR: Bruce Buttermore, Director Human Resources
CNO: Jared Beasley, R.N., Vice President Patient Care
Web address: www.parkview.com
Control: Other not–for–profit (including NFP Corporation) **Service**: General medical and surgical

Staffed Beds: 25 **Admissions**: 1111 **Census**: 10 **Outpatient Visits**: 27498
Births: 205 **Total Expense ($000)**: 36375 **Payroll Expense ($000)**: 10125
Personnel: 157

LAWRENCEBURG—Dearborn County

COMMUNITY MENTAL HEALTH CENTER (154011), 285 Bielby Road, Zip 47025–1055; tel. 812/537–1302, (Nonreporting) **A**10
Primary Contact: Tom Talbot, Chief Executive Officer
CFO: Georgii Zhirkin, Chief Financial Officer
CMO: Hasan Bakhtier, M.D., Medical Director
CIO: John McKinley, Director, Information Technology
CHR: Kelly Stewart, Director of Human Resources
Web address: www.cmhcinc.org
Control: Other not–for–profit (including NFP Corporation) **Service**: Psychiatric

Staffed Beds: 16

★ ○ **HIGHPOINT HEALTH (150086)**, 600 Wilson Creek Road, Zip 47025–2751; tel. 812/537–1010, **A**10 11 **F**3 11 13 15 20 28 29 30 34 35 37 40 43 44 45 46 47 49 50 57 59 62 63 64 70 75 76 77 79 81 84 85 86 87 92 93 107 108 110 111 115 116 117 118 119 129 130 131 132 146 148 **P**7
Primary Contact: Michael W. Schwebler, President and Chief Executive Officer
CMO: Nancy A. Kennedy, M.D., Chief Medical Officer
CIO: Kathy Dickman, Director of Information Systems
CNO: Angela K. Scudder, MSN, R.N., Vice President Patient Care Services
Web address: www.dch.org
Control: County, Government, nonfederal **Service**: General medical and surgical

Staffed Beds: 62 **Admissions**: 3873 **Census**: 36 **Outpatient Visits**: 145326
Births: 381 **Total Expense ($000)**: 79502 **Payroll Expense ($000)**: 34447
Personnel: 599

LEBANON—Boone County

☒ **WITHAM HEALTH SERVICES (150104)**, 2605 North Lebanon Street, Zip 46052–1476, Mailing Address: P.O. Box 1200, Zip 46052–3005; tel. 765/485–8000, **A**1 10 **F**3 7 8 13 15 18 20 22 24 28 29 30 34 40 45 53 54 56 57 59 64 65 69 70 75 76 77 79 81 82 83 85 86 87 93 94 97 98 107 111 116 121 128 129 130 132 135 143 144 146 147 148 **P**1
Primary Contact: Raymond V. Ingham, Ph.D., President and Chief Executive Officer
COO: Diane Feder, R.N., FACHE, Senior Vice President and Chief Operating Officer
CFO: George Pogas, CPA, Senior Vice President and Chief Financial Officer
CMO: Anthony Steele, M.D., Chief Medical Officer
CIO: George Pogas, CPA, Senior Vice President and Chief Financial Officer
CHR: Gary A Deater, Vice President Administration, Human Resources and Risk Management
CNO: Diane Feder, R.N., FACHE, Senior Vice President and Chief Operating Officer
Web address: www.witham.org
Control: County, Government, nonfederal **Service**: General medical and surgical

Staffed Beds: 70 **Admissions**: 2830 **Census**: 42 **Outpatient Visits**: 193863
Births: 499 **Total Expense ($000)**: 124252 **Payroll Expense ($000)**: 52836
Personnel: 788

LINTON—Greene County

☒ **GREENE COUNTY GENERAL HOSPITAL (151317)**, 1185 North 1000 West, Zip 47441–5282; tel. 812/847–2281, **A**1 10 18 **F**1 3 6 11 13 15 18 19 26 27 28 29 30 31 34 35 40 41 45 50 55 57 58 59 62 64 65 66 67 68 70 75 76 77 78 79 81 85 86 87 90 91 93 107 108 110 111 114 119 125 128 130 133 135 146 147 148 149 154
Primary Contact: Brenda Reetz, FACHE, Chief Executive Officer
CFO: April Settles, Chief Financial Officer
CMO: Frederick R. Ridge, M.D., Chief of Staff
CIO: Steve Phillips, Information Officer
CHR: Jean Prather, Director of Human Resources
CNO: Kristin Crynes, Executive Director of Nursing
Web address: www.greenecountyhospital.com
Control: County, Government, nonfederal **Service**: General medical and surgical

Staffed Beds: 25 **Admissions**: 693 **Census**: 6 **Outpatient Visits**: 729399
Births: 87 **Total Expense ($000)**: 29920 **Payroll Expense ($000)**: 12854
Personnel: 257

LOGANSPORT—Cass County

FOUR COUNTY COUNSELING CENTER (154035), 1015 Michigan Avenue, Zip 46947–1526; tel. 574/722–5151, (Nonreporting) **A**10
Primary Contact: C.J. Davis, Chief Executive Officer and Executive Director
COO: Carrie Cadwell, M.D., Chief Clinical Officer
CFO: Jason Cadwell, Chief Financial Officer
CMO: John Yarling, M.D., Medical Director
CIO: Becky Mulis, Director of Health Information Management Systems
CHR: Steve Curry, Regional Director Human Resources
CNO: Donna Henry, Vice President of Nursing Services
Web address: www.fourcounty.org
Control: Other not–for–profit (including NFP Corporation) **Service**: Psychiatric

Staffed Beds: 15

★ ○ **LOGANSPORT MEMORIAL HOSPITAL (150072)**, 1101 Michigan Avenue, Zip 46947–1528, Mailing Address: P.O. Box 7013, Zip 46947–7013; tel. 574/753–7541, **A**10 11 20 **F**3 11 13 15 28 29 32 34 35 36 40 44 45 48 49 50 51 57 59 64 65 68 69 70 75 76 77 78 79 81 85 86 87 93 97 107 108 110 111 114 119 124 129 130 132 135 146 147 149 **P**6
Primary Contact: Perry Gay, President and Chief Executive Officer
CFO: Sherri Gehlhausen, Assistant Chief Financial Officer
CMO: Todd S Weinstein, M.D., Chief of Staff
CIO: Beth Jump, Chief Information Officer
CHR: Lynda J Shrock, Vice President Human Resources
CNO: Tara McVay, Chief Nursing Officer
Web address: www.logansportmemorial.org
Control: County, Government, nonfederal **Service**: General medical and surgical

Staffed Beds: 83 **Admissions**: 1790 **Census**: 14 **Outpatient Visits**: 113912
Births: 513 **Total Expense ($000)**: 70688 **Payroll Expense ($000)**: 31576
Personnel: 504

☐ **LOGANSPORT STATE HOSPITAL**, 1098 South State Road 25, Zip 46947–6723; tel. 574/737–3633, (Nonreporting) **A**1
Primary Contact: Robert Clover, Superintendent and Chief Executive Officer
CFO: Misty Moss, Director Business Administration
CMO: Danny Meadows, M.D., Medical Director
CIO: Joe McIntosh, Director Management Information Systems
CHR: Dianne Renner, Director Human Resources
Web address: www.lshonline.org
Control: State, Government, nonfederal **Service**: Psychiatric

Staffed Beds: 170

MADISON—Jefferson County

★ ○ **KING'S DAUGHTERS' HEALTH (150069)**, 1373 East State Road 62, Zip 47250–3357, Mailing Address: P.O. Box 447, Zip 47250–0447; tel. 812/801–0800, **A**2 10 11 **F**3 7 8 12 13 15 18 20 22 28 29 30 31 32 34 35 40 45 48 50 55 57 59 62 63 64 65 68 70 74 75 76 77 78 79 81 82 84 85 86 87 89 91 93 94 97 107 108 110 111 115 119 120 121 123 129 130 131 132 134 135 144 145 146 147 148 149 150 **P**6
Primary Contact: Carol Dozier, President and Chief Executive Officer
CFO: John Price, Chief Financial Officer
CIO: Linda Darnell, Director Management Information Systems
CHR: Susan Poling, Director Human Resources
CNO: Jennifer Lynn Liter, Vice President of Inpatient Services
Web address: www.kdhhs.org
Control: Other not–for–profit (including NFP Corporation) **Service**: General medical and surgical

Staffed Beds: 77 **Admissions**: 3247 **Census**: 32 **Outpatient Visits**: 198329
Births: 474 **Total Expense ($000)**: 123563 **Payroll Expense ($000)**: 51988
Personnel: 788

☐ **MADISON STATE HOSPITAL (154019)**, 711 Green Road, Zip 47250–2199; tel. 812/265–2611, (Nonreporting) **A**1 10
Primary Contact: Peggy Stephens, M.D., Superintendent and Medical Director
COO: Peggy Stephens, M.D., Superintendent and Medical Director
CFO: Carolyn Copeland, Business Administrator
CMO: Peggy Stephens, M.D., Superintendent and Medical Director
CIO: Ric Martin, Information Specialist
Web address: www.in.gov/fssa/msh
Control: State, Government, nonfederal **Service**: Psychiatric

Staffed Beds: 150

MARION—Grant County

☐ **GRANT–BLACKFORD MENTAL HEALTH CENTER (154021)**, 505 North Wabash Avenue, Zip 46952–2608; tel. 765/662–3971, (Nonreporting) **A**1 10
Primary Contact: Paul Kuczora, Chief Executive Officer
Web address: www.cornerstone.org/
Control: Other not–for–profit (including NFP Corporation) **Service**: Psychiatric

Staffed Beds: 16

Many Facility Codes have changed. Please refer to the AHA Guide Code Chart. © 2018 AHA Guide

IN

★ ○ **MARION GENERAL HOSPITAL (150011)**, 441 North Wabash Avenue, Zip 46952–2690; tel. 765/660–6000, **A**2 10 11 **F**3 7 8 11 13 15 18 20 22 26 28 29 30 31 34 35 40 41 44 45 47 50 54 57 58 59 64 68 70 76 77 78 79 81 82 85 86 87 89 90 91 92 93 96 97 107 108 110 111 114 115 117 118 119 129 130 132 135 146 147 148 149 154 **P**6
Primary Contact: Stephanie Hilton–Siebert, MSN, President and Chief Executive Officer
CFO: Jeff Wakefield, CPA, Chief Financial Officer
CMO: Edward L. Keppler, M.D., Chief Medical Officer
CIO: Emmanuel Ndow, Chief Information Officer
CHR: Karen Jones, Administrative Director Human Resources
CNO: Cynthia Futrell, MSN, R.N., Chief Nursing Officer
Web address: www.mgh.net
Control: Other not–for–profit (including NFP Corporation) **Service**: General medical and surgical

Staffed Beds: 117 **Admissions**: 5192 **Census**: 58 **Outpatient Visits**: 243064 **Births**: 553 **Total Expense ($000)**: 171554 **Payroll Expense ($000)**: 65950 **Personnel**: 1024

VETERANS AFFAIRS NORTHERN INDIANA HEALTH CARE SYSTEM–MARION CAMPUS See Veterans Affairs Northern Indiana Health Care System, Fort Wayne

MERRILLVILLE—Lake County

REGIONAL MENTAL HEALTH CENTER (154020), 8555 Taft Street, Zip 46410–6123; tel. 219/769–4005, (Nonreporting) **A**10
Primary Contact: Robert D. Krumwied, President and Chief Executive Officer
Web address: www.regionalmentalhealth.org/
Control: Corporation, Investor–owned (for–profit) **Service**: Psychiatric

Staffed Beds: 16

SOUTHLAKE CAMPUS See Methodist Hospitals, Gary

MICHIGAN CITY—Laporte County

○ **FRANCISCAN HEALTH MICHIGAN CITY (150015)**, 301 West Homer Street, Zip 46360–4358; tel. 219/879–8511, (Nonreporting) **A**2 10 11 19 **S** Franciscan Health, Mishawaka, IN
Primary Contact: Dean Mazzoni, President and Chief Executive Officer
CFO: Marc Golan, Regional Chief Financial Officer
CIO: Tim Loosemore, Regional Director Information Systems
CHR: John Barrett, Regional Director Human Resources
CNO: Trish Weber, R.N., FACHE, Vice President Operations and Chief Nursing Officer
Web address: www.franciscanalliance.org
Control: Church operated, Nongovernment, not–for–profit **Service**: General medical and surgical

Staffed Beds: 171

SAINT ANTHONY MEMORIAL See Franciscan Health Michigan City

MISHAWAKA—St. Joseph County

☒ **SAINT JOSEPH HEALTH SYSTEM (150012)**, 5215 Holy Cross Parkway, Zip 46545–1469; tel. 574/335–5000, **A**1 2 3 5 10 **F**3 11 13 15 17 18 19 20 21 22 23 24 26 28 29 30 31 34 35 36 37 39 40 41 44 45 46 47 48 49 50 51 52 54 55 57 58 59 60 61 63 64 65 66 68 70 71 72 73 74 75 76 77 78 79 80 81 82 83 84 85 86 87 89 90 91 92 93 96 97 100 107 108 110 114 115 117 118 119 120 121 124 126 129 130 131 132 135 144 146 147 148 149 154 **S** Trinity Health, Livonia, MI
Primary Contact: Chad Towner, Chief Executive Officer
COO: Christopher J Karam, Chief Operating Officer
CFO: Kevin J Higdon, Chief Financial Officer
CMO: Stephen Anderson, M.D., Chief Medical Officer
CIO: Gary L Miller, Senior Director Information Systems
CHR: Kurt A Meyer, Chief Human Resource Officer
CNO: Kenneth C Hall, R.N., Chief Nursing Officer
Web address: www.sjmed.com
Control: Other not–for–profit (including NFP Corporation) **Service**: General medical and surgical

Staffed Beds: 300 **Admissions**: 14646 **Census**: 181 **Outpatient Visits**: 162102 **Births**: 1826 **Total Expense ($000)**: 312382 **Payroll Expense ($000)**: 89489 **Personnel**: 1610

○ **UNITY MEDICAL & SURGICAL HOSPITAL (150177)**, 4455 Edison Lakes Parkway, Zip 46545–1442; tel. 574/968–0867, (Nonreporting) **A**10 11
Primary Contact: John M. Day, Chief Executive Officer
COO: Donald Allen, Chief Operating Officer
CFO: Matthew M Sherwood, Chief Financial Officer
CMO: Viraj Patel, M.D., Chief Medical Officer
CIO: Richard Leighton, Financial Application Analyst
CHR: Emyle Kruyer–Collins, Chief Human Resources Officer
CNO: Sylvia K Coffing, R.N., MSN, Chief Nursing and Compliance Officer
Web address: www.umsh.net
Control: Partnership, Investor–owned (for–profit) **Service**: Surgical

Staffed Beds: 15

MONTICELLO—White County

★ **INDIANA UNIVERSITY HEALTH WHITE MEMORIAL HOSPITAL (151312)**, 720 South Sixth Street, Zip 47960–8182; tel. 574/583–7111, **A**10 18 **F**3 11 15 29 30 31 34 35 40 45 50 57 59 64 69 75 77 78 79 81 85 93 107 108 110 111 114 119 129 133 135 146 147 148 149 150 **S** Indiana University Health, Indianapolis, IN
Primary Contact: Mary Minier, President
CMO: Adel Khdour, M.D., Chief Medical Officer
CIO: Michelle Baker, Director Information Systems
CHR: JoEllyn Brockmeyer, Director Human Resources
CNO: Robin C Smith, Chief Nursing Officer
Web address: www.iuhealth.org/white–memorial
Control: Other not–for–profit (including NFP Corporation) **Service**: General medical and surgical

Staffed Beds: 25 **Admissions**: 572 **Census**: 6 **Outpatient Visits**: 39487 **Births**: 0 **Total Expense ($000)**: 24934 **Payroll Expense ($000)**: 7684 **Personnel**: 131

MOORESVILLE—Morgan County

○ **FRANCISCAN HEALTH MOORESVILLE (150057)**, 1201 Hadley Road, Zip 46158–1789; tel. 317/831–1160, (Nonreporting) **A**3 5 10 11 **S** Franciscan Health, Mishawaka, IN
Primary Contact: Peter J. Murphy, Senior Vice President and Chief Operating Officer
CIO: Barbara Coulter, Director Information Systems
CHR: John Ross, Vice President
CNO: Agnes Therady, MSN, FACHE, Vice President and Chief Nursing Officer
Web address: www.franciscanalliance.org/hospitals/mooresville/Pages/default.aspx
Control: Church operated, Nongovernment, not–for–profit **Service**: General medical and surgical

Staffed Beds: 115

ST. FRANCIS HOSPITAL–MOORESVILLE See Franciscan Health Mooresville

MUNCIE—Delaware County

○ **AMG SPECIALTY HOSPITAL – MUNCIE (152025)**, 2401 West University Avenue, 8th Floor, Zip 47303–3428; tel. 765/751–5253, **A**10 11 **F**1 29 85
Primary Contact: Victor J. Galfano, FACHE, Chief Executive Officer
CNO: Lisa G. Hayes, Chief Clinical Officer
Web address: www.amgmuncie.com/
Control: Corporation, Investor–owned (for–profit) **Service**: Acute long–term care hospital

Staffed Beds: 32 **Admissions**: 378 **Census**: 24 **Outpatient Visits**: 0 **Births**: 0

BALL MEMORIAL HOSPITAL See Indiana University Health Ball Memorial Hospital

---

Hospital, Medicare Provider Number, Address, Telephone, Approval, Facility, and Physician Codes, Health Care System

★ American Hospital Association (AHA) membership
□ The Joint Commission accreditation
○ Healthcare Facilities Accreditation Program
◇ DNV Healthcare Inc. accreditation
⇑ Center for Improvement in Healthcare Quality Accreditation
△ Commission on Accreditation of Rehabilitation Facilities (CARF) accreditation

IN

☒ △ **INDIANA UNIVERSITY HEALTH BALL MEMORIAL HOSPITAL (150089)**,
2401 University Avenue, Zip 47303–3499; tel. 765/747-3111, **A**1 2 3 5 7 10
19 **F**7 11 12 13 15 17 18 20 22 24 26 28 29 30 31 32 34 35 39 40 43 45 49
50 51 53 54 56 57 58 59 60 64 65 66 69 70 72 73 74 75 76 77 78 79 80 81
82 84 85 86 87 89 90 92 93 94 96 97 98 100 101 102 105 107 108 110 111
114 115 116 117 118 119 120 121 123 124 126 129 130 146 147 148 149 **S**
Indiana University Health, Indianapolis, IN
Primary Contact: Jeffrey C. Bird, M.D., President
COO: Lori Luther, CPA, Chief Operating Officer
CFO: John Vanator, CPA, Chief Financial Officer
CMO: Peter Voss, M.D., Chief Medical Officer
CHR: Ann M. McGuire, Regional Vice President Human Resources
CNO: Carla C. Cox, Chief Nursing Officer
Web address: www.iuhealth.org
Control: Other not–for–profit (including NFP Corporation) **Service**: General
medical and surgical

Staffed Beds: 346 Admissions: 16110 Census: 241 Outpatient Visits:
291058 **Births:** 1352 **Total Expense ($000):** 355574 **Payroll Expense
($000):** 111366 **Personnel:** 1819

MERIDIAN HEALTH SERVICES (154053), 240 North Tillotson Avenue,
Zip 47304; tel. 765/747-3281, (Nonreporting) **A**10
Primary Contact: Hank A. Milius, Chief Executive Officer
CMO: Sarfraz Khan, Medical Director
Web address: www.meridianhs.org
Control: Other not–for–profit (including NFP Corporation) **Service**: Psychiatric

Staffed Beds: 20

RENAISSANCE SPECIALTY HOSPITAL OF CENTRAL INDIANA See AMG
Specialty Hospital – Muncie

MUNSTER—Lake County

☐ **COMMUNITY HOSPITAL (150125)**, 901 Macarthur Boulevard, Zip 46321–2959;
tel. 219/836-1600, **A**1 2 10 **F**3 8 11 12 13 15 17 18 20 22 24 26 28 29 30
31 34 35 36 38 39 40 45 46 47 49 50 53 54 55 57 58 59 62 64 67 70 72 73
74 75 77 78 79 80 81 82 85 86 87 90 92 93 96 107 108 110 111 114 115
116 119 120 121 123 124 126 129 130 131 132 135 144 146 147 148 **S**
Community Healthcare System, Hammond, IN
Primary Contact: Luis F. Molina, Chief Executive Officer and Administrator
CFO: Daniel R. O'Brien, Vice President and Chief Financial Officer
CMO: David Robinson, President Medical and Dental Staff
CIO: Gary Weiner, Vice President Information Technology, Chief Information Officer
CHR: Debbie Brandt, Director Human Resources
CNO: Ronda McKay, R.N., Vice President Patient Care Services, Chief Nursing Officer
Web address: www.comhs.org
Control: Other not–for–profit (including NFP Corporation) **Service**: General
medical and surgical

Staffed Beds: 510 Admissions: 18320 Census: 326 Outpatient Visits:
341047 **Births:** 1885 **Total Expense ($000):** 474674 **Payroll Expense
($000):** 164468 **Personnel:** 2516

○ **FRANCISCAN HEALTHCARE MUNSTER (150165)**, 701 Superior Avenue,
Zip 46321–4037; tel. 219/924-1300, (Nonreporting) **A**3 10 11 **S** Franciscan
Health, Mishawaka, IN
Primary Contact: Patrick J. Maloney, Chief Executive Officer
CFO: Harold E Collins, JD, Chief Financial Officer
CMO: Vijay D Gupta, M.D., President and Chief Executive Officer
CIO: Steven Krause, Manager Information Technology
Web address: www.franciscanphysicianshospital.org
Control: Partnership, Investor–owned (for–profit) **Service**: General medical and surgical

Staffed Beds: 32

NEW ALBANY—Floyd County

★ ○ **BAPTIST HEALTH FLOYD (150044)**, 1850 State Street, Zip 47150–4997;
tel. 812/949-5500, **A**2 3 5 10 11 **F**3 8 11 12 13 15 17 18 20 22 24 26 28 29
30 31 34 35 40 43 45 48 49 50 53 54 55 57 58 59 62 64 70 74 75 76 77 78
79 80 81 82 84 85 86 87 89 92 93 100 107 108 109 110 111 114 115 116
117 118 119 120 121 123 129 130 131 132 135 144 146 147 148 149 **S**
Baptist Health, Louisville, KY
Primary Contact: Daniel J. Eichenberger, M.D., President and Chief Executive Officer
COO: Mark Truman, Vice President of Operations
CIO: Brian Cox, Director Information Systems
CHR: Sue Christopher, Vice President, Human Resources
CNO: Kelly McMinoway, R.N., Vice President, Nursing
Web address: www.floydmemorial.com
Control: Other not–for–profit (including NFP Corporation) **Service**: General
medical and surgical

Staffed Beds: 216 Admissions: 12685 Census: 142 Outpatient Visits:
238583 **Births:** 1115 **Total Expense ($000):** 251451 **Payroll Expense
($000):** 90458 **Personnel:** 2196

PHYSICIANS' MEDICAL CENTER (150172), 4023 Reas Lane,
Zip 47150–2228; tel. 812/206-7660, **A**1 10 **F**3 12 29 45 51 77 79 81 82 85
89 94 107 111 144
Primary Contact: Dennis Medley, Chief Executive Officer and Administrator
COO: Rob Jones, Director of Nursing and Operations
CFO: Dennis Medley, Chief Executive Officer
CMO: Perry Cassady, M.D., Medical Director
CIO: Rob Jones, Director of Nursing and Operations
CHR: Mary Arntz, Manager Business Office and Executive Assistant
CNO: Rob Jones, Director of Nursing and Operations
Web address: www.pmcindiana.com
Control: Partnership, Investor–owned (for–profit) **Service**: General medical and
surgical

**Staffed Beds: 19 Admissions: 1205 Census: 7 Outpatient Visits: 25365
Births: 0 Total Expense ($000):** 47801 **Payroll Expense ($000):** 9494
Personnel: 236

☒ △ **SOUTHERN INDIANA REHABILITATION HOSPITAL (153037)**, 3104
Blackiston Boulevard, Zip 47150–9579; tel. 812/941-8300, (Nonreporting) **A**1 3
7 10 **S** Vibra Healthcare, Mechanicsburg, PA
Primary Contact: William Boso, Executive Director, Administrator
CFO: Robert Steltenpohl, Vice President
CMO: John C Shaw, M.D., Medical Director
CHR: Lisa Burris, Director Human Resources
CNO: Suzann Byers, Director of Nursing
Web address: www.sirh.org
Control: Other not–for–profit (including NFP Corporation) **Service**: Rehabilitation

Staffed Beds: 60

NEW CASTLE—Henry County

★ ○ **HENRY COMMUNITY HEALTH (150030)**, 1000 North 16th Street,
Zip 47362–4319, Mailing Address: P.O. Box 490, Zip 47362–0490;
tel. 765/521-0890, **A**10 11 **F**3 13 15 28 29 30 32 34 35 40 45 46 48 49 50
51 53 54 57 59 62 63 64 65 68 70 75 76 77 79 81 82 85 86 87 89 91 92 93
96 97 107 108 109 110 111 113 114 115 119 127 129 130 131 132 135 144
146 147 148 149 154 **P**6
Primary Contact: Paul Janssen, President and Chief Executive Officer
COO: Brian K Ring, Chief Operating Officer
CFO: Darin Brown, Vice President Finance
CMO: Arun Tewari, M.D., Chief Medical Officer
CIO: Mike Spencer, Chief Information Officer
CHR: Deanna Malott, Director Human Resources
CNO: Leslie Cowan, R.N., Chief Nursing Officer
Web address: www.hcmhcares.org
Control: County, Government, nonfederal **Service**: General medical and surgical

**Staffed Beds: 90 Admissions: 2509 Census: 22 Outpatient Visits: 105084
Births: 316 Total Expense ($000):** 107664 **Payroll Expense ($000):** 45355
Personnel: 834

NEWBURGH—Warrick County

☐ **BRENTWOOD SPRINGS (154055)**, 4455 Roslin Road, Zip 47630;
tel. 812/858-7200, (Nonreporting) **A**1 10 **S** Springstone, Louisville, KY
Primary Contact: Jessica Black, Chief Executive Officer
Web address: www.brentwoodmeadows.com
Control: Partnership, Investor–owned (for–profit) **Service**: Psychiatric

Staffed Beds: 48

★ ○ **THE HEART HOSPITAL AT DEACONESS GATEWAY (150175)**, 4007
Gateway Boulevard, Zip 47630–8947; tel. 812/842-4784, **A**10 11 **F**3 17 18 20
22 24 26 28 29 30 34 35 57 58 59 60 62 63 64 68 81 83 84 85 86 87 107
108 109 111 114 115 116 117 118 119 130 132 149 **S** Deaconess Health
System, Evansville, IN
Primary Contact: Rebecca Malotte, Executive Director and Chief Nursing Officer
COO: Rebecca Malotte, Executive Director and Chief Nursing Officer
CFO: Tracy Hoefling, Chief Financial Officer
CMO: Lee Wagmeister, M.D., President Medical Staff
CIO: Lisa Hobgood, Chief Information Officer
CHR: Sarah Bryan, Manager Human Resources
CNO: Rebecca Malotte, Executive Director and Chief Nursing Officer
Web address: www.deaconess.com/
Control: Partnership, Investor–owned (for–profit) **Service**: Heart

**Staffed Beds: 24 Admissions: 1495 Census: 16 Outpatient Visits: 19364
Births: 0 Total Expense ($000):** 44730 **Payroll Expense ($000):** 9163
Personnel: 145

★ ○ **THE WOMEN'S HOSPITAL (150149)**, 4199 Gateway Boulevard, Zip 47630–8940; tel. 812/842–4200, **A**3 10 11 **F**3 13 15 29 30 34 35 36 40 50 53 55 57 59 63 64 65 72 75 76 77 81 84 85 86 87 93 110 119 126 130 132 134 135 147 154 **P**6 **S** Deaconess Health System, Evansville, IN
Primary Contact: Christina M. Ryan, R.N., Chief Executive Officer
CFO: Tina Cady, Controller
CIO: Jenny Skelton, System Integration Manager
CHR: Jerri Sue Traylor, Director Human Resources
CNO: Christina M Ryan, R.N., Chief Executive Officer and Chief Nursing Officer
Web address: www.deaconess.com
Control: Partnership, Investor–owned (for–profit) **Service:** Obstetrics and gynecology

Staffed Beds: 74 Admissions: 3715 Census: 47 Outpatient Visits: 39195 Births: 3100 Total Expense ($000): 84873 Payroll Expense ($000): 36391 Personnel: 558

NOBLESVILLE—Hamilton County

○ △ **RIVERVIEW HEALTH (150059)**, 395 Westfield Road, Zip 46060–1425, Mailing Address: P.O. Box 220, Zip 46061–0220; tel. 317/773–0760, **A**2 7 10 11 **F**3 8 11 13 15 17 18 20 22 24 26 28 29 30 31 34 35 37 40 45 46 49 50 53 54 56 57 59 60 62 63 64 65 70 73 74 75 76 77 78 79 81 82 85 86 87 89 90 91 93 94 97 107 108 110 111 114 115 116 118 119 120 121 123 128 129 130 131 132 144 146 147 148 149
Primary Contact: Seth Warren, President and Chief Executive Officer
COO: Lawrence Christman, Chief Financial Officer and Chief Operating Officer
CFO: Brenda Baker, Chief Financial Officer
CMO: Eric Marcotte, M.D., Chief Medical Officer
CIO: Brant Bucciarelli, Chief Information Officer
CHR: Ann Kuzee, Executive Director Human Resources
CNO: Joyce Wood, Vice President Organizational Improvement and Chief Nursing Officer
Web address: www.riverview.org
Control: County, Government, nonfederal **Service:** General medical and surgical

Staffed Beds: 156 Admissions: 4272 Census: 65 Outpatient Visits: 453683 Births: 588 Total Expense ($000): 192764 Payroll Expense ($000): 70488 Personnel: 1151

NORTH VERNON—Jennings County

☒ **ST. VINCENT JENNINGS HOSPITAL (151303)**, 301 Henry Street, Zip 47265–1097; tel. 812/352–4200, **A**1 10 18 **F**3 15 29 30 32 34 35 40 44 45 50 56 57 59 64 65 66 77 79 81 85 97 103 107 111 115 119 128 133 135 144 146 148 **S** Ascension Healthcare, Saint Louis, MO
Primary Contact: Christina Crank, Chief Nursing Officer
CFO: Joseph Kubala, Chief Financial Officer
CMO: Jennifer Stanley, M.D., Chief Medical Officer
CHR: Kathryn Johnson, Manager Human Resources, Marketing and Public Relations
Web address: www.stvincent.org
Control: Other not–for–profit (including NFP Corporation) **Service:** General medical and surgical

Staffed Beds: 17 Admissions: 504 Census: 2 Births: 0 Total Expense ($000): 16879 Payroll Expense ($000): 5302 Personnel: 57

PAOLI—Orange County

BLOOMINGTON HOSPITAL OF ORANGE COUNTY See Indiana University Health Paoli Hospital

☒ **INDIANA UNIVERSITY HEALTH PAOLI HOSPITAL (151306)**, 642 West Hospital Road, Zip 47454–9672, Mailing Address: P.O. Box 499, Zip 47454–0499; tel. 812/723–2811, **A**1 10 18 **F**3 13 15 29 30 35 40 45 50 57 59 64 76 77 81 84 85 89 93 107 110 111 114 119 129 132 133 135 146 148 149 150 **S** Indiana University Health, Indianapolis, IN
Primary Contact: Larry Bailey, President
COO: Sonya M. Zeller, R.N., Vice President, Chief Operating Officer and Chief Nursing Officer
CMO: Jose Lopez, M.D., Medical Staff President
CNO: Sonya M. Zeller, R.N., Vice President, Chief Operating Officer and Chief Nursing Officer
Web address: www.iuhealth.org/paoli
Control: Other not–for–profit (including NFP Corporation) **Service:** General medical and surgical

Staffed Beds: 25 Admissions: 204 Census: 2 Outpatient Visits: 27927 Births: 105 Total Expense ($000): 23804 Payroll Expense ($000): 7618 Personnel: 119

PERU—Miami County

☒ **DUKES MEMORIAL HOSPITAL (151318)**, 275 West 12th Street, Zip 46970–1638; tel. 765/472–8000, **A**1 10 18 **F**3 7 8 13 15 17 18 28 29 34 35 40 41 50 51 57 59 64 68 69 70 75 76 77 79 81 85 87 89 90 93 97 107 108 110 111 115 118 119 129 130 132 133 135 144 146 147 **S** Community Health Systems, Inc., Franklin, TN
Primary Contact: Debra Close, Chief Executive Officer
CFO: Adam Cumbo, Chief Financial Officer
CMO: Neil Stalker, M.D., Chief of Staff
Web address: www.dukesmemorialhosp.com
Control: Corporation, Investor–owned (for–profit) **Service:** General medical and surgical

Staffed Beds: 25 Admissions: 1299 Census: 10

PLYMOUTH—Marshall County

☐ **MICHIANA BEHAVIORAL HEALTH CENTER (154047)**, 1800 North Oak Drive, Zip 46563–3492; tel. 574/936–3784, (Nonreporting) **A**1 10 **S** Universal Health Services, Inc., King of Prussia, PA
Primary Contact: Michael Perry, Chief Executive Officer
CFO: Jeff Calvin, Chief Financial Officer
CMO: Robert Raster, M.D., Medical Director
CIO: Leslie McLaughlin, Director of Business Development
CHR: Becky Nowicki, Director Human Resources
CNO: Brandi Richard, Chief Nursing Officer
Web address: www.michianabhc.com
Control: Corporation, Investor–owned (for–profit) **Service:** Psychiatric

Staffed Beds: 75

☒ **PLYMOUTH MEDICAL CENTER (150076)**, 1915 Lake Avenue, Zip 46563–9366, Mailing Address: P.O. Box 670, Zip 46563–0670; tel. 574/948–4000, **A**1 10 **F**3 8 13 15 18 20 29 30 31 34 35 40 45 46 50 51 54 57 59 64 65 66 68 70 74 75 76 78 79 81 84 85 86 87 89 91 92 93 97 107 108 110 114 115 118 119 120 121 123 124 129 132 135 146 149 154 **S** Trinity Health, Livonia, MI
Primary Contact: Christopher J. Karam, President
COO: Tamara Awald, Chief Nursing Officer and Chief Operating Officer
CFO: Janice Dunn, Chief Financial Officer
CMO: Stephen Anderson, M.D., Chief Medical Officer
CIO: Gary L Miller, Regional Director Information Systems
CHR: Kurt A Meyer, Chief Human Resources Officer
CNO: Tamara Awald, Chief Nursing Officer and Chief Operating Officer
Web address: www.sjmed.com
Control: Other not–for–profit (including NFP Corporation) **Service:** General medical and surgical

Staffed Beds: 48 Admissions: 2044 Census: 16 Outpatient Visits: 82601 Births: 297 Total Expense ($000): 50301 Payroll Expense ($000): 17810 Personnel: 316

PORTLAND—Jay County

☒ **INDIANA UNIVERSITY HEALTH JAY HOSPITAL (151320)**, 500 West Votaw Street, Zip 47371–1322; tel. 260/726–7131, **A**1 10 18 **F**3 8 11 13 15 28 29 30 32 34 35 40 45 50 57 59 68 70 75 76 77 81 85 86 87 104 107 108 110 111 114 119 129 130 132 133 135 146 148 154 **S** Indiana University Health, Indianapolis, IN
Primary Contact: David W. Hyatt, President
CIO: Jeff Horn, Director of Support Services
CHR: Linda Guise, Senior Human Resource Consultant
CNO: Lisa Craiger, Chief Nursing Officer
Web address: www.jaycountyhospital.com
Control: County, Government, nonfederal **Service:** General medical and surgical

Staffed Beds: 35 Admissions: 953 Census: 10 Outpatient Visits: 103313 Births: 93 Total Expense ($000): 38274 Payroll Expense ($000): 17523 Personnel: 303

PRINCETON—Gibson County

☒ **GIBSON GENERAL HOSPITAL (151319)**, 1808 Sherman Drive, Zip 47670–1043; tel. 812/385–3401, (Total facility includes 45 beds in nursing home–type unit) **A**1 10 18 **F**3 11 15 28 29 30 31 34 35 38 40 45 49 50 56 57 58 59 62 64 68 70 75 77 79 81 82 89 93 97 102 107 110 111 115 119 127 128 129 130 131 133 148 **P**6 **S** Deaconess Health System, Evansville, IN
Primary Contact: Mike Carney, Interim President and Chief Executive Officer
CFO: James R Childers, Vice President & Chief Financial Officer
CMO: Krishna Murthy, M.D., Chief of Medical Staff
CIO: Steve Paddock, Director of Information Services
CHR: D Deann Hunt, Director of Human Resources
CNO: Lois Morgan, R.N., MSN, Vice President and Chief Nursing Officer
Web address: www.gibsongeneral.com
Control: Other not–for–profit (including NFP Corporation) **Service:** General medical and surgical

Staffed Beds: 70 Admissions: 440 Census: 44 Outpatient Visits: 30276 Births: 0

IN

Hospital, Medicare Provider Number, Address, Telephone, Approval, Facility, and Physician Codes, Health Care System

★ American Hospital Association (AHA) membership ○ Healthcare Facilities Accreditation Program ⇧ Center for Improvement in Healthcare Quality Accreditation
☐ The Joint Commission accreditation ◇ DNV Healthcare Inc. accreditation △ Commission on Accreditation of Rehabilitation Facilities (CARF) accreditation

RENSSELAER—Jasper County

FRANCISCAN HEALTH RENSSELAER (151324), 1104 East Grace Street, Zip 47978–3296; tel. 219/866–5141, (Total facility includes 21 beds in nursing home–type unit) **A**10 18 **F**1 3 15 28 29 31 34 35 40 49 50 51 54 57 62 63 64 69 70 75 77 78 79 81 85 91 93 94 107 108 110 111 115 118 119 127 129 130 132 133 135 145 148 154 **S** Franciscan Health, Mishawaka, IN
Primary Contact: Terrance E. Wilson, President and Chief Executive Officer
CFO: Jeffrey D Webb, CPA, Chief Financial Officer
CIO: Kirby Reed, Director Information Systems
CHR: Deana Brown, Director Administrative Services
CNO: Stacie Klingler, R.N., Vice President of Patient Services
Web address: www.franciscanhealth.org
Control: Church operated, Nongovernment, not–for–profit **Service**: General medical and surgical

Staffed Beds: 46 **Admissions:** 442 **Census:** 17 **Outpatient Visits:** 81297 **Births:** 0 **Total Expense ($000):** 39666 **Payroll Expense ($000):** 12186 **Personnel:** 210

RICHMOND—Wayne County

★ ○ **REID HEALTH (150048)**, 1100 Reid Parkway, Zip 47374–1157; tel. 765/983–3000, **A**2 3 10 11 13 **F**3 8 11 13 15 18 20 22 24 26 28 29 30 31 32 34 35 37 40 43 44 45 47 49 50 51 54 55 56 57 58 59 61 63 64 68 69 70 74 75 77 78 79 81 82 84 85 86 87 90 91 92 93 95 96 97 98 100 101 102 103 104 107 108 110 111 114 115 116 117 118 119 120 121 123 124 126 127 129 130 131 132 135 144 146 147 148 149 154 **P**6 8
Primary Contact: Craig C. Kinyon, President
CFO: Christopher D. Knight, Vice President Finance and Chief Financial Officer
CMO: Thomas Huth, M.D., Vice President Medical Affairs
CIO: Tim Love, Director Information Services
CHR: Scott C Rauch, Vice President Human Resources
CNO: Misti Foust-Cofield, R.N., Vice President and Chief Nursing Officer
Web address: www.reidhealth.org
Control: Other not–for–profit (including NFP Corporation) **Service**: General medical and surgical

Staffed Beds: 221 **Admissions:** 12280 **Census:** 139 **Outpatient Visits:** 366810 **Births:** 742 **Total Expense ($000):** 433532 **Payroll Expense ($000):** 178360 **Personnel:** 2515

☐ **RICHMOND STATE HOSPITAL (154018)**, 498 NW 18th Street, Zip 47374–2851; tel. 765/966–0511, (Nonreporting) **A**1 10
Primary Contact: Warren Fournier, Chief Executive Officer and Medical Director
CFO: Dave Shelford, Assistant Superintendent
CMO: Donald Graber, M.D., Medical Director
CIO: Robert Boatman, Director Information Technology
CHR: Sarah Witt, Director Human Resources
Web address: www.richmondstatehospital.org
Control: State, Government, nonfederal **Service**: Psychiatric

Staffed Beds: 213

ROCHESTER—Fulton County

★ **WOODLAWN HOSPITAL (151313)**, 1400 East Ninth Street, Zip 46975–8937; tel. 574/223–3141, **A**10 18 **F**3 11 15 28 29 30 31 34 40 46 56 57 59 65 68 69 70 75 76 77 78 79 81 82 93 94 97 107 108 111 115 119 129 130 132 133 135 146 147 148 149 **P**6
Primary Contact: John L. Alley, Chief Executive Officer
CFO: Dave Cholger, Chief Financial Officer
CHR: Debra J Lemasters, Director Human Resources
Web address: www.woodlawnhospital.com
Control: County, Government, nonfederal **Service**: General medical and surgical

Staffed Beds: 25 **Admissions:** 991 **Census:** 10 **Outpatient Visits:** 51250 **Births:** 164 **Total Expense ($000):** 56580 **Payroll Expense ($000):** 25217 **Personnel:** 357

RUSHVILLE—Rush County

★ **RUSH MEMORIAL HOSPITAL (151304)**, 1300 North Main Street, Zip 46173–1198; tel. 765/932–4111, **A**10 18 **F**3 7 11 15 18 24 28 29 31 35 36 40 46 50 51 57 59 63 64 65 74 75 77 78 79 81 82 85 93 97 107 111 114 117 120 121 122 129 130 131 132 133 135 146 147 148 **P**6
Primary Contact: Bradley Smith, President and Chief Executive Officer
COO: Gretchen Smith, Vice President of Operations, Risk and Compliance, and Chief Operating Officer
CFO: Karen Meyer, Vice President Finance and Chief Financial Officer
CMO: Daniel Stahl, D.O., Chief Medical Officer
CIO: Jim Boyer, Vice President Information Technology and Chief Information Officer
CHR: Brian R Bane, Vice President Human Resources
CNO: Carrie Tressler, Vice President of Nursing and Chief Nursing Officer
Web address: www.rushmemorial.com
Control: County, Government, nonfederal **Service**: General medical and surgical

Staffed Beds: 25 **Admissions:** 568 **Census:** 4 **Outpatient Visits:** 36062 **Births:** 0 **Total Expense ($000):** 32441 **Payroll Expense ($000):** 14273 **Personnel:** 245

SALEM—Washington County

⊞ **ST. VINCENT SALEM HOSPITAL (151314)**, 911 North Shelby Street, Zip 47167–1694; tel. 812/883–5881, **A**1 10 18 **F**3 11 15 28 29 30 32 34 40 45 47 49 57 59 75 77 79 81 82 85 93 107 111 114 119 124 129 130 131 132 133 144 148 154 **P**6 **S** Ascension Healthcare, Saint Louis, MO
Primary Contact: Dana M. Muntz, Chief Executive Officer
CFO: Joseph Kubala, Director Financial and Support Services
CMO: S E Kemker, M.D., President Medical Staff
CIO: Jeremy Long, Manager Information Systems
CHR: Val Potter, Director Human Resources
Web address: www.stvincent.org/St-Vincent-Salem/Default.aspx
Control: Other not–for–profit (including NFP Corporation) **Service**: General medical and surgical

Staffed Beds: 25 **Admissions:** 108 **Census:** 1 **Outpatient Visits:** 32507 **Births:** 0 **Total Expense ($000):** 16691 **Payroll Expense ($000):** 6167 **Personnel:** 71

SCOTTSBURG—Scott County

⊞ **SCOTT MEMORIAL HOSPITAL (151334)**, 1415 North Gardner Street, Zip 47170, Mailing Address: Box 430, Zip 47170–0430; tel. 812/752–3456, (Nonreporting) **A**1 10 18 **S** LifePoint Health, Brentwood, TN
Primary Contact: Michael Everett, Chief Executive Officer
CFO: Angela Doan, Chief Financial Officer
CNO: Dawn Mays, Chief Nursing Officer
Web address: www.scottmemorial.com
Control: County, Government, nonfederal **Service**: General medical and surgical

Staffed Beds: 25

SEYMOUR—Jackson County

⊞ **SCHNECK MEDICAL CENTER (150065)**, 411 West Tipton Street, Zip 47274–2363, Mailing Address: P.O. Box 2349, Zip 47274–5000; tel. 812/522–2349, **A**1 2 10 **F**3 5 12 13 15 18 28 29 30 31 34 35 36 40 45 48 53 56 57 59 62 63 64 65 68 69 70 74 75 76 77 78 79 81 82 84 85 87 89 93 97 100 101 104 107 108 110 111 114 115 116 117 119 120 121 123 124 126 129 130 131 132 133 135 144 146 147 148 **P**1
Primary Contact: Warren Forgey, CPA, FACHE, President and Chief Executive Officer
CFO: Deborah Ridlen, CPA, Vice President Finance and Chief Financial Officer
CMO: Eric Fish, M.D., Vice President of Medical Affairs and Chief Medical Officers
CIO: Craig Rice, Director Information Technology
CHR: Kathy Covert, MSN, Vice President Workforce Development and Organizational Development
CNO: Amy Pettit, R.N., Vice President Nursing Services and Chief Nursing Officer
Web address: www.schneckmed.org
Control: County, Government, nonfederal **Service**: General medical and surgical

Staffed Beds: 93 **Admissions:** 2728 **Census:** 28 **Outpatient Visits:** 269704 **Births:** 729 **Total Expense ($000):** 136856 **Payroll Expense ($000):** 61613 **Personnel:** 915

SHELBYVILLE—Shelby County

★ ○ **MAJOR HOSPITAL (150097)**, 150 West Washington Street, Zip 46176–1236, Mailing Address: 2451 Intelliplex Drive, Zip 46176; tel. 317/392–3211, **A**2 10 11 **F**3 13 15 28 29 30 31 34 35 40 45 47 50 56 57 59 62 64 65 68 69 70 73 74 75 76 77 78 79 81 82 84 85 87 92 93 94 104 107 108 109 110 111 114 115 118 119 120 121 123 127 129 130 131 132 135 144 146 147 148 **P**6
Primary Contact: John M. Horner, President and Chief Executive Officer
CFO: Ralph Mercuri, Vice President and Chief Financial Officer
CMO: Douglas S Carter, M.D., Vice President and Chief Medical Officer
CIO: Carol Huesman, Chief Information Officer
CHR: Nicki Sparling, Manager Human Resources
CNO: Valerie L Miller, MSN, R.N., Director of Nursing
Web address: www.majorhospital.org
Control: City–county, Government, nonfederal **Service**: General medical and surgical

Staffed Beds: 52 **Admissions:** 3064 **Census:** 29 **Outpatient Visits:** 168482 **Births:** 362 **Total Expense ($000):** 117379 **Payroll Expense ($000):** 47743 **Personnel:** 1019

Many Facility Codes have changed. Please refer to the AHA Guide Code Chart.
© 2018 AHA Guide

IN

SOUTH BEND—St. Joseph County

✣ △ **MEMORIAL HOSPITAL OF SOUTH BEND (150058)**, 615 North Michigan Street, Zip 46601-1033; tel. 574/647-1000, (Includes BEACON CHILDREN'S HOSPITAL, 615 North Michigan Street, South Bend, IN, Zip 46601; tel. 574/647-1000) **A**1 2 3 7 10 **F**3 7 8 11 12 13 15 17 18 19 20 22 24 26 28 29 30 31 35 36 38 40 43 46 49 50 53 55 56 58 59 60 61 64 65 67 68 70 72 73 74 75 76 77 78 79 81 82 84 85 86 87 88 89 90 91 92 93 96 98 99 102 103 107 108 110 114 115 116 117 118 119 120 121 123 124 126 129 130 131 132 135 146 147 148 150 **P**8 **S** Beacon Health System, South Bend, IN
Primary Contact: Larry A. Tracy Jr, FACHE, President
CFO: Jeff Costello, Chief Financial Officer, Beacon Health System
CMO: Cheryl Wibbens, M.D., Vice President Medical Staff Affairs
CIO: Mark Warlick, Chief Information Officer
CHR: Steven M Eller, Chief Human Resources Officer
Web address: www.beaconhealthsystem.org
Control: Other not-for-profit (including NFP Corporation) **Service**: General medical and surgical

Staffed Beds: 445 **Admissions:** 18831 **Census:** 267 **Outpatient Visits:** 193796 **Births:** 2453 **Total Expense ($000):** 423221 **Payroll Expense ($000):** 143361 **Personnel:** 2540

SULLIVAN—Sullivan County

★ **SULLIVAN COUNTY COMMUNITY HOSPITAL (151327)**, 2200 North Section Street, Zip 47882-7523, Mailing Address: P.O. Box 10, Zip 47882-0010; tel. 812/268-4311, **A**10 18 **F**3 8 11 13 15 28 29 32 34 35 40 44 45 47 48 50 53 56 57 59 61 62 65 69 70 75 76 77 78 79 81 86 87 93 97 107 110 111 114 116 117 118 119 127 129 130 131 133 146 147 148 **P**7 **S** QHR, Brentwood, TN
Primary Contact: Michelle Franklin, Chief Executive Officer
CFO: Jim Bishop, Chief Financial Officer
CMO: Divyesh Purohit, M.D., Chief of Staff
CIO: Hap Beckes, Director Information Systems
CHR: Denise Hart, Director Human Resources
CNO: Lori Resler, R.N., Chief Nurse
Web address: www.schosp.com
Control: County, Government, nonfederal **Service**: General medical and surgical

Staffed Beds: 25 **Admissions:** 721 **Census:** 6 **Outpatient Visits:** 77749 **Births:** 120 **Total Expense ($000):** 33033 **Payroll Expense ($000):** 16364 **Personnel:** 207

TELL CITY—Perry County

★ **PERRY COUNTY MEMORIAL HOSPITAL (151322)**, 8885 State Road 237, Zip 47586-2750; tel. 812/547-7011, **A**10 18 **F**3 7 11 13 15 17 18 28 29 30 31 34 35 40 41 45 50 53 56 57 59 62 64 65 68 70 76 77 78 79 81 82 85 87 89 107 110 111 115 119 124 127 128 129 130 133 135 144 146 148 154 **S** Alliant Management Services, Louisville, KY
Primary Contact: Brian J. Herwig, Chief Executive Officer
CMO: Juan Cornejo, M.D., Chief of Staff
CIO: Mark Miller, Director Information Systems
CHR: Sheila Gaynor, Director Human Resources
CNO: Michele Howard, Vice President Nursing Services
Web address: www.pchospital.org
Control: County, Government, nonfederal **Service**: General medical and surgical

Staffed Beds: 25 **Admissions:** 671 **Census:** 6 **Outpatient Visits:** 51359 **Births:** 91 **Total Expense ($000):** 38160 **Payroll Expense ($000):** 13419 **Personnel:** 224

TERRE HAUTE—Vigo County

HAMILTON CENTER (154009), 620 Eighth Avenue, Zip 47804-2744; tel. 812/231-8323, **A**10 **F**5 29 34 38 50 54 56 59 98 101 102 104 106
Primary Contact: Melvin Burks, Chief Executive Officer
COO: Robb Johnson, Director Operations
CFO: Renee Utley, Chief Financial Officer
CMO: Ahsan Mahmood, M.D., Chief Medical Officer
CIO: Hans Eilbracht, Chief Information Officer
CHR: Margie Anshutz, Chief Development Officer
CNO: Rose Christy, Executive Director of Medical Services
Web address: www.hamiltoncenter.org
Control: State, Government, nonfederal **Service**: Psychiatric

Staffed Beds: 16 **Admissions:** 780 **Census:** 15 **Births:** 0

☐ **HARSHA BEHAVIORAL CENTER (154054)**, 1980 East Woodsmall Drive, Zip 47802-4937; tel. 866/644-8880, (Nonreporting) **A**1 10
Primary Contact: Roopam Harshawat, Chief Executive Officer
COO: Holly Near, Chief Administrative Officer
CFO: Holly Near, Chief Administrative Officer
CMO: Paras Harshawat, M.D., Medical Director
CHR: Karen Hunt, Executive Director
CNO: Cindy Dowers, Chief Nursing Officer
Web address: www.harshacenter.com
Control: Corporation, Investor-owned (for-profit) **Service**: Psychiatric

Staffed Beds: 44

✣ **TERRE HAUTE REGIONAL HOSPITAL (150046)**, 3901 South Seventh Street, Zip 47802-5709; tel. 812/232-0021, (Nonreporting) **A**1 2 10 **S** HCA Healthcare, Nashville, TN
Primary Contact: Nathan Vooys, Chief Executive Officer
COO: Andrea Gwyn, Chief Operating Officer
CIO: Mike Kuckewich, Director Information Systems
CNO: Angela Ellis, R.N., Chief Nursing Officer
Web address: www.regionalhospital.com
Control: Corporation, Investor-owned (for-profit) **Service**: General medical and surgical

Staffed Beds: 208

★ ○ **UNION HOSPITAL (150023)**, 1606 North Seventh Street, Zip 47804-2780; tel. 812/238-7000, **A**2 3 10 11 19 **F**3 8 13 15 18 20 22 24 26 28 29 30 31 34 36 40 43 45 46 47 48 49 50 51 53 54 57 59 64 68 70 72 73 74 75 76 77 78 79 81 83 85 86 87 89 90 91 92 93 94 95 96 97 107 108 110 111 112 114 115 116 117 118 119 120 121 123 124 126 127 130 131 132 135 144 146 147 **P**6
Primary Contact: Steve M. Holman, Chief Executive Officer
CFO: Wayne Hutson, Executive Vice President and Chief Financial Officer
CMO: John Bolinger, M.D., Vice President Medical Affairs
CIO: Kym Pfrank, Senior Vice President and Chief Operating Officer
CHR: Sally Zuel, Vice President Human Resources
Web address: www.uhhg.org
Control: Other not-for-profit (including NFP Corporation) **Service**: General medical and surgical

Staffed Beds: 214 **Admissions:** 16553 **Census:** 175 **Outpatient Visits:** 412356 **Births:** 1892 **Total Expense ($000):** 393959 **Payroll Expense ($000):** 107396 **Personnel:** 1701

TIPTON—Tipton County

✣ **INDIANA UNIVERSITY HEALTH TIPTON HOSPITAL (151311)**, 1000 South Main Street, Zip 46072-9799; tel. 765/675-8500, **A**1 10 18 **F**3 11 15 18 28 29 30 31 34 35 39 40 45 46 47 48 57 59 70 74 75 77 78 79 81 82 85 86 87 93 107 108 110 111 115 119 129 131 132 133 135 146 147 148 **S** Indiana University Health, Indianapolis, IN
Primary Contact: Michael Harlowe, President and Chief Executive Officer
CFO: Randall C Yust, Chief Financial Officer NCR
CMO: Larry Hopkins, Chief Medical Officer
CHR: Shelly E Huff, Manager Human Resources
CNO: Jo Ellen Scott, R.N., MS, Senior Vice President of Patient Care Services and Chief Nursing Officer
Web address: www.iuhealth.org
Control: Other not-for-profit (including NFP Corporation) **Service**: General medical and surgical

Staffed Beds: 25 **Admissions:** 792 **Census:** 8 **Outpatient Visits:** 49283 **Births:** 0 **Total Expense ($000):** 35908 **Payroll Expense ($000):** 11124 **Personnel:** 174

TIPTON HOSPITAL See Indiana University Health Tipton Hospital

VALPARAISO—Porter County

✣ **PORTER REGIONAL HOSPITAL (150035)**, 85 East U.S. Highway 6, Zip 46383-8947; tel. 219/983-8300, (Nonreporting) **A**1 5 10 **S** Community Health Systems, Inc., Franklin, TN
Primary Contact: Sean T. Dardeau, FACHE, Chief Executive Officer
COO: Lauren Hull, Chief Operating Officer
CFO: Jeffrey Daneff, Chief Financial Officer
CMO: Ramireddy K Tummuru, M.D., Chief Medical Officer
CIO: Robert Richardson, Information Technology Administrator
CHR: Angie Hampton, Director Human Resources
CNO: Judy Davidson, R.N., I Chief Nursing Officer
Web address: www.porterhealth.com
Control: Corporation, Investor-owned (for-profit) **Service**: General medical and surgical

Staffed Beds: 276

Hospital, Medicare Provider Number, Address, Telephone, Approval, Facility, and Physician Codes, Health Care System

★ American Hospital Association (AHA) membership   ○ Healthcare Facilities Accreditation Program   ⇑ Center for Improvement in Healthcare Quality Accreditation
☐ The Joint Commission accreditation   ◇ DNV Healthcare Inc. accreditation   △ Commission on Accreditation of Rehabilitation Facilities (CARF) accreditation

IN

PORTER–STARKE SERVICES (154052), 601 Wall Street, Zip 46383–2512; tel. 219/531–3500, (Nonreporting) **A**10
Primary Contact: Rocco Schiralli, President and Chief Executive Officer
CFO: Mary Idstein, Chief Financial Officer
CMO: Anand Popli, Medical Director
Web address: www.porterstarke.org
Control: Other not–for–profit (including NFP Corporation) **Service:** Psychiatric

Staffed Beds: 16

VINCENNES—Knox County

✠ △ **GOOD SAMARITAN HOSPITAL (150042)**, 520 South Seventh Street, Zip 47591–1038; tel. 812/882–5220, **A**1 2 7 10 19 **F**3 4 5 8 13 15 18 20 22 28 29 30 31 34 35 36 38 40 41 43 44 45 46 47 48 49 50 51 53 56 57 58 59 60 63 64 65 66 67 70 74 75 76 77 78 79 80 81 82 84 85 86 87 89 90 93 94 96 97 98 102 104 107 110 111 115 118 119 120 121 123 127 129 130 131 132 134 135 144 147 148 149 150 154 **P**6
Primary Contact: Robert D. McLin, President and Chief Executive Officer
COO: Adam Thacker, Chief Operating Officer
CFO: Thomas M Cook, Chief Financial Officer
CMO: Charles C Hedde, M.D., Chief Medical Officer
CIO: Daniel Scott, Director of Information Systems
CHR: Dean Wagoner, Director Human Resources
CNO: Karen S. Haak, R.N., MSN, Chief Nursing Officer
Web address: www.gshvin.org/goodsamaritan
Control: County, Government, nonfederal **Service:** General medical and surgical

Staffed Beds: 170 Admissions: 6949 Census: 93 Outpatient Visits: 545449 Births: 494 Total Expense ($000): 241241 Payroll Expense ($000): 106210 Personnel: 1664

WABASH—Wabash County

✠ **PARKVIEW WABASH COUNTY HOSPITAL (151310)**, 710 North East Street, Zip 46992–1924; tel. 260/563–3131, **A**1 10 18 **F**3 15 28 29 30 31 34 35 40 44 45 46 47 50 56 57 59 62 63 68 69 70 75 77 78 79 81 85 93 107 108 110 111 119 129 130 131 132 133 135 146 148 154 **P**6 **S** Parkview Health, Fort Wayne, IN
Primary Contact: Marilyn J. Custer–Mitchell, President
CMO: Jeff Miller, M.D., Chief of Staff
CIO: David Brinson, Director Information Technology
CHR: Kimberly R Shininger, Manger, Human Resources
CNO: Cathy Allyson Wolfe, Chief Nursing Officer
Web address: www.wchospital.com
Control: Other not–for–profit (including NFP Corporation) **Service:** General medical and surgical

Staffed Beds: 25 Admissions: 700 Census: 6 Outpatient Visits: 30102 Births: 0 Total Expense ($000): 42194 Payroll Expense ($000): 9208 Personnel: 133

WARSAW—Kosciusko County

✠ **KOSCIUSKO COMMUNITY HOSPITAL (150133)**, 2101 East Dubois Drive, Zip 46580–3288; tel. 574/267–3200, **A**1 10 19 **F**3 7 8 13 15 18 28 29 30 31 32 35 40 49 50 51 54 55 57 58 59 64 65 68 69 70 74 75 76 77 78 79 81 85 86 89 90 93 107 108 110 111 114 115 116 117 118 119 120 121 129 130 131 132 144 146 147 148 154 **P**6 **S** Community Health Systems, Inc., Franklin, TN
Primary Contact: Kim Finch, Interim Chief Executive Officer Chief Nursing Officer
CFO: Douglas J BeMent, Chief Financial Officer
CMO: Patrick Silveus, M.D., Medical Director
CIO: Tammy Lukens, Director Information
CHR: Joe Jarboe, Director Human Resources
CNO: Kim Finch, Chief Nursing Officer
Web address: www.kch.com
Control: Corporation, Investor–owned (for–profit) **Service:** General medical and surgical

Staffed Beds: 72 Admissions: 3016 Census: 26 Outpatient Visits: 107286 Births: 504 Total Expense ($000): 73154 Payroll Expense ($000): 23029 Personnel: 486

★ **OTIS R. BOWEN CENTER FOR HUMAN SERVICES (154014)**, 2621 East Jefferson Street, Zip 46580–3880; tel. 574/267–7169, (Nonreporting) **A**10
Primary Contact: Kurt Carlson, Chief Executive Officer
Web address: www.bowencenter.org
Control: Other not–for–profit (including NFP Corporation) **Service:** Psychiatric

Staffed Beds: 16

WASHINGTON—Daviess County

✠ △ **DAVIESS COMMUNITY HOSPITAL (150061)**, 1314 East Walnut Street, Zip 47501–2860; Mailing Address: P.O. Box 760, Zip 47501–0760; tel. 812/254–2760, **A**1 7 10 **F**3 11 13 15 18 28 29 30 31 34 35 36 40 41 43 45 51 54 56 57 59 61 63 64 65 66 68 70 71 74 75 76 77 78 79 81 85 86 87 89 90 92 93 94 96 97 98 100 101 102 103 104 107 108 110 111 115 118 119 127 129 130 131 132 135 148 149 153 **P**6 **S** Ascension Healthcare, Saint Louis, MO
Primary Contact: Tracy Conroy, Chief Executive Officer
COO: Keith Miller, Chief Operating Officer
CFO: Amanda Rodewald, Interim Chief Financial Officer
CNO: Nancy Case, Chief Nursing Officer
Web address: www.dchosp.org
Control: County, Government, nonfederal **Service:** General medical and surgical

Staffed Beds: 72 Admissions: 2074 Census: 34 Outpatient Visits: 104573 Births: 498 Total Expense ($000): 59844 Payroll Expense ($000): 24807 Personnel: 537

WEST LAFAYETTE—Tippecanoe County

★ **RIVER BEND HOSPITAL (154005)**, 2900 North River Road, Zip 47906–3744; tel. 765/464–0400, (Nonreporting) **A**10
Primary Contact: Stephanie Long, President and Chief Executive Officer
COO: Tom Gillian, Chief Operating Officer
CFO: Jeff Nagy, Chief Financial Officer
CMO: Richard Rahdert, M.D., Medical Director
CIO: Craig Anderson, Director Management Information Systems
CHR: Jan Shaw, Director Personnel
CNO: Megan Gibson, Nurse Manager
Web address: www.nchsi.com/riverbendhospital.cfm
Control: Other not–for–profit (including NFP Corporation) **Service:** Psychiatric

Staffed Beds: 16

WABASH VALLEY HOSPITAL See River Bend Hospital

WILLIAMSPORT—Warren County

✠ **ST. VINCENT WILLIAMSPORT HOSPITAL (151307)**, 412 North Monroe Street, Zip 47993–1049; tel. 765/762–4000, **A**1 10 18 **F**3 7 15 29 30 34 35 40 45 50 57 59 64 75 77 79 81 85 86 87 93 97 107 110 111 114 119 127 131 132 133 135 143 146 149 **S** Ascension Healthcare, Saint Louis, MO
Primary Contact: Jane Craigin, Chief Executive Officer
CFO: Janet Merritt, Chief Financial Officer
Web address: www.stvincent.org
Control: Other not–for–profit (including NFP Corporation) **Service:** General medical and surgical

Staffed Beds: 16 Admissions: 511 Census: 6 Births: 0

WINAMAC—Pulaski County

★ **PULASKI MEMORIAL HOSPITAL (151305)**, 616 East 13th Street, Zip 46996–1117, Mailing Address: P.O. Box 279, Zip 46996–0279; tel. 574/946–2100, **A**10 18 **F**3 11 12 13 15 18 28 29 30 31 34 35 40 43 45 50 53 56 57 59 62 63 64 65 68 73 75 77 78 79 81 82 85 86 87 89 90 93 96 97 103 107 110 111 114 119 127 128 131 133 135 146 147 148 149 153 154 **P**6
Primary Contact: Thomas Barry, Chief Executive Officer
CFO: Gregg Malott, Chief Financial Officer
CMO: Rex Allman, M.D., President Medical Staff
CIO: Jeff Boer, Director Information Technology
CHR: Mark Fenn, Director Human Resources
CNO: Linda Webb, R.N., Chief Nursing Executive
Web address: www.pmhnet.com
Control: County, Government, nonfederal **Service:** General medical and surgical

Staffed Beds: 25 Admissions: 708 Census: 8 Outpatient Visits: 28943 Births: 110 Total Expense ($000): 33346 Payroll Expense ($000): 15740 Personnel: 266

WINCHESTER—Randolph County

✠ **ST. VINCENT RANDOLPH HOSPITAL (151301)**, 473 Greenville Avenue, Zip 47394–9436; tel. 765/584–0004, **A**1 10 18 **F**3 11 13 15 18 28 29 30 31 34 35 40 44 45 50 57 59 64 65 68 75 76 77 79 81 85 86 87 89 93 107 110 111 115 119 129 130 131 132 133 135 146 147 148 149 150 154 **S** Ascension Healthcare, Saint Louis, MO
Primary Contact: Carla Fouse, Administrator and Chief Nursing Officer
CFO: John Arthur, Chief Financial Officer
CNO: Carla Fouse, Chief Nursing Officer
Web address: www.stvincent.org
Control: Other not–for–profit (including NFP Corporation) **Service:** General medical and surgical

Staffed Beds: 18 Admissions: 518 Census: 4 Outpatient Visits: 44039 Births: 231 Total Expense ($000): 22550 Payroll Expense ($000): 8090 Personnel: 157

IN

Many Facility Codes have changed. Please refer to the AHA Guide Code Chart.

IOWA

ALBIA—Monroe County

★ **MONROE COUNTY HOSPITAL AND CLINICS (161342)**, 6580 165th Street, Zip 52531–8793; tel. 641/932–2134, **A**10 18 **F**1 4 7 11 15 16 17 28 29 31 34 40 43 47 50 57 59 67 70 72 73 77 80 81 88 89 90 93 98 107 110 114 119 127 128 130 132 133 **P**6
Primary Contact: Veronica Fuhs, Chief Executive Officer
Web address: www.mchalbia.com
Control: County, Government, nonfederal **Service:** General medical and surgical

Staffed Beds: 25 **Admissions:** 333 **Census:** 4 **Outpatient Visits:** 46035
Births: 0 **Total Expense ($000):** 20498 **Payroll Expense ($000):** 8831
Personnel: 135

ALGONA—Kossuth County

★ **KOSSUTH REGIONAL HEALTH CENTER (161353)**, 1515 South Phillips Street, Zip 50511–3649; tel. 515/295–2451, **A**10 18 **F**11 13 15 17 28 29 30 31 32 34 35 36 40 41 43 50 56 57 59 62 63 64 65 67 68 70 75 76 77 78 81 82 84 86 87 89 92 93 97 107 114 119 127 128 130 131 132 133 135 146 147 148 149 154 **P**8 **S** Trinity Health, Livonia, MI
Primary Contact: Scott A. Curtis, Administrator and Chief Executive Officer
CFO: Jason Feucht, Chief Financial Officer
CMO: Michael Lampe, M.D., Chief of Staff
CIO: Nancy Erickson, Administrator Information Systems
CHR: Paula Seely, Manager Human Resources
CNO: Darlene M Elbert, R.N., MS, Assistant Administrator and Chief Nursing Officer
Web address: www.krhc.com
Control: County, Government, nonfederal **Service:** General medical and surgical

Staffed Beds: 23 **Admissions:** 883 **Census:** 11 **Outpatient Visits:** 29740
Births: 126 **Total Expense ($000):** 36169 **Payroll Expense ($000):** 11994
Personnel: 207

AMES—Story County

⊞ △ ⇑ **MARY GREELEY MEDICAL CENTER (160030)**, 1111 Duff Avenue, Zip 50010–5745; tel. 515/239–2011, **A**1 2 7 10 19 21 **F**3 7 11 12 13 17 18 20 22 26 28 29 30 31 34 35 36 37 38 40 43 45 46 47 48 49 50 53 55 57 58 59 61 62 63 64 65 69 70 72 74 75 76 77 78 79 81 82 84 85 86 89 90 92 93 96 98 100 101 102 104 107 108 110 111 114 115 118 119 120 121 123 124 126 129 130 131 132 135 145 146 148 149
Primary Contact: Brian Dieter, President and Chief Executive Officer
CFO: Gary Botine, Vice President, Chief Financial Officer
CIO: Scott Carlson, Director
CHR: Betsy V Schoeller, Director Human Resources and Education
Web address: www.mgmc.org
Control: City, Government, nonfederal **Service:** General medical and surgical

Staffed Beds: 172 **Admissions:** 8368 **Census:** 99 **Outpatient Visits:** 155641 **Births:** 1177 **Total Expense ($000):** 182260 **Payroll Expense ($000):** 64361 **Personnel:** 1058

ANAMOSA—Jones County

★ **UNITYPOINT HEALTH – JONES REGIONAL MEDICAL CENTER (161306)**, 1795 Highway 64 East, Zip 52205–2112; tel. 319/462–6131, **A**10 18 **F**3 7 11 12 15 28 29 30 31 34 35 38 40 43 45 50 56 57 59 64 65 68 71 75 77 81 82 84 85 87 91 93 96 97 100 102 104 107 110 114 118 119 127 128 129 130 131 132 133 135 146 148 149 150 154 **P**6 **S** UnityPoint Health, West Des Moines, IA
Primary Contact: Eric Briesemeister, Chief Executive Officer
CFO: Rachel Von Behren, Director Financial Services
CMO: Victor Salas, M.D., President Medical Staff
CHR: Donna Condry, Director Human Resources
Web address: www.jonesregional.org
Control: Other not–for–profit (including NFP Corporation) **Service:** General medical and surgical

Staffed Beds: 22 **Admissions:** 388 **Census:** 5 **Outpatient Visits:** 87153
Births: 0 **Total Expense ($000):** 27886 **Payroll Expense ($000):** 8782
Personnel: 206

ATLANTIC—Cass County

★ **CASS COUNTY MEMORIAL HOSPITAL (161376)**, 1501 East Tenth Street, Zip 50022–1997; tel. 712/243–3250, **A**10 18 **F**3 13 15 28 29 31 34 35 40 45 50 57 59 64 65 70 75 76 77 78 79 81 82 85 93 97 98 101 102 107 108 110 111 115 119 124 127 129 130 131 132 133 135 146 147 148 154 **P**6 8
Primary Contact: Brett Altman, Chief Executive Officer
COO: Alison Bruckner, Chief Operating Officer
CFO: Abbey Stangl, Chief Financial Officer
CMO: Todd Bean, Chief Medical Officer
CIO: Jeff Osegard, Chief Information Officer
CHR: Denise Coder, Chief Human Resource Officer
Web address: www.casshealth.org
Control: County, Government, nonfederal **Service:** General medical and surgical

Staffed Beds: 29 **Admissions:** 945 **Census:** 10 **Outpatient Visits:** 98344
Births: 121 **Total Expense ($000):** 48663 **Payroll Expense ($000):** 17422
Personnel: 333

AUDUBON—Audubon County

AUDUBON COUNTY MEMORIAL HOSPITAL (161330), 515 Pacific Street, Zip 50025–1056; tel. 712/563–2611, **A**10 18 **F**3 15 28 31 34 40 43 45 53 57 59 64 67 78 79 81 82 85 93 110 119 127 128 133 135
Primary Contact: Suzanne Cooner, R.N., MSN, Chief Executive Officer
CFO: Melinda Alt, Chief Financial Officer
CMO: James Cunnigham, D.O., Chief of Staff
CIO: Mike Card, Chief Information Officer
CNO: Holly Kjergaard, Chief Nursing Officer
Web address: www.acmhhosp.org
Control: County, Government, nonfederal **Service:** General medical and surgical

Staffed Beds: 25 **Admissions:** 182 **Census:** 3 **Outpatient Visits:** 14698
Births: 0 **Total Expense ($000):** 13077 **Payroll Expense ($000):** 5398
Personnel: 98

BELMOND—Wright County

★ ⇑ **IOWA SPECIALTY HOSPITAL–BELMOND (161301)**, 403 1st Street SE, Zip 50421–1201; tel. 641/444–3223, **A**10 18 21 **F**7 11 12 15 28 29 32 34 35 40 43 45 46 50 56 57 59 62 63 64 65 67 68 70 75 77 79 81 82 85 87 89 92 93 96 97 100 101 102 104 107 110 119 127 128 129 130 131 132 133 135 146 148 149 150 154 **P**6 **S** Iowa Specialty Hospitals, Clarion, IA
Primary Contact: Amy McDaniel, Chief Executive Officer
CFO: Greg Polzin, Chief Financial Officer
CMO: Charles B Brindle, M.D., Chief Medical Staff
CHR: Holly Martin, Director Human Resource
CNO: Lisa Weatherwax, R.N., Chief Nursing Officer
Web address: www.iowaspecialtyhospital.com
Control: City, Government, nonfederal **Service:** General medical and surgical

Staffed Beds: 22 **Admissions:** 531 **Census:** 4 **Outpatient Visits:** 45766
Births: 0 **Total Expense ($000):** 26982 **Payroll Expense ($000):** 6354
Personnel: 146

BETTENDORF—Scott County

⊞ **UNITYPOINT HEALTH – TRINITY BETTENDORF (160104)**, 4500 Utica Ridge Road, Zip 52722–1626; tel. 563/742–5000, **A**1 10 13 **F**3 11 13 15 18 20 22 24 26 29 30 34 35 37 40 44 45 46 48 50 57 59 64 68 70 73 74 75 76 79 81 82 85 86 87 89 93 96 97 102 104 107 108 110 114 119 130 132 135 146 147 148 149 150 154 **P**8 **S** UnityPoint Health, West Des Moines, IA
Primary Contact: Richard A. Seidler, FACHE, President and Chief Executive Officer
COO: Jay Willsher, Chief Operating Officer
CFO: Greg Pagliuzza, Chief Financial Officer
CMO: Paul McLoone, M.D., Chief Medical Officer
CHR: Cara Fuller, Vice President Human Resources
CNO: Jean B Doerge, MS, R.N., Chief Nursing Executive
Web address: www.trinityqc.com
Control: Other not–for–profit (including NFP Corporation) **Service:** General medical and surgical

Staffed Beds: 86 **Admissions:** 4681 **Census:** 37 **Outpatient Visits:** 78038
Births: 938 **Total Expense ($000):** 79521 **Payroll Expense ($000):** 27145
Personnel: 435

IA

Hospital, Medicare Provider Number, Address, Telephone, Approval, Facility, and Physician Codes, Health Care System

★ American Hospital Association (AHA) membership
□ The Joint Commission accreditation
○ Healthcare Facilities Accreditation Program
◇ DNV Healthcare Inc. accreditation
⇑ Center for Improvement in Healthcare Quality Accreditation
△ Commission on Accreditation of Rehabilitation Facilities (CARF) accreditation

BLOOMFIELD—Davis County

★ **DAVIS COUNTY HOSPITAL (161327)**, 509 North Madison Street, Zip 52537-1271; tel. 641/664-2145, **A**10 18 **F**3 7 11 15 28 29 34 35 40 44 45 50 57 59 63 64 65 69 75 79 81 84 85 86 87 97 107 110 111 115 119 127 132 133 135 146 **P**6
Primary Contact: Catherine Hillestad, Interim Chief Executive Officer
CFO: Kendra Warning, Chief Financial Officer
CMO: Robert Floyd, D.O., Chief Medical Staff
CIO: Kendra Warning, Chief Financial Officer
CHR: Pam Young, Director Human Resources
CNO: Susan Kay Pankey, Chief Nursing Officer
Web address: www.daviscountyhospital.org
Control: County, Government, nonfederal **Service**: General medical and surgical

Staffed Beds: 13 **Admissions**: 274 **Census**: 3 **Outpatient Visits**: 39897 **Births**: 0 **Total Expense ($000)**: 24907 **Payroll Expense ($000)**: 8609 **Personnel**: 163

BOONE—Boone County

★ **BOONE COUNTY HOSPITAL (161372)**, 1015 Union Street, Zip 50036-4821; tel. 515/432-3140, **A**10 18 **F**2 3 7 11 13 15 28 29 30 31 34 35 40 43 45 50 56 57 59 62 64 65 69 70 75 76 77 78 79 81 82 85 86 87 89 91 93 97 107 110 111 114 119 131 132 133 134 145 146 147 148 **P**6 **S** QHR, Brentwood, TN
Primary Contact: Joseph S. Smith, Chief Executive Officer
CFO: Joseph Devin, Chief Financial Officer
CMO: Brian Mehlhaus, M.D., Chief of Staff
CIO: Paul Sliva, Chief Information Officer
CHR: Kim Schwartz, Assistant Administrator Human Resources and Operations
Web address: www.boonehospital.com
Control: County, Government, nonfederal **Service**: General medical and surgical

Staffed Beds: 25 **Admissions**: 1068 **Census**: 12 **Outpatient Visits**: 84113 **Births**: 121 **Total Expense ($000)**: 46601 **Payroll Expense ($000)**: 19658 **Personnel**: 368

BRITT—Hancock County

★ **HANCOCK COUNTY HEALTH SYSTEM (161307)**, 532 First Street NW, Zip 50423-1227; tel. 641/843-5000, **A**10 18 **F**3 15 28 29 34 35 36 40 43 45 46 50 53 56 57 59 62 64 65 75 77 81 82 85 93 97 100 104 107 110 114 119 129 130 131 132 133 135 146 148 154 **P**1 **S** Trinity Health, Livonia, MI
Primary Contact: Laura Zwiefel, Chief Executive Officer
CFO: Julie Damm, Chief Financial Officer
CMO: Catherine Butler, M.D., Chief Medical Staff
CIO: Julie Damm, Chief Financial Officer
CHR: Denise Jakoubeck, Director Human Resources
Web address: www.trusthchs.com/hancock-county-health-system
Control: County, Government, nonfederal **Service**: General medical and surgical

Staffed Beds: 25 **Admissions**: 463 **Census**: 9 **Outpatient Visits**: 21473 **Births**: 0 **Total Expense ($000)**: 23903 **Payroll Expense ($000)**: 7842 **Personnel**: 174

CARROLL—Carroll County

★ **ST. ANTHONY REGIONAL HOSPITAL (160005)**, 311 South Clark Street, Zip 51401-3038, Mailing Address: P.O. Box 628, Zip 51401-0628; tel. 712/792-3581, (Total facility includes 79 beds in nursing home-type unit) **A**10 20 **F**6 11 13 15 28 29 30 31 34 35 37 38 39 40 43 44 45 46 50 51 56 57 59 60 61 62 63 64 65 67 68 69 70 74 75 76 77 78 79 81 82 84 85 86 87 89 93 97 98 100 101 102 103 104 107 108 110 111 115 118 119 125 126 127 129 130 131 132 133 134 135 145 146 147 148 **P**6
Primary Contact: Edward H. Smith, President and Chief Executive Officer
CFO: John Munson, Vice President and Chief Financial Officer
CMO: Kyle Ulveling, M.D., Chief of Staff
CIO: Chad Lawson, Chief Information Officer
CHR: Anna Fitzpatrick, Director Human Resources
CNO: Karen Timm, R.N., MSN, Vice President Patient Services
Web address: www.stanthonyhospital.org
Control: Church operated, Nongovernment, not-for-profit **Service**: General medical and surgical

Staffed Beds: 155 **Admissions**: 2369 **Census**: 108 **Outpatient Visits**: 119061 **Births**: 407 **Total Expense ($000)**: 77860 **Payroll Expense ($000)**: 32428 **Personnel**: 580

CEDAR FALLS—Black Hawk County

⊞ **SARTORI MEMORIAL HOSPITAL (160040)**, 515 College Street, Zip 50613-2500; tel. 319/268-3000, **A**1 10 **F**3 7 8 11 12 15 29 30 35 40 43 44 46 53 57 59 64 68 70 75 77 79 81 91 93 97 98 103 107 110 111 119 130 131 132 146 **P**1 6 **S** Trinity Health, Livonia, MI
Primary Contact: MaryJo Kavalier, Administrator
CFO: Timothy Huber, Vice President and Chief Financial Officer
CMO: James Lehman, M.D., Vice President Medical Affairs
CNO: Kelly Richards, MSN, Senior Vice President and Chief Nursing Officer
Web address: www.wheatoniowa.org
Control: Church operated, Nongovernment, not-for-profit **Service**: General medical and surgical

Staffed Beds: 50 **Admissions**: 1494 **Census**: 20 **Outpatient Visits**: 43743 **Births**: 0 **Total Expense ($000)**: 36815 **Payroll Expense ($000)**: 11721 **Personnel**: 192

CEDAR RAPIDS—Linn County

⊞ **MERCY MEDICAL CENTER (160079)**, 701 Tenth Street SE, Zip 52403-1292; tel. 319/398-6011, (Total facility includes 76 beds in nursing home-type unit) **A**1 2 3 5 10 **F**3 4 5 6 11 12 13 15 18 20 22 26 28 29 30 31 32 34 35 37 38 40 43 44 45 46 48 49 50 51 54 55 56 57 58 59 60 61 62 63 64 65 67 68 70 72 74 75 76 77 78 79 81 82 84 85 86 87 88 89 90 91 92 93 96 98 99 100 101 102 103 104 107 108 109 110 114 115 116 117 118 119 120 121 123 124 126 128 130 131 132 135 145 146 147 148 149 153 154 **P**2 8
Primary Contact: Timothy L. Charles, President and Chief Executive Officer
CFO: Nathan Van Genderen, Executive Vice President and Chief Financial Officer
CMO: Tim Quinn, M.D., Executive Vice President and Chief of Clinical Operations and President Mercy Care Management
CIO: Jeff Cash, Senior Vice President and Chief Information Officer
CHR: Doug Jontz, Senior Vice President Human Resources
CNO: Mary Brobst, R.N., MSN, Senior Vice President Patient Care Services and Chief Nursing Officer
Web address: www.mercycare.org
Control: Church operated, Nongovernment, not-for-profit **Service**: General medical and surgical

Staffed Beds: 302 **Admissions**: 11278 **Census**: 173 **Outpatient Visits**: 349624 **Births**: 874 **Total Expense ($000)**: 307962 **Payroll Expense ($000)**: 117867 **Personnel**: 1924

ST. LUKE'S HOSPITAL See Unitypoint Health – St. Luke's Hospital

⊞ △ **UNITYPOINT HEALTH – ST. LUKE'S HOSPITAL (160045)**, 1026 'A' Avenue NE, Zip 52402-3026, Mailing Address: P.O. Box 3026, Zip 52406-3026; tel. 319/369-7211, **A**1 2 3 5 7 10 **F**3 5 11 12 13 15 17 18 19 20 22 24 26 28 29 30 31 32 34 35 36 37 39 40 43 45 46 49 50 54 55 56 57 59 60 61 62 63 64 65 66 68 70 72 74 75 76 77 78 79 81 82 84 85 86 87 88 89 90 91 92 93 95 96 98 99 100 101 103 104 105 107 108 110 115 117 118 119 120 121 123 124 126 130 131 132 134 135 145 146 147 148 149 152 153 154 **P**6 **S** UnityPoint Health, West Des Moines, IA
Primary Contact: Theodore E. Townsend, FACHE, President and Chief Executive Officer
COO: Michelle Niermann, Executive Vice President and Chief Operating Officer
CFO: Michael G. Heinrich, Senior Vice President and Chief Financial Officer
CMO: Dustin Arnold, D.O., Chief Medical Officer
CHR: Susan L Slattery, Director Human Resources
CNO: Carmen Kleinsmith, MSN, R.N., Vice President, Chief Nurse Executive
Web address: www.unitypoint.org
Control: Other not-for-profit (including NFP Corporation) **Service**: General medical and surgical

Staffed Beds: 348 **Admissions**: 16111 **Census**: 199 **Outpatient Visits**: 476099 **Births**: 2376 **Total Expense ($000)**: 349060 **Payroll Expense ($000)**: 124231 **Personnel**: 2142

CENTERVILLE—Appanoose County

★ **MERCY MEDICAL CENTER–CENTERVILLE (161377)**, 1 St Joseph's Drive, Zip 52544-8055; tel. 641/437-4111, (Total facility includes 20 beds in nursing home-type unit) **A**10 18 **F**1 3 4 8 11 13 15 16 17 28 29 30 31 34 40 45 46 50 54 57 59 64 67 70 72 73 75 76 77 78 80 81 85 86 87 88 89 90 93 97 98 107 110 111 113 115 117 119 127 128 129 130 132 133 135 **P**6 **S** Catholic Health Initiatives, Englewood, CO
Primary Contact: Ann Young, Interim President
CHR: Tonya Clawson, Manager Human Resources
CNO: Sherri L Doggett, Vice President Patient Services
Web address: www.mercycenterville.org
Control: Church operated, Nongovernment, not-for-profit **Service**: General medical and surgical

Staffed Beds: 45 **Admissions**: 573 **Census**: 25 **Outpatient Visits**: 89959 **Births**: 49 **Total Expense ($000)**: 27065 **Payroll Expense ($000)**: 11714 **Personnel**: 200

IA

CHARITON—Lucas County

★ **LUCAS COUNTY HEALTH CENTER (161341)**, 1200 North Seventh Street, Zip 50049–1258; tel. 641/774–3000, **A**10 18 **F**3 5 7 11 13 15 28 29 30 31 34 38 40 43 44 45 47 50 64 66 68 70 75 76 81 85 87 89 90 93 97 107 115 119 127 128 130 132 133 143 145 146 148 **S** UnityPoint Health, West Des Moines, IA
Primary Contact: Brian Sims, Chief Executive Officer
CMO: David Marcowitz, M.D., Chief of Staff
CIO: Terri Black, Network Manager
CHR: Lana Kuball, Director Administrative Services
CNO: JoBeth Lawless, Chief Nursing Officer, Nursing Services and Director Emergency Management Services
Web address: www.lchcia.com
Control: County, Government, nonfederal **Service:** General medical and surgical

Staffed Beds: 25 **Admissions:** 374 **Census:** 5 **Outpatient Visits:** 18277 **Births:** 69 **Total Expense ($000):** 20681 **Payroll Expense ($000):** 9334 **Personnel:** 182

CHARLES CITY—Floyd County

FLOYD COUNTY MEDICAL CENTER (161347), 800 Eleventh Street, Zip 50616–3499; tel. 641/228–6830, **A**10 18 **F**11 13 15 28 29 34 35 40 45 57 59 64 75 79 81 86 91 93 97 107 115 119 127 130 132 133 146 148 149 154 **S** Mayo Clinic, Rochester, MN
Primary Contact: Rod Nordeng, Administrator
CFO: Ron Timpe, Chief Financial Officer
CHR: Don Nosbisch, Director Human Resources
CNO: Viva Boerschel, Director of Nursing
Web address: www.fcmc.us.com/
Control: County, Government, nonfederal **Service:** General medical and surgical

Staffed Beds: 25 **Admissions:** 733 **Census:** 11 **Outpatient Visits:** 58205 **Births:** 80 **Total Expense ($000):** 25857 **Payroll Expense ($000):** 9404 **Personnel:** 173

CHEROKEE—Cherokee County

★ **CHEROKEE REGIONAL MEDICAL CENTER (161362)**, 300 Sioux Valley Drive, Zip 51012–1205; tel. 712/225–5101, **A**10 18 **F**7 11 13 15 17 28 29 34 35 40 43 45 53 56 57 59 62 63 64 65 67 68 69 75 76 77 78 81 84 86 87 89 93 96 97 107 111 114 119 125 127 128 129 130 131 132 133 135 146 147 148 **P**6 **S** UnityPoint Health, West Des Moines, IA
Primary Contact: Matthew Johnson, Chief Executive Officer and President
CFO: Joan Bierman, Vice President Finance
CIO: Kevin Naslund, Manager Information Technology
CHR: Theresa Conley, Manager Human Resources
CNO: Christy Syndergaard, Vice President Nursing
Web address: www.cherokeermc.org
Control: Other not-for-profit (including NFP Corporation) **Service:** General medical and surgical

Staffed Beds: 25 **Admissions:** 973 **Census:** 10 **Outpatient Visits:** 49024 **Births:** 123 **Total Expense ($000):** 22539 **Payroll Expense ($000):** 9686 **Personnel:** 181

☐ **MENTAL HEALTH INSTITUTE (164002)**, 1251 West Cedar Loop, Zip 51012–1599; tel. 712/225–2594, **A**1 10 **F**29 30 68 75 98 99 100 101 130 135 149 **P**6
Primary Contact: Chris Tosteberg, Superintendent
CFO: Tony Morris, Business Manager
CHR: Mary Ann Hanson, Director Personnel
Web address: www.dhs.state.ia.us
Control: State, Government, nonfederal **Service:** Psychiatric

Staffed Beds: 36 **Admissions:** 420 **Census:** 29 **Outpatient Visits:** 59 **Births:** 0 **Total Expense ($000):** 16714 **Payroll Expense ($000):** 9272 **Personnel:** 155

CLARINDA—Page County

★ **CLARINDA REGIONAL HEALTH CENTER (161352)**, 220 Essie Davison Drive, Zip 51632–2915, Mailing Address: P.O. Box 217, Zip 51632–0217; tel. 712/542–2176, **A**10 18 **F**3 7 11 15 28 29 31 34 36 40 43 50 57 59 64 65 69 75 79 81 85 86 87 93 97 107 110 111 114 118 119 127 128 129 130 133 135 143 146 148 150 152 154 **P**3 6 **S** Bryan Health, Lincoln, NE
Primary Contact: Charles Nordyke, Chief Executive Officer
COO: Elaine Otte, Chief Operating Officer
CFO: Milton Trabal, Chief Financial Officer
CMO: Autumn Morales, Chief Medical Staff Officer
CIO: Richard Morgan–Fine, IT Director
CHR: Melissa Walter, Director Human Resources
CNO: Sherrie L Laubenthal, R.N., Chief Nursing Officer
Web address: www.clarindahealth.com
Control: City, Government, nonfederal **Service:** General medical and surgical

Staffed Beds: 25 **Admissions:** 450 **Census:** 3 **Outpatient Visits:** 66323 **Births:** 0 **Total Expense ($000):** 31204 **Payroll Expense ($000):** 12171 **Personnel:** 245

CLARION—Wright County

★ ⇑ **IOWA SPECIALTY HOSPITAL–CLARION (161302)**, 1316 South Main Street, Zip 50525–2019; tel. 515/532–2811, **A**10 18 21 **F**11 13 15 28 29 31 32 34 35 40 43 45 46 50 56 57 59 63 64 65 68 69 75 76 77 79 81 82 85 86 87 92 93 96 97 107 110 111 114 119 125 127 131 132 133 134 135 146 147 148 149 154 **P**6 **S** Iowa Specialty Hospitals, Clarion, IA
Primary Contact: Steven J. Simonin, President and Chief Executive Officer
COO: Kirk Rier, Chief Operating Officer
CFO: Greg Polzin, Chief Financial Officer
CMO: Dennis Colby, M.D., Chief of Staff
CHR: Holly Martin, Human Resources Leader
CNO: Abby Young, Chief Nursing Officer
Web address: www.iowaspecialtyhospital.com
Control: City, Government, nonfederal **Service:** General medical and surgical

Staffed Beds: 25 **Admissions:** 1092 **Census:** 7 **Outpatient Visits:** 57578 **Births:** 368 **Total Expense ($000):** 51231 **Payroll Expense ($000):** 19356 **Personnel:** 330

CLINTON—Clinton County

⊞ **MERCY MEDICAL CENTER–CLINTON (160080)**, 1410 North Fourth Street, Zip 52732–2940; tel. 563/244–5555, (Includes MERCY SERVICES FOR AGING, 600 14th Avenue North, Clinton, IA, Zip 52732; tel. 563/244–3888) (Total facility includes 183 beds in nursing home–type unit) **A**1 10 **F**3 11 13 15 18 20 22 28 29 30 31 34 35 36 38 40 44 45 47 49 50 53 55 56 57 59 60 61 62 63 64 68 70 74 75 76 77 78 79 80 81 82 84 85 87 89 93 98 100 101 102 107 108 110 111 115 118 119 121 123 128 129 130 132 146 148 **S** Trinity Health, Livonia, MI
Primary Contact: Amy Berentes, R.N., MSN, Executive Vice President and Chief Operating Officer
CFO: Paul Mangin, Vice President Finance
CHR: Shane Buer, Vice President, Human Resources
CNO: Amy Berentes, R.N., MSN, Vice President Patient Care Services
Web address: www.mercyclinton.com
Control: Church operated, Nongovernment, not-for-profit **Service:** General medical and surgical

Staffed Beds: 290 **Admissions:** 4807 **Census:** 171 **Outpatient Visits:** 68319 **Births:** 384 **Total Expense ($000):** 94769 **Payroll Expense ($000):** 38731 **Personnel:** 730

CORALVILLE—Johnson County

IOWA MEDICAL AND CLASSIFICATION CENTER, 2700 Coral Ridge Avenue, Zip 52241–4708, Mailing Address: 2700 Coral Rigde Avenue, Zip 52241; tel. 319/626–2391, **F**29 30 38 39 59 75 98 101 102 103 130 132 143 154
Primary Contact: James McKinney, Warden
Web address: www.oakdaleprison.com/
Control: State, Government, nonfederal **Service:** Psychiatric

Staffed Beds: 20 **Admissions:** 112 **Census:** 12 **Outpatient Visits:** 0 **Births:** 0 **Personnel:** 26

CORNING—Adams County

★ **CHI HEALTH MERCY CORNING (161304)**, 603 Rosary Drive, Zip 50841–1683; tel. 641/322–3121, **A**10 18 **F**3 11 15 28 30 31 34 40 43 46 50 53 56 57 59 64 67 74 75 77 78 79 81 85 89 90 97 107 110 115 119 127 128 129 130 132 133 135 146 147 148 149 154 **P**6 **S** Catholic Health Initiatives, Englewood, CO
Primary Contact: Lisa Wolfe, President
CMO: Maen Haddadin, M.D., President Medical Staff
CIO: Kenneth Lawonn, Senior Vice President and Chief Information Officer
CHR: Sandra Lammers, Coordinator Human Resources and Finance
Web address: www.alegent.com
Control: Church operated, Nongovernment, not-for-profit **Service:** General medical and surgical

Staffed Beds: 22 **Admissions:** 197 **Census:** 3 **Outpatient Visits:** 21186 **Births:** 0 **Total Expense ($000):** 13804 **Payroll Expense ($000):** 4386 **Personnel:** 85

Hospital, Medicare Provider Number, Address, Telephone, Approval, Facility, and Physician Codes, Health Care System

★ American Hospital Association (AHA) membership
☐ The Joint Commission accreditation
○ Healthcare Facilities Accreditation Program
◇ DNV Healthcare Inc. accreditation
⇑ Center for Improvement in Healthcare Quality Accreditation
△ Commission on Accreditation of Rehabilitation Facilities (CARF) accreditation

IA

CORYDON—Wayne County

★ **WAYNE COUNTY HOSPITAL (161358)**, 417 South East Street, Zip 50060–1860, Mailing Address: P.O. Box 305, Zip 50060–0305; tel. 641/872–2260, **A**10 18 **F**7 13 15 28 29 31 34 35 40 43 51 56 57 59 60 64 69 70 75 76 77 78 79 81 85 87 89 91 92 93 97 107 110 115 119 126 127 130 131 133 148 149 154 **P**6
Primary Contact: Daren Relph, Chief Executive Officer
COO: Michael Thomas, Associate Administrator
CFO: Diane Hook, Chief Financial Officer
CMO: Joel Baker, D.O., Chief Medical Officer
CIO: Laurie Ehrich, Chief Communications Officer
CHR: Dave Carlyle, Director Human Resources
CNO: Sheila Mattly, Chief Nursing Officer
Web address: www.waynecountyhospital.org
Control: County, Government, nonfederal **Service**: General medical and surgical

> **Staffed Beds**: 25 **Admissions**: 543 **Census**: 6 **Outpatient Visits**: 28898
> **Births**: 144 **Total Expense ($000)**: 25258 **Payroll Expense ($000)**: 11712
> **Personnel**: 223

COUNCIL BLUFFS—Pottawattamie County

✠ **CHI HEALTH MERCY COUNCIL BLUFFS (160028)**, 800 Mercy Drive, Zip 51503–3128; tel. 712/328–5000, **A**1 2 5 10 **F**3 11 13 15 18 20 22 26 28 29 30 31 34 35 40 41 44 47 48 49 50 57 59 68 70 73 74 76 77 78 79 81 82 84 85 87 89 91 93 98 99 100 101 102 104 105 107 108 110 111 114 115 119 129 130 132 146 147 154 **P**8 **S** Catholic Health Initiatives, Englewood, CO
Primary Contact: Marie E. Knedler, R.N., FACHE, President
COO: Joan E Neuhaus, Chief Operating Officer
CFO: Jeanette Wojtalewicz, Chief Financial Officer
CMO: Joseph Hoagbin, M.D., Chief Quality Officer
CIO: Thomas Haley, Information Technology Services Site Director
CHR: Nancy Wallace, Senior Vice President Human Resources
CNO: Kathy Bressler, Chief Nursing Officer
Web address: www.chihealth.com/chi–health–mercy–council–bluffs
Control: Church operated, Nongovernment, not–for–profit **Service**: General medical and surgical

> **Staffed Beds**: 148 **Admissions**: 7200 **Census**: 79 **Outpatient Visits**: 80475
> **Births**: 412 **Total Expense ($000)**: 91149 **Payroll Expense ($000)**: 31597
> **Personnel**: 460

JENNIE EDMUNDSON HOSPITAL See Methodist Jennie Edmundson Hospital

✠ **METHODIST JENNIE EDMUNDSON HOSPITAL (160047)**, 933 East Pierce Street, Zip 51503–4652, Mailing Address: P.O. Box 2C, Zip 51502–3002; tel. 712/396–6000, **A**1 2 3 5 10 **F**3 11 13 15 18 20 22 26 28 29 30 31 34 35 39 40 43 44 45 47 49 50 57 58 59 61 64 68 70 74 75 76 78 79 81 82 85 86 87 89 92 93 98 100 101 102 107 108 110 111 115 118 119 120 121 123 124 129 130 131 132 135 143 145 146 147 148 149 **P**6 8 **S** Nebraska Methodist Health System, Inc., Omaha, NE
Primary Contact: Steven P. Baumert, President and Chief Executive Officer
CFO: Jeffrey Francis, Vice President Finance and Chief Financial Officer
CMO: Scott Bomgaars, M.D., Vice President Medical Affairs
CIO: Steven Zuber, Vice President
CHR: Holly Huerter, Vice President Human Resources
CNO: Peggy Helget, R.N., MSN, Vice President Patient Services and Chief Nursing Officer
Web address: www.bestcare.org
Control: Other not–for–profit (including NFP Corporation) **Service**: General medical and surgical

> **Staffed Beds**: 114 **Admissions**: 5867 **Census**: 64 **Outpatient Visits**: 61999
> **Births**: 574 **Total Expense ($000)**: 103202 **Payroll Expense ($000)**: 40517
> **Personnel**: 542

CRESCO—Howard County

★ **REGIONAL HEALTH SERVICES OF HOWARD COUNTY (161328)**, 235 Eighth Avenue West, Zip 52136–1098; tel. 563/547–2101, **A**10 18 **F**3 7 11 13 15 28 29 34 35 36 40 41 43 45 50 56 57 59 62 63 64 65 68 75 76 81 82 85 89 96 102 107 110 115 119 127 128 130 132 133 146 147 148 149 154 **P**8 **S** Trinity Health, Livonia, MI
Primary Contact: Robin M. Schluter, Chief Executive Officer
CFO: Greg Burkel, Chief Financial Officer
CMO: Paul Jensen, M.D., Chief of Staff
CIO: Greg Burkel, Chief Financial Officer
CHR: Jennalee Pedretti, Vice President Operations
CNO: Carol Kerian–Masters, RN, Chief Nursing Officer
Web address: www.rhshc.com
Control: County, Government, nonfederal **Service**: General medical and surgical

> **Staffed Beds**: 19 **Admissions**: 253 **Census**: 3 **Outpatient Visits**: 22285
> **Births**: 65 **Total Expense ($000)**: 21990 **Payroll Expense ($000)**: 7409
> **Personnel**: 148

CRESTON—Union County

★ ⇑ **GREATER REGIONAL MEDICAL CENTER (161365)**, 1700 West Townline Street Suite 3, Zip 50801–1099; tel. 641/782–7091, **A**10 18 21 **F**3 7 8 11 13 15 28 29 31 34 35 40 43 44 45 47 48 50 56 57 59 64 65 66 70 75 76 77 78 79 81 82 85 86 93 96 97 104 107 108 110 111 115 119 120 121 122 123 124 125 127 128 129 131 132 133 146 147 148 149 **P**6 **S** UnityPoint Health, West Des Moines, IA
Primary Contact: Monte Neitzel, Chief Executive Officer
CFO: Matt McCutchan, Chief Financial Officer
CMO: Steve Reeves, M.D., Chief Medical Staff
CIO: Karla Alford, Chief Information Officer
CHR: Amy Rieck, Human Resources Officer
CNO: Amanda Mohr, Chief Nursing Officer
Web address: www.greaterregional.org
Control: County, Government, nonfederal **Service**: General medical and surgical

> **Staffed Beds**: 25 **Admissions**: 858 **Census**: 7 **Outpatient Visits**: 111667
> **Births**: 190 **Total Expense ($000)**: 55026 **Payroll Expense ($000)**: 23781
> **Personnel**: 370

DAVENPORT—Scott County

✠ △ **GENESIS MEDICAL CENTER, DAVENPORT (160033)**, 1227 East Rusholme Street, Zip 52803–2498; tel. 563/421–1000, (Includes GENESIS MEDICAL CENTER–EAST CAMPUS, 1227 East Rusholme Street, Davenport, IA, Zip 52803; tel. 563/421–1000; GENESIS MEDICAL CENTER–WEST CAMPUS, 1401 West Central Park, Davenport, IA, Zip 52804–1769; tel. 563/421–1000) **A**1 2 3 5 7 10 **F**3 7 11 12 13 15 17 18 20 22 24 26 28 29 30 31 34 35 37 38 40 43 44 46 49 50 53 54 57 58 59 63 64 68 70 72 74 75 77 78 79 81 82 84 85 86 87 90 91 92 93 94 96 97 98 100 102 107 111 114 115 118 119 120 121 123 124 126 129 130 131 132 135 146 147 148 153 154 **P**6 **S** Genesis Health System, Davenport, IA
Primary Contact: Jordan Voigt, Administrator
CFO: Mark G Rogers, Interim Vice President Finance and Chief Financial Officer
CMO: Frank Claudy, M.D., Vice President Medical Staff Affairs
CIO: Robert Frieden, Vice President Information Systems
CHR: Heidi Kahly–McMahon, Interim Vice President Human Resources
Web address: www.genesishealth.com
Control: Other not–for–profit (including NFP Corporation) **Service**: General medical and surgical

> **Staffed Beds**: 368 **Admissions**: 19435 **Census**: 202 **Outpatient Visits**: 206105 **Births**: 1817 **Total Expense ($000)**: 341216 **Payroll Expense ($000)**: 92959 **Personnel**: 1393

✠ **SELECT SPECIALTY HOSPITAL–QUAD CITIES (162001)**, 1111 West Kimberly Road, Zip 52806–5711; tel. 563/468–2000, **A**1 10 **F**1 3 29 45 75 85 119 130 148 **S** Select Medical Corporation, Mechanicsburg, PA
Primary Contact: Codie Dillie, Chief Executive Officer
Web address: www.selectmedicalcorp.com
Control: Corporation, Investor–owned (for–profit) **Service**: Acute long–term care hospital

> **Staffed Beds**: 50 **Admissions**: 324 **Census**: 23 **Outpatient Visits**: 0
> **Births**: 0 **Total Expense ($000)**: 14768 **Payroll Expense ($000)**: 6123
> **Personnel**: 107

DE WITT—Clinton County

✠ **GENESIS MEDICAL CENTER, DEWITT (161313)**, 1118 11th Street, Zip 52742–1296; tel. 563/659–4200, (Total facility includes 75 beds in nursing home–type unit) **A**1 10 18 **F**3 7 8 11 15 28 29 30 34 35 38 40 41 43 44 45 49 50 53 57 59 64 68 69 74 77 79 81 82 85 86 87 93 102 107 110 115 119 129 130 131 132 133 135 146 148 149 **P**6 **S** Genesis Health System, Davenport, IA
Primary Contact: Curt Coleman, FACHE, Chief Executive Officer
CMO: Steven Fowler, M.D., President Medical Staff
CHR: Kristin Nicholson, Coordinator Human Resources
CNO: Wanda Haack, MSN, R.N., Chief Nursing Officer
Web address: www.genesishealth.com
Control: Other not–for–profit (including NFP Corporation) **Service**: General medical and surgical

> **Staffed Beds**: 88 **Admissions**: 315 **Census**: 76 **Outpatient Visits**: 20556
> **Births**: 0 **Total Expense ($000)**: 19688 **Payroll Expense ($000)**: 7652
> **Personnel**: 83

Many Facility Codes have changed. Please refer to the AHA Guide Code Chart. © 2018 AHA Guide

DECORAH—Winneshiek County

⊞ **WINNESHIEK MEDICAL CENTER (161371)**, 901 Montgomery Street, Zip 52101–2325; tel. 563/382–2911, **A**1 10 18 **F**3 7 8 11 13 15 28 29 31 34 35 36 38 40 43 44 45 50 56 57 59 61 62 63 64 65 68 69 75 77 78 79 81 82 86 87 93 94 97 102 104 107 110 111 115 119 129 130 131 132 133 135 144 146 147 148 149 153 **S** Mayo Clinic, Rochester, MN
Primary Contact: Lisa Radtke, Chief Administrative Officer
COO: David Rooney, Administrator Operations
CFO: Lynn Luloff, Chief Financial Officer
CMO: Robert Flinchbaugh, D.O., Chief Medical Officer
CHR: Laurie Bulman, Director Human Resources
Web address: www.winmedical.org
Control: County, Government, nonfederal **Service**: General medical and surgical

Staffed Beds: 25 **Admissions**: 1030 **Census**: 13 **Outpatient Visits**: 71333
Births: 222 **Total Expense ($000)**: 58319 **Payroll Expense ($000)**: 20785
Personnel: 409

DENISON—Crawford County

★ **CRAWFORD COUNTY MEMORIAL HOSPITAL (161369)**, 100 Medical Parkway, Zip 51442–2299; tel. 712/265–2500, **A**10 18 **F**3 7 8 11 13 15 17 28 29 31 34 35 40 45 50 54 56 57 59 64 65 67 68 70 75 76 77 78 79 81 82 85 87 89 93 97 101 104 107 110 111 115 119 127 128 133 135 143 148 **P**6
Primary Contact: Bill Bruce, FACHE, Chief Executive Officer
CFO: Rachel Melby, Vice President, Chief Financial Officer
CIO: Angie Anderson, Director Information Technology
CHR: Brad L. Bonner, Executive Director, Human Resources and General Counsel
CNO: Erin Muck, Vice President, Clinical Nursing
Web address: www.ccmhia.com
Control: County, Government, nonfederal **Service**: General medical and surgical

Staffed Beds: 25 **Admissions**: 655 **Census**: 6 **Outpatient Visits**: 47913
Births: 133 **Total Expense ($000)**: 36425 **Payroll Expense ($000)**: 15493
Personnel: 240

DES MOINES—Polk County

⊞ **BROADLAWNS MEDICAL CENTER (160101)**, 1801 Hickman Road, Zip 50314–1597; tel. 515/282–2200, **A**1 3 5 10 **F**3 5 11 13 15 18 29 30 31 32 34 35 38 39 40 43 44 45 48 50 52 53 56 57 58 59 64 65 66 68 70 74 75 76 77 78 79 81 82 85 86 87 92 93 94 97 98 99 100 101 102 103 104 105 106 107 111 114 119 127 129 130 131 132 135 144 146 147 148 153 154 **P**6
Primary Contact: Jody J. Jenner, President and Chief Executive Officer
CFO: Karlis Vilums, Chief Financial Officer
CMO: Vincent Mandracchia, DPM, Chief Medical Officer
CHR: Julie Kilgore, Vice President, Human Resources
CNO: Susan N. Kirstein, R.N., MSN, Chief Nursing Officer
Web address: www.broadlawns.org
Control: County, Government, nonfederal **Service**: General medical and surgical

Staffed Beds: 113 **Admissions**: 2552 **Census**: 51 **Outpatient Visits**: 255827 **Births**: 377 **Total Expense ($000)**: 157501 **Payroll Expense ($000)**: 75245 **Personnel**: 980

DES MOINES DIVISION See Veterans Affairs Central Iowa Health Care System, Des Moines

⇑ **IOWA LUTHERAN HOSPITAL** See Unitypoint Health–Iowa Lutheran Hospital

⊞ △ **MERCY MEDICAL CENTER–DES MOINES (160083)**, 1111 6th Avenue, Zip 50314–2611; tel. 515/247–3121, (Includes MERCY MEDICAL CENTER – WEST LAKES, 1755 59th Place, West Des Moines, IA, Zip 50266–7737; tel. 515/358–8000; Karl Keeler, President) **A**1 2 3 7 10 13 **F**3 4 5 6 7 8 9 11 12 13 15 16 17 18 19 20 21 22 23 24 25 26 27 28 29 30 31 32 34 35 36 38 39 40 41 43 44 46 48 49 50 53 54 55 56 57 58 59 60 61 62 63 64 65 66 68 70 71 72 73 74 75 76 77 78 79 81 82 84 85 86 87 88 89 90 91 92 93 94 96 97 98 99 100 101 102 103 104 105 107 108 109 110 111 114 115 116 117 118 119 120 121 123 124 126 129 130 131 132 134 135 138 141 142 143 144 145 146 147 148 149 150 151 152 153 154 **P**6 **S** Catholic Health Initiatives, Englewood, CO
Primary Contact: Karl Keeler, President
COO: Linda Goodwin, Chief Operating Officer and Chief Nursing Executive
CFO: Randy Rubin, Senior Vice President and Chief Financial Officer
CIO: James Strother, Site Director Information Technology Systems
CHR: Kevin Elsberry, Senior Vice President Human Resources
CNO: Linda Goodwin, Chief Operating Officer and Chief Nursing Executive
Web address: www.mercydesmoines.org
Control: Church operated, Nongovernment, not–for–profit **Service**: General medical and surgical

Staffed Beds: 620 **Admissions**: 33460 **Census**: 429 **Outpatient Visits**: 258262 **Births**: 4535 **Total Expense ($000)**: 706220 **Payroll Expense ($000)**: 269276 **Personnel**: 3915

⊞ **SELECT SPECIALTY HOSPITAL–DES MOINES (162003)**, 1111 6th Avenue, 4th Floor Main, Zip 50314–2610; tel. 515/247–4400, **A**1 10 **F**1 29 75 148 **S** Select Medical Corporation, Mechanicsburg, PA
Primary Contact: Glen Griesheim, Chief Executive Officer
Web address: www.selectspecialtyhospitals.com
Control: Corporation, Investor–owned (for–profit) **Service**: Acute long–term care hospital

Staffed Beds: 30 **Admissions**: 262 **Census**: 17 **Outpatient Visits**: 0
Births: 0 **Total Expense ($000)**: 10975 **Payroll Expense ($000)**: 4418
Personnel: 69

★ △ ⇑ **UNITYPOINT HEALTH – IOWA METHODIST MEDICAL CENTER (160082)**, 1200 Pleasant Street, Zip 50309–1406; tel. 515/241–6212, (Includes POWELL CONVALESCENT CENTER, 1200 Pleasant, Des Moines, IA, Zip 50309; tel. 515/241–6212; UNITY POINT HEALTH – JOHN STODDARD CANCER CENTER, 1221 Pleasant Street, Des Moines, IA, Zip 50309–1423; tel. 515/241–6212; UNITYPOINT HEALTH – BLANK CHILDREN'S HOSPITAL, 1200 Pleasant Street, Des Moines, IA, Zip 50309–1406; tel. 515/241–5437; Steve R. Stephenson, M.D., President and Chief Operating Officer; UNITYPOINT HEALTH – METHODIST WEST HOSPITAL, 1660 60th Street, West Des Moines, IA, Zip 50266–7700; tel. 515/343–1000; David A. Stark, FACHE, President and Chief Executive Officer; YOUNKER MEMORIAL REHABILITATION CENTER, 1200 Pleasant Road, Des Moines, IA, Zip 50308; tel. 515/241–6212) **A**2 5 7 8 10 21 **F**3 7 8 11 12 13 17 18 20 22 24 26 28 29 30 31 32 34 35 39 40 41 43 44 45 46 47 48 49 50 53 54 55 56 57 58 59 60 61 64 65 68 70 71 72 74 75 76 77 78 79 81 82 84 85 86 87 88 89 90 91 92 93 95 96 97 100 107 108 111 114 115 116 117 118 119 120 121 123 124 126 129 130 131 132 134 135 138 146 147 148 149 **P**6 **S** UnityPoint Health, West Des Moines, IA
Primary Contact: David A. Stark, FACHE, President and Chief Executive Officer
COO: Eric L Lothe, FACHE, Executive Vice President and Chief Operating Officer
CFO: Michael Dewerff, Chief Financial Officer
CMO: Mark Purtle, M.D., Vice President Medical Affairs
CHR: Joyce McDanel, Vice President Human Resources and Education
CNO: Debra Moyer, R.N., Chief Nursing Executive and Vice President Nursing Services
Web address: www.unitypoint.org
Control: Other not–for–profit (including NFP Corporation) **Service**: General medical and surgical

Staffed Beds: 448 **Admissions**: 21835 **Census**: 319 **Outpatient Visits**: 281218 **Births**: 3910 **Total Expense ($000)**: 526618 **Payroll Expense ($000)**: 232058 **Personnel**: 3729

★ ⇑ **UNITYPOINT HEALTH–IOWA LUTHERAN HOSPITAL (160024)**, 700 East University Avenue, Zip 50316–2392; tel. 515/263–5612, (Total facility includes 16 beds in nursing home–type unit) **A**5 10 21 **F**3 4 5 8 11 13 15 17 18 20 22 26 28 29 30 34 35 38 39 40 43 44 45 49 50 51 53 56 57 58 59 60 61 64 65 68 70 71 74 75 76 79 81 82 84 85 86 87 91 92 93 95 96 97 98 99 100 101 102 103 104 105 107 108 110 111 114 115 118 119 128 130 132 134 135 146 147 148 149 152 153 **P**6 **S** UnityPoint Health, West Des Moines, IA
Primary Contact: David A. Stark, FACHE, President and Chief Executive Officer
COO: Eric L Lothe, FACHE, Senior Vice President and Chief Operating Officer
CFO: Joe Corfits, Chief Financial Officer
CMO: Mark Purtle, M.D., Vice President Medical Affairs
CHR: Joyce McDanel, Vice President Human Resources and Education
CNO: Debra Moyer, R.N., Chief Nurse Executive
Web address: www.unitypoint.org
Control: Other not–for–profit (including NFP Corporation) **Service**: General medical and surgical

Staffed Beds: 206 **Admissions**: 7956 **Census**: 117 **Outpatient Visits**: 61474 **Births**: 416 **Total Expense ($000)**: 135623 **Payroll Expense ($000)**: 57721 **Personnel**: 872

⊞ △ **VETERANS AFFAIRS CENTRAL IOWA HEALTH CARE SYSTEM**, 3600 30th Street, Zip 50310–5753; tel. 515/699–5999, (Includes DES MOINES DIVISION, 3600 30th Street, Des Moines, IA, Zip 50310–5774; tel. 515/699–5999; KNOXVILLE DIVISION, 1515 West Pleasant, Knoxville, IA, Zip 50138–3399; tel. 515/842–3101) (Total facility includes 108 beds in nursing home–type unit) **A**1 3 5 7 **F**3 5 6 8 11 12 15 18 20 22 24 28 29 30 31 33 34 35 36 37 38 39 40 44 45 46 50 53 54 55 56 57 59 61 62 63 64 65 66 70 71 74 75 77 78 79 80 81 82 83 84 85 86 87 93 94 96 97 98 100 101 102 103 104 106 107 110 111 115 117 118 119 127 128 129 130 132 135 137 138 139 140 141 143 146 147 148 149 153 154 **S** Department of Veterans Affairs, Perry Point, MD
Primary Contact: Gail L. Graham, Director
CMO: Fredrick Bahls, M.D., Chief of Staff
CIO: James Danuser, Chief Information Officer
CHR: Sabrina Owen, Human Resources Officer
Web address: www.centraliowa.va.gov/
Control: Veterans Affairs, Government, federal **Service**: General medical and surgical

Staffed Beds: 220 **Admissions**: 2371 **Census**: 156 **Outpatient Visits**: 366184 **Births**: 0 **Total Expense ($000)**: 325354 **Payroll Expense ($000)**: 149902 **Personnel**: 1492

IA

DUBUQUE—Dubuque County

FINLEY HOSPITAL See Unitypoint Health – Finley Hospital

✠ △ **MERCY MEDICAL CENTER–DUBUQUE (160069)**, 250 Mercy Drive,
Zip 52001–7360; tel. 563/589–8000, (Total facility includes 40 beds in nursing
home–type unit) **A**1 7 10 **F**3 4 5 8 11 13 15 18 20 22 24 26 28 29 30 31 32 34
35 36 38 39 40 43 44 49 50 51 53 56 57 58 59 61 62 64 65 67 70 72 74 75
76 77 78 79 80 81 84 85 86 87 89 90 91 93 97 98 99 100 101 102 103 104
107 108 110 111 114 115 117 118 119 126 128 129 130 131 132 134 135
144 146 147 148 149 150 **P**8 **S** Trinity Health, Livonia, MI
Primary Contact: Kay Takes, R.N., President
CFO: Robert Shafer, Vice President Finance
CIO: Joe Billmeyer, Director, Information Services
CHR: Kathryn Roberts, Director Human Resources
CNO: Robert Wethal, R.N., Vice President and Chief Nursing Officer
Web address: www.mercydubuque.com
Control: Church operated, Nongovernment, not–for–profit **Service**: General
medical and surgical

> **Staffed Beds: 231 Admissions: 9284 Census: 143 Outpatient Visits:**
> 47107 **Births: 749 Total Expense ($000): 167077 Payroll Expense**
> **($000): 50492 Personnel: 1046**

✠ △ **UNITYPOINT HEALTH – FINLEY HOSPITAL (160117)**, 350 North
Grandview Avenue, Zip 52001–6393; tel. 563/582–1881, **A**1 7 10 **F**3 11 12 13
15 18 20 22 26 28 29 30 31 34 35 39 40 43 44 45 46 48 49 50 56 57 59 60
61 62 64 65 70 72 74 75 76 77 78 79 81 82 84 85 86 87 90 91 92 93 96 97
98 103 107 108 110 111 114 115 117 118 119 120 121 123 124 126 129
130 131 132 135 144 146 147 148 149 153 **P**1 5 **S** UnityPoint Health, West
Des Moines, IA
Primary Contact: Theodore E. Townsend, FACHE, Interim Chief Executive Officer
COO: Tim Ahlers, Chief Operating Officer
CFO: Tim Ahlers, Chief Financial Officer
CMO: Bryan Pechous, M.D., Vice President Medical Affairs
CIO: Tim Loeffelholz, Account Executive Information Technology
CHR: Karla Waldbillig, Director Human Resources
CNO: Mary Peters, Chief Nursing Officer
Web address: www.unitypoint.org
Control: Other not–for–profit (including NFP Corporation) **Service**: General
medical and surgical

> **Staffed Beds: 109 Admissions: 4746 Census: 54 Outpatient Visits: 95113**
> **Births: 771 Total Expense ($000): 127411 Payroll Expense ($000): 55352**
> **Personnel: 795**

DYERSVILLE—Dubuque County

★ **MERCY MEDICAL CENTER–DYERSVILLE (161378)**, 1111 Third Street SW,
Zip 52040–1725; tel. 563/875–7101, **A**10 18 **F**11 15 34 35 36 39 40 44 50 56
57 59 64 65 75 79 81 85 86 93 119 130 131 132 133 134 135 146 147 149
P8 **S** Trinity Health, Livonia, MI
Primary Contact: Kay Takes, R.N., President
CFO: Robert Shafer, Vice President Finance
Web address: www.mercydubuque.com/mercy–dyersville
Control: Church operated, Nongovernment, not–for–profit **Service**: General
medical and surgical

> **Staffed Beds: 20 Admissions: 97 Census: 3 Outpatient Visits: 3085**
> **Births: 0 Total Expense ($000): 5750 Payroll Expense ($000): 2476**
> **Personnel: 51**

ELKADER—Clayton County

★ **CENTRAL COMMUNITY HOSPITAL (161319)**, 901 Davidson Street NW,
Zip 52043–9015; tel. 563/245–7000, **A**10 18 **F**7 11 15 28 34 35 40 43 45 50
57 59 64 67 68 75 81 85 87 91 93 102 107 110 114 128 133 146 **S** Trinity
Health, Livonia, MI
Primary Contact: Brooke Kensinger, Chief Executive Officer
CFO: Patricia Borel, Chief Financial Officer
CIO: Jonathan Holliday, Manager Information Technology
CHR: Angie Gerndt, Human Resources Manager
CNO: Natalie Shea, Chief Nursing Officer
Web address: www.centralcommunityhospital.com
Control: Other not–for–profit (including NFP Corporation) **Service**: General
medical and surgical

> **Staffed Beds: 15 Admissions: 131 Census: 2 Outpatient Visits: 6727**
> **Births: 0 Total Expense ($000): 7397 Payroll Expense ($000): 2576**
> **Personnel: 61**

EMMETSBURG—Palo Alto County

★ **PALO ALTO COUNTY HEALTH SYSTEM (161357)**, 3201 First Street,
Zip 50536–2516; tel. 712/852–5500, (Total facility includes 22 beds in nursing
home–type unit) **A**10 18 **F**3 7 11 13 15 28 29 34 35 40 43 45 46 50 57 59 62
63 64 65 67 69 71 75 76 77 81 82 85 87 93 107 110 114 119 125 127 130
132 133 135 143 146 154 **S** Trinity Health, Livonia, MI
Primary Contact: Brett Antczak, Chief Executive Officer
CFO: Collette Johnson, Chief Financial Officer
CMO: Madhan Prabhakaran, M.D., Chief Medical Officer
CHR: Tara Helle, Human Resources Lead
CNO: Sara Travis, Chief Nursing Officer and Assistant Administrator
Web address: www.pachs.com
Control: County, Government, nonfederal **Service**: General medical and surgical

> **Staffed Beds: 47 Admissions: 343 Census: 26 Outpatient Visits: 20060**
> **Births: 83 Total Expense ($000): 26185 Payroll Expense ($000): 10181**
> **Personnel: 192**

ESTHERVILLE—Emmet County

★ **AVERA HOLY FAMILY HOSPITAL (161351)**, 826 North Eighth Street,
Zip 51334–1598; tel. 712/362–2631, **A**10 18 **F**3 11 13 15 28 29 30 31 34 35
37 40 45 57 59 64 68 69 70 75 76 77 78 79 81 85 87 93 97 107 110 111
114 119 130 131 132 133 146 154 **P**4 **S** Avera Health, Sioux Falls, SD
Primary Contact: Kayleen R. Lee, Interim Chief Executive Officer
CFO: Shannon Adams, Chief Financial Officer
CMO: Anthony Cook, M.D., Chief of Staff
CHR: Janette Jensen, Manager Human Resources
CNO: Cathi Rae Scharnberg, R.N., M.P.H., Vice President Patient Services
Web address: www.avera–holyfamily.org
Control: Church operated, Nongovernment, not–for–profit **Service**: General
medical and surgical

> **Staffed Beds: 25 Admissions: 751 Census: 6 Outpatient Visits: 70448**
> **Births: 84 Total Expense ($000): 25304 Payroll Expense ($000): 10826**
> **Personnel: 176**

FAIRFIELD—Jefferson County

★ **JEFFERSON COUNTY HEALTH CENTER (161364)**, 2000 S Main,
Zip 52556–9572; Mailing Address: P.O. Box 588, Zip 52556–0010;
tel. 641/472–4111, **A**10 18 **F**11 15 28 30 31 34 35 36 40 43 45 50 57 59 67
68 70 75 77 78 79 81 85 89 93 96 102 107 110 111 112 114 115 119 127
128 129 132 133 135 143 144 146 148 **P**5
Primary Contact: Bryan Hunger, Chief Executive Officer
CFO: Larry Peach, Chief Financial Officer
CHR: Nanette Everly, Manager Human Resources and Administrative Assistant
Web address: www.jeffersoncountyhealthcenter.org
Control: County, Government, nonfederal **Service**: General medical and surgical

> **Staffed Beds: 25 Admissions: 698 Census: 11 Outpatient Visits: 69831**
> **Births: 0 Total Expense ($000): 44683 Payroll Expense ($000): 16339**
> **Personnel: 313**

FORT DODGE—Webster County

★ ⇑ **UNITYPOINT HEALTH – TRINITY REGIONAL MEDICAL CENTER (160016)**,
802 Kenyon Road, Zip 50501–5795; tel. 515/573–3101, **A**2 10 21 **F**3 7 8 11 13
15 18 20 22 26 28 29 30 31 32 34 35 36 38 40 43 44 45 46 47 48 49 50 53
57 59 64 68 70 74 75 76 77 78 79 81 82 84 85 86 87 89 91 92 93 102 107
108 110 111 115 118 119 120 121 123 129 130 131 132 135 145 146 148
149 150 **P**6 **S** UnityPoint Health, West Des Moines, IA
Primary Contact: Susan K. Thompson, RN, Interim President and Chief Executive
Officer
COO: Troy Martens, Chief Operating Officer
CFO: Brent Feickert, Chief Financial Officer
CHR: Ted W Vaughn, Director Human Resources
CNO: Debra Shriver, R.N., MSN, Chief Nurse Executive
Web address: www.trmc.org
Control: Other not–for–profit (including NFP Corporation) **Service**: General
medical and surgical

> **Staffed Beds: 49 Admissions: 3959 Census: 35 Outpatient Visits: 90250**
> **Births: 484 Total Expense ($000): 97728 Payroll Expense ($000): 47506**
> **Personnel: 641**

IA

FORT MADISON—Lee County

⊞ **FORT MADISON COMMUNITY HOSPITAL (160122)**, 5445 Avenue
'O', Zip 52627–9611, Mailing Address: P.O. Box 174, Zip 52627–0174;
tel. 319/372–6530, **A**1 10 **F**3 11 13 15 28 29 31 34 40 43 45 50 51 53 57 59
62 64 67 68 70 74 75 76 77 78 79 81 85 86 87 90 91 93 94 96 97 99 100
101 102 103 104 107 108 110 111 115 117 118 119 128 129 130 131 132
133 143 144 146 147 148 149 **P**6 **S** QHR, Brentwood, TN
Primary Contact: Jeremy Alexander, Chief Executive Officer
CFO: Bradley J Kokjohn, Chief Financial Officer
CMO: David Wenger–Keller, M.D., Chief of Staff
CIO: Shane Tapper, Director Management Information Systems
CHR: Vicki Kokjohn, Director Employee Relations
CNO: Shelby Dickens, Director, Patient Care Services
Web address: www.fmchosp.com
Control: Other not-for-profit (including NFP Corporation) **Service:** General
medical and surgical

Staffed Beds: 50 **Admissions:** 1231 **Census:** 11 **Outpatient Visits:** 98421
Births: 379 **Total Expense ($000):** 59098 **Payroll Expense ($000):** 28036
Personnel: 473

GREENFIELD—Adair County

★ **ADAIR COUNTY HEALTH SYSTEM (161310)**, 609 SE Kent Street,
Zip 50849–9454; tel. 641/743–2123, **A**10 18 **F**3 7 8 11 15 18 28 34 35 40 43
45 50 57 59 64 65 69 75 81 97 107 108 110 114 119 127 128 133 144 149
P6
Primary Contact: Marcia Hendricks, FACHE, R.N., Chief Executive Officer
CFO: Heather Shaull, Chief Financial Officer
CMO: Jessica Kennedy, D.O., Chief Medical Officer
CIO: Gary Bateman, Chief Information Technology
CHR: Angie Frankl, Director Human Resources
CNO: Cindy K Peeler, R.N., Chief Nursing Officer
Web address: www.adaircountyhealthsystem.org
Control: County, Government, nonfederal **Service:** General medical and surgical

Staffed Beds: 17 **Admissions:** 66 **Census:** 1 **Outpatient Visits:** 8696
Births: 0 **Total Expense ($000):** 13319 **Payroll Expense ($000):** 5423
Personnel: 105

GRINNELL—Poweshiek County

★ ○ **UNITYPOINT HEALTH – GRINNELL REGIONAL MEDICAL CENTER
(160147)**, 210 Fourth Avenue, Zip 50112–1898; tel. 641/236–7511, **A**10 11 **F**3
11 12 13 15 28 29 30 31 32 34 35 36 38 40 43 44 45 46 47 50 53 54 56 57
59 61 62 63 64 65 66 70 75 76 77 78 81 84 85 86 87 89 93 97 107 110 111
115 118 119 126 127 130 131 132 133 134 135 144 146 147 148 149 150
154 **P**6 7 **S** UnityPoint Health, West Des Moines, IA
Primary Contact: Jennifer Havens, Chief Executive Officer
CFO: Kyle M Wilcox, Vice President Finance
CIO: David L Ness, Vice President Operations
CHR: Debra S. Nowachek, Director Human Resources
CNO: Doris Rindels, Vice President Operations
Web address: www.grmc.us
Control: Other not-for-profit (including NFP Corporation) **Service:** General
medical and surgical

Staffed Beds: 49 **Admissions:** 1406 **Census:** 12 **Outpatient Visits:** 44488
Births: 172 **Total Expense ($000):** 52569 **Payroll Expense ($000):** 21638
Personnel: 354

GRUNDY CENTER—Grundy County

★ **GRUNDY COUNTY MEMORIAL HOSPITAL (161303)**, 201 East 'J' Avenue,
Zip 50638–2096; tel. 319/824–5421, (Total facility includes 55 beds in nursing
home–type unit) **A**10 18 **F**15 28 29 34 35 40 43 50 57 59 63 64 67 68 75 78
79 81 82 86 87 93 107 110 111 114 119 128 129 130 131 132 133 135 146
148 154 **S** UnityPoint Health, West Des Moines, IA
Primary Contact: Adam Scherling, President and Chief Executive Officer
COO: Ryan Bingman, Director Operations
CFO: Lisa Zinkula, Chief Financial Officer
CMO: Douglas Cooper, M.D., Chief Medical Officer
CIO: Steve Bantz, Manager Information Technology
CHR: Keagan Brunscheon, Manager, Human Resources
CNO: Jody Schipper, Director of Nursing
Web address: www.grundycountyhospital.com
Control: County, Government, nonfederal **Service:** General medical and surgical

Staffed Beds: 80 **Admissions:** 317 **Census:** 52 **Outpatient Visits:** 43994
Births: 0 **Total Expense ($000):** 20977 **Payroll Expense ($000):** 8848
Personnel: 168

GUTHRIE CENTER—Guthrie County

★ **GUTHRIE COUNTY HOSPITAL (161314)**, 710 North 12th Street,
Zip 50115–1544; tel. 641/332–2201, **A**10 18 **F**11 15 18 28 29 31 34 35 40
43 45 53 56 57 59 64 69 75 79 81 85 93 107 110 114 119 128 130 132 133
143 148 154 **S** UnityPoint Health, West Des Moines, IA
Primary Contact: Patrick Peters, Chief Executive Officer
CFO: Troy Eller, Chief Financial Officer
CMO: Donald Fillman, M.D., Chief Medical Officer
CIO: Jeff Cobb, Information Technologist
CHR: Kimberly Myers, Director Human Resources
CNO: Gregory Opseth, Chief Nursing Officer
Web address: www.guthriecountyhospital.org
Control: County, Government, nonfederal **Service:** General medical and surgical

Staffed Beds: 17 **Admissions:** 371 **Census:** 4 **Outpatient Visits:** 34408
Births: 0 **Total Expense ($000):** 16282 **Payroll Expense ($000):** 7111
Personnel: 103

GUTTENBERG—Clayton County

⊞ **GUTTENBERG MUNICIPAL HOSPITAL (161312)**, 200 Main Street,
Zip 52052–9108, Mailing Address: P.O. Box 550, Zip 52052–0550;
tel. 563/252–1121, **A**1 10 18 **F**3 11 15 28 34 35 40 43 45 50 57 59 64 68
76 81 85 89 93 97 102 107 110 111 115 119 126 127 128 130 132 133 **P**5 6
Primary Contact: Kelly Dybvig, Chief Executive Officer
COO: Lisa Manson, Director Ambulatory Services
CFO: Jill DeMoss, Finance Manager
CMO: Chris Hugo, M.D., Chief of Staff
CIO: Scott R Pauls, Director Information Technology– HealthNet Connect
CHR: Chelsea Greene, Manager Human Resources
Web address: www.guttenberghospital.org
Control: City, Government, nonfederal **Service:** General medical and surgical

Staffed Beds: 20 **Admissions:** 349 **Census:** 4 **Outpatient Visits:** 26836
Births: 34 **Total Expense ($000):** 16580 **Payroll Expense ($000):** 6698
Personnel: 122

HAMBURG—Fremont County

GEORGE C GRAPE COMMUNITY HOSPITAL (161324), 2959 US Highway 275,
Zip 51640–5067; tel. 712/382–1515, (Total facility includes 6 beds in nursing
home–type unit) **A**10 18 **F**11 15 18 28 31 34 35 40 43 45 50 53 59 62 64 65
68 75 77 78 79 81 82 85 91 93 107 114 119 128 129 130 133 135 148
Primary Contact: Michael O'Neal, Administrator and Chief Executive Officer
CFO: Hilary Christiansen, Chief Financial Officer
CMO: Kelli Woltemath, D.O., Chief Medical Staff
CIO: Craig Wells, Chief Information Officer
CHR: Jackie Wertz, Director Human Resources
CNO: Gloria Mattice, R.N., Director Patient Care
Web address: www.grapehospital.com
Control: Other not-for–profit (including NFP Corporation) **Service:** General
medical and surgical

Staffed Beds: 25 **Admissions:** 158 **Census:** 3 **Outpatient Visits:** 18175
Births: 0 **Total Expense ($000):** 10618 **Payroll Expense ($000):** 4158
Personnel: 85

HAMPTON—Franklin County

★ **FRANKLIN GENERAL HOSPITAL (161308)**, 1720 Central Avenue East, Suite A,
Zip 50441–1867; tel. 641/456–5000, (Total facility includes 52 beds in nursing
home–type unit) **A**10 18 **F**7 10 11 15 28 30 34 40 43 57 59 63 64 65 67 68 75
77 79 81 82 85 86 89 90 93 103 107 111 115 119 127 128 129 130 131 132
133 135 146 147 148 154 **S** Trinity Health, Livonia, MI
Primary Contact: Kim Price, Chief Executive Officer
CFO: Deb Rosburg, Chief Financial Officer
CHR: Victoria Kruse, Manager Human Resources
CNO: Ronda Reimer, R.N., Chief Nursing Officer and Assistant Administrator
Web address: www.franklingeneral.com
Control: County, Government, nonfederal **Service:** General medical and surgical

Staffed Beds: 77 **Admissions:** 253 **Census:** 53 **Outpatient Visits:** 23504
Births: 0 **Total Expense ($000):** 19678 **Payroll Expense ($000):** 6038
Personnel: 133

IA

HARLAN—Shelby County

★ **MYRTUE MEDICAL CENTER (161374)**, 1213 Garfield Avenue,
Zip 51537–2057; tel. 712/755–5161, **A**10 18 **F**3 11 13 15 28 29 31 32 34 35
38 40 43 45 46 50 53 56 57 59 62 63 64 65 68 75 76 77 78 81 85 87 92 93
97 99 101 102 103 104 107 110 114 119 127 129 130 131 132 133 135 146
148 154 **P**6 8
Primary Contact: Barry Jacobsen, CPA, Chief Executive Officer
CFO: Kristy Hansen, CPA, Chief Financial Officer
CMO: Brian A. Anderson, D.O., Chief of Staff
CIO: David Sirek, Chief Information Officer
CHR: Donna Christensen–Mores, JD, Director Human Resources
CNO: Karen Buman, MSN, Chief Nursing Executive
Web address: www.myrtuemedical.org
Control: County, Government, nonfederal **Service**: General medical and surgical

Staffed Beds: 25 **Admissions**: 967 **Census**: 11 **Outpatient Visits**: 111792
Births: 72 **Total Expense ($000)**: 39625 **Payroll Expense ($000)**: 15313
Personnel: 360

HAWARDEN—Sioux County

★ **HAWARDEN REGIONAL HEALTHCARE (161311)**, 1111 11th Street,
Zip 51023–1999; tel. 712/551–3100, **A**10 18 **F**11 15 28 29 31 34 35 40 43 53
59 64 68 75 77 81 90 92 93 107 108 110 114 119 127 128 131 132 133 135
148 **P**3 **S** Trinity Health, Livonia, MI
Primary Contact: Jayson Pullman, Chief Executive Officer
CFO: Jessica Hughes, Director Finance
CMO: Dale Nystrom, M.D., Chief Medical Officer, Physician
CHR: Maggie Hofer, Human Resources Representative
Web address: www.hawardenregionalhealthcare.com/
Control: City, Government, nonfederal **Service**: General medical and surgical

Staffed Beds: 18 **Admissions**: 153 **Census**: 3 **Outpatient Visits**: 18736
Births: 0 **Total Expense ($000)**: 9496 **Payroll Expense ($000)**: 3225
Personnel: 66

HUMBOLDT—Humboldt County

★ **HUMBOLDT COUNTY MEMORIAL HOSPITAL (161334)**, 1000 North 15th
Street, Zip 50548–1008; tel. 515/332–4200, (Total facility includes 28 beds in
nursing home–type unit) **A**10 18 **F**7 8 10 11 12 14 15 28 29 31 34 35 40 41 43
45 47 50 51 59 62 63 65 68 69 75 77 78 79 81 82 84 85 87 93 102 104 107
110 111 114 119 125 127 128 129 130 133 134 135 **S** UnityPoint Health, West
Des Moines, IA
Primary Contact: Michelle Sleiter, Chief Executive Officer
CFO: Betty Etherington, Chief Financial Officer
CHR: Mary Moritz, Administrator Human Resources
Web address: www.humboldthospital.org
Control: County, Government, nonfederal **Service**: General medical and surgical

Staffed Beds: 49 **Admissions**: 540 **Census**: 32 **Outpatient Visits**: 85178
Births: 0 **Total Expense ($000)**: 18485 **Payroll Expense ($000)**: 7847
Personnel: 159

IDA GROVE—Ida County

★ **HORN MEMORIAL HOSPITAL (161354)**, 701 East Second Street,
Zip 51445–1699; tel. 712/364–3311, **A**10 18 **F**11 15 28 29 34 40 45 50 57
59 62 63 64 65 66 68 75 77 79 81 82 85 89 93 97 100 107 108 110 111 115
117 119 127 128 129 130 131 132 133 135 146 147 148 154 **P**6
Primary Contact: Glen Winekauf, Chief Executive Officer
CFO: Marcia Fehring, Chief Financial Officer
CIO: Robbie Todd, Director Information Technology
CHR: Lorraine Davis, Vice President Human Resources
CNO: Jo Hayes, Chief Nursing Officer
Web address: www.hornmemorialhospital.org
Control: Other not–for–profit (including NFP Corporation) **Service**: General
medical and surgical

Staffed Beds: 20 **Admissions**: 414 **Census**: 6 **Outpatient Visits**: 47249
Births: 0 **Total Expense ($000)**: 19317 **Payroll Expense ($000)**: 8792
Personnel: 165

INDEPENDENCE—Buchanan County

★ **BUCHANAN COUNTY HEALTH CENTER (161335)**, 1600 First Street East,
Zip 50644–3155; tel. 319/332–0999, (Total facility includes 39 beds in nursing
home–type unit) **A**10 18 **F**3 11 15 28 29 32 34 35 40 43 45 50 53 56 57 59 64
65 67 75 77 79 81 82 84 86 87 91 93 97 107 110 111 114 119 125 127 128
129 130 131 132 133 135 146 148 **P**6 **S** UnityPoint Health, West Des Moines, IA
Primary Contact: Steve Robert. Slessor, Chief Executive Officer
CFO: Ben Stevens, Chief Financial Officer
CNO: Rachel Goldenstein, R.N., Chief Nursing Officer
Web address: www.bchealth.info
Control: County, Government, nonfederal **Service**: General medical and surgical

Staffed Beds: 58 **Admissions**: 320 **Census**: 40 **Outpatient Visits**: 61851
Births: 0 **Total Expense ($000)**: 26123 **Payroll Expense ($000)**: 11312
Personnel: 190

☐ **MENTAL HEALTH INSTITUTE (164003)**, 2277 Iowa Avenue, Zip 50644–9106;
tel. 319/334–2583, **A**1 10 **F**59 65 75 98 99 101 102 130 135 143 146 149 **P**6
Primary Contact: Bhasker J. Dave, M.D., Superintendent
CFO: Kevin Jimmerson, Business Manager
CMO: Bhasker J Dave, M.D., Superintendent
Web address: www.dhs.state.ia.us
Control: State, Government, nonfederal **Service**: Psychiatric

Staffed Beds: 60 **Admissions**: 159 **Census**: 52 **Outpatient Visits**: 19
Births: 0 **Total Expense ($000)**: 20322 **Payroll Expense ($000)**: 11755
Personnel: 191

IOWA CITY—Johnson County

⊞ **IOWA CITY VETERANS AFFAIRS HEALTH CARE SYSTEM**, 601 Highway 6
West, Zip 52246–2208; tel. 319/338–0581, **A**1 3 5 8 **F**3 5 8 11 12 17 18 20
22 24 29 30 31 33 34 35 36 38 39 40 43 44 45 46 47 50 51 53 54 56 57 58
59 60 61 62 64 65 70 71 74 75 78 79 81 82 83 84 85 86 87 91 92 93 94 97
98 100 101 102 103 104 105 107 108 110 111 114 115 116 117 118 119
129 130 135 138 142 143 146 147 148 149 152 153 154 **P**6 **S** Department of
Veterans Affairs, Perry Point, MD
Primary Contact: Judith Johnson–Mekota, Director
COO: Kevin Kosek, Associate Director Operations
CFO: Jennifer Ruppert, Chief Financial Officer
CMO: Richard A Charlat, Chief of Staff
CIO: Dwight Schuessler, Chief Information Officer
CHR: Dan Helle, Human Resources Officer
CNO: Dawn Oxley, R.N., Associate Director Patient Care Services and Nurse
Executive
Web address: www.iowacity.va.gov/
Control: Veterans Affairs, Government, federal **Service**: General medical and
surgical

Staffed Beds: 78 **Admissions**: 3504 **Census**: 55 **Outpatient Visits**: 542397
Births: 0 **Total Expense ($000)**: 384376 **Payroll Expense ($000)**: 144375
Personnel: 2027

⊞ **MERCY IOWA CITY (160029)**, 500 East Market Street, Zip 52245–2689;
tel. 319/339–0300, **A**1 2 10 **F**3 5 8 11 12 13 15 18 20 22 24 26 28 29 30 31
34 35 38 40 41 43 44 45 47 48 50 51 54 58 59 62 63 64 65 70 72 73
74 75 76 77 78 79 81 85 86 87 89 97 98 100 101 102 104 107 108 110 111
114 115 116 117 119 126 127 129 130 132 135 144 145 146 148 **P**8
Primary Contact: Sean J. Williams, President and Chief Executive Officer
CFO: Douglas Davenport, Interim Chief Financial Officer
CMO: Martin Izakovic, M.D., Vice President Medical Staff Affairs and Chief Medical
Officer
CIO: David Fishbaugher, Chief Medical Information
CHR: Dena M Brockhouse, Director Human Resources
CNO: Cindy L Penney, R.N., Vice President Nursing
Web address: www.mercyiowacity.org
Control: Church operated, Nongovernment, not–for–profit **Service**: General
medical and surgical

Staffed Beds: 223 **Admissions**: 6844 **Census**: 70 **Outpatient Visits**:
346162 **Births**: 1186 **Total Expense ($000)**: 159845 **Payroll Expense
($000)**: 61770 **Personnel**: 829

UNIVERSITY HOSPITAL SCHOOL See Center for Disabilities and Development

⊞ **UNIVERSITY OF IOWA HOSPITALS AND CLINICS (160058)**, 200
Hawkins Drive, Zip 52242–1009; tel. 319/356–1616, (Includes CENTER FOR
DISABILITIES AND DEVELOPMENT, 200 Hawkins Drive, Iowa City, IA, Zip 52242;
tel. 319/356–1347; CHEMICAL DEPENDENCY CENTER, 200 Hawkins Drive, Iowa
City, IA, Zip 52242–1007; tel. 319/384–8765; STATE PSYCHIATRIC HOSPITAL,
200 Hawkins Drive, Iowa City, IA, Zip 52242; tel. 319/356–4658; UNIVERSITY
OF IOWA STEAD FAMILY CHILDREN'S HOSPITAL, 200 Hawkins Drive, Iowa City, IA,
Zip 52242–1009; tel. 888/573–5437) **A**1 2 3 5 8 10 **F**3 5 6 7 8 9 11 12 13 14
15 16 17 18 19 20 21 22 23 24 25 26 27 28 29 30 31 32 33 34 35 36 37 38
39 40 41 43 44 45 46 47 48 49 50 51 52 53 54 55 56 57 58 59 60 61 62 63
64 65 66 68 70 72 73 74 75 76 77 78 79 80 81 82 83 84 85 86 87 88 89 90
91 92 93 94 96 97 98 99 100 101 102 103 104 105 107 108 109 110 111
114 115 116 117 118 119 120 121 123 124 126 127 129 130 131 132 135
136 137 138 139 140 141 142 143 145 146 147 148 152 153 154 **P**1
Primary Contact: Kenneth P. Kates, Chief Executive Officer
COO: Scott Turner, Chief Operating Officer
CFO: Bradley Haws, Chief Financial Officer
CMO: Theresa Brennan, M.D., Chief Medical Officer
CIO: Lee Carmen, Associate Vice President Health Care Information Systems
CHR: Jana Wessels, Associate Vice President Human Resources
CNO: Cindy Dawson, MSN, R.N., Chief Nursing Executive
Web address: www.uihealthcare.org
Control: State, Government, nonfederal **Service**: General medical and surgical

Staffed Beds: 745 **Admissions**: 34216 **Census**: 621 **Outpatient Visits**:
1476668 **Births**: 2256 **Total Expense ($000)**: 1483016 **Payroll Expense
($000)**: 509046 **Personnel**: 8785

IA

IOWA FALLS—Hardin County

★ **HANSEN FAMILY HOSPITAL (161380)**, 920 South Oak, Zip 50126–9506;
tel. 641/648–4631, **A**10 18 **F**1 3 4 11 13 15 16 17 28 29 30 34 40 41 43 45
50 53 57 59 64 65 67 70 72 73 75 76 77 80 81 82 85 86 87 88 89 90 93 97
98 100 104 107 110 115 119 128 133 135 147 **P**6 **S** Trinity Health, Livonia, MI
Primary Contact: Douglas E. Morse, Chief Executive Officer
CFO: Mike White, Chief Financial Officer
CMO: George Pfaltzgraff, Chief Medical Officer
CHR: Cheri Geitz, Director Human Resources
CNO: Katie Rieks, Chief Nursing Officer
Web address: www.hansenfamilyhospital.com
Control: City, Government, nonfederal **Service**: General medical and surgical

Staffed Beds: 21 **Admissions**: 501 **Census**: 6 **Outpatient Visits**: 24895
Births: 82 **Total Expense ($000)**: 24255 **Payroll Expense ($000)**: 9207
Personnel: 228

JEFFERSON—Greene County

★ **GREENE COUNTY MEDICAL CENTER (161325)**, 1000 West Lincolnway,
Zip 50129–1645; tel. 515/386–2114, (Total facility includes 60 beds in nursing
home–type unit) **A**10 18 **F**3 11 15 28 29 31 34 35 36 40 46 55 56 57 59 63 64
65 67 68 75 77 79 81 82 85 93 107 110 114 119 125 128 130 131 132 133
147 149 150 **S** UnityPoint Health, West Des Moines, IA
Primary Contact: Carl P. Behne, Chief Executive Officer
CFO: Mark A VanderLinden, Chief Financial Officer
CMO: Jon Van Der Veer, D.O., Vice President Medical Affairs
CIO: Roger Overby, Executive Director Information Systems
CHR: Cathy Krieger, Human Resources Director
CNO: Katie Heldt, Chief Nursing Officer
Web address: www.gcmchealth.com
Control: County, Government, nonfederal **Service**: General medical and surgical

Staffed Beds: 85 **Admissions**: 370 **Census**: 43 **Outpatient Visits**: 18684
Births: 3 **Total Expense ($000)**: 25765 **Payroll Expense ($000)**: 9439
Personnel: 207

KEOKUK—Lee County

✠ **UNITYPOINT HEALTH–KEOKUK (160008)**, 1600 Morgan Street,
Zip 52632–3456; tel. 319/524–7150, **A**1 10 **F**3 11 15 28 29 34 35 40 43 45
46 57 59 62 64 68 70 79 81 85 86 87 93 96 107 108 111 115 118 119 129
132 133 146 148 149 **P**6 **S** UnityPoint Health, West Des Moines, IA
Primary Contact: Donza T. Worden, M.D., Chief Clinical Officer
CFO: Kris Karre, Director Finance and Accounting
CMO: Neville Crenshaw, D.O., Chief of Staff
CIO: Linda Atterberg, Chief Information Officer
CHR: Lora Taylor, Director Human Resources and Compliance Officer
CNO: Vickie White, Director of Nursing
Web address: www.keokukhealthsystems.org
Control: Other not–for–profit (including NFP Corporation) **Service**: General
medical and surgical

Staffed Beds: 42 **Admissions**: 882 **Census**: 8 **Outpatient Visits**: 30651
Births: 0 **Total Expense ($000)**: 19474 **Payroll Expense ($000)**: 8851
Personnel: 207

KEOSAUQUA—Van Buren County

★ **VAN BUREN COUNTY HOSPITAL (161337)**, 304 Franklin Street,
Zip 52565–1164; tel. 319/293–3171, **A**10 18 **F**3 7 10 11 13 15 28 29 32 34
35 40 43 45 46 50 56 57 59 64 65 70 75 76 81 82 85 89 93 97 102 107 110
115 119 125 127 128 130 132 133 135 146 147 154 **P**6
Primary Contact: Ray Brownsworth, Chief Executive Officer
CFO: Kara McEntee, Chief Financial Officer
CIO: Chris McEntee, Network Specialist
CNO: Rhonda Fellows, R.N., Chief Nursing Officer
Web address: www.vbch.org
Control: County, Government, nonfederal **Service**: General medical and surgical

Staffed Beds: 25 **Admissions**: 302 **Census**: 4 **Outpatient Visits**: 15261
Births: 41 **Total Expense ($000)**: 15970 **Payroll Expense ($000)**: 7720
Personnel: 160

KNOXVILLE—Marion County

KNOXVILLE DIVISION See Veterans Affairs Central Iowa Health Care System, Des
Moines

★ **KNOXVILLE HOSPITAL & CLINICS (161355)**, 1002 South Lincoln Street,
Zip 50138–3155; tel. 641/842–2151, **A**10 18 **F**3 8 11 15 28 29 34 35 37 40
43 45 47 48 49 50 54 57 59 64 65 75 77 79 81 85 86 93 97 107 108 110
111 114 118 119 126 129 130 131 132 133 135 146 148 154 **P**6 **S** Catholic
Health Initiatives, Englewood, CO
Primary Contact: Kevin Kincaid, Chief Executive Officer
CFO: Maggie Hamilton–Beyer, Chief Financial Officer
CMO: Brent Hoehns, M.D., Chief of Medical Staff
CIO: Thom Richards, Director Information Technology
CNO: MaryJane Hunt, Chief Clinical Officer
Web address: www.knoxvillehospital.org
Control: Other not–for–profit (including NFP Corporation) **Service**: General
medical and surgical

Staffed Beds: 25 **Admissions**: 1031 **Census**: 8 **Outpatient Visits**: 65957
Births: 0 **Total Expense ($000)**: 30363 **Payroll Expense ($000)**: 12439
Personnel: 248

LAKE CITY—Calhoun County

★ **STEWART MEMORIAL COMMUNITY HOSPITAL (161350)**, 1301 West Main,
Zip 51449–1585; tel. 712/464–3171, **A**10 18 **F**11 12 13 15 28 29 30 31 34 40
43 45 50 59 62 63 64 65 69 75 76 77 80 81 82 86 93 94 107 110 114 119
127 130 133 135 147 **P**6 **S** UnityPoint Health, West Des Moines, IA
Primary Contact: Cynthia L. Carstens, R.N., President and Chief Executive Officer
CFO: Jim Henkenius, Chief Financial Officer
CHR: Bill Albright, Director Human Resources
Web address: www.stewartmemorial.org
Control: Other not–for–profit (including NFP Corporation) **Service**: General
medical and surgical

Staffed Beds: 25 **Admissions**: 452 **Census**: 4 **Outpatient Visits**: 48193
Births: 92 **Total Expense ($000)**: 32507 **Payroll Expense ($000)**: 14543
Personnel: 232

LE MARS—Plymouth County

★ **FLOYD VALLEY HEALTHCARE (161368)**, 714 Lincoln Street NE,
Zip 51031–3314; tel. 712/546–7871, **A**10 18 **F**3 10 11 13 15 28 29 31 32 34
35 40 43 45 50 53 57 59 62 64 65 67 68 76 78 79 80 81 85 86 87 89 107
110 111 114 119 128 130 132 133 135 146 148 154 **S** Avera Health, Sioux
Falls, SD
Primary Contact: Michael T. Donlin, FACHE, Administrator
CFO: Daryl Friedenbach, Director Fiscal Services
CMO: Andrew Geha, D.O., President Medical Staff
CIO: Jacob Jorgensen, Chief Information Officer
CHR: Mary Helen Gibson, Director Human Resources
CNO: Lorrie Mortensen, MSN, R.N., Director, Patient Care
Web address: www.floydvalley.org
Control: City, Government, nonfederal **Service**: General medical and surgical

Staffed Beds: 25 **Admissions**: 601 **Census**: 6 **Outpatient Visits**: 50050
Births: 84 **Total Expense ($000)**: 37368 **Payroll Expense ($000)**: 13296
Personnel: 276

LEON—Decatur County

★ **DECATUR COUNTY HOSPITAL (161340)**, 1405 NW Church Street,
Zip 50144–1299; tel. 641/446–4871, **A**10 18 **F**3 7 11 15 28 29 31 34 40 41
45 50 57 59 64 68 69 71 75 78 79 81 82 85 93 107 111 114 117 119 130
133 146 148 149
Primary Contact: Daren Relph, Interim Administrator
CFO: Tara Spidle, Chief Financial Officer
CMO: Ed Wehling, Chief Medical Staff
CHR: Jo Beth Smith, Vice President Human Resources
Web address: www.decaturcountyhospital.org
Control: County, Government, nonfederal **Service**: General medical and surgical

Staffed Beds: 11 **Admissions**: 216 **Census**: 2 **Outpatient Visits**: 9722
Births: 0 **Total Expense ($000)**: 13563 **Payroll Expense ($000)**: 4365
Personnel: 90

IA

Hospital, Medicare Provider Number, Address, Telephone, Approval, Facility, and Physician Codes, Health Care System

★ American Hospital Association (AHA) membership ○ Healthcare Facilities Accreditation Program ⇑ Center for Improvement in Healthcare Quality Accreditation
□ The Joint Commission accreditation ◇ DNV Healthcare Inc. accreditation △ Commission on Accreditation of Rehabilitation Facilities (CARF) accreditation

MANCHESTER—Delaware County

★ **REGIONAL MEDICAL CENTER (161343)**, 709 West Main Street,
Zip 52057–1526, Mailing Address: P.O. Box 359, Zip 52057–0359;
tel. 563/927–3232, **A**10 18 **F**3 7 11 13 15 17 28 29 34 35 36 40 43 44 50 53
57 59 61 62 63 64 65 66 68 70 75 76 77 79 81 82 85 86 89 93 94 97 104
107 110 111 114 119 126 127 128 129 130 131 132 133 146 148 **P**6
Primary Contact: Charlie A. Button, Chief Executive Officer
CFO: Danette Kramer, Chief Financial Officer
CIO: Amy Mensen, Chief Administrative Officer
CHR: Amy Mensen, Chief Administrative Officer
CNO: Heather Ries, MSN, R.N., Chief Nursing Officer
Web address: www.regmedctr.org
Control: County, Government, nonfederal **Service**: General medical and surgical

> **Staffed Beds**: 25 **Admissions**: 837 **Census**: 8 **Outpatient Visits**: 179605
> **Births**: 181 **Total Expense ($000)**: 53003 **Payroll Expense ($000)**: 24436
> **Personnel**: 391

MANNING—Carroll County

★ **MANNING REGIONAL HEALTHCARE CENTER (161332)**, 1550 6th Street,
Zip 51455–1093; tel. 712/655–2072, (Total facility includes 56 beds in nursing
home–type unit) **A**10 18 **F**3 4 5 11 15 31 34 35 38 40 43 45 50 56 57 59 64
68 75 81 85 89 92 93 97 107 110 114 119 128 130 132 133 152 154 **P**6
Primary Contact: John O'Brien, Chief Executive Officer
CFO: Amy McLaughlin, CPA, Chief Financial Officer
CMO: Douglas McLaws, D.O., Chief Medical Officer
CIO: Kim C Jahn, Chief Plant Operations and Chief Information Officer
CHR: Shelli Lorenzen, Chief Human Resources Officer
CNO: Linn Block, R.N., Chief Nursing Officer
Web address: www.mrhcia.com
Control: Other not–for–profit (including NFP Corporation) **Service**: General medical and surgical

> **Staffed Beds**: 73 **Admissions**: 209 **Census**: 44 **Outpatient Visits**: 8466
> **Births**: 0 **Total Expense ($000)**: 17760 **Payroll Expense ($000)**: 7049
> **Personnel**: 160

MAQUOKETA—Jackson County

⊞ **JACKSON COUNTY REGIONAL HEALTH CENTER (161329)**, 700 West Grove
Street, Zip 52060–2163; tel. 563/652–2474, **A**1 10 18 **F**3 7 11 15 28 34 40
43 45 50 53 64 75 81 82 85 87 93 107 110 114 119 128 129 133 146 148 **S**
Genesis Health System, Davenport, IA
Primary Contact: Curt Coleman, FACHE, Administrator
CFO: Donna Roeder, Chief Financial Officer
CHR: Shannon Langenberg, Director Human Resources
Web address: www.jcrhc.org
Control: County, Government, nonfederal **Service**: General medical and surgical

> **Staffed Beds**: 12 **Admissions**: 191 **Census**: 4 **Outpatient Visits**: 18053
> **Births**: 0 **Total Expense ($000)**: 15171 **Payroll Expense ($000)**: 5413
> **Personnel**: 118

MARENGO—Iowa County

★ **COMPASS MEMORIAL HEALTHCARE (161317)**, 300 West May Street,
Zip 52301–1261; tel. 319/642–5543, **A**10 18 **F**3 15 28 29 31 34 35 38 40 43 45
50 59 64 65 69 75 77 81 93 96 97 107 110 111 119 127
129 130 131 133 135 145 146 149 **P**6 **S** UnityPoint Health, West Des Moines, IA
Primary Contact: Barry Goettsch, FACHE, Chief Executive Officer
COO: Mikaela Gehring, Chief Operating Officer
CFO: Matthew Murphy, Chief Financial Officer
CHR: Lesa Waddell, Director Human Resources
CNO: Teresa Sauerbrei, Chief Nursing Officer
Web address: www.compassmemorial.org
Control: City, Government, nonfederal **Service**: General medical and surgical

> **Staffed Beds**: 25 **Admissions**: 312 **Census**: 6 **Outpatient Visits**: 14017
> **Births**: 0 **Total Expense ($000)**: 20743 **Payroll Expense ($000)**: 8610
> **Personnel**: 158

MARSHALLTOWN—Marshall County

★ **UNITYPOINT HEALTH – MARSHALLTOWN (160001)**, 3 South Fourth Avenue,
Zip 50158–2998; tel. 641/754–5151, **A**10 **F**3 7 11 12 13 15 18 20 22 28 30
34 39 40 43 44 45 50 53 54 56 57 59 62 65 68 69 70 75 76 79 81 85 86 87
88 89 97 107 108 110 111 114 115 119 127 129 130 132 135 143 144 146
147 149 **S** UnityPoint Health, West Des Moines, IA
Primary Contact: Jennifer Friedly, President
COO: Dustin Wright, Vice President of Operations
CMO: Russell Adams, M.D., Chief Medical Officer
CHR: Jill Petermeier, Senior Executive Human Resources
Web address: www.https://marshalltown.unitypoint.org
Control: Other not–for–profit (including NFP Corporation) **Service**: General medical and surgical

> **Staffed Beds**: 34 **Admissions**: 1888 **Census**: 16 **Outpatient Visits**: 186051
> **Births**: 446 **Total Expense ($000)**: 71109 **Payroll Expense ($000)**: 24344
> **Personnel**: 433

MASON CITY—Cerro Gordo County

⊞ **MERCY MEDICAL CENTER–NORTH IOWA (160064)**, 1000 Fourth Street SW,
Zip 50401–2800; tel. 641/428–7000, **A**1 2 3 5 10 13 **F**3 11 12 13 15 18 20 22
24 26 28 29 30 31 34 35 37 40 43 44 45 46 50 54 55 56 57 58 59 61 62 63
64 65 68 69 70 71 72 74 75 76 77 78 79 81 82 84 85 87 89 90 91 92 93 96
97 98 100 101 102 104 105 107 108 110 111 114 115 116 117 118 119 120
121 122 123 125 126 127 128 129 130 131 132 135 144 146 147 148 149
153 154 **P**1 6 **S** Trinity Health, Livonia, MI
Primary Contact: Rod G. Schlader, Interim Chief Executive Officer
COO: Diane Fischels, Senior Vice President and Chief Operating Officer
CFO: Danette Zook, Chief Financial Officer
CMO: Paul Manternach, M.D., Senior Vice President Physician Integration
CIO: Terry Chartier, Director, Information Systems
CHR: Jackie Luecht, Chief Human Resources Officer
CNO: Kim Chamberlin, Vice President Patient Services and Chief Nursing Officer
Web address: www.mercynorthiowa.com
Control: Church operated, Nongovernment, not–for–profit **Service**: General medical and surgical

> **Staffed Beds**: 205 **Admissions**: 10911 **Census**: 121 **Outpatient Visits**:
> 444391 **Births**: 928 **Total Expense ($000)**: 358778 **Payroll Expense
> ($000)**: 143459 **Personnel**: 2145

MISSOURI VALLEY—Harrison County

★ **CHI HEALTH MISSOURI VALLEY (161309)**, 631 North Eighth Street,
Zip 51555–1102; tel. 712/642–2784, **A**10 18 **F**3 28 34 40 44 45 47 50 54 57
58 59 60 61 75 81 82 83 84 86 87 93 94 97 99 100 101 107 110 119 127
129 133 135 144 146 154 **P**8 **S** Catholic Health Initiatives, Englewood, CO
Primary Contact: Robert A. Valentine, President
CMO: Daniel Richter, M.D., Chief of Staff
CIO: Ravae Smallwood, IS Coordinator
CHR: Heidi Winters, Business Partner Human Resources
CNO: Darcy Behrendt, R.N., Vice President, Patient Care Services
Web address: www.chihealth.com/chi–health–missouri–valley
Control: Other not–for–profit (including NFP Corporation) **Service**: General medical and surgical

> **Staffed Beds**: 16 **Admissions**: 637 **Census**: 5 **Outpatient Visits**: 26134
> **Births**: 0 **Total Expense ($000)**: 17541 **Payroll Expense ($000)**: 6251
> **Personnel**: 87

MOUNT AYR—Ringgold County

RINGGOLD COUNTY HOSPITAL (161373), 504 North Cleveland Street,
Zip 50854–2201; tel. 641/464–3226, **A**10 18 **F**3 7 15 28 29 31 34 35 36 38
40 43 56 57 59 64 65 81 93 97 119 127 133 148 **P**6
Primary Contact: Gordon W. Winkler, Administrator and Chief Executive Officer
CFO: Teresa Roberts, Chief Financial Officer
CIO: Beth Kosman, Director Health Information Management
CHR: Mitzi Hymbaugh, Chief Personnel
Web address: www.rchmtayr.org
Control: Hospital district or authority, Government, nonfederal **Service**: General medical and surgical

> **Staffed Beds**: 16 **Admissions**: 285 **Census**: 3 **Outpatient Visits**: 34944
> **Births**: 0 **Total Expense ($000)**: 19953 **Payroll Expense ($000)**: 7126
> **Personnel**: 137

MOUNT PLEASANT—Henry County

★ **HENRY COUNTY HEALTH CENTER (161356)**, 407 South White Street,
Zip 52641–2263; tel. 319/385–3141, (Total facility includes 49 beds in nursing
home–type unit) **A**10 18 **F**3 7 11 13 15 28 29 31 32 34 35 40 41 43 45 50 53
57 59 64 65 68 70 75 76 77 78 79 81 82 85 86 87 89 93 97 102 107 108
110 115 118 119 128 129 130 131 132 133 146 147 **P**6
Primary Contact: Robb Gardner, Chief Executive Officer
CFO: David Muhs, Chief Financial Officer
CMO: Joel Ryon, M.D., Chief of Staff
CHR: Lynn Humphreys, Director Human Resources
CNO: Jodi Geerts, Chief Nursing Officer
Web address: www.hchc.org
Control: County, Government, nonfederal **Service**: General medical and surgical

> **Staffed Beds**: 74 **Admissions**: 624 **Census**: 50 **Outpatient Visits**: 50701
> **Births**: 129 **Total Expense ($000)**: 37231 **Payroll Expense ($000)**: 14053
> **Personnel**: 229

Many Facility Codes have changed. Please refer to the AHA Guide Code Chart.

MUSCATINE—Muscatine County

✠ **UNITYPOINT HEALTH – TRINITY MUSCATINE (160013)**, 1518 Mulberry Avenue, Zip 52761–3499; tel. 563/264–9100, **A**1 10 20 **F**3 5 11 13 15 18 28 29 34 38 40 43 45 50 55 56 57 59 61 64 65 68 69 70 75 76 77 81 85 87 97 102 107 108 110 111 114 119 124 129 130 131 132 134 135 147 148 149 **S** UnityPoint Health, West Des Moines, IA
Primary Contact: Angela Johnson, Executive Director
CFO: Katie A Marchik, Vice President, Consolidated Services, UnityPoint Health and Chief Financial Officer, Trinity Regional Health System
CMO: Manasi Nadkarni, M.D., Vice President Medical Affairs
CIO: Sean Liddell, Manager Regional Service Information Technology
CHR: Karla Blaser, Director Human Resources
CNO: Pam Askew, R.N., Vice President Patient Care Services
Web address: www.unitypoint.org/quadcities/trinity–muscatine.aspx
Control: Other not–for–profit (including NFP Corporation) **Service:** General medical and surgical

Staffed Beds: 45 **Admissions:** 1333 **Census:** 10 **Outpatient Visits:** 93056 **Births:** 280 **Total Expense ($000):** 45019 **Payroll Expense ($000):** 15333 **Personnel:** 256	

NEVADA—Story County

★ **STORY COUNTY MEDICAL CENTER (161333)**, 640 South 19th Street, Zip 50201–2902; tel. 515/382–2111, (Total facility includes 65 beds in nursing home–type unit) **A**10 18 **F**3 7 11 28 29 32 34 35 36 40 43 50 53 57 59 64 65 75 81 85 87 97 107 114 116 119 127 130 133 146 147 **P**6 **S** UnityPoint Health, West Des Moines, IA
Primary Contact: Nate Thompson, Chief Executive Officer
CFO: Jane Ramthun, Chief Financial Officer
CMO: Arthur Check, M.D., Chief Medical Officer
CHR: Jessica Lingo, Human Resource Generalist
CNO: Beth Rehbein, Chief Nursing and Quality Officer
Web address: www.storymedical.org
Control: County, Government, nonfederal **Service:** General medical and surgical

Staffed Beds: 82 **Admissions:** 350 **Census:** 65 **Outpatient Visits:** 56007 **Births:** 0 **Total Expense ($000):** 26436 **Payroll Expense ($000):** 11046 **Personnel:** 228	

NEW HAMPTON—Chickasaw County

★ **MERCY MEDICAL CENTER–NEW HAMPTON (161331)**, 308 North Maple Avenue, Zip 50659–1142; tel. 641/394–4121, **A**10 18 **F**3 11 13 15 28 29 34 35 40 43 45 48 56 57 59 64 65 68 74 75 76 77 79 81 85 93 97 107 110 119 131 133 146 149 **P**1 **S** Trinity Health, Livonia, MI
Primary Contact: Aaron Flugum, Chief Executive Officer
CFO: Jennifer Rapenske, Manager Financial Services
CMO: Jack Kline, M.D., Chief of Staff
CIO: Terry Chartier, Director, Information Systems
CHR: Jackie Luecht, Director, Human Resources
CNO: Cheryl Kay Haggerty, Chief Nursing Officer, Assistant Chief Executive Officer
Web address: www.mercynewhampton.com
Control: Church operated, Nongovernment, not–for–profit **Service:** General medical and surgical

Staffed Beds: 18 **Admissions:** 344 **Census:** 3 **Outpatient Visits:** 22922 **Births:** 65 **Total Expense ($000):** 17967 **Payroll Expense ($000):** 6675 **Personnel:** 120	

NEWTON—Jasper County

★ **SKIFF MEDICAL CENTER (160032)**, 204 North Fourth Avenue East, Zip 50208–3100; tel. 641/792–1273, **A**10 **F**3 11 13 15 17 28 29 30 31 34 35 40 43 44 45 50 57 59 63 64 70 75 76 77 78 79 81 82 85 89 90 93 96 102 107 108 110 111 115 119 128 130 131 132 133 135 145 146 148 149 **S** Catholic Health Initiatives, Englewood, CO
Primary Contact: Laurie A. Conner, FACHE, Chief Executive Officer
COO: Sonja Ranck, MSN, R.N., Chief Operating Officer and Chief Nursing Officer
CIO: Amber Wentz, Director of Clinical Information Systems & Clinical Informatics
CHR: Heather Wolf, Human Resources Business Partner
CNO: Sonja Ranck, MSN, R.N., Chief Operating Officer and Chief Nursing Officer
Web address: www.skiffmed.com
Control: Other not–for–profit (including NFP Corporation) **Service:** General medical and surgical

Staffed Beds: 26 **Admissions:** 1144 **Census:** 12 **Outpatient Visits:** 75014 **Births:** 180 **Total Expense ($000):** 32509 **Payroll Expense ($000):** 11371 **Personnel:** 204	

OELWEIN—Fayette County

★ **MERCY HOSPITAL OF FRANCISCAN SISTERS (161338)**, 201 Eighth Avenue SE, Zip 50662–2447; tel. 319/283–6000, (Total facility includes 39 beds in nursing home–type unit) **A**10 18 **F**7 11 15 29 30 34 35 40 57 59 69 75 79 81 93 97 107 110 111 119 127 128 130 132 133 146 147 **P**1 **S** Trinity Health, Livonia, MI
Primary Contact: Terri Derflinger, Site Administrator
CFO: Timothy Huber, Vice President and Chief Financial Officer
CMO: James Lehman, M.D., Vice President Medical Affairs
CNO: Kelly Richards, MSN, Senior Vice President and Chief Nursing Officer
Web address: www.wheatoniowa.org
Control: Church operated, Nongovernment, not–for–profit **Service:** General medical and surgical

Staffed Beds: 64 **Admissions:** 321 **Census:** 36 **Outpatient Visits:** 25232 **Births:** 0 **Total Expense ($000):** 13652 **Payroll Expense ($000):** 5559 **Personnel:** 94	

ONAWA—Monona County

★ **BURGESS HEALTH CENTER (161359)**, 1600 Diamond Street, Zip 51040–1548; tel. 712/423–2311, **A**10 18 **F**3 7 11 13 15 28 31 32 34 35 40 45 47 50 53 56 57 59 62 63 64 65 67 68 70 75 76 77 78 79 81 82 85 93 97 107 111 114 119 127 128 130 132 133 135 146 148 149 **P**6
Primary Contact: Francis G. Tramp, President
CFO: Shawn Gosch, Chief Financial Officer
CMO: John Garred, M.D., Sr Chief Medical Officer
CIO: Grady Warner, Director of Information Technology
CHR: Erin Brekke, Director Human Resources
CNO: Patty Sandmann, Senior Director of Nursing
Web address: www.burgesshc.org
Control: Other not–for–profit (including NFP Corporation) **Service:** General medical and surgical

Staffed Beds: 25 **Admissions:** 678 **Census:** 7 **Outpatient Visits:** 67726 **Births:** 68 **Total Expense ($000):** 29593 **Payroll Expense ($000):** 12983 **Personnel:** 248	

ORANGE CITY—Sioux County

★ **ORANGE CITY AREA HEALTH SYSTEM (161360)**, 1000 Lincoln Circle SE, Zip 51041–1862; tel. 712/737–4984, (Total facility includes 89 beds in nursing home–type unit) **A**10 18 **F**7 10 11 13 15 18 28 29 31 34 35 40 45 50 53 56 57 59 60 62 63 64 67 68 69 70 75 76 77 78 79 81 82 85 86 87 89 93 97 99 100 101 102 103 104 107 110 111 114 117 119 125 127 130 131 132 133 146 147 148 **P**6 **S** Sanford Health, Sioux Falls, SD
Primary Contact: Martin W. Guthmiller, Chief Executive Officer
COO: Daniel P McCarty, Chief Operating Officer
CFO: Dina Baas, Director Financial Services
CMO: Alan Laird, M.D., Chief Medical Officer
CHR: Jason Jauron, Director Human Resources
CNO: Laurie Gebauer, Director Patient Care
Web address: www.ochealthsystem.org
Control: City, Government, nonfederal **Service:** General medical and surgical

Staffed Beds: 114 **Admissions:** 947 **Census:** 93 **Outpatient Visits:** 77108 **Births:** 227 **Total Expense ($000):** 47882 **Payroll Expense ($000):** 19018 **Personnel:** 421	

OSAGE—Mitchell County

★ **MITCHELL COUNTY REGIONAL HEALTH CENTER (161323)**, 616 North Eighth Street, Zip 50461–1498; tel. 641/732–6000, **A**10 18 **F**7 8 11 15 18 28 29 34 35 40 45 50 56 57 59 63 64 65 75 81 85 93 107 110 114 119 127 129 130 132 133 144 146 **P**8 **S** Trinity Health, Livonia, MI
Primary Contact: Shelly Russell, Chief Executive Officer
CFO: Gregory Burkel, Chief Financial Officer
CMO: Jeff Nasstrom, D.O., Chief of Staff
CHR: Jodie Anderson, Director Human Resources
CNO: Shelly Russell, Chief Nursing Officer
Web address: www.mitchellcohospital–clinics.com
Control: County, Government, nonfederal **Service:** General medical and surgical

Staffed Beds: 25 **Admissions:** 336 **Census:** 5 **Outpatient Visits:** 62751 **Births:** 0 **Total Expense ($000):** 23762 **Payroll Expense ($000):** 8074 **Personnel:** 156	

IA

Hospital, Medicare Provider Number, Address, Telephone, Approval, Facility, and Physician Codes, Health Care System

★ American Hospital Association (AHA) membership   ○ Healthcare Facilities Accreditation Program   ⇈ Center for Improvement in Healthcare Quality Accreditation
□ The Joint Commission accreditation   ◇ DNV Healthcare Inc. accreditation   △ Commission on Accreditation of Rehabilitation Facilities (CARF) accreditation

OSCEOLA—Clarke County

★ **CLARKE COUNTY HOSPITAL (161348)**, 800 South Fillmore Street,
Zip 50213–1619; tel. 641/342–2184, **A**10 18 **F**7 11 15 18 28 29 31 34 35 40
45 50 57 59 64 67 68 75 77 78 79 81 82 89 90 93 94 96 107 110 111 115
116 117 118 119 128 129 130 131 132 133 135 148 **S** UnityPoint Health, West
Des Moines, IA
Primary Contact: Brian G. Evans, FACHE, Chief Executive Officer
CFO: Michael Thilges, Chief Financial Officer
CMO: George Fotiadis, M.D., Chief of Staff
CIO: Dennis Blazek, Chief Information Officer
CHR: Kate Emanuel, Director Human Resources
Web address: www.clarkehosp.org
Control: County, Government, nonfederal **Service**: General medical and surgical

Staffed Beds: 25 **Admissions**: 322 **Census**: 12 **Outpatient Visits**: 24373
Births: 0 **Total Expense ($000)**: 21447 **Payroll Expense ($000)**: 7150
Personnel: 149

OSKALOOSA—Mahaska County

⊠ **MAHASKA HEALTH PARTNERSHIP (161379)**, 1229 'C' Avenue East,
Zip 52577–4298; tel. 641/672–3100, **A**1 10 18 **F**3 5 7 8 11 13 15 28 29 31
34 35 40 43 45 46 47 50 54 56 57 59 62 63 64 65 68 70 75 76 77 78 79 81
84 85 87 93 94 97 100 101 102 104 107 110 111 114 119 126 129 130 132
133 135 146 148 149 150 **P**6
Primary Contact: Kevin DeRonde, Chief Executive Officer
COO: Erin Baldwin, M.P.H., Chief Operating Officer
CMO: Matt Whitis, Chief Medical Officer
CHR: Sarah J. Dickey, Human Resource Directory of People and Culture
CNO: Christinia Jepsen, R.N., Chief Nursing Officer
Web address: www.mahaskahealth.com
Control: County, Government, nonfederal **Service**: General medical and surgical

Staffed Beds: 25 **Admissions**: 1280 **Census**: 17 **Outpatient Visits**: 154665
Births: 185 **Total Expense ($000)**: 57168 **Payroll Expense ($000)**: 29160
Personnel: 410

OTTUMWA—Wapello County

☐ △ **OTTUMWA REGIONAL HEALTH CENTER (160089)**, 1001 Pennsylvania
Avenue, Zip 52501–2186; tel. 641/684–2300, **A**1 7 10 **F**3 7 11 13 15 18 20 22
26 28 29 30 34 35 40 41 43 45 46 47 48 50 51 53 54 56 57 59 60 62 64 73
74 75 76 77 79 81 82 85 87 89 90 93 96 98 102 103 107 108 110 111 114
115 116 117 118 119 120 121 123 126 129 130 131 132 135 146 147 148
154 **P**6 **S** RCCH HealthCare Partners, Brentwood, TN
Primary Contact: Philip J. Noel III, Chief Executive Officer
COO: Dennis Hunger, Chief Operating Officer
CFO: Jason Hotchkiss, CPA, Chief Financial Officer
CMO: Sandro Younadam, M.D., Chief Medical Officer
CIO: Scott Garrett, Director of IS
CHR: Lidia Bryant, Director Human Resources
CNO: Lori Bailey, R.N., Vice President and Chief Nursing Officer
Web address: www.ottumwaregionalhealth.com
Control: Corporation, Investor–owned (for–profit) **Service**: General medical and
surgical

Staffed Beds: 101 **Admissions**: 3312 **Census**: 43 **Outpatient Visits**:
143949 **Births**: 451 **Total Expense ($000)**: 78173 **Payroll Expense
($000)**: 23317 **Personnel**: 506

PELLA—Marion County

⊠ **PELLA REGIONAL HEALTH CENTER (161367)**, 404 Jefferson Street,
Zip 50219–1257; tel. 641/628–3150, **A**1 10 18 **F**3 11 13 15 18 28 29 30 31
32 34 35 40 43 45 50 51 53 57 59 62 63 64 65 66 70 74 75 76 77 78 79 81
82 84 85 86 87 91 93 94 97 102 107 108 110 111 115 119 126 127 129 130
131 132 133 146 147 148 149 154 **P**6
Primary Contact: Robert D. Kroese, FACHE, Chief Executive Officer
COO: Robert D Kroese, FACHE, Chief Executive Officer
CFO: Bruce Heifner, Chief Financial Officer
CIO: Tait Smock, Manager Information Systems
CHR: Ashley Arkema, Manager Human Resources
CNO: Deborah Willyard, R.N., MSN, Chief Nursing Officer
Web address: www.pellahealth.org
Control: Other not–for–profit (including NFP Corporation) **Service**: General
medical and surgical

Staffed Beds: 25 **Admissions**: 1360 **Census**: 13 **Outpatient Visits**: 138824
Births: 525 **Total Expense ($000)**: 53304 **Payroll Expense ($000)**: 20299
Personnel: 595

PERRY—Dallas County

★ **DALLAS COUNTY HOSPITAL (161322)**, 610 10th Street, Zip 50220–2221;
tel. 515/465–3547, **A**10 18 **F**15 18 28 29 31 34 35 39 40 41 43 45 47 50 56 57 59
68 75 77 78 79 81 82 85 89 93 107 110 114 119 128 130 132 133 135 146 148
Primary Contact: Angela Mortoza, Chief Executive Officer
CFO: Randy Loomis, Chief Financial Officer
CMO: Steven Sohn, M.D., President Medical Staff
CHR: Sherry Smith, Manager Human Resources
CNO: Tonya Summerson, Chief Clinical Officer
Web address: www.dallascohospital.org
Control: County, Government, nonfederal **Service**: General medical and surgical

Staffed Beds: 15 **Admissions**: 172 **Census**: 2 **Outpatient Visits**: 21606
Births: 0 **Total Expense ($000)**: 14423 **Payroll Expense ($000)**: 4404
Personnel: 81

POCAHONTAS—Pocahontas County

★ **POCAHONTAS COMMUNITY HOSPITAL (161305)**, 606 NW Seventh Street,
Zip 50574–1099; tel. 712/335–3501, **A**10 18 **F**7 11 15 17 28 29 30 31 35 40
43 45 59 62 63 64 67 70 75 77 78 79 81 84 85 89 90 93 107 110 115 119
128 130 132 133 135 146 148 **P**6 **S** UnityPoint Health, West Des Moines, IA
Primary Contact: James D. Roetman, President and Chief Executive Officer
CFO: Lynn Raveling, Chief Financial Officer
CNO: Susie Aden, Director of IP Services
Web address: www.pocahontashospital.org
Control: City, Government, nonfederal **Service**: General medical and surgical

Staffed Beds: 20 **Admissions**: 199 **Census**: 3 **Outpatient Visits**: 22979
Births: 0 **Total Expense ($000)**: 10695 **Payroll Expense ($000)**: 3869
Personnel: 82

PRIMGHAR—O'brien County

★ **BAUM HARMON MERCY HOSPITAL (161300)**, 255 North Welch Avenue,
Zip 51245–7765, Mailing Address: P.O. Box 528, Zip 51245–0528;
tel. 712/957–2300, **A**10 18 **F**11 15 28 29 34 35 40 45 53 59 64 67 75 77 81
89 107 110 119 127 128 132 133 **P**6 **S** Trinity Health, Livonia, MI
Primary Contact: Misty Dulin, CAH, Director
CFO: Sue E McCauley, Director Finance
CMO: Shailesh Desai, M.D., Chief of Staff
Web address: www.baumharmon.org
Control: Church operated, Nongovernment, not–for–profit **Service**: General
medical and surgical

Staffed Beds: 11 **Admissions**: 97 **Census**: 1 **Outpatient Visits**: 20851
Births: 0 **Total Expense ($000)**: 8643 **Payroll Expense ($000)**: 4191
Personnel: 61

RED OAK—Montgomery County

★ **MONTGOMERY COUNTY MEMORIAL HOSPITAL (161363)**, 2301 Eastern
Avenue, Zip 51566–1300, Mailing Address: P.O. Box 498, Zip 51566–0498;
tel. 712/623–7000, **A**10 18 **F**3 11 12 13 15 28 29 31 34 35 40 44 45 50 53
57 59 63 64 68 69 70 71 75 76 77 78 79 81 82 85 86 87 93 107 110 111
114 115 118 119 128 129 130 133 135 146 147 148 154
Primary Contact: David E. Abercrombie, Chief Executive Officer
CFO: Rick J Leinen, Chief Financial Officer
CMO: Warren Hayes, Chief of Staff
CIO: Ron Kloewer, Chief Information Officer
CHR: Shayla Jennings, Human Resources Director
CNO: Diane McGrew, Chief Nurse Executive
Web address: www.mcmh.org
Control: County, Government, nonfederal **Service**: General medical and surgical

Staffed Beds: 25 **Admissions**: 927 **Census**: 12 **Outpatient Visits**: 47787
Births: 64 **Total Expense ($000)**: 41003 **Payroll Expense ($000)**: 17204
Personnel: 296

ROCK RAPIDS—Lyon County

SANFORD MERRILL MEDICAL CENTER See Sanford Rock Rapids Medical
Center

★ **SANFORD ROCK RAPIDS MEDICAL CENTER (161321)**, 801 South Greene
Street, Zip 51246–1998; tel. 712/472–2591, **A**10 18 **F**11 28 31 34 40 45 53
57 59 65 66 75 77 81 87 89 97 107 114 119 127 130 131 133 146 149 154
P6 **S** Sanford Health, Sioux Falls, SD
Primary Contact: Tammy Loosbrock, Chief Executive Officer
CFO: Stanley Knobloch, Director Fiscal Services
CMO: Beta Hamon, Chief Medical Officer
CHR: Holly Anderson, Supervisor Human Resources
CNO: Jack Johnson, R.N., Director of Nursing
Web address: www.sanfordrockrapids.org
Control: Other not–for–profit (including NFP Corporation) **Service**: General
medical and surgical

Staffed Beds: 14 **Admissions**: 300 **Census**: 3 **Outpatient Visits**: 21091 **Births**: 0
Total Expense ($000): 8999 **Payroll Expense ($000)**: 4102 **Personnel**: 75

IA

Many Facility Codes have changed. Please refer to the AHA Guide Code Chart. © 2018 AHA Guide

ROCK VALLEY—Sioux County

★ **HEGG HEALTH CENTER AVERA (161336)**, 1202 21st Avenue, Zip 51247–1497; tel. 712/476–8000, (Total facility includes 60 beds in nursing home–type unit) **A**10 18 **F**3 11 13 15 17 28 29 31 34 35 36 40 41 43 44 45 50 53 57 59 62 64 65 67 68 70 73 75 76 77 78 79 81 82 85 89 91 93 96 97 107 110 115 119 128 130 131 132 133 135 144 146 147 148 **S** Avera Health, Sioux Falls, SD
Primary Contact: Glenn Zevenbergen, Chief Executive Officer
CFO: Kari Timmer, Chief Financial Officer
CMO: Jon Engbers, M.D., President
CHR: Tammy Faber, Director Human Resources
Web address: www.hegghc.org
Control: Other not–for–profit (including NFP Corporation) **Service:** General medical and surgical

Staffed Beds: 85 **Admissions:** 261 **Census:** 63 **Outpatient Visits:** 36594 **Births:** 54 **Total Expense ($000):** 18606 **Payroll Expense ($000):** 9886 **Personnel:** 186

SAC CITY—Sac County

★ **LORING HOSPITAL (161370)**, 211 Highland Avenue, Zip 50583–2424; tel. 712/662–7105, **A**10 18 **F**3 11 15 28 29 30 31 34 35 40 43 45 50 57 59 64 68 75 77 78 79 81 86 87 93 107 110 115 125 130 132 133 146 148 154 **S** UnityPoint Health, West Des Moines, IA
Primary Contact: Brian Martin, Chief Executive Officer
CFO: Stacy Johnson, Chief Financial Officer
CMO: Les Marczewski, M.D., Chief Medical Officer
CIO: Leah Snyder, Director Health Information Services
CHR: Becky Pontious, Human Resources/Accounting
Web address: www.loringhospital.org
Control: Other not–for–profit (including NFP Corporation) **Service:** General medical and surgical

Staffed Beds: 25 **Admissions:** 310 **Census:** 3 **Outpatient Visits:** 23979 **Births:** 0 **Total Expense ($000):** 12050 **Payroll Expense ($000):** 4080 **Personnel:** 106

SHELDON—O'brien County

★ **SANFORD SHELDON MEDICAL CENTER (161381)**, 118 North Seventh Avenue, Zip 51201–1235, Mailing Address: P.O. Box 250, Zip 51201–0250; tel. 712/324–5041, (Total facility includes 70 beds in nursing home–type unit) **A**10 18 **F**3 11 13 15 28 29 31 32 34 35 38 40 43 45 50 53 57 59 62 63 64 65 67 68 74 75 76 77 78 79 81 82 84 86 87 91 93 96 97 99 100 101 102 103 104 107 108 110 111 114 119 127 129 130 131 132 133 135 146 148 149 150 154 **P**6 **S** Sanford Health, Sioux Falls, SD
Primary Contact: Richard E. Nordahl, Chief Executive Officer
CFO: Richard E Nordahl, Chief Financial Officer
CMO: Scott Lichty, M.D., Physician
CIO: Jason Brown, Director Information Systems
CHR: Dianne Wolthuizen, Director Human Resources
CNO: Joni DeKok, Chief Nursing Officer
Web address: www.sanfordsheldon.org
Control: Other not–for–profit (including NFP Corporation) **Service:** General medical and surgical

Staffed Beds: 95 **Admissions:** 949 **Census:** 69 **Outpatient Visits:** 108926 **Births:** 121 **Total Expense ($000):** 28642 **Payroll Expense ($000):** 13378 **Personnel:** 252

SHENANDOAH—Page County

★ **SHENANDOAH MEDICAL CENTER (161366)**, 300 Pershing Avenue, Zip 51601–2355; tel. 712/246–1230, (Total facility includes 50 beds in nursing home–type unit) **A**10 18 **F**3 13 15 18 28 29 31 34 36 38 40 41 43 45 50 53 56 57 59 62 63 64 65 67 68 69 70 74 75 76 77 78 79 81 83 84 85 87 91 93 104 107 108 110 111 115 117 118 119 127 129 130 131 132 133 135 144 146 147 148 149 154 **P**6
Primary Contact: Matt Sells, Chief Executive Officer
COO: Jonathan Moe, Chief Operating Officer
CFO: Kaley Neal, Chief Financial Officer
CMO: Heather Babe, M.D., Chief of Staff
CIO: Chuck Dougherty, Chief Information Officer
CHR: Keli Royal, Chief Human Resources Officer
CNO: Laura Stofferson, Chief Nursing Officer
Web address: www.smchospital.com/
Control: Other not–for–profit (including NFP Corporation) **Service:** General medical and surgical

Staffed Beds: 75 **Admissions:** 544 **Census:** 46 **Outpatient Visits:** 192623 **Births:** 106 **Total Expense ($000):** 43934 **Payroll Expense ($000):** 21094 **Personnel:** 273

SIBLEY—Page County

★ **OSCEOLA COMMUNITY HOSPITAL (161345)**, 600 Ninth Avenue North, Zip 51249–1012, Mailing Address: P.O. Box 258, Zip 51249–0258; tel. 712/754–2574, **A**10 18 **F**3 8 9 10 11 12 13 15 17 18 26 28 29 31 32 34 35 36 40 43 45 46 53 56 57 59 61 62 64 65 67 68 70 75 76 77 78 79 81 82 84 85 86 87 89 107 108 110 114 119 125 128 129 130 131 132 133 135 143 144 145 146 147 148 149 **P**5 **S** Avera Health, Sioux Falls, SD
Primary Contact: Ben Davis, Chief Executive Officer
CFO: Lorrie Reed, Chief Financial Officer
CMO: Gregory J Kosters, D.O., Chief Medical Officer
Web address: www.osceolacommunityhospital.org
Control: Other not–for–profit (including NFP Corporation) **Service:** General medical and surgical

Staffed Beds: 25 **Admissions:** 276 **Census:** 3 **Outpatient Visits:** 20329 **Births:** 15 **Total Expense ($000):** 13332 **Payroll Expense ($000):** 4487 **Personnel:** 68

SIGOURNEY—Keokuk County

KEOKUK COUNTY HEALTH CENTER (161315), 23019 Highway 149, Zip 52591–8341; tel. 641/622–2720, **A**10 18 **F**3 8 15 17 18 28 29 30 34 35 38 40 43 44 45 46 50 56 57 59 63 64 65 66 67 75 77 82 84 86 87 90 91 93 97 107 110 127 128 129 130 131 132 133 135 146 147 148 **P**5 6
Primary Contact: Matthew Ives, Administrator and Chief Financial Officer
CFO: Matthew Ives, Interim Chief Executive Officer and Chief Financial Officer
Web address: www.kchc.net
Control: County, Government, nonfederal **Service:** General medical and surgical

Staffed Beds: 14 **Admissions:** 161 **Census:** 7 **Outpatient Visits:** 25160 **Births:** 0 **Total Expense ($000):** 11081 **Payroll Expense ($000):** 5752 **Personnel:** 98

SIOUX CENTER—Sioux County

★ **SIOUX CENTER HEALTH (161346)**, 1101 9th Street SE, Zip 51250; tel. 712/722–8107, (Total facility includes 69 beds in nursing home–type unit) **A**10 18 **F**3 8 10 13 15 17 18 28 29 30 31 34 35 40 41 43 45 50 56 57 59 62 63 64 65 67 68 74 75 76 77 78 79 81 82 84 85 86 87 89 93 96 97 107 110 111 114 119 125 128 130 131 132 133 144 146 147 148 149 154 **P**6 **S** Avera Health, Sioux Falls, SD
Primary Contact: Cory D. Nelson, Administrator
CFO: Jackson Schuiteman, Chief Financial Officer
CHR: Theresa Tucker, Human Resources Officer
Web address: www.siouxcenterhealth.org
Control: Other not–for–profit (including NFP Corporation) **Service:** General medical and surgical

Staffed Beds: 88 **Admissions:** 610 **Census:** 73 **Outpatient Visits:** 51985 **Births:** 184 **Total Expense ($000):** 40003 **Payroll Expense ($000):** 16949 **Personnel:** 347

SIOUX CITY—Woodbury County

⊠ **MERCY MEDICAL CENTER–SIOUX CITY (160153)**, 801 Fifth Street, Zip 51101–1326, Mailing Address: P.O. Box 3168, Zip 51102–3168; tel. 712/279–2010, **A**1 2 3 5 10 **F**3 5 8 11 12 13 15 17 18 20 22 24 26 28 29 30 31 32 34 35 36 37 38 40 43 44 45 49 50 52 55 56 57 59 64 65 68 70 71 74 75 76 77 78 79 81 82 84 85 87 89 90 91 93 96 97 98 100 102 107 108 110 111 114 115 118 119 124 126 127 128 129 130 132 134 135 144 146 147 148 149 150 **P**6 8 **S** Trinity Health, Livonia, MI
Primary Contact: Beth Hughes, President
CFO: Hugh DePaulis, Interim Vice President and Chief Financial Officer
CMO: Jerome Pierson, Chief Medical Officer
CIO: Steve Larson, M.D., Director Information Systems
CHR: Julie Anfinson, Director Human Resources
CNO: Tracy Larson, MS, Vice President Patient Care Services and Chief Nursing Officer
Web address: www.mercysiouxcity.com
Control: Church operated, Nongovernment, not–for–profit **Service:** General medical and surgical

Staffed Beds: 186 **Admissions:** 8384 **Census:** 116 **Outpatient Visits:** 206676 **Births:** 211 **Total Expense ($000):** 193772 **Payroll Expense ($000):** 79966 **Personnel:** 1329

IA

Hospital, Medicare Provider Number, Address, Telephone, Approval, Facility, and Physician Codes, Health Care System

★ American Hospital Association (AHA) membership   ○ Healthcare Facilities Accreditation Program   ⇑ Center for Improvement in Healthcare Quality Accreditation
□ The Joint Commission accreditation   ◇ DNV Healthcare Inc. accreditation   △ Commission on Accreditation of Rehabilitation Facilities (CARF) accreditation

★ ⇑ **UNITYPOINT HEALTH – ST. LUKES'S SIOUX CITY (160146)**, 2720 Stone Park Boulevard, Zip 51104–3734; tel. 712/279–3500, **A3** 5 10 21 **F3** 11 13 15 17 18 20 22 26 28 29 30 31 34 35 39 40 43 45 49 50 51 54 56 57 58 59 60 64 68 70 72 73 74 75 76 77 78 79 81 82 84 85 86 88 89 90 91 92 93 96 97 98 102 104 107 108 111 114 118 119 126 129 130 131 132 135 142 143 144 145 146 147 149 **P6 S** UnityPoint Health, West Des Moines, IA
Primary Contact: Lynn Wold, President and Chief Executive Officer
COO: Lynn Wold, Chief Operation Officer
CFO: James Gobell, Chief Financial Officer
CIO: James Gobell, Chief Financial Officer
CHR: Tammy Hartnett, Employee Relations Manager
CNO: Priscilla Stokes, MS, R.N., Vice President Patient Care and Hospital Operations
Web address: www.stlukes.org
Control: Other not–for–profit (including NFP Corporation) **Service**: General medical and surgical

Staffed Beds: 150 **Admissions**: 8722 **Census**: 100 **Outpatient Visits**: 84722 **Births**: 1978 **Total Expense ($000)**: 162360 **Payroll Expense ($000)**: 68057 **Personnel**: 1248

SPENCER—Clay County

★ **SPENCER HOSPITAL (160112)**, 1200 First Avenue East, Suite 1, Zip 51301–4342; tel. 712/264–6111, **A10 F3** 7 8 11 13 15 28 29 30 31 34 35 37 39 40 43 45 50 53 57 59 60 62 63 64 65 70 75 76 77 78 79 81 82 85 86 87 93 96 98 107 108 109 110 111 115 118 119 120 121 123 126 127 129 130 131 132 133 135 144 146 147 148 149
Primary Contact: William J. Bumgarner, President
CFO: Stacy E Mol, CPA, Director Finance
CMO: Sonia Sather, M.D., President Medical Staff
CIO: Brenda Marie Tiefenthaler, R.N., MSN, Vice President Patient Care and Informatics
CHR: Stephen Deutsch, Vice President Operations and Support
CNO: Brenda Marie Tiefenthaler, R.N., MSN, Vice President Patient Care and Informatics
Web address: www.spencerhospital.org
Control: City, Government, nonfederal **Service**: General medical and surgical

Staffed Beds: 64 **Admissions**: 2319 **Census**: 26 **Outpatient Visits**: 127487 **Births**: 261 **Total Expense ($000)**: 86926 **Payroll Expense ($000)**: 23237 **Personnel**: 423

SPIRIT LAKE—Dickinson County

★ **LAKES REGIONAL HEALTHCARE (160124)**, 2301 Highway 71 South, Zip 51360–0159, Mailing Address: P.O. Box AB, Zip 51360–0159; tel. 712/336–1230, **A10 F3** 7 11 13 15 28 29 30 31 34 35 37 40 41 43 45 50 57 59 62 63 64 65 70 75 76 77 78 79 81 85 89 91 93 97 107 111 115 119 126 128 129 130 132 133 143 146 148 149 154 **P5 S** Avera Health, Sioux Falls, SD
Primary Contact: Jason Harrington, FACHE, President and Chief Executive Officer
CFO: Steve Alger, Senior Vice President and Chief Financial Officer
CMO: Zachary A. Borus, M.D., Medical Chief of Staff
CIO: Derek Larson, Information Technology Network
CHR: Sonja Hamm, Vice President Human and Foundation Resources
CNO: Connie Lange, R.N., Vice President Quality, Inpatient and Community Services
Web address: www.lakeshealth.org
Control: County, Government, nonfederal **Service**: General medical and surgical

Staffed Beds: 30 **Admissions**: 780 **Census**: 8 **Outpatient Visits**: 98767 **Births**: 125 **Total Expense ($000)**: 38344 **Payroll Expense ($000)**: 11587 **Personnel**: 217

STORM LAKE—Buena Vista County

⊠ **BUENA VISTA REGIONAL MEDICAL CENTER (161375)**, 1525 West Fifth Street, Zip 50588–3027, Mailing Address: P.O. Box 309, Zip 50588–0309; tel. 712/732–4030, **A1** 10 18 **F3** 7 8 11 13 15 18 28 29 30 31 34 40 43 45 53 55 56 57 59 63 64 68 70 74 75 76 77 78 79 81 82 84 85 86 87 93 96 98 103 107 108 110 111 115 117 118 119 128 129 130 131 132 135 146 147 148 **S** UnityPoint Health, West Des Moines, IA
Primary Contact: Steven Colerick, Chief Executive Officer
CFO: Krista Ketcham, Chief Financial Officer
CMO: Lisa Shepherd, M.D., Chief of Staff
CIO: Steve Spurlock, Director Information Systems
CHR: Carrie Turnquist, Director Human Resources
CNO: Dawn M Bach, MS, Chief Clinical Officer
Web address: www.bvrmc.org
Control: County, Government, nonfederal **Service**: General medical and surgical

Staffed Beds: 35 **Admissions**: 1246 **Census**: 16 **Outpatient Visits**: 67832 **Births**: 380 **Total Expense ($000)**: 47992 **Payroll Expense ($000)**: 19167 **Personnel**: 344

SUMNER—Bremer County

★ **COMMUNITY MEMORIAL HOSPITAL (161320)**, 909 West First Street, Zip 50674–1203, Mailing Address: P.O. Box 148, Zip 50674–0148; tel. 563/578–3275, **A10** 18 **F3** 11 15 28 29 34 40 45 57 59 64 81 82 85 86 97 107 114 119 128 129 131 133 135 148 149 **P5** 6 **S** UnityPoint Health, West Des Moines, IA
Primary Contact: Dawn Everding, President and Chief Financial Officer
CFO: Dawn Everding, President and Chief Financial Officer
CMO: Jeff Roske, D.O., Chief Medical Staff
CHR: Robin Elliott, Personnel Officer
CNO: Lynne Niemann, Director Nurses and Patient Care
Web address: www.cmhsumner.org
Control: Other not–for–profit (including NFP Corporation) **Service**: General medical and surgical

Staffed Beds: 16 **Admissions**: 196 **Census**: 3 **Outpatient Visits**: 33251 **Births**: 0 **Total Expense ($000)**: 13594 **Payroll Expense ($000)**: 4810 **Personnel**: 86

VINTON—Benton County

★ **VIRGINIA GAY HOSPITAL (161349)**, 502 North 9th Avenue, Zip 52349–2299; tel. 319/472–6200, (Total facility includes 40 beds in nursing home–type unit) **A10** 18 **F3** 15 28 29 34 40 43 45 53 57 59 62 63 64 75 77 81 85 86 87 96 97 107 111 114 119 125 127 129 130 131 132 133 143 146 **P6**
Primary Contact: Michael J. Riege, Chief Executive Officer
CFO: Barry Dietsch, Chief Financial Officer
CMO: Brian Meeker, D.O., President Medical Staff
CIO: Sherri Isbell, Chief Information Officer
CHR: Kim Frank, Chief Human Resources Officer
CNO: Tina M Eden, Director of Nursing
Web address: www.myvgh.org
Control: Other not–for–profit (including NFP Corporation) **Service**: General medical and surgical

Staffed Beds: 65 **Admissions**: 382 **Census**: 41 **Outpatient Visits**: 86813 **Births**: 0 **Total Expense ($000)**: 26581 **Payroll Expense ($000)**: 12527 **Personnel**: 232

WASHINGTON—Washington County

★ **WASHINGTON COUNTY HOSPITAL AND CLINICS (161344)**, 400 East Polk Street, Zip 52353–1237, Mailing Address: P.O. Box 909, Zip 52353–0909; tel. 319/653–5481, (Total facility includes 43 beds in nursing home–type unit) **A10** 18 **F3** 13 15 18 28 29 34 40 43 45 50 57 59 64 67 68 74 75 76 77 81 85 86 93 96 97 107 110 111 115 119 127 130 132 133 146 147 148 **P6**
Primary Contact: Steve Schomer, M.D., Interim Chief Executive Officer
CFO: Steve Sanders, Chief Financial Officer
CMO: Matt Prihoda, M.D., Chief of Staff
CIO: Makyla Maize, Director Information Services
CHR: Tracy Ousey, Director Human Resources
CNO: Andrea Leyden RN Chief Nursing Officer
Web address: www.wchc.org
Control: County, Government, nonfederal **Service**: General medical and surgical

Staffed Beds: 68 **Admissions**: 1077 **Census**: 46 **Outpatient Visits**: 72154 **Births**: 114 **Total Expense ($000)**: 41332 **Payroll Expense ($000)**: 17480 **Personnel**: 308

WATERLOO—Black Hawk County

ALLEN MEMORIAL HOSPITAL See Unitypoint Health – Allen Hospital

⊠ △ **COVENANT MEDICAL CENTER (160067)**, 3421 West Ninth Street, Zip 50702–5401; tel. 319/272–8000, (Includes KIMBALL–RIDGE CENTER, 2101 Kimball Avenue, Waterloo, IA, Zip 50702; tel. 319/272–8000; Jack Dusenbery, President and Chief Executive Officer) **A1** 2 3 5 7 10 **F3** 4 5 7 11 13 15 18 19 20 22 26 28 29 30 31 33 34 35 40 43 44 46 49 50 51 53 56 57 58 59 60 61 62 64 68 70 71 72 74 75 76 77 78 79 81 82 86 87 89 90 93 97 98 99 100 101 102 104 107 108 110 111 114 115 116 118 119 120 126 127 129 130 131 132 135 143 144 146 147 148 152 154 **P1** 6 **S** Trinity Health, Livonia, MI
Primary Contact: Jack Dusenbery, President and Chief Executive Officer
CFO: Timothy Huber, Vice President and Chief Financial Officer
CMO: James Lehman, M.D., Vice President Medical Affairs
CIO: Marge Ray, Director Information Systems
CHR: Suzanne M. Burt, Director Human Resources
CNO: Kelly Richards, MSN, Senior Vice President and Chief Nursing Officer
Web address: www.wheatoniowa.com
Control: Church operated, Nongovernment, not–for–profit **Service**: General medical and surgical

Staffed Beds: 229 **Admissions**: 7719 **Census**: 96 **Outpatient Visits**: 658830 **Births**: 1321 **Total Expense ($000)**: 292528 **Payroll Expense ($000)**: 135206 **Personnel**: 2031

IA

⊠ △ **UNITYPOINT HEALTH – ALLEN HOSPITAL (160110)**, 1825 Logan Avenue, Zip 50703–1916; tel. 319/235–3941, **A**1 3 5 7 10 **F**3 8 11 13 15 18 20 22 24 26 28 29 30 31 34 35 37 40 43 45 46 48 49 50 51 54 56 57 59 63 64 66 68 70 72 74 75 76 77 78 79 81 82 84 85 86 87 88 90 91 92 93 96 97 98 99 100 101 102 103 104 107 108 110 111 114 115 118 119 126 127 129 130 132 135 146 147 148 149 153 **P**6 **S** UnityPoint Health, West Des Moines, IA
Primary Contact: Pamela K. Delagardelle, President and Chief Executive Officer
COO: Jennifer Friedly, Chief Operating Officer and Vice President
CFO: Craig Flanagan, Chief Financial Officer
CMO: Timothy Horrigan, M.D., Chief Quality Officer
CIO: Daniel Norman, Regional Service Manager
CHR: Steven Sesterhenn, Vice President
CNO: Mary Hagen, R.N., MSN, VP and Chief Nursing Officer
Web address: www.unitypoint.org/waterloo
Control: Other not–for–profit (including NFP Corporation) **Service:** General medical and surgical

Staffed Beds: 201 **Admissions:** 9302 **Census:** 98 **Outpatient Visits:** 261612 **Births:** 1065 **Total Expense ($000):** 259096 **Payroll Expense ($000):** 99327 **Personnel:** 1562

WAUKON—Allamakee County

★ **VETERANS MEMORIAL HOSPITAL (161318)**, 40 First Street SE, Zip 52172–2099; tel. 563/568–3411, **A**10 18 **F**7 11 13 15 28 34 35 40 45 46 50 57 59 62 64 65 75 76 77 79 81 91 93 107 110 111 119 131 132 133 134 144 146
Primary Contact: Michael D. Myers, R.N., Chief Executive Officer
CFO: Scott Knode, Chief Financial Officer
CHR: Erin Berns, Director Human Resources
Web address: www.vmhospital.com
Control: City, Government, nonfederal **Service:** General medical and surgical

Staffed Beds: 25 **Admissions:** 558 **Census:** 7 **Outpatient Visits:** 44180 **Births:** 153 **Total Expense ($000):** 18086 **Payroll Expense ($000):** 8397 **Personnel:** 157

WAVERLY—Bremer County

⊠ **WAVERLY HEALTH CENTER (161339)**, 312 Ninth Street SW, Zip 50677–2999; tel. 319/352–4120, **A**1 10 18 **F**3 7 8 11 13 15 18 26 28 29 34 35 36 40 43 45 50 57 59 63 64 75 76 77 81 85 86 97 104 107 110 111 114 119 127 130 132 133 134 135 144 146 147 **P**6
Primary Contact: James Atty, Chief Executive Officer
CFO: Lisa Bennett, Chief Financial Officer
CMO: Clay Dahlquist, M.D., Chief Medical Officer
CIO: Jerry Tiedt, Director Information Systems
CHR: Angie Tye, Director Human Resources
CNO: Joanne Nathem, MSN, R.N., Chief Clinical and Nursing Officer
Web address: www.waverlyhealthcenter.org
Control: City, Government, nonfederal **Service:** General medical and surgical

Staffed Beds: 25 **Admissions:** 763 **Census:** 7 **Outpatient Visits:** 120533 **Births:** 238 **Total Expense ($000):** 56274 **Payroll Expense ($000):** 26612 **Personnel:** 326

WEBSTER CITY—Hamilton County

HAMILTON HOSPITAL See Van Diest Medical Center

★ **VAN DIEST MEDICAL CENTER (161361)**, 2350 Hospital Drive, Zip 50595–6600, Mailing Address: P.O. Box 430, Zip 50595–0430; tel. 515/832–9400, **A**10 18 **F**3 7 8 11 13 15 28 29 30 31 34 35 36 38 40 41 43 45 47 50 56 64 68 75 76 78 79 81 82 85 86 87 89 93 97 100 103 104 107 110 111 115 117 119 128 129 130 132 133 143 146 147 148 149 **P**6
Primary Contact: Lisa Ridge, Chief Executive Officer
CFO: Alice Heinrichs, CPA, Chief Financial Officer
CMO: Nicole Ehn, M.D., Chief of Staff
CIO: Erick Schrier, Supervisor Information Technology
CHR: Jodie Harker, Director Human Resources
CNO: Janet Naset–Payne, MS, R.N., Chief Nursing Officer
Web address: www.vandiestmc.org
Control: County, Government, nonfederal **Service:** General medical and surgical

Staffed Beds: 25 **Admissions:** 900 **Census:** 10 **Outpatient Visits:** 44769 **Births:** 77 **Total Expense ($000):** 32229 **Payroll Expense ($000):** 12903 **Personnel:** 233

WEST BURLINGTON—Des Moines County

⊠ △ **GREAT RIVER MEDICAL CENTER (160057)**, 1221 South Gear Avenue, Zip 52655–1681; tel. 319/768–1000, (Total facility includes 160 beds in nursing home–type unit) **A**1 7 10 19 **F**3 4 5 7 11 13 15 18 20 22 28 29 30 31 32 34 35 36 38 40 43 45 48 50 53 57 59 60 62 63 64 67 68 69 70 73 75 76 77 78 79 81 82 84 85 86 87 89 90 91 92 93 96 98 99 100 101 102 103 104 107 108 110 111 114 115 116 117 118 119 120 121 123 128 129 130 131 132 143 146 147 148 **P**6
Primary Contact: Matthew Wenzel, President and Chief Executive Officer
CFO: Todd J. Sladky, Chief Financial Officer and Vice President Finance
CMO: Michael Jerry McCoy, M.D., Chief Medical Officer
CIO: Levi Nathan Gause, M.D., Chief Information Officer and Vice President Health System Informatics
CHR: James M. Kammerer, Vice President Support Services
CNO: Teresa Colgan, Vice President Nursing
Web address: www.greatrivermedical.org
Control: Other not–for–profit (including NFP Corporation) **Service:** General medical and surgical

Staffed Beds: 314 **Admissions:** 6490 **Census:** 219 **Outpatient Visits:** 279819 **Births:** 496 **Total Expense ($000):** 174676 **Payroll Expense ($000):** 70091 **Personnel:** 1190

WEST UNION—Fayette County

★ **GUNDERSEN PALMER LUTHERAN HOSPITAL AND CLINICS (161316)**, 112 Jefferson Street, Zip 52175–1022; tel. 563/422–3811, **A**10 18 **F**3 8 11 13 15 28 29 30 31 34 35 40 43 45 50 53 56 57 59 62 63 64 65 68 70 76 77 78 79 81 82 85 86 93 96 107 110 111 114 119 127 128 129 130 131 132 133 135 144 146 148 154 **P**1
Primary Contact: Tanya Tysland, Chief Executive Officer
CFO: Joni Gisleson, Director Finance
CMO: Chaudri Rasool, D.O., Chief of Staff
CIO: Kurt Chicken, Director Support Services
CHR: Cheryl Meyer, Director Human Resources
CNO: Kathy Begalske, Chief Nursing Officer
Web address: www.palmerlutheran.org
Control: Other not–for–profit (including NFP Corporation) **Service:** General medical and surgical

Staffed Beds: 25 **Admissions:** 262 **Census:** 4 **Outpatient Visits:** 90869 **Births:** 85 **Total Expense ($000):** 29518 **Payroll Expense ($000):** 9124 **Personnel:** 193

WINTERSET—Madison County

★ **MADISON COUNTY HEALTH CARE SYSTEM (161326)**, 300 West Hutchings Street, Zip 50273–2109; tel. 515/462–2373, **A**10 18 **F**3 15 18 28 31 35 37 40 43 45 57 59 64 78 79 81 89 93 97 107 110 114 119 127 128 130 131 133 135 144 146 149 **P**6 **S** Catholic Health Initiatives, Englewood, CO
Primary Contact: Marcia Hendricks, FACHE, R.N., Chief Executive Officer
CFO: Rebekah Mitchell, Chief Financial Officer
CMO: David Smith, D.O., Chief of Staff
CIO: Dan VandenBosch, Chief Information Officer
CHR: Jennifer Jackson, Director Human Resources
CNO: Kim Hulbert, R.N., Chief Clinical Officer
Web address: www.madisonhealth.com
Control: County, Government, nonfederal **Service:** General medical and surgical

Staffed Beds: 25 **Admissions:** 328 **Census:** 4 **Outpatient Visits:** 59896 **Births:** 0 **Total Expense ($000):** 20562 **Payroll Expense ($000):** 7818 **Personnel:** 146

IA

Hospital, Medicare Provider Number, Address, Telephone, Approval, Facility, and Physician Codes, Health Care System

★ American Hospital Association (AHA) membership
□ The Joint Commission accreditation
○ Healthcare Facilities Accreditation Program
◇ DNV Healthcare Inc. accreditation
⇑ Center for Improvement in Healthcare Quality Accreditation
△ Commission on Accreditation of Rehabilitation Facilities (CARF) accreditation

© 2018 AHA Guide   *Many Facility Codes have changed. Please refer to the AHA Guide Code Chart.*   Hospitals **A231**

KANSAS

ABILENE—Dickinson County

★ **MEMORIAL HEALTH SYSTEM (171381)**, 511 NE Tenth Street,
Zip 67410–2153; tel. 785/263–2100, (Total facility includes 74 beds in nursing
home–type unit) **A**10 18 **F**2 3 11 13 15 18 28 29 31 34 36 40 45 53 57 59 62
63 64 68 69 75 76 77 78 79 81 82 85 87 89 93 98 103 104 107 108 110 111
115 119 127 128 129 130 131 132 133 143 145 146 148 154 **P**6
Primary Contact: Harold Courtois, Chief Executive Officer
CFO: Elgin Glanzer, Chief Financial Officer
CMO: W L Short, M.D., Chief Medical Officer
CIO: Blaine Cappel, Director Information Systems
CNO: Brenda L. Moffitt, Chief Nursing Officer
Web address: www.mhsks.org
Control: Hospital district or authority, Government, nonfederal **Service:** General
medical and surgical

Staffed Beds: 109 **Admissions:** 744 **Census:** 80 **Outpatient Visits:** 25337
Births: 19 **Total Expense ($000):** 33222 **Payroll Expense ($000):** 14205
Personnel: 316

ANDOVER—Butler County

KANSAS MEDICAL CENTER (170197), 1124 West 21st Street,
Zip 67002–5500; tel. 316/300–4000, **A**10 **F**3 18 20 22 24 28 29 30 40 49 51
60 64 68 70 75 77 79 81 85 87 93 102 107 108 111 115 119 126 130 131
146 148
Primary Contact: Badr Idbeis, M.D., Chief Executive Officer
COO: Daryl W Thornton, Chief Operating Officer
CFO: Steven N Hadley, Chief Financial Officer
CMO: G. Whitney Reader, M.D., Chief Medical Officer
CIO: Mike Buffington, Manager Information Technology
CHR: Norm Nevins, Manager Human Resources
CNO: Janet Kaiser, R.N., Chief Nursing Officer
Web address: www.ksmedcenter.com/
Control: Corporation, Investor–owned (for–profit) **Service:** General medical and
surgical

Staffed Beds: 58 **Admissions:** 2508 **Census:** 26 **Outpatient Visits:** 12992
Births: 0 **Personnel:** 224

ARKANSAS CITY—Cowley County

★ **SOUTH CENTRAL KANSAS MEDICAL CENTER (170150)**, 6401 Patterson
Parkway, Zip 67005–5701, Mailing Address: P.O. Box 1107, Zip 67005–1107;
tel. 620/442–2500, **A**10 20 **F**3 11 12 13 15 29 30 34 35 39 40 45 47 48 50
52 56 57 59 64 68 70 75 76 77 79 81 82 85 87 91 93 97 98 103 107 108
110 111 115 119 127 129 130 132 133 135 146 147 148 149 154
Primary Contact: Jeff Bowman, Interim Chief Executive Officer
CFO: Holly Beaty, Chief Financial Officer
CMO: Kamran Shahzada, M.D., Chief Medical Staff
CHR: Clayton Pappan, Director Human Resources and Marketing
CNO: Patricia Davis, Chief Nursing Officer
Web address: www.sckrmc.org
Control: City, Government, nonfederal **Service:** General medical and surgical

Staffed Beds: 44 **Admissions:** 1029 **Census:** 17 **Outpatient Visits:** 24985
Births: 106 **Total Expense ($000):** 27926 **Payroll Expense ($000):** 7543
Personnel: 172

ASHLAND—Clark County

★ **ASHLAND HEALTH CENTER (171304)**, 709 Oak Street, Zip 67831–0188,
Mailing Address: P.O. Box 188, Zip 67831–0188; tel. 620/635–2241, **A**10 18 **F**2
30 34 40 53 59 62 64 67 68 85 87 93 107 127 128 133 143 154 **P**6 **S** Great
Plains Health Alliance, Inc., Wichita, KS
Primary Contact: Michael Mages, Chief Executive Officer
CFO: Debbie Filson, Chief Financial Officer
CMO: Daniel Shuman, D.O., Chief Medical Officer
CIO: Alan Romans, Director Information Technology
CHR: Debbie Filson, Chief Financial Officer
CNO: Patty Young, R.N., Chief Nursing Officer
Web address: www.ashlandhc.org
Control: Hospital district or authority, Government, nonfederal **Service:** General
medical and surgical

Staffed Beds: 25 **Admissions:** 84 **Census:** 18 **Outpatient Visits:** 4283
Births: 0 **Total Expense ($000):** 6881 **Payroll Expense ($000):** 2983
Personnel: 71

ATCHISON—Atchison County

★ **ATCHISON HOSPITAL (171382)**, 800 Raven Hill Drive, Zip 66002–9204;
tel. 913/367–2131, **A**10 18 **F**3 11 13 15 28 29 30 31 34 35 39 40 45 49
50 57 59 62 63 64 65 68 70 75 76 77 79 81 82 85 87 89 92 93 96 97 107
108 110 111 114 118 119 127 129 130 131 132 133 135 144 146 147 148
149 **P**6
Primary Contact: John L. Jacobson, Chief Executive Officer
COO: Sandra Leggett, Chief Operating Officer
CFO: Gary R Foll, Chief Financial Officer
CMO: McGarrett Groth, Chief of Staff
CIO: Terry Davis, Manager Information Systems
CHR: Jill Wenger, Director Human Resources
Web address: www.atchisonhospital.org
Control: Other not–for–profit (including NFP Corporation) **Service:** General
medical and surgical

Staffed Beds: 25 **Admissions:** 1099 **Census:** 12 **Outpatient Visits:** 80201
Births: 125 **Total Expense ($000):** 41175 **Payroll Expense ($000):** 18789
Personnel: 269

ATWOOD—Rawlins County

★ **RAWLINS COUNTY HEALTH CENTER (171307)**, 707 Grant Street,
Zip 67730–1526, Mailing Address: P.O. Box 47, Zip 67730–0047;
tel. 785/626–3211, **A**10 18 **F**3 28 29 30 34 40 41 45 59 64 65 66 75 81 83
85 87 89 93 97 107 114 125 127 128 130 131 132 133 135 147 148 **P**6
Primary Contact: Sharon K. Cox, FACHE, Chief Executive Officer
COO: Ryan Marvin, Support Services Director
CFO: Heather Prideaux, Chief Financial Officer
CMO: Brewster Kellogg, D.O., Chief Medical Officer
CIO: Destiny Schroeder, Information Systems Director
CHR: Tara Bowles, Employee Relations Director
CNO: Amber Withington, RN, Chief Clinical Officer
Web address: www.rchc.us
Control: County, Government, nonfederal **Service:** General medical and surgical

Staffed Beds: 24 **Admissions:** 135 **Census:** 3 **Outpatient Visits:** 13089
Births: 0 **Total Expense ($000):** 7892 **Payroll Expense ($000):** 2961
Personnel: 62

BELLEVILLE—Republic County

★ **REPUBLIC COUNTY HOSPITAL (171361)**, 2420 'G' Street, Zip 66935–2400;
tel. 785/527–2254, **A**10 18 **F**3 13 15 28 29 30 31 34 35 39 40 43 45 56 57
64 67 68 75 76 77 78 79 81 82 85 86 87 89 91 93 107 108 114 119 128 129
130 131 133 **S** Great Plains Health Alliance, Inc., Wichita, KS
Primary Contact: David–Paul Cavazos, Chief Executive Officer
CFO: Barry Bottger, Chief Financial Officer
Web address: www.rphospital.org
Control: Other not–for–profit (including NFP Corporation) **Service:** General
medical and surgical

Staffed Beds: 63 **Admissions:** 760 **Census:** 31 **Outpatient Visits:** 16453
Births: 59 **Total Expense ($000):** 14247 **Payroll Expense ($000):** 6650
Personnel: 120

BELOIT—Mitchell County

★ **MITCHELL COUNTY HOSPITAL HEALTH SYSTEMS (171375)**, 400 West
Eighth, Zip 67420–1605, Mailing Address: P.O. Box 399, Zip 67420–0399;
tel. 785/738–2266, (Total facility includes 40 beds in nursing home–type unit) **A**10
18 **F**3 11 13 15 28 29 31 34 40 43 45 48 50 56 59 63 64 68 69 74 76 77 81
82 84 86 87 93 98 103 107 111 114 119 128 129 130 132 133 148 149
Primary Contact: Jeremy Armstrong, FACHE, Chief Executive Officer
CFO: Eldon Koepke, Chief Financial Officer
CIO: Nate Richards, Director Information Technology
CHR: Phyllis Oetting, Director Human Resources
CNO: Jan Kemmerer, Director of Nursing
Web address: www.mchks.com
Control: County, Government, nonfederal **Service:** General medical and surgical

Staffed Beds: 75 **Admissions:** 1311 **Census:** 62 **Outpatient Visits:** 16717
Births: 83 **Total Expense ($000):** 25488 **Payroll Expense ($000):** 11588
Personnel: 267

Many Facility Codes have changed. Please refer to the AHA Guide Code Chart.   © 2018 AHA Guide

BURLINGTON—Coffey County

★ **COFFEY COUNTY HOSPITAL (170094)**, 801 North 4th Street, Zip 66839–2602; tel. 620/364–2121, (Total facility includes 42 beds in nursing home–type unit) **A**10 20 **F**3 7 10 11 13 15 17 29 30 31 34 40 45 50 57 59 62 64 65 67 68 70 75 76 77 78 79 81 82 85 87 93 107 110 111 114 119 125 127 128 130 133 146 149 **P**6
Primary Contact: Leonard Hernandez, Chief Executive Officer
CFO: Jim Van Hoet, Chief Financial Officer
CMO: John Shell, M.D., Chief Medical Officer
CIO: Adam Haag, Manager Information Technology
CHR: Theresa Thoele, Director Human Resources
CNO: Melissa Hall, Chief Nursing Officer
Web address: www.coffeyhealth.org
Control: County, Government, nonfederal **Service**: General medical and surgical

Staffed Beds: 67 **Admissions:** 510 **Census:** 30 **Outpatient Visits:** 25644 **Births:** 96 **Total Expense ($000):** 24765 **Payroll Expense ($000):** 13749 **Personnel:** 156

CALDWELL—Sumner County

★ **SUMNER COUNTY HOSPITAL DISTRICT ONE (171329)**, 601 South Osage Street, Zip 67022–1654; tel. 620/845–6492, **A**10 18 **F**7 40 50 57 59 64 67 75 81 90 93 107 111 114 119 133 146 **P**5
CFO: Jennifer Marcrum, Chief Financial Officer
CMO: Jim Blunk, D.O., Chief Medical Officer
CIO: Trey Watson, Network Administrator
Web address: www.schd1.com
Control: Hospital district or authority, Government, nonfederal **Service**: General medical and surgical

Staffed Beds: 16 **Admissions:** 100 **Census:** 2 **Outpatient Visits:** 1020 **Births:** 0 **Total Expense ($000):** 4846 **Payroll Expense ($000):** 2003 **Personnel:** 43

CHANUTE—Neosho County

★ ⇪ **NEOSHO MEMORIAL REGIONAL MEDICAL CENTER (171380)**, 629 South Plummer, Zip 66720–1928, Mailing Address: P.O. Box 426, Zip 66720–0426; tel. 620/431–4000, **A**10 18 21 **F**3 7 13 15 28 29 30 40 43 47 48 50 62 63 64 76 79 81 85 107 108 110 111 114 119 126 127 129 130 133 143 146 147 149 154 **P**8 **S** QHR, Brentwood, TN
Primary Contact: Dennis Franks, FACHE, Chief Executive Officer
COO: Wendy Brazil, Chief Operating Officer
CFO: Nancy Woodyard, Chief Financial Officer
CMO: Charles Van Houden, M.D., Chief Medical Officer
CIO: Gretchen Keller, Director Health Information
CHR: R C Rowan, Director Human Resources
CNO: Jennifer Newton, R.N., Chief Nursing Officer
Web address: www.nmrmc.com
Control: County, Government, nonfederal **Service**: General medical and surgical

Staffed Beds: 25 **Admissions:** 1692 **Census:** 10 **Outpatient Visits:** 61233 **Births:** 338 **Total Expense ($000):** 55884 **Payroll Expense ($000):** 23802 **Personnel:** 388

CLAY CENTER—Clay County

★ **CLAY COUNTY MEDICAL CENTER (171371)**, 617 Liberty Street, Zip 67432–1564, Mailing Address: P.O. Box 512, Zip 67432–0512; tel. 785/632–2144, **A**10 18 **F**13 15 18 19 28 29 30 31 40 45 50 53 55 59 63 64 68 70 74 75 76 77 78 79 81 82 84 85 86 87 93 96 107 108 111 114 119 127 130 132 133 148 149
Primary Contact: Austin M. Gillard, Chief Executive Officer
CFO: James Garbarino, Chief Financial Officer
CIO: Chris Wolf, Director Information Technology
CHR: Cindy Rush, Director Human Resources
CNO: Sara Beikman, Director of Nursing
Web address: www.ccmcks.org
Control: County, Government, nonfederal **Service**: General medical and surgical

Staffed Beds: 25 **Admissions:** 766 **Census:** 11 **Outpatient Visits:** 84624 **Births:** 59 **Total Expense ($000):** 21200 **Payroll Expense ($000):** 11065 **Personnel:** 215

COFFEYVILLE—Montgomery County

⊠ **COFFEYVILLE REGIONAL MEDICAL CENTER (170145)**, 1400 West Fourth, Zip 67337–3306; tel. 620/251–1200, (Total facility includes 20 beds in nursing home–type unit) **A**1 10 20 **F**3 7 11 13 15 28 29 30 31 34 40 45 50 51 57 59 62 64 70 74 75 76 77 78 79 81 82 85 86 87 93 97 107 108 109 110 111 113 117 119 120 121 123 127 128 130 131 132 135 146 154 **P**6 8
Primary Contact: Lori Rexwinkle, Chief Executive Officer
CIO: Kris Penco, Director Information Systems
CHR: Becky McCune, Director Human Resources, Community Relations and Education
CNO: Lori Rexwinkle, Chief Nursing Officer
Web address: www.crmcinc.com
Control: Other not–for–profit (including NFP Corporation) **Service**: General medical and surgical

Staffed Beds: 69 **Admissions:** 2047 **Census:** 20 **Outpatient Visits:** 46576 **Births:** 268 **Total Expense ($000):** 48582 **Payroll Expense ($000):** 18679 **Personnel:** 361

COLBY—Thomas County

★ **CITIZENS MEDICAL CENTER (171362)**, 100 East College Drive, Zip 67701–3799; tel. 785/462–7511, (Total facility includes 60 beds in nursing home–type unit) **A**10 18 **F**3 11 13 15 28 30 31 34 35 40 43 50 64 67 68 76 77 78 81 85 86 87 93 97 107 108 110 111 114 119 127 130 133 146 148 **P**6
Primary Contact: Greg Unruh, Chief Executive Officer
CFO: Darcy Howard, Chief Financial Officer
CMO: Kelly Gabel, Chief of Staff
CIO: Jacee Dobbs, Chief Information Officer
CHR: Margaret Kummer, Chief Human Resource Officer
CNO: Jenny Niblock, Chief Clinical Officer
Web address: www.cmciks.com
Control: Other not–for–profit (including NFP Corporation) **Service**: General medical and surgical

Staffed Beds: 85 **Admissions:** 788 **Census:** 58 **Outpatient Visits:** 59384 **Births:** 175 **Total Expense ($000):** 34442 **Payroll Expense ($000):** 17438 **Personnel:** 294

COLDWATER—Comanche County

★ **COMANCHE COUNTY HOSPITAL (171312)**, 202 South Frisco Street, Zip 67029–9101, Mailing Address: HC 65, Box 8A, Zip 67029–9500; tel. 620/582–2144, **A**10 18 **F**3 11 30 31 40 43 53 59 61 68 75 78 93 102 107 128 133 **P**6 **S** Great Plains Health Alliance, Inc., Wichita, KS
Primary Contact: Nancy Zimmerman, R.N., Administrator
CFO: Lisa Brooks, Chief Financial Officer
CMO: Daniel Schowengerdt, M.D., Chief of Staff
CIO: LaNell Wagnon, Director Medical Records
CHR: Lisa Brooks, Chief Financial Officer
CNO: Sandra Dobrinski, Director of Nursing
Web address: www.gpha.com
Control: County, Government, nonfederal **Service**: General medical and surgical

Staffed Beds: 12 **Admissions:** 99 **Census:** 2 **Outpatient Visits:** 11234 **Births:** 0 **Total Expense ($000):** 5544 **Payroll Expense ($000):** 2629 **Personnel:** 57

COLUMBUS—Cherokee County

★ **MERCY HOSPITAL COLUMBUS (171308)**, 220 North Pennsylvania Avenue, Zip 66725–1110; tel. 620/429–2545, (Nonreporting) **A**10 18 **S** Mercy, Chesterfield, MO
Primary Contact: Angie Saporito, Administrator
Web address: www.mercy.net/newsroom–mercy–maude–norton–hospital–quick–facts
Control: Church operated, Nongovernment, not–for–profit **Service**: General medical and surgical

Staffed Beds: 18

Hospital, Medicare Provider Number, Address, Telephone, Approval, Facility, and Physician Codes, Health Care System

★ American Hospital Association (AHA) membership
□ The Joint Commission accreditation
○ Healthcare Facilities Accreditation Program
◇ DNV Healthcare Inc. accreditation
⇪ Center for Improvement in Healthcare Quality Accreditation
△ Commission on Accreditation of Rehabilitation Facilities (CARF) accreditation

KS

CONCORDIA—Cloud County

★ **CLOUD COUNTY HEALTH CENTER (171349)**, 1100 Highland Drive,
Zip 66901–3923; tel. 785/243–1234, **A**10 18 **F**3 11 15 28 31 34 35 40 41 45
56 57 59 64 65 70 74 75 77 79 81 82 85 86 87 93 96 97 102 107 108 114
118 119 127 130 133 135 146 148 154 **P**6 **S** Salina Regional Health Center,
Salina, KS
Primary Contact: David Garnas, Administrator
CFO: Pamela Blochlinger, Acting Vice President Finance
CMO: Justin Poore, D.O., Chief Medical Staff
CIO: Jenny Bergstrom, Project Manager Information Technology
CHR: Dawn Thoman, Vice President Human Resources
CNO: Michelle Metro, Vice President Nursing
Web address: www.cchc.com
Control: Other not–for–profit (including NFP Corporation) **Service**: General
medical and surgical

Staffed Beds: 25 **Admissions:** 296 **Census:** 4 **Outpatient Visits:** 38875
Births: 0 **Total Expense ($000):** 14713 **Payroll Expense ($000):** 7882
Personnel: 133

COUNCIL GROVE—Morris County

★ **MORRIS COUNTY HOSPITAL (171379)**, 600 North Washington Street,
Zip 66846–1422; tel. 620/767–6811, **A**10 18 **F**7 11 13 15 18 28 35 40 45 59
64 65 70 76 77 81 87 93 94 96 107 110 111 130 132 133 146 148 149 **P**5
Primary Contact: Kevin Leeper, Chief Executive Officer
CFO: Ron Christenson, Chief Financial Officer
CMO: Lora Siegle, M.D., Chief Medical Officer
CIO: Bill Lauer, Chief Information Officer
CHR: Don Zimmerman, Director Human Resources
CNO: Stephanne Wolf, Chief Nursing Officer
Web address: www.mrcohosp.com
Control: County, Government, nonfederal **Service**: General medical and surgical

Staffed Beds: 25 **Admissions:** 303 **Census:** 3 **Outpatient Visits:** 12807
Births: 18 **Total Expense ($000):** 9703 **Payroll Expense ($000):** 3381
Personnel: 81

DIGHTON—Lane County

★ **LANE COUNTY HOSPITAL (171303)**, 235 West Vine, Zip 67839–0969, Mailing
Address: P.O. Box 969, Zip 67839–0969; tel. 620/397–5321, **A**10 18 **F**30 40 56
77 93 97 127 128 131 133 **P**6 **S** Great Plains Health Alliance, Inc., Wichita, KS
Primary Contact: Brian Sarpy, Chief Executive Officer
CFO: Marcia Gabel, Chief Financial Officer
CMO: Paul Chinburg, M.D., Medical Director
CHR: Dina Casey, Human Resources Officer
CNO: Jennifer Whipple, Director Nursing
Web address: www.lanecountyhospital.com/
Control: County, Government, nonfederal **Service**: General medical and surgical

Staffed Beds: 25 **Admissions:** 57 **Census:** 19 **Outpatient Visits:** 8847
Births: 0 **Total Expense ($000):** 5740 **Payroll Expense ($000):** 2574
Personnel: 66

DODGE CITY—Ford County

⊞ **WESTERN PLAINS MEDICAL COMPLEX (170175)**, 3001 Avenue 'A',
Zip 67801–6508, Mailing Address: P.O. Box 1478, Zip 67801–1478;
tel. 620/225–8400, **A**1 3 5 10 20 **F**1 3 4 8 11 13 15 16 17 18 20 22 28 29
30 34 35 40 50 57 60 64 67 70 72 73 74 75 76 77 79 80 81 85 88 89 90
93 98 107 108 110 111 115 119 128 130 131 132 133 146 149 150 **P**5 7 **S**
LifePoint Health, Brentwood, TN
Primary Contact: Scott M. Smith, Interim Chief Executive Officer
CFO: Ryan Pugh, Chief Financial Officer
CMO: Merrill Conant, M.D., Chief of Staff
CIO: Shawna Culver, Director Information Systems
CHR: Corry Israel, Director Human Resources
CNO: Jay Trevor Fogg, R.N., Chief Nursing Officer
Web address: www.westernplainsmc.com
Control: Corporation, Investor–owned (for–profit) **Service**: General medical and
surgical

Staffed Beds: 45 **Admissions:** 1903 **Census:** 14 **Outpatient Visits:** 29210
Births: 620 **Total Expense ($000):** 33564 **Payroll Expense ($000):** 12942
Personnel: 203

EL DORADO—Butler County

⊞ **SUSAN B. ALLEN MEMORIAL HOSPITAL (170017)**, 720 West Central Avenue,
Zip 67042–2112; tel. 316/321–3300, **A**1 10 **F**3 11 13 15 28 30 40 45 59 60
62 69 70 76 79 81 85 92 93 96 97 107 108 110 111 115 119 120 121 123
130 133 144 146 148
Primary Contact: James B. Kirkbride, President and Chief Executive Officer
COO: Mark Rooker, Chief Operations and Information Officer
CFO: Gene Kaberline, Chief Financial Officer
CMO: Paige Dodson, M.D., M.P.H., Chief Medical Officer
CIO: Mark Rooker, Chief Operations and Information Officer
CHR: D. Gay Kimble, Chief Human Resource Officer
CNO: Cecilia B Goebel, R.N., Chief Nursing Officer
Web address: www.sbamh.com
Control: Other not–for–profit (including NFP Corporation) **Service**: General
medical and surgical

Staffed Beds: 38 **Admissions:** 1685 **Census:** 17 **Outpatient Visits:** 85124
Births: 184 **Total Expense ($000):** 54326 **Payroll Expense ($000):** 23046
Personnel: 387

ELKHART—Morton County

★ **MORTON COUNTY HEALTH SYSTEM (170166)**, 445 Hilltop Street,
Zip 67950–0937, Mailing Address: P.O. Box 937, Zip 67950–0937;
tel. 620/697–2141, **A**10 20 **F**3 34 40 50 54 56 57 59 70 83 86 87 93 94 96
97 104 107 114 119 127 130 131 132 133 154 **P**6
Primary Contact: Richard Q. Bergling, Chief Executive Officer
CHR: Sonja May, Director Human Resources
Web address: www.mchswecare.com
Control: County, Government, nonfederal **Service**: General medical and surgical

Staffed Beds: 28 **Admissions:** 173 **Census:** 2 **Outpatient Visits:** 6523
Births: 0 **Total Expense ($000):** 7003 **Payroll Expense ($000):** 3301
Personnel: 73

ELLINWOOD—Barton County

★ **ELLINWOOD DISTRICT HOSPITAL (171301)**, 605 North Main Street,
Zip 67526–1440; tel. 620/564–2548, **A**10 18 **F**11 40 64 65 93 107 127 128
133 154 **P**6 **S** Great Plains Health Alliance, Inc., Wichita, KS
Primary Contact: Kile Magner, Administrator
CFO: Summer Zink, Chief Financial Officer
CMO: Charlie Joslin, M.D., Chief of Staff
CIO: Becky L Burns, Manager Health Information Management
CHR: Chris Robl, Human Resources
CNO: Jill Ritchie, Director of Nursing
Web address: www.ellinwooddistricthospital.org
Control: Other not–for–profit (including NFP Corporation) **Service**: General
medical and surgical

Staffed Beds: 25 **Admissions:** 234 **Census:** 7 **Outpatient Visits:** 13381
Births: 0 **Total Expense ($000):** 6772 **Payroll Expense ($000):** 3276
Personnel: 77

ELLSWORTH—Ellsworth County

★ **ELLSWORTH COUNTY MEDICAL CENTER (171327)**, 1604 Aylward
Street, Zip 67439–0087, Mailing Address: P.O. Box 87, Zip 67439–0087;
tel. 785/472–3111, **A**10 18 **F**3 11 28 29 34 35 40 45 47 53 57 59 64 67 75
77 85 86 87 93 97 107 115 119 127 128 130 133 146 **P**6
Primary Contact: John R. Broberg, FACHE, Interim Chief Executive Officer
CFO: Preston Sauers, Chief Financial Officer
CIO: Lynette Dick, Director of Support Services
CHR: Christa N Bohnen, Director Human Resources
CNO: Amanda Thrasher, Director Nursing
Web address: www.ewmed.com
Control: County, Government, nonfederal **Service**: General medical and surgical

Staffed Beds: 20 **Admissions:** 558 **Census:** 6 **Outpatient Visits:** 16147
Births: 0 **Total Expense ($000):** 16957 **Payroll Expense ($000):** 8288
Personnel: 150

EMPORIA—Lyon County

NEWMAN REGIONAL HEALTH (171384), 1201 West 12th Avenue,
Zip 66801–2597; tel. 620/343–6800, (Nonreporting) **A**10 18
Primary Contact: Robert N. Wright, Chief Executive Officer
CFO: Holly French, Chief Financial Officer
CMO: James Geitz, M.D., Chief of Staff
CHR: Kathy Orear, Director Human Resources
CNO: Julia Pyle, R.N., Chief Nursing Officer
Web address: www.newmanrh.org
Control: County, Government, nonfederal **Service**: General medical and surgical

Staffed Beds: 32

Many Facility Codes have changed. Please refer to the AHA Guide Code Chart. © 2018 AHA Guide

EUREKA—Greenwood County

GREENWOOD COUNTY HOSPITAL (171339), 100 West 16th Street, Zip 67045–1064; tel. 620/583–7451, **A**10 18 **F**3 40 43 53 57 62 81 93 96 107 119 127 128 133 135 146 **P**6
Primary Contact: Sandra Dickerson, Chief Executive Officer
CFO: Marian Drake, Chief Financial Officer
CIO: Jason Clark, Director Quality Improvement, Risk Management and Information System
CHR: Janel M Palmer, Director Human Resources
CNO: Tracy Harrod, Director of Nursing
Web address: www.gwch.org
Control: County, Government, nonfederal **Service:** General medical and surgical

Staffed Beds: 25 **Admissions:** 425 **Census:** 8 **Outpatient Visits:** 16080 **Births:** 0 **Total Expense ($000):** 11403 **Payroll Expense ($000):** 6356 **Personnel:** 119

FORT SCOTT—Bourbon County

⊞ **MERCY HOSPITAL FORT SCOTT (170058)**, 401 Woodland Hills Boulevard, Zip 66701–8797; tel. 620/223–2200, **A**1 10 **F**3 7 11 13 15 28 29 30 34 35 40 57 59 62 63 65 70 75 76 77 79 81 84 85 93 97 107 108 110 111 114 118 119 127 129 130 131 132 133 143 144 145 146 148 149 150 154 **P**6 **S** Mercy, Chesterfield, MO
Primary Contact: Reta K. Baker, President
CFO: Shelly Hunter, Chief Financial Officer
CMO: Robert R Nichols, M.D., Vice President Medical Affairs
CIO: Lori Sturgill, Vice President Business Partnership
CHR: Timothy Murphy, Vice President Human Resources
CNO: Patrick Callanan, Vice President Patient Care Services
Web address: www.mercykansas.com
Control: Church operated, Nongovernment, not–for–profit **Service:** General medical and surgical

Staffed Beds: 46 **Admissions:** 1155 **Census:** 10 **Outpatient Visits:** 102449 **Births:** 240 **Total Expense ($000):** 29983 **Payroll Expense ($000):** 13520 **Personnel:** 263

FREDONIA—Wilson County

★ **FREDONIA REGIONAL HOSPITAL (171374)**, 1527 Madison Street, Zip 66736–1751, Mailing Address: P.O. Box 579, Zip 66736–0579; tel. 620/378–2121, **A**10 18 **F**3 7 11 15 30 40 57 59 81 82 85 91 93 98 103 107 110 111 115 119 128 133 154 **S** Great Plains Health Alliance, Inc., Wichita, KS
Primary Contact: Johnathan Durrett, Chief Executive Officer
CFO: Tracy Row, Manager Business Office
CMO: Jennifer McKenney, M.D., Chief Medical Officer
CIO: Tyler Row, Director Information Technology
CHR: Debbie Marr, Administrative Assistant and Director Human Resources
CNO: Ryan Duft, R.N., Chief Nursing Officer
Web address: www.fredoniaregionalhospital.org
Control: City, Government, nonfederal **Service:** General medical and surgical

Staffed Beds: 34 **Admissions:** 557 **Census:** 11 **Outpatient Visits:** 28115 **Births:** 0 **Total Expense ($000):** 15168 **Payroll Expense ($000):** 5905 **Personnel:** 135

GALENA—Cherokee County

⇑ **PREMIER SURGICAL INSTITUTE (170203)**, 1619 West 7th Street, Zip 66739; tel. 620/783–1732, (Nonreporting) **A**10 21
Primary Contact: Travis W. Roderick, Chief Executive Officer
Web address: www.premiersurgicalinstitute.com/
Control: City, Government, nonfederal **Service:** General medical and surgical

Staffed Beds: 25

GARDEN CITY—Finney County

⊞ **ST. CATHERINE HOSPITAL (170023)**, 401 East Spruce Street, Zip 67846–5679; tel. 620/272–2561, **A**1 10 20 **F**3 8 13 15 18 20 22 29 30 31 34 35 40 45 49 51 57 59 60 63 64 65 68 69 70 73 74 75 77 78 79 81 82 83 84 85 86 87 90 91 92 93 94 96 97 98 100 102 107 108 109 110 111 112 113 114 115 116 117 118 119 120 121 122 123 124 127 130 131 132 135 144 146 147 148 **P**5 6 **S** Catholic Health Initiatives, Englewood, CO
Primary Contact: Scott J. Taylor, President and Chief Executive Officer
CFO: Amanda Vaughan, Chief Financial Officer
CMO: Matthew C Byrnes, M.D., Chief Medical Officer
CIO: Lance Kellenbarger, Site Director Information Systems
CHR: Kathy E Morrison, Executive Director Human Resources
CNO: Margaret Elizabeth Prewitt, Vice President Patient Services and Chief Nursing Officer
Web address: www.StCatherineHosp.org
Control: Church operated, Nongovernment, not–for–profit **Service:** General medical and surgical

Staffed Beds: 104 **Admissions:** 4267 **Census:** 48 **Outpatient Visits:** 176611 **Births:** 674 **Total Expense ($000):** 114454 **Payroll Expense ($000):** 43370 **Personnel:** 453

GARDNER—Johnson County

★ △ **MEADOWBROOK REHABILITATION HOSPITAL (173033)**, 427 West Main Street, Zip 66030–1183; tel. 913/856–8747, (Nonreporting) **A**7 10
Primary Contact: Peter Kautz, Chief Executive Officer
CFO: Kelly Taul, Business Manager
CMO: David Edalati, M.D., Medical Director
CHR: Carrie Moore, Director Human Resources
CNO: Lisa Perez, R.N., Director Nursing
Web address: www.meadowbrookrehab.com
Control: Partnership, Investor–owned (for–profit) **Service:** Rehabilitation

Staffed Beds: 96

GARNETT—Anderson County

★ **ANDERSON COUNTY HOSPITAL (171316)**, 421 South Maple, Zip 66032–1334, Mailing Address: P.O. Box 309, Zip 66032–0309; tel. 785/448–3131, (Total facility includes 36 beds in nursing home–type unit) **A**10 18 **F**3 7 11 15 18 29 30 34 35 40 41 43 45 56 57 59 64 65 67 75 77 79 81 82 86 87 91 93 97 100 107 108 110 115 118 119 127 130 131 133 146 149 154 **P**6 **S** Saint Luke's Health System, Kansas City, MO
Primary Contact: Rick McKain, Chief Executive Officer
CFO: Vicki L Mills, Chief Financial Officer
CMO: Mackenzie Peterson, Chief of Staff
CHR: Karen Gillespie, Director Human Resources
CNO: Margo L Williams, R.N., Chief Nursing Officer
Web address: www.saint–lukes.org
Control: Other not–for–profit (including NFP Corporation) **Service:** General medical and surgical

Staffed Beds: 48 **Admissions:** 222 **Census:** 34 **Outpatient Visits:** 48591 **Births:** 0 **Total Expense ($000):** 26008 **Payroll Expense ($000):** 10591 **Personnel:** 218

GIRARD—Crawford County

★ **GIRARD MEDICAL CENTER (171376)**, 302 North Hospital Drive, Zip 66743–2000; tel. 620/724–8291, **A**10 18 **F**3 6 8 11 12 15 28 29 34 35 40 43 44 45 47 50 51 53 56 57 59 62 64 65 68 75 77 79 81 86 87 93 97 98 100 101 103 104 107 114 119 127 130 131 132 133 144 146 148 149 **P**6
Primary Contact: Ruth Duling, Chief Executive Officer
CFO: Holly Koch, Chief Financial Officer
CIO: Jeff Barnes, Director Information Technology
CHR: Gregory Sullivan, Manager Human Resources
CNO: Joyce Geier, Director Nursing
Web address: www.girardmedicalcenter.com
Control: Hospital district or authority, Government, nonfederal **Service:** General medical and surgical

Staffed Beds: 35 **Admissions:** 553 **Census:** 12 **Outpatient Visits:** 19134 **Births:** 0 **Total Expense ($000):** 19239 **Payroll Expense ($000):** 9514 **Personnel:** 176

GOODLAND—Sherman County

★ **GOODLAND REGIONAL MEDICAL CENTER (171370)**, 220 West Second Street, Zip 67735–1602; tel. 785/890–3625, **A**10 18 **F**3 11 13 15 28 29 31 34 35 40 45 57 59 60 62 64 65 69 75 76 77 78 79 81 82 87 93 96 97 107 110 115 119 127 129 130 132 133 135 148 154 **P**6
Primary Contact: Chris Smolik, Chief Executive Officer
CFO: Donald Lee Wade, Chief Financial Officer
CIO: Christopher Biel, Chief Information Officer
CHR: Linda Taylor, Chief Human Resources Officer
Web address: www.goodlandregional.com
Control: County, Government, nonfederal **Service:** General medical and surgical

Staffed Beds: 25 **Admissions:** 516 **Census:** 6 **Outpatient Visits:** 51059 **Births:** 56 **Total Expense ($000):** 20490 **Payroll Expense ($000):** 9567 **Personnel:** 158

KS

GREAT BEND—Barton County

UNIVERSITY OF KANSAS HEALTH SYSTEM GREAT BEND CAMPUS (170191), 514 Cleveland Street, Zip 67530–3562; tel. 620/792–8833, **A**10 20 22 **F**3 8 13 15 29 30 34 40 43 45 57 59 64 65 68 70 75 76 79 81 82 89 107 110 111 114 119 127 130 133 135 144 146 147 **S** The University of Kansas Health System, Kansas City, KS
Primary Contact: Jodi A. Schmidt, Interim Chief Executive Officer
COO: Adina Gregory, Chief Operating Officer
CFO: Timothy Latimer, Chief Financial Officer
CMO: Randall Hildebrand, M.D., Chief Medical Officer
CHR: Brenda Kaiser, Director Human Resources
CNO: Adina Gregory, Chief Nursing Officer
Web address: www.gbregional.com
Control: Partnership, Investor–owned (for–profit) **Service**: General medical and surgical

Staffed Beds: 33 **Admissions**: 1845 **Census**: 17 **Outpatient Visits**: 61061 **Births**: 283 **Total Expense ($000)**: 38832 **Payroll Expense ($000)**: 14957 **Personnel**: 284

GREENSBURG—Kiowa County

★ **KIOWA COUNTY MEMORIAL HOSPITAL (171332)**, 721 West Kansas Avenue, Zip 67054–1633; tel. 620/723–3341, **A**10 18 **F**3 7 34 40 50 53 59 64 68 107 114 127 128 133 149 **P**6 **S** Great Plains Health Alliance, Inc., Wichita, KS
Primary Contact: Mary Sweet, Administrator
CFO: Ron Tucker, Business Office Manager
CMO: Nizar Kibar, M.D., Chief Medical Staff
CIO: Jeremy Steven Hoover, Chief Information Officer
CHR: Cathy McFall, Human Resources Manager
CNO: Vanessa Kirk, Director of Nursing
Web address: www.kcmh.net
Control: Other not–for–profit (including NFP Corporation) **Service**: General medical and surgical

Staffed Beds: 15 **Admissions**: 119 **Census**: 5 **Outpatient Visits**: 10834 **Births**: 0 **Total Expense ($000)**: 8991 **Payroll Expense ($000)**: 3448 **Personnel**: 76

HANOVER—Washington County

★ **HANOVER HOSPITAL (171365)**, 205 South Hanover, Zip 66945–8924, Mailing Address: P.O. Box 38, Zip 66945–0038; tel. 785/337–2214, **A**10 18 **F**2 7 28 40 53 69 81 127 133 **P**4
Primary Contact: Brittni Oehmke, Administrator
CFO: Sheryl Adam, Chief Financial Officer
Control: Hospital district or authority, Government, nonfederal **Service**: General medical and surgical

Staffed Beds: 25 **Admissions**: 125 **Census**: 4 **Outpatient Visits**: 1836 **Births**: 0 **Total Expense ($000)**: 3916 **Payroll Expense ($000)**: 2103 **Personnel**: 50

HARPER—Harper County

★ **HOSPITAL DISTRICT 6 – HARPER CAMPUS (171346)**, 700 West 13th Street, Zip 67058–1401; tel. 620/896–7324, (Includes HOSPITAL DISTRICT 6 – ANTHONY CAMPUS, 1101 East Spring Street, Anthony, KS, Zip 67003–2122; tel. 620/842–5111; Pat Patton, Chief Executive Officer) (Nonreporting) **A**10 18
Primary Contact: Pat Patton, Chief Executive Officer
CFO: Sandra Owen, Director Fiscal and Accounting
CMO: Ralph Imlay, M.D., Chief of Staff
CIO: Cindi Beadman, Director Medical Records
CHR: Troy Hickman, Director Human Resources
CNO: Karen Aldis, Director of Nursing
Web address: www.hhd5.com
Control: Hospital district or authority, Government, nonfederal **Service**: General medical and surgical

Staffed Beds: 25

HAYS—Ellis County

★ ⇧ **HAYS MEDICAL CENTER (170013)**, 2220 Canterbury Drive, Zip 67601–2370, Mailing Address: P.O. Box 8100, Zip 67601–8100; tel. 785/623–5000, **A**5 10 21 **F**3 11 12 13 15 18 20 22 24 26 28 29 30 31 32 34 35 36 37 38 40 41 43 45 51 53 55 56 57 59 60 63 64 65 66 68 69 70 71 72 73 75 76 77 78 79 80 81 82 84 85 86 87 89 92 93 96 97 107 108 110 111 115 118 119 120 121 123 124 126 127 129 130 131 132 135 144 146 147 148 149 154 **P**6 **S** The University of Kansas Health System, Kansas City, KS
Primary Contact: Edward Herrman, R.N., FACHE, President and Chief Executive Officer
COO: Bryce A Young, Chief Operating Officer
CFO: George Harms, Chief Financial Officer
CIO: Scott Rohleder, Chief Information Officer
CHR: Bryce A Young, Chief Operating Officer
CNO: Terry Siek, MSN, R.N., Chief Nursing Officer
Web address: www.haysmed.com
Control: Other not–for–profit (including NFP Corporation) **Service**: General medical and surgical

Staffed Beds: 127 **Admissions**: 4458 **Census**: 54 **Outpatient Visits**: 178563 **Births**: 627 **Total Expense ($000)**: 178278 **Payroll Expense ($000)**: 76763 **Personnel**: 1291

HERINGTON—Dickinson County

HERINGTON MUNICIPAL HOSPITAL (171340), 100 East Helen Street, Zip 67449–1606; tel. 785/258–2207, (Nonreporting) **A**10 18
Primary Contact: Isabel Schmedemann, R.N., Chief Executive Officer and Administrator
CFO: Alan Meisinger, Chief Financial Officer
CMO: John Mosier, D.O., Chief of Staff
CHR: Nicole Will, Human Resources Officer
CNO: Roni Baker, Director of Nursing
Web address: www.heringtonhospital.org
Control: City, Government, nonfederal **Service**: General medical and surgical

Staffed Beds: 25

HIAWATHA—Brown County

★ **HIAWATHA COMMUNITY HOSPITAL (171341)**, 300 Utah Street, Zip 66434–2314; tel. 785/742–2131, **A**10 18 **F**8 11 13 15 28 29 40 43 45 67 69 70 76 81 85 107 111 114 119 127 128 130 133 143 146 149 **P**6
Primary Contact: Jeffrey Shelton, Chief Executive Officer
CFO: Jenny Knudson, Controller
CMO: Steffen Shamburg, M.D., Chief of Staff
CIO: Cheryl Wenger, Manager Health Information and Quality Assurance
CHR: Alison Keri, Director Human Resources
CNO: Lisa Thompson, MSN, R.N., Director of Nursing
Web address: www.hch-ks.org
Control: Other not–for–profit (including NFP Corporation) **Service**: General medical and surgical

Staffed Beds: 25 **Admissions**: 912 **Census**: 10 **Outpatient Visits**: 34394 **Births**: 80 **Total Expense ($000)**: 22586 **Payroll Expense ($000)**: 9302 **Personnel**: 223

HILL CITY—Graham County

★ **GRAHAM COUNTY HOSPITAL (171325)**, 304 West Prout Street, Zip 67642–1435; tel. 785/421–2121, **A**10 18 **F**3 11 34 40 50 53 59 64 65 67 68 81 82 84 93 107 114 127 128 133 148 149 154
Primary Contact: Melissa Atkins, CPA, Chief Executive Officer
CHR: Donella Belleau, Director Human Resources
Web address: www.grahamcountyhospital.org
Control: County, Government, nonfederal **Service**: General medical and surgical

Staffed Beds: 20 **Admissions**: 268 **Census**: 4 **Outpatient Visits**: 862 **Births**: 0 **Total Expense ($000)**: 7004 **Payroll Expense ($000)**: 3514 **Personnel**: 64

HILLSBORO—Marion County

HILLSBORO COMMUNITY HOSPITAL (171357), 701 South Main Street, Zip 67063–1553; tel. 620/947–3114, (Nonreporting) **A**10 18 **S** Rural Community Hospitals of America, Kansas City, MO
Primary Contact: Marion Regier, Chief Executive Officer
COO: Johna Magnuson, Director Nursing
CIO: Marsha Setzkorn–Meyer, Director Public Relations and Marketing
CHR: Wendy McCarty, Director Human Resources
Web address: www.hchks.com
Control: Corporation, Investor–owned (for–profit) **Service**: General medical and surgical

Staffed Beds: 10

HOISINGTON—Barton County

★ **CLARA BARTON HOSPITAL (171333)**, 250 West Ninth Street, Zip 67544–1706; tel. 620/653–2114, **A**10 18 **F**11 15 28 40 56 57 59 64 77 81 85 92 93 97 107 114 127 128 133 148 **P**6
Primary Contact: James Blackwell, President and Chief Executive Officer
CMO: Nathan Knackstedt, D.O., Chief of Staff
CHR: John Moshier, Director Human Resources
CNO: Jane Schepman, Vice President and Chief Nursing Officer
Web address: www.clarabartonhospital.org
Control: Other not–for–profit (including NFP Corporation) **Service**: General medical and surgical

Staffed Beds: 23 **Admissions**: 554 **Census**: 9 **Outpatient Visits**: 45639 **Births**: 0 **Total Expense ($000)**: 21668 **Payroll Expense ($000)**: 10438 **Personnel**: 207

Many Facility Codes have changed. Please refer to the AHA Guide Code Chart.

© 2018 AHA Guide

HOLTON—Jackson County

★ **HOLTON COMMUNITY HOSPITAL (171319)**, 1110 Columbine Drive,
Zip 66436–8824; tel. 785/364–2116, **A**10 18 **F**3 11 13 15 18 28 29 34 40 43
45 50 57 59 62 63 64 65 75 77 79 81 82 87 93 97 107 114 119 127 130 131
132 133 135 146 147 148
Primary Contact: Carrie L. Saia, Chief Executive Officer
CFO: Bart Kenton, Chief Financial Officer
CMO: Joel Hutchsin, M.D., Chief Medical Staff
CIO: Holli Peters, Director Health Information Management
CHR: Gretchen Snavely, Director Human Resources
CNO: Mandy Bontrager, Director Nursing
Web address: www.holtonhospital.com
Control: Other not–for–profit (including NFP Corporation) **Service:** General
medical and surgical

Staffed Beds: 12 **Admissions:** 292 **Census:** 4 **Outpatient Visits:** 47765
Births: 41 **Total Expense ($000):** 14920 **Payroll Expense ($000):** 7424
Personnel: 154

HORTON—Brown County

HORTON COMMUNITY HOSPITAL (171320), 240 West 18th Street,
Zip 66439–1245; tel. 785/486–2642, **A**10 18 **F**7 18 28 29 40 45 64 75 81
82 89 93 98 107 114 119 127 128 133 **P**6 **S** Rural Community Hospitals of
America, Kansas City, MO
Primary Contact: James D. Noble, Chief Executive Officer
CFO: Sue Kidd, Chief Financial Officer
CMO: William Buck, Chief of Staff
CHR: Barbara McClain, Human Resources
CNO: Ty Compton, Chief Nursing Officer
Web address: www.horton–hospital.com
Control: Corporation, Investor–owned (for–profit) **Service:** General medical and
surgical

Staffed Beds: 25 **Admissions:** 165 **Census:** 2 **Outpatient Visits:** 5185
Births: 0 **Total Expense ($000):** 5080 **Payroll Expense ($000):** 2814
Personnel: 57

HOXIE—Sheridan County

SHERIDAN COUNTY HEALTH COMPLEX (171347), 826 18th Street,
Zip 67740–0167, Mailing Address: P.O. Box 167, Zip 67740–0167;
tel. 785/675–3281, (Total facility includes 32 beds in nursing home–type unit) **A**10
18 **F**7 10 11 29 34 35 40 45 50 53 56 57 59 64 66 67 68 69 75 81 85 87 93
107 115 119 130 133 **P**6
Primary Contact: Niceta Farber, Chief Executive Officer
CFO: Michael O'Dell, Chief Financial Officer
CMO: Victor Nemechek, M.D., Chief of Staff and Chief Medical Officer
CHR: Shelby Moss, Human Resource Officer
CNO: Hannah Schoendaler, Chief Nursing Officer
Web address: www.sheridancountyhospital.com
Control: County, Government, nonfederal **Service:** General medical and surgical

Staffed Beds: 50 **Admissions:** 293 **Census:** 32 **Outpatient Visits:** 5836
Births: 0 **Total Expense ($000):** 11305 **Payroll Expense ($000):** 5753
Personnel: 136

HUGOTON—Stevens County

★ **STEVENS COUNTY HOSPITAL (171335)**, 1006 South Jackson Street,
Zip 67951–2858, Mailing Address: P.O. Box 10, Zip 67951–0010;
tel. 620/544–8511, (Total facility includes 77 beds in nursing home–type unit) **A**10
18 **F**3 11 15 28 29 30 40 45 50 57 59 67 68 81 93 107 119 125 127 128 130
132 133 135 143 147 149
Primary Contact: Linda Stalcup, Chief Executive Officer
CMO: Samer Al–hashmi, M.D., Chief Medical Staff
Web address: www.stevenscountyhospital.com/
Control: County, Government, nonfederal **Service:** General medical and surgical

Staffed Beds: 94 **Admissions:** 239 **Census:** 73 **Outpatient Visits:** 11413
Births: 0 **Total Expense ($000):** 16825 **Payroll Expense ($000):** 7985
Personnel: 193

HUTCHINSON—Reno County

☒ △ **HUTCHINSON REGIONAL MEDICAL CENTER (170020)**, 1701 East 23rd
Avenue, Zip 67502–1191; tel. 620/665–2000, **A**1 7 10 **F**3 7 11 13 18 20 22 24
26 28 29 30 31 34 35 40 43 45 47 48 49 50 51 53 57 60 64 68 70 74 76 77
78 79 81 82 83 85 87 89 90 93 98 102 106 107 108 111 114 115 119 120
121 123 126 128 129 130 143 146 148 154 **P**6
Primary Contact: Ken Johnson, President and Chief Executive Officer
CFO: Cassie Dolen, Vice President Finance and Chief Financial Officer
CMO: Thomas Smith, M.D., Vice President Medical Affairs
CIO: Calvin Wright, Chief Information Officer
CHR: Kevin Chiles, Vice President Human Resources
CNO: Julie R. Ward, MSN, R.N., Vice President Patient Care Services
Web address: www.hutchregional.com
Control: Other not–for–profit (including NFP Corporation) **Service:** General
medical and surgical

Staffed Beds: 146 **Admissions:** 6184 **Census:** 70 **Outpatient Visits:**
116838 **Births:** 597 **Total Expense ($000):** 122704 **Payroll Expense
($000):** 42791 **Personnel:** 857

SUMMIT SURGICAL (170198), 1818 East 23rd Avenue, Zip 67502–1106;
tel. 620/663–4800, **A**10 **F**29 45 64 77 79 81 85 87 93 94 **P**2
Primary Contact: Ann Hentzen Page, M.D., Chief Executive Officer
COO: Nancy Corwin, Chief Operating Officer
CMO: Ann Hentzen Page, M.D., Medical Director
CNO: Nancy Corwin, Chief Nursing Officer
Web address: www.summitks.com/index_surgical.htm
Control: Corporation, Investor–owned (for–profit) **Service:** Surgical

Staffed Beds: 10 **Admissions:** 254 **Census:** 1 **Outpatient Visits:** 21367
Births: 0 **Total Expense ($000):** 7333 **Payroll Expense ($000):** 2080
Personnel: 22

IOLA—Allen County

☒ **ALLEN COUNTY REGIONAL HOSPITAL (171373)**, 3066 N. Kentucky St,
Zip 66749, Mailing Address: P.O. Box 540, Zip 66749–0540; tel. 620/365–1000,
A1 10 18 **F**3 11 13 29 30 31 34 35 40 43 45 57 59 62 63 64 65 75 76 77 78
79 81 82 84 85 86 89 92 103 104 107 115 119 127 129 130 133 146 148
149
Primary Contact: Marion A. Thompson, FACHE, Chief Executive Officer
CFO: Larry Peterson, Chief Financial Officer
CMO: Brian Wolfe, Chief of Staff
CHR: Paula Sell, Director Human Resources
CNO: Patty McGuffin, R.N., Chief Nursing Officer
Web address: www.allencountyhospital.com
Control: County, Government, nonfederal **Service:** General medical and surgical

Staffed Beds: 25 **Admissions:** 717 **Census:** 10 **Outpatient Visits:** 19688
Births: 74 **Total Expense ($000):** 24763 **Payroll Expense ($000):** 7513
Personnel: 155

JETMORE—Hodgeman County

★ **HODGEMAN COUNTY HEALTH CENTER (171369)**, 809 Bramley Street,
Zip 67854–9320, Mailing Address: P.O. Box 310, Zip 67854–0310;
tel. 620/357–8361, (Total facility includes 25 beds in nursing home–type unit) **A**10
18 **F**3 40 53 67 81 107 114 125 127 130 133 143 **P**4
Primary Contact: Phil Ginder, Chief Executive Officer
Web address: www.hchonline.org
Control: County, Government, nonfederal **Service:** General medical and surgical

Staffed Beds: 38 **Admissions:** 264 **Census:** 28 **Outpatient Visits:** 4283
Births: 0 **Total Expense ($000):** 8291 **Payroll Expense ($000):** 3812
Personnel: 79

JOHNSON—Stanton County

STANTON COUNTY HOSPITAL (171343), 404 North Chestnut Street,
Zip 67855–5001, Mailing Address: P.O. Box 779, Zip 67855–0779;
tel. 620/492–6250, (Total facility includes 25 beds in nursing home–type unit) **A**10
18 **F**3 11 34 35 40 41 45 50 54 56 57 59 64 68 75 76 81 82 86 87 89 93
97 107 114 127 130 131 133 143 154 **P**6
Primary Contact: Jay Tusten, Chief Executive Officer
CFO: Robert Nahmensen, Chief Financial Officer and Chief Operations Officer
CMO: Bill Troup, M.D., Chief of Staff
CIO: Marco Medina, Chief Information Officer
CHR: Camille Davidson, Director Human Resources
CNO: Marianne Mills, R.N., Chairperson
Web address: www.stantoncountyhospital.com
Control: County, Government, nonfederal **Service:** General medical and surgical

Staffed Beds: 40 **Admissions:** 96 **Census:** 22 **Outpatient Visits:** 12279
Births: 20 **Total Expense ($000):** 7790 **Payroll Expense ($000):** 4604
Personnel: 87

JUNCTION CITY—Geary County

☒ **GEARY COMMUNITY HOSPITAL (170074)**, 1102 St Mary's Road,
Zip 66441–4196, Mailing Address: P.O. Box 490, Zip 66441–0490;
tel. 785/238–4131, (Nonreporting) **A**1 10
Primary Contact: Joseph Stratton, FACHE, Chief Executive Officer
CFO: William Kloppe, Chief Financial Officer
CMO: Jimmy Jenkins, M.D., Chief Medical Officer
CIO: Kyle Ibarra, Director Information Systems
CHR: Loren Streit, Director Human Resources
CNO: Dawn M Engel, Chief Nursing Officer
Web address: www.gchks.org
Control: County, Government, nonfederal **Service**: General medical and surgical

Staffed Beds: 49

☒ **IRWIN ARMY COMMUNITY HOSPITAL**, 600 Caisson Hill Road,
Zip 66442–7037; tel. 785/239–7000, (Nonreporting) **A**1 3 5 **S** Department of the
Army, Office of the Surgeon General, Falls Church, VA
Primary Contact: Colonel Risa Ware, Commander
CMO: Lieutenant Colonel Mark S Ochoa, M.D., Deputy Commander, Clinical
Services
CIO: David Dougherty, Chief Information Management Officer
CHR: Hope Brunton, Chief Manpower Branch
Web address: www.iach.amedd.army.mil
Control: Army, Government, federal **Service**: General medical and surgical

Staffed Beds: 44

KANSAS CITY—Wyandotte County

☐ **KVC PRAIRIE RIDGE PSYCHIATRIC HOSPITAL**, 4300 Brenner Drive,
Zip 66104–1163; tel. 913/334–0294, (Nonreporting) **A**1 5
Primary Contact: Jason R. Hooper, President and Chief Executive Officer
COO: Ryan Speier, Vice President Administration
CMO: Vishal Adma, M.D., Medical Director
Web address: www.kvc.org
Control: Other not–for–profit (including NFP Corporation) **Service**: Children's
hospital psychiatric

Staffed Beds: 100

☒ **PROVIDENCE MEDICAL CENTER (170146)**, 8929 Parallel Parkway,
Zip 66112–1689; tel. 913/596–4000, (Total facility includes 45 beds in nursing
home–type unit) **A**1 10 **F**3 13 15 17 18 20 22 24 28 29 30 31 34 35 40 41 44
45 49 50 53 56 57 59 64 70 74 75 76 77 78 79 81 82 84 85 87 93 97 102
107 108 110 111 114 119 120 121 123 124 126 128 129 130 131 132 135
143 146 147 148 149 **P**6 **S** Prime Healthcare, Ontario, CA
Primary Contact: Karen Orr, Administrator and Chief Nursing Officer
CFO: David Dulny, Chief Financial Officer
CMO: Sabato Sisillo, M.D., Chief Medical Officer
CIO: Charles Soeken, Director Information Technology
CHR: Brenda Farwell, Director Human Resources
CNO: Karen Orr, Chief Nursing Officer
Web address: www.providencekc.com
Control: Individual, Investor–owned (for–profit) **Service**: General medical and
surgical

Staffed Beds: 215 Admissions: 9478 Census: 122 Outpatient Visits:
208401 Births: 485 Total Expense ($000): 155543 Payroll Expense
($000): 57871 Personnel: 903

☒ **SELECT SPECIALTY HOSPITAL–KANSAS CITY (172005)**, 1731 North 90th
Street, Zip 66112–1515; tel. 913/732–5900, (Nonreporting) **A**1 10 **S** Select
Medical Corporation, Mechanicsburg, PA
Primary Contact: Bridgette Hunter, Chief Executive Officer
Web address: www.selectspecialtyhospitals.com
Control: Corporation, Investor–owned (for–profit) **Service**: Acute long–term care
hospital

Staffed Beds: 40

☒ **THE UNIVERSITY OF KANSAS HOSPITAL (170040)**, 4000 Cambridge Street,
MS 3011, Zip 66160; tel. 913/588–5000, (Includes THE UNIVERSITY OF KANSAS
HOSPITAL – INDIAN CREEK CAMPUS, 10720 Nall Avenue, Overland Park, KS,
Zip 66211–1206; tel. 913/754–5000) **A**1 2 3 5 8 10 **F**3 5 8 9 11 12 13 15 16
17 18 20 22 24 25 26 27 28 29 30 31 32 34 35 36 37 38 39 40 41 43 44 45
46 47 48 49 50 51 52 54 55 56 57 58 59 60 61 63 64 65 68 70 71 72 74 75
76 77 78 79 80 81 82 83 84 85 86 87 88 89 90 92 93 96 97 98 99 100 101
102 103 104 105 107 108 110 111 114 115 116 117 118 119 120 121 123
124 126 129 130 131 132 135 136 137 138 139 141 142 144 145 146 147
148 149 154 **P**6 **S** The University of Kansas Health System, Kansas City, KS
Primary Contact: Bob Page, Chief Executive Officer
COO: Tammy Peterman, R.N., MS, Executive Vice President, Chief Operating
Officer and Chief Nursing Officer
CFO: Bill Marting, Senior Vice President and Chief Financial Officer
CMO: Lou Wetzel, M.D., Chief of Staff
CIO: Chris Hansen, Senior Vice President Ambulatory Services and Chief
Information Officer
CHR: Alisa Ford, Vice President Human Resources
CNO: Tammy Peterman, R.N., MS, Executive Vice President, Chief Operating
Officer and Chief Nursing Officer
Web address: www.kumed.com
Control: Hospital district or authority, Government, nonfederal **Service**: General
medical and surgical

Staffed Beds: 792 Admissions: 38245 Census: 600 Outpatient Visits:
1321558 Births: 1989 Total Expense ($000): 1969345 Payroll Expense
($000): 894929 Personnel: 10485

KINGMAN—Kingman County

★ **KINGMAN COMMUNITY HOSPITAL (171378)**, 750 Avenue D West,
Zip 67068–0376; tel. 620/532–3147, **A**10 18 **F**3 11 15 17 18 28 29 31 34 35
40 45 50 54 56 57 59 64 70 75 77 78 81 86 87 89 90 93 97 107 114 119
127 128 129 130 132 133 145 146 148 **P**6
Primary Contact: Shannan Flach, Chief Executive Officer
CFO: Kent Hudson, Chief Financial Officer
CIO: Jay Gehring, Director Information Systems
CHR: Nancy Stucky, Director Human Resources and Public Relations
CNO: Nita McFarland, Director of Nursing
Web address: www.kchks.com
Control: Other not–for–profit (including NFP Corporation) **Service**: General
medical and surgical

Staffed Beds: 25 Admissions: 483 Census: 8 Outpatient Visits: 19992
Births: 0 Total Expense ($000): 10861 Payroll Expense ($000): 5488
Personnel: 104

KINSLEY—Edwards County

★ **EDWARDS COUNTY MEDICAL CENTER (171317)**, 620 West Eighth
Street, Zip 67547–2329, Mailing Address: P.O. Box 99, Zip 67547–0099;
tel. 620/659–3621, (Nonreporting) **A**10 18
Primary Contact: Jimmie W. Hansel, Ph.D., Chief Executive Officer
CHR: Tammy K Lampe, Director Human Resources
Web address: www.edwardscohospital.com
Control: County, Government, nonfederal **Service**: General medical and surgical

Staffed Beds: 22

KIOWA—Barber County

★ **KIOWA DISTRICT HEALTHCARE (171331)**, 810 Drumm Street,
Zip 67070–1626, Mailing Address: P.O. Box 184, Zip 67070–0184;
tel. 620/825–4131, (Total facility includes 29 beds in nursing home–type unit) **A**10
18 **F**1 2 3 4 12 16 17 34 40 41 45 55 56 57 59 64 65 67 69 70 72 73 80 81
84 85 87 88 89 90 91 92 93 97 98 107 114 119 127 128 133 148 150 154
P6
Primary Contact: Robert Whitaker, Chief Executive Officer
CFO: Robin Lewis, Chief Financial Officer
CMO: Paul Wilhelm, M.D., Chief of Staff
CHR: Tara Girty, Director Human Resources
Web address: www.k–d–h.com
Control: Hospital district or authority, Government, nonfederal **Service**: General
medical and surgical

Staffed Beds: 39 Admissions: 371 Census: 19 Outpatient Visits: 6302
Births: 0 Total Expense ($000): 8491 Payroll Expense ($000): 3188
Personnel: 67

LA CROSSE—Rush County

★ **RUSH COUNTY MEMORIAL HOSPITAL (171342)**, 801 Locust Street, Zip 67548–9673, Mailing Address: P.O. Box 520, Zip 67548–0520; tel. 785/222–2545, **A**10 18 **F**3 34 40 45 53 59 64 67 77 82 93 97 107 114 119 127 128 133 **P**6
Primary Contact: Brenda Legleiter, R.N., Chief Executive Officer
CFO: Jane Oborny, Chief Financial Officer
CMO: Harley Calvin, D.O., Chief Medical Officer
CHR: Charlene Goodman, Director Human Resources
Web address: www.rushcountymemorialhospital.com
Control: County, Government, nonfederal **Service**: General medical and surgical

**Staffed Beds: 25 Admissions: 178 Census: 15 Outpatient Visits: 13362
Births: 0 Total Expense ($000): 5584 Payroll Expense ($000): 2584**

LAKIN—Kearny County

★ **KEARNY COUNTY HOSPITAL (171313)**, 500 Thorpe Street, Zip 67860–9625; tel. 620/355–7111, (Total facility includes 75 beds in nursing home–type unit) **A**10 18 **F**2 3 6 10 13 15 28 29 34 35 40 45 50 56 57 58 59 62 64 67 68 69 75 76 79 81 82 85 86 87 89 93 97 107 111 114 119 125 127 128 130 131 132 133 143 149 **P**6
Primary Contact: Benjamin Anderson, Chief Executive Officer and Administrator
COO: Shari Campbell, Chief Operating Officer
CFO: Kelly Ann Speckman, Chief Financial Officer
CMO: Arlo Reimer, M.D., Chief of Staff
CIO: Lisa Kay–Garcia, Chief Information Officer
CHR: Laci Williams, Director Human Resources
CNO: Susan D Stingley, Chief Nursing Officer
Web address: www.kearnycountyhospital.com
Control: County, Government, nonfederal **Service**: General medical and surgical

**Staffed Beds: 100 Admissions: 579 Census: 76 Outpatient Visits: 44926
Births: 284 Total Expense ($000): 24029 Payroll Expense ($000): 12733
Personnel: 250**

LARNED—Pawnee County

☐ **LARNED STATE HOSPITAL (174006)**, 1301 Kansas Highway 264, Zip 67550; tel. 620/285–2131, **A**1 10 **F**3 30 50 53 57 68 75 77 86 87 97 98 100 101 102 103 130 132 135 143 146 149 154
Primary Contact: Thomas Kinlen, Superintendent
COO: Steve Spain, Chief Operating Officer
CMO: Sayed Jehan, M.D., Interim Medical Director
CIO: Sid Smith, Director Information Resources
CHR: Kerri Barnard, Director Human Resources
CNO: Holly Hertel, Director Nursing
Web address: www.larnedstatehospital.org
Control: State, Government, nonfederal **Service**: Psychiatric

**Staffed Beds: 532 Admissions: 1362 Census: 485 Outpatient Visits: 0
Births: 0 Total Expense ($000): 63949 Payroll Expense ($000): 34626
Personnel: 637**

★ **PAWNEE VALLEY COMMUNITY HOSPITAL (171345)**, 923 Carroll Avenue, Zip 67550–2429; tel. 620/285–3161, **A**10 18 **F**3 11 28 29 30 34 40 43 45 46 57 68 77 81 82 84 85 86 87 93 94 102 107 111 115 127 129 130 131 132 133 135 147 148 149 **P**6 **S** The University of Kansas Health System, Kansas City, KS
Primary Contact: Kendra Barker, Administrator
COO: Bryce A Young, Chief Operating Officer
CFO: George Harms, Chief Financial Officer
CMO: David Sanger, M.D., Chief Medical Officer
CHR: Bruce Whittington, Vice President Human Resources
Web address: www.pawneevalleyhospital.com
Control: County, Government, nonfederal **Service**: General medical and surgical

**Staffed Beds: 22 Admissions: 209 Census: 4 Outpatient Visits: 14836
Births: 0 Total Expense ($000): 13213 Payroll Expense ($000): 6839
Personnel: 102**

LAWRENCE—Douglas County

⊞ **LAWRENCE MEMORIAL HOSPITAL (170137)**, 325 Maine Street, Zip 66044–1360; tel. 785/505–5000, (Total facility includes 17 beds in nursing home–type unit) **A**1 3 5 10 20 **F**3 11 13 15 18 19 20 22 26 28 29 30 31 34 35 38 39 40 43 44 45 49 50 51 54 55 56 57 59 61 64 65 67 69 70 73 74 75 76 77 78 79 81 82 84 85 86 87 89 90 93 94 96 97 100 102 107 110 111 114 115 118 119 120 124 126 128 130 131 132 135 145 146 147 148 154 **P**6 8
Primary Contact: Russell W. Johnson, President and Chief Executive Officer
COO: Karen J Shumate, R.N., Chief Operating Officer
CFO: Joe Pedley, CPA, Vice President and Chief Financial Officer
CIO: Michael Williams, Chief Information Officer
CHR: Carolyn Bowmer
CNO: Traci Hoopingarner, R.N., Chief Nursing Officer
Web address: www.lmh.org
Control: City, Government, nonfederal **Service**: General medical and surgical

**Staffed Beds: 142 Admissions: 6919 Census: 67 Outpatient Visits:
207349 Births: 1052 Total Expense ($000): 239773 Payroll Expense
($000): 98616 Personnel: 1588**

LEAVENWORTH—Leavenworth County

⊞ **SAINT JOHN HOSPITAL (170009)**, 3500 South Fourth Street, Zip 66048–5043; tel. 913/680–6000, **A**1 10 **F**3 15 18 29 30 34 40 44 45 46 50 54 56 57 59 64 68 70 74 75 77 84 85 87 93 98 100 103 107 114 119 130 133 146 148 149 154 **P**6 **S** Prime Healthcare, Ontario, CA
Primary Contact: Paula Ellis, Administrator
CFO: David Dulny, Chief Financial Officer
CMO: Sabato Sisillo, M.D., Chief Medical Officer
CIO: Charles Soeken, Director Information Technology
CHR: Brenda Farwell, Director Human Resources
CNO: Jodi Fincher, Vice President Patient Care Services
Web address: www.providence–health.org/sjh
Control: Individual, Investor–owned (for–profit) **Service**: General medical and surgical

**Staffed Beds: 58 Admissions: 1548 Census: 27 Outpatient Visits: 26665
Births: 0 Total Expense ($000): 27209 Payroll Expense ($000): 10843
Personnel: 151**

⊞ **SAINT LUKE'S CUSHING HOSPITAL (170133)**, 711 Marshall Street, Zip 66048–3235; tel. 913/684–1100, **A**1 10 **F**3 11 13 15 18 28 29 31 34 35 38 40 44 45 50 57 59 64 65 68 70 74 75 76 77 78 79 81 82 84 85 86 87 89 93 94 100 102 107 108 110 111 115 119 129 130 131 132 135 141 146 149 154 **S** Saint Luke's Health System, Kansas City, MO
Primary Contact: Bobby Olm–Shipman, President and Chief Executive Officer
CFO: Jackie Martin, Chief Financial Officer
CMO: Nicholas Brockert, President
CHR: Donna Kunz, System Director Human Resources
CNO: Karin Sundblom, MSN, R.N., Chief Nursing Officer
Web address: www.saintlukeshealthsystem.org/locations/saint–lukes–cushing–hospital
Control: Other not–for–profit (including NFP Corporation) **Service**: General medical and surgical

**Staffed Beds: 25 Admissions: 863 Census: 7 Outpatient Visits: 37292
Births: 149 Total Expense ($000): 36451 Payroll Expense ($000): 12063
Personnel: 198**

VETERANS AFFAIRS EASTERN KANSAS HEALTH CARE SYSTEM–DWIGHT D. EISENHOWER VETERANS AFFAIRS MEDICAL CENTER See Veterans Affairs Eastern Kansas Health Care System, Topeka

LEAWOOD—Johnson County

☐ **DOCTOR'S HOSPITAL (170194)**, 4901 College Boulevard, Zip 66211–1602; tel. 913/529–1801, **A**1 10 **F**39 79 81 82 111 **P**5
Primary Contact: Phil Harness, Chief Executive Officer
Web address: www.dshospital.net
Control: Partnership, Investor–owned (for–profit) **Service**: General medical and surgical

**Staffed Beds: 9 Admissions: 87 Census: 1 Outpatient Visits: 12714
Births: 0 Total Expense ($000): 18391 Payroll Expense ($000): 2611
Personnel: 45**

Hospital, Medicare Provider Number, Address, Telephone, Approval, Facility, and Physician Codes, Health Care System

★ American Hospital Association (AHA) membership
☐ The Joint Commission accreditation
○ Healthcare Facilities Accreditation Program
◇ DNV Healthcare Inc. accreditation
⇑ Center for Improvement in Healthcare Quality Accreditation
△ Commission on Accreditation of Rehabilitation Facilities (CARF) accreditation

KS

KANSAS CITY ORTHOPAEDIC INSTITUTE (170188), 3651 College Boulevard, Zip 66211–1910; tel. 913/338–4100, **A**3 5 10 **F**29 77 79 81 82 93 111 **P**5
Primary Contact: Charles E. Rhoades, M.D., Chief Executive Officer
CIO: Jim Leveling, Director Information Technology
CHR: Laura Sinclair, Director Human Resources
Web address: www.kcoi.com
Control: Partnership, Investor–owned (for–profit) **Service:** Orthopedic

Staffed Beds: 9 **Admissions:** 982 **Census:** 5 **Outpatient Visits:** 32011
Births: 0 **Personnel:** 123

SAINT LUKE'S COMMUNITY HOSPITAL AT LEAWOOD, 13200 State Line Road, Zip 66209; tel. 913/222–8380, (Nonreporting) **S** Saint Luke's Health System, Kansas City, MO
Primary Contact: Teresa Collins, R.N., Chief Executive Officer and Chief Nursing Officer
Web address: www.saintlukescommunityhospital.org
Control: Church operated, Nongovernment, not–for–profit **Service:** General medical and surgical

Staffed Beds: 8

LENEXA—Johnson County

☐ **MINIMALLY INVASIVE SURGERY HOSPITAL (170199)**, 11217 Lakeview Avenue, Zip 66219–1399; tel. 913/322–7401, **A**1 10 **F**3 18 26 31 45 64 68 70 78 81 82 85 86 107 111 115 119 129 **P**6
Primary Contact: Parajeet Sabharrwal, Chief Executive Officer
Web address: www.mishhospital.com
Control: Corporation, Investor–owned (for–profit) **Service:** Surgical

Staffed Beds: 9 **Admissions:** 350 **Census:** 1 **Outpatient Visits:** 5246
Births: 0 **Personnel:** 29

LEOTI—Wichita County

★ **WICHITA COUNTY HEALTH CENTER (171306)**, 211 East Earl Street, Zip 67861–9620; tel. 620/375–2233, (Total facility includes 17 beds in nursing home–type unit) **A**10 18 **F**2 3 11 29 34 35 40 41 45 50 56 57 59 64 69 75 77 86 87 93 97 102 107 119 127 130 133 135 146 148 **P**6 **S** Great Plains Health Alliance, Inc., Wichita, KS
Primary Contact: Teresa Clark, Chief Executive Officer and Administrator
CFO: Janice Campas, Chief Financial Officer
CMO: Jeffrey Alpert, M.D., Medical Director
CHR: Patti Whalen, Manager Human Resources
Web address: www.wichitacountyhealthcenter.com
Control: County, Government, nonfederal **Service:** General medical and surgical

Staffed Beds: 42 **Admissions:** 166 **Census:** 27 **Outpatient Visits:** 5955
Births: 0 **Total Expense ($000):** 8802 **Payroll Expense ($000):** 3893
Personnel: 78

LIBERAL—Seward County

☐ **SOUTHWEST MEDICAL CENTER (170068)**, 315 West 15th Street, Zip 67901–2455, Mailing Address: Box 1340, Zip 67905–1340; tel. 620/624–1651, (Total facility includes 18 beds in nursing home–type unit) **A**1 10 **F**3 11 13 15 28 29 31 34 40 45 48 49 57 59 68 70 73 75 76 77 79 81 85 87 89 93 96 98 103 107 108 110 111 114 118 119 128 129 130 131 145 146 147 148 149 154
Primary Contact: William Ermann, President and Chief Executive Officer
CFO: Amber Williams, Vice President and Chief Financial Officer
CHR: Lisa L Mathes, Human Resources Director
CNO: Jo L Harrison, Vice President of Patient Care Services
Web address: www.swmedcenter.com
Control: County, Government, nonfederal **Service:** General medical and surgical

Staffed Beds: 101 **Admissions:** 2338 **Census:** 21 **Outpatient Visits:** 52149
Births: 754 **Total Expense ($000):** 49977 **Payroll Expense ($000):** 22484
Personnel: 414

LINCOLN—Lincoln County

LINCOLN COUNTY HOSPITAL (171360), 624 North Second Street, Zip 67455–1738, Mailing Address: P.O. Box 406, Zip 67455–0406; tel. 785/524–4403, **A**10 18 **F**3 11 15 34 40 57 69 107 110 111 112 114 119 127 129 133 **P**6
Primary Contact: Steven L. Granzow, Chief Executive Officer
CFO: Tawnya Seitz, Chief Financial Officer
CNO: Christa Haesemeyer, Chief Nursing Officer
Web address: www.lincolncountyhospital.net
Control: County, Government, nonfederal **Service:** General medical and surgical

Staffed Beds: 14 **Admissions:** 99 **Census:** 1 **Outpatient Visits:** 5519
Births: 0 **Total Expense ($000):** 8537 **Payroll Expense ($000):** 3214
Personnel: 68

LINDSBORG—Mcpherson County

★ **LINDSBORG COMMUNITY HOSPITAL (171358)**, 605 West Lincoln Street, Zip 67456–2328; tel. 785/227–3308, **A**10 18 **F**3 28 29 36 40 53 57 59 62 64 65 67 81 87 93 97 107 115 119 128 130 133 144 **P**6 **S** Salina Regional Health Center, Salina, KS
Primary Contact: Larry VanDerWege, Administrator
CFO: Laraine Gengler, Chief Financial Officer
CIO: Jeremy Snapp, Director Information Systems
CHR: Brad Malm, Director Human Resources and Education
CNO: Beth Hedberg, R.N., Director Nursing
Web address: www.lindsborghospital.org
Control: Other not–for–profit (including NFP Corporation) **Service:** General medical and surgical

Staffed Beds: 21 **Admissions:** 181 **Census:** 4 **Outpatient Visits:** 21400
Births: 0 **Total Expense ($000):** 10725 **Payroll Expense ($000):** 4816
Personnel: 96

LYONS—Rice County

★ **HOSPITAL DISTRICT NO 1 OF RICE COUNTY (171330)**, 619 South Clark Street, Zip 67554–3003, Mailing Address: P.O. Box 828, Zip 67554–0828; tel. 620/257–5173, **A**10 18 **F**3 13 28 29 30 34 35 40 43 45 65 75 77 81 93 107 125 127 130 132 133 143
Primary Contact: George M. Stover, Chief Executive Officer
CFO: Terry Pound, Chief Financial Officer
CMO: Kristina Darnauer, M.D., Chief of Staff
CNO: Judy Hogdson, R.N., Chief Nursing Officer
Web address: www.ricecountyhospital.com
Control: Hospital district or authority, Government, nonfederal **Service:** General medical and surgical

Staffed Beds: 25 **Admissions:** 258 **Census:** 13 **Outpatient Visits:** 17414
Births: 75 **Total Expense ($000):** 14775 **Payroll Expense ($000):** 7239
Personnel: 123

MANHATTAN—Riley County

MANHATTAN SURGICAL (170190), 1829 College Avenue, Zip 66502–3381; tel. 785/776–5100, (Nonreporting) **A**10
Primary Contact: Christopher R. Stipe, FACHE, Chief Executive Officer
Web address: www.manhattansurgical.com
Control: Corporation, Investor–owned (for–profit) **Service:** Surgical

Staffed Beds: 13

★ ○ **VIA CHRISTI HOSPITAL MANHATTAN, INC. (170142)**, 1823 College Avenue, Zip 66502–3346; tel. 785/776–3322, **A**10 11 19 **F**3 11 12 13 15 18 22 28 29 30 31 34 35 37 40 41 44 45 49 50 51 60 67 70 76 77 79 81 82 83 84 85 86 87 89 90 92 94 95 96 102 104 107 108 109 110 111 115 119 126 129 130 132 133 145 146 147 148 149 154 **S** Ascension Healthcare, Saint Louis, MO
Primary Contact: Robert C. Copple, FACHE, Senior Administrator
CFO: James Fraser, Administrator Finance
CIO: Andy Gagnon, Manager Information Technology
CHR: Renee Reed, Director Human Resources
CNO: Jennifer Goehring, R.N., Assistant Chief Nursing Officer
Web address: www.viachristi.org/manhattan
Control: Other not–for–profit (including NFP Corporation) **Service:** General medical and surgical

Staffed Beds: 96 **Admissions:** 4503 **Census:** 42 **Outpatient Visits:** 101776
Births: 1132 **Total Expense ($000):** 91738 **Payroll Expense ($000):** 31024
Personnel: 396

MANKATO—Jewell County

JEWELL COUNTY HOSPITAL (171309), 100 Crestvue Avenue, Zip 66956–2407, Mailing Address: P.O. Box 327, Zip 66956–0327; tel. 785/378–3137, **A**10 18 **F**2 3 29 40 50 64 75 77 87 93 107 127 128 130 133 148 **P**6
Primary Contact: Doyle L. McKimmy, FACHE, Chief Executive Officer
COO: Eric Borden, Chief Operating Officer and Chief Financial Officer
CFO: Eric Borden, Chief Operating Officer and Chief Financial Officer
Web address: www.jewellcountyhospital.com
Control: County, Government, nonfederal **Service:** General medical and surgical

Staffed Beds: 25 **Admissions:** 100 **Census:** 19 **Outpatient Visits:** 19003
Births: 0 **Total Expense ($000):** 5454 **Payroll Expense ($000):** 2767
Personnel: 79

MARION—Marion County

ST. LUKE HOSPITAL AND LIVING CENTER (171356), 535 South Freeborn, Zip 66861–1256; tel. 620/382–2177, (Nonreporting) **A**10 18
Primary Contact: Jeremy Ensey, Chief Executive Officer
CFO: Bev Reid, Chief Financial Officer
CMO: Don Hodson, M.D., Chief Medical Officer
CIO: Jeff Methvin, Manager Information Technology
CHR: Sharon Zogelman, Director Human Resources
Web address: www.slhmarion.org
Control: Hospital district or authority, Government, nonfederal **Service:** General medical and surgical

Staffed Beds: 37

MARYSVILLE—Marshall County

★ **COMMUNITY MEMORIAL HEALTHCARE (171363)**, 708 North 18th Street, Zip 66508–1338; tel. 785/562–2311, **A**10 18 **F**3 13 15 28 29 30 34 35 40 43 45 47 50 57 59 62 64 68 69 75 76 77 81 85 87 93 97 107 108 114 119 127 128 129 130 131 132 133 135 146 147 148 **P**6
Primary Contact: Curtis R. Hawkinson, Chief Executive Officer
CFO: Therese Landoll, Interim Chief Financial Officer
CMO: John Haefele, M.D., Chief Medical Officer
CIO: Colleen Behrens, Director Information Technology
CHR: Jessie Schneider, Director Human Resources
CNO: Diane Luebcke, R.N., Director Nursing
Web address: www.cmhcare.org
Control: Other not–for–profit (including NFP Corporation) **Service:** General medical and surgical

Staffed Beds: 25 Admissions: 736 Census: 9 Outpatient Visits: 26782 Births: 63 Total Expense ($000): 22168 Payroll Expense ($000): 9816 Personnel: 190

MCPHERSON—McPherson County

★ **MCPHERSON HOSPITAL (170105)**, 1000 Hospital Drive, Zip 67460–2326; tel. 620/241–2250, **A**10 **F**3 7 11 13 15 28 29 34 35 40 45 50 53 54 59 64 65 70 75 76 77 81 82 85 86 87 97 107 110 114 119 130 133 144 146 148 **P**6
Primary Contact: Terri Gehring, President and Chief Executive Officer
COO: Terri Gehring, Vice President Operations
CFO: George Halama, Vice President Finance
CHR: Cathy Dunham, Vice President Human Resources
CNO: Beth Worden, Director Nursing Services
Web address: www.mcphersonhospital.org
Control: Other not–for–profit (including NFP Corporation) **Service:** General medical and surgical

Staffed Beds: 33 Admissions: 849 Census: 8 Outpatient Visits: 67154 Births: 107 Total Expense ($000): 33806 Payroll Expense ($000): 14739 Personnel: 269

MEMORIAL HOSPITAL See Mcpherson Hospital

MEADE—Meade County

★ **MEADE DISTRICT HOSPITAL (171321)**, 510 East Carthage Street, Zip 67864–6401, Mailing Address: P.O. Box 820, Zip 67864–0820; tel. 620/873–2141, (Nonreporting) **A**10 18
Primary Contact: Tara Ramlochan, Chief Executive Officer
CIO: Matt Bobo, Chief Information Officer
Web address: www.meadehospital.com
Control: Hospital district or authority, Government, nonfederal **Service:** General medical and surgical

Staffed Beds: 65

MEDICINE LODGE—Barber County

MEDICINE LODGE MEMORIAL HOSPITAL (171334), 710 North Walnut Street, Zip 67104–1019; tel. 620/886–3771, **A**10 18 **F**3 7 11 40 44 45 56 64 81 93 107 119 127 128 133 148 154 **P**6 **S** Great Plains Health Alliance, Inc., Wichita, KS
Primary Contact: Kevin A. White, Administrator
CFO: Thomas G Lee, Chief Financial Officer
CHR: Johnnie Davis, Director Human Resources
CNO: Kathryn I. Burns, R.N., Director of Nursing
Web address: www.mlmh.net/
Control: Hospital district or authority, Government, nonfederal **Service:** General medical and surgical

Staffed Beds: 25 Admissions: 200 Census: 15 Outpatient Visits: 19963 Births: 0 Total Expense ($000): 10375 Payroll Expense ($000): 4873 Personnel: 89

MINNEAPOLIS—Ottawa County

★ **OTTAWA COUNTY HEALTH CENTER (171328)**, 215 East Eighth, Zip 67467–1902, Mailing Address: P.O. Box 290, Zip 67467–0290; tel. 785/392–2122, (Total facility includes 20 beds in nursing home–type unit) **A**10 18 **F**28 35 40 53 56 64 67 85 86 93 107 128 130 133 143 154 **S** Great Plains Health Alliance, Inc., Wichita, KS
Primary Contact: Jody Parks, Administrator
CFO: Cheryl Lanoue, Chief Financial Officer
CIO: Linda Wright, Director Information
CNO: Marlene Gawith, Director of Nursing
Web address: www.ottawacountyhealthcenter.com
Control: Other not–for–profit (including NFP Corporation) **Service:** General medical and surgical

Staffed Beds: 45 Admissions: 239 Census: 24 Outpatient Visits: 6207 Births: 0 Total Expense ($000): 6673 Payroll Expense ($000): 3036 Personnel: 73

MINNEOLA—Ford County

★ **MINNEOLA DISTRICT HOSPITAL (171368)**, 212 Main Street, Zip 67865–8511, Mailing Address: P.O. Box 127, Zip 67865–0127; tel. 620/885–4264, (Total facility includes 36 beds in nursing home–type unit) **A**10 18 **F**29 40 45 46 56 57 64 65 67 81 83 93 102 107 127 128 130 133 148 **P**6 **S** Great Plains Health Alliance, Inc., Wichita, KS
Primary Contact: Deborah Bruner, Chief Executive Officer and Administrator
CFO: Marion Zirger, Chief Financial Officer
CMO: Tony Luna, M.D., Chief of Staff
CHR: Vena Harris, Director Human Resources
CNO: Amanda Stout, Chief Nursing Officer
Web address: www.minneolahealthcare.com
Control: Hospital district or authority, Government, nonfederal **Service:** General medical and surgical

Staffed Beds: 54 Admissions: 314 Census: 36 Outpatient Visits: 24338 Births: 0 Total Expense ($000): 12693 Payroll Expense ($000): 5889 Personnel: 112

MOUNDRIDGE—Mcpherson County

★ **MERCY HOSPITAL (170075)**, 218 East Pack Street, Zip 67107–8815, Mailing Address: P.O. Box 180, Zip 67107–0180; tel. 620/345–6391, **A**10 **F**29 30 40 45 59 67 75 76 77 81 86 87 89 93 107 128 130 133 146 149 154
Primary Contact: Aaron Herbel, Administrator
CFO: Royce Holdeman, Chief Financial Officer
Web address: www.mercyh.org/
Control: Church operated, Nongovernment, not–for–profit **Service:** General medical and surgical

Staffed Beds: 16 Admissions: 302 Census: 5 Outpatient Visits: 7844 Births: 2 Total Expense ($000): 3240 Payroll Expense ($000): 1604 Personnel: 39

NEODESHA—Wilson County

★ **WILSON MEDICAL CENTER (171344)**, 2600 Ottawa Road, Zip 66757–1897, Mailing Address: P.O. Box 360, Zip 66757–0127; tel. 620/325–2611, **A**10 18 **F**3 11 12 15 29 32 34 35 40 44 45 53 57 59 64 75 77 81 82 85 86 87 89 90 93 107 110 114 119 127 128 130 133 146 148 154 **P**6 **S** QHR, Brentwood, TN
Primary Contact: Dennis R. Shelby, Chief Executive Officer
CFO: John Gutschenritter, Chief Financial Officer
CIO: Kevin Myers, Director Information Technology
CHR: Laura L Dean, Director Human Resources
CNO: Temple Monroe, Director Nursing Operations
Web address: www.wilsonmedical.org
Control: County, Government, nonfederal **Service:** General medical and surgical

Staffed Beds: 15 Admissions: 275 Census: 6 Outpatient Visits: 20324 Births: 0 Total Expense ($000): 17458 Payroll Expense ($000): 7587 Personnel: 159

Hospital, Medicare Provider Number, Address, Telephone, Approval, Facility, and Physician Codes, Health Care System

★ American Hospital Association (AHA) membership
□ The Joint Commission accreditation
○ Healthcare Facilities Accreditation Program
◇ DNV Healthcare Inc. accreditation
⇑ Center for Improvement in Healthcare Quality Accreditation
△ Commission on Accreditation of Rehabilitation Facilities (CARF) accreditation

KS

NESS CITY—Ness County

★ **NESS COUNTY HOSPITAL DISTRICT NO 2 (171336)**, 312 Custer Street, Zip 67560–1654; tel. 785/798–2291, (Total facility includes 43 beds in nursing home–type unit) **A**10 18 **F**7 15 40 45 59 62 67 93 111 114 119 125 127 133
Primary Contact: Curt Thomas, Administrator
CFO: Debra Frank, Chief Financial Officer
CMO: Mikhail Imseis, M.D., Chief of Staff
CIO: Vicki Howe, Health Information Management
CHR: Shelly McDonald, Chief Human Resources Officer
CNO: Cindy Maier, R.N., Director of Nursing
Web address: www.nchospital.org
Control: Hospital district or authority, Government, nonfederal **Service:** General medical and surgical

Staffed Beds: 63	**Admissions:** 169	**Census:** 38 **Outpatient Visits:** 9229
Births: 0	**Total Expense ($000):** 9735	**Payroll Expense ($000):** 4336
Personnel: 123		

NEWTON—Harvey County

★ ○ **NEWTON MEDICAL CENTER (170103)**, 600 Medical Center Drive, Zip 67114–8780, Mailing Address: P.O. Box 308, Zip 67114–0308; tel. 316/283–2700, **A**3 10 11 **F**3 11 13 15 20 22 28 29 30 31 34 35 40 45 51 59 62 64 68 70 73 74 75 76 77 79 81 85 86 90 98 102 103 107 108 110 111 115 119 126 130 131 132 133 146 147 148 149 154 **P**6
Primary Contact: Vallerie L. Gleason, President and Chief Executive Officer
COO: Todd Tangeman, Chief Operating Officer
CFO: Todd Kasitz, Vice President Finance
CIO: Mike Cottle, Chief Information Officer
CHR: Todd Tangeman, Chief Operating Officer and Chief Human Resource Officer
CNO: Heather Renee Porter, Chief Clinical Officer
Web address: www.newtonmedicalcenter.com
Control: Other not–for–profit (including NFP Corporation) **Service:** General medical and surgical

Staffed Beds: 103	**Admissions:** 2585	**Census:** 33 **Outpatient Visits:** 55935
Births: 467	**Total Expense ($000):** 76003	**Payroll Expense ($000):** 37429
Personnel: 679		

☐ **PRAIRIE VIEW (174016)**, 1901 East First Street, Zip 67114–5010, Mailing Address: P.O. Box 467, Zip 67114–0467; tel. 316/284–6400, (Nonreporting) **A**1 10
Primary Contact: Jessie Kaye, Chief Executive Officer
CFO: Lisa Ramsey, Chief Financial Officer
CMO: Gary Fast, M.D., Medical Director
CIO: Chad Roth, Director Information Services
CHR: Joy Robb, Vice President Human Resources
CNO: Patrick Flaming, R.N., Director Inpatient Operations
Web address: www.prairieview.org
Control: Other not–for–profit (including NFP Corporation) **Service:** Psychiatric

Staffed Beds: 38

NORTON—Norton County

★ **NORTON COUNTY HOSPITAL (171348)**, 102 East Holme, Zip 67654–1406, Mailing Address: P.O. Box 250, Zip 67654–0250; tel. 785/877–3351, **A**10 18 **F**3 13 15 18 28 29 30 31 34 35 40 45 50 59 64 65 67 76 77 78 79 81 85 86 87 93 97 107 110 119 127 128 129 130 131 133 154 **P**6
Primary Contact: Gina Frack, Chief Executive Officer
CHR: Shannan Hempler, Director Human Resources
Web address: www.ntcohosp.com
Control: County, Government, nonfederal **Service:** General medical and surgical

Staffed Beds: 25	**Admissions:** 377	**Census:** 8 **Outpatient Visits:** 41050
Births: 36	**Total Expense ($000):** 15360	**Payroll Expense ($000):** 7154
Personnel: 134		

OAKLEY—Logan County

LOGAN COUNTY HOSPITAL (171326), 211 Cherry Street, Zip 67748–1201; tel. 785/672–3211, (Nonreporting) **A**10 18
Primary Contact: Meldon L. Snow, Chief Executive Officer
COO: Aimee Zimmerman, R.N., Chief Operations Officer
CFO: Bonnie Hagel, Chief Financial Officer
CMO: Celeste Rains, D.O., Chief of Staff
CIO: Russ Kahle, Chief Information Officer
CHR: Steve Allison, Director Human Resources
CNO: Marcia Kruse, R.N., Director Nursing
Web address: www.logancountyhospital.org
Control: County, Government, nonfederal **Service:** General medical and surgical

Staffed Beds: 59

OBERLIN—Decatur County

DECATUR HEALTH SYSTEMS (171352), 810 West Columbia Street, Zip 67749–2450, Mailing Address: P.O. Box 268, Zip 67749–0268; tel. 785/475–2208, **A**10 18 **F**3 15 34 40 45 50 53 56 59 64 69 77 82 84 85 86 90 93 97 107 110 114 125 127 128 130 133 148 149 154 **P**6
Primary Contact: Kristopher Matthews, Chief Operating Officer
CFO: Amanda Fortin, Manager Finance
CMO: Elizabeth Sliter, M.D., Chairman Medical Staff
CIO: Natasha Weishapl, Manager Business Office and Human Resources
CHR: Natasha Weishapl, Manager Business Office and Human Resources
Web address: www.decaturhealthsystems.org
Control: Other not–for–profit (including NFP Corporation) **Service:** General medical and surgical

Staffed Beds: 24	**Admissions:** 179	**Census:** 3 **Outpatient Visits:** 11646
Births: 0	**Total Expense ($000):** 7590	**Payroll Expense ($000):** 3628
Personnel: 74		

OLATHE—Johnson County

COTTONWOOD SPRINGS HOSPITAL (174020), 13351 South Arapaho Drive, Zip 66062–1520; tel. 913/353–3000, (Nonreporting) **S** Springstone, Louisville, KY
Primary Contact: Jason Toalson, Chief Executive Officer
Web address: www.cottonwoodsprings.com
Control: Corporation, Investor–owned (for–profit) **Service:** Psychiatric

Staffed Beds: 72

☐ **OLATHE MEDICAL CENTER (170049)**, 20333 West 151st Street, Zip 66061–5350; tel. 913/791–4200, **A**1 2 5 10 **F**3 11 12 13 15 18 20 22 24 26 28 29 30 31 34 35 39 40 45 46 47 48 49 56 57 58 59 61 62 63 64 65 68 70 73 74 75 76 77 78 79 80 81 82 84 85 86 87 89 92 93 107 108 110 111 115 116 117 118 119 121 124 129 130 131 132 135 144 145 146 147 148 149
Primary Contact: Frank H. Devocelle, President and Chief Executive Officer
COO: John Staton, Senior Vice President Operations
CFO: Tierney Lynn Grasser, Senior Vice President and Chief Financial Officer
CMO: James L Wetzel, M.D., Senior Vice President, Chief Medical Officer
CIO: Randy Rahman, Vice President and Chief Information Officer
CHR: David Klimek, Vice President Human Resources
CNO: Amy J Meglemre, R.N., MSN, Senior Vice President and Chief Nursing Officer
Web address: www.olathehealth.org
Control: Other not–for–profit (including NFP Corporation) **Service:** General medical and surgical

Staffed Beds: 254	**Admissions:** 11056	**Census:** 115 **Outpatient Visits:** 337902
Births: 1261	**Total Expense ($000):** 220367	**Payroll Expense ($000):** 81751
Personnel: 1322		

ONAGA—Pottawatomie County

★ **COMMUNITY HEALTHCARE SYSTEM (171354)**, 120 West Eighth Street, Zip 66521–9574; tel. 785/889–4272, (Total facility includes 78 beds in nursing home–type unit) **A**10 18 **F**2 3 15 29 31 32 35 36 40 43 45 50 53 56 57 59 62 64 65 67 74 75 77 78 81 82 84 85 86 87 93 97 99 100 101 102 103 104 105 106 107 110 111 114 119 125 127 128 130 131 132 133 134 135 143 144 145 146 147 148 151 152 153 154 **P**6
Primary Contact: Todd Willert, Chief Executive Officer
COO: Marcia S Walsh, M.P.H., Chief Operating Officer
CFO: Monica Holthaus, Chief Financial Officer
CMO: Marcus Weiser, D.O., Chief of Staff
CIO: Rod Evans, Chief Information Officer
CHR: Terry D. Bernatis, Director Human Resources
CNO: Rosalind Lewis, R.N., MSN, Director of Ancillary Services
Web address: www.chcsks.org
Control: Other not–for–profit (including NFP Corporation) **Service:** General medical and surgical

Staffed Beds: 150	**Admissions:** 1068	**Census:** 78 **Outpatient Visits:** 108402
Births: 76	**Total Expense ($000):** 34432	**Payroll Expense ($000):** 19102
Personnel: 264		

OSAWATOMIE—Miami County

☐ **OSAWATOMIE STATE HOSPITAL AT ADAIR ACUTE CARE (174022)**, 500 State Hospital Drive, Zip 66064–1813, Mailing Address: P.O. Box 500, Zip 66064–0500; tel. 913/755–7000, **A**1 10 **F**30 50 86 87 98 101 130 135 146 **P**6
Primary Contact: Sherman W. Cole, Interim Chief Executive Officer
CMO: Maria Gustilo, M.D., Medical Director
CHR: Dezerae Curran, Director Human Resources
Web address: www.srskansas.org/osh/osh–rmhf_info.html
Control: State, Government, nonfederal **Service:** Psychiatric

Staffed Beds: 106	**Admissions:** 152	**Census:** 91 **Outpatient Visits:** 0
Births: 0	**Total Expense ($000):** 23922	**Payroll Expense ($000):** 11680
Personnel: 381		

KS

Many Facility Codes have changed. Please refer to the AHA Guide Code Chart. © 2018 AHA Guide

OSBORNE—Osborne County

OSBORNE COUNTY MEMORIAL HOSPITAL (171364), 424 West New Hampshire Street, Zip 67473–2314, Mailing Address: P.O. Box 70, Zip 67473–0070; tel. 785/346–2121, **A**10 18 **F**3 11 13 40 45 50 64 67 69 81 82 91 93 107 119 127 128 133 154 **P**6 **S** Great Plains Health Alliance, Inc., Wichita, KS
Primary Contact: Marianna Harris, Administrator
CFO: Linda Murphy, Chief Financial Officer
CMO: Erin Baxa, M.D., Chief Medical Officer
CNO: Monica Mullender, Director of Nursing
Web address: www.ocmh.org
Control: County, Government, nonfederal **Service**: General medical and surgical

Staffed Beds: 25 **Admissions:** 182 **Census:** 1 **Outpatient Visits:** 7077 **Births:** 13 **Total Expense ($000):** 4219 **Payroll Expense ($000):** 2726	

OSWEGO—Labette County

OSWEGO COMMUNITY HOSPITAL (171302), 800 Barker Drive, Zip 67356–9014; tel. 620/795–2921, (Nonreporting) **A**10 18 **S** Rural Community Hospitals of America, Kansas City, MO
Primary Contact: Bill Cochran, Interim Chief Executive Officer
CFO: Christina Schlatter, Chief Financial Officer
CMO: Gordon Kern, M.D., Medical Director
CHR: Christina Schlatter, Chief Financial Officer
Web address: www.oswegocommunityhospital.com
Control: Corporation, Investor–owned (for–profit) **Service**: General medical and surgical

Staffed Beds: 12	

OTTAWA—Franklin County

☒ **RANSOM MEMORIAL HOSPITAL (170014)**, 1301 South Main Street, Zip 66067–3598; tel. 785/229–8200, **A**1 10 20 **F**3 11 13 15 28 29 30 32 34 35 40 41 43 45 50 53 56 57 59 64 65 68 70 75 76 77 78 79 81 82 85 86 87 89 92 93 94 96 102 107 108 111 114 115 118 119 127 129 130 131 132 134 135 144 146 147 148 149 154 **P**6
Primary Contact: Matthew M. Heyn, Chief Executive Officer
Web address: www.ransom.org
Control: County, Government, nonfederal **Service**: General medical and surgical

Staffed Beds: 44 **Admissions:** 1280 **Census:** 10 **Outpatient Visits:** 134465 **Births:** 139 **Total Expense ($000):** 45177 **Payroll Expense ($000):** 20679 **Personnel:** 309	

OVERLAND PARK—Johnson County

○ **BLUE VALLEY HOSPITAL (170201)**, 12850 Metcalf Avenue, Zip 66213–2622; tel. 913/220–2866, (Nonreporting) **A**11
Primary Contact: Todd Wells, Chief Executive Officer
COO: Todd Wells, Chief Operating Officer
CMO: Lee Nigro, M.D., Chief Medical Officer
Web address: www.bluevalleysurgical.com/
Control: Other not–for–profit (including NFP Corporation) **Service**: General medical and surgical

Staffed Beds: 7	

☐ **CHILDREN'S MERCY HOSPITAL KANSAS (173300)**, 5808 West 110th Street, Zip 66211–2504; tel. 913/696–8000, **A**1 10 **F**3 7 9 12 29 30 32 35 36 38 40 41 44 48 50 54 58 59 62 64 68 75 77 79 81 82 85 87 93 100 101 104 107 111 115 119 129 130 131 132 134 144 146 148 149 150 154 **P**6
Primary Contact: Jo W. Stueve, Executive Vice President and Co–Chief Operating Officer
CFO: Sandra A J Lawrence, Executive Vice President and Chief Financial Officer
CMO: Charles Roberts, M.D., Medical Director
CIO: Jean Ann Breedlove, Chief Information Officer
CHR: Dan Wright, Vice President Human Resources
Web address: www.childrens–mercy.org
Control: Other not–for–profit (including NFP Corporation) **Service**: Children's general medical and surgical

Staffed Beds: 50 **Admissions:** 2147 **Census:** 14 **Outpatient Visits:** 149065 **Births:** 0 **Total Expense ($000):** 111139 **Payroll Expense ($000):** 64668 **Personnel:** 786	

HEARTLAND SPINE & SPECIALTY HOSPITAL See The University of Kansas Hospital – Indian Creek Campus

☒ **MENORAH MEDICAL CENTER (170182)**, 5721 West 119th Street, Zip 66209–3722; tel. 913/498–6000, **A**1 2 3 10 **F**3 12 13 15 18 20 22 24 26 28 29 30 31 34 35 38 40 45 46 47 49 55 57 58 59 60 64 65 68 70 72 74 75 76 77 78 79 81 82 84 85 86 87 90 93 100 102 107 108 110 111 114 115 116 117 119 120 121 126 129 130 131 132 135 145 146 148 149 154 **S** HCA Healthcare, Nashville, TN
Primary Contact: Charles Laird, Chief Executive Officer
CFO: Deborah Gafford, Chief Financial Officer
CMO: James Cheray, M.D., Chief Medical Officer
CIO: Christina McGinnis, Director Information Technology
CHR: Amy Hunt, Director Human Resources
CNO: Kelly Reno, R.N., Chief Nursing Officer
Web address: www.menorahmedicalcenter.com
Control: Corporation, Investor–owned (for–profit) **Service**: General medical and surgical

Staffed Beds: 158 **Admissions:** 8257 **Census:** 95 **Outpatient Visits:** 69449 **Births:** 610 **Total Expense ($000):** 195886 **Payroll Expense ($000):** 54625 **Personnel:** 720	

☒ **OVERLAND PARK REGIONAL MEDICAL CENTER (170176)**, 10500 Quivira Road, Zip 66215–2306, Mailing Address: P.O. Box 15959, Zip 66215–5959; tel. 913/541–5000, **A**1 2 3 5 10 **F**3 8 13 15 18 19 20 22 24 26 28 29 30 34 35 37 40 41 43 45 49 50 56 57 59 60 61 64 65 67 70 72 73 74 75 76 77 78 79 81 82 83 84 85 86 87 88 91 92 93 107 108 110 111 114 115 119 126 129 130 131 135 144 145 146 147 149 **S** HCA Healthcare, Nashville, TN
Primary Contact: Matt Sogard, Chief Executive Officer
COO: Jim Beatty, Chief Operating Officer
CFO: Steven R Cleary, Chief Financial Officer
CMO: George D. Stamos, M.D., Chief Medical Officer
CHR: Connie Miller, Vice President Human Resources
Web address: www.oprmc.com
Control: Corporation, Investor–owned (for–profit) **Service**: General medical and surgical

Staffed Beds: 275 **Admissions:** 11018 **Census:** 140 **Outpatient Visits:** 94590 **Births:** 2853 **Total Expense ($000):** 191428 **Payroll Expense ($000):** 68843 **Personnel:** 859	

☐ **PROMISE HOSPITAL OF OVERLAND PARK (172004)**, 6509 West 103rd Street, Zip 66212–1728; tel. 913/649–3701, (Nonreporting) **A**1 10 **S** Promise Healthcare, Boca Raton, FL
Primary Contact: Kristen Barrett, Chief Executive Officer
CFO: William Scott, Chief Financial Officer
CHR: Darren Enochs, Director Human Resources
Web address: www.promise–overlandpark.com
Control: Corporation, Investor–owned (for–profit) **Service**: Acute long–term care hospital

Staffed Beds: 104	

REHABILITATION HOSPITAL OF OVERLAND PARK (173032), 5100 Indian Creek Parkway, Zip 66207–4115; tel. 913/544–1957, (Nonreporting) **S** Post Acute Medical, LLC, Enola, PA
Primary Contact: Portlyn Brogger, Divisional President
Web address: www.warmsprings.org
Control: Corporation, Investor–owned (for–profit) **Service**: Rehabilitation

Staffed Beds: 45	

☒ **SAINT LUKE'S SOUTH HOSPITAL (170185)**, 12300 Metcalf Avenue, Zip 66213–1324; tel. 913/317–7000, **A**1 10 **F**3 12 13 15 18 20 22 26 28 29 30 31 34 35 38 39 40 44 45 47 48 49 50 54 58 59 60 64 65 68 70 73 74 75 76 77 78 79 80 81 82 84 85 86 87 89 90 91 93 94 95 96 100 102 107 108 110 111 114 115 117 118 119 126 129 130 131 132 135 141 146 147 148 149 154 **S** Saint Luke's Health System, Kansas City, MO
Primary Contact: Bobby Olm–Shipman, Chief Executive Officer
CFO: Shelby Frigon, Chief Financial Officer
CMO: Lisa Heath, M.D., President Medical Staff
CIO: Deborah Gash, Chief Information Officer
CHR: Donna Kunz, System Director Human Resources
CNO: Julia Woods, R.N., MSN, Vice President and Chief Nursing Officer
Web address: www.saintlukeshealthsystem.org/south
Control: Church operated, Nongovernment, not–for–profit **Service**: General medical and surgical

Staffed Beds: 104 **Admissions:** 5642 **Census:** 57 **Outpatient Visits:** 92903 **Births:** 531 **Total Expense ($000):** 127579 **Payroll Expense ($000):** 35029 **Personnel:** 517	

Hospital, Medicare Provider Number, Address, Telephone, Approval, Facility, and Physician Codes, Health Care System

★ American Hospital Association (AHA) membership
☐ The Joint Commission accreditation
○ Healthcare Facilities Accreditation Program
◇ DNV Healthcare Inc. accreditation
⇑ Center for Improvement in Healthcare Quality Accreditation
△ Commission on Accreditation of Rehabilitation Facilities (CARF) accreditation

KS

PAOLA—Miami County

☐ **MIAMI COUNTY MEDICAL CENTER (170109)**, 2100 Baptiste Drive,
Zip 66071–1314, Mailing Address: P.O. Box 365, Zip 66071–0365;
tel. 913/294–2327, **A**1 5 10 **F**3 11 15 18 28 34 40 43 57 59 61 64 68 75 77 78 79
81 82 85 87 89 90 93 107 108 110 111 115 119 127 130 131 135 145 146 148
Primary Contact: Paul W. Luce, R.N., MSN, Vice President Operations
CFO: Cheryl Sharp, Chief Financial Office
CMO: Christopher Eckland, M.D., Chief Medical Officer
CIO: Randy Rahman, Chief Information Officer
CHR: David Klimek, Chief Human Resources Officer
CNO: Aubree Slayman, Director Patient Services
Web address: www.olathehealth.org
Control: Other not–for–profit (including NFP Corporation) **Service**: General
medical and surgical

Staffed Beds: 18 **Admissions**: 555 **Census**: 3 **Outpatient Visits**: 29775
Births: 0 **Personnel**: 118

PARSONS—Labette County

★ ○ **LABETTE HEALTH (170120)**, 1902 South US Highway 59,
Zip 67357–7404; tel. 620/421–4880, **A**10 11 **F**3 11 13 15 29 30 34 40 43 50
53 59 62 70 74 75 76 77 79 81 86 90 93 97 107 108 110 111 114 119 126
127 129 130 143 144 146 147 148 149 154 **P**6
Primary Contact: Brian A. Williams, Chief Executive Officer
CFO: Thomas Macaronas, Chief Financial Officer
CHR: Christina Sykes, Director Human Resources
Web address: www.labettehealth.com
Control: County, Government, nonfederal **Service**: General medical and surgical

Staffed Beds: 56 **Admissions**: 1973 **Census**: 19 **Outpatient Visits**: 80235
Births: 200 **Total Expense ($000)**: 67138 **Payroll Expense ($000)**: 28658
Personnel: 556

PARSONS STATE HOSPITAL AND TRAINING CENTER, 2601 Gabriel
Avenue, Zip 67357–2341, Mailing Address: P.O. Box 738, Zip 67357–0738;
tel. 620/421–6550, **F**35 39 67 130 146
Primary Contact: Jerry A. Rea, Ph.D., Superintendent
CFO: John Spare, Accountant
CMO: Rema Menon, M.D., Clinical Director
CIO: Ron Malmstrom, Information Research Specialist
CHR: Tim B Posch, Business Manager and Director Personnel
Web address: www.pshtc.org
Control: State, Government, nonfederal **Service**: Intellectual disabilities

Staffed Beds: 188 **Admissions**: 15 **Census**: 163 **Outpatient Visits**: 0
Births: 0 **Total Expense ($000)**: 27189 **Payroll Expense ($000)**: 16188
Personnel: 491

PHILLIPSBURG—Phillips County

★ **PHILLIPS COUNTY HOSPITAL (171353)**, 1150 State Street, Zip 67661–1743,
Mailing Address: P.O. Box 607, Zip 67661–0607; tel. 785/543–5226, **A**10 18
F3 11 15 28 30 31 40 45 50 59 64 68 75 77 78 81 86 87 91 93 107 114 119
127 128 130 132 133 145 146 148 154 **P**6 **S** Great Plains Health Alliance, Inc.,
Wichita, KS
Primary Contact: Rex D. Walk, Chief Executive Officer
CFO: Christi Driggs, Chief Financial Officer
CMO: Ben Stephenson, M.D., Chief of Staff
CIO: Steven Seems, Director of Information Technology
CHR: Peggy Fabin, Director Human Resources
CNO: Vickie Gibbs, Director Nursing
Web address: www.phillipshospital.org
Control: Other not–for–profit (including NFP Corporation) **Service**: General
medical and surgical

Staffed Beds: 25 **Admissions**: 246 **Census**: 7 **Outpatient Visits**: 22200
Births: 0 **Total Expense ($000)**: 13003 **Payroll Expense ($000)**: 5683
Personnel: 107

PITTSBURG—Crawford County

⊞ **VIA CHRISTI HOSPITAL PITTSBURG (170006)**, 1 Mt. Carmel Way,
Zip 66762–7587; tel. 620/231–6100, **A**1 2 10 **F**3 5 11 12 13 15 18 20 22 26
28 29 31 34 35 40 43 45 46 47 48 50 51 53 54 56 57 58 59 62 64 68 69
70 74 75 76 77 78 79 81 82 84 85 86 89 90 93 104 107 108 109 110 111
112 114 115 116 117 118 119 120 121 122 123 126 129 130 131 132 133
135 143 144 145 146 147 148 154 **P**8 **S** Ascension Healthcare, Saint Louis, MO
Primary Contact: Randall R. Cason, FACHE, Senior Administrator
CFO: Mike Joy, Administrator, Finance
CIO: Missy McDown, Director Information Systems
CHR: Laurie Johnson, Director – Human Resources
CNO: Amy Katherine Renn, Interim Administrator, Patient Care and Nursing
Web address: www.viachristi.org/pittsburg
Control: Church operated, Nongovernment, not–for–profit **Service**: General
medical and surgical

Staffed Beds: 89 **Admissions**: 3092 **Census**: 34 **Outpatient Visits**: 78808
Births: 565 **Total Expense ($000)**: 92819 **Payroll Expense ($000)**: 32740
Personnel: 433

PLAINVILLE—Rooks County

★ **ROOKS COUNTY HEALTH CENTER (171311)**, 1210 North Washington
Street, Zip 67663–1632, Mailing Address: P.O. Box 389, Zip 67663–0389;
tel. 785/434–4553, **A**10 18 **F**3 13 15 28 29 31 34 35 40 43 45 47 50 57 59
64 67 76 77 79 81 82 85 86 87 93 96 107 108 110 114 119 125 128 130
131 133 135 143 144 146 147 148 149
Primary Contact: Anthony Thomas, Chief Executive Officer
COO: William D Stahl, Chief Operating Officer
CFO: Frank A Rajewski, Chief Financial Officer
CMO: Lynn Fisher, M.D., Chief of Staff
CHR: Cindi Knipp, Director Human Resources
Web address: www.rookscountyhealthcenter.com
Control: Hospital district or authority, Government, nonfederal **Service**: General
medical and surgical

Staffed Beds: 20 **Admissions**: 424 **Census**: 5 **Outpatient Visits**: 25746
Births: 55 **Total Expense ($000)**: 16224 **Payroll Expense ($000)**: 6312
Personnel: 129

PRATT—Pratt County

★ **PRATT REGIONAL MEDICAL CENTER (170027)**, 200 Commodore Street,
Zip 67124–2903; tel. 620/672–7451, (Total facility includes 45 beds in nursing
home–type unit) **A**10 20 **F**3 11 13 15 30 31 34 40 45 49 56 57 59 61 62 64 68
70 75 76 77 79 81 82 85 86 87 89 90 93 107 108 114 118 119 124 127 128
130 131 133 145 146 147 148 **P**6
Primary Contact: Susan M. Page, President and Chief Executive Officer
CFO: Vincent Scot Wilczek, Controller
CIO: Vikki Mader, Director Health Information Services
CHR: Kenneth A Brown, Vice President and Chief Human Resource Officer
CNO: Jack L Kennedy, R.N., MS, Vice President and Chief Nursing Officer
Web address: www.prmc.org
Control: Other not–for–profit (including NFP Corporation) **Service**: General
medical and surgical

Staffed Beds: 80 **Admissions**: 1396 **Census**: 50 **Outpatient Visits**: 106143
Births: 238 **Total Expense ($000)**: 52558 **Payroll Expense ($000)**: 23823
Personnel: 497

QUINTER—Gove County

GOVE COUNTY MEDICAL CENTER (171367), 520 West Fifth Street,
Zip 67752–0129, Mailing Address: P.O. Box 129, Zip 67752–0129;
tel. 785/754–3341, (Total facility includes 39 beds in nursing home–type unit) **A**10
18 **F**3 11 13 28 29 34 40 45 57 67 75 81 86 93 107 114 119 125 129 133
135 143 148
Primary Contact: Coleen Tummons, Chief Executive Officer
CFO: Alan Waites, Chief Financial Officer
CIO: Brad Mullins, Director Information Technology
CHR: Valerie Schneider, Director Human Resources
CNO: Renee Wagoner, R.N., Director of Nursing
Web address: www.govecountymedicalcenter.org
Control: County, Government, nonfederal **Service**: General medical and surgical

Staffed Beds: 60 **Admissions**: 353 **Census**: 40 **Outpatient Visits**: 10441
Births: 60 **Total Expense ($000)**: 13279 **Payroll Expense ($000)**: 5726
Personnel: 150

RANSOM—Ness County

★ **GRISELL MEMORIAL HOSPITAL DISTRICT ONE (171300)**, 210 South Vermont
Avenue, Zip 67572–9525; tel. 785/731–2231, (Total facility includes 30 beds in
nursing home–type unit) **A**10 18 **F**3 40 56 67 69 85 93 97 127 128 133 **P**6 **S**
Great Plains Health Alliance, Inc., Wichita, KS
Primary Contact: David Caudill, Administrator
CFO: Jolene Schuster, Chief Financial Officer
CMO: Allen McLain, M.D., Chief of Staff
CNO: Joni Pfaff, Chief Nursing Officer
Web address: www.grisellmemorialhospital.org
Control: Hospital district or authority, Government, nonfederal **Service**: General
medical and surgical

Staffed Beds: 42 **Admissions**: 60 **Census**: 22 **Outpatient Visits**: 4430
Births: 0 **Total Expense ($000)**: 6078 **Payroll Expense ($000)**: 2566
Personnel: 84

Many Facility Codes have changed. Please refer to the AHA Guide Code Chart. © 2018 AHA Guide

RUSSELL—Russell County

★ **RUSSELL REGIONAL HOSPITAL (171350)**, 200 South Main Street, Zip 67665–2920; tel. 785/483–3131, (Total facility includes 22 beds in nursing home–type unit) **A**10 18 **F**9 11 15 29 34 40 45 46 50 53 57 59 64 65 66 67 69 75 81 85 87 93 97 107 108 109 110 115 119 127 129 130 131 133 135 145 146 147 148 154 **P**6
Primary Contact: Sharon Collins, Interim Chief Executive Officer
COO: Sharon Collins, Director Human Resources and Chief Operating Officer
CFO: Kevin Kreutzer, Chief Financial Officer
CMO: Tyrel Somers, M.D., Chief Medical Officer
CIO: David Schraeder, Director Information Systems
CHR: Sharon Collins, Director Human Resources and Chief Operating Officer
CNO: Deb Strobel, R.N., Chief Nursing Officer
Web address: www.russellhospital.org
Control: Other not–for–profit (including NFP Corporation) **Service**: General medical and surgical

Staffed Beds: 47 **Admissions**: 386 **Census**: 27 **Outpatient Visits**: 36430 **Births**: 0 **Total Expense ($000)**: 17515 **Payroll Expense ($000)**: 9076 **Personnel**: 169

SABETHA—Nemaha County

★ **SABETHA COMMUNITY HOSPITAL (171338)**, 14th and Oregon Streets, Zip 66534–0229, Mailing Address: P.O. Box 229, Zip 66534–0229; tel. 785/284–2121, **A**10 18 **F**3 11 13 15 28 34 35 40 43 45 50 56 57 59 62 63 64 68 75 76 77 78 79 81 82 84 85 86 93 107 110 114 119 128 130 132 133 146 148 **P**6 **S** Great Plains Health Alliance, Inc., Wichita, KS
Primary Contact: Lora Key, Chief Executive Officer
CFO: Lori Lackey, Chief Financial Officer
CMO: James Longabaugh, M.D., Chief Medical Staff
CIO: Garrett Colglazier, Director Health Information Management
CHR: Julie K Holthaus, Director Human Resources
CNO: Rhonda Spellmeier, R.N., Director of Nursing
Web address: www.sabethahospital.com
Control: Other not–for–profit (including NFP Corporation) **Service**: General medical and surgical

Staffed Beds: 25 **Admissions**: 314 **Census**: 5 **Outpatient Visits**: 37266 **Births**: 43 **Total Expense ($000)**: 11881 **Payroll Expense ($000)**: 5622 **Personnel**: 101

SAINT FRANCIS—Cheyenne County

★ **CHEYENNE COUNTY HOSPITAL (171310)**, 210 West First Street, Zip 67756–3540, Mailing Address: P.O. Box 547, Zip 67756–0547; tel. 785/332–2104, **A**10 18 **F**3 8 11 13 28 29 31 40 57 59 64 65 66 68 76 77 78 81 85 89 93 97 107 119 127 128 133 148 **P**6 **S** Great Plains Health Alliance, Inc., Wichita, KS
Primary Contact: Kelly Pottorff, Chief Executive Officer
CFO: Heidi Tice, Chief Financial Officer
CMO: Mary Beth Miller, M.D., Chief of Staff
CIO: Carol Sloper, Manager Information Technology
CHR: Sara Wilson, Director Human Resources
CNO: Judith Ann Hodgson, Chief Nursing Officer
Web address: www.cheyennecountyhospital.com
Control: Other not–for–profit (including NFP Corporation) **Service**: General medical and surgical

Staffed Beds: 16 **Admissions**: 267 **Census**: 4 **Outpatient Visits**: 21643 **Births**: 15 **Total Expense ($000)**: 10951 **Payroll Expense ($000)**: 4619 **Personnel**: 80

SALINA—Saline County

★ ○ **SALINA REGIONAL HEALTH CENTER (170012)**, 400 South Santa Fe Avenue, Zip 67401–4198, Mailing Address: P.O. Box 5080, Zip 67402–5080; tel. 785/452–7000, (Includes SALINA REGIONAL HEALTH CENTER– PENN CAMPUS, 139 North Penn Street, Salina, KS, Zip 67401, Mailing Address: P.O. Box 5080, Zip 67402–5080, tel. 913/452–7000; SALINA REGIONAL HEALTH CENTER–SANTA FE CAMPUS, 400 South Santa Fe Avenue, Salina, KS, Zip 67401, Mailing Address: Box 5080, Zip 67402–5080, tel. 913/452–7000) **A**3 5 10 11 20 **F**3 13 15 18 19 20 22 24 28 29 30 31 40 43 45 46 47 48 49 51 53 54 55 57 59 63 64 65 68 70 71 72 73 74 76 77 78 79 81 85 86 87 89 90 98 100 101 102 104 105 107 108 110 111 114 115 116 117 118 119 120 121 122 123 124 126 129 130 143 144 145 146 147 148 149 153 154 **P**6 **S** Salina Regional Health Center, Salina, KS
Primary Contact: Micheal Terry, President and Chief Executive Officer
COO: Joel Phelps, Chief Operating Officer
CFO: Joe Tallon, Vice President Finance
CIO: Larry Barnes, Vice President Information Technology
CHR: David Moody, Vice President Human Resources
Web address: www.srhc.com
Control: Other not–for–profit (including NFP Corporation) **Service**: General medical and surgical

Staffed Beds: 205 **Admissions**: 8766 **Census**: 114 **Outpatient Visits**: 265932 **Births**: 1156 **Total Expense ($000)**: 232823 **Payroll Expense ($000)**: 103222 **Personnel**: 1713

SALINA SURGICAL HOSPITAL (170187), 401 South Santa Fe Avenue, Zip 67401–4143, Mailing Address: 401 South Sante Fe Avenue, Zip 67401–4143; tel. 785/827–0610, **A**5 10 **F**29 45 48 49 51 59 74 79 81 85 89 131
Primary Contact: LuAnn Puvogel, R.N., Chief Executive Officer
CFO: Elizabeth Bishop, Business Office Manager
CMO: Michael Johnson, M.D., Medical Director
CIO: Earl Akers, Supervisor Information Technology
CHR: Elizabeth Bishop, Business Office Manager
CNO: Jolene Glavin, R.N., MSN, Director Nursing
Web address: www.salinasurgical.com/
Control: Partnership, Investor–owned (for–profit) **Service**: Surgical

Staffed Beds: 16 **Admissions**: 882 **Census**: 6 **Outpatient Visits**: 7691 **Births**: 0 **Total Expense ($000)**: 19501 **Payroll Expense ($000)**: 6013 **Personnel**: 96

SATANTA—Haskell County

★ **SATANTA DISTRICT HOSPITAL AND LONG TERM CARE (171324)**, 401 South Cheyenne Street, Zip 67870–0159, Mailing Address: P.O. Box 159, Zip 67870–0159; tel. 620/649–2761, (Total facility includes 44 beds in nursing home–type unit) **A**10 18 **F**3 11 40 43 45 57 64 67 68 75 81 87 93 104 107 119 127 128 130 133 **P**4 **S** Great Plains Health Alliance, Inc., Wichita, KS
Primary Contact: Jeremy Clingenpeel, Administrator
CFO: Libby Anderson, Chief Financial Officer
CMO: Virgilio Taduran, M.D., Chief Medical Officer
CIO: Ben Leppke, Chief Information Officer
CHR: Samantha Hett, Manager Human Resources
CNO: Tina Pendergraft, Chief Nursing Officer
Web address: www.satantahospital.org
Control: Hospital district or authority, Government, nonfederal **Service**: General medical and surgical

Staffed Beds: 57 **Admissions**: 123 **Census**: 37 **Outpatient Visits**: 19255 **Births**: 0 **Total Expense ($000)**: 12754 **Payroll Expense ($000)**: 5974 **Personnel**: 129

SCOTT CITY—Scott County

★ **SCOTT COUNTY HOSPITAL (171372)**, 201 East Albert Avenue, Zip 67871–1203; tel. 620/872–5811, **A**10 18 **F**3 7 11 13 15 28 29 30 31 32 34 40 41 45 46 57 59 64 69 74 75 76 77 81 82 85 87 93 97 107 108 110 111 114 119 127 128 129 130 133 135 148 149 152 154 **P**6
Primary Contact: Mark Burnett, President and Chief Executive Officer
COO: Karma Huck, Chief Operating Officer
CFO: Joe S Meyer, Chief Financial Officer
CMO: Elizabeth Hineman, M.D., Chief Medical Staff
CHR: Pamela R Wheeler, Director Human Resources
Web address: www.scotthospital.net
Control: Other not–for–profit (including NFP Corporation) **Service**: General medical and surgical

Staffed Beds: 22 **Admissions**: 503 **Census**: 8 **Outpatient Visits**: 34461 **Births**: 46 **Total Expense ($000)**: 20874 **Payroll Expense ($000)**: 10915 **Personnel**: 216

SEDAN—Chautauqua County

SEDAN CITY HOSPITAL (171318), 300 North Street, Zip 67361–1051, Mailing Address: P.O. Box 'C', Zip 67361–0427; tel. 620/725–3115, **A**10 18 **F**29 34 40 57 64 93 107 119 128 130 133 148
Primary Contact: Michelle Williams, Administrator
CFO: Jennifer Seever, Regional Chief Financial Officer
CMO: James McDermott, M.D., Chief of Staff
Control: City, Government, nonfederal **Service**: General medical and surgical

Staffed Beds: 20 **Admissions**: 234 **Census**: 3 **Outpatient Visits**: 9810 **Births**: 0 **Total Expense ($000)**: 4757 **Payroll Expense ($000)**: 2226 **Personnel**: 39

SENECA—Nemaha County

★ **NEMAHA VALLEY COMMUNITY HOSPITAL (171315)**, 1600 Community Drive, Zip 66538–9739; tel. 785/336–6181, **A**10 18 **F**11 12 13 15 28 31 40 56 57 59 64 65 75 76 77 78 79 81 84 85 89 93 107 114 119 127 129 130 131 132 133 **P**6
Primary Contact: Kiley Floyd, Chief Executive Officer
CFO: Connie Ingwerson, Chief Financial Officer
CMO: Angela Stueve, M.D., Chief Medical Officer
CHR: Lynn E Hartter Jr Director Human Resources
CNO: Lynda Cross, R.N., Director of Nurses
Web address: www.nemvch.org
Control: Other not–for–profit (including NFP Corporation) **Service**: General medical and surgical

Staffed Beds: 24 **Admissions**: 375 **Census**: 5 **Outpatient Visits**: 21286 **Births**: 57 **Total Expense ($000)**: 14987 **Payroll Expense ($000)**: 7432 **Personnel**: 154

SHAWNEE MISSION—Johnson County

⊞ **MID–AMERICA REHABILITATION HOSPITAL (173026)**, 5701 West 110th
Street, Zip 66211–2503, Mailing Address: Overland Park, tel. 913/491–2400,
A1 10 **F**29 34 35 38 62 82 87 90 93 94 95 96 100 130 132 135 148 **S**
Encompass Health Corporation, Birmingham, AL
Primary Contact: Tiffany Kiehl, Chief Executive Officer
CFO: Richard Lane, Chief Financial Officer
CMO: Cielo Dehning, M.D., Medical Director
CHR: Elizabeth Gibson, Director Human Resources
CNO: Amy McKay, Chief Nursing Officer
Web address: www.midamericarehabhospital.com
Control: Corporation, Investor–owned (for–profit) **Service**: Rehabilitation

Staffed Beds: 98 **Admissions**: 1722 **Census**: 58 **Outpatient Visits**: 8662
Births: 0 **Total Expense ($000)**: 25481 **Payroll Expense ($000)**: 13020
Personnel: 181

⊞ **SHAWNEE MISSION MEDICAL CENTER (170104)**, 9100 West 74th
Street, Zip 66204–4004, Mailing Address: Box 2923, Zip 66201–1323;
tel. 913/676–2000, **A**1 2 3 5 10 **F**3 4 5 8 11 12 13 15 17 18 20 22 24 26 28
29 30 31 32 34 35 36 40 45 46 47 48 49 52 53 54 55 56 57 58 59 60 61 62
64 65 70 72 74 75 76 77 78 79 80 81 82 83 84 85 86 87 89 93 96 97 98 100
101 102 103 104 105 106 107 108 110 111 114 115 117 118 121 122
123 124 126 129 130 131 132 135 144 145 146 147 148 149 153 154 **P**6 **S**
Adventist Health System Sunbelt Health Care Corporation, Altamonte Springs, FL
Primary Contact: Sam D. Huenergardt, Chief Executive Officer
CFO: Karsten Randolph, Executive Vice President and Chief Financial Officer
CMO: Sherri Martin, M.D., President Medical Staff
CIO: Mike Allen, Director Information Services
CHR: Brad Hoffman, Administrative Director Human Resources
CNO: Sheri Hawkins, Chief Nursing Officer
Web address: www.shawneemission.org
Control: Church operated, Nongovernment, not–for–profit **Service**: General
medical and surgical

Staffed Beds: 397 **Admissions**: 22304 **Census**: 247 **Outpatient Visits**:
597954 **Births**: 5317 **Total Expense ($000)**: 433686 **Payroll Expense
($000)**: 176519 **Personnel**: 2550

SMITH CENTER—Smith County

★ **SMITH COUNTY MEMORIAL HOSPITAL (171377)**, 614 South Main Street,
Zip 66967–3001; tel. 785/282–6845, (Total facility includes 28 beds in nursing
home–type unit) **A**10 18 **F**3 13 15 28 29 30 31 34 40 43 45 53 64 65 67 68
69 75 76 81 85 89 91 93 107 110 114 119 127 128 130 133 135 154 **P**6 **S**
Great Plains Health Alliance, Inc., Wichita, KS
Primary Contact: Allen Van Driel, FACHE, Administrator
CFO: Julie Williams, Chief Financial Officer
CIO: Tammy Gaston, Chief Information Officer
CHR: Jody Maxwell, Manager Business Office
CNO: Sarah Ragsdale, R.N., Chief Nursing Officer
Web address: www.gpha.com
Control: Other not–for–profit (including NFP Corporation) **Service**: General
medical and surgical

Staffed Beds: 53 **Admissions**: 562 **Census**: 24 **Outpatient Visits**: 13413
Births: 42 **Total Expense ($000)**: 15027 **Payroll Expense ($000)**: 6146
Personnel: 106

STAFFORD—Stafford County

★ **STAFFORD COUNTY HOSPITAL (171323)**, 502 South Buckeye Street,
Zip 67578–2035, Mailing Address: P.O. Box 190, Zip 67578–0190;
tel. 620/234–5221, (Nonreporting) **A**10 18
Primary Contact: Todd Taylor, Chief Executive Officer
Web address: www.staffordcounty.org
Control: County, Government, nonfederal **Service**: General medical and surgical

Staffed Beds: 25

SYRACUSE—Hamilton County

★ **HAMILTON COUNTY HOSPITAL (171322)**, 700 North Huser Street,
Zip 67878–0948, Mailing Address: P.O. Box 948, Zip 67878–0948;
tel. 620/384–7461, **A**10 18 **F**3 34 40 41 57 59 64 75 85 86 87 91 93 94 96
97 107 111 114 127 148 **P**6
Primary Contact: Chad Thompson, Administrator
CMO: Richard Carter, M.D., Chief Medical Director
CIO: Merlin Kuder, Chief Information Officer
CHR: Angela Talbot, Manager Human Resources
CNO: Stacey Perry, Director, Nursing
Web address: www.myhch.org
Control: County, Government, nonfederal **Service**: General medical and surgical

Staffed Beds: 25 **Admissions**: 42 **Census**: 1 **Outpatient Visits**: 7455
Births: 0 **Total Expense ($000)**: 5785 **Payroll Expense ($000)**: 230
Personnel: 38

TOPEKA—Shawnee County

KANSAS NEUROLOGICAL INSTITUTE, 3107 West 21st Street,
Zip 66604–3298; tel. 785/296–5301, (Nonreporting)
Primary Contact: Brent Widick, Superintendent
CFO: Sara Hoyer, Director Administrative Services
CMO: Mary Gingrich, Director Health Care Services
CIO: Cheryl Fuller, Director Information Resources
CHR: Shawna Mercer, Director Human Resources
Web address: www.kdads.ks.gov/state–hospitals–and–institutions/kansas–
neurological–institute
Control: State, Government, nonfederal **Service**: Intellectual disabilities

Staffed Beds: 142

⊞ **KANSAS REHABILITATION HOSPITAL (173025)**, 1504 SW Eighth Avenue,
Zip 66606–1632; tel. 785/235–6600, **A**1 10 **F**29 75 86 90 91 95 96 130 132
148 **S** Encompass Health Corporation, Birmingham, AL
Primary Contact: William J. Overbey, Chief Executive Officer
CMO: Joseph Sankoorikal, M.D., Chief Medical Staff
CHR: Dina Cox, Director Human Resources
CNO: Carol Swanger, Chief Nursing Officer
Web address: www.kansasrehabhospital.com
Control: Corporation, Investor–owned (for–profit) **Service**: Rehabilitation

Staffed Beds: 57 **Admissions**: 1155 **Census**: 36 **Outpatient Visits**: 0
Births: 0 **Total Expense ($000)**: 15716 **Payroll Expense ($000)**: 7613
Personnel: 140

⊞ **STORMONT VAIL HEALTH (170086)**, 1500 SW Tenth Avenue, Zip 66604–1353;
tel. 785/354–6000, **A**1 2 5 10 **F**3 11 12 13 15 17 18 19 20 22 24 26 28 29 30
31 34 35 37 40 43 44 45 47 49 50 51 54 55 56 57 58 59 60 61 64 65 68 70
71 72 74 75 76 77 78 79 81 82 84 85 86 87 88 89 91 92 93 97 98 99 101
102 103 104 105 107 108 110 111 112 114 115 116 117 118 119 120 121
123 129 130 131 132 135 143 144 145 146 147 148 149 150 153 154 **P**6
Primary Contact: Randall Peterson, President and Chief Executive Officer
COO: Janet Stanek, Senior Vice President and Chief Operating Officer
CFO: Robert Langland, Senior Vice President and Chief Financial Officer
CMO: Rob Kenagy, M.D., Senior Vice President and Chief Medical Officer
CIO: Judy Corzine, Administrative Director and Chief Information Officer
CNO: Carol Perry, R.N., Vice President and Chief Nursing Officer
Web address: www.stormontvail.org
Control: Other not–for–profit (including NFP Corporation) **Service**: General
medical and surgical

Staffed Beds: 394 **Admissions**: 23827 **Census**: 279 **Outpatient Visits**:
141319 **Births**: 1812 **Total Expense ($000)**: 636802 **Payroll Expense
($000)**: 323510 **Personnel**: 4117

⊞ **UNIVERSITY OF KANSAS HEALTH SYSTEM ST. FRANCIS CAMPUS
(170016)**, 1700 SW 7th Street, Zip 66606–1690; tel. 785/295–8000, **A**1 2 10
F3 12 13 15 18 20 22 24 26 28 29 30 31 34 35 36 37 38 40 45 47 48 49 50
51 53 54 56 57 58 59 60 61 62 64 65 66 70 71 73 74 75 76 77 78 79 80 81
82 85 86 87 89 90 92 93 95 96 107 108 110 111 114 115 116 117 118 119
120 121 123 126 130 131 132 135 144 146 147 148 149 **P**6 **S** Ardent Health
Services, Nashville, TN
Primary Contact: Steven Anderson, Chief Executive Officer
CFO: Samuel Moore, Chief Financial Officer
CMO: Jaquelyn Hyland, M.D., Chief Medical Officer
CIO: Jamie Hilliard, Director of Information Technology
CHR: Steve Saffa, Director Human Resources
CNO: Lisa Alexander, Vice President Patient Services and Chief Nursing Officer
Web address: www.stfrancistopeka.org
Control: Partnership, Investor–owned (for–profit) **Service**: General medical and
surgical

Staffed Beds: 259 **Admissions**: 7715 **Census**: 99 **Outpatient Visits**:
223179 **Births**: 851 **Total Expense ($000)**: 178685 **Payroll Expense
($000)**: 61941 **Personnel**: 1203

⊞ **VETERANS AFFAIRS EASTERN KANSAS HEALTH CARE SYSTEM**, 2200
South West Gage Boulevard, Zip 66622–0002; tel. 785/350–3111, (Includes
VETERANS AFFAIRS EASTERN KANSAS HEALTH CARE SYSTEM–COLMERY–O'NEIL
VETERANS AFFAIRS MEDICAL CENTER, 2200 South West Gage Boulevard, Topeka,
KS, Zip 66622–0002; tel. 785/350–3111; VETERANS AFFAIRS EASTERN KANSAS
HEALTH CARE SYSTEM–DWIGHT D. EISENHOWER VETERANS AFFAIRS MEDICAL
CENTER, 4101 South 4th Street Trafficway, Leavenworth, KS, Zip 66048–5055;
tel. 913/682–2000) (Nonreporting) **A**1 3 5 **S** Department of Veterans Affairs,
Perry Point, MD
Primary Contact: Anthony Rudy. Klopfer, FACHE, Director
COO: John Moon, Associate Director
CMO: Rajeev Trehan, M.D., M.P.H., Chief of Staff
CIO: Joni Davin, Director Information and Business Management Service Line
Web address: www.topeka.va.gov/
Control: Veterans Affairs, Government, federal **Service**: General medical and
surgical

Staffed Beds: 213

Many Facility Codes have changed. Please refer to the AHA Guide Code Chart.   © 2018 AHA Guide

VETERANS AFFAIRS EASTERN KANSAS HEALTH CARE SYSTEM–COLMERY–O'NEIL VETERANS AFFAIRS MEDICAL CENTER See Veterans Affairs Eastern Kansas Health Care System, Topeka

TRIBUNE—Greeley County

★ **GREELEY COUNTY HEALTH SERVICES (171359)**, 506 Third Street, Zip 67879–9684, Mailing Address: P.O. Box 338, Zip 67879–0338; tel. 620/376–4221, (Total facility includes 32 beds in nursing home–type unit) **A**10 18 **F**1 3 4 16 17 28 34 40 45 59 64 65 66 67 69 70 72 73 76 80 81 88 89 90 98 107 127 128 133 147 151 **S** QHR, Brentwood, TN
Primary Contact: Burke Kline, Chief Executive Officer
CMO: Wendel Ellis, D.O., Chief Medical Staff
CIO: Shanon Schneider, Chief Information Officer
CHR: Katelyn Reynolds, Manager Human Resources
CNO: Janie Schmidt, Director of Nursing
Web address: www.mygchs.com
Control: Other not–for–profit (including NFP Corporation) **Service**: General medical and surgical

> **Staffed Beds: 50 Admissions: 274 Census: 35 Outpatient Visits: 12478 Births: 0 Total Expense ($000): 10800 Payroll Expense ($000): 5508 Personnel: 126**

ULYSSES—Grant County

★ **BOB WILSON MEMORIAL GRANT COUNTY HOSPITAL (170110)**, 415 North Main Street, Zip 67880–2133; tel. 620/356–1266, **A**10 20 **F**3 11 15 29 30 34 35 40 45 50 57 59 64 68 75 76 79 81 82 85 86 87 91 93 96 97 107 119 127 130 133 146 148 154 **P**6 **S** Catholic Health Initiatives, Englewood, CO
Primary Contact: Amanda Vaughan, Interim Administrator
CFO: Amanda Vaughan, Chief Financial Officer
CIO: Chris Moffet, Director Information Services
CHR: Tammy Oxford, Director Human Resources
Web address: www.bwmgch.com
Control: Corporation, Investor–owned (for–profit) **Service**: General medical and surgical

> **Staffed Beds: 26 Admissions: 210 Census: 3 Outpatient Visits: 6689 Births: 12 Total Expense ($000): 12622 Payroll Expense ($000): 5041 Personnel: 79**

WAKEENEY—Trego County

★ **TREGO COUNTY–LEMKE MEMORIAL HOSPITAL (171355)**, 320 North 13th Street, Zip 67672–2099; tel. 785/743–2182, (Total facility includes 37 beds in nursing home–type unit) **A**10 18 **F**3 8 10 11 15 28 29 34 40 45 53 57 59 62 64 67 69 71 81 86 89 93 107 110 114 127 128 130 133 143 146 148 154 **P**6 **S** Great Plains Health Alliance, Inc., Wichita, KS
Primary Contact: David Augustine, Chief Executive Officer
CFO: ReChelle Horinek, Chief Financial Officer
CMO: Gordon Lang, M.D., Chief of Staff
CHR: Jeff Bieker, Director Human Resource
CNO: Sandy Purinton, Chief Nursing Officer
Web address: www.tclmh.org
Control: County, Government, nonfederal **Service**: General medical and surgical

> **Staffed Beds: 62 Admissions: 569 Census: 51 Outpatient Visits: 31714 Births: 0 Total Expense ($000): 17650 Payroll Expense ($000): 7919 Personnel: 175**

WAMEGO—Pottawatomie County

★ **WAMEGO HEALTH CENTER (171337)**, 711 Genn Drive, Zip 66547–1179; tel. 785/456–2295, **A**10 18 **F**3 11 15 28 29 32 34 35 40 45 56 59 64 65 75 77 81 93 97 107 114 119 127 130 131 132 133 143 146 147 148 149 **P**6
Primary Contact: Steve Land, Senior Administrator
COO: Brian Smith, Director of Operations
CFO: Keith Zachariasen, Chief Financial Officer
CMO: Roland Darey, M.D., Medical Director
CIO: Wes Janzen, Chief Information Officer
CHR: Renee Reed, Director Human Resources
CNO: Tresha Flanary, R.N., Chief Clinical Services Officer
Web address: www.wamegohealthcenter.com
Control: Other not–for–profit (including NFP Corporation) **Service**: General medical and surgical

> **Staffed Beds: 18 Admissions: 221 Census: 5 Outpatient Visits: 39425 Births: 0 Total Expense ($000): 11933 Payroll Expense ($000): 6001 Personnel: 86**

WASHINGTON—Washington County

WASHINGTON COUNTY HOSPITAL (171351), 304 East Third Street, Zip 66968–2033; tel. 785/325–2211, **A**10 18 **F**3 11 13 15 28 29 31 34 35 40 41 44 45 64 67 68 69 81 83 85 91 93 97 107 110 114 127 133 144 148 149 **P**6
Primary Contact: Roxanne Schottel, Chief Executive Officer
CFO: Linda Rettig, Director Financial Services
CNO: Kelly Otott, R.N., Chief Nursing Officer
Web address: www.washingtoncountyhospital.net
Control: County, Government, nonfederal **Service**: General medical and surgical

> **Staffed Beds: 18 Admissions: 193 Census: 6 Outpatient Visits: 7223 Births: 11 Total Expense ($000): 5852 Payroll Expense ($000): 2441 Personnel: 44**

WELLINGTON—Sumner County

SUMNER REGIONAL MEDICAL CENTER (170039), 1323 North 'A' Street, Zip 67152–4350; tel. 620/326–7451, (Total facility includes 9 beds in nursing home–type unit) **A**10 **F**10 11 13 15 31 35 40 45 56 59 64 76 77 78 79 81 82 85 98 103 107 108 110 111 119 128 129 130
Primary Contact: Les Dean, President and Chief Executive Officer
CFO: Barry Harding, Interim Chief Executive Officer and Chief Financial Officer
CHR: Allen Keller, Director Human Resources
CNO: Darlene Cooney, Director Nursing
Web address: www.srmcks.org
Control: City, Government, nonfederal **Service**: General medical and surgical

> **Staffed Beds: 61 Admissions: 348 Census: 6 Outpatient Visits: 20206 Births: 69 Total Expense ($000): 12285 Payroll Expense ($000): 6002 Personnel: 131**

WICHITA—Sedgwick County

☐ **AMG SPECIALTY HOSPITAL–WICHITA (172003)**, 8080 East Pawnee Street, Zip 67207–5475; tel. 316/682–0004, (Nonreporting) **A**1 10 **S** AMG Integrated Healthcare Management, Lafayette, LA
Primary Contact: Robert A. Loepp Jr, FACHE, Chief Executive Officer
CFO: Myra Dick, Manager Business Office
CIO: Michelle Bradley, Director Health Information Management
CHR: Adrienne Burkholder, Director Human Resources
Web address: www.amgwichita.com/
Control: Corporation, Investor–owned (for–profit) **Service**: Acute long–term care hospital

> **Staffed Beds: 26**

KANSAS HEART HOSPITAL (170186), 3601 North Webb Road, Zip 67226–8129; tel. 316/630–5000, (Nonreporting) **A**10
Primary Contact: Thomas L. Ashcom, M.D., Ph.D., Chief Executive Officer
COO: Joyce Heismeyer, Chief Operating Officer
CFO: Steve Smith, Chief Financial Officer
CHR: Teresa E Wolfe, Manager Human Resources
CNO: Susan Bradford, Director Nursing
Web address: www.kansasheart.com
Control: Corporation, Investor–owned (for–profit) **Service**: Heart

> **Staffed Beds: 54**

KANSAS SPINE AND SPECIALTY HOSPITAL (170196), 3333 North Webb Road, Zip 67226–8123; tel. 316/462–5000, **A**10 **F**3 29 79 81 82 85 87 107 111 114 126 149
Primary Contact: Thomas M. Schmitt, Chief Executive Officer
CFO: Kevin P Vaughn, Chief Financial Officer
CIO: Michael Knocke, Chief Information Officer
CHR: Jean–Marie Jimeson, Manager Human Resources
CNO: John Coslett, R.N., Chief Nursing Officer
Web address: www.ksspine.com
Control: Corporation, Investor–owned (for–profit) **Service**: General medical and surgical

> **Staffed Beds: 36 Admissions: 2149 Census: 13 Outpatient Visits: 8401 Births: 0 Personnel: 156**

Hospital, Medicare Provider Number, Address, Telephone, Approval, Facility, and Physician Codes, Health Care System

★ American Hospital Association (AHA) membership ○ Healthcare Facilities Accreditation Program ⇧ Center for Improvement in Healthcare Quality Accreditation
☐ The Joint Commission accreditation ◇ DNV Healthcare Inc. accreditation △ Commission on Accreditation of Rehabilitation Facilities (CARF) accreditation

KS

KANSAS SURGERY AND RECOVERY CENTER (170183), 2770 North Webb Road, Zip 67226–8112; tel. 316/634–0090, **A**10 **F**45 51 64 68 79 81 85 87 93 107 111 114 119 126
Primary Contact: Ely Bartal, M.D., Chief Executive Officer
CFO: Ashley Simon, Chief Financial Officer
CMO: Ely Bartal, M.D., Chief Executive Officer and Medical Director
CIO: Jonathan Wells, Supervisor Information Technology
CNO: Becky Bailey, R.N., Director Nursing
Web address: www.ksrc.org
Control: Partnership, Investor–owned (for–profit) **Service:** Surgical

Staffed Beds: 32 **Admissions:** 1950 **Census:** 11 **Outpatient Visits:** 9540 **Births:** 0 **Total Expense ($000):** 27930 **Payroll Expense ($000):** 7500 **Personnel:** 137

✠ **ROBERT J. DOLE VETERANS AFFAIRS MEDICAL CENTER**, 5500 East Kellogg, Zip 67218–1607; tel. 316/685–2221, (Nonreporting) **A**1 3 5 **S** Department of Veterans Affairs, Perry Point, MD
Primary Contact: Rick Ament, Chief Executive Officer
CFO: Ronald Dreher, Finance Officer
CMO: Kent Murray, M.D., Chief of Staff
CIO: Sharon Williamson, Chief Information Technology
CHR: Nancy Gerstner, Manager Human Resources
Web address: www.wichita.va.gov
Control: Veterans Affairs, Government, federal **Service:** General medical and surgical

Staffed Beds: 41

✠ **SELECT SPECIALTY HOSPITAL–WICHITA (172007)**, 929 North St Francis Street, Zip 67214–3821; tel. 316/261–8303, (Nonreporting) **A**1 10 **S** Select Medical Corporation, Mechanicsburg, PA
Primary Contact: Christopher Keith, Chief Executive Officer
CHR: Renee Schaffer, Coordinator Human Resources
CNO: Lindsey Cahoj, Chief Nursing Officer
Web address: www.selectspecialtyhospitals.com/company/locations/wichita.aspx
Control: Corporation, Investor–owned (for–profit) **Service:** Acute long–term care hospital

Staffed Beds: 48

✠ **VIA CHRISTI HOSPITAL ON ST. FRANCIS (170122)**, 929 North St Francis Street, Zip 67214–3882; tel. 316/268–5000, (Includes GOOD SHEPHERD CAMPUS, 8901 East Orme, Wichita, KS, Zip 67207; tel. 316/858–0333; ST. FRANCIS CAMPUS, 929 North St Francis Street, Wichita, KS, Zip 67214–3882; tel. 316/268–5000; ST. JOSEPH CAMPUS, 3600 East Harry Street, Wichita, KS, Zip 67218–3713; tel. 316/685–1111) **A**1 2 3 5 10 13 **F**3 7 11 12 13 15 16 17 18 19 20 22 23 24 26 27 28 29 30 31 32 34 35 38 40 43 44 45 46 48 49 50 51 54 56 57 58 59 60 61 62 64 68 70 72 74 75 76 77 78 79 80 81 82 84 85 86 87 88 89 92 93 97 98 99 100 103 104 105 107 108 110 111 114 115 117 118 119 120 121 123 124 126 130 131 132 135 136 141 142 143 146 147 148 153 154 **P**6 **S** Ascension Healthcare, Saint Louis, MO
Primary Contact: Kevin Strecker, President
CFO: Jeff Seirer, Interim Chief Financial Officer
CMO: Darrell Youngman, D.O., Chief Medical Officer
CIO: Donna Roach, Chief Information Officer
CHR: Judy Espinoza, Chief Human Resources Officer
Web address: www.via–christi.org
Control: Church operated, Nongovernment, not–for–profit **Service:** General medical and surgical

Staffed Beds: 675 **Admissions:** 30859 **Census:** 422 **Outpatient Visits:** 290298 **Births:** 2400 **Total Expense ($000):** 530519 **Payroll Expense ($000):** 166780 **Personnel:** 3401

✠ **VIA CHRISTI HOSPITAL ON ST. TERESA (170200)**, 14800 West St. Teresa, Zip 67235–9602; tel. 316/796–7000, **A**1 10 **F**3 8 18 20 22 29 30 34 35 40 45 50 64 68 70 75 78 79 81 85 87 90 92 93 96 107 108 111 114 118 119 130 146 147 148 154 **S** Ascension Healthcare, Saint Louis, MO
Primary Contact: Robyn Chadwick, President
Web address: www.via–christi.org/st–teresa
Control: Church operated, Nongovernment, not–for–profit **Service:** General medical and surgical

Staffed Beds: 48 **Admissions:** 1763 **Census:** 22 **Outpatient Visits:** 23014 **Births:** 0 **Total Expense ($000):** 32875 **Payroll Expense ($000):** 9582 **Personnel:** 158

VIA CHRISTI REGIONAL MEDICAL CENTER See Via Christi Hospital On St. Francis

✠ **VIA CHRISTI REHABILITATION HOSPITAL (173028)**, 1151 North Rock Road, Zip 67206–1262; tel. 316/634–3400, **A**1 10 **F**11 29 30 34 35 44 50 54 57 59 64 77 78 85 87 90 92 93 95 96 119 129 130 131 132 143 146 148 **S** Ascension Healthcare, Saint Louis, MO
CMO: Kevin Rieg, M.D., President Medical Staff
CNO: Cindy Hagerty, Assistant Chief Nurse Officer and Administrator of Operations
Web address: www.via–christi.org
Control: Church operated, Nongovernment, not–for–profit **Service:** Rehabilitation

Staffed Beds: 58 **Admissions:** 740 **Census:** 22 **Outpatient Visits:** 103706 **Births:** 0 **Total Expense ($000):** 22387 **Payroll Expense ($000):** 9833 **Personnel:** 198

✠ **WESLEY HEALTHCARE CENTER (170123)**, 550 North Hillside, Zip 67214–4976; tel. 316/962–2000, (Includes WESLEY CHILDREN'S HOSPITAL, 550 North Hillside Street, Wichita, KS, Zip 67214–4910; tel. 316/962–2000; WESLEY WOODLAWN HOSPITAL & ER, 2610 North Woodlawn, Wichita, KS, Zip 67220; tel. 316/858–2610; Thomas Owings, Chief Executive Officer) (Nonreporting) **A**1 2 3 5 10 **S** HCA Healthcare, Nashville, TN
Primary Contact: Bill Voloch, President and Chief Executive Officer
CFO: Bradley Schultz, Chief Financial Officer
CMO: Francie H Ekengren, M.D., Chief Medical Officer
CIO: Jeffrey Schauf, Director Information Systems
CHR: Jennifer Krier, Vice President Human Resources
Web address: www.wesleymc.com
Control: Corporation, Investor–owned (for–profit) **Service:** General medical and surgical

Staffed Beds: 562

✠ **WESLEY REHABILITATION HOSPITAL (173027)**, 8338 West 13th Street North, Zip 67212–2984; tel. 316/729–9999, **A**1 10 **F**29 34 35 64 68 90 91 93 95 96 132 148 **S** Encompass Health Corporation, Birmingham, AL
Primary Contact: James F. Grocholski, FACHE, Chief Executive Officer
CFO: Bob Peck, Chief Financial Officer
CIO: Debbie Patterson, Director Health Information Management
CHR: Betty Shuman, Director Human Resources
CNO: Jessika M Workman, Chief Nursing Officer
Web address: www.wesleyrehabhospital.com
Control: Corporation, Investor–owned (for–profit) **Service:** Rehabilitation

Staffed Beds: 65 **Admissions:** 1034 **Census:** 39 **Outpatient Visits:** 8320 **Births:** 0 **Total Expense ($000):** 18739 **Payroll Expense ($000):** 8467 **Personnel:** 151

WICHITA SPECIALTY HOSPITAL See AMG Specialty Hospital–Wichita

WINCHESTER—Jefferson County

★ **F. W. HUSTON MEDICAL CENTER (171314)**, 408 Delaware Street, Zip 66097–4003; tel. 913/774–4340, (Total facility includes 38 beds in nursing home–type unit) **A**10 18 **F**3 10 40 56 57 64 67 69 75 77 93 97 103 104 107 111 125 128 130 133 143 144 **P**6 8
Primary Contact: LaMont Cook, Administrator
CFO: Jason Johnson, Controller
CMO: William Greiner, M.D., Chief of Staff
CIO: Jason Johnson, Controller
CHR: Melody Keirns, Manager Human Resources
CNO: Heather R Aranda, R.N., MSN, Chief Nursing Officer
Web address: www.jcmhospital.org
Control: Other not–for–profit (including NFP Corporation) **Service:** General medical and surgical

Staffed Beds: 69 **Admissions:** 85 **Census:** 33 **Outpatient Visits:** 7135 **Births:** 0 **Total Expense ($000):** 5751 **Payroll Expense ($000):** 3677 **Personnel:** 71

JEFFERSON COUNTY MEMORIAL HOSPITAL See F. W. Huston Medical Center

WINFIELD—Cowley County

★ **WILLIAM NEWTON HOSPITAL (171383)**, 1300 East Fifth Street, Zip 67156–2407; tel. 620/221–2300, **A**3 5 10 18 **F**3 8 11 13 15 28 29 34 35 40 43 45 57 59 62 64 67 68 69 70 76 77 79 81 82 84 85 86 87 89 90 91 93 94 107 108 110 111 114 118 119 127 128 130 133 146 148 149 150 154
Primary Contact: J Ben. Quinton, Administrator
COO: Shona Salzman, Chief Operating Officer
CFO: Debbie Hockenbury, Assistant Administrator and Chief Financial Officer
CMO: Bryan Dennett, M.D., Chief of Staff
CIO: Randy Mayo, Director Information Technology
CHR: Cathy McClurg, Director Human Resources
CNO: Tina Wheeler, R.N., MSN, Director Nursing
Web address: www.wnmh.org
Control: Other not–for–profit (including NFP Corporation) **Service:** General medical and surgical

Staffed Beds: 25 **Admissions:** 1061 **Census:** 10 **Outpatient Visits:** 74690 **Births:** 269 **Total Expense ($000):** 36024 **Payroll Expense ($000):** 14476 **Personnel:** 279

KENTUCKY

ALBANY—Clinton County

THE MEDICAL CENTER ALBANY (180106), 723 Burkesville Road, Zip 42602–1654; tel. 606/387–8000, (Nonreporting) **A**10 **S** Med Center Health, Bowling Green, KY
Primary Contact: Laura Belcher, Administrator
CFO: Ronald G. Sowell, FACHE, Executive Vice President, Chief Financial Officer
CIO: Mark Brookman, Chief Information Officer
CHR: Lynn Williams, Vice President, Human Resources
Web address: www.chc.net/services/hospitals/the_medical_center_at_albany.aspx
Control: Other not–for–profit (including NFP Corporation) **Service:** General medical and surgical

Staffed Beds: 42

ASHLAND—Boyd County

☐ **KING'S DAUGHTERS MEDICAL CENTER (180009)**, 2201 Lexington Avenue, Zip 41101–2874, Mailing Address: P.O. Box 151, Zip 41105–0151; tel. 606/408–4000, (Nonreporting) **A**1 2 3 10
Primary Contact: Kristie Whitlatch, President
COO: Bob Lucas, Vice President Operations
CFO: Paul L McDowell, Vice President Finance and Chief Financial Officer
CMO: Phil Fioret, M.D., Vice President Medical Affairs
CIO: David Oliver, Director Information Systems
CHR: Larry Higgins, Vice President Human Resources
Web address: www.kdmc.com
Control: Other not–for–profit (including NFP Corporation) **Service:** General medical and surgical

Staffed Beds: 448

⊞ **OUR LADY OF BELLEFONTE HOSPITAL (180036)**, St Christopher Drive, Zip 41101, Mailing Address: P.O. Box 789, Zip 41105–0789; tel. 606/833–3333, **A**1 2 10 12 13 **F**3 4 8 11 15 18 20 22 28 29 30 31 34 35 37 39 40 44 48 49 50 53 54 55 56 57 58 59 62 64 65 66 69 70 74 75 77 78 79 81 82 84 85 86 87 89 93 96 97 98 100 101 102 103 104 105 106 107 108 110 111 114 115 118 119 129 130 131 132 135 143 144 145 146 147 148 154 **P**6 8 **S** Bon Secours Health System, Inc., Marriottsville, MD
Primary Contact: Kevin Halter, Chief Executive Officer
CFO: Joe Buchheit, Chief Financial Officer
CMO: Dan Goulson, M.D., Chief Medical Officer
CIO: Mike Gomez, Site Manager Medical Information Systems
CHR: Judy Daniels, Vice President Human Resources
Web address: www.olbh.com
Control: Church operated, Nongovernment, not–for–profit **Service:** General medical and surgical

Staffed Beds: 140 Admissions: 7277 Census: 92 Outpatient Visits: 271596 Births: 0 Total Expense ($000): 166396 Payroll Expense ($000): 51927 Personnel: 868

BARBOURVILLE—Knox County

☐ **BARBOURVILLE ARH HOSPITAL (181328)**, 80 Hospital Drive, Zip 40906–7363, Mailing Address: P.O. Box 10, Zip 40906–0010; tel. 606/546–4175, **A**1 10 18 **F**3 28 29 34 35 39 40 45 46 47 48 49 50 57 59 64 70 81 85 87 107 108 110 114 119 127 130 133 146 **P**6 **S** Pacer Health Corporation, Miami Lakes, FL
Primary Contact: Charles D. Lovell Jr, FACHE, Chief Executive Officer
CFO: Amanda Ellis, Chief Financial Officer
CMO: Kamran Hasni, M.D., Chief of Medical Staff
CIO: Evan Davis, Director Technology and Environmental Services
CHR: Janet Wilder, Director Human Resources
CNO: Brenda Graham, Chief Nursing Officer
Web address: www.knoxcohospital.com
Control: Other not–for–profit (including NFP Corporation) **Service:** General medical and surgical

Staffed Beds: 25 Admissions: 1080 Census: 10 Births: 0

BARDSTOWN—Nelson County

⊞ **FLAGET MEMORIAL HOSPITAL (180025)**, 4305 New Shepherdsville Road, Zip 40004–9019; tel. 502/350–5000, **A**1 2 3 10 **F**3 11 12 13 15 18 29 30 31 34 35 37 40 45 49 55 59 60 62 63 64 70 76 78 79 81 82 84 85 87 91 93 96 107 111 116 117 119 120 128 129 130 132 144 146 147 148 **P**6 **S** Catholic Health Initiatives, Englewood, CO
Primary Contact: Jennifer Nolan, President and Chief Executive Officer
CFO: Jim Wentz, Chief Financial Officer
CMO: Mickey Anderson, M.D., Vice President Medical Affairs
CHR: Tanja Oquendo, Chief Human Resources Officer
CNO: Norma Goss, R.N., Chief Nursing Officer
Web address: www.kentuckyonehealth.org/flaget
Control: Other not–for–profit (including NFP Corporation) **Service:** General medical and surgical

Staffed Beds: 42 Admissions: 1914 Census: 19 Outpatient Visits: 73917 Births: 277 Total Expense ($000): 61320 Payroll Expense ($000): 15909 Personnel: 265

BENTON—Marshall County

⊞ **MARSHALL COUNTY HOSPITAL (181327)**, 615 Old Symsonia Road, Zip 42025–5042; tel. 270/527–4800, **A**1 10 18 **F**3 11 15 18 19 28 29 30 34 35 40 57 59 62 77 79 81 85 89 90 93 107 108 119 127 130 132 133 135 149 **P**6
Primary Contact: David G. Fuqua, Chief Executive Officer
CFO: Janice Kelley, Chief Financial Officer
CMO: Edwin Perez, M.D., Chief of Medical Staff
CIO: Dave Cope, Director Information Systems
CHR: Janice Bone, Human Resources
Web address: www.marshallcountyhospital.org
Control: Hospital district or authority, Government, nonfederal **Service:** General medical and surgical

Staffed Beds: 25 Admissions: 629 Census: 7 Outpatient Visits: 18172 Births: 0 Total Expense ($000): 21605 Payroll Expense ($000): 9041 Personnel: 252

BEREA—Madison County

⊞ **SAINT JOSEPH BEREA (181329)**, 305 Estill Street, Zip 40403–1909; tel. 859/986–3151, **A**1 5 10 18 **F**3 29 40 45 70 77 79 81 82 91 97 107 111 114 119 133 **P**4 **S** Catholic Health Initiatives, Englewood, CO
Primary Contact: Terrence G. Deis, CPA, FACHE, President
CFO: Christy Spitser, Vice President Finance
CMO: Joshua Huffman, M.D., Chief Medical Staff
CHR: Sandra Turqueza, Human Resources Business Partner
CNO: Leslie Adams, Chief Nursing Executive
Web address: www.kentuckyonehealth.org/berea
Control: Other not–for–profit (including NFP Corporation) **Service:** General medical and surgical

Staffed Beds: 25 Admissions: 937 Census: 11 Outpatient Visits: 55135 Births: 0 Total Expense ($000): 30393 Payroll Expense ($000): 10714 Personnel: 202

BOWLING GREEN—Warren County

☐ **COMMONWEALTH REGIONAL SPECIALTY HOSPITAL (182005)**, 250 Park Drive, 6th Floor, Zip 42101–1760, Mailing Address: P.O. Box 90010, Zip 42102–9010; tel. 270/796–6200, **A**1 10 **F**1 3 29 30 34 35 50 57 68 85 87 130 135 143 146 148 149 **S** Med Center Health, Bowling Green, KY
Primary Contact: Christa Atkins, Administrator
CFO: Ronald G. Sowell, FACHE, Executive Vice President
CMO: Doug Thomson, M.D., Chief Medical Officer
CIO: Jean Cherry, Executive Vice President
CHR: Lynn Williams, Vice President Human Resources
Web address: www.commonwealthregionalspecialtyhospital.org
Control: Other not–for–profit (including NFP Corporation) **Service:** Acute long–term care hospital

Staffed Beds: 28 Admissions: 207 Census: 15 Outpatient Visits: 0 Births: 0 Personnel: 56

□ **MEDICAL CENTER AT BOWLING GREEN (180013)**, 250 Park Street,
Zip 42101–1795, Mailing Address: P.O. Box 90010, Zip 42102–9010;
tel. 270/745–1000, **A**1 2 3 10 13 19 **F**1 3 7 12 13 15 17 18 20 22 24 26 28
29 30 31 34 37 39 40 45 46 47 48 49 50 51 56 57 58 59 60 62 64 68 70 73 74
75 76 78 79 81 82 85 86 87 91 92 93 98 100 102 103 104 107 108 110 111
114 115 116 117 118 119 120 121 122 123 124 126 129 130 132 135 145
146 147 148 149 154 **P6 S** Med Center Health, Bowling Green, KY
Primary Contact: Connie Smith, FACHE, MSN, R.N., Chief Executive Officer
CFO: Ronald G. Sowell, FACHE, Executive Vice President
CIO: Mark Brookman, Chief Information Officer
CHR: Lynn Williams, Vice President Human Resources
CNO: Betsy Kullman, R.N., MSN, Executive Vice President and Chief Nursing Officer
Web address: www.themedicalcenter.org
Control: Other not–for–profit (including NFP Corporation) **Service:** General
medical and surgical

Staffed Beds: 337 **Admissions:** 16067 **Census:** 230 **Outpatient Visits:**
140350 **Births:** 2469 **Personnel:** 1788

□ **RIVENDELL BEHAVIORAL HEALTH (184017)**, 1035 Porter Pike,
Zip 42103–9581; tel. 270/843–1199, (Nonreporting) **A**1 10 **S** Universal Health
Services, Inc., King of Prussia, PA
Primary Contact: Matt Ours, Chief Executive Officer and Managing Director
CFO: Tim Gore, Chief Financial Officer
Web address: www.rivendellbehavioral.com
Control: Corporation, Investor–owned (for–profit) **Service:** Psychiatric

Staffed Beds: 125

⊠ △ **SOUTHERN KENTUCKY REHABILITATION HOSPITAL (183029)**, 1300
Campbell Lane, Zip 42104–4162; tel. 270/782–6900, (Nonreporting) **A**1 7 10 **S**
Vibra Healthcare, Mechanicsburg, PA
Primary Contact: Stuart Locke, Chief Executive Officer
COO: Dana Lewis, Director Clinical Services
CMO: Jim Farrage, M.D., Medical Director
CHR: Suzanne Cornett, Director Human Resources
Web address: www.skyrehab.com
Control: Corporation, Investor–owned (for–profit) **Service:** Rehabilitation

Staffed Beds: 60

⊠ **TRISTAR GREENVIEW REGIONAL HOSPITAL (180124)**, 1801 Ashley
Circle, Zip 42104–3362; tel. 270/793–1000, (Nonreporting) **A**1 10 19 **S** HCA
Healthcare, Nashville, TN
Primary Contact: Michael Sherrod, Chief Executive Officer
COO: Andrew Bedi, Chief Operating Officer
CMO: Wayne Bush, M.D., Chief of Staff
CIO: Cyndi Talley, Director Information Systems
CHR: Judy Fulkerson, Director Human Resources
CNO: Anne Leonard, R.N., Chief Nursing Officer
Web address: www.greenviewhospital.com
Control: Corporation, Investor–owned (for–profit) **Service:** General medical and
surgical

Staffed Beds: 167

BURKESVILLE—Cumberland County

CUMBERLAND COUNTY HOSPITAL (181317), 299 Glasgow Road,
Zip 42717–9696, Mailing Address: P.O. Box 280, Zip 42717–0280;
tel. 270/864–2511, (Nonreporting) **A**10 18
Primary Contact: Richard Neikirk, Chief Executive Officer
COO: Steve Burns, Chief Operating Officer
CFO: Rick Capps, Chief Financial Officer
CMO: Christian Konsavage, M.D., Chief of Staff
CHR: Martha Young, Director Human Resources
CNO: Susan S Flowers, MSN, R.N., Chief Nursing Officer
Web address: www.cchospital.org
Control: Other not–for–profit (including NFP Corporation) **Service:** General
medical and surgical

Staffed Beds: 25

CADIZ—Trigg County

TRIGG COUNTY HOSPITAL (181304), 254 Main Street, Zip 42211–9153,
Mailing Address: P.O. Box 312, Zip 42211–0312; tel. 270/522–3215,
(Nonreporting) **A**10 18
Primary Contact: John Sumner, Chief Executive Officer
CFO: Liz Snodgrass, Chief Financial Officer
CMO: Stuart Harris, M.D., Chief of Staff
CHR: Janet James, Director Human Resources
Web address: www.trigghospital.org
Control: County, Government, nonfederal **Service:** General medical and surgical

Staffed Beds: 25

CAMPBELLSVILLE—Taylor County

⊞ **TAYLOR REGIONAL HOSPITAL (180087)**, 1700 Old Lebanon Road,
Zip 42718–9600; tel. 270/465–3561, **A**1 2 10 **F**3 8 11 13 15 18 20 28 29 30 31
32 34 35 39 40 41 43 45 46 48 49 50 51 54 56 57 59 64 65 68 70 74 75 76 77
78 79 81 85 86 87 93 97 107 108 110 111 115 118 119 127 129 130 131 132
134 135 141 143 146 147 148 149 150 **S** Catholic Health Initiatives, Englewood, CO
Primary Contact: Jane Wheatley, Chief Executive Officer
CFO: Paul Phillips, Chief Financial Officer
CIO: Christopher Michael Gibbs, Director Information Management Systems
CHR: Andrea Settle, Director Human Resources
CNO: Dana M. Garrett, R.N., Nursing Services Administrator
Web address: www.trhosp.org
Control: Hospital district or authority, Government, nonfederal **Service:** General
medical and surgical

Staffed Beds: 90 **Admissions:** 2516 **Census:** 26 **Outpatient Visits:** 96916
Births: 330 **Total Expense ($000):** 78643 **Payroll Expense ($000):** 35504
Personnel: 619

CARROLLTON—Carroll County

★ **CARROLL COUNTY MEMORIAL HOSPITAL (181310)**, 309 11th Street,
Zip 41008–1400; tel. 502/732–4321, (Nonreporting) **A**10 18 **S** Alliant
Management Services, Louisville, KY
Primary Contact: Harry Hays, Chief Executive Officer
CMO: Winston Yap, M.D., Chief Medical Officer
CHR: Kimberly Adams, Manager Human Resources
CNO: Lisa Penick, R.N., Chief Nursing Officer
Web address: www.ccmhosp.com
Control: County, Government, nonfederal **Service:** General medical and surgical

Staffed Beds: 25

COLUMBIA—Adair County

□ **T.J. HEALTH COLUMBIA (180149)**, 901 Westlake Drive, Zip 42728–1123,
Mailing Address: P.O. Box 1269, Zip 42728–6269; tel. 270/384–4753,
(Nonreporting) **A**1 10
Primary Contact: Neil Thornbury, Chief Executive Officer
CFO: David R Hayes, Chief Financial Officer
CMO: Charles Giles, M.D., President Medical Staff
CHR: Tonya Grant, Director Human Resources
CNO: Gidgett Warren, Director of Nursing
Web address: www.healthiercolumbia.org/
Control: Hospital district or authority, Government, nonfederal **Service:** General
medical and surgical

Staffed Beds: 32

CORBIN—Whitley County

★ ⇑ **BAPTIST HEALTH CORBIN (180080)**, 1 Trillium Way, Zip 40701–8420;
tel. 606/528–1212, **A**10 19 21 **F**1 3 4 5 13 15 18 20 22 26 28 29 30 31 32
34 35 36 38 40 45 47 48 49 51 53 54 57 59 64 67 68 70 73 76 78 79 81 84
85 86 87 89 90 93 96 98 100 101 102 104 105 106 107 108 110 111 114
115 118 119 126 130 132 133 135 145 146 147 148 152 153 154 **S** Baptist
Health, Louisville, KY
Primary Contact: Anthony Powers, Interim President and Vice President of Patient
Services
CFO: Pamela K. Jones, Executive Director of Finance
CMO: David Worthy, M.D., Vice President and Chief Medical Officer
CIO: Rodney Richardson, Director of Information Technology
CHR: Tim Perry, Executive Director of Human Resources
CNO: Sherrie Mays, MSN, R.N., Vice President and Chief Nursing Officer
Web address: www.baptisthealth.com/corbin
Control: Other not–for–profit (including NFP Corporation) **Service:** General
medical and surgical

Staffed Beds: 273 **Admissions:** 9158 **Census:** 119 **Outpatient Visits:**
150720 **Births:** 827 **Total Expense ($000):** 164999 **Payroll Expense
($000):** 61230 **Personnel:** 1104

★ **CONTINUECARE HOSPITAL AT BAPTIST HEALTH CORBIN (182006)**, 1
Trillium Way, Lower Level, Zip 40701–8727; tel. 606/523–5150, **A**10 22 **F**1 3 29
30 34 57 59 85 148 **S** Community Hospital Corporation, Plano, TX
Primary Contact: Tuan Le, Chief Executive Officer
COO: Wilson Weber, Chief Operating Officer
CFO: Lisa Young, CPA, Chief Financial Officer
CMO: Steve Morton, M.D., Chief Medical Officer
CIO: Brian Doerr, Chief Information Officer
CHR: Amie Marcum, Human Resources Coordinator
CNO: Della Rains, Chief Nursing Officer
Web address: www.continuecare.org
Control: Other not–for–profit (including NFP Corporation) **Service:** Acute long–
term care hospital

Staffed Beds: 32 **Admissions:** 275 **Census:** 25 **Outpatient Visits:** 0
Births: 0 **Total Expense ($000):** 11495 **Payroll Expense ($000):** 5013
Personnel: 75

COVINGTON—Kenton County

ST. ELIZABETH MEDICAL CENTER–NORTH See St. Elizabeth Covington

CYNTHIANA—Harrison County

☒ **HARRISON MEMORIAL HOSPITAL (180079)**, 1210 KY Highway 36E, Zip 41031–7498; tel. 859/234–2300, **A**1 10 **F**3 11 13 15 18 20 22 28 29 30 31 34 35 36 39 40 43 44 45 47 49 50 53 57 59 61 64 68 69 70 74 75 76 77 78 79 81 82 85 86 87 89 93 97 107 108 111 115 118 119 129 130 131 132 133 135 144 146 147 148 **P**6
Primary Contact: Sheila Currans, Chief Executive Officer
CFO: David Mellett, Chief Financial Officer
CIO: Martha Sullivan, Chief Information Officer
CHR: Rebecca Jenkins, Director Human Resources Management
CNO: Wendy Reeder, R.N., Chief Nursing Officer
Web address: www.harrisonmemhosp.com
Control: Other not–for–profit (including NFP Corporation) **Service:** General medical and surgical

Staffed Beds: 34 **Admissions:** 1460 **Census:** 14 **Outpatient Visits:** 78557 **Births:** 197 **Total Expense ($000):** 45156 **Payroll Expense ($000):** 19776 **Personnel:** 452

DANVILLE—Boyle County

☐ **EPHRAIM MCDOWELL REGIONAL MEDICAL CENTER (180048)**, 217 South Third Street, Zip 40422–1823; tel. 859/239–1000, (Nonreporting) **A**1 3 5 10 19 **S** Ephraim McDowell Health, Danville, KY
Primary Contact: Daniel E. McKay, Chief Executive Officer
COO: Burt Piper, Chief Operating Officer
CFO: William R Snapp III Executive Vice President Finance and Chief Financial Officer
CMO: Kryder Van Buskirk III Medical Staff President at EMRMC
CIO: Gary Neat, Chief Information Officer
CHR: Libby Mayes, Human Resource Director
CNO: Mark W Milner, Chief Nursing Officer
Web address: www.emrmc.org
Control: Other not–for–profit (including NFP Corporation) **Service:** General medical and surgical

Staffed Beds: 159

EDGEWOOD—Kenton County

☒ **HEALTHSOUTH NORTHERN KENTUCKY REHABILITATION HOSPITAL (183027)**, 201 Medical Village Drive, Zip 41017–3407; tel. 859/341–2044, **A**1 10 **F**28 29 64 79 82 90 91 93 94 95 96 148 154 **S** Encompass Health Corporation, Birmingham, AL
Primary Contact: Jeremy Yates, Chief Executive Officer
CFO: Lisa McGue, Controller
CMO: Neal Moser, M.D., Medical Director
CHR: Bridgette Keith, Director Human Resources
CNO: Terri Ballard, Chief Nursing Officer
Web address: www.healthsouthkentucky.com
Control: Corporation, Investor–owned (for–profit) **Service:** Rehabilitation

Staffed Beds: 40 **Admissions:** 1305 **Census:** 39 **Outpatient Visits:** 3104 **Births:** 0 **Personnel:** 129

☐ **ST. ELIZABETH EDGEWOOD (180035)**, 1 Medical Village Drive, Zip 41017–3403; tel. 859/301–2000, (Includes ST. ELIZABETH COVINGTON, 1500 James Simpson Jr. Way, Covington, KY, Zip 41014–1585; tel. 859/655–8800) **A**1 2 3 5 10 **F**3 5 8 9 13 14 15 17 18 20 22 24 26 28 29 30 31 34 35 36 37 38 39 40 44 45 46 47 48 49 50 53 55 57 58 59 60 61 63 64 65 70 71 72 73 74 75 76 77 78 79 80 81 82 83 84 85 86 87 92 93 97 98 100 101 102 103 104 105 107 108 109 110 111 114 115 117 118 119 120 121 123 124 126 129 130 131 132 135 141 145 146 147 148 149 150 152 153 154 **S** St. Elizabeth Healthcare, Edgewood, KY
Primary Contact: Garren Colvin, Chief Executive Officer
CMO: Karl Schmitt, M.D., Chief of Staff
CIO: Alex Rodriguez, Vice President and Chief Information Officer
CHR: Martin Oscadal, Vice President Human Resources
Web address: www.stelizabeth.com
Control: Church operated, Nongovernment, not–for–profit **Service:** General medical and surgical

Staffed Beds: 508 **Admissions:** 28357 **Census:** 349 **Outpatient Visits:** 1273309 **Births:** 4490 **Total Expense ($000):** 730356 **Payroll Expense ($000):** 277914 **Personnel:** 3288

ST. ELIZABETH HEALTHCARE–EDGEWOOD See St. Elizabeth Edgewood

ELIZABETHTOWN—Hardin County

☒ **HARDIN MEMORIAL HEALTH (180012)**, 913 North Dixie Avenue, Zip 42701–2503; tel. 270/737–1212, (Total facility includes 15 beds in nursing home–type unit) **A**1 2 5 10 19 **F**3 8 11 12 13 15 17 18 20 22 24 28 29 30 31 32 34 35 37 39 40 44 45 48 49 50 51 52 54 57 58 59 64 68 70 71 72 74 75 76 77 78 79 80 81 82 84 85 86 87 89 93 94 96 98 102 107 108 110 111 114 115 117 118 119 120 121 124 126 127 128 129 130 131 132 134 135 144 146 147 148 149 154 **S** Baptist Health, Louisville, KY
Primary Contact: Dennis B. Johnson, President and Chief Executive Officer
COO: Tom Carrico, Vice President of Operations
CFO: Lennis Thompson II Vice President and Chief Financial Officer
CMO: John Godfrey, M.D., Vice President and Chief Executive Officer
CIO: Trey Hyberger, Director Information Technology
CHR: Myra Covault, Associate Vice President of Human Resources
CNO: Sharon Wright, R.N., Vice President and Chief Nursing Officer
Web address: www.hmh.net
Control: County, Government, nonfederal **Service:** General medical and surgical

Staffed Beds: 268 **Admissions:** 13128 **Census:** 162 **Outpatient Visits:** 451641 **Births:** 1712 **Total Expense ($000):** 318143 **Payroll Expense ($000):** 143463 **Personnel:** 2423

☒ **HEALTHSOUTH LAKEVIEW REHABILITATION HOSPITAL (183028)**, 134 Heartland Drive, Zip 42701–2778; tel. 270/769–3100, (Nonreporting) **A**1 10 **S** Encompass Health Corporation, Birmingham, AL
Primary Contact: Lori Jarboe, Chief Executive Officer
CFO: Scott Hart, Controller
CMO: Toni Abang, M.D., Medical Director
CHR: Janet Morris, Director Human Resources
Web address: www.healthsouthlakeview.com
Control: Corporation, Investor–owned (for–profit) **Service:** Rehabilitation

Staffed Beds: 40

ERLANGER—Kenton County

★ **SUN BEHAVIORAL KENTUCKY (184006)**, 820 Dolwick Drive, Zip 41018, Mailing Address: 3900 Olympic Blvd., Ste 400, Zip 41018; tel. 859/429–5188, (Nonreporting)
Primary Contact: Chris Lockey, Chief Executive Officer
COO: Carol Parke, Chief Operating Officer, SUN Kentucky
Web address: www.sunkentucky.com/
Control: Corporation, Investor–owned (for–profit) **Service:** Psychiatric

Staffed Beds: 197

FLEMINGSBURG—Fleming County

☒ **FLEMING COUNTY HOSPITAL (180053)**, 55 Foundation Drive, Zip 41041–9815, Mailing Address: P.O. Box 388, Zip 41041–0388; tel. 606/849–5000, (Nonreporting) **A**1 10 **S** LifePoint Health, Brentwood, TN
Primary Contact: Brian Springate, Chief Executive Officer
CFO: Theresa Fite, R.N., Chief Financial Officer
CMO: Samuel Gehring, M.D., Chief of Staff
CIO: Don Daugherty, Director Information Systems
CHR: Marsha Mitchell, Director Human Resources
CNO: Lynda Skaggs, Chief Nursing Officer
Web address: www.flemingcountyhospital.org
Control: Other not–for–profit (including NFP Corporation) **Service:** General medical and surgical

Staffed Beds: 52

FLORENCE—Boone County

☐ **GATEWAY REHABILITATION HOSPITAL (183030)**, 5940 Merchant Street, Zip 41042–1158; tel. 859/426–2400, (Nonreporting) **A**1 10 **S** Vibra Healthcare, Mechanicsburg, PA
Primary Contact: Frank Schneider, FACHE, Chief Executive Officer
CFO: Margaret Cesarez, Chief Financial Officer
CNO: Jenna Wellbrock, Chief Nursing Officer
Web address: www.gatewayflorence.com/
Control: Corporation, Investor–owned (for–profit) **Service:** Rehabilitation

Staffed Beds: 40

Hospital, Medicare Provider Number, Address, Telephone, Approval, Facility, and Physician Codes, Health Care System

★ American Hospital Association (AHA) membership
☐ The Joint Commission accreditation
○ Healthcare Facilities Accreditation Program
◇ DNV Healthcare Inc. accreditation
⇑ Center for Improvement in Healthcare Quality Accreditation
△ Commission on Accreditation of Rehabilitation Facilities (CARF) accreditation

☐ **ST. ELIZABETH FLORENCE (180045)**, 4900 Houston Road, Zip 41042–4824; tel. 859/212–5200, (Total facility includes 16 beds in nursing home–type unit) **A**1 10 **F**3 9 11 12 15 20 28 29 30 34 35 39 40 44 45 47 48 49 50 53 55 56 57 59 60 61 64 65 70 71 74 75 77 78 79 80 81 82 84 86 87 92 93 97 98 100 101 102 107 108 110 111 115 118 119 126 128 129 130 132 135 141 145 146 147 148 149 150 152 153 154 **S** St. Elizabeth Healthcare, Edgewood, KY
Primary Contact: Garren Colvin, Chief Executive Officer
COO: Chris Carle, Senior Vice President and Chief Operating Officer
CMO: George Hall, M.D., Vice President Medical Affairs
CIO: Alex Rodriguez, Vice President and Chief Information Officer
CHR: Martin Oscadal, Senior Vice President Human Resources
Web address: www.stelizabeth.com
Control: Church operated, Nongovernment, not–for–profit **Service:** General medical and surgical

Staffed Beds: **169** Admissions: **11083** Census: **122** Outpatient Visits: **179429** Births: **0** Total Expense ($000): **140811** Payroll Expense ($000): **60688** Personnel: **851**

ST. ELIZABETH HEALTHCARE FLORENCE See St. Elizabeth Florence

FORT CAMPBELL—Christian County

✠ **COLONEL FLORENCE A. BLANCHFIELD ARMY COMMUNITY HOSPITAL**, 650 Joel Drive, Zip 42223–5318; tel. 270/798–8040, (Nonreporting) **A**1 3 5 **S** Department of the Army, Office of the Surgeon General, Falls Church, VA
Primary Contact: Colonel Telita Crosland, Commander
CHR: Major Travis Burchett, Troop Commander Human Resources
Web address: www.campbell.amedd.army.mil/
Control: Army, Government, federal **Service:** General medical and surgical

Staffed Beds: **66**

FORT THOMAS—Campbell County

CARDINAL HILL SPECIALTY HOSPITAL See Select Specialty Hospital–Northern Kentucky

✠ **SELECT SPECIALTY HOSPITAL–NORTHERN KENTUCKY (182004)**, 85 North Grand Avenue, Zip 41075–1793; tel. 859/572–3880, (Nonreporting) **A**1 10 **S** Select Medical Corporation, Mechanicsburg, PA
Primary Contact: Mavis Bechtle, MSN, R.N., FACHE, Chief Executive Officer
Web address: www.selectspecialtyhospitals.com
Control: Corporation, Investor–owned (for–profit) **Service:** Acute long–term care hospital

Staffed Beds: **33**

☐ **ST. ELIZABETH FORT THOMAS (180001)**, 85 North Grand Avenue, Zip 41075–1796; tel. 859/572–1796, (Includes ST. ELIZABETH FALMOUTH, 512 South Maple Avenue, Falmouth, KY, Zip 41040–1422; tel. 859/572–3500; Garren Colvin, Chief Executive Officer) (Total facility includes 26 beds in nursing home–type unit) **A**1 2 10 **F**3 4 5 9 11 15 17 18 20 28 29 30 31 34 35 39 40 44 45 47 48 49 50 51 53 55 56 57 58 59 60 61 63 64 65 70 71 74 75 77 78 79 80 81 82 85 86 87 91 92 93 94 97 100 102 107 108 110 111 115 118 119 120 121 123 126 128 129 130 135 141 146 147 149 150 152 153 154 **S** St. Elizabeth Healthcare, Edgewood, KY
Primary Contact: Garren Colvin, Chief Executive Officer
COO: Thomas Saalfeld, Senior Vice President and Chief Operating Officer
CMO: George Hall, M.D., Vice President Medical Affairs
CIO: Alex Rodriguez, Vice President and Chief Information Officer
CHR: Martin Oscadal, Senior Vice President Human Resources
Web address: www.stelizabeth.com
Control: Church operated, Nongovernment, not–for–profit **Service:** General medical and surgical

Staffed Beds: **171** Admissions: **7603** Census: **102** Outpatient Visits: **149834** Births: **0** Total Expense ($000): **130247** Payroll Expense ($000): **53909** Personnel: **676**

ST. ELIZABETH HEALTHCARE FORT THOMAS See St. Elizabeth Fort Thomas

FRANKFORT—Franklin County

✠ **FRANKFORT REGIONAL MEDICAL CENTER (180127)**, 299 King's Daughters Drive, Zip 40601–4186; tel. 502/875–5240, **A**1 2 10 19 **F**3 13 15 18 20 22 28 29 30 31 34 40 43 45 49 50 51 57 60 64 68 70 72 74 75 76 77 78 79 81 82 84 85 87 89 93 98 102 103 107 111 119 124 129 130 133 135 145 146 147 148 154 **S** HCA Healthcare, Nashville, TN
Primary Contact: Chip Peal, Chief Executive Officer
CMO: Willis P McKee, M.D., Jr Chief Medical Officer
CIO: Craig Willard, Director Information Technology and Systems
CHR: Bev Young, Director Human Resources
Web address: www.frankfortregional.com
Control: Corporation, Investor–owned (for–profit) **Service:** General medical and surgical

Staffed Beds: **116** Admissions: **5930** Census: **77** Outpatient Visits: **93563** Births: **752** Total Expense ($000): **108878** Payroll Expense ($000): **32702** Personnel: **436**

FRANKLIN—Simpson County

✠ **MEDICAL CENTER AT FRANKLIN (181318)**, 1100 Brookhaven Road, Zip 42134–2746; tel. 270/598–4800, **A**1 10 18 **F**3 15 28 29 30 34 35 40 46 50 57 59 64 68 75 77 81 82 86 87 93 107 108 110 111 114 119 127 130 133 135 146 148 149 **S** Med Center Health, Bowling Green, KY
Primary Contact: Annette Runyon, Vice President and Administrator
CFO: Ronald G. Sowell, FACHE, Executive Vice President
CIO: Mark Brookman, Vice President and Chief Information Officer
Web address: www.themedicalcenterfranklin.org
Control: Other not–for–profit (including NFP Corporation) **Service:** General medical and surgical

Staffed Beds: **25** Admissions: **1043** Census: **19** Outpatient Visits: **21904** Births: **0** Personnel: **125**

GEORGETOWN—Scott County

✠ **GEORGETOWN COMMUNITY HOSPITAL (180101)**, 1140 Lexington Road, Zip 40324–9362; tel. 502/868–1100, **A**1 5 10 **F**3 11 12 13 15 18 28 29 30 31 34 35 40 45 46 47 48 49 50 51 57 59 60 64 65 66 70 74 75 76 77 78 79 81 82 85 87 92 93 100 107 108 109 110 111 114 115 116 119 124 126 129 130 131 132 133 135 144 146 147 148 149 154 **S** LifePoint Health, Brentwood, TN
Primary Contact: William Haugh, Administrator
CFO: Patrick C Bolander, Chief Financial Officer
CMO: Brian Allen, M.D., President Medical Staff
CHR: Marrianne Slonina, Director Human Resources
Web address: www.georgetowncommunityhospital.com
Control: Corporation, Investor–owned (for–profit) **Service:** General medical and surgical

Staffed Beds: **58** Admissions: **2150** Census: **17** Outpatient Visits: **71453** Births: **335** Total Expense ($000): **52332** Payroll Expense ($000): **17491** Personnel: **387**

GLASGOW—Barren County

☐ **T. J. SAMSON COMMUNITY HOSPITAL (180017)**, 1301 North Race Street, Zip 42141–3483; tel. 270/651–4444, (Nonreporting) **A**1 3 5 10 19
Primary Contact: Neil Thornbury, Chief Executive Officer
COO: Margie Gentry, Controller
CFO: Mei Deng, Chief Financial Officer
CIO: Chad Friend, Director
CHR: LaDonna Rogers, Director Human Resources
CNO: Shea Wilson, Chief Nursing Officer
Web address: www.tjsamson.org
Control: Other not–for–profit (including NFP Corporation) **Service:** General medical and surgical

Staffed Beds: **141**

GREENSBURG—Green County

JANE TODD CRAWFORD HOSPITAL (181325), 202–206 Milby Street, Zip 42743–1100, Mailing Address: P.O. Box 220, Zip 42743–0220; tel. 270/932–4211, (Nonreporting) **A**10 18
Primary Contact: Rex A. Tungate, Chief Executive Officer
CFO: Richard Hendershot, Chief Financial Officer
CMO: Shane DeSimone, M.D., Chief of Staff
CHR: Mary Ann Quinn, Administrative Assistant
CNO: Roxie Montgomery, Director of Nursing
Web address: www.janetoddhospital.com
Control: County, Government, nonfederal **Service:** General medical and surgical

Staffed Beds: **45**

GREENVILLE—Muhlenberg County

☐ **OWENSBORO HEALTH MUHLENBERG COMMUNITY HOSPITAL (180004)**, 440 Hopkinsville Street, Zip 42345–1172, Mailing Address: P.O. Box 387, Zip 42345–0378; tel. 270/338–8000, (Nonreporting) **A**1 10 **S** Owensboro Health, Owensboro, KY
Primary Contact: Ed Heath, FACHE, Chief Executive Officer
CMO: Vincent P Genovese, M.D., President Medical Staff
CIO: Alan Trail, Director Information Systems
CHR: Lisa R Hope, Director Human Resources
CNO: Kathy Mitchell, Chief Nursing Officer
Web address: www.mchky.org
Control: Other not–for–profit (including NFP Corporation) **Service:** General medical and surgical

Staffed Beds: **105**

HARDINSBURG—Breckinridge County

⊠ **BRECKINRIDGE MEMORIAL HOSPITAL (181319)**, 1011 Old Highway 60, Zip 40143–2597; tel. 270/756–7000, (Nonreporting) **A**1 5 10 18 **S** Alliant Management Services, Louisville, KY
Primary Contact: Angela Portman, Chief Executive Officer
CFO: Timothy D Crockett, Chief Financial Officer
CMO: Brian O'Donoghue, M.D., Chief Medical Officer
CHR: James Turpin, Human Resources
CNO: Tiffany Kennedy, Chief Nursing Officer
Web address: www.breckinridgehealth.org/
Control: Other not–for–profit (including NFP Corporation) **Service:** General medical and surgical

Staffed Beds: 43

HARLAN—Harlan County

☐ **HARLAN ARH HOSPITAL (180050)**, 81 Ball Park Road, Zip 40831–1792; tel. 606/573–8100, **A**1 10 19 **F**3 11 13 15 18 20 28 29 30 32 34 35 40 43 50 54 57 59 62 64 70 75 76 77 78 79 81 82 85 86 87 89 93 97 98 99 102 103 107 108 111 115 118 119 127 129 130 132 146 147 148 **P**6 **S** Appalachian Regional Healthcare, Inc., Lexington, KY
Primary Contact: Donald R. Fields, Community Chief Executive Officer
CFO: Brad Burkhart, Assistant Administrator
CHR: Sabra Howard, Manager Human Resources
Web address: www.arh.org
Control: Other not–for–profit (including NFP Corporation) **Service:** General medical and surgical

Staffed Beds: 103 **Admissions:** 4744 **Census:** 51 **Outpatient Visits:** 73750 **Births:** 202 **Total Expense ($000):** 45156 **Payroll Expense ($000):** 19776

HARRODSBURG—Mercer County

⊠ **EPHRAIM MCDOWELL JAMES B. HAGGIN MEMORIAL HOSPITAL (181302)**, 464 Linden Avenue, Zip 40330–1862; tel. 859/734–5441, **A**1 5 10 18 **F**7 15 17 29 30 93 107 111 115 119 127 132 133 146 **P**5 **S** Ephraim McDowell Health, Danville, KY
Primary Contact: Lynne Warner Lynn, DNP, RN, Administrator
CFO: Tony Patterson, Chief Financial Officer
Web address: www.hagginhosp.org
Control: Other not–for–profit (including NFP Corporation) **Service:** General medical and surgical

Staffed Beds: 25 **Admissions:** 375 **Census:** 3 **Outpatient Visits:** 121867 **Births:** 0 **Personnel:** 221

HARTFORD—Ohio County

⊠ **OHIO COUNTY HOSPITAL (181323)**, 1211 Main Street, Zip 42347–1619; tel. 270/298–7411, **A**1 10 18 **F**3 15 18 26 28 29 30 35 36 40 48 49 50 59 63 64 65 74 75 77 79 81 82 84 85 87 92 93 97 100 107 110 111 115 119 127 129 130 132 133 135 146 147 148 149 154 **S** QHR, Brentwood, TN
Primary Contact: Blaine Pieper, Chief Executive Officer
CFO: John Tichenor, Chief Financial Officer
CMO: Joshua Skibba, Chief Medical Officer
CHR: Sue Wydick, Director Human Resources
CNO: Athena Minor, Chief Nursing Officer
Web address: www.ohiocountyhospital.com
Control: Other not–for–profit (including NFP Corporation) **Service:** General medical and surgical

Staffed Beds: 30 **Admissions:** 833 **Census:** 9 **Outpatient Visits:** 16173 **Births:** 0 **Total Expense ($000):** 38809 **Payroll Expense ($000):** 18615 **Personnel:** 427

HAZARD—Perry County

☐ **HAZARD ARH REGIONAL MEDICAL CENTER (180029)**, 100 Medical Center Drive, Zip 41701–9421; tel. 606/439–6600, **A**1 2 3 5 10 19 **F**3 11 12 13 15 17 18 20 22 24 26 28 29 30 31 32 34 35 40 43 46 47 48 49 50 54 55 57 59 61 62 64 70 71 73 74 75 76 77 78 79 81 82 85 86 87 89 90 93 97 98 101 102 103 107 108 110 116 120 121 124 127 129 130 132 146 147 148 **S** Appalachian Regional Healthcare, Inc., Lexington, KY
Primary Contact: Dan Stone, Senior Community Chief Executive Officer
CMO: J D Miller, M.D., Chief Medical Officer
CIO: Jeff Brady, Director Information Systems
CHR: Sheila Cornett, Manager Human Resources
Web address: www.arh.org
Control: Other not–for–profit (including NFP Corporation) **Service:** General medical and surgical

Staffed Beds: 358 **Admissions:** 10921 **Census:** 184 **Outpatient Visits:** 126923 **Births:** 341

HENDERSON—Henderson County

☐ **METHODIST HOSPITAL (180056)**, 1305 North Elm Street, Zip 42420–2775, Mailing Address: P.O. Box 48, Zip 42419–0048; tel. 270/827–7700, **A**1 2 10 13 **F**3 11 13 15 18 29 30 31 34 35 36 40 45 46 47 49 50 51 53 54 57 58 59 64 66 68 70 72 74 75 76 77 78 79 81 82 85 86 87 92 93 107 108 110 111 114 115 118 119 126 127 129 130 131 132 135 146 147 148 149 **P**8
Primary Contact: Benny Nolen, President and Chief Executive Officer
CFO: David Massengale, Vice President and Chief Financial Officer
CMO: John Logan, M.D., Chief Medical Officer
CIO: Randy McCleese, Chief Information Officer
CHR: Ty Kahle, Vice President Human Resources
Web address: www.methodisthospital.net
Control: Church operated, Nongovernment, not–for–profit **Service:** General medical and surgical

Staffed Beds: 124 **Admissions:** 4003 **Census:** 50 **Outpatient Visits:** 332799 **Births:** 655 **Total Expense ($000):** 110153 **Payroll Expense ($000):** 39631 **Personnel:** 958

HOPKINSVILLE—Christian County

☐ **CUMBERLAND HALL HOSPITAL (184014)**, 270 Walton Way, Zip 42240–6808; tel. 270/886–1919, **A**1 10 **F**98 100 101 102 130 133 143 **S** Universal Health Services, Inc., King of Prussia, PA
Primary Contact: Jason Staats, Chief Executive Officer
CFO: Mark Wallace, Chief Financial Officer
CMO: Deepak Patel, M.D., Medical Director
CIO: Patricia Gray, Director Health Information Management
CHR: Kelly Hagy, Director Human Resources
CNO: Denise Lyons, Chief Nursing Officer
Web address: www.cumberlandhallhospital.com
Control: Corporation, Investor–owned (for–profit) **Service:** Psychiatric

Staffed Beds: 97 **Admissions:** 1713 **Census:** 64 **Outpatient Visits:** 0 **Births:** 0 **Total Expense ($000):** 11656 **Payroll Expense ($000):** 6507 **Personnel:** 126

☐ **JENNIE STUART MEDICAL CENTER (180051)**, 320 West 18th Street, Zip 42240–1965, Mailing Address: P.O. Box 2400, Zip 42241–2400; tel. 270/887–0100, (Nonreporting) **A**1 3 10 20 **S** QHR, Brentwood, TN
Primary Contact: Eric A. Lee, President and Chief Executive Officer
CMO: Casey Covington, M.D., President Elect, Medical Staff
CIO: Jerry Houston, Director Information Systems
CHR: Austin Moss, Vice President Human Resources
Web address: www.jsmc.org
Control: Other not–for–profit (including NFP Corporation) **Service:** General medical and surgical

Staffed Beds: 139

☐ **WESTERN STATE HOSPITAL (184002)**, Russellville Road, Zip 42240–3017, Mailing Address: P.O. Box 2200, Zip 42241–2200; tel. 270/889–6025, **A**1 10 **F**98 102 103 130 149 **P**5
Primary Contact: Roger Westfall, Director
CFO: Jessica Cates, Fiscal Manager
CMO: Nayyar Iqbal, M.D., Director Medical Staff
CIO: Valerie Majors, Director Information Services
CHR: James L Hayes, Director Human Resources
CNO: Jill Thomas, Director of Nursing
Web address: www.westernstatehospital.ky.gov
Control: State, Government, nonfederal **Service:** Psychiatric

Staffed Beds: 205 **Admissions:** 1958 **Census:** 109 **Outpatient Visits:** 0 **Births:** 0 **Total Expense ($000):** 18104 **Payroll Expense ($000):** 8438 **Personnel:** 641

HORSE CAVE—Hart County

THE MEDICAL CENTER AT CAVERNA (181314), 1501 South Dixie Street, Zip 42749–1477; tel. 270/786–2191, (Nonreporting) **A**10 18 **S** Med Center Health, Bowling Green, KY
Primary Contact: Alan B. Alexander, FACHE, Vice President and Administrator
CFO: Ronald G. Sowell, FACHE, Executive Vice President and Chief Financial Officer
CIO: Mark Brookman, Vice President, Chief Information Officer
CHR: Lynn Williams, Vice President, Human Resources
Web address: www.TheMedicalCenterCaverna.org
Control: Corporation, Investor–owned (for–profit) **Service:** General medical and surgical

Staffed Beds: 25

Hospital, Medicare Provider Number, Address, Telephone, Approval, Facility, and Physician Codes, Health Care System

★ American Hospital Association (AHA) membership
☐ The Joint Commission accreditation
○ Healthcare Facilities Accreditation Program
◇ DNV Healthcare Inc. accreditation
⇑ Center for Improvement in Healthcare Quality Accreditation
△ Commission on Accreditation of Rehabilitation Facilities (CARF) accreditation

HYDEN—Leslie County

MARY BRECKINRIDGE ARH HOSPITAL (181316), 130 Kate Ireland Drive, Zip 41749–9071, Mailing Address: P.O. Box 447–A, Zip 41749–0717; tel. 606/672–2901, **A**10 18 **F**2 3 11 15 29 30 32 34 35 40 50 57 59 62 65 68 75 77 81 86 87 93 107 110 115 119 130 132 133 135 146 **P**6 **S** Appalachian Regional Healthcare, Inc., Lexington, KY
Primary Contact: Mallie S. Noble, Administrator
COO: Nathan W Lee, Chief Executive Officer
CFO: Robert Besten, Chief Financial Officer
CMO: Roy Varghese, M.D., Chief of Staff
CIO: Frank Baker, Chief Information Officer
CHR: Beulah Couch, Director Human Resources
Web address: www.frontiernursing.org
Control: Other not–for–profit (including NFP Corporation) **Service**: General medical and surgical

Staffed Beds: 25 Admissions: 384 Census: 10 Outpatient Visits: 21633 Births: 0

IRVINE—Estill County

★ **MERCY HEALTH – MARCUM AND WALLACE (181301)**, 60 Mercy Court, Zip 40336–1331; tel. 606/723–2115, **A**10 18 **F**3 15 29 30 34 35 40 43 45 50 56 57 59 64 75 77 81 93 107 115 119 127 129 130 131 133 146 147 **S** Mercy Health, Cincinnati, OH
Primary Contact: Susan Starling, President and Chief Executive Officer
CFO: Lori Witt, Site Finance Director
CMO: Maher Kassis, M.D., Chief Medical Staff
CHR: Dana Stepp, Human Resources Officer
CNO: Trena Stocker, Chief Nursing Executive
Web address: www.marcumandwallace.org
Control: Church operated, Nongovernment, not–for–profit **Service**: General medical and surgical

Staffed Beds: 25 Admissions: 1153 Census: 13 Outpatient Visits: 73455 Births: 0 Total Expense ($000): 22051 Payroll Expense ($000): 9016 Personnel: 159

JACKSON—Breathitt County

▣ **KENTUCKY RIVER MEDICAL CENTER (180139)**, 540 Jett Drive, Zip 41339–9622; tel. 606/666–6000, (Nonreporting) **A**1 10 20 **S** Quorum Health, Brentwood, TN
Primary Contact: John Ballard, Ph.D., Chief Executive Officer
CFO: Michael Ackley, Chief Financial Officer
CMO: Eunice Johnson, M.D., Chief Medical Staff
CIO: Diana Tyra, Director Health Information
CHR: Naomi Mitchell, Director Human Resources
Web address: www.kentuckyrivermc.com
Control: Corporation, Investor–owned (for–profit) **Service**: General medical and surgical

Staffed Beds: 54

LA GRANGE—Oldham County

▣ **BAPTIST HEALTH LA GRANGE (180138)**, 1025 New Moody Lane, Zip 40031–9154; tel. 502/222–5388, (Total facility includes 24 beds in nursing home–type unit) **A**1 5 10 **F**3 7 11 13 15 18 28 29 30 31 34 35 40 43 45 46 49 50 54 56 57 59 64 70 74 75 76 77 78 79 81 82 85 86 87 93 97 107 108 110 111 114 119 128 130 131 132 133 135 146 147 148 149 **S** Baptist Health, Louisville, KY
Primary Contact: Clint Kaho, President
CFO: Jim Morris, Vice President Finance
CMO: Matt McDanald, M.D., Chief Medical Officer
CIO: David Bensema, Chief Information Officer
CHR: Kayla Batts, Manager Human Resources
CNO: Nathan Wilson, R.N., Vice President and Chief Nursing Officer
Web address: www.baptisthealthlagrange.com
Control: Other not–for–profit (including NFP Corporation) **Service**: General medical and surgical

Staffed Beds: 65 Admissions: 2330 Census: 35 Outpatient Visits: 148032 Births: 489 Total Expense ($000): 92217 Payroll Expense ($000): 25623 Personnel: 382

LEBANON—Marion County

▣ **SPRING VIEW HOSPITAL (180024)**, 320 Loretto Road, Zip 40033–1300; tel. 270/692–3161, (Nonreporting) **A**1 10 **S** LifePoint Health, Brentwood, TN
Primary Contact: Timothy R. Trottier, Chief Executive Officer
CFO: Denise Thomas, Chief Financial Officer
CIO: Douglas Bland, Manager Information Services
CHR: Ann Dabney, Manager Human Resources
CNO: Linda Hunter, Chief Nursing Officer
Web address: www.springviewhospital.com
Control: Corporation, Investor–owned (for–profit) **Service**: General medical and surgical

Staffed Beds: 60

LEITCHFIELD—Grayson County

☐ **TWIN LAKES REGIONAL MEDICAL CENTER (180070)**, 910 Wallace Avenue, Zip 42754–2414; tel. 270/259–9400, (Nonreporting) **A**1 10 **S** Alliant Management Services, Louisville, KY
Primary Contact: Wayne Meriwether, Chief Executive Officer
COO: Deneace Clemons, Chief Operating Officer
CFO: Scott Arndell, Chief Financial Officer
CIO: Robbie Lindsey, Chief Information Officer
CHR: Kim Rayls, Director Human Resources
CNO: David Logdson, Chief Nursing Officer
Web address: www.tlrmc.com
Control: Other not–for–profit (including NFP Corporation) **Service**: General medical and surgical

Staffed Beds: 75

LEXINGTON—Fayette County

▣ **BAPTIST HEALTH LEXINGTON (180103)**, 1740 Nicholasville Road, Zip 40503–1499; tel. 859/260–6100, **A**1 2 3 10 **F**3 11 12 13 15 17 18 20 22 24 26 28 29 30 31 34 35 36 40 44 45 46 47 48 49 53 54 55 56 57 58 59 60 64 65 68 70 72 74 75 76 77 78 79 81 82 84 85 86 87 92 93 97 107 108 110 111 114 115 117 118 119 120 121 124 126 129 130 131 132 135 144 146 147 148 154 **S** Baptist Health, Louisville, KY
Primary Contact: William G. Sisson, FACHE, President
COO: Karen S Hill, R.N., FACHE, Chief Operating Officer and Chief Nursing Officer
CFO: John Franke, Chief Financial Officer
CMO: James Borders, M.D., Chief Medical Officer
CIO: Lisa Fluty, Director Information Services
CHR: Lynette Walker, R.N., Ph.D., Vice President Human Resources
CNO: Karen S Hill, R.N., FACHE, Chief Operating Officer and Chief Nursing Officer
Web address: www.baptisthealthlexington.com
Control: Other not–for–profit (including NFP Corporation) **Service**: General medical and surgical

Staffed Beds: 391 Admissions: 19555 Census: 252 Outpatient Visits: 321066 Births: 3507 Total Expense ($000): 462425 Payroll Expense ($000): 142502 Personnel: 2731

★ △ **CARDINAL HILL REHABILITATION HOSPITAL (183026)**, 2050 Versailles Road, Zip 40504–1405; tel. 859/254–5701, (Total facility includes 74 beds in nursing home–type unit) **A**3 5 7 10 **F**3 28 29 56 58 62 64 87 90 91 93 95 96 128 130 **S** Encompass Health Corporation, Birmingham, AL
Primary Contact: Tara Diebling, Chief Executive Officer
CFO: Marty Lautner, Vice President Finance and Chief Financial Officer
CMO: William Lester, M.D., Vice President Medical Affairs
CIO: LouAnn Hyder, Director Information Integrity Management
CHR: Barry K Lindeman, Director Human Resources
CNO: Maureen Couture, Chief Nursing Officer and Vice President Nursing
Web address: www.cardinalhillhealthsouth.com
Control: Corporation, Investor–owned (for–profit) **Service**: Rehabilitation

Staffed Beds: 232 Admissions: 3983 Census: 147 Outpatient Visits: 43878 Births: 0 Total Expense ($000): 65357 Payroll Expense ($000): 33909 Personnel: 557

★ **CONTINUING CARE HOSPITAL (182002)**, 1 Saint Joseph Drive, Zip 40504–3742; tel. 859/967–5744, **A**10 **F**1 3 29 30 **S** Catholic Health Initiatives, Englewood, CO
Primary Contact: Robert C. Desotelle, President and Chief Executive Officer
CMO: Michael Miedler, M.D., Chief Medical Officer
CNO: Regina Masters, R.N., MSN, Director of Nursing
Web address: www.kentuckyonehealth.org
Control: Church operated, Nongovernment, not–for–profit **Service**: Acute long–term care hospital

Staffed Beds: 23 Admissions: 362 Census: 23 Outpatient Visits: 0 Births: 0 Total Expense ($000): 14683 Payroll Expense ($000): 4906 Personnel: 72

☐ **EASTERN STATE HOSPITAL (184004)**, 1350 Bull Lea Road, Zip 40511; tel. 859/246–8000, **A**1 3 5 10 **F**30 35 98 101 103 130 132 135 143 146 149 150
Primary Contact: Carrie Rudzik, Chief Administrative Officer
CFO: Brett Russell, Finance Business Partner Specialist
CMO: Andrew Cooley, M.D., Chief Medical Officer
CIO: Steve Kincaid, Information Technology Manager
CHR: Daniel Hacker, Human Resource Business Partner
CNO: Marc Anthony Woods, Assistant Chief Nurse Executive
Web address: www.ukhealthcare.uky.edu/ESH/
Control: State, Government, nonfederal **Service**: Psychiatric

Staffed Beds: 140 Admissions: 2725 Census: 129 Outpatient Visits: 0 Births: 0 Total Expense ($000): 31948 Payroll Expense ($000): 24016 Personnel: 426

Many Facility Codes have changed. Please refer to the AHA Guide Code Chart.
© 2018 AHA Guide

FEDERAL MEDICAL CENTER, 3301 Leestown Road, Zip 40511–8799; tel. 859/255–6812, (Nonreporting)
Primary Contact: Francisco Quintana, Warden
CFO: Mike Kinsel, Controller
CMO: Michael Growse, M.D., Clinical Director
Control: Department of Justice, Government, federal **Service:** Hospital unit of an institution (prison hospital, college infirmary, etc.)

Staffed Beds: 22

☒ **LEXINGTON VETERANS AFFAIRS MEDICAL CENTER**, 1101 Veterans Drive, Zip 40502–2235; tel. 859/281–4901, (Total facility includes 50 beds in nursing home–type unit) **A**1 3 5 **F**3 4 5 8 11 17 18 20 22 26 29 30 31 34 35 36 38 39 40 46 47 49 51 54 56 57 58 59 60 61 63 64 65 67 70 74 75 77 78 79 81 82 83 84 86 87 90 91 92 93 94 96 97 98 100 102 104 106 107 108 111 114 115 116 117 118 119 126 127 128 129 130 132 135 143 144 146 147 148 149 152 153 154 **P**6 **S** Department of Veterans Affairs, Perry Point, MD
Primary Contact: Emma Metcalf, MSN, R.N., Director
CFO: Patricia Swisshelm, Acting Chief Fiscal Service
CMO: Patricia Breeden, M.D., Chief of Staff
CIO: Jeffrey Sutton, Chief Information Officer
CHR: Laura Faulkner, Chief Human Resource Management Service
CNO: Mary Kelly McCullough, Associate Director Patient Care Services
Web address: www.lexington.va.gov/
Control: Veterans Affairs, Government, federal **Service:** General medical and surgical

Staffed Beds: 168 Admissions: 5412 Census: 66 Outpatient Visits: 517777 Births: 0 Personnel: 2096

☐ **RIDGE BEHAVIORAL HEALTH SYSTEM (184009)**, 3050 Rio Dosa Drive, Zip 40509–1540; tel. 859/269–2325, (Nonreporting) **A**1 5 10 **S** Universal Health Services, Inc., King of Prussia, PA
Primary Contact: Nina W. Eisner, Chief Executive Officer and Managing Director
CFO: Richard McDowell, Chief Financial Officer
CMO: Michael Rieser, M.D., Medical Director
CNO: Georgia Swank, Chief Nursing Officer
Web address: www.ridgebhs.com
Control: Corporation, Investor–owned (for–profit) **Service:** Psychiatric

Staffed Beds: 110

☒ **SAINT JOSEPH EAST (180143)**, 150 North Eagle Creek Drive, Zip 40509–1805; tel. 859/967–5000, (Includes WOMEN'S HOSPITAL SAINT JOSEPH EAST, 170 North Eagle Creek Drive, Lexington, KY, Zip 40509–9087; tel. 859/572–3500) **A**1 2 5 10 **F**3 8 12 13 15 18 20 22 24 26 28 29 30 31 40 47 49 50 60 68 70 72 74 75 76 77 78 79 81 82 85 86 93 107 108 111 114 119 120 121 122 123 126 129 142 146 147 148 **S** Catholic Health Initiatives, Englewood, CO
Primary Contact: Eric Gilliam, President
COO: Christine Mays, R.N., MSN, Chief Operating Officer and Chief Nurse Executive
CFO: Melinda S Evans, Vice President Finance
CIO: Janie Fergus, Director and Chief Information Officer
Web address: www.sjhlex.org
Control: Church operated, Nongovernment, not–for–profit **Service:** General medical and surgical

Staffed Beds: 150 Admissions: 9165 Census: 91 Outpatient Visits: 133005 Total Expense ($000): 181950 Payroll Expense ($000): 51228 Personnel: 701

☒ **SAINT JOSEPH HOSPITAL (180010)**, One St Joseph Drive, Zip 40504–3754; tel. 859/278–3436, **A**1 2 3 10 **F**3 8 11 12 15 17 18 19 20 22 24 25 26 27 28 29 30 31 34 35 37 40 41 45 47 49 50 51 54 55 56 57 58 59 64 65 66 68 70 74 77 78 79 81 82 83 84 85 86 87 91 92 93 94 97 107 110 111 114 115 116 117 118 119 120 121 122 126 127 129 130 132 135 144 146 147 148 **S** Catholic Health Initiatives, Englewood, CO
Primary Contact: Bruce J. Tassin, President
COO: Christine Mays, R.N., MSN, Chief Operating Officer and Chief Nurse Executive
CFO: Melinda S Evans, Vice President Finance
CIO: Janie Fergus, Director and Chief Information Officer
Web address: www.sjhlex.org
Control: Church operated, Nongovernment, not–for–profit **Service:** General medical and surgical

Staffed Beds: 307 Admissions: 12745 Census: 182 Outpatient Visits: 94994 Births: 0 Total Expense ($000): 280458 Payroll Expense ($000): 82951 Personnel: 1095

☒ **SELECT SPECIALTY HOSPITAL–LEXINGTON (182003)**, 310 South Limestone Street, 3rd Floor, Zip 40508–3008; tel. 859/226–7096, (Nonreporting) **A**1 10 **S** Select Medical Corporation, Mechanicsburg, PA
Primary Contact: Kim Pennington, Chief Executive Officer
CMO: Fadi Bacha, M.D., Chief Medical Officer
CHR: Tina Kirkland–Rose, Coordinator Human Resources
CNO: Katie Meredith, Chief Nursing Officer
Web address: www.lexington.selectspecialtyhospitals.com/
Control: Corporation, Investor–owned (for–profit) **Service:** Acute long–term care hospital

Staffed Beds: 41

☒ **UNIVERSITY OF KENTUCKY ALBERT B. CHANDLER HOSPITAL (180067)**, 800 Rose Street, Zip 40536–0293; tel. 859/323–5000, (Includes KENTUCKY CHILDREN'S HOSPITAL, N–100 – 800 Rose Street, Lexington, KY, Zip 40536–0293; tel. 859/257–1000; UK HEALTHCARE GOOD SAMARITAN HOSPITAL, 310 South Limestone Street, Lexington, KY, Zip 40508–3008; tel. 859/226–7000) **A**1 2 3 5 8 10 12 **F**3 5 6 7 9 11 12 13 15 16 17 18 19 20 21 22 23 24 25 26 27 28 29 30 31 32 34 35 36 37 38 39 40 41 43 44 45 46 47 48 49 50 52 54 55 56 57 58 59 60 61 64 65 66 68 70 72 73 74 75 76 77 78 79 81 82 84 85 86 87 88 89 91 92 93 94 95 96 97 98 99 100 102 103 104 107 108 110 111 114 115 116 117 118 119 120 121 124 126 129 130 131 132 134 135 136 137 138 139 140 141 142 145 146 147 148 149 150 154 **P**6
Primary Contact: Mark Newman, M.D., Executive Vice President of Health Affairs
CHR: Kimberly P Wilson, Director Human Resources
Web address: www.ukhealthcare.uky.edu
Control: State, Government, nonfederal **Service:** General medical and surgical

Staffed Beds: 888 Admissions: 38739 Census: 722 Outpatient Visits: 1602378 Births: 1907 Total Expense ($000): 1359881 Payroll Expense ($000): 462537 Personnel: 7949

UNIVERSITY OF KENTUCKY HOSPITAL See University of Kentucky Albert B. Chandler Hospital

LIBERTY—Casey County

☐ **CASEY COUNTY HOSPITAL (181309)**, 187 Wolford Avenue, Zip 42539–3278; tel. 606/787–6275, (Nonreporting) **A**1 10 18
Primary Contact: Rex A. Tungate, Chief Executive Officer
CFO: Richard Hendershot, Chief Financial Officer
CMO: Housam Haddad, M.D., Chief of Staff
CHR: Mary Ann Quinn, Administrative Assistant
CNO: Sue Antle, Director of Nursing
Web address: www.caseycountyhospital.com
Control: County, Government, nonfederal **Service:** General medical and surgical

Staffed Beds: 24

LONDON—Laurel County

☒ **SAINT JOSEPH LONDON (180011)**, 1001 Saint Joseph Lane, Zip 40741–8345; tel. 606/330–6000, **A**1 10 19 **F**3 13 15 20 22 26 28 29 30 31 34 35 40 45 47 49 50 51 57 59 60 61 64 70 74 75 76 78 79 80 81 82 85 87 89 92 93 97 107 108 110 111 114 115 119 127 129 130 131 135 146 147 149 150 **S** Catholic Health Initiatives, Englewood, CO
Primary Contact: Terrence G. Deis, CPA, FACHE, President
CFO: Christy Spitser, Vice President Finance and Business Development
CMO: Shelley Stanko, M.D., Chief Medical Officer
CHR: Sandra Turqueza, Senior Human Resources Business Partner
CNO: Lewis Stephen O'Neal, R.N., MSN, Chief Nursing Officer
Web address: www.saintjosephhealthsystem.com
Control: Church operated, Nongovernment, not–for–profit **Service:** General medical and surgical

Staffed Beds: 116 Admissions: 5764 Census: 61 Outpatient Visits: 108526 Births: 1198 Total Expense ($000): 117104 Payroll Expense ($000): 31009 Personnel: 554

LOUISA—Lawrence County

☒ **THREE RIVERS MEDICAL CENTER (180128)**, 2485 Highway 644, Zip 41230–9242, Mailing Address: P.O. Box 769, Zip 41230–0769; tel. 606/638–9451, **A**1 10 20 **F**3 5 12 15 18 29 40 45 49 50 51 68 70 75 79 81 85 86 87 93 98 101 102 104 107 108 110 111 113 115 119 129 130 133 146 147 **S** Quorum Health, Brentwood, TN
Primary Contact: Greg Kiser, Chief Executive Officer
CFO: Michael Ackley, Chief Financial Officer
CHR: Pat Hart, Director Human Resources
CNO: Cathy Heston, Chief Nursing Officer
Web address: www.threeriversmedicalcenter.com
Control: Corporation, Investor–owned (for–profit) **Service:** General medical and surgical

Staffed Beds: 90 Admissions: 2454 Census: 26 Outpatient Visits: 51443 Births: 0

Hospital, Medicare Provider Number, Address, Telephone, Approval, Facility, and Physician Codes, Health Care System

★ American Hospital Association (AHA) membership   ○ Healthcare Facilities Accreditation Program   ⇑ Center for Improvement in Healthcare Quality Accreditation
☐ The Joint Commission accreditation   ◇ DNV Healthcare Inc. accreditation   △ Commission on Accreditation of Rehabilitation Facilities (CARF) accreditation

LOUISVILLE—Jefferson County

☒ △ **BAPTIST HEALTH LOUISVILLE (180130)**, 4000 Kresge Way,
Zip 40207–4676; tel. 502/897–8100, **A**1 2 3 5 7 10 **F**3 5 6 8 11 12 13 15 17
18 20 22 24 26 28 29 30 31 34 35 36 37 38 40 44 45 46 47 48 49 50 51 54
56 57 58 59 61 62 64 70 72 74 75 76 78 79 81 82 83 84 85 86 87 90 91 92
93 98 100 101 102 103 104 105 107 108 110 111 114 115 116 117 118 119
120 121 123 124 126 129 130 132 135 141 146 147 148 149 153 **S** Baptist
Health, Louisville, KY
Primary Contact: Larry W. Gray, President
COO: Clint Kaho, Vice President
CFO: Jim Morris, Vice President Finance
CMO: Kenneth Anderson, M.D., Vice President and Chief Medical Officer
CIO: Shari Price, Director Information Services
CHR: Kim Scaglione, Vice President Human Resources
CNO: Karen Newman, Ed.D., MSN, R.N., Vice President and Chief Nursing Officer
Web address: www.baptisthealthlouisville.com
Control: Other not–for–profit (including NFP Corporation) **Service**: General
medical and surgical

Staffed Beds: 500 **Admissions:** 27281 **Census:** 326 **Outpatient Visits:**
353355 **Births:** 3318 **Total Expense ($000):** 485296 **Payroll Expense
($000):** 165906 **Personnel:** 2573

☐ **CENTRAL STATE HOSPITAL (184015)**, 10510 LaGrange Road,
Zip 40223–1228; tel. 502/253–7060, (Nonreporting) **A**1 3 5 10
Primary Contact: Josie Goodman, Hospital Director
CFO: Robert Underhill, Director of Business Services
CMO: Vital Shah, M.D., Associate Director and Chief Medical Officer
CIO: Randy Spicer, Information Technology Supervisor
CHR: Sonya Wheatley, Human Resources Manager
CNO: Jennifer Fowler
Control: State, Government, nonfederal **Service**: Psychiatric

Staffed Beds: 112

☒ **JEWISH HOSPITAL (180040)**, 200 Abraham Flexner Way, Zip 40202–1886;
tel. 502/587–4011, (Includes FRAZIER REHAB INSTITUTE, 220 Abraham Flexner
Way, Louisville, KY, Zip 40202–1887; tel. 502/582–7400) Cathy Spalding, Vice
President of Operations) **A**1 2 3 5 10 **F**3 8 11 14 18 20 22 24 26 28 29 30 31
34 35 36 37 40 44 45 46 47 48 49 50 53 54 56 57 58 59 60 61 64 67 68 70
74 75 78 79 81 82 84 85 87 92 100 107 108 111 112 114 115 118 119 121
123 124 126 130 131 132 135 136 137 138 139 140 141 142 145 146 148
154 **P**6 **S** Catholic Health Initiatives, Englewood, CO
Primary Contact: Charles W. Neumann, President and Chief Medical Officer
CFO: Ronald Farr, Chief Financial Officer
CMO: James P Ketterhagen, M.D., Senior Vice President and Chief Medical Officer
CIO: Thomas Wittman, Chief Information Officer
CHR: Julie McGregor, Vice President and Chief People Officer
CNO: Cheryl Fugatte, MSN, Vice President and Chief Nursing Officer
Web address: www.kentuckyonehealth.org/jewish–hospital
Control: Other not–for–profit (including NFP Corporation) **Service**: General
medical and surgical

Staffed Beds: 321 **Admissions:** 16426 **Census:** 249 **Outpatient Visits:**
104712 **Births:** 0 **Total Expense ($000):** 413500 **Payroll Expense
($000):** 121964 **Personnel:** 1622

KINDRED HOSPITAL LOUISVILLE AT JEWISH HOSPITAL See Kindred Hospital–
Louisville, Louisville

☒ **KINDRED HOSPITAL–LOUISVILLE (182001)**, 1313 Saint Anthony Place,
Zip 40204–1740; tel. 502/587–7001, (Includes KINDRED HOSPITAL LOUISVILLE
AT JEWISH HOSPITAL, 200 Abraham Flexner Way, 2nd Floor, Louisville, KY,
Zip 40202; tel. 502/587–3999; David Johnson, Chief Executive Officer)
(Nonreporting) **A**1 3 5 10 **S** Kindred Healthcare, Louisville, KY
Primary Contact: Jack Nicholson, Chief Executive Officer
Web address: www.kindredlouisville.com
Control: Corporation, Investor–owned (for–profit) **Service**: Acute long–term care
hospital

Staffed Beds: 117

★ **NORTON CHILDREN'S HOSPITAL (189801)**, 231 East Chestnut Street,
Zip 40202–1821; tel. 502/629–6000, **A**2 3 5 **F**3 8 11 16 18 19 21 23 25 27
29 30 31 32 34 35 38 39 40 41 43 44 45 50 51 54 57 58 59 64 65 68 72
73 74 75 78 79 81 82 84 85 86 87 88 89 91 92 93 96 98 99 101 102 107
108 111 114 115 119 130 131 132 134 136 137 138 146 149 150 **S** Norton
Healthcare, Louisville, KY
Primary Contact: Emmett Ramser, Chief Administrative Officer
Web address: www.kosairchildrens.com/
Control: Other not–for–profit (including NFP Corporation) **Service**: Children's
general medical and surgical

Staffed Beds: 267 **Admissions:** 10004 **Census:** 209 **Outpatient Visits:**
135095 **Births:** 0 **Total Expense ($000):** 312335 **Payroll Expense
($000):** 109407 **Personnel:** 1638

NORTON HEALTHCARE PAVILION See Norton Hospital, Louisville

☒ **NORTON HOSPITAL (180088)**, 200 East Chestnut Street, Zip 40202–1800,
Mailing Address: P.O. Box 35070, Zip 40232–5070; tel. 502/629–8000,
(Includes NORTON AUDUBON HOSPITAL, One Audubon Plaza Drive, Louisville,
KY, Zip 40217–1300, Mailing Address: P.O. Box 17550, Zip 40217–0550,
tel. 502/636–7111; Jon Cooper, Chief Administrative Officer; NORTON
BROWNSBORO HOSPITAL, 4960 Norton Healthcare Boulevard, Louisville,
KY, Zip 40241–2831; tel. 502/446–8000; Andrew Strausbaugh, Chief
Administrative Officer; NORTON HEALTHCARE PAVILION, 315 East Broadway,
Louisville, KY, Zip 40202–1703; tel. 502/629–2000; NORTON WOMEN'S AND
CHILDREN'S HOSPITAL, 4001 Dutchmans Lane, Louisville, KY, Zip 40207–4799;
tel. 502/893–1000; Charlotte Ipsan, Chief Administrative Officer) **A**1 2 3 5 10 **F**3
11 12 13 15 17 18 20 22 24 26 28 29 30 31 34 35 36 38 40 44 45 46 50
51 53 55 56 57 59 64 68 70 74 75 76 78 79 81 82 84 85 86 87 91 92 93 95
96 98 100 101 102 107 108 110 111 114 115 116 117 118 119 126 130 132
146 147 148 149 150 **S** Norton Healthcare, Louisville, KY
Primary Contact: Matthew Ayers, Chief Administrative Officer
CFO: Carl Amorose, Vice President Finance
Web address: www.nortonhealthcare.com/nortonhospital
Control: Other not–for–profit (including NFP Corporation) **Service**: General
medical and surgical

Staffed Beds: 1158 **Admissions:** 62122 **Census:** 797 **Outpatient Visits:**
520279 **Births:** 7871 **Total Expense ($000):** 1037751 **Payroll Expense
($000):** 349814 **Personnel:** 5712

★ **OUR LADY OF PEACE**, 2020 Newburg Road, Zip 40205–1879;
tel. 502/479–4500, **A**5 **F**5 29 30 35 98 99 100 101 104 105 130 132 143 152
153 154 **S** Catholic Health Initiatives, Englewood, CO
Primary Contact: Jennifer Nolan, President and Chief Executive Officer
COO: Martha S Mather, Chief Operating Officer and Vice President
CFO: Beckie Kistler, Director of Finance
CHR: Jan Ostbloom, Human Resources Consultant
CNO: Brad Lincks, R.N., Chief Nursing Officer and Vice President
Web address: www.kentuckyonehealth.org/our–lady–of–peace
Control: Other not–for–profit (including NFP Corporation) **Service**: Psychiatric

Staffed Beds: 220 **Admissions:** 8688 **Census:** 183 **Outpatient Visits:**
34079 **Births:** 0 **Total Expense ($000):** 54224 **Payroll Expense
($000):** 29426 **Personnel:** 479

☒ **ROBLEY REX VETERANS AFFAIRS MEDICAL CENTER**, 800 Zorn Avenue,
Zip 40206–1499; tel. 502/287–4000, (Nonreporting) **A**1 3 5 **S** Department of
Veterans Affairs, Perry Point, MD
Primary Contact: Dr. Marylee Rothschild, MD, Chief of Staff
CFO: Barbara Roberts, Chief Financial Officer
CMO: Marylee Rothschild, M.D., Chief of Staff
CIO: Augustine Bittner, Chief Information Officer
CHR: Angela Dutton, Chief Human Resources Management Service
Web address: www.louisville.va.gov
Control: Veterans Affairs, Government, federal **Service**: General medical and
surgical

Staffed Beds: 116

★ **STS. MARY & ELIZABETH HOSPITAL**, 1850 Bluegrass Avenue,
Zip 40215–1199; tel. 502/361–6000, **A**3 5 **F**3 11 12 15 18 20 22 29 30 31 34
35 40 44 45 47 49 50 53 56 59 60 63 64 68 69 70 74 75 78 79 81 82 84 85
86 87 107 108 110 111 114 115 118 119 130 132 135 154 **S** Catholic Health
Initiatives, Englewood, CO
Primary Contact: Charles Powell, President
COO: Kenneth Johnson, Vice President
CFO: Elaine Hayes, Controller
CMO: Val Slayton, M.D., Vice President Medical Affairs
CHR: Julie McGregor, Director Human Resources
Web address: www.jhsmh.org
Control: Other not–for–profit (including NFP Corporation) **Service**: General
medical and surgical

Staffed Beds: 173 **Admissions:** 8112 **Census:** 95 **Outpatient Visits:** 95313
Births: 0 **Total Expense ($000):** 125990 **Payroll Expense ($000):** 45476
Personnel: 568

TEN BROECK DUPONT See The Brook at Dupont

☐ **THE BROOK AT DUPONT (184007)**, 1405 Browns Lane, Zip 40207–4608;
tel. 502/896–0495, **A**1 10 **F**4 5 64 98 99 100 101 102 103 104 105 130 151
152 153 **S** Universal Health Services, Inc., King of Prussia, PA
Primary Contact: Paul Andrews, Chief Executive Officer
Web address: www.thebrookhospitals.com/
Control: Corporation, Investor–owned (for–profit) **Service**: Psychiatric

Staffed Beds: 88 **Admissions:** 2144 **Census:** 54 **Outpatient Visits:** 15883
Births: 0 **Total Expense ($000):** 13227 **Payroll Expense ($000):** 7880
Personnel: 134

Many Facility Codes have changed. Please refer to the AHA Guide Code Chart.

☐ **THE BROOK HOSPITAL – KMI (184008)**, 8521 Old LaGrange Road, Zip 40242–3800; tel. 502/426–6380, **A**1 3 5 10 **F**4 5 38 64 98 99 100 101 102 104 105 106 130 151 152 153 **S** Universal Health Services, Inc., King of Prussia, PA
Primary Contact: Paul Andrews, Chief Executive Officer
COO: Kim Peabody, Chief Operating Officer
CFO: Dennis Collins, Chief Financial Officer
CMO: Timothy Burke, M.D., Medical Director
CIO: Joel Roy, Manager Information Systems
CHR: Christina Taylor, Director Human Resources
Web address: www.thebrookhospitals.com
Control: Corporation, Investor–owned (for–profit) **Service**: Psychiatric

Staffed Beds: 110 **Admissions**: 2337 **Census**: 82 **Outpatient Visits**: 19785 **Births**: 0 **Total Expense ($000)**: 14356 **Payroll Expense ($000)**: 8759 **Personnel**: 190

⊞ **UNIVERSITY OF LOUISVILLE HOSPITAL (180141)**, 530 South Jackson Street, Zip 40202–3611; tel. 502/562–3000, **A**1 2 3 5 8 10 **F**3 8 12 13 15 16 17 18 20 22 24 26 28 29 30 31 34 35 36 37 38 40 43 45 46 47 48 49 50 51 54 56 57 58 59 60 64 66 68 70 71 72 73 74 75 76 77 78 79 80 81 82 84 85 86 87 91 92 93 96 98 100 101 102 103 107 108 109 110 111 112 114 115 116 117 118 119 120 121 123 124 126 130 132 135 136 144 145 146 147 148 149 150 154 **P**1 **S** Catholic Health Initiatives, Englewood, CO
Primary Contact: Kenneth P. Marshall, President and Chief Executive Officer
CMO: Mark P Pfeifer, M.D., Senior Vice President and Chief Medical Officer
CIO: Troy May, Chief Information Officer
CNO: Mary Jane Adams, R.N., MSN, Senior Vice President and Chief Nursing Officer
Web address: www.ulh.org
Control: Other not–for–profit (including NFP Corporation) **Service**: General medical and surgical

Staffed Beds: 329 **Admissions**: 15622 **Census**: 253 **Outpatient Visits**: 172846 **Births**: 1829 **Total Expense ($000)**: 507768 **Payroll Expense ($000)**: 126129 **Personnel**: 2090

VETERANS AFFAIRS MEDICAL CENTER–LOUISVILLE See Robley Rex Veterans Affairs Medical Center

MADISONVILLE—Hopkins County

⊞ **BAPTIST HEALTH MADISONVILLE (180093)**, 900 Hospital Drive, Zip 42431–1694; tel. 270/825–5100, **A**1 2 3 5 10 22 **F**3 8 11 13 14 18 20 22 24 26 28 29 30 31 34 40 44 45 49 51 53 57 58 59 60 62 63 70 73 75 76 78 79 81 85 87 88 89 90 93 94 96 98 100 102 103 107 108 111 114 115 117 118 119 120 121 123 129 130 131 132 146 148 149 **S** Baptist Health, Louisville, KY
Primary Contact: Robert L. Ramey, President
COO: Kevin Moser, Vice President of Operations
CFO: Kim Ashby, Vice President of Finance
CMO: Wayne Lipson, M.D., Chief Physician Executive
CIO: Karla Durham, Director of Information Systems
CHR: Lorie A. Oglesby, Director of Human Resources
CNO: Denise Dunn, R.N., Chief Nursing Officer
Web address: www.baptisthealthmadisonville.com
Control: Other not–for–profit (including NFP Corporation) **Service**: General medical and surgical

Staffed Beds: 175 **Admissions**: 7543 **Census**: 104 **Outpatient Visits**: 148653 **Births**: 801 **Total Expense ($000)**: 184867 **Payroll Expense ($000)**: 66296 **Personnel**: 1176

★ **CONTINUECARE HOSPITAL AT MADISONVILLE (182009)**, 900 Hospital Drive, 4th Floor, Zip 42431–1644; tel. 270/825–5450, **A**10 **F**1 3 28 29 34 50 57 85 87 91 **S** Community Hospital Corporation, Plano, TX
Primary Contact: Lea Ann H. Klarner, Chief Executive Officer
Web address: www.continuecare.org/madisonville/
Control: Other not–for–profit (including NFP Corporation) **Service**: Acute long–term care hospital

Staffed Beds: 35 **Admissions**: 204 **Census**: 15 **Outpatient Visits**: 0 **Births**: 0 **Total Expense ($000)**: 6895 **Payroll Expense ($000)**: 2820 **Personnel**: 79

MANCHESTER—Clay County

⊞ ○ **MANCHESTER MEMORIAL HOSPITAL (180043)**, 210 Marie Langdon Drive, Zip 40962–6388; tel. 606/598–5104, **A**1 10 11 **F**3 13 15 18 29 30 32 34 35 40 45 50 57 59 62 65 68 70 71 75 76 77 79 81 85 86 87 93 97 107 108 110 111 115 119 127 130 135 143 146 147 149 151 154 **S** Adventist Health System Sunbelt Health Care Corporation, Altamonte Springs, FL
Primary Contact: Erika Skula, President and Chief Executive Officer
COO: Chris Self, Chief Operating Officer
CFO: Paul Merklin, Vice President Finance and Chief Financial Officer
CMO: Jeff Newswanger, M.D., Chief Medical Officer
CHR: Joe Skula, Director Human Resources
Web address: www.manchestermemorial.org
Control: Church operated, Nongovernment, not–for–profit **Service**: General medical and surgical

Staffed Beds: 49 **Admissions**: 2024 **Census**: 17 **Outpatient Visits**: 63045 **Births**: 179 **Total Expense ($000)**: 60526 **Payroll Expense ($000)**: 27684 **Personnel**: 424

MARION—Crittenden County

☐ **CRITTENDEN COUNTY HOSPITAL (180095)**, 520 West Gum Street, Zip 42064–1516, Mailing Address: P.O. Box 386, Zip 42064–0386; tel. 270/965–5281, (Nonreporting) **A**1 10 20
Primary Contact: Daniel Hiben, Chief Executive Officer
COO: Robin Curnel, MSN, Chief Operating Officer and Chief Nursing Officer
CFO: Karen Paris, Controller
CMO: Steven Burkhart, M.D., Chief Medical Officer
CIO: Reese Baker, Director Information Systems
CHR: Jan Gregory, Chief of Human Resources
CNO: Robin Curnel, MSN, Chief Operating Officer and Chief Nursing Officer
Web address: www.crittenden–health.org
Control: Other not–for–profit (including NFP Corporation) **Service**: General medical and surgical

Staffed Beds: 48

MARTIN—Floyd County

⊞ **ARH OUR LADY OF THE WAY (181305)**, 11203 Main Street, Zip 41649; tel. 606/285–6400, (Nonreporting) **A**1 10 18 **S** Catholic Health Initiatives, Englewood, CO
Primary Contact: Kathy Stumbo, President
CFO: Robert Brock, Vice President Finance
CMO: John Triplett, D.O., President Medical Staff
CIO: Chris Dye, Director Information Systems
Web address: www.saintjosephmartin.org
Control: Church operated, Nongovernment, not–for–profit **Service**: General medical and surgical

Staffed Beds: 25

MAYFIELD—Graves County

⊞ **JACKSON PURCHASE MEDICAL CENTER (180116)**, 1099 Medical Center Circle, Zip 42066–1159; tel. 270/251–4100, (Nonreporting) **A**1 10 19 **S** LifePoint Health, Brentwood, TN
Primary Contact: David Anderson, Chief Executive Officer
CFO: Vicki Parks, Chief Financial Officer
CMO: Rudy Triana, M.D., Chief of Staff
CIO: Randy McDaniel, Information Systems Director
CHR: Tressa B Hargrove, Director Human Resources
CNO: Julia Grove, Chief Nursing Officer
Web address: www.jacksonpurchase.com
Control: Corporation, Investor–owned (for–profit) **Service**: General medical and surgical

Staffed Beds: 227

MAYSVILLE—Mason County

⊞ **MEADOWVIEW REGIONAL MEDICAL CENTER (180019)**, 989 Medical Park Drive, Zip 41056–8750; tel. 606/759–5311, **A**1 10 **F**3 13 15 18 20 22 26 28 29 30 31 34 35 40 45 50 51 57 59 60 68 70 75 76 77 78 79 81 85 87 92 93 107 108 110 111 115 118 119 129 130 131 133 144 145 154 **S** LifePoint Health, Brentwood, TN
Primary Contact: Joseph G. Koch, Chief Executive Officer
CFO: Clayton Kolodziejczyk, Chief Financial Officer
CMO: Eric Lohman, M.D., Chief of Staff
CHR: Diana Kennedy, Director Human Resources
Web address: www.meadowviewregional.com
Control: Corporation, Investor–owned (for–profit) **Service**: General medical and surgical

Staffed Beds: 100 **Admissions**: 2386 **Census**: 22

Hospital, Medicare Provider Number, Address, Telephone, Approval, Facility, and Physician Codes, Health Care System

★ American Hospital Association (AHA) membership   ○ Healthcare Facilities Accreditation Program   ⇑ Center for Improvement in Healthcare Quality Accreditation
☐ The Joint Commission accreditation   ◇ DNV Healthcare Inc. accreditation   △ Commission on Accreditation of Rehabilitation Facilities (CARF) accreditation

MCDOWELL—Floyd County

☐ **MCDOWELL ARH HOSPITAL (181331)**, Route 122, Zip 41647, Mailing Address: P.O. Box 247, Zip 41647–0247; tel. 606/377–3400, **A**1 10 18 **F**3 11 15 29 30 34 35 40 50 57 59 62 64 65 75 77 81 82 86 87 89 93 97 107 111 115 119 127 130 131 133 146 **P**6 **S** Appalachian Regional Healthcare, Inc., Lexington, KY
Primary Contact: Russell Barker, Community Chief Executive Officer
COO: Russell Barker, Community Chief Executive Officer
CMO: Mary A Hall, Chief Medical Staff
CIO: Jeff Brady, Director Information Systems
CHR: Stephanie Owens, Manager Human Resources
Web address: www.arh.org
Control: Other not-for-profit (including NFP Corporation) **Service:** General medical and surgical

Staffed Beds: 25 **Admissions:** 407 **Census:** 5 **Outpatient Visits:** 25464 **Births:** 0 **Personnel:** 126

MIDDLESBORO—Bell County

☐ **MIDDLESBORO ARH HOSPITAL (180020)**, 3600 West Cumberland Avenue, Zip 40965–2614, Mailing Address: P.O. Box 340, Zip 40965–0340; tel. 606/242–1100, **A**1 10 **F**3 11 13 15 17 18 20 28 29 30 34 35 39 40 45 46 49 50 57 59 62 64 65 70 75 76 77 79 81 85 86 87 89 90 93 97 107 108 110 111 115 118 119 127 129 132 133 146 147 148 **P**6 **S** Appalachian Regional Healthcare, Inc., Lexington, KY
Primary Contact: Michael Slusher, Community Chief Executive Officer
CFO: Jeremy Hall, Assistant Administrator and Chief Financial Officer
CMO: Maria Hortillosa, M.D., Chief of Staff
CIO: Lisa Dooley, Health Information Officer
CHR: Marina Cawood, Administrative Assistant
CNO: Stacy England, Community Chief Nursing Officer
Web address: www.arh.org/middlesboro
Control: Other not-for-profit (including NFP Corporation) **Service:** General medical and surgical

Staffed Beds: 73 **Admissions:** 1532 **Census:** 21 **Outpatient Visits:** 73941 **Births:** 236

MONTICELLO—Wayne County

WAYNE COUNTY HOSPITAL (181321), 166 Hospital Street, Zip 42633–2416; tel. 606/348–9343, **A**10 18 **F**3 15 29 30 40 47 75 81 107 108 114 119 127 133 135 146 **P**6
Primary Contact: Joseph Murrell, Chief Executive Officer
CFO: Anne Sawyer, Chief Financial Officer
CMO: David Mayer, Chief of Staff
CIO: Angela Burton, Privacy Officer
CHR: Mollie Dick, Coordinator Human Resources
CNO: Lora Elam, R.N., Chief Nursing Officer
Web address: www.waynehospital.org
Control: Other not-for-profit (including NFP Corporation) **Service:** General medical and surgical

Staffed Beds: 25 **Admissions:** 537 **Census:** 9 **Outpatient Visits:** 14522 **Births:** 0 **Total Expense ($000):** 13674 **Payroll Expense ($000):** 5776 **Personnel:** 164

MOREHEAD—Rowan County

☒ **ST. CLAIRE HEALTHCARE (180018)**, 222 Medical Circle, Zip 40351–1179; tel. 606/783–6500, (Nonreporting) **A**1 2 3 5 10 13
Primary Contact: Mark J. Neff, FACHE, President and Chief Executive Officer
CFO: Chris McClurg, Vice President Finance and Chief Financial Officer
CMO: William L Melahn, M.D., Vice President Medical Affairs and Chief Medical Officer
CIO: Randy McCleese, Vice President Information Services and Chief Information Officer
CHR: Travis A Bailey, Vice President Administration
CNO: Lerae Wilson, Vice President Patient Services and Chief Nursing Officer
Web address: www.st-claire.org
Control: Church operated, Nongovernment, not-for-profit **Service:** General medical and surgical

Staffed Beds: 133

MORGANFIELD—Union County

☒ **METHODIST HOSPITAL UNION COUNTY (181306)**, 4604 Highway 60 West, Zip 42437–9570; tel. 270/389–5000, **A**1 10 18 **F**3 11 15 29 30 34 40 43 45 57 68 75 77 81 85 87 93 107 114 119 130 133 135 146 149
Primary Contact: Lynn R. Steinwachs, Vice President and Administrator
CFO: David Massengale, Chief Financial Officer
CMO: William Clapp, M.D., Chief of Medical Staff
CIO: Randy McCleese, Chief Information Officer
CHR: Ty Kahle, Assistant Vice President Human Resources
CNO: Peggy F Creighton, R.N., Director of Nursing
Web address: www.methodisthospital.net
Control: Church operated, Nongovernment, not-for-profit **Service:** General medical and surgical

Staffed Beds: 25 **Admissions:** 602 **Census:** 12 **Outpatient Visits:** 24920 **Births:** 0 **Total Expense ($000):** 15830 **Payroll Expense ($000):** 6188 **Personnel:** 132

MOUNT STERLING—Montgomery County

☒ **SAINT JOSEPH MOUNT STERLING (180064)**, 225 Falcon Drive, Zip 40353–1158, Mailing Address: P.O. Box 7, Zip 40353–0007; tel. 859/497–5000, **A**1 5 10 **F**3 13 15 17 28 29 34 35 40 45 46 57 59 64 68 70 74 75 76 77 78 79 81 86 87 93 97 107 114 119 129 130 132 133 135 146 147 148 **S** Catholic Health Initiatives, Englewood, CO
Primary Contact: Terrence G. Deis, CPA, FACHE, President
CFO: Amanda Kinman, Director of Finance
CMO: Jeff McGinnis, M.D., President Medical Staff
CIO: Jeff Ryder, Director Information Systems
CHR: Annette Saadat, Human Resources Business Partner
CNO: Cinda Fluke, R.N., Chief Nursing Officer
Web address: www.sjhlex.org
Control: Other not-for-profit (including NFP Corporation) **Service:** General medical and surgical

Staffed Beds: 42 **Admissions:** 1716 **Census:** 18 **Outpatient Visits:** 73562 **Births:** 250 **Total Expense ($000):** 46992 **Payroll Expense ($000):** 12713 **Personnel:** 212

MOUNT VERNON—Rockcastle County

☒ **ROCKCASTLE REGIONAL HOSPITAL AND RESPIRATORY CARE CENTER (180115)**, 145 Newcomb Avenue, Zip 40456–2728, Mailing Address: P.O. Box 1310, Zip 40456–1310; tel. 606/256–2195, (Nonreporting) **A**1 10
Primary Contact: Stephen A. Estes, Chief Executive Officer
CFO: Charles Black Jr Chief Financial Officer
CMO: Jon A Arvin, M.D., Chief Medical Officer
CIO: Maleigha Amyx, Chief Information Officer
CHR: Carmen Poynter, Director Human Resources
CNO: Cynthia Burton, R.N., Chief Nursing Officer
Web address: www.rockcastleregional.org
Control: Other not-for-profit (including NFP Corporation) **Service:** General medical and surgical

Staffed Beds: 105

MURRAY—Calloway County

☒ **MURRAY–CALLOWAY COUNTY HOSPITAL (180027)**, 803 Poplar Street, Zip 42071–2432; tel. 270/762–1100, (Total facility includes 150 beds in nursing home–type unit) **A**1 2 3 10 19 **F**3 7 11 12 13 14 15 18 20 28 29 30 31 34 35 40 45 47 49 50 51 53 57 59 62 63 66 68 70 74 75 76 77 78 79 81 82 84 85 87 90 92 93 94 98 103 104 107 108 111 114 115 119 121 127 128 129 130 131 132 135 141 146 147 148 **P**5
Primary Contact: Colonel Jerome Penner, Chief Executive Officer
COO: John R Wilson, Chief Operating Officer
CFO: John Bradford, Chief Financial Officer
CIO: Brian Benedict, Director of Information Technology
CHR: John R Wilson, Vice President, Human Resources
CNO: Jeffrey L Eye, R.N., Vice President Patient Care Services
Web address: www.murrayhospital.org
Control: City–county, Government, nonfederal **Service:** General medical and surgical

Staffed Beds: 259 **Admissions:** 4646 **Census:** 189 **Outpatient Visits:** 86790 **Births:** 633 **Total Expense ($000):** 119643 **Payroll Expense ($000):** 48882 **Personnel:** 948

OWENSBORO—Daviess County

☒ △ **OWENSBORO HEALTH REGIONAL HOSPITAL (180038)**, 1201 Pleasant Valley Road, Zip 42303; tel. 270/417–2000, (Includes HEALTHPARK, 1006 Ford Avenue, Owensboro, KY, Zip 42301, Mailing Address: P.O. Box 2839, Zip 42302, tel. 270/688–5433) (Total facility includes 30 beds in nursing home–type unit) **A**1 2 3 5 7 10 **F**3 5 11 13 15 17 18 20 22 24 26 28 29 30 31 32 34 35 40 43 44 45 46 49 53 54 56 57 58 59 61 62 64 65 66 70 72 74 75 76 77 78 79 81 82 83 84 85 86 87 89 90 91 92 93 97 98 100 101 102 103 104 105 107 108 110 111 114 115 117 118 119 120 121 123 124 126 127 128 129 130 131 132 135 144 145 146 147 148 149 153 **P**6 8 **S** Owensboro Health, Owensboro, KY
Primary Contact: Greg Strahan, Interim Chief Executive Officer
COO: Greg Strahan, Chief Operating Officer
CFO: John Hackbarth, CPA, Senior Vice President Finance and Chief Financial Officer
CMO: Wathen Medley, M.D., Chief Medical Officer
CIO: Michael Elley, Chief Information Officer
CHR: Mia Suter, Chief Administration Officer
CNO: Vicki Stogsdill, R.N., MSN, Chief Nursing Officer
Web address: www.owensborohealth.org
Control: Other not-for-profit (including NFP Corporation) **Service:** General medical and surgical

Staffed Beds: 360 **Admissions:** 17119 **Census:** 231 **Outpatient Visits:** 965031 **Births:** 2059 **Total Expense ($000):** 537839 **Payroll Expense ($000):** 152061 **Personnel:** 2453

RIVERVALLEY BEHAVIORAL HEALTH HOSPITAL (184013), 1000 Industrial Drive, Zip 42301–8715; tel. 270/689–6500, **A**10 **F**29 34 35 38 40 41 50 59 68 98 99 100 101 102 104 130 132 **P**6
Primary Contact: Wanda Figuerora Peralta, President and Chief Executive Officer
COO: Michelle Parks, Administrator
CFO: J Michael Mountain, Chief Financial Officer
CMO: David Harmon, D.O., Vice President Medical Services
CIO: Travis Taggart, Director Information Technology
CHR: Cathryn H Gaddis, Director Human Resources
Web address: www.rvbh.com
Control: Other not–for–profit (including NFP Corporation) **Service**: Children's hospital psychiatric

Staffed Beds: 80 **Admissions**: 968 **Census**: 36 **Outpatient Visits**: 1498 **Births**: 0 **Total Expense ($000)**: 7289 **Payroll Expense ($000)**: 3279 **Personnel**: 85	

PADUCAH—Mccracken County

✠ **BAPTIST HEALTH PADUCAH (180104)**, 2501 Kentucky Avenue, Zip 42003–3200; tel. 270/575–2100, **A**1 2 10 19 22 **F**3 11 12 13 15 17 18 20 22 24 26 28 29 30 31 32 34 35 40 45 46 48 50 51 57 58 59 64 68 70 73 74 75 76 77 78 79 81 82 84 85 86 87 91 92 93 96 107 108 109 110 111 112 113 114 115 116 117 118 119 120 121 124 126 129 130 131 132 134 135 145 146 147 148 149 **S** Baptist Health, Louisville, KY
Primary Contact: Christopher Roty, Interim President
COO: Bonnie W Schrock, FACHE, Chief Operating Officer
CMO: Bradley W. Housman, M.D., Chief Medical Officer
CIO: Jay Orazine, Director Information Services
CHR: Kal Keitel, Executive Director Human Resources
CNO: Sharon Freyer, R.N., Chief Nursing Officer
Web address: www.baptisthealthpaducah.com
Control: Other not–for–profit (including NFP Corporation) **Service**: General medical and surgical

Staffed Beds: 210 **Admissions**: 10073 **Census**: 119 **Outpatient Visits**: 164273 **Births**: 1301 **Total Expense ($000)**: 256152 **Payroll Expense ($000)**: 80211 **Personnel**: 1501	

★ **CONTINUECARE HOSPITAL AT BAPTIST HEALTH PADUCAH (180153)**, 2501 Kentucky Avenue, 5th Floor, Zip 42003–3813; tel. 270/575–2598, **F**1 3 29 34 35 148 154 **S** Community Hospital Corporation, Plano, TX
Primary Contact: Len McDade, Chief Executive Officer
CNO: Mary Lou Young, Chief Nursing Officer
Web address: www.continuecare.org/paducah//
Control: Other not–for–profit (including NFP Corporation) **Service**: Acute long–term care hospital

Staffed Beds: 37 **Admissions**: 194 **Census**: 14 **Outpatient Visits**: 0 **Births**: 0 **Total Expense ($000)**: 8643 **Payroll Expense ($000)**: 3399 **Personnel**: 66	

✠ △ **LOURDES HOSPITAL (180102)**, 1530 Lone Oak Road, Zip 42003–7900, Mailing Address: P.O. Box 7100, Zip 42002–7100; tel. 270/444–2444, **A**1 7 10 19 **F**3 7 8 11 13 15 17 18 20 22 24 26 28 29 30 31 34 35 40 45 49 55 57 59 60 62 63 64 68 70 73 74 75 76 77 78 79 81 82 83 84 85 87 90 93 96 97 98 100 101 102 103 104 105 107 108 110 111 114 115 116 118 119 126 129 130 131 132 135 141 143 144 146 147 148 149 150 153 154 **P**6 **S** Mercy Health, Cincinnati, OH
Primary Contact: Michael Yungmann, President and Chief Executive Officer
CHR: Kim Lindsey, Chief Human Resources Officer
Web address: www.lourdes–pad.org
Control: Church operated, Nongovernment, not–for–profit **Service**: General medical and surgical

Staffed Beds: 281 **Admissions**: 11047 **Census**: 137 **Outpatient Visits**: 550377 **Births**: 462 **Total Expense ($000)**: 258765 **Payroll Expense ($000)**: 102186	

PAINTSVILLE—Johnson County

✠ **PAUL B. HALL REGIONAL MEDICAL CENTER (180078)**, 625 James S. Trimble Boulevard, Zip 41240–0000; tel. 606/789–3511, (Nonreporting) **A**1 10 **S** Quorum Health, Brentwood, TN
Primary Contact: Deborah Trimble, R.N., Chief Executive Officer
CFO: Pattie Major, Chief Financial Officer
CMO: F K Belhasen, M.D., Medical Director
CHR: Carla J. Stapleton, Director Human Resources
Web address: www.pbhrmc.com
Control: Corporation, Investor–owned (for–profit) **Service**: General medical and surgical

Staffed Beds: 72	

PARIS—Bourbon County

✠ **BOURBON COMMUNITY HOSPITAL (180046)**, 9 Linville Drive, Zip 40361–2196; tel. 859/987–3600, (Nonreporting) **A**1 10 **S** LifePoint Health, Brentwood, TN
Primary Contact: Matt Smith, Interim Chief Executive Officer
CFO: Michael Snedegar, Chief Financial Officer
CMO: C. Ray Young, M.D., Chief Medical Officer
CIO: Phil Osborne, Director Information Technology
CHR: Roger K Davis, Director Human Resources
Web address: www.bourbonhospital.com
Control: Corporation, Investor–owned (for–profit) **Service**: General medical and surgical

Staffed Beds: 58	

PIKEVILLE—Pike County

☐ **PIKEVILLE MEDICAL CENTER (180044)**, 911 Bypass Road, Zip 41501–1689; tel. 606/218–3500, **A**1 2 3 10 13 **F**3 11 12 13 15 18 20 22 24 26 28 29 30 31 32 34 35 39 40 43 45 49 50 51 55 57 59 60 61 62 64 66 68 69 70 72 74 75 76 77 78 79 81 82 84 85 86 87 89 90 93 95 96 97 107 108 110 111 115 116 117 118 119 121 123 124 126 127 129 130 131 132 135 146 147 148 154 **P**6
Primary Contact: Donovan Blackburn, Chief Executive Officer
COO: Kansas Justice, Senior Vice President and Chief Operating Officer
CFO: Michelle Hagy, Senior Vice President and Chief Financial Officer
CMO: Aaron Crum, M.D., Senior Vice President, Assistant Chief Executive Officer and Chief Medical Officer
CIO: Tony Damron, Senior Vice President and Chief Information Officer
CNO: Michelle L. Rainey, Senior Vice President and Chief Nursing Officer
Web address: www.pikevillehospital.org
Control: Other not–for–profit (including NFP Corporation) **Service**: General medical and surgical

Staffed Beds: 284 **Admissions**: 15642 **Census**: 263 **Outpatient Visits**: 468703 **Births**: 932 **Total Expense ($000)**: 542086 **Payroll Expense ($000)**: 222482 **Personnel**: 3175	

PINEVILLE—Bell County

SOUTHEASTERN KENTUCKY MEDICAL CENTER (180021), 850 Riverview Avenue, Zip 40977–1452; tel. 606/337–3051, (Nonreporting) **A**10
Primary Contact: Grant White, Chief Executive Officer
CFO: Colan Kelly, Chief Financial Officer
CMO: Michael Peterson, M.D., Chief of Staff
CIO: David Hall, Chief Information Officer
CHR: Josh Collett, Director Human Resources
CNO: Dinah Jarvis, Director of Nursing
Web address: www.pinevillehospital.com
Control: Other not–for–profit (including NFP Corporation) **Service**: General medical and surgical

Staffed Beds: 150	

PRESTONSBURG—Floyd County

★ ⇑ **HIGHLANDS REGIONAL MEDICAL CENTER (180005)**, 5000 Kentucky Route 321, Zip 41653–1273, Mailing Address: P.O. Box 668, Zip 41653–0668; tel. 606/886–8511, **A**2 5 10 19 22 **F**3 11 13 15 18 20 22 28 30 31 34 35 40 44 51 53 56 57 59 62 64 68 70 74 75 76 77 78 79 81 85 86 89 93 97 98 100 107 111 114 115 119 124 128 134 135 146
Primary Contact: Harold C. Warman Jr, FACHE, President and Chief Executive Officer
COO: Chris Hoffman, Chief Operating Officer
CFO: Jack Blackwell, Chief Financial Officer
CIO: Michael Roberts, Chief Information Officer
CHR: Susan Renee' Ellis, R.N., MSN, Vice President of Human Resources
CNO: Teresa O. Booher, Vice President of Patient Care Services
Web address: www.hrmc.org
Control: Other not–for–profit (including NFP Corporation) **Service**: General medical and surgical

Staffed Beds: 139 **Admissions**: 4130 **Census**: 50	

Hospital, Medicare Provider Number, Address, Telephone, Approval, Facility, and Physician Codes, Health Care System

★ American Hospital Association (AHA) membership   ○ Healthcare Facilities Accreditation Program   ⇑ Center for Improvement in Healthcare Quality Accreditation
☐ The Joint Commission accreditation   ◇ DNV Healthcare Inc. accreditation   △ Commission on Accreditation of Rehabilitation Facilities (CARF) accreditation

PRINCETON—Caldwell County

☒ **CALDWELL MEDICAL CENTER (181322)**, 100 Medical Center Drive,
Zip 42445–2430, Mailing Address: P.O. Box 410, Zip 42445–0410;
tel. 270/365–0300, **A**1 10 18 **F**3 8 15 28 29 39 40 45 57 81 85 89 90 97 107
108 110 111 115 119 128 129 130 133 146 149 **S** QHR, Brentwood, TN
Primary Contact: Daniel Odegaard, FACHE, Chief Executive Officer
CFO: Shane Whittington, Chief Financial Officer
CHR: Rhonda Burns, Director Human Resources
CNO: Douglas James, Chief Nursing Officer
Web address: www.caldwellhosp.org
Control: Other not–for–profit (including NFP Corporation) **Service**: General
medical and surgical

Staffed Beds: 25 **Admissions**: 299 **Census**: 3 **Outpatient Visits**: 22431
Births: 0 **Total Expense ($000)**: 14857 **Payroll Expense ($000)**: 4501
Personnel: 118

RADCLIFF—Hardin County

☐ **LINCOLN TRAIL BEHAVIORAL HEALTH SYSTEM (184012)**, 3909 South
Wilson Road, Zip 40160–8944, Mailing Address: P.O. Box 369, Zip 40159–0369;
tel. 270/351–9444, (Nonreporting) **A**1 10 **S** Universal Health Services, Inc., King
of Prussia, PA
Primary Contact: Charles L. Webb Jr, Chief Executive Officer
CFO: Debbie Ditto, CPA, Controller
CMO: Muhammad W. Sajid, M.D., Medical Director
CHR: Charlotte C Davis, Director Human Resources
Web address: www.lincolnbehavioral.com
Control: Corporation, Investor–owned (for–profit) **Service**: Psychiatric

Staffed Beds: 140

RICHMOND—Madison County

★ ○ **BAPTIST HEALTH RICHMOND (180049)**, 801 Eastern Bypass,
Zip 40475–2405, Mailing Address: P.O. Box 1600, Zip 40476–2603;
tel. 859/623–3131, **A**1 10 19 **F**3 11 12 15 18 20 22 28 29 30 31 34 35
40 45 49 50 51 54 59 68 70 74 75 76 77 78 79 81 85 87 92 107 108 110
111 114 115 118 119 129 130 132 135 146 147 148 **S** Baptist Health,
Louisville, KY
Primary Contact: Greg Donavan. Gerard, President
CMO: Richard Shelton, M.D., Chief Medical Officer
CIO: Kelly Bonzo, Director
CHR: Joy M Benedict, Director Human Resources
CNO: Melinda Lee Blair, MSN, Vice President and Chief Nursing Officer
Web address: www.baptisthealthrichmond.com
Control: Other not–for–profit (including NFP Corporation) **Service**: General
medical and surgical

Staffed Beds: 60 **Admissions**: 2824 **Census**: 31 **Outpatient Visits**: 85061
Births: 558 **Total Expense ($000)**: 87259 **Payroll Expense ($000)**: 27623
Personnel: 487

RUSSELL SPRINGS—Russell County

★ **RUSSELL COUNTY HOSPITAL (181330)**, 153 Dowell Road, Zip 42642–4579,
Mailing Address: P.O. Box 1610, Zip 42642–1610; tel. 270/866–4141, **A**10 18
F3 11 15 28 29 30 34 40 45 57 59 70 81 85 91 93 107 111 118 119 127 129
130 133 135 146 147 148
Primary Contact: Scott Thompson, Chief Executive Officer
CFO: Janie Landis, Chief Financial Officer
CMO: Jerry D. Westerfield, M.D., Chief of Medical Staff
CIO: Monte Monsanto, Chief Information Systems
CHR: Jennifer Goode, Director Human Resources
CNO: Judy Chenoweth, Chief Nursing Officer
Web address: www.russellcohospital.org
Control: Hospital district or authority, Government, nonfederal **Service**: General
medical and surgical

Staffed Beds: 25 **Admissions**: 557 **Census**: 6 **Births**: 0

RUSSELLVILLE—Logan County

☒ **LOGAN MEMORIAL HOSPITAL (180066)**, 1625 South Nashville Road,
Zip 42276–8834, Mailing Address: P.O. Box 10, Zip 42276–0010;
tel. 270/726–4011, **A**1 10 **F**3 15 28 29 30 34 40 45 50 51 57 64 70 75 79
81 87 93 107 108 110 111 114 119 127 129 130 133 146 **S** LifePoint Health,
Brentwood, TN
Primary Contact: James Bills, Chief Executive Officer
CFO: Tim Prestridge, Interim Chief Financial Officer
CIO: Randy Compton, Information Technology and System Director
CHR: Susan Renodin Deaton, Human Resources Director
CNO: Deborah Brown, Chief Nursing Officer
Web address: www.loganmemorial.com
Control: Corporation, Investor–owned (for–profit) **Service**: General medical and
surgical

Staffed Beds: 30 **Admissions**: 913 **Census**: 11 **Outpatient Visits**: 35793
Births: 0 **Total Expense ($000)**: 19776 **Payroll Expense ($000)**: 7366
Personnel: 196

SALEM—Livingston County

LIVINGSTON HOSPITAL AND HEALTHCARE SERVICES (181320), 131
Hospital Drive, Zip 42078–8043; tel. 270/988–2299, (Nonreporting) **A**10 18
Primary Contact: Elizabeth Snodgrass, Chief Executive Officer
CMO: William Guyette, M.D., President Medical Staff
CIO: Shannan Landreth, Information Systems
CHR: Carla Wiggins, Director Human Resources
CNO: Joanna Stone, Chief Nursing Officer
Web address: www.lhhs.org
Control: Other not–for–profit (including NFP Corporation) **Service**: General
medical and surgical

Staffed Beds: 25

SCOTTSVILLE—Allen County

MEDICAL CENTER AT SCOTTSVILLE (181324), 456 Burnley Road,
Zip 42164–6355; tel. 270/622–2800, (Total facility includes 110 beds in nursing
home–type unit) **A**10 18 **F**3 15 28 29 30 34 35 40 45 50 56 57 59 64 68 75 81
82 85 86 87 93 97 103 104 107 110 111 114 119 127 128 130 132 133 135
143 146 148 149 154 **S** Med Center Health, Bowling Green, KY
Primary Contact: Eric Hagan, R.N., Executive Vice President and Administrator
CFO: Ronald G. Sowell, FACHE, Chief Financial Officer
CIO: Mark Brookman, Chief Information Officer
CHR: Lynn Williams, Vice President Human Resources
Web address: www.themedicalcenterscottsville.org/
Control: Other not–for–profit (including NFP Corporation) **Service**: General
medical and surgical

Staffed Beds: 135 **Admissions**: 771 **Census**: 124 **Outpatient Visits**: 23633
Births: 0 **Personnel**: 208

SHELBYVILLE—Shelby County

☒ **JEWISH HOSPITAL–SHELBYVILLE (180016)**, 727 Hospital Drive,
Zip 40065–1699; tel. 502/647–4000, **A**1 10 **F**3 11 15 18 28 29 34 35 39 40
44 45 46 50 57 59 64 68 75 79 80 81 82 84 85 87 93 107 108 110 111 114
119 129 132 146 147 148 **P**6 **S** Catholic Health Initiatives, Englewood, CO
Primary Contact: Annessa Baker, Site Executive and Chief Nursing Officer
CFO: Erika McGimsey, Controller
CMO: Tony Perez, M.D., President Medical Staff
CHR: Cindy Stewart Rattray, Director Human Resources
Web address: www.kentuckyonehealth.org/jewish–hospital–shelbyville
Control: Other not–for–profit (including NFP Corporation) **Service**: General
medical and surgical

Staffed Beds: 30 **Admissions**: 863 **Census**: 7 **Outpatient Visits**: 37404
Births: 0 **Total Expense ($000)**: 27564 **Payroll Expense ($000)**: 8700
Personnel: 123

SOMERSET—Pulaski County

☒ **LAKE CUMBERLAND REGIONAL HOSPITAL (180132)**, 305 Langdon
Street, Zip 42503–2750, Mailing Address: P.O. Box 620, Zip 42502–0620;
tel. 606/679–7441, (Total facility includes 12 beds in nursing home–type unit)
A1 2 3 10 13 **F**3 8 11 12 13 15 17 18 20 22 24 29 30 31 34 39 40 41 45 46
49 50 51 54 56 57 58 64 65 68 70 73 74 76 77 78 79 81 82 85 86 87
89 90 91 93 96 97 98 100 102 103 107 108 110 111 114 115 119 120 121
123 127 128 129 130 131 132 135 144 146 147 148 149 **S** LifePoint Health,
Brentwood, TN
Primary Contact: Elizabeth Jones, Interim Chief Executive Officer
COO: Elizabeth Jones, Chief Operating Officer
CFO: Steve Sloan, Chief Financial Officer
CMO: Michael Citak, M.D., Chief Medical Officer
CIO: Thomas Gilbert, Director Information Technology Services
CHR: James Hughes, Director Human Resources
CNO: Sheryl Glasscock, Chief Nursing Officer
Web address: www.lakecumberlandhospital.com
Control: Corporation, Investor–owned (for–profit) **Service**: General medical and
surgical

Staffed Beds: 295 **Admissions**: 9485 **Census**: 127 **Outpatient Visits**:
117261 **Births**: 1159 **Total Expense ($000)**: 153818 **Payroll Expense
($000)**: 51914 **Personnel**: 1056

SOUTH WILLIAMSON—Pike County

☐ **TUG VALLEY ARH REGIONAL MEDICAL CENTER (180069)**, 260 Hospital
Drive, Zip 41503–4072; tel. 606/237–1710, (Nonreporting) **A**1 10 19 **S**
Appalachian Regional Healthcare, Inc., Lexington, KY
Primary Contact: Timothy A. Hatfield, Community Chief Executive Officer
CMO: J D Miller, M.D., Vice President Medical Affairs
CIO: Jeff Brady, Chief Information Officer
Web address: www.arh.org/locations/tug_valley/about_us.aspx
Control: Other not–for–profit (including NFP Corporation) **Service**: General
medical and surgical

Staffed Beds: 141

Many Facility Codes have changed. Please refer to the AHA Guide Code Chart. © 2018 AHA Guide

STANFORD—Lincoln County

☐ **EPHRAIM MCDOWELL FORT LOGAN HOSPITAL (181315)**, 110 Metker Trail, Zip 40484–1020; tel. 606/365–4600, (Nonreporting) **A**1 10 18 **S** Ephraim McDowell Health, Danville, KY
Primary Contact: Ina Louise. Glass, Administrator
CFO: William R Snapp III Vice President and Chief Financial Officer
CMO: James Turpin, Chief of Staff
CIO: Gary Neat, Director Information Systems
CHR: Carl Metz, Vice President
CNO: Ina Louise Glass, Administrator
Web address: www.fortloganhospital.org
Control: Other not–for–profit (including NFP Corporation) **Service:** General medical and surgical

Staffed Beds: 25

TOMPKINSVILLE—Monroe County

☒ **MONROE COUNTY MEDICAL CENTER (180105)**, 529 Capp Harlan Road, Zip 42167–1840; tel. 270/487–9231, (Nonreporting) **A**1 10 **S** QHR, Brentwood, TN
Primary Contact: Vicky McFall, Chief Executive Officer
CFO: Rickie F Brown, Chief Financial Officer
CIO: Paul McKiddy, Director Information Technology
CHR: Sue Page, Director Human Resources
Web address: www.mcmccares.com
Control: Other not–for–profit (including NFP Corporation) **Service:** General medical and surgical

Staffed Beds: 49

VERSAILLES—Woodford County

★ **BLUEGRASS COMMUNITY HOSPITAL (181308)**, 360 Amsden Avenue, Zip 40383–1286; tel. 859/873–3111, (Nonreporting) **A**10 18 **S** LifePoint Health, Brentwood, TN
Primary Contact: Tommy Haggard, Chief Executive Officer
CFO: Shellie Shouse, Chief Financial Officer
CMO: Michele Welling, M.D., Chief of Staff
CHR: Marcia Carter, Director Human Resources
CNO: Kathy Russell, R.N., Chief Nursing Officer
Web address: www.bluegrasscommunityhospital.com
Control: Other not–for–profit (including NFP Corporation) **Service:** General medical and surgical

Staffed Beds: 16

WEST LIBERTY—Morgan County

☐ **MORGAN COUNTY ARH HOSPITAL (181307)**, 476 Liberty Road, Zip 41472–2049, Mailing Address: P.O. Box 579, Zip 41472–0579; tel. 606/743–3186, **A**1 10 18 **F**11 15 28 29 30 34 35 40 43 57 59 62 64 75 82 85 86 87 93 107 110 115 119 129 130 132 133 146 148 **S** Appalachian Regional Healthcare, Inc., Lexington, KY
Primary Contact: Stephen M. Gavalchik, FACHE, Community Chief Executive Officer
COO: Paul V Miles, Chief Operating Officer
CMO: J D Miller, M.D., Vice President Medical Affairs
CIO: Jeff Brady, Director Information Systems
CHR: Lisa Redding, Manager Human Resources
Web address: www.arh.org
Control: Other not–for–profit (including NFP Corporation) **Service:** General medical and surgical

Staffed Beds: 25 Admissions: 179 Census: 3 Outpatient Visits: 26627
Births: 0 Total Expense ($000): 13794 Payroll Expense ($000): 4484
Personnel: 104

WHITESBURG—Letcher County

☐ **WHITESBURG ARH HOSPITAL (180002)**, 240 Hospital Road, Zip 41858–7627; tel. 606/633–3500, **A**1 10 20 **F**3 11 13 15 18 20 28 29 30 31 32 34 35 40 43 50 54 57 59 62 64 70 75 76 77 81 82 85 86 87 89 93 97 107 108 110 111 114 118 119 127 129 130 133 146 147 **S** Appalachian Regional Healthcare, Inc., Lexington, KY
Primary Contact: Dena C. Sparkman, FACHE, Community Chief Executive Officer
COO: Paul V Miles, Vice President Administration
CMO: Ricky M Collins, M.D., Chief of Staff
CIO: Brent Styer, Director Information Technology
CHR: Daniel Fitzpatrick, Director Human Resources
Web address: www.arh.org/whitesburg
Control: Other not–for–profit (including NFP Corporation) **Service:** General medical and surgical

Staffed Beds: 89 Admissions: 3236 Census: 38 Outpatient Visits: 60442
Births: 408 Total Expense ($000): 45533 Payroll Expense ($000): 13659

WILLIAMSTOWN—Grant County

ST. ELIZABETH GRANT (181311), 238 Barnes Road, Zip 41097–9482; tel. 859/824–8240, **A**10 18 **F**3 9 11 15 18 26 29 30 31 34 35 38 40 44 45 50 53 57 59 63 64 65 74 75 78 79 84 93 97 107 108 110 111 115 119 129 130 131 132 135 141 146 148 149 150 152 153 154 **S** St. Elizabeth Healthcare, Edgewood, KY
Primary Contact: Garren Colvin, Chief Executive Officer
Web address: www.stelizabeth.com
Control: Church operated, Nongovernment, not–for–profit **Service:** General medical and surgical

Staffed Beds: 16 Admissions: 217 Census: 2 Outpatient Visits: 56096
Births: 0 Total Expense ($000): 23196 Payroll Expense ($000): 8534
Personnel: 97

ST. ELIZABETH MEDICAL CENTER–GRANT COUNTY See St. Elizabeth Grant

WINCHESTER—Clark County

☒ **CLARK REGIONAL MEDICAL CENTER (180092)**, 175 Hospital Drive, Zip 40391–9591; tel. 859/745–3500, (Nonreporting) **A**1 5 10 **S** LifePoint Health, Brentwood, TN
Primary Contact: Robert Parker, Chief Executive Officer and Market President
CFO: Amber Goodpaster, Chief Financial Officer
CMO: Ben McQuaide, M.D., Chief of Staff
CHR: Deidre Bradley, Vice President Human Resources
CNO: Barbara Kinder, R.N., Chief Clinical Officer
Web address: www.clarkregional.org
Control: Corporation, Investor–owned (for–profit) **Service:** General medical and surgical

Staffed Beds: 79

Hospital, Medicare Provider Number, Address, Telephone, Approval, Facility, and Physician Codes, Health Care System

★ American Hospital Association (AHA) membership
☐ The Joint Commission accreditation
○ Healthcare Facilities Accreditation Program
◇ DNV Healthcare Inc. accreditation
⇑ Center for Improvement in Healthcare Quality Accreditation
△ Commission on Accreditation of Rehabilitation Facilities (CARF) accreditation

LOUISIANA

ABBEVILLE—Vermilion Parish

⊞ **ABBEVILLE GENERAL HOSPITAL (190034)**, 118 North Hospital Drive, Zip 70510–4077, Mailing Address: P.O. Box 580, Zip 70511–0580; tel. 337/893–5466, **A**1 10 **F**3 11 13 15 29 30 31 34 40 45 50 54 59 60 64 66 68 70 75 76 79 81 82 85 86 87 89 97 98 103 105 107 108 114 119 127 128 130 133 146 149 153 **P**6
Primary Contact: Ray A. Landry, Chief Executive Officer
COO: Charles W Guidry, Chief Operating Officer
CFO: Troy Hair, Chief Financial Officer
CMO: Weston Miller, M.D., Chief Medical Officer
CIO: Kelly Hair, Director Information Systems and Data Analytics
CNO: Heidi Broussard, Chief Nursing Officer
Web address: www.abbgen.net
Control: Hospital district or authority, Government, nonfederal **Service**: General medical and surgical

Staffed Beds: 60 **Admissions**: 1939 **Census**: 30 **Outpatient Visits**: 108215
Births: 247 **Total Expense ($000)**: 46727 **Payroll Expense ($000)**: 23325
Personnel: 423

ALEXANDRIA—Rapides Parish

⇑ **CENTRAL LOUISIANA SURGICAL HOSPITAL (190298)**, 651 North Bolton Avenue, Zip 71301–7449, Mailing Address: P.O. Box 8646, Zip 71306–1646; tel. 318/443–3511, (Nonreporting) **A**10 21
Primary Contact: Louise Barker, R.N., Chief Executive Officer
CFO: Michael Fuselier, FACHE, CPA, R.N., Chief Financial Officer
CMO: Renick Webb, M.D., Chief Medical Director
CHR: Debbie Norman, Director Human Resources
CNO: Carol Wells, R.N., MSN, Chief Nursing Officer
Web address: www.clshospital.com
Control: Corporation, Investor–owned (for–profit) **Service**: Surgical

Staffed Beds: 24

⊞ **CHRISTUS DUBUIS HOSPITAL OF ALEXANDRIA (192012)**, 3330 Masonic Drive, 4th Floor, Zip 71301–3841; tel. 318/448–4938, **A**1 10 **F**1 3 29 77 84 85 148 **S** LHC Group, Lafayette, LA
Primary Contact: Beth Parsons, R.N., Administrator
CNO: Kimberly Bennett, R.N., Director of Nursing
Web address: www.christusdubuis.org/CHRISTUSDubuisHospitalofAlexandriaLA
Control: Church operated, Nongovernment, not–for–profit **Service**: Acute long–term care hospital

Staffed Beds: 25 **Admissions**: 209 **Census**: 15 **Outpatient Visits**: 0
Births: 0 **Personnel**: 57

⊞ **CHRISTUS ST. FRANCES CABRINI HOSPITAL (190019)**, 3330 Masonic Drive, Zip 71301–3899; tel. 318/487–1122, **A**1 2 10 **F**3 11 12 13 15 18 20 22 24 26 28 29 30 31 34 40 45 46 49 57 58 59 64 66 70 72 74 75 76 78 79 81 82 84 85 86 87 89 90 91 93 98 102 104 105 107 108 111 114 115 116 117 118 119 120 121 124 126 129 130 131 132 135 144 146 147 148 149 **P**6 **S** CHRISTUS Health, Irving, TX
Primary Contact: Chris Karam, FACHE, President and Chief Executive Officer, Senior Vice President Group Operations
COO: Lisa R. Lauve, R.N., Regional Chief Nursing Executive and Chief Operating Officer
CFO: Gary Karg, Interim Vice President Finance
CHR: Wendy Chandler, Regional Vice President Human Resources
Web address: www.cabrini.org/
Control: Church operated, Nongovernment, not–for–profit **Service**: General medical and surgical

Staffed Beds: 281 **Admissions**: 11948 **Census**: 182 **Outpatient Visits**: 188950 **Births**: 1174 **Total Expense ($000)**: 236864 **Payroll Expense ($000)**: 78213 **Personnel**: 1243

☐ **COMPASS BEHAVIORAL CENTER OF ALEXANDRIA (194106)**, 6410 Masonic Drve, Zip 71301–2319; tel. 318/442–3163, (Nonreporting) **A**1 10 **S** Compass Health, Crowley, LA
Primary Contact: Andre' Robichaux, Interim Administrator
CNO: Cheryl Lachney, Director of Nursing
Web address: www.compasshealthcare.com/site191.php
Control: Other not–for–profit (including NFP Corporation) **Service**: Psychiatric

Staffed Beds: 16

⊞ **HEALTHSOUTH REHABILITATION HOSPITAL OF ALEXANDRIA (193031)**, 104 North Third Street, Zip 71301–8581; tel. 318/449–1370, (Nonreporting) **A**1 10 **S** Encompass Health Corporation, Birmingham, AL
Primary Contact: James W. McClung, Chief Executive Officer
CFO: Linda Wright, Chief Financial Officer
CMO: Vasudeva Dhulipala, M.D., Medical Director
CHR: Suzie Wagner, Director Human Resources
Web address: www.healthsouthalexandria.com
Control: Partnership, Investor–owned (for–profit) **Service**: Rehabilitation

Staffed Beds: 47

LONGLEAF HOSPITAL (194022), 44 Versailles Boulevard, Zip 71303–3960; tel. 318/445–5111, **A**10 **F**4 5 29 34 35 38 68 98 99 100 101 102 103 104 105 130 132 151 152 153 **S** Acadia Healthcare Company, Inc., Franklin, TN
Primary Contact: Claire Hick, Chief Executive Officer
CFO: John Montanio, Chief Financial Officer
Web address: www.longleafhospital.com/
Control: Corporation, Investor–owned (for–profit) **Service**: Psychiatric

Staffed Beds: 92 **Admissions**: 3409 **Census**: 79 **Births**: 0

☐ **OCEANS BEHAVIORAL HOSPITAL OF ALEXANDRIA (194096)**, 2621 North Bolton Avenue, Zip 71303–4506; tel. 318/448–8473, (Nonreporting) **A**1 10 **S** Oceans Healthcare, Lake Charles, LA
Primary Contact: Ben Cooper, Administrator
Web address: www.obha.info/
Control: Corporation, Investor–owned (for–profit) **Service**: Psychiatric

Staffed Beds: 24

⊞ **RAPIDES REGIONAL MEDICAL CENTER (190026)**, 211 4th ST, Zip 71301–8421, Mailing Address: 211 Fourth Street, Zip 71301–8421; tel. 318/769–3000, **A**1 2 3 5 10 **F**3 11 13 15 17 18 19 20 22 24 26 28 29 30 31 32 34 35 36 38 40 41 43 44 45 46 47 48 49 50 51 52 54 55 57 59 60 61 64 65 66 68 70 72 74 75 76 77 78 79 81 82 84 85 86 87 88 89 97 107 108 110 111 114 115 118 119 120 121 123 124 126 129 130 131 132 135 144 146 147 148 149 154 **P**1 **S** HCA Healthcare, Nashville, TN
Primary Contact: Jason E. Cobb, FACHE, Chief Executive Officer
CFO: Nathan Crabdree, Chief Financial Officer
CMO: David Rhodes, M.D., Senior Vice President Medical Affairs and Chief Medical Officer
CHR: Stephen W Scull, Vice President Ethics and Compliance officer
CNO: Barbara J Griffin, MSN, R.N., Chief Nursing Officer
Web address: www.rapidesregional.com
Control: Partnership, Investor–owned (for–profit) **Service**: General medical and surgical

Staffed Beds: 357 **Admissions**: 15858 **Census**: 239 **Outpatient Visits**: 233912 **Births**: 1728 **Total Expense ($000)**: 235561 **Payroll Expense ($000)**: 83716 **Personnel**: 1422

☐ **RIVERSIDE HOSPITAL OF LOUISIANA (192043)**, 211 Fourth Street, 5th Floor, Zip 71301–8421; tel. 318/767–2900, (Nonreporting) **A**1 10
Primary Contact: Wade K Lester, Administrator
Web address: www.riversidehospital.net
Control: Corporation, Investor–owned (for–profit) **Service**: Acute long–term care hospital

Staffed Beds: 27

AMITE—Tangipahoa Parish

★ **HOOD MEMORIAL HOSPITAL (191309)**, 301 West Walnut Street, Zip 70422–2098; tel. 985/748–9485, **A**10 18 **F**3 29 35 40 50 57 59 64 65 75 83 84 86 87 97 107 108 111 115 119 127 130 133 135 144 146 149 **P**6
Primary Contact: Edward Dugar, R.N., Chief Executive Officer
CFO: Mike Estay, Chief Financial Officer
CMO: Richard Bridges, M.D., Chief of Staff
CIO: Schley Harvin, Information Technology Technician
CHR: Alicia Chatelain, Director Human Resource
CNO: Fran St. Pierre, Chief Nursing Officer
Web address: www.hoodmemorial.com
Control: Hospital district or authority, Government, nonfederal **Service**: General medical and surgical

Staffed Beds: 25 **Admissions**: 427 **Census**: 17 **Outpatient Visits**: 25512
Births: 0 **Total Expense ($000)**: 16738 **Payroll Expense ($000)**: 7355
Personnel: 167

Many Facility Codes have changed. Please refer to the AHA Guide Code Chart.

ARCADIA—Bienville Parish

BIENVILLE MEDICAL CENTER (191320), 1175 Pine Street, Suite 200, Zip 71001–3122; tel. 318/263–4700, (Nonreporting) **A**10 18 **S** Allegiance Health Management, Shreveport, LA
Primary Contact: Kirk Lemoine, Chief Executive Officer
Web address: www.bienvillemedicalcenter.net/
Control: Other not–for–profit (including NFP Corporation) **Service:** General medical and surgical

Staffed Beds: 21

BASTROP—Morehouse Parish

☐ **CYPRESS GROVE BEHAVIORAL HEALTH (194083)**, 4673 Eugene Ware Boulevard, Zip 71220–1425; tel. 318/281–2448, (Nonreporting) **A**1 10
Primary Contact: Venicea Austin Preston, Administrator
COO: Christine Murphy, MS, Chief Operating Officer
CFO: Paul Coburn, Chief Financial Officer
CMO: Tommy Dansby, Chief Medical Officer
CHR: Lindsay Cobb, Director Human Resources
CNO: Carla Sams, R.N., Director of Nursing
Web address: www.libertybh.com/
Control: Corporation, Investor–owned (for–profit) **Service:** Psychiatric

Staffed Beds: 60

★ **MOREHOUSE GENERAL HOSPITAL (190116)**, 323 West Walnut Avenue, Zip 71220–4521, Mailing Address: P.O. Box 1060, Zip 71221–1060; tel. 318/283–3600, (Nonreporting) **A**3 10 **S** Community Hospital Corporation, Plano, TX
Primary Contact: Derrick A. Frazier, FACHE, Chief Executive Officer
CFO: Tom Ramsey, Chief Financial Officer
CMO: John Coats, M.D., Chief Medical Staff
CIO: B J Vail, Director Information Systems
CHR: Debbie Spann, Director Human Resources
CNO: Melinda Jones, R.N., Chief Nursing Officer
Web address: www.mghospital.com
Control: Hospital district or authority, Government, nonfederal **Service:** General medical and surgical

Staffed Beds: 49

STERLINGTON REHABILITATION HOSPITAL (193069), 370 W Hickory Ave, Zip 71220–4442, Mailing Address: P.O. Box 627, Sterlington, Zip 71280–0627; tel. 318/665–9950, **A**10 **F**28 34 35 50 54 56 57 59 64 65 66 68 70 72 74 75 86 87 90 91 93 94 95 96 97 100 104 127 132 135 143 147 148 153 **P**6
Primary Contact: Catherine M. Waldrop, Administrator
Web address: www.https://sterlingtonrehab.com/
Control: Corporation, Investor–owned (for–profit) **Service:** Rehabilitation

Staffed Beds: 10 **Admissions:** 285 **Census:** 10 **Outpatient Visits:** 1350
Births: 0

BATON ROUGE—East Baton Rouge Parish

APOLLO BEHAVIORAL HEALTH HOSPITAL (194105), 9938 Airline Highway, Zip 70816–8193; tel. 225/663–2881, (Nonreporting)
Primary Contact: Gopinath Gopalam, Chief Executive Officer
Web address: www.apollo–bhh.com/about–us/
Control: Other not–for–profit (including NFP Corporation) **Service:** Psychiatric

Staffed Beds: 25

☐ **BATON ROUGE BEHAVIORAL HOSPITAL (194107)**, 4040 North Boulevard, Zip 70806–3829; tel. 225/300–8470, (Nonreporting) **A**1 10
Primary Contact: Michael Gomila, Administrator
COO: James O'Shea, Chief Operating Officer
CFO: Warren Knight, Chief Financial Officer
CMO: Richard Capiola, M.D., Chief Medical Officer
CNO: Francine Mineau, Chief Nursing Officer
Web address: www.batonrougebehavioral.com
Control: Corporation, Investor–owned (for–profit) **Service:** Psychiatric

Staffed Beds: 15

⊞ **BATON ROUGE GENERAL MEDICAL CENTER (190065)**, 8585 Picardy Avenue, Zip 70809–3679; tel. 225/763–4000, (Includes BATON ROUGE GENERAL MEDICAL CENTER–BLUEBONNET, 8585 Picardy Avenue, Baton Rouge, LA, Zip 70809–3679, Mailing Address: P.O. Box 84330, Zip 70884–4330, tel. 225/763–4000; Edgardo J Tenreiro, Chief Executive Officer and Chief Operating Officer) **A**1 2 3 5 8 10 **F**3 8 11 12 15 16 18 19 20 22 24 26 28 29 30 31 34 35 38 40 41 44 45 46 50 53 56 57 58 59 60 61 64 65 68 70 72 74 75 76 77 78 79 81 82 84 86 87 89 90 91 93 96 97 98 99 101 102 103 104 107 108 110 111 114 115 117 118 119 120 121 123 124 126 128 129 130 131 132 135 143 144 146 147 148 154 **P**4 6
Primary Contact: Edgardo J. Tenreiro, Chief Executive Officer and Chief Operating Officer
COO: Stephen Mumford, Chief Operating Officer
CFO: Kendall Johnson, Chief Financial Officer
CIO: Bennett Cheramie, Vice President Information Technology
CHR: Paul Douglas, Vice President Human Resources
CNO: Monica Nijoka, Chief Nursing Officer
Web address: www.brgeneral.org
Control: Other not–for–profit (including NFP Corporation) **Service:** General medical and surgical

Staffed Beds: 365 **Admissions:** 16781 **Census:** 249 **Outpatient Visits:** 257174 **Births:** 819 **Total Expense ($000):** 432576 **Payroll Expense ($000):** 120975 **Personnel:** 2862

☐ **BATON ROUGE REHABILITATION HOSPITAL (193028)**, 8595 United Plaza Boulevard, Zip 70809–2251; tel. 225/927–0567, (Nonreporting) **A**1 10
Primary Contact: Trisha Guidry, Administrator
CFO: Nicholas Hluchy, Business Analyst, Support Services Manager
CMO: Sundararama R Vatsavai, M.D., Medical Director
CIO: John Derrick Landreneau, Director of Nursing and Marketing Manager
CHR: Michelle Smith, Coordinator Human Resources
CNO: John Derrick Landreneau, Director of Nursing
Web address: www.brrehab.com
Control: Corporation, Investor–owned (for–profit) **Service:** Rehabilitation

Staffed Beds: 80

BETHESDA REHABILITATION HOSPITAL (193092), 7414 Sumrall Drive, Zip 70812–1240, Mailing Address: 8225 Summa Avenue, Suite B, Zip 70809–3422; tel. 225/767–2034, (Nonreporting) **A**10
Primary Contact: Lionel Murphy, Chief Executive Officer and Administrator
Web address: www.bethesdarh.com/
Control: Corporation, Investor–owned (for–profit) **Service:** Rehabilitation

Staffed Beds: 18

HEALTHSOUTH REHABILITATION HOSPITAL OF BATON ROUGE See Baton Rouge Rehabilitation Hospital

OCEANS BEHAVIORAL HOSPITAL OF BATON ROUGE (194086), 11135 Florida Boulevard, Zip 70815–2013; tel. 225/356–7030, (Nonreporting) **A**10 **S** Oceans Healthcare, Lake Charles, LA
Primary Contact: Valerie Dalton, R.N., Administrator
Web address: www.obhbr.info/
Control: Corporation, Investor–owned (for–profit) **Service:** Psychiatric

Staffed Beds: 20

⊞ **OCHSNER MEDICAL CENTER – BATON ROUGE (190202)**, 17000 Medical Center Drive, Zip 70816–3224; tel. 225/752–2470, **A**1 10 **F**3 11 12 13 15 18 20 22 24 26 28 29 30 31 34 35 36 40 41 44 45 46 47 48 49 51 54 57 58 59 60 64 68 70 72 74 75 76 77 78 79 81 82 85 86 87 93 97 102 104 107 108 110 111 114 116 117 119 126 129 130 131 132 135 144 146 147 148 **P**6 **S** Ochsner Health System, New Orleans, LA
Primary Contact: Eric McMillen, Chief Executive Officer
CFO: Stephanie Bushart, Chief Financial Officer
CMO: F Ralph Dauterive, M.D., Vice President Medical Affairs
CHR: Jan Rivers, Director Human Resources
Web address: www.ochsner.org/page.cfm?id=103
Control: Other not–for–profit (including NFP Corporation) **Service:** General medical and surgical

Staffed Beds: 154 **Admissions:** 7290 **Census:** 75 **Outpatient Visits:** 104638 **Births:** 1578 **Total Expense ($000):** 190556 **Payroll Expense ($000):** 64137 **Personnel:** 957

Hospital, Medicare Provider Number, Address, Telephone, Approval, Facility, and Physician Codes, Health Care System

★ American Hospital Association (AHA) membership
☐ The Joint Commission accreditation
○ Healthcare Facilities Accreditation Program
◇ DNV Healthcare Inc. accreditation
⇑ Center for Improvement in Healthcare Quality Accreditation
△ Commission on Accreditation of Rehabilitation Facilities (CARF) accreditation

LA

⊞ **OUR LADY OF THE LAKE REGIONAL MEDICAL CENTER (190064)**, 5000 Hennessy Boulevard, Zip 70808–4375; tel. 225/765–6565, (Includes OUR LADY OF THE LAKE CHILDREN'S HOSPITAL, 5000 Hennessy Boulevard, Baton Rouge, LA, Zip 70808–4375; tel. 225/765–8886) (Total facility includes 390 beds in nursing home–type unit) **A**1 2 3 5 8 10 **F**3 4 5 8 9 11 12 14 15 17 18 19 20 21 22 24 26 28 29 30 31 32 34 35 37 38 39 40 41 43 45 46 47 48 49 50 51 53 54 55 56 57 58 59 60 61 64 66 68 70 71 74 75 77 78 79 81 83 84 85 86 87 88 89 90 91 92 93 94 96 97 98 100 101 102 103 104 105 107 108 110 111 114 115 116 117 118 119 124 125 126 127 129 130 131 132 135 141 142 143 144 145 146 148 149 153 154 **P**6 **S** Franciscan Missionaries of Our Lady Health System, Inc., Baton Rouge, LA
Primary Contact: K Scott. Wester, FACHE, President and Chief Executive Officer
COO: Stephanie Manson, Chief Operating Officer
CFO: Jeff Limbocker, Chief Financial Officer
CMO: Richard Vath, M.D., Vice President Medical Affairs
CIO: Vindell Washington, M.D., Vice President Performance Excellence and Technology
CHR: Cora Ford, Vice President Human Resources
CNO: Nicole Telhiard, MSN, Chief Nursing Officer
Web address: www.ololrmc.com
Control: Church operated, Nongovernment, not–for–profit **Service:** General medical and surgical

Staffed Beds: 1219 **Admissions:** 35613 **Census:** 782 **Outpatient Visits:** 1688531 **Births:** 0 **Total Expense ($000):** 1177895 **Payroll Expense ($000):** 419669 **Personnel:** 5474

☐ **PROMISE HOSPITAL BATON ROUGE – MAIN CAMPUS (192004)**, 5130 Mancuso Lane, Zip 70809–3583; tel. 225/490–9600, (Nonreporting) **A**1 **S** Promise Healthcare, Boca Raton, FL
Primary Contact: Kiley P. Cedotal, FACHE, Chief Executive Officer
COO: Michael R Sanders, MS, Chief Operating Officer
CFO: Trina Arceneaux, Assistant Chief Financial Officer
CMO: Subhaker Gummadi, M.D., Chief Medical Staff
CIO: Charmaine T Mosby, Area Director Health Information Management
CHR: Marilyn Hamilton, Director Human Resources
CNO: Larrie Arceneaux, Chief Clinical Officer
Web address: www.promise–batonrouge.com
Control: Corporation, Investor–owned (for–profit) **Service:** Acute long–term care hospital

Staffed Beds: 54

PROMISE HOSPITAL OF BATON ROUGE – OCHSNER CAMPUS (192049), 17000 Medical Center Drive, 3rd Floor, Zip 70816–3246; tel. 225/236–5440, (Includes PROMISE HOSPITAL OF BATON ROUGE – MID–CITY CAMPUS, 3600 Florida Boulevard, 4th Floor, Baton Rouge, LA, Zip 70806–3842; tel. 225/387–7770; Kiley P Cedotal, FACHE, Chief Executive Officer) (Nonreporting) **A**10 **S** Promise Healthcare, Boca Raton, FL
Primary Contact: Kiley P. Cedotal, FACHE, Chief Executive Officer
CMO: Venkat Banda, M.D., President Medical Staff
CHR: Wendy Cobbs, Director of Human Resources
Web address: www.promise–batonrougeochsner.com
Control: Corporation, Investor–owned (for–profit) **Service:** Acute long–term care hospital

Staffed Beds: 86

SAGE REHABILITATION HOSPITAL (193078), 8000 Summa Avenue, Zip 70809–3423, Mailing Address: P.O. Box 82681, Zip 70884–2681; tel. 225/819–0703, (Total facility includes 24 beds in nursing home–type unit) **A**10 **F**29 54 74 75 77 90 91 93 96 128 130 148 **S** The Carpenter Health Network, Baton Rouge, LA
Primary Contact: Scott McClelland, Administrator
CMO: Christopher Belleau, M.D., Medical Director
CHR: Kathy Ringe, Director Human Resources
CNO: Beth Sibley, Director of Nursing
Web address: www.sage–rehab.org
Control: Individual, Investor–owned (for–profit) **Service:** Rehabilitation

Staffed Beds: 42 **Admissions:** 624 **Census:** 28 **Outpatient Visits:** 0 **Births:** 0

☐ **SEASIDE HEALTH SYSTEM (194103)**, 4363 Convention Street, Zip 70806–3906, Mailing Address: 4363 Convention Stret, Zip 70806–3906; tel. 225/238–3043, (Nonreporting) **A**1 10
Primary Contact: Eric Gintoli, Administrator
Web address: www.seasidehc.com/seaside–health–system–locations/
Control: Partnership, Investor–owned (for–profit) **Service:** Psychiatric

Staffed Beds: 24

SPINE HOSPITAL OF LOUISIANA (FORMALLY THE NEUROMEDICAL CENTER SURGICAL HOSPITAL) (190266), 10105 Park Rowe Circle, Suite 250, Zip 70810–1684; tel. 225/763–9900, (Nonreporting) **A**10
Primary Contact: Robert D. Blair, Chief Executive Officer
CFO: Allison Doherty, Chief Financial Officer
CMO: Greg Fautheree, M.D., Medical Director
CIO: Jeremy Deprato, Director Information Technology
CHR: Kimberly Jones, Director Human Resources
CNO: Kim Pettijohn, R.N., MSN, Chief Nursing Officer
Web address: www.theneuromedicalcenter.com
Control: Corporation, Investor–owned (for–profit) **Service:** Surgical

Staffed Beds: 23

☐ **SURGICAL SPECIALTY CENTER OF BATON ROUGE (190251)**, 8080 Bluebonnet Boulevard, Zip 70810–7827; tel. 225/408–8080, (Nonreporting) **A**1 10
Primary Contact: Ann Heine, Chief Executive Officer
CNO: Kelli Firmin, Interim Chief Nursing Officer, Pre–Op and PACU Manager
Web address: www.sscbr.com
Control: Corporation, Investor–owned (for–profit) **Service:** Surgical

Staffed Beds: 14

THE NEUROMEDICAL CENTER REHABILITATION HOSPITAL (193090), 10101 Park Rowe Avenue, Suite 500, Zip 70810–1685; tel. 225/906–2999, (Nonreporting) **A**10 **S** AMG Integrated Healthcare Management, Lafayette, LA
Primary Contact: Sherry Mix, Chief Executive Officer and Administrator
Web address: www.theneuromedicalcenter.com
Control: Corporation, Investor–owned (for–profit) **Service:** Rehabilitation

Staffed Beds: 23

⊞ **WOMAN'S HOSPITAL (190128)**, 100 Woman's Way, Zip 70817–5100, Mailing Address: P.O. Box 95009, Zip 70895–9009; tel. 225/927–1300, **A**1 2 3 5 10 **F**3 11 12 13 15 29 31 32 34 35 36 38 40 45 50 53 54 57 58 59 61 64 65 66 68 70 71 72 74 75 76 77 78 79 81 85 86 87 93 102 107 110 111 115 119 126 129 130 131 132 134 135 146 147 148 149 154 **P**6
Primary Contact: Teri G. Fontenot, FACHE, President and Chief Executive Officer
COO: Stephanie Anderson, Executive Vice President and Chief Operating Officer
CFO: Gina Dugas, Chief Financial Officer
CMO: Susan Puyau, M.D., Medical Director
CIO: Paul Kirk, Vice President
CHR: Donna L Bodin, Vice President
CNO: Patricia Johnson, R.N., Senior Vice President
Web address: www.womans.org
Control: Other not–for–profit (including NFP Corporation) **Service:** Obstetrics and gynecology

Staffed Beds: 228 **Admissions:** 11245 **Census:** 140 **Outpatient Visits:** 142671 **Births:** 8295 **Total Expense ($000):** 308298 **Payroll Expense ($000):** 133898 **Personnel:** 1816

BERNICE—Union Parish

REEVES MEMORIAL MEDICAL CENTER (191326), 409 First Street, Zip 71222–4001, Mailing Address: P.O. Box 697, Zip 71222–0697; tel. 318/285–9066, (Nonreporting) **A**10 18
Primary Contact: Kerry Goff, Chief Executive Officer
COO: Beth Jones, Chief Operating Officer
CFO: Charolette Thompson, Chief Financial Officer
CMO: R Brian Harris, M.D., Chief of Staff
CIO: Scott Dickson, Director Information Technology
CHR: Robin Adams, Director Human Resources
CNO: Beth Jones, Director of Nursing
Web address: www.reevesmemorial.com/
Control: Hospital district or authority, Government, nonfederal **Service:** General medical and surgical

Staffed Beds: 11

TRI–WARD GENERAL HOSPITAL See Reeves Memorial Medical Center

BOGALUSA—Washington Parish

⊞ **OUR LADY OF THE ANGELS HOSPITAL (190312)**, 433 Plaza Street, Zip 70427–3793; tel. 985/730–6700, (Includes BOGALUSA COMMUNITY MEDICAL CENTER, 433 Plaza Street, Bogalusa, LA, Zip 70427–3793; tel. 985/730–6700) (Nonreporting) **A**1 3 5 10 **S** Franciscan Missionaries of Our Lady Health System, Inc., Baton Rouge, LA
Primary Contact: Rene J. Ragas, Chief Operating Officer
COO: Rene J. Ragas, Chief Operating Officer
CFO: Brooke Cummings, Chief Financial Officer
CMO: Hamid Hussain, M.D., Medical Director
CIO: Mike Gilly, Chief Information Officer
CHR: Christi Brown, Director Human Resources
CNO: Mark Kellar, R.N., Interim Chief Nursing Officer
Web address: www.oloah.org
Control: Church operated, Nongovernment, not–for–profit **Service:** General medical and surgical

Staffed Beds: 57

BOSSIER CITY—Bossier Parish

☐ **CORNERSTONE HOSPITAL OF BOSSIER CITY (192006)**, 4900 Medical Drive, Zip 71112–4521; tel. 318/747–9500, (Nonreporting) **A**1 10 **S** Cornerstone Healthcare Group, Dallas, TX
Primary Contact: Sheri Burnette, R.N., Chief Executive Officer and Administrator
CMO: James Jackson, M.D., Chief of Staff
CNO: Tamara Grimm, R.N., Chief Clinical Officer and Chief Nursing Officer
Web address: www.chghospitals.com/
Control: Corporation, Investor–owned (for–profit) **Service:** Acute long–term care hospital

Staffed Beds: 54

⇑ **PATHWAY REHABILITATION HOSPITAL (193094)**, 4900 Medical Drive, Zip 71112–4521; tel. 318/841–5555, (Nonreporting) **A**10 21
Primary Contact: James Manning, Administrator
Web address: www.pathrehab.com
Control: Corporation, Investor–owned (for–profit) **Service:** Rehabilitation

Staffed Beds: 24

RED RIVER BEHAVIORAL CENTER (194079), 2800 Melrose Avenue, Zip 71111–5870; tel. 318/549–2033, **A**10 **F**29 38 56 98 100 101 103 130 135 143 154
Primary Contact: Susan Kottenbrook, Chief Executive Officer
Web address: www.redriverbc.com
Control: Partnership, Investor–owned (for–profit) **Service:** Psychiatric

Staffed Beds: 20 **Admissions:** 325 **Census:** 16 **Outpatient Visits:** 0 **Births:** 0 **Total Expense ($000):** 3531 **Payroll Expense ($000):** 1512

WILLIS–KNIGHTON BOSSIER HEALTH CENTER See Wk Bossier Health Center

BREAUX BRIDGE—St. Martin Parish

GENESIS BEHAVIORAL HOSPITAL (194089), 606 Latiolais Drive, Zip 70517–4231, Mailing Address: PO BOX 159, Zip 70517–0159; tel. 337/442–6084, (Nonreporting) **A**10
Primary Contact: William Arledge, Administrator and Chief Financial Officer
COO: Gretchen Kaltenbach, R.N., Chief Operating Officer
CFO: William Arledge, Administrator and Chief Financial Officer
Web address: www.genesisbh.com/
Control: Corporation, Investor–owned (for–profit) **Service:** Psychiatric

Staffed Beds: 18

★ **ST. MARTIN HOSPITAL (191302)**, 210 Champagne Boulevard, Zip 70517–3700, Mailing Address: P.O. Box 357, Zip 70517–0357; tel. 337/332–2178, **A**10 18 **F**3 15 18 28 29 30 34 35 40 54 57 59 64 68 75 77 87 91 93 107 110 111 114 119 130 133 146 149 154 **S** Lafayette General Health, Lafayette, LA
Primary Contact: Karen O. Wyble, R.N., Chief Executive Officer
CFO: Shadelle Huval, Director Finance
CHR: Rena B Mouisset, Director Human Resources and Contract Compliance
Web address: www.stmartinhospital.org
Control: Other not–for–profit (including NFP Corporation) **Service:** General medical and surgical

Staffed Beds: 25 **Admissions:** 380 **Census:** 14 **Outpatient Visits:** 152786 **Births:** 0 **Total Expense ($000):** 16622 **Payroll Expense ($000):** 7026 **Personnel:** 120

BROUSSARD—Lafayette Parish

☐ **OCEANS BEHAVIORAL HOSPITAL OF BROUSSARD (194073)**, 418 Albertson Parkway, Zip 70518–4971; tel. 337/237–6444, (Nonreporting) **A**1 10 **S** Oceans Healthcare, Lake Charles, LA
Primary Contact: Amy Dysart–Credeur, Administrator
Web address: www.obhb.info/
Control: Corporation, Investor–owned (for–profit) **Service:** Psychiatric

Staffed Beds: 38

BUNKIE—Avoyelles Parish

BEACON BEHAVIORAL HOSPITAL (194112), 323 Evergreen Street, Zip 71322–1307; tel. 318/346–3143, (Nonreporting) **S** Beacon Health System, South Bend, IN
Primary Contact: Randall Johnson, Administrator
Web address: www.beaconbh.com
Control: Other not–for–profit (including NFP Corporation) **Service:** Psychiatric

Staffed Beds: 17

BUNKIE GENERAL HOSPITAL (191311), 427 Evergreen Highway, Zip 71322, Mailing Address: P.O. Box 380, Zip 71322–0380; tel. 318/346–6681, (Nonreporting) **A**10 18
Primary Contact: Linda F. Deville, Chief Executive Officer
CFO: Layla Chase, Interim Chief Financial Officer
CMO: Mohit Srivastava, M.D., Chief of Staff
CIO: Kiland Jackson, Chief Information Officer
CHR: Tina Louise Juneau, Director Human Resources
CNO: Corey Jeansonne, Chief Nursing Officer
Web address: www.bunkiegeneral.com
Control: Hospital district or authority, Government, nonfederal **Service:** General medical and surgical

Staffed Beds: 18

CAMERON—Cameron Parish

SOUTH CAMERON MEMORIAL HOSPITAL (190307), 5360 West Creole Highway, Zip 70631–5127; tel. 337/542–4111, (Includes CALCASIEU OAKS GERIATRIC PSYCHIATRIC HOSPITAL, 2837 Ernest Street, Lake Charles, LA, Zip 70601–8785; tel. 337/439–8111; Erica Williams, Assistant Chief Executive Officer) **A**10 **F**40 64 98 107
Primary Contact: Leslie Trahan, Chief Executive Officer
Control: Corporation, Investor–owned (for–profit) **Service:** General medical and surgical

Staffed Beds: 30 **Admissions:** 812 **Census:** 17 **Outpatient Visits:** 1341 **Births:** 0

CHALMETTE—Saint Bernard Parish

⊞ **ST. BERNARD PARISH HOSPITAL (190308)**, 8000 West Judge Perez Drive, Zip 70043–1668; tel. 504/826–9500, (Nonreporting) **A**1 10
Primary Contact: Kimberly Keene, Chief Executive Officer
CFO: Anthony Bonnecarrere, Controller
CMO: Paul Verrette, M.D., Chief Medical Officer
CIO: Zane Looney, Chief Information Officer
CHR: Melody M O'Connell, Director Human Resources
CNO: Janice Kishner, R.N., FACHE, Chief Clinical Officer
Web address: www.sbph.net
Control: Hospital district or authority, Government, nonfederal **Service:** General medical and surgical

Staffed Beds: 40

CHURCH POINT—Acadia Parish

ACADIA–ST. LANDRY HOSPITAL (191319), 810 South Broadway Street, Zip 70525–4497; tel. 337/684–5435, (Nonreporting) **A**10 18
Primary Contact: Cindy Walters, Chief Executive Officer
CFO: Lucille LeJeune, Assistant Administrator and Chief Financial Officer
CMO: Ty Hargroder, M.D., Chief of Staff
Web address: www.aslh.org
Control: Other not–for–profit (including NFP Corporation) **Service:** General medical and surgical

Staffed Beds: 25

COLUMBIA—Caldwell Parish

CALDWELL MEMORIAL HOSPITAL (190190), 411 Main Street, Zip 71418–6704, Mailing Address: P.O. Box 899, Zip 71418–0899; tel. 318/649–6111, **A**10 **F**34 50 59 90 107 119 127 149
Primary Contact: Danielle Williams, Administrator
COO: Lisa Patrick, Chief Operating Officer
CFO: William H Clark, Chief Financial Officer
Control: Other not–for–profit (including NFP Corporation) **Service:** General medical and surgical

Staffed Beds: 47 **Admissions:** 912 **Census:** 12 **Outpatient Visits:** 0 **Births:** 0

Hospital, Medicare Provider Number, Address, Telephone, Approval, Facility, and Physician Codes, Health Care System

★ American Hospital Association (AHA) membership
☐ The Joint Commission accreditation
○ Healthcare Facilities Accreditation Program
◇ DNV Healthcare Inc. accreditation
⇑ Center for Improvement in Healthcare Quality Accreditation
△ Commission on Accreditation of Rehabilitation Facilities (CARF) accreditation

LA

CITIZENS MEDICAL CENTER (190184), 7939 US Highway 165, Zip 71418–1079, Mailing Address: P.O. Box 1079, Zip 71418–1079; tel. 318/649–6106, (Nonreporting) **A**10
Primary Contact: Steve Barbo, RN, Chief Executive Officer
Web address: www.citizensmedcenter.com/
Control: Hospital district or authority, Government, nonfederal **Service:** General medical and surgical

Staffed Beds: 40

COUSHATTA—Red River Parish

CHRISTUS COUSHATTA HEALTH CARE CENTER (191312), 1635 Marvel Street, Zip 71019–9022, Mailing Address: P.O. Box 589, Zip 71019–0589; tel. 318/932–2000, (Nonreporting) **A**1 10 18 **S** CHRISTUS Health, Irving, TX
Primary Contact: Brandon Hillman, Interim Administrator, Director of Hospital Services
CFO: Scott Merryman, Chief Financial Officer
CMO: Jonathan Weisul, M.D., Vice President Medical Affairs and Chief Medical Officer
CIO: Bruce Honea, Director Information Services
CHR: Donnette Craig, Director Human Resources
Web address: www.christuscoushatta.org
Control: Church operated, Nongovernment, not–for–profit **Service:** General medical and surgical

Staffed Beds: 25

SPECIALTY REHABILITATION HOSPITAL OF COUSHATTA (193080), 1110 Ringgold Avenue Suite B, Zip 71019–9073; tel. 318/932–1770, (Nonreporting) **A**10
Primary Contact: Craig Ball, Chief Executive Officer
COO: Charlie Ball, Chief Operating Officer
CFO: Connie Ball, Chief Financial Officer
CMO: Jalal Joudeh, M.D., Chief Medical Officer
CHR: Denise Logan, Director Human Resources
Web address: www.specialtyhealthcare.com
Control: Individual, Investor–owned (for–profit) **Service:** Rehabilitation

Staffed Beds: 12

COVINGTON—St. Tammany Parish

AMG PHYSICAL REHABILITATION HOSPITAL (193097), 5025 Keystone Boulevard, Suite 200, Zip 70433; tel. 985/888–0301, **A**10 **F**29 74 75 77 82 86 87 90 91 97 **S** AMG Integrated Healthcare Management, Lafayette, LA
Primary Contact: Natalie Stols, Interim Chief Executive Officer
Web address: www.amgcovingtonprh.com/
Control: Individual, Investor–owned (for–profit) **Service:** Rehabilitation

Staffed Beds: 24 **Admissions:** 467 **Census:** 17 **Outpatient Visits:** 0 **Births:** 0

⇑ **AVALA (190267)**, 67252 Industry Lane, Zip 70433–8704; tel. 985/809–9888, (Nonreporting) **A**10 21
Primary Contact: Scott Boudreaux, Chief Executive Officer
CFO: Denise Businelle, Chief Financial Officer
CMO: William Preau, M.D., Medical Director
CIO: Skip Federico, Director Information Systems
CHR: Pam Collins, Director Human Resources
Web address: www.fairwaymedical.com
Control: Corporation, Investor–owned (for–profit) **Service:** General medical and surgical

Staffed Beds: 21

COVINGTON BEHAVIOR HEALTH (194069), 201 Greenbrier Boulevard, Zip 70433–7236; tel. 985/893–2970, (Nonreporting) **A**10 **S** Acadia Healthcare Company, Inc., Franklin, TN
Primary Contact: Wes Crawford, Chief Executive Officer
CFO: Terri Logsdon, Chief Financial Officer
CMO: Jason Coe, M.D., Medical Director
Web address: www.greenbrierhospital.com/
Control: Corporation, Investor–owned (for–profit) **Service:** Psychiatric

Staffed Beds: 60

NORTHSHORE SPECIALTY HOSPITAL See Pam Specialty Hospital of Covington

PAM SPECIALTY HOSPITAL OF COVINGTON (192048), 20050 Crestwood Boulevard, Zip 70433–5207; tel. 985/875–7525, **A**1 10 **F**1 29 64 75 130 143 154 **S** Post Acute Medical, LLC, Enola, PA
Primary Contact: J Cullen. Meyers, Chief Executive Officer
COO: John Bauer, Chief Operating Officer
CFO: Karick Stober, Chief Financial Officer
CMO: Adam Burick, M.D., Chief Medical Officer
CIO: Bryan Munchel, Senior Vice President and Chief Information Officer
CHR: Waynea Finley, Senior Vice President Human Resources
CNO: Marsha Medlin, Senior Vice President of Clinical and Operations
Web address: www.postacutemedical.com
Control: Partnership, Investor–owned (for–profit) **Service:** Acute long–term care hospital

Staffed Beds: 58 **Admissions:** 500 **Census:** 32 **Outpatient Visits:** 0 **Births:** 0 **Total Expense ($000):** 17243 **Payroll Expense ($000):** 6634 **Personnel:** 120

ST. TAMMANY PARISH HOSPITAL (190045), 1202 South Tyler Street, Zip 70433–2330; tel. 985/898–4000, **A**1 2 10 **F**3 8 11 12 13 15 17 18 20 22 24 26 28 29 30 31 34 35 37 40 41 44 45 46 48 49 50 54 57 59 62 63 64 65 69 70 72 74 75 76 77 78 79 81 82 84 85 86 87 89 90 92 93 96 97 107 108 109 110 111 114 115 119 124 126 129 130 132 135 146 147 148 154 **P**6
Primary Contact: Joan Coffman, FACHE, President and Chief Executive Officer
COO: Sharon A Toups, Senior Vice President and Chief Operating Officer
CFO: Sandra P Dipietro, Chief Financial Officer
CMO: Robert Capitelli, M.D., Senior Vice President and Chief Medical Officer
CIO: Craig Doyle, Director and Chief Information Officer
CHR: Carolyn Adema, Vice President, Human Resources
CNO: Kerry K. Milton, R.N., Chief Nursing Officer
Web address: www.stph.org
Control: Hospital district or authority, Government, nonfederal **Service:** General medical and surgical

Staffed Beds: 218 **Admissions:** 11955 **Census:** 145 **Outpatient Visits:** 373477 **Births:** 1875 **Total Expense ($000):** 285350 **Payroll Expense ($000):** 122168 **Personnel:** 1957

CROWLEY—Acadia Parish

★ **ACADIA GENERAL HOSPITAL (190044)**, 1305 Crowley Rayne Highway, Zip 70526–8202; tel. 337/783–3222, (Nonreporting) **A**10 **S** Lafayette General Health, Lafayette, LA
Primary Contact: Joe J. Mitchell, Chief Executive Officer
CNO: Caroline Marceaux, MSN, R.N., Chief Nursing Officer
Web address: www.acadiageneral.com
Control: Other not–for–profit (including NFP Corporation) **Service:** General medical and surgical

Staffed Beds: 140

CUT OFF—Lafourche Parish

★ ⇑ **LADY OF THE SEA GENERAL HOSPITAL (191325)**, 200 West 134th Place, Zip 70345–4143; tel. 985/632–6401, **A**10 18 21 **F**15 29 34 35 40 45 50 57 59 60 62 70 81 85 87 107 108 110 111 114 119 127 130 132 133 146 148 154
Primary Contact: Karen S. Collins, R.N., Chief Executive Officer
COO: Lloyd Guidry, Chief Operating Officer
CFO: Jacquelyn Richoux, Chief Financial Officer
CMO: William Crenshaw, M.D., Chief of Staff
CIO: Bennie Smith, Chief Information Officer
CHR: Bennie Smith, Director Human Resources and Risk Management
CNO: Holly Griffin, R.N., Chief Nursing Officer
Web address: www.losgh.org
Control: Hospital district or authority, Government, nonfederal **Service:** General medical and surgical

Staffed Beds: 25 **Admissions:** 661 **Census:** 8 **Outpatient Visits:** 94964 **Births:** 0 **Total Expense ($000):** 32888 **Payroll Expense ($000):** 13734 **Personnel:** 275

DE RIDDER—Beauregard Parish

BEAUREGARD HEALTH SYSTEM (190050), 600 South Pine Street, Zip 70634–4942, Mailing Address: P.O. Box 730, Zip 70634–0730; tel. 337/462–7100, **A**1 10 **F**3 11 13 15 18 20 26 28 29 30 31 34 35 39 40 45 46 50 53 57 64 70 75 76 78 81 85 89 91 93 96 107 108 110 111 114 119 129 130 131 133 144 148 154 **P**6
Primary Contact: William F. Barrow II, Chief Executive Officer
CFO: Darrell L Kingham, CPA, Vice President Finance
CMO: David Jones, M.D., Chief Medical Officer
CIO: Meg Jackson, Director Information Technology
CHR: Kelli C Broocks, Director Human Resources, Public Relations and Physician Recruitment
CNO: Anita Thibodeaux, Chief Nursing Officer
Web address: www.beauregard.org
Control: Hospital district or authority, Government, nonfederal **Service:** General medical and surgical

Staffed Beds: 49 **Admissions:** 2206 **Census:** 22 **Outpatient Visits:** 79976 **Births:** 345 **Total Expense ($000):** 37362 **Payroll Expense ($000):** 18175 **Personnel:** 346

Many Facility Codes have changed. Please refer to the AHA Guide Code Chart.
© 2018 AHA Guide

DELHI—Richland Parish

RICHLAND PARISH HOSPITAL (191323), 407 Cincinnati Street,
Zip 71232–3007; tel. 318/878–5171, (Nonreporting) **A**10 18
Primary Contact: Michael W. Carroll, Administrator
CIO: Barbra Hutchison, Director Medical Records
CHR: Patsy Stout, Director Personnel
Web address: www.delhihospital.com
Control: Hospital district or authority, Government, nonfederal **Service:** General medical and surgical

Staffed Beds: 25

DENHAM SPRINGS—Livingston Parish

SAGE SPECIALTY HOSPITAL (LTAC) (192008), 8375 Florida Boulevard,
Zip 70726–7806; tel. 225/665–2664, (Nonreporting) **A**10 **S** The Carpenter Health Network, Baton Rouge, LA
Primary Contact: Sharon Faulkner, Administrator
CFO: Jessica McGee, Chief Financial Officer
CMO: Durwin Walker, M.D., Chief Medical Officer
CHR: Kim Hernandez, Chief Human Resources Officer
CNO: Sharon Faulkner, Chief Nursing Officer
Web address: www.amgdenham.com/
Control: Individual, Investor–owned (for–profit) **Service:** Acute long–term care hospital

Staffed Beds: 117

DEQUINCY—Calcasieu Parish

☐ **DEQUINCY MEMORIAL HOSPITAL (191307)**, 110 West Fourth Street,
Zip 70633–3508, Mailing Address: P.O. Box 1166, Zip 70633–1166;
tel. 337/786–1200, (Nonreporting) **A**1 10 18
Primary Contact: John A. Matheson, Interim Chief Executive Officer
CFO: Vicky Kelley, Chief Financial Officer
CMO: Jalal Joudeh, M.D., Chief of Staff
Web address: www.dequincymemorial.com/
Control: City, Government, nonfederal **Service:** General medical and surgical

Staffed Beds: 19

DERIDDER—Beauregard Parish

☐ **OCEANS BEHAVIORAL HOSPITAL OF DE RIDDER (194081)**, 1420
Blankenship Drive, Zip 70634–4604; tel. 337/460–9472, (Nonreporting) **A**1 10 **S**
Oceans Healthcare, Lake Charles, LA
Primary Contact: Stuart Archer, Chief Executive Officer
Web address: www.obhd.info/
Control: Corporation, Investor–owned (for–profit) **Service:** Psychiatric

Staffed Beds: 20

DONALDSONVILLE—Ascension Parish

⊞ **PREVOST MEMORIAL HOSPITAL (191308)**, 301 Memorial Drive,
Zip 70346–4376; tel. 225/473–7931, (Nonreporting) **A**1 10 18
Primary Contact: Vincent A. Cataldo, Administrator
CFO: Nobie Landry, Chief Financial Officer
CMO: Glenn Schexnayder, M.D., Chief of Staff
CHR: Linda Cataldo, Human Resources Secretary
Web address: www.prevosthospital.net
Control: Hospital district or authority, Government, nonfederal **Service:** General medical and surgical

Staffed Beds: 25

FARMERVILLE—Union Parish

UNION GENERAL HOSPITAL (191301), 901 James Avenue, Zip 71241–2234,
Mailing Address: P.O. Box 398, Zip 71241–0398; tel. 318/368–9751, **A**10 18 **F**15
29 32 35 40 45 50 56 81 93 104 107 110 114 119 127 128 133 143 149 153 **P**6
Primary Contact: Evalyn Ormond, Chief Executive Officer
COO: Dianne Davidson, Chief Operating Officer
CFO: William Adcock, Chief Financial Officer
CHR: Sheri Taylor, Director Human Resources
CNO: Darra Jung, Director of Nursing
Web address: www.uniongen.com
Control: Other not-for-profit (including NFP Corporation) **Service:** General medical and surgical

Staffed Beds: 15 **Admissions:** 340 **Census:** 5 **Outpatient Visits:** 35594
Births: 0 **Total Expense ($000):** 13186 **Payroll Expense ($000):** 5190
Personnel: 105

FERRIDAY—Concordia Parish

RIVERLAND MEDICAL CENTER (191318), 1700 EE Wallace Boulevard,
Zip 71334–0111, Mailing Address: P.O. Box 111, Zip 71334–0111;
tel. 318/757–6551, **A**10 18 **F**3 15 29 34 35 40 45 57 59 68 70 75 77 81 85
86 87 93 104 107 110 119 133 **P**6
Primary Contact: William H. Rucker, Administrator
CFO: Spencer Holder, Chief Financial Officer
CMO: Carrie Bonomo, M.D., Chief of Staff
CIO: Nekisha Smith, Director Health Information Systems
CHR: Debra Stephens, Director Personnel
CNO: Shelia James, Director of Nursing
Web address: www.riverlandmedical.com/
Control: Hospital district or authority, Government, nonfederal **Service:** General medical and surgical

Staffed Beds: 25 **Admissions:** 888 **Census:** 11 **Outpatient Visits:** 99985
Births: 0 **Total Expense ($000):** 18306 **Payroll Expense ($000):** 8127
Personnel: 153

FORT POLK—Vernon Parish

⊞ **BAYNE–JONES ARMY COMMUNITY HOSPITAL**, 1585 3rd Street,
Zip 71459–5102; tel. 337/531–3928, (Nonreporting) **A**1 **S** Department of the
Army, Office of the Surgeon General, Falls Church, VA
Primary Contact: Colonel Marla J. Ferguson, Commanding Officer
COO: Larry R. Patterson, Deputy Commander Administration
CFO: Captain Dustin Mullins, Chief Resource Management
CIO: Major William Callahan, Chief Information Management Division
CHR: Captain Dustin Mullins, Chief Human Resources
Web address: www.polk.amedd.army.mil
Control: Army, Government, federal **Service:** General medical and surgical

Staffed Beds: 13

FRANKLIN—St. Mary Parish

⊞ **FRANKLIN FOUNDATION HOSPITAL (191310)**, 1097 Northwest Boulevard,
Zip 70538–3407, Mailing Address: P.O. Box 577, Zip 70538–0577;
tel. 337/828–0760, **A**1 10 18 **F**3 11 13 15 18 26 29 34 35 40 45 50 57 59 68
70 74 75 76 77 79 81 85 93 107 110 111 119 130 132 133 135 145 147 148
149 154 **P**6 **S** QHR, Brentwood, TN
Primary Contact: Stephanie Guidry, Chief Executive Officer
CFO: Ron Bailey, Chief Financial Officer
CMO: Jesus Chua, M.D., Chief of Staff
CIO: John Spradlin, Information Systems Director
CHR: Elmo Vinas, Director Human Resources
CNO: Michelle Skillings, Chief Nursing Officer
Web address: www.franklinfoundation.org
Control: Hospital district or authority, Government, nonfederal **Service:** General medical and surgical

Staffed Beds: 22 **Admissions:** 516 **Census:** 9 **Outpatient Visits:** 27264
Births: 61 **Total Expense ($000):** 25108 **Payroll Expense ($000):** 11717
Personnel: 160

FRANKLINTON—Washington Parish

☐ **RIVERSIDE MEDICAL CENTER (191313)**, 1900 Main Street, Zip 70438–3688;
tel. 985/839–4431, (Nonreporting) **A**1 10 18
Primary Contact: Peter Sullivan, Chief Executive Officer
CFO: Michael J Magee, Chief Financial Officer
CMO: Chris Foret, M.D., Chief of Staff
CHR: John Seal, Director Human Resources
Web address: www.rmchospital.com
Control: Hospital district or authority, Government, nonfederal **Service:** General medical and surgical

Staffed Beds: 25

GONZALES—Ascension Parish

SOUTH BATON ROUGE REHABILITATION HOSPITAL See United Medical
Rehabilitation Hospital – Gonzales

Hospital, Medicare Provider Number, Address, Telephone, Approval, Facility, and Physician Codes, Health Care System

★ American Hospital Association (AHA) membership   ○ Healthcare Facilities Accreditation Program   ⇑ Center for Improvement in Healthcare Quality Accreditation
☐ The Joint Commission accreditation   ◇ DNV Healthcare Inc. accreditation   △ Commission on Accreditation of Rehabilitation Facilities (CARF) accreditation

LA

⊞ **ST. ELIZABETH HOSPITAL (190242)**, 1125 West Highway 30, Zip 70737–5004; tel. 225/647–5000, **A**1 10 **F**3 8 11 12 15 18 20 28 29 30 34 35 40 44 46 47 49 51 54 57 59 66 68 70 74 75 77 79 81 82 84 85 87 92 107 108 110 111 112 114 115 119 129 130 132 135 146 147 149 154 **P**6 **S** Franciscan Missionaries of Our Lady Health System, Inc., Baton Rouge, LA
Primary Contact: Robert L. Burgess, President and Chief Executive Officer
COO: Sue Knight, CPA, Chief Operating Officer
CFO: Scott Richard, Vice President Finance and Chief Financial Officer
CMO: Chris Trevino, M.D., Chief Medical Officer
CIO: Shannon Simpson, Director Information Services
CHR: Melissa Miller, Director Human Resources
CNO: Yvonne Pellerin, Chief Nursing Officer
Web address: www.steh.com
Control: Church operated, Nongovernment, not–for–profit **Service**: General medical and surgical

Staffed Beds: 57 Admissions: 2608 Census: 33 Outpatient Visits: 347264 Births: 0 Total Expense ($000): 122211 Payroll Expense ($000): 46730 Personnel: 809

⊞ **ST. JAMES BEHAVIORAL HEALTH HOSPITAL (194088)**, 3136 South Saint Landry Road, Zip 70737–5801; tel. 225/647–7524, (Nonreporting) **A**1 10
Primary Contact: Andrew Hines, Administrator
COO: Wendell Smith, Chief Operating Officer
CFO: Rama Kongara, Chief Financial Officer
CMO: Lance Bullock, M.D., Medical Director
CHR: Dessa Frederick, Manager Human Resources
Web address: www.sjbhh.net
Control: Corporation, Investor–owned (for–profit) **Service**: Psychiatric

Staffed Beds: 10

GREENSBURG—St. Helena Parish

ST. HELENA PARISH HOSPITAL (191300), 16874 Highway 43, Zip 70441–4834; tel. 225/222–6111, (Nonreporting) **A**10 18
Primary Contact: Naveed Awan, FACHE, Chief Executive Officer
CFO: Theresa Brinkhaus, Chief Financial Officer
CMO: Anjanette Varnado, M.D., Chief Medical Officer
CHR: Lorraine L Ballard, Director Human Resources
Web address: www.sthelenaparishhospital.com
Control: Other not–for–profit (including NFP Corporation) **Service**: General medical and surgical

Staffed Beds: 75

GRETNA—Jefferson Parish

UNITED MEDICAL REHABILITATION HOSPITAL (193074), 3201 Wall Boulevard, Suite B, Zip 70056–7755; tel. 504/433–5551, (Nonreporting) **A**10 **S** United Medical Rehabilitation Hospitals, Gretna, LA
Primary Contact: Jerry Deller, Administrator
Web address: www.umrhospital.com/
Control: Individual, Investor–owned (for–profit) **Service**: Rehabilitation

Staffed Beds: 21

HAMMOND—Tangipahoa Parish

⇑ **CYPRESS POINTE SURGICAL HOSPITAL (190303)**, 42570 South Airport Road, Zip 70403–0946; tel. 985/510–6200, (Nonreporting) **A**10 21
Primary Contact: Glenda Dobson, Chief Executive Officer
COO: Scot Treitler, Chief Operating Officer
CFO: Donna Varnado, Vice President Finance
CNO: Denise Fortenberry, Chief Nursing Officer and Chief Compliance Officer
Web address: www.cpsh.org
Control: Corporation, Investor–owned (for–profit) **Service**: Surgical

Staffed Beds: 24

⊞ △ **NORTH OAKS MEDICAL CENTER (190015)**, 15790 Paul Vega, MD, Drive, Zip 70403–1436, Mailing Address: P.O. Box 2668, Zip 70404–2668; tel. 985/345–2700, **A**1 3 7 10 19 **F**3 12 13 15 18 20 22 24 26 28 29 30 31 32 34 40 43 45 49 50 54 56 57 58 59 63 64 68 70 72 73 74 75 76 77 78 79 81 82 84 85 86 87 89 93 94 96 102 107 108 110 111 114 115 118 119 126 129 130 131 132 135 143 144 146 147 148 149 154 **P**6 **S** North Oaks Health System, Hammond, LA
Primary Contact: Michele K. Sutton, FACHE, President and Chief Executive Officer
COO: Michael Watkins, Chief Operating Officer
CFO: Mark Anderson, Chief Financial Officer
CMO: Robert Peltier, M.D., Chief Medical Officer
CIO: Doug Bankston, Director Technical Services
CHR: Jeff Jarreau, Chief Human Resources Officer
Web address: www.northoaks.org
Control: Hospital district or authority, Government, nonfederal **Service**: General medical and surgical

Staffed Beds: 231 Admissions: 11478 Census: 157 Outpatient Visits: 481300 Births: 1260 Total Expense ($000): 296127 Payroll Expense ($000): 159660 Personnel: 1741

☐ **NORTH OAKS REHABILITATION HOSPITAL (193044)**, 1900 South Morrison Boulevard, Zip 70403–5742; tel. 985/542–7777, **A**1 10 **F**29 56 75 86 87 90 130 132 143 154 **P**6 **S** North Oaks Health System, Hammond, LA
Primary Contact: Sybil K. Paulson, Administrator
CFO: Mark Anderson, Chief Financial Officer
CMO: Robert Peltier, M.D., Senior Vice President, Chief Medical Officer, North Oaks Health System
CIO: Herbert Robinson, M.D., Vice President, Chief Medical Information Officer, North Oaks Health System
CHR: Jeff Jarreau, Senior Vice President, Human Resources, North Oaks Health System
Web address: www.northoaks.org
Control: Hospital district or authority, Government, nonfederal **Service**: Rehabilitation

Staffed Beds: 27 Admissions: 571 Census: 17 Outpatient Visits: 0 Births: 0 Total Expense ($000): 11804 Payroll Expense ($000): 2473 Personnel: 44

⊞ **PAM SPECIALTY HOSPITAL OF HAMMOND (192036)**, 42074 Veterans Avenue, Zip 70403–1408; tel. 985/902–8148, **A**1 10 **F**1 29 75 77 148 149 **S** Post Acute Medical, LLC, Enola, PA
Primary Contact: Nicholas Paul. Mendez, Chief Executive Officer
Web address: www.postacutemedical.com
Control: Partnership, Investor–owned (for–profit) **Service**: Acute long–term care hospital

Staffed Beds: 40 Admissions: 531 Census: 30 Outpatient Visits: 0 Births: 0 Total Expense ($000): 13583 Payroll Expense ($000): 5301 Personnel: 111

UNITED MEDICAL REHABILITATION HOSPITAL (193079), 15717 Belle Drive, Zip 70403–1439; tel. 985/340–5998, (Includes UNITED MEDICAL REHABILITATION HOSPITAL – GONZALES, 333 East Worthy Road, Gonzales, LA, Zip 70737–4234; tel. 225/450–2231; Laura Begnaud, Administrator) (Nonreporting) **A**10 **S** United Medical Rehabilitation Hospitals, Gretna, LA
Primary Contact: Jonathan Landreth, Administrator
CFO: Warren Swenson, Chief Financial Officer
CMO: Luis Franco, M.D., Medical Director
CHR: Mark Gros, Director Human Resources
Web address: www.umrhospital.com
Control: Corporation, Investor–owned (for–profit) **Service**: Rehabilitation

Staffed Beds: 20

HOMER—Claiborne Parish

★ ⇑ **CLAIBORNE MEMORIAL MEDICAL CENTER (190114)**, 620 East College Street, Zip 71040–3202; tel. 318/927–2024, **A**10 21 **F**3 15 29 34 35 38 40 45 50 53 54 55 56 57 59 62 64 65 68 70 81 85 86 87 98 100 101 102 103 104 105 107 108 110 111 114 115 116 117 119 130 132 133 134 143 146 147 148 149 150 153 154
Primary Contact: Antonia M. Goodin, Chief Executive Officer and Chief Financial Officer
CFO: Michelle Stillwell, Chief Financial Officer
CMO: Mark Haynes, M.D., Chief of Staff
CIO: Angie Costakis, Chief Information Officer
CHR: William Colvin, Human Resources Officer
CNO: Kristie M. Copeland, Interim Chief Nursing Officer
Web address: www.clairbornemedical.com/
Control: Hospital district or authority, Government, nonfederal **Service**: General medical and surgical

Staffed Beds: 57 Admissions: 1153 Census: 19 Outpatient Visits: 20644 Births: 0

HOUMA—Terrebonne Parish

AMG SPECIALTY HOSPITAL–HOUMA (192037), 629 Dunn Street, Zip 70360–4707; tel. 985/274–0001, (Nonreporting) **A**10 **S** AMG Integrated Healthcare Management, Lafayette, LA
Primary Contact: Jody Robichaux, Chief Executive Officer
Web address: www.amghouma.com/
Control: Corporation, Investor–owned (for–profit) **Service**: Acute long–term care hospital

Staffed Beds: 40

☐ **COMPASS BEHAVIORAL CENTER OF HOUMA (194109)**, 4701 West Park Avenue, Zip 70364–4426; tel. 985/876–1715, (Nonreporting) **A**1 10 **S** Compass Health, Crowley, LA
Primary Contact: Andre' Robichaux, Interim Administrator
Web address: www.compasshealthcare.com/site83.php
Control: Corporation, Investor–owned (for–profit) **Service**: Psychiatric

Staffed Beds: 20

Many Facility Codes have changed. Please refer to the AHA Guide Code Chart.

⊠ **LEONARD J. CHABERT MEDICAL CENTER (190183)**, 1978 Industrial Boulevard, Zip 70363–7094; tel. 985/873–2200, **A**1 3 5 10 **F**3 4 15 17 18 20 29 31 34 35 38 40 44 45 46 48 49 50 51 57 58 59 61 64 65 66 68 70 74 75 77 78 79 81 82 85 86 87 89 93 97 98 100 101 102 107 108 110 111 115 119 130 132 146 147 148 **S** Ochsner Health System, New Orleans, LA
Primary Contact: Timothy J. Allen, FACHE, Chief Executive Officer
COO: Kendrick Duet, Chief Operating Officer
CNO: Jana Semere, Chief Nursing Officer
Web address: www.ochsner.org/locations/leonard_j_chabert_medical_center/
Control: State, Government, nonfederal **Service:** General medical and surgical

Staffed Beds: 72 **Admissions:** 3291 **Census:** 45 **Outpatient Visits:** 179261 **Births:** 0 **Total Expense ($000):** 94618 **Payroll Expense ($000):** 31901 **Personnel:** 798

PHYSICIANS ALLIANCE HOSPITAL OF HOUMA See Amg Specialty Hospital–Houma

PHYSICIANS MEDICAL CENTER (190241), 218 Corporate Drive, Zip 70360–2768; tel. 985/853–1390, (Nonreporting) **A**10
Primary Contact: Connie Martin, Chief Executive Officer and Administrator
Web address: www.physicianshouma.com/
Control: Partnership, Investor–owned (for–profit) **Service:** Surgical

Staffed Beds: 10

⊠ △ **TERREBONNE GENERAL MEDICAL CENTER (190008)**, 8166 Main Street, Zip 70360–3498; tel. 985/873–4141, (Total facility includes 8 beds in nursing home–type unit) **A**1 2 7 10 **F**8 11 13 14 15 17 18 20 22 24 26 29 30 31 34 35 44 44 49 50 53 55 57 58 59 64 65 68 70 72 74 75 76 77 78 79 81 84 85 86 87 89 90 91 92 93 96 102 107 108 109 110 111 112 115 116 117 118 119 121 123 124 128 130 131 132 134 135 143 146 147 148 149 **P**3 5 6
Primary Contact: Phyllis L. Peoples, President and Chief Executive Officer
COO: Diane Yeates, Chief Operating Officer
CFO: Dean Verret, Vice President Financial Services
CMO: Robert Gamble, M.D., Chief of Staff
CIO: Jeff Sardella, Director Information Technology
CHR: Mickie Rousseau, Director Human Resources
CNO: Teresita McNabb, R.N., FACHE, Vice President Nursing Services
Web address: www.tgmc.com
Control: Hospital district or authority, Government, nonfederal **Service:** General medical and surgical

Staffed Beds: 230 **Admissions:** 8933 **Census:** 123 **Outpatient Visits:** 137290 **Births:** 1692 **Total Expense ($000):** 193280 **Payroll Expense ($000):** 73773 **Personnel:** 1329

☐ **LALLIE KEMP MEDICAL CENTER (191321)**, 52579 Highway 51 South, Zip 70443–2231; tel. 985/878–9421, (Nonreporting) **A**1 3 5 10 18
Primary Contact: Rhonda G. Green, Administrator
COO: Lisa G Bruhl, Chief Operating Officer
CFO: Chad Thompson, Chief Financial Officer
CMO: Kathy Willis, M.D., Medical Director
CIO: Charles Tate, Director Information Technology
CHR: Diane Farnham, Acting Director Human Resources
Web address: www.lsuhospitals.org/Hospitals/LK/LK.aspx
Control: State, Government, nonfederal **Service:** General medical and surgical

Staffed Beds: 25

☐ **EASTERN LOUISIANA MENTAL HEALTH SYSTEM (194008)**, 4502 Highway 951, Zip 70748–5842, Mailing Address: P.O. Box 498, Zip 70748–0498; tel. 225/634–0100, (Nonreporting) **A**1 3 10 **S** Louisiana State Hospitals, Baton Rouge, LA
Primary Contact: Hampton P S. Lea, Acting Chief Executive Officer
CFO: Laura Lott, Administrative Director
CMO: John W Thompson, M.D., Chief of Staff
CIO: Deborah Brandon, Director Total Quality Management
CHR: Vikki Riggle, Director Human Resources
CNO: Mary Fontenelle, Executive Nurse Director
Web address: www.new.dhh.louisiana.gov/index.cfm/directory/detail/219
Control: State, Government, nonfederal **Service:** Psychiatric

Staffed Beds: 473

VILLA FELICIANA MEDICAL COMPLEX (190199), 5002 Highway 10, Zip 70748–3627, Mailing Address: P.O. Box 438, Zip 70748–0438; tel. 225/634–4017, (Total facility includes 289 beds in nursing home–type unit) **A**10 **F**1 3 29 65 85 86 91 94 106 130 132 135 143 148 149 **P**8
Primary Contact: Mark Anders, Administrator
CFO: Kim Jelks, Fiscal Officer
CMO: John F Piker, M.D., Medical Director
CIO: Michael James, Information Technology Technical Support Specialist 1
CHR: Sandra Delatte, Director Human Resources
CNO: Linda Williams, Director of Nursing
Web address: www.dhh.state.la.us/
Control: State, Government, nonfederal **Service:** Acute long–term care hospital

Staffed Beds: 299 **Admissions:** 75 **Census:** 153 **Outpatient Visits:** 0 **Births:** 0 **Total Expense ($000):** 19054 **Payroll Expense ($000):** 8946 **Personnel:** 194

★ **LASALLE GENERAL HOSPITAL (190145)**, 187 Ninth Street, Zip 71342–3901, Mailing Address: P.O. Box 2780, Zip 71342–2780; tel. 318/992–9200, **A**3 10 **F**7 11 15 18 29 33 34 35 40 53 57 59 62 64 81 89 93 98 103 107 108 110 111 115 119 127 130 133 149 **P**6
Primary Contact: Lana B. Francis, Chief Executive Officer
CHR: Allyson Fannin, Human Resources Officer
CNO: Carolyn Francis, R.N., MSN, Director of Nursing
Web address: www.lasallegeneralhospital.com
Control: Hospital district or authority, Government, nonfederal **Service:** General medical and surgical

Staffed Beds: 46 **Admissions:** 614 **Census:** 10 **Outpatient Visits:** 55488 **Births:** 0 **Total Expense ($000):** 18324 **Payroll Expense ($000):** 8181 **Personnel:** 199

☐ **JENNINGS AMERICAN LEGION HOSPITAL (190053)**, 1634 Elton Road, Zip 70546–3614; tel. 337/616–7000, **A**1 10 **F**3 15 18 20 28 29 40 45 64 70 76 79 81 89 107 108 111 115 119 127 133 146 147 149 154
Primary Contact: Dana D. Williams, Chief Executive Officer
COO: Keith J Simpson, Chief Operating Officer
CIO: Gary Courrege, Chief Information Officer
CHR: Ruth Carnes, Manager Human Resources
CNO: Theresa L Woods, MSN, R.N., FACHE, Chief Nursing Officer
Web address: www.jalh.com
Control: Other not–for–profit (including NFP Corporation) **Service:** General medical and surgical

Staffed Beds: 49 **Admissions:** 2629 **Census:** 28 **Outpatient Visits:** 41019 **Births:** 421 **Total Expense ($000):** 43619 **Payroll Expense ($000):** 19954 **Personnel:** 415

JENNINGS SENIOR CARE HOSPITAL (194082), 1 Hospital Drive, Suite 201, Zip 70546–3641; tel. 337/824–1558, (Nonreporting) **A**10
Primary Contact: Kirk Perron, Administrator and Chief Administrative Officer
Web address: www.compasshealthcare.com/site74.php
Control: Corporation, Investor–owned (for–profit) **Service:** Psychiatric

Staffed Beds: 16

REHABILITATION HOSPITAL OF JENNINGS (193067), 1 Hospital Drive, Suite 101, Zip 70546–3641; tel. 337/821–5353, **A**10 **F**29 30 34 35 56 57 65 68 75 77 87 90 91 130 148 149
Primary Contact: Michael Holland, M.D., Chief Executive Officer
Web address: www.jenningsrehab.com
Control: Partnership, Investor–owned (for–profit) **Service:** Rehabilitation

Staffed Beds: 16 **Admissions:** 276 **Census:** 10 **Outpatient Visits:** 0 **Births:** 0 **Personnel:** 44

★ **JACKSON PARISH HOSPITAL (191317)**, 165 Beech Springs Road, Zip 71251–2059; tel. 318/259–4435, (Nonreporting) **A**10 18
Primary Contact: John Morgan, R.N., Chief Executive Officer
CFO: Bill Stansbury, Chief Financial Officer
CMO: W. James (Jamie) Slusher, M.D., Chief of Staff
CIO: Monie Phillips III Director Clinical Informatics
CHR: Phillip Thomas Jr Director Human Resources
CNO: Christy Wyatt, R.N., Interim Chief Nursing Officer
Web address: www.jacksonparishhospital.com
Control: Hospital district or authority, Government, nonfederal **Service:** General medical and surgical

Staffed Beds: 25

Hospital, Medicare Provider Number, Address, Telephone, Approval, Facility, and Physician Codes, Health Care System

★ American Hospital Association (AHA) membership
☐ The Joint Commission accreditation
○ Healthcare Facilities Accreditation Program
◇ DNV Healthcare Inc. accreditation
⇑ Center for Improvement in Healthcare Quality Accreditation
△ Commission on Accreditation of Rehabilitation Facilities (CARF) accreditation

LA

KAPLAN—Vermilion Parish

ABROM KAPLAN MEMORIAL HOSPITAL (191322), 1310 West Seventh Street, Zip 70548–2910; tel. 337/643–8300, (Nonreporting) **A**10 18 **S** Lafayette General Health, Lafayette, LA
Primary Contact: Bryce Quebodeaux, Chief Executive Officer
CFO: Michael G. Johnson, CPA, Chief Financial Officer
CMO: Scott Bergeaux, M.D., Chief Medical Staff
CIO: Michael Cardiff, Systems Supervisor
CHR: Linda Guidry, Human Resources Generalist
CNO: Sally Roberts, R.N., Director of Nursing
Web address: www.lafayettegeneral.com
Control: Hospital district or authority, Government, nonfederal **Service:** General medical and surgical

Staffed Beds: 35

KENNER—Jefferson Parish

☐ **LAKE PINES HOSPITAL**, 3639 Loyola Drive, Zip 70065; tel. 504/305–2700, (Nonreporting) **A**1
Primary Contact: Debbie Tullier, Chief Executive Officer
Web address: www.lakepineshospital.com/
Control: Individual, Investor–owned (for–profit) **Service:** Psychiatric

Staffed Beds: 36

LOUISIANA EXTENDED CARE HOSPITAL OF KENNER See Ochsner Extended Care Hospital of Kenner

☐ **OCEANS BEHAVIORAL HOSPITAL OF GREATER NEW ORLEANS (194098)**, 716 Village Road, Zip 70065–2751; tel. 504/464–8895, (Nonreporting) **A**1 10 **S** Oceans Healthcare, Lake Charles, LA
Primary Contact: Deborah Spier, Administrator
Web address: www.obhgno.info/
Control: Corporation, Investor–owned (for–profit) **Service:** Psychiatric

Staffed Beds: 30

☐ **EXTENDED CARE HOSPITAL (192015)**, 180 West Esplanade Avenue, 5th Floor, Zip 70065–2467; tel. 504/464–8658, (Nonreporting) **A**1 3 10 **S** LHC Group, Lafayette, LA
Primary Contact: Jan Turk, Administrator
Web address: www.lhcgroup.com/
Control: Corporation, Investor–owned (for–profit) **Service:** Acute long–term care hospital

Staffed Beds: 32

⊞ **OCHSNER MEDICAL CENTER – KENNER (190274)**, 180 West Esplanade Avenue, Zip 70065–6001; tel. 504/468–8600, **A**1 3 5 10 **F**3 13 15 18 20 22 29 30 31 34 35 37 38 40 41 44 45 46 47 49 50 51 53 54 56 57 58 59 60 61 64 65 66 68 70 72 74 75 76 77 78 79 81 82 84 85 86 87 93 97 102 107 110 111 114 116 117 119 120 129 130 131 132 135 146 147 148 **S** Ochsner Health System, New Orleans, LA
Primary Contact: Stephen Robinson Jr, FACHE, Chief Executive Officer
COO: Eddy Ramirez, Assistant Vice President Business Development
CFO: Mark Eckert, Vice President Finance
CMO: James Tebbe, M.D., Vice President Medical Affairs
CIO: Dere Krummel, Director Information Systems
Web address: www.ochsner.org/locations/ochsner–medical–center–kenner/
Control: Other not–for–profit (including NFP Corporation) **Service:** General medical and surgical

Staffed Beds: 110 **Admissions:** 6720 **Census:** 70 **Outpatient Visits:** 165835 **Births:** 1065 **Total Expense ($000):** 138752 **Payroll Expense ($000):** 47966 **Personnel:** 753

☐ **ST. THERESA SPECIALTY HOSPITAL (192030)**, 3601 Loyola Drive, Zip 70065–1797; tel. 504/904–7600, (Nonreporting) **A**1 10
Primary Contact: Sam Liljebert, Chief Executive Officer
CMO: Ricardo Febry, M.D., Medical Director
CHR: Nicole Wilson, Manager Human Resources
CNO: Collette Jackson, R.N., Director of Clinical Services
Web address: www.stmck.com
Control: Corporation, Investor–owned (for–profit) **Service:** Acute long–term care hospital

Staffed Beds: 73

KENTWOOD—Tangipahoa Parish

OCEANS BEHAVIORAL HOSPITAL OF KENTWOOD (194091), 921 Avenue G, Zip 70444–2636; tel. 985/229–0717, (Nonreporting) **A**10 **S** Oceans Healthcare, Lake Charles, LA
Primary Contact: Frederick Nelson, MA, Administrator
Web address: www.obhk.info/
Control: Corporation, Investor–owned (for–profit) **Service:** Psychiatric

Staffed Beds: 16

SOUTHEAST REGIONAL MEDICAL CENTER (192040), 719 Avenue G, Zip 70444–2601; tel. 985/229–9193, (Nonreporting) **A**10
Primary Contact: Lionel Murphy, Chief Executive Officer
Control: Corporation, Investor–owned (for–profit) **Service:** Acute long–term care hospital

Staffed Beds: 14

KINDER—Allen Parish Parish

★ **ALLEN PARISH HOSPITAL (190133)**, 108 Sixth Avenue, Zip 70648–3187, Mailing Address: P.O. Box 1670, Zip 70648–1670; tel. 337/738–2527, (Nonreporting) **A**10
Primary Contact: Jackie Reviel, R.N., Chief Executive Officer
COO: Terry Willet, Chief Financial Officer
CFO: Stephen Thames, Chief Financial Officer
CMO: Ejiro Ughouwa, M.D., Chief of Staff
CIO: Bill Marcantel, Chief Information Systems
CHR: Amand Lambert, Director Human Resources
Web address: www.allenparishhospital.com
Control: Hospital district or authority, Government, nonfederal **Service:** General medical and surgical

Staffed Beds: 49

LA PLACE—St. John The Baptist Parish

☐ **RIVER PLACE BEHAVIORAL HEALTH**, 500 Rue De Sante, Zip 70068–5418; tel. 985/303–2327, (Nonreporting) **A**1 **S** Acadia Healthcare Company, Inc., Franklin, TN
Primary Contact: Rick Bennett, Chief Executive Officer
Web address: www.riverplacebh.com
Control: Corporation, Investor–owned (for–profit) **Service:** Psychiatric

Staffed Beds: 82

LACOMBE—St. Tammany Parish

BEACON BEHAVIORAL HOSPITAL NORTHSHORE (194080), 64026 Highway 434, Suite 300, Zip 70445–5417; tel. 985/882–0226, (Nonreporting) **A**10
Primary Contact: Jessika Scallion, Administrator
Web address: www.magnoliabh.com/
Control: Corporation, Investor–owned (for–profit) **Service:** Psychiatric

Staffed Beds: 22

LAFAYETTE—Lafayette Parish

AMG SPECIALTY HOSPITAL–LAFAYETTE (192029), 310 Youngsville Highway, Zip 70508–4524; tel. 337/839–9880, (Nonreporting) **A**10 **S** AMG Integrated Healthcare Management, Lafayette, LA
Primary Contact: Rachel Mayeaux, Chief Executive Officer
CFO: Jessica McGee, Chief Financial Officer
CMO: Maximo LaMarche, M.D., Chief Medical Officer
CHR: Heather Lamarche, Manager Human Resources
CNO: Mary Bollich, Director of Nurses
Web address: www.amglafayette.com
Control: Corporation, Investor–owned (for–profit) **Service:** Acute long–term care hospital

Staffed Beds: 58

★ **COMPASS BEHAVIORAL CENTER OF LAFAYETTE (194085)**, 312 Youngsville Highway, Zip 70508; tel. 337/534–4655, (Nonreporting) **S** Compass Health, Crowley, LA
Primary Contact: Jason Branson, Administrator
Web address: www.compasshealthcare.com/site184.php
Control: Other not–for–profit (including NFP Corporation) **Service:** Psychiatric

Staffed Beds: 16

Many Facility Codes have changed. Please refer to the AHA Guide Code Chart.
© 2018 AHA Guide

⊞ **HEART HOSPITAL OF LAFAYETTE (190263)**, 1105 Kaliste Saloom Road, Zip 70508–5705; tel. 337/521–1000, **A**1 10 **F**1 3 4 16 17 18 20 22 24 26 28 29 30 34 35 40 46 50 57 59 64 67 68 70 72 73 74 75 80 81 85 87 88 89 90 98 107 108 115 128 135 **P**5 7 8
Primary Contact: Michelle B. Crain, R.N., MSN, Administrator and Chief Operating Officer
CFO: Rachel Hebert, Chief Financial Officer
CHR: Thomas Duhon, Director Human Resources
Web address: www.hearthospitaloflafayette.com
Control: Partnership, Investor–owned (for–profit) **Service:** Heart

> **Staffed Beds:** 32 **Admissions:** 1688 **Census:** 16 **Outpatient Visits:** 19808
> **Births:** 0 **Total Expense ($000):** 38780 **Payroll Expense ($000):** 11877
> **Personnel:** 222

⊞ **LAFAYETTE GENERAL MEDICAL CENTER (190002)**, 1214 Coolidge Avenue, Zip 70503–2696, Mailing Address: P.O. Box 52009 OCS, Zip 70505–2009; tel. 337/289–7991, (Includes LAFAYETTE BEHAVIORAL HEALTH, 302 Dulles Drive, Lafayette, LA, Zip 70506–3008; tel. 337/289–8595; Sandra Armand, Director; LAFAYETTE GENERAL ORTHOPEDIC HOSPITAL, 2810 Ambassador Caffery Parkway, Lafayette, LA, Zip 70506–5906; tel. 337/981–2949; Jude Fontenot, Administrator) **A**1 2 3 5 10 **F**3 8 11 12 13 15 18 20 22 24 26 28 29 30 31 34 35 37 40 41 43 45 46 47 48 49 50 53 54 55 56 57 58 59 64 65 70 72 74 75 77 78 79 81 82 85 87 90 92 93 96 98 107 108 110 111 115 117 118 119 120 121 123 124 126 129 130 132 135 146 147 148 149 **P**8 **S** Lafayette General Health, Lafayette, LA
Primary Contact: Patrick W. Gandy Jr, CPA, Executive Vice President and Chief Executive Officer
COO: Court LeMaistre, FACHE, Chief Operating Officer
CFO: Lana Adams, Chief Financial Officer
CMO: Stephen G. Rees, M.D., Vice President Medical Affairs
CIO: Michael Dozier, Vice President, Chief Information Officer
CHR: Sheena Bouquet, Vice President
CNO: Rebecca Benoit, R.N., Chief Nursing Officer
Web address: www.lafayettegeneral.com
Control: Other not–for–profit (including NFP Corporation) **Service:** General medical and surgical

> **Staffed Beds:** 420 **Admissions:** 22618 **Census:** 309 **Outpatient Visits:** 266644 **Births:** 3020 **Total Expense ($000):** 432587 **Payroll Expense ($000):** 133615 **Personnel:** 1946

LAFAYETTE GENERAL SURGICAL HOSPITAL (190268), 1000 West Pinhook Road, Zip 70503–2460; tel. 337/289–8088, (Nonreporting) **A**10 **S** Lafayette General Health, Lafayette, LA
Primary Contact: Kimberly H. Dooley, Administrator
CFO: Sandi Hernandez, Controller
CHR: Sheena Bouquet, Vice President
CNO: Veronica Els, Chief Nursing Officer
Web address: www.lafayettegeneral.com/our_facilities/main_facilities/lafayette_general_surgical_hospital.aspx
Control: Partnership, Investor–owned (for–profit) **Service:** General medical and surgical

> **Staffed Beds:** 10

LAFAYETTE PHYSICAL REHABILITATION HOSPITAL (193093), 307 Polly Lane, Zip 70508–4960; tel. 337/314–1111, (Nonreporting) **A**10 **S** AMG Integrated Healthcare Management, Lafayette, LA
Primary Contact: Bruce J. Bartels, Interim Chief Executive Officer
Web address: www.lafayettephysicalrehab.com/
Control: Corporation, Investor–owned (for–profit) **Service:** Rehabilitation

> **Staffed Beds:** 32

☐ **LAFAYETTE SURGICAL SPECIALTY HOSPITAL (190259)**, 1101 Kaliste Saloom Road, Zip 70508–5705; tel. 337/769–4100, (Nonreporting) **A**1 10 **S** National Surgical Healthcare, Chicago, IL
Primary Contact: Buffy Domingue, Chief Executive Officer
CFO: Chris Kohlenberg, Chief Financial Officer
CNO: Ruth Guidry, Chief Nursing Officer
Web address: www.lafayettesurgical.com
Control: Corporation, Investor–owned (for–profit) **Service:** Surgical

> **Staffed Beds:** 20

LONG TERM ACUTE CARE OF ACADIANA See Amg Specialty Hospital–Lafayette

LOUISIANA EXTENDED CARE HOSPITAL OF LAFAYETTE (192032), 1214 Coolidge Boulevard, Floors 9 & 10, Zip 70503–2621; tel. 337/289–8180, (Includes EUNICE EXTENDED CARE HOSPITAL, 3879 Highway 190, Eunice, LA, Zip 70535; tel. 337/546–0024; Kevin Frank, Administrator; IBERIA EXTENDED CARE HOSPITAL, 2315 East Main Street, 3rd Floor, New Iberia, LA, Zip 70560–4031; tel. 337/369–1100; Kevin Frank, Administrator) (Nonreporting) **A**10 **S** LHC Group, Lafayette, LA
Primary Contact: Kevin Frank, Administrator
CMO: David Ashton Reed, M.D., Chief Medical Officer
CNO: Monica Lake, Chief Nursing Officer
Web address: www.lhcgroup.com
Control: Other not–for–profit (including NFP Corporation) **Service:** Acute long–term care hospital

> **Staffed Beds:** 42

OPTIMA SPECIALTY HOSPITAL See Vermilion Behavioral Health Systems South

⊞ **OUR LADY OF LOURDES REGIONAL MEDICAL CENTER (190102)**, 4801 Ambassador Caffery Parkway, Zip 70508–6917; tel. 337/470–2000, **A**1 10 **F**3 9 11 12 15 16 18 20 22 24 26 28 29 30 31 32 34 35 38 39 40 43 46 48 49 50 51 53 54 56 57 58 59 60 61 64 65 66 68 70 74 75 77 78 79 81 82 84 85 86 87 90 93 94 96 107 108 110 111 114 115 117 118 119 126 127 129 130 132 134 135 143 144 146 147 148 149 150 154 **P**6 **S** Franciscan Missionaries of Our Lady Health System, Inc., Baton Rouge, LA
Primary Contact: W. Bryan. Lee, Chief Executive Officer
COO: Donna F. Landry, Chief Operating Officer
CMO: Anthony P. Blalock, M.D., Chief Medical Officer
CIO: Ryan J Latiolais, Director Information Systems
CHR: Jennifer Lynch Trahan, Assistant Vice President Human Resources
CNO: Sherelle James, Interim Chief Nursing Officer and Clinical Manager
Web address: www.lourdesrmc.com
Control: Church operated, Nongovernment, not–for–profit **Service:** General medical and surgical

> **Staffed Beds:** 186 **Admissions:** 9408 **Census:** 131 **Outpatient Visits:** 144849 **Births:** 0 **Total Expense ($000):** 229987 **Payroll Expense ($000):** 59679 **Personnel:** 1267

⇑ **PARK PLACE SURGICAL HOSPITAL (190255)**, 4811 Ambassador Caffery Parkway, Zip 70508–6917; tel. 337/237–8119, (Nonreporting) **A**10 21
Primary Contact: Brandon Moore, FACHE, Administrator and Chief Executive Officer
Web address: www.parkplacesurgery.com/
Control: Partnership, Investor–owned (for–profit) **Service:** Surgical

> **Staffed Beds:** 10

☐ **UNIVERSITY HOSPITAL AND CLINICS (190006)**, 2390 West Congress Street, Zip 70506–4298; tel. 337/261–6000, (Nonreporting) **A**1 2 3 5 10 **S** Lafayette General Health, Lafayette, LA
Primary Contact: Katherine D. Hebert, Chief Executive Officer
CMO: James B Falterman, M.D., Jr Medical Director
CNO: Laurence Marie Vincent, Chief Nursing Officer
Web address: www.lafayettegeneral.com
Control: Other not–for–profit (including NFP Corporation) **Service:** General medical and surgical

> **Staffed Beds:** 52

VERMILION BEHAVIORAL HEALTH SYSTEMS (194044), 2520 North University Avenue, Zip 70507–5306; tel. 337/234–5614, (Includes VERMILION BEHAVIORAL HEALTH SYSTEMS SOUTH, 1131 Rue De Belier, Lafayette, LA, Zip 70506–6532; tel. 337/991–0571; Stephanie Hrdlicka, Chief Executive Officer) **A**10 **F**4 5 68 98 99 102 104 105 130 132 151 152 153 **P**5 6 **S** Acadia Healthcare Company, Inc., Franklin, TN
Primary Contact: Stephanie Hrdlicka, Chief Executive Officer
CFO: Margot Mokdessi, Interim Chief Financial Officer
CMO: Bob Winston, M.D., Medical Director
CHR: Claire Rowland, Director Human Resources
CNO: Amy LaHood, R.N., Director of Nursing
Web address: www.acadiavermilion.com
Control: Corporation, Investor–owned (for–profit) **Service:** Psychiatric

> **Staffed Beds:** 78 **Admissions:** 3715 **Census:** 69 **Outpatient Visits:** 4205
> **Births:** 0 **Total Expense ($000):** 15346 **Payroll Expense ($000):** 8054
> **Personnel:** 154

Hospital, Medicare Provider Number, Address, Telephone, Approval, Facility, and Physician Codes, Health Care System

★ American Hospital Association (AHA) membership   ○ Healthcare Facilities Accreditation Program   ⇑ Center for Improvement in Healthcare Quality Accreditation
☐ The Joint Commission accreditation   ◇ DNV Healthcare Inc. accreditation   △ Commission on Accreditation of Rehabilitation Facilities (CARF) accreditation

LA

✠ **WOMEN'S AND CHILDREN'S HOSPITAL (190205)**, 4600 Ambassador Caffery Parkway, Zip 70508–6923, Mailing Address: P.O. Box 88030, Zip 70598–8030; tel. 337/521–9100, **A**1 3 5 10 **F**3 13 15 19 29 30 31 35 39 40 41 50 52 55 57 59 65 68 70 72 74 75 76 77 78 79 81 85 86 87 88 89 91 93 107 111 114 115 117 119 126 129 130 132 146 147 148 **S** HCA Healthcare, Nashville, TN
Primary Contact: Leona Boullion, R.N., Interim Chief Executive Officer
COO: Leona Boullion, R.N., Chief Operating Officer
CFO: James Miller, Chief Financial Officer
CMO: Donald Mickal, M.D., Chief Medical Officer
CIO: John Trahan, Director Information Systems
CHR: Candice Chopin, Vice President Human Resources
Web address: www.womens–childrens.com
Control: Corporation, Investor–owned (for–profit) **Service**: Obstetrics and gynecology

Staffed Beds: **161** Admissions: **6259** Census: **83** Outpatient Visits: **54168** Births: **3210** Total Expense ($000): **86070** Payroll Expense ($000): **32251** Personnel: **487**

LAKE CHARLES—Calcasieu Parish

✠ **CHRISTUS OCHSNER LAKE AREA HOSPITAL (190201)**, 4200 Nelson Road, Zip 70605–4118; tel. 337/474–6370, (Nonreporting) **A**1 10 **S** CHRISTUS Health, Irving, TX
Primary Contact: Kevin Holland, MHSA, MBA, Chief Executive Officer, CHRISTUS Southwestern Louisiana
CFO: Dawn Johnson–Hatcher, Chief Financial Officer
CIO: Aaron Cook, Director Information Services
CHR: Lisa Friday, Director Human Resources
CNO: Robbin Odom, Chief Nursing Officer
Web address: www.Lakeareamc.com
Control: Corporation, Investor–owned (for–profit) **Service**: Other specialty treatment

Staffed Beds: **88**

✠ △ **CHRISTUS OCHSNER ST. PATRICK HOSPITAL SOUTHWEST LOUISIANA (190027)**, 524 Dr Michael Debakey Drive, Zip 70601–5799, Mailing Address: P.O. Box 3401, Zip 70602–3401; tel. 337/436–2511, **A**1 2 7 10 **F**3 11 15 17 18 20 22 24 26 28 29 30 31 32 34 35 37 38 40 44 45 46 47 48 49 50 56 57 59 61 64 65 70 74 75 78 79 81 84 85 86 87 89 90 93 96 97 98 100 101 102 103 104 105 107 108 110 115 118 119 120 121 122 123 124 126 130 131 132 134 135 146 147 148 153 **P**8 **S** CHRISTUS Health, Irving, TX
Primary Contact: Kevin Holland, MHSA, MBA, Chief Executive Officer, CHRISTUS Southwestern Louisiana
CFO: Scott Merryman, Chief Financial Officer
CMO: Timothy Haman, M.D., Vice President Medical Affairs
CHR: Wendy Chandler, Assistant Administrator Human Resources
CNO: Marsha White, Chief Nursing Executive
Web address: www.stpatrickhospital.org
Control: Church operated, Nongovernment, not–for–profit **Service**: General medical and surgical

Staffed Beds: **160** Admissions: **7512** Census: **102** Outpatient Visits: **70071** Births: **0** Total Expense ($000): **153884** Payroll Expense ($000): **42354** Personnel: **729**

✠ **LAKE CHARLES MEMORIAL HOSPITAL (190060)**, 1701 Oak Park Boulevard, Zip 70601–8911; tel. 337/494–3000, (Includes LAKE CHARLES MEMORIAL HOSPITAL FOR WOMEN, 1900 West Gauthier Road, Lake Charles, LA, Zip 70605–7170; tel. 337/480–7000; Marilyn McSwain, MSN, R.N., Administrator) **A**1 2 3 5 10 **F**3 8 11 13 15 17 18 20 22 24 26 28 29 30 31 34 37 40 45 49 50 53 54 56 62 64 66 70 72 73 74 75 76 77 78 79 81 82 85 86 87 88 89 90 93 98 99 102 103 107 108 110 111 114 115 119 120 121 123 124 126 127 129 130 131 132 144 146 147 148 149 153 **P**1 6 7
Primary Contact: Larry M. Graham, FACHE, President and Chief Executive Officer
COO: Anna Leah Cazes, Senior Vice President, Chief Operating Officer
CFO: Charles P Whitson, CPA, Senior Vice President Finance
CMO: Manley Jordan, M.D., Chief Medical Officer
CIO: Belinda Sommers, Chief Information Officer
CHR: Ginger Consigney, Vice President Human Resources
CNO: Anna Leah Cazes, Interim Chief Nursng Officer, Senior Vice President, Chief Operating Officer
Web address: www.lcmh.com
Control: Other not–for–profit (including NFP Corporation) **Service**: General medical and surgical

Staffed Beds: **324** Admissions: **13008** Census: **188** Outpatient Visits: **300859** Births: **2075** Total Expense ($000): **285834** Payroll Expense ($000): **94108** Personnel: **2428**

MEMORIAL SPECIALTY HOSPITAL (192019), 524 Doctor Michael Debakey Drive, 3rd Floor, Zip 70601–5725; tel. 337/480–8990, **A**10 **F**1 3 130
Primary Contact: Angelita Dugas, Administrator
CNO: Julie LeBlanc, Director of Nursing
Web address: www.lcmh.com/
Control: Other not–for–profit (including NFP Corporation) **Service**: Acute long–term care hospital

Staffed Beds: **29** Admissions: **310** Census: **19** Outpatient Visits: **0** Births: **0**

OCEANS BEHAVIORAL HOSPITAL OF LAKE CHARLES (194090), 302 West Mcneese Street, Zip 70605–5604; tel. 337/474–7581, (Nonreporting) **A**10 **S** Oceans Healthcare, Lake Charles, LA
Primary Contact: Monica Tatum, Administrator
Web address: www.obhlc.info/
Control: Corporation, Investor–owned (for–profit) **Service**: Psychiatric

Staffed Beds: **40**

LAKE PROVIDENCE—East Carroll Parish

EAST CARROLL PARISH HOSPITAL (190208), 336 North Hood Street, Zip 71254–2140; tel. 318/559–4023, (Nonreporting) **A**10
Primary Contact: LaDonna Englerth, Administrator
Control: Hospital district or authority, Government, nonfederal **Service**: General medical and surgical

Staffed Beds: **11**

LEESVILLE—Vernon Parish

✠ **BYRD REGIONAL HOSPITAL (190164)**, 1020 West Fertitta Boulevard, Zip 71446–4645; tel. 337/239–9041, (Nonreporting) **A**1 10 **S** Allegiance Health Management, Shreveport, LA
Primary Contact: F. Peter. Savoy III, Chief Executive Officer
CFO: Jared Graves, Chief Financial Officer
CMO: Charles Caldwell, M.D., Chief of Staff
CHR: Karolyne Christian, Director Human Resources
CNO: Beth Westerchil, Chief Nursing Officer
Web address: www.byrdregional.com
Control: Corporation, Investor–owned (for–profit) **Service**: General medical and surgical

Staffed Beds: **60**

DOCTOR'S HOSPITAL OF DEER CREEK (190297), 815 South 10th Street, Zip 71446–4611, Mailing Address: P.O. Box 1391, Zip 71496–1391; tel. 337/392–5088, (Nonreporting) **A**10
Primary Contact: William F. Barrow II, Chief Executive Officer
COO: Traci Thibodeaux, Chief Operating Officer
CMO: Gregory D Lord, M.D., Medical Director
CIO: Kim Smith, Director Business Office
CHR: Annette Hillman, Director Human Resources
CNO: Brenda Willis, Director of Nursing
Web address: www.dhdc.md
Control: Corporation, Investor–owned (for–profit) **Service**: General medical and surgical

Staffed Beds: **10**

☐ **LEESVILLE REHABILITATION HOSPITAL (193086)**, 900 South 6th Street, Zip 71446–4723; tel. 337/392–8118, (Nonreporting) **A**1 10
Primary Contact: Jack M. Causey, Chief Executive Officer
CMO: Gregory D Lord, M.D., Chief Medical Officer
CHR: Jackie Rubar, Administrative Assistant and Director Human Resources
Web address: www.leesvillerehab.com
Control: Corporation, Investor–owned (for–profit) **Service**: Rehabilitation

Staffed Beds: **16**

☐ **TRI PARISH REHABILITATION HOSPITAL (193050)**, 8088 Hawks Road, Zip 71446–6649; tel. 337/462–8880, **A**1 10 **F**3 29 34 90 143 **P**6
Primary Contact: Elizabeth Bennett, Interim Chief Executive Officer
Web address: www.triparishrehab.com
Control: Corporation, Investor–owned (for–profit) **Service**: Rehabilitation

Staffed Beds: **36** Admissions: **352** Census: **13** Outpatient Visits: **0** Births: **0** Personnel: **75**

LULING—St. Charles Parish

✠ **ST. CHARLES PARISH HOSPITAL (190079)**, 1057 Paul Maillard Road, Zip 70070–4349, Mailing Address: P.O. Box 87, Zip 70070–0087; tel. 985/785–6242, **A**1 10 **F**3 7 11 15 20 22 28 29 30 34 40 45 50 51 59 60 64 68 70 75 79 81 82 85 86 87 93 96 97 98 100 102 107 108 110 111 115 119 130 131 135 146 148 154 **S** Ochsner Health System, New Orleans, LA
Primary Contact: Austin Reeder, Chief Executive Officer
COO: Terrell Neal, R.N., Chief Operating Officer and Chief Nursing Officer
CFO: Peter Torsch, Chief Financial Officer
CMO: Vadakkipalayam N. Devarajan, Chief Medical Staff
CIO: Angela Boudreaux, Director Information Technology
CHR: Karen Ann Judlin, Director Human Resources
CNO: Terrell Neal, R.N., Chief Operating Officer and Chief Nursing Officer
Web address: www.ochsner.org/locations/st-charles-parish-hospital/
Control: Hospital district or authority, Government, nonfederal **Service**: General medical and surgical

Staffed Beds: 59 **Admissions**: 1813 **Census**: 27 **Outpatient Visits**: 29877 **Births**: 0 **Total Expense ($000)**: 40880 **Payroll Expense ($000)**: 9108 **Personnel**: 86

LUTCHER—St. James Parish

BEACON BEHAVIORAL HOSPITAL (194102), 2471 Louisiana Avenue, Zip 70071–5413; tel. 225/258–6103, (Nonreporting)
Primary Contact: Sean Wendell, Chief Executive Officer
Web address: www.beaconbh.com
Control: Other not–for–profit (including NFP Corporation) **Service**: Psychiatric

Staffed Beds: 19

✠ **ST. JAMES PARISH HOSPITAL (191305)**, 1645 Lutcher Avenue, Zip 70071–5150; tel. 225/869–5512, **A**1 10 18 **F**3 15 29 30 34 35 40 45 50 57 59 64 75 77 80 81 85 107 110 111 114 119 128 129 132 133 135 144 149 154
Primary Contact: Mary Ellen. Pratt, FACHE, Chief Executive Officer
CFO: Tracy L George, Chief Financial Officer
CIO: Jeremy Martin, Chief Support Services Officer
CHR: Lisa Faucheux, Director Human Resources
CNO: Rhonda Zeringue, R.N., Chief Nursing Officer
Web address: www.sjph.org
Control: Hospital district or authority, Government, nonfederal **Service**: General medical and surgical

Staffed Beds: 25 **Admissions**: 565 **Census**: 8 **Outpatient Visits**: 32859 **Births**: 0 **Total Expense ($000)**: 26406 **Payroll Expense ($000)**: 10715 **Personnel**: 219

MAMOU—Evangeline Parish

✠ **SAVOY MEDICAL CENTER (190025)**, 801 Poinciana Avenue, Zip 70554–2298; tel. 337/468–5261, **A**1 10 **F**3 4 5 17 70 78 81 89 90 93 98 104 107 119 127 146 152 154 **S** CHRISTUS Health, Irving, TX
Primary Contact: Eugene H. Burge, Chief Executive Officer
COO: Gerald Fuselier, Chief Operating Officer
CMO: Greg Savoy, M.D., Chief Medical Officer
CIO: Daniel Lahaye, Manager
CHR: Annette Thibodeaux, Director Human Resources
Web address: www.savoymedical.com/
Control: City, Government, nonfederal **Service**: General medical and surgical

Staffed Beds: 172 **Admissions**: 1884 **Census**: 34 **Outpatient Visits**: 90204 **Births**: 0

MANDEVILLE—St. Tammany Parish

☐ **NORTHLAKE BEHAVIORAL HEALTH SYSTEM (194007)**, 23515 Highway 190, Zip 70448–7334; tel. 985/626–6300, **A**1 3 5 10 **F**100 102 104 130
Primary Contact: Marty Dean, Chief Executive Officer
CFO: Melissa S. Clayton, CPA, Chief Financial Officer
CMO: Hyon Su Kim, M.D., Medical Director
CIO: Archie Carriere, Information Technology Technician
CHR: Nicole Messa–Gill, Manager Human Resources
CNO: Jo Nell King, Director of Nursing
Web address: www.northlakebehavioralhealth.com
Control: Other not–for–profit (including NFP Corporation) **Service**: Psychiatric

Staffed Beds: 122 **Admissions**: 2400 **Census**: 82 **Outpatient Visits**: 0 **Births**: 0

MANSFIELD—De Soto Parish

DE SOTO REGIONAL HEALTH SYSTEM (190118), 207 Jefferson Street, Zip 71052–2603, Mailing Address: P.O. Box 1636, Zip 71052–1636; tel. 318/872–4610, (Nonreporting) **A**10 20 **S** Willis–Knighton Health System, Shreveport, LA
Primary Contact: Todd Eppler, FACHE, Chief Executive Officer
CFO: Eric Cripps, Chief Financial Officer
CMO: Denis Kamberov, M.D., Chief of Staff
CNO: Shane Goodman, Chief Nursing Officer
Web address: www.desotoregional.com
Control: Other not–for–profit (including NFP Corporation) **Service**: General medical and surgical

Staffed Beds: 10

MANY—Sabine Parish

SABINE MEDICAL CENTER (190218), 240 Highland Drive, Zip 71449–3718; tel. 318/256–5691, (Nonreporting) **A**10 20 **S** Allegiance Health Management, Shreveport, LA
COO: Doug Plummer, Chief Operating Officer
CFO: Frances F Hopkins, Chief Financial Officer
CNO: Karen Ford, Chief Nursing Officer
Web address: www.sabinemedicalcenter.net
Control: Individual, Investor–owned (for–profit) **Service**: General medical and surgical

Staffed Beds: 24

MARKSVILLE—Avoyelles Parish

☐ **AVOYELLES HOSPITAL (190099)**, 4231 Highway 1192, Zip 71351–4711, Mailing Address: P.O. Box 249, Zip 71351–0249; tel. 318/253–8611, **A**1 10 **F**3 15 29 30 34 40 54 56 57 64 65 70 75 79 81 85 86 107 110 114 119 127 133 135 146
Primary Contact: L Rene'. Goux, Chief Executive Officer
COO: Tim Curry, Chief Operating Officer
CFO: Douglas Lahasky, Chief Financial Officer
CMO: Donna Breen, M.D., Chief of Staff
CIO: Johnny Bergeron, Manager Information Technology
CHR: Allison Ferguson, Director Human Resources
CNO: Cindy K Juneau, Chief Nursing Officer, Manger Quality and Risk
Web address: www.avoyelleshospital.com
Control: Corporation, Investor–owned (for–profit) **Service**: General medical and surgical

Staffed Beds: 35 **Admissions**: 1633 **Census**: 13 **Outpatient Visits**: 40171 **Births**: 0 **Total Expense ($000)**: 15500 **Payroll Expense ($000)**: 6725 **Personnel**: 176

MARRERO—Jefferson Parish

BRIDGEPOINT CONTINUING CARE HOSPITAL (192007), 1111 Medical Center Boulevard, Suite S–550, Zip 70072–3151; tel. 504/349–2470, (Nonreporting) **A**10
Primary Contact: Paul Konske, Chief Executive Officer
Control: Corporation, Investor–owned (for–profit) **Service**: Acute long–term care hospital

Staffed Beds: 56

✠ △ **WEST JEFFERSON MEDICAL CENTER (190039)**, 1101 Medical Center Boulevard, Zip 70072–3191; tel. 504/347–5511, **A**1 2 3 5 7 10 **F**3 6 7 8 11 12 13 15 17 18 20 22 24 26 28 29 30 31 34 35 37 38 39 40 41 43 45 46 47 49 50 51 53 56 57 59 61 64 65 68 70 72 74 75 76 78 79 81 82 84 85 86 87 90 91 93 96 97 98 100 101 102 104 105 107 108 110 111 114 115 117 118 119 120 121 124 126 127 129 130 132 135 144 146 147 148 149 154 **P**6 7 **S** LCMC Health, New Orleans, LA
Primary Contact: Nancy R. Cassagne, FACHE, Chief Executive Officer
CFO: Bryan McCauley, Chief Financial Officer
CMO: Robert Chugden, M.D., Chief Medical Officer
CHR: Floyd Riedlinger, Director Human Resources
CNO: Monica Bologna, R.N., Chief Nursing Officer
Web address: www.wjmc.org
Control: Other not–for–profit (including NFP Corporation) **Service**: General medical and surgical

Staffed Beds: 243 **Admissions**: 10557 **Census**: 163 **Outpatient Visits**: 325478 **Births**: 1114 **Total Expense ($000)**: 274106 **Payroll Expense ($000)**: 97242 **Personnel**: 1481

Hospital, Medicare Provider Number, Address, Telephone, Approval, Facility, and Physician Codes, Health Care System

★ American Hospital Association (AHA) membership
☐ The Joint Commission accreditation
◯ Healthcare Facilities Accreditation Program
◇ DNV Healthcare Inc. accreditation
⇑ Center for Improvement in Healthcare Quality Accreditation
△ Commission on Accreditation of Rehabilitation Facilities (CARF) accreditation

LA

METAIRIE—Jefferson Parish

☐ △ **EAST JEFFERSON GENERAL HOSPITAL (190146)**, 4200 Houma Boulevard, Zip 70006–2996; tel. 504/503–4000, (Includes DOCTORS HOSPITAL OF JEFFERSON, 4320 Houma Boulevard, Metairie, LA, Zip 70006–2973; tel. 504/849–4000) **A**1 2 3 5 7 10 **F**3 7 8 11 13 14 15 17 18 20 22 24 26 28 29 30 31 34 35 36 37 40 44 45 46 47 48 49 50 51 53 54 55 56 57 58 59 60 64 65 70 72 73 74 75 76 77 78 79 81 82 84 85 86 87 90 91 92 93 96 97 98 102 103 107 108 110 111 114 115 117 118 119 120 121 123 124 126 128 129 130 131 132 135 141 142 145 146 147 148 149 **P**6
Primary Contact: Gerald L. Parton, FACHE, Chief Executive Officer
COO: Judy Brown, Executive Vice President and Chief Operating Officer
CFO: Robert Riley, Interim Chief Financial Officer
CMO: Raymond P DeCorte, M.D., Chief Medical Officer
CHR: Frank Martinez, Senior Vice President Human Resources
CNO: Ruby Brewer RN Senior Vice President, Chief Nursing and Quality Officer
Web address: www.ejgh.org
Control: Hospital district or authority, Government, nonfederal **Service:** General medical and surgical

Staffed Beds: 424 **Admissions:** 14781 **Census:** 204 **Outpatient Visits:** 225712 **Births:** 1098 **Total Expense ($000):** 363059 **Payroll Expense ($000):** 97105 **Personnel:** 2011

⇑ **OMEGA HOSPITAL (190302)**, 2525 Severn Avenue, Zip 70002–5932; tel. 504/832–4200, (Nonreporting) **A**10 21
Primary Contact: Karen Rousselle, Administrator
Web address: www.omegahospital.com
Control: Individual, Investor–owned (for–profit) **Service:** Surgical

Staffed Beds: 10

MINDEN—Webster Parish

⊞ **MINDEN MEDICAL CENTER (190144)**, 1 Medical Plaza, Zip 71055–3330, Mailing Address: P.O. Box 5003, Zip 71058–5003; tel. 318/377–2321, **A**1 10 19 **F**11 13 15 18 20 22 29 30 34 40 45 46 56 57 59 64 70 75 76 77 79 81 82 87 89 90 93 98 103 107 111 115 119 129 130 131 132 146 147 148 154 **S** Allegiance Health Management, Shreveport, LA
Primary Contact: Gregory Pearson, Chief Executive Officer
CFO: James R. Williams, Chief Financial Officer
CMO: G Max Stell, M.D., Medical Director
CIO: Mace Morgan, Director Information Systems
CHR: Mary Winget, Director Human Resources
CNO: Donna Carter, MSN, R.N., Chief Nursing Officer
Web address: www.mindenmedicalcenter.com
Control: Corporation, Investor–owned (for–profit) **Service:** General medical and surgical

Staffed Beds: 161 **Admissions:** 3209 **Census:** 40 **Outpatient Visits:** 50929 **Births:** 622 **Total Expense ($000):** 50070 **Payroll Expense ($000):** 20694 **Personnel:** 436

MONROE—Ouachita Parish

BASTROP REHABILITATION HOSPITAL (193058), 4310 South Grand Street, Zip 71202–6322; tel. 318/654–8300, (Nonreporting) **A**10
Primary Contact: William H. Means Jr, Administrator
CMO: Jeffery Combetta, M.D., Medical Director
CHR: Rhonda Church, Director Human Resources
Control: Corporation, Investor–owned (for–profit) **Service:** Rehabilitation

Staffed Beds: 10

E. A. CONWAY MEDICAL CENTER See University Health Conway

⇑ **MONROE SURGICAL HOSPITAL (190245)**, 2408 Broadmoor Boulevard, Zip 71201–2963; tel. 318/410–0002, (Nonreporting) **A**10 21
Primary Contact: Robyn Hemphill, Chief Executive Officer and Chief Nursing Officer
Web address: www.monroesurgical.com
Control: Corporation, Investor–owned (for–profit) **Service:** Surgical

Staffed Beds: 10

★ ⇑ **P & S SURGICAL HOSPITAL (190246)**, 312 Grammont Street Suite 101, Zip 71201–7403; tel. 318/388–4040, (Nonreporting) **A**10 21
Primary Contact: Linda S. Holyfield, R.N., MSN, President and Chief Executive Officer
COO: Terri Hicks, Chief Operating Officer and Chief Financial Officer
CFO: Terri Hicks, Chief Operating Officer and Chief Financial Officer
CMO: Bart Liles, M.D., Chief of Staff
CIO: Christy Childers, Director Information Technology
CHR: Cheniere Craig, Director Human Resources
CNO: Debbie W Austin, MSN, R.N., Vice President Patient Care Services
Web address: www.pssurgery.com
Control: Partnership, Investor–owned (for–profit) **Service:** Surgical

Staffed Beds: 22

SPECIALTY HOSPITAL (192016), 309 Jackson Street, 7th Floor, Zip 71201–7407, Mailing Address: P.O. Box 1532, Zip 71210–1532; tel. 318/966–7045, (Nonreporting) **A**10 **S** LHC Group, Lafayette, LA
Primary Contact: Cleta Munholland, Administrator
COO: Pamela Chappell, R.N., Assistant Administrator
CNO: Jerry Rogers, R.N., Director Nurses and Infection Control
Web address: www.lhcgroup.com
Control: Church operated, Nongovernment, not–for–profit **Service:** Acute long–term care hospital

Staffed Beds: 32

⊞ **ST. FRANCIS MEDICAL CENTER (190125)**, 309 Jackson Street, Zip 71201–7407, Mailing Address: P.O. Box 1901, Zip 71210–1901; tel. 318/966–4000, **A**1 10 **F**3 12 13 15 17 18 19 20 21 22 23 24 25 26 27 28 29 30 31 32 34 35 37 39 40 44 45 46 49 50 54 55 56 57 59 64 65 68 69 70 71 72 74 75 76 77 78 79 81 84 85 87 88 89 90 92 93 96 97 107 108 110 111 114 115 118 119 124 126 128 129 130 131 132 135 146 147 148 **P**8 **S** Franciscan Missionaries of Our Lady Health System, Inc., Baton Rouge, LA
Primary Contact: Kristin Wolkart, R.N., President and Chief Executive Officer
CFO: Jeremy Rogers, Chief Financial Officer
CNO: Kayla Johnson, R.N., Vice President Patient Care Services and Chief Nursing Officer
Web address: www.stfran.com
Control: Church operated, Nongovernment, not–for–profit **Service:** General medical and surgical

Staffed Beds: 365 **Admissions:** 14041 **Census:** 192 **Outpatient Visits:** 220492 **Births:** 1681 **Total Expense ($000):** 259951 **Payroll Expense ($000):** 95386 **Personnel:** 1368

ST. FRANCIS SPECIALTY HOSPITAL See Specialty Hospital

☐ **UNIVERSITY HEALTH CONWAY (190011)**, 4864 Jackson Street, Zip 71202–6497, Mailing Address: P.O. Box 1881, Zip 71210–8005; tel. 318/330–7000, **A**1 3 5 10 **F**1 3 4 13 15 16 17 18 20 22 26 29 30 31 32 34 35 38 40 45 50 54 56 57 58 59 61 63 64 65 66 67 68 70 72 73 74 75 76 77 78 79 80 81 83 84 85 86 87 88 89 90 91 93 94 97 98 100 101 102 107 108 110 111 112 114 115 119 124 128 130 135 143 144 146 147 149 150 **P**8 **S** University Health System, Shreveport, LA
Primary Contact: Jonathan Phillips, Interim Administrator
CFO: Dorothy Whittington, Chief Financial Officer
CMO: Richard Cavell, M.D., Medical Director
CIO: Todd Walters, Director of UHC Information Technology Services
CHR: Rob Hartmann, Assistant Director Human Resources Management
CNO: Traci S. Jordan, MS, R.N., Chief Nursing Officer
Web address: www.uhsystem.com
Control: Other not–for–profit (including NFP Corporation) **Service:** General medical and surgical

Staffed Beds: 123 **Admissions:** 4342 **Census:** 67 **Outpatient Visits:** 145315 **Births:** 956 **Total Expense ($000):** 114974 **Payroll Expense ($000):** 37603 **Personnel:** 677

MORGAN CITY—St. Mary Parish

⊞ **TECHE REGIONAL MEDICAL CENTER (190014)**, 1125 Marguerite Street, Zip 70380–1855, Mailing Address: P.O. Box 2308, Zip 70381–2308; tel. 985/384–2200, **A**1 10 20 **F**3 13 15 18 29 30 34 40 45 50 57 59 70 76 79 81 82 84 85 89 90 93 98 100 101 102 107 108 110 111 114 117 118 119 129 130 146 147 154 **S** LifePoint Health, Brentwood, TN
Primary Contact: Aphreikah DuHaney–West, Chief Executive Officer
COO: Don Knight, Assistant Administrator and Risk Manager
CFO: James R. Williams, Chief Financial Officer, Louisiana Market
CMO: Eric Melancon, Chief of Staff
CIO: Rene Bilello, Manager Information System
CHR: Timothy Hebert, Director Human Resources
Web address: www.techeregional.com
Control: Corporation, Investor–owned (for–profit) **Service:** General medical and surgical

Staffed Beds: 164 **Admissions:** 2696 **Census:** 38 **Outpatient Visits:** 52434 **Births:** 389 **Total Expense ($000):** 39184 **Payroll Expense ($000):** 15223 **Personnel:** 273

NAPOLEONVILLE—Assumption Parish

★ **ASSUMPTION COMMUNITY HOSPITAL (191303)**, 135 Highway 402, Zip 70390–2217; tel. 985/369–3600, (Nonreporting) **A**10 18 **S** Franciscan Missionaries of Our Lady Health System, Inc., Baton Rouge, LA
Primary Contact: Christina Hockaday, FACHE, Chief Executive Officer
CHR: Letonia Pierre, Coordinator Human Resources
CNO: Donna Mullings, Director of Nursing
Web address: www.https://ololrmc.com
Control: Other not–for–profit (including NFP Corporation) **Service:** General medical and surgical

Staffed Beds: 6

NATCHITOCHES—Natchitoches Parish

LOUISIANA EXTENDED CARE HOSPITAL OF NATCHITOCHES (192035), 501 Keyser Avenue, Zip 71457–6018; tel. 318/354–2044, **A**10 **F**1 3 4 16 17 28 29 30 34 50 57 59 67 68 70 72 73 74 75 76 80 85 86 87 88 89 90 91 97 98 128 130 148 **S** LHC Group, Lafayette, LA
Primary Contact: John Rivoire, R.N., MSN, Administrator
Web address: www.lhcgroup.com
Control: Partnership, Investor–owned (for–profit) **Service:** Acute long–term care hospital

Staffed Beds: 21 **Admissions:** 284 **Census:** 16 **Outpatient Visits:** 0
Births: 0 **Personnel:** 52

☒ **NATCHITOCHES REGIONAL MEDICAL CENTER (190007)**, 501 Keyser Avenue, Zip 71457–6036, Mailing Address: P.O. Box 2009, Zip 71457–2009; tel. 318/214–4200, **A**1 10 20 **F**3 5 7 8 10 11 13 15 18 28 29 30 31 32 34 35 36 37 38 39 40 41 43 45 46 47 50 51 53 54 56 57 58 59 60 61 65 66 69 70 71 74 75 77 78 79 81 82 85 86 87 93 94 97 98 100 101 102 103 104 105 106 107 108 109 110 111 112 114 119 120 121 124 125 126 127 129 130 131 132 133 135 143 144 145 146 147 148 152 153 154 **P**5 7 8 **S** CHRISTUS Health, Irving, TX
Primary Contact: D. Kirk. Soileau, FACHE, Chief Executive Officer
CFO: Brad McCormick, Chief Financial Officer
CMO: Phyllis Mason, M.D., Chief Medical Officer
CHR: Ernie Scott, Director Human Resources
CNO: Dawna DeBlieux, Vice President Patient Care Services and Chief Nurse Executive
Web address: www.nrmchospital.org
Control: Hospital district or authority, Government, nonfederal **Service:** General medical and surgical

Staffed Beds: 91 **Admissions:** 2700 **Census:** 32 **Outpatient Visits:** 67506
Births: 596

NEW IBERIA—Iberia Parish

☐ **IBERIA MEDICAL CENTER (190054)**, 2315 East Main Street, Zip 70560–4031, Mailing Address: P.O. Box 13338, Zip 70562–3338; tel. 337/364–0441, **A**1 10 **F**1 3 4 11 13 15 16 17 18 20 22 28 29 30 31 34 39 40 45 46 47 48 49 50 57 67 68 70 72 73 74 75 76 77 78 79 80 81 85 88 89 90 93 97 98 103 107 108 110 111 115 119 127 128 130 135 146 149 **P**6 **S** HealthTech Management Services, Brentwood, TN
Primary Contact: Parker A. Templeton, FACHE, Chief Executive Officer
COO: Shane P Myers, Chief Operating Officer
CFO: Dionne Viator, CPA, FACHE, Chief Financial Officer
CMO: Shawn Baquet, Chief of Staff
CIO: Vance Robinson, Chief Information Officer
CHR: Lori Spann, Director Human Resources
CNO: Josie Fletcher, Interim Chief Nursing Officer
Web address: www.iberiamedicalcenter.com
Control: Hospital district or authority, Government, nonfederal **Service:** General medical and surgical

Staffed Beds: 123 **Admissions:** 4444 **Census:** 51 **Outpatient Visits:** 128687 **Births:** 204 **Total Expense ($000):** 87234 **Payroll Expense ($000):** 33605 **Personnel:** 638

☐ **IBERIA REHABILITATION HOSPITAL (193096)**, 532 Jefferson Terrace, Zip 70560–4948; tel. 337/364–6923, (Nonreporting) **A**1 10
Primary Contact: Athan Olivier III, R.N., FACHE, Administrator and Chief Executive Officer
Web address: www.iberiarehab.net/
Control: Partnership, Investor–owned (for–profit) **Service:** Rehabilitation

Staffed Beds: 24

NEW ORLEANS—Orleans Parish

☐ **BEACON BEHAVIORAL HOSPITAL – NEW ORLEANS (194084)**, 14500 Hayne Boulevard, Suite 200, Zip 70128–1751; tel. 504/210–0460, (Nonreporting) **A**1 10
Primary Contact: Jessika Scallion, Administrator
Control: Corporation, Investor–owned (for–profit) **Service:** Psychiatric

Staffed Beds: 24

☐ △ **CHILDREN'S HOSPITAL (193300)**, 200 Henry Clay Avenue, Zip 70118–5720; tel. 504/899–9511, **A**1 2 3 5 7 10 **F**9 11 17 19 21 23 25 27 29 30 31 32 34 35 39 41 44 45 50 51 54 55 57 58 60 61 65 68 72 74 75 77 78 79 81 82 84 85 86 87 88 89 93 96 97 99 100 101 102 105 107 111 115 119 121 126 129 130 131 132 134 136 138 146 148 149 150 **S** LCMC Health, New Orleans, LA
Primary Contact: John R. Nickens IV, President and Chief Executive Officer
COO: Matthew Schaefer, Chief Operating Officer
CFO: Courtney Garrett, CPA, Senior Vice President, Chief Financial Officer
CMO: George Bisset, M.D., III Chief Medical Officer
CIO: Tanya Townsend, Senior Vice President, Chief Information Officer (part of LCMC)
CHR: Wendy L Willis, Vice President Human Resources
CNO: Diane Michel, Senior Vice President, Chief Nursing Officer
Web address: www.chnola.org
Control: Other not–for–profit (including NFP Corporation) **Service:** Children's general medical and surgical

Staffed Beds: 177 **Admissions:** 6269 **Census:** 121 **Outpatient Visits:** 277873 **Total Expense ($000):** 266069 **Payroll Expense ($000):** 97051 **Personnel:** 1496

COBALT REHABILITATION HOSPITAL OF NEW ORLEANS (193098), 3801 Bienville Street, Zip 70119; tel. 504/930–3500, (Nonreporting) **A**10 22
Primary Contact: Scott Tranchina, R.N., MSN, Administrator
Control: Partnership, Investor–owned (for–profit) **Service:** Rehabilitation

Staffed Beds: 60

☐ **COMMUNITY CARE HOSPITAL (194056)**, 1421 General Taylor Street, Zip 70115–3717; tel. 504/899–2500, (Nonreporting) **A**1 10
Primary Contact: Paul B. Kavanaugh, President and Chief Executive Officer
Web address: www.communitycarehospital.com
Control: State, Government, nonfederal **Service:** Psychiatric

Staffed Beds: 36

☒ **CURAHEALTH NEW ORLEANS (192009)**, 3601 Coliseum Street, Zip 70115–3606; tel. 504/899–1555, (Nonreporting) **A**1 10 **S** Curahealth Hospitals, Garland, TX
Primary Contact: Richard Daughdrill, R.N., Chief Executive Officer
CFO: Laurie Champagne, Controller
Web address: www.curahealth.com
Control: Corporation, Investor–owned (for–profit) **Service:** Acute long–term care hospital

Staffed Beds: 80

MEDICAL CENTER OF LOUISIANA AT NEW ORLEANS See University Medical Center

☐ **NEW ORLEANS EAST HOSPITAL (190313)**, 5620 Read Boulevard, Zip 70127–3106, Mailing Address: 5620 Read Blvd, Zip 70127–3106; tel. 504/592–6600, **A**1 **F**3 11 15 18 20 22 26 29 30 34 35 38 40 44 45 50 57 59 63 64 68 70 74 75 77 79 81 82 85 86 87 91 93 107 108 110 111 115 118 119 129 130 131 146 147 149 **P**8 **S** LCMC Health, New Orleans, LA
Primary Contact: Takeisha C. Davis, M.D., M.P.H., President and Chief Executive Officer
COO: Dante Green, Assistant Vice President Operations
CFO: Anthony Saul, Chief Financial Officer
CHR: Brion Stanford, Director Human Resources
CNO: Martha Smith, R.N., Chief Nursing Officer
Web address: www.noehospital.org
Control: Hospital district or authority, Government, nonfederal **Service:** General medical and surgical

Staffed Beds: 34 **Admissions:** 1026 **Census:** 9 **Outpatient Visits:** 63139 **Births:** 0 **Total Expense ($000):** 63550 **Payroll Expense ($000):** 16624 **Personnel:** 241

Hospital, Medicare Provider Number, Address, Telephone, Approval, Facility, and Physician Codes, Health Care System

★ American Hospital Association (AHA) membership
☐ The Joint Commission accreditation
○ Healthcare Facilities Accreditation Program
◇ DNV Healthcare Inc. accreditation
⇑ Center for Improvement in Healthcare Quality Accreditation
△ Commission on Accreditation of Rehabilitation Facilities (CARF) accreditation

NEW ORLEANS—Jefferson Parish

☒ △ **OCHSNER MEDICAL CENTER (190036)**, 1514 Jefferson Highway, Zip 70121–2429; tel. 504/842–3000, (Includes OCHSNER BAPTIST MEDICAL CENTER, 2700 Napoleon Avenue, New Orleans, LA, Zip 70115–6914; tel. 504/899–9311; Dawn Anuszkiewicz, Chief Executive Officer; OCHSNER MEDICAL CENTER – WEST BANK, 2500 Belle Chasse Highway, Gretna, LA, Zip 70056–7127; tel. 504/392–3131; Mary Deynoodt, Interim Chief Executive Officer and Chief Operating Officer; OCHSNER MEDICAL CENTER FOR CHILDREN, 1514 Jefferson Highway, New Orleans, LA, Zip 70121–2429; tel. 504/842–3000) (Total facility includes 38 beds in nursing home–type unit) **A**1 2 5 7 8 10 **F**3 4 5 6 7 8 9 11 12 13 14 15 17 18 19 20 21 22 23 24 25 26 27 28 29 30 31 32 34 35 36 37 38 40 41 43 44 45 46 47 48 49 50 53 54 55 56 57 58 59 60 61 63 64 65 68 70 71 72 73 74 75 76 77 78 79 80 81 82 84 85 86 87 88 89 90 91 92 93 94 96 97 98 99 100 101 102 103 104 105 107 108 110 111 114 115 116 117 118 119 120 121 123 124 126 128 129 130 131 132 134 135 136 137 138 139 140 141 142 145 146 147 148 151 152 153 154 **P**6 **S** Ochsner Health System, New Orleans, LA
Primary Contact: Robert K. Wolterman, Chief Executive Officer
CFO: Scott J Posecai, Executive Vice President and Chief Financial Officer
CMO: Patrick J Quinlan, M.D., Chief Executive Officer
CIO: Lynn Witherspoon, Vice President and Chief Information Officer
CHR: Joan Mollohan, Vice President Human Resources
Web address: www.ochsner.org
Control: Other not–for–profit (including NFP Corporation) **Service:** General medical and surgical

Staffed Beds: 823 **Admissions:** 42189 **Census:** 676 **Outpatient Visits:** 276842 **Births:** 4458 **Total Expense ($000):** 1393827 **Payroll Expense ($000):** 475601 **Personnel:** 7659

NEW ORLEANS—Orleans Parish

PSYCHIATRIC PAVILION NEW ORLEANS See Beacon Behavioral Hospital – New Orleans

NEW ORLEANS—Jefferson Parish

☐ **RIVER OAKS HOSPITAL (194031)**, 1525 River Oaks Road West, Zip 70123–2162; tel. 504/734–1740, (Includes RIVER OAKS CHILD AND ADOLESCENT HOSPITAL, 1525 River Oaks Road West, New Orleans, LA, Zip 70123–2162; tel. 504/734–1740) (Nonreporting) **A**1 3 10 **S** Universal Health Services, Inc., King of Prussia, PA
Primary Contact: Deagan Watson, Chief Executive Officer
CFO: Brandon Frazier, Chief Financial Officer
CMO: Lincoln Paine, M.D., Medical Director
CIO: Vincent Chatelain, Director Business Development
CHR: Wanda Hoffmann, Director Human Resources
CNO: Michelle Wells, Director of Nursing
Web address: www.riveroakshospital.com
Control: Corporation, Investor–owned (for–profit) **Service:** Psychiatric

Staffed Beds: 126

NEW ORLEANS—Orleans Parish

SEASIDE BEHAVIORAL CENTER (194100), 4201 Woodland Drive, Zip 70131–7339; tel. 504/393–4223, **A**3 10 **F**35 98 100 101 102 103 105 130 143 153
Primary Contact: Mary L. Matamoros, R.N., Chief Executive Officer
CHR: Sherry May Campbell, Director of Human Resources, Medical Records
CNO: Justin Bernier, R.N., Director of Nursing
Web address: www.seasidehc.com
Control: Corporation, Investor–owned (for–profit) **Service:** Psychiatric

Staffed Beds: 47 **Admissions:** 1783 **Census:** 43 **Outpatient Visits:** 0 **Births:** 0

☐ **ST. CATHERINE MEMORIAL HOSPITAL (192023)**, 14500 Hayne Boulevard, Zip 70128–1751; tel. 504/210–3000, **A**1 10 **F**29 128
Primary Contact: Lexis Landry Nunez, Chief Executive Officer
Web address: www.stcatherine–hospital.com
Control: Partnership, Investor–owned (for–profit) **Service:** Children's acute long–term Care

Staffed Beds: 21 **Admissions:** 146 **Census:** 14 **Outpatient Visits:** 0 **Births:** 0

⇑ **ST. CHARLES SURGICAL HOSPITAL (190300)**, 1717 Saint Charles Avenue, Zip 70130–5223; tel. 504/529–6600, (Nonreporting) **A**10 21
Primary Contact: Cheri Saltaformaggio, Chief Executive Officer
Web address: www.scsh.com
Control: Corporation, Investor–owned (for–profit) **Service:** Surgical

Staffed Beds: 39

☒ △ **TOURO INFIRMARY (190046)**, 1401 Foucher Street, Zip 70115–3593; tel. 504/897–7011, (Includes TOURO REHABILITATION CENTER, 1401 Foucher Street, New Orleans, LA, Zip 70115–3515; tel. 504/897–8560; Susan E. Andrews, Chief Executive Officer) **A**1 2 3 5 7 10 11 13 15 18 20 22 24 26 28 29 30 31 34 35 37 39 40 44 45 46 50 53 54 55 57 58 59 60 61 62 64 68 70 72 74 75 76 77 78 79 81 83 84 85 86 87 90 92 93 96 107 108 109 110 111 114 115 116 117 118 119 120 121 123 124 125 126 130 131 132 135 143 144 146 147 148 149 154 **S** LCMC Health, New Orleans, LA
Primary Contact: Susan E. Andrews, Chief Executive Officer
CFO: Mark Wack, Senior Vice President and Chief Financial Officer
CMO: Jeffrey Coco, M.D., Chief Medical Officer
CIO: Leann Hughes–Mickel, Chief Information Officer
CHR: Cindy Mousa, Director Human Resources
CNO: Danita S Sullivan, R.N., Chief Nursing Officer
Web address: www.touro.com
Control: Other not–for–profit (including NFP Corporation) **Service:** General medical and surgical

Staffed Beds: 280 **Admissions:** 10965 **Census:** 185 **Outpatient Visits:** 294071 **Births:** 3268 **Total Expense ($000):** 252578 **Payroll Expense ($000):** 92371 **Personnel:** 1294

☒ **TULANE HEALTH SYSTEM (190176)**, 1415 Tulane Avenue, Zip 70112–2600; tel. 504/988–5263, (Includes LAKEVIEW REGIONAL MEDICAL CENTER, 95 Judge Tanner Boulevard, Covington, LA, Zip 70433–7507; tel. 985/867–3800; Hiral Patel, Interim Chief Executive Officer and Chief Operating Officer; TULANE–LAKESIDE HOSPITAL, 4700 South I 10 Service Road West, Metairie, LA, Zip 70001–1269; tel. 504/780–4200) **A**1 2 3 5 8 10 **F**3 12 13 15 17 18 20 21 22 23 24 25 26 27 28 29 30 31 32 34 35 40 41 43 45 46 47 48 49 50 51 52 55 58 60 61 64 65 70 72 74 75 76 77 78 79 80 81 85 87 88 89 90 91 92 93 97 98 100 102 104 107 108 109 110 111 114 115 118 119 120 121 122 123 124 126 129 130 131 132 136 138 139 141 142 146 147 148 154 **S** HCA Healthcare, Nashville, TN
Primary Contact: William Lunn, MD, President and Chief Executive Officer
COO: Thomas Patrias, FACHE, Chief Operating Officer
CFO: Regina Ramazani, Chief Financial Officer
CMO: John Pigott, M.D., Chief Medical Officer
CIO: Sue Rachuig, Director Information Services
CHR: Leah Grau, Director Human Resources
CNO: Jana S Stonestreet, R.N., Ph.D., Chief Nursing Officer
Web address: www.tuhc.com
Control: Corporation, Investor–owned (for–profit) **Service:** General medical and surgical

Staffed Beds: 552 **Admissions:** 17951 **Census:** 262 **Outpatient Visits:** 419792 **Births:** 2288 **Total Expense ($000):** 501146 **Payroll Expense ($000):** 144568 **Personnel:** 1945

☐ **UNIVERSITY MEDICAL CENTER (190005)**, 2000 Canal Street, Zip 70112–3018; tel. 504/903–3000, **A**1 2 3 5 8 10 **F**3 11 15 18 20 22 24 26 29 30 31 34 35 39 40 43 49 50 51 53 55 57 58 59 61 64 65 66 70 74 78 79 81 83 84 85 86 87 93 94 97 98 100 102 107 108 110 111 112 114 115 116 117 118 119 123 126 130 135 141 146 147 148 **S** LCMC Health, New Orleans, LA
Primary Contact: William J. Masterton, President and Chief Executive Officer
COO: Lisa Miranda, Vice President Operations
CFO: Christine Williams, Chief Financial Officer
CNO: Denise Danna Esq Chief Nursing Officer
Web address: www.umcno.org
Control: Other not–for–profit (including NFP Corporation) **Service:** General medical and surgical

Staffed Beds: 298 **Admissions:** 13436 **Census:** 230 **Outpatient Visits:** 355435 **Births:** 0 **Total Expense ($000):** 598612 **Payroll Expense ($000):** 134359 **Personnel:** 1937

NEW ROADS—Pointe Coupee Parish

★ **POINTE COUPEE GENERAL HOSPITAL (191316)**, 2202 False River Drive, Zip 70760–2614; tel. 225/638–6331, **A**10 18 **F**3 40 45 64 75 77 81 87 93 107 111 119 128 129 130 133 146 148 154
Primary Contact: Chad E. Olinde, CPA, Administrator and Chief Executive Officer
CFO: John Cazayoux, Chief Financial Officer
CMO: Paul Rachal, M.D., Chief Medical Officer
CIO: Anthony Sauro, Chief Information Officer
CHR: Lisa Patterson, Director Human Resources
CNO: Valerie Sparks Jarreau, R.N., Chief Nursing Officer
Web address: www.pcgh.org
Control: Hospital district or authority, Government, nonfederal **Service:** General medical and surgical

Staffed Beds: 25 **Admissions:** 236 **Census:** 2 **Outpatient Visits:** 49646 **Births:** 0 **Total Expense ($000):** 16483 **Payroll Expense ($000):** 7370 **Personnel:** 184

OAK GROVE—West Carroll Parish

WEST CARROLL MEMORIAL HOSPITAL (190081), 706 Ross Street,
Zip 71263–9798; tel. 318/428–3237, (Nonreporting) **A**10
Primary Contact: R Randall. Morris, Administrator
Control: Other not–for–profit (including NFP Corporation) **Service:** General
medical and surgical

Staffed Beds: 21

OAKDALE—Allen Parish

☐ **OAKDALE COMMUNITY HOSPITAL (190106)**, 130 North Hospital
Drive, Zip 71463–3035, Mailing Address: P.O. Box 629, Zip 71463–0629;
tel. 318/335–3700, (Nonreporting) **A**1 10
Primary Contact: Patrick C. Robinson, M.D., Chief Executive Officer
CFO: Suzette Fatula, Chief Financial Officer
CMO: Tommy Davis, M.D., Chief of Staff
CIO: Sheri Dugas, Director Health Information Management
CHR: Becky Johnson, Director Human Resources
CNO: Kari Broussard, Chief Nursing Officer
Web address: www.oakdalecommunityhospital.com/
Control: Partnership, Investor–owned (for–profit) **Service:** General medical and
surgical

Staffed Beds: 27

OLLA—Caldwell Parish

HARDTNER MEDICAL CENTER (191315), 1102 North Pine Road,
Zip 71465–4804; tel. 318/495–3131, (Nonreporting) **A**10 18
Primary Contact: Paul G. Mathews, CPA, Administrator
CIO: Sarah Thompson, Director Health Information Management
CNO: Cherry B Salter, Director of Nursing
Web address: www.hardtnermedical.com
Control: Hospital district or authority, Government, nonfederal **Service:** General
medical and surgical

Staffed Beds: 35

OPELOUSAS—St. Landry Parish

☐ **OCEANS BEHAVIORAL HOSPITAL OF OPELOUSAS (194095)**, 1310 Heather
Drive, Zip 70570–7714; tel. 337/948–8820, (Nonreporting) **A**1 10 **S** Oceans
Healthcare, Lake Charles, LA
Primary Contact: Katherine Simoneaux, Administrator
Web address: www.obho.info/
Control: Corporation, Investor–owned (for–profit) **Service:** Psychiatric

Staffed Beds: 20

✠ **OPELOUSAS GENERAL HEALTH SYSTEM (190017)**, 539 East Prudhomme
Street, Zip 70570–6499, Mailing Address: P.O. Box 1389, Zip 70571–1389;
tel. 337/948–3011, (Includes OPELOUSAS GENERAL HEALTH SYSTEM–SOUTH
CAMPUS, 3983 I–49 South Service Road, Opelousas, LA, Zip 70570–8975;
tel. 337/948–2100; Kenneth Cochran, R.N., FACHE, President and Chief Executive
Officer) **A**1 2 10 19 **F**3 13 15 28 31 34 37 40 44 45 48 49 50 57 60 64 68 70
73 76 77 78 79 80 81 85 87 89 90 91 93 96 97 98 102 103 104 105 107 108
110 111 112 114 115 116 117 119 121 129 130 131 132 146 147 148 149
153 **P**6
Primary Contact: Kenneth Cochran, R.N., FACHE, President and Chief Executive
Officer
COO: Bob Hardy, Chief Operating Officer
CFO: James B Juneau, Chief Financial Officer
CMO: Hunt Deblanc, M.D., Chief of Staff
CIO: Jared Lormand, Vice President Information Technology
CHR: Suzanne F Kidder, Human Resources Officer
CNO: Kimberly Probus, Chief Nursing Officer
Web address: www.opelousasgeneral.com
Control: Other not–for–profit (including NFP Corporation) **Service:** General
medical and surgical

Staffed Beds: 201 Admissions: 6903 Census: 92 Outpatient Visits:
147263 Births: 1037 Total Expense ($000): 130566 Payroll Expense
($000): 45812 Personnel: 906

ST. LANDRY EXTENDED CARE HOSPITAL (192034), 3983 1–49 South

Service Road, 2nd Floor, Zip 70570; tel. 337/948–2251, (Nonreporting) **A**10 **S**
LHC Group, Lafayette, LA
Primary Contact: Biff David, R.N., Administrator
CNO: Shelia B. Johnson, Director of Nursing
Web address: www.lhcgroup.com
Control: Corporation, Investor–owned (for–profit) **Service:** Acute long–term care
hospital

Staffed Beds: 41

PINEVILLE—Rapides Parish

✠ **ALEXANDRIA VETERANS AFFAIRS HEALTH CARE SYSTEM**, 2495 Shreveport
Highway, 71 N, Zip 71360–4044, Mailing Address: P.O. Box 69004, Alexandria,
Zip 71306–9004; tel. 318/473–0010, (Nonreporting) **A**1 5 **S** Department of
Veterans Affairs, Perry Point, MD
Primary Contact: Peter C. Dancy Jr, Director
CFO: Bianca A. Obey, Chief Financial Officer
CMO: Robert Bernard, M.D., Chief of Staff
CIO: Robin McBryde, Chief Information Officer
CHR: Alex Love, Acting Manager Human Resources
CNO: Amy Lesniewski, Associate Director Patient Care Services
Web address: www.alexandria.va.gov/
Control: Veterans Affairs, Government, federal **Service:** General medical and
surgical

Staffed Beds: 143

☐ **CENTRAL LOUISIANA STATE HOSPITAL (194025)**, 242 West Shamrock
Avenue, Zip 71360–6439, Mailing Address: P.O. Box 5031, Zip 71361–5031;
tel. 318/484–6200, (Nonreporting) **A**1 10 **S** Louisiana State Hospitals, Baton
Rouge, LA
Primary Contact: Ronald G. Williams, Administrator
COO: Paul Benoit, Associate Administrator
CFO: Tina Darbonne, Chief Financial Officer
CMO: L Lee Tynes, M.D., Ph.D., Jr Medical Director
CIO: William Haynes, Director Information Technology
CHR: Tom Crout, MS, Director Human Resources
Web address: www.dhh.louisiana.gov/index.cfm/directory/detail/217
Control: State, Government, nonfederal **Service:** Psychiatric

Staffed Beds: 120

VETERANS AFFAIRS MEDICAL CENTER – ALEXANDRIA See Alexandria
Veterans Affairs Health Care System

PLAQUEMINE—Iberville Parish

ACCORD REHABILIATION HOSPITAL (193070), 59213 Riverwest Drive,
Zip 70764–6552; tel. 225/687–8100, (Nonreporting) **A**10
Primary Contact: Julene Mcalister, Administrator
Web address: www.mmoinc.com
Control: Other not–for–profit (including NFP Corporation) **Service:** Rehabilitation

Staffed Beds: 8

RACELAND—Lafourche Parish

✠ **OCHSNER ST. ANNE GENERAL HOSPITAL (191324)**, 4608 Highway 1,
Zip 70394–2623; tel. 985/537–6841, **A**1 10 18 **F**3 4 13 15 17 18 29 34 35 38
40 44 57 59 64 65 70 74 75 76 77 81 85 86 87 89 98 100 101 102 103 104
107 108 110 111 114 118 119 130 133 146 147 **S** Ochsner Health System,
New Orleans, LA
Primary Contact: Timothy J. Allen, FACHE, Chief Executive Officer
COO: Fernis LeBlanc, Chief Operating Officer
CNO: Jana Semere, Chief Nursing Officer
Web address: www.ochsner.org/locations/ochsner–st–anne
Control: Other not–for–profit (including NFP Corporation) **Service:** General
medical and surgical

Staffed Beds: 35 Admissions: 1940 Census: 18 Outpatient Visits: 81369
Births: 335 Total Expense ($000): 50860 Payroll Expense ($000): 16669
Personnel: 473

Hospital, Medicare Provider Number, Address, Telephone, Approval, Facility, and Physician Codes, Health Care System

★ American Hospital Association (AHA) membership ○ Healthcare Facilities Accreditation Program ⇧ Center for Improvement in Healthcare Quality Accreditation
☐ The Joint Commission accreditation ◇ DNV Healthcare Inc. accreditation △ Commission on Accreditation of Rehabilitation Facilities (CARF) accreditation

LA

RAYNE—Acadia Parish

☐ **OCEANS BEHAVIORAL HOSPITAL OF CROWLEY (194097)**, 2021 Crowley Rayne Highway, Zip 70578–4027; tel. 337/788–0091, (Nonreporting) **A**1 10
Primary Contact: Katherine Simoneaux, Administrator
Control: Corporation, Investor–owned (for–profit) **Service:** Psychiatric

Staffed Beds: 16

RAYVILLE—Richland Parish

RICHARDSON MEDICAL CENTER (190151), 254 Highway 3048 Christian Drive, Zip 71269–0388, Mailing Address: P.O. Box 388, Zip 71269–0388; tel. 318/728–4181, **A**10 **F**17 18 20 29 34 40 45 48 50 53 56 57 59 65 70 71 77 81 83 93 97 103 104 107 108 110 111 119 127 129 130 133 146 147 154 **P**5
Primary Contact: James W. Barrett Jr, Chief Executive Officer
CFO: Mallory Gulley Wells, CPA, Chief Financial Officer
CMO: David Thompson, M.D., Chief of Staff
CHR: Rita Brown, Director Human Resources
CNO: Earlene Chriceol, Chief Nursing Officer
Web address: www.richardsonmed.org
Control: Hospital district or authority, Government, nonfederal **Service:** General medical and surgical

Staffed Beds: 38 **Admissions:** 805 **Census:** 9 **Outpatient Visits:** 51320 **Births:** 0 **Personnel:** 206

RUSTON—Lincoln Parish

LIBERTY HEALTHCARE SYSTEMS See Serenity Springs Specialty Hospital

✠ **NORTHERN LOUISIANA MEDICAL CENTER (190086)**, 401 East Vaughn Avenue, Zip 71270–5950; tel. 318/254–2100, (Includes GREEN CLINIC SURGICAL HOSPITAL, 1118 Farmerville Street, Ruston, LA, Zip 71270–5914; tel. 318/232–7700; Chad Conner, Administrator) (Nonreporting) **A**1 10 19 **S** Community Health Systems, Inc., Franklin, TN
Primary Contact: Keith Newton, Interim Chief Executive Officer
CFO: Michael Lockridge, Chief Financial Officer
CMO: Derek McClusky, M.D., Chief of Staff
CIO: Heather Nolan, Director Information Services
CHR: Tonya Duggan, Director Human Resources
CNO: Hartland Hintze, Chief Nursing Officer
Web address: www.northernlouisianamedicalcenter.com
Control: Other not–for–profit (including NFP Corporation) **Service:** General medical and surgical

Staffed Beds: 104

✠ **RUSTON REGIONAL SPECIALTY HOSPITAL (192022)**, 1401 Ezell Street, Zip 71270–7218; tel. 318/251–3126, (Nonreporting) **A**1 10
Primary Contact: Mark J. Rice, Administrator
Web address: www.lifecare-hospitals.com/hospital.php?id=19
Control: Corporation, Investor–owned (for–profit) **Service:** Acute long–term care hospital

Staffed Beds: 55

SERENITY SPRINGS SPECIALTY HOSPITAL (194074), 1495 Frazier Road, Zip 71270–1632; tel. 318/202–3860, (Nonreporting) **A**10
Primary Contact: Adrian Williams, Chief Executive Officer
Web address: www.serenityhospital.com
Control: Corporation, Investor–owned (for–profit) **Service:** Psychiatric

Staffed Beds: 18

SAINT FRANCISVILLE—West Feliciana Parish

✠ **WEST FELICIANA PARISH HOSPITAL (191306)**, 5266 Commerce Street, Zip 70775, Mailing Address: P.O. Box 368, Zip 70775–0368; tel. 225/635–3811, **A**1 10 18 **F**3 7 15 34 40 57 59 68 77 93 97 107 110 111 114 115 119 128 129 133 143 148 149 153 154 **P**5 6
Primary Contact: Lee Chastant, Chief Executive Officer
CFO: Linda Harvey, Chief Financial Officer
CHR: Neta F Leake, Administrative Assistant Human Resources
CNO: Angela Noble, Director of Nursing
Web address: www.wfph.org
Control: Hospital district or authority, Government, nonfederal **Service:** General medical and surgical

Staffed Beds: 12 **Admissions:** 49 **Census:** 1 **Outpatient Visits:** 23687 **Births:** 0 **Total Expense ($000):** 19362 **Payroll Expense ($000):** 7424 **Personnel:** 164

SHREVEPORT—Caddo Parish

☐ **BRENTWOOD HOSPITAL (194020)**, 1006 Highland Avenue, Zip 71101–4103; tel. 318/678–7500, **A**1 3 10 **F**4 5 29 35 38 56 87 98 99 100 102 103 104 105 135 151 152 153 154 **P**6 **S** Universal Health Services, Inc., King of Prussia, PA
Primary Contact: William Weaver, Chief Executive Officer
COO: Charles Lee, Director Clinical Operations
CFO: Kae Bell, Chief Financial Officer
CMO: Colonel Daniel Feeney, M.D., Medical Director
CHR: Talicia Johnson, Director Human Resources
CNO: Ravon Dominique, Chief Nursing Officer
Web address: www.brentwoodbehavioral.com
Control: State, Government, nonfederal **Service:** Psychiatric

Staffed Beds: 176 **Admissions:** 6228 **Census:** 159 **Outpatient Visits:** 11657 **Births:** 0 **Total Expense ($000):** 29419 **Payroll Expense ($000):** 14961 **Personnel:** 343

✠ **CHRISTUS HEALTH SHREVEPORT–BOSSIER (190041)**, 1453 East Bert Kouns Industrial Loop, Zip 71105–6800; tel. 318/681–5000, (Includes CHRISTUS BOSSIER EMERGENCY HOSPITAL, 2531 Viking Drive, Bossier City, LA, Zip 71111; tel. 318/681–7000; Jennifer Varnadore, Administrator; CHRISTUS HIGHLAND MEDICAL CENTER, 1453 East Bert Kouns Industrial Loop, Shreveport, LA, Zip 71105–6050; tel. 318/681–5000; Isaac Palmer, Chief Executive Officer) **A**1 2 5 10 **F**3 11 12 13 15 17 18 20 22 24 26 28 29 30 31 32 34 35 40 45 46 47 48 49 50 53 54 55 56 57 58 59 61 64 70 72 73 74 75 76 77 78 79 80 81 82 84 85 86 87 90 93 96 97 102 107 108 110 111 114 115 119 120 121 123 124 126 130 131 132 134 135 146 147 148 149 **S** CHRISTUS Health, Irving, TX
Primary Contact: Isaac Palmer, Chief Executive Officer
COO: Joshua Lamb, Vice President Operations
CFO: Scott Merryman, Chief Financial Officer
CMO: Marisa Johnson, M.D., Vice President Medical Affairs
CIO: Mary Merryman, Regional Director Information Management
CHR: Wendy Chandler, Vice President Human Resources
CNO: Ginger Disante, Chief Nursing Executive
Web address: www.christushealthsb.org
Control: Church operated, Nongovernment, not–for–profit **Service:** General medical and surgical

Staffed Beds: 185 **Admissions:** 8492 **Census:** 107 **Outpatient Visits:** 111484 **Births:** 921 **Total Expense ($000):** 184385 **Payroll Expense ($000):** 51961 **Personnel:** 837

★ **LIFECARE HOSPITALS OF SHREVEPORT–WILLIS KNIGHTON (192011)**, 8001 Youree Drive, Zip 71115–2302; tel. 318/212–2200, (Includes LIFECARE HOSPITALS OF SOUTH SHREVEPORT–WILLIS KNIGHTON NORTH, 2550 Kings Highway, Shreveport, LA, Zip 71103–3922; tel. 318/681–7000; Keith Cox, Chief Executive Officer and Administrator) (Nonreporting)
Primary Contact: Brent Martin, Administrator
Web address: www.lifecarehealthpartners.com/region/shreveport
Control: Corporation, Investor–owned (for–profit) **Service:** Acute long–term care hospital

Staffed Beds: 30

✠ **OVERTON BROOKS VETERANS AFFAIRS MEDICAL CENTER**, 510 East Stoner Avenue, Zip 71101–4295; tel. 318/221–8411, (Nonreporting) **A**1 2 3 5 **S** Department of Veterans Affairs, Perry Point, MD
Primary Contact: Richard Crockett, Director
CFO: Kim Lane, Chief Fiscal Service
CIO: Janey Taylor, Chief Information and Technology
CHR: Michael L Palmier, Chief Human Resources Management
Web address: www.shreveport.va.gov/
Control: Veterans Affairs, Government, federal **Service:** General medical and surgical

Staffed Beds: 100

PHYSICIANS BEHAVIORAL HOSPITAL (194094), 2025 Desoto Street, Zip 71103–4717; tel. 318/550–0520, (Nonreporting) **A**10
Primary Contact: Allison Cooper, Administrator
Control: Corporation, Investor–owned (for–profit) **Service:** Psychiatric

Staffed Beds: 24

☐ **PROMISE HOSPITAL OF LOUISIANA – SHREVEPORT CAMPUS (192010)**, 1800 Irving Place, Zip 71101–4608; tel. 318/425–4096, (Includes PROMISE HOSPITAL OF LOUISIANA – BOSSIER CITY CAMPUS, 2525 Viking Drive, Bossier City, LA, Zip 71111–2103; tel. 318/841–2525) (Nonreporting) **A**1 3 10 **S** Promise Healthcare, Boca Raton, FL
Primary Contact: Rick Stockton, Chief Executive Officer
Web address: www.promise–shreveport.com
Control: Corporation, Investor–owned (for–profit) **Service:** Acute long–term care hospital

Staffed Beds: 146

PROMISE SPECIALTY HOSPITAL OF SHREVEPORT See Promise Hospital of Louisiana – Shreveport Campus

☐ **SHRINERS HOSPITALS FOR CHILDREN–SHREVEPORT (193301)**, 3100 Samford Avenue, Zip 71103–4289; tel. 318/222–5704, **A**1 3 5 10 **F**34 50 55 59 64 68 77 79 81 85 89 93 94 119 130 131 146 154 **S** Shriners Hospitals for Children, Tampa, FL
Primary Contact: Garry Kim. Green, FACHE, Administrator
CFO: Clarissa Brown–Smith, Director Fiscal Services
CMO: John A. Fox, M.D., Chief of Staff
CIO: Michael Lyons, Regional Information Systems Director
CHR: Rena Arbuthnot, Director Human Resources
CNO: Kathleen A. Redler, Director Patient Care Services
Web address: www.shrinershospitalsforchildren.org/Hospitals/Locations/Shreveport.aspx
Control: Other not–for–profit (including NFP Corporation) **Service:** Children's orthopedic

Staffed Beds: 45 **Admissions:** 249 **Census:** 2 **Outpatient Visits:** 15148 **Births:** 0 **Personnel:** 202

SPECIALISTS HOSPITAL – SHREVEPORT (190278), 1500 Line Avenue, Zip 71101–4639; tel. 318/213–3800, (Nonreporting) **A**10
Primary Contact: Kandi Moore, Administrator
CFO: Daniel Montgomery, Chief Financial Officer
CNO: Mary Virginia Loftus, Chief Nursing Officer
Web address: www.specialistshospitalshreveport.com/
Control: Corporation, Investor–owned (for–profit) **Service:** Orthopedic

Staffed Beds: 15

UNIVERSITY HEALTH SHREVEPORT (190098), 1501 Kings Highway, Zip 71103–4228, Mailing Address: Zip 71130–3932, Zip 71130–3932; tel. 318/675–5000, (Includes CHILDREN'S HOSPITAL OF SHREVEPORT, 1501 Kings Highway, Shreveport, LA, Zip 71103–4228, Mailing Address: PO Box 33932, Zip 71130–3932, tel. 318/675–5000) **A**2 3 5 10 **F**3 13 15 16 18 19 20 21 22 23 24 25 26 27 29 30 31 32 34 39 40 41 47 48 49 50 51 54 59 60 61 64 65 66 70 72 73 75 76 77 78 79 81 82 85 87 88 89 93 98 102 104 107 108 109 110 111 112 114 115 116 117 118 119 120 121 123 126 129 130 131 135 136 146 147 148 149 154 **P**1 **S** University Health System, Shreveport, LA
Primary Contact: Mark Randolph, President
COO: Betty Johnson, Associate Administrator
CFO: Harold White, Vice Chancellor
CMO: Kevin Sittig, M.D., Senior Associate Dean and Chief Medical Officer
CIO: Marcus Hobgood, Director Information Services
CHR: David Fuqua, Director Human Resources Management
Web address: www.lsuhscshreveport.edu
Control: Other not–for–profit (including NFP Corporation) **Service:** General medical and surgical

Staffed Beds: 386 **Admissions:** 16334 **Census:** 290 **Outpatient Visits:** 391102 **Births:** 1561 **Total Expense ($000):** 482396 **Payroll Expense ($000):** 145009 **Personnel:** 2413

⊠ △ **WILLIS–KNIGHTON MEDICAL CENTER (190111)**, 2600 Greenwood Road, Zip 71103–3908, Mailing Address: P.O. Box 32600, Zip 71130–2600; tel. 318/212–4600, (Includes WILLIS–KNIGHTON PIERREMONT HEALTH CENTER, 8001 Youree Drive, Shreveport, LA, Zip 71115; tel. 318/212–3000; WILLIS–KNIGHTON SOUTH – THE CENTER FOR WOMEN'S HEALTH, 2510 Bert Kouns Industrial Loop, Shreveport, LA, Zip 71118; tel. 318/212–5000; Keri Elrod, Administrator; WK BOSSIER HEALTH CENTER, 2400 Hospital Drive, Bossier City, LA, Zip 71111–2385; tel. 318/212–7000; Todd Blanchard, Administrator) (Total facility includes 155 beds in nursing home–type unit) **A**1 2 3 5 7 10 **F**3 4 5 7 8 12 13 15 18 20 22 24 26 28 29 30 31 32 33 34 35 39 40 44 45 46 47 48 49 50 51 52 53 54 55 56 57 58 59 60 62 63 64 65 66 68 70 72 74 75 76 77 78 79 81 82 84 85 86 87 88 89 90 91 92 93 94 96 97 98 100 101 102 103 104 105 107 108 109 110 111 112 114 115 116 117 118 119 120 121 122 123 124 125 126 127 128 129 130 131 132 134 135 138 139 142 143 144 145 147 148 149 152 153 **P**7 **S** Willis–Knighton Health System, Shreveport, LA
Primary Contact: James K. Elrod, FACHE, Chief Executive Officer
CMO: Dan Moller, M.D., Chief Medical Officer
CHR: Mike Chandler, Administrator
CNO: Debbie D Olds, R.N., MSN, Director of Nursing
Web address: www.wkhs.com
Control: Other not–for–profit (including NFP Corporation) **Service:** General medical and surgical

Staffed Beds: 799 **Admissions:** 51365 **Census:** 590 **Outpatient Visits:** 782985 **Births:** 3280 **Personnel:** 5926

NORTHSHORE REGIONAL MEDICAL CENTER See Ochsner Medical Center – North Shore

⊠ **OCHSNER MEDICAL CENTER – NORTH SHORE (190204)**, 100 Medical Center Drive, Zip 70461–5520; tel. 985/649–7070, **A**1 10 **F**3 12 15 18 24 29 30 31 32 34 35 38 40 41 44 45 46 49 50 51 57 59 60 61 64 68 70 74 75 77 78 79 81 84 85 86 87 88 89 90 91 93 95 96 97 102 107 108 110 111 117 118 119 126 130 132 135 146 147 148 **S** Ochsner Health System, New Orleans, LA
Primary Contact: John William Bill"". Davis, Chief Executive Officer
CFO: Forrest Whichard, Chief Financial Officer
CMO: James Newcomb, M.D., Vice President Medical
CHR: Terri Joseph–Taylor, Chief Human Resource Manager
CNO: Cheryl Woods, Chief Nursing Officer
Web address: www.ochsner.org/locations/ochsner–medical–center–north–shore/
Control: Other not–for–profit (including NFP Corporation) **Service:** General medical and surgical

Staffed Beds: 168 **Admissions:** 5147 **Census:** 60 **Outpatient Visits:** 90103 **Births:** 0 **Total Expense ($000):** 88419 **Payroll Expense ($000):** 35697 **Personnel:** 556

⊠ **SLIDELL MEMORIAL HOSPITAL (190040)**, 1001 Gause Boulevard, Zip 70458–2987; tel. 985/280–2200, **A**1 2 3 5 10 **F**3 11 13 15 17 18 20 22 24 26 28 29 30 31 32 34 35 40 45 47 49 54 56 57 59 62 64 65 70 72 75 76 78 79 81 82 85 86 87 90 91 93 96 97 102 107 108 110 111 114 115 116 117 118 119 120 121 124 129 130 132 135 154 **S** Ochsner Health System, New Orleans, LA
Primary Contact: John William Bill"". Davis, Chief Executive Officer
COO: Bruce Clement, Chief Operating Officer
CFO: Sandy Badinger, Chief Financial Officer
CMO: James Newcomb, M.D., Vice President Medical Affairs
CNO: Lynn Strain, R.N., MSN, Chief Nursing Officer
Web address: www.slidellmemorial.org
Control: Hospital district or authority, Government, nonfederal **Service:** General medical and surgical

Staffed Beds: 175 **Admissions:** 8749 **Census:** 92 **Outpatient Visits:** 146994 **Births:** 1203 **Total Expense ($000):** 186557 **Payroll Expense ($000):** 73951 **Personnel:** 1085

☐ **SOUTHERN SURGICAL HOSPITAL (190270)**, 1700 Lindberg Drive, Zip 70458–8062; tel. 985/641–0600, **A**1 10 **F**8 12 18 26 29 34 35 37 45 47 51 57 59 60 64 68 74 75 79 81 82 85 86 87 107 111 112 114 119 126 130 131 132 135 **P**2 7 8
Primary Contact: Michael J. Pisciotta, Chief Executive Officer
CFO: Michael J Maurin, Chief Financial Officer
CMO: J Gosey, M.D., Medical Director
CIO: Buddy Graves, Chief Information Officer
CHR: Lorrie Alfred, Director Human Resources
Web address: www.sshla.com/
Control: Corporation, Investor–owned (for–profit) **Service:** General medical and surgical

Staffed Beds: 37 **Admissions:** 1333 **Census:** 12 **Outpatient Visits:** 5210 **Births:** 0 **Total Expense ($000):** 24550 **Payroll Expense ($000):** 8500 **Personnel:** 108

STERLING SURGICAL HOSPITAL (190256), 989 Robert Boulevard, Zip 70458–2009; tel. 985/690–8200, (Nonreporting) **A**10
Primary Contact: Christopher W. Daniel, Administrator
Web address: www.sterlingsurgical.net/
Control: Corporation, Investor–owned (for–profit) **Service:** Surgical

Staffed Beds: 10

☐ **SPRINGHILL MEDICAL CENTER (190088)**, 2001 Doctors Drive, Zip 71075–4526, Mailing Address: P.O. Box 920, Zip 71075–0920; tel. 318/539–1000, **A**1 10 20 **F**15 18 29 30 34 35 40 45 47 48 49 50 56 57 59 64 65 66 68 70 75 77 81 82 85 86 87 89 93 97 98 103 107 108 110 111 114 119 127 129 130 131 133 135 146 147 148 149 154 **P**6 **S** Willis–Knighton Health System, Shreveport, LA
Primary Contact: Vince Sedminik, Chief Executive Officer
COO: Dana R. Jones, R.N., MSN, Chief Nursing Officer and Chief Operating Officer
CFO: David Sanders, Chief Financial Officer
CMO: Jerry W. Sessions, M.D., Chief Medical Staff
CIO: Brian Griffin, Director Information Services
CHR: Ashley Ortego, Director Human Resources and Marketing
CNO: Dana R. Jones, R.N., MSN, Chief Nursing Officer and Chief Operating Officer
Web address: www.smccare.com
Control: Other not–for–profit (including NFP Corporation) **Service:** General medical and surgical

Staffed Beds: 32 **Admissions:** 1010 **Census:** 13 **Outpatient Visits:** 63935 **Births:** 0

Hospital, Medicare Provider Number, Address, Telephone, Approval, Facility, and Physician Codes, Health Care System

★ American Hospital Association (AHA) membership
☐ The Joint Commission accreditation
○ Healthcare Facilities Accreditation Program
◇ DNV Healthcare Inc. accreditation
⇑ Center for Improvement in Healthcare Quality Accreditation
△ Commission on Accreditation of Rehabilitation Facilities (CARF) accreditation

LA

SULPHUR—Calcasieu Parish

☐ **CORNERSTONE HOSPITAL OF SOUTHWEST LOUISIANA (192013)**, 703 Cypress Street, Zip 70663–5053; tel. 337/310–6000, (Nonreporting) **A**1 10 **S** Cornerstone Healthcare Group, Dallas, TX
Primary Contact: Jeffrey Clark, Chief Executive Officer
CFO: Amy Bryant, Chief Financial Officer
Web address: www.chghospitals.com/sulphur/
Control: Partnership, Investor–owned (for–profit) **Service:** Acute long–term care hospital

Staffed Beds: 30

☐ **WEST CALCASIEU CAMERON HOSPITAL (190013)**, 701 Cypress Street, Zip 70663–5000, Mailing Address: P.O. Box 2509, Zip 70664–2509; tel. 337/527–7034, **A**1 10 **F**3 7 8 11 13 15 18 20 22 26 28 29 30 31 34 35 37 38 40 44 45 46 50 51 53 54 57 59 62 65 68 70 75 76 77 78 79 81 85 86 87 89 91 93 94 96 97 100 108 110 111 114 115 118 119 127 129 130 132 134 135 141 145 146 147 148 149 154
Primary Contact: Janie Fruge, R.N., MSN, FACHE, Chief Executive Officer
CFO: Jobie James, Chief Financial Officer
CIO: Trey Rion, Chief Information Officer
CHR: Christi Kingsley, Vice President Human Resources
CNO: Brenda Quesnel, R.N., Vice President of Patient Care and Chief Nursing Officer
Web address: www.wcch.com
Control: Hospital district or authority, Government, nonfederal **Service:** General medical and surgical

Staffed Beds: 79 Admissions: 2729 Census: 27 Outpatient Visits: 138171 Births: 321 Total Expense ($000): 71939 Payroll Expense ($000): 30820 Personnel: 640

TALLULAH—Madison Parish

MADISON PARISH HOSPITAL (191314), 900 Johnson Street, Zip 71282–4537; tel. 318/574–2374, (Nonreporting) **A**10 18
Primary Contact: Ted Topolewski, Chief Executive Officer
CFO: W Robert Laurents, CPA, Chief Financial Officer
CIO: Charles Whitaker, Director Information Technology
CHR: Chasity Whitaker, Administrative Assistant
Web address: www.madisonparishhospital.com
Control: Other not–for–profit (including NFP Corporation) **Service:** General medical and surgical

Staffed Beds: 25

THIBODAUX—Lafourche Parish

✠ △ **THIBODAUX REGIONAL MEDICAL CENTER (190004)**, 602 North Acadia Road, Zip 70301–4847, Mailing Address: P.O. Box 1118, Zip 70302–1118; tel. 985/447–5500, **A**1 2 7 10 **F**3 8 11 12 13 15 18 19 20 22 24 28 29 30 31 32 34 39 40 46 49 50 53 57 59 62 64 70 73 74 75 76 78 79 81 82 85 86 87 89 90 92 93 96 97 98 103 104 107 108 110 111 115 116 117 119 120 121 123 124 126 127 129 130 131 132 134 135 146 147 148 149 153
Primary Contact: Greg K. Stock, FACHE, Chief Executive Officer
COO: Scott Flowers, Vice President Professional Services
CFO: Steve C Gaubert, Chief Financial Officer
CMO: Allen Vander, M.D., Chief Medical Staff
CIO: Bernie Clement, Chief Information Officer
CHR: Eric Degravelle, Director Human Resources
Web address: www.thibodaux.com
Control: Hospital district or authority, Government, nonfederal **Service:** General medical and surgical

Staffed Beds: 154 Admissions: 7618 Census: 88 Outpatient Visits: 186836 Births: 1095 Total Expense ($000): 172406 Payroll Expense ($000): 67684 Personnel: 1087

VIDALIA—Concordia Parish

☐ **PROMISE HOSPITAL OF MISS LOU (192028)**, 209 Front Street, Zip 71373–2837; tel. 318/336–6500, (Nonreporting) **A**1 10 **S** Promise Healthcare, Boca Raton, FL
Primary Contact: Michael Harrell, R.N., Chief Executive Officer
COO: Howard B Koslow, President and Chief Executive Officer
CFO: James Hopwood, Chief Financial Officer
CMO: Randy Tillman, M.D., Chief Medical Staff
CIO: Robert Greene, Director Information Technology
CHR: Roxan Houghton, Director Human Resources
CNO: Regetta Woods, Chief Nursing Officer and Chief Clinical Officer
Web address: www.promise–misslou.com
Control: Corporation, Investor–owned (for–profit) **Service:** Acute long–term care hospital

Staffed Beds: 40

VILLE PLATTE—Evangeline Parish

✠ **MERCY REGIONAL MEDICAL CENTER (190167)**, 800 East Main Street, Zip 70586–4618; tel. 337/363–5684, (Includes ACADIAN MEDICAL CENTER, 3501 Highway 190, Eunice, LA, Zip 70535–5129; tel. 337/580–7500; Calvin Green, Chief Executive Officer) (Nonreporting) **A**1 10 **S** Allegiance Health Management, Shreveport, LA
Primary Contact: Calvin Green, Chief Executive Officer
CFO: Janice G Jones, Interim Chief Financial Officer, Controller and Compliance Officer
CMO: Zebediah Stearns, M.D., Chief of Staff
CIO: Courtney Bieber, Director Information Systems
CHR: Cody Ardoin, Director Human Resources
CNO: Sandy Morein, Chief Nursing Officer
Web address: www.mercyregionalmedicalcenter.com
Control: Corporation, Investor–owned (for–profit) **Service:** General medical and surgical

Staffed Beds: 109

VIVIAN—Caddo Parish

NORTH CADDO MEDICAL CENTER (191304), 815 South Pine Street, Zip 71082–3353, Mailing Address: P.O. Box 792, Zip 71082–0792; tel. 318/375–3235, (Nonreporting) **A**3 5 10 18
Primary Contact: David C. Jones, Administrator
CFO: Dakota Robinson, Interim Chief Financial Officer and Controller
CMO: John H Haynes, M.D., Jr Chief of Medical Staff
Web address: www.ncmcla.com/
Control: Hospital district or authority, Government, nonfederal **Service:** General medical and surgical

Staffed Beds: 27

WEST MONROE—Ouachita Parish

ALLEGIANCE BEHAVIORAL HEALTH CENTERS OF MONROE (194087), 222 Bell Lane, Suite 3, Zip 71291–6302; tel. 318/329–2174, (Includes ALLEGIANCE HEALTH CENTER OF RUSTON, 1401 Ezell Street, Ruston, LA, Zip 71270–7218; tel. 318/255–8085; Chris Young, Chief Executive Officer) (Nonreporting)
Primary Contact: Chris Young, Chief Executive Officer
Web address: www.ahmgt.com
Control: Corporation, Investor–owned (for–profit) **Service:** Psychiatric

Staffed Beds: 38

CORNERSTONE HOSPITAL–WEST MONROE (192031), 6198 Cypress Street, Zip 71291–9010; tel. 318/396–5600, (Nonreporting) **A**10 22 **S** Cornerstone Healthcare Group, Dallas, TX
Primary Contact: Chris Simpson, Chief Executive Officer
COO: Jay Quintana, Vice President Operations
CFO: Kurt Schultz, Chief Financial Officer
CMO: Khaled Shafici, M.D., President Medical Staff
CIO: Adam Davis, Chief Information Officer
CHR: Dan Perkins, Corporate Director Human Resources
Web address: www.chghospitals.com/chwm.html
Control: Corporation, Investor–owned (for–profit) **Service:** Acute long–term care hospital

Staffed Beds: 40

⇑ **GLENWOOD REGIONAL MEDICAL CENTER (190160)**, 503 McMillan Road, Zip 71291–5327; tel. 318/329–4200, (Includes GLENWOOD SURGERY CENTER, 1275 Glenwood Drive, West Monroe, LA, Zip 71291–5539, Mailing Address: 503 McMillan Road, Zip 71291–5327; tel. 318/322–1339; Jeremy Tinnerello, MSN, R.N., Chief Executive Officer, Chief Operating Officer) (Total facility includes 14 beds in nursing home–type unit) **A**10 21 **F**3 8 12 13 15 17 18 20 22 24 26 28 29 30 31 34 35 37 38 40 41 45 46 47 48 49 50 51 54 55 56 57 58 59 60 61 62 63 64 68 70 71 72 74 75 76 78 79 81 82 83 84 85 86 87 89 90 91 92 93 94 96 97 98 100 101 102 103 104 107 108 110 111 113 114 115 116 117 119 120 121 126 128 129 130 131 132 134 146 147 148 149 153 154 **S** Steward Health Care System, LLC, Dallas, TX
Primary Contact: Jeremy M. Tinnerello, CEN, MSN, RN, President
COO: Jeremy M. Tinnerello, CEN, MSN, RN, President
CFO: Lisa Bradley, CPA, Chief Financial Officer
CMO: Steve McMahan, M.D., Chief Medical Officer
CIO: Ronnie Maxwell, Director Information Systems
CHR: Jan Walker, Director Human Resources
CNO: Lori Mathieu, MSN, Chief Nursing Officer
Web address: www.grmc.com
Control: Corporation, Investor–owned (for–profit) **Service:** General medical and surgical

Staffed Beds: 278 Admissions: 12538 Census: 180 Outpatient Visits: 64939 Births: 766 Personnel: 907

Many Facility Codes have changed. Please refer to the AHA Guide Code Chart. © 2018 AHA Guide

LOUISIANA EXTENDED CARE HOSPITAL WEST MONROE (192055), 503 McMillan Road, 3rd Floor, Zip 71291–5327; tel. 318/329–4378, (Nonreporting) **A**10 **S** LHC Group, Lafayette, LA
Primary Contact: Cleta Munholland, Administrator
COO: Pamela Chappell, R.N., Assistant Administrator
CNO: Shelly Nugent, R.N., Director Nurses and Infection Control
Control: Corporation, Investor–owned (for–profit) **Service**: Acute long–term care hospital

Staffed Beds: 18

WINNFIELD—Winn Parish

☐ **SPECIALTY HOSPITAL OF WINNFIELD (192052)**, 915 First Street, Zip 71483–2945; tel. 318/209–4507, (Nonreporting) **A**1 10
Primary Contact: Chuck Jurek, Interim Administrator and Chief Operating Officer
CFO: Chuck Jurek, Business Office Manager
CIO: Shamada Venzant, Manager Health Information
Control: Corporation, Investor–owned (for–profit) **Service**: Acute long–term care hospital

Staffed Beds: 20

WINN PARISH MEDICAL CENTER (190090), 301 West Boundary Street, Zip 71483–3427, Mailing Address: P.O. Box 152, Zip 71483–0152; tel. 318/648–3000, (Nonreporting) **A**10
Primary Contact: Bryan Bogle, Chief Executive Officer
CFO: Suzette Fatula, Chief Financial Officer
CMO: Mark Shelton, Chief of Staff
CHR: Ashley S Files, Director Human Resources and Public Relations and Marketing
CNO: Toby Wise, Chief Nursing Officer
Web address: www.winnparishmedical.com
Control: Partnership, Investor–owned (for–profit) **Service**: General medical and surgical

Staffed Beds: 60

WINNSBORO—Franklin Parish

FRANKLIN MEDICAL CENTER (190140), 2106 Loop Road, Zip 71295–3344, Mailing Address: P.O. Box 1300, Zip 71295–1300; tel. 318/435–9411, (Nonreporting) **A**3 10
Primary Contact: Blake Kramer, Chief Executive Officer
CFO: William E Page, CPA, Chief Financial Officer
CMO: Jay Busby, M.D., President Medical Staff
CIO: Judy Ogden, Director Information Technology
Web address: www.fmc–cares.com
Control: Hospital district or authority, Government, nonfederal **Service**: General medical and surgical

Staffed Beds: 43

ZACHARY—East Baton Rouge Parish

AMG SPECIALTY HOSPITAL–ZACHARY (192041), 4601 McHugh Road, Zip 70791–5348; tel. 225/683–1600, (Nonreporting) **A**10 **S** AMG Integrated Healthcare Management, Lafayette, LA
Primary Contact: April Ebeling, Chief Executive Officer
Web address: www.amgzachary.com/
Control: Corporation, Investor–owned (for–profit) **Service**: Acute long–term care hospital

Staffed Beds: 16

⊞ **LANE REGIONAL MEDICAL CENTER (190020)**, 6300 Main Street, Zip 70791–4037; tel. 225/658–4000, (Total facility includes 38 beds in nursing home–type unit) **A**1 10 **F**3 8 11 13 15 20 22 26 29 34 35 36 39 40 45 46 50 54 57 59 62 64 67 70 73 75 76 77 79 80 81 85 87 90 107 108 110 111 114 115 119 130 132 144 146 148 **P**6
Primary Contact: Larry Meese, Chief Executive Officer
COO: David Beck, Chief Operating Officer
CFO: Phil Hacker, Chief Financial Officer
CMO: Thomas Trahan, M.D., Chief of Medical Staff
CIO: Paul Murphy, Chief Information Officer
CNO: Staci Sullivan, R.N., Chief Nursing Officer
Web address: www.lanermc.org
Control: Hospital district or authority, Government, nonfederal **Service**: General medical and surgical

Staffed Beds: 179 Admissions: 4575 Census: 91 Outpatient Visits: 148640 Births: 439 Total Expense ($000): 90576 Payroll Expense ($000): 34291 Personnel: 701

MAINE

AUGUSTA—Kennebec County

MAINE VETERANS AFFAIRS MEDICAL CENTER, 1 VA Center, Zip 04330–6719; tel. 207/623–8411, **A**1 3 **F**3 5 18 20 28 29 30 31 34 35 36 38 39 40 44 45 53 54 56 57 58 59 60 61 62 63 64 65 66 68 70 71 74 75 77 78 79 81 82 83 84 85 87 93 94 97 98 100 102 104 105 107 108 111 114 115 118 119 127 129 130 132 135 143 146 147 148 149 153 154 **S** Department of Veterans Affairs, Perry Point, MD
Primary Contact: Ryan S. Lilly, Director
CFO: Daniel Howard, Chief Financial Officer
CMO: Timothy J Richardson, M.D., Chief of Staff
CIO: Richard McNaughton, Chief Information Management Service
CHR: Christine Miller, Chief Human Resources Management Services
Web address: www.maine.va.gov/
Control: Veterans Affairs, Government, federal **Service**: General medical and surgical

Staffed Beds: 167 **Admissions**: 2544 **Census**: 42 **Outpatient Visits**: 460895 **Births**: 0 **Total Expense ($000)**: 336744 **Payroll Expense ($000)**: 166130 **Personnel**: 1482

MAINEGENERAL MEDICAL CENTER (200039), 35 Medical Center Parkway, Zip 4330; tel. 207/626–1000, (Includes MAINEGENERAL MEDICAL CENTER–AUGUSTA CAMPUS, 35 Medical Center Parkway, Augusta, ME, Zip 04330–9988; tel. 207/626–1000; Chuck Hays, President and Chief Executive Officer) **A**1 2 3 10 19 **F**3 4 5 8 11 12 13 15 17 18 20 26 28 29 30 31 34 35 36 40 44 45 46 47 48 49 50 51 54 55 56 57 58 59 61 64 65 70 73 74 75 76 77 78 79 81 82 84 85 86 87 89 90 92 93 96 97 98 99 100 101 102 104 107 108 110 115 116 117 118 119 120 121 123 124 126 129 130 131 132 134 135 144 145 146 147 148 149 153 154 **P**6 8
Primary Contact: Chuck Hays, President and Chief Executive Officer
COO: Paul Stein, Chief Operating Officer
CFO: Terry Brann, Chief Financial Officer
CMO: Steve Diaz, M.D., Chief Medical Officer
CIO: Daniel Burgess, Chief Information Officer
CHR: Rebecca Lamey, Vice President Human Resources
CNO: Jennifer Riggs, R.N., Chief Nurse Officer
Web address: www.mainegeneral.org
Control: Other not–for–profit (including NFP Corporation) **Service**: General medical and surgical

Staffed Beds: 197 **Admissions**: 9319 **Census**: 156 **Outpatient Visits**: 766723 **Births**: 1009 **Total Expense ($000)**: 467732 **Payroll Expense ($000)**: 197505 **Personnel**: 3484

MAINEGENERAL MEDICAL CENTER–AUGUSTA CAMPUS See Mainegeneral Medical Center, Augusta

RIVERVIEW PSYCHIATRIC CENTER (204007), 250 Arsenal Street, Zip 04330–5742; tel. 207/624–3900, (Nonreporting) **A**1 10
Primary Contact: Rodney Bouffard, Superintendent
COO: David Lovejoy, Chief Operations Officer
CFO: Samantha Kavanaugh, Chief Financial Officer
CMO: Brendan Kirby, M.D., Medical Director
CHR: Aimee Rice, Human Resources Manager
CNO: Roland Pushard, Director of Nursing
Web address: www.state.me.us/dhhs/riverview
Control: State, Government, nonfederal **Service**: Psychiatric

Staffed Beds: 92

VETERANS AFFAIRS MEDICAL CENTER See Maine Veterans Affairs Medical Center

BANGOR—Penobscot County

DOROTHEA DIX PSYCHIATRIC CENTER (204004), 656 State Street, Zip 04401–5609, Mailing Address: P.O. Box 926, Zip 04402–0926; tel. 207/941–4000, **A**1 10 **F**98 104
Primary Contact: Carolyn Dimek, Acting Superintendent
CMO: Michelle Gardner, M.D., Clinical Director
CHR: Tamra Hanson, Human Resource Manager
CNO: Christine Bellatty, Acting Director of Nursing
Web address: www.maine.gov/dhhs/ddpc/index.shtml
Control: State, Government, nonfederal **Service**: Psychiatric

Staffed Beds: 45 **Admissions**: 86 **Census**: 43 **Outpatient Visits**: 156 **Births**: 0 **Total Expense ($000)**: 22063 **Payroll Expense ($000)**: 10631 **Personnel**: 200

EASTERN MAINE MEDICAL CENTER (200033), 489 State Street, Zip 04401–6674, Mailing Address: P.O. Box 404, Zip 04402–0404; tel. 207/973–7000, **A**1 2 3 5 10 13 **F**3 11 12 13 15 17 18 19 20 22 24 26 27 28 29 30 31 32 34 36 37 39 40 43 44 45 46 47 48 49 50 51 53 54 55 56 57 58 59 61 64 70 72 74 75 76 77 78 79 81 82 84 85 86 87 88 89 90 92 93 94 96 97 107 108 110 111 114 115 117 118 119 120 121 123 124 126 129 130 131 132 144 145 146 147 148 149 154 **P**6 **S** Eastern Maine Healthcare Systems, Brewer, ME
Primary Contact: Donna Russell–Cook, FACHE, President
CMO: James Raczek, M.D., Sr. Vice President of Operations and Chief Medical Officer
CIO: Catherine Bruno, FACHE, Chief Information Officer
CHR: Greg Howat, Vice President Human Resources
Web address: www.emh.org
Control: Other not–for–profit (including NFP Corporation) **Service**: General medical and surgical

Staffed Beds: 385 **Admissions**: 19985 **Census**: 300 **Outpatient Visits**: 617632 **Births**: 1837 **Total Expense ($000)**: 828216 **Payroll Expense ($000)**: 333248 **Personnel**: 3807

ST. JOSEPH HOSPITAL (200001), 360 Broadway, Zip 04401–3979, Mailing Address: P.O. Box 403, Zip 04402–0403; tel. 207/262–1000, **A**1 10 **F**3 8 15 18 29 30 31 35 40 45 46 48 49 51 55 56 57 62 64 70 75 77 81 82 84 85 86 87 97 107 108 110 111 114 118 119 129 130 132 135 145 146 147 148 149 154 **S** Covenant Health, Tewksbury, MA
Primary Contact: Mary Prybylo, President and Chief Executive Officer
CFO: Michael A. Hendrix Jr Chief Financial Officer
CMO: William Wood, M.D., Vice President Medical Affairs
CHR: Paige A Hagerstrom, System Director of Talent Management
CNO: Dianne Swandal, R.N., MSN, Vice President Patient Care
Web address: www.sjhhealth.com
Control: Church operated, Nongovernment, not–for–profit **Service**: General medical and surgical

Staffed Beds: 84 **Admissions**: 4124 **Census**: 48 **Outpatient Visits**: 137156 **Births**: 0 **Total Expense ($000)**: 138374 **Payroll Expense ($000)**: 58890 **Personnel**: 963

THE ACADIA HOSPITAL (204006), 268 Stillwater Avenue, Zip 04401–3945, Mailing Address: P.O. Box 422, Zip 04402–0422; tel. 207/973–6100, **A**1 10 **F**5 6 29 30 50 56 57 66 68 75 77 87 98 99 100 101 103 104 105 130 132 152 153 154 **P**6 **S** Eastern Maine Healthcare Systems, Brewer, ME
Primary Contact: Scott Oxley, President
CFO: Marie Suitter, Chief Financial Officer
CMO: Anthony Ng, M.D., Vice President and Chief Medical Officer
CIO: Jeanne Paradis, Director Information Services
CHR: Paul Bolin, Vice President and Chief Human Resources Officer
CNO: Wayne Steller, Vice President Chief Nursing Officer
Web address: www.acadiahospital.org
Control: Other not–for–profit (including NFP Corporation) **Service**: Psychiatric

Staffed Beds: 68 **Admissions**: 1357 **Census**: 62 **Outpatient Visits**: 118786 **Births**: 0 **Total Expense ($000)**: 54853 **Payroll Expense ($000)**: 30775 **Personnel**: 545

BAR HARBOR—Hancock County

★ **MOUNT DESERT ISLAND HOSPITAL (201304)**, 10 Wayman Lane, Zip 04609–1625, Mailing Address: P.O. Box 8, Zip 04609–0008; tel. 207/288–5081, **A**5 10 18 **F**3 5 6 10 11 13 15 28 29 31 34 35 36 39 40 50 54 56 57 59 64 65 70 74 75 76 77 78 79 81 82 84 85 87 91 92 93 97 99 100 101 104 107 108 111 114 119 125 127 130 131 132 133 135 145 146 147 **P**6
Primary Contact: Arthur J. Blank, President and Chief Executive Officer
CFO: Christina Harding, Vice President Finance
CMO: Stuart Davidson, President Medical Staff
CIO: Bruce Donlin, Director Information Services
CHR: Joanne Harris, Director Human Resources
CNO: Karen Mueller, R.N., Chief Nursing Officer
Web address: www.mdihospital.org
Control: Other not–for–profit (including NFP Corporation) **Service**: General medical and surgical

Staffed Beds: 25 **Admissions**: 835 **Census**: 8 **Outpatient Visits**: 184595 **Births**: 63 **Total Expense ($000)**: 55330 **Payroll Expense ($000)**: 23978 **Personnel**: 362

Many Facility Codes have changed. Please refer to the AHA Guide Code Chart. © 2018 AHA Guide

BELFAST—Waldo County

WALDO COUNTY GENERAL HOSPITAL MAINE HEALTH (201312), 118 Northport Avenue, Zip 04915–6072, Mailing Address: P.O. Box 287, Zip 04915–0287; tel. 207/338–2500, (Nonreporting) **A**10 18 **S** MaineHealth, Portland, ME
Primary Contact: Mark Fourre, Chief Executive Officer
CFO: Linda Drinkwater, Chief Financial Officer
CMO: Kent Clark, M.D., Chief Medical Affairs and Quality
CIO: David Felton, Manager Information Systems
CHR: Karen Littlefield, Director Human Resources
CNO: Paula Delahanty, Regional Chief Nursing Officer
Web address: www.wcgh.org
Control: Other not–for–profit (including NFP Corporation) **Service:** General medical and surgical

Staffed Beds: 25

BIDDEFORD—York County

✠ **SOUTHERN MAINE HEALTH CARE – BIDDEFORD MEDICAL CENTER (200019)**, One Medical Center Drive, Zip 04005–9496, Mailing Address: P.O. Box 626, Zip 04005–0626; tel. 207/283–7000, (Includes SOUTHERN MAINE HEALTH CARE – BIDDEFORD MEDICAL CENTER, One Medical Center Drive, Biddeford, ME, Zip 04005–9496, Mailing Address: P.O. Box 626, Zip 04005–0626, tel. 207/283–7000; Edward J McGeachey, President and Chief Executive Officer) (Total facility includes 112 beds in nursing home–type unit) **A**1 2 3 10 **F**5 6 8 10 11 12 13 15 18 20 22 26 28 29 30 31 33 34 35 40 44 45 46 49 50 54 56 57 59 61 64 65 68 70 74 75 76 77 78 79 81 82 84 86 87 89 93 97 98 100 102 104 105 107 108 110 111 117 119 128 129 130 131 132 135 144 146 147 148 149 154 **P**6
Primary Contact: Nathan Howell, Chief Executive Officer
COO: Patricia Aprile, Chief Operating Officer
CFO: Norman Belair, Senior Vice President and Chief Financial Officer
CMO: Michael Albaum, M.D., Senior Vice President and Chief Medical Officer
CIO: Ralph Johnson, Chief Information Officer
CHR: Yvonne McAllister, Senior Director Human Resources
CNO: Joanna Salamone, Senior Vice President Clinical Services and Chief Nursing Officer
Web address: www.smhc.org
Control: Other not–for–profit (including NFP Corporation) **Service:** General medical and surgical

Staffed Beds: 196 **Admissions:** 7298 **Census:** 179 **Outpatient Visits:** 363691 **Births:** 529 **Total Expense ($000):** 281716 **Payroll Expense ($000):** 132242

BLUE HILL—Hancock County

★ **BLUE HILL MEMORIAL HOSPITAL (201300)**, 57 Water Street, Zip 04614–5231, Mailing Address: P.O. Box 1029, Zip 04614–1029; tel. 207/374–3400, **A**10 18 **F**8 15 18 28 29 31 32 34 35 40 41 43 44 45 50 51 57 59 64 65 66 75 78 79 80 81 82 85 86 87 91 93 96 97 107 110 119 130 132 133 135 146 147 148 **S** Eastern Maine Healthcare Systems, Brewer, ME
Primary Contact: John Ronan, President
CFO: Wendy Jones, Interim Chief Financial Officer
CHR: David Wheaton, Director Human Resources
CNO: Kathy Lirakis, R.N., Chief Nursing Officer
Web address: www.bhmh.org
Control: Other not–for–profit (including NFP Corporation) **Service:** General medical and surgical

Staffed Beds: 23 **Admissions:** 619 **Census:** 11 **Outpatient Visits:** 165310 **Births:** 0 **Total Expense ($000):** 39649 **Payroll Expense ($000):** 17257 **Personnel:** 264

BRIDGTON—Cumberland County

★ **BRIDGTON HOSPITAL (201310)**, 10 Hospital Drive, Zip 04009–1148; tel. 207/647–6000, **A**10 18 **F**3 7 8 11 13 15 18 29 30 31 34 35 40 43 44 45 50 57 59 64 65 67 68 75 76 77 78 79 80 81 85 87 90 91 93 94 96 97 107 108 110 114 119 128 130 131 132 133 135 143 144 146 148 **P**8 **S** Central Maine Healthcare, Lewiston, ME
Primary Contact: R David. Frum, President
COO: Robert Slattery, Vice President of Operations
CMO: Alan Verrill, M.D., President Medical Staff
CHR: Kirk Miklavic, Director Human Resources
Web address: www.bridgtonhospital.org
Control: Other not–for–profit (including NFP Corporation) **Service:** General medical and surgical

Staffed Beds: 22 **Admissions:** 961 **Census:** 12 **Outpatient Visits:** 157598 **Births:** 96 **Total Expense ($000):** 48002 **Payroll Expense ($000):** 19535 **Personnel:** 289

BRUNSWICK—Cumberland County

✠ **MID COAST HOSPITAL (200021)**, 123 Medical Center Drive, Zip 04011–2652; tel. 207/373–6000, (Nonreporting) **A**1 2 5 10
Primary Contact: Lois N. Skillings, R.N., MSN, President and Chief Executive Officer
COO: Philip A Ortolani, Vice President Operations
CFO: Robert N McCue, Vice President Finance
CMO: Scott Mills, M.D., Vice President Medical Staff Administration and Chief Medical Officer
CIO: Gale Stoy, Manager Information Systems
CHR: Coleen M Farrell, Vice President Human Resources
CNO: Deborah MacLeod, MS, R.N., Vice President Nursing and Patient Care Services
Web address: www.midcoasthealth.com
Control: Other not–for–profit (including NFP Corporation) **Service:** General medical and surgical

Staffed Beds: 93

CALAIS—Washington County

★ **CALAIS REGIONAL HOSPITAL (201305)**, 24 Hospital Lane, Zip 04619–1398; tel. 207/454–7521, **A**10 18 **F**3 8 11 13 15 28 29 31 32 34 35 36 40 41 45 46 50 54 57 59 62 63 64 65 68 76 77 79 81 82 83 84 85 87 90 93 96 97 107 108 110 111 114 119 127 128 129 130 132 133 146 147 148 149 154 **P**6
Primary Contact: Rodney Boula, Chief Executive Officer
CFO: Nancy Glidden, Chief Financial Officer
CMO: Francis Lee, M.D., Chief Medical Officer
CIO: Dee Dee Travis, Vice President Community Relations
CHR: Kristi K Saunders, Director and Compliance Officer
CNO: Erika Marshall, Interim Chief Nursing Officer
Web address: www.calaishospital.com
Control: Other not–for–profit (including NFP Corporation) **Service:** General medical and surgical

Staffed Beds: 25 **Admissions:** 918 **Census:** 10 **Outpatient Visits:** 36611 **Births:** 39 **Total Expense ($000):** 36288 **Payroll Expense ($000):** 19521 **Personnel:** 232

CARIBOU—Aroostook County

✠ **CARY MEDICAL CENTER (200031)**, 163 Van Buren Road, Suite 1, Zip 04736–3567; tel. 207/498–3111, (Total facility includes 9 beds in nursing home–type unit) **A**1 10 **F**3 8 11 13 15 28 29 31 32 34 35 36 38 40 43 44 51 53 54 56 57 59 61 64 67 68 70 75 76 77 78 79 81 82 84 85 86 87 89 90 93 97 107 108 111 115 118 119 121 130 131 132 135 144 146 147 148 **S** QHR, Brentwood, TN
Primary Contact: Kris A. Doody, R.N., Chief Executive Officer
COO: Shawn Anderson, Chief Operating Officer
CFO: Galen Dickinson, Chief Financial Officer
CMO: Regen Gallagher, D.O., Chief Medical Officer
CIO: Dave Silsbee, Chief Information Officer
CHR: Paula A. Parent, Chief Nursing Officer and Director of Human Resources
CNO: Paula A. Parent, Chief Nursing Officer
Web address: www.carymedicalcenter.org
Control: City, Government, nonfederal **Service:** General medical and surgical

Staffed Beds: 49 **Admissions:** 1609 **Census:** 29 **Outpatient Visits:** 72469 **Births:** 222 **Total Expense ($000):** 52464 **Payroll Expense ($000):** 21261 **Personnel:** 392

DAMARISCOTTA—Lincoln County

★ **LINCOLNHEALTH (201302)**, 35 Miles Street, Zip 04543–4047; tel. 207/563–1234, (Includes LINCOLNHEALTH MILES CAMPUS, 35 Miles Street, Damariscotta, ME, Zip 04543–4047; tel. 207/563–1234; James W Donovan, President and Chief Executive Officer; LINCOLNHEALTH ST. ANDREWS CAMPUS, 6 St Andrews Lane, Boothbay Harbor, ME, Zip 04538–1732, Mailing Address: P.O. Box 417, Zip 04538–0417, tel. 207/633–2121) (Total facility includes 66 beds in nursing home–type unit) **A**10 18 **F**3 10 11 13 15 29 30 32 34 35 40 44 45 50 57 59 64 65 67 70 75 76 79 81 85 86 87 93 96 97 107 108 110 111 114 115 119 125 127 128 130 132 133 135 144 146 147 148 149 **P**6 **S** MaineHealth, Portland, ME
Primary Contact: James W. Donovan, President and Chief Executive Officer
COO: Cynthia Wade, R.N., RN, BSN, Executive Vice President and Chief Operating Officer
CFO: Wayne Printy, Chief Financial Officer and Senior Vice President Finance
CIO: David Felton, Regional Chief Information Officer
CHR: Thomas R Girard, Vice President Human Resources
CNO: Christine Anderson, Chief Nursing Officer and Vice President of Patient Care Services
Web address: www.lchcare.org
Control: Other not–for–profit (including NFP Corporation) **Service:** General medical and surgical

Staffed Beds: 91 **Admissions:** 1958 **Census:** 70 **Outpatient Visits:** 115756 **Births:** 108 **Total Expense ($000):** 79402 **Payroll Expense ($000):** 24017 **Personnel:** 454

Hospital, Medicare Provider Number, Address, Telephone, Approval, Facility, and Physician Codes, Health Care System

★ American Hospital Association (AHA) membership
☐ The Joint Commission accreditation
○ Healthcare Facilities Accreditation Program
◇ DNV Healthcare Inc. accreditation
⇑ Center for Improvement in Healthcare Quality Accreditation
△ Commission on Accreditation of Rehabilitation Facilities (CARF) accreditation

ME

DOVER—FOXCROFT–Piscataquis County

★ **MAYO REGIONAL HOSPITAL (201309)**, 897 West Main Street,
Zip 04426–1099; tel. 207/564–8401, **A**10 18 **F**3 7 8 11 13 15 28 29 30 31 34
35 38 40 45 50 57 59 64 65 71 75 76 77 78 79 80 81 82 85 86 87 93 96 97
104 107 110 111 114 119 127 129 130 132 133 135 146 147 148 149
Primary Contact: Marie E. Vienneau, FACHE, President and Chief Executive Officer
CFO: Nancy Glidden, Chief Financial Officer and Vice President Finance
CMO: Challa Reddy, M.D., President Medical Staff
CHR: James R Godley, Vice President of Human Resources
CNO: Denise Scuderi, Vice President Patient Care Services
Web address: www.mayohospital.com
Control: Hospital district or authority, Government, nonfederal **Service**: General
medical and surgical

Staffed Beds: 25 **Admissions**: 1156 **Census**: 12 **Outpatient Visits**: 137299
Births: 100 **Total Expense ($000)**: 51416 **Payroll Expense ($000)**: 26017
Personnel: 381

ELLSWORTH—Hancock County

⊞ **MAINE COAST MEMORIAL HOSPITAL (200050)**, 50 Union Street,
Zip 04605–1599; tel. 207/664–5311, (Nonreporting) **A**1 10 **S** Eastern Maine
Healthcare Systems, Brewer, ME
Primary Contact: John Ronan, President
CFO: Chris Frauenhofer, Chief Financial Officer
CMO: Sheena Whittaker, M.D., Chief Medical Officer
CIO: Scott Burtchell, Director Information Systems
CHR: Noah Lundy, Director of Human Resources
CNO: Kristin Cyr, R.N., MSN, Senior Nursing Executive and Vice President of
Patient Care Services
Web address: www.mainehospital.org
Control: Other not–for–profit (including NFP Corporation) **Service**: General
medical and surgical

Staffed Beds: 48

FARMINGTON—Franklin County

⊞ **FRANKLIN MEMORIAL HOSPITAL (200037)**, 111 Franklin Health Commons,
Zip 04938–6144; tel. 207/778–6031, **A**1 5 10 20 **F**3 5 7 8 11 13 15 28 29 30
31 32 34 40 45 46 50 51 54 59 61 64 65 70 75 76 77 78 79 81 83 85 86 87
89 93 94 97 101 102 107 108 110 111 115 118 119 129 130 131 135 143
146 147 148 149
Primary Contact: Timothy A. Churchill, Interim Chief Executive Officer
CFO: Wayne Bennett, Chief Financial Officer
CMO: Michael Rowland, M.D., Vice President Medical Affairs
CIO: Ralph Johnson, Chief Information Officer
CHR: Joline Hart, Vice President Human Resources
Web address: www.fchn.org
Control: Other not–for–profit (including NFP Corporation) **Service**: General
medical and surgical

Staffed Beds: 48 **Admissions**: 1715 **Census**: 17 **Outpatient Visits**: 105266
Births: 230 **Total Expense ($000)**: 83670 **Payroll Expense ($000)**: 37366
Personnel: 532

FORT FAIRFIELD—Aroostook County

COMMUNITY GENERAL HEALTH CENTER See The Aroostook Medical Center,
Presque Isle

FORT KENT—Aroostook County

⊞ **NORTHERN MAINE MEDICAL CENTER (200052)**, 194 East Main Street,
Zip 04743–1497; tel. 207/834–3155, (Total facility includes 45 beds in nursing
home–type unit) **A**1 10 20 **F**3 13 15 29 31 34 40 45 50 54 57 59 62 64 67 68
70 75 76 77 78 79 81 82 86 87 89 98 99 100 101 102 103 104 107 108 110
111 115 119 127 128 130 131 132 133 135 146 147 148 **P**6
Primary Contact: Peter Sirois, Chief Executive Officer
CFO: Cindy Daigle, Chief Financial Officer
CMO: Michael Sullivan, M.D., Chief Medical Officer
CIO: Adam Landry, Director of Information Systems
CHR: Robin Damboise, Director Human Resources
CNO: Alain Bois, R.N., Director of Nursing
Web address: www.nmmc.org
Control: Other not–for–profit (including NFP Corporation) **Service**: General
medical and surgical

Staffed Beds: 81 **Admissions**: 1656 **Census**: 68 **Outpatient Visits**: 52795
Births: 47 **Total Expense ($000)**: 51504 **Payroll Expense ($000)**: 28121
Personnel: 390

GREENVILLE—Piscataquis County

★ **CHARLES A. DEAN MEMORIAL HOSPITAL (201301)**, 364 Pritham
Avenue, Zip 04441–1395, Mailing Address: P.O. Box 1129, Zip 04441–1129;
tel. 207/695–5200, (Nonreporting) **A**10 18 **S** Eastern Maine Healthcare Systems,
Brewer, ME
Primary Contact: Terri Vieira, President
CFO: Edward Olivier, Chief Financial Officer
CMO: Darin Peck, M.D., Chief of Staff
Web address: www.cadean.org
Control: Other not–for–profit (including NFP Corporation) **Service**: General
medical and surgical

Staffed Beds: 23

HOULTON—Aroostook County

★ **HOULTON REGIONAL HOSPITAL (201308)**, 20 Hartford Street, Zip 04730–1891;
tel. 207/532–9471, **A**10 18 **F**1 3 4 11 13 15 16 17 28 29 30 34 40 43 45 46 50
59 65 67 70 72 73 75 76 77 79 80 81 83 84 85 86 87 88 89 90 93 97 98 107
108 110 111 114 119 127 128 129 130 132 133 146 148 149
Primary Contact: Thomas J. Moakler, Chief Executive Officer
CHR: Vicky Moody, Director of Human Resources
Web address: www.houlton.net/hrh
Control: Other not–for–profit (including NFP Corporation) **Service**: General
medical and surgical

Staffed Beds: 25 **Admissions**: 1215 **Census**: 15 **Outpatient Visits**: 97895
Births: 125 **Total Expense ($000)**: 47891 **Payroll Expense ($000)**: 21568
Personnel: 353

LEWISTON—Androscoggin County

⊞ △ **CENTRAL MAINE MEDICAL CENTER (200024)**, 300 Main Street,
Zip 04240–7027; tel. 207/795–0111, **A**1 2 3 5 7 10 13 **F**3 11 12 13 15 18 19
20 22 24 26 28 29 30 31 32 34 35 36 40 41 43 44 45 46 47 48 49 50 51 52
54 55 56 57 58 59 61 64 65 66 67 68 70 71 73 74 75 76 77 78 79 81 82 84
85 86 87 89 90 91 92 93 97 101 104 107 108 110 114 115 118 119 120 121
123 124 129 130 131 132 135 143 146 147 148 149 150 **P**8 **S** Central Maine
Healthcare, Lewiston, ME
Primary Contact: David Tupponce, M.D., President
CFO: David Thompson, Chief Financial Officer
CMO: David Lauver, M.D., Chief Division Hospital Based Care
CIO: Denis Tanguay, Chief Information Officer
CHR: Kirk Miklavic, Director, Human Resources
Web address: www.cmmc.org
Control: Other not–for–profit (including NFP Corporation) **Service**: General
medical and surgical

Staffed Beds: 190 **Admissions**: 10986 **Census**: 132 **Outpatient Visits**:
748689 **Births**: 644 **Total Expense ($000)**: 386960 **Payroll Expense
($000)**: 156069 **Personnel**: 1687

⊞ **ST. MARY'S REGIONAL MEDICAL CENTER (200034)**, 93 Campus
Avenue, Zip 04240–6030, Mailing Address: P.O. Box 291, Zip 04243–0291;
tel. 207/777–8100, (Total facility includes 210 beds in nursing home–type unit) **A**1
2 3 5 10 **F**3 4 5 7 13 15 17 18 20 28 29 30 31 34 35 36 37 38 39 40 44 45
49 50 53 54 56 57 59 61 64 65 68 70 74 75 76 77 78 79 80 81 82 84 85 86
87 89 92 93 97 98 99 100 101 102 103 104 105 107 108 110 111 114 115
118 119 128 129 130 131 132 134 135 143 144 146 147 148 149 152 153
154 **S** Covenant Health, Tewksbury, MA
Primary Contact: Steven C. Jorgensen, Chief Executive Officer
CFO: Michael Hendrix, Chief Financial Officer
CMO: Christopher Bowe, M.D., Chief Medical Officer, Medical Affairs
CIO: Karen Bowling, Chief Information Officer
CHR: Nicole Morin–Scribner, Director Human Resources
CNO: Karen Clark, Vice President Patient Care Services
Web address: www.stmarysmaine.com
Control: Church operated, Nongovernment, not–for–profit **Service**: General
medical and surgical

Staffed Beds: 350 **Admissions**: 5624 **Census**: 266 **Outpatient Visits**:
301749 **Births**: 591 **Total Expense ($000)**: 193544 **Payroll Expense
($000)**: 89788 **Personnel**: 1524

LINCOLN—Penobscot County

★ **PENOBSCOT VALLEY HOSPITAL (201303)**, 7 Transalpine Road,
Zip 04457–4222, Mailing Address: P.O. Box 368, Zip 04457–0368;
tel. 207/794–3321, (Nonreporting) **A**10 18 **S** QHR, Brentwood, TN
Primary Contact: Gary R. Poquette, FACHE, Chief Executive Officer
CFO: Ann Marie Rush, Chief Financial Officer
CHR: Sarah Loman, Director Human Resources
Web address: www.pvhme.org
Control: Other not–for–profit (including NFP Corporation) **Service**: General
medical and surgical

Staffed Beds: 25

Many Facility Codes have changed. Please refer to the AHA Guide Code Chart. © 2018 AHA Guide

MACHIAS—Washington County

★ **DOWN EAST COMMUNITY HOSPITAL (201311)**, 11 Hospital Drive, Zip 04654–3325; tel. 207/255–3356, (Total facility includes 28 beds in nursing home–type unit) **A**10 18 **F**3 13 15 28 29 34 35 40 45 51 57 59 64 65 75 77 79 81 82 83 84 85 93 97 107 108 110 111 114 119 127 128 130 133 146 147
Primary Contact: Dennis Welsh, President and CEO
COO: Steve Lail, Vice President Operations and Chief Operating Officer
CFO: Lynnette Parr, Chief Financial Officer
CMO: Aziz Massaad, M.D., Medical Staff President
CHR: Ernestine O Reisman, Vice President Human Resources
CNO: Kevin K McEwan, MSN, R.N., Vice President of Patient Care Service and Chief Nursing Officer
Web address: www.dech.org
Control: Other not–for–profit (including NFP Corporation) **Service**: General medical and surgical

Staffed Beds: 53 **Admissions**: 960 **Census**: 31 **Outpatient Visits**: 31641
Births: 152 **Total Expense ($000)**: 45040 **Payroll Expense ($000)**: 20030
Personnel: 290

MARS HILL—Aroostook County

AROOSTOOK HEALTH CENTER See The Aroostook Medical Center, Presque Isle

MILLINOCKET—Penobscot County

★ **MILLINOCKET REGIONAL HOSPITAL (201307)**, 200 Somerset Street, Zip 04462–1298; tel. 207/723–5161, **A**10 18 **F**3 8 11 15 29 31 34 35 40 41 45 50 53 54 56 57 59 64 65 68 75 77 78 79 80 81 85 87 93 96 97 107 108 110 111 114 118 119 127 130 131 133 135 144 145 148 154
Primary Contact: Robert Peterson I, Chief Executive Officer
CFO: Catherine LeMay, Vice President Finance
CMO: Daniel Herbert, M.D., Medical Administrative Officer
CHR: Lisa Arsenault, Vice President Human Resources and Compliance
CNO: Mary Tatro Esq Chief Nursing Officer
Web address: www.mrhme.org
Control: Other not–for–profit (including NFP Corporation) **Service**: General medical and surgical

Staffed Beds: 25 **Admissions**: 754 **Census**: 8 **Outpatient Visits**: 27078
Births: 2 **Total Expense ($000)**: 30850 **Payroll Expense ($000)**: 15045
Personnel: 222

NORWAY—Oxford County

★ **STEPHENS MEMORIAL HOSPITAL (201315)**, 181 Main Street, Zip 04268–5664; tel. 207/743–5933, **A**3 5 10 18 **F**3 7 13 15 28 29 30 31 34 35 40 43 45 57 59 61 64 65 68 75 76 78 79 80 81 85 87 89 93 96 97 102 107 108 110 111 115 119 127 130 132 146 148 149 **S** MaineHealth, Portland, ME
Primary Contact: Timothy A. Churchill, President
CMO: James Eshleman, D.O., President Medical Staff
CHR: Roberta Metivier, Vice President Human Resources and Administrator, Western Main Nursing Home
Web address: www.wmhcc.com
Control: Other not–for–profit (including NFP Corporation) **Service**: General medical and surgical

Staffed Beds: 25 **Admissions**: 1295 **Census**: 12 **Outpatient Visits**: 102288
Births: 144 **Total Expense ($000)**: 64167 **Payroll Expense ($000)**: 26801
Personnel: 431

PITTSFIELD—Somerset County

⊞ **SEBASTICOOK VALLEY HEALTH (201313)**, 447 North Main Street, Zip 04967–3707; tel. 207/487–4000, **A**1 10 18 **F**3 7 11 15 18 28 29 30 32 34 35 40 45 46 50 51 57 59 64 65 70 75 77 78 79 81 87 93 96 97 104 107 108 111 119 127 129 130 132 133 135 143 146 147 148 **P**6 **S** Eastern Maine Healthcare Systems, Brewer, ME
Primary Contact: Terri Vieira, President and Chief Executive Officer
COO: Michael Peterson, FACHE, Chief Operating Officer
CFO: Randal Clark, Vice President Finance
CMO: Robert Schlager, M.D., Chief Medical Officer
CIO: Michael Peterson, FACHE, Chief Operating Officer
CHR: Tammy Hatch, Manager
Web address: www.sebasticookvalleyhealth.org
Control: Other not–for–profit (including NFP Corporation) **Service**: General medical and surgical

Staffed Beds: 25 **Admissions**: 817 **Census**: 12 **Outpatient Visits**: 78746
Births: 0 **Total Expense ($000)**: 37795 **Payroll Expense ($000)**: 17690
Personnel: 304

PORTLAND—Cumberland County

⊞ **MAINE MEDICAL CENTER (200009)**, 22 Bramhall Street, Zip 04102–3175; tel. 207/662–0111, (Includes BARBARA BUSH CHILDREN'S HOSPITAL, 22 Bramhall Street, Portland, ME, Zip 04102–3134; tel. 207/662–0111; Richard W Petersen, President and Chief Executive Officer; MAINE MEDICAL CENTER, BRIGHTON CAMPUS, 335 Brighton Avenue, Portland, ME, Zip 04102–9735, Mailing Address: P.O. Box 9735, Zip 04102–9735, tel. 207/879–8000; Richard W Petersen, President and Chief Executive Officer) **A**1 2 3 5 8 10 **F**1 3 5 6 11 12 13 15 16 17 18 19 20 21 22 23 24 25 26 27 28 29 30 31 32 34 35 36 38 40 41 43 44 45 46 47 48 49 51 54 55 56 57 58 59 60 61 64 65 66 68 70 72 73 74 75 76 78 79 80 81 82 84 85 86 87 88 89 91 92 97 98 99 100 101 102 103 104 107 108 110 111 115 116 117 118 119 120 121 123 124 126 128 129 130 131 132 134 135 138 141 144 146 147 148 149 151 154 **P**6 8 **S** MaineHealth, Portland, ME
Primary Contact: Richard W. Petersen, President and Chief Executive Officer
COO: Jeff Sanders, Senior Vice President, Chief Operating Officer
CFO: Lou Inzana, Senior Vice President and Chief Financial Officer
CMO: Joel Botler, M.D., Chief Medical Officer
CHR: Judith M West, Senior Vice President Human Resources and Chief Human Resources Officer
CNO: Marjorie Wiggins, Senior Vice President, Chief Nursing Officer
Web address: www.mmc.org
Control: Other not–for–profit (including NFP Corporation) **Service**: General medical and surgical

Staffed Beds: 637 **Admissions**: 28533 **Census**: 421 **Outpatient Visits**: 302117 **Births**: 2670 **Total Expense ($000)**: 1231213 **Payroll Expense ($000)**: 485719 **Personnel**: 8100

⊞ **MERCY HOSPITAL OF PORTLAND (200008)**, 144 State Street, Zip 04101–3795; tel. 207/879–3000, **A**1 2 10 **F**3 11 13 15 18 20 29 30 31 34 35 36 40 44 45 48 49 50 51 54 55 56 57 58 59 61 64 68 70 72 74 75 76 78 79 81 82 84 86 87 93 96 97 100 102 104 107 108 110 111 114 115 119 130 132 135 143 144 146 147 148 149 154 **P**6 **S** Eastern Maine Healthcare Systems, Brewer, ME
Primary Contact: Charles D. Therrien, President
CFO: Michael Hachey, Senior Vice President and Chief Financial Officer
CIO: Craig Dreher, Chief Information Officer
CHR: Elizabeth B Christensen, Director Human Resources
CNO: Bette Neville, R.N., MSN, Vice President and Chief Nursing Officer
Web address: www.mercyhospital.org
Control: Other not–for–profit (including NFP Corporation) **Service**: General medical and surgical

Staffed Beds: 104 **Admissions**: 4945 **Census**: 43 **Outpatient Visits**: 365457 **Births**: 777 **Total Expense ($000)**: 216097 **Payroll Expense ($000)**: 85170 **Personnel**: 1011

⊞ **NEW ENGLAND REHABILITATION HOSPITAL OF PORTLAND (203025)**, 335 Brighton Avenue, Zip 04102–2363; tel. 207/775–4000, **A**1 3 10 **F**29 34 35 75 79 82 90 93 95 96 131 132 135 146 **S** Encompass Health Corporation, Birmingham, AL
Primary Contact: Jeanine Chesley, Chief Executive Officer
CFO: James Paladino, Controller
CMO: Thomas Morrione, Medical Director
CHR: Mary Cote, Director Human Resources
CNO: Sharon Kuhrt, Chief Nursing Officer
Web address: www.nerhp.org
Control: Partnership, Investor–owned (for–profit) **Service**: Rehabilitation

Staffed Beds: 90 **Admissions**: 1956 **Census**: 67 **Outpatient Visits**: 10162 **Births**: 0 **Total Expense ($000)**: 27315 **Payroll Expense ($000)**: 14829 **Personnel**: 222

Hospital, Medicare Provider Number, Address, Telephone, Approval, Facility, and Physician Codes, Health Care System

★ American Hospital Association (AHA) membership   ○ Healthcare Facilities Accreditation Program   ⇑ Center for Improvement in Healthcare Quality Accreditation
☐ The Joint Commission accreditation   ◇ DNV Healthcare Inc. accreditation   △ Commission on Accreditation of Rehabilitation Facilities (CARF) accreditation

ME

PRESQUE ISLE—Aroostook County

⊠ **THE AROOSTOOK MEDICAL CENTER (200018)**, 140 Academy Street, Zip 04769–3171, Mailing Address: P.O. Box 151, Zip 04769–0151; tel. 207/768–4000, (Includes AROOSTOOK HEALTH CENTER, 15 Highland Avenue, Mars Hill, ME, Zip 4758; tel. 207/768–4900; ARTHUR R. GOULD MEMORIAL HOSPITAL, 140 Academy Street, Presque Isle, ME, Zip 4769, Mailing Address: P.O. Box 151, Zip 4769, tel. 207/768–4000; COMMUNITY GENERAL HEALTH CENTER, 3 Green Street, Fort Fairfield, ME, Zip 4742; tel. 207/768–4700) (Total facility includes 64 beds in nursing home–type unit) **A**1 10 **F**3 7 8 12 13 15 18 20 28 29 30 31 32 34 35 36 38 40 43 45 46 51 52 53 54 56 57 59 60 61 64 65 67 70 74 75 76 78 79 81 82 84 85 86 87 89 90 91 93 96 97 104 107 108 110 114 115 116 117 118 119 120 121 123 128 129 130 131 132 133 134 135 143 144 146 147 148 149 150 154 **P**6 **S** Eastern Maine Healthcare Systems, Brewer, ME
Primary Contact: Gregory LaFrancois, President
COO: Jay Reynolds, M.D., Chief Medical Officer and Chief Clinical Officer
CFO: C Bruce Sandstrom, Vice President and Chief Financial Officer
CMO: Jay Reynolds, M.D., Chief Medical Officer and Chief Clinical Officer
CIO: Kyle Johnson, Chief Information Officer
CHR: Joseph Siddiqui, Vice President Human Resources
Web address: www.tamc.org
Control: Other not–for–profit (including NFP Corporation) **Service**: General medical and surgical

Staffed Beds: 115 **Admissions:** 2412 **Census:** 86 **Outpatient Visits:** 213142 **Births:** 170 **Total Expense ($000):** 131826 **Payroll Expense ($000):** 62911 **Personnel:** 974

ROCKPORT—Knox County

☐ **PEN BAY MEDICAL CENTER (200063)**, 6 Glen Cove Drive, Zip 04856–4240; tel. 207/921–8000, (Nonreporting) **A**1 2 5 10 20 **S** MaineHealth, Portland, ME
Primary Contact: Mark Fourre, President and Chief Executive Officer
COO: Eric Waters, Vice President Operations
CFO: Maura Kelly, Vice President Fiscal Services
CMO: Dana L Goldsmith, M.D., Vice President Medical Affairs
CIO: Brooks Betts, Director Information Systems and Chief Information Officer
CHR: Thomas R Girard, Vice President Human Resources
CNO: Paula Delahanty, Regional Chief Nursing Officer
Web address: www.penbayhealthcare.org
Control: Other not–for–profit (including NFP Corporation) **Service**: General medical and surgical

Staffed Beds: 165

PENOBSCOT BAY MEDICAL CENTER See Pen Bay Medical Center

RUMFORD—Oxford County

★ **RUMFORD HOSPITAL (201306)**, 420 Franklin Street, Zip 04276–2145; tel. 207/369–1000, **A**3 10 18 **F**3 8 11 13 15 18 28 29 30 31 34 35 40 43 44 45 50 53 57 59 64 65 67 68 75 76 77 78 79 80 81 85 87 89 90 91 93 94 96 97 107 110 114 119 127 128 130 132 133 135 143 144 146 148 **P**8 **S** Central Maine Healthcare, Lewiston, ME
Primary Contact: R David. Frum, President
CNO: Becky Hall, R.N., Director Nursing
Web address: www.rumfordhospital.org
Control: Other not–for–profit (including NFP Corporation) **Service**: General medical and surgical

Staffed Beds: 25 **Admissions:** 1127 **Census:** 13 **Outpatient Visits:** 125035 **Births:** 91 **Total Expense ($000):** 40779 **Payroll Expense ($000):** 16099 **Personnel:** 244

SKOWHEGAN—Somerset County

★ **REDINGTON–FAIRVIEW GENERAL HOSPITAL (201314)**, 46 Fairview Avenue, Zip 4976, Mailing Address: PO Box 468, Zip 04976–0468; tel. 207/474–5121, **A**5 10 18 **F**3 7 11 13 15 18 28 29 31 34 35 40 45 47 50 53 56 57 59 65 68 70 74 75 76 77 78 79 81 82 84 85 91 92 93 97 107 108 110 114 115 118 119 130 131 132 133 134 135 146 147 148 149 **P**6
Primary Contact: Richard Willett, Chief Executive Officer
CFO: Elmer H Doucette, Chief Financial Officer
CMO: Gust Stringos, M.D., Medical Staff Director
CHR: Lisa G. Landry, Human Resources Director
CNO: Sherry L Rogers, MS, R.N., Chief Nursing Officer
Web address: www.rfgh.net
Control: Other not–for–profit (including NFP Corporation) **Service**: General medical and surgical

Staffed Beds: 25 **Admissions:** 1538 **Census:** 14 **Outpatient Visits:** 26286 **Births:** 157 **Total Expense ($000):** 88674 **Payroll Expense ($000):** 42507 **Personnel:** 593

WATERVILLE—Kennebec County

★ ○ **INLAND HOSPITAL (200041)**, 200 Kennedy Memorial Drive, Zip 04901–4595; tel. 207/861–3000, **A**10 11 **F**3 13 15 18 28 29 30 34 35 40 45 46 50 51 56 57 59 64 68 70 74 75 76 77 79 81 82 85 92 93 97 107 108 109 110 111 115 119 127 129 130 132 146 147 148 149 151 154 **P**6 **S** Eastern Maine Healthcare Systems, Brewer, ME
Primary Contact: John Dalton, President and Chief Executive Officer
COO: Daniel Booth, Vice President Operations and Chief Human Resources Officer
CFO: Dean Bither, Chief Financial Officer
CMO: Michael Palumbo, D.O., Vice President Medical Affairs and Chief Education
CIO: Kevin Dieterich, Director Information Services
CHR: Daniel Booth, Vice President Operations
Web address: www.inlandhospital.org
Control: Other not–for–profit (including NFP Corporation) **Service**: General medical and surgical

Staffed Beds: 29 **Admissions:** 1241 **Census:** 13 **Outpatient Visits:** 15493 **Births:** 324 **Total Expense ($000):** 77323 **Payroll Expense ($000):** 32120 **Personnel:** 514

WESTBROOK—Cumberland County

⊠ **SPRING HARBOR HOSPITAL (204005)**, 123 Andover Road, Zip 04092–3850; tel. 207/761–2200, **A**1 3 10 **F**50 59 68 75 77 80 87 98 **S** MaineHealth, Portland, ME
Primary Contact: Mary Jane Krebs, FACHE, President
CFO: Michael Abbatiello, Chief Financial Officer
CMO: Girard Robinson, M.D., Senior Vice President Medical and Clinical Affairs
CIO: Susan Moulton, Director Health Information Management
CHR: Timothy McNulty, Director Human Resources
Web address: www.springharbor.org
Control: Other not–for–profit (including NFP Corporation) **Service**: Psychiatric

Staffed Beds: 88 **Admissions:** 2571 **Census:** 86

YORK—York County

★ **YORK HOSPITAL (200020)**, 15 Hospital Drive, Zip 03909–1099; tel. 207/363–4321, **A**10 **F**3 5 13 15 18 20 22 26 28 29 30 31 32 34 35 36 37 40 45 48 50 53 54 55 57 59 62 63 64 65 66 68 69 70 71 74 75 76 77 78 79 81 85 87 89 91 92 93 96 97 100 104 107 108 110 111 112 114 119 126 129 130 132 135 143 144 146 148 149 154 **P**6
Primary Contact: Jud Knox, Chief Executive Officer
CFO: Robin LaBonte, Leader Financial Care
CMO: Lawrence Petrovich, M.D., Chief Medical Officer
CIO: Robin LaBonte, Leader Financial Care
CHR: Olivia Chayer, Director, Human Resources
Web address: www.yorkhospital.com
Control: Other not–for–profit (including NFP Corporation) **Service**: General medical and surgical

Staffed Beds: 58 **Admissions:** 3695 **Census:** 35 **Outpatient Visits:** 336606 **Births:** 658 **Total Expense ($000):** 168610 **Payroll Expense ($000):** 80239 **Personnel:** 1010

Many Facility Codes have changed. Please refer to the AHA Guide Code Chart. © 2018 AHA Guide

MARYLAND

ANNAPOLIS—Anne Arundel County

✠ **ANNE ARUNDEL MEDICAL CENTER (210023)**, 2001 Medical Parkway, Zip 21401–3019; tel. 443/481–1000, (Total facility includes 40 beds in nursing home–type unit) **A**1 2 3 5 10 **F**3 4 5 6 9 11 12 13 14 15 18 19 20 22 26 28 29 30 31 32 34 35 36 37 38 39 40 41 44 45 46 47 49 50 51 53 54 55 56 57 58 59 60 61 63 64 65 66 68 70 72 74 75 76 77 78 79 81 82 83 84 85 86 87 89 91 92 93 94 96 99 100 101 102 103 107 108 110 111 114 115 116 117 118 119 120 121 123 124 126 129 130 131 132 134 135 146 147 148 149 150 151 152 154 **P**6 7 8
Primary Contact: Victoria Bayless, President and Chief Executive Officer
COO: Maulik Joshi, Executive Vice President, Integrated Care Delivery and Chief Operating Officer
CFO: Robert Reilly, Vice President and Chief Financial Officer
CMO: Mitchell B Schwartz, M.D., Chief Medical Officer
CIO: Barbara Baldwin, Chief Information Officer
CHR: Julie McGovern, Vice President Human Resources
CNO: Barbara S Jacobs, MSN, Vice President, Nursing and Chief Nursing Officer
Web address: www.aahs.org
Control: Other not–for–profit (including NFP Corporation) **Service:** General medical and surgical

Staffed Beds: 440 Admissions: 27059 Census: 292 Outpatient Visits: 480981 Births: 5500 Total Expense ($000): 546372 Payroll Expense ($000): 208458 Personnel: 4011

BALTIMORE—Baltimore City County

✠ **BON SECOURS BALTIMORE HEALTH SYSTEM (210013)**, 2000 West Baltimore Street, Zip 21223–1558; tel. 410/362–3000, **A**1 10 **F**3 5 18 20 26 29 30 40 44 49 58 59 60 64 66 70 77 78 79 81 84 85 87 97 98 99 100 101 102 103 104 105 107 108 110 111 115 119 130 143 146 148 153 154 **S** Bon Secours Health System, Inc., Marriottsville, MD
Primary Contact: Samuel Lee. Ross, M.D., MS, Chief Executive Officer
CFO: Laura Ellison, Chief Financial Officer
CMO: Arsalan Sheikh, Chief of Medicine
CIO: Sanjay Purushotham, Executive Director Information Systems
CHR: Danielle Jorden–Ellis, Director
CNO: Shelly Buck, Chief Nursing Executive and Chief Operating Officer
Web address: www.bonsecoursbaltimore.com
Control: Church operated, Nongovernment, not–for–profit **Service:** General medical and surgical

Staffed Beds: 69 Admissions: 3673 Census: 49 Outpatient Visits: 322557 Births: 0 Total Expense ($000): 113068 Payroll Expense ($000): 41465 Personnel: 650

FRANKLIN SQUARE HOSPITAL CENTER See Medstar Franklin Square Medical Center

GOOD SAMARITAN HOSPITAL OF MARYLAND See Medstar Good Samaritan Hospital

BALTIMORE—Baltimore County

✠ **GREATER BALTIMORE MEDICAL CENTER (210044)**, 6701 North Charles Street, Zip 21204–6892; tel. 443/849–2000, (Total facility includes 27 beds in nursing home–type unit) **A**1 2 3 5 10 **F**3 8 11 12 13 18 20 22 26 29 30 31 34 35 40 41 44 45 46 47 48 49 50 51 55 56 57 58 59 60 61 63 64 68 70 72 73 74 75 76 77 78 79 81 82 83 84 85 86 87 89 92 93 96 97 102 107 108 114 115 119 120 121 123 124 126 128 129 130 132 135 136 142 145 146 147 148 **P**4
Primary Contact: John B. Chessare, M.D., M.P.H., FACHE, President and Chief Executive Officer
COO: Keith R Poisson, Executive Vice President and Chief Operating Officer
CFO: Eric L Melchior, Executive Vice President and Chief Financial Officer
CMO: John R Saunders, M.D., Senior Vice President Medical Affairs and Chief Medical Officer
CHR: Deloris Simpson–Tuggle, Vice President Human Resources and Organizational Development and Chief Human Resources Officer
CNO: Jody Porter, R.N., Senior Vice President Patient Care Services and Chief Nursing Officer
Web address: www.gbmc.org
Control: Other not–for–profit (including NFP Corporation) **Service:** General medical and surgical

Staffed Beds: 401 Admissions: 16256 Census: 164 Outpatient Visits: 127163 Births: 3854 Total Expense ($000): 419397 Payroll Expense ($000): 215064 Personnel: 3453

BALTIMORE—Baltimore City County

HARBOR HOSPITAL See Medstar Harbor Hospital

✠ △ **JOHNS HOPKINS BAYVIEW MEDICAL CENTER (210029)**, 4940 Eastern Avenue, Zip 21224–2780; tel. 410/550–0100, **A**1 3 5 7 8 10 **F**1 2 3 4 5 6 8 9 11 12 13 15 16 17 18 20 22 26 28 29 30 31 32 34 35 36 38 40 41 43 44 45 46 47 48 49 50 51 54 55 56 57 58 59 60 61 64 65 66 68 70 71 72 74 75 76 77 78 79 80 81 82 84 85 86 87 89 90 91 92 93 94 97 98 99 100 101 102 103 104 107 108 110 111 115 116 117 118 119 120 121 123 126 130 131 132 134 135 141 143 146 147 148 149 153 154 **S** Johns Hopkins Health System, Baltimore, MD
Primary Contact: Richard G. Bennett, M.D., President
COO: Charles B. Reuland, Sc.D., Executive Vice President and Chief Operating Officer
CFO: Carl H Francioli, Vice President Finance
CIO: Sandy Reckert, Director Communications and Public Affairs
CHR: Craig R Brodian, Vice President Human Resources
Web address: www.hopkinsbayview.org
Control: Other not–for–profit (including NFP Corporation) **Service:** General medical and surgical

Staffed Beds: 420 Admissions: 20330 Census: 314 Outpatient Visits: 433795 Births: 1265 Total Expense ($000): 551536 Payroll Expense ($000): 188710 Personnel: 3280

✠ △ **JOHNS HOPKINS HOSPITAL (210009)**, 600 North Wolfe Street, Admin 104, Zip 21287–1629; tel. 410/955–5000, (Includes JOHNS HOPKINS CHILDREN'S CENTER, 1800 Orleans Street, Baltimore, MD, Zip 21287–0010; tel. 410/955–5000) **A**1 2 3 5 7 8 10 **F**3 5 6 7 8 9 11 13 14 15 16 17 18 19 20 21 22 23 24 25 26 27 28 29 30 31 32 34 35 36 38 39 40 41 43 44 45 46 47 48 49 50 51 52 54 55 56 57 58 59 60 61 63 64 65 66 68 70 72 74 75 76 77 78 79 80 81 82 83 84 85 86 87 88 89 90 91 92 93 94 96 97 98 99 100 101 102 103 104 105 107 108 110 111 112 114 115 116 117 118 119 120 121 123 124 126 129 130 131 132 134 135 136 137 138 139 140 141 142 143 145 146 147 148 149 150 153 154 **S** Johns Hopkins Health System, Baltimore, MD
Primary Contact: Redonda G. Miller, M.D., President
COO: Charles B. Reuland, Sc.D., Executive Vice President and Chief Operations Officer
CFO: Ronald J Werthman, Senior Vice President Finance, Chief Financial Officer and Treasurer
CIO: Stephanie L Reel, Senior Vice President Information Services
CHR: Bonnie Windsor, Senior Vice President Human Resources
CNO: Deborah Baker, Vice President, Nursing
Web address: www.hopkinsmedicine.org
Control: Other not–for–profit (including NFP Corporation) **Service:** General medical and surgical

Staffed Beds: 976 Admissions: 45721 Census: 838 Outpatient Visits: 651624 Births: 2354 Total Expense ($000): 2275759 Payroll Expense ($000): 613038 Personnel: 10023

☐ △ **KENNEDY KRIEGER INSTITUTE (213301)**, 707 North Broadway, Zip 21205–1890; tel. 443/923–9200, (Nonreporting) **A**1 3 5 7 10
Primary Contact: Bradley Schlagger, M.D., President and Chief Executive Officer
COO: James M Anders Jr Administrator and Chief Operating Officer
CFO: Michael J Neuman, Vice President Finance
CMO: Michael V Johnston, M.D., Chief Medical Officer and Senior Vice President Medical Programs
CIO: Kenneth Davis, Assistant Vice President Information Systems
CHR: Michael Loughran, Vice President Human Resources
Web address: www.kennedykrieger.org
Control: Other not–for–profit (including NFP Corporation) **Service:** Children's other specialty

Staffed Beds: 70

Hospital, Medicare Provider Number, Address, Telephone, Approval, Facility, and Physician Codes, Health Care System

★ American Hospital Association (AHA) membership
☐ The Joint Commission accreditation
○ Healthcare Facilities Accreditation Program
◇ DNV Healthcare Inc. accreditation
⇑ Center for Improvement in Healthcare Quality Accreditation
△ Commission on Accreditation of Rehabilitation Facilities (CARF) accreditation

☐ △ **LEVINDALE HEBREW GERIATRIC CENTER AND HOSPITAL (210064)**, 2434 West Belvedere Avenue, Zip 21215–5267; tel. 410/601–2400, (Nonreporting) **A**1 7 10 **S** LifeBridge Health, Baltimore, MD
Primary Contact: Idriz Limaj, Chief Operating Officer and Executive Director
CMO: Susan M Levy, M.D., Vice President Medical Affairs
CIO: Tressa Springmann, Vice President and Chief Information Officer
CHR: Cheryl T. Boyer, Vice President Human Resources
CNO: Candy Hamner, Vice President and Chief Nursing Officer
Web address: www.sinai-balt.com
Control: Other not–for–profit (including NFP Corporation) **Service**: Acute long–term care hospital

Staffed Beds: 490

MD

BALTIMORE—Baltimore County

✠ **MEDSTAR FRANKLIN SQUARE MEDICAL CENTER (210015)**, 9000 Franklin Square Drive, Zip 21237–3901; tel. 443/777–7000, **A**1 2 3 5 8 10 **F**3 5 9 11 12 13 15 18 20 22 26 28 29 30 31 32 34 35 36 37 38 39 40 41 44 45 46 47 48 49 50 51 55 56 57 58 59 60 61 63 64 65 66 68 70 71 72 74 75 76 77 78 79 81 82 84 85 86 87 89 92 93 94 97 98 99 100 101 102 104 107 108 110 111 114 115 118 119 120 121 123 124 126 129 130 131 132 134 135 145 146 147 148 149 154 **P**6 **S** MedStar Health, Columbia, MD
Primary Contact: Samuel E. Moskowitz, President
CFO: Robert P Lally Jr Vice President Finance
CMO: Tony Sclama, M.D., Vice President Medical Affairs
CIO: Stephen Mannion, Assistant Vice President Information Systems Customer Service
CNO: Lawrence F Strassner III, Ph.D., FACHE, R.N., MS, Senior Vice President Operations and Chief Nursing Officer
Web address: www.medstarfranklin.org
Control: Other not–for–profit (including NFP Corporation) **Service**: General medical and surgical

Staffed Beds: 373 **Admissions**: 23616 **Census**: 261 **Outpatient Visits**: 414746 **Births**: 2722 **Total Expense ($000)**: 508535 **Payroll Expense ($000)**: 235240 **Personnel**: 2828

BALTIMORE—Baltimore City County

✠ △ **MEDSTAR GOOD SAMARITAN HOSPITAL (210056)**, 5601 Loch Raven Boulevard, Zip 21239–2995; tel. 443/444–8000, (Total facility includes 30 beds in nursing home–type unit) **A**1 2 3 5 7 10 **F**3 6 9 11 15 17 18 20 26 28 29 30 31 34 35 36 37 38 40 44 45 49 50 51 53 55 56 57 58 59 60 61 63 64 65 66 68 70 74 75 77 78 79 80 81 82 84 85 86 87 90 91 92 93 96 97 100 101 104 107 108 110 111 114 115 116 117 118 119 120 121 123 129 130 131 132 135 143 146 148 149 **S** MedStar Health, Columbia, MD
Primary Contact: Bradley Chambers, President and Senior Vice President, MedStar Health
CFO: Deana Stout, Vice President Financial Services
Web address: www.goodsam-md.org
Control: Other not–for–profit (including NFP Corporation) **Service**: General medical and surgical

Staffed Beds: 230 **Admissions**: 9185 **Census**: 129 **Outpatient Visits**: 311452 **Births**: 0 **Total Expense ($000)**: 285676 **Payroll Expense ($000)**: 126987 **Personnel**: 1500

✠ **MEDSTAR HARBOR HOSPITAL (210034)**, 3001 South Hanover Street, Zip 21225–1290; tel. 410/350–3200, **A**1 2 3 5 10 **F**3 9 11 13 15 18 20 26 29 30 34 35 36 40 43 44 45 46 48 49 50 51 53 54 55 56 57 58 59 60 61 63 64 65 66 68 70 72 74 75 76 77 78 79 81 82 84 85 86 87 89 92 93 94 97 98 100 102 103 104 105 118 119 120 129 130 131 132 135 146 147 149 153 **P**6 **S** MedStar Health, Columbia, MD
Primary Contact: Stuart M. Levine, M.D., President and Chief Medical Officer
COO: Jill Donaldson, Vice President Operations
CFO: David R Pitman, Vice President Finance
CMO: Allan Birenberg, Vice President Medical Affairs
CIO: Cynthia Tanebaum, Director Information Services
CHR: Karen Evelius, Director Human Resources
CNO: Lenora Addison, Vice President Patient Care and Nursing
Web address: www.harborhospital.org
Control: Other not–for–profit (including NFP Corporation) **Service**: General medical and surgical

Staffed Beds: 127 **Admissions**: 7437 **Census**: 89 **Outpatient Visits**: 153108 **Births**: 1279 **Total Expense ($000)**: 186860 **Payroll Expense ($000)**: 82847 **Personnel**: 1025

✠ **MEDSTAR UNION MEMORIAL HOSPITAL (210024)**, 201 East University Parkway, Zip 21218–2895; tel. 410/554–2000, **A**1 2 3 5 10 **F**3 9 11 15 17 18 20 22 24 26 28 29 30 31 34 35 37 38 39 40 43 44 45 46 47 48 49 50 51 53 54 55 56 57 58 59 60 61 63 64 65 66 68 70 74 75 77 78 79 80 81 82 84 85 86 87 91 92 93 94 96 97 100 101 102 104 105 107 108 110 111 114 115 118 119 120 121 123 130 131 132 135 141 145 146 149 153 **S** MedStar Health, Columbia, MD
Primary Contact: Bradley Chambers, President
COO: Neil MacDonald, Vice President, Operations
CFO: Deana Stout, Vice President, Finance
CMO: Stuart Bell, M.D., Vice President, Medical Affairs
CIO: Janet Decker, Assistant Vice President, Information Systems
CHR: Ashley Handwerk, Director, Human Resources
CNO: Karen Owings, MSN, Vice President, Patient Care Services
Web address: www.medstarunionmemorial.org
Control: Other not–for–profit (including NFP Corporation) **Service**: General medical and surgical

Staffed Beds: 199 **Admissions**: 11004 **Census**: 133 **Outpatient Visits**: 180479 **Births**: 0 **Total Expense ($000)**: 447451 **Payroll Expense ($000)**: 191017 **Personnel**: 1991

BALTIMORE—Baltimore (City) County

✠ **MERCY MEDICAL CENTER (210008)**, 301 St Paul Place, Zip 21202–2165; tel. 410/332–9000, **A**1 2 3 10 **F**3 4 8 11 13 14 15 18 20 29 30 31 34 35 36 37 39 40 41 44 45 46 47 48 49 50 51 55 57 58 59 64 65 66 68 70 72 74 75 76 77 78 79 81 82 85 86 87 89 92 93 94 100 102 107 108 110 111 114 115 116 117 118 119 120 121 123 126 128 129 130 131 132 135 141 142 143 144 145 146 147 148 149 150 **P**6
Primary Contact: Thomas R. Mullen, President and Chief Executive Officer
COO: Susan D Finlayson, MSN, R.N., Senior Vice President of MMC Operations
CFO: Justin Deibel, Senior Vice President and Chief Financial Officer
CMO: Wilma Rowe, M.D., Senior Vice President Medical Affairs
CIO: Kathleen Perry, Senior Vice President and Chief Information Officer
CHR: Tammy Janus, Senior Vice President Human Resources
CNO: Kim Bushnell, MSN, R.N., Vice President, Patient Care Services
Web address: www.mdmercy.com
Control: Church operated, Nongovernment, not–for–profit **Service**: General medical and surgical

Staffed Beds: 238 **Admissions**: 14032 **Census**: 165 **Outpatient Visits**: 280735 **Births**: 2780 **Total Expense ($000)**: 467919 **Payroll Expense ($000)**: 172813 **Personnel**: 3655

BALTIMORE—Baltimore City County

✠ △ **MT. WASHINGTON PEDIATRIC HOSPITAL (213300)**, 1708 West Rogers Avenue, Zip 21209–4545; tel. 410/578–8600, (Nonreporting) **A**1 3 5 7 10 **S** University of Maryland Medical System, Baltimore, MD
Primary Contact: Sheldon J. Stein, President and Chief Executive Officer
CFO: Mary Miller, Vice President Finance and Business Development
CMO: Richard Katz, M.D., Vice President Medical Affairs
CIO: Tim Brady, Director Information Systems
CHR: Thomas J Ellis, Vice President Human Resources
Web address: www.mwph.org
Control: Other not–for–profit (including NFP Corporation) **Service**: Children's other specialty

Staffed Beds: 61

✠ **SAINT AGNES HEALTHCARE (210011)**, 900 Caton Avenue, Zip 21229–5201; tel. 667/234–6000, **A**1 2 3 5 10 **F**3 8 11 12 13 14 15 17 18 20 22 26 28 29 30 31 32 34 35 40 41 44 46 49 50 53 54 55 56 57 58 59 60 61 64 65 68 70 72 74 75 76 77 78 79 81 82 84 85 86 87 88 89 92 93 96 97 100 107 108 110 111 114 115 117 118 119 120 121 123 124 126 129 130 131 132 134 135 144 146 147 148 149 150 154 **P**6 **S** Ascension Healthcare, Saint Louis, MO
Primary Contact: Keith Vander Kolk, President and Chief Executive Officer
CFO: Scott Furniss, Vice President and Chief Financial Officer
CMO: Nancy Hammond, M.D., Vice President, Chief Medical Officer
CHR: James Bobbitt, Vice President Human Resources, Group Ministry Market
CNO: Yolanda Copeland, R.N., Senior Vice President Patient Care Services and Chief Nursing Officer
Web address: www.stagnes.org
Control: Church operated, Nongovernment, not–for–profit **Service**: General medical and surgical

Staffed Beds: 367 **Admissions**: 15610 **Census**: 190 **Outpatient Visits**: 442700 **Births**: 2018 **Total Expense ($000)**: 433588 **Payroll Expense ($000)**: 215585 **Personnel**: 2519

Many Facility Codes have changed. Please refer to the AHA Guide Code Chart. © 2018 AHA Guide

BALTIMORE—Baltimore County

✠ **SHEPPARD PRATT HEALTH SYSTEM (214000)**, 6501 North Charles Street, Zip 21204–6819, Mailing Address: P.O. Box 6815, Zip 21285–6815; tel. 410/938–3000, **A**1 3 5 10 **F**10 30 35 38 56 58 64 75 87 98 99 101 103 104 105 106 130 132 135 143 144 146 152 153 154
Primary Contact: Harsh Trivedi, M.D., President and Chief Executive Officer
COO: Armando Colombo, Chief Operating Officer
CFO: Ray R Dziesinski, Vice President and Chief Financial Officer
CMO: Robert Roca, M.D., Vice President Medical Affairs
CIO: Matthew Knudsen, Director, Information Systems
CHR: Cathy Doughty, Vice President Human Resources
CNO: Ernestine Y. Cosby, Vice President Clinical Services and Chief Nursing Officer
Web address: www.sheppardpratt.org
Control: Other not–for–profit (including NFP Corporation) **Service:** Psychiatric

Staffed Beds: 336 Admissions: 8630 Census: 289 Outpatient Visits:
87783 Births: 0 Total Expense ($000): 217156 Payroll Expense
($000): 115363 Personnel: 2409

BALTIMORE—Baltimore City County

✠ △ **SINAI HOSPITAL OF BALTIMORE (210012)**, 2401 West Belvedere Avenue, Zip 21215–5271; tel. 410/601–9000, **A**1 2 3 5 7 10 **F**3 5 6 8 9 11 12 13 15 17 18 19 20 22 24 26 28 29 30 31 32 34 35 36 38 39 40 41 43 44 45 46 47 49 50 51 54 55 56 57 58 59 60 61 63 64 65 66 68 70 72 73 74 75 76 77 78 79 80 81 82 83 84 85 86 87 88 89 90 92 93 94 95 96 97 98 100 101 102 103 104 105 107 108 110 111 113 114 115 116 117 118 119 120 121 123 124 126 129 130 131 132 134 135 143 146 147 148 154 **P**6 **S** LifeBridge Health, Baltimore, MD
Primary Contact: Jonathan Ringo, M.D., President and Chief Operating Officer
CFO: David Krajewski, Senior Vice President and Chief Financial Officer
CMO: Daniel C Silverman, M.D., Vice President and Chief Medical Officer
CIO: Karen Barker, Vice President and Chief Information Officer
CHR: Cheryl T. Boyer, Vice President Human Resources
CNO: Linda Kosnik, R.N., MSN, Chief Nursing Officer and Vice President, Patient Care Services
Web address: www.lifebridgehealth.org
Control: Other not–for–profit (including NFP Corporation) **Service:** General medical and surgical

Staffed Beds: 378 Admissions: 17930 Census: 299 Outpatient Visits:
183942 Births: 1920 Total Expense ($000): 741848 Payroll Expense
($000): 306199 Personnel: 4123

BALTIMORE—Baltimore County

☐ **SPRING GROVE HOSPITAL CENTER (214018)**, 55 Wade Avenue, Zip 21228–4663; tel. 410/402–6000, **A**1 3 5 10 **F**30 39 50 68 86 87 91 98 99 100 101 103 130 132 135 146 149 **P**6
Primary Contact: David S. Helsel, M.D., Chief Executive Officer
CFO: Edward Swartz, Chief Financial Officer
CMO: Kelly Phillips, M.D., M.P.H., Clinical Director and Chief Staff
Web address: www.springgrove.com
Control: State, Government, nonfederal **Service:** Psychiatric

Staffed Beds: 377 Admissions: 324 Census: 342 Outpatient Visits: 0
Births: 0 Total Expense ($000): 85000 Payroll Expense ($000): 34000
Personnel: 758

BALTIMORE—Baltimore City County

UNION MEMORIAL HOSPITAL See Medstar Union Memorial Hospital

✠ **UNIVERSITY OF MARYLAND MEDICAL CENTER (210002)**, 22 South Greene Street, Zip 21201–1595; tel. 410/328–9199, (Includes UNIVERSITY OF MARYLAND HOSPITAL FOR CHILDREN, 22 South Greene Street, Baltimore, MD, Zip 21201–1544; tel. 800/492–5538) **A**1 2 3 5 8 10 **F**3 5 6 7 8 9 11 12 13 14 15 17 18 19 20 21 22 23 24 25 26 27 28 29 30 31 32 34 35 36 37 38 39 40 41 43 44 45 46 47 48 49 50 51 54 55 56 57 58 59 60 61 62 64 65 66 68 70 71 72 74 75 76 77 78 79 81 82 85 86 87 88 89 92 93 94 97 98 99 100 101 102 103 104 105 106 107 108 109 110 111 114 115 116 117 118 119 120 121 122 123 124 126 129 130 131 132 134 135 136 137 138 139 140 141 142 143 144 145 146 147 148 149 150 153 154 **P**6 **S** University of Maryland Medical System, Baltimore, MD
Primary Contact: Mohan Suntha, M.D., President and Chief Executive Officer
CFO: Joseph E Hoffman III Senior Vice President and Chief Financial Officer
CMO: Jonathan Gottlieb, M.D., Senior Vice President and Chief Medical Officer
CIO: Jon P Burns, Chief Information Officer
CHR: R Keith Allen, Senior Vice President Human Resources
CNO: Lisa Rowen, R.N., Senior Vice President and Chief Nursing Officer
Web address: www.umm.edu
Control: Other not–for–profit (including NFP Corporation) **Service:** General medical and surgical

Staffed Beds: 680 Admissions: 27416 Census: 593 Outpatient Visits:
322914 Births: 1760 Total Expense ($000): 1470085 Payroll Expense
($000): 614664 Personnel: 8459

✠ **UNIVERSITY OF MARYLAND MEDICAL CENTER MIDTOWN CAMPUS (210038)**, 827 Linden Avenue, Zip 21201–4606; tel. 410/225–8000, **A**1 3 5 10 **F**1 5 11 15 18 20 29 30 31 34 35 40 44 45 49 56 57 59 60 61 64 65 66 68 70 74 75 77 78 79 81 82 84 87 91 93 94 96 97 98 100 101 102 104 106 107 108 111 114 115 118 119 129 130 143 146 148 149 153 154 **P**7 **S** University of Maryland Medical System, Baltimore, MD
Primary Contact: Mohan Suntha, M.D., President and Chief Executive Officer
COO: Donald Ray, Vice President Operations
CFO: Craig Fleischmann, Vice President Finance
CMO: W Eugene Egerton, M.D., Chief Medical Officer
CIO: Jon P Burns, Senior Vice President and Chief Information Officer
CHR: Paula Henderson, Vice President Human Resources
CNO: Lisa Rowen, R.N., Chief Nursing Officer
Web address: www.ummidtown.org/
Control: Other not–for–profit (including NFP Corporation) **Service:** General medical and surgical

Staffed Beds: 170 Admissions: 4525 Census: 92 Outpatient Visits:
131729 Births: 0 Total Expense ($000): 204226 Payroll Expense
($000): 75264 Personnel: 1193

✠ △ **UNIVERSITY OF MARYLAND REHABILITATION & ORTHOPAEDIC INSTITUTE (210058)**, 2200 Kernan Drive, Zip 21207–6697; tel. 410/448–2500, **A**1 3 5 7 10 **F**8 29 30 34 35 39 57 64 68 74 75 77 79 81 82 86 87 90 91 93 94 95 96 100 107 131 132 133 146 148 149 154 **S** University of Maryland Medical System, Baltimore, MD
Primary Contact: Cynthia Kelleher, M.P.H., President and Chief Executive Officer
CFO: W Walter Augustin, CPA, III Vice President Financial Services and Chief Financial Officer
CMO: John P. Straumanis, M.D., Vice President Medical Affairs and Chief Medical Officer
CIO: Linda Hines, Vice President Information Technology and Information Systems
CHR: Paula Henderson, Vice President Human Resources
CNO: Cheryl D Lee, R.N., MSN, Vice President of Patient Care Services and Chief Nursing Officer
Web address: www.umrehabortho.org
Control: Other not–for–profit (including NFP Corporation) **Service:** Rehabilitation

Staffed Beds: 141 Admissions: 2635 Census: 92 Outpatient Visits: 60261
Births: 0 Total Expense ($000): 107006 Payroll Expense ($000): 42979
Personnel: 631

✠ **VETERANS AFFAIRS MARYLAND HEALTH CARE SYSTEM–BALTIMORE DIVISION**, 10 North Greene Street, Zip 21201–1524; tel. 410/605–7001, (Includes VETERANS AFFAIRS MARYLAND HEALTH CARE SYSTEM–PERRY POINT DIVISION, Circle Drive, Perry Point, MD, Zip 21902; tel. 410/642–2411; Adam M. Robinson, Director) (Nonreporting) **A**1 2 3 5 8 **S** Department of Veterans Affairs, Perry Point, MD
Primary Contact: Adam M. Robinson, Director
CFO: Major Tom Scheffler, Chief Fiscal Officer
CMO: Dorothy Snow, M.D., Chief of Staff
CIO: Sharon Zielinski, Chief Information Resource Officer
CHR: Jeff Craig, Chief Human Resource Management
Web address: www.maryland.va.gov/
Control: Veterans Affairs, Government, federal **Service:** General medical and surgical

Staffed Beds: 727

BEL AIR—Harford County

✠ **UNIVERSITY OF MARYLAND UPPER CHESAPEAKE MEDICAL CENTER (210049)**, 500 Upper Chesapeake Drive, Zip 21014–4324; tel. 443/643–1000, **A**1 3 10 **F**11 13 15 18 20 22 26 28 29 30 31 34 35 36 38 40 41 45 46 49 50 51 54 57 59 60 64 65 68 70 71 74 75 76 77 78 79 81 82 84 85 86 87 89 92 93 96 107 108 110 111 114 115 118 119 120 121 124 130 131 132 143 146 147 **S** University of Maryland Medical System, Baltimore, MD
Primary Contact: Lyle Ernest. Sheldon, FACHE, President and Chief Executive Officer
CMO: Peggy Vaughan, M.D., Senior Vice President Medical Affairs
CIO: Rick Casteel, Vice President Management Information Systems and Chief Information Officer
CHR: Toni M Shivery, Vice President Human Resources
Web address: www.uchs.org
Control: Other not–for–profit (including NFP Corporation) **Service:** General medical and surgical

Staffed Beds: 170 Admissions: 11357 Census: 118 Outpatient Visits:
190234 Births: 1312 Total Expense ($000): 265985 Payroll Expense
($000): 98410 Personnel: 1272

MD

Hospital, Medicare Provider Number, Address, Telephone, Approval, Facility, and Physician Codes, Health Care System

★ American Hospital Association (AHA) membership
☐ The Joint Commission accreditation
○ Healthcare Facilities Accreditation Program
◇ DNV Healthcare Inc. accreditation
⇑ Center for Improvement in Healthcare Quality Accreditation
△ Commission on Accreditation of Rehabilitation Facilities (CARF) accreditation

MD

BERLIN—Worcester County

✠ **ATLANTIC GENERAL HOSPITAL (210061)**, 9733 Healthway Drive, Zip 21811–1155; tel. 410/641–1100, (Nonreporting) **A**1 10
Primary Contact: Michael A. Franklin, FACHE, President and Chief Executive Officer
COO: Kim Justice, Vice President Planning and Operations
CFO: Cheryl Nottingham, Chief Financial Officer
CMO: Stephen F Waters, M.D., Medical Director
CIO: Andrew Fowler, Vice President Information Services
CHR: Jim Brannon, Vice President Human Resources
CNO: Colleen Wareing, Vice President Patient Care Services
Web address: www.atlanticgeneral.org
Control: Other not–for–profit (including NFP Corporation) **Service**: General medical and surgical

| Staffed Beds: 45 |

BETHESDA—Montgomery County

✠ **NATIONAL INSTITUTES OF HEALTH CLINICAL CENTER**, 9000 Rockville Pike, Building 10, Room 6–2551, Zip 20892–1504; tel. 301/496–4000, (Includes CHILDREN'S INN AT NIH, 7 West Drive, Bethesda, MD, Zip 20814–1509; tel. 301/496–5672) **A**1 5 8 **F**3 4 5 14 20 22 26 30 31 36 39 45 55 58 59 60 61 64 65 67 68 70 74 75 77 78 79 81 82 84 85 86 87 89 91 92 93 94 95 96 98 99 100 101 103 104 107 108 111 112 114 115 116 117 118 119 120 121 124 126 129 130 132 135 136 141 142 145 146 148 149 152 **S** U.S. Indian Health Service, Rockville, MD
Primary Contact: James K. Gilman, M.D., Chief Executive Officer
COO: Captain Pius Aiyelawo, Chief Operating Officer
CFO: Maria Joyce, Chief Financial Officer
CMO: David K Henderson, M.D., Deputy Director Clinical Care
CIO: Jon W McKeeby, Chief Information Officer
CHR: Bonnie Tuma, Human Resources Team Lead
CNO: Clare Hastings, R.N., Ph.D., Chief Nurse Officer
Web address: www.clinicalcenter.nih.gov
Control: Public Health Service other than 47, Government, federal **Service**: Other specialty treatment

| Staffed Beds: 121 Admissions: 4563 Census: 112 Outpatient Visits: 92329 Births: 0 Total Expense ($000): 460196 Payroll Expense ($000): 181606 Personnel: 1824 |

NATIONAL NAVAL MEDICAL CENTER See Walter Reed National Military Medical Center

✠ **SUBURBAN HOSPITAL (210022)**, 8600 Old Georgetown Road, Zip 20814–1497; tel. 301/896–3100, **A**1 2 3 5 10 **F**3 5 8 11 15 17 18 20 22 24 26 28 29 30 31 34 35 36 37 38 39 40 41 43 44 45 46 49 50 51 56 57 58 59 60 64 70 71 74 75 77 78 79 81 82 84 85 87 92 93 98 99 100 101 102 103 104 105 106 107 108 110 111 115 118 119 120 121 123 126 130 132 135 146 148 152 153 **P**6 **S** Johns Hopkins Health System, Baltimore, MD
Primary Contact: Jacky Schultz, MSN, R.N., President
COO: Joseph Linstrom, Vice President Operations
CFO: Marty Basso, Senior Vice President Finance
CMO: Eric D Dobkin, M.D., Vice President Medical Affairs
CIO: Jason Cole, Senior Director, Management Information Systems
CNO: LeighAnn Sidone, MSN, R.N., Chief Nursing Officer
Web address: www.suburbanhospital.org
Control: Other not–for–profit (including NFP Corporation) **Service**: General medical and surgical

| Staffed Beds: 208 Admissions: 12430 Census: 167 Outpatient Visits: 65895 Births: 0 Total Expense ($000): 281845 Payroll Expense ($000): 104776 Personnel: 1578 |

✠ **WALTER REED NATIONAL MILITARY MEDICAL CENTER**, 8901 Wisconsin Avenue, Zip 20889–5600; tel. 301/295–4611, (Nonreporting) **A**1 2 3 5 **S** Bureau of Medicine and Surgery, Department of the Navy, Falls Church, VA
Primary Contact: Capt. Mark A. Kobelja, MC, USN, Director
CFO: Commander Joseph Pickel, Director Resource Management
CIO: Commander Cayetano Thornton, Chief Information Officer
CHR: Captain Jaime Carroll, Department Head
Web address: www.wrnmmc.capmed.mil/SitePages/home.aspx
Control: Navy, Government, federal **Service**: General medical and surgical

| Staffed Beds: 247 |

CAMBRIDGE—Dorchester County

☐ **EASTERN SHORE HOSPITAL CENTER (214002)**, 5262 Woods Road, Zip 21613–3796, Mailing Address: P.O. Box 800, Zip 21613–0800; tel. 410/221–2300, (Nonreporting) **A**1 10
Primary Contact: Randy L. Bradford, Chief Executive Officer
COO: William Webb, Assistant Superintendent
CFO: William Webb, Assistant Superintendent
CMO: Evangeline Garcia, M.D., Clinical Director
CHR: Cassandra Stanley, Director Personnel
CNO: Lisa Hines, Director Nursing
Web address: www.dhmh.state.md.us/eshc
Control: State, Government, nonfederal **Service**: Psychiatric

| Staffed Beds: 80 |

✠ **UNIVERSITY OF MARYLAND SHORE MEDICAL CENTER AT DORCHESTER**, 300 Byrn Street, Zip 21613–1908; tel. 410/228–5511, (Nonreporting) **A**1 **S** University of Maryland Medical System, Baltimore, MD
Primary Contact: Kenneth D. Kozel, FACHE, President and Chief Executive Officer
COO: Robert A Frank, Senior Vice President Operations
CFO: Joanne A Hahey, Senior Vice President and Chief Financial Officer
CMO: William Huffner, M.D., Vice President Medical Affairs
CIO: Elizabeth Fish, Chief Information Officer
CHR: Susan Coe, Regional Vice President Human Resources
Web address: www.shorehealth.org
Control: Other not–for–profit (including NFP Corporation) **Service**: General medical and surgical

| Staffed Beds: 47 |

CHESTERTOWN—Kent County

CHESTER RIVER HOSPITAL CENTER See University of Maryland Shore Medical Center At Chestertown

✠ **UNIVERSITY OF MARYLAND SHORE MEDICAL CENTER AT CHESTERTOWN (210030)**, 100 Brown Street, Zip 21620–1499; tel. 410/778–3300, (Nonreporting) **A**1 10 **S** University of Maryland Medical System, Baltimore, MD
Primary Contact: Kenneth D. Kozel, FACHE, President and Chief Executive Officer
COO: Robert A Frank, Senior Vice President of Operations
CFO: Joanne A Hahey, Vice President Finance and Chief Financial Officer
CMO: William Huffner, M.D., Chief Medical Officer
CIO: Elizabeth Fish, Senior Director Site Executive and Information Technology
CHR: Susan Coe, Vice President Human Resources
CNO: Ruth Ann Jones, Ed.D., MSN, R.N., Senior Vice President, Chief Nursing Officer
Web address: www.umms.org/hospitals/shore–health–system.htm
Control: Other not–for–profit (including NFP Corporation) **Service**: General medical and surgical

| Staffed Beds: 124 |

CHEVERLY—Prince George's County

GLADYS SPELLMAN SPECIALTY HOSPITAL AND NURSING CENTER, 2900 Mercy Lane, Zip 20785–1157; tel. 301/618–2010, (Nonreporting)
Primary Contact: Stewart R. Seitz, Chief Executive Officer
CFO: Ketty Taboado, Chief Financial Officer
CMO: Paul A Devore, M.D., Medical Director
CHR: Michael Jacobs, Vice President Human Resources
Web address: www.dimensionshealth.org
Control: Corporation, Investor–owned (for–profit) **Service**: Chronic disease

| Staffed Beds: 30 |

☐ **UNIVERSITY OF MARYLAND CAPITAL REGION HEALTH PRINCE GEORGE'S HOSPITAL CENTER (210003)**, 3001 Hospital Drive, Zip 20785–1189; tel. 301/618–2000, **A**1 3 5 10 **F**3 11 13 15 17 18 20 22 24 26 28 29 31 34 35 38 40 43 45 46 47 48 50 54 55 56 57 59 60 61 63 64 65 66 68 69 70 72 74 75 76 77 78 79 81 82 84 85 86 87 92 93 97 98 100 101 102 103 104 105 107 108 110 111 114 115 118 119 130 131 132 134 135 142 144 146 147 148 153 **P**6 **S** University of Maryland Medical System, Baltimore, MD
Primary Contact: Sherry B. Perkins, Ph.D., R.N., President and Chief Executive Officer
CFO: William Brosius, Chief Financial Officer
CIO: Henry Archibong, Vice President, Information Services and Technology
CHR: Veronica Ford, Vice President Human Resources
CNO: Katie Boston–Leary, Vice President and Chief Nursing Officer, UMPGHC
Web address: www.princegeorgeshospital.org
Control: Other not–for–profit (including NFP Corporation) **Service**: General medical and surgical

| Staffed Beds: 227 Admissions: 11039 Census: 163 Outpatient Visits: 86551 Births: 1367 Total Expense ($000): 306738 Payroll Expense ($000): 125589 Personnel: 1608 |

CLINTON—Prince George's County

✠ **MEDSTAR SOUTHERN MARYLAND HOSPITAL CENTER (210062)**, 7503 Surratts Road, Zip 20735–3358; tel. 301/868–8000, **A**1 2 10 **F**3 13 15 17 18 20 22 26 28 29 30 34 35 37 39 40 44 46 47 48 49 50 57 58 59 60 61 64 66 68 70 74 75 76 77 78 79 80 81 82 85 86 87 93 98 100 101 102 105 107 108 114 115 118 119 126 129 130 132 135 141 143 146 147 148 149 **S** MedStar Health, Columbia, MD
Primary Contact: Christine R. Wray, President
CFO: Daniel Feeley, Interim Chief Financial Officer
CMO: Yvette Johnson–Threat, Vice President Medical Affairs
CIO: Lou Mavromatis, Vice President Information Technology
CHR: Paul Zeller, Vice President Human Resources
CNO: Patricia A Scalfari, Vice President Nursing
Web address: www.medstarsouthernmaryland.org
Control: Other not–for–profit (including NFP Corporation) **Service**: General medical and surgical

| Staffed Beds: 216 Admissions: 10514 Census: 129 Outpatient Visits: 140671 Births: 1212 Total Expense ($000): 226249 Payroll Expense ($000): 92415 Personnel: 1178 |

Many Facility Codes have changed. Please refer to the AHA Guide Code Chart. © 2018 AHA Guide

SOUTHERN MARYLAND HOSPITAL CENTER See Medstar Southern Maryland Hospital Center

COLUMBIA—Howard County

☒ **HOWARD COUNTY GENERAL HOSPITAL (210048)**, 5755 Cedar Lane, Zip 21044–2999; tel. 410/740–7890, **A**1 2 3 5 10 **F**3 8 11 13 15 18 20 22 26 28 29 30 31 32 34 35 36 39 40 41 44 45 46 47 49 50 51 55 56 57 58 59 60 61 64 65 68 70 72 74 75 76 77 78 79 81 82 84 85 86 87 89 91 92 93 96 98 99 100 101 102 103 107 108 110 111 115 119 130 131 132 134 135 146 147 148 149 **S** Johns Hopkins Health System, Baltimore, MD
Primary Contact: Steven C. Snelgrove, President
CFO: Claro M Pio Roda, Dr.PH, Vice President, Finance and Chief Financial Officer
CMO: Mohammed Shafeeq Ahmed, M.D., Vice President of Medical Affairs and Chief Medical Officer
CHR: Jon Oravec, Vice President, Human Resources
CNO: Karen Davis, Chief Nursing Officer and Vice President, Nursing
Web address: www.hcgh.org
Control: Other not–for–profit (including NFP Corporation) **Service**: General medical and surgical

Staffed Beds: 262 **Admissions:** 17121 **Census:** 188 **Outpatient Visits:** 140875 **Births:** 3537 **Total Expense ($000):** 258420 **Payroll Expense ($000):** 99775 **Personnel:** 1584

CRISFIELD—Somerset County

☐ **MCCREADY HEALTH (210045)**, 201 Hall Highway, Zip 21817–1299; tel. 410/968–1200, (Nonreporting) **A**1 10
Primary Contact: Kathleen Harrison, Chief Executive Officer
CFO: Gary W Broadwater, Chief Financial Officer
Web address: www.mccreadyhealth.org
Control: Other not–for–profit (including NFP Corporation) **Service**: General medical and surgical

Staffed Beds: 89

CUMBERLAND—Allegany County

☐ **THOMAS B. FINAN CENTER (214012)**, 10102 Country Club Road SE, Zip 21502–8339, Mailing Address: P.O. Box 1722, Zip 21501–1722; tel. 301/777–2405, (Nonreporting) **A**1 10
Primary Contact: John Cullen, Chief Executive Officer
COO: Craig Alexander, Chief Operating Officer
CFO: Gina Spears, Chief Financial Officer
CMO: David Millis, M.D., Clinical Director
CHR: Chris Loney, Director Personnel
CNO: Gayle Walter, Director of Nursing
Web address: www.dhmh.state.md.us
Control: State, Government, nonfederal **Service**: Psychiatric

Staffed Beds: 80

☒ △ **WESTERN MARYLAND REGIONAL MEDICAL CENTER (210027)**, 12500 Willowbrook Road SE, Zip 21502–6393, Mailing Address: P.O. Box 539, Zip 21501–0539; tel. 240/964–7000, (Total facility includes 88 beds in nursing home–type unit) **A**1 2 7 10 **F**3 5 11 13 14 15 17 18 20 22 24 26 28 29 30 31 32 34 35 40 43 44 45 49 50 53 54 56 57 58 59 60 62 63 64 66 68 70 73 74 75 76 77 78 79 80 81 82 84 85 86 87 89 90 93 94 96 97 98 100 101 102 104 107 108 110 111 114 116 117 119 120 121 124 126 128 129 130 132 134 135 144 145 146 148 150 153 154 **P**6
Primary Contact: Barry P. Ronan, President and Chief Executive Officer
COO: Nancy D. Adams, R.N., Senior Vice President and Chief Operating Officer
CFO: Kimberly S Repac, Senior Vice President and Chief Financial Officer
CMO: Gerald Goldstein, M.D., Senior Vice President and Chief Medical Officer
CIO: William J. Byers, Chief Information Officer
CHR: Christopher Bumbaugh, Executive Director Human Resource and Organizational Development
CNO: James M. Karstetter, R.N., II Vice President & Chief Nursing Officer
Web address: www.wmhs.com
Control: Other not–for–profit (including NFP Corporation) **Service**: General medical and surgical

Staffed Beds: 321 **Admissions:** 11673 **Census:** 234 **Outpatient Visits:** 584172 **Births:** 915 **Total Expense ($000):** 322864 **Payroll Expense ($000):** 109581 **Personnel:** 1548

EASTON—Talbot County

☒ △ **UNIVERSITY OF MARYLAND SHORE MEDICAL CENTER AT EASTON (210037)**, 219 South Washington Street, Zip 21601–2996; tel. 410/822–1000, (Nonreporting) **A**1 2 7 10 **S** University of Maryland Medical System, Baltimore, MD
Primary Contact: Kenneth D. Kozel, FACHE, President and Chief Executive Officer
COO: Robert A Frank, Senior Vice President of Operations
CFO: Joanne A Hahey, Senior Vice President and Chief Financial Officer
CMO: William Huffner, M.D., Chief Medical Officer
CIO: Elizabeth Fish, Chief Information Officer
CHR: Susan Coe, Regional Vice President Human Resources
CNO: Ruth Ann Jones, Ed.D., MSN, R.N., Senior Vice President, Chief Nursing Officer
Web address: www.shorehealth.org
Control: Other not–for–profit (including NFP Corporation) **Service**: General medical and surgical

Staffed Beds: 132

ELKTON—Cecil County

☒ **UNION HOSPITAL (210032)**, 106 Bow Street, Zip 21921–5596; tel. 410/398–4000, **A**1 2 3 5 10 **F**2 3 11 12 13 15 18 26 29 30 31 34 35 38 40 44 45 46 49 50 51 53 54 57 59 61 64 69 70 74 75 76 77 78 79 81 82 84 85 86 87 89 92 93 97 98 100 102 104 107 108 110 111 114 118 119 129 130 131 132 135 146 147 148 149 154 **P**6
Primary Contact: Richard C. Szumel, M.D., Chief Executive Officer
CFO: Laurie Beyer, Senior Vice President and Chief Financial Officer
CMO: Cydney Teal, M.D., Vice President Medical Affairs
CIO: Anne Lara, Chief Information Officer
CHR: Terrence Lovell, Vice President Human Resources
Web address: www.uhcc.com
Control: Other not–for–profit (including NFP Corporation) **Service**: General medical and surgical

Staffed Beds: 109 **Admissions:** 5442 **Census:** 56 **Outpatient Visits:** 140205 **Births:** 577 **Total Expense ($000):** 157260 **Payroll Expense ($000):** 69771 **Personnel:** 994

FREDERICK—Frederick County

☒ **FREDERICK REGIONAL HEALTH SYSTEM (210005)**, 400 West Seventh Street, Zip 21701–4593; tel. 240/566–3300, (Nonreporting) **A**1 2 5 10
Primary Contact: Thomas A. Kleinhanzl, President and Chief Executive Officer
COO: John R Verbus, Senior Vice President and Chief Operating Officer
CFO: Michelle K Mahan, Senior Vice President and Chief Financial Officer
CMO: Manuel Casiano, M.D., Senior Vice President Medical Affairs
CIO: David Quirke, Vice President Information Services
CNO: Cheryl Cioffi, R.N., Senior Vice President Patient Care Services and Chief Nursing Officer
Web address: www.fmh.org
Control: Other not–for–profit (including NFP Corporation) **Service**: General medical and surgical

Staffed Beds: 281

GERMANTOWN—Montgomery County

★ **HOLY CROSS GERMANTOWN HOSPITAL (210065)**, 19801 Observation Drive, Zip 20876–4070; tel. 301/754–7000, **A**3 **F**3 11 12 13 18 26 29 30 31 35 39 40 45 46 49 50 56 58 59 60 64 66 68 70 73 74 75 76 77 78 79 81 84 85 86 87 93 97 98 100 102 107 108 111 115 118 119 120 126 130 132 144 146 147 149 **S** Trinity Health, Livonia, MI
Primary Contact: Doug Ryder, President
Web address: www.holycrosshealth.org/germantown
Control: Church operated, Nongovernment, not–for–profit **Service**: General medical and surgical

Staffed Beds: 101 **Admissions:** 5523 **Census:** 56 **Outpatient Visits:** 30909 **Births:** 855 **Total Expense ($000):** 97125 **Payroll Expense ($000):** 34022 **Personnel:** 545

MD

GLEN BURNIE—Anne Arundel County

⊠ **UNIVERSITY OF MARYLAND BALTIMORE WASHINGTON MEDICAL CENTER (210043)**, 301 Hospital Drive, Zip 21061-5899; tel. 410/787-4000, **A**1 2 3 5 10 **F**3 11 13 15 18 20 22 26 28 29 30 31 32 34 35 36 37 38 39 40 41 43 44 45 46 48 49 50 54 55 56 57 58 59 60 63 64 68 70 74 75 76 77 79 81 82 84 85 86 87 89 93 98 100 101 102 104 107 111 114 115 118 119 120 121 122 123 124 126 129 130 131 132 134 135 146 147 148 149 150 153 **P**6 **S** University of Maryland Medical System, Baltimore, MD
Primary Contact: Karen E. Olscamp, President and Chief Executive Officer
COO: Kathleen McCollum, Senior Vice President, Clinical Integration and Chief Operating Officer
CFO: Al Pietsch, CPA, Senior Vice President and Chief Financial Officer
CMO: Neel Vibhakar, M.D., Senior Vice President and Chief Medical Officer
CIO: Jon P Burns, Senior Vice President and Chief Information Officer
CHR: Kathy Poehler, Vice President, Human Resources
CNO: Catherine Whitaker, MSN, R.N., Vice President and Chief Nursing Officer
Web address: www.mybwmc.org
Control: Other not-for-profit (including NFP Corporation) **Service**: General medical and surgical

Staffed Beds: 326 **Admissions**: 16843 **Census**: 201 **Outpatient Visits**: 126816 **Births**: 972 **Total Expense ($000)**: 337057 **Payroll Expense ($000)**: 134212 **Personnel**: 2307

HAGERSTOWN—Washington County

☐ **BROOK LANE HEALTH SERVICES (214003)**, 13121 Brook Lane, Zip 21742-1435, Mailing Address: P.O. Box 1945, Zip 21742-1945; tel. 301/733-0330, (Nonreporting) **A**1 10
Primary Contact: R Lynn. Rushing, Chief Executive Officer
COO: Jason Allen, Chief Operating Officer
CFO: David Schey, Chief Financial Officer
CMO: David Gonzalez, M.D., Medical Director
CIO: Robert Fritz, Chief Information Officer
CHR: Nicole Twigg, Director Human Resources
CNO: Jason Allen, Director Patient Care Services
Web address: www.brooklane.org
Control: Other not-for-profit (including NFP Corporation) **Service**: Psychiatric

Staffed Beds: 57

⊠ △ **MERITUS MEDICAL CENTER (210001)**, 11116 Medical Campus Road, Zip 21742-6710; tel. 301/790-8000, **A**1 2 7 10 13 **F**3 5 11 12 13 15 17 18 20 22 26 28 29 30 31 34 35 38 40 44 49 51 52 54 56 57 58 59 60 61 62 64 65 70 74 75 76 77 78 79 81 82 83 84 85 86 87 89 90 93 94 96 97 98 99 100 101 102 103 104 107 108 111 114 115 118 119 120 121 123 130 131 132 135 143 144 145 146 147 148 153 154 **P**6 8
Primary Contact: Joseph P. Ross, President and Chief Executive Officer
CFO: Thomas T. Chan, Chief Financial Officer
CMO: Heather Lorenzo, M.D., Vice President and Chief Medical Officer
CHR: Laura Minteer, Chief Human Resource Officer
CNO: Melanie M Heuston, Chief Nursing Office
Web address: www.meritushealth.com
Control: Other not-for-profit (including NFP Corporation) **Service**: General medical and surgical

Staffed Beds: 278 **Admissions**: 15794 **Census**: 183 **Outpatient Visits**: 198530 **Births**: 1757 **Total Expense ($000)**: 309164 **Payroll Expense ($000)**: 105644 **Personnel**: 1812

WASHINGTON COUNTY HEALTH SYSTEM See Meritus Medical Center

☐ △ **WESTERN MARYLAND HOSPITAL CENTER (212002)**, 1500 Pennsylvania Avenue, Zip 21742-3194; tel. 301/745-4200, (Nonreporting) **A**1 7 10
Primary Contact: Michael Reyka, Ph.D., Chief Executive Officer
COO: David Davis, Chief Operating Officer
CFO: Kelly Edmonds, Chief Financial Officer
CMO: Monica Stallworth, M.D., Chief of Staff
CIO: Ron Keplinger, Chief Information Officer
CHR: David Davis, Chief Operating Officer
Web address: www.wmhc.us
Control: State, Government, nonfederal **Service**: Acute long-term care hospital

Staffed Beds: 120

HAVRE DE GRACE—Harford County

⊠ **UNIVERSITY OF MARYLAND HARFORD MEMORIAL HOSPITAL (210006)**, 501 South Union Avenue, Zip 21078-3493; tel. 443/843-5000, **A**1 10 **F**11 12 15 29 30 31 34 35 36 38 40 46 49 50 51 57 59 60 64 65 66 68 70 71 74 75 77 78 79 81 82 84 85 86 87 92 93 98 102 103 104 107 108 110 111 114 115 118 119 129 130 131 132 135 146 148 **S** University of Maryland Medical System, Baltimore, MD
Primary Contact: Lyle Ernest. Sheldon, FACHE, President and Chief Executive Officer
CMO: Peggy Vaughan, M.D., Senior Vice President Medical Affairs
CIO: Rick Casteel, Vice President Management Information Systems and Chief Information Officer
CHR: Toni M Shivery, Vice President Human Resources
Web address: www.uchs.org
Control: Other not-for-profit (including NFP Corporation) **Service**: General medical and surgical

Staffed Beds: 85 **Admissions**: 4429 **Census**: 60 **Outpatient Visits**: 53128 **Births**: 0 **Total Expense ($000)**: 84926 **Payroll Expense ($000)**: 39649 **Personnel**: 558

JESSUP—Howard County

☐ **CLIFTON T. PERKINS HOSPITAL CENTER**, 8450 Dorsey Run Road, Zip 20794-9486; tel. 410/724-3000, (Nonreporting) **A**1 3 5
Primary Contact: John Robison, Chief Executive Officer
COO: Thomas D Lewis, Chief Operating Officer
CFO: George Parnel, Chief Financial Officer
CMO: Muhammed Ajanah, M.D., Clinical Director
CIO: Chanda Hamilton, Chief Information Officer
CHR: Beverly Stacie, Director Human Resources
Web address: www.dhmh.state.md.us/perkins/
Control: State, Government, nonfederal **Service**: Psychiatric

Staffed Beds: 250

LA PLATA—Charles County

⊠ **UNIVERSITY OF MARYLAND CHARLES REGIONAL MEDICAL CENTER (210035)**, 5 Garrett Avenue, Zip 20646-5960, Mailing Address: P.O. Box 1070, Zip 20646-1070; tel. 301/609-4000, **A**1 2 10 **F**3 11 13 15 28 29 30 31 34 35 38 40 44 45 50 51 56 57 59 61 64 70 74 76 77 78 79 81 82 84 85 86 87 89 91 92 93 107 108 110 111 115 118 119 130 132 135 144 145 146 148 149 **S** University of Maryland Medical System, Baltimore, MD
Primary Contact: Noel A. Cervino, President and Chief Executive Officer
CFO: Erik Boas, Chief Financial Officer
CMO: Joseph Moser, M.D., Chief Medical Officer
CIO: John Czahor, IT Site Executive
CHR: Stacey M Cook, MS, Vice President, Human Resources
CNO: Dana Levy, Chief Nursing Officer
Web address: www.charlesregional.org
Control: Other not-for-profit (including NFP Corporation) **Service**: General medical and surgical

Staffed Beds: 89 **Admissions**: 6646 **Census**: 76 **Outpatient Visits**: 77419 **Births**: 874 **Total Expense ($000)**: 117918 **Payroll Expense ($000)**: 46758 **Personnel**: 742

LANHAM—Prince George's County

⊠ **DOCTORS COMMUNITY HOSPITAL (210051)**, 8118 Good Luck Road, Zip 20706-3574; tel. 301/552-8118, **A**1 10 **F**3 8 12 15 18 20 26 27 28 29 30 31 34 35 40 44 49 50 51 53 54 57 59 64 70 71 75 77 78 79 81 84 85 86 87 93 107 108 111 114 115 118 119 123 126 129 130 131 132 135 146 149 **P**6
Primary Contact: Philip B. Down, Chief Executive Officer
COO: Paul Grenaldo, Executive Vice President and Chief Operating Officer
CFO: Camille Bash, Chief Financial Officer
CMO: Sunil Madan, M.D., Chief Medical Officer and Chief Population Health Officer
CIO: Joyce Hanscome, Chief Information Officer
CHR: Paul Hagens, Vice President Human Resources
Web address: www.dchweb.org
Control: Other not-for-profit (including NFP Corporation) **Service**: General medical and surgical

Staffed Beds: 144 **Admissions**: 9977 **Census**: 149 **Outpatient Visits**: 62581 **Births**: 0 **Total Expense ($000)**: 193854 **Payroll Expense ($000)**: 86344 **Personnel**: 1382

LAUREL—Prince George's County

☐ △ **UNIVERSITY OF MARYLAND CAPITAL REGION HEALTH AT LAUREL REGIONAL HOSPITAL (210055)**, 7300 Van Dusen Road, Zip 20707-9463; tel. 301/725-4300, **A**1 7 10 **F**1 3 11 18 26 27 29 30 31 34 35 39 40 41 45 47 49 50 51 56 57 59 60 61 64 65 66 68 69 70 74 75 77 78 79 81 82 84 85 86 87 90 93 96 98 100 101 102 103 105 107 108 110 111 114 115 119 130 132 135 146 148 149 153 **P**6 **S** University of Maryland Medical System, Baltimore, MD
Primary Contact: Trudy Hall, M.D., Vice President Medical Affairs and Interim Chief Executive Officer
CFO: Lisa Goodlett, Senior Vice President and Chief Financial Officer
CMO: Trudy Hall, M.D., Vice President Medical Affairs
CIO: David Peterson, Chief Information Officer
CHR: John Peeples, Senior Vice President Human Resources
CNO: June Meyer, MSN, R.N., Vice President Chief Nursing Officer
Web address: www.laurelregionalhospital.org
Control: Other not-for-profit (including NFP Corporation) **Service**: General medical and surgical

Staffed Beds: 70 **Admissions**: 3766 **Census**: 60 **Outpatient Visits**: 28319 **Births**: 0 **Total Expense ($000)**: 93884 **Payroll Expense ($000)**: 37366 **Personnel**: 454

LEONARDTOWN—St. Mary's County

⊠ **MEDSTAR ST. MARY'S HOSPITAL (210028)**, 25500 Point Lookout Road, Zip 20650-2015, Mailing Address: PO Box 527, Zip 20650-0527; tel. 301/475-6001, **A**1 2 10 **F**3 11 13 15 18 28 29 30 31 32 34 35 36 39 40 44 45 48 50 51 53 54 57 59 63 64 65 66 68 70 71 74 75 76 77 78 79 81 82 84 85 86 87 89 93 97 100 101 102 103 104 105 107 108 110 111 114 115 116 117 118 119 129 130 132 134 135 143 144 146 147 148 149 150 **S** MedStar Health, Columbia, MD
Primary Contact: Christine R. Wray, President
COO: Stephen T. Michaels, M.D., Chief Operating Officer and Chief Medical Officer
CIO: Donald Sirk, Director Information Systems
Web address: www.medstarstmarys.org
Control: Other not-for-profit (including NFP Corporation) **Service**: General medical and surgical

Staffed Beds: 103 **Admissions**: 7423 **Census**: 82 **Outpatient Visits**: 181111 **Births**: 1188 **Total Expense ($000)**: 169121 **Payroll Expense ($000)**: 68634 **Personnel**: 995

Many Facility Codes have changed. Please refer to the AHA Guide Code Chart.   © 2018 AHA Guide

OAKLAND—Garrett County

✠ **GARRETT REGIONAL MEDICAL CENTER (210017)**, 251 North Fourth Street, Zip 21550–1375; tel. 301/533–4000, (Total facility includes 10 beds in nursing home–type unit) **A**1 10 **F**3 11 13 28 29 30 31 32 34 35 38 40 45 50 53 56 57 59 64 65 68 70 75 76 77 78 79 81 83 84 85 87 89 102 107 108 114 119 128 130 132 135 141 143 144 146 147 148 149 154 **P**6
Primary Contact: Mark G. Boucot, FACHE, President and Chief Executive Officer
CFO: Tracy Lipscomb, CPA, Vice President Financial Services and Chief Financial Officer
CMO: Marjorie Fridkin, M.D., Chief Medical Officer
CIO: Steven Peterson, Chief Information Officer, Vice President of Operations
CHR: Laura M Waters, Vice President Human Resources
CNO: Kendra Thayer, MSN, R.N., Chief Nursing Officer, Vice President Clinical Services
Web address: www.gcmh.com
Control: Other not–for–profit (including NFP Corporation) **Service**: General medical and surgical

Staffed Beds: 59 **Admissions**: 2075 **Census**: 20 **Outpatient Visits**: 77590 **Births**: 289 **Total Expense ($000)**: 52656 **Payroll Expense ($000)**: 21341 **Personnel**: 377

OLNEY—Montgomery County

✠ **MEDSTAR MONTGOMERY MEDICAL CENTER (210018)**, 18101 Prince Philip Drive, Zip 20832–1512; tel. 301/774–8882, **A**1 2 3 10 **F**3 4 5 9 11 12 13 15 18 20 26 28 29 30 31 34 35 36 37 38 40 41 44 45 46 48 49 50 51 53 55 56 57 58 59 60 61 64 65 68 70 74 75 76 77 78 79 80 81 82 84 85 86 87 89 92 93 97 98 99 102 103 104 105 107 108 110 111 114 115 118 119 120 121 123 124 126 129 130 131 132 134 135 146 147 148 149 153 **P**6 **S** MedStar Health, Columbia, MD
Primary Contact: Thomas J. Senker, FACHE, President
CFO: David A Havrilla, Chief Financial Officer
CMO: Frederick Finelli, M.D., Vice President Medical Affairs
CIO: Chistiane Brown, Assistant Vice President
CHR: Kevin Mell, Vice President Operations
CNO: Connie Stone, R.N., Chief Nursing Officer
Web address: www.medstarmontgomery.org
Control: Other not–for–profit (including NFP Corporation) **Service**: General medical and surgical

Staffed Beds: 147 **Admissions**: 7221 **Census**: 85 **Outpatient Visits**: 80661 **Births**: 524 **Total Expense ($000)**: 160660 **Payroll Expense ($000)**: 62580 **Personnel**: 866

OXEN HILL—Prince George's County

✠ **FORT WASHINGTON MEDICAL CENTER (210060)**, 174 Waterfront Street, Suite 225, Zip 20744; tel. 301/292–7000, **A**1 10 **F**3 15 29 30 34 35 40 41 45 47 50 51 57 59 60 61 64 68 70 74 75 77 79 81 82 85 86 87 100 107 108 110 114 118 119 130
Primary Contact: Joseph B. Tucker, Acting President and Chief Executive Officer
COO: Al Campbell, Senior Vice President and Chief Operating Officer
CFO: Joseph B Tucker, Senior Vice President and Chief Financial Officer
CMO: Elias Debbas, M.D., President Medical Staff
CIO: Fred Ashby, Director Information Technology
CHR: Alexander Morris, Corporate Director Human Resources
CNO: Marjorie Quint–Bouzid, Chief Nursing Officer and Vice President Patient Care Services
Web address: www.fortwashingtonmc.org
Control: Other not–for–profit (including NFP Corporation) **Service**: General medical and surgical

Staffed Beds: 37 **Admissions**: 2107 **Census**: 21 **Outpatient Visits**: 42718 **Births**: 2 **Total Expense ($000)**: 42237 **Payroll Expense ($000)**: 20470 **Personnel**: 315

PERRY POINT—Cecil County

VETERANS AFFAIRS MARYLAND HEALTH CARE SYSTEM–PERRY POINT DIVISION See Veterans Affairs Maryland Health Care System–Baltimore Division, Baltimore

PRINCE FREDERICK—Calvert County

✠ **CALVERTHEALTH MEDICAL CENTER (210039)**, 100 Hospital Road, Zip 20678–4017; tel. 410/535–4000, (Total facility includes 18 beds in nursing home–type unit) **A**1 10 **F**3 8 11 13 18 20 26 28 29 30 31 32 34 35 36 38 39 40 41 43 45 46 47 48 49 50 51 54 56 57 59 61 64 65 66 68 70 71 74 75 76 77 78 79 81 82 84 85 86 87 89 93 98 99 100 101 102 104 105 107 108 111 112 114 115 119 124 127 129 130 132 133 134 135 144 146 147 148 149 153 154 **P**4
Primary Contact: Dean Teague, FACHE, Chief Executive Officer
CFO: Carolyn Heithaus, Chief Financial Officer
CMO: J Michael Brooks, M.D., Chief Medical Officer
CIO: Philip Campbell, Vice President Information Services
CHR: Anthony M. Bladen, Vice President Human Resources
CNO: Diane Couchman, Vice President Patient Care Services and Chief Nursing Executive
Web address: www.calverthospital.com
Control: Other not–for–profit (including NFP Corporation) **Service**: General medical and surgical

Staffed Beds: 112 **Admissions**: 5525 **Census**: 64 **Outpatient Visits**: 163290 **Births**: 648 **Total Expense ($000)**: 135480 **Payroll Expense ($000)**: 58639 **Personnel**: 1042

RANDALLSTOWN—Baltimore County

☐ **NORTHWEST HOSPITAL (210040)**, 5401 Old Court Road, Zip 21133–5185; tel. 410/521–2200, (Nonreporting) **A**1 2 3 10 **S** LifeBridge Health, Baltimore, MD
Primary Contact: Faraaz Yousuf, President and Chief Operating Officer
COO: Kelly Corbi, Chief Operating Officer
CFO: Nancy Kane, Assistant Vice President Finance LifeBridge Health
CMO: Ronald L Ginsberg, M.D., Vice President Medical Affairs
CIO: Tressa Springmann, Vice President and Chief Information Officer
CHR: Valerie Brandenburg, Director Human Resources
CNO: Susan L Jalbert, R.N., MS, Vice President Patient Care Services and Chief Nursing Officer
Web address: www.lifebridgehealth.org
Control: Other not–for–profit (including NFP Corporation) **Service**: General medical and surgical

Staffed Beds: 253

ROCKVILLE—Montgomery County

☐ **ADVENTIST BEHAVIORAL HEALTH AND WELLNESS SERVICES (214013)**, 14901 Broschart Road, Zip 20850–3318; tel. 301/251–4500, (Nonreporting) **A**1 3 10 **S** Adventist HealthCare, Gaithersburg, MD
Primary Contact: Kevin Young, FACHE, President
CFO: Randy Reimer, Chief Financial Officer
CMO: Peter H Levine, M.D., Executive Medical Director Behavioral Health Services
CIO: Kathleen Dyer, Vice President and Chief Information Officer
CHR: Mary Cloutier, Director Human Resources
Web address: www.adventistbehavioralhealth.com
Control: Other not–for–profit (including NFP Corporation) **Service**: Psychiatric

Staffed Beds: 220

☐ △ **ADVENTIST HEALTHCARE PHYSICAL HEALTH AND REHABILITATION (213029)**, 9909 Medical Center Drive, Zip 20850–6361; tel. 240/864–6000, (Nonreporting) **A**1 7 10 **S** Adventist HealthCare, Gaithersburg, MD
Primary Contact: Brent Reitz, President
COO: Jason Makaroff, Chief Operating Officer and Associate Vice President
CMO: Terrence P Sheehan, M.D., Medical Director
CHR: Carrie Hibbard, Human Resource Business Partner
CNO: Valerie Summerlin, R.N., MS, Chief Nursing Officer
Web address: www.adventistrehab.com
Control: Other not–for–profit (including NFP Corporation) **Service**: Rehabilitation

Staffed Beds: 77

MD

Hospital, Medicare Provider Number, Address, Telephone, Approval, Facility, and Physician Codes, Health Care System

★ American Hospital Association (AHA) membership ☐ The Joint Commission accreditation ○ Healthcare Facilities Accreditation Program ◇ DNV Healthcare Inc. accreditation ⇧ Center for Improvement in Healthcare Quality Accreditation △ Commission on Accreditation of Rehabilitation Facilities (CARF) accreditation

☐ **ADVENTIST HEALTHCARE SHADY GROVE MEDICAL CENTER (210057)**, 9901 Medical Center Drive, Zip 20850–3395; tel. 240/826–6000, **A**1 2 3 10 **F**3 12 13 15 18 20 22 26 28 29 30 31 36 39 40 41 45 46 47 48 50 51 53 55 57 60 61 64 66 68 70 72 74 75 76 77 78 79 81 82 83 84 85 87 89 102 107 108 110 111 114 115 116 117 119 120 121 126 129 130 135 146 148 149 **P**8 **S** Adventist HealthCare, Gaithersburg, MD
Primary Contact: John Sackett, President SGMC and Executive Vice President and Chief Operating Officer
COO: Eunmee Shim, R.N., MSN, Vice President Operations
CFO: Daniel Cochran, Vice President and Chief Financial Officer
CMO: Kevin Smothers, M.D., Vice President Chief Medical Officer
CIO: christopher Ghion, Vice President and Chief Information Officer
CNO: Joan M Vincent, MSN, MS, R.N., Vice President Patient Care Services and Chief Nurse Executive
Web address: www.adventisthealthcare.com
Control: Church operated, Nongovernment, not-for-profit **Service:** General medical and surgical

Staffed Beds: 315 **Admissions:** 16653 **Census:** 179 **Outpatient Visits:** 91097 **Births:** 4550 **Total Expense ($000):** 347981 **Payroll Expense ($000):** 127152 **Personnel:** 1674

POTOMAC RIDGE BEHAVIORAL HEALTH See Adventist Behavioral Health and Wellness Services

SALISBURY—Wicomico County

✠ **DEER'S HEAD HOSPITAL CENTER (212003)**, 351 Deer's Head Hospital Road, Zip 21801–3201, Mailing Address: PO Box 2018, Zip 21802–2018; tel. 410/543–4000, (Total facility includes 61 beds in nursing home–type unit) **A**1 10 **F**1 3 11 28 29 30 44 50 56 57 59 60 61 65 68 75 77 82 84 85 86 87 90 91 93 94 96 128 130 132 135 146 148 149 **P**6
Primary Contact: Mary Beth Waide, JD, MS, R.N., Chief Executive Officer
CFO: Kenneth Waller, Fiscal Administrator
CMO: Michael P. Buchness, M.D., Director Medical
CIO: Mac Beattie, Computer Network Specialist
CHR: Luanne G Dashield, Personnel Administrator
CNO: Cheri Porcelli, MSN, R.N., Chief Nursing Officer
Web address: www.deershead.org
Control: State, Government, nonfederal **Service:** Chronic disease

Staffed Beds: 73 **Admissions:** 100 **Census:** 46 **Outpatient Visits:** 8830 **Births:** 0 **Total Expense ($000):** 24729 **Payroll Expense ($000):** 9773 **Personnel:** 234

✠ △ **HEALTHSOUTH CHESAPEAKE REHABILITATION HOSPITAL (213028)**, 220 Tilghman Road, Zip 21804–1921; tel. 410/546–4600, (Nonreporting) **A**1 7 10 **S** Encompass Health Corporation, Birmingham, AL
Primary Contact: Steven Walas, Chief Executive Officer
CFO: Karen Rounsley, Controller
CHR: Belinda Thompson, Coordinator Human Resources
CNO: Belle Goslee, Chief Nursing Officer
Web address: www.healthsouthchesapeake.com
Control: Corporation, Investor–owned (for-profit) **Service:** Rehabilitation

Staffed Beds: 54

✠ **PENINSULA REGIONAL MEDICAL CENTER (210019)**, 100 East Carroll Street, Zip 21801–5422; tel. 410/546–6400, **A**1 2 3 10 **F**3 11 12 13 15 17 18 20 22 24 26 28 29 30 31 32 34 35 37 40 43 44 45 46 47 48 49 50 51 53 54 57 58 59 60 61 64 68 70 71 73 74 75 76 77 78 79 81 82 84 85 86 87 89 92 97 98 100 102 104 105 107 108 110 111 114 115 118 119 120 121 123 124 126 130 132 135 143 144 145 146 147 148 149 153 154 **P**5 8
Primary Contact: Steven E. Leonard, President and Chief Executive Officer
COO: Cindy Lunsford, Executive Vice President and Chief Operating Officer
CFO: Bruce Ritchie, Vice President of Finance and Chief Financial Officer
CMO: Charles B Silvia, M.D., Chief Medical Officer and Vice President Medical Affairs
CIO: Raymond Adkins, Chief Information Officer
CHR: Scott Peterson, Vice President of People and Organizational Development
CNO: Karen C Poisker, MSN, Vice President Patient Care Services and Chief Nursing Officer
Web address: www.peninsula.org
Control: Other not-for-profit (including NFP Corporation) **Service:** General medical and surgical

Staffed Beds: 291 **Admissions:** 17237 **Census:** 207 **Outpatient Visits:** 562568 **Births:** 1873 **Total Expense ($000):** 440221 **Payroll Expense ($000):** 175710 **Personnel:** 2616

SILVER SPRING—Montgomery County

✠ **HOLY CROSS HOSPITAL (210004)**, 1500 Forest Glen Road, Zip 20910–1487; tel. 301/754–7000, **A**1 2 3 5 10 **F**3 7 11 12 13 15 17 18 20 22 26 29 30 31 40 41 45 46 49 50 56 58 60 64 66 68 69 70 72 74 75 76 77 78 79 81 82 84 85 86 87 89 93 97 100 102 107 108 110 111 115 118 119 120 121 123 124 126 129 130 132 144 146 147 148 149 154 **S** Trinity Health, Livonia, MI
Primary Contact: Louis Damiano, M.D., President
CFO: Anne Gillis, Chief Financial Officer
CMO: Blair Eig, M.D., Senior Vice President Medical Affairs
CIO: Matthew Trimmer, Director Information Services
CHR: J Manuel Ocasio, Vice President Human Resources
CNO: Celia Guarino, R.N., MSN, Vice President and Chief Nursing Officer
Web address: www.holycrosshealth.org
Control: Church operated, Nongovernment, not-for-profit **Service:** General medical and surgical

Staffed Beds: 415 **Admissions:** 31464 **Census:** 359 **Outpatient Visits:** 164798 **Births:** 9599 **Total Expense ($000):** 430741 **Payroll Expense ($000):** 194594 **Personnel:** 2425

SILVER SPRING—Prince George's County

☐ **SAINT LUKE INSTITUTE**, 8901 New Hampshire Avenue, Zip 20903–3611; tel. 301/445–7970, (Nonreporting) **A**1
Primary Contact: David Songy, President and Chief Executive Officer
COO: Sister Danile Lynch, Chief Operating Officer
Web address: www.sli.org
Control: Other not-for-profit (including NFP Corporation) **Service:** Psychiatric

Staffed Beds: 24

SYKESVILLE—Carroll County

☐ **SPRINGFIELD HOSPITAL CENTER (214004)**, 6655 Sykesville Road, Zip 21784–7966; tel. 410/970–7000, **A**1 10 **F**11 30 35 39 44 50 53 56 57 68 75 77 86 87 98 101 103 130 132 135 146 149 **P**6
Primary Contact: Paula A. Langmead, Chief Executive Officer
COO: Daniel Triplett, Acting Chief Operating Officer
CFO: Keith Hardesty, Chief Financial Officer
CMO: Kim Bright, M.D., Clinical Director
CIO: Denise Maskell, Chief Information Officer
CNO: Gloria Merek, Director of Nursing
Web address: www.dhmh.state.md.us/springfield
Control: State, Government, nonfederal **Service:** Psychiatric

Staffed Beds: 220 **Admissions:** 280 **Census:** 217 **Outpatient Visits:** 0 **Births:** 0 **Total Expense ($000):** 74263 **Payroll Expense ($000):** 40146 **Personnel:** 654

TAKOMA PARK—Montgomery County

☐ △ **ADVENTIST HEALTHCARE WASHINGTON ADVENTIST HOSPITAL (210016)**, 7600 Carroll Avenue, Zip 20912–6392; tel. 301/891–7600, (Nonreporting) **A**1 2 3 5 7 10 **S** Adventist HealthCare, Gaithersburg, MD
Primary Contact: Erik Wangsness, President
Web address: www.adventisthealthcare.com
Control: Other not-for-profit (including NFP Corporation) **Service:** General medical and surgical

Staffed Beds: 230

TOWSON—Baltimore County

✠ **UNIVERSITY OF MARYLAND ST. JOSEPH MEDICAL CENTER (210063)**, 7601 Osler Drive, Zip 21204–7582; tel. 410/337–1000, **A**1 2 3 10 **F**3 11 13 15 17 18 20 22 24 26 28 29 30 31 34 35 36 37 40 41 44 45 46 47 48 49 50 54 55 56 57 58 59 60 61 64 65 66 68 70 71 72 74 75 76 77 78 79 81 82 84 85 86 87 89 91 92 93 97 98 100 101 102 103 104 107 108 114 115 118 119 120 121 122 123 124 128 132 134 135 144 146 147 148 149 153 **P**6 **S** University of Maryland Medical System, Baltimore, MD
Primary Contact: Thomas Smyth, President and Chief Executive Officer
COO: Craig Carmichael, Vice President, Operations
CMO: Gail Cunningham, Interim Chief Medical Officer
CIO: Thomas Gronert, Chief Information Officer
CNO: Pamela Jamieson, Vice President Patient Care Services and Chief Nursing Officer
Web address: www.stjosephtowson.com/home.aspx
Control: Other not-for-profit (including NFP Corporation) **Service:** General medical and surgical

Staffed Beds: 287 **Admissions:** 15131 **Census:** 157 **Outpatient Visits:** 110233 **Births:** 2261 **Total Expense ($000):** 341333 **Payroll Expense ($000):** 110501 **Personnel:** 1856

WESTMINSTER—Carroll County

✠ **CARROLL HOSPITAL CENTER (210033)**, 200 Memorial Avenue, Zip 21157–5799; tel. 410/848–3000, **A**1 2 10 **F**3 5 11 13 15 18 19 20 22 26 28 29 30 31 32 34 35 36 37 38 39 40 44 45 46 49 50 51 54 55 56 57 58 59 62 63 64 68 70 74 75 76 77 78 79 81 82 83 84 85 86 87 89 93 94 96 98 99 100 101 102 103 104 105 107 108 109 111 114 115 118 119 120 121 126 129 130 131 132 134 135 145 146 147 148 149 153 **P**6 **S** LifeBridge Health, Baltimore, MD
Primary Contact: Leslie Simmons, FACHE, R.N., President
CFO: Kevin Kelbly, Senior Vice President Finance and Corporate Fiscal Affairs
CMO: Mark Olszyk, M.D., Vice President Medical Affairs and Chief Medical Officer
CHR: Holly Phipps Adams, Vice President of Human Resources
CNO: Stephanie Reid, R.N., Vice President of Patient Care Services and Chief Nursing Officer
Web address: www.carrollhospitalcenter.org
Control: Other not-for-profit (including NFP Corporation) **Service:** General medical and surgical

Staffed Beds: 143 **Admissions:** 9937 **Census:** 105 **Outpatient Visits:** 167991 **Births:** 1037 **Personnel:** 1575

MASSACHUSETTS

ATHOL—Worcester County

☐ **ATHOL HOSPITAL (221303)**, 2033 Main Street, Zip 01331–3598;
tel. 978/249–3511, (Nonreporting) **A**1 10 18 **S** Heywood Healthcare, Gardner, MA
Primary Contact: Winfield S. Brown, FACHE, President and Chief Executive Officer
COO: Michael Grimmer, Chief Operating Officer
CFO: Robert Crosby, Chief Financial Officer
CMO: Mohsen Noreldin, M.D., President Medical Staff
CIO: Carol Roosa, Vice President Information Services and Chief Information Officer
CNO: Lucille Songer, Chief Nursing Officer
Web address: www.atholhospital.org
Control: Other not–for–profit (including NFP Corporation) **Service:** General medical and surgical

Staffed Beds: 25

ATTLEBORO—Bristol County

☐ **ARBOUR–FULLER HOSPITAL (224021)**, 200 May Street, Zip 02703–5520;
tel. 508/761–8500, (Nonreporting) **A**1 10 **S** Universal Health Services, Inc., King of Prussia, PA
Primary Contact: Rachel Legend, Chief Executive Officer
CFO: James Rollins, Chief Financial Officer
CMO: Aminadav Zakai, M.D., Medical Director
CHR: Brian Jenkins, Director Human Resources
Web address: www.arbourhealth.com
Control: Corporation, Investor–owned (for–profit) **Service:** Psychiatric

Staffed Beds: 46

★ ⇑ **STURDY MEMORIAL HOSPITAL (220008)**, 211 Park Street,
Zip 02703–3137, Mailing Address: PO Box 2963, Zip 02703–0963;
tel. 508/222–5200, **A**2 5 10 21 **F**3 8 12 13 15 18 20 28 29 30 31 32 34 35 36 39 40 44 45 46 49 50 56 57 58 59 61 64 70 74 75 76 77 78 79 81 82 85 86 87 89 93 97 100 107 108 109 110 111 115 118 119 129 130 131 132 134 144 146 147 148 **P**5 6
Primary Contact: Joseph Casey, Interim President and Chief Executive Officer
CFO: Amy Pfeffer, Chief Financial Officer
CMO: Brian Kelly, M.D., Vice President Medical Affairs and Medical Director
CHR: Cheryl Barrows, Vice President Human Resources
CNO: David Spoor, R.N., Vice President, Patient Care Services and Chief Nursing Officer
Web address: www.sturdymemorial.org
Control: Other not–for–profit (including NFP Corporation) **Service:** General medical and surgical

Staffed Beds: 132 **Admissions:** 6811 **Census:** 80 **Outpatient Visits:** 217911 **Births:** 666 **Total Expense ($000):** 169427 **Payroll Expense ($000):** 85932 **Personnel:** 1062

AYER—Middlesex County

☐ **NASHOBA VALLEY MEDICAL CENTER (220098)**, 200 Groton Road,
Zip 01432–3300; tel. 978/784–9000, (Nonreporting) **A**1 10 **S** Steward Health Care System, LLC, Dallas, TX
Primary Contact: Korry Dow, Interim President
CFO: Ben Moll, Assistant Chief Financial Officer
CMO: Michael Older, M.D., President Medical Staff
CNO: Cheryl L Bonasoro, MSN, R.N., Vice President of Nursing and Chief Operating Officer
Web address: www.nashobamed.org
Control: Corporation, Investor–owned (for–profit) **Service:** General medical and surgical

Staffed Beds: 48

BEDFORD—Middlesex County

⊞ **BEDFORD VETERANS AFFAIRS MEDICAL CENTER, EDITH NOURSE ROGERS MEMORIAL VETERANS HOSPITAL**, 200 Springs Road, Zip 01730–1198;
tel. 781/687–2000, (Nonreporting) **A**1 3 5 **S** Department of Veterans Affairs, Perry Point, MD
Primary Contact: Joan Clifford, R.N., FACHE, Director
COO: Mark Fontaine–Westhart, Associate Director
CFO: Edward Koetting, Chief Financial Officer
CMO: Dan Berlowitz, M.D., M.P.H., Acting Chief of Staff
CHR: Robert Colpitts, Chief Human Resource Service
CNO: Mary Ann Petrillo, R.N., MSN, Acting Associate Director Nursing and Patient Clinical Services
Web address: www.bedford.va.gov
Control: Veterans Affairs, Government, federal **Service:** Psychiatric

Staffed Beds: 461

BELMONT—Middlesex County

⊞ **MCLEAN HOSPITAL (224007)**, 115 Mill Street, Zip 02478–1064;
tel. 617/855–2000, **A**1 3 5 10 **F**4 5 29 50 53 56 58 68 77 86 98 100 101 103 104 105 106 111 119 130 132 134 146 152 153 **P**6 **S** Partners HealthCare System, Inc., Boston, MA
Primary Contact: Scott L. Rauch, M.D., President and Psychiatrist in Chief
COO: Michele L Gougeon, Executive Vice President and Chief Operating Officer
CFO: David A Lagasse, Senior Vice President Fiscal Affairs
CMO: Joseph Gold, M.D., Chief Medical Officer
CHR: Lisa D. Pratt, Vice President, Human Resources
CNO: Linda Flaherty, R.N., Senior Vice President, Patient Care Services
Web address: www.mcleanhospital.org
Control: Other not–for–profit (including NFP Corporation) **Service:** Psychiatric

Staffed Beds: 217 **Admissions:** 6371 **Census:** 189 **Outpatient Visits:** 51005 **Births:** 0 **Total Expense ($000):** 226026 **Payroll Expense ($000):** 96098 **Personnel:** 1712

BEVERLY—Essex County

⊞ **BEVERLY HOSPITAL (220033)**, 85 Herrick Street, Zip 01915–1777;
tel. 978/922–3000, (Includes ADDISON GILBERT HOSPITAL, 298 Washington Street, Gloucester, MA, Zip 01930–4887; tel. 978/283–4000) (Nonreporting) **A**1 2 3 5 10 **S** Lahey Health, Burlington, MA
Primary Contact: Philip M. Cormier, Chief Executive Officer
COO: Pauline Pike, Chief Operating Officer
CFO: Gary P Marlow, Chief Financial Officer
CMO: Peter H Short, M.D., Senior Vice President Medical Affairs
CIO: Robert Laramie, Chief Information Officer
CHR: Althea C Lyons, Vice President Human Resources and Development
Web address: www.beverlyhospital.org
Control: Other not–for–profit (including NFP Corporation) **Service:** General medical and surgical

Staffed Beds: 320

BOSTON—Suffolk County

☐ **ARBOUR HOSPITAL (224013)**, 49 Robinwood Avenue, Zip 02130–2156;
tel. 617/522–4400, (Nonreporting) **A**1 10 **S** Universal Health Services, Inc., King of Prussia, PA
Primary Contact: Eric Kennedy, Chief Executive Officer
Web address: www.arbourhealth.com
Control: Other not–for–profit (including NFP Corporation) **Service:** Psychiatric

Staffed Beds: 118

Hospital, Medicare Provider Number, Address, Telephone, Approval, Facility, and Physician Codes, Health Care System			
★ American Hospital Association (AHA) membership	○ Healthcare Facilities Accreditation Program	⇑ Center for Improvement in Healthcare Quality Accreditation	
☐ The Joint Commission accreditation	◇ DNV Healthcare Inc. accreditation	△ Commission on Accreditation of Rehabilitation Facilities (CARF) accreditation	

MA

✠ **BETH ISRAEL DEACONESS MEDICAL CENTER (220086)**, 330 Brookline Avenue, Zip 02215–5491; tel. 617/667–7000, **A**1 2 3 5 8 10 **F**3 5 6 9 11 12 13 14 15 17 18 20 22 24 26 28 29 30 31 32 34 35 36 37 38 40 43 44 45 46 47 48 49 50 51 52 53 54 55 56 57 58 59 60 61 63 64 65 66 68 70 71 72 73 74 75 77 78 79 81 82 84 85 86 87 92 93 97 98 100 101 102 103 104 107 108 109 110 111 112 113 114 115 116 117 118 119 120 121 123 124 126 129 130 131 132 135 136 138 139 141 142 143 144 145 146 147 148 149 150 154 **P**8
Primary Contact: Kevin Tabb, M.D., Chief Executive Officer
CFO: Steven P Fischer, Chief Financial Officer
CMO: Anthony Weiss, M.D., Chief Medical Officer
CIO: John Halamka, M.D., Chief Information Officer
CHR: Judi Bieber, Senior Vice President Human Resources
CNO: Marsha L. Maurer, R.N., MS, Chief Nursing Officer Patient Care Services
Web address: www.bidmc.harvard.edu
Control: Other not–for–profit (including NFP Corporation) **Service**: General medical and surgical

Staffed Beds: 704 **Admissions:** 35917 **Census:** 577 **Outpatient Visits:** 696718 **Births:** 5023 **Total Expense ($000):** 1658387 **Payroll Expense ($000):** 667605 **Personnel:** 8521

☐ **BOSTON CHILDREN'S HOSPITAL (223302)**, 300 Longwood Avenue, Zip 02115–5737; tel. 617/355–6000, **A**1 3 5 8 10 **F**3 8 11 12 14 18 19 20 21 22 23 24 25 26 27 28 29 30 31 32 34 35 36 37 38 39 40 41 43 44 45 46 48 49 50 51 54 55 57 58 59 60 61 62 63 64 65 67 68 72 74 75 77 78 79 80 81 82 83 84 85 86 87 88 89 92 93 94 97 98 99 100 101 102 104 105 106 107 108 109 111 112 113 114 115 116 117 118 119 120 121 123 124 126 129 130 131 132 134 135 136 137 138 139 140 141 142 143 144 146 147 148 149 150 151 153 154 **P**3 5
Primary Contact: Sandra L. Fenwick, M.P.H., President and Chief Executive Officer
COO: Kevin B Churchwell, M.D., Chief Operating Officer and Executive Vice President Health Affairs
CFO: Douglas M Vanderslice, Senior Vice President and Chief Financial Officer
CIO: Daniel Nigrin, M.D., Vice President Information Services and Chief Information Officer
CHR: Inez Stewart, Vice President
Web address: www.childrenshospital.org/
Control: Other not–for–profit (including NFP Corporation) **Service**: Children's general medical and surgical

Staffed Beds: 415 **Admissions:** 14790 **Census:** 321 **Outpatient Visits:** 703373 **Births:** 0 **Total Expense ($000):** 1645169 **Payroll Expense ($000):** 578536 **Personnel:** 10101

✠ **BOSTON MEDICAL CENTER (220031)**, 1 Boston Medical Center Place, Zip 02118–2908; tel. 617/638–8000, **A**1 2 3 5 8 10 **F**3 5 8 9 12 13 15 17 18 20 22 24 26 28 29 30 31 32 34 35 36 38 40 41 43 44 45 46 47 48 49 50 54 55 56 57 58 59 60 61 64 65 66 68 70 72 74 75 76 77 78 79 81 82 84 85 86 87 88 89 93 97 99 100 101 102 103 104 107 108 110 111 114 116 117 118 119 120 121 123 124 126 129 130 131 132 134 135 136 138 142 143 144 145 146 147 148 149 150 **P**7
Primary Contact: Kate Walsh, M.P.H., President and Chief Executive Officer
CFO: Ronald E Bartlett, Chief Financial Officer
CMO: Ravin Davidoff, M.D., Chief Medical Officer
CHR: Stephanie Lovell, Vice President and General Counsel
Web address: www.bmc.org
Control: Other not–for–profit (including NFP Corporation) **Service**: General medical and surgical

Staffed Beds: 449 **Admissions:** 23148 **Census:** 335 **Outpatient Visits:** 1281475 **Births:** 2821 **Total Expense ($000):** 1274372 **Payroll Expense ($000):** 475340 **Personnel:** 6488

✠ **BRIGHAM AND WOMEN'S FAULKNER HOSPITAL (220119)**, 1153 Centre Street, Zip 02130–3446; tel. 617/983–7000, **A**1 3 5 10 **F**3 4 5 9 11 12 15 18 28 29 30 32 34 35 40 41 45 46 47 49 50 51 54 56 57 58 59 64 65 68 70 74 75 77 79 81 82 84 85 86 87 91 93 94 96 98 100 101 102 103 104 105 107 108 110 111 114 115 118 119 126 129 130 131 132 135 145 146 147 148 149 154 **P**6 **S** Partners HealthCare System, Inc., Boston, MA
Primary Contact: David O. McCready, President
CFO: Gerard Hadley, Vice President Finance for Brigham & Women's Faulkner Hospital and Vice President Finance and Controller
CMO: Margaret M. Duggan, M.D., Chief Medical Officer
CIO: Catherine Schroeder, Deputy Chief Information Officer
CHR: Laura Barnett, Executive Director, Human Resources
CNO: Cori Loescher, R.N., Chief Nursing Officer and Vice President of Patient Care Services
Web address: www.brighamandwomensfaulkner.org/index.asp
Control: Other not–for–profit (including NFP Corporation) **Service**: General medical and surgical

Staffed Beds: 144 **Admissions:** 10032 **Census:** 106 **Outpatient Visits:** 202461 **Births:** 0 **Total Expense ($000):** 258173 **Payroll Expense ($000):** 100841 **Personnel:** 1218

✠ **BRIGHAM AND WOMEN'S HOSPITAL (220110)**, 75 Francis Street, Zip 02115–6110; tel. 617/732–5500, **A**1 2 3 5 8 10 **F**3 5 6 8 9 11 12 13 14 15 16 17 18 20 22 24 26 28 29 30 31 32 33 34 35 36 37 38 39 40 43 44 45 46 47 48 49 50 51 52 53 54 55 56 57 58 59 60 61 64 65 66 68 70 71 72 74 75 76 77 78 79 81 82 83 84 85 86 87 92 93 97 99 100 101 102 103 104 105 107 108 110 111 112 114 115 116 117 118 119 120 121 123 124 126 129 130 131 132 133 134 135 136 137 138 140 141 142 143 144 145 146 147 148 149 150 151 152 153 154 **P**6 **S** Partners HealthCare System, Inc., Boston, MA
Primary Contact: Elizabeth Nabel, M.D., President
COO: Ron Walls, M.D., Executive Vice President and Chief Operating Officer
CFO: Christopher Dunleavy, Senior Vice President Finance and Chief Financial Officer
CMO: Stanley Ashley, M.D., Senior Vice President Medical Affairs and Chief Medical Officer
CIO: Adam Landman, M.D., Chief Information Officer
CHR: Sabrina Williams, Interim Vice President Human Resources
CNO: Madelyn Pearson, R.N., Senior Vice President Patient Care Services and Chief Nursing Officer
Web address: www.brighamandwomens.org
Control: Other not–for–profit (including NFP Corporation) **Service**: General medical and surgical

Staffed Beds: 761 **Admissions:** 41015 **Census:** 688 **Outpatient Visits:** 1150136 **Births:** 6346 **Total Expense ($000):** 2883064 **Payroll Expense ($000):** 786243 **Personnel:** 13434

☐ **CARNEY HOSPITAL (220017)**, 2100 Dorchester Avenue, Zip 02124–5615; tel. 617/296–4000, (Nonreporting) **A**1 3 5 10 **S** Steward Health Care System, LLC, Dallas, TX
Primary Contact: Tom Sands, Interim Chief Executive Officer
COO: Christian Stroucken, Chief Operating Officer
CFO: David McGrail, Vice President Finance
CMO: Alexander White, Vice President Medical Affairs
CHR: Mary Orlandi, Manager Human Resources
Web address: www.carneyhospital.org
Control: Corporation, Investor–owned (for–profit) **Service**: General medical and surgical

Staffed Beds: 81

✠ **DANA–FARBER CANCER INSTITUTE (220162)**, 450 Brookline Avenue, Zip 02215–5418; tel. 617/632–3000, **A**1 2 3 5 8 10 **F**3 11 15 29 30 31 32 34 35 36 44 50 54 55 56 57 58 59 64 65 66 68 71 75 77 78 82 83 84 85 86 87 99 100 101 104 107 108 110 111 114 115 117 118 119 120 121 123 124 130 132 134 135 136 146 147 148 149 150 154 **P**6
Primary Contact: Laurie H. Glimcher, M.D., President and Chief Executive Officer
COO: Dorothy E Puhy, Executive VP and Chief Operating Officer
CIO: Jeffrey R Kessler, Vice President Information Services
CHR: Emily Barclay, Vice President Human Resources
Web address: www.dana–farber.org
Control: Other not–for–profit (including NFP Corporation) **Service**: Cancer

Staffed Beds: 30 **Admissions:** 1043 **Census:** 28 **Outpatient Visits:** 435316 **Births:** 0 **Total Expense ($000):** 1519072 **Payroll Expense ($000):** 411518 **Personnel:** 4992

DR. SOLOMON CARTER FULLER MENTAL HEALTH CENTER (224040), 85 East Newton Street, Zip 02118–2340; tel. 617/626–8700, (Nonreporting) **A**3 5 10
Primary Contact: Mary–Louise White, M.D., Chief Operating Officer
Web address: www.mass.gov/service–details/metro–boston–area
Control: Other not–for–profit (including NFP Corporation) **Service**: Psychiatric

Staffed Beds: 32

✠ **MASSACHUSETTS EYE AND EAR (220075)**, 243 Charles Street, Zip 02114–3002; tel. 617/523–7900, **A**1 3 5 10 **F**3 7 8 11 29 30 31 34 35 36 40 41 44 50 54 55 56 57 58 59 64 65 66 68 74 75 77 78 81 82 85 86 87 89 107 111 114 119 130 132 141 143 144 146 148 149 **P**6 **S** Partners HealthCare System, Inc., Boston, MA
Primary Contact: John R. Fernandez, President and Chief Executive Officer
CFO: CarolAnn Williams, Chief Financial Officer
CIO: Leo Hill, Chief Information Officer
CHR: Martha Pyle Farrell, Vice President Human Resources and General Counsel
Web address: www.masseyeandear.org
Control: Other not–for–profit (including NFP Corporation) **Service**: Eye, ear, nose and throat

Staffed Beds: 41 **Admissions:** 1292 **Census:** 13 **Outpatient Visits:** 449447 **Births:** 0 **Total Expense ($000):** 276045 **Payroll Expense ($000):** 74504 **Personnel:** 1838

⊞ **MASSACHUSETTS GENERAL HOSPITAL (220071)**, 55 Fruit Street,
Zip 02114–2696; tel. 617/726–2000, (Includes MASSGENERAL HOSPITAL FOR
CHILDREN, 55 Fruit Street, Boston, MA, Zip 02114–2621; tel. 888/644–3248)
A1 3 5 8 10 **F**3 5 6 8 9 11 12 13 14 15 16 17 18 19 20 21 22 23 24 25 26 27
28 29 30 31 32 33 34 35 36 37 38 39 40 41 43 44 45 46 47 48 49 50 51 52
53 54 55 56 57 58 59 60 61 62 63 64 65 66 68 70 71 72 73 74 75 76 77 78
79 80 81 82 84 85 86 87 88 89 91 92 93 94 96 97 98 99 100 101 102 103
104 105 107 108 110 111 112 113 114 115 116 117 118 119 120 121 122
123 124 126 129 130 131 132 134 135 136 137 138 139 140 141 142 143
144 145 146 147 148 149 150 151 152 153 154 **P**6 7 **S** Partners HealthCare
System, Inc., Boston, MA
Primary Contact: Peter L. Slavin, M.D., President
CFO: Sally Mason Boemer, Senior Vice President Finance
CMO: Britain Nicholson, M.D., Chief Medical Officer
CIO: Keith Jennings, Chief Information Officer
CHR: Jeff Davis, Senior Vice President Human Resources
CNO: Jeanette R Ives Erickson, MS, R.N., Senior Vice President Patient Care and
Chief Nurse
Web address: www.massgeneral.org
Control: Other not–for–profit (including NFP Corporation) **Service**: General
medical and surgical

Staffed Beds: 1032 **Admissions:** 51446 **Census:** 867 **Outpatient Visits:**
926719 **Births:** 3849 **Total Expense ($000):** 3719141 **Payroll Expense
($000):** 1080553 **Personnel:** 17529

⊞ **NEW ENGLAND BAPTIST HOSPITAL (220088)**, 125 Parker Hill Avenue,
Zip 02120–2847; tel. 617/754–5800, **A**1 3 5 10 **F**3 8 9 14 18 29 30 34 35 37
44 45 50 53 54 57 58 59 64 65 66 70 74 75 77 79 81 82 85 86 87 92 93 97
107 108 111 115 119 130 131 141 146 148
Primary Contact: David Passafaro, Chief Executive Officer
CFO: Thomas Gheringhelli, Senior Vice President, Chief Financial Officer
CHR: Linda Thompson, Senior Vice President, Human Resources and Service
Excellence
CNO: Mary Sullivan Smith, R.N., MS, Senior Vice President, Chief Operating Officer
and Chief Nursing Officer
Web address: www.nebh.org
Control: Other not–for–profit (including NFP Corporation) **Service**: Orthopedic

Staffed Beds: 113 **Admissions:** 8332 **Census:** 61 **Outpatient Visits:**
117481 **Births:** 0 **Total Expense ($000):** 244109 **Payroll Expense
($000):** 83909 **Personnel:** 893

☐ **SHRINERS HOSPITALS FOR CHILDREN–BOSTON (223304)**, 51 Blossom
Street, Zip 02114–2601; tel. 617/722–3000, (Nonreporting) **A**1 3 5 10 **S**
Shriners Hospitals for Children, Tampa, FL
Primary Contact: Eileen F. Skinner, FACHE, Administrator
CFO: Maria Chung, CPA, Director Fiscal Services
CMO: Matthias B Donelan, M.D., Chief of Staff
CIO: Mary Dolan, Regional Director Information Services and HIPAA Security Official
CHR: John Donlin, Regional Director Human Resources – Boston, Erie, and
Springfield
Web address: www.shrinershospitalsforchildren.org/Hospitals/Locations/Boston
Control: Other not–for–profit (including NFP Corporation) **Service**: Children's other
specialty

Staffed Beds: 14

⊞ **TUFTS MEDICAL CENTER (220116)**, 800 Washington Street, Zip 02111–1552;
tel. 617/636–5000, **A**1 2 3 5 8 10 **F**3 12 13 14 15 17 18 19 20 21 22 23 24
25 26 27 28 29 30 31 32 34 35 39 40 41 43 44 45 47 49 50 51 52 55 56 57
58 59 61 64 65 68 70 71 72 74 75 76 77 78 79 81 82 84 85 86 87 88 89 93
97 98 100 102 104 107 108 111 114 116 117 118 119 120 121 123 124
126 129 130 131 132 134 135 136 137 138 143 146 147 148 149 **P**5
Primary Contact: Michael Apkon, MD, PhD, Chief Executive Officer
CFO: Kristine Hanscom, Chief Financial Officer
CMO: David Fairchild, M.D., Chief Medical Officer
CIO: William Shickolovich, Chief Information Officer
CNO: Therese M. Hudson–Jinks, R.N., MSN, Chief Nursing Officer
Web address: www.tuftsmedicalcenter.org
Control: Other not–for–profit (including NFP Corporation) **Service**: General
medical and surgical

Staffed Beds: 284 **Admissions:** 17227 **Census:** 270 **Outpatient Visits:**
429097 **Births:** 1321 **Total Expense ($000):** 769781 **Payroll Expense
($000):** 297372 **Personnel:** 4752

BRADFORD—Essex County

⊞ **WHITTIER REHABILITATION HOSPITAL (222047)**, 145 Ward Hill Avenue,
Zip 01835–6928; tel. 978/372–8000, (Nonreporting) **A**1 10 **S** Whittier Health
Network, Haverhill, MA
Primary Contact: Alfred J. Arcidi, M.D., Senior Vice President
Web address: www.whittierhealth.com
Control: Partnership, Investor–owned (for–profit) **Service**: Acute long–term care
hospital

Staffed Beds: 60

BRAINTREE—Norfolk County

⊞ **HEALTHSOUTH BRAINTREE REHABILITATION HOSPITAL (223027)**, 250
Pond Street, Zip 02184–5351; tel. 781/348–2500, (Nonreporting) **A**1 5 10 **S**
Encompass Health Corporation, Birmingham, AL
Primary Contact: Randy Doherty, CPA, Chief Executive Officer
CFO: Barry Leonard I Vice President of Finance
CMO: Arthur Williams, M.D., Medical Director
CHR: Cathryn Wigman, Director Human Resources
CNO: Jinia Drinkwater, R.N., Director Patient Care Services
Web address: www.braintreerehabhospital.com
Control: Corporation, Investor–owned (for–profit) **Service**: Rehabilitation

Staffed Beds: 187

BRIDGEWATER—Plymouth County

BRIDGEWATER STATE HOSPITAL, 20 Administration Road, Zip 02324–3201;
tel. 508/279–4521, (Nonreporting) **A**3 5
Primary Contact: Daniel Calais Jr, Superintendent
CFO: Diane Wholley, Director Fiscal Services
Control: State, Government, nonfederal **Service**: Psychiatric

Staffed Beds: 350

BRIGHTON—Suffolk County

CARITAS ST. ELIZABETH'S MEDICAL CENTER See St. Elizabeth's Medical
Center

⊞ **FRANCISCAN CHILDREN'S (223300)**, 30 Warren Street, Zip 02135–3680;
tel. 617/254–3800, **A**1 10 **F**1 29 30 38 39 50 58 59 64 65 68 75 77 81 86 87
90 91 93 97 98 99 100 101 104 105 106 130 132 146 **P**8
Primary Contact: John D. Nash, FACHE, President and Chief Executive Officer
COO: Donna Polselli, Chief Operating Officer
CFO: Alex Denucci, Chief Financial Officer
CMO: Jane E O'Brien, M.D., Medical Director
CIO: Sean McKeon, Director, Information Technology
CHR: Nancy Murphy, Vice President, Human Resources
CNO: Mary Lou Kelleher, R.N., MSN, Vice President, Nursing
Web address: www.franciscanhospital.org
Control: Other not–for–profit (including NFP Corporation) **Service**: Children's
rehabilitation

Staffed Beds: 74 **Admissions:** 821 **Census:** 64 **Outpatient Visits:** 36366
Births: 0 **Total Expense ($000):** 58784 **Payroll Expense ($000):** 34755
Personnel: 497

☐ **ST. ELIZABETH'S MEDICAL CENTER (220036)**, 736 Cambridge Street,
Zip 02135–2997; tel. 617/789–3000, (Nonreporting) **A**1 2 5 8 10 **S** Steward
Health Care System, LLC, Dallas, TX
Primary Contact: Craig T. Williams, President
CFO: Jeffrey P. Dion, Vice President Finance
CMO: Dicken S.C. Ko, M.D., Vice President of Medical Affairs and Chief Medical
Officer
CIO: Joseph Schmitt, Chief Information Officer
CHR: Claudia Henderson, Chief Human Resources
Web address: www.semc.org/
Control: Corporation, Investor–owned (for–profit) **Service**: General medical and
surgical

Staffed Beds: 338

BROCKTON—Plymouth County

CARITAS GOOD SAMARITAN MEDICAL CENTER See Good Samaritan Medical
Center

MA

Hospital, Medicare Provider Number, Address, Telephone, Approval, Facility, and Physician Codes, Health Care System

★ American Hospital Association (AHA) membership ○ Healthcare Facilities Accreditation Program ⇑ Center for Improvement in Healthcare Quality Accreditation
☐ The Joint Commission accreditation ◇ DNV Healthcare Inc. accreditation △ Commission on Accreditation of Rehabilitation Facilities (CARF) accreditation

☐ **GOOD SAMARITAN MEDICAL CENTER (220111)**, 235 North Pearl Street, Zip 02301–1794; tel. 508/427–3000, (Includes GOOD SAMARITAN MEDICAL CENTER – CUSHING CAMPUS, 235 North Pearl Street, Brockton, MA, Zip 02401–1794; tel. 508/427–3000) (Nonreporting) **A**1 2 3 5 10 **S** Steward Health Care System, LLC, Dallas, TX
Primary Contact: Harrison Bane, President
COO: Donna Rubinate, R.N., Chief Operating Officer
CFO: Thomas Whalen, Vice President Finance
CMO: Scott Stewart, M.D., Vice President Medical Management
CIO: Lori Caswell, Director Information Technology
CHR: David J Cronin, Regional Vice President Human Resources
Web address: www.goodsamaritanmedical.org
Control: Corporation, Investor–owned (for–profit) **Service**: General medical and surgical

Staffed Beds: 190

⊞ **SIGNATURE HEALTHCARE BROCKTON HOSPITAL (220052)**, 680 Centre Street, Zip 02302–3395; tel. 508/941–7000, **A**1 2 3 10 **F**3 12 13 15 17 18 20 22 24 28 29 30 31 32 34 35 38 40 45 46 47 48 49 50 51 52 54 55 56 57 58 59 61 64 65 66 68 70 73 74 75 76 77 78 79 81 82 85 86 87 89 93 97 98 100 102 104 107 108 110 111 114 115 116 117 118 119 120 121 123 124 130 131 132 135 144 146 147 148 149 154 **P**6 8
Primary Contact: Kim Norton. Hollon, FACHE, President and Chief Executive Officer
CFO: James Papadakos, Chief Financial Officer
CIO: Gerald Greeley, Chief Information Officer
CHR: David Fisher, Vice President Human Resources
CNO: Kim Walsh, Chief Nursing Officer
Web address: www.signature–healthcare.org
Control: Other not–for–profit (including NFP Corporation) **Service**: General medical and surgical

Staffed Beds: 216 **Admissions**: 10584 **Census**: 129 **Outpatient Visits**: 359044 **Births**: 992 **Total Expense ($000)**: 264538 **Payroll Expense ($000)**: 115244 **Personnel**: 1397

★ **VETERANS AFFAIRS BOSTON HEALTHCARE SYSTEM BROCKTON DIVISION**, 940 Belmont Street, Zip 02301–5596; tel. 508/583–4500, (Includes VETERANS AFFAIRS MEDICAL CENTER WEST ROXBURY DIVISION, 1400 VFW Parkway, West Roxbury, MA, Zip 2132, Mailing Address: 1400 VVF Parkway, West Roxbury, Boston, Zip 2132, tel. 617/323–7700; William H Kelleher, Director) (Nonreporting) **A**3 5 8 **S** Department of Veterans Affairs, Perry Point, MD
Primary Contact: Vincent Ng, Director
CFO: Joe Costa, Acting Chief Fiscal Officer
Web address: www.boston.va.gov/
Control: Veterans Affairs, Government, federal **Service**: General medical and surgical

Staffed Beds: 375

BROOKLINE—Norfolk County

☐ **ARBOUR H. R. I. HOSPITAL (224018)**, 227 Babcock Street, Zip 02446–6799; tel. 617/731–3200, **A**1 10 **F**4 29 30 34 35 38 57 59 61 68 75 77 82 86 87 98 100 101 102 105 119 130 132 135 143 147 149 150 152 153 154 **S** Universal Health Services, Inc., King of Prussia, PA
Primary Contact: Jameson Pinette, Chief Executive Officer
CFO: James Rollins, Chief Financial Officer
CMO: Anthony Raynes, M.D., Psychiatrist in Chief
CHR: Kris Munson, Director Human Resources
Web address: www.arbourhealth.com
Control: Corporation, Investor–owned (for–profit) **Service**: Psychiatric

Staffed Beds: 76 **Admissions**: 4595 **Census**: 58 **Outpatient Visits**: 22446 **Births**: 0 **Personnel**: 131

BOURNEWOOD HEALTH SYSTEMS (224022), 300 South Street, Zip 02467–3658; tel. 617/469–0300, (Nonreporting) **A**3 5 10
Primary Contact: Marcia Fowler, Chief Executive Officer
CFO: Michael Gale, Chief Financial Officer
CMO: Carmel Heinsohn, M.D., Medical Director
CHR: Paula Berardi, Manager Human Resources
Web address: www.bournewood.com
Control: Corporation, Investor–owned (for–profit) **Service**: Psychiatric

Staffed Beds: 90

BURLINGTON—Middlesex County

⊞ **LAHEY HOSPITAL & MEDICAL CENTER, BURLINGTON (220171)**, 41 Mall Road, Zip 01805–0001; tel. 781/744–5100, (Includes LAHEY MEDICAL CENTER, PEABODY, 1 Essex Center Drive, Peabody, MA, Zip 01960–2901; tel. 978/538–4000) **A**1 2 3 5 8 10 **F**3 6 8 9 11 13 15 17 18 20 22 24 26 28 29 30 31 34 35 36 37 38 40 43 44 45 46 47 48 49 50 51 52 54 55 56 57 58 59 60 61 63 64 65 68 70 74 75 77 78 79 81 82 84 85 86 87 91 92 93 96 97 100 101 102 104 107 108 110 111 114 115 116 117 118 119 120 121 123 124 126 129 130 131 132 135 136 138 139 141 142 144 145 146 147 148 149 150 153 **P**6 **S** Lahey Health, Burlington, MA
Primary Contact: David L. Longworth, MD, Chief Executive Officer
COO: Richard R Bias, Chief Operating Officer
CFO: Timothy P. O'Connor, Executive Vice President and Chief Financial Officer
CMO: Andrew Villanueva, M.D., Interim Chief Medical Officer
CIO: Bruce Metz, Ph.D., Senior Vice President and Chief Information Officer
CHR: Elizabeth P. Conrad, Senior Vice President and Chief Human Resource Officer
Web address: www.lahey.org
Control: Other not–for–profit (including NFP Corporation) **Service**: General medical and surgical

Staffed Beds: 345 **Admissions**: 23556 **Census**: 307 **Outpatient Visits**: 774942 **Births**: 0 **Total Expense ($000)**: 924196 **Payroll Expense ($000)**: 290575 **Personnel**: 5988

CAMBRIDGE—Middlesex County

⊞ **CAMBRIDGE HEALTH ALLIANCE (220011)**, 1493 Cambridge Street, Zip 02139–1099; tel. 617/665–1000, (Includes CAMBRIDGE HOSPITAL, 1493 Cambridge Street, Cambridge, MA, Zip 02139–1099; tel. 617/498–1000; SOMERVILLE HOSPITAL, 230 Highland Avenue, Somerville, MA, Zip 2143; tel. 617/666–4400; WHIDDEN MEMORIAL HOSPITAL, 103 Garland Street, Everett, MA, Zip 02149–5095; tel. 617/389–6270) **A**1 2 3 5 8 10 **F**2 4 5 8 11 12 13 15 29 30 31 32 34 35 36 38 39 40 44 45 46 47 48 49 50 56 57 58 59 61 64 65 66 68 70 75 76 77 78 79 81 82 86 87 93 97 98 99 100 101 102 103 104 107 108 110 111 114 115 119 129 130 131 132 134 135 141 143 145 146 147 148 149 150 152 153 **P**6
Primary Contact: Patrick R. Wardell, Chief Executive Officer
CFO: Jill I Batty, Chief Financial Officer
CMO: Assaad Sayah, M.D., Chief Medical Officer
CIO: Judith S Klickstein, Chief Information Officer
CHR: Joy U Curtis, Senior Vice President Human Resources
CNO: Elizabeth Cadigan, R.N., MSN, Senior Vice President Patient Care Services and Chief Nursing Officer
Web address: www.challiance.org
Control: Hospital district or authority, Government, nonfederal **Service**: General medical and surgical

Staffed Beds: 274 **Admissions**: 10888 **Census**: 153 **Outpatient Visits**: 704356 **Births**: 1109 **Total Expense ($000)**: 601120 **Payroll Expense ($000)**: 324443 **Personnel**: 3321

⊞ **MOUNT AUBURN HOSPITAL (220002)**, 330 Mount Auburn Street, Zip 02138–5597; tel. 617/492–3500, **A**1 2 3 5 8 10 **F**3 5 11 12 13 14 15 17 18 20 22 24 26 28 29 30 31 34 35 36 37 40 45 49 50 51 52 55 56 57 58 59 60 61 63 64 65 68 70 73 74 75 76 77 78 79 81 82 86 87 93 97 98 100 101 102 103 104 107 108 110 111 114 115 117 118 119 120 121 123 124 126 129 130 131 132 135 144 145 146 147 154 **P**5 6 7
Primary Contact: Jeanette G. Clough, President and Chief Executive Officer
COO: Nicholas T Dileso, R.N., Chief Operating Officer
CFO: William Sullivan
CIO: Kendall White, Chief Information Officer
CHR: Tom Fabiano, Director Human Resources
CNO: Deborah Baker, Vice President, Patient Care Services
Web address: www.mountauburnhospital.org
Control: Other not–for–profit (including NFP Corporation) **Service**: General medical and surgical

Staffed Beds: 205 **Admissions**: 12094 **Census**: 147 **Outpatient Visits**: 202753 **Births**: 2731 **Total Expense ($000)**: 330021 **Payroll Expense ($000)**: 146963 **Personnel**: 2533

SPAULDING HOSPITAL CAMBRIDGE See Spaulding Hospital for Continuing Medical Care Cambridge

⊞ **SPAULDING HOSPITAL FOR CONTINUING MEDICAL CARE CAMBRIDGE (222000)**, 1575 Cambridge Street, Zip 02138–4308; tel. 617/876–4344, **A**1 10 **F**1 3 7 30 31 34 44 50 54 57 58 60 64 68 77 78 86 91 93 94 95 96 100 130 131 132 146 148 154 **P**8 **S** Partners HealthCare System, Inc., Boston, MA
Primary Contact: Maureen Banks, FACHE, MS, R.N., President
CFO: Mary Shaughnessy, Vice President Finance
CMO: Jonathon Schwartz, M.D., Chief Medical Officer
CIO: John Campbell, Chief Information Officer
CHR: Jack Carroll, Director Human Resources
CNO: Adrienne Sarnecki, R.N., Chief Nurse Executive
Web address: www.spauldingnetwork.org
Control: Other not–for–profit (including NFP Corporation) **Service**: Acute long–term care hospital

Staffed Beds: 128 **Admissions**: 1334 **Census**: 116 **Outpatient Visits**: 0 **Births**: 0 **Total Expense ($000)**: 77551 **Payroll Expense ($000)**: 35210 **Personnel**: 384

Many Facility Codes have changed. Please refer to the AHA Guide Code Chart.   © 2018 AHA Guide

MA

CANTON—Norfolk County

☐ **PAPPAS REHABILITATION HOSPITAL FOR CHILDREN (222025)**, 3 Randolph Street, Zip 02021–2351; tel. 781/828–2440, (Nonreporting) **A**1 10 **S** Massachusetts Department of Public Health, Boston, MA
Primary Contact: Brian V. Devin, Chief Executive Officer
CFO: Sharon Porter, Chief Financial Officer
CMO: Aruna Sachdev, M.D., Medical Director
CIO: Robert Lima, Director Information Systems
CHR: Trish Scully, Manager Employment Services
Web address: www.mhsf.us/
Control: State, Government, nonfederal **Service**: Children's acute long–term Care

Staffed Beds: 80

CHARLESTOWN—Suffolk County

☒ △ **SPAULDING REHABILITATION HOSPITAL (223034)**, 300 First Avenue, Zip 02129–3109; tel. 617/952–5000, (Nonreporting) **A**1 3 5 7 10 **S** Partners HealthCare System, Inc., Boston, MA
Primary Contact: David E. Storto, President
COO: Maureen Banks, FACHE, MS, R.N., Chief Operating Officer
CFO: Mary Shaughnessy, Vice President Finance
CMO: Ross Zafonte, D.O., Chief, Physical Medicine and Rehabilitation and Vice President Medical Affairs, Research and Education
CIO: John Campbell, Chief Information Officer
CHR: Russell Averna, Vice President Human Resources
Web address: www.spauldingrehab.org
Control: Other not–for–profit (including NFP Corporation) **Service**: Rehabilitation

Staffed Beds: 132

CONCORD—Middlesex County

☒ **EMERSON HOSPITAL (220084)**, 133 Old Road to Nine Acre Corner, Zip 01742–9120; tel. 978/369–1400, **A**1 5 10 **F**3 5 7 8 11 12 13 14 15 17 18 28 29 30 31 32 34 35 36 37 38 40 45 48 49 50 51 54 57 59 60 62 64 65 68 70 72 73 74 75 76 77 78 79 81 82 85 86 87 89 93 98 100 101 102 103 104 105 107 110 111 114 115 119 128 129 130 131 132 135 144 145 146 148 152 153 **P**5 8
Primary Contact: Christine C. Schuster, R.N., President and Chief Executive Officer
CFO: Michael Hachey, Senior Vice President and Chief Financial Officer
CMO: Barrett Kitch, MD, Senior Vice President, Clinical Affairs and Chief Medical Officer
CIO: Renee Fosberg, Chief Information Officer
CNO: Joyce Welsh, R.N., MS, Vice President of Clinical Services and Chief Nursing Officer
Web address: www.emersonhospital.org
Control: Other not–for–profit (including NFP Corporation) **Service**: General medical and surgical

Staffed Beds: 170 Admissions: 7475 Census: 97 Outpatient Visits: 287440 Births: 1262 Total Expense ($000): 233679 Payroll Expense ($000): 107654 Personnel: 1204

DARTMOUTH—Bristol County

SOUTHCOAST BEHAVIORAL HEALTH (224041), 581 Faunce Corner Road, Zip 02747–1242; tel. 888/210–2475, **F**29 56 98 101 102 103 130 **S** Acadia Healthcare Company, Inc., Franklin, TN
Primary Contact: Richard Remley, Chief Executive Officer
Web address: www.southcoastbehavioral.com
Control: Partnership, Investor–owned (for–profit) **Service**: Psychiatric

Staffed Beds: 120 Admissions: 3123 Census: 90 Outpatient Visits: 0 Births: 0 Total Expense ($000): 26223 Payroll Expense ($000): 15861 Personnel: 12

EAST SANDWICH—Barnstable County

☒ △ **SPAULDING REHABILITATION HOSPITAL CAPE COD (223032)**, 311 Service Road, Zip 02537–1370; tel. 508/833–4000, **A**1 7 10 **F**3 28 29 30 34 35 36 50 56 60 64 74 75 77 79 82 90 91 92 93 94 96 130 131 132 146 147 148 **P**4 6 **S** Partners HealthCare System, Inc., Boston, MA
Primary Contact: Maureen Banks, FACHE, MS, R.N., President
COO: Stephanie Nadolny, Vice President of Hospital Operations
CFO: Mary Shaughnessy, Vice President Finance
CMO: David Lowell, M.D., Chief Medical Officer
CIO: John Campbell, Chief Information Officer
CHR: Russell Averna, Vice President of Human Resources
CNO: Adrienne Sarnecki, R.N., Chief Nursing Officer
Web address: www.spauldingrehab.org
Control: State, Government, nonfederal **Service**: Rehabilitation

Staffed Beds: 60 Admissions: 1111 Census: 40 Outpatient Visits: 112673 Births: 0 Total Expense ($000): 43826 Payroll Expense ($000): 23586 Personnel: 390

EVERETT—Middlesex County

WHIDDEN MEMORIAL HOSPITAL See Cambridge Health Alliance, Cambridge

FALL RIVER—Bristol County

CHARLTON MEMORIAL HOSPITAL See Southcoast Hospitals Group, Fall River

☐ **DR. J. CORRIGAN MENTAL HEALTH CENTER (224028)**, 49 Hillside Street, Zip 02720–5266; tel. 508/235–7200, (Nonreporting) **A**1 3 10 **S** Massachusetts Department of Mental Health, Boston, MA
Primary Contact: Frank O'Reilly, Director
Control: State, Government, nonfederal **Service**: Psychiatric

Staffed Beds: 16

☐ **SAINT ANNE'S HOSPITAL (220020)**, 795 Middle Street, Zip 02721–1798; tel. 508/674–5741, (Nonreporting) **A**1 2 3 10 **S** Steward Health Care System, LLC, Dallas, TX
Primary Contact: Michael Bushell, President
CMO: John Conlon, M.D., Chief Medical Officer
CIO: Julie Berry, Chief Information Officer
CHR: Sandra Dellicker, Director of Human Resources
CNO: Carole Billington, R.N., MSN, Vice President Operations, Chief Nursing Officer
Web address: www.saintanneshospital.org
Control: Corporation, Investor–owned (for–profit) **Service**: General medical and surgical

Staffed Beds: 160

☒ **SOUTHCOAST HOSPITALS GROUP (220074)**, 363 Highland Avenue, Zip 02720–3703; tel. 508/679–3131, (Includes CHARLTON MEMORIAL HOSPITAL, 363 Highland Avenue, Fall River, MA, Zip 02720–3703; tel. 508/679–3131; Keith A Hovan, R.N., President and Chief Executive Officer; ST. LUKE'S HOSPITAL, 101 Page Street, New Bedford, MA, Zip 2740; tel. 508/997–1515; Keith A Hovan, R.N., President and Chief Executive Officer; TOBEY HOSPITAL, 43 High Street, Wareham, MA, Zip 2571; tel. 508/295–0880; Keith A Hovan, R.N., President and Chief Executive Officer) **A**1 2 10 **F**3 8 11 12 13 15 17 18 20 22 24 26 28 29 30 31 34 35 37 40 41 44 45 46 47 48 49 50 51 54 56 57 58 59 60 61 64 65 68 70 71 73 74 75 76 77 78 79 81 82 84 85 86 87 89 90 91 92 93 96 100 102 107 108 110 111 114 115 116 117 118 119 120 121 123 124 126 130 131 132 134 135 144 146 147 148 149 154 **P**1 6
Primary Contact: Keith A. Hovan, R.N., President and Chief Executive Officer
COO: Renee Clark, Senior Vice President and Chief Operating Officer
CFO: Wade Broughman, Chief Financial Officer
CMO: Robert Caldas, D.O., Chief Medical Officer
CIO: Jim Feen, Senior Vice President and Chief Information Officer
CHR: David DeJesus, Senior Vice President Human Resources
CNO: Timothy D. Eixenberger, Chief Nursing Officer
Web address: www.southcoast.org
Control: Other not–for–profit (including NFP Corporation) **Service**: General medical and surgical

Staffed Beds: 645 Admissions: 34486 Census: 418 Outpatient Visits: 898784 Births: 3394 Total Expense ($000): 763926 Payroll Expense ($000): 330667 Personnel: 4205

FALMOUTH—Barnstable County

☒ **FALMOUTH HOSPITAL (220135)**, 100 Ter Heun Drive, Zip 02540–2599; tel. 508/548–5300, **A**1 2 10 **F**3 8 11 13 15 18 28 29 30 34 35 36 38 40 45 50 53 54 58 59 61 64 65 68 70 74 75 76 77 79 81 82 85 86 87 89 93 96 100 101 102 104 107 108 110 111 115 119 120 121 122 123 124 129 130 131 132 135 143 144 146 147 148 149 **P**6 8 **S** Cape Cod Healthcare, Inc., Hyannis, MA
Primary Contact: Lori Jewett, R.N., Chief Executive Officer
CFO: Michael Connors, Senior Vice President and Chief Financial Officer
CMO: Alex Heard, M.D., Chief Medical Officer
CIO: Jeanne M. Fallon, Chief Information Officer
CHR: Emily Schorer, Vice President, Human Resources
CNO: Mary Johnson, Chief Nursing Officer
Web address: www.capecodhealth.org
Control: Other not–for–profit (including NFP Corporation) **Service**: General medical and surgical

Staffed Beds: 95 Admissions: 5660 Census: 61 Outpatient Visits: 159544 Births: 371 Total Expense ($000): 152614 Payroll Expense ($000): 69854 Personnel: 490

Hospital, Medicare Provider Number, Address, Telephone, Approval, Facility, and Physician Codes, Health Care System

★ American Hospital Association (AHA) membership
☐ The Joint Commission accreditation
○ Healthcare Facilities Accreditation Program
◇ DNV Healthcare Inc. accreditation
⇑ Center for Improvement in Healthcare Quality Accreditation
△ Commission on Accreditation of Rehabilitation Facilities (CARF) accreditation

MA

FRAMINGHAM—Middlesex County

⊞ **METROWEST MEDICAL CENTER (220175)**, 115 Lincoln Street,
Zip 01702–6342; tel. 508/383–1000, (Includes FRAMINGHAM UNION HOSPITAL,
115 Lincoln Street, Framingham, MA, Zip 1702; tel. 508/383–1000; LEONARD
MORSE HOSPITAL, 67 Union Street, Natick, MA, Zip 1760; tel. 508/650–7000)
A1 2 3 5 10 **F**3 4 5 11 12 13 14 15 18 20 22 26 28 29 30 31 32 34 35 36 40
41 44 45 49 50 54 56 57 59 61 64 65 68 70 73 74 75 76 77 78 79 81 84 85
87 89 93 97 98 99 100 102 103 104 105 107 108 110 114 115 118 119 120
121 129 130 131 132 134 135 143 146 147 148 149 152 **S** TENET Healthcare
Corporation, Dallas, TX
Primary Contact: Andrew D. Harding, R.N., Interim Chief Executive Officer
CHR: Rebecca Heffernan, Director Human Resources
CNO: Andrew D. Harding, R.N., Chief Nursing Officer
Web address: www.mwmc.com
Control: Corporation, Investor–owned (for–profit) **Service:** General medical and surgical

Staffed Beds: 160 **Admissions:** 10094 **Census:** 139 **Outpatient Visits:**
307596 **Births:** 1046 **Total Expense ($000):** 232451 **Payroll Expense
($000):** 111525 **Personnel:** 1983

GARDNER—Worcester County

☐ **HEYWOOD HOSPITAL (220095)**, 242 Green Street, Zip 01440–1373;
tel. 978/632–3420, (Nonreporting) **A**1 3 5 10 **S** Heywood Healthcare,
Gardner, MA
Primary Contact: Winfield S. Brown, FACHE, President and Chief Executive Officer
CFO: Robert Crosby, Senior Vice President and Chief Financial Officer
CHR: Thomas Cady, Vice President Human Resources
Web address: www.heywood.org
Control: Other not–for–profit (including NFP Corporation) **Service:** General
medical and surgical

Staffed Beds: 93

GEORGETOWN—Essex County

BALDPATE HOSPITAL (224033), 83 Baldpate Road, Zip 01833–2303;
tel. 978/352–2131, (Nonreporting) **A**10
Primary Contact: Lucille M. Batal, Administrator
Web address: www.detoxma.com/
Control: Corporation, Investor–owned (for–profit) **Service:** Psychiatric

Staffed Beds: 59

GLOUCESTER—Essex County

ADDISON GILBERT HOSPITAL See Beverly Hospital, Beverly

GREAT BARRINGTON—Berkshire County

⊞ **FAIRVIEW HOSPITAL (221302)**, 29 Lewis Avenue, Zip 01230–1713;
tel. 413/528–0790, **A**1 10 18 **F**3 11 13 15 18 28 29 32 34 35 36 40 50 54 56
57 59 64 65 68 70 75 76 77 79 81 85 86 87 89 92 93 94 107 108 110 115
119 130 131 132 133 134 135 145 146 147 148 149 150 154 **P**8 **S** Berkshire
Health Systems, Inc., Pittsfield, MA
Primary Contact: Eugene A. Dellea, President
COO: Doreen M Sylvia–Hutchinson, Vice President Operations and Chief Nurse
Executive
CFO: Anthony Rinaldi, Executive Vice President
CMO: Brian Burke, M.D., President Medical Staff
CHR: Laura Farkas, Director Human Resources
Web address: www.bhs1.org/body_fh.cfm?id=39
Control: Other not–for–profit (including NFP Corporation) **Service:** General
medical and surgical

Staffed Beds: 25 **Admissions:** 819 **Census:** 8 **Outpatient Visits:** 79803
Births: 113 **Total Expense ($000):** 48501 **Payroll Expense ($000):** 24015
Personnel: 263

GREENFIELD—Franklin County

⊞ **BAYSTATE FRANKLIN MEDICAL CENTER (220016)**, 164 High Street,
Zip 01301–2613; tel. 413/773–0211, **A**1 3 10 **F**3 11 12 13 14 15 18 26 28 29
30 31 34 35 36 40 45 46 47 48 49 50 51 55 57 59 64 68 70 74 75 76 77 78
79 81 82 85 86 87 89 93 98 100 101 105 107 108 110 111 115 118 119 129
130 131 132 146 147 148 154 **P**8 **S** Baystate Health, Inc., Springfield, MA
Primary Contact: Ronald Bryant, President
CFO: Andrea Nathanson, Director Finance
CMO: Thomas Higgins, M.D., Chief Medical Officer
CHR: Kerry Damon, Director Human Resources
CNO: Deborah A Provost, Chief Nursing Officer
Web address: www.baystatehealth.org
Control: Other not–for–profit (including NFP Corporation) **Service:** General
medical and surgical

Staffed Beds: 89 **Admissions:** 4704 **Census:** 50 **Outpatient Visits:** 111147
Births: 452 **Total Expense ($000):** 97007 **Payroll Expense ($000):** 36812
Personnel: 412

HAVERHILL—Essex County

WHITTIER PAVILION (224039), 76 Summer Street, Zip 01830–5814;
tel. 978/373–8222, (Nonreporting) **A**10 **S** Whittier Health Network, Haverhill, MA
Primary Contact: Alfred L. Arcidi, M.D., Chief Executive Officer
Web address: www.whittierhealth.com
Control: Partnership, Investor–owned (for–profit) **Service:** Psychiatric

Staffed Beds: 65

HOLYOKE—Hampden County

⇑ **HOLYOKE MEDICAL CENTER (220024)**, 575 Beech Street, Zip 01040–2223;
tel. 413/534–2500, **A**2 5 10 21 **F**3 12 13 14 15 18 26 28 29 30 31 34 35 38
40 46 50 51 54 55 57 58 59 60 64 65 67 68 70 74 75 76 77 78 79 81 82 85
87 89 93 96 97 98 101 102 104 105 107 108 110 111 114 115 118 119 129
130 132 135 143 145 146 147 148 149 **P**8
Primary Contact: Spiros Hatiras, FACHE, President and Chief Executive Officer
CFO: Michael J Koziol, Chief Financial Officer
CMO: Karen Ferroni, M.D., Medical Director
CIO: Carl Cameron, Director Information Systems
CHR: Mary Kelleher, Vice President Human Resources
CNO: Colleen Desai, Chief Nursing Officer
Web address: www.holyokehealth.com
Control: Other not–for–profit (including NFP Corporation) **Service:** General
medical and surgical

Staffed Beds: 196 **Admissions:** 6219 **Census:** 75 **Outpatient Visits:**
309800 **Births:** 457 **Total Expense ($000):** 150550 **Payroll Expense
($000):** 77194 **Personnel:** 850

HYANNIS—Barnstable County

⊞ **CAPE COD HOSPITAL (220012)**, 27 Park Street, Zip 02601–5230;
tel. 508/771–1800, **A**1 2 3 5 10 20 **F**3 11 13 14 15 17 18 20 22 24 26 28 29
30 31 34 35 37 38 40 45 49 50 51 54 57 58 61 64 65 68 70 74 75 76 77 78
79 81 82 85 86 87 89 93 97 98 99 100 101 102 103 104 105 107 108 110
111 114 115 119 120 121 122 123 124 126 130 131 132 143 144 146 147
148 149 153 **P**6 8 **S** Cape Cod Healthcare, Inc., Hyannis, MA
Primary Contact: Michael K. Lauf, President and Chief Executive Officer
COO: Michael N Bundy, Chief Operating Officer
CFO: Michael Connors, Senior Vice President and Chief Financial Officer
CMO: Donald Guadagnoli, M.D., Chief Medical Officer
CIO: Jeanne M. Fallon, Senior Vice President and Chief Information Officer
CHR: Emily Schorer, Senior Vice President Human Resources
CNO: Judith Quinn, Vice President Patient Care Services
Web address: www.capecodhealth.org
Control: Other not–for–profit (including NFP Corporation) **Service:** General
medical and surgical

Staffed Beds: 259 **Admissions:** 15613 **Census:** 185 **Outpatient Visits:**
620050 **Births:** 835 **Total Expense ($000):** 493353 **Payroll Expense
($000):** 188392 **Personnel:** 1592

JAMAICA PLAIN—Suffolk County

☐ **LEMUEL SHATTUCK HOSPITAL (222006)**, 170 Morton Street,
Zip 02130–3735; tel. 617/522–8110, (Nonreporting) **A**1 3 5 10 **S** Massachusetts
Department of Public Health, Boston, MA
Primary Contact: Rosette Martinez, Acting Chief Executive Officer
CFO: Mike Donovan, Chief Financial Officer
CMO: Kenneth Freedman, M.D., Chief Medical Officer
CIO: Kathryn Noonan, Director Information Management
CHR: Jill Sampson, Director Human Resources
Web address: www.mass.gov/shattuckhospital
Control: State, Government, nonfederal **Service:** Acute long–term care hospital

Staffed Beds: 260

LAWRENCE—Essex County

⊞ **LAWRENCE GENERAL HOSPITAL (220010)**, 1 General Street,
Zip 01841–2961, Mailing Address: P.O. Box 189, Zip 01842–0389;
tel. 978/683–4000, **A**1 2 3 5 10 **F**3 7 11 12 13 15 16 18 20 22 26 28 29 30
34 35 43 44 45 46 47 49 50 51 56 57 59 60 64 65 68 70 73 74 75 76 77
78 79 81 82 84 85 87 89 90 93 100 107 108 110 114 115 119 120 121 122
123 129 130 132 135 144 146 147 148 149 150 **P**5 6 8
Primary Contact: Dianne J. Anderson, MS, R.N., President and Chief Executive Officer
CFO: Felix V. Mercado, Chief Financial Officer
CMO: Pracha Eamranond, M.D., Senior Vice President Population Health and
Medical Affairs
CHR: Cynthia Phelan, Vice President Human Resources
CNO: Karen O. Moore, FACHE, Senior Vice President Operations and Chief Nursing
Officer
Web address: www.lawrencegeneral.org
Control: Other not–for–profit (including NFP Corporation) **Service:** General
medical and surgical

Staffed Beds: 189 **Admissions:** 11221 **Census:** 121 **Outpatient Visits:**
178213 **Births:** 1490 **Total Expense ($000):** 247771 **Payroll Expense
($000):** 115871 **Personnel:** 1253

Many Facility Codes have changed. Please refer to the AHA Guide Code Chart. © 2018 AHA Guide

MA

LEEDS—Hampshire County

☒ **VETERANS AFFAIRS CENTRAL WESTERN MASSACHUSETTS HEALTHCARE SYSTEM**, 421 North Main Street, Zip 01053–9764; tel. 413/582–3000, (Nonreporting) **A**1 3 5 **S** Department of Veterans Affairs, Perry Point, MD
Primary Contact: John P. Collins, FACHE, Medical Center Director
COO: Joyce Fredrick, Associate Director
CFO: Andrew McMahon, Chief Fiscal Officer
CMO: Neil Nusbaum, M.D., Chief of Staff
CIO: Michael Marley, Chief Information Officer
CHR: Pablo Feliciano, Manager Human Resources
Web address: www.centralwesternmass.va.gov/
Control: Veterans Affairs, Government, federal **Service**: Psychiatric

Staffed Beds: 117

LEOMINSTER—Worcester County

☒ **UMASS MEMORIAL HEALTHALLIANCE–CLINTON HOSPITAL (220001)**, 60 Hospital Road, Zip 01453–2205; tel. 978/466–2000, (Includes UMASS MEMORIAL HEALTHALLIANCE–CLINTON HOSPITAL, 201 Highland Street, Clinton, MA, Zip 01510–1096; tel. 978/368–3000; Deborah K Weymouth, FACHE, President and Chief Executive Officer) **A**1 2 3 5 10 **F**3 5 13 15 27 28 29 30 31 34 35 36 40 45 46 47 49 50 51 54 57 59 60 62 63 64 66 68 70 74 75 76 77 78 79 80 81 82 84 85 89 91 92 93 97 104 107 108 110 114 115 118 119 127 130 131 132 133 135 144 146 149 153 154 **P**6 **S** UMass Memorial Health Care, Inc., Worcester, MA
Primary Contact: Deborah K. Weymouth, FACHE, President and Chief Executive Officer
COO: Paul MacKinnon, R.N., Chief Operating Officer
CFO: John Bronhard, CPA, II Corporate Vice President, Chief Financial Officer and Treasurer
CMO: Daniel H O'Leary, M.D., Chief Medical Officer
CHR: Julie DeBono, Director, Human Resources
CNO: Judith Thorpe, R.N., MSN, Vice President and Chief Nursing Officer
Web address: www.healthalliance.com
Control: Other not–for–profit (including NFP Corporation) **Service**: General medical and surgical

Staffed Beds: 103 **Admissions:** 6942 **Census:** 73 **Outpatient Visits:** 272082 **Births:** 818 **Total Expense ($000):** 182298 **Payroll Expense ($000):** 74253 **Personnel:** 861

LOWELL—Middlesex County

☒ **LOWELL GENERAL HOSPITAL (220063)**, 295 Varnum Avenue, Zip 01854–2134; tel. 978/937–6000, (Includes LOWELL GENERAL HOSPITAL, SAINTS CAMPUS, 1 Hospital Drive, Lowell, MA, Zip 01852–1311, Mailing Address: 295 Varnum Ave, Zip 01854–2134, tel. 978/458–1411; Normand E. Deschene, FACHE, Chief Executive Officer) **A**1 2 3 5 10 **F**3 11 12 13 15 18 20 22 26 28 29 30 31 32 34 35 36 40 41 43 44 45 46 47 48 49 50 51 54 56 57 58 59 60 61 64 65 68 70 73 74 75 76 78 79 81 82 83 84 85 86 87 89 92 93 97 100 107 108 110 114 115 118 120 121 123 124 126 129 130 131 132 133 134 143 144 146 149 150 **P**5 6 8
Primary Contact: Joseph White, FACHE, President and Chief Executive Officer
COO: Amy J Hoey, R.N., MS, Executive Vice President and Chief Operating Officer
CFO: Susan Green, Senior Vice President Finance, Chief Financial Officer
CMO: Arthur Lauretano, M.D., Chief Medical Officer
CIO: Brian Sandager, Chief Information Officer
CHR: Sabrina M Granville, Senior Vice President and Chief Human Resources Officer
CNO: Cecelia Lynch, R.N., MS, Vice President Patient Care Services and Chief Nursing Officer
Web address: www.lowellgeneral.org
Control: Other not–for–profit (including NFP Corporation) **Service**: General medical and surgical

Staffed Beds: 325 **Admissions:** 20070 **Census:** 231 **Outpatient Visits:** 515877 **Births:** 2269 **Total Expense ($000):** 447616 **Payroll Expense ($000):** 176062 **Personnel:** 2748

SAINTS MEDICAL CENTER See Lowell General Hospital, Saints Campus

LUDLOW—Hampden County

☒ **HEALTHSOUTH REHABILITATION HOSPITAL OF WESTERN MASSACHUSETTS (223030)**, 222 State Street, Zip 01056–3437; tel. 413/308–3300, (Nonreporting) **A**1 10 **S** Encompass Health Corporation, Birmingham, AL
Primary Contact: John R. Hunt, Chief Executive Officer
CFO: John Flaherty, Chief Financial Officer
CMO: Adnan Dahdul, M.D., Medical Director
CHR: Mary Mazza, Director Human Resources
CNO: Deborah Santos, R.N., Chief Nursing Officer
Web address: www.healthsouthrehab.org
Control: Corporation, Investor–owned (for–profit) **Service**: Rehabilitation

Staffed Beds: 53

LYNN—Essex County

UNION CAMPUS See North Shore Medical Center, Salem

UNION HOSPITAL See Union Campus

MARLBOROUGH—Middlesex County

☒ **UMASS MEMORIAL–MARLBOROUGH HOSPITAL (220049)**, 157 Union ST, Zip 01752–1297; tel. 508/481–5000, **A**1 3 5 10 **F**3 11 15 18 24 28 29 30 34 35 40 49 50 51 53 57 63 68 70 77 79 81 82 85 93 98 100 101 107 115 119 132 146 147 149 154 **S** UMass Memorial Health Care, Inc., Worcester, MA
Primary Contact: Steven P. Roach, FACHE, President and Chief Executive Officer
COO: John Kelly, R.N., Chief Nursing Officer and Chief Operating Officer
CFO: Steven McCue, Chief Financial Officer
CMO: Habib Sioufi, M.D., Chief Medical Officer
CHR: Francis Meringolo, Vice President Human Resources
CNO: John Kelly, R.N., Chief Nursing Officer and Chief Operating Officer
Web address: www.marlboroughhospital.org
Control: Other not–for–profit (including NFP Corporation) **Service**: General medical and surgical

Staffed Beds: 67 **Admissions:** 4093 **Census:** 47 **Outpatient Visits:** 28316 **Births:** 0 **Total Expense ($000):** 81265 **Payroll Expense ($000):** 30948 **Personnel:** 433

MEDFORD—Middlesex County

LAWRENCE MEMORIAL HOSPITAL OF MEDFORD See Melrosewakefield Healthcare, Melrose

MELROSE—Middlesex County

☒ **MELROSEWAKEFIELD HEALTHCARE (220070)**, 585 Lebanon Street, Zip 02176–3225; tel. 781/979–3000, (Includes LAWRENCE MEMORIAL HOSPITAL OF MEDFORD, 170 Governors Avenue, Medford, MA, Zip 02155–1643; tel. 781/306–6000; MELROSE–WAKEFIELD HOSPITAL, 585 Lebanon Street, Melrose, MA, Zip 2176; tel. 781/979–3000; Michael V Sack, FACHE, Chief Executive Officer) **A**1 2 3 10 **F**3 11 12 13 15 18 20 22 26 28 29 30 31 34 35 38 40 41 45 46 47 49 50 51 54 55 56 57 58 59 60 61 62 63 64 65 68 70 72 74 75 76 78 79 81 82 84 85 86 87 93 97 98 100 101 102 103 104 105 107 108 110 111 114 115 116 117 118 119 120 121 123 124 129 130 131 132 135 141 144 146 147 148 149 **P**5 6
Primary Contact: Susan Sandberg, R.N., Chief Executive Officer
CFO: Michael P. Connelly, CPA, FACHE, Executive Vice President and Chief Financial Officer
CMO: Steven P. Sbardella, M.D., FABC, President Clinical Operations and Chief Medical Officer
CHR: David P. Ryan, Vice President Human Resources
CNO: Deborah L Cronin–Waelde, MSN, R.N., Senior Vice President Clinical Operations and Chief Nursing Officer
Web address: www.melrosewakefield.org
Control: Other not–for–profit (including NFP Corporation) **Service**: General medical and surgical

Staffed Beds: 267 **Admissions:** 10124 **Census:** 145 **Outpatient Visits:** 509586 **Births:** 877 **Total Expense ($000):** 260828 **Payroll Expense ($000):** 128338 **Personnel:** 1265

Hospital, Medicare Provider Number, Address, Telephone, Approval, Facility, and Physician Codes, Health Care System

★ American Hospital Association (AHA) membership ○ Healthcare Facilities Accreditation Program ⇑ Center for Improvement in Healthcare Quality Accreditation
□ The Joint Commission accreditation ◇ DNV Healthcare Inc. accreditation △ Commission on Accreditation of Rehabilitation Facilities (CARF) accreditation

© 2018 AHA Guide *Many Facility Codes have changed. Please refer to the AHA Guide Code Chart.* Hospitals **A301**

MA

METHUEN—Essex County

☐ **HOLY FAMILY HOSPITAL (220080)**, 70 East Street, Zip 01844–4597;
tel. 978/687–0151, (Includes HOLY FAMILY HOSPITAL AT MERRIMACK VALLEY,
140 Lincoln Avenue, Haverhill, MA, Zip 01830–6798; tel. 978/374–2000; Craig
A Jesiolowski, FACHE, President) (Nonreporting) **A**1 2 3 10 **S** Steward Health Care
System, LLC, Dallas, TX
Primary Contact: Craig A. Jesiolowski, FACHE, President
COO: Martha M McDrury, R.N., Chief Operating Officer and Chief Nursing Officer
CFO: Kevin Kilday, Vice President Finance
CHR: Patricia Gauron, Director Human Resources
CNO: Martha M McDrury, R.N., Chief Operating Officer and Chief Nursing Officer
Web address: www.stewardhealth.org/Holy–Family–Hospital
Control: Corporation, Investor–owned (for–profit) **Service:** General medical and
surgical

Staffed Beds: 329

MILFORD—Worcester County

⊞ **MILFORD REGIONAL MEDICAL CENTER (220090)**, 14 Prospect Street,
Zip 01757–3003; tel. 508/473–1190, (Includes WHITINSVILLE MEDICAL CENTER,
18 Granite Street, Whitinsville, MA, Zip 1588; tel. 508/234–6311) **A**1 2 3 5 10
F3 11 12 13 15 18 20 28 29 30 31 32 34 35 40 41 45 46 47 48 49 50 51 52
57 59 64 65 68 70 74 75 76 77 79 80 81 84 85 86 87 89 93 96 107 108 110
115 118 119 126 130 131 132 134 135 146 147 148 149 154
Primary Contact: Edward Kelly, Chief Executive Officer and President
COO: Peggy Novick, Vice President, Clinical Support and Outpatient Services
CFO: Jeanne Lynskey, Vice President and Chief Financial Officer
CMO: Mary Czymbor, Chief Medical Officer
CIO: Nicole Heim, Chief Information Officer
CHR: Linda Greason, Vice President Human Resources
CNO: Nancy Tomaso, Vice President, Patient Care Services
Web address: www.milfordregional.org
Control: Other not–for–profit (including NFP Corporation) **Service:** General
medical and surgical

Staffed Beds: 145 Admissions: 8448 Census: 81 Outpatient Visits:
427789 Births: 969 Total Expense ($000): 205885 Payroll Expense
($000): 93370 Personnel: 1798

MILTON—Norfolk County

☐ **BETH ISRAEL DEACONESS HOSPITAL–MILTON (220108)**, 199 Reedsdale
Road, Zip 02186–3926; tel. 617/696–4600, (Nonreporting) **A**1 3 10
Primary Contact: Richard W. Fernandez, President and Chief Executive Officer
CIO: Jean Fernandez, Chief Information Officer
CHR: Kathleen Harrington, Vice President Human Resources
Web address: www.miltonhospital.org
Control: Other not–for–profit (including NFP Corporation) **Service:** General
medical and surgical

Staffed Beds: 88

NANTUCKET—Nantucket County

⊞ **NANTUCKET COTTAGE HOSPITAL (220177)**, 57 Prospect Street,
Zip 02554–2799; tel. 508/825–8100, **A**1 10 **F**13 15 29 35 40 45 50 57 59
60 64 68 70 75 76 77 78 79 81 82 84 85 86 87 89 93 100 102 107 110 111
115 119 130 132 133 147 148 154 **P**5 **S** Partners HealthCare System, Inc.,
Boston, MA
Primary Contact: Margot Hartmann, M.D., Ph.D., President and Chief Executive
Officer
COO: Jim Kelly, Chief Operating Officer
CFO: David J Burke, Director Finance and Chief Financial Officer
CMO: Jock Lawrason, M.D., Chief Medical Officer
CIO: Terry Hughes, Director Information Systems
CHR: Susan Partridge, Director Human Resources
CNO: Bonnie J Kester, R.N., MSN, Vice President Patient Care Services and Chief
Nursing Officer
Web address: www.nantuckethospital.org
Control: Other not–for–profit (including NFP Corporation) **Service:** General
medical and surgical

Staffed Beds: 19 Admissions: 826 Census: 7 Outpatient Visits: 63249
Births: 111 Total Expense ($000): 52706 Payroll Expense ($000): 18594
Personnel: 230

NATICK—Middlesex County

LEONARD MORSE HOSPITAL See Metrowest Medical Center, Framingham

NEEDHAM—Norfolk County

☐ **BETH ISRAEL DEACONESS HOSPITAL–NEEDHAM CAMPUS (220083)**, 148
Chestnut Street, Zip 2492; tel. 781/453–3000, **A**1 2 3 **F**3 15 18 29 30 34 35 40
45 50 51 54 59 60 64 65 68 69 70 74 75 77 79 81 82 84 85 87 92 93 100
102 107 108 110 111 114 115 118 119 129 130 131 144 145 146 148 149
154
Primary Contact: John M. Fogarty, President and Chief Executive Officer
CFO: Brian Smith, Chief Financial Officer
CMO: Peter Ostrow, M.D., President Medical Staff
Web address: www.bidneedham.org/
Control: Other not–for–profit (including NFP Corporation) **Service:** General
medical and surgical

Staffed Beds: 46 Admissions: 2686 Census: 33 Outpatient Visits: 177789
Births: 0 Total Expense ($000): 85469 Payroll Expense ($000): 34458
Personnel: 501

NEW BEDFORD—Bristol County

ST. LUKE'S HOSPITAL See Southcoast Hospitals Group, Fall River

⊞ **VIBRA HOSPITAL OF SOUTHEASTERN MASSACHUSETTS (222043)**, 4499
Acushnet Avenue, Zip 02745–4707; tel. 508/995–6900, **A**1 10 **F**1 12 18 28
29 50 56 57 64 74 75 77 79 87 93 94 96 104 130 135 146 148 **P**6 **S** Vibra
Healthcare, Mechanicsburg, PA
Primary Contact: Edward B. Leary, Chief Executive Officer
CFO: Cheryl Perry, Chief Financial Officer
CMO: Albert Loerinc, M.D., Medical Director
CHR: Ilene Mirabella, Director Human Resources
CNO: Emmanuel Berthil, Chief Clinical Officer
Web address: www.newbedfordrehab.com
Control: Corporation, Investor–owned (for–profit) **Service:** Children's acute long–
term Care

Staffed Beds: 90 Admissions: 549 Census: 61 Outpatient Visits: 1875
Births: 0 Total Expense ($000): 23236 Payroll Expense ($000): 1085
Personnel: 139

NEWBURYPORT—Essex County

⊞ **ANNA JAQUES HOSPITAL (220029)**, 25 Highland Avenue, Zip 01950–3894;
tel. 978/463–1000, **A**1 10 **F**3 8 13 14 15 18 20 26 28 29 31 34 37 40 43 45
46 50 59 65 70 75 76 77 78 79 80 81 82 85 89 92 93 98 99 102 105 107
108 110 114 115 118 119 129 130 135 146 148 149 **P**5 8
Primary Contact: Mark L. Goldstein, President and Chief Executive Officer
CFO: Kevin Kilday, Chief Financial Officer
CMO: Gail Fayre, M.D., Medical Director
CIO: Robert Buchanan, Chief Information Officer
CHR: Stephen Salvo, Vice President Human Resources
CNO: Richard Maki, R.N., Vice President Nursing and Chief Nursing Officer
Web address: www.ajh.org
Control: Other not–for–profit (including NFP Corporation) **Service:** General
medical and surgical

Staffed Beds: 123 Admissions: 6465 Census: 74 Outpatient Visits:
262650 Births: 676 Total Expense ($000): 126575 Payroll Expense
($000): 55668 Personnel: 706

NEWTON LOWER FALLS—Middlesex County

⊞ **NEWTON–WELLESLEY HOSPITAL (220101)**, 2014 Washington Street,
Zip 02462–1699; tel. 617/243–6000, (Includes MASSGENERAL FOR CHILDREN
AT NEWTON–WELLESLEY HOSPITAL, 2000 Washington Street, Newton, MA,
Zip 02462–1650; tel. 617/243–6585) **A**1 2 3 5 10 **F**3 8 12 13 15 17 18 19 26
28 29 30 31 32 34 35 36 40 41 45 46 47 49 50 51 52 53 54 55 56 58 59
60 64 65 66 68 70 73 74 75 76 77 78 79 81 82 84 85 86 87 89 92 93 97 98
100 101 102 104 107 108 110 111 114 115 117 118 119 126 129 130 131
132 134 135 144 145 146 147 148 149 150 154 **P**1 6 **S** Partners HealthCare
System, Inc., Boston, MA
Primary Contact: Michael R. Jaff, D.O., President
CFO: Jeffrey P. Dion, Vice President Finance and Chief Financial Officer
CMO: Timothy Foster, Acting Chief Medical Officer
CIO: Beth Downie, Chief Information Officer
CHR: Beth Taylor, Vice President, Human Resources
Web address: www.nwh.org
Control: Other not–for–profit (including NFP Corporation) **Service:** General
medical and surgical

Staffed Beds: 220 Admissions: 15391 Census: 185 Outpatient Visits:
534433 Births: 3750 Total Expense ($000): 467456 Payroll Expense
($000): 192492 Personnel: 2515

MA

NORTHAMPTON—Hampshire County

☒ **COOLEY DICKINSON HOSPITAL (220015)**, 30 Locust Street, Zip 01060–2093, Mailing Address: P.O. Box 5001, Zip 01061–5001; tel. 413/582–2000, (Nonreporting) **A**1 2 10 **S** Partners HealthCare System, Inc., Boston, MA
Primary Contact: Joanne Marqusee, President and Chief Executive Officer
CFO: Laurie Lamoureux, Director of Finance
CMO: Estevan Garcia, M.D., Chief Medical Officer
CIO: Lee Martinez, Chief Information Officer
CHR: Lori A Kerwood, Director Human Resources
Web address: www.cooleydickinson.org
Control: Other not–for–profit (including NFP Corporation) **Service**: General medical and surgical

Staffed Beds: 86

NORWOOD—Norfolk County

☐ **NORWOOD HOSPITAL (220126)**, 800 Washington Street, Zip 02062–3487; tel. 781/769–4000, (Nonreporting) **A**1 2 5 10 **S** Steward Health Care System, LLC, Dallas, TX
Primary Contact: Salvatore Perla, President
COO: William P Fleming, Chief Operating Officer
CFO: Mark Johnson, Chief Financial Officer
CHR: Kimberly Brosnan, Director Human Resources
CNO: Mary Kinneman, R.N., MSN, Chief Nursing Officer, Vice President Patient Care Services
Web address: www.norwood–hospital.org
Control: Corporation, Investor–owned (for–profit) **Service**: General medical and surgical

Staffed Beds: 188

OAK BLUFFS—Dukes County

☒ **MARTHA'S VINEYARD HOSPITAL (221300)**, One Hospital Road, Zip 2557, Mailing Address: P.O. Box 1477, Zip 02557–1477; tel. 508/693–0410, **A**1 10 18 **F**3 8 13 15 28 29 30 31 37 39 40 45 50 57 59 60 64 69 70 75 76 78 79 81 82 85 86 87 89 93 97 107 110 111 113 115 119 120 130 133 135 146 147 **P**6 **S** Partners HealthCare System, Inc., Boston, MA
Primary Contact: Denise Schepici, M.P.H., Chief Executive Officer and President
CFO: Edward Olivier, Chief Financial Officer
CMO: Pieter Pil, M.D., Chief Medical Staff
CHR: Christine Gould, Director Human Resources
CNO: Carol A Bardwell, R.N., MSN, Chief Nurse Executive
Web address: www.mvhospital.com/
Control: Other not–for–profit (including NFP Corporation) **Service**: General medical and surgical

Staffed Beds: 25 Admissions: 1342 Census: 17

PALMER—Hampden County

☒ **BAYSTATE WING HOSPITAL (220030)**, 40 Wright Street, Zip 01069–1138; tel. 413/283–7651, **A**1 5 10 **F**3 5 11 15 18 29 33 34 35 36 38 40 45 46 49 50 54 56 57 59 61 64 65 68 70 74 75 77 79 81 82 85 86 87 93 97 98 100 101 103 104 107 108 110 115 119 129 130 132 135 146 147 149 150 154 **S** Baystate Health, Inc., Springfield, MA
Primary Contact: Michael Francis. Moran, President and Chief Administrative Officer
CFO: Keary T Allicon, Vice President Finance and Chief Financial Officer
CMO: David L Maguire, M.D., Vice President Medical Affairs
CIO: Kenneth Riley, Director Information Systems
CHR: Thomas Guilfoil, Director Human Resources
Web address: www.baystatewinghospital.org/
Control: Other not–for–profit (including NFP Corporation) **Service**: General medical and surgical

Staffed Beds: 74 Admissions: 3125 Census: 46 Outpatient Visits: 164310 Births: 0 Total Expense ($000): 95018 Payroll Expense ($000): 37038 Personnel: 682

PEMBROKE—Plymouth County

☐ **PEMBROKE HOSPITAL**, 199 Oak Street, Zip 02359–1953; tel. 781/829–7000, (Nonreporting) **A**1 **S** Universal Health Services, Inc., King of Prussia, PA
Primary Contact: Raymond Robinson, Chief Executive Officer
CFO: Diane Airosus, Chief Financial Officer
CMO: Gary Jacobson, M.D., Chief Medical Officer
Web address: www.arbourhealth.com/organizations/pembroke–hospital/
Control: Partnership, Investor–owned (for–profit) **Service**: Psychiatric

Staffed Beds: 115

PITTSFIELD—Berkshire County

☒ **BERKSHIRE MEDICAL CENTER (220046)**, 725 North ST, Zip 01201–4124, Mailing Address: 725 North Street, Zip 01201–4124; tel. 413/447–2000, (Includes HILLCREST HOSPITAL, 165 Tor Court, Pittsfield, MA, Zip 01201–3099, Mailing Address: Box 1155, Zip 01202–1155, tel. 413/443–4761) **A**1 2 3 5 8 10 12 13 **F**3 4 5 8 12 13 14 15 17 18 20 26 28 29 30 31 32 34 35 37 38 40 43 44 45 46 48 49 50 51 53 54 55 56 57 58 59 60 61 62 63 64 65 68 70 71 74 75 76 77 78 79 81 82 83 85 86 87 89 90 92 93 98 100 101 102 104 107 108 110 111 112 114 115 116 117 118 119 120 121 122 123 124 126 129 130 131 132 134 135 144 145 146 147 148 149 150 **P**6 8 **S** Berkshire Health Systems, Inc., Pittsfield, MA
Primary Contact: David E. Phelps, President and Chief Executive Officer
CFO: Darlene Rodowicz, Chief Financial Officer
CIO: William Young, Chief Information Officer
CHR: Arthur D Milano, Vice President Human Resources
CNO: Brenda E Cadorette, Chief Nursing Officer
Web address: www.berkshirehealthsystems.org
Control: Other not–for–profit (including NFP Corporation) **Service**: General medical and surgical

Staffed Beds: 275 Admissions: 14272 Census: 180 Outpatient Visits: 352111 Births: 700 Total Expense ($000): 467481 Payroll Expense ($000): 206186 Personnel: 2460

PLYMOUTH—Plymouth County

☐ **BETH ISRAEL DEACONESS HOSPITAL PLYMOUTH (220060)**, 275 Sandwich Street, Zip 02360–2196; tel. 508/746–2000, (Nonreporting) **A**1 2 5 10
Primary Contact: Kevin B. Coughlin, President and Chief Executive Officer
CFO: Jason Radzevich, Vice President Finance
CIO: Ronald Rutherford, Chief Information Officer
CHR: Lisa Berry–Barbosa, Vice President Human Resources
CNO: Donna Doherty, R.N., Vice President of Nursing and Chief Nursing Officer
Web address: www.bidplymouth.org
Control: Other not–for–profit (including NFP Corporation) **Service**: General medical and surgical

Staffed Beds: 155

POCASSET—Barnstable County

☐ **CAPE COD & ISLAND COMMUNITY MENTAL HEALTH CENTER (224031)**, 830 County Road, Zip 02559–2110; tel. 508/564–9600, (Nonreporting) **A**1 10
Primary Contact: Steven Jochim, Administrator
Control: Other not–for–profit (including NFP Corporation) **Service**: Psychiatric

Staffed Beds: 24

ROCHDALE—Worcester County

VIBRA HOSPITAL OF WESTERN MASSACHUSETTS–CENTRAL CAMPUS See Vibra Hospital of Western Massachusetts, Springfield

ROSLINDALE—Suffolk County

★ △ **HEBREW REHABILITATION CENTER (222007)**, 1200 Centre Street, Zip 02131–1097; tel. 617/363–8000, (Total facility includes 675 beds in nursing home–type unit) **A**7 10 **F**1 2 6 29 30 35 39 50 58 59 60 64 65 68 69 75 77 82 83 84 93 97 100 103 104 119 128 130 132 143 146 148 149 **P**6
Primary Contact: Mary K. Moscato, FACHE, President
COO: Brian Murphy, Senior Director Admissions and Referral Services
CFO: Lise Paul, Vice President Reimbursement and Network Planning
CMO: Helen Chen, M.D., Chief Medical Officer
CIO: Eric Rogers, Chief Information Officer
CHR: Deborah Lemmerman, Chief People Officer
CNO: Tammy B. Retalic, R.N., MS, Chief Nursing Officer
Web address: www.hebrewseniorlife.org
Control: Other not–for–profit (including NFP Corporation) **Service**: Acute long–term care hospital

Staffed Beds: 725 Admissions: 1340 Census: 657 Outpatient Visits: 66352 Births: 0 Total Expense ($000): 127033 Payroll Expense ($000): 74124 Personnel: 981

SALEM—Essex County

NORTH SHORE CHILDREN'S HOSPITAL See Massgeneral for Children At North Shore Medical Center

---

Hospital, Medicare Provider Number, Address, Telephone, Approval, Facility, and Physician Codes, Health Care System

★ American Hospital Association (AHA) membership
☐ The Joint Commission accreditation
○ Healthcare Facilities Accreditation Program
◇ DNV Healthcare Inc. accreditation
⇑ Center for Improvement in Healthcare Quality Accreditation
△ Commission on Accreditation of Rehabilitation Facilities (CARF) accreditation

MA

✠ **NORTH SHORE MEDICAL CENTER (220035)**, 81 Highland Avenue, Zip 01970–2714; tel. 978/741–1200, (Includes MASSGENERAL FOR CHILDREN AT NORTH SHORE MEDICAL CENTER, 57 Highland Avenue, Salem, MA, Zip 01970–6508; tel. 978/745–2100; SALEM CAMPUS, 81 Highland Avenue, Salem, MA, Zip 1970; tel. 978/741–1200; Robert G Norton, President; UNION CAMPUS, 500 Lynnfield Street, Lynn, MA, Zip 01904–1487; tel. 781/581–9200; Robert G Norton, President) **A**1 3 5 10 **F**5 12 13 15 17 18 20 22 24 26 28 29 30 32 34 35 36 38 40 41 43 44 45 46 48 49 50 51 55 56 57 59 60 63 64 68 70 73 74 75 76 77 79 81 82 84 85 86 87 89 92 93 98 99 100 101 102 103 104 105 107 108 110 111 114 115 119 129 130 132 135 143 146 147 148 149 150 152 153 **P**6 8 **S** Partners HealthCare System, Inc., Boston, MA
Primary Contact: David J. Roberts, M.D., President
CFO: Sally Mason Boemer, Chief Financial Officer
CMO: Mitchell S Rein, M.D., Chief Medical Officer
CIO: Fran X. Hinckley, Chief Information Officer
CHR: Arthur Bowes, Senior Vice President Human Resources
CNO: Cheryl Bhima Merrill, MSN, R.N., Senior Vice President Patient Care Services and Chief Nursing Officer
Web address: www.nsmc.partners.org/
Control: Other not–for–profit (including NFP Corporation) **Service**: General medical and surgical

Staffed Beds: 408 **Admissions:** 18723 **Census:** 256 **Outpatient Visits:** 633675 **Births:** 1300 **Total Expense ($000):** 471650 **Payroll Expense ($000):** 203856 **Personnel:** 2305	

SALEM HOSPITAL See Salem Campus

SOMERVILLE—Middlesex County

SOMERVILLE HOSPITAL See Cambridge Health Alliance, Cambridge

SOUTH WEYMOUTH—Norfolk County

✠ **SOUTH SHORE HOSPITAL (220100)**, 55 Fogg Road, Zip 02190–2432; tel. 781/624–8000, **A**1 2 3 5 10 **F**3 7 11 13 15 17 18 20 22 24 26 28 29 30 31 32 34 35 36 37 40 41 43 44 45 46 49 50 51 53 54 55 57 58 59 60 62 63 64 65 68 70 72 74 75 76 78 79 81 82 84 85 86 87 89 91 92 93 96 107 108 110 111 114 115 118 119 124 126 129 130 132 134 135 143 146 147 148 149 150 **P**1
Primary Contact: Gene E. Green, M.D., President and Chief Executive Officer
COO: Joseph Cahill, Executive Vice President and Chief Operating Officer
CFO: Michael Cullen, Senior Vice President and Chief Financial Officer
CMO: John Stevenson, M.D., Senior Vice President and Chief Medical Officer
CIO: Del Dixon, Chief Information Officer
CHR: Robert Wheeler, Vice President Human Resources
Web address: www.southshorehospital.org
Control: Other not–for–profit (including NFP Corporation) **Service**: General medical and surgical

Staffed Beds: 387 **Admissions:** 25899 **Census:** 304 **Outpatient Visits:** 562256 **Births:** 3422 **Total Expense ($000):** 592433 **Payroll Expense ($000):** 334820 **Personnel:** 3465	

SOUTHBRIDGE—Worcester County

✠ **HARRINGTON HOSPITAL (220019)**, 100 South Street, Zip 01550–4051; tel. 508/765–9771, **A**1 2 5 10 **F**3 5 11 15 17 18 19 28 29 30 31 32 34 35 38 39 40 45 48 49 50 51 54 57 59 61 64 65 68 70 71 74 75 76 77 78 79 81 82 85 86 87 89 92 93 94 96 98 99 100 101 102 103 104 105 107 108 110 111 114 115 117 118 119 129 130 131 132 134 135 145 146 147 148 149 150 152 153 **P**6 8
Primary Contact: Edward H. Moore, President and Chief Executive Officer
COO: Kristin Morales, Chief Operating Officer
CFO: Thomas Sullivan, Vice President Fiscal Services
CMO: Arthur Russo, M.D., Director Medical Affairs
CIO: Harry Lemieux, Chief Information Officer
CHR: Christopher Canniff, Executive Director, Human Resources
CNO: Thomas W. Hijeck, R.N., MS, Vice President Nursing Services and Chief Nursing Officer
Web address: www.harringtonhospital.org
Control: Other not–for–profit (including NFP Corporation) **Service**: General medical and surgical

Staffed Beds: 130 **Admissions:** 4236 **Census:** 61 **Outpatient Visits:** 360949 **Births:** 225 **Total Expense ($000):** 133384 **Payroll Expense ($000):** 65104 **Personnel:** 930	

SPRINGFIELD—Hampden County

✠ **BAYSTATE MEDICAL CENTER (220077)**, 759 Chestnut Street, Zip 01199–0001; tel. 413/794–0000, (Includes BAYSTATE CHILDREN'S HOSPITAL, 759 Chestnut Street, Springfield, MA, Zip 01199–1001; tel. 413/794–0000; Mark A. Keroack, M.D., M.P.H., President and Chief Executive Officer, Baystate Health) **A**1 3 5 8 10 **F**3 8 12 13 14 15 17 18 19 20 22 24 26 28 29 30 31 32 34 35 37 38 40 41 43 44 45 46 47 48 49 50 51 52 54 55 56 57 58 59 60 61 64 65 66 68 70 72 74 75 76 77 78 79 81 82 83 84 85 86 87 88 89 93 96 97 98 100 101 102 104 105 107 108 110 111 114 115 118 119 120 121 123 124 126 129 130 131 132 135 138 141 143 145 146 147 148 149 154 **P**8 **S** Baystate Health, Inc., Springfield, MA
Primary Contact: Nancy Shendell–Falik, R.N., President
COO: Tejas Gandhi, Ph.D., Chief Operating Officer
CFO: Dennis Chalke, Senior Vice President, Chief Financial Officer and Treasurer
CMO: Andrew Artenstein, M.D., Chief Physician Executive, Chief Academic Officer and President, Baystate Medical Practices
CIO: Joel L. Vengco, MS, Vice President, Chief Information Officer
CHR: Paula C Squires, Senior Vice President, Chief Human Resources Officer and Chief Human Resources Officer
CNO: Nancy Shendell–Falik, R.N., Senior Vice President, Chief Operating Officer and Chief Nursing Officer
Web address: www.baystatehealth.org/bmc
Control: Other not–for–profit (including NFP Corporation) **Service**: General medical and surgical

Staffed Beds: 720 **Admissions:** 38238 **Census:** 537 **Outpatient Visits:** 872839 **Births:** 3799 **Total Expense ($000):** 1138545 **Payroll Expense ($000):** 413861 **Personnel:** 7433	

KINDRED HOSPITAL PARK VIEW See Vibra Hospital of Western Massachusetts

✠ △ **MERCY MEDICAL CENTER (220066)**, 271 Carew Street, Zip 01104–2398, Mailing Address: P.O. Box 9012, Zip 01102–9012; tel. 413/748–9000, (Nonreporting) **A**1 2 7 10 **S** Trinity Health, Livonia, MI
Primary Contact: Mark M. Fulco, President
CFO: Thomas W. Robert, Senior Vice President of Finance and Chief Financial Officer
CMO: Mark Dumais, M.D., Chief Medical Officer
CIO: Joan Methe, Chief Information Officer
CHR: Leonard F Pansa, Senior Vice President Human Resources and Administrative Services
CNO: Frances Marthone, Ph.D., R.N., Chief Nursing Officer
Web address: www.mercycares.com
Control: Other not–for–profit (including NFP Corporation) **Service**: General medical and surgical

Staffed Beds: 336	

☐ **SHRINERS HOSPITALS FOR CHILDREN–SPRINGFIELD (223303)**, 516 Carew Street, Zip 01104–2396; tel. 413/787–2000, **A**1 3 5 10 **F**29 32 34 35 37 39 44 55 57 58 59 64 66 68 75 77 79 81 82 85 86 87 89 91 92 93 94 95 96 119 130 131 132 134 143 146 148 154 **P**1 **S** Shriners Hospitals for Children, Tampa, FL
Primary Contact: H Lee. Kirk Jr, FACHE, Administrator
CFO: Richard Fulkerson, Director Fiscal Services
CMO: David M Drvaric, M.D., Chief of Staff
CIO: Eric Kamens, Regional Director Information Systems
CHR: John Donlin, Director Human Resources
CNO: Diane Brunelle, MSN, R.N., Director Patient Care Services and Chief Nursing Officer
Web address: www.shrinershospitalsforchildren.org/Hospitals/Locations/Springfield.aspx
Control: Other not–for–profit (including NFP Corporation) **Service**: Children's orthopedic

Staffed Beds: 10 **Admissions:** 133 **Census:** 2 **Outpatient Visits:** 15980 **Births:** 0 **Total Expense ($000):** 22326 **Payroll Expense ($000):** 11193 **Personnel:** 169	

✠ **VIBRA HOSPITAL OF WESTERN MASSACHUSETTS (222046)**, 1400 State Street, Zip 01109–2550; tel. 413/726–6700, (Includes VIBRA HOSPITAL OF WESTERN MASSACHUSETTS–CENTRAL CAMPUS, 111 Huntoon Memorial Highway, Rochdale, MA, Zip 1542; tel. 508/892–6000; Scott MacLean, Administrator) (Nonreporting) **A**1 10 **S** Vibra Healthcare, Mechanicsburg, PA
Primary Contact: Edward B. Leary, Interim Chief Executive Officer
CFO: Anna Dyrkacz, Chief Financial Officer
CHR: Donna Ciarefella, Director Human Resources
Web address: www.vhwmass.com
Control: Corporation, Investor–owned (for–profit) **Service**: Acute long–term care hospital

Staffed Beds: 155	

Many Facility Codes have changed. Please refer to the AHA Guide Code Chart. © 2018 AHA Guide

STOCKBRIDGE—Berkshire County

✠ **AUSTEN RIGGS CENTER**, 25 Main Street, Zip 1262, Mailing Address: P.O. Box 962, Zip 01262–0962; tel. 413/298–5511, **A**1 3 5 **F**98 104 106 130 **P**6
Primary Contact: Andrew Gerber, M.D., Ph.D., Medical Director and Chief Executive Officer
COO: Chauncey Collins, Chief Operating Officer and Chief Financial Officer
CFO: Chauncey Collins, Chief Operating Officer and Chief Financial Officer
CIO: Ave Schwartz, Chief Information Officer
CHR: Bertha Mary Connelley, Director Human Resources
CNO: Barbara Turner, Director of Nursing
Web address: www.austenriggs.org
Control: Other not–for–profit (including NFP Corporation) **Service**: Psychiatric

Staffed Beds: 69 **Admissions:** 64 **Census:** 1 **Outpatient Visits:** 1874
Births: 0 **Total Expense ($000):** 19114 **Payroll Expense ($000):** 11075
Personnel: 138

STOUGHTON—Norfolk County

✠ **CURAHEALTH HOSPITAL STOUGHTON (222002)**, 909 Sumner Street, 1st Floor, Zip 02072–3396; tel. 781/297–8200, (Nonreporting) **A**1 10 **S** Curahealth Hospitals, Garland, TX
Primary Contact: MacGregor Morgan, R.N., Chief Executive Officer
Web address: www.curahealth.com
Control: Corporation, Investor–owned (for–profit) **Service**: Acute long–term care hospital

Staffed Beds: 111

☐ **NEW ENGLAND SINAI HOSPITAL AND REHABILITATION CENTER (222027)**, 150 York Street, Zip 02072–1881; tel. 781/344–0600, (Nonreporting) **A**1 3 5 10 **S** Steward Health Care System, LLC, Dallas, TX
Primary Contact: Mary Beth. Urquhart, Interim President, Vice President Patient Care Services and Chief Nursing Officer
CFO: Victoria Lobban, Vice President Finance
CMO: Lawrence S Hotes, M.D., Chief Medical Officer
CIO: Michael West, Manager Systems Account
CHR: Julie Burke, Director Human Resources
CNO: Mary Beth Urquhart, Vice President Patient Care Services and Director of Quality
Web address: www.newenglandsinai.org
Control: Other not–for–profit (including NFP Corporation) **Service**: Acute long–term care hospital

Staffed Beds: 212

TAUNTON—Bristol County

☐ **MORTON HOSPITAL AND MEDICAL CENTER (220073)**, 88 Washington Street, Zip 02780–2465; tel. 508/828–7000, (Nonreporting) **A**1 2 10 **S** Steward Health Care System, LLC, Dallas, TX
Primary Contact: Deborah Bitsoli, CPA, President
COO: Donna Maher, R.N., Chief Operating Officer
CFO: Heidi Taylor, Chief Financial Officer
CMO: Charles Thayer, M.D., Chief Medical Officer
CNO: Lisa Coggins, Chief Nursing Officer
Web address: www.mortonhospital.org
Control: Other not–for–profit (including NFP Corporation) **Service**: General medical and surgical

Staffed Beds: 153

☐ **TAUNTON STATE HOSPITAL (224001)**, 60 Hodges Avenue Extension, Zip 02780–3034, Mailing Address: PO Box 4007, Zip 02780–0997; tel. 508/977–3000, (Nonreporting) **A**1 10 **S** Massachusetts Department of Mental Health, Boston, MA
Primary Contact: Joyce O Connor, Chief Operating Officer
CHR: Trish Scully, Director Human Resources
Control: State, Government, nonfederal **Service**: Psychiatric

Staffed Beds: 45

TEWKSBURY—Middlesex County

☐ **TEWKSBURY HOSPITAL (222003)**, 365 East Street, Zip 01876–1998; tel. 978/851–7321, (Nonreporting) **A**1 3 10 **S** Massachusetts Department of Public Health, Boston, MA
Primary Contact: Debra Tosti, Chief Executive Officer
COO: Betsy L Schwechheimer, Chief Operating Officer
CFO: Maureen DiPalma, Chief Financial Officer
CMO: James DeVita, M.D., Chief Medical Officer
CNO: Janice E Bishop, R.N., Chief Nursing Officer
Web address: www.mass.gov
Control: State, Government, nonfederal **Service**: Acute long–term care hospital

Staffed Beds: 381

WALTHAM—Middlesex County

☐ **WALDEN BEHAVIORAL CARE (224038)**, 9 Hope Avenue, Zip 02453–2741; tel. 781/647–6700, **A**1 10 **F**98 99 101 104 105 106 153 **P**6
Primary Contact: Stuart Koman, Ph.D., President and Chief Executive Officer
COO: Paula Vass, Vice President Clinical Operations
CFO: Lawrence Behan, Vice President Administration and Finance, Chief Financial Officer
CMO: James Greenblatt, M.D., Chief Medical Officer, Vice President Medical Clinical Services
CIO: Lawrence Behan, Vice President Administration and Finance, Chief Financial Officer
CHR: Carol Pender, Assistant Vice President Human Resources
Web address: www.waldenbehavioralcare.com/
Control: Corporation, Investor–owned (for–profit) **Service**: Psychiatric

Staffed Beds: 69 **Admissions:** 1304 **Census:** 45 **Outpatient Visits:** 7954
Births: 0

WAREHAM—Plymouth County

TOBEY HOSPITAL See Southcoast Hospitals Group, Fall River

WEST ROXBURY—Suffolk County

★ △ **VETERANS AFFAIRS BOSTON HEALTHCARE SYSTEM**, 1400 VFW Parkway, Zip 02132–4927; tel. 617/323–7700, (Nonreporting) **A**3 5 7 8 **S** Department of Veterans Affairs, Perry Point, MD
Primary Contact: Vincent Ng, Director
CFO: Joe Costa, Chief Financial Officer
CMO: Brian Hoffman, M.D., Chief Medical Services
CIO: David M Goodman, Ph.D., Chief Information Officer
CHR: William Warfield, Chief Human Resources Management
Web address: www.boston.va.gov/
Control: Veterans Affairs, Government, federal **Service**: General medical and surgical

Staffed Beds: 361

VETERANS AFFAIRS MEDICAL CENTER WEST ROXBURY DIVISION See Veterans Affairs Boston Healthcare System Brockton Division, Brockton

WESTBOROUGH—Worcester County

☐ **WHITTIER REHABILITATION HOSPITAL (222048)**, 150 Flanders Road, Zip 01581–1017; tel. 508/871–2000, (Nonreporting) **A**1 10 **S** Whittier Health Network, Haverhill, MA
Primary Contact: Alfred J. Arcidi, M.D., Senior Vice President
Web address: www.whittierhealth.com
Control: Partnership, Investor–owned (for–profit) **Service**: Acute long–term care hospital

Staffed Beds: 60

WESTFIELD—Hampden County

✠ **BAYSTATE NOBLE HOSPITAL (220065)**, 115 West Silver Street, Zip 01085–3628; tel. 413/568–2811, **A**1 2 5 10 **F**8 14 15 18 28 29 30 31 34 40 57 59 68 70 75 77 78 79 80 81 86 89 90 93 98 100 101 102 104 105 107 108 110 111 115 116 117 119 130 132 144 146 147 148 **P**8 **S** Baystate Health, Inc., Springfield, MA
Primary Contact: Ronald Bryant, President
CFO: John Shaver, Chief Financial Officer
CMO: Stanley Strzempko, M.D., Vice President Medical Affairs and Chief Medical Officer
CIO: Steven Cummings, Chief Operating Officer and Chief Information Officer
CHR: Joanne Ollson, Vice President Human Resources
Web address: www.baystatehealth.org/locations/noble–hospital
Control: Other not–for–profit (including NFP Corporation) **Service**: General medical and surgical

Staffed Beds: 97 **Admissions:** 2883 **Census:** 43 **Outpatient Visits:** 68278
Births: 0 **Total Expense ($000):** 56992 **Payroll Expense ($000):** 27275
Personnel: 424

Hospital, Medicare Provider Number, Address, Telephone, Approval, Facility, and Physician Codes, Health Care System

★ American Hospital Association (AHA) membership	○ Healthcare Facilities Accreditation Program	⇑ Center for Improvement in Healthcare Quality Accreditation
☐ The Joint Commission accreditation	◇ DNV Healthcare Inc. accreditation	△ Commission on Accreditation of Rehabilitation Facilities (CARF) accreditation

☐ **WESTERN MASSACHUSETTS HOSPITAL (222023)**, 91 East Mountain Road, Zip 01085–1801; tel. 413/562–4131, (Nonreporting) **A**1 10 **S** Massachusetts Department of Public Health, Boston, MA
Primary Contact: Valenda M. Liptak, Chief Executive Officer
CMO: Chabilal Neergheen, M.D., Medical Director
CHR: James E Duggan, Director Human Resources
Web address: www.mass.gov/eohhs/gov/departments/dph/programs/western–massachusetts–hospital.html
Control: State, Government, nonfederal **Service**: Acute long–term care hospital

Staffed Beds: 80

WHITINSVILLE—Worcester County

WHITINSVILLE MEDICAL CENTER See Milford Regional Medical Center, Milford

WINCHESTER—Middlesex County

⊞ **WINCHESTER HOSPITAL (220105)**, 41 Highland Avenue, Zip 01890–1496; tel. 781/729–9000, **A**1 2 3 5 10 **F**3 8 12 13 15 18 26 28 29 30 31 32 34 35 36 38 40 41 44 45 46 49 50 51 54 55 56 57 59 62 64 70 73 74 75 76 77 78 79 81 82 85 86 87 89 91 92 93 107 108 110 114 115 118 119 120 121 126 129 130 131 132 135 144 145 146 147 148 149 **S** Lahey Health, Burlington, MA
Primary Contact: Richard I. Weiner, M.D., Chief Executive Officer and Chief Medical Officer
COO: Kathy Schuler, R.N., MS, Chief Operating Officer and Chief Nursing Officer
CFO: Matthew Woods, Vice President Finance
CMO: Richard I. Weiner, M.D., Chief Executive Officer and Chief Medical Officer
CHR: Stephanie M Bettinelli, Vice President of Human Resources
CNO: Kathy Schuler, R.N., MS, Chief Operating Officer and Chief Nursing Officer
Web address: www.winchesterhospital.org
Control: Other not–for–profit (including NFP Corporation) **Service**: General medical and surgical

Staffed Beds: 197 Admissions: 10594 Census: 118 Outpatient Visits: 482276 Births: 2181 Total Expense ($000): 277866 Payroll Expense ($000): 114809 Personnel: 1704

WOBURN—Middlesex County

⊞ **HEALTHSOUTH NEW ENGLAND REHABILITATION HOSPITAL (223026)**, Two Rehabilitation Way, Zip 01801–6098; tel. 781/935–5050, **A**1 3 10 **F**28 29 30 34 58 59 64 75 77 82 96 90 91 93 94 96 100 101 103 104 132 146 148 **S** Encompass Health Corporation, Birmingham, AL
Primary Contact: David Coggins, MS, Chief Executive Officer
CFO: Lester Felege, Controller
CHR: Annamarie Cronin, Director Human Resources
Web address: www.newenglandrehab.com
Control: Corporation, Investor–owned (for–profit) **Service**: Rehabilitation

Staffed Beds: 210 Admissions: 2887 Census: 106 Outpatient Visits: 27594 Births: 0 Total Expense ($000): 37306 Payroll Expense ($000): 22991

WORCESTER—Worcester County

ADCARE HOSPITAL OF WORCESTER (220062), 107 Lincoln Street, Zip 01605–2499; tel. 508/799–9000, (Nonreporting) **A**3 5 10
Primary Contact: David W. Hillis, Chairman and Chief Executive Officer
COO: Jeffrey W Hillis, Chief Operating Officer
CFO: Christine Judycki–Crepeault, Chief Financial Officer
CMO: Ronald F Pike, M.D., Medical Director
CHR: Joan L. Bertrand, Vice President Human Resources
CNO: Judith Richards, Director of Nursing
Web address: www.adcare.com
Control: Other not–for–profit (including NFP Corporation) **Service**: Alcoholism and other chemical dependency

Staffed Beds: 114

⊞ **FAIRLAWN REHABILITATION HOSPITAL (223029)**, 189 May Street, Zip 01602–4339; tel. 508/791–6351, (Nonreporting) **A**1 3 5 10 **S** Encompass Health Corporation, Birmingham, AL
Primary Contact: William P. Johnson, Interim Chief Executive Officer
CFO: John Flaherty, Controller
CMO: Debra Twehous, Medical Director
CHR: Rosalie Lawless, Director Human Resources
CNO: Sonja Cooley–Johnson, Chief Nursing Officer
Web address: www.fairlawnrehab.org
Control: Corporation, Investor–owned (for–profit) **Service**: Rehabilitation

Staffed Beds: 110

⊞ **SAINT VINCENT HOSPITAL (220176)**, 123 Summer Street, Zip 01608–1216; tel. 508/363–5000, **A**1 2 3 5 10 **F**3 8 12 13 15 17 18 20 22 24 26 28 29 30 31 34 35 36 38 40 45 46 48 49 50 54 55 56 57 59 60 64 68 70 74 75 76 77 78 79 81 82 84 85 86 87 92 93 97 98 100 101 102 105 107 108 110 111 114 115 116 117 119 120 121 123 124 126 129 130 131 132 135 144 146 147 **P**5 **S** TENET Healthcare Corporation, Dallas, TX
Primary Contact: Ava Jo. Collins, FACHE, Interim Chief Executive Officer
COO: Ava Jo Collins, FACHE, Chief Operating Officer
CFO: Peter D'Elia, Chief Financial Officer
CMO: Douglas Waite, M.D., Chief Medical Officer
CHR: Jan Peters, Vice President Human Resources
CNO: JoAnn Piedrafite, R.N., Chief Nursing Officer
Web address: www.stvincenthospital.com
Control: Corporation, Investor–owned (for–profit) **Service**: General medical and surgical

Staffed Beds: 283 Admissions: 17257 Census: 197 Outpatient Visits: 250247 Births: 1774 Total Expense ($000): 400540 Payroll Expense ($000): 152062 Personnel: 1514

⊞ **UMASS MEMORIAL MEDICAL CENTER (220163)**, 119 Belmont Street, Zip 01605–2982; tel. 508/334–1000, (Includes HAHNEMANN CAMPUS, 281 Lincoln Street, Worcester, MA, Zip 1605; tel. 508/334–1000; MEMORIAL CAMPUS, 119 Belmont Street, Worcester, MA, Zip 1605; tel. 508/334–1000; UMASS MEMORIAL CHILDREN'S MEDICAL CENTER, 55 Lake Avenue North, Worcester, MA, Zip 01655–0002; tel. 508/334–1000; UNIVERSITY CAMPUS, 55 Lake Avenue North, Worcester, MA, Zip 01655–0002; tel. 508/334–1000) **A**1 2 3 5 8 10 **F**3 5 6 7 8 9 12 13 14 15 16 17 18 19 20 22 24 26 29 30 31 32 38 40 41 43 45 46 47 48 49 50 51 52 55 56 58 59 60 61 64 65 68 70 71 72 73 74 75 76 77 78 79 81 82 84 85 86 87 88 89 92 93 97 98 100 101 102 104 107 108 110 114 115 118 119 120 121 123 124 126 127 131 132 135 136 138 140 141 145 146 147 148 149 150 152 154 **P**5 6 **S** UMass Memorial Health Care, Inc., Worcester, MA
Primary Contact: Michael Gustafson, M.D., President
COO: Andrew Sussman, M.D., Chief Operating Officer
CFO: Therese Day, Chief Financial Officer
CMO: Charles E Cavagnaro, M.D., III Interim Chief Medical officer
CIO: George Brenkle, Chief Information Officer
CNO: Lisa Colombo, R.N., Senior Vice President Patient Care Services and Chief Nursing Officer
Web address: www.umassmemorial.org
Control: Other not–for–profit (including NFP Corporation) **Service**: General medical and surgical

Staffed Beds: 654 Admissions: 37701 Census: 566 Outpatient Visits: 1007953 Births: 4137 Total Expense ($000): 1654304 Payroll Expense ($000): 531102 Personnel: 8027

☐ **WORCESTER RECOVERY CENTER AND HOSPITAL (224032)**, 309 Belmont Street, Zip 01604–1695; tel. 508/368–3300, (Nonreporting) **A**1 3 5 10 **S** Massachusetts Department of Mental Health, Boston, MA
Primary Contact: Anthony Riccitelli, Chief Operating Officer
COO: Anthony Riccitelli, Chief Operating Officer
CIO: Ron Medciros, Director Applied Information Technology
Control: State, Government, nonfederal **Service**: Psychiatric

Staffed Beds: 126

Many Facility Codes have changed. Please refer to the AHA Guide Code Chart. © 2018 AHA Guide

MICHIGAN

ADRIAN—Lenawee County

★ ○ **PROMEDICA BIXBY HOSPITAL (230005)**, 818 Riverside Avenue, Zip 49221–1446; tel. 517/265–0900, **A**2 10 11 **F**3 8 11 12 15 18 19 26 28 29 31 34 35 38 39 40 45 48 49 54 57 59 62 64 65 68 70 74 76 77 78 79 81 82 85 87 92 93 97 100 102 104 107 108 109 111 114 115 119 121 126 127 129 130 132 135 146 148 154 **P**8 **S** ProMedica Health System, Toledo, OH
Primary Contact: Julie Yaroch, D.O., President
CFO: Bernie Nawrocki, Administrative Director Finance
CIO: Stephanie Sonnenberg, Director Information Technology
CHR: Kim Langley, Business Partner
CNO: Kathryn M Greenlee, R.N., Vice President, Clinical Services/CNO
Web address: www.promedica.org
Control: Other not–for–profit (including NFP Corporation) **Service:** General medical and surgical

Staffed Beds: 66 **Admissions:** 3798 **Census:** 31 **Outpatient Visits:** 122351 **Births:** 591 **Total Expense ($000):** 79998 **Payroll Expense ($000):** 25930 **Personnel:** 420

ALLEGAN—Allegan County

★ ⇑ **ALLEGAN GENERAL HOSPITAL (231328)**, 555 Linn Street, Zip 49010–1524; tel. 269/673–8424, **A**3 10 18 21 **F**3 12 15 28 29 31 34 35 40 43 45 47 48 50 57 59 70 75 77 78 79 81 82 85 86 87 96 97 99 100 101 104 107 108 110 114 115 119 127 129 130 131 132 135 146 149 153 **S** Quorum Health, Brentwood, TN
Primary Contact: Gerald J. Barbini, President and Chief Executive Officer
CFO: Woody White, Interim Chief Financial Officer
CMO: Nabil Nouna, M.D., Chief of Staff
CIO: David Federinko, Chief Information Officer
CHR: Denise A Eberth, Chief Human Resources Officer
CNO: Kathy Chapman, R.N., Chief Clinical Officer and Vice President of Patient Services
Web address: www.aghosp.org
Control: Other not–for–profit (including NFP Corporation) **Service:** General medical and surgical

Staffed Beds: 25 **Admissions:** 729 **Census:** 6 **Outpatient Visits:** 73612 **Births:** 0 **Total Expense ($000):** 47163 **Payroll Expense ($000):** 16129

ALMA—Gratiot County

GRATIOT MEDICAL CENTER See Midmichigan Medical Center–Gratiot

⊞ △ **MIDMICHIGAN MEDICAL CENTER–GRATIOT (230030)**, 300 East Warwick Drive, Zip 48801–1014; tel. 989/463–1101, **A**1 3 5 7 10 **F**3 12 13 15 18 20 28 29 31 34 35 38 40 43 45 50 51 56 57 59 61 64 65 68 70 74 76 77 78 79 81 82 85 86 87 89 90 92 93 96 97 98 100 101 103 104 105 107 108 110 111 115 117 118 119 127 129 130 132 135 144 145 146 148 149 154 **S** MidMichigan Health, Midland, MI
Primary Contact: Marita Hattem–Schiffman, President
CFO: Jeff Provenzano, Vice President and Chief Financial Officer
CNO: Robin Whitmore, Chief Nursing Officer
Web address: www.midmichigan.org/gratiot
Control: Other not–for–profit (including NFP Corporation) **Service:** General medical and surgical

Staffed Beds: 96 **Admissions:** 4138 **Census:** 51 **Outpatient Visits:** 137913 **Births:** 469 **Total Expense ($000):** 108709 **Payroll Expense ($000):** 32458 **Personnel:** 626

ALPENA—Alpena County

⊞ **MIDMICHIGAN MEDICAL CENTER – ALPENA (230036)**, 1501 West Chisholm Street, Zip 49707–1401; tel. 989/356–7000, **A**1 2 10 **F**3 11 13 15 20 26 28 29 31 34 35 40 44 45 46 47 48 49 50 59 60 62 64 65 70 71 73 74 75 76 77 78 79 81 82 85 86 87 90 92 93 96 97 98 100 101 102 103 104 107 108 110 111 114 115 118 119 129 130 131 132 135 146 147 148 149 154 **P**6 **S** MidMichigan Health, Midland, MI
Primary Contact: Charles H. Sherwin, President
CFO: George J Smart, Vice President Finance and Information Technology
CMO: Richard Bates, Vice President of Medical Affairs
CHR: Diane Shields, Chief Human Resources Officer
Web address: www.alpenaregionalmedicalcenter.org
Control: Other not–for–profit (including NFP Corporation) **Service:** General medical and surgical

Staffed Beds: 125 **Admissions:** 4553 **Census:** 50 **Outpatient Visits:** 239073 **Births:** 401 **Total Expense ($000):** 135517 **Payroll Expense ($000):** 54109 **Personnel:** 853

ANN ARBOR—Washtenaw County

⊞ **UNIVERSITY OF MICHIGAN HEALTH SYSTEM (230046)**, 1500 East Medical Center Drive, Zip 48109; tel. 734/936–4000, (Includes C. S. MOTT CHILDREN'S HOSPITAL, 1540 East Hospital Drive, Ann Arbor, MI, Zip 48109–5475; tel. 734/936–4000; Paul A King, Executive Director) **A**1 2 3 5 8 10 **F**3 5 6 8 9 11 12 13 15 16 17 18 19 20 21 22 23 24 25 26 27 28 29 30 31 32 34 35 36 37 38 39 40 41 43 44 45 46 47 48 49 50 51 52 53 54 55 56 57 58 59 60 61 62 64 65 66 68 69 70 72 74 75 76 77 78 79 80 81 82 84 85 86 87 88 89 90 91 92 93 94 95 96 97 98 99 100 101 102 103 104 107 108 110 111 112 114 115 116 117 118 119 120 121 123 124 126 127 129 130 131 132 134 135 136 137 138 139 140 141 142 145 146 147 148 149 150 151 153 154 **P**1
Primary Contact: David Spahlinger, M.D., President
COO: Tony Denton, JD, Senior Vice President and Chief Operating Officer, University of Michigan Health System
CFO: Paul Castillo, Chief Financial Officer
CMO: Jeffrey Desmond, M.D., Chief Medical Officer
CIO: Andrew Rosenberg, M.D., Chief Information Officer
CHR: Deloris Hunt, Chief Human Resources Officer
CNO: Marge Calarco, Chief Nursing Executive
Web address: www.med.umich.edu
Control: Other not–for–profit (including NFP Corporation) **Service:** General medical and surgical

Staffed Beds: 982 **Admissions:** 50441 **Census:** 847 **Outpatient Visits:** 3155088 **Births:** 4621 **Total Expense ($000):** 3035104 **Payroll Expense ($000):** 1153978 **Personnel:** 16756

⊞ **VETERANS AFFAIRS ANN ARBOR HEALTHCARE SYSTEM**, 2215 Fuller Road, Zip 48105–2399; tel. 734/769–7100, **A**1 2 3 5 8 **F**3 5 12 18 20 22 24 26 28 29 30 31 34 35 36 38 39 40 45 49 50 54 56 57 58 59 60 61 62 63 64 65 68 70 71 74 75 77 78 79 81 82 83 84 85 86 87 91 92 93 94 96 97 98 100 101 102 103 104 107 108 111 114 115 116 117 118 119 120 121 123 126 128 129 130 132 135 143 144 146 147 148 149 153 154 **S** Department of Veterans Affairs, Perry Point, MD
Primary Contact: Andrew Pacyna, Acting Director
COO: Himanshu Singh, M.D., Associate Director
CFO: Joel Wallinga, Chief Financial Officer
CMO: Eric Young, M.D., Chief of Staff
CIO: Rob Whitehurst, Chief, Office of Information and Technology
CHR: Stephanie Hunter, Chief Human Resources Officer
CNO: Stacey Breedveld, R.N., MSN, Associate Director for Patient Care
Web address: www.annarbor.va.gov
Control: Veterans Affairs, Government, federal **Service:** General medical and surgical

Staffed Beds: 109 **Admissions:** 5378 **Census:** 85 **Outpatient Visits:** 630107 **Births:** 0 **Total Expense ($000):** 528466 **Payroll Expense ($000):** 222775

AUBURN HILLS—Oakland County

☐ **HAVENWYCK HOSPITAL (234023)**, 1525 University Drive, Zip 48326–2673; tel. 248/373–9200, **A**1 10 **F**98 99 102 103 105 106 130 154 **P**8 **S** Universal Health Services, Inc., King of Prussia, PA
Primary Contact: Julie Szyska, Chief Executive Officer and Managing Director
CFO: Steve Sacharski, Chief Financial Officer
CMO: Hani Mekhael, M.D., Chief Staff
CHR: Amy Giannosa, Director Human Resources
CNO: Mitzi Sawicki, Director of Nursing
Web address: www.havenwyckhospital.com
Control: Corporation, Investor–owned (for–profit) **Service:** Psychiatric

Staffed Beds: 243 **Admissions:** 7089 **Census:** 200 **Outpatient Visits:** 5814 **Births:** 0 **Total Expense ($000):** 48037 **Payroll Expense ($000):** 18788 **Personnel:** 431

Hospital, Medicare Provider Number, Address, Telephone, Approval, Facility, and Physician Codes, Health Care System

★ American Hospital Association (AHA) membership   ○ Healthcare Facilities Accreditation Program   ⇑ Center for Improvement in Healthcare Quality Accreditation
☐ The Joint Commission accreditation   ◇ DNV Healthcare Inc. accreditation   △ Commission on Accreditation of Rehabilitation Facilities (CARF) accreditation

BAD AXE—Huron County

MCLAREN THUMB REGION (230118), 1100 South Van Dyke Road, Zip 48413–9615; tel. 989/269–9521, **A**5 10 20 **F**3 11 13 14 15 18 20 28 29 31 32 34 35 40 45 53 56 57 59 64 70 74 75 76 77 78 79 81 82 85 93 97 107 108 114 119 127 130 132 134 135 144 146 148 149 **P**6 **S** McLaren Health Care Corporation, Grand Blanc, MI
Primary Contact: Michael Eric. Johnston, President and Chief Executive Officer
CFO: Kevin J Cawley, Interim Chief Financial Officer
CMO: Craig McManaman, M.D., Chief of Staff
CHR: Nancy Bouck, Senior Director of Human Resources
CNO: Jane Christner, Chief Nursing Officer
Web address: www.huronmedicalcenter.org
Control: Other not–for–profit (including NFP Corporation) **Service**: General medical and surgical

Staffed Beds: 46 **Admissions**: 1429 **Census**: 12 **Outpatient Visits**: 49043 **Births**: 423 **Total Expense ($000)**: 44235 **Payroll Expense ($000)**: 16521 **Personnel**: 302

BATTLE CREEK—Calhoun County

BATTLE CREEK VETERANS AFFAIRS MEDICAL CENTER, 5500 Armstrong Road, Zip 49037–7314; tel. 269/966–5600, (Total facility includes 75 beds in nursing home–type unit) **A**1 3 5 **F**3 4 5 7 12 18 29 30 33 34 35 36 38 39 50 53 54 56 57 58 59 61 62 63 64 65 68 74 75 77 82 83 84 86 87 93 94 96 97 98 100 101 102 103 104 106 107 108 111 114 115 119 127 128 130 132 135 143 144 146 147 148 153 154 **P**6 **S** Department of Veterans Affairs, Perry Point, MD
Primary Contact: Ketan Shah, M.D., Acting Director
COO: Edward G. Dornoff, Associate Director
CFO: James M. Rupert, Chief Fiscal Services
CMO: Wilfredo Rodriguez, M.D., Chief of Staff
CIO: Scott Hershberger, Acting Chief Information Management Services
CHR: Palma Simkins, Chief Human Resources Management Services
CNO: Kay Bower, Associate Director for Patient Care Services
Web address: www.battlecreek.va.gov/
Control: Veterans Affairs, Government, federal **Service**: Psychiatric

Staffed Beds: 242 **Admissions**: 1720 **Census**: 189 **Outpatient Visits**: 560089 **Births**: 0 **Personnel**: 1718

BRONSON BATTLE CREEK HOSPITAL (230075), 300 North Avenue, Zip 49017–3307; tel. 269/245–8000, (Includes FIELDSTONE CENTER, 165 North Washington Avenue, Battle Creek, MI, Zip 49037; tel. 269/245–8570; MAIN CAMPUS, 300 North Avenue, Battle Creek, MI, Zip 49017; tel. 616/966–8000) **A**1 2 10 **F**3 4 6 9 11 15 18 19 28 29 30 31 34 35 36 38 40 44 45 46 49 50 51 54 55 56 57 58 59 60 61 63 64 65 66 68 70 71 74 75 76 77 78 79 81 82 84 85 86 87 90 92 93 97 98 100 101 102 103 104 107 110 111 114 115 117 118 119 120 121 123 126 129 130 131 132 134 135 143 144 146 147 148 149 **P**6 **S** Bronson Healthcare Group, Kalamazoo, MI
Primary Contact: Frank J. Sardone, President and Chief Executive Officer
COO: James E. Mckernan, Chief Operating Officer
CMO: Daniel Stewart, M.D., Vice President Medical Affairs
CHR: John Hayden, Senior Vice President and Human Resources Officer
CNO: Susan Watson, MSN, R.N., Vice President
Web address: www.bronsonhealth.com
Control: Other not–for–profit (including NFP Corporation) **Service**: General medical and surgical

Staffed Beds: 198 **Admissions**: 8287 **Census**: 108 **Outpatient Visits**: 519413 **Births**: 757 **Total Expense ($000)**: 248772 **Payroll Expense ($000)**: 130076 **Personnel**: 1502

SELECT SPECIALTY HOSPITAL–BATTLE CREEK (232035), 300 North Avenue, Zip 49017–3307; tel. 269/245–4675, (Nonreporting) **A**1 10 **S** Select Medical Corporation, Mechanicsburg, PA
Primary Contact: Robert Mach, Chief Executive Officer
Web address: www.battlecreek.selectspecialtyhospitals.com/
Control: Corporation, Investor–owned (for–profit) **Service**: Acute long–term care hospital

Staffed Beds: 25

VETERANS AFFAIRS MEDICAL CENTER See Battle Creek Veterans Affairs Medical Center

BAY CITY—Bay County

☐ △ **MCLAREN BAY REGION (230041)**, 1900 Columbus Avenue, Zip 48708–6831; tel. 989/894–3000, (Includes MCLAREN BAY REGION–WEST CAMPUS, 3250 East Midland Road, Bay City, MI, Zip 48706; tel. 989/667–6750; Monica Baranski, MS, R.N., President) **A**1 2 3 5 7 10 12 13 **F**3 7 11 13 15 17 18 20 22 24 26 28 29 30 31 32 34 35 36 38 40 44 45 46 47 48 49 50 54 57 58 59 64 65 68 70 73 74 75 76 78 79 81 82 85 86 87 89 90 92 93 96 97 98 100 102 103 107 108 110 111 114 115 119 120 121 123 124 129 130 131 132 135 141 143 144 146 147 148 149 **S** McLaren Health Care Corporation, Grand Blanc, MI
Primary Contact: Clarence Sevillian, President and Chief Executive Officer
COO: Mitch Southwick, Chief Operating Officer
CFO: Damon Sorensen, Chief Financial Officer
CMO: Jason White, M.D., Chief Medical Officer
CIO: Ronald Strachan, Chief Information Officer
CHR: Carolyn Potter, Chief Human Resources Officer
CNO: Ellen E Talbott, MSN, R.N., Vice President Patient Care Services
Web address: www.mclaren.org/bayregion
Control: Other not–for–profit (including NFP Corporation) **Service**: General medical and surgical

Staffed Beds: 338 **Admissions**: 15423 **Census**: 207 **Outpatient Visits**: 333103 **Births**: 821 **Total Expense ($000)**: 299256 **Payroll Expense ($000)**: 130769 **Personnel**: 1864

○ **MCLAREN BAY SPECIAL CARE (232020)**, 3250 East Midland Road, Suite 1, Zip 48706–2835; tel. 989/667–6851, **A**10 11 **F**1 3 29 79 87 96 148 **S** McLaren Health Care Corporation, Grand Blanc, MI
Primary Contact: Monica Baranski, MS, R.N., President
CMO: Janet Sutton, D.O., Medical Director
CIO: Greg Jacobs, Manager
CHR: Carolyn Potter, Vice President Human Resources
Web address: www.mclaren/bayspecialcare
Control: Other not–for–profit (including NFP Corporation) **Service**: Acute long–term care hospital

Staffed Beds: 10 **Admissions**: 117 **Census**: 8 **Outpatient Visits**: 0 **Births**: 0 **Total Expense ($000)**: 4869 **Payroll Expense ($000)**: 2229 **Personnel**: 33

BIG RAPIDS—Mecosta County

SPECTRUM HEALTH BIG RAPIDS HOSPITAL (230093), 605 Oak Street, Zip 49307–2099; tel. 231/796–8691, **A**1 5 10 20 **F**3 8 13 15 28 29 30 34 35 40 45 50 53 54 57 59 62 63 64 65 70 75 76 77 79 81 85 86 87 89 91 93 97 107 108 110 111 115 118 119 126 127 129 130 131 132 135 146 147 148 149 154 **S** Spectrum Health, Grand Rapids, MI
Primary Contact: Mary Kay VanDriel, President
CFO: Thomas Khoerl, Vice President Finance
CMO: Christopher Skinner, Chief of Staff
CIO: Patrick Whiteside, Manager Information Services
CHR: Melonie Jackson, Human Resource Business Partner
CNO: Caroline A Ring, Chief Nursing Officer
Web address: www.spectrumhealth.org
Control: Other not–for–profit (including NFP Corporation) **Service**: General medical and surgical

Staffed Beds: 48 **Admissions**: 1918 **Census**: 14 **Outpatient Visits**: 471509 **Births**: 582 **Total Expense ($000)**: 66878 **Payroll Expense ($000)**: 24374 **Personnel**: 446

BRIGHTON—Livingston County

★ **BRIGHTON CENTER FOR RECOVERY (230279)**, 12851 Grand River Road, Zip 48116–8506; tel. 810/227–1211, **A**10 **F**4 5 30 34 35 36 38 44 57 68 75 86 100 101 104 130 132 135 146 149 150 152 **S** Ascension Healthcare, Saint Louis, MO
Primary Contact: Raymond A. Waller, Director
COO: Raymond A. Waller, Director
CFO: Marie Allard, Finance Manager
CMO: Ismael David Yanga, M.D., Chief Medical Officer
CIO: Frank Sanzone, Manager Information Technology
CHR: Marney Daugherty, Worklife Services Consultant
CNO: Barbara Shoup, R.N., Chief Nursing Officer
Web address: www.brightonrecovery.org
Control: Church operated, Nongovernment, not–for–profit **Service**: Alcoholism and other chemical dependency

Staffed Beds: 99 **Admissions**: 3612 **Census**: 74 **Outpatient Visits**: 18074 **Births**: 0 **Total Expense ($000)**: 15518 **Payroll Expense ($000)**: 7443 **Personnel**: 117

Many Facility Codes have changed. Please refer to the AHA Guide Code Chart.

CADILLAC—Wexford County

☒ **MUNSON HEALTHCARE CADILLAC HOSPITAL (230081)**, 400 Hobart Street, Zip 49601–2389; tel. 231/876–7200, **A**1 10 20 **F**3 11 13 15 18 28 29 30 31 34 35 40 44 45 50 51 59 64 68 70 76 77 78 79 81 85 87 93 97 107 111 114 115 116 119 127 129 130 132 146 154 **P**8 **S** Munson Healthcare, Traverse City, MI
Primary Contact: Tonya Smith, President
COO: Michael Zdrodowski, Vice President of Operations and Ambulatory Services
CFO: Kristin Ellis, Controller
CMO: Joe Santangelo, M.D., Vice President of Medical Affairs
CIO: Randi Terry, Site Director Management Information Systems
CHR: Kelley Whittington–Geppert, Director Human Resources
CNO: Kathryn Bandfield–Keough, Vice President Patient Care Services
Web address: www.mercyhealthcadillac.com/welcome–cadillac
Control: Other not–for–profit (including NFP Corporation) **Service**: General medical and surgical

Staffed Beds: 49 **Admissions**: 3425 **Census**: 31 **Outpatient Visits**: 155121
Births: 337 **Total Expense ($000)**: 86660 **Payroll Expense ($000)**: 34252
Personnel: 594

CARO—Tuscola County

☐ **CARO CENTER (234025)**, 2000 Chambers Road, Zip 48723–9296; tel. 989/673–3191, (Nonreporting) **A**1 10
Primary Contact: Rose Laskowski, R.N., Director
COO: Rose Laskowski, R.N., Director
CFO: Mary Jo Drzewiecki–Burger, Administrative Manager
CMO: William Clark, M.D., Chief Clinical Affairs
CIO: Michele Wills, Registered Health Information Administrator
CHR: Barbara Frank, Human Resource Specialist
Control: State, Government, nonfederal **Service**: Psychiatric

Staffed Beds: 193

★ **MCLAREN CARO REGION (231329)**, 401 North Hooper Street, Zip 48723–1476, Mailing Address: P.O. Box 435, Zip 48723–0435; tel. 989/673–3141, **A**5 10 18 **F**3 11 15 29 34 35 40 45 50 54 57 59 65 75 77 81 85 87 92 93 97 107 108 110 115 119 130 135 144 149 154 **S** McLaren Health Care Corporation, Grand Blanc, MI
Primary Contact: Marc Augsburger, R.N., President and Chief Executive Officer
CFO: Ron Srebinski, Chief Financial Officer
CMO: T Gard Adams, M.D., Chief of Staff
CHR: Allyson Joyce, Vice President Human Resources
CNO: Kelly Whittaker, Vice President Nursing
Web address: www.cch–mi.org
Control: Other not–for–profit (including NFP Corporation) **Service**: General medical and surgical

Staffed Beds: 25 **Admissions**: 123 **Census**: 1 **Outpatient Visits**: 30329
Births: 0 **Total Expense ($000)**: 15010 **Payroll Expense ($000)**: 6090
Personnel: 117

CARSON CITY—Montcalm County

★ ○ **SPARROW CARSON HOSPITAL (230208)**, 406 East Elm Street, Zip 48811–9693, Mailing Address: P.O. Box 879, Zip 48811–0879; tel. 989/584–3131, **A**3 5 10 11 19 **F**3 11 13 31 34 35 40 45 46 50 57 59 62 64 65 68 70 75 76 78 79 81 82 85 86 87 93 97 107 108 110 111 115 118 119 126 127 130 146 147 148 **P**6 8 **S** Sparrow Health System, Lansing, MI
Primary Contact: William Roeser, Interim President and Chief Executive Officer
CFO: Richard Reid, Vice President Chief Finance Officer
CMO: Robert Seals, D.O., Medical Director
CIO: Richard Terry, Vice President & Chief Information Officer
CHR: Georgette Russell, Vice President of Talent & Organizational Effectiveness
Web address: www.carsoncityhospital.com
Control: Other not–for–profit (including NFP Corporation) **Service**: General medical and surgical

Staffed Beds: 48 **Admissions**: 965 **Census**: 7 **Outpatient Visits**: 102339
Births: 228 **Total Expense ($000)**: 54257 **Payroll Expense ($000)**: 26223
Personnel: 373

CASS CITY—Tuscola County

★ **HILLS & DALES GENERAL HOSPITAL (231316)**, 4675 Hill Street, Zip 48726–1099; tel. 989/872–2121, **A**5 10 18 **F**3 11 15 29 30 31 32 34 35 40 45 46 53 56 57 59 61 64 68 74 75 77 79 81 86 87 93 97 107 108 109 110 115 118 119 127 129 130 131 132 133 135 144 146 147 148 149 **P**6
Primary Contact: Jean Anthony, R.N., President and Chief Executive Officer
CFO: Kenneth Baranski, Chief Financial Officer
CMO: Donald Robbins, M.D., Jr Chief Staff
CNO: Jennifer TerBush, Vice President, Patient Services
Web address: www.hdghmi.org
Control: Other not–for–profit (including NFP Corporation) **Service**: General medical and surgical

Staffed Beds: 25 **Admissions**: 353 **Census**: 6 **Outpatient Visits**: 96021
Births: 0 **Total Expense ($000)**: 35502 **Payroll Expense ($000)**: 15264
Personnel: 263

CHARLEVOIX—Charlevoix County

☒ **MUNSON HEALTHCARE CHARLEVOIX HOSPITAL (231322)**, 14700 Lake Shore Drive, Zip 49720–1999; tel. 231/547–4024, **A**1 5 10 18 **F**3 11 13 14 15 28 29 30 31 34 35 40 50 55 56 59 64 75 76 77 78 79 81 85 87 89 93 97 100 104 107 114 115 119 127 129 130 131 132 133 135 143 144 146 147 **P**6 **S** Munson Healthcare, Traverse City, MI
Primary Contact: Joanne Schroeder, President
COO: John Singer IV Chief Operating Officer
CFO: Robert Wilcox, Chief Financial Officer
CMO: James Jeakle, Chief Medical Officer
CIO: David Priest, Director Information Systems
CHR: Patty Fitzgerald, Staff Services
CNO: Bernadette Green Cole, R.N., Chief Nursing Officer
Web address: www.cah.org
Control: Other not–for–profit (including NFP Corporation) **Service**: General medical and surgical

Staffed Beds: 25 **Admissions**: 921 **Census**: 7

CHARLOTTE—Eaton County

☒ **HAYES GREEN BEACH MEMORIAL HOSPITAL (231327)**, 321 East Harris Street, Zip 48813–1629; tel. 517/543–1050, **A**1 3 10 18 **F**3 7 11 15 18 26 28 29 31 34 35 36 40 45 46 50 53 59 64 65 68 69 75 77 79 81 82 85 87 89 92 93 97 107 108 110 111 114 118 119 129 130 131 132 135 143 144 146 147 148 149 154 **P**6 **S** QHR, Brentwood, TN
Primary Contact: Matthew Rush, FACHE, President and Chief Executive Officer
CFO: Kim Capps, Chief Financial Officer
CMO: Hugh Lindsey, M.D., Chief Medical Officer
CIO: Kevin Neugent, Chief Information Officer
CHR: Jennifer C Bucienski, Vice President Human Resources
CNO: Maureen Hillary, Chief Nursing Officer
Web address: www.hgbhealth.com
Control: Other not–for–profit (including NFP Corporation) **Service**: General medical and surgical

Staffed Beds: 25 **Admissions**: 673 **Census**: 5 **Outpatient Visits**: 166564
Births: 0 **Total Expense ($000)**: 52040 **Payroll Expense ($000)**: 21889
Personnel: 388

CHELSEA—Washtenaw County

☒ **ST. JOSEPH MERCY CHELSEA (230259)**, 775 South Main Street, Zip 48118–1383; tel. 734/593–6000, **A**1 3 5 10 **F**3 5 8 11 15 18 28 29 30 31 34 35 40 45 50 51 56 57 59 64 65 70 74 75 77 78 79 81 82 84 85 86 87 90 91 92 93 97 98 100 101 102 103 104 107 110 111 114 115 119 120 121 129 130 131 132 134 135 146 147 149 154 **P**6 **S** Trinity Health, Livonia, MI
Primary Contact: Nancy Kay. Graebner, President and Chief Executive Officer
CFO: Barb Fielder, Vice President Finance
CMO: Randall T Forsch, M.D., M.P.H., Chief Medical Officer
CHR: Jeremy Stephens, Vice President and Chief Human Resources Officer
CNO: Kathy M. Brubaker, R.N., MSN, Vice President and Chief Nursing Officer
Web address: www.cch.org
Control: Church operated, Nongovernment, not–for–profit **Service**: General medical and surgical

Staffed Beds: 96 **Admissions**: 4372 **Census**: 48 **Outpatient Visits**: 230916
Births: 0 **Total Expense ($000)**: 149931 **Payroll Expense ($000)**: 60768
Personnel: 818

MI

CLARE—Clare County

⊞ **MIDMICHIGAN MEDICAL CENTER–CLARE (230180)**, 703 North McEwan Street, Zip 48617–1440; tel. 989/802–5000, **A**1 5 10 **F**3 11 15 18 20 28 29 30 34 35 40 43 45 50 53 57 58 59 61 64 75 77 79 80 81 85 86 87 93 97 107 108 110 111 115 118 119 127 129 130 135 144 146 148 154 **S** MidMichigan Health, Midland, MI
Primary Contact: Raymond Stover, President and Chief Executive Officer
CFO: Jeff Provenzano, Vice President and Chief Financial Officer
CMO: David Bremer, D.O., Chief of Staff
CIO: Michael Larson, Vice President Chief Information Officer
CNO: Glenn King, R.N., MSN, Vice President, Chief Nursing Officer
Web address: www.midmichigan.org
Control: Other not–for–profit (including NFP Corporation) **Service:** General medical and surgical

Staffed Beds: 49 **Admissions:** 1036 **Census:** 8 **Outpatient Visits:** 91724 **Births:** 0 **Total Expense ($000):** 49195 **Payroll Expense ($000):** 13371 **Personnel:** 200

CLINTON TOWNSHIP—Macomb County

⊞ **HENRY FORD MACOMB HOSPITALS (230047)**, 15855 19 Mile Road, Zip 48038–6324; tel. 586/263–2300, (Includes HENRY FORD MACOMB HOSPITAL – MOUNT CLEMENS CAMPUS, 215 North Avenue, Mount Clemens, MI, Zip 48043; tel. 586/466–9300; ST. JOSEPH'S MERCY HOSPITAL–WEST, 15855 19 Mile Road, Clinton Township, MI, Zip 48038; tel. 586/263–2707; ST. JOSEPH'S MERCY– NORTH, 80650 North Van Dyke, Romeo, MI, Zip 48065; tel. 810/798–3551) **A**1 2 3 10 13 **F**3 7 8 11 12 13 15 18 20 22 24 26 28 29 30 31 32 34 35 36 38 40 41 43 44 45 46 47 49 50 51 54 56 57 58 59 60 61 62 63 64 65 66 68 69 70 73 74 75 76 77 78 79 81 82 84 85 86 87 89 90 92 93 96 97 98 100 101 102 103 107 108 110 111 114 115 116 117 118 119 120 121 123 124 126 129 130 131 132 134 135 144 146 147 148 149 150 154 **P**6 **S** Henry Ford Health System, Detroit, MI
Primary Contact: Barbara W. Rossmann, R.N., President and Chief Executive Officer
COO: Gary Beaulac, Chief Operating Officer
CFO: Terry Goodbalian, Vice President Finance and Chief Financial Officer
CMO: Charles Kelly, D.O., Vice President Medical Affairs and Chief Medical Officer
CHR: Joel Gibson, Vice President Human Resources
Web address: www.henryfordmacomb.com
Control: Other not–for–profit (including NFP Corporation) **Service:** General medical and surgical

Staffed Beds: 415 **Admissions:** 21316 **Census:** 290 **Outpatient Visits:** 641047 **Births:** 1632 **Total Expense ($000):** 478988 **Payroll Expense ($000):** 178158 **Personnel:** 2647

COLDWATER—Branch County

⊞ **PROMEDICA COLDWATER REGIONAL HOSPITAL (230022)**, 274 East Chicago Street, Zip 49036–2041; tel. 517/279–5400, **A**1 10 13 19 **F**3 8 11 13 15 18 28 29 30 31 32 34 40 45 50 57 59 62 63 64 70 74 75 76 77 78 79 81 85 87 91 92 93 96 97 98 100 101 102 106 107 108 110 111 115 119 127 129 130 132 146 154 **P**6 **S** ProMedica Health System, Toledo, OH
Primary Contact: Randy DeGroot, President and Chief Executive Officer
COO: Mary R Rose, R.N., Chief Clinical Officer
CFO: Amy Crouch, Chief Financial Officer
CMO: Joudat Daoud, M.D., Chief of Staff
CIO: Joel Lederman, Director Information Systems
CHR: Amy Jensen, Director Human Resources
Web address: www.chcbc.com
Control: County, Government, nonfederal **Service:** General medical and surgical

Staffed Beds: 62 **Admissions:** 2789 **Census:** 29 **Outpatient Visits:** 137092 **Births:** 201 **Total Expense ($000):** 61614 **Payroll Expense ($000):** 28640 **Personnel:** 459

COMMERCE TOWNSHIP—Oakland County

⊞ **DMC HURON VALLEY–SINAI HOSPITAL (230277)**, 1 William Carls Drive, Zip 48382–2201; tel. 248/937–3300, **A**1 3 5 10 **F**3 11 12 13 15 18 20 22 26 28 29 30 31 34 35 37 39 40 44 47 48 49 50 51 54 56 57 58 59 61 64 65 70 73 74 75 76 77 78 79 81 82 85 86 87 89 91 96 107 108 110 111 114 115 116 117 118 119 121 123 124 126 129 130 131 132 135 141 145 146 147 148 149 150 154 **P**1 6 **S** TENET Healthcare Corporation, Dallas, TX
Primary Contact: Karima Bentounsi, Chief Executive Officer
COO: Samuel Pieh, Chief Operating Officer
CFO: William Lantzy, Chief Financial Officer
CHR: Nicole Williams, Director of Human Resources Operations
CNO: Lori Stallings–Sicard, R.N., Chief Nursing Officer
Web address: www.hvsh.org
Control: Corporation, Investor–owned (for–profit) **Service:** General medical and surgical

Staffed Beds: 156 **Admissions:** 8400 **Census:** 80 **Outpatient Visits:** 100515 **Births:** 1068 **Total Expense ($000):** 162901 **Payroll Expense ($000):** 55810 **Personnel:** 858

DEARBORN—Wayne County

⊞ **BEAUMONT HOSPITAL – DEARBORN (230020)**, 18101 Oakwood Boulevard, Zip 48124–4089, Mailing Address: P.O. Box 2500, Zip 48123–2500; tel. 313/593–7000, **A**1 2 3 5 10 **F**3 11 12 13 15 17 18 19 20 22 24 26 28 29 30 31 32 34 35 37 38 39 40 41 43 44 45 46 47 49 50 52 54 55 56 57 58 59 60 61 64 65 68 70 72 74 75 76 77 78 79 81 82 84 85 86 87 89 92 93 96 97 100 102 107 108 110 111 114 115 117 118 119 120 121 123 124 126 129 130 131 132 135 146 147 149 **P**6 **S** Beaumont Health, Southfield, MI
Primary Contact: David Claeys, FACHE, Chief Executive Officer
COO: Carolyn Wilson, Chief Operating Officer
CFO: Timothy Jodway, Chief Financial Administrator
CMO: Paolo G Marciano, M.D., Chief Medical Officer
CIO: Subra Sripada, Executive Vice President, Chief Transformation Officer and Chief Information Officer
CHR: Sherry Huffman, Administrator Human Resources
CNO: Mary Ellen Kochis, MSN, R.N., Administrator Nursing Operations
Web address: www.beaumont.org
Control: Other not–for–profit (including NFP Corporation) **Service:** General medical and surgical

Staffed Beds: 632 **Admissions:** 30717 **Census:** 419 **Outpatient Visits:** 349618 **Births:** 4324 **Total Expense ($000):** 567210 **Payroll Expense ($000):** 227688 **Personnel:** 3738

DECKERVILLE—Sanilac County

DECKERVILLE COMMUNITY HOSPITAL (231311), 3559 Pine Street, Zip 48427–7703, Mailing Address: P.O. Box 126, Zip 48427–0126; tel. 810/376–2835, (Nonreporting) **A**10 18
Primary Contact: Angela McConnachie, Chief Executive Officer and Chief Nursing Officer
CFO: Kim Gentner, Chief Financial Officer
CMO: Josh White, Chief Medical Officer
Web address: www.deckervillehosp.org
Control: Other not–for–profit (including NFP Corporation) **Service:** General medical and surgical

Staffed Beds: 15

DETROIT—Wayne County

⊞ **ASCENSION ST. JOHN HOSPITAL (230165)**, 22101 Moross Road, Zip 48236–2148; tel. 313/343–4000, **A**1 2 3 5 8 10 **F**3 8 9 11 12 13 14 15 17 18 20 22 24 26 28 29 30 31 32 34 35 36 37 38 39 40 41 43 44 45 46 47 48 49 50 54 55 56 57 58 59 60 61 63 64 65 66 68 70 72 74 75 76 77 78 79 80 81 82 84 85 86 87 88 89 90 92 93 95 96 97 98 100 101 102 107 108 110 111 114 115 118 119 120 121 123 124 126 130 131 132 135 138 141 143 144 146 147 148 149 150 154 **P**8 **S** Ascension Healthcare, Saint Louis, MO
Primary Contact: Robert E. Hoban, President
COO: Brant Russell, R.N., Chief Operating Officer
CMO: Kevin Grady, M.D., Chief Medical Officer
CIO: Ralph Tenney, Chief Information Officer
CHR: Joanne E Tuscany, Director Human Resources
Web address: www.stjohnprovidence.org/stjohnhospital/
Control: Church operated, Nongovernment, not–for–profit **Service:** General medical and surgical

Staffed Beds: 621 **Admissions:** 28163 **Census:** 398 **Outpatient Visits:** 906421 **Births:** 3023 **Total Expense ($000):** 773828 **Payroll Expense ($000):** 262154 **Personnel:** 3167

BCA STONECREST HOSPITAL See Stonecrest Center

⊞ △ **DMC – CHILDREN'S HOSPITAL OF MICHIGAN (233300)**, 3901 Beaubien Street, Zip 48201–2119; tel. 313/745–5852, **A**1 3 5 7 10 **F**3 7 8 11 16 17 18 19 20 21 22 23 24 25 26 27 29 30 31 32 34 35 37 38 39 40 41 43 44 45 48 49 50 51 54 55 57 58 59 60 61 63 64 65 66 68 72 74 75 77 78 79 80 81 82 84 85 86 87 88 89 90 91 92 93 95 96 97 99 100 107 108 111 114 115 116 117 119 120 121 123 124 129 130 131 132 134 136 137 138 139 141 146 148 149 150 154 **S** TENET Healthcare Corporation, Dallas, TX
Primary Contact: Luanne T. Ewald, Chief Executive Officer
COO: Monique Butler, Chief Operating Officer
CFO: Lisa Hutchings, Chief Financial Officer
CMO: Rudolph Valentini, M.D., Chief Medical Officer
CHR: Jonita Edwards, Director Human Resources
CNO: Brenda VanWallaghen, Interim Chief Nursing Officer
Web address: www.chmkids.org
Control: Corporation, Investor–owned (for–profit) **Service:** Children's general medical and surgical

Staffed Beds: 227 **Admissions:** 10825 **Census:** 152 **Outpatient Visits:** 303702 **Births:** 0 **Total Expense ($000):** 371601 **Payroll Expense ($000):** 136693 **Personnel:** 2161

MI

Many Facility Codes have changed. Please refer to the AHA Guide Code Chart. © 2018 AHA Guide

⊞ **DMC – DETROIT RECEIVING HOSPITAL (230273)**, 4201 Saint Antoine Street, Zip 48201–2153; tel. 313/745–3000, **A**1 3 5 10 **F**3 16 17 18 29 30 34 35 38 39 40 41 43 44 49 50 56 57 58 59 60 61 64 65 66 67 70 74 75 77 79 81 82 84 85 86 87 93 97 98 100 102 103 104 107 114 115 119 129 130 131 132 135 141 144 145 146 148 149 150 **P**1 6 **S** TENET Healthcare Corporation, Dallas, TX
Primary Contact: Scott Steiner, FACHE, Chief Executive Officer
COO: Tina Wood, Chief Operations Officer
CFO: Bridgett Feagin, Chief Financial Officer
CMO: Patricia Wilkerson–Uddyback, M.D., Chief Medical Officer
CIO: Michael LeRoy, Senior Vice President and Chief Information Officer
Web address: www.dmc.org
Control: Corporation, Investor–owned (for–profit) **Service**: General medical and surgical

Staffed Beds: 187 Admissions: 12630 Census: 180 Outpatient Visits: 144910 Births: 0 Total Expense ($000): 252536 Payroll Expense ($000): 88982 Personnel: 1461

⊞ △ **DMC – REHABILITATION INSTITUTE OF MICHIGAN (233027)**, 261 Mack Avenue, Zip 48201–2495; tel. 313/745–1203, **A**1 3 5 7 10 **F**11 28 29 30 34 35 44 50 53 54 58 59 64 65 75 82 86 87 90 91 92 93 95 96 119 130 131 132 134 146 149 **P**1 6 **S** TENET Healthcare Corporation, Dallas, TX
Primary Contact: William Restum, Chief Executive Officer
COO: Patty Jobbitt, Chief Operating Officer
CFO: Dan Babb, Chief Financial Officer
CMO: Ali Bitar, M.D., Vice President Medical Affairs
CHR: Paul Sturgis, Director Human Resources
CNO: Julia Libcke, R.N., MSN, VP Patient Care Services
Web address: www.rimrehab.org
Control: Corporation, Investor–owned (for–profit) **Service**: Rehabilitation

Staffed Beds: 69 Admissions: 1222 Census: 54 Outpatient Visits: 241337 Births: 0 Total Expense ($000): 73177 Payroll Expense ($000): 38220 Personnel: 578

⊞ **DMC – SINAI–GRACE HOSPITAL (230024)**, 6071 West Outer Drive, Zip 48235–2679; tel. 313/966–3300, **A**1 3 5 10 12 13 **F**3 8 11 13 15 18 20 22 24 26 28 29 30 31 34 37 38 39 40 43 44 45 46 49 50 51 53 54 55 57 58 59 60 61 64 65 66 70 72 74 75 77 78 79 80 81 82 84 85 86 87 90 93 96 97 98 100 102 104 107 108 110 111 114 115 117 118 119 120 121 123 126 129 130 131 132 134 135 141 144 146 147 148 149 150 154 **P**1 6 **S** TENET Healthcare Corporation, Dallas, TX
Primary Contact: Conrad L. Mallett Jr, Chief Executive Officer
COO: London Quicci, Chief Operating Officer
CFO: Michael Prusatis, Vice President Finance
CHR: Paulette Griffin, Director Human Resources
Web address: www.sinaigrace.org
Control: Corporation, Investor–owned (for–profit) **Service**: General medical and surgical

Staffed Beds: 301 Admissions: 20187 Census: 272 Outpatient Visits: 209429 Births: 1328 Total Expense ($000): 345978 Payroll Expense ($000): 133439 Personnel: 1945

⊞ **DMC HARPER UNIVERSITY HOSPITAL (230104)**, 3990 John 'R' Street, Zip 48201–2018; tel. 313/745–8040, (Includes DMC HUTZEL WOMEN'S HOSPITAL, 3980 John R Street, Detroit, MI, Zip 48201; tel. 313/745–7555; Scott Steiner, FACHE, Chief Executive Officer) **A**1 3 5 10 **F**3 8 9 11 12 18 20 22 24 26 28 29 30 31 34 35 37 40 44 45 46 47 48 49 50 51 52 54 55 57 58 59 60 61 64 65 66 70 72 74 75 76 77 78 79 81 82 84 85 86 87 92 93 97 100 107 108 111 115 118 119 126 130 131 132 134 135 138 141 145 146 147 148 149 150 **P**1 6 **S** TENET Healthcare Corporation, Dallas, TX
Primary Contact: Scott Steiner, FACHE, Chief Executive Officer
COO: Tina Wood, Chief Operating Officer
CFO: Bridgett Feagin, Chief Financial Officer
CMO: Patricia Wilkerson–Uddyback, M.D., Chief Medical Officer
CIO: Michael LeRoy, Senior Vice President and Chief Information Officer
CNO: Christine Bowen, R.N., Chief Nursing Officer
Web address: www.harperhospital.org
Control: Corporation, Investor–owned (for–profit) **Service**: General medical and surgical

Staffed Beds: 364 Admissions: 21610 Census: 259 Outpatient Visits: 206366 Births: 4058 Total Expense ($000): 481113 Payroll Expense ($000): 153875 Personnel: 2291

HARPER UNIVERSITY HOSPITAL See DMC Harper University Hospital

⊞ **HENRY FORD HOSPITAL (230053)**, 2799 West Grand Boulevard, Zip 48202–2608; tel. 313/916–2600, **A**1 2 3 5 8 10 **F**3 5 6 8 9 11 12 13 15 17 18 19 20 22 24 26 28 29 30 31 32 33 34 35 36 38 40 41 43 44 45 46 47 48 49 50 51 52 53 54 55 56 57 58 59 60 61 62 63 64 65 66 68 70 71 72 73 74 75 76 77 78 79 80 81 82 83 84 85 86 87 91 93 96 97 99 100 101 102 103 104 107 108 110 111 112 113 114 115 116 117 118 119 120 121 123 124 126 129 130 132 134 135 136 137 138 139 140 141 142 144 145 146 147 148 149 150 154 **P**6 **S** Henry Ford Health System, Detroit, MI
Primary Contact: Veronica Hall, R.N., Interim President and Chief Executive Officer
CFO: Joseph Schmitt III Senior Vice President Finance and Chief Financial Officer
CIO: Mary Alice Annecharico, System Vice President and Chief Information Officer
CHR: Antonina Ramsey, Senior Vice President and Chief Human Resource Officer
CNO: Gwen Gnam, R.N., MSN, Chief Nursing Officer
Web address: www.henryfordhealth.org
Control: Other not–for–profit (including NFP Corporation) **Service**: General medical and surgical

Staffed Beds: 725 Admissions: 38709 Census: 565 Outpatient Visits: 3116761 Births: 2688 Total Expense ($000): 2016942 Payroll Expense ($000): 1001671 Personnel: 11852

⊞ △ **JOHN D. DINGELL VETERANS AFFAIRS MEDICAL CENTER**, 4646 John 'R' Street, Zip 48201–1932; tel. 313/576–1000, (Total facility includes 44 beds in nursing home–type unit) **A**1 2 3 5 7 **F**3 4 5 8 9 11 12 18 20 26 28 29 30 31 34 35 36 37 38 39 40 44 45 46 49 50 53 54 56 57 58 59 60 61 62 63 64 65 66 67 70 74 75 77 78 79 81 82 83 84 85 86 87 90 91 92 93 94 97 98 100 101 102 103 104 105 107 108 111 114 115 118 119 121 123 127 128 129 130 132 135 143 144 146 147 148 149 152 153 154 **P**6 **S** Department of Veterans Affairs, Perry Point, MD
Primary Contact: Pamela J. Reeves, M.D., Director
COO: Annette Walker, Associate Director
CFO: Sherry Riedel, Chief Financial Management Service
CMO: Scott Gruber, M.D., Chief of Staff
CIO: Jonathan Small, Chief Operations Information and Technology
CHR: Kathleen Osinski, Chief Human Resources Service
CNO: Belina Brown–Tezera, MSN, Associate Director Patient Care Services
Web address: www.detroit.va.gov/
Control: Veterans Affairs, Government, federal **Service**: General medical and surgical

Staffed Beds: 216 Admissions: 5613 Census: 88 Outpatient Visits: 538372 Births: 0 Total Expense ($000): 404825 Payroll Expense ($000): 153354 Personnel: 1995

☐ **KARMANOS CANCER CENTER (230297)**, 4100 John 'R' Street, Zip 48201–2013; tel. 313/576–8670, **A**1 2 3 5 10 **F**3 8 14 15 29 30 31 34 35 36 39 44 45 46 47 49 50 54 55 57 58 59 60 63 64 68 70 74 75 78 79 80 81 82 83 84 85 86 87 100 107 108 110 111 112 113 114 115 116 117 118 119 120 121 123 124 126 130 132 135 136 146 147 148 149 **P**4
Primary Contact: Gerold Bepler, M.D., Ph.D., President and Chief Executive Officer
CFO: Brian Gamble, Chief Financial Officer
CMO: George Yoo, M.D., Chief Medical Officer
CIO: Scott McCarter, Chief Information Officer
CHR: David Jansen, Vice President Human Resources
Web address: www.karmanos.org
Control: Other not–for–profit (including NFP Corporation) **Service**: Cancer

Staffed Beds: 84 Admissions: 3218 Census: 67 Outpatient Visits: 136132 Births: 0 Total Expense ($000): 245169 Payroll Expense ($000): 53539 Personnel: 953

⊞ **SELECT SPECIALTY HOSPITAL–NORTHWEST DETROIT (232032)**, 6071 West Outer Drive, Zip 48235–2624; tel. 313/966–4747, (Nonreporting) **A**1 10 **S** Select Medical Corporation, Mechanicsburg, PA
Primary Contact: Marilouise Riska, Chief Executive Officer
Web address: www.selectspecialtyhospitals.com/company/locations/northwestdetroit.aspx
Control: Corporation, Investor–owned (for–profit) **Service**: Acute long–term care hospital

Staffed Beds: 36

☐ **STONECREST CENTER (234038)**, 15000 Gratiot Avenue, Zip 48205–1973; tel. 313/245–0600, **A**1 10 **F**98 99 100 101 103 130 149 **S** Acadia Healthcare Company, Inc., Franklin, TN
Primary Contact: Steve Savage, Chief Executive Officer
Web address: www.stonecrestcenter.com
Control: Corporation, Investor–owned (for–profit) **Service**: Psychiatric

Staffed Beds: 134 Admissions: 3666 Census: 124 Outpatient Visits: 0 Births: 0 Total Expense ($000): 26332 Payroll Expense ($000): 12141 Personnel: 257

MI

DOWAGIAC—Cass County

✠ **BORGESS–LEE MEMORIAL HOSPITAL (231315)**, 420 West High Street, Zip 49047–1943; tel. 269/782–8681, **A**1 10 18 **F**3 11 15 18 28 29 30 31 34 35 40 41 50 54 57 59 64 65 68 70 75 77 78 79 81 85 86 87 93 97 100 104 107 108 110 114 119 127 128 130 132 133 135 146 148 149 **P**6 **S** Ascension Healthcare, Saint Louis, MO
Primary Contact: Natalie Ryder, Chief Administrative Officer
CMO: Robert Hill, M.D., Chief Medical Officer
CIO: James Keller, Chief Information Officer
Web address: www.borgess.com
Control: Church operated, Nongovernment, not–for–profit **Service:** General medical and surgical

Staffed Beds: 25 **Admissions:** 343 **Census:** 3 **Outpatient Visits:** 100864 **Births:** 0 **Total Expense ($000):** 25922 **Payroll Expense ($000):** 11922 **Personnel:** 155

EAST CHINA—St. Clair County

✠ **ST. JOHN RIVER DISTRICT HOSPITAL (230241)**, 4100 River Road, Zip 48054–2909; tel. 810/329–7111, **A**1 3 10 **F**3 7 11 13 15 18 20 29 30 34 35 36 40 44 45 49 50 57 59 60 64 65 68 70 74 75 76 77 79 80 81 82 84 85 86 87 92 93 97 101 107 108 110 111 115 119 129 130 132 141 144 146 147 149 **P**8 **S** Ascension Healthcare, Saint Louis, MO
Primary Contact: Robert E. Hoban, President
CMO: H Lee Bacheldor, D.O., Chief Medical Officer
CHR: Dawn Beindit, Labor Relations Partner
CNO: Kim Ronnisch, R.N., Vice President Nursing and Operations
Web address: www.stjohnprovidence.org/RiverDistrict/
Control: Church operated, Nongovernment, not–for–profit **Service:** General medical and surgical

Staffed Beds: 68 **Admissions:** 1773 **Census:** 14 **Outpatient Visits:** 50404 **Births:** 337 **Total Expense ($000):** 39761 **Payroll Expense ($000):** 16890 **Personnel:** 196

EATON RAPIDS—Eaton County

★ ⇑ **EATON RAPIDS MEDICAL CENTER (231324)**, 1500 South Main Street, Zip 48827–1952, Mailing Address: P.O. Box 130, Zip 48827–0130; tel. 517/663–2671, **A**10 18 21 **F**3 11 15 18 28 29 34 35 38 40 41 45 50 53 54 57 59 64 65 66 68 75 77 81 86 87 91 93 94 97 107 110 115 119 127 129 130 131 132 133 144 146 148 149
Primary Contact: Timothy Johnson, President and Chief Executive Officer
CFO: Shari Glynn, Vice President Finance and Chief Financial Officer
CMO: Ashok K Gupta, M.D., Chief of Staff
CIO: Mark Rodge, Director Information Systems
CHR: Laurie Field, Director Human Resources
Web address: www.eatonrapidsmedicalcenter.org
Control: Other not–for–profit (including NFP Corporation) **Service:** General medical and surgical

Staffed Beds: 20 **Admissions:** 508 **Census:** 5 **Outpatient Visits:** 69923 **Births:** 0 **Total Expense ($000):** 26890 **Payroll Expense ($000):** 11049 **Personnel:** 210

ESCANABA—Delta County

✠ **OSF ST. FRANCIS HOSPITAL AND MEDICAL GROUP (231337)**, 3401 Ludington Street, Zip 49829–1377; tel. 906/786–3311, **A**1 10 18 **F**3 11 13 15 18 28 29 30 31 34 35 40 44 45 46 53 56 57 59 62 63 64 65 66 68 70 75 76 77 78 79 81 82 83 84 85 86 92 93 96 97 107 108 110 111 115 119 127 129 130 131 132 133 144 146 147 148 149 **S** OSF Healthcare, Peoria, IL
Primary Contact: David Lord, President
COO: Kelly Jefferson, Vice President, Operations
CFO: Fred Wagner, Chief Financial Officer
CMO: Mark Povich, D.O., Medical Director
CIO: Mark Irving, Manager Management Information Systems
CHR: Elizabeth Zorza, Assistant Administrator
CNO: Joy Hopkins, Vice President Patient Care Services
Web address: www.osfstfrancis.org
Control: Church operated, Nongovernment, not–for–profit **Service:** General medical and surgical

Staffed Beds: 25 **Admissions:** 1773 **Census:** 12 **Outpatient Visits:** 108691 **Births:** 312 **Total Expense ($000):** 83048 **Payroll Expense ($000):** 30253 **Personnel:** 374

FARMINGTON HILLS—Oakland County

★ ○ **BEAUMONT HOSPITAL – FARMINGTON HILLS (230151)**, 28050 Grand River Avenue, Zip 48336–5933; tel. 248/471–8000, **A**2 3 10 11 12 13 **F**3 11 13 15 18 20 22 28 29 30 31 32 34 35 36 38 39 40 41 43 44 45 46 47 48 49 50 51 54 56 57 58 59 60 61 64 65 68 70 74 75 76 77 78 79 81 82 84 85 87 89 90 92 93 96 97 98 100 101 102 103 107 110 111 114 119 120 121 123 124 126 130 131 132 134 135 144 146 147 148 149 **P**6 **S** Beaumont Health, Southfield, MI
Primary Contact: Constance O'Malley, President
COO: Carolyn Wilson, R.N., Chief Operating Officer
CFO: Barbara Hrit, Controller
CMO: Michael Rebock, Chief Medical Officer
CIO: Subra Sripada, Executive Vice President, Chief Transportation Officer and Chief Information Officer
CHR: Dalph Watson, Director of Human Resources
CNO: Kim Guesman, R.N., Chief Nursing Officer
Web address: www.beaumont.org
Control: Other not–for–profit (including NFP Corporation) **Service:** General medical and surgical

Staffed Beds: 330 **Admissions:** 14118 **Census:** 201 **Outpatient Visits:** 342563 **Births:** 681 **Total Expense ($000):** 392964 **Payroll Expense ($000):** 169267 **Personnel:** 2362

FERNDALE—Oakland County

✠ **HENRY FORD KINGSWOOD HOSPITAL (234011)**, 10300 West Eight Mile Road, Zip 48220–2100; tel. 248/398–3200, **A**1 10 **F**29 30 32 34 35 44 56 57 59 68 75 77 82 86 87 98 99 101 103 104 105 106 130 134 135 153 154 **P**6 **S** Henry Ford Health System, Detroit, MI
Primary Contact: Cathrine Frank, M.D., Chairperson
CMO: Robert Lagrou, D.O., Medical Director
CNO: Cheryl Taylor, R.N., Director of Nursing
Web address: www.henryford.com
Control: Other not–for–profit (including NFP Corporation) **Service:** Psychiatric

Staffed Beds: 91 **Admissions:** 3840 **Census:** 70 **Outpatient Visits:** 0 **Births:** 0 **Total Expense ($000):** 23430 **Payroll Expense ($000):** 15256 **Personnel:** 217

FLINT—Genesee County

✠ **HURLEY MEDICAL CENTER (230132)**, One Hurley Plaza, Zip 48503–5993; tel. 810/262–9000, (Includes HURLEY CHILDREN'S HOSPITAL, 1 Hurley Plaza, Flint, MI, Zip 48503–5902; tel. 313/745–7555) **A**1 2 3 5 8 10 **F**3 5 11 12 13 15 16 17 18 19 20 22 26 28 29 30 31 32 35 39 40 41 43 45 46 49 50 52 54 55 56 57 58 59 61 64 66 70 72 74 75 76 77 78 79 80 81 82 84 85 86 87 88 89 90 93 96 97 98 100 101 102 103 104 107 108 110 111 114 115 118 119 120 121 123 124 126 129 130 131 132 135 141 143 144 146 147 148 154
Primary Contact: Melany Gavulic, President & Chief Executive Officer
COO: Melany Gavulic, Senior Vice President Operations & COO
CFO: Cass Wisniewski, Interim Chief Financial Officer
CMO: Michael Jaggi, D.O., Vice President and Chief Medical Officer
CIO: Gary Townsend, Chief Information Officer
CHR: Beth Brophy, Interim VP for Human Resources
CNO: Teresa Bourque, Sr. Administrator for Nursing/Chief Nurse
Web address: www.hurleymc.com
Control: City, Government, nonfederal **Service:** General medical and surgical

Staffed Beds: 418 **Admissions:** 19310 **Census:** 281 **Outpatient Visits:** 507686 **Births:** 2856 **Total Expense ($000):** 434732 **Payroll Expense ($000):** 175056 **Personnel:** 2498

☐ **MCLAREN FLINT (230141)**, 401 South Ballenger Highway, Zip 48532–3685; tel. 810/342–2000, **A**1 2 3 5 8 10 **F**3 8 11 12 13 15 17 18 20 22 24 26 28 29 30 31 32 34 35 36 38 39 40 41 43 44 45 46 47 48 49 50 53 54 55 56 57 58 59 60 61 64 66 68 70 74 75 76 77 78 79 81 82 85 86 87 90 91 93 95 96 97 98 101 102 104 105 107 108 110 111 114 115 118 119 120 121 123 124 126 129 130 131 132 135 141 144 145 146 147 148 149 154 **S** McLaren Health Care Corporation, Grand Blanc, MI
Primary Contact: Chad M. Grant, President and Chief Executive Officer
COO: Brent Wheeler, Vice President of Operations
CFO: Fred Korte, Chief Financial Officer
CMO: Binesh Patel, M.D., Chief Medical Officer
CIO: Ronald Strachan, Chief Information Officer
CHR: Rachelle Hulett, Vice President Human Resources
CNO: James Williams, Vice President and Chief Nursing Officer
Web address: www.mclaren.org/flint
Control: Other not–for–profit (including NFP Corporation) **Service:** General medical and surgical

Staffed Beds: 358 **Admissions:** 19589 **Census:** 273 **Outpatient Visits:** 320513 **Births:** 609 **Total Expense ($000):** 410834 **Payroll Expense ($000):** 185592 **Personnel:** 2121

Many Facility Codes have changed. Please refer to the AHA Guide Code Chart. © 2018 AHA Guide

☒ **SELECT SPECIALTY HOSPITAL–FLINT (232012)**, 401 South Ballenger Highway, 5th Floor Central, Zip 48532–3638; tel. 810/342–4545, (Nonreporting) **A**1 10 **S** Select Medical Corporation, Mechanicsburg, PA
Primary Contact: Christina DeBlouw, Chief Executive Officer
CMO: Jitendra P. Katneni, M.D., Medical Director
CHR: Gayle Barthel, Coordinator Human Resources
CNO: Kathleen Gallardo, Chief Nursing Officer
Web address: www.selectspecialtyhospitals.com/company/locations/flint.aspx
Control: Corporation, Investor–owned (for–profit) **Service:** Acute long–term care hospital

Staffed Beds: 26

FRANKFORT—Benzie County

★ **PAUL OLIVER MEMORIAL HOSPITAL (231300)**, 224 Park Avenue, Zip 49635–9658; tel. 231/352–2200, (Total facility includes 39 beds in nursing home–type unit) **A**10 18 **F**11 15 28 30 34 35 40 45 50 53 57 59 60 64 75 77 81 86 87 93 107 110 111 115 119 129 130 132 133 143 146 148 154 **S** Munson Healthcare, Traverse City, MI
Primary Contact: Peter Marinoff, President
CMO: George Ryckman, D.O., Chief of Staff
CHR: Julie Banktson, Manager Human Resources
Web address: www.munsonhealthcare.org
Control: Other not–for–profit (including NFP Corporation) **Service:** General medical and surgical

Staffed Beds: 47 Admissions: 120 Census: 29 Outpatient Visits: 55010 Births: 0 Total Expense ($000): 17634 Payroll Expense ($000): 6644 Personnel: 139

FREMONT—Newaygo County

☒ **SPECTRUM HEALTH GERBER MEMORIAL (231338)**, 212 South Sullivan Avenue, Zip 49412–1548; tel. 231/924–3300, **A**1 3 10 13 15 28 29 30 31 32 34 35 36 40 43 45 50 53 59 64 68 70 75 76 77 78 79 81 86 87 93 96 107 108 110 111 115 118 119 127 129 130 131 132 135 146 147 **S** Spectrum Health, Grand Rapids, MI
Primary Contact: Randall Kelley, FACHE, President
COO: Shelly Johnson, Chief Operating Officer
CMO: P. Kevin Gerth, Chief of Staff
CIO: Dave Mitchell, Manager Information Services
CHR: Christine Schurkamp, Senior Human Resources Business Partner
CNO: Meleah Mariani, Chief Nursing Officer
Web address: www.spectrumhealth.org
Control: Other not–for–profit (including NFP Corporation) **Service:** General medical and surgical

Staffed Beds: 25 Admissions: 2013 Census: 15 Outpatient Visits: 121255 Births: 527 Total Expense ($000): 89786 Payroll Expense ($000): 31162 Personnel: 607

GARDEN CITY—Wayne County

★ ○ **GARDEN CITY HOSPITAL (230244)**, 6245 Inkster Road, Zip 48135–4001; tel. 734/421–3300, **A**3 10 11 12 13 **F**3 4 11 13 15 17 18 20 22 26 28 29 31 34 35 36 40 43 44 45 46 47 49 50 59 62 64 65 68 70 71 74 75 76 77 78 79 80 81 82 85 87 89 90 91 92 93 96 107 109 110 111 112 114 115 119 129 130 131 132 135 143 146 147 148 149 152 154 **P**6 **S** Prime Healthcare, Ontario, CA
Primary Contact: Saju George, Chief Executive Officer
CFO: Gina Butcher, Chief Financial Officer
CMO: H. Rex Reuttinger, D.O., Chief Medical Officer, Administration
CIO: Randall Sanborn, Director Information Systems
CHR: Josie Ciccone, Director, Human Resources
Web address: www.gch.org
Control: Corporation, Investor–owned (for–profit) **Service:** General medical and surgical

Staffed Beds: 164 Admissions: 8807 Census: 99 Outpatient Visits: 121799 Births: 678 Total Expense ($000): 134153 Payroll Expense ($000): 54738 Personnel: 865

GAYLORD—Otsego County

☒ **MUNSON HEALTHCARE OTSEGO MEMORIAL HOSPITAL (230133)**, 825 North Center Avenue, Zip 49735–1592; tel. 989/731–2100, (Total facility includes 34 beds in nursing home–type unit) **A**1 5 10 20 **F**3 13 15 28 29 31 32 34 35 36 40 43 44 45 46 49 50 51 54 56 57 59 64 65 70 74 75 76 77 78 79 81 82 85 86 87 93 96 97 100 104 107 108 110 111 115 118 119 124 126 127 128 130 131 132 134 135 144 146 147 148 149 **P**6 **S** Munson Healthcare, Traverse City, MI
Primary Contact: Thomas R. Lemon, Chief Executive Officer
COO: James Flickema, Vice President Market Development
CFO: Robert Courtois, Vice President Finance
CMO: Kevin Smith, D.O., Chief of Staff
CIO: Timothy Hella, Chief Information Officer
CHR: Terra Deming, Director Human Resources
CNO: Diane Fisher, R.N., VP, Patient Care Services
Web address: www.myomh.org
Control: Other not–for–profit (including NFP Corporation) **Service:** General medical and surgical

Staffed Beds: 80 Admissions: 2273 Census: 47 Outpatient Visits: 308116 Births: 374 Total Expense ($000): 96853 Payroll Expense ($000): 49475 Personnel: 700

GLADWIN—Gladwin County

☒ **MIDMICHIGAN MEDICAL CENTER–GLADWIN (231325)**, 515 Quarter Street, Zip 48624–1959; tel. 989/426–9286, **A**1 5 10 18 **F**3 11 15 18 28 29 30 31 34 35 40 45 53 57 59 64 75 77 81 85 86 93 97 107 108 110 111 114 118 119 127 129 130 132 135 144 146 154 **S** MidMichigan Health, Midland, MI
Primary Contact: Raymond Stover, President and Chief Executive Officer
CFO: Jeff Provenzano, Vice President and Chief Financial Officer
CMO: Cheryl Loubert, M.D., Chief Medical Staff
CIO: Dan Waltz, Vice President and Chief Information Officer
CNO: Glenn King, R.N., MSN, Vice President and Chief Nursing Officer
Web address: www.midmichigan.org
Control: Other not–for–profit (including NFP Corporation) **Service:** General medical and surgical

Staffed Beds: 25 Admissions: 564 Census: 4 Outpatient Visits: 53920 Births: 0 Total Expense ($000): 27838 Payroll Expense ($000): 8215 Personnel: 130

GRAND BLANC—Genesee County

☒ **GENESYS REGIONAL MEDICAL CENTER (230197)**, One Genesys Parkway, Zip 48439–8066; tel. 810/606–5000, (Total facility includes 12 beds in nursing home–type unit) **A**1 3 5 10 12 13 **F**3 11 13 18 20 22 24 26 28 29 30 31 32 34 35 40 43 44 45 46 47 48 49 50 51 57 58 60 61 64 68 70 73 74 75 76 78 79 81 82 84 85 86 87 89 90 91 92 96 97 102 107 108 110 111 114 115 117 118 119 126 128 129 130 132 135 145 146 147 148 154 **S** Ascension Healthcare, Saint Louis, MO
Primary Contact: Chris Palazzolo, President and Chief Executive Officer
COO: Joy Finkenbiner, Vice President, Operations
CFO: Nancy Haywood, Chief Financial Officer
CMO: Charles Husson, Regional Chief Medical Officer
CIO: Daniel Stross, Chief Information Officer
CNO: Julie A Gorczyca, R.N., Chief Nursing Officer
Web address: www.genesys.org
Control: Church operated, Nongovernment, not–for–profit **Service:** General medical and surgical

Staffed Beds: 427 Admissions: 19841 Census: 267 Outpatient Visits: 518056 Births: 1604 Total Expense ($000): 410062 Payroll Expense ($000): 177162 Personnel: 2635

GRAND HAVEN—Ottawa County

★ ⇑ **NORTH OTTAWA COMMUNITY HOSPITAL (230174)**, 1309 Sheldon Road, Zip 49417–2488; tel. 616/842–3600, **A**10 21 **F**3 7 11 12 13 15 29 30 34 35 37 40 43 45 46 50 51 57 59 61 63 64 65 68 70 74 75 76 77 79 81 83 84 85 86 87 89 92 97 107 108 115 119 124 126 129 130 131 132 133 135 143 144 145 146 147 148 149 **P**5
Primary Contact: Shelleye Yaklin, President and Chief Executive Officer
CFO: Mark Gross, Vice President Finance and Chief Financial Officer
CMO: Haney Assaad, Vice President Medical Affairs
CHR: Tim F Gengle, Director Human Resources
CNO: Cindy Van Kampen, Chief Nursing Officer
Web address: www.noch.org
Control: Other not–for–profit (including NFP Corporation) **Service:** General medical and surgical

Staffed Beds: 58 Admissions: 1520 Census: 11 Outpatient Visits: 121308 Births: 292 Total Expense ($000): 50929 Payroll Expense ($000): 27902 Personnel: 442

MI

Hospital, Medicare Provider Number, Address, Telephone, Approval, Facility, and Physician Codes, Health Care System

★ American Hospital Association (AHA) membership ○ Healthcare Facilities Accreditation Program ⇑ Center for Improvement in Healthcare Quality Accreditation
□ The Joint Commission accreditation ◇ DNV Healthcare Inc. accreditation △ Commission on Accreditation of Rehabilitation Facilities (CARF) accreditation

GRAND RAPIDS—Kent County

☐ **FOREST VIEW PSYCHIATRIC HOSPITAL (234030)**, 1055 Medical Park Drive SE, Zip 49546–3607; tel. 616/942–9610, **A**1 10 **F**87 98 99 100 101 102 103 104 130 132 154 **S** Universal Health Services, Inc., King of Prussia, PA
Primary Contact: Andrew Hotaling, Chief Executive Officer
CFO: Andre Pierre, Chief Financial Officer
CMO: James VanHaren, M.D., Medical Director
CHR: Mike Henderson, Human Resources Director
CNO: Jo ell Harris, R.N., Chief Nursing Officer
Web address: www.forestviewhospital.com
Control: Corporation, Investor–owned (for–profit) **Service:** Psychiatric

Staffed Beds: 108 **Admissions:** 3371 **Census:** 87 **Outpatient Visits:** 14902 **Births:** 0 **Total Expense ($000):** 22081 **Payroll Expense ($000):** 9798 **Personnel:** 173

⊞ △ **MARY FREE BED REHABILITATION HOSPITAL (233026)**, 235 Wealthy Street SE, Zip 49503–5247; tel. 616/840–8000, **A**1 3 5 7 10 **F**30 34 54 57 58 62 64 68 75 77 78 79 82 86 90 91 92 93 94 95 96 100 104 119 128 130 131 132 143 146 **P**6
Primary Contact: Kent Riddle, Chief Executive Officer
CFO: Randall DeNeff, Vice President Finance
CMO: Michael Jakubowski, M.D., Chief Medical Officer
CIO: Jeff Burns, Manager of Information Technology
CHR: Karen S. Richter, Vice President, Human Resources
CNO: Ingrid Cheslek, R.N., Chief Nursing Officer
Web address: www.maryfreebed.com
Control: Other not–for–profit (including NFP Corporation) **Service:** Rehabilitation

Staffed Beds: 167 **Admissions:** 1733 **Census:** 87 **Outpatient Visits:** 93203 **Births:** 0 **Total Expense ($000):** 87634 **Payroll Expense ($000):** 51615 **Personnel:** 946

⊞ **MERCY HEALTH SAINT MARY'S (230059)**, 200 Jefferson Avenue Southeast, Zip 49503–4598, Mailing Address: 200 Jefferson Avenue SE, Zip 49503–4598; tel. 616/685–5000, (Includes MERCY HEALTH ROCKFORD, 6050 Northland Drive NE, Rockford, MI, Zip 49341–9244; tel. 616/685–7950) **A**1 2 3 5 10 **F**3 6 13 15 18 20 22 26 28 29 30 34 35 36 37 38 39 40 41 43 44 45 46 48 49 50 54 55 56 57 58 59 61 64 65 66 68 70 72 74 75 76 77 78 79 80 81 82 83 84 85 86 87 97 98 100 102 107 108 110 111 114 115 116 117 118 119 120 121 123 124 126 129 130 132 135 138 144 146 147 148 149 154 **P**6 8 **S** Trinity Health, Livonia, MI
Primary Contact: Bill Manns, President
COO: Randall J Wagner, Chief Operating Officer
CFO: Steve Eavenson, Vice President Finance
CMO: Rolland Mambourg, M.D., Vice President Medical Affairs
CIO: Jim Keller, Site Director Information Services
CHR: Thomas L Karel, Vice President Organization and Talent Effectiveness
CNO: Elizabeth A Murphy, R.N., FACHE, Vice President for Patient Care Services
Web address: www.mercyhealthsaintmarys.org
Control: Church operated, Nongovernment, not–for–profit **Service:** General medical and surgical

Staffed Beds: 371 **Admissions:** 22661 **Census:** 285 **Outpatient Visits:** 1134070 **Births:** 2233 **Total Expense ($000):** 568069 **Payroll Expense ($000):** 186795 **Personnel:** 3611

☐ **PINE REST CHRISTIAN MENTAL HEALTH SERVICES (234006)**, 300 68th Street SE, Zip 49548–6927, Mailing Address: P.O. Box 165, Zip 49501–0165; tel. 616/455–5000, **A**1 3 5 10 **F**4 5 6 29 30 32 34 35 38 56 58 59 66 68 75 77 82 86 87 98 99 100 101 102 103 104 105 106 130 132 134 135 146 147 149 150 154 **P**6
Primary Contact: Mark C. Eastburg, Ph.D., President and Chief Executive Officer
COO: Robert Nykamp, Vice President and Chief Operating Officer
CFO: Paul H Karsten, Vice President Finance and Chief Financial Officer
CMO: Alan Armstrong, M.D., Chief Medical Officer
Web address: www.pinerest.org
Control: Other not–for–profit (including NFP Corporation) **Service:** Psychiatric

Staffed Beds: 457 **Admissions:** 6580 **Census:** 167 **Outpatient Visits:** 304590 **Births:** 0 **Total Expense ($000):** 142970 **Payroll Expense ($000):** 82570 **Personnel:** 1394

★ **SELECT SPECIALTY HOSPITAL – SPECTRUM HEALTH (232029)**, 1840 Wealthy Street, Southeast, Zip 49506–2921; tel. 616/774–3800, (Nonreporting) **S** Select Medical Corporation, Mechanicsburg, PA
Primary Contact: Jim Aldrich, Chief Executive Officer
Web address: www.https://grandrapids.selectspecialtyhospitals.com
Control: Corporation, Investor–owned (for–profit) **Service:** Acute long–term care hospital

Staffed Beds: 36

⊞ **SPECTRUM HEALTH – BUTTERWORTH HOSPITAL (230038)**, 100 Michigan Street NE, Zip 49503–2560; tel. 616/391–1774, (Includes HELEN DEVOS CHILDREN'S HOSPITAL, 100 Michigan Street NE, Grand Rapids, MI, Zip 49503–2560; tel. 616/391–9000; Robert Connors, M.D., President, Helen DeVos Children's Hospital; SPECTRUM HEALTH – BLODGETT CAMPUS, 1840 Wealthy Street SE, Grand Rapids, MI, Zip 49506–2921; tel. 616/774–7444; Julie Wolowitz, Vice President, Imaging, Lab; SPECTRUM HEALTH, 100 Michigan Street NE, Grand Rapids, MI, Zip 49503–2551; tel. 616/391–1774; Christina Freese Decker, FACHE, Executive Vice President and Chief Operating Officer) **A**1 2 3 5 8 10 **F**3 5 8 9 11 12 13 15 16 17 18 19 20 21 22 23 24 25 26 27 28 29 30 31 32 34 35 36 37 38 40 41 43 44 45 46 47 48 49 50 51 52 54 55 56 57 58 59 60 61 64 65 66 68 70 71 72 73 74 75 76 77 78 79 80 81 82 84 85 86 87 88 89 90 93 96 100 101 102 104 107 108 110 111 112 114 115 116 117 118 119 120 121 123 124 126 130 131 132 134 135 136 137 138 140 145 146 147 148 149 **P**6 **S** Spectrum Health, Grand Rapids, MI
Primary Contact: Gwen Sandefur, President, Spectrum Health Hospital Group
CFO: Doug Welday, Senior Vice President Finance
CMO: David Krhovsky, M.D., Vice President, Medical Affairs
CIO: Jason Joseph, Vice President, Information Services
CHR: Ovell Barbee, Senior Vice President, Human Resources
CNO: Shawn Ulreich, R.N., MSN, Vice President Clinical Operations and Chief Nursing Executive
Web address: www.spectrumhealth.org
Control: Other not–for–profit (including NFP Corporation) **Service:** General medical and surgical

Staffed Beds: 1126 **Admissions:** 61119 **Census:** 809 **Outpatient Visits:** 1490404 **Births:** 7658 **Total Expense ($000):** 1909234 **Payroll Expense ($000):** 511458 **Personnel:** 9198

GRAYLING—Crawford County

⊞ **MUNSON HEALTHCARE GRAYLING HOSPITAL (230058)**, 1100 East Michigan Avenue, Zip 49738–1312; tel. 989/348–5461, (Total facility includes 39 beds in nursing home–type unit) **A**1 5 10 20 **F**3 11 13 15 28 29 30 32 34 35 36 38 40 44 45 51 53 54 56 57 58 59 60 64 65 66 70 75 76 77 78 79 81 85 86 87 93 97 107 108 111 115 119 127 129 130 131 135 146 147 148 154 **P**8 **S** Munson Healthcare, Traverse City, MI
Primary Contact: Kirsten Korth–White, Interim President
COO: Kirsten Korth–White, Vice President Physician Network and Ambulatory Service
CFO: Lori Shively, Vice President of Finance
CMO: Vince Schultz, M.D., Chief Medical Officer
CHR: Kirsten Korth–White, Vice President Physician Network and Ambulatory Services
CNO: Carla Gardner, Director of Nursing
Web address: www.mercygrayling.munsonhealthcare.org/
Control: Other not–for–profit (including NFP Corporation) **Service:** General medical and surgical

Staffed Beds: 110 **Admissions:** 2974 **Census:** 57 **Outpatient Visits:** 142020 **Births:** 370 **Total Expense ($000):** 82349 **Payroll Expense ($000):** 34587 **Personnel:** 656

GREENVILLE—Montcalm County

⊞ **SPECTRUM HEALTH UNITED HOSPITAL (230035)**, 615 South Bower Street, Zip 48838–2614; tel. 616/754–4691, (Includes SPECTRUM HEALTH KELSEY HOSPITAL, 418 Washington Avenue, Lakeview, MI, Zip 48850; tel. 989/352–7211; Andrea M. Leslie, MSN, R.N., President) (Total facility includes 70 beds in nursing home–type unit) **A**1 3 10 **F**3 8 11 13 15 18 28 29 30 31 34 35 40 41 43 44 45 46 47 50 54 57 59 64 65 66 68 70 71 75 76 78 79 81 85 87 93 96 97 107 108 110 111 115 119 124 127 128 129 130 133 134 135 143 146 147 148 **P**6 **S** Spectrum Health, Grand Rapids, MI
Primary Contact: Andrea M. Leslie, MSN, R.N., President
COO: Priscilla Mahar, Chief Operating Officer
CFO: Ryan K Johnson, Controller
CMO: Kevin O'Connor, D.O., President, Medical Staff
CIO: David Dutmers, Manager, Information Services
CHR: Jennifer Nelson, Senior Human Resource Business Partner
CNO: Linda Schaltz, MSN, R.N., Chief Nursing Officer
Web address: www.spectrumhealth.org
Control: Other not–for–profit (including NFP Corporation) **Service:** General medical and surgical

Staffed Beds: 116 **Admissions:** 3097 **Census:** 88 **Outpatient Visits:** 202600 **Births:** 449 **Total Expense ($000):** 102344 **Payroll Expense ($000):** 38079 **Personnel:** 711

MI

Many Facility Codes have changed. Please refer to the AHA Guide Code Chart.
© 2018 AHA Guide

MI

GROSSE POINTE—Wayne County

☒ **BEAUMONT HOSPITAL – GROSSE POINTE (230089)**, 468 Cadieux Road, Zip 48230–1507; tel. 313/473–1000, **A**1 2 3 5 10 **F**3 6 11 12 13 15 18 20 22 26 28 29 30 31 34 35 36 39 40 43 45 46 47 48 49 50 51 53 54 55 56 57 58 59 60 61 63 64 65 66 68 69 70 71 74 75 76 77 78 79 80 81 82 84 85 86 87 91 92 93 94 96 100 107 108 110 111 114 115 116 117 118 119 126 129 130 131 132 134 135 145 146 147 148 149 150 **P**6 **S** Beaumont Health, Southfield, MI
Primary Contact: Richard P. Swaine, President
COO: Carolyn Wilson, R.N., Chief Operating Officer
CFO: Maria Miller, Controller
CMO: Donna Hoban, M.D., Senior Vice President and Chief Medical Officer
CIO: Subra Sripada, Executive Vice President, Chief Transportation Officer and Chief Information Officer
CHR: Pandora Walker, Director, Human Resources
CNO: Anne Stewart, Vice President and Chief Nursing Officer
Web address: www.beaumont.org
Control: Other not–for–profit (including NFP Corporation) **Service:** General medical and surgical

Staffed Beds: 280 **Admissions:** 12830 **Census:** 134 **Outpatient Visits:** 342925 **Births:** 745 **Total Expense ($000):** 208016 **Payroll Expense ($000):** 79946 **Personnel:** 1406

☒ **SELECT SPECIALTY HOSPITAL–GROSSE POINTE (232038)**, 468 Cadieux Road, 3 North East, Zip 48230–1507, Mailing Address: 22101 Moross Road, 6th Floor, Detroit, Zip 48236; tel. 313/473–6131, (Nonreporting) **A**1 10 **S** Select Medical Corporation, Mechanicsburg, PA
Primary Contact: Zaahra Butt, Chief Executive Officer
Web address: www.grossepointe.selectspecialtyhospitals.com/
Control: Corporation, Investor–owned (for–profit) **Service:** Acute long–term care hospital

Staffed Beds: 30

HANCOCK—Houghton County

☒ **UP HEALTH SYSTEM–PORTAGE (230108)**, 500 Campus Drive, Zip 49930–1569; tel. 906/483–1000, (Total facility includes 60 beds in nursing home–type unit) **A**1 5 10 20 **F**3 5 8 11 13 15 28 29 30 31 32 34 35 40 43 50 53 56 57 59 60 64 65 67 68 70 75 76 77 78 79 81 84 85 86 87 89 90 93 94 97 100 102 107 108 110 111 115 119 129 130 131 132 133 144 145 146 148 151 152 154 **P**6 **S** LifePoint Health, Brentwood, TN
Primary Contact: Randy Neiswonger, Chief Executive Officer
CFO: Steve Bishop, Chief Financial Officer
CMO: Mary Beth Hines, D.O., Chief Medical Officer
CHR: Robbyn Lucier, Director Human Resources
CNO: Debra Young, R.N., MSN, Vice President, Patient Services and Chief Nursing Officer
Web address: www.portagehealth.org
Control: Corporation, Investor–owned (for–profit) **Service:** General medical and surgical

Staffed Beds: 96 **Admissions:** 1234 **Census:** 70 **Outpatient Visits:** 83520 **Births:** 234 **Total Expense ($000):** 67847 **Payroll Expense ($000):** 30196 **Personnel:** 635

HARBOR BEACH—Huron County

HARBOR BEACH COMMUNITY HOSPITAL (231313), 210 South First Street, Zip 48441–1236; tel. 989/479–3201, (Total facility includes 30 beds in nursing home–type unit) **A**5 10 18 **F**3 15 29 30 32 34 35 40 43 45 46 50 56 57 59 64 65 68 75 77 79 81 93 97 107 110 119 128 130 131 133 144 146 147 148 149 154 **P**6
Primary Contact: Paul Clabuesch, President and Chief Executive Officer
CFO: Jill Wehner, Vice President Financial Services
CMO: Richard Lloyd, D.O., Chief of Staff
CIO: Tami Nickrand, Director Information Technology
CHR: Tina Osantoski, Director Human Resources
CNO: Deb Geiger, Executive Director of Acute Care
Web address: www.hbch.org
Control: Other not–for–profit (including NFP Corporation) **Service:** General medical and surgical

Staffed Beds: 45 **Admissions:** 150 **Census:** 27 **Births:** 0

HASTINGS—Barry County

☒ **SPECTRUM HEALTH PENNOCK (230040)**, 1009 West Green Street, Zip 49058–1710; tel. 269/945–3451, **A**1 10 **F**3 11 13 15 29 30 31 32 34 35 36 39 40 44 45 50 53 54 56 57 59 62 63 64 65 68 70 74 75 76 77 79 81 82 84 85 86 87 89 91 92 93 96 97 107 108 110 115 119 125 126 127 130 131 132 135 144 146 147 148 **S** Spectrum Health, Grand Rapids, MI
Primary Contact: Sheryl Lewis. Blake, FACHE, President
COO: Carla Wilson–Neil, FACHE, Chief Operating Officer
CFO: Micheal King, Controller
CMO: Douglas Smendik, M.D., Hospital Medical Director
CIO: Teri VanTongeren, Director Information Services
CHR: Sherri Thrasher, Executive Human Resources Partner
CNO: Steve Marzolf, R.N., Chief Nursing Officer
Web address: www.spectrumhealth.org
Control: Other not–for–profit (including NFP Corporation) **Service:** General medical and surgical

Staffed Beds: 39 **Admissions:** 2242 **Census:** 20 **Outpatient Visits:** 427231 **Births:** 303 **Total Expense ($000):** 78690 **Payroll Expense ($000):** 28463 **Personnel:** 474

HILLSDALE—Hillsdale County

★ ○ **HILLSDALE HOSPITAL (230037)**, 168 South Howell Street, Zip 49242–2081; tel. 517/437–4451, (Total facility includes 39 beds in nursing home–type unit) **A**10 11 12 13 19 **F**3 11 12 13 15 28 29 31 34 35 38 40 45 46 48 49 50 57 59 62 70 74 75 76 78 79 81 82 87 93 97 98 102 105 106 107 110 111 115 119 127 128 130 131 132 135 146 147 148 154
Primary Contact: Duke Anderson, President and Chief Executive Officer
COO: Terri Draper, Director of Operations
CFO: Leya VanDeusen, Interim Chief Financial Officer
CMO: Nichole Ellis, Chief Medical Officer
CIO: Sheila Puffenberger, Manager Information Technology
CHR: Stacy Feltz, Manager Human Resource
CNO: Julie Walters, Chief Nursing Officer
Web address: www.hillsdalehospital.com
Control: Other not–for–profit (including NFP Corporation) **Service:** General medical and surgical

Staffed Beds: 93 **Admissions:** 2776 **Census:** 55 **Outpatient Visits:** 99410 **Births:** 326 **Total Expense ($000):** 59167 **Payroll Expense ($000):** 21641 **Personnel:** 416

HOLLAND—Ottawa County

★ ⇑ **HOLLAND HOSPITAL (230072)**, 602 Michigan Avenue, Zip 49423–4999; tel. 616/392–5141, (Nonreporting) **A**10 21
Primary Contact: Dale Sowders, President and Chief Executive Officer
CFO: Terry L Steele, Vice President Finance and Chief Financial Officer
CMO: William Vandervliet, M.D., Vice President Medical Affairs
CIO: Randy J Paruch, Director, Information Systems
CHR: Michael Matthews, Vice President Human Resources
CNO: Patti J VanDort, MSN, R.N., Vice President Nursing/Chief Nursing Officer
Web address: www.hollandhospital.org
Control: Other not–for–profit (including NFP Corporation) **Service:** General medical and surgical

Staffed Beds: 130

HOWELL—Livingston County

☒ **ST. JOSEPH MERCY LIVINGSTON HOSPITAL (230069)**, 620 Byron Road, Zip 48843–1093; tel. 517/545–6000, **A**1 3 5 10 13 **F**3 5 8 11 12 15 18 28 29 30 31 34 35 40 41 45 50 51 54 56 57 59 62 63 64 65 66 68 70 74 75 77 78 79 81 82 84 85 86 87 93 97 100 104 107 108 110 111 115 117 118 119 120 121 123 129 130 131 132 134 135 141 145 146 147 148 149 153 154 **P**1 **S** Trinity Health, Livonia, MI
Primary Contact: John F. O'Malley, FACHE, President
COO: Robin Damschroder, Chief Operating Officer
CFO: Kathy O'Connor, Vice President Finance and Controller
CMO: Rosalie Tocco–Bradley, Ph.D., M.D., Chief Medical Officer
CIO: Frank Rademacher, Director, Information Systems
CHR: Tonia Schemer, Interim Chief Human Resources
CNO: Joyce Young, Ph.D., R.N., Vice President, Patient Services and Chief Nursing Officer
Web address: www.stjoeslivingston.org/livingston
Control: Church operated, Nongovernment, not–for–profit **Service:** General medical and surgical

Staffed Beds: 38 **Admissions:** 2691 **Census:** 23 **Outpatient Visits:** 288335 **Births:** 0 **Total Expense ($000):** 113884 **Payroll Expense ($000):** 37387 **Personnel:** 528

Hospital, Medicare Provider Number, Address, Telephone, Approval, Facility, and Physician Codes, Health Care System

★ American Hospital Association (AHA) membership
☐ The Joint Commission accreditation
○ Healthcare Facilities Accreditation Program
◇ DNV Healthcare Inc. accreditation
⇑ Center for Improvement in Healthcare Quality Accreditation
△ Commission on Accreditation of Rehabilitation Facilities (CARF) accreditation

IONIA—Ionia County

✠ **SPARROW IONIA HOSPITAL (231331)**, 3565 South State Road,
Zip 48846–1870; tel. 616/523–1400, **A1** 10 18 **F3** 12 15 18 29 31 34 35 40
45 50 54 57 59 64 65 68 70 75 77 78 79 81 85 93 107 108 110 111 115 119
127 129 130 131 146 148 149 **P6 S** Sparrow Health System, Lansing, MI
Primary Contact: William Roeser, President and Chief Executive Officer
COO: Kevin A Price, Vice President and Chief Operating Officer
CFO: Mark Brisboe, VP and Chief Financial Officer
CMO: Amy Jentz, M.D., Chief of Staff
CIO: Bob Neal, Information Technology
CHR: Debbie Olsen, Human Resource Partner
Web address: www.sparrow.org/sparrowionia
Control: Other not–for–profit (including NFP Corporation) **Service**: General
medical and surgical

Staffed Beds: 22 **Admissions**: 768 **Census**: 6 **Outpatient Visits**: 148644
Births: 1 **Total Expense ($000)**: 48444 **Payroll Expense ($000)**: 20601
Personnel: 281

IRON MOUNTAIN—Dickinson County

✠ **DICKINSON COUNTY HEALTHCARE SYSTEM (230055)**, 1721 South
Stephenson Avenue, Zip 49801–3637; tel. 906/774–1313, **A1** 10 20 **F3** 11 13
15 28 29 30 31 32 34 35 40 45 46 50 53 59 62 64 65 70 75 76 77 78 79 80
81 85 87 89 91 92 93 96 107 108 110 111 114 115 119 120 121 127 129
130 131 132 133 144 145 146 147 148 149 **P6**
Primary Contact: John Schon, Administrator and Chief Executive Officer
COO: Peggy Freeman, Chief Physicians Services Officer
CFO: Debbie Hanson, Interim Chief Financial Officer
CMO: Don Kube, M.D., Chief Medical Officer
CIO: Dean Decremer, Information Systems Manager
CHR: Paula Swartout, Human Resources Manager
CNO: Susan Hadley, MS, Chief Nursing Officer
Web address: www.dchs.org
Control: County, Government, nonfederal **Service**: General medical and surgical

Staffed Beds: 49 **Admissions**: 2793 **Census**: 26 **Outpatient Visits**: 308754
Births: 416 **Total Expense ($000)**: 118238 **Payroll Expense ($000)**: 46992
Personnel: 634

✠ **OSCAR G. JOHNSON VETERANS AFFAIRS MEDICAL CENTER**, 325 East 'H'
Street, Zip 49801–4792; tel. 906/774–3300, (Nonreporting) **A1 S** Department of
Veterans Affairs, Perry Point, MD
Primary Contact: James W. Rice, Director
Web address: www.ironmountain.va.gov/
Control: Veterans Affairs, Government, federal **Service**: General medical and surgical

Staffed Beds: 17

VETERANS AFFAIRS MEDICAL CENTER See Oscar G. Johnson Veterans Affairs
Medical Center

IRON RIVER—Iron County

✠ **ASPIRUS IRON RIVER HOSPITALS & CLINICS, INC. (231318)**, 1400 West Ice
Lake Road, Zip 49935–9526; tel. 906/265–6121, **A1** 10 18 **F**11 15 28 29 31
32 34 35 40 43 50 54 56 57 59 60 63 64 70 75 77 78 79 81 86 87 89 93 97
107 111 115 119 128 130 131 132 133 135 144 145 146 147 148 **S** Aspirus,
Inc., Wausau, WI
Primary Contact: Connie L. Koutouzos, R.N., MSN, Chief Executive Officer
CFO: Glenn E Dobson, Vice President, Finance and Chief Financial Officer
CMO: Nasseem Rizkalla, M.D., Chief Medical Officer
CHR: Carol Bastianello, Director Human Resources
CNO: Nancy Lynn Ponozzo, MSN, R.N., Chief Nursing Officer
Web address: www.aspirus.org
Control: Other not–for–profit (including NFP Corporation) **Service**: General
medical and surgical

Staffed Beds: 12 **Admissions**: 778 **Census**: 6 **Outpatient Visits**: 66179
Births: 0 **Total Expense ($000)**: 42357 **Payroll Expense ($000)**: 14874
Personnel: 275

IRONWOOD—Gogebic County

✠ **ASPIRUS IRONWOOD HOSPITALS & CLINICS, INC. (231333)**, N10561 Grand
View Lane, Zip 49938–9622; tel. 906/932–2525, **A1** 10 18 **F3** 11 13 15 28 29
31 34 35 40 46 50 57 59 64 65 70 75 78 79 81 85 87 93 104 107 110 114
115 119 127 130 132 133 135 146 147 148 149 **P6 S** Aspirus, Inc., Wausau, WI
Primary Contact: Paula L. Chermside, Chief Executive Officer
COO: Paula L Chermside, Chief Executive Officer
CFO: Shane Jacques, Regional Chief Financial Officer
CMO: Chris Pogliano, M.D., Chief Medical Staff
CIO: John Steenport, Information Systems Manager
CHR: Keri Van Epern, Manager Human Resources
CNO: Grace Tousignant, R.N., MSN, Chief Nursing Officer
Web address: www.aspirus.org
Control: Other not–for–profit (including NFP Corporation) **Service**: General
medical and surgical

Staffed Beds: 25 **Admissions**: 1099 **Census**: 10 **Outpatient Visits**: 65811
Births: 136 **Total Expense ($000)**: 61032 **Payroll Expense ($000)**: 23388

ISHPEMING—Marquette County

★ **UP HEALTH SYSTEM–BELL (231321)**, 901 Lakeshore Drive, Zip 49849–1367;
tel. 906/486–4431, **A**10 18 **F**3 11 13 15 29 30 34 40 50 53 57 59 64 65 68
70 75 76 77 79 81 82 85 87 92 93 96 97 107 108 110 114 119 129 133 135
144 145 146 147 **P6 S** LifePoint Health, Brentwood, TN
Primary Contact: Mitchell D. Leckelt, Chief Executive Officer
CFO: Teresa J Perry, Chief Financial Officer
CMO: Douglas LaBelle, M.D., Chief Medical Officer
CIO: Mike Brady, Director Information Technology
CHR: Tami Ketchem, Human Resource Director
CNO: Sandra McGovern, Chief Nursing Officer
Web address: www.bellhospital.org
Control: Corporation, Investor–owned (for–profit) **Service**: General medical and
surgical

Staffed Beds: 25 **Admissions**: 1017 **Census**: 8 **Outpatient Visits**: 54624
Births: 292 **Total Expense ($000)**: 36830 **Payroll Expense ($000)**: 13228
Personnel: 212

JACKSON—Jackson County

DUANE L. WATERS HOSPITAL, 3857 Cooper Street, Zip 49201–7521;
tel. 517/780–5600, (Nonreporting)
Primary Contact: Carol Griffes, Administrator
Control: State, Government, nonfederal **Service**: Hospital unit of an institution
(prison hospital, college infirmary, etc.)

Staffed Beds: 150

✠ **HENRY FORD ALLEGIANCE HEALTH (230092)**, 205 North East Avenue,
Zip 49201–1753; tel. 517/205–4800, **A**1 2 3 5 10 12 13 **F**1 3 4 5 7 8 9 11 13
15 17 18 20 22 24 26 28 29 30 31 34 35 38 40 43 44 45 46 47 48 49 50 51
53 56 57 58 59 61 62 64 65 68 69 70 71 73 74 75 76 77 78 79 81 82 84 85
87 89 91 92 93 96 97 98 99 100 101 102 103 104 105 107 108 110 111 115
118 119 121 123 126 128 129 130 131 132 135 146 147 148 149 151 152
153 154 **P6 S** Henry Ford Health System, Detroit, MI
Primary Contact: Georgia R. Fojtasek, President and Chief Executive Officer
COO: Ondrea Bates, Senior Vice President, Operations and Continuum of Care
CFO: Kevin Leonard, Vice President, Finance
CMO: Ray King, M.D., Senior Vice President, Medical Affairs and Chief Medical
Officer
CIO: Aaron Wootton, Vice President, Health Information Systems and Chief
Information Officer
CHR: Patricia Seagram, Vice President Human Resources
CNO: Wendy Boersma, Vice President, Nursing and Chief Nursing Officer
Web address: www.allegiancehealth.org
Control: Other not–for–profit (including NFP Corporation) **Service**: General
medical and surgical

Staffed Beds: 401 **Admissions**: 18546 **Census**: 221 **Outpatient Visits**:
493628 **Births**: 1619 **Total Expense ($000)**: 525335 **Payroll Expense
($000)**: 258121 **Personnel**: 3851

✠ **HENRY FORD ALLEGIANCE SPECIALTY HOSPITAL (232036)**, 110 North Elm
Avenue, Zip 49202–3595; tel. 517/205–4463, **A1** 10 **F**1 3 29 30 31 50 57 60
77 85 87 130 146 148 **S** Henry Ford Health System, Detroit, MI
Primary Contact: J Mark. Fall, Chief Executive Officer
COO: Charlotte Hyatt, MSN, R.N., Chief Operating Officer and Chief Nursing Officer
CFO: Dale L Friesen, Chief Financial Officer
CMO: Robert Albertson, M.D., Chief Medical Officer
CNO: Charlotte Hyatt, MSN, R.N., Chief Operating Officer and Chief Nursing Officer
Web address: www.carelinkofjackson.org
Control: Other not–for–profit (including NFP Corporation) **Service**: Acute long–
term care hospital

Staffed Beds: 44 **Admissions**: 472 **Census**: 29 **Outpatient Visits**: 0
Births: 0 **Total Expense ($000)**: 15619 **Payroll Expense ($000)**: 5762
Personnel: 107

KALAMAZOO—Kalamazoo County

✠ △ **BORGESS MEDICAL CENTER (230117)**, 1521 Gull Road,
Zip 49048–1640; tel. 269/226–7000, (Includes BORGESS–PIPP HOSPITAL, 411
Naomi Street, Plainwell, MI, Zip 49080–1222; tel. 269/685–6811; Donna Cassidy,
Administrator) **A1** 3 5 7 10 12 13 **F3** 7 8 9 11 12 13 15 17 18 20 22 24 26 28
29 30 31 32 33 34 35 36 37 38 39 40 43 44 45 46 47 49 50 53 54 56 57
58 59 60 61 64 68 70 74 75 76 77 78 79 81 82 83 84 85 86 87 90 91 92 93
94 96 97 98 99 100 101 102 103 104 105 107 108 110 114 118 119 126
127 129 130 131 132 135 144 146 147 148 149 154 **P3** 6 8 **S** Ascension
Healthcare, Saint Louis, MO
Primary Contact: Tim Stover, M.D., Interim Chief Executive Officer
COO: Mark Anthony, Executive Vice President and Chief Operating Officer
CMO: Robert Hill, M.D., Vice President Medical Staff Affairs
CHR: Laura Lentenbrink, Vice President, Human Resources
CNO: Lori J Brown, R.N., FACHE, Vice President and Chief Nursing Executive
Web address: www.borgess.com
Control: Church operated, Nongovernment, not–for–profit **Service**: General
medical and surgical

Staffed Beds: 422 **Admissions**: 18546 **Census**: 241 **Outpatient Visits**:
391610 **Births**: 1064 **Total Expense ($000)**: 404825 **Payroll Expense
($000)**: 145509 **Personnel**: 2622

Many Facility Codes have changed. Please refer to the AHA Guide Code Chart.

© 2018 AHA Guide

☒ **BRONSON METHODIST HOSPITAL (230017)**, 601 John Street, Zip 49007–5346; tel. 269/341–6000, (Includes BRONSON VICKSBURG HOSPITAL, 13326 North Boulevard, Vicksburg, MI, Zip 49097–1099; tel. 269/649–2321; Frank J Sardone, President and Chief Executive Officer; CHILDREN'S HOSPITAL AT BRONSON, 601 John Street, Kalamazoo, MI, Zip 49007–5341; tel. 269/341–7654) **A**1 3 5 10 12 13 **F**3 8 9 11 12 15 16 17 18 19 20 22 24 26 28 29 30 31 32 34 35 36 37 39 40 41 43 44 45 46 47 48 49 50 51 54 55 56 57 58 59 60 61 63 64 65 66 68 70 71 72 74 75 76 77 78 79 80 81 82 84 85 86 87 88 89 90 92 93 97 101 102 107 110 111 114 115 117 118 119 126 129 130 131 132 134 135 141 143 144 146 147 148 149 154 **P**6 **S** Bronson Healthcare Group, Kalamazoo, MI
Primary Contact: Frank J. Sardone, President and Chief Executive Officer
COO: Kenneth L Taft, Executive Vice President and Chief Operating Officer
CMO: Scott Larson, M.D., Vice President Medical Affairs and Chief Medical Officer
CHR: John Hayden, Vice President and Chief Human Resources Officer
CNO: Denise Neely, R.N., Vice President and Chief Nursing Officer
Web address: www.bronsonhealth.com
Control: Other not–for–profit (including NFP Corporation) **Service**: General medical and surgical

Staffed Beds: 415 Admissions: 22952 Census: 286 Outpatient Visits: 1002253 Births: 3736 Total Expense ($000): 765174 Payroll Expense ($000): 356608 Personnel: 4002

☐ **KALAMAZOO PSYCHIATRIC HOSPITAL (234026)**, 1312 Oakland Drive, Zip 49008–1205; tel. 269/337–3000, **A**1 10 12 13 **F**3 39 50 53 56 65 75 77 86 87 97 98 101 103 130 132 135 143 146 148 149 **P**6
Primary Contact: Jill A. Krause, Director
CMO: V.R. Kanaparti, M.D., Director Medical Services
CIO: Brian Bayer, Information Technology Site Leader
CHR: Holly Hiday, Director Human Resources
CNO: Kathleen Millard, Acting Director Nursing
Control: State, Government, nonfederal **Service**: Psychiatric

Staffed Beds: 203 Admissions: 139 Census: 141 Outpatient Visits: 0 Births: 0 Total Expense ($000): 61609 Payroll Expense ($000): 28877 Personnel: 459

KALKASKA—Kalkaska County

★ **KALKASKA MEMORIAL HEALTH CENTER (231301)**, 419 South Coral Street, Zip 49646–2503; tel. 231/258–7500, (Total facility includes 104 beds in nursing home–type unit) **A**10 18 **F**2 10 15 28 34 35 40 44 45 50 53 56 57 59 60 64 65 66 79 81 84 87 93 97 107 110 111 115 119 127 128 129 130 132 134 143 144 146 147 148 154 **S** Munson Healthcare, Traverse City, MI
Primary Contact: Kevin L. Rogols, FACHE, Administrator
CHR: Kimberly Babcock, Administrative Director of Operations
CNO: Christine Bissonette, R.N., Service Line Director for Acute Services
Web address: www.munsonhealthcare.org
Control: Hospital district or authority, Government, nonfederal **Service**: General medical and surgical

Staffed Beds: 112 Admissions: 286 Census: 97 Outpatient Visits: 75461 Births: 0 Total Expense ($000): 42379 Payroll Expense ($000): 19328 Personnel: 332

LAKEVIEW—Montcalm County

SPECTRUM HEALTH KELSEY HOSPITAL See Spectrum Health United Hospital, Greenville

L'ANSE—L'Anse County

☐ **BARAGA COUNTY MEMORIAL HOSPITAL (231307)**, 18341 U.S. Highway 41, Zip 49946–8024; tel. 906/524–3300, **A**1 10 18 **F**3 11 15 28 31 34 35 40 45 50 53 57 59 62 63 64 74 75 77 78 79 81 82 84 85 89 93 107 108 110 114 118 119 127 130 132 133 146 154 **P**6
Primary Contact: Margie Hale, R.N., MSN, Chief Executive Officer
CFO: Gail Jestila–Peltola, Chief Financial Officer
CMO: Sharon Gilliland, Chief of Staff
CIO: Taylor Makela, Director Information Technology
CHR: Janelle E Beeler, Human Resource Manager
CNO: Bonny Cotter, Chief Nursing Officer
Web address: www.bcmh.org
Control: County, Government, nonfederal **Service**: General medical and surgical

Staffed Beds: 15 Admissions: 502 Census: 6 Outpatient Visits: 23711 Births: 0 Total Expense ($000): 22570 Payroll Expense ($000): 8431 Personnel: 126

LANSING—Ingham County

○ **MCLAREN GREATER LANSING (230167)**, 401 West Greenlawn Avenue, Zip 48910–2819; tel. 517/975–6000, (Includes MCLAREN GREATER LANSING, 401 West Greenlawn Avenue, Lansing, MI, Zip 48910–2819; tel. 517/795–6000; MCLAREN ORTHOPEDIC HOSPITAL, 2727 South Pennsylvania Avenue, Lansing, MI, Zip 48910–3490; tel. 517/975–6000; Casey Kandow, Interim President and Chief Executive Officer) (Nonreporting) **A**2 3 5 10 11 13 **S** McLaren Health Care Corporation, Grand Blanc, MI
Primary Contact: Kirk M. Ray, President and Chief Executive Officer
COO: Casey Kandow, Chief Operating Officer
CFO: Dale Thompson, Chief Financial Officer
CMO: Linda Peterson, M.D., Vice President Medical Affairs
CHR: Amy Dorr, Vice President Human Resources
CNO: Camille Jensen, R.N., Chief Nursing Officer
Web address: www.mclaren.org
Control: Other not–for–profit (including NFP Corporation) **Service**: General medical and surgical

Staffed Beds: 321

☒ △ **SPARROW HOSPITAL (230230)**, 1215 East Michigan Avenue, Zip 48912–1811; tel. 517/364–1000, (Includes SPARROW CHILDREN'S CENTER, 1215 East Michigan Avenue, Lansing, MI, Zip 48912–1811; tel. 517/364–1000) **A**1 2 3 5 7 8 10 12 13 **F**3 5 11 12 13 15 17 18 20 22 24 26 28 29 30 31 34 35 36 38 40 41 43 44 45 46 49 50 51 54 56 57 58 59 60 63 64 65 67 70 72 74 75 76 77 78 79 81 82 84 85 86 87 88 89 90 91 92 93 94 96 97 98 99 100 101 102 103 104 105 107 108 109 110 111 114 115 116 117 118 119 120 121 123 124 126 129 130 131 132 135 144 146 147 148 149 **P**1 6 **S** Sparrow Health System, Lansing, MI
Primary Contact: Mark Brett, Chief Executive Officer
COO: Joseph Ruth, Executive Vice President and Chief Operating Officer
CFO: Paula Reichle, Senior Vice President and Chief Operating Officer
CMO: Brian D. Schroeder, M.D., Senior Vice President and Chief Medical Officer
CIO: Thomas Bres, Senior Vice President and Chief Administrative Officer
CHR: Paul Sturgis, Vice President and Chief Human Resources Officer
CNO: Mary Lou Wesley, R.N., Senior Vice President and Chief Nursing Officer
Web address: www.sparrow.org
Control: Other not–for–profit (including NFP Corporation) **Service**: General medical and surgical

Staffed Beds: 631 Admissions: 32558 Census: 452 Outpatient Visits: 852597 Births: 4201 Total Expense ($000): 917329 Payroll Expense ($000): 428155 Personnel: 5353

★ ○ **SPARROW SPECIALTY HOSPITAL (232037)**, 8 West Sparrow Hospital Tower, Zip 48912; tel. 517/364–4840, **A**10 11 **F**1 3 29 30 60 68 85 100 101 119 130 148 **S** Sparrow Health System, Lansing, MI
Primary Contact: Lou Little, President and Chief Executive Officer
CFO: David Przybylski, Controller
CMO: Paul Entler, D.O., Medical Director
CHR: Paul Sturgis, Chief Human Resource Officer
CNO: Tina Gross, MSN, R.N., Chief Nursing Officer
Web address: www.sparrowspecialty.org
Control: Other not–for–profit (including NFP Corporation) **Service**: Acute long–term care hospital

Staffed Beds: 30 Admissions: 264 Census: 22 Outpatient Visits: 0 Births: 0 Total Expense ($000): 12155 Payroll Expense ($000): 5825 Personnel: 92

LAPEER—Lapeer County

○ **MCLAREN LAPEER REGION (230193)**, 1375 North Main Street, Zip 48446–1350; tel. 810/667–5500, (Total facility includes 19 beds in nursing home–type unit) **A**2 10 11 **F**3 13 15 18 20 26 28 29 30 31 34 35 40 43 44 45 49 54 56 57 59 61 64 68 70 74 76 77 79 81 82 84 85 86 87 92 93 94 97 98 100 101 102 107 108 110 111 114 115 119 128 129 130 131 135 143 144 146 148 149 154 **S** McLaren Health Care Corporation, Grand Blanc, MI
Primary Contact: Chris Candela, President and Chief Executive Officer
CFO: Mary Beth Callahan, Chief Financial Officer
CMO: Gary Salem, M.D., Vice President Medical Affairs
CIO: Gayle Consiglio, Chief Information Officer
CHR: Amy Dorr, Vice President Human Resources
Web address: www.lapeerregional.org
Control: Other not–for–profit (including NFP Corporation) **Service**: General medical and surgical

Staffed Beds: 159 Admissions: 6917 Census: 87 Outpatient Visits: 148496 Births: 263 Total Expense ($000): 109700 Payroll Expense ($000): 50590 Personnel: 618

Hospital, Medicare Provider Number, Address, Telephone, Approval, Facility, and Physician Codes, Health Care System

★ American Hospital Association (AHA) membership
☐ The Joint Commission accreditation
○ Healthcare Facilities Accreditation Program
◇ DNV Healthcare Inc. accreditation
⇑ Center for Improvement in Healthcare Quality Accreditation
△ Commission on Accreditation of Rehabilitation Facilities (CARF) accreditation

LAURIUM—Houghton County

⊞ **ASPIRUS KEWEENAW HOSPITAL, INC. (231319)**, 205 Osceola Street,
Zip 49913–2134; tel. 906/337–6500, **A**1 10 18 **F**3 11 13 15 17 18 28 29 30
31 34 35 36 40 43 45 52 53 56 57 59 61 64 65 66 68 70 75 76 77 78 79 81
85 87 89 93 97 107 108 110 115 118 119 127 129 130 131 132 133 135
146 147 148 154 **P6 S** Aspirus, Inc., Wausau, WI
Primary Contact: Jesse G. Tischer, Interim Presidnet
CFO: Shane Jacques, Regional Chief Financial Officer – U.P.
CMO: Michael Luoma, M.D., Chief of Staff
CIO: Dave Olsson, Director of Marketing
CHR: Chad Rowe, Human Resource Director
CNO: Grace Tousignant, R.N., MSN, Chief Nursing Officer
Web address: www.aspirus.org
Control: Other not–for–profit (including NFP Corporation) **Service**: General
medical and surgical

Staffed Beds: 25 **Admissions**: 1135 **Census**: 9 **Outpatient Visits**: 48309
Births: 142 **Total Expense ($000)**: 51127 **Payroll Expense ($000)**: 20022
Personnel: 290

LINCOLN PARK—Wayne County

⊞ **VIBRA HOSPITAL OF SOUTHEASTERN MICHIGAN, LLC (232019)**, 26400
West Outer Drive, Zip 48146–2088; tel. 313/386–2000, (Nonreporting) **A**1 10 **S**
Vibra Healthcare, Mechanicsburg, PA
Primary Contact: Reginald Lee, Chief Executive Officer
COO: Cindy Brassinger, Chief Operating Officer
CFO: Douglas Morris, Chief Financial Officer
CHR: Karen D Gray, Director Human Resources
Web address: www.vhsemichigan.com/
Control: Corporation, Investor–owned (for–profit) **Service**: Acute long–term care
hospital

Staffed Beds: 220

LIVONIA—Wayne County

⊞ **ST. MARY MERCY HOSPITAL (230002)**, 36475 Five Mile Road,
Zip 48154–1988; tel. 734/655–4800, **A**1 2 3 10 12 13 **F**3 4 5 8 12 13 15 18
20 22 26 28 29 30 31 34 35 38 40 43 44 45 46 47 49 50 51 53 54 55 56 57
58 59 63 64 68 70 74 75 76 77 78 79 81 84 85 87 90 93 97 98 100 101 102
107 108 110 111 114 115 116 117 118 119 120 121 126 129 130 131 132
135 143 144 145 146 147 148 149 153 154 **P6 S** Trinity Health, Livonia, MI
Primary Contact: David A. Spivey, President and Chief Executive Officer
CFO: Mike Samyn, Vice President, Finance and Chief Financial Officer
CMO: Matthew Griffin, M.D., Chief Medical Officer
CIO: Janet Yim, Director Information Services
CHR: Kenneth Antczak, Vice President Human Resources
Web address: www.stmarymercy.org
Control: Church operated, Nongovernment, not–for–profit **Service**: General
medical and surgical

Staffed Beds: 303 **Admissions**: 17749 **Census**: 213 **Outpatient Visits**:
291759 **Births**: 730 **Total Expense ($000)**: 299045 **Payroll Expense
($000)**: 128384 **Personnel**: 1625

LUDINGTON—Mason County

★ ⇑ **SPECTRUM HEALTH LUDINGTON HOSPITAL (230110)**, One Atkinson Drive,
Zip 49431–1906, Mailing Address: PO Box 2408, Grand Rapids, Zip 49501–2408;
tel. 231/843–2591, **A**10 20 21 **F**3 8 11 13 15 28 29 31 32 34 35 40 41 45 49
50 53 54 57 59 64 65 68 70 75 76 77 78 79 81 82 85 86 87 92 93 98 100
102 107 108 110 111 114 115 118 119 127 129 130 131 132 135 146 147
148 149 154 **S** Spectrum Health, Grand Rapids, MI
Primary Contact: Randall Kelley, FACHE, President
CFO: Kerri Nelson, Chief Financial Officer
CMO: Steve Strbich, D.O., Chief of Staff
CIO: Jeremy Vronko, Manager, Information Services
CHR: Jill Vasquez, Manager Human Resources
CNO: Helen Johnson, R.N., MSN, Vice President Patient Services
Web address: www.mmcwm.org
Control: Other not–for–profit (including NFP Corporation) **Service**: General
medical and surgical

Staffed Beds: 41 **Admissions**: 2143 **Census**: 20 **Outpatient Visits**: 111560
Births: 287 **Total Expense ($000)**: 82518 **Payroll Expense ($000)**: 25797
Personnel: 431

MANISTEE—Manistee County

★ **MUNSON HEALTHCARE MANISTEE HOSPITAL (230303)**, 1465 East Parkdale
Avenue, Zip 49660–9709; tel. 231/398–1000, **A**10 20 **F**3 7 11 13 15 28 29 31
34 35 39 40 45 48 50 51 53 54 57 59 64 74 76 77 78 79 80 81 85 86 87 92
93 96 97 107 108 110 111 115 118 119 127 129 131 146 147 148 149 **P6 S**
Munson Healthcare, Traverse City, MI
Primary Contact: James Barker, Chief Executive Officer
COO: Donn J Lemmer, Chief Financial Officer and Chief Operating Officer
CFO: Donn J Lemmer, Chief Financial Officer and Chief Operating Officer
CMO: Marion Fuller, Chief of Staff
CHR: Kim Weckesser, Director Human Resources
CNO: Thomas Kane, R.N., Vice President Patient Services and Chief Nursing
Officer
Web address: www.westshoremedcenter.org
Control: Other not–for–profit (including NFP Corporation) **Service**: General
medical and surgical

Staffed Beds: 45 **Admissions**: 1397 **Census**: 14 **Outpatient Visits**: 95833
Births: 216 **Total Expense ($000)**: 64688 **Payroll Expense ($000)**: 26697
Personnel: 335

MANISTIQUE—Schoolcraft County

★ **SCHOOLCRAFT MEMORIAL HOSPITAL (231303)**, 7870W US Highway 2,
Zip 49854–8992; tel. 906/341–3200, **A**10 18 **F**3 11 15 18 19 28 29 30 31 32
34 35 44 45 50 53 56 57 59 62 63 64 65 68 70 75 77 78 79 81 85 93 97
100 107 108 110 114 118 119 127 129 130 132 133 144 146 147 148 154
P6
Primary Contact: Robert Crumb, MS, Chief Executive Officer
CMO: John P Galey, M.D., Chief Medical Officer
CIO: Kent La Croix, Chief Information Officer
CHR: Fawn Freeborn, Human Resources Generalist
CNO: Cindy Olli, R.N., Chief Nursing Officer
Web address: www.scmh.org
Control: County, Government, nonfederal **Service**: General medical and surgical

Staffed Beds: 12 **Admissions**: 407 **Census**: 5 **Outpatient Visits**: 49646
Births: 0 **Total Expense ($000)**: 33894 **Payroll Expense ($000)**: 15416
Personnel: 240

MARLETTE—Sanilac County

MARLETTE REGIONAL HOSPITAL (231330), 2770 Main Street,
Zip 48453–1141, Mailing Address: P.O. Box 307, Zip 48453–0307;
tel. 989/635–4000, (Nonreporting) **A**5 10 18
Primary Contact: Daniel Babcock, Chief Executive Officer
CFO: James L Singles, Chief Financial Officer
CMO: Daniel Kulick, M.D., Chief of Staff
CIO: Paul Gugel, Manager Information Technology
CHR: Connie Kennedy, Director Human Resources
CNO: Hilda Hebberd, R.N., MSN, Senior Director Clinical Services
Web address: www.marletteregionalhospital.org
Control: Other not–for–profit (including NFP Corporation) **Service**: General
medical and surgical

Staffed Beds: 74

MARQUETTE—Marquette County

⊞ **UP HEALTH SYSTEM–MARQUETTE (230054)**, 580 West College Avenue,
Zip 49855–2736; tel. 906/228–9440, **A**1 2 3 5 10 13 **F**3 4 5 7 8 11 12 13 14
15 17 18 19 20 22 24 26 28 29 30 31 32 34 35 37 38 40 43 45 46 49 50 51
53 55 56 57 58 59 60 64 65 68 70 72 74 75 76 77 78 79 81 82 84 85 86 87
89 90 93 94 98 100 101 104 107 108 110 111 114 115 116 119 120
121 123 124 127 129 130 131 132 135 145 147 148 149 **P6 S** Duke LifePoint
Healthcare, Brentwood, TN
Primary Contact: Brian Sinotte, Chief Executive Officer
COO: Steven Salyer, Chief Operating Officer
CFO: Steve Embree, Chief Financial Officer
CMO: Tom Noren, M.D., Chief Medical Officer
CIO: Doug Stacy, Director Information Technology
CHR: Ruth Solinski, Senior Director Human Resources
Web address: www.mgh.org
Control: Corporation, Investor–owned (for–profit) **Service**: General medical and
surgical

Staffed Beds: 260 **Admissions**: 10153 **Census**: 143 **Outpatient Visits**:
181682 **Births**: 575 **Total Expense ($000)**: 319445 **Payroll Expense
($000)**: 119940 **Personnel**: 1747

MARSHALL—Calhoun County

★ ⇑ **OAKLAWN HOSPITAL (230217)**, 200 North Madison Street, Zip 49068–1199; tel. 269/781–4271, (Nonreporting) **A**10 21
Primary Contact: Gregg M. Beeg, FACHE, Interim President and Chief Executive Officer
COO: Sharon Thomas–Boyd, Chief Operating Officer
CFO: Andrew J. Poole III Interim Chief Financial Officer
CNO: Theresa Dawson, MSN, R.N., Chief Nursing Officer
Web address: www.oaklawnhospital.org
Control: Other not–for–profit (including NFP Corporation) **Service**: General medical and surgical

Staffed Beds: 78

MIDLAND—Midland County

⊞ **MIDMICHIGAN MEDICAL CENTER–MIDLAND (230222)**, 4000 Wellness Drive, Zip 48670–2000; tel. 989/839–3000, **A**1 2 3 5 10 **F**3 7 8 11 12 13 15 17 18 19 20 22 24 26 28 29 30 31 32 34 35 36 37 40 43 45 46 47 48 49 50 51 53 54 56 57 58 59 60 61 62 63 64 65 68 70 71 74 75 77 78 79 80 81 82 84 85 86 87 91 92 93 94 97 98 100 101 102 103 104 107 108 109 110 111 114 115 116 117 118 119 121 122 123 124 126 127 130 131 132 135 143 144 145 146 147 148 149 154 **S** MidMichigan Health, Midland, MI
Primary Contact: Gregory H. Rogers, President
CFO: Scott D Currie, Vice President and Chief Financial Officer
CMO: Margueritte Kuhn, M.D., Vice President Medical Affairs
CIO: C Harlan Goodrich, Vice President and Chief Information Officer
CNO: Jan Penney, R.N., Vice President and Chief Nursing Officer
Web address: www.midmichigan.org
Control: Other not–for–profit (including NFP Corporation) **Service**: General medical and surgical

Staffed Beds: 304 **Admissions**: 13546 **Census**: 140 **Outpatient Visits**: 265992 **Births**: 1382 **Total Expense ($000)**: 384351 **Payroll Expense ($000)**: 114944 **Personnel**: 2183

MONROE—Monroe County

⊞ **PROMEDICA MONROE REGIONAL HOSPITAL (230099)**, 718 North Macomb Street, Zip 48162–7815; tel. 734/240–8400, **A**1 2 3 10 **F**3 5 11 13 15 18 20 21 28 29 30 31 34 35 36 38 40 41 43 44 45 46 49 50 51 53 54 56 57 59 65 66 69 70 71 74 75 76 77 78 79 81 82 85 86 87 92 93 97 98 100 101 102 104 107 108 109 110 111 113 114 115 116 117 118 119 124 126 129 130 132 135 145 146 147 148 149 150 154 **S** ProMedica Health System, Toledo, OH
Primary Contact: Daniel Schwanke, President
CMO: Gary L. Moorman, D.O., Chief Medical Officer and Senior Vice President Medical Affairs
CNO: Pamela A Urbanski, R.N., MSN, Chief Nursing Officer, Senior Vice President, Patient Care Services
Web address: www.promedica.org
Control: Other not–for–profit (including NFP Corporation) **Service**: General medical and surgical

Staffed Beds: 100 **Admissions**: 6450 **Census**: 77 **Outpatient Visits**: 154590 **Births**: 672 **Total Expense ($000)**: 131306 **Payroll Expense ($000)**: 50087 **Personnel**: 797

MOUNT CLEMENS—Macomb County

MCLAREN MACOMB (230227), 1000 Harrington Boulevard, Zip 48043–2992; tel. 586/493–8000, **A**2 3 10 12 13 **F**3 8 11 12 13 14 15 18 19 20 22 24 26 28 29 30 31 34 35 36 37 40 41 43 45 46 47 48 49 50 51 54 55 56 59 62 63 64 65 66 68 70 71 74 75 76 77 78 79 81 82 85 87 89 92 93 96 97 98 100 102 107 110 111 114 118 119 120 121 122 123 124 126 129 130 131 132 135 144 145 146 147 148 154 **P**8 **S** McLaren Health Care Corporation, Grand Blanc, MI
Primary Contact: Thomas M. Brisse, President and Chief Executive Officer
COO: Sue Durst, R.N., MS, Vice President Plant Operations
CFO: Brian Baluntanski, Chief Financial Officer
CMO: Dennis J. Cunningham, M.D., Chief Medical Officer
CNO: Julia Libcke, R.N., MSN, Chief Nursing Officer
Web address: www.mclaren.org/macomb/macomb.aspx
Control: Other not–for–profit (including NFP Corporation) **Service**: General medical and surgical

Staffed Beds: 288 **Admissions**: 15274 **Census**: 164 **Outpatient Visits**: 159241 **Births**: 1161 **Total Expense ($000)**: 313520 **Payroll Expense ($000)**: 132572 **Personnel**: 1907

⊞ **SELECT SPECIALTY HOSPITAL–MACOMB COUNTY (232023)**, 215 North Avenue, Zip 48043–1700; tel. 586/307–9000, (Nonreporting) **A**1 10 **S** Select Medical Corporation, Mechanicsburg, PA
Primary Contact: Jon P. O'Malley, Chief Executive Officer
CFO: Sharon Ryan, Regional Controller
CMO: Arsenio V Deleon, M.D., Chief Medical Officer
CHR: Katelyn Andre, Human Resource Coordinator
CNO: Lydia Alaszewski, Chief Nursing Officer
Web address: www.macomb.selectspecialtyhospitals.com/
Control: Corporation, Investor–owned (for–profit) **Service**: Acute long–term care hospital

Staffed Beds: 36

MOUNT PLEASANT—Isabella County

☐ **MCLAREN CENTRAL MICHIGAN (230080)**, 1221 South Drive, Zip 48858–3257; tel. 989/772–6700, **A**1 2 5 10 19 **F**3 12 13 15 18 20 22 26 28 29 30 31 34 35 40 44 45 48 49 50 51 54 57 59 62 64 65 68 70 74 75 77 78 79 81 82 85 86 87 89 96 97 107 108 110 111 114 117 118 119 120 121 123 124 129 130 131 132 144 145 146 147 148 **S** McLaren Health Care Corporation, Grand Blanc, MI
Primary Contact: Martin Tursky, President and Chief Executive Officer
CMO: Ashok Vashishta, M.D., Vice President Medical Affairs
CIO: Nicolette Zalud, Customer Site Manager
CHR: Carolyn Potter, Vice President Human Resources
CNO: Sheri Myers, Vice President Patient Care Services
Web address: www.cmch.org
Control: Other not–for–profit (including NFP Corporation) **Service**: General medical and surgical

Staffed Beds: 78 **Admissions**: 3037 **Census**: 25 **Outpatient Visits**: 123090 **Births**: 529 **Total Expense ($000)**: 86154 **Payroll Expense ($000)**: 38591 **Personnel**: 478

MUNISING—Alger County

MUNISING MEMORIAL HOSPITAL (231308), 1500 Sand Point Road, Zip 49862–1406; tel. 906/387–4110, **A**10 18 **F**3 10 15 29 34 35 40 56 57 59 65 68 75 77 81 82 90 93 97 107 119 127 129 131 133 135 144 146 147 154
Primary Contact: Melissa Hall, Chief Executive Officer
CFO: Wendy Rautio, Chief Financial Officer
CMO: Christine Krueger, M.D., Chief of Staff
CNO: Andrea Wills, R.N., Chief Nursing Executive
Web address: www.munisingmemorial.org
Control: Other not–for–profit (including NFP Corporation) **Service**: General medical and surgical

Staffed Beds: 11 **Admissions**: 100 **Census**: 2 **Outpatient Visits**: 17495 **Births**: 0 **Total Expense ($000)**: 9078 **Payroll Expense ($000)**: 4419 **Personnel**: 64

MUSKEGON—Muskegon County

⊞ **MERCY HEALTH HACKLEY CAMPUS (230066)**, 1700 Clinton Street, Zip 49442–5502, Mailing Address: P.O. Box 3302, Zip 49443–3302; tel. 231/726–3511, (Includes MERCY HEALTH, GENERAL CAMPUS, 1700 Oak Avenue, Muskegon, MI, Zip 49442; tel. 231/672–3311; Greg Loomis, Interim President and Chief Operating Officer; MERCY HEALTH, MERCY CAMPUS, 1500 East Sherman Boulevard, Muskegon, MI, Zip 49444–1849; tel. 231/672–2000; Gary Allore, President) **A**1 2 3 10 13 **F**3 7 11 12 13 15 20 22 24 26 28 29 30 33 35 36 40 43 45 49 50 51 53 54 56 57 59 61 64 68 70 76 77 79 81 82 84 85 87 89 90 91 93 96 97 98 104 107 108 110 111 114 115 118 119 122 123 124 127 129 130 131 132 144 146 147 148 149 154 **S** Trinity Health, Livonia, MI
Primary Contact: Gary Allore, President
CMO: F. Remington Sprague, M.D., Chief Medical Officer
CIO: William Stefl, Director Information Systems
CNO: Kimberly Maguire, R.N., Chief Nursing Officer
Web address: www.mercyhealthmuskegon.com
Control: Other not–for–profit (including NFP Corporation) **Service**: General medical and surgical

Staffed Beds: 401 **Admissions**: 18972 **Census**: 214 **Outpatient Visits**: 1064684 **Births**: 1903 **Total Expense ($000)**: 537942 **Payroll Expense ($000)**: 232190 **Personnel**: 3345

✠ **SELECT SPECIALTY HOSPITAL–MUSKEGON (232021)**, 1700 Clinton Street, 3 South, Zip 49442–5502; tel. 231/728–5811, (Nonreporting) **A**1 10 **S** Select Medical Corporation, Mechanicsburg, PA
Primary Contact: Kerry McLane, Chief Executive Officer
Web address: www.greatlakesspecialtyhospital.com
Control: Corporation, Investor–owned (for–profit) **Service**: Acute long–term care hospital

Staffed Beds: 31

SELECT SPECIALTY HOSPITAL–WESTERN MICHIGAN See Select Specialty Hospital–Muskegon

NEW BALTIMORE—Macomb County

HARBOR OAKS HOSPITAL (234021), 35031 23 Mile Road, Zip 48047–3649; tel. 586/725–5777, **A**10 **F**4 98 99 103 105 **S** Acadia Healthcare Company, Inc., Franklin, TN
Primary Contact: Sari Abromovich, Chief Executive Officer
CFO: Michael Ferguson, Chief Financial Officer
CMO: James D. Adamo, M.D., Medical Director
CHR: Zena Ridley, Director Human Resources
CNO: Leeann Duncan, Director Patient Care Services
Web address: www.harboroaks.com
Control: Corporation, Investor–owned (for–profit) **Service**: Psychiatric

Staffed Beds: 99 Admissions: 3180 Census: 90

NEWBERRY—Luce County

★ ⇑ **HELEN NEWBERRY JOY HOSPITAL (231304)**, 502 West Harrie Street, Zip 49868–1209; tel. 906/293–9200, (Total facility includes 39 beds in nursing home–type unit) **A**10 18 21 **F**3 15 28 29 31 34 35 40 45 53 57 59 64 65 75 78 79 81 87 93 97 107 108 115 118 119 127 128 129 130 131 132 133 143 144 148 154 **P**6
Primary Contact: Scott Pillion, Chief Executive Officer
CFO: Hunter Nostrant, Chief Financial Officer
CMO: Michael Gregory Beaulieu, M.D., Chief Medical Officer
CIO: Howard Bliss, Director of Information Systems
CNO: Deborah Baker, Chief Nursing Officer
Web address: www.hnjh.org
Control: County, Government, nonfederal **Service**: General medical and surgical

Staffed Beds: 64 Admissions: 458 Census: 44 Outpatient Visits: 32338 Births: 0 Total Expense ($000): 32808 Payroll Expense ($000): 13987 Personnel: 267

NORTHVILLE—Wayne County

☐ **HAWTHORN CENTER**, 18471 Haggerty Road, Zip 48168–9575; tel. 248/735–6771, (Nonreporting) **A**1 3
Primary Contact: George Mellows, Facility Director
CIO: Robert W Bailey, Chief Information Officer
Web address: www.michigan.gov
Control: State, Government, nonfederal **Service**: Children's hospital psychiatric

Staffed Beds: 69

NOVI—Oakland County

PROVIDENCE – PROVIDENCE PARK HOSPITAL, NOVI CAMPUS See Providence–Providence Park Hospitals, Southfield

ONTONAGON—Ontonagon County

✠ **ASPIRUS ONTONAGON HOSPITAL, INC. (231309)**, 601 South Seventh Street, Zip 49953–1459; tel. 906/884–8000, (Total facility includes 46 beds in nursing home–type unit) **A**1 10 18 **F**3 15 28 29 31 34 35 40 41 45 47 53 56 59 64 65 68 75 77 78 79 81 85 87 93 94 97 107 110 114 119 127 128 131 132 133 147 149 154 **P**6 **S** Aspirus, Inc., Wausau, WI
Primary Contact: Jesse G. Tischer, Interim President
CMO: Richard Chaltry, M.D., Director Medical Staff
CHR: Gina Linna, Manager Human Resources
CNO: Deanna Wilson, VP Patient Care Services/Site Manager
Web address: www.aspirus.org
Control: Other not–for–profit (including NFP Corporation) **Service**: General medical and surgical

Staffed Beds: 64 Admissions: 219 Census: 41 Outpatient Visits: 13725 Births: 0 Total Expense ($000): 15425 Payroll Expense ($000): 5835 Personnel: 94

OWOSSO—Shiawassee County

✠ **MEMORIAL HEALTHCARE (230121)**, 826 West King Street, Zip 48867–2120; tel. 989/723–5211, (Total facility includes 32 beds in nursing home–type unit) **A**1 2 5 10 **F**3 11 13 15 28 29 30 31 32 34 35 36 38 40 45 50 51 56 57 58 59 62 63 64 65 69 70 74 75 76 77 78 79 81 82 85 87 89 93 97 98 100 101 102 107 108 110 111 115 119 127 128 129 130 131 132 143 144 146 147 148 154 **P**6 7
Primary Contact: Brian Long, FACHE, President and Chief Executive Officer
COO: Tim Susterich, Chief Financial Officer and Chief Operating Officer
CFO: Tim Susterich, Chief Financial Officer and Chief Operating Officer
CMO: Wael Salman, M.D., Vice President Medical Affairs
CIO: Tom Kurtz, Vice President Information Services and Chief Information Officer
CNO: Jim Nemeth, Senior Vice President of Patient Care Services and Chief Nursing Officer
Web address: www.memorialhealthcare.org
Control: Other not–for–profit (including NFP Corporation) **Service**: General medical and surgical

Staffed Beds: 150 Admissions: 3842 Census: 69 Outpatient Visits: 383346 Births: 424 Total Expense ($000): 136024 Payroll Expense ($000): 63281 Personnel: 1072

PAW PAW—Van Buren County

✠ **BRONSON LAKEVIEW HOSPITAL (231332)**, 408 Hazen Street, Zip 49079–1019, Mailing Address: P.O. Box 209, Zip 49079–0209; tel. 269/657–3141, **A**1 10 18 **F**3 6 9 11 15 18 29 30 34 35 36 40 44 50 55 56 57 58 59 63 64 65 66 68 71 74 75 77 79 81 82 84 85 86 87 90 93 97 98 100 101 102 103 107 110 111 115 118 119 127 129 130 132 135 143 146 147 148 149 **P**6 **S** Bronson Healthcare Group, Kalamazoo, MI
Primary Contact: Kirk Richardson, R.N., Vice President, Chief Operating Officer, and Chief Nursing Officer
COO: Kirk Richardson, R.N., Vice President, Chief Operating Officer, and Chief Nursing Officer
CFO: Becky East, CPA, Senior Vice President, Chief Financial Officer
CMO: Matthew Dommer, M.D., Chief Medical Officer
CIO: Ash Goel, Senior Vice President Information Technology & Chief Information Officer
CHR: John Hayden, Senior Vice President and Chief Human Resources Officer
CNO: Kirk Richardson, R.N., Vice President, Chief Operating Officer, and Chief Nursing Officer
Web address: www.bronsonhealth.com/lakeview
Control: Other not–for–profit (including NFP Corporation) **Service**: General medical and surgical

Staffed Beds: 35 Admissions: 801 Census: 12 Outpatient Visits: 98589 Births: 0 Total Expense ($000): 47519 Payroll Expense ($000): 25792 Personnel: 308

PETOSKEY—Emmet County

☐ **MCLAREN NORTHERN MICHIGAN (230105)**, 416 Connable Avenue, Zip 49770–2297; tel. 231/487–4000, **A**1 2 5 10 **F**3 13 15 17 18 20 22 24 26 28 29 30 31 32 34 35 36 38 40 44 45 49 50 51 53 57 58 59 60 64 68 70 74 75 76 77 78 79 81 82 85 86 87 89 90 91 93 94 96 107 108 110 114 115 119 120 121 123 124 129 130 132 135 146 148 149 154 **S** McLaren Health Care Corporation, Grand Blanc, MI
Primary Contact: David M. Zechman, FACHE, President and Chief Executive Officer
CFO: David Bellamy, Chief Financial Officer
CMO: Kirk Lufkin, M.D., VPMA
CIO: David Bellamy, Chief Financial Officer
CHR: Gene Kaminski, Vice President Human Resources and Hospitality Services
CNO: Jennifer Woods, R.N., MSN, Chief Nursing Officer
Web address: www.northernhealth.org
Control: Other not–for–profit (including NFP Corporation) **Service**: General medical and surgical

Staffed Beds: 188 Admissions: 10000 Census: 111 Outpatient Visits: 194813 Births: 579 Total Expense ($000): 242575 Payroll Expense ($000): 80867 Personnel: 1296

PIGEON—Huron County

✠ **SCHEURER HOSPITAL (231310)**, 170 North Caseville Road, Zip 48755–9781; tel. 989/453–3223, (Total facility includes 19 beds in nursing home–type unit) **A**1 5 10 18 **F**3 7 8 10 11 15 28 29 30 31 32 34 35 40 44 45 50 53 54 56 57 59 64 65 68 69 75 77 78 79 81 85 86 87 91 93 97 107 108 110 115 119 125 127 130 131 132 133 134 144 146 149 **P**6
Primary Contact: Terrance Lerash, President and Chief Executive Officer
CFO: Terry Lutz, Chief Financial Officer
CMO: Ross Ramsey, M.D., Chief of Staff
CIO: Carleen Giddings, Information Technology System Leader
CHR: Gregory S. Foy, Human Resources System Leader
CNO: Kendra Kretzschmer, Patient Care System Leader
Web address: www.scheurer.org
Control: Other not–for–profit (including NFP Corporation) **Service**: General medical and surgical

Staffed Beds: 44 Admissions: 433 Census: 28 Outpatient Visits: 42257 Births: 0 Total Expense ($000): 42210 Payroll Expense ($000): 20498 Personnel: 352

PONTIAC—Oakland County

☐ **DOCTORS' HOSPITAL OF MICHIGAN (230013)**, 461 West Huron Street, Zip 48341–1601; tel. 248/857–7200, (Nonreporting) **A**1 10
Primary Contact: Robert Barrow, Chief Executive Officer
COO: Dennis Franks, Vice President Operations
CFO: Dennis Franks, Interim Chief Financial Officer
CMO: Ray Breitenbach, M.D., Chief of Staff
CIO: Albert Sinisi, Director Information Systems
Web address: www.dhofm.com
Control: Other not–for–profit (including NFP Corporation) **Service**: General medical and surgical

Staffed Beds: 106

☐ **MCLAREN OAKLAND (230207)**, 50 North Perry Street, Zip 48342–2253; tel. 248/338–5000, (Total facility includes 120 beds in nursing home–type unit) **A**1 2 3 10 12 13 **F**3 4 7 8 11 12 14 15 18 20 24 26 28 29 30 31 32 33 34 35 36 40 43 44 45 50 53 54 57 59 62 63 64 65 66 68 70 74 75 77 78 79 81 82 85 90 92 93 94 98 103 107 108 111 114 118 119 124 126 128 129 130 131 132 135 136 137 138 139 140 141 142 143 144 146 148 149 **P**4 8 **S** McLaren Health Care Corporation, Grand Blanc, MI
Primary Contact: Margaret Dimond, Ph.D., President and Chief Executive Officer
COO: Nicholle Mehr, Vice President Operations
CFO: Lynn Marcotte, Chief Financial Officer
CMO: Steven Calkin, D.O., Vice President Medical Affairs
CIO: Kelly Finley, Customer Site Executive
CHR: Dwan Cosby, Manager Human Resources
CNO: Calandra Anderson, Vice President Patient Care and Chief Nursing Officer
Web address: www.mclaren.org/oakland
Control: Other not–for–profit (including NFP Corporation) **Service**: General medical and surgical

Staffed Beds: 263 Admissions: 5704 Census: 198 Outpatient Visits: 180421 Births: 0 Total Expense ($000): 183967 Payroll Expense ($000): 73014 Personnel: 1244

PIONEER SPECIALTY HOSPITAL (230304), 50 North Perry Street, 6th Floor, Zip 48342–2217; tel. 248/338–5430, (Nonreporting)
Primary Contact: Denise Wayne, Chief Executive Officer
Web address: www.pioneerspecialtyhospital.com
Control: Individual, Investor–owned (for–profit) **Service**: Acute long–term care hospital

Staffed Beds: 30

⊞ **SELECT SPECIALTY HOSPITAL–PONTIAC (232030)**, 44405 Woodward Avenue, 8th Floor, Zip 48341–5023; tel. 248/452–5252, (Nonreporting) **A**1 10 **S** Select Medical Corporation, Mechanicsburg, PA
Primary Contact: Peggy Kingston, Chief Executive Officer
CMO: Fadi Salloum, M.D., Medical Director
CNO: Cathy Boyd, Chief Nursing Officer
Web address: www.selectspecialtyhospitals.com/company/locations/pontiac.aspx
Control: Corporation, Investor–owned (for–profit) **Service**: Acute long–term care hospital

Staffed Beds: 30

⊞ **ST. JOSEPH MERCY OAKLAND (230029)**, 44405 Woodward Avenue, Zip 48341–5023; tel. 248/858–3000, **A**1 2 3 5 10 13 **F**3 8 11 12 13 15 17 18 20 22 24 26 28 29 30 31 34 35 36 39 40 41 43 44 45 46 48 49 50 53 54 55 56 57 58 59 61 64 65 66 68 70 72 74 75 76 77 78 79 81 82 84 85 86 87 89 90 93 94 96 97 98 100 102 105 107 108 110 111 114 115 119 126 130 131 132 135 144 146 147 148 149 150 154 **P**6 **S** Trinity Health, Livonia, MI
Primary Contact: Shannon Striebich, Chief Executive Officer
CFO: Michael Gusho, Chief Financial Officer
CMO: Fabian Fregoli, M.D., Chief Medical Officer
CIO: Robert Jones, Director Management Information Systems
CHR: Ane McNeil, Vice President Human Resources
CNO: Douglas R Dascenzo, MSN, R.N., Chief Nursing Officer
Web address: www.stjoesoakland.com
Control: Church operated, Nongovernment, not–for–profit **Service**: General medical and surgical

Staffed Beds: 411 Admissions: 19911 Census: 267 Outpatient Visits: 376491 Births: 1794 Total Expense ($000): 425245 Payroll Expense ($000): 166556 Personnel: 2601

PORT HURON—St. Clair County

⊞ **LAKE HURON MEDICAL CENTER (230031)**, 2601 Electric Avenue, Zip 48060–6518; tel. 810/985–1500, **A**1 2 10 **F**3 12 15 18 20 28 29 30 31 34 35 37 40 45 49 50 54 55 57 58 59 61 64 66 70 74 75 77 78 79 81 82 85 86 87 90 91 93 96 97 107 108 110 114 118 119 120 121 123 130 131 132 135 144 146 147 148 149 154 **P**6 8 **S** Prime Healthcare, Ontario, CA
Primary Contact: Jay De los Reyes, Chief Executive Officer
COO: Ken Sanger, R.N., Chief Nursing Officer and Chief Operations Officer
CFO: Chris Fulks, Vice President Finance
CMO: Sridhar Reddy, M.D., Chief Medical Officer
CIO: Jefferey Wagner, Director, Information Technology
CHR: Debra A Seifert, Director Human Resources
CNO: Ken Sanger, R.N., Chief Nursing Officer and Chief Operations Officer
Web address: www.mymercy.us
Control: Corporation, Investor–owned (for–profit) **Service**: General medical and surgical

Staffed Beds: 119 Admissions: 3743 Census: 37 Outpatient Visits: 96500 Births: 0 Total Expense ($000): 73247 Payroll Expense ($000): 24533 Personnel: 555

⊞ **MCLAREN PORT HURON (230216)**, 1221 Pine Grove Avenue, Zip 48060–3511; tel. 810/987–5000, **A**1 2 10 **F**1 3 4 5 11 12 13 15 16 17 18 20 22 24 26 28 29 30 31 32 34 35 36 39 40 43 44 45 46 48 49 50 51 54 56 57 58 59 61 64 65 66 67 68 70 71 72 73 74 75 76 77 78 79 80 81 82 84 85 86 87 88 89 90 92 93 94 96 97 98 99 100 101 102 103 104 107 108 110 111 114 115 116 117 118 119 120 121 126 128 129 130 131 132 134 135 144 145 146 147 148 149 153 154 **P**6 **S** McLaren Health Care Corporation, Grand Blanc, MI
Primary Contact: Jennifer Montgomery, FACHE, R.N., President and Chief Executive Officer
COO: John Liston, Chief Operating Officer
CFO: Bridget Sholtis, Chief Financial Officer
CMO: Michael W Tawney, D.O., Vice President Medical Affairs
CIO: John McGrath, Chief Information Officer
CHR: Doris A Seidl, Vice President Human Resources
CNO: Christine R Sansom, Chief Nursing Officer
Web address: www.porthuronhospital.org
Control: Other not–for–profit (including NFP Corporation) **Service**: General medical and surgical

Staffed Beds: 186 Admissions: 12175 Census: 126 Outpatient Visits: 220686 Births: 932 Total Expense ($000): 195276 Payroll Expense ($000): 82600 Personnel: 1138

REED CITY—Osceola County

⊞ **SPECTRUM HEALTH REED CITY HOSPITAL (231323)**, 300 North Patterson Road, Zip 49677–8041, Mailing Address: P.O. Box 75, Zip 49677–0075; tel. 231/832–3271, (Total facility includes 50 beds in nursing home–type unit) **A**1 5 10 18 **F**3 8 15 28 29 30 31 34 35 36 40 45 50 53 54 57 59 64 65 75 78 81 85 86 87 91 93 97 107 108 110 115 118 119 120 121 123 124 127 128 129 130 132 133 135 144 146 149 154 **S** Spectrum Health, Grand Rapids, MI
Primary Contact: Mary Kay VanDriel, President
COO: Cathy Rybicki, Chief Operating Officer
CFO: Thomas Knoerl, Vice President Finance
CMO: Thomas Campana, M.D., Chief of Staff
CIO: Brandi Johnson, Site Manager Technology Information Systems
CHR: Kris Miller, Senior Human Resources Business Partner
Web address: www.spectrumhealth.org/reedcity
Control: Other not–for–profit (including NFP Corporation) **Service**: General medical and surgical

Staffed Beds: 72 Admissions: 844 Census: 54 Outpatient Visits: 316196 Births: 0 Total Expense ($000): 56959 Payroll Expense ($000): 17996 Personnel: 292

ROCHESTER—Oakland County

⊞ △ **ASCENSION CRITTENTON HOSPITAL MEDICAL CENTER (230254)**, 1101 West University Drive, Zip 48307–1831; tel. 248/652–5000, **A**1 3 5 7 10 **F**3 8 13 15 17 18 20 22 24 26 28 29 30 34 35 36 38 40 43 44 48 49 50 51 53 54 56 57 58 59 64 65 66 68 70 73 74 75 76 77 79 81 85 86 87 90 93 97 98 100 107 108 110 111 114 115 119 126 129 130 131 132 134 135 143 146 147 148 149 154 **S** Ascension Healthcare, Saint Louis, MO
Primary Contact: Chris Palazzolo, President and Chief Executive Officer
COO: Tomasine Marx, Chief Financial Officer and Chief Operating Officer
CFO: Tomasine Marx, Chief Financial Officer and Chief Operating Officer
CMO: Sheryl Wissman, M.D., Chief Medical Officer
CIO: Ralph Tenney, Chief Information Officer
CHR: Ann Vano, Vice President, Human Resources
Web address: www.crittenton.com
Control: Other not–for–profit (including NFP Corporation) **Service**: General medical and surgical

Staffed Beds: 226 Admissions: 10116 Census: 124 Outpatient Visits: 157686 Births: 636 Total Expense ($000): 196087 Payroll Expense ($000): 75335 Personnel: 1122

Hospital, Medicare Provider Number, Address, Telephone, Approval, Facility, and Physician Codes, Health Care System

★ American Hospital Association (AHA) membership
☐ The Joint Commission accreditation
○ Healthcare Facilities Accreditation Program
◇ DNV Healthcare Inc. accreditation
⇑ Center for Improvement in Healthcare Quality Accreditation
△ Commission on Accreditation of Rehabilitation Facilities (CARF) accreditation

ROMEO—Macomb County

ST. JOSEPH'S MERCY–NORTH See Henry Ford Macomb Hospitals, Clinton Township

ROYAL OAK—Oakland County

✠ **BEAUMONT HOSPITAL – ROYAL OAK (230130)**, 3601 West Thirteen Mile Road, Zip 48073–6712; tel. 248/898–5000, (Includes BEAUMONT CHILDREN'S HOSPITAL, 3601 West 13 Mile Road, Royal Oak, MI, Zip 48073–6712; tel. 248/898–5000) **A**1 2 3 5 8 10 **F**3 6 7 8 11 12 13 15 17 18 19 20 22 24 26 28 29 30 31 32 34 35 36 37 38 39 40 41 43 44 45 46 47 48 49 50 51 54 55 56 57 58 59 60 61 62 63 64 65 66 68 70 71 72 74 75 76 77 78 79 80 81 82 83 84 85 86 87 88 89 90 91 92 93 94 95 96 97 98 100 101 102 103 104 105 107 108 109 110 111 114 115 116 117 118 119 120 121 122 123 124 126 129 130 131 132 134 135 138 139 141 142 143 144 145 146 147 148 149 150 **P**6 **S** Beaumont Health, Southfield, MI
Primary Contact: Rosanna Morris, R.N., President Royal Oak Hospital
COO: Carolyn Wilson, R.N., Chief Operating Officer
CFO: John Kerndl, Executive Vice President and Chief Financial Officer
CMO: Leslie Rocher, Senior Vice President and Chief Medical Officer
CIO: Subra Sripada, Executive Vice President, Chief Transportation Officer and Chief Information Officer
CHR: Michael L Dixon, Vice President, Human Resources
CNO: Maureen Bowman, Vice President and Chief Nursing Officer
Web address: www.beaumont.org
Control: Other not–for–profit (including NFP Corporation) **Service:** General medical and surgical

Staffed Beds: 1100 **Admissions:** 59419 **Census:** 862 **Outpatient Visits:** 1565405 **Births:** 6749 **Total Expense ($000):** 1298302 **Payroll Expense ($000):** 492075 **Personnel:** 8811

SAGINAW—Saginaw County

✠ **ALEDA E. LUTZ VETERANS AFFAIRS MEDICAL CENTER**, 1500 Weiss Street, Zip 48602–5298; tel. 989/497–2500, (Total facility includes 81 beds in nursing home–type unit) **A**1 3 **F**3 5 8 11 12 15 18 29 30 31 34 35 36 38 39 44 45 50 53 54 56 57 58 59 61 63 64 68 74 75 77 78 81 82 83 84 85 86 87 93 94 97 100 101 102 103 104 107 108 119 127 128 130 131 132 133 135 136 137 138 139 140 141 142 143 144 146 147 148 149 154 **P**6 **S** Department of Veterans Affairs, Perry Point, MD
Primary Contact: Karandeep Sraon, Interim Director
COO: Stephanie Young, Associate Director
CFO: Jeff Drew, Fiscal Officer
CMO: Gregory Movsesian, M.D., Acting Chief of Staff
CIO: Angie Schmus, Chief Information Technology
CHR: Thomas Stredney, Chief Human Resources Management Service
CNO: Penny Holland, Associate Director for Patient Care Services
Web address: www.saginaw.va.gov/
Control: Veterans Affairs, Government, federal **Service:** General medical and surgical

Staffed Beds: 89 **Admissions:** 991 **Census:** 37 **Outpatient Visits:** 422850 **Births:** 0 **Total Expense ($000):** 225198 **Payroll Expense ($000):** 88360 **Personnel:** 1203

★ ○ △ **COVENANT HEALTHCARE (230070)**, 1447 North Harrison Street, Zip 48602–4727; tel. 989/583–0000, (Includes COVENANT MEDICAL CENTER–COOPER, 700 Cooper Avenue, Saginaw, MI, Zip 48602–5399; tel. 989/583–0000; Edward Bruff, President and Chief Executive Officer; COVENANT MEDICAL CENTER–HARRISON, 1447 North Harrison Street, Saginaw, MI, Zip 48602–4785; tel. 989/583–0000; Edward Bruff, President and Chief Executive Officer) (Total facility includes 20 beds in nursing home–type unit) **A**2 3 5 7 10 11 **F**3 8 11 12 13 15 17 18 19 20 22 24 25 26 27 28 29 30 31 35 36 40 41 43 45 46 47 48 49 50 54 57 58 59 60 61 62 63 64 65 70 72 74 75 76 77 78 79 81 82 83 84 86 87 88 89 90 91 92 93 94 97 107 108 110 111 113 114 115 118 119 120 121 123 124 126 128 129 130 131 132 135 143 144 146 147 148 154 **P**7 8
Primary Contact: Edward Bruff, President and Chief Executive Officer
COO: Daniel M George, Executive Vice President, Operations
CFO: Kevin Albosta, Vice President, Chief Financial Officer
CMO: John Kosanovich, M.D., Executive Vice President Physician Enterprise and Chief Executive Officer, Covenant Medical Group
CHR: Kevin Birchmeier, Director Human Resources
CNO: Beth Charlton, Vice President Patient Services and Chief Nursing Officer
Web address: www.covenanthealthcare.com
Control: Other not–for–profit (including NFP Corporation) **Service:** General medical and surgical

Staffed Beds: 530 **Admissions:** 27445 **Census:** 404 **Outpatient Visits:** 445559 **Births:** 2984 **Total Expense ($000):** 596392 **Payroll Expense ($000):** 270413 **Personnel:** 4328

☐ **HEALTHSOURCE SAGINAW, INC. (230275)**, 3340 Hospital Road, Zip 48603–9622; tel. 989/790–7700, (Total facility includes 213 beds in nursing home–type unit) **A**1 3 5 10 **F**4 5 64 90 91 93 96 98 99 100 101 104 128 130 143 146
Primary Contact: Lisa Lapham, President and Chief Executive Officer
CFO: Glen Chipman, Chief Financial Officer
CMO: Daniel Duffy, D.O., Chief Medical Director
CIO: Greg Sieg, Director Information Technology
CHR: Krystal Hadaway, Director Human Resources
CNO: Susan Graham, R.N., Nurse Executive
Web address: www.healthsourcesaginaw.org
Control: Other not–for–profit (including NFP Corporation) **Service:** Psychiatric

Staffed Beds: 343 **Admissions:** 4329 **Census:** 282 **Outpatient Visits:** 11187 **Births:** 0 **Total Expense ($000):** 50990 **Payroll Expense ($000):** 24131 **Personnel:** 494

✠ **SELECT SPECIALTY HOSPITAL–SAGINAW (232033)**, 1447 North Harrison Street, 8th Floor, Zip 48602–4785; tel. 989/583–4235, (Nonreporting) **A**1 10 **S** Select Medical Corporation, Mechanicsburg, PA
Primary Contact: Matthew J. Campbell Esq, Chief Executive Officer
CNO: Shannon Sequin, MSN, Chief Nursing Officer
Web address: www.selectspecialtyhospitals.com/company/locations/saginaw.aspx
Control: Corporation, Investor–owned (for–profit) **Service:** Acute long–term care hospital

Staffed Beds: 32

✠ **ST. MARY'S OF MICHIGAN (230077)**, 800 South Washington Avenue, Zip 48601–2594; tel. 989/907–8000, **A**1 2 3 5 10 **F**2 3 11 12 15 17 18 20 22 24 26 28 29 30 31 34 35 40 43 44 45 49 50 54 57 58 59 64 66 68 70 74 77 78 79 80 81 82 84 85 86 87 92 93 96 97 100 102 107 108 110 111 114 115 118 119 120 121 123 124 126 128 129 130 131 132 133 135 146 149 154 **P**6 8 **S** Ascension Healthcare, Saint Louis, MO
Primary Contact: Chris Palazzolo, Health System President and Chief Executive Officer Mid–Michigan
CFO: Nancy Haywood, Chief Financial Officer
CMO: Raghu Sarvepalli, M.D., Vice President of Medical Affairs
CIO: Daniel Stross, Chief Information Officer
CHR: Paula Coffee, Director Human Resources
CNO: Bernie Jore, Chief Nursing Officer
Web address: www.stmarysofmichigan.org
Control: Church operated, Nongovernment, not–for–profit **Service:** General medical and surgical

Staffed Beds: 286 **Admissions:** 11247 **Census:** 167 **Outpatient Visits:** 241345 **Births:** 0 **Total Expense ($000):** 291390 **Payroll Expense ($000):** 110429 **Personnel:** 1587

SAINT IGNACE—Mackinac County

★ ⇑ **MACKINAC STRAITS HEALTH SYSTEM, INC. (231306)**, 1140 North State Street, Zip 49781–1048; tel. 906/643–8585, (Total facility includes 48 beds in nursing home–type unit) **A**10 18 21 **F**3 8 15 28 29 31 40 45 51 54 56 59 64 65 74 75 77 78 79 81 91 93 97 107 110 111 114 119 127 128 130 133 135 146 147 148
Primary Contact: Karen Cheeseman, Chief Executive Officer
CFO: Jason Anderson, Chief Financial Officer
CMO: Edward Smith, Chief of Staff
CHR: Kevin McElroy, Chief Human Resources Officer
CNO: Mary Kaye Ruegg, Chief Nursing Officer
Web address: www.mackinacstraitshealth.org
Control: Other not–for–profit (including NFP Corporation) **Service:** General medical and surgical

Staffed Beds: 63 **Admissions:** 471 **Census:** 53 **Outpatient Visits:** 35873 **Births:** 0 **Total Expense ($000):** 39955 **Payroll Expense ($000):** 13746 **Personnel:** 185

SAINT JOHNS—Clinton County

✠ **SPARROW CLINTON HOSPITAL (231326)**, 805 South Oakland Street, Zip 48879–2253; tel. 989/227–3400, **A**1 10 18 **F**3 11 15 18 31 32 34 35 40 43 45 50 53 57 59 64 68 70 75 77 78 79 81 85 93 107 108 110 111 115 119 129 130 131 133 146 148 149 **P**6 **S** Sparrow Health System, Lansing, MI
Primary Contact: Edward Bruun, President and Chief Executive Officer
COO: Kevin A Price, Vice President and Chief Operating Officer
CFO: Mark Brisboe, VP and Chief Financial Officer
CMO: Christopher Beal, M.D., Chief of Staff
CNO: Beth Ann Daugherty, R.N., M.P.H., Vice President Care Services and Chief Nursing Executive
Web address: www.sparrowclinton.org
Control: Other not–for–profit (including NFP Corporation) **Service:** General medical and surgical

Staffed Beds: 25 **Admissions:** 685 **Census:** 6 **Outpatient Visits:** 91646 **Births:** 0 **Total Expense ($000):** 41632 **Payroll Expense ($000):** 16789 **Personnel:** 217

Many Facility Codes have changed. Please refer to the AHA Guide Code Chart.
© 2018 AHA Guide

SAINT JOSEPH—Berrien County

☒ **LAKELAND MEDICAL CENTER, ST. JOSEPH (230021)**, 1234 Napier Avenue, Zip 49085–2158; tel. 269/983–8300, (Includes LAKELAND HOSPITAL, NILES, 31 North Saint Joseph Avenue, Niles, MI, Zip 49120; tel. 269/683–5510; Debra Johnson, R.N., Chief Administrator) **A**1 2 3 10 13 **F**70 76 90 98 **S** Lakeland Health, Saint Joseph, MI
Primary Contact: Loren Hamel, M.D., President and Chief Executive Officer
CFO: Timothy Calhoun, Vice President Finance and Chief Financial Officer
CMO: Stephen Hempel, M.D., President Medical Staff
CIO: Emily Gallay, Vice President and Chief Information Officer
Web address: www.lakelandhealth.org
Control: Other not–for–profit (including NFP Corporation) **Service:** General medical and surgical

Staffed Beds: 300 Admissions: 12064 Census: 135 Births: 1726

SALINE—Washtenaw County

☐ **CENTER FOR FORENSIC PSYCHIATRY (234041)**, 8303 Platt Rd, Zip 48176–9773, Mailing Address: P.O. Box 2060, Ann Arbor, Zip 48106–2060; tel. 734/429–2531, (Nonreporting) **A**1 3 10
Primary Contact: Diane Heisel, Acting Director
Web address: www.michigan.gov
Control: County, Government, nonfederal **Service:** Psychiatric

Staffed Beds: 210

SANDUSKY—Sanilac County

MCKENZIE HEALTH SYSTEM (231314), 120 North Delaware Street, Zip 48471–1087; tel. 810/648–3770, (Nonreporting) **A**10 18
Primary Contact: Steve Barnett, President and Chief Executive Officer
COO: Billi Jo Hennika, Vice President Operations
CFO: Amy Ruedisueli, Vice President of Finance
CMO: James C. Sams, Chief of Staff
CHR: Carrie Krampits, Director Human Resources
CNO: Patricia Schafsnitz, Director of Nursing Services
Web address: www.mckenziehealth.org
Control: Other not–for–profit (including NFP Corporation) **Service:** General medical and surgical

Staffed Beds: 25

SAULT SAINTE MARIE—Chippewa County

★ ⇧ **WAR MEMORIAL HOSPITAL (230239)**, 500 Osborn Boulevard, Zip 49783–1884; tel. 906/635–4460, (Total facility includes 51 beds in nursing home–type unit) **A**5 10 20 21 **F**3 11 12 13 15 18 28 29 30 31 34 35 36 38 40 43 44 50 51 53 54 56 57 59 62 65 66 68 70 74 75 76 77 78 79 81 82 85 87 92 93 96 97 98 100 101 103 104 106 107 108 110 111 115 119 126 127 128 129 130 131 132 133 135 143 144 146 147 148 154 **P**6
Primary Contact: David B. Jahn, President and Chief Executive Officer
COO: Marla Bunker, Vice President Nursing and Chief Operating Officer
CFO: Kevin Kalchik, Chief Financial Officer
CMO: Paula Rechner, M.D., Chief Medical Officer
CIO: Sandy DePlonty, Senior Director Clinical Services
CHR: Susan Sliger, Director Human Resources
CNO: Marla Bunker, Vice President Nursing and Chief Operating Officer
Web address: www.warmemorialhospital.org
Control: Other not–for–profit (including NFP Corporation) **Service:** General medical and surgical

Staffed Beds: 133 Admissions: 3198 Census: 86 Outpatient Visits: 183123 Births: 321 Total Expense ($000): 110763 Payroll Expense ($000): 49046 Personnel: 871

SHELBY—Oceana County

☒ **MERCY HEALTH, LAKESHORE CAMPUS (231320)**, 72 South State Street, Zip 49455–1299; tel. 231/861–2156, **A**1 10 18 **F**3 11 15 29 30 34 35 40 45 47 50 57 59 68 81 83 84 85 87 89 97 107 110 111 114 119 127 129 131 132 146 **S** Trinity Health, Livonia, MI
Primary Contact: Jay Bryan, President and Chief Executive Officer
CFO: Mark Gross, Senior Business Director Finance
Web address: www.mercyhealthmuskegon.com
Control: Other not–for–profit (including NFP Corporation) **Service:** General medical and surgical

Staffed Beds: 24 Admissions: 283 Census: 3 Outpatient Visits: 94270 Births: 0 Total Expense ($000): 27919 Payroll Expense ($000): 13350 Personnel: 207

SHERIDAN—Montcalm County

SHERIDAN COMMUNITY HOSPITAL (231312), 301 North Main Street, Zip 48884–9235, Mailing Address: P.O. Box 279, Zip 48884–0279; tel. 989/291–3261, **A**5 10 18 **F**1 15 18 34 40 45 50 54 57 59 64 65 66 77 79 81 85 89 90 93 97 107 115 119 127 129 132 133 146
Primary Contact: Randolph K. Flechsig, Administrator
COO: Steve Scott, Chief Operating Officer
CFO: Randolph K Flechsig, Administrator
CMO: Maria Charlotte Alvarez, M.D., Chief of Staff
CIO: David Bussler, Chief Information Officer
CHR: Sharon Bowers, R.N., Manager of Community, Public and Employee Relations
CNO: Kim Christensen, Interim Chief Nursing Executive
Web address: www.sheridanhospital.com
Control: Other not–for–profit (including NFP Corporation) **Service:** General medical and surgical

Staffed Beds: 22 Admissions: 132 Census: 1

SOUTH HAVEN—Van Buren County

☒ **BRONSON SOUTH HAVEN HOSPITAL (230085)**, 955 South Bailey Avenue, Zip 49090–6743; tel. 269/637–5271, **A**1 10 **F**3 11 15 18 28 29 30 31 34 35 36 39 40 45 50 53 54 57 59 62 65 68 70 75 77 78 79 81 82 84 85 86 87 89 93 97 107 110 111 114 115 117 118 119 127 129 130 131 132 135 144 146 147 148 149 **P**6 **S** Bronson Healthcare Group, Kalamazoo, MI
Primary Contact: Kirk Richardson, R.N., Vice President, Chief Operating Officer and Chief Nursing Officer
CFO: Mark Gross, Executive Vice President and Chief Financial Officer
CMO: Allan Caudill, M.D., Chief of Staff
CIO: Dennis Sorenson, Supervisor Information Technology
CHR: Kim Wise, Director Human Resources
CNO: Donna Cassidy, Chief Nursing Executive
Web address: www.sh–hs.org
Control: Other not–for–profit (including NFP Corporation) **Service:** General medical and surgical

Staffed Beds: 49 Admissions: 594 Census: 4 Outpatient Visits: 85506 Births: 0 Total Expense ($000): 38909 Payroll Expense ($000): 20031 Personnel: 251

SOUTH HAVEN COMMUNITY HOSPITAL See Bronson South Haven Hospital

SOUTHFIELD—Oakland County

★ ○ **OAKLAND REGIONAL HOSPITAL (230301)**, 22401 Foster Winter Drive, Zip 48075–3724; tel. 248/423–5100, **A**10 11 **F**12 45 64 79 81 82 85 87 90 93 111 115 119 128 130 149
Primary Contact: Steven Craig, Ph.D., Chief Operating Officer and Acting Chief Executive Officer
COO: Steven Craig, Ph.D., Chief Operating Officer and Acting Chief Executive Officer
CMO: John Jack Ryan, M.D., Chief Medical Officer
CIO: William Moncrief, ORH IT Client Executive
CHR: Gordon Meyer, Director Human Resources
CNO: Lola Evans, Director of Nursing
Web address: www.oaklandregionalhospital.com
Control: Corporation, Investor–owned (for–profit) **Service:** General medical and surgical

Staffed Beds: 71 Admissions: 813 Census: 22 Outpatient Visits: 13080 Births: 0 Total Expense ($000): 30234 Payroll Expense ($000): 8419 Personnel: 162

☒ **PROVIDENCE–PROVIDENCE PARK HOSPITALS (230019)**, 16001 West Nine Mile Road, Zip 48075; tel. 248/849–3400, (Includes PROVIDENCE – PROVIDENCE PARK HOSPITAL, NOVI CAMPUS, 47601 Grand River Avebue, Novi, MI, Zip 48374–1233; tel. 248/465–4100; Joseph R Hurshe, President) **A**1 2 3 5 10 **F**3 4 9 11 12 13 15 17 18 20 22 24 26 28 29 30 31 34 35 36 39 40 43 44 45 46 47 48 49 50 51 54 55 56 57 58 59 60 61 63 64 65 66 68 70 72 74 75 76 77 78 79 80 81 82 84 85 86 87 88 89 90 92 93 96 97 98 100 101 102 105 107 108 110 111 114 115 118 119 120 121 123 124 126 129 130 131 132 135 141 146 147 148 149 150 154 **P**8 **S** Ascension Healthcare, Saint Louis, MO
Primary Contact: Joseph R. Hurshe, President
CFO: Douglas Winner, Chief Financial Officer, Acute Care Operations
CHR: Ann Vano, Vice President Human Resources
Web address: www.https://ascension.org/michigan
Control: Church operated, Nongovernment, not–for–profit **Service:** General medical and surgical

Staffed Beds: 635 Admissions: 32704 Census: 398 Outpatient Visits: 320664 Births: 3616 Total Expense ($000): 687794 Payroll Expense ($000): 239540 Personnel: 2944

MI

Hospital, Medicare Provider Number, Address, Telephone, Approval, Facility, and Physician Codes, Health Care System

★ American Hospital Association (AHA) membership   ○ Healthcare Facilities Accreditation Program   ⇧ Center for Improvement in Healthcare Quality Accreditation
☐ The Joint Commission accreditation   ◇ DNV Healthcare Inc. accreditation   △ Commission on Accreditation of Rehabilitation Facilities (CARF) accreditation

⊞ **STRAITH HOSPITAL FOR SPECIAL SURGERY (230071)**, 23901 Lahser Road, Zip 48033–6035; tel. 248/357–3360, (Nonreporting) **A**1 10
Primary Contact: Jan Rys, R.N., Chief Executive Officer
CFO: Bradley Bescoe, Chief Financial Officer
CNO: Michelle Holder, Nurse Executive
Web address: www.straith.org/
Control: Other not–for–profit (including NFP Corporation) **Service:** Surgical

Staffed Beds: 24

STANDISH—Arenac County

⊞ **ST. MARY'S OF MICHIGAN STANDISH HOSPITAL (231305)**, 805 West Cedar Street, Zip 48658–9526; tel. 989/846–4521, (Nonreporting) **A**1 5 10 18 **S** Ascension Healthcare, Saint Louis, MO
Primary Contact: Chris Palazzolo, President and Chief Executive Officer
CFO: Tony Doud, Controller
CMO: Jaya Sankaran, M.D., Chief of Staff
CIO: Tammy Copes, Director Information Systems
CHR: Renee Reetz, Director Human Resources
Web address: www.stmarysofmichigan.org/standish
Control: Other not–for–profit (including NFP Corporation) **Service:** General medical and surgical

Staffed Beds: 25

STURGIS—St. Joseph County

★ ⇑ **STURGIS HOSPITAL (230096)**, 916 Myrtle Street, Zip 49091–2326; tel. 269/651–7824, **A**10 21 **F**3 11 13 15 28 29 30 31 34 35 40 45 49 50 57 59 62 63 64 65 68 70 75 76 77 79 81 82 85 87 89 93 97 102 107 108 110 115 118 119 127 129 130 132 144 145 146 147 148 149 154 **P**6 **S** QHR, Brentwood, TN
Primary Contact: Robert J. LaBarge, President and Chief Executive Officer
CFO: Robert J. Morin, Vice President Finance and Chief Financial Officer
CMO: James Grannell, Chief Medical Officer
CIO: Rita Denison, Director of Information Systems
CHR: Mary Kay Schultz, Director Human Resources
CNO: Charlotte J Pavilanis, R.N., Vice President of Clinical Services and Chief Nursing Officer
Web address: www.sturgishospital.com
Control: Other not–for–profit (including NFP Corporation) **Service:** General medical and surgical

Staffed Beds: 49 Admissions: 1469 Census: 11 Outpatient Visits: 160544 Births: 322 Total Expense ($000): 51000 Payroll Expense ($000): 22646 Personnel: 304

TAWAS CITY—Iosco County

⊞ **ST. JOSEPH HEALTH SYSTEM (230100)**, 200 Hemlock Street, Zip 48763–9237, Mailing Address: P.O. Box 659, Zip 48764–0659; tel. 989/362–3411, (Nonreporting) **A**1 10 20 **S** Ascension Healthcare, Saint Louis, MO
Primary Contact: Jan Jacob, R.N., Interim Administrator
CFO: Tony Doud, Controller
CIO: Daniel Stross, Chief Information Officer
CHR: Nancy Bodenner, Director Human Resources
Web address: www.sjhsys.org
Control: Other not–for–profit (including NFP Corporation) **Service:** General medical and surgical

Staffed Beds: 20

TAYLOR—Wayne County

⊞ **BEAUMONT HOSPITAL – TAYLOR (230270)**, 10000 Telegraph Road, Zip 48180–3330; tel. 313/295–5000, **A**1 3 5 10 **F**3 11 15 29 30 34 35 37 38 39 40 44 46 49 50 56 57 59 61 64 65 68 70 74 75 79 81 82 85 86 87 90 92 93 96 98 100 101 102 104 105 107 108 111 114 117 118 119 130 131 132 135 146 148 149 152 **P**6 **S** Beaumont Health, Southfield, MI
Primary Contact: Lee Ann Odom, Division President
COO: Carolyn Wilson, R.N., Chief Operating Officer
CFO: Mark Deming, Administrator, Finance and Support
CMO: Kassem Charara, Chief Medical Officer
CIO: Subra Sripada, Exec. Vice President, Chief Transformation Officer and Chief Information Officer
CHR: Karen Krolicki, Director, Human Resources
CNO: Kristine Marie Donahue, Administrator, Clinical Operations
Web address: www.beaumont.org
Control: Other not–for–profit (including NFP Corporation) **Service:** General medical and surgical

Staffed Beds: 189 Admissions: 7336 Census: 122 Outpatient Visits: 79221 Births: 0 Total Expense ($000): 134268 Payroll Expense ($000): 60682 Personnel: 1012

TECUMSEH—Lenawee County

★ **PROMEDICA HERRICK HOSPITAL (231334)**, 500 East Pottawatamie Street, Zip 49286–2018; tel. 517/424–3000, **A**10 18 **F**8 11 15 18 26 29 34 35 36 39 40 50 53 57 59 65 68 75 77 81 82 87 91 92 93 96 97 104 107 108 110 114 119 129 130 132 135 146 147 148 149 154 **P**8 **S** ProMedica Health System, Toledo, OH
Primary Contact: Julie Yaroch, D.O., President
CFO: Bernie Nawrocki, Administrative Director Finance
CIO: Stephanie Sonnenberg, Director Information Technology
CHR: Kim Langley, Business Partner
CNO: Kathryn M Greenlee, R.N., Vice President, Clinical Services/CNO
Web address: www.promedica.org
Control: Other not–for–profit (including NFP Corporation) **Service:** General medical and surgical

Staffed Beds: 25 Admissions: 248 Census: 3 Outpatient Visits: 39325 Births: 0 Total Expense ($000): 27996 Payroll Expense ($000): 6773 Personnel: 79

THREE RIVERS—St. Joseph County

★ ○ △ **THREE RIVERS HEALTH (230015)**, 701 South Health Parkway, Zip 49093–8352; tel. 269/278–1145, **A**7 10 11 **F**3 13 15 50 62 63 65 70 71 75 76 77 80 90 107 111 119 129 130 131 147 **S** QHR, Brentwood, TN
Primary Contact: David A. Shannon, Interim Chief Executive Officer
COO: Laurie Herbert, Vice President Operations
CFO: Steve Andrews, Chief Financial Officer
CIO: Dave Parks, Chief Information Officer
Web address: www.threerivershealth.org
Control: Other not–for–profit (including NFP Corporation) **Service:** General medical and surgical

Staffed Beds: 60 Admissions: 1088 Census: 11 Outpatient Visits: 149969 Births: 181 Total Expense ($000): 58731 Payroll Expense ($000): 21303

TRAVERSE CITY—Grand Traverse County

⊞ **MUNSON MEDICAL CENTER (230097)**, 1105 Sixth Street, Zip 49684–2386; tel. 231/935–5000, **A**1 2 3 5 10 13 **F**2 4 10 15 17 28 34 35 39 40 43 44 45 47 48 49 50 53 54 55 56 57 58 59 60 61 62 63 64 65 68 70 71 72 74 75 76 77 78 79 81 82 84 85 86 87 89 90 92 93 94 96 97 98 100 101 102 103 104 105 107 108 110 111 115 116 117 118 119 120 121 123 124 126 129 130 131 132 134 135 141 142 143 144 145 146 147 148 149 154 **P**6 **S** Munson Healthcare, Traverse City, MI
Primary Contact: Alfred E. Pilong Jr, FACHE, President, Munson Medical Center & Chief Operating Officer, Munson Healthcare
COO: Derk F Pronger, Chief Operating Officer
CFO: Mark A Helper, Corporate Vice President and Chief Financial Officer
CMO: Christine Nefcy, Chief Medical Officer, Munson Healthcare
CIO: Christopher J Podges, Vice President Outpatient Services and Chief Information Officer
CHR: Suzanne K Peters, Vice President Human Resources
CNO: Loraine Frank–Lightfoot, Vice President, Patient Care Services and Chief Nursing Officer
Web address: www.munsonhealthcare.org
Control: Other not–for–profit (including NFP Corporation) **Service:** General medical and surgical

Staffed Beds: 439 Admissions: 22056 Census: 280 Outpatient Visits: 556766 Births: 1825 Total Expense ($000): 576999 Payroll Expense ($000): 206531 Personnel: 2999

TRENTON—Wayne County

⊞ **BEAUMONT HOSPITAL – TRENTON (230176)**, 5450 Fort Street, Zip 48183–4625; tel. 734/671–3800, **A**1 3 10 12 13 **F**3 8 11 13 15 18 20 22 26 28 29 30 34 35 38 39 40 43 44 45 46 47 49 50 51 56 57 59 60 61 62 63 64 65 68 70 74 75 76 78 79 80 81 82 84 85 87 91 92 93 100 102 107 108 110 111 114 115 117 118 119 126 130 131 132 135 146 147 148 149 150 **P**6 **S** Beaumont Health, Southfield, MI
Primary Contact: Christine Stesney–Ridenour, FACHE, President
COO: Carolyn Wilson, R.N., Chief Operating Officer
CFO: Paul Lauzau, Controller
CMO: Jonathan Kaper, Chief Medical Officer
CIO: Subra Sripada, Executive Vice President, Chief Transformation Officer and Chief Information Officer
CHR: Michelle Cora, Director Human Resources
CNO: Susan G Schulz, Director Patient Care Services
Web address: www.beaumont.org
Control: Other not–for–profit (including NFP Corporation) **Service:** General medical and surgical

Staffed Beds: 173 Admissions: 9461 Census: 104 Outpatient Visits: 100558 Births: 606 Total Expense ($000): 166246 Payroll Expense ($000): 69326 Personnel: 882

Many Facility Codes have changed. Please refer to the AHA Guide Code Chart.

© 2018 AHA Guide

TROY—Oakland County

☒ **BEAUMONT HOSPITAL – TROY (230269)**, 44201 Dequindre Road,
Zip 48085–1117; tel. 248/964–5000, **A**1 2 3 5 10 13 **F**3 8 11 12 13 15 17 18
19 20 22 24 26 28 29 30 31 32 34 35 36 37 38 39 40 41 43 44 45 46 47 48
49 50 53 54 55 57 58 59 60 61 62 63 64 65 66 68 70 71 72 74 75 76 77 78
79 80 81 82 84 85 86 87 89 90 91 92 93 94 96 97 100 102 107 108 109 110
111 114 115 116 117 118 119 120 121 123 124 126 129 130 131 132 135
141 142 143 145 146 147 148 149 150 **P**6 **S** Beaumont Health, Southfield, MI
Primary Contact: Nancy Susick, MSN, President
COO: Carolyn Wilson, R.N., Chief Operating Officer
CFO: Mark Leonard, Vice President Finance
CMO: James Lynch, Senior Vice President and Chief Medical Officer
CIO: Subra Sripada, Executive Vice President, Chief Transportation Officer and
Chief Information Officer
CHR: Lisa Ouelette, Director Human Resources
CNO: Debra Guido–Allen, Vice President and Chief Nursing Officer
Web address: www.beaumont.org
Control: Other not–for–profit (including NFP Corporation) **Service**: General
medical and surgical

Staffed Beds: 520 **Admissions**: 35022 **Census**: 401 **Outpatient Visits**:
995157 **Births**: 3584 **Total Expense ($000)**: 596975 **Payroll Expense
($000)**: 237839 **Personnel**: 3887

VICKSBURG—Kalamazoo County

BRONSON VICKSBURG HOSPITAL See Bronson Methodist Hospital, Kalamazoo

WARREN—Macomb County

☐ **BEHAVIORAL CENTER OF MICHIGAN (234042)**, 4050 East 12 Mile Road,
Zip 48092–2534; tel. 586/261–2266, (Nonreporting) **A**1 10
Primary Contact: Ryan Gunabalan, Chief Executive Officer
COO: Efren Lusterio, Director of Nursing
CFO: Mark Corey, Chief Financial Officer
CMO: Eleanor Medina, M.D., Chief Medical Officer
CIO: Kashmira Khade, Coordinator Non–Clinical Services
CHR: Erin R Youngblood, Chief Human Resources Officer
Web address: www.behavioralcenter.com
Control: Corporation, Investor–owned (for–profit) **Service**: Psychiatric

Staffed Beds: 42

☐ **SOUTHEAST MICHIGAN SURGICAL HOSPITAL (230264)**, 21230 Dequindre,
Zip 48091–2287; tel. 586/427–1000, (Nonreporting) **A**1 10 **S** National Surgical
Healthcare, Chicago, IL
Primary Contact: Barry Cullen, Chief Executive Officer
CMO: Benjamin Paolucci, D.O., Chief of Staff
CHR: Dawn Meiers, Coordinator Medical Staff and Personnel Services
Web address: www.nshinc.com
Control: Corporation, Investor–owned (for–profit) **Service**: Surgical

Staffed Beds: 13

☒ **ST. JOHN MACOMB–OAKLAND HOSPITAL (230195)**, 11800 East 12 Mile
Road, Zip 48093–3472; tel. 586/573–5000, (Includes ST. JOHN MACOMB–
OAKLAND HOSPITAL, MADISON HEIGHTS CAMPUS, 27351 Dequindre, Madison
Heights, MI, Zip 48071–3487; tel. 248/967–7000; Terry Hamilton, President;
ST. JOHN MACOMB–OAKLAND HOSPITAL, WARREN CAMPUS, 11800 East Twelve
Mile Road, Warren, MI, Zip 48093–3472; tel. 586/573–5000; Terry Hamilton,
President) **A**1 2 3 10 12 13 **F**3 11 12 13 15 17 18 20 22 24 26 28 29 30 31 34
35 36 38 39 40 43 44 45 46 47 49 50 51 56 57 58 59 60 61 63 64 65 68
70 74 75 76 77 78 79 80 81 82 84 85 86 87 90 91 92 93 95 96 97 98 100
101 102 105 107 108 111 115 116 118 119 121 123 126 129 130 131 132
135 141 146 147 148 149 150 **S** Ascension Healthcare, Saint Louis, MO
Primary Contact: Terry Hamilton, President
COO: William Mott, Chief Operating Officer
CFO: Patrick McGuire, Chief Financial Officer, Michigan Market
CMO: Gary L Berg, D.O., Chief Medical Officer
CIO: Ralph Tenney, Chief Information Officer
CHR: Joanne E Tuscany, Senior Director Human Resources
Web address: www.stjohnprovidence.org/macomb–oakland/
Control: Church operated, Nongovernment, not–for–profit **Service**: General
medical and surgical

Staffed Beds: 535 **Admissions**: 25401 **Census**: 352 **Outpatient Visits**:
435886 **Births**: 733 **Total Expense ($000)**: 382436 **Payroll Expense
($000)**: 154955 **Personnel**: 2183

WATERVLIET—Berrien County

COMMUNITY HOSPITAL See Lakeland Hospital, Watervliet

☒ △ **LAKELAND HOSPITAL, WATERVLIET (230078)**, 400 Medical Park Drive,
Zip 49098–9225; tel. 269/463–3111, **A**1 7 10 **F**3 11 15 29 30 34 35 38 40 45
50 54 57 59 64 68 75 77 79 81 86 87 90 93 94 96 97 107 119 127 130 131
132 135 144 146 148 149 154 **S** Lakeland Health, Saint Joseph, MI
Primary Contact: Ray Cruse, Chief Executive Officer
CFO: Timothy Calhoun, Vice President Finance, Chief Financial Officer
CIO: Norma Tirado, Vice President, Human Resources and Health Information
Technology
CHR: Norma Tirado, Vice President, Human Resources and Health Information
Technology
CNO: Connie Harmon, Director of Nursing
Control: Other not–for–profit (including NFP Corporation) **Service**: General
medical and surgical

Staffed Beds: 44 **Admissions**: 527 **Census**: 12 **Outpatient Visits**: 136153
Births: 0 **Total Expense ($000)**: 38494 **Payroll Expense ($000)**: 17886
Personnel: 255

WAYNE—Wayne County

☒ **BEAUMONT HOSPITAL, WAYNE (230142)**, 33155 Annapolis Street,
Zip 48184–2405; tel. 734/467–4000, **A**1 3 10 **F**3 11 12 13 15 18 20 22 26 28
29 30 31 34 35 38 40 43 44 45 46 47 49 50 57 59 60 61 64 65 68 70 74 75
76 77 78 79 81 82 84 85 86 87 91 92 93 96 100 102 107 108 110 111 115
116 117 118 119 126 130 131 132 134 135 143 146 147 148 149 154 **P**6 **S**
Beaumont Health, Southfield, MI
Primary Contact: Eric W. Widner, FACHE, Division President
COO: Carolyn Wilson, R.N., Chief Operating Officer
CFO: Jacqueline Nash, Controller
CMO: Ashok Jain, M.D., Senior Vice President and Chief Medical Officer
CIO: Subra Sripada, Executive Vice President, Chief Transformation Officer and
Chief Information Officer
CHR: Robert L James, Director Human Resources
CNO: Diane L Hartley, Director of Patient Care Services
Web address: www.beaumont.org
Control: Other not–for–profit (including NFP Corporation) **Service**: General
medical and surgical

Staffed Beds: 185 **Admissions**: 8297 **Census**: 88 **Outpatient Visits**: 52177
Births: 992 **Total Expense ($000)**: 170564 **Payroll Expense ($000)**: 78292
Personnel: 1050

WEST BLOOMFIELD—Oakland County

☒ **HENRY FORD WEST BLOOMFIELD HOSPITAL (230302)**, 6777 West Maple
Road, Zip 48322–3013; tel. 248/661–4100, **A**1 2 3 10 **F**3 6 11 12 13 15 18 20
22 26 28 29 30 31 32 34 35 36 37 38 40 41 43 44 45 46 49 50 51 53 54 55
56 57 58 59 60 61 62 63 64 65 66 68 70 73 74 75 76 77 78 79 80 81 82 84
85 86 87 89 92 93 96 97 100 102 107 108 110 111 114 115 117 118 119
120 121 123 124 126 130 131 132 134 135 146 147 148 149 150 154 **P**6 **S**
Henry Ford Health System, Detroit, MI
Primary Contact: Lynn M. Torossian, President and Chief Executive Officer
COO: Karen Harris, R.N., Chief Nursing and Operations Officer
CFO: Terry Goodbalian, Regional Chief Financial Officer
CMO: Betty Chu, M.D., Chief Medical Officer and Vice President of Medical Affairs
CIO: Mary Alice Annecharico, System Vice President and Chief Information Officer
CNO: Karen Harris, R.N., Chief Nursing and Operations Officer
Web address: www.henryford.com
Control: Other not–for–profit (including NFP Corporation) **Service**: General
medical and surgical

Staffed Beds: 212 **Admissions**: 12729 **Census**: 125 **Outpatient Visits**:
223180 **Births**: 1932 **Total Expense ($000)**: 274664 **Payroll Expense
($000)**: 105854 **Personnel**: 1835

MI

Hospital, Medicare Provider Number, Address, Telephone, Approval, Facility, and Physician Codes, Health Care System

★ American Hospital Association (AHA) membership
☐ The Joint Commission accreditation
○ Healthcare Facilities Accreditation Program
◇ DNV Healthcare Inc. accreditation
⇑ Center for Improvement in Healthcare Quality Accreditation
△ Commission on Accreditation of Rehabilitation Facilities (CARF) accreditation

WEST BRANCH—Ogemaw County

★ ○ **MIDMICHIGAN MEDICAL CENTER – WEST BRANCH (230095)**, 2463 South M–30, Zip 48661–1199; tel. 989/345-3660, **A**5 10 11 20 **F**3 11 15 17 20 28 29 30 34 35 40 50 57 59 63 64 75 77 79 81 93 97 107 111 115 117 119 130 135 146 148 **P**6 **S** MidMichigan Health, Midland, MI
Primary Contact: Robert McGrail, Chief Executive Officer
CFO: Kathy Kohr, Chief Financial Officer
CMO: Mark Weber, M.D., President Medical Staff
CHR: Kent Allen, Director Human Resources
CNO: Nicole Gillette, R.N., Chief Nursing Officer
Web address: www.wbrmc.com
Control: Other not–for–profit (including NFP Corporation) **Service**: General medical and surgical

Staffed Beds: 88 **Admissions:** 2402 **Census:** 22 **Outpatient Visits:** 64371 **Births:** 0 **Total Expense ($000):** 45567 **Payroll Expense ($000):** 14277 **Personnel:** 321

WESTLAND—Wayne County

□ **WALTER P. REUTHER PSYCHIATRIC HOSPITAL (234035)**, 30901 Palmer Road, Zip 48186–5389; tel. 734/367-8400, (Nonreporting) **A**1 10
Primary Contact: Richard T. Young, FACHE, Director
CMO: H. Bandla, M.D., Chief Clinical Affairs
CHR: Deborah Moore, Director Human Resources
Web address: www.mhweb.org/wayne/reuther.htm
Control: State, Government, nonfederal **Service**: Psychiatric

Staffed Beds: 239

WYANDOTTE—Wayne County

⊞ △ **HENRY FORD WYANDOTTE HOSPITAL (230146)**, 2333 Biddle Avenue, Zip 48192–4668; tel. 734/246-6000, **A**1 3 7 10 12 13 **F**3 8 11 12 13 15 18 19 20 22 26 28 29 30 31 32 34 35 36 38 40 41 43 44 45 46 47 49 50 51 54 56 57 58 59 60 61 62 63 64 65 66 68 70 73 74 75 76 77 78 79 80 81 82 84 85 86 87 90 92 93 96 97 98 100 101 102 103 107 108 110 111 114 115 116 117 118 119 126 129 130 131 132 135 144 146 147 148 149 150 154 **P**6 **S** Henry Ford Health System, Detroit, MI
Primary Contact: Denise Brooks–Williams, President and Chief Executive Officer
CFO: Terry Goodbalian, Vice President, Finance and Chief Financial Officer
CMO: Dennis R Lemanski, D.O., Senior Vice President Medical Affairs and Medical Education/CMO
CIO: Mary Alice Annecharico, System Vice President and Chief Information Officer
CNO: Josephine Sclafani Wahl, R.N., MS, FACHE, VP, Patient Care Services & CNO
Web address: www.henryfordhealth.org
Control: Other not–for–profit (including NFP Corporation) **Service**: General medical and surgical

Staffed Beds: 345 **Admissions:** 16585 **Census:** 212 **Outpatient Visits:** 404911 **Births:** 1586 **Total Expense ($000):** 307455 **Payroll Expense ($000):** 127124 **Personnel:** 2011

⊞ **SELECT SPECIALTY HOSPITAL–DOWNRIVER (232031)**, 2333 Biddle Avenue, 8th Floor, Zip 48192–4668; tel. 734/246-5500, (Nonreporting) **A**1 10 **S** Select Medical Corporation, Mechanicsburg, PA
Primary Contact: John Ponczocha, Chief Executive Officer
CMO: Roderick Boyer, M.D., Medical Director
CHR: Barb Wierzbicki, Manager Human Resources
CNO: Angela Kudla, MSN, R.N., Chief Nursing Officer
Web address: www.downriver.selectspecialtyhospitals.com/
Control: Corporation, Investor–owned (for–profit) **Service**: Acute long–term care hospital

Staffed Beds: 35

WYOMING—Kent County

★ ○ **METRO HEALTH – UNIVERSITY OF MICHIGAN HEALTH (230236)**, 5900 Byron Center Avenue SW, Zip 49519–9606, Mailing Address: P.O. Box 916, Zip 49509–0916; tel. 616/252-7200, **A**3 5 10 11 12 13 **F**3 12 13 15 18 19 20 22 26 28 29 30 31 34 35 40 43 44 45 48 49 50 54 57 58 59 64 65 66 70 74 75 76 77 78 79 80 81 85 86 87 92 94 97 107 108 110 111 115 119 126 129 130 131 132 135 144 146 147 148 149 150 154 **P**6 8
Primary Contact: Michael D. Faas, President and Chief Executive Officer
COO: David R Olejniczak, Chief Operating Officer
CFO: Kris Kurtz, Chief Financial Officer
CMO: Peter Hahn, Chief Medical Officer
CIO: Joshua Wilda, Chief Information Officer
CNO: Steve Polega, Chief Nursing Officer
Web address: www.metrohealth.net
Control: Other not–for–profit (including NFP Corporation) **Service**: General medical and surgical

Staffed Beds: 208 **Admissions:** 9476 **Census:** 110 **Outpatient Visits:** 552594 **Births:** 1473 **Total Expense ($000):** 399965 **Payroll Expense ($000):** 151818 **Personnel:** 2311

YPSILANTI—Washtenaw County

□ **FOREST HEALTH MEDICAL CENTER (230144)**, 135 South Prospect Street, Zip 48198–7914; tel. 734/547-4700, **A**1 10 **F**12 30 64 74 75 79 81 82 85 111 119 130 132 149
Primary Contact: Trevor J. Dyksterhouse, President
COO: Andrea Walrath, Chief Operating Officer
CFO: David Althoen, Director Financial Planning and Analysis
CMO: Jason Adams, M.D., Medical Staff President
CIO: Andrea Walrath, Chief Operating Officer
CHR: Amy Mohr, Coordinator Human Resources
Web address: www.fhmc-mi.com
Control: Corporation, Investor–owned (for–profit) **Service**: General medical and surgical

Staffed Beds: 24 **Admissions:** 1333 **Census:** 5 **Outpatient Visits:** 14907 **Births:** 0 **Personnel:** 48

⊞ **SELECT SPECIALTY HOSPITAL–ANN ARBOR (232024)**, 5301 East Huron River Drive, 7th Floor, Zip 48197–1051; tel. 734/712-6751, (Nonreporting) **A**1 10 **S** Select Medical Corporation, Mechanicsburg, PA
Primary Contact: Bryan Cutliff, Chief Executive Officer
CMO: Hamid Halimi, M.D., Medical Director
CHR: Cindy Hardick, Human Resources Coordinator
CNO: Tim Varney, R.N., Chief Nursing Officer
Web address: www.annarbor.selectspecialtyhospitals.com/
Control: Corporation, Investor–owned (for–profit) **Service**: Acute long–term care hospital

Staffed Beds: 36

★ **ST. JOSEPH MERCY ANN ARBOR (230156)**, 5301 Mcauley Drive, Zip 48197–1051, Mailing Address: P.O. Box 995, Ann Arbor, Zip 48106–0995; tel. 734/712-3456, **A**2 5 10 **F**3 4 5 8 11 12 13 15 17 18 20 22 24 26 28 29 30 31 32 34 35 36 37 38 40 41 43 44 47 48 49 50 51 53 54 55 56 57 58 59 61 64 65 66 68 70 71 72 73 74 75 76 77 78 79 80 81 82 83 84 85 86 87 89 90 91 92 93 94 95 96 97 98 99 100 101 102 103 104 105 107 108 109 110 111 114 115 118 119 120 121 123 124 126 129 130 131 132 134 135 141 143 144 146 147 148 149 153 154 **P**5 6 **S** Trinity Health, Livonia, MI
Primary Contact: David Brooks, President
CFO: Kathy O'Connor, Vice President Finance
CMO: Rosalie Tocco–Bradley, Ph.D., M.D., Chief Medical Officer
CIO: Frank Rademacher, Senior Director Information Systems
CNO: Joyce Young, Ph.D., R.N., Vice President, Patient Services and Chief Nursing Officer
Web address: www.sjmercyhealth.org
Control: Church operated, Nongovernment, not–for–profit **Service**: General medical and surgical

Staffed Beds: 483 **Admissions:** 31588 **Census:** 380 **Outpatient Visits:** 1109813 **Births:** 3837 **Total Expense ($000):** 770418 **Payroll Expense ($000):** 278294 **Personnel:** 4786

ZEELAND—Ottawa County

⊞ **SPECTRUM HEALTH ZEELAND COMMUNITY HOSPITAL (230003)**, 8333 Felch Street, Zip 49464–2608; tel. 616/772-4644, **A**1 10 **F**3 12 13 15 18 29 32 34 35 39 40 43 45 46 57 59 64 65 68 70 74 75 76 78 79 81 85 86 87 89 91 92 93 107 108 110 111 115 118 129 130 132 134 135 144 146 147 148 154 **S** Spectrum Health, Grand Rapids, MI
Primary Contact: Ron Lewis, President
CFO: Ryan J. Powers, Vice President Finance
CMO: Ruel R. Lirio, M.D., Clinical Physician Advisor
CIO: Imran Syed, Manager Technology Information Services
CHR: Jennifer F Becksvoort, Senior Human Resource Business Partner
CNO: Jane Czerew, Vice President Clinical Services and Quality
Web address: www.spectrumhealth.org/zeeland
Control: Other not–for–profit (including NFP Corporation) **Service**: General medical and surgical

Staffed Beds: 50 **Admissions:** 2609 **Census:** 19 **Outpatient Visits:** 94476 **Births:** 543 **Total Expense ($000):** 55691 **Payroll Expense ($000):** 19194 **Personnel:** 349

ZEELAND COMMUNITY HOSPITAL See Spectrum Health Zeeland Community Hospital

MINNESOTA

ADA—Norman County

BRIDGES MEDICAL CENTER See Essentia Health ADA

★ **ESSENTIA HEALTH ADA (241313)**, 201 9th Street West, Zip 56510–1279;
tel. 218/784–5000, (Nonreporting) **A**10 18 **S** Essentia Health, Duluth, MN
Primary Contact: Erin Stoltman, Administrator
CMO: Jeff Peterson, M.D., Chief of Staff
CHR: Shayla Hennenberg, Director Human Resources
Web address: www.essentiahealth.org
Control: Other not–for–profit (including NFP Corporation) **Service:** General medical and surgical

Staffed Beds: 14

AITKIN—Aitkin County

⊠ **RIVERWOOD HEALTHCARE CENTER (241305)**, 200 Bunker Hill Drive,
Zip 56431–1865; tel. 218/927–2121, (Nonreporting) **A**1 2 10 18
Primary Contact: Todd Sandberg, Chief Executive Officer
COO: Cindi Baker, Chief Operating Officer
CFO: Casey R Johnson, Chief Financial Officer
CMO: Mark Heggem, M.D., Chief Medical Officer
CIO: Daryl Kallevig, Chief Information Officer
CHR: Cindi Hills, Director Human Resources
CNO: Kristine Layne, R.N., Chief Nursing Officer
Web address: www.riverwoodhealthcare.org
Control: Other not–for–profit (including NFP Corporation) **Service:** General medical and surgical

Staffed Beds: 25

ALBERT LEA—Freeborn County

☐ **MAYO CLINIC HEALTH SYSTEM – ALBERT LEA AND AUSTIN (240043)**, 404
West Fountain Street, Zip 56007–2473; tel. 507/373–2384, (Includes MAYO CLINIC
HEALTH SYSTEM – ALBERT LEA AND AUSTIN, 1000 First Drive NW, Austin, MN,
Zip 55912–2904; tel. 507/433–7351; Mark Ciota, M.D., Chief Executive Officer) **A**1
3 5 10 20 **F**3 13 15 18 28 29 30 31 32 34 35 36 40 43 45 46 57 59 63 64 65
70 74 75 76 77 78 79 81 82 85 86 87 92 93 97 98 104 106 107 110 111 115
119 129 130 131 132 144 146 147 148 149 **P**6 **S** Mayo Clinic, Rochester, MN
Primary Contact: Mark Ciota, M.D., Chief Executive Officer
CMO: John Grzybowski, M.D., Medical Director
CHR: Monica Fleegel, Director Human Resources
CNO: Lori Routh, R.N., Nurse Administrator
Web address: www.almedcenter.org
Control: Other not–for–profit (including NFP Corporation) **Service:** General medical and surgical

Staffed Beds: 69 Admissions: 4513 Census: 42 Outpatient Visits: 365114 Births: 675 Personnel: 1099

ALEXANDRIA—Douglas County

★ ○ **ALOMERE HEALTH (240030)**, 111 17th Avenue East, Zip 56308–3798;
tel. 320/762–1511, **A**2 10 11 **F**3 8 11 13 15 28 29 30 31 32 34 35 36 40 43
45 50 57 61 64 65 68 70 76 77 78 79 81 82 85 86 87 89 91 93 97 107 108
111 115 117 118 119 129 130 131 132 135 144 146 149 154 **P**6
Primary Contact: Carl P. Vaagenes, Chief Executive Officer
CFO: Nate Meyer, Director Finance
CHR: Shelly Gompf, Director Human Resources
Web address: www.dchospital.com
Control: County, Government, nonfederal **Service:** General medical and surgical

Staffed Beds: 99 Admissions: 3419 Census: 29 Outpatient Visits: 64235 Births: 663 Total Expense ($000): 144446 Payroll Expense ($000): 43878 Personnel: 704

ALEXANDRIA—Sherburne County

☐ **COMMUNITY BEHAVIORAL HEALTH HOSPITAL – ALEXANDRIA (244012)**,
1610 8th Avenue East, Zip 56308–2472; tel. 320/335–6201, (Nonreporting) **A**1
10 **S** Minnesota Department of Human Services, Saint Paul, MN
Primary Contact: Jennifer Westrum, Administrator
CFO: Shirley Jacobson, Chief Financial Officer
Web address: www.health.state.mn.us
Control: State, Government, nonfederal **Service:** Psychiatric

Staffed Beds: 16

ANNANDALE—Wright County

☐ **COMMUNITY BEHAVIORAL HEALTH HOSPITAL – ANNANDALE (244011)**,
400 Annandale Boulevard, Zip 55302–3141; tel. 651/259–3850, (Nonreporting)
A1 10 **S** Minnesota Department of Human Services, Saint Paul, MN
Primary Contact: James P. Kelly, FACHE, Administrator
CMO: Shabeer A Ahmed, M.D., Clinical Director
CNO: Lennetta M Reynolds, Administrative Supervisor
Web address: www.health.state.mn.us
Control: State, Government, nonfederal **Service:** Psychiatric

Staffed Beds: 16

ANOKA—Anoka County

☐ **ANOKA–METROPOLITAN REGIONAL TREATMENT CENTER (244002)**,
3301 Seventh Avenue, Zip 55303–4516, Mailing Address: 3301 Seventh Avenue
North, Zip 55303–4516; tel. 651/431–5000, (Nonreporting) **A**1 10 **S** Minnesota
Department of Human Services, Saint Paul, MN
Primary Contact: Wade Brost, Executive Director
Web address: www.health.state.mn.us
Control: State, Government, nonfederal **Service:** Psychiatric

Staffed Beds: 200

APPLETON—Swift County

APPLETON AREA HEALTH SERVICES (241341), 30 South Behl Street,
Zip 56208–1699; tel. 320/289–2422, (Nonreporting) **A**10 18
Primary Contact: Lori Andreas, Chief Executive Officer and Administrator
CFO: Anne Kells, Interim Chief Financial Officer
Web address: www.appletonareahealth.com
Control: City, Government, nonfederal **Service:** General medical and surgical

Staffed Beds: 15

ARLINGTON—Sibley County

★ ⇑ **RIDGEVIEW SIBLEY MEDICAL CENTER (241311)**, 601 West Chandler
Street, Zip 55307–2127; tel. 507/964–2271, (Nonreporting) **A**10 18 21 **S**
Ridgeview Medical Center, Waconia, MN
CFO: Darla Anderson, Chief Financial Officer
CMO: Ehtaisham Mohammed, M.D., Chief Medical Officer
CIO: Chris Bulau, Manager Information Technology
CHR: Sara Christiansen, Interim Director Human Resources
CNO: Sandy Domeier, Director Patient Care Services
Web address: www.sibleymedical.org
Control: City, Government, nonfederal **Service:** General medical and surgical

Staffed Beds: 16

AURORA—St. Louis County

★ **ESSENTIA HEALTH NORTHERN PINES MEDICAL CENTER (241340)**, 5211
Highway 110, Zip 55705–1599; tel. 218/229–2211, (Total facility includes 50
beds in nursing home–type unit) **A**10 18 **F**3 28 29 34 40 43 50 56 57 59 64 65
75 81 82 85 87 93 96 97 100 102 107 127 128 130 133 135 148 149 154 **P**6
S Essentia Health, Duluth, MN
Primary Contact: Laura Ackman, Chief Operating Officer and Administrator
CFO: Kevin Boren, Chief Financial Officer
CMO: Michelle Oman, D.O., Chief Medical Officer
CHR: Kim Carlson, Director Human Resources
CNO: Cindy Loe, R.N., Director of Nursing
Web address: www.essentiahealth.org/NorthernPines/FindaClinic/Essentia–
HealthNorthern–Pines–36.aspx
Control: Other not–for–profit (including NFP Corporation) **Service:** General medical and surgical

Staffed Beds: 58 Admissions: 185 Census: 29 Outpatient Visits: 18169 Births: 0 Total Expense ($000): 15713 Payroll Expense ($000): 7840 Personnel: 102

WHITE COMMUNITY HOSPITAL See Essentia Health Northern Pines Medical Center

MN

Hospital, Medicare Provider Number, Address, Telephone, Approval, Facility, and Physician Codes, Health Care System

★ American Hospital Association (AHA) membership
☐ The Joint Commission accreditation
○ Healthcare Facilities Accreditation Program
◇ DNV Healthcare Inc. accreditation
⇑ Center for Improvement in Healthcare Quality Accreditation
△ Commission on Accreditation of Rehabilitation Facilities (CARF) accreditation

BAGLEY—Clearwater County

★ **SANFORD BAGLEY MEDICAL CENTER (241328)**, 203 Fourth Street NW, Zip 56621–8307; tel. 218/694–6501, **A**10 18 **F**3 7 15 28 34 40 45 53 59 65 66 75 77 79 81 87 89 93 97 104 107 114 119 127 128 133 143 149 150 **P**6 **S** Sanford Health, Sioux Falls, SD
Primary Contact: Robert Belanger, Administrator Director
CMO: Andre Spence, Chief Medical Staff
CNO: Stephanie McKnight, Hospital Nursing Manager
Web address: www.sanfordhealth.org
Control: Other not–for–profit (including NFP Corporation) **Service:** General medical and surgical

Staffed Beds: 8 **Admissions:** 137 **Census:** 2 **Outpatient Visits:** 20494 **Births:** 0 **Total Expense ($000):** 11448 **Payroll Expense ($000):** 4884 **Personnel:** 74

BAUDETTE—Lake Of The Woods County

★ **CHI LAKEWOOD HEALTH (241301)**, 600 Main Avenue South, Zip 56623–2855; tel. 218/634–2120, (Nonreporting) **A**10 18 **S** Catholic Health Initiatives, Englewood, CO
Primary Contact: Benjamin Koppelman, Interim President
CFO: Jay Ross, Vice President of Finance
CMO: Justin Quo, Chief of Staff
CIO: Dan Leadbetter, Information Technology Systems Site Lead
CNO: Danielle Abel, Vice President of Patient Care Services
Web address: www.lakewoodhealthcenter.org
Control: Church operated, Nongovernment, not–for–profit **Service:** General medical and surgical

Staffed Beds: 55

BAXTER—Crow Wing County

☐ **COMMUNITY BEHAVIORAL HEALTH HOSPITAL – BAXTER (244015)**, 14241 Grand Oaks Drive, Zip 56425–8749; tel. 218/316–3101, (Nonreporting) **A**1 10 **S** Minnesota Department of Human Services, Saint Paul, MN
Primary Contact: James Coughenour, Administrator
Web address: www.business.explorebrainerdlakes.com/list/member/community–behavioral–health–hospital–baxter–8647
Control: State, Government, nonfederal **Service:** Psychiatric

Staffed Beds: 16

BEMIDJI—Beltrami County

☐ **COMMUNITY BEHAVIORAL HEALTH HOSPITAL – BEMIDJI (244014)**, 800 Bemidji Avenue North, Zip 56601–3054; tel. 218/308–2400, (Nonreporting) **A**1 10 **S** Minnesota Department of Human Services, Saint Paul, MN
Primary Contact: Larry A. Laudon, Administrator
Control: State, Government, nonfederal **Service:** Psychiatric

Staffed Beds: 16

NORTH COUNTRY REGIONAL HOSPITAL See Sanford Bemidji Medical Center

★ **SANFORD BEMIDJI MEDICAL CENTER (240100)**, 1300 Anne Street NW, Zip 56601–5103; tel. 218/751–5430, (Total facility includes 78 beds in nursing home–type unit) **A**2 10 **F**3 7 8 10 11 13 14 15 18 20 22 28 29 30 31 34 35 40 43 44 45 46 49 54 55 56 57 58 59 60 62 63 64 65 66 68 70 74 75 76 77 78 79 81 82 85 86 87 90 93 96 97 104 107 108 110 111 114 115 117 119 120 121 123 124 125 126 127 128 129 130 131 132 133 135 141 142 143 144 146 147 148 149 150 154 **P**6 **S** Sanford Health, Sioux Falls, SD
Primary Contact: Bryan Nermoe, Executive Vice President
CFO: Craig Boyer, Vice President Finance
CMO: Daniel DeKrey, M.D., Chief of Staff
CIO: Dan Moffatt, Chief Information Officer
Web address: www.sanfordhealth.org/bemidji
Control: Other not–for–profit (including NFP Corporation) **Service:** General medical and surgical

Staffed Beds: 196 **Admissions:** 5976 **Census:** 139 **Outpatient Visits:** 285312 **Births:** 914 **Total Expense ($000):** 156946 **Payroll Expense ($000):** 55323 **Personnel:** 1108

BENSON—Swift County

★ **SWIFT COUNTY – BENSON HEALTH SERVICES (241365)**, 1815 Wisconsin Avenue, Zip 56215–1653; tel. 320/843–1311, (Nonreporting) **A**10 18
Primary Contact: Kurt Waldbillig, Chief Executive Officer
CFO: Jayne Thielke, Chief Financial Officer
CMO: Richard Horecka, Chief Medical Officer
CIO: Jayne Thielke, Chief Financial Officer
CHR: Naomi Sands, Administrative Assistant and Manager Human Resources
Web address: www.scbh.org
Control: Hospital district or authority, Government, nonfederal **Service:** General medical and surgical

Staffed Beds: 18

BIGFORK—Itasca County

★ **BIGFORK VALLEY HOSPITAL (241316)**, 258 Pine Tree Drive, Zip 56628, Mailing Address: P.O. Box 258, Zip 56628–0258; tel. 218/743–3177, (Nonreporting) **A**10 18
Primary Contact: Aaron Saude, Chief Executive Officer
CFO: Christine Lokken, Chief Financial Officer
CMO: Edwin Anderson, M.D., Chief of Staff and Chief Medical Officer
CIO: Amanda Niemala, Director of Information Services
CHR: Angela Kleffman, Director of Ancillary Services
CNO: Nancy Probst, R.N., Chief Nursing Officer
Web address: www.bigforkvalley.org
Control: Hospital district or authority, Government, nonfederal **Service:** General medical and surgical

Staffed Beds: 67

BLUE EARTH—Faribault County

⊞ **UNITED HOSPITAL DISTRICT (241369)**, 515 South Moore Street, Zip 56013–2158, Mailing Address: P.O. Box 160, Zip 56013–0160; tel. 507/526–3273, **A**1 10 18 **F**3 5 7 8 11 13 15 17 28 29 30 34 35 40 43 45 47 48 50 53 56 57 59 62 63 64 65 68 69 70 75 76 77 79 81 82 85 86 91 93 96 97 104 107 110 111 114 115 119 129 130 131 132 133 135 144 146 148 149 154 **P**6
Primary Contact: Richard M. Ash, Chief Executive Officer
CFO: Patrick Justin, Chief Financial Officer
CMO: Bob Karp, M.D., Chief Medical Officer
CIO: Mary Hynes, Manager Information Services
CHR: Shanna Gudahl, Manager Human Resources
CNO: Candace Arends, R.N., Chief Nursing Officer
Web address: www.uhd.org
Control: Other not–for–profit (including NFP Corporation) **Service:** General medical and surgical

Staffed Beds: 25 **Admissions:** 605 **Census:** 7 **Outpatient Visits:** 57829 **Births:** 53 **Total Expense ($000):** 30751 **Payroll Expense ($000):** 13270 **Personnel:** 188

BRAINERD—Crow Wing County

⊞ **ESSENTIA HEALTH ST. JOSEPH'S MEDICAL CENTER (240075)**, 523 North Third Street, Zip 56401–3098; tel. 218/829–2861, **A**1 2 10 **F**3 4 5 11 13 15 18 20 22 26 28 29 30 31 32 34 35 40 43 45 49 50 51 54 57 59 64 65 70 74 75 76 77 78 81 82 86 87 89 91 93 96 97 98 100 102 105 107 111 118 119 126 130 131 132 135 144 145 148 152 154 **P**6 **S** Essentia Health, Duluth, MN
Primary Contact: Adam Rees, President
COO: Mike Larson, Chief Operating Officer
CFO: Dave Pilot, Chief Financial Officer
CMO: Peter Henry, M.D., Chief Medical Officer
CIO: Pam Marlatt, Business Systems Director
CHR: Sarah Carlson, Director Human Resources
CNO: Patricia DeLong, Chief Nursing Officer
Web address: www.essentiahealth.org
Control: Church operated, Nongovernment, not–for–profit **Service:** General medical and surgical

Staffed Beds: 136 **Admissions:** 5029 **Census:** 53 **Outpatient Visits:** 298663 **Births:** 468 **Total Expense ($000):** 176826 **Payroll Expense ($000):** 84738 **Personnel:** 1094

ST. JOSEPH'S MEDICAL CENTER See Essentia Health St. Joseph's Medical Center

BRECKENRIDGE—Wilkin County

★ **CHI ST. FRANCIS HEALTH (241377)**, 2400 St Francis Drive, Zip 56520–1025; tel. 218/643–3000, (Total facility includes 80 beds in nursing home–type unit) **A**5 10 18 **F**3 8 11 13 15 28 29 30 34 35 38 40 43 45 50 56 57 59 64 65 75 79 81 87 93 96 97 99 100 104 107 110 111 115 119 125 127 128 129 130 131 132 133 146 154 **S** Catholic Health Initiatives, Englewood, CO
Primary Contact: David A. Nelson, President and Chief Executive Officer
CFO: Joshua Senger, Chief Financial Officer
CHR: Gail Grant, Director Human Resources
CNO: Alice Pesonen–Johnson, Chief Nursing Officer
Web address: www.sfcare.org
Control: Church operated, Nongovernment, not–for–profit **Service:** General medical and surgical

Staffed Beds: 105 **Admissions:** 681 **Census:** 83 **Outpatient Visits:** 18988 **Births:** 119 **Total Expense ($000):** 29459 **Payroll Expense ($000):** 11666 **Personnel:** 92

MN

BROOKLYN PARK—Hennepin County

PRAIRIECARE – BROOKLYN PARK (244016), 9400 Zane Avenue North, Zip 55443, Mailing Address: 12915 63rd Avenue North, Maple Grove, Zip 55369–6001; tel. 763/383–5800, (Nonreporting)
Primary Contact: Joel V. Oberstar, M.D., Chief Executive Officer and Chief Medical Officer
Web address: www.prairie-care.com
Service: Psychiatric

Staffed Beds: 50

BUFFALO—Wright County

☒ **BUFFALO HOSPITAL (240076)**, 303 Catlin Street, Zip 55313–1947; tel. 763/682–1212, **A**1 10 **F**3 13 15 18 28 29 30 31 32 34 35 36 40 43 44 45 50 53 57 59 64 75 76 77 78 79 80 81 85 86 87 93 107 110 111 114 115 119 129 130 131 132 135 144 148 149 150 154 **S** Allina Health, Minneapolis, MN
Primary Contact: Jennifer Myster, President
COO: Heather Johnson, Director of Finance, Operations and Business Development
CFO: Heather Johnson, Director of Finance, Operations and Business Development
CMO: Corey Martin, M.D., Director Medical Affairs
CIO: Jonathan Cloutier, Manager, Information Services
CHR: Leah Schmoyer, Human Resources Director
CNO: Gretchen A Frederick, R.N., Director Patient Care Services
Web address: www.buffalohospital.org
Control: Other not–for–profit (including NFP Corporation) **Service:** General medical and surgical

Staffed Beds: 44 **Admissions:** 2165 **Census:** 14 **Outpatient Visits:** 76840 **Births:** 610 **Total Expense ($000):** 72056 **Payroll Expense ($000):** 28461 **Personnel:** 325

BURNSVILLE—Dakota County

☒ **FAIRVIEW RIDGES HOSPITAL (240207)**, 201 East Nicollet Boulevard, Zip 55337–5799; tel. 952/892–2000, **A**1 2 3 5 10 **F**3 13 15 18 20 22 28 29 30 31 34 35 40 41 43 44 45 46 49 50 53 57 59 64 65 68 70 72 74 75 76 77 78 79 81 82 84 85 86 87 89 93 96 107 108 110 111 114 115 116 117 118 119 126 130 132 146 148 149 154 **P**6 **S** Fairview Health Services, Minneapolis, MN
Primary Contact: Patrick Belland, Chief Operating Officer, Acute Care Services
COO: Brian A Knapp, Vice President Operations
CFO: Alan Lem, Vice President Finance
CMO: Paul Kettler, M.D., Vice President Medical Affairs
CHR: Michelle LeDell, Director Human Resource
CNO: Julie Sethney, R.N., Vice President Patient Care
Web address: www.fairview.org
Control: Other not–for–profit (including NFP Corporation) **Service:** General medical and surgical

Staffed Beds: 150 **Admissions:** 10876 **Census:** 117 **Outpatient Visits:** 122225 **Births:** 2219 **Total Expense ($000):** 228188 **Payroll Expense ($000):** 98555 **Personnel:** 1029

CAMBRIDGE—Isanti County

☒ **CAMBRIDGE MEDICAL CENTER (240020)**, 701 South Dellwood Street, Zip 55008–1920; tel. 763/689–7700, **A**1 2 10 **F**3 4 5 11 13 14 15 18 28 29 30 31 32 34 35 38 40 43 45 50 55 56 57 59 61 64 65 69 70 74 75 76 77 78 79 81 82 85 86 87 89 93 97 98 100 101 102 104 107 108 111 114 115 129 130 131 132 134 135 144 145 146 147 148 149 154 **P**5 6 **S** Allina Health, Minneapolis, MN
Primary Contact: Gary Shaw, President
CFO: Nancy Treacy, Director Finance
CHR: Diane Rasmussen, Director Human Resources
CNO: Sherri Abrahamson–Baty, Director Patient Care Services
Web address: www.allina.com/ahs/cambridge.nsf
Control: Other not–for–profit (including NFP Corporation) **Service:** General medical and surgical

Staffed Beds: 73 **Admissions:** 2712 **Census:** 27 **Outpatient Visits:** 88900 **Births:** 332 **Total Expense ($000):** 77415 **Payroll Expense ($000):** 33879 **Personnel:** 652

CANBY—Yellow Medicine County

★ **SANFORD CANBY MEDICAL CENTER (241347)**, 112 St Olaf Avenue South, Zip 56220–1433; tel. 507/223–7277, (Total facility includes 58 beds in nursing home–type unit) **A**10 18 **F**3 7 10 11 13 15 28 29 31 34 35 39 40 45 46 53 56 59 60 62 64 65 70 71 75 79 81 85 89 92 93 107 110 119 127 128 130 132 133 135 144 149 **P**6 **S** Sanford Health, Sioux Falls, SD
Primary Contact: Lori Sisk, R.N., Chief Executive Officer
CFO: Allison Nelson, Chief Financial Officer
CMO: Maritza Lopez, M.D., Chief of Staff
CIO: Cheryl L Ferguson, Associate Administrator
Web address: www.sanfordcanby.org
Control: Other not–for–profit (including NFP Corporation) **Service:** General medical and surgical

Staffed Beds: 83 **Admissions:** 278 **Census:** 45 **Outpatient Visits:** 32132 **Births:** 0 **Total Expense ($000):** 20579 **Payroll Expense ($000):** 10059 **Personnel:** 194

CANNON FALLS—Goodhue County

☐ **MAYO CLINIC HEALTH SYSTEM IN CANNON FALLS (241346)**, 32021 County Road 24 Boulevard, Zip 55009–1898; tel. 507/263–4221, **A**1 10 18 **F**3 11 15 18 28 29 34 35 40 45 53 57 59 64 65 67 74 75 77 79 81 87 93 97 104 107 111 115 119 130 133 149 **P**6 **S** Mayo Clinic, Rochester, MN
Primary Contact: Brian Whited, M.D., Vice Chair Mayo Clinic Health System
COO: Glenn Christian, Administrator
CFO: Edward A Tusa, Chief Financial Officer
CMO: Tarlochan Turna, M.D., Medical Director
CHR: Mary Garlets, Director Human Resources
Web address: www.mayoclinichealthsystem.org/locations/cannon–falls
Control: Other not–for–profit (including NFP Corporation) **Service:** General medical and surgical

Staffed Beds: 15 **Admissions:** 502 **Census:** 9 **Outpatient Visits:** 26070 **Births:** 0 **Personnel:** 113

CASS LAKE—Cass County

★ **U.S. PUBLIC HEALTH SERVICE INDIAN HOSPITAL (241358)**, 425 7th Street North West, Zip 56633; tel. 218/335–3200, (Nonreporting) **A**5 10 18 **S** U.S. Indian Health Service, Rockville, MD
Primary Contact: Louis P. Erdrich, Acting Chief Executive Officer
CMO: Antonio Guimaraes, M.D., Clinical Director
CHR: Terrance Lascano, Administrative Officer
CNO: Roberta A Williams, Director of Nursing
Web address: www.ihs.gov
Control: PHS, Indian Service, Government, federal **Service:** General medical and surgical

Staffed Beds: 9

CLOQUET—Carlton County

★ **COMMUNITY MEMORIAL HOSPITAL (241364)**, 512 Skyline Boulevard, Zip 55720–1199; tel. 218/879–4641, (Nonreporting) **A**10 18
Primary Contact: Rick Breuer, Chief Executive Officer and Administrator
CFO: Brad Anderson, Chief Financial Officer
CIO: Sam Jacobson, Director Management Information Systems
Web address: www.cloquethospital.com
Control: Other not–for–profit (including NFP Corporation) **Service:** General medical and surgical

Staffed Beds: 69

COOK—St. Louis County

★ **COOK HOSPITAL & CARE CENTER (241312)**, 10 Fifth Street SE, Zip 55723–9745; tel. 218/666–5945, (Total facility includes 28 beds in nursing home–type unit) **A**10 18 **F**2 3 11 15 28 29 35 40 43 50 53 56 57 64 77 81 93 96 107 110 111 114 119 128 130 133 148 149 154
Primary Contact: Teresa Debevec, Chief Executive Officer and Administrator
CFO: Kaylee S. Hoard, Chief Financial Officer
Web address: www.cookhospital.org
Control: Hospital district or authority, Government, nonfederal **Service:** General medical and surgical

Staffed Beds: 42 **Admissions:** 199 **Census:** 28 **Outpatient Visits:** 13593 **Births:** 0 **Total Expense ($000):** 13831 **Payroll Expense ($000):** 5851 **Personnel:** 103

Hospital, Medicare Provider Number, Address, Telephone, Approval, Facility, and Physician Codes, Health Care System

★ American Hospital Association (AHA) membership
☐ The Joint Commission accreditation
○ Healthcare Facilities Accreditation Program
◇ DNV Healthcare Inc. accreditation
⇑ Center for Improvement in Healthcare Quality Accreditation
△ Commission on Accreditation of Rehabilitation Facilities (CARF) accreditation

MN

COON RAPIDS—Anoka County

☒ ⇧ **MERCY HOSPITAL (240115)**, 4050 Coon Rapids Boulevard,
Zip 55433–2586; tel. 763/236–6000, (Includes UNITY HOSPITAL, 550 Osborne
Road NE, Fridley, MN, Zip 55432–2799; tel. 763/236–5000; Helen J Strike, R.N.,
President) **A**1 2 3 5 10 21 **F**3 4 5 8 11 13 17 18 20 22 24 26 28 29 30 31 34
35 36 37 38 40 43 45 46 49 50 53 55 56 57 59 64 65 68 69 70 74 75 76 77
78 79 81 82 85 86 87 93 96 97 98 99 100 101 102 103 104 105 107 108
111 114 115 119 126 130 131 132 135 145 146 151 152 154 **S** Allina Health,
Minneapolis, MN
Primary Contact: Sara J. Criger, President
CFO: Gerald Pietz, Vice President Finance
CMO: Ryan Else, M.D., Vice President Medical Affairs
CIO: Susan Heichert, Chief Information Officer
CHR: Nancy Watson, Director Human Resources
CNO: MariBeth Olson, R.N., Vice President Patient Care Services
Web address: www.allinamercy.org
Control: Other not–for–profit (including NFP Corporation) **Service**: General
medical and surgical

Staffed Beds: 412 **Admissions:** 29745 **Census:** 322 **Outpatient Visits:**
232561 **Births:** 3095 **Total Expense ($000):** 637448 **Payroll Expense
($000):** 240176 **Personnel:** 3085

CROOKSTON—Polk County

☒ **RIVERVIEW HEALTH (241320)**, 323 South Minnesota Street, Zip 56716–1601;
tel. 218/281–9200, (Nonreporting) **A**1 5 10 18
Primary Contact: Carrie Michalski, President and Chief Executive Officer
COO: Chris Bruggeman, Chief Operating Officer
CFO: Betty Arvidson, Chief Financial Officer
CMO: Colin Fennell, M.D., Chief Medical Officer
CIO: Nichole Beauchane, Director Information Technology
CHR: Jean Tate, Vice President Human Resources
CNO: April Grunhovd, Chief Nursing Officer
Web address: www.riverviewhealth.org
Control: Other not–for–profit (including NFP Corporation) **Service**: General
medical and surgical

Staffed Beds: 49

CROSBY—Crow Wing County

☒ **CUYUNA REGIONAL MEDICAL CENTER (241353)**, 320 East Main Street,
Zip 56441–1690; tel. 218/546–7000, (Total facility includes 117 beds in nursing
home–type unit) **A**1 2 3 5 10 18 **F**3 7 12 13 15 18 28 29 31 34 35 40 45 46 47
48 49 50 51 56 57 59 62 63 64 65 68 70 75 76 77 78 79 81 82 84 85 86 87
91 92 93 94 97 99 100 101 103 104 107 110 111 115 116 117 118 119 124
127 128 130 131 132 133 143 144 146 147 148 149 150 154 **P**6
Primary Contact: Kyle Bauer, Chief Executive Officer
COO: Amy Hart, Chief Operating Officer
CFO: Katie Berg, Chief Financial Officer
CMO: Robert Westin, M.D., Chief Medical Officer
CHR: Caity Eggen, Chief Human Resource Officer
CNO: Renee Steffin, Chief Nursing Officer
Web address: www.cuyunamed.org
Control: Other not–for–profit (including NFP Corporation) **Service**: General
medical and surgical

Staffed Beds: 142 **Admissions:** 2091 **Census:** 96 **Outpatient Visits:**
182949 **Births:** 246 **Total Expense ($000):** 111568 **Payroll Expense
($000):** 45402 **Personnel:** 656

DAWSON—Lac Qui Parle County

JOHNSON MEMORIAL HEALTH SERVICES (241314), 1282 Walnut Street,
Zip 56232–2333; tel. 320/769–4323, (Total facility includes 56 beds in nursing
home–type unit) **A**10 18 **F**7 8 10 11 12 15 28 31 32 34 40 41 43 45 50 56 57
59 62 64 65 66 69 71 75 77 81 93 97 107 110 111 115 119 127 128 129
130 133 135 145 147 148 154 **P**6
Primary Contact: Stacey Lee, CPA, JD, Chief Executive Officer
CFO: Crystal Bothun, Chief Financial Officer
CMO: Ayaz Virji, M.D., Chief of Staff
CIO: Derrick Ochsendorf, Manager Information Technology and Systems
CHR: Megan Lynch, Manager Human Resources
Web address: www.jmhsmn.org
Control: Hospital district or authority, Government, nonfederal **Service**: General
medical and surgical

Staffed Beds: 76 **Admissions:** 331 **Census:** 52 **Outpatient Visits:** 9740
Births: 0 **Total Expense ($000):** 16626 **Payroll Expense ($000):** 8530
Personnel: 151

DEER RIVER—Itasca County

★ **ESSENTIA HEALTH–DEER RIVER (241360)**, 115 10th Avenue NE,
Zip 55636–8795; tel. 218/246–2900, (Total facility includes 32 beds in nursing
home–type unit) **A**10 18 **F**3 7 11 12 13 15 28 29 31 34 35 40 45 46 50 56 57
59 62 64 65 70 71 74 75 76 77 79 81 82 85 91 92 93 96 97 107 108 110
115 118 119 125 127 128 130 131 133 135 143 146 147 148 149 154 **P**6 **S**
Essentia Health, Duluth, MN
Primary Contact: Marsha Green, Administrator and Chief Operating Officer
COO: Marsha Green, Administrator and Chief Operating Officer
CMO: David Goodall, M.D., Chief Medical Staff
CHR: Brittany Mohler, Director Human Resources
Web address: www.essentiahealth.org
Control: Other not–for–profit (including NFP Corporation) **Service**: General
medical and surgical

Staffed Beds: 52 **Admissions:** 486 **Census:** 28 **Outpatient Visits:** 51227
Births: 64 **Total Expense ($000):** 30156 **Payroll Expense ($000):** 14601
Personnel: 204

DETROIT LAKES—Becker County

☒ **ESSENTIA HEALTH ST. MARY'S – DETROIT LAKES (240101)**, 1027
Washington Avenue, Zip 56501–3409; tel. 218/847–5611, (Total facility includes
96 beds in nursing home–type unit) **A**1 5 10 20 **F**10 11 13 15 18 28 29 30 31
34 35 40 41 43 45 56 57 59 62 64 65 70 75 76 77 78 79 81 82 85 87 89 91
93 97 104 107 110 111 114 115 119 125 127 128 130 131 132 135 144 146
147 148 149 154 **S** Essentia Health, Duluth, MN
Primary Contact: Peter Jacobson, President
CMO: Rich Vetter, M.D., Associate Chief
CIO: Ken Gilles, Associate Chief Information Officer
CHR: Diane Sundrud, Human Resource Service Partner
CNO: Kay Larson, R.N., Chief Nursing Officer
Web address: www.essentiahealth.org
Control: Other not–for–profit (including NFP Corporation) **Service**: General
medical and surgical

Staffed Beds: 132 **Admissions:** 2412 **Census:** 101 **Outpatient Visits:**
322747 **Births:** 519 **Total Expense ($000):** 114586 **Payroll Expense
($000):** 54461 **Personnel:** 726

ST. MARY'S INNOVIS HEALTH See Essentia Health St. Mary's – Detroit Lakes

DULUTH—St. Louis County

☒ △ **ESSENTIA HEALTH DULUTH (240019)**, 502 East Second Street,
Zip 55805–1982; tel. 218/727–8762, **A**1 3 5 7 10 **F**3 5 11 12 15 16 29 30 31
32 34 35 49 50 51 52 54 55 56 57 59 61 64 65 70 74 75 77 78 79 81 82 84
85 86 87 90 91 92 93 94 96 97 98 99 100 101 103 104 105 107 108 110
111 115 116 117 118 119 120 121 123 124 130 131 132 134 135 141
144 146 147 148 149 151 153 **P**6 **S** Essentia Health, Duluth, MN
Primary Contact: James Garvey, Hospital Operations
CFO: Kevin Boren, Chief Financial Officer
CMO: Hugh Renier, M.D., Vice President Medical Affairs
CIO: Dennis Dassenko, Chief Information Officer
CHR: Diane Davidson, Senior Vice President Human Resources
CNO: Sandee Carlson, Director of Nursing
Web address: www.smdcmedicalcenter.org
Control: Other not–for–profit (including NFP Corporation) **Service**: General
medical and surgical

Staffed Beds: 154 **Admissions:** 3137 **Census:** 72 **Outpatient Visits:**
543319 **Births:** 9 **Total Expense ($000):** 406047 **Payroll Expense
($000):** 225608 **Personnel:** 2133

☒ **ESSENTIA HEALTH ST. MARY'S MEDICAL CENTER (240002)**, 407 East
Third Street, Zip 55805–1984; tel. 218/786–4000, (Includes ST. MARY'S
CHILDREN'S HOSPITAL, 407 East Third Street, Duluth, MN, Zip 55805–1950;
tel. 218/786–5437) **A**1 2 3 5 10 **F**3 11 12 13 17 18 20 22 24 26 28 29 30 34
35 37 38 40 41 43 45 46 47 48 49 50 57 59 63 65 67 70 72 74 76 78 79 81
83 84 85 86 87 88 89 91 102 107 108 111 115 119 126 129 130 132 135
141 146 149 154 **P**6 **S** Essentia Health, Duluth, MN
Primary Contact: James Garvey, Senior Vice President Hospital Practice, Essentia
Health East
CMO: Hugh Renier, M.D., Vice President Medical Affairs
CIO: Tess Jettergren, Director Clinical Informatics
CHR: Glen Porter, Vice President Human Resources
Web address: www.essentiahealth.org/StMarysMedicalCenter/FindaClinic/
Essentia–HealthSt–Marys–Medical–Center–46.aspx
Control: Other not–for–profit (including NFP Corporation) **Service**: General
medical and surgical

Staffed Beds: 310 **Admissions:** 18313 **Census:** 223 **Outpatient Visits:**
131865 **Births:** 1311 **Total Expense ($000):** 394080 **Payroll Expense
($000):** 159437 **Personnel:** 2114

SMDC MEDICAL CENTER See Essentia Health Duluth

Many Facility Codes have changed. Please refer to the AHA Guide Code Chart. © 2018 AHA Guide

★ △ ⇧ **ST. LUKE'S HOSPITAL (240047)**, 915 East First Street,
Zip 55805–2193; tel. 218/249–5555, **A**2 3 7 10 21 **F**3 8 9 11 12 13 15 18 20
22 24 26 28 29 30 31 34 35 39 40 43 45 46 47 48 49 51 53 54 57 58 59 60
61 62 63 64 65 70 74 75 76 77 78 79 81 82 83 84 85 86 87 89 90 91 92 93
97 98 100 102 104 107 108 110 114 115 117 118 119 120 121 123 124 126
129 130 131 132 144 145 146 147 148 149 154 **P**6
Primary Contact: John Strange, President and Chief Executive Officer
CFO: Eric Lohn, Vice President and Chief Financial Officer
CMO: Gary Peterson, M.D., Vice President Medical Affairs and Chief Medical Officer
CIO: Clark Averill, Director Information Technology
CHR: Marla Halvorson, Director Human Resources
CNO: Susan Hamel, Chief Nursing Officer
Web address: www.slhduluth.com
Control: Other not–for–profit (including NFP Corporation) **Service**: General
medical and surgical

Staffed Beds: 267 **Admissions:** 11711 **Census:** 160 **Outpatient Visits:**
818697 **Births:** 810 **Total Expense ($000):** 439681 **Payroll Expense
($000):** 215009 **Personnel:** 2222

ST. MARY'S MEDICAL CENTER See Essentia Health St. Mary's Medical Center

EDINA—Hennepin County

⊠ ⇧ **FAIRVIEW SOUTHDALE HOSPITAL (240078)**, 6401 France Avenue South,
Zip 55435–2199; tel. 952/924–5000, **A**1 2 3 5 10 21 **F**3 8 13 15 17 18 20 22
24 26 28 29 30 31 34 35 40 43 44 45 46 49 50 51 56 57 59 64 65 70 71
74 75 76 77 78 79 81 84 85 87 92 93 98 100 101 107 108 110 111 114 115
116 117 118 119 121 126 130 132 146 148 149 154 **P**6 **S** Fairview Health
Services, Minneapolis, MN
Primary Contact: Patrick Belland, Chief Operating Officer, Acute Care Services
COO: Patrick Belland, Chief Operating Officer, Acute Care Services
CFO: Alan Lem, Vice President Finance
CHR: Michelle LeDell, Director Human Resources
Web address: www.fairview.org
Control: Other not–for–profit (including NFP Corporation) **Service**: General
medical and surgical

Staffed Beds: 316 **Admissions:** 18101 **Census:** 205 **Outpatient Visits:**
133534 **Births:** 3099 **Total Expense ($000):** 419580 **Payroll Expense
($000):** 169511 **Personnel:** 1767

ELBOW LAKE—Grant County

ELEAH MEDICAL CENTER See Prairie Ridge Hospital and Health Services

★ **PRAIRIE RIDGE HOSPITAL AND HEALTH SERVICES (241379)**, 1411 Highway
79 East, Zip 56531–4645; tel. 218/685–7300, **A**10 18 **F**3 7 8 15 18 24 26 28
34 40 43 45 48 53 54 59 64 68 77 79 81 90 91 93 94 96 97 104 107 108
110 111 114 119 127 128 132 133 135 148 149 154 **P**3
Primary Contact: Danielle Lesmeister, Chief Executive Officer
CFO: Brett Longtin, Chief Financial Officer
CMO: Phillip Walter Holmes, M.D., Chief of Staff
CHR: Kim Blank, Director Human Resources
CNO: Alycia Athey, Director of Nursing
Web address: www.prairiehealth.org
Control: Other not–for–profit (including NFP Corporation) **Service**: General
medical and surgical

Staffed Beds: 9 **Admissions:** 155 **Census:** 2 **Outpatient Visits:** 26021
Births: 2 **Total Expense ($000):** 18758 **Payroll Expense ($000):** 4838
Personnel: 121

ELY—St. Louis County

★ **ELY–BLOOMENSON COMMUNITY HOSPITAL (241318)**, 328 West Conan
Street, Zip 55731–1198; tel. 218/365–3271, **A**10 18 **F**3 15 28 31 40 45 53 62
64 81 107 110 119 130 133 148 149 **P**6
Primary Contact: Michael F. Coyle, Chief Executive Officer
CFO: Scott Kellerman, Chief Financial Officer
CHR: Rochelle Sjoberg, Director Human Resources
CNO: Becky Gaulke, Chief Nursing Officer
Web address: www.ebch.org
Control: Other not–for–profit (including NFP Corporation) **Service**: General
medical and surgical

Staffed Beds: 21 **Admissions:** 249 **Census:** 2 **Outpatient Visits:** 10321
Births: 0 **Total Expense ($000):** 16694 **Payroll Expense ($000):** 5497
Personnel: 87

FAIRMONT—Martin County

☐ **MAYO CLINIC HEALTH SYSTEM IN FAIRMONT (240166)**, 800 Medical Center
Drive, Zip 56031–4575; tel. 507/238–8100, **A**1 10 20 **F**3 11 12 13 15 18 28
29 30 31 34 35 36 40 43 45 57 59 64 65 68 74 75 76 77 78 79 81 82 85 86
87 92 93 97 100 101 104 107 108 110 111 115 118 119 129 130 132 133
144 146 148 149 **P**6 **S** Mayo Clinic, Rochester, MN
Primary Contact: Amy Long, Administrator
COO: Gayle B Hansen, R.N., Chief Operating Officer
CFO: Brian Suter, Chief Financial Officer
CMO: Rufus Rodriguez, M.D., Medical Director
Web address: www.fairmontmedicalcenter.org
Control: Other not–for–profit (including NFP Corporation) **Service**: General
medical and surgical

Staffed Beds: 23 **Admissions:** 1409 **Census:** 14 **Outpatient Visits:** 73631
Births: 218 **Personnel:** 294

FARIBAULT—Rice County

★ **DISTRICT ONE HOSPITAL (240071)**, 200 State Avenue, Zip 55021–6345;
tel. 507/334–6451, (Nonreporting) **A**2 10 **S** Allina Health, Minneapolis, MN
Primary Contact: David L. Albrecht, President
COO: Rick Miller, Director, Operations and Finance
CFO: Rick Miller, Chief Financial Officer
CMO: Amy Elliott, M.D., Director Medical Affairs
Web address: www.allinahealth.org/District–One–Hospital/
Control: Hospital district or authority, Government, nonfederal **Service**: General
medical and surgical

Staffed Beds: 42

FERGUS FALLS—Otter Tail County

☐ **COMMUNITY BEHAVIORAL HEALTH HOSPITAL – FERGUS FALLS (244013)**,
1801 West Alcott Avenue, Zip 56537–2661, Mailing Address: P.O. Box 478,
Zip 56538–0478; tel. 218/332–5001, (Nonreporting) **A**1 10 **S** Minnesota
Department of Human Services, Saint Paul, MN
Primary Contact: Brenda Schleske, Administrator
Control: State, Government, nonfederal **Service**: Psychiatric

Staffed Beds: 16

⊠ △ **LAKE REGION HEALTHCARE (240052)**, 712 South Cascade
Street, Zip 56537–2900, Mailing Address: P.O. Box 728, Zip 56538–0728;
tel. 218/736–8000, (Nonreporting) **A**1 7 10 20
Primary Contact: Kyle Richards, Chief Executive Officer
CFO: Brett Longtin, Chief Financial Officer
CMO: Greg Smith, Chief Medical Officer
CIO: Wade A Jyrkas, Director Computer Information Systems
CHR: Kim Blank, Director Human Resources
CNO: Lucia E Anderson, Senior Vice President Operations and Chief Nurse
Executive
Web address: www.lrhc.org
Control: Other not–for–profit (including NFP Corporation) **Service**: General
medical and surgical

Staffed Beds: 108

FOSSTON—Polk County

★ **ESSENTIA HEALTH FOSSTON (241357)**, 900 Hilligoss Boulevard SE,
Zip 56542–1599; tel. 218/435–1133, (Total facility includes 50 beds in nursing
home–type unit) **A**10 18 **F**3 7 10 11 13 15 18 28 29 31 34 35 40 43 44 50
56 57 59 62 63 65 68 70 75 76 77 78 79 80 81 82 84 85 87 93 97 104 107
110 114 127 128 129 130 131 132 133 135 146 148 149 154 **P**6 **S** Essentia
Health, Duluth, MN
Primary Contact: Kevin Gish, Administrator and Vice President
CFO: Kim Bodensteiner, Chief Financial Officer
CHR: Diane Sundrud, Director Human Resources
Web address: www.essentiahealth.org
Control: Other not–for–profit (including NFP Corporation) **Service**: General
medical and surgical

Staffed Beds: 74 **Admissions:** 532 **Census:** 44 **Outpatient Visits:** 58392
Births: 89 **Total Expense ($000):** 28040 **Payroll Expense ($000):** 16573
Personnel: 219

FIRST CARE MEDICAL SERVICES See Essentia Health Fosston

MN

Hospital, Medicare Provider Number, Address, Telephone, Approval, Facility, and Physician Codes, Health Care System

★ American Hospital Association (AHA) membership ○ Healthcare Facilities Accreditation Program ⇧ Center for Improvement in Healthcare Quality Accreditation
☐ The Joint Commission accreditation ◇ DNV Healthcare Inc. accreditation △ Commission on Accreditation of Rehabilitation Facilities (CARF) accreditation

GLENCOE—Mcleod County

★ **GLENCOE REGIONAL HEALTH SERVICES (241355)**, 1805 Hennepin Avenue North, Zip 55336–1416; tel. 320/864–3121, (Total facility includes 110 beds in nursing home–type unit) **A**10 18 **F**3 11 13 15 28 29 31 34 40 43 45 48 50 56 64 68 75 76 77 78 79 81 85 86 87 89 93 97 107 110 111 115 118 119 125 128 130 132 133 135 144 146 148 149 **P**6 **S** HealthPartners, Bloomington, MN
Primary Contact: Jeffrey Mason, President and Chief Executive Officer
CFO: John C Doidge, Vice President Finance
CMO: Kristine Knudten, M.D., Vice President Medical Affairs
CIO: Ryan Lake, Director Information Technology
CHR: Jill Hatlestad, Vice President Human Resources and Marketing
CNO: Patricia Henderson, R.N., Vice President Nursing and Clinical Services
Web address: www.grhsonline.org
Control: Other not–for–profit (including NFP Corporation) **Service:** General medical and surgical

Staffed Beds: 135 **Admissions:** 819 **Census:** 102 **Outpatient Visits:** 27826 **Births:** 138 **Total Expense ($000):** 61147 **Payroll Expense ($000):** 29792 **Personnel:** 403

GLENWOOD—Pope County

★ **GLACIAL RIDGE HEALTH SYSTEM (241376)**, 10 Fourth Avenue SE, Zip 56334–1898; tel. 320/634–4521, **A**10 18 **F**7 11 12 13 15 17 28 31 34 35 40 41 43 53 59 62 63 64 75 76 79 81 93 107 110 111 115 119 127 130 133 146 148 149 154 **P**6
Primary Contact: Kirk A. Stensrud, Chief Executive Officer
CFO: Kyle Chase, Chief Financial Officer
CMO: Gustave Mellgren, M.D., Chief of Staff
CIO: Jeff Ofstedal, Manager Information Technology
CHR: Gordon Paulson, Manager Human Resources
CNO: Lynn Flesner, Director of Nursing
Web address: www.glacialridge.org
Control: Hospital district or authority, Government, nonfederal **Service:** General medical and surgical

Staffed Beds: 19 **Admissions:** 807 **Census:** 10 **Outpatient Visits:** 22203 **Births:** 79 **Total Expense ($000):** 33274 **Payroll Expense ($000):** 16382 **Personnel:** 283

GOLDEN VALLEY—Hennepin County

⊞ **REGENCY HOSPITAL OF MINNEAPOLIS (242005)**, 1300 Hidden Lakes Parkway, Zip 55422–4286; tel. 763/588–2750, (Nonreporting) **A**1 10 **S** Select Medical Corporation, Mechanicsburg, PA
Primary Contact: Sean Stricker, Chief Executive Officer
CMO: Alaka Nagaraj, M.D., Medical Director
CNO: Caren Gaytko, Chief Nursing Officer
Web address: www.regencyhospital.com
Control: Corporation, Investor–owned (for–profit) **Service:** Acute long–term care hospital

Staffed Beds: 92

GRACEVILLE—Big Stone County

★ **ESSENTIA HEALTH–GRACEVILLE (241321)**, 115 West Second Street, Zip 56240–4845, Mailing Address: P.O. Box 157, Zip 56240–0157; tel. 320/748–7223, (Nonreporting) **A**10 18 **S** Essentia Health, Duluth, MN
Primary Contact: Julie Rosenberg, Administrator
CMO: Arthur Van Vranken, M.D., Chief Medical Officer
CIO: Brad Tostenson, Chief Information Officer
CHR: Jenny Lee, Human Resources Generalist
CNO: Jill Johnsrud, Director of Nursing
Web address: www.essentiahealth.org/HolyTrinityHospital/FindaClinic/Essentia–HealthHoly–Trinity–Hospital–96.aspx
Control: Other not–for–profit (including NFP Corporation) **Service:** General medical and surgical

Staffed Beds: 60

GRACEVILLE HEALTH CENTER See Essentia Health–Graceville

GRAND MARAIS—Cook County

★ **NORTH SHORE HEALTH (241317)**, 515 5th Avenue West, Zip 55604–3017; tel. 218/387–3040, (Total facility includes 37 beds in nursing home–type unit) **A**10 18 **F**3 7 15 28 40 45 50 56 59 62 64 75 84 85 89 93 107 110 111 115 119 128 130 133 148 149
Primary Contact: Kimber L. Wraalstad, FACHE, Administrator
CFO: Vera Schumann, Director of Finance and Controller
CMO: Milan Schmidt, Medical Director
CIO: Greg Johnson, IT Coordinator
CHR: Robert Willis, Director Human Resources
CNO: Amy Lacina, R.N., Director of Nursing
Web address: www.nshorehospitalhealthgm.com
Control: Hospital district or authority, Government, nonfederal **Service:** General medical and surgical

Staffed Beds: 53 **Admissions:** 188 **Census:** 31 **Outpatient Visits:** 11970 **Births:** 3 **Total Expense ($000):** 17113 **Payroll Expense ($000):** 6181 **Personnel:** 134

GRAND RAPIDS—Itasca County

⊞ **GRAND ITASCA CLINIC AND HOSPITAL (240064)**, 1601 Golf Course Road, Zip 55744–8648; tel. 218/326–5000, (Nonreporting) **A**1 10 20 **S** Fairview Health Services, Minneapolis, MN
Primary Contact: Laura Reed, R.N., President, Acute Care Hospitals
CFO: Todd Christensen, Vice President, Finance
CMO: Dan Soular, M.D., Vice President, Medical Affairs
CHR: Katherine Burns–Chistenson, Human Resource Director
CNO: Sandy Lenarz, Chief Nursing Officer
Web address: www.granditasca.org
Control: Other not–for–profit (including NFP Corporation) **Service:** General medical and surgical

Staffed Beds: 31

GRANITE FALLS—Yellow Medicine County

★ **GRANITE FALLS HEALTH (241343)**, 345 Tenth Avenue, Zip 56241–1499; tel. 320/564–3111, (Nonreporting) **A**10 18
Primary Contact: Thomas Kooiman, Chief Executive Officer
CFO: Val Hoffman, Chief Financial Officer
CIO: Kris Wilke, Manager Health Information
CHR: Sue Tollefson, Coordinator Payroll Personnel
CNO: Patty Massman, Director of Nursing
Web address: www.granitefallshealthcare.com
Control: City, Government, nonfederal **Service:** General medical and surgical

Staffed Beds: 82

HALLOCK—Kittson County

★ **KITTSON MEMORIAL HEALTHCARE CENTER (241336)**, 1010 South Birch Street, Zip 56728–4215, Mailing Address: P.O. Box 700, Zip 56728–0700; tel. 218/843–3612, (Nonreporting) **A**10 18
Primary Contact: Ashley Rivera, Chief Financial Officer and Chief Executive Officer
CMO: Thomas Lohstreter, M.D., Chief of Staff
CIO: Holly Knutson, Manager Information Technology
CHR: Carlene Cole, Manager Human Resources
CNO: Tawnya Sorenson, Director of Nursing
Web address: www.kmhc.net
Control: Other not–for–profit (including NFP Corporation) **Service:** General medical and surgical

Staffed Beds: 75

HASTINGS—Dakota County

⊞ **REGINA HOSPITAL (240059)**, 1175 Nininger Road, Zip 55033–1098; tel. 651/480–4100, **A**1 10 **F**3 8 11 13 15 28 29 30 31 34 35 40 43 45 46 50 57 59 75 76 77 78 79 80 81 82 87 93 98 103 107 110 111 114 119 129 130 132 145 146 148 149 154 **S** Allina Health, Minneapolis, MN
Primary Contact: Thomas R. Thompson, President
CFO: Andy Rolling, Director of Finance
CMO: James Noreen, M.D., Chief Medical Officer
Web address: www.reginamedical.org
Control: Other not–for–profit (including NFP Corporation) **Service:** General medical and surgical

Staffed Beds: 43 **Admissions:** 1606 **Census:** 19 **Outpatient Visits:** 52581 **Births:** 255 **Total Expense ($000):** 51458 **Payroll Expense ($000):** 19530 **Personnel:** 283

HENDRICKS—Lincoln County

★ **HENDRICKS COMMUNITY HOSPITAL ASSOCIATION (241339)**, 503 East Lincoln Street, Zip 56136–9598, Mailing Address: P.O. Box 106, Zip 56136–0106; tel. 507/275–3134, (Total facility includes 55 beds in nursing home–type unit) **A**10 18 **F**2 3 7 10 11 15 17 28 31 34 35 40 50 59 62 63 70 81 89 93 107 125 127 128 130 132 133 146 148
Primary Contact: Jeffrey Gollaher, Chief Executive Officer
CMO: Tabb McCluskey, M.D., Chief Medical Officer
CHR: Lynn R Olson, Director Human Resources
Web address: www.hendrickshosp.org
Control: Other not–for–profit (including NFP Corporation) **Service:** General medical and surgical

Staffed Beds: 67 **Admissions:** 173 **Census:** 60 **Outpatient Visits:** 11442 **Births:** 0 **Total Expense ($000):** 13648 **Payroll Expense ($000):** 7377 **Personnel:** 106

MN

Many Facility Codes have changed. Please refer to the AHA Guide Code Chart.
© 2018 AHA Guide

HIBBING—St. Louis County

⊞ **RANGE REGIONAL HEALTH SERVICES (240040)**, 750 East 34th Street,
Zip 55746–4600; tel. 218/262–4881, **A**1 2 10 **F**3 6 11 13 15 18 28 29 30 31
33 34 35 36 40 43 50 54 56 57 59 62 63 64 65 68 70 75 76 77 78 79 81 82
83 84 85 87 89 93 97 98 100 102 104 105 107 108 110 111 115 118 119
120 121 123 129 130 131 133 144 145 146 147 148 149 154 **P**5 6
S Fairview Health Services, Minneapolis, MN
Primary Contact: Laura Reed, R.N., President, Acute Care Hospitals
CFO: Tom Fink, Vice President Regional Finance Officer
CMO: Susan Rudberg, M.D., Chief Medical Officer
CIO: Jessica Valento, Director Information Systems
CHR: Mitchell S Vincent, Vice President Organizational Support
CNO: Connie Harle, Chief Nursing Officer
Web address: www.range.fairview.org
Control: Other not–for–profit (including NFP Corporation) **Service**: General
medical and surgical

Staffed Beds: 73 **Admissions:** 2392 **Census:** 37 **Outpatient Visits:** 51018
Births: 369 **Total Expense ($000):** 117762 **Payroll Expense ($000):** 62390
Personnel: 862

HUTCHINSON—Mcleod County

⊞ **HUTCHINSON HEALTH (240187)**, 1095 Highway 15 South, Zip 55350–3182;
tel. 320/234–5000, **A**1 10 20 **F**3 5 11 13 15 28 29 31 34 35 36 38 40 43 45
47 56 57 59 64 65 69 70 75 76 77 78 79 81 82 85 86 87 93 96 97 98 99 100
103 104 107 110 111 115 119 127 129 130 131 132 144 146 147 148 149
154 **P**6 **S** HealthPartners, Bloomington, MN
Primary Contact: Steven Mulder, M.D., President and Chief Executive Officer
COO: Glen Kegley, Chief Operating Officer
CFO: Pamela Larson, Division Director Financial Services
CMO: Brian Pollman, Chief Medical Officer
CIO: Jim Lyons, Chief Clinic Officer
CHR: Rebecca Streich, Manager Human Resources and Education Manager
CNO: Terry J. Graner, R.N., Chief Nursing Officer
Web address: www.hutchhealth.com
Control: Other not–for–profit (including NFP Corporation) **Service**: General
medical and surgical

Staffed Beds: 49 **Admissions:** 1889 **Census:** 20 **Outpatient Visits:** 225613
Births: 240 **Total Expense ($000):** 88487 **Payroll Expense ($000):** 33758
Personnel: 469

INTERNATIONAL FALLS—Koochiching County

☐ **RAINY LAKE MEDICAL CENTER (241322)**, 1400 Highway 71,
Zip 56649–2189; tel. 218/283–4481, (Nonreporting) **A**1 10 18
Primary Contact: Robert Pastor II, R.N., Chief Executive Officer
CFO: Melissa Marcotte, Chief Financial Officer
CIO: Michael Blesi, Director Information Technology
CNO: Donita Ettestad, R.N., MS, Chief Nursing Officer
Web address: www.rainylakemedical.com
Control: Other not–for–profit (including NFP Corporation) **Service**: General
medical and surgical

Staffed Beds: 25

JACKSON—Jackson County

★ **SANFORD JACKSON MEDICAL CENTER (241315)**, 1430 North Highway,
Zip 56143–1093; tel. 507/847–2420, (Nonreporting) **A**10 18 **S** Sanford Health,
Sioux Falls, SD
Primary Contact: Dawn Schnell, Chief Nursing Officer and Interim Senior Director
CFO: Gail Eike, Chief Financial Officer
CMO: Sister Marie Paul Lockerd, M.D., Chief Medical Officer
CNO: Dawn Schnell, Chief Nursing Officer
Web address: www.sanfordjackson.org
Control: Other not–for–profit (including NFP Corporation) **Service**: General
medical and surgical

Staffed Beds: 14

LAKE CITY—Goodhue County

☐ **MAYO CLINIC HEALTH SYSTEM IN LAKE CITY (241338)**, 500 West Grant
Street, Zip 55041–1143; tel. 651/345–3321, (Total facility includes 90 beds in
nursing home–type unit) **A**1 10 18 **F**15 18 28 29 30 34 35 40 45 57 59 64 67
69 75 79 81 87 92 93 97 103 110 111 114 119 128 130 132 133 146 148
149 **P**6 **S** Mayo Clinic, Rochester, MN
Primary Contact: Brian Whited, M.D., President and Chief Executive Officer
CFO: David Biren, Chief Financial Officer
CMO: Dennis Spano, M.D., Medical Director
CHR: Jacqueline Ryan, Director Human Resources
Web address: www.lakecitymedicalcenter.org
Control: Other not–for–profit (including NFP Corporation) **Service**: General
medical and surgical

Staffed Beds: 105 **Admissions:** 625 **Census:** 91 **Outpatient Visits:** 40700
Births: 0 **Personnel:** 101

LE SUEUR—Le Sueur County

★ **RIDGEVIEW LE SUEUR MEDICAL CENTER (241375)**, 621 South Fourth Street,
Zip 56058–2298; tel. 507/665–3375, (Nonreporting) **A**10 18 **S** Ridgeview
Medical Center, Waconia, MN
Primary Contact: Pamela Williams, Vice President
CFO: Patricia Schlegel, Executive Director Finance
CMO: Carolyn Stelter, M.D., Chief of Staff
CHR: Bonnie Barnhardt, Executive Director Human Resources
CNO: Kim Putz, R.N., Director, Nursing Hospital
Web address: www.mvhc.org
Control: Other not–for–profit (including NFP Corporation) **Service**: General
medical and surgical

Staffed Beds: 9

LITCHFIELD—Meeker County

★ **MEEKER MEMORIAL HOSPITAL (241366)**, 612 South Sibley Avenue,
Zip 55355–3398; tel. 320/693–4500, **A**10 18 **F**11 13 15 28 29 31 34 40 43 45
57 59 70 75 76 77 78 81 93 107 110 111 114 119 130 133 146 148 149
Primary Contact: Stacie Voss, Executive Assistant
CFO: Stephen Plaisance, Chief Financial Officer
CMO: Tim Peterson, M.D., Chief of Staff
CIO: Troy Bruning, Director Information Technology
CHR: Cindi Twardy, Manager Human Resources
CNO: Joan Bitz, Chief Nursing Officer
Web address: www.meekermemorial.org
Control: County, Government, nonfederal **Service**: General medical and surgical

Staffed Beds: 38 **Admissions:** 960 **Census:** 14 **Outpatient Visits:** 30946
Births: 136 **Total Expense ($000):** 32868 **Payroll Expense ($000):** 11893
Personnel: 172

LITTLE FALLS—Morrison County

⊞ **CHI ST. GABRIEL'S HEALTH (241370)**, 815 Second Street SE,
Zip 56345–3596; tel. 320/632–5441, (Nonreporting) **A**1 10 18 **S** Catholic Health
Initiatives, Englewood, CO
Primary Contact: Lee Boyles, President
CFO: Steve Smith, Assistant Vice President Finance
CMO: Susan Okoniewski, M.D., Chief of Staff
Web address: www.stgabriels.com
Control: Church operated, Nongovernment, not–for–profit **Service**: General
medical and surgical

Staffed Beds: 25

LONG PRAIRIE—Todd County

★ **CENTRACARE HEALTH–LONG PRAIRIE (241326)**, 20 Ninth Street SE,
Zip 56347–1404; tel. 320/732–2141, (Nonreporting) **A**5 10 18 **S** CentraCare
Health, Saint Cloud, MN
Primary Contact: Daniel J. Swenson, FACHE, Administrator
CFO: Larry Knutson, Director Finance
CMO: Rene Eldidy, M.D., Chief of Staff
Web address: www.centracare.com
Control: Other not–for–profit (including NFP Corporation) **Service**: General
medical and surgical

Staffed Beds: 20

LONG PRAIRIE MEMORIAL HOSPITAL AND HOME See Centracare Health–Long
Prairie

LUVERNE—Rock County

★ **SANFORD LUVERNE MEDICAL CENTER (241371)**, 1600 North Kniss Avenue, Zip 56156–1067; tel. 507/283–2321, **A**10 18 **F**3 4 5 7 8 11 13 15 18 19 28 29 31 32 34 35 40 43 45 56 57 59 63 64 65 67 68 74 75 76 77 78 79 81 82 83 84 85 86 87 90 93 96 97 107 111 114 118 119 128 129 131 132 133 135 146 147 148 149 152 154 **P**6 **S** Sanford Health, Sioux Falls, SD
Primary Contact: Tammy Loosbrock, Senior Director
COO: Nancy E Drenth, R.N., Director Ancillary Services
CFO: Stanley Knobloch, Director Fiscal Services
CMO: Judy S Chesley, M.D., Chief of Staff
CNO: Nyla H Sandbulte, R.N., Director of Nursing
Web address: www.sanfordluverne.org
Control: Other not–for–profit (including NFP Corporation) **Service**: General medical and surgical

Staffed Beds: 25 **Admissions:** 539 **Census:** 6 **Outpatient Visits:** 33220 **Births:** 86 **Total Expense ($000):** 22870 **Payroll Expense ($000):** 10223 **Personnel:** 155

MADELIA—Watonwan County

⊞ **MADELIA COMMUNITY HOSPITAL (241323)**, 121 Drew Avenue SE, Zip 56062–1899; tel. 507/642–3255, **A**1 5 10 18 **F**3 11 13 15 34 35 40 57 59 62 64 68 69 75 76 77 81 84 85 86 93 102 107 110 114 128 130 132 133 144 145 149 154
Primary Contact: Candace Fenske, Chief Executive Officer
CFO: Donna M Klinkner, Chief Financial Officer
CMO: Todd Gavin, Chief Medical Officer
CIO: Valerie Juhl, Director of Health
CHR: Donna M Klinkner, Chief Financial Officer
CNO: Deidre Hruby, Director of Patient Care
Web address: www.mchospital.org
Control: Other not–for–profit (including NFP Corporation) **Service**: General medical and surgical

Staffed Beds: 21 **Admissions:** 155 **Census:** 2 **Outpatient Visits:** 9670 **Births:** 0 **Total Expense ($000):** 11211 **Payroll Expense ($000):** 4273 **Personnel:** 70

MADISON—Lac Qui Parle County

★ **MADISON HEALTHCARE SERVICES (241372)**, 900 Second Avenue, Zip 56256–1006; tel. 320/598–7556, **A**10 18 **F**10 11 15 28 29 30 34 40 43 57 59 62 64 65 77 78 79 81 82 84 93 97 107 110 111 119 127 130 132 133 145 147 149 **P**5
Primary Contact: Erik Bjerke, Chief Executive Officer
CFO: Carol Borgerson, Chief Financial Officer
CIO: Jerry Harberts, Information Technologist
CHR: Kelly Johnson, Director Human Resources
Web address: www.mlhmn.org/
Control: Other not–for–profit (including NFP Corporation) **Service**: General medical and surgical

Staffed Beds: 12 **Admissions:** 190 **Census:** 2 **Outpatient Visits:** 13403 **Births:** 5 **Total Expense ($000):** 11225 **Payroll Expense ($000):** 4041 **Personnel:** 53

MAHNOMEN—Mahnomen County

★ **MAHNOMEN HEALTH CENTER (241300)**, 414 West Jefferson Avenue, Zip 56557–4912, Mailing Address: P.O. Box 396, Zip 56557–0396; tel. 218/935–2511, (Nonreporting) **A**10 18 **S** Sanford Health, Sioux Falls, SD
Primary Contact: Dale K. Kruger, Chief Executive Officer
CFO: Mary Pazdernik, Chief Financial Officer
CMO: Anju Gurung, M.D., Chief Medical Officer
CHR: Kristi Stall, Chief Human Resources Officer
Web address: www.mahnomenhealthcenter.com
Control: City–county, Government, nonfederal **Service**: General medical and surgical

Staffed Beds: 56

MANKATO—Blue Earth County

⊞ **MAYO CLINIC HEALTH SYSTEM IN MANKATO (240093)**, 1025 Marsh Street, Zip 56001–4752; tel. 507/625–4031, **A**1 3 5 10 13 **F**3 11 12 13 15 18 19 20 22 26 28 29 30 31 33 34 35 36 38 40 41 43 45 49 53 54 56 57 58 59 60 61 63 64 65 68 70 73 74 75 76 77 78 79 81 82 83 84 85 87 89 91 92 93 97 98 100 102 104 107 108 110 111 114 115 118 119 120 121 126 129 130 131 132 135 144 146 147 148 149 154 **P**6 **S** Mayo Clinic, Rochester, MN
Primary Contact: James Hebl, M.D., Regional Vice President
CMO: Susan Pearson, M.D., Chief Medical Officer
CIO: Sarah Daniels, Vice President, Information Technology
CHR: Beth Dittbenner, Regional Director, Human Resources
CNO: Laura Evenson, Chief Nursing Officer
Web address: www.mayoclinichealthsystem.org
Control: Other not–for–profit (including NFP Corporation) **Service**: General medical and surgical

Staffed Beds: 145 **Admissions:** 9107 **Census:** 100 **Outpatient Visits:** 247605 **Births:** 1359 **Personnel:** 1524

MAPLE GROVE—Hennepin County

☐ ⇑ **MAPLE GROVE HOSPITAL (240214)**, 9875 Hospital Drive, Zip 55369–4648; tel. 763/581–1000, **A**1 3 10 21 **F**3 13 15 18 29 30 40 43 45 47 53 60 68 70 72 76 77 79 81 84 85 89 100 102 107 108 111 115 118 119 126 130 146 148 149 **P**8 **S** North Memorial Health Care, Robbinsdale, MN
Primary Contact: Andrew S. Cochrane, Chief Executive Officer
CFO: Aaron Bloomquist, Chief Financial Officer
CMO: Pamela Doorenbos, M.D., Vice President, Medical Affairs
CHR: Rebecca A. Rauen, Director Human Resources
CNO: Wendy Ulferts, Vice President and Chief Nursing Officer
Web address: www.maplegrovehospital.org
Control: Other not–for–profit (including NFP Corporation) **Service**: General medical and surgical

Staffed Beds: 108 **Admissions:** 9105 **Census:** 64 **Outpatient Visits:** 229419 **Births:** 4567 **Total Expense ($000):** 161174 **Payroll Expense ($000):** 56739 **Personnel:** 745

MAPLEWOOD—Ramsey County

⊞ **ST. JOHN'S HOSPITAL (240210)**, 1575 Beam Avenue, Zip 55109–1126; tel. 651/232–7000, **A**1 3 5 10 **F**3 5 13 15 18 28 29 30 31 34 35 36 37 38 40 43 44 45 46 49 50 51 53 55 57 59 61 63 64 68 70 72 74 75 76 77 78 79 81 82 85 86 87 93 96 97 100 102 104 107 108 110 111 114 115 116 117 118 119 120 121 123 126 129 130 131 132 135 146 147 148 149 **P**8 **S** Fairview Health Services, Minneapolis, MN
Primary Contact: Lia Christiansen, Chief Operating Officer, Acute Care Hospitals
COO: M. Osman Akhtar, Chief Operating Officer
CFO: Daniel Fromm, Chief Financial Officer
CMO: Mark Welton, M.D., Chief Medical Officer
CIO: Alistar Jacques, Chief Information Officer
CHR: Carolyn Jacobson, Chief Human Resources Officer
CNO: Laura Reed, R.N., Chief Nursing Executive
Web address: www.stjohnshospital-mn.org
Control: Other not–for–profit (including NFP Corporation) **Service**: General medical and surgical

Staffed Beds: 192 **Admissions:** 12080 **Census:** 107 **Outpatient Visits:** 119392 **Births:** 2243 **Total Expense ($000):** 244241 **Payroll Expense ($000):** 91658 **Personnel:** 1007

MARSHALL—Lyon County

★ **AVERA MARSHALL REGIONAL MEDICAL CENTER (241359)**, 300 South Bruce Street, Zip 56258–3900; tel. 507/532–9661, (Total facility includes 76 beds in nursing home–type unit) **A**10 18 **F**2 3 11 12 13 15 17 18 28 29 30 31 33 34 35 40 41 43 45 50 56 57 59 62 63 64 65 70 75 76 78 79 81 82 84 85 87 89 97 98 101 102 104 107 110 111 115 119 120 121 123 128 129 130 131 132 133 144 146 148 149 **S** Avera Health, Sioux Falls, SD
Primary Contact: Mary B. Maertens, FACHE, President and Chief Executive Officer
CFO: Sharon Williams, Vice President Finance and Information Technology
CMO: Edward Woiske, M.D., Chief Medical Officer
CIO: Sharon Williams, Vice President Finance and Information Technology
CHR: Sonya J Kayser, Human Resources Officer
CNO: Dodie Derynck, Chief Nursing Officer
Web address: www.avera.org
Control: Church operated, Nongovernment, not–for–profit **Service**: General medical and surgical

Staffed Beds: 111 **Admissions:** 2092 **Census:** 91 **Outpatient Visits:** 57068 **Births:** 478 **Total Expense ($000):** 56574 **Payroll Expense ($000):** 22163 **Personnel:** 390

MELROSE—Stearns County

★ **CENTRACARE HEALTH–MELROSE (241330)**, 525 Main Street West, Zip 56352–1043; tel. 320/256–4231, (Total facility includes 75 beds in nursing home–type unit) **A**10 18 **F**2 3 6 7 10 13 15 28 30 34 35 40 41 43 56 57 76 77 78 79 81 82 85 89 91 92 93 96 103 107 110 111 115 119 121 127 128 129 130 132 133 135 146 148 154 **S** CentraCare Health, Saint Cloud, MN
Primary Contact: Gerry Gilbertson, FACHE, Administrator
COO: Gerry Gilbertson, FACHE, Administrator
CFO: Adam Paulson, Director Finance
CMO: Dante Beretta, M.D., Chief of Staff
CIO: Janet Kruzel, Business Office Manager
CHR: Joyce Chan, Chief Human Resources Officer
CNO: Keri Wimmer, R.N., Patient Care Director
Web address: www.centracare.com
Control: Other not–for–profit (including NFP Corporation) **Service**: General medical and surgical

Staffed Beds: 93 **Admissions:** 544 **Census:** 80 **Total Expense ($000):** 32635 **Payroll Expense ($000):** 14944

Many Facility Codes have changed. Please refer to the AHA Guide Code Chart.   © 2018 AHA Guide

MINNEAPOLIS—Hennepin County

⌖ ⇑ **ABBOTT NORTHWESTERN HOSPITAL (240057)**, 800 East 28th
Street, Zip 55407–3799; tel. 612/863–4000, (Includes SISTER KENNY
REHABILITATION INSTITUTE, 810 East 27th Street, Minneapolis, MN, Zip 55407;
tel. 612/874–4000) (Total facility includes 48 beds in nursing home–type unit) **A**1
2 3 5 10 21 **F**3 8 9 12 13 15 17 18 19 20 22 24 26 28 29 30 31 34 35 36 38
39 40 43 44 45 46 47 48 49 50 51 52 53 54 55 56 57 58 59 60 61 63 64 65
66 68 70 71 74 75 76 77 78 79 81 82 83 84 85 86 87 90 91 92 93 95 96 97
98 99 100 101 102 104 105 107 108 109 110 111 112 113 114 115 116 117
118 119 120 121 123 124 126 128 129 130 131 132 135 137 138 141 143
144 145 146 147 148 149 153 154 **P**6 **S** Allina Health, Minneapolis, MN
Primary Contact: Thomas O'Connor, Interim Chief Executive Officer
CFO: Brian Weinreis, Vice President Operations and Finance
CMO: Penny Ann Wheeler, M.D., President and Chief Medical Officer
CIO: Susan Heichert, Senior Vice President and Chief Information Officer
CHR: Margaret Butler, Vice President Human Resources
Web address: www.abbottnorthwestern.com
Control: Other not–for–profit (including NFP Corporation) **Service**: General
medical and surgical

> **Staffed Beds**: 679 **Admissions**: 36324 **Census**: 458 **Outpatient Visits**:
> 524107 **Births**: 5102 **Total Expense ($000)**: 1179631 **Payroll Expense
> ($000)**: 496719 **Personnel**: 4951

⌖ **CHILDREN'S HOSPITALS AND CLINICS OF MINNESOTA (243302)**, 2525
Chicago Avenue South, Zip 55404–4518; tel. 612/813–6100, (Includes
CHILDREN'S HOSPITALS AND CLINICS OF MINNESOTA, 345 North Smith Avenue,
Saint Paul, MN, Zip 55102–2346; tel. 651/220–6000; Robert Bonar Jr, Chief
Executive Officer) **A**1 3 5 10 **F**3 8 9 17 18 19 20 21 22 23 24 25 26 27 28 29
30 31 32 34 35 36 38 39 40 43 45 50 51 54 55 57 58 59 61 62 63 64 65 68
71 72 73 74 75 77 78 79 80 81 82 84 85 86 87 88 89 92 93 97 100 101 102
104 107 108 111 112 114 115 119 129 130 131 132 134 135 136 143 145
146 148 154
Primary Contact: Marc Gorelick, M.D., President and Chief Executive Officer
COO: Trevor Sawallish, Senior Vice President Clinical Operations and Chief
Operating Officer
CFO: Rebecca Woitalewicz, Chief Financial Officer
CMO: Emily Chapman, Chief Medical Officer
CIO: Jeffrey D Young, Chief Information Officer
CHR: Samantha Hanson, Chief Human Resources Officer
CNO: Roxanne Fernandes, R.N., Chief Nursing Officer
Web address: www.childrensmn.org
Control: Other not–for–profit (including NFP Corporation) **Service**: Children's
general medical and surgical

> **Staffed Beds**: 430 **Admissions**: 15482 **Census**: 285 **Outpatient Visits**:
> 489646 **Births**: 0 **Total Expense ($000)**: 869390 **Payroll Expense
> ($000)**: 398017 **Personnel**: 3956

FAIRVIEW RIVERSIDE HOSPITAL See University of Minnesota Medical Center,
Fairview, Minneapolis

□ △ **HENNEPIN HEALTHCARE (240004)**, 701 Park Avenue South,
Zip 55415–1829; tel. 612/873–3000, (Includes HCMC DEPARTMENT
OF PEDIATRICS, 701 Park Avenue, Minneapolis, MN, Zip 55415–1623;
tel. 612/873–2064) **A**1 2 3 5 7 8 10 **F**3 5 7 12 13 15 16 18 20 22 24 26 28 29
30 31 32 33 34 35 36 38 39 40 41 43 44 45 46 47 48 49 50 51 53 54 55 56
57 58 59 60 61 62 63 64 65 66 68 70 72 74 75 76 77 78 79 81 82 84 85 86
87 88 89 90 92 93 94 96 97 98 99 100 101 102 103 104 105 106 107 108
110 111 112 114 115 117 118 119 120 121 126 129 130 131 132 134 135
136 138 139 140 141 144 145 146 147 148 149 150 153 154 **P**6
Primary Contact: Jon Pryor, M.D., Chief Executive Officer
COO: Emily Blomberg, Chief Operating Officer
CFO: Larry Kryzaniak, Chief Financial Officer
CMO: William Heegaard, M.D., Chief Medical Officer
CIO: Nancy Garrett, Chief Analytics and Information Technology Officer
CHR: Walter Chesley, Senior Vice President Human Resources
CNO: Kathy R Wilde, R.N., Chief Nursing Officer
Web address: www.hcmc.org
Control: County, Government, nonfederal **Service**: General medical and surgical

> **Staffed Beds**: 461 **Admissions**: 22954 **Census**: 333 **Outpatient Visits**:
> 725241 **Births**: 1965 **Total Expense ($000)**: 1026567 **Payroll Expense
> ($000)**: 546071 **Personnel**: 5722

⌖ △ **MINNEAPOLIS VETERANS AFFAIRS HEALTH CARE SYSTEM**, One
Veterans Drive, Zip 55417–2399; tel. 612/725–2000, (Nonreporting) **A**1 2 3 5 7
8 **S** Department of Veterans Affairs, Perry Point, MD
Primary Contact: Patrick J. Kelly, FACHE, Director
COO: Kurt Thielen, Associate Director
CFO: LeAnn Stomberg, Chief Financial Officer
CMO: Kent Crossley, M.D., Chief of Staff
CIO: Brian Bornick, Chief Information Officer
CHR: Tom Johnson, Chief Human Resource Officer
CNO: Helen Pearlman, Nurse Executive
Web address: www.minneapolis.va.gov
Control: Veterans Affairs, Government, federal **Service**: General medical and
surgical

> **Staffed Beds**: 309

⌖ **PHILLIPS EYE INSTITUTE (240196)**, 2215 Park Avenue, Zip 55404–3756;
tel. 612/775–8800, (Nonreporting) **A**1 10 **S** Allina Health, Minneapolis, MN
Primary Contact: Daniel S. Conrad, M.D., President
CFO: Chris Verdon, Director Finance
CMO: Emmett Carpel, M.D., Medical Director and Chief of Staff
CNO: Margaret Watry, Director of Patient Care Services and Nurse Executive
Web address: www.allinahealth.org/ahs/pei.nsf/
Control: Other not–for–profit (including NFP Corporation) **Service**: Eye, ear, nose
and throat

> **Staffed Beds**: 8

□ **SHRINERS HOSPITALS FOR CHILDREN–TWIN CITIES (243303)**, 2025 East
River Parkway, Zip 55414–3696; tel. 612/596–6100, (Nonreporting) **A**1 3 5 10 **S**
Shriners Hospitals for Children, Tampa, FL
Primary Contact: Charles C. Lobeck, Administrator
CMO: Kenneth Guidera, M.D., Chief of Staff
CHR: Karen Frigen, Director Human Resources
Web address: www.shrinershospitalsforchildren.org/Hospitals/Locations/twincities.
aspx
Control: Other not–for–profit (including NFP Corporation) **Service**: Children's
orthopedic

> **Staffed Beds**: 40

SISTER KENNY REHABILITATION INSTITUTE See Abbott Northwestern
Hospital, Minneapolis

ST. MARY'S HOSPITAL AND REHABILITATION CENTER See University of
Minnesota Medical Center, Fairview, Minneapolis

UNIVERSITY OF MINNESOTA HOSPITAL AND CLINIC See University of
Minnesota Medical Center, Fairview, Minneapolis

⌖ **UNIVERSITY OF MINNESOTA MEDICAL CENTER, FAIRVIEW (240080)**, 2450
Riverside Avenue, Zip 55454–1400; tel. 612/672–6000, (Includes FAIRVIEW
RIVERSIDE HOSPITAL, 2312 South Sixth Street, Minneapolis, MN, Zip 55454;
tel. 612/371–6300; ST. MARY'S HOSPITAL AND REHABILITATION CENTER,
2414 South Seventh Street, Minneapolis, MN, Zip 55454; tel. 612/338–2229;
UNIVERSITY OF MINNESOTA HOSPITAL AND CLINIC, 420 SE Delaware Street,
Minneapolis, MN, Zip 55455–0392; tel. 612/626–3000; UNIVERSITY OF
MINNESOTA MASONIC CHILDREN'S HOSPITAL, 420 Delaware Street, SE,
Minneapolis, MN, Zip 55455–0341; tel. 888/543–7866) (Total facility includes 20
beds in nursing home–type unit) **A**1 3 5 8 10 **F**2 3 4 5 11 12 13 15 17 18 19 20
21 22 23 24 25 26 27 28 29 30 31 32 33 34 35 36 37 38 39 40 41 43 44 45
46 47 48 49 50 51 54 55 56 57 58 59 60 61 64 65 68 70 72 74 75 76 77 78
79 80 81 82 84 85 86 87 88 89 90 91 92 93 96 97 98 99 100 101 102 104
105 106 107 108 109 110 111 112 113 114 115 116 117 118 119 120 121
123 124 126 128 130 131 132 134 135 136 137 138 139 140 141 142 145
146 147 148 149 151 153 **S** Fairview Health Services, Minneapolis, MN
Primary Contact: John Doherty, Co–President, M Health
CFO: John Doherty, Vice President Finance
CMO: Barbara Gold, M.D., Chief Medical Officer
CHR: Don Moschkau, Senior Director Human Resources
Web address: www.fairview.org
Control: Other not–for–profit (including NFP Corporation) **Service**: General
medical and surgical

> **Staffed Beds**: 860 **Admissions**: 33863 **Census**: 642 **Outpatient Visits**:
> 565921 **Births**: 2381 **Total Expense ($000)**: 1577959 **Payroll Expense
> ($000)**: 570068 **Personnel**: 6755

VETERANS AFFAIRS MEDICAL CENTER See Minneapolis Veterans Affairs Health
Care System

MN

Hospital, Medicare Provider Number, Address, Telephone, Approval, Facility, and Physician Codes, Health Care System

★ American Hospital Association (AHA) membership   ○ Healthcare Facilities Accreditation Program   ⇑ Center for Improvement in Healthcare Quality Accreditation
□ The Joint Commission accreditation   ◇ DNV Healthcare Inc. accreditation   △ Commission on Accreditation of Rehabilitation Facilities (CARF) accreditation

MN

MONTEVIDEO—Chippewa County

★ **CHIPPEWA COUNTY–MONTEVIDEO HOSPITAL (241325)**, 824 North 11th Street, Zip 56265–1683; tel. 320/269–8877, (Nonreporting) **A**10 18
Primary Contact: Brian A. Lovdahl, Chief Executive Officer
CFO: Darlene Boike, Chief Financial Officer
CIO: Jeff Plemel, Director Health Information
CHR: Vonnie Erickson, Human Resource Manager
CNO: Terry Anderson, R.N., Director of Nursing Services
Web address: www.montevideomedical.com
Control: City–county, Government, nonfederal **Service:** General medical and surgical

Staffed Beds: 25

MONTICELLO—Wright County

⊞ **CENTRACARE HEALTH–MONTICELLO (241362)**, 1013 Hart Boulevard, Zip 55362–8230; tel. 763/295–2945, (Nonreporting) **A**1 5 10 18 **S** CentraCare Health, Saint Cloud, MN
Primary Contact: Mary Ellen Wells, FACHE, Administrator
CFO: Kristine Hammer, Director of Finance
CMO: John Hering, M.D., Chief Medical Officer
CNO: Lynn Christian, R.N., MSN, Division Director, Acute Care Nursing
Web address: www.centracare.com
Control: Hospital district or authority, Government, nonfederal **Service:** General medical and surgical

Staffed Beds: 126

MOOSE LAKE—Carlton County

★ **MERCY HOSPITAL (241350)**, 4572 County Road 61, Zip 55767–9405; tel. 218/485–4481, **A**10 18 **F**3 7 8 11 13 15 28 29 31 34 35 40 43 45 46 53 57 59 62 64 68 70 75 76 77 79 81 85 86 87 93 107 110 111 114 119 124 129 130 131 132 133 135 144 146 148 149 **P**5
Primary Contact: Michael Delfs, Chief Executive Officer
CHR: Sonya Towle, Director Human Resources
CNO: Donita Korpela, R.N., Director of Patient Care Services
Web address: www.mercymooselake.org
Control: Hospital district or authority, Government, nonfederal **Service:** General medical and surgical

Staffed Beds: 25 Admissions: 735 Census: 8 Outpatient Visits: 33367 Births: 111 Total Expense ($000): 35665 Payroll Expense ($000): 13498 Personnel: 194

MORA—Kanabec County

⊞ **FIRSTLIGHT HEALTH SYSTEM (241367)**, 301 South Highway 65 South, Zip 55051–1899; tel. 320/679–1212, **A**1 10 18 **F**3 7 11 13 15 28 30 31 34 35 40 43 51 53 57 59 70 75 76 77 78 79 81 84 85 87 93 94 107 110 111 115 118 119 127 130 131 132 133 135 144 146 148 149
Primary Contact: Randy Ulseth, Chief Executive Officer
COO: Sandy Zutz–Wiczek, Chief Operating Officer
CFO: Gordy Forbort, Chief Financial Officer
CIO: Becky Gallik, Information Systems Manager
CHR: Kim Carlson, Senior Vice President Human Resources
CNO: Diane Bankers, Senior Vice President, Nursing Services
Web address: www.firstlighthealthsystem.org
Control: County, Government, nonfederal **Service:** General medical and surgical

Staffed Beds: 25 Admissions: 1282 Census: 9 Outpatient Visits: 37235 Births: 217 Total Expense ($000): 76417 Payroll Expense ($000): 25116 Personnel: 406

MORRIS—Stevens County

★ **STEVENS COMMUNITY MEDICAL CENTER (241363)**, 400 East First Street, Zip 56267–1408; tel. 320/589–1313, **A**10 18 **F**3 11 13 15 28 29 31 34 35 40 43 44 45 50 54 57 59 64 70 75 76 77 79 81 85 86 87 89 97 107 110 111 115 119 127 130 131 132 135 146 148 149 **P**6
Primary Contact: John Rau, President and Chief Executive Officer
CFO: Kerrie Erickson, Vice President Finance
CIO: Kerrie Erickson, Vice President Finance
CHR: Karla Larson, Director Human Resources
Web address: www.scmcinc.org
Control: Other not–for–profit (including NFP Corporation) **Service:** General medical and surgical

Staffed Beds: 25 Admissions: 789 Census: 7 Outpatient Visits: 71308 Births: 97 Total Expense ($000): 38312 Payroll Expense ($000): 18011 Personnel: 247

NEW PRAGUE—Scott County

☐ **MAYO CLINIC HEALTH SYSTEM IN NEW PRAGUE (241361)**, 301 Second Street NE, Zip 56071–1799; tel. 952/758–4431, **A**1 10 18 **F**11 13 15 18 28 29 30 31 34 35 36 40 43 45 46 53 57 59 64 68 74 75 76 77 78 79 81 82 85 86 87 93 97 107 108 110 111 114 116 117 119 125 128 129 130 131 132 133 146 147 149 **P**6 **S** Mayo Clinic, Rochester, MN
Primary Contact: Mary J. Klimp, FACHE, Interim Administrator
Web address: www.mayoclinichealthsystem.org/locations/new-prague
Control: Other not–for–profit (including NFP Corporation) **Service:** General medical and surgical

Staffed Beds: 20 Admissions: 783 Census: 10 Outpatient Visits: 46605 Births: 167 Personnel: 180

NEW ULM—Brown County

⊞ **NEW ULM MEDICAL CENTER (241378)**, 1324 Fifth Street North, Zip 56073–1553; tel. 507/217–5000, **A**1 3 10 18 **F**3 4 5 8 13 15 28 29 31 32 34 35 36 40 43 45 50 55 56 57 59 64 65 68 70 75 76 77 78 79 81 82 84 85 87 89 93 94 97 98 100 101 102 104 107 108 111 115 119 129 130 131 132 135 144 146 148 149 154 **S** Allina Health, Minneapolis, MN
Primary Contact: Toby Freier, President
CFO: Steve Schneider, Manager Behavioral Services and Director Operations
CMO: Daniel Holmberg, M.D., Director of Medical Affairs
CHR: Anne Makepeace, Director Human Resources
CNO: Jennifer Brehmer, Director of Patient Care
Web address: www.newulmmedicalcenter.com
Control: Other not–for–profit (including NFP Corporation) **Service:** General medical and surgical

Staffed Beds: 45 Admissions: 2244 Census: 19 Outpatient Visits: 123768 Births: 304 Total Expense ($000): 85511 Payroll Expense ($000): 29745 Personnel: 411

NORTHFIELD—Dakota County

★ **NORTHFIELD HOSPITAL AND CLINICS (240014)**, 2000 North Avenue, Zip 55057–1498; tel. 507/646–1000, (Total facility includes 40 beds in nursing home–type unit) **A**10 18 **F**3 7 11 13 15 30 31 40 43 48 62 63 64 68 69 70 75 76 77 78 79 81 85 87 89 93 107 110 111 115 119 128 129 130 131 132 133 144 146 149 154 **P**6
Primary Contact: Steve Underdahl, President and Chief Executive Officer
COO: Jerry Ehn, Chief Operating Officer
CFO: Scott D Edin, Vice President, Finance and Chief Financial Officer
CMO: Jeff Meland, M.D., Vice President, Chief Medical Officer
CHR: Vicki Stevens, Human Resources Executive
CNO: Tammy A. Hayes, R.N., MS, Chief Nurse Executive and Long Term Care Administrator
Web address: www.northfieldhospital.org
Control: City, Government, nonfederal **Service:** General medical and surgical

Staffed Beds: 77 Admissions: 2014 Census: 51 Outpatient Visits: 140694 Births: 541 Total Expense ($000): 108117 Payroll Expense ($000): 46736 Personnel: 552

OLIVIA—Renville County

★ **RC HOSPITAL AND CLINICS (241306)**, 100 Healthy Way, Zip 56277–1117; tel. 320/523–1261, **A**10 18 **F**3 8 15 17 28 29 34 35 40 41 43 45 46 57 59 63 64 65 68 70 75 76 77 79 81 82 85 86 89 93 94 96 97 107 111 114 119 126 127 129 130 131 132 133 146 148 149
Primary Contact: Nathan Blad, Chief Executive Officer
CFO: Nathan Blad, Chief Financial Officer
CIO: Cherry Weigel, Director Health Information Management
Web address: www.rchospital.com
Control: County, Government, nonfederal **Service:** General medical and surgical

Staffed Beds: 16 Admissions: 390 Census: 4 Outpatient Visits: 66772 Births: 43 Total Expense ($000): 26429 Payroll Expense ($000): 10074 Personnel: 151

ONAMIA—Mille Lacs County

★ **MILLE LACS HEALTH SYSTEM (241356)**, 200 North Elm Street, Zip 56359–7901; tel. 320/532–3154, (Total facility includes 57 beds in nursing home–type unit) **A**10 18 **F**7 11 15 28 29 31 33 34 40 43 45 50 59 62 63 64 75 77 81 85 93 98 103 107 110 114 115 127 129 130 132 133 135 144 149 **P**6
Primary Contact: Bill Nelson, Chief Executive Officer
COO: Kim Kucera, Chief Operating Officer
CFO: John Unzen, Chief Financial Officer
CMO: Thomas H Bracken, M.D., Vice President Medical Affairs
Web address: www.mlhealth.org
Control: Other not–for–profit (including NFP Corporation) **Service:** General medical and surgical

Staffed Beds: 85 Admissions: 875 Census: 63 Outpatient Visits: 23984 Births: 5 Total Expense ($000): 40060 Payroll Expense ($000): 20240 Personnel: 370

Many Facility Codes have changed. Please refer to the AHA Guide Code Chart. © 2018 AHA Guide

ORTONVILLE—Big Stone County

★ **ORTONVILLE AREA HEALTH SERVICES (241342)**, 450 Eastvold Avenue, Zip 56278–1133; tel. 320/839–2502, (Total facility includes 51 beds in nursing home–type unit) **A**5 10 18 **F**2 3 6 7 8 10 11 13 15 18 19 20 21 28 29 30 31 32 34 36 40 44 45 46 47 50 56 59 60 62 63 64 65 68 69 74 75 76 77 78 79 81 85 86 87 93 94 96 97 100 101 102 104 107 110 111 112 115 116 117 118 119 125 127 128 129 130 131 132 133 135 143 147 148 149 154 **P**4 **S** Sanford Health, Sioux Falls, SD
Primary Contact: David Rogers, Chief Executive Officer
CFO: Kevin Benson, Chief Financial Officer
CMO: Stacy Longnecker, Chief of Staff
CIO: Barbara Voecks, Chief Information Officer
CHR: Kim McCrea, Chief Human Resources Officer
CNO: Jennifer Wiik, Chief Nursing Officer
Web address: www.oahs.us
Control: City, Government, nonfederal **Service:** General medical and surgical

Staffed Beds: 90 **Admissions:** 575 **Census:** 54 **Outpatient Visits:** 23112 **Births:** 72 **Total Expense ($000):** 29276 **Payroll Expense ($000):** 10179

OWATONNA—Steele County

☒ **OWATONNA HOSPITAL (240069)**, 2250 NW 26th Street, Zip 55060–5503; tel. 507/451–3850, **A**1 10 **F**11 13 28 29 34 35 40 57 77 79 80 81 93 98 100 101 102 107 108 119 129 130 131 145 149 154 **S** Allina Health, Minneapolis, MN
Primary Contact: David L. Albrecht, President
COO: Mark T Gillen, Director of Operations
CFO: Mark T Gillen, Director Finance and Operations
CHR: Sarah Stumme, Director Human Resources
CNO: Anne Draeger, Chief Nursing Officer
Web address: www.owatonnahospital.com
Control: Other not–for–profit (including NFP Corporation) **Service:** General medical and surgical

Staffed Beds: 43 **Admissions:** 2577 **Census:** 24 **Outpatient Visits:** 41420 **Births:** 470 **Total Expense ($000):** 52205 **Payroll Expense ($000):** 19262 **Personnel:** 239

PARK RAPIDS—Hubbard County

☒ **CHI ST. JOSEPH'S HEALTH (241380)**, 600 Pleasant Avenue, Zip 56470–1431; tel. 218/732–3311, **A**1 5 10 18 **F**3 11 12 13 15 28 29 30 32 34 35 39 40 43 45 47 50 57 59 63 64 65 70 75 76 77 79 81 82 84 85 93 107 108 110 115 118 129 130 131 132 133 134 146 149 150 154 **S** Catholic Health Initiatives, Englewood, CO
Primary Contact: Benjamin Koppelman, President
CFO: Jay Ross, Chief Financial Officer
CMO: Kia Parsi, M.D., Chief Medical Officer
CHR: John Tormanen, Director Mission and Human Resources
CNO: Deb Haagenson, R.N., Vice President of Patient Care
Web address: www.sjahs.org
Control: Church operated, Nongovernment, not–for–profit **Service:** General medical and surgical

Staffed Beds: 25 **Admissions:** 1423 **Census:** 14 **Outpatient Visits:** 45220 **Births:** 98 **Total Expense ($000):** 47194 **Payroll Expense ($000):** 18309 **Personnel:** 254

PAYNESVILLE—Stearns County

★ **CENTRACARE HEALTH–PAYNESVILLE (241349)**, 200 West 1st Street, Zip 56362–1496; tel. 320/243–3767, (Total facility includes 52 beds in nursing home–type unit) **A**10 18 **F**2 7 10 11 13 15 28 31 34 40 43 45 50 56 57 64 65 71 81 82 85 93 107 110 111 115 119 125 128 130 133 135 145 146 148 149 **S** CentraCare Health, Saint Cloud, MN
Primary Contact: Brandon E. Pietsch, Administrator
CFO: Jennifer Holtz, Director Finance
CMO: Timothy Malling, M.D., Chief of Staff
CHR: Paulette Hagen, Human Resources and Administrative Services Director
CNO: Rachel A Walz, Director Patient Care
Web address: www.centracare.com
Control: Other not–for–profit (including NFP Corporation) **Service:** General medical and surgical

Staffed Beds: 67 **Admissions:** 559 **Census:** 56 **Outpatient Visits:** 37889 **Births:** 80 **Total Expense ($000):** 37443 **Payroll Expense ($000):** 19174 **Personnel:** 140

PERHAM—Otter Tail County

☒ **PERHAM HEALTH (241373)**, 1000 Coney Street West, Zip 56573–1108; tel. 218/347–4500, (Total facility includes 96 beds in nursing home–type unit) **A**1 10 18 **F**2 3 8 10 13 15 28 29 30 33 34 36 40 41 43 45 50 56 57 59 62 64 65 69 75 76 77 81 85 86 89 91 93 97 107 110 111 119 125 128 130 131 132 133 135 144 146 147 148 149 154 **S** Sanford Health, Sioux Falls, SD
Primary Contact: Chuck Hofius, Chief Executive Officer
CFO: Brad D Wurgler, Chief Financial Officer
CMO: Tim Studer, President Medical Staff
CIO: Jim Rieber, Director Information Systems
CNO: Bonnie Johnson, R.N., Vice President of Patient Services
Web address: www.perhamhealth.org
Control: Hospital district or authority, Government, nonfederal **Service:** General medical and surgical

Staffed Beds: 121 **Admissions:** 650 **Census:** 96 **Outpatient Visits:** 321282 **Births:** 139 **Total Expense ($000):** 53894 **Payroll Expense ($000):** 23751 **Personnel:** 269

PIPESTONE—Pipestone County

★ **PIPESTONE COUNTY MEDICAL CENTER AVERA (241374)**, 916 4th Avenue SW, Zip 56164–1890; tel. 507/825–5811, **A**10 18 **F**3 8 13 15 28 29 30 31 34 35 40 45 46 47 48 50 53 56 57 59 62 63 64 65 68 75 76 77 79 81 82 85 93 96 97 107 110 111 115 119 130 131 132 133 135 146 148 149 **P**6 **S** Avera Health, Sioux Falls, SD
Primary Contact: Bradley D. Burris, Chief Executive Officer
CFO: Dave Keeler, Chief Financial Officer
CHR: Judy Raschke, Director Human Resources
CNO: Jessica Smidt, R.N., Director of Nursing
Web address: www.pcmchealth.org
Control: County, Government, nonfederal **Service:** General medical and surgical

Staffed Beds: 18 **Admissions:** 352 **Census:** 3 **Outpatient Visits:** 34538 **Births:** 89 **Total Expense ($000):** 29126 **Payroll Expense ($000):** 9149 **Personnel:** 166

PRINCETON—Sherburne County

☒ **FAIRVIEW NORTHLAND MEDICAL CENTER (240141)**, 911 Northland Drive, Zip 55371–2173; tel. 763/389–1313, **A**1 5 10 **F**3 11 13 15 18 34 35 40 41 43 47 48 50 51 57 59 64 69 70 75 76 77 78 79 81 85 86 87 89 93 94 101 107 110 111 115 119 130 131 132 146 148 149 154 **P**6 **S** Fairview Health Services, Minneapolis, MN
Primary Contact: Lia Christiansen, Chief Operating Officer, Acute Care Hospitals
CFO: Kim Ericson, Vice President Finance
CMO: Greg Schoen, M.D., Regional Medical Director
CHR: Erich Spencer, Chief Human Resource Officer
CNO: Karen Whiley, Vice President Patient Care Services
Web address: www.northland.fairview.org
Control: Other not–for–profit (including NFP Corporation) **Service:** General medical and surgical

Staffed Beds: 23 **Admissions:** 1701 **Census:** 13 **Outpatient Visits:** 50925 **Births:** 374 **Total Expense ($000):** 58892 **Payroll Expense ($000):** 27827 **Personnel:** 248

RED LAKE—Beltrami County

☐ **RED LAKE INDIAN HEALTH SERVICE HOSPITAL (240206)**, 24760 Hospital Drive, Zip 56671, Mailing Address: P.O. Box 497, Zip 56671–0497; tel. 218/679–3912, (Nonreporting) **A**1 10 **S** U.S. Indian Health Service, Rockville, MD
Primary Contact: Norine Smith, Chief Executive Officer
CMO: Paul Ditmanson, M.D., Clinical Director
CNO: Mary Ann Cook, R.N., Director of Nursing
Web address: www.rlnnredlakehospital.com/
Control: PHS, Indian Service, Government, federal **Service:** General medical and surgical

Staffed Beds: 19

MN

RED WING—Goodhue County

☐ **MAYO CLINIC HEALTH SYSTEM IN RED WING (240018)**, 701 Hewitt Boulevard, Zip 55066–2848, Mailing Address: P.O. Box 95, Zip 55066–0095; tel. 651/267–5000, **A**1 3 10 **F**3 11 13 15 18 28 29 30 31 34 35 36 40 43 45 57 59 63 64 65 70 74 75 76 77 78 79 81 87 93 94 97 100 104 107 111 115 119 129 130 131 132 146 147 149 **P**6 **S** Mayo Clinic, Rochester, MN
Primary Contact: Brian Whited, M.D., President and Chief Executive Officer
CMO: Jack Alexander, M.D., Chief Medical Officer
CHR: Kim Trittin, Manager Human Resources
Web address: www.mayoclinichealthsystem.org/locations/red–wing
Control: Other not–for–profit (including NFP Corporation) **Service**: General medical and surgical

Staffed Beds: 22 **Admissions**: 1934 **Census**: 13 **Outpatient Visits**: 172078
Births: 319 **Personnel**: 470

REDWOOD FALLS—Redwood County

★ **REDWOOD AREA HOSPITAL (241351)**, 100 Fallwood Road, Zip 56283–1828; tel. 507/637–4500, **A**10 18 **F**2 3 11 13 15 29 31 34 35 40 45 46 57 59 62 63 75 77 79 81 84 93 107 111 115 119 129 130 131 133 146 148 149 154
Primary Contact: Bryan Lydick, Chief Executive Officer
CFO: Thomas Richard, Director Budget and Revenue Cycle
CIO: Tom Balko, Manager Information Systems
CHR: Jody Rindfleisch, Manager Human Resources
CNO: Dawn Allen, R.N., Chief Nursing Officer
Web address: www.redwoodareahospital.org
Control: City, Government, nonfederal **Service**: General medical and surgical

Staffed Beds: 25 **Admissions**: 515 **Census**: 5 **Outpatient Visits**: 22329
Births: 90 **Total Expense ($000)**: 24853 **Payroll Expense ($000)**: 9138
Personnel: 141

ROBBINSDALE—Hennepin County

△ ⇑ **NORTH MEMORIAL HEALTH HOSPITAL (240001)**, 3300 Oakdale Avenue North, Zip 55422–2926; tel. 763/520–5200, **A**2 3 5 7 10 21 **F**3 7 11 12 13 15 17 18 20 22 24 26 28 29 30 31 34 35 38 40 44 49 50 53 54 55 56 57 58 59 60 61 63 64 68 70 72 73 74 75 76 77 78 79 80 81 82 84 85 86 87 88 89 90 91 92 93 96 97 98 100 102 103 104 105 107 108 110 111 114 115 117 118 119 124 126 129 130 132 135 144 146 147 148 149 150 153 154 **P**8 **S** North Memorial Health Care, Robbinsdale, MN
Primary Contact: Jeff Wicklander, President
COO: Steve Horstmann, Vice President Operations
CFO: Aaron Bloomquist, Chief Financial Officer
CMO: Andrew Houlton, M.D., Chief Medical Officer
CIO: Patrick Taffe, Vice President Information Services
CHR: Melissa Smith, Interim Vice President Human Resources
CNO: Kelly Lynn White, Vice President of Patient Care and Chief Nursing Officer
Web address: www.northmemorial.com
Control: Other not–for–profit (including NFP Corporation) **Service**: General medical and surgical

Staffed Beds: 358 **Admissions**: 19345 **Census**: 251 **Outpatient Visits**: 170083 **Births**: 909 **Total Expense ($000)**: 786242 **Payroll Expense ($000)**: 378180 **Personnel**: 3188

ROCHESTER—Olmsted County

☐ **COMMUNITY BEHAVIORAL HEALTH HOSPITAL – ROCHESTER (244017)**, 251 Wood Lake Drive SE, Zip 55904–5530; tel. 507/206–2561, (Nonreporting) **A**1 10 **S** Minnesota Department of Human Services, Saint Paul, MN
Primary Contact: James Pierce, Administrator
CFO: Shirley Jacobson, Chief Financial Officer
CMO: Peter S Millen, Chief Medical Officer MHSATS
CIO: Thomas Baden Jr Chief Information Officer
CHR: Connie Jones, Director Human Resources
CNO: Pamela R Bajari, R.N., Nurse Executive MHSATS
Web address: www.health.state.mn.us
Control: State, Government, nonfederal **Service**: Psychiatric

Staffed Beds: 8

☒ △ **MAYO CLINIC HOSPITAL – ROCHESTER (240010)**, 1216 Second Street SW, Zip 55902–1906; tel. 507/255–5123, (Includes MAYO CLINIC HOSPITAL – METHODIST CAMPUS, 201 West Center Street, Rochester, MN, Zip 55902–3084; tel. 507/266–7890; MAYO CLINIC HOSPITAL – SAINT MARYS CAMPUS, 1216 Second Street SW, Rochester, MN, Zip 55902–1970; tel. 507/255–5123; F. Kenneth Ackerman, FACHE, Chair, Hospital Operation; MAYO EUGENIO LITTA CHILDREN'S HOSPITAL, 200 First Street, SW, Rochester, MN, Zip 55905–0001; tel. 507/255–5123) **A**1 2 3 5 7 8 10 20 **F**3 6 8 9 11 12 13 14 15 17 18 19 20 21 22 23 24 25 26 27 28 29 30 31 34 35 36 37 38 39 40 41 43 44 45 46 47 48 49 50 51 52 53 54 55 56 57 58 59 60 61 63 64 65 68 70 71 72 73 74 75 76 77 78 79 80 81 82 84 85 86 87 88 89 90 91 92 93 94 95 96 97 98 99 100 101 102 103 104 105 107 108 110 111 112 114 115 116 117 118 119 120 121 122 123 124 126 130 132 134 135 136 137 138 139 140 141 142 143 145 146 147 148 149 150 153 154 **P**6 **S** Mayo Clinic, Rochester, MN
Primary Contact: F. Kenneth, FACHE, Hospital Administrator
COO: Jeffrey W. Bolton, Chief Administrative Officer
CFO: Kedrick D. Adkins, Chief Financial Officer
CMO: Robert R. Cima, M.D., Medical Director, Hospital Operations
CIO: Christopher J. Ross, Chief Information Technology Officer
CHR: Cathryn H. Fraser, Chief Human Resources Officer
CNO: Pamela O. Johnson, MS, R.N., Chief Nursing Officer
Web address: www.mayoclinic.org
Control: Other not–for–profit (including NFP Corporation) **Service**: General medical and surgical

Staffed Beds: 1287 **Admissions**: 57174 **Census**: 874 **Outpatient Visits**: 312779 **Births**: 2475 **Personnel**: 31808

★ ⇑ **OLMSTED MEDICAL CENTER (240006)**, 1650 Fourth Street SE, Zip 55904–4717, Mailing Address: 210 Ninth Street SE, Zip 55904–6756; tel. 507/288–3443, **A**10 21 **F**3 11 12 15 18 26 28 29 30 34 40 44 45 46 50 53 54 57 58 59 64 65 68 74 75 76 77 79 80 81 82 84 85 86 87 92 93 97 100 102 104 107 108 110 111 115 119 129 130 131 132 135 146 147 148 149 154 **P**6
Primary Contact: Tim W. Weir, FACHE, Chief Executive Officer
CFO: Kevin A Higgins, Chief Financial Officer
CIO: Michelle Majerus, Chief Information Officer
CHR: Tom Hunsberger, Director Human Resources
CNO: Susan Klenner, Chief Nursing Officer and Vice President of Hospital Operations
Web address: www.olmmed.org
Control: Other not–for–profit (including NFP Corporation) **Service**: General medical and surgical

Staffed Beds: 42 **Admissions**: 2234 **Census**: 14 **Outpatient Visits**: 340458 **Births**: 971 **Total Expense ($000)**: 187203 **Payroll Expense ($000)**: 95196 **Personnel**: 854

ROSEAU—Roseau County

☒ **LIFECARE MEDICAL CENTER (241344)**, 715 Delmore Drive, Zip 56751–1599; tel. 218/463–2500, (Total facility includes 90 beds in nursing home–type unit) **A**1 5 10 18 **F**3 7 10 11 13 15 28 29 30 31 32 34 35 36 40 43 45 53 56 57 59 62 63 64 65 68 75 76 77 81 82 84 85 86 93 104 107 110 111 115 118 119 128 129 130 132 133 135 144 146 147 148 149 **P**6
Primary Contact: Keith Okeson, President and Chief Executive Officer
COO: Susan C Lisell, Vice President of Clinical Services
CFO: Cathy Huss, Chief Financial Officer
CIO: Kevin Schumacher, Director of Information Systems
CHR: Lois Slick, Director Human Resources
CNO: Roxanne Fabian, Director of Nursing–Acute Care
Web address: www.lifecaremedicalcenter.org
Control: Other not–for–profit (including NFP Corporation) **Service**: General medical and surgical

Staffed Beds: 115 **Admissions**: 839 **Census**: 94 **Outpatient Visits**: 42514
Births: 196 **Total Expense ($000)**: 43087 **Payroll Expense ($000)**: 19779
Personnel: 337

SAINT CLOUD—Stearns County

☒ △ **ST. CLOUD HOSPITAL (240036)**, 1406 Sixth Avenue North, Zip 56303–1901; tel. 320/251–2700, **A**1 2 3 5 7 10 20 **F**3 5 11 12 13 14 15 17 18 19 20 22 24 26 27 28 29 30 31 32 34 35 36 37 38 39 40 43 44 45 46 47 48 49 50 51 54 56 57 58 59 60 61 62 63 64 66 68 69 70 72 74 75 76 77 78 79 80 81 82 84 85 86 87 88 89 90 92 93 96 97 98 99 100 101 102 103 104 105 106 107 108 110 111 115 117 118 119 120 121 123 126 129 130 131 132 134 135 141 144 145 146 147 148 149 150 151 152 153 **P**6 **S** CentraCare Health, Saint Cloud, MN
Primary Contact: Craig J. Broman, FACHE, President
COO: Joy Plamann, R.N., Chief Nursing and Operating Officer
CFO: Greg Klugherz, Vice President Corporate Services and Chief Financial Officer
CMO: Mark Matthias, M.D., Vice President of Medical Affairs
CIO: Amy Porwoll, Vice President of Information Systems
CHR: Duane Rasmusson, Vice President Human Resources
CNO: Joy Plamann, R.N., Chief Nursing and Operating Officer
Web address: www.centracare.com
Control: Other not–for–profit (including NFP Corporation) **Service**: General medical and surgical

Staffed Beds: 487 **Admissions**: 27607 **Census**: 324 **Outpatient Visits**: 509953 **Births**: 2590 **Total Expense ($000)**: 736290 **Payroll Expense ($000)**: 324045 **Personnel**: 4161

Many Facility Codes have changed. Please refer to the AHA Guide Code Chart. © 2018 AHA Guide

MN

☒ **ST. CLOUD VETERANS AFFAIRS HEALTH CARE SYSTEM**, 4801 Veterans Drive, Zip 56303–2099; tel. 320/252–1670, (Nonreporting) **A**1 3 **S** Department of Veterans Affairs, Perry Point, MD
Primary Contact: Stephen Black, MS, Health Care System Director
COO: Barry I Bahl, Director
CFO: Joseph Schmitz, Chief Financial Officer
CMO: Susan Markstrom, M.D., Chief of Staff
CIO: Denise Hanson, Information Technology Specialist
CHR: Lisa Rosendahl, Director Human Resources
CNO: Meri Hauge, R.N., MSN, Associate Director of Patient Care Services and Nurse Executive
Web address: www.stcloud.va.gov
Control: Veterans Affairs, Government, federal **Service**: Psychiatric

> **Staffed Beds**: 388

VETERANS AFFAIRS MEDICAL CENTER See St. Cloud Veterans Affairs Health Care System

SAINT JAMES—Watonwan County

☐ **MAYO CLINIC HEALTH SYSTEM IN SAINT JAMES (241333)**, 1101 Moulton and Parsons Drive, Zip 56081–5550; tel. 507/375–3261, **A**1 10 18 **F**3 15 18 28 34 35 40 43 53 57 59 64 75 81 86 87 93 97 107 110 114 119 128 129 130 132 133 144 146 148 149 **P**6 **S** Mayo Clinic, Rochester, MN
Primary Contact: Scott D. Thoreson, FACHE, Administrator
COO: Richard Grace, Chief Administrative Officer
CFO: James Tarasovich, Chief Financial Officer
CMO: Jennifer Langbehn, Medical Director
CHR: Gayle B Hansen, R.N., Chief Integration Officer
Web address: www.mayoclinichealthsystem.org/locations/st-james
Control: Other not–for–profit (including NFP Corporation) **Service**: General medical and surgical

> **Staffed Beds**: 13 **Admissions**: 242 **Census**: 6 **Outpatient Visits**: 23350 **Births**: 0 **Personnel**: 64

SAINT LOUIS PARK—Hennepin County

☐ **PARK NICOLLET METHODIST HOSPITAL (240053)**, 6500 Excelsior Boulevard, Zip 55426–4702, Mailing Address: Minneapolis, tel. 952/993–5000, **A**1 2 3 5 10 **F**3 8 11 12 13 15 17 18 20 22 24 26 28 29 30 31 34 38 40 43 44 45 46 47 49 50 51 53 54 55 56 57 58 59 62 63 64 68 70 71 73 74 75 76 77 78 79 81 82 83 84 85 86 87 89 93 94 97 100 102 107 108 111 114 115 117 119 120 121 123 124 126 129 130 132 144 145 146 147 148 149 154 **P**6 **S** HealthPartners, Bloomington, MN
Primary Contact: Roxanna L. Gapstur, Ph.D., R.N., President
COO: Michael Kaupa, Executive Vice President and Chief Operating Officer
CFO: Sheila McMillan, Chief Financial Officer
CMO: Steven Connelly, M.D., President and Chief Medical Officer
CIO: Julie Flaschenriem, Chief Information Officer
CHR: Paul Dominski, Vice President Human Resources
Web address: www.parknicollet.com
Control: Other not–for–profit (including NFP Corporation) **Service**: General medical and surgical

> **Staffed Beds**: 420 **Admissions**: 23263 **Census**: 232 **Outpatient Visits**: 62641 **Births**: 3158 **Total Expense ($000)**: 549083 **Payroll Expense ($000)**: 231268 **Personnel**: 3056

SAINT PAUL—Ramsey County

☒ **BETHESDA HOSPITAL (242004)**, 559 Capitol Boulevard, Zip 55103–2101; tel. 651/232–2000, **A**1 5 10 **F**1 3 6 11 29 30 38 44 50 53 56 64 68 74 75 77 82 84 85 86 87 91 93 96 100 104 107 119 130 132 148 **P**8 **S** Fairview Health Services, Minneapolis, MN
Primary Contact: Patrick Belland, Chief Operating Officer, Acute Care Services
COO: Patrick Belland, Chief Operating Officer, Acute Care Services
CFO: Daniel Fromm, Chief Financial Officer
CMO: Mark Welton, M.D., Chief Medical Officer
CIO: Alistar Jacques, Chief Information Officer
CHR: Carolyn Jacobson, Chief Human Resources Officer
CNO: Laura Reed, R.N., Chief Nursing Executive
Web address: www.healtheast.org
Control: Other not–for–profit (including NFP Corporation) **Service**: Acute long–term care hospital

> **Staffed Beds**: 114 **Admissions**: 965 **Census**: 77 **Outpatient Visits**: 6673 **Births**: 0 **Total Expense ($000)**: 74590 **Payroll Expense ($000)**: 32688 **Personnel**: 393

☒ △ **GILLETTE CHILDREN'S SPECIALTY HEALTHCARE (243300)**, 200 University Avenue East, Zip 55101–2507; tel. 651/291–2848, **A**1 3 5 7 10 **F**3 29 32 34 35 36 39 43 44 50 54 55 58 64 68 74 75 79 81 82 83 84 85 86 87 88 89 90 91 92 93 94 95 96 100 104 107 111 114 115 119 127 129 130 146 148 149 154 **P**6
Primary Contact: Barbara Walczyk–Joers, President and Chief Executive Officer
CFO: Patrick Nolan, Vice President Finance and Chief Financial Officer
CMO: Steven Koop, M.D., Chief Medical Officer, Medical Director
CIO: Timothy Getsay, Chief Information Officer, Vice President of Performance & Information Mgmt
CHR: Kit Brady, Vice President Human Resources, Education and Guest Experience
CNO: Karen Brill, R.N., Chief Nursing Officer, Vice President Care
Web address: www.gillettechildrens.org
Control: Other not–for–profit (including NFP Corporation) **Service**: Children's general medical and surgical

> **Staffed Beds**: 60 **Admissions**: 2128 **Census**: 33 **Outpatient Visits**: 140587 **Births**: 0 **Total Expense ($000)**: 238464 **Payroll Expense ($000)**: 124529 **Personnel**: 1088

☐ △ **REGIONS HOSPITAL (240106)**, 640 Jackson Street, Zip 55101–2595; tel. 651/254–3456, **A**1 2 3 5 7 8 10 **F**3 4 5 7 8 13 15 16 17 18 20 22 24 26 28 29 30 31 34 35 36 38 40 43 45 46 47 48 49 50 51 53 54 55 56 57 58 59 60 64 65 68 70 71 72 74 75 76 77 78 79 81 82 84 85 86 87 88 90 91 93 95 96 98 100 101 102 103 104 105 106 107 108 110 111 114 115 116 117 118 119 120 121 124 126 129 130 131 132 135 143 146 147 148 149 152 154 **P**8 **S** HealthPartners, Bloomington, MN
Primary Contact: Megan Remark, President and Chief Executive Officer
CFO: Heidi Conrad, Vice President and Chief Financial Officer
CMO: Charles Fazio, Chief Health Officer and Medical Director Health Plan
CIO: Kim LaReau, Vice President and Chief Information Officer
CHR: Kim Egan, Executive Director Human Resources
CNO: Chris Boese, Vice President and Chief Nursing Officer
Web address: www.regionshospital.com
Control: Other not–for–profit (including NFP Corporation) **Service**: General medical and surgical

> **Staffed Beds**: 463 **Admissions**: 27074 **Census**: 370 **Outpatient Visits**: 145566 **Births**: 2369 **Total Expense ($000)**: 741742 **Payroll Expense ($000)**: 351494 **Personnel**: 3846

☒ **ST. JOSEPH'S HOSPITAL (240063)**, 45 West 10th Street, Zip 55102–1053; tel. 651/232–3000, **A**1 2 3 5 10 **F**3 4 5 12 15 17 18 20 22 24 26 28 29 30 35 36 37 38 40 43 44 45 49 50 53 56 63 68 70 74 75 77 79 81 84 85 86 87 92 93 96 97 98 100 101 102 103 104 107 108 110 111 114 115 118 119 120 121 124 130 132 146 148 149 152 **P**8 **S** Fairview Health Services, Minneapolis, MN
Primary Contact: Lia Christiansen, Chief Operating Officer, Acute Care Hospitals
COO: Lia Christiansen, Chief Operating Officer, Acute Care Hospitals
CFO: Daniel Fromm, Chief Financial Officer
CMO: Kevin C. Garrett, M.D., Medical Executive East Region
CIO: Joanne Sunquist, Chief Information Officer East Region
CHR: Carolyn Jacobson, Chief Human Resource Officer
CNO: Debra J. Hurd, MS, R.N., Vice President and Chief Nursing Officer
Web address: www.healtheast.org
Control: Other not–for–profit (including NFP Corporation) **Service**: General medical and surgical

> **Staffed Beds**: 237 **Admissions**: 11698 **Census**: 165 **Outpatient Visits**: 52716 **Births**: 584 **Total Expense ($000)**: 291825 **Payroll Expense ($000)**: 107546 **Personnel**: 1316

☒ △ ⇑ **UNITED HOSPITAL (240038)**, 333 North Smith Avenue, Zip 55102–2389; tel. 651/241–8000, **A**1 2 3 5 7 10 21 **F**3 8 12 13 15 17 18 20 22 24 26 28 29 30 31 34 35 36 37 40 43 44 45 46 47 48 49 50 51 53 54 56 58 59 60 61 64 65 68 70 74 75 76 77 78 79 81 82 83 85 86 87 90 91 92 93 95 97 98 99 100 102 103 104 105 107 108 110 111 112 113 114 115 118 119 120 121 123 124 126 129 130 132 134 146 148 149 153 154 **P**6 **S** Allina Health, Minneapolis, MN
Primary Contact: Thomas O'Connor, President
CFO: John Bien, Vice President Finance
CMO: Alison Peterson, Vice President Medical Affairs
CIO: Susan Heichert, Senior Vice President
CHR: James McGlade, Director Human Resources
CNO: Mandy Richards, R.N., MSN, Vice President Patient Care
Web address: www.allina.com
Control: Other not–for–profit (including NFP Corporation) **Service**: General medical and surgical

> **Staffed Beds**: 377 **Admissions**: 24081 **Census**: 271 **Outpatient Visits**: 186620 **Births**: 3645 **Total Expense ($000)**: 550774 **Payroll Expense ($000)**: 220732 **Personnel**: 2647

MN

SAINT PETER—Nicollet County

★ ⇧ **RIVER'S EDGE HOSPITAL AND CLINIC (241334)**, 1900 North Sunrise Drive, Zip 56082–5376; tel. 507/931–2200, **A**10 18 21 **F**7 15 28 34 40 43 53 64 75 79 81 93 107 133 143 144
Primary Contact: George A. Rohrich, FACHE, Chief Executive Officer
CFO: Lori Zook, Chief Financial Officer
CIO: Kevin Schaefer, Manager Information Services
CHR: Jackie Kimmet, Chief Human Resource Officer
CNO: Paula Meskan, R.N., Chief Nursing Officer
Web address: www.rehc.org
Control: City, Government, nonfederal **Service**: General medical and surgical

Staffed Beds: 17 **Admissions**: 995 **Census**: 7 **Outpatient Visits**: 21086
Births: 0 **Total Expense ($000)**: 32927 **Payroll Expense ($000)**: 8847
Personnel: 134

SANDSTONE—Pine County

★ **ESSENTIA HEALTH SANDSTONE (241309)**, 705 Lundorff Drive, Zip 55072–5009; tel. 320/245–2212, (Total facility includes 22 beds in nursing home–type unit) **A**10 18 **F**3 7 11 12 15 28 29 30 34 35 40 45 59 64 65 75 77 80 81 82 85 87 91 92 93 107 110 115 119 128 129 130 132 133 135 143 144 148 149 154 **P**5 6 **S** Essentia Health, Duluth, MN
Primary Contact: Michael D. Hedrix, Administrator and President
CMO: Sarah Aldredge, M.D., Chief Medical Officer
Web address: www.pinemedicalcenter.org
Control: Hospital district or authority, Government, nonfederal **Service**: General medical and surgical

Staffed Beds: 31 **Admissions**: 230 **Census**: 22 **Outpatient Visits**: 10786
Births: 0 **Total Expense ($000)**: 18475 **Payroll Expense ($000)**: 8356
Personnel: 103

SAUK CENTRE—Stearns County

★ **CENTRACARE HEALTH–SAUK CENTRE (241368)**, 425 North Elm Street, Zip 56378–1010; tel. 320/352–2221, (Nonreporting) **A**5 10 18 **S** CentraCare Health, Saint Cloud, MN
Primary Contact: Delano Christianson, Administrator
CFO: Delano Christianson, Administrator
Web address: www.centracare.com/hospitals/sauk_centre/index.html
Control: City, Government, nonfederal **Service**: General medical and surgical

Staffed Beds: 85

SHAKOPEE—Scott County

⊞ **ST. FRANCIS REGIONAL MEDICAL CENTER (240104)**, 1455 St Francis Avenue, Zip 55379–3380; tel. 952/428–3000, **A**1 2 5 10 **F**3 12 13 15 28 29 30 31 34 35 36 38 40 41 43 45 46 50 57 58 59 64 68 75 76 77 78 79 80 81 82 84 86 87 89 93 107 108 110 111 114 117 118 119 124 129 130 131 132 144 146 147 148 154 **S** Allina Health, Minneapolis, MN
Primary Contact: Mike McMahan, President
CFO: Cynthia Vincent, Vice President Finance and Operations
CMO: Monte Johnson, Vice President, Medical Affairs
CIO: Joe Delveaux, Manager Information Services
CHR: Sally Haack, Vice President and Director of Human Resources
CNO: Debora Ryan, R.N., Vice President Patient Care
Web address: www.stfrancis-shakopee.com
Control: Other not–for–profit (including NFP Corporation) **Service**: General medical and surgical

Staffed Beds: 85 **Admissions**: 6085 **Census**: 44 **Outpatient Visits**: 129998 **Births**: 1209 **Total Expense ($000)**: 140428 **Payroll Expense ($000)**: 55998 **Personnel**: 582

SLAYTON—Murray County

★ **MURRAY COUNTY MEDICAL CENTER (241319)**, 2042 Juniper Avenue, Zip 56172–1017; tel. 507/836–6111, (Nonreporting) **A**10 18 **S** Sanford Health, Sioux Falls, SD
Primary Contact: Dennis Goebel, Chief Executive Officer
CFO: Renee Logan, Chief Financial Officer
CMO: Joyce Tarbet, M.D., Chief Medical Officer
CIO: Justin Keller, Chief Information Officer
CHR: Nancy Andert, Director Human Resources
Web address: www.murraycountymed.org
Control: County, Government, nonfederal **Service**: General medical and surgical

Staffed Beds: 18

SLEEPY EYE—Brown County

SLEEPY EYE MEDICAL CENTER (241327), 400 Fourth Avenue NW, Zip 56085–1109, Mailing Address: P.O. Box 323, Zip 56085–0323; tel. 507/794–3571, (Nonreporting) **A**10 18
Primary Contact: Kevin Sellheim, Administrator
CHR: Connie Dahlberg, Director Business and Employee
CNO: Karee Schmiesing, Director of Nursing
Web address: www.semedicalcenter.org
Control: City, Government, nonfederal **Service**: General medical and surgical

Staffed Beds: 16

SPRINGFIELD—Brown County

☐ **MAYO CLINIC HEALTH SYSTEM IN SPRINGFIELD (241352)**, 625 North Jackson Avenue, Zip 56087–1714, Mailing Address: P.O. Box 146, Zip 56087–0146; tel. 507/723–6201, **A**1 10 18 **F**3 15 28 29 32 34 35 40 45 57 59 64 65 75 81 85 93 97 107 110 114 128 133 135 146 148 149 **P**6 **S** Mayo Clinic, Rochester, MN
Primary Contact: Scott D. Thoreson, FACHE, Administrator
CFO: James Tarasovich, Chief Financial Officer
CMO: Jennifer White, Chief of Staff
Web address: www.mayoclinichealthsystem.org
Control: Other not–for–profit (including NFP Corporation) **Service**: General medical and surgical

Staffed Beds: 10 **Admissions**: 183 **Census**: 4 **Outpatient Visits**: 12231
Births: 0 **Personnel**: 58

STAPLES—Todd County

LAKEWOOD HEALTH SYSTEM (241329), 49725 County 83, Zip 56479–5280; tel. 218/894–1515, (Total facility includes 100 beds in nursing home–type unit) **A**10 18 **F**3 6 7 8 10 11 12 13 15 28 29 30 31 34 35 36 39 40 43 50 52 53 56 57 59 62 63 64 65 68 75 77 78 79 81 82 84 85 86 87 93 97 98 99 100 101 102 103 104 107 110 114 119 125 127 128 129 130 131 132 133 135 143 146 147 148 149
Primary Contact: Tim Rice, President and Chief Executive Officer
CMO: John Halfen, M.D., Medical Director
CHR: Janet Jacobson, Director Human Resources
CNO: Teresa Fisher, Chief Nursing Officer
Web address: www.lakewoodhealthsystem.com
Control: Other not–for–profit (including NFP Corporation) **Service**: General medical and surgical

Staffed Beds: 135 **Admissions**: 1505 **Census**: 114 **Outpatient Visits**: 130126 **Births**: 461 **Total Expense ($000)**: 102284 **Payroll Expense ($000)**: 40149 **Personnel**: 712

STILLWATER—Washington County

⊞ **LAKEVIEW HOSPITAL (240066)**, 927 Churchill Street West, Zip 55082–6605; tel. 651/439–5330, **A**1 3 5 10 **F**3 7 13 15 18 26 28 29 30 31 34 35 36 40 41 43 45 50 51 57 62 63 64 70 73 75 76 78 79 81 84 85 87 89 107 108 110 111 115 117 118 119 129 130 132 135 146 147 149 **S** HealthPartners, Bloomington, MN
Primary Contact: Theodore Wegleitner, Chief Executive Officer and President
CFO: Douglas E Johnson, Chief Financial Officer
CMO: Thomas Anderson, Vice President Medical Affairs
CIO: Emad Awwad, Director Care Delivery Sites Information Systems and Technology
CHR: Angy Duchesneau, Senior Director Human Resources
CNO: Robbi Hagelberg, Vice President Nursing Services and Chief Nursing Officer
Web address: www.lakeview.org
Control: Other not–for–profit (including NFP Corporation) **Service**: General medical and surgical

Staffed Beds: 67 **Admissions**: 4066 **Census**: 31 **Outpatient Visits**: 61437
Births: 570 **Total Expense ($000)**: 109643 **Payroll Expense ($000)**: 49536
Personnel: 599

THIEF RIVER FALLS—Pennington County

MERITCARE THIEF RIVER FALLS NORTHWEST MEDICAL CENTER See Sanford Medical Center Thief River Falls

★ **SANFORD MEDICAL CENTER THIEF RIVER FALLS (241381)**, 3001 Sanford Parkway, Zip 56701–2700; tel. 218/681–4747, **A**10 18 **F**3 8 11 13 15 28 29 31 32 33 34 35 39 40 45 53 57 64 65 68 76 78 79 81 82 85 86 87 97 107 110 111 115 119 129 130 131 132 133 135 144 146 147 148 **P**6 **S** Sanford Health, Sioux Falls, SD
Primary Contact: Brian J. Carlson, FACHE, Executive Director
COO: Rob Lovejoy, Director, Operations
CMO: Brook Redd, M.D., Chief of Staff
CNO: Janell Hudson, Director, Nursing and Clinical Services
Web address: www.sanfordhealth.org
Control: Other not–for–profit (including NFP Corporation) **Service**: General medical and surgical

Staffed Beds: 25 **Admissions**: 1166 **Census**: 9 **Outpatient Visits**: 95635
Births: 217 **Total Expense ($000)**: 65342 **Payroll Expense ($000)**: 26421
Personnel: 372

SANFORD THIEF RIVER FALLS BEHAVIORAL HEALTH CENTER (244018), 120 LaBree Avenue South, Zip 56701–2819, Mailing Address: 3001 Sanford Parkway, Zip 56701–2819; tel. 218/683–4349, **F**38 64 98 100 101 102 104 154 **P**6 **S** Sanford Health, Sioux Falls, SD
Primary Contact: Brian J. Carlson, FACHE, Chief Executive Officer
COO: Rob Lovejoy, Chief Operating Officer
Web address: www.sanfordhealth.org/Locations/1766896362
Control: Other not–for–profit (including NFP Corporation) **Service:** Psychiatric

Staffed Beds: 16 Admissions: 503 Census: 10 Outpatient Visits: 0
Births: 0 **Total Expense ($000):** 11017 **Payroll Expense ($000):** 5811
Personnel: 84

TRACY—Lyon County

★ **SANFORD TRACY MEDICAL CENTER (241303)**, 251 Fifth Street East, Zip 56175–1536; tel. 507/629–8400, **A**10 18 **F**3 28 29 31 32 34 40 41 43 45 50 56 57 59 62 64 65 68 77 81 85 87 89 91 93 97 107 108 111 114 125 127 129 130 131 132 133 135 143 149 154 **S** Sanford Health, Sioux Falls, SD
Primary Contact: Stacy Barstad, Chief Executive Officer
CMO: Muhammad Ali, M.D., Chief Medical Officer
CIO: Janet Theisen, Chief Information Officer
CHR: Becky Foster, Employee Relations Specialist
CNO: Jeri Schons, R.N., Chief Nursing Officer
Web address: www.sanfordtracy.org
Control: Other not–for–profit (including NFP Corporation) **Service:** General medical and surgical

Staffed Beds: 25 Admissions: 110 Census: 1 Outpatient Visits: 17011
Births: 0 **Total Expense ($000):** 10069 **Payroll Expense ($000):** 4023
Personnel: 86

TWO HARBORS—Lake County

LAKE VIEW HOSPITAL (241308), 325 11th Avenue, Zip 55616–1360; tel. 218/834–7300, (Nonreporting) **A**10 18
Primary Contact: Greg Ruberg, President and Chief Executive Officer
CFO: Eric Lohn, Chief Financial Officer
Web address: www.lvmhospital.com
Control: Other not–for–profit (including NFP Corporation) **Service:** General medical and surgical

Staffed Beds: 16

TYLER—Lincoln County

AVERA TYLER HOSPITAL (241348), 240 Willow Street, Zip 56178–1166; tel. 507/247–5521, (Nonreporting) **A**10 18 **S** Avera Health, Sioux Falls, SD
Primary Contact: Allen Anderson, Administrator
CNO: Kris Vollmer, Director Patient Care Services
Web address: www.avera.org
Control: Other not–for–profit (including NFP Corporation) **Service:** General medical and surgical

Staffed Beds: 25

VIRGINIA—St. Louis County

⊞ △ **ESSENTIA HEALTH–VIRGINIA (240084)**, 901 Ninth Street North, Zip 55792–2398; tel. 218/741–3340, (Total facility includes 90 beds in nursing home–type unit) **A**1 7 10 **F**3 11 13 15 18 28 29 30 31 34 35 40 41 43 45 47 48 56 59 63 64 65 70 75 76 77 81 84 85 87 89 90 93 96 97 104 107 108 110 111 115 119 128 129 130 132 135 144 146 147 148 149 **P**6 **S** Essentia Health, Duluth, MN
Primary Contact: Sam Stone, Operations Administrator
CFO: Steven Feltman, CPA, Chief Financial Officer
CMO: Michelle Oman, D.O., Chief Medical Officer
Web address: www.essentiahealth.org
Control: Other not–for–profit (including NFP Corporation) **Service:** General medical and surgical

Staffed Beds: 144 Admissions: 1684 Census: 83 Outpatient Visits: 158909 **Births:** 220 **Total Expense ($000):** 88452 **Payroll Expense ($000):** 43034 **Personnel:** 539

WABASHA—Wabasha County

★ **SAINT ELIZABETH'S MEDICAL CENTER (241335)**, 1200 Grant Boulevard West, Zip 55981–1042; tel. 651/565–4531, (Total facility includes 143 beds in nursing home–type unit) **A**10 18 **F**2 6 10 11 12 15 28 29 30 34 35 40 43 45 46 49 50 53 56 59 62 64 65 75 77 79 81 82 84 85 86 93 94 97 107 114 119 125 127 128 130 133 135 143 145 146 147 148 149 154 **S** Ascension Healthcare, Saint Louis, MO
Primary Contact: Thomas Crowley, President and Chief Executive Officer
CFO: John Wolfe, Chief Financial Officer
CMO: Brian E. Kelly, M.D., President Medical Staff
CHR: Jim Root, Vice President Human Resources
CNO: Kathy Lueders, R.N., Director of Nursing–Acute Care
Web address: www.stelizabethswabasha.org
Control: Church operated, Nongovernment, not–for–profit **Service:** General medical and surgical

Staffed Beds: 153 Admissions: 415 Census: 132 Outpatient Visits: 23067
Births: 0 **Total Expense ($000):** 30781 **Payroll Expense ($000):** 13049
Personnel: 244

WACONIA—Carver County

★ ⇑ **RIDGEVIEW MEDICAL CENTER (240056)**, 500 South Maple Street, Zip 55387–1791; tel. 952/442–2191, **A**2 10 21 **F**3 7 12 13 15 18 20 22 28 29 30 31 32 34 35 36 38 40 41 43 45 46 48 49 54 57 58 59 62 63 64 65 70 73 74 75 76 77 78 79 81 82 84 85 86 87 89 93 96 98 103 107 108 110 111 114 115 118 119 126 127 129 130 131 132 135 144 146 147 148 149 **P**6 **S** Ridgeview Medical Center, Waconia, MN
Primary Contact: Michael Phelps, President and Chief Executive Officer
CFO: Gordon Gablenz, Vice President Finance
CMO: Alvaro Sanchez, M.D., Chief Medical Officer
CIO: Tamara Korbel, Director Management Information Systems
CHR: Sarah M Hastings, Executive Director
Web address: www.ridgeviewmedical.org
Control: Other not–for–profit (including NFP Corporation) **Service:** General medical and surgical

Staffed Beds: 108 Admissions: 5196 Census: 64 Outpatient Visits: 312720 **Births:** 1151 **Total Expense ($000):** 247008 **Payroll Expense ($000):** 118795 **Personnel:** 1193

WADENA—Wadena County

⊞ **TRI–COUNTY HOSPITAL (241354)**, 415 Jefferson Street North, Zip 56482–1297; tel. 218/631–3510, **A**1 10 18 **F**3 7 11 13 15 17 28 31 34 35 40 43 45 48 50 54 57 59 64 65 68 70 75 76 77 81 85 86 87 89 93 104 107 108 110 111 114 115 118 119 127 129 130 131 132 133 135 146 147 148 149 154 **P**6
Primary Contact: Joel Beiswenger, Chief Executive Officer
CFO: Kim Aagard, Chief Financial Officer
CMO: John Pate, M.D., Chief Medical Officer
CIO: Bill Blaha, Manager Information Technology
CHR: Bryan Pederson, Human Resources Manager
CNO: Kathy Kleen, Chief Nursing Officer
Web address: www.tchc.org
Control: Other not–for–profit (including NFP Corporation) **Service:** General medical and surgical

Staffed Beds: 25 Admissions: 760 Census: 6 Outpatient Visits: 133536
Births: 162 **Total Expense ($000):** 60209 **Payroll Expense ($000):** 23853
Personnel: 377

WARREN—Marshall County

★ **NORTH VALLEY HEALTH CENTER (241337)**, 300 West Good Samaritan Drive, Zip 56762; tel. 218/745–4211, (Nonreporting) **A**10 18
Primary Contact: Jon E. Linnell, Interim Chief Executive Officer
CFO: Mitchell Kotrba, Chief Financial Officer
CNO: Sara Marie Kazmierczak, R.N., Director of Nursing
Web address: www.northvalleyhealth.org
Control: Other not–for–profit (including NFP Corporation) **Service:** General medical and surgical

Staffed Beds: 20

MN

Hospital, Medicare Provider Number, Address, Telephone, Approval, Facility, and Physician Codes, Health Care System

★ American Hospital Association (AHA) membership   ○ Healthcare Facilities Accreditation Program   ⇑ Center for Improvement in Healthcare Quality Accreditation
☐ The Joint Commission accreditation   ◇ DNV Healthcare Inc. accreditation   △ Commission on Accreditation of Rehabilitation Facilities (CARF) accreditation

© 2018 AHA Guide   *Many Facility Codes have changed. Please refer to the AHA Guide Code Chart.*   Hospitals **A341**

WASECA—Waseca County

☐ **MAYO CLINIC HEALTH SYSTEM IN WASECA (241345)**, 501 North State Street, Zip 56093–2811; tel. 507/835–1210, **A**1 3 5 10 18 **F**3 11 15 18 28 29 30 34 35 40 45 53 57 59 64 65 74 75 77 81 82 85 86 87 93 97 107 110 114 119 128 130 132 133 144 146 148 149 **P**6 **S** Mayo Clinic, Rochester, MN
Primary Contact: April Lanz, Interim Administrator
CMO: Christopher Schimming, M.D., Medical Director
Web address: www.mayoclinichealthsystem.org
Control: Other not–for–profit (including NFP Corporation) **Service**: General medical and surgical

Staffed Beds: 12 **Admissions:** 285 **Census:** 7 **Outpatient Visits:** 27334
Births: 0 **Personnel:** 91

WESTBROOK—Cottonwood County

★ **SANFORD WESTBROOK MEDICAL CENTER (241302)**, 920 Bell Avenue, Zip 56183–9669, Mailing Address: P.O. Box 188, Zip 56183–0188; tel. 507/274–6121, **A**10 18 **F**3 29 31 34 35 40 43 56 57 59 62 64 65 68 71 75 77 81 85 86 87 89 91 93 97 99 100 101 102 103 104 107 108 114 125 127 130 131 132 133 135 143 154 **P**6 **S** Sanford Health, Sioux Falls, SD
Primary Contact: Stacy Barstad, Chief Executive Officer
COO: Gordon Kopperud, Director Operations
CIO: Janet Theisen, Chief Information Officer
CHR: Becky Foster, Employee Relations Specialist
Web address: www.sanfordwestbrook.org
Control: Other not–for–profit (including NFP Corporation) **Service**: General medical and surgical

Staffed Beds: 6 **Admissions:** 102 **Census:** 1 **Outpatient Visits:** 12610
Births: 0 **Total Expense ($000):** 6922 **Payroll Expense ($000):** 2671
Personnel: 40

WHEATON—Traverse County

★ **SANFORD WHEATON MEDICAL CENTER (241304)**, 401 12th Street North, Zip 56296–1099; tel. 320/563–8226, (Nonreporting) **A**10 18 **S** Sanford Health, Sioux Falls, SD
Primary Contact: JoAnn M. Foltz, R.N., Chief Executive Officer
CFO: Shane Ayres, Chief Financial Officer
CHR: Brenda Petersen, Human Resources
CNO: Chelsie Falk, Chief Nursing Officer
Web address: www.sanfordhealth.org
Control: City, Government, nonfederal **Service**: General medical and surgical

Staffed Beds: 15

WILLMAR—Kandiyohi County

☐ **CHILD AND ADOLESCENT BEHAVIORAL HEALTH SERVICES (244005)**, 1701 Technology Drive Northeast, Zip 56201–2275; tel. 320/231–5421, (Nonreporting) **A**1 10
Primary Contact: Jacquelyn Sammons, R.N., Supervisor
Web address: www.dhs.state.mn.us
Control: County, Government, nonfederal **Service**: Psychiatric

Staffed Beds: 16

⊞ **RICE MEMORIAL HOSPITAL (240088)**, 301 Becker Avenue SW, Zip 56201–3395; tel. 320/235–4543, (Total facility includes 78 beds in nursing home–type unit) **A**1 2 10 **F**3 7 11 12 13 28 29 30 34 35 39 40 43 45 47 48 49 50 57 59 60 63 64 65 68 70 73 75 76 78 79 81 82 85 86 87 89 90 93 98 100 101 102 103 104 105 107 108 111 115 118 119 121 130 132 143 146 147 148 149 150 153 154 **S** CentraCare Health, Saint Cloud, MN
Primary Contact: Michael Schramm, Chief Executive Officer
CFO: Bill Fenske, Chief Financial Officer
CMO: Kenneth Flowe, M.D., Chief Medical Officer
CIO: Teri Beyer, Chief Information Officer, Quality
Web address: www.ricehospital.com
Control: City, Government, nonfederal **Service**: General medical and surgical

Staffed Beds: 164 **Admissions:** 3953 **Census:** 106 **Outpatient Visits:** 69309 **Births:** 747 **Total Expense ($000):** 116044 **Payroll Expense ($000):** 47219 **Personnel:** 551

WINDOM—Cottonwood County

★ **WINDOM AREA HOSPITAL (241332)**, 2150 Hospital Drive, Zip 56101–0339, Mailing Address: P.O. Box 339, Zip 56101–0339; tel. 507/831–2400, (Nonreporting) **A**10 18 **S** Sanford Health, Sioux Falls, SD
Primary Contact: Shelby Medina, Chief Executive Officer
CFO: Kim Armstrong, Chief Financial Officer
CIO: Lori Ling, Information Technician
CHR: Emily Masters, Chief Human Relations Officer
CNO: Kari Witte, Director Patient Care
Web address: www.windomareahospital.com
Control: City, Government, nonfederal **Service**: General medical and surgical

Staffed Beds: 18

WINONA—Winona County

★ **WINONA HEALTH (240044)**, 855 Mankato Avenue, Zip 55987–4868, Mailing Address: P.O. Box 5600, Zip 55987–0600; tel. 507/454–3650, **A**2 10 20 **F**11 13 15 28 29 30 31 32 34 35 38 40 43 50 53 56 57 58 59 61 62 63 70 75 76 77 78 79 81 82 83 84 85 86 87 89 93 96 97 98 100 101 102 104 107 108 110 111 115 118 119 127 129 130 131 132 133 135 144 146 147 148 153 154
Primary Contact: Rachelle H. Schultz, Ed.D., President and Chief Executive Officer
CFO: Jan Brosnahan, Chief Financial Officer
CMO: Brett Whyte, M.D., Chief of Medical Staff
CIO: Luke Keninger, Information Technology Client Leader
CHR: Kathy Wade, Chief Human Resource Officer
Web address: www.winonahealth.org
Control: Other not–for–profit (including NFP Corporation) **Service**: General medical and surgical

Staffed Beds: 46 **Admissions:** 2253 **Census:** 22 **Outpatient Visits:** 221404
Births: 246 **Total Expense ($000):** 123940 **Payroll Expense ($000):** 53472
Personnel: 931

WOODBURY—Washington County

⊞ **WOODWINDS HEALTH CAMPUS (240213)**, 1925 Woodwinds Drive, Zip 55125–4445; tel. 651/232–0228, **A**1 5 10 **F**3 13 15 28 29 30 31 35 36 37 38 40 43 49 50 59 64 68 70 74 75 76 77 78 79 81 85 86 87 93 96 97 100 102 107 108 110 111 115 118 119 120 121 124 130 132 146 149 **S** Fairview Health Services, Minneapolis, MN
Primary Contact: Lia Christiansen, Chief Operating Officer, Acute Care Hospitals
COO: Lia Christiansen, Chief Operating Officer, Acute Care Hospitals
CFO: Daniel Fromm, Chief Financial Officer
CMO: Kevin C. Garrett, M.D., Medical Executive, East Region
CIO: Joanne Sunquist, Chief Information Officer
CHR: Carolyn Jacobson, Chief Human Resource Officer
CNO: Debra J. Hurd, MS, R.N., Vice President and Chief Nursing Officer
Web address: www.woodwinds.org
Control: Other not–for–profit (including NFP Corporation) **Service**: General medical and surgical

Staffed Beds: 86 **Admissions:** 7804 **Census:** 57 **Outpatient Visits:** 62324 **Births:** 1678 **Total Expense ($000):** 140515 **Payroll Expense ($000):** 48496 **Personnel:** 551

WORTHINGTON—Nobles County

SANFORD REGIONAL HOSPITAL WORTHINGTON See Sanford Worthington Medical Center

★ **SANFORD WORTHINGTON MEDICAL CENTER (240022)**, 1018 Sixth Avenue, Zip 56187–2202, Mailing Address: P.O. Box 997, Zip 56187–0997; tel. 507/372–2941, **A**10 20 **F**3 7 11 13 15 18 19 26 27 28 31 34 35 40 43 45 50 57 59 60 62 64 68 69 70 75 76 78 79 81 85 86 93 97 107 110 111 114 116 119 120 121 126 129 130 131 132 135 144 146 147 148 149 154 **S** Sanford Health, Sioux Falls, SD
Primary Contact: Jennifer Weg, MS, R.N., Executive Director
CFO: Linda Wagner, Chief Financial Officer
CMO: Charles Dike, M.D., Chief of Staff
CIO: Brad Klassen, Information Technology Coordinator
CNO: Gwen Post, R.N., Chief Nursing Officer
Web address: www.sanfordhealth.org
Control: Other not–for–profit (including NFP Corporation) **Service**: General medical and surgical

Staffed Beds: 48 **Admissions:** 1062 **Census:** 7 **Outpatient Visits:** 57522
Births: 401 **Total Expense ($000):** 35152 **Payroll Expense ($000):** 13827
Personnel: 202

WYOMING—Chisago County

⊞ **FAIRVIEW LAKES HEALTH SERVICES (240050)**, 5200 Fairview Boulevard, Zip 55092–8013; tel. 651/982–7000, **A**1 10 **F**3 11 13 15 18 28 29 30 34 35 40 41 43 45 50 51 57 59 64 65 68 70 75 76 81 84 85 86 87 89 93 96 101 107 110 111 115 119 130 131 132 134 144 146 148 149 154 **P**6 **S** Fairview Health Services, Minneapolis, MN
Primary Contact: Lia Christiansen, Chief Operating Officer, Acute Care Hospitals
CFO: Kim Ericson, Vice President Finance
CMO: David Milbrandt, M.D., Vice President Medical Affairs
CNO: Karen Whiley, Vice President Patient Care Services
Web address: www.fairview.org/
Control: Other not–for–profit (including NFP Corporation) **Service**: General medical and surgical

Staffed Beds: 34 **Admissions:** 3060 **Census:** 25 **Outpatient Visits:** 83551
Births: 627 **Total Expense ($000):** 80061 **Payroll Expense ($000):** 42554
Personnel: 424

MN

Many Facility Codes have changed. Please refer to the AHA Guide Code Chart.
© 2018 AHA Guide

MISSISSIPPI

ABERDEEN—Monroe County

★ ⇧ **MONROE REGIONAL HOSPITAL (251302)**, 400 South Chestnut Street, Zip 39730–3335, Mailing Address: P.O. Box 548, Zip 39730–0548; tel. 662/369–2455, (Nonreporting) **A**10 18 21
Primary Contact: Christopher Chandler, Chief Executive Officer
CFO: Julie Gieger, Chief Financial Officer
CMO: Kevin Hayes, M.D., Chief of Staff
CHR: Lee Rob, Director Human Resources
Control: Corporation, Investor–owned (for–profit) **Service:** General medical and surgical

Staffed Beds: 35

ACKERMAN—Choctaw County

⇧ **CHOCTAW REGIONAL MEDICAL CENTER (251334)**, 8613 Highway 12, Zip 39735–8708; tel. 662/285–6235, (Total facility includes 60 beds in nursing home–type unit) **A**10 18 21 **F**3 29 34 40 43 50 57 58 65 77 80 87 93 104 107 114 119 127 128 130 133 **P**4
Primary Contact: Jamie Rodgers, Interim Chief Executive Officer
Control: County, Government, nonfederal **Service:** General medical and surgical

Staffed Beds: 75 **Admissions:** 354 **Census:** 63 **Outpatient Visits:** 37743
Births: 0 **Total Expense ($000):** 19829 **Payroll Expense ($000):** 10660
Personnel: 274

AMORY—Monroe County

⊞ **GILMORE MEMORIAL HOSPITAL (250025)**, 1105 Earl Frye Boulevard, Zip 38821–5500, Mailing Address: P.O. Box 459, Zip 38821–0459; tel. 662/256–7111, **A**1 10 **F**3 13 15 17 18 29 32 34 35 40 41 43 45 49 50 53 55 57 59 64 65 68 70 72 73 75 76 77 81 85 86 87 88 89 90 107 108 110 111 114 115 119 126 130 135 146 147 **P**8 **S** Curae Health, Clinton, TN
Primary Contact: J Allen. Tyra, Chief Executive
COO: Carol Upton, Regional Area Practice Manager
CFO: Bert Pickard, Chief Financial Officer
CMO: William Rogers, Chief Medical Officer
CIO: Jeff Wideman, Director Information Systems
CHR: Angie L Weaver, Director Human Resources
Web address: www.gilmorehealth.com
Control: Other not–for–profit (including NFP Corporation) **Service:** General medical and surgical

Staffed Beds: 95 **Admissions:** 2488 **Census:** 25 **Outpatient Visits:** 57831
Births: 644 **Total Expense ($000):** 40468 **Payroll Expense ($000):** 12427
Personnel: 273

BATESVILLE—Panola County

★ **PANOLA MEDICAL CENTER (250128)**, 303 Medical Center Drive, Zip 38606–8608; tel. 662/563–5611, (Data for 214 days) **A**10 **F**3 4 5 11 12 13 15 18 19 28 29 30 32 34 35 38 40 43 45 48 50 56 57 59 64 65 68 70 76 77 81 85 87 89 97 98 100 101 102 103 107 108 114 119 127 129 130 132 146 147 **S** Curae Health, Clinton, TN
Primary Contact: Travis Sisson, Chief Executive Officer
COO: Vince Brummett, Director Administrative Services
CMO: Michael R. Hovens, M.D., Chief Medical Officer
CIO: Will Morris, Director Information Technology
CHR: Arthur A Wasek, Director Human Resources
Web address: www.panolamedicalcenter.org/
Control: Other not–for–profit (including NFP Corporation) **Service:** General medical and surgical

Staffed Beds: 112 **Admissions:** 1526 **Census:** 29 **Outpatient Visits:** 18427
Births: 179 **Total Expense ($000):** 22053 **Payroll Expense ($000):** 8939
Personnel: 309

BAY SAINT LOUIS—Hancock County

⊞ **HANCOCK MEDICAL CENTER (250162)**, 149 Drinkwater Boulevard, Zip 39520–1658, Mailing Address: Bay St Louis, tel. 228/467–8600, **A**1 10 **F**3 13 15 17 18 28 29 34 35 39 40 43 45 54 57 59 64 65 70 75 76 77 79 81 85 86 87 89 90 93 97 107 108 110 111 114 115 118 119 127 129 130 131 146 147 **S** Ochsner Health System, New Orleans, LA
Primary Contact: Alan Hodges, Chief Executive Officer
CFO: Thomas Ramsey, Chief Financial Officer
CIO: Craig Hodges, Director Information Services
CHR: Cathy Benvenutti, Human Resource Director
CNO: Virginia Kenny, Chief Nursing Officer
Web address: www.hmc.org
Control: County, Government, nonfederal **Service:** General medical and surgical

Staffed Beds: 102 **Admissions:** 1448 **Census:** 13 **Outpatient Visits:** 45085
Births: 185 **Total Expense ($000):** 34832 **Payroll Expense ($000):** 15851
Personnel: 243

BAY SPRINGS—Jasper County

★ **JASPER GENERAL HOSPITAL (250018)**, 15 'A' South Sixth Street, Zip 39422–9738, Mailing Address: P.O. Box 527, Zip 39422–0527; tel. 601/764–2101, (Total facility includes 110 beds in nursing home–type unit) **A**10 **F**10 55 59 62 64 108 119 128 130 133
Primary Contact: Clinton Eaves, Administrator
CFO: Steve Green, Comptroller
CMO: A K Lay, M.D., Jr Chief Medical Officer
CHR: Beth Gable, Administrative Assistant
CNO: Becky Ulmer, R.N., Director of Nursing
Web address: www.jaspergeneralhospital.com
Control: County, Government, nonfederal **Service:** General medical and surgical

Staffed Beds: 126 **Admissions:** 155 **Census:** 117 **Outpatient Visits:** 0
Births: 0 **Total Expense ($000):** 10941 **Payroll Expense ($000):** 6917
Personnel: 193

BILOXI—Harrison County

⊞ **MERIT HEALTH BILOXI (250007)**, 150 Reynoir Street, Zip 39530–4199, Mailing Address: P.O. Box 128, Zip 39533–0128; tel. 228/432–1571, (Nonreporting) **A**1 10 **S** Community Health Systems, Inc., Franklin, TN
Primary Contact: Robert Calhoun, Chief Executive Officer
COO: Tonda V. Haigler, Chief Operating Officer
CFO: Charles Brinkley III Chief Financial Officer
CMO: George Loukatos, M.D., President Medical Staff Affairs
CIO: George Bickel, Director, Information Systems
CNO: James Wells, Chief Nursing Officer
Web address: www.merithealthbiloxi.com
Control: Corporation, Investor–owned (for–profit) **Service:** General medical and surgical

Staffed Beds: 198

⊞ **VETERANS AFFAIRS GULF COAST VETERANS HEALTH CARE SYSTEM**, 400 Veterans Avenue, Zip 39531–2410; tel. 228/523–5000, (Nonreporting) **A**1 3 5 **S** Department of Veterans Affairs, Perry Point, MD
Primary Contact: Christopher M. Saslo, Acting Director
COO: Alexander Murray, Interim Associate Director
CFO: John D Williams Jr Chief Financial Officer
CMO: Kenneth B Simon, M.D., Chief of Staff
CIO: David D Wagner, Chief Information Management Service
CHR: Andrew Roberts, Interim Chief Human Resources Officer
CNO: Deatosha D. Haynes, Interim Associates Director for Patient
Web address: www.biloxi.va.gov/
Control: Veterans Affairs, Government, federal **Service:** General medical and surgical

Staffed Beds: 392

Hospital, Medicare Provider Number, Address, Telephone, Approval, Facility, and Physician Codes, Health Care System

★ American Hospital Association (AHA) membership
□ The Joint Commission accreditation
○ Healthcare Facilities Accreditation Program
◇ DNV Healthcare Inc. accreditation
⇧ Center for Improvement in Healthcare Quality Accreditation
△ Commission on Accreditation of Rehabilitation Facilities (CARF) accreditation

---

BOONEVILLE—Prentiss County

☒ **BAPTIST MEMORIAL HOSPITAL–BOONEVILLE (250044)**, 100 Hospital Street, Zip 38829–3359; tel. 662/720–5000, **A**1 10 **F**3 15 17 28 29 30 34 35 40 41 43 56 57 59 63 68 70 74 75 77 81 85 86 87 89 90 93 98 103 107 108 111 115 118 119 129 130 132 133 145 146 148 154 **S** Baptist Memorial Health Care Corporation, Memphis, TN
Primary Contact: James Grantham, Administrator and Chief Executive Officer
CFO: Donavan Leonard, Chief Financial Officer
CMO: Nathan Baldwin, M.D., President Medical Staff
CIO: Linda Chaffin, Director Medical Review
CHR: Shannon Bolen, Director Human Resources
Web address: www.bmhcc.org/booneville
Control: Other not–for–profit (including NFP Corporation) **Service:** General medical and surgical

Staffed Beds: 63 **Admissions:** 1010 **Census:** 19 **Outpatient Visits:** 23909 **Births:** 0 **Total Expense ($000):** 15787 **Payroll Expense ($000):** 7946 **Personnel:** 154

BRANDON—Rankin County

☒ **MERIT HEALTH RANKIN (250096)**, 350 Crossgates Boulevard, Zip 39042–2698; tel. 601/825–2811, **A**1 5 10 **F**3 6 15 17 29 30 34 40 43 45 50 57 59 64 70 78 79 81 85 87 90 93 97 98 103 107 108 109 110 111 112 114 119 129 130 146 **P**1 **S** Community Health Systems, Inc., Franklin, TN
Primary Contact: Heather Sistrunk, MHSA, RN, BSN, Chief Executive Officer
CFO: Christy Wilson, Chief Financial Officer
CMO: Edward Rigdon, M.D., Chief Medical Officer
CIO: Heather Holmes, Director Health Information Systems
CHR: Joy M Hutson, Director Human Resources
CNO: Cynthia Ellis, Chief Nursing Officer
Web address: www.crossgatesriveroaks.com
Control: Corporation, Investor–owned (for–profit) **Service:** General medical and surgical

Staffed Beds: 134 **Admissions:** 2145 **Census:** 34 **Outpatient Visits:** 54706 **Births:** 0 **Total Expense ($000):** 44081 **Payroll Expense ($000):** 13236 **Personnel:** 256

BROOKHAVEN—Lincoln County

★ ⇧ **KING'S DAUGHTERS MEDICAL CENTER (250057)**, 427 Highway 51 North, Zip 39601–2350, Mailing Address: P.O. Box 948, Zip 39602–0948; tel. 601/833–6011, **A**10 20 21 **F**3 7 11 13 15 17 29 30 34 35 40 41 45 53 54 57 59 64 65 68 70 73 74 75 76 77 79 80 81 82 86 89 93 96 97 107 108 110 111 114 115 119 126 129 130 131 132 135 143 146 147 149 **S** QHR, Brentwood, TN
Primary Contact: Alvin Hoover, FACHE, Chief Executive Officer
COO: Thomas Hood, Chief Operating Officer
CFO: Randy B Pirtle, Chief Financial Officer
CMO: Jeffrey Ross, M.D., Chief of Staff
CIO: Carl Smith, Director Information Systems
CHR: Celine H Craig, Director Human Resources
CNO: Cheri Walker, R.N., Chief Nursing Officer
Web address: www.kdmc.org
Control: Other not–for–profit (including NFP Corporation) **Service:** General medical and surgical

Staffed Beds: 79 **Admissions:** 2845 **Census:** 33 **Outpatient Visits:** 167079 **Births:** 643 **Total Expense ($000):** 86504 **Payroll Expense ($000):** 36815 **Personnel:** 595

CALHOUN CITY—Calhoun County

★ **BAPTIST MEMORIAL HOSPITAL – CALHOUN (251331)**, 140 Burke–Calhoun City Road, Zip 38916–9690; tel. 662/628–6611, (Total facility includes 120 beds in nursing home–type unit) **A**10 18 **F**30 40 43 59 64 68 81 87 89 93 103 107 114 119 128 130 133 151 **S** Baptist Memorial Health Care Corporation, Memphis, TN
Primary Contact: Collin Cheek, Administrator
CFO: Kenneth Conley, Chief Financial Officer
CMO: Bruce Longest, M.D., President Medical Staff
Web address: www.baptistonline.org/calhoun/
Control: Other not–for–profit (including NFP Corporation) **Service:** General medical and surgical

Staffed Beds: 145 **Admissions:** 400 **Census:** 106 **Births:** 0 **Personnel:** 193

CANTON—Madison County

☒ **MERIT HEALTH MADISON (250038)**, 161 River Oaks Drive, Zip 39046–5375, Mailing Address: PO Box 1607, Zip 39046–5375; tel. 601/855–4000, **A**1 10 **F**13 15 29 35 40 43 70 73 76 81 82 87 89 108 119 130 146 **P**8 **S** Community Health Systems, Inc., Franklin, TN
Primary Contact: Britton Phelps, Chief Executive Officer
CFO: Shea Sutherland, Chief Financial Officer
CMO: Vibha Vig, Chief of Staff
CIO: Rick Hartzog, Chief Information Officer
CHR: Jackie Williams, Director Human Resources
CNO: Tim Lolley, MSN, Chief Nursing Officer
Web address: www.merithealthmadison.com
Control: Corporation, Investor–owned (for–profit) **Service:** General medical and surgical

Staffed Beds: 43 **Admissions:** 1363 **Census:** 12 **Outpatient Visits:** 39802 **Births:** 338 **Personnel:** 219

CARTHAGE—Leake County

★ **BAPTIST MEDICAL CENTER LEAKE (251315)**, 1100 Highway 16 E, Zip 39051–3809, Mailing Address: P.O. Box 909, Zip 39051–0909; tel. 601/267–1100, **A**10 18 **F**15 29 35 40 43 45 56 59 81 87 107 109 111 114 115 119 127 130 133 146 148 154 **P**6 **S** Baptist Memorial Health Care Corporation, Memphis, TN
Primary Contact: Daryl W. Weaver, Chief Executive Officer
COO: C Gerald Cotton, Interim Chief Operating Officer
CFO: David Jackson, Chief Financial Officer
CMO: Doug Perry, M.D., Chief of Staff
Web address: www.mbhs.com/locations/baptist–medical–center–leake/
Control: Other not–for–profit (including NFP Corporation) **Service:** General medical and surgical

Staffed Beds: 25 **Admissions:** 768 **Census:** 17 **Outpatient Visits:** 24248 **Births:** 2 **Total Expense ($000):** 23683 **Payroll Expense ($000):** 7205 **Personnel:** 160

CENTREVILLE—Wilkinson County

☒ **FIELD MEMORIAL COMMUNITY HOSPITAL (251309)**, 178 Highway 24, Zip 39631–4171; tel. 601/645–5221, **A**1 10 18 **F**15 18 29 34 39 40 43 45 57 59 64 75 77 79 81 89 90 93 107 108 110 118 119 133 148 **P**6
Primary Contact: Chad Netterville, Administrator
CFO: Bryan N Stevens, Chief Financial Officer
CIO: Locke Wheeles, Information Technology Manager
CHR: Dana McNabb, Human Resources Manager
CNO: Robin Walker, Chief Nursing Officer
Web address: www.fmch.org
Control: County, Government, nonfederal **Service:** General medical and surgical

Staffed Beds: 16 **Admissions:** 449 **Census:** 8 **Outpatient Visits:** 13004 **Births:** 0 **Total Expense ($000):** 14963 **Payroll Expense ($000):** 8379 **Personnel:** 156

CHARLESTON—Tallahatchie County

⇧ **TALLAHATCHIE GENERAL HOSPITAL (251304)**, 201 South Market, Zip 38921–2236, Mailing Address: P.O. Box 230, Zip 38921–0240; tel. 662/647–5535, (Total facility includes 98 beds in nursing home–type unit) **A**10 18 21 **F**29 34 40 43 53 57 64 86 87 93 107 127 128 130 133 143 **P**6
Primary Contact: Jim Blackwood, Chief Executive Officer
CFO: Sammie Bell Jr Chief Financial Officer
Control: County, Government, nonfederal **Service:** General medical and surgical

Staffed Beds: 116 **Admissions:** 600 **Census:** 109 **Births:** 0 **Total Expense ($000):** 33673 **Payroll Expense ($000):** 17043 **Personnel:** 303

CLARKSDALE—Coahoma County

☒ **NORTHWEST MISSISSIPPI MEDICAL CENTER (250042)**, 1970 Hospital Drive, Zip 38614–7202, Mailing Address: P.O. Box 1218, Zip 38614–1218; tel. 662/627–3211, **A**1 10 19 **F**3 13 15 18 20 22 28 29 30 31 34 35 40 43 53 57 59 64 70 73 74 76 79 81 85 89 93 107 108 110 111 114 115 118 119 126 130 131 132 **P**8 **S** Curae Health, Clinton, TN
Primary Contact: Joel Southern, R.N., MSN, Chief Executive Officer
CFO: Charles H. Hester, CPA, Jr Chief Financial Officer
CMO: Richard Brownstein, M.D., Chief of Staff
CIO: Adrienne Taylor, Director of Health Information Management
CHR: Devasha Patterson, Director of Human Resources
CNO: Steven W Brackeen, R.N., Chief Nursing Officer
Web address: www.merithealthnorthwestms.com
Control: Other not–for–profit (including NFP Corporation) **Service:** General medical and surgical

Staffed Beds: 181 **Admissions:** 2882 **Census:** 33 **Outpatient Visits:** 55034 **Births:** 665 **Personnel:** 384

MS

Many Facility Codes have changed. Please refer to the AHA Guide Code Chart. © 2018 AHA Guide

CLEVELAND—Bolivar County

☒ **BOLIVAR MEDICAL CENTER (250093)**, 901 East Sunflower Road,
Zip 38732–2833, Mailing Address: P.O. Box 1380, Zip 38732–1380;
tel. 662/846–0061, (Total facility includes 35 beds in nursing home–type unit) **A**1
10 20 **F**13 15 24 25 29 30 35 39 40 43 56 60 70 73 76 81 82 87 88 89 93 98
103 107 108 111 116 118 119 128 130 132 133 146 148 **S** LifePoint Health,
Brentwood, TN
Primary Contact: Robert L. Marshall Jr, FACHE, Chief Executive Officer
CMO: Mark Blackwood, M.D., Chief of Staff
CIO: Cagri Sapmaz, Information Technology Director
CHR: Ben Bufkin, Human Resource Director
CNO: Joann McCollum, Chief Nursing Officer
Web address: www.bolivarmedical.com
Control: Corporation, Investor–owned (for–profit) **Service:** General medical and
surgical

> **Staffed Beds:** 129 **Admissions:** 3217 **Census:** 67 **Births:** 383 **Total
> Expense ($000):** 31023 **Payroll Expense ($000):** 19060 **Personnel:** 374

COLLINS—Covington County

★ ⇑ **COVINGTON COUNTY HOSPITAL (251325)**, 701 South Holly Avenue,
Zip 39428–3894, Mailing Address: P.O. Box 1149, Zip 39428–1149;
tel. 601/765–6711, (Total facility includes 60 beds in nursing home–type unit) **A**10
18 21 **F**3 7 29 34 35 40 43 45 50 54 57 59 64 65 66 68 81 89 93 94 98 104
107 114 119 127 128 130 133 143 144 146 147
Primary Contact: Gregg Gibbes, Chief Executive Officer
CFO: Delilah Hudson, Controller
CMO: Word Johnston, Medical Director
CHR: Beverly K Ponder, Executive Assistant and Human Resources Coordinator
CNO: Martha Lynn Scott, Chief Patient Care Officer
Web address: www.covingtoncountyhospital.com
Control: County, Government, nonfederal **Service:** General medical and surgical

> **Staffed Beds:** 95 **Admissions:** 557 **Census:** 68 **Outpatient Visits:** 23588
> **Births:** 0 **Total Expense ($000):** 22499 **Payroll Expense ($000):** 10229
> **Personnel:** 255

COLUMBIA—Marion County

MARION GENERAL HOSPITAL (250085), 1560 Sumrall Road,
Zip 39429–2654, Mailing Address: P.O. Box 630, Zip 39429–0630;
tel. 601/736–6303, **A**10 **F**3 11 29 34 35 39 40 41 43 64 65 66 68 70 81 85
87 90 97 107 115 119 127 130 133 146 154
Primary Contact: Alaina Cedillo, Interim Administrator
CMO: Mark Stevens, M.D., Chief Medical Staff
CIO: Donny Bracey, Director Information Services
CNO: Patricia Reid, Director of Nursing
Web address: www.mgh.net/
Control: County, Government, nonfederal **Service:** General medical and surgical

> **Staffed Beds:** 49 **Admissions:** 598 **Census:** 7 **Outpatient Visits:** 27522
> **Births:** 0 **Total Expense ($000):** 11121 **Payroll Expense ($000):** 5974
> **Personnel:** 115

COLUMBUS—Lowndes County

☒ **BAPTIST MEMORIAL HOSPITAL–GOLDEN TRIANGLE (250100)**, 2520
Fifth Street North, Zip 39705–2095, Mailing Address: P.O. Box 1307,
Zip 39703–1307; tel. 662/244–1000, **A**1 3 10 19 **F**3 4 5 7 11 13 15 17 18
20 22 24 26 28 29 30 31 34 38 39 40 43 45 49 51 57 59 61 64 70 73 75 76
77 79 80 81 84 85 87 88 89 91 93 94 96 98 100 102 104 106 107 108 109
110 111 114 115 116 117 118 119 120 121 123 124 126 129 130 132 134
146 147 148 149 153 154 **P**6 7 **S** Baptist Memorial Health Care Corporation,
Memphis, TN
Primary Contact: Paul Cade, Administrator and Chief Executive Officer
CFO: David Webb, Chief Financial Officer
CMO: John E Reed, M.D., Medical Director
CIO: Sheila Bardwell, Director Information Systems
CHR: Bob McCallister, Director Human Resources
CNO: Mary Ellen Sumrall, Chief Nursing Officer
Web address: www.baptistonline.org/golden–triangle/
Control: Other not–for–profit (including NFP Corporation) **Service:** General
medical and surgical

> **Staffed Beds:** 236 **Admissions:** 9279 **Census:** 107 **Outpatient Visits:**
> 128180 **Births:** 928 **Total Expense ($000):** 168395 **Payroll Expense
> ($000):** 45164 **Personnel:** 972

CORINTH—Alcorn County

☐ **MAGNOLIA REGIONAL HEALTH CENTER (250009)**, 611 Alcorn Drive,
Zip 38834–9321; tel. 662/293–1000, **A**1 3 10 13 19 **F**13 15 17 22 24 29 30
35 39 40 43 51 53 60 62 63 70 75 76 77 81 82 86 87 89 93 98 100 101 102
103 107 108 111 116 118 119 121 129 130 131 132 143 146 147 148 **P**7 8
Primary Contact: Ronny Humes, Chief Executive Officer
COO: Angela Nowlin, R.N., FACHE, Senior VP, Operations
CFO: Brian Craven, Senior Vice President Finance
CMO: Felton Combest, M.D., Vice President Medical Affairs
CIO: David Parker, VP Information Technology
CHR: Regenia Brown, Vice President Human Resources
CNO: Pam B Wallis, MSN, Vice President Nursing Services
Web address: www.mrhc.org
Control: City–county, Government, nonfederal **Service:** General medical and surgical

> **Staffed Beds:** 200 **Admissions:** 8760 **Census:** 97 **Outpatient Visits:**
> 189920 **Births:** 644 **Personnel:** 1301

DE KALB—Kemper County

JOHN C. STENNIS MEMORIAL HOSPITAL (251335), 14365 Highway 16 West,
Zip 39328–7974; tel. 769/486–1000, **A**10 18 **F**29 40 43 75 81 107 119 127
128 133 **P**6 **S** Rush Health Systems, Meridian, MS
Primary Contact: Justin Palmer, Administrator
Web address: www.johncstennismemorialhospital.com/jcsmh/
Control: Other not–for–profit (including NFP Corporation) **Service:** General
medical and surgical

> **Staffed Beds:** 25 **Admissions:** 354 **Census:** 10 **Outpatient Visits:** 6666
> **Births:** 0 **Total Expense ($000):** 12682 **Payroll Expense ($000):** 2852
> **Personnel:** 162

EUPORA—Webster County

☒ **NORTH MISSISSIPPI MEDICAL CENTER–EUPORA (250020)**, 70 Medical
Plaza, Zip 39744–4018; tel. 662/258–6221, (Total facility includes 35 beds in
nursing home–type unit) **A**1 10 20 **F**3 11 15 28 29 30 32 34 35 38 40 43 50 53
57 59 64 65 68 71 74 84 87 89 90 97 107 114 119 127 129 130 132 133
135 146 148 149 150 154 **S** North Mississippi Health Services, Inc., Tupelo, MS
Primary Contact: Robin Mixon, Interim Chief Executive Officer
CFO: Adonna Mitchell, Director Fiscal Services
CMO: Christy Vowell, D.O., Chief of Staff
CIO: Helen Reed, Director Health Information
CHR: Dorothy Castle, Director Human Resources
Web address: www.nmhs.net/eupora
Control: Other not–for–profit (including NFP Corporation) **Service:** General
medical and surgical

> **Staffed Beds:** 73 **Admissions:** 949 **Census:** 44 **Births:** 0 **Total Expense
> ($000):** 25592 **Payroll Expense ($000):** 11853 **Personnel:** 169

FAYETTE—Jefferson County

★ **JEFFERSON COUNTY HOSPITAL (250060)**, 870 South Main Street,
Zip 39069–5695, Mailing Address: P.O. Box 577, Zip 39069–0577;
tel. 601/786–3401, **A**10 **F**3 40 107 130
Primary Contact: Ada Wilson, R.N., Interim Chief Executive Officer
CMO: Khar Omolara, M.D., Chief Medical Staff
CHR: Patricia Selmon, Director Public Relations and Chief Human Resources
Control: County, Government, nonfederal **Service:** General medical and surgical

> **Staffed Beds:** 30 **Admissions:** 230 **Census:** 4 **Outpatient Visits:** 21608
> **Births:** 1 **Personnel:** 93

FLOWOOD—Rankin County

☒ **MERIT HEALTH RIVER OAKS (250138)**, 1030 River Oaks Drive,
Zip 39232–9553, Mailing Address: P.O. Box 5100, Jackson, Zip 39296–5100;
tel. 601/932–1030, **A**1 3 10 **F**3 11 12 13 15 18 20 29 30 31 35 39 40 43 45
49 51 60 61 63 70 72 73 74 75 76 77 78 79 81 82 85 87 89 93 107 108
110 111 115 119 126 130 144 146 147 **P**5 **S** Community Health Systems, Inc.,
Franklin, TN
Primary Contact: L Dwayne. Blaylock, Chief Executive Officer
COO: Heather Sistrunk, R.N., Chief Operating Officer
CFO: Brad Sinclair, Chief Financial Officer
CIO: Pat Jones, Director Information Systems
CHR: Warren Weed, Director Human Resources
CNO: Sherry P Cook, R.N., MSN, Chief Nursing Executive
Web address: www.riveroakshosp.com
Control: Corporation, Investor–owned (for–profit) **Service:** General medical and
surgical

> **Staffed Beds:** 158 **Admissions:** 4745 **Census:** 66 **Births:** 1457 **Total
> Expense ($000):** 108030 **Payroll Expense ($000):** 31125 **Personnel:** 542

MS

Hospital, Medicare Provider Number, Address, Telephone, Approval, Facility, and Physician Codes, Health Care System

★ American Hospital Association (AHA) membership ○ Healthcare Facilities Accreditation Program ⇑ Center for Improvement in Healthcare Quality Accreditation
☐ The Joint Commission accreditation ◇ DNV Healthcare Inc. accreditation △ Commission on Accreditation of Rehabilitation Facilities (CARF) accreditation

---

⌧ **MERIT HEALTH WOMAN'S HOSPITAL (250136)**, 1026 North Flowood Drive, Zip 39232–9532, Mailing Address: 1026 North Flowood Drive, Zip 39232; tel. 601/932–1000, (Nonreporting) **A**1 3 10 **S** Community Health Systems, Inc., Franklin, TN
Primary Contact: Sherry J. Pitts, Chief Executive Officer
CFO: Nick Renda, Chief Financial Officer
CMO: Ed Barham, M.D., Chief of Staff
CHR: Warren Weed, Director Associate Relations
CNO: Linda Atwood, Chief Nursing Officer
Web address: www.merithealthwomanshospital.com
Control: Corporation, Investor–owned (for–profit) **Service**: Obstetrics and gynecology

Staffed Beds: 60

FOREST—Scott County

★ ⇑ **LACKEY MEMORIAL HOSPITAL (251300)**, 330 Broad Street, Zip 39074–3508, Mailing Address: P.O. Box 428, Zip 39074–0428; tel. 601/469–4151, (Total facility includes 20 beds in nursing home–type unit) **A**10 18 21 **F**3 8 11 15 18 29 34 35 38 39 40 41 43 45 50 54 55 56 57 59 64 65 66 68 81 86 87 89 92 97 98 103 104 107 108 110 111 119 127 128 130 133 **P**6
Primary Contact: Sydney Sawyer, R.N., Chief Executive Officer
CFO: Julie Gieger, Chief Financial Officer
CMO: John Paul Lee, M.D., Chief of Staff
CIO: Eddie Pope, Chief Information Officer
CHR: Donn Paul, Chief Human Resources
Web address: www.lackeymemorialhospital.com
Control: Other not–for–profit (including NFP Corporation) **Service**: General medical and surgical

Staffed Beds: 55 **Admissions**: 1048 **Census**: 30 **Outpatient Visits**: 21680 **Births**: 0 **Total Expense ($000)**: 22286 **Payroll Expense ($000)**: 9431 **Personnel**: 212

GREENVILLE—Washington County

★ ⇑ **ALLEGIANCE SPECIALTY HOSPITAL OF GREENVILLE (252013)**, 300 South Washington Avenue, 3rd Floor, Zip 38701–4719; tel. 662/332–7344, **A**10 21 **F**1 3 29 34 68 85 130 149 153 **S** Allegiance Health Management, Shreveport, LA
Primary Contact: Vearnail Herzog, Chief Executive Officer
CMO: Parvez Karim, M.D., Chief Medical Officer
CIO: Sharon Scott, Health Information Director
CHR: Sharon Taylor, Human Resources Director
CNO: John Read, Chief Nursing Officer
Web address: www.ahmgt.com
Control: Corporation, Investor–owned (for–profit) **Service**: Acute long–term care hospital

Staffed Beds: 39 **Admissions**: 357 **Census**: 20 **Outpatient Visits**: 0 **Births**: 0 **Personnel**: 101

★ **DELTA REGIONAL MEDICAL CENTER (250082)**, 1400 East Union Street, Zip 38704–5247; tel. 662/378–3783, (Includes THE KING'S DAUGHTERS HOSPITAL, 300 Washington Avenue, Greenville, MS, Zip 38701–3614, Mailing Address: P.O. Box 1857, Zip 38702–1857, tel. 662/378–2020; Scott Christensen, FACHE, Chief Executive Officer) **A**10 19 **F**3 4 8 11 13 15 18 20 22 28 29 30 31 34 35 39 40 43 45 47 50 55 56 57 59 60 62 63 64 65 68 70 72 73 75 76 78 79 81 85 87 89 90 92 93 96 97 98 100 102 103 104 105 107 108 110 111 115 116 118 119 124 127 129 130 131 132 135 144 145 146 147 148 149
Primary Contact: Scott Christensen, FACHE, Chief Executive Officer
CFO: C Thomas Moore, FACHE, Chief Financial Officer
CHR: Chrissy Nicholson, Vice President of Human Resources
CNO: Amy Walker, MSN, Chief Nursing Officer
Web address: www.deltaregional.com
Control: County, Government, nonfederal **Service**: General medical and surgical

Staffed Beds: 171 **Admissions**: 6734 **Census**: 94 **Outpatient Visits**: 93611 **Births**: 689 **Personnel**: 903

GREENWOOD—Leflore County

AMG SPECIALTY HOSPITAL–GREENWOOD (252010), 1401 River Road Floor 2, Zip 38930–4030; tel. 662/459–2681, (Nonreporting) **A**10 **S** AMG Integrated Healthcare Management, Lafayette, LA
Primary Contact: Jennifer Wallace, Chief Executive Officer
CMO: Gutti Rao, M.D., Medical Director
CNO: Brenda Small, Chief Clinical Officer
Web address: www.amggreenwood.com/
Control: Partnership, Investor–owned (for–profit) **Service**: Acute long–term care hospital

Staffed Beds: 40

☐ △ **GREENWOOD LEFLORE HOSPITAL (250099)**, 1401 River Road, Zip 38930–4030, Mailing Address: Drawer 1410, Zip 38935–1410; tel. 662/459–7000, **A**1 7 10 19 **F**3 13 15 17 18 20 28 29 31 32 34 35 39 40 43 44 45 46 50 53 56 57 58 59 64 65 70 74 75 76 79 81 82 85 86 87 89 90 93 96 98 103 107 108 109 110 111 114 118 119 120 121 129 130 132 146 147 149 **P**6 8
Primary Contact: Dawne Holmes, Interim Chief Executive Officer
COO: Dodie McElmurray, Chief Operating Officer
CFO: Dawne Holmes, Chief Financial Officer
CMO: Abhash Thakur, M.D., Chief of Staff
CHR: Key Britt, Associate Director
Web address: www.glh.org
Control: City–county, Government, nonfederal **Service**: General medical and surgical

Staffed Beds: 208 **Admissions**: 5618 **Census**: 72 **Outpatient Visits**: 156684 **Births**: 495 **Total Expense ($000)**: 119730 **Payroll Expense ($000)**: 56197 **Personnel**: 819

GRENADA—Grenada County

★ ⇑ **UNIVERSITY OF MISSISSIPPI MEDICAL CENTER GRENADA (250168)**, 960 Avent Drive, Zip 38901–5230; tel. 662/227–7000, **A**10 21 **F**3 7 8 11 13 15 17 29 30 33 34 40 43 53 56 57 60 62 64 65 70 73 76 77 79 80 81 82 85 87 89 90 93 94 96 97 98 103 107 108 110 111 115 116 118 119 127 130 143 146 147 **P**6 **S** University Hospitals and Health System, Jackson, MS
Primary Contact: Wes Sigler, Chief Executive Officer
COO: Molly B. Brown, Chief Operating Officer
CFO: Scott Whittemore, Chief Financial Officer
CIO: John Farrish, Health Information Director
CHR: Claudette Hathcock, Administrative Director Human Resources
Web address: www.glmc.net/
Control: State, Government, nonfederal **Service**: General medical and surgical

Staffed Beds: 58 **Admissions**: 2384 **Census**: 28 **Outpatient Visits**: 59347 **Births**: 397 **Total Expense ($000)**: 46711 **Payroll Expense ($000)**: 25198 **Personnel**: 367

GULFPORT—Harrison County

⌧ **GARDEN PARK MEDICAL CENTER (250123)**, 15200 Community Road, Zip 39503–3085, Mailing Address: P.O. Box 1240, Zip 39502–1240; tel. 228/575–7000, **A**1 10 **F**3 8 9 11 12 13 15 18 29 30 34 35 37 40 41 43 45 46 49 57 59 64 65 70 74 76 79 81 85 86 89 90 98 103 105 106 107 108 109 110 111 112 115 118 119 126 129 147 148 149 152 154 **S** HCA Healthcare, Nashville, TN
Primary Contact: Randy Rogers, FACHE, Chief Executive Officer
COO: Regina Ramazani, Chief Operating Officer
CFO: Regina Ramazani, Chief Financial Officer
CMO: T. Paul Mace, Chief Medical Officer
CIO: Chris Oubre, Information Technology Director
CHR: Michael Pocchiari, Director Human Resources
CNO: Cheryl Thompson, Chief Nursing Officer
Web address: www.gpmedical.com
Control: Corporation, Investor–owned (for–profit) **Service**: General medical and surgical

Staffed Beds: 130 **Admissions**: 3865 **Census**: 50 **Outpatient Visits**: 58483 **Births**: 467 **Total Expense ($000)**: 73964 **Payroll Expense ($000)**: 24789 **Personnel**: 328

☐ △ **HEALTHSOUTH REHABILITATION HOSPITAL OF GULFPORT (253027)**, 4500 13th Street, Suite 900, Zip 39501–2515; tel. 228/822–6965, (Data for 183 days) **A**1 7 **F**29 90 **S** Encompass Health Corporation, Birmingham, AL
Primary Contact: Amber Hester, Chief Executive Officer
Web address: www.healthsouthgulfport.com
Control: Corporation, Investor–owned (for–profit) **Service**: Rehabilitation

Staffed Beds: 33 **Admissions**: 306 **Census**: 18 **Outpatient Visits**: 0 **Births**: 0 **Total Expense ($000)**: 5400 **Payroll Expense ($000)**: 2719 **Personnel**: 86

⌧ △ **MEMORIAL HOSPITAL AT GULFPORT (250019)**, 4500 13th Street, Zip 39501–2569, Mailing Address: P.O. Box 1810, Zip 39502–1810; tel. 228/867–4000, (Includes MEMORIAL BEHAVIORAL HEALTH, 11150 Highway 49 North, Gulfport, MS, Zip 39503–4110; tel. 228/831–1700; Michael A Zieman, FACHE, Administrator) **A**1 2 3 7 10 **F**2 3 14 17 18 20 22 24 28 29 30 31 34 35 40 43 44 45 46 47 48 49 50 53 54 57 59 64 65 68 70 71 72 73 74 76 77 78 79 80 81 84 85 87 89 90 98 99 100 101 102 104 105 107 108 110 111 114 115 116 117 118 119 120 121 123 124 126 130 132 145 146 148 149 151 **P**8
Primary Contact: Kent Nicaud, President and Chief Executive Officer
CFO: Jeffrey T Steiner, Vice President Finance
CMO: Larry Couvillon, M.D., Chief Medical Officer
CIO: Gene Thomas, Vice President, Information Systems, Chief Information Officer
CHR: Cathy Wood, Vice President, Human Resources
CNO: Jennifer Dumal, R.N., Chief Operating Officer of Clinical and Chief Nursing Officer
Web address: www.gulfportmemorial.com
Control: City–county, Government, nonfederal **Service**: General medical and surgical

Staffed Beds: 412 **Admissions**: 16497 **Census**: 232 **Outpatient Visits**: 722957 **Births**: 1322 **Total Expense ($000)**: 513394 **Payroll Expense ($000)**: 236174 **Personnel**: 3073

⊞ **SELECT SPECIALTY HOSPITAL–GULFPORT (252005)**, 1520 Broad Avenue, Suite 300, Zip 39501–3601; tel. 228/575–7500, **A**1 10 **F**1 29 75 82 87 90 **S** Select Medical Corporation, Mechanicsburg, PA
Primary Contact: John O'Keefe, Chief Executive Officer
Web address: www.selectspecialtyhospitals.com/company/locations/gulfcoast.aspx
Control: Corporation, Investor–owned (for–profit) **Service:** Acute long–term care hospital

Staffed Beds: 61 **Admissions:** 359 **Census:** 27 **Outpatient Visits:** 0 **Births:** 0 **Total Expense ($000):** 16171 **Payroll Expense ($000):** 6798 **Personnel:** 130

HATTIESBURG—Forrest County

★ △ ⇑ **FORREST GENERAL HOSPITAL (250078)**, 6051 US Highway 49, Zip 39401–7200, Mailing Address: P.O. Box 16389, Zip 39404–6389; tel. 601/288–7000, (Includes PINE GROVE BEHAVIORAL HEALTH AND ADDICTION SERVICES, 2255 Broadway Drive, Hattiesburg, MS, Zip 39402–3254; tel. 888/574–4673; Debbie F Sanford, R.N., MS, Administrator) **A**2 3 5 7 10 19 21 **F**3 4 5 8 12 13 15 17 18 20 22 24 26 28 29 30 31 34 35 37 39 40 43 45 46 47 48 49 53 57 58 59 62 63 64 68 70 72 73 75 76 77 79 81 84 85 86 87 89 90 91 92 93 95 96 98 99 100 101 102 103 104 107 108 111 114 115 118 119 120 121 123 124 126 128 130 132 135 146 147 149 152 154 **P**1
Primary Contact: Evan S. Dillard, M.P.H., FACHE, Chief Executive Officer
COO: Douglas A Jones, Chief Operating Officer
CMO: Steven E Farrell, M.D., Chief Medical Officer
CHR: Troy P Daniels, Chief Human Resources Officer
CNO: Micah Rehm, Chief Nursing Officer
Web address: www.forrestgeneral.com
Control: County, Government, nonfederal **Service:** General medical and surgical

Staffed Beds: 512 **Admissions:** 29766 **Census:** 367 **Outpatient Visits:** 155716 **Births:** 2537 **Total Expense ($000):** 402412 **Payroll Expense ($000):** 165631 **Personnel:** 3233

HATTIESBURG—Lamar County

⊞ **MERIT HEALTH WESLEY (250094)**, 5001 Hardy Street, Zip 39402–1308, Mailing Address: P.O. Box 16509, Zip 39404–6509; tel. 601/268–8000, **A**1 3 10 19 **F**3 8 11 12 13 15 17 18 20 22 24 26 28 29 30 32 34 35 37 39 40 41 43 45 46 49 53 54 57 58 59 60 61 64 65 70 71 72 73 74 75 76 77 78 79 81 82 85 87 89 90 91 93 96 97 103 107 108 110 111 114 115 117 118 119 126 129 130 132 135 146 148 **S** Community Health Systems, Inc., Franklin, TN
Primary Contact: Carol Upton, Interim Chief Executive Officer
CFO: Randy Humphrey, Chief Financial Officer
CMO: William Reno, M.D., III President Medical Staff
CIO: Jesse Folds, Director of Information Technologies
CHR: Terry Trigg, Director Human Resources
Web address: www.wesley.com
Control: Corporation, Investor–owned (for–profit) **Service:** General medical and surgical

Staffed Beds: 211 **Admissions:** 6741 **Census:** 93 **Outpatient Visits:** 77107 **Births:** 1140 **Personnel:** 785

HAZLEHURST—Copiah County

★ **COPIAH COUNTY MEDICAL CENTER (251327)**, 27190 Highway 28, Zip 39083–2228, Mailing Address: P.O. Box 889, Zip 39083–0889; tel. 601/574–7000, **A**10 18 **F**3 8 15 24 25 29 30 34 35 39 40 50 51 57 59 66 69 77 81 93 104 107 110 111 115 119 133 148 153
Primary Contact: Benjamin Lott, Chief Executive Officer
CFO: Bryan N Stevens, Interim Chief Financial Officer
CNO: Alison Mathis, Chief Nursing Officer
Web address: www.myccmc.org/
Control: County, Government, nonfederal **Service:** General medical and surgical

Staffed Beds: 25 **Admissions:** 659 **Census:** 14 **Births:** 0 **Total Expense ($000):** 7607 **Payroll Expense ($000):** 5525 **Personnel:** 158

HOLLY SPRINGS—Marshall County

ALLIANCE HEALTHCARE SYSTEM (250012), 1430 Highway 4 East, Zip 38635–2140, Mailing Address: P.O. Box 6000, Zip 38634–6000; tel. 662/252–1212, **A**10 20 **F**15 29 35 40 43 57 63 75 81 84 87 89 98 103 107 114 119 130 132 133
Primary Contact: Perry E. Williams Sr, Administrator and Chief Executive Officer
COO: Cecelia Bost, Chief Operating Officer
CFO: William F Magee, Chief Financial Officer
CMO: Subbu Rayudu, M.D., Chief of Staff
CIO: Saul Mbenga, Manager Information Technology
CHR: Judy Eggers, Manager Human Resources
Web address: www.alliancehealth.us
Control: Corporation, Investor–owned (for–profit) **Service:** General medical and surgical

Staffed Beds: 40 **Admissions:** 377 **Census:** 7 **Outpatient Visits:** 7490 **Births:** 0 **Total Expense ($000):** 9714 **Payroll Expense ($000):** 4678 **Personnel:** 94

HOUSTON—Chickasaw County

TRACE REGIONAL HOSPITAL (250017), Highway 8 East, Zip 38851–9396, Mailing Address: P.O. Box 626, Zip 38851–0626; tel. 662/456–3700, **A**10 **F**3 11 15 30 34 35 45 57 59 61 64 66 75 82 90 91 93 98 101 102 103 107 111 119 127 130 133 135 146 148 **P**6
Primary Contact: Gary L. Staten, Chief Executive Officer
CFO: Pamela W Cook, Chief Financial Officer
CMO: Bill Brohawn, Chief of Staff
CHR: Sherry Craig, Director Human Resources
CNO: Marianne Johnson, Chief Nursing Officer
Web address: www.traceregional.com
Control: Corporation, Investor–owned (for–profit) **Service:** General medical and surgical

Staffed Beds: 84 **Admissions:** 640 **Census:** 19 **Outpatient Visits:** 7482 **Births:** 0 **Total Expense ($000):** 14728 **Payroll Expense ($000):** 8707 **Personnel:** 194

INDIANOLA—Sunflower County

★ **SOUTH SUNFLOWER COUNTY HOSPITAL (250095)**, 121 East Baker Street, Zip 38751–2498; tel. 662/635–7201, **A**10 20 **F**3 8 13 34 40 43 50 64 65 76 80 81 85 89 107 119 127 133 **P**8
Primary Contact: Courtney Phillips, Chief Executive Officer
COO: Holly H. Sparks, Chief Clinical Officer
CFO: Katie Yates, Chief Financial Officer
CMO: Eric Lessmann, Chief of Staff
CIO: Benjamin Rosenthal, Information Systems Director
CHR: Meredith Taylor, Controller
Web address: www.southsunflower.com
Control: County, Government, nonfederal **Service:** General medical and surgical

Staffed Beds: 48 **Admissions:** 898 **Census:** 10 **Births:** 100 **Total Expense ($000):** 19124 **Payroll Expense ($000):** 5539 **Personnel:** 110

IUKA—Tishomingo County

⊞ **NORTH MISSISSIPPI MEDICAL CENTER–IUKA (250002)**, 1777 Curtis Drive, Zip 38852–1001, Mailing Address: P.O. Box 860, Zip 38852–0860; tel. 662/423–6051, **A**1 10 **F**15 29 35 40 53 80 82 86 87 89 90 93 107 108 111 114 119 129 130 132 133 134 146 151 **S** North Mississippi Health Services, Inc., Tupelo, MS
Primary Contact: Fred A. Truesdale Jr, Administrator
CFO: Betty Moore, Business Manager
CMO: Margaret Glynn, M.D., Chief Medical Officer
CIO: Fred A Truesdale Jr Administrator
CHR: Jane Chamblee, Manager Human Resources
Web address: www.nmhs.net
Control: Other not–for–profit (including NFP Corporation) **Service:** General medical and surgical

Staffed Beds: 48 **Admissions:** 613 **Census:** 5 **Outpatient Visits:** 23010 **Births:** 0 **Total Expense ($000):** 11711 **Payroll Expense ($000):** 6487 **Personnel:** 107

MS

Hospital, Medicare Provider Number, Address, Telephone, Approval, Facility, and Physician Codes, Health Care System

★ American Hospital Association (AHA) membership
☐ The Joint Commission accreditation
◯ Healthcare Facilities Accreditation Program
◇ DNV Healthcare Inc. accreditation
⇑ Center for Improvement in Healthcare Quality Accreditation
△ Commission on Accreditation of Rehabilitation Facilities (CARF) accreditation

JACKSON—Hinds County

☐ **BRENTWOOD BEHAVIORAL HEALTHCARE OF MISSISSIPPI (254007)**, 3531 East Lakeland Drive, Zip 39232–8839; tel. 601/936–2024, **A**1 10 **F**35 98 99 101 102 104 105 130 132 134 153 **S** Universal Health Services, Inc., King of Prussia, PA
Primary Contact: Michael J. Carney, Chief Executive Officer
Web address: www.brentwoodjackson.com
Control: Corporation, Investor–owned (for–profit) **Service**: Psychiatric

Staffed Beds: 105 **Admissions**: 2565 **Census**: 66 **Outpatient Visits**: 3748
Births: 0 **Personnel**: 250

☒ **G.V. (SONNY) MONTGOMERY VETERANS AFFAIRS MEDICAL CENTER**, 1500 East Woodrow Wilson Drive, Zip 39216–5199; tel. 601/362–4471, (Nonreporting) **A**1 3 5 **S** Department of Veterans Affairs, Perry Point, MD
Primary Contact: David M. Walker, M.D., Medical Center Director
COO: Jed Fillingim, Acting Chief Operating Officer and Associate Director
CFO: Joy Willis, Acting Chief Fiscal Service
CMO: Kent Kirchner, M.D., Chief of Staff
CIO: Robert Wolak, Chief Information Resource Management Service
CHR: Sam Evans, Chief Human Resources Management
Web address: www.jackson.va.gov/
Control: Veterans Affairs, Government, federal **Service**: General medical and surgical

Staffed Beds: 323

☒ **MERIT HEALTH CENTRAL (250072)**, 1850 Chadwick Drive, Zip 39204–3479, Mailing Address: P.O. Box 59001, Zip 39284–9001; tel. 601/376–1000, **A**1 3 10 **F**13 15 16 17 29 35 40 43 70 72 75 76 77 78 81 86 87 89 90 93 98 100 102 107 108 111 116 118 119 130 132 146 **S** Community Health Systems, Inc., Franklin, TN
Primary Contact: Barry Moss, Chief Executive Officer
CFO: Justin Stroud, Chief Financial Officer
CMO: Greg Oden, Chief Medical Officer
CIO: Tracy Holifield, Director Information Systems
CHR: Sean Jones, Director Human Resources
CNO: Laura Knight, Chief Nursing Officer
Web address: www.merithealthcentral.com/
Control: Corporation, Investor–owned (for–profit) **Service**: General medical and surgical

Staffed Beds: 319 **Admissions**: 7473 **Census**: 117 **Outpatient Visits**: 178949 **Births**: 751 **Total Expense ($000)**: 144176 **Payroll Expense ($000)**: 43447 **Personnel**: 634

☒ △ **METHODIST REHABILITATION CENTER (250152)**, 1350 Woodrow Wilson Drive, Zip 39216–5198; tel. 601/981–2611, (Total facility includes 60 beds in nursing home–type unit) **A**1 5 7 10 **F**30 34 35 50 57 58 59 64 68 74 81 82 86 87 90 91 92 93 94 95 96 119 130 131 132 135 146
Primary Contact: Mark A. Adams, President and Chief Executive Officer
COO: Joseph M Morette, Executive Vice President
CFO: Gary Armstrong, Executive Vice President
CIO: Gary Armstrong, Executive Vice President
CHR: Steve Hope, Vice President Corporate Services
Web address: www.methodistrehab.org
Control: Other not–for–profit (including NFP Corporation) **Service**: Rehabilitation

Staffed Beds: 184 **Admissions**: 1332 **Census**: 116 **Outpatient Visits**: 52188 **Births**: 0 **Total Expense ($000)**: 46491 **Payroll Expense ($000)**: 26123 **Personnel**: 608

☒ **MISSISSIPPI BAPTIST MEDICAL CENTER (250102)**, 1225 North State Street, Zip 39202–2064; tel. 601/968–1000, **A**1 2 3 5 10 **F**3 12 13 15 17 18 20 22 24 26 28 29 30 31 34 35 37 40 46 47 49 50 53 57 58 59 60 64 65 68 70 72 74 75 76 79 80 81 84 85 87 89 92 93 98 100 103 107 108 110 111 114 115 116 117 118 119 120 121 122 123 124 126 129 130 132 141 146 147 149 **S** Baptist Memorial Health Care Corporation, Memphis, TN
Primary Contact: Bobbie K. Ware, R.N., FACHE, Chief Executive Officer
COO: Bobbie K. Ware, R.N., FACHE, Vice President Patient Care and Chief Nursing Officer
CFO: William Thompson, Chief Financial Officer
CMO: Michael Maples, M.D., Vice President and Chief Medical Officer
CIO: Steve M Stanic, Vice President and Chief Information Officer
CHR: Lee Ann Foreman, Vice President Human Resources
CNO: Bobbie K. Ware, R.N., FACHE, Vice President Patient Care and Chief Nursing Officer
Web address: www.mbhs.org
Control: Other not–for–profit (including NFP Corporation) **Service**: General medical and surgical

Staffed Beds: 450 **Admissions**: 20685 **Census**: 276 **Outpatient Visits**: 238694 **Births**: 1866 **Total Expense ($000)**: 317345 **Payroll Expense ($000)**: 137697 **Personnel**: 2867

☒ **SELECT SPECIALTY HOSPITAL – BELHAVEN (252003)**, 1225 North State Street, Zip 39202–2097, Mailing Address: P.O. Box 23695, Zip 39225–3695; tel. 601/968–1000, **A**1 10 **F**1 3 29 56 61 82 130 **S** Select Medical Corporation, Mechanicsburg, PA
Primary Contact: Bobbie K. Ware, MHS, BSN, RN, FACHE, Chief Executive Officer
CFO: Russell W York, Vice President and Chief Financial Officer
CMO: Holland M Addison, M.D., Medical Director
CIO: Steve M Stanic, Vice President and Chief Information Officer
CHR: Lee Ann Foreman, Vice President Human Resources
Web address: www.mbhs.org
Control: Corporation, Investor–owned (for–profit) **Service**: Acute long–term care hospital

Staffed Beds: 25 **Admissions**: 232 **Census**: 20 **Outpatient Visits**: 0 **Births**: 0 **Total Expense ($000)**: 14200 **Payroll Expense ($000)**: 6315 **Personnel**: 118

☒ **SELECT SPECIALTY HOSPITAL–JACKSON (252007)**, 5903 Ridgewood Road, Suite 100, Zip 39211–3700; tel. 601/899–3800, **A**1 10 **F**1 107 119 **P**7 **S** Select Medical Corporation, Mechanicsburg, PA
Primary Contact: Chandler Ewing, Chief Executive Officer
CFO: Melissa Smith, Controller
CIO: Jacqueline Barnes, Manager Health Information
CHR: Vicki Watson, Manager Human Resources
Web address: www.selectspecialtyhospitals.com/company/locations/jackson.aspx
Control: Corporation, Investor–owned (for–profit) **Service**: Acute long–term care hospital

Staffed Beds: 53 **Admissions**: 596 **Census**: 44 **Outpatient Visits**: 0 **Births**: 0 **Total Expense ($000)**: 23887 **Payroll Expense ($000)**: 10634 **Personnel**: 216

☒ **ST. DOMINIC–JACKSON MEMORIAL HOSPITAL (250048)**, 969 Lakeland Drive, Zip 39216–4606; tel. 601/200–2000, **A**1 2 3 5 10 **F**3 4 11 12 13 15 17 18 20 22 24 26 28 29 30 31 34 36 37 38 40 43 46 47 49 50 51 53 58 60 61 64 65 68 70 72 73 74 75 76 77 79 80 81 82 84 85 86 87 89 90 92 93 96 97 98 100 101 102 103 107 108 110 111 114 115 116 117 118 119 120 121 123 124 126 130 131 146 147 148 154 **P**6 8
Primary Contact: Lester K. Diamond, President
CFO: Sam Scott, Vice President Financial Services
CMO: Eric A McVey, M.D., Executive Vice President Medical Affairs and Quality
CIO: Keith Van Camp, Vice President Information Services
CHR: Frank Lenior, Vice President Human Resources
Web address: www.stdom.com
Control: Church operated, Nongovernment, not–for–profit **Service**: General medical and surgical

Staffed Beds: 502 **Admissions**: 37853 **Census**: 418 **Outpatient Visits**: 220006 **Births**: 1553 **Total Expense ($000)**: 480692 **Payroll Expense ($000)**: 202818 **Personnel**: 2973

☒ △ **UNIVERSITY OF MISSISSIPPI MEDICAL CENTER (250001)**, 2500 North State Street, Zip 39216–4505; tel. 601/984–1000, (Includes BLAIR E. BATSON HOSPITAL FOR CHILDREN, 2500 North State State Room W019, Zip 39216–4500; tel. 601/984–1000; CHILDREN'S HEALTHCARE OF MISSISSIPPI, 2500 North State Street, Jackson, MS, Zip 39216–4500; tel. 601/984–1000) **A**1 2 3 5 7 8 10 13 **F**3 6 7 8 11 12 13 15 17 18 19 20 21 22 23 24 25 28 29 30 31 32 34 35 38 39 40 41 43 45 46 47 48 49 50 52 53 54 55 56 57 58 59 60 61 64 65 66 68 70 71 72 73 74 75 76 77 79 80 81 82 84 85 86 87 88 89 90 92 93 94 96 97 98 99 100 101 102 103 104 107 108 110 111 112 114 115 116 117 118 119 120 121 123 124 126 127 129 130 131 132 134 135 136 137 138 139 141 142 143 144 146 147 148 149 152 154 **P**6 **S** University Hospitals and Health System, Jackson, MS
Primary Contact: Kevin S. Cook, Chief Executive Officer
CFO: Dan Janicak, Chief Financial Officer
CMO: William H Cleland, M.D., Chief Medical Officer
CHR: Paula Henderson, Chief Human Resources Officer
Web address: www.umc.edu
Control: State, Government, nonfederal **Service**: General medical and surgical

Staffed Beds: 680 **Admissions**: 30211 **Census**: 539 **Outpatient Visits**: 562573 **Births**: 2184 **Total Expense ($000)**: 730013 **Payroll Expense ($000)**: 317934 **Personnel**: 4616

KEESLER AFB—Harrison County

☒ **U.S. AIR FORCE MEDICAL CENTER KEESLER**, 301 Fisher Street, Room 1A132, Zip 39534–2519; tel. 228/376–2550, (Nonreporting) **A**1 2 3 5 **S** Department of the Air Force, Washington, DC
Primary Contact: Colonel Thomas Harrell, M.D., Commander
COO: Brigadier General James Dougherty, Commander
CFO: Major Brenda Yi, Director Medical Resource Management and Chief Financial Officer
CMO: Colonel James Gasque, M.D., Chief Hospital Services
CIO: Major Samuel Silverthorne, Chief Information Officer
CHR: Major Brenda Yi, Director Medical Resource Management and Chief Financial Officer
Web address: www.keesler.af.mil
Control: Air Force, Government, federal **Service**: General medical and surgical

Staffed Beds: 56

Many Facility Codes have changed. Please refer to the AHA Guide Code Chart.

© 2018 AHA Guide

MS

KOSCIUSKO—Attala County

★ ⇑ **BAPTIST MEDICAL CENTER ATTALA (251336)**, 220 Highway 12 West, Zip 39090–3208, Mailing Address: P.O. Box 887, Zip 39090–0887; tel. 662/289–4311, **A**10 18 21 **F**2 3 8 15 30 40 45 64 65 68 81 89 90 107 108 110 115 118 119 127 133 148 153 **S** Baptist Memorial Health Care Corporation, Memphis, TN
Primary Contact: Robert Coleman, Chief Executive Officer
CHR: Stephanie Washington, Human Resources Director
CNO: Allison Schuler, R.N., Chief Nursing Officer
Web address: www.mbhs.org/locations/baptist–medical–center–attala/
Control: Other not–for–profit (including NFP Corporation) **Service**: General medical and surgical

Staffed Beds: 25 **Admissions**: 724 **Census**: 11 **Outpatient Visits**: 19300 **Births**: 0 **Total Expense ($000)**: 15770 **Payroll Expense ($000)**: 5245 **Personnel**: 132		

LAUREL—Jones County

★ ⇑ **SOUTH CENTRAL REGIONAL MEDICAL CENTER (250058)**, 1220 Jefferson Street, Zip 39440–4374, Mailing Address: P.O. Box 607, Zip 39441–0607; tel. 601/426–4000, (Total facility includes 248 beds in nursing home–type unit) **A**10 **F**3 4 7 10 11 12 13 15 17 18 20 28 29 31 32 34 35 39 40 41 43 45 46 47 48 49 50 51 53 54 57 59 62 63 64 65 68 70 71 73 74 75 76 77 78 79 81 82 84 85 86 87 89 90 93 100 102 104 107 108 109 110 111 115 117 119 126 128 129 130 131 132 134 143 144 146 147 **P**6
Primary Contact: G Douglas Higginbotham, President and Chief Executive Officer
CFO: Tom Canizaro, Vice President and Chief Financial Officer
CIO: Dell Blakeney, Vice President and Chief Information Officer
CHR: Janet Staples, Vice President Human Resources
CNO: Beth W Endom, R.N., MSN, Vice President and Chief Nursing Officer
Web address: www.scrmc.com
Control: County, Government, nonfederal **Service**: General medical and surgical

Staffed Beds: 424 **Admissions**: 7864 **Census**: 351 **Outpatient Visits**: 201451 **Births**: 861 **Total Expense ($000)**: 138250 **Payroll Expense ($000)**: 76358 **Personnel**: 1697		

LEAKESVILLE—Greene County

GREENE COUNTY HOSPITAL (251329), 1017 Jackson Avenue, Zip 39451–9105; tel. 601/394–4139, **A**10 18 **F**40 43 107 133
Primary Contact: Deborah Berry, Director of Operations
CFO: Debbie Brannan, Chief Financial Officer
CMO: Larry Henderson, M.D., Medical Director
CHR: Carla Shows, Payroll Clerk
Web address: www.georgeregional.com
Control: County, Government, nonfederal **Service**: General medical and surgical

Staffed Beds: 7 **Admissions**: 137 **Census**: 4 **Births**: 0 **Total Expense ($000)**: 5017 **Payroll Expense ($000)**: 2027 **Personnel**: 45		

LEXINGTON—Holmes County

✉ **UNIVERSITY OF MISSISSIPPI MEDICAL CENTER HOLMES COUNTY (251319)**, 239 Bowling Green Road, Zip 39095–5167; tel. 601/496–5200, **A**1 10 18 **F**3 15 29 34 40 43 50 56 57 59 64 86 87 89 93 104 107 114 119 127 130 133 146 148 149 153 **P**6 **S** University Hospitals and Health System, Jackson, MS
Primary Contact: Wes Sigler, Chief Executive Officer
COO: Paige Lawrence, Assistant Administrator
CFO: Scott Whittemore, Chief Financial Officer
CMO: Mark Smothers, M.D., Chief Medical Officer
CIO: Sammuel Townsend, LAN Administrator
CHR: Claudette Hathcock, Human Resources Director
Web address: www.ummchealth.com/holmes/
Control: State, Government, nonfederal **Service**: General medical and surgical

Staffed Beds: 25 **Admissions**: 327 **Census**: 7 **Outpatient Visits**: 18079 **Births**: 0 **Total Expense ($000)**: 13406 **Payroll Expense ($000)**: 7038 **Personnel**: 114		

LOUISVILLE—Winston County

WINSTON MEDICAL CENTER (250027), 562 East Main Street, Zip 39339–2742, Mailing Address: P.O. Box 967, Zip 39339–0967; tel. 662/773–6211, (Total facility includes 120 beds in nursing home–type unit) **A**10 20 **F**15 29 34 35 40 43 57 59 65 89 93 98 103 107 110 114 119 127 128 130 133 146
Primary Contact: Paul S. Black, Chief Executive Officer
Web address: www.winstonmedical.org
Control: Other not–for–profit (including NFP Corporation) **Service**: General medical and surgical

Staffed Beds: 144 **Admissions**: 947 **Census**: 89 **Outpatient Visits**: 27328 **Births**: 0 **Total Expense ($000)**: 27708 **Payroll Expense ($000)**: 9074 **Personnel**: 270		

LUCEDALE—George County

GEORGE REGIONAL HOSPITAL (250036), 859 Winter Street, Zip 39452–6603, Mailing Address: P.O. Box 607, Zip 39452–0607; tel. 601/947–3161, **A**10 20 **F**3 11 13 15 18 29 30 34 35 40 43 45 47 48 49 53 54 57 59 65 68 70 76 77 81 82 86 87 93 97 107 108 111 119 127 129 130 133 135 146 148 **P**8
Primary Contact: Greg Havard, Chief Executive Officer
CFO: Debbie Brannan, Chief Financial Officer
CMO: Jay Pinkerton, Chief Medical Officer
CIO: Anthoney Fryfogle, Chief Information Officer
CHR: Carla Shows, Human Resource and Payroll Clerk
CNO: Tabatha Pinter, Director of Nursing
Web address: www.georgeregional.com
Control: County, Government, nonfederal **Service**: General medical and surgical

Staffed Beds: 48 **Admissions**: 1046 **Census**: 10 **Outpatient Visits**: 46493 **Births**: 271 **Total Expense ($000)**: 23059 **Payroll Expense ($000)**: 12497 **Personnel**: 265		

MACON—Noxubee County

NOXUBEE GENERAL HOSPITAL (251307), 606 North Jefferson Street, Zip 39341–2242, Mailing Address: P.O. Box 480, Zip 39341–0480; tel. 662/726–4231, (Total facility includes 60 beds in nursing home–type unit) **A**10 18 **F**40 89 107 111 127 128 130 133
Primary Contact: Danny H. McKay, Administrator
Web address: www.noxubeecountyms.com/quality–of–life–noxubee–mississipp/health–care–noxubee–mississippi/
Control: County, Government, nonfederal **Service**: General medical and surgical

Staffed Beds: 85 **Admissions**: 714 **Census**: 66 **Outpatient Visits**: 31429 **Births**: 0 **Total Expense ($000)**: 13381 **Payroll Expense ($000)**: 6818 **Personnel**: 177		

MAGEE—Simpson County

MAGEE GENERAL HOSPITAL (250124), 300 Third Avenue SE, Zip 39111–3698; tel. 601/849–5070, **A**10 **F**15 29 35 40 43 81 89 107 108 111 119 129 130 133 146 148
Primary Contact: Amy Tolliver, Administrator
CMO: Kelli Smith, M.D., Chief of Staff
CIO: Kirby Craft, Chief Information Officer
CHR: Steve Beckham, Director Human Resources
CNO: Cindy McIntyre, R.N., Administrative Director Clinical Services
Web address: www.mghosp.org
Control: Other not–for–profit (including NFP Corporation) **Service**: General medical and surgical

Staffed Beds: 44 **Admissions**: 814 **Census**: 13 **Births**: 0 **Total Expense ($000)**: 20553 **Payroll Expense ($000)**: 6848 **Personnel**: 177		

MAGNOLIA—Pike County

BEACHAM MEMORIAL HOSPITAL (250049), 205 North Cherry Street, Zip 39652–2819, Mailing Address: P.O. Box 351, Zip 39652–0351; tel. 601/783–2351, **A**10 **F**3 34 35 36 57 59 65 68 98 100 101 103 107 114 127 130 133 146 148
Primary Contact: Jason Reed, Chief Executive Officer
CMO: Lucius Lampton, M.D., Medical Director
CHR: Jackie McKenzie, Director Administrative Services
Web address: www.beachammemorial.org
Control: Other not–for–profit (including NFP Corporation) **Service**: General medical and surgical

Staffed Beds: 31 **Admissions**: 1262 **Census**: 25 **Outpatient Visits**: 0 **Births**: 0 **Personnel**: 50		

Hospital, Medicare Provider Number, Address, Telephone, Approval, Facility, and Physician Codes, Health Care System

★ American Hospital Association (AHA) membership   ◯ Healthcare Facilities Accreditation Program   ⇑ Center for Improvement in Healthcare Quality Accreditation
☐ The Joint Commission accreditation   ◇ DNV Healthcare Inc. accreditation   △ Commission on Accreditation of Rehabilitation Facilities (CARF) accreditation

MCCOMB—Pike County

★ �û **SOUTHWEST MISSISSIPPI REGIONAL MEDICAL CENTER (250097)**, 215 Marion Avenue, Zip 39648-2705, Mailing Address: P.O. Box 1307, Zip 39649-1307; tel. 601/249-5500, **A**10 19 21 **F**3 11 12 13 15 17 18 20 22 24 28 29 31 34 35 37 39 40 41 43 44 45 46 47 48 49 50 53 57 59 64 65 68 70 72 73 74 75 76 77 79 81 84 85 86 87 93 94 96 107 108 110 111 115 118 119 120 121 129 130 131 132 145 146 149 154 **P**6 **S** Southwest Health Systems, Mccomb, MS
Primary Contact: Norman M. Price, FACHE, Chief Executive Officer
COO: Richard Williams, Chief Operating Officer
CFO: Charla Rowley, Chief Financial Officer
CMO: Kevin Richardson, M.D., Chief of Staff
CIO: David Hamilton, Chief Information Officer
CHR: Don Haskins, Administrative Director Human Resources
CNO: Michelle Gough MSN, RN–B Chief Nursing Officer
Web address: www.smrmc.com
Control: Hospital district or authority, Government, nonfederal **Service**: General medical and surgical

Staffed Beds: 145 **Admissions**: 5304 **Census**: 48 **Personnel**: 821

MEADVILLE—Franklin County

FRANKLIN COUNTY MEMORIAL HOSPITAL (251330), 40 Union Church Road, Zip 39653-8336, Mailing Address: P.O. Box 636, Zip 39653-0636; tel. 601/384-5801, **A**10 18 **F**29 35 39 40 43 56 86 93 104 107 119 127 130 133 143 148 **P**6
Primary Contact: Mike Boleware, Administrator
Web address: www.fcmh.net
Control: County, Government, nonfederal **Service**: General medical and surgical

Staffed Beds: 25 **Admissions**: 297 **Census**: 18 **Outpatient Visits**: 20473 **Births**: 0 **Total Expense ($000)**: 18568 **Payroll Expense ($000)**: 9735 **Personnel**: 204

MENDENHALL—Simpson County

SIMPSON GENERAL HOSPITAL (251317), 1842 Simpson Highway 149, Zip 39114-3438; tel. 601/847-2221, **A**10 18 **F**3 11 29 30 34 35 40 43 44 54 56 57 59 61 64 65 66 68 81 85 86 87 93 98 100 101 102 103 104 105 107 114 119 127 130 132 133 134 143 146 **P**5
Primary Contact: Randall Neely, Chief Executive Officer
COO: Al Gary, COO
CFO: Al Gary, COO
CMO: Chip Holbrook, M.D., Chief of Staff
CIO: David Welch, Director Information Technology
CHR: Randall Neely, CEO
CNO: Sharon Burnham, Director of Nursing
Web address: www.simpsongeneralhospital.com
Control: Other not–for–profit (including NFP Corporation) **Service**: General medical and surgical

Staffed Beds: 35 **Admissions**: 686 **Census**: 18 **Outpatient Visits**: 12828 **Births**: 2 **Total Expense ($000)**: 14366 **Payroll Expense ($000)**: 8002 **Personnel**: 179

MERIDIAN—Lauderdale County

☐ **ALLIANCE HEALTH CENTER (250151)**, 5000 Highway 39 North, Zip 39301-1021; tel. 601/483-6211, **A**1 10 **F**4 6 35 38 64 86 87 98 99 101 102 103 105 106 135 152 153 154 **P**6 **S** Universal Health Services, Inc., King of Prussia, PA
Primary Contact: Jay Shehi, Chief Executive Officer
CFO: Robert Jackson, Chief Financial Officer
CMO: Terry Jordan, M.D., Chief of Staff
CIO: Brenda Smith, Director Financial Services
CHR: Shrea Johnson, Director Human Resources
Web address: www.alliancehealthcenter.com
Control: Corporation, Investor–owned (for–profit) **Service**: Psychiatric

Staffed Beds: 154 **Admissions**: 3556 **Census**: 131 **Outpatient Visits**: 0 **Births**: 0 **Total Expense ($000)**: 37176 **Payroll Expense ($000)**: 11491 **Personnel**: 216

⊞ **ANDERSON REGIONAL HEALTH SYSTEM (250104)**, 2124 14th Street, Zip 39301-4040; tel. 601/553-6000, **A**1 2 3 10 19 **F**3 7 11 12 13 15 17 18 20 22 24 26 28 29 30 31 32 34 35 40 41 43 44 45 47 48 49 50 53 54 57 58 59 64 65 68 70 72 73 75 76 77 79 80 81 85 86 87 88 89 90 91 92 93 96 107 110 111 114 115 116 119 120 121 123 124 126 127 129 130 131 132 135 146 148 149 **P**7 8
Primary Contact: John G. Anderson, FACHE, President and Chief Executive Officer
CFO: Steven Brown, Vice President Finance
CMO: Scot Bell, Chief Medical Officer
CHR: Joel Windham, Vice President Human Resources
CNO: Matt Edwards, Vice President Nursing Services and Chief Nursing Officer
Web address: www.andersonregional.org
Control: Other not–for–profit (including NFP Corporation) **Service**: General medical and surgical

Staffed Beds: 260 **Admissions**: 10313 **Census**: 153 **Outpatient Visits**: 138184 **Births**: 1308 **Total Expense ($000)**: 159941 **Payroll Expense ($000)**: 52304 **Personnel**: 1039

☐ △ **ANDERSON REGIONAL HEALTH SYSTEM SOUTH (250081)**, 1102 Constitution Avenue, Zip 39301-4001; tel. 601/553-6000, **A**1 7 10 19 **F**3 29 34 35 54 60 65 68 81 82 86 87 90 91 92 96 97 98 103 105 119 127 130 132 133 135 146 148 **P**7 8
Primary Contact: John G. Anderson, FACHE, President and Chief Executive Officer
CFO: Steven Brown, Vice President Finance
CIO: Steve Taylor, Chief Information Officer
CHR: Joel Windham, Vice President Human Resources
CNO: Betty Cryer, R.N., Administrator/Chief Nursing Officer
Web address: www.andersonregional.org
Control: Other not–for–profit (including NFP Corporation) **Service**: General medical and surgical

Staffed Beds: 69 **Admissions**: 1136 **Census**: 40 **Outpatient Visits**: 33198 **Births**: 0 **Total Expense ($000)**: 19857 **Payroll Expense ($000)**: 6339 **Personnel**: 170

☐ **EAST MISSISSIPPI STATE HOSPITAL**, 1818 College Drive, Zip 39307, Mailing Address: Box 4128, West Station, Zip 39304-4128; tel. 601/482-6186, (Total facility includes 210 beds in nursing home–type unit) **A**1 **F**29 34 38 39 59 82 86 87 98 103 106 128 130 143 146 149 **S** Mississippi State Department of Mental Health, Jackson, MS
Primary Contact: Charles Carlisle, Director
CFO: Geri Doggett, Director Business
CMO: Gloria Gomez, M.D., Medical Director
CIO: Scotty Taylor, Information Technology Director
CHR: Shearmaine Calaway, Director Human Resources
CNO: Diane Nobles, Nurse Executive
Web address: www.emsh.state.ms.us
Control: State, Government, nonfederal **Service**: Psychiatric

Staffed Beds: 310 **Admissions**: 662 **Census**: 295 **Outpatient Visits**: 0 **Births**: 0 **Total Expense ($000)**: 57094 **Payroll Expense ($000)**: 27736 **Personnel**: 896

⊞ **REGENCY HOSPITAL OF MERIDIAN (252006)**, 1102 Constitution Avenue, 2nd Floor, Zip 39301-4001; tel. 601/484-7900, **A**1 10 **F**1 **S** Select Medical Corporation, Mechanicsburg, PA
Primary Contact: Clifton Quinn, Chief Executive Officer
Web address: www.regencyhospital.com
Control: Corporation, Investor–owned (for–profit) **Service**: Acute long–term care hospital

Staffed Beds: 40 **Admissions**: 254 **Census**: 19 **Outpatient Visits**: 0 **Births**: 0 **Total Expense ($000)**: 10399 **Payroll Expense ($000)**: 4787 **Personnel**: 100

RILEY HOSPITAL See Anderson Regional Health System South

★ �û **RUSH FOUNDATION HOSPITAL (250069)**, 1314 19th Avenue, Zip 39301-4195; tel. 601/483-0011, **A**3 10 19 21 **F**13 15 17 22 24 29 35 39 40 43 70 72 73 76 77 81 82 86 89 90 93 97 107 108 118 119 130 131 146 147 **P**3 8 **S** Rush Health Systems, Meridian, MS
Primary Contact: Larkin Kennedy, Chief Executive Officer
COO: Jason Payne, Executive Vice President and Chief Operating Officer
CMO: W Scot Bell, M.D., Chief Medical Officer
CIO: Angela Sherrill, Corporate Director Information System
CHR: Donnie Smith, Director Human Resources
CNO: Casey Bland, Director of Nursing
Web address: www.rushhealthsystems.org/rfh/
Control: Other not–for–profit (including NFP Corporation) **Service**: General medical and surgical

Staffed Beds: 182 **Admissions**: 6927 **Census**: 81 **Outpatient Visits**: 179095 **Births**: 969 **Personnel**: 681

SPECIALTY HOSPITAL OF MERIDIAN (252004), 1314 19th Avenue, Zip 39301-4116; tel. 601/703-4211, **A**10 **F**1 3 18 20 34 50 57 59 68 74 79 85 87 94 96 112 133 144 145 149 **S** Rush Health Systems, Meridian, MS
Primary Contact: Elizabeth C. Mitchell, Chief Executive Officer and Chief Operating Officer
COO: Elizabeth C Mitchell, Chief Operating Officer
CFO: Christopher Rush, Chief Financial Officer
CMO: John Johnston, Chief Medical Officer
CIO: Angela Sherrill, Corporate Director Information System
CHR: Donnie Smith, Director of Human Resources
CNO: Kawanda Johnson, Director of Nursing
Web address: www.specialtyhospitalofmeridian.com/shm/
Control: Other not–for–profit (including NFP Corporation) **Service**: Acute long–term care hospital

Staffed Beds: 49 **Admissions**: 598 **Census**: 42 **Outpatient Visits**: 0 **Births**: 0 **Personnel**: 118

Many Facility Codes have changed. Please refer to the AHA Guide Code Chart. © 2018 AHA Guide

MONTICELLO—Lawrence County

LAWRENCE COUNTY HOSPITAL (251305), Highway 84 East, Zip 39654–0788, Mailing Address: P.O. Box 788, Zip 39654–0788; tel. 601/587–4051, **A**10 18 **F**3 18 34 40 43 50 57 59 64 107 115 119 127 133 149 153 **P**5 **S** Southwest Health Systems, Mccomb, MS
Primary Contact: Semmes Ross Jr, Administrator
CFO: Jennifer Moak, Business Office Manager
Web address: www.smrmc.com
Control: County, Government, nonfederal **Service:** General medical and surgical

Staffed Beds: 25 **Admissions:** 477 **Census:** 10 **Outpatient Visits:** 7955 **Births:** 0 **Total Expense ($000):** 9892 **Payroll Expense ($000):** 5542 **Personnel:** 106

MORTON—Scott County

SCOTT REGIONAL HOSPITAL (251323), 317 Highway 13 South, Zip 39117–3353, Mailing Address: P.O. Box 259, Zip 39117–0259; tel. 601/732–6301, **A**10 18 **F**3 30 35 40 43 55 57 77 81 89 93 107 111 112 114 119 127 130 133 **S** Rush Health Systems, Meridian, MS
Primary Contact: Heather Davis, Administrator
CFO: Paul S Black, Chief Financial Officer
CHR: Amy Sugg, Director Human Resources
Web address: www.scottregional.org/srh/
Control: Other not–for–profit (including NFP Corporation) **Service:** General medical and surgical

Staffed Beds: 25 **Admissions:** 382 **Census:** 8 **Outpatient Visits:** 9016 **Births:** 1 **Total Expense ($000):** 8265 **Payroll Expense ($000):** 3816 **Personnel:** 129

NATCHEZ—Adams County

☒ △   **MERIT HEALTH NATCHEZ (250084)**, 54 Seargent 'S' Prentiss Drive, Zip 39120–4726; tel. 601/443–2100, **A**1 7 10 **F**13 15 17 29 35 40 43 60 70 73 75 76 77 78 81 82 86 87 88 89 90 93 98 103 107 108 111 116 118 119 130 131 132 134 146 147 **P**5 **S** Community Health Systems, Inc., Franklin, TN
Primary Contact: Lance Boyd, Chief Executive Officer
CFO: Charles Mack, Vice President Finance and Chief Financial Officer
CMO: Leslie England, Chief of Staff
CIO: Leslie Makoro, Director Information management Systems
CHR: Jean E Juchnowicz, Director Human Resources
CNO: Lee Hinson, Chief Nursing Officer
Web address: www.natchezregional.com
Control: Corporation, Investor–owned (for–profit) **Service:** General medical and surgical

Staffed Beds: 136 **Admissions:** 4657 **Census:** 58 **Outpatient Visits:** 50624 **Births:** 883 **Total Expense ($000):** 92666 **Payroll Expense ($000):** 26028 **Personnel:** 430

NEW ALBANY—Union County

☒   **BAPTIST MEMORIAL HOSPITAL–UNION COUNTY (250006)**, 200 Highway 30 West, Zip 38652–3112; tel. 662/538–7631, **A**1 10 **F**3 11 13 15 17 29 30 31 34 35 40 45 51 57 59 64 68 70 75 76 77 79 81 84 85 86 87 89 90 91 92 93 94 96 107 108 110 111 114 115 118 119 124 130 132 133 135 146 147 148 149 154 **P**3 **S** Baptist Memorial Health Care Corporation, Memphis, TN
Primary Contact: Walter Grace, Chief Executive Officer and Administrator
CFO: Kim High, Chief Financial Officer
CMO: Justin Lohmeier, M.D., Chief of Staff
CIO: Missy Coltharp, Director
CHR: Lori Goode, Director Human Resources
CNO: Randy White, Chief Nursing Officer
Web address: www.baptistonline.org/union–county/
Control: Other not–for–profit (including NFP Corporation) **Service:** General medical and surgical

Staffed Beds: 153 **Admissions:** 3023 **Census:** 25 **Outpatient Visits:** 66457 **Births:** 932 **Total Expense ($000):** 55711 **Payroll Expense ($000):** 19964 **Personnel:** 335

OCEAN SPRINGS—Jackson County

OCEAN SPRINGS HOSPITAL See Singing River Health System, Pascagoula

OLIVE BRANCH—Desoto County

☒   **METHODIST HEALTHCARE OLIVE BRANCH HOSPITAL (250167)**, 4250 Bethel Road, Zip 38654–8737; tel. 662/932–9000, **A**1 10 **F**3 15 18 20 22 29 30 34 35 40 43 58 59 64 68 70 74 76 77 79 80 81 82 86 87 88 90 93 107 108 109 110 111 114 119 130 132 136 137 139 141 142 144 146 147 154 **P**8 **S** Methodist Le Bonheur Healthcare, Memphis, TN
Primary Contact: David G. Baytos, President
CFO: Kris Sanders, Chief Financial Officer
CHR: Robin Mathis, Director Human Resources
CNO: Annelise Jensen, Vice President and Chief Nursing Officer
Web address: www.methodisthealth.org/olivebranch
Control: Other not–for–profit (including NFP Corporation) **Service:** General medical and surgical

Staffed Beds: 69 **Admissions:** 2391 **Census:** 23 **Births:** 501 **Total Expense ($000):** 52369 **Payroll Expense ($000):** 19987 **Personnel:** 355

☐   **PARKWOOD BEHAVIORAL HEALTH SYSTEM (254005)**, 8135 Goodman Road, Zip 38654–2103; tel. 662/895–4900, (Total facility includes 40 beds in nursing home–type unit) **A**1 10 **F**4 5 29 34 35 54 57 64 71 75 82 86 87 98 99 100 101 102 103 104 105 128 130 135 153 **P**5 **S** Universal Health Services, Inc., King of Prussia, PA
Primary Contact: Ethan Permenter, Chief Executive Officer
CFO: David Denegri, Chief Financial Officer
CMO: Paul King, M.D., Medical Director
CHR: Julie Dorman, Human Resources Director
CNO: Alicia Plunkett, Chief Nurse Executive
Web address: www.parkwoodbhs.com
Control: Corporation, Investor–owned (for–profit) **Service:** Psychiatric

Staffed Beds: 148 **Admissions:** 3189 **Census:** 108 **Outpatient Visits:** 5208 **Births:** 0 **Personnel:** 136

OXFORD—Lafayette County

☒ △   **BAPTIST MEMORIAL HOSPITAL–NORTH MISSISSIPPI (250034)**, 2301 South Lamar Boulevard, Zip 38655–5373, Mailing Address: P.O. Box 946, Zip 38655–6002; tel. 662/232–8100, **A**1 2 3 7 10 19 **F**3 8 9 11 12 13 15 17 18 20 22 24 26 28 29 30 31 34 35 40 43 45 46 47 48 49 54 57 58 59 64 65 70 73 74 76 79 81 83 84 85 86 87 89 90 91 93 96 107 108 110 111 114 115 116 117 118 119 120 121 123 124 126 129 130 132 146 148 154 **P**7 **S** Baptist Memorial Health Care Corporation, Memphis, TN
Primary Contact: William C. Henning, Administrator and Chief Executive Officer
CFO: Dana Williams, Chief Financial Officer
CMO: Dennis P Morgan, Chief of Staff
CIO: Linda Britt, Director Information Systems
CHR: Josh Lowery, Director of Human Resources
CNO: Mark Ottens, Chief Nursing Officer
Web address: www.baptistonline.org/north–mississippi/
Control: Other not–for–profit (including NFP Corporation) **Service:** General medical and surgical

Staffed Beds: 172 **Admissions:** 8657 **Census:** 96 **Outpatient Visits:** 103143 **Births:** 881 **Personnel:** 750

PASCAGOULA—Jackson County

☐ △   **SINGING RIVER HEALTH SYSTEM (250040)**, 2809 Denny Avenue, Zip 39581–5301; tel. 228/809–5000, (Includes OCEAN SPRINGS HOSPITAL, 3109 Bienville Boulevard, Ocean Springs, MS, Zip 39564–4361; tel. 228/818–1111; Heath Thompson, R.N., Administrator; SINGING RIVER HOSPITAL, 2809 Denny Avenue, Pascagoula, MS, Zip 39581–5301; tel. 228/809–5000; Laurin St. Pe', Administrator – Singing River Hospital) **A**1 2 7 10 **F**3 7 8 9 11 12 13 15 17 18 20 22 24 26 28 29 30 31 32 34 38 39 40 41 43 44 45 46 47 48 49 50 53 54 55 56 57 58 59 61 64 65 66 68 70 71 73 74 76 78 79 80 81 82 83 84 85 86 87 88 89 90 91 92 94 95 96 98 99 100 101 102 103 104 105 106 107 108 110 111 114 115 118 119 120 121 123 124 126 127 129 130 135 144 145 146 148 152 153 154 **P**8
Primary Contact: Lee Bond, Chief Executive Officer
CFO: Sandra Albrecht, Interim Chief Financial Officer
CMO: Randy Roth, Chief Medical Officer
CHR: Craig Summerlin, Chief Human Resources Officer
CNO: Susan Russell, Chief Nursing Officer
Web address: www.singingriverhealthsystem.com
Control: County, Government, nonfederal **Service:** General medical and surgical

Staffed Beds: 361 **Admissions:** 17026 **Census:** 201 **Outpatient Visits:** 211955 **Births:** 1466 **Personnel:** 2110

Hospital, Medicare Provider Number, Address, Telephone, Approval, Facility, and Physician Codes, Health Care System

★ American Hospital Association (AHA) membership
☐ The Joint Commission accreditation
○ Healthcare Facilities Accreditation Program
◇ DNV Healthcare Inc. accreditation
⇧ Center for Improvement in Healthcare Quality Accreditation
△ Commission on Accreditation of Rehabilitation Facilities (CARF) accreditation

MS

PHILADELPHIA—Neshoba County

⇧ **CHOCTAW HEALTH CENTER (250127)**, 210 Hospital Circle, Zip 39350–6781; tel. 601/656–2211, (Nonreporting) **A**10 21
Primary Contact: Tina Scott, Acting Health Director
CFO: Myrna Hancock, Director Financial Services
CMO: Juantina Johnson, Chief of Staff
CIO: Raymond Willis, IT Manager
CHR: Anna Denson, Human Resources Specialist
CNO: Regina Isaac, Director of Nursing
Web address: www.choctaw.org
Control: Public Health Service other than 47, Government, federal **Service:** General medical and surgical

Staffed Beds: 26

NESHOBA COUNTY GENERAL HOSPITAL (250043), 1001 Holland Avenue, Zip 39350–2161, Mailing Address: P.O. Box 648, Zip 39350–0648; tel. 601/663–1200, (Total facility includes 160 beds in nursing home–type unit) **A**10 20 **F**3 6 7 11 15 29 31 32 34 40 43 45 57 59 64 65 81 82 89 90 92 93 96 103 104 106 107 108 110 111 115 118 119 127 128 129 130 132 133 143 144 146 148 149 153 154
Primary Contact: Lee McCall, Chief Executive Officer
CFO: Scott McNair, Chief Financial Officer
CMO: Heather Cannon, M.D., Medical Director
CHR: Hedda Stewart, Director Human Resources
CNO: Scott Breazeale, Chief Nursing Officer
Web address: www.neshobageneral.com
Control: County, Government, nonfederal **Service:** General medical and surgical

Staffed Beds: 208 **Admissions:** 1799 **Census:** 172 **Outpatient Visits:** 58109 **Births:** 0 **Total Expense ($000):** 47964 **Payroll Expense ($000):** 23361 **Personnel:** 517

PICAYUNE—Pearl River County

HIGHLAND COMMUNITY HOSPITAL (250117), 130 Highland Parkway, Zip 39466–5574, Mailing Address: P.O. Box 909, Zip 39466–0909; tel. 601/358–9400, **A**10 **F**3 11 13 15 18 29 34 40 41 43 44 45 46 50 56 57 59 64 65 70 75 76 81 85 86 87 89 93 96 103 107 108 110 111 114 119 131 135 146 147 148
Primary Contact: Mark Stockstill, R.N., Administrator
CMO: Robert Lopez, Chief Medical Officer
CHR: Cynthia Render–Leach, Director Human Resources
CNO: Kim Varnado, R.N., Chief Nursing Officer
Web address: www.highlandch.com
Control: County, Government, nonfederal **Service:** General medical and surgical

Staffed Beds: 60 **Admissions:** 1821 **Census:** 19 **Outpatient Visits:** 75602 **Births:** 266 **Total Expense ($000):** 39181 **Payroll Expense ($000):** 15225 **Personnel:** 240

PONTOTOC—Pontotoc County

✪ **NORTH MISSISSIPPI MEDICAL CENTER–PONTOTOC (251308)**, 176 South Main Street, Zip 38863–3311, Mailing Address: P.O. Box 790, Zip 38863–0790; tel. 662/488–7640, (Total facility includes 44 beds in nursing home–type unit) **A**1 10 18 **F**3 11 34 35 40 43 57 65 68 82 83 84 86 87 93 104 107 114 119 128 130 133 146 **S** North Mississippi Health Services, Inc., Tupelo, MS
Primary Contact: Leslia Carter, Administrator
CFO: M Denise Heard, Director Business Services
CHR: P. Marie Barnes, Director, Human Resources
CNO: Cathy Waldrop, Director, Hospital Nursing Services
Web address: www.nmhs.net
Control: Other not–for–profit (including NFP Corporation) **Service:** General medical and surgical

Staffed Beds: 69 **Admissions:** 462 **Census:** 62 **Births:** 0 **Personnel:** 184

POPLARVILLE—Pearl River County

★ **PEARL RIVER COUNTY HOSPITAL (251333)**, 305 West Moody Street, Zip 39470–7338, Mailing Address: P.O. Box 392, Zip 39470–0392; tel. 601/795–4543, **A**10 18 **F**3 35 40 43 64 65 90 107 119 127 128 130 133 143 146
Primary Contact: James Williams, Chief Executive Officer
CNO: Lisa Brown, Director of Nursing
Web address: www.prc–med.com/
Control: County, Government, nonfederal **Service:** General medical and surgical

Staffed Beds: 24 **Admissions:** 189 **Census:** 8 **Births:** 0 **Total Expense ($000):** 19005 **Payroll Expense ($000):** 10111 **Personnel:** 209

PORT GIBSON—Claiborne County

CLAIBORNE COUNTY MEDICAL CENTER (251320), 123 McComb Avenue, Zip 39150–2915, Mailing Address: P.O. Box 1004, Zip 39150–1004; tel. 601/437–5141, **A**10 18 **F**40 43 86 89 98 100 101 103 104 106 107 119 130 133 146
Primary Contact: Ada Ratliff, Chief Executive Officer
CFO: Linda Caho–Mooney, Chief Financial Officer
CIO: Ada Ratliff, Chief Information Officer
Control: County, Government, nonfederal **Service:** General medical and surgical

Staffed Beds: 32 **Admissions:** 263 **Census:** 9 **Births:** 0 **Personnel:** 132

PRENTISS—Jefferson Davis County

JEFFERSON DAVIS COMMUNITY HOSPITAL (251326), 1102 Rose Street, Zip 39474–5200, Mailing Address: P.O. Box 1288, Zip 39474–1288; tel. 601/792–4276, (Total facility includes 60 beds in nursing home–type unit) **A**10 18 **F**3 35 40 43 53 56 64 86 87 89 93 98 103 104 107 115 119 127 128 130 132 133
Primary Contact: Jimmy Graves, Interim Chief Executive Officer
CHR: Diane Daughdrill, Director Human Resources
Web address: www.jdchospital.com
Control: County, Government, nonfederal **Service:** General medical and surgical

Staffed Beds: 95 **Admissions:** 363 **Census:** 49 **Outpatient Visits:** 12367 **Births:** 0 **Total Expense ($000):** 8572 **Payroll Expense ($000):** 3063 **Personnel:** 106

PURVIS—Lamar County

☐ **SOUTH MISSISSIPPI STATE HOSPITAL (254008)**, 823 Highway 589, Zip 39475–4194; tel. 601/794–0100, **A**1 10 **F**3 34 50 98 130 146 **S** Mississippi State Department of Mental Health, Jackson, MS
Primary Contact: Sabrina Young, Director
CFO: Andy Tucker, Chief Financial Officer
CMO: Allen Harris, M.D., Clinical Director
CIO: Sabrina Young, Administrative Support Director
CHR: Kelly Reid, Human Resources Director
CNO: Pam Brinson, Nurse Executive
Web address: www.smsh.ms.gov/
Control: State, Government, nonfederal **Service:** Psychiatric

Staffed Beds: 50 **Admissions:** 593 **Census:** 43 **Outpatient Visits:** 0 **Births:** 0 **Total Expense ($000):** 8559 **Payroll Expense ($000):** 5047 **Personnel:** 89

QUITMAN—Clarke County

H. C. WATKINS MEMORIAL HOSPITAL (251316), 605 South Archusa Avenue, Zip 39355–2331; tel. 601/776–6925, **A**10 18 **F**29 40 43 89 104 107 119 127 130 133 **P**6 **S** Rush Health Systems, Meridian, MS
Primary Contact: Michael Nester, Administrator
CFO: Paul S Black, Controller
CMO: O Wayne Byrd, M.D., Chief of Staff
CIO: Melinda Smith, Chief Information Systems
CHR: Leigh Moore, Administrative Assistant Human Resources
Web address: www.watkinsmemorialhospital.com/hcwmh/
Control: Other not–for–profit (including NFP Corporation) **Service:** General medical and surgical

Staffed Beds: 25 **Admissions:** 432 **Census:** 11 **Outpatient Visits:** 28650 **Births:** 0 **Personnel:** 159

RALEIGH—Smith County

PATIENTS CHOICE MEDICAL CENTER OF SMITH COUNTY (250163), 347 Magnolia Drive, Zip 39153–6011; tel. 601/782–9997, **A**10 **F**98 101 103 104 130 **P**6
Primary Contact: Tim Cockrell, Chief Executive Officer
Control: Corporation, Investor–owned (for–profit) **Service:** General medical and surgical

Staffed Beds: 20 **Admissions:** 147 **Census:** 5 **Births:** 0

RICHTON—Perry County

PERRY COUNTY GENERAL HOSPITAL (251306), 206 Bay Avenue, Zip 39476–2941; tel. 601/788–6316, **A**10 18 **F**3 34 40 57 59 64 65 107 119 127 130 133 146
Primary Contact: David Paris, Chief Executive Officer
Web address: www.pcghospital.com/
Control: Partnership, Investor–owned (for–profit) **Service:** General medical and surgical

Staffed Beds: 22 **Admissions:** 125 **Census:** 3 **Births:** 0 **Total Expense ($000):** 5770 **Payroll Expense ($000):** 3130 **Personnel:** 53

RIPLEY—Tippah County

★ **TIPPAH COUNTY HOSPITAL (251337)**, 1005 City Avenue North,
Zip 38663–1414, Mailing Address: P.O. Box 499, Zip 38663–0499;
tel. 662/837–9221, (Total facility includes 40 beds in nursing home–type unit) **A**10
18 **F**29 40 43 53 81 90 93 98 103 107 119 128 130 131 133 **P**1
Primary Contact: Patrick Chapman, Ed.D., Chief Executive Officer
CFO: Stephanie McAlister, Controller
CMO: Troy Cappleman, M.D., Chief of Staff
CHR: Heather Taylor, Human Resources Manager
CNO: Carol Anne Hurt, Chief Nursing Officer
Web address: www.tippahcountyhospital.com/
Control: County, Government, nonfederal **Service**: General medical and surgical

Staffed Beds: 65 **Admissions:** 615 **Census:** 46 **Outpatient Visits:** 12938
Births: 0 **Total Expense ($000):** 12979 **Payroll Expense ($000):** 4997
Personnel: 199

ROLLING FORK—Sharkey County

SHARKEY–ISSAQUENA COMMUNITY HOSPITAL (250079), 108 South Fourth
Street, Zip 39159–5146, Mailing Address: P.O. Box 339, Zip 39159–0339;
tel. 662/873–4395, **A**10 **F**40 53 56 98 103 104 105 107 133
Primary Contact: Jerry Keever, Administrator
Control: County, Government, nonfederal **Service**: General medical and surgical

Staffed Beds: 29 **Admissions:** 403 **Census:** 6 **Births:** 0 **Total Expense
($000):** 9798 **Payroll Expense ($000):** 4411 **Personnel:** 71

RULEVILLE—Sunflower County

★ **NORTH SUNFLOWER MEDICAL CENTER (251318)**, 840 North Oak
Avenue, Zip 38771–3227, Mailing Address: P.O. Box 369, Zip 38771–0369;
tel. 662/756–2711, (Total facility includes 60 beds in nursing home–type unit) **A**10
18 **F**15 28 29 30 34 35 40 41 43 45 47 50 53 56 59 63 64 65 74 75 77 81 82
83 84 85 87 90 93 97 98 100 103 104 105 107 110 115 119 127 128 129
130 132 133 143 147 149 153 **P**6
Primary Contact: Sam Miller, Chief Executive Officer
COO: Rodney Clark, Chief Operating Officer
CFO: Drew Weissinger, Chief Financial Officer
CMO: Michael W Montesi, M.D., Chief of Staff
CIO: Roger Goss, Chief Information Officer
CHR: Robbie Taylor, Director Human Resources
CNO: Hannah Barrett, Director of Nursing
Web address: www.northsunflower.com
Control: County, Government, nonfederal **Service**: General medical and surgical

Staffed Beds: 95 **Admissions:** 869 **Census:** 68 **Outpatient Visits:** 52586
Births: 0 **Total Expense ($000):** 64100 **Payroll Expense ($000):** 29318
Personnel: 605

SENATOBIA—Tate County

☐ **NORTH OAK REGIONAL MEDICAL CENTER (250126)**, 401 Getwell
Drive, Zip 38668–2213, Mailing Address: P.O. Box 648, Zip 38668–0648;
tel. 662/562–3100, **A**1 10 **F**3 29 34 35 40 43 45 56 57 63 64 81 86 98 103
107 114 119 130 132
Primary Contact: Philip S. Hanna, Chief Executive Officer
CHR: Olga Burris, Human Resource/Executive Assistant
CNO: Pam Ayers, Chief Nursing Officer
Web address: www.northoakregional.com/
Control: Corporation, Investor–owned (for–profit) **Service**: General medical and
surgical

Staffed Beds: 41 **Admissions:** 619 **Census:** 9 **Outpatient Visits:** 11129
Births: 0 **Total Expense ($000):** 15513 **Payroll Expense ($000):** 5582
Personnel: 129

SOUTHAVEN—Desoto County

✉ △ **BAPTIST MEMORIAL HOSPITAL–DESOTO (250141)**, 7601 Southcrest
Parkway, Zip 38671–4742; tel. 662/772–4000, **A**1 3 7 10 **F**3 9 11 13 15 17 18
20 22 24 26 28 29 30 31 35 39 40 43 44 45 46 47 48 49 50 57 59 60 68 70
73 74 75 76 77 79 80 82 84 85 86 87 90 93 96 107 108 109 110 111 114
115 116 117 118 119 120 121 123 124 126 129 130 131 132 135 143 144
146 147 148 154 **P**7 **S** Baptist Memorial Health Care Corporation, Memphis, TN
Primary Contact: James Huffman, Chief Executive Officer and Administrator
CFO: Joe McWherter, Chief Financial Officer
CMO: Joann Wood, M.D., Chief Medical Officer
CHR: Walter Banks, Director Human Resources
Web address: www.baptistonline.org/desoto/
Control: Other not–for–profit (including NFP Corporation) **Service**: General
medical and surgical

Staffed Beds: 339 **Admissions:** 16006 **Census:** 203 **Outpatient Visits:**
126024 **Births:** 1512 **Total Expense ($000):** 224765 **Payroll Expense
($000):** 88021 **Personnel:** 1220

STARKVILLE—Oktibbeha County

★ ⇧ **OCH REGIONAL MEDICAL CENTER (250050)**, 400 Hospital Road,
Zip 39759–2163, Mailing Address: P.O. Box 1506, Zip 39760–1506;
tel. 662/323–4320, **A**10 21 **F**3 7 11 13 15 17 28 29 32 34 35 40 41 43 45 47
48 51 53 57 59 61 64 65 70 73 74 75 76 77 79 81 82 87 88 89 90 93 94 97 98
107 108 110 111 114 115 118 119 126 129 130 131 132 133 134 146 147 **P**6
Primary Contact: James H. Jackson Jr, Chief Executive Officer
COO: Mike Andrews, Associate Administrator and Chief Operating Officer
CFO: Susan Russell, Chief Financial Officer
CIO: Chamath Wijewardane, Chief Information Technology Officer
CHR: Mike Andrews, Associate Administrator and Chief Operating Officer
CNO: Martha Fulcher, Chief Nursing Officer
Web address: www.och.org
Control: County, Government, nonfederal **Service**: General medical and surgical

Staffed Beds: 96 **Admissions:** 2446 **Census:** 24 **Outpatient Visits:** 246337
Births: 900 **Total Expense ($000):** 75559 **Payroll Expense ($000):** 37242
Personnel: 615

TUPELO—Lee County

✉ △ **NORTH MISSISSIPPI MEDICAL CENTER – TUPELO (250004)**, 830 South
Gloster Street, Zip 38801–4934; tel. 662/377–3000, (Total facility includes 107
beds in nursing home–type unit) **A**1 2 3 5 7 10 **F**3 4 5 6 7 8 9 11 12 13 15 17
18 20 22 24 26 28 29 30 31 32 34 35 38 40 43 44 45 46 47 48 49 50 51 53
54 55 56 57 58 59 61 62 63 64 65 66 68 70 71 72 73 74 75 76 77 78 79 81
83 84 85 86 87 89 90 91 92 93 94 95 96 97 98 100 101 103 104 107 108
109 110 111 112 113 114 115 116 117 118 119 120 121 122 123 124 126
128 129 130 131 132 134 135 146 147 148 152 154 **P**6 7 **S** North Mississippi
Health Services, Inc., Tupelo, MS
Primary Contact: M. Shane. Spees, Chief Executive Officer
CFO: Sharon Nobles, Chief Financial Officer
CMO: C K White, M.D., Esq Chief Medical Officer
CIO: James Weldon, Chief Information Officer
CHR: Laura M Land, Chief Human Resource Officer
Web address: www.nmhs.net
Control: Other not–for–profit (including NFP Corporation) **Service**: General
medical and surgical

Staffed Beds: 747 **Admissions:** 27220 **Census:** 465 **Personnel:** 4178

☐ **NORTH MISSISSIPPI STATE HOSPITAL (254009)**, 1937 Briar Ridge Road,
Zip 38804–5963; tel. 662/690–4200, **A**1 10 **F**3 29 30 34 87 98 101 130 143
146 **S** Mississippi State Department of Mental Health, Jackson, MS
Primary Contact: Paul A. Callens, Ph.D., Director
CFO: Joe Rials, Director Fiscal Services
CMO: Ken Lippincott, M.D., Chief of Staff
CIO: James Wilhite, Director Systems Information
Web address: www.nmsh.state.ms.us
Control: State, Government, nonfederal **Service**: Psychiatric

Staffed Beds: 50 **Admissions:** 571 **Census:** 50 **Outpatient Visits:** 0
Births: 0 **Personnel:** 99

TYLERTOWN—Walthall County

★ **WALTHALL COUNTY GENERAL HOSPITAL (251324)**, 100 Hospital Drive,
Zip 39667–2099; tel. 601/876–2122, **A**10 18 **F**3 40 43 45 64 81 89 93 107
111 115 119 127 133 146
Primary Contact: Bryan K. Maxie, Administrator
Web address: www.walthallhospitalms.org
Control: County, Government, nonfederal **Service**: General medical and surgical

Staffed Beds: 25 **Admissions:** 313 **Census:** 5 **Outpatient Visits:** 15959
Births: 0 **Total Expense ($000):** 8340 **Payroll Expense ($000):** 4303
Personnel: 87

UNION—Newton County

LAIRD HOSPITAL (251322), 25117 Highway 15, Zip 39365–9099;
tel. 601/774–8214, **A**10 18 **F**15 29 35 40 43 81 87 89 93 104 107 119 130
132 133 146 **S** Rush Health Systems, Meridian, MS
Primary Contact: Thomas G. Bartlett III, Administrator
COO: Morris A Reece, EVP/COO
CFO: Jennifer Flint, Chief Financial Officer
CMO: John Mutziger, M.D., Chief Medical Officer
CIO: Angela Sherrill, Chief Information Officer
CHR: Donnie Smith, Chief Human Resources Officer
CNO: Pam Rigdon, Director Nursing
Web address: www.lairdhospital.com/lh/
Control: Other not–for–profit (including NFP Corporation) **Service**: General
medical and surgical

Staffed Beds: 25 **Admissions:** 500 **Census:** 11 **Outpatient Visits:** 19195
Births: 0 **Total Expense ($000):** 19277 **Payroll Expense ($000):** 4714
Personnel: 245

MS

Hospital, Medicare Provider Number, Address, Telephone, Approval, Facility, and Physician Codes, Health Care System

★ American Hospital Association (AHA) membership   ○ Healthcare Facilities Accreditation Program   ⇧ Center for Improvement in Healthcare Quality Accreditation
☐ The Joint Commission accreditation   ◇ DNV Healthcare Inc. accreditation   △ Commission on Accreditation of Rehabilitation Facilities (CARF) accreditation

VICKSBURG—Warren County

✠ **MERIT HEALTH RIVER REGION (250031)**, 2100 Highway 61 North,
Zip 39183–8211, Mailing Address: P.O. Box 590, Zip 39181–0590;
tel. 601/883–5000, (Includes RIVER REGION WEST CAMPUS, 1111 North
Frontage Road, Vicksburg, MS, Zip 39180–5102; tel. 601/883–5000) **A**1 10 **F**3 4
11 13 15 17 18 19 20 22 24 28 29 34 35 38 39 40 43 49 50 51 56 59 60 64
68 70 73 75 76 77 81 82 87 89 90 93 97 98 103 107 108 110 111 115 118
119 126 130 131 132 146 147 149 151 **S** Community Health Systems, Inc.,
Franklin, TN
Primary Contact: Benjamin Richaud, Interim Chief Executive Officer
CFO: John Milazzo, Chief Financial Officer
CMO: W Briggs Hopson, M.D., Clinical Medical Director
CIO: J B White, Director Information Systems
CHR: Hal Harrington, Vice President Human Resources
Web address: www.riverregion.com
Control: Corporation, Investor–owned (for–profit) **Service**: General medical and
surgical

Staffed Beds: 361 **Admissions**: 6955 **Census**: 104 **Outpatient Visits**:
187140 **Births**: 549 **Total Expense ($000)**: 102938 **Payroll Expense
($000)**: 31391 **Personnel**: 590

PROMISE HOSPITAL OF VICKSBURG (252008), 1111 North Frontage Road,
2nd Floor, Zip 39180–5102; tel. 601/619–3526, **A**10 **F**1 3 11 29 77 148 **S**
Promise Healthcare, Boca Raton, FL
Primary Contact: Michael Harrell, R.N., Chief Executive Officer
COO: Dawn Posey, Chief Operating Officer
CFO: Christopher A Stegall, Regional Chief Financial Officer and Chief Operating
Officer
CMO: Daniel Edney, M.D., Chief of Staff
CIO: Barbara Whiting, Director Health Information Management
CHR: Debbie Carson, Director Human Resources
Web address: www.promise–vicksburg.com
Control: Corporation, Investor–owned (for–profit) **Service**: Acute long–term care
hospital

Staffed Beds: 33 **Admissions**: 390 **Census**: 26 **Outpatient Visits**: 0
Births: 0 **Personnel**: 85

WATER VALLEY—Yalobusha County

★ **YALOBUSHA GENERAL HOSPITAL (250061)**, 630 South Main,
Zip 38965–3468, Mailing Address: P.O. Box 728, Zip 38965–0728;
tel. 662/473–1411, (Total facility includes 122 beds in nursing home–type unit)
A10 **F**3 7 15 29 33 34 59 65 107 110 114 119 128 130 133 143 146 **P**6
Primary Contact: Terry Varner, Administrator
COO: Ashlee Langdon, Controller
CHR: Katie Rotenberry–Baggett, Administrative Assistant and Human Resources
Web address: www.yalobushageneral.com/
Control: County, Government, nonfederal **Service**: General medical and surgical

Staffed Beds: 148 **Admissions**: 770 **Census**: 131 **Births**: 0 **Total
Expense ($000)**: 23433 **Payroll Expense ($000)**: 14918 **Personnel**: 206

WAYNESBORO—Wayne County

⇑ **WAYNE GENERAL HOSPITAL (250077)**, 950 Matthew Drive, Zip 39367–2590,
Mailing Address: P.O. Box 1249, Zip 39367–1249; tel. 601/735–5151, **A**3 10 20
21 **F**3 7 11 13 15 29 34 40 43 53 59 62 63 64 70 76 81 85 89 93 107 108
115 119 127 130 133 146 148 154
Primary Contact: Kathy Waddell, Administrator
Web address: www.waynegeneralhospital.org
Control: County, Government, nonfederal **Service**: General medical and surgical

Staffed Beds: 80 **Admissions**: 1763 **Census**: 28 **Outpatient Visits**: 30845
Births: 198 **Total Expense ($000)**: 31323 **Payroll Expense ($000)**: 16487
Personnel: 368

WEST POINT—Clay County

✠ **NORTH MISSISSIPPI MEDICAL CENTER–WEST POINT (250067)**, 835 Medical
Center Drive, Zip 39773–9320; tel. 662/495–2300, **A**1 10 **F**3 8 11 13 15 17 28
29 30 31 32 34 35 40 43 45 48 53 57 59 64 65 70 73 75 76 80 81 85 86 87
89 97 107 108 109 110 114 119 120 127 129 130 132 133 135 145 146 147
S North Mississippi Health Services, Inc., Tupelo, MS
Primary Contact: Barry L. Keel, Administration
CFO: Kay Lawler, Business Office Manager
CMO: B Keith Watson, M.D., Chief Medical Staff
CIO: Stacie Griggs, MIS Analyst
CHR: Brenda Johnson, Director Human Resources
CNO: Pam White, Chief Nursing Officer
Web address: www.nmhs.net/westpoint
Control: Other not–for–profit (including NFP Corporation) **Service**: General
medical and surgical

Staffed Beds: 49 **Admissions**: 1313 **Census**: 15 **Outpatient Visits**: 49501
Births: 345 **Total Expense ($000)**: 32159 **Payroll Expense ($000)**: 13362
Personnel: 242

WHITFIELD—Rankin County

✠ **MISSISSIPPI STATE HOSPITAL (254010)**, 3550 Highway 468 West,
Zip 39193–5529, Mailing Address: P.O. Box 157–A, Zip 39193–0157;
tel. 601/351–8000, (Includes WHITFIELD MEDICAL SURGICAL HOSPITAL, 3550
Highway 468 West, Building 60, Whitfield, MS, Zip 39193–5529, Mailing Address:
P.O. Box 157A, Zip 39193–0157, tel. 601/351–8023) **A**1 3 10 **F**3 4 29 32 39
50 55 56 59 65 68 74 75 86 87 98 99 100 101 103 104 107 115 119 128
130 143 146 149 151 **P**1 **S** Mississippi State Department of Mental Health,
Jackson, MS
Primary Contact: James G. Chastain, FACHE, Director
COO: Kelly R Breland, CPA, Director Support Services
CFO: Alicia Harris, Director Fiscal Services
CMO: Duncan Stone, D.D.S., Chief Medical Staff
CIO: Bart Uharriet, Director Information Services
CHR: Katie Storr, Director of Human Resources
CNO: Jackie Yates, R.N., Nurse Executive
Web address: www.msh.state.ms.us
Control: State, Government, nonfederal **Service**: Psychiatric

Staffed Beds: 395 **Admissions**: 1893 **Census**: 328 **Outpatient Visits**: 1691
Births: 0 **Total Expense ($000)**: 128482 **Payroll Expense ($000)**: 60670
Personnel: 1073

WIGGINS—Stone County

STONE COUNTY HOSPITAL (251303), 1434 East Central Avenue,
Zip 39577–9602; tel. 601/928–6600, **A**10 18 **F**3 5 7 29 34 35 40 43 46 57 59
64 81 82 89 97 99 100 101 103 104 112 114 115 119 130 133 143 146
Primary Contact: Lynn Truelove, Chief Executive Officer
Web address: www.schospital.net/
Control: Corporation, Investor–owned (for–profit) **Service**: General medical and
surgical

Staffed Beds: 25 **Admissions**: 513 **Census**: 18 **Births**: 0 **Total Expense
($000)**: 20719 **Payroll Expense ($000)**: 7114 **Personnel**: 162

WINONA—Montgomery County

TYLER HOLMES MEMORIAL HOSPITAL (251312), 409 Tyler Holmes Drive,
Zip 38967–1599; tel. 662/283–4114, **A**10 18 **F**3 11 15 34 35 40 43 44 50 57
59 64 68 87 104 107 110 111 115 119 130 133 149 153 **P**8
Primary Contact: Eddie Rutherford, Administrator
CFO: Cori Bailey, Accountant
CHR: Becky Corley, Director Human Resources
Web address: www.thmh.org/
Control: County, Government, nonfederal **Service**: General medical and surgical

Staffed Beds: 25 **Admissions**: 503 **Census**: 13 **Outpatient Visits**: 12051
Births: 0 **Total Expense ($000)**: 12667 **Payroll Expense ($000)**: 6333
Personnel: 136

YAZOO CITY—Yazoo County

★ **BAPTIST MEDICAL CENTER YAZOO (251313)**, 823 Grand Avenue,
Zip 39194–3233; tel. 662/746–2261, **A**10 18 **F**8 11 15 18 28 29 30 40 41 54
56 64 68 81 97 107 108 110 111 112 114 115 119 127 133 145 148 149
153 154 **S** Baptist Memorial Health Care Corporation, Memphis, TN
Primary Contact: Robert Coleman, Chief Executive Officer
COO: Marsha Jones, R.N., Director Nursing
CFO: James L Miller, Chief Financial Officer
CMO: Marion Sigrest, M.D., Chief of Staff
CIO: Benton D Estes, Materials Management
CHR: Stephanie Washington, Director Community Relations and Human Resources
CNO: Marsha Jones, R.N., Director of Nursing
Web address: www.kdhyazoo.com
Control: Other not–for–profit (including NFP Corporation) **Service**: General
medical and surgical

Staffed Beds: 25 **Admissions**: 703 **Census**: 13 **Outpatient Visits**: 31497
Births: 0 **Total Expense ($000)**: 19525 **Payroll Expense ($000)**: 8581
Personnel: 171

MISSOURI

ALBANY—Gentry County

NORTHWEST MEDICAL CENTER (261328), 705 North College Street,
Zip 64402–1433; tel. 660/726–3941, **A**10 18 **F**3 11 15 18 28 29 34 35 40 41
44 45 47 50 53 56 57 59 62 64 65 68 74 75 77 79 81 84 85 86 87 89 90 93
97 99 104 107 108 110 111 114 118 119 127 128 130 131 133 135 143 148
149 154 **P**6
Primary Contact: Jon D. Doolittle, Regional President
COO: Nate Blackford, Chief Operating Officer
CMO: Angelia Martin, M.D., Chief of Staff
CIO: James Crouch, Vice President Technical Services
CHR: Vickie Cline, Director Human Resources
CNO: Miranda Floyd, R.N., Chief Nursing Officer
Web address: www.northwestmedicalcenter.org
Control: Other not–for–profit (including NFP Corporation) **Service:** General
medical and surgical

Staffed Beds: 25 **Admissions:** 458 **Census:** 6 **Outpatient Visits:** 42283
Births: 0 **Total Expense ($000):** 18526 **Payroll Expense ($000):** 8457
Personnel: 146

APPLETON CITY—St. Clair County

ELLETT MEMORIAL HOSPITAL (261301), 610 North Ohio Avenue,
Zip 64724–1609, Mailing Address: P.O. Box 6, Zip 64724–0006;
tel. 660/476–2111, **A**10 18 **F**3 7 11 18 34 40 45 50 57 59 64 77 79 81 97
107 111 114 119 127 129 133 143 **P**6
Primary Contact: Melissa Fletcher, Chief Executive Officer
CMO: Richard R Dailey, D.O., President Medical Staff
CIO: Gina Raybourn, Director Health Information
CHR: Cathy Grishow, Director Human Resources
CNO: Laura Smith, Chief Nursing Officer and Director of Infection Control
Web address: www.ellettmemorial.com
Control: Hospital district or authority, Government, nonfederal **Service:** General
medical and surgical

Staffed Beds: 12 **Admissions:** 173 **Census:** 2 **Outpatient Visits:** 4959
Births: 0 **Total Expense ($000):** 9398 **Payroll Expense ($000):** 3131
Personnel: 57

AURORA—Lawrence County

MERCY HOSPITAL AURORA (261316), 500 Porter Street, Zip 65605–2365;
tel. 417/678–2122, **A**1 10 18 **F**3 11 13 15 28 29 30 34 35 40 41 45 50 57 59
64 65 75 76 77 81 85 86 87 89 93 94 96 107 108 110 111 114 119 129 132
133 135 148 149 154 **P**6 **S** Mercy, Chesterfield, MO
Primary Contact: Nicki Gamet, R.N., Administrator
CFO: Sherry Clouse Day, CPA, Vice President Finance and Regional Chief Financial
Officer
CMO: Christie Hurt, M.D., Chief of Staff and Medical Director
CHR: George Roden, Vice President Human Resources
Web address: www.stjohns.com/aboutus/aurora.aspx
Control: Church operated, Nongovernment, not–for–profit **Service:** General
medical and surgical

Staffed Beds: 25 **Admissions:** 633 **Census:** 6 **Outpatient Visits:** 31374
Births: 230 **Total Expense ($000):** 18017 **Payroll Expense ($000):** 8542
Personnel: 151

BELTON—Cass County

BELTON REGIONAL MEDICAL CENTER (260214), 17065 South 71 Highway,
Zip 64012–4631; tel. 816/348–1200, **A**1 2 10 **F**3 15 18 20 29 30 31 34 35
37 40 43 45 57 59 65 68 70 74 75 77 78 79 81 82 85 87 90 93 107 108 110
111 114 115 118 119 129 130 131 132 146 **S** HCA Healthcare, Nashville, TN
Primary Contact: Todd Krass, Chief Executive Officer
COO: Patrick Avila, Chief Operating Officer
CFO: Ronnie Thompson, Chief Financial Officer
CMO: Douglas Bradley, M.D., Chief Medical Officer
CIO: Sarah Richardson, Director Information Systems
CHR: Jessica Sulzen, Director Human Resources
CNO: Karen Lee, MSN, R.N., Chief Nursing Officer
Web address: www.beltonregionalmedicalcenter.com
Control: Corporation, Investor–owned (for–profit) **Service:** General medical and
surgical

Staffed Beds: 48 **Admissions:** 3242 **Census:** 27 **Outpatient Visits:** 104323
Births: 0 **Total Expense ($000):** 58352 **Payroll Expense ($000):** 18738
Personnel: 232

RESEARCH BELTON HOSPITAL See Belton Regional Medical Center

BETHANY—Harrison County

HARRISON COUNTY COMMUNITY HOSPITAL (261312), 2600 Miller
Street, Zip 64424–2701, Mailing Address: P.O. Box 428, Zip 64424–0428;
tel. 660/425–2211, **A**10 18 **F**3 11 15 28 29 34 40 41 44 45 50 53 54 57 59
62 64 67 74 75 77 81 82 87 89 90 92 93 94 96 97 98 102 103 104 107 108
110 111 115 119 127 128 129 130 131 133 135 143 147 148 149 **P**5
Primary Contact: Tina Gillespie, Chief Executive Officer
CFO: Lee Ann Miles, Chief Financial Officer
CMO: Terry E. Hall, Chief of Staff
CIO: Will Holt, Director Information Technology
CHR: Cathie Chalfant, Director Human Resources
CNO: Crystal Hicks, R.N., Chief Nursing Officer
Web address: www.hcchospital.org
Control: Hospital district or authority, Government, nonfederal **Service:** General
medical and surgical

Staffed Beds: 19 **Admissions:** 410 **Census:** 6 **Outpatient Visits:** 69081
Births: 0 **Total Expense ($000):** 25198 **Payroll Expense ($000):** 10918
Personnel: 207

BLUE SPRINGS—Jackson County

ST. MARY'S MEDICAL CENTER (260193), 201 Northwest R D Mize Road,
Zip 64014–2518; tel. 816/228–5900, **A**1 10 13 **F**3 8 15 18 20 22 29 30 34 35
40 49 50 53 57 59 60 62 63 64 68 70 74 77 78 79 80 81 82 83 84 85 87 90
93 96 107 108 110 111 113 114 115 119 129 130 131 135 143 145 146 148
154 **P**6 **S** Prime Healthcare, Ontario, CA
Primary Contact: Steven D. Wilkinson, Interim Chief Executive Officer
Web address: www.stmaryskc.com/
Control: Corporation, Investor–owned (for–profit) **Service:** General medical and
surgical

Staffed Beds: 83 **Admissions:** 4827 **Census:** 54 **Outpatient Visits:** 62160
Births: 0 **Total Expense ($000):** 79213 **Payroll Expense ($000):** 27696
Personnel: 496

BOLIVAR—Polk County

CITIZENS MEMORIAL HOSPITAL (260195), 1500 North Oakland Avenue,
Zip 65613–3011; tel. 417/326–6000, **A**1 10 20 **F**3 7 11 13 15 18 20 22 26
28 29 31 34 36 40 43 44 50 51 54 56 57 59 64 66 70 74 75 76 77 78 79 80
81 82 84 85 86 87 89 90 93 94 96 97 98 100 102 103 104 107 108 110 111
115 117 119 127 128 129 130 131 132 133 135 146 147 148 149 154 **P**6
Primary Contact: Donald J. Babb, Chief Executive Officer
COO: Jeff Miller, Chief Operating Officer
CFO: Gary D. Fullbright, Comptroller
CMO: Ronald A. Evans, M.D., Chief Medical Officer
CIO: Denni McColm, Chief Information Officer
CHR: Jeremy MacLaughlin, Director Human Resources
CNO: Lesa Stock, R.N., Chief Clinical Officer
Web address: www.citizensmemorial.com
Control: Hospital district or authority, Government, nonfederal **Service:** General
medical and surgical

Staffed Beds: 72 **Admissions:** 3499 **Census:** 31 **Outpatient Visits:** 372541
Births: 539 **Total Expense ($000):** 149896 **Payroll Expense ($000):** 67650
Personnel: 1105

BONNE TERRE—St. Francois County

PARKLAND HEALTH CENTER–BONNE TERRE (261315), 7245 Raider Road,
Zip 63628, Mailing Address: 1101 West Liberty Street, Farmington, Zip 63640;
tel. 573/358–1400, **A**10 18 20 **F**3 11 29 30 31 34 35 40 50 53 57 59 64 65
75 77 78 86 90 107 129 130 146 149 **P**8 **S** BJC HealthCare, Saint Louis, MO
Primary Contact: Laura Lynn Rasnick, RN, BSN, CLNC, Administrator
CFO: Cheri L. Goldsmith, Director Financial Services
CHR: Sheri Graham, Director Human Resources and Administrative Services
Web address: www.parklandhealthcenter.org
Control: Other not–for–profit (including NFP Corporation) **Service:** General
medical and surgical

Staffed Beds: 3 **Admissions:** 4 **Census:** 1 **Outpatient Visits:** 25467
Births: 0 **Personnel:** 40

MO

Hospital, Medicare Provider Number, Address, Telephone, Approval, Facility, and Physician Codes, Health Care System

★ American Hospital Association (AHA) membership   ○ Healthcare Facilities Accreditation Program   ⇑ Center for Improvement in Healthcare Quality Accreditation
□ The Joint Commission accreditation   ◇ DNV Healthcare Inc. accreditation   △ Commission on Accreditation of Rehabilitation Facilities (CARF) accreditation

BOONVILLE—Cooper County

COOPER COUNTY COMMUNITY HOSPITAL (260004), 17651 'B'
Highway, Zip 65233–2839, Mailing Address: P.O. Box 88, Zip 65233–0088;
tel. 660/882–7461, (Total facility includes 14 beds in nursing home–type unit) **A**10
20 **F**3 7 11 29 34 35 40 45 53 57 59 64 67 68 75 79 81 85 89 93 94 107 111
114 119 127 128 130 131 132 133 146 148 **S** Rural Community Hospitals of
America, Kansas City, MO
Primary Contact: Randy Simmons, Chief Executive Officer
CFO: Patricia Nowlin, Director Accounting
CMO: Mona Brownfield, M.D., Chief Medical Staff
CIO: Bill Fletcher, Director Information Technology
CHR: Patricia Nowlin, Director Human Resources
CNO: Nancy Fredrich, R.N., Chief Clinical Officer
Web address: www.coopercmh.com
Control: County, Government, nonfederal **Service:** General medical and surgical

Staffed Beds: 32 **Admissions:** 331 **Census:** 17 **Outpatient Visits:** 28251
Births: 0 **Total Expense ($000):** 11268 **Payroll Expense ($000):** 6284
Personnel: 116

BRANSON—Taney County

COX MEDICAL CENTER BRANSON (260094), 251 Skaggs Road,
Zip 65616–2031, Mailing Address: P.O. Box 650, Zip 65615–0650;
tel. 417/335–7000, **A**7 10 21 **F**3 11 13 15 17 18 20 22 26 28 29 30 31 32 34
35 40 41 45 46 48 50 53 56 57 59 60 61 62 64 65 66 68 70 74 75 76 77 78
79 80 81 85 86 87 89 90 98 107 108 110 111 114 115 117 119 120 121 123
129 130 131 132 135 143 144 146 147 148 149 150 154 **P**3 6 **S** CoxHealth,
Springfield, MO
Primary Contact: William K. Mahoney, FACHE, President and Chief Executive Officer
CFO: David Strong, Chief Financial Officer/Vice President Finance
CMO: James Duff, M.D., Chief Medical Officer
CHR: Carol Murrow, Vice President Business Development
Web address: www.coxhealth.com
Control: Other not–for–profit (including NFP Corporation) **Service:** General
medical and surgical

Staffed Beds: 120 **Admissions:** 6541 **Census:** 83 **Outpatient Visits:**
323568 **Births:** 556 **Total Expense ($000):** 172674 **Payroll Expense
($000):** 63193 **Personnel:** 1104

BRIDGETON—St. Louis County

SSM HEALTH DEPAUL HOSPITAL – ST. LOUIS (260104), 12303 De Paul Drive,
Zip 63044–2512; tel. 314/344–6000, (Total facility includes 52 beds in nursing
home–type unit) **A**1 2 5 7 10 **F**3 4 5 11 12 13 15 17 18 20 22 24 26 28 29 30
31 34 35 36 38 40 43 44 45 49 50 51 53 55 56 57 58 59 60 61 64 68 70 73
74 75 76 78 79 81 82 84 85 86 87 89 98 99 100 101 102 104 105 107 108
110 111 114 115 117 118 119 120 121 126 128 129 130 132 135 144 146
147 148 153 154 **P**6 8 **S** SSM Health, Saint Louis, MO
Primary Contact: Ellis Hawkins, President
CFO: Hal Holder, Director Finance
CMO: John Moore, M.D., Vice President Medical Affairs
CIO: Scott Feldmann, Director Information Technology
CHR: Gloria Reed, Leader Human Resources
CNO: Shelly L. Cordum, R.N., MSN, Vice President Nursing and Chief Nursing
Officer
Web address: www.ssmdepaul.com
Control: Church operated, Nongovernment, not–for–profit **Service:** General
medical and surgical

Staffed Beds: 529 **Admissions:** 24265 **Census:** 352 **Outpatient Visits:**
264693 **Births:** 1039 **Total Expense ($000):** 403700 **Payroll Expense
($000):** 130082 **Personnel:** 1992

BROOKFIELD—Linn County

PERSHING MEMORIAL HOSPITAL (261307), 130 East Lockling Avenue,
Zip 64628–2337, Mailing Address: P.O. Box 408, Zip 64628–0408;
tel. 660/258–2222, **A**10 18 **F**11 15 28 29 34 40 57 59 64 75 77 81 85 87 89
93 97 107 111 114 119 127 129 130 133 146 149 **P**6
Primary Contact: Phil Hamilton, R.N., Chief Executive Officer
CFO: Gary R Tandy, Chief Financial Officer
CMO: B K Knowles, D.O., Chief of Staff
CIO: Elaine Sutton, Chief Information Officer
CHR: Amy Sayre, Director Human Resources
Web address: www.phsmo.org
Control: Other not–for–profit (including NFP Corporation) **Service:** General
medical and surgical

Staffed Beds: 25 **Admissions:** 325 **Census:** 6 **Outpatient Visits:** 49322
Births: 0 **Total Expense ($000):** 16527 **Payroll Expense ($000):** 6502
Personnel: 139

BUTLER—Bates County

BATES COUNTY MEMORIAL HOSPITAL (260034), 615 West Nursery
Street, Zip 64730–1840, Mailing Address: P.O. Box 370, Zip 64730–0370;
tel. 660/200–7000, **A**10 20 **F**3 7 11 15 28 29 30 31 34 40 45 50 59 64 68 70
77 78 79 81 87 90 93 107 108 109 110 111 115 118 119 127 129 130 132
133 154 **P**5 6
Primary Contact: John P. Bustle, M.D., Chief Executive Officer
CFO: Terri Floyd, Chief Financial Officer
CMO: William F. Joyce, D.O., Chief of Staff
CIO: Marcia Cook, Director Information Technology
CHR: Melinda R Jackson, Director Human Resources
CNO: Rebecca Tarver, Chief Nursing Officer
Web address: www.bcmhospital.com
Control: County, Government, nonfederal **Service:** General medical and surgical

Staffed Beds: 49 **Admissions:** 915 **Census:** 9 **Outpatient Visits:** 74151
Births: 0 **Total Expense ($000):** 37769 **Payroll Expense ($000):** 14344
Personnel: 275

CAMERON—Clinton County

CAMERON REGIONAL MEDICAL CENTER (260057), 1600 East Evergreen,
Zip 64429–2400, Mailing Address: P.O. Box 557, Zip 64429–0557;
tel. 816/632–2101, **A**3 5 10 **F**3 11 12 13 15 28 29 30 31 34 35 39 40 46 47
49 56 57 59 61 62 63 64 70 74 75 76 77 78 79 81 82 84 85 86 87 89 90 98
100 103 104 107 110 111 115 119 129 130 131 133 143 146 147 148 **P**6
Primary Contact: Joseph F. Abrutz Jr, Administrator
CFO: Rosa Patti, Chief Financial Officer
CIO: Bill Walser, Coordinator Technology
CHR: Pat Bestgen, Manager Human Resources
Web address: www.cameronregional.org
Control: Other not–for–profit (including NFP Corporation) **Service:** General
medical and surgical

Staffed Beds: 58 **Admissions:** 1823 **Census:** 29 **Outpatient Visits:** 279756
Births: 144 **Total Expense ($000):** 58858 **Payroll Expense ($000):** 26294
Personnel: 377

CAPE GIRARDEAU—Cape Girardeau County

LANDMARK HOSPITAL OF CAPE GIRARDEAU (262015), 3255 Independence
Street, Zip 63701–4914; tel. 573/335–1091, **A**1 10 22 **F**1 3 29 130 148 **S**
Landmark Hospitals, Cape Girardeau, MO
Primary Contact: Deborah Sabella, R.N., Chief Executive Officer
COO: Michael L Norman, Executive Vice President and Chief Operating Officer
CFO: Richard H Hogan, CPA, Chief Financial Officer
CMO: William Fritsch, M.D., Medical Director
CIO: Renee Hesselrode, Director Health Information Management
CHR: Angela Kisner, Director Human Resources and Coordinator Medical Staff
Web address: www.landmarkhospitals.com
Control: Corporation, Investor–owned (for–profit) **Service:** Acute long–term care
hospital

Staffed Beds: 30 **Admissions:** 242 **Census:** 18 **Outpatient Visits:** 0
Births: 0 **Total Expense ($000):** 10301 **Payroll Expense ($000):** 4004
Personnel: 48

SAINT FRANCIS MEDICAL CENTER (260183), 211 St Francis Drive,
Zip 63703–5049; tel. 573/331–3000, **A**1 2 10 19 **F**3 9 11 12 13 15 17 18 20
22 24 26 28 29 34 44 45 46 47 48 49 50 51 53 54 56 57 58 59 60 61 62 63
64 65 68 70 72 73 74 75 76 77 78 79 80 81 82 83 84 85 86 87 89 90 91 92
93 96 97 119 126 127 129 130 131 132 135 141 142 143 144 145 146 147
148 149 **P**6
Primary Contact: Maryann Reese, R.N., FACHE, President and Chief Executive
Officer
CFO: Tony Balsano, Vice President Finance
CMO: James Schell, M.D., Vice President Medical Affairs
CIO: Edward E Duryee, Director Information Systems
CHR: Teri Kreitzer, Director Human Resources
CNO: Jeannie Fadler, R.N., Vice President Patient Care Services
Web address: www.sfmc.net
Control: Church operated, Nongovernment, not–for–profit **Service:** General
medical and surgical

Staffed Beds: 308 **Admissions:** 12678 **Census:** 164 **Outpatient Visits:**
794981 **Births:** 1011 **Total Expense ($000):** 465883 **Payroll Expense
($000):** 182973 **Personnel:** 2369

Many Facility Codes have changed. Please refer to the AHA Guide Code Chart. © 2018 AHA Guide

SOUTHEAST HOSPITAL (260110), 1701 Lacey Street, Zip 63701–5230; tel. 573/334–4822, **A**1 10 19 **F**3 11 13 15 17 18 20 22 24 26 28 29 30 31 32 34 35 40 44 45 48 50 51 53 54 57 58 59 60 61 62 63 64 65 70 72 73 74 75 76 77 78 79 80 81 82 84 85 86 87 88 89 90 92 93 96 97 98 100 102 107 108 110 111 114 115 117 119 120 123 124 126 127 129 130 131 132 135 146 147 148 149 154 **S** SoutheastHEALTH, Cape Girardeau, MO
Primary Contact: Kenneth Bateman, CPA, President and Chief Executive Officer
COO: Sylvia Moore, Vice President and Chief Operating Officer
CFO: Bruce Fairbanks, Vice President and Chief Financial Officer
CMO: Matt Shoemaker, D.O., Vice President and Chief Medical Officer
CIO: Mike Dozier, Chief Information Officer
CHR: Lincoln Scott, Vice President Human Resources
CNO: Judy Aslin, MSN, R.N., Vice President and Chief Nursing Officer
Web address: www.sehealth.org/
Control: Other not–for–profit (including NFP Corporation) **Service:** General medical and surgical

Staffed Beds: 209 Admissions: 8800 Census: 113 Outpatient Visits: 427088 **Births: 980 Total Expense ($000):** 318509 **Payroll Expense ($000):** 119830 **Personnel:** 1954

CARROLLTON—Carroll County

CARROLL COUNTY MEMORIAL HOSPITAL (261332), 1502 North Jefferson Street, Zip 64633–1948; tel. 660/542–1695, **A**10 18 **F**3 11 15 28 29 30 31 34 35 38 40 45 50 53 56 57 59 62 64 65 69 74 75 77 78 79 81 82 86 87 90 91 92 93 96 103 104 108 110 111 114 119 125 127 129 130 131 132 133 135 143 146 148 149 153 154 **P**6
Primary Contact: Jeff A. Tindle, Chief Executive Officer
COO: Tim Braun, Chief Operation Officer
CFO: Amy Ireland, Chief Financial Officer
CMO: Richard Smith, Chief of Staff
CIO: Bill Bollinger, Chief Information Officer
CHR: Michael Schubach, Chief People Officer
CNO: Jeanne Rector, Chief Nursing Officer
Web address: www.carrollcountyhospital.org
Control: Other not–for–profit (including NFP Corporation) **Service:** General medical and surgical

Staffed Beds: 25 Admissions: 265 Census: 6 Outpatient Visits: 57127 **Births: 0 Total Expense ($000):** 25389 **Payroll Expense ($000):** 8934 **Personnel:** 211

CARTHAGE—Jasper County

MERCY HOSPITAL CARTHAGE (261338), 3125 Dr Russell Smith Way, Zip 64836–7402; tel. 417/358–8121, **A**10 18 **F**3 7 11 15 28 29 30 31 34 35 40 45 50 53 57 59 62 64 67 68 69 75 79 81 89 98 104 107 108 110 111 115 119 126 127 129 130 131 132 133 135 146 147 154 **P**6 **S** Mercy, Chesterfield, MO
Primary Contact: Scott Watson, Administrator
CFO: Douglas Culver, Chief Financial Officer
CIO: Cheryl Lease–Homeyer, Lead Information Technology Business Partner
CHR: Colette St. Peter, Senior Manager Human Resources
Web address: www.mercy.net
Control: Church operated, Nongovernment, not–for–profit **Service:** General medical and surgical

Staffed Beds: 13 Admissions: 776 Census: 12 Outpatient Visits: 94905 **Births: 0 Total Expense ($000):** 37198 **Payroll Expense ($000):** 15221 **Personnel:** 233

CASSVILLE—Barry County

MERCY HOSPITAL CASSVILLE (261317), 94 Main Street, Zip 65625–1610; tel. 417/847–6000, **A**1 10 18 **F**3 11 15 28 29 30 34 35 40 44 45 50 53 57 59 64 65 68 75 77 81 85 86 87 89 90 93 94 96 103 107 108 110 111 114 119· 132 133 135 148 149 153 154 **P**6 **S** Mercy, Chesterfield, MO
Primary Contact: Nicki Gamet, R.N., Administrator
CFO: Sherry Clouse Day, CPA, Chief Financial Officer
CMO: Jamie Zengotita, M.D., Chief Medical Staff
CHR: George Roden, Vice President Human Resources
Web address: www.mercy.net/northweststar/practice/mercy–hospital–cassville
Control: Church operated, Nongovernment, not–for–profit **Service:** General medical and surgical

Staffed Beds: 18 Admissions: 292 Census: 3 Outpatient Visits: 33565 **Births: 0 Total Expense ($000):** 14999 **Payroll Expense ($000):** 7094 **Personnel:** 97

CHESTERFIELD—St. Louis County

MERCY REHABILITATION HOSPITAL ST. LOUIS (263029), 14561 North Outer Forty Road, Zip 63017; tel. 314/881–4000, **A**1 7 10 **F**16 29 30 90 130 132 148 **S** Kindred Healthcare, Louisville, KY
Primary Contact: Jerald W. Rumph, Chief Executive Officer
CMO: Siresha Samudrala, M.D., Medical Director
Web address: www.mercy.net/practice/mercy–rehabilitation–hospital–st–louis/
Control: Partnership, Investor–owned (for–profit) **Service:** Rehabilitation

Staffed Beds: 90 Admissions: 1816 Census: 68 Outpatient Visits: 0 Births: 0 Total Expense ($000): 29415 **Payroll Expense ($000):** 13122 **Personnel:** 229

ST. LUKE'S HOSPITAL (260179), 232 South Woods Mill Road, Zip 63017–3417; tel. 314/434–1500, (Total facility includes 140 beds in nursing home–type unit) **A**1 2 3 10 **F**3 10 11 13 15 17 18 20 22 24 26 28 29 30 31 32 34 35 36 38 39 40 41 44 45 46 49 50 52 53 54 57 58 59 60 61 62 63 64 65 66 68 69 70 71 73 74 75 76 77 78 79 81 82 83 84 85 86 87 89 90 93 97 107 110 111 114 115 117 118 119 120 121 123 124 126 128 129 130 131 132 135 144 145 146 147 148 149 **P**6 8
Primary Contact: Christine M. Candio, R.N., FACHE, President and Chief Executive Officer
COO: Donald L Miller, FACHE, Vice President, Operations
CFO: Scott H. Johnson, Vice President Finance and Chief Financial Officer
CIO: William Meyers, Chief Information Officer
CHR: Janette Taaffe, Vice President, Human Resource
CNO: Diane Ray, R.N., FACHE, Vice President and Chief Nursing Officer Patient Services
Web address: www.stlukes–stl.com
Control: Church operated, Nongovernment, not–for–profit **Service:** General medical and surgical

Staffed Beds: 542 Admissions: 14934 Census: 273 Outpatient Visits: 1066007 **Births: 1873 Total Expense ($000):** 512561 **Payroll Expense ($000):** 227798 **Personnel:** 3062

ST. LUKE'S REHABILITATION HOSPITAL (263030), 14709 Olive Boulevard, Zip 63017–2221; tel. 314/317–5700, **A**1 7 10 **F**3 12 18 28 29 34 75 79 90 96 100 130 132 148
Primary Contact: Don Foster, Chief Executive Officer
Web address: www.khrehabstluke.com
Control: Partnership, Investor–owned (for–profit) **Service:** Rehabilitation

Staffed Beds: 35 Admissions: 705 Census: 23 Outpatient Visits: 0 Births: 0 Total Expense ($000): 8800 **Payroll Expense ($000):** 4739 **Personnel:** 49

CHILLICOTHE—Livingston County

HEDRICK MEDICAL CENTER (261321), 2799 North Washington Street, Zip 64601–2902; tel. 660/646–1480, **A**1 10 18 **F**3 11 13 15 18 28 29 30 31 34 35 39 40 43 44 45 50 57 59 64 68 69 70 74 75 76 77 78 79 81 85 86 87 89 90 92 93 96 97 100 102 104 107 108 110 111 115 118 119 127 130 131 133 141 146 147 148 154 **P**6 **S** Saint Luke's Health System, Kansas City, MO
Primary Contact: Steven M. Schieber, FACHE, Chief Executive Officer
CHR: Lisa Hecker, Director Human Resources
CNO: Catherine Hamilton, Chief Nursing Officer
Web address: www.saintlukeskc.org
Control: Other not–for–profit (including NFP Corporation) **Service:** General medical and surgical

Staffed Beds: 25 Admissions: 1301 Census: 14 Outpatient Visits: 96344 **Births: 363 Total Expense ($000):** 48445 **Payroll Expense ($000):** 18869 **Personnel:** 324

CLINTON—Henry County

GOLDEN VALLEY MEMORIAL HEALTHCARE (260175), 1600 North Second Street, Zip 64735–1192; tel. 660/885–5511, **A**1 10 **F**3 7 11 13 15 17 18 28 29 30 31 34 35 40 45 47 48 49 53 57 59 61 62 64 68 70 74 75 76 77 78 79 81 85 86 87 89 90 93 96 107 108 111 115 118 127 128 129 130 131 132 133 143 146 147 148 149
Primary Contact: Craig Thompson, Chief Executive Officer
CFO: Tammy R Nadler, Chief Financial Officer
CIO: Mike Gaul, Director Information Technology
CHR: Greg Shannon, Chief Human Resources Officer
CNO: Lynnette Hayes, Chief Nursing Officer
Web address: www.gvmh.org
Control: Hospital district or authority, Government, nonfederal **Service:** General medical and surgical

Staffed Beds: 53 Admissions: 2061 Census: 19 Outpatient Visits: 305070 **Births: 0 Total Expense ($000):** 95605 **Payroll Expense ($000):** 41073 **Personnel:** 709

MO

Hospital, Medicare Provider Number, Address, Telephone, Approval, Facility, and Physician Codes, Health Care System

★ American Hospital Association (AHA) membership   ○ Healthcare Facilities Accreditation Program   ⇑ Center for Improvement in Healthcare Quality Accreditation
☐ The Joint Commission accreditation   ◇ DNV Healthcare Inc. accreditation   △ Commission on Accreditation of Rehabilitation Facilities (CARF) accreditation

© 2018 AHA Guide   *Many Facility Codes have changed. Please refer to the AHA Guide Code Chart.*   Hospitals **A357**

COLUMBIA—Boone County

BOONE HOSPITAL CENTER (260068), 1600 East Broadway, Zip 65201–5844; tel. 573/815–8000, **A**1 2 3 5 10 **F**3 7 11 12 13 15 17 18 20 22 24 26 28 29 31 34 35 36 40 45 46 47 48 49 50 51 53 54 56 57 59 60 61 64 65 68 70 71 72 73 74 75 76 77 78 79 80 81 82 84 85 86 87 90 93 96 107 108 110 111 115 117 118 119 126 129 130 131 132 133 135 143 144 145 146 147 148 149 **S** BJC HealthCare, Saint Louis, MO
Primary Contact: James J. Sinek, FACHE, President
CFO: Randy Morrow, Vice President and Chief Operating Officer
CMO: Jerry Kennett, M.D., Chief Medical Officer
CHR: Michelle Zvanut, Vice President Human Resources
Web address: www.boone.org
Control: Other not–for–profit (including NFP Corporation) **Service**: General medical and surgical

Staffed Beds: 311 **Admissions**: 14038 **Census**: 168 **Outpatient Visits**: 175194 **Births**: 1626 **Total Expense ($000)**: 321920 **Payroll Expense ($000)**: 88454 **Personnel**: 1248

ELLIS FISCHEL CANCER CENTER See University of Missouri Health Care, Columbia

HARRY S. TRUMAN MEMORIAL VETERANS HOSPITAL, 800 Hospital Drive, Zip 65201–5275; tel. 573/814–6000, (Total facility includes 35 beds in nursing home–type unit) **A**1 3 5 **F**3 4 5 17 18 20 22 24 26 28 29 31 34 35 36 38 39 40 45 46 49 56 57 58 59 60 61 62 63 64 65 70 74 78 79 81 82 84 85 86 87 90 92 93 97 98 100 102 104 105 106 107 111 115 116 117 118 119 128 130 132 135 146 147 149 153 154 **S** Department of Veterans Affairs, Perry Point, MD
Primary Contact: David Isaacks, Director
COO: Robert G Ritter, FACHE, Associate Director
CFO: Deborah Henderson, Acting Chief Financial Officer
CMO: Lana Zerrer, M.D., Chief of Staff
CIO: Donna Krause, Chief Information Officer
CHR: Jimmy Powell, Manager Human Resources
Web address: www.columbiamo.va.gov
Control: Veterans Affairs, Government, federal **Service**: General medical and surgical

Staffed Beds: 126 **Admissions**: 4419 **Census**: 91 **Outpatient Visits**: 523939 **Births**: 0 **Total Expense ($000)**: 328910 **Payroll Expense ($000)**: 132391 **Personnel**: 1023

HOWARD A. RUSK REHABILITATION CENTER (263027), 315 Business Loop 70 West, Zip 65203–3248; tel. 573/817–2703, **A**1 3 5 10 **F**29 30 34 68 75 90 91 94 95 96 132 143 148 **S** Encompass Health Corporation, Birmingham, AL
Primary Contact: John M. Dawes, FACHE, Chief Executive Officer
CFO: Jeff Reese, Chief Financial Officer
CMO: Gregory Worsowicz, M.D., Medical Director
CHR: Robin Prater, Director Human Resources
CNO: Lori Mann, R.N., MSN, Chief Nursing Officer
Web address: www.ruskrehab.com
Control: Partnership, Investor–owned (for–profit) **Service**: Rehabilitation

Staffed Beds: 60 **Admissions**: 1129 **Census**: 42 **Outpatient Visits**: 0 **Births**: 0 **Total Expense ($000)**: 19985 **Payroll Expense ($000)**: 9228 **Personnel**: 141

LANDMARK HOSPITAL OF COLUMBIA (262020), 604 Old 63 North, Zip 65201–6308; tel. 573/499–6600, **A**3 5 10 22 **F**1 60 70 148 **P**5 6 **S** Landmark Hospitals, Cape Girardeau, MO
Primary Contact: Laura D. Peckham, Chief Executive Officer
Web address: www.landmarkhospitals.com
Control: Corporation, Investor–owned (for–profit) **Service**: Acute long–term care hospital

Staffed Beds: 42 **Admissions**: 283 **Census**: 20 **Outpatient Visits**: 0 **Births**: 0 **Total Expense ($000)**: 13338 **Payroll Expense ($000)**: 4888 **Personnel**: 65

UNIVERSITY OF MISSOURI HEALTH CARE (260141), One Hospital Drive, Zip 65212–0001; tel. 573/882–4141, (Includes ELLIS FISCHEL CANCER CENTER, 115 Business Loop 70 West, Columbia, MO, Zip 65203; tel. 573/882–5460; WOMEN'S AND CHILDREN'S HOSPITAL, 404 Keene Street, Columbia, MO, Zip 65201–6626; tel. 573/875–9000; Keri Simon, Executive Director) **A**1 2 3 5 8 10 **F**3 4 7 9 11 12 13 15 16 17 18 19 20 22 24 26 28 29 30 31 32 33 34 35 36 37 38 39 40 41 43 44 45 46 47 48 49 50 51 52 53 54 55 56 57 58 59 60 61 64 65 66 68 70 71 72 73 74 75 76 77 78 79 81 82 83 84 85 86 87 88 89 91 92 93 97 98 99 100 101 102 103 104 107 108 110 111 115 116 117 118 119 120 121 123 124 126 127 129 130 131 132 134 135 138 141 142 143 144 146 147 148 154 **P**1 6 **S** University of Missouri Health Care, Columbia, MO
Primary Contact: Jonathan W. Curtright, Chief Executive Officer and Chief Operating Officer
CFO: Kevin Necas, Chief Financial Officer
CMO: Stevan Whitt, M.D., Chief Medical Officer
CHR: Sue Kopfle, Chief Human Resources Officer
Web address: www.muhealth.org
Control: State, Government, nonfederal **Service**: General medical and surgical

Staffed Beds: 595 **Admissions**: 26874 **Census**: 390 **Outpatient Visits**: 978253 **Births**: 2320 **Total Expense ($000)**: 889499 **Payroll Expense ($000)**: 273069 **Personnel**: 5176

CRYSTAL CITY—Jefferson County

MERCY HOSPITAL JEFFERSON (260023), Highway 61 South, Zip 63019, Mailing Address: P.O. Box 350, Zip 63019–0350; tel. 636/933–1000, **A**1 7 10 **F**3 8 11 12 13 15 18 20 22 24 26 28 29 30 31 34 35 40 44 45 47 49 50 51 53 54 57 59 60 62 63 64 68 70 74 75 76 77 78 79 81 82 84 85 86 87 89 90 93 96 97 98 103 104 107 108 110 111 114 115 117 118 119 129 130 131 132 135 143 144 146 147 148 153 154 **P**6 8 **S** Mercy, Chesterfield, MO
Primary Contact: Eric Ammons, President
COO: Michele C Meyer, Vice President of Operations
CMO: Mark Briete, M.D., Vice President Medical Affairs
CIO: Jan Poneta, Director Information Services
CHR: Saundra G Turner, Director Human Resources
Web address: www.mercy.net/crystalcitymo
Control: Other not–for–profit (including NFP Corporation) **Service**: General medical and surgical

Staffed Beds: 205 **Admissions**: 9443 **Census**: 120 **Outpatient Visits**: 170548 **Births**: 406 **Total Expense ($000)**: 153165 **Payroll Expense ($000)**: 62824 **Personnel**: 1124

DEXTER—Stoddard County

SOUTHEAST HEALTH CENTER OF STODDARD COUNTY (260160), 1200 North One Mile Road, Zip 63841–1000; tel. 573/624–5566, **A**10 **F**3 11 15 28 29 31 34 39 40 45 59 62 65 70 75 77 78 81 85 89 90 93 97 107 108 111 115 118 119 127 129 130 133 135 146 **P**6 **S** SoutheastHEALTH, Cape Girardeau, MO
Primary Contact: Sue Ann Williams, Chief Executive Officer
Web address: www.sehealth.org
Control: Other not–for–profit (including NFP Corporation) **Service**: General medical and surgical

Staffed Beds: 16 **Admissions**: 817 **Census**: 6 **Outpatient Visits**: 104101 **Births**: 0 **Total Expense ($000)**: 28284 **Payroll Expense ($000)**: 10959 **Personnel**: 191

DONIPHAN—Ripley County

SOUTHEAST HEALTH CENTER OF RIPLEY COUNTY (260080), 109 Plum Street, Zip 63935–1299; tel. 573/996–2141, **A**10 **F**3 29 34 35 40 59 62 64 65 93 107 111 115 119 127 129 133 149 **P**6 **S** SoutheastHEALTH, Cape Girardeau, MO
Primary Contact: Cheryl Lynne. Barton, R.N., Chief Executive Officer
CFO: Rickie Maples, Interim Chief Financial Officer
CMO: Ureej Mansoor, M.D., Chief of Staff
CIO: Riley March, Manager Information Technology
CHR: Peggy Teasdale, Director Human Resources
Web address: www.sehealth.org/southeast-health-center-of-ripley-county/SoutheastHEALTH.aspx?nd=41
Control: Other not–for–profit (including NFP Corporation) **Service**: General medical and surgical

Staffed Beds: 8 **Admissions**: 233 **Census**: 2 **Outpatient Visits**: 42079 **Births**: 0 **Total Expense ($000)**: 10599 **Payroll Expense ($000)**: 4692 **Personnel**: 73

EL DORADO SPRINGS—Cedar County

CEDAR COUNTY MEMORIAL HOSPITAL (261323), 1401 South Park Street, Zip 64744–2037; tel. 417/876–2511, **A**10 18 **F**11 15 18 28 29 30 34 35 40 45 53 56 57 59 62 64 65 74 77 81 85 87 89 90 93 102 103 107 110 111 114 119 127 129 130 133 147 148 149 153 **P**6
Primary Contact: Jana Witt, Chief Executive Officer
CFO: Carla Gilbert, Director Finance
CMO: R. John Torontow, M.D., Chief Medical Staff
CIO: Lois Willmore, Supervisor Health Information Management
CHR: Diana Pyle, Director Human Resources and Executive Assistant to Chief Executive Officer
CNO: Drew Alexander, Chief Nursing Officer
Web address: www.cedarcountyhospital.org
Control: County, Government, nonfederal **Service**: General medical and surgical

Staffed Beds: 25 **Admissions**: 340 **Census**: 6 **Outpatient Visits**: 20070 **Births**: 0 **Total Expense ($000)**: 12878 **Payroll Expense ($000)**: 4195 **Personnel**: 116

MO

Many Facility Codes have changed. Please refer to the AHA Guide Code Chart.

© 2018 AHA Guide

EXCELSIOR SPRINGS—Clay County

EXCELSIOR SPRINGS HOSPITAL (261322), 1700 Rainbow Boulevard, Zip 64024–1190; tel. 816/630–6081, (Total facility includes 80 beds in nursing home–type unit) **A**10 18 **F**3 10 11 15 18 29 31 32 34 35 39 40 45 56 57 59 62 63 64 67 68 70 75 77 78 79 81 82 84 85 86 87 89 90 93 102 107 108 110 111 115 116 117 118 119 125 128 129 130 133 143 146
Primary Contact: Kristen DeHart, Chief Executive Officer
CFO: Cameron Meyer, CPA, Chief Financial Officer
CMO: H. Andrew Pickett, M.D., Medical Staff President
CHR: Joni Schwan, Director Human Resources
CNO: Nanette Houck, R.N., Chief Nursing Executive
Web address: www.ESHospital.org
Control: City, Government, nonfederal **Service:** General medical and surgical

Staffed Beds: 105 **Admissions:** 381 **Census:** 65 **Outpatient Visits:** 35431 **Births:** 0 **Total Expense ($000):** 27761 **Payroll Expense ($000):** 12003 **Personnel:** 260

FAIRFAX—Atchison County

COMMUNITY HOSPITAL ASSOCIATION See Community Hospital–Fairfax

COMMUNITY HOSPITAL–FAIRFAX (261303), 26136 US Highway 59, Zip 64446–9105, Mailing Address: P.O. Box 107, Zip 64446–0107; tel. 660/686–2211, **A**10 18 21 **F**3 11 13 15 18 28 29 30 34 40 45 50 57 59 62 64 75 76 79 81 85 87 89 90 93 96 97 101 103 104 107 110 114 119 127 130 131 132 133 148 149
Primary Contact: Roger W. Steinkruger, Chief Executive Officer
COO: Ann Schlueter, Chief Operating Officer
CFO: Jon Davis, Chief Financial Officer
CMO: Richard Aron Burke, M.D., Chief Medical Officer
CIO: Chris Hedlund, Director Information Systems
CNO: Julie L Jones, Chief Nursing Officer
Web address: www.fairfaxmed.com
Control: Other not–for–profit (including NFP Corporation) **Service:** General medical and surgical

Staffed Beds: 18 **Admissions:** 461 **Census:** 5 **Outpatient Visits:** 25269 **Births:** 32 **Total Expense ($000):** 15729 **Payroll Expense ($000):** 5727 **Personnel:** 112

FARMINGTON—St. Francois County

PARKLAND HEALTH CENTER – FARMINGTON COMMUNITY (260163), 1101 West Liberty Street, Zip 63640–1921; tel. 573/756–6451, **A**1 10 **F**3 11 13 15 18 29 30 34 35 40 45 46 49 50 53 57 59 65 68 69 70 75 76 77 79 81 85 86 87 93 98 102 103 107 108 111 115 118 119 130 143 146 147 148 149 154 **P**6 **S** BJC HealthCare, Saint Louis, MO
Primary Contact: Thomas P. Karl, President
COO: Steven R Marler, Assistant Administrator
CFO: Cheri L. Goldsmith, Director Financial Services
CMO: Scott Kirkley, M.D., BJC CHief Medical Officer Group Liaison
CHR: Sheri Graham, Director Human Resources and Administrative Services
Web address: www.parklandhealthcenter.org
Control: Other not–for–profit (including NFP Corporation) **Service:** General medical and surgical

Staffed Beds: 103 **Admissions:** 3613 **Census:** 33 **Outpatient Visits:** 91608 **Births:** 674 **Total Expense ($000):** 103055 **Payroll Expense ($000):** 39611 **Personnel:** 589

SOUTHEAST MISSOURI MENTAL HEALTH CENTER (264005), 1010 West Columbia Street, Zip 63640–2997; tel. 573/218–6792, **A**1 10 **F**4 11 30 39 53 65 75 77 86 87 97 98 101 103 106 130 132 135 143 146
Primary Contact: Julie Inman, Regional Executive Officer
CMO: Jay Englehart, M.D., Medical Director
CHR: Mark Remspecher, Director Human Resources
Web address: www.dmh.missouri.gov/southeast/
Control: State, Government, nonfederal **Service:** Psychiatric

Staffed Beds: 331 **Admissions:** 45 **Census:** 311 **Outpatient Visits:** 0 **Births:** 0 **Total Expense ($000):** 65081 **Payroll Expense ($000):** 34805 **Personnel:** 1010

FENTON—St. Louis County

SSM HEALTH ST. CLARE HOSPITAL – FENTON (260081), 1015 Bowles Avenue, Zip 63026–2394; tel. 636/496–2000, **A**1 10 **F**3 11 13 15 17 18 20 22 24 28 29 30 31 34 35 40 41 44 45 49 50 51 53 54 56 57 58 59 61 64 70 73 74 75 76 78 79 81 82 84 85 86 87 89 100 102 103 105 107 108 110 111 115 117 119 120 121 124 130 132 135 143 144 146 147 148 **P**6 8 **S** SSM Health, Saint Louis, MO
Primary Contact: Tina Garrison, President
COO: Lee Bernstein, Regional Executive Vice President and Chief Operating Officer
CFO: Hal Holder, Regional Chief Financial Officer–Hospital Operations
CMO: Timothy J Pratt, M.D., Vice President Medical Affairs and Chief Medical Officer
CIO: Michael Paasch, Vice President, Regional Chief Information Officer
CHR: Renee Roach, System Vice President, Human Resources
CNO: Wayne Laramie, Vice President Nursing
Web address: www.ssmstclare.com
Control: Church operated, Nongovernment, not–for–profit **Service:** General medical and surgical

Staffed Beds: 184 **Admissions:** 10910 **Census:** 117 **Outpatient Visits:** 142394 **Births:** 1144 **Total Expense ($000):** 191126 **Payroll Expense ($000):** 62440 **Personnel:** 867

FORT LEONARD WOOD—Pulaski County

GENERAL LEONARD WOOD ARMY COMMUNITY HOSPITAL, 4430 Missouri Avenue, Zip 65473–8952, Mailing Address: PO Box 4430, Zip 65473–8952; tel. 573/596–0414, **A**1 **F**3 7 8 12 13 14 15 18 29 30 32 33 34 35 38 39 40 45 46 50 53 54 56 57 59 61 64 65 68 70 75 76 77 79 81 82 86 87 91 92 93 98 99 101 102 104 107 110 111 114 115 118 119 130 131 132 135 141 143 144 147 148 154 **S** Department of the Army, Office of the Surgeon General, Falls Church, VA
Primary Contact: Colonel Kimberlie Biever, Hospital Commander
CFO: Major Michael Hogan, Chief Resource Management
CMO: Lieutenant Colonel John Lowery, M.D., Deputy Commander Clinical Services
CHR: Major Sandra Roper, Chief Human Resources
Web address: www.glwach.amedd.army.mil/
Control: Army, Government, federal **Service:** General medical and surgical

Staffed Beds: 46 **Admissions:** 2285 **Census:** 25 **Outpatient Visits:** 164912 **Births:** 368 **Personnel:** 687

FREDERICKTOWN—Madison County

MADISON MEDICAL CENTER (261302), 611 West Main Street, Zip 63645–1111; tel. 573/783–3341, (Total facility includes 80 beds in nursing home–type unit) **A**10 18 **F**6 11 15 18 28 35 40 45 59 62 64 67 70 77 78 79 81 85 87 92 93 97 103 107 111 119 127 128 130 133 144 146
Primary Contact: Lisa Twidwell, Administrator
CMO: P A George, M.D., Chief of Staff
CHR: Jennifer Penuel, Director Human Resources
Web address: www.madisonmedicalcenter.net
Control: County, Government, nonfederal **Service:** General medical and surgical

Staffed Beds: 97 **Admissions:** 430 **Census:** 77 **Outpatient Visits:** 55972 **Births:** 0 **Total Expense ($000):** 19139 **Payroll Expense ($000):** 9434 **Personnel:** 256

FULTON—Callaway County

FULTON MEDICAL CENTER (260209), 10 South Hospital Drive, Zip 65251–2510; tel. 573/642–3376, (Nonreporting) **A**1 5 10
Primary Contact: Mike Reece, Chief Executive Officer
Web address: www.fultonmed.com
Control: Corporation, Investor–owned (for–profit) **Service:** General medical and surgical

Staffed Beds: 37

FULTON STATE HOSPITAL (264004), 600 East Fifth Street, Zip 65251–1753; tel. 573/592–4100, **A**1 3 5 10 **F**3 4 11 29 30 39 44 50 53 56 57 58 59 65 75 77 82 86 87 98 100 101 102 103 130 132 135 143 146 149 **P**6
Primary Contact: Robert Reitz, Ph.D., Chief Executive Officer
COO: Andrew Atkinson, Chief Operating Officer
CFO: Susie Kemp, Chief Financial Officer
CMO: Sanjiv Sethi, M.D., Medical Director
CIO: Keith Jones, Chief Information Officer
CHR: Lori French, Manager Human Resources
CNO: Susan Knoepflein, Chief Nurse Executive
Web address: www.dmh.missouri.gov/fulton
Control: State, Government, nonfederal **Service:** Psychiatric

Staffed Beds: 399 **Admissions:** 115 **Census:** 399 **Outpatient Visits:** 0 **Births:** 0 **Total Expense ($000):** 97996 **Payroll Expense ($000):** 50546 **Personnel:** 1246

MO

Hospital, Medicare Provider Number, Address, Telephone, Approval, Facility, and Physician Codes, Health Care System

★ American Hospital Association (AHA) membership
□ The Joint Commission accreditation
○ Healthcare Facilities Accreditation Program
◇ DNV Healthcare Inc. accreditation
⇑ Center for Improvement in Healthcare Quality Accreditation
△ Commission on Accreditation of Rehabilitation Facilities (CARF) accreditation

---

HANNIBAL—Marion County

HANNIBAL REGIONAL HOSPITAL (260025), 6000 Hospital Drive, Zip 63401–6887, Mailing Address: P.O. Box 551, Zip 63401–0551; tel. 573/248–1300, **A**1 2 10 **F**3 13 15 20 22 26 28 29 31 34 35 40 45 47 49 51 57 59 62 64 68 70 74 75 76 78 79 81 85 86 87 89 90 92 107 108 110 111 115 117 118 120 121 123 124 129 130 132 135 148 **P**1
Primary Contact: C Todd. Ahrens, President and Chief Executive Officer
CFO: Roger J Dix, Vice President Finance
CMO: Bryson McHardy, M.D., President Medical Staff
CIO: Jeff W. Evans, Vice President Information and Technology
CHR: Susan R Wathen, Vice President Human Resources
Web address: www.hrhonline.org
Control: Other not–for–profit (including NFP Corporation) **Service:** General medical and surgical

Staffed Beds: 99 **Admissions:** 4170 **Census:** 46 **Outpatient Visits:** 177875 **Births:** 587 **Total Expense ($000):** 141557 **Payroll Expense ($000):** 64733 **Personnel:** 759

HARRISONVILLE—Cass County

CASS REGIONAL MEDICAL CENTER (261324), 2800 East Rock Haven Road, Zip 64701–4411; tel. 816/380–3474, **A**1 10 18 **F**3 11 12 15 17 18 28 29 30 31 32 34 35 40 43 44 45 46 48 50 54 56 57 59 64 65 66 70 74 75 77 78 79 81 82 84 85 86 87 92 97 98 103 110 111 114 115 119 127 129 130 131 132 133 135 146 147 149 **P**6
Primary Contact: John Christopher. Lang, Chief Executive Officer
CFO: Brent Probasco, Chief Financial Officer
CIO: Lester Vohs, Manager Information Systems
CHR: Carla Wallen, Manager Human Resources
CNO: Twila Buckner, R.N., Chief Nursing Officer
Web address: www.cassregional.org
Control: County, Government, nonfederal **Service:** General medical and surgical

Staffed Beds: 35 **Admissions:** 1148 **Census:** 15 **Outpatient Visits:** 116273 **Births:** 0 **Total Expense ($000):** 63651 **Payroll Expense ($000):** 24665 **Personnel:** 392

HAYTI—Pemiscot County

PEMISCOT MEMORIAL HEALTH SYSTEM (260070), 946 East Reed Street, Zip 63851–1245, Mailing Address: P.O. Box 489, Zip 63851–0489; tel. 573/359–1372, (Total facility includes 66 beds in nursing home–type unit) **A**10 **F**3 4 15 28 29 30 34 39 49 50 57 59 64 67 68 70 75 79 81 85 87 90 93 97 98 99 103 104 107 119 127 128 130 133 143 144 149 **P**6
Primary Contact: Jim Marshall, Chief Executive Officer and Administrator
CFO: Kerry L Noble, Chief Financial Officer
CHR: Jackie Powell, Director Human Resources
Web address: www.pemiscot.org/
Control: County, Government, nonfederal **Service:** General medical and surgical

Staffed Beds: 167 **Admissions:** 1288 **Census:** 69 **Outpatient Visits:** 25950 **Births:** 0 **Total Expense ($000):** 31882 **Payroll Expense ($000):** 14558 **Personnel:** 406

HERMANN—Gasconade County

HERMANN AREA DISTRICT HOSPITAL (261314), 509 West 18th Street, Zip 65041–1547, Mailing Address: P.O. Box 470, Zip 65041–0470; tel. 573/486–2191, **A**10 18 **F**3 11 12 15 18 28 29 34 35 40 41 44 45 53 56 57 59 62 64 67 69 71 75 77 78 81 85 86 87 89 90 93 96 97 104 107 110 111 114 119 127 128 129 130 133 143 146 **P**6
Primary Contact: Dan McKinney, Administrator
COO: Matt Siebert, Assistant Administrator Ancillary Services
CFO: Christine Lewis, Assistant Administrator, Finance
CMO: Michael Rothermich, M.D., Chief of Staff
CIO: Jeffrey Wehmeyer, Director Information Technology
CHR: Brandon Hughes, Director Human Resources
CNO: Sue Daller, R.N., Assistant Administrator Nursing
Web address: www.hadh.org
Control: Hospital district or authority, Government, nonfederal **Service:** General medical and surgical

Staffed Beds: 24 **Admissions:** 441 **Census:** 10 **Outpatient Visits:** 58359 **Births:** 0 **Total Expense ($000):** 18926 **Payroll Expense ($000):** 9694 **Personnel:** 187

HOUSTON—Texas County

TEXAS COUNTY MEMORIAL HOSPITAL (260024), 1333 South Sam Houston Boulevard, Zip 65483–2046; tel. 417/967–3311, **A**10 20 **F**3 28 29 34 40 45 57 59 62 63 64 70 76 81 85 86 89 93 97 107 110 111 115 119 127 129 130 133 143 148 149 **P**6
Primary Contact: Wesley E. Murray, Chief Executive Officer
CFO: Linda Pamperien, Chief Financial Officer
CMO: Charles Mueller, M.D., Chief of Staff
CHR: Anita Kuhn, Controller
Web address: www.tcmh.org
Control: County, Government, nonfederal **Service:** General medical and surgical

Staffed Beds: 47 **Admissions:** 1451 **Census:** 14 **Outpatient Visits:** 104254 **Births:** 209 **Total Expense ($000):** 31763 **Payroll Expense ($000):** 15495 **Personnel:** 324

INDEPENDENCE—Jackson County

CENTERPOINT MEDICAL CENTER (260095), 19600 East 39th Street, Zip 64057–2301; tel. 816/698–7000, **A**1 2 10 **F**3 8 12 13 15 18 20 22 24 26 28 29 30 31 34 35 38 40 43 46 47 48 49 50 52 54 55 56 57 59 60 64 68 70 72 74 75 76 77 78 79 80 81 82 85 86 87 92 93 107 108 110 111 114 115 117 118 119 120 121 123 126 129 130 131 132 144 145 146 147 148 149 154 **S** HCA Healthcare, Nashville, TN
Primary Contact: Bret Kolman, CPA, FACHE, Chief Executive Officer
COO: Phil Buttell, Chief Operating Officer
CFO: James H Brown, Chief Financial Officer
CMO: Christopher Sullivan, M.D., Chief Medical Officer
CIO: Carl Sifers, Director Information Technology and System Services
CHR: Kyla Stoltz, Vice President Human Resources
CNO: Lynn Barrett, Chief Nursing Officer
Web address: www.centerpointmedical.com
Control: Corporation, Investor–owned (for–profit) **Service:** General medical and surgical

Staffed Beds: 221 **Admissions:** 14773 **Census:** 167 **Outpatient Visits:** 161568 **Births:** 1542 **Total Expense ($000):** 249812 **Payroll Expense ($000):** 77740 **Personnel:** 964

JEFFERSON CITY—Cole County

CAPITAL REGION MEDICAL CENTER (260047), 1125 Madison Street, Zip 65101–5200, Mailing Address: P.O. Box 1128, Zip 65102–1128; tel. 573/632–5000, **A**1 3 5 10 12 13 **F**3 5 11 15 17 18 20 22 24 26 28 29 30 31 34 35 36 38 40 45 46 47 48 51 53 57 59 60 61 62 64 65 66 68 70 73 75 76 77 78 79 80 81 82 85 87 89 90 92 93 97 100 103 107 108 110 111 114 115 116 118 119 120 121 123 126 129 130 131 132 135 144 146 147 148 149 150 154 **P**2 6 **S** University of Missouri Health Care, Columbia, MO
Primary Contact: Gaspare Calvaruso, President
COO: Janet Weckenborg, Vice President Operations
CFO: Tom Luebbering, Vice President Finance
CMO: Mitchell Godbee, Chief of Staff
CIO: Jason Cecil, Vice President, Information
CHR: Sarah Morrow, Vice President Human Resources
Web address: www.crmc.org
Control: Other not–for–profit (including NFP Corporation) **Service:** General medical and surgical

Staffed Beds: 114 **Admissions:** 5142 **Census:** 52 **Outpatient Visits:** 454958 **Births:** 639 **Total Expense ($000):** 185668 **Payroll Expense ($000):** 80654 **Personnel:** 1284

SSM HEALTH ST. MARY'S HOSPITAL – JEFFERSON CITY (260011), 2505 Mission Drive, Zip 65109; tel. 573/681–3000, **A**1 10 19 **F**3 5 11 13 15 17 18 20 22 24 28 29 30 31 34 40 45 46 47 48 49 50 51 53 54 57 59 60 62 64 68 70 73 74 75 76 77 78 79 81 82 85 86 87 89 93 96 98 100 101 102 104 107 108 110 111 115 118 119 120 121 122 123 127 129 130 131 132 135 144 146 147 148 149 150 153 154 **P**6 **S** SSM Health, Saint Louis, MO
Primary Contact: Philip P. Gustafson, Interim President
CFO: James Stratton, Vice President Finance
CMO: Stephen Stewart, M.D., Vice President Medical Affairs
CHR: Susan Mankoski, Vice President Human Resources
CNO: Alice M Chatley, R.N., MSN, Vice President Acute Care Services
Web address: www.lethealingbegin.com
Control: Church operated, Nongovernment, not–for–profit **Service:** General medical and surgical

Staffed Beds: 95 **Admissions:** 6750 **Census:** 70 **Outpatient Visits:** 225309 **Births:** 837 **Total Expense ($000):** 162453 **Payroll Expense ($000):** 50947 **Personnel:** 860

MO

JOPLIN—Newton County

FREEMAN HEALTH SYSTEM (260137), 1102 West 32nd Street, Zip 64804–3503; tel. 417/347–1111, (Includes FREEMAN HOSPITAL EAST, 932 East 34th Street, Joplin, MO, Zip 64804–3999, Mailing Address: 1102 West 32nd Street, Zip 64804–3999, tel. 417/347–1111; Paula F Baker, President and Chief Executive Officer) **A**10 11 13 **F**3 8 11 12 13 15 17 18 20 22 24 26 28 30 31 34 35 40 43 44 46 47 48 49 50 54 56 57 59 60 61 62 64 65 68 70 72 73 74 75 76 77 78 79 81 82 83 84 85 86 87 89 90 93 96 97 98 100 102 103 107 108 110 111 115 117 119 120 121 124 129 130 131 132 144 145 146 147 148 **P**1 6 **S** Freeman Health System, Joplin, MO
Primary Contact: Paula F. Baker, President and Chief Executive Officer
CFO: Steve W Graddy, Chief Financial Officer
CMO: Saba Habis, M.D., Chief Medical Officer
CIO: Skip Rollins, Chief Information Officer
CHR: Mary Frerer, Chief Human Resources Officer
CNO: Jeffrey Carrier, R.N., Chief Clinical Officer
Web address: www.freemanhealth.com
Control: Other not–for–profit (including NFP Corporation) **Service:** General medical and surgical

Staffed Beds: 381 Admissions: 17395 Census: 242 Outpatient Visits: 743915 Births: 1967 Total Expense ($000): 477578 Payroll Expense ($000): 225006 Personnel: 3205

LANDMARK HOSPITAL OF JOPLIN (262016), 2040 West 32nd Street, Zip 64804–3512; tel. 417/627–1300, **A**10 22 **F**1 3 29 60 75 77 83 90 119 130 148 **S** Landmark Hospitals, Cape Girardeau, MO
Primary Contact: Kevin J. Clement, Chief Executive Officer
CMO: Jack Rhoads, M.D., Medical Director
CHR: Janice Nordstrom, Director Human Resources
CNO: Stephanie Slater–Nesuold, Director of Nursing
Web address: www.landmarkhospitals.com
Control: Corporation, Investor–owned (for–profit) **Service:** Acute long–term care hospital

Staffed Beds: 30 Admissions: 278 Census: 20 Outpatient Visits: 0 Births: 0 Total Expense ($000): 11806 Payroll Expense ($000): 4812

MERCY HOSPITAL JOPLIN (260001), 100 Mercy Way, Zip 64804–1626; tel. 417/781–2727, (Includes ST. JOHN'S REHABILITATION CENTER, 2727 McClelland Boulevard, Joplin, MO, Zip 64804; tel. 417/659–6716) **A**1 2 10 13 **F**3 5 7 11 12 13 15 17 18 19 20 22 24 26 28 29 30 31 34 35 38 39 40 43 44 45 46 47 48 49 50 51 54 57 58 59 60 61 62 63 64 65 66 68 70 72 73 74 75 76 77 78 79 81 82 84 85 86 87 89 93 94 97 98 100 101 102 104 107 108 110 111 114 115 117 118 119 120 121 123 124 126 127 129 130 131 132 135 144 146 147 148 154 **P**6 **S** Mercy, Chesterfield, MO
Primary Contact: Gary W. Pulsipher, President and Chief Executive Officer
COO: Michele Stewart, R.N., Chief Operating Officer
CFO: Shelly Hunter, Chief Financial Officer
CHR: Timothy Murphy, Vice President Human Resources
CNO: Dennis Manley, R.N., Chief Nursing Officer
Web address: www.mercy.net/joplinmo
Control: Church operated, Nongovernment, not–for–profit **Service:** General medical and surgical

Staffed Beds: 229 Admissions: 9749 Census: 146 Outpatient Visits: 252882 Births: 1092 Total Expense ($000): 231314 Payroll Expense ($000): 84719 Personnel: 1192

KANSAS CITY—Jackson County

CENTER FOR BEHAVIORAL MEDICINE (264008), 1000 East 24th Street, Zip 64108–2776; tel. 816/512–7000, (Total facility includes 68 beds in nursing home–type unit) **A**1 3 5 10 **F**4 35 50 53 86 87 98 106 128
Primary Contact: Denise Norbury, Regional Chief Executive Officer
COO: Jeanette Simmons, Chief Operating Officer
CFO: Randy Riley, Chief Financial Officer
CMO: Nashaat Boutros, M.D., Clinical Director
CIO: Robert Curren, Director Information Technology
CHR: Silva Ward, Director Human Resources
CNO: John Tucker, Chief Nursing Executive
Web address: www.dmhonline.dmh.state.mo.us
Control: State, Government, nonfederal **Service:** Psychiatric

Staffed Beds: 133 Admissions: 44 Census: 108 Outpatient Visits: 0 Births: 0 Total Expense ($000): 25121 Payroll Expense ($000): 14131 Personnel: 385

CHILDREN'S MERCY HOSPITAL KANSAS CITY (263302), 2401 Gillham Road, Zip 64108–4619; tel. 816/234–3000, **A**1 2 3 5 8 10 **F**3 7 8 9 11 12 16 19 20 21 22 23 24 25 26 27 29 30 31 32 34 35 36 38 39 40 41 43 44 48 50 54 55 57 58 59 60 61 62 64 65 68 72 73 74 75 77 78 79 81 82 84 85 86 87 88 89 90 91 92 93 94 96 97 100 101 104 107 108 111 115 117 118 119 130 131 132 134 136 137 138 139 141 142 144 146 148 149 150 154 **P**6
Primary Contact: Jo W. Stueve, Interim Chief Executive Officer
COO: Jo W. Stueve, Executive Vice President and Co–Chief Operating Officer
CFO: David Cauble, Executive Vice President and Chief Financial Officer
CMO: Charles Roberts, M.D., Executive Vice President and Executive Medical Director
CIO: David Chou, Vice President, Chief Information and Digital Officer
CNO: Cheri Hunt, R.N., Vice President Patient Care Services and Chief Nursing Officer
Web address: www.childrensmercy.org
Control: Other not–for–profit (including NFP Corporation) **Service:** Children's general medical and surgical

Staffed Beds: 314 Admissions: 12222 Census: 230 Outpatient Visits: 450357 Births: 146 Total Expense ($000): 1149985 Payroll Expense ($000): 556079 Personnel: 6231

KANSAS CITY VETERANS AFFAIRS MEDICAL CENTER, 4801 East Linwood Boulevard, Zip 64128–2226; tel. 816/861–4700, (Nonreporting) **A**1 2 3 5 **S** Department of Veterans Affairs, Perry Point, MD
Primary Contact: Kathleen R. Fogarty, MS, Director
CFO: Bryan Bieri, Manager Finance
CMO: Ahmad Batrash, Chief of Staff
CIO: Eddie Johnson, Chief Information Technology Officer
CHR: Kathi Nippert, Acting Chief Human Resources Officer
Web address: www.kansascity.va.gov/
Control: Veterans Affairs, Government, federal **Service:** General medical and surgical

Staffed Beds: 157

KINDRED HOSPITAL NORTHLAND (262018), 500 Northwest 68th Street, Zip 64118–2455; tel. 816/420–6300, **A**1 10 **F**1 3 29 80 85 130 148 149 **S** Kindred Healthcare, Louisville, KY
Primary Contact: Laura Inge, Chief Executive Officer
CFO: Brett Stevenson, Controller
CMO: Sean R Muldoon, M.D., Senior Vice President and Chief Medical Officer–Kindred Healthcare, Hospital Division
Web address: www.khnorthland.com
Control: Corporation, Investor–owned (for–profit) **Service:** Acute long–term care hospital

Staffed Beds: 35 Admissions: 359 Census: 26 Outpatient Visits: 0 Births: 0 Total Expense ($000): 16397 Payroll Expense ($000): 6523 Personnel: 95

NORTHLAND LTAC HOSPITAL See Kindred Hospital Northland

RESEARCH MEDICAL CENTER (260027), 2316 East Meyer Boulevard, Zip 64132–1136; tel. 816/276–4000, (Includes RESEARCH PSYCHIATRIC CENTER, 2323 East 63rd Street, Kansas City, MO, Zip 64130–3462; tel. 816/444–8161; Shannon Griggs, Interim Chief Executive Officer) **A**1 2 3 5 10 **F**3 4 8 11 13 15 16 17 18 20 22 24 26 28 29 30 31 34 35 38 39 40 43 44 45 46 47 49 50 52 53 54 55 57 58 59 60 61 64 68 70 72 73 74 75 76 77 78 79 81 82 84 85 86 87 90 91 93 94 96 97 98 99 100 101 102 103 104 105 107 108 110 111 112 114 115 116 117 118 119 120 121 122 124 126 129 130 131 132 134 135 138 142 143 146 147 148 149 153 154 **S** HCA Healthcare, Nashville, TN
Primary Contact: Jacqueline DeSouza, Chief Executive Officer
COO: Eric Becker, Chief Operating Officer
CFO: Susan Shreeve, Chief Financial Officer
CMO: James Bower, M.D., Chief Medical Officer
CIO: Shawn Kegley, Director Information Services
CHR: Charlotte O'Neal, Vice President Human Resources
Web address: www.researchmedicalcenter.com
Control: Corporation, Investor–owned (for–profit) **Service:** General medical and surgical

Staffed Beds: 463 Admissions: 19374 Census: 313 Outpatient Visits: 171068 Births: 1112 Total Expense ($000): 474568 Payroll Expense ($000): 134052 Personnel: 2013

MO

Hospital, Medicare Provider Number, Address, Telephone, Approval, Facility, and Physician Codes, Health Care System

★ American Hospital Association (AHA) membership
□ The Joint Commission accreditation
○ Healthcare Facilities Accreditation Program
◇ DNV Healthcare Inc. accreditation
⇑ Center for Improvement in Healthcare Quality Accreditation
△ Commission on Accreditation of Rehabilitation Facilities (CARF) accreditation

SAINT LUKE'S HOSPITAL OF KANSAS CITY (260138), 4401 Wornall Road, Zip 64111–3220; tel. 816/932–3800, (Includes CRITTENTON CHILDREN'S CENTER, 10918 Elm Avenue, Kansas City, MO, Zip 64134–4108; tel. 816/765–6600; Margaret Donnelly, Interim President) **A**1 2 3 5 8 10 **F**3 6 8 9 11 12 13 15 17 18 20 22 24 25 26 28 29 30 31 32 34 35 36 37 38 39 40 43 44 45 46 47 48 49 50 55 56 57 58 59 60 61 64 65 66 68 70 72 73 74 75 76 77 78 79 80 81 82 84 85 86 87 89 90 91 92 93 94 95 96 97 98 99 100 101 102 103 104 106 107 108 110 111 114 115 116 117 118 119 120 121 123 124 126 129 130 131 132 134 135 137 138 139 141 145 146 147 148 149 151 152 153 **P**6 **S** Saint Luke's Health System, Kansas City, MO
Primary Contact: Jani L. Johnson, R.N., MSN, Chief Executive Officer
COO: Brad Simmons, Chief Operating Officer
CFO: Amy Nachtigal, Chief Financial Officer
CMO: Peter Holt, M.D., Director Medical Affairs
CIO: Deborah Gash, Chief Information Officer
CHR: Doris Rogers, Vice President Human Resources
CNO: Debra Wilson, Vice President and Chief Nursing Officer
Web address: www.saint–lukes.org
Control: Church operated, Nongovernment, not–for–profit **Service**: General medical and surgical

Staffed Beds: 478 **Admissions**: 22633 **Census**: 357 **Outpatient Visits**: 296169 **Births**: 2531 **Total Expense ($000)**: 743275 **Payroll Expense ($000)**: 194954 **Personnel**: 3318

KANSAS CITY—Platte County

SAINT LUKE'S NORTH HOSPITAL – BARRY ROAD (260062), 5830 NW Barry Road, Zip 64154–2778; tel. 816/891–6000, (Includes SAINT LUKE'S NORTH HOSPITAL–SMITHVILLE CAMPUS, 601 South 169 Highway, Smithville, MO, Zip 64089–9317; tel. 816/532–3700; Adele Ducharme, MSN, R.N., Chief Executive Officer) **A**1 2 10 **F**3 11 12 13 15 18 20 22 26 28 29 30 31 34 35 38 40 44 45 46 49 50 53 56 57 58 59 60 64 68 69 70 73 74 75 76 77 78 79 80 81 82 84 85 86 87 89 90 91 92 93 96 98 100 101 102 107 108 110 111 114 115 116 117 118 119 129 130 131 132 135 141 143 146 147 148 149 154 **S** Saint Luke's Health System, Kansas City, MO
Primary Contact: Adele Ducharme, MSN, R.N., Chief Executive Officer
CFO: Julie Murphy, Chief Financial Officer
CMO: Leonardo J Lozada, M.D., Chief Physician Executive
CIO: LaDonna Seger, Director Information Services
CHR: Donna Kunz, System Director Human Resources
CNO: Amy Brummer, R.N., MSN, Chief Nursing Officer
Web address: www.saint–lukes.org
Control: Church operated, Nongovernment, not–for–profit **Service**: General medical and surgical

Staffed Beds: 137 **Admissions**: 7752 **Census**: 85 **Outpatient Visits**: 91405 **Births**: 740 **Total Expense ($000)**: 129491 **Payroll Expense ($000)**: 43043 **Personnel**: 652

KANSAS CITY—Clay County

SIGNATURE PSYCHIATRIC HOSPITAL (264030), 2900 Clay Edwards Drive, Zip 64116–3235; tel. 816/691–5101, **F**2 34 59 98 101 102 103 104 105 130 132 153
Primary Contact: Lisa St. Aubyn, Chief Executive Officer
CFO: Robert Jackson, Chief Financial Officer
CMO: Azfar Malik, M.D., Chief Medical Officer
CIO: Tariq Nazir, Interim Director Information Technology
CHR: Maria Griffith, Director Human Resources
Web address: www.sphkc.net
Control: Corporation, Investor–owned (for–profit) **Service**: Psychiatric

Staffed Beds: 24 **Admissions**: 1138 **Census**: 23 **Outpatient Visits**: 0 **Births**: 0 **Total Expense ($000)**: 7877 **Payroll Expense ($000)**: 3892 **Personnel**: 71

KANSAS CITY—Jackson County

ST. JOSEPH MEDICAL CENTER (260085), 1000 Carondelet Drive, Zip 64114–4673; tel. 816/942–4400, **A**1 2 10 **F**3 11 12 15 17 18 20 22 24 26 28 29 30 31 34 35 40 45 48 49 50 51 57 58 60 62 64 68 70 74 75 77 78 79 80 81 82 84 85 87 90 93 107 108 110 111 114 115 119 126 129 130 132 146 148 154 **P**6 **S** Prime Healthcare, Ontario, CA
Primary Contact: Jodi Fincher, Administrator
CFO: Debra Cartwright, Chief Financial Officer
CMO: Tommy Ko, M.D., Chief Medical Officer
CIO: Cheryl Johnson, Regional Chief Information Officer
CHR: Donna Sumner, Director, Human Resources and Organizational Development
CNO: Greg Simpson, Chief Nursing Officer
Web address: www.stjosephkc.com/
Control: Individual, Investor–owned (for–profit) **Service**: General medical and surgical

Staffed Beds: 116 **Admissions**: 7212 **Census**: 85 **Outpatient Visits**: 90713 **Births**: 0 **Total Expense ($000)**: 151857 **Payroll Expense ($000)**: 47326 **Personnel**: 1122

TRUMAN MEDICAL CENTER–HOSPITAL HILL (260048), 2301 Holmes Street, Zip 64108–2640; tel. 816/404–1000, **A**1 2 3 5 8 10 13 **F**3 4 5 8 11 12 13 14 15 17 20 22 26 28 29 30 31 34 35 36 37 38 39 40 41 43 44 45 46 48 49 50 52 53 55 57 58 59 61 64 65 66 68 70 71 72 73 74 75 76 77 78 79 81 82 84 85 86 87 90 93 94 97 98 99 100 101 102 103 104 107 108 110 111 114 115 119 129 130 131 132 134 135 142 143 146 147 148 **P**5 6 **S** Truman Medical Centers, Kansas City, MO
Primary Contact: Charlie Shields, President and Chief Executive Officer
CFO: Allen Johnson, Chief Financial Officer
CMO: Mark Steele, M.D., Chief Medical Officer
CIO: Mitzi Cardenas, Chief Information Officer
CHR: Marcos DeLeon, Vice President Community Engagement
Web address: www.trumed.org
Control: Other not–for–profit (including NFP Corporation) **Service**: General medical and surgical

Staffed Beds: 249 **Admissions**: 14261 **Census**: 199 **Outpatient Visits**: 552646 **Births**: 1696 **Total Expense ($000)**: 377634 **Payroll Expense ($000)**: 162263 **Personnel**: 2577

TRUMAN MEDICAL CENTER–LAKEWOOD (260102), 7900 Lee's Summit Road, Zip 64139–1236; tel. 816/404–7000, (Total facility includes 188 beds in nursing home–type unit) **A**1 3 5 10 **F**3 4 6 11 13 15 18 29 30 32 33 34 35 36 38 39 40 44 45 50 53 56 57 58 59 64 65 66 67 68 70 71 72 74 75 76 77 78 79 81 85 86 87 89 90 92 93 94 97 98 100 101 102 103 104 107 112 115 119 126 128 129 130 131 132 134 135 143 146 147 **P**5 6 **S** Truman Medical Centers, Kansas City, MO
Primary Contact: Lynette Wheeler, MSN, Chief Operating Officer
CFO: Allen Johnson, Chief Financial Officer
CMO: Mark Steele, M.D., Chief Medical Officer
CIO: Mitzi Cardenas, Chief Information Officer
CHR: Marcos DeLeon, Vice President Community Engagement
CNO: Amy Peters, R.N., Chief Nursing Officer
Web address: www.trumed.org
Control: Other not–for–profit (including NFP Corporation) **Service**: General medical and surgical

Staffed Beds: 298 **Admissions**: 5051 **Census**: 220 **Outpatient Visits**: 426215 **Births**: 1560 **Total Expense ($000)**: 141725 **Payroll Expense ($000)**: 63237 **Personnel**: 1041

TWO RIVERS BEHAVIORAL HEALTH SYSTEM (264017), 5121 Raytown Road, Zip 64133–2141; tel. 816/382–6300, **A**1 10 **F**4 5 34 38 98 99 101 102 105 130 132 143 152 153 154 **P**6 **S** Universal Health Services, Inc., King of Prussia, PA
Primary Contact: Greg Shannon, Chief Executive Officer
CMO: Shahbaz Khan, M.D., Medical Director
CNO: Cindy Bearden, Chief Nursing Officer
Web address: www.tworivershospital.com
Control: Corporation, Investor–owned (for–profit) **Service**: Psychiatric

Staffed Beds: 105 **Admissions**: 2126 **Census**: 32 **Outpatient Visits**: 0 **Births**: 0 **Total Expense ($000)**: 13204 **Payroll Expense ($000)**: 5779 **Personnel**: 112

VETERANS AFFAIRS MEDICAL CENTER See Kansas City Veterans Affairs Medical Center

KIRKSVILLE—Adair County

NORTHEAST REGIONAL MEDICAL CENTER (260022), 315 South Osteopathy, Zip 63501–6401, Mailing Address: P.O. Box C8502, Zip 63501–8599; tel. 660/785–1000, **A**3 10 11 12 13 **F**3 13 15 17 18 20 22 24 28 29 34 35 39 40 43 45 46 48 49 50 53 57 59 60 62 64 68 70 73 74 75 76 77 79 81 82 85 86 87 89 90 93 107 108 110 111 115 119 127 129 130 131 132 133 135 146 147 148 154 **P**5 **S** Community Health Systems, Inc., Franklin, TN
Primary Contact: Ranee C. Brayton, FACHE, MSN, R.N., Chief Executive Officer
CFO: Carol Cross, CPA, Chief Financial Officer
CMO: Benjamin Schrant, M.D., Chief of Staff
CIO: Chad Tatro, Supervisor Information Systems
CHR: Jim Bergman, Director Human Resources
CNO: Peggy Parks, R.N., Chief Nursing Officer
Web address: www.nermc.com
Control: Corporation, Investor–owned (for–profit) **Service**: General medical and surgical

Staffed Beds: 76 **Admissions**: 2451 **Census**: 27 **Outpatient Visits**: 65774 **Births**: 524 **Total Expense ($000)**: 48715 **Payroll Expense ($000)**: 18112 **Personnel**: 429

Many Facility Codes have changed. Please refer to the AHA Guide Code Chart.

LAKE SAINT LOUIS—St. Charles County

SSM HEALTH ST. JOSEPH HOSPITAL – LAKE SAINT LOUIS (260200), 100 Medical Plaza, Zip 63367–1366; tel. 636/625–5200, **A**1 2 10 **F**3 11 13 15 17 18 20 22 28 29 30 31 34 35 36 38 40 41 43 44 46 49 50 51 53 54 55 56 57 59 60 61 64 68 70 73 74 75 76 78 79 81 82 84 85 86 87 89 102 107 108 110 111 115 117 119 129 130 132 135 145 146 147 148 149 **P**6 8 **S** SSM Health, Saint Louis, MO
Primary Contact: Lisle Wescott, President
COO: Lee Bernstein, Regional Executive Vice President of Hospital and Chief Operating Officer
CFO: Hal Holder, Regional Chief Financial Officer
CMO: Michael Handler, M.D., Vice President Medical Affairs and Chief Medical Officer
CIO: Sharon Gardner, Manager Information Systems
CHR: Renee Roach, System Vice President
CNO: Janet K. Pestle, R.N., MSN, Vice President Nursing and Chief Nursing Officer
Web address: www.ssmstjoseph.com
Control: Church operated, Nongovernment, not–for–profit **Service**: General medical and surgical

Staffed Beds: 215 **Admissions**: 9685 **Census**: 104 **Outpatient Visits**: 179678 **Births**: 898 **Total Expense ($000)**: 166641 **Payroll Expense ($000)**: 60831 **Personnel**: 856

LAMAR—Barton County

COX BARTON COUNTY MEMORIAL HOSPITAL (261325), 29 NW First Lane, Zip 64759–8105; tel. 417/681–5100, **A**10 18 **F**3 11 15 18 28 30 34 35 36 40 44 45 50 57 59 64 65 68 74 75 77 79 81 84 85 86 87 89 90 92 93 97 107 108 110 111 114 119 127 128 129 130 132 133 135 146 148 149 **S** CoxHealth, Springfield, MO
Primary Contact: Wendy Duvall, Chief Executive Officer
CIO: Brad Butler, Network Administrator
CNO: Marlys Buckner, Chief Nursing Officer
Web address: www.bcmh.net
Control: County, Government, nonfederal **Service**: General medical and surgical

Staffed Beds: 25 **Admissions**: 693 **Census**: 8 **Outpatient Visits**: 41434 **Births**: 0 **Total Expense ($000)**: 18368 **Payroll Expense ($000)**: 7887 **Personnel**: 147

LEBANON—Laclede County

MERCY HOSPITAL LEBANON (260059), 100 Hospital Drive, Zip 65536–9210; tel. 417/533–6100, **A**1 10 20 **F**3 11 13 15 28 29 30 31 35 36 40 45 47 50 51 57 59 64 65 68 70 71 74 75 76 77 78 79 81 82 83 85 86 87 89 90 93 94 102 107 108 110 111 114 119 129 130 131 132 135 146 147 148 149 **S** Mercy, Chesterfield, MO
Primary Contact: Scott W. Childers, Administrator
CFO: Douglas M Hoban, Vice President and Chief Financial Officer
CNO: Judy O'Connor–Snyder, Chief Nursing Officer
Web address: www.mercy.net/practice/mercy–hospital–lebanon
Control: Church operated, Nongovernment, not–for–profit **Service**: General medical and surgical

Staffed Beds: 58 **Admissions**: 2332 **Census**: 19 **Outpatient Visits**: 135826 **Births**: 329 **Total Expense ($000)**: 69901 **Payroll Expense ($000)**: 28162 **Personnel**: 420

LEE'S SUMMIT—Jackson County

LEE'S SUMMIT MEDICAL CENTER (260190), 2100 SE Blue Parkway, Zip 64063–1007; tel. 816/282–5000, **A**1 3 10 **F**12 15 18 20 22 28 29 30 31 34 40 49 57 59 60 64 65 68 70 74 77 78 79 81 82 84 87 93 107 108 109 110 111 115 119 126 129 130 131 145 146 148 149 154 **S** HCA Healthcare, Nashville, TN
Primary Contact: Patrick Kueny, Interim Chief Executive Officer
COO: Patrick Kueny, Chief Operating Officer
CFO: John Heurtin, Chief Financial Officer
CIO: Andrew Beechy, Manager Information Technology Systems
CHR: Linda Duncan, Director Human Resources
CNO: Paige Baker, MSN, R.N., Chief Nursing Officer
Web address: www.leessummitmedicalcenter.com
Control: Corporation, Investor–owned (for–profit) **Service**: General medical and surgical

Staffed Beds: 64 **Admissions**: 3944 **Census**: 38 **Outpatient Visits**: 107763 **Births**: 0 **Total Expense ($000)**: 78147 **Payroll Expense ($000)**: 26141 **Personnel**: 340

SAINT LUKE'S EAST HOSPITAL (260216), 100 NE Saint Luke's Boulevard, Zip 64086–6000; tel. 816/347–5000, **A**1 10 **F**3 12 13 15 18 20 22 26 28 29 30 31 34 35 38 40 44 45 46 49 50 56 57 58 59 60 64 65 70 71 72 73 74 75 76 77 78 79 80 81 82 84 85 86 87 89 90 91 92 93 94 96 100 102 107 108 110 111 114 115 117 118 119 120 121 123 126 129 130 131 132 135 141 145 146 147 148 149 154 **S** Saint Luke's Health System, Kansas City, MO
Primary Contact: Ron Baker, FACHE, Chief Executive Officer
CFO: Joseph P Stasi, Chief Financial Officer
CHR: John Clabaugh, Director Human Resources
CNO: Gloria Solis, R.N., MSN, Chief Nursing Officer
Web address: www.saintlukeskc.org
Control: Church operated, Nongovernment, not–for–profit **Service**: General medical and surgical

Staffed Beds: 203 **Admissions**: 13466 **Census**: 138 **Outpatient Visits**: 150910 **Births**: 1679 **Total Expense ($000)**: 228053 **Payroll Expense ($000)**: 65239 **Personnel**: 1041

LEXINGTON—Lafayette County

LAFAYETTE REGIONAL HEALTH CENTER (261320), 1500 State Street, Zip 64067–1107; tel. 660/259–2203, **A**1 10 18 **F**11 15 29 31 40 64 68 70 75 78 79 81 85 93 107 110 111 114 116 119 127 130 133 147 149 **P**6 **S** HCA Healthcare, Nashville, TN
Primary Contact: Darrel Box, Chief Executive Officer
COO: Daniel Astleford, Vice President Operations
CFO: Teri James, Chief Financial Officer
CIO: Keith Richcreek, Manager Technical Services
CHR: Stephen Davidson, Director Human Resources
CNO: Kim Leakey, R.N., Chief Nursing Officer
Web address: www.lafayetteregionalhealthcenter.com
Control: Corporation, Investor–owned (for–profit) **Service**: General medical and surgical

Staffed Beds: 25 **Admissions**: 847 **Census**: 8 **Outpatient Visits**: 65757 **Births**: 0 **Total Expense ($000)**: 27882 **Payroll Expense ($000)**: 9101 **Personnel**: 188

LIBERTY—Clay County

LIBERTY HOSPITAL (260177), 2525 Glenn Hendren Dive, Zip 64068–9600, Mailing Address: P.O. Box 1002, Zip 64069–1002; tel. 816/781–7200, **A**1 2 10 **F**3 8 9 11 13 15 17 18 20 22 24 28 29 30 31 34 35 37 40 43 44 45 46 47 49 51 53 54 59 61 62 63 64 65 68 69 70 73 74 75 76 77 78 79 80 81 82 83 84 85 86 87 89 90 92 93 96 97 107 108 110 111 114 115 117 118 119 126 129 130 131 135 144 146 147 148 154
Primary Contact: David Feess, President and Chief Executive Officer
CFO: Dan Williams, Vice President Finance and Support
CMO: Robert Haas, M.D., Chief Medical Officer
CIO: Paul Klehn, Chief Information Technology Officer
CHR: Nancy E Cattell, Vice President Human Resources
CNO: Shirley Heintz, R.N., MS, Vice President Patient Care
Web address: www.Libertyhospital.org
Control: Hospital district or authority, Government, nonfederal **Service**: General medical and surgical

Staffed Beds: 212 **Admissions**: 7898 **Census**: 85 **Outpatient Visits**: 299355 **Births**: 1090 **Total Expense ($000)**: 202708 **Payroll Expense ($000)**: 94601 **Personnel**: 1391

LOUISIANA—Pike County

PIKE COUNTY MEMORIAL HOSPITAL (261333), 2305 Georgia Street, Zip 63353–2559; tel. 573/754–5531, **A**1 10 18 **F**3 7 11 15 18 28 29 30 34 35 40 45 50 53 54 56 57 59 64 65 68 74 75 77 79 81 85 86 87 89 90 93 97 100 107 110 114 127 130 131 132 133 147 148 149
Primary Contact: Tylie Mills, Chief Executive Officer
CFO: Ann Tran, Chief Financial Officer
CIO: Jeremy Gruen, Director Information Systems
CHR: Connie Bair, Human Resources Assistant
CNO: Judith Prater, Director of Nursing
Web address: www.pcmh–mo.org
Control: County, Government, nonfederal **Service**: General medical and surgical

Staffed Beds: 25 **Admissions**: 384 **Census**: 5 **Outpatient Visits**: 43102 **Births**: 0 **Total Expense ($000)**: 16925 **Payroll Expense ($000)**: 8098 **Personnel**: 182

MO

Hospital, Medicare Provider Number, Address, Telephone, Approval, Facility, and Physician Codes, Health Care System

★ American Hospital Association (AHA) membership
☐ The Joint Commission accreditation
◯ Healthcare Facilities Accreditation Program
◇ DNV Healthcare Inc. accreditation
⇑ Center for Improvement in Healthcare Quality Accreditation
△ Commission on Accreditation of Rehabilitation Facilities (CARF) accreditation

MACON—Macon County

SAMARITAN HOSPITAL (261313), 1205 North Missouri Street,
Zip 63552–2095; tel. 660/385–8700, **A**10 18 **F**3 7 8 11 34 35 40 45 46 53 56
57 59 63 64 65 68 74 75 77 79 81 82 84 85 86 87 89 90 93 94 107 111 115
119 127 128 129 130 133 146 148 **P**5
Primary Contact: Bernard A. Orman Jr, FACHE, Chief Executive Officer
CFO: Susan Spencer, Chief Financial Officer
CHR: Suzanne Britt, Director Human Resources
Web address: www.samaritanhospital.net
Control: County, Government, nonfederal **Service**: General medical and surgical

Staffed Beds: 25 **Admissions:** 727 **Census:** 12 **Outpatient Visits:** 60367
Births: 0 **Total Expense ($000):** 25592 **Payroll Expense ($000):** 9168
Personnel: 190

MARSHALL—Saline County

FITZGIBBON HOSPITAL (260142), 2305 South 65 Highway, Zip 65340–0250,
Mailing Address: P.O. Box 250, Zip 65340–0250; tel. 660/886–7431, **A**5 10 20
F3 11 13 15 30 31 33 34 35 40 45 56 57 59 62 63 64 65 68 70 74 75 76 77
78 79 81 85 87 89 90 93 98 99 103 104 107 108 110 111 115 118 119 120
121 127 128 129 130 131 132 133 146 147 148
Primary Contact: Darin L. Haug, D.O., President and Chief Executive Officer
COO: Angela P. Littrell, CPA, Chief Financial Officer and Chief Operating Officer
CFO: Angela P. Littrell, CPA, Chief Financial Officer and Chief Operating Officer
CMO: Darin L. Haug, D.O., President & Chief Executive Officer
CIO: Tom Jones, Chief Information Officer
CHR: Jessica Henderson, Manager Human Resources
CNO: Angela Igo, MSN, R.N., Chief Nursing Officer
Web address: www.fitzgibbon.org
Control: Other not–for–profit (including NFP Corporation) **Service**: General
medical and surgical

Staffed Beds: 52 **Admissions:** 1950 **Census:** 17 **Outpatient Visits:** 112121
Births: 207 **Total Expense ($000):** 51223 **Payroll Expense ($000):** 23792
Personnel: 465

MARYLAND HEIGHTS—St. Louis County

RANKEN JORDAN PEDIATRIC BRIDGE HOSPITAL (263303), 11365 Dorsett
Road, Zip 63043–3411; tel. 314/872–6400, **A**3 10 **F**1 3 12 29 30 32 34 35 44
50 68 80 86 87 89 90 91 92 93 94 96 99 130 132 146 148 149 **P**6
Primary Contact: Brett Moorehouse, FACHE, Interim Chief Executive Officer and
Chief Operating Officer
COO: Brett Moorehouse, FACHE, Vice President and Chief Operating Officer
CFO: Kenneth Marx, Chief Financial Officer
CMO: Nicholas Holekamp, M.D., Chief Medical Officer
CHR: Erin Bachelier, Human Resource Administrator
Web address: www.rankenjordan.org
Control: Other not–for–profit (including NFP Corporation) **Service**: Children's
rehabilitation

Staffed Beds: 34 **Admissions:** 232 **Census:** 29 **Outpatient Visits:** 6350
Births: 0 **Total Expense ($000):** 30003 **Payroll Expense ($000):** 15733
Personnel: 254

MARYVILLE—Nodaway County

SSM HEALTH ST. FRANCIS HOSPITAL – MARYVILLE (260050), 2016 South
Main Street, Zip 64468–2655; tel. 660/562–2600, **A**1 10 20 **F**3 11 13 15 18 28
29 30 31 34 35 38 40 45 57 59 64 65 68 70 75 76 77 78 79 81 82 84 85 86
89 90 93 96 97 98 102 103 104 107 110 111 115 116 117 118 119 127 128
130 131 132 133 136 146 149 **P**6 **S** SSM Health, Saint Louis, MO
Primary Contact: Michael A. Baumgartner, President
COO: Frank Grispino, Vice President Operations
CFO: Jocelyn Skidmore, Director Finance
CMO: Shirley Harris, M.D., President Medical Staff
CIO: Dave Lewis, Director Information Services
CHR: Krista Barcus, Human Resources Leader
CNO: Debbie Hoffman, Vice President Patient Services
Web address: www.ssmhealthstfrancis.com
Control: Church operated, Nongovernment, not–for–profit **Service**: General
medical and surgical

Staffed Beds: 52 **Admissions:** 1503 **Census:** 18 **Outpatient Visits:** 129674
Births: 237 **Total Expense ($000):** 65223 **Payroll Expense ($000):** 27474
Personnel: 382

MEMPHIS—Scotland County

SCOTLAND COUNTY HOSPITAL (261310), 450 Sigler Avenue,
Zip 63555–1726, Mailing Address: 450 E Sigler Avenue, Zip 63555–1726;
tel. 660/465–8511, **A**10 18 **F**3 7 8 9 11 15 18 28 29 30 31 32 33 34 35 39 40
45 46 47 48 50 56 57 59 64 65 67 70 75 76 77 78 79 81 82 85 86 87 89 90
97 107 119 127 128 130 131 132 135 146 147 148 **P**6
Primary Contact: Randy Tobler, M.D., Chief Executive Officer
CFO: Sheryl Templeton, Chief Financial Officer
CMO: Randy Tobler, M.D., Chief Medical Officer
CIO: Ken McMinn, Director Information Technology
CHR: Missy Smith, Coordinator Human Resources
CNO: Carla Cook, Director of Nursing
Web address: www.scotlandcountyhospital.com
Control: Hospital district or authority, Government, nonfederal **Service**: General
medical and surgical

Staffed Beds: 25 **Admissions:** 621 **Census:** 10 **Outpatient Visits:** 100688
Births: 212 **Total Expense ($000):** 22590 **Payroll Expense ($000):** 9947
Personnel: 189

SCOTLAND COUNTY MEMORIAL HOSPITAL See Scotland County Hospital

MEXICO—Audrain County

SSM HEALTH ST. MARY'S HOSPITAL – AUDRAIN (260064), 620 East Monroe
Street, Zip 65265–2919; tel. 573/582–5000, **A**1 2 10 **F**3 11 13 15 18 20 22
26 28 29 30 31 34 45 54 57 59 64 65 70 73 74 75 76 77 78 79 81 82 85
86 87 89 90 93 98 103 107 108 110 111 115 118 119 121 123 127 129 130
131 132 144 146 147 149 **P**6 **S** SSM Health, Saint Louis, MO
Primary Contact: Donna K. Jacobs, FACHE, President
CFO: James Stratton, Regional Vice President Finance
CMO: Diane Jacobi, Chief of Staff
CIO: Dawn Evans, Manager Information Technology
CHR: Christy Smiley, Leader Human Resources
CNO: Kari Wilson, MHA, FNP, RN, Chief Nursing Officer
Web address: www.ssmhealthmidmo.com
Control: Church operated, Nongovernment, not–for–profit **Service**: General
medical and surgical

Staffed Beds: 57 **Admissions:** 1938 **Census:** 24 **Outpatient Visits:** 142209
Births: 197 **Total Expense ($000):** 65370 **Payroll Expense ($000):** 23642
Personnel: 362

MILAN—Sullivan County

SULLIVAN COUNTY MEMORIAL HOSPITAL (261306), 630 West Third Street,
Zip 63556–1076; tel. 660/265–4212, **A**10 18 **F**28 29 32 33 34 40 57 59 64 65
67 68 77 93 97 99 104 107 111 114 119 127 128 130 133 147 148 149 154
P5 6
Primary Contact: Jerry Dover, Chief Executive Officer
COO: Amy J Michael, Chief Operating Officer
CMO: Dale Essmyer, M.D., Chief of Staff
CIO: Vern Johnson, Director Information Technology
CHR: Rae A. Ashby, Director Human Resources
CNO: Tina Sears, Director Patient Care Services
Web address: www.scmhospital.org
Control: County, Government, nonfederal **Service**: General medical and surgical

Staffed Beds: 25 **Admissions:** 262 **Census:** 18 **Outpatient Visits:** 29652
Births: 0 **Total Expense ($000):** 10629 **Payroll Expense ($000):** 3248
Personnel: 90

MOBERLY—Randolph County

MOBERLY REGIONAL MEDICAL CENTER (260074), 1515 Union Avenue,
Zip 65270–9449; tel. 660/263–8400, **A**1 10 20 **F**3 18 20 22 26 28 29 30 34
35 38 40 44 45 50 53 54 56 57 59 64 65 70 74 75 77 79 81 85 86 87 89 93
94 97 98 100 103 107 111 115 118 119 126 127 128 129 130 133 135 146
148 149 **P**5 **S** Community Health Systems, Inc., Franklin, TN
Primary Contact: Ranee C. Brayton, FACHE, MSN, R.N., Chief Executive Officer
COO: Tracey Matheis, Chief Operating Officer
CFO: Tracey Matheis, Chief Financial Officer
CMO: Heather Gessling, M.D., Chief Medical Officer
CHR: Michael Turner, Director Human Resources
CNO: Patsy Lewellen, Interim Chief Nursing Officer
Web address: www.moberlyhospital.com
Control: Corporation, Investor–owned (for–profit) **Service**: General medical and
surgical

Staffed Beds: 100 **Admissions:** 1355 **Census:** 21 **Outpatient Visits:** 52777
Births: 0 **Total Expense ($000):** 45908 **Payroll Expense ($000):** 13761
Personnel: 280

MO

MONETT—Barry County

COX MONETT HOSPITAL (261329), 801 North Lincoln Avenue,
Zip 65708–1641; tel. 417/235–3144, **A**10 18 21 **F**3 11 13 15 28 29 30 32 34
35 40 45 50 53 56 57 59 64 76 77 81 85 89 90 93 107 111 114 119 127 128
129 130 131 133 135 144 146 147 154 **P**6 **S** CoxHealth, Springfield, MO
Primary Contact: Darren Bass, President
CFO: Josh Powell, Facility Controller
CMO: Frank Romero, M.D., Vice President Medical Affairs and Chief Medical Officer
CHR: Debra Isenmann, Human Resources Generalist
CNO: Bev Eli, Chief Nursing Officer
Web address: www.coxhealth.com
Control: Other not–for–profit (including NFP Corporation) **Service**: General
medical and surgical

**Staffed Beds: 25 Admissions: 846 Census: 8 Outpatient Visits: 111970
Births: 243 Total Expense ($000): 39102 Payroll Expense ($000): 18970
Personnel: 313**

MOUNTAIN VIEW—Howell County

MERCY ST. FRANCIS HOSPITAL (261335), 100 West Highway 60,
Zip 65548–7125; tel. 417/934–7000, **A**1 10 18 **F**3 11 15 28 29 30 34 40 45
50 57 59 64 65 75 77 81 85 89 90 93 107 110 111 114 119 129 131 132
133 148 **P**6 **S** Mercy, Chesterfield, MO
Primary Contact: Cynthia Weatherford, Administrator and Director of Nursing
CFO: Sherry Clouse Day, CPA, Chief Financial Officer
CMO: Barry Spoon, M.D., Chief of Staff
CHR: Tracy Smith, Director Human Resources
Web address: www.stjohns.com/aboutus/stfrancis.aspx
Control: Church operated, Nongovernment, not–for–profit **Service**: General
medical and surgical

**Staffed Beds: 20 Admissions: 227 Census: 3 Outpatient Visits: 25064
Births: 0 Total Expense ($000): 13856 Payroll Expense ($000): 6379
Personnel: 96**

NEOSHO—Newton County

FREEMAN NEOSHO HOSPITAL (261331), 113 West Hickory Street,
Zip 64850–1705; tel. 417/455–4352, **A**10 18 **F**3 11 15 28 30 34 35 40 44 45
47 50 56 57 59 64 68 70 75 77 79 81 84 85 86 87 90 93 97 107 110 111
114 119 127 130 131 132 133 146 147 148 **P**1 6 **S** Freeman Health System,
Joplin, MO
Primary Contact: Renee Denton, Chief Operating Officer
CFO: Steve W Graddy, Chief Financial Officer
CMO: Rodney McFarland, M.D., Medical Director
CIO: Sue Annesser, Director Information Systems
CHR: Mary Frerer, Chief Human Resources Officer
Web address: www.freemanhealth.com
Control: Other not–for–profit (including NFP Corporation) **Service**: General
medical and surgical

**Staffed Beds: 25 Admissions: 883 Census: 9 Outpatient Visits: 80734
Births: 0 Total Expense ($000): 25019 Payroll Expense ($000): 11186
Personnel: 189**

NEVADA—Vernon County

HEARTLAND BEHAVIORAL HEALTH SERVICES, 1500 West Ashland Street,
Zip 64772–1710; tel. 417/667–2666, **A**1 3 **F**98 99 101 **S** Universal Health
Services, Inc., King of Prussia, PA
Primary Contact: Alyson Wysong–Harder, Chief Executive Officer
CFO: Bryan Bishop, Chief Financial Officer
CMO: Ahmad Tarar, M.D., Medical Director
CHR: Carri Compton, Administrative Officer
CNO: Nathan Taylor, Director of Nursing
Web address: www.heartlandbehavioral.com
Control: Corporation, Investor–owned (for–profit) **Service**: Psychiatric

**Staffed Beds: 69 Admissions: 1930 Census: 41 Outpatient Visits: 0
Births: 0 Total Expense ($000): 14132 Payroll Expense ($000): 7715
Personnel: 139**

NEVADA REGIONAL MEDICAL CENTER (260061), 800 South Ash Street,
Zip 64772–3223; tel. 417/667–3355, **A**10 22 **F**3 4 11 13 14 15 18 26 27 28
29 30 31 32 34 35 39 40 41 45 50 54 57 59 62 63 64 65 66 70 74 75 76
77 78 79 81 82 83 84 85 86 87 89 90 91 93 94 96 98 101 102 103 104 107
111 115 119 127 129 130 131 132 133 135 143 144 146 147 148 **S** Freeman
Health System, Joplin, MO
Primary Contact: Wes Braman, Chief Executive Officer
CMO: Warren Lovinger, M.D., Chief Medical Officer
CIO: Marci Hardin, Manager Information Technology
CHR: Heather Brockmeyer, Human Resource Administrative Officer
CNO: Cory Vokoun, Chief Nursing Officer
Web address: www.nrmchealth.com
Control: City, Government, nonfederal **Service**: General medical and surgical

**Staffed Beds: 71 Admissions: 2155 Census: 27 Outpatient Visits: 61418
Births: 290 Total Expense ($000): 41189 Payroll Expense ($000): 15189
Personnel: 264**

NORTH KANSAS CITY—Clay County

NORTH KANSAS CITY HOSPITAL (260096), 2800 Clay Edwards Drive,
Zip 64116–3220; tel. 816/691–2000, **A**1 2 3 5 10 **F**3 11 12 13 15 17 18 20 22
24 26 28 29 30 31 34 35 37 40 43 44 45 46 47 48 49 50 51 53 54 57 58 59
60 62 64 70 72 74 75 76 77 78 79 80 81 82 83 84 85 86 87 89 90 93 96 100
107 108 110 111 114 115 116 117 118 119 120 121 123 124 126 129 130
132 135 146 147 148 149
Primary Contact: Peggy Schmitt, President and Chief Executive Officer
COO: Jody Abbott, Senior Vice President and Chief Operating Officer
CFO: Jim McNey, Senior Vice President Finance and Chief Financial Officer
CMO: Gary L Carter, M.D., Vice President and Chief Medical Officer
CIO: Doug Abel, Chief Information Officer
CHR: Dawn Bryant, Vice President Human Resources
CNO: Sarah G Oakley, Vice President Nursing
Web address: www.nkch.org
Control: City, Government, nonfederal **Service**: General medical and surgical

**Staffed Beds: 413 Admissions: 21348 Census: 284 Outpatient Visits:
294483 Births: 1781 Total Expense ($000): 500596 Payroll Expense
($000): 178896 Personnel: 2690**

O'FALLON—St. Charles County

PROGRESS WEST HOSPITAL (260219), Two Progress Point Parkway,
Zip 63368–2208; tel. 636/344–1000, **A**1 10 **F**3 4 13 15 18 20 22 26 29 30
34 35 40 41 45 49 51 57 59 60 70 76 77 79 81 85 86 87 89 90 107 108 110
111 115 118 119 130 135 146 148 149 154 **S** BJC HealthCare, Saint Louis, MO
Primary Contact: Chris Watts, President
CFO: Glen Schwaegel, Chief Financial Officer
CMO: Dane Glueck, M.D., Chief of Staff
CHR: Michael J Miller, Director Human Resources
Web address: www.progresswest.org
Control: Other not–for–profit (including NFP Corporation) **Service**: General
medical and surgical

**Staffed Beds: 74 Admissions: 3199 Census: 28 Outpatient Visits: 53628
Births: 723 Total Expense ($000): 75221 Payroll Expense ($000): 27632
Personnel: 323**

OSAGE BEACH—Camden County

LAKE REGIONAL HEALTH SYSTEM (260186), 54 Hospital Drive,
Zip 65065–3050; tel. 573/348–8000, (Total facility includes 16 beds in nursing
home–type unit) **A**1 2 10 **F**3 11 12 13 15 17 18 20 22 24 28 29 30 31 32 34
35 38 39 40 43 44 45 48 49 50 51 53 57 59 60 62 63 64 65 68 70 73 74 75
76 77 78 79 81 82 84 85 86 87 89 93 96 107 108 111 114 115 118 119 120
121 122 123 124 127 128 129 130 131 132 135 144 145 146 148 149 150
P6
Primary Contact: Dane W. Henry, Chief Executive Officer
COO: Kevin G McRoberts, FACHE, Senior Vice President of Operations
CFO: David Halsell, Senior Vice President and Chief Financial Officer
CMO: Patrick O'Neil, Senior Vice President Medical Affairs
CIO: Scott Poest, Chief Information Officer
CHR: Tom Williams, Vice President Employee and Community Development
CNO: Melissa Hunter, Senior Vice President Clinical Services
Web address: www.lakeregional.com
Control: Other not–for–profit (including NFP Corporation) **Service**: General
medical and surgical

**Staffed Beds: 116 Admissions: 4613 Census: 55 Outpatient Visits:
405801 Births: 593 Total Expense ($000): 181583 Payroll Expense
($000): 72485 Personnel: 1144**

MO

OSAGE BEACH CENTER FOR COGNITIVE DISORDERS, 840 Passover Road, Zip 65065; tel. 573/302–0319, **A**1 **F**50 56 68 74 75 86 87 98 101 103 104 130 132 135 149 154 **P**6
Primary Contact: Tom Flanagan, Chief Executive Officer
CNO: Lorri Steffen, Director of Nursing
Web address: www.osagebeachccd.com
Control: Partnership, Investor–owned (for–profit) **Service**: Psychiatric

Staffed Beds: 14 **Admissions**: 475 **Census**: 10 **Outpatient Visits**: 260 **Births**: 0 **Total Expense ($000)**: 4405 **Payroll Expense ($000)**: 2224 **Personnel**: 38

PERRYVILLE—Perry County

PERRY COUNTY MEMORIAL HOSPITAL (261311), 434 North West Street, Zip 63775–1398; tel. 573/547–2536, **A**1 10 18 **F**3 7 8 11 13 15 28 29 30 31 34 35 40 44 45 49 53 54 56 57 59 62 64 66 68 75 76 77 78 79 81 85 87 89 90 92 93 97 100 101 102 103 104 107 111 115 117 119 129 130 131 132 133 135 143 144 145 146 147 148 154
Primary Contact: Patrick E. Carron, FACHE, President and Chief Executive Officer
CFO: Randall Wolf, Vice President Finance
CMO: Michael Steele, M.D., Chief of Staff
CIO: Ron Heuring, Director Information Systems
CHR: Christopher Wibbenmeyer, Director Human Resources
Web address: www.pchmo.org
Control: Other not–for–profit (including NFP Corporation) **Service**: General medical and surgical

Staffed Beds: 25 **Admissions**: 1428 **Census**: 17 **Outpatient Visits**: 50049 **Births**: 146 **Total Expense ($000)**: 37940 **Payroll Expense ($000)**: 14869 **Personnel**: 312

PILOT KNOB—Iron County

IRON COUNTY MEDICAL CENTER (261336), 301 North Highway 21, Zip 63663–0548, Mailing Address: P.O. Box 548, Zip 63663–0548; tel. 573/546–1260, **A**10 18 **F**3 11 15 18 29 34 35 38 40 44 45 57 59 64 66 79 81 82 89 90 93 96 97 102 107 111 114 119 127 130 133 147 148 **P**6
Primary Contact: Joshua Gilmore, Chief Executive Officer
CNO: Cindy Sadler, Chief Nursing Officer
Web address: www.icmedcenter.org/
Control: Hospital district or authority, Government, nonfederal **Service**: General medical and surgical

Staffed Beds: 15 **Admissions**: 250 **Census**: 5 **Outpatient Visits**: 23530 **Births**: 0 **Personnel**: 127

POPLAR BLUFF—Butler County

BLACK RIVER MEDICAL CENTER (260227), 217 Physicians Park Drive, Zip 63901–3956; tel. 573/727–9080, **A**1 10 **F**3 15 29 34 39 40 45 51 57 59 64 65 81 107 108 111 115 118 119 135 149
Primary Contact: Christy Shawan, Chief Executive Officer
CMO: Christopher Pinderski, M.D., Medical Director of Emergency Room
CIO: Matthew Wallace, Manager Information Technology, Biomed
CHR: Meagan Tucker, Director Human Resources
CNO: E. Kay Fox, Director of Nursing
Web address: www.blackrivermedical.com
Control: Other not–for–profit (including NFP Corporation) **Service**: General medical and surgical

Staffed Beds: 8 **Admissions**: 407 **Census**: 3 **Outpatient Visits**: 36799 **Births**: 0 **Total Expense ($000)**: 18821 **Payroll Expense ($000)**: 5479 **Personnel**: 125

JOHN J. PERSHING VETERANS AFFAIRS MEDICAL CENTER, 1500 North Westwood Boulevard, Zip 63901–3318; tel. 573/686–4151, (Nonreporting) **A**1 **S** Department of Veterans Affairs, Perry Point, MD
Primary Contact: Patricia Hall, MSN, Ph.D., R.N., Director
COO: Seth Barlage, Associate Medical Center Director
CFO: Kristy Williams, Manager Finance
CMO: Vijayachandran Nair, M.D., Chief of Staff
CIO: Michael Gustin, Information Technology
CHR: Genise Denton, Manager Human Resources
CNO: Chandra Miller, Director of Nursing
Web address: www.poplarbluff.va.gov
Control: Veterans Affairs, Government, federal **Service**: General medical and surgical

Staffed Beds: 58

POPLAR BLUFF REGIONAL MEDICAL CENTER (260119), 3100 Oak Grove Road, Zip 63901, Mailing Address: P.O. Box 88, Zip 63902–0088; tel. 573/776–2000, (Includes POPLAR BLUFF REGIONAL MEDICAL CENTER–SOUTH CAMPUS, 621 Pine Boulevard, Poplar Bluff, MO, Zip 63901; tel. 573/785–7721) **A**1 2 10 **F**3 11 13 15 17 18 20 22 24 29 30 31 34 35 40 45 46 49 50 51 53 54 56 57 59 60 64 65 68 70 74 75 76 77 78 79 80 81 85 87 89 90 93 98 102 107 108 111 114 117 118 119 120 121 126 127 129 130 131 132 146 148 154 **S** Community Health Systems, Inc., Franklin, TN
Primary Contact: Bryan Bateman, Chief Executive Officer
COO: Christian Jones, Chief Operating Officer
CFO: Steve Dorris, Chief Financial Officer
CMO: Steve Pu, D.O., Chief Medical Officer
CIO: Gary Dollins, Director Management Information Systems
CHR: Denise Rushin, Director Human Resources
Web address: www.poplarbluffregional.com
Control: Individual, Investor–owned (for–profit) **Service**: General medical and surgical

Staffed Beds: 296 **Admissions**: 10557 **Census**: 120 **Outpatient Visits**: 82082 **Births**: 1385 **Total Expense ($000)**: 154198 **Payroll Expense ($000)**: 41201 **Personnel**: 935

POTOSI—Washington County

WASHINGTON COUNTY MEMORIAL HOSPITAL (261308), 300 Health Way, Zip 63664–1420; tel. 573/438–5451, **A**10 18 **F**3 15 28 29 33 34 35 40 45 57 59 64 65 74 75 77 79 81 82 85 87 90 93 97 98 104 107 108 110 111 115 119 127 129 130 133 135 143 144 145 146 154 **P**6
Primary Contact: Michele C. Meyer, Chief Executive Officer
CFO: Yvonne Fourez, Chief Financial Officer
CMO: Jonathan Borchers, M.D., Chief Medical Officer
CIO: Jim Smith, Director Information Systems
CHR: Christy Aubuchon, Director Personnel
CNO: Beverly Williams, R.N., Chief Nursing Officer
Web address: www.wcmhosp.org
Control: County, Government, nonfederal **Service**: General medical and surgical

Staffed Beds: 25 **Admissions**: 856 **Census**: 10 **Outpatient Visits**: 85126 **Births**: 0 **Total Expense ($000)**: 23893 **Payroll Expense ($000)**: 10388 **Personnel**: 195

RICHMOND—Ray County

RAY COUNTY MEMORIAL HOSPITAL (261327), 904 Wollard Boulevard, Zip 64085–2229; tel. 816/470–5432, **A**10 18 **F**3 11 15 28 29 30 31 40 44 45 56 57 62 64 68 75 78 79 81 82 85 87 93 103 105 107 108 110 111 115 117 119 130 133 146 153
Primary Contact: Earl Nielsen. Sheehy, Chief Executive Officer
CFO: Donald Harr, Controller
CHR: Donna Strain, Director Human Resources
Web address: www.raycountyhospital.com
Control: County, Government, nonfederal **Service**: General medical and surgical

Staffed Beds: 25 **Admissions**: 674 **Census**: 8 **Outpatient Visits**: 16498 **Births**: 0 **Total Expense ($000)**: 23630 **Payroll Expense ($000)**: 10540 **Personnel**: 213

RICHMOND HEIGHTS—St. Louis County

SSM SELECT REHABILITATION HOSPITAL (263031), 1027 Bellevue Avenue, 3rd Floor, Zip 63117–1851, Mailing Address: 1027 Bellevue Avenue, Zip 63117–1851; tel. 314/768–5300, (Includes SSM HEALTH REHABILITATION HOSPITAL – LAKE SAINT LOUIS, 100 Medical Plaza, Fifth Floor, Lake Saint Louis, MO, Zip 63367–1366; tel. 636/755–6500; Robert Pritts, Chief Executive Officer and Market Executive; SSM SELECT REHABILITATION HOSPITAL, 12380 De Paul Drive, Bridgeton, MO, Zip 63044–2511; tel. 314/447–9700; Robert Pritts, Chief Executive Officer) **A**1 7 10 **F**3 29 44 64 74 77 78 79 85 87 90 91 93 96 130 131 132 143 148 149 **P**2 6 **S** Select Medical Corporation, Mechanicsburg, PA
Primary Contact: Robert Pritts, Chief Executive Officer
Web address: www.ssm–select.com
Control: Partnership, Investor–owned (for–profit) **Service**: Rehabilitation

Staffed Beds: 125 **Admissions**: 2296 **Census**: 86 **Outpatient Visits**: 433093 **Births**: 0 **Total Expense ($000)**: 106593 **Payroll Expense ($000)**: 58830 **Personnel**: 852

ROLLA—Phelps County

PHELPS COUNTY REGIONAL MEDICAL CENTER (260017), 1000 West Tenth Street, Zip 65401–2905; tel. 573/458–8899, (Total facility includes 20 beds in nursing home–type unit) **A**1 2 7 10 **F**3 7 8 11 13 15 18 20 22 26 28 29 30 31 34 35 39 40 45 47 49 50 51 54 56 57 58 59 60 62 63 68 70 73 74 75 76 77 78 79 81 82 84 85 86 87 89 90 93 94 96 98 102 107 108 110 111 114 115 117 118 119 120 121 123 126 127 128 129 130 132 135 143 146 147 148 149 **P**6
Primary Contact: Edward Clayton, Chief Executive Officer
COO: Jason Shenefield, Senior Vice President and Chief Operating Officer
CFO: Jana Cook, Vice President and Chief Financial Officer
CMO: Donald James, D.O., Senior Vice President and Chief Medical Officer
CIO: Jeff McKune, Chief Health Informatics Officer
CHR: Frank A. Lazzaro III Chief Human Resources Officer
CNO: Keri S. Brookshire–Heavin, Senior Vice President and Chief Nursing Officer
Web address: www.pcrmc.com
Control: County, Government, nonfederal **Service**: General medical and surgical

Staffed Beds: 181 **Admissions**: 6343 **Census**: 85 **Outpatient Visits**: 412518 **Births**: 801 **Total Expense ($000)**: 235095 **Payroll Expense ($000)**: 103763 **Personnel**: 1116

Many Facility Codes have changed. Please refer to the AHA Guide Code Chart. © 2018 AHA Guide

MO

SAINT CHARLES—St. Charles County

CENTERPOINTE HOSPITAL (264012), 4801 Weldon Spring Parkway, Zip 63304–9101; tel. 636/441–7300, **A**1 10 **F**4 5 34 35 38 44 54 80 87 98 99 100 101 102 103 104 105 106 143 152 153
Primary Contact: Scott Williams, Chief Executive Officer
CFO: Tom Croffut, Chief Financial Officer
CMO: Azfar Malik, M.D., Chief Medical Officer
CIO: Jennifer Bourn, Director, Health Information Services and Medical Staff Services
CHR: Kelli White, Director, Human Resources
Web address: www.centerpointehospital.com
Control: Corporation, Investor–owned (for–profit) **Service**: Psychiatric

Staffed Beds: 150 Admissions: 4565 Census: 114 Outpatient Visits: 0
Births: 0 Total Expense ($000): 39495 Payroll Expense ($000): 20716
Personnel: 354

SAINT CHARLES—Saint Charles County

SELECT SPECIALTY HOSPITAL–ST. LOUIS (262013), 300 First Capitol Drive, Unit 1, Zip 63301–2844; tel. 636/947–5010, (Includes SELECT SPECIALTY HOSPITAL – TOWN AND COUNTRY, 3015 North Ballas Road, Fifth Floor, St. Louis, MO, Zip 63131–2329; tel. 314/996–6500; Marie T Droege, Chief Executive Officer) **A**1 10 **F**1 29 74 75 148 **S** Select Medical Corporation, Mechanicsburg, PA
Primary Contact: Phillip Readinger, Chief Executive Officer
Web address: www.selectspecialtyhospitals.com/company/locations/stlouis.aspx
Control: Corporation, Investor–owned (for–profit) **Service**: Acute long–term care hospital

Staffed Beds: 33 Admissions: 314 Census: 27 Outpatient Visits: 0
Births: 0 Total Expense ($000): 17177 Payroll Expense ($000): 7373
Personnel: 96

SAINT CHARLES—St. Charles County

SSM HEALTH ST. JOSEPH – ST. CHARLES (260005), 300 First Capitol Drive, Zip 63301–2844; tel. 636/947–5000, (Includes SSM HEALTH ST. JOSEPH – WENTZVILLE, 500 Medical Drive, Wentzville, MO, Zip 63385–3421; tel. 636/327–1000; Lisle Wescott, President) **A**1 2 3 10 **F**3 4 5 11 13 15 17 18 20 22 24 26 28 29 30 31 34 35 38 40 41 43 44 45 46 49 50 53 54 55 56 57 58 59 60 64 68 70 73 74 75 76 78 79 81 82 84 85 86 87 90 96 97 98 99 100 101 102 103 104 105 107 108 110 111 114 118 119 120 121 129 130 132 135 144 146 147 148 153 154 **P**6 8 **S** SSM Health, Saint Louis, MO
Primary Contact: Lisle Wescott, President
COO: Lee Bernstein, Regional Executive Vice President and Chief Operating Officer
CFO: Karen Rewerts, System Vice President Finance
CMO: Douglas Barton, M.D., Chief Medical Officer
CIO: Margaret Feilner, Director Information Services
CHR: Debbie G Walkenhorst, System Vice President Talent Management
Web address: www.ssmstjoseph.com
Control: Church operated, Nongovernment, not–for–profit **Service**: General medical and surgical

Staffed Beds: 341 Admissions: 14227 Census: 199 Outpatient Visits: 202771 Births: 667 Total Expense ($000): 252602 Payroll Expense ($000): 87919 Personnel: 1265

SAINT JOSEPH—Buchanan County

LONG–TERM ACUTE CARE HOSPITAL, MOSAIC LIFE CARE AT ST. JOSEPH (262019), 5325 Faraon Street, Zip 64506–3488; tel. 816/271–6000, **A**10 **F**1 3 29 85 130 148 149 150
Primary Contact: Dana Anderson, Administrator
CNO: Douglas Schmitz, Director of Nursing
Web address: www.mymosaiclifecare.org/General/Long–Term–Acute–Care–Hospital/
Control: Other not–for–profit (including NFP Corporation) **Service**: Acute long–term care hospital

Staffed Beds: 41 Admissions: 242 Census: 22 Outpatient Visits: 0
Births: 0 Total Expense ($000): 12618 Payroll Expense ($000): 3564
Personnel: 59

MOSAIC LIFE CARE (260006), 5325 Faraon Street, Zip 64506–3488; tel. 816/271–6000, **A**1 2 10 20 **F**3 8 9 11 12 13 15 17 18 20 22 24 26 28 29 30 31 32 33 34 35 36 40 43 45 46 48 49 50 53 54 57 58 59 62 63 64 65 70 74 75 76 77 78 79 80 81 82 84 85 86 87 89 90 92 93 94 96 97 98 102 103 104 107 108 110 111 114 115 118 119 120 121 123 124 129 130 131 134 135 143 144 146 147 148 149 150 154 **P**6
Primary Contact: Samuel Mark. Laney, M.D., Chief Executive Officer
COO: Curt Kretzinger, Chief Operating Officer
CFO: Dwain Stilson, Chief Financial Officer
CIO: Brennan Lehman, Chief Information Officer
CHR: Michael Pulido, Chief Administrative Officer
Web address: www.mymosaiclifecare.org/Main/Location/st–joseph–mo/mosaic–life–care–at–st.–joseph/
Control: Other not–for–profit (including NFP Corporation) **Service**: General medical and surgical

Staffed Beds: 352 Admissions: 16201 Census: 186 Outpatient Visits: 1171561 Births: 1584 Total Expense ($000): 635581 Payroll Expense ($000): 274027 Personnel: 3697

NORTHWEST MISSOURI PSYCHIATRIC REHABILITATION CENTER (264007), 3505 Frederick Avenue, Zip 64506–2914; tel. 816/387–2300, **A**1 3 10 **F**4 29 30 65 68 75 77 86 87 97 98 101 102 103 130 132 135 143 146 **P**6
Primary Contact: Denise Norbury, Regional Executive Officer
COO: Mary Attebury, Chief Operating Officer
CFO: Randy Riley, Fiscal and Administrative Manager
CMO: James B Reynolds, M.D., Medical Director
CIO: Robert Curren, Western Region Chief Information Technology Officer
CHR: Mary Blakey Gorman, Director Human Resources
CNO: Pam Nold, Chief Nurse Executive
Web address: www.https://dmh.mo.gov
Control: State, Government, nonfederal **Service**: Psychiatric

Staffed Beds: 108 Admissions: 56 Census: 107 Outpatient Visits: 0
Births: 0 Total Expense ($000): 23127 Payroll Expense ($000): 11855
Personnel: 294

SAINT LOUIS—St. Louis City County

BARNES–JEWISH HOSPITAL (260032), 1 Barnes–Jewish Hospital Plaza, Zip 63110–1003; tel. 314/747–3000, (Includes BARNES–JEWISH HOSPITAL PSYCHIATRIC SUPPORT CENTER, 5355 Delmar Boulevard, Saint Louis, MO, Zip 63112–3146; tel. 314/286–1700; John M. Eiler, Administrative Director) (Total facility includes 120 beds in nursing home–type unit) **A**1 2 3 5 8 10 **F**3 4 5 6 8 9 11 12 13 14 15 16 17 18 20 22 24 26 28 29 30 31 34 35 36 37 38 39 40 43 44 45 46 47 48 49 50 51 52 53 54 55 56 57 58 59 60 61 63 64 65 66 68 70 71 73 74 75 76 77 78 79 80 81 82 84 85 86 87 89 90 91 92 93 94 95 96 97 98 100 101 102 103 104 107 108 109 110 111 112 114 115 116 117 118 119 120 121 122 123 124 126 128 129 130 131 132 134 135 136 137 138 139 140 141 142 143 145 146 147 148 149 154 **P**6 **S** BJC HealthCare, Saint Louis, MO
Primary Contact: Robert W. Cannon, President
CFO: Mark Krieger, Vice President and Chief Financial Officer
CMO: John Lynch, M.D., Vice President and Chief Medical Officer
CIO: Jerry Vuchak, Vice President Healthcare Delivery
CHR: Betsy Rodriguez, Vice President Human Resources
CNO: Coreen Vlodarchyk, R.N., Vice President, Patient Care Services and Chief Nursing Officer
Web address: www.barnesjewish.org
Control: Other not–for–profit (including NFP Corporation) **Service**: General medical and surgical

Staffed Beds: 1396 Admissions: 54780 Census: 971 Outpatient Visits: 671888 Births: 3357 Total Expense ($000): 2018303 Payroll Expense ($000): 622613 Personnel: 11222

SAINT LOUIS—St. Louis County

BARNES–JEWISH WEST COUNTY HOSPITAL (260162), 12634 Olive Boulevard, Zip 63141–6337; tel. 314/996–8000, **A**1 3 5 10 **F**3 12 15 18 29 34 35 40 45 46 47 49 50 51 57 59 60 64 65 70 74 75 77 78 79 81 82 85 90 93 107 110 114 115 119 120 121 126 129 130 131 142 145 146 148 149 154 **S** BJC HealthCare, Saint Louis, MO
Primary Contact: Trisha Lollo, President
CFO: Diane M Glen, Assistant Administrator
CMO: Sam B Bhayani, M.D., Chief Medical Officer
CIO: Jerry Vuchak, Vice President Information Systems
CNO: Yoany Finetti, R.N., Chief Nursing Officer
Web address: www.barnesjewishwestcounty.org
Control: Other not–for–profit (including NFP Corporation) **Service**: General medical and surgical

Staffed Beds: 77 Admissions: 2736 Census: 17 Outpatient Visits: 160958
Births: 0 Total Expense ($000): 117520 Payroll Expense ($000): 36327
Personnel: 439

MO

Hospital, Medicare Provider Number, Address, Telephone, Approval, Facility, and Physician Codes, Health Care System

★ American Hospital Association (AHA) membership
□ The Joint Commission accreditation
○ Healthcare Facilities Accreditation Program
◇ DNV Healthcare Inc. accreditation
⇑ Center for Improvement in Healthcare Quality Accreditation
△ Commission on Accreditation of Rehabilitation Facilities (CARF) accreditation

CHRISTIAN HOSPITAL (260180), 11133 Dunn Road, Zip 63136–6119; tel. 314/653–5000, **A**1 2 3 10 **F**3 4 5 7 8 11 15 17 18 20 22 24 26 28 29 30 34 35 36 38 40 44 45 46 47 49 50 53 56 57 58 59 60 63 64 65 68 69 70 74 75 77 78 79 80 81 82 83 84 85 86 87 90 92 93 94 96 102 104 107 108 109 110 111 112 113 114 115 116 117 118 119 120 121 123 126 130 132 135 143 146 147 148 149 153 **P**6 **S** BJC HealthCare, Saint Louis, MO
Primary Contact: Rick Stevens, President
CMO: Sebastian Rueckert, M.D., Chief Medical Officer
CIO: Michael Kelly, Vice President
CHR: Bryan Hartwick, Vice President Human Resources
CNO: Jennifer Cordia, Vice President and Chief Nursing Executive
COO: Douglas Black, Vice President of Operations
Web address: www.christianhospital.org
Control: Other not–for–profit (including NFP Corporation) **Service**: General medical and surgical

Staffed Beds: 220 **Admissions:** 12142 **Census:** 195 **Outpatient Visits:** 297821 **Births:** 0 **Total Expense ($000):** 323161 **Payroll Expense ($000):** 123698 **Personnel:** 1696

HAWTHORN CHILDREN PSYCHIATRIC HOSPITAL (264028), 1901 Pennsylvania, Zip 63133–1325, Mailing Address: 1901 Pennsylvania Avenue, Zip 63133–1325; tel. 314/512–7800, **A**1 3 10 **F**98 99 106 **P**6
Primary Contact: Laurent D. Javois, Regional Executive Officer
COO: Marcia F Ford, Chief Operating Officer
CFO: James D Martin, Chief Financial Officer
CMO: Joshua Calhoun, M.D., Medical Director
CHR: Michael McFarlane, Director Human Resource
CNO: Melody Chilese, Chief Nurse Executive
Web address: www.dmh.missouri.gov/hcph/
Control: State, Government, nonfederal **Service**: Children's hospital psychiatric

Staffed Beds: 52 **Admissions:** 141 **Census:** 37 **Outpatient Visits:** 0 **Births:** 0 **Total Expense ($000):** 14909 **Payroll Expense ($000):** 8836 **Personnel:** 227

SAINT LOUIS—St. Louis City County

KINDRED HOSPITAL–ST. LOUIS (262010), 4930 Lindell Boulevard, Zip 63108–1510; tel. 314/361–8700, (Includes KINDRED HOSPITAL ST. LOUIS–ST. ANTHONY'S, 10018 Kennerly Road, 3rd Floor, Saint Louis, MO, Zip 63128; tel. 314/525–8100; Angela Green, Chief Executive Officer) **A**1 10 **F**1 107 111 148 **S** Kindred Healthcare, Louisville, KY
Primary Contact: Lourene Money, R.N., Resource Chief Executive Officer
COO: Dakota Redd, R.N., Chief Clinical Officer
CFO: Maureen Roach, Senior Chief Financial Officer
CMO: Michael Holtzman, M.D., Medical Director
CIO: Thomas C Christman, Director Plant Operations
CHR: Cindy Sander, Coordinator Human Resources
Web address: www.kindredstlouis.com/
Control: Corporation, Investor–owned (for–profit) **Service**: Acute long–term care hospital

Staffed Beds: 98 **Admissions:** 809 **Census:** 56 **Outpatient Visits:** 0 **Births:** 0 **Total Expense ($000):** 34025 **Payroll Expense ($000):** 13856 **Personnel:** 188

SAINT LOUIS—St. Louis County

MERCY HOSPITAL ST. LOUIS (260020), 615 South New Ballas Road, Zip 63141–8277; tel. 314/251–6000, (Includes MERCY CHILDREN'S HOSPITAL ST. LOUIS, 615 South New Ballas Road, Saint Louis, MO, Zip 63141–8221; tel. 314/251–6000) **A**1 2 3 5 8 10 **F**3 4 5 8 11 12 13 14 15 16 17 18 19 20 22 24 25 26 27 28 29 30 31 32 33 34 35 36 38 39 40 41 43 45 46 47 48 49 50 51 52 53 54 55 56 57 58 59 60 61 64 66 68 69 70 71 72 73 74 75 76 77 78 79 80 81 82 84 85 86 87 88 89 90 92 93 94 96 98 99 100 101 102 103 104 105 106 107 108 110 111 114 115 116 117 118 119 120 121 123 124 126 129 130 131 132 134 135 143 144 146 147 148 149 153 154 **P**6 8 **S** Mercy, Chesterfield, MO
Primary Contact: Stephen Mackin, President
CFO: Cheryl Matejka, Chief Financial Officer
CMO: Paul Hintze, M.D., Vice President Medical Affairs
CIO: Eugene Roth, Vice President Information Services
CHR: Rocky Ruello, Vice President Human Resources
Web address: www.mercy.net/stlouismo
Control: Other not–for–profit (including NFP Corporation) **Service**: General medical and surgical

Staffed Beds: 859 **Admissions:** 40004 **Census:** 555 **Outpatient Visits:** 1215444 **Births:** 8778 **Total Expense ($000):** 924442 **Payroll Expense ($000):** 323218 **Personnel:** 5250

SAINT LOUIS—St. Louis City County

METROPOLITAN ST. LOUIS PSYCHIATRIC CENTER (264025), 5351 Delmar, Zip 63112–3198; tel. 314/877–0501, **A**1 3 10 **F**11 30 98 146 149
Primary Contact: Laurent D. Javois, Regional Executive Officer
COO: Michael Bruce Anderson, Ph.D., Chief Operating Officer
CFO: James D Martin, Chief Financial Officer
CMO: Davinder Hayreh, M.D., Medical Director
CHR: Michael McFarlane, Director Human Resources
CNO: Sarah Jones, Chief Nurse Executive
Web address: www.dmh.missouri.gov/mpc
Control: State, Government, nonfederal **Service**: Psychiatric

Staffed Beds: 50 **Admissions:** 71 **Census:** 50 **Outpatient Visits:** 0 **Births:** 0 **Total Expense ($000):** 15672 **Payroll Expense ($000):** 7212 **Personnel:** 78

SAINT LOUIS—St. Louis County

MISSOURI BAPTIST MEDICAL CENTER (260108), 3015 North Ballas Road, Zip 63131–2329; tel. 314/996–5000, **A**1 2 3 5 10 **F**3 11 13 14 15 17 18 20 22 24 26 28 29 30 31 32 34 35 36 40 41 45 46 48 49 50 51 54 56 57 58 59 60 63 64 65 68 70 71 72 74 75 76 77 78 79 81 82 83 84 85 86 87 89 90 92 93 94 96 97 102 107 108 110 111 114 115 116 117 118 119 120 121 123 124 126 130 132 135 145 146 147 148 149 150 154 **P**6 **S** BJC HealthCare, Saint Louis, MO
Primary Contact: John Antes, President
COO: Michael Kelly, Vice President Operations
CFO: Amy Desart, Vice President, Chief Financial Officer
CMO: Mitchell Botney, M.D., Vice President Medical Affairs and Chief Medical Officer
CIO: Tracie Jones, Director Information Services
CHR: Cyndy Donato, Vice President, Human Resources
CNO: Tim Mislan, MS, Vice President and Chief Nurse Executive
Web address: www.missouribaptist.org
Control: Other not–for–profit (including NFP Corporation) **Service**: General medical and surgical

Staffed Beds: 443 **Admissions:** 20171 **Census:** 247 **Outpatient Visits:** 387004 **Births:** 3825 **Total Expense ($000):** 605621 **Payroll Expense ($000):** 191483 **Personnel:** 2538

SHRINERS HOSPITALS FOR CHILDREN–ST. LOUIS (263304), 4400 Clayton Avenue, Zip 63110–1624; tel. 314/432–3600, **A**1 3 5 10 **F**3 29 58 64 74 75 79 81 85 86 87 89 93 94 130 131 146 **S** Shriners Hospitals for Children, Tampa, FL
Primary Contact: Phillip L. Grady, Administrator
CFO: Sandra K. Lawson, Interim Director Fiscal Services
CMO: Perry L Schoenecker, M.D., Chief of Staff
CIO: Jeanne Hall, Director Information Systems
CHR: Mark Venable, Interim Director Human Resources
Web address: www.shrinershospitalsforchildren.org
Control: Other not–for–profit (including NFP Corporation) **Service**: Children's orthopedic

Staffed Beds: 12 **Admissions:** 313 **Census:** 4 **Outpatient Visits:** 9292 **Births:** 0 **Total Expense ($000):** 26956 **Payroll Expense ($000):** 8262 **Personnel:** 142

SAINT LOUIS—St. Louis City County

SSM CARDINAL GLENNON CHILDREN'S HOSPITAL (269807), 1465 South Grand Boulevard, Zip 63104–1095; tel. 314/577–5600, **A**3 5 10 **F**3 11 19 21 23 25 27 29 30 31 32 34 35 38 39 40 41 43 44 45 46 47 48 49 50 51 54 55 57 59 60 61 64 66 68 72 73 74 75 77 78 79 80 81 82 84 85 86 87 88 89 90 93 94 97 99 100 101 102 104 107 108 111 115 118 119 124 127 129 130 131 132 134 136 137 138 139 141 142 146 148 154 **P**6 8 **S** SSM Health, Saint Louis, MO
Primary Contact: Steven Burghart, President
CFO: Karen Rewerts, System Vice President of Finance
CMO: John Peter, M.D., Vice President Medical Affairs
CIO: Michael Paasch, Regional Vice President and Chief Information Officer
CHR: Debbie G Walkenhorst, Network Vice President
Web address: www.cardinalglennon.com
Control: Church operated, Nongovernment, not–for–profit **Service**: Children's general medical and surgical

Staffed Beds: 176 **Admissions:** 7155 **Census:** 131 **Outpatient Visits:** 250971 **Births:** 0 **Total Expense ($000):** 348240 **Payroll Expense ($000):** 106177 **Personnel:** 1661

SSM HEALTH SAINT LOUIS UNIVERSITY HOSPITAL (260105), 3635 Vista at Grand Boulevard, Zip 63110–0250, Mailing Address: P.O. Box 15250, Zip 63110–0250; tel. 314/577–8000, (Includes SSM HEALTH SAINT LOUIS UNIVERSITY HOSPITAL–SOUTH, 1755 South Grand Boulevard, Saint Louis, MO, Zip 63104–1540; tel. 314/577–6027; Raymond Alvey, Chief Financial Officer) **A**1 2 3 5 8 10 **F**3 4 6 7 8 9 11 14 15 17 18 20 22 24 26 28 29 30 31 34 35 36 37 38 39 40 43 44 45 46 47 48 49 50 51 55 56 57 58 59 60 61 63 64 65 68 70 74 75 77 78 79 81 82 84 85 86 87 90 91 92 93 94 96 97 98 100 101 102 104 107 108 110 111 112 113 114 115 116 117 118 119 121 123 124 126 129 130 131 132 135 136 138 139 141 142 146 147 148 149 150 **P**1 6 **S** SSM Health, Saint Louis, MO
Primary Contact: Patti Kelley, Vice President, Nurisng and Chief Nursing Officer
COO: Gretchen Leiterman, Chief Operating Officer
CFO: Raymond Alvey, Chief Financial Officer
CMO: Nirav Patel, M.D., Interim Chief Medical Officer
CIO: Patrick Brennan, Director Information System Technology
CNO: Patti Kelley, Vice President, Nurisng and Chief Nursing Officer
Web address: www.sluhospital.com
Control: Church operated, Nongovernment, not–for–profit **Service:** General medical and surgical

Staffed Beds: 356 Admissions: 16362 Census: 269 Outpatient Visits: 189353 **Births:** 0 **Total Expense ($000):** 547047 **Payroll Expense ($000):** 141152 **Personnel:** 1629

SSM HEALTH ST. MARY'S HOSPITAL – ST. LOUIS (260091), 6420 Clayton Road, Zip 63117–1811, Mailing Address: Richmond Heights, tel. 314/768–8000, **A**2 3 5 **F**3 4 13 15 17 18 19 20 28 29 30 31 34 35 37 38 40 44 45 48 49 50 51 52 55 56 57 58 59 60 61 64 66 70 72 73 74 75 76 78 79 81 82 84 85 86 87 97 98 100 101 102 103 104 107 108 110 111 114 115 119 120 121 126 129 130 132 135 143 144 146 147 148 149 153 154 **P**6 8 **S** SSM Health, Saint Louis, MO
Primary Contact: Travis Capers, FACHE, President
CFO: Karen Rewerts, System Vice President of Finance
CMO: Stephen Kelly, M.D., Chief Medical Officer
CIO: Michael Paasch, Regional Chief Information Officer
Web address: www.stmarys–stlouis.com
Control: Church operated, Nongovernment, not–for–profit **Service:** General medical and surgical

Staffed Beds: 394 Admissions: 18655 Census: 262 Outpatient Visits: 244043 **Births:** 3396 **Total Expense ($000):** 375707 **Payroll Expense ($000):** 121901 **Personnel:** 1783

ST. ALEXIUS HOSPITAL – BROADWAY CAMPUS (260210), 3933 South Broadway, Zip 63118–4601; tel. 314/865–7000, (Includes SOUTHPOINTE HOSPITAL, 2639 Miami Street, Saint Louis, MO, Zip 63118–3929; tel. 314/772–1456; ST. ALEXIUS HOSPITAL – FOREST PARK CAMPUS, 6150 Oakland Avenue, Saint Louis, MO, Zip 63139–3215; tel. 314/768–3000; Michael J. Motte, Chief Executive Officer) **A**1 3 5 10 **F**3 11 12 20 29 34 35 38 39 40 43 45 50 51 56 57 59 60 65 68 70 74 79 81 85 86 87 98 101 102 103 104 107 108 111 118 119 130 135 143 146 148 149 **P**6 **S** Success Healthcare, Boca Raton, FL
Primary Contact: Michael J. Motte, Chief Executive Officer
CFO: Matthew Brandt, Chief Financial Officer
Web address: www.stalexiushospital.com
Control: Corporation, Investor–owned (for–profit) **Service:** General medical and surgical

Staffed Beds: 190 Admissions: 3537 Census: 100 Outpatient Visits: 26851 **Births:** 0 **Total Expense ($000):** 60820 **Payroll Expense ($000):** 34894 **Personnel:** 574

ST. ANTHONY'S MERCY (260077), 10010 Kennerly Road, Zip 63128–2106; tel. 314/525–1000, **A**1 2 3 5 7 10 **F**3 4 5 11 12 13 15 17 18 20 22 24 26 28 29 30 31 34 35 36 38 40 41 43 47 48 49 50 51 53 54 56 57 58 59 60 61 62 63 64 65 68 69 70 74 75 76 77 78 79 80 81 82 84 85 86 87 90 91 92 93 94 95 96 97 98 99 100 101 102 103 104 105 107 108 110 111 114 115 116 117 118 119 120 121 122 123 124 126 129 130 131 132 135 143 144 146 147 148 149 153 **P**6 **S** Mercy, Chesterfield, MO
Primary Contact: Sean Hogan, FACHE, President
COO: Bill Hoefer, Chief Operating Officer
Web address: www.stanthonysmedcenter.com
Control: Other not–for–profit (including NFP Corporation) **Service:** General medical and surgical

Staffed Beds: 520 Admissions: 26044 Census: 324 Outpatient Visits: 717925 **Births:** 959 **Total Expense ($000):** 536922 **Payroll Expense ($000):** 246075 **Personnel:** 3178

ST. JOHN'S MERCY CHILDREN'S HOSPITAL See Mercy Children's Hospital St. Louis

ST. JOHN'S MERCY MEDICAL CENTER See Mercy Hospital St. Louis

ST. LOUIS CHILDREN'S HOSPITAL (263301), One Children's Place, Zip 63110–1002; tel. 314/454–6000, **A**1 3 5 7 8 10 **F**3 7 8 11 16 17 19 20 21 22 23 25 26 27 29 30 31 32 34 35 38 39 40 41 43 44 45 46 47 48 49 50 52 54 57 58 59 60 61 62 63 64 65 68 71 72 74 75 77 78 79 81 82 83 84 85 86 87 88 89 90 91 92 93 95 96 99 100 101 102 104 107 108 109 111 112 114 115 118 119 126 129 130 131 132 134 135 136 137 138 139 140 141 142 143 145 146 148 149 150 154 **S** BJC HealthCare, Saint Louis, MO
Primary Contact: Joan Magruder, President
CFO: Michele McKee, Vice President and Chief Financial Officer
CMO: F Sessions Cole, M.D., Chief Medical Officer
Web address: www.stlouischildrens.org
Control: Other not–for–profit (including NFP Corporation) **Service:** Children's general medical and surgical

Staffed Beds: 274 Admissions: 10238 Census: 214 Outpatient Visits: 371148 **Births:** 0 **Total Expense ($000):** 618640 **Payroll Expense ($000):** 212524 **Personnel:** 2768

ST. LOUIS PSYCHIATRIC REHABILITATION CENTER (264010), 5300 Arsenal Street, Zip 63139–1463; tel. 314/877–6501, **A**1 10 **F**11 30 39 65 68 75 86 87 98 100 101 106 130 143 146
Primary Contact: Laurent D. Javois, Chief Executive Officer
COO: Felix T Vincenz, Chief Operating Officer
CFO: James D Martin, Chief Financial Officer
CMO: Roy Wilson, M.D., Medical Director
CHR: Michael McFarlane, Chief Human Resource Officer
CNO: Deborah Mokry, Chief Nurse Executive
Web address: www.dmh.missouri.gov
Control: State, Government, nonfederal **Service:** Psychiatric

Staffed Beds: 180 Admissions: 37 Census: 178 Outpatient Visits: 0 **Births:** 0 **Total Expense ($000):** 35234 **Payroll Expense ($000):** 18549 **Personnel:** 516

ST. LUKE'S DES PERES HOSPITAL (260176), 2345 Dougherty Ferry Road, Zip 63122–3313; tel. 314/966–9100, **A**1 3 5 10 12 13 **F**3 12 15 18 20 22 24 26 29 34 35 36 37 40 44 48 49 50 58 59 60 64 68 69 70 75 77 79 81 85 86 87 93 107 108 110 111 115 119 126 130 132 146 149
Primary Contact: David E. Loving, FACHE, Chief Executive Officer
CFO: Steven Downs, Chief Financial Officer
CIO: Mary Estes, Director Information Systems
CHR: Kathaleen Clutts, Chief Human Resources Officer
CNO: Mary Ann Hampton, MSN, R.N., Chief Nursing Officer
Web address: www.despereshospital.com
Control: Corporation, Investor–owned (for–profit) **Service:** General medical and surgical

Staffed Beds: 88 Admissions: 4305 Census: 37 Outpatient Visits: 24541 **Births:** 0 **Total Expense ($000):** 107005 **Payroll Expense ($000):** 29384 **Personnel:** 492

THE REHABILITATION INSTITUTE OF ST. LOUIS (263028), 4455 Duncan Avenue, Zip 63110–1111; tel. 314/658–3800, **A**1 3 7 10 **F**29 34 44 56 58 60 64 68 74 75 79 82 87 90 91 93 94 100 130 132 143 146 148 149 150 **S** Encompass Health Corporation, Birmingham, AL
Primary Contact: Mark Dwyer, Chief Executive Officer
CMO: David Carr, M.D., Physician Medical Director
CHR: Heather Savage, Director Human Resources
CNO: Angelina Sherman, R.N., MSN, Chief Nursing Officer
Web address: www.rehabinstitutestl.com
Control: Partnership, Investor–owned (for–profit) **Service:** Rehabilitation

Staffed Beds: 131 Admissions: 2174 Census: 84 Outpatient Visits: 26601 **Births:** 0 **Total Expense ($000):** 58661 **Payroll Expense ($000):** 20038 **Personnel:** 297

MO

Hospital, Medicare Provider Number, Address, Telephone, Approval, Facility, and Physician Codes, Health Care System

★ American Hospital Association (AHA) membership
□ The Joint Commission accreditation
○ Healthcare Facilities Accreditation Program
◇ DNV Healthcare Inc. accreditation
⇑ Center for Improvement in Healthcare Quality Accreditation
△ Commission on Accreditation of Rehabilitation Facilities (CARF) accreditation

VETERANS AFFAIRS ST. LOUIS HEALTH CARE SYSTEM, 915 North Grand, Zip 63106–1621; tel. 314/652–4100, (Nonreporting) **A**1 3 5 7 **S** Department of Veterans Affairs, Perry Point, MD
Primary Contact: Keith D. Repko, Director
CFO: Karen Westerheide, Chief Financial Officer
CIO: Steve Warmbold, Director Information Management Service Line
CHR: Marie Lewis, Human Resources Liaison
CNO: Richard Holt, R.N., Associate Director Patient Care Services
Web address: www.stlouis.va.gov/
Control: Veterans Affairs, Government, federal **Service**: General medical and surgical

Staffed Beds: 356

SAINT PETERS—St. Charles County

BARNES–JEWISH ST. PETERS HOSPITAL (260191), 10 Hospital Drive, Zip 63376–1659; tel. 636/916–9000, **A**1 3 5 10 **F**3 4 11 15 18 20 22 26 28 29 30 31 34 35 40 45 46 49 51 57 59 60 64 70 75 77 78 79 81 85 86 90 93 107 108 110 111 115 117 118 119 120 121 123 129 130 132 135 146 147 148 149 154 **S** BJC HealthCare, Saint Louis, MO
Primary Contact: Chris Watts, President
CFO: Glen Schwaegel, Vice President and Chief Financial Officer
CMO: Feliipe Orellana, Chief Medical Officer
CIO: Cindy Gross, Director of Finance
CHR: Michael J Miller, Director Human Resources
CNO: Lauren Beckmann, Vice President Patient Services and Chief Nursing Officer
Web address: www.bjsph.org/
Control: Other not–for–profit (including NFP Corporation) **Service**: General medical and surgical

Staffed Beds: 101 Admissions: 5027 Census: 57 Outpatient Visits: 86483 Births: 0 Total Expense ($000): 123126 Payroll Expense ($000): 42727 Personnel: 522

SALEM—Dent County

SALEM MEMORIAL DISTRICT HOSPITAL (261318), Highway 72 North, Zip 65560–0774, Mailing Address: P.O. Box 774, Zip 65560–0774; tel. 573/729–6626, (Total facility includes 18 beds in nursing–type unit) **A**10 18 **F**3 7 11 29 30 34 40 59 60 62 67 75 81 85 87 89 107 115 119 127 128 130 133 135 146 149
Primary Contact: Kasey Lucas, Chief Executive Officer, Hospital Administrator
CFO: Becky Cunningham, Controller
CMO: John Demorlis, M.D., Chief Medical Staff
CHR: Jodie Gorman, Director Human Resources
Web address: www.smdh.net
Control: Hospital district or authority, Government, nonfederal **Service**: General medical and surgical

Staffed Beds: 43 Admissions: 534 Census: 26 Outpatient Visits: 36002 Births: 0 Total Expense ($000): 20294 Payroll Expense ($000): 8508 Personnel: 195

SEDALIA—Pettis County

BOTHWELL REGIONAL HEALTH CENTER (260009), 601 East 14th Street, Zip 65301–5972, Mailing Address: P.O. Box 1706, Zip 65302–1706; tel. 660/826–8833, (Total facility includes 10 beds in nursing home–type unit) **A**1 10 **F**3 9 11 13 14 15 18 20 22 28 29 30 31 34 35 39 40 51 54 56 57 59 60 64 65 68 70 73 74 75 76 77 78 79 80 81 82 84 85 86 87 89 92 93 107 108 110 111 114 115 116 117 118 119 120 121 123 124 127 128 129 130 131 132 135 146 147 148
Primary Contact: James A. Robertson Jr, President and Chief Executive Officer
COO: Thomas Bailey, Chief Operating Officer
CIO: Tom Fairfax, Director Information Systems
CHR: Deb Clemmer, Vice President Human Resources
CNO: Regina W Crow, R.N., Chief Nursing Officer
Web address: www.brhc.org
Control: City, Government, nonfederal **Service**: General medical and surgical

Staffed Beds: 137 Admissions: 4334 Census: 58 Outpatient Visits: 132698 Births: 493 Total Expense ($000): 107914 Payroll Expense ($000): 41348 Personnel: 681

SIKESTON—Scott County

MISSOURI DELTA MEDICAL CENTER (260113), 1008 North Main Street, Zip 63801–5044; tel. 573/471–1600, **A**1 10 **F**3 13 15 18 28 29 30 31 34 35 37 40 45 50 51 53 54 56 57 59 60 62 64 68 70 74 75 76 77 78 79 81 82 85 86 87 89 90 93 97 98 103 107 108 109 110 111 115 116 117 118 119 126 127 129 130 131 132 144 146 147 148 149
Primary Contact: Jason Schrumpf, President
CFO: Greg Carda, Vice President Finance
Web address: www.missouridelta.com
Control: Other not–for–profit (including NFP Corporation) **Service**: General medical and surgical

Staffed Beds: 110 Admissions: 3895 Census: 50 Outpatient Visits: 217765 Births: 399 Total Expense ($000): 92621 Payroll Expense ($000): 40828 Personnel: 753

SPRINGFIELD—Greene County

COX MEDICAL CENTERS (260040), 1423 North Jefferson Street, Zip 65802–1988; tel. 417/269–3000, (Includes COX MEDICAL CENTER NORTH, 1423 North Jefferson Avenue, Springfield, MO, Zip 65802; tel. 417/269–3000; COX MEDICAL CENTER SOUTH, 3801 South National Avenue, Springfield, MO, Zip 65807; tel. 417/269–6000) **A**3 5 10 21 **F**3 4 5 7 11 12 13 15 17 18 19 20 22 24 26 28 29 30 31 32 34 35 38 39 40 41 43 44 45 46 47 48 49 50 51 52 53 54 55 56 57 58 59 60 61 62 64 65 68 69 70 71 72 74 75 76 77 78 79 80 81 82 84 85 86 87 88 89 90 92 93 94 95 96 97 98 99 100 101 102 103 104 107 108 110 111 114 115 116 117 118 119 120 121 124 126 127 128 129 130 131 132 134 135 143 144 146 147 148 149 150 152 154 **P**3 6 **S** CoxHealth, Springfield, MO
Primary Contact: Steven D. Edwards, President and Chief Executive Officer
CFO: Jacob McWay, Senior Vice President and Chief Financial Officer
CMO: Frank Romero, M.D., Chief Medical Officer
CIO: Bruce Robison, Vice President and Chief Information Officer
CHR: John Hursh, Vice President Human Resources
CNO: Karen Kramer, R.N., Vice President and System Chief Nursing Officer
Web address: www.coxhealth.com
Control: Other not–for–profit (including NFP Corporation) **Service**: General medical and surgical

Staffed Beds: 640 Admissions: 33072 Census: 471 Outpatient Visits: 1575736 Births: 3596 Total Expense ($000): 1036812 Payroll Expense ($000): 342388 Personnel: 8035

LAKELAND BEHAVIORAL HEALTH SYSTEM (264024), 440 South Market Street, Zip 65806–2026; tel. 417/865–5581, **A**1 10 **F**98 99 103 106 130 **P**6 **S** Acadia Healthcare Company, Inc., Franklin, TN
Primary Contact: Nathan Duncan, Chief Executive Officer
COO: Randy Fox, Director Performance Improvement and Risk Management
CFO: Rick Crump, Chief Financial Officer
CMO: Richard Aiken, M.D., Medical Director
CIO: Brad Strothkamp, Chief Information Systems
CHR: Dave England, Director Human Resources
Web address: www.lakeland–hospital.com
Control: Corporation, Investor–owned (for–profit) **Service**: Psychiatric

Staffed Beds: 100 Admissions: 2400 Census: 85 Outpatient Visits: 0 Births: 0 Total Expense ($000): 23263 Payroll Expense ($000): 13500 Personnel: 316

MERCY HOSPITAL SPRINGFIELD (260065), 1235 East Cherokee Street, Zip 65804–2263; tel. 417/820–2000, (Includes MERCY CHILDREN'S HOSPITAL SPRINGFIELD, 1235 East Cherokee Street, Springfield, MO, Zip 65804–2203; tel. 417/820–2000; MERCY ORTHOPEDIC HOSPITAL SPRINGFIELD, 3050 East Riverbluff Boulevard, Ozark, MO, Zip 65721; tel. 417/820–5611; Robert Steele, M.D., President) (Total facility includes 97 beds in nursing home–type unit) **A**1 3 5 10 **F**3 4 5 7 9 11 12 13 15 16 17 18 19 20 22 24 26 28 29 30 31 32 34 35 37 38 39 40 43 44 45 46 49 50 51 54 55 56 57 58 59 60 61 62 63 64 65 66 67 68 70 71 72 73 74 75 76 77 78 79 81 82 84 85 86 87 88 89 90 91 92 93 94 96 97 98 103 104 107 108 110 111 114 115 117 118 119 120 121 123 124 126 128 129 130 131 132 135 143 146 147 148 149 **P**6 8 **S** Mercy, Chesterfield, MO
Primary Contact: Jon D. Swope, Interim President
COO: Brent Hubbard, Chief Operating Officer
CFO: Scott Reynolds, Vice President Finance
CMO: Allan Allphin, M.D., Chief of Staff
CIO: Lori Sturgill, Vice President Business Partnership
CHR: Tanya Maricn, Interim Vice President Human Resources
Web address: www.mercy.net/springfieldmo
Control: Church operated, Nongovernment, not–for–profit **Service**: General medical and surgical

Staffed Beds: 744 Admissions: 34547 Census: 462 Outpatient Visits: 559866 Births: 2851 Total Expense ($000): 934605 Payroll Expense ($000): 347569 Personnel: 7949

MERCY REHABILITION HOSPITAL SPRINGFIELD (263032), 5904 South Southwood Road, Zip 65804–5234; tel. 417/227–9000, **A**1 10 **F**3 29 30 90 96 130 132 148
Primary Contact: Jay Guffey, Chief Executive Officer
CFO: Melissa Campbell, Chief Financial Officer and Controller
CMO: Hollis Bell, M.D., Esq Medical Director
CHR: Melissa Mooney, Director Human Resources
CNO: Paul Moore, R.N., Chief Clinical Officer
Web address: www.mercy.net
Control: Partnership, Investor–owned (for–profit) **Service**: Rehabilitation

Staffed Beds: 60 Admissions: 1332 Census: 44 Outpatient Visits: 0 Births: 0 Total Expense ($000): 17061 Payroll Expense ($000): 7822 Personnel: 194

MO

SELECT SPECIALTY HOSPITAL–SPRINGFIELD (262017), 1630 East Primrose Street, Zip 65804–7929; tel. 417/885–4700, **A**1 10 **F**1 3 29 45 85 107 114 148 **S** Select Medical Corporation, Mechanicsburg, PA
Primary Contact: Steve Patterson, Chief Executive Officer
CHR: Tonya Eddington, Coordinator Human Resources
Web address: www.selectspecialtyhospitals.com/company/locations/springfield.aspx
Control: Corporation, Investor–owned (for–profit) **Service**: Acute long–term care hospital

Staffed Beds: 44 **Admissions:** 421 **Census:** 28 **Outpatient Visits:** 0 **Births:** 0 **Total Expense ($000):** 19321 **Payroll Expense ($000):** 8475 **Personnel:** 135

STE GENEVIEVE—Ste. Genevieve County

STE. GENEVIEVE COUNTY MEMORIAL HOSPITAL (261330), 800 Ste Genevieve Drive, Zip 63670–1434; tel. 573/883–2751, **A**1 10 18 **F**2 3 11 13 14 15 18 28 29 31 34 35 40 50 53 56 57 59 62 64 65 66 68 75 76 77 78 79 81 82 85 86 87 89 92 93 107 110 111 115 119 124 127 129 130 131 132 133 135 145 146 147 148 154 **P**6
Primary Contact: Thomas Keim, Chief Executive Officer
CFO: Susan Eckenfels, Chief Financial Officer
CMO: Joseph Sharlow, M.D., Chief of Staff
CHR: Sarah Jo Kelley, Executive Director of Human Resources and Support Services
CNO: Rita Brumfield, R.N., MSN, Chief Nursing Officer
Web address: www.stegenevievehospital.org
Control: County, Government, nonfederal **Service**: General medical and surgical

Staffed Beds: 25 **Admissions:** 865 **Census:** 10 **Outpatient Visits:** 115171 **Births:** 168 **Total Expense ($000):** 45239 **Payroll Expense ($000):** 18758 **Personnel:** 351

SULLIVAN—Crawford County

MISSOURI BAPTIST SULLIVAN HOSPITAL (261337), 751 Sappington Bridge Road, Zip 63080–2354; tel. 573/468–4186, **A**10 18 **F**3 4 7 11 12 13 15 28 29 30 31 34 35 40 53 56 57 59 63 64 65 70 75 76 77 78 79 81 82 83 84 85 86 87 89 90 93 97 98 102 103 104 107 111 115 119 127 129 130 131 132 133 146 148 152 154 **S** BJC HealthCare, Saint Louis, MO
Primary Contact: Tony Schwarm, President
CFO: Angela Wilks, Finance Director
CMO: Alison Baker, M.D., Chief of Staff
CHR: Kathleen Reed, Manager Human Resources
CNO: Carmen J. Bartolotta, Chief Nursing Officer
Web address: www.missouribaptistsullivan.org
Control: Other not–for–profit (including NFP Corporation) **Service**: General medical and surgical

Staffed Beds: 35 **Admissions:** 2057 **Census:** 22 **Outpatient Visits:** 101861 **Births:** 313 **Total Expense ($000):** 51177 **Payroll Expense ($000):** 20570 **Personnel:** 360

SWEET SPRINGS—Saline County

I–70 COMMUNITY HOSPITAL (261334), 105 Hospital Drive, Zip 65351–2229; tel. 660/335–4700, **A**10 18 **F**3 11 29 32 30 40 45 59 64 65 68 75 77 79 81 83 87 90 93 98 102 107 111 127 128 130 133 143 148 154 **S** Rural Community Hospitals of America, Kansas City, MO
Primary Contact: Jeff Bloemker, Chief Executive Officer
CFO: Cathy Berube, Chief Financial Officer
CMO: Deborah Herrmann, M.D., Chief of Staff
CIO: Diane Swift, Director Medical Records
CHR: Tina Bredehoeft, Human Resources
CNO: Nancy Gardner, Chief Nursing Officer
Web address: www.i70medcenter.com
Control: Corporation, Investor–owned (for–profit) **Service**: General medical and surgical

Staffed Beds: 11 **Admissions:** 154 **Census:** 4 **Outpatient Visits:** 10377 **Births:** 0 **Total Expense ($000):** 9080 **Payroll Expense ($000):** 3729 **Personnel:** 59

TRENTON—Grundy County

WRIGHT MEMORIAL HOSPITAL (261309), 191 Iowa Boulevard, Zip 64683–8343; tel. 660/358–5700, **A**10 18 **F**3 11 15 18 28 29 30 31 34 35 40 44 45 50 59 64 68 74 75 77 78 79 81 82 85 87 89 90 93 97 102 104 107 108 110 111 115 119 127 129 130 133 141 146 148 **P**6 **S** Saint Luke's Health System, Kansas City, MO
Primary Contact: Steven M Schieber, MBA, FACMPE, FACHE, Chief Executive Officer
CFO: Leslie Reed, Chief Financial Officer
CMO: Gerald C Zabielski, M.D., Chief Medical Staff
CHR: Jenny Donovan, Director Human Resources
Web address: www.saintlukeshealthsystem.org
Control: Other not–for–profit (including NFP Corporation) **Service**: General medical and surgical

Staffed Beds: 15 **Admissions:** 503 **Census:** 8 **Outpatient Visits:** 66524 **Births:** 0 **Total Expense ($000):** 31209 **Payroll Expense ($000):** 10886 **Personnel:** 157

TROY—Lincoln County

MERCY HOSPITAL LINCOLN (261319), 1000 East Cherry Street, Zip 63379–1513; tel. 636/528–8551, **A**1 10 18 **F**3 11 15 18 28 29 30 34 35 40 44 45 50 51 57 59 62 63 64 65 68 70 75 77 79 81 85 86 87 90 93 104 107 110 111 113 114 119 127 129 130 131 132 133 135 144 146 149 154 **P**6 8 **S** Mercy, Chesterfield, MO
Primary Contact: Anthony Rothermich, Administrator
CFO: Mark Thorn, FACHE, Executive Director, Finance
CIO: Travis Boyd, Manager, Information Technology
CHR: Mary Kay Kunza, Manager Human Resources
Web address: www.mercy.net
Control: Other not–for–profit (including NFP Corporation) **Service**: General medical and surgical

Staffed Beds: 25 **Admissions:** 667 **Census:** 9 **Outpatient Visits:** 88158 **Births:** 0 **Total Expense ($000):** 33615 **Payroll Expense ($000):** 15679 **Personnel:** 232

UNIONVILLE—Putnam County

PUTNAM COUNTY MEMORIAL HOSPITAL (261305), 1926 Oak Street, Zip 63565–1180, Mailing Address: P.O. Box 389, Zip 63565–0389; tel. 660/947–2411, **A**10 18 **F**3 15 29 32 34 35 40 45 48 50 57 59 75 77 81 82 85 90 93 97 102 107 110 111 115 119 127 128 130 133 135 145 147 148 149 **P**5
Primary Contact: Gayle Pickens, Chief Executive Officer
COO: Jerry Cummings, Chief Operating Officer
CMO: Dawn Ann Fairley, M.D., Chief of Staff
CHR: Debbie Douglas, Director Human Resources
CNO: Nathan Baughman, Chief Nursing Officer
Web address: www.pcmhosp.com
Control: County, Government, nonfederal **Service**: General medical and surgical

Staffed Beds: 15 **Admissions:** 306 **Census:** 4 **Outpatient Visits:** 15033 **Births:** 0 **Total Expense ($000):** 127336 **Payroll Expense ($000):** 4100 **Personnel:** 84

WARRENSBURG—Johnson County

WESTERN MISSOURI MEDICAL CENTER (260097), 403 Burkarth Road, Zip 64093–3101; tel. 660/747–2500, **A**1 10 20 **F**3 8 11 12 13 15 17 18 28 29 30 31 32 34 35 40 43 45 47 56 57 59 61 64 65 68 70 74 75 76 77 78 79 81 82 85 89 90 93 98 102 103 107 108 110 111 115 117 118 119 127 129 130 131 132 133 135 144 146 147 148 154 **P**6
Primary Contact: Darinda Reberry, MSN, R.N., President and Chief Executive Officer
CFO: Dean Ohmart, Vice President Financial Services and Chief Financial Officer
CIO: Bill Ladd, Director Information Services
CHR: Dennis Long, Director Human Resources
CNO: Jennifer Koepke, R.N., Vice President of Patient Care Services and Chief Nursing Officer
Web address: www.wmmc.com
Control: County, Government, nonfederal **Service**: General medical and surgical

Staffed Beds: 69 **Admissions:** 3002 **Census:** 27 **Outpatient Visits:** 158759 **Births:** 697 **Total Expense ($000):** 101433 **Payroll Expense ($000):** 40942 **Personnel:** 612

MO

Hospital, Medicare Provider Number, Address, Telephone, Approval, Facility, and Physician Codes, Health Care System

★ American Hospital Association (AHA) membership
□ The Joint Commission accreditation
○ Healthcare Facilities Accreditation Program
◇ DNV Healthcare Inc. accreditation
⇑ Center for Improvement in Healthcare Quality Accreditation
△ Commission on Accreditation of Rehabilitation Facilities (CARF) accreditation

WASHINGTON—Franklin County

MERCY HOSPITAL WASHINGTON (260052), 901 East Fifth Street,
Zip 63090–3127; tel. 636/239–8000, **A**1 10 **F**3 5 8 11 12 13 14 15 17 18 20
22 26 28 29 30 31 32 34 35 39 40 43 44 46 48 49 50 51 52 53 54 57 59
61 64 66 68 69 70 73 74 75 76 77 78 79 80 81 82 84 85 87 89 90 93 94
96 97 98 99 100 101 104 107 108 110 111 114 116 117 118 119 120 121
123 127 129 130 131 132 134 135 143 144 146 147 149 154 **P**6 8 **S** Mercy,
Chesterfield, MO
Primary Contact: Eric J. Eoloff, President
COO: Joan Frost, R.N., Chief Operating Officer
CFO: Cheryl Matejka, Chief Financial Officer
CMO: Thomas Riechers, M.D., Chief Medical Staff
CIO: Michael McCreary, Chief of Services
CHR: Barbara Grayson, Vice President Human Resources
CNO: Anna Landon, Chief Nursing Officer
Web address: www.mercy.net
Control: Other not–for–profit (including NFP Corporation) **Service**: General
medical and surgical

Staffed Beds: 148 **Admissions:** 5740 **Census:** 49 **Outpatient Visits:**
346434 **Births:** 802 **Total Expense ($000):** 162259 **Payroll Expense
($000):** 60731 **Personnel:** 821

WENTZVILLE—St. Charles County

SSM HEALTH ST. JOSEPH – WENTZVILLE See Ssm Health St. Joseph –
St. Charles, Saint Charles

WEST PLAINS—Howell County

OZARKS MEDICAL CENTER (260078), 1100 Kentucky Avenue,
Zip 65775–2029, Mailing Address: P.O. Box 1100, Zip 65775–1100;
tel. 417/256–9111, **A**1 10 **F**2 3 5 11 12 13 15 17 18 20 22 24 28 29 30 31 34
38 40 44 45 49 50 57 59 61 62 63 64 68 70 74 75 76 77 78 79 81 82 84 85
86 87 89 90 91 93 94 98 99 100 101 102 103 104 107 108 110 111 115 118
119 120 121 127 129 130 131 132 135 144 145 146 147 148 154 **P**8
Primary Contact: Thomas Keller, President and Chief Executive Officer
COO: Pamela R. Lee, Chief Operating Officer
CFO: Kim Thompson, Vice President and Chief Financial Officer
CMO: Walter R Holloway, Chief Medical Officer
CIO: John Wilcox, Chief Information Officer
CHR: Connie Schott, Vice President, Human Resources
CNO: Kurt Abbey, Chief Nursing Officer
Web address: www.ozarksmedicalcenter.com
Control: Other not–for–profit (including NFP Corporation) **Service**: General
medical and surgical

Staffed Beds: 103 **Admissions:** 5464 **Census:** 50 **Outpatient Visits:**
544601 **Births:** 587 **Total Expense ($000):** 150652 **Payroll Expense
($000):** 66861 **Personnel:** 1022

WINDSOR—Henry County

ROYAL OAKS HOSPITAL (264020), 307 North Main, Zip 65360–1449;
tel. 660/647–2182, (Nonreporting) **A**1 3 5 10
Primary Contact: Alan W. Greiman, Chief Executive Officer and President
CFO: Jake Matthew Krafve, Chief Financial Officer
CMO: Syed Arshad Husain, M.D., Executive Vice President and Chief Medical
Officer
CIO: Richard Colvert, Chief Information Officer
CHR: Diane Coletta, Vice President Human Resources
CNO: Saundra Overton, R.N., Chief Nursing Officer
Web address: www.compasshealthnetwork.org
Control: Other not–for–profit (including NFP Corporation) **Service**: Psychiatric

Staffed Beds: 41

MO

Many Facility Codes have changed. Please refer to the AHA Guide Code Chart.   © 2018 AHA Guide

MONTANA

ANACONDA—Deer Lodge County

★ **COMMUNITY HOSPITAL OF ANACONDA (271335)**, 401 West Pennsylvania Street, Zip 59711; tel. 406/563–8500, (Total facility includes 32 beds in nursing home–type unit) **A**10 18 **F**3 8 11 13 15 29 30 31 34 35 40 43 45 50 54 57 59 62 63 64 70 74 75 76 77 78 79 81 82 87 89 93 97 99 104 107 111 114 116 119 128 130 133 135 143 144 146 148 154 **P**6
Primary Contact: Steve McNeece, President and Chief Executive Officer
CFO: Laura Austin, Vice President Finance and Chief Financial Officer
CMO: Freddy Bartoletti, M.D., Chief of Staff
CHR: Meg Hickey–Boynton, Director Human Resources and Marketing
CNO: Jamie Johnson, R.N., Vice President Nursing
Web address: www.communityhospitalofanaconda.org
Control: Other not–for–profit (including NFP Corporation) **Service:** General medical and surgical

Staffed Beds: 57 **Admissions:** 1193 **Census:** 44 **Outpatient Visits:** 61246 **Births:** 187 **Total Expense ($000):** 61540 **Payroll Expense ($000):** 28691 **Personnel:** 361

BAKER—Fallon County

FALLON MEDICAL COMPLEX (271301), 202 South 4th Street West, Zip 59313–9156, Mailing Address: P.O. Box 820, Zip 59313–0820; tel. 406/778–3331, **A**10 18 **F**11 15 32 34 40 56 57 59 62 64 65 66 68 69 75 93 97 107 110 114 119 127 130 133 146 148 149 **P**6
Primary Contact: David Espeland, Chief Executive Officer
CFO: Selena Nelson, Chief Financial Officer
CMO: Darryl Espeland, D.O., Chief Medical Staff
CIO: Susan Stevens, Information Technology Specialist
CHR: Theresa Myers, Personnel Director
CNO: Susan Lunde, R.N., Director of Nursing
Web address: www.fallonmedical.org
Control: Other not–for–profit (including NFP Corporation) **Service:** General medical and surgical

Staffed Beds: 25 **Admissions:** 150 **Census:** 18 **Outpatient Visits:** 17837 **Births:** 0 **Total Expense ($000):** 10320 **Payroll Expense ($000):** 4225 **Personnel:** 78

BIG SANDY—Chouteau County

★ **BIG SANDY MEDICAL CENTER (271311)**, 166 Montana Avenue East, Zip 59520–8474, Mailing Address: P.O. Box 530, Zip 59520–0530; tel. 406/378–2188, (Total facility includes 22 beds in nursing home–type unit) **A**10 18 **F**40 64 93 127 128 133 154
Primary Contact: Leah Griffith, Chief Executive Officer
CFO: Nora Grubb, Chief Financial Officer
Web address: www.bsmc.org
Control: Other not–for–profit (including NFP Corporation) **Service:** General medical and surgical

Staffed Beds: 30 **Admissions:** 74 **Census:** 17 **Outpatient Visits:** 2285 **Births:** 0 **Total Expense ($000):** 3102 **Payroll Expense ($000):** 1302 **Personnel:** 39

BIG SKY—Gallatin County

BOZEMAN HEALTH BIG SKY MEDICAL CENTER (270089), 334 Town Center Avenue, Zip 59716, Mailing Address: P.O. Box 161529, Zip 59716–1529; tel. 406/995–6995, **A**10 **F**3 34 35 40 45 50 57 59 65 68 87 97 107 111 114 135
Primary Contact: Tracy Reamy, Administrator
Web address: www.bigskymedicalcenter.org/
Control: Other not–for–profit (including NFP Corporation) **Service:** General medical and surgical

Staffed Beds: 4 **Admissions:** 26 **Census:** 1 **Outpatient Visits:** 12663 **Births:** 0 **Personnel:** 38

BIG TIMBER—Sweet Grass County

★ **PIONEER MEDICAL CENTER (271313)**, 301 West Seventh Avenue, Zip 59011–7893, Mailing Address: P.O. Box 1228, Zip 59011–1228; tel. 406/932–4603, (Nonreporting) **A**10 18
Primary Contact: Gary Hamilton, Chief Executive Officer
CFO: Kyle Gee, Chief Financial Officer
CMO: Benjamin P Bullington, M.D., Chief of Staff
CHR: Miki Gregorich, Director Human Resources
CNO: Randi Pike, Director of Nursing
Web address: www.pmcmt.org/
Control: County, Government, nonfederal **Service:** General medical and surgical

Staffed Beds: 50

BILLINGS—Yellowstone County

☐ **ADVANCED CARE HOSPITAL OF MONTANA (272001)**, 3528 Gabel Road, Zip 59102–7307; tel. 406/373–8000, (Nonreporting) **A**1 10 **S** Ernest Health, Inc., Albuquerque, NM
Primary Contact: Judi Powers, Chief Executive Officer
Web address: www.achm.ernesthealth.com
Control: Corporation, Investor–owned (for–profit) **Service:** Acute long–term care hospital

Staffed Beds: 40

⊞ **BILLINGS CLINIC (270004)**, 2800 10th Avenue North, Zip 59101–0703, Mailing Address: P.O. Box 37000, Zip 59107–7000; tel. 406/657–4000, (Total facility includes 125 beds in nursing home–type unit) **A**1 2 3 10 19 **F**3 7 8 9 10 11 12 13 15 17 18 19 20 22 24 26 27 28 29 30 31 32 34 35 36 38 40 41 43 44 45 46 47 48 49 50 51 52 54 55 56 57 58 59 60 61 64 65 66 68 70 71 72 74 75 76 77 78 79 81 82 84 85 86 87 89 91 92 93 97 98 99 100 101 102 103 104 105 107 108 110 111 114 115 116 117 118 119 120 121 124 126 128 129 130 132 134 135 136 143 146 147 148 154 **P**6
Primary Contact: Randall K. Gibb, M.D., Chief Executive Officer
CFO: Connie F Prewitt, Chief Financial Officer
CMO: Randall K. Gibb, M.D., Chief Executive Officer
CIO: Chris E Stevens, Chief Information Officer
CHR: Karla Stauffer, Executive Director People Resources
CNO: Lu Byrd, R.N., MSN, Vice President Hospital Operations and Chief Nursing Officer
Web address: www.billingsclinic.com
Control: Other not–for–profit (including NFP Corporation) **Service:** General medical and surgical

Staffed Beds: 400 **Admissions:** 16203 **Census:** 274 **Outpatient Visits:** 846021 **Births:** 1171 **Total Expense ($000):** 655607 **Payroll Expense ($000):** 324199 **Personnel:** 3623

⊞ △ **ST. VINCENT HEALTHCARE (270049)**, 1233 North 30th Street, Zip 59101–0165, Mailing Address: P.O. Box 35200, Zip 59107–5200; tel. 406/237–7000, **A**1 2 3 7 10 **F**3 7 11 12 13 15 18 19 20 22 24 26 28 29 30 31 32 34 35 36 37 38 40 43 44 46 47 49 50 51 56 57 58 59 60 61 64 68 70 71 72 74 75 76 77 78 79 81 82 84 85 86 87 88 89 90 92 93 97 100 101 107 108 110 111 114 115 116 117 118 119 120 121 123 124 126 129 130 131 132 134 135 143 144 145 146 147 148 149 154 **P**6 **S** SCL Health, Broomfield, CO
Primary Contact: Steve Loveless, President and Chief Executive Officer
CMO: Michael Schweitzer, M.D., Chief Medical Officer
CIO: Al Rooney, Director Information Systems
Web address: www.svh–mt.org
Control: Church operated, Nongovernment, not–for–profit **Service:** General medical and surgical

Staffed Beds: 221 **Admissions:** 12041 **Census:** 150 **Outpatient Visits:** 145360 **Births:** 1561 **Total Expense ($000):** 346248 **Payroll Expense ($000):** 110225 **Personnel:** 1790

MT

Hospital, Medicare Provider Number, Address, Telephone, Approval, Facility, and Physician Codes, Health Care System

★ American Hospital Association (AHA) membership
☐ The Joint Commission accreditation
○ Healthcare Facilities Accreditation Program
◇ DNV Healthcare Inc. accreditation
⇑ Center for Improvement in Healthcare Quality Accreditation
△ Commission on Accreditation of Rehabilitation Facilities (CARF) accreditation

© 2018 AHA Guide   *Many Facility Codes have changed. Please refer to the AHA Guide Code Chart.*   Hospitals **A373**

BOZEMAN—Gallatin County

✚ **BOZEMAN HEALTH DEACONESS HOSPITAL (270057)**, 915 Highland Boulevard, Zip 59715–6902; tel. 406/585–5000, **A**1 2 10 20 **F**3 10 13 18 19 20 22 28 29 30 31 32 34 35 36 37 38 39 40 43 45 49 50 54 56 57 58 59 64 65 70 71 74 75 76 77 78 79 81 82 83 84 85 86 87 92 93 96 97 100 107 108 111 115 118 119 120 121 123 125 129 130 132 135 146 147 148 149 154 **P**6 7
Primary Contact: John Hill, President and Chief Executive Officer
CIO: Brad Ludford, Chief Financial Officer
Web address: www.bozemandeaconess.org
Control: Other not–for–profit (including NFP Corporation) **Service**: General medical and surgical

Staffed Beds: 83 **Admissions**: 5467 **Census**: 51 **Outpatient Visits**: 422968
Births: 1295 **Personnel**: 1326

BUTTE—Silver Bow County

✚ **ST. JAMES HEALTHCARE (270017)**, 400 South Clark Street, Zip 59701–2328; tel. 406/723–2500, **A**1 10 **F**3 11 13 15 18 20 22 28 29 30 31 34 35 40 43 45 47 48 50 51 56 57 59 64 65 68 70 71 72 75 76 77 78 79 81 82 85 86 87 89 93 97 107 108 110 111 114 115 117 118 119 120 121 124 126 127 130 131 132 135 146 147 148 149 **S** SCL Health, Broomfield, CO
Primary Contact: Jay Doyle, President and Chief Executive Officer
CFO: David Brain, Interim Vice President Finance
CMO: Dennis Salisbury, M.D., Vice President for Medical Affairs
CHR: Trisha Palmer, Director
CNO: Mary Winters, Interim Chief Nursing Officer
Web address: www.stjameshealthcare.org
Control: Other not–for–profit (including NFP Corporation) **Service**: General medical and surgical

Staffed Beds: 67 **Admissions**: 3431 **Census**: 37 **Outpatient Visits**: 53753
Births: 267 **Total Expense ($000)**: 100865 **Payroll Expense ($000)**: 34482
Personnel: 507

CHESTER—Liberty County

LIBERTY MEDICAL CENTER (271334), 315 West Madison Avenue, Zip 59522, Mailing Address: P.O. Box 705, Zip 59522–0705; tel. 406/759–5181, **A**10 18 **F**2 3 10 11 34 35 40 43 45 56 59 64 67 81 86 87 93 97 107 114 119 127 128 130 133 **P**6
Primary Contact: Matthew Waller, Chief Executive Officer
CMO: Gladys Young, M.D., Chief of Staff
CHR: Bev Halter, Director Human Resources and Payroll
CNO: Shirley Morkrid, Chief Nursing Officer
Web address: www.lchnh.org
Control: Other not–for–profit (including NFP Corporation) **Service**: General medical and surgical

Staffed Beds: 25 **Admissions**: 63 **Census**: 1 **Outpatient Visits**: 8548
Births: 0 **Total Expense ($000)**: 7166 **Payroll Expense ($000)**: 3513
Personnel: 92

CHOTEAU—Teton County

BENEFIS TETON MEDICAL CENTER (271307), 915 4th Street North West, Zip 59422–9123; tel. 406/466–5763, (Total facility includes 36 beds in nursing home–type unit) **A**10 18 **F**34 35 40 41 43 53 56 57 59 63 64 68 93 107 127 128 133 143 154 **P**6 **S** Benefis Health System, Great Falls, MT
Primary Contact: Louie King, Chief Executive Officer
Web address: www.tetonmedicalcenter.net
Control: Other not–for–profit (including NFP Corporation) **Service**: General medical and surgical

Staffed Beds: 46 **Admissions**: 71 **Census**: 26 **Outpatient Visits**: 6678
Births: 0 **Total Expense ($000)**: 8012 **Payroll Expense ($000)**: 3517
Personnel: 59

CIRCLE—McCone County

★ **MCCONE COUNTY HEALTH CENTER (271305)**, 605 Sullivan Avenue, Zip 59215, Mailing Address: P.O. Box 48, Zip 59215–0048; tel. 406/485–3381, **A**10 18 **F**2 3 11 34 40 41 57 58 59 65 69 86 87 93 133 135 143 146 149 154
Primary Contact: Nancy Rosaaen, Chief Executive Officer
CFO: Nancy Rosaaen, Chief Executive Officer
CHR: Jacque Gardner, Administrative Assistant, Clinic Manager, Co–Chief Financial Officer and Chief Human Resources
Web address: www.mcconehealth.org/
Control: County, Government, nonfederal **Service**: General medical and surgical

Staffed Beds: 30 **Admissions**: 46 **Census**: 20 **Outpatient Visits**: 660
Births: 0 **Total Expense ($000)**: 3725 **Payroll Expense ($000)**: 1488
Personnel: 37

COLUMBUS—Stillwater County

★ **STILLWATER BILLINGS CLINIC (271330)**, 44 West Fourth Avenue North, Zip 59019–0959, Mailing Address: P.O. Box 959, Zip 59019–0959; tel. 406/322–5316, **A**10 18 **F**3 15 28 32 34 35 40 43 45 50 59 62 64 65 68 75 83 93 107 110 114 127 133 144 154 **P**1
Primary Contact: David Ryerse, Chief Executive Officer
Web address: www.billingsclinic.com
Control: Other not–for–profit (including NFP Corporation) **Service**: General medical and surgical

Staffed Beds: 10 **Admissions**: 148 **Census**: 2 **Outpatient Visits**: 12203
Births: 0 **Total Expense ($000)**: 10134 **Payroll Expense ($000)**: 3774
Personnel: 79

CONRAD—Pondera County

PONDERA MEDICAL CENTER (271324), 805 Sunset Boulevard, Zip 59425–1717, Mailing Address: P.O. Box 668, Zip 59425–0668; tel. 406/271–3211, (Nonreporting) **A**10 18
Primary Contact: Bill O'Leary, Chief Executive Officer
CFO: Brigid Burke, Chief Financial Officer
CMO: Jay Taylor, M.D., Chief of Medical Staff
CIO: Sean Kavanagh, Director Information Technology
CHR: Patrick Johnson, Director Human Resources
CNO: Laura Erickson, R.N., Chief Nursing Officer
Web address: www.ponderamedical.org
Control: Other not–for–profit (including NFP Corporation) **Service**: General medical and surgical

Staffed Beds: 79

CROW AGENCY—Big Horn County

CROW/NORTHERN CHEYENNE HOSPITAL (271339), 10110 South 7650 East, Zip 59022–0009, Mailing Address: P.O. Box 9, Zip 59022–0009; tel. 406/638–2626, (Nonreporting) **A**3 10 18 **S** U.S. Indian Health Service, Rockville, MD
Primary Contact: Darren Crowe, Chief Executive Officer
CMO: Jim Upchurch, M.D., Chief Medical Officer
CIO: Melanie Falls Down, Site Manager
Web address: www.ihs.gov/billings/healthcarefacilities/crow/
Control: PHS, Indian Service, Government, federal **Service**: General medical and surgical

Staffed Beds: 24

CULBERTSON—Roosevelt County

★ **ROOSEVELT MEDICAL CENTER (271308)**, 818 Second Avenue East, Zip 59218, Mailing Address: P.O. Box 419, Zip 59218–0419; tel. 406/787–6401, (Total facility includes 27 beds in nursing home–type unit) **A**10 18 **F**2 7 15 34 35 40 43 50 56 57 59 65 69 77 82 93 97 119 127 128 130 133 143 146 147 154 **P**6
Primary Contact: Audrey Stromberg, Administrator
CFO: Jennifer Kessner, Financial Director
CMO: Don Helland, M.D., Chief Medical Officer
CIO: Brian Fordyce, Director Information Technology
CHR: Elizabeth Raaum, Manger Business Office
CNO: Jessica Schmitz, Director of Nursing
Web address: www.roosmem.org
Control: Other not–for–profit (including NFP Corporation) **Service**: General medical and surgical

Staffed Beds: 33 **Admissions**: 58 **Census**: 22 **Outpatient Visits**: 7927
Births: 0 **Total Expense ($000)**: 5490 **Payroll Expense ($000)**: 3097
Personnel: 55

CUT BANK—Glacier County

★ **NORTHERN ROCKIES MEDICAL CENTER (271337)**, 802 Second Street SE, Zip 59427–3329; tel. 406/873–2251, **A**10 18 **F**13 34 40 57 59 64 65 76 81 93 107 119 127 128 133 149 154
Primary Contact: Cherie Taylor, Chief Executive Officer
CFO: Treasure Berkram, Chief Financial Officer
CMO: Adron Medley, M.D., Chief Medical Staff
CHR: Kandie Lemieux, Administrative Assistant and Director Human Resources
Web address: www.nrmcinc.org
Control: Other not–for–profit (including NFP Corporation) **Service**: General medical and surgical

Staffed Beds: 29 **Admissions**: 124 **Census**: 1 **Outpatient Visits**: 14511
Births: 43 **Total Expense ($000)**: 9190 **Payroll Expense ($000)**: 4908
Personnel: 79

MT

DEER LODGE—Powell County

DEER LODGE MEDICAL CENTER (271314), 1100 Hollenbeck Lane,
Zip 59722–2317; tel. 406/846–2212, **A**10 18 **F**8 11 15 18 32 33 34 35 40 43
45 50 55 56 57 59 64 65 79 81 82 84 85 86 87 91 93 97 107 108 110 119
127 133 147 148 154 **P**6
Primary Contact: Tony Pfaff, Chief Executive Officer
CFO: Jaena Richards, Chief Financial Officer
CMO: Michelle Corbin, M.D., Chief of Staff
CIO: Chris Foster, Director Health Information Management
Web address: www.dlmed.org/
Control: Corporation, Investor–owned (for–profit) **Service:** General medical and surgical

Staffed Beds: 16 **Admissions:** 290 **Census:** 4 **Outpatient Visits:** 9966 **Births:** 0 **Total Expense ($000):** 12798 **Payroll Expense ($000):** 5396 **Personnel:** 104	

DILLON—Beaverhead County

★ **BARRETT HOSPITAL & HEALTHCARE (271318)**, 600 Mt Highway 91 South,
Zip 59725–7379; tel. 406/683–3000, **A**5 10 18 **F**3 13 15 28 31 34 40 45 50
57 59 62 63 64 65 69 75 76 77 79 80 81 83 84 85 87 89 93 96 97 107 110
111 115 119 130 133 135 146 148 154 **S** HealthTech Management Services,
Brentwood, TN
Primary Contact: Ken Westman, Chief Executive Officer
CFO: Dick Achter, Chief Financial Officer
CMO: Carol Kennedy, Chief Clinical Officer
CIO: Dick Achter, Chief Financial Officer
CHR: Geoff Roach, Director Human Resources
Web address: www.barretthospital.org
Control: Other not–for–profit (including NFP Corporation) **Service:** General
medical and surgical

Staffed Beds: 18 **Admissions:** 521 **Census:** 5 **Outpatient Visits:** 29488 **Births:** 76 **Total Expense ($000):** 31889 **Payroll Expense ($000):** 14574 **Personnel:** 227	

EKALAKA—Carter County

DAHL MEMORIAL HEALTHCARE ASSOCIATION (271302), 215 Sandy Street,
Zip 59324, Mailing Address: P.O. Box 46, Zip 59324–0046; tel. 406/775–8730,
(Nonreporting) **A**10 18
Primary Contact: Ryan Tooke, Chief Executive Officer
CFO: Nadine Elmore, Chief Executive Officer
CMO: Darryl Espeland, D.O., Medical Director
CIO: Davie Ann Barrere, Coordinator Information Technology
CHR: Melissa Matthews, Director Human Resources
CNO: Patricia Rogers, Director of Nursing
Web address: www.dahlmemorial.com
Control: Other not–for–profit (including NFP Corporation) **Service:** General
medical and surgical

Staffed Beds: 31	

ENNIS—Madison County

MADISON VALLEY MEDICAL CENTER (271329), 305 North Main Street,
Zip 59729–8001; tel. 406/682–4222, **A**10 18 **F**3 8 11 28 29 32 34 35 36 38
40 43 45 46 50 53 56 57 59 64 65 66 71 75 77 87 92 93 94 97 107 114 119
127 128 130 131 132 133 135 148 **P**6
Primary Contact: Allen Rohrback, Chief Executive Officer
CMO: Cindy Sharp, M.D., Chief Medical Officer
CIO: Bo Nix, Chief Information Officer
Web address: www.mvmedcenter.org
Control: Other not–for–profit (including NFP Corporation) **Service:** General
medical and surgical

Staffed Beds: 10 **Admissions:** 250 **Census:** 4 **Outpatient Visits:** 6061 **Births:** 0 **Total Expense ($000):** 7939 **Payroll Expense ($000):** 3485 **Personnel:** 51	

FORSYTH—Rosebud County

★ **ROSEBUD HEALTH CARE CENTER (271327)**, 383 North 17th Avenue,
Zip 59327–0268, Mailing Address: P.O. Box 268, Zip 59327–0268;
tel. 406/346–2161, (Nonreporting) **A**10 18
CMO: William Anderson, M.D., Medical Director
CHR: Karla Allies, Director Human Resources
Web address: www.rosebudhealthcare.com/
Control: Other not–for–profit (including NFP Corporation) **Service:** General
medical and surgical

Staffed Beds: 55	

FORT BENTON—Chouteau County

MISSOURI RIVER MEDICAL CENTER (271304), 1501 St Charles
Street, Zip 59442–0249, Mailing Address: P.O. Box 249, Zip 59442–0249;
tel. 406/622–3331, **A**10 18 **F**2 40 41 50 59 65 67 84 107 127 128 130 133
135 143 148 154 **S** Benefis Health System, Great Falls, MT
Primary Contact: Louie King, President, Harry Bold Nursing Home Administrator
CMO: Jace Bird, M.D., Chief Medical Officer
CIO: Bryan Cartwright, Chief Information Technology Officer
CHR: Carolyn Johnsrud, Manager Human Resources
CNO: Janice Woodhouse, Director of Nursing
Web address: www.mrmcfb.org
Control: Hospital district or authority, Government, nonfederal **Service:** Acute
long–term care hospital

Staffed Beds: 25 **Admissions:** 34 **Census:** 1 **Outpatient Visits:** 6620 **Births:** 0 **Total Expense ($000):** 5089 **Payroll Expense ($000):** 2702 **Personnel:** 67	

FORT HARRISON—Lewis And Clark County

▣ **VETERANS AFFAIRS MONTANA HEALTH CARE SYSTEM**, 3687 Veterans
Drive, Zip 59636–9703, Mailing Address: P.O. Box 1500, Zip 59636–1500;
tel. 406/442–6410, (Total facility includes 30 beds in nursing home–type unit) **A**1
F3 4 5 7 8 28 29 30 31 33 35 36 38 39 40 44 45 50 53 54 55 56 61 63 64
65 66 70 71 74 75 77 78 79 81 82 83 84 85 87 91 92 93 94 97 100 101 102
104 106 107 108 111 115 118 119 127 129 130 132 135 143 144 146 147
148 149 152 154 **P**6 **S** Department of Veterans Affairs, Perry Point, MD
Primary Contact: Kathy Berger, R.N., Director
CFO: Brian Gustafson, Chief Financial Officer
CMO: Kurt Werner, M.D., Chief of Staff
CIO: Paul Gauthier, Chief Information Resources Management
CHR: Aggie Hamilton, Chief Human Resources
Web address: www.montana.va.gov/
Control: Veterans Affairs, Government, federal **Service:** General medical and
surgical

Staffed Beds: 94 **Admissions:** 1333 **Census:** 31 **Outpatient Visits:** 455090 **Births:** 0 **Total Expense ($000):** 260386 **Payroll Expense ($000):** 123539 **Personnel:** 1152	

GLASGOW—Valley County

▣ **FRANCES MAHON DEACONESS HOSPITAL (271316)**, 621 Third Street South,
Zip 59230–2699; tel. 406/228–3500, **A**1 10 18 **F**3 7 11 13 15 28 29 31 34
35 40 43 53 56 57 59 61 64 70 75 76 78 79 81 82 86 87 89 93 100 102 107
108 110 111 114 118 119 127 128 130 131 133 135 145 146 149 **P**6 7
Primary Contact: Randall G. Holom, Chief Executive Officer
COO: Ellen Guttenberg, Chief Operating Officer
CFO: Cami Kalinski, Director Financial Services
CMO: Gordon Bell, M.D., Chief of Staff
CIO: David L Nixdorf, Director Support Services
CHR: Charam Orth, Director Human Resources
CNO: Brenda Koessl, R.N., Director of Nursing Services
Web address: www.fmdh.org
Control: Other not–for–profit (including NFP Corporation) **Service:** General
medical and surgical

Staffed Beds: 25 **Admissions:** 486 **Census:** 5 **Outpatient Visits:** 33956 **Births:** 139 **Total Expense ($000):** 22492 **Payroll Expense ($000):** 10703 **Personnel:** 167	

GLENDIVE—Dawson County

★ **GLENDIVE MEDICAL CENTER (271332)**, 202 Prospect Drive,
Zip 59330–1999; tel. 406/345–3306, **A**10 18 **F**1 8 10 11 13 15 28 29 30 31
34 40 41 45 51 56 57 59 62 63 64 65 67 70 75 76 77 79 81 85 89 90 93 97
100 102 104 107 110 111 115 119 125 127 128 130 132 133 146 147 148
154 **P**6
Primary Contact: Parker Powell, Chief Executive Officer
CFO: Barbara Markham, Chief Financial Officer
CMO: Joseph M Leal, M.D., Jr Chief of Staff
CIO: Barbara Markham, Chief Financial Officer
CHR: Joetta J Pearcy, Director, Human Resources
Web address: www.gmc.org
Control: Other not–for–profit (including NFP Corporation) **Service:** General
medical and surgical

Staffed Beds: 88 **Admissions:** 546 **Census:** 4 **Births:** 87 **Total Expense ($000):** 34658 **Payroll Expense ($000):** 13897	

MT

Hospital, Medicare Provider Number, Address, Telephone, Approval, Facility, and Physician Codes, Health Care System		
★ American Hospital Association (AHA) membership	○ Healthcare Facilities Accreditation Program	⇧ Center for Improvement in Healthcare Quality Accreditation
□ The Joint Commission accreditation	◇ DNV Healthcare Inc. accreditation	△ Commission on Accreditation of Rehabilitation Facilities (CARF) accreditation

GREAT FALLS—Cascade County

△ **BENEFIS HEALTH SYSTEM (270012)**, 1101 26th Street South,
Zip 59405–5104; tel. 406/455–5000, (Includes BENEFIS HEALTH CARE–EAST
CAMPUS, 1101 26th Street, Great Falls, MT, Zip 59405; tel. 406/455–5000;
BENEFIS HEALTH CARE–WEST CAMPUS, 500 15th Avenue South, Great Falls, MT,
Zip 59405; tel. 406/455–5000) (Total facility includes 237 beds in nursing home–
type unit) **A**2 7 10 20 **F**3 4 5 6 8 10 11 12 13 15 18 20 22 24 26 28 29 30 31
34 35 36 37 38 40 43 45 46 48 49 50 52 53 54 55 56 57 58 59 61 62 63 64
65 70 71 72 73 74 75 76 77 78 79 81 82 83 84 85 86 87 88 89 90 91 92 93
96 97 98 100 101 102 104 105 107 108 110 111 114 115 117 119 120 121
123 124 126 127 128 130 131 132 133 135 141 143 144 146 147 148 149
152 154 **P**8 **S** Benefis Health System, Great Falls, MT
Primary Contact: John H. Goodnow, Chief Executive Officer
CFO: Forrest Ehlinger, System Chief Financial Officer
CMO: Gregory Tierney, M.D., President, BMG and BHS Chief Medical Officer
CIO: Mark Simon, System Chief Information Officer
CNO: Rayn Ginnaty, Vice President Nursing
Web address: www.benefis.org
Control: Other not–for–profit (including NFP Corporation) **Service**: General
medical and surgical

> **Staffed Beds:** 502 **Admissions:** 10945 **Census:** 369 **Outpatient Visits:**
> 497189 **Births:** 1396 **Total Expense ($000):** 415126 **Payroll Expense**
> **($000):** 198217 **Personnel:** 2550

GREAT FALLS CLINIC HOSPITAL (270086), 3010 15th Avenue South,
Zip 59405–5240, Mailing Address: 3010 15th Street South, Zip 59405–5240;
tel. 406/216–8000, **A**10 **F**3 15 18 19 24 26 27 29 30 31 34 35 38 40 41 45
46 47 50 51 57 58 69 68 74 75 77 78 79 81 82 85 86 87 91 92 93 94 107
108 109 110 111 114 115 119 120 121 123 124 126 130 135 143 144 146
147 148 149
Primary Contact: Vicki Newmiller, Chief Executive Officer
CFO: Cheryl Cornwell, Chief Financial Officer
CMO: Nicholas Bonfilio, M.D., Chief of Staff
Web address: www.gfclinic.com/location/great–falls–clinic–hospital/
Control: Partnership, Investor–owned (for–profit) **Service**: Surgical

> **Staffed Beds:** 20 **Admissions:** 1303 **Census:** 12 **Outpatient Visits:** 111663
> **Births:** 0 **Total Expense ($000):** 56348 **Payroll Expense ($000):** 16969
> **Personnel:** 284

HAMILTON—Ravalli County

★ **MARCUS DALY MEMORIAL HOSPITAL (271340)**, 1200 Westwood Drive,
Zip 59840–2345; tel. 406/363–2211, (Nonreporting) **A**10 18 **F**3 7 8 11 13 15 17
28 29 30 34 40 45 50 57 59 62 63 64 65 70 74 75 76 77 79 81 83 84 89 93
97 102 107 110 111 115 119 127 129 130 131 132 133 144 145 146 148 **P**8
Primary Contact: John Bishop, Chief Executive Officer
CFO: Donja Erdman, Chief Financial Officer
CMO: John Moreland, M.D., Chief Medical Officer
CIO: Brad Kowalski, Director Information Technology
CHR: Debbie M Morris, Director Human Resources
CNO: Kathy Padilla, Director of Nursing
Web address: www.mdmh.org
Control: Other not–for–profit (including NFP Corporation) **Service**: General
medical and surgical

> **Staffed Beds:** 25 **Admissions:** 1734 **Census:** 14 **Outpatient Visits:** 46781
> **Births:** 115 **Total Expense ($000):** 59289 **Payroll Expense ($000):** 32014
> **Personnel:** 468

HARDIN—Big Horn County

★ **BIG HORN COUNTY MEMORIAL HOSPITAL (271338)**, 17 North Miles Avenue,
Zip 59034–2323; **A**10 18
Primary Contact: Bill Forbes, Interim Chief Executive Officer
CFO: Roxie Cain, Chief Financial Officer
CNO: Kirsten Willoughby, Director of Nursing
Control: Other not–for–profit (including NFP Corporation) **Service**: General
medical and surgical

> **Staffed Beds:** 61

HARLEM—Blaine County

FORT BELKNAP SERVICE UNIT (271315), 669 Agency Main Street,
Zip 59526–9455; tel. 406/353–3100, (Nonreporting) **A**10 18 **S** U.S. Indian Health
Service, Rockville, MD
Primary Contact: Gregory Smith, M.D., Chief Executive Officer
CMO: Ethel L Moore, M.D., Director of Medical Affairs
CIO: Mikki Grant, Chief Information Officer
CHR: Charlotte Lamebull, Administrative Officer
CNO: Diana Hunter, Director of Nursing
Web address: www.ihs.gov
Control: PHS, Indian Service, Government, federal **Service**: General medical and surgical

> **Staffed Beds:** 6

HARLOWTON—Wheatland County

★ **WHEATLAND MEMORIAL HEALTHCARE (271321)**, 530 Third Street
North West, Zip 59036, Mailing Address: P.O. Box 287, Zip 59036–0287;
tel. 406/632–4351, (Nonreporting) **A**10 18
Primary Contact: Mary J. Ruyter, Interim Chief Executive Officer
CFO: Doug Lewis, Chief Financial Officer
CMO: Kathy Jutila, M.D., Chief of Staff
CIO: Ray Hetherington, Network Administrator
CHR: Peggy Hiner, Director Human Resources
CNO: Lauri Ann Cooney, Director Nursing
Web address: www.wheatlandmemorial.org
Control: Other not–for–profit (including NFP Corporation) **Service**: General
medical and surgical

> **Staffed Beds:** 25

HAVRE—Hill County

★ **NORTHERN MONTANA HEALTH CARE (270032)**, 30 13th Street,
Zip 59501–5222, Mailing Address: P.O. Box 1231, Zip 59501–1231;
tel. 406/265–2211, (Total facility includes 115 beds in nursing home–type unit)
A10 20 **F**2 5 10 11 13 15 28 29 34 35 36 38 40 43 45 53 56 57 59 60 63 64
68 70 75 76 77 78 79 81 82 84 85 89 93 97 99 101 102 103 104 107 108
110 111 115 118 119 127 128 129 130 132 133 135 146 148 153 154 **P**6
Primary Contact: David Henry, President and Chief Executive Officer
CFO: Kim Lucke, Vice President Finance
CNO: Eric Koch, Chief Nursing Officer
Web address: www.nmhcare.org
Control: Other not–for–profit (including NFP Corporation) **Service**: General
medical and surgical

> **Staffed Beds:** 142 **Admissions:** 1380 **Census:** 101 **Outpatient Visits:**
> 99220 **Births:** 375 **Total Expense ($000):** 62123 **Payroll Expense**
> **($000):** 32779 **Personnel:** 542

HELENA—Lewis And Clark County

⊞ **SHODAIR CHILDREN'S HOSPITAL (274004)**, 2755 Colonial Drive,
Zip 59601–4926, Mailing Address: P.O. Box 5539, Zip 59604–5539;
tel. 406/444–7500, **A**1 10 **F**55 98 99 101 106 130 149 154 **P**6
Primary Contact: Craig E. Aasved, Chief Executive Officer
CFO: Ron Wiens, Chief Financial Officer
CMO: Heather Zaluski, M.D., President Medical Staff
CIO: Judy Jackson, Director Health Information Management and Privacy Officer
CNO: Christine Bates, Chief Nursing Officer
Web address: www.shodair.org
Control: Other not–for–profit (including NFP Corporation) **Service**: Children's
hospital psychiatric

> **Staffed Beds:** 84 **Admissions:** 917 **Census:** 58 **Outpatient Visits:** 2297
> **Births:** 0 **Total Expense ($000):** 24198 **Payroll Expense ($000):** 14316
> **Personnel:** 248

⊞ **ST. PETER'S HOSPITAL (270003)**, 2475 Broadway, Zip 59601–4928;
tel. 406/442–2480, (Nonreporting) **A**1 2 10 20
Primary Contact: Wade C. Johnson, MS, FACHE, Chief Executive Officer
CFO: John Green, Vice President Finance
CMO: Shelly Harkins, M.D., Chief Medical Officer
CHR: Karla Smith, Director Human Resources
CNO: Cheryl Hunt Esq Chief Nursing Officer
Web address: www.stpetes.org
Control: Other not–for–profit (including NFP Corporation) **Service**: General
medical and surgical

> **Staffed Beds:** 123

JORDAN—Garfield County

GARFIELD COUNTY HEALTH CENTER (271310), 332 Leavitt Avenue,
Zip 59337, Mailing Address: P.O. Box 389, Zip 59337–0389; tel. 406/557–2500,
(Total facility includes 24 beds in nursing home–type unit) **A**10 18 **F**7 34 40 57 59
64 67 107 143 148
Primary Contact: Chris Hopkins, Chief Executive Officer
CFO: Charlotte Herbold, Manager Business Officer
CMO: David M. Kidder, D.O., Chief Medical Officer
CIO: Charlotte Herbold, Manager Business Officer
CNO: Sarah Nordlund, Director of Nursing
Web address: www.garfieldco.us/garfield–county–health–center.html
Control: County, Government, nonfederal **Service**: General medical and surgical

> **Staffed Beds:** 32 **Admissions:** 2 **Census:** 32 **Outpatient Visits:** 1220
> **Births:** 0 **Total Expense ($000):** 2148 **Payroll Expense ($000):** 1048
> **Personnel:** 22

KALISPELL—Flathead County

HEALTHCENTER NORTHWEST See The Healthcenter

MT

★ △ **KALISPELL REGIONAL HEALTHCARE (270051)**, 310 Sunnyview Lane, Zip 59901-3129; tel. 406/752-5111, (Includes PATHWAYS TREATMENT CENTER, 200 Heritage Way, Kalispell, MT, Zip 59901; tel. 406/756-3950) **A**2 3 5 7 10 **F**3 4 5 7 8 13 15 18 19 20 22 24 26 28 29 31 34 35 36 40 43 45 46 49 50 55 57 58 59 62 63 64 70 71 72 74 75 77 78 79 81 83 84 85 86 87 88 89 93 97 98 99 100 101 102 103 104 105 107 114 115 118 119 120 121 123 126 129 130 131 132 143 144 145 146 147 148 149 151 152 153 154 **P**6
Primary Contact: Pamela Robertson, Chief Executive Officer
COO: Ted W Hirsch, Senior Executive Director
CFO: Tracey Talley, Chief Financial and Information Officer
CHR: Deb Wilson, Director Human Resources
Web address: www.krmc.org
Control: Other not-for-profit (including NFP Corporation) **Service:** General medical and surgical

Staffed Beds: 167 **Admissions:** 8232 **Census:** 99 **Outpatient Visits:** 211976 **Births:** 672 **Total Expense ($000):** 373627 **Payroll Expense ($000):** 171012 **Personnel:** 2358

★ **THE HEALTHCENTER (270087)**, 320 Sunnyview Lane, Zip 59901-3129; tel. 406/751-7550, **A**10 **F**3 15 33 36 39 45 59 64 71 81 82 85 90 91 95 96 107 110 111 112 114 115 117 119 124 126 147 149 **P**6
Primary Contact: Tate J. Kreitinger, Chief Executive Officer
CFO: Charles T Pearce, Chief Financial and Information Officer
CIO: Charles T Pearce, Chief Financial and Information Officer
CHR: Susan Stevens, Director Human Resources
CNO: Victoria Johnson, R.N., Nursing Director of Surgical and Medical Services
Web address: www.krmc.org
Control: Corporation, Investor-owned (for-profit) **Service:** General medical and surgical

Staffed Beds: 28 **Admissions:** 667 **Census:** 8 **Outpatient Visits:** 49217 **Births:** 0 **Total Expense ($000):** 56856 **Payroll Expense ($000):** 15428 **Personnel:** 241

LEWISTOWN—Fergus County

★ **CENTRAL MONTANA MEDICAL CENTER (271345)**, 408 Wendell Avenue, Zip 59457-2261; tel. 406/535-7711, **A**10 18 **F**3 7 11 13 15 28 29 31 34 35 40 43 45 50 53 57 59 62 63 64 65 75 76 77 81 84 85 86 87 89 91 92 93 94 97 107 108 110 111 115 119 129 130 131 132 133 135 146 148 **P**6
Primary Contact: Michael Dowdy, Chief Executive Officer
CFO: Alan Aldrich, Chief Financial Officer
CHR: Torie A Lynch, Manager Human Resources
CNO: Karen White, Chief Nursing Officer
Web address: www.cmmccares.com
Control: Other not-for-profit (including NFP Corporation) **Service:** General medical and surgical

Staffed Beds: 25 **Admissions:** 702 **Census:** 5 **Outpatient Visits:** 30449 **Births:** 85 **Total Expense ($000):** 30258 **Payroll Expense ($000):** 14483 **Personnel:** 259

LIBBY—Lincoln County

★ **CABINET PEAKS MEDICAL CENTER (271320)**, 209 Health Park Drive, Zip 59923-2130; tel. 406/283-7000, **A**5 10 18 **F**3 11 13 15 17 28 29 30 31 34 35 40 45 50 54 56 57 59 64 70 75 76 77 79 81 84 85 86 87 89 93 97 102 107 110 111 114 119 128 129 130 131 132 133 135 144 146 147 148 154 **P**6
Primary Contact: Bruce Whitfield, CPA, Chief Executive Officer and Chief Financial Officer
CFO: Bruce Whitfield, CPA, Chief Executive Officer and Chief Financial Officer
CMO: Jay Maloney, M.D., Chief of Staff
Web address: www.sjlh.com
Control: Other not-for-profit (including NFP Corporation) **Service:** General medical and surgical

Staffed Beds: 25 **Admissions:** 844 **Census:** 7 **Outpatient Visits:** 41867 **Births:** 120 **Total Expense ($000):** 30945 **Payroll Expense ($000):** 13140 **Personnel:** 228

LIVINGSTON—Park County

★ **LIVINGSTON HEALTHCARE (271317)**, 320 Alpenglow Lane, Zip 59047-8506; tel. 406/222-3541, **A**5 10 18 **F**3 13 15 17 28 29 30 31 34 35 38 40 41 43 45 46 50 55 56 57 59 62 63 64 65 66 67 70 75 76 77 78 79 81 84 85 86 87 89 93 100 101 102 104 107 108 110 111 114 119 124 127 128 129 130 131 133 135 144 146 147 149 150 154 **P**6
Primary Contact: Deb Anczak, Director Performance Improvement
CFO: Ryan Speas, Director Finance
CMO: D. Scott Coleman, M.D., Medical Director
CIO: Jody Duran, Manager Information Systems
CHR: Vicki Axtell, Director Human Resources
CNO: Dave Noble, Director of Nursing
Web address: www.livingstonhealthcare.org
Control: Other not-for-profit (including NFP Corporation) **Service:** General medical and surgical

Staffed Beds: 25 **Admissions:** 1044 **Census:** 11 **Outpatient Visits:** 28459 **Births:** 116 **Total Expense ($000):** 44217 **Payroll Expense ($000):** 18715 **Personnel:** 293

MALTA—Phillips County

★ **PHILLIPS COUNTY HOSPITAL (271312)**, 311 South 8th Avenue East, Zip 59538-0640, Mailing Address: P.O. Box 640, Zip 59538-0640; tel. 406/654-1100, **A**10 18 **F**3 29 31 34 40 41 56 57 59 62 66 68 82 84 90 91 93 107 114 119 127 130 132 133 **P**4
Primary Contact: Ward C. VanWichen, Chief Executive Officer
CFO: Stephanie Denham, Chief Financial Officer and Human Resources Officer
CMO: Ed Medina, M.D., Medical Director
CHR: Stephanie Denham, Chief Financial Officer and Human Resources Officer
CNO: Lonna Crowder, Director of Nursing
Web address: www.pchospital.us/
Control: Other not-for-profit (including NFP Corporation) **Service:** General medical and surgical

Staffed Beds: 8 **Admissions:** 183 **Census:** 1 **Outpatient Visits:** 6689 **Births:** 0 **Total Expense ($000):** 6104 **Payroll Expense ($000):** 3046 **Personnel:** 55

MILES CITY—Custer County

⊞ **HOLY ROSARY HEALTHCARE (271347)**, 2600 Wilson Street, Zip 59301-5094; tel. 406/233-2600, (Total facility includes 65 beds in nursing home–type unit) **A**1 10 18 **F**3 13 15 28 29 30 31 32 34 40 48 50 55 57 59 63 64 65 68 70 75 76 77 78 79 81 84 85 87 89 93 94 97 102 107 108 110 111 115 119 124 127 129 130 131 133 135 143 146 147 148 149 154 **P**6 **S** SCL Health, Broomfield, CO
Primary Contact: Paul Lewis, Chief Executive Officer
CFO: Travis Scheving, Chief Financial Officer
CMO: Michael Bush, M.D., Chief Medical Officer
CHR: Cathy Rodenbaugh, Director Human Resources
CNO: Lisa Sanford, VP Patient Care/CNO
Web address: www.holyrosaryhealthcare.org
Control: Church operated, Nongovernment, not-for-profit **Service:** General medical and surgical

Staffed Beds: 90 **Admissions:** 1223 **Census:** 57 **Outpatient Visits:** 27566 **Births:** 220 **Total Expense ($000):** 35772 **Payroll Expense ($000):** 13701 **Personnel:** 241

MISSOULA—Missoula County

☐ △ **COMMUNITY MEDICAL CENTER (270023)**, 2827 Fort Missoula Road, Zip 59804-7408; tel. 406/728-4100, **A**1 3 5 7 10 19 **F**3 11 13 15 17 18 20 22 26 28 29 30 31 34 35 37 40 43 46 47 48 49 51 54 55 57 59 64 65 68 70 72 74 75 76 78 79 81 82 83 84 85 87 88 89 90 91 92 93 94 96 97 106 107 108 110 111 114 115 116 117 118 119 120 121 123 124 126 130 132 134 135 141 143 144 145 146 147 148 149 154 **P**6 7 **S** RCCH HealthCare Partners, Brentwood, TN
Primary Contact: Dean French, M.D., Chief Executive Officer
COO: Devin Huntley, Vice President Operations
CMO: David Lechner, M.D., Chief Medical Officer and Vice President Innovation
CNO: Jan Perry, R.N., Vice President Patient Care Services
Web address: www.communitymed.org
Control: Corporation, Investor-owned (for-profit) **Service:** General medical and surgical

Staffed Beds: 135 **Admissions:** 4812 **Census:** 64 **Outpatient Visits:** 135678 **Births:** 1129 **Total Expense ($000):** 163111 **Payroll Expense ($000):** 62678 **Personnel:** 1029

MT

Hospital, Medicare Provider Number, Address, Telephone, Approval, Facility, and Physician Codes, Health Care System

★ American Hospital Association (AHA) membership
☐ The Joint Commission accreditation
○ Healthcare Facilities Accreditation Program
◇ DNV Healthcare Inc. accreditation
⇑ Center for Improvement in Healthcare Quality Accreditation
△ Commission on Accreditation of Rehabilitation Facilities (CARF) accreditation

✠ **ST. PATRICK HOSPITAL (270014)**, 500 West Broadway, Zip 59802–4096, Mailing Address: P.O. Box 4587, Zip 59806–4587; tel. 406/543–7271, **A**1 2 3 5 10 19 **F**3 11 12 13 15 18 20 22 24 26 28 29 30 31 34 35 38 40 43 45 46 48 49 50 53 57 58 59 60 61 64 65 68 70 74 75 76 77 78 79 81 82 84 85 86 88 89 90 92 93 96 97 98 99 100 101 102 103 104 105 107 108 109 110 111 113 114 115 116 117 118 119 120 121 123 124 126 127 129 130 131 132 135 141 146 147 148 149 154 **P**4 **S** Providence St. Joseph Health, Renton, WA
Primary Contact: Joyce Dombrouski, R.N., Chief Executive Officer
CFO: Kirk Bodlovic, WMSA Chief Financial Officer
CHR: Karyn Trainor, Director Human Resources
CNO: Carol Bensen, MSN, R.N., Chief Nursing Officer
Web address: www.montana.providence.org
Control: Church operated, Nongovernment, not–for–profit **Service:** General medical and surgical

> **Staffed Beds: 180 Admissions: 10394 Census: 127 Outpatient Visits:** 335977 **Births: 453 Total Expense ($000): 238193 Payroll Expense ($000):** 75838 **Personnel:** 1526

PHILIPSBURG—Granite County

★ **GRANITE COUNTY MEDICAL CENTER (271303)**, 310 Sansome Street, Zip 59858–0729, Mailing Address: P.O. Box 729, Zip 59858–0729; tel. 406/859–3271, **A**10 18 **F**2 32 34 35 39 40 41 50 56 57 59 64 67 68 93 97 100 102 104 105 119 127 128 130 133 135 143 146 148 154 **S** Providence St. Joseph Health, Renton, WA
Primary Contact: Maria Stoppler, Chief Executive Officer
CFO: Susan Ossello, Chief Financial Officer
CMO: John Moore, M.D., Medical Director
Web address: www.gcmedcenter.org/
Control: Hospital district or authority, Government, nonfederal **Service:** General medical and surgical

> **Staffed Beds: 25 Admissions: 14 Census: 1 Outpatient Visits:** 2652 **Births:** 0

PLAINS—Sanders County

★ **CLARK FORK VALLEY HOSPITAL (271323)**, 10 Kruger Road, Zip 59859, Mailing Address: P.O. Box 768, Zip 59859–0768; tel. 406/826–4800, (Total facility includes 28 beds in nursing home–type unit) **A**10 18 **F**3 11 13 15 28 29 30 32 34 35 36 40 43 44 45 50 57 58 59 62 63 64 65 70 75 76 77 81 82 83 84 85 87 89 91 93 97 100 115 118 119 127 128 129 130 132 133 135 143 146 147 148 149 154 **P**3 6
Primary Contact: Gregory S. Hanson, M.D., Chief Executive Officer
CFO: Carla A Neiman, Chief Financial Officer
CMO: Ronald Black, M.D., Chief Medical Officer
CIO: Carla A Neiman, Chief Financial Officer
CHR: Barry Fowler, Director Human and System Resources
CNO: Lisa Eberhardt, Chief Nursing Officer
Web address: www.cfvh.org
Control: Other not–for–profit (including NFP Corporation) **Service:** General medical and surgical

> **Staffed Beds: 44 Admissions: 509 Census: 36 Outpatient Visits:** 30359 **Births: 28 Total Expense ($000): 20914 Payroll Expense ($000):** 8773 **Personnel:** 204

PLENTYWOOD—Sheridan County

SHERIDAN MEMORIAL HOSPITAL (271322), 440 West Laurel Avenue, Zip 59254–1596; tel. 406/765–3700, (Nonreporting) **A**10 18
Primary Contact: Gregory L. Maurer, Chief Executive Officer
CIO: Troy McClymont, Chief Information Technology Officer
Web address: www.sheridanmemorial.net/
Control: Other not–for–profit (including NFP Corporation) **Service:** General medical and surgical

> **Staffed Beds:** 97

POLSON—Lake County

✠ **PROVIDENCE ST. JOSEPH MEDICAL CENTER (271343)**, 6 Thirteenth Avenue East, Zip 59860–5315, Mailing Address: P.O. Box 1010, Zip 59860–1010; tel. 406/883–5377, **A**1 10 18 **F**3 10 13 15 28 29 30 31 34 35 40 43 45 50 57 59 64 68 75 76 77 79 81 82 85 87 89 93 97 107 110 111 115 119 125 127 129 130 131 133 146 147 148 149 154 **P**6 **S** Providence St. Joseph Health, Renton, WA
Primary Contact: Lynn Weddle, Interim Chief Executive Officer
COO: Colleen Nielsen, Director Operations
CFO: Kirk Bodlovic, Vice President and Chief Financial Officer
CMO: Kelly Bagnell, M.D., Chief of Staff
Web address: www.saintjoes.org
Control: Church operated, Nongovernment, not–for–profit **Service:** General medical and surgical

> **Staffed Beds: 22 Admissions: 733 Census: 7 Outpatient Visits:** 93337 **Births: 105 Total Expense ($000): 29356 Payroll Expense ($000):** 16688 **Personnel:** 195

POPLAR—Richland County

★ **POPLAR COMMUNITY HOSPITAL (271300)**, 211 H Street, Zip 59255–9519, Mailing Address: P.O. Box 38, Zip 59255–0038; tel. 406/768–6100, **A**10 18 **F**3 7 31 40 43 50 57 59 75 87 97 100 101 102 104 107 114 127 130 133 143 147 **P**3 6
Primary Contact: Margaret B. Norgaard, Chief Executive Officer
CHR: Annie Block, Director Human Resources
Web address: www.nemhs.net
Control: Other not–for–profit (including NFP Corporation) **Service:** General medical and surgical

> **Staffed Beds: 20 Admissions: 115 Census: 4 Outpatient Visits:** 7750 **Births: 3 Total Expense ($000): 7761 Payroll Expense ($000):** 3440 **Personnel:** 88

RED LODGE—Carbon County

★ **BEARTOOTH BILLINGS CLINIC (271326)**, 2525 North Broadway Avenue, Zip 59068–9222, Mailing Address: P.O. Box 590, Zip 59068–0590; tel. 406/446–2345, **A**10 18 **F**3 11 15 18 28 29 34 35 40 43 44 45 50 56 57 59 62 63 64 65 68 75 77 81 84 85 86 87 91 93 94 96 97 107 110 114 119 130 131 133 135 146 147 148 149 154 **P**6
Primary Contact: Kelley Evans, Chief Administrative Officer
CFO: Kyle Gee, Chief Financial Officer
CMO: William George, M.D., Chief of Staff
CHR: Katie Nordstrom, Director Human Resources
CNO: Bridgett Chartier, Director of Nursing
Web address: www.beartoothbillingsclinic.org
Control: Other not–for–profit (including NFP Corporation) **Service:** General medical and surgical

> **Staffed Beds: 10 Admissions: 162 Census: 2 Outpatient Visits:** 60876 **Births: 1 Total Expense ($000): 14079 Payroll Expense ($000):** 5031 **Personnel:** 109

RONAN—Lake County

★ **ST. LUKE COMMUNITY HEALTHCARE (271325)**, 107 Sixth Avenue SW, Zip 59864–2634; tel. 406/676–4441, (Total facility includes 75 beds in nursing home–type unit) **A**10 18 **F**2 13 15 28 29 31 34 40 43 45 53 54 56 57 59 61 64 65 68 75 76 78 79 81 85 93 97 107 108 110 111 115 119 127 128 129 130 131 132 133 135 144 145 147 154 **P**6
Primary Contact: Steve J. Todd, Chief Executive Officer
COO: Sarah Teaff, Chief Operating Officer
CFO: Paul Soukup, Chief Financial Officer
CMO: Edred T. Vizcarra, M.D., Chief of Staff
CHR: Theresa L. Jones, Manager Human Resources
CNO: Leah Emerson, Director of Nursing
Web address: www.stlukehealthcare.org
Control: Other not–for–profit (including NFP Corporation) **Service:** General medical and surgical

> **Staffed Beds: 100 Admissions: 1012 Census: 56 Outpatient Visits:** 69794 **Births: 122 Total Expense ($000): 36003 Payroll Expense ($000):** 19287 **Personnel:** 335

ROUNDUP—Musselshell County

★ **ROUNDUP MEMORIAL HEALTHCARE (271346)**, 1202 Third Street West, Zip 59072–1816, Mailing Address: P.O. Box 40, Zip 59072–0040; tel. 406/323–2301, **A**10 18 **F**3 11 29 30 34 35 40 57 59 65 66 67 87 93 97 102 107 119 127 130 132 133 146 147 148
Primary Contact: Bradley Howell, Chief Executive Officer
CFO: Kyle Gee, Regional Vice President Financial Operations
CMO: Mark Ward, M.D., Chief of Staff
CHR: Michelle Clement, Executive Assistant/Human Resources Director
CNO: Emily Shoup, Director Nursing Services
Web address: www.rmhmt.org/
Control: Other not–for–profit (including NFP Corporation) **Service:** General medical and surgical

> **Staffed Beds: 25 Admissions: 170 Census: 19 Outpatient Visits:** 23297 **Births: 0 Total Expense ($000): 7196 Payroll Expense ($000):** 3308 **Personnel:** 71

MT

Many Facility Codes have changed. Please refer to the AHA Guide Code Chart.   © 2018 AHA Guide

SAINT MARY—Glacier County

BLACKFEET COMMUNITY HOSPITAL (270074), 760 New Hospital Circle, Zip 59417–0760, Mailing Address: P.O. Box 760, Browning, Zip 59417–0760; tel. 406/338–6100, (Nonreporting) **A**5 10 **S** U.S. Indian Health Service, Rockville, MD
Primary Contact: Garland Stiffarm, Chief Executive Officer
CFO: Cleo Main, Finance Officer
CMO: Neil Sun Rhodes, M.D., Chief Medical Officer
CNO: Susan Head, Director Nursing Services
Web address: www.ihs.gov
Control: PHS, Indian Service, Government, federal **Service:** General medical and surgical

Staffed Beds: 25

SCOBEY—Daniels County

DANIELS MEMORIAL HEALTHCARE CENTER (271342), 105 Fifth Avenue East, Zip 59263, Mailing Address: P.O. Box 400, Zip 59263–0400; tel. 406/487–2296, **A**10 18 **F**2 11 29 40 44 50 56 59 64 65 67 69 75 85 91 93 97 107 114 119 127 130 133 143 146 148 **P**6
Primary Contact: David Ryerse, Chief Executive Officer
CMO: Don Sawdey, M.D., Medical Director
CHR: Edith Huda, Director Human Resources
CNO: Kathy Ware, Director of Nursing
Web address: www.danielsmemorialhealthcare.org
Control: Hospital district or authority, Government, nonfederal **Service:** General medical and surgical

Staffed Beds: 25 **Admissions:** 93 **Census:** 20 **Outpatient Visits:** 4517
Births: 0 **Total Expense ($000):** 7723 **Payroll Expense ($000):** 3376
Personnel: 103

SHELBY—Toole County

MARIAS MEDICAL CENTER (271328), 640 Park Drive, Zip 59474–1663, Mailing Address: P.O. Box 915, Zip 59474–0915; tel. 406/434–3200, (Nonreporting) **A**10 18
Primary Contact: Jessica Brusven, Chief Executive Officer
CFO: Melissa Ostberg, Chief Financial Officer
CMO: Melanie Hardy, D.O., Chief of Staff
CIO: Jayce Yarn, Director Information Technology
CHR: Cindy Lamb, Director Human Resources
CNO: Tamra Fender, Chief Nursing Officer
Web address: www.mmcmt.org
Control: County, Government, nonfederal **Service:** General medical and surgical

Staffed Beds: 147

SHERIDAN—Madison County

RUBY VALLEY HOSPITAL (271319), 220 East Crofoot Street, Zip 59749–7714, Mailing Address: P.O. Box 336, Zip 59749–0336; tel. 406/842–5453, (Nonreporting) **A**10 18
Primary Contact: John H. Semingson, Chief Executive Officer
CFO: Dennis Holschbach, Chief Financial Officer
CMO: Roman Hendrickson, M.D., Medical Director
CHR: Jenny Rohrback, Director Human Resource
CNO: Brenda Green, Director of Nursing
Web address: www.rubyvalleyhospital.com/
Control: Hospital district or authority, Government, nonfederal **Service:** General medical and surgical

Staffed Beds: 8

SIDNEY—Richland County

★ **SIDNEY HEALTH CENTER (271344)**, 216 14th Avenue SW, Zip 59270–3586; tel. 406/488–2100, (Total facility includes 56 beds in nursing home–type unit) **A**10 18 **F**2 3 13 15 17 28 30 31 34 35 40 41 45 50 55 56 58 59 62 63 64 68 70 75 76 78 79 81 82 84 85 86 87 89 93 96 97 105 107 108 110 111 115 119 120 121 122 123 124 128 129 133 144 145 146 147 148 149 154 **P**6
Primary Contact: Richard Haraldson, Chief Executive Officer
CFO: Tina Montgomery, Chief Financial Officer
CMO: Rajohn Karanjai, M.D., Chief Medical Officer
CIO: Brian Fay, Director Information Systems
CHR: Lisa Aisenbrey, Administrator Human Resources and Support Services
Web address: www.sidneyhealth.org
Control: Other not–for–profit (including NFP Corporation) **Service:** General medical and surgical

Staffed Beds: 81 **Admissions:** 1222 **Census:** 61 **Outpatient Visits:** 48249
Births: 159 **Total Expense ($000):** 61276 **Payroll Expense ($000):** 23064
Personnel: 351

SUPERIOR—Mineral County

MINERAL COMMUNITY HOSPITAL (271331), 1208 6th Avenue East, Zip 59872–9618; tel. 406/822–4841, **A**10 18 **F**29 40 45 57 69 75 77 81 93 107 110 114 119 133 143 154
Primary Contact: Steve McNeece, Interim Chief Executive Officer
CFO: Cliff Case, Chief Financial Officer
CMO: Roger Pafford, M.D., Medical Director
CHR: Stacy Conrow–Ververis, Director Human Resources
CNO: Jenifer Mitchell, R.N., Director of Nursing Services
Web address: www.mineralcommunityhospital.com/
Control: Other not–for–profit (including NFP Corporation) **Service:** General medical and surgical

Staffed Beds: 25 **Admissions:** 129 **Census:** 16 **Outpatient Visits:** 5292
Births: 0 **Total Expense ($000):** 5900 **Payroll Expense ($000):** 3119
Personnel: 70

TERRY—Prairie County

PRAIRIE COMMUNITY HEALTH CENTER See Prairie Community Hospital

★ **PRAIRIE COMMUNITY HOSPITAL (271309)**, 312 South Adams Avenue, Zip 59349–0156, Mailing Address: P.O. Box 156, Zip 59349–0156; tel. 406/635–5511, **A**10 18 **F**2 34 40 41 57 59 64 65 69 75 87 93 127 133 135 146 148 154 **P**6
Primary Contact: Laurie Lea Durham, Chief Executive Officer
CFO: Laurie Chandler, Financial Officer
CIO: Laurie Chandler, Chairman
CNO: Susan Morgan, Director of Nursing Services
Web address: www.prairiecommunityhospital.org/
Control: Hospital district or authority, Government, nonfederal **Service:** General medical and surgical

Staffed Beds: 22 **Admissions:** 51 **Census:** 19 **Outpatient Visits:** 4041
Births: 0 **Total Expense ($000):** 2983 **Payroll Expense ($000):** 1185
Personnel: 32

TOWNSEND—Broadwater County

BROADWATER HEALTH CENTER (271333), 110 North Oak Street, Zip 59644–2306; tel. 406/266–3186, **A**10 18 **F**3 7 9 15 29 32 34 40 41 43 50 53 54 55 57 59 64 66 71 75 77 79 87 91 93 97 107 111 130 131 133 135 143 144 146 147 148 154 **P**6
Primary Contact: Kyle Hopstad, Chief Executive Officer
CFO: Jennifer Clowes, Chief Financial Officer
CMO: Carol Bridges, M.D., Medical Director
CHR: April Campbell, Director Human Resources
CNO: Fran Wright, Director of Nursing
Web address: www.broadwaterhealthcenter.com
Control: Other not–for–profit (including NFP Corporation) **Service:** General medical and surgical

Staffed Beds: 25 **Admissions:** 75 **Census:** 2 **Outpatient Visits:** 1018
Births: 0

WARM SPRINGS—Deer Lodge County

MONTANA STATE HOSPITAL (274086), 100 Garnet Way, Zip 59756–9705, Mailing Address: P.O. Box 300, tel. 406/693–7000, **A**10 **F**98
Primary Contact: Jay Pottenger, Administrator
CFO: Tracey Thun, Director Business and Support Services
CMO: Thomas Gray, M.D., Medical Director
CIO: Melinda Bridgewater, Director, Information Services
CHR: Todd Thun, Director Human Resources
CNO: Dave Olson, Director of Nursing
Web address: www.msh.mt.gov
Control: State, Government, nonfederal **Service:** Psychiatric

Staffed Beds: 270 **Admissions:** 790 **Census:** 232 **Outpatient Visits:** 0
Births: 0 **Total Expense ($000):** 47283 **Payroll Expense ($000):** 22111
Personnel: 528

MT

Hospital, Medicare Provider Number, Address, Telephone, Approval, Facility, and Physician Codes, Health Care System

★ American Hospital Association (AHA) membership
□ The Joint Commission accreditation
○ Healthcare Facilities Accreditation Program
◇ DNV Healthcare Inc. accreditation
⇧ Center for Improvement in Healthcare Quality Accreditation
△ Commission on Accreditation of Rehabilitation Facilities (CARF) accreditation

WHITE SULPHUR SPRINGS—Meagher County

MOUNTAINVIEW MEDICAL CENTER (271306), 16 West Main Street, Zip 59645–9036, Mailing Address: P.O. Box 'Q', Zip 59645–0817; tel. 406/547–3321, (Nonreporting) **A**10 18
Primary Contact: Rob Brandt, Chief Executive Officer
Web address: www.mvmc.org
Control: Other not–for–profit (including NFP Corporation) **Service**: General medical and surgical

Staffed Beds: 21

WHITEFISH—Flathead County

★ **NORTH VALLEY HOSPITAL (271336)**, 1600 Hospital Way, Zip 59937–7849; tel. 406/863–3500, **A**10 18 **F**3 11 13 15 28 29 30 31 34 35 37 40 43 50 51 54 56 59 64 65 68 70 75 76 79 81 85 86 87 97 104 107 110 111 114 119 126 127 129 131 132 133 135 146 148 **P**6
Primary Contact: Kevin Abel, Chief Executive Officer
COO: Christina Bogers, Chief Clinical Officer
CFO: David Richhart, Chief Financial Officer
CMO: Jason Cohen, M.D., Chief Medical Officer
CIO: Michael Barnes, Chief Information Officer
CHR: Joseph Schmier, Interim Director Human Resources
Web address: www.nvhosp.org
Control: Other not–for–profit (including NFP Corporation) **Service**: General medical and surgical

Staffed Beds: 25 **Admissions:** 1615 **Census:** 13 **Outpatient Visits:** 78867
Births: 595 **Total Expense ($000):** 56241 **Payroll Expense ($000):** 20624
Personnel: 371

WOLF POINT—Roosevelt County

★ **TRINITY HOSPITAL (271341)**, 315 Knapp Street, Zip 59201–1826; tel. 406/653–6500, (Total facility includes 60 beds in nursing home–type unit) **A**10 18 **F**2 3 6 7 8 13 15 29 31 32 34 40 43 45 50 56 57 59 64 70 75 76 78 81 92 93 110 119 120 125 127 128 130 133 143 145 154 **P**5
Primary Contact: Margaret B. Norgaard, Chief Executive Officer
Web address: www.nemhs.net
Control: Other not–for–profit (including NFP Corporation) **Service**: General medical and surgical

Staffed Beds: 82 **Admissions:** 493 **Census:** 56 **Outpatient Visits:** 12821
Births: 103 **Total Expense ($000):** 17245 **Payroll Expense ($000):** 8993
Personnel: 225

MT

Many Facility Codes have changed. Please refer to the AHA Guide Code Chart.

NEBRASKA

AINSWORTH—Brown County

BROWN COUNTY HOSPITAL (281325), 945 East Zero Street,
Zip 69210–1547; tel. 402/387–2800, (Nonreporting) **A**10 18
Primary Contact: John W. Werner, Chief Executive Officer
CFO: Lisa Wood, Chief Financial Officer
CMO: Melvin Campbell, M.D., Medical Staff Chairman
CIO: Mike Depko, Director Information Technology
CHR: Lisa Fischer, Director Human Resources
CNO: Matt Lentz, R.N., Director of Patient Services
Web address: www.browncountyhospital.org
Control: County, Government, nonfederal **Service**: General medical and surgical

Staffed Beds: 18

ALBION—Boone County

★ **BOONE COUNTY HEALTH CENTER (281334)**, 723 West Fairview
Street, Zip 68620–1725, Mailing Address: P.O. Box 151, Zip 68620–0151;
tel. 402/395–2191, **A**5 10 18 **F**13 15 26 28 29 31 34 35 40 43 45 50 57 59
62 64 68 75 77 78 79 81 82 93 107 110 111 115 116 119 127 129 130 131
132 133 135 148 154 **P**6
Primary Contact: Tanya Sharp, President and Chief Executive Officer
CFO: Rita Liss, Vice President Fiscal Services and Chief Financial Officer
CMO: Lynette Kramer, M.D., Chief Medical Officer
CIO: Larry Zoucha, Chief Information Officer
CHR: Jennifer Beierman, Director Human Resources
CNO: Cindy Lesiak, Vice President Patient Care Services and Director of Nursing
Web address: www.boonecohealth.org
Control: County, Government, nonfederal **Service**: General medical and surgical

Staffed Beds: 25 Admissions: 815 Census: 9 Outpatient Visits: 28766
Births: 82 Total Expense ($000): 30494 **Payroll Expense ($000):** 14140
Personnel: 232

ALLIANCE—Box Butte County

⊠ **BOX BUTTE GENERAL HOSPITAL (281360)**, 2101 Box Butte Avenue,
Zip 69301–4445, Mailing Address: P.O. Box 810, Zip 69301–0810;
tel. 308/762–6660, **A**1 5 10 18 **F**3 5 11 13 15 28 29 32 34 35 36 38 40 43 47
48 50 53 57 59 60 64 68 69 75 77 78 79 81 82 85 86 87 92 93 97 100 101
104 107 108 111 114 116 118 119 127 129 130 131 132 133 134 135 146
148
Primary Contact: Lori Mazanec, Interim Chief Executive Officer
COO: Lori Mazanec, Chief Operating Officer
CFO: Tracy E Jatczak, CPA, Chief Financial Officer
CHR: Lisa L Hillyer, Human Resources Manager
CNO: Carolyn Jones, R.N., MSN, Chief Nursing Officer
Web address: www.bbgh.org
Control: County, Government, nonfederal **Service**: General medical and surgical

Staffed Beds: 25 Admissions: 920 Census: 9 Outpatient Visits: 32754
Births: 89 Total Expense ($000): 40500 **Payroll Expense ($000):** 14777
Personnel: 262

ALMA—Harlan County

★ **HARLAN COUNTY HEALTH SYSTEM (281300)**, 717 North Brown
Street, Zip 68920–2132, Mailing Address: P.O. Box 836, Zip 68920–0836;
tel. 308/928–2151, **A**10 18 **F**1 3 4 11 15 16 17 29 31 40 45 50 57 59 64 67
70 72 73 80 81 85 88 89 90 93 98 107 110 114 119 127 128 130 133
135 146 **P**6 **S** Great Plains Health Alliance, Inc., Wichita, KS
Primary Contact: Mark A. Miller, FACHE, Interim Chief Executive Officer
CFO: Heidi Cushing, Chief Financial Officer
CMO: Cameron Knackstedt, D.O., Chief Medical Staff
CIO: Michael Andrews, Coordinator Information Systems
CHR: Ana Schluntz, Director of Human Resources
CNO: Elizabeth Miller, Director of Nursing
Web address: www.harlancountyhealth.com
Control: County, Government, nonfederal **Service**: General medical and surgical

Staffed Beds: 19 Admissions: 121 Census: 3 Outpatient Visits: 17853
Births: 0 Total Expense ($000): 9158 **Payroll Expense ($000):** 3878
Personnel: 88

ATKINSON—Holt County

WEST HOLT MEDICAL SERVICES (281343), 406 West Neely Street,
Zip 68713–4801; tel. 402/925–2811, (Nonreporting) **A**10 18 **S** Faith Regional
Health Services, Norfolk, NE
Primary Contact: Bradley D. Pfeifer, FACHE, Chief Executive Officer
CFO: Karen Nollette, Chief Financial Officer
CMO: John Tubbs, M.D., Chief of Staff
CIO: Mark Johnson, Chief Information Officer
CHR: Margaret Linse, Administrative Secretary and Director Human Resources
CNO: Tana O'Neill, R.N., Chief Nursing Officer
Web address: www.westholtmed.org
Control: Other not–for–profit (including NFP Corporation) **Service**: General
medical and surgical

Staffed Beds: 17

AUBURN—Nemaha County

★ ⇑ **NEMAHA COUNTY HOSPITAL (281324)**, 2022 13th Street,
Zip 68305–1799; tel. 402/274–4366, **A**10 18 21 **F**3 7 12 15 28 29 30 31 34
35 40 43 62 64 68 74 75 77 78 79 81 85 86 87 93 94 107 110 111 114 117
119 128 129 130 131 133 135 141 148 149
Primary Contact: Marty Fattig, Chief Executive Officer
COO: Kermit Moore, R.N., Chief Operating Officer and Chief Nursing Officer
CFO: Stacy Taylor, Chief Financial Officer
CIO: Kathy McNaughton, Chief Information Officer
CHR: Susan Shupp, Chief Human Resources Officer
Web address: www.nchnet.org
Control: County, Government, nonfederal **Service**: General medical and surgical

Staffed Beds: 16 Admissions: 233 Census: 3 Outpatient Visits: 18418
Births: 0 Total Expense ($000): 12541 **Payroll Expense ($000):** 5115
Personnel: 87

AURORA—Hamilton County

★ **MEMORIAL COMMUNITY HEALTH (281320)**, 1423 Seventh Street,
Zip 68818–1197; tel. 402/694–3171, (Total facility includes 47 beds in nursing
home–type unit) **A**10 18 **F**10 11 13 15 28 29 31 34 35 40 41 43 45 50 51 57
59 64 65 67 75 76 77 78 79 81 82 85 86 87 93 94 97 107 108 110 114 119
130 131 132 133 146 154 **P**6
Primary Contact: Diane R. Keller, Chief Executive Officer
CFO: Phil Fendt, Chief Financial Officer
CMO: Jeff Muilenburg, Chief of Staff
CIO: Brad Tiede, Director Information Systems
CHR: Laura Teichmeier, Director Human Resources
CNO: Lindy Mosel, Director of Nursing
Web address: www.memorialcommunityhealth.org
Control: Other not–for–profit (including NFP Corporation) **Service**: General
medical and surgical

Staffed Beds: 63 Admissions: 274 Census: 46 Outpatient Visits: 25737
Births: 27 Total Expense ($000): 22274 **Payroll Expense ($000):** 11067
Personnel: 231

MEMORIAL HOSPITAL See Memorial Community Health

BASSETT—Rock County

ROCK COUNTY HOSPITAL (281333), 102 East South Street, Zip 68714–5508;
tel. 402/684–3366, (Total facility includes 30 beds in nursing home–type unit) **A**10
18 **F**7 11 15 28 40 53 57 81 84 107 110 119 127 128 133 154
Primary Contact: Stacey A. Knox, Administrator
CMO: John Tubbs, M.D., Chief of Staff
CIO: Cal Alder, Director Information Technology
CHR: Jackie Carpenter, Office Manager
CNO: Katie Ogier, Director of Nursing
Web address: www.rockcountyhospital.com
Control: County, Government, nonfederal **Service**: General medical and surgical

Staffed Beds: 54 Admissions: 142 Census: 30 Outpatient Visits: 5878
Births: 0 Total Expense ($000): 10789 **Payroll Expense ($000):** 3850
Personnel: 97

NE

Hospital, Medicare Provider Number, Address, Telephone, Approval, Facility, and Physician Codes, Health Care System

★ American Hospital Association (AHA) membership   ○ Healthcare Facilities Accreditation Program   ⇑ Center for Improvement in Healthcare Quality Accreditation
□ The Joint Commission accreditation   ◇ DNV Healthcare Inc. accreditation   △ Commission on Accreditation of Rehabilitation Facilities (CARF) accreditation

BEATRICE—Gage County

✠ **BEATRICE COMMUNITY HOSPITAL AND HEALTH CENTER (281364)**, 4800 Hospital Parkway, Zip 68310–6906, Mailing Address: P.O. Box 278, Zip 68310–0278; tel. 402/228–3344, **A**1 10 18 **F**3 13 15 28 29 31 34 35 40 45 57 62 63 64 65 68 69 70 75 76 78 79 81 82 84 85 87 93 107 110 111 114 119 127 129 130 131 132 133 135 146 147 149
Primary Contact: Richard Haraldson, CPA, FACHE, Chief Executive Officer
CFO: Alan W Streeter, Chief Financial Officer
CMO: John T Findley, M.D., Chief Medical Officer
CHR: Kathryn G. Humble, Chief Human Resources Officer
CNO: Arlinda K Ament, R.N., Interim Chief Nursing Officer
Web address: www.beatricecommunityhospital.com
Control: Other not–for–profit (including NFP Corporation) **Service:** General medical and surgical

Staffed Beds: 25 **Admissions:** 982 **Census:** 9 **Outpatient Visits:** 195550 **Births:** 204 **Total Expense ($000):** 71286 **Payroll Expense ($000):** 33551 **Personnel:** 493

BELLEVUE—Sarpy County

MADONNA REHABILITATION SPECIALTY HOSPITAL (280136), 2500 Bellevue Medical Center Drive, Fourth Floor, Zip 68123–1591; tel. 402/401–3000, (Nonreporting)
Primary Contact: Paul Dongilli Jr, Ph.D., FACHE, President and Chief Executive Officer
Web address: www.madonna.org
Control: Other not–for–profit (including NFP Corporation) **Service:** General medical and surgical

Staffed Beds: 32

☐ **NEBRASKA MEDICINE – BELLEVUE (280132)**, 2500 Bellevue Medical Center Drive, Zip 68123–1591; tel. 402/763–3000, **A**1 3 5 10 **F**3 13 15 18 20 22 28 29 30 31 34 35 40 41 44 45 47 48 49 50 51 53 55 57 58 59 60 63 64 65 68 70 74 75 76 77 78 79 81 82 84 85 86 87 91 92 93 96 97 107 108 110 111 114 119 130 131 132 135 141 143 145 146 147 148 149 150 154
Primary Contact: Matt E. Pospisil, Vice President Perioperative Services
CFO: Stephanie Daubert, Chief Financial Officer
CMO: Jeffrey D. Akerson, M.D., Chief Medical Officer
CIO: Brian Lancaster, Executive Director Information Management
CNO: Ray D. Dial, Director of Nursing
Web address: www.nebraskamed.com
Control: Other not–for–profit (including NFP Corporation) **Service:** General medical and surgical

Staffed Beds: 55 **Admissions:** 4386 **Census:** 37 **Outpatient Visits:** 115048 **Births:** 678 **Total Expense ($000):** 68608 **Payroll Expense ($000):** 27828 **Personnel:** 377

BENKELMAN—Dundy County

★ **DUNDY COUNTY HOSPITAL (281340)**, 1313 North Cheyenne Street, Zip 69021–3074, Mailing Address: P.O. Box 626, Zip 69021–0626; tel. 308/423–2204, **A**10 18 **F**3 25 34 40 43 50 56 57 59 65 78 79 81 82 87 89 93 107 110 114 119 127 128 130 131 133 154
Primary Contact: Rita A. Jones, Chief Executive Officer
COO: Wendy Elkins, Director Operations
CFO: Renee Fink, CPA, Chief Financial Officer
CMO: Jose Garcia, M.D., Chief Medical Staff
CIO: David Craw, Coordinator Information Technology
CHR: Sandy Noffsinger, Executive Assistant, Risk Manager and Director Marketing
CNO: Laken Vrbas, R.N., Director of Nursing
Web address: www.dchbenkelman.com
Control: County, Government, nonfederal **Service:** General medical and surgical

Staffed Beds: 14 **Admissions:** 103 **Census:** 1 **Outpatient Visits:** 8985 **Births:** 0 **Total Expense ($000):** 9454 **Payroll Expense ($000):** 4128 **Personnel:** 83

BLAIR—Washington County

★ **MEMORIAL COMMUNITY HOSPITAL AND HEALTH SYSTEM (281359)**, 810 North 22nd Street, Zip 68008–1199, Mailing Address: P.O. Box 250, Zip 68008–0250; tel. 402/426–2182, **A**10 18 **F**3 11 13 15 28 29 31 32 34 35 40 41 43 45 46 55 57 59 65 67 75 76 77 85 89 93 97 107 110 111 119 127 128 129 130 132 133 135 154
Primary Contact: Manuela Wolf, R.N., President and Chief Executive Officer
CMO: John F Simonson, M.D., President Medical Staff
CHR: Kristine Nielsen, Manager Human Resources
CNO: Laura Stawniak, R.N., Chief Nursing Executive
Web address: www.mchhs.org
Control: Other not–for–profit (including NFP Corporation) **Service:** General medical and surgical

Staffed Beds: 10 **Admissions:** 304 **Census:** 2 **Outpatient Visits:** 41079 **Births:** 55 **Total Expense ($000):** 32407 **Payroll Expense ($000):** 15078 **Personnel:** 212

BRIDGEPORT—Morrill County

MORRILL COUNTY COMMUNITY HOSPITAL (281318), 1313 'S' Street, Zip 69336–0579; tel. 308/262–1616, **A**10 18 **F**7 28 34 35 40 41 43 45 57 59 62 64 65 69 75 77 79 81 82 93 97 107 119 127 133 135 144 148 149 **P**6
Primary Contact: Robin Stuart, Chief Executive Officer
CFO: Connie Christensen, Chief Financial Officer
CMO: John Post, M.D., Medical Director
CIO: Lori Shengle, Director Information Technology
CHR: Rhea Basa, Director Human Resources
CNO: Sylvia Marie Lichius, R.N., Chief Nursing Officer
Web address: www.morrillcountyhospital.com
Control: County, Government, nonfederal **Service:** General medical and surgical

Staffed Beds: 6 **Admissions:** 114 **Census:** 1 **Outpatient Visits:** 4356 **Births:** 0 **Total Expense ($000):** 12581 **Payroll Expense ($000):** 5899 **Personnel:** 108

BROKEN BOW—Custer County

★ **JENNIE M. MELHAM MEMORIAL MEDICAL CENTER (281365)**, 145 Memorial Drive, Zip 68822–1378, Mailing Address: P.O. Box 250, Zip 68822–0250; tel. 308/872–4100, (Nonreporting) **A**10 18
Primary Contact: Veronica Schmidt, Chief Executive Officer
CFO: Tim Schuckman, Chief Financial Officer
CIO: Tim Schuckman, Chief Financial Officer
CHR: Teri Sell, Payroll and Personnel Coordinator
CNO: Shelly Amsberry, Director of Nursing
Web address: www.brokenbow-ne.com/community/healthcare/melham.htm
Control: Other not–for–profit (including NFP Corporation) **Service:** General medical and surgical

Staffed Beds: 73

CALLAWAY—Custer County

★ **CALLAWAY DISTRICT HOSPITAL (281335)**, 211 East Kimball, Zip 68825–2589, Mailing Address: P.O. Box 100, Zip 68825–0100; tel. 308/836–2228, **A**10 18 **F**3 17 18 31 40 45 56 57 59 64 65 67 70 97 107 110 114 115 119 127 128 133 154
Primary Contact: Marvin Neth, Chief Executive Officer
CFO: Brett Eggleston, Chief Financial Officer
CHR: Toni French, Manager Human Resources
Web address: www.callawayhospital.org
Control: Hospital district or authority, Government, nonfederal **Service:** General medical and surgical

Staffed Beds: 12 **Admissions:** 162 **Census:** 2 **Outpatient Visits:** 6575 **Births:** 0 **Total Expense ($000):** 7509 **Payroll Expense ($000):** 3563 **Personnel:** 61

CAMBRIDGE—Furnas County

★ **TRI VALLEY HEALTH SYSTEM (281348)**, 1305 West Highway 6 and 34, Zip 69022–0488, Mailing Address: P.O. Box 488, Zip 69022–0488; tel. 308/697–3329, (Total facility includes 32 beds in nursing home–type unit) **A**10 18 **F**3 8 10 11 13 15 28 29 30 31 32 34 35 40 41 45 46 53 56 57 59 64 65 67 68 69 71 75 76 77 78 79 81 82 86 87 91 93 107 110 115 116 119 125 127 128 129 130 131 132 133 135 143 145 146 147 148 **P**6
Primary Contact: Deborah L. Herzberg, R.N., MS, FACHE, Chief Executive Officer
COO: Keith Luedders, Chief Operations Officer
CFO: Diana Swindler, Chief Financial Officer
CMO: Shiuvaun Jaeger, M.D., Chief of Staff
CIO: Ciprian Galarneau, Director Information Systems
CHR: Tammy Claussen, Chief Human Resource Officer
CNO: Melissa Bodkins, R.N., Chief Clinical Officer
Web address: www.trivalleyhealth.com
Control: Other not–for–profit (including NFP Corporation) **Service:** General medical and surgical

Staffed Beds: 52 **Admissions:** 411 **Census:** 29 **Outpatient Visits:** 14648 **Births:** 67 **Total Expense ($000):** 21227 **Payroll Expense ($000):** 8847

CENTRAL CITY—Merrick County

★ **MERRICK MEDICAL CENTER (281328)**, 1715 26th Street, Zip 68826–9620; tel. 308/946–3015, (Nonreporting) **A**10 18 **S** Bryan Health, Lincoln, NE
Primary Contact: Julie Murray, Chief Executive Officer
CHR: Shauna Graham, Director of Professional Services Human Resources, Marketing Foundation
Web address: www.bryanhealth.com
Control: County, Government, nonfederal **Service:** General medical and surgical

Staffed Beds: 65

Many Facility Codes have changed. Please refer to the AHA Guide Code Chart.

© 2018 AHA Guide

NE

CHADRON—Dawes County

★ **CHADRON COMMUNITY HOSPITAL AND HEALTH SERVICES (281341)**, 825 Centennial Drive, Zip 69337–9400; tel. 308/432–5586, **A**10 18 **F**3 7 10 11 12 13 15 28 29 31 34 35 38 39 40 43 44 45 57 59 60 61 62 63 64 65 66 68 70 75 77 78 79 81 82 84 86 87 91 93 94 96 107 110 111 114 119 125 127 130 131 132 133 134 135 143 146 148 149
Primary Contact: Anna Turman, Chief Executive Officer
CFO: Russ Bohnenkamp, Chief Financial Officer
CMO: Ed Pelton, Chief of Staff
CHR: Ellen Krueger, Director Human Resources
CNO: Cheryl Cassiday, R.N., Director of Nursing
Web address: www.chadronhospital.com
Control: Other not–for–profit (including NFP Corporation) **Service:** General medical and surgical

Staffed Beds: 25 **Admissions:** 464 **Census:** 3 **Outpatient Visits:** 34425 **Births:** 105 **Total Expense ($000):** 25459 **Payroll Expense ($000):** 9859 **Personnel:** 168	

COLUMBUS—Platte County

✠ **COLUMBUS COMMUNITY HOSPITAL (280111)**, 4600 38th Street, Zip 68601–1664, Mailing Address: P.O. Box 1800, Zip 68602–1800; tel. 402/564–7118, (Nonreporting) **A**1 10 20
Primary Contact: Michael T. Hansen, FACHE, President and Chief Executive Officer
COO: James P Goulet, Vice President Operations
CFO: Chad Van Cleave, Chief Financial Officer
CMO: Mark Howerter, M.D., President Medical Staff
CIO: Cheryl Tira, Director Information Systems
CHR: Scott E Messersmith, Director Human Resources
CNO: Linda K Walline, R.N., Ph.D., MSN, Vice President Nursing
Web address: www.columbushosp.org
Control: Other not–for–profit (including NFP Corporation) **Service:** General medical and surgical

Staffed Beds: 51	

COZAD—Dawson County

★ **COZAD COMMUNITY HEALTH SYSTEM (281327)**, 300 East 12th Street, Zip 69130–1505, Mailing Address: P.O. Box 108, Zip 69130–0108; tel. 308/784–2261, (Nonreporting) **A**3 5 10 18
Primary Contact: Lyle E. Davis, Administrator
Web address: www.cozadhealthcare.com
Control: Hospital district or authority, Government, nonfederal **Service:** General medical and surgical

Staffed Beds: 20	

CREIGHTON—Knox County

★ **AVERA CREIGHTON HOSPITAL (281331)**, 1503 Main Street, Zip 68729–3007, Mailing Address: P.O. Box 186, Zip 68729–0186; tel. 402/358–5700, (Total facility includes 47 beds in nursing home–type unit) **A**10 18 **F**2 7 15 18 28 29 34 35 40 41 43 44 45 53 56 59 65 67 68 77 79 81 82 89 93 94 97 100 102 104 107 108 110 115 118 127 128 129 131 133 143 146 149 154 **P**6 **S** Avera Health, Sioux Falls, SD
Primary Contact: Todd Consbruck, Chief Executive Officer
CHR: Jane E. Miller, Director Human Resources
CNO: Jean M. Henes, MSN, R.N., Director of Nursing
Web address: www.avera.org/creighton/
Control: Other not–for–profit (including NFP Corporation) **Service:** General medical and surgical

Staffed Beds: 64 **Admissions:** 180 **Census:** 45 **Outpatient Visits:** 8102 **Births:** 0 **Total Expense ($000):** 14240 **Payroll Expense ($000):** 6723 **Personnel:** 88	

CRETE—Saline County

★ **CRETE AREA MEDICAL CENTER (281354)**, 2910 Betten Drive, Zip 68333–3084, Mailing Address: P.O. Box 220, Zip 68333–0220; tel. 402/826–2102, (Nonreporting) **A**10 18 **S** Bryan Health, Lincoln, NE
Primary Contact: Rebekah Mussman, Chief Executive Officer
CFO: Doug Kucera, Chief Financial Officer
CMO: Amy Vertin, M.D., Chief of Staff
CIO: Drew Kotil, Director Information Technology
CHR: Bobbie Wilson, Director Human Resources
CNO: Jeaniffr P. Snide, Chief Nursing Officer
Web address: www.creteareamedicalcenter.com
Control: Other not–for–profit (including NFP Corporation) **Service:** General medical and surgical

Staffed Beds: 24	

DAVID CITY—Butler County

★ **BUTLER COUNTY HEALTH CARE CENTER (281332)**, 372 South Ninth Street, Zip 68632–2116; tel. 402/367–1200, (Nonreporting) **A**5 10 18
Primary Contact: Donald T. Naiberk, Administrator
CFO: Jodi Prochaska, Chief Financial Officer
CMO: Victor Thoendel, M.D., Chief Medical Officer
CIO: Cindy Neesen, Director of Information Technology
CHR: Andra Vandenberg, Director Human Resources
CNO: Sue M Birkel, R.N., Director of Nursing
Web address: www.bchccnet.org
Control: County, Government, nonfederal **Service:** General medical and surgical

Staffed Beds: 20	

ELKHORN—Douglas County

METHODIST WOMEN'S HOSPITAL See Nebraska Methodist Hospital, Omaha

FAIRBURY—Jefferson County

★ **JEFFERSON COMMUNITY HEALTH AND LIFE (281319)**, 2200 'H' Street, Zip 68352–1119, Mailing Address: P.O. Box 277, Zip 68352–0277; tel. 402/729–3351, (Total facility includes 40 beds in nursing home–type unit) **A**10 18 **F**2 3 13 15 28 29 30 31 34 35 40 45 50 53 57 59 62 64 75 76 77 78 79 81 85 86 87 93 107 110 114 119 127 128 130 131 132 133 135 146 149 **P**6
Primary Contact: Chad Jurgens, Chief Executive Officer
CFO: Chance Klasek, CPA, Chief Financial Officer
CIO: Dennis Ahl, Director Information Technology
CHR: Sandra A. Bauer, Director Human Resources
Web address: www.jchealthandlife.org
Control: Other not–for–profit (including NFP Corporation) **Service:** General medical and surgical

Staffed Beds: 57 **Admissions:** 354 **Census:** 42 **Outpatient Visits:** 27500 **Births:** 16 **Total Expense ($000):** 21292 **Payroll Expense ($000):** 10336 **Personnel:** 201	

FALLS CITY—Richardson County

★ **COMMUNITY MEDICAL CENTER, INC. (281352)**, 3307 Barada Street, Zip 68355–2470, Mailing Address: P.O. Box 399, Zip 68355–0399; tel. 402/245–2428, **A**10 18 **F**3 13 15 28 31 34 35 40 43 45 59 75 76 78 79 81 85 93 97 107 111 114 119 127 130 133 135 154 **P**6
Primary Contact: Ryan C. Larsen, FACHE, Administrator
CFO: Scott Sawyer, Chief Financial Officer
CMO: David E. Borg, Chief of Medical Staff
CIO: Joe Buckminster, Manager Information Technology
CHR: Shannon Weinmann, Human Resources Manager
CNO: Ivy Campbell, Director of Nursing
Web address: www.cmcfc.org
Control: Other not–for–profit (including NFP Corporation) **Service:** General medical and surgical

Staffed Beds: 24 **Admissions:** 773 **Census:** 8 **Outpatient Visits:** 57812 **Births:** 47 **Total Expense ($000):** 24910 **Payroll Expense ($000):** 8710 **Personnel:** 178	

FRANKLIN—Franklin County

★ **FRANKLIN COUNTY MEMORIAL HOSPITAL (281311)**, 1406 'Q' Street, Zip 68939–0315, Mailing Address: 1406 Q Street, Zip 68939–0315; tel. 308/425–6221, (Nonreporting) **A**10 18
Primary Contact: Theresa Rizzo, Administrator
CFO: Amy Kahrs, Director of Finance
CMO: Linda Mazour, M.D., President
CIO: Cathy Webber, Director of Health Information Management
CNO: Kari Yelken, R.N., Director of Nursing
Web address: www.fcmh.com
Control: County, Government, nonfederal **Service:** General medical and surgical

Staffed Beds: 14	

NE

Hospital, Medicare Provider Number, Address, Telephone, Approval, Facility, and Physician Codes, Health Care System

★ American Hospital Association (AHA) membership   ○ Healthcare Facilities Accreditation Program   ⇑ Center for Improvement in Healthcare Quality Accreditation
□ The Joint Commission accreditation   ◇ DNV Healthcare Inc. accreditation   △ Commission on Accreditation of Rehabilitation Facilities (CARF) accreditation

FREMONT—Dodge County

⊞ **FREMONT HEALTH (280077)**, 450 East 23rd Street, Zip 68025–2387;
tel. 402/721–1610, (Total facility includes 106 beds in nursing home–type unit) **A**1
2 3 5 10 20 **F**3 8 11 13 15 17 18 20 22 26 28 29 30 31 34 35 37 38 40 45
56 57 59 62 63 64 68 70 75 76 77 78 79 81 85 86 87 89 93 98 100 103 104
107 108 110 111 114 119 120 121 123 124 126 128 129 130 131 132 135
143 144 146 **P**8
Primary Contact: Patrick M. Booth, FACHE, President and Chief Executive Officer
COO: Brett Richmond, Senior Vice President, Chief Operating Officer
CFO: Michael Sindelar, Vice President and Chief Financial Officer
CIO: Matt Sakalosky, Director Information Services and Chief Information Officer
CHR: Bethany Childers, Director Human Resources
CNO: Melinda Johanna Kentfield, R.N., Director of Nursing and Interim Chief
Nursing Officer
Web address: www.fremonthealth.com
Control: County, Government, nonfederal **Service**: General medical and surgical

Staffed Beds: 176 Admissions: 4208 Census: 108 Outpatient Visits:
85522 **Births: 309 Total Expense ($000): 121208 Payroll Expense**
($000): 53280 Personnel: 744

FRIEND—Saline County

FRIEND COMMUNITY HEALTHCARE SYSTEM (281330), 905 Second Street,
Zip 68359–1133; tel. 402/947–2541, (Nonreporting) **A**10 18
Primary Contact: Chad Thompson, President and Chief Executive Officer
CFO: Mackenzie Svarc, Finance Director
CMO: Roger Meyer, M.D., Chief of Staff
CHR: Shyanne Scholl, Interim Human Resources Director
CNO: Dayna Pulver, Director of Nursing
Web address: www.friendmed.org/
Control: City, Government, nonfederal **Service**: General medical and surgical

Staffed Beds: 63

GENEVA—Fillmore County

FILLMORE COUNTY HOSPITAL (281301), 1900 'F' Street, Zip 68361–1325,
Mailing Address: P.O. Box 193, Zip 68361–0193; tel. 402/759–3167, **A**10 18 **F**7
11 13 15 18 28 29 31 34 40 41 45 46 47 48 49 50 56 57 59 64 67 68 74 75
76 77 78 79 81 82 85 87 92 93 94 98 99 100 101 102 103 104 107 110 111
114 119 128 130 131 132 133 143 148 153 154 **P**6
Primary Contact: Christopher Nichols, Chief Executive Officer
COO: Debbie Domann, Director of Operations
CFO: Jeanne Ackland, Director of Finance
CMO: Jason Bespalec, M.D., Chief of Staff
CIO: Tyler Gewecke, Information Technology Technician
CHR: Abby Tuberville, Human Resource Manager
Web address: www.fhsofgeneva.org
Control: County, Government, nonfederal **Service**: General medical and surgical

Staffed Beds: 30 Admissions: 517 Census: 9 Outpatient Visits: 18640
Births: 49 Total Expense ($000): 19354 Payroll Expense ($000): 7168
Personnel: 139

GENOA—Nance County

GENOA MEDICAL FACILITIES (281312), 706 Ewing Avenue, Zip 68640–3035,
Mailing Address: P.O. Box 310, Zip 68640–0310; tel. 402/993–2283,
(Nonreporting) **A**10 18
Primary Contact: Amanda Roebuck, Interim Chief Executive Officer and Director
Patient Care Services
CFO: Angie Sutton, Chief Financial Officer
CMO: Brian Buhlke, M.D., Medical Director
CHR: Brianna Molt, Human Resources Director
CNO: Amanda Roebuck, Director Patient Care Services
Web address: www.genoamedical.org/
Control: City–county, Government, nonfederal **Service**: General medical and
surgical

Staffed Beds: 58

GORDON—Sheridan County

★ **GORDON MEMORIAL HEALTH SERVICES (281358)**, 300 East Eighth Street,
Zip 69343–1123; tel. 308/282–0401, (Nonreporting) **A**10 18
Primary Contact: Allen J. Gamble, Interim Chief Executive Officer
CMO: Christopher P. Costa, M.D., Chief of Staff
CIO: Ray Waldron, Director Information Technology
CHR: Lisa Woodcock, Director Human Resources
CNO: Megan Heath, Chief Nursing Officer
Web address: www.gordonmemorial.org
Control: Hospital district or authority, Government, nonfederal **Service**: General
medical and surgical

Staffed Beds: 25

GOTHENBURG—Dawson County

★ **GOTHENBURG HEALTH (281313)**, 910 20th Street, Zip 69138–1237, Mailing
Address: P.O. Box 469, Zip 69138–0469; tel. 308/537–3661, **A**10 18 **F**3 13 15
28 29 30 31 34 35 36 37 38 40 41 43 45 50 53 56 57 59 64 65 75 76 77 78
79 81 85 97 107 110 111 115 119 127 128 129 133 147 **P**1
Primary Contact: Mick Brant, FACHE, Chief Executive Officer
CFO: Michael Pracheil, Chief Financial Officer
CMO: Carol Shackleton, M.D., Medical Director
CIO: Tinna Therrien, R.N., Chief Information Officer and Senior Director Ancillary
Services
CHR: Jim Imler, Director Human Resources
CNO: Susan Moore, MS, R.N., Chief Nursing Officer
Web address: www.gothenburghealth.org
Control: Hospital district or authority, Government, nonfederal **Service**: General
medical and surgical

Staffed Beds: 12 Admissions: 344 Census: 3 Outpatient Visits: 30262
Births: 74 Total Expense ($000): 17333 Payroll Expense ($000): 6903
Personnel: 112

GRAND ISLAND—Hall County

⊞ **CHI HEALTH SAINT FRANCIS (280023)**, 2620 West Faidley Avenue,
Zip 68803–4297, Mailing Address: P.O. Box 9804, Zip 68802–9804;
tel. 308/384–4600, (Includes ST. FRANCIS MEDICAL PLAZA, 2116 West Faidley
Avenue, Grand Island, NE, Zip 68803, Mailing Address: P.O. Box 9804, Zip 68802,
tel. 308/384–4600) **A**1 2 3 5 10 19 **F**3 5 11 12 13 15 17 18 19 20 22 28 30
31 34 35 40 43 45 47 50 51 53 59 60 62 63 64 65 68 70 72 74 75 76 77 78
79 81 82 84 85 89 90 91 97 110 120 121 123 128 129 130 132 135 145 146
148 **P**8 **S** Catholic Health Initiatives, Englewood, CO
Primary Contact: Edward J. Hannon, FACHE, President
CFO: Lisa Webb, Vice President Operational Finance
CMO: Shu–Ming Wang, MD, Vice President Medical Affairs
CHR: Nancy Wallace, Vice President Human Resources, CHI Health
CNO: Beth Bartlett, MSN, R.N., Vice President Nursing
Web address: www.saintfrancisgi.org
Control: Church operated, Nongovernment, not–for–profit **Service**: General
medical and surgical

Staffed Beds: 159 Admissions: 6171 Census: 89 Outpatient Visits: 83887
Births: 878 Total Expense ($000): 142227 Payroll Expense ($000): 36990
Personnel: 622

GRANT—Perkins County

★ **PERKINS COUNTY HEALTH SERVICES (281356)**, 900 Lincoln Avenue,
Zip 69140–3095; tel. 308/352–7200, (Nonreporting) **A**10 18
Primary Contact: Neil A. Hilton, FACHE, President and Chief Executive Officer
CFO: Derick Lorentz, Chief Financial Officer
CMO: Ruth Demmel, M.D., Chief Medical Officer
CIO: Jennifer Baumgartner, Chief Information Officer
CHR: Julie Bevard, Vice President Human Resources
CNO: Dana McArtor, R.N., Director of Nursing
Web address: www.pchsgrant.com
Control: Hospital district or authority, Government, nonfederal **Service**: General
medical and surgical

Staffed Beds: 20

HASTINGS—Adams County

⊞ **MARY LANNING HEALTHCARE (280032)**, 715 North St Joseph Avenue,
Zip 68901–4497; tel. 402/463–4521, (Nonreporting) **A**1 2 3 10
Primary Contact: Eric A. Barber, President and Chief Executive Officer
COO: Mark Callahan, Chief Operating Officer
CFO: Shawn A Nordby, Chief Financial Officer
CMO: Donald R. Snodgrass, M.D., Chief Medical Officer
CIO: Lisa Nonneman, Director Information Technology Services
CHR: Bruce E Cutright, MS, Vice President Human Resources
CNO: Ronda S Ehly, R.N., Chief Nursing Officer
Web address: www.marylanning.org
Control: Other not–for–profit (including NFP Corporation) **Service**: General
medical and surgical

Staffed Beds: 148

HEBRON—Thayer County

★ **THAYER COUNTY HEALTH SERVICES (281304)**, 120 Park Avenue,
Zip 68370–2019, Mailing Address: P.O. Box 49, Zip 68370–0049;
tel. 402/768–6041, (Nonreporting) **A**10 18
Primary Contact: David Burd, Chief Executive Officer
COO: Stephanie Boldt, Chief Operating Officer
CFO: Doug Wismer, Chief Financial Officer
CMO: Leann Heinrichs, M.D., Chief of Staff
CIO: Randy Levendofsky, Director Information Technology
CHR: Tamara Brose, Director Human Resources
CNO: Jamie Koch, R.N., Chief Nursing Officer
Web address: www.thayercountyhealth.com
Control: County, Government, nonfederal **Service**: General medical and surgical

Staffed Beds: 19

NE

Many Facility Codes have changed. Please refer to the AHA Guide Code Chart. © 2018 AHA Guide

HENDERSON—York County

HENDERSON HEALTH CARE SERVICES (281308), 1621 Front Street,
Zip 68371–8902; tel. 402/723–4512, (Nonreporting) **A**10 18
Primary Contact: Cheryl Brown, Chief Executive Officer
CMO: James M Ohrt, M.D., Director Medical Staff
CHR: Lynette Friesen, Manager Human Resources
CNO: Carrie Peterson, Director of Nursing
Web address: www.hendersonhealthcare.org/getpage.php?name=message
Control: Other not–for–profit (including NFP Corporation) **Service:** General
medical and surgical

Staffed Beds: 56

HOLDREGE—Phelps County

★ ⇑ **PHELPS MEMORIAL HEALTH CENTER (281362)**, 1215 Tibbals Street,
Zip 68949–1255; tel. 308/995–2211, (Nonreporting) **A**10 18 21 **S** QHR,
Brentwood, TN
Primary Contact: Mark Harrel, Chief Executive Officer
CFO: Loren D Schroder, Chief Financial Officer
CMO: Stuart Embury, M.D., Chief Medical Officer
CIO: Leora Smith, Information System and Health Information Management Team
Leader
CHR: Cindy Jackson, Director Human Resources
Web address: www.phelpsmemorial.com
Control: Other not–for–profit (including NFP Corporation) **Service:** General
medical and surgical

Staffed Beds: 25

IMPERIAL—Chase County

★ **CHASE COUNTY COMMUNITY HOSPITAL (281351)**, 600 West 12th
Street, Zip 69033–3130, Mailing Address: P.O. Box 819, Zip 69033–0819;
tel. 308/882–7111, **A**10 18 **F**11 13 15 28 29 30 31 34 35 40 41 43 45 57 59
64 75 81 91 93 107 110 114 127 133 **P**6
Primary Contact: Stephen Lewis, Chief Executive Officer
CFO: Abigail Cyboron, Chief Financial Officer
CMO: Jonathan Richman, M.D., Chief of Staff
CIO: Jen Harris, Director Health Information Management
CHR: Julie Sharp, Supervisor Human Resources
CNO: Kathy Geier, Director of Nursing
Web address: www.chasecountyhospital.com
Control: County, Government, nonfederal **Service:** General medical and surgical

Staffed Beds: 20 **Admissions:** 161 **Census:** 2 **Outpatient Visits:** 16437
Births: 15 **Total Expense ($000):** 12400 **Payroll Expense ($000):** 4905
Personnel: 83

KEARNEY—Buffalo County

⊞ **CHI HEALTH GOOD SAMARITAN (280009)**, 10 East 31st Street,
Zip 68847–2926, Mailing Address: P.O. Box 1990, Zip 68848–1990;
tel. 308/865–7100, (Includes RICHARD H. YOUNG BEHAVIORAL HEALTH CENTER,
1755 Prairie View Place, Kearney, NE, Zip 68848, Mailing Address: P.O. Box
1750, Zip 68848–1705; tel. 308/865–2000; Michelle Hansen, Director) **A**1 2 3
5 10 **F**3 7 11 13 15 18 20 22 24 28 29 30 31 34 35 40 41 43 45 46 50 53
54 55 56 57 58 59 60 62 67 68 70 72 74 75 76 77 78 79 81 82 84 85 89 90
91 93 97 100 101 102 104 107 108 110 111 112 113 114 115 117 119 124
126 129 130 131 132 134 135 146 148 149 150 154 **P**8 **S** Catholic Health
Initiatives, Englewood, CO
Primary Contact: Michael H. Schnieders, FACHE, President
CFO: Lisa Webb, Vice President for Operational Finance
CMO: Dennis Edwards, M.D., Vice President Medical Affairs
CIO: Katie Gartner, Director Health Information Management
CNO: Kimber Bonner, R.N., Vice President Patient Care Services
Web address: www.chihealthgoodsamaritan.org
Control: Church operated, Nongovernment, not–for–profit **Service:** General
medical and surgical

Staffed Beds: 217 **Admissions:** 7636 **Census:** 111 **Outpatient Visits:**
51986 **Births:** 797 **Total Expense ($000):** 172348 **Payroll Expense
($000):** 49201 **Personnel:** 703

GOOD SAMARITAN HEALTH SYSTEMS See Chi Health Good Samaritan

★ ○ **KEARNEY REGIONAL MEDICAL CENTER (280134)**, 804 22nd Avenue,
Zip 68845–2206; tel. 855/404–5762, (Nonreporting) **A**10 11
Primary Contact: William Calhoun, Chief Executive Officer
COO: John Lanning, Chief Operating Officer
CFO: Steve Regier, Chief Financial Officer
CIO: Travis Gregg, Director Support Services
CHR: Steve Beck, MS, Director Human Resources
CNO: Adrienne Carney, R.N., Director Nursing and Surgical Services
Web address: www.kearneyregional.com
Control: Partnership, Investor–owned (for–profit) **Service:** General medical and
surgical

Staffed Beds: 92

KIMBALL—Kimball County

★ **KIMBALL HEALTH SERVICES (281305)**, 505 South Burg Street,
Zip 69145–1398; tel. 308/235–1952, (Nonreporting) **A**10 18
Primary Contact: Ken Hunter, R.N., Chief Executive Officer
CFO: Melissa Prante, Chief Financial Officer
CMO: James Plate, M.D., Chief of Staff
CIO: Charles Walker, Director Information Technology
CHR: Jim Imler, Director Human Resources
CNO: Richard Harriger, Director of Emergency Services
Web address: www.kimballhealth.org
Control: County, Government, nonfederal **Service:** General medical and surgical

Staffed Beds: 10

LEXINGTON—Dawson County

★ ⇑ **LEXINGTON REGIONAL HEALTH CENTER (281361)**, 1201 North Erie
Street, Zip 68850–1560, Mailing Address: P.O. Box 980, Zip 68850–0980;
tel. 308/324–5651, (Nonreporting) **A**3 5 10 18 21
Primary Contact: Leslie Marsh, Chief Executive Officer
COO: Jim Hain, Chief Operating Officer
CFO: Wade Eschenbrenner, Chief Financial Officer
CMO: Francisca Acosta–Carlson, M.D., Chief of Staff
CIO: Robb Hanna, Executive Director Information Technology
CHR: Jill Denker, Executive Director Human Resources
CNO: Nicole Thorell, R.N., MSN, Chief Nursing Officer
Web address: www.lexingtonregional.org
Control: Hospital district or authority, Government, nonfederal **Service:** General
medical and surgical

Staffed Beds: 25

LINCOLN—Lancaster County

⊞ △ **BRYAN MEDICAL CENTER (280003)**, 1600 South 48th Street,
Zip 68506–1299; tel. 402/481–1111, (Includes BRYAN MEDICAL CENTER–EAST,
1600 South 48th Street, Lincoln, NE, Zip 68506–1299; tel. 402/481–1111;
BRYAN MEDICAL CENTER–WEST, 2300 South 16th Street, Lincoln, NE,
Zip 68502–3781; tel. 402/475–1011) **A**1 2 3 7 10 **F**3 4 5 12 13 15 17 18 19
20 22 24 26 28 29 30 31 34 35 37 38 39 40 43 45 46 47 48 49 50 54 56 57
58 59 61 64 68 70 71 72 74 75 76 77 78 79 81 82 84 85 86 87 89 90 92 93
96 98 99 102 103 104 105 107 108 110 111 114 115 116 117 118 119 121
123 126 129 130 131 132 135 145 146 147 148 149 151 152 **S** Bryan Health,
Lincoln, NE
Primary Contact: John T. Woodrich, President and Chief Operating Officer
CFO: Russell Gronewold, Chief Financial Officer
CMO: John Trapp, Vice President Medical Affairs
CIO: George Carr, Chief Information Officer
CHR: Jan Garvin, Vice President Human Resources
CNO: Lisa M Vail, R.N., Chief Nursing Officer and Vice President of Patient Care
Services
Web address: www.bryanhealth.com
Control: Other not–for–profit (including NFP Corporation) **Service:** General
medical and surgical

Staffed Beds: 540 **Admissions:** 27376 **Census:** 345 **Outpatient Visits:**
201742 **Births:** 3299 **Total Expense ($000):** 548620 **Payroll Expense
($000):** 205087 **Personnel:** 3315

NE

Hospital, Medicare Provider Number, Address, Telephone, Approval, Facility, and Physician Codes, Health Care System

★ American Hospital Association (AHA) membership   ○ Healthcare Facilities Accreditation Program   ⇑ Center for Improvement in Healthcare Quality Accreditation
□ The Joint Commission accreditation   ◇ DNV Healthcare Inc. accreditation   △ Commission on Accreditation of Rehabilitation Facilities (CARF) accreditation

★ **CHI HEALTH NEBRASKA HEART (280128)**, 7500 South 91st Street, Zip 68526–9437; tel. 402/327–2700, **A**10 **F**17 18 20 22 24 26 29 30 34 45 57 58 59 64 81 107 115 119 130 **P**8 **S** Catholic Health Initiatives, Englewood, CO
Primary Contact: Derek Vance, President
CFO: Dan Schonlau, Vice President Operational Finance
Web address: www.CHIhealthNebraskaHeart.com
Control: Church operated, Nongovernment, not–for–profit **Service:** Heart

Staffed Beds: 63 Admissions: 2038 Census: 19 Outpatient Visits: 12296 Births: 0 Total Expense ($000): 65517 Payroll Expense ($000): 16774 Personnel: 292

⊞ **CHI HEALTH ST ELIZABETH (280020)**, 555 South 70th Street, Zip 68510–2494; tel. 402/219–8000, **A**1 2 3 5 10 **F**3 8 11 12 13 15 16 29 30 31 34 35 37 39 40 44 45 46 47 48 49 50 51 53 55 58 59 60 61 64 65 68 70 72 74 75 76 78 79 80 81 84 85 86 87 89 92 107 108 110 111 114 115 116 117 118 119 122 123 124 126 129 130 131 132 144 145 146 147 148 154 **P**8 **S** Catholic Health Initiatives, Englewood, CO
Primary Contact: Derek Vance, President
CFO: Dan Schonlau, Chief Financial Officer and Vice President of Finance
CMO: Michael Ferris, M.D., Chief Medical Officer
CIO: Richard Bohaty, Director Information Technology
CHR: Nancy Wallace, Senior Vice President, Chief Human Resources Officer
CNO: Elizabeth A Raetz, R.N., MSN, Vice President Nursing and Chief Nursing Officer
Web address: www.saintelizabethonline.com
Control: Other not–for–profit (including NFP Corporation) **Service:** General medical and surgical

Staffed Beds: 260 Admissions: 8760 Census: 105 Outpatient Visits: 96165 Births: 1553 Total Expense ($000): 190588 Payroll Expense ($000): 53261 Personnel: 752

LINCOLN DIVISION See Veterans Affairs Nebraska–Western Iowa Health Care System – Lincoln, Lincoln

☐ **LINCOLN REGIONAL CENTER (284003)**, West Prospector Place and South Folsom, Zip 68522–2299, Mailing Address: P.O. Box 94949, Zip 68509–4949; tel. 402/471–4444, (Nonreporting) **A**1 10
Primary Contact: Mark LaBouchardiere, Interim Facility Administrator
COO: Stacey Werth–Sweeney, Facility Operating Officer
CFO: Randy Willey, Business Manager
CMO: Vijay Dewan, M.D., Clinical Director
CHR: Scott Rasmussen, Director Human Resources
Web address: www.hhs.state.ne.us/beh/rc
Control: State, Government, nonfederal **Service:** Psychiatric

Staffed Beds: 244

LINCOLN SURGICAL HOSPITAL (280127), 1710 South 70th Street, Suite 200, Zip 68506–1677; tel. 402/484–9090, (Nonreporting) **A**10
Primary Contact: Robb Linafelter, Chief Executive Officer
Web address: www.lincolnsurgery.com
Control: Corporation, Investor–owned (for–profit) **Service:** Surgical

Staffed Beds: 7

△ **MADONNA REHABILITATION HOSPITAL (283025)**, 5401 South Street, Zip 68506–2134; tel. 402/489–7102, (Nonreporting) **A**3 7 10
Primary Contact: Paul Dongilli Jr, Ph.D., FACHE, President and Chief Executive Officer
CFO: Victor J Witkowicz, Senior Vice President and Chief Financial Officer
CMO: Thomas Stadler, M.D., Vice President Medical Affairs and Chief Medical Officer
CIO: David Rolfe, Chief Information Officer
CHR: Lou Ann Manske, Director Human Resources
Web address: www.madonna.org
Control: Other not–for–profit (including NFP Corporation) **Service:** Rehabilitation

Staffed Beds: 308

MADONNA REHABILITATION HOSPITAL (282000), 5401 South Street, Zip 68506–2150; tel. 402/413–3000, (Nonreporting) **A**3
Primary Contact: Paul Dongilli Jr, Ph.D., FACHE, President and Chief Executive Officer
Web address: www.madonna.org/
Control: Other not–for–profit (including NFP Corporation) **Service:** Acute long–term care hospital

Staffed Beds: 300

NEBRASKA PENAL AND CORRECTIONAL HOSPITAL, 14th And Pioneer Streets, Zip 68501, Mailing Address: P.O. Box 94661, Zip 94661; tel. 402/471–3161, (Nonreporting)
Primary Contact: Randy T. Kohl, M.D., Deputy Director, Health Services
Web address: www.corrections.nebraska.gov
Control: State, Government, nonfederal **Service:** Hospital unit of an institution (prison hospital, college infirmary, etc.)

Staffed Beds: 12

⊞ **SELECT SPECIALTY HOSPITAL – LINCOLN (282002)**, 2300 South 16th Street, 7th Floor, Zip 68502–3704; tel. 402/483–8444, (Nonreporting) **A**1 10 **S** Select Medical Corporation, Mechanicsburg, PA
Primary Contact: Connie K. Siffring, Chief Executive Officer
CHR: Bob Dorsey, Human Resources Coordinator
CNO: Trisha Smolik, R.N., MSN, Chief Nursing Officer
Web address: www.selectmedical.com
Control: Corporation, Investor–owned (for–profit) **Service:** Acute long–term care hospital

Staffed Beds: 24

★ **VETERANS AFFAIRS NEBRASKA–WESTERN IOWA HEALTH CARE SYSTEM – LINCOLN**, 600 South 70th Street, Zip 68510–2493; tel. 402/489–3802, (Includes LINCOLN DIVISION, 600 South 70th Street, Lincoln, NE, Zip 68510–2493; tel. 402/489–3802) (Nonreporting) **S** Department of Veterans Affairs, Perry Point, MD
Primary Contact: Don Burman, Director
CIO: David Daiker, Chief Information Resource Management
CHR: Dave Peters, Chief Human Resources Officer
Web address: www.nebraska.va.gov/
Control: Veterans Affairs, Government, federal **Service:** General medical and surgical

Staffed Beds: 132

LYNCH—Boyd County

NIOBRARA VALLEY HOSPITAL (281303), 401 South Fifth Street, Zip 68746–0118, Mailing Address: P.O. Box 118, Zip 68746–0118; tel. 402/569–2451, (Nonreporting) **A**10 18 **S** Faith Regional Health Services, Norfolk, NE
Primary Contact: Kelly Kalkowski, Chief Executive Officer
CFO: Martha Nelson, Chief Financial Officer
CMO: James Keil, M.D., Chief Medical Officer
CHR: Trudy Nelson, Chief Human Resource Officer
CNO: Debra Dawn Hanzlik, R.N., Director of Nursing
Web address: www.nvhcares.org
Control: Other not–for–profit (including NFP Corporation) **Service:** General medical and surgical

Staffed Beds: 20

MCCOOK—Red Willow County

★ ⊞ **COMMUNITY HOSPITAL (281363)**, 1301 East 'H' Street, Zip 69001–1328, Mailing Address: P.O. Box 1328, Zip 69001–1328; tel. 308/344–2650, **A**3 10 18 21 **F**3 11 13 15 28 29 31 34 35 40 41 45 48 50 51 57 62 63 64 75 77 78 79 81 82 85 93 96 107 110 111 114 119 120 121 127 129 130 131 132 133 135 145 146 148 154
Primary Contact: Troy Bruntz, President and Chief Executive Officer
CFO: Sean Wolfe, Vice President Finance and Chief Financial Officer
CMO: Jason Blomstedt, Chief of Staff
CIO: Lori Beeby, Director Information Systems
CHR: Leanne R Miller, Director Human Resources
CNO: Brad Langdorf, Vice President Clinical Services and Chief Nursing Officer
Web address: www.chmccook.org
Control: Other not–for–profit (including NFP Corporation) **Service:** General medical and surgical

Staffed Beds: 25 Admissions: 848 Census: 6 Outpatient Visits: 28551 Births: 148 Total Expense ($000): 44410 Payroll Expense ($000): 16428 Personnel: 249

MINDEN—Kearney County

KEARNEY COUNTY HEALTH SERVICES (281306), 727 East First Street, Zip 68959–1705; tel. 308/832–3400, (Total facility includes 34 beds in nursing home–type unit) **A**10 18 **F**3 10 15 28 29 34 35 40 41 55 57 59 64 65 67 68 81 87 97 104 107 110 115 119 127 128 129 130 131 133 135 145 146 147 148 149 154 **P**6
Primary Contact: Luke David. Poore, Chief Executive Officer
CFO: Kayla Rhynalds, Interim Chief Financial Officer
CMO: Douglas Althouse, Chief Medical Staff
CHR: Rebecca L Cooke, Director Human Resources
CNO: Kendra Brown, MSN, R.N., Director of Nursing
Web address: www.kchs.org
Control: County, Government, nonfederal **Service:** General medical and surgical

Staffed Beds: 44 Admissions: 113 Census: 22 Outpatient Visits: 4737 Births: 0

Many Facility Codes have changed. Please refer to the AHA Guide Code Chart. © 2018 AHA Guide

NEBRASKA CITY—Otoe County

★ **CHI HEALTH ST. MARY'S (281342)**, 1301 Grundman Boulevard, Zip 68410; tel. 402/873–3321, **A**10 18 **F**3 13 15 18 28 31 34 35 40 43 45 57 59 64 66 68 69 75 76 78 79 81 82 85 87 97 107 110 111 114 115 118 119 127 128 129 130 132 133 135 146 147 148 154 **S** Catholic Health Initiatives, Englewood, CO
Primary Contact: Daniel DeFreece, M.D., Interim President
CFO: Tim H. Schnack, Vice President Operations Finance
CMO: Jonathan Stelling, M.D., Vice President Medical Affairs
CNO: Brenda Jean Sebek, R.N., Administrator
Web address: www.chihealthstmarys.com
Control: Church operated, Nongovernment, not–for–profit **Service:** General medical and surgical

Staffed Beds: 18 **Admissions:** 434 **Census:** 4 **Outpatient Visits:** 35861 **Births:** 146 **Total Expense ($000):** 22566 **Payroll Expense ($000):** 6519 **Personnel:** 143	

NELIGH—Antelope County

★ **ANTELOPE MEMORIAL HOSPITAL (281326)**, 102 West Ninth Street, Zip 68756–1114, Mailing Address: P.O. Box 229, Zip 68756–0229; tel. 402/887–4151, **A**10 18 **F**7 13 15 28 34 35 36 40 41 45 53 56 57 59 62 63 64 67 68 75 76 77 79 81 82 87 89 93 94 107 115 119 127 128 129 130 131 133 147 154 **P**6
Primary Contact: Jack W. Green, Administrator
CFO: Martha Nelson, Chief Financial Officer
CMO: Troy Dawson, M.D., President Medical Staff
CIO: Kevin Trease, Chief Information Officer
CHR: Mary A Schwager, Director Human Resources
CNO: Merry Sprout, R.N., Chief Nursing Officer
Web address: www.amhne.org/
Control: Other not–for–profit (including NFP Corporation) **Service:** General medical and surgical

Staffed Beds: 23 **Admissions:** 325 **Census:** 5 **Outpatient Visits:** 10409 **Births:** 9 **Total Expense ($000):** 14975 **Payroll Expense ($000):** 6815 **Personnel:** 121	

NORFOLK—Madison County

⊞ **FAITH REGIONAL HEALTH SERVICES (280125)**, 2700 West Norfolk Avenue, Zip 68701–4438, Mailing Address: P.O. Box 869, Zip 68702–0869; tel. 402/371–4880, (Includes EAST CAMPUS, 1500 Koenigstein Avenue, Norfolk, NE, Zip 68701; tel. 402/371–3402; WEST CAMPUS, 2700 Norfolk Avenue, Norfolk, NE, Zip 68701, Mailing Address: P.O. Box 869, Zip 68702–0869; tel. 402/371–4880) (Total facility includes 62 beds in nursing home–type unit) **A**1 2 3 5 10 20 **F**3 8 10 11 13 15 18 20 22 24 26 28 29 30 31 34 35 40 41 43 44 45 46 49 50 53 57 58 59 61 62 63 64 65 67 70 71 73 74 75 76 77 78 79 80 81 82 84 85 86 87 89 90 91 92 93 96 98 102 107 108 110 111 114 115 119 120 121 123 128 129 130 131 132 135 146 147 148 149 154 **P**6 7 8 **S** Faith Regional Health Services, Norfolk, NE
Primary Contact: Kelly Driscoll, R.N., Interim President and Chief Executive Officer
CFO: Johnathan Wilker, Vice President Finance and Chief Financial Officer
CMO: Dean O French, M.D., Chief of Staff
CIO: Brian Sterud, Chief Information Officer
CHR: Janet Pinkelman, Director Human Resources
Web address: www.frhs.org
Control: Other not–for–profit (including NFP Corporation) **Service:** General medical and surgical

Staffed Beds: 136 **Admissions:** 5032 **Census:** 136 **Outpatient Visits:** 82220 **Births:** 812 **Total Expense ($000):** 155313 **Payroll Expense ($000):** 51796 **Personnel:** 1109	

NORTH PLATTE—Lincoln County

⊞ **GREAT PLAINS HEALTH (280065)**, 601 West Leota Street, Zip 69101–6598, Mailing Address: P.O. Box 1167, Zip 69103–1167; tel. 308/568–8000, **A**1 2 3 5 10 **F**3 8 11 12 13 15 18 20 22 28 29 30 31 34 35 40 43 45 48 50 51 57 59 60 62 63 68 70 73 74 75 76 78 79 81 82 84 85 86 87 89 93 98 101 102 104 107 108 110 111 115 116 117 119 120 121 122 124 129 130 131 132 135 145 146 147 148 154 **P**8
Primary Contact: Melvin McNea, Chief Executive Officer
COO: Ivan Mitchell, Chief Operating Officer
CFO: Krystal Claymore, Chief Financial Officer
CIO: Brandon Kelliher, Chief Information Officer
CHR: Jayne Johnson, Director Human Resources
CNO: Tamara Martin–Linnard, R.N., Chief Clinical Officer
Web address: www.gphealth.org
Control: Other not–for–profit (including NFP Corporation) **Service:** General medical and surgical

Staffed Beds: 114 **Admissions:** 5712 **Census:** 60 **Outpatient Visits:** 196552 **Births:** 537 **Total Expense ($000):** 198756 **Payroll Expense ($000):** 78249 **Personnel:** 989	

OAKLAND—Burt County

★ **OAKLAND MERCY HOSPITAL (281321)**, 601 East Second Street, Zip 68045–1499; tel. 402/685–5601, (Nonreporting) **A**10 18 **S** Trinity Health, Livonia, MI
Primary Contact: Laura Gamble, Director of Critical Access Hospitals
CFO: Terri Mentink, Chief Financial Officer
CMO: Tracie Martin, M.D., Chief Medical Officer
CNO: Jayma Brown, R.N., Director of Nursing
Web address: www.oaklandhospital.org
Control: Church operated, Nongovernment, not–for–profit **Service:** General medical and surgical

Staffed Beds: 18	

OGALLALA—Keith County

★ **OGALLALA COMMUNITY HOSPITAL (281355)**, 2601 North Spruce Street, Zip 69153–2465; tel. 308/284–4011, **A**10 18 **F**3 13 15 29 31 40 43 45 68 76 77 79 81 85 93 107 110 111 115 119 128 130 133 148 154 **S** Banner Health, Gilbert, AZ
Primary Contact: Drew H. Dostal, R.N., FACHE, Chief Executive Officer
CFO: Dena Klockman, Chief Financial Officer
CMO: Gabriel Godina, M.D., Chief of Staff
CHR: Gracie Ramos, Chief Human Resources Officer
CNO: Linda Baldwin, Chief Nursing Officer
Web address: www.bannerhealth.com/locations/ogallala/ogallala–community–hospital
Control: Other not–for–profit (including NFP Corporation) **Service:** General medical and surgical

Staffed Beds: 18 **Admissions:** 379 **Census:** 4 **Outpatient Visits:** 20667 **Births:** 56 **Total Expense ($000):** 17946 **Payroll Expense ($000):** 6715 **Personnel:** 129	

OMAHA—Douglas County

☐ **BOYS TOWN NATIONAL RESEARCH HOSPITAL (283300)**, 555 North 30th Street, Zip 68131–2198; tel. 402/498–6511, **A**1 3 5 10 **F**3 34 35 58 65 68 79 81 86 87 89 97 104 106 107 108 111 119 129 130 131 154 **P**6
Primary Contact: John K. Arch, FACHE, Director
CFO: Leigh Jean Koinzan, Director Finance
CMO: Edward Kolb, M.D., Medical Director
CIO: Ann Ducey, Chief Information Officer
CHR: Michael Gell, Director Human Resources
CNO: Patricia Allgeier, R.N., Chief Nursing Officer
Web address: www.boystownhospital.org
Control: Other not–for–profit (including NFP Corporation) **Service:** Children's general medical and surgical

Staffed Beds: 141 **Admissions:** 130 **Census:** 1 **Outpatient Visits:** 214509 **Births:** 0 **Total Expense ($000):** 123965 **Payroll Expense ($000):** 56731 **Personnel:** 922	

⊞ **CHI HEALTH CREIGHTON UNIVERSITY MEDICAL CENTER – BERGAN MERCY (280060)**, 7500 Mercy Road, Zip 68124–2319; tel. 402/398–6060, (Includes LASTING HOPE RECOVERY CENTER, 415 South 25th Avenue, Omaha, NE, Zip 68131; tel. 402/717–5300; Robin Conyers, Administrator) **A**1 2 3 5 8 10 **F**3 8 11 13 15 17 18 20 22 24 26 28 29 30 31 32 34 35 37 38 40 43 44 45 46 47 48 49 50 51 53 54 55 56 57 58 59 60 61 62 63 64 65 68 70 72 74 75 76 77 78 79 81 82 83 84 85 86 87 89 92 93 97 98 100 107 108 109 110 111 114 115 116 117 118 119 120 121 123 124 126 130 131 132 134 143 144 145 146 147 148 154 **P**8 **S** Catholic Health Initiatives, Englewood, CO
Primary Contact: Kevin J. Nokels, FACHE, President
COO: Patricia Townley, Director Operations
CFO: Tim H. Schnack, Vice President Financial Services
CMO: Devin Fox, M.D., Vice President Medical Operations
CIO: Thomas Haley, Division Assistant Vice President Business Relationship Management
CHR: Nancy Wallace, Vice President Human Resources
Web address: www.chihealth.com/chi–health–bergan–mercy
Control: Church operated, Nongovernment, not–for–profit **Service:** General medical and surgical

Staffed Beds: 336 **Admissions:** 13424 **Census:** 169 **Outpatient Visits:** 121400 **Births:** 3808 **Total Expense ($000):** 266237 **Payroll Expense ($000):** 79940 **Personnel:** 1615	

NE

Hospital, Medicare Provider Number, Address, Telephone, Approval, Facility, and Physician Codes, Health Care System	
★ American Hospital Association (AHA) membership	⇧ Center for Improvement in Healthcare Quality Accreditation
☐ The Joint Commission accreditation	○ Healthcare Facilities Accreditation Program
	◇ DNV Healthcare Inc. accreditation
	△ Commission on Accreditation of Rehabilitation Facilities (CARF) accreditation

☒ △ **CHI HEALTH IMMANUEL (280081)**, 6901 North 72nd Street, Zip 68122–1799; tel. 402/572–2121, **A**1 2 3 5 7 10 **F**3 4 5 11 12 13 15 17 18 20 22 26 28 29 30 31 32 34 35 36 37 38 40 43 45 46 49 50 51 53 55 56 57 58 59 64 68 70 74 75 76 77 78 79 81 82 84 85 86 87 90 91 92 93 94 95 96 97 98 99 100 102 103 105 107 108 110 111 114 115 117 118 119 120 121 123 124 126 128 129 130 131 132 136 141 142 146 154 **P**8 **S** Catholic Health Initiatives, Englewood, CO
Primary Contact: Ann Schumacher, R.N., MSN, FACHE, President
CFO: Tim H. Schnack, Chief Financial Officer
CMO: Joseph Hoagbin, M.D., Chief Medical Officer
CHR: Nancy Wallace, Vice President Human Resources
Web address: www.alegent.com/immanuel
Control: Church operated, Nongovernment, not–for–profit **Service:** General medical and surgical

Staffed Beds: 272 **Admissions:** 10333 **Census:** 163 **Outpatient Visits:** 113270 **Births:** 541 **Total Expense ($000):** 162833 **Payroll Expense ($000):** 55349 **Personnel:** 874

☒ **CHI HEALTH LAKESIDE (280130)**, 16901 Lakeside Hills Court, Zip 68130–2318; tel. 402/717–8000, **A**1 2 3 5 10 **F**3 8 12 13 15 18 20 22 26 28 29 30 31 32 34 35 36 38 44 45 46 49 53 54 55 56 59 60 63 64 68 70 72 74 75 76 77 78 79 81 82 83 84 85 86 93 94 97 99 100 102 103 104 107 108 110 111 114 115 118 119 120 121 122 123 124 126 129 130 131 132 134 143 146 147 148 **P**8 **S** Catholic Health Initiatives, Englewood, CO
Primary Contact: Kevin Miller, President
COO: Joan E Neuhaus, Division Senior Vice President Chief Operating Officer
CFO: Nick O'Tool, Vice President Operational Finance
CMO: Patricia Murdock–Langan, M.D., Chief Medical Officer
CIO: Thomas Haley, Information Technology Systems Site Director
CHR: Nancy Wallace, Division Senior Vice President, Chief Human Resource Officer
CNO: Kathy Bressler, Division Senior Vice President, Chief Nursing Officer
Web address: www.CHIhealth.com
Control: Church operated, Nongovernment, not–for–profit **Service:** General medical and surgical

Staffed Beds: 128 **Admissions:** 7359 **Census:** 75 **Outpatient Visits:** 98126 **Births:** 1003 **Total Expense ($000):** 129266 **Payroll Expense ($000):** 37439 **Personnel:** 545

☒ **CHILDREN'S HOSPITAL AND MEDICAL CENTER (283301)**, 8200 Dodge St, Zip 68114–4113; tel. 402/955–5400, **A**1 3 5 10 **F**3 7 8 11 12 13 19 21 23 25 27 29 30 31 32 34 35 36 41 43 45 46 47 48 49 50 54 55 59 60 62 64 65 68 72 74 75 76 77 78 79 81 82 84 85 87 88 89 92 93 104 107 108 111 115 119 129 130 131 132 137 144 145 146 148 149 154 **P**6
Primary Contact: Richard G. Azizkhan, M.D., President and Chief Executive Officer
COO: Kathy L English, R.N., MSN, Executive Vice President and Chief Operating Officer
CFO: Amy Hatcher, Senior Vice President and Chief Financial Officer
CMO: Christopher Maloney, M.D., Senior Vice President, Medical Affairs and Chief Medical Officer
CIO: Mark Stastny, Vice President and Chief Information Officer
CHR: Suzanne Nocita, Senior Vice President and Chief Human Resource Officer
Web address: www.childrensomaha.org
Control: Other not–for–profit (including NFP Corporation) **Service:** Children's general medical and surgical

Staffed Beds: 140 **Admissions:** 4716 **Census:** 101 **Outpatient Visits:** 389343 **Births:** 17 **Total Expense ($000):** 393000 **Payroll Expense ($000):** 180037 **Personnel:** 2147

★ ○ **DOUGLAS COUNTY COMMUNITY MENTAL HEALTH CENTER (284009)**, 4102 Woolworth Avenue, Zip 68105–1899; tel. 402/444–7449, **A**5 10 11 **F**98 **P**6
Primary Contact: Sherry L. Glasnapp, Director
CFO: DeDe Will, Director Finance
CMO: Sidney A. Kauzlarich, M.D., Medical Director
CIO: Dianne Wallace, County Information Manager
CHR: Karen Buche, Chief Human Resource Officer
CNO: Marti Christensen, Director of Psychiatric Nursing
Web address: www.co.douglas.ne.us
Control: County, Government, nonfederal **Service:** Psychiatric

Staffed Beds: 16 **Admissions:** 842 **Census:** 10 **Outpatient Visits:** 9406 **Births:** 0

MIDWEST SURGICAL HOSPITAL (280131), 7915 Farnam Drive, Zip 68114–4504; tel. 402/399–1900, (Nonreporting) **A**3 10
Primary Contact: Charles Livingston, Chief Executive Officer
Web address: www.mwsurgicalhospital.com
Control: Corporation, Investor–owned (for–profit) **Service:** Surgical

Staffed Beds: 19

☒ **NEBRASKA MEDICINE – NEBRASKA MEDICAL CENTER (280013)**, 987400 Nebraska Medical Center, Zip 68198–7400; tel. 402/552–2000, **A**1 2 3 5 8 10 **F**3 6 8 9 11 12 13 15 16 17 18 20 22 24 26 28 29 30 31 32 34 35 36 37 38 39 40 41 43 44 45 46 47 48 49 50 51 53 54 55 56 57 58 59 60 61 62 63 64 65 66 68 70 71 72 74 75 76 77 78 79 80 81 82 84 85 86 87 88 89 91 92 93 94 96 97 98 100 104 107 108 110 111 113 114 115 116 117 118 119 120 121 123 124 126 127 129 130 131 132 134 135 136 137 138 139 140 141 142 143 145 146 147 148 149 150 154 **P**5 6 8
Primary Contact: James Linder, M.D., Chief Executive Officer
COO: Dennis Bierle, Chief Operating Officer
CFO: Stephanie Daubert, Chief Financial Officer
CMO: Harris Frankel, M.D., Interim Chief Medical Officer
CIO: Michael A Ash, Chief Transformation Officer
CHR: Frank Venuto, Chief Human Capital Officer
CNO: Suzanne Langan Nuss, M.D., Chief Nursing Officer
Web address: www.nebraskamed.com
Control: Other not–for–profit (including NFP Corporation) **Service:** General medical and surgical

Staffed Beds: 569 **Admissions:** 26227 **Census:** 410 **Outpatient Visits:** 1008942 **Births:** 1651 **Total Expense ($000):** 1243285 **Payroll Expense ($000):** 581846 **Personnel:** 7128

☒ △ **NEBRASKA METHODIST HOSPITAL (280040)**, 8303 Dodge Street, Zip 68114–4199; tel. 402/354–4000, (Includes METHODIST WOMEN'S HOSPITAL, 707 North 190th Plaza, Elkhorn, NE, Zip 68022–3974; tel. 402/815–4000; Susan Korth, M.P.H., Ph.D., Vice President and Chief Operating Officer) **A**1 2 3 5 7 10 **F**3 8 11 12 15 18 20 22 24 26 28 29 30 31 34 35 40 45 46 47 48 49 50 51 52 53 54 55 56 57 58 59 62 63 64 65 66 68 70 72 74 75 76 77 78 79 80 81 82 83 84 85 86 87 90 91 92 93 96 100 101 102 107 108 110 111 114 115 116 117 118 119 120 121 123 124 126 129 130 132 135 142 143 146 147 148 154 **S** Nebraska Methodist Health System, Inc., Omaha, NE
Primary Contact: Stephen L. Goeser, FACHE, President and Chief Executive Officer
CFO: Linda K Burt, Corporate Vice President Finance
CMO: William Shiffermiller, M.D., Vice President Medical Affairs
CHR: Holly Huerter, Vice President Human Resources
CNO: Teri Tipton Bruening, MSN, Chief Nursing Officer and Vice President Patient Care Services
Web address: www.bestcare.org
Control: Other not–for–profit (including NFP Corporation) **Service:** General medical and surgical

Staffed Beds: 400 **Admissions:** 18674 **Census:** 260 **Outpatient Visits:** 146133 **Births:** 5046 **Total Expense ($000):** 493856 **Payroll Expense ($000):** 185379 **Personnel:** 2632

☒ **NEBRASKA SPINE HOSPITAL (280133)**, 6901 North 72nd Street, Suite 20300, Zip 68122–1755, Mailing Address: 6901 North 72nd Street, Zip 68122–1709; tel. 402/572–3000, (Nonreporting) **A**1 10
Primary Contact: Christopher M. Palumbo, President and Chief Executive Officer
CNO: Teresa Hawlik, MSN, Chief Nurse Executive
Web address: www.nebraskaspinehospital.com
Control: Partnership, Investor–owned (for–profit) **Service:** Orthopedic

Staffed Beds: 34

☐ **ORTHONEBRASKA HOSPITAL (280129)**, 2808 South 143rd Plaza, Zip 68144–5611; tel. 402/609–1600, **A**1 3 5 10 **F**3 37 40 64 68 79 81 82 85 93 94 96 107 111 119 131 141 **P**8
Primary Contact: Levi Scheppers, Chief Executive Officer
COO: Mark E Longacre, FACHE, Chief Operating Officer
CFO: Anna McCaslin, Chief Financial Officer
CMO: Ian Crabb, M.D., Chief Medical Officer
CIO: Tim Pugsley, Chief Information Officer
CHR: Lori L Thompson, Manager Human Resources
Web address: www.neorthohospital.com
Control: Partnership, Investor–owned (for–profit) **Service:** Orthopedic

Staffed Beds: 24 **Admissions:** 1846 **Census:** 10 **Outpatient Visits:** 58121 **Births:** 0 **Total Expense ($000):** 68335 **Payroll Expense ($000):** 22774 **Personnel:** 354

☒ **SELECT SPECIALTY HOSPITAL–OMAHA (282001)**, 1870 South 75th Street, Zip 68124–1700; tel. 402/361–5700, (Nonreporting) **A**1 10 **S** Select Medical Corporation, Mechanicsburg, PA
Primary Contact: Nancy Laughlin Wagner, R.N., Chief Executive Officer
COO: Joel White, Chief Operating Officer
CMO: Guillermo Huerta, M.D., Chief Medical Officer
CHR: Laurna Hoss, Human Resource Coordinator
CNO: Amanda Wellman, MSN, R.N., Chief Nursing Officer
Web address: www.https://omaha.selectspecialtyhospitals.com
Control: Corporation, Investor–owned (for–profit) **Service:** Acute long–term care hospital

Staffed Beds: 52

Many Facility Codes have changed. Please refer to the AHA Guide Code Chart. © 2018 AHA Guide

NE

☒ **VETERANS AFFAIRS NEBRASKA–WESTERN IOWA HEALTH CARE SYSTEM,** 4101 Woolworth Avenue, Zip 68105–1873; tel. 402/346–8800, (Nonreporting) **A**1 2 3 5 8 **S** Department of Veterans Affairs, Perry Point, MD
Primary Contact: Don Burman, Director
COO: Denise Harrison, Associate Director
CFO: Kirk Kay, Chief Financial Officer
CMO: Grace Stringfellow, M.D., Chief of Staff
CIO: Jennifer Rosenbalm, Manager Business Office
CHR: Cheryl M DeWispelare, Chief Human Resources Officer
CNO: Eileen M Kingston, R.N., Nurse Executive, Associate Director Patient Care
Web address: www.nebraska.va.gov/
Control: Veterans Affairs, Government, federal **Service**: General medical and surgical

Staffed Beds: 137

O'NEILL—Holt County

★ **AVERA ST. ANTHONY'S HOSPITAL (281329)**, 300 North Second Street, Zip 68763–1514, Mailing Address: P.O. Box 270, Oneill, Zip 68763–0270; tel. 402/336–2611, (Nonreporting) **A**5 10 18 **S** Avera Health, Sioux Falls, SD
Primary Contact: Todd Consbruck, President and Chief Executive Officer
CFO: Michael Garman, Chief Financial Officer
CIO: Michael Garman, Chief Financial Officer
CHR: Kathryn Benson, Human Resources Partner
Web address: www.avera.org/st-anthonys
Control: Church operated, Nongovernment, not–for–profit **Service**: General medical and surgical

Staffed Beds: 25

ORD—Valley County

★ **VALLEY COUNTY HEALTH SYSTEM (281353)**, 2707 L Street, Zip 68862–1275; tel. 308/728–4200, **A**10 18 **F**3 7 15 28 29 31 34 35 40 41 43 45 46 50 56 57 59 62 63 64 65 68 74 75 77 78 79 81 82 84 87 90 93 94 97 103 107 110 111 119 127 128 129 130 131 132 133 148 154
Primary Contact: Nancy Glaubke, Chief Executive Officer
CFO: Ashley Woodward, Director Financial Services
CMO: Jennifer Bengston, M.D., Chief Medical Officer
CIO: Shane Molacek, Chief Information Officer
CHR: Danielle Proskocil, Director Human Resources
CNO: Vicki Bredthauer, R.N., Director of Nursing
Web address: www.valleycountyhealthsystem.org
Control: County, Government, nonfederal **Service**: General medical and surgical

Staffed Beds: 16 Admissions: 363 Census: 6 Outpatient Visits: 25000 Births: 0 Total Expense ($000): 21809 Payroll Expense ($000): 8963 Personnel: 163

OSCEOLA—Polk County

ANNIE JEFFREY MEMORIAL COUNTY HEALTH CENTER (281314), 531 Beebe Street, Zip 68651–5537, Mailing Address: P.O. Box 428, Zip 68651–0428; tel. 402/747–2031, (Nonreporting) **A**10 18
Primary Contact: Joseph W. Lohrman, Chief Executive Officer
CFO: Joseph W Lohrman, Chief Executive Officer
CMO: David Jameson, M.D., Chief of Staff
CIO: Frank Vrba, Chief Information Officer
CHR: Sue Leif, R.N., Director Human Resources
Web address: www.ajhc.org
Control: County, Government, nonfederal **Service**: General medical and surgical

Staffed Beds: 12

OSHKOSH—Garden County

★ **REGIONAL WEST GARDEN COUNTY (281310)**, 1100 West Second Street, Zip 69154–6152; tel. 308/772–3283, (Nonreporting) **A**10 18
Primary Contact: William Giles, Chief Executive Officer
CFO: Jennifer Moffat, Staff Accountant
CMO: Steve Boyer, M.D., Chief Medical Officer
CHR: Ricca Sanford, Director Human Resources
CNO: Trish Davison, R.N., Chief Nursing Officer
Web address: www.gchealth.org
Control: County, Government, nonfederal **Service**: General medical and surgical

Staffed Beds: 50

OSMOND—Pierce County

★ **OSMOND GENERAL HOSPITAL (281347)**, 402 North Maple Street, Zip 68765–5726, Mailing Address: P.O. Box 429, Zip 68765–0429; tel. 402/748–3393, **A**10 18 **F**3 28 34 40 57 59 64 67 69 81 90 97 107 114 127 128 133 143 **P**6
Primary Contact: Lon Knievel, Chief Executive Officer
CFO: Jodi Aschoff, Chief Financial Officer
CMO: David Mwebe, M.D., Chief of Staff
CNO: Kristen Colsden, Director of Nursing
Web address: www.osmondhospital.com
Control: Other not–for–profit (including NFP Corporation) **Service**: General medical and surgical

Staffed Beds: 20 Admissions: 169 Census: 2 Outpatient Visits: 65290 Births: 0 Total Expense ($000): 6890 Payroll Expense ($000): 3237 Personnel: 64

PAPILLION—Sarpy County

☒ **CHI HEALTH MIDLANDS (280105)**, 11111 South 84th Street, Zip 68046–4122; tel. 402/593–3000, **A**1 2 5 10 **F**3 11 15 17 18 20 22 26 28 29 30 34 35 36 38 40 43 44 45 46 49 50 51 53 56 57 59 60 61 62 63 64 65 68 70 77 79 81 84 85 86 87 93 97 107 110 111 114 115 117 118 119 129 130 131 132 135 143 146 147 154 **P**8 **S** Catholic Health Initiatives, Englewood, CO
Primary Contact: Kevin Miller, President
COO: Joan E Neuhaus, Division Senior Vice President, Chief Operating Officer
CFO: Tyler DeJong, Director of Operational Finance
CMO: Patricia Murdock–Langan, M.D., Chief Medical Officer
CIO: Thomas Haley, Information Technology Systems Site Director
CHR: Nancy Wallace, Division Senior Vice President, Chief Human Resource Officer
CNO: Brenda Bergman–Evans, Chief Nursing Officer
Web address: www.CHIhealth.com
Control: Church operated, Nongovernment, not–for–profit **Service**: General medical and surgical

Staffed Beds: 28 Admissions: 1406 Census: 14 Outpatient Visits: 43039 Births: 0 Total Expense ($000): 43342 Payroll Expense ($000): 12579 Personnel: 196

PAWNEE CITY—Pawnee County

★ **PAWNEE COUNTY MEMORIAL HOSPITAL AND RURAL HEALTH CLINIC (281302)**, 600 'I' Street, Zip 68420–3001, Mailing Address: P.O. Box 433, Zip 68420–0433; tel. 402/852–2231, **A**10 18 **F**3 7 15 28 29 30 40 43 45 59 81 107 110 119 127 128 130 133 147 154 **P**6
Primary Contact: Ruth M. Stephens, MSN, R.N., Chief Executive Officer
CFO: Susan Daniels, Chief Financial Officer
CHR: Jennifer Bartels, Director Human Resources
CNO: Kelly Findlay, Director of Nurses
Web address: www.pawneehospital.com
Control: County, Government, nonfederal **Service**: General medical and surgical

Staffed Beds: 11 Admissions: 55 Census: 1 Outpatient Visits: 7801 Births: 0 Total Expense ($000): 8037 Payroll Expense ($000): 3096 Personnel: 52

PENDER—Thurston County

★ **PENDER COMMUNITY HOSPITAL (281349)**, 100 Hospital Drive, Zip 68047–0100, Mailing Address: P.O. Box 100, Zip 68047–0100; tel. 402/385–3083, (Total facility includes 40 beds in nursing home–type unit) **A**10 18 **F**10 11 13 15 18 28 29 34 35 40 45 50 57 59 67 74 75 76 77 78 79 81 82 86 93 94 96 97 101 104 107 110 111 114 119 127 129 130 131 133 135 143 148 149 150 153 154 **P**6 **S** Trinity Health, Livonia, MI
Primary Contact: Melissa Kelly, Chief Executive Officer and Chief Financial Officer
CFO: Melissa Kelly, Chief Executive Officer and Chief Financial Officer
CMO: Matt Timm, M.D., Medical Director
CIO: Teresa Heise, Coordinator Management Information Systems
CHR: Nancy Suhr, Manager Human Resources
CNO: Katie Peterson, R.N., Chief Nursing Officer
Web address: www.pendercommunityhospital.com
Control: Hospital district or authority, Government, nonfederal **Service**: General medical and surgical

Staffed Beds: 61 Admissions: 469 Census: 37 Outpatient Visits: 60783 Total Expense ($000): 23502 Payroll Expense ($000): 9503 Personnel: 215

NE

PLAINVIEW—Pierce County

★ **CHI HEALTH PLAINVIEW (281346)**, 704 North Third Street, Zip 68769–2047, Mailing Address: P.O. Box 489, Zip 68769–0489; tel. 402/582–4245, (Nonreporting) **A**10 18 **S** Catholic Health Initiatives, Englewood, CO
Primary Contact: Gregory Beckmann, Chief Executive Officer
CFO: Tim H. Schnack, Chief Financial Officer
CMO: Steve Peterson, M.D., Chief of Staff
CHR: Diane Blair, Human Resources and Admissions
CNO: Debra K Rutledge, R.N., Vice President Nursing Services
Web address: www.alegentcreighton.com/plainview–hospital
Control: Church operated, Nongovernment, not–for–profit **Service:** General medical and surgical

Staffed Beds: 15

RED CLOUD—Webster County

★ **WEBSTER COUNTY COMMUNITY HOSPITAL (281316)**, Sixth Avenue and Franklin Street, Zip 68970–0465, Mailing Address: P.O. Box 465, Zip 68970–0465; tel. 402/746–5600, **A**10 18 **F**3 15 18 28 29 30 32 34 35 40 41 45 50 56 57 59 64 65 68 70 75 77 78 79 81 82 83 84 90 93 94 96 97 107 110 111 112 115 119 127 128 129 130 133 135 145 146 147 148 149 150 154
Primary Contact: Mirya Hallock, Administrator
CFO: Marcia Olson, Business Office Manager
CMO: Amy Springer, Medical Director
CHR: Marcia Olson, Business Office Manager
CNO: Candace Peters, R.N., Director of Nursing
Web address: www.websterhospital.org
Control: County, Government, nonfederal **Service:** General medical and surgical

Staffed Beds: 13 Admissions: 87 Census: 1 Outpatient Visits: 601 Births: 0 Total Expense ($000): 5686 Payroll Expense ($000): 2223 Personnel: 47

SAINT PAUL—Howard County

HOWARD COUNTY COMMUNITY HOSPITAL See Howard County Medical Center

★ **HOWARD COUNTY MEDICAL CENTER (281338)**, 1113 Sherman Street, Zip 68873–1546, Mailing Address: P.O. Box 406, Zip 68873–0406; tel. 308/754–4421, (Nonreporting) **A**10 18
Primary Contact: Arlan D. Johnson, Chief Executive Officer
COO: Jillyn Klein, Chief Operating Officer
CFO: Morgan Meyer, Chief Financial Officer
CMO: Angela Brennan, M.D., Chief of Staff
CIO: Cheryl Watson, Chief Information Officer
CHR: Leslie Belzer, Director Human Resources
CNO: Janelle Morgan, Interim Director of Nursing
Web address: www.hcmc.us.com
Control: County, Government, nonfederal **Service:** General medical and surgical

Staffed Beds: 25

SCHUYLER—Colfax County

★ **CHI HEALTH SCHUYLER (281323)**, 104 West 17th Street, Zip 68661–1304; tel. 402/352–2441, (Nonreporting) **A**10 18 **S** Catholic Health Initiatives, Englewood, CO
Primary Contact: Connie Peters, R.N., President
CFO: Tim H. Schnack, Chief Financial Officer
CIO: Kenneth Lawonn, Senior Vice President and Chief Information Officer
CHR: Nancy Wallace, Vice President Human Resources
Web address: www.alegent.org
Control: Church operated, Nongovernment, not–for–profit **Service:** General medical and surgical

Staffed Beds: 25

SCOTTSBLUFF—Scotts Bluff County

✠ △ **REGIONAL WEST MEDICAL CENTER (280061)**, 4021 Avenue 'B', Zip 69361–4695; tel. 308/635–3711, (Nonreporting) **A**1 2 3 5 7 10
Primary Contact: John Mentgen, FACHE, President and Chief Executive Officer
COO: Tadd Greenfield, Executive Vice President and Chief Operating Officer
CFO: Michael F Ickowski, Vice President and Chief Financial Officer
CMO: Lisa Scheppers, Chief Medical Officer
CIO: Montie Hodge, Vice President Information Technology and Chief Information Officer
CHR: Brenda J Forge, Vice President, Human Resources
CNO: Connie Rupp, MSN, R.N., Executive Vice President and Chief Nursing Officer
Web address: www.rwhs.org
Control: Other not–for–profit (including NFP Corporation) **Service:** General medical and surgical

Staffed Beds: 122

SEWARD—Seward County

★ **MEMORIAL HEALTH CARE SYSTEMS (281339)**, 300 North Columbia Avenue, Zip 68434–2228; tel. 402/643–2971, **A**10 18 **F**3 10 11 13 15 28 29 30 31 32 34 35 40 43 45 46 50 57 59 62 64 65 68 75 76 77 78 79 81 82 87 93 94 96 97 104 107 108 110 111 114 116 119 127 128 129 130 131 132 133 135 146 147 148 149 **P**5 8
Primary Contact: Roger J. Reamer, Chief Executive Officer
CFO: Greg Jerger, Chief Financial Officer
CMO: James Plasek, M.D., Chief of Staff
CIO: Mark Criner, Director Information Technology
CHR: Corey Mann, Director Human Resources
Web address: www.mhcs.us
Control: Other not–for–profit (including NFP Corporation) **Service:** General medical and surgical

Staffed Beds: 24 Admissions: 750 Census: 7 Outpatient Visits: 32267 Births: 76 Total Expense ($000): 30670 Payroll Expense ($000): 14274

SIDNEY—Cheyenne County

★ **SIDNEY REGIONAL MEDICAL CENTER (281357)**, 1000 Pole Creek Crossing, Zip 69162–1799; tel. 308/254–5825, (Total facility includes 63 beds in nursing home–type unit) **A**5 10 18 **F**2 10 11 12 13 15 18 26 27 28 29 30 31 34 35 40 41 45 49 50 56 57 59 62 63 64 65 68 70 75 76 77 79 81 84 85 86 87 89 91 92 93 94 97 107 111 115 119 127 129 130 131 132 133 135 143 144 148 154 **P**6
Primary Contact: Jason Petik, Chief Executive Officer
CMO: Mandy Shaw, M.D., Chief of Staff
CIO: Jennifer Brockhaus, Chief Information Officer
CHR: Catherine T Arterburn, R.N., Vice President Human Resources
CNO: Julie A Slagle, R.N., MSN, Vice President Patient Care Services
Web address: www.sidneyrmc.com
Control: Other not–for–profit (including NFP Corporation) **Service:** General medical and surgical

Staffed Beds: 88 Admissions: 635 Census: 52 Outpatient Visits: 17608 Births: 62 Total Expense ($000): 52304 Payroll Expense ($000): 22561 Personnel: 346

SUPERIOR—Nuckolls County

★ **BRODSTONE MEMORIAL HOSPITAL (281315)**, 520 East Tenth Street, Zip 68978–1225, Mailing Address: P.O. Box 187, Zip 68978–0187; tel. 402/879–3281, **A**10 18 **F**3 8 11 13 15 17 28 29 30 34 35 40 41 45 50 57 59 64 65 67 70 74 75 76 77 79 81 82 85 86 87 89 93 94 97 107 110 111 115 119 127 128 129 130 131 132 133 135 146 148 154
Primary Contact: Treg Vyzourek, Chief Executive Officer
COO: Dena C Alvarez, R.N., COO & Chief Compliance Officer
CFO: Sandy Borden, Chief Financial Officer
CMO: Timothy Blecha, M.D., Medical Director
CIO: Tim Hiatt, Chief Information Officer
CHR: Beth A Schlichtman, Manager Human Resources
CNO: Kori Field, Director of Nursing
Web address: www.brodstonehospital.org
Control: Other not–for–profit (including NFP Corporation) **Service:** General medical and surgical

Staffed Beds: 25 Admissions: 459 Census: 4 Outpatient Visits: 18500 Births: 32 Total Expense ($000): 23089 Payroll Expense ($000): 9385 Personnel: 172

SYRACUSE—Otoe County

★ **COMMUNITY MEMORIAL HOSPITAL (281309)**, 1579 Midland Street, Zip 68446–9732, Mailing Address: P.O. Box N, Zip 68446–0518; tel. 402/269–2011, **A**10 18 **F**1 3 11 15 28 29 40 43 45 53 59 64 67 79 81 82 85 89 93 107 110 114 119 127 128 133
Primary Contact: Michael Harvey, FACHE, President and Chief Executive Officer
CFO: Karrie Beach, Vice President Finance
CMO: Zak Tempelmeyer, M.D., Chief Medical Staff
CIO: Matthew Steinblock, Director Information Systems
CHR: Nancy R Brack, Vice President Human Resources
CNO: Pat Howell, Chief Nursing Officer
Web address: www.syracusecmh.org
Control: Hospital district or authority, Government, nonfederal **Service:** General medical and surgical

Staffed Beds: 10 Admissions: 153 Census: 1 Outpatient Visits: 15040 Births: 0 Total Expense ($000): 15259 Payroll Expense ($000): 6794 Personnel: 118

NE

Many Facility Codes have changed. Please refer to the AHA Guide Code Chart.

TECUMSEH—Johnson County

★ **JOHNSON COUNTY HOSPITAL (281350)**, 202 High Street, Zip 68450–2443,
Mailing Address: P.O. Box 599, Zip 68450–0599; tel. 402/335–3361,
(Nonreporting) **A**10 18
Primary Contact: Diane Newman, FACHE, Administrator
COO: Diane Newman, FACHE, Administrator
CMO: Benjamin Biehl, M.D., Chief Medical Officer
CIO: Joseph Randall Stollar, Chief Information Officer
CHR: Susan Hessheimer, Director Human Resources
CNO: Matthew Snyder, R.N., Director of Nursing
Web address: www.jchosp.com
Control: County, Government, nonfederal **Service:** General medical and surgical

Staffed Beds: 25

VALENTINE—Cherry County

★ **CHERRY COUNTY HOSPITAL (281344)**, 510 North Green Street,
Zip 69201–1932, Mailing Address: P.O. Box 410, Zip 69201–0410;
tel. 402/376–2525, (Nonreporting) **A**3 10 18
Primary Contact: Brent A. Peterson, Administrator
CFO: Peggy Snell, Chief Finance Officer
CNO: Kathryn Renning, Director of Nursing
Web address: www.cherrycountyhospital.org
Control: County, Government, nonfederal **Service:** General medical and surgical

Staffed Beds: 25

WAHOO—Saunders County

★ **SAUNDERS MEDICAL CENTER (281307)**, 1760 County Road J,
Zip 68066–4152; tel. 402/443–4191, (Nonreporting) **A**10 18 **S** Bryan Health,
Lincoln, NE
Primary Contact: Tyler Toline, FACHE, Chief Executive Officer
COO: Julie A Rezac, R.N., Chief Operating Officer
CFO: Chase Manstedt, Chief Financial Officer
CMO: Lorance Newburn, M.D., Medical Chief of Staff
CIO: Carrie Stephens, Director Information Technology
CNO: Lalah Landers, R.N., Director of Nursing
Web address: www.saundersmedicalcenter.com
Control: County, Government, nonfederal **Service:** General medical and surgical

Staffed Beds: 16

WAYNE—Wayne County

★ **PROVIDENCE MEDICAL CENTER (281345)**, 1200 Providence Road,
Zip 68787–1299; tel. 402/375–3800, **A**10 18 **F**3 7 13 15 28 29 30 31 34 35
36 40 50 53 57 59 62 63 64 68 75 76 81 82 84 85 93 107 110 111 115 119
128 130 132 133 135 154
Primary Contact: James Frank, CPA, Chief Executive Officer
COO: Kristine A Giese, Chief Operating Officer
CFO: Kim Hixson, Vice President of Financial Officer and Chief Financial Officer
CNO: Nicole Haglund, Vice President of Nursing Services
Web address: www.providencemedical.com
Control: Other not–for–profit (including NFP Corporation) **Service:** General
medical and surgical

Staffed Beds: 25 **Admissions:** 351 **Census:** 5 **Outpatient Visits:** 14053
Births: 64 **Total Expense ($000):** 20006 **Payroll Expense ($000):** 8368
Personnel: 183

WEST POINT—Cuming County

★ **ST. FRANCIS MEMORIAL HOSPITAL (281322)**, 430 North Monitor Street,
Zip 68788–1555; tel. 402/372–2404, (Total facility includes 63 beds in nursing
home–type unit) **A**10 18 **F**3 6 11 13 15 28 29 30 31 34 35 40 43 45 50 53
57 59 62 63 64 68 75 76 77 78 79 81 82 85 86 90 92 93 94 98 99 100 103
107 111 114 119 127 128 129 130 131 132 133 135 146 147 148 154 **P**6 **S**
Franciscan Sisters of Christian Charity Sponsored Ministries, Inc., Manitowoc, WI
Primary Contact: Jerry Wordekemper, President and Chief Executive Officer
CFO: Dennis Dinslage, Vice President Finance and Chief Financial Officer
CMO: Kenneth Pitz, M.D., Chief of Staff
CIO: Jean Meiergerd, Chief Information Officer
CHR: Terri Ridder, Director Human Resources
CNO: Carol Kampschnieder, Vice President Clinical and Regulatory Services
Web address: www.fcswp.org
Control: Church operated, Nongovernment, not–for–profit **Service:** General
medical and surgical

Staffed Beds: 88 **Admissions:** 498 **Census:** 51 **Outpatient Visits:** 72924
Births: 62 **Total Expense ($000):** 32479 **Payroll Expense ($000):** 15426
Personnel: 238

WINNEBAGO—Thurston County

☐ ⇑ **U.S. PUBLIC HEALTH SERVICE INDIAN HOSPITAL (280119)**, Highway
7577, Zip 68071; tel. 402/878–2231, (Nonreporting) **A**1 10 21 **S** U.S. Indian
Health Service, Rockville, MD
Primary Contact: Gary Wabaunsee, Service Unit Director
CFO: Audrey Parker, Budget Analyst
Web address: www.ihs.gov
Control: PHS, Indian Service, Government, federal **Service:** General medical and
surgical

Staffed Beds: 30

YORK—York County

★ **YORK GENERAL (281336)**, 2222 North Lincoln Avenue, Zip 68467–1095;
tel. 402/362–6671, (Total facility includes 129 beds in nursing home–type unit)
A10 18 **F**3 10 11 12 13 15 28 29 31 34 35 40 45 53 56 57 59 60 62 64 68 70
75 76 77 78 79 81 82 85 86 87 89 93 96 107 108 110 111 115 117 118 119
125 128 129 130 131 132 133 145 146 148
Primary Contact: James P. Ulrich Jr, Chief Executive Officer
COO: Jenny Obermier, Senior Vice President, Chief Operating Officer and Chief
Nursing Officer
CFO: Bob McQuistan, Vice President Finance
CMO: Patrick Hotovy, M.D., Chief of Staff
CIO: Chris Kraft, Director Information Systems
CHR: Cathy Norquest, Director Human Resources
CNO: Jenny Obermier, Senior Vice President, Chief Operating Officer and Chief
Nursing Officer
Web address: www.yorkgeneral.org
Control: Other not–for–profit (including NFP Corporation) **Service:** General
medical and surgical

Staffed Beds: 154 **Admissions:** 1145 **Census:** 118 **Outpatient Visits:**
40254 **Births:** 78 **Total Expense ($000):** 42872 **Payroll Expense
($000):** 19672 **Personnel:** 401

NE

Hospital, Medicare Provider Number, Address, Telephone, Approval, Facility, and Physician Codes, Health Care System

★ American Hospital Association (AHA) membership   ◯ Healthcare Facilities Accreditation Program   ⇑ Center for Improvement in Healthcare Quality Accreditation
☐ The Joint Commission accreditation   ◇ DNV Healthcare Inc. accreditation   △ Commission on Accreditation of Rehabilitation Facilities (CARF) accreditation

NEVADA

BATTLE MOUNTAIN—Lander County

BATTLE MOUNTAIN GENERAL HOSPITAL (291303), 535 South Humboldt Street, Zip 89820–1988; tel. 775/635–2550, (Nonreporting) **A**10 18
Primary Contact: Kelley Price, R.N., Interim Chief Executive Officer
CFO: Cindy Fagg, Fiscal Officer
CMO: Mark S. Meyers, M.D., Chief of Staff
CIO: Terry Dunn, Director Information Technology
CHR: Lori Sherbondy, Director Human Resources
CNO: Kelley Price, R.N., Chief Nursing Officer
Web address: www.bmgh.org
Control: Hospital district or authority, Government, nonfederal **Service:** General medical and surgical

Staffed Beds: 7

BOULDER CITY—Clark County

BOULDER CITY HOSPITAL (291309), 901 Adams Boulevard, Zip 89005–2213; tel. 702/293–4111, (Total facility includes 47 beds in nursing home–type unit) **A**10 18 **F**28 29 34 35 40 45 57 59 62 63 64 65 75 77 81 83 84 86 93 96 98 102 103 104 105 106 107 111 114 119 128 130 132 133 143 146 150
Primary Contact: Thomas Maher, Chief Executive Officer and Administrator
CFO: Douglas Lewis, Chief Financial Officer
CMO: Herve Bezard, M.D., Chief of Staff
CHR: Belinda McGraw, Director Human Resources
CNO: Andre Pastian, R.N., MSN, Chief Nursing Officer
Web address: www.bouldercityhospital.org
Control: Other not–for–profit (including NFP Corporation) **Service:** General medical and surgical

Staffed Beds: 82 **Admissions:** 596 **Census:** 59 **Outpatient Visits:** 18348 **Births:** 0 **Total Expense ($000):** 26004 **Payroll Expense ($000):** 12117 **Personnel:** 162

CALIENTE—Lincoln County

GROVER C. DILS MEDICAL CENTER (291312), 700 North Spring Street, Zip 89008, Mailing Address: P.O. Box 1010, Zip 89008–1010; tel. 775/726–3171, (Nonreporting) **A**10 18
Primary Contact: Jason Bleak, Administrator and Chief Executive Officer
COO: Jason Bleak, Administrator and Chief Executive Officer
CFO: Sherlyn Fackrell, Finance Controller
CMO: R William Katschke, M.D., Jr Medical Director
CHR: Rozanne Mangum, Administrative Assistant and Director Human Resources
Web address: www.gcdmc.org
Control: Other not–for–profit (including NFP Corporation) **Service:** Other specialty treatment

Staffed Beds: 20

CARSON CITY—Carson City County

CARSON TAHOE CONTINUING CARE HOSPITAL (292008), 775 Fleischmann Way, 2nd Floor, Zip 89703–2995; tel. 775/445–7795, **A**10 **F**1 3 29 68 85 130 148
Primary Contact: Michelle L. Joy, FACHE, Chief Executive Officer
CFO: Ann Beck, Vice President and Chief Financial Officer
CMO: Jose Aguirre, M.D., Medical Director
CHR: Larry Fagerhaug
CNO: Cynthia Parker, Administrator and Director of Nursing
Web address: www.carsontahoe.com
Control: Other not–for–profit (including NFP Corporation) **Service:** Acute long–term care hospital

Staffed Beds: 29 **Admissions:** 279 **Census:** 19 **Outpatient Visits:** 0 **Births:** 0 **Total Expense ($000):** 11069 **Payroll Expense ($000):** 4563 **Personnel:** 49

⊠ **CARSON TAHOE HEALTH (290019)**, 1600 Medical Parkway, Zip 89703–4625, Mailing Address: P.O. Box 2168, Zip 89702–2168; tel. 775/445–8672, (Includes SIERRA SURGERY HOSPITAL, 1400 Medical Parkway, Carson City, NV, Zip 89703–4624; tel. 775/883–1700; Ken Doran, Interim Chief Executive Officer) **A**1 2 5 10 22 **F**3 5 8 11 13 15 17 18 20 22 24 26 28 29 30 31 34 35 38 40 46 47 49 50 51 54 56 57 59 64 65 68 70 74 75 76 77 78 79 81 82 85 86 87 89 93 96 98 100 101 102 103 104 105 107 108 110 111 115 116 117 118 119 130 132 135 144 146 147 148 149 152 153 154
Primary Contact: Edward L. Epperson, Chief Executive Officer
COO: Michelle L Joy, FACHE, Chief Operating Officer
CFO: Ann Beck, Vice President Finance
CMO: Jeffrey Sanders, M.D., Chief of Staff
CHR: Jim Lewandowski, Interim Director of Human Resources
CNO: Anna Anders, Vice President and Chief Nursing Officer
Web address: www.carsontahoe.com
Control: Other not–for–profit (including NFP Corporation) **Service:** General medical and surgical

Staffed Beds: 211 **Admissions:** 12783 **Census:** 156 **Outpatient Visits:** 312713 **Births:** 980 **Total Expense ($000):** 255768 **Payroll Expense ($000):** 88836 **Personnel:** 1302

ELKO—Elko County

⊠ **NORTHEASTERN NEVADA REGIONAL HOSPITAL (290008)**, 2001 Errecart Boulevard, Zip 89801–8333; tel. 775/738–5151, **A**1 3 10 20 **F**3 8 11 13 15 18 20 22 28 29 30 31 34 38 40 41 45 46 50 51 57 59 60 68 70 75 76 77 79 81 85 93 102 107 108 111 114 115 119 129 148 154 **S** LifePoint Health, Brentwood, TN
Primary Contact: Steve Simpson, Chief Executive Officer
CFO: Grant Trollope, Chief Financial Officer
CIO: Jeff Morgan, Director Information Systems
CHR: Laura Elliott, Director Human Resources
Web address: www.nnrhospital.com
Control: Corporation, Investor–owned (for–profit) **Service:** General medical and surgical

Staffed Beds: 50 **Admissions:** 1866 **Census:** 14 **Outpatient Visits:** 51855 **Births:** 542 **Total Expense ($000):** 55383 **Payroll Expense ($000):** 23718 **Personnel:** 420

ELY—White Pine County

⊠ **WILLIAM BEE RIRIE HOSPITAL (291302)**, 1500 Avenue 'H', Zip 89301–2699; tel. 775/289–3001, **A**1 10 18 **F**1 4 8 11 13 15 16 17 29 31 34 40 41 45 50 56 57 59 64 65 66 67 70 72 73 75 76 79 80 81 82 85 86 87 88 89 90 92 97 98 100 102 104 107 108 111 115 119 127 128 129 130 133 135 147 148 **P**6
Primary Contact: Matthew Walker, Chief Executive Officer and Administrator
CMO: G N Christensen, M.D., Chief Medical Officer
CIO: Destin Brandis, Chief Information Officer
CHR: Vicki Pereace, Manager Human Resources
Web address: www.wbrhely.org/getpage.php?name=index
Control: County, Government, nonfederal **Service:** General medical and surgical

Staffed Beds: 25 **Admissions:** 381 **Census:** 3 **Outpatient Visits:** 19802 **Births:** 66 **Total Expense ($000):** 30486 **Payroll Expense ($000):** 13531

FALLON—Churchill County

⊠ **BANNER CHURCHILL COMMUNITY HOSPITAL (291313)**, 801 East Williams Avenue, Zip 89406–3052; tel. 775/423–3151, **A**1 10 18 **F**3 7 11 13 15 31 34 35 40 41 45 47 50 57 59 64 65 68 70 75 76 79 81 85 86 87 89 93 97 107 110 111 115 119 129 130 146 154 **S** Banner Health, Gilbert, AZ
Primary Contact: Robert H. Carnahan II, R.N., Chief Executive Officer
CFO: Steve Fraker, Chief Financial Officer
CMO: Tedd McDonald, M.D., Chief Medical Officer
CHR: Darlene Hanefeld, Chief Human Resources Officer
Web address: www.bannerhealth.com/churchill
Control: Other not–for–profit (including NFP Corporation) **Service:** General medical and surgical

Staffed Beds: 25 **Admissions:** 1372 **Census:** 13 **Births:** 360 **Total Expense ($000):** 36912 **Payroll Expense ($000):** 16123 **Personnel:** 267

NV

Many Facility Codes have changed. Please refer to the AHA Guide Code Chart.

GARDNERVILLE—Douglas County

★ **CARSON VALLEY MEDICAL CENTER (291306)**, 1107 Highway 395, Zip 89410; tel. 775/782–1500, **A**3 10 18 **F**3 15 18 29 30 31 34 35 40 45 46 47 48 50 56 57 59 64 65 66 68 70 75 77 78 79 81 82 85 87 93 104 107 108 110 111 115 119 127 128 129 130 132 133 144 146 148 149 **P**6
Primary Contact: Jeffrey Prater, Chief Executive Officer
COO: Linda Lilleboe, R.N., MSN, Director Operations
CMO: Evan Easley, M.D., Chief Medical Officer
CIO: Jason Roberts, Director Information System
CHR: Lisa Tremaine, Manager Human Resources
CNO: Kathy Cocking, R.N., Director of Clinical Services
Web address: www.cvmchospital.org
Control: Other not–for–profit (including NFP Corporation) **Service**: General medical and surgical

Staffed Beds: 23 **Admissions:** 1139 **Census:** 10 **Outpatient Visits:** 82001 **Births:** 0 **Personnel:** 331

HAWTHORNE—Mineral County

MOUNT GRANT GENERAL HOSPITAL (291300), First and 'A' Street, Zip 89415, Mailing Address: P.O. Box 1510, Zip 89415–1510; tel. 775/945–2461, **A**10 18 **F**40 93 107 119 128 154 **P**6
Primary Contact: Richard Munger, Administrator
Web address: www.mtgrantgenhospital.org/
Control: Hospital district or authority, Government, nonfederal **Service**: General medical and surgical

Staffed Beds: 35 **Admissions:** 315 **Census:** 24 **Outpatient Visits:** 12278

HENDERSON—Clark County

⊞ **HEALTHSOUTH REHABILITATION HOSPITAL – HENDERSON (293032)**, 10301 Jeffreys Street, Zip 89052–3922; tel. 702/939–9400, (Nonreporting) **A**1 10 **S** Encompass Health Corporation, Birmingham, AL
Primary Contact: Samantha Billig, Chief Executive Officer
CFO: Robert Bollard, Chief Financial Officer
Web address: www.hendersonrehabhospital.com
Control: Corporation, Investor–owned (for–profit) **Service**: Rehabilitation

Staffed Beds: 90

HENDERSON HOSPITAL (290057), 1050 West Galleria Drive, Zip 89011; tel. 702/963–7000, (Nonreporting) **A**10 **S** Universal Health Services, Inc., King of Prussia, PA
Primary Contact: Samuel Kaufman, Chief Executive Officer
CNO: Tina Coker, MSN, Chief Nursing Officer
Web address: www.hendersonhospital.com/
Control: Corporation, Investor–owned (for–profit) **Service**: General medical and surgical

Staffed Beds: 145

⊞ **KINDRED HOSPITAL LAS VEGAS–SAHARA (292002)**, 102 East Mead Parkway, 3rd Floor, Zip 89015; tel. 702/871–1418, (Includes KINDRED HOSPITAL–FLAMINGO, 2250 East Flamingo Road, Las Vegas, NV, Zip 89119; tel. 702/871–1418) (Nonreporting) **A**1 10 **S** Kindred Healthcare, Louisville, KY
Primary Contact: Doug McCoy, Chief Executive Officer
CFO: William Lysaght, Chief Financial Officer
CMO: Paul Stewart, M.D., Medical Director
CHR: Jim Sturgeon, Area Director Human Resources
Web address: www.kindredhospitallvs.com/
Control: Corporation, Investor–owned (for–profit) **Service**: Acute long–term care hospital

Staffed Beds: 238

SEVEN HILLS HOSPITAL (294012), 3021 West Horizon Ridge Parkway, Zip 89052–3990; tel. 702/646–5000, (Nonreporting) **A**3 10 **S** Acadia Healthcare Company, Inc., Franklin, TN
Primary Contact: Christopher West, Chief Executive Officer
CFO: Mars Patricio Jr Chief Financial Officer
CMO: Jonathan Wirjo, M.D., Medical Director
CIO: Jessica Raub, Director Health Information Management
CHR: Teresa Sulit, Director of Human Resources
CNO: Rustin Park, Director of Nursing
Web address: www.sevenhillsbi.com
Control: Corporation, Investor–owned (for–profit) **Service**: Psychiatric

Staffed Beds: 94

⊞ **ST. ROSE DOMINICAN HOSPITALS – ROSE DE LIMA CAMPUS (290012)**, 102 East Lake Mead Parkway, Zip 89015–5524; tel. 702/616–5000, **A**1 10 **F**3 8 15 18 20 29 30 31 32 34 35 38 40 44 45 49 50 57 59 61 62 64 65 68 70 74 75 77 78 79 80 81 82 84 85 86 87 90 91 95 96 102 107 110 111 115 119 130 131 132 135 143 146 147 148 149 **S** Dignity Health, San Francisco, CA
Primary Contact: Teressa Conley, President and Chief Executive Officer
COO: Teressa Conley, Vice President and Chief Operating Officer
CFO: Kevin Walters, Chief Financial Officer
CMO: Stephen K Jones, M.D., Vice President Medical Staff Affairs
Web address: www.strosehospitals.org
Control: Church operated, Nongovernment, not–for–profit **Service**: General medical and surgical

Staffed Beds: 110 **Admissions:** 4512 **Census:** 64 **Outpatient Visits:** 38287 **Births:** 0 **Total Expense ($000):** 140111 **Payroll Expense ($000):** 54979 **Personnel:** 537

⊞ **ST. ROSE DOMINICAN HOSPITALS – SIENA CAMPUS (290045)**, 3001 St Rose Parkway, Zip 89052; tel. 702/616–5000, **A**1 3 5 10 **F**3 7 8 13 15 17 18 19 20 22 24 26 28 29 30 31 32 34 35 38 40 41 43 44 45 46 47 48 49 50 51 57 59 61 63 64 68 70 72 73 74 75 76 78 79 80 81 82 84 85 87 88 89 93 102 107 108 110 111 115 116 117 119 126 130 131 132 135 146 147 148 149 154 **S** Dignity Health, San Francisco, CA
Primary Contact: Eugene Bassett, President and Chief Executive Officer
COO: Kimberly Shaw, Chief Operating Officer
CFO: Brian Kleven, Chief Financial Officer
CMO: Robert Pretzlaff, M.D., Chief Medical Officer
CIO: Russ Patterson, Director Information Technology
CHR: Linda Gerstenberger, Vice President Human Resources
CNO: Cathleen Hamel, Chief Nurse Executive
Web address: www.strosehospitals.com
Control: Church operated, Nongovernment, not–for–profit **Service**: General medical and surgical

Staffed Beds: 326 **Admissions:** 18702 **Census:** 241 **Outpatient Visits:** 94844 **Births:** 3697 **Total Expense ($000):** 432205 **Payroll Expense ($000):** 169991 **Personnel:** 1989

INCLINE VILLAGE—Washoe County

★ **INCLINE VILLAGE COMMUNITY HOSPITAL (291301)**, 880 Alder Avenue, Zip 89451–8335; tel. 775/833–4100, (Nonreporting) **A**5 10 18 **S** Tahoe Forest Health System, Truckee, CA
Primary Contact: Judy Newland, R.N., Chief Nursing Officer
CFO: Crystal Betts, Chief Financial Officer
CIO: Mark Griffiths, Director Management Information Systems
CHR: Jayne O'Flanagan, Director Human Resources
Web address: www.tfhd.com
Control: Hospital district or authority, Government, nonfederal **Service**: General medical and surgical

Staffed Beds: 6

LAS VEGAS—Clark County

AMG SPECIALTY HOSPITAL – LAS VEGAS (292007), 4015 Mcleod Drive, Zip 89121–4305; tel. 702/433–2200, (Nonreporting) **A**10 **S** AMG Integrated Healthcare Management, Lafayette, LA
Primary Contact: William Fox, Chief Executive Officer
CMO: Anthony Pollard, D.O., Chief Medical Officer
Web address: www.amgihm.com/locations/#map_top
Control: Partnership, Investor–owned (for–profit) **Service**: Acute long–term care hospital

Staffed Beds: 24

☐ **CENTENNIAL HILLS HOSPITAL MEDICAL CENTER (290054)**, 6900 North Durango Drive, Zip 89149–4409; tel. 702/835–9700, (Nonreporting) **A**1 10 **S** Universal Health Services, Inc., King of Prussia, PA
Primary Contact: Sajit Pullarkat, Chief Executive Officer and Managing Director
Web address: www.centennialhillshospital.com
Control: Corporation, Investor–owned (for–profit) **Service**: General medical and surgical

Staffed Beds: 165

NV

☒ **COMPLEX CARE HOSPITAL AT TENAYA (292006)**, 2500 North Tenaya, Zip 89128–0482; tel. 702/562–2021, (Nonreporting) **A**1 10 **S** LifeCare Management Services, Plano, TX
Primary Contact: Matt Archer, Chief Executive Officer
COO: Paul D'Ambrosio, Chief Operating Officer
CFO: Anna Rich, Chief Financial Officer
CMO: C Dean Milne, D.O., Medical Director
CIO: Lynn Tunson, Manager Medical Records
CHR: Belinda McGraw, Director Human Resources
CNO: Robin Wolf, Chief Nursing Officer
Web address: www.lifecare–hospitals.com
Control: Corporation, Investor–owned (for–profit) **Service**: Acute long–term care hospital

Staffed Beds: 70

DESERT PARKWAY BEHAVIORAL HEALTHCARE HOSPITAL (294013), 3247 South Maryland Parkway, Zip 89109–2412; tel. 702/776–3500, (Nonreporting) **S** Signature Healthcare Services, Corona, CA
Primary Contact: Steve Shell, Chief Executive Officer
Control: Other not–for–profit (including NFP Corporation) **Service**: Psychiatric

Staffed Beds: 83

☐ **DESERT SPRINGS HOSPITAL MEDICAL CENTER (290022)**, 2075 East Flamingo Road, Zip 89119–8800, tel. 702/733–8800, **A**1 3 10 **F**3 12 17 18 20 22 24 26 28 29 30 31 40 45 46 47 48 49 50 54 58 60 64 68 70 74 75 77 78 79 81 85 86 87 90 93 96 98 102 103 107 108 110 111 112 114 115 116 117 119 120 121 122 123 124 126 130 132 135 146 148 149 154 **P**7 **S** Universal Health Services, Inc., King of Prussia, PA
Primary Contact: Ryan Jensen, Chief Executive Officer
CFO: George Wiley, Chief Financial Officer
CMO: Golam Choudhury, Chief of Staff
CIO: Alan Woratschek, System Director of Information Services
CNO: Elena McNutt, Chief Nursing Officer
Web address: www.desertspringshospital.com
Control: Corporation, Investor–owned (for–profit) **Service**: General medical and surgical

Staffed Beds: 293 **Admissions**: 13497 **Census**: 157

DESERT WILLOW TREATMENT CENTER, 6171 West Charleston Boulevard, Zip 89146–1126; tel. 702/486–8900, **A**3 5 **F**29 98 99 106 **P**6
Primary Contact: Jacqueline Wade, Ph.D., Director
Web address: www.dcfs.nv.gov/
Control: State, Government, nonfederal **Service**: Children's hospital psychiatric

Staffed Beds: 58 **Admissions**: 199 **Census**: 18 **Outpatient Visits**: 0
Births: 0 **Total Expense ($000)**: 8469

HARMON MEDICAL AND REHABILITATION HOSPITAL (290042), 2170 East Harmon Avenue, Zip 89119–7840; tel. 702/794–0100, (Nonreporting) **A**10 **S** Fundamental Long Term Care Holdings, LLC, Sparks Glencoe, MD
Primary Contact: Bonnie Essex. Hillegass, Chief Executive Officer
Control: Corporation, Investor–owned (for–profit) **Service**: Rehabilitation

Staffed Beds: 118

☒ **HEALTHSOUTH DESERT CANYON REHABILITATION HOSPITAL (293033)**, 9175 West Oquendo Road, Zip 89148–1234; tel. 702/252–7342, (Nonreporting) **A**1 10 **S** Encompass Health Corporation, Birmingham, AL
Primary Contact: Andrea Davis, Chief Executive Officer
CMO: Bevins Chue, M.D., Medical Director
CNO: Timothy Murphy, R.N., Chief Nursing Officer
Web address: www.healthsouthdesertcanyon.com
Control: Corporation, Investor–owned (for–profit) **Service**: Rehabilitation

Staffed Beds: 50

☒ **HEALTHSOUTH REHABILITATION HOSPITAL–LAS VEGAS (293026)**, 1250 South Valley View Boulevard, Zip 89102–1861; tel. 702/877–8898, (Nonreporting) **A**1 10 **S** Encompass Health Corporation, Birmingham, AL
Primary Contact: Michael Ward, Chief Executive Officer
CFO: Raymond Hardy, Controller
CMO: John D. Reneau, Medical Director
CHR: Cheryl Ballew, Human Resources Director
CNO: Susan Ramirez, Chief Nursing Officer
Web address: www.healthsouthlasvegas.com
Control: Corporation, Investor–owned (for–profit) **Service**: Rehabilitation

Staffed Beds: 79

☐ **HORIZON SPECIALTY HOSPITAL (292003)**, 640 Desert Lane, Zip 89106–4207; tel. 702/382–3155, (Nonreporting) **A**1 10 **S** Fundamental Long Term Care Holdings, LLC, Sparks Glencoe, MD
Primary Contact: Darrin Cook, Chief Executive Officer and Administrator
CFO: Darnell Bennett, Director Finance
CMO: Syed Rahman, M.D., Chief of Staff
CIO: Azena Ansi, Manager Health Information Management
CHR: Melvin Layugan, Director Human Resources
Web address: www.horizonspecialtyhosp.com/
Control: Corporation, Investor–owned (for–profit) **Service**: Acute long–term care hospital

Staffed Beds: 49

☐ **MONTEVISTA HOSPITAL (294009)**, 5900 West Rochelle Avenue, Zip 89103–3327; tel. 702/364–1111, **A**1 10 **F**4 5 38 98 99 100 103 104 105 106 130 151 152 153 154 **S** Strategic Behavioral Health, LLC, Memphis, TN
Primary Contact: Richard Failla, Chief Executive Officer
CMO: William Bauer, M.D., Medical Director
CHR: Carol Nelson, Director Human Resources
Web address: www.montevistahospital.com
Control: Partnership, Investor–owned (for–profit) **Service**: Psychiatric

Staffed Beds: 202 **Admissions**: 5575 **Census**: 99

MOUNTAIN'S EDGE HOSPITAL (290056), 8656 West Patrick Lane, Zip 89148–5043; tel. 702/777–7100, (Nonreporting)
Primary Contact: Melissa War, Chief Executive Officer
Web address: www.mountainsedgehospital.com/
Control: Other not–for–profit (including NFP Corporation) **Service**: General medical and surgical

Staffed Beds: 130

☒ **MOUNTAINVIEW HOSPITAL (290039)**, 3100 North Tenaya Way, Zip 89128–0436; tel. 702/255–5000, (Nonreporting) **A**1 3 5 10 **S** HCA Healthcare, Nashville, TN
Primary Contact: Jeremy Bradshaw, Chief Executive Officer
CFO: Lana Arad, Chief Financial Officer
CMO: Jack Collier, M.D., Chief of Staff
CHR: Robert Nettles, Director Human Resources
CNO: Natalie Ransom, Chief Nursing Officer
Web address: www.mountainview–hospital.com
Control: Corporation, Investor–owned (for–profit) **Service**: General medical and surgical

Staffed Beds: 340

☐ **RED ROCK BEHAVIORAL HOSPITAL (294008)**, 5975 West Twain Avenue, Zip 89103–1237; tel. 702/214–8099, (Nonreporting) **A**1 10 **S** Strategic Behavioral Health, LLC, Memphis, TN
Primary Contact: Richard Failla, Chief Executive Officer
Web address: www.redrockhospital.com
Control: Other not–for–profit (including NFP Corporation) **Service**: Psychiatric

Staffed Beds: 21

☒ **SOUTHERN HILLS HOSPITAL AND MEDICAL CENTER (290047)**, 9300 West Sunset Road, Zip 89148–4844; tel. 702/880–2100, (Nonreporting) **A**1 3 10 **S** HCA Healthcare, Nashville, TN
Primary Contact: Adam Rudd, Chief Executive Officer
CFO: Jennifer Le, Chief Financial Officer
CMO: Eric Ramos, M.D., Division Chief Medical Officer
CIO: Joe Grandiosi, Director Information Technology
CHR: Brian Wood, Director Human Resources
CNO: Maura Wright, Chief Nursing Officer
Web address: www.southernhillshospital.com
Control: Corporation, Investor–owned (for–profit) **Service**: General medical and surgical

Staffed Beds: 134

☐ **SOUTHERN NEVADA ADULT MENTAL HEALTH SERVICES (294002)**, 6161 West Charleston Boulevard, Zip 89146–1126; tel. 702/486–6000, (Nonreporting) **A**1 3 5 10
Primary Contact: Chelsea Szklany, Hospital Administrator
Web address: www.mhds.state.nv.us
Control: State, Government, nonfederal **Service**: Psychiatric

Staffed Beds: 289

NV

☐ **SPRING MOUNTAIN SAHARA (294010)**, 5460 West Sahara, Zip 89146–3307; tel. 702/216–8900, **A**1 10 **F**29 56 64 98 103 104 130 **S** Universal Health Services, Inc., King of Prussia, PA
Primary Contact: Darryl S. Dubroca, Chief Executive Officer and Managing Director
Web address: www.springmountainsahara.com
Control: Corporation, Investor–owned (for–profit) **Service:** Psychiatric

Staffed Beds: 30 **Admissions:** 831 **Census:** 23 **Outpatient Visits:** 2181
Births: 0 **Total Expense ($000):** 6358 **Payroll Expense ($000):** 3074
Personnel: 56

☐ **SPRING MOUNTAIN TREATMENT CENTER (294011)**, 7000 West Spring Mountain Road, Zip 89117–3816; tel. 702/873–2400, **A**1 10 **F**29 98 104 130 143 149 **S** Universal Health Services, Inc., King of Prussia, PA
Primary Contact: C. Alan. Eaks, Chief Executive Officer and Managing Director
CFO: Sherilene DeLeon, Chief Financial Officer
CMO: Jerome Nwokike, M.D., Medical Director
CNO: Norma Ferris, R.N., MS, Chief Nursing Officer
Web address: www.springmountaintreatmentcenter.com/
Control: Corporation, Investor–owned (for–profit) **Service:** Psychiatric

Staffed Beds: 110 **Admissions:** 5341 **Census:** 88 **Outpatient Visits:** 1135
Births: 0 **Total Expense ($000):** 20766 **Payroll Expense ($000):** 9597
Personnel: 179

☐ **SPRING VALLEY HOSPITAL MEDICAL CENTER (290046)**, 5400 South Rainbow Boulevard, Zip 89118–1859; tel. 702/853–3000, (Nonreporting) **A**1 3 10 **S** Universal Health Services, Inc., King of Prussia, PA
Primary Contact: Leonard Freehof, Chief Executive Officer and Managing Director
COO: Matthew Wheelus, Chief Operating Officer
CFO: Carl Caley, Chief Financial Officer
CMO: S. Daniel, M.D., Chief Medical Officer
CHR: Angelique Ford, Administrator Human Resources
CNO: Margaret Covelli, R.N., Chief Nursing Officer
Web address: www.springvalleyhospital.com
Control: Corporation, Investor–owned (for–profit) **Service:** General medical and surgical

Staffed Beds: 169

☒ **ST. ROSE DOMINICAN HOSPITALS – SAN MARTIN CAMPUS (290053)**, 8280 West Warm Springs Road, Zip 89113–3612; tel. 702/492–8000, **A**1 10 **F**3 8 13 15 18 19 20 22 24 26 28 29 30 31 34 35 38 40 44 45 47 49 50 57 59 61 62 64 68 70 72 74 75 76 77 78 79 80 81 84 85 86 87 93 102 107 108 110 111 115 119 126 130 131 132 135 146 147 148 149 **S** Dignity Health, San Francisco, CA
Primary Contact: Lawrence Barnard, President and Chief Executive Officer
CFO: Dev Ramsamy, Chief Financial Officer
CMO: Robert Pretzlaff, M.D., Chief Medical Officer
CIO: Russ Patterson, Site Manager Information Technology
CHR: Linda Gerstenberger, Vice President Human Resources
CNO: Katherine Raymond, Chief Nursing Officer
Web address: www.strosehospitals.org
Control: Church operated, Nongovernment, not–for–profit **Service:** General medical and surgical

Staffed Beds: 147 **Admissions:** 6729 **Census:** 81 **Outpatient Visits:** 36702 **Births:** 1351 **Total Expense ($000):** 183512 **Payroll Expense ($000):** 62569 **Personnel:** 673

☐ **SUMMERLIN HOSPITAL MEDICAL CENTER (290041)**, 657 Town Center Drive, Zip 89144–6367; tel. 702/233–7000, (Nonreporting) **A**1 3 10 **S** Universal Health Services, Inc., King of Prussia, PA
Primary Contact: Robert S. Freymuller, Chief Executive Officer
Web address: www.summerlinhospital.com
Control: Corporation, Investor–owned (for–profit) **Service:** General medical and surgical

Staffed Beds: 148

☒ △ **SUNRISE HOSPITAL AND MEDICAL CENTER (290003)**, 3186 South Maryland Parkway, Zip 89109–2306, Mailing Address: P.O. Box 98530, Zip 89193; tel. 702/731–8000, (Nonreporting) **A**1 2 3 5 7 10 **S** HCA Healthcare, Nashville, TN
Primary Contact: Todd Sklamberg, President
COO: Mark J. Amox, Chief Operating Officer
CFO: Daniel Perritt, Chief Financial Officer
CMO: Katherine Keeley, M.D., Chief of Staff
CIO: Alan Burt, Director Information Services
Web address: www.sunrisehospital.com
Control: Corporation, Investor–owned (for–profit) **Service:** General medical and surgical

Staffed Beds: 668

☒ **UNIVERSITY MEDICAL CENTER (290007)**, 1800 West Charleston Boulevard, Zip 89102–2386; tel. 702/383–2000, (Includes CHILDREN'S HOSPITAL OF NEVADA AT UMC, 800 Hope Place, Las Vegas, NV, Zip 89106; tel. 702/383–2000) **A**1 2 3 5 10 **F**3 8 11 13 15 16 17 18 20 22 24 26 28 29 31 32 34 35 36 37 40 41 43 45 48 49 50 57 58 59 61 68 70 72 73 74 75 76 77 78 79 80 81 83 84 85 86 87 88 89 97 107 108 110 111 114 115 116 117 119 124 126 130 131 132 135 136 138 141 143 144 146 148 149 150 **P**1 5 8
Primary Contact: Mason VanHouweling, Chief Executive Officer
COO: Anthony Marinello, Chief Operating Officer
CFO: Jennifer Wakem, Chief Financial Officer
CHR: John Espinoza, Chief Human Resources Officer
CNO: Debra Fox, Chief Nursing Officer
Web address: www.umcsn.com
Control: County, Government, nonfederal **Service:** General medical and surgical

Staffed Beds: 510 **Admissions:** 20794 **Census:** 349 **Outpatient Visits:** 427914 **Births:** 2493 **Total Expense ($000):** 636679 **Payroll Expense ($000):** 247161 **Personnel:** 3264

☐ **VALLEY HOSPITAL MEDICAL CENTER (290021)**, 620 Shadow Lane, Zip 89106–4119; tel. 702/388–4000, (Nonreporting) **A**1 3 10 **S** Universal Health Services, Inc., King of Prussia, PA
Primary Contact: Elaine Glaser, Chief Executive Officer
CFO: Betsy A Sponsler, Chief Financial Officer
CMO: Dost Wattoo, M.D., Chief of Staff
CIO: Tom Schoenig, Regional Director Information Services
CHR: Dana Thorne, Administrator Human Resources
Web address: www.valleyhospital.net
Control: Corporation, Investor–owned (for–profit) **Service:** General medical and surgical

Staffed Beds: 365

LOVELOCK—Pershing County

★ **PERSHING GENERAL HOSPITAL (291304)**, 855 Sixth Street, Zip 89419, Mailing Address: P.O. Box 661, Zip 89419–0661; tel. 775/273–2621, (Nonreporting) **A**10 18
Primary Contact: Patty Bianchi, Chief Executive Officer
CFO: Marjorie Skinner, Director Finance
CMO: Yousri Gadallah, M.D., Chief Medical Officer
CIO: Jim Weeldreyer, Manager Information Technology
CHR: Cynthia Hixenbaugh, Director Human Resources
Web address: www.pershinghospital.org
Control: Hospital district or authority, Government, nonfederal **Service:** General medical and surgical

Staffed Beds: 38

MESQUITE—Clark County

☒ **MESA VIEW REGIONAL HOSPITAL (291307)**, 1299 Bertha Howe Avenue, Zip 89027–7500; tel. 702/346–8040, **A**1 10 18 **F**3 11 13 15 18 29 30 34 35 40 45 46 51 56 57 59 63 64 70 75 76 79 81 85 87 107 108 110 111 114 119 130 132 133 135 146 147 148 **P**7 **S** Quorum Health, Brentwood, TN
Primary Contact: Ned Hill, Chief Executive Officer
CFO: Mitchell Fransen, Chief Financial Officer
CHR: Steve Siegrist, Director of Human Resources
CNO: Leslie Woodson, Chief Nursing Officer
Web address: www.mesaviewhospital.com
Control: Corporation, Investor–owned (for–profit) **Service:** General medical and surgical

Staffed Beds: 25 **Admissions:** 646 **Census:** 5 **Outpatient Visits:** 35497 **Births:** 68 **Total Expense ($000):** 28553 **Payroll Expense ($000):** 13395

NELLIS AFB—Clark County

☒ **MIKE O'CALLAGHAN FEDERAL HOSPITAL**, 4700 Las Vegas Boulevard North, Suite 2419, Zip 89191–6600; tel. 702/653–2000, (Nonreporting) **A**1 3 5 **S** Department of the Air Force, Washington, DC
Primary Contact: Colonel Christian Benjamin, USAF, MC, Commander
COO: Colonel Linnes L Chester, USAF, MSC, Administrator
CFO: Major Kari Turkal–Barrett, Flight Commander Resource Management Officer
CMO: Lieutenant Colonel Markham Brown, M.D., Chief Medical Staff
CIO: Major Kevin Seeley, Chief Information Officer
Web address: www.nellis.af.mil/
Control: Air Force, Government, federal **Service:** General medical and surgical

Staffed Beds: 46

NV

Hospital, Medicare Provider Number, Address, Telephone, Approval, Facility, and Physician Codes, Health Care System

★ American Hospital Association (AHA) membership
☐ The Joint Commission accreditation
○ Healthcare Facilities Accreditation Program
◇ DNV Healthcare Inc. accreditation
⇑ Center for Improvement in Healthcare Quality Accreditation
△ Commission on Accreditation of Rehabilitation Facilities (CARF) accreditation

NORTH LAS VEGAS—Clark County

★ ⇧ **NORTH VISTA HOSPITAL (290005)**, 1409 East Lake Mead Boulevard, Zip 89030–7197; tel. 702/649–7711, (Nonreporting) **A**10 21 **S** Prime Healthcare, Ontario, CA
Primary Contact: Vincenzo Variale, Chief Executive Officer
CFO: Peter S Miller, Chief Financial Officer
CHR: Abayomi Fibiyi, Chief Human Resources Officer
Web address: www.northvistahospital.com
Control: Corporation, Investor–owned (for–profit) **Service:** General medical and surgical

Staffed Beds: 177

⊞ **VETERANS AFFAIRS SOUTHERN NEVADA HEALTHCARE SYSTEM**, 6900 North Pecos Road, Zip 89086–4400; tel. 702/791–9000, **A**1 5 **F**3 5 8 12 15 18 20 22 28 29 30 31 33 34 35 36 38 39 40 44 45 47 48 50 51 54 56 57 58 59 60 61 62 64 65 66 68 70 74 75 77 78 79 81 82 84 85 86 87 91 92 93 94 97 98 100 101 102 103 104 107 108 110 111 114 115 116 117 118 119 126 127 130 132 135 143 144 146 147 148 149 153 154 **S** Department of Veterans Affairs, Perry Point, MD
Primary Contact: Peggy W. Kearns, MS, FACHE, Executive Director
CFO: Richard O Hays, Chief Fiscal Service
CMO: Ramanujam Komanduri, M.D., Chief of Staff
Web address: www.lasvegas.va.gov/
Control: Veterans Affairs, Government, federal **Service:** General medical and surgical

Staffed Beds: 90 **Admissions:** 5368 **Census:** 73 **Outpatient Visits:** 892172 **Births:** 0 **Total Expense ($000):** 566857 **Payroll Expense ($000):** 190786 **Personnel:** 2558

PAHRUMP—Nye County

★ **DESERT VIEW HOSPITAL (291311)**, 360 South Lola Lane, Zip 89048–0884; tel. 775/751–7500, **A**10 18 **F**3 15 29 34 40 45 46 59 81 85 87 107 108 110 111 114 119 133 154 **S** Universal Health Services, Inc., King of Prussia, PA
Primary Contact: Susan Davila, Chief Executive Officer
CFO: Ryan Eggleston, Chief Financial Officer
CMO: Fredric Siegel, M.D., Chief of Staff
CIO: Chad Andres, Chief Information Officer
CHR: Lisa Doty, Manager Human Resources
CNO: Markeeta Araujo, Chief Nursing Officer
Web address: www.desertviewhospital.com
Control: Corporation, Investor–owned (for–profit) **Service:** General medical and surgical

Staffed Beds: 25 **Admissions:** 1331 **Census:** 10 **Outpatient Visits:** 35406 **Births:** 0

DESERT VIEW REGIONAL MEDICAL CENTER See Desert View Hospital

RENO—Washoe County

⊞ **RENOWN REGIONAL MEDICAL CENTER (290001)**, 1155 Mill Street, Zip 89502–1576; tel. 775/982–4100, (Includes RENOWN CHILDREN'S HOSPITAL, 1155 Mill Street, Reno, NV, Zip 89502–1576; tel. 775/982–5437) **A**1 2 3 5 10 **F**3 5 11 13 15 17 18 19 20 21 22 23 24 25 26 27 28 29 30 31 32 34 35 40 41 43 44 45 46 48 49 54 56 57 58 59 61 64 65 66 68 70 72 73 74 75 76 77 78 79 80 81 85 86 87 88 89 92 100 101 102 104 105 107 108 111 114 115 118 119 120 121 123 124 126 130 131 132 135 145 146 148 149 153 **S** Renown Health, Reno, NV
Primary Contact: Erik Olson, Chief Executive Officer
COO: Sy Johnson, Executive Vice President, Chief Operating Officer
CFO: Sam King, Chief Financial Officer
CMO: Charles Johnson, M.D., Chief of Staff
CIO: Charles Scully, Chief Information Officer
CHR: Michelle Sanchez–Bickley, Vice President Human Resources
Web address: www.renown.org
Control: Other not–for–profit (including NFP Corporation) **Service:** General medical and surgical

Staffed Beds: 661 **Admissions:** 30826 **Census:** 476 **Outpatient Visits:** 535948 **Births:** 4065 **Total Expense ($000):** 620296 **Payroll Expense ($000):** 208377 **Personnel:** 4189

⊞ △ **RENOWN REHABILITATION HOSPITAL**, 1495 Mill Street, Zip 89502–1479; tel. 775/982–3500, **A**1 5 7 **F**29 54 77 82 90 93 95 96 143 148 **S** Renown Health, Reno, NV
Primary Contact: Chris Nicholas, Administrator of Rehabilitation Hospital
CFO: Dawn Ahner, Chief Financial Officer
CMO: Doug Merrill, Executive Vice President Chielf Medical and Acad Officer
CIO: Ronald Fuschillo, Chief Information Officer
CHR: Michelle Sanchez–Bickley, Vice President Human Resources
CNO: Melodie Osborn, Vice President and Chief Nursing Officer, Transitional Care Services
Web address: www.renown.org
Control: Other not–for–profit (including NFP Corporation) **Service:** Rehabilitation

Staffed Beds: 62 **Admissions:** 819 **Census:** 36 **Outpatient Visits:** 22650 **Births:** 0 **Total Expense ($000):** 22480 **Payroll Expense ($000):** 10696 **Personnel:** 154

⊞ **RENOWN SOUTH MEADOWS MEDICAL CENTER (290049)**, 10101 Double 'R' Boulevard, Zip 89521–5931; tel. 775/982–7000, **A**1 5 10 **F**8 10 12 29 30 35 38 40 44 46 68 70 74 75 79 81 82 85 87 92 93 97 107 108 111 119 125 130 131 146 **S** Renown Health, Reno, NV
Primary Contact: Siri Nelson, Chief Executive Officer
COO: Sy Johnson, Executive Vice President, Chief Operating Officer
CFO: Gina Nelson, Chief Financial Officer
CMO: Dennis Rochier, Chief Medical Officer
CIO: Ronald Fuschillo, Chief Information Officer
CHR: Michelle Sanchez–Bickley, Vice President Human Resources
CNO: Melodie Osborn, Vice President and Chief Nursing Officer, Transitional Care Services
Web address: www.renown.org
Control: Other not–for–profit (including NFP Corporation) **Service:** General medical and surgical

Staffed Beds: 76 **Admissions:** 4070 **Census:** 34 **Outpatient Visits:** 69349 **Births:** 0 **Total Expense ($000):** 76047 **Payroll Expense ($000):** 23639 **Personnel:** 337

⊞ **SAINT MARY'S REGIONAL MEDICAL CENTER (290009)**, 235 West Sixth Street, Zip 89503–4548; tel. 775/770–3000, **A**1 2 3 5 10 **F**11 12 13 15 17 18 20 22 24 26 28 29 30 31 34 35 40 45 46 47 49 50 51 53 54 56 57 62 63 64 65 68 70 72 74 75 76 77 78 79 81 82 84 85 86 87 89 91 92 93 94 95 96 97 107 110 111 114 115 119 120 121 123 124 126 129 130 132 143 146 148 149 154 **S** Prime Healthcare, Ontario, CA
Primary Contact: Helen Lidholm, Chief Executive Officer
CFO: John R Deakyne, Chief Financial Officer
CIO: Cindy Mullins, Director Information Technology
CHR: David Milovich, Vice President Human Resources
Web address: www.saintmarysreno.org
Control: Corporation, Investor–owned (for–profit) **Service:** General medical and surgical

Staffed Beds: 281 **Admissions:** 14418 **Census:** 173 **Outpatient Visits:** 138767 **Births:** 1189 **Total Expense ($000):** 249792 **Payroll Expense ($000):** 88335 **Personnel:** 1372

⊞ **VETERANS AFFAIRS SIERRA NEVADA HEALTH CARE SYSTEM**, 975 Kirman Avenue, Zip 89502–0993; tel. 775/786–7200, (Total facility includes 60 beds in nursing home–type unit) **A**1 3 5 **F**3 5 8 18 20 22 28 29 30 31 33 34 35 36 38 39 40 45 46 47 48 51 56 57 58 59 60 61 62 63 65 68 70 71 74 75 77 78 79 81 82 83 84 85 86 87 93 94 96 97 98 100 101 102 103 104 107 108 109 118 119 127 128 129 130 132 135 143 144 147 148 149 152 153 154 **S** Department of Veterans Affairs, Perry Point, MD
Primary Contact: Lisa M. Howard, Director
COO: Lisa M Howard, Associate Director
CFO: Kelly Manson, Chief Financial Officer
CMO: Steven Brilliant, M.D., Chief of Staff
CIO: Jack Smith, Acting Chief Information Resources Management Service
CHR: Debbie Jenkins, Chief Human Resources Management Service
Web address: www.reno.va.gov/
Control: Veterans Affairs, Government, federal **Service:** General medical and surgical

Staffed Beds: 124 **Admissions:** 3606 **Census:** 104 **Births:** 0 **Total Expense ($000):** 308165 **Payroll Expense ($000):** 116210 **Personnel:** 1460

☐ **WEST HILLS HOSPITAL (294003)**, 1240 East Ninth Street, Zip 89512–2964; tel. 775/323–0478, (Nonreporting) **A**1 10 **S** Universal Health Services, Inc., King of Prussia, PA
Primary Contact: Allison Zednicek, Chief Executive Officer
CMO: Philip Rich, M.D., Chief Medical Officer
CHR: Don Gay, Director Human Resources
Web address: www.westhillshospital.net
Control: Corporation, Investor–owned (for–profit) **Service:** Psychiatric

Staffed Beds: 190

☐ **WILLOW SPRINGS CENTER**, 690 Edison Way, Zip 89502–4135; tel. 775/858–3303, (Nonreporting) **A**1 3 5
Primary Contact: Ann Schaack, Chief Executive Officer
CFO: Chris Farley, Chief Financial Officer
CMO: Dana Arlien, M.D., Chief Medical Officer
CIO: Wallace Marsh, Director of Information Technology
CHR: Kristine Anglin, Human Resources Manager
CNO: Laurie MacAffee, Director of Nursing
Web address: www.willowspringscenter.com
Control: Corporation, Investor–owned (for–profit) **Service:** Children's hospital psychiatric

Staffed Beds: 116

Many Facility Codes have changed. Please refer to the AHA Guide Code Chart. © 2018 AHA Guide

NV

SPARKS—Washoe County

☐ **NORTHERN NEVADA ADULT MENTAL HEALTH SERVICES (294000)**, 480 Galletti Way, Zip 89431–5564; tel. 775/688–2001, **A**1 3 5 10 **F**29 50 98 104 130 149
Primary Contact: Cody Phinney, Administrator
CFO: Elizabeth O'Brien, Chief Financial Officer
CIO: Lois Repass, Quality Assurance Specialist and Coordinator Performance Improvement
Web address: www.mhds.state.nv.us/
Control: State, Government, nonfederal **Service:** Psychiatric

Staffed Beds: 30 **Admissions:** 798 **Census:** 28 **Outpatient Visits:** 35576
Births: 0 **Total Expense ($000):** 29555 **Payroll Expense ($000):** 11164
Personnel: 221

☐ **NORTHERN NEVADA MEDICAL CENTER (290032)**, 2375 East Prater Way, Zip 89434–9641; tel. 775/331–7000, (Nonreporting) **A**1 10 **S** Universal Health Services, Inc., King of Prussia, PA
Primary Contact: Alan C. Olive, Chief Executive Officer
COO: Tiffany Coury, Chief Operating Officer
CFO: Ryan Heit, Chief Financial Officer
CHR: Patricia Downs, Director Human Resources
CNO: Carla Adams, Chief Nursing Officer
Web address: www.nnmc.com
Control: Corporation, Investor–owned (for–profit) **Service:** General medical and surgical

Staffed Beds: 108

⊞ **TAHOE PACIFIC HOSPITALS (292004)**, 2375 East Prater Way, Zip 89434; tel. 775/355–5600, (Includes TAHOE PACIFIC HOSPITALS – WEST, 235 West Sixth Street, 5th Floor, Reno, NV, Zip 89503–4548; tel. 775/982–5437; TAHOE PACIFIC HOSPITALS, 10101 Double R Boulevard, Reno, NV, Zip 89521–5931; tel. 775/331–1044) **A**1 10 **F**1 3 29 30 77 107 111 114 117 148 **P**5 **S** LifeCare Management Services, Plano, TX
Primary Contact: Matt Archer, Chief Executive Officer
COO: Theresa Fegan, R.N., Chief Clinical Officer
CFO: Nena Swenson, Financial Manager
CMO: T Brian Callister, M.D., Chief Medical Officer
CIO: Kaylene Reeves, Director
CHR: Nelson Coy, Director Human Resources
Web address: www.lifecare–hospitals.com
Control: Corporation, Investor–owned (for–profit) **Service:** Children's acute long–term Care

Staffed Beds: 60 **Admissions:** 408 **Census:** 40 **Outpatient Visits:** 0
Births: 0 **Total Expense ($000):** 18921 **Payroll Expense ($000):** 10779

WINNEMUCCA—Humboldt County

★ **HUMBOLDT GENERAL HOSPITAL (291308)**, 118 East Haskell Street, Zip 89445–3299; tel. 775/623–5222, (Nonreporting) **A**3 10 18
Primary Contact: Arthur H. Frable, Chief Executive Officer
CFO: Sandi Lehman, Chief Financial Officer
CMO: Brad Granath, M.D., Chief of Staff
CHR: Rose Marie Green, Director Human Resources
CNO: Darlene Bryan, R.N., Chief Nursing Officer
Web address: www.hghospital.org
Control: Hospital district or authority, Government, nonfederal **Service:** General medical and surgical

Staffed Beds: 88

YERINGTON—Lyon County

SOUTH LYON MEDICAL CENTER (290002), 213 South Whitacre, Zip 89447–2561, Mailing Address: P.O. Box 940, Zip 89447–0940; tel. 775/463–2301, (Nonreporting) **A**10
Primary Contact: Toni A. Inserra, Interim Administrator
Web address: www.southlyonmedicalcenter.org
Control: Other not–for–profit (including NFP Corporation) **Service:** General medical and surgical

Staffed Beds: 14

NV

NEW HAMPSHIRE

BERLIN—Coos County

★ **ANDROSCOGGIN VALLEY HOSPITAL (301310)**, 59 Page Hill Road, Zip 03570–3531; tel. 603/752–2200, **A**10 18 **F**3 8 11 12 13 15 17 28 29 30 34 40 41 43 45 47 57 59 61 64 67 68 70 74 75 76 77 79 81 82 85 89 92 93 102 107 108 110 115 119 128 129 130 131 132 133 146 147 149 **P**6 **S** North Country Healthcare, Littleton, NH
Primary Contact: Michael Peterson, FACHE, President
CFO: Jeremy Roberge, Director Reimbursement
CMO: Keith M Shute, M.D., Senior Vice President Medical Affairs and Clinical Services
CIO: Linda M Laperle, Vice President Administrative Services
CHR: James A Wheeler, Vice President Human Relations and Community Development
Web address: www.avhnh.org
Control: Other not-for-profit (including NFP Corporation) **Service**: General medical and surgical

Staffed Beds: 25 Admissions: 1209 Census: 13 Outpatient Visits: 67184 Births: 83 Total Expense ($000): 54438 Payroll Expense ($000): 22821 Personnel: 312

CLAREMONT—Sullivan County

⊞ **VALLEY REGIONAL HOSPITAL (301308)**, 243 Elm Street, Zip 03743–4921; tel. 603/542–7771, **A**1 10 18 **F**3 11 14 15 28 29 31 34 35 38 40 43 45 49 50 51 54 57 59 64 68 75 77 79 81 83 84 85 87 93 97 107 108 110 114 118 119 130 131 132 133 144 146 147 148 **P**6
Primary Contact: Peter J. Wright, FACHE, Chief Executive Officer
CFO: Jean Shaw, Chief Financial Officer
CMO: Oliver Herfort, M.D., Chief Medical Officer
CIO: Patricia Witthaus, Director Information Services
CHR: Cheryl Cavanaugh, Senior Director Human Resources
Web address: www.vrh.org
Control: Other not-for-profit (including NFP Corporation) **Service**: General medical and surgical

Staffed Beds: 25 Admissions: 726 Census: 8 Outpatient Visits: 75870 Births: 0 Total Expense ($000): 41858 Payroll Expense ($000): 16841 Personnel: 248

COLEBROOK—Coos County

★ **UPPER CONNECTICUT VALLEY HOSPITAL (301300)**, 181 Corliss Lane, Zip 03576–3207; tel. 603/237–4971, **A**10 18 **F**3 15 28 29 31 34 35 40 45 50 56 57 59 64 67 68 75 78 79 81 84 85 93 102 107 110 111 114 119 128 130 133 146 147 148 **S** North Country Healthcare, Littleton, NH
Primary Contact: Scott Colby, President
CFO: Celeste Pitts, Chief Financial Officer
CMO: Robert Rose, M.D., Chief Medical Officer
CIO: Heather Leighton, Director, Revenue Cycle and Privacy Officer
CHR: Heidi L Saari, Director, Human Resources
CNO: Lindsay Rancourt, Director of Nursing
Web address: www.ucvh.org
Control: Other not-for-profit (including NFP Corporation) **Service**: General medical and surgical

Staffed Beds: 12 Admissions: 307 Census: 4 Outpatient Visits: 17946 Births: 0 Total Expense ($000): 16601 Payroll Expense ($000): 5929 Personnel: 98

CONCORD—Merrimack County

★ ⇑ **CONCORD HOSPITAL (300001)**, 250 Pleasant Street, Zip 03301–2598; tel. 603/225–2711, **A**2 3 5 10 21 **F**3 8 12 13 14 15 17 18 20 22 24 26 28 29 30 31 33 34 35 36 37 38 39 40 43 44 45 46 49 50 51 53 54 55 56 57 58 59 61 64 65 66 68 69 70 71 74 75 76 77 78 79 80 81 82 83 84 85 86 87 89 90 93 97 98 99 100 101 102 103 104 105 107 108 110 111 114 115 118 119 120 121 123 124 126 129 130 132 134 135 144 145 146 147 148 149 150 152 153 154 **P**6
Primary Contact: Robert P. Steigmeyer, President and Chief Executive Officer
COO: Timothy P. Jones, Chief Operating Officer
CFO: Bruce R. Burns, Chief Financial Officer
CMO: David F. Green, M.D., Chief Medical Officer
CIO: Deane Morrison, Chief Information Officer
CHR: Robin A. Moore, Chief Human Resources Officer
CNO: Amy Dumont, R.N., MSN, Chief Nursing Officer
Web address: www.concordhospital.org
Control: Other not-for-profit (including NFP Corporation) **Service**: General medical and surgical

Staffed Beds: 242 Admissions: 13677 Census: 163 Outpatient Visits: 681878 Births: 1221 Total Expense ($000): 456826 Payroll Expense ($000): 219512 Personnel: 2853

⊞ **HEALTHSOUTH REHABILITATION HOSPITAL (303027)**, 254 Pleasant Street, Zip 03301–2508; tel. 603/226–9800, (Nonreporting) **A**1 10 **S** Encompass Health Corporation, Birmingham, AL
Primary Contact: Diana Lachapelle, CPA, Chief Executive Officer
CMO: Muhammad Salmanullah, Chief Medical Director
CHR: Myra Nixon, Director Human Resources
CNO: Joseph Adamski, Chief Nursing Officer
Web address: www.healthsouthrehabconcordnh.com
Control: Corporation, Investor–owned (for–profit) **Service**: Rehabilitation

Staffed Beds: 50

☐ **NEW HAMPSHIRE HOSPITAL (304000)**, 36 Clinton Street, Zip 03301–2359; tel. 603/271–5300, **A**1 3 10 **F**3 29 30 32 35 44 50 56 57 58 59 65 68 74 75 77 86 87 91 98 99 101 103 130 132 135 146 149 **P**4
Primary Contact: Lori Shibinette, Chief Executive Officer
COO: Geoffrey C Souther, Chief Operating Officer
CFO: Jamie Dall, Chief Financial Officer
CIO: David Levesque, Director, Information Systems
CHR: Mark Bussiere, Administrator Human Resources
CNO: Roberta A Vitale-Nolen, Administrator, Patient Care Services
Web address: www.dhhs.nh.gov/dcbcs/nhh/
Control: State, Government, nonfederal **Service**: Psychiatric

Staffed Beds: 168 Admissions: 1774 Census: 146 Outpatient Visits: 0 Births: 0 Total Expense ($000): 66140 Payroll Expense ($000): 32373 Personnel: 595

DERRY—Rockingham County

⊞ **PARKLAND MEDICAL CENTER (300017)**, One Parkland Drive, Zip 03038–2750; tel. 603/432–1500, (Nonreporting) **A**1 2 10 **S** HCA Healthcare, Nashville, TN
Primary Contact: Jeff Scionti, Chief Executive Officer
CFO: Jacob Wisemann, Chief Financial Officer
CMO: Edward Yourtee, M.D., Chief Medical Officer
CIO: Brad George, Director Information Systems
CHR: Molly Lahti, Director Human Resources
CNO: Eileen Keefe, Chief Nursing Officer
Web address: www.parklandmedicalcenter.com
Control: Corporation, Investor–owned (for–profit) **Service**: General medical and surgical

Staffed Beds: 82

DOVER—Strafford County

⊞ **WENTWORTH–DOUGLASS HOSPITAL (300018)**, 789 Central Avenue, Zip 3820; tel. 603/742–5252, **A**1 2 10 **F**3 5 8 13 17 18 19 20 22 26 28 29 30 31 32 34 35 36 38 39 40 41 43 44 45 46 47 48 49 50 51 52 53 54 55 57 58 59 61 62 63 64 65 68 70 73 74 75 76 77 78 79 81 82 84 85 86 87 89 91 92 93 94 96 97 100 101 102 104 107 108 111 114 115 118 119 120 121 123 124 126 129 130 131 132 134 135 143 144 145 146 147 148 149 154 **P**6 8 **S** Partners HealthCare System, Inc., Boston, MA
Primary Contact: Gregory J. Walker, Chief Executive Officer
COO: Daniel N Dunn, Vice President Operations
CFO: Peter Walcek, Vice President Finance
CMO: Paul Cass, D.O., Chief Medical & Clinical Integration Officer
CIO: Jeffrey Pollock, Chief Information Officer
CHR: Erin Flanigan, Vice President Human Resources
CNO: Sheila Woolley, R.N., M.P.H., Vice President, Patient Care Services
Web address: www.wdhospital.com
Control: Other not-for-profit (including NFP Corporation) **Service**: General medical and surgical

Staffed Beds: 148 Admissions: 8397 Census: 88 Outpatient Visits: 311673 Births: 1210 Total Expense ($000): 278957 Payroll Expense ($000): 111260 Personnel: 2117

NH

Many Facility Codes have changed. Please refer to the AHA Guide Code Chart.

EXETER—Rockingham County

★ ⇑ **EXETER HOSPITAL (300023)**, 5 Alumni Drive, Zip 03833–2128;
tel. 603/778–7311, **A**2 10 21 **F**3 8 13 14 15 18 20 22 26 28 29 30 31 32 34
35 36 37 38 40 44 45 46 47 48 49 50 51 52 54 55 57 58 59 64 70 74 75 76
77 78 79 80 81 84 85 86 87 89 93 107 108 110 111 114 115 117 118 119
120 121 123 124 126 129 130 131 132 135 143 144 145 146 147 148 149
Primary Contact: Kevin J. Callahan, President and Chief Executive Officer
CFO: Kevin J O'Leary, Senior Vice President and Chief Financial Officer
CMO: Richard Hollister, President of Medical Staff
CIO: David Briden, Chief Information Officer
CHR: Christopher M Callahan, Vice President Human Resources
CNO: Susan Burns–Tisdale, Senior Vice President Clinical Operations, Interim CNO
Web address: www.ehr.org
Control: Other not–for–profit (including NFP Corporation) **Service:** General
medical and surgical

Staffed Beds: 99 **Admissions:** 5313 **Census:** 58 **Outpatient Visits:** 213817
Births: 631 **Total Expense ($000):** 210059 **Payroll Expense ($000):** 77316
Personnel: 1194

FRANKLIN—Merrimack County

★ ⇑ **FRANKLIN REGIONAL HOSPITAL (301306)**, 15 Aiken Avenue,
Zip 03235–1299; tel. 603/934–2060, **A**10 18 21 **F**3 5 11 15 18 29 30 34 35
39 40 44 45 49 50 57 58 59 61 64 65 68 74 75 77 79 81 82 84 85 87 93 97
98 100 101 102 107 110 114 119 127 130 132 133 135 146 147 148 149 **P**4
6 **S** LRGHealthcare, Laconia, NH
Primary Contact: Kevin Donovan, FACHE, President and Chief Executive Officer
CFO: Henry D Lipman, Senior Vice President, Financial Strategy and External
Relations
CMO: Peter Doane, M.D., Chief Medical Officer
CIO: Kevin Irish, Chief Information Officer
CHR: Cass Walker, Vice President Administrative & Support Services
CNO: Patti Strohla, R.N., Chief Nursing Officer
Web address: www.lrgh.org
Control: Other not–for–profit (including NFP Corporation) **Service:** General
medical and surgical

Staffed Beds: 31 **Admissions:** 808 **Census:** 19 **Outpatient Visits:** 42154
Births: 0 **Total Expense ($000):** 24388 **Payroll Expense ($000):** 13080
Personnel: 141

HAMPSTEAD—Rockingham County

☐ **HAMPSTEAD HOSPITAL (304001)**, 218 East Road, Zip 03841–2305;
tel. 603/329–5311, (Nonreporting) **A**1 10
Primary Contact: Phillip J. Kubiak, President
COO: Cynthia A Gove, Chief Operating Officer
CFO: Cherie Clough–Berry, Vice President, Finance
CMO: Michael Knight, M.D., Medical Director
CIO: Sandra J Lucia, Director Health Information and Corporate Compliance Officer
CHR: Lisa M Ryan, Coordinator Human Resources
CNO: Julie D'Apollo, R.N., Director of Nursing
Web address: www.hampsteadhospital.com
Control: Corporation, Investor–owned (for–profit) **Service:** Psychiatric

Staffed Beds: 60

KEENE—Cheshire County

⊞ **CHESHIRE MEDICAL CENTER (300019)**, 580 Court Street, Zip 03431–1718;
tel. 603/354–5400, **A**1 2 3 10 **F**3 13 15 18 28 29 30 31 34 35 36 40 41 43 44
45 46 49 50 54 55 56 58 59 61 64 65 68 70 74 75 77 78 79 80 81 82 84 85
86 87 90 91 92 93 94 96 97 100 102 104 107 108 110 111 115 118 119 120
121 123 130 131 132 133 135 146 147 148 149 **P**6
Primary Contact: Don Caruso, M.D., Chief Executive Officer and President
CMO: Don Caruso, M.D., Chief Medical Officer
CIO: Peter Malloy, Chief Information Officer
CHR: Julie Green, Vice President Human Resources
CNO: Cynthia Coughlin, MS, R.N., Chief Nursing Officer
Web address: www.cheshire–med.com
Control: Other not–for–profit (including NFP Corporation) **Service:** General
medical and surgical

Staffed Beds: 91 **Admissions:** 4154 **Census:** 52 **Outpatient Visits:** 441789
Births: 391 **Total Expense ($000):** 207490 **Payroll Expense ($000):** 97725
Personnel: 1261

LACONIA—Belknap County

★ ⇑ **LAKES REGION GENERAL HOSPITAL (300005)**, 80 Highland Street,
Zip 03246–3298; tel. 603/524–3211, **A**10 21 **F**3 5 8 11 12 13 15 18 28 29 30
31 32 33 34 35 37 39 40 44 45 49 50 53 54 56 57 58 59 61 64 65 68 70 74
75 76 77 78 79 81 82 84 85 86 87 93 97 98 100 101 102 103 107 108 110
115 118 119 126 129 130 131 132 133 135 144 146 147 148 149 **P**4 6 **S**
LRGHealthcare, Laconia, NH
Primary Contact: Kevin Donovan, FACHE, President and Chief Executive Officer
CFO: Henry D Lipman, Senior Vice President, Financial Strategy and External
Relations
CMO: Peter Doane, M.D., Chief Medical Officer
CIO: Kevin Irish, Chief Information Officer
CHR: Cass Walker, Vice President Administrative & Support Services
CNO: Jacqueline Dawe, R.N., Chief Nursing Officer
Web address: www.lrgh.org
Control: Other not–for–profit (including NFP Corporation) **Service:** General
medical and surgical

Staffed Beds: 96 **Admissions:** 4293 **Census:** 55 **Outpatient Visits:** 202493
Births: 296 **Total Expense ($000):** 196960 **Payroll Expense ($000):** 97611
Personnel: 882

LANCASTER—Coos County

★ **WEEKS MEDICAL CENTER (301303)**, 173 Middle Street, Zip 03584–3508;
tel. 603/788–4911, **A**10 18 **F**3 11 15 18 28 29 31 32 34 35 36 40 45 50 51
56 57 59 61 62 63 64 65 66 68 70 77 79 81 85 86 87 91 92 93 94 97
100 104 107 108 110 111 114 116 117 118 119 127 130 131 132 133 134
135 146 147 148 **P**6 **S** North Country Healthcare, Littleton, NH
Primary Contact: Michael Lee, President
CMO: Lars Nielson, M.D., Chief Medical Officer
CIO: Darrell Bodnar, Director Information
CHR: Linda Rexford, Director Human Resources
CNO: Donna Walker, Chief Nurse Executive
Web address: www.weeksmedical.org
Control: Other not–for–profit (including NFP Corporation) **Service:** General
medical and surgical

Staffed Beds: 25 **Admissions:** 739 **Census:** 9 **Outpatient Visits:** 87844
Births: 0 **Total Expense ($000):** 45115 **Payroll Expense ($000):** 21997
Personnel: 280

LEBANON—Grafton County

★ **ALICE PECK DAY MEMORIAL HOSPITAL (301305)**, 10 Alice Peck Day Drive,
Zip 03766–2650; tel. 603/448–3121, (Data for 273 days) **A**10 18 **F**3 11 13 15
29 34 35 36 37 39 40 41 44 45 47 50 54 56 57 59 64 65 67 75 76 77 79 81
82 85 93 97 107 110 119 128 129 130 133 135 146 147 148 **P**6
Primary Contact: Susan E. Mooney, M.D., MS, President and Chief Executive
Officer
CFO: Evalie M Crosby, CPA, Vice President Finance and Chief Financial Officer
CMO: Randy Lea, M.D., M.P.H., Vice President and Chief Medical Officer
CIO: Kristin Kneisel, Interim Director, Information Services
CHR: Brenda Blair, Vice President Human Resources
CNO: Barbra Brown, MS, R.N., Interim Chief Nursing Officer and Vice President of
Nursing
Web address: www.alicepeckday.org
Control: Other not–for–profit (including NFP Corporation) **Service:** General
medical and surgical

Staffed Beds: 25 **Admissions:** 1268 **Census:** 18 **Outpatient Visits:** 119812
Births: 240 **Total Expense ($000):** 65005 **Payroll Expense ($000):** 29073
Personnel: 387

⊞ **DARTMOUTH–HITCHCOCK MEDICAL CENTER (300003)**, One Medical
Center Drive, Zip 03756–0001; tel. 603/650–5000, (Includes CHILDREN'S
HOSPITAL AT DARTMOUTH, One Medical Center Drive, Lebanon, NH, Zip 3756;
tel. 603/650–5000) **A**1 3 5 8 10 **F**3 5 6 7 8 9 11 12 13 14 15 17 18 19 20 21
22 23 24 25 26 27 28 29 30 31 32 33 34 35 36 37 38 39 40 41 43 44 45 46
47 48 49 50 51 52 53 54 55 56 57 58 59 60 61 63 64 65 66 68 70 71 72 74
75 76 77 78 79 80 81 82 83 84 85 86 87 88 89 91 92 93 94 96 97 98 99 100
101 102 103 104 107 108 110 111 112 114 115 116 117 118 119 120 121
123 124 126 129 130 131 132 134 135 136 138 141 142 143 145 146 147
148 149 150 153 154 **P**6
Primary Contact: Joanne M. Conroy, M.D., President and Chief Executive Officer
COO: Patrick Jordan III Chief Operating Officer
CFO: Daniel Jantzen, Chief Financial Officer
CMO: Alexander de Nesherea, M.D., Chief Medical Officer
CHR: Aimee M. Giglio, Chief Human Resources Officer
CNO: Susan A Reeves, Chief Nursing Executive
Web address: www.hitchcock.org
Control: Other not–for–profit (including NFP Corporation) **Service:** General
medical and surgical

Staffed Beds: 404 **Admissions:** 18895 **Census:** 320 **Outpatient Visits:**
797960 **Births:** 1201 **Total Expense ($000):** 1333129 **Payroll Expense
($000):** 613121 **Personnel:** 6509

NH

LITTLETON—Grafton County

★ **LITTLETON REGIONAL HEALTHCARE (301302)**, 600 Saint Johnsbury Road, Zip 03561–3442; tel. 603/444–9000, **A**10 18 **F**3 11 13 15 18 26 28 29 31 32 34 35 36 38 40 44 45 50 56 57 59 64 65 67 70 74 75 76 77 78 79 81 84 85 86 87 89 90 92 93 96 97 107 108 110 111 114 115 118 119 127 128 129 130 131 133 143 146 147 148 **P**6 **S** North Country Healthcare, Littleton, NH
Primary Contact: Robert Nutter, President
CFO: Robert L Fotter, Chief Financial Officer
CIO: Scott Vachon, Director Information Technology
CHR: Georgene Novak, Director Human Resources
Web address: www.littletonhospital.org
Control: Other not–for–profit (including NFP Corporation) **Service**: General medical and surgical

Staffed Beds: 25 Admissions: 1534 Census: 12 Outpatient Visits: 58582 **Births:** 306 **Total Expense ($000):** 84554 **Payroll Expense ($000):** 36014 **Personnel:** 424

MANCHESTER—Hillsborough County

⊞ **CATHOLIC MEDICAL CENTER (300034)**, 100 McGregor Street, Zip 03102–3770; tel. 603/668–3545, **A**1 2 3 10 **F**3 5 9 12 13 15 18 20 22 24 26 28 29 30 31 34 35 36 37 38 39 40 41 43 44 45 46 47 48 49 50 53 57 58 59 60 63 64 65 66 70 71 73 74 75 76 77 78 79 80 81 82 84 85 90 91 93 94 96 97 100 102 104 107 110 111 114 115 118 119 126 129 130 131 132 134 135 143 144 146 147 148 149 154 **P**6
Primary Contact: Joseph Pepe, M.D., President and Chief Executive Officer
COO: Alexander J. Walker, Executive Vice President Operations and Strategic Development
CFO: Edward L Dudley III Executive Vice President and Chief Financial Officer
CMO: William H. Goodman, Vice President Medical Affairs, Chief Medical Officer
CIO: Thomas Della Flora, Vice President and Chief Information Officer
CHR: Merryll Rosenfeld, Vice President, Human Resources
CNO: Robert A Duhaime, R.N., Senior Vice President Clinical Operations and Chief Nursing Officer
Web address: www.catholicmedicalcenter.org
Control: Other not–for–profit (including NFP Corporation) **Service**: General medical and surgical

Staffed Beds: 258 Admissions: 12453 Census: 176 Outpatient Visits: 187018 **Births:** 1131 **Total Expense ($000):** 370640 **Payroll Expense ($000):** 163151 **Personnel:** 1839

□ △ **ELLIOT HOSPITAL (300012)**, One Elliot Way, Zip 03103–3502; tel. 603/669–5300, **A**1 2 3 7 10 **F**3 8 9 11 12 13 15 18 20 22 26 28 29 30 31 32 34 35 36 37 38 39 40 41 43 44 45 46 47 48 49 50 51 53 54 55 56 57 59 62 64 65 68 70 72 74 75 76 77 78 79 81 82 83 84 85 86 87 89 91 93 97 98 100 101 102 103 104 107 108 110 111 114 115 118 119 120 121 123 124 126 129 130 131 132 134 135 144 146 147 148 149 **P**6
Primary Contact: Douglas F. Dean Jr, Chief Executive Officer
CFO: Richard Elwell, Senior Vice President and Chief Financial Officer
CMO: Greg Baxter, M.D., Senior Vice President Medical Affairs and Chief Medical Officer
CIO: Denise Purington, Vice President and Chief Information Officer
CHR: Catherine Bardier, Vice President, Human Resources
CNO: Martha Leighton, Senior Vice President and Chief Nursing Officer
Web address: www.elliothospital.org
Control: Other not–for–profit (including NFP Corporation) **Service**: General medical and surgical

Staffed Beds: 258 Admissions: 12831 Census: 175 Outpatient Visits: 506060 **Births:** 1891 **Total Expense ($000):** 394671 **Payroll Expense ($000):** 141082 **Personnel:** 3128

★ **MANCHESTER VETERANS AFFAIRS MEDICAL CENTER**, 718 Smyth Road, Zip 03104–4098; tel. 603/624–4366, **A**5 **F**5 8 9 12 18 29 30 31 33 34 35 36 38 39 45 54 55 56 58 61 62 63 64 65 68 74 75 77 78 79 81 82 83 84 86 87 93 94 97 100 101 104 107 108 111 115 119 126 129 130 132 135 143 144 146 147 148 149 154 **S** Department of Veterans Affairs, Perry Point, MD
Primary Contact: Alfred Montoya, Director
COO: Richard T Rose, Associate Director
CFO: Frank Ryan, Chief Financial Officer
CMO: Andrew Breuder, M.D., Chief of Staff
CIO: John Foote, Chief Information Officer
CHR: Mary Ellen Kenney, Chief Human Services
Web address: www.manchester.va.gov/
Control: Veterans Affairs, Government, federal **Service**: General medical and surgical

Staffed Beds: 41 Admissions: 120 Census: 44 Outpatient Visits: 261029 **Births:** 0 **Total Expense ($000):** 167600 **Payroll Expense ($000):** 67048 **Personnel:** 803

VETERANS AFFAIRS MEDICAL CENTER See Manchester Veterans Affairs Medical Center

NASHUA—Hillsborough County

★ △ ⇑ **SOUTHERN NEW HAMPSHIRE MEDICAL CENTER (300020)**, 8 Prospect Street, Zip 03060–3925, Mailing Address: P.O. Box 2014, Zip 03061–2014; tel. 603/577–2000, **A**2 3 5 7 10 21 **F**3 11 13 15 18 20 22 26 28 29 30 31 34 35 40 43 45 49 50 51 52 57 59 61 65 68 70 72 74 75 76 77 78 79 81 84 85 86 87 89 93 96 98 100 102 104 105 107 110 111 115 118 119 126 129 130 131 132 135 143 146 147 148 149 150 153 154 **P**6
Primary Contact: Michael S. Rose, President and Chief Executive Officer
COO: Tate Curti, Senior Vice President and Chief Operating Officer
CFO: Paul Trainor, Senior Vice President Finance and Chief Financial Officer
CMO: Timothy Scherer, M.D., Chief Medical Officer
CIO: Andrew Watt, M.D., Vice President, Information Technology & Services, Chief Information Officer, Chief Medical Information Officer
CHR: Jacqueline Woolley, Vice President Human Resources
CNO: Cheryl Gagne I Vice President Patient Care Services and Chief Nursing Officer
Web address: www.snhhs.org
Control: Other not–for–profit (including NFP Corporation) **Service**: General medical and surgical

Staffed Beds: 162 Admissions: 8496 Census: 102 Outpatient Visits: 232444 **Births:** 1248 **Total Expense ($000):** 196360 **Payroll Expense ($000):** 94704 **Personnel:** 1502

★ △ ⇑ **ST. JOSEPH HOSPITAL (300011)**, 172 Kinsley Street, Zip 03060–3648; tel. 603/882–3000, **A**2 7 10 21 **F**3 13 15 18 20 22 28 29 30 31 32 34 35 36 37 40 43 44 45 46 47 48 49 50 51 54 55 56 57 58 59 61 63 64 65 68 70 71 74 75 76 77 78 79 81 82 83 84 85 86 87 89 90 91 92 93 94 96 97 102 107 108 109 110 111 115 116 117 118 119 126 129 130 131 132 135 144 145 146 147 148 149 **S** Covenant Health, Tewksbury, MA
Primary Contact: John A. Jurczyk, FACHE, Senior Vice President and President
COO: Pam Duchene, R.N., Vice President Patient Care Services
CFO: Richard Plamondon, Vice President Finance and Chief Financial Officer
CIO: Keith A Choinka, Vice President Information Systems and Chief Information Officer
CHR: Jacqueline Woolley, Vice President Human Resources
Web address: www.stjosephhospital.com
Control: Church operated, Nongovernment, not–for–profit **Service**: General medical and surgical

Staffed Beds: 135 Admissions: 5323 Census: 72 Outpatient Visits: 177244 **Births:** 411 **Total Expense ($000):** 205108 **Payroll Expense ($000):** 77126 **Personnel:** 1258

NEW LONDON—Merrimack County

★ **NEW LONDON HOSPITAL (301304)**, 273 County Road, Zip 03257–5736; tel. 603/526–2911, **A**3 10 18 **F**3 7 11 15 18 29 30 31 32 34 35 36 38 40 41 45 50 51 53 54 55 56 57 59 64 70 74 75 77 78 79 81 82 84 85 86 87 89 93 94 97 100 102 104 107 110 111 114 115 119 127 128 130 131 133 134 146 147 149 150 154 **P**6
Primary Contact: Bruce King, President and Chief Executive Officer
CFO: Lisa Cohen, Chief Financial Officer
CMO: James M. Murphy, M.D., Chief Medical Officer Regional Development and Outpatient Services
CIO: David Foss, Chief Information Officer
CHR: Shari Bostwick, Director Human Resources
CNO: Sally K Patton, R.N., MS, Chief Nursing Officer
Web address: www.newlondonhospital.org
Control: Other not–for–profit (including NFP Corporation) **Service**: General medical and surgical

Staffed Beds: 25 Admissions: 1101 Census: 9 Outpatient Visits: 169651 **Births:** 0 **Total Expense ($000):** 63942 **Payroll Expense ($000):** 30311 **Personnel:** 466

NORTH CONWAY—Carroll County

★ **MEMORIAL HOSPITAL (301307)**, 3073 White Mountain Highway, Zip 03860–7101; tel. 603/356–5461, (Total facility includes 45 beds in nursing home–type unit) **A**10 18 **F**3 11 13 15 28 29 30 31 32 34 35 36 40 41 45 50 51 57 59 64 67 68 70 75 76 77 78 79 81 82 85 86 87 90 93 94 96 97 100 101 103 104 110 115 119 128 129 130 131 132 133 144 146 147 148 **P**6 **S** MaineHealth, Portland, ME
Primary Contact: Scott McKinnon, President and Chief Executive Officer
CFO: Diane Maheux, Vice President Finance
CMO: Ray Rabideau, M.D., Senior Vice President and Chief Medical Officer
CIO: Curtis Kerbs, Regional Chief Information Officer
CHR: Melanie Sleime, Director Human Resources
CNO: Ethnee Garner, R.N., Vice President Patient Care Services
Web address: www.memorialhospitalnh.org
Control: Other not–for–profit (including NFP Corporation) **Service**: General medical and surgical

Staffed Beds: 70 Admissions: 1576 Census: 58 Outpatient Visits: 60024 **Births:** 206 **Total Expense ($000):** 71136 **Payroll Expense ($000):** 29731 **Personnel:** 398

NH

PETERBOROUGH—Hillsborough County

★ **MONADNOCK COMMUNITY HOSPITAL (301309)**, 452 Old Street Road,
Zip 03458–1295; tel. 603/924–7191, **A**5 10 18 **F**3 11 13 15 28 29 31 34 35
36 38 40 41 44 50 53 59 64 65 70 75 76 77 78 79 81 82 85 86 90 91 92 93
97 98 99 100 101 102 103 104 107 108 110 114 118 119 124 127 128 130
131 132 133 134 135 146 147 148 149 **P**6
Primary Contact: Cynthia McGuire, FACHE, President and Chief Executive Officer
CFO: Richard Scheinblum, Chief Financial Officer
CMO: Michael Lindberg, M.D., Chief Medical Officer
CIO: Peter A Johnson, Interim Chief Information Officer
CHR: John Sansone, Vice President, Human Resources
CNO: Vicki Loughery, R.N., MS, Chief Nursing Officer
Web address: www.monadnockhospital.org
Control: Other not–for–profit (including NFP Corporation) **Service**: General
medical and surgical

Staffed Beds: 25 **Admissions:** 1294 **Census:** 10 **Outpatient Visits:** 80257
Births: 332 **Total Expense ($000):** 81545 **Payroll Expense ($000):** 34003
Personnel: 449

PLYMOUTH—Grafton County

★ **SPEARE MEMORIAL HOSPITAL (301311)**, 16 Hospital Road, Zip 03264–1199;
tel. 603/536–1120, **A**10 18 **F**3 13 15 28 29 30 31 32 35 40 45 47 50 53 54
57 59 64 70 75 76 77 78 79 81 83 84 85 87 89 93 97 107 110 111 113 114
119 127 129 130 131 132 133 146 147 148 **P**8
Primary Contact: Michelle McEwen, President and Chief Executive Officer
CFO: Thomas Lenkowski, Chief Financial Officer
CMO: Joseph Ebner, M.D., Chief Medical Officer
CHR: Laurie Bolognani, Human Resources Officer
CNO: Kristine Hering, R.N., Chief Nursing Officer
Web address: www.spearehospital.com
Control: Other not–for–profit (including NFP Corporation) **Service**: General
medical and surgical

Staffed Beds: 25 **Admissions:** 1439 **Census:** 13 **Outpatient Visits:** 61397
Births: 159 **Total Expense ($000):** 52939 **Payroll Expense ($000):** 25355
Personnel: 337

PORTSMOUTH—Rockingham County

✠ **PORTSMOUTH REGIONAL HOSPITAL (300029)**, 333 Borthwick Avenue,
Zip 03801–7128; tel. 603/436–5110, (Nonreporting) **A**1 2 10 **S** HCA Healthcare,
Nashville, TN
Primary Contact: Dean Carucci, Chief Executive Officer
COO: Stuart Hemming, Chief Operating Officer
CFO: Richard Senger, Chief Financial Officer
CMO: Tim Pike, M.D., Chief Medical Officer
CIO: Ed Sovetskhy, Director Information Services
CHR: Jackie Brayton, Vice President Human Resources
Web address: www.portsmouthhospital.com
Control: Corporation, Investor–owned (for–profit) **Service**: General medical and
surgical

Staffed Beds: 165

ROCHESTER—Strafford County

★ **FRISBIE MEMORIAL HOSPITAL (300014)**, 11 Whitehall Road, Zip 03867–3297;
tel. 603/332–5211, **A**10 **F**7 11 13 17 18 20 29 31 34 35 40 45 46 49 50 55
59 68 70 71 75 76 77 78 79 81 82 85 89 91 93 97 98 103 104 107 111 114
118 119 129 130 135 143 144 146 149 **P**5 8
Primary Contact: Jocelyn Caple, M.D., Interim President and Chief Executive Officer
CFO: Robert K. Cochrane, Vice President Finance and Chief Financial Officer
CMO: Jocelyn Caple, M.D., Chief Medical Officer
CHR: Christi Green, R.N., MS, Vice President, Human Resources
CNO: John Levitow, Vice President Patient Care Services and Chief Nursing Officer
Web address: www.frisbiehospital.com
Control: Other not–for–profit (including NFP Corporation) **Service**: General
medical and surgical

Staffed Beds: 96 **Admissions:** 3067 **Census:** 44 **Outpatient Visits:** 156826
Births: 307 **Total Expense ($000):** 157089 **Payroll Expense ($000):** 67369
Personnel: 882

SALEM—Rockingham County

☐ △ **NORTHEAST REHABILITATION HOSPITAL (303026)**, 70 Butler Street,
Zip 03079–3925; tel. 603/893–2900, **A**1 7 10 **F**29 62 68 77 82 87 90 91 93
96 100 130 131 133 147 148 149
Primary Contact: John F. Prochilo Jr, Chief Executive Officer
CFO: Charles D. Champagne, Chief Financial Officer
CMO: A Deniz Ozel, M.D., Chief Medical Officer
CHR: Shirley G Lussier, Vice President Human Resources
CNO: Helene Thibodeau, R.N., MSN, Vice President Patient Care Services
Web address: www.northeastrehab.com
Control: Corporation, Investor–owned (for–profit) **Service**: Rehabilitation

Staffed Beds: 135 **Admissions:** 3707 **Census:** 118 **Outpatient Visits:**
191574 **Births:** 0 **Total Expense ($000):** 92640 **Payroll Expense
($000):** 54320 **Personnel:** 687

WOLFEBORO—Carroll County

★ **HUGGINS HOSPITAL (301312)**, 240 South Main Street, Zip 03894–4455,
Mailing Address: P.O. Box 912, Zip 03894–0912; tel. 603/569–7500, **A**10 18 **F**2
3 10 15 28 29 34 35 36 40 45 50 53 57 59 64 65 68 70 75 79 81 85 86 87
93 96 97 107 108 110 115 119 130 131 132 133 146 147 148 149 **P**6
Primary Contact: Jeremy Roberge, President and Chief Executive Officer
CFO: Jeremy Roberge, Chief Financial Officer
CMO: John Boornazian, M.D., Chief Medical Officer
CIO: Pam McGovern, Director Technology
CHR: Laura Stauss, Director of Human Resources
Web address: www.hugginshospital.org
Control: Other not–for–profit (including NFP Corporation) **Service**: General
medical and surgical

Staffed Beds: 25 **Admissions:** 920 **Census:** 12 **Outpatient Visits:** 70496
Births: 0 **Total Expense ($000):** 57254 **Payroll Expense ($000):** 24558
Personnel: 340

WOODSVILLE—Grafton County

★ **COTTAGE HOSPITAL (301301)**, 90 Swiftwater Road, Zip 03785–1421, Mailing
Address: P.O. Box 2001, Zip 03785–2001; tel. 603/747–9000, (Nonreporting)
A10 18
Primary Contact: Maria Ryan, Ph.D., Chief Executive Officer
COO: Lori Hughes, R.N., MSN, Chief Nursing Officer, Vice President Operations and
Patient Care Services
CFO: Steven L Plant, Chief Financial Officer
CIO: Rick Fredrick, Director Information Technology
CNO: Lori Hughes, R.N., MSN, Chief Nursing Officer, Vice President Operations &
Patient Care Services
Web address: www.cottagehospital.org
Control: Other not–for–profit (including NFP Corporation) **Service**: General
medical and surgical

Staffed Beds: 25

NH

NEW JERSEY

ATLANTIC CITY—Atlantic County

★ ⇑ **ACUITY SPECIALTY HOSPITAL OF NEW JERSEY (312023)**, 1925 Pacific Avenue, 7th Floor, Zip 08401–6713; tel. 609/441–2122, (Nonreporting) **A**10 21 **S** AcuityHealthcare, LP, Charlotte, NC
Primary Contact: Monica B. Titus, BSN, MBA, RN, Regional Chief Executive Officer
CFO: Cheryl Lambert, Chief Financial Officer
CHR: Maria Ciro, Director Human Resources
CNO: Kathleen Kerstetter, R.N., MSN, Chief Clinical Officer
Web address: www.acuityhealthcare.net
Control: Corporation, Investor–owned (for–profit) **Service**: Acute long–term care hospital

Staffed Beds: 30

⊞ **ATLANTICARE REGIONAL MEDICAL CENTER (310064)**, 1925 Pacific Avenue, Zip 08401–6713; tel. 609/441–8994, (Includes ATLANTICARE REGIONAL MEDICAL CENTER–MAINLAND DIVISION, Jimmie Leeds Road, Pomona, NJ, Zip 8240, Mailing Address: 65 West Jimmie Leeds Road, Zip 8240, tel. 609/652–1000; Lori Herdon, President and Chief Executive Officer) **A**1 2 3 10 13 **F**3 7 11 12 13 15 17 18 20 22 24 26 28 29 30 31 34 35 36 37 38 40 41 43 45 46 47 48 49 50 54 55 57 58 59 60 61 64 66 68 70 71 72 73 74 75 76 78 79 81 82 83 84 85 86 87 89 97 98 100 102 104 105 107 108 110 111 114 115 116 117 118 119 120 121 123 124 126 130 132 135 143 146 147 148 149 150 153 154 **P**6 **S** Geisinger, Danville, PA
Primary Contact: Lori S. Herndon, R.N., President and Chief Executive Officer
CFO: Walter Greiner, Chief Financial Officer
CMO: Marilouise Vendetti, M.D., Chief Medical Officer
CIO: Christopher A Scanzera, Vice President and Chief Information Officer
CHR: Richard Lovering, Corporate Vice President Human Resources and Organizational Development
CNO: Robyn Begley, R.N., Chief Nursing Officer
Web address: www.atlanticare.org
Control: Other not–for–profit (including NFP Corporation) **Service**: General medical and surgical

Staffed Beds: 533 **Admissions**: 28313 **Census**: 347 **Outpatient Visits**: 335128 **Births**: 1115 **Total Expense ($000)**: 655927 **Payroll Expense ($000)**: 294259 **Personnel**: 3159

BAYONNE—Hudson County

☐ **CAREPOINT HEALTH BAYONNE MEDICAL CENTER (310025)**, 29th Street & Avenue E, Zip 07002–4699, Mailing Address: 29 East 29 Street, Zip 07002–4699; tel. 201/858–5000, (Nonreporting) **A**1 2 3 10 12 13 **S** CarePoint Health, Jersey City, NJ
Primary Contact: W. Peter Daniels, FACHE, Executive Vice President and Chief Operating Officer
CFO: Gary Bryant, Chief Financial Officer
CMO: Vijayant Singh, M.D., Chief Medical Officer
CIO: Joel Taylor, Chief Information Officer
CHR: Jennifer Dobin, Executive Vice President Human Resources
Web address: www.carepointhealth.org
Control: Corporation, Investor–owned (for–profit) **Service**: General medical and surgical

Staffed Beds: 178

BELLE MEAD—Somerset County

⊞ **CARRIER CLINIC (314012)**, 252 County Route 601, Zip 08502–0147, Mailing Address: P.O. Box 147, Zip 08502–0147; tel. 908/281–1000, **A**1 3 5 10 **F**4 5 30 38 98 99 100 101 102 103 130 132 149
Primary Contact: Donald J. Parker, President and Chief Executive Officer
CFO: Randolph Jacobson, Chief Financial Officer
CMO: Umesh Mehta, M.D., Interim Chief Medical Officer
CIO: Peter Schwartz, Director of Information Systems
CHR: Trish Toole, Vice President Administrative Services
CNO: Shaun Sweeney, Vice President Patient Care Services
Web address: www.carrierclinic.org
Control: Other not–for–profit (including NFP Corporation) **Service**: Psychiatric

Staffed Beds: 320 **Admissions**: 6716 **Census**: 256 **Outpatient Visits**: 1402 **Births**: 0 **Total Expense ($000)**: 75731 **Payroll Expense ($000)**: 46160

EAST MOUNTAIN HOSPITAL (314026), 252 County Route 601, Zip 8502; tel. 908/281–1500, **A**10 **F**98 102
Primary Contact: Michael Voorhees, MS, Executive Director
CFO: Randolph Jacobson, Chief Financial Officer
CMO: Bohdan Cehelyk, M.D., Chief Medical Officer
CIO: Peter Schwartz, Director Information Systems
CHR: Patricia Toole, Vice President Human Resources
CNO: Deborah Charette, Director of Nursing
Web address: www.eastmountainhospital.com
Control: Other not–for–profit (including NFP Corporation) **Service**: Psychiatric

Staffed Beds: 16 **Admissions**: 499 **Census**: 14 **Outpatient Visits**: 0 **Births**: 0 **Total Expense ($000)**: 4946 **Payroll Expense ($000)**: 2109 **Personnel**: 28

BELLEVILLE—Essex County

⊞ **CLARA MAASS MEDICAL CENTER (310009)**, One Clara Maass Drive, Zip 07109–3557; tel. 973/450–2000, **A**1 3 5 10 **F**1 3 8 11 12 13 15 18 19 20 22 26 28 29 30 31 34 35 36 38 40 41 46 47 49 50 51 53 55 56 57 59 60 61 63 64 65 66 68 70 71 73 74 75 76 77 78 79 81 82 83 84 85 86 87 89 92 93 94 98 100 101 102 103 105 107 108 110 111 114 115 119 120 121 123 126 129 130 131 132 135 143 146 147 148 149 154 **P**3 6 **S** RWJBarnabas Health, West Orange, NJ
Primary Contact: Mary Ellen Clyne, Ph.D., President and Chief Executive Officer
COO: Domenic Segalla, Chief Operating Officer and Chief Financial Officer
CFO: Domenic Segalla, Chief Operating Officer and Chief Financial Officer
CMO: Frank Mazzarella, M.D., Chief Medical Officer
CIO: Michael McTigue, Chief Information Officer
CHR: Jim Rolek, Chief Human Resources Officer, Vice President
CNO: Bonnie Geissler, R.N., Chief Nursing Officer, Vice President Patient Care Services
Web address: www.barnabashealth.org/hospitals/clara_maass/index.html
Control: Other not–for–profit (including NFP Corporation) **Service**: General medical and surgical

Staffed Beds: 364 **Admissions**: 15732 **Census**: 228 **Outpatient Visits**: 145665 **Births**: 1529 **Total Expense ($000)**: 254544 **Payroll Expense ($000)**: 112507 **Personnel**: 1365

BERKELEY HEIGHTS—Union County

CORNERSTONE BEHAVIORAL HEALTH HOSPITAL OF UNION COUNTY (314027), 40 Watchung Way, Zip 07922–2600; tel. 908/790–5300, (Nonreporting)
Primary Contact: Michael Flemming, Administrator
Control: County, Government, nonfederal **Service**: Psychiatric

Staffed Beds: 44

BLACKWOOD—Camden County

NORTHBROOK BEHAVIORAL HEALTH HOSPITAL (314018), 425 Woodbury Turnersville Road, Zip 08012–2960; tel. 856/374–6500, (Nonreporting)
Primary Contact: Avi Feigenbaum, LNHA, Chief Executive Officer
Web address: www.northbrookbhh.com
Control: Corporation, Investor–owned (for–profit) **Service**: Psychiatric

Staffed Beds: 153

BOONTON TOWNSHIP—Morris County

SAINT CLARE'S HOSPITAL/BOONTON TOWNSHIP See Saint Clare's Denville Hospital, Denville

BRICK—Ocean County

⊞ △ **HACKENSACK MERIDIAN HEALTH SHORE REHABILITATION INSTITUTE (313033)**, 425 Jack Martin Boulevard, Zip 08724–7732; tel. 732/836–4500, **A**1 7 10 **F**29 36 50 75 90 91 93 94 95 96 130 132 148 149 **P**6 **S** Hackensack Meridian Health, Edison, NJ
Primary Contact: Kerri Fitzgerald, Executive Director
CFO: Richard C. Smith, Senior Vice President Finance
CMO: Lisa Luciano, D.O., Medical Director
CNO: Maria Clohsey, Director of Nursing
Web address: www.shorerehabilitationinstitute.com
Control: Other not–for–profit (including NFP Corporation) **Service**: Rehabilitation

Staffed Beds: 40 **Admissions**: 899 **Census**: 30 **Outpatient Visits**: 6465 **Births**: 0 **Total Expense ($000)**: 16448 **Payroll Expense ($000)**: 8302 **Personnel**: 153

NJ

Many Facility Codes have changed. Please refer to the AHA Guide Code Chart. © 2018 AHA Guide

BRICK TOWNSHIP—Ocean County

⊞ **HACKENSACK MERIDIAN HEALTH OCEAN MEDICAL CENTER (310052)**, 425 Jack Martin Boulevard, Zip 08724–7732; tel. 732/840–2200, **A**1 2 10 **F**3 11 12 13 15 17 18 20 22 28 29 30 31 32 34 35 36 38 40 41 44 45 46 47 48 49 50 54 55 56 57 58 59 60 61 63 64 65 66 68 70 71 73 74 75 76 77 78 79 80 81 82 84 85 86 87 91 92 93 94 96 97 99 100 101 102 104 107 108 109 110 111 114 115 116 117 118 119 120 121 123 124 126 129 130 132 134 135 141 144 146 147 148 149 154 **S** Hackensack Meridian Health, Edison, NJ
Primary Contact: Dean Q. Lin, FACHE, Regional President
COO: Regina Foley, R.N., FACHE, Vice President Nursing and Operations
CFO: Robert Palermo, Vice President Finance
CMO: James Clarke, M.D., Vice President Medical Affairs and Clinical Effectiveness
CIO: Rebecca Weber, Senior Vice President and Chief Information Officer
CHR: Sherrie String, Senior Vice President Human Resources
Web address: www.meridianhealth.com
Control: Other not–for–profit (including NFP Corporation) **Service:** General medical and surgical

Staffed Beds: 317 **Admissions:** 27307 **Census:** 197 **Outpatient Visits:** 176292 **Births:** 874 **Total Expense ($000):** 307536 **Payroll Expense ($000):** 121457 **Personnel:** 1692

BRIDGETON—Cumberland County

BRIDGETON HEALTH CENTER See Inspira Medical Center–Vineland, Vineland

BROWNS MILLS—Burlington County

☐ **DEBORAH HEART AND LUNG CENTER (310031)**, 200 Trenton Road, Zip 08015–1705; tel. 609/893–6611, (Nonreporting) **A**1 3 5 10 13
Primary Contact: Joseph Chirichella, President and Chief Executive Officer
COO: Joseph Manni, Executive Vice President and Chief Operating Officer
CFO: R. Grant Leidy, Chief Financial Officer
CMO: Lynn McGrath, M.D., Vice President Medical Affairs
CIO: Richard Temple, Chief Information Officer
CHR: Marion Stamopoulos, Vice President Human Resouces
CNO: Rita Zenna, R.N., Vice President Patient Care Services
Web address: www.deborah.org
Control: Other not–for–profit (including NFP Corporation) **Service:** Other specialty treatment

Staffed Beds: 89

CAMDEN—Camden County

⊞ **COOPER UNIVERSITY HEALTH CARE (310014)**, One Cooper Plaza, Zip 08103–1489; tel. 856/342–2000, (Includes CHILDEN'S REGIONAL HOSPITAL AT COOPER, Three Cooper Plaza, Camden, NJ, Zip 8103; tel. 800/826–6737) **A**1 2 3 5 8 10 **F**3 5 7 8 9 11 12 13 15 17 18 19 20 22 24 26 29 30 31 32 34 35 36 37 39 40 41 43 44 45 46 47 49 50 51 52 54 55 56 57 58 59 60 61 63 64 65 66 68 70 72 73 74 75 78 79 80 81 82 84 85 86 87 88 92 93 96 97 98 99 100 101 102 103 104 107 108 110 111 114 115 117 118 119 120 121 123 124 126 130 131 132 135 144 146 147 148 149 **P**6
Primary Contact: Adrienne Kirby, Ph.D., FACHE, President and Executive Chairman/Chief Executive Chair
CFO: Douglas E. Shirley, Senior Executive Vice President and Chief Financial Officer
CMO: Anthony J Mazzarelli, JD, M.D., Co–President
CIO: Stephanie Conners, Senior Executive Vice President Chief Operating Officer and Chief Nursing Officer
CHR: Elizabeth Green, Chief Human Resources Officer
Web address: www.cooperhealth.org
Control: Other not–for–profit (including NFP Corporation) **Service:** General medical and surgical

Staffed Beds: 578 **Admissions:** 28298 **Census:** 429 **Outpatient Visits:** 340584 **Births:** 2040 **Total Expense ($000):** 902850 **Payroll Expense ($000):** 311959 **Personnel:** 6388

⊞ **OUR LADY OF LOURDES MEDICAL CENTER (310029)**, 1600 Haddon Avenue, Zip 08103–3117; tel. 856/757–3500, **A**1 2 3 10 **F**3 7 11 12 13 15 17 18 20 22 24 26 28 29 30 31 32 34 35 36 37 38 40 44 46 47 49 50 55 56 57 58 59 60 61 64 65 66 68 70 73 74 75 76 78 79 81 82 84 85 86 87 90 95 96 107 108 110 111 114 115 118 119 126 130 132 134 135 138 139 142 146 147 148 149 **P**8 **S** Trinity Health, Livonia, MI
Primary Contact: Reginald Blaber, M.D., FACC, President
COO: Mark Nessel, Chief Operating Officer
CFO: Michael Hammond, Chief Financial Officer
CMO: Alan R Pope, M.D., Chief Medical Officer
CIO: Maureen Hetu, Chief Information Officer
CHR: Jennifer L Moughan, Chief Human Resources Officer
CNO: Audrey Jadczak, R.N., FACHE, Vice President Chief Nursing Officer
Web address: www.lourdesnet.org
Control: Other not–for–profit (including NFP Corporation) **Service:** General medical and surgical

Staffed Beds: 340 **Admissions:** 12969 **Census:** 175 **Outpatient Visits:** 149931 **Births:** 1032 **Total Expense ($000):** 311577 **Payroll Expense ($000):** 111533 **Personnel:** 1450

CAPE MAY COURT HOUSE—Cape May County

⊞ **CAPE REGIONAL HEALTH SYSTEM (310011)**, Two Stone Harbor Boulevard, Zip 08210–9990; tel. 609/463–2000, **A**1 2 10 **F**3 8 11 13 15 18 20 28 29 30 31 34 35 40 44 45 46 49 50 57 59 64 70 74 75 76 77 78 79 81 82 85 86 87 89 93 97 107 111 114 118 119 120 121 123 124 129 130 132 135 143 146 149
Primary Contact: Joanne Carrocino, FACHE, President and Chief Executive Officer
CFO: Mark Gill, Vice President Finance and Chief Financial Officer
CMO: Andrea C.S. McCoy, M.D., Chief Medical Officer
CIO: Richard Wheatley, Chief Information Officer
CHR: Byron Hunter, Vice President Human Resources
CNO: Rosemary Dunn, R.N., Chief Nursing Officer
Web address: www.caperegional.com
Control: Other not–for–profit (including NFP Corporation) **Service:** General medical and surgical

Staffed Beds: 178 **Admissions:** 6735 **Census:** 77 **Outpatient Visits:** 203245 **Births:** 364 **Total Expense ($000):** 126166 **Payroll Expense ($000):** 55008 **Personnel:** 898

CEDAR GROVE—Essex County

☐ **ESSEX COUNTY HOSPITAL CENTER (314020)**, 204 Grove Avenue, Zip 07009–1436; tel. 973/571–2800, (Nonreporting) **A**1 10
Primary Contact: Frank J. Del Gaudio, Director and Chief Executive Officer
CFO: Jacqueline Campoverde, Business Manager
CMO: Bolivar Pascual, M.D., Medical Director
CIO: Vijay Prakash, Information Technology Officer
CHR: Marlon Brown, Human Resources
CNO: Fern Papalia, Director of Nursing
Web address: www.essexcountynj.org
Control: County, Government, nonfederal **Service:** Psychiatric

Staffed Beds: 180

CHESTER—Morris County

KESSLER INSTITUTE FOR REHABILITATION See Kessler Institute for Rehabilitation, West Orange

DENVILLE—Morris County

⊞ **SAINT CLARE'S DENVILLE HOSPITAL (310050)**, 25 Pocono Road, Zip 07834–2954; tel. 973/625–6000, (Includes SAINT CLARE'S HEALTH CENTER AT SUSSEX, 20 Walnut Street, Sussex, NJ, Zip 7461; tel. 973/702–2200; SAINT CLARE'S HOSPITAL/BOONTON TOWNSHIP, 130 Powerville Road, Boonton Township, NJ, Zip 7005; tel. 973/316–1800; SAINT CLARE'S HOSPITAL/DENVILLE, 25 Pocono Road, Denville, NJ, Zip 7834; tel. 973/625–6000; SAINT CLARE'S HOSPITAL/DOVER, 400 West Blackwell Street, Dover, NJ, Zip 07801–3311; tel. 973/989–3000) (Nonreporting) **A**1 2 10 **S** Prime Healthcare, Ontario, CA
Primary Contact: Brian Finestein, Chief Executive Officer
COO: Joe Nolan, Chief Operating Officer
CFO: Dianne Halford, Chief Financial Officer
CMO: Alma Ratcliffe, M.D., Executive Vice President Medical Staff and Business Development
CIO: Tero Caamano, Director Information Technology
CHR: Kay Bryant, Executive Director Human Resources
Web address: www.saintclares.org
Control: Church operated, Nongovernment, not–for–profit **Service:** General medical and surgical

Staffed Beds: 412

NJ

SAINT CLARE'S HOSPITAL/DENVILLE See Saint Clare's Denville Hospital, Denville

DOVER—Morris County

☒ **KINDRED HOSPITAL–NEW JERSEY MORRIS COUNTY (312020)**, 400 West Blackwell Street, Zip 07801–2525; tel. 973/537–3818, (Includes KINDRED HOSPITAL NEW JERSEY – RAHWAY, 865 Stone Street, Rahway, NJ, Zip 7065; tel. 732/669–8200; Christopher Cannara, Chief Executive Officer; KINDRED HOSPITAL NEW JERSEY – WAYNE, 224 Hamburg Turnpike, Wayne, NJ, Zip 7470; tel. 973/636–7200; Alice M O'Connor, Chief Executive Officer) (Nonreporting) **A**1 10 **S** Kindred Healthcare, Louisville, KY
Primary Contact: Tarra Washington, Chief Executive Officer
COO: Kent Wallace, Chief Operating Officer
CFO: Stephen D. Farber, Chief Financial Officer
CMO: Sean R Muldoon, M.D., Chief Medical Officer
Web address: www.khmorriscounty.com/
Control: Corporation, Investor–owned (for–profit) **Service**: Acute long–term care hospital

Staffed Beds: 117

EAST ORANGE—Essex County

☐ **EAST ORANGE GENERAL HOSPITAL (310083)**, 300 Central Avenue, Zip 07018–2897; tel. 973/672–8400, **A**1 10 **F**3 5 8 12 15 17 18 29 30 34 35 38 40 44 49 50 51 53 57 59 60 64 65 68 70 75 77 79 81 82 84 85 87 93 94 96 98 101 104 105 106 107 108 110 111 119 130 132 135 143 146 147 148 149 152 **P**5 **S** Prospect Medical Holdings, Los Angeles, CA
Primary Contact: Paige Dworak, FACHE, Chief Executive Officer
CMO: Valentine Burroughs, M.D., Chief Medical Officer
CIO: Thomas Ciccarelli, Chief Information Officer
CHR: Chester Banks, Director Human Resources
Web address: www.evh.org
Control: Corporation, Investor–owned (for–profit) **Service**: General medical and surgical

Staffed Beds: 186 **Admissions:** 6081 **Census:** 93 **Outpatient Visits:** 48495 **Births:** 0 **Total Expense ($000):** 104089 **Payroll Expense ($000):** 43125 **Personnel:** 711

☒ **VETERANS AFFAIRS NEW JERSEY HEALTH CARE SYSTEM**, 385 Tremont Avenue, Zip 07018–1095; tel. 973/676–1000, (Includes EAST ORANGE DIVISION, 385 Tremont Avenue, East Orange, NJ, Zip 07018–1095; tel. 973/676–1000; LYONS DIVISION, 151 Knollcroft Road, Lyons, NJ, Zip 07939–9998; tel. 908/647–0180) (Total facility includes 270 beds in nursing home–type unit) **A**1 2 5 **F**3 4 5 11 15 18 20 29 30 31 34 35 38 39 40 45 46 50 53 54 56 57 58 59 60 61 62 64 68 70 71 74 75 77 78 79 81 82 83 84 85 86 87 91 92 93 94 96 97 98 100 101 102 104 105 106 107 111 114 119 120 123 128 129 130 132 133 135 143 147 148 152 **P**6 **S** Department of Veterans Affairs, Perry Point, MD
Primary Contact: Vincent F. Immiti, FACHE, Director
CFO: Tyrone Taylor, Chief Financial Officer
CMO: Steven L Lieberman, M.D., Chief of Staff
CIO: Kamesha Scarlett, Chief Information Resource Management
CHR: Nancy Hamilton, Chief Human and Learning Resources
CNO: Patrick J Troy, R.N., MSN, Associate Director Patient Care Services
Web address: www.newjersey.va.gov/
Control: Veterans Affairs, Government, federal **Service**: General medical and surgical

Staffed Beds: 429 **Admissions:** 5907 **Census:** 489 **Outpatient Visits:** 17904 **Births:** 0 **Total Expense ($000):** 568051 **Payroll Expense ($000):** 301946 **Personnel:** 3065

EDISON—Middlesex County

★ △ **HACKENSACK MERIDIAN HEALTH JFK JOHNSON REHABILITATION INSTITUTE**, 65 James Street, Zip 8818; tel. 732/321–7050, **A**7 **F**3 9 28 29 30 35 36 44 50 53 54 64 82 87 90 91 92 93 94 96 130 131 132 143 149 150 **P**6 **S** JFK Health, Edison, NJ
Primary Contact: Anthony Cuzzola, Vice President and Administrator
COO: Scott Gebhard, Chief Operating Officer
CFO: Richard C. Smith, Chief Financial Officer
CMO: William F. Oser, M.D., Chief Medical Officer
CIO: Neal Ganguly, Chief Information Officer
CNO: James Lindquist, Chief Nursing Officer
Web address: www.njrehab.org
Control: Other not–for–profit (including NFP Corporation) **Service**: Rehabilitation

Staffed Beds: 94 **Admissions:** 1877 **Census:** 77 **Outpatient Visits:** 147263 **Births:** 0 **Total Expense ($000):** 74233 **Payroll Expense ($000):** 48929 **Personnel:** 538

☒ **HACKENSACK MERIDIAN HEALTH JFK MEDICAL CENTER (310108)**, 65 James Street, Zip 8818; tel. 732/321–7000, **A**1 2 3 10 **F**2 3 5 7 8 11 12 13 14 15 17 18 20 22 26 28 29 30 31 34 35 36 37 38 39 40 41 44 45 47 49 50 51 53 54 56 57 58 59 60 61 63 64 66 69 70 71 73 74 75 76 77 78 79 80 81 82 84 85 86 87 89 90 91 92 93 94 96 97 100 101 102 104 107 108 109 110 111 113 114 115 116 117 118 119 120 121 123 124 126 129 130 131 132 135 141 143 144 145 146 147 148 149 153 154 **P**6 7 **S** JFK Health, Edison, NJ
Primary Contact: Raymond F Fredericks, President and Chief Executive Officer
COO: Scott Gebhard, Executive VP and Chief Operating Officer
CFO: Richard C. Smith, Senior Vice President and Chief Financial Officer
CMO: William F. Oser, M.D., Senior Vice President and Chief Medical Officer
CIO: Indranil Ganguly, Vice President and Chief Information Officer
CHR: Shirley Higgins Bowers, Senior Vice President Human Resources
CNO: James Lindquist, Chief Nursing Officer
Web address: www.jfkmc.org
Control: Other not–for–profit (including NFP Corporation) **Service**: General medical and surgical

Staffed Beds: 388 **Admissions:** 18083 **Census:** 249 **Outpatient Visits:** 288608 **Births:** 2255 **Total Expense ($000):** 441530 **Payroll Expense ($000):** 205533 **Personnel:** 3191

ELIZABETH—Union County

CAREONE AT TRINITAS REGIONAL MEDICAL CENTER, 225 Williamson Street, Zip 07202–3625; tel. 908/994–5288, (Nonreporting)
Primary Contact: Sharon Bready, R.N., Chief Executive Officer
Web address: www.care-one.com/locations/ltach-careone-at-trinitas-regional-medical-center/
Control: Other not–for–profit (including NFP Corporation) **Service**: Acute long–term care hospital

Staffed Beds: 25

☒ **TRINITAS REGIONAL MEDICAL CENTER (310027)**, 225 Williamson Street, Zip 07202–3625; tel. 908/994–5000, (Includes TRINITAS HOSPITAL, 225 Williamson Street, Elizabeth, NJ, Zip 7207; tel. 908/994–5000; Gary S Horan, FACHE, President and Chief Executive Officer; TRINITAS REGIONAL MEDICAL CENTER – NEW POINT CAMPUS, 655 East Jersey Street, Elizabeth, NJ, Zip 7206; tel. 908/994–5000; Gary S Horan, FACHE, President and Chief Executive Officer) (Total facility includes 124 beds in nursing home–type unit) **A**1 2 3 5 10 13 **F**3 5 7 8 11 13 15 17 18 20 22 28 29 30 31 32 34 35 36 38 40 44 45 46 48 49 53 55 56 57 58 59 60 61 64 65 66 68 70 73 74 75 77 78 79 81 82 84 85 86 87 91 93 97 98 99 100 101 102 103 104 105 106 107 108 110 111 115 117 118 119 120 121 123 124 126 128 129 130 132 134 135 141 143 146 147 148 149 153 154 **P**6
Primary Contact: Gary S. Horan, FACHE, President and Chief Executive Officer
CFO: Karen Lumpp, Senior Vice President and Chief Financial Officer
CMO: William McHugh, M.D., Medical Director and Chief Medical Officer
CIO: Judy Comitto, Vice President Information Services and Chief Information Officer
CHR: Glenn Nacion, Vice President Human Resources
CNO: Mary McTigue, Vice President Patient Care Services and Chief Nursing Officer
Web address: www.trinitasrmc.com
Control: Other not–for–profit (including NFP Corporation) **Service**: General medical and surgical

Staffed Beds: 464 **Admissions:** 13390 **Census:** 360 **Outpatient Visits:** 428487 **Births:** 1665 **Total Expense ($000):** 291643 **Payroll Expense ($000):** 137453 **Personnel:** 2240

ELMER—Salem County

★ ⇑ **INSPIRA MEDICAL CENTER–ELMER (310069)**, 501 West Front Street, Zip 08318–2101; tel. 856/363–1000, **A**10 21 **F**3 7 8 11 12 13 15 18 20 22 28 29 30 34 37 38 40 44 50 57 59 64 68 70 74 75 76 77 78 79 81 82 85 86 87 93 107 108 110 111 114 115 116 117 118 119 120 121 123 124 126 130 131 132 134 146 147 148 154 **S** Inspira Health Network, Mullica Hill, NJ
Primary Contact: John A. DiAngelo, President and Chief Executive Officer
COO: David Yhlen, Chief Operating Officer
CFO: Thomas Baldosaro, Chief Financial Officer
CMO: Steven C Linn, M.D., Chief Medical Officer
CIO: Thomas Pacek, Vice President Information Systems and Chief Information Officer
CHR: Erich Florentine, Chief People Officer
CNO: Elizabeth Sheridan, Chief Operating Officer and Chief Nursing Executive
Web address: www.inspirahealthnetwork.org/?id=5281&sid=1
Control: Other not–for–profit (including NFP Corporation) **Service**: General medical and surgical

Staffed Beds: 96 **Admissions:** 3119 **Census:** 32 **Outpatient Visits:** 71315 **Births:** 281 **Total Expense ($000):** 63186 **Payroll Expense ($000):** 27690 **Personnel:** 281

Many Facility Codes have changed. Please refer to the AHA Guide Code Chart.

ENGLEWOOD—Bergen County

☒ **ENGLEWOOD HOSPITAL AND MEDICAL CENTER (310045)**, 350 Engle Street, Zip 07631–1898; tel. 201/894–3000, **A**1 2 3 5 10 **F**3 5 6 7 8 9 11 12 13 15 17 18 19 20 22 24 26 28 29 30 31 32 34 35 36 37 38 39 40 41 44 45 46 47 48 49 50 51 53 54 55 56 57 58 59 60 61 62 63 64 65 68 70 72 73 74 75 76 77 78 79 80 81 82 83 84 85 86 87 89 91 92 93 94 96 97 98 100 101 102 103 104 107 108 110 111 114 115 116 117 118 119 120 121 123 124 126 129 130 131 132 133 134 135 143 144 145 146 147 148 149 150 154 **P**3 5 6
Primary Contact: Warren Geller, President and Chief Executive Officer
CFO: Anthony T Orlando, Senior Vice President Finance
CMO: Michael Harris, M.D., Chief Medical Officer
CHR: Patricia Wilson, Senior Vice President Human Resources
CNO: MaryAnn Donohue–Ryan, Ph.D., Vice President Patient Care Services
Web address: www.englewoodhealth.org
Control: Other not–for–profit (including NFP Corporation) **Service**: General medical and surgical

Staffed Beds: 271 Admissions: 15092 Census: 199 Outpatient Visits: 1243830 Births: 2690 Total Expense ($000): 597373 Payroll Expense ($000): 153958 Personnel: 2332

FLEMINGTON—Hunterdon County

☒ **HUNTERDON MEDICAL CENTER (310005)**, 2100 Wescott Drive, Zip 08822–4604; tel. 908/788–6100, **A**1 2 3 5 10 13 **F**3 5 8 11 12 13 14 15 17 18 20 22 28 29 30 31 32 34 35 38 40 45 46 47 48 49 53 54 55 56 57 58 59 60 61 62 63 65 66 68 70 71 73 74 75 76 77 78 79 81 82 83 84 85 86 87 89 91 92 93 94 97 98 99 100 101 102 103 104 105 106 107 108 110 114 115 118 119 121 123 126 127 129 130 131 132 134 135 144 146 147 148 149 150 153 154
Primary Contact: Robert J. Cody, MD, MBA, Interim President and Chief Executive Officer
COO: Lawrence N Grand, MS, R.N., Chief Operating Officer
CFO: Gail Kosyla, Chief Financial Officer and Senior Vice President Strategy
CMO: Robert Coates, M.D., Vice President, Medical Affairs
CIO: Daniel Morreale, Chief Information Officer
CHR: Violet Kocsis, Chief Human Resources Officer
CNO: Patricia Steingall, MS, R.N., R.N., MS, Vice President, Patient Care Services
Web address: www.hunterdonhealthcare.org
Control: Other not–for–profit (including NFP Corporation) **Service**: General medical and surgical

Staffed Beds: 184 Admissions: 8738 Census: 103 Outpatient Visits: 708478 Births: 936 Total Expense ($000): 305206 Payroll Expense ($000): 151275 Personnel: 2310

FREEHOLD—Monmouth County

☒ **CENTRASTATE HEALTHCARE SYSTEM (310111)**, 901 West Main Street, Zip 07728–2549; tel. 732/431–2000, **A**1 2 3 5 10 **F**3 11 12 13 15 18 19 20 28 29 30 31 32 34 35 36 37 38 40 41 45 46 47 49 56 57 58 59 61 64 65 66 70 73 74 75 76 77 78 79 81 82 84 86 87 89 92 93 97 98 100 101 102 107 108 110 114 118 119 120 121 123 124 126 129 130 131 132 134 135 146 147 148 149 154 **P**1 6
Primary Contact: John Gribbin, FACHE, President and Chief Executive Officer
COO: Thomas W. Scott, Senior Vice President and Chief Operating Officer
CFO: John Dellocono, Senior Vice President and Chief Financial Officer
CMO: Jack H Dworkin, M.D., Vice President Medical Affairs and Chief Medical Officer
CIO: John Ulett, Vice President and Chief Information Officer
CHR: Fran Keane, Vice President Human Resources
CNO: Linda W Geisler, R.N., FACHE, Vice President Patient Services
Web address: www.centrastate.com
Control: Other not–for–profit (including NFP Corporation) **Service**: General medical and surgical

Staffed Beds: 260 Admissions: 13409 Census: 159 Outpatient Visits: 256550 Births: 956 Total Expense ($000): 274851 Payroll Expense ($000): 110366 Personnel: 1532

HACKENSACK—Bergen County

☒ **HACKENSACK MERIDIAN HEALTH HACKENSACK UNIVERSITY MEDICAL CENTER (310001)**, 30 Prospect Avenue, Zip 07601–1914; tel. 201/996–2000, (Includes THE JOSEPH M. SANZARI CHILDREN'S HOSPITAL, 30 Prospect Avenue, Hackensack, NJ, Zip 07601–1914; tel. 201/996–2000) **A**1 2 3 5 8 10 **F**2 3 4 5 6 7 9 11 12 13 14 15 16 17 18 19 20 22 24 28 29 30 31 32 33 34 35 36 37 38 39 40 41 43 44 45 46 47 48 49 50 51 52 53 54 55 56 57 58 59 60 61 63 64 65 66 68 69 70 71 72 73 74 75 76 77 78 79 80 81 82 84 85 86 87 88 89 90 91 92 93 94 96 97 98 99 100 101 102 103 104 107 108 109 110 111 112 113 114 115 116 117 118 119 120 121 123 124 126 129 130 131 132 134 135 136 138 141 142 143 144 145 146 147 148 149 150 153 154 **P**1 6 7 **S** Hackensack Meridian Health, Edison, NJ
Primary Contact: Ihor S. Sawczuk, M.D., President
CFO: Robert Glenning, Executive Vice President Finance and Chief Financial Officer
CMO: Peter A Gross, M.D., Senior Vice President and Chief Medical Officer
CHR: Nancy R Corcoran, Senior Vice President Human Resources and Quality Service
Web address: www.hackensackumc.org
Control: Other not–for–profit (including NFP Corporation) **Service**: General medical and surgical

Staffed Beds: 737 Admissions: 74912 Census: 584 Outpatient Visits: 511449 Births: 6321 Total Expense ($000): 1529809 Payroll Expense ($000): 579310 Personnel: 7592

HACKETTSTOWN—Warren County

☒ **HACKETTSTOWN MEDICAL CENTER (310115)**, 651 Willow Grove Street, Zip 07840–1799; tel. 908/852–5100, **A**1 10 **F**3 5 7 11 12 15 18 28 29 30 31 34 35 36 38 39 40 41 44 45 46 47 49 51 53 54 56 57 59 60 61 62 63 64 65 68 70 74 75 77 78 79 81 82 84 85 86 87 91 93 94 97 100 101 102 104 107 108 110 111 114 116 117 118 119 120 129 130 131 132 135 141 143 146 147 148 149 150 154 **P**3 5 6 **S** Atlantic Health System, Morristown, NJ
Primary Contact: Joseph DiPaolo, FACHE, MBA, President
COO: Donna Watridge, R.N., Director of Operations
CFO: Robert Peterson, CPA, Chief Financial Officer
CMO: Paul Owens, M.D., Chief Medical Officer
CIO: Dorothy Cox, Manager Information Systems
CHR: Kimberly McGovern, Manager Human Resources
CNO: Donna Watridge, R.N., Chief Nursing Officer
Web address: www.atlantichealth.org
Control: Other not–for–profit (including NFP Corporation) **Service**: General medical and surgical

Staffed Beds: 80 Admissions: 3093 Census: 34 Outpatient Visits: 53897 Births: 0 Total Expense ($000): 75402 Payroll Expense ($000): 34123 Personnel: 564

HAMILTON—Mercer County

☒ **ROBERT WOOD JOHNSON UNIVERSITY HOSPITAL AT HAMILTON (310110)**, One Hamilton Health Place, Zip 08690–3599; tel. 609/586–7900, **A**1 2 5 10 **F**11 15 18 20 22 28 29 30 31 34 35 37 40 41 45 46 47 48 49 51 53 54 57 59 64 66 68 70 74 75 77 78 79 81 82 85 87 92 93 94 95 96 97 107 108 110 111 114 115 116 119 121 124 126 129 130 131 144 145 146 147 148 149 **P**5 6 **S** RWJBarnabas Health, West Orange, NJ
Primary Contact: Richard Freeman, President and Chief Executive Officer
COO: Barbara H Smith, Senior Vice President & Chief Operating Officer
CMO: Ronald Ryder, D.O., President of the Medical Staff
CIO: L. Gill Gottle, Senior Vice President and Chief Financial Officer
CNO: Lisa Breza, R.N., Vice President and Chief Nursing Officer
Web address: www.rwjhamilton.org
Control: Other not–for–profit (including NFP Corporation) **Service**: General medical and surgical

Staffed Beds: 164 Admissions: 7994 Census: 104 Outpatient Visits: 135714 Births: 0 Total Expense ($000): 180924 Payroll Expense ($000): 64603 Personnel: 1064

HAMMONTON—Camden County

☐ **ANCORA PSYCHIATRIC HOSPITAL (314005)**, 301 Spring Garden Road, Zip 08037–9699; tel. 609/561–1700, **A**1 3 10 **F**30 39 56 68 75 87 97 98 103 130 135 143 149 154 **P**6 **S** Division of Mental Health and Addiction Services, Department of Human Services, State of New Jersey, Trenton, NJ
Primary Contact: Christopher Morrison, Chief Executive Officer
CFO: John Holmes, Business Manager
CIO: Charlene Ruberti, Director Information Technology Development
CHR: Alfred Filipini, Manager Human Resources
Web address: www.state.nj.us/humanservices/dmhs/oshm/aph/
Control: State, Government, nonfederal **Service**: Psychiatric

Staffed Beds: 449 Admissions: 564 Census: 397 Outpatient Visits: 0 Births: 0

NJ

HOBOKEN—Hudson County

☐ **CAREPOINT HEALTH HOBOKEN UNIVERSITY MEDICAL CENTER (310040)**, 308 Willow Avenue, Zip 07030–3889; tel. 201/418–1000, **A**1 3 5 10 **F**15 29 30 31 34 38 40 41 43 46 49 54 57 59 60 61 64 65 66 68 69 71 74 75 76 77 78 79 81 82 84 85 86 87 89 93 97 101 102 104 105 107 110 111 114 115 119 129 130 132 143 146 147 148 149 153 154 **P**3 7 **S** CarePoint Health, Jersey City, NJ
Primary Contact: Ann P. Logan, R.N., Ph.D., Chief Operating Officer
COO: Ann P. Logan, R.N., Ph.D., Chief Operating Officer
CMO: Meika Roberson, M.D., Chief Medical Officer
CIO: Joel Taylor, Chief Information Officer
CHR: Roberto Gonzalez, Executive Director Human Resources
CNO: Neena S. Philip, R.N., Assistant Vice President Nursing
Web address: www.hobokenumc.com
Control: Partnership, Investor–owned (for–profit) **Service:** General medical and surgical

Staffed Beds: 228 Admissions: 8325 Census: 110 Births: 1049

HOLMDEL—Monmouth County

✠ **HACKENSACK MERIDIAN HEALTH BAYSHORE COMMUNITY HOSPITAL (310112)**, 727 North Beers Street, Zip 07733–1598; tel. 732/739–5900, **A**1 2 10 **F**3 11 12 15 18 20 22 28 29 30 31 32 34 35 36 38 39 40 41 44 45 46 49 50 51 54 55 56 57 58 59 60 61 63 64 65 66 68 69 70 71 74 75 77 78 79 80 81 82 84 85 86 87 92 93 94 96 97 100 101 102 103 107 108 110 111 114 116 117 118 119 129 130 131 132 134 135 141 144 146 147 148 149 150 154 **S** Hackensack Meridian Health, Edison, NJ
Primary Contact: Timothy J. Hogan, FACHE, President, RMC and BMC
CFO: Joseph M Lemaire, Executive Vice President Finance and Partner Company Operations
CMO: Ian Leber, M.D., Chief Medical Officer
CIO: Rebecca Weber, Senior Vice President and Chief Information Officer
CHR: Sherrie String, Senior Vice President Human Resources
CNO: Linda Walsh, R.N., MSN, Vice President Chief Nursing Executive
Web address: www.bchs.com
Control: Other not–for–profit (including NFP Corporation) **Service:** General medical and surgical

Staffed Beds: 160 Admissions: 17045 Census: 112 Outpatient Visits: 82790 Births: 0 Total Expense ($000): 149997 Payroll Expense ($000): 65640 Personnel: 952

JERSEY CITY—Hudson County

☐ **CAREPOINT HEALTH CHRIST HOSPITAL (310016)**, 176 Palisade Avenue, Zip 07306–1196, Mailing Address: 176 Palisades Avenue, Zip 07306–1196; tel. 201/795–8200, (Nonreporting) **A**1 3 10 12 13 **S** CarePoint Health, Jersey City, NJ
Primary Contact: Marie Theresa Duffy, Chief Operating Officer
COO: Marie Theresa Duffy, Chief Operating Officer
CFO: Gary Bryant, Executive Vice President and Chief Financial Officer
CMO: William Holubek, M.D., Chief Medical Officer
CHR: Josiane Deroncerey, Director Human Resources
CNO: Denise Cimmino, MSN, R.N., Assistant Vice President, Nursing and Patient Care Services
Web address: www.carepointhealth.org
Control: Other not–for–profit (including NFP Corporation) **Service:** General medical and surgical

Staffed Beds: 376

★ ⇑ **JERSEY CITY MEDICAL CENTER (310074)**, 355 Grand Street, Zip 07302–4321; tel. 201/915–2000, **A**3 5 10 13 21 **F**3 5 7 8 11 13 15 17 18 20 22 24 26 29 30 31 34 35 38 39 40 41 43 45 46 47 48 49 50 54 55 56 57 59 60 61 64 65 66 68 70 71 72 73 74 75 76 77 78 79 81 84 85 87 89 91 92 93 96 98 100 101 102 104 107 108 110 111 112 114 115 119 130 132 143 146 147 148 149 154 **P**6 **S** RWJBarnabas Health, West Orange, NJ
Primary Contact: Joseph F. Scott, FACHE, President and Chief Executive Officer
COO: Michael Prilutsky, Chief Operating Officer
CFO: Paul R Goldberg, Chief Financial Officer
CMO: Kenneth Garay, M.D., Chief Medical Officer
CIO: Stephen Li, Vice President Management Information Systems
CHR: Mary Cataudella, Corporate Director Human Resources
CNO: Joanne Reich, R.N., Chief Nursing Officer
Web address: www.barnabashealth.org/Jersey–City–Medical–Center.aspx
Control: Other not–for–profit (including NFP Corporation) **Service:** General medical and surgical

Staffed Beds: 316 Admissions: 14915 Census: 220 Outpatient Visits: 244192 Births: 2110 Total Expense ($000): 375640 Payroll Expense ($000): 169592 Personnel: 2301

LAKEWOOD—Ocean County

✠ **MONMOUTH MEDICAL CENTER, SOUTHERN CAMPUS (310084)**, 600 River Avenue, Zip 08701–5237; tel. 732/363–1900, **A**1 2 10 **F**3 15 18 28 29 30 31 34 35 36 38 40 41 44 50 56 57 58 59 60 61 64 68 70 74 75 77 78 79 81 82 85 86 87 93 98 100 101 102 103 107 108 110 111 117 119 130 131 132 134 146 148 149 154 **P**6 **S** RWJBarnabas Health, West Orange, NJ
Primary Contact: Frank J. Vozos, M.D., FACS, Chief Executive Officer, MMC Southern Campus
CFO: Joanna Zimmerman, Regional Chief Financial Officer
CMO: Rajesh Mohan, M.D., Chief Medical Officer
CIO: Ray Duarte, Director, Information Technology and Services
CHR: Richard Kiernan, Regional Chief Human Resources Officer
CNO: Judy Colorado, R.N., Chief Nursing Officer
Web address: www.rwjbarnabashealth.org/monmouth–medical–center–southern–campus.aspx
Control: Other not–for–profit (including NFP Corporation) **Service:** General medical and surgical

Staffed Beds: 124 Admissions: 5845 Census: 94 Outpatient Visits: 77967 Births: 0 Total Expense ($000): 109601 Payroll Expense ($000): 46132 Personnel: 613

☐ **SPECIALTY HOSPITAL OF CENTRAL JERSEY (312017)**, 600 River Avenue, 4 and 5 West, Zip 08701–5237; tel. 732/942–3588, (Nonreporting) **A**1 10
Primary Contact: Violeta Peters, RN, MA, LNHA, Chief Executive Officer
CFO: Kristin Prentiss, Chief Financial Officer
CMO: Howard Lebowitz, M.D., Chief Medical Officer
CHR: Mary Pat Napolitano, Director Human Resources
CNO: Judy Boccellato, R.N., MSN, Chief Nursing Officer
Web address: www.acutecarehs.com
Control: Corporation, Investor–owned (for–profit) **Service:** Acute long–term care hospital

Staffed Beds: 50

LAWRENCEVILLE—Mercer County

✠ **ST. LAWRENCE REHABILITATION CENTER (313027)**, 2381 Lawrenceville Road, Zip 08648–2025; tel. 609/896–9500, (Total facility includes 56 beds in nursing home–type unit) **A**1 10 **F**34 57 64 90 91 93 96 104 108 119 128 130 132 135 143 146 148 149 154
Primary Contact: Darlene S. Hanley, R.N., President and Chief Executive Officer
COO: Shirley Pukala, R.N., Assistant Administrator Operations
CFO: Thomas W Boyle, Chief Financial Officer
CMO: Kevin McGuigan, M.D., Medical Director
CIO: Joseph Castronuevo, Director Information Management
CHR: John Levi, Director Human Resources
CNO: Hsiu–chin Brix, R.N., Director of Nursing
Web address: www.slrc.org
Control: Church operated, Nongovernment, not–for–profit **Service:** Rehabilitation

Staffed Beds: 116 Admissions: 2156 Census: 88 Outpatient Visits: 22833 Births: 0 Total Expense ($000): 36095 Payroll Expense ($000): 20293 Personnel: 315

LIVINGSTON—Essex County

✠ **SAINT BARNABAS MEDICAL CENTER (310076)**, 94 Old Short Hills Rd, Zip 07039–5672; tel. 973/322–5000, **A**1 2 3 5 8 10 13 **F**3 7 8 11 12 13 16 17 18 19 20 22 24 26 28 29 30 31 32 34 35 36 37 38 39 40 41 44 45 46 47 48 49 50 53 54 55 56 57 59 60 61 64 65 66 68 69 70 71 72 73 74 75 76 77 78 79 81 82 84 85 86 87 88 89 91 92 93 94 96 97 100 102 107 108 111 114 115 118 119 120 121 123 124 126 129 130 131 132 134 135 138 141 142 143 144 146 147 148 149 154 **P**3 6 **S** RWJBarnabas Health, West Orange, NJ
Primary Contact: Stephen P. Zieniewicz, FACHE, President and Chief Executive Officer
COO: Patrick Ahearn, Chief Operating Officer and Senior Vice President
CFO: Richard Davis, Chief Financial Officer
CMO: Gregory Rokosz, D.O., Senior Vice President Medical and Academic Affairs
CIO: Michael McTigue, Chief Information Officer
CHR: Arnold D Manzo, Vice President Human Resources
CNO: Jennifer A O'Neill, R.N., Chief Nursing Officer, Vice President Patient Care Services
Web address: www.barnabashealth.org/hospitals/saint_barnabas/index.html
Control: Other not–for–profit (including NFP Corporation) **Service:** General medical and surgical

Staffed Beds: 553 Admissions: 28776 Census: 414 Outpatient Visits: 340787 Births: 5888 Total Expense ($000): 723763 Payroll Expense ($000): 261403 Personnel: 3373

NJ

Many Facility Codes have changed. Please refer to the AHA Guide Code Chart. © 2018 AHA Guide

LONG BRANCH—Monmouth County

✶ **MONMOUTH MEDICAL CENTER, LONG BRANCH CAMPUS (310075)**, 300
Second Avenue, Zip 07740–6303; tel. 732/222–5200, (Includes CHILDREN'S
HOSPITAL AT MONMOUTH MEDICAL CENTER, 300 Second Avenue, Long Branch,
NJ, Zip 07740–6303; tel. 732/222–5200) **A**1 2 3 5 8 10 **F**3 8 9 11 12 13 14
15 17 18 20 22 28 29 30 31 34 35 37 38 39 40 41 43 44 45 46 47 48 49 50
51 53 54 55 56 57 58 59 60 61 63 64 66 68 69 70 72 73 74 75 76 77 78 79
81 82 84 85 86 87 88 89 96 97 98 99 100 101 102 104 105 107 108 109
110 111 114 115 116 117 118 119 120 121 123 124 126 129 130 131 132
135 141 143 145 146 147 148 149 153 154 **P**3 6 **S** RWJBarnabas Health, West
Orange, NJ
Primary Contact: Bill Arnold, President and Chief Executive Officer
CMO: Eric Burkett, M.D., Vice President Medical Affairs
CIO: Chris Butler, Chief Information Officer
CHR: Richard Kiernan, Vice President Human Resources
CNO: Diann Johnston, R.N., MSN, Vice President of Patient Care Services
Web address: www.barnabashealth.org/hospitals/monmouth_medical/index.html
Control: Other not–for–profit (including NFP Corporation) **Service:** General
medical and surgical

Staffed Beds: 296 Admissions: 17604 Census: 204 Outpatient Visits:
230050 **Births:** 5426 **Total Expense ($000):** 365938 **Payroll Expense**
($000): 140161 **Personnel:** 1818

LYONS—Somerset County

LYONS DIVISION See Veterans Affairs New Jersey Health Care System, East
Orange

MANAHAWKIN—Ocean County

✶ **HACKENSACK MERIDIAN HEALTH SOUTHERN OCEAN MEDICAL CENTER**
(310113), 1140 Route 72 West, Zip 08050–2499; tel. 609/597–6011, (Total
facility includes 20 beds in nursing home–type unit) **A**1 2 10 **F**3 11 12 13 15 18
20 28 29 30 31 32 34 35 38 39 40 41 44 45 46 48 49 50 51 54 55 56 57
58 59 60 61 63 64 65 66 68 70 71 74 75 76 77 78 79 80 81 82 84 85 86 87
92 93 94 96 97 100 101 102 103 107 108 110 111 114 115 116 117 118
119 120 121 123 128 129 130 131 132 134 135 141 144 145 146 147 148
149 154 **S** Hackensack Meridian Health, Edison, NJ
Primary Contact: Regina Foley, R.N., FACHE, Chief Operating Officer
CFO: Joseph M Lemaire, Executive Vice President
CMO: Theodore Zaleski, M.D., Vice President Clinical Effectiveness
CIO: Rebecca Weber, Senior Vice President and Chief Information Officer
CHR: Susan Tillman–Taylor, Manager Human Resources
CNO: Donna Ciufo, R.N., Vice President and Chief Nurse Executive
Web address: www.soch.com
Control: Other not–for–profit (including NFP Corporation) **Service:** General
medical and surgical

Staffed Beds: 172 Admissions: 16420 Census: 91 Outpatient Visits:
115353 **Births:** 359 **Total Expense ($000):** 177794 **Payroll Expense**
($000): 69253 **Personnel:** 952

MARLTON—Burlington County

✶ △ **KESSLER MARLTON REHABILITATION (313032)**, 92 Brick Road,
Zip 08053–2177; tel. 856/988–8778, **A**1 7 10 **F**3 29 50 65 85 90 130 132 **P**8
S Select Medical Corporation, Mechanicsburg, PA
Primary Contact: Phyllis J. Schlichtmann, BSN, RN, MBA, Chief Executive Officer
CFO: Stuart Moss, Chief Financial Officer
CMO: Kenneth Wu, M.D., Medical Director
CHR: Joanne Cernava, Director Human Resources
CNO: Chris Kreeley, Director Nursing
Web address: www.marltonrehab.com
Control: Corporation, Investor–owned (for–profit) **Service:** Rehabilitation

Staffed Beds: 61 Admissions: 1532 Census: 54 Outpatient Visits: 11130
Births: 0 **Total Expense ($000):** 20646 **Payroll Expense ($000):** 12052
Personnel: 162

✶ **VIRTUA MARLTON**, 90 Brick Road, Zip 08053–2177; tel. 856/355–6000, **A**1
2 5 **F**3 12 18 20 22 29 30 31 40 45 46 47 49 56 60 64 70 75 77 78 79 81
82 84 85 87 91 92 107 108 111 114 115 118 119 130 141 146 149 **S** Virtua
Health, Marlton, NJ
Primary Contact: Lisa Ferraro, Senior Vice President and Chief Operating Officer
COO: Lisa Ferraro, Senior Vice President and Chief Operating Officer
CFO: Robert Segin, Executive Vice President & Chief Financial Officer
CMO: John Matsinger, D.O., Chief Medical Officer
CIO: Thomas Gordon, Chief Information Officer
CHR: Rhonda R Jordan, Chief Human Resources Officer
CNO: Tracy Carlino, R.N., Chief Nursing Officer
Web address: www.virtua.org
Control: Other not–for–profit (including NFP Corporation) **Service:** General
medical and surgical

Staffed Beds: 187 Admissions: 7391 Census: 96 Outpatient Visits: 48120
Births: 0 **Total Expense ($000):** 155578 **Payroll Expense ($000):** 50413
Personnel: 576

☐ **WEISMAN CHILDREN'S REHABILITATION HOSPITAL (313302)**, 92 Brick Road
3rd Floor, Zip 08053–2177; tel. 856/489–4520, (Nonreporting) **A**1 10
Primary Contact: Kathy Hall–Olsen, MA, Administrator
COO: Michael Rosiak, Chief Operating Officer
CMO: Connie Domingo, M.D., Medical Director
CIO: Darren Pedersen, Coordinator Information Technology
CHR: Jill Koerner, Manager Employee Relations
CNO: Daniel William Pfeffer, Chief Nurse Executive
Web address: www.weismanchildrens.com
Control: Corporation, Investor–owned (for–profit) **Service:** Children's rehabilitation

Staffed Beds: 24

MONTCLAIR—Essex County

✶ **HACKENSACK MERIDIAN HEALTH MOUNTAINSIDE MEDICAL CENTER**
(310054), 1 Bay Avenue, Zip 07042–4898; tel. 973/429–6000, **A**1 2 3 5 10 **F**3
5 12 13 15 17 18 20 22 28 29 30 31 32 34 35 38 39 40 44 45 46 47 48 49
50 51 53 54 55 56 57 58 59 60 64 67 68 70 73 74 75 76 77 78 79 80 81
82 84 85 86 87 93 94 96 97 98 100 101 102 103 104 105 107 108 110 111
114 115 116 117 118 119 121 126 129 130 131 132 135 141 146 147 148
149 152 153 154 **P**5 **S** Ardent Health Services, Nashville, TN
Primary Contact: John A. Fromhold, FACHE, President and Chief Executive Officer
CFO: Al Aboud, CPA, Chief Financial Officer
CMO: Valerie Alluson, M.D., Chief Medical Officer
CIO: Max Siu, Chief Information Officer
CNO: Debbie Regen, R.N., Chief Nursing Officer
Web address: www.mountainsidenow.com
Control: Partnership, Investor–owned (for–profit) **Service:** General medical and
surgical

Staffed Beds: 202 Admissions: 12119 Census: 145 Outpatient Visits:
100172 **Births:** 797 **Total Expense ($000):** 203446 **Payroll Expense**
($000): 85941 **Personnel:** 1304

MORRIS PLAINS—Morris County

☐ **GREYSTONE PARK PSYCHIATRIC HOSPITAL (314016)**, 59 Koch Avenue,
Zip 07950–4400; tel. 973/538–1800, **A**1 3 5 10 **F**30 39 98 103 **P**6 **S** Division
of Mental Health and Addiction Services, Department of Human Services, State of
New Jersey, Trenton, NJ
Primary Contact: Tomika Carter, Deputy Chief Executive Officer
COO: Stacey Provenzano, Chief Operating Officer
CFO: Jack Frey, Acting Business Manager
CMO: Cherry Monroy–Miller, M.D., Acting Medical Director
CIO: David Saleem, Director Information Technology
CHR: James Frey Jr Acting Manager Human Resources
Web address: www.state.nj.us/humanservices/dmhs/oshm/gpph/
Control: State, Government, nonfederal **Service:** Psychiatric

Staffed Beds: 468 Admissions: 419 Census: 548 Outpatient Visits: 0
Births: 0 **Total Expense ($000):** 124998 **Payroll Expense ($000):** 95521
Personnel: 1353

NJ

MORRISTOWN—Morris County

✠ **MORRISTOWN MEDICAL CENTER (310015)**, 100 Madison Avenue,
Zip 07960–6136; tel. 973/971–5000, (Includes GORYEB CHILDREN'S HOSPITAL,
100 Madison Avenue, Morristown, NJ, Zip 07960–6136; tel. 973/971–5000)
(Total facility includes 40 beds in nursing home–type unit) **A**1 2 3 5 8 10 13 **F**3 5
6 7 8 9 11 12 13 14 15 17 18 19 20 22 24 26 28 29 30 31 32 33 34 35 36
37 38 39 40 41 43 44 45 46 47 48 49 50 51 52 53 54 55 56 57 58 59 60 61
62 63 64 65 66 68 69 70 71 72 73 74 75 76 77 78 79 81 82 83 84 85 86 87
88 89 90 91 92 93 94 95 96 97 98 100 101 102 103 104 107 108 109 110
111 114 115 116 117 118 119 120 121 123 124 126 128 129 130 131 132
134 135 141 143 144 145 146 147 148 149 150 153 154 **P**2 3 5 6 **S** Atlantic
Health System, Morristown, NJ
Primary Contact: Trish O'Keefe, Ph.D., R.N., President
CFO: Joseph D'Auria, Director Finance
CMO: Louis Brusco, M.D., Chief Medical Officer
CNO: Carol S. Jones, MSN, R.N., Interim Chief Nursing Officer
Web address: www.atlantichealth.org/Morristown/
Control: Other not–for–profit (including NFP Corporation) **Service**: General
medical and surgical

Staffed Beds: 727 **Admissions:** 38840 **Census:** 571 **Outpatient Visits:**
578078 **Births:** 4601 **Total Expense ($000):** 1297643 **Payroll Expense
($000):** 539695 **Personnel:** 6484

MOUNT HOLLY—Burlington County

✠ **VIRTUA MEMORIAL (310057)**, 175 Madison Avenue, Zip 08060–2099;
tel. 609/267–0700, **A**1 3 5 10 **F**3 11 12 13 15 18 20 22 28 29 30 31 40 41
45 46 48 49 60 70 73 74 75 76 77 78 79 81 84 85 86 87 89 92 98 100 102
107 108 110 111 114 115 118 119 120 121 123 126 129 130 143 146 149 **S**
Virtua Health, Marlton, NJ
Primary Contact: John Kirby, Senior Vice President and Chief Operating Officer
COO: John Kirby, Senior Vice President and Chief Financial Officer
CFO: Robert Segin, Chief Financial Officer
CMO: James P Dwyer, D.O., Executive Vice President and Chief Medical Officer
CHR: E D Dunn, Vice President Human Resources
Web address: www.virtua.org
Control: Other not–for–profit (including NFP Corporation) **Service**: General
medical and surgical

Staffed Beds: 334 **Admissions:** 16610 **Census:** 206 **Outpatient Visits:**
172244 **Births:** 2306 **Total Expense ($000):** 302122 **Payroll Expense
($000):** 96432 **Personnel:** 1238

VIRTUA MEMORIAL HOSPITAL BURLINGTON COUNTY See Virtua Memorial

NEPTUNE—Monmouth County

✠ **HACKENSACK MERIDIAN HEALTH JERSEY SHORE UNIVERSITY MEDICAL
CENTER (310073)**, 1945 Route 33, Zip 07754–0397; tel. 732/775–5500,
(Includes K. HOVNANIAN CHILDREN'S HOSPITAL, 1945 State Route 33, Neptune,
NJ, Zip 07753–4859; tel. 800/560–9990) **A**1 2 3 5 8 10 13 **F**3 4 5 9 11 12 13
15 16 17 18 19 20 22 24 26 28 29 30 31 32 34 35 36 37 38 39 40 41 43 44
45 46 47 48 49 50 52 54 55 56 57 58 59 60 61 63 64 65 66 68 70 71 72 73
74 75 76 77 78 79 80 81 82 84 85 86 87 88 89 90 92 93 94 96 97 98 99 100
101 102 103 104 105 107 108 111 114 115 116 117 118 119 120 121 123
126 129 130 131 132 134 135 141 144 145 146 147 148 149 150 152 153
154 **S** Hackensack Meridian Health, Edison, NJ
Primary Contact: Kenneth N. Sable, M.D., President
COO: Robert H Adams, Vice President Operations
CMO: David Kountz, M.D., Senior Vice President Medical Affairs
CIO: Rebecca Weber, Senior Vice President and Chief Information Officer
Web address: www.meridianhealth.com
Control: Other not–for–profit (including NFP Corporation) **Service**: General
medical and surgical

Staffed Beds: 579 **Admissions:** 60295 **Census:** 355 **Outpatient Visits:**
208216 **Births:** 2478 **Total Expense ($000):** 725561 **Payroll Expense
($000):** 270792 **Personnel:** 3651

NEW BRUNSWICK—Middlesex County

☐ **CHILDREN'S SPECIALIZED HOSPITAL (313300)**, 200 Somerset Street,
Zip 08901–1942; tel. 732/258–7000, (Includes CHILDREN'S SPECIALIZED
HOSPITAL, 200 Somerset Street, New Brunswick, NJ, Zip 08901–1942;
tel. 732/258–7134; Warren E. Moore, FACHE, President and Chief Executive
Officer) (Total facility includes 72 beds in nursing home–type unit) **A**1 3 5 10
F29 32 33 54 64 65 74 75 82 90 91 93 94 97 104 130 131 132 146 154 **S**
RWJBarnabas Health, West Orange, NJ
Primary Contact: Warren E. Moore, FACHE, President and Chief Executive Officer
COO: Charles Chianese, Vice President, Chief Operating Officer
CFO: Joseph J Dobosh Jr Vice President and Chief Financial Officer
CMO: Christopher Haines, D.O., Vice President and Chief Medical Officer
CHR: William Dwyer, Vice President and Chief Human Resources Officer
CNO: Bonnie Baloga–Altieri, Ph.D., R.N., Vice President Patient Care Services and
Chief Nursing Officer
Web address: www.childrens-specialized.org
Control: Other not–for–profit (including NFP Corporation) **Service**: Children's
rehabilitation

Staffed Beds: 140 **Admissions:** 586 **Census:** 116 **Outpatient Visits:**
198307 **Births:** 0 **Total Expense ($000):** 135968 **Payroll Expense
($000):** 80039 **Personnel:** 1092

✠ **ROBERT WOOD JOHNSON UNIVERSITY HOSPITAL (310038)**, 1 Robert
Wood Johnson Place, Zip 08901–1928; tel. 732/828–3000, (Includes BRISTOL–
MYERS SQUIBB CHILDREN'S HOSPITAL, One Robert Wood Johnson Place, New
Brunswick, NJ, Zip 8901, Mailing Address: P.O. Box 2601, Zip 08903–2601,
tel. 732/828–3000) **A**1 2 3 5 8 10 **F**3 6 7 8 9 11 12 13 14 15 17 18 19 20 22
24 26 28 29 30 31 32 34 35 36 37 38 39 40 41 43 44 45 46 47 48 49 50 51
52 53 54 55 56 57 58 59 60 61 62 63 64 65 66 68 70 71 72 73 74 75 76 77
78 79 81 82 84 85 86 87 88 89 91 92 93 94 96 97 100 101 102 104 107 108
109 110 111 114 115 116 117 118 119 120 121 122 123 124 126 129 130
131 132 134 135 136 137 138 141 142 143 144 145 146 147 148 149 150
154 **P**5 6 **S** RWJBarnabas Health, West Orange, NJ
Primary Contact: John J. Gantner, President and Chief Executive Officer
COO: Jessie Lee Tucker, Ph.D., III Senior Vice President and Chief Operating Officer
CFO: Brian M Reilly, Chief Financial Officer
CMO: Joshua M Bershad, M.D., Senior Vice President Medical Affairs and Chief
Medical Officer
CIO: Robert G Irwin, Vice President Information Systems
CHR: Martin S Everhart, Senior Vice President Human Resources
CNO: Lori Colineri, R.N., Senior Vice President Nursing and Chief Nursing Officer
Web address: www.rwjuh.edu
Control: Other not–for–profit (including NFP Corporation) **Service**: General
medical and surgical

Staffed Beds: 610 **Admissions:** 29683 **Census:** 476 **Outpatient Visits:**
229592 **Births:** 2576 **Total Expense ($000):** 1006424 **Payroll Expense
($000):** 337128 **Personnel:** 4248

✠ **SAINT PETER'S UNIVERSITY HOSPITAL (310070)**, 254 Easton Avenue,
Zip 08901–1780; tel. 732/745–8600, (Includes THE CHILDREN'S HOSPITAL
AT SAINT PETER'S UNIVERSITY, 254 Easton Avenue, New Brunswick, NJ,
Zip 08901–1766; tel. 732/565–5437) **A**1 2 3 5 8 10 **F**2 3 12 13 15 18 19 20
22 26 27 29 30 31 32 34 35 37 38 39 40 41 44 45 46 47 49 50 51 54 55 56
57 58 59 60 61 63 64 65 66 67 68 70 71 72 73 74 75 76 77 78 79 81 82 83
84 85 86 87 88 89 91 92 93 94 96 97 100 101 102 104 105 107 108 110
111 113 114 115 118 119 120 121 123 124 126 129 130 131 132 134 135
143 145 146 147 148 149 150 153 154 **P**6
Primary Contact: Leslie D. Hirsch, FACHE, Interim Chief Executive Officer and President
CFO: Garrick J Stoldt, Vice President and Chief Financial Officer
CHR: Susan Ballestero, Vice President and Chief Human Resources Officer
CNO: Elizabeth Wise, R.N., MS, Chief Nursing Officer and Vice President, Patient
Care Services
Web address: www.saintpetersuh.com
Control: Church operated, Nongovernment, not–for–profit **Service**: General
medical and surgical

Staffed Beds: 361 **Admissions:** 19021 **Census:** 228 **Outpatient Visits:**
253758 **Births:** 5568 **Total Expense ($000):** 459277 **Payroll Expense
($000):** 220263 **Personnel:** 2415

NEWARK—Essex County

⇑ **COLUMBUS HOSPITAL LTACH (312024)**, 495 North Thirteenth Street,
Zip 07107–1317; tel. 973/587–7777, **A**10 21 **F**1 3 50 68 82 87 90 130 148
149 **P**8
Primary Contact: Peter Callaghan, President and Chief Executive Officer
CFO: Alexey Gololobov, Chief Financial Officer
CHR: Patrice Ricciardi, Director Human Resources
CNO: Arthur Kharonov, Vice President Nursing
Web address: www.columbusltach.org
Control: State, Government, nonfederal **Service**: Acute long–term care hospital

Staffed Beds: 63 **Admissions:** 628 **Census:** 60 **Outpatient Visits:** 0
Births: 0

✠ **NEWARK BETH ISRAEL MEDICAL CENTER (310002)**, 201 Lyons Avenue at
Osborne Terrace, Zip 07112–2027; tel. 973/926–7000, (Includes CHILDREN'S
HOSPITAL OF NEW JERSEY, 201 Lyons Avenue, Newark, NJ, Zip 07112–2027;
tel. 973/926–7000; Darrell K. Terry Sr, M.P.H., FACHE, President and Chief
Executive Officer) **A**1 2 3 5 8 10 12 13 **F**3 15 17 18 19 20 21 22 23 24 25 26
27 28 29 30 31 32 34 35 38 39 40 41 44 45 46 47 48 49 50 51 53 55 56 57
58 59 60 61 64 65 66 68 70 71 72 73 74 75 76 77 78 79 81 82 84 85 86 87
88 89 91 92 93 94 97 98 99 100 101 102 104 107 108 109 110 111 114 115
117 118 119 120 121 123 126 129 130 131 132 137 140 141 143 145 146
147 148 149 153 **P**6 **S** RWJBarnabas Health, West Orange, NJ
Primary Contact: Darrell K. Terry Sr, M.P.H., FACHE, President and Chief Executive
Officer
CFO: Douglas A Zehner, Chief Financial Officer
CMO: Jeremias Murillo, M.D., Chief Medical Officer
CHR: Zach Lipner, Vice President Human Resources
CNO: Mary Fuhro, Chief Nursing Officer
Web address: www.barnabashealth.org/hospitals/newark_beth_israel/index.html
Control: Other not–for–profit (including NFP Corporation) **Service**: General
medical and surgical

Staffed Beds: 333 **Admissions:** 20537 **Census:** 354 **Outpatient Visits:**
298378 **Births:** 3157 **Total Expense ($000):** 583851 **Payroll Expense
($000):** 259790 **Personnel:** 3171

Many Facility Codes have changed. Please refer to the AHA Guide Code Chart.   © 2018 AHA Guide

☒ **SAINT MICHAEL'S MEDICAL CENTER (310096)**, 111 Central Avenue, Zip 07102–1909; tel. 973/877–5350, **A**1 3 5 10 13 **F**3 5 15 17 18 20 22 24 26 29 30 31 34 37 40 45 47 49 50 57 58 59 61 64 66 68 70 71 74 75 77 78 79 81 85 87 97 98 100 107 108 109 110 111 114 115 119 121 122 123 126 129 130 132 143 147 148 149 **S** Prime Healthcare, Ontario, CA
Primary Contact: Robert C. Iannaccone, JD, Chief Executive Officer
COO: Dennis Pettigrew, Chief Operating Officer
CFO: Dennis Pettigrew, Chief Financial Officer
CMO: Joseph DePasquale, M.D., Interim Chief Medical Officer
CIO: Tom Addington, Chief Information Officer
CHR: Dennis W. Sparks, Vice President Human Resources
CNO: Johanna Magner, Interim Chief Nursing Officer
Web address: www.smmcnj.org
Control: Corporation, Investor–owned (for–profit) **Service**: General medical and surgical

Staffed Beds: 162 **Admissions**: 7961 **Census**: 93 **Outpatient Visits**: 94708
Births: 0 **Total Expense ($000)**: 185192 **Payroll Expense ($000)**: 75623
Personnel: 1059

☒ **UNIVERSITY HOSPITAL (310119)**, 150 Bergen Street, Zip 07103–2496; tel. 973/972–4300, **A**1 2 3 5 10 **F**3 7 8 11 15 17 18 19 20 22 24 26 28 29 30 31 34 35 37 38 39 40 41 43 44 45 46 47 49 50 54 55 57 58 59 60 61 64 65 67 68 70 71 72 73 74 75 76 78 79 81 82 84 85 87 88 89 90 92 93 97 98 100 102 104 107 108 110 111 114 118 119 120 121 123 124 126 130 131 132 134 135 139 140 141 142 145 146 147 148 149 150
Primary Contact: John N. Kastanis, FACHE, President and Chief Executive Officer
COO: Nancy Hamstra, Chief Operating Officer
CFO: Thomas M Daly, CPA, Chief Financial Officer
CMO: Suzanne Atkin, M.D., Chief Medical Officer
CIO: Richard Tunnell, Chief Information Officer
CHR: Gerard Garcia, Chief Human Resource Officer
CNO: Carl Kirton, Ph.D., Chief Nursing Officer
Web address: www.uhnj.org
Control: Other not–for–profit (including NFP Corporation) **Service**: General medical and surgical

Staffed Beds: 519 **Admissions**: 15598 **Census**: 279 **Outpatient Visits**: 255043 **Births**: 1183 **Total Expense ($000)**: 655743 **Payroll Expense ($000)**: 317851 **Personnel**: 3401

NEWTON—Sussex County

☒ **NEWTON MEDICAL CENTER (310028)**, 175 High Street, Zip 07860–1004; tel. 973/383–2121, **A**1 2 10 **F**3 5 7 8 9 11 12 13 15 18 19 28 29 30 31 32 34 35 36 38 39 40 41 44 45 46 47 49 50 54 55 56 57 58 59 60 61 62 63 64 65 66 68 69 70 71 73 74 75 76 77 78 79 81 82 84 86 87 91 92 93 94 95 96 97 98 100 101 102 104 105 106 107 108 109 110 111 114 115 118 119 120 130 131 132 134 135 141 143 144 146 147 148 149 150 153 154 **P**3 5 6 **S** Atlantic Health System, Morristown, NJ
Primary Contact: Joseph DiPaolo, FACHE, MBA, President
CFO: Kevin Lenahan, Director Corporate Accounting, Budgets, Grants and Reimbursements
CMO: David Lazarus, M.D., Medical Director Clinical Affairs
CIO: Linda Reed, Vice President Information Systems and Chief Information Officer
CHR: Andrew L Kovach, Vice President Human Resources and Chief Administrative Officer
Web address: www.atlantichealth.org/newton/
Control: Other not–for–profit (including NFP Corporation) **Service**: General medical and surgical

Staffed Beds: 148 **Admissions**: 7997 **Census**: 99 **Outpatient Visits**: 90314
Births: 625 **Total Expense ($000)**: 166893 **Payroll Expense ($000)**: 77091
Personnel: 1099

NORTH BERGEN—Hudson County

☒ **HACKENSACK MERIDIAN HEALTH PALISADES MEDICAL CENTER (310003)**, 7600 River Road, Zip 07047–6217; tel. 201/854–5000, **A**1 3 5 10 12 13 **F**3 7 11 12 13 15 17 18 20 28 29 30 31 34 35 38 40 44 45 46 49 50 56 57 59 60 64 65 68 70 73 74 75 76 77 78 79 80 81 82 84 85 86 87 89 92 93 97 100 101 102 104 107 108 110 111 114 115 119 129 130 132 141 143 145 146 147 148 149 154 **S** Hackensack Meridian Health, Edison, NJ
Primary Contact: Anthony Passannante Jr, M.D., FACC, President
COO: David J Berkowitz, Vice President and Chief Operating Officer
CFO: John Calandriello, Vice President and Chief Financial Officer
CMO: Suresh Raina, M.D., Vice President Medical Staff and Chief Medical Officer
CIO: Albert Porco, Director Management Information Systems
CNO: Ruben D Fernandez, R.N., Vice President and Chief Nursing Officer
Web address: www.palisadesmedical.org
Control: Other not–for–profit (including NFP Corporation) **Service**: General medical and surgical

Staffed Beds: 228 **Admissions**: 15769 **Census**: 109 **Outpatient Visits**: 104690 **Births**: 1276 **Total Expense ($000)**: 176715 **Payroll Expense ($000)**: 85995 **Personnel**: 1157

PARAMUS—Bergen County

☒ **NEW BRIDGE MEDICAL CENTER (310058)**, 230 East Ridgewood Avenue, Zip 07652–4142; tel. 201/967–4000, (Total facility includes 574 beds in nursing home–type unit) **A**1 3 10 **F**4 5 9 15 17 18 29 30 31 34 35 38 40 41 45 46 48 49 50 57 58 59 60 61 64 65 66 68 70 74 77 78 79 81 82 87 92 93 97 98 99 100 101 102 103 104 105 107 108 110 111 115 118 119 128 130 131 132 135 146 147 148 149 152 153 **P**3
Primary Contact: Deborah D. Visconi, President and Chief Executive Officer
COO: Susan Mendelowitz, R.N., FACHE, Executive Vice President and Chief Operating Officer
CFO: Connie Magdangal, Executive Vice President and Chief Financial Officer
CMO: Robert M Harris, M.D., President Medical and Dental Staff
CIO: Ronald Li, Vice President Management Information Systems
CHR: Guy Mennonna, Senior Vice President Human Resources
Web address: www.bergenregional.com
Control: County, Government, nonfederal **Service**: General medical and surgical

Staffed Beds: 1020 **Admissions**: 14335 **Census**: 919 **Outpatient Visits**: 153934 **Births**: 0 **Total Expense ($000)**: 220358 **Payroll Expense ($000)**: 114521 **Personnel**: 1488

PASSAIC—Passaic County

☒ **ST. MARY'S GENERAL HOSPITAL (310006)**, 350 Boulevard, Zip 07055–2840; tel. 973/365–4300, (Nonreporting) **A**1 10 **S** Prime Healthcare, Ontario, CA
Primary Contact: Edward Condit, President and Chief Executive Officer
CFO: Nicholas Lanza, Controller
CMO: Ronald Poblete, M.D., President Medical and Dental Staff
CHR: Cathy Lynch–Kilic, Vice President Human Resources
Web address: www.smh–passaic.org
Control: Other not–for–profit (including NFP Corporation) **Service**: General medical and surgical

Staffed Beds: 287

PATERSON—Passaic County

★ ⇧ **ST. JOSEPH'S UNIVERSITY MEDICAL CENTER (310019)**, 703 Main Street, Zip 07503–2691; tel. 973/754–2000, (Includes ST. JOSEPH'S CHILDREN'S HOSPITAL, 703 Main Street, Paterson, NJ, Zip 07503–2621; tel. 973/754–2500; Kevin J Slavin, FACHE, President and Chief Executive Officer; ST. JOSEPH'S WAYNE HOSPITAL, 224 Hamburg Turnpike, Wayne, NJ, Zip 07470–2100; tel. 973/942–6900; Daniel B Kline, Vice President, Site Administrator) (Total facility includes 151 beds in nursing home–type unit) **A**2 3 5 10 13 21 **F**3 8 11 12 13 15 17 18 19 20 21 22 23 24 25 26 27 28 29 30 31 32 34 35 36 37 38 39 40 41 43 44 45 46 47 48 49 50 51 54 55 56 57 58 59 60 61 62 63 64 65 66 68 70 72 73 74 75 76 77 78 79 81 82 84 85 86 87 88 89 90 92 93 94 96 97 98 100 101 102 103 104 105 106 107 108 110 111 114 115 116 117 118 119 121 123 126 128 129 130 131 132 133 134 135 146 147 148 149 150 153 154 **P**5
Primary Contact: Kevin J. Slavin, FACHE, President and Chief Executive Officer
COO: Lisa Brady, Senior Vice President and Chief Operating Officer
CFO: David Alexander, Senior Vice President and Chief Financial Officer
CMO: James Labagnara, M.D., Vice President Medical Affairs
CIO: Linda Reed, Vice President and Chief Information Officer
CHR: John P Bruno, Senior Vice President Human Resources
CNO: Judy Padula, MSN, R.N., Vice President Patient Care Services and Chief Nursing Officer
Web address: www.stjosephshealth.org
Control: Church operated, Nongovernment, not–for–profit **Service**: General medical and surgical

Staffed Beds: 1031 **Admissions**: 30299 **Census**: 621 **Births**: 3606 **Total Expense ($000)**: 795459 **Payroll Expense ($000)**: 381036

PEAPACK—Somerset County

☐ **MATHENY MEDICAL AND EDUCATIONAL CENTER (312014)**, 65 Highland Avenue, Zip 7977, Mailing Address: P.O. Box 339, Zip 07977–0339; tel. 908/234–0011, (Nonreporting) **A**1 5 10
Primary Contact: Kendell R. Sprott, M.D., JD, Chief Executive Officer
COO: Christopher King, Director Operations and Administrative Services
CFO: Wayne Guberman, Director Finance
CMO: Gary E Eddey, M.D., Medical Director
CIO: Ron Daniel, Manager Information Systems
CHR: Nancy Petrillo, Director Human Resources
Web address: www.matheny.org
Control: Other not–for–profit (including NFP Corporation) **Service**: Acute long–term care hospital

Staffed Beds: 101

NJ

Hospital, Medicare Provider Number, Address, Telephone, Approval, Facility, and Physician Codes, Health Care System

★ American Hospital Association (AHA) membership
☐ The Joint Commission accreditation
○ Healthcare Facilities Accreditation Program
◇ DNV Healthcare Inc. accreditation
⇧ Center for Improvement in Healthcare Quality Accreditation
△ Commission on Accreditation of Rehabilitation Facilities (CARF) accreditation

PENNINGTON—Mercer County

☒ **CAPITAL HEALTH MEDICAL CENTER–HOPEWELL (310044)**, 1 Capital Way, Zip 08534–2520; tel. 609/303–4000, **A**1 2 5 10 **F**3 8 11 12 13 15 18 20 22 28 29 30 31 32 34 35 36 40 41 44 45 46 47 48 49 50 51 52 55 57 58 59 60 61 64 65 68 70 72 73 74 75 76 78 79 81 82 84 85 86 87 89 90 93 96 97 107 108 109 110 111 112 114 115 117 118 119 120 121 123 124 126 129 130 132 135 143 145 146 147 148 **P**6 **S** Capital Health, Trenton, NJ
Primary Contact: Al Maghazehe, Ph.D., FACHE, President and Chief Executive Officer
CFO: Shane Fleming, Chief Financial Officer
CMO: Eugene McMahon, Senior Vice President and Chief Medical Officer
CIO: Eugene Grochala, Vice President Information Systems
CHR: Scott Clemmensen, Vice President Human Resources and Leadership Enhancement
CNO: Deborah Mican, R.N., Chief Nursing Officer
Web address: www.capitalhealth.org
Control: Other not–for–profit (including NFP Corporation) **Service**: General medical and surgical

Staffed Beds: 170 Admissions: 14124 Census: 163 Outpatient Visits: 168729 Births: 3360 Personnel: 1636

PERTH AMBOY—Middlesex County

☐ **CAREONE AT RARITAN BAY MEDICAL CENTER (312018)**, 530 New Brunswick Avenue, Zip 08861–3654; tel. 732/324–6090, (Nonreporting) **A**1 10
Primary Contact: Sharon Bready, R.N., Chief Executive Officer
CFO: Richard Burguillos, Chief Financial Officer
Web address: www.care-one.com
Control: Corporation, Investor–owned (for–profit) **Service**: Acute long–term care hospital

Staffed Beds: 30

☒ **HACKENSACK MERIDIAN HEALTH RARITAN BAY MEDICAL CENTER (310039)**, 530 New Brunswick Avenue, Zip 08861–3654; tel. 732/442–3700, (Includes OLD BRIDGE DIVISION, One Hospital Plaza, Old Bridge, NJ, Zip 8857; tel. 732/360–1000; PERTH AMBOY DIVISION, 530 New Brunswick Avenue, Perth Amboy, NJ, Zip 08861–3685; tel. 732/442–3700) **A**1 3 5 10 **F**3 4 7 8 11 12 13 15 17 18 20 22 29 30 31 32 34 35 36 48 49 54 55 56 57 58 59 60 61 63 64 65 66 68 70 73 74 75 76 77 78 79 80 81 82 84 85 86 87 89 91 92 93 94 96 97 98 99 100 101 102 103 104 107 108 110 111 114 115 116 117 119 126 129 130 131 132 141 143 144 146 147 148 149 150 154 **P**6 **S** Hackensack Meridian Health, Edison, NJ
Primary Contact: Thomas Shanahan, Chief Operating Officer
CFO: Thomas Shanahan, Chief Financial Officer and Senior Vice President
CMO: Michael Ciencewicki, M.D., Vice President Medical Affairs
CHR: Vincent Costantino, Vice President Operations and Human Resources
Web address: www.rbmc.org
Control: Other not–for–profit (including NFP Corporation) **Service**: General medical and surgical

Staffed Beds: 282 Admissions: 25804 Census: 154 Outpatient Visits: 133698 Births: 1121 Total Expense ($000): 240437 Payroll Expense ($000): 120007 Personnel: 1769

PHILLIPSBURG—Warren County

☐ **ST. LUKE'S HOSPITAL – WARREN CAMPUS (310060)**, 185 Roseberry Street, Zip 08865–1690; tel. 908/859–6700, **A**1 2 3 5 10 13 **F**2 3 8 11 15 18 20 28 29 30 31 34 35 39 40 44 45 47 49 50 51 53 54 56 59 60 61 63 64 65 66 70 74 75 77 78 79 81 82 85 86 87 91 92 93 97 100 101 102 104 107 108 110 111 115 118 119 124 129 130 131 132 134 144 146 147 148 149 154 **S** St. Luke's University Health Network, Bethlehem, PA
Primary Contact: Scott R. Wolfe, CPA, President
COO: Alice Wilson, FACHE, Vice President Administration
CMO: Edward Gilkey, M.D., Vice President Medical Affairs
CHR: Morgan G Mahl, Director Human Resources
CNO: Gail Newton, R.N., MSN, Vice President Patient Care Services
Web address: www.slhn.org
Control: Other not–for–profit (including NFP Corporation) **Service**: General medical and surgical

Staffed Beds: 103 Admissions: 4134 Census: 55 Outpatient Visits: 97926 Births: 0 Total Expense ($000): 104013 Payroll Expense ($000): 43852 Personnel: 543

PISCATAWAY—Middlesex County

UNIVERSITY BEHAVIORAL HEALTHCARE (314011), 671 Hoes Lane West, Zip 08854–8021; tel. 732/235–5900, (Nonreporting) **A**3 5 10
Primary Contact: Frank A. Ghinassi, Ph.D., President and Chief Executive Officer
COO: Rosemarie Rosati, Chief Operating Officer
CFO: Alan Weinkrantz, Chief Financial Officer, Finance
CMO: Theresa Miskimen, M.D., Vice President Medical Services
CIO: Adam Levinson, Associate Director, Information Services
CNO: Michele A Miller, R.N., MSN, Vice President, Acute and Nursing Services
Web address: www.ubhc.rutgers.edu
Control: State, Government, nonfederal **Service**: Psychiatric

Staffed Beds: 48

PLAINSBORO—Middlesex County

☒ △ **PENN MEDICINE PRINCETON MEDICAL CENTER (310010)**, One Plainsboro Road, Zip 08536–1913; tel. 609/853–7100, **A**1 2 3 5 7 10 **F**3 4 5 8 11 12 13 14 15 17 18 19 20 22 28 29 30 31 34 35 36 37 38 39 40 41 45 46 47 48 49 50 51 53 54 55 56 57 58 59 60 61 62 63 64 65 66 67 68 70 72 73 74 75 76 77 78 79 80 81 82 83 85 86 87 89 90 91 92 93 96 97 98 99 100 101 102 103 104 105 107 108 110 111 114 115 116 117 118 119 120 121 123 124 126 129 130 131 132 134 135 143 145 146 147 148 152 153 154 **P**6 **S** University of Pennsylvania Health System, Philadelphia, PA
Primary Contact: Barry S. Rabner, President and Chief Executive Officer, Princeton Healthcare System
COO: James Demetriades, Vice President, Operations
CMO: Donald Denny, M.D., Senior Vice President, Medical Affairs
CIO: Anne Searle, Chief Information Officer
CHR: Marcia M Telthorster, M.Ed, Vice President Human Resources
CNO: Barbara Christiano, Vice President, Patient Care Services and Chief Nursing Officer
Web address: www.princetonhcs.org
Control: Other not–for–profit (including NFP Corporation) **Service**: General medical and surgical

Staffed Beds: 355 Admissions: 17907 Census: 264 Outpatient Visits: 222094 Births: 2232 Total Expense ($000): 427732 Payroll Expense ($000): 162579 Personnel: 3247

UNIVERSITY MEDICAL CENTER AT PRINCETON See Penn Medicine Princeton Medical Center, Plainsboro

POMONA—Atlantic County

ATLANTICARE REGIONAL MEDICAL CENTER–MAINLAND DIVISION See Atlanticare Regional Medical Center, Atlantic City

☒ △ **BACHARACH INSTITUTE FOR REHABILITATION (313030)**, 61 West Jimmie Leeds Road, Zip 08240–9102, Mailing Address: P.O. Box 723, Zip 08240–0723; tel. 609/652–7000, (Nonreporting) **A**1 7 10
Primary Contact: Richard J. Kathrins, Ph.D., President and Chief Executive Officer
CFO: Jeanne Vuksta, Chief Financial Officer
CMO: Craig Anmuth, M.D., Medical Director
CIO: Jeff Rees, Director Information Systems
CHR: Diane S Croshaw, Vice President Human Resources
Web address: www.bacharach.org
Control: Other not–for–profit (including NFP Corporation) **Service**: Rehabilitation

Staffed Beds: 80

POMPTON PLAINS—Morris County

☒ **CHILTON MEDICAL CENTER (310017)**, 97 West Parkway, Zip 07444–1696; tel. 973/831–5000, **A**1 2 10 **F**3 7 8 9 11 12 13 15 18 20 22 28 29 30 31 32 34 35 36 38 39 40 41 44 45 46 47 49 50 54 55 56 57 58 59 60 61 62 63 64 65 66 68 70 73 74 75 76 77 78 79 81 82 84 85 86 87 89 93 97 100 101 102 107 108 110 111 114 115 116 117 118 119 120 121 123 124 126 129 130 131 132 134 135 141 143 146 147 148 149 150 154 **P**3 5 6 **S** Atlantic Health System, Morristown, NJ
Primary Contact: Stephanie L Schwartz, FACHE, MA, Vice President AHS and President CMC
CFO: Michael Richetti, Chief Financial Officer
CMO: Charles Ross, M.D., Vice President Medical Affairs
CIO: Karen S Smith, Director Information Services
CHR: Julia McGovern, Vice President Human Resources
Web address: www.chiltonmemorial.org
Control: Other not–for–profit (including NFP Corporation) **Service**: General medical and surgical

Staffed Beds: 131 Admissions: 8379 Census: 107 Outpatient Visits: 110857 Births: 657 Total Expense ($000): 198715 Payroll Expense ($000): 92547 Personnel: 1198

RAHWAY—Union County

KINDRED HOSPITAL NEW JERSEY – RAHWAY See Kindred Hospital–New Jersey Morris County, Dover

NJ

✠ **ROBERT WOOD JOHNSON UNIVERSITY HOSPITAL RAHWAY (310024)**, 865 Stone Street, Zip 07065–2797; tel. 732/381–4200, **A**1 10 **F**3 11 12 15 17 20 29 30 31 34 35 38 40 44 46 47 49 53 56 57 59 64 65 68 70 74 75 77 78 79 81 86 87 93 97 100 101 102 107 108 111 117 118 119 129 130 132 134 143 146 147 148 149 **P**5 **S** RWJBarnabas Health, West Orange, NJ
Primary Contact: Kirk C. Tice, President and Chief Executive Officer
CFO: Peter Bihuniak, Vice President Finance
CMO: Juan Baez, M.D., President Medical Staff
CIO: Denine Izzi, Senior Director Information Technology
CHR: Barbara M Mullery, Vice President Administration
CNO: Ann Marie Shears, Vice President Patient Care Services
Web address: www.rwjuhr.com
Control: Other not–for–profit (including NFP Corporation) **Service**: General medical and surgical

Staffed Beds: 106 **Admissions**: 4801 **Census**: 67 **Outpatient Visits**: 70505 **Births**: 0 **Total Expense ($000)**: 108342 **Payroll Expense ($000)**: 46412 **Personnel**: 643

RED BANK—Monmouth County

✠ △ **HACKENSACK MERIDIAN HEALTH RIVERVIEW MEDICAL CENTER (310034)**, 1 Riverview Plaza, Zip 07701–1864; tel. 732/741–2700, **A**1 2 7 10 **F**3 4 5 9 11 13 15 17 18 20 22 28 29 30 31 32 34 35 36 37 38 39 40 41 44 45 46 47 49 50 51 54 55 56 57 58 59 60 61 63 64 65 66 68 70 71 73 74 75 76 77 78 79 80 81 82 84 85 86 87 90 91 92 93 94 96 97 98 99 100 101 102 103 104 105 107 108 110 111 114 115 116 117 118 119 120 121 123 124 126 130 131 132 134 135 141 144 145 146 147 148 149 150 152 153 154 **S** Hackensack Meridian Health, Edison, NJ
Primary Contact: Timothy J. Hogan, FACHE, President, RMC and BMC
COO: Kelly O'Brien, Chief Operating Officer
CFO: Joseph M Lemaire, Executive Vice President Finance
CMO: Joseph Reichman, M.D., Vice President Medical Affairs and Clinical Effectiveness
CIO: Rebecca Weber, Senior Vice President Information Technology
CHR: Sherrie String, Senior Vice President Human Resources
CNO: Rebecca Graboso, Vice President and Chief Nurse Executive
Web address: www.riverviewmedicalcenter.com
Control: Other not–for–profit (including NFP Corporation) **Service**: General medical and surgical

Staffed Beds: 321 **Admissions**: 25542 **Census**: 172 **Outpatient Visits**: 143162 **Births**: 1370 **Total Expense ($000)**: 272460 **Payroll Expense ($000)**: 111103 **Personnel**: 1460

RIDGEWOOD—Bergen County

✠ **VALLEY HOSPITAL (310012)**, 223 North Van Dien Avenue, Zip 07450–2726; tel. 201/447–8000, **A**1 2 3 5 10 **F**3 7 8 11 17 18 19 20 22 24 26 28 29 30 31 32 34 35 36 37 38 40 41 44 45 46 47 48 49 50 51 52 53 54 55 56 57 58 59 60 61 64 65 66 68 69 70 71 72 73 74 75 76 77 78 79 80 81 82 83 84 85 86 87 88 89 91 92 93 94 96 97 100 101 102 107 108 109 110 111 114 115 117 118 119 120 121 123 124 126 129 130 131 132 134 135 141 143 145 146 147 148 149 150 **P**6
Primary Contact: Audrey Meyers, FACHE, President and Chief Executive Officer
COO: Peter Diestel, Senior Vice President and Chief Operating Officer
CFO: Richard Keenan, Senior Vice President Finance and Chief Financial Officer
CMO: Joseph Yallowitz, M.D., Vice President and Chief Medical Officer
CIO: Eric R Carey, Vice President Information Systems and Chief Information Officer
CHR: Jose Balderrama, Vice President Human Resources
CNO: Ann Marie Leichman, MSN, R.N., Esq Senior Vice President Patient Care Services and Chief Nursing Officer
Web address: www.valleyhealth.com
Control: Other not–for–profit (including NFP Corporation) **Service**: General medical and surgical

Staffed Beds: 446 **Admissions**: 27803 **Census**: 292 **Outpatient Visits**: 289841 **Births**: 3319 **Total Expense ($000)**: 589631 **Payroll Expense ($000)**: 244321 **Personnel**: 3245

ROCHELLE PARK—Bergen County

✠ **SELECT SPECIALTY HOSPITAL–NORTHEAST NEW JERSEY (312019)**, 96 Parkway, Zip 07662–4200; tel. 201/221–2352, (Nonreporting) **A**1 10 **S** Select Medical Corporation, Mechanicsburg, PA
Primary Contact: Patrick T. Swift, PhD, MBA, FACHE, Chief Executive Officer
Web address: www.northeastnewjersey.selectspecialtyhospitals.com/about/
Control: Corporation, Investor–owned (for–profit) **Service**: Acute long–term care hospital

Staffed Beds: 62

SADDLE BROOK—Bergen County

KESSLER INSTITUTE FOR REHABILITATION See Kessler Institute For Rehabilitation, West Orange

SALEM—Salem County

✠ **MEMORIAL HOSPITAL OF SALEM COUNTY (310091)**, 310 Woodstown Road, Zip 08079–2080; tel. 856/935–1000, (Nonreporting) **A**1 10 **S** Community Health Systems, Inc., Franklin, TN
Primary Contact: Tammy Torres, R.N., MSN, Chief Executive Officer
CFO: Donald Bevers, Chief Financial Officer
CIO: Brian McCarthy, Director Information Systems
CHR: Victoria A. Bates, Director Human Resources
Web address: www.salemhospitalnj.org
Control: Corporation, Investor–owned (for–profit) **Service**: General medical and surgical

Staffed Beds: 110

SECAUCUS—Hudson County

HUDSON COUNTY MEADOWVIEW PSYCHIATRIC HOSPITAL (314024), 595 County Avenue, Zip 07094–2605; tel. 201/369–5252, (Nonreporting)
Primary Contact: Joanne Reilly, Administrator
Web address: www.hudsoncountynj.org
Control: County, Government, nonfederal **Service**: Psychiatric

Staffed Beds: 84

⇑ **HUDSON REGIONAL HOSPITAL (310118)**, 55 Meadowlands Parkway, Zip 07094–2977; tel. 201/392–3100, (Nonreporting) **A**10 12 13 21
Primary Contact: Felicia Karsos, R.N., President and Chief Executive Officer
COO: Lynn McVey, Chief Operating Officer
CMO: Michael Sciarra, M.D., Chief Medical Officer
CHR: Elizabeth Garrity, Director Human Resources
CNO: Felicia Karsos, R.N., Chief Nursing Officer
Web address: www.hudsonregionalhospital.com/
Control: Partnership, Investor–owned (for–profit) **Service**: General medical and surgical

Staffed Beds: 230

⇑ **LIBERTYHEALTH–MEADOWLANDS HOSPITAL MEDICAL CENTER** See Hudson Regional Hospital

SOMERS POINT—Atlantic County

☐ **SHORE MEDICAL CENTER (310047)**, 100 Medical Center Way, Zip 8244; tel. 609/653–3500, (Nonreporting) **A**1 2 10
Primary Contact: Ronald W. Johnson, FACHE, President and Chief Executive Officer
COO: Linda S Kenwood, R.N., MSN, Chief Nursing Officer and Chief Operating Officer
CFO: James T Foley, CPA, Vice President and Chief Financial Officer
CMO: Jeanne M Rowe, M.D., Chief Medical Officer
CIO: Fred Banner, Chief Information Officer
CHR: Alan L Beatty, Vice President Human Resources
CNO: Linda S Kenwood, R.N., MSN, Chief Nursing Officer and Chief Operating Officer
Web address: www.shoremedicalcenter.org
Control: Other not–for–profit (including NFP Corporation) **Service**: General medical and surgical

Staffed Beds: 198

SOMERVILLE—Somerset County

✠ **ROBERT WOOD JOHNSON UNIVERSITY HOSPITAL SOMERSET (310048)**, 110 Rehill Avenue, Zip 08876–2598; tel. 908/685–2200, **A**1 2 3 5 10 **F**3 5 7 8 11 13 14 15 18 20 22 26 28 30 31 34 35 36 38 40 41 44 45 46 47 48 49 50 51 52 55 56 57 58 59 61 62 63 64 65 66 68 70 71 73 74 75 76 77 78 79 81 82 84 85 86 87 91 92 93 94 97 98 99 100 101 102 104 105 107 108 110 111 114 115 116 117 118 119 120 121 123 124 126 129 130 131 132 134 135 143 144 145 146 147 148 149 150 152 153 154 **P**5 6 **S** RWJBarnabas Health, West Orange, NJ
Primary Contact: Anthony V. Cava, MS, RPH, FACHE, President
COO: Patrick Delaney, Administrative Director, Operations
CMO: Salvatore Moffa, Vice President, Medical Affairs and Chief Medical Officer
CIO: Jordan Ruch, Vice President and Chief Information Officer
CHR: Anastasia Jacobs, Chief Human Resources Officer
CNO: Lynn Kearney, Vice President Nursing
Web address: www.rwjuh.edu
Control: Other not–for–profit (including NFP Corporation) **Service**: General medical and surgical

Staffed Beds: 285 **Admissions**: 13219 **Census**: 172 **Outpatient Visits**: 173742 **Births**: 821 **Total Expense ($000)**: 257228 **Payroll Expense ($000)**: 107159 **Personnel**: 1686

NJ

Hospital, Medicare Provider Number, Address, Telephone, Approval, Facility, and Physician Codes, Health Care System

★ American Hospital Association (AHA) membership
☐ The Joint Commission accreditation
○ Healthcare Facilities Accreditation Program
◇ DNV Healthcare Inc. accreditation
⇑ Center for Improvement in Healthcare Quality Accreditation
△ Commission on Accreditation of Rehabilitation Facilities (CARF) accreditation

STRATFORD—Camden County

☒ **JEFFERSON STRATFORD HOSPITAL (310086)**, 18 East Laurel Road, Zip 08084–1327; tel. 856/346–6000, (Includes JEFFERSON STRATFORD HOSPITAL, 18 East Laurel Road, Stratford, NJ, Zip 8084; tel. 609/346–6000; JEFFERSON WASHINGTON TOWNSHIP HOSPITAL, 435 Hurffville–Cross Keys Road, Turnersville, NJ, Zip 8012; tel. 609/582–2500; Joseph W Devine, FACHE, President, New Jersey Division Jefferson Health) (Total facility includes 190 beds in nursing home–type unit) **A**1 2 3 10 **F**3 5 7 8 11 12 13 15 18 20 22 24 29 30 31 32 34 35 38 39 40 41 44 46 49 50 51 54 55 56 57 59 60 61 62 64 65 66 70 72 73 74 75 76 77 78 79 81 82 84 85 86 87 89 93 97 98 99 100 101 102 103 104 105 107 108 110 111 114 115 117 118 119 120 121 123 124 126 129 130 131 132 134 143 144 146 147 148 149 154 **P**6 **S** Jefferson Health, Philadelphia, PA
Primary Contact: Jill Ostrem, Senior Vice President and Chief Operating Officer
CFO: Glenn Zirbser, Senior Vice President Finance and Chief Financial Officer
CMO: David Condoluci, M.D., Senior Vice President and Chief Medical Officer
CIO: Thomas Balcavage, Vice President Chief Patient Safety and Quality Officer
CHR: Anneliese McMenamin, Senior Vice President Information Technology and Program Services
CNO: Helene M Burns, MSN, R.N., Chief Nursing Executive
Web address: www.kennedyhealth.org
Control: Other not–for–profit (including NFP Corporation) **Service**: General medical and surgical

Staffed Beds: 527 **Admissions:** 27122 **Census:** 331 **Outpatient Visits:** 395343 **Births:** 990 **Total Expense ($000):** 550678 **Payroll Expense ($000):** 233564 **Personnel:** 4463

KENNEDY MEMORIAL HOSPITALS–UNIVERSITY MEDICAL CENTER See Jefferson Stratford Hospital

SUMMIT—Union County

☒ **OVERLOOK MEDICAL CENTER (310051)**, 99 Beauvoir Avenue, Zip 07901–3533; tel. 908/522–2000, **A**1 2 3 5 8 10 13 **F**3 5 6 7 8 9 11 12 13 15 17 18 20 22 28 29 30 31 32 34 35 36 37 38 39 40 41 44 45 46 47 48 49 50 51 52 53 54 55 56 57 58 59 60 61 62 63 64 65 66 68 69 70 71 72 74 75 76 77 78 79 81 82 84 85 86 87 89 91 92 93 94 95 96 97 98 100 101 102 103 104 105 107 108 110 111 113 114 115 116 117 118 119 120 121 123 124 126 129 130 131 132 134 135 141 143 144 145 146 147 148 149 150 153 154 **P**3 5 6 **S** Atlantic Health System, Morristown, NJ
Primary Contact: Alan R. Lieber, President
CFO: Kevin Lenahan, Vice President Finance and Chief Financial Officer
CMO: John R Audett, M.D., Medical Director Clinical Affairs
CIO: Elizabeth Lindsay–Wood, Interim Chief Information Officer
CNO: Mary Patricia Sullivan, R.N., MSN, Chief Nursing Officer
Web address: www.atlantichealth.org/Overlook
Control: Other not–for–profit (including NFP Corporation) **Service**: General medical and surgical

Staffed Beds: 384 **Admissions:** 21842 **Census:** 279 **Outpatient Visits:** 258341 **Births:** 2733 **Total Expense ($000):** 734665 **Payroll Expense ($000):** 331107 **Personnel:** 3695

☐ **SUMMIT OAKS HOSPITAL (314001)**, 19 Prospect Street, Zip 07901–2530; tel. 908/522–7000, (Nonreporting) **A**1 10 **S** Universal Health Services, Inc., King of Prussia, PA
Primary Contact: Ross Friedman, Chief Executive Officer
Web address: www.summitoakshospital.com/
Control: Corporation, Investor–owned (for–profit) **Service**: Psychiatric

Staffed Beds: 90

SUSSEX—Sussex County

SAINT CLARE'S HEALTH CENTER AT SUSSEX See Saint Clare's Denville Hospital, Denville

TEANECK—Bergen County

HOLY NAME HOSPITAL See Holy Name Medical Center

☒ **HOLY NAME MEDICAL CENTER (310008)**, 718 Teaneck Road, Zip 07666–4281; tel. 201/833–3000, **A**1 2 5 10 **F**1 2 3 4 7 8 11 12 13 15 16 17 18 20 22 28 29 30 31 32 34 35 36 37 38 39 40 41 44 45 46 47 48 49 50 51 53 54 55 56 57 58 59 60 62 63 64 65 66 67 68 70 71 72 73 74 75 76 77 78 79 80 81 82 83 84 85 86 87 88 89 90 91 92 93 94 96 97 98 100 101 102 103 107 108 110 111 114 115 116 117 118 119 120 121 123 124 126 128 129 130 131 132 133 135 143 144 145 146 147 148 149 151 154 **P**4 6 7
Primary Contact: Michael Maron, President and Chief Executive Officer
CFO: Ryan Kennedy, Chief Financial Officer
CMO: Adam D Jarrett, M.D., Executive Vice President and Chief Medical Officer
CIO: Michael Skvarenina, Assistant Vice President Information Systems
CHR: April Rodgers, Vice President, Human Resources
CNO: Sheryl A Slonim, Executive Vice President and Chief Nursing Officer
Web address: www.holyname.org
Control: Other not–for–profit (including NFP Corporation) **Service**: General medical and surgical

Staffed Beds: 318 **Admissions:** 19953 **Census:** 211 **Outpatient Visits:** 343691 **Births:** 1230 **Total Expense ($000):** 351067 **Payroll Expense ($000):** 149428 **Personnel:** 2285

TINTON FALLS—Monmouth County

★ **HEALTHSOUTH REHABILITATION HOSPITAL OF TINTON FALLS (313035)**, 2 Centre Plaza, Zip 07724–9744; tel. 732/460–5320, **A**10 **F**28 29 64 90 93 94 95 148 149 **S** Encompass Health Corporation, Birmingham, AL
Primary Contact: Jason Dan Hudson, RN, BSN, Chief Executive Officer
CFO: Lynne Traister, Controller
CMO: Todd Cooperman, M.D., Medical Director
CHR: Anita Saum, Director Human Resources
Web address: www.rehabnjtintonfalls.com/
Control: Corporation, Investor–owned (for–profit) **Service**: Rehabilitation

Staffed Beds: 60 **Admissions:** 1390 **Census:** 51 **Outpatient Visits:** 663 **Births:** 0

TOMS RIVER—Ocean County

☒ **BARNABAS HEALTH BEHAVIORAL HEALTH CENTER (314022)**, 1691 Highway 9, Zip 8754; tel. 732/914–1688, **A**1 10 **F**35 68 98 100 101 103 153 **S** RWJBarnabas Health, West Orange, NJ
Primary Contact: Deanna Sperling, R.N., President and Chief Executive Officer
Web address: www.barnabashealth.org/hospitals/psychiatric/index.html
Control: Other not–for–profit (including NFP Corporation) **Service**: Psychiatric

Staffed Beds: 40 **Admissions:** 1402 **Census:** 29 **Outpatient Visits:** 5987 **Births:** 0 **Total Expense ($000):** 9822 **Payroll Expense ($000):** 5230 **Personnel:** 85

☒ **COMMUNITY MEDICAL CENTER (310041)**, 99 Route 37 West, Zip 08755–6423; tel. 732/557–8000, **A**1 2 3 10 **F**3 11 12 13 15 18 20 22 28 29 30 31 32 34 35 36 37 38 40 41 43 44 50 54 55 56 57 58 59 60 61 63 64 68 70 73 74 75 76 77 78 79 81 82 84 85 86 87 89 93 96 97 100 107 108 109 110 111 114 115 118 119 120 121 123 124 126 129 130 131 132 133 134 135 143 146 147 148 149 154 **P**3 6 **S** RWJBarnabas Health, West Orange, NJ
Primary Contact: Michael Mimoso, FACHE, President and Chief Executive Officer
COO: Patrick Ahearn, Chief Operating Officer
CFO: Thomas Percello, Chief Financial Officer
CMO: Yeshavanth Nayak, M.D., Interim Chief Medical Officer
CIO: Shaun Fitzsimmons, Director Information Technology Services
CHR: Vanessa Smith, Chief Human Resources Officer
CNO: Donna Bonacorso, Interim Chief Nursing Officer
Web address: www.barnabashealth.org/hospitals/community_medical/index.html
Control: Other not–for–profit (including NFP Corporation) **Service**: General medical and surgical

Staffed Beds: 338 **Admissions:** 20201 **Census:** 284 **Outpatient Visits:** 237362 **Births:** 2083 **Total Expense ($000):** 352673 **Payroll Expense ($000):** 136292 **Personnel:** 1862

☒ **HEALTHSOUTH REHABILITATION HOSPITAL OF TOMS RIVER (313029)**, 14 Hospital Drive, Zip 08755–6470; tel. 732/244–3100, (Nonreporting) **A**1 10 **S** Encompass Health Corporation, Birmingham, AL
Primary Contact: Patricia Ostaszewski, MS, Chief Executive Officer
COO: Patricia Ostaszewski, MS, Chief Executive Officer
CFO: Janet Turso, Controller
CMO: Carol Sonatore, D.O., Medical Director
CIO: Coleen Rossi, Director Quality Services
CHR: Lori Munyan, Director, Human Resources
CNO: Susan Castor, Chief Nursing Officer
Web address: www.rehabnjtomsriver.com/
Control: Corporation, Investor–owned (for–profit) **Service**: Rehabilitation

Staffed Beds: 92

NJ

Many Facility Codes have changed. Please refer to the AHA Guide Code Chart.
© 2018 AHA Guide

SAINT BARNABAS BEHAVIORAL HEALTH CENTER See Barnabas Health Behavioral Health Center

TRENTON—Mercer County

CAPITAL HEALTH REGIONAL MEDICAL CENTER (310092), 750 Brunswick Avenue, Zip 08638–4143; tel. 609/394–6000, **A**1 3 5 10 **F**3 7 11 15 18 29 30 34 35 40 43 44 45 46 47 48 50 54 57 58 59 60 61 64 65 66 68 70 74 75 78 79 81 82 84 85 87 89 93 96 97 98 100 101 102 107 108 109 111 112 114 115 118 119 129 130 132 135 143 145 146 147 148 154 **P**6 **S** Capital Health, Trenton, NJ
Primary Contact: Al Maghazehe, Ph.D., FACHE, President and Chief Executive Officer
CFO: Shane Fleming, Chief Financial Officer
CMO: Eugene McMahon, Senior Vice President and Chief Medical Officer
CIO: Eugene Grochala, Vice President Information Systems
CHR: Scott Clemmensen, Vice President Human Resources and Leadership Enhancement
CNO: Gina Mumolie, Senior Vice President Hospital Administration
Web address: www.capitalhealth.org
Control: Other not–for–profit (including NFP Corporation) **Service**: General medical and surgical

Staffed Beds: 167 **Admissions:** 7037 **Census:** 120 **Outpatient Visits:** 151540 **Births:** 0 **Personnel:** 1384

ST. FRANCIS MEDICAL CENTER (310021), 601 Hamilton Avenue, Zip 08629–1986; tel. 609/599–5000, **A**1 3 10 **F**2 3 10 11 12 15 17 18 20 22 24 26 29 30 31 34 35 40 45 46 50 56 57 58 59 60 61 62 64 65 66 70 74 77 78 79 81 82 84 85 86 87 92 93 98 100 101 102 104 107 108 110 111 114 115 118 119 121 123 124 126 129 130 132 135 143 144 146 147 148 149 **P**5 6 **S** Trinity Health, Livonia, MI
Primary Contact: Daniel P. Moen, President
CFO: Mark Kelly, Vice President Finance
CMO: C. James Romano, M.D., Chief Medical Officer
CIO: Richard Dowgun, Chief Information Officer
CHR: Laura James, Director Human Resources
CNO: Mary Anne Suttles, Chief Nursing Officer
Web address: www.stfrancismedical.org/
Control: Church operated, Nongovernment, not–for–profit **Service**: General medical and surgical

Staffed Beds: 142 **Admissions:** 4343 **Census:** 63 **Outpatient Visits:** 89940 **Births:** 0 **Total Expense ($000):** 133015 **Payroll Expense ($000):** 45152 **Personnel:** 846

TRENTON PSYCHIATRIC HOSPITAL (314013), Route 29 and Sullivan Way, Zip 08628–3425, Mailing Address: P.O. Box 7500, West Trenton, Zip 08628–0500; tel. 609/633–1500, (Nonreporting) **A**1 3 10 **S** Division of Mental Health and Addiction Services, Department of Human Services, State of New Jersey, Trenton, NJ
Primary Contact: Robyn Caporoso, Chief Executive Officer
CFO: Joseph Canale, Business Manager
CMO: Lawrence Rossi, M.D., Clinical Director
CIO: Scott Eustace, Director Health Information Technology
CHR: Marybeth Longo, Manager Human Resources
CNO: Colleen Birkhofer, Chief Nursing Officer
Web address: www.state.nj.us/humanservices/dmhs/oshm/tph/
Control: State, Government, nonfederal **Service**: Psychiatric

Staffed Beds: 431

TURNERSVILLE—Camden County

JEFFERSON WASHINGTON TOWNSHIP HOSPITAL See Jefferson Stratford Hospital, Stratford

VINELAND—Cumberland County

HEALTHSOUTH REHABILITATION HOSPITAL OF VINELAND (313036), 1237 West Sherman Avenue, Zip 08360–6920; tel. 856/696–7100, **A**1 10 **F**29 30 65 75 90 130 132 148 149 **S** Encompass Health Corporation, Birmingham, AL
Primary Contact: Tammy Feuer, Chief Executive Officer
CHR: Dawn Pearson, Director Human Resources
Web address: www.healthsouthvineland.com
Control: Corporation, Investor–owned (for–profit) **Service**: Rehabilitation

Staffed Beds: 41 **Admissions:** 973 **Census:** 37 **Outpatient Visits:** 0 **Births:** 0 **Total Expense ($000):** 13736 **Payroll Expense ($000):** 7586 **Personnel:** 115

★ ⇧ **INSPIRA MEDICAL CENTER–VINELAND (310032)**, 1505 West Sherman Avenue, Zip 08360–6912; tel. 856/641–8000, (Includes BRIDGETON HEALTH CENTER, 333 Irving Avenue, Bridgeton, NJ, Zip 08302–2100; tel. 856/575–4500) **A**2 3 10 12 13 21 **F**3 7 8 11 12 13 15 17 18 20 22 28 29 30 34 35 37 38 40 41 44 49 50 54 57 59 64 68 70 72 73 74 75 76 77 78 79 81 82 85 86 87 89 93 98 99 100 104 105 107 108 110 111 114 115 116 117 118 119 120 121 123 124 126 130 131 132 134 144 146 147 148 153 154 **P**8 **S** Inspira Health Network, Mullica Hill, NJ
Primary Contact: John A. DiAngelo, President and Chief Executive Officer
COO: Elizabeth Sheridan, Chief Operating Officer and Chief Nursing Executive
CFO: Thomas Baldosaro, Chief Financial Officer
CMO: Steven C Linn, M.D., Chief Medical Officer
CIO: Thomas Pacek, Vice President Information Systems and Chief Information Officer
CHR: Erich Florentine, Chief People Officer
CNO: Elizabeth Sheridan, Chief Operating Officer and Chief Nursing Executive
Web address: www.inspirahealthnetwork.org/?id=5280&sid=1
Control: Other not–for–profit (including NFP Corporation) **Service**: General medical and surgical

Staffed Beds: 335 **Admissions:** 17938 **Census:** 239 **Outpatient Visits:** 312055 **Births:** 1838 **Total Expense ($000):** 350050 **Payroll Expense ($000):** 152139 **Personnel:** 1650

VOORHEES—Camden County

VIRTUA VOORHEES (310022), 100 Bowman Drive, Zip 08043–9612; tel. 856/325–3000, (Includes VOORHEES PEDIATRIC FACILITY, 1304 Laurel Oak Road, Voorhees, NJ, Zip 08043–4310; tel. 888/873–5437) **A**1 3 5 10 **F**3 11 13 28 29 30 31 34 35 37 39 40 41 45 46 50 55 64 66 68 70 72 73 74 75 76 78 79 81 84 85 87 88 89 92 93 107 108 111 115 116 117 119 126 129 130 143 145 146 147 148 149 **S** Virtua Health, Marlton, NJ
Primary Contact: Dennis W. Pullin, FACHE, President and Chief Executive Officer
COO: Paul E Minnick, R.N., MSN, Senior Vice President and Chief Operating Officer
CFO: Robert Rosvold, Director Finance
CMO: James P Dwyer, D.O., Executive Vice President and Chief Medical Officer
CIO: Alfred Campanella, Chief Information Officer
Web address: www.virtua.org
Control: Other not–for–profit (including NFP Corporation) **Service**: General medical and surgical

Staffed Beds: 402 **Admissions:** 23182 **Census:** 273 **Outpatient Visits:** 292655 **Births:** 4756 **Total Expense ($000):** 524274 **Payroll Expense ($000):** 153436 **Personnel:** 1848

WAYNE—Passaic County

KINDRED HOSPITAL NEW JERSEY – WAYNE See Kindred Hospital–New Jersey Morris County, Dover

WEST ORANGE—Essex County

KESSLER INSTITUTE FOR REHABILITATION See Kessler Institute for Rehabilitation, West Orange

△ **KESSLER INSTITUTE FOR REHABILITATION (313025)**, 1199 Pleasant Valley Way, Zip 07052–1424; tel. 973/731–3600, (Includes KESSLER INSTITUTE FOR REHABILITATION, 1199 Pleasant Valley Way, West Orange, NJ, Zip 07052–1424; tel. 973/731–3600; Bonnie A. Evans, Chief Executive Officer; KESSLER INSTITUTE FOR REHABILITATION, 201 Pleasant Hill Road, Chester, NJ, Zip 07930–2141; tel. 973/252–6300; Sue Kida, Chief Executive Officer; KESSLER INSTITUTE FOR REHABILITATION, 300 Market Street, Saddle Brook, NJ, Zip 07663–5309; tel. 201/368–6000; Philip J Driscoll Jr, Chief Executive Officer) (Nonreporting) **A**1 3 5 7 10 **S** Select Medical Corporation, Mechanicsburg, PA
Primary Contact: Sue Kida, PT, MHA, President
CMO: Bruce M Gans, M.D., Executive Vice President and Chief Medical Officer
CHR: Ken Caldera, Director Human Resources
Web address: www.kessler–rehab.com
Control: Corporation, Investor–owned (for–profit) **Service**: Rehabilitation

Staffed Beds: 336

WESTAMPTON—Burlington County

☐ **HAMPTON BEHAVIORAL HEALTH CENTER (314021)**, 650 Rancocas Road, Zip 08060–5613; tel. 609/267–7000, **A**1 10 **F**30 35 98 99 100 103 104 105 130 132 143 149 153 **P**6 **S** Universal Health Services, Inc., King of Prussia, PA
Primary Contact: Craig Hilton, Chief Executive Officer and Managing Director
COO: Joanne Wijaya, MSN, R.N., Chief Operating Officer and Risk Manager
CFO: Melissa Zinni, Chief Financial Officer
CMO: Anusuya Balasundaram, M.D., Medical Director
CHR: Lori DeCelis, Director Human Resources
CNO: Kathleena Cohen, MSN, R.N., Director of Nursing
Web address: www.hamptonhospital.com
Control: Corporation, Investor–owned (for–profit) **Service:** Psychiatric

Staffed Beds: 120 **Admissions:** 2508 **Census:** 105 **Outpatient Visits:** 20634 **Births:** 0 **Total Expense ($000):** 25743 **Payroll Expense ($000):** 17278 **Personnel:** 332

WESTWOOD—Bergen County

CAREONE AT HACKENSACK UNIVERSITY MEDICAL CENTER AT PASCACK VALLEY, 250 Old Hook Road, Zip 07675–3123, Mailing Address: 250 Old Hook Road, 4 Central, Zip 07675–3123; tel. 201/781–1555, (Nonreporting)
Primary Contact: Sharon Bready, R.N., Chief Executive Officer
Web address: www.care-one.com/locations/ltach-careone-at-hackensack-university-medical-center-pascack-valley/
Control: Other not–for–profit (including NFP Corporation) **Service:** Acute long–term care hospital

Staffed Beds: 25

⊞ **HACKENSACK MERIDIAN HEALTH PASCACK VALLEY MEDICAL CENTER (310130)**, 250 Old Hook Road, Zip 07675–3123; tel. 201/383–1035, **A**1 **F**3 12 13 15 17 18 20 28 29 30 34 35 40 44 45 46 47 49 50 51 57 59 60 64 68 70 73 74 75 76 77 78 79 81 82 85 87 93 107 108 110 111 115 119 129 130 135 141 146 147 148 149 **S** Ardent Health Services, Nashville, TN
Primary Contact: Emily L. Holliman, Chief Executive Officer
COO: Colleen Smorra, Assistant Administrator
CFO: Jason Pritchard, Chief Financial Officer
CMO: George Lin, M.D., Physician Advisor
CIO: Anthony Teri, Director Information Technology
CNO: Susan Giordano, R.N., Chief Nursing Officer
Web address: www.hackensackumcpv.com/
Control: Partnership, Investor–owned (for–profit) **Service:** General medical and surgical

Staffed Beds: 128 **Admissions:** 4895 **Census:** 47 **Outpatient Visits:** 30680 **Births:** 1211 **Total Expense ($000):** 100917 **Payroll Expense ($000):** 34128 **Personnel:** 486

WILLINGBORO—Burlington County

⊞ **ACUITY SPECIALTY HOSPITAL OF SOUTHERN NEW JERSEY (312022)**, 218 A Sunset Road, Zip 08046–1110, Mailing Address: 220 Sunset Road, Zip 08046–1110; tel. 609/835–3650, (Nonreporting) **A**1 10 **S** AcuityHealthcare, LP, Charlotte, NC
Primary Contact: Monica B. Titus, R.N., Regional Chief Executive Officer
COO: Garrett Arneson, FACHE, R.N., Chief Operating Officer
CMO: Edward G. Hamaty, D.O., Chief Medical Officer
CHR: Lisa M Sinnott, Director Human Resources
CNO: Kim Fetterolf, R.N., Chief Clinical Officer
Web address: www.willingboro.acuityhealthcare.net
Control: Corporation, Investor–owned (for–profit) **Service:** Acute long–term care hospital

Staffed Beds: 53

⊞ **LOURDES MEDICAL CENTER OF BURLINGTON COUNTY (310061)**, 218–A Sunset Road, Zip 08046–1162; tel. 609/835–2900, **A**1 2 3 10 **F**3 7 11 12 15 17 18 29 30 31 34 35 36 38 40 44 45 46 47 49 50 55 56 57 59 60 61 64 66 68 70 74 75 78 79 81 82 85 86 87 93 98 100 103 107 108 109 110 111 114 118 119 121 129 130 131 132 135 146 147 148 149 **P**8 **S** Trinity Health, Livonia, MI
Primary Contact: Mark Nessel, Executive Vice President and Chief Operating Officer
CFO: Michael Hammond, Chief Financial Officer
CMO: Alan R Pope, M.D., Vice President, Medical Affairs
CIO: Mike Elfert, Director Information Services
CNO: Audrey Jadczak, R.N., FACHE, Vice President/Chief Nursing Officer
Web address: www.lourdesnet.org
Control: Other not–for–profit (including NFP Corporation) **Service:** General medical and surgical

Staffed Beds: 169 **Admissions:** 6101 **Census:** 82 **Outpatient Visits:** 114726 **Births:** 0 **Total Expense ($000):** 121445 **Payroll Expense ($000):** 46772 **Personnel:** 705

WOODBURY—Gloucester County

★ ⇑ **INSPIRA MEDICAL CENTER–WOODBURY (310081)**, 509 North Broad Street, Zip 08096–1697; tel. 856/845–0100, (Nonreporting) **A**3 5 10 21 **S** Inspira Health Network, Mullica Hill, NJ
Primary Contact: John A. DiAngelo, President and Chief Executive Officer
COO: Patrick B Nolan, Chief Operating Officer
CIO: Robert Mizia, Director Information Systems and Chief Information Officer
CHR: Robert Manestrina, Vice President Human Resources
CNO: Gina Mumolie, Senior Vice President and Chief Nurse Executive
Web address: www.inspirahealthnetwork.org/?id=5282&sid=1
Control: Other not–for–profit (including NFP Corporation) **Service:** General medical and surgical

Staffed Beds: 261

WYCKOFF—Bergen County

⊞ **CHRISTIAN HEALTH CARE CENTER (314019)**, 301 Sicomac Avenue, Zip 07481–2194; tel. 201/848–5200, (Total facility includes 294 beds in nursing home–type unit) **A**1 10 **F**2 10 35 63 69 93 98 100 104 105 106 128 131 153 **P**6
Primary Contact: Douglas A. Struyk, CPA, President and Chief Executive Officer
COO: Steve Dumke, FACHE, Executive Vice President and Chief Operating Officer
CFO: Kevin Stagg, Executive Vice President Finance and Chief Financial Officer
CMO: Howard Gilman, M.D., Medical Executive
CIO: Jennifer D'Angelo, Vice President Information Services
CHR: Bob Zierold, Senior Vice President Human Resources
CNO: Marianne Guerriero, Nurse Executive
Web address: www.chccnj.org
Control: Church operated, Nongovernment, not–for–profit **Service:** Rehabilitation

Staffed Beds: 857 **Admissions:** 2270 **Census:** 496 **Outpatient Visits:** 57274 **Births:** 0 **Total Expense ($000):** 80982 **Payroll Expense ($000):** 44600 **Personnel:** 789

Many Facility Codes have changed. Please refer to the AHA Guide Code Chart.   © 2018 AHA Guide

NJ

NEW MEXICO

ACOMA—Bergen County

☐ **ACOMA–CANONCITO–LAGUNA HOSPITAL (320070)**, 80B Veterans Boulevard, Zip 87034, Mailing Address: P.O. Box 130, San Fidel, Zip 87049–0130; tel. 505/552–5300, **A**1 10 **F**29 34 39 40 41 55 59 64 97 119 129 130 144 147 154 **S** U.S. Indian Health Service, Rockville, MD
Primary Contact: Melody Price–Yonts, Chief Executive Officer
Web address: www.ihs.gov/albuquerque/index.cfm?module=dsp_abq_acoma_canoncito_laguna
Control: PHS, Indian Service, Government, federal **Service:** General medical and surgical

Staffed Beds: 6 **Admissions:** 5 **Census:** 1 **Births:** 0 **Personnel:** 208

ALAMOGORDO—Otero County

★ ⇑ **GERALD CHAMPION REGIONAL MEDICAL CENTER (320004)**, 2669 North Scenic Drive, Zip 88310–8799; tel. 575/439–6100, **A**3 10 13 20 21 **F**3 8 11 12 13 18 20 22 26 28 29 30 31 34 35 38 40 43 44 50 51 56 57 58 59 60 64 70 74 75 76 77 78 79 81 82 85 86 87 90 92 96 97 98 100 101 102 103 104 107 108 111 114 115 117 119 129 130 131 132 145 146 147 148 149 153 **P**8
Primary Contact: Robert J. Heckert Jr, Chief Executive Officer
CFO: Bashar Naser, Chief Financial Officer
CMO: Lee Saltzgaber, Chief Medical Officer
CIO: Ana Castro, Director Information Technology
CHR: Karen O'Brien, Director Human Resources
CNO: Robert Eldon Middleton, MSN, R.N., III Chief Nursing Officer
Web address: www.gcrmc.org
Control: Other not–for–profit (including NFP Corporation) **Service:** General medical and surgical

Staffed Beds: 86 **Admissions:** 4180 **Census:** 55 **Outpatient Visits:** 92505 **Births:** 584 **Total Expense ($000):** 129284 **Payroll Expense ($000):** 49630 **Personnel:** 757

ALBUQUERQUE—Bernalillo County

☐ **AMG SPECIALTY HOSPITAL–ALBUQUERQUE (322003)**, 235 Elm Street NE, Zip 87102–3672; tel. 505/842–5550, (Nonreporting) **A**1 10 **S** AMG Integrated Healthcare Management, Lafayette, LA
Primary Contact: Kendra Camp, R.N., Chief Executive Officer
CFO: Julie Lenzo, Director Business Office
CMO: Jeffrey Ross, M.D., Medical Director
CHR: Robin Stendel–Freels, Coordinator Human Resources
Web address: www.amgalbuquerque.com/
Control: Partnership, Investor–owned (for–profit) **Service:** Acute long–term care hospital

Staffed Beds: 24

☐ **HAVEN BEHAVIORAL SENIOR CARE OF ALBUQUERQUE (324013)**, 5400 Gibson Boulevard SE, 4th Floor, Zip 87108–4729; tel. 505/336–1247, (Nonreporting) **A**1 10
Primary Contact: Sheila McDermott–Lord, Chief Executive Officer
Web address: www.https://albuquerque.havenbehavioral.com/
Control: Corporation, Investor–owned (for–profit) **Service:** Psychiatric

Staffed Beds: 32

⊞ **HEALTHSOUTH REHABILITATION HOSPITAL OF NEW MEXICO (323027)**, 7000 Jefferson Street NE, Zip 87109–4313; tel. 505/344–9478, **A**1 10 **F**28 29 34 35 56 57 59 60 62 64 74 75 77 79 90 91 93 94 95 96 130 132 143 148 **S** Encompass Health Corporation, Birmingham, AL
Primary Contact: David S. Nevill, Chief Executive Officer
CFO: Michelle Martinez, Controller
CMO: Angela Walker, M.D., Medical Director
CHR: Kristen Hernandez, Director Human Resources
CNO: Karin Jones, Interim Chief Nursing Officer
Web address: www.healthsouthnewmexico.com
Control: Corporation, Investor–owned (for–profit) **Service:** Rehabilitation

Staffed Beds: 87 **Admissions:** 1673 **Census:** 60 **Births:** 0

⊞ **KINDRED HOSPITAL–ALBUQUERQUE (322002)**, 700 High Street NE, Zip 87102–2565; tel. 505/242–4444, **A**1 10 **F**1 3 16 29 30 67 70 75 80 90 91 98 107 130 135 148 **S** Kindred Healthcare, Louisville, KY
Primary Contact: Bud Schawl, Chief Executive Officer
CFO: Sheila Bova, Chief Financial Officer
CMO: Jon Marinaro, M.D., Chief Medical Officer
CHR: Donald Whitney, Director Human Resources
CNO: Diane Nelson, R.N., Chief Nursing Officer
Web address: www.kindredalbuquerque.com/
Control: Corporation, Investor–owned (for–profit) **Service:** General medical and surgical

Staffed Beds: 61 **Admissions:** 437 **Census:** 40 **Births:** 0

★ ⇑ **LOVELACE MEDICAL CENTER (320009)**, 601 Martin Luther King Avenue NE, Zip 87102–3619; tel. 505/727–8000, (Includes HEART HOSPITAL OF NEW MEXICO, 504 Elm Street, Albuquerque, NM, Zip 87102; tel. 505/724–2000; Ronald C Winger, President) (Nonreporting) **A**3 5 10 21 **S** Ardent Health Services, Nashville, TN
Primary Contact: Troy Greer, Chief Executive Officer
CHR: Helen V Nielsen, Director Human Resources
CNO: Laurie S Bigham, R.N., FACHE, Chief Nursing Officer
Web address: www.lovelace.com/albuquerque–hospital/lovelace–medical–center#.UDZ1laDhf48
Control: Corporation, Investor–owned (for–profit) **Service:** General medical and surgical

Staffed Beds: 263

★ △ **LOVELACE REHABILITATION HOSPITAL (323028)**, 505 Elm Street NE, Zip 87102–2500; tel. 505/727–4700, (Nonreporting) **A**5 7 10 **S** Ardent Health Services, Nashville, TN
Primary Contact: Derrick Jones, Chief Executive Officer
CFO: Andrea Solin, Chief Financial Officer
CHR: Helen V Nielsen, Director Human Resources
CNO: Cynthia Rankin, Chief Nursing Officer
Web address: www.lovelace.com
Control: Corporation, Investor–owned (for–profit) **Service:** Rehabilitation

Staffed Beds: 52

★ ⇑ **LOVELACE WESTSIDE HOSPITAL (320074)**, 10501 Golf Course Road NW, Mailing Address: P.O. Box 25555, Zip 87125–0555; tel. 505/727–8000, **A**5 10 21 **F**3 12 13 15 29 30 34 39 40 41 49 51 57 59 68 70 75 76 79 81 85 93 107 110 111 115 119 130 133 135 146 148 **S** Ardent Health Services, Nashville, TN
Primary Contact: Amy Blasing, Chief Executive Officer
COO: Nancye Cole, R.N., Chief Operating Officer
CFO: Andrea Solin, Chief Financial Officer
CNO: Nancye Cole, R.N., Chief Nursing Officer and Chief Operating Officer
Web address: www.lovelace.com/albuquerque–hospital/lovelace–westside–hospital#.UDZ1t6Dhf48
Control: Corporation, Investor–owned (for–profit) **Service:** General medical and surgical

Staffed Beds: 80 **Admissions:** 3088 **Census:** 24

★ ⇑ **LOVELACE WOMEN'S HOSPITAL (320017)**, 4701 Montgomery Boulevard NE, Zip 87109–1251, Mailing Address: P.O. Box 25555, Zip 87125–0555; tel. 505/727–7800, (Nonreporting) **A**5 10 21 **S** Ardent Health Services, Nashville, TN
Primary Contact: Sheri Milone, Chief Executive Officer and Administrator
COO: Janelle Raborn, Chief Operating Officer
CFO: Joseph Sereno, Chief Financial Officer
CHR: Carol Shelton, Director Human Resources
Web address: www.lovelace.com/albuquerque–hospital/lovelace–womens–hospital#.UDZ17KDhf48
Control: Corporation, Investor–owned (for–profit) **Service:** General medical and surgical

Staffed Beds: 78

NM

Hospital, Medicare Provider Number, Address, Telephone, Approval, Facility, and Physician Codes, Health Care System

★ American Hospital Association (AHA) membership   ○ Healthcare Facilities Accreditation Program   ⇑ Center for Improvement in Healthcare Quality Accreditation
☐ The Joint Commission accreditation   ◇ DNV Healthcare Inc. accreditation   △ Commission on Accreditation of Rehabilitation Facilities (CARF) accreditation

⊞ △ **NEW MEXICO VETERANS AFFAIRS HEALTH CARE SYSTEM – RAYMOND G. MURPHY MEDICAL CENTER**, 1501 San Pedro SE, Zip 87108–5153; tel. 505/265–1711, (Nonreporting) **A**1 2 3 5 7 8 **S** Department of Veterans Affairs, Perry Point, MD
Primary Contact: Andrew Welch, Director
CFO: Michael McNeill, Chief Financial Management
CMO: Meghan Gerety, M.D., Chief of Staff
CIO: Ronald Ferrell, Chief Information Officer
CHR: Melvin Hooker, Chief Human Resources
CNO: Tina Prince, R.N., Associate Director Patient Care Services, Chief Nursing Officer
Web address: www.albuquerque.va.gov/
Control: Veterans Affairs, Government, federal **Service**: General medical and surgical

Staffed Beds: 203

⊞ **PRESBYTERIAN HOSPITAL (320021)**, 1100 Central Avenue SE, Zip 87106–4934, Mailing Address: P.O. Box 26666, Zip 87125–6666; tel. 505/841–1234, (Includes PRESBYTERIAN KASEMAN HOSPITAL, 8300 Constitution Avenue NE, Albuquerque, NM, Zip 87110–7624, Mailing Address: P.O. Box 26666, Zip 87125–6666, tel. 505/291–2000; Doyle Boykin, R.N., MSN, Administrator; PRESBYTERIAN RUST MEDICAL CENTER, 2400 Unser Boulevard SE, Rio Rancho, NM, Zip 87124–4740; tel. 505/253–7878; Jeff McBee, Administrator) **A**1 2 3 5 10 **F**7 8 11 12 13 17 18 19 20 21 22 23 24 25 26 27 28 29 30 31 32 34 35 38 40 45 47 48 49 50 51 53 55 56 57 58 59 61 62 63 64 65 68 70 72 74 75 76 77 78 79 80 81 82 84 85 86 87 88 89 91 92 93 96 97 98 99 100 102 103 104 107 108 110 111 112 114 115 116 117 118 119 121 126 127 128 129 130 131 132 135 138 144 146 147 148 149 153 154 **P**6 **S** Presbyterian Healthcare Services, Albuquerque, NM
Primary Contact: Devon Hyde, Vice President, Chief Administrative Officer
COO: Paul Briggs, Executive Vice President and Chief Operating Officer
CFO: Dale Maxwell, Executive Vice President and Chief Financial Officer
CMO: Jayne McCormick, M.D., Chief Medical Officer CDS
CIO: Lee Marley, VP/Information Services Chief Application Officer
CHR: Lee Patchell, Lead Human Resources Business Partner
CNO: Ann L Wright, R.N., MSN, Assistant Central Delivery System CNO
Web address: www.phs.org
Control: Other not–for–profit (including NFP Corporation) **Service**: General medical and surgical

Staffed Beds: 616 Admissions: 42152 Census: 522 Outpatient Visits: 2141729 Births: 4231 Total Expense ($000): 1518435 Payroll Expense ($000): 487964 Personnel: 5598

TURQUOISE LODGE HOSPITAL, 5901 Zuni Road SE, Zip 87108–3073; tel. 505/841–8978, (Nonreporting)
Primary Contact: Shauna Hartley, Administrator
CFO: Juliette Aragon, Finance Director
CIO: Eric Gurule, Chief Information Officer
CHR: Mario Lechuga, Director Human Resources
CNO: Debra Jane Green, R.N., Director of Nursing
Web address: www.health.state.nm.us
Control: State, Government, nonfederal **Service**: Alcoholism and other chemical dependency

Staffed Beds: 52

⊞ **UNIVERSITY OF NEW MEXICO HOSPITALS (320001)**, 2211 Lomas Boulevard NE, Zip 87106–2745; tel. 505/272–2111, (Includes CARRIE TINGLEY HOSPITAL, 1127 University Boulevard NE, Albuquerque, NM, Zip 87102–1715; tel. 505/272–5200; Doris Tinagero, Executive Director; MENTAL HEALTH CENTER, 2600 Marble NE, Albuquerque, NM, Zip 87131–2600; tel. 505/272–2800; UNIVERSITY OF NEW MEXICO Children's hospital psychiatric HOSPITAL, 1001 Yale Boulevard NE, Albuquerque, NM, Zip 87131–3830; tel. 505/272–2890; UNM CHILDREN'S HOSPITAL, 2211 Lomas Boulevard, NE, 3rd Floor of UNM Hospital, Albuquerque, NM, Zip 87106–2745; tel. 505/272–2111) **A**1 2 3 5 8 10 **F**3 8 9 11 13 15 16 18 19 20 21 22 23 24 25 26 27 28 29 30 31 32 34 35 38 40 41 43 44 45 46 47 48 49 50 51 54 56 57 59 60 61 63 64 65 68 70 72 73 74 75 76 77 78 79 81 82 83 84 85 86 87 88 89 90 92 93 94 95 96 97 107 108 109 110 111 114 116 117 118 119 121 123 126 129 132 135 136 138 144 146 147 148 **S** University of New Mexico Hospitals, Albuquerque, NM
Primary Contact: Kathleen R. Becker, M.P.H., JD, Chief Executive Officer
CFO: Ella Watt, Chief Financial Officer
CMO: Irene Agostini, M.D., Chief Medical Officer
CIO: Dawn Harrington, Chief Information Officer
CHR: Sara Frasch, Chief Human Resource Officer
Web address: www.unm.edu
Control: State, Government, nonfederal **Service**: General medical and surgical

Staffed Beds: 537 Admissions: 25078 Census: 485

★ **ARTESIA GENERAL HOSPITAL (320030)**, 702 North 13th Street, Zip 88210–1199; tel. 575/748–3333, (Nonreporting) **A**3 10 20
Primary Contact: Robert C. Tyk, Interim Chief Executive Officer
CFO: Carl Hollingsworth, Chief Financial Officer
CMO: Joe Salgado, M.D., Chief of Staff
CHR: Bruce Hinshaw, Director Human Resources
CNO: Wendi Hulett, Chief Nursing Officer
Web address: www.artesiageneral.com
Control: Other not–for–profit (including NFP Corporation) **Service**: General medical and surgical

Staffed Beds: 30

⊞ **CARLSBAD MEDICAL CENTER (320063)**, 2430 West Pierce Street, Zip 88220–3597; tel. 575/887–4100, (Total facility includes 15 beds in nursing home–type unit) **A**1 10 **F**11 13 15 18 20 22 28 29 30 34 35 39 40 41 43 45 46 50 51 54 57 59 64 65 66 70 74 75 76 77 78 79 81 83 85 86 87 90 91 92 93 107 108 110 111 115 119 120 121 122 123 128 129 135 144 146 147 148 149 **S** Community Health Systems, Inc., Franklin, TN
Primary Contact: Cathy Hibbs, Chief Executive Officer
CFO: Craig Morse, Chief Financial Officer
CIO: Thomas Motejzik, Director Information Systems
CNO: Connie Shofner, Chief Nursing Officer
Web address: www.carlsbadmedicalcenter.com
Control: Corporation, Investor–owned (for–profit) **Service**: General medical and surgical

Staffed Beds: 130 Admissions: 2376 Census: 27 Outpatient Visits: 65189 Births: 370 Total Expense ($000): 53263 Payroll Expense ($000): 19219 Personnel: 400

★ **UNION COUNTY GENERAL HOSPITAL (321304)**, 300 Wilson Street, Zip 88415–3304, Mailing Address: P.O. Box 489, Zip 88415–0489; tel. 575/374–2585, (Nonreporting) **A**10 18 **S** Community Hospital Corporation, Plano, TX
Primary Contact: Tammie Stump, R.N., Chief Executive Officer
CFO: Alexander B Altman III Chief Financial Officer
CMO: Daniel Radunsky, M.D., Medical Staff President
CIO: Kelsey Lawrence, Manager Information Technology
CHR: Jill Swagerty, Director Human Resources
CNO: Stacye Bradley, R.N., Chief Nursing Officer
Web address: www.ucgh.net/
Control: Other not–for–profit (including NFP Corporation) **Service**: General medical and surgical

Staffed Beds: 21

⊞ **PLAINS REGIONAL MEDICAL CENTER (320022)**, 2100 North Doctor Martin Luther King Boulevard, Zip 88101–9412, Mailing Address: P.O. Box 1688, Zip 88102–1688; tel. 575/769–2141, **A**1 10 **F**3 11 13 15 18 20 28 29 30 31 35 39 40 45 47 48 50 51 53 56 57 61 62 63 64 65 68 69 70 75 76 77 78 79 81 84 85 87 89 93 97 107 108 110 111 112 114 115 116 119 120 121 123 129 130 135 146 147 148 149 150 154 **P**6 **S** Presbyterian Healthcare Services, Albuquerque, NM
Primary Contact: Troy Clark, Interim Administrator
CMO: Brian Willmon, M.D., Medical Director
CHR: Cindy Duncan, Manager Human Resources
CNO: Terri A Marney, R.N., Director of Nursing
Web address: www.phs.org
Control: Other not–for–profit (including NFP Corporation) **Service**: General medical and surgical

Staffed Beds: 60 Admissions: 3349 Census: 26 Outpatient Visits: 132561 Births: 1096 Total Expense ($000): 93654 Payroll Expense ($000): 31916 Personnel: 461

⊞ **U.S. PUBLIC HEALTH SERVICE INDIAN HOSPITAL (320062)**, Route 9 and State Road 371, Zip 87313, Mailing Address: P.O. Box 358, Zip 87313–0358; tel. 505/786–5291, (Nonreporting) **A**10 **S** U.S. Indian Health Service, Rockville, MD
Primary Contact: Anslem Roanhorse, Chief Executive Officer
CFO: Darlene Kirk, Manager Finance
CMO: John Johnson, M.D., Clinical Director
CIO: Jimmy Burbank, Chief Information Officer
CHR: Christina Bitsilly, Human Resource Specialist
CNO: Alex Daniels, Chief Nurse Executive
Web address: www.ihs.gov
Control: PHS, Indian Service, Government, federal **Service**: General medical and surgical

Staffed Beds: 12

DEMING—Luna County

☒ **MIMBRES MEMORIAL HOSPITAL (321309)**, 900 West Ash Street, Zip 88030–4098, Mailing Address: P.O. Box 710, Zip 88031–0710; tel. 575/546–5800, **A**1 10 18 **F**11 13 15 18 20 22 29 30 34 35 40 41 44 45 46 48 51 57 59 64 68 70 75 76 77 79 81 82 87 91 97 107 110 111 114 115 119 120 126 127 130 131 132 146 147 154 **S** Quorum Health, Brentwood, TN
Primary Contact: Steve Westenhofer, Interim Chief Executive Officer
CFO: Trisha Smith, Chief Financial Officer
CHR: Johanna Gramer, Director Human Resources
CNO: Joy Harrell, R.N., Chief Nursing Officer
Web address: www.mimbresmemorial.com
Control: Corporation, Investor–owned (for–profit) **Service**: General medical and surgical

Staffed Beds: 25 Admissions: 1461 Census: 18

ESPANOLA—Rio Arriba County

☒ **PRESBYTERIAN ESPANOLA HOSPITAL (320011)**, 1010 Spruce Street, Zip 87532–2746; tel. 505/753–7111, **A**1 10 20 **F**3 7 8 11 13 15 29 30 34 35 40 45 50 51 53 57 59 62 64 68 70 76 79 81 85 93 107 108 110 115 119 129 130 146 **P**6 **S** Presbyterian Healthcare Services, Albuquerque, NM
Primary Contact: Brenda Romero, Administrator
CFO: Lupe Lucero, Manager Business Office
CMO: Fernando Bayardo, M.D., Chief Medical Officer
CHR: Joshua Griffith, Manager Human Resources
CNO: Nancy Santiesteban, Director Patient Care Services
Web address: www.phs.org
Control: Other not–for–profit (including NFP Corporation) **Service**: General medical and surgical

Staffed Beds: 46 Admissions: 2202 Census: 21 Outpatient Visits: 144183 Births: 273 Total Expense ($000): 70097 Payroll Expense ($000): 31768 Personnel: 307

FARMINGTON—San Juan County

☒ ⇑ **SAN JUAN REGIONAL MEDICAL CENTER (320005)**, 801 West Maple Street, Zip 87401–5630; tel. 505/609–2000, (Includes SAN JUAN REGIONAL MEDICAL CENTER REHABILITATION HOSPITAL, 525 South Schwartz Avenue, Farmington, NM, Zip 87401–5955; tel. 505/609–2625; Jeff A. Bourgeois, President and Chief Executive Officer) **A**1 10 21 **F**3 7 8 11 13 15 18 20 22 26 28 29 30 31 32 34 35 39 40 43 45 46 47 48 49 50 53 54 57 59 60 61 64 65 68 70 74 75 76 77 78 79 81 82 85 86 87 89 90 92 93 96 97 98 100 102 104 107 108 110 111 112 114 115 117 119 121 130 132 135 143 144 146 147 148 154 **P**5 6
Primary Contact: Jeff A. Bourgeois, President and Chief Executive Officer
COO: John Buffington, Chief Operating Officer
CFO: Karen Miller, Chief Financial Officer
CMO: Melania Yeats, M.D., Chief Medical Officer
CIO: Sheri Rawlings, Chief Information Officer
CHR: Elizabeth Volkerding, Director Workforce Excellence
CNO: Suzanne E Smith, R.N., MSN, Chief Nursing Officer
Web address: www.sanjuanregional.com
Control: Other not–for–profit (including NFP Corporation) **Service**: General medical and surgical

Staffed Beds: 198 Admissions: 9894 Census: 124 Outpatient Visits: 785301 Total Expense ($000): 304848 Payroll Expense ($000): 148894 Personnel: 1747

GALLUP—Mckinley County

☒ **GALLUP INDIAN MEDICAL CENTER (320061)**, 516 East Nizhoni Boulevard, Zip 87301–5748, Mailing Address: P.O. Box 1337, Zip 87305–1337; tel. 505/722–1000, **A**1 5 10 **F**3 5 8 13 15 18 29 34 35 39 40 43 45 50 54 55 56 57 59 61 64 65 68 70 74 75 76 77 79 81 82 84 85 87 89 93 97 100 101 102 104 107 119 127 130 132 135 147 148 **S** U.S. Indian Health Service, Rockville, MD
Primary Contact: John Meese, Acting Director
CFO: Agnes Kee, Financial Manager
CMO: Douglas G Peter, M.D., Chief Medical Officer
CIO: Adrian C Haven, Site Manager
CHR: Karen Lee, Director Human Resources
CNO: Selva Thompson, R.N., Chief Nurse Executive
Web address: www.ihs.gov/navajo/index.cfm?module=nao_hcc_gallup
Control: PHS, Indian Service, Government, federal **Service**: General medical and surgical

Staffed Beds: 57 Admissions: 2247 Census: 33 Outpatient Visits: 258291 Births: 426 Total Expense ($000): 168181 Payroll Expense ($000): 75185

GALLUP—McKinley County

★ ⇑ **REHOBOTH MCKINLEY CHRISTIAN HEALTH CARE SERVICES (320038)**, 1901 Red Rock Drive, Zip 87301–5683; tel. 505/863–7000, **A**10 20 21 **F**3 4 5 11 13 15 28 29 30 32 34 35 40 45 50 57 59 62 63 64 65 68 70 74 75 76 77 79 81 82 84 85 86 87 89 93 97 100 104 107 108 110 111 115 118 119 129 130 131 132 135 144 146 149 154 **P**8
Primary Contact: David Conejo, Chief Executive Officer
COO: William Kiefer, Chief Operating Officer
CFO: John McMullin, Chief Financial Officer
CIO: Randy Myers, Chief Information Officer
CHR: Ronnye Etcitty, Director Human Resources
CNO: Bill Norton, Chief Nursing Officer
Web address: www.rmch.org
Control: Other not–for–profit (including NFP Corporation) **Service**: General medical and surgical

Staffed Beds: 62 Admissions: 2525 Census: 63 Outpatient Visits: 174250 Births: 328 Total Expense ($000): 68908 Payroll Expense ($000): 29539 Personnel: 506

GRANTS—Cibola County

☒ **CIBOLA GENERAL HOSPITAL (321308)**, 1016 East Roosevelt Avenue, Zip 87020–2118; tel. 505/287–4446, **A**1 10 18 **F**3 13 15 29 30 34 40 45 46 50 56 57 59 64 65 66 68 70 75 76 77 81 85 93 97 107 110 115 119 129 130 133 135 147 148 **S** QHR, Brentwood, TN
Primary Contact: Thomas Whelan, Chief Executive Officer
CFO: Ed Brown, Chief Financial Officer
CMO: Janice Shipley, M.D., Chief Medical Officer
CIO: Rick Smith, Director Information Services
CHR: Sheila Cox, Director Human Resources
CNO: Glenna Losito, R.N., MSN, Chief Nursing Officer
Web address: www.cibolahospital.com
Control: Other not–for–profit (including NFP Corporation) **Service**: General medical and surgical

Staffed Beds: 25 Admissions: 825 Census: 7 Outpatient Visits: 39501 Births: 186 Total Expense ($000): 27936 Payroll Expense ($000): 12433 Personnel: 184

HOBBS—Lea County

☒ **LEA REGIONAL MEDICAL CENTER (320065)**, 5419 North Lovington Highway, Zip 88240–9125, Mailing Address: P.O. Box 3000, Zip 88241–9501; tel. 575/492–5000, (Nonreporting) **A**1 10 **S** Community Health Systems, Inc., Franklin, TN
Primary Contact: Timothy Thornell, FACHE, Chief Executive Officer
CFO: Jorge Latibeaudiere, Chief Financial Officer
CMO: Ali Sherif, M.D., Chief of Staff
CIO: Terrance J. Purcell, Director Information Services
CHR: Laurie Russell, Director Human Resources
CNO: Patrick A Dunn, R.N., Chief Nursing Officer
Web address: www.learegionalmedical.com
Control: Corporation, Investor–owned (for–profit) **Service**: General medical and surgical

Staffed Beds: 195

LAS CRUCES—Dona Ana County

☐ **ADVANCED CARE HOSPITAL OF SOUTHERN NEW MEXICO (322004)**, 4451 East Lohman Avenue, Zip 88011–8267; tel. 575/521–6600, (Nonreporting) **A**1 10 **S** Ernest Health, Inc., Albuquerque, NM
Primary Contact: Claudia Saiz, Chief Executive Officer
Web address: www.achsnm.ernesthealth.com
Control: Corporation, Investor–owned (for–profit) **Service**: Acute long–term care hospital

Staffed Beds: 40

NM

☒ **MEMORIAL MEDICAL CENTER (320018)**, 2450 South Telshor Boulevard, Zip 88011–5076; tel. 575/522–8641, **A**1 2 3 10 13 **F**3 8 11 13 15 17 18 20 22 24 28 29 30 31 34 35 40 45 49 50 51 54 57 60 64 65 66 68 70 72 73 74 75 76 78 79 81 84 85 88 89 98 102 107 108 109 110 111 114 115 118 119 120 121 123 144 146 147 148 149 **S** LifePoint Health, Brentwood, TN
Primary Contact: John Harris, Chief Executive Officer
COO: Steven T Ruwoldt, Chief Operating Officer
CFO: Raymond Grenier, Chief Financial Officer
CMO: Bruce San Filippo, M.D., Chief Medical Officer
CHR: Laura Pierce, Director Human Resources
CNO: Ann Debooy, R.N., Chief Nursing Officer
Web address: www.mmclc.org
Control: Corporation, Investor–owned (for–profit) **Service**: General medical and surgical

Staffed Beds: 173 **Admissions**: 9062 **Census**: 112 **Outpatient Visits**: 135472 **Births**: 1123 **Total Expense ($000)**: 218185 **Payroll Expense ($000)**: 81752 **Personnel**: 1268

☒ **MESILLA VALLEY HOSPITAL (324010)**, 3751 Del Rey Boulevard, Zip 88012–8526; tel. 575/382–3500, (Nonreporting) **A**1 10 **S** Universal Health Services, Inc., King of Prussia, PA
Primary Contact: Anna Laliotis, Chief Executive Officer
CFO: Dana McRimmon, Chief Financial Officer
CMO: Arthur L. Ramirez, M.D., Medical Director
CIO: Rebecca Mumpower, Director Marketing
CHR: Linda Moya, Director Human Resources
CNO: Veronica Hughes, Chief Nursing Officer
Web address: www.mesillavalleyhospital.com
Control: Corporation, Investor–owned (for–profit) **Service**: Psychiatric

Staffed Beds: 120

☒ **MOUNTAINVIEW REGIONAL MEDICAL CENTER (320085)**, 4311 East Lohman Avenue, Zip 88011–8255; tel. 575/556–7600, (Nonreporting) **A**1 10 12 13 **S** Community Health Systems, Inc., Franklin, TN
Primary Contact: Derrick Cuenca, Chief Executive Officer
COO: Warren Yehl, Chief Operating Officer
CIO: Donald Harlow, Director of Information Services
CHR: Delilah Doss, Director, Human Resources
CNO: Gayle Nash, R.N., M.P.H., Chief Nursing Officer
Web address: www.mountainviewregional.com
Control: Corporation, Investor–owned (for–profit) **Service**: General medical and surgical

Staffed Beds: 142

☒ **REHABILITATION HOSPITAL OF SOUTHERN NEW MEXICO (323032)**, 4441 East Lohman Avenue, Zip 88011–8267; tel. 575/521–6400, (Nonreporting) **A**1 10 **S** Ernest Health, Inc., Albuquerque, NM
Primary Contact: Sabrina Martin, Chief Executive Officer
CFO: Elizabeth Striplin, Chief Financial Officer
CMO: Kimberly Encapera, M.D., Medical Director
CIO: Ricky Molina, Director Marketing and Business Development
CHR: Yolanda Mendoza, Director Human Resources
CNO: Carole Carson, Director of Nursing Operations
Web address: www.rhsnm.ernesthealth.com
Control: Corporation, Investor–owned (for–profit) **Service**: Rehabilitation

Staffed Beds: 40

LAS VEGAS—San Miguel County

☒ **ALTA VISTA REGIONAL HOSPITAL (320003)**, 104 Legion Drive, Zip 87701–4804; tel. 505/426–3500, (Nonreporting) **A**1 10 20 **S** Quorum Health, Brentwood, TN
Primary Contact: Caleb F. O'Rear, Chief Executive Officer
CMO: Nancy Wright, M.D., Chief Medical Staff
CIO: Laird Thornton, Director Information Systems
CHR: Michael Freeman, Director Human Resources
CNO: Rhonda Clark, Interim Chief Nursing Officer
Web address: www.altavistaregionalhospital.com
Control: Corporation, Investor–owned (for–profit) **Service**: General medical and surgical

Staffed Beds: 54

☐ **NEW MEXICO BEHAVIORAL HEALTH INSTITUTE AT LAS VEGAS**, 3695 Hot Springs Boulevard, Zip 87701–9549; tel. 505/454–2100, (Nonreporting) **A**1
Primary Contact: Frances Tweed, R.N., Executive Director and Administrator
COO: Charles Jaramillo, Chief Operating Officer
CFO: Darlene Martinez, Director Finance
CMO: Daniel Collins, M.D., Clinical Director
CNO: Mabel Arguello–Vasquez, R.N., Executive Nurse Administrator
Web address: www.nmbhi.org
Control: State, Government, nonfederal **Service**: Psychiatric

Staffed Beds: 257

LOS ALAMOS—Los Alamos County

☒ **LOS ALAMOS MEDICAL CENTER (320033)**, 3917 West Road, Zip 87544–2293; tel. 505/661–9500, **A**1 10 20 **F**3 8 11 13 15 28 29 30 31 34 35 40 45 46 49 50 57 59 64 65 68 70 73 75 76 78 81 85 87 90 93 107 108 110 111 114 119 124 129 130 143 146 147 150 **P**8 **S** LifePoint Health, Brentwood, TN
Primary Contact: John Whiteside, Chief Executive Officer
CFO: Steve Weingart, Chief Financial Officer
CMO: Barbara Van Eeckhout, M.D., Chief of Staff
CIO: Kevin Vigil, Director Information Systems
CHR: Jacqueline Carroll, Director Human Resources
CNO: Tracie Stratton, Chief Nursing Officer
Web address: www.losalamosmedicalcenter.com
Control: Corporation, Investor–owned (for–profit) **Service**: General medical and surgical

Staffed Beds: 29 **Admissions**: 805 **Census**: 7 **Outpatient Visits**: 51482 **Births**: 195 **Total Expense ($000)**: 37824 **Payroll Expense ($000)**: 12761

LOVINGTON—Lea County

★ ⇑ **NOR–LEA HOSPITAL DISTRICT (321305)**, 1600 North Main Avenue, Zip 88260–2871; tel. 575/396–6611, **A**10 18 21 **F**3 8 9 15 18 26 28 29 30 31 32 34 35 39 40 43 45 46 49 50 54 57 59 64 65 66 68 69 74 75 77 78 81 82 89 92 93 97 100 101 102 104 107 108 110 111 115 119 127 129 130 132 133 135 146 147 148 149 154 **P**6
Primary Contact: David B. Shaw, Chief Executive Officer and Administrator
COO: Dan Hamilton, Chief Operating Officer
CFO: Allyson Roberts, CPA, Chief Financial Officer
CMO: Ronald Hopkins, D.O., Chief of Staff
CIO: Brent Kelley, Director Information Technology
CHR: Angela Carrejo, Director Human Resources
CNO: Marcia Patterson, MSN, R.N., Chief Nursing Officer
Web address: www.norlea.org/
Control: Hospital district or authority, Government, nonfederal **Service**: General medical and surgical

Staffed Beds: 25 **Admissions**: 546 **Census**: 5 **Outpatient Visits**: 231845 **Births**: 0 **Total Expense ($000)**: 73238 **Payroll Expense ($000)**: 29252 **Personnel**: 411

MESCALERO—Otero County

☐ **MESCALERO PUBLIC HEALTH SERVICE INDIAN HOSPITAL (320058)**, 318 Abalone Loop, Zip 88340, Mailing Address: Box 210, Zip 88340–0210; tel. 505/464–3801, (Nonreporting) **A**1 10 **S** U.S. Indian Health Service, Rockville, MD
Primary Contact: Dorlynn Simmons, Chief Executive Officer
CFO: Rainey Enjady, Administrative Officer
CIO: Kathy Murphy, Site Manager
Web address: www.ihs.gov
Control: PHS, Indian Service, Government, federal **Service**: General medical and surgical

Staffed Beds: 13

PORTALES—Roosevelt County

⇑ **ROOSEVELT GENERAL HOSPITAL (320084)**, 42121 US Highway 70, Zip 88130, Mailing Address: P.O. Box 868, Zip 88130–0868; tel. 575/359–1800, (Nonreporting) **A**10 21
Primary Contact: Kaye Green, FACHE, Chief Executive Officer
CFO: Eva Steven, Chief Financial Officer
CMO: Les Donaldson, M.D., Chief of Staff
CHR: Cindy Duncan, Director Human Resources
Web address: www.myrgh.org
Control: Hospital district or authority, Government, nonfederal **Service**: General medical and surgical

Staffed Beds: 22

RATON—Colfax County

★ **MINERS' COLFAX MEDICAL CENTER (321307)**, 200 Hospital Drive, Zip 87740–2099; tel. 575/445–7700, (Includes MINERS' COLFAX MEDICAL CENTER, 203 Hospital Drive, Raton, NM, Zip 87740, Mailing Address: Box 1067, Zip 87740, tel. 575/445–3661; Bo Beames, Chief Executive Officer) **A**10 18 **F**11 13 15 18 34 40 45 46 50 53 54 56 57 58 59 65 70 71 75 76 77 78 81 82 85 86 87 97 107 115 119 127 129 130 132 133 135 146 147 148
Primary Contact: Bo Beames, Interim Chief Executive Officer
CFO: Albino Martinez, Director Budget and Finance
CIO: Richard Laner Jr Manager Information Systems
CHR: Jamie Johnson, Director Human Resources
Web address: www.minershosp.com
Control: State, Government, nonfederal **Service**: General medical and surgical

Staffed Beds: 25 **Admissions**: 925 **Census**: 9

NM

RIO RANCHO—Sandoval County

☐ **UNM SANDOVAL REGIONAL MEDICAL CENTER, INC. (320089)**, 3001 Broadmoor Boulevard NE, Zip 87131; tel. 505/994–7000, **A**1 3 5 10 **F**3 18 29 30 35 40 45 46 47 48 49 50 70 74 79 80 81 87 93 94 97 100 107 108 110 111 114 115 119 126 129 130 131 143 146 154 **P**8 **S** University of New Mexico Hospitals, Albuquerque, NM
Primary Contact: Jamie A. Silva–Steele, FACHE, R.N., President and Chief Executive Officer
CFO: Darlene Fernandez, Chief Financial Officer
CMO: Robb McLean, M.D., Chief Medical Officer
CIO: Matthew Braun, Chief Information Officer
CHR: Correen Bales, Executive Director Human Resources
CNO: Pamela Demarest, MSN, R.N., Chief Nursing Officer
Web address: www.hsc.unm.edu/health/locations/sandoval–regional–medical–center.html
Control: Other not–for–profit (including NFP Corporation) **Service:** General medical and surgical

Staffed Beds: 60 **Admissions:** 4527 **Census:** 41 **Outpatient Visits:** 66798 **Births:** 0 **Total Expense ($000):** 85877 **Payroll Expense ($000):** 31030 **Personnel:** 601

ROSWELL—Chaves County

☒ **EASTERN NEW MEXICO MEDICAL CENTER (320006)**, 405 West Country Club Road, Zip 88201–5209; tel. 575/622–8170, (Nonreporting) **A**1 10 19 **S** Community Health Systems, Inc., Franklin, TN
Primary Contact: Warren Yehl, Interim Chief Executive Officer
CFO: Leanne Hacker, Chief Financial Officer
CMO: Richard Pinon, Chief Medical Officer
CIO: Deepak Surl, Chief Information Officer
CHR: Sheila Nunez, Director Human Resources
CNO: Kathy Williams, Chief Nursing Officer
Web address: www.enmmc.com
Control: Corporation, Investor–owned (for–profit) **Service:** General medical and surgical

Staffed Beds: 149

★ **LOVELACE REGIONAL HOSPITAL – ROSWELL (320086)**, 117 East 19th Street, Zip 88201–5151; tel. 575/627–7000, **A**10 13 **F**3 13 17 18 22 29 34 40 45 57 59 70 76 79 81 82 85 89 90 91 93 111 119 130 146 147 **S** Ardent Health Services, Nashville, TN
Primary Contact: Heather L. Harper, FACHE, Chief Executive Officer
CFO: Veronica Galaviz, Chief Financial Officer
CNO: Rhonda Rauch, Chief Nursing Officer
Web address: www.lovelace.com
Control: Corporation, Investor–owned (for–profit) **Service:** General medical and surgical

Staffed Beds: 26 **Admissions:** 2231 **Census:** 17

☐ **NEW MEXICO REHABILITATION CENTER (323026)**, 72 Gail Harris Street, Zip 88203–8116; tel. 575/347–3400, (Includes PECOS VALLEY LODGE, 31 Gail Harris Avenue, Roswell, NM, Zip 88201; tel. 505/347–5491) (Nonreporting) **A**1 10
Primary Contact: Jose Gurrola, Administrator
CFO: Shirley Donaldson, Chief Financial Officer
CMO: Stephen Dorman, M.D., Chief Medical Officer
CIO: Dennis Hoefs, Manager Information Technology
CHR: Teresa Casarez, Director Human Resources
CNO: William Chaltry, Chief Nursing Officer
Control: State, Government, nonfederal **Service:** Rehabilitation

Staffed Beds: 41

RUIDOSO—Lincoln County

☒ **LINCOLN COUNTY MEDICAL CENTER (321306)**, 211 Sudderth Drive, Zip 88345–6043, Mailing Address: P.O. Box 8000, Zip 88355–8000; tel. 575/257–8200, **A**1 10 18 **F**7 11 13 15 29 34 35 39 40 45 46 50 53 56 57 59 64 65 68 70 74 76 77 79 81 85 87 91 93 97 107 110 111 115 119 127 130 131 132 135 144 146 148 **P**6 **S** Presbyterian Healthcare Services, Albuquerque, NM
Primary Contact: Todd Oberheu, Administrator
CFO: Dudley McCauley, Controller
CMO: Gary Jackson, D.O., Medical Director
CHR: Susanne Johnston, Manager Human Resources
Web address: www.phs.org
Control: Other not–for–profit (including NFP Corporation) **Service:** General medical and surgical

Staffed Beds: 25 **Admissions:** 1101 **Census:** 9 **Outpatient Visits:** 87946 **Births:** 250 **Total Expense ($000):** 42294 **Payroll Expense ($000):** 19138 **Personnel:** 240

SANTA FE—Santa Fe County

☒ △ **CHRISTUS ST. VINCENT REGIONAL MEDICAL CENTER (320002)**, 455 Saint Michaels Drive, Zip 87505–7601, Mailing Address: P.O. Box 2107, Zip 87505; tel. 505/983–3361, (Includes CHRISTUS ST. VINCENT PHYSICIANS MEDICAL CENTER, 2990 Rodeo Park Drive East, Santa Fe, NM, Zip 87505; tel. 505/428–5400; J. Alex Valdez, JD, President and Chief Executive Officer) **A**1 2 3 7 10 20 **F**8 12 13 15 17 18 19 20 21 22 24 26 28 29 30 31 32 34 35 36 37 38 39 40 41 43 45 46 47 48 49 50 51 53 54 56 57 64 65 66 68 70 73 74 75 76 77 78 79 81 82 83 84 85 86 87 88 89 90 91 92 93 97 98 100 101 102 104 107 108 109 110 111 112 113 114 115 119 120 121 122 124 126 129 130 131 132 135 143 144 146 147 148 149 150 154 **S** CHRISTUS Health, Irving, TX
Primary Contact: Lillian Montoya, President and Chief Executive Officer
COO: Jason Adams, Chief Operating Officer
CFO: Bob Moon, Chief Financial Officer
CMO: John C Beeson, M.D., Chief Medical Officer
CIO: Ron Dekeyzer, Regional Director Information Systems
CHR: Pearl Mohnkern, Vice President and Director Human Resources
Web address: www.stvin.org
Control: Other not–for–profit (including NFP Corporation) **Service:** General medical and surgical

Staffed Beds: 219 **Admissions:** 12131 **Census:** 142 **Outpatient Visits:** 144606 **Births:** 1303 **Total Expense ($000):** 396536 **Payroll Expense ($000):** 153579 **Personnel:** 1806

☐ **PHS SANTA FE INDIAN HOSPITAL (320057)**, 1700 Cerrillos Road, Zip 87505–3554; tel. 505/988–9821, (Nonreporting) **A**1 5 10 **S** U.S. Indian Health Service, Rockville, MD
Primary Contact: Leslie Dye, Chief Executive Officer
CMO: Bret Smoker, M.D., Clinical Director
CIO: Vernita Jones, Site Manager
Control: PHS, Indian Service, Government, federal **Service:** General medical and surgical

Staffed Beds: 4

SANTA ROSA—Guadalupe County

★ **GUADALUPE COUNTY HOSPITAL (320067)**, 117 Camino de Vida, Zip 88435–2267; tel. 575/472–3417, **A**10 20 **F**3 29 34 35 40 50 57 59 64 65 81 82 87 107 114 119 130 148 **P**5
Primary Contact: Christina Campos, Administrator
CFO: Bret Goebel, Chief Financial Officer
CMO: Randal Brown, M.D., Chief of Medical Staff
CIO: Emilio Campos, Deparment Head Information Technology
CHR: Colleen Gallegos, Director Human Resources
CNO: Mandelyn Cordova, R.N., Director of Nurses
Web address: www.gchnm.org
Control: County, Government, nonfederal **Service:** General medical and surgical

Staffed Beds: 10 **Admissions:** 269 **Census:** 2 **Outpatient Visits:** 8760 **Births:** 2 **Total Expense ($000):** 10231 **Payroll Expense ($000):** 2051 **Personnel:** 45

SANTA TERESA—Dona Ana County

☐ **PEAK BEHAVIORAL HEALTH SERVICES (324012)**, 5065 McNutt Road, Zip 88008–9442; tel. 575/589–3000, (Nonreporting) **A**1 10 **S** Strategic Behavioral Health, LLC, Memphis, TN
Primary Contact: Peggy Cunningham, Chief Executive Officer
COO: Doug Ginn, Executive Vice President Operations
CFO: Espie Herrara, Chief Financial Officer
CHR: Norma Oaxaca, Director Human Resources
Web address: www.peakbehavioral.com/
Control: Corporation, Investor–owned (for–profit) **Service:** Psychiatric

Staffed Beds: 36

NM

Hospital, Medicare Provider Number, Address, Telephone, Approval, Facility, and Physician Codes, Health Care System
★ American Hospital Association (AHA) membership ☐ The Joint Commission accreditation ○ Healthcare Facilities Accreditation Program ◇ DNV Healthcare Inc. accreditation ⇑ Center for Improvement in Healthcare Quality Accreditation △ Commission on Accreditation of Rehabilitation Facilities (CARF) accreditation

SHIPROCK—San Juan County

⊞ **NORTHERN NAVAJO MEDICAL CENTER (320059)**, Highway 491 North, Zip 87420–0160, Mailing Address: P.O. Box 160, Zip 87420–0160; tel. 505/368–6001, (Nonreporting) **A**1 10 **S** U.S. Indian Health Service, Rockville, MD
Primary Contact: Fannessa Comer, Chief Executive Officer
CFO: Shawn Morgan, Finance Officer
CMO: Ira Salom, M.D., Clinical Director
CIO: Roland Chapman, Chief Information Officer
CHR: Gloria Redhorse–Charley, Director Human Resources
CNO: Lavenia Diswood, R.N., Chief Nurse Executive
Web address: www.ihs.gov/
Control: PHS, Indian Service, Government, federal **Service**: General medical and surgical

Staffed Beds: 68

SILVER CITY—Grant County

☐ **GILA REGIONAL MEDICAL CENTER (320016)**, 1313 East 32nd Street, Zip 88061–7251; tel. 575/538–4000, **A**1 3 10 20 **F**3 11 13 14 15 18 29 30 31 35 40 45 50 51 53 64 68 70 76 77 78 79 81 82 85 87 89 93 97 98 100 102 103 107 110 111 115 119 120 123 129 130 132 148 149
Primary Contact: Taffy J. Arias, Chief Executive Officer
CFO: Richard W Stokes, CPA, Jr Chief Financial Officer
CIO: David Furnas, Chief Information Officer
CHR: Barbara Barela, Director Human Resources
CNO: Patricia Sheyka, Chief Nursing Officer
Web address: www.grmc.org
Control: County, Government, nonfederal **Service**: General medical and surgical

Staffed Beds: 47 **Admissions**: 1988 **Census**: 18

SOCORRO—Socorro County

⊞ **SOCORRO GENERAL HOSPITAL (321301)**, 1202 Highway 60 West, Zip 87801–3914, Mailing Address: P.O. Box 1009, Zip 87801–1009; tel. 575/835–1140, **A**1 10 18 **F**3 11 13 15 18 29 30 34 35 40 45 57 59 62 63 64 65 68 75 76 77 81 83 85 91 93 100 103 107 115 119 130 132 133 134 135 146 147 **P**6 **S** Presbyterian Healthcare Services, Albuquerque, NM
Primary Contact: Veronica Pound, R.N., Administrator
CFO: Scott Shannon, Director Finance
CMO: Darla Bejnar, M.D., Chief Medical Officer
CHR: Pam Miller–Balfour, Director Human Resources
CNO: Veronica Pound, R.N., Interim Administrator and Director of Patient Care
Web address: www.phs.org
Control: Other not–for–profit (including NFP Corporation) **Service**: General medical and surgical

Staffed Beds: 19 **Admissions**: 449 **Census**: 5 **Outpatient Visits**: 56268
Births: 91 **Total Expense ($000)**: 28324 **Payroll Expense ($000)**: 13814
Personnel: 168

TAOS—Taos County

★ ⇑ **HOLY CROSS HOSPITAL (320013)**, 1397 Weimer Road, Zip 87571–6253; tel. 575/758–8883, **A**3 10 20 21 **F**3 11 13 15 18 29 30 32 34 35 40 45 46 50 59 64 68 75 77 79 80 81 85 86 87 91 93 97 100 102 107 110 114 115 118 119 130 132 133 145 146 147 148 149 **P**6 8 **S** QHR, Brentwood, TN
Primary Contact: William D. Patten Jr, Chief Executive Officer
CFO: Steve Rozenboom, Chief Financial Officer
CHR: Judy Marshall, Director Human Resources
CNO: Denise Clark, Chief Nursing Officer
Web address: www.taoshospital.org
Control: Other not–for–profit (including NFP Corporation) **Service**: General medical and surgical

Staffed Beds: 29 **Admissions**: 1537 **Census**: 15 **Outpatient Visits**: 45752
Births: 232 **Total Expense ($000)**: 59439 **Payroll Expense ($000)**: 26959
Personnel: 353

TRUTH OR CONSEQUENCES—Sierra County

★ ⇑ **SIERRA VISTA HOSPITAL (321300)**, 800 East Ninth Avenue, Zip 87901–1961; tel. 575/894–2111, **A**10 18 21 **F**7 11 15 16 30 34 40 54 57 59 65 67 93 99 102 104 107 110 127 128 130 133 **S** QHR, Brentwood, TN
Primary Contact: David Faulkner, Interim Chief Executive Officer
CFO: Bret Gobel, Chief Financial Officer
CMO: James F Malcolmson, M.D., Chief of Staff
CIO: Dan Morrell, Manager Information Systems
CHR: Mindee Holguin, Manager Human Resources
CNO: Palmer Greene, R.N., Chief Nursing Officer
Web address: www.svhnm.org
Control: City–county, Government, nonfederal **Service**: General medical and surgical

Staffed Beds: 15 **Admissions**: 485 **Census**: 4

TUCUMCARI—Quay County

★ **DR. DAN C. TRIGG MEMORIAL HOSPITAL (321302)**, 301 East Miel De Luna Avenue, Zip 88401–3810; tel. 575/461–7000, **A**10 18 **F**11 15 29 35 40 59 62 63 64 65 68 81 85 87 97 104 107 110 114 119 130 133 135 146 148 **P**6 **S** Presbyterian Healthcare Services, Albuquerque, NM
Primary Contact: Troy Clark, Interim Administrator
CMO: Darrell Willis, M.D., Chief of Staff
CNO: Vickie Gutierrez, Director of Patient Care
Web address: www.phs.org
Control: Other not–for–profit (including NFP Corporation) **Service**: General medical and surgical

Staffed Beds: 10 **Admissions**: 161 **Census**: 2 **Outpatient Visits**: 22858
Births: 0 **Total Expense ($000)**: 16863 **Payroll Expense ($000)**: 5332
Personnel: 75

ZUNI—McKinley County

☐ **U.S. PUBLIC HEALTH SERVICE INDIAN HOSPITAL (320060)**, Route 301 North B Street, Zip 87327, Mailing Address: P.O. Box 467, Zip 87327–0467; tel. 505/782–4431, (Nonreporting) **A**1 10 **S** U.S. Indian Health Service, Rockville, MD
Primary Contact: Jean Othole, Chief Executive Officer
CFO: Clyde Yatsattie, Administrative Officer
CMO: David Kessler, M.D., Clinical Director
CHR: Cynthia Tsalate, Human Resource Specialist
Web address: www.ihs.gov
Control: PHS, Indian Service, Government, federal **Service**: General medical and surgical

Staffed Beds: 32

NM

Many Facility Codes have changed. Please refer to the AHA Guide Code Chart. © 2018 AHA Guide

NEW YORK

ALBANY—Albany County

☐ **ALBANY MEDICAL CENTER (330013)**, 43 New Scotland Avenue, Zip 12208–3478; tel. 518/262–3125, (Includes ALBANY MEDICAL CENTER SOUTH–CLINICAL CAMPUS, 25 Hackett Boulevard, Albany, NY, Zip 12208–3499; tel. 518/242–1200; Timothy W Duffy, General Director) **A**1 2 3 5 8 10 19 **F**3 6 7 8 11 12 13 15 17 18 19 20 21 22 23 24 25 26 27 28 29 30 31 32 34 35 38 39 40 41 43 44 45 46 47 49 50 51 52 53 54 55 56 57 58 59 60 61 64 65 68 70 72 73 74 75 76 77 78 79 81 82 84 85 86 87 88 89 90 92 93 96 98 100 102 103 104 105 107 108 109 110 111 114 115 116 117 118 119 120 121 122 123 124 126 130 131 132 135 138 142 145 146 148
Primary Contact: James J. Barba, President and Chief Executive Officer
COO: Bernadette R Pedlow, Senior Vice President Business and Chief Operating Officer
CFO: Frances Spreer–Albert, Chief Financial Officer and Executive Vice President
CMO: Dennis McKenna, M.D., Interim Vice President Medical Affairs
CIO: George Hickman, Executive Vice President and Chief Information Officer
Web address: www.amc.edu
Control: Other not–for–profit (including NFP Corporation) **Service:** General medical and surgical

Staffed Beds: 784 **Admissions:** 40635 **Census:** 639 **Outpatient Visits:** 376236 **Births:** 2071 **Total Expense ($000):** 998515 **Payroll Expense ($000):** 311366 **Personnel:** 6062

★ **ALBANY MEMORIAL HOSPITAL (330003)**, 600 Northern Boulevard, Zip 12204–1083; tel. 518/471–3221, **A**10 **F**3 8 15 29 30 31 34 40 45 46 49 50 54 57 59 60 63 64 68 70 77 79 81 84 85 87 93 107 111 119 130 135 146 147 148 149 **S** Trinity Health, Livonia, MI
Primary Contact: James K. Reed, M.D., Chief Executive Officer
CFO: Lori Santos, Vice President Finance
CMO: Robert Cella, M.D., Chief Medical Officer
CHR: Judy Gray, Vice President Human Resources
Web address: www.nehealth.com
Control: Other not–for–profit (including NFP Corporation) **Service:** General medical and surgical

Staffed Beds: 74 **Admissions:** 2604 **Census:** 33 **Outpatient Visits:** 144120 **Births:** 0 **Total Expense ($000):** 87957 **Payroll Expense ($000):** 35780 **Personnel:** 472

⊞ △ **ALBANY STRATTON VETERANS AFFAIRS MEDICAL CENTER**, 113 Holland Avenue, Zip 12208–3410; tel. 518/626–5000, (Total facility includes 50 beds in nursing home–type unit) **A**1 2 3 5 7 8 **F**2 3 4 5 15 17 18 20 22 28 29 30 31 34 35 38 39 40 44 45 46 47 49 54 55 56 57 58 59 60 61 62 63 64 65 68 70 74 75 77 78 79 81 82 83 84 85 86 87 91 92 93 94 97 98 100 101 102 103 104 105 106 107 108 110 111 115 117 118 119 120 121 122 123 126 127 128 129 130 132 133 135 143 144 146 147 148 149 150 152 153 154 **S** Department of Veterans Affairs, Perry Point, MD
Primary Contact: Darlene DeLancey, Interim Director
CFO: Gerard Scorzelli, Chief Financial Officer
CMO: Lourdes Irizarry, M.D., Chief of Staff
CIO: Ron Diaz, Manager Operations
CHR: Kenneth Kio, Manager Human Resources
CNO: Deborah Spath, R.N., MSN, Associate Director Patient and Nurses Services
Web address: www.albany.va.gov/
Control: Veterans Affairs, Government, federal **Service:** General medical and surgical

Staffed Beds: 121 **Admissions:** 3402 **Census:** 97 **Outpatient Visits:** 375313 **Births:** 0 **Total Expense ($000):** 237384 **Payroll Expense ($000):** 132239 **Personnel:** 1293

☐ **CAPITAL DISTRICT PSYCHIATRIC CENTER (334046)**, 75 New Scotland Avenue, Zip 12208–3474; tel. 518/549–6000, (Nonreporting) **A**1 3 5 10 **S** New York State Office of Mental Health, Albany, NY
Primary Contact: William Dickson, Executive Director
COO: Catherine McGregor, Deputy Director Facility and Administrative Services
CMO: Kren K Shriver, M.D., Clinical Director
CNO: Charlene Puorto, Chief Nursing Officer
Web address: www.omh.ny.gov/omhweb/facilities/cdpc/facility.htm
Control: State, Government, nonfederal **Service:** Psychiatric

Staffed Beds: 200

⊞ **ST. PETER'S HOSPITAL (330057)**, 315 South Manning Boulevard, Zip 12208–1789; tel. 518/525–1550, **A**1 2 3 5 10 19 **F**4 5 8 11 12 13 15 17 18 19 20 21 22 23 24 26 27 28 29 30 31 34 35 36 37 38 39 40 45 46 47 48 49 50 51 53 54 56 57 59 60 61 62 63 64 65 66 68 69 70 71 72 73 74 75 76 77 78 79 81 82 84 85 86 87 89 92 93 97 107 108 109 110 111 114 115 116 117 118 119 120 121 123 124 126 129 130 132 133 135 143 145 146 147 148 151 152 **P**6 **S** Trinity Health, Livonia, MI
Primary Contact: James K. Reed, M.D., Chief Executive Officer
CFO: Lori Santos, Chief Financial Officer
CMO: Robert Cella, M.D., Chief Medical Officer
CHR: Judy Gray, Vice President Human Resources
CNO: Jane O'Rourke, R.N., Chief Nursing Officer, Vice President Operations
Web address: www.sphcs.org
Control: Church operated, Nongovernment, not–for–profit **Service:** General medical and surgical

Staffed Beds: 442 **Admissions:** 27307 **Census:** 378 **Outpatient Visits:** 497904 **Births:** 2875 **Total Expense ($000):** 569638 **Payroll Expense ($000):** 195277 **Personnel:** 3177

ALEXANDRIA BAY—Jefferson County

RIVER HOSPITAL (331309), 4 Fuller Street, Zip 13607–1316; tel. 315/482–2511, (Nonreporting) **A**10 18
Primary Contact: Ben Moore III, President and Chief Executive Officer
COO: William Connor, Assistant Administrator and Director Human Resources
CFO: Traci Mintonye, Chief Financial Officer
CMO: Prasad Yitta, M.D., Medical Director
CIO: John Smithers, Network Specialist
CHR: William Connor, Assistant Administrator and Director Human Resources
CNO: Ann Narrow, Director of Nursing
Web address: www.riverhospital.org
Control: Other not–for–profit (including NFP Corporation) **Service:** General medical and surgical

Staffed Beds: 11

AMITYVILLE—Suffolk County

☐ **BRUNSWICK PSYCH CENTER (334026)**, 81 Louden Avenue, Zip 11701–2736; tel. 631/789–7421, (Nonreporting) **A**1 10
Primary Contact: Amarjit Singh, M.D., President and Chief Executive Officer
Control: Corporation, Investor–owned (for–profit) **Service:** Psychiatric

Staffed Beds: 124

⊞ **SOUTH OAKS HOSPITAL (334027)**, 400 Sunrise Highway, Zip 11701–2508; tel. 631/264–4000, **A**1 3 10 **F**4 5 53 68 98 99 101 102 103 104 105 135 153 **P**5 6 **S** Northwell Health, New Hyde Park, NY
Primary Contact: Carolyn Sweetapple, Ph.D., R.N., CPA, Executive Director
CMO: Tina Walch, M.D., Medical Director
CHR: Irene Calvin, Vice President Human Resources
Web address: www.longislandhome.org
Control: Other not–for–profit (including NFP Corporation) **Service:** Psychiatric

Staffed Beds: 258 **Admissions:** 5041 **Census:** 152 **Outpatient Visits:** 103233 **Births:** 0 **Total Expense ($000):** 82509 **Payroll Expense ($000):** 49961 **Personnel:** 845

AMSTERDAM—Montgomery County

⊞ **ST. MARY'S HEALTHCARE (330047)**, 427 Guy Park Avenue, Zip 12010–1054; tel. 518/842–1900, (Includes ST. MARY'S HEALTHCARE, 427 Guy Park Avenue, Amsterdam, NY, Zip 12010–1054; tel. 518/842–1900; Victor Giulianelli, FACHE, President and Chief Executive Officer) (Total facility includes 160 beds in nursing home–type unit) **A**1 10 **F**2 3 4 5 8 11 13 15 17 28 29 30 31 34 35 36 38 40 45 46 49 50 51 54 56 57 59 60 61 65 66 68 70 71 74 75 76 77 78 79 81 84 85 86 87 89 90 93 94 96 97 98 99 100 101 102 103 104 107 108 110 111 115 116 126 127 128 130 131 132 135 144 145 146 147 149 150 154 **S** Ascension Healthcare, Saint Louis, MO
Primary Contact: Victor Giulianelli, FACHE, President and Chief Executive Officer
COO: Scott Bruce, Vice President Operations
CFO: Rick Henze, Chief Financial Officer
CMO: William Mayer, M.D., Vice President Medical Staff Services
CHR: Albert Turo, Vice President Human Resources
CNO: Michele M Walsh, Chief Nursing Officer
Web address: www.smha.org
Control: Other not–for–profit (including NFP Corporation) **Service:** General medical and surgical

Staffed Beds: 290 **Admissions:** 6705 **Census:** 248 **Outpatient Visits:** 436530 **Births:** 443 **Total Expense ($000):** 175365 **Payroll Expense ($000):** 87534 **Personnel:** 1435

NY

Hospital, Medicare Provider Number, Address, Telephone, Approval, Facility, and Physician Codes, Health Care System

★ American Hospital Association (AHA) membership
☐ The Joint Commission accreditation
○ Healthcare Facilities Accreditation Program
◇ DNV Healthcare Inc. accreditation
⇑ Center for Improvement in Healthcare Quality Accreditation
△ Commission on Accreditation of Rehabilitation Facilities (CARF) accreditation

ST. MARY'S HEALTHCARE See St. Mary's Healthcare, Amsterdam

AUBURN—Cayuga County

✠ **AUBURN COMMUNITY HOSPITAL (330235)**, 17 Lansing Street,
Zip 13021–1943; tel. 315/255–7011, (Total facility includes 80 beds in nursing
home–type unit) **A**1 10 20 **F**1 3 12 13 15 18 26 28 29 30 31 34 35 40 45 50
51 53 54 55 57 59 60 64 70 76 79 81 82 85 89 93 97 98 104 105 107 108
110 111 114 115 119 129 130 131 132 135 144 146 147
Primary Contact: Scott A. Berlucchi, FACHE, President and Chief Executive Officer
CFO: Jason Lesch, Chief Financial Officer
CMO: John A. Riccio, M.D., Chief Medical Officer
CIO: Chris Ryan, Chief Information Officer
CHR: Linda Daly, Vice President Human Resources
CNO: Tammy Sunderlin, Director of Nursing
Web address: www.auburnhospital.org
Control: Other not–for–profit (including NFP Corporation) **Service**: General
medical and surgical

Staffed Beds: 179 Admissions: 5274 Census: 135 Outpatient Visits:
156656 **Births: 415 Total Expense ($000): 124293 Payroll Expense**
($000): 61804 Personnel: 705

BATAVIA—Genesee County

✠ **UNITED MEMORIAL MEDICAL CENTER (330073)**, 127 North Street,
Zip 14020–1631; tel. 585/343–6030, (Includes UNITED MEMORIAL MEDICAL
CENTER–BANK STREET, 16 Bank Street, Batavia, NY, Zip 14020–2260;
tel. 585/343–6030; UNITED MEMORIAL MEDICAL CENTER–NORTH STREET, 127
North Street, Batavia, NY, Zip 14020–1697; tel. 585/343–6030) **A**1 3 10 13 **F**3
4 8 13 15 17 18 28 29 30 31 34 35 40 43 49 50 54 57 59 64 65 68 70 75 76
77 78 79 81 82 84 85 86 87 89 93 97 107 111 114 115 119 120 121 122
127 129 130 131 132 135 144 146 147 148 149 154 **P**5 **S** Rochester Regional
Health, Rochester, NY
Primary Contact: Daniel P. Ireland, FACHE, President
CFO: Robert Chiavetta, Vice President Finance
CMO: Tara L Gellasch, Chief Medical Officer
CIO: Chad Caccamise, Director Information Services
CHR: Eileen Herkimer, Director Human Resources
CNO: Marilyn Almeter, Chief Nursing Officer
Web address: www.ummc.org
Control: Other not–for–profit (including NFP Corporation) **Service**: General
medical and surgical

Staffed Beds: 133 Admissions: 4208 Census: 51 Outpatient Visits:
252445 **Births: 575 Total Expense ($000): 104740 Payroll Expense**
($000): 43335 Personnel: 680

★ **VETERANS AFFAIRS WESTERN NEW YORK HEALTHCARE SYSTEM–BATAVIA**
DIVISION, 222 Richmond Avenue, Zip 14020–1288; tel. 585/297–1000,
(Nonreporting) **A**5 **S** Department of Veterans Affairs, Perry Point, MD
Primary Contact: Michael J. Swartz, FACHE, Interim Director
Web address: www.buffalo.va.gov/batavia.asp
Control: Veterans Affairs, Government, federal **Service**: General medical and
surgical

Staffed Beds: 128

BATH—Steuben County

✠ **BATH VETERANS AFFAIRS MEDICAL CENTER**, 76 Veterans Avenue,
Zip 14810–0842; tel. 607/664–4000, (Total facility includes 94 beds in nursing
home–type unit) **A**1 **F**3 4 5 7 11 12 18 29 30 33 34 35 36 38 39 44 50 53 54
56 57 59 61 62 63 64 65 66 68 71 74 75 77 79 82 83 84 86 87 90 91 93 94
97 100 101 103 104 106 107 119 127 128 129 130 132 133 135 143 144
146 147 148 149 154 **P**6 **S** Department of Veterans Affairs, Perry Point, MD
Primary Contact: Kenneth P. Piazza, Medical Center Director
CFO: Jill Haynes, Financial Coach
CMO: Robert Babcock, M.D., Interim Chief of Staff
CHR: Susan DeSalvo, Manager Human Resources
Web address: www.bath.va.gov
Control: Veterans Affairs, Government, federal **Service**: General medical and
surgical

Staffed Beds: 274 Admissions: 1333 Census: 218 Outpatient Visits:
163840 **Births: 0 Total Expense ($000): 106672 Payroll Expense**
($000): 64504 Personnel: 735

⇧ **IRA DAVENPORT MEMORIAL HOSPITAL (330144)**, 7571 State Route 54,
Zip 14810–9590; tel. 607/776–8500, (Nonreporting) **A**10 21 **S** Arnot Health, Elmira, NY
Primary Contact: Elizabeth Weir, MSN, R.N., Chief Executive Officer
CFO: Ronald J Kintz, Chief Financial Officer
CMO: Dennis O'Connor, M.D., Medical Director
CIO: Gregg Martin, Chief Information Officer
CHR: Dave Stanbro, Director Human Resources
CNO: Linda Donley, Vice President Operations
Web address: www.arnothealth.org
Control: Other not–for–profit (including NFP Corporation) **Service**: General
medical and surgical

Staffed Beds: 132

BAY SHORE—Suffolk County

✠ △ **SOUTHSIDE HOSPITAL (330043)**, 301 East Main Street, Zip 11706–8458;
tel. 631/968–3000, **A**1 2 3 5 7 10 **F**3 5 8 11 13 15 17 18 19 20 22 24 26 28
29 30 31 32 34 35 36 38 40 41 43 44 45 46 49 50 54 56 57 58 59 60 61 62
63 64 65 66 68 70 73 74 75 76 77 78 79 80 81 82 84 85 86 87 89 92 93 96
97 100 101 102 107 108 111 118 119 126 129 130 131 132 135 145 146
147 148 149 152 154 **P**5 6 **S** Northwell Health, New Hyde Park, NY
Primary Contact: Donna Moravick, R.N., MSN, Executive Director
CFO: Michele Cusack, Senior Vice President and Chief Financial Officer
CMO: Jay Enden, M.D., Medical Director
CHR: Anne J Barrett, Associate Executive Director Human Resources
Web address: www.northwell.edu/find–care/locations/southside–hospital
Control: Other not–for–profit (including NFP Corporation) **Service**: General
medical and surgical

Staffed Beds: 275 Admissions: 21375 Census: 278 Outpatient Visits:
149631 **Births: 2607 Total Expense ($000): 600609 Payroll Expense**
($000): 303472 Personnel: 2937

BETHPAGE—Nassau County

☐ **ST. JOSEPH HOSPITAL (330332)**, 4295 Hempstead Turnpike, Zip 11714–5769;
tel. 516/579–6000, **A**1 10 **F**3 8 15 18 29 30 31 34 35 39 40 45 46 47 49 50
51 56 57 59 60 64 65 68 70 74 75 78 79 80 81 82 85 86 87 93 107 108
110 111 114 115 119 129 130 131 132 141 146 148 149 **S** Catholic Health
Services of Long Island, Rockville Centre, NY
Primary Contact: Peter Scaminaci, Executive Vice President and Chief
Administrative Officer
CFO: John Morahan, Vice President Finance
CMO: Howard Sussman, M.D., Chief Medical Officer
CHR: Peter Chiacchiaro, Vice President Human Resources
CNO: Barbara Gibbons, Vice President Patient Care Services
Web address: www.stjosephhospital.chsli.org/
Control: Other not–for–profit (including NFP Corporation) **Service**: General
medical and surgical

Staffed Beds: 128 Admissions: 6205 Census: 91 Outpatient Visits: 43709
Births: 0 Total Expense ($000): 124168 Payroll Expense ($000): 49474
Personnel: 698

BINGHAMTON—Broome County

BINGHAMTON GENERAL HOSPITAL See United Health Services Hospitals–
Binghamton, Binghamton

☐ **GREATER BINGHAMTON HEALTH CENTER (334012)**, 425 Robinson Street,
Zip 13904–1735; tel. 607/724–1391, **A**1 3 10 **F**29 30 50 54 56 65 66 68 71
75 77 86 98 99 100 101 103 104 106 130 132 135 143 146 149 153 **P**1 **S**
New York State Office of Mental Health, Albany, NY
Primary Contact: David Peppel, Executive Director
CFO: Cherry Randall, Business Officer
CHR: Renee O'Brien, Director Human Resources
Web address: www.omh.ny.gov/omhweb/facilities/bipc/facility.htm
Control: State, Government, nonfederal **Service**: Psychiatric

Staffed Beds: 86 Admissions: 358 Census: 84 Births: 0

✠ **OUR LADY OF LOURDES MEMORIAL HOSPITAL, INC. (330011)**, 169
Riverside Drive, Zip 13905–4246; tel. 607/798–5111, **A**1 2 10 13 19 **F**3 11 12
13 15 18 19 28 29 30 31 32 34 35 36 39 40 44 45 46 47 49 50 51 53 54 56
57 59 60 62 63 64 65 66 68 70 71 74 75 76 77 78 79 81 84 85 86 87 89
93 97 100 101 104 107 108 110 111 114 115 118 119 120 121 123 124
126 127 129 130 131 132 134 135 143 144 145 146 147 148 149 154 **P**6 **S**
Ascension Healthcare, Saint Louis, MO
Primary Contact: Kathryn Connerton, President and Chief Executive Officer
CFO: Sean Mills, Chief Financial Officer
CMO: Richard Blansky, M.D., Chief Medical Officer
CIO: Thomas Ellerson, Chief Information Officer
CHR: Mary Hughs, Chief Human Resources Officer
Web address: www.lourdes.com
Control: Church operated, Nongovernment, not–for–profit **Service**: General
medical and surgical

Staffed Beds: 154 Admissions: 10108 Census: 108 Outpatient Visits:
1609726 **Births: 1061 Total Expense ($000): 330664 Payroll Expense**
($000): 138267 Personnel: 2068

Many Facility Codes have changed. Please refer to the AHA Guide Code Chart.

UNITED HEALTH SERVICES HOSPITALS–BINGHAMTON (330394), 10–42 Mitchell Avenue, Zip 13903–1678; tel. 607/763–6000, (Includes BINGHAMTON GENERAL HOSPITAL, 10–42 Mitchell Avenue, Binghamton, NY, Zip 13903; tel. 607/762–2200; John M. Carrigg, President and Chief Executive Officer; WILSON MEMORIAL REGIONAL MEDICAL CENTER, 33–57 Harrison Street, Johnson City, NY, Zip 13790; tel. 607/763–6000; John M. Carrigg, President and Chief Executive Officer) **A**8 10 **F**1 3 4 5 8 11 12 13 15 17 18 20 22 24 26 28 29 30 31 32 33 34 35 38 39 40 43 45 46 47 49 50 51 54 56 57 58 59 61 64 65 68 70 72 74 75 76 77 78 79 81 82 84 85 86 87 89 90 92 93 96 97 98 100 101 102 103 104 106 107 108 110 114 115 118 119 120 121 123 124 127 129 130 131 132 135 144 145 146 147 148 149 154 **P**3 **S** United Health Services, Binghamton, NY
Primary Contact: John M. Carrigg, President and Chief Executive Officer
COO: John M. Carrigg, Executive Vice President and Chief Operating Officer
CFO: David MacDougall, Chief Financial Officer
CMO: Rajesh J Dave', M.D., Executive Vice President and Chief Medical Officer
CIO: Susan Carman, Chief Information Officer
CHR: Michael McNally, Vice President Human Resources
CNO: E. Kay Boland, R.N., MS, Vice President and Chief Nursing Officer
Web address: www.uhs.net
Control: Other not–for–profit (including NFP Corporation) **Service:** General medical and surgical

Staffed Beds: 464 **Admissions:** 16666 **Census:** 285 **Outpatient Visits:** 1095379 **Births:** 1333 **Total Expense ($000):** 633736 **Payroll Expense ($000):** 230807 **Personnel:** 4206

BRENTWOOD—Suffolk County

☐ **PILGRIM PSYCHIATRIC CENTER (334013)**, 998 Crooked Hill Road, Zip 11717–1019; tel. 631/761–3500, (Nonreporting) **A**1 10 **S** New York State Office of Mental Health, Albany, NY
Primary Contact: Kathy O'Keefe, Executive Director
Web address: www.omh.ny.gov/omhweb/facilities/pgpc/facility.htm
Control: State, Government, nonfederal **Service:** Psychiatric

Staffed Beds: 569

BRONX—Bronx County; See New York City

BROOKLYN—Kings County; See New York City

BUFFALO—Erie County

BRYLIN HOSPITALS (334022), 1263 Delaware Avenue, Zip 14209–2402; tel. 716/886–8200, (Nonreporting) **A**10
Primary Contact: Eric D. Pleskow, President and Chief Executive Officer
CFO: E Paul Hettich, Chief Financial Officer
CMO: Maria Cartagena, M.D., Chief Medical Officer
CIO: Pawel Wieczorek, Director Information Technology
CHR: Pamela Nicastro, Director Human Resources
Web address: www.brylin.com
Control: Corporation, Investor–owned (for–profit) **Service:** Psychiatric

Staffed Beds: 88

☐ **BUFFALO PSYCHIATRIC CENTER (334052)**, 400 Forest Avenue, Zip 14213–1298; tel. 716/885–2261, (Nonreporting) **A**1 3 5 10 **S** New York State Office of Mental Health, Albany, NY
Primary Contact: Beatrix Souza, Chief Executive Officer
COO: Celia Spacone, M.D., Director Operations
CFO: Pamela Esposito, Director Administration
CMO: Jeffery Grace, M.D., Clinical Director
CIO: Anne Buchheit, Coordinator Mental Health Local Information Systems
CHR: Charles Siewert, Director Human Resources
CNO: Susan Fallis, Chief Nursing Officer
Web address: www.omh.ny.gov
Control: State, Government, nonfederal **Service:** Psychiatric

Staffed Beds: 240

⊞ △ **ERIE COUNTY MEDICAL CENTER (330219)**, 462 Grider Street, Zip 14215–3098; tel. 716/898–3000, (Total facility includes 390 beds in nursing home–type unit) **A**1 3 5 7 10 **F**3 4 5 12 16 18 20 29 30 31 33 34 35 38 39 40 43 45 49 50 53 54 56 57 58 59 60 61 63 64 65 66 68 70 71 74 75 77 78 79 81 82 83 84 85 87 90 91 93 94 96 97 98 99 100 101 102 103 104 105 107 110 111 115 119 128 130 131 132 135 138 146 148 149 **P**6 7
Primary Contact: Thomas J. Quatroche Jr, Chief Executive Officer
COO: Andrew L Davis Jr Chief Operating Officer
CFO: Michael Sammarco, M.D., Chief Financial Officer
CMO: Brian Murray, M.D., Medical Director
CIO: Leslie Feidt, Chief Information Officer
CHR: Kathleen O'Hara, Vice President Human Resources
CNO: Karen Ziemianski, R.N., MS, Senior Vice President Nursing
Web address: www.ecmc.edu
Control: Hospital district or authority, Government, nonfederal **Service:** General medical and surgical

Staffed Beds: 890 **Admissions:** 20221 **Census:** 786 **Outpatient Visits:** 314927 **Births:** 0 **Total Expense ($000):** 644189 **Payroll Expense ($000):** 226648 **Personnel:** 3195

△ ⇑ **KALEIDA HEALTH (330005)**, 100 High Street, Zip 14203–1154; tel. 716/859–5600, (Includes DE GRAFF MEMORIAL HOSPITAL, 445 Tremont Street, North Tonawanda, NY, Zip 14120–0750, Mailing Address: P.O. Box 0750, Zip 14120–0750, tel. 716/694–4500; Darcy Craven, President; MILLARD FILLMORE SUBURBAN HOSPITAL, 1540 Maple Road, Williamsville, NY, Zip 14221; tel. 716/688–3100; Darcy Craven, President; WOMEN AND CHILDREN'S HOSPITAL, 219 Bryant Street, Buffalo, NY, Zip 14222–2099; tel. 716/878–7000; Cheryl Klass, President) (Total facility includes 380 beds in nursing home–type unit) **A**3 5 7 10 21 **F**1 2 3 6 8 9 11 12 13 15 17 18 19 20 21 22 24 26 27 28 29 30 31 32 34 35 36 37 38 39 40 41 43 44 45 46 47 48 49 50 51 54 55 57 58 59 60 61 62 63 64 65 66 67 68 70 71 72 73 74 75 76 77 78 79 80 81 82 83 84 85 86 87 88 89 90 91 92 93 94 96 97 99 100 101 102 103 104 107 108 109 110 111 114 115 118 119 120 124 126 128 130 131 132 134 135 136 143 146 147 148 154 **P**2 4 5 6 7
Primary Contact: Jody Lomeo, Chief Executive Officer
CFO: Joseph Kessler, Executive Vice President and Chief Financial Officer
CMO: Margaret Paroski, M.D., Executive Vice President and Chief Medical Officer
CIO: Francis Meyer, Vice President Information Systems Technology
Web address: www.kaleidahealth.org
Control: Other not–for–profit (including NFP Corporation) **Service:** General medical and surgical

Staffed Beds: 1409 **Admissions:** 50956 **Census:** 1078 **Outpatient Visits:** 333579 **Births:** 5385 **Total Expense ($000):** 1364397 **Payroll Expense ($000):** 579269 **Personnel:** 8487

⊞ **MERCY HOSPITAL (330279)**, 565 Abbott Road, Zip 14220–2095; tel. 716/826–7000, (Total facility includes 84 beds in nursing home–type unit) **A**1 3 5 10 **F**3 13 15 17 18 20 22 24 26 28 29 30 34 35 38 39 40 41 44 45 49 50 54 56 57 58 59 60 64 65 66 68 70 72 74 75 76 77 79 81 84 85 87 90 92 93 95 97 100 107 108 110 111 114 115 118 119 126 128 129 130 131 132 141 146 147 148 149 **P**5 6 **S** Catholic Health System, Buffalo, NY
Primary Contact: Charles J. Urlaub, President and Chief Executive Officer
COO: Eddie Bratko, Chief Operating Officer
CFO: James H Dunlop, CPA, Jr Senior Vice President Finance and Chief Financial Officer
CMO: Timothy Gabryel, M.D., Vice President Medical Affairs and Medical Director
CIO: Michael Galang, M.D., Chief Information Officer
CHR: Joseph A Scrivo Jr Director Human Resources
CNO: Shari McDonald, Vice President Patient Care Services
Web address: www.chsbuffalo.org
Control: Church operated, Nongovernment, not–for–profit **Service:** General medical and surgical

Staffed Beds: 420 **Admissions:** 19650 **Census:** 347 **Outpatient Visits:** 300423 **Births:** 2329 **Total Expense ($000):** 419242 **Payroll Expense ($000):** 180004 **Personnel:** 2245

☐ **ROSWELL PARK CANCER INSTITUTE (330354)**, Elm and Carlton Streets, Zip 14263–0001; tel. 716/845–2300, **A**1 2 3 5 8 10 **F**3 14 15 29 30 31 32 34 35 36 38 39 44 45 46 47 49 50 54 55 57 58 59 63 64 65 66 67 70 74 75 77 78 79 80 81 82 84 85 86 87 89 90 92 93 94 96 98 100 104 107 108 110 111 112 114 115 116 117 118 119 120 121 123 124 126 130 132 134 135 136 141 145 146 147 148 149 **P**6
Primary Contact: Candace Johnson, Ph.D., President and Chief Executive Officer
COO: Victor A Filadora, M.D., MS, II Chief Clinical Services
CFO: Gregory McDonald, Vice President Finance and Chief Financial Officer
CMO: Boris Kuvshinoff, M.D., II Chief Medical Officer
CIO: Kerry Kerlin, Chief Information Officer
CHR: Errol A. Douglas, MS, Vice President, Human Resources
CNO: Shirley Johnson, MS, R.N., Senior Vice President Nursing and Patient Care Services, Chief Nursing Officer
Web address: www.roswellpark.org
Control: Hospital district or authority, Government, nonfederal **Service:** Cancer

Staffed Beds: 133 **Admissions:** 5077 **Census:** 107 **Outpatient Visits:** 231744 **Births:** 0 **Total Expense ($000):** 595989 **Payroll Expense ($000):** 197468 **Personnel:** 3088

NY

✠ **SISTERS OF CHARITY HOSPITAL OF BUFFALO (330078)**, 2157 Main Street, Zip 14214–2692; tel. 716/862–1000, (Includes ELIZABETH SETON PEDIATRIC CENTER, 300 Corporate Boulevard South, Yonkers, NY, Zip 10701–6862; tel. 914/294–6300; ST. JOSEPH HOSPITAL, 2605 Harlem Road, Cheektowaga, NY, Zip 14225–4097; tel. 716/891–2400) (Total facility includes 80 beds in nursing home–type unit) **A**1 2 3 5 10 12 13 **F**2 3 5 11 12 13 15 18 28 29 30 31 32 34 35 36 37 38 40 41 44 45 46 47 49 50 53 54 55 57 58 59 60 64 65 66 68 70 72 73 74 75 76 77 78 79 81 82 84 85 87 92 93 97 100 107 108 110 111 114 115 118 119 126 128 129 130 131 132 141 146 147 148 149 **P**5 6 **S** Catholic Health System, Buffalo, NY
Primary Contact: Martin Boryszak, President and Chief Executive Officer
COO: John Sperrazza, Chief Operating Officer
CFO: James H Dunlop, CPA, Jr Chief Financial Officer
CMO: Nady Shehata, M.D., Vice President Medical Affairs
CIO: Michael Galang, M.D., Chief Information Officer
CHR: David DeLorenzo, Senior Director Human Resources
CNO: Mary E Dillon, MS, R.N., Vice President Patient Care Services
Web address: www.chsbuffalo.org
Control: Church operated, Nongovernment, not–for–profit **Service:** General medical and surgical

Staffed Beds: 378 Admissions: 16098 Census: 291 Outpatient Visits: 752355 Births: 3468 Total Expense ($000): 330486 Payroll Expense ($000): 149842 Personnel: 1968

✠ **VETERANS AFFAIRS WESTERN NEW YORK HEALTHCARE SYSTEM–BUFFALO DIVISION**, 3495 Bailey Avenue, Zip 14215–1129; tel. 716/834–9200, (Nonreporting) **A**1 3 5 8 **S** Department of Veterans Affairs, Perry Point, MD
Primary Contact: Brian G. Stiller, Director Medical Center
CFO: Susan Gage, Financial Manager
CMO: Ali El–Solh, M.D., Interim Chief of Staff
CIO: Margaret Senker, Chief Information Officer
Web address: www.buffalo.va.gov/index.asp
Control: Veterans Affairs, Government, federal **Service:** General medical and surgical

Staffed Beds: 113

WOMEN AND CHILDREN'S HOSPITAL See Kaleida Health, Buffalo

CALLICOON—Sullivan County

★ **GROVER M. HERMANN HOSPITAL (331303)**, 8881 Route 97, Zip 12723; tel. 845/887–5530, **A**10 18 **F**3 11 15 29 30 34 35 40 50 57 59 64 75 85 93 97 107 130 132 133 146 149 **S** Greater Hudson Valley Health System, Middletown, NY
Primary Contact: Rolland Bojo, R.N., Administrator
Web address: www.crmcny.org
Control: Other not–for–profit (including NFP Corporation) **Service:** General medical and surgical

Staffed Beds: 10 Admissions: 107 Census: 3 Outpatient Visits: 9749 Births: 0 Total Expense ($000): 5364 Payroll Expense ($000): 2503 Personnel: 33

CANANDAIGUA—Ontario County

★ **CANANDAIGUA VETERANS AFFAIRS MEDICAL CENTER**, 400 Fort Hill Avenue, Zip 14424–1159; tel. 585/394–2000, (Nonreporting) **A**3 5 **S** Department of Veterans Affairs, Perry Point, MD
Primary Contact: Kenneth P. Piazza, Medical Center Director
CIO: Bob Corrado, Chief Information Officer
Web address: www.canandaigua.va.gov/
Control: Veterans Affairs, Government, federal **Service:** Psychiatric

Staffed Beds: 196

✠ **F. F. THOMPSON HOSPITAL (330074)**, 350 Parrish Street, Zip 14424–1731; tel. 585/396–6000, (Total facility includes 178 beds in nursing home–type unit) **A**1 3 10 **F**3 8 11 13 15 17 18 28 29 30 32 33 34 35 38 40 43 44 45 46 50 54 56 57 59 60 64 68 70 75 76 77 79 81 84 85 86 87 89 91 93 95 96 97 107 108 110 111 115 118 119 125 126 128 129 130 131 132 135 144 145 146 147 148 149 **S** University of Rochester Medical Center, Rochester, NY
Primary Contact: Michael Stapleton, President and Chief Executive Officer
COO: Kurt Koczent, Executive Vice President and Chief Operating Officer
CFO: Mark Prunoske, Chief Financial Officer and Senior Vice President Finance
CMO: David Baum, M.D., Senior Vice President Medical Services
CHR: Jennifer DeVault, Vice President Associate Services
CNO: Hazel Robertshaw, R.N., Ph.D., Chief Nursing Officer, Vice President Patient Services
Web address: www.thompsonhealth.com
Control: Other not–for–profit (including NFP Corporation) **Service:** General medical and surgical

Staffed Beds: 291 Admissions: 5425 Census: 226 Outpatient Visits: 287788 Births: 642 Total Expense ($000): 146235 Payroll Expense ($000): 67838

THOMPSON HEALTH See F. F. Thompson Hospital

CARMEL—Putnam County

ARMS ACRES, 75 Seminary Hill Road, Zip 10512–1921; tel. 845/225–3400, **F**4 5 34 35 39 54 68 75 86 87 100 101 133 134 135 151
Primary Contact: Patrice Wallace–Moore, Chief Executive Officer and Executive Director
CFO: Jason Burczeuski, Controller
CMO: Fred Hesse, M.D., Medical Director
CIO: Dolores Watson, Director Health Information Management
CHR: Kim Halpin, Director Human Resources
CNO: Barbara Klein, R.N., Director of Nursing
Web address: www.armsacres.com
Control: State, Government, nonfederal **Service:** Alcoholism and other chemical dependency

Staffed Beds: 183 Admissions: 4903 Census: 183 Outpatient Visits: 6193 Births: 0 Personnel: 324

☐ **PUTNAM HOSPITAL CENTER (330273)**, 670 Stoneleigh Avenue, Zip 10512–3997; tel. 845/279–5711, **A**1 2 10 **F**3 8 12 13 15 18 28 29 30 31 34 35 37 38 40 41 45 46 49 55 56 57 59 61 64 65 68 70 74 75 76 77 78 79 81 82 83 84 85 87 89 91 92 93 94 98 100 101 102 103 104 105 107 108 110 111 114 118 119 120 121 126 129 130 131 132 143 146 149 **P**6 **S** Health Quest Systems, Inc., LaGrangeville, NY
Primary Contact: Peter Kelly, President
CFO: Joseph Hart, Director Finance and Support Services
CNO: Luanne Convery, Vice President Patient Care Services
Web address: www.healthquest.org/carmel/putnam–hospital–center.aspx
Control: Other not–for–profit (including NFP Corporation) **Service:** General medical and surgical

Staffed Beds: 164 Admissions: 6743 Census: 72 Outpatient Visits: 120813 Births: 375 Total Expense ($000): 156997 Payroll Expense ($000): 53436 Personnel: 707

CARTHAGE—Jefferson County

✠ **CARTHAGE AREA HOSPITAL (331318)**, 1001 West Street, Zip 13619–9703; tel. 315/493–1000, (Nonreporting) **A**1 10 18
Primary Contact: Richard Duvall, Chief Executive Officer
CFO: Rob Bloom, Chief Financial Officer
CMO: Mirza Ashraf, M.D., Medical Director
CIO: Joe Virkler, Chief Information Officer
CHR: Cathy Siedlecki, Director Human Resources
CNO: Susan Kellogg, Administrator Patient Care Services
Web address: www.carthagehospital.com
Control: Other not–for–profit (including NFP Corporation) **Service:** General medical and surgical

Staffed Beds: 55

CLIFTON SPRINGS—Ontario County

★ ⇑ **CLIFTON SPRINGS HOSPITAL AND CLINIC (330265)**, 2 Coulter Road, Zip 14432–1189; tel. 315/462–9561, (Total facility includes 108 beds in nursing home–type unit) **A**10 21 **F**3 4 5 11 15 28 29 30 31 34 35 38 40 45 48 49 50 51 57 59 60 64 65 68 70 75 77 78 79 81 82 85 87 93 97 98 100 101 102 103 104 107 108 110 111 114 117 118 119 120 121 123 128 130 132 146 148 149 154 **P**5 6 **S** Rochester Regional Health, Rochester, NY
Primary Contact: Dustin Riccio, M.D., President
CFO: Sharon Kelley, Chief Financial Officer
CIO: Joel Majauskas, Chief Information Officer
CHR: Kathy Babb, Manager Human Resources
CNO: Donna P Smith, R.N., Vice President Chief Operating Officer and Chief Nursing Officer
Web address: www.cliftonspringshospital.org
Control: Other not–for–profit (including NFP Corporation) **Service:** General medical and surgical

Staffed Beds: 181 Admissions: 2552 Census: 150 Outpatient Visits: 102575 Births: 0 Total Expense ($000): 62438 Payroll Expense ($000): 33243 Personnel: 559

COBLESKILL—Schoharie County

✠ **COBLESKILL REGIONAL HOSPITAL (330268)**, 178 Grandview Drive, Zip 12043–5144; tel. 518/254–3456, (Nonreporting) **A**1 10 20 **S** Bassett Healthcare Network, Cooperstown, NY
Primary Contact: Eric H. Stein, FACHE, President
CFO: James Vielkind, Chief Financial Officer
CMO: Roy Korn, M.D., Medical Director
CIO: Bridgette West, Director Patient Access Services
CNO: Susan Oakes Ferrucci, MS, Vice President Patient Services and Chief Nursing Officer
Web address: www.bassett.org
Control: Other not–for–profit (including NFP Corporation) **Service:** General medical and surgical

Staffed Beds: 40

Many Facility Codes have changed. Please refer to the AHA Guide Code Chart. © 2018 AHA Guide

COOPERSTOWN—Otsego County

BASSETT MEDICAL CENTER (330136), One Atwell Road, Zip 13326–1394; tel. 607/547–3456, (Nonreporting) **A**1 2 3 5 8 10 **S** Bassett Healthcare Network, Cooperstown, NY
Primary Contact: William W. LeCates, M.D., President
COO: Ronette Wiley, R.N., Executive Vice President and Chief Operating Officer
CFO: Michael A. Tengeres, Corporate Vice President and Chief Financial Officer
CMO: William W LeCates, M.D., Vice President Medical Affairs and Medical Director
CHR: Sara Z Albright, Vice President Human Resources
CNO: Judi Brendle, Vice President Clinical Support and Chief Nursing Officer
Web address: www.bassett.org
Control: Other not–for–profit (including NFP Corporation) **Service:** General medical and surgical

Staffed Beds: 152

CORNING—Steuben County

GUTHRIE CORNING HOSPITAL (330277), One Guthrie Drive, Zip 14830–3696; tel. 607/937–7200, **A**1 10 **F**8 11 13 15 18 20 22 24 26 28 29 30 31 34 37 38 40 45 46 47 48 49 50 51 53 57 59 64 68 70 76 77 78 79 81 85 86 87 91 93 107 108 110 111 112 114 115 116 117 118 119 120 121 123 126 129 130 131 146 148 **S** Guthrie Clinic, Sayre, PA
Primary Contact: Garrett W. Hoover, FACHE, President
CFO: Francis M Macafee, Vice President Finance and Chief Financial Officer
CMO: Chris Wentzel, M.D., Interim Medical Director
CHR: Laura Manning, Administrative Director
CNO: Deb Raupers, MSN, R.N., Chief Nursing Officer
Web address: www.corninghospital.com
Control: Other not–for–profit (including NFP Corporation) **Service:** General medical and surgical

Staffed Beds: 65 **Admissions:** 4132 **Census:** 38 **Outpatient Visits:** 98234 **Births:** 561 **Total Expense ($000):** 104287 **Payroll Expense ($000):** 29922 **Personnel:** 544

CORNWALL—Orange County

ST. LUKE'S CORNWALL HOSPITAL – CORNWALL CAMPUS See St. Luke's Cornwall Hospital, Newburgh

CORTLAND—Cortland County

CORTLAND REGIONAL MEDICAL CENTER (330175), 134 Homer Avenue, Zip 13045–1206; tel. 607/756–3500, (Total facility includes 82 beds in nursing home–type unit) **A**1 10 20 **F**2 3 8 11 13 15 18 28 29 30 31 34 35 38 40 44 45 49 50 51 54 56 57 59 62 64 70 75 76 77 78 79 81 82 85 86 87 91 93 96 98 100 102 103 107 108 110 111 114 115 118 119 128 130 131 132 133 135 146 147 148 149 150 154 **P**6
Primary Contact: Tracy Gates, President and Chief Executive Officer
COO: Tracy Gates, Vice President Operations and Chief Operating Officer
CFO: Denise Wrinn, Vice President Finance and Chief Financial Officer
CMO: Russell Firman, M.D., Chief Medical Officer
CIO: Robert J Duthe, Director Information Systems and Chief Information Officer
CNO: Mary Wright, Vice President Nursing Services and Chief Nursing Officer
Web address: www.cortlandregional.org
Control: Other not–for–profit (including NFP Corporation) **Service:** General medical and surgical

Staffed Beds: 154 **Admissions:** 4042 **Census:** 115 **Outpatient Visits:** 109080 **Births:** 423 **Total Expense ($000):** 86590 **Payroll Expense ($000):** 36903 **Personnel:** 703

CORTLANDT MANOR—Westchester County

NEW YORK–PRESBYTERIAN/HUDSON VALLEY HOSPITAL (330267), 1980 Crompond Road, Zip 10567–4182; tel. 914/737–9000, **A**1 10 **F**3 8 11 12 13 15 18 28 29 30 31 34 35 36 37 40 41 45 46 47 49 53 54 56 57 59 64 70 73 74 75 76 77 78 79 81 82 85 87 89 93 94 102 107 108 110 111 114 115 116 117 119 120 124 129 130 131 132 145 146 147 148 149 154 **P**6 **S** NewYork–Presbyterian, New York, NY
Primary Contact: Stacey Petrower, President
COO: Deborah Neuendorf, Vice President Administration
CFO: Mark Webster, Vice President Finance
CMO: William Higgins, M.D., Vice President Medical Affairs
CIO: Bud Sorbello, Director Management Information Systems
CHR: Jeane L Costella, Vice President
CNO: Kathleen Webster, R.N., MSN, Vice President Patient Services
Web address: www.hvhc.org
Control: Other not–for–profit (including NFP Corporation) **Service:** General medical and surgical

Staffed Beds: 128 **Admissions:** 8614 **Census:** 100 **Outpatient Visits:** 176804 **Births:** 756 **Total Expense ($000):** 205099 **Payroll Expense ($000):** 81156 **Personnel:** 994

CUBA—Allegany County

CUBA MEMORIAL HOSPITAL (331301), 140 West Main Street, Zip 14727–1398; tel. 585/968–2000, (Nonreporting) **A**10 18
Primary Contact: Andrew Boser, Chief Executive Officer
CFO: Jack Ormond, Chief Financial Officer
Web address: www.cubamemorialhospital.com
Control: Other not–for–profit (including NFP Corporation) **Service:** General medical and surgical

Staffed Beds: 81

DANSVILLE—Livingston County

NICHOLAS H. NOYES MEMORIAL HOSPITAL (330238), 111 Clara Barton Street, Zip 14437–9503; tel. 585/335–6001, **A**1 10 **F**3 8 11 13 15 29 30 32 34 35 40 45 47 49 50 51 53 54 57 59 60 64 68 70 75 76 78 79 81 82 84 85 87 93 100 102 104 107 110 111 115 119 120 121 123 130 131 132 133 144 146 149 **P**5 **S** University of Rochester Medical Center, Rochester, NY
Primary Contact: Amy Pollard, R.N., President and Chief Executive Officer
CMO: Douglas Mayhle, M.D., Medical Director
CNO: Tamara West, R.N., MSN, Vice President Patient Care
Web address: www.noyes–health.org
Control: Other not–for–profit (including NFP Corporation) **Service:** General medical and surgical

Staffed Beds: 40 **Admissions:** 2074 **Census:** 21 **Outpatient Visits:** 197552 **Births:** 330 **Total Expense ($000):** 57387 **Payroll Expense ($000):** 26955 **Personnel:** 444

DELHI—Delaware County

O'CONNOR HOSPITAL (331305), 460 Andes Road, State Route 28, Zip 13753–7407; tel. 607/746–0300, **A**1 10 18 **F**15 29 34 35 40 45 50 56 57 59 64 65 75 77 79 81 85 86 87 91 92 93 96 107 110 119 130 131 132 133 135 147 148 149 **S** Bassett Healthcare Network, Cooperstown, NY
Primary Contact: Scott Bonderoff, President
CFO: Sue E. Andrews, Chief Financial Officer
CMO: Peter L Sosnow, Medical Director
CHR: Barbara Green, Director Human Resources
CNO: Debra Neale, R.N., Chief Nursing Officer
Web address: www.bassett.org/oconnor
Control: Other not–for–profit (including NFP Corporation) **Service:** General medical and surgical

Staffed Beds: 16 **Admissions:** 344 **Census:** 7 **Outpatient Visits:** 33889 **Births:** 0 **Personnel:** 147

DIX HILLS—Suffolk County

SAGAMORE Children's hospital psychiatric CENTER, 197 Half Hollow Road, Zip 11746–5861; tel. 631/370–1700, (Nonreporting) **A**1 **S** New York State Office of Mental Health, Albany, NY
Primary Contact: Kathy O'Keefe, Interim Executive Director
COO: Cathy Stein, Chief Inpatient Services
CFO: Jane Alexander, Director Facility Administrative Services
CIO: Bryan Doherty, Management Information Technology Services I
CHR: Nancy Angell, Associate Administrator Personnel
CNO: Sandra King, Chief Nursing Officer
Web address: www.omh.ny.gov
Control: State, Government, nonfederal **Service:** Children's hospital psychiatric

Staffed Beds: 69

DUNKIRK—Chautauqua County

BROOKS MEMORIAL HOSPITAL (330229), 529 Central Avenue, Zip 14048–2599; tel. 716/366–1111, (Includes TLC HEALTH NETWORK – LAKE SHORE HOSPITAL, 845 Route 5 and 20, Irving, NY, Zip 14081–9716; tel. 716/951–7000; John P Galati, Chief Executive Officer) (Nonreporting) **A**10 21
Primary Contact: Mary E. LaRowe, FACHE, President and Chief Executive Officer
CFO: Jeffrey H. Morgan, Vice President Finance and Chief Financial Officer
CIO: Kevin Kimball, Director Information Technology
CHR: Tracie Luther, Director Employee and Labor Relations
CNO: Jodi Witherell, Vice President Patient Care and Quality
Web address: www.brookshospital.org
Control: Other not–for–profit (including NFP Corporation) **Service:** General medical and surgical

Staffed Beds: 145

NY

EAST MEADOW—Nassau County

⊞ **NASSAU UNIVERSITY MEDICAL CENTER (330027)**, 2201 Hempstead Turnpike, Zip 11554–1859; tel. 516/572–0123, (Nonreporting) **A**1 3 5 10 12 13
Primary Contact: Paul A. Pipia, M.D., Interim President and Chief Executive Officer
COO: Donald L Ashkenase, Executive Vice President and Chief Operating Officer
CFO: John P Maher, Executive Vice President and Chief Financial Officer
CMO: Victor Scarmato, M.D., Acting Medical Director
CIO: Farooq Ajmal, Vice President and Chief Information Officer
CHR: Maureen Roarty, Executive Vice President Human Resources
CNO: Kathy Skarka, MSN, R.N., Executive Vice President Patient Care Services
Web address: www.nuhealth.net
Control: Hospital district or authority, Government, nonfederal **Service:** General medical and surgical

Staffed Beds: 481

ELIZABETHTOWN—Essex County

⊞ **THE UNIVERSITY OF VERMONT HEALTH NETWORK ELIZABETHTOWN COMMUNITY HOSPITAL (331302)**, 75 Park Street, Zip 12932, Mailing Address: P.O. Box 277, Zip 12932–0277; tel. 518/873–6377, (Includes MOSES LUDINGTON HOSPITAL, 1019 Wicker Street, Ticonderoga, NY, Zip 12883–1097; tel. 518/585–2831; John R Remillard, President and Chief Executive Officer) **A**1 10 18 **F**3 7 11 15 28 29 31 34 40 44 45 46 50 53 54 57 62 64 65 68 75 77 78 81 86 87 90 91 93 96 97 107 110 114 115 119 127 130 132 133 135 145 146 147
Primary Contact: John R. Remillard, President and Chief Executive Officer
COO: Matthew Nolan, Chief Operating Officer
CFO: Alan Chardavoyne, Chief Financial Officer
CMO: Rob DeMuro, M.D., Chief Medical Officer
CIO: Darrin Goodrow, Chief Information Officer
CHR: Michelle Meachem, Director Human Resources
CNO: Julie Tromblee, R.N., Chief Nursing Officer
Web address: www.ech.org
Control: Other not–for–profit (including NFP Corporation) **Service:** General medical and surgical

Staffed Beds: 40 **Admissions:** 625 **Census:** 12 **Outpatient Visits:** 62060 **Births:** 0 **Total Expense ($000):** 38168 **Payroll Expense ($000):** 18174 **Personnel:** 283

ELLENVILLE—Ulster County

★ **ELLENVILLE REGIONAL HOSPITAL (331310)**, 10 Healthy Way, Zip 12428–5612; tel. 845/647–6400, **A**10 18 **F**3 11 15 34 40 41 45 46 47 48 59 68 77 79 81 85 87 93 107 108 110 111 114 119 132 133 135 146 147 148
Primary Contact: Steven L. Kelley, President and Chief Executive Officer
CFO: Robert Rue, Chief Financial Officer
CMO: Walter Sperling, M.D., Medical Director
CHR: Deborah Briggs, Vice President Human Resources, Marketing, Volunteer Services and Community Relations
CNO: Ann Marie Guntlow, Chief Nursing Officer
Web address: www.ellenvilleregional.org
Control: Other not–for–profit (including NFP Corporation) **Service:** General medical and surgical

Staffed Beds: 25 **Admissions:** 421 **Census:** 11 **Outpatient Visits:** 29020 **Births:** 0 **Total Expense ($000):** 17169 **Payroll Expense ($000):** 9298 **Personnel:** 147

ELMHURST—Queens County; See New York City

ELMIRA—Chemung County

★ ⇑ **ARNOT OGDEN MEDICAL CENTER (330090)**, 600 Roe Avenue, Zip 14905–1629; tel. 607/737–4100, **A**2 3 10 12 13 21 **F**3 8 11 12 13 15 17 18 19 20 22 24 26 28 29 30 31 34 35 40 41 43 51 57 65 68 70 71 72 73 75 76 77 79 89 102 107 108 110 111 114 115 118 119 120 121 124 129 130 132 135 143 144 146 147 148 154 **S** Arnot Health, Elmira, NY
Primary Contact: Jonathan I. Lawrence, System Chief Operating Officer
CFO: Ronald J Kintz, Vice President and Treasurer
CMO: Kenneth Herzl–Betz, M.D., Chief Medical Officer
CIO: Gregg Martin, Chief Information Officer
CHR: Dave Stanbro, Director Human Resources
CNO: Sandra Mac"" McCarthy, Chief Nursing Officer
Web address: www.arnothealth.org
Control: Other not–for–profit (including NFP Corporation) **Service:** General medical and surgical

Staffed Beds: 266 **Admissions:** 10716 **Census:** 122 **Personnel:** 3006

☐ **ELMIRA PSYCHIATRIC CENTER (334045)**, 100 Washington Street, Zip 14901–2898; tel. 607/737–4739, **A**1 3 10 **F**98 99 103 **S** New York State Office of Mental Health, Albany, NY
Primary Contact: David Peppel, Executive Director
COO: Karen Patterson, Deputy Director Operations
CFO: J. Paul Bedzyk, Deputy Director Administration
CMO: Kurt Hahn, M.D., Acting Clinical Director
CIO: Jeremy Newcomer, Director Information Services
CHR: Patricia Santulli, Director Human Resources
CNO: Pam Seeley, Chief Nursing Officer
Web address: www.omh.ny.gov/omhweb/facilities/elpc/facility.htm
Control: State, Government, nonfederal **Service:** Psychiatric

Staffed Beds: 60 **Admissions:** 258 **Census:** 65 **Births:** 0

⇑ **ST. JOSEPH'S HOSPITAL (330108)**, 555 St. Joseph's Boulevard, Zip 14901–3223; tel. 607/733–6541, (Nonreporting) **A**10 21 **S** Arnot Health, Elmira, NY
Primary Contact: Jonathan I. Lawrence, President and Chief Executive Officer
CFO: Ronald J Kintz, Senior Vice President Finance and Chief Financial Officer
CMO: Kenneth Herzl–Betz, M.D., Chief Medical Officer and Senior Vice President Medical Affairs
CIO: Gregg Martin, Chief Information Officer
CHR: Dave Stanbro, Director Human Resources
CNO: Sandra Mac"" McCarthy, Chief Nursing Officer
Web address: www.arnothealth.org
Control: Other not–for–profit (including NFP Corporation) **Service:** General medical and surgical

Staffed Beds: 141

FAR ROCKAWAY—Queens County; See New York City

FLUSHING—Queens County; See New York City

FRESH MEADOWS—Queens County

CORNERSTONE OF MEDICAL ARTS CENTER HOSPITAL, 159–05 Union Turnpike, Zip 11366–1950; tel. 212/755–0200, (Nonreporting)
Primary Contact: Thomas C. Puzo, President and Chief Executive Officer
CFO: Jeff OniFather, Chief Financial Officer
CMO: Sami Kaddouri, M.D., Medical Director
CHR: Gloria Burtch, Director Human Resources
Web address: www.cornerstoneny.com
Control: Corporation, Investor–owned (for–profit) **Service:** Alcoholism and other chemical dependency

Staffed Beds: 162

GENEVA—Ontario County

⊞ **FINGER LAKES HOSPITAL (330058)**, 196 North Street, Zip 14456–1694; tel. 315/787–4000, **A**1 3 10 **F**3 8 11 13 15 17 18 28 29 31 32 34 35 40 45 50 54 57 59 60 61 64 66 70 74 75 76 77 79 81 85 86 87 90 92 93 96 97 107 108 110 115 118 119 128 129 130 131 132 135 146 147 **P**6 **S** Finger Lakes Health, Geneva, NY
Primary Contact: Frank Korich, FACHE, Senior Vice President, Operations
COO: Frank Korich, FACHE, Senior Vice President, Operations
CFO: Pamela Johnson, Treasurer and Chief Financial Officer
CMO: Jason Feinberg, M.D., Vice President Medical Affairs and Chief Medical Officer
CIO: Guy W Mosher III Manager Information Systems
CHR: Patrick R Boyle, Vice President Human Resources
CNO: Eileen Gage, R.N., Vice President Nursing
Web address: www.flhealth.org
Control: Other not–for–profit (including NFP Corporation) **Service:** General medical and surgical

Staffed Beds: 132 **Admissions:** 3821 **Census:** 47 **Outpatient Visits:** 535891 **Births:** 0 **Total Expense ($000):** 91417 **Payroll Expense ($000):** 51645 **Personnel:** 766

GLEN COVE—Nassau County

⊞ **GLEN COVE HOSPITAL (330181)**, 101 St Andrews Lane, Zip 11542–2254; tel. 516/674–7300, **A**1 2 3 5 10 **F**3 5 8 9 11 15 17 18 28 29 30 31 32 33 34 35 36 38 39 40 43 45 46 47 48 49 50 51 54 55 56 57 58 59 60 61 63 64 65 66 68 69 70 74 75 77 78 81 84 85 86 87 90 91 92 93 94 95 96 97 100 102 104 107 110 111 115 118 119 121 130 131 132 135 143 146 147 149 152 154 **P**5 6 **S** Northwell Health, New Hyde Park, NY
Primary Contact: Susan Kwiatek, R.N., Executive Director
COO: Michele Frankel, Associate Executive Director Finance
CFO: Michele Frankel, Associate Executive Director Finance
Web address: www.northshorelij.com
Control: Other not–for–profit (including NFP Corporation) **Service:** General medical and surgical

Staffed Beds: 119 **Admissions:** 4835 **Census:** 93 **Outpatient Visits:** 74675 **Births:** 0 **Total Expense ($000):** 149416 **Payroll Expense ($000):** 81667 **Personnel:** 794

GLEN OAKS—Queens County; See New York City

GLENS FALLS—Warren County

☒ **GLENS FALLS HOSPITAL (330191)**, 100 Park Street, Zip 12801–4413; tel. 518/926–1000, **A**1 2 5 10 **F**3 5 8 11 13 15 17 18 20 22 26 28 29 30 31 32 34 35 36 37 38 40 43 44 45 46 47 49 50 53 54 57 59 60 64 68 70 71 73 74 75 76 77 78 79 81 82 84 85 86 87 89 90 92 93 96 97 98 100 102 104 107 108 110 114 115 118 119 120 121 123 124 126 127 129 130 132 135 144 145 146 147 148 **P**6
Primary Contact: Dianne Shugrue, President and Chief Executive Officer
COO: Paul Scimeca, Senior Vice President Operations and Chief Operating Officer
CFO: Mitchell Amado, Senior Vice President Finance and Chief Financial Officer
CMO: Benjamin Katz, M.D., Vice President Medical Affairs
CHR: Kyle Brock, Vice President Human Resources
CNO: Donna Kirker, R.N., MS, Vice President Patient Services and Chief Nursing Officer
Web address: www.glensfallshospital.org
Control: Other not–for–profit (including NFP Corporation) **Service**: General medical and surgical

Staffed Beds: 314 **Admissions**: 13058 **Census**: 178 **Outpatient Visits**: 739474 **Births**: 1046 **Total Expense ($000)**: 348210 **Payroll Expense ($000)**: 162876 **Personnel**: 2187

GLENVILLE—Schenectady County

CONIFER PARK, 79 Glenridge Road, Zip 12302–4523; tel. 518/399–6446, (Nonreporting)
Primary Contact: Jeanne Gluchowski, Executive Director
COO: Jeanne Gluchowski, Executive Director
CFO: Jason Burczeuski, Controller
CMO: John Melbourne, M.D., Medical Director
CIO: Amy Kentera, Chief Information Officer
CHR: Maureen Fowler, Director Human Resources
Web address: www.coniferpark.com/
Control: Corporation, Investor–owned (for–profit) **Service**: Alcoholism and other chemical dependency

Staffed Beds: 225

GLOVERSVILLE—Fulton County

★ ⇑ **NATHAN LITTAUER HOSPITAL AND NURSING HOME (330276)**, 99 East State Street, Zip 12078–1203; tel. 518/725–8621, (Total facility includes 84 beds in nursing home–type unit) **A**5 10 21 **F**3 8 11 13 15 18 28 29 30 31 32 34 35 36 37 40 45 50 53 54 57 59 61 64 65 70 74 75 76 77 78 79 81 82 85 86 87 89 93 97 107 108 110 115 118 119 128 130 131 132 135 144 145 146 147 149 150 **P**6
Primary Contact: Laurence E. Kelly, President and Chief Executive Officer
CMO: Frederick Goldberg, M.D., Vice President Medical Affairs and Chief Medical Officer
CIO: Martin Brown, Vice President Information Services and Chief Information Officer
CHR: Lana Wydra, Vice President Human Resources
CNO: Stephanie Fishel, Vice President Patient Care Services and Chief Nursing Officer
Web address: www.nlh.org
Control: Other not–for–profit (including NFP Corporation) **Service**: General medical and surgical

Staffed Beds: 146 **Admissions**: 2800 **Census**: 107 **Outpatient Visits**: 252773 **Births**: 384 **Total Expense ($000)**: 102408 **Payroll Expense ($000)**: 52418 **Personnel**: 816

GOUVERNEUR—St. Lawrence County

★ ⇑ **GOUVERNEUR HOSPITAL (331315)**, 77 West Barney Street, Zip 13642–1040; tel. 315/287–1000, **A**10 18 21 **F**3 11 15 29 34 35 40 50 57 59 64 68 81 87 89 93 97 107 110 111 119 129 130 133 149 154 **P**6 **S** St. Lawrence Health System, Potsdam, NY
Primary Contact: David Bender, Chief Executive Officer
CFO: Richard T Lang, Chief Financial Officer
CMO: George Dodds, M.D., Medical Director
CNO: Jennifer Shaver, Director of Nursing
Web address: www.gvnrhospital.org
Control: Other not–for–profit (including NFP Corporation) **Service**: General medical and surgical

Staffed Beds: 25 **Admissions**: 388 **Census**: 6 **Outpatient Visits**: 42964 **Births**: 0 **Total Expense ($000)**: 20792 **Payroll Expense ($000)**: 9408 **Personnel**: 167

GREENPORT—Suffolk County

☒ **EASTERN LONG ISLAND HOSPITAL (330088)**, 201 Manor Place, Zip 11944–1298; tel. 631/477–1000, **A**1 10 **F**3 4 5 7 8 11 14 15 17 18 28 29 34 35 38 40 45 47 49 50 53 56 59 62 64 65 68 70 75 79 81 82 84 85 93 98 102 103 107 110 111 114 115 119 130 131 132 135 146 148
Primary Contact: Paul J. Connor III, President and Chief Executive Officer
CFO: Robert A Ragona, Senior Vice President Finance and Chief Financial Officer
CMO: Lloyd Simon, M.D., Medical Director
CIO: Dan Scotto, Director Information Technology
CHR: Frank Dumont, Assistant Vice President Human Resources and Corporate Compliance
CNO: D. Patricia Pispisa, Senior Vice President, Patient Care Services and Chief Nursing Officer
Web address: www.elih.org
Control: Other not–for–profit (including NFP Corporation) **Service**: General medical and surgical

Staffed Beds: 90 **Admissions**: 2840 **Census**: 51 **Outpatient Visits**: 47352 **Births**: 0 **Total Expense ($000)**: 52785 **Payroll Expense ($000)**: 25175 **Personnel**: 298

HAMILTON—Madison County

☒ **COMMUNITY MEMORIAL HOSPITAL (331316)**, 150 Broad Street, Zip 13346–9518; tel. 315/824–1100, **A**1 10 18 **F**3 11 15 18 26 29 34 35 40 45 50 53 54 57 59 64 75 79 81 84 85 89 93 97 100 107 108 110 111 114 119 127 130 133 135 144 146 **P**6
Primary Contact: Sean Fadale, President and Chief Executive Officer
CFO: Christopher W Graham, Chief Financial Officer
CMO: Robert Delorme, Vice President Medical Affairs
CHR: Jennifer Montana, Manager Human Resources
CNO: Denise Hummer, R.N., Vice President Administrative Services
Web address: www.communitymemorial.org
Control: Other not–for–profit (including NFP Corporation) **Service**: General medical and surgical

Staffed Beds: 25 **Admissions**: 1692 **Census**: 15 **Outpatient Visits**: 35372 **Births**: 0 **Total Expense ($000)**: 44462 **Payroll Expense ($000)**: 17177 **Personnel**: 266

HARRIS—Sullivan County

☒ **CATSKILL REGIONAL MEDICAL CENTER (330386)**, 68 Harris Bushville Road, Zip 12742–5030, Mailing Address: P.O. Box 800, Zip 12742–0800; tel. 845/794–3300, (Total facility includes 58 beds in nursing home–type unit) **A**1 2 10 **F**2 3 13 15 17 18 28 29 30 31 32 34 35 40 45 57 59 64 66 70 74 75 76 77 78 79 81 85 87 89 93 97 98 100 102 104 107 108 110 111 114 115 127 128 130 132 133 135 144 146 147 148 149 153 154 **S** Greater Hudson Valley Health System, Middletown, NY
Primary Contact: Jonathan Schiller, Chief Executive Officer
CFO: Rick Caprico, Chief Financial Officer
CMO: Gerard Galarneau, M.D., Regional Chief Medical Officer
CIO: Brian Tew, Chief Information Officer
CNO: Rolland Bojo, R.N., Chief Nursing Officer, Administrator Patient Care and Services
Web address: www.crmcny.org
Control: Other not–for–profit (including NFP Corporation) **Service**: General medical and surgical

Staffed Beds: 119 **Admissions**: 4159 **Census**: 112 **Outpatient Visits**: 68666 **Births**: 596 **Total Expense ($000)**: 85422 **Payroll Expense ($000)**: 35512 **Personnel**: 542

HORNELL—Steuben County

☒ **ST. JAMES MERCY HOSPITAL (330151)**, 411 Canisteo Street, Zip 14843–2197; tel. 607/324–8000, (Nonreporting) **A**1 10 20 **S** University of Rochester Medical Center, Rochester, NY
Primary Contact: Leo P. Brideau, FACHE, Interim President and Chief Executive Officer
CMO: John Carroll, M.D., Chief Medical Officer
CIO: Jason Soles, Manager Information Systems
CHR: Jennifer Spike, Director Human Resources
CNO: Kathleen Brodbeck MSN, RN–B Chief Nursing Officer
Web address: www.stjamesmercy.org
Control: Other not–for–profit (including NFP Corporation) **Service**: General medical and surgical

Staffed Beds: 222

Hospital, Medicare Provider Number, Address, Telephone, Approval, Facility, and Physician Codes, Health Care System

★ American Hospital Association (AHA) membership
☐ The Joint Commission accreditation
○ Healthcare Facilities Accreditation Program
◇ DNV Healthcare Inc. accreditation
⇑ Center for Improvement in Healthcare Quality Accreditation
△ Commission on Accreditation of Rehabilitation Facilities (CARF) accreditation

HUDSON—Columbia County

★ **COLUMBIA MEMORIAL HOSPITAL (330094)**, 71 Prospect Avenue,
Zip 12534–2907; tel. 518/828–7601, (Nonreporting) **A**10 19
Primary Contact: Jay P. Cahalan, Chief Executive Officer
COO: Karen Tassey, FACHE, Chief Operating Officer
CFO: Bryan Mahoney, Chief Financial Officer
CMO: Lawrence Perl, M.D., Chief Medical Officer
CIO: Bonnie Ratliff, Chief Information Officer
CNO: Mary Ellen Plass, MS, R.N., Senior Vice President and Chief Nursing Officer
Web address: www.columbiamemorialhealth.org
Control: Other not–for–profit (including NFP Corporation) **Service**: General medical and surgical

Staffed Beds: 192

HUNTINGTON—Suffolk County

⊞ **HUNTINGTON HOSPITAL (330045)**, 270 Park Avenue, Zip 11743–2799;
tel. 631/351–2000, **A**1 2 3 10 **F**3 5 8 11 12 13 15 17 18 20 22 26 29 30 31
32 34 35 36 37 38 40 41 43 44 45 46 47 48 49 50 51 54 55 56 57 58 59 60
61 63 64 65 66 68 69 70 73 74 75 76 78 79 81 82 84 85 86 87 89 91 97 98
100 101 102 103 107 108 110 111 114 115 118 119 126 130 132 146 147
148 149 150 152 154 **P**5 6 **S** Northwell Health, New Hyde Park, NY
Primary Contact: Gerard Brogan Jr, M.D., Executive Director
CFO: Peter Costalas, Chief Financial Officer
CMO: Michael Grosso, M.D., Senior Vice President Medical Affairs
CIO: Scott C Groom, Senior Vice President and Chief Information Officer
CHR: Lisa Khavkin, Vice President Human Resources
CNO: Susan Knoepffler, R.N., Vice President Nursing
Web address: www.northwell.edu
Control: Other not–for–profit (including NFP Corporation) **Service**: General medical and surgical

Staffed Beds: 290 Admissions: 16202 Census: 199 Outpatient Visits: 110200 Births: 1315 Total Expense ($000): 420797 Payroll Expense ($000): 205245 Personnel: 1907

ITHACA—Tompkins County

⊞ **CAYUGA MEDICAL CENTER AT ITHACA (330307)**, 101 Dates Drive,
Zip 14850–1342; tel. 607/274–4011, **A**1 2 5 10 20 **F**3 8 12 13 15 18 20 22 28
29 30 31 34 35 38 40 41 45 48 49 50 51 54 57 59 61 64 68 70 72 74 75 76
77 78 79 81 82 84 85 86 87 90 93 98 99 100 101 102 103 107 108 110
111 114 115 116 117 118 119 121 129 130 131 132 133 135 144 145 146
147 148 149 154 **P**6 **S** Cayuga Health System, Ithaca, NY
Primary Contact: John B. Rudd, President and Chief Executive Officer
CFO: John Collett, Vice President and Chief Financial Officer
CMO: David M Evelyn, M.D., Vice President Medical Affairs
CIO: Brett Mello, Chief Information Officer
CHR: Brian Forrest, Vice President Human Resources
CNO: Deb Raupers, MSN, R.N., Vice President Patient Services and Chief Nursing Officer
Web address: www.cayugamed.org
Control: Other not–for–profit (including NFP Corporation) **Service**: General medical and surgical

Staffed Beds: 193 Admissions: 6596 Census: 80 Outpatient Visits: 272753 Births: 857 Total Expense ($000): 200782 Payroll Expense ($000): 73765 Personnel: 1399

JAMAICA—Queens County; See New York City

JAMESTOWN—Chautauqua County

⊞ **UPMC CHAUTAUQUA WCA (330239)**, 207 Foote Avenue, Zip 14701–7077,
Mailing Address: P.O. Box 840, Zip 14702–0840; tel. 716/487–0141, **A**1 2 10
F3 4 5 8 11 12 13 15 18 19 20 28 29 31 34 35 38 40 45 46 57 59 60 64 68
69 70 74 75 76 77 78 79 81 82 83 84 85 86 87 90 93 94 96 98 99 100 101
102 104 107 108 110 111 116 117 126 129 130 131 132 135 141 146
147 148 149 154 **P**5 7 **S** UPMC, Pittsburgh, PA
Primary Contact: Betsy T. Wright, President and Chief Executive Officer
CMO: Marlene Garone, M.D., Vice President Medical Affairs and Medical Director
CIO: Keith Robison, Chief Information Officer
CHR: Karen Bohall, Director Human Resources
Web address: www.wcahospital.org
Control: Other not–for–profit (including NFP Corporation) **Service**: General medical and surgical

Staffed Beds: 111 Admissions: 6930 Census: 101 Outpatient Visits: 271357 Births: 647 Total Expense ($000): 113442 Payroll Expense ($000): 43866 Personnel: 969

JOHNSON CITY—Broome County

WILSON MEMORIAL REGIONAL MEDICAL CENTER See United Health Services Hospitals–Binghamton, Binghamton

KATONAH—Westchester County

☐ **FOUR WINDS HOSPITAL (334002)**, 800 Cross River Road, Zip 10536–3549;
tel. 914/763–8151, (Nonreporting) **A**1 10
Primary Contact: Martin A. Buccolo, Ph.D., Chief Executive Officer
COO: Moira Morrissey, Chief Operating Officer and General Counsel
CFO: Barry S Weinstein, Chief Financial Officer
CMO: Jonathan Bauman, M.D., Chief Medical Officer
CIO: Barry S Weinstein, Chief Financial Officer
CHR: Susan Cusano, Director Human Resources
Web address: www.fourwindshospital.com
Control: Partnership, Investor–owned (for–profit) **Service**: Psychiatric

Staffed Beds: 181

KENMORE—Erie County

⊞ **KENMORE MERCY HOSPITAL (330102)**, 2950 Elmwood Avenue,
Zip 14217–1390, Mailing Address: 2950 Elmwood Avenue, Room 4024,
Zip 14217–1390; tel. 716/447–6100, (Total facility includes 160 beds in nursing home–type unit) **A**1 3 10 **F**3 11 15 18 29 30 31 34 35 37 38 40 41 44 45 49
50 53 54 57 58 59 60 64 65 66 68 70 74 75 77 79 81 84 85 87 90 92 93 97
100 107 108 110 115 118 119 126 128 129 130 131 132 141 146 147 148
149 **P**5 6 **S** Catholic Health System, Buffalo, NY
Primary Contact: Walter Ludwig, President and Chief Executive Officer
CFO: James H Dunlop, CPA, Jr Executive Vice President and Chief Financial Officer
CMO: James Fitzpatrick, M.D., Vice President Medical Affairs
CHR: Laura Cianflone, Director Human Resources
Web address: www.chsbuffalo.org
Control: Church operated, Nongovernment, not–for–profit **Service**: General medical and surgical

Staffed Beds: 329 Admissions: 9530 Census: 226 Outpatient Visits: 125101 Births: 0 Total Expense ($000): 169010 Payroll Expense ($000): 71498 Personnel: 1032

KINGSTON—Ulster County

⇑ **BENEDICTINE HOSPITAL** See Health Alliance Hospital – Mary's Avenue Campus

⇑ **HEALTH ALLIANCE HOSPITAL – BROADWAY CAMPUS (330004)**, 396
Broadway, Zip 12401–4692; tel. 845/331–3131, **A**10 19 21 **F**3 5 11 13 18 20
22 28 29 30 31 35 36 40 45 49 50 54 56 57 59 60 63 68 70 74 75 76 77
78 79 81 83 84 85 86 87 92 93 102 107 108 111 114 119 130 131 132
135 146 148 154 **S** WMCHealth, Valhalla, NY
Primary Contact: David Scarpino, President and Chief Executive Officer
COO: Robert Seidman, Chief Operating Officer
CFO: Steven J Haas, Chief Financial Officer
CMO: Frank Ehrlich, M.D., Chief Medical Officer
CIO: John Finch, Vice President Information Services
CHR: Greg M Howard, Director Human Resource
Web address: www.hahv.org
Control: Other not–for–profit (including NFP Corporation) **Service**: General medical and surgical

Staffed Beds: 150 Admissions: 6695 Census: 82 Outpatient Visits: 85522 Births: 286 Total Expense ($000): 114782 Payroll Expense ($000): 50897 Personnel: 773

⇑ **HEALTH ALLIANCE HOSPITAL – MARY'S AVENUE CAMPUS (330224)**, 105
Marys Avenue, Zip 12401–5894; tel. 845/338–2500, **A**2 10 19 21 **F**3 4 8 11 15
18 20 29 30 31 34 35 36 50 54 56 57 59 63 64 66 68 70 74 75 78 79 81 83
84 85 86 87 90 98 105 107 108 114 119 120 121 123 129 130 131 132 146
147 148 154 **P**5 **S** WMCHealth, Valhalla, NY
Primary Contact: David Scarpino, President and Chief Executive Officer
COO: Robert Seidman, Chief Operating Officer
CFO: Steven J Haas, Chief Financial Officer
CMO: Frank Ehrlich, M.D., Chief Medical Officer
CIO: John Finch, Chief Information and Community Officer
CHR: Greg M Howard, Vice President Human Resources
Web address: www.hahv.org
Control: Other not–for–profit (including NFP Corporation) **Service**: General medical and surgical

Staffed Beds: 105 Admissions: 2946 Census: 58 Outpatient Visits: 16557 Births: 0 Total Expense ($000): 62851 Payroll Expense ($000): 24192 Personnel: 524

⇑ **KINGSTON HOSPITAL** See Health Alliance Hospital – Broadway Campus

Many Facility Codes have changed. Please refer to the AHA Guide Code Chart. © 2018 AHA Guide

LEWISTON—Niagara County

⊞ **MOUNT ST. MARY'S HOSPITAL AND HEALTH CENTER (330188)**, 5300 Military Road, Zip 14092–1903; tel. 716/297–4800, **A**1 10 **F**3 4 11 13 15 18 28 29 30 34 35 38 40 41 44 45 49 50 51 54 56 57 58 59 60 64 65 66 68 70 74 75 76 77 79 81 84 85 87 92 93 97 100 107 108 110 111 114 115 118 119 130 132 141 143 **P**5 6 **S** Catholic Health System, Buffalo, NY
Primary Contact: Gary C. Tucker, President and Chief Executive Officer
CFO: Stephen Franko, Vice President Finance and Chief Financial Officer
CNO: Jessica Visser, R.N., Vice President Patient Care Services and Chief Nursing Officer
Web address: www.msmh.org
Control: Church operated, Nongovernment, not–for–profit **Service:** General medical and surgical

Staffed Beds: 145 **Admissions:** 4912 **Census:** 76 **Outpatient Visits:** 175065 **Births:** 327 **Total Expense ($000):** 99721 **Payroll Expense ($000):** 49235 **Personnel:** 621

LITTLE FALLS—Herkimer County

★ **LITTLE FALLS HOSPITAL (331311)**, 140 Burwell Street, Zip 13365–1725; tel. 315/823–1000, (Nonreporting) **A**10 18 **S** Bassett Healthcare Network, Cooperstown, NY
Primary Contact: Michael L. Ogden, President and Chief Executive Officer
CFO: James Vielkind, Chief Financial Officer
CMO: Louis Oceguera, M.D., Medical Director
CIO: Duane Merry, Chief Information Officer
CHR: Christine Pirri, Vice President Human Resources
CNO: Heidi Camardello, Vice President Patient Care Services and Chief Nursing Officer
Web address: www.bassett.org
Control: Other not–for–profit (including NFP Corporation) **Service:** General medical and surgical

Staffed Beds: 25

LOCKPORT—Niagara County

★ **EASTERN NIAGARA HOSPITAL (330163)**, 521 East Avenue, Zip 14094–3299; tel. 716/514–5700, (Includes EASTERN NIAGARA HOSPITAL LOCKPORT, 521 East Avenue, Lockport, NY, Zip 14094–3299; tel. 716/514–5700; EASTERN NIAGARA HOSPITAL NEWFANE, 2600 William Street, Newfane, NY, Zip 14108–1093; tel. 716/778–5111) **A**10 13 **F**3 4 8 13 15 18 19 28 29 30 31 34 40 45 46 47 48 49 50 51 54 57 59 60 63 65 68 70 74 75 76 77 79 81 82 83 84 85 87 89 93 94 97 98 99 100 102 107 108 110 111 115 119 126 130 132 135 144 146 147 148
Primary Contact: Anne E. McCaffrey, President and Chief Executive Officer
CMO: Bruce J Cusenz, M.D., Medical Director
CHR: Joseph Farrauto, Director Human Resources
CNO: Mary Beth Campo, MS, R.N., Director of Nursing
Web address: www.enhs.org
Control: Other not–for–profit (including NFP Corporation) **Service:** General medical and surgical

Staffed Beds: 125 **Admissions:** 3938 **Census:** 73 **Outpatient Visits:** 112040 **Births:** 305 **Total Expense ($000):** 63745 **Payroll Expense ($000):** 28842 **Personnel:** 513

LOWVILLE—Lewis County

⊞ **LEWIS COUNTY GENERAL HOSPITAL (331317)**, 7785 North State Street, Zip 13367–1297; tel. 315/376–5200, (Total facility includes 160 beds in nursing home–type unit) **A**1 10 18 **F**2 13 11 13 15 29 30 34 35 36 40 50 56 57 59 62 63 70 75 77 79 81 82 93 96 97 107 110 111 115 119 128 129 130 132 133 141 143 146 147 154 **P**3
Primary Contact: Gerald Cayer, Chief Executive Officer
COO: Michele Prince, Chief Operating Officer
CMO: Catherine Williams, M.D., Medical Director
CIO: Rob Uttendorfsky, Director Information Management
CNO: Jennifer Shaver, Director of Nursing
Web address: www.lcgh.net
Control: County, Government, nonfederal **Service:** General medical and surgical

Staffed Beds: 185 **Admissions:** 1310 **Census:** 161 **Outpatient Visits:** 95313 **Births:** 238 **Total Expense ($000):** 72162 **Payroll Expense ($000):** 28145 **Personnel:** 546

MALONE—Franklin County

⊞ **THE UNIVERSITY OF VERMONT HEALTH NETWORK – ALICE HYDE MEDICAL CENTER (330084)**, 133 Park Street, Zip 12953–1243, Mailing Address: P.O. Box 729, Zip 12953–0729; tel. 518/483–3000, (Total facility includes 165 beds in nursing home–type unit) **A**1 10 20 **F**3 10 11 13 15 17 18 28 29 31 34 35 39 40 45 57 59 64 67 68 70 75 76 77 78 79 81 82 84 85 86 87 90 92 93 96 97 107 108 110 111 115 117 119 121 127 128 129 130 131 132 135 146 147 149 154 **P**6
Primary Contact: Michelle Lebeau, President
COO: Matthew Jones, Vice President Support Services and Facilities
CFO: Sean Curtin, Chief Financial Officer
CMO: William Latreille, M.D., Chief Medical Officer
CIO: Darrin Goodrow, Chief Information Officer
CHR: Emily Campbell, Vice President Human Resources
CNO: Julie Marshall, Chief Nursing Officer
Web address: www.UVMHealth.org/AHMC
Control: Other not–for–profit (including NFP Corporation) **Service:** General medical and surgical

Staffed Beds: 213 **Admissions:** 1795 **Census:** 173 **Outpatient Visits:** 204134 **Births:** 230 **Total Expense ($000):** 92166 **Payroll Expense ($000):** 46474 **Personnel:** 674

MANHASSET—Nassau County

⊞ **NORTH SHORE UNIVERSITY HOSPITAL (330106)**, 300 Community Drive, Zip 11030–3816; tel. 516/562–0100, **A**1 2 3 5 8 10 **F**3 5 6 7 8 9 11 12 13 14 15 17 18 20 22 24 26 28 29 30 31 34 36 37 38 39 40 41 43 44 45 46 47 48 49 50 51 52 54 55 56 57 58 59 60 61 62 63 64 65 66 68 69 70 71 72 73 74 75 76 77 78 79 80 81 82 83 84 85 86 87 91 92 93 94 97 100 101 102 104 107 108 110 111 112 114 115 117 118 119 120 121 123 126 129 130 131 132 134 135 136 137 138 141 142 143 144 145 146 147 148 149 150 152 154 **P**5 6 **S** Northwell Health, New Hyde Park, NY
Primary Contact: Alessandro Bellucci, M.D., Executive Director
CFO: Frank Rizzo, Chief Financial Officer, Central Region
CMO: Michael Gitman, M.D., Medical Director
CIO: Nympha Meindel, R.N., Chief Information Officer
CHR: Debra Bierman, Associate Executive Director Human Resources
CNO: Kerri Scanlon, MSN, Chief Nursing Officer
Web address: www.northwell.edu/find–care/locations/north–shore–university–hospital
Control: Other not–for–profit (including NFP Corporation) **Service:** General medical and surgical

Staffed Beds: 738 **Admissions:** 46735 **Census:** 737 **Outpatient Visits:** 975234 **Births:** 6671 **Total Expense ($000):** 2257632 **Payroll Expense ($000):** 1171393 **Personnel:** 11882

MARCY—Oneida County

☐ **CENTRAL NEW YORK PSYCHIATRIC CENTER**, 9005 Old River Road, Zip 13403–3000, Mailing Address: P.O. Box 300, Zip 13403–0300; tel. 315/765–3600, (Nonreporting) **A**1 3 **S** New York State Office of Mental Health, Albany, NY
Primary Contact: Maureen Bosco, Executive Director
Web address: www.omh.ny.gov
Control: State, Government, nonfederal **Service:** Psychiatric

Staffed Beds: 226

MARGARETVILLE—Delaware County

⇑ **MARGARETVILLE HOSPITAL (331304)**, 42084 State Highway 28, Zip 12455–2820; tel. 845/586–2631, (Nonreporting) **A**10 18 21 **S** WMCHealth, Valhalla, NY
Primary Contact: Mark Pohar, Executive Director
CHR: Linda Mead, Director Human Resources
Web address: www.margaretvillehospital.org
Control: Other not–for–profit (including NFP Corporation) **Service:** General medical and surgical

Staffed Beds: 15

NY

MASSENA—St. Lawrence County

☐ **MASSENA MEMORIAL HOSPITAL (330223)**, One Hospital Drive,
Zip 13662–1097; tel. 315/764–1711, (Nonreporting) **A**1 10 20
Primary Contact: Charles Gijanto, Interim Chief Executive Officer
CFO: Patrick M. Facteau, Chief Financial Officer
CMO: Nimesh Desai, M.D., Medical Director
CHR: Jonnie Dorothy, Senior Director Human Resources
CNO: Ralene North, Chief Nurse Executive
Web address: www.massenahospital.org
Control: City, Government, nonfederal **Service:** General medical and surgical

Staffed Beds: 50

MEDINA—Orleans County

△ ⇑ **MEDINA MEMORIAL HOSPITAL (331319)**, 200 Ohio Street,
Zip 14103–1095; tel. 585/798–2000, (Total facility includes 30 beds in nursing home–type unit) **A**7 10 18 21 **F**3 11 15 18 26 29 34 35 40 45 46 50 51 53 54 57 59 60 64 68 75 77 79 81 85 86 87 90 91 92 93 96 97 107 108 110 111 115 118 119 127 128 130 132 133 135 146 148 149
Primary Contact: Mark Cye, Chief Executive Officer
CFO: David Britton, Interim Chief Financial Officer
CMO: Joseph Misiti, M.D., President Medical Staff
CHR: Mary Williams, Director Human Resources
Web address: www.medinamemorial.org
Control: Other not–for–profit (including NFP Corporation) **Service:** General medical and surgical

Staffed Beds: 60 **Admissions:** 416 **Census:** 33 **Outpatient Visits:** 51824 **Births:** 0 **Total Expense ($000):** 25260 **Payroll Expense ($000):** 13405 **Personnel:** 232

MIDDLETOWN—Orange County

⊠ △ **ORANGE REGIONAL MEDICAL CENTER (330126)**, 707 East Main Street,
Zip 10940–2650; tel. 845/333–1000, **A**1 2 3 7 10 12 13 **F**3 5 8 11 12 13 15 17 18 20 22 26 28 29 30 31 34 35 36 40 41 43 45 46 47 48 49 50 51 54 57 58 59 63 64 66 70 72 74 75 76 77 78 79 81 82 84 85 86 87 89 90 91 93 96 97 98 100 101 102 104 107 108 110 111 114 115 116 117 119 120 121 122 123 124 126 129 130 132 133 135 144 146 148 149 **S** Greater Hudson Valley Health System, Middletown, NY
Primary Contact: Scott Batulis, President and Chief Executive Officer
COO: Timothy P Selz, Vice President
CFO: Mitch Amodo, Vice President and Chief Financial Officer
CMO: James Oxley, D.O., Vice President Medical Affairs
CHR: Deborah Carr, Vice President Human Resources
Web address: www.ormc.org
Control: Other not–for–profit (including NFP Corporation) **Service:** General medical and surgical

Staffed Beds: 340 **Admissions:** 24091 **Census:** 299 **Outpatient Visits:** 754441 **Births:** 1877 **Total Expense ($000):** 450809 **Payroll Expense ($000):** 173229 **Personnel:** 2196

MINEOLA—Nassau County

⊠ **NYU WINTHROP HOSPITAL (330167)**, 259 First Street, Zip 11501–3957;
tel. 516/663–0333, (Includes CHILDREN'S MEDICAL CENTER, 259 First Street, Mineola, NY, Zip 11501–3957; tel. 516/663–0333) **A**1 2 3 5 8 10 **F**3 5 6 8 9 11 12 13 14 15 17 18 19 20 22 24 26 28 29 30 31 32 34 35 36 37 38 39 40 41 43 44 45 46 47 48 49 50 51 52 54 55 56 57 58 59 60 61 62 63 64 65 66 68 70 72 73 74 75 76 77 78 79 81 82 84 85 86 87 88 89 92 93 94 96 97 100 101 102 104 107 108 110 111 114 115 116 117 118 119 120 121 123 124 126 129 130 131 132 134 135 136 141 142 144 145 146 147 148 149 150 154 **P**5 6 7 8 **S** NYU Langone Health, New York, NY
Primary Contact: John F. Collins, President and Chief Executive Officer
COO: Garry Schwall, Chief Operating Officer
CFO: Palmira Cataliotti, Senior Vice President, Chief Financial Officer and Treasurer
CMO: Michael Ammazzalorso, M.D., Chief Medical Officer
CIO: Nicholas Casabona, Chief Information Officer
CHR: Stacey Pfeffer, Senior Vice President Human Resources
CNO: Valerie Terzano, MSN, R.N., Senior Vice President Nursing
Web address: www.winthrop.org
Control: Other not–for–profit (including NFP Corporation) **Service:** General medical and surgical

Staffed Beds: 511 **Admissions:** 32967 **Census:** 458 **Outpatient Visits:** 453871 **Births:** 4879 **Total Expense ($000):** 1506060 **Payroll Expense ($000):** 740298 **Personnel:** 8360

MONTOUR FALLS—Schuyler County

⊠ **SCHUYLER HOSPITAL (331313)**, 220 Steuben Street, Zip 14865–9709;
tel. 607/535–7121, (Total facility includes 120 beds in nursing home–type unit) **A**1 10 18 **F**3 11 14 15 29 30 34 35 40 50 59 64 70 74 75 77 81 82 85 87 91 92 93 94 97 107 110 111 114 119 128 129 130 133 135 146 149 **P**6 **S** Cayuga Health System, Ithaca, NY
Primary Contact: James B. Watson, President
CMO: Michael Eisman, M.D., Medical Director
Web address: www.schuylerhospital.org
Control: Other not–for–profit (including NFP Corporation) **Service:** General medical and surgical

Staffed Beds: 145 **Admissions:** 858 **Census:** 116 **Outpatient Visits:** 56629 **Births:** 0 **Total Expense ($000):** 32342 **Payroll Expense ($000):** 17231 **Personnel:** 335

MONTROSE—Westchester County

⊠ **VETERANS AFFAIRS HUDSON VALLEY HEALTH CARE SYSTEM**, 2094 Albany Post Road, Zip 10548–1454, Mailing Address: P.O. Box 100, Zip 10548–0100; tel. 914/737–4400, (Includes VETERAN AFFAIRS HUDSON VALLEY HEALTH CARE SYSTEM–CASTLE POINT CAMPUS, 41 Castle Point Road, Wappingers, NY, Zip 12590; tel. 914/831–2000; VETERANS AFFAIRS HUDSON VALLEY HEALTH CARE SYSTEM–MONTROSE CAMPUS, 2094 Albany Post Road, Montrose, NY, Zip 10548; tel. 914/737–4400) **A**1 3 5 **F**1 3 4 5 7 8 12 15 18 20 22 26 28 29 30 31 34 35 36 38 39 44 45 46 47 48 49 53 54 56 57 58 59 60 61 63 65 66 67 68 71 74 75 77 78 79 81 82 83 84 86 87 90 93 94 97 98 100 101 102 103 104 107 108 109 111 112 113 114 115 116 117 118 119 120 121 123 124 127 130 132 135 143 144 146 147 148 149 151 153 154 **P**6 **S** Department of Veterans Affairs, Perry Point, MD
Primary Contact: Margaret B. Caplan, Director
COO: John M Grady, Associate Director
CFO: John Walsh, Chief Fiscal Services
CMO: Joanne J Malina, M.D., Chief of Staff
CIO: Thomas Rooney, Chief Information Resource Management
CHR: Dardanella Russell, Chief Human Resources Management Service
Web address: www.hudsonvalley.va.gov/
Control: Veterans Affairs, Government, federal **Service:** Psychiatric

Staffed Beds: 272 **Admissions:** 1238 **Census:** 98 **Outpatient Visits:** 156848 **Births:** 0 **Total Expense ($000):** 267127 **Payroll Expense ($000):** 124441 **Personnel:** 1456

MOUNT KISCO—Westchester County

⊠ **NORTHERN WESTCHESTER HOSPITAL (330162)**, 400 East Main Street,
Zip 10549–3477, Mailing Address: 400 East Main Street, G–02, Zip 10549–3477; tel. 914/666–1200, **A**1 2 10 **F**3 5 7 8 12 13 15 17 18 28 29 30 31 32 34 35 36 37 40 46 47 48 49 50 51 54 55 56 57 59 60 61 64 65 68 70 72 73 74 75 76 78 79 81 82 84 85 86 87 89 91 92 93 97 98 100 101 102 107 108 109 110 111 114 115 118 119 120 121 123 124 126 129 130 131 132 135 146 147 148 152 **P**5 6 **S** Northwell Health, New Hyde Park, NY
Primary Contact: Joel Seligman, President and Chief Executive Officer
CFO: John Partenza, Vice President and Treasurer
CMO: Marla Koroly, M.D., Chief Medical Officer and Senior Vice President Medical Affairs
CIO: Sue Prince, Director Information Systems
CHR: Kerry Flynn Barrett, Vice President Human Resources
CNO: Lauraine Szekely, R.N., Senior Vice President, Patient Care
Web address: www.nwhc.net
Control: Other not–for–profit (including NFP Corporation) **Service:** General medical and surgical

Staffed Beds: 195 **Admissions:** 9309 **Census:** 114 **Outpatient Visits:** 155482 **Births:** 1532 **Total Expense ($000):** 261573 **Payroll Expense ($000):** 123413 **Personnel:** 1379

MOUNT VERNON—Westchester County

☐ **MONTEFIORE MOUNT VERNON (330086)**, 12 North Seventh Avenue,
Zip 10550–2098; tel. 914/664–8000, **A**1 3 5 10 **F**3 14 15 18 29 30 31 34 35 40 45 50 59 60 61 64 65 66 68 70 74 75 77 78 79 81 84 85 86 87 92 93 97 98 100 102 104 106 107 110 111 114 119 130 146 147 **P**5 **S** Montefiore Health System, Bronx, NY
Primary Contact: Jaccel Kouns, R.N., MS, Vice President and Executive Director
CFO: Albert M Farina, Chief Financial Officer
CMO: Gary Ishkanian, M.D., Vice President Medical Affairs
CIO: Barbara Cooke, Director Health Information Systems
CHR: Dennis H Ashley, Vice President Human Resources
Web address: www.montefiorehealthsystem.org/landing.cfm?id=17
Control: Other not–for–profit (including NFP Corporation) **Service:** General medical and surgical

Staffed Beds: 63 **Admissions:** 3367 **Census:** 60 **Outpatient Visits:** 137701 **Births:** 0 **Total Expense ($000):** 98512 **Payroll Expense ($000):** 39105 **Personnel:** 588

NEW HAMPTON—Orange County

☐ **MID–HUDSON FORENSIC PSYCHIATRIC CENTER (334061)**, Route 17M, Zip 10958, Mailing Address: P.O. Box 158, Zip 10958–0158; tel. 845/374–8700, **A**1 3 10 **F**39 59 75 77 78 82 86 87 98 130 135 154 **S** New York State Office of Mental Health, Albany, NY
Primary Contact: Joseph Freebern, Executive Director
COO: Kristin Orlando, Director Operations
Web address: www.omh.ny.gov
Control: State, Government, nonfederal **Service**: Psychiatric

Staffed Beds: 285 **Admissions:** 342 **Census:** 263 **Outpatient Visits:** 0 **Births:** 0 **Total Expense ($000):** 96644 **Payroll Expense ($000):** 49026 **Personnel:** 549	

NEW HYDE PARK—Queens County; See New York City

NEW HYDE PARK—Nassau County

STEVEN AND ALEXANDRA COHEN CHILDREN'S MEDICAL CENTER OF NEW YORK See Long Island Jewish Medical Center, New Hyde Park

NEW ROCHELLE—Westchester County

✠ **MONTEFIORE NEW ROCHELLE (330184)**, 16 Guion Place, Zip 10801–5502; tel. 914/632–5000, (Total facility includes 150 beds in nursing home–type unit) **A**1 2 3 5 10 **F**2 3 12 13 14 15 18 28 29 30 31 32 34 35 37 40 45 50 55 59 64 65 66 68 70 72 74 75 76 77 78 79 81 82 84 85 86 87 90 92 93 97 100 107 108 110 114 119 128 130 132 135 146 **P**5 **S** Montefiore Health System, Bronx, NY
Primary Contact: Anthony Alfano, Vice President Executive Director
CMO: Richard Barone, M.D., Medical Director
CHR: Dennis H Ashley, Vice President Human Resources
CNO: Pamela M Dupuis, R.N., Senior Vice President Patient Care Services
Web address: www.montefiorehealthsystem.org
Control: Other not–for–profit (including NFP Corporation) **Service**: General medical and surgical

Staffed Beds: 301 **Admissions:** 7193 **Census:** 225 **Outpatient Visits:** 89023 **Births:** 928 **Total Expense ($000):** 205996 **Payroll Expense ($000):** 91094 **Personnel:** 1226	

NEW YORK (Includes all hospitals located within the five boroughs)
BRONX—Bronx County (Mailing Address – Bronx)
BROOKLYN—Kings County (Mailing Address – Brooklyn)
MANHATTAN—New York County (Mailing Address – New York)
QUEENS—Queens County (Mailing Addresses – Bellerose, Elmhurst, Far Rockaway, Flushing, Forest Hills, Glen Oaks, Holliswood, Jackson Heights, Jamaica, Little Neck, Long Island City, New Hyde Park, and Queens Village)
RICHMOND VALLEY—Richmond County (Mailing Address – Staten Island)

BETH ISRAEL MEDICAL CENTER See Mount Sinai Beth Israel

BETH ISRAEL MEDICAL CENTER–KINGS HIGHWAY DIVISION See Mount Sinai Beth Israel Brooklyn

☐ **BRONX PSYCHIATRIC CENTER (334053)**, 1500 Waters Place, Zip 10461–2796; tel. 718/931–0600, (Nonreporting) **A**1 3 5 10 **S** New York State Office of Mental Health, Albany, NY
Primary Contact: Anita Daniels, Director
CFO: Robert Erway, Director for Administration
Web address: www.omh.ny.gov
Control: State, Government, nonfederal **Service**: Psychiatric

Staffed Beds: 450	

✠ **BRONXCARE HEALTH SYSTEM (330009)**, 1276 Fulton Avenue, Zip 10456–3499; tel. 718/590–1800, (Includes BRONX–LEBANON SPECIAL CARE CENTER, 1265 Fulton Avenue, Bronx, NY, Zip 10465; tel. 718/579–7000; Octavio Marin, Vice President Long Term Care and Ambulatory Care Services; CONCOURSE DIVISION, 1650 Grand Concourse, Bronx, NY, Zip 10457, Mailing Address: 1276 Fulton Ave, Zip 10456–3402, tel. 718/590–1800; Miguel A Fuentes Jr, President and Chief Executive Officer; FULTON DIVISION, 1276 Fulton Avenue, Bronx, NY, Zip 10456, Mailing Address: 1650 Grand Concourse, Zip 10457–7606, tel. 718/590–1800; Miguel A Fuentes Jr, President and Chief Executive Officer; HIGHBRIDGE WOODYCREST CENTER, 936 Woodycrest Avenue, Bronx, NY, Zip 10452; tel. 718/579–8875; Leonardo Vicent III, Executive Director) (Total facility includes 240 beds in nursing home–type unit) **A**1 3 5 10 **F**3 4 8 9 11 12 13 15 17 18 19 20 21 22 26 28 29 30 31 32 34 35 37 38 39 40 41 43 44 45 46 47 48 49 50 51 52 54 55 56 57 58 59 60 61 64 65 66 68 70 71 72 73 74 75 76 77 78 79 81 82 83 84 85 86 87 88 89 91 92 93 95 96 97 98 99 100 101 102 103 104 105 106 107 108 110 111 114 115 118 119 126 128 129 130 131 132 133 134 135 143 144 146 147 148 149 150 151 152 153 **P**5
Primary Contact: Miguel A. Fuentes Jr, President and Chief Executive Officer
CFO: Victor DeMarco, Chief Financial Officer
CMO: Milton A Gumbs, M.D., Vice President and Medical Director
CIO: Ivan Durbak, Chief Information Officer
CHR: Selena Griffin–Mahon, Assistant Vice President Human Resources
CNO: Patricia Cahill, R.N., Vice President, Patient Care Services and Chief Nursing Officer
Web address: www.bronxcare.org
Control: Other not–for–profit (including NFP Corporation) **Service**: General medical and surgical

Staffed Beds: 859 **Admissions:** 30333 **Census:** 756 **Outpatient Visits:** 1108297 **Births:** 2047 **Total Expense ($000):** 834000 **Payroll Expense ($000):** 402023 **Personnel:** 4169	

☐ **BROOKDALE HOSPITAL MEDICAL CENTER (330233)**, 125 Worth Street, 4th Fl Ste 418, Zip 10013, Mailing Address: One Brookdale Plaza, Brooklyn, Zip 11212–3139; tel. 718/240–5000, (Nonreporting) **A**1 3 5 10
Primary Contact: Dominick Stanzione, President and Chief Executive Officer
CFO: James Porter, Chief Financial Officer
CIO: David Reitzel, Chief Information Officer
CHR: Margaret M Brubaker, Senior Vice President Human Resources
Web address: www.brookdalehospital.org
Control: Other not–for–profit (including NFP Corporation) **Service**: General medical and surgical

Staffed Beds: 789	

☐ **BROOKLYN HOSPITAL CENTER (330056)**, 121 DeKalb Avenue, Zip 11201–5425; tel. 718/250–8000, **A**1 3 5 10 **F**3 4 7 8 12 13 15 17 18 19 20 26 29 30 31 32 34 35 39 40 41 45 46 47 48 49 50 52 54 55 56 57 58 59 60 61 63 64 65 68 70 72 74 75 77 78 79 81 82 83 84 85 86 87 88 90 93 94 97 100 101 103 107 109 110 111 112 114 115 116 117 119 120 121 122 123 129 130 131 132 133 134 135 143 144 145 146 147 148 149 150
Primary Contact: Gary G. Terrinoni, President and Chief Executive Officer
COO: John Gupta, Executive Vice President and Chief Operating Officer
CIO: Irene Farrelly, Vice President and Chief Information Officer
CHR: Ira Warm, Senior Vice President Human Resources
Web address: www.tbh.org
Control: Other not–for–profit (including NFP Corporation) **Service**: General medical and surgical

Staffed Beds: 297 **Admissions:** 15503 **Census:** 210 **Outpatient Visits:** 328145 **Births:** 2373 **Total Expense ($000):** 432570 **Payroll Expense ($000):** 219848 **Personnel:** 4362	

✠ **CALVARY HOSPITAL (332006)**, 1740 Eastchester Road, Zip 10461–2392; tel. 718/863–6900, **A**1 3 5 10 **F**1 29 30 35 39 62 63 64 68 74 78 82 84 87 119 121 130 132 134 146 148 149 **P**6
Primary Contact: Frank A. Calamari, President and Chief Executive Officer
COO: Richard J Kutilek, Chief Operating Officer
CFO: Andrew Greco, Chief Financial Officer
CMO: Michael J Brescia, M.D., Executive Medical Director
CIO: Patrick Martin, Director Information Systems
CHR: Michael T Troncone, Chief Human Resources Officer
CNO: Margaret Pelkowski, R.N., Vice President Patient Care Services
Web address: www.calvaryhospital.org
Control: Church operated, Nongovernment, not–for–profit **Service**: Other specialty treatment

Staffed Beds: 225 **Admissions:** 2625 **Census:** 217 **Outpatient Visits:** 114336 **Births:** 0 **Total Expense ($000):** 122125 **Payroll Expense ($000):** 64836 **Personnel:** 890	

NY

COLER–GOLDWATER SPECIALTY HOSPITAL AND NURSING FACILITY See NYC Health + Hospitals / Henry J Carter Specialty Hospital and Medical Center

CONCOURSE DIVISION See Bronxcare Health System, Bronx

☐ **CREEDMOOR PSYCHIATRIC CENTER (334004)**, 79–25 Winchester Boulevard, Zip 11427–2128; tel. 718/264–3600, (Nonreporting) **A**1 10 **S** New York State Office of Mental Health, Albany, NY
Primary Contact: Ann Marie. Barbarotta, Executive Director
CFO: Viodelda Ho–Shing, Deputy Director Administration
CIO: Ed Yunusov, Chief Information Officer
CHR: Adrienne Jones, Director Human Resources
CNO: Marie S Jean–Louis, R.N., Chief Nursing Officer
Web address: www.omh.ny.gov
Control: State, Government, nonfederal **Service**: Psychiatric

Staffed Beds: 322

✕ **FLUSHING HOSPITAL MEDICAL CENTER (330193)**, 4500 Parsons Boulevard, Zip 11355–2205; tel. 718/670–5000, **A**1 3 5 10 **F**3 4 5 6 7 8 12 13 15 17 18 19 29 30 31 32 34 35 36 39 40 41 45 49 50 51 55 56 57 59 60 61 64 65 68 70 71 72 73 74 75 76 77 78 79 81 82 84 85 87 89 91 92 93 97 98 100 101 103 104 105 106 107 110 111 114 119 126 128 130 132 135 146 147 148 149 150 154 **P**5 **S** MediSys Health Network, Jamaica, NY
Primary Contact: Bruce J. Flanz, President and Chief Executive Officer
COO: Robert V Levine, Executive Vice President and Chief Operating Officer
CFO: Mounir F Doss, Executive Vice President and Chief Financial Officer
CIO: Tony Gatto, Director Management Information Systems
Web address: www.flushinghospital.org
Control: Other not–for–profit (including NFP Corporation) **Service**: General medical and surgical

Staffed Beds: 299 Admissions: 14628 Census: 213 Outpatient Visits: 148613 Births: 2928 Total Expense ($000): 700407 Payroll Expense ($000): 128265 Personnel: 1766

FULTON DIVISION See Bronxcare Health System, Bronx

☐ **GRACIE SQUARE HOSPITAL (334048)**, 420 East 76th Street, Zip 10021–3396; tel. 212/988–4400, (Nonreporting) **A**1 10
Primary Contact: David Wyman, President and Chief Executive Officer
Web address: www.nygsh.org
Control: Other not–for–profit (including NFP Corporation) **Service**: Psychiatric

Staffed Beds: 157

HENRY J. CARTER SPECIALTY HOSPITAL & NURSING FACILITY See NYC Health + Hospitals / Henry J Carter Specialty Hospital and Medical Center, New York

✕ **HOSPITAL FOR SPECIAL SURGERY (330270)**, 535 East 70th Street, Zip 10021–4898, Mailing Address: 535 East 70th Street, Belaire 10–08, Zip 10021–4898; tel. 212/606–1000, **A**1 3 5 10 **F**3 8 9 29 30 32 33 34 35 36 37 38 43 44 50 53 54 56 57 58 60 64 66 68 70 74 75 77 79 80 81 82 84 85 86 87 89 92 93 94 97 100 107 109 111 114 115 116 117 119 121 123 126 130 131 132 134 141 142 143 146 147 148 149 154 **P**8
Primary Contact: Louis A. Shapiro, President and Chief Executive Officer
COO: Lisa Goldstein, Executive Vice President and Chief Operating Officer
CFO: Stacey Malakoff, Executive Vice President and Chief Financial Officer
CMO: Todd Albert, M.D., Surgeon–in–Chief and Medical Director
CIO: Jamie Nelson, Vice President and Chief Information Officer
CHR: Bruce Slawitsky, Vice President Human Resources
CNO: Stephanie J Goldberg, MSN, R.N., Senior Vice President and Chief Nursing Officer
Web address: www.hss.edu
Control: Other not–for–profit (including NFP Corporation) **Service**: Orthopedic

Staffed Beds: 215 Admissions: 16271 Census: 142 Outpatient Visits: 429624 Births: 0 Total Expense ($000): 1059614 Payroll Expense ($000): 475235 Personnel: 4754

☐ **INTERFAITH MEDICAL CENTER (330397)**, 1545 Atlantic Avenue, Zip 11213–1122; tel. 718/613–4000, **A**1 3 5 10 **F**4 5 8 15 18 20 22 29 30 34 35 38 39 40 41 43 44 45 46 50 54 56 57 59 60 61 64 68 70 77 79 81 82 89 93 94 97 98 100 101 102 104 105 114 115 130 132 135 143 146 148 152 154
Primary Contact: LaRay Brown, President and Chief Executive Officer
CMO: Jochanan Weisenfreund, M.D., Senior Vice President Academic and Medical Affairs
CIO: Mark Lederman, Chief Information Officer
CHR: Venra Mathurin, Vice President Human Resources
Web address: www.interfaithmedical.com
Control: Other not–for–profit (including NFP Corporation) **Service**: General medical and surgical

Staffed Beds: 243 Admissions: 9592 Census: 197 Outpatient Visits: 157518 Births: 0 Total Expense ($000): 228388 Payroll Expense ($000): 120415 Personnel: 1309

JACK D WEILER HOSPITAL OF ALBERT EINSTEIN COLLEGE OF MEDICINE See Montefiore Medical Center, Bronx

✕ **JAMAICA HOSPITAL MEDICAL CENTER (330014)**, 8900 Van Wyck Expressway, Zip 11418–2832; tel. 718/206–6000, (Total facility includes 228 beds in nursing home–type unit) **A**1 3 5 10 13 **F**1 3 7 11 13 15 17 18 19 20 22 26 29 30 31 32 34 35 36 38 39 40 41 43 44 45 49 50 52 53 54 55 56 57 58 59 60 61 62 64 65 66 68 70 71 72 73 74 75 76 77 78 79 80 81 82 83 84 85 86 87 89 90 92 93 96 97 98 100 101 102 103 104 107 108 110 111 114 115 118 119 128 129 130 131 132 134 135 143 144 146 147 149 150 **P**5 7 8 **S** MediSys Health Network, Jamaica, NY
Primary Contact: Bruce J. Flanz, President and Chief Executive Officer
COO: William Lynch, Executive Vice President and Chief Operating Officer
CFO: Mounir F Doss, Executive Vice President and Chief Financial Officer
CMO: Antonietta Morisco, M.D., Medical Director, Chairman Anesthesiology
CIO: Sami Boshut, Chief Information Officer
CHR: Trina Cornet, JD, Vice President Human Resources
CNO: Kathleen Scher, Ed.D., R.N., Chief Nursing Officer
Web address: www.Jamaicahospital.org
Control: Other not–for–profit (including NFP Corporation) **Service**: General medical and surgical

Staffed Beds: 632 Admissions: 21193 Census: 529 Outpatient Visits: 351156 Births: 2214 Total Expense ($000): 733066 Payroll Expense ($000): 269343 Personnel: 3400

✕ △ **JAMES J. PETERS VETERANS AFFAIRS MEDICAL CENTER**, 130 West Kingsbridge Road, Zip 10468–3904; tel. 718/584–9000, (Total facility includes 80 beds in nursing home–type unit) **A**1 2 3 5 7 8 **F**1 3 5 8 12 15 17 18 26 29 30 31 34 35 39 40 46 47 48 49 51 53 54 56 57 58 59 60 61 63 64 65 70 71 74 75 77 78 79 80 81 82 83 84 85 86 87 90 91 92 93 95 97 98 100 101 102 104 105 107 108 110 111 112 114 116 117 118 119 120 121 122 123 126 129 130 132 135 138 143 145 146 147 148 149 152 153 154 **S** Department of Veterans Affairs, Perry Point, MD
Primary Contact: Erik Langhoff, M.D., Ph.D., Director
CFO: Gregory Angelo, Chief Fiscal Program
CIO: Linda Bund, Chief Information Officer and Director Education
CNO: Kathleen Capitulo, Ph.D., R.N., Chief Nurse Executive
Web address: www.bronx.va.gov/
Control: Veterans Affairs, Government, federal **Service**: General medical and surgical

Staffed Beds: 378 Admissions: 3785 Census: 79 Outpatient Visits: 359407 Births: 0 Total Expense ($000): 475432 Payroll Expense ($000): 174063 Personnel: 1964

☐ **KINGSBORO PSYCHIATRIC CENTER (334063)**, 681 Clarkson Avenue, Zip 11203–2125; tel. 718/221–7395, (Nonreporting) **A**1 3 5 10 **S** New York State Office of Mental Health, Albany, NY
Primary Contact: Deborah Parchment, Executive Director
CFO: Yinusa Awolowo, Business Officer
CMO: Jeffery Lucey, M.D., Clinical Director
CIO: George Gavora, Director Program Evaluation
CHR: Vera Thompson, Director Human Resources
CNO: Deborah Denigris, Chief Nursing Officer
Web address: www.omh.ny.gov/omhweb/facilities/kbpc/facility/htm
Control: State, Government, nonfederal **Service**: Psychiatric

Staffed Beds: 290

NY

□ △ **KINGSBROOK JEWISH MEDICAL CENTER (330201)**, 585 Schenectady Avenue, Zip 11203–1891; tel. 718/604–5000, (Total facility includes 398 beds in nursing home–type unit) **A**1 3 5 7 10 **F**3 8 14 15 17 18 28 29 30 31 34 35 39 40 45 46 48 49 50 54 56 57 59 60 61 64 65 68 70 74 75 77 78 79 80 81 82 84 85 87 90 91 92 94 96 97 98 100 101 103 104 107 108 110 111 115 119 128 130 131 132 135 146 147 148 149 **P**6
Primary Contact: Kurt Kodroff, M.D., Chief Executive Officer
COO: Robert Dubicki, Executive Vice President and Chief Operating Officer
CFO: John Schmitt, Senior Vice President and Chief Financial Officer
CMO: Sibte Burney, M.D., Senior Vice President Medical Affairs and Chief Medical Officer
CIO: Daniel Morreale, Vice President and Chief Information Officer
CHR: John McKeon, Vice President Human Resources
CNO: Jane Lederer, R.N., Ed.D., Vice President and Chief Nursing Officer
Web address: www.kingsbrook.org
Control: Other not–for–profit (including NFP Corporation) **Service:** General medical and surgical

Staffed Beds: 740 **Admissions:** 9563 **Census:** 635 **Outpatient Visits:** 127359 **Births:** 0 **Total Expense ($000):** 308048 **Payroll Expense ($000):** 156088 **Personnel:** 1916

KIRBY FORENSIC PSYCHIATRIC CENTER (334060), 600 East 125th Street, Zip 10035–6000; tel. 646/672–5800, (Nonreporting) **A**3 **S** New York State Office of Mental Health, Albany, NY
Primary Contact: Vincent Miccoli, Executive Director
Web address: www.omh.ny.gov/omhweb/facilities/krpc/
Control: Other not–for–profit (including NFP Corporation) **Service:** Psychiatric

Staffed Beds: 193

☒ **LENOX HILL HOSPITAL (330119)**, 100 East 77th Street, Zip 10075–1850; tel. 212/434–2000, (Includes MANHATTAN EYE, EAR AND THROAT HOSPITAL, 210 East 64th Street, New York, NY, Zip 10021–9885; tel. 212/838–9200; Philip P Rosenthal, Executive Director) **A**1 3 5 8 10 **F**3 5 7 8 9 11 12 13 14 15 17 18 19 20 21 22 24 26 29 30 31 32 34 35 36 37 40 43 44 45 47 49 50 51 52 54 55 56 57 58 59 60 61 62 63 64 65 66 68 70 72 74 75 76 77 78 79 81 82 84 85 86 87 89 91 92 93 94 97 98 100 101 102 103 104 107 108 110 111 114 115 116 117 118 119 120 121 123 124 126 129 130 131 132 135 141 143 146 147 148 149 150 152 154 **P**5 6 **S** Northwell Health, New Hyde Park, NY
Primary Contact: Jill Kalman, Executive Director
CIO: Beth Dituro, Divisional Chief Information Officer
Web address: www.lenoxhillhospital.org
Control: Other not–for–profit (including NFP Corporation) **Service:** General medical and surgical

Staffed Beds: 440 **Admissions:** 29560 **Census:** 332 **Outpatient Visits:** 248501 **Births:** 4146 **Total Expense ($000):** 1207515 **Payroll Expense ($000):** 599688 **Personnel:** 5231

☒ **LONG ISLAND JEWISH MEDICAL CENTER (330195)**, 270–05 76th Avenue, Zip 11040–1496; tel. 718/470–7000, (Includes LONG ISLAND JEWISH FOREST HILLS, 102–01 66th Road, Forest Hills, NY, Zip 11375–2029; tel. 718/830–4000; Susan Browning, Executive Director; LONG ISLAND JEWISH VALLEY STREAM, 900 Franklin Avenue, Valley Stream, NY, Zip 11580–2190; tel. 516/256–6000; Stephen Bello, Executive Director; MANHASSET AMBULATORY CARE PAVILION, 1554 Northern Boulevard, Manhasset, NY, Zip 11030; tel. 516/365–2070; STEVEN AND ALEXANDRA COHEN CHILDREN'S MEDICAL CENTER OF NEW YORK, 270–05 76th Avenue, New Hyde Park, NY, Zip 11040; tel. 718/470–3000; ZUCKER HILLSIDE HOSPITAL, 75–59 263rd Street, Glen Oaks, NY, Zip 11004; tel. 718/470–8000) **A**1 2 3 5 8 10 13 **F**2 3 4 5 6 7 8 9 11 12 13 14 15 17 18 19 20 21 22 23 24 25 26 27 28 29 30 31 32 34 35 38 39 40 41 43 44 45 46 47 48 49 50 51 52 53 54 55 56 57 58 59 60 61 62 63 64 65 66 67 68 70 72 73 74 75 76 77 78 79 80 81 82 84 85 86 87 88 89 92 93 97 98 99 100 101 102 103 104 105 107 108 109 110 111 114 115 116 117 118 119 120 121 123 124 126 129 130 131 132 134 136 141 142 143 144 145 146 147 148 149 151 152 153 154 **P**5 6 **S** Northwell Health, New Hyde Park, NY
Primary Contact: Michael Goldberg, Executive Director
CIO: John Bosco, Senior Vice President and Chief Information Officer
CHR: Ronald W Stone, Regional Chief Human Resource Officer
Web address: www.lij.edu
Control: Other not–for–profit (including NFP Corporation) **Service:** General medical and surgical

Staffed Beds: 1211 **Admissions:** 81756 **Census:** 1302 **Outpatient Visits:** 1068465 **Births:** 10860 **Total Expense ($000):** 2711329 **Payroll Expense ($000):** 1341526 **Personnel:** 13844

☒ **MAIMONIDES MEDICAL CENTER (330194)**, 4802 Tenth Avenue, Zip 11219–2916; tel. 718/283–6000, (Includes MAIMONIDES INFANTS AND CHILDREN'S HOSPITAL OF BROOKLYN, 4802 Tenth Avenue, Brooklyn, NY, Zip 11219–2916; tel. 718/283–6000) **A**1 2 3 5 8 10 12 13 **F**2 3 7 8 9 11 12 13 14 15 17 18 19 20 22 24 26 28 29 30 31 32 34 35 38 39 40 41 43 44 45 46 47 48 49 50 51 52 54 55 56 57 58 59 60 61 64 65 66 68 70 72 73 74 75 76 77 78 79 81 82 84 85 86 87 88 89 91 92 93 96 97 98 99 100 101 102 103 104 107 108 110 111 114 115 117 118 119 120 121 123 124 126 129 130 131 132 135 144 145 146 147 148 149 150 154 **P**5 6
Primary Contact: Kenneth Gibbs, President and Chief Executive Officer
COO: Mark McDougle, Executive Vice President and Chief Operating Officer
CFO: Robert Naldi, Chief Financial Officer
CMO: Samuel Kopel, M.D., Medical Director
CIO: Walter Fahey, Chief Information Officer
Web address: www.maimonidesmed.org/
Control: Other not–for–profit (including NFP Corporation) **Service:** General medical and surgical

Staffed Beds: 598 **Admissions:** 36695 **Census:** 550 **Outpatient Visits:** 530288 **Births:** 8378 **Total Expense ($000):** 1256879 **Payroll Expense ($000):** 610693 **Personnel:** 5807

□ **MANHATTAN PSYCHIATRIC CENTER–WARD'S ISLAND (334054)**, 600 East 125th Street, Zip 10035–6000; tel. 646/672–6767, (Nonreporting) **A**1 3 5 10 **S** New York State Office of Mental Health, Albany, NY
Primary Contact: Vincent Miccoli, Executive Director
Web address: www.omh.ny.gov
Control: State, Government, nonfederal **Service:** Psychiatric

Staffed Beds: 745

☒ **MEMORIAL SLOAN–KETTERING CANCER CENTER (330154)**, 1275 York Avenue, Zip 10065–6007; tel. 212/639–2000, **A**1 2 3 5 8 10 **F**3 8 11 14 15 29 31 32 34 35 36 37 39 44 45 46 47 48 49 50 54 55 56 57 58 59 60 61 64 66 68 70 74 75 77 78 79 81 82 84 85 86 87 88 89 92 93 94 96 99 100 103 104 107 108 110 111 112 114 115 117 118 120 121 123 124 126 130 132 135 136 142 143 144 145 146 147 148 149 154 **P**6
Primary Contact: Craig B. Thompson, M.D., President and Chief Executive Officer
COO: Ned Groves, Executive Vice President and Administrator
CFO: Michael Gutnick, Executive Vice President and Chief Financial Officer
CMO: Lisa DeAngelis, MD, Acting Physician–in–Chief
CIO: Patricia Skarulis, Senior Vice President and Chief Information Systems Officer
CHR: Kerry Bessey, Senior Vice President and Chief Human Resources Officer
CNO: Elizabeth Nelkin McCormick, MSN, R.N., Senior Vice President and Chief Nursing Officer
Web address: www.mskcc.org
Control: Other not–for–profit (including NFP Corporation) **Service:** Cancer

Staffed Beds: 473 **Admissions:** 23506 **Census:** 443 **Outpatient Visits:** 1757534 **Births:** 0 **Total Expense ($000):** 3421667 **Payroll Expense ($000):** 1318918 **Personnel:** 16587

☒ **MONTEFIORE MEDICAL CENTER (330059)**, 111 East 210th Street, Zip 10467–2401; tel. 718/920–4321, (Includes CHILDREN'S HOSPITAL OF MONTEFIORE, 3415 Bainbridge Avenue, Bronx, NY, Zip 10467–2403; tel. 718/741–2426; JACK D WEILER HOSPITAL OF ALBERT EINSTEIN COLLEGE OF MEDICINE, 1825 Eastchester Road, Bronx, NY, Zip 10461–2373; tel. 718/904–2000; MONTEFIORE MEDICAL CENTER – NORTH DIVISION, 600 East 233rd Street, Bronx, NY, Zip 10466–2697; tel. 718/920–9000) **A**1 2 3 5 8 10 **F**1 3 5 6 7 8 9 12 13 14 15 17 18 19 20 21 22 23 24 25 26 27 28 29 30 31 32 34 35 36 37 38 39 40 41 43 44 45 46 47 48 49 50 51 52 53 54 55 56 57 58 59 60 61 62 63 64 65 66 67 68 70 71 72 73 74 75 76 77 78 79 80 81 82 83 84 85 86 87 88 89 90 91 92 93 94 97 98 99 100 101 102 103 104 107 108 110 111 114 115 117 118 119 120 121 123 124 126 128 129 130 131 132 134 135 136 137 138 139 140 141 142 143 144 145 146 147 148 149 150 154 **P**5 6 **S** Montefiore Health System, Bronx, NY
Primary Contact: Steven M. Safyer, M.D., President and Chief Executive Officer
COO: Philip O. Ozuah, M.D., Ph.D., Executive Vice President and Chief Operating Officer
CFO: Colleen M Blye, Executive Vice President and Chief Financial Officer
CMO: Gary Kalkut, M.D., Senior Vice President and Chief Medical Officer
CIO: Jack Wolf, Vice President Information Systems
Web address: www.montefiore.org
Control: Other not–for–profit (including NFP Corporation) **Service:** General medical and surgical

Staffed Beds: 1519 **Admissions:** 88125 **Census:** 1407 **Outpatient Visits:** 1749897 **Births:** 5961 **Total Expense ($000):** 3743460 **Payroll Expense ($000):** 1761775 **Personnel:** 19042

MORGAN STANLEY CHILDREN'S HOSPITAL OF NEW YORK–PRESBYTERIAN
See New York–Presbyterian Hospital, New York

Hospital, Medicare Provider Number, Address, Telephone, Approval, Facility, and Physician Codes, Health Care System

★ American Hospital Association (AHA) membership
□ The Joint Commission accreditation
○ Healthcare Facilities Accreditation Program
◇ DNV Healthcare Inc. accreditation
⇑ Center for Improvement in Healthcare Quality Accreditation
△ Commission on Accreditation of Rehabilitation Facilities (CARF) accreditation

☒ **MOUNT SINAI BETH ISRAEL (330169)**, First Avenue and 16th Street, Zip 10003–3803; tel. 212/420–2000, (Includes MOUNT SINAI BETH ISRAEL BROOKLYN, 3201 Kings Highway, Brooklyn, NY, Zip 11234; tel. 718/252–3000; Lin H Mo, M.P.H., President) **A**1 2 3 5 8 10 **F**3 4 5 7 8 9 11 12 14 15 17 18 19 20 22 26 29 30 31 34 35 36 38 39 40 41 43 44 45 46 47 48 49 50 51 53 54 55 56 57 58 59 60 61 63 64 65 66 68 70 74 75 77 78 79 81 82 83 84 85 86 87 92 93 94 97 98 100 101 102 103 104 107 108 110 111 114 115 117 118 119 120 121 123 124 126 130 131 132 134 141 144 146 147 148 149 150 154 **P**5 6 **S** Mount Sinai Health System, New York, NY
Primary Contact: Jeremy Boal, M.D., President
COO: Kevin Molloy, Senior Vice President and Chief Operating Officer
CFO: Donald Scanlon, Chief Corporate Services, Mount Sinai Health System
CIO: Kumar Chatani, Senior Vice President and Chief Information Officer Mount Sinai Health System
CHR: Jane Maksoud, R.N., Senior Vice President Human Resources and Labor Relations, Mount Sinai Health System
CNO: Mary Walsh, R.N., MSN, Vice President Patient Care Services and Chief Nursing Officer
Web address: www.bethisraelny.org
Control: Other not–for–profit (including NFP Corporation) **Service:** General medical and surgical

Staffed Beds: 649 **Admissions:** 29900 **Census:** 475 **Outpatient Visits:** 380163 **Births:** 791 **Total Expense ($000):** 1074146 **Payroll Expense ($000):** 393256 **Personnel:** 5816

☒ △ **MOUNT SINAI HOSPITAL (330024)**, One Gustave L Levy Place, Zip 10029–0310; tel. 212/241–6500, (Includes KRAVIS CHILDREN'S HOSPITAL, 1184 Fifth Avenue, New York, NY, Zip 10029–6503, Mailing Address: One Gustave L Levy Place, Zip 10029–0312, tel. 212/241–9500; MOUNT SINAI QUEENS, 25–10 30th Avenue, Long Island City, NY, Zip 11102–2448; tel. 718/932–1000; Caryn A Schwab, Executive Director) **A**1 2 5 7 8 10 **F**1 3 4 6 7 8 9 11 12 13 14 15 17 18 19 20 21 22 23 24 25 26 27 28 29 30 31 32 34 35 36 37 39 41 43 44 45 46 47 48 49 50 51 52 54 55 56 57 58 59 60 61 63 64 65 66 67 68 70 71 72 73 74 75 76 77 78 79 80 81 82 83 84 85 86 87 88 89 90 91 92 93 94 95 96 97 98 99 100 101 102 103 104 105 107 108 110 111 114 115 116 117 118 119 120 121 123 124 126 128 129 130 131 132 134 135 136 137 138 139 141 142 143 144 145 146 147 148 149 150 153 154 **P**5 6 **S** Mount Sinai Health System, New York, NY
Primary Contact: David L. Reich, M.D., President and Chief Operating Officer
COO: David L Reich, M.D., President and Chief Operating Officer
CFO: Donald Scanlon, Chief Financial Officer
CMO: Vicki LoPachin, M.D., Chief Medical Officer
CIO: Kumar Chatani, Senior Vice President and Chief Information Officer Mount Sinai Health System
CHR: Jane Maksoud, R.N., Senior Vice President Human Resources and Labor Relations
Web address: www.mountsinai.org
Control: Other not–for–profit (including NFP Corporation) **Service:** General medical and surgical

Staffed Beds: 1113 **Admissions:** 58646 **Census:** 985 **Outpatient Visits:** 1041291 **Births:** 7737 **Total Expense ($000):** 2454033 **Payroll Expense ($000):** 937165 **Personnel:** 10868

☒ **MOUNT SINAI WEST (330046)**, 1111 Amsterdam Avenue, Zip 10025–1716; tel. 212/523–4000, (Includes MOUNT SINAI WEST HOSPITAL, 1000 Tenth Avenue, New York, NY, Zip 10019; tel. 212/523–4000; Evan Flatow, M.D., President) **A**1 2 3 5 8 10 **F**3 4 5 7 8 11 12 13 15 17 18 20 22 24 26 29 30 31 32 34 35 36 37 38 39 40 41 43 44 45 46 48 49 50 51 52 54 55 56 57 58 59 60 61 64 65 66 68 70 72 74 75 76 77 78 79 81 82 84 85 86 87 90 92 93 94 96 97 98 99 100 101 102 103 104 107 108 110 111 114 115 118 119 120 121 123 124 126 130 131 132 135 141 143 144 145 146 147 148 149 150 **P**5 6 **S** Mount Sinai Health System, New York, NY
Primary Contact: Arthur A. Gianelli, M.P.H., President
COO: Kevin Molloy, Senior Vice President and Chief Operating Officer
CFO: Donald Scanlon, Chief Corporate Services, Mount Sinai Health System
CIO: Kumar Chatani, Chief Information Officer, Mount Sinai Health System
CHR: Jane Maksoud, R.N., Senior Vice President Human Resources and Labor Relations, Mount Sinai Health System
CNO: Mary Walsh, R.N., MSN, Vice President Patient Care Services and Chief Nursing Officer
Web address: www.stlukeshospitalnyc.org
Control: Other not–for–profit (including NFP Corporation) **Service:** General medical and surgical

Staffed Beds: 672 **Admissions:** 35354 **Census:** 604 **Outpatient Visits:** 466202 **Births:** 5506 **Total Expense ($000):** 1170237 **Payroll Expense ($000):** 475142 **Personnel:** 5822

MOUNT SINAI WEST HOSPITAL See Mount Sinai West, New York

☐ **NEW YORK CITY CHILDREN'S CENTER**, 74–03 Commonwealth Boulevard, Zip 11426–1890; tel. 718/264–4506, (Includes BRONX Children's hospital psychiatric CENTER, 1000 Waters Place, Bronx, NY, Zip 10461–2799; tel. 718/239–3600; BROOKLYN Children's hospital psychiatric CENTER, 1819 Bergen Street, Brooklyn, NY, Zip 11233–4513; tel. 718/221–4500) **A**1 3 **F**32 35 39 57 58 59 68 79 87 98 99 104 105 130 135 146 149 **S** New York State Office of Mental Health, Albany, NY
Primary Contact: Kanika Jefferies, Executive Director
CMO: David M Rube, M.D., Clinical Director
CIO: Ed Yunusov, Coordinator Facility Information Center
Web address: www.omh.ny.gov/omhweb/facilities/nyccc/
Control: State, Government, nonfederal **Service:** Children's hospital psychiatric

Staffed Beds: 102 **Admissions:** 275 **Census:** 134 **Births:** 0 **Personnel:** 556

☐ **NEW YORK COMMUNITY HOSPITAL (330019)**, 2525 Kings Highway, Zip 11229–1705; tel. 718/692–5300, (Nonreporting) **A**1 5 10
Primary Contact: Barry Stern, President and Chief Executive Officer
COO: Una E Morrissey, R.N., MSN, Senior Vice President Operations, Chief Operating Officer and Chief Nursing Officer
CFO: Leonardo Tamburello, Chief Financial Officer
CMO: Herbert Rader, M.D., Advisor for Medical Affairs
CIO: Edward B. Stolyar, D.O., Divisional Chief Informational Officer
CHR: Raquel Collado, Vice President Human Resources
CNO: Una E Morrissey, R.N., MSN, Senior Vice President Operations, Chief Operating Officer and Chief Nursing Officer
Web address: www.nych.com
Control: Other not–for–profit (including NFP Corporation) **Service:** General medical and surgical

Staffed Beds: 134

☒ **NEW YORK EYE AND EAR INFIRMARY OF MOUNT SINAI (330100)**, 310 East 14th Street, Zip 10003–4201; tel. 212/979–4000, **A**1 3 5 8 10 **F**3 11 29 30 34 35 44 50 57 58 59 64 66 68 81 82 87 92 107 114 119 129 130 132 146 **P**5 6 **S** Mount Sinai Health System, New York, NY
Primary Contact: James Tsai, M.D., President
CFO: Donald Scanlon, Chief Corporate Services, Mount Sinai Health System
CIO: Kumar Chatani, Chief Information Officer, Mount Sinai Health System
CHR: Jane Maksoud, R.N., Senior Vice President Human Resources and Labor Relations, Mount Sinai Health System
Web address: www.nyee.edu
Control: Other not–for–profit (including NFP Corporation) **Service:** Eye, ear, nose and throat

Staffed Beds: 32 **Admissions:** 305 **Census:** 2 **Outpatient Visits:** 197660 **Births:** 0 **Total Expense ($000):** 143674 **Payroll Expense ($000):** 51302 **Personnel:** 726

☐ **NEW YORK STATE PSYCHIATRIC INSTITUTE (334009)**, 1051 Riverside Drive, Zip 10032–1007; tel. 646/774–5000, (Nonreporting) **A**1 3 5 10 **S** New York State Office of Mental Health, Albany, NY
Primary Contact: Jeffrey A. Lieberman, M.D., Executive Director
COO: Janelle Dierkens, Chief Administration Officer
CFO: Jonathan Segal, Chief Financial Officer
CMO: David Lowenthal, M.D., Clinical Director
CIO: Joseph Grun, Chief Information Officer
CHR: Rebecca Dechabert, Acting Director Personnel
Web address: www.nyspi.org
Control: State, Government, nonfederal **Service:** Psychiatric

Staffed Beds: 58

☒ △ **NEW YORK–PRESBYTERIAN HOSPITAL (330101)**, 525 East 68th Street, Zip 10065–4870; tel. 212/746–5454, (Includes MORGAN STANLEY CHILDREN'S HOSPITAL OF NEW YORK–PRESBYTERIAN, 3959 Broadway, New York, NY, Zip 10032–3784; tel. 212/305–2500; NEW YORK PRESBYTERIAN LOWER MANHATTAN HOSPITAL, 170 William Street, New York, NY, Zip 10038–2649; tel. 212/312–5000; Robert E Kelly, M.D., President; NEW YORK–PRESBYTERIAN HOSPITAL, WESTCHESTER DIVISION, 21 Bloomingdale Road, White Plains, NY, Zip 10605; tel. 914/682–9100; NEW YORK–PRESBYTERIAN HOSPITAL/WEILL CORNELL MEDICAL CENTER, 525 East 68th Street, New York, NY, Zip 10021–4885; tel. 212/746–5454; NEW YORK–PRESBYTERIAN/COLUMBIA UNIVERSITY MEDICAL CENTER, 161 Fort Washington Avenue, New York, NY, Zip 10032; tel. 212/305–2500; NEW YORK–PRESBYTERIAN/LAWRENCE HOSPITAL, 55 Palmer Avenue, Bronxville, NY, Zip 10708–3403; tel. 914/787–1000; Michael Fosina, M.P.H., FACHE, President; PAYNE WHITNEY PSYCHIATRIC CLINIC, 525 East 68th Street, New York, NY, Zip 10021; tel. 212/746–3800; PHYLLIS AND DAVID KOMANSKY CENTER FOR CHILDREN'S HEALTH, 525 East 68th Street, New York, NY, Zip 10065–4870; tel. 212/746–5454; THE ALLEN PAVILION, 5141 Broadway, New York, NY, Zip 10032; tel. 212/932–5000) **A**1 2 3 5 7 8 10 **F**3 4 5 6 7 8 9 11 12 13 14 15 16 17 18 19 20 21 22 23 24 25 26 27 28 29 30 31 32 34 35 36 37 38 39 40 41 43 44 45 46 47 48 49 50 51 52 53 54 55 56 57 58 59 60 61 62 63 64 65 66 68 70 71 72 73 74 75 76 77 78 79 80 81 82 83 84 85 86 87 88 89 90 91 92 93 94 96 97 98 99 100 101 102 103 104 105 107 108 110 111 112 114 115 116 117 118 119 120 121 123 124 126 129 130 131 132 134 135 136 137 138 139 140 141 142 143 144 145 146 147 148 149 150 152 153 154 **P**6 **S** NewYork–Presbyterian, New York, NY
Primary Contact: Steven J. Corwin, M.D., President and Chief Executive Officer
CFO: Phyllis R Lantos, Executive Vice President, Corporate Chief Financial Officer and Treasurer
CMO: Laura Forese, M.D., M.P.H., Executive Vice President and Chief Medical Officer
CIO: Aurelia Boyer, Senior Vice President and Chief Information Officer
CHR: G Thomas Ferguson, Senior Vice President and Chief Human Resources Officer
CNO: Rosemary Ventura, M.D., Chief Nursing Informatics Officer
Web address: www.nyp.org
Control: Other not–for–profit (including NFP Corporation) **Service:** General medical and surgical

Staffed Beds: 2540 **Admissions:** 121091 **Census:** 2087 **Outpatient Visits:** 2451940 **Births:** 16897 **Total Expense ($000):** 5543478 **Payroll Expense ($000):** 2603221 **Personnel:** 24496

NY

Many Facility Codes have changed. Please refer to the AHA Guide Code Chart. © 2018 AHA Guide

☒ **NEW YORK–PRESBYTERIAN QUEENS (330055)**, 56–45 Main Street,
Zip 11355–5045; tel. 718/670–1231, **A**1 2 3 5 10 **F**3 7 11 12 13 15 17 18 19
20 22 24 26 28 29 30 31 32 34 35 39 40 41 43 44 45 46 47 48 49 50 51 54
55 56 57 58 59 60 61 63 64 65 66 68 70 72 73 74 75 76 77 78 79 80 81 82
83 84 85 87 89 91 92 93 96 97 100 101 107 108 110 111 114 115 116 119
120 121 123 124 126 130 131 141 145 146 147 148 149 154 **P**6 **S** NewYork–
Presbyterian, New York, NY
Primary Contact: Jaclyn Mucaria, President
COO: Robert Blenderman, Senior Vice President and Chief Operating Officer
CFO: Kevin J Ward, Vice President and Chief Financial Officer
CMO: Amir Jaffer, M.D., Senior Vice President Medical Affairs
CIO: Mark Greaker, Chief Information Officer
CHR: Lorraine Orlando, Vice President Human Resources
CNO: Alan M. Levin, MSN, R.N., Chief Nursing Officer
Web address: www.nyhq.org
Control: Other not–for–profit (including NFP Corporation) **Service:** General
medical and surgical

Staffed Beds: 482 **Admissions:** 31136 **Census:** 450 **Outpatient Visits:**
419052 **Births:** 3991 **Total Expense ($000):** 833734 **Payroll Expense
($000):** 419385 **Personnel:** 4556

☒ **NEWYORK–PRESBYTERIAN BROOKLYN METHODIST HOSPITAL (330236)**,
506 Sixth Street, Zip 11215–3609; tel. 718/780–3000, **A**1 2 3 5 10 **F**3 6 7 9
11 12 13 15 17 18 19 20 22 24 26 29 30 31 32 34 35 36 39 40 41 43 44 45
46 47 48 49 50 51 52 54 55 56 57 58 59 61 64 65 66 68 70 72 73 74 75 76
77 78 79 81 82 84 85 87 88 89 90 91 92 93 95 96 97 98 100 102 103 107
108 109 110 111 112 114 115 118 119 120 121 123 124 126 129 130 131
132 145 146 147 148 149 154 **P**6 **S** NewYork–Presbyterian, New York, NY
Primary Contact: Robert Guimento, President
CFO: Michael Fagan, Senior Vice President Finance
CMO: Steven Silber, M.D., Senior Vice President Medical Affairs
CHR: Rick Pogue, Vice President, Human Resources
CNO: Ernesto Perez–Mir, Vice President, Chief Nursing Officer
Web address: www.nym.org
Control: Other not–for–profit (including NFP Corporation) **Service:** General
medical and surgical

Staffed Beds: 591 **Admissions:** 35271 **Census:** 516 **Outpatient Visits:**
552521 **Births:** 5337 **Total Expense ($000):** 974177 **Payroll Expense
($000):** 433805 **Personnel:** 4354

☒ **NYC HEALTH + HOSPITALS / BELLEVUE (330204)**, 462 First Avenue,
Zip 10016–9198; tel. 212/562–4141, **A**1 3 5 10 **F**3 4 5 8 11 12 15 17 18 19
20 22 23 24 25 26 27 28 29 30 31 34 35 36 37 38 39 40 41 43 45 46 47 48
49 50 52 53 55 56 57 58 59 61 64 65 66 68 69 70 71 72 73 74 75 76 77 78
79 81 82 83 84 85 86 87 88 89 90 91 92 93 94 96 97 98 99 100 101 102 103
104 105 107 108 110 111 114 115 118 119 130 132 134 135 141 143
144 146 147 148 149 152 153 154 **P**6 **S** NYC Health + Hospitals, New York, NY
Primary Contact: William Hicks, Chief Executive Officer
COO: Michael Rawlings, Interim Chief Operating Officer
CFO: Rebecca J Fischer, Chief Financial Officer
CMO: Nathan Link, M.D., Medical Director
CIO: James Carr, Chief Information Officer
CNO: Kim K Mendez, Ed.D., R.N., Chief Nurse Officer
Web address: www.nyc.gov/bellevue
Control: City, Government, nonfederal **Service:** General medical and surgical

Staffed Beds: 719 **Admissions:** 27303 **Census:** 610 **Outpatient Visits:**
573177 **Births:** 1375 **Total Expense ($000):** 951588 **Payroll Expense
($000):** 337334 **Personnel:** 4493

☒ **NYC HEALTH + HOSPITALS / CONEY ISLAND (330196)**, 2601 Ocean
Parkway, Zip 11235–7795; tel. 718/616–3000, **A**1 3 5 10 12 13 **F**3 4 5 13 15
17 18 20 29 30 31 34 39 40 41 44 45 49 50 51 56 57 58 59 60 61 64
65 66 68 70 71 72 73 74 75 76 77 78 79 81 82 83 84 85 87 89 90 91 92 93
94 96 97 98 100 102 104 107 108 110 111 114 115 118 129 130 132
134 135 143 146 147 148 149 150 **S** NYC Health + Hospitals, New York, NY
Primary Contact: William A. Brown, FACHE, Chief Executive Officer
COO: Mei Kong, Chief Operating Officer
CMO: Wehbeh Wehbeh, M.D., Chief Medical Officer
CIO: Robert Kee, Chief Information Officer
CHR: Andrew Campbell, Associate Executive Director
CNO: Patricia Ruiz, R.N., Chief Nursing Officer
Web address: www.nyc.gov/html/hhc/html/facilities/coneyisland.shtml
Control: City, Government, nonfederal **Service:** General medical and surgical

Staffed Beds: 371 **Admissions:** 13834 **Census:** 302 **Outpatient Visits:**
315516 **Births:** 1139 **Total Expense ($000):** 500706 **Payroll Expense
($000):** 186968 **Personnel:** 2865

☒ **NYC HEALTH + HOSPITALS / ELMHURST (330128)**, 79–01 Broadway,
Zip 11373–1329; tel. 718/334–4000, **A**1 2 3 5 10 **F**2 5 13 14 15 17 18 20
22 26 29 30 31 34 35 38 39 40 41 43 45 46 49 50 51 52 54 55 56 57 58 59
60 61 65 66 68 70 72 73 74 76 77 78 79 80 81 82 83 84 85 86 87 89
90 91 92 93 94 96 97 98 99 100 101 102 104 105 107 108 109 110 111 114
115 119 120 121 126 130 135 141 143 145 146 147 149 152 153 154
P6 **S** NYC Health + Hospitals, New York, NY
Primary Contact: Israel Rocha Jr, Chief Executive Officer
COO: Wayne Zimmermann, Chief Operating Officer
CFO: David Guzman, Chief Financial Officer
CMO: Jasmin Moshirpur, M.D., Dean and Medical Director
CIO: Jeannith Michelen, Chief Implementation Officer
CHR: Peter Maris, Director Human Resources
CNO: Joann Bernadette Gull, Chief Nursing Officer
Web address: www.nyc.gov/html/hhc/ehc/html/home/home.shtml
Control: City, Government, nonfederal **Service:** General medical and surgical

Staffed Beds: 506 **Admissions:** 18318 **Census:** 372 **Outpatient Visits:**
539676 **Births:** 2632 **Total Expense ($000):** 678025 **Payroll Expense
($000):** 244080 **Personnel:** 2993

☒ △ **NYC HEALTH + HOSPITALS / HARLEM (330240)**, 506 Lenox Avenue,
Zip 10037–1802; tel. 212/939–1000, **A**1 3 5 7 10 **F**3 4 5 8 11 12 13 15 16
17 18 19 20 29 30 32 34 35 38 39 40 41 43 44 45 46 47 49 50 52 53 55
57 58 59 60 61 64 65 68 70 71 72 74 75 76 77 79 81 82 84 85 86 87 88 89
90 93 94 96 97 98 100 101 102 104 107 108 110 111 114 115 118 119 130
132 134 135 141 144 146 147 148 149 154 **P**6 **S** NYC Health + Hospitals, New
York, NY
Primary Contact: Ebone' Carrington, Chief Executive Officer and Chief Operating
Officer
COO: Ebone' Carrington, Chief Executive Officer and Chief Operating Officer
Web address: www.nyc.gov/html/hhc/harlem
Control: City, Government, nonfederal **Service:** General medical and surgical

Staffed Beds: 252 **Admissions:** 12688 **Census:** 210 **Outpatient Visits:**
302946 **Births:** 942 **Total Expense ($000):** 471376 **Payroll Expense
($000):** 168350 **Personnel:** 2218

☒ **NYC HEALTH + HOSPITALS / HENRY J CARTER SPECIALTY HOSPITAL
AND MEDICAL CENTER (332008)**, 1752 Park Avenue, Zip 10035;
tel. 646/686–0000, (Includes COLER REHABILITATION AND NURSING CARE
CENTER, 900 Main Street, Roosevelt Island, New York, NY, Zip 10044;
tel. 212/848–6300; Robert K. Hughes, Chief Executive Officer; HENRY J. CARTER
SPECIALTY HOSPITAL & NURSING FACILITY, 1752 Park Avenue, New York, NY,
Zip 10035; tel. 646/686–0000; Floyd R Long, Chief Executive Officer) (Total
facility includes 164 beds in nursing home–type unit) **A**1 10 **F**1 3 11 28 29 30 39
56 58 68 74 75 77 79 84 85 87 100 103 107 114 119 128 130 132 135 146
148 149 **P**4 **S** NYC Health + Hospitals, New York, NY
Primary Contact: Robert K. Hughes, Chief Executive Officer
CFO: Manuela Brito, Chief Financial Officer Post Acute Care
CMO: Vasudeva Raju, M.D., Suffix Chief, Long Term Acute Care Medicine
CIO: Steve ONeill, Chief Information Officer
CHR: Jamie Grecco, Director Human Resources Post Acute
CNO: Stanlee Richards, R.N., Chief Nurse Executive
Web address: www.nychealthandhospitals.org/Carter
Control: City, Government, nonfederal **Service:** Acute long–term care hospital

Staffed Beds: 365 **Admissions:** 379 **Census:** 314 **Outpatient Visits:** 0
Births: 0 **Total Expense ($000):** 163477 **Payroll Expense ($000):** 55958
Personnel: 793

☒ **NYC HEALTH + HOSPITALS / JACOBI (330127)**, 1400 Pelham Parkway South,
Zip 10461–1197; tel. 718/918–5000, **A**1 3 5 10 **F**3 4 5 8 11 12 13 15 16 17
18 20 26 29 30 31 32 34 35 38 39 40 41 43 44 45 46 47 49 50 51 55 56 57
58 59 60 61 64 65 66 68 70 72 73 74 75 76 77 78 79 81 82 84 85 86 87
88 89 90 92 93 94 96 97 98 100 101 102 104 107 108 110 111 114 115
118 119 130 132 134 135 141 144 146 147 148 149 150 **P**6 **S** NYC Health +
Hospitals, New York, NY
Primary Contact: Christopher Mastromanno, Interim Chief Executive Officer
COO: Christopher Mastromanno, Chief Operating Officer
CFO: Ellen Barlis, Chief Financial Officer
CMO: Michael Zinaman, M.D., Acting Chief Medical Officer
CIO: Md Alam, Chief Information Officer
CHR: Jamie Grecco, Chief Human Resource Executive
CNO: Suzanne Pennacchio, Chief Nursing Officer
Web address: www.nyc.gov/html/hhc/jacobi/home.html
Control: City, Government, nonfederal **Service:** General medical and surgical

Staffed Beds: 457 **Admissions:** 18410 **Census:** 361 **Outpatient Visits:**
408507 **Births:** 1964 **Total Expense ($000):** 772440 **Payroll Expense
($000):** 267927 **Personnel:** 3397

NY

Hospital, Medicare Provider Number, Address, Telephone, Approval, Facility, and Physician Codes, Health Care System

★ American Hospital Association (AHA) membership ◯ Healthcare Facilities Accreditation Program ⇑ Center for Improvement in Healthcare Quality Accreditation
☐ The Joint Commission accreditation ◇ DNV Healthcare Inc. accreditation △ Commission on Accreditation of Rehabilitation Facilities (CARF) accreditation

⊞ **NYC HEALTH + HOSPITALS / KINGS COUNTY (330202)**, 451 Clarkson Avenue, Zip 11203–2054; tel. 718/245–3131, **A**1 3 5 10 **F**3 4 5 8 9 11 12 13 15 17 18 19 20 24 26 28 29 30 31 32 34 35 38 39 40 41 43 45 46 47 49 50 51 52 53 56 57 58 59 60 61 64 65 66 68 70 71 72 73 74 75 76 77 78 79 81 82 84 85 86 87 88 89 90 91 92 93 94 97 98 99 100 101 102 103 104 105 106 107 108 110 111 114 115 116 119 120 121 123 129 130 131 132 134 135 143 144 145 146 147 148 149 153 154 **P**6 **S** NYC Health + Hospitals, New York, NY
Primary Contact: Sheldon Mcleod, Chief Executive Officer
CNO: Opal Sinclair–Chung, R.N., MS, Chief Nursing Officer, Deputy Executive Director
Web address: www.nyc.gov/html/hhc/kchc/html/home/home.shtml
Control: City, Government, nonfederal **Service:** General medical and surgical

> **Staffed Beds:** 589 **Admissions:** 21069 **Census:** 467 **Outpatient Visits:** 659571 **Births:** 2073 **Total Expense ($000):** 851317 **Payroll Expense ($000):** 392984 **Personnel:** 4762

⊞ **NYC HEALTH + HOSPITALS / LINCOLN (330080)**, 234 East 149th Street, Zip 10451–5504, Mailing Address: 234 East 149th Street, Room 923, Zip 10451–5504; tel. 718/579–5700, **A**1 2 3 5 10 **F**3 5 8 11 13 15 18 19 29 30 31 32 34 35 38 39 40 41 43 45 50 55 56 57 58 59 60 61 64 65 66 68 70 71 73 74 75 76 77 78 79 81 82 84 85 86 87 89 93 97 98 99 100 101 102 103 104 107 108 110 111 114 115 119 121 123 130 132 134 135 143 144 146 147 148 151 **P**6 **S** NYC Health + Hospitals, New York, NY
Primary Contact: Milton Nunez, Executive Director
CFO: Caswell Samms, Network Chief Financial Officer
CMO: Anita Soni, M.D., Chief Medical Officer
CIO: James Carr, Chief Information Officer
CHR: Jeannith Michelen, Senior Associate Executive Director
Web address: www.nyc.gov/html/hhc/lincoln/
Control: City, Government, nonfederal **Service:** General medical and surgical

> **Staffed Beds:** 367 **Admissions:** 20888 **Census:** 295 **Outpatient Visits:** 525662 **Births:** 2065 **Total Expense ($000):** 634568 **Payroll Expense ($000):** 231880 **Personnel:** 3374

⊞ **NYC HEALTH + HOSPITALS / METROPOLITAN (330199)**, 1901 First Avenue, Zip 10029–7404; tel. 212/423–6262, **A**1 3 5 10 **F**3 4 5 8 9 11 13 15 17 18 28 29 30 31 32 34 35 38 39 40 41 43 48 49 50 51 53 54 55 56 57 58 59 60 61 64 65 66 67 68 70 71 72 73 74 75 76 77 78 79 80 81 82 84 85 86 87 88 89 90 92 93 94 96 97 98 99 100 101 102 104 107 108 110 111 114 119 128 130 131 132 134 135 144 146 147 148 149 153 **P**6 **S** NYC Health + Hospitals, New York, NY
Primary Contact: Alina Moran, Chief Executive Officer
COO: William Norberto Wang, M.D., Chief Operating Officer
CFO: Tracy V. Green, Chief Financial Officer
CMO: John T Pellicone, M.D., Chief Medical Officer
CIO: Md Alam, Chief Information Officer
CHR: April Alexander, Director Human Resources
CNO: Noreen Brennan, Chief Nursing Officer
Web address: www.nyc.gov/html/hhc/mhc/html/home/home.shtml
Control: City, Government, nonfederal **Service:** General medical and surgical

> **Staffed Beds:** 302 **Admissions:** 11277 **Census:** 217 **Outpatient Visits:** 367213 **Births:** 949 **Total Expense ($000):** 376703 **Payroll Expense ($000):** 144214 **Personnel:** 1876

⊞ **NYC HEALTH + HOSPITALS / NORTH CENTRAL BRONX (330385)**, 3424 Kossuth Avenue, Zip 10467–2489; tel. 718/519–3500, **A**1 3 5 10 **F**3 5 8 11 12 13 15 18 28 29 30 32 34 35 38 39 40 41 43 44 45 46 48 50 51 55 56 57 58 59 60 61 64 65 66 68 70 73 74 75 76 77 79 81 82 84 85 87 92 93 94 96 97 98 100 101 102 103 104 107 108 110 111 115 119 130 131 132 135 146 147 148 152 154 **P**6 **S** NYC Health + Hospitals, New York, NY
Primary Contact: Maureen Pode, Co–Interim Executive Director
COO: Sheldon McLeod, Chief Operating Officer
CMO: Joseph Skarzynski, M.D., Medical Director
CIO: Diane Carr, Chief Information Officer
CNO: Elizabeth Gerdts, Chief Nursing Officer
Web address: www.nyc.gov/html/hhc/ncbh/html/home/home.shtml
Control: City, Government, nonfederal **Service:** General medical and surgical

> **Staffed Beds:** 232 **Admissions:** 6769 **Census:** 117 **Outpatient Visits:** 204661 **Births:** 1244 **Total Expense ($000):** 222539 **Payroll Expense ($000):** 81790 **Personnel:** 1142

⊞ **NYC HEALTH + HOSPITALS / QUEENS (330231)**, 82–68 164th Street, Zip 11432–1104; tel. 718/883–3000, **A**1 2 3 5 10 **F**3 5 8 9 11 13 15 18 19 28 29 30 31 32 34 35 38 39 40 41 45 46 47 49 50 52 53 54 55 56 58 59 60 61 64 65 66 68 70 71 72 73 74 75 76 77 78 81 82 84 85 86 87 90 93 97 98 100 101 102 104 105 107 108 110 111 114 116 117 118 119 120 121 123 129 130 132 141 143 144 146 147 148 149 152 153 154 **P**6 **S** NYC Health + Hospitals, New York, NY
Primary Contact: Christopher Roker, Chief Executive Officer
COO: Dean Milhaltses, Chief Operating Officer
CFO: Brian Stacey, Chief Financial Officer
CMO: Jasmin Moshirpur, M.D., Chief Medical Officer
CIO: Vincent Smith, Chief Information Officer
CHR: Jeannith Michelen, Senior Associate Executive Director
CNO: Joan Gabriele, Deputy Executive Director
Web address: www.nyc.gov/html/hhc/qhc/html/home/home.shtml
Control: City, Government, nonfederal **Service:** General medical and surgical

> **Staffed Beds:** 259 **Admissions:** 13013 **Census:** 200 **Outpatient Visits:** 379095 **Births:** 1535 **Total Expense ($000):** 451724 **Payroll Expense ($000):** 159203 **Personnel:** 1936

⊞ **NYC HEALTH + HOSPITALS / WOODHULL (330396)**, 760 Broadway, Zip 11206–5383; tel. 718/963–8000, **A**1 3 5 10 **F**3 4 5 11 13 15 18 19 29 30 31 32 34 35 36 38 39 40 41 43 44 45 49 50 54 55 56 57 59 60 61 64 65 68 70 71 72 73 74 75 76 77 78 79 80 81 82 84 87 89 92 93 94 97 98 100 102 104 107 108 110 111 115 118 119 130 131 132 135 141 142 143 145 146 147 148 149 154 **P**6 **S** NYC Health + Hospitals, New York, NY
Primary Contact: Gregory Calliste, Ph.D., FACHE, Chief Executive Officer
COO: Eve Borzon, R.N., Chief Operating Officer
CFO: Erika Soiman, CPA, Chief Financial Officer
CMO: Edward Fishkin, M.D., Medical Director
CHR: Irma Suarez, Deputy Executive Director
CNO: Angela Imelda Edwards, R.N., Chief Nurse Executive
Web address: www.nyc.gov/html/hhc
Control: City–county, Government, nonfederal **Service:** General medical and surgical

> **Staffed Beds:** 272 **Admissions:** 11083 **Census:** 228 **Outpatient Visits:** 434325 **Births:** 1454 **Total Expense ($000):** 479405 **Payroll Expense ($000):** 175140 **Personnel:** 2428

NYU HOSPITAL FOR JOINT DISEASES See NYU Langone Orthopedic Hospital

⊞ **NYU LANGONE HOSPITALS (330214)**, 550 First Avenue, Zip 10016–6402; tel. 212/263–7300, (Includes HASSENFELD CHILDRENS HOSPITAL OF NEW YORK AT NYU LANGONE MEDICAL CENTER, 550 First Avenue, New York, NY, Zip 10016–6401; tel. 212/263–7300; NYU LANGONE HOSPITAL–BROOKLYN, 150 55th Street, Brooklyn, NY, Zip 11220–2559; tel. 718/630–7000; Bret Rudy, M.D., Executive Director and Senior Vice President; NYU LANGONE ORTHOPEDIC HOSPITAL, 301 East 17th Street, New York, NY, Zip 10003–3890; tel. 212/598–6000; David A Dibner, FACHE, Senior Vice President Hospital Operations and Musculoskeletal Strategic Areas; RUSK INSTITUTE AT NYU–HJD, 301 E 17th ST, New York, NY, Zip 10003–3804; tel. 212/598–6000; David A Dibner, FACHE, Senior Vice President Hospital Operations and Musculoskeletal Strategic Areas) **A**1 2 3 5 8 10 **F**3 5 6 7 8 9 11 12 13 15 17 18 19 20 21 22 23 24 25 26 27 28 29 30 31 32 33 34 35 36 37 38 39 40 41 43 44 45 46 47 48 49 50 51 52 53 54 55 64 65 66 68 70 72 73 74 75 76 77 78 79 80 81 82 84 85 86 87 88 89 90 91 92 93 94 95 96 97 98 100 101 102 103 104 107 108 110 111 113 114 115 116 117 118 119 120 121 123 124 126 129 130 131 132 134 135 136 138 139 141 142 143 145 146 147 148 149 150 153 154 **P**5 6 **S** NYU Langone Health, New York, NY
Primary Contact: Robert I. Grossman, M.D., Chief Executive Officer
COO: Robert Press, M.D., Senior Vice President, Vice Dean and Chief Hospital Operations
CFO: Michael Burke, Senior Vice President and Corporate Chief Financial Officer
CMO: Fritz Francois, M.D., Chief Medical Officer
CIO: Nader Mherabi, Senior Vice President and Vice Dean, Chief Information Officer
CHR: Nancy Sanchez, Senior Vice President and Vice Dean Human Resources
CNO: Kimberly S Glassman, Ph.D., R.N., Chief Nursing Officer
Web address: www.nyumedicalcenter.org
Control: Other not–for–profit (including NFP Corporation) **Service:** General medical and surgical

> **Staffed Beds:** 1096 **Admissions:** 59719 **Census:** 834 **Outpatient Visits:** 1780843 **Births:** 9753 **Total Expense ($000):** 3830406 **Payroll Expense ($000):** 1342682 **Personnel:** 16880

PAYNE WHITNEY PSYCHIATRIC CLINIC See New York–Presbyterian Hospital, New York

QUEENS CHILDREN'S HOSPITAL PSYCHIATRIC CENTER See New York City Children's Center

☒ **RICHMOND UNIVERSITY MEDICAL CENTER (330028)**, 355 Bard Avenue, Zip 10310–1664; tel. 718/818–1234, (Nonreporting) **A**1 2 3 5 10
Primary Contact: Daniel J. Messina, Ph.D., FACHE, President and Chief Executive Officer
CMO: Edward Arsura, M.D., Chief Medical Officer
CHR: Patricia Caldari, Vice President
Web address: www.rumcsi.org
Control: Other not–for–profit (including NFP Corporation) **Service:** General medical and surgical

Staffed Beds: 374

☐ **ROCKEFELLER UNIVERSITY HOSPITAL (330387)**, 1230 York Avenue, Zip 10065–6399; tel. 212/327–8000, (Nonreporting) **A**1 10
Primary Contact: James G. Krueger, M.D., Ph.D., Chief Executive Officer
CMO: Barbara O'Sullivan, M.D., M.P.H., Medical Director
Web address: www.rucares.org
Control: Other not–for–profit (including NFP Corporation) **Service:** Other specialty treatment

Staffed Beds: 17

ROOSEVELT HOSPITAL See Mount Sinai West Hospital

☐ **SOUTH BEACH PSYCHIATRIC CENTER (334043)**, 777 Seaview Avenue, Zip 10305–3409; tel. 718/667–2300, (Nonreporting) **A**1 3 10 **S** New York State Office of Mental Health, Albany, NY
Primary Contact: Doreen Piazza, Acting Executive Director
CHR: George Bouquio, Director Human Resources
Web address: www.omh.ny.gov/omhweb/facilities/sbpc/facility.htm
Control: State, Government, nonfederal **Service:** Psychiatric

Staffed Beds: 340

☒ △ **STATEN ISLAND UNIVERSITY HOSPITAL (330160)**, 475 Seaview Avenue, Zip 10305–3436; tel. 718/226–9000, **A**1 2 3 5 7 8 10 **F**3 4 5 7 8 11 12 13 14 15 16 17 18 19 20 22 24 26 28 29 30 31 32 34 35 36 38 39 40 41 43 44 45 46 47 48 49 50 51 52 54 55 57 58 59 60 61 62 64 70 72 73 74 75 76 77 78 79 81 82 84 85 86 87 88 89 90 92 93 94 95 96 97 98 100 101 102 104 105 107 108 110 111 114 115 116 117 118 119 120 121 123 124 126 129 130 131 132 134 135 145 146 147 148 152 153 154 **P**5 6 **S** Northwell Health, New Hyde Park, NY
Primary Contact: Joseph Schulman, Interim Chief Executive Officer
CFO: Thomas Reca Sr Deputy Executive Director and Chief Financial Officer
CMO: Theodore Maniatis, M.D., Medical Director
CIO: Kathy Kania, Associate Executive Director and Chief Information Officer
CHR: Margaret DiAlto, Regional Chief Human Resource Officer
CNO: Terry Pando, R.N., Associate Executive Director and Chief Nursing Officer
Web address: www.siuh.edu
Control: Other not–for–profit (including NFP Corporation) **Service:** General medical and surgical

Staffed Beds: 634 **Admissions:** 38926 **Census:** 577 **Outpatient Visits:** 950760 **Births:** 2810 **Total Expense ($000):** 881785 **Payroll Expense ($000):** 421934 **Personnel:** 5521

☒ **ST. BARNABAS HOSPITAL (330399)**, 4422 Third Avenue, Zip 10457–2545; tel. 718/960–9000, **A**1 3 5 10 12 13 **F**3 4 5 11 13 15 18 19 20 22 26 29 30 31 32 34 35 36 38 39 40 41 43 44 45 46 47 49 50 51 54 55 56 57 58 59 60 61 64 65 66 68 70 71 72 74 75 76 77 78 79 81 82 83 84 85 86 87 89 91 92 93 94 97 98 100 101 102 104 107 108 109 110 111 114 115 117 118 119 123 129 130 131 132 134 135 143 146 147 149 150 **P**6
Primary Contact: David A. Perlstein, M.D., President and Chief Executive Officer
COO: Len Walsh, Executive Vice President and Chief Operating Officer
CFO: Todd Gorlewski, Senior Vice President and Chief Financial Officer
CIO: Jitendra Barmecha, M.D., M.P.H., Senior Vice President and Chief Information Officer
CHR: Marc Wolf, Assistant Vice President Human Resources
CNO: Denise Richardson, R.N., MSN, Senior Vice President and Chief Nursing Officer
Web address: www.sbhny.org
Control: Other not–for–profit (including NFP Corporation) **Service:** General medical and surgical

Staffed Beds: 422 **Admissions:** 14136 **Census:** 204 **Outpatient Visits:** 574536 **Births:** 917 **Total Expense ($000):** 436729 **Payroll Expense ($000):** 198709 **Personnel:** 2705

☐ **ST. JOHN'S EPISCOPAL HOSPITAL–SOUTH SHORE (330395)**, 327 Beach 19th Street, Zip 11691–4423; tel. 718/869–7000, **A**1 3 5 10 12 13 **F**3 12 13 15 17 18 19 29 30 31 32 34 35 38 40 41 45 49 50 54 55 56 57 59 60 61 64 65 66 70 73 74 75 76 77 78 79 81 82 84 85 87 89 92 93 97 98 100 101 102 103 104 107 108 110 111 114 118 119 130 132 134 135 141 146 148 149
Primary Contact: Gerard W. Walsh, Chief Executive Officer
COO: Patrick L Sullivan, Chief Operating Officer
CFO: Kathleen Garcia, Controller
CMO: Raymond Pastore, M.D., Chief Medical Officer
CIO: Michael J Piro, Chief Information Officer
CHR: Roger Franco, Director Human Resources
Web address: www.ehs.org
Control: State, Government, nonfederal **Service:** General medical and surgical

Staffed Beds: 213 **Admissions:** 7851 **Census:** 151 **Outpatient Visits:** 115273 **Births:** 670 **Total Expense ($000):** 223358 **Payroll Expense ($000):** 115295 **Personnel:** 1342

☒ **SUNY DOWNSTATE MEDICAL CENTER UNIVERSITY HOSPITAL (330350)**, 450 Clarkson Avenue, Zip 11203–2012, Mailing Address: 450 Clarkson Avenue, MSC#75, Zip 11203–2012; tel. 718/270–1000, (Includes UNIVERSITY HOSPITAL OF BROOKLYN AT LONG ISLAND COLLEGE HOSPITAL, 339 Hicks Street, Brooklyn, NY, Zip 11201–5509; tel. 718/780–1000; George P Caralis, Interim Chief Executive Officer) **A**1 3 5 8 10 **F**8 13 14 15 17 18 19 20 22 24 26 29 30 31 34 35 36 38 40 41 44 45 46 47 48 49 50 51 54 55 56 57 58 59 60 61 64 65 66 68 70 72 73 74 75 76 77 78 79 80 81 82 84 86 87 88 89 90 92 93 94 95 96 97 104 107 108 110 111 114 115 118 119 126 129 130 131 138 143 144 146 147 149 150 **P**6
Primary Contact: Wayne J. Riley, M.D., M.P.H., President
COO: Patricia A Winston, FACHE, MS, R.N., Vice President, Chief Administrative Officer and Chief Operating Officer
CFO: Richard B. Miller, Ph.D., Vice President Hospital Affairs and Chief Financial Officer
CMO: Michael Lucchesi, M.D., Chief Medical Officer; Chair, Emergency Medicine
CIO: Dilip Nath, Sc.D., Associate Chief Information Officer
CHR: Maria Silas, Manager Human Resources
CNO: Margaret G. Jackson, R.N., Vice President Patient Care Services and Chief Nursing Officer
Web address: www.downstate.edu
Control: State, Government, nonfederal **Service:** General medical and surgical

Staffed Beds: 323 **Admissions:** 11397 **Census:** 214 **Outpatient Visits:** 304896 **Births:** 882 **Total Expense ($000):** 560716 **Payroll Expense ($000):** 263159 **Personnel:** 2607

TERENCE CARDINAL COOKE HEALTH CARE CENTER (332022), 1249 Fifth Avenue, Zip 10029–4413; tel. 212/360–1000, (Nonreporting) **A**10
Primary Contact: Mitch Marsh, Interim Executive Director
COO: Neil Pollack, Senior Administrator
CFO: Ann Marie Covone, Senior Vice President and Chief Financial Officer
CMO: Anthony Lechich, M.D., Chief Medical Officer
CIO: Mitze Amoroso, Chief Information Officer
CHR: Hugo A Pizarro, Vice President Human Resources
CNO: Monica McGibbon, Chief Nursing Officer
Web address: www.tcchcc.org/
Control: Church operated, Nongovernment, not–for–profit **Service:** Acute long–term care hospital

Staffed Beds: 28

THE ALLEN PAVILION See New York–Presbyterian Hospital, New York

VETERANS AFFAIRS MEDICAL CENTER See James J. Peters Veterans Affairs Medical Center

☒ **VETERANS AFFAIRS NEW YORK HARBOR HEALTHCARE SYSTEM**, 800 Poly Place, Zip 11209–7104; tel. 718/630–3500, (Includes VETERANS AFFAIRS NEW YORK HARBOR HEALTHCARE SYSTEM – MANHATTAN CAMPUS, 423 East 23rd Street, New York, NY, Zip 10010–5050; tel. 212/686–7500; Martina A Parauda, Director) (Nonreporting) **A**1 2 3 5 **S** Department of Veterans Affairs, Perry Point, MD
Primary Contact: Martina A. Parauda, Director
COO: Jodie A. Jackson, Associate Director
CFO: Andre Chance, Chief Financial Officer
CMO: Patrick C. Malloy, M.D., Chief of Staff
CIO: Luis Barrios, Chief Information Officer
CHR: Kevin Grundig, Chief Human Resource Officer
CNO: Cynthia A. Caroselli, R.N., Ph.D., Chief Nursing Officer
Web address: www.nyharbor.va.gov
Control: Veterans Affairs, Government, federal **Service:** General medical and surgical

Staffed Beds: 522

NY

Hospital, Medicare Provider Number, Address, Telephone, Approval, Facility, and Physician Codes, Health Care System

★ American Hospital Association (AHA) membership
☐ The Joint Commission accreditation
○ Healthcare Facilities Accreditation Program
◇ DNV Healthcare Inc. accreditation
⇑ Center for Improvement in Healthcare Quality Accreditation
△ Commission on Accreditation of Rehabilitation Facilities (CARF) accreditation

☐ **WYCKOFF HEIGHTS MEDICAL CENTER (330221)**, 374 Stockholm Street, Zip 11237–4006; tel. 718/963–7272, (Nonreporting) **A**1 3 5 10 12 13
Primary Contact: Ramon J. Rodriguez, President and Chief Executive Officer
COO: David Rock, Executive Vice President and Chief Operating Officer
CFO: Frank A Vutrano, Chief Financial Officer
CMO: Gustavo Del Toro, M.D., Chief Medical Officer
CIO: Jebashini Jesurasa, Vice President, Chief Information Technology Officer
CHR: Margaret E Cornelius, Vice President Human Resources
CNO: Catherine A Gallogly–Simon, R.N., MS, Chief Nursing Officer
Web address: www.wyckoffhospital.org
Control: Other not-for-profit (including NFP Corporation) **Service**: General medical and surgical

Staffed Beds: 276

ZUCKER HILLSIDE HOSPITAL See Long Island Jewish Medical Center, New Hyde Park

NEWARK—Wayne County

⊞ **NEWARK–WAYNE COMMUNITY HOSPITAL (330030)**, 1200 Driving Park Avenue, Zip 14513–1057, Mailing Address: P.O. Box 111, Zip 14513–0111; tel. 315/332–2022, (Total facility includes 180 beds in nursing home–type unit) **A**1 10 **F**2 3 5 6 8 11 13 15 35 38 40 44 50 51 54 55 56 57 59 61 64 68 70 74 75 76 77 79 80 81 85 86 87 90 93 97 98 100 101 102 103 104 107 108 110 111 114 118 119 126 128 130 131 132 135 143 146 147 148 149 154 **P**5 6 **S** Rochester Regional Health, Rochester, NY
Primary Contact: Dustin Riccio, M.D., President Eastern Region
CFO: Tom Crilly, Executive Vice President, Chief Financial Officer, Rochester Regional Health
CMO: Robert Mayo, M.D., Executive Vice President, Chief Medical Officer, Rochester Regional Health
CIO: John Glynn, Executive Vice President, Chief Information Officer, Rochester Regional Health
CHR: Janine Schue, Executive Vice President, Chief Human Resources Officer, Rochester Regional Health
CNO: Theresa Glessner, Chief Nursing Officer, Eastern Region
Web address: www.rochesterregional.org
Control: Other not-for-profit (including NFP Corporation) **Service**: General medical and surgical

Staffed Beds: 289 Admissions: 6292 Census: 233 Outpatient Visits: 99777 **Births: 722 Total Expense ($000): 97629 Payroll Expense ($000): 50220 Personnel: 726**

NEWBURGH—Orange County

⊞ **ST. LUKE'S CORNWALL HOSPITAL (330264)**, 70 Dubois Street, Zip 12550–4851; tel. 845/561–4400, (Includes ST. LUKE'S CORNWALL HOSPITAL – CORNWALL CAMPUS, 19 Laurel Avenue, Cornwall, NY, Zip 12518–1499; tel. 845/534–7711; ST. LUKE'S CORNWALL HOSPITAL – NEWBURGH CAMPUS, 70 Dubois Street, Newburgh, NY, Zip 12550–4898; tel. 845/561–4400; Joan Cusack–McGuirk, President and Chief Executive Officer) **A**1 2 10 **F**3 11 12 13 15 18 20 22 26 28 29 31 34 35 37 40 43 46 49 51 54 57 59 60 61 64 70 72 74 75 76 77 78 79 81 82 84 85 86 87 89 93 100 102 107 108 110 114 115 118 119 120 121 123 124 126 129 130 131 132 146 147 149 154 **S** Montefiore Health System, Bronx, NY
Primary Contact: Joan Cusack–McGuirk, President and Chief Executive Officer
CFO: Thomas Gibney, Senior Vice President and Chief Financial Officer
CMO: Christine Jelalian, M.D., Medical Director
CIO: Dwayne Simmons, Interim Chief Information Officer
CHR: Daniel Bengyak, Vice President, Administrative Services
CNO: Margaret Deyo–Allers, Vice President, Chief Nursing Officer
Web address: www.stlukescornwallhospital.org
Control: Other not-for-profit (including NFP Corporation) **Service**: General medical and surgical

Staffed Beds: 128 Admissions: 9694 Census: 125 Outpatient Visits: 178193 **Births: 780 Total Expense ($000): 197535 Payroll Expense ($000): 72785 Personnel: 1021**

NIAGARA FALLS—Niagara County

○ **NIAGARA FALLS MEMORIAL MEDICAL CENTER (330065)**, 621 Tenth Street, Zip 14301–1813, Mailing Address: P.O. Box 708, Zip 14302–0708; tel. 716/278–4000, (Nonreporting) **A**3 5 10 11 13
Primary Contact: Joseph A. Ruffolo, President and Chief Executive Officer
CMO: Fatma Patel, M.D., Vice President Medical Affairs
CIO: Diane Martin–Pratt, Director Information Systems
Web address: www.nfmmc.org
Control: Other not-for-profit (including NFP Corporation) **Service**: General medical and surgical

Staffed Beds: 288

NORTH TONAWANDA—Niagara County

DE GRAFF MEMORIAL HOSPITAL See Kaleida Health, Buffalo

NORTHPORT—Suffolk County

⊞ △ **NORTHPORT VETERANS AFFAIRS MEDICAL CENTER**, 79 Middleville Road, Zip 11768–2200; tel. 631/261–4400, (Total facility includes 134 beds in nursing home–type unit) **A**1 2 3 5 7 **F**1 3 4 5 8 9 18 20 26 28 29 30 31 34 35 36 38 39 40 45 50 51 52 53 54 56 57 58 59 60 61 62 63 64 65 68 70 71 74 75 77 78 79 81 82 83 84 85 86 87 92 93 94 96 97 98 100 101 102 103 104 105 106 107 108 109 111 114 115 118 119 120 121 127 129 130 132 133 135 143 144 146 147 148 149 150 153 154 **S** Department of Veterans Affairs, Perry Point, MD
Primary Contact: D. Scott. Guermonprez, FACHE, Director
COO: Michael McCully, Chief Operating Officer
CFO: Mary Pat Hessman, Chief Fiscal
CIO: Robert Ziskin, Chief Information Officer
CHR: Wilmino Sainbert, Chief Human Resources Management Service
Web address: www.northport.va.gov/index.asp
Control: Veterans Affairs, Government, federal **Service**: General medical and surgical

Staffed Beds: 254 Admissions: 3231 Census: 180 Outpatient Visits: 279074 **Births: 0 Personnel: 1754**

NORWICH—Chenango County

★ ○ **UHS CHENANGO MEMORIAL HOSPITAL (330033)**, 179 North Broad Street, Zip 13815–1097; tel. 607/337–4111, (Total facility includes 80 beds in nursing home–type unit) **A**10 11 **F**3 8 11 13 15 17 18 29 32 34 35 38 39 40 45 47 50 54 56 57 59 61 64 65 68 70 75 76 77 79 81 82 85 86 87 89 93 97 107 108 110 111 115 119 127 128 130 132 133 146 147 148 149 **P**6 **S** United Health Services, Binghamton, NY
Primary Contact: Drake M. Lamen, M.D., President, Chief Executive Officer and Chief Medical Officer
COO: Christina A Kisacky, Vice President, Operations
CFO: Peggy Swartwood, Assistant Vice President, Finance and Controller
CIO: Richard Stone, Manager, Technical Services
CHR: Anne L English, Director Human Resources
CNO: David Finney, R.N., Vice President Nursing
Web address: www.uhs.net/cmh
Control: Other not-for-profit (including NFP Corporation) **Service**: General medical and surgical

Staffed Beds: 138 Admissions: 1309 Census: 79 Outpatient Visits: 258463 **Births: 248 Total Expense ($000): 68622 Payroll Expense ($000): 21079 Personnel: 420**

NYACK—Rockland County

☐ **NYACK HOSPITAL (330104)**, 160 North Midland Avenue, Zip 10960–1998; tel. 845/348–2000, (Nonreporting) **A**1 2 5 10 **S** Montefiore Health System, Bronx, NY
Primary Contact: Mark Geller, M.D., President and Chief Executive Officer
COO: John Volanto, Vice President, Chief Operating Officer
CFO: John Burke, Chief Financial Officer
CMO: Anthony Matejicka, D.O., M.P.H., Vice President, Chief Medical Officer
CHR: Mary K Shinick, Vice President Human Resources
CNO: Kathleen Lunney, MS, R.N., Vice President Patient Care Services and Chief Nursing Officer
Web address: www.nyackhospital.org
Control: Other not-for-profit (including NFP Corporation) **Service**: General medical and surgical

Staffed Beds: 245

OCEANSIDE—Nassau County

⊞ **SOUTH NASSAU COMMUNITIES HOSPITAL (330198)**, One Healthy Way, Zip 11572–1551; tel. 516/632–3000, **A**1 2 3 5 10 12 13 **F**3 5 11 12 13 15 17 18 20 22 26 28 29 30 31 34 35 37 38 40 43 44 45 46 47 49 50 54 55 56 57 58 59 60 62 64 66 68 69 70 73 74 77 78 79 81 82 83 84 85 86 87 89 91 92 93 97 98 99 100 102 103 104 105 107 108 109 110 111 114 115 117 118 119 120 121 123 124 126 128 129 130 131 132 135 145 146 148 149 153 154 **P**8
Primary Contact: Richard J. Murphy, President and Chief Executive Officer
COO: William E. Allison, Senior Vice President and Chief Operating Officer, Administration
CFO: Mark A. Bogen, CPA, Senior Vice President, Finance
CMO: Adhi Sharma, M.D., Senior Vice President, Medical Affairs and Chief Medical Officer
CIO: Noah Caldwell, Vice President and Chief Information Officer
CHR: Paul D. Giordano, Senior Vice President, Human Resources
CNO: Sue Penque, Ph.D., R.N., Senior Vice President and Chief Nursing Officer
Web address: www.southnassau.org
Control: Other not-for-profit (including NFP Corporation) **Service**: General medical and surgical

Staffed Beds: 381 Admissions: 20546 Census: 322 Outpatient Visits: 333467 **Births: 1923 Total Expense ($000): 523570 Payroll Expense ($000): 259738 Personnel: 2951**

OGDENSBURG—St. Lawrence County

★ ⇑ **CLAXTON–HEPBURN MEDICAL CENTER (330211)**, 214 King Street, Zip 13669–1142; tel. 315/393–3600, (Nonreporting) **A**2 10 20 21
Primary Contact: Charles Gijanto, Interim Chief Executive Officer
COO: Vicki Perrine, FACHE, Chief Operating Officer
CFO: Kelley Tiernan, Chief Financial Officer
CIO: James Flood, Director Information Systems
CHR: Lou–Ann McNally, Executive Director Human Resources and Staff Development
CNO: David Ferris, Chief Nursing Officer and Vice President Patient Care Services
Web address: www.claxtonhepburn.org
Control: Other not–for–profit (including NFP Corporation) **Service:** General medical and surgical

Staffed Beds: 97

☐ **ST. LAWRENCE PSYCHIATRIC CENTER (334003)**, 1 Chimney Point Drive, Zip 13669–2291; tel. 315/541–2001, (Nonreporting) **A**1 3 10 **S** New York State Office of Mental Health, Albany, NY
Primary Contact: Timothy Farrell, Executive Director
CMO: Harishankar Sanghi, M.D., Clinical Director
CHR: Rosie Turnbull, Director Human Resources
Web address: www.omh.ny.gov/omhweb/facilities/slpc/facility.htm
Control: State, Government, nonfederal **Service:** Psychiatric

Staffed Beds: 146

OLEAN—Cattaraugus County

✉ **OLEAN GENERAL HOSPITAL (330103)**, 515 Main Street, Zip 14760–1513; tel. 716/373–2600, **A**1 3 5 10 19 **F**3 8 11 13 15 17 18 20 22 28 29 30 31 34 35 38 39 40 45 46 47 48 49 50 51 54 57 58 59 60 61 62 64 65 70 71 74 75 76 77 78 79 81 82 83 84 85 86 87 89 91 92 93 94 96 97 98 100 101 102 103 107 108 109 110 111 114 115 117 118 119 120 121 123 127 129 130 131 132 133 134 135 143 144 145 146 147 148 149 154 **P**6 8 **S** Upper Allegheny Health System, Olean, NY
Primary Contact: Timothy J. Finan, FACHE, President and Chief Executive Officer
COO: Jeff S Zewe, R.N., Senior Vice President, Chief Operating Officer
CFO: Richard G Braun, CPA, Jr Senior Vice President and Chief Financial Officer
CMO: William Mills, M.D., Senior Vice President Quality and Professional Affairs
CIO: Jason Yaworsky, Senior Vice President Information Systems and Chief Information Officer
CHR: Timothy M McNamara, Senior Vice President Human Resources
CNO: Vi–Anne Antrum, Chief Nursing Officer
Web address: www.ogh.org
Control: Other not–for–profit (including NFP Corporation) **Service:** General medical and surgical

Staffed Beds: 186 Admissions: 6114 Census: 88 Outpatient Visits: 232343 Births: 663 Total Expense ($000): 121048 Payroll Expense ($000): 44692 Personnel: 819

ONEIDA—Madison County

✉ **ONEIDA HEALTHCARE (330115)**, 321 Genesee Street, Zip 13421–2611; tel. 315/363–6000, (Total facility includes 160 beds in nursing home–type unit) **A**1 10 **F**3 11 13 15 18 29 34 40 45 49 50 54 57 59 64 65 68 70 74 75 76 77 78 79 81 85 86 87 89 92 93 97 107 108 110 111 115 117 118 119 126 128 129 130 135 146 149 **P**6 8
Primary Contact: Gene Morreale, President and Chief Executive Officer
COO: Mary Parry, Vice President Operations and Chief Operating Officer
CMO: Dan J. Vick, M.D., Vice President of Medical Affairs and Chief Medical Officer
CIO: Mary McGuirl, Director Information Systems
CHR: Michael Fifield, Vice President Human Resources
Web address: www.oneidahealthcare.org
Control: Other not–for–profit (including NFP Corporation) **Service:** General medical and surgical

Staffed Beds: 231 Admissions: 2828 Census: 181 Outpatient Visits: 210445 Births: 535 Total Expense ($000): 94339 Payroll Expense ($000): 45077 Personnel: 862

ONEONTA—Otsego County

★ ⇑ **AURELIA OSBORN FOX MEMORIAL HOSPITAL (330085)**, 1 Norton Avenue, Zip 13820–2629; tel. 607/432–2000, (Total facility includes 131 beds in nursing home–type unit) **A**10 21 **F**2 3 11 15 26 28 29 30 34 35 37 39 40 45 46 47 48 51 53 54 56 57 59 64 65 68 75 77 81 85 86 87 93 96 97 104 107 108 110 111 115 118 119 120 121 123 128 129 130 135 146 147 154 **P**6 **S** Bassett Healthcare Network, Cooperstown, NY
Primary Contact: Jeff Joyner, President
COO: Gary Smith, Chief Operating Officer
CFO: Mark J. Wright, Chief Financial Officer
CMO: Reginald Q. Knight, Chief Medical Officer
CHR: Jennie Gliha, Chief Human Resource Officer
CNO: Joan MacDonald, R.N., MSN, Chief Nursing Officer
Web address: www.bassett.org/ao-fox-hospital/
Control: Other not–for–profit (including NFP Corporation) **Service:** General medical and surgical

Staffed Beds: 184 Admissions: 2308 Census: 146 Outpatient Visits: 127470 Births: 0 Total Expense ($000): 74798 Payroll Expense ($000): 29523 Personnel: 616

ORANGEBURG—Rockland County

☐ **ROCKLAND Children's hospital psychiatric CENTER**, 599 Convent Road, Zip 10962–1162; tel. 845/359–7400, (Nonreporting) **A**1 3 5 **S** New York State Office of Mental Health, Albany, NY
Primary Contact: Christopher Tavella, Acting Executive Director
COO: Kenneth Perrotte, Director Operations
CFO: Peter Gorey, Administrative Coordinator
CMO: Sadhana Sardana, M.D., Clinical Director
CIO: Mary Pivonka, Director Quality Management
Web address: www.omh.ny.gov/
Control: State, Government, nonfederal **Service:** Children's hospital psychiatric

Staffed Beds: 54

☐ **ROCKLAND PSYCHIATRIC CENTER (334015)**, 140 Old Orangeburg Road, Zip 10962–1157; tel. 845/359–1000, (Nonreporting) **A**1 3 5 10 **S** New York State Office of Mental Health, Albany, NY
Primary Contact: Christopher Tavella, Executive Director
Web address: www.omh.ny.gov/
Control: State, Government, nonfederal **Service:** Psychiatric

Staffed Beds: 525

OSSINING—Westchester County

OSSINING CORRECTIONAL FACILITIES HOSPITAL, 354 Hunter Street, Zip 10562–5498; tel. 914/941–0108, (Nonreporting) **A**3
Primary Contact: Riza Ferdous, Health Services Director
Control: State, Government, nonfederal **Service:** Hospital unit of an institution (prison hospital, college infirmary, etc.)

Staffed Beds: 25

OSWEGO—Oswego County

✉ **OSWEGO HOSPITAL (330218)**, 110 West Sixth Street, Zip 13126–2507; tel. 315/349–5511, **A**1 3 10 20 **F**2 3 11 12 13 15 18 29 34 37 38 40 41 45 49 50 51 57 59 62 70 75 76 77 79 81 85 86 87 89 93 97 98 100 101 102 104 107 108 110 111 114 115 118 119 130 131 132 135 144 146 **P**6
Primary Contact: Michael Harlovic, R.N., President and Chief Executive Officer
COO: Jeff Coakley, Executive Vice President and Chief Operating Officer
CFO: Eric Campbell, Chief Financial Officer
CMO: Renato Mandanas, M.D., Chief Medical Officer
CIO: Barry W. Ryle, Chief Information Officer
CHR: James E Marco Jr Interim Vice President, Human Resources
CNO: Valerie Favata, R.N., MS, Chief Nursing Officer
Web address: www.oswegohealth.org
Control: Other not–for–profit (including NFP Corporation) **Service:** General medical and surgical

Staffed Beds: 99 Admissions: 3996 Census: 52 Outpatient Visits: 328427 Births: 507 Total Expense ($000): 114728 Payroll Expense ($000): 55280 Personnel: 841

NY

PATCHOGUE—Suffolk County

★ ⇑ **LONG ISLAND COMMUNITY HOSPITAL (330141)**, 101 Hospital Road, Zip 11772–4897; tel. 631/654–7100, (Nonreporting) **A**3 10 12 13 21
Primary Contact: Richard T. Margulis, President and Chief Executive Officer
COO: Ron Stephenson, Chief Operating Officer
CFO: Brenda Farrell, Vice President Finance
CMO: Nejat Zeyneloglu, Vice President and Chief Quality Medical Officer
CIO: Joseph Wood, Vice President and Chief Information Officer
CNO: Debra Grimm, DPN, MS, RN, Vice President and Chief Nursing Officer
Web address: www.bmhmc.org
Control: Other not–for–profit (including NFP Corporation) **Service**: General medical and surgical

Staffed Beds: 247

PENN YAN—Yates County

SOLDIERS AND SAILORS MEMORIAL HOSPITAL OF YATES COUNTY (331314), 418 North Main Street, Zip 14527–1085; tel. 315/531–2000, **A**10 18 **F**2 3 11 15 18 28 29 34 35 38 40 54 56 57 59 64 65 66 68 70 75 81 87 91 93 97 98 100 101 104 107 110 114 119 128 130 132 133 135 146 147 154 **P**6 **S** Finger Lakes Health, Geneva, NY
Primary Contact: Frank Korich, FACHE, Senior Vice President, Operations
COO: Lina Brennan, Site Administrator
CFO: Pamela Johnson, Treasurer and Chief Financial Officer
CMO: Jason Feinberg, M.D., Vice President Medical Affairs and Chief Medical Officer
CIO: Guy W Mosher III Manager Information Systems
CHR: Patrick R Boyle, Vice President Human Resources
CNO: Eileen Gage, R.N., Vice President Nursing
Web address: www.flhealth.org
Control: Other not–for–profit (including NFP Corporation) **Service**: General medical and surgical

Staffed Beds: 186 Admissions: 936 Census: 145 Outpatient Visits: 159174 **Births:** 0 **Total Expense ($000):** 28515 **Payroll Expense ($000):** 16393 **Personnel:** 326

PLAINVIEW—Nassau County

☒ **PLAINVIEW HOSPITAL (330331)**, 888 Old Country Road, Zip 11803–4978; tel. 516/719–3000, **A**1 3 10 12 13 **F**3 5 8 9 15 17 18 29 30 31 34 35 36 38 40 43 44 45 46 49 50 51 57 58 59 60 63 64 65 68 69 70 71 74 75 78 79 81 84 85 86 87 97 100 101 102 107 108 110 111 114 115 116 119 130 132 135 146 148 152 154 **P**5 6 **S** Northwell Health, New Hyde Park, NY
Primary Contact: Michael Fener, Executive Director
CMO: Alan Mensch, M.D., Senior Vice President Medical Affairs
Web address: www.planview.com/
Control: Other not–for–profit (including NFP Corporation) **Service**: General medical and surgical

Staffed Beds: 150 Admissions: 8622 Census: 109 Outpatient Visits: 62226 **Births:** 0 **Total Expense ($000):** 217634 **Payroll Expense ($000):** 108423 **Personnel:** 1218

PLATTSBURGH—Clinton County

☒ **THE UNIVERSITY OF VERMONT HEALTH NETWORK–CHAMPLAIN VALLEY PHYSICIANS HOSPITAL (330250)**, 75 Beekman Street, Zip 12901–1438; tel. 518/561–2000, (Total facility includes 54 beds in nursing home–type unit) **A**1 2 3 10 **F**3 7 8 13 14 15 18 20 22 26 28 29 30 31 34 35 36 38 40 41 43 45 46 49 50 53 56 58 59 64 68 70 76 77 78 79 81 83 84 85 87 89 93 94 96 98 99 102 107 108 110 111 114 115 116 117 118 119 120 121 123 126 128 129 130 132 143 144 145 146 147 148 149 154 **P**6
Primary Contact: Michelle Lebeau, President and Chief Operating Officer
COO: Michelle Lebeau, President and Chief Operating Officer
CFO: Joyce Rafferty, Vice President Finance
CMO: Kent Hall, M.D., Vice President and Chief Medical Officer
CIO: Wouter Rietsema, M.D., Chief Quality and Information Officer
CHR: Dean Civitello, Vice President, Human Resources, Public Relations and Development
Web address: www.https://profiles.health.ny.gov/hospital/view/103048
Control: Other not–for–profit (including NFP Corporation) **Service**: General medical and surgical

Staffed Beds: 260 Admissions: 8777 Census: 168 Outpatient Visits: 382352 **Births:** 825 **Total Expense ($000):** 323289 **Payroll Expense ($000):** 166597 **Personnel:** 2022

PORT JEFFERSON—Suffolk County

☒ **JOHN T. MATHER MEMORIAL HOSPITAL (330185)**, 75 North Country Road, Zip 11777–2190; tel. 631/473–1320, **A**1 2 3 10 **F**5 8 11 12 14 15 17 18 29 31 34 35 36 37 38 40 44 45 46 49 51 55 56 57 59 60 64 65 69 70 74 75 77 78 79 81 82 84 85 86 87 93 98 99 100 101 102 103 104 105 107 108 110 111 114 115 118 119 124 126 129 130 132 146 147 148 152 **P**6 **S** Northwell Health, New Hyde Park, NY
Primary Contact: Kenneth D. Roberts, President
COO: Kevin J Murray, Senior Vice President
CFO: Joseph Wisnoski, Chief Financial Officer
CMO: Joan Faro, M.D., Chief Medical Officer
CIO: Thomas Heiman, Vice President Information Services and Chief Information Officer
CHR: Diane Marotta, Vice President Human Resources
CNO: Marie Mulligan, R.N., MSN, Vice President Nursing
Web address: www.matherhospital.com
Control: Other not–for–profit (including NFP Corporation) **Service**: General medical and surgical

Staffed Beds: 248 Admissions: 12815 Census: 207 Outpatient Visits: 170127 **Births:** 0 **Total Expense ($000):** 366977 **Payroll Expense ($000):** 172212 **Personnel:** 2095

☐ △ **ST. CHARLES HOSPITAL (330246)**, 200 Belle Terre Road, Zip 11777–1928; tel. 631/474–6000, **A**1 2 3 7 10 **F**3 4 5 8 11 12 13 15 17 28 29 30 31 32 34 35 37 39 40 41 44 45 46 47 48 49 50 54 57 58 59 64 65 66 68 69 70 72 73 74 75 76 77 78 79 80 81 82 84 85 86 87 89 90 91 92 93 96 97 107 108 110 111 114 115 119 126 129 130 131 132 134 135 136 141 142 146 148 149 151 153 **P**5 6 **S** Catholic Health Services of Long Island, Rockville Centre, NY
Primary Contact: James O'Connor, Executive Vice President and Chief Administrative Officer
COO: Ronald Weingartner, Vice President Administration
CFO: Kathleen Vasil, Vice President Finance
CMO: Michael Sauter, M.D., Chief Medical Officer
CIO: Felix Pabon–Ramirez, Chief Information Officer
CNO: Nicolette Fiore–Lopez, R.N., Chief Nursing Officer
Web address: www.stcharleshospital.chsli.org
Control: Church operated, Nongovernment, not–for–profit **Service**: General medical and surgical

Staffed Beds: 243 Admissions: 9200 Census: 165 Outpatient Visits: 216650 **Births:** 1220 **Total Expense ($000):** 216787 **Payroll Expense ($000):** 90481 **Personnel:** 1334

PORT JERVIS—Orange County

☒ **BON SECOURS COMMUNITY HOSPITAL (330135)**, 160 East Main Street, Zip 12771–2245, Mailing Address: P.O. Box 1014, Zip 12771–0268; tel. 845/858–7000, (Nonreporting) **A**1 10 **S** WMCHealth, Valhalla, NY
Primary Contact: Mary Leahy, M.D., Chief Executive Officer
COO: Gaynor Rosenstein, Vice President Operations
CHR: Kim Hirkaler, Director Human Resources
Web address: www.bonsecourscommunityhosp.org
Control: Church operated, Nongovernment, not–for–profit **Service**: General medical and surgical

Staffed Beds: 189

POTSDAM—St. Lawrence County

★ ⇑ **CANTON–POTSDAM HOSPITAL (330197)**, 50 Leroy Street, Zip 13676–1799; tel. 315/265–3300, **A**10 20 21 **F**3 5 11 13 15 18 26 28 29 30 31 34 35 36 38 40 43 46 51 54 57 58 59 64 65 68 75 76 77 78 79 81 82 85 86 87 92 93 94 95 96 97 100 101 102 104 107 108 110 111 115 116 117 118 119 120 121 123 127 129 130 131 132 133 135 144 145 146 147 149 150 **S** St. Lawrence Health System, Potsdam, NY
Primary Contact: David B. Acker, FACHE, President and Chief Executive Officer
CFO: Richard Jacobs, Vice President Finance and Chief Financial Officer
CMO: Robert T Rogers, M.D., II Medical Director
CIO: Jorge C Grillo, Chief Information Officer
CHR: Darlene Lewis, Vice President Human Resources
CNO: Jan Carroll, MSN, M.P.H., R.N., Chief Nursing Officer
Web address: www.cphospital.org
Control: Other not–for–profit (including NFP Corporation) **Service**: General medical and surgical

Staffed Beds: 87 Admissions: 4964 Census: 63 Outpatient Visits: 323683 **Births:** 488 **Total Expense ($000):** 182079 **Payroll Expense ($000):** 93769 **Personnel:** 1078

POUGHKEEPSIE—Dutchess County

☐ **VASSAR BROTHERS MEDICAL CENTER (330023)**, 45 Reade Place, Zip 12601–3947; tel. 845/454–8500, **A**1 2 10 **F**3 8 11 12 13 15 17 18 20 22 24 26 28 29 30 31 34 35 36 37 40 43 44 45 46 47 48 49 50 51 54 55 57 58 59 60 68 70 72 73 74 75 76 77 78 79 81 82 84 85 86 87 89 92 93 97 100 107 108 109 110 111 114 115 117 118 119 120 121 123 124 126 129 130 131 132 135 146 147 148 149 **S** Health Quest Systems, Inc., LaGrangeville, NY
Primary Contact: Ann McMackin, President
COO: Robert Rosenbaum, Vice President Operations
CFO: Tony Perugino, Assistant Vice President Decision Support
CMO: Michael Doyle, M.D., Vice President Medical Affairs
CNO: Lore Bogolin, MSN, R.N., Chief Nursing Officer and Vice President Care Services
Web address: www.health–quest.org
Control: Other not–for–profit (including NFP Corporation) **Service:** General medical and surgical

Staffed Beds: 365 **Admissions:** 21500 **Census:** 272 **Outpatient Visits:** 305974 **Births:** 2199 **Total Expense ($000):** 560877 **Payroll Expense ($000):** 163596 **Personnel:** 1866

RHINEBECK—Dutchess County

☐ △ **NORTHERN DUTCHESS HOSPITAL (330049)**, 6511 Springbrook Avenue, Zip 12572–3709, Mailing Address: P.O. Box 5002, Zip 12572–5002; tel. 845/876–3001, **A**1 7 10 **F**3 11 13 15 18 28 29 34 35 36 37 40 45 50 53 56 64 68 70 74 75 76 77 78 79 81 82 84 85 87 90 93 100 107 108 110 111 115 118 119 125 126 129 130 146 147 148 149 154 **S** Health Quest Systems, Inc., LaGrangeville, NY
Primary Contact: Denise George, R.N., President
CMO: John Sabia, M.D., Vice President Medical Affairs
Web address: www.health–quest.org/home_nd.cfm?id=9
Control: Other not–for–profit (including NFP Corporation) **Service:** General medical and surgical

Staffed Beds: 68 **Admissions:** 5001 **Census:** 55 **Outpatient Visits:** 127274 **Births:** 897 **Total Expense ($000):** 107255 **Payroll Expense ($000):** 37634 **Personnel:** 564

RIVERHEAD—Suffolk County

☒ **PECONIC BAY MEDICAL CENTER (330107)**, 1300 Roanoke Avenue, Zip 11901–2031; tel. 631/548–6000, **A**1 3 10 12 13 **F**3 5 7 8 11 12 13 15 18 20 22 28 29 30 31 33 34 35 40 41 43 44 45 46 49 50 51 53 54 56 57 59 62 64 67 68 70 74 75 76 77 78 79 80 81 82 83 84 85 86 87 93 96 107 108 110 111 115 118 119 126 130 131 132 143 144 146 147 148 149 152 154 **P**5 6 **S** Northwell Health, New Hyde Park, NY
Primary Contact: Andrew J. Mitchell, President and Chief Executive Officer
COO: Ronald McManus, Senior Vice President Clinical Services and Business Entities
CFO: Michael F. O'Donnell, CPA, Chief Financial Officer
CIO: Arthur Crowe, Director Information Systems
CHR: Monica Chestnut–Rauls, Vice President Human Resources
CNO: Amy E Loeb, Ed.D., R.N., Chief Nursing Officer
Web address: www.pbmchealth.org
Control: Other not–for–profit (including NFP Corporation) **Service:** General medical and surgical

Staffed Beds: 101 **Admissions:** 8303 **Census:** 90 **Outpatient Visits:** 97719 **Births:** 329 **Total Expense ($000):** 178948 **Payroll Expense ($000):** 77396 **Personnel:** 960

ROCHESTER—Monroe County

☒ **HIGHLAND HOSPITAL (330164)**, 1000 South Avenue, Zip 14620–2733; tel. 585/473–2200, **A**1 3 5 10 19 **F**3 12 13 15 18 29 30 31 34 35 37 40 44 45 46 47 49 50 54 55 56 57 58 59 60 63 64 65 66 68 70 74 75 76 77 78 79 81 83 84 85 86 87 91 93 97 100 107 108 110 111 114 115 118 119 120 121 122 123 126 130 132 134 135 141 145 146 147 148 149 154 **P**5 **S** University of Rochester Medical Center, Rochester, NY
Primary Contact: Steven I. Goldstein, President and Chief Executive Officer
COO: Cindy Becker, Vice President and Chief Operating Officer
CFO: Adam Anolik, Chief Financial Officer
CMO: Raymond Mayewski, M.D., Chief Medical Officer
CIO: Tom Barnett, Chief Information Officer
CHR: Amy Taney, Chief Human Resource Officer
Web address: www.urmc.rochester.edu/highland
Control: Other not–for–profit (including NFP Corporation) **Service:** General medical and surgical

Staffed Beds: 261 **Admissions:** 16139 **Census:** 201 **Outpatient Visits:** 427317 **Births:** 3019 **Total Expense ($000):** 353761 **Payroll Expense ($000):** 162480 **Personnel:** 2298

☒ **ROCHESTER GENERAL HOSPITAL (330125)**, 1425 Portland Avenue, Zip 14621–3099; tel. 585/922–4000, **A**1 2 3 5 10 **F**3 5 8 9 11 12 13 15 17 18 20 22 24 26 29 30 31 32 34 35 38 39 40 41 44 45 47 49 50 51 54 55 57 58 59 60 61 63 64 65 66 68 70 73 74 75 76 77 78 79 80 81 82 84 85 86 87 89 92 93 96 97 98 100 101 102 103 104 107 108 110 111 114 115 116 117 118 119 121 122 123 124 126 130 131 132 134 135 145 146 147 148 149 154 **P**5 6 **S** Rochester Regional Health, Rochester, NY
Primary Contact: Nancy M. Tinsley, R.N., President
CMO: Robert Mayo, M.D., Chief Medical Officer
CIO: John Glynn, Chief Information Officer
CHR: Janine Schue, Senior Vice President Human Resources
CNO: Cheryl Sheridan, R.N., Senior Vice President Patient Care Services
Web address: www.rochestergeneral.org
Control: Other not–for–profit (including NFP Corporation) **Service:** General medical and surgical

Staffed Beds: 528 **Admissions:** 31062 **Census:** 437 **Outpatient Visits:** 1236912 **Births:** 2174 **Total Expense ($000):** 999067 **Payroll Expense ($000):** 485152 **Personnel:** 6608

☐ **ROCHESTER PSYCHIATRIC CENTER (334020)**, 1111 Elmwood Avenue, Zip 14620–3005; tel. 585/241–1200, (Nonreporting) **A**1 3 5 10 **S** New York State Office of Mental Health, Albany, NY
Primary Contact: Philip Griffin, Director of Operations
COO: Joseph Coffey, Director Facility Administration
CFO: Rosanne Minnis, Business Officer
CMO: Laurence Guttmacher, M.D., Clinical Director
CIO: Lori Hintz, Coordinator Information Systems
CHR: Colomba Misseritti, Director Human Resources
CNO: Christopher Kirisits, Chief Nursing Officer
Web address: www.omh.ny.gov/omhweb/facilities/ropc/facility.htm
Control: State, Government, nonfederal **Service:** Psychiatric

Staffed Beds: 180

☒ △ **STRONG MEMORIAL HOSPITAL OF THE UNIVERSITY OF ROCHESTER (330285)**, 601 Elmwood Avenue, Zip 14642–0002, Mailing Address: 601 Elmwood Avenue, Box 612, Zip 14642–0002; tel. 585/275–2100, (Includes GOLISANO CHILDREN'S HOSPITAL, 601 Elmwood Avenue, Rochester, NY, Zip 14610; tel. 585/275–2182) **A**1 2 3 5 7 8 10 19 **F**3 5 6 8 9 11 12 13 14 15 16 17 18 19 20 21 22 23 24 25 26 27 28 29 30 31 32 33 34 35 36 38 39 40 41 43 44 45 46 47 48 49 50 51 52 53 54 55 56 57 58 59 60 61 63 64 65 66 68 70 71 72 73 74 75 76 77 78 79 80 81 82 83 84 85 86 87 88 89 90 91 92 93 94 95 96 97 98 99 100 101 102 103 104 105 107 108 110 111 114 115 116 117 118 119 120 121 123 124 126 127 129 130 131 132 134 135 136 137 138 139 141 142 143 144 145 146 147 148 149 150 152 154 **P**6 **S** University of Rochester Medical Center, Rochester, NY
Primary Contact: Steven I. Goldstein, President and Chief Executive Officer
COO: Kathleen M Parrinello, Ph.D., Chief Operating Officer
CFO: David L. Kirshner, Chief Financial Officer
CMO: Raymond Mayewski, M.D., Chief Medical Officer
CIO: D Jerome Powell, M.D., Chief Information Officer
CHR: Charles J Murphy, Associate Vice President Human Resources
Web address: www.urmc.rochester.edu
Control: Other not–for–profit (including NFP Corporation) **Service:** General medical and surgical

Staffed Beds: 835 **Admissions:** 40423 **Census:** 795 **Outpatient Visits:** 1633199 **Births:** 2758 **Total Expense ($000):** 1646237 **Payroll Expense ($000):** 660888 **Personnel:** 11097

☒ **UNITY HOSPITAL (330226)**, 1555 Long Pond Road, Zip 14626–4182; tel. 585/723–7000, (Total facility includes 120 beds in nursing home–type unit) **A**1 3 5 10 **F**3 4 5 13 15 18 20 22 26 28 29 30 31 33 34 35 38 39 40 44 45 47 48 49 50 52 55 56 57 59 60 61 63 64 65 66 70 71 73 74 75 77 78 79 80 81 82 84 85 86 87 90 91 92 93 96 97 98 100 101 102 103 104 107 108 114 118 119 126 128 129 130 131 132 134 135 141 144 146 147 148 149 151 **P**5 6 **S** Rochester Regional Health, Rochester, NY
Primary Contact: Douglas Stewart, PsyD, President
COO: Stewart C Putnam, Executive Vice President and Chief Operating Officer
CFO: Tom Crilly, Executive Vice President and Chief Financial Officer
CMO: James Haley, M.D., Senior Vice President and Chief Medical Officer
CIO: John Glynn, Senior Vice President and Chief Information Officer
CHR: Maryalice Keller, Vice President Brand and Talent Management
CNO: Jane McCormack, R.N., MSN, Vice President, Chief Nursing Officer and Nursing and Patient Care Services
Web address: www.unityhealth.org
Control: Other not–for–profit (including NFP Corporation) **Service:** General medical and surgical

Staffed Beds: 454 **Admissions:** 18388 **Census:** 326 **Outpatient Visits:** 716210 **Births:** 1443 **Total Expense ($000):** 469524 **Payroll Expense ($000):** 233589 **Personnel:** 4261

ROCKVILLE CENTRE—Nassau County

☐ **MERCY MEDICAL CENTER (330259)**, 1000 North Village Avenue, Zip 11570–1000; tel. 516/705–2525, **A**1 2 3 10 13 **F**3 5 8 12 13 15 20 26 29 30 31 34 35 37 38 40 41 43 46 48 49 50 51 56 57 58 59 60 64 65 66 68 70 72 74 75 76 77 78 79 81 82 84 85 87 90 92 93 94 96 97 98 100 102 103 104 105 107 108 110 111 115 119 129 130 131 132 135 141 142 143 146 147 148 152 153 154 **P**5 **S** Catholic Health Services of Long Island, Rockville Centre, NY
Primary Contact: Ronald Steimel, Executive Vice President and Chief Administrative Officer
CFO: William C Armstrong, Senior Vice President and Chief Financial Officer
CMO: John Reilly, M.D., Vice President Medical Affairs and Chief Medical Officer
CIO: Marcy Dunn, Vice President Information Services and Chief Information Officer
CHR: Allison Cianciotto Croyle, Vice President of Human Resources
CNO: Beth Vlahavas, R.N., MSN, Vice President Patient Care Services and Chief Nursing Officer
Web address: www.mercymedicalcenter.chsli.org
Control: Church operated, Nongovernment, not–for–profit **Service:** General medical and surgical

Staffed Beds: 191 **Admissions:** 10201 **Census:** 187 **Outpatient Visits:** 116532 **Births:** 898 **Total Expense ($000):** 229599 **Payroll Expense ($000):** 98600 **Personnel:** 1172

ROME—Oneida County

★ ○ **ROME MEMORIAL HOSPITAL (330215)**, 1500 North James Street, Zip 13440–2844; tel. 315/338–7000, (Total facility includes 82 beds in nursing home–type unit) **A**10 11 **F**3 5 8 11 13 15 18 28 29 30 34 45 47 48 49 50 54 57 59 64 65 68 70 74 75 76 77 78 79 80 81 85 86 87 89 93 98 101 102 103 104 107 108 109 110 111 112 113 114 115 116 117 119 120 121 122 123 124 128 129 130 132 135 143 144 146 147 148 149 154
Primary Contact: David W. Lundquist, President and Chief Executive Officer
CFO: Dewey R Rowlands, Vice President and Chief Financial Officer
CMO: Andrew Bushnell, M.D., Interim Chief Medical Officer
CIO: Mark Rowan, Interim Chief Information Officer
CHR: Regina Chambers, Vice President Human Resource
CNO: Durinda Durr, Vice President and Chief Nursing Officer
Web address: www.romehospital.org
Control: Other not–for–profit (including NFP Corporation) **Service:** General medical and surgical

Staffed Beds: 203 **Admissions:** 3497 **Census:** 117 **Outpatient Visits:** 165145 **Births:** 560 **Total Expense ($000):** 83780 **Payroll Expense ($000):** 40271 **Personnel:** 726

ROSLYN—Nassau County

☒ **ST. FRANCIS HOSPITAL, THE HEART CENTER (330182)**, 100 Port Washington Boulevard, Zip 11576–1353; tel. 516/562–6000, **A**1 3 10 **F**3 7 8 11 12 14 15 17 18 19 20 21 22 23 24 26 27 28 29 30 31 34 35 36 37 38 39 40 44 45 46 47 49 50 53 54 55 56 57 58 59 60 61 62 63 64 65 66 68 70 71 74 75 77 78 79 81 82 84 85 86 87 93 97 100 102 107 108 109 110 111 114 115 116 117 118 119 120 121 123 126 130 131 132 135 146 147 148 149 **P**6 **S** Catholic Health Services of Long Island, Rockville Centre, NY
Primary Contact: Ruth Hennessey, Executive Vice President and Chief Administrative Officer
CFO: William C Armstrong, Vice President and Chief Financial Officer
CMO: Jack Soterakis, M.D., Executive Vice President Medical Affairs
CIO: Marcy Dunn, Vice President Information Services and Chief Information Officer
CHR: Barbara Fierro, Director, Human Resources
CNO: Ann S Cella, R.N., Senior Vice President, Patient Care Services
Web address: www.stfrancisheartcenter.com/index.html
Control: Church operated, Nongovernment, not–for–profit **Service:** General medical and surgical

Staffed Beds: 320 **Admissions:** 17027 **Census:** 278 **Outpatient Visits:** 215950 **Births:** 0 **Total Expense ($000):** 619786 **Payroll Expense ($000):** 262322 **Personnel:** 2949

SARANAC LAKE—Franklin County

★ ○ **ADIRONDACK HEALTH (330079)**, 2233 State Route 86, Zip 12983–5644, Mailing Address: P.O. Box 471, Zip 12983–0471; tel. 518/891–4141, (Total facility includes 60 beds in nursing home–type unit) **A**5 10 11 **F**3 8 9 12 13 15 18 28 29 30 31 34 35 37 38 39 40 41 43 45 46 49 50 53 54 56 57 59 60 64 70 71 74 75 76 77 78 79 81 82 84 85 86 89 90 92 93 94 97 98 102 103 104 107 108 110 111 114 116 119 127 128 129 130 131 132 135 146 147 148 153 154 **P**6
Primary Contact: Sylvia Getman, President and Chief Executive Officer
COO: Patti Hammond, Chief Operating Officer
CFO: Tristan Glanville, Chief Financial Officer
CMO: Joahd Toure', M.D., Chief Medical Officer
CHR: Michael D Lee, Chief Human Resources Officer
CNO: Linda McClarigan, R.N., Chief Nursing Officer
Web address: www.adirondackhealth.org
Control: Other not–for–profit (including NFP Corporation) **Service:** General medical and surgical

Staffed Beds: 120 **Admissions:** 2488 **Census:** 81 **Outpatient Visits:** 139774 **Births:** 171 **Total Expense ($000):** 102831 **Payroll Expense ($000):** 47578 **Personnel:** 857

SARATOGA SPRINGS—Saratoga County

☐ **FOUR WINDS HOSPITAL (334049)**, 30 Crescent Avenue, Zip 12866–5142; tel. 518/584–3600, **A**1 10 **F**30 35 98 99 100 101 103 104 105 153
Primary Contact: Samuel A. Bastien IV, Ph.D., Chief Executive Officer
CFO: Juanita Wheeler–Moore, Director Financial Services
CMO: Kevin P. Martin, M.D., Chief Medical Officer
CIO: Susan Snowdon, Director Information Technology
CHR: Susan M Kirchner, Director Human Resources
CNO: James Colamaria, Director of Nursing
Web address: www.fourwindshospital.com
Control: Individual, Investor–owned (for–profit) **Service:** Psychiatric

Staffed Beds: 88 **Admissions:** 2793 **Census:** 88 **Births:** 0 **Total Expense ($000):** 33898

☒ **SARATOGA HOSPITAL (330222)**, 211 Church Street, Zip 12866–1003; tel. 518/587–3222, **A**1 2 3 5 10 **F**3 5 8 11 12 13 15 18 20 22 28 29 30 31 34 35 36 38 39 40 45 46 47 48 49 50 51 53 54 55 57 59 60 63 64 65 66 70 74 75 76 77 78 79 81 82 84 85 86 87 89 92 93 96 97 98 100 101 102 104 107 108 110 111 114 115 116 117 119 120 121 123 126 129 130 131 132 135 144 145 146 147 149 **P**6
Primary Contact: Angelo G. Calbone, President and Chief Executive Officer
CFO: Gary Foster, Vice President and Chief Financial Officer
CMO: Richard Falivena, D.O., M.P.H., Vice President and Chief Medical Officer
CIO: John Mangona, Vice President, Chief Information Officer and Compliance Officer
CHR: Jeffrey M Methven, Vice President Ambulatory Services and Chief Human Resources Officer
CNO: Mary Jo LaPosta, Ph.D., R.N., Senior Vice President Patient Care and Organizational Excellence
Web address: www.saratogacare.org
Control: Other not–for–profit (including NFP Corporation) **Service:** General medical and surgical

Staffed Beds: 171 **Admissions:** 10055 **Census:** 134 **Outpatient Visits:** 451935 **Births:** 749 **Total Expense ($000):** 305879 **Payroll Expense ($000):** 149533 **Personnel:** 2151

SCHENECTADY—Schenectady County

☒ **ELLIS HOSPITAL (330153)**, 1101 Nott Street, Zip 12308–2425; tel. 518/243–4000, (Includes BELLEVUE WOMAN'S CARE CENTER, 2210 Troy Road, Schenectady, NY, Zip 12309–4797; tel. 518/346–9400; ELLIS HOSPITAL HEALTH CENTER, 600 McClellan Street, Schenectady, NY, Zip 12304–1090; tel. 518/382–2000) (Nonreporting) **A**1 3 5 10 13
Primary Contact: Paul A. Milton, President and Chief Executive Officer
COO: Paul A Milton, Executive Vice President and Chief Operating Officer
CFO: Marc Mesick, Vice President and Chief Financial Officer
CMO: David Liebers, M.D., Chief Medical Officer and Vice President Medical Affairs
CIO: Ron McKinnon, Chief Information Officer
CHR: Joseph Giansante, Vice President Human Resources
Web address: www.ellismedicine.org
Control: Other not–for–profit (including NFP Corporation) **Service:** General medical and surgical

Staffed Beds: 436

ELLIS HOSPITAL HEALTH CENTER See Ellis Hospital, Schenectady

ELLIS HOSPITAL MCCLELLAN CAMPUS See Ellis Hospital Health Center

☒ △ **SUNNYVIEW REHABILITATION HOSPITAL (330406)**, 1270 Belmont Avenue, Zip 12308–2104; tel. 518/382–4500, (Nonreporting) **A**1 3 5 7 10 **S** Trinity Health, Livonia, MI
Primary Contact: Edward Eisenman, Chief Executive Officer
CFO: Kristin Signor, Director Finance
CMO: Lynne T Nicolson, M.D., Medical Director
CIO: Patrick Clark, Manager Information Technology
CHR: Meghan Glowa, Director Human Resources
Web address: www.sunnyview.org
Control: Other not–for–profit (including NFP Corporation) **Service:** Rehabilitation

Staffed Beds: 115

SLEEPY HOLLOW—Westchester County

☒ **PHELPS MEMORIAL HOSPITAL CENTER (330261)**, 701 North Broadway, Zip 10591–1020; tel. 914/366–3000, **A**1 2 3 5 10 **F**3 4 5 8 9 11 13 14 15 17 18 28 29 30 31 34 35 37 39 40 45 46 47 48 49 50 53 55 56 57 58 59 60 61 63 64 65 68 70 74 75 76 77 78 79 81 82 84 85 86 87 89 90 91 92 93 94 96 97 98 100 101 102 104 107 108 110 111 114 115 118 119 129 130 131 132 135 141 143 145 146 147 148 152 153 154 **P**5 6 **S** Northwell Health, New Hyde Park, NY
Primary Contact: Daniel Blum, President
CFO: Vincent DeSantis, Vice President Finance
CHR: Jussi Maijala, Vice President, Human Resources
CNO: Mary McDermott, MSN, MS, R.N., Senior Vice President Patient Care Services and Chief Nursing Officer
Web address: www.phelpshospital.org
Control: Other not–for–profit (including NFP Corporation) **Service:** General medical and surgical

Staffed Beds: 158 **Admissions:** 7306 **Census:** 126 **Outpatient Visits:** 182345 **Births:** 1037 **Total Expense ($000):** 261126 **Payroll Expense ($000):** 147333 **Personnel:** 1574

SMITHTOWN—Suffolk County

☐ **ST. CATHERINE OF SIENA MEDICAL CENTER (330401)**, 50 Route 25–A, Zip 11787–1348; tel. 631/862–3000, (Nonreporting) **A**1 10 **S** Catholic Health Services of Long Island, Rockville Centre, NY
Primary Contact: James O'Connor, Chief Administrative Officer
CFO: John Pohlman, Vice President Finance and Administration
CMO: Jason Golbin, M.D., Chief Medical Officer
CNO: Mary Jane Finnegan, Chief Nursing Officer
Web address: www.stcatherines.chsli.org/
Control: Church operated, Nongovernment, not–for–profit **Service:** General medical and surgical

Staffed Beds: 503

SPRINGVILLE—Erie County

BERTRAND CHAFFEE HOSPITAL (330111), 224 East Main Street, Zip 14141–1497; tel. 716/592–2871, (Nonreporting) **A**10
Primary Contact: Nils Gunnersen, Administrator
CMO: J Matthew Baker, M.D., President Medical Staff
CHR: Mary Beth Brown, Director Human Resources
Web address: www.chaffeehospitalandhome.com
Control: Other not–for–profit (including NFP Corporation) **Service:** General medical and surgical

Staffed Beds: 24

STAR LAKE—St. Lawrence County

★ **CLIFTON–FINE HOSPITAL (331307)**, 1014 Oswegatchie Trail, Zip 13690–3143; tel. 315/848–3351, (Nonreporting) **A**10 18
Primary Contact: Dierdra Sorrell, R.N., Interim Chief Executive Officer
COO: Cathy Rice, Director Support Services
CFO: Heather Cockayne, Chief Financial Officer
CMO: David Welch, M.D., Medical Director
CIO: Joe Deeter, MS, Director Information Systems
CNO: John Schaffer, R.N., Director of Nursing
Web address: www.cliftonfinehospital.org
Control: Other not–for–profit (including NFP Corporation) **Service:** General medical and surgical

Staffed Beds: 20

STATEN ISLAND—Richmond County; See New York City

STONY BROOK—Suffolk County

☒ **STONY BROOK UNIVERSITY HOSPITAL (330393)**, State University of New York, Zip 11794–8410; tel. 631/444–1077, (Includes STONY BROOK CHILDREN'S HOSPITAL, 100 Nicolls Road, Stony Brook, NY, Zip 11794–0001; tel. 631/444–4000; STONY BROOK SOUTHAMPTON HOSPITAL, 240 Meeting House Lane, Southampton, NY, Zip 11968–5090; tel. 631/726–8200; Robert S Chaloner, Chief Administrative Officer) **A**1 2 5 8 10 **F**3 6 7 8 9 11 12 13 14 15 16 17 18 19 20 22 24 26 28 29 30 31 32 34 35 36 37 38 39 40 41 43 44 45 46 47 48 49 50 51 52 53 54 55 56 57 58 59 60 61 62 63 64 65 66 68 70 72 73 74 75 76 77 78 79 81 82 83 84 85 86 87 88 89 91 92 93 96 97 98 99 100 101 102 103 104 107 108 110 111 112 114 115 116 117 118 119 120 121 122 123 124 126 129 130 131 132 134 135 136 138 141 143 144 145 146 147 148 149 150 154 **P**1 6
Primary Contact: Ernest J. Baptiste, Chief Executive Officer
COO: Carol Gomes, FACHE, Chief Operating Officer
CFO: Gary E Bie, CPA, Chief Financial Officer
CMO: Joseph H. Laver, M.D., Chief Medical Officer
CIO: Jim Murry, Chief Information Officer
CHR: Luis de Onis, Interim Chief Human Resources Officer
CNO: Mary Ann T Donohue, Ph.D., R.N., Chief Patient Care Services Officer
Web address: www.stonybrookmedicalcenter.edu
Control: State, Government, nonfederal **Service:** General medical and surgical

Staffed Beds: 687 Admissions: 38499 Census: 586 Outpatient Visits: 1169614 Births: 3349 Total Expense ($000): 1400279 Payroll Expense ($000): 610538 Personnel: 6662

SUFFERN—Rockland County

☒ **GOOD SAMARITAN REGIONAL MEDICAL CENTER (330158)**, 255 Lafayette Avenue, Zip 10901–4869; tel. 845/368–5000, (Nonreporting) **A**1 2 10 **S** WMCHealth, Valhalla, NY
Primary Contact: Mary Leahy, M.D., Chief Executive Officer
COO: Gerry Durney, Chief Operating Officer
CMO: Rodney W Williams, M.D., JD, MS, Vice President Medical Affairs
CIO: Deborah K Marshall, Vice President Public Relations
CHR: Pamela Tarulli, Senior Vice President Human Resources
Web address: www.goodsamhosp.org
Control: Church operated, Nongovernment, not–for–profit **Service:** General medical and surgical

Staffed Beds: 308

SYOSSET—Nassau County

★ **SYOSSET HOSPITAL**, 221 Jericho Turnpike, Zip 11791–4515; tel. 516/496–6500, **A**3 **F**3 5 8 12 15 18 29 30 31 34 35 36 38 40 43 44 45 50 57 58 59 60 62 63 64 65 68 70 74 78 79 81 82 84 85 87 96 97 98 100 101 102 107 108 114 119 126 130 132 135 146 152 154 **P**5 6 **S** Northwell Health, New Hyde Park, NY
Primary Contact: Michael Fener, Executive Director
COO: Mark J Solazzo, Regional Chief Operating Officer
CFO: Richard Reilly, Deputy Executive Director
CMO: Randolph DiLorenzo, M.D., Medical Director
CHR: Andrew S Goldberg, Associate Executive Director
Web address: www.northshorelij.com
Control: Other not–for–profit (including NFP Corporation) **Service:** General medical and surgical

Staffed Beds: 75 Admissions: 3961 Census: 55 Outpatient Visits: 63570 Births: 0 Total Expense ($000): 180041 Payroll Expense ($000): 93731 Personnel: 811

SYRACUSE—Onondaga County

COMMUNITY–GENERAL HOSPITAL OF GREATER SYRACUSE See Upstate University Hospital At Community General

★ ⇧ **CROUSE HEALTH (330203)**, 736 Irving Avenue, Zip 13210–1690; tel. 315/470–7375, **A**3 5 10 21 **F**3 4 5 8 11 12 13 15 18 19 20 21 22 23 26 27 29 31 34 35 36 37 40 49 50 53 58 59 60 64 66 68 70 72 73 74 75 76 77 78 79 81 83 84 86 87 89 91 93 96 107 108 110 112 114 115 116 117 118 119 126 129 130 131 132 135 144 145 146 147 148 149 150
Primary Contact: Kimberly Boynton, President and Chief Executive Officer
CFO: Michael A. Tengeres, Chief Financial Officer
CMO: Seth Kronenberg, M.D., Chief Medical Officer
CIO: Kim Rose, Chief Information Technology
CHR: John Bergemann, Director Human Resources
CNO: Betty O'Connor, Chief Nursing Officer
Web address: www.crouse.org
Control: Other not–for–profit (including NFP Corporation) **Service:** General medical and surgical

Staffed Beds: 487 Admissions: 18746 Census: 296 Outpatient Visits: 463165 Births: 3862 Total Expense ($000): 434395 Payroll Expense ($000): 168724 Personnel: 1969

☐ **RICHARD H. HUTCHINGS PSYCHIATRIC CENTER (334001)**, 620 Madison Street, Zip 13210–2319; tel. 315/426–3632, (Nonreporting) **A**1 3 5 10 **S** New York State Office of Mental Health, Albany, NY
Primary Contact: Colleen A. Sawyer, R.N., MSN, Executive Director
CFO: Robert Stapleton, Director Administration
CMO: Mark Cattalani, M.D., Clinical Director
CIO: Neil Nemi, Administrator Facility Information Center
CHR: Katherine Herron, Director Human Resources
Web address: www.omh.ny.gov
Control: State, Government, nonfederal **Service:** Psychiatric

Staffed Beds: 131

NY

★ ⇧ **ST. JOSEPH'S HOSPITAL HEALTH CENTER (330140)**, 301 Prospect Avenue, Zip 13203–1807; tel. 315/448–5111, **A**3 5 10 21 **F**3 8 11 12 13 14 15 17 18 20 22 24 26 28 29 30 31 34 35 37 38 39 40 45 46 47 48 49 50 51 54 57 58 59 60 61 62 64 65 66 68 70 72 73 74 75 76 77 78 79 81 82 83 84 85 87 90 92 93 94 97 98 100 101 102 103 104 106 107 108 110 111 114 115 118 119 126 129 130 131 132 135 144 146 147 148 149 **S** Trinity Health, Livonia, MI
Primary Contact: Leslie Paul. Luke, President and Chief Executive Officer
COO: Mary W Brown, Senior Vice President Operations
CFO: Meredith Price, Vice President Fiscal Services and Chief Financial Officer
CMO: Joseph W Spinale, D.O., Chief Medical Officer
CIO: Charles Fennell, Vice President Information Management
CHR: Erika Duncan, Vice President Human Resources
CNO: AnneMarie Czyz, R.N., MS, Ed.D., Senior Vice President Operations, Chief Operating Officer and Chief Nursing Officer
Web address: www.sjhsyr.org
Control: Other not–for–profit (including NFP Corporation) **Service**: General medical and surgical

Staffed Beds: 451 **Admissions**: 26595 **Census**: 340 **Outpatient Visits**: 589707 **Births**: 2031 **Total Expense ($000)**: 600490 **Payroll Expense ($000)**: 250821 **Personnel**: 3963

✠ △ **SYRACUSE VETERANS AFFAIRS MEDICAL CENTER**, 800 Irving Avenue, Zip 13210–2716; tel. 315/425–4400, **A**1 3 5 7 8 **F**1 2 3 4 5 8 12 18 20 22 26 28 29 30 31 33 34 35 36 38 39 40 45 46 47 49 50 53 54 56 57 58 59 60 61 62 63 64 65 67 70 71 74 75 77 78 79 81 82 84 85 86 87 90 91 92 94 95 97 98 100 101 104 105 106 107 108 111 126 128 132 135 146 147 148 152 153 154 **S** Department of Veterans Affairs, Perry Point, MD
Primary Contact: Judy A. Hayman, Ph.D., Director
CFO: Deborah Angell, Chief Financial Officer
CMO: Syed Asif Ali, M.D., Chief of Staff
CIO: James Stenson, Chief Information Officer
CHR: Mark Antinelli, Manager Human Resources
CNO: Cheryl Czajkowski, Associate Director Patient and Nursing Services
Web address: www.syracuse.va.gov/
Control: Veterans Affairs, Government, federal **Service**: General medical and surgical

Staffed Beds: 160 **Admissions**: 4598 **Census**: 119 **Outpatient Visits**: 535977 **Births**: 0 **Personnel**: 1857

★ ⇧ **UPSTATE UNIVERSITY HOSPITAL (330241)**, 750 East Adams Street, Zip 13210–2342; tel. 315/464–5540, (Includes GOLISANO CHILDREN'S HOSPITAL, 750 East Adams Street, Syracuse, NY, Zip 13210–2342; tel. 315/464–4570; UPSTATE UNIVERSITY HOSPITAL AT COMMUNITY GENERAL, 4900 Broad Road, Syracuse, NY, Zip 13215–2293; tel. 315/492–5011) **A**2 3 8 10 21 **F**3 5 6 9 12 13 15 16 17 18 19 20 22 24 25 26 28 29 30 31 33 34 35 36 37 38 39 40 41 43 44 45 46 47 48 49 50 51 52 53 54 55 56 57 58 59 61 64 65 66 68 70 74 76 78 79 81 82 84 85 86 87 88 89 90 92 93 95 96 97 98 100 101 102 104 107 108 109 110 111 112 114 115 118 119 120 121 123 124 126 128 129 130 131 132 135 136 138 141 142 145 146 147 148 149 150 154 **P**4
Primary Contact: Robert Corona, D.O., Interim Chief Executive Officer
COO: Robert Marzella, Chief Operations Officer
CFO: Stuart M Wright, CPA, Chief Financial Officer
CIO: Terry Wagner, Chief Information Officer
CHR: Eric Frost, Associate Vice President Human Resources
CMO: Amy Tucker, MD, Interim Chief Medical Officer
CNO: Nancy E. Page, MS, R.N., Chief Nursing Officer
Web address: www.upstate.edu/hospital
Control: State, Government, nonfederal **Service**: General medical and surgical

Staffed Beds: 612 **Admissions**: 33144 **Census**: 516 **Outpatient Visits**: 808732 **Births**: 900 **Total Expense ($000)**: 1038791 **Payroll Expense ($000)**: 364727 **Personnel**: 5402

VETERANS AFFAIRS MEDICAL CENTER See Syracuse Veterans Affairs Medical Center

TROY—Rensselaer County

BURDETT BIRTH CENTER (330409), 2215 Burdett Avenue, Suite 200, Zip 12180–2466; tel. 518/271–3393, (Nonreporting) **S** Trinity Health, Livonia, MI
Primary Contact: , MS, R.N.
Web address: www.burdettbirthcenter.org/
Control: Church operated, Nongovernment, not–for–profit **Service**: Obstetrics and gynecology

Staffed Beds: 15

★ **SAMARITAN HOSPITAL (330180)**, 2215 Burdett Avenue, Zip 12180–2475; tel. 518/271–3300, **A**3 10 **F**3 8 11 12 15 18 20 22 28 29 30 31 32 34 35 36 38 40 44 45 46 49 50 51 56 59 60 63 64 65 66 68 70 74 75 77 78 79 81 84 85 87 93 94 97 98 100 101 102 103 104 107 108 109 111 114 119 120 121 123 126 130 132 135 145 146 148 149 150 153 154 **S** Trinity Health, Livonia, MI
Primary Contact: James K. Reed, M.D., Chief Executive Officer
CFO: Daniel A Kochie, CPA, Chief Financial Officer
CMO: Daniel C Silverman, M.D., Chief Medical Officer, Acute Care Troy
CIO: Karen LeBlanc, Director, Applications
CNO: Jacqueline Priore, Chief Nursing Officer
Web address: www.nehealth.com
Control: Other not–for–profit (including NFP Corporation) **Service**: General medical and surgical

Staffed Beds: 183 **Admissions**: 8188 **Census**: 132 **Outpatient Visits**: 395060 **Births**: 0 **Total Expense ($000)**: 161399 **Payroll Expense ($000)**: 76467 **Personnel**: 1054

★ **SETON HEALTH ST. MARY'S HOSPITAL (330232)**, 1300 Massachusetts Avenue, Zip 12180–1695; tel. 518/268–5000, (Includes SETON HEALTH SYSTEM–ST. MARY'S HOSPITAL, 1300 Massachusetts Avenue, Troy, NY, Zip 12180; tel. 518/272–5000) **A**10 **F**5 11 15 34 35 40 44 45 46 47 48 49 51 54 57 59 66 75 93 108 111 115 130 135 144 146 147 148 149 150 **S** Trinity Health, Livonia, MI
Primary Contact: James K. Reed, M.D., Chief Executive Officer
CFO: Daniel A Kochie, CPA, Chief Financial Officer
CMO: Daniel C Silverman, M.D., Chief Medical Officer
CHR: Barbara McCandless, Vice President Human Resources
CNO: Carol Crucetti, R.N., Chief Nursing Officer
Web address: www.setonhealth.org
Control: Other not–for–profit (including NFP Corporation) **Service**: General medical and surgical

Staffed Beds: 20 **Admissions**: 1042 **Census**: 24 **Outpatient Visits**: 336845 **Births**: 0 **Total Expense ($000)**: 106936 **Payroll Expense ($000)**: 46441 **Personnel**: 491

UTICA—Oneida County

★ △ ⇧ **FAXTON ST. LUKE'S HEALTHCARE (330044)**, 1656 Champlin Avenue, Zip 13502–4830, Mailing Address: P.O. Box 479, Zip 13503–0479; tel. 315/624–6000, (Includes FAXTON CAMPUS, 1676 Sunset Avenue, Utica, NY, Zip 13502–5475; tel. 315/624–6000; ST. LUKE'S CAMPUS, 1656 Champlin Avenue, Utica, NY, Zip 13502–4830, Mailing Address: P.O. Box 479, Zip 13503–0479; tel. 315/624–6000) **A**2 3 7 10 21 **F**2 3 8 11 12 13 15 28 29 30 31 34 35 36 39 40 45 46 47 48 49 50 51 53 54 56 57 58 59 60 62 64 65 66 68 70 73 74 75 76 77 78 79 80 81 84 85 86 87 89 90 92 93 97 98 100 101 102 104 107 108 109 114 115 116 117 118 119 120 121 123 124 127 130 132 135 143 144 146 147 149 150 154 **P**6
Primary Contact: Scott H. Perra, FACHE, President and Chief Executive Officer
COO: Robert Scholefield, MS, R.N., Executive Vice President and Chief Operating Officer
CFO: Louis Aiello, Senior Vice President and Chief Financial Officer
CMO: Michael F Trevisani, M.D., Senior Vice President and Chief Medical Officer
CIO: John Lynch, Vice President and Chief Information Officer
CHR: Jack Davis, Vice President Human Resources
CNO: Linda McCormack–Miller, Chief Nursing Officer
Web address: www.mvhealthsystem.org
Control: Other not–for–profit (including NFP Corporation) **Service**: General medical and surgical

Staffed Beds: 278 **Admissions**: 13239 **Census**: 174 **Outpatient Visits**: 422684 **Births**: 1865 **Total Expense ($000)**: 297180 **Payroll Expense ($000)**: 143154 **Personnel**: 2029

☐ **MOHAWK VALLEY PSYCHIATRIC CENTER (334021)**, 1400 Noyes Street, Zip 13502–3854; tel. 315/738–3800, (Nonreporting) **A**1 10 **S** New York State Office of Mental Health, Albany, NY
Primary Contact: Colleen A. Sawyer, R.N., MSN, Executive Director
Web address: www.omh.ny.gov/omhweb/facilities/mvpc/facility.htm
Control: State, Government, nonfederal **Service**: Psychiatric

Staffed Beds: 614

★ ⇧ **ST. ELIZABETH MEDICAL CENTER (330245)**, 2209 Genesee Street, Zip 13501–5999; tel. 315/798–8100, **A**3 10 13 21 **F**3 11 15 17 18 20 22 24 26 29 30 32 34 35 36 37 40 43 45 50 54 57 58 59 61 64 65 66 68 70 74 75 77 79 80 81 84 85 87 89 92 93 97 98 100 101 102 104 107 108 110 114 115 119 126 127 129 130 131 132 135 146 147 148 149 150 **P**6
Primary Contact: Scott H. Perra, FACHE, Chief Executive Officer
CFO: Louis Aiello, Chief Financial Officer
CMO: Albert D'Accurzio, M.D., Medical Director
CIO: Robert Gillette, Chief Information Officer
CNO: Varinya Sheppard, R.N., Chief Nursing Officer
Web address: www.stemc.org
Control: Church operated, Nongovernment, not–for–profit **Service**: General medical and surgical

Staffed Beds: 181 **Admissions**: 10223 **Census**: 144 **Outpatient Visits**: 406689 **Births**: 0 **Total Expense ($000)**: 215138 **Payroll Expense ($000)**: 104446 **Personnel**: 1682

ST. LUKE'S CAMPUS See Faxton St. Luke's Healthcare, Utica

Many Facility Codes have changed. Please refer to the AHA Guide Code Chart.
© 2018 AHA Guide

VALHALLA—Westchester County

⊠ **BLYTHEDALE CHILDREN'S HOSPITAL (333301)**, 95 Bradhurst Avenue, Zip 10595–1697; tel. 914/592–7555, (Nonreporting) **A**1 3 10
Primary Contact: Larry L. Levine, President and Chief Executive Officer
COO: Maureen Desimone, Chief Operating Officer
CFO: John Canning, Chief Financial Officer
CMO: Joelle Mast, Ph.D., M.D., Chief Medical Officer
CHR: Ronald Gallo, Director Human Resources
Web address: www.blythedale.org
Control: Other not–for–profit (including NFP Corporation) **Service:** Children's rehabilitation

Staffed Beds: 92

⇑ **WESTCHESTER MEDICAL CENTER (330234)**, 100 Woods Road, Zip 10595–1530; tel. 914/493–7000, (Includes MARIA FARERI CHILDREN'S HOSPITAL, 100 Woods Road, Valhalla, NY, Zip 10595–1652; tel. 866/962–7337; MIDHUDSON REGIONAL HOSPITAL OF WESTCHESTER MEDICAL CENTER, 241 North Road, Poughkeepsie, NY, Zip 12601–1154; tel. 845/483–5000; Paul S Hochenberg, Executive Director) **A**2 3 5 8 10 21 **F**3 4 5 8 12 13 14 15 16 17 18 19 20 21 22 23 24 25 26 27 28 29 30 31 32 34 35 36 37 38 39 40 41 43 44 45 46 47 48 49 50 51 52 54 55 56 57 58 59 60 61 62 64 65 66 68 70 71 72 73 74 75 76 77 78 79 80 81 82 84 85 86 87 88 89 90 91 92 93 94 97 98 99 100 101 102 103 104 107 108 110 111 114 115 116 117 118 119 120 121 123 124 126 129 130 131 132 134 135 136 137 138 139 141 142 145 146 147 148 149 151 154 **P**6 **S** WMCHealth, Valhalla, NY
Primary Contact: Michael D. Israel, President and Chief Executive Officer
COO: Gary F Brudnicki, Senior Executive Vice President, Chief Operating Officer and Chief Financial Officer
CFO: Gary F Brudnicki, Senior Executive Vice President, Chief Operating Officer and Chief Financial Officer
CMO: Renee Garrick, M.D., Executive Medical Director
CIO: John Moustakakis, Senior Vice President Information Systems and Chief Information Officer
CHR: Jordy Rabinowitz, Senior Vice President Human Resources Operations
CNO: Patricia A. Wrobbel, Senior Vice President and Chief Nurse Executive
Web address: www.wmchealth.org
Control: Hospital district or authority, Government, nonfederal **Service:** General medical and surgical

Staffed Beds: 872 **Admissions:** 27184 **Census:** 648 **Outpatient Visits:** 269416 **Births:** 955 **Total Expense ($000):** 1248066 **Payroll Expense ($000):** 328155 **Personnel:** 4945

WALTON—Delaware County

UHS DELAWARE VALLEY HOSPITAL (331312), 1 Titus Place, Zip 13856–1498; tel. 607/865–2100, **A**10 18 **F**3 4 5 11 15 18 28 29 30 34 35 40 45 50 57 59 64 75 77 82 85 87 93 97 107 110 114 119 130 131 133 146 147 148 **S** United Health Services, Binghamton, NY
Primary Contact: Paul Summers, President and Chief Executive Officer
CFO: Paul Summers, Interim Chief Financial Officer
CMO: John Giannone, M.D., Delaware Valley Hospital Medical Director
CHR: Cynthia Gardepe, Director, Human Resources
CNO: Victoria Conkling, Vice President, Patient Services and Chief Nursing Officer
Web address: www.uhs.net/locations/
Control: Other not–for–profit (including NFP Corporation) **Service:** General medical and surgical

Staffed Beds: 25 **Admissions:** 460 **Census:** 12 **Outpatient Visits:** 171698 **Births:** 0 **Total Expense ($000):** 22581 **Payroll Expense ($000):** 7524 **Personnel:** 164

WAPPINGERS—Dutchess County

VETERAN AFFAIRS HUDSON VALLEY HEALTH CARE SYSTEM–CASTLE POINT CAMPUS See Veterans Affairs Hudson Valley Health Care System, Montrose

WARSAW—Wyoming County

☐ **WYOMING COUNTY COMMUNITY HOSPITAL (330008)**, 400 North Main Street, Zip 14569–1025; tel. 585/786–2233, (Nonreporting) **A**1 10 20
Primary Contact: Donald T. Eichenauer, Chief Executive Officer
COO: Michael Corcimiglia, Chief Operating Officer
CFO: John (Jack) T. Ormond, Director Finance and Revenue
CMO: Bilal Ahmed, M.D., Medical Director
CIO: Jane Beechler, Director Healthcare Information Systems
CHR: Peter J. Bendyna, Director Human Resources and Civil Service Administrator
CNO: Connie Almeter, Director of Nursing (Acute)
Web address: www.wcchs.net
Control: County, Government, nonfederal **Service:** General medical and surgical

Staffed Beds: 75

WARWICK—Orange County

⊠ **ST. ANTHONY COMMUNITY HOSPITAL (330205)**, 15 Maple Avenue, Zip 10990–1028; tel. 845/986–2276, (Nonreporting) **A**1 10 **S** WMCHealth, Valhalla, NY
Primary Contact: Mary Leahy, M.D., Chief Executive Officer
Web address: www.stanthonycommunityhosp.org
Control: Church operated, Nongovernment, not–for–profit **Service:** General medical and surgical

Staffed Beds: 60

WATERTOWN—Jefferson County

⊠ **SAMARITAN MEDICAL CENTER (330157)**, 830 Washington Street, Zip 13601–4034; tel. 315/785–4000, **A**1 3 10 12 13 20 **F**3 5 8 13 15 18 28 29 30 31 35 40 47 49 50 51 57 60 62 64 68 70 73 75 76 77 78 81 82 87 89 90 93 94 97 98 100 102 104 107 108 111 114 115 116 119 120 121 126 129 130 135 146 147 148 154 **P**6
Primary Contact: Thomas H. Carman, President and Chief Executive Officer
CFO: Sean Mills, Chief Financial Officer
CMO: Mario Victoria, M.D., Vice President, Medical Affairs
CIO: M Andrew Short, Vice President Information Services
CHR: Thomas Shatraw, Director Human Resources
CNO: Kimberly Thibert, R.N., MSN, Vice President Patient Care Services and Chief Nursing Officer
Web address: www.samaritanhealth.com
Control: Other not–for–profit (including NFP Corporation) **Service:** General medical and surgical

Staffed Beds: 195 **Admissions:** 8541 **Census:** 126 **Outpatient Visits:** 296560 **Births:** 1660 **Total Expense ($000):** 213249 **Payroll Expense ($000):** 99664 **Personnel:** 1331

WELLSVILLE—Allegany County

⊠ **JONES MEMORIAL HOSPITAL (330096)**, 191 North Main Street, Zip 14895–1150, Mailing Address: P.O. Box 72, Zip 14895–0072; tel. 585/593–1100, **A**1 10 20 **F**8 11 13 15 17 28 29 30 31 34 35 36 40 43 50 57 59 61 64 68 70 75 77 78 79 81 85 93 97 107 110 114 119 129 131 132 133 146 147 149 **S** University of Rochester Medical Center, Rochester, NY
Primary Contact: Eva Benedict, R.N., President and Chief Executive Officer
CFO: James Helms, Vice President Finance
CMO: William Coch, M.D., Medical Director
CIO: James Helms, Vice President Finance
CHR: Brenda Sobeck, Director of Human Resources
CNO: Donna Bliven, Vice President Patient Care Services and Chief Nursing Officer
Web address: www.jmhny.org
Control: Other not–for–profit (including NFP Corporation) **Service:** General medical and surgical

Staffed Beds: 33 **Admissions:** 1806 **Census:** 19 **Outpatient Visits:** 134171 **Births:** 375 **Total Expense ($000):** 39769 **Payroll Expense ($000):** 18950 **Personnel:** 345

WEST HAVERSTRAW—Rockland County

☐ △ **HELEN HAYES HOSPITAL (330405)**, Route 9W, Zip 10993–1127; tel. 845/786–4000, (Nonreporting) **A**1 3 5 7 10
Primary Contact: Edmund Coletti, Chief Executive Officer
COO: Kathleen Martucci, Chief Operating Officer
CFO: Lori A. Meszler, Chief Financial Officer
CIO: Virgil Ennis, Chief Information Officer
CHR: Patrick J. Ryan, Chief Human Resources Officer
Web address: www.helenhayeshospital.org
Control: State, Government, nonfederal **Service:** Rehabilitation

Staffed Beds: 155

WEST ISLIP—Suffolk County

⊠ **GOOD SAMARITAN HOSPITAL MEDICAL CENTER (330286)**, 1000 Montauk Highway, Zip 11795–4927; tel. 631/376–3000, (Total facility includes 100 beds in nursing home–type unit) **A**1 2 3 5 10 12 13 **F**3 8 11 12 13 15 17 18 20 22 24 26 28 29 30 31 32 34 35 40 41 43 45 46 47 48 49 50 51 54 55 56 57 59 64 65 66 68 70 72 73 74 75 76 77 78 79 80 81 82 84 85 86 87 88 89 91 93 94 96 97 99 100 102 107 108 110 111 115 117 119 120 121 123 124 126 128 129 130 131 132 142 146 147 149 154 **S** Catholic Health Services of Long Island, Rockville Centre, NY
Primary Contact: Thomas Ockers, Executive Vice President and Chief Administrative Officer
CFO: Dan Macksood, Regional Senior Vice President and Chief Financial Officer
CMO: Jerome Weiner, M.D., Senior Vice President Medical Affairs
CIO: Marcy Dunn, Vice President Information Services and Chief Information Officer
CHR: Lori Spina, Vice President Human Resources
Web address: www.good–samaritan–hospital.org
Control: Church operated, Nongovernment, not–for–profit **Service:** General medical and surgical

Staffed Beds: 522 **Admissions:** 24442 **Census:** 464 **Outpatient Visits:** 208261 **Births:** 2601 **Total Expense ($000):** 680446 **Payroll Expense ($000):** 310589 **Personnel:** 3238

NY

Hospital, Medicare Provider Number, Address, Telephone, Approval, Facility, and Physician Codes, Health Care System

★ American Hospital Association (AHA) membership
☐ The Joint Commission accreditation
○ Healthcare Facilities Accreditation Program
◇ DNV Healthcare Inc. accreditation
⇑ Center for Improvement in Healthcare Quality Accreditation
△ Commission on Accreditation of Rehabilitation Facilities (CARF) accreditation

WEST POINT—Orange County

⊞ **KELLER ARMY COMMUNITY HOSPITAL**, 900 Washington Road,
Zip 10996–1197, Mailing Address: US Military Academy, Building 900,
Zip 10996–1197; tel. 845/938–5169, **A**1 3 5 **F**3 4 5 7 8 13 15 29 34 35 36 38
39 40 43 45 50 52 54 58 59 65 67 68 70 75 76 77 79 81 82 87 89 91 93 97
98 99 100 101 102 104 107 110 111 112 115 119 128 130 131 135 143 144
147 149 151 154 **S** Department of the Army, Office of the Surgeon General, Falls
Church, VA
Primary Contact: Colonel Eric B. Sones, Commander
CIO: Patrick McGuinness, Chief Information Management
CHR: Margaret Greco, Chief Human Resources
Web address: www.kach.amedd.army.mil/SitePages/Home.aspx
Control: Army, Government, federal **Service**: General medical and surgical

**Staffed Beds: 16 Admissions: 972 Census: 5 Outpatient Visits: 66884
Births: 110 Personnel: 602**

WEST SENECA—Erie County

☐ **WESTERN NEW YORK Children's hospital psychiatric CENTER**, 1010 East
and West Road, Zip 14224–3602; tel. 716/677–7000, **A**1 3 5 **F**32 34 38 54 59
64 75 77 99 100 101 104 130 132 134 135 146 149 **S** New York State Office
of Mental Health, Albany, NY
Primary Contact: Kathe Hayes, Executive Director
COO: David Privett, Deputy Director
CMO: Patrick Stein, M.D., Clinical Director
CIO: Dan Hrubiak, Associate Computer Program Analyst
CHR: Charles Siewert, Director Human Resources
Web address: www.omh.ny.gov
Control: State, Government, nonfederal **Service**: Children's hospital psychiatric

**Staffed Beds: 46 Admissions: 151 Census: 37 Outpatient Visits: 2086
Births: 0**

WESTFIELD—Chautauqua County

★ **WESTFIELD MEMORIAL HOSPITAL (330166)**, 189 East Main Street,
Zip 14787–1195; tel. 716/326–4921, (Nonreporting) **A**10 **S** Allegheny Health
Network, Pittsburgh, PA
Primary Contact: Valarie Jackson, President
COO: Patricia Ballman, Director
CFO: Tina Gowen, System Controller
CMO: Russell Elwell, M.D., Medical Director
CIO: Cindy Harper, Manager Patient Data
Web address: www.wmhinc.org
Control: Other not–for–profit (including NFP Corporation) **Service**: General
medical and surgical

Staffed Beds: 4

WHITE PLAINS—Westchester County

⊞ △ **BURKE REHABILITATION HOSPITAL (330404)**, 785 Mamaroneck Avenue,
Zip 10605–2523; tel. 914/597–2500, **A**1 3 5 7 10 **F**11 28 29 30 34 35 53 54
57 58 59 74 75 77 87 90 92 93 94 95 96 99 100 104 130 131 132 133 146
148 149 **S** Montefiore Health System, Bronx, NY
Primary Contact: Jeffrey Menkes, President and Chief Executive Officer
COO: Brian M Swift, Senior Administrator Plant Operations
CFO: John Stewart, Director Finance
CIO: Cathy Dwyer, Senior Administrator Information Systems
CHR: Annette Bucci, Vice President Human Resources
CNO: Marie Spencer, Chief Nursing Officer and Senior Administrator
Web address: www.burke.org
Control: Other not–for–profit (including NFP Corporation) **Service**: Rehabilitation

**Staffed Beds: 150 Admissions: 2521 Census: 129 Outpatient Visits:
124897 Births: 0 Total Expense ($000): 85160 Payroll Expense
($000): 49025 Personnel: 665**

NEW YORK–PRESBYTERIAN HOSPITAL, WESTCHESTER DIVISION See New
York–Presbyterian Hospital, New York

⊞ **WHITE PLAINS HOSPITAL CENTER (330304)**, 41 East Post Road,
Zip 10601–4699; tel. 914/681–0600, **A**1 2 3 5 10 **F**3 11 12 13 14 15 17 18 20
22 26 29 30 31 32 34 35 36 38 40 41 43 44 45 46 47 49 50 51 54 55 56 57
58 59 60 61 63 64 65 66 68 70 72 73 74 75 76 77 78 79 81 82 84 85 86 87
89 92 93 97 100 101 102 104 107 108 110 111 115 116 117 118 119 120
121 122 123 124 126 129 130 131 132 135 144 145 146 147 148 149 150
153 154 **P**5 6 **S** Montefiore Health System, Bronx, NY
Primary Contact: Susan Fox, President and Chief Executive Officer
COO: Edward F Leonard, Executive Vice President and Chief Operating Officer
CFO: Joseph Guarracino, Senior Vice President and Chief Financial Officer
CMO: Michael Palumbo, M.D., Executive Vice President and Medical Director
CIO: Rick McCarthy, Chief Information Officer
CHR: John Sanchez, Vice President Human Resources
CNO: Leigh McMahon, MS, R.N., Senior Vice President Patient Care Services and
Chief Nursing Officer
Web address: www.wphospital.org
Control: Other not–for–profit (including NFP Corporation) **Service**: General
medical and surgical

**Staffed Beds: 292 Admissions: 18162 Census: 224 Outpatient Visits:
366575 Births: 1895 Total Expense ($000): 606582 Payroll Expense
($000): 298821 Personnel: 2993**

WILLIAMSVILLE—Erie County

MILLARD FILLMORE SUBURBAN HOSPITAL See Kaleida Health, Buffalo

YONKERS—Westchester County

ANDRUS PAVILION See St. John's Riverside Hospital, Yonkers

⊞ **SAINT JOSEPH'S MEDICAL CENTER (330006)**, 127 South Broadway,
Zip 10701–4006; tel. 914/378–7000, (Total facility includes 200 beds in nursing
home–type unit) **A**1 3 5 10 **F**2 3 4 5 7 11 15 17 18 29 30 31 34 35 38 39 40
45 47 48 49 54 56 57 58 59 60 61 62 64 68 70 74 75 77 78 79 81 82 85 87
89 93 94 97 98 99 100 101 102 103 104 105 106 107 108 110 111 115 118
119 128 130 132 134 135 143 144 146 152 153 154 **P**5
Primary Contact: Michael J. Spicer, President and Chief Executive Officer
COO: Frances Casola, Senior Vice President Operations
CFO: Frank Hagan, Senior Vice President Finance
CMO: James Neuendorf, M.D., Medical Director
CIO: Deborah Di Bernardo, Chief Information Officer
CHR: Dean Civitello, Vice President Human Resources
CNO: Margaret M Cusumano, R.N., MSN, Vice President Patient Care Services and
Chief Nursing Officer
Web address: www.saintjosephs.org
Control: Other not–for–profit (including NFP Corporation) **Service**: General
medical and surgical

**Staffed Beds: 473 Admissions: 7460 Census: 398 Outpatient Visits:
1088207 Births: 0 Total Expense ($000): 253478 Payroll Expense
($000): 119092 Personnel: 1737**

☐ **ST. JOHN'S RIVERSIDE HOSPITAL (330208)**, 967 North Broadway,
Zip 10701–1399; tel. 914/964–4444, (Includes ANDRUS PAVILION, 967 North
Broadway, Yonkers, NY, Zip 10701–1399; tel. 914/964–4444; ST. JOHN'S
RIVERSIDE HOSPITAL – PARK CARE PAVILION, Two Park Avenue, Yonkers, NY,
Zip 10703–3497; tel. 914/964–7300; ST. JOHN'S RIVERSIDE HOSPITAL – DOBBS
FERRY PAVILION, 128 Ashford Avenue, Dobbs Ferry, NY, Zip 10522–1896;
tel. 914/693–0700) **A**1 2 3 10 **F**3 4 5 8 11 12 13 15 18 29 30 31 34 35 36 37
40 41 45 49 50 51 55 56 57 59 60 61 64 68 70 73 74 76 77 78 79 81 82 83
84 85 93 97 107 108 110 111 114 115 118 119 124 126 129 130 131 132
135 136 143 146 147 148 149 151 152 154 **P**5
Primary Contact: Ronald J. Corti, President and Chief Executive Officer
COO: Lynn M. Nelson, R.N., R.N., Chief Nursing Officer and Chief Operating Officer
CFO: Dennis M. Keane, Vice President Finance and Chief Financial Officer
CMO: Paul Antonecchia, M.D., Vice President Medical Affairs and Chief Medical
Officer
CIO: Peter Weidner, Director Information Technology
CHR: Marc Leff, Vice President Human Resources
CNO: Lynn M. Nelson, R.N., R.N., Chief Nursing Officer and Chief Operating Officer
Web address: www.riversidehealth.org
Control: Other not–for–profit (including NFP Corporation) **Service**: General
medical and surgical

**Staffed Beds: 376 Admissions: 16191 Census: 243 Outpatient Visits:
235308 Births: 1142 Total Expense ($000): 261187 Payroll Expense
($000): 116165 Personnel: 1453**

Many Facility Codes have changed. Please refer to the AHA Guide Code Chart.   © 2018 AHA Guide

NY

NORTH CAROLINA

AHOSKIE—Hertford County

⊞ **VIDANT ROANOKE–CHOWAN HOSPITAL (340099)**, 500 South Academy Street, Zip 27910–3261, Mailing Address: P.O. Box 1385, Zip 27910–1385; tel. 252/209–3000, **A**1 10 20 **F**3 11 13 15 28 29 30 31 34 35 40 43 44 45 53 56 57 59 64 68 70 75 76 77 78 79 81 82 85 86 87 89 92 98 100 101 102 103 107 108 110 111 114 118 119 120 121 123 129 130 132 146 148 149 154 **S** Vidant Health, Greenville, NC
Primary Contact: Patrick Heins, President
CFO: Jon Graham, Chief Finance Officer
CMO: David Lingle, Directors Council Chairman and Chief of Staff
CHR: Debbie Sisler, Director, Human Resource
CNO: Judy Bruno, Chief Nursing Officer
Web address: www.vidanthealth.com
Control: Other not–for–profit (including NFP Corporation) **Service:** General medical and surgical

Staffed Beds: 71 **Admissions:** 4937 **Census:** 61 **Outpatient Visits:** 67600 **Births:** 339 **Total Expense ($000):** 73889 **Payroll Expense ($000):** 27177 **Personnel:** 565

ALBEMARLE—Stanly County

⊞ **CAROLINAS HEALTHCARE SYSTEM STANLY (340119)**, 301 Yadkin Street, Zip 28001–3441, Mailing Address: P.O. Box 1489, Zip 28002–1489; tel. 704/984–4000, **A**1 2 10 **F**3 11 13 15 18 28 29 30 31 34 35 39 40 45 46 49 55 57 59 61 63 64 68 70 74 75 76 77 78 79 81 82 85 86 87 89 91 93 98 100 101 102 103 107 108 110 111 114 115 118 119 120 121 123 129 130 131 132 146 148 149 154 **S** Atrium Health, Charlotte, NC
Primary Contact: Brian Freeman, President
CFO: Nick Samilo, Vice President Fiscal Services and Chief Financial Officer
CMO: Paul D'Amico, M.D., Chief of Staff
CNO: Judy Doran, R.N., Vice President of Hospital Services and Chief Nurse Executive
Web address: www.stanly.org
Control: Hospital district or authority, Government, nonfederal **Service:** General medical and surgical

Staffed Beds: 109 **Admissions:** 3987 **Census:** 43 **Outpatient Visits:** 78048 **Births:** 560 **Total Expense ($000):** 84382 **Payroll Expense ($000):** 30512 **Personnel:** 477

ASHEBORO—Randolph County

⊞ **RANDOLPH HOSPITAL (340123)**, 364 White Oak Street, Zip 27203–5400, Mailing Address: P.O. Box 1048, Zip 27204–1048; tel. 336/625–5151, **A**1 2 10 **F**3 8 13 15 18 28 29 30 31 34 35 40 45 49 50 53 56 57 64 68 70 74 75 76 77 78 79 80 81 84 85 86 87 89 91 92 93 94 96 97 107 109 110 111 114 115 119 120 121 123 130 131 132 135 143 146 148 154 **P**6 **S** Atrium Health, Charlotte, NC
Primary Contact: Steven E. Eblin, Chief Executive Officer and President
CMO: Charles West, M.D., Chief Medical Officer
CIO: Angela Burgess, Chief Information Officer
Web address: www.randolphhospital.org
Control: Other not–for–profit (including NFP Corporation) **Service:** General medical and surgical

Staffed Beds: 85 **Admissions:** 4967 **Census:** 49 **Outpatient Visits:** 96697 **Births:** 696 **Total Expense ($000):** 97291 **Payroll Expense ($000):** 38598 **Personnel:** 901

ASHEVILLE—Buncombe County

★ **ASHEVILLE SPECIALTY HOSPITAL (342017)**, 428 Biltmore Avenue, 4th Floor, Zip 28801–4502; tel. 828/213–5400, (Nonreporting) **A**3 10 **S** Mission Health System, Asheville, NC
Primary Contact: Julie A. Dikos, MSN, R.N., President and Chief Executive Officer
CFO: Gregg Dixon, Chief Financial Officer
CMO: Ronnie Jacobs, M.D., Chief Medical Officer
CIO: Megan Serzan, Director of Quality, Compliance, Risk & Safety
CNO: Josephine Picker, MSN, R.N., Director of Nursing
Web address: www.missionhospitals.org/acute–care
Control: Partnership, Investor–owned (for–profit) **Service:** Acute long–term care hospital

Staffed Beds: 34

⊞ △ **CAREPARTNERS HEALTH SERVICES (343025)**, 68 Sweeten Creek Road, Zip 28803–2318, Mailing Address: P.O. Box 15025, Zip 28813–0025; tel. 828/277–4800, (Nonreporting) **A**1 3 7 10 **S** Mission Health System, Asheville, NC
Primary Contact: Tracy Buchanan, Chief Executive Officer and President
CFO: Gregg Dixon, Chief Financial Officer
CMO: Michael Parmer, Chief Medical Officer
CIO: Jennifer Scott, Director of Informatics
CHR: Katy Pless, Director of Human Resources
CNO: Cathleen Adams, Chief Nursing Officer
Web address: www.carepartners.org
Control: Other not–for–profit (including NFP Corporation) **Service:** Rehabilitation

Staffed Beds: 80

⊞ **CHARLES GEORGE VETERANS AFFAIRS MEDICAL CENTER**, 1100 Tunnel Road, Zip 28805–2087; tel. 828/298–7911, (Total facility includes 73 beds in nursing home–type unit) **A**1 3 5 **F**3 4 5 12 18 20 22 24 26 28 29 30 31 34 35 36 38 39 40 45 49 50 54 56 57 58 59 61 63 64 65 68 70 74 75 77 78 79 81 82 83 84 85 86 87 91 92 93 94 97 98 100 101 102 104 107 108 111 114 115 119 128 129 130 132 135 143 145 146 147 148 149 153 154 **S** Department of Veterans Affairs, Perry Point, MD
Primary Contact: Cynthia Breyfogle, FACHE, Director
CFO: Margaret Wilkes, Chief Fiscal Officer
CMO: Webster Carl Bazemore, M.D., Interim Chief of Staff
CIO: Carla McLendon, Director Information Resource Management Services
CHR: James Sitlinger, Chief Human Resources Management
CNO: David Przestrzelski, Associate Director, Patient Care Services and Chief Nursing Executive
Web address: www.asheville.va.gov/
Control: Veterans Affairs, Government, federal **Service:** General medical and surgical

Staffed Beds: 174 **Admissions:** 4843 **Census:** 130 **Outpatient Visits:** 546340 **Births:** 0 **Total Expense ($000):** 324733 **Payroll Expense ($000):** 159903 **Personnel:** 1927

⊞ **MISSION HOSPITAL (340002)**, 509 Biltmore Avenue, Zip 28801–4690; tel. 828/213–1111, (Includes MISSION CHILDREN'S HOSPITAL, 509 Biltmore Avenue, Asheville, NC, Zip 28801–4601; tel. 828/213–1111; MISSION HOSPITAL – ST. JOSEPH'S CAMPUS, 428 Biltmore Avenue, Asheville, NC, Zip 28801–9839; tel. 828/213–1111; MISSION HOSPITAL, 509 Biltmore Avenue, Asheville, NC, Zip 28801–4690; tel. 828/213–1111; Jill Hoggard Green, Ph.D., R.N., President) **A**1 2 3 5 10 **F**3 7 8 12 13 15 17 18 19 20 22 24 26 28 29 30 31 32 34 35 36 37 38 39 40 43 44 45 46 47 48 49 50 51 53 54 55 56 57 58 59 61 64 65 68 70 71 72 73 74 75 76 77 78 79 80 81 82 84 85 86 87 88 89 91 92 93 94 95 97 98 99 100 102 103 104 107 108 110 111 114 115 116 117 118 119 120 121 123 124 126 129 130 131 132 135 142 143 145 146 148 149 150 153 154 **P**6 **S** Mission Health System, Asheville, NC
Primary Contact: Jill Hoggard Green, Ph.D., R.N., President
CFO: Paul L McDowell, Deputy Chief Financial Officer
CMO: William Hathaway, M.D., Chief Medical Officer
CIO: Jon Brown, Chief Information Officer
CHR: Sheila M Meadows, Chief Human Resources Officer
CNO: Karen M Olsen, R.N., Chief Nursing Officer
Web address: www.mission–health.org
Control: Other not–for–profit (including NFP Corporation) **Service:** General medical and surgical

Staffed Beds: 763 **Admissions:** 41428 **Census:** 584 **Outpatient Visits:** 561336 **Births:** 3945 **Total Expense ($000):** 1119374 **Payroll Expense ($000):** 309925 **Personnel:** 5405

Hospital, Medicare Provider Number, Address, Telephone, Approval, Facility, and Physician Codes, Health Care System

★ American Hospital Association (AHA) membership
☐ The Joint Commission accreditation
○ Healthcare Facilities Accreditation Program
◇ DNV Healthcare Inc. accreditation
⇑ Center for Improvement in Healthcare Quality Accreditation
△ Commission on Accreditation of Rehabilitation Facilities (CARF) accreditation

NC

BERMUDA RUN—Davie County

★ **WAKE FOREST BAPTIST HEALTH–DAVIE MEDICAL CENTER (341313)**, 329 NC Highway 801 North, Zip 27006; tel. 336/998–1300, **A**10 **F**3 15 28 29 30 34 35 40 45 50 56 57 59 64 68 74 75 77 79 81 85 87 93 102 107 115 119 129 130 131 133 146 **S** Wake Forest Baptist Health, Winston–Salem, NC
Primary Contact: Chad J. Brown, M.P.H., President
CFO: Danny Squires, Chief Financial Officer
CMO: Bret Nicks, M.D., Chief Medical Officer and Chief of Staff
CIO: William Showalter, Senior Vice President and Chief Information Officer, Information Technology Services
CHR: Jennifer Bandy, Human Resource Business Partner
CNO: Susan T. Bachmeier, MSN, R.N., Chief Nursing Officer
Web address: www.wakehealth.edu/Davie–Medical–Center
Control: Other not–for–profit (including NFP Corporation) **Service**: General medical and surgical

Staffed Beds: 50 **Admissions**: 363 **Census**: 6 **Outpatient Visits**: 50101
Births: 0 **Total Expense ($000)**: 43704 **Payroll Expense ($000)**: 13542
Personnel: 231

BLACK MOUNTAIN—Buncombe County

JULIAN F. KEITH ALCOHOL AND DRUG ABUSE TREATMENT CENTER (344023), 201 Tabernacle Road, Zip 28711–2599; tel. 828/669–3400, (Nonreporting) **A**10
Primary Contact: W Douglas. Baker, Director
CFO: Jackie Maurer, Fiscal Officer
CMO: Anthony Burnett, M.D., Medical Director
CHR: Faye Hamlin, Manager Human Resources
Web address: www.jfkadatc.net
Control: State, Government, nonfederal **Service**: Alcoholism and other chemical dependency

Staffed Beds: 80

BOLIVIA—Brunswick County

⊞ **NOVANT HEALTH BRUNSWICK MEDICAL CENTER (340158)**, 240 Hospital Drive NE, Zip 28422–8346; tel. 910/721–1000, (Nonreporting) **A**1 10 **S** Novant Health, Winston Salem, NC
Primary Contact: Shelbourn Stevens, President and Chief Operating Officer
CFO: Fred M Hargett, Executive Vice President and Chief Financial Officer
CMO: Thomas Zweng, Executive Vice President and Chief Medical Officer
CIO: David B Garrett, Senior Vice President and Chief Information Officer
CHR: Janet Smith-Hill, Executive Vice President and Chief Human Resources Officer
CNO: Lorna J Ward, MSN, R.N., Chief Nursing Officer
Web address: www.novanthealth.org
Control: Other not–for–profit (including NFP Corporation) **Service**: General medical and surgical

Staffed Beds: 53

BOONE—Watauga County

⊞ **WATAUGA MEDICAL CENTER (340051)**, 336 Deerfield Road, Zip 28607–5008, Mailing Address: P.O. Box 2600, Zip 28607–2600; tel. 828/262–4100, **A**1 2 10 **F**3 5 13 15 17 18 20 22 26 28 29 30 31 32 34 35 38 40 44 45 46 47 48 49 50 53 54 57 59 64 70 73 75 76 77 78 81 82 84 85 86 87 91 92 93 96 107 108 110 111 114 115 118 119 120 121 122 123 124 129 130 131 132 135 144 145 146 147 148 149 154 **P**6 **S** Appalachian Regional Healthcare System, Boone, NC
Primary Contact: Charles Mantooth, President and Chief Executive Officer
CFO: Kevin B May, Chief Financial Officer
CMO: Herman A Godwin, M.D., Jr Senior Vice President and Medical Director
CIO: Mike Quinto, Chief Information Officer
CHR: Amy J. Crabbe, Senior Vice President Human Resources
Web address: www.https://apprhs.org/contact-us
Control: Other not–for–profit (including NFP Corporation) **Service**: General medical and surgical

Staffed Beds: 99 **Admissions**: 3982 **Census**: 36 **Outpatient Visits**: 124683
Births: 621 **Total Expense ($000)**: 119124 **Payroll Expense ($000)**: 37941
Personnel: 634

BREVARD—Transylvania County

⊞ **TRANSYLVANIA REGIONAL HOSPITAL (341319)**, 260 Hospital Drive, Zip 28712–3378; tel. 828/884–9111, (Total facility includes 10 beds in nursing home–type unit) **A**1 10 18 **F**3 11 15 18 28 29 30 31 34 35 40 45 49 51 53 54 56 64 70 75 77 78 79 80 81 85 91 93 96 97 101 104 107 108 110 111 114 118 119 128 129 130 131 133 135 146 147 149 154 **P**6 **S** Mission Health System, Asheville, NC
Primary Contact: Michele Pilon, President and Chief Nursing Officer
CFO: Theresa M Parker, Regional Finance Director
CMO: Mark Lemel, Chief of Staff
CIO: Ed Coye, Director Information Technology
CHR: Susan Stevens, Human Resources Strategic Business Partner
CNO: Melina Arrowood, Interim President and Chief Nursing Officer
Web address: www.trhospital.org
Control: Other not–for–profit (including NFP Corporation) **Service**: General medical and surgical

Staffed Beds: 40 **Admissions**: 1646 **Census**: 23 **Outpatient Visits**: 84680
Births: 0 **Total Expense ($000)**: 66535 **Payroll Expense ($000)**: 18072
Personnel: 283

BRYSON CITY—Swain County

★ **SWAIN COMMUNITY HOSPITAL (341305)**, 45 Plateau Street, Zip 28713–4200; tel. 828/488–2155, (Nonreporting) **A**10 18 **S** Duke LifePoint Healthcare, Brentwood, TN
Primary Contact: Steve Heatherly, Chief Executive Officer
CMO: David Zimmerman, M.D., Chief of Staff
Web address: www.westcare.org
Control: Other not–for–profit (including NFP Corporation) **Service**: General medical and surgical

Staffed Beds: 25

BURGAW—Pender County

⊞ **PENDER MEMORIAL HOSPITAL (341307)**, 507 East Freemont Street, Zip 28425–5131; tel. 910/259–5451, (Total facility includes 43 beds in nursing home–type unit) **A**1 10 18 **F**3 11 15 29 34 35 40 45 54 56 57 59 62 64 81 85 87 93 96 107 110 114 119 128 130 133 143 146 148 149 **S** New Hanover Regional Medical Center, Wilmington, NC
Primary Contact: Ruth Glaser, President
CFO: Morrison Hall, Chief Financial Officer
CMO: Heather Davis, M.D., Chief of Staff
CIO: Ashley Hernandez, Chief Information Technology Officer
CHR: Lori McKoy, Business Partner
CNO: Cynthia Faulkner, R.N., Chief Nursing Executive
Web address: www.pendermemorial.org
Control: County, Government, nonfederal **Service**: General medical and surgical

Staffed Beds: 68 **Admissions**: 764 **Census**: 45 **Outpatient Visits**: 48775
Births: 0 **Total Expense ($000)**: 22610 **Payroll Expense ($000)**: 7613
Personnel: 217

BURLINGTON—Alamance County

⊞ **ALAMANCE REGIONAL MEDICAL CENTER (340070)**, 1240 Huffman Mill Road, Zip 27215–8700, Mailing Address: P.O. Box 202, Zip 27216–0202; tel. 336/538–7000, **A**1 2 10 **F**3 8 9 12 13 15 18 20 22 24 26 28 29 30 31 32 34 35 36 38 39 40 44 45 46 47 49 50 53 54 57 58 59 60 64 66 68 70 73 74 75 76 77 78 79 81 82 84 85 86 87 89 91 93 94 96 97 98 100 101 102 103 107 108 110 111 115 117 118 119 120 121 123 126 130 131 132 135 144 145 146 147 148 154 **P**6 **S** Cone Health, Greensboro, NC
Primary Contact: Preston W. Hammock, President
CFO: Rex Street, Senior Vice President and Chief Financial Officer
CMO: Andrew Lamb, M.D., Chief of Staff
CIO: Terri Andrews, Director Information Technology
Web address: www.armc.com
Control: Other not–for–profit (including NFP Corporation) **Service**: General medical and surgical

Staffed Beds: 200 **Admissions**: 10126 **Census**: 112 **Outpatient Visits**: 294926 **Births**: 1305 **Total Expense ($000)**: 228062 **Payroll Expense ($000)**: 74691 **Personnel**: 1579

BUTNER—Granville County

☐ **CENTRAL REGIONAL HOSPITAL (344004)**, 300 Veazey Road, Zip 27509–1668; tel. 919/764–2000, (Nonreporting) **A**1 3 5 10
Primary Contact: Walter Edwin. Beal, Chief Executive Officer
COO: Cliff Hood, Chief Operating Officer
CFO: Pamela Richardson, Business Manager
CMO: Alan Cook, Chief Medical Officer
CIO: Joe Thurber, Director Information Technology
CHR: Kathleen Tardif, Director of Human Resources
CNO: Diana Holmes, Chief Nursing Officer
Control: State, Government, nonfederal **Service**: Psychiatric

Staffed Beds: 382

NC

CAMP LEJEUNE—Onslow County

☒ **NAVAL HOSPITAL CAMP LEJEUNE**, 100 Brewster Boulevard, Zip 28547–2538, Mailing Address: P.O. Box 10100, Zip 28547–0100; tel. 910/450–4300, (Nonreporting) **A**1 3 5 **S** Bureau of Medicine and Surgery, Department of the Navy, Falls Church, VA
Primary Contact: Captain Rick Freedman, Commanding Officer
Web address: www.med.navy.mil/sites/nhcl/Pages/default.aspx
Control: Navy, Government, federal **Service**: General medical and surgical

Staffed Beds: 117

CARY—Wake County

☒ **WAKEMED CARY HOSPITAL (340173)**, 1900 Kildaire Farm Road, Zip 27518–6616; tel. 919/350–8000, **A**1 10 **F**3 7 12 13 15 18 20 26 28 29 30 31 35 40 44 45 46 48 49 50 54 61 64 68 70 73 74 75 76 77 79 81 82 85 86 92 100 107 110 111 114 115 118 119 126 129 130 132 146 147 154 **P**6 **S** WakeMed Health & Hospitals, Raleigh, NC
Primary Contact: Donald R. Gintzig, President and Chief Executive Officer
COO: Denise Wilder Warren, R.N., Executive Vice President and Chief Operating Officer
CMO: West Paul, M.D., Ph.D., Senior Vice President, Chief Quality and Medical Staff Officer
CIO: Denton Arledge, Vice President and Chief Information Officer
CHR: Jeanene R Martin, M.P.H., Senior Vice President Human Resources and Chief People Officer
CNO: Cindy Boily, MSN, R.N., Senior Vice President and Chief Nursing Officer
Web address: www.wakemed.org
Control: Other not–for–profit (including NFP Corporation) **Service**: General medical and surgical

Staffed Beds: 156 Admissions: 11152 Census: 123 Outpatient Visits: 262271 **Births:** 2352 **Total Expense ($000):** 184247 **Payroll Expense ($000):** 66962 **Personnel:** 1065

CHAPEL HILL—Orange County

☒ △ **UNIVERSITY OF NORTH CAROLINA HOSPITALS (340061)**, 101 Manning Drive, Zip 27514–4220; tel. 984/974–1000, (Includes N.C. WOMEN'S HOSPITAL, 101 Manning Drive, Chapel Hill, NC, Zip 27514–4220; tel. 984/974–1000; Gary L Park, President; NORTH CAROLINA CHILDREN'S HOSPITAL, 101 Manning Drive, Chapel Hill, NC, Zip 27514–4220; tel. 984/974–1000; UNC HEALTH CARE HILLSBOROUGH CAMPUS, 430 Waterstone Drive, Hillsborough, NC, Zip 27278–9078; tel. 984/215–2000; Gary L Park, Chief Executive Officer; UNC LINEBERGER COMPREHENSIVE CANCER CENTER, 450 West Drive, Chapel Hill, NC, Zip 27599–5020; tel. 919/966–3036) **A**1 2 3 5 7 8 10 **F**3 4 5 7 8 9 11 12 13 14 15 16 17 18 19 20 21 22 23 24 25 26 27 28 29 30 31 32 34 35 36 38 39 40 41 43 44 45 46 47 48 49 50 51 52 53 54 55 56 57 58 59 60 61 62 63 64 65 66 68 70 72 73 74 75 76 77 78 79 80 81 82 83 84 85 86 87 88 89 90 91 92 93 94 96 97 98 99 100 101 102 103 104 106 107 108 110 111 114 115 116 117 118 119 120 121 123 124 126 129 130 131 132 134 135 136 137 138 139 140 141 142 143 144 145 146 147 148 149 150 151 154 **S** UNC Health Care, Chapel Hill, NC
Primary Contact: Gary L. Park, President
CFO: Christopher Ellington, Executive Vice President and Chief Financial Officer
CMO: Tony Lindsey, M.D., Chief of Staff
CIO: Tracy Parham
CHR: Scott Doak, System Vice President, Human Resources
CNO: Catherine Madigan, Chief Nursing Officer
Web address: www.unchealthcare.org
Control: State, Government, nonfederal **Service**: General medical and surgical

Staffed Beds: 929 Admissions: 39984 Census: 761 Outpatient Visits: 1441160 **Births:** 3724 **Total Expense ($000):** 1570064 **Payroll Expense ($000):** 518616 **Personnel:** 8410

CHARLOTTE—Mecklenburg County

☒ **CAROLINAS CONTINUECARE HOSPITAL AT PINEVILLE (342015)**, 10648 Park Road, Zip 28210; tel. 704/667–8050, **A**1 5 10 **F**1 3 18 20 29 34 35 45 46 59 65 68 74 75 77 82 84 85 91 96 130 148 154 **P**5 **S** Community Hospital Corporation, Plano, TX
Primary Contact: Derek Murzyn, Market Chief Executive Officer
CFO: Joanne Tyo, Chief Financial Officer
CMO: Joseph Lang, M.D., Chief of Staff
CHR: Doug Gallagher, Director Human Resources
CNO: Teshia Davis, Chief Clinical Officer
Web address: www.continuecare.org/pineville/
Control: Other not–for–profit (including NFP Corporation) **Service**: Acute long–term care hospital

Staffed Beds: 40 Admissions: 400 Census: 29 Outpatient Visits: 0 **Births:** 0 **Total Expense ($000):** 17844 **Payroll Expense ($000):** 7190 **Personnel:** 129

★ **CAROLINAS CONTINUECARE HOSPITAL AT UNIVERSITY (342021)**, 8800 North Tryon Street, Zip 28262–3300; tel. 704/863–8300, (Nonreporting) **S** Community Hospital Corporation, Plano, TX
Primary Contact: Derek Murzyn, Chief Executive Officer
Web address: www.continuecare.org/charlotte//
Control: Other not–for–profit (including NFP Corporation) **Service**: Acute long–term care hospital

Staffed Beds: 35

☒ △ **CAROLINAS HEALTHCARE SYSTEM PINEVILLE (340098)**, 10628 Park Road, Zip 28210–8407; tel. 704/667–1000, **A**1 2 3 7 10 **F**3 13 17 18 20 22 24 26 28 29 30 31 40 45 49 50 64 68 70 73 74 75 76 77 78 79 81 82 84 85 86 87 90 91 92 93 100 107 108 111 114 115 119 120 121 123 126 129 130 132 135 146 147 148 149 154 **S** Atrium Health, Charlotte, NC
Primary Contact: Christopher R. Hummer, President
Web address: www.carolinashealthcare.org/pineville
Control: Hospital district or authority, Government, nonfederal **Service**: General medical and surgical

Staffed Beds: 235 Admissions: 17035 Census: 204 Outpatient Visits: 165616 **Births:** 2311 **Total Expense ($000):** 313173 **Payroll Expense ($000):** 100811 **Personnel:** 1458

☒ **CAROLINAS HEALTHCARE SYSTEM UNIVERSITY (340166)**, 8800 North Tryon Street, Zip 28262–3300, Mailing Address: P.O. Box 560727, Zip 28256–0727; tel. 704/863–6000, **A**1 2 3 10 22 **F**3 8 13 15 18 20 26 29 30 31 34 40 43 44 45 46 49 50 51 57 59 60 64 65 68 70 72 74 75 76 78 79 81 82 84 85 86 87 93 107 111 114 115 118 119 126 129 130 145 146 148 149 150 154 **S** Atrium Health, Charlotte, NC
Primary Contact: William H. Leonard, President
CFO: Greg A Gombar, Chief Financial Officer
CIO: John Knox, Senior Vice President and Chief Information Officer
Web address: www.carolinashealthcare.org/university
Control: Hospital district or authority, Government, nonfederal **Service**: General medical and surgical

Staffed Beds: 100 Admissions: 6442 Census: 68 Outpatient Visits: 155343 **Births:** 1461 **Total Expense ($000):** 157548 **Payroll Expense ($000):** 53359 **Personnel:** 770

☒ △ **CAROLINAS MEDICAL CENTER (340113)**, 1000 Blythe Boulevard, Zip 28203–5871, Mailing Address: P.O. Box 32861, Zip 28232–2861; tel. 704/355–2000, (Includes CAROLINAS MEDICAL CENTER–MERCY, 2001 Vail Avenue, Charlotte, NC, Zip 28207–1289; tel. 704/304–5000; Scott Jones, Vice President and Facility Executive; LEVINE CHILDREN'S HOSPITAL, 1000 Blythe Boulevard, Charlotte, NC, Zip 28203; tel. 704/381–2000) **A**1 2 3 5 7 8 10 **F**3 4 6 7 8 12 13 15 17 18 19 20 21 22 23 24 25 26 27 28 29 30 31 32 34 35 36 37 38 39 40 41 43 44 45 46 47 48 49 50 52 54 55 56 57 58 59 60 61 62 64 65 66 68 70 71 72 73 74 75 76 77 78 79 80 81 82 84 85 86 87 88 89 90 93 96 97 98 99 100 101 102 103 104 105 107 108 111 114 115 117 118 119 120 121 123 124 126 130 131 132 134 135 136 137 138 139 141 142 145 146 147 148 151 153 154 **P**6 **S** Atrium Health, Charlotte, NC
Primary Contact: Christopher Bowe, FACHE, Interim Chief Executive Officer
CFO: Anthony C DeFurio, Executive Vice President Chief Financial Officer
CMO: Roger A Ray, M.D., Executive Vice President and Chief Medical Officer
CHR: Jim Dunn, Ph.D., Chief Human Resource Officer
Web address: www.carolinashealthcare.org/cmc
Control: Hospital district or authority, Government, nonfederal **Service**: General medical and surgical

Staffed Beds: 1246 Admissions: 61329 Census: 990 Outpatient Visits: 1052027 **Births:** 7250 **Total Expense ($000):** 2037390 **Payroll Expense ($000):** 585488 **Personnel:** 8837

☒ △ **CAROLINAS REHABILITATION (343026)**, 1100 Blythe Boulevard, Zip 28203–5864; tel. 704/355–4300, **A**1 3 7 10 **F**29 30 64 68 82 90 91 93 95 96 119 130 143 144 146 147 148 149 **P**1 **S** Atrium Health, Charlotte, NC
Primary Contact: Robert G. Larrison Jr, President
CFO: William Hopkins, Director Finance
CMO: William Bockenek, M.D., Chief Medical Officer
CHR: Deonca Leach, Director, Human Resources
CNO: Susan Chase, Vice President
Web address: www.carolinashealthcare.org/rehabilitation
Control: Other not–for–profit (including NFP Corporation) **Service**: Rehabilitation

Staffed Beds: 150 Admissions: 2769 Census: 116 Outpatient Visits: 85063 **Births:** 0 **Total Expense ($000):** 90419 **Payroll Expense ($000):** 38078 **Personnel:** 699

Hospital, Medicare Provider Number, Address, Telephone, Approval, Facility, and Physician Codes, Health Care System

★ American Hospital Association (AHA) membership
☐ The Joint Commission accreditation
◯ Healthcare Facilities Accreditation Program
◇ DNV Healthcare Inc. accreditation
⇑ Center for Improvement in Healthcare Quality Accreditation
△ Commission on Accreditation of Rehabilitation Facilities (CARF) accreditation

NC

★ **NOVANT HEALTH CHARLOTTE ORTHOPAEDIC HOSPITAL (340153)**, 1901 Randolph Road, Zip 28207–1195; tel. 704/316-2000, (Nonreporting) **A**10 **S** Novant Health, Winston Salem, NC
Primary Contact: Jason Bernd, Vice President
CFO: Fred M Hargett, Executive Vice President and Chief Financial Officer
CMO: Thomas Zweng, Executive Vice President and Chief Medical Officer
CIO: David B Garrett, Senior Vice President and Chief Information Officer
CHR: Janet Smith–Hill, Executive Vice Presideent and Chief Human Resource Officer
CNO: Kelli S Sadler Bell, R.N., Vice President, Chief Nursing Officer
Web address: www.novanthealth.org
Control: Other not–for–profit (including NFP Corporation) **Service**: Orthopedic

Staffed Beds: 33

✠ **NOVANT HEALTH PRESBYTERIAN MEDICAL CENTER (340053)**, 200 Hawthorne Lane, Zip 28204–2528, Mailing Address: P.O. Box 33549, Zip 28233–3549; tel. 704/384-4000, (Includes PRESBYTERIAN HEMBY CHILDREN'S HOSPITAL, 200 Hawthorne Lane, Charlotte, NC, Zip 28204–2515; tel. 704/384–5134) (Nonreporting) **A**1 2 3 10 **S** Novant Health, Winston Salem, NC
Primary Contact: Paula Vincent, MSN, President and Chief Operating Officer
CFO: Fred M Hargett, Executive Vice President and Chief Financial Officer
CMO: Thomas Zweng, Executive Vice President and Chief Medical Officer
CIO: David B Garrett, Senior Vice President Information Technology
CHR: Janet Smith–Hill, Senior Vice President Human Resources
CNO: Kelli S Sadler Bell, R.N., Vice President, Chief Nursing Officer
Web address: www.novanthealth.org
Control: Other not–for–profit (including NFP Corporation) **Service**: General medical and surgical

Staffed Beds: 419

PRESBYTERIAN HOSPITAL See Novant Health Presbyterian Medical Center

PRESBYTERIAN–ORTHOPAEDIC HOSPITAL See Novant Health Charlotte Orthopaedic Hospital

STRATEGIC BEHAVIORAL HEALTH – CHARLOTTE (344031), 1715 Sharon Road West, Zip 28210–5663; tel. 704/944-0650, (Nonreporting) **S** Strategic Behavioral Health, LLC, Memphis, TN
Primary Contact: George G. Boykin, Chief Executive Officer
Web address: www.sbccharlotte.com/
Control: Corporation, Investor–owned (for–profit) **Service**: Children's hospital psychiatric

Staffed Beds: 60

CHEROKEE—Swain County

✠ **CHEROKEE INDIAN HOSPITAL (340156)**, 1 Hospital Road, Zip 28719; tel. 828/497-9163, (Nonreporting) **A**1 3 10
Primary Contact: Casey Cooper, Chief Executive Officer
COO: Beth Greene, Chief Operating Officer
CFO: Chrissy Arch, Chief Financial Officer
CMO: Michael E Toedt, M.D., Director Clinical Services
CIO: Anthony Taylor, Manager Information Technology
Web address: www.cherokeehospital.org
Control: Other not–for–profit (including NFP Corporation) **Service**: General medical and surgical

Staffed Beds: 15

CLINTON—Sampson County

✠ **SAMPSON REGIONAL MEDICAL CENTER (340024)**, 607 Beaman Street, Zip 28328–2697, Mailing Address: P.O. Box 260, Zip 28329–0260; tel. 910/592-8511, **A**1 10 12 13 **F**3 13 14 15 29 34 35 40 45 46 47 50 51 53 57 59 62 64 68 70 75 76 77 79 81 82 85 86 89 91 93 107 110 111 114 119 130 132 133 144 146 148
Primary Contact: Shawn Howerton, M.D., Chief Executive Officer and President, Medical Staff
COO: Geraldine H Shipp, Director of Risk Management
CFO: Jerry Heinzman, Senior Vice President and Chief Financial Officer
CMO: Shawn Howerton, M.D., Chief Executive Officer and President, Medical Staff
CIO: Kelly Lucas, Chief Information Officer
CHR: Michael W. Gilpin, Vice President Human Resources
CNO: Allison H Taylor, R.N., Chief Nursing Officer and Vice President Clinical Services
Web address: www.sampsonrmc.org
Control: County, Government, nonfederal **Service**: General medical and surgical

Staffed Beds: 83 Admissions: 2752 Census: 29 Outpatient Visits: 77405 Births: 453 Total Expense ($000): 47758 Payroll Expense ($000): 17671 Personnel: 491

CLYDE—Haywood County

✠ **HAYWOOD REGIONAL MEDICAL CENTER (340184)**, 262 Leroy George Drive, Zip 28721–7430; tel. 828/456-7311, (Nonreporting) **A**1 3 10 **S** Duke LifePoint Healthcare, Brentwood, TN
Primary Contact: Rod Harkleroad, R.N., Chief Executive Officer
COO: Teresa Reynolds, Chief Operating Officer
CFO: Rose Coyne, Interim CFO
CMO: Tyson Smith, M.D., Chief Medical Officer
CIO: Greg Copen, Chief Information Officer
CHR: Janet Millsaps, Vice President Human Resources
Web address: www.haymed.org
Control: Hospital district or authority, Government, nonfederal **Service**: General medical and surgical

Staffed Beds: 146

COLUMBUS—Polk County

✠ **ST. LUKE'S HOSPITAL (341322)**, 101 Hospital Drive, Zip 28722–6418; tel. 828/894-3311, **A**1 10 18 **F**3 11 15 29 30 31 34 35 40 45 56 57 59 64 70 75 77 78 79 81 82 85 87 93 98 103 107 108 110 115 119 127 130 133 135 146 149 153 154 **P**6 **S** Atrium Health, Charlotte, NC
Primary Contact: James B. Bross, President
CFO: Elizabeth Presnell, Assistant Vice President of Finance
CMO: James Holleman, M.D., Chief of Staff
CIO: Nick Whichard, Chief Information Officer
CHR: Amy Norville, Vice President Support Services
CNO: Katherine Hefner, MSN, Chief Nursing Officer
Web address: www.saintlukeshospital.com
Control: Other not–for–profit (including NFP Corporation) **Service**: General medical and surgical

Staffed Beds: 35 Admissions: 1518 Census: 21 Outpatient Visits: 30069 Births: 0 Total Expense ($000): 41478 Payroll Expense ($000): 17887

CONCORD—Cabarrus County

✠ **CAROLINAS HEALTHCARE SYSTEM NORTHEAST (340001)**, 920 Church Street North, Zip 28025–2983; tel. 704/403-3000, **A**1 2 3 10 **F**3 5 6 8 9 11 12 13 15 17 18 20 22 24 26 28 29 30 32 34 35 36 38 40 43 44 45 46 47 48 49 50 53 54 55 56 57 58 59 60 61 64 65 68 70 71 72 73 74 75 76 78 79 81 82 84 85 86 87 88 89 92 93 94 97 98 100 102 103 104 105 107 108 110 111 114 115 117 118 119 120 121 124 126 129 130 131 132 135 145 146 147 148 149 150 153 154 **P**6 **S** Atrium Health, Charlotte, NC
Primary Contact: Phyllis A. Wingate, FACHE, President
COO: Bill Hubbard, Vice President, Operations
CFO: Rodney Ball, Vice President Finance
CMO: Dan Hagler, M.D., Vice President and Chief Medical Officer
CIO: Lisa Sykes, Manager, Information Services
CHR: Lesley Chambless, Assistant Vice President Workforce Relations
CNO: Kate Grew, MSN, R.N., Vice President/Chief Nurse Executive
Web address: www.carolinashealthcare.org/northeast
Control: Hospital district or authority, Government, nonfederal **Service**: General medical and surgical

Staffed Beds: 455 Admissions: 22393 Census: 284 Outpatient Visits: 368734 Births: 2874 Total Expense ($000): 487206 Payroll Expense ($000): 163810 Personnel: 2625

DANBURY—Stokes County

★ ⇑ **LIFEBRITE COMMUNITY HOSPITAL OF STOKES (341317)**, 1570 NC 8 & 89 Highway North, Zip 27016, Mailing Address: P.O. Box 10, Zip 27016–0010; tel. 336/593-2831, (Nonreporting) **A**10 18 21
Primary Contact: Pamela P. Tillman, Administrator
CFO: Warren S. Binderman, Chief Financial Officer
CMO: Samuel C Newsome, M.D., Chief of Staff
CIO: Ada Ashley, HIM Director
CHR: Lee Sykes, Human Resources Director
CNO: Amanda Parks, Chief Nursing Officer
Web address: www.lifebritestokes.com
Control: Corporation, Investor–owned (for–profit) **Service**: General medical and surgical

Staffed Beds: 65

NC

DUNN—Harnett County

☐ **HARNETT HEALTH SYSTEM (340071)**, 800 Tilghman Drive, Zip 28334–5599, Mailing Address: P.O. Box 1706, Zip 28335–1706; tel. 910/892–1000, (Includes CENTRAL HARTNETT HOSPITAL, 215 Brightwater Drive, Lillington, NC, Zip 27546; tel. 910/892–1000) **A**1 3 10 12 13 **F**3 11 13 15 18 28 29 30 34 35 39 40 45 50 56 57 59 70 73 75 76 77 79 81 85 86 87 89 92 93 96 102 107 108 110 111 114 118 119 130 146 148 **S** Cape Fear Valley Health System, Fayetteville, NC
Primary Contact: Kevin Jackson, Interim Chief Executive Officer
COO: Kenneth E Bryan, FACHE, President and Chief Executive Officer
CFO: Lynn Lambert, Chief Financial Officer
CIO: Tim Krieger, Director Information Systems
CHR: Sondra Davis, Vice President Human Resources & System Development
CNO: Vicki Allen, R.N., MS, Vice President Patient Care Services and Chief Nursing Officer
Web address: www.myharnetthealth.org/
Control: Other not–for–profit (including NFP Corporation) **Service**: General medical and surgical

Staffed Beds: 105 **Admissions**: 5659 **Census**: 59 **Outpatient Visits**: 116207 **Births**: 516 **Total Expense ($000)**: 96533 **Payroll Expense ($000)**: 41279 **Personnel**: 709

DURHAM—Durham County

✠ **DUKE REGIONAL HOSPITAL (340155)**, 3643 North Roxboro Street, Zip 27704–2763; tel. 919/470–4000, **A**1 3 5 10 **F**3 8 11 12 13 15 17 18 20 22 24 26 29 30 31 34 35 40 41 44 45 47 48 50 51 57 58 59 60 64 66 68 70 73 74 75 76 77 78 79 80 81 82 84 85 86 87 90 93 96 98 100 101 102 107 108 110 111 115 118 119 120 121 123 124 126 130 131 132 135 146 147 148 149 154 **P**6 **S** Duke University Health System, Durham, NC
Primary Contact: Kathleen B. Galbraith, FACHE, President
COO: A. Mitch Babb, Vice President, Operations
CFO: Jonathan B Hoy, Chief Financial Officer
CMO: Barbara Griffith, M.D., Chief Medical Officer
CIO: Terry Mears, Director Information Systems
CHR: Dexter Nolley, Chief Human Resources Officer
CNO: Victoria K Orto, R.N., Chief Nursing and Patient Care Services Officer
Web address: www.dukehealth.org
Control: Other not–for–profit (including NFP Corporation) **Service**: General medical and surgical

Staffed Beds: 214 **Admissions**: 16394 **Census**: 214 **Outpatient Visits**: 165953 **Births**: 2367 **Total Expense ($000)**: 319016 **Payroll Expense ($000)**: 143962 **Personnel**: 1985

✠ **DUKE UNIVERSITY HOSPITAL (340030)**, 2301 Erwin Road, Zip 27705–4699, Mailing Address: P.O. Box 3814, Zip 27710–3708; tel. 919/684–8111, (Includes DUKE CHILDREN'S HOSPITAL & HEALTH CENTER, 2301 Erwin Road, Durham, NC, Zip 27710–0001, Mailing Address: PO Box 3708, Zip 27702, tel. 919/684–8111) **A**1 2 3 5 8 10 **F**3 5 6 7 8 9 11 12 13 15 17 18 19 20 21 22 23 24 25 26 27 28 29 30 31 32 33 34 35 37 39 40 41 43 44 45 46 47 48 49 50 51 52 53 54 55 57 58 59 60 61 64 66 68 70 72 73 74 75 76 77 78 79 80 81 82 84 85 86 87 88 89 91 92 93 94 96 97 98 99 100 101 102 103 104 107 108 110 111 112 114 115 116 117 118 119 120 121 123 124 126 129 130 131 132 134 135 136 137 138 139 140 141 142 145 146 147 148 149 154 **P**1 **S** Duke University Health System, Durham, NC
Primary Contact: Thomas Owens, M.D., President
CFO: Sabrina Olsen, Chief Financial Officer
CMO: Lisa C Pickett, M.D., Chief Medical Officer
CIO: Jeffrey Ferranti, M.D., Chief Information Officer
CHR: Deborah Page, Chief Human Resources Officer
CNO: Mary Ann Fuchs, R.N., Vice President Patient Care and System Chief Nurse Executive
Web address: www.dukehealth.org
Control: Other not–for–profit (including NFP Corporation) **Service**: General medical and surgical

Staffed Beds: 962 **Admissions**: 42020 **Census**: 794 **Outpatient Visits**: 1085741 **Births**: 3429 **Total Expense ($000)**: 2294174 **Payroll Expense ($000)**: 748918 **Personnel**: 10906

DURHAM REGIONAL HOSPITAL See Duke Regional Hospital

✉ **DURHAM VETERANS AFFAIRS MEDICAL CENTER**, 508 Fulton Street, Zip 27705–3897; tel. 919/286–0411, (Total facility includes 75 beds in nursing home–type unit) **A**1 3 5 8 **F**3 5 6 8 9 10 11 12 15 17 18 20 22 24 26 28 29 30 31 34 35 36 38 39 40 44 45 46 47 48 49 50 51 52 54 55 56 57 58 59 60 61 62 63 64 65 66 70 71 74 75 77 78 79 81 82 83 84 85 86 87 91 92 93 94 96 97 98 100 101 102 103 104 105 107 108 110 111 114 115 116 117 118 119 120 121 126 127 128 129 130 131 132 133 135 143 144 146 147 148 149 150 152 153 154 **S** Department of Veterans Affairs, Perry Point, MD
Primary Contact: Paul Crews, Director
COO: Sara Haigh, Associate Director
CFO: David Kuboushek, Chief, Fiscal Service
CMO: John D Shelburne, M.D., Chief of Staff
CIO: Toby Dickerson, Chief Information Resources Management Services
CHR: Jerry Freeman, Chief, Human Resources Management Services
CNO: Gregory S Eagerton, Ph.D., R.N., Nurse Executive
Web address: www.durham.va.gov/
Control: Veterans Affairs, Government, federal **Service**: General medical and surgical

Staffed Beds: 251 **Admissions**: 7013 **Census**: 189 **Outpatient Visits**: 381818 **Births**: 0 **Total Expense ($000)**: 622430 **Personnel**: 3179

☐ **NORTH CAROLINA SPECIALTY HOSPITAL (340049)**, 3916 Ben Franklin Boulevard, Zip 27704–2383, Mailing Address: PO Box 15819, Zip 27704–2383; tel. 919/956–9300, **A**1 10 **F**3 29 30 51 64 79 81 82 85 86 87 107 119 126 130 131 148 **S** National Surgical Healthcare, Chicago, IL
Primary Contact: Randi L. Shults, Chief Executive Officer
CFO: Bill Wilson, Chief Financial Officer
CMO: David Musante, M.D., Medical Director
CHR: Sarah Bohlin, Human Resources Director
CNO: John Medlin, Chief Nursing Officer
Web address: www.ncspecialty.com
Control: Partnership, Investor–owned (for–profit) **Service**: Surgical

Staffed Beds: 18 **Admissions**: 1627 **Census**: 10 **Outpatient Visits**: 11319 **Births**: 0 **Total Expense ($000)**: 45073 **Payroll Expense ($000)**: 12219 **Personnel**: 204

✉ **SELECT SPECIALTY HOSPITAL–DURHAM (342018)**, 3643 North Roxboro Road, 6th Floor, Zip 27704–2702; tel. 919/470–9159, (Nonreporting) **A**1 10 **S** Select Medical Corporation, Mechanicsburg, PA
Primary Contact: Jennifer Rawley, PharmD, Chief Executive Officer
CHR: Michael Stinson, Human Resources Coordinator
CNO: Cole Oren, R.N., Chief Nursing Officer
Web address: www.selectspecialtyhospitals.com/company/locations/durham.aspx
Control: Corporation, Investor–owned (for–profit) **Service**: Acute long–term care hospital

Staffed Beds: 30

☐ **VERITAS COLLABORATIVE**, 4024 Stirrup Creek Drive, Zip 27703–9464; tel. 919/908–9730, (Nonreporting) **A**1 **S** Veritas Collaborative, Durham, NC
Primary Contact: Sara Hofmeier, Executive Director
Web address: www.https://veritascollaborative.com
Control: Partnership, Investor–owned (for–profit) **Service**: Psychiatric

Staffed Beds: 40

☐ **VERITAS COLLABORATIVE**, 615 Douglas Street, Suite 500, Zip 27705–6616; tel. 919/908–9730, (Nonreporting) **A**1 **S** Veritas Collaborative, Durham, NC
Primary Contact: Becca Eckstein, Executive Director
Web address: www.https://veritascollaborative.com
Control: Partnership, Investor–owned (for–profit) **Service**: Psychiatric

Staffed Beds: 25

EDEN—Rockingham County

★ ⇑ **UNC ROCKINGHAM HEALTH CARE (340060)**, 117 East King's Highway, Zip 27288–5201; tel. 336/623–9711, (Total facility includes 121 beds in nursing home–type unit) **A**2 10 21 **F**3 11 13 15 26 29 30 34 35 40 45 47 48 49 50 57 59 64 68 70 74 76 77 78 79 81 82 85 87 89 90 93 107 108 110 111 114 118 119 122 123 128 129 130 132 143 144 146 147 148 154 **P**6 **S** UNC Health Care, Chapel Hill, NC
Primary Contact: Dana Weston, Chief Executive Officer
CFO: Raymond C. Owings, Interim Chief Financial Officer
CIO: Wade Williams, Chief Information Officer
CHR: Tom Stevens, Director Personnel
CNO: JoAnn P. Smith, R.N., Chief Nursing Officer, and Vice President Patient Care Services
Web address: www.morehead.org
Control: Other not–for–profit (including NFP Corporation) **Service**: General medical and surgical

Staffed Beds: 188 **Admissions**: 3773 **Census**: 131 **Outpatient Visits**: 152834 **Births**: 486 **Total Expense ($000)**: 77846 **Payroll Expense ($000)**: 30117 **Personnel**: 468

EDENTON—Chowan County

☒ **VIDANT CHOWAN HOSPITAL (341318)**, 211 Virginia Road, Zip 27932–9668, Mailing Address: P.O. Box 629, Zip 27932–0629; tel. 252/482–8451, **A**1 3 10 18 **F**3 11 13 15 28 29 30 31 34 35 40 45 46 57 59 64 70 74 75 76 77 78 79 81 82 84 85 93 107 108 110 111 114 119 130 132 135 146 147 148 **S** Vidant Health, Greenville, NC
Primary Contact: Jeffrey Sackrison, President
CFO: Brian Harvill, Vice President Financial Services
CMO: William Hope IV Chief of Medical Staff
CIO: Brian White, Director Strategic Operations
CHR: Nicole Spell, Director Human Resources
CNO: Cindy Coker, Vice President, Patient Care Services
Web address: www.vidanthealth.com
Control: Other not–for–profit (including NFP Corporation) **Service:** General medical and surgical

Staffed Beds: 19 **Admissions:** 1395 **Census:** 16 **Outpatient Visits:** 41445 **Births:** 210 **Total Expense ($000):** 42503 **Payroll Expense ($000):** 15571 **Personnel:** 307

ELIZABETH CITY—Pasquotank County

★ ⇑ **SENTARA ALBEMARLE MEDICAL CENTER (340109)**, 1144 North Road Street, Zip 27909–3473, Mailing Address: P.O. Box 1587, Zip 27906–1587; tel. 252/335–0531, **A**10 21 **F**3 11 13 15 18 20 22 28 29 30 31 34 35 36 37 38 39 40 41 44 45 46 47 48 49 50 51 53 54 55 56 57 58 59 60 61 64 65 68 70 74 75 76 77 78 79 81 84 85 86 87 91 92 93 94 96 97 100 102 107 108 110 111 114 116 117 118 119 121 126 129 130 131 132 135 141 146 147 148 149 154 **P**6 **S** Sentara Healthcare, Norfolk, VA
Primary Contact: Coleen F. Santa Ana, President
CFO: Craig Lewis, Chief Financial Officer
CMO: Charles Nicholson, Vice President, Medical Affairs
CHR: Deborah Ferguson, Director, Human Resources
CNO: Jaime Carroll, R.N., Vice President Nursing
Web address: www.albemarlehealth.org
Control: Other not–for–profit (including NFP Corporation) **Service:** General medical and surgical

Staffed Beds: 109 **Admissions:** 5224 **Census:** 58 **Outpatient Visits:** 129710 **Births:** 590 **Total Expense ($000):** 131735 **Payroll Expense ($000):** 49733 **Personnel:** 793

ELIZABETHTOWN—Bladen County

BLADEN COUNTY HOSPITAL See Cape Fear Valley – Bladen County Hospital

☒ **CAPE FEAR VALLEY – BLADEN COUNTY HOSPITAL (341315)**, 501 South Poplar Street, Zip 28337–9375, Mailing Address: P.O. Box 398, Zip 28337–0398; tel. 910/862–5100, (Nonreporting) **A**1 10 18 **S** Cape Fear Valley Health System, Fayetteville, NC
Primary Contact: Roxie Cannon. Wells, M.D., Chief Executive Officer
CFO: Stephen Fife, Chief Financial Officer
CMO: Pearly Graham Hoskins, M.D., President Medical Staff
CIO: Craig Kellum, Director Management Information Systems
CHR: Ginger Parks, Director Human Resources
CNO: Diana Harris, Chief Nursing Officer
Web address: www.bchn.org
Control: County, Government, nonfederal **Service:** General medical and surgical

Staffed Beds: 25

ELKIN—Surry County

☒ **HUGH CHATHAM MEMORIAL HOSPITAL (340097)**, 180 Parkwood Drive, Zip 28621–2430, Mailing Address: P.O. Box 560, Zip 28621–0560; tel. 336/527–7000, **A**1 10 **F**3 11 13 15 28 29 30 34 40 45 49 53 57 59 62 64 70 74 75 76 77 79 81 85 87 93 96 107 108 110 111 118 119 120 121 125 127 130 131 132 133 135 144 146 147 148 149 **P**6
Primary Contact: Paul Hammes, Chief Executive Officer
COO: Mary Blackburn, Vice President Operations and Chief Practice Officer
CFO: Donald E Trippel, Chief Financial Officer
CMO: Dominick Carbone, M.D., Chief of Staff
CIO: Lee Powe, Director Management Information Systems
CHR: Kathy Poteate, Interim Director Human Resources
CNO: Paula Moore, R.N., Chief Clinical Officer
Web address: www.hughchatham.org
Control: Other not–for–profit (including NFP Corporation) **Service:** General medical and surgical

Staffed Beds: 81 **Admissions:** 3729 **Census:** 35 **Outpatient Visits:** 69946 **Births:** 505 **Total Expense ($000):** 63670 **Payroll Expense ($000):** 23335 **Personnel:** 804

FAYETTEVILLE—Cumberland County

☒ △ **CAPE FEAR VALLEY MEDICAL CENTER (340028)**, 1638 Owen Drive, Zip 28304–3431, Mailing Address: P.O. Box 2000, Zip 28302–2000; tel. 910/615–4000, (Includes BEHAVIORAL HEALTH CARE OF CAPE FEAR VALLEY HEALTH SYSTEM, 711 Executive Place, Fayetteville, NC, Zip 28301; tel. 910/615–3700; CAPE FEAR VALLEY REHABILITATION CENTER, 1638 Owen Drive, Fayetteville, NC, Zip 28304; tel. 910/615–4000) **A**1 2 3 5 7 10 12 13 **F**3 4 5 7 12 13 14 15 17 18 20 22 24 26 28 29 30 31 34 35 38 39 40 41 43 44 45 46 47 48 49 53 54 55 56 57 58 59 60 61 64 65 68 70 72 73 74 75 76 77 78 79 81 82 84 85 86 87 88 89 90 91 92 93 96 97 98 100 101 102 103 104 105 107 108 109 110 111 114 115 116 117 118 119 120 121 122 123 124 126 127 129 130 132 135 143 144 146 147 148 149 150 152 153 **P**6 **S** Cape Fear Valley Health System, Fayetteville, NC
Primary Contact: Michael Nagowski, Chief Executive Officer
COO: Daniel R Weatherly, Chief Operating Officer
CFO: Sandra Williams, Chief Financial Officer
CMO: Samuel A Fleishman, M.D., Chief Medical Officer
CIO: Phillip E. Wood Jr Chief Information Officer
CHR: William B Pryor, Chief Human Resources Officer
CNO: Deborah Marshburn, R.N., Chief Nursing Executive
Web address: www.capefearvalley.com
Control: Other not–for–profit (including NFP Corporation) **Service:** General medical and surgical

Staffed Beds: 608 **Admissions:** 32423 **Census:** 446 **Outpatient Visits:** 246360 **Births:** 4614 **Total Expense ($000):** 689737 **Payroll Expense ($000):** 305347 **Personnel:** 4967

☒ **FAYETTEVILLE VETERANS AFFAIRS MEDICAL CENTER**, 2300 Ramsey Street, Zip 28301–3899; tel. 910/488–2120, (Nonreporting) **A**1 3 5 **S** Department of Veterans Affairs, Perry Point, MD
Primary Contact: Elizabeth Goolsby, Director
COO: James Galkowski, Associate Director for Operations
CFO: Patrick Bullard, Chief Financial Officer
CMO: Greg Antoine, M.D., Chief of Staff
CIO: Kenneth Williams, Chief Information Officer
CHR: Joseph Whaley, Chief, Human Resources Management Service
CNO: Joyce Alexander–Hines, R.N., MSN, Associate Director, Patient Care Services
Web address: www.fayettevillenc.va.gov
Control: Veterans Affairs, Government, federal **Service:** General medical and surgical

Staffed Beds: 58

☐ **HIGHSMITH–RAINEY SPECIALTY HOSPITAL (342014)**, 150 Robeson Street, Zip 28301–5570; tel. 910/615–1000, **A**1 10 **F**1 3 8 11 29 30 35 39 50 51 58 68 70 81 85 107 114 119 130 144 146 148 149 150 **P**6 **S** Cape Fear Valley Health System, Fayetteville, NC
Primary Contact: Kevin Jackson, On Site Administrator
Web address: www.capefearvalley.com
Control: Other not–for–profit (including NFP Corporation) **Service:** Acute long–term care hospital

Staffed Beds: 66 **Admissions:** 353 **Census:** 54 **Outpatient Visits:** 32417 **Births:** 0 **Total Expense ($000):** 37353 **Payroll Expense ($000):** 21792 **Personnel:** 303

VETERANS AFFAIRS MEDICAL CENTER See Fayetteville Veterans Affairs Medical Center

FORT BRAGG—Cumberland County

☒ **WOMACK ARMY MEDICAL CENTER**, 2817 Reilly Road, Zip 28310–7302; tel. 910/907–6000, (Nonreporting) **A**1 3 5 **S** Department of the Army, Office of the Surgeon General, Falls Church, VA
Primary Contact: Colonel Lance C. Raney, Commander
CIO: Mary Peters, Chief Information Officer
Web address: www.wamc.amedd.army.mil/
Control: Army, Government, federal **Service:** General medical and surgical

Staffed Beds: 156

FRANKLIN—Macon County

☒ **ANGEL MEDICAL CENTER (341326)**, 120 Riverview Street, Zip 28734–2612, Mailing Address: P.O. Box 1209, Zip 28744–0569; tel. 828/524–8411, **A**1 3 10 18 **F**3 11 13 15 28 29 30 31 34 35 40 44 45 47 49 50 54 57 59 64 70 77 78 79 81 85 86 87 93 96 97 107 108 110 111 114 119 127 130 131 132 133 135 144 146 147 148 149 **S** Mission Health System, Asheville, NC
Primary Contact: Karen S. Gorby, R.N., MSN, FACHE, President and Chief Nursing Officer
COO: Martin Wadewitz, Chief Operations Officer/ Vice President, Operations
CFO: George Kimbro, Vice President Finance
CIO: Ed Coye, Director Information Technology Mission Health System Hospitals
CHR: Teresa Mallonee, Director Human Resources
Web address: www.angelmed.org
Control: Other not–for–profit (including NFP Corporation) **Service:** General medical and surgical

Staffed Beds: 36 **Admissions:** 2163 **Census:** 15 **Outpatient Visits:** 108350 **Births:** 288 **Total Expense ($000):** 63347 **Payroll Expense ($000):** 16055 **Personnel:** 354

Many Facility Codes have changed. Please refer to the AHA Guide Code Chart.

GARNER—Wake County

☐ **STRATEGIC BEHAVIORAL HEALTH – RALEIGH (344028)**, 3200 Waterfield Drive, Zip 27529–7727; tel. 919/800–4400, (Nonreporting) **A**1 10 **S** Strategic Behavioral Health, LLC, Memphis, TN
Primary Contact: Matt Doyle, Chief Executive Officer
CMO: Karen Miles, M.D., Medical Director
CHR: Christina Meeker, Director Human Resources
CNO: Shawanna Royal, R.N., Director Nursing
Web address: www.sbcraleigh.com/
Control: Corporation, Investor–owned (for–profit) **Service:** Children's hospital psychiatric

Staffed Beds: 50

GASTONIA—Gaston County

✠ **CAROMONT REGIONAL MEDICAL CENTER (340032)**, 2525 Court Drive, Zip 28054–2140, Mailing Address: P.O. Box 1747, Zip 28053–1747; tel. 704/834–2000, **A**1 2 10 **F**3 13 15 17 18 20 22 24 26 28 29 30 31 34 35 40 41 43 44 45 46 48 49 50 53 54 55 57 58 59 60 64 68 70 71 72 73 74 75 76 78 79 81 82 83 87 89 93 94 96 98 99 100 101 102 104 107 108 110 111 114 115 116 117 118 119 120 121 123 124 126 129 130 131 132 135 146 147 148
Primary Contact: Chris Peek, Chief Executive Officer
COO: Kathleen Besson, Executive Vice President and Chief Operating Officer
CFO: David O'Connor, Executive Vice President and Chief Financial Officer
CMO: Todd Davis, M.D., Vice President Medical Affairs, Patient Safety Officer
CIO: Mike Johnson, Vice President, Chief Information Officer
CHR: Elizabeth McCraw, Vice President, Human Resources
CNO: Scott E Wells, MSN, R.N., Vice President Patient Care Services
Web address: www.caromont.org
Control: Other not–for–profit (including NFP Corporation) **Service:** General medical and surgical

Staffed Beds: 423 **Admissions:** 21133 **Census:** 267 **Outpatient Visits:** 438894 **Births:** 1971 **Total Expense ($000):** 393866 **Payroll Expense ($000):** 157168 **Personnel:** 2747

GASTON MEMORIAL HOSPITAL See Caromont Regional Medical Center

GOLDSBORO—Wayne County

☐ **CHERRY HOSPITAL (344026)**, 1401 West Ash Street, Zip 27530–1057; tel. 919/947–7000, **A**1 3 10 **F**30 39 98 103 106 119 130 143 146 149 154
Primary Contact: J. Luckey. Welsh Jr, Chief Executive Officer
CFO: Susie Sherrod Sanders, Chief Financial Officer
CMO: Jim Mayo, M.D., Clinical Director
CIO: Mike Letchworth, Manager Information Systems
CHR: Carol Thornton, Director Human Resources
CNO: Debbie Wall, Chief Nursing Officer
Web address: www.cherryhospital.org
Control: State, Government, nonfederal **Service:** Psychiatric

Staffed Beds: 243 **Admissions:** 808 **Census:** 183 **Outpatient Visits:** 0 **Births:** 0 **Total Expense ($000):** 91478 **Payroll Expense ($000):** 56159 **Personnel:** 1061

✠ **WAYNE UNC HEALTH CARE (340010)**, 2700 Wayne Memorial Drive, Zip 27534–9494, Mailing Address: P.O. Box 8001, Zip 27533–8001; tel. 919/736–1110, **A**1 10 **F**3 8 13 15 18 20 22 28 29 30 31 34 35 39 40 45 47 49 50 57 58 59 60 64 68 70 73 74 75 76 77 78 79 80 81 85 86 87 89 92 93 96 98 100 101 102 107 108 110 111 114 118 119 126 129 130 132 145 146 147 148 **P**6 **S** UNC Health Care, Chapel Hill, NC
Primary Contact: Janie Jaberg, FACHE, President and Chief Executive Officer
COO: Thomas A Bradshaw, Vice President Operations
CFO: Rebecca W Craig, Vice President and Chief Financial Officer
CIO: Lori Cole, Director Information Technology
CNO: Shirley S Harkey, FACHE, R.N., Vice President, Patient Services
Web address: www.waynehealth.org
Control: Other not–for–profit (including NFP Corporation) **Service:** General medical and surgical

Staffed Beds: 274 **Admissions:** 10866 **Census:** 139 **Outpatient Visits:** 148150 **Births:** 1213 **Total Expense ($000):** 236393 **Payroll Expense ($000):** 86812 **Personnel:** 1488

GREENSBORO—Guilford County

✠ **KINDRED HOSPITAL–GREENSBORO (342012)**, 2401 Southside Boulevard, Zip 27406–3311; tel. 336/271–2800, (Nonreporting) **A**1 10 **S** Kindred Healthcare, Louisville, KY
Primary Contact: Chad Lovett, Chief Executive Officer
CFO: Anthony Grate, Controller
CMO: Saad Amin, Medical Director Hospital
CIO: Little Shuford, Health Information Manager
CNO: Anne Correll, Chief Clinical Officer
Web address: www.khgreensboro.com
Control: Corporation, Investor–owned (for–profit) **Service:** Acute long–term care hospital

Staffed Beds: 101

✠ △ **MOSES H. CONE MEMORIAL HOSPITAL (340091)**, 1200 North Elm Street, Zip 27401–1020; tel. 336/832–7000, (Includes ANNIE PENN HOSPITAL, 618 South Main Street, Reidsville, NC, Zip 27320–5094; tel. 336/951–4000; Cynthia B Farrand, President; BEHAVIORAL HEALTH CENTER, 700 Walter Reed Drive, Greensboro, NC, Zip 27403–1129; tel. 336/832–9600; Debbie Cunningham, R.N., Senior Vice President, Cone Health and President, Maternal, Child and Behavioral Health Services; CONE HEALTH, 1200 North Elm Street, Greensboro, NC, Zip 27401; tel. 336/832–7000; Judith A Schanel, R.N., MSN, FACHE, Chief Operating Officer; WESLEY LONG COMMUNITY HOSPITAL, 501 North Elam Avenue, Greensboro, NC, Zip 27403; tel. 336/832–1000; Paul A Jeffrey, President; WOMEN'S HOSPITAL OF GREENSBORO, 801 Green Valley Road, Greensboro, NC, Zip 27408; tel. 336/832–6500; Debbie Cunningham, R.N., President) (Total facility includes 92 beds in nursing home–type unit) **A**1 2 3 5 7 10 **F**3 5 7 8 11 12 13 15 17 18 19 20 22 24 26 28 29 30 31 32 34 35 36 37 39 40 41 43 44 45 46 47 49 50 54 55 56 57 58 59 60 61 63 64 66 68 70 72 74 75 76 77 78 79 80 81 82 83 84 85 86 87 88 89 90 92 93 95 96 97 98 99 100 101 102 103 104 105 107 108 110 111 114 115 117 118 119 120 121 123 124 126 127 128 129 130 131 132 134 135 144 145 146 147 148 149 152 153 154 **P**8 **S** Cone Health, Greensboro, NC
Primary Contact: Mickey Foster, President
CFO: Jeffrey Jones, Chief Financial Officer
CMO: William Bowman, M.D., Vice President Medical Affairs
CIO: Steve Horsley, Vice President and Chief Information Officer
CHR: Noel F Burt, Ph.D., Chief Human Resources Officer
CNO: Ann Marie Madden, MS, R.N., Vice President of Patient Care Services and Chief Nursing Officer
Web address: www.conehealth.com/locations/moses–cone–hospital/
Control: Other not–for–profit (including NFP Corporation) **Service:** General medical and surgical

Staffed Beds: 921 **Admissions:** 49135 **Census:** 654 **Outpatient Visits:** 1756954 **Births:** 6133 **Total Expense ($000):** 1361379 **Payroll Expense ($000):** 488876 **Personnel:** 9254

✠ **SELECT SPECIALTY HOSPITAL–GREENSBORO (342020)**, 1200 North Elm Street, 5th Floor, Zip 27401–1004; tel. 336/832–8571, (Nonreporting) **A**1 10 **S** Select Medical Corporation, Mechanicsburg, PA
Primary Contact: Deana Knight, Chief Executive Officer
CHR: Karen Tracey, Chief Human Resources
CNO: Robin Clark, Chief Nursing Officer
Web address: www.selectspecialtyhospitals.com/company/locations/greensboro.aspx
Control: Corporation, Investor–owned (for–profit) **Service:** Acute long–term care hospital

Staffed Beds: 30

GREENVILLE—Pitt County

PITT COUNTY MEMORIAL HOSPITAL See Vidant Medical Center

Hospital, Medicare Provider Number, Address, Telephone, Approval, Facility, and Physician Codes, Health Care System

★ American Hospital Association (AHA) membership   ○ Healthcare Facilities Accreditation Program   ⇑ Center for Improvement in Healthcare Quality Accreditation
☐ The Joint Commission accreditation   ◇ DNV Healthcare Inc. accreditation   △ Commission on Accreditation of Rehabilitation Facilities (CARF) accreditation

NC

© 2018 AHA Guide   *Many Facility Codes have changed. Please refer to the AHA Guide Code Chart.*   Hospitals **A453**

✠ △ **VIDANT MEDICAL CENTER (340040)**, 2100 Stantonsburg Road, Zip 27834–2818, Mailing Address: P.O. Box 6028, Zip 27835–6028; tel. 252/847–4100, (Includes JAMES AND CONNIE MAYNARD CHILDREN'S HOSPITAL, 2101 Stantonsburg Road, Greenville, NC, Zip 27834–2817; tel. 252/847–5712; UNIVERSITY HEALTH SYSTEMS CHILDREN'S HOSPITAL, 2100 Stantonsburg Road, Greenville, NC, Zip 27834–2818, Mailing Address: PO Box 6028, Zip 27835–6028, tel. 252/847–4100) **A**1 2 3 5 7 8 10 **F**3 7 12 13 14 15 17 18 19 20 21 22 23 24 25 27 28 29 30 31 34 35 38 40 41 43 44 45 46 47 48 49 50 51 52 55 56 57 58 59 60 61 64 65 68 70 71 72 73 74 75 76 77 78 79 80 81 82 83 84 85 86 87 88 89 90 92 93 94 95 96 97 98 100 101 102 104 107 108 110 111 114 115 117 118 119 124 126 129 130 131 132 134 135 138 139 143 145 146 147 148 149 150 **P**6 **S** Vidant Health, Greenville, NC
Primary Contact: William Brian. Floyd, President
CFO: David S Hughes, Chief Financial Officer
CMO: Paul Shackelford, M.D., Chief Medical Officer
CIO: Donnette Herring, Chief Information Officer
CHR: Tyree Walker, Chief Human Resources Officer
CNO: Linda D Hofler, Ph.D., R.N., FACHE, Senior Vice President, Nurse Executive
Web address: www.vidanthealth.com/
Control: Other not–for–profit (including NFP Corporation) **Service:** General medical and surgical

Staffed Beds: 974 **Admissions:** 37446 **Census:** 675 **Outpatient Visits:** 404193 **Births:** 3581 **Total Expense ($000):** 1012959 **Payroll Expense ($000):** 349220 **Personnel:** 7303

WALTER B. JONES ALCOHOL AND DRUG ABUSE TREATMENT CENTER (344024), 2577 West Fifth Street, Zip 27834–7813; tel. 252/830–3426, (Nonreporting) **A**3 10
Primary Contact: Ben Gregory, Chief Executive Officer
CFO: Roy Carlton, Chief Financial Officer
CMO: Sonya Longest, M.D., Chief Medical Officer
CIO: Jed Hayn, Chief Information Officer
CHR: Amy Marion, Chief Human Resource Officer
CNO: Linda Roy, R.N., Chief Nursing Officer
Web address: www.ncdhhs.gov
Control: State, Government, nonfederal **Service:** Alcoholism and other chemical dependency

Staffed Beds: 80

HENDERSON—Vance County

✠ **MARIA PARHAM MEDICAL CENTER (340132)**, 566 Ruin Creek Road, Zip 27536–2927; tel. 252/438–4143, (Nonreporting) **A**1 2 3 10 **S** Duke LifePoint Healthcare, Brentwood, TN
Primary Contact: Bert Beard, Chief Executive Officer
CFO: Jim Chatman, Chief Financial Officer
CIO: Randy Williams, Director Management Information Systems
Web address: www.mariaparham.com
Control: Other not–for–profit (including NFP Corporation) **Service:** General medical and surgical

Staffed Beds: 102

HENDERSONVILLE—Henderson County

★ ⇑ **MARGARET R. PARDEE MEMORIAL HOSPITAL (340017)**, 800 North Justice Street, Zip 28791–3410; tel. 828/696–1000, (Data for 273 days) **A**2 3 10 21 **F**3 4 5 11 13 15 18 20 22 24 26 28 29 30 31 34 35 36 38 39 40 44 45 46 47 48 49 50 54 56 57 58 59 62 63 64 65 68 69 70 74 75 76 77 78 79 81 82 85 86 87 89 93 94 97 98 100 101 102 103 104 107 108 110 111 114 115 118 119 120 121 123 129 130 131 132 135 143 144 146 147 148 149 **P**6 **S** UNC Health Care, Chapel Hill, NC
Primary Contact: James M. Kirby II, President and Chief Executive Officer
CFO: Andrew Wampler, Chief Financial Officer
CMO: Robert Kiskaddon, M.D., Chief Medical Officer
CHR: Hope Reynolds, Vice President, Human Resources and Service Excellence
CNO: Denise Lucas, R.N., MSN, Vice President Clinical Services and Chief Nursing Officer
Web address: www.pardeehospital.org
Control: County, Government, nonfederal **Service:** General medical and surgical

Staffed Beds: 160 **Admissions:** 6316 **Census:** 84 **Outpatient Visits:** 246097 **Births:** 253 **Total Expense ($000):** 161648 **Payroll Expense ($000):** 60195 **Personnel:** 1174

✠ ○ **PARK RIDGE HEALTH (340023)**, 100 Hospital Drive, Zip 28792–5272; tel. 828/684–8501, **A**1 2 3 10 11 19 **F**3 11 13 15 18 26 28 29 30 31 34 35 39 40 45 46 47 48 49 50 54 59 62 65 68 70 71 74 75 76 77 78 79 80 81 85 87 93 97 98 101 102 103 104 105 107 108 110 111 114 115 117 118 119 126 129 130 131 135 142 146 147 148 153 154 **P**6 **S** Adventist Health System Sunbelt Health Care Corporation, Altamonte Springs, FL
Primary Contact: Jimm Bunch, President and Chief Executive Officer
CFO: Wendi Barber, Vice President Finance and Chief Financial Officer
CMO: Carlo Mainardi, M.D., Vice President Medical Affairs and Chief Medical Officer
CIO: Lee Strickland, Regional Director Information Technology
CHR: Sharon J Campbell, Director, Human Resources
CNO: Roland Eugene Joy Jr Vice President and Chief Nursing Officer
Web address: www.parkridgehealth.org
Control: Other not–for–profit (including NFP Corporation) **Service:** General medical and surgical

Staffed Beds: 87 **Admissions:** 3965 **Census:** 49 **Outpatient Visits:** 359429 **Births:** 566 **Total Expense ($000):** 165571 **Payroll Expense ($000):** 67023 **Personnel:** 1012

HICKORY—Catawba County

✠ △ **CATAWBA VALLEY MEDICAL CENTER (340143)**, 810 Fairgrove Church Road SE, Zip 28602–9643; tel. 828/326–3000, **A**1 2 5 7 10 **F**3 11 12 13 15 18 20 22 26 28 29 30 31 34 35 39 40 44 45 49 50 51 53 54 56 57 58 59 61 64 65 68 70 71 73 74 75 76 77 78 79 81 84 85 86 87 89 90 91 92 93 96 97 98 100 101 102 103 104 107 108 109 110 111 114 115 117 118 119 120 121 122 123 124 126 129 130 131 132 135 143 144 145 146 147 148 149 154 **P**3 8
Primary Contact: Edward L. Beard, R.N., President and Chief Executive Officer
CFO: Kimberly Crews, Vice President and Chief Financial Officer
CMO: Andrew Chesson, Chief Medical Officer
CIO: Tim Blanchat, Chief Information Officer
CHR: Phyllis M. Johnston, Vice President
Web address: www.catawbavalleymc.org
Control: County, Government, nonfederal **Service:** General medical and surgical

Staffed Beds: 250 **Admissions:** 11359 **Census:** 143 **Outpatient Visits:** 478994 **Births:** 2031 **Total Expense ($000):** 273190 **Payroll Expense ($000):** 120388 **Personnel:** 1799

✠ **FRYE REGIONAL MEDICAL CENTER (340116)**, 420 North Center Street, Zip 28601–5049; tel. 828/315–5000, (Includes FRYE REGIONAL MEDICAL CENTER–SOUTH CAMPUS, One Third Avenue NW, Hickory, NC, Zip 28601, Mailing Address: 420 North Center St., Zip 28603, tel. 828/315–5777) **A**1 2 10 **F**3 11 12 13 15 17 18 20 22 24 26 28 29 30 31 34 37 40 44 45 46 49 54 57 59 64 70 72 74 75 76 77 78 79 81 82 85 86 87 89 90 93 96 98 101 103 107 108 110 111 114 115 118 119 128 129 130 131 132 144 146 147 148 **P**6 **S** Duke LifePoint Healthcare, Brentwood, TN
Primary Contact: Garfield Atchison, Chief Executive Officer
COO: Chris Fensterle, Chief Operating Officer
CFO: Jamey Stoner, Chief Financial Officer
CNO: Michelle Dickerson, Chief Nursing Officer
Web address: www.fryemedctr.com
Control: Corporation, Investor–owned (for–profit) **Service:** General medical and surgical

Staffed Beds: 271 **Admissions:** 10744 **Census:** 163 **Outpatient Visits:** 95313 **Births:** 386 **Personnel:** 1277

HIGH POINT—Guilford County

✠ △ **HIGH POINT REGIONAL HEALTH SYSTEM (340004)**, 601 North Elm Street, Zip 27262–4398, Mailing Address: P.O. Box HP–5, Zip 27261–1899; tel. 336/878–6000, **A**1 7 10 **F**3 4 5 7 8 11 12 13 15 17 18 20 22 24 26 28 29 30 34 35 38 39 40 44 45 47 48 49 50 51 53 54 55 57 58 59 60 61 62 64 66 67 68 70 73 74 75 76 77 78 79 81 82 84 85 86 87 89 90 91 92 93 96 97 98 100 101 102 104 107 108 109 110 111 114 115 118 119 120 121 123 124 126 129 130 131 132 135 144 145 146 147 148 149 151 154 **P**6 **S** UNC Health Care, Chapel Hill, NC
Primary Contact: Ernest L. Bovio Jr, Chief Executive Officer
COO: Gregory W Taylor, M.D., Vice President and Chief Operating Officer
CMO: L Dale Williams, M.D., Vice President and Chief Medical Director
CIO: Nancy Waters, Interim Chief Information Officer
CHR: Katherine Burns, Vice President Human Resources
CNO: Tammi Erving–Mengel, R.N., MSN, Vice President, Chief Nursing Officer
Web address: www.highpointregional.com
Control: Other not–for–profit (including NFP Corporation) **Service:** General medical and surgical

Staffed Beds: 297 **Admissions:** 17148 **Census:** 192 **Outpatient Visits:** 226452 **Births:** 1453 **Total Expense ($000):** 248067 **Payroll Expense ($000):** 99416 **Personnel:** 1625

NC

Many Facility Codes have changed. Please refer to the AHA Guide Code Chart. © 2018 AHA Guide

Hospitals, U.S. / NORTH CAROLINA

HIGHLANDS—Macon County

HIGHLANDS–CASHIERS HOSPITAL (341316), 190 Hospital Drive, Zip 28741–7600, Mailing Address: P O Drawer 190, Zip 28741–0190; tel. 828/526–1200, (Total facility includes 80 beds in nursing home–type unit) **A**1 10 18 **F**3 11 15 28 29 30 34 35 40 45 46 47 48 53 56 57 59 64 65 74 75 77 79 81 91 93 96 107 108 110 111 119 128 130 131 133 146 **P**6 **S** Mission Health System, Asheville, NC
Primary Contact: Jacqueline Medland, MS, Ph.D., President and Chief Nursing Officer
CFO: Lena Cochran, Director of Finance
CHR: Ruby Rowland, Strategic Partner
CNO: Cindy Pierson, Interim Chief Nursing Officer
Web address: www.hchospital.org
Control: Other not–for–profit (including NFP Corporation) **Service:** General medical and surgical

Staffed Beds: 104 **Admissions:** 621 **Census:** 75 **Outpatient Visits:** 36801 **Births:** 0 **Total Expense ($000):** 22528 **Payroll Expense ($000):** 5771 **Personnel:** 115

HUNTERSVILLE—Mecklenburg County

NOVANT HEALTH HUNTERSVILLE MEDICAL CENTER (340183), 10030 Gilead Road, Zip 28078–7545, Mailing Address: P.O. Box 3508, Zip 28070–3508; tel. 704/316–4000, (Nonreporting) **A**1 2 3 10 13 **S** Novant Health, Winston Salem, NC
Primary Contact: Mike Riley, President and Chief Operating Officer
CFO: Fred M Hargett, Executive Vice President and Chief Financial Officer
CMO: Thomas Zweng, Executive Vice President and Chief Medical Officer
CIO: David B Garrett, Senior Vice President and Chief Information Officer
CHR: Janet Smith–Hill, Executive Vice President and Chief Human Resources
CNO: Katrina King, R.N., Senior Director, Nursing
Web address: www.novanthealth.org
Control: Other not–for–profit (including NFP Corporation) **Service:** General medical and surgical

Staffed Beds: 78

JACKSONVILLE—Onslow County

BRYNN MARR HOSPITAL (344016), 192 Village Drive, Zip 28546–7299; tel. 910/577–1400, (Nonreporting) **A**1 10 **S** Universal Health Services, Inc., King of Prussia, PA
Primary Contact: Jay Kortemeyer, Chief Executive Officer
CFO: David Warmerdam, Chief Financial Officer
CMO: Ashraf Mikhail, M.D., Medical Director
CIO: Amy Black, Risk Manager/PI Director
CHR: Jennifer Gier, Director Human Resources
CNO: Sheila Maraan, Director of Nursing
Web address: www.brynnmarr.org
Control: Corporation, Investor–owned (for–profit) **Service:** Psychiatric

Staffed Beds: 99

ONSLOW MEMORIAL HOSPITAL (340042), 317 Western Boulevard, Zip 28546–6379, Mailing Address: P.O. Box 1358, Zip 28541–1358; tel. 910/577–2345, **A**1 2 10 20 **F**3 8 11 13 15 19 20 28 29 34 35 40 45 46 47 48 49 54 57 59 60 64 68 70 72 73 75 76 77 79 81 82 84 85 86 87 89 93 96 107 108 110 111 114 115 117 118 119 126 131 132 135 146 147 148 154 **P**7
Primary Contact: Penney Burlingame Deal, FACHE, R.N., Chief Executive Officer
CFO: Roy Smith, Chief Financial Officer
CMO: Scott Johnston, Chief of Staff
CIO: Rob Lowe, Director, Healthcare Information Management
CHR: Taylor Flowers, Senior Vice President Human Resources
CNO: Regina Lanier, MSN, R.N., Senior Vice President and Chief Nursing Officer
Web address: www.onslow.org
Control: Hospital district or authority, Government, nonfederal **Service:** General medical and surgical

Staffed Beds: 149 **Admissions:** 6629 **Census:** 77 **Outpatient Visits:** 136270 **Births:** 1464 **Total Expense ($000):** 143873 **Payroll Expense ($000):** 52543 **Personnel:** 961

JEFFERSON—Ashe County

ASHE MEMORIAL HOSPITAL (341325), 200 Hospital Avenue, Zip 28640–9244; tel. 336/846–7101, **A**1 10 18 **F**3 11 13 15 28 30 31 34 35 40 45 48 56 57 59 64 75 76 78 79 80 81 85 86 89 91 93 102 107 108 110 111 114 118 119 127 130 132 133 135 141 142 146 147 154 **S** Novant Health, Winston Salem, NC
Primary Contact: Laura Lambeth, Chief Executive Officer
COO: Joe Thore, Chief Operating Officer
CFO: Charles Wright, Chief Financial Officer
CMO: Jayne Leonard, M.D., Family Medicine
CIO: William Baldwin, Chief Information Officer
CHR: Lana Smith, Human Resources Director
CNO: Sara Houser, Chief Nursing Officer
Web address: www.ashememorial.org
Control: Other not–for–profit (including NFP Corporation) **Service:** General medical and surgical

Staffed Beds: 25 **Admissions:** 1339 **Census:** 14 **Outpatient Visits:** 71225 **Births:** 112 **Total Expense ($000):** 30573 **Payroll Expense ($000):** 14104 **Personnel:** 310

KENANSVILLE—Duplin County

VIDANT DUPLIN HOSPITAL (340120), 401 North Main Street, Zip 28349–8801, Mailing Address: P.O. Box 278, Zip 28349–0278; tel. 910/296–0941, **A**1 10 **F**3 11 13 15 18 19 29 30 31 34 35 39 40 45 56 57 59 68 70 75 76 77 78 79 81 91 93 97 98 101 102 103 107 108 110 111 115 116 119 129 130 131 132 135 146 147 154 **S** Vidant Health, Greenville, NC
Primary Contact: Jay Briley, President
COO: Matthew Gitzinger, Director of Operations
CFO: Lucinda Crawford, Vice President Financial Services
CMO: Dyrek Miller, M.D., Chief Medical Staff
CIO: Lucinda Crawford, Vice President Financial Services
CHR: Pansy Chase, Director Human Resources
CNO: Sue O. Taylor, Vice President Nursing
Web address: www.vidanthealth.com
Control: Other not–for–profit (including NFP Corporation) **Service:** General medical and surgical

Staffed Beds: 42 **Admissions:** 3809 **Census:** 48 **Outpatient Visits:** 54694 **Births:** 436 **Total Expense ($000):** 49666 **Payroll Expense ($000):** 20267 **Personnel:** 430

KINGS MOUNTAIN—Cleveland County

★ **CAROLINAS CONTINUECARE HOSPITAL AT KINGS MOUNTAIN (342019)**, 706 West King Street, 2nd Floor, Zip 28086–2708, Mailing Address: P.O. Box 159, Zip 28086–0159; tel. 980/487–5520, **F**1 3 29 30 34 35 59 60 68 77 86 87 91 94 95 96 130 148 149 154 **S** Community Hospital Corporation, Plano, TX
Primary Contact: Derek Murzyn, Chief Executive Officer
CFO: Lisa Young, CPA, Chief Financial Officer
Web address: www.continuecare.org/kings–mountain/
Control: Other not–for–profit (including NFP Corporation) **Service:** Acute long–term care hospital

Staffed Beds: 28 **Admissions:** 187 **Census:** 14 **Outpatient Visits:** 0 **Births:** 0 **Total Expense ($000):** 7923 **Payroll Expense ($000):** 3066 **Personnel:** 66

CAROLINAS HEALTHCARE SYSTEM KINGS MOUNTAIN (340037), 706 West King Street, Zip 28086–2708; tel. 980/487–5000, **A**1 10 **F**3 4 15 29 30 34 40 45 49 59 70 79 81 82 85 93 98 100 107 110 111 115 119 130 133 146 148 149 154 **S** Atrium Health, Charlotte, NC
Primary Contact: Brian Gwyn, President and Chief Executive Officer
CFO: Terry Edwards, Controller
CHR: Debra Kale, Director Human Resources
Web address: www.clevelandregional.org/kings–mountain–hospital.html
Control: Hospital district or authority, Government, nonfederal **Service:** General medical and surgical

Staffed Beds: 59 **Admissions:** 2701 **Census:** 35 **Outpatient Visits:** 59753 **Births:** 0 **Total Expense ($000):** 42522 **Payroll Expense ($000):** 15084 **Personnel:** 258

Hospital, Medicare Provider Number, Address, Telephone, Approval, Facility, and Physician Codes, Health Care System

★ American Hospital Association (AHA) membership
□ The Joint Commission accreditation
○ Healthcare Facilities Accreditation Program
◇ DNV Healthcare Inc. accreditation
⇑ Center for Improvement in Healthcare Quality Accreditation
△ Commission on Accreditation of Rehabilitation Facilities (CARF) accreditation

NC

KINSTON—Lenoir County

☐ **UNC LENOIR HEALTHCARE (340027)**, 100 Airport Road, Zip 28501-1634, Mailing Address: P.O. Box 1678, Zip 28503-1678; tel. 252/522-7000, **A**1 10 **F**3 8 11 12 13 18 20 22 28 29 30 31 34 35 38 40 43 45 47 48 49 50 53 56 57 59 60 61 64 65 68 70 74 75 76 77 78 79 81 85 86 87 89 90 93 102 107 108 111 115 118 119 120 121 123 129 130 132 134 135 143 145 146 147 148 154 **S** UNC Health Care, Chapel Hill, NC
Primary Contact: Gary E. Black, President and Chief Executive Officer
CFO: Sarah Mayo, Vice President Financial Services
CMO: John Herlong, Medical Staff President
CIO: Karl Vanderstouw, Vice President Information Systems
CHR: Jim Dobbins, Vice President Human Resources
CNO: Laurel Molloy, Vice President Nursing and Rehab Services
Web address: www.lenoirmemorial.org
Control: Other not-for-profit (including NFP Corporation) **Service**: General medical and surgical

Staffed Beds: 155 **Admissions**: 5784 **Census**: 73 **Outpatient Visits**: 95833 **Births**: 417 **Total Expense ($000)**: 102799 **Payroll Expense ($000)**: 43891 **Personnel**: 797

LAURINBURG—Scotland County

⊠ **SCOTLAND HEALTH CARE SYSTEM (340008)**, 500 Lauchwood Drive, Zip 28352-5599; tel. 910/291-7000, **A**1 2 3 10 **F**3 11 13 15 18 28 29 31 34 37 40 45 54 57 59 64 70 71 73 74 75 76 77 78 79 81 85 86 87 89 90 92 93 96 97 107 110 111 114 115 119 120 121 123 126 127 130 132 135 143 144 145 146 147 148 149 **S** Atrium Health, Charlotte, NC
Primary Contact: Gregory C. Wood, President and Chief Executive Officer
CFO: Matthew Pracht, Vice President Finance
CMO: Cheryl Davis, M.D., Chief Medical Officer
CIO: Gary Liuzzo, Director Information Systems
CHR: Ann Locklear, Vice President, Human Resources
CNO: Camille Utter, R.N., Chief Nursing Officer
Web address: www.scotlandhealth.org
Control: Other not-for-profit (including NFP Corporation) **Service**: General medical and surgical

Staffed Beds: 104 **Admissions**: 5555 **Census**: 55 **Outpatient Visits**: 134915 **Births**: 726 **Total Expense ($000)**: 125066 **Payroll Expense ($000)**: 46489 **Personnel**: 980

LELAND—Brunswick County

☐ **STRATEGIC BEHAVIORAL HEALTH – WILMINGTON (344030)**, 2050 Mercantile Drive, Zip 28451-4053; tel. 910/371-2500, **A**1 10 **F**56 98 99 101 103 **S** Strategic Behavioral Health, LLC, Memphis, TN
Primary Contact: Daniel Kern, Chief Executive Officer
CHR: Kelly Pace, Director Human Resource
CNO: Brooke Cook, Director of Nursing
Web address: www.sbcwilmington.com/
Control: Corporation, Investor-owned (for-profit) **Service**: Psychiatric

Staffed Beds: 112 **Admissions**: 831 **Census**: 16 **Outpatient Visits**: 0 **Births**: 0 **Total Expense ($000)**: 14284 **Payroll Expense ($000)**: 8999 **Personnel**: 274

LENOIR—Caldwell County

⊠ **CALDWELL UNC HEALTH CARE (340041)**, 321 Mulberry Street SW, Zip 28645-5720, Mailing Address: P.O. Box 1890, Zip 28645-1890; tel. 828/757-5100, **A**1 10 **F**3 8 11 13 15 18 20 22 29 30 31 34 35 37 40 45 46 48 49 50 53 54 55 57 59 64 65 70 75 76 77 78 79 81 82 85 86 87 93 97 107 108 109 110 111 114 119 120 121 122 123 129 132 135 145 146 147 148 149 154 **P**6 **S** UNC Health Care, Chapel Hill, NC
Primary Contact: Laura J. Easton, President and Chief Executive Officer
COO: Rebecca T Smith, Chief Operating Officer and Chief Nursing Officer
CFO: Shawn Hartley, Chief Financial Officer
CMO: David Lowry, M.D., Chief Medical Officer
CIO: Deborah Purcell, Director of Information Technology
CHR: Laura J Easton, President and Chief Executive Officer
CNO: Rebecca T Smith, Chief Operating Officer and Chief Nursing Officer
Web address: www.caldwellmemorial.org
Control: Other not-for-profit (including NFP Corporation) **Service**: General medical and surgical

Staffed Beds: 82 **Admissions**: 3724 **Census**: 50 **Outpatient Visits**: 76659 **Births**: 341 **Total Expense ($000)**: 111705 **Payroll Expense ($000)**: 45401 **Personnel**: 760

LEXINGTON—Davidson County

LEXINGTON MEMORIAL HOSPITAL See Wake Forest Baptist Health–Lexington Medical Center

WAKE FOREST BAPTIST HEALTH–LEXINGTON MEDICAL CENTER (340096)

⊠ **WAKE FOREST BAPTIST HEALTH–LEXINGTON MEDICAL CENTER (340096)**, 250 Hospital Drive, Zip 27292-6728, Mailing Address: P.O. Box 1817, Zip 27293-1817; tel. 336/248-5161, **A**1 3 10 **F**3 13 15 18 28 29 30 31 34 35 40 45 46 50 57 58 59 61 64 65 68 70 74 75 76 78 79 81 82 85 87 91 92 93 97 102 107 108 110 111 115 119 120 121 123 129 130 131 146 147 148 154 **S** Wake Forest Baptist Health, Winston-Salem, NC
Primary Contact: William B. James, FACHE, President
CFO: Danny Squires, Vice President and Chief Financial Officer
CMO: Raghava Nagaraj, Chief Medical Officer
CIO: Dee Emon, R.N., Chief Information Officer
CNO: Clyde A. Bristow, R.N., III Senior Director Nursing and Clinical Services, Chief Nursing Officer
Web address: www.lexington.wakehealth.edu
Control: Other not-for-profit (including NFP Corporation) **Service**: General medical and surgical

Staffed Beds: 85 **Admissions**: 3115 **Census**: 26 **Outpatient Visits**: 121391 **Births**: 389 **Total Expense ($000)**: 80030 **Payroll Expense ($000)**: 32996 **Personnel**: 530

LINCOLNTON—Lincoln County

⊠ **CAROLINAS HEALTHCARE SYSTEM LINCOLN (340145)**, 433 McAlister Road, Zip 28092-4147, Mailing Address: PO Box 677, Zip 28093-0677; tel. 980/212-2000, **A**1 10 **F**3 8 11 13 15 18 28 29 30 31 34 40 44 45 50 51 57 59 64 70 73 74 75 76 77 78 79 81 82 84 85 87 91 93 94 96 107 108 114 115 118 119 129 130 131 132 135 146 148 149 150 154 **S** Atrium Health, Charlotte, NC
Primary Contact: Peter W. Acker, President and Chief Executive Officer
COO: Teresa C Watson, Vice President Administration
CFO: Jarrett L Morris, Controller
CMO: Vineet Goel, Chief Medical Officer
CIO: Jarrett L Morris, Controller and Chief Information Officer
CHR: Lesley Chambless, Assistant Vice President Human Resources
CNO: Elaine S Haynes, R.N., MSN, Vice President Patient Services and Chief Nursing Executive
Web address: www.carolinashealthcare.org/lincoln
Control: Hospital district or authority, Government, nonfederal **Service**: General medical and surgical

Staffed Beds: 101 **Admissions**: 4374 **Census**: 46 **Outpatient Visits**: 100697 **Births**: 440 **Total Expense ($000)**: 104901 **Payroll Expense ($000)**: 32013 **Personnel**: 541

LUMBERTON—Robeson County

★ ⇑ **SOUTHEASTERN HEALTH (340050)**, 300 West 27th Street, Zip 28358-3075, Mailing Address: P.O. Box 1408, Zip 28359-1408; tel. 910/671-5000, (Nonreporting) **A**2 3 10 12 13 21
Primary Contact: Joann Anderson, President and Chief Executive Officer
CFO: C Thomas Johnson III Vice President Finance and Chief Financial Officer
CMO: Barry Williamson, President Medical Staff
CIO: Eric Harper, Chief Information Officer
CHR: Susan Hayes, Director Human Resources
CNO: Renae Taylor, Chief Nursing Officer
Web address: www.srmc.org
Control: Other not-for-profit (including NFP Corporation) **Service**: General medical and surgical

Staffed Beds: 380

MARION—Mcdowell County

⊠ **MCDOWELL HOSPITAL (340087)**, 430 Rankin Drive, Zip 28752-6568, Mailing Address: P.O. Box 730, Zip 28752-0730; tel. 828/659-5000, **A**1 10 **F**3 13 15 18 28 29 30 31 34 35 40 45 57 59 64 70 76 77 78 79 81 82 85 87 93 97 107 108 110 111 115 119 127 129 130 131 132 135 144 146 147 148 149 154 **S** Mission Health System, Asheville, NC
Primary Contact: Carol C. Wolfenbarger, FACHE, MSN, President
CFO: Clint Stewart, Regional Director of Finance East
CMO: Rex Henderson, M.D., Chief of Staff
CIO: Pam Blevins, R.N., Director Information Technology Member Hospitals Mission
CHR: Tonya Revels, Senior Strategic Business Partner
CNO: Kathy Hefner, Chief Nursing Officer
Web address: www.mission-health.org
Control: Other not-for-profit (including NFP Corporation) **Service**: General medical and surgical

Staffed Beds: 49 **Admissions**: 2003 **Census**: 20 **Outpatient Visits**: 187877 **Births**: 183 **Total Expense ($000)**: 59336 **Payroll Expense ($000)**: 30013 **Personnel**: 342

NC

Many Facility Codes have changed. Please refer to the AHA Guide Code Chart.

✠ **NOVANT HEALTH MATTHEWS MEDICAL CENTER (340171)**, 1500 Matthews Township Parkway, Zip 28105–4656; tel. 704/384–6500, (Nonreporting) **A**1 2 10 **S** Novant Health, Winston Salem, NC
Primary Contact: Roland R. Bibeau, President and Chief Operating Officer
CFO: Fred M Hargett, Executive Vice President and Chief Financial Officer
CMO: Thomas Zweng, Executive Vice President and Chief Medical Officer
CIO: David B Garrett, Senior Vice President and Chief Information Officer
CHR: Janet Smith–Hill, Executive Vice President and Chief HR Officer
CNO: Tracy B Forster, R.N., Senior Director of Nursing
Web address: www.novanthealth.org
Control: Other not–for–profit (including NFP Corporation) **Service**: General medical and surgical

Staffed Beds: 111

MONROE—Union County

✠ **CAROLINAS HEALTHCARE SYSTEM UNION (340130)**, 600 Hospital Drive, Zip 28112–6000, Mailing Address: P.O. Box 5003, Zip 28111–5003; tel. 980/993–3100, (Total facility includes 70 beds in nursing home–type unit) **A**1 2 3 10 **F**3 4 5 8 13 18 20 22 26 27 28 29 30 31 34 35 39 40 45 49 53 56 57 59 60 64 66 68 70 72 74 75 76 77 78 79 81 82 84 85 86 87 89 93 97 102 107 108 111 114 117 118 119 120 121 123 126 128 129 130 132 135 143 146 147 148 152 154 **S** Atrium Health, Charlotte, NC
Primary Contact: Michael Lutes, President
COO: Dave Anderson, FACHE, Vice President Administration
CFO: John G Moore, Vice President and Chief Financial Officer
CMO: Craig M Slater, M.D., Chief Medical Officer
CIO: Lisa Sykes, Director Information Services
CHR: Rhonda McFarland, Director Human Resources
CNO: Denise White, MSN, Chief Nurse Executive
Web address: www.carolinashealthcare.org/union
Control: Hospital district or authority, Government, nonfederal **Service**: General medical and surgical

Staffed Beds: 228 Admissions: 9099 Census: 147 Outpatient Visits: 181640 Births: 1087 Total Expense ($000): 210093 Payroll Expense ($000): 64694 Personnel: 1028

MOORESVILLE—Iredell County

✠ **LAKE NORMAN REGIONAL MEDICAL CENTER (340129)**, 171 Fairview Road, Zip 28117–9500, Mailing Address: P.O. Box 3250, Zip 28117–3250; tel. 704/660–4000, (Nonreporting) **A**1 2 10 19 **S** Community Health Systems, Inc., Franklin, TN
Primary Contact: Stephen L. Midkiff, Chief Executive Officer
CFO: Claire Polk, Chief Financial Officer
CHR: Stephanie Williams, Market Director Human Resources
CNO: Marie Marks, Chief Nursing Officer
Web address: www.lnrmc.com
Control: Corporation, Investor–owned (for–profit) **Service**: General medical and surgical

Staffed Beds: 123

MOREHEAD CITY—Carteret County

✠ **CARTERET HEALTH CARE (340142)**, 3500 Arendell Street, Zip 28557–2901, Mailing Address: P.O. Box 1619, Zip 28557–1619; tel. 252/499–6000, **A**1 2 10 **F**3 7 11 12 13 15 18 20 22 28 29 30 31 34 35 37 40 45 46 54 57 59 62 63 64 65 68 70 74 75 76 77 78 79 81 82 84 85 86 87 89 91 93 97 107 108 110 111 114 115 118 119 120 121 123 129 130 132 135 143 145 146 148 154
Primary Contact: Richard A. Brvenik, President
CFO: Joanie King, Chief Financial Officer
CMO: Donald Pocock, Vice–President Medical Affairs
CIO: Kyle Marek, Chief Information Officer
CHR: Elizabeth Beswick, Vice President Human Resources and Public Relations
Web address: www.carterethealth.org
Control: County, Government, nonfederal **Service**: General medical and surgical

Staffed Beds: 104 Admissions: 5654 Census: 67 Outpatient Visits: 168130 Births: 758 Total Expense ($000): 137446 Payroll Expense ($000): 53629 Personnel: 904

MORGANTON—Burke County

☐ **BROUGHTON HOSPITAL (344025)**, 1000 South Sterling Street, Zip 28655–3999; tel. 828/433–2111, (Nonreporting) **A**1 3 5 10
Primary Contact: Vivian Streater, Co–Acting Chief Executive Officer
CFO: Bea Tullis, Chief Financial Officer and Budget Officer
CMO: George Krebs, M.D., Chief Medical Officer
CIO: Darin Kiracofe, Director Information Resource Management
CHR: Jean Buchanan, Director Human Resources
CNO: Vivian Streater, Chief Nursing Officer and Co–Acting Chief Executive Officer
Web address: www.ncdhhs.gov/dsohf/broughton
Control: State, Government, nonfederal **Service**: Psychiatric

Staffed Beds: 297

✠ **CAROLINAS HEALTHCARE SYSTEM BLUE RIDGE (340075)**, 2201 South Sterling Street, Zip 28655–4058; tel. 828/580–5000, (Includes CAROLINAS HEALTHCARE SYSTEM – BLUE RIDGE – MORGANTON, 2201 South Sterling Street, Morganton, NC, Zip 28655–4058; tel. 828/580–5000; VALDESE GENERAL HOSPITAL, 720 Malcolm Boulevard, Valdese, NC, Zip 28690–2872, Mailing Address: P.O. Box 700, Zip 28690–0700, tel. 828/874–2251) **A**1 2 3 10 13 **F**3 13 15 18 20 22 28 29 30 31 34 35 40 45 49 50 53 56 57 59 64 68 69 70 71 72 76 77 78 81 82 85 86 87 93 96 97 98 107 108 110 111 114 115 119 120 121 123 130 131 132 146 147 148 **S** Atrium Health, Charlotte, NC
Primary Contact: Kathy C. Bailey, Ph.D., FACHE, President and Chief Executive Officer
CFO: Robert G Fritts, Chief Financial Officer and Senior Vice President
CMO: Joe Mazzola, D.O., Senior Vice President Medical Affairs and Chief Medical Officer
CHR: Thomas Eure, Vice President Administration
Web address: www.blueridgehealth.org
Control: Other not–for–profit (including NFP Corporation) **Service**: General medical and surgical

Staffed Beds: 156 Admissions: 7481 Census: 85 Births: 888

MOUNT AIRY—Surry County

✠ **NORTHERN HOSPITAL OF SURRY COUNTY (340003)**, 830 Rockford Street, Zip 27030–5365, Mailing Address: P.O. Box 1101, Zip 27030–1101; tel. 336/719–7000, (Total facility includes 33 beds in nursing home–type unit) **A**1 10 **F**3 12 13 15 18 28 29 30 31 34 35 40 45 50 53 54 55 56 57 59 64 65 67 70 75 76 77 79 80 81 82 85 86 87 89 97 107 108 110 111 114 115 118 119 128 130 131 132 133 135 145 146 147 148 149 **P**6 **S** QHR, Brentwood, TN
Primary Contact: Chris A. Lumsden, President and Chief Executive Officer
CFO: Andrea Hickling, Vice President of Finance and Chief Financial Officer
CMO: Druery DeVore, Chief of Medical Staff
CIO: Rodney Bond, Director of Information Technology
CHR: Julia Nelson, Vice President of Human Resources
CNO: Robin Hodgin, R.N., Vice President of Patient Services and Chief Nursing Officer
Web address: www.northernhospital.com
Control: Hospital district or authority, Government, nonfederal **Service**: General medical and surgical

Staffed Beds: 108 Admissions: 3961 Census: 67 Outpatient Visits: 121483 Births: 339 Total Expense ($000): 90523 Payroll Expense ($000): 39382 Personnel: 533

MURPHY—Cherokee County

✠ **ERLANGER MURPHY MEDICAL CENTER (341328)**, 3990 US Highway 64 East Alt, Zip 28906–7917; tel. 828/837–8161, (Nonreporting) **A**1 10 18 **S** Erlanger Health System, Chattanooga, TN
Primary Contact: Mark E. Kimball, Chief Executive Officer
COO: Toni Lovingood, Chief Operating Officer
CFO: Steve Gilgen, Chief Financial Officer
CMO: Jeffrey H Martin, M.D., Chief of Staff
CIO: Connie Stalcup, Manager Information Systems
CHR: Russ Paine, Human Resources Officer
CNO: Teresa Bowleg, R.N., Chief Nursing Officer
Web address: www.murphymedical.org
Control: Other not–for–profit (including NFP Corporation) **Service**: General medical and surgical

Staffed Beds: 191

Hospital, Medicare Provider Number, Address, Telephone, Approval, Facility, and Physician Codes, Health Care System

★ American Hospital Association (AHA) membership
☐ The Joint Commission accreditation
○ Healthcare Facilities Accreditation Program
◇ DNV Healthcare Inc. accreditation
⇑ Center for Improvement in Healthcare Quality Accreditation
△ Commission on Accreditation of Rehabilitation Facilities (CARF) accreditation

NC

© 2018 AHA Guide   *Many Facility Codes have changed. Please refer to the AHA Guide Code Chart.*   Hospitals **A457**

NAGS HEAD—Dare County

☒ **THE OUTER BANKS HOSPITAL (341324)**, 4800 South Croatan Highway, Zip 27959–9704; tel. 252/449–4500, **A**1 2 10 18 **F**13 15 28 29 30 31 34 35 36 38 40 45 50 51 54 57 59 64 65 68 71 75 77 78 79 81 82 84 85 86 87 93 100 107 108 109 110 111 114 115 118 119 120 121 129 130 133 135 141 144 146 147 149 154 **P**5 **S** Vidant Health, Greenville, NC
Primary Contact: Ronald A. Sloan, FACHE, President
CFO: Todd Warlitner, Vice President Business Operations
CMO: Roger Lever, M.D., President Medical Staff
CHR: Mary Kelley, Director Human Resources
CNO: Marcia Bryant, R.N., Vice President, Clinical Operations
Web address: www.theouterbankshospital.com
Control: Other not–for–profit (including NFP Corporation) **Service:** General medical and surgical

Staffed Beds: 21 **Admissions:** 1028 **Census:** 6 **Outpatient Visits:** 39485 **Births:** 334 **Total Expense ($000):** 66926 **Payroll Expense ($000):** 19209 **Personnel:** 318

NEW BERN—Craven County

☒ △ **CAROLINAEAST HEALTH SYSTEM (340131)**, 2000 Neuse Boulevard, Zip 28560–3499, Mailing Address: P.O. Box 12157, Zip 28561–2157; tel. 252/633–8111, **A**1 2 7 10 **F**3 7 8 11 13 15 17 18 20 22 24 26 28 29 30 31 34 35 36 40 45 47 48 49 53 54 57 58 59 62 64 67 70 75 76 77 78 79 81 84 85 86 87 89 90 91 92 93 94 96 98 101 102 107 108 110 111 113 114 115 116 117 118 119 120 121 123 126 130 132 135 146 147 148 **P**4
Primary Contact: G Raymond. Leggett III, President and Chief Executive Officer
CFO: Tammy M. Sherron, Vice President Finance
CMO: Ronald B May, M.D., Vice President Medical Affairs
CIO: Ronald B May, M.D., Vice President Medical Affairs
CHR: Bruce A Martin, Vice President Human Resources
CNO: Rosanne Leahy, Vice President Nursing Services
Web address: www.carolinaeasthealth.com
Control: Hospital district or authority, Government, nonfederal **Service:** General medical and surgical

Staffed Beds: 201 **Admissions:** 12702 **Census:** 176 **Outpatient Visits:** 174509 **Births:** 1099 **Total Expense ($000):** 271047 **Payroll Expense ($000):** 97705 **Personnel:** 1874

NEWLAND—Avery County

☒ **CHARLES A. CANNON MEMORIAL HOSPITAL (341323)**, 434 Hospital Drive, Zip 28646, Mailing Address: P.O. Box 767, Linville, Zip 28646–0767; tel. 828/737–7000, **A**1 10 18 **F**3 11 15 28 29 30 40 45 64 68 70 81 85 93 98 100 101 102 104 107 110 115 119 130 133 135 146 149 154 **S** Appalachian Regional Healthcare System, Boone, NC
Primary Contact: Carmen Lacey, MSN, R.N., President
CFO: Kevin B May, System Director Finance
CMO: Thomas M Haizlip, M.D., Jr Chief of Staff
CIO: Nathan White, Chief Information Officer
CHR: Amy J. Crabbe, Vice President People Services
CNO: Carmen Lacey, MSN, R.N., President and Director of Patient Care Services
Web address: www.https://apprhs.org/locations/cannon–memorial–hospital
Control: Other not–for–profit (including NFP Corporation) **Service:** General medical and surgical

Staffed Beds: 35 **Admissions:** 1200 **Census:** 14 **Outpatient Visits:** 33175 **Births:** 0 **Total Expense ($000):** 22672 **Payroll Expense ($000):** 8352 **Personnel:** 157

NORTH WILKESBORO—Wilkes County

☒ **WAKE FOREST BAPTIST HEALTH – WILKES MEDICAL CENTER (340064)**, 1370 West 'D' Street, Zip 28659–3506, Mailing Address: P.O. Box 609, Zip 28659–0609; tel. 336/651–8100, (Total facility includes 10 beds in nursing home–type unit) (Data for 273 days) **A**1 10 **F**3 11 13 15 18 29 30 34 35 40 45 49 57 59 60 64 67 68 70 74 76 77 79 81 85 87 91 92 93 107 108 110 111 114 115 119 124 128 130 146 154 **S** Wake Forest Baptist Health, Winston–Salem, NC
Primary Contact: J Gene. Faile, Chief Executive Officer and President
CFO: Barry Wald, Chief Financial Officer
CMO: Richard Barber, M.D., Chief Medical Officer
CIO: William Hofman, Manager Information Technology
CHR: Vanya Baker, Director
CNO: Sandy Sheppard, Vice President Patient Services
Web address: www.wilkesregional.com/
Control: City, Government, nonfederal **Service:** General medical and surgical

Staffed Beds: 92 **Admissions:** 2862 **Census:** 40 **Outpatient Visits:** 79600 **Births:** 269 **Total Expense ($000):** 55846 **Payroll Expense ($000):** 20685 **Personnel:** 602

OXFORD—Granville County

☒ **GRANVILLE HEALTH SYSTEM (340127)**, 1010 College Street, Zip 27565–2507, Mailing Address: P.O. Box 947, Zip 27565–0947; tel. 919/690–3000, (Total facility includes 80 beds in nursing home–type unit) **A**1 3 10 **F**2 3 7 11 13 15 18 19 29 30 34 35 38 39 40 45 50 54 55 56 57 59 64 66 70 75 76 77 79 81 82 85 86 93 100 101 104 107 108 110 111 112 114 115 118 119 124 127 128 129 130 132 133 143 144 146 147 148 **P**3 6 8
Primary Contact: John Snow, Chief Executive Officer
COO: Cristina Rigsbee Carroll, Chief Operating Officer
CFO: Jeffery Armstrong, CPA, Chief Financial Officer
CMO: Richard Pacca, M.D., Chief of Staff
CIO: Geoff Tanthorey, Director, Information Systems
CHR: Scott Thomas, Administrative Director Human Resources and Communications
CNO: Bill Hughes, Chief Nursing Officer
Web address: www.ghshospital.com
Control: County, Government, nonfederal **Service:** General medical and surgical

Staffed Beds: 142 **Admissions:** 2180 **Census:** 88 **Outpatient Visits:** 52079 **Births:** 280 **Total Expense ($000):** 52044 **Payroll Expense ($000):** 28417 **Personnel:** 587

PINEHURST—Moore County

☒ △ **FIRSTHEALTH MOORE REGIONAL HOSPITAL (340115)**, 155 Memorial Drive, Zip 28374–8710, Mailing Address: P.O. Box 3000, Zip 28374–3000; tel. 910/715–1000, (Includes FIRSTHEALTH MOORE REGIONAL HOSPITAL – HOKE, 6408 Fayetteville Road, Raeford, NC, Zip 28376–7977; tel. 910/878–6000; Susan R Beaty, R.N., Administrator; FIRSTHEALTH MOORE REGIONAL HOSPITAL – RICHMOND, 925 Long Drive, Rockingham, NC, Zip 28379–4835; tel. 910/417–3000; John J Jackson, President) **A**1 2 7 10 13 19 **F**3 4 5 11 12 13 15 17 18 20 22 24 26 28 29 30 31 34 35 40 44 45 46 47 48 49 50 51 53 54 55 56 57 58 59 60 64 65 68 70 72 74 75 76 77 78 79 81 82 86 87 89 90 91 93 96 98 99 100 101 102 103 104 105 107 108 111 114 115 118 119 120 121 124 126 129 130 132 134 135 143 146 147 148 153 154 **S** FirstHealth of the Carolinas, Pinehurst, NC
Primary Contact: David J. Kilarski, FACHE, Chief Executive Officer
COO: Brian Canfield, Chief Operating Officer
CFO: Lynn S DeJaco, Chief Financial Officer
CMO: John F Krahnert, M.D., Chief Medical Officer
CIO: David B Dillehunt, Chief Information Officer
CHR: Daniel F Biediger, Vice President Human Resources
CNO: Karen Robeano, R.N., Chief Nursing Officer and Vice President Patient Care Services
Web address: www.firsthealth.org
Control: Other not–for–profit (including NFP Corporation) **Service:** General medical and surgical

Staffed Beds: 376 **Admissions:** 20618 **Census:** 257 **Outpatient Visits:** 190094 **Births:** 1980 **Total Expense ($000):** 402546 **Payroll Expense ($000):** 180277 **Personnel:** 3460

PLYMOUTH—Washington County

⇑ **WASHINGTON COUNTY HOSPITAL (341314)**, 958 US Highway 64 East, Zip 27962–9591, Mailing Address: PO Box 707, Zip 27962–9591; tel. 252/793–4135, (Nonreporting) **A**10 18 21 **S** Rural Community Hospitals of America, Kansas City, MO
Primary Contact: Al Arrowood, Interim President
CMO: Robert Venable, M.D., Chief Medical Staff
CIO: Christina Craft, Director Information Systems
CNO: Kimberly Manning, Chief Nursing Officer
Control: County, Government, nonfederal **Service:** General medical and surgical

Staffed Beds: 25

RAEFORD—Hoke County

HOKE HOSPITAL (340188), 210 Medical Pavilion Drive, Zip 28376–9111; tel. 910/904–8000, (Nonreporting) **S** Cape Fear Valley Health System, Fayetteville, NC
Primary Contact: Roxie Cannon. Wells, M.D., President
Web address: www.capefearvalley.com
Control: County, Government, nonfederal **Service:** General medical and surgical

Staffed Beds: 41

RALEIGH—Wake County

CENTRAL PRISON HOSPITAL, 1300 Western Boulevard, Zip 27606–2148; tel. 919/743–2440, (Nonreporting) **A**3
Primary Contact: Dean Doering, Chief Executive Officer
CMO: Olushola Metiko, M.D., Medical Director
CHR: Bruce McKinney, Business Officer, Administrative Services
CNO: Cindy J McLean, R.N., MSN, Director of Nursing
Web address: www.ncdps.gov/index2.cfm?a=000003,002240,002381,002252
Control: State, Government, nonfederal **Service:** Hospital unit of an institution (prison hospital, college infirmary, etc.)

Staffed Beds: 230

Many Facility Codes have changed. Please refer to the AHA Guide Code Chart.

☒ **DUKE RALEIGH HOSPITAL (340073)**, 3400 Wake Forest Road, Zip 27609–7373; tel. 919/954–3000, **A**1 2 3 10 **F**3 11 12 15 18 20 22 26 28 29 30 31 34 35 36 39 40 44 46 47 49 50 51 53 55 57 58 59 60 64 68 70 74 75 77 78 79 80 81 82 84 85 87 92 93 94 96 100 102 103 107 108 110 111 114 115 117 118 119 120 121 123 126 129 130 131 132 135 142 146 147 148 149 154 **P**6 **S** Duke University Health System, Durham, NC
Primary Contact: David William. Zaas, M.D., Chief Executive Officer
COO: Brian Sloan, Chief Operating Officer
CMO: Ted Kunstling, M.D., Chief Medical Officer
CIO: Janis Curtis, Interim Director Information Technology
CHR: Donald K Barnes, Chief Human Resources Officer
Web address: www.dukehealthraleigh.org
Control: Other not–for–profit (including NFP Corporation) **Service**: General medical and surgical

Staffed Beds: 171 **Admissions:** 9560 **Census:** 117 **Outpatient Visits:** 230957 **Births:** 0 **Total Expense ($000):** 389819 **Payroll Expense ($000):** 102610 **Personnel:** 1707	

☐ **HOLLY HILL HOSPITAL (344014)**, 3019 Falstaff Road, Zip 27610–1812; tel. 919/250–7000, **A**1 10 **F**4 5 29 38 56 68 98 99 103 105 151 152 154 **S** Universal Health Services, Inc., King of Prussia, PA
Primary Contact: Amanda Johanson, Chief Executive Officer
COO: Jessica Knudsen, Chief Operating Officer and Director Performance Improvement and Risk Management
CFO: Ron Howard, Chief Financial Officer
CMO: Thomas Cornwall, M.D., Medical Director
CHR: Ebuni McFall–Roberts, Director Human Resources
CNO: Michael Hartley, MS, Chief Nursing Officer
Web address: www.hollyhillhospital.com
Control: Corporation, Investor–owned (for–profit) **Service**: Psychiatric

Staffed Beds: 228 **Admissions:** 8381 **Census:** 204 **Outpatient Visits:** 6087 **Births:** 0 **Total Expense ($000):** 43459 **Payroll Expense ($000):** 19652 **Personnel:** 458	

LARRY B. ZIEVERINK, SR. ALCOHOLISM TREATMENT CENTER, 3000 Falstaff Road, Zip 27610–1897; tel. 919/250–1500, (Nonreporting)
Primary Contact: Martin D. Woodward, Director Acute Care Services
COO: Martin D Woodward, Director Acute Care Services
CFO: Paul Gross, Human Services and Finance Officer
CMO: Enrique Lopez, M.D., Medical Director
CIO: Wil A Glenn, Director Communications
Web address: www.wakegov.com/county/family/atc
Control: County, Government, nonfederal **Service**: Alcoholism and other chemical dependency

Staffed Beds: 34	

☐ **TRIANGLE SPRINGS HOSPITAL**, 10901 World Trade Boulevard, Zip 27617–4203; tel. 919/372–4408, (Nonreporting) **A**1 **S** Springstone, Louisville, KY
Primary Contact: Carla Hollis, Chief Executive Officer
Web address: www.trianglesprings.com
Control: Corporation, Investor–owned (for–profit) **Service**: Psychiatric

Staffed Beds: 77	

☒ **UNC REX HEALTH CARE (340114)**, 4420 Lake Boone Trail, Zip 27607–6599; tel. 919/784–3100, (Total facility includes 227 beds in nursing home–type unit) **A**1 2 3 5 10 **F**3 7 8 11 12 13 14 15 17 18 20 22 24 26 28 29 30 31 34 35 36 40 44 45 46 47 48 49 50 53 54 56 57 58 59 60 62 64 65 68 69 71 72 73 74 75 76 77 78 79 81 82 84 85 86 87 89 92 93 96 97 100 102 107 108 110 111 114 115 116 117 118 119 120 121 123 126 128 129 130 131 132 135 142 143 144 145 146 147 148 149 154 **P**6 **S** UNC Health Care, Chapel Hill, NC
Primary Contact: Stephen W. Burriss, President
COO: Sue Sandberg, R.N., Chief Operating Officer
CFO: Andrew Zukowski, Chief Financial Officer
CMO: Linda H. Butler, M.D., Chief Medical Officer
CIO: Tracy Parham, Health Care System Chief Information Officer
CHR: Scott Doak, Vice President, Human Resources
CNO: Colonel Joel Ray, MSN, Vice President and Chief Nursing Officer
Web address: www.rexhealth.com
Control: Other not–for–profit (including NFP Corporation) **Service**: General medical and surgical

Staffed Beds: 666 **Admissions:** 29431 **Census:** 523 **Outpatient Visits:** 937491 **Births:** 5121 **Total Expense ($000):** 955311 **Payroll Expense ($000):** 382505 **Personnel:** 4970	

☒ △ **WAKEMED RALEIGH CAMPUS (340069)**, 3000 New Bern Avenue, Zip 27610–1295; tel. 919/350–8000, (Includes WAKEMED NORTH FAMILY HEALTH AND WOMEN'S HOSPITAL, 10000 Falls Of Neuse Road, Raleigh, NC, Zip 27614–7838; tel. 919/350–8000; Sherri De Shazo, R.N., Senior Vice President and Hospital Administrator) **A**1 3 5 7 10 **F**3 7 8 12 13 15 17 18 20 22 24 26 28 29 30 31 32 34 35 37 38 40 41 43 44 45 46 48 49 50 53 54 56 57 58 59 60 61 62 64 65 66 68 70 71 72 73 74 75 76 77 78 79 80 81 85 86 87 88 89 90 92 93 95 96 97 100 107 110 111 114 115 118 119 126 130 131 132 135 143 144 146 147 148 154 **P**6 **S** WakeMed Health & Hospitals, Raleigh, NC
Primary Contact: Donald R. Gintzig, President and Chief Executive Officer
COO: Denise Wilder Warren, R.N., Executive Vice President and Chief Operating Officer
CMO: West Paul, M.D., Ph.D., Senior Vice President and Chief Quality and Medical Staff Officer
CIO: Peter Marks, Vice President & Chief Information Officer
CHR: Jeanene R Martin, M.P.H., Senior Vice President Human Resources
CNO: Cindy Boily, MSN, R.N., Senior Vice President and Chief Nursing Officer
Web address: www.wakemed.org
Control: Other not–for–profit (including NFP Corporation) **Service**: General medical and surgical

Staffed Beds: 695 **Admissions:** 29798 **Census:** 511 **Outpatient Visits:** 1489684 **Births:** 5373 **Total Expense ($000):** 1010647 **Payroll Expense ($000):** 551843 **Personnel:** 7230	

REIDSVILLE—Rockingham County

ANNIE PENN HOSPITAL See Moses H. Cone Memorial Hospital, Greensboro

ROANOKE RAPIDS—Halifax County

☒ **HALIFAX REGIONAL MEDICAL CENTER (340151)**, 250 Smith Church Road, Zip 27870–4914, Mailing Address: P.O. Box 1089, Zip 27870–1089; tel. 252/535–8011, (Nonreporting) **A**1 10 20 **S** Novant Health, Winston Salem, NC
Primary Contact: William Mahone, President and Chief Executive Officer
CFO: Sherry Jensen, Chief Financial Officer
CIO: Robert Gordon, Manager Information Systems
CHR: Thomas Mastroianni, Administrative Director of Human Resources
CNO: Karen Daniels, MSN, R.N., Chief Nursing Officer
Web address: www.halifaxmedicalcenter.org
Control: Other not–for–profit (including NFP Corporation) **Service**: General medical and surgical

Staffed Beds: 142	

ROCKY MOUNT—Nash County

☒ **LIFECARE HOSPITALS OF NORTH CAROLINA (342013)**, 1051 Noell Lane, Zip 27804–1761; tel. 252/451–2300, **A**1 10 **F**1 3 29 30 77 91 148 **S** LifeCare Management Services, Plano, TX
Primary Contact: Robyn Perkerson, R.N., Administrator
COO: Robyn Perkerson, R.N., Administrator
CMO: Daniel Crocker, M.D., Chief Medical Officer
CHR: Vicky Goode, Director Human Resources
CNO: Brandee Chappell, Director of Nursing
Web address: www.lifecare-hospitals.com
Control: Corporation, Investor–owned (for–profit) **Service**: Acute long–term care hospital

Staffed Beds: 43 **Admissions:** 520 **Census:** 42 **Outpatient Visits:** 0 **Births:** 0 **Personnel:** 184	

☒ **NASH HEALTH CARE SYSTEMS (340147)**, 2460 Curtis Ellis Drive, Zip 27804–2237; tel. 252/962–8000, **A**1 2 10 **F**3 4 11 12 13 15 18 20 22 28 29 30 31 34 35 38 40 41 44 45 48 49 50 54 55 57 59 60 63 64 70 73 74 75 76 77 78 79 80 81 82 84 85 86 87 90 93 96 98 100 101 102 107 108 110 111 114 115 117 118 119 120 121 123 126 127 129 130 131 132 135 146 147 148 **P**6 **S** UNC Health Care, Chapel Hill, NC
Primary Contact: L Lee. Isley, FACHE, Ph.D., President and Chief Executive Officer
COO: Brad Weisner, Executive Vice President and Chief Operating Officer
CFO: Shawn Hartley, Chief Financial Officer
CHR: Katie Davison, Executive Director, Human Resources
CNO: Crystal Hayden, MSN, R.N., Senior Vice President and Chief Nursing Officer
Web address: www.nhcs.org
Control: Hospital district or authority, Government, nonfederal **Service**: General medical and surgical

Staffed Beds: 273 **Admissions:** 12078 **Census:** 177 **Outpatient Visits:** 179775 **Births:** 1063 **Total Expense ($000):** 233030 **Payroll Expense ($000):** 97374 **Personnel:** 1634	

ROXBORO—Person County

✠ **PERSON MEMORIAL HOSPITAL (340159)**, 615 Ridge Road, Zip 27573–4629; tel. 336/599–2121, (Total facility includes 60 beds in nursing home–type unit) **A**1 10 **F**3 11 15 18 28 29 34 40 45 57 59 64 70 75 77 79 81 85 87 93 96 97 107 108 110 111 114 119 124 128 130 132 146 149 154 **P**6 **S** Duke LifePoint Healthcare, Brentwood, TN
Primary Contact: David Ziolkowski, Chief Executive Officer
CFO: Jessi Ayers, Chief Financial Officer
CIO: Rhonda M. Elliott, Director Information Technology and Meaningful Use
CHR: Mary Barksdale, Director Human Resources
CNO: Lynn Peoples, Interim Chief Nursing Officer
Web address: www.personhospital.com
Control: Partnership, Investor–owned (for–profit) **Service**: General medical and surgical

Staffed Beds: 98 **Admissions**: 1305 **Census**: 56 **Outpatient Visits**: 19695
Births: 0 **Total Expense ($000)**: 32985 **Payroll Expense ($000)**: 10176
Personnel: 191

RUTHERFORDTON—Rutherford County

✠ **RUTHERFORD REGIONAL HEALTH SYSTEM (340013)**, 288 South Ridgecrest Avenue, Zip 28139–2838; tel. 828/286–5000, **A**1 2 10 **F**3 13 15 18 20 28 29 30 31 34 35 40 45 48 50 57 59 64 70 75 76 77 78 79 81 85 86 87 89 93 97 98 100 101 102 104 107 108 110 111 114 115 118 119 130 131 132 135 146 147 149 **S** Duke LifePoint Healthcare, Brentwood, TN
Primary Contact: Rebecca Segal, Chief Executive Officer
COO: John Domansky, Vice President Operations
CFO: Jeff Rush, Chief Financial Officer
CIO: Tommy Finley, Chief Information Officer
CHR: Robin B Callas, R.N., Vice President Human Resources
Web address: www.rutherfordhosp.org
Control: Partnership, Investor–owned (for–profit) **Service**: General medical and surgical

Staffed Beds: 112 **Admissions**: 3866 **Census**: 48 **Outpatient Visits**: 73984
Births: 433 **Total Expense ($000)**: 71978 **Payroll Expense ($000)**: 30836
Personnel: 604

SALISBURY—Rowan County

✠ **NOVANT HEALTH ROWAN MEDICAL CENTER (340015)**, 612 Mocksville Avenue, Zip 28144–2799; tel. 704/210–5000, (Nonreporting) **A**1 2 10 19 **S** Novant Health, Winston Salem, NC
Primary Contact: Dari Caldwell, R.N., Ph.D., FACHE, President and Chief Operating Officer
CFO: Fred M Hargett, Executive Vice President and Chief Financial Officer
CMO: Thomas Zweng, Executive Vice President and Chief Medical Officer
CIO: David B Garrett, Senior Vice President and Chief Information Officer
CHR: Janet Smith-Hill, Executive Vice President and Chief Human Resource Officer
CNO: Cora Greene, Senior Director, Chief Nursing Officer
Web address: www.novanthealth.org/rowan–medical–center.aspx
Control: Other not–for–profit (including NFP Corporation) **Service**: General medical and surgical

Staffed Beds: 147

VETERANS AFFAIRS MEDICAL CENTER See W. G. (Bill) Heffner Veterans Affairs Medical Center

✠ **W. G. (BILL) HEFFNER VETERANS AFFAIRS MEDICAL CENTER**, 1601 Brenner Avenue, Zip 28144–2559; tel. 704/638–9000, (Nonreporting) **A**1 3 5 **S** Department of Veterans Affairs, Perry Point, MD
Primary Contact: Joseph Vaughn, Director
CFO: Steve Patil, Chief Financial Officer
CIO: Deborah Gunn, Chief Information Officer
CHR: Sandra Fischer, Director Human Resources
Web address: www.salisbury.va.gov
Control: Veterans Affairs, Government, federal **Service**: Psychiatric

Staffed Beds: 171

SANFORD—Lee County

✠ **CENTRAL CAROLINA HOSPITAL (340020)**, 1135 Carthage Street, Zip 27330–4162; tel. 919/774–2100, (Nonreporting) **A**1 10 **S** Duke LifePoint Healthcare, Brentwood, TN
Primary Contact: Spencer Thomas, Chief Executive Officer
CFO: Jared Stimpson, Chief Financial Officer
CIO: Jimmy Whitaker, Director Information Systems
CHR: Deanna Lamb, Director Human Resources
CNO: Jan P. Phillips, R.N., Chief Nursing Officer
Web address: www.centralcarolinahosp.com
Control: Corporation, Investor–owned (for–profit) **Service**: General medical and surgical

Staffed Beds: 137

SHELBY—Cleveland County

✠ **CAROLINAS HEALTHCARE SYSTEM CLEVELAND (340021)**, 201 East Grover Street, Zip 28150–3917; tel. 980/487–3000, **A**1 2 10 19 **F**3 8 13 15 18 20 28 29 30 31 32 34 35 39 40 43 45 47 48 49 50 51 53 56 57 59 64 65 70 74 75 76 77 78 79 80 81 85 86 87 89 93 100 107 108 110 111 114 115 118 119 121 123 126 129 130 131 132 135 143 145 146 147 148 149 154 **S** Atrium Health, Charlotte, NC
Primary Contact: Brian Gwyn, President and Chief Executive Officer
COO: Brian Gwyn, President Chief Operating Officer
CFO: Christine M Martin, Vice President and Chief Financial Officer
CMO: Charles M Tomlinson, M.D., Chief Medical Officer
CHR: Debra Kale, Vice President Human Resources
CNO: Veronica Poole–Adams, R.N., Vice President, Chief Operating Officer and Chief Nursing Executive
Web address: www.clevelandregional.org
Control: Hospital district or authority, Government, nonfederal **Service**: General medical and surgical

Staffed Beds: 161 **Admissions**: 7303 **Census**: 80 **Outpatient Visits**: 173515 **Births**: 1011 **Total Expense ($000)**: 177839 **Payroll Expense ($000)**: 56111 **Personnel**: 954

SILER CITY—Chatham County

✠ **CHATHAM HOSPITAL (341311)**, 475 Progress Boulevard, Zip 27344–6787, Mailing Address: P.O. Box 649, Zip 27344–0649; tel. 919/799–4000, **A**1 10 18 **F**3 15 18 26 28 29 30 34 35 39 40 45 46 57 59 68 70 75 77 79 81 85 92 93 107 110 111 114 119 130 133 135 154 **S** UNC Health Care, Chapel Hill, NC
Primary Contact: Robert A. Enders Jr, President
CFO: Jeff LeGay, Chief Financial Officer
CMO: Andrew Hannapel, Chief Medical Officer
CIO: Deborah Taylor, Chief Information Officer
CHR: Jodie Sartor Solow, Director of Human Resources
CNO: Tammy Needham, Chief Nursing Officer
Web address: www.chathamhospital.org
Control: Other not–for–profit (including NFP Corporation) **Service**: General medical and surgical

Staffed Beds: 25 **Admissions**: 815 **Census**: 13 **Outpatient Visits**: 44316
Births: 0 **Total Expense ($000)**: 32926 **Payroll Expense ($000)**: 9946
Personnel: 187

SMITHFIELD—Johnston County

✠ **JOHNSTON HEALTH (340090)**, 509 North Bright Leaf Blvd, Zip 27577–4407, Mailing Address: P.O. Box 1376, Zip 27577–1376; tel. 919/934–8171, **A**1 2 10 **F**3 11 13 15 17 18 20 22 26 28 29 30 31 32 34 35 38 40 45 49 50 53 57 59 61 62 63 64 66 68 70 73 74 75 76 79 81 85 86 87 89 92 93 98 100 107 108 110 111 115 119 120 121 126 130 132 144 146 147 148 149 154 **S** UNC Health Care, Chapel Hill, NC
Primary Contact: Charles W. Elliott Jr, Chief Executive Officer
COO: Ruth Marler, Chief Nursing Officer and Chief Operating Officer
CFO: Edward A Klein, Chief Financial Officer
CMO: Peter Charvat, Chief Medical Officer
CIO: Teresa Chappell, Chief Information Officer
CHR: Timothy A Hays, Vice President Human Resources
CNO: Ruth Marler, Chief Nursing Officer and Chief Operating Officer
Web address: www.johnstonhealth.org
Control: Hospital district or authority, Government, nonfederal **Service**: General medical and surgical

Staffed Beds: 153 **Admissions**: 9966 **Census**: 102 **Outpatient Visits**: 170085 **Births**: 1457 **Total Expense ($000)**: 199166 **Payroll Expense ($000)**: 79020 **Personnel**: 1360

SOUTHPORT—Brunswick County

✠ **J. ARTHUR DOSHER MEMORIAL HOSPITAL (341327)**, 924 North Howe Street, Zip 28461–3099; tel. 910/457–3800, **A**1 10 18 **F**3 11 12 15 28 30 34 35 40 45 47 50 54 57 59 64 68 75 77 79 81 91 93 97 107 110 111 114 115 118 119 127 129 130 131 132 133 144 146 148 149 154 **P**6
Primary Contact: Thomas R. Siemers, Chief Executive Officer
COO: Carol Northup, R.N., Chief Nursing Officer and Chief Operating Officer
CFO: Daniel J. Porter, Senior Vice President and Chief Financial Officer
CMO: Brad L Hilaman, M.D., Chief Medical Officer
CIO: Susan Shomaker, Director Information Management Systems
CHR: Deanna Parker, Director Human Resources
CNO: Carol Northup, R.N., Chief Nursing Officer and Chief Operating Officer
Web address: www.dosher.org
Control: Hospital district or authority, Government, nonfederal **Service**: General medical and surgical

Staffed Beds: 25 **Admissions**: 953 **Census**: 7 **Outpatient Visits**: 69030
Births: 0 **Total Expense ($000)**: 43346 **Payroll Expense ($000)**: 16150
Personnel: 246

Many Facility Codes have changed. Please refer to the AHA Guide Code Chart. © 2018 AHA Guide

SPARTA—Alleghany County

☒ **ALLEGHANY MEMORIAL HOSPITAL (341320)**, 233 Doctors Street, Zip 28675–9247; tel. 336/372–5511, **A**1 10 18 **F**3 15 18 28 29 30 34 35 40 43 45 59 64 67 70 77 78 79 81 82 87 90 93 97 107 111 114 119 129 130 131 133 135 146 154
Primary Contact: Craig James, President
CFO: Brett Liverman, Chief Financial Officer
CMO: Joe Arocha, Chief of Staff
CIO: Darlene Keith, Chief Information Systems
CHR: Courtney Bennett, Human Resource Manager
CNO: Wendy Orton, Chief Nursing Officer
Web address: www.amhsparta.org
Control: Other not–for–profit (including NFP Corporation) **Service:** General medical and surgical

Staffed Beds: 25 **Admissions:** 400 **Census:** 4 **Outpatient Visits:** 25268 **Births:** 0 **Total Expense ($000):** 12275 **Payroll Expense ($000):** 5232 **Personnel:** 134

SPRUCE PINE—Mitchell County

☒ **BLUE RIDGE REGIONAL HOSPITAL (341329)**, 125 Hospital Drive, Zip 28777–3035; tel. 828/765–4201, (Includes BLUE RIDGE MEDICAL CENTER – YANCEY CAMPUS, 800 Medical Campus Drive, Burnsville, NC, Zip 28714–9010; tel. 828/682–0200) **A**1 10 18 **F**3 13 15 17 28 29 30 31 32 34 35 40 45 50 54 59 64 66 70 75 76 77 78 79 81 82 85 87 90 93 96 97 107 108 111 114 118 119 127 128 129 130 131 132 133 135 146 147 148 154 **P**6 **S** Mission Health System, Asheville, NC
Primary Contact: Rebecca W. Carter, MSN, R.N., FACHE, Chief Executive Officer and Chief Nursing Officer
CFO: Clint Stewart, Chief Financial Officer
CMO: Jennifer Larson, M.D., Chief of Staff
CIO: Pam Blevins, R.N., Director, Clinical Informatics
CNO: Rebecca W Carter, MSN, R.N., FACHE, Chief Executive Officer and Chief Nursing Officer
Web address: www.spchospital.org
Control: Other not–for–profit (including NFP Corporation) **Service:** General medical and surgical

Staffed Beds: 25 **Admissions:** 1362 **Census:** 11 **Outpatient Visits:** 131031 **Births:** 175 **Total Expense ($000):** 46781 **Payroll Expense ($000):** 22526 **Personnel:** 234

STATESVILLE—Iredell County

☒ **DAVIS REGIONAL MEDICAL CENTER (340144)**, 218 Old Mocksville Road, Zip 28625–1930, Mailing Address: P.O. Box 1823, Zip 28687–1823; tel. 704/873–0281, (Nonreporting) **A**1 10 19 **S** Community Health Systems, Inc., Franklin, TN
Primary Contact: Matthew Banks, Chief Executive Officer
CFO: Hugh Tobin, Chief Financial Officer
CMO: Christopher Lariscy, M.D., Chief of Staff
CIO: Janie Stikeleather, Director Marketing and Community Relations
CHR: Christine McKenzie, Director Human Resources
CNO: Janice S Martin, R.N., Chief Nursing Officer
Web address: www.davisregional.com
Control: Corporation, Investor–owned (for–profit) **Service:** General medical and surgical

Staffed Beds: 130

☒ **IREDELL HEALTH SYSTEM (340039)**, 557 Brookdale Drive, Zip 28677–4107, Mailing Address: P.O. Box 1828, Zip 28687–1828; tel. 704/873–5661, (Total facility includes 48 beds in nursing home–type unit) **A**1 2 10 **F**3 11 13 15 17 18 20 22 28 29 30 31 32 34 35 40 41 44 45 47 49 50 56 57 58 59 60 62 64 68 70 74 75 76 77 78 79 81 82 85 86 87 89 91 93 97 107 108 110 111 114 115 116 117 118 119 120 121 123 127 128 129 130 132 135 146 147 148 **P**6
Primary Contact: Ed Rush, President and Chief Executive Officer
COO: John Green, Chief Operating Officer
CFO: Skip Smith, Vice President Finance
CMO: Brent Warren, President Medical Staff
CIO: Kyle Smith, Director Information Systems
CHR: Cindy Smale, Director, Human Resources
CNO: Becky Quate, Vice President Nursing and Patient Care Services
Web address: www.iredellhealth.org
Control: Other not–for–profit (including NFP Corporation) **Service:** General medical and surgical

Staffed Beds: 199 **Admissions:** 7884 **Census:** 114 **Outpatient Visits:** 123350 **Births:** 632 **Total Expense ($000):** 168044 **Payroll Expense ($000):** 74098 **Personnel:** 1620

SYLVA—Jackson County

☒ **HARRIS REGIONAL HOSPITAL (340016)**, 68 Hospital Road, Zip 28779–2722; tel. 828/586–7000, (Nonreporting) **A**1 10 **S** Duke LifePoint Healthcare, Brentwood, TN
Primary Contact: Steve Heatherly, Chief Executive Officer
CHR: Janet Millsaps, Chief Human Resources Officer
Web address: www.westcare.org
Control: Other not–for–profit (including NFP Corporation) **Service:** General medical and surgical

Staffed Beds: 86

TARBORO—Edgecombe County

☒ △ **VIDANT EDGECOMBE HOSPITAL (340107)**, 111 Hospital Drive, Zip 27886–2011; tel. 252/641–7700, **A**1 2 3 7 10 **F**3 11 13 15 28 29 30 31 34 35 40 45 50 57 59 60 64 70 73 75 78 79 81 82 85 87 90 92 93 96 107 110 111 119 127 130 131 132 135 145 146 149 154 **S** Vidant Health, Greenville, NC
Primary Contact: Wendell H. Baker Jr, President
CFO: Charles Alford, Vice President Financial Services
CMO: Barry Bunn, M.D., Chief of Staff
CHR: David Prafka, Ed.D., Director of Human Resources
Web address: www.vidanthealth.com/edgecombe/default.aspx
Control: Other not–for–profit (including NFP Corporation) **Service:** General medical and surgical

Staffed Beds: 94 **Admissions:** 3353 **Census:** 45 **Outpatient Visits:** 75414 **Births:** 443 **Total Expense ($000):** 73543 **Payroll Expense ($000):** 25994 **Personnel:** 466

THOMASVILLE—Davidson County

☒ ⇑ **NOVANT HEALTH THOMASVILLE MEDICAL CENTER (340085)**, 207 Old Lexington Road, Zip 27360–3428, Mailing Address: P.O. Box 789, Zip 27361–0789; tel. 336/472–2000, (Nonreporting) **A**1 3 10 21 **S** Novant Health, Winston Salem, NC
Primary Contact: Jon D. Applebaum, President and Chief Operating Officer
CFO: Fred M Hargett, Executive Vice President and Chief Financial Officer
CMO: Thomas Zweng, Executive Vice President and Chief Medical Officer
CIO: David B Garrett, Senior Vice President and Chief Information Officer
CHR: Janet Smith–Hill, Executive Vice Presideent and Chief Human Resource Officer
CNO: Nancy Pearson, MSN, R.N., Director, Nursing
Web address: www.thomasvillemedicalcenter.org
Control: Other not–for–profit (including NFP Corporation) **Service:** General medical and surgical

Staffed Beds: 80

TROY—Montgomery County

☒ **FIRSTHEALTH MONTGOMERY MEMORIAL HOSPITAL (341303)**, 520 Allen Street, Zip 27371–2802; tel. 910/571–5000, **A**1 10 18 **F**3 11 15 40 45 47 49 59 64 81 85 87 91 93 97 107 110 114 119 127 133 135 146 154 **S** FirstHealth of the Carolinas, Pinehurst, NC
Primary Contact: Beth Walker, R.N., President
CFO: Bryan Hawkins, Controller
CIO: David B Dillehunt, Chief Information Officer
CHR: Tina H Thompson, Coordinator Human Resources
CNO: Pam Gaddy, Director, Patient Care Services and Chief Nursing Officer
Web address: www.firsthealth.org
Control: Other not–for–profit (including NFP Corporation) **Service:** General medical and surgical

Staffed Beds: 5 **Admissions:** 185 **Census:** 1 **Outpatient Visits:** 21534 **Births:** 0 **Personnel:** 106

WADESBORO—Anson County

☒ **CAROLINAS HEALTHCARE SYSTEM ANSON (340084)**, 2301 US Highway 74 W, Zip 28170–7554, Mailing Address: 2301 U.S Highway 74 West, Zip 28170; tel. 704/994–4500, **A**1 10 **F**15 18 28 29 34 35 40 57 59 64 71 75 77 81 86 87 93 97 100 107 110 114 119 129 130 131 132 135 143 145 146 154 **S** Atrium Health, Charlotte, NC
Primary Contact: Dave Anderson, FACHE, Vice President and Administrator
CFO: Jeff Griffin, Assistant Vice President Finance
CMO: Edward Blasko, Chief of Staff
CIO: Lisa Sykes, IS/Communications Director
CHR: Rhonda McFarland, Director Human Resources
CNO: Denise White, MSN, Chief Nurse Executive
Web address: www.carolinashealthcare.org/anson
Control: Hospital district or authority, Government, nonfederal **Service:** General medical and surgical

Staffed Beds: 15 **Admissions:** 186 **Census:** 1 **Outpatient Visits:** 32665 **Births:** 0 **Total Expense ($000):** 16370 **Payroll Expense ($000):** 6038 **Personnel:** 103

Hospital, Medicare Provider Number, Address, Telephone, Approval, Facility, and Physician Codes, Health Care System

★ American Hospital Association (AHA) membership
☐ The Joint Commission accreditation
○ Healthcare Facilities Accreditation Program
◇ DNV Healthcare Inc. accreditation
⇑ Center for Improvement in Healthcare Quality Accreditation
△ Commission on Accreditation of Rehabilitation Facilities (CARF) accreditation

NC

WASHINGTON—Beaufort County

BEAUFORT COUNTY HOSPITAL See Vidant Beaufort Hospital

✠ **VIDANT BEAUFORT HOSPITAL (340186)**, 628 East 12th Street, Zip 27889–3409; tel. 252/975–4100, (Nonreporting) **A**1 3 10 **S** Vidant Health, Greenville, NC
Primary Contact: Harvey Case, President
CFO: Lucinda Crawford, Vice President of Patient Care Services
CMO: James Egbert, Chief of Staff
CHR: Jenny Brown, Director of Human Resources
CNO: Lou Montana–Rhodes, Vice President of Patient Care Services
Web address: www.vidanthealth.com
Control: Hospital district or authority, Government, nonfederal **Service:** General medical and surgical

Staffed Beds: 142

WHITEVILLE—Columbus County

✠ **COLUMBUS REGIONAL HEALTHCARE SYSTEM (340068)**, 500 Jefferson Street, Zip 28472–3634; tel. 910/642–8011, **A**1 10 19 **F**3 11 12 13 15 28 29 30 31 34 35 40 45 46 47 48 50 57 59 65 68 70 74 75 76 77 78 79 81 85 86 87 89 91 92 93 94 107 108 114 115 118 119 126 129 130 132 145 146 148 149 **P**7 **S** Atrium Health, Charlotte, NC
Primary Contact: John E. Young, Interim Chief Executive Officer
CFO: Carl Biber, Chief Financial Officer
CMO: Samuel N Wheatley, Chief Medical Officer
CIO: Lisa Ward, Director Information Systems
CHR: Andrea West, MS, Vice President of Human Resources
CNO: Terri Veneziano, Interim Chief Nursing Officer
Web address: www.crhealthcare.org/
Control: Other not–for–profit (including NFP Corporation) **Service:** General medical and surgical

Staffed Beds: 85 Admissions: 3786 Census: 43 Outpatient Visits: 121169 Births: 351 Total Expense ($000): 75148 Payroll Expense ($000): 27100 Personnel: 576

WILLIAMSTON—Martin County

✠ **MARTIN GENERAL HOSPITAL (340133)**, 310 South McCaskey Road, Zip 27892–2150, Mailing Address: P.O. Box 1128, Zip 27892–1128; tel. 252/809–6300, (Nonreporting) **A**1 10 **S** Quorum Health, Brentwood, TN
Primary Contact: John Jacobson, Interim Chief Executive Officer
CFO: John Jacobson, Chief Financial Officer
CIO: James Griffin, Manager Information Systems
CHR: Rebecca Edwards, Director Human Resources
CNO: Gregory Hornick, MSN, Chief Nursing Officer
Web address: www.martingeneral.com
Control: Corporation, Investor–owned (for–profit) **Service:** General medical and surgical

Staffed Beds: 49

WILMINGTON—New Hanover County

✠ △ **NEW HANOVER REGIONAL MEDICAL CENTER (340141)**, 2131 South 17th Street, Zip 28401–7483, Mailing Address: P.O. Box 9000, Zip 28402–9000; tel. 910/343–7000, (Includes CAPE FEAR HOSPITAL, 5301 Wrightsville Avenue, Wilmington, NC, Zip 28403–6599; tel. 910/452–8100) **A**1 2 3 5 7 10 13 **F**3 7 8 11 12 13 15 17 18 20 22 24 26 28 29 30 31 34 35 36 37 39 40 43 44 45 46 47 48 49 50 53 54 56 57 58 59 60 61 64 65 66 68 70 72 73 74 75 76 77 78 79 80 81 82 84 85 86 87 88 89 90 92 93 94 96 97 98 100 101 102 107 108 110 111 114 115 117 118 119 121 123 126 130 131 132 135 144 146 147 148 149 **S** New Hanover Regional Medical Center, Wilmington, NC
Primary Contact: Andre Boyd Sr, Executive Vice President, Hospital Division
CFO: Edwin J Ollie, Executive Vice President and Chief Financial Officer
CMO: Sam Spicer, M.D., Vice President Medical Affairs
CIO: Avery Cloud, Vice President and Chief Information Officer
CHR: Keith A Strawn, Vice President Human Resources
CNO: Mary Ellen Bonczek, R.N., Chief Nursing Executive
Web address: www.nhrmc.org
Control: County, Government, nonfederal **Service:** General medical and surgical

Staffed Beds: 711 Admissions: 41576 Census: 572 Outpatient Visits: 439033 Births: 4182 Total Expense ($000): 898160 Payroll Expense ($000): 331566 Personnel: 5079

WILMINGTON TREATMENT CENTER (340168), 2520 Troy Drive, Zip 28401–7643; tel. 910/762–2727, (Nonreporting) **A**10 **S** CRC Health Group, Inc., Cupertino, CA
Primary Contact: Robert Pitts, Executive Director
COO: Paige Bottom, Director Operations
CFO: Virginia Powell, Director Finance
CMO: Patrick Martin, M.D., Medical Director
Web address: www.wilmtreatment.com
Control: Corporation, Investor–owned (for–profit) **Service:** Alcoholism and other chemical dependency

Staffed Beds: 44

WILSON—Wilson County

TRIANGLE EAST NURSING CARE CENTER See Wilmed Nursing Care Center

✠ **WILSON MEDICAL CENTER (340126)**, 1705 Tarboro Street, SW, Zip 27893–3428; tel. 252/399–8040, (Total facility includes 90 beds in nursing home–type unit) **A**1 2 10 19 **F**3 11 13 15 18 20 22 26 28 29 30 31 34 35 39 40 45 47 48 50 54 57 60 64 68 70 73 74 75 76 77 78 79 81 82 85 86 87 89 92 93 94 97 98 102 103 107 108 110 111 114 115 118 119 120 121 123 128 129 130 132 135 146 148 154 **P**5 **S** Duke LifePoint Healthcare, Brentwood, TN
Primary Contact: William E. Caldwell Jr, FACHE, Chief Executive Officer
CMO: Rick Guarino, M.D., Vice President Medical Affairs
CIO: Brian Dietrick, Director Information Systems
CHR: Denise O'Hara, Vice President Human Resources
Web address: www.wilmed.org
Control: Corporation, Investor–owned (for–profit) **Service:** General medical and surgical

Staffed Beds: 244 Admissions: 7119 Census: 156 Outpatient Visits: 66634 Births: 879 Total Expense ($000): 100680 Payroll Expense ($000): 45672 Personnel: 871

WINDSOR—Bertie County

✠ **VIDANT BERTIE HOSPITAL (341304)**, 1403 South King Street, Zip 27983–9666, Mailing Address: P.O. Box 40, Zip 27983–0040; tel. 252/794–6600, **A**1 10 18 **F**3 15 29 30 34 35 40 45 46 47 48 49 57 59 64 77 79 81 82 93 94 97 107 110 114 119 127 132 135 146 148 **S** Vidant Health, Greenville, NC
Primary Contact: Jeffrey Sackrison, President
CFO: Brian Harvill, Vice President Financial Services
CMO: William Ballance, Chief of Medical Staff
CIO: Brian White, Director Strategic Planning
CHR: Nicole Spell, Director Human Resources
CNO: Silvia Rose, Director Patient Care Services
Web address: www.vidanthealth.com
Control: Other not–for–profit (including NFP Corporation) **Service:** General medical and surgical

Staffed Beds: 6 Admissions: 369 Census: 4 Outpatient Visits: 25213 Births: 0 Total Expense ($000): 18339 Payroll Expense ($000): 7665 Personnel: 107

WINSTON SALEM—Forsyth County

BRENNER CHILDREN'S HOSPITAL & HEALTH SERVICES See Wake Forest Baptist Medical Center, Winston–Salem

WINSTON—SALEM—Forsyth County

MEDICAL PARK HOSPITAL See Novant Health Medical Park Hospital

✠ △ **NOVANT HEALTH FORSYTH MEDICAL CENTER (340014)**, 3333 Silas Creek Parkway, Zip 27103–3090; tel. 336/718–5000, (Includes KERNERSVILLE MEDICAL CENTER, 2911750 Kernersville Medical Parkway, Kernersville, NC, Zip 27284–2932, Mailing Address: 1750 Kernersville Medical Parkway, Zip 27284–2932, tel. 336/564–4000; Chad Setliff, President and Chief Operating Officer; NOVANT HEALTH CLEMMONS MEDICAL CENTER, 6915 Village Medical Circle, Clemmons, NC, Zip 27012–8002; tel. 336/893–1000; Chad Setliff, President and Chief Operating Officer) (Nonreporting) **A**1 2 3 5 7 10 **S** Novant Health, Winston Salem, NC
Primary Contact: Chad Setliff, President and Chief Operating Officer
CFO: Fred M Hargett, Executive Vice President and Chief Financial Officer
CMO: Thomas Zweng, Executive Vice President and Chief Medical Officer
CIO: David B Garrett, Senior Vice President and Chief Information Officer
CHR: Janet Smith–Hill, Senior Vice President Human Resources
CNO: Janet L Bright, Vice President, Chief Nursing Officer
Web address: www.novanthealth.org
Control: Other not–for–profit (including NFP Corporation) **Service:** General medical and surgical

Staffed Beds: 706

Many Facility Codes have changed. Please refer to the AHA Guide Code Chart. © 2018 AHA Guide

✠ **NOVANT HEALTH MEDICAL PARK HOSPITAL (340148)**, 1950 South Hawthorne Road, Zip 27103–3993; tel. 336/718–0600, (Nonreporting) **A**1 2 10 **S** Novant Health, Winston Salem, NC
Primary Contact: Kirsten Royster, President and Chief Operating Officer
CFO: Fred M Hargett, Executive Vice President and Chief Financial Officer
CMO: Thomas Zweng, Executive Vice President and Chief Medical Officer
CIO: David B Garrett, Senior Vice President and Chief Information Officer
CHR: Janet Smith–Hill, Executive Vice President and Chief Human Resource Officer
CNO: Carol A Smith, R.N., Director Operations and Nursing
Web address: www.novanthealth.org
Control: Other not–for–profit (including NFP Corporation) **Service**: General medical and surgical

Staffed Beds: 14

☐ **OLD VINEYARD BEHAVIORAL HEALTH SERVICES (344007)**, 3637 Old Vineyard Road, Zip 27104–4842; tel. 336/794–3550, **A**1 10 **F**4 29 40 50 75 87 98 99 101 102 103 104 105 130 149 153 154 **S** Universal Health Services, Inc., King of Prussia, PA
Primary Contact: Kevin Patton, Chief Executive Officer
CFO: Ernest C Priddy III Chief Financial Officer
CMO: Raj Thotakura, M.D., Medical Director
CHR: Jackie Pennino, Director Human Resources
CNO: Susan Evans, Chief Nursing Officer
Web address: www.oldvineyardbhs.com
Control: Corporation, Investor–owned (for–profit) **Service**: Psychiatric

Staffed Beds: 148 **Admissions:** 4805 **Census:** 108 **Outpatient Visits:** 5565 **Births:** 0 **Total Expense ($000):** 24168 **Payroll Expense ($000):** 12208 **Personnel:** 224

✠ **WAKE FOREST BAPTIST MEDICAL CENTER (340047)**, Medical Center Boulevard, Zip 27157–0001; tel. 336/716–2011, (Includes BRENNER CHILDREN'S HOSPITAL & HEALTH SERVICES, Medical Center Boulevard, Winston Salem, NC, Zip 27157, Mailing Address: One Medical Center Boulevard, Zip 27157, tel. 336/716–2255) **A**1 2 3 5 8 10 **F**3 5 6 7 9 11 12 15 16 17 18 19 20 21 22 23 24 25 26 27 28 29 30 31 32 34 35 36 37 40 41 43 44 45 46 47 48 49 50 52 53 54 55 56 57 58 59 60 61 62 64 65 66 67 68 70 72 73 74 75 77 78 79 81 82 84 85 86 87 88 89 90 92 93 96 97 98 99 100 101 102 104 107 108 110 111 113 114 115 116 117 118 119 120 121 123 124 126 129 130 131 132 135 136 137 138 141 142 143 144 145 146 147 148 149 153 154 **P6 S** Wake Forest Baptist Health, Winston–Salem, NC
Primary Contact: Julie Ann. Freischlag, M.D., Chief Executive Officer
CMO: Russell M Howerton, M.D., Chief Medical Officer
CHR: Cheryl Locke, Vice President and Chief Human Resource Officer
Web address: www.wakehealth.edu
Control: Other not–for–profit (including NFP Corporation) **Service**: General medical and surgical

Staffed Beds: 798 **Admissions:** 39867 **Census:** 679 **Outpatient Visits:** 1117526 **Births:** 13 **Total Expense ($000):** 1518680 **Payroll Expense ($000):** 497157 **Personnel:** 9420

Hospital, Medicare Provider Number, Address, Telephone, Approval, Facility, and Physician Codes, Health Care System

★ American Hospital Association (AHA) membership
☐ The Joint Commission accreditation
○ Healthcare Facilities Accreditation Program
◇ DNV Healthcare Inc. accreditation
⇑ Center for Improvement in Healthcare Quality Accreditation
△ Commission on Accreditation of Rehabilitation Facilities (CARF) accreditation

NC

NORTH DAKOTA

ASHLEY—Mcintosh County

★ **ASHLEY MEDICAL CENTER (351322)**, 612 North Center Avenue, Zip 58413–7013, Mailing Address: P.O. Box 450, Zip 58413–0450; tel. 701/288–3433, (Total facility includes 40 beds in nursing home–type unit) **A**10 18 **F**3 8 15 28 29 40 41 45 49 56 57 59 60 64 65 70 75 81 83 87 93 97 107 110 114 125 127 128 130 131 132 133 144 146 147 148
Primary Contact: Holly Wolff, Chief Executive Officer
CMO: Udom Tinsa, M.D., Medical Director
Web address: www.amctoday.org
Control: Other not–for–profit (including NFP Corporation) **Service**: General medical and surgical

> **Staffed Beds: 60 Admissions: 118 Census: 43 Outpatient Visits: 5608 Births: 0 Total Expense ($000): 7492 Payroll Expense ($000): 4025 Personnel: 110**

BELCOURT—Rolette County

☐ **INDIAN HEALTH SERVICE – QUENTIN N. BURDICK MEMORIAL HEALTH CARE FACILITY (350063)**, 1300 Hospital Loop, Zip 58316, Mailing Address: P.O. Box 160, Zip 58316–0160; tel. 701/477–6111, **A**1 5 10 **F**3 7 13 15 29 34 35 39 40 45 50 59 65 75 76 77 81 82 83 85 89 91 93 107 108 119 130 135 143 147 154 **S** U.S. Indian Health Service, Rockville, MD
Primary Contact: Shelly Harris, Chief Executive Officer
CFO: Deland Davis, Chief Financial Officer
CMO: Vernon Azure, Clinical Director
CIO: Chance Wilkie, Information Technology Specialist
CHR: Donna Belgarde, Human Resources Specialist
CNO: Lynelle Hunt, Director of Nursing
Web address: www.ihs.gov
Control: PHS, Indian Service, Government, federal **Service**: General medical and surgical

> **Staffed Beds: 29 Admissions: 881 Census: 8 Outpatient Visits: 25258 Births: 99 Total Expense ($000): 65500 Payroll Expense ($000): 21600 Personnel: 327**

BISMARCK—Burleigh County

✠ **CHI ST. ALEXIUS HEALTH (350002)**, 900 East Broadway, Zip 58501–4586, Mailing Address: P.O. Box 5510, Zip 58506–5510; tel. 701/530–7000, (Total facility includes 19 beds in nursing home–type unit) **A**1 2 3 5 10 **F**3 5 8 9 11 12 13 15 17 18 19 20 21 22 23 24 25 26 28 29 30 31 32 34 35 38 40 43 45 46 49 53 56 57 58 59 60 64 65 68 70 72 73 74 75 76 77 78 79 81 82 83 84 85 87 88 89 91 92 93 94 96 97 98 99 100 101 102 103 104 105 107 110 111 114 115 118 119 126 128 129 130 131 132 135 146 147 148 149 150 152 **P**8 **S** Catholic Health Initiatives, Englewood, CO
Primary Contact: Kurt Schley, Market Chief Executive Officer
CFO: Susan Sisk, Chief Financial Officer
CMO: Shiraz Hyder, M.D., Director Medical Affairs
CIO: Todd Bortke, Director Information Systems
CHR: Tom Gregg, Vice President Human Resources
CNO: Rosanne Schmidt, R.N., Chief Nursing Officer
Web address: www.st.alexius.org
Control: Church operated, Nongovernment, not–for–profit **Service**: General medical and surgical

> **Staffed Beds: 237 Admissions: 9871 Census: 123 Outpatient Visits: 157699 Births: 1330 Total Expense ($000): 316137 Payroll Expense ($000): 143850 Personnel: 1622**

✠ △ **SANFORD BISMARCK (350015)**, 300 North Seventh Street, Zip 58501–4439, Mailing Address: P.O. Box 5525, Zip 58506–5525; tel. 701/323–6000, **A**1 2 3 5 7 10 19 **F**3 7 9 11 12 13 15 17 18 20 22 24 26 28 29 30 31 33 34 35 36 37 38 40 43 44 45 48 49 50 51 52 53 54 55 56 57 58 59 60 61 62 63 64 65 66 68 69 70 72 73 74 75 76 77 78 79 81 82 85 86 87 88 89 90 91 92 93 96 97 98 99 100 101 102 103 104 105 107 108 110 111 114 115 116 117 118 119 126 128 129 130 131 132 135 138 144 146 147 148 149 150 153 154 **P**6 **S** Sanford Health, Sioux Falls, SD
Primary Contact: Craig Lambrecht, M.D., President
COO: Al Hurley, Clinic Operating Officer
CFO: Kirk Cristy, Chief Financial Officer
CMO: Chris Meeker, M.D., Chief Medical Officer
CHR: Scott D Boehm, Executive Vice President Human Resources and Facilities
CNO: Jan Kamphuis, Ph.D., R.N., Executive Vice President and Chief Nurse Executive
Web address: www.bismarck.sanfordhealth.org/
Control: Other not–for–profit (including NFP Corporation) **Service**: General medical and surgical

> **Staffed Beds: 208 Admissions: 11825 Census: 142 Outpatient Visits: 203287 Births: 1292 Total Expense ($000): 473364 Payroll Expense ($000): 224915 Personnel: 2606**

SANFORD HEALTH See Sanford Bismarck

BOTTINEAU—Bottineau County

ST. ANDREW'S HEALTH CENTER (351307), 316 Ohmer Street, Zip 58318–1045; tel. 701/228–9300, **A**5 10 18 **F**1 3 4 15 16 17 28 29 30 34 35 40 43 57 59 67 70 72 73 76 80 81 88 89 90 93 98 107 108 110 125 127 128 130 132 133 143 144 146 149 **P**3 5 **S** Sisters of Mary of the Presentation Health System, Fargo, ND
Primary Contact: Jodi Atkinson, President and Chief Executive Officer
CFO: Sean Rinkenberger, Chief Financial Officer
CMO: Jessica Skjolden, M.D., Chief of Staff
CHR: Brenda Arneson, Administrative Assistant
CNO: Karla Spence, Director of Nursing
Web address: www.standrewshealth.com
Control: Church operated, Nongovernment, not–for–profit **Service**: General medical and surgical

> **Staffed Beds: 25 Admissions: 135 Census: 17 Outpatient Visits: 8800 Births: 0 Total Expense ($000): 8902 Payroll Expense ($000): 3708 Personnel: 93**

BOWMAN—Bowman County

SOUTHWEST HEALTHCARE SERVICES (351313), 802 2nd Street Northwest, Zip 58623–4483, Mailing Address: P O Drawer 'C', Zip 58623; tel. 701/523–5265, (Nonreporting) **A**10 18
Primary Contact: Jerry Wiesner, Administrator and Chief Executive Officer
Web address: www.swhealthcare.net
Control: Other not–for–profit (including NFP Corporation) **Service**: General medical and surgical

> **Staffed Beds: 55**

CANDO—Towner County

★ **TOWNER COUNTY MEDICAL CENTER (351331)**, State Highway 281 North, Zip 58324, Mailing Address: P.O. Box 688, Zip 58324–0688; tel. 701/968–4411, (Total facility includes 35 beds in nursing home–type unit) **A**5 10 18 **F**4 5 11 14 15 29 31 32 33 34 35 40 41 45 50 53 55 56 57 59 65 67 75 78 81 85 89 93 97 102 107 110 114 119 125 127 128 129 130 133 135 144 148 152 154
Primary Contact: Ben Bucher, Chief Executive Officer
CFO: Tammy Larson, Chief Financial Officer
CMO: Russ Petty, M.D., Chief of Staff
CIO: David Fite, Director Information Technology
CHR: Pat Klingenberg, Director Human Resources
Web address: www.tcmedcenter.org
Control: Other not–for–profit (including NFP Corporation) **Service**: General medical and surgical

> **Staffed Beds: 55 Admissions: 126 Census: 31 Outpatient Visits: 8250 Births: 0 Total Expense ($000): 10185 Payroll Expense ($000): 4669 Personnel: 106**

CARRINGTON—Foster County

★ **CHI ST ALEXIUS HEALTH CARRINGTON MEDICAL CENTER (351318)**, 800 North Fourth Street, Zip 58421–1217, Mailing Address: P.O. Box 461, Zip 58421–0461; tel. 701/652–3141, **A**5 10 18 **F**7 11 15 28 30 34 40 45 46 64 75 81 87 107 108 110 114 119 127 133 143 146 154 **P**6 **S** Catholic Health Initiatives, Englewood, CO
Primary Contact: Mariann Doeling, R.N., President
COO: Brenda Rask, Vice President Operations
CFO: Kurt Sargent, CPA, Vice President, Operational Finance
CIO: Keith Stauffer, Regional Chief Information Officer
CHR: Carol Risovi, Human Resources
CNO: Jodi Lynn Hovdenes, Vice President Patient Care
Web address: www.carringtonhealthcenter.org
Control: Other not–for–profit (including NFP Corporation) **Service**: General medical and surgical

> **Staffed Beds: 25 Admissions: 447 Census: 5 Outpatient Visits: 21537 Births: 0 Total Expense ($000): 11788 Payroll Expense ($000): 3370 Personnel: 78**

Many Facility Codes have changed. Please refer to the AHA Guide Code Chart. © 2018 AHA Guide

CAVALIER—Pembina County

★ **PEMBINA COUNTY MEMORIAL HOSPITAL AND WEDGEWOOD MANOR (351319)**, 301 Mountain Street East, Zip 58220–4015, Mailing Address: P.O. Box 380, Zip 58220–0380; tel. 701/265–8461, (Total facility includes 50 beds in nursing home–type unit) **A**5 10 18 **F**2 3 28 29 31 40 43 45 56 59 65 68 78 81 82 84 87 93 97 107 114 119 127 128 130 131 132 133 135 146 154
Primary Contact: Lisa LeTexier, Interim Chief Executive Officer
CMO: K S Sumra, M.D., Chief of Staff
CIO: Robert Heidt, Director Information Systems
Web address: www.cavalierhospital.com
Control: Other not–for–profit (including NFP Corporation) **Service:** General medical and surgical

Staffed Beds: 70 Admissions: 354 Census: 42 Outpatient Visits: 21629 Births: 0 Total Expense ($000): 14956 Payroll Expense ($000): 5791

COOPERSTOWN—Griggs County

★ **COOPERSTOWN MEDICAL CENTER (351306)**, 1200 Roberts Avenue NorthEast, Zip 58425–7101; tel. 701/797–2221, (Nonreporting) **A**10 18
Primary Contact: Nikki Johnson, Interim Chief Executive Officer
CMO: Jeffrey Peterson, M.D., Medical Director
CHR: Pamela VenHuizen, Chief Human Resources Officer
Web address: www.coopermc.com
Control: Other not–for–profit (including NFP Corporation) **Service:** General medical and surgical

Staffed Beds: 62

CROSBY—Divide County

★ **ST. LUKE'S MEDICAL CENTER (351325)**, 702 First Street Southwest, Zip 58730–3329, Mailing Address: P.O. Box 10, Zip 58730–0010; tel. 701/965–6384, (Nonreporting) **A**10 18
Primary Contact: Jodi Nelson, Interim Chief Executive Officer
Web address: www.dcstlukes.org/
Control: Other not–for–profit (including NFP Corporation) **Service:** General medical and surgical

Staffed Beds: 15

DEVILS LAKE—Ramsey County

☒ **CHI ST. ALEXIUS HEALTH DEVILS LAKE HOSPITAL (351333)**, 1031 Seventh Street NE, Zip 58301–2798; tel. 701/662–2131, **A**1 5 10 18 **F**3 11 13 28 29 30 34 35 40 45 57 70 75 76 81 85 87 93 107 108 111 115 119 130 131 133 **S** Catholic Health Initiatives, Englewood, CO
Primary Contact: Andrew Lankowicz, FACHE, President
CFO: Kurt Sargent, CPA, Vice President Operational Finance
CMO: Richard Johnson, M.D., Chief of Medical Staff
CHR: Bonnie Mattern, Director Human Resources
CNO: Aaron Johnson, Vice President Patient Care Services and Chief Nursing Officer
Web address: www.mercyhospitaldl.com
Control: Other not–for–profit (including NFP Corporation) **Service:** General medical and surgical

Staffed Beds: 25 Admissions: 908 Census: 10 Outpatient Visits: 21037 Births: 301 Total Expense ($000): 20711 Payroll Expense ($000): 8492 Personnel: 124

DICKINSON—Stark County

☒ **CHI ST. ALEXIUS HEALTH – DICKINSON MEDICAL CENTER (351336)**, 2500 Fairway Street, Zip 58601–4399; tel. 701/456–4000, **A**1 5 10 18 **F**3 8 11 13 15 28 29 30 34 35 40 53 57 59 64 70 75 76 79 81 84 85 86 87 89 97 107 108 111 114 119 127 129 130 132 133 146 149 **S** Catholic Health Initiatives, Englewood, CO
Primary Contact: Reed Reyman, President
CFO: Stephanie Franken, Vice President Operational Finance
CHR: Denise Lutz, Chief Human Resources Officer
CNO: DeeAnna Opstedahl, R.N., Vice President Patient Care Services
Web address: www.stjoeshospital.org
Control: Church operated, Nongovernment, not–for–profit **Service:** General medical and surgical

Staffed Beds: 25 Admissions: 1892 Census: 15 Outpatient Visits: 53666 Births: 650 Total Expense ($000): 66037 Payroll Expense ($000): 25954 Personnel: 287

ELGIN—Grant County

★ **JACOBSON MEMORIAL HOSPITAL CARE CENTER (351314)**, 601 East Street North, Zip 58533–7105, Mailing Address: P.O. Box 367, Zip 58533–0367; tel. 701/584–2792, **A**10 18 **F**1 15 28 32 35 40 41 43 59 62 64 65 69 75 77 93 97 104 107 110 111 114 119 127 128 130 131 132 133 146 154
Primary Contact: Theo Stoller, Chief Executive Officer
CFO: Scott Ostenson, Chief Financial Officer
CMO: Deepak Goyal, M.D., Chief of Staff
CHR: Rynae Golke, Director Human Resources
CNO: Connie Gustafson, Director of Nursing
Web address: www.jacobsonhospital.org
Control: Other not–for–profit (including NFP Corporation) **Service:** General medical and surgical

Staffed Beds: 30 Admissions: 154 Census: 26 Outpatient Visits: 7821 Births: 0 Total Expense ($000): 7298 Payroll Expense ($000): 2467 Personnel: 61

FARGO—Cass County

☒ **ESSENTIA HEALTH FARGO (350070)**, 3000 32nd Avenue South, Zip 58103–6132; tel. 701/364–8000, **A**1 2 3 5 10 **F**3 9 11 12 13 15 17 18 20 22 24 25 26 28 29 30 31 32 33 34 35 38 40 41 43 44 45 46 47 48 49 50 51 56 57 58 59 60 61 64 65 70 72 74 75 76 77 78 79 81 82 83 84 85 86 87 89 91 92 93 97 107 108 109 110 111 112 113 114 115 116 117 118 119 120 121 122 123 124 126 129 130 131 132 135 144 145 146 147 148 154 **P**6 **S** Essentia Health, Duluth, MN
Primary Contact: Timothy Sayler, Chief Operating Officer
COO: Timothy Sayler, Chief Operating Officer
CFO: Dennis Fuhrman, Vice President Finance
CMO: Michael Briggs, M.D., Chief Medical Officer
CIO: Ken Gilles, Chief Information Officer
CHR: Keith Wahlund, Vice President Human Resources
Web address: www.essentiahealth.com
Control: Other not–for–profit (including NFP Corporation) **Service:** General medical and surgical

Staffed Beds: 137 Admissions: 7710 Census: 93 Outpatient Visits: 137143 Births: 1441 Total Expense ($000): 354477 Payroll Expense ($000): 161517 Personnel: 1927

☒ **FARGO VETERANS AFFAIRS HEALTH CARE SYSTEM**, 2101 Elm Street North, Zip 58102; tel. 701/232–3241, **A**1 3 5 **F**3 5 8 11 12 18 29 30 31 33 34 35 36 38 39 40 44 45 50 54 56 57 58 59 60 61 62 63 64 65 70 71 74 75 77 78 79 81 82 83 84 85 86 87 93 94 96 97 98 100 101 102 103 104 107 111 114 115 119 127 128 129 130 132 133 135 136 137 138 139 140 141 142 143 144 146 147 148 149 150 153 154 **P**6 **S** Department of Veterans Affairs, Perry Point, MD
Primary Contact: Lavonne Liversage, Director
COO: Dale DeKrey, MS, Associate Director Operations and Resources
CFO: Roger Sayler, Finance Officer
CMO: J Brian Hancock, M.D., Chief of Staff
CIO: Raymond Nelson, Acting Chief Information Resource Management
CHR: Jason Wells, Chief Human Resources Management Service
CNO: Julie Bruhn, R.N., MS, Associate Director Patient Care and Nurse Executive
Web address: www.fargo.va.gov/
Control: Veterans Affairs, Government, federal **Service:** General medical and surgical

Staffed Beds: 72 Admissions: 2465 Census: 27 Outpatient Visits: 232225 Births: 0 Total Expense ($000): 256171 Payroll Expense ($000): 78466 Personnel: 1207

INNOVIS HEALTH See Essentia Health Fargo

KINDRED HOSPITAL FARGO See Vibra Hospital of Fargo

MERITCARE MEDICAL CENTER See Sanford Medical Center Fargo

Hospital, Medicare Provider Number, Address, Telephone, Approval, Facility, and Physician Codes, Health Care System

★ American Hospital Association (AHA) membership
☐ The Joint Commission accreditation
○ Healthcare Facilities Accreditation Program
◇ DNV Healthcare Inc. accreditation
⇑ Center for Improvement in Healthcare Quality Accreditation
△ Commission on Accreditation of Rehabilitation Facilities (CARF) accreditation

☐ **PRAIRIE ST. JOHN'S (354004)**, 510 4th Street South, Zip 58103–1914; tel. 701/476–7200, (Nonreporting) **A**1 3 10 **S** Universal Health Services, Inc., King of Prussia, PA
Primary Contact: Jeff Herman, Chief Executive Officer
COO: Jennifer Faul, Chief Operating Officer
CFO: Tom Eide, Chief Financial Officer
CMO: Eduardo Meza, M.D., Medical Director
CHR: Michelle A Parkinson, Director Human Resources
CNO: Jacki Toppen, Director of Nursing
Web address: www.prairie-stjohns.com
Control: Partnership, Investor–owned (for–profit) **Service:** Psychiatric

Staffed Beds: 94

⊞ △ **SANFORD MEDICAL CENTER FARGO (350011)**, 801 Broadway North, Zip 58122–3641; tel. 701/234–2000, (Includes SANFORD SOUTH UNIVERSITY, 1720 South University Drive, Fargo, ND, Zip 58103–4994; tel. 701/234–2000; Nate White, Executive Vice President) **A**1 2 3 5 7 8 10 19 **F**3 7 8 9 11 12 13 15 17 18 19 20 21 22 23 24 25 26 27 28 29 30 31 32 33 34 35 36 37 38 39 40 43 44 45 46 47 48 49 50 51 52 53 54 55 56 57 58 59 60 61 62 63 64 65 66 68 70 71 72 73 74 75 76 78 79 80 81 82 83 84 85 86 87 88 89 90 91 92 93 94 96 97 98 99 100 101 102 103 104 105 107 108 110 111 112 114 115 116 117 118 119 120 121 123 124 126 129 130 131 132 135 138 141 142 143 144 145 146 147 148 149 150 153 154 **P**6 **S** Sanford Health, Sioux Falls, SD
Primary Contact: Nate White, Executive Vice President
COO: Susan Jarvis, Vice President Operations
CFO: Tiffany Lawrence, Vice President of Finance
CMO: Douglas Griffin, M.D., Vice President Medical Officer
CIO: Arlyn Broekhuis, Chief Information Officer
CHR: Bill Gassen, Chief Human Resource Officer
CNO: Roberta Young, Vice President Nursing
Web address: www.sanfordhealth.org
Control: Other not–for–profit (including NFP Corporation) **Service:** General medical and surgical

Staffed Beds: 490 Admissions: 23602 Census: 350 Outpatient Visits: 411581 Births: 2752 Total Expense ($000): 1006643 Payroll Expense ($000): 429776 Personnel: 4987

VETERANS AFFAIRS HEALTH CARE SYSTEM See Fargo Veterans Affairs Health Care System

⊞ **VIBRA HOSPITAL OF FARGO (352004)**, 1720 University Drive South, Zip 58103–4940; tel. 701/241–9099, (Nonreporting) **A**1 10 **S** Vibra Healthcare, Mechanicsburg, PA
Primary Contact: Custer Huseby, Chief Executive Officer
Web address: www.vhfargo.com
Control: Corporation, Investor–owned (for–profit) **Service:** Acute long–term care hospital

Staffed Beds: 31

FORT YATES—Sioux County

⇑ **STANDING ROCK SERVICE UNIT, FORT YATES HOSPITAL, INDIAN HEALTH SERVICE, DHHS (350064)**, 10 North River Road, Zip 58538, Mailing Address: P.O. Box 'J', Zip 58538; tel. 701/854–3831, (Nonreporting) **A**5 10 21 **S** U.S. Indian Health Service, Rockville, MD
Primary Contact: Jana Gipp, Chief Executive Officer
CFO: Byron Wilcox, Chief Financial Management Officer
CMO: Sara Jumping Eagle, Clinical Director
CNO: Joelle Keepseagle, Director of Nursing
Web address: www.ihs.gov
Control: PHS, Indian Service, Government, federal **Service:** General medical and surgical

Staffed Beds: 14

GARRISON—Mclean County

★ **CHI ST. ALEXIUS HEALTH GARRISON (351303)**, 407 Third Avenue SE, Zip 58540–7235; tel. 701/463–2275, (Total facility includes 28 beds in nursing home–type unit) **A**5 10 18 **F**2 15 28 29 30 34 35 40 56 57 59 64 65 66 68 71 77 93 97 107 110 115 127 128 130 131 132 133 154 **P**6 **S** Catholic Health Initiatives, Englewood, CO
Primary Contact: Tod Graeber, Administrator
CMO: Vern Harchenko, M.D., Chief of Staff
CNO: Beth Hetletved, Director of Nurses
Web address: www.garrisonmh.com
Control: Church operated, Nongovernment, not–for–profit **Service:** General medical and surgical

Staffed Beds: 50 Admissions: 168 Census: 43 Outpatient Visits: 12365 Births: 0 Total Expense ($000): 9901 Payroll Expense ($000): 5154 Personnel: 61

GRAFTON—Walsh County

★ **UNITY MEDICAL CENTER (351320)**, 164 West 13th Street, Zip 58237–1896; tel. 701/352–1620, (Nonreporting) **A**5 10 18
Primary Contact: Alan O'Neil, Chief Executive Officer
CFO: Rachel Ray, Chief Financial Officer
Web address: www.unitymedcenter.com
Control: Other not–for–profit (including NFP Corporation) **Service:** General medical and surgical

Staffed Beds: 14

GRAND FORKS—Grand Forks County

⊞ △ **ALTRU HEALTH SYSTEM (350019)**, 1200 South Columbia Road, Zip 58201–4036, Mailing Address: P.O. Box 6002, Zip 58206–6002; tel. 701/780–5000, (Includes ALTRU HOSPITAL, 1200 South Columbia Road, Grand Forks, ND, Zip 58201, Mailing Address: PO Box 6002, Zip 58206–6002, tel. 701/780–5000; David R Molmen, M.P.H., Chief Executive Officer; ALTRU REHABILITATION CENTER, 1300 South Columbia Road, Grand Forks, ND, Zip 58201; tel. 701/780–2311; David R Molmen, M.P.H., Chief Executive Officer) (Nonreporting) **A**1 2 3 5 7 10 20
Primary Contact: David R. Molmen, M.P.H., Chief Executive Officer
COO: Brad Wehe, Chief Operating Officer
CFO: Dwight Thompson, Chief Financial Officer
CMO: Colleen Swank, Chief Medical Officer
CIO: Mark Waind, Chief Information Officer
CHR: Kellee J Fisk, Chief People Officer
CNO: Margaret M Reed, R.N., Chief Nursing Officer
Web address: www.altru.org
Control: Other not–for–profit (including NFP Corporation) **Service:** General medical and surgical

Staffed Beds: 299

⇑ **RED RIVER BEHAVIORAL HEALTH SYSTEM (354005)**, 1451 44th Avenue South Unit A, Zip 58201–3434; tel. 701/772–2500, **A**10 21 **F**4 98 102 106 151 **P**1
Primary Contact: Susan Tabor, Interim Chief Executive Officer
CFO: Michelle Currie, Chief Financial Officer
CHR: Amanda Altendorf, Chief Human Resources and Quality Management
Web address: www.redriverbhs.com
Control: Corporation, Investor–owned (for–profit) **Service:** Psychiatric

Staffed Beds: 70 Admissions: 810 Census: 21 Outpatient Visits: 0 Births: 0 Total Expense ($000): 10403 Payroll Expense ($000): 4603 Personnel: 106

HARVEY—Wells County

★ **ST. ALOISIUS MEDICAL CENTER (351327)**, 325 East Brewster Street, Zip 58341–1653; tel. 701/324–4651, (Total facility includes 91 beds in nursing home–type unit) **A**5 10 18 **F**15 28 30 40 45 53 56 57 59 77 81 93 107 110 114 125 128 130 131 132 133 146 147 **S** Sisters of Mary of the Presentation Health System, Fargo, ND
Primary Contact: Mike Zwicker, Chief Executive Officer
CFO: Sandra Teubner, Chief Financial Officer
Web address: www.staloisius.com
Control: Church operated, Nongovernment, not–for–profit **Service:** General medical and surgical

Staffed Beds: 116 Admissions: 339 Census: 88 Outpatient Visits: 7617 Births: 0 Total Expense ($000): 16078 Payroll Expense ($000): 6924 Personnel: 202

HAZEN—Mercer County

★ **SAKAKAWEA MEDICAL CENTER (351310)**, 510 Eighth Avenue NE, Zip 58545–4637; tel. 701/748–2225, (Nonreporting) **A**5 10 18
Primary Contact: Darrold Bertsch, Chief Executive Officer
CFO: Renae Snyder, Chief Financial Officer
CHR: Laurie Miller, Administrative Assistant
CNO: Marcie Schulz, Director Patient Care
Web address: www.smcnd.org
Control: Other not–for–profit (including NFP Corporation) **Service:** General medical and surgical

Staffed Beds: 18

Many Facility Codes have changed. Please refer to the AHA Guide Code Chart.

© 2018 AHA Guide

HETTINGER—Adams County

WEST RIVER REGIONAL MEDICAL CENTER (351330), 1000 Highway 12, Zip 58639–7530; tel. 701/567–4561, (Nonreporting) **A**3 5 10 18
Primary Contact: Matthew Shahan, Chief Executive Officer
CFO: Nathan Stadheim, Chief Financial Officer
CMO: Jennifer Shefield, M.D., Chief of Staff
CIO: Julia Gochenour, Manager Information Systems
CHR: Tera Fried, Manager Human Resources
CNO: Barbara Stadheim, Chief Nursing Officer
Web address: www.wrhs.com
Control: Other not–for–profit (including NFP Corporation) **Service:** General medical and surgical

Staffed Beds: 25

HILLSBORO—Traill County

★ **SANFORD HILLSBORO MEDICAL CENTER (351329)**, 12 Third Street SE, Zip 58045–4840, Mailing Address: P.O. Box 609, Zip 58045–0609; tel. 701/636–3200, (Total facility includes 36 beds in nursing home–type unit) **A**5 10 18 **F**7 10 11 34 35 40 64 65 68 75 93 97 103 125 128 130 131 133 143 146 148 **P**6 **S** Sanford Health, Sioux Falls, SD
Primary Contact: Jac McTaggart, Chief Executive Officer
CFO: Scott Awalt, Chief Financial Officer
CMO: Charles J Breen, M.D., Medical Director
CHR: Jenny Jacobson, Manager Human Resources
Web address: www.hillsboromedicalcenter.com
Control: Other not–for–profit (including NFP Corporation) **Service:** General medical and surgical

Staffed Beds: 52 **Admissions:** 218 **Census:** 40 **Outpatient Visits:** 16701 **Births:** 0 **Total Expense ($000):** 11324 **Payroll Expense ($000):** 4920 **Personnel:** 89

JAMESTOWN—Stutsman County

⊞ **JAMESTOWN REGIONAL MEDICAL CENTER (351335)**, 2422 20th Street SW, Zip 58401–6201; tel. 701/252–1050, **A**1 5 10 18 **F**3 11 13 15 28 29 31 34 35 40 43 45 50 53 57 59 62 63 64 68 70 75 77 79 81 82 84 85 86 87 93 107 108 110 111 115 118 119 130 131 132 133 135 146 148 149
Primary Contact: Trisha Jungels, R.N., Interim Chief Executive Officer
COO: Ricki Ramlo, Chief Operating Officer and Human Resources
CFO: Brandon Vaughan, Chief Financial Officer and Vice President Finance
CMO: Derek Brickner, President Medical Staff
CIO: Jeff Gunkel, Chief Information Officer
CHR: Ricki Ramlo, Chief Operating Officer and Human Resources
CNO: Trisha Jungels, R.N., Chief Nursing Officer and Vice President Clinical Services
Web address: www.jamestownhospital.com
Control: Other not–for–profit (including NFP Corporation) **Service:** General medical and surgical

Staffed Beds: 25 **Admissions:** 1295 **Census:** 10 **Outpatient Visits:** 34201 **Births:** 323 **Total Expense ($000):** 46179 **Payroll Expense ($000):** 18123 **Personnel:** 268

☐ **NORTH DAKOTA STATE HOSPITAL (354003)**, 2605 Circle Drive SE, Zip 58401–6905; tel. 701/253–3964, (Nonreporting) **A**1 3 5 10
Primary Contact: Rosalie Etherington, Superintendent and Chief Executive Officer
COO: Ken Schulz, Chief Operating Officer
CMO: Eduardo Yabut, M.D., Medical Director
CIO: Amy Shape, Information Technology
CNO: Leah Schulz, Director of Nursing
Web address: www.nd.gov/
Control: State, Government, nonfederal **Service:** Psychiatric

Staffed Beds: 100

KENMARE—Ward County

★ **KENMARE COMMUNITY HOSPITAL (351305)**, 317 First Avenue NW, Zip 58746–7104, Mailing Address: P.O. Box 697, Zip 58746–0697; tel. 701/385–4296, (Nonreporting) **A**10 18
Primary Contact: Danielle Alsadon, Clinic/Hospital Manager
COO: Bev Heninger, Director of Nursing
CFO: Dennis Empey, Chief Financial Officer
CMO: Buki Oni, M.D., Chief Medical Officer
CIO: David Wanner, Director Information Technology
CHR: Ranae Ehlke, Administrative Secretary and Coordinator Risk Management and Human Resources
CNO: Bev Heninger, Director of Nursing
Web address: www.kenmarend.net/hospital.htm
Control: Corporation, Investor–owned (for–profit) **Service:** General medical and surgical

Staffed Beds: 25

LANGDON—Cavalier County

★ **CAVALIER COUNTY MEMORIAL HOSPITAL AND CLINICS (351323)**, 909 Second Street, Zip 58249–2407; tel. 701/256–6100, (Nonreporting) **A**5 10 18
Primary Contact: Darla Roder, Chief Operating Officer and Interim Chief Executive Officer
COO: Darla Roder, Chief Operating Officer
CFO: Richard Fromme, Chief Financial Officer
CMO: Lynne Didrikson, M.D., Chief Medical Officer
CHR: Linda Benoit, Human Resource Officer
CNO: Jamie Nienhuis, Chief Nursing Officer
Web address: www.cavaliercountyhospital.com
Control: Other not–for–profit (including NFP Corporation) **Service:** General medical and surgical

Staffed Beds: 20

LINTON—Emmons County

★ **LINTON HOSPITAL (351328)**, 518 North Broadway, Zip 58552–7308, Mailing Address: P.O. Box 850, Zip 58552–0850; tel. 701/254–4511, (Nonreporting) **A**5 10 18
Primary Contact: Robert O. Black, Chief Executive Officer
CMO: John Knecht, Chief Medical Staff
CHR: Sue Meidinger, Manager Business Office
Web address: www.lintonhospital.com
Control: Other not–for–profit (including NFP Corporation) **Service:** General medical and surgical

Staffed Beds: 14

LISBON—Ransom County

★ **CHI LISBON HEALTH (351311)**, 905 Main Street, Zip 58054–4334, Mailing Address: P.O. Box 353, Zip 58054–0353; tel. 701/683–6400, (Nonreporting) **A**10 18 **S** Catholic Health Initiatives, Englewood, CO
Primary Contact: Peggy Reinke, R.N., Administrator
COO: Sheri Heinisch, Compliance Officer
CFO: Amber Stowman, Controller
CHR: Janet Froemke, Human Resources Officer
Web address: www.lisbonhospital.com
Control: Church operated, Nongovernment, not–for–profit **Service:** General medical and surgical

Staffed Beds: 25

MANDAN—Morton County

TRIUMPH HOSPITAL – CENTRAL DAKOTAS See Vibra Hospital of Central Dakotas

⊞ **VIBRA HOSPITAL OF CENTRAL DAKOTAS (352005)**, 1000 18th Street NW, Zip 58554–1612; tel. 701/667–2000, (Nonreporting) **A**1 10 **S** Vibra Healthcare, Mechanicsburg, PA
Primary Contact: Glynda Troyo–Sauviac, Chief Executive Officer
Web address: www.vhcentraldakotas.com
Control: Corporation, Investor–owned (for–profit) **Service:** Acute long–term care hospital

Staffed Beds: 41

MAYVILLE—Traill County

MERITCARE MAYVILLE UNION HOSPITAL See Sanford Mayville Medical Center

★ **SANFORD MAYVILLE MEDICAL CENTER (351309)**, 42 Sixth Avenue SE, Zip 58257–1598; tel. 701/786–3800, **A**5 10 18 **F**7 40 43 45 50 65 77 81 93 97 107 119 128 129 130 133 **P**6 **S** Sanford Health, Sioux Falls, SD
Primary Contact: Jac McTaggart, Chief Executive Officer
CFO: Shauna Slabik, Chief Financial Officer
CMO: Jane Ostlig, Chief Medical Officer
Web address: www.unionhospital.com
Control: Other not–for–profit (including NFP Corporation) **Service:** General medical and surgical

Staffed Beds: 18 **Admissions:** 194 **Census:** 3 **Outpatient Visits:** 19604 **Births:** 0 **Total Expense ($000):** 8488 **Payroll Expense ($000):** 4340 **Personnel:** 62

Hospital, Medicare Provider Number, Address, Telephone, Approval, Facility, and Physician Codes, Health Care System

★ American Hospital Association (AHA) membership
☐ The Joint Commission accreditation
○ Healthcare Facilities Accreditation Program
◇ DNV Healthcare Inc. accreditation
⇧ Center for Improvement in Healthcare Quality Accreditation
△ Commission on Accreditation of Rehabilitation Facilities (CARF) accreditation

MCVILLE—Nelson County

NELSON COUNTY HEALTH SYSTEM (351308), 200 Main Street, Zip 58254,
Mailing Address: P.O. Box 367, Zip 58254–0367; tel. 701/322–4328,
(Nonreporting) **A**10 18
Primary Contact: Steve Forde, Chief Executive Officer
CMO: Erling Martinson, M.D., Medical Director
Web address: www.nelsoncountyhealthsystem.org
Control: Other not–for–profit (including NFP Corporation) **Service**: General
medical and surgical

Staffed Beds: 58

MINOT—Ward County

✠ △ **TRINITY HEALTH (350006)**, One Burdick Expressway West,
Zip 58701–4406, Mailing Address: P.O. Box 5020, Zip 58702–5020;
tel. 701/857–5766, (Includes TRINITY HOSPITAL–ST. JOSEPH'S, 407 3rd Street
SE, Minot, ND, Zip 58702–5001; tel. 701/857–2000) (Total facility includes 215
beds in nursing home–type unit) **A**1 2 3 5 7 10 **F**3 4 5 7 8 10 11 13 15 18 20 22
24 28 29 30 31 34 35 38 39 40 43 45 46 50 54 55 56 57 59 60 62 63 64 65
68 70 72 73 74 75 76 77 78 79 81 82 84 85 86 87 89 90 92 93 94 97 98 99
100 101 103 104 105 107 108 110 111 114 115 116 117 118 119 120 121
124 126 127 128 129 130 131 132 133 143 144 146 147 148 151 152 154
Primary Contact: John M. Kutch, President
CFO: Dennis Empey, Chief Financial Officer
CIO: David Wanner, Chief Information Officer
CHR: Paul Simonson, Vice President
Web address: www.trinityhealth.org
Control: Other not–for–profit (including NFP Corporation) **Service**: General
medical and surgical

Staffed Beds: 580 Admissions: 9060 Census: 310 Outpatient
Visits: 225585 Births: 1634 Total Expense ($000): 434584 Payroll
Expense ($000): 214531 Personnel: 2702

NORTHWOOD—Grand Forks County

★ **NORTHWOOD DEACONESS HEALTH CENTER (351312)**, 4 North Park
Street, Zip 58267–4102, Mailing Address: P.O. Box 190, Zip 58267–0190;
tel. 701/587–6060, (Nonreporting) **A**5 10 18 **S** Sanford Health, Sioux Falls, SD
Primary Contact: Pete Antonson, Chief Executive Officer
CMO: Jon Berg, M.D., Chief of Staff
CIO: Chad Peterson, Chief Information Officer
Web address: www.ndhc.net
Control: Church operated, Nongovernment, not–for–profit **Service**: General
medical and surgical

Staffed Beds: 57

OAKES—Dickey County

★ **CHI OAKES HOSPITAL (351315)**, 1200 North Seventh Street, Zip 58474–2502;
tel. 701/742–3291, (Nonreporting) **A**5 10 18 **S** Catholic Health Initiatives,
Englewood, CO
Primary Contact: Becki Thompson, President
CFO: Bethany Smith, Director of Finance
CMO: Katie O'Brien–Paradis, M.D., Chief Medical Officer
CHR: Julie Entzminger, Manager Human Resources
CNO: Kimberly A. Ketterling, R.N., Vice President of Nursing
Web address: www.oakeshospital.com
Control: Other not–for–profit (including NFP Corporation) **Service**: General
medical and surgical

Staffed Beds: 20

PARK RIVER—Walsh County

★ **FIRST CARE HEALTH CENTER (351326)**, 115 Vivian Street, Zip 58270–4540,
Mailing Address: PO Box I, Zip 58270–0708; tel. 701/284–7500, **A**5 10 18 **F**11
15 28 29 31 33 34 35 40 45 50 57 59 64 65 68 75 77 78 79 81 82 86 87 93
104 107 108 110 111 115 119 127 129 130 133 135 146 147 148 154 **P**6
Primary Contact: Marcus Lewis, Chief Executive Officer and Administrator
CFO: Layne Ensrude, Chief Financial Officer
CMO: Joel Johnson, M.D., Chief Medical Staff
CNO: Lori Seim, R.N., Director Nursing Services
Web address: www.firstcarehc.com
Control: Other not–for–profit (including NFP Corporation) **Service**: General
medical and surgical

Staffed Beds: 14 Admissions: 330 Census: 6 Outpatient Visits: 29546
Births: 0 Total Expense ($000): 11568 Payroll Expense ($000): 4559
Personnel: 90

ROLLA—Rolette County

PRESENTATION MEDICAL CENTER (351316), 213 Second Avenue
NE, Zip 58367–7153, Mailing Address: P.O. Box 759, Zip 58367–0759;
tel. 701/477–3161, (Nonreporting) **A**5 10 18 **S** Sisters of Mary of the
Presentation Health System, Fargo, ND
Primary Contact: Chris Albertson, Chief Executive Officer
CFO: Paula Wilkie, Chief Financial Officer
CMO: Roy Cordy, M.D., President Medical Staff
CHR: Chris Albertson, Director Human Resources
Web address: www.pmc–rolla.com
Control: Church operated, Nongovernment, not–for–profit **Service**: General
medical and surgical

Staffed Beds: 25

RUGBY—Pierce County

★ **HEART OF AMERICA MEDICAL CENTER (351332)**, 800 Main Avenue South,
Zip 58368–2198; tel. 701/776–5261, (Nonreporting) **A**5 10 18
Primary Contact: Patrick J. Branco, Chief Executive Officer
CFO: Bonnie Kuehnemund, Comptroller
CIO: Jeremy Schonebery, Director Information Technology
Web address: www.hamc.com
Control: Other not–for–profit (including NFP Corporation) **Service**: General
medical and surgical

Staffed Beds: 20

STANLEY—Mountrail County

★ **MOUNTRAIL COUNTY MEDICAL CENTER (351301)**, 615 6th Street
SE, Zip 58784–4444, Mailing Address: P.O. Box 399, Zip 58784–0399;
tel. 701/628–2424, (Nonreporting) **A**10 18
Primary Contact: Rockford Zastoupil, Administrator
CFO: Susan Weston, CPA, Chief Financial Officer
CMO: Marla Longmuir, M.D., Chief Medical Officer
CIO: Kathy Janssen, Director Medical Records
CHR: Alisha McMahon, Director Human Resources
CNO: Belinda Moen, R.N., MSN, Interim Director of Nursing
Web address: www.stanleyhealth.org
Control: Other not–for–profit (including NFP Corporation) **Service**: General
medical and surgical

Staffed Beds: 11

TIOGA—Williams County

★ **TIOGA MEDICAL CENTER (351300)**, 810 North Welo Street, Zip 58852–7157,
Mailing Address: P.O. Box 159, Zip 58852–0159; tel. 701/664–3305,
(Nonreporting) **A**5 10 18
Primary Contact: Randall K. Pederson, Chief Executive Officer
CMO: Swami P Gade, M.D., Medical Director
CHR: Mary Ann Holm, Office Clerk
Web address: www.tiogahealth.org
Control: Other not–for–profit (including NFP Corporation) **Service**: General
medical and surgical

Staffed Beds: 55

TURTLE LAKE—McLean County

★ **COMMUNITY MEMORIAL HOSPITAL (351304)**, 220 Fifth Avenue,
Zip 58575–4005, Mailing Address: P.O. Box 280, Zip 58575–0280;
tel. 701/448–2331, (Nonreporting) **A**10 18 **S** Catholic Health Initiatives,
Englewood, CO
Primary Contact: Tod Graeber, Administrator
CFO: Tom Spain, Director Operations Finance
CNO: Jessie Martin, R.N., Chief Nursing Executive
Web address: www.wrtc.com/cullum/hospital
Control: Church operated, Nongovernment, not–for–profit **Service**: General
medical and surgical

Staffed Beds: 25

VALLEY CITY—Barnes County

★ **CHI MERCY HEALTH (351324)**, 570 Chautauqua Boulevard, Zip 58072–3199;
tel. 701/845–6400, (Nonreporting) **A**10 18 **S** Catholic Health Initiatives,
Englewood, CO
Primary Contact: Keith E. Heuser, Market President
CFO: Joshua Senger, Vice President, Operational Finance
CHR: Nicole Nestler, Division Director Human Resources
Web address: www.mercyhospitalvalleycity.org
Control: Church operated, Nongovernment, not–for–profit **Service**: General
medical and surgical

Staffed Beds: 19

A468 Hospitals

Many Facility Codes have changed. Please refer to the AHA Guide Code Chart.

© 2018 AHA Guide

★ **MCKENZIE COUNTY HEALTHCARE SYSTEM (351302)**, 516 North Main
Street, Zip 58854–7310; tel. 701/842–3000, **A**10 18 **F**3 11 28 29 34 40 43 45
50 56 57 59 64 65 68 77 81 85 86 87 93 94 97 107 114 119 127 129 131
133 144 146 154
Primary Contact: Daniel R. Kelly, Chief Executive Officer
COO: Michael Curtis, Chief Administrative Officer
CFO: Kenneth Cox, Interim Chief Financial Officer
CMO: Gary Ramage, M.D., Chief Medical Officer
CIO: Karn Pederson, Manager Health Information Management
CHR: Amy Gonzales, Director of Human Resources
CNO: Cheryl Faulkner, Director of Nursing
Web address: www.mckenziehealth.com
Control: Other not–for–profit (including NFP Corporation) **Service**: General
medical and surgical

Staffed Beds: 24 **Admissions:** 101 **Census:** 2 **Outpatient Visits:** 13448
Births: 0 **Total Expense ($000):** 17296 **Payroll Expense ($000):** 7142
Personnel: 62

⊠ **CHI ST. ALEXIUS HEALTH – WILLISTON MEDICAL CENTER (351334)**, 1301
15th Avenue West, Zip 58801–3896; tel. 701/774–7400, (Nonreporting) **A**1 3 10
18 **S** Catholic Health Initiatives, Englewood, CO
Primary Contact: Dan Bjerknes, Market Leader
CMO: Brett Vibeto, M.D., Chief of Staff
CIO: Jeff Rust, Information Technology Systems Site Manager
CHR: Dan Bjerknes, Director Human Resources
CNO: Lori Hahn, Vice President Nursing Services
Web address: www.mercy–williston.org
Control: Church operated, Nongovernment, not–for–profit **Service**: General
medical and surgical

Staffed Beds: 25

★ **WISHEK COMMUNITY HOSPITAL AND CLINICS (351321)**, 1007 Fourth
Avenue South, Zip 58495–7527, Mailing Address: P.O. Box 647, Zip 58495–0647;
tel. 701/452–2326, **A**5 10 18 **F**3 7 11 15 17 18 28 29 32 34 35 36 40 44 45
50 53 56 57 59 64 65 68 75 81 82 83 87 91 92 93 97 107 114 127 128 130
131 133 143 146 147 148 149 **P**6
Primary Contact: Beverly Vilhauer, Chief Executive Officer
CFO: Megan Rath, Chief Financial Officer
CMO: Joseph Thirumalareddy, M.D., Chief of Staff
CIO: Kari Buchholz, Director Health Information Management
CHR: Shar Bauer, Executive Secretary
Web address: www.wishekhospital.com
Control: Other not–for–profit (including NFP Corporation) **Service**: General
medical and surgical

Staffed Beds: 19 **Admissions:** 284 **Census:** 4 **Outpatient Visits:** 9032
Births: 0 **Total Expense ($000):** 7636 **Payroll Expense ($000):** 3496
Personnel: 75

Hospital, Medicare Provider Number, Address, Telephone, Approval, Facility, and Physician Codes, Health Care System

★ American Hospital Association (AHA) membership
□ The Joint Commission accreditation
○ Healthcare Facilities Accreditation Program
◇ DNV Healthcare Inc. accreditation
⇑ Center for Improvement in Healthcare Quality Accreditation
△ Commission on Accreditation of Rehabilitation Facilities (CARF) accreditation

© 2018 AHA Guide   *Many Facility Codes have changed. Please refer to the AHA Guide Code Chart.*   Hospitals **A469**

OHIO

AKRON—Summit County

☒ **AKRON CHILDREN'S HOSPITAL (363303)**, One Perkins Square,
Zip 44308–1063; tel. 330/543–1000, **A**1 2 3 5 8 10 **F**3 7 11 13 16 18 19 20
21 22 23 25 26 27 29 30 31 32 33 34 35 36 38 39 40 41 43 44 48 50 54 55
57 58 59 60 61 62 63 64 65 66 68 72 73 74 75 76 77 78 79 81 82 84 85 86
87 88 89 91 92 93 94 96 97 98 99 100 101 102 104 105 106 107 108 111
112 114 115 116 117 118 119 129 130 131 132 134 135 136 141 143 144
146 148 149 153 154 **P**6
Primary Contact: William H. Considine, President
COO: Lisa Aurilio, R.N., MSN, Chief Operating Officer
CFO: Michael Trainer, Chief Financial Officer
CMO: Robert McGregor, M.D., Chief Medical Officer
CIO: Harun Rashid, Vice President and Chief Information Officer
CHR: Bernett Williams, Interim Chief Human Resource Officer
CNO: Christine Young, MSN, R.N., Vice President of Patient Services and Chief
Nursing Officer
Web address: www.akronchildrens.org
Control: Other not–for–profit (including NFP Corporation) **Service**: Children's
general medical and surgical

Staffed Beds: 434 **Admissions:** 10214 **Census:** 213 **Outpatient Visits:**
1089251 **Births:** 2 **Total Expense ($000):** 800516 **Payroll Expense**
($000): 401365 **Personnel:** 5085

☒ **CLEVELAND CLINIC AKRON GENERAL (360027)**, 1 Akron General Avenue,
Zip 44307–2433; tel. 330/344–6000, **A**1 2 3 5 8 10 **F**3 5 8 11 12 13 15 17 18
20 22 24 26 28 29 30 31 34 35 36 37 38 40 43 44 45 46 47 48 49 50 51 52
53 54 58 59 60 61 62 63 64 65 66 68 70 71 72 74 75 76 77 78 79 81 82 84
85 87 93 94 96 97 98 100 101 102 103 104 105 107 108 110 111 112 114
115 117 118 119 120 121 123 124 126 129 130 131 132 135 138 144 146
147 148 149 152 153 154 **S** Cleveland Clinic Health System, Cleveland, OH
Primary Contact: Alan Papa, President
CFO: Dave Frigo, Vice President Financial Planning and Treasury
CMO: David Peter, M.D., Senior Vice President Medical Affairs and Chief Medical
Director
CIO: David Fiser, Vice President and Chief Information Officer
CHR: Don Corpora, Executive Vice President and Chief Human Resources Officer
CNO: Cherie M Guster, R.N., MSN, Senior Vice President and Chief Nursing Officer
Web address: www.akrongeneral.org
Control: Other not–for–profit (including NFP Corporation) **Service**: General
medical and surgical

Staffed Beds: 450 **Admissions:** 25531 **Census:** 328 **Outpatient Visits:**
734126 **Births:** 2943 **Total Expense ($000):** 563030 **Payroll Expense**
($000): 230596 **Personnel:** 2966

☒ **SELECT SPECIALTY HOSPITAL–AKRON (362027)**, 200 East Market Street,
Zip 44308–2015; tel. 330/761–7500, (Nonreporting) **A**1 10 **S** Select Medical
Corporation, Mechanicsburg, PA
Primary Contact: Sonda Burns, Chief Executive Officer
Web address: www.selectspecialtyhospitals.com/company/locations/akron.aspx
Control: Corporation, Investor–owned (for–profit) **Service**: Acute long–term care
hospital

Staffed Beds: 60

SUMMA AKRON CITY HOSPITAL See Summa Health System, Akron

SUMMA HEALTH SYSTEM See Summa Health System

☒ **SUMMA HEALTH SYSTEM (360020)**, 525 East Market Street,
Zip 44304–1619; tel. 330/375–3000, (Includes SUMMA AKRON CITY HOSPITAL,
525 East Market Street, Akron, OH, Zip 44309–2090, Mailing Address: P.O.
Box 2090, Zip 44309–2090, tel. 330/375–3000; SUMMA HEALTH SYSTEM
BARBERTON HOSPITAL, 155 Fifth Street NE, Barberton, OH, Zip 44203–3332;
tel. 330/615–3000; Michael Hughes, M.D., President, Summa Health System
Barberton; SUMMA SAINT THOMAS HOSPITAL, 444 North Main Street, Akron, OH,
Zip 44310; tel. 330/375–3000) **A**1 2 5 8 10 13 **F**3 4 5 8 11 12 13 15 17 18 20
22 24 26 28 29 30 31 34 35 36 37 38 39 40 43 44 45 46 47 49 50 51 53 54
56 57 58 59 61 62 63 64 65 66 70 71 74 75 76 77 78 79 80 81 82 83 84 85
86 87 90 92 93 96 97 98 100 101 102 103 104 105 107 108 110 111 114
115 116 117 119 120 121 123 124 126 129 130 131 132 134 135 144 146
147 148 149 153 **P**6 8 **S** Summa Health, Akron, OH
Primary Contact: David Custodio, M.D., President Summa Health System Akron
CMO: Erik N Steele, D.O., Senior Vice President and Chief Medical Officer
CIO: Greg Kall, Chief Information Officer
CHR: Kyle Klawitter, Vice President Human Resources
Web address: www.summahealth.org
Control: Other not–for–profit (including NFP Corporation) **Service**: General
medical and surgical

Staffed Beds: 639 **Admissions:** 31433 **Census:** 414 **Outpatient Visits:**
479625 **Births:** 3834 **Total Expense ($000):** 840857 **Payroll Expense**
($000): 260146 **Personnel:** 6587

☐ △ **SUMMA REHAB HOSPITAL (363035)**, 29 North Adams Street,
Zip 44304–1641; tel. 330/572–7300, (Nonreporting) **A**1 7 10 **S** Summa Health,
Akron, OH
Primary Contact: Cheryl Henthorn, Chief Executive Officer
Web address: www.summarehabhospital.com/
Control: Corporation, Investor–owned (for–profit) **Service**: Rehabilitation

Staffed Beds: 60

SUMMA SAINT THOMAS HOSPITAL See Summa Health System, Akron

ALLIANCE—Stark County

○ **ALLIANCE COMMUNITY HOSPITAL (360131)**, 200 East State Street,
Zip 44601–4936; tel. 330/596–6000, (Total facility includes 78 beds in nursing
home–type unit) **A**2 5 10 11 **F**3 8 11 12 15 28 29 30 31 34 35 36 40 45 49 50
51 56 57 59 60 62 63 64 68 69 70 74 75 77 79 81 82 84 85 86 87 90 93 96
98 103 107 108 110 111 114 115 118 119 128 129 130 132 135 143 144
146 147 148 154 **P**5 7 8 **S** Aultman Health Foundation, Canton, OH
Primary Contact: Ryan Jones, Chief Executive Officer
COO: Dale W. Wells, Chief Financial and Operating Officer
CFO: Dale W. Wells, Chief Financial and Operating Officer
CMO: Ashraf Ahmed, M.D., Senior Vice President Physician and Hospital Services
CIO: David W Shroades, Vice President Technology Services
CHR: Nicole L Russ, Director Colleague Relations
CNO: Amy Antonacci, MSN, R.N., Vice President Nursing Services
Web address: www.achosp.org
Control: Other not–for–profit (including NFP Corporation) **Service**: General
medical and surgical

Staffed Beds: 202 **Admissions:** 2969 **Census:** 99 **Outpatient Visits:**
180714 **Births:** 0 **Total Expense ($000):** 88465 **Payroll Expense**
($000): 38070 **Personnel:** 741

AMHERST—Lorain County

☐ **SPECIALTY HOSPITAL OF LORAIN (362025)**, 254 Cleveland Avenue,
Zip 44001–1620; tel. 440/988–6260, (Nonreporting) **A**1 10
Primary Contact: Rajive Khanna, Chief Executive Officer
COO: Susan Adams, Chief Nursing Officer and Chief Operating Officer
CNO: Susan Adams, Chief Nursing Officer and Chief Operating Officer
Control: Other not–for–profit (including NFP Corporation) **Service**: Acute long–
term care hospital

Staffed Beds: 30

ARCHBOLD—Fulton County

ARCHBOLD HOSPITAL See Community Hospitals and Wellness Centers, Bryan

ASHLAND—Ashland County

☒ **UNIVERSITY HOSPITALS SAMARITAN MEDICAL CENTER (360002)**, 1025
Center Street, Zip 44805–4011; tel. 419/289–0491, **A**1 5 10 **F**11 13 15 18 20
28 29 30 31 34 35 40 45 50 51 57 59 62 64 68 75 76 77 78 79 81 82 86
87 93 96 107 111 114 119 129 130 131 132 135 146 147 148 149 154 **S**
University Hospitals, Cleveland, OH
Primary Contact: Karen McNeil, President
CFO: Mary Griest, Vice President Finance and Chief Financial Officer
CMO: Philip Myers, M.D., Vice President Medical Affairs
CIO: Kathleen Metcalf, Chief Information Officer
CHR: Alyce Legg, Vice President Human Resources
CNO: Karin Schwan, Chief Nursing Officer, Vice President Patient Care Services
Web address: www.samaritanhospital.org
Control: Other not–for–profit (including NFP Corporation) **Service**: General
medical and surgical

Staffed Beds: 39 **Admissions:** 2379 **Census:** 18 **Outpatient Visits:** 155772
Births: 294 **Total Expense ($000):** 67700 **Payroll Expense ($000):** 22630
Personnel: 429

Many Facility Codes have changed. Please refer to the AHA Guide Code Chart.

ASHTABULA—Ashtabula County

⊞ **ASHTABULA COUNTY MEDICAL CENTER (360125)**, 2420 Lake Avenue,
Zip 44004–4954; tel. 440/997–2262, (Total facility includes 15 beds in nursing
home–type unit) **A**1 5 10 20 **F**3 11 13 15 18 19 20 26 28 29 30 31 34 35 40
44 45 49 51 53 54 57 59 61 62 63 64 68 70 74 76 78 79 81 82 85 87 89 92
93 97 98 100 102 103 104 107 108 110 111 114 115 116 117 118 119 128
129 130 131 132 135 144 146 147 148 149 153 154 **P**6 8
Primary Contact: Michael J. Habowski, President and Chief Executive Officer
COO: Lewis Hutchison, Vice President Operations and Quality
CFO: Donald L Kepner, Chief Financial Officer
CMO: Jude Cauwenberg, M.D., Chief of Staff
CIO: Jared Swiger, Director Information Systems
CHR: Jonathan Forbes, Director Human Resources
CNO: Ken Frame, Chief Nursing Officer
Web address: www.acmchealth.org
Control: Other not–for–profit (including NFP Corporation) **Service**: General
medical and surgical

Staffed Beds: 151 **Admissions:** 6284 **Census:** 73 **Outpatient Visits:**
266855 **Births:** 379 **Total Expense ($000):** 127734 **Payroll Expense
($000):** 60134 **Personnel:** 894

ATHENS—Athens County

☐ **APPALACHIAN BEHAVIORAL HEALTHCARE (364015)**, 100 Hospital Drive,
Zip 45701–2301; tel. 740/594–5000, (Nonreporting) **A**1 3 10 **S** Ohio Department
of Mental Health, Columbus, OH
Primary Contact: Jane E. Krason, R.N., Chief Executive Officer
COO: Kelly Sole, Chief Operating Officer
CMO: Mark F McGee, M.D., Chief Clinical Officer
CHR: Donovan Workman, Director Human Capital Management
CNO: Karen Durniat–Sushrstedt, Nurse Executive
Web address: www.mh.state.oh.us
Control: State, Government, nonfederal **Service**: Psychiatric

Staffed Beds: 224

⊞ **O'BLENESS MEMORIAL HOSPITAL (360014)**, 55 Hospital Drive,
Zip 45701–2302; tel. 740/593–5551, (Nonreporting) **A**1 3 10 12 13 **S**
OhioHealth, Columbus, OH
Primary Contact: Mark R. Seckinger, President
CFO: Robert Melaragno, Vice President Finance
CIO: Kristine Barr, Vice President Communication Services
CHR: Sandie Leasure, Senior Vice President Human Resources
CNO: Sandy Wood, MSN, R.N., Vice President Patient Services and Chief Nursing
Officer
Web address: www.obleness.org
Control: Other not–for–profit (including NFP Corporation) **Service**: General
medical and surgical

Staffed Beds: 64

AVON—Lorain County

★ **CLEVELAND CLINIC AVON HOSPITAL (360364)**, 33300 Cleveland Clinic
Boulevard, Zip 44011; tel. 440/695–5000, **A**10 **F**3 15 18 20 29 30 34 35 40 45
49 51 64 68 70 74 75 77 79 80 81 82 85 87 92 100 107 108 110 111 114
115 119 130 146 147 148 154 **S** Cleveland Clinic Health System, Cleveland, OH
Primary Contact: Rebecca Starck, M.D., President
COO: John Mills, Chief Operating Officer
CFO: Lori Koenig, Assistant Finance Director
CNO: Mary R Sauer, R.N., Chief Nursing Officer
Web address: www.my.clevelandclinic.org
Control: Other not–for–profit (including NFP Corporation) **Service**: General
medical and surgical

Staffed Beds: 126 **Admissions:** 5964 **Census:** 57 **Outpatient Visits:** 88483
Births: 0 **Total Expense ($000):** 106219 **Payroll Expense ($000):** 38534
Personnel: 550

★ **CLEVELAND CLINIC REHABILITATION HOSPITAL (363038)**, 33355 Health
Campus Boulevard, Zip 44011; tel. 440/937–9099, (Includes CLEVELAND
CLINIC REHABILITATION HOSPITAL, 3025 Science Park Drive, Beachwood,
OH, Zip 44122; tel. 216/455–6400; R David Richer, Chief Executive Officer)
(Nonreporting) **A**3 **S** Select Medical Corporation, Mechanicsburg, PA
Primary Contact: Sam Bayoumy, Chief Executive Officer
Web address: www.my.clevelandclinic.org
Control: Partnership, Investor–owned (for–profit) **Service**: Rehabilitation

Staffed Beds: 120

UH AVON REHABILITATION HOSPITAL (363039), 37900 Chester Road,
Zip 44011–1044; tel. 440/695–7100, (Nonreporting) **S** Kindred Healthcare,
Louisville, KY
Primary Contact: Andrew Goldfrach, Chief Executive Officer
CFO: Jason DiGuilio, Controller
CHR: Abby Hoag, Director, Human Resources
CNO: Katie Kasper, Chief Clinical Officer
Web address: www.uhhospitals.org/uh–avon–rehabilitation–hospital
Control: Corporation, Investor–owned (for–profit) **Service**: Rehabilitation

Staffed Beds: 50

BARNESVILLE—Belmont County

⊞ **BARNESVILLE HOSPITAL (361321)**, 639 West Main Street, Zip 43713–1039,
Mailing Address: P.O. Box 309, Zip 43713–0309; tel. 740/425–3941,
(Nonreporting) **A**1 10 18
Primary Contact: David D. Phillips, Chief Executive Officer and Administrator
CFO: Willie Cooper–Lohr, Chief Financial Officer
CMO: David J Hilliard, D.O., Chief of Staff
CHR: Beth K. Brill, Senior Director Human Resources
CNO: Cynthia Touvelle, R.N., Senior Director Care Management and Chief Nursing
Officer
Web address: www.barnesvillehospital.com
Control: Other not–for–profit (including NFP Corporation) **Service**: General
medical and surgical

Staffed Beds: 25

BATAVIA—Clermont County

⊞ **MERCY HEALTH – CLERMONT HOSPITAL (360236)**, 3000 Hospital Drive,
Zip 45103–1921; tel. 513/732–8200, **A**1 2 10 **F**3 4 8 11 15 16 17 18 19 20
21 22 23 24 25 26 27 28 29 30 34 35 36 37 38 40 41 44 45 46 49 50 51 56
57 59 60 61 64 67 68 70 74 75 77 79 81 83 84 86 87 88 89 90 92 93 94 95
98 99 100 101 102 103 105 107 110 111 115 118 119 126 130 131 132 134
146 148 149 152 153 154 **S** Mercy Health, Cincinnati, OH
Primary Contact: Justin Krueger, FACHE, President
CFO: Philip Wheeler, Director Finance
CMO: Parma Hariharan, M.D., Chief of Staff
CHR: Angie Ferrell, Director Human Resources
CNO: Melissa A Samuelson, R.N., Vice President and Chief Nursing Officer
Web address: www.e–mercy.com
Control: Church operated, Nongovernment, not–for–profit **Service**: General
medical and surgical

Staffed Beds: 147 **Admissions:** 7339 **Census:** 76 **Outpatient Visits:**
128271 **Births:** 3

BEACHWOOD—Cuyahoga County

UH REHABILITATION HOSPITAL (363036), 23333 Harvard Road,
Zip 44122–6232; tel. 216/593–2200, (Nonreporting) **A**3 **S** Kindred Healthcare,
Louisville, KY
Primary Contact: Mirza Baig, M.D., Medical Director
Web address: www.uhhospitals.org
Control: Corporation, Investor–owned (for–profit) **Service**: Rehabilitation

Staffed Beds: 50

⊞ **UNIVERSITY HOSPITALS AHUJA MEDICAL CENTER (360359)**, 3999
Richmond Road, Zip 44122–6046; tel. 216/593–5500, **A**1 3 10 **F**3 5 9 14 15 17
18 19 20 22 24 26 28 29 30 34 35 36 37 40 41 45 46 47 48 49 50 51 56 57
58 59 60 61 64 65 68 70 74 75 77 78 79 80 81 82 84 85 87 91 92 93 97 102
107 108 109 110 111 115 119 126 130 131 144 145 146 148 149 152 154 **S**
University Hospitals, Cleveland, OH
Primary Contact: Susan V. Juris, President
Web address: www.uhhospitals.org/ahuja/tabid/7051/uhahujamedicalcenter.aspx
Control: Other not–for–profit (including NFP Corporation) **Service**: General
medical and surgical

Staffed Beds: 138 **Admissions:** 8544 **Census:** 91 **Outpatient Visits:**
182969 **Births:** 0 **Total Expense ($000):** 158361 **Payroll Expense
($000):** 54200 **Personnel:** 892

Hospital, Medicare Provider Number, Address, Telephone, Approval, Facility, and Physician Codes, Health Care System

★ American Hospital Association (AHA) membership
☐ The Joint Commission accreditation
○ Healthcare Facilities Accreditation Program
◇ DNV Healthcare Inc. accreditation
⇑ Center for Improvement in Healthcare Quality Accreditation
△ Commission on Accreditation of Rehabilitation Facilities (CARF) accreditation

OH

BEAVERCREEK—Greene County

★ ○ **SOIN MEDICAL CENTER (360360)**, 3535 Pentagon Boulevard, Zip 45431–1705; tel. 937/702–4000, **A**2 3 10 11 **F**3 11 13 15 18 20 22 29 30 31 34 35 36 38 39 40 43 44 45 46 47 48 50 51 53 56 57 59 60 61 64 66 68 70 73 74 75 76 77 78 79 81 82 84 85 86 87 92 102 107 108 111 114 115 116 117 118 119 126 130 132 135 146 147 148 149 154 **S** Kettering Health Network, Dayton, OH
Primary Contact: Rick A. Dodds, President
COO: Ron D Connovich, Chief Financial Officer and Chief Operating Officer
CFO: Ron D Connovich, Chief Financial Officer and Chief Operating Officer
CMO: Michael Caccamo, M.D., Chief Medical Officer
CIO: Andy Lehman, Vice President Information Systems
CNO: Belinda Mallett, R.N., MS, Vice President, Patient Care and Clinical Services
Web address: www.khnetwork.org/soin
Control: Church operated, Nongovernment, not–for–profit **Service**: General medical and surgical

Staffed Beds: 133 **Admissions:** 6801 **Census:** 65 **Outpatient Visits:** 87677 **Births:** 713 **Total Expense ($000):** 167444 **Payroll Expense ($000):** 59239 **Personnel:** 839	

BELLAIRE—Belmont County

☐ **BELMONT COMMUNITY HOSPITAL (360153)**, 4697 Harrison Street, Zip 43906–1338, Mailing Address: P.O. Box 653, Zip 43906–0653; tel. 740/671–1200, (Nonreporting) **A**1 10
Primary Contact: John DeBlasis, Vice President
CFO: James B Murdy, Chief Financial Officer
CMO: Jeffrey A Patey, M.D., Chief of Staff
CHR: Serge Gentile, Director Human Resources
Web address: www.wheelinghospital.org/facilities/bch/
Control: Other not–for–profit (including NFP Corporation) **Service**: General medical and surgical

Staffed Beds: 66	

BELLEFONTAINE—Logan County

★ ⇑ **MARY RUTAN HOSPITAL (360197)**, 205 Palmer Avenue, Zip 43311–2281; tel. 937/592–4015, **A**5 10 20 21 **F**3 11 12 13 14 15 18 20 28 29 30 31 32 34 50 51 54 57 59 64 66 68 70 75 76 77 79 81 82 85 86 87 89 107 108 110 111 115 118 119 129 130 132 133 135 146 147 149
Primary Contact: Mandy C. Goble, President and Chief Executive Officer
CFO: Steven Brown, Vice President Fiscal Affairs
CMO: Grant Varian, M.D., Medical Director
CIO: Robert Reynolds, Director Information Systems
CHR: Vickie L Crumley, Chief Human Resources Officer
CNO: Frank Gliha, Vice President of Patient Care
Web address: www.maryrutan.org
Control: Other not–for–profit (including NFP Corporation) **Service**: General medical and surgical

Staffed Beds: 46 **Admissions:** 1465 **Census:** 11 **Outpatient Visits:** 125622 **Births:** 382 **Total Expense ($000):** 93359 **Payroll Expense ($000):** 43886 **Personnel:** 596	

BELLEVUE—Sandusky County

✚ **BELLEVUE HOSPITAL (360107)**, 1400 West Main Street, Zip 44811–9088, Mailing Address: P.O. Box 8004, Zip 44811–8004; tel. 419/483–4040, **A**1 3 5 10 **F**3 13 15 28 29 30 31 34 35 40 41 45 46 50 53 56 57 59 61 68 70 74 75 76 77 79 81 82 85 89 93 107 110 111 115 118 119 127 129 130 131 132 133 135 143 144 146 147 148 149 151 **P**8
Primary Contact: Michael Winthrop, President
CFO: Timothy Buit, Executive Vice President and Chief Financial Officer
CMO: Donald Smith, President Medical Staff
CIO: Kim Stults, Director, Information Systems
CHR: Lisa M. Sartain, Vice President, Human Resources
CNO: Sara Brokaw, Vice President Patient Care Services
Web address: www.bellevuehospital.com
Control: Other not–for–profit (including NFP Corporation) **Service**: General medical and surgical

Staffed Beds: 50 **Admissions:** 1514 **Census:** 12 **Outpatient Visits:** 87383 **Births:** 378 **Total Expense ($000):** 48978 **Payroll Expense ($000):** 17751 **Personnel:** 357	

BLUFFTON—Allen County

★ **BLUFFTON HOSPITAL (361322)**, 139 Garau Street, Zip 45817–1027; tel. 419/358–9010, **A**10 18 **F**3 8 11 13 15 18 40 45 57 59 63 64 68 70 76 77 79 81 82 91 93 107 110 114 119 126 127 146 147 154 **S** Blanchard Valley Health System, Findlay, OH
Primary Contact: Christine Keller, Chief Administrative Officer
CFO: David Cytlak, Vice President Finance
CMO: William H Kose, M.D., Vice President Quality and Medical Affairs
CIO: David Cytlak, Vice President Finance
CHR: Ryan Fisher, Director Human Resources
CNO: Barbara J. Pasztor, R.N., Vice President Nursing and Patient Care Services
Web address: www.bvhealthsystem.org/
Control: Other not–for–profit (including NFP Corporation) **Service**: General medical and surgical

Staffed Beds: 25 **Admissions:** 335 **Census:** 2 **Outpatient Visits:** 22830 **Births:** 282 **Total Expense ($000):** 13737 **Payroll Expense ($000):** 8369 **Personnel:** 109	

BOARDMAN—Mahoning County

MAHONING VALLEY HOSPITAL See Vibra Hospital of Mahoning Valley

✠ **MERCY HEALTH – ST. ELIZABETH BOARDMAN HOSPITAL (360276)**, 8401 Market Street, Zip 44512–6777; tel. 330/729–2929, **A**1 3 10 13 **F**3 8 11 13 15 18 29 30 31 34 35 37 40 45 46 49 59 60 68 70 74 75 76 77 78 79 81 84 87 93 107 108 110 111 114 115 116 117 118 119 120 121 123 126 129 130 146 147 148 149 154 **S** Mercy Health, Cincinnati, OH
Primary Contact: Eugenia Aubel, President, St. Elizabeth Boardman Hospital
CFO: Anthony J. Seminaro, Chief Financial Youngstown
CMO: Heath Dorion, Physician Administrator
CIO: Maureen Kordupel, Director Information Technology Relationship Manager
CNO: Stacie Call, Chief Nursing Officer
Web address: www.mercy.com/youngstown
Control: Church operated, Nongovernment, not–for–profit **Service**: General medical and surgical

Staffed Beds: 217 **Admissions:** 13760 **Census:** 139 **Outpatient Visits:** 120688 **Births:** 2972 **Total Expense ($000):** 170664 **Payroll Expense ($000):** 50642 **Personnel:** 873	

✠ **SELECT SPECIALTY HOSPITAL – BOARDMAN (360363)**, 8401 Market Street, 7 South, Zip 44512–6725; tel. 330/729–1750, (Nonreporting) **A**1 10 **S** Select Medical Corporation, Mechanicsburg, PA
Primary Contact: Varun Chauhan, Chief Executive Officer
Web address: www.selectspecialtyhospitals.com/
Control: Corporation, Investor–owned (for–profit) **Service**: Acute long–term care hospital

Staffed Beds: 24	

✠ **VIBRA HOSPITAL OF MAHONING VALLEY (362023)**, 8049 South Avenue, Zip 44512–6154; tel. 330/726–5000, (Includes VIBRA HOSPITAL OF MAHONING VALLEY–TRUMBULL CAMPUS, 1350 E Market Street, 9th Floor, Warren, OH, Zip 44483–6608; tel. 330/675–5555; Nathan Mast, Chief Executive Officer) (Nonreporting) **A**1 10 **S** Vibra Healthcare, Mechanicsburg, PA
Primary Contact: Nathan Mast, Chief Executive Officer
CMO: Lawrence Goldstein, M.D., Chief Medical Officer
Web address: www.vhmvalley.com
Control: Corporation, Investor–owned (for–profit) **Service**: Acute long–term care hospital

Staffed Beds: 42	

BOWLING GREEN—Wood County

✠ **WOOD COUNTY HOSPITAL (360029)**, 950 West Wooster Street, Zip 43402–2603; tel. 419/354–8900, **A**1 5 10 **F**3 11 12 13 15 17 28 29 30 31 32 33 34 35 36 40 44 45 50 54 57 59 64 65 68 69 70 74 75 76 77 78 79 81 82 85 87 89 93 107 108 110 111 115 118 119 120 121 123 124 129 130 131 132 135 144 146 147 148 154 **P**6 8
Primary Contact: Stanley R. Korducki, President
CFO: Karol Bortel, Vice President Financial Services
CMO: Shawn Stansbery, M.D., Chief of Staff
CIO: Joanne White, Chief Information Officer
CHR: Michael Ford, Vice President Patient Services
CNO: Sandra Beidelschies, MSN, R.N., Vice President Patient Services
Web address: www.woodcountyhospital.org
Control: Other not–for–profit (including NFP Corporation) **Service**: General medical and surgical

Staffed Beds: 108 **Admissions:** 2580 **Census:** 20 **Outpatient Visits:** 100423 **Births:** 317 **Total Expense ($000):** 88511 **Payroll Expense ($000):** 32419 **Personnel:** 405	

Many Facility Codes have changed. Please refer to the AHA Guide Code Chart. © 2018 AHA Guide

BRYAN—Williams County

☐ **COMMUNITY HOSPITALS AND WELLNESS CENTERS (360121)**, 433 West High Street, Zip 43506–1679; tel. 419/636–1131, (Includes ARCHBOLD HOSPITAL, 121 Westfield Drive, Archbold, OH, Zip 43502; tel. 419/445–4415; BRYAN HOSPITAL, 433 West High Street, Bryan, OH, Zip 43506; tel. 419/636–1131; MONTPELIER HOSPITAL, 909 East Snyder Avenue, Montpelier, OH, Zip 43543; tel. 419/485–3154) (Nonreporting) **A**1 2 5 10
Primary Contact: Philip L. Ennen, Vice President and Chief Executive Officer
CFO: Leroy P Feather, Vice President Finance
CIO: Greg Slattery, Vice President Information
CHR: Mary Ann Potts, Director Personnel
Web address: www.chwchospital.com
Control: Other not–for–profit (including NFP Corporation) **Service**: General medical and surgical

Staffed Beds: 113

BUCYRUS—Crawford County

★ ⇑ **BUCYRUS HOSPITAL (361316)**, 629 North Sandusky Avenue, Zip 44820–1821; tel. 419/562–4677, (Nonreporting) **A**5 10 18 21 **S** Avita Health System, Galion, OH
Primary Contact: Jerome Morasko, Chief Executive Officer
COO: Andy Daniels, Chief Operating Officer
CMO: Michael A Johnson, M.D., Chief of Staff
CIO: Joann Riedlinger, Vice President Nursing and Manager Information Systems
CHR: Jeanne Perkins, Vice President Nursing and Interim Manager Human Resources
Web address: www.bchonline.org
Control: Other not–for–profit (including NFP Corporation) **Service**: General medical and surgical

Staffed Beds: 25

CADIZ—Harrison County

☒ **HARRISON COMMUNITY HOSPITAL (361311)**, 951 East Market Street, Zip 43907–9799; tel. 740/942–4631, (Nonreporting) **A**1 10 18
Primary Contact: John DeBlasis, Vice President
CFO: Donald Huelskamp, Interim Chief Financial Officer
CMO: Anandhi Murthy, Chief Medical Officer
CIO: Will Combs, Director Information Technology
CHR: Peter Giordano, Senior Director Human Resources
CNO: Janis Olinski, R.N., Vice President Clinical Services
Web address: www.harrisoncommunity.com
Control: Other not–for–profit (including NFP Corporation) **Service**: General medical and surgical

Staffed Beds: 25

CAMBRIDGE—Guernsey County

CAMBRIDGE BEHAVIORAL HOSPITAL (364027), 66755 State Street, Zip 43725–8757; tel. 740/432–4906, **F**29 98 102
Primary Contact: Pamela Braden, Administrator
Web address: www.cbhohio.com
Control: State, Government, nonfederal **Service**: Psychiatric

Staffed Beds: 66 **Admissions:** 1214 **Census:** 51 **Births:** 0

☒ **SOUTHEASTERN OHIO REGIONAL MEDICAL CENTER (360203)**, 1341 North Clark Street, Zip 43725–9614, Mailing Address: P.O. Box 610, Zip 43725–0610; tel. 740/439–8000, **A**1 2 3 10 20 **F**3 11 13 15 28 29 30 31 32 34 35 40 43 44 45 48 49 50 51 57 59 60 62 64 66 68 70 75 76 77 78 79 81 83 84 85 86 87 89 90 91 93 96 107 108 110 111 114 115 118 119 120 121 123 130 131 132 135 146 147 148 149 **P**6 8
Primary Contact: Raymond M. Chorey, President and Chief Executive Officer
CFO: Timothy R. Evancho, Chief Financial Officer
CMO: E Edwin Conaway, M.D., Vice President Medical Affairs and Chief Medical Officer
CIO: Kevin Ludwigsen, Chief Information Officer
CHR: Steven Michael Brooks, Vice President Human Resources
CNO: Angela S Long, Vice President Clinical Services and Chief Nursing Officer
Web address: www.seormc.org
Control: Other not–for–profit (including NFP Corporation) **Service**: General medical and surgical

Staffed Beds: 90 **Admissions:** 3307 **Census:** 30 **Outpatient Visits:** 138832 **Births:** 409 **Total Expense ($000):** 91945 **Payroll Expense ($000):** 31948 **Personnel:** 684

CANAL WINCHESTER—Fairfield County

☐ **DILEY RIDGE MEDICAL CENTER (360358)**, 7911 Diley Road, Zip 43110–9653; tel. 614/838–7911, **A**1 10 **F**3 15 29 35 40 50 54 64 68 85 87 107 110 111 114 119 130 147 **P**8
Primary Contact: Jodi Wilson, President and Chief Operating Officer
COO: Jodi Wilson, President and Chief Operating Officer
Web address: www.dileyridgemedicalcenter.com
Control: Other not–for–profit (including NFP Corporation) **Service**: General medical and surgical

Staffed Beds: 10 **Admissions:** 20 **Census:** 1 **Outpatient Visits:** 51504 **Births:** 0 **Total Expense ($000):** 12653 **Payroll Expense ($000):** 4761 **Personnel:** 75

CANTON—Stark County

☒ △ **AULTMAN HOSPITAL (360084)**, 2600 Sixth Street SW, Zip 44710–1702; tel. 330/452–9911, (Includes AULTMAN HOSPITAL PEDIATRIC SERVICES, 2600 Sixth Street, SW, Canton, OH, Zip 44710–1702; tel. 330/363–5455) (Total facility includes 60 beds in nursing home–type unit) **A**1 2 3 5 7 10 **F**3 7 8 11 12 13 14 15 17 18 20 22 24 26 28 29 30 31 34 35 39 40 43 44 45 48 49 50 51 53 54 55 56 57 58 59 60 61 62 63 64 68 70 71 72 74 75 76 77 78 79 81 82 83 84 85 86 87 89 90 93 96 97 98 102 103 104 105 107 108 109 110 111 114 115 117 118 119 120 121 123 127 128 129 130 131 132 133 134 135 143 144 145 146 147 148 149 150 154 **P**6 **S** Aultman Health Foundation, Canton, OH
Primary Contact: Edward J. Roth III, President and Chief Executive Officer
CFO: Mark Wright, Vice President
CMO: Allison Oprandi, M.D., Chief Medical Officer
CIO: Liz Getz, Chief Information Officer
CHR: Sue Olivera, Vice President
CNO: Nicole Kolacz, Chief Nursing Officer
Web address: www.aultman.com
Control: Other not–for–profit (including NFP Corporation) **Service**: General medical and surgical

Staffed Beds: 532 **Admissions:** 23140 **Census:** 341 **Outpatient Visits:** 481201 **Births:** 2691 **Total Expense ($000):** 446510 **Payroll Expense ($000):** 169924 **Personnel:** 4903

☐ **AULTMAN SPECIALTY HOSPITAL (362032)**, 2600 Sixth Street, SW, Zip 44710–1702; tel. 330/363–4000, **A**1 10 **F**1 18 29 30 31 56 60 74 78 84 130 148 154 **S** Aultman Health Foundation, Canton, OH
Primary Contact: Ryan J. Kuharich, Chief Executive Officer
CFO: Mark Wright, Chief Financial Officer
CMO: George Kefalas, Chief Medical Officer
Web address: www.aultman.org
Control: Other not–for–profit (including NFP Corporation) **Service**: Acute long–term care hospital

Staffed Beds: 16 **Admissions:** 181 **Census:** 11 **Outpatient Visits:** 0 **Births:** 0

☒ △ **MERCY MEDICAL CENTER (360070)**, 1320 Mercy Drive NW, Zip 44708–2641; tel. 330/489–1000, **A**1 2 3 5 7 10 **F**3 11 13 15 17 18 20 22 24 26 28 29 30 31 34 35 39 40 43 44 46 48 49 50 51 53 54 57 58 59 60 61 62 63 64 66 68 70 72 74 75 76 77 78 79 80 81 82 84 85 86 87 89 90 91 92 93 96 97 107 108 110 111 114 115 116 117 118 119 120 121 123 124 126 129 130 131 132 135 144 146 147 148 149 150 **P**6 7 **S** Sisters of Charity Health System, Cleveland, OH
Primary Contact: Paul C. Hiltz, FACHE, Interim Chief Executive Officer
COO: David D Cemate, FACHE, Senior Vice President and Chief Operating Officer
CFO: David K Stewart, Senior Vice President and Chief Financial Officer
CMO: David Gormsen, D.O., Vice President and Chief Medical Officer
CIO: Trevor Clere, Director Information Technology
CHR: Patti Bresnahan, Director Human Resources
CNO: Barbara Yingling, R.N., Vice President Patient Care Services and Chief Nursing Officer
Web address: www.cantonmercy.org
Control: Other not–for–profit (including NFP Corporation) **Service**: General medical and surgical

Staffed Beds: 304 **Admissions:** 14950 **Census:** 196 **Outpatient Visits:** 641484 **Births:** 1505 **Total Expense ($000):** 337587 **Payroll Expense ($000):** 138780 **Personnel:** 2067

Hospital, Medicare Provider Number, Address, Telephone, Approval, Facility, and Physician Codes, Health Care System

★ American Hospital Association (AHA) membership	◯ Healthcare Facilities Accreditation Program	⇑ Center for Improvement in Healthcare Quality Accreditation
☐ The Joint Commission accreditation	◇ DNV Healthcare Inc. accreditation	△ Commission on Accreditation of Rehabilitation Facilities (CARF) accreditation

OH

⊞ **SELECT SPECIALTY HOSPITAL–CANTON (362016)**, 1320 Mercy Drive NW, 6th Floor, Zip 44708–2614; tel. 330/489–8189, (Nonreporting) **A**1 10 **S** Select Medical Corporation, Mechanicsburg, PA
Primary Contact: Dawne Wheeler, Chief Executive Officer
Web address: www.selectspecialtyhospitals.com/company/locations/canton.aspx
Control: Corporation, Investor–owned (for–profit) **Service**: Acute long–term care hospital

Staffed Beds: 30

CHARDON—Geauga County

☐ **HEATHERHILL CARE COMMUNITIES (362014)**, 12340 Bass Lake Road, Zip 44024–8327; tel. 440/285–4040, (Nonreporting) **A**1 10
Primary Contact: Jim Homa, Chief Executive Officer
COO: Lisa Deering, Administrator
CFO: Valerie Love, Manager Business Office
CMO: Beejadi Makunda, M.D., Chief Medical Officer
CHR: Pam McCall, Director Human Resources
CNO: Alice Harvey, Director of Nursing
Web address: www.heatherhill.com
Control: Other not–for–profit (including NFP Corporation) **Service**: Acute long–term care hospital

Staffed Beds: 214

⊞ **UNIVERSITY HOSPITALS GEAUGA MEDICAL CENTER (360192)**, 13207 Ravenna Road, Zip 44024–7032; tel. 440/269–6000, **A**1 2 3 10 **F**3 8 11 12 13 15 18 20 22 26 28 29 30 31 32 34 35 36 38 39 40 41 43 44 47 49 50 51 54 56 57 58 59 60 62 63 64 65 68 70 74 75 76 77 78 79 81 82 84 85 86 87 91 92 93 96 97 98 100 101 103 107 108 109 110 111 114 115 116 117 118 119 120 121 123 124 129 130 131 132 134 135 143 145 146 147 148 149 154 **S** University Hospitals, Cleveland, OH
Primary Contact: M Steven. Jones, President
COO: M Steven Jones, President
CFO: Paul Amantea, Director Finance
CMO: David Kosnosky, M.D., Chief Medical Officer
CIO: Lou Ciraldo, Information Services Representative
CHR: Danialle Lynce, Manager Human Resources
CNO: Peggy A Kuhar, R.N., MSN, Chief Nursing Officer
Web address: www.uhhospitals.org/geauga/
Control: Other not–for–profit (including NFP Corporation) **Service**: General medical and surgical

Staffed Beds: 142 **Admissions**: 7899 **Census**: 87 **Outpatient Visits**: 160521 **Births**: 1000 **Total Expense ($000)**: 125396 **Payroll Expense ($000)**: 42997 **Personnel**: 776

CHILLICOTHE—Ross County

⊞ **ADENA MEDICAL CENTER (360159)**, 272 Hospital Road, Zip 45601–9031; tel. 740/779–7500, **A**1 2 3 5 10 12 13 19 **F**3 5 8 13 15 18 20 22 24 26 28 29 30 31 32 34 35 37 38 40 41 45 46 48 49 50 51 54 57 59 62 63 64 66 70 73 74 75 76 77 78 79 81 82 83 84 85 87 89 91 93 96 97 98 100 101 102 103 104 107 108 111 114 115 119 120 121 123 126 127 129 130 131 132 133 135 144 146 147 148 **P**6 **S** Adena Health System, Chillicothe, OH
Primary Contact: Jeff Graham, President and Chief Executive Officer
COO: Eric Cecava, Chief Operating Officer
CFO: Robert Rosenberger, Chief Financial Officer
CMO: John Fortney, Senior System Medical Advisor
CIO: Linn Weimer, Chief Information Officer
CHR: Jay D. Justice, Chief Human Resource Officer
Web address: www.adena.org
Control: Other not–for–profit (including NFP Corporation) **Service**: General medical and surgical

Staffed Beds: 192 **Admissions**: 10481 **Census**: 105 **Outpatient Visits**: 644992 **Births**: 677 **Total Expense ($000)**: 309937 **Payroll Expense ($000)**: 113649 **Personnel**: 2273

⊞ **CHILLICOTHE VETERANS AFFAIRS MEDICAL CENTER**, 17273 State Route 104, Zip 45601–9718; tel. 740/773–1141, (Total facility includes 162 beds in nursing home–type unit) **A**1 3 5 **F**3 5 12 18 28 29 30 33 34 35 36 38 39 44 45 47 49 50 53 56 57 58 59 60 61 62 63 64 65 68 71 74 75 77 79 80 83 84 86 87 91 92 93 94 96 97 98 100 101 102 103 104 106 107 108 111 114 119 127 128 129 130 132 135 143 144 146 147 148 149 153 154 **P**6 **S** Department of Veterans Affairs, Perry Point, MD
Primary Contact: Mark Murdock, FACHE, Director
CFO: Rick Deckard, Chief Fiscal Service
CMO: Deborah Meesig, M.D., Chief of Staff
CIO: William Gawler, Chief Information Officer
CHR: Angela Young, Human Resources Officer
Web address: www.chillicothe.va.gov/
Control: Veterans Affairs, Government, federal **Service**: General medical and surgical

Staffed Beds: 295 **Admissions**: 2899 **Census**: 237 **Outpatient Visits**: 417996 **Births**: 0 **Total Expense ($000)**: 232222 **Payroll Expense ($000)**: 104639 **Personnel**: 1557

VETERANS AFFAIRS MEDICAL CENTER See Chillicothe Veterans Affairs Medical Center

CINCINNATI—Hamilton County

⊞ **BETHESDA NORTH HOSPITAL (360179)**, 10500 Montgomery Road, Zip 45242–4402; tel. 513/865–1111, (Includes BETHESDA BUTLER HOSPITAL, 3125 Hamilton Mason Road, Hamilton, OH, Zip 45011–5307; tel. 513/894–8888; Chuck Brown, Administrator) **A**1 3 5 10 **F**3 5 8 9 11 12 13 15 17 18 20 22 24 26 28 29 30 31 34 35 36 37 38 39 40 41 43 44 45 46 47 48 49 50 53 54 55 56 57 58 59 61 63 64 65 66 68 70 71 73 74 75 76 77 78 79 81 82 83 84 85 86 87 91 92 93 94 96 97 100 101 102 104 107 108 109 110 111 114 115 116 117 118 119 120 121 123 124 126 129 130 131 132 134 135 141 143 144 145 146 147 148 149 153 154 **P**6 8
Primary Contact: Barbara Boyne, Executive Director, Operations
COO: Jenny Oliphant, Executive Vice President and Chief Operating Officer
CFO: Michael Crofton, Senior Vice President and Chief Financial Officer
CMO: Georges Feghali, M.D., Senior Vice President Quality and Chief Medical Officer
CIO: Rick Moore, Chief Information Officer
CHR: Walter L McLarty, Chief Human Resources Officer
CNO: Mary Irvin, R.N., MSN, Senior Vice President and Chief Nursing Officer
Web address: www.trihealth.com
Control: Other not–for–profit (including NFP Corporation) **Service**: General medical and surgical

Staffed Beds: 369 **Admissions**: 23212 **Census**: 254 **Outpatient Visits**: 364315 **Births**: 4019 **Total Expense ($000)**: 518801 **Payroll Expense ($000)**: 167867 **Personnel**: 3143

☐ △ **CHRIST HOSPITAL (360163)**, 2139 Auburn Avenue, Zip 45219–2906; tel. 513/585–2000, **A**1 2 3 5 7 10 **F**1 3 6 8 9 12 13 15 17 18 20 22 24 26 28 29 30 31 34 35 36 37 38 39 40 44 45 46 47 48 49 50 51 53 54 55 56 57 58 59 60 61 64 65 66 68 70 73 74 75 76 77 78 79 80 81 82 83 84 85 91 92 93 94 96 97 98 100 103 107 108 109 110 111 114 115 116 117 118 119 120 121 123 124 126 129 130 131 132 135 138 141 143 144 145 146 147 148 149 154 **P**6
Primary Contact: Michael Keating, President and Chief Executive Officer
COO: Deborah Marie Hayes, R.N., MS, MSN, Chief Operating Officer
CMO: Bernard B Gawne, M.D., Vice President and Chief Medical Officer
CIO: Alex Vaillancourt, Chief Information Officer
CHR: Rick Tolson, Chief Administrative Officer and Chief Human Resources Officer
Web address: www.thechristhospital.com
Control: Other not–for–profit (including NFP Corporation) **Service**: General medical and surgical

Staffed Beds: 539 **Admissions**: 24496 **Census**: 288 **Outpatient Visits**: 615641 **Births**: 3121 **Total Expense ($000)**: 684149 **Payroll Expense ($000)**: 225408 **Personnel**: 3716

⊞ △ **CINCINNATI CHILDREN'S HOSPITAL MEDICAL CENTER (363300)**, 3333 Burnet Avenue MLC 8006, Zip 45229–3039, Mailing Address: 3333 Burnet Avenue, Zip 45229–3039; tel. 513/636–4200, (Includes CHILDREN'S HOSPITAL, 3300 Elland Avenue, Cincinnati, OH, Zip 45229–2804; tel. 513/894–8888) **A**1 2 3 5 7 8 10 **F**3 7 9 11 12 17 18 19 20 21 22 23 24 25 26 27 28 29 30 31 32 34 35 36 37 38 39 40 41 43 44 45 46 48 49 50 51 54 55 57 58 59 60 61 62 63 64 65 66 68 72 74 75 76 77 78 79 81 82 84 85 86 87 88 89 90 91 92 93 94 95 96 97 98 99 100 101 102 104 105 106 107 108 111 112 113 115 117 118 119 120 122 126 129 130 131 132 134 135 136 137 138 139 140 141 142 144 146 148 149 150 154 **P**1
Primary Contact: Michael Fisher, President and Chief Executive Officer
CIO: Marianne Speight, Vice President Information System and Chief Information Officer
CHR: Nerissa E. Morris, Senior Vice President and Chief Human Resource Officer
CNO: Barbara F. Tofani, R.N., MSN, Senior Vice President and Chief Nursing Officer
Web address: www.cincinnatichildrens.org
Control: Other not–for–profit (including NFP Corporation) **Service**: Children's general medical and surgical

Staffed Beds: 625 **Admissions**: 19382 **Census**: 424 **Outpatient Visits**: 1287945 **Births**: 21 **Total Expense ($000)**: 2139128 **Payroll Expense ($000)**: 1093470 **Personnel**: 13293

⊞ **CINCINNATI VETERANS AFFAIRS MEDICAL CENTER**, 3200 Vine Street, Zip 45220–2288; tel. 513/475–6300, (Nonreporting) **A**1 2 3 5 **S** Department of Veterans Affairs, Perry Point, MD
Primary Contact: Colonel Vivian T. Hutson, Director
COO: David Ninneman, Associate Director
CFO: Sandra Selvidge, Chief Fiscal Service
CIO: Vique Caro, Chief Information Officer
CHR: Sandra Stenger, Acting Chief Human Resources
CNO: Katheryn Cook, R.N., Nurse Executive
Web address: www.cincinnati.va.gov/
Control: Veterans Affairs, Government, federal **Service**: General medical and surgical

Staffed Beds: 268

DANIEL DRAKE CENTER FOR POST ACUTE CARE (362004), 151 West Galbraith Road, Zip 45216–1015; tel. 513/418–2500, (Nonreporting) **A**1 3 5 10 **S** UC Health, Cincinnati, OH
Primary Contact: Lafe Bauer, Vice President, Post Acute Care Services and Chief Administrative Officer
CFO: Duane Pifko, Interim Director Financial Services
Web address: www.uchealth.com/danieldrakecenter/
Control: Other not–for–profit (including NFP Corporation) **Service**: Acute long–term care hospital

Staffed Beds: 202

GOOD SAMARITAN HOSPITAL (360134), 375 Dixmyth Avenue, Zip 45220–2489; tel. 513/862–1400, **A**1 2 3 5 8 10 **F**3 5 6 8 9 11 12 13 15 17 18 20 22 24 26 28 29 30 31 34 35 36 37 38 39 40 41 44 45 46 47 48 49 50 53 54 55 56 57 58 59 61 63 64 65 66 68 70 71 72 74 75 76 77 78 79 81 82 83 84 85 86 87 91 92 93 94 96 97 98 100 101 102 103 104 105 107 108 109 110 111 114 115 116 117 118 119 120 121 123 124 126 129 130 131 132 134 135 141 143 144 145 146 147 148 149 152 153 154 **P**6 8 **S** Catholic Health Initiatives, Englewood, CO
Primary Contact: Jamie Easterling, Executive Director, Operations
COO: Gerald P Oliphant, Executive Vice President and Chief Operating Officer
CFO: Michael Crofton, Chief Financial Officer
CMO: Georges Feghali, M.D., Senior Vice President Quality and Chief Medical Officer
CIO: Rick Moore, Chief Information Officer
CHR: Walter L McLarty, Chief Human Resources Officer
Web address: www.trihealth.com
Control: Church operated, Nongovernment, not–for–profit **Service**: General medical and surgical

Staffed Beds: 438 **Admissions**: 22431 **Census**: 297 **Outpatient Visits**: 291338 **Births**: 5164 **Total Expense ($000)**: 514795 **Payroll Expense ($000)**: 171470 **Personnel**: 2684

HEALTHSOUTH REHABILITATION HOSPITAL AT DRAKE (363034), 151 West Galbraith Road, Zip 45216–1015; tel. 513/418–5600, (Includes HEALTHSOUTH REHABILITATION HOSPITAL OF CINCINNATI AT NORWOOD, 4953 Section Avenue, Cincinnati, OH, Zip 45212–2120; tel. 513/712–9200; Ryan Smokovitz, Chief Executive Officer) **A**1 3 10 **F**29 34 35 56 74 90 91 130 148 **S** Encompass Health Corporation, Birmingham, AL
Primary Contact: Ryan Smokovitz, Chief Executive Officer
CFO: Scott Corder, Controller
CMO: Mark Goddard, M.D., Medical Director
CHR: Jason Sparks, Director, Human Resources
CNO: Kathy McNally, Chief Nursing Officer
Web address: www.healthsouthatdrake.com
Control: Corporation, Investor–owned (for–profit) **Service**: Rehabilitation

Staffed Beds: 100 **Admissions**: 1610 **Census**: 64 **Outpatient Visits**: 0 **Births**: 0 **Total Expense ($000)**: 24498 **Payroll Expense ($000)**: 11989 **Personnel**: 180

MERCY HEALTH – ANDERSON HOSPITAL (360001), 7500 State Road, Zip 45255–2492; tel. 513/624–4500, **A**1 2 3 10 **F**3 8 9 11 12 13 14 15 17 18 20 22 24 26 28 29 30 31 34 35 37 38 39 40 44 45 46 47 48 49 50 51 53 54 55 56 57 58 59 61 63 64 65 68 70 71 74 75 76 77 78 79 81 82 84 85 86 87 90 93 96 97 107 110 111 114 115 116 117 118 119 120 121 123 126 127 129 130 131 132 134 135 144 146 147 148 154 **S** Mercy Health, Cincinnati, OH
Primary Contact: Ken James, President and Chief Executive Officer of East Market
COO: Robert Maloney Jr Chief Operating Officer
CFO: Patrick A Kowalski, Chief Financial Officer
CMO: Dan Roth, M.D., Vice President Medical Affairs
CIO: Matt Eversole, Regional Vice President Information Services
CHR: Angie Ferrell, Director Human Resources
CNO: Melissa A Samuelson, R.N., Vice President and Chief Nursing Officer
Web address: www.e–mercy.com
Control: Church operated, Nongovernment, not–for–profit **Service**: General medical and surgical

Staffed Beds: 281 **Admissions**: 13206 **Census**: 145 **Outpatient Visits**: 123635 **Births**: 1791

MERCY HEALTH – WEST HOSPITAL (360234), 3300 Mercy Health Boulevard, Zip 45211–1103; tel. 513/215–5000, (Nonreporting) **A**1 2 10 **S** Mercy Health, Cincinnati, OH
Primary Contact: Michael Kramer, Chief Executive Officer
COO: Jason Asic, Chief Operating Officer
CFO: Kyle Klein, Assistant Chief Financial Officer
CMO: Creighton Wright, M.D., Vice President Medical Administration
CHR: Bridget Mentzel, Director Human Resources
CNO: Stephanie Meade, R.N., MSN, Chief Nursing Officer
Web address: www.e–mercy.com/west–hospital
Control: Church operated, Nongovernment, not–for–profit **Service**: General medical and surgical

Staffed Beds: 250

SELECT SPECIALTY HOSPITAL – CINCINNATI NORTH (362034), 10500 Montgomery Road, Zip 45242–4402; tel. 513/865–5300, (Nonreporting) **A**1 10 **S** Select Medical Corporation, Mechanicsburg, PA
Primary Contact: Raymond Carnevale, Interim Chief Executive Officer
CMO: Sunil Dama, M.D., Medical Director
CHR: Elizabeth M Wilson, Coordinator Human Resources
Web address: www.cincinnatinorth.selectspecialtyhospitals.com/
Control: Corporation, Investor–owned (for–profit) **Service**: Acute long–term care hospital

Staffed Beds: 41

SELECT SPECIALTY HOSPITAL–CINCINNATI (362019), 375 Dixmyth Avenue, 15th Floor, Zip 45220–2475; tel. 513/862–4444, **A**1 10 **F**1 3 29 35 50 53 60 68 74 75 77 79 83 84 87 91 100 130 135 143 148 149 154 **P**5 **S** Select Medical Corporation, Mechanicsburg, PA
Primary Contact: David D. Muggli, FACHE, Chief Executive Officer
CMO: Brian Boster, M.D., Medical Director
CNO: Bobbi Schmidt, Chief Nursing Officer
Web address: www.selectspecialtyhospitals.com/company/locations/cincinnati.aspx
Control: Corporation, Investor–owned (for–profit) **Service**: Acute long–term care hospital

Staffed Beds: 30 **Admissions**: 267 **Census**: 22 **Outpatient Visits**: 0 **Births**: 0

SHRINERS HOSPITALS FOR CHILDREN – CINCINNATI (363308), 3229 Burnet Avenue, Zip 45229–3095; tel. 513/872–6000, (Nonreporting) **A**1 3 10 **S** Shriners Hospitals for Children, Tampa, FL
Primary Contact: Mark D. Shugarman, Administrator
CFO: Susan Harris, Director Fiscal Services
CMO: Petra Warner, Chief of Staff
CIO: David Brian, Chief Information Officer
CHR: Gretchen Long, Manager Human Resources
Web address: www.shrinershospitalsforchildren.org/Hospitals/Locations/Cincinnati.aspx
Control: Other not–for–profit (including NFP Corporation) **Service**: Children's other specialty

Staffed Beds: 30

SUMMIT BEHAVIORAL HEALTHCARE (364035), 1101 Summit Road, Zip 45237–2652; tel. 513/948–3600, (Nonreporting) **A**1 3 10 **S** Ohio Department of Mental Health, Columbus, OH
Primary Contact: Elizabeth Banks, Chief Executive Officer
COO: Steven Burns, Director Fiscal Services
CFO: Steven Burns, Director Fiscal Services
CMO: Patrick McCullough, M.D., Chief Medical Services
CIO: Eric Bradley, Director Computer Information Services
CHR: Bobbie Carrelli, Director Human Resources
CNO: Kathy A. Smith, MSN, R.N., Nurse Executive
Web address: www.mh.state.oh.us/
Control: State, Government, nonfederal **Service**: Psychiatric

Staffed Beds: 291

Hospital, Medicare Provider Number, Address, Telephone, Approval, Facility, and Physician Codes, Health Care System

★ American Hospital Association (AHA) membership
□ The Joint Commission accreditation
○ Healthcare Facilities Accreditation Program
◇ DNV Healthcare Inc. accreditation
⇑ Center for Improvement in Healthcare Quality Accreditation
△ Commission on Accreditation of Rehabilitation Facilities (CARF) accreditation

OH

⊞ **THE JEWISH HOSPITAL – MERCY HEALTH (360016)**, 4777 East Galbraith Road, Zip 45236–2725; tel. 513/686–3000, (Nonreporting) **A**1 2 3 5 10 **S** Mercy Health, Cincinnati, OH
Primary Contact: Patricia Davis–Hagens, R.N., Central Market Leader and President
COO: Jack Hill, Chief Operating Officer and Administrator
Web address: www.jewishhospitalcincinnati.com/
Control: Other not–for–profit (including NFP Corporation) **Service**: General medical and surgical

Staffed Beds: 209

☐ **TRIHEALTH EVENDALE HOSPITAL (360362)**, 3155 Glendale Milford Road, Zip 45241–3134; tel. 513/454–2222, **A**1 2 10 **F**3 8 29 30 34 35 44 46 50 57 59 64 68 70 75 79 81 82 85 86 87 107 109 111 115 119 130 131 143 146 149 **P**6 8
Primary Contact: Kelvin Hanger, Chief Executive Officer
CFO: Michael Crofton, Chief Financial Officer
Web address: www.evendalemedical.com
Control: Other not–for–profit (including NFP Corporation) **Service**: Surgical

Staffed Beds: 8 Admissions: 759 Census: 3 Outpatient Visits: 36386 Births: 0 Total Expense ($000): 49517 Payroll Expense ($000): 13887 Personnel: 177

★ **TRIHEALTH REHABILITATION HOSPITAL (363041)**, 2155 Dana Avenue, Zip 45207; tel. 513/601–0600, (Nonreporting) **S** Select Medical Corporation, Mechanicsburg, PA
Primary Contact: Daphne Glenn, Chief Executive Officer
Web address: www.trihealthrehab.com
Control: Corporation, Investor–owned (for–profit) **Service**: Rehabilitation

Staffed Beds: 60

⊞ **UNIVERSITY OF CINCINNATI MEDICAL CENTER (360003)**, 234 Goodman Street, Zip 45219–2316; tel. 513/584–1000, **A**1 2 3 5 8 10 **F**3 7 9 11 12 13 15 16 17 18 20 22 24 26 29 30 31 34 35 37 38 39 40 41 43 44 45 46 47 48 49 50 51 54 55 56 63 64 66 68 70 71 72 74 75 76 77 78 79 80 81 82 84 85 86 87 91 92 97 98 100 101 102 103 104 107 108 110 111 112 114 115 116 117 118 119 120 121 122 123 124 126 129 130 131 132 134 135 136 137 138 139 141 142 143 145 146 147 148 149 150 154 **P**6 **S** UC Health, Cincinnati, OH
Primary Contact: Beverly A. Bokovitz, R.N., Chief Nursing Officer
CFO: Matthew Nealon, Vice President, Chief Financial Officer
CMO: Bill Hurford, Chief Medical Officer
CIO: Jay Brown, Vice President and Chief Information Officer
CHR: Clarence Pauley, Senior Vice President and Chief Human Resources Officer
Web address: www.uchealth.com/university–of–cincinnati–medical–center/
Control: Other not–for–profit (including NFP Corporation) **Service**: General medical and surgical

Staffed Beds: 555 Admissions: 26599 Census: 434 Outpatient Visits: 669925 Births: 2307 Total Expense ($000): 914823 Payroll Expense ($000): 283419 Personnel: 4656

VETERANS AFFAIRS MEDICAL CENTER See Cincinnati Veterans Affairs Medical Center

CIRCLEVILLE—Pickaway County

⊞ **BERGER HEALTH SYSTEM (360170)**, 600 North Pickaway Street, Zip 43113–1447; tel. 740/474–2126, **A**1 5 10 **F**3 13 15 18 20 28 29 30 31 34 35 40 45 46 50 53 54 59 63 64 70 76 77 78 81 85 87 92 93 96 107 108 110 111 115 119 124 129 130 131 132 135 146 148
Primary Contact: Tim A. Colburn, President and Chief Executive Officer
CFO: Richard Filler, Chief Financial Officer
CMO: Jill Barno, M.D., Chief Medical Officer
CIO: Andy Chileski, Chief Information Officer and Vice President Facilities
CHR: Diane Guglielmi, Vice President, Human Resources
CNO: Kristin Day Gardner, Chief Nursing Officer
Web address: www.bergerhealth.com
Control: City–county, Government, nonfederal **Service**: General medical and surgical

Staffed Beds: 56 Admissions: 2110 Census: 17 Outpatient Visits: 89326 Births: 419 Total Expense ($000): 76276 Payroll Expense ($000): 24245 Personnel: 431

CLEVELAND—Cuyahoga County

⊞ **CLEVELAND CLINIC (360180)**, 9500 Euclid Avenue, Zip 44195–5108; tel. 216/444–2200, (Includes CLEVELAND CLINIC CHILDREN'S HOSPITAL, 9500 Euclid Avenue, Cleveland, OH, Zip 44103; tel. 800/223–2273) **A**1 3 5 8 10 **F**3 6 7 8 9 12 13 14 15 17 18 19 20 21 22 23 24 25 26 27 28 29 30 31 32 33 34 35 36 37 38 39 40 44 45 46 47 48 49 50 51 52 53 54 55 56 57 58 59 60 61 63 64 65 66 68 70 71 72 74 75 76 77 78 79 80 81 82 83 84 85 86 87 88 89 90 91 92 93 94 95 96 97 100 101 104 107 108 109 110 111 112 113 114 115 116 117 118 119 120 121 123 124 126 129 130 131 132 134 135 136 137 138 139 140 141 142 143 144 145 146 147 148 149 150 154 **P**6 **S** Cleveland Clinic Health System, Cleveland, OH
Primary Contact: Tomislav Mihaljevic, M.D., President and Chief Executive Officer
CFO: Steven Glass, Chief Financial Officer
CMO: Joseph Hahn, M.D., Chief of Staff
CIO: Edward Marx, Chief Information Officer
CNO: Katherine Hancock, R.N., Executive Chief Nursing Officer
Web address: www.clevelandclinic.org
Control: Other not–for–profit (including NFP Corporation) **Service**: General medical and surgical

Staffed Beds: 1275 Admissions: 52169 Census: 1003 Outpatient Visits: 6297877 Births: 117 Total Expense ($000): 5415535 Payroll Expense ($000): 2702995 Personnel: 29444

⊞ △ **CLEVELAND CLINIC CHILDREN'S HOSPITAL FOR REHABILITATION (363304)**, 2801 Martin Luther King Jr Drive, Zip 44104–3865; tel. 216/448–6400, **A**1 3 7 10 **F**28 29 30 32 34 35 36 44 50 60 74 75 79 80 82 90 91 93 94 96 99 100 130 131 132 143 146 148 **S** Cleveland Clinic Health System, Cleveland, OH
Primary Contact: Michelle Marks, D.O., Medical Director
COO: Alec G Kulik, Administrator
CFO: Debra Nyikes, Director Finance and Chief Financial Officer
CMO: Roberta Bauer, M.D., Acting Chair Medical Staff
CIO: C Martin Harris, M.D., Chief Information Officer
CHR: Jan Hlahol, Manager Human Resources
Web address: www.my.clevelandclinic.org/childrens–hospital/default.aspx
Control: Other not–for–profit (including NFP Corporation) **Service**: Children's rehabilitation

Staffed Beds: 25 Admissions: 183 Census: 15 Outpatient Visits: 104925 Births: 0 Total Expense ($000): 45384 Payroll Expense ($000): 26888 Personnel: 398

⊞ **CLEVELAND CLINIC FAIRVIEW HOSPITAL (360077)**, 18101 Lorain Avenue, Zip 44111–5656; tel. 216/476–7000, **A**1 2 3 5 10 13 **F**3 8 11 12 13 15 17 18 19 20 22 24 26 28 29 30 31 32 34 35 36 40 41 43 45 46 47 49 50 51 53 55 57 58 59 60 64 65 66 68 69 70 71 72 73 74 75 76 77 78 79 80 81 82 84 85 86 87 89 92 93 97 98 99 100 107 108 110 111 114 115 117 118 119 120 121 123 124 126 130 131 132 133 146 147 148 149 150 154 **S** Cleveland Clinic Health System, Cleveland, OH
Primary Contact: Neil Smith, D.O., President
COO: John C Mills, Senior Vice President Operations
CFO: Ankit Chhabra, Director Finance
CIO: C Martin Harris, M.D., Chief Information Officer
CHR: Ann Beatty, Director Human Resources
Web address: www.fairviewhospital.org
Control: Other not–for–profit (including NFP Corporation) **Service**: General medical and surgical

Staffed Beds: 460 Admissions: 25110 Census: 294 Outpatient Visits: 222962 Births: 5263 Total Expense ($000): 402440 Payroll Expense ($000): 153585 Personnel: 2321

☐ **GRACE HOSPITAL (362015)**, 2307 West 14th Street, Zip 44113–3698; tel. 216/687–1500, (Nonreporting) **A**1 10
Primary Contact: Rajive Khanna, Chief Executive Officer
COO: Rajive Khanna, Chief Executive Officer
CFO: Michelle Hennis, Administrative Director Financial Services
CMO: John Nickels, M.D., President Medical Staff
Web address: www.gracehospital.org
Control: Other not–for–profit (including NFP Corporation) **Service**: Acute long–term care hospital

Staffed Beds: 87

⊞ **HILLCREST HOSPITAL (360230)**, 6780 Mayfield Road, Zip 44124–2203; tel. 440/312–4500, **A**1 2 3 10 **F**3 12 13 15 17 18 20 22 24 26 28 29 30 31 34 35 36 37 38 40 41 43 46 49 50 51 53 54 55 56 57 59 60 64 65 68 70 72 74 75 76 77 78 79 81 82 84 85 86 89 93 97 99 100 107 108 110 111 114 115 116 117 118 119 120 121 126 129 130 131 132 135 143 145 146 147 148 149 154 **S** Cleveland Clinic Health System, Cleveland, OH
Primary Contact: Richard Parker, M.D., President, Hillcrest Hospital
Web address: www.hillcresthospital.org
Control: Other not–for–profit (including NFP Corporation) **Service**: General medical and surgical

Staffed Beds: 440 Admissions: 23210 Census: 307 Outpatient Visits: 223003 Births: 4503 Total Expense ($000): 393348 Payroll Expense ($000): 137204 Personnel: 2111

Many Facility Codes have changed. Please refer to the AHA Guide Code Chart. © 2018 AHA Guide

LOUIS STOKES CLEVELAND VETERANS AFFAIRS MEDICAL CENTER, 10701 East Boulevard, Zip 44106–1702; tel. 216/791–3800, (Total facility includes 123 beds in nursing home–type unit) **A**1 2 3 5 7 8 **F**3 4 5 8 9 10 12 15 17 18 20 22 24 26 28 29 30 31 33 34 35 36 38 39 40 44 45 46 47 48 49 50 51 53 54 55 56 57 58 59 60 61 62 63 64 65 67 68 70 71 74 75 77 78 79 80 81 82 83 84 85 86 87 90 91 92 93 94 95 96 97 98 100 101 102 103 104 105 106 107 110 111 113 116 117 119 120 121 126 127 128 129 130 132 135 143 146 147 148 149 150 152 153 154 **S** Department of Veterans Affairs, Perry Point, MD
Primary Contact: Susan Fuehrer, Director
COO: Andrew Pacyna, Deputy Director
CFO: Michael Pappas, Chief Fiscal Service Officer
CMO: Murray Altose, M.D., Chief of Staff
CIO: Steve Gaj, Facility Chief Information Officer
CHR: Charles Franks, Chief Human Resources
CNO: Innette Mary Sarduy, M.P.H., R.N., Associate Director Patient Care Services and Nurse Executive
Web address: www.cleveland.va.gov/
Control: Veterans Affairs, Government, federal **Service**: General medical and surgical

Staffed Beds: 578 **Admissions**: 11894 **Census**: 491 **Outpatient Visits**: 1514954 **Births**: 0 **Personnel**: 4962

LUTHERAN HOSPITAL (360087), 1730 West 25th Street, Zip 44113–3170; tel. 216/696–4300, **A**1 3 10 **F**3 4 5 15 29 30 34 35 37 40 45 50 56 57 58 59 60 64 65 68 70 74 75 77 79 81 82 85 86 87 93 94 98 100 102 103 104 107 108 110 111 114 115 119 126 130 132 135 143 146 148 149 152 153 **S** Cleveland Clinic Health System, Cleveland, OH
Primary Contact: Donald A. Malone Jr, President
COO: Matthew Mattner, Chief Operating Officer
CFO: Don Urbancsik, Director Finance
CMO: Ronald Golovan, M.D., Vice President Medical Operations
CIO: C Martin Harris, M.D., Chief Information Officer
CHR: Judith Santora, Chief Human Resource Officer
CNO: Janet Schuster, Chief Nursing Officer
Web address: www.lutheranhospital.org
Control: Other not–for–profit (including NFP Corporation) **Service**: General medical and surgical

Staffed Beds: 194 **Admissions**: 8791 **Census**: 107 **Outpatient Visits**: 75943 **Births**: 0 **Total Expense ($000)**: 109566 **Payroll Expense ($000)**: 44956 **Personnel**: 653

METROHEALTH MEDICAL CENTER (360059), 2500 MetroHealth Drive, Zip 44109–1998; tel. 216/778–7800, (Total facility includes 120 beds in nursing home–type unit) **A**1 2 3 5 7 8 10 13 **F**3 5 6 7 8 9 11 12 13 15 16 17 18 19 20 22 24 26 27 28 29 30 31 32 34 35 36 38 39 40 43 44 45 46 47 49 50 51 52 53 54 55 56 57 58 59 60 61 63 64 65 66 68 70 71 72 74 75 76 77 78 79 80 81 82 83 84 85 86 87 88 89 90 91 92 93 94 95 96 97 98 100 101 102 104 105 107 108 110 111 114 115 116 117 118 119 120 121 123 124 126 128 129 130 131 132 134 135 143 144 146 147 148 149 150 153 154 **P**6
Primary Contact: Akram Boutros, M.D., FACHE, President and Chief Executive Officer
COO: Daniel Lewis, Executive Vice President and Chief Operating Officer
CFO: Craig Richmond, Senior Vice President and Chief Financial Officer
CMO: Alfred Connors, M.D., Executive Vice President and Chief Quality Officer and Interim Chief Medical Officer
CIO: Don Reichert, Vice President Associate Chief Information Officer
CHR: Debbie Warman, Vice President Human Resources
CNO: Melissa Kline, Chief Nursing Officer
Web address: www.metrohealth.org
Control: County, Government, nonfederal **Service**: General medical and surgical

Staffed Beds: 680 **Admissions**: 22336 **Census**: 485 **Outpatient Visits**: 1395984 **Births**: 3167 **Total Expense ($000)**: 1211748 **Payroll Expense ($000)**: 578015 **Personnel**: 6628

SELECT SPECIALTY HOSPITAL – CLEVELAND FAIRHILL See Select Specialty Hospital – Cleveland Gateway, Cleveland

★ **SELECT SPECIALTY HOSPITAL – CLEVELAND GATEWAY (362026)**, 2351 East 22nd Street, 7th Floor, Zip 44115–3111; tel. 216/363–2671, (Includes SELECT SPECIALTY HOSPITAL – CLEVELAND FAIRHILL, 11900 Fairhill Road, Cleveland, OH, Zip 44120–1062; tel. 216/983–8030; Laurie Kozorosky, Chief Executive Officer) (Nonreporting) **A**10 **S** Select Medical Corporation, Mechanicsburg, PA
Primary Contact: Julie Idoine–Fries, Chief Executive Officer
Web address: www.selectspecialtyhospitals.com/
Control: Corporation, Investor–owned (for–profit) **Service**: Acute long–term care hospital

Staffed Beds: 143

☐ **ST. VINCENT CHARITY MEDICAL CENTER (360037)**, 2351 East 22nd Street, Zip 44115–3111; tel. 216/861–6200, (Nonreporting) **A**1 2 3 5 10 **S** Sisters of Charity Health System, Cleveland, OH
Primary Contact: David F. Perse, M.D., President and Chief Executive Officer
COO: Joan Ross, Senior Vice President and Chief Operating Officer
CFO: John Rusnaczyk, Senior Vice President and Chief Financial Officer
CMO: Joseph A. Sopko, M.D., Chief Medical Officer
CIO: Robin Stursa, Chief Information Officer
CHR: Ted Monczewski, Vice President Human Resources
CNO: Beverly Lozar, Chief Nursing Executive
Web address: www.stvincentcharity.com/
Control: Other not–for–profit (including NFP Corporation) **Service**: General medical and surgical

Staffed Beds: 199

UH REGIONAL HOSPITALS (360075), 27100 Chardon Road, Zip 44143–1116; tel. 440/585–6500, (Includes UNIVERSITY HOSPITALS BEDFORD MEDICAL CENTER, 44 Blaine Avenue, Cleveland, OH, Zip 44146–2709; tel. 440/735–3900; UNIVERSITY HOSPITALS RICHMOND MEDICAL CENTER, 27100 Chardon Road, Cleveland, OH, Zip 44143–1116; tel. 440/585–6500) **A**1 3 10 12 13 **F**8 14 15 18 20 26 29 30 34 35 39 40 50 56 57 59 60 64 65 66 68 70 74 75 77 78 79 81 82 84 85 86 87 91 92 93 96 97 100 107 108 109 110 111 114 116 117 118 119 130 131 132 133 135 143 146 147 148 149 154 **S** University Hospitals, Cleveland, OH
Primary Contact: Brian Monter, MSN, R.N., President
CFO: Scott Platz, Director Finance
CMO: Rosemary Leeming, M.D., Chief Medical Officer
CHR: Stephanie W Neonakis, Manager Human Resources
CNO: Michelle Giltner, Interim Chief Nursing Officer
Web address: www.uhhospitals.org
Control: Other not–for–profit (including NFP Corporation) **Service**: General medical and surgical

Staffed Beds: 101 **Admissions**: 4624 **Census**: 46 **Outpatient Visits**: 138834 **Births**: 0 **Total Expense ($000)**: 113447 **Payroll Expense ($000)**: 43132 **Personnel**: 772

UNIVERSITY HOSPITALS CLEVELAND MEDICAL CENTER (360137), 11100 Euclid Avenue, Zip 44106–1716; tel. 216/844–1000, (Includes HANNA HOUSE SKILLED NURSING FACILITY, 11100 Euclid Avenue, Cleveland, OH, Zip 44106; tel. 216/844–3911; RAINBOW BABIES AND CHILDREN'S HOSPITAL, 2101 Adelbert Road, Cleveland, OH, Zip 44106–2624; tel. 216/844–3911; Patricia DePompei, President; UNIVERSITY MACDONALD WOMEN'S HOSPITAL, 2101 Adelbert Road, Cleveland, OH, Zip 44106–2624; tel. 216/844–3911; Patricia DePompei, President) (Total facility includes 38 beds in nursing home–type unit) **A**1 2 3 5 8 10 **F**3 6 8 9 11 12 13 14 15 17 18 19 20 21 22 23 24 25 26 27 28 29 30 31 32 34 35 36 37 38 39 40 41 43 44 45 46 47 48 49 50 51 52 53 54 55 56 57 58 59 60 61 62 63 64 65 66 68 70 71 72 73 74 75 76 77 78 79 80 81 82 83 84 85 86 87 88 89 91 92 93 94 96 97 98 99 100 101 102 104 107 108 109 110 111 112 114 115 116 117 118 119 120 121 122 123 124 126 128 129 130 131 132 133 134 135 136 137 138 139 140 141 142 143 144 145 146 147 148 149 150 153 154 **P**6 7 **S** University Hospitals, Cleveland, OH
Primary Contact: Daniel I. Simon, M.D., President
COO: Ron Dziedzicki, R.N., Chief Operating Officer
CFO: Sonia Salvino, Vice President Finance
CIO: Sue Schade, Interim Chief Information Officer
CHR: Julie Chester, Vice President Human Resources
CNO: Jean Blake, Chief Nursing Officer
Web address: www.UHhospitals.org
Control: Other not–for–profit (including NFP Corporation) **Service**: General medical and surgical

Staffed Beds: 871 **Admissions**: 42743 **Census**: 685 **Outpatient Visits**: 523110 **Births**: 4068 **Total Expense ($000)**: 1296682 **Payroll Expense ($000)**: 495158 **Personnel**: 8682

VETERANS AFFAIRS MEDICAL CENTER See Louis Stokes Cleveland Veterans Affairs Medical Center

---

Hospital, Medicare Provider Number, Address, Telephone, Approval, Facility, and Physician Codes, Health Care System

★ American Hospital Association (AHA) membership ☐ The Joint Commission accreditation ○ Healthcare Facilities Accreditation Program ◇ DNV Healthcare Inc. accreditation ⇑ Center for Improvement in Healthcare Quality Accreditation △ Commission on Accreditation of Rehabilitation Facilities (CARF) accreditation

© 2018 AHA Guide *Many Facility Codes have changed. Please refer to the AHA Guide Code Chart.* Hospitals **A477**

OH

COLDWATER—Mercer County

☒ **MERCER HEALTH (360058)**, 800 West Main Street, Zip 45828–1698;
tel. 419/678–2341, **A**1 10 **F**3 7 11 12 13 15 18 28 29 30 31 34 35 40 44 45
47 50 51 54 57 59 61 62 64 65 70 75 76 77 78 79 81 82 85 87 92 93 94 95
97 107 108 110 111 114 118 119 130 131 132 133 134 135 143 144 145
146 147 148 149 150
Primary Contact: Lisa R. Klenke, R.N., Chief Executive Officer
CFO: George Boyles, Senior Vice President of Finance and Chief Financial Officer
CMO: James Reichert, Chief Medical Officer
CIO: DeWayne Marsee, Director Information Systems
CHR: Jon Dingledine, Senior Director Human Resources and Support Services
CNO: Cindy Liette, Vice President Patient Care Services
Web address: www.mercer–health.com
Control: Hospital district or authority, Government, nonfederal **Service**: General
medical and surgical

> **Staffed Beds**: 60 **Admissions**: 1692 **Census**: 14 **Births**: 341 **Total Expense**
> **($000)**: 55737 **Payroll Expense ($000)**: 18776 **Personnel**: 516

COLUMBUS—Franklin County

☒ **JAMES CANCER HOSPITAL AND SOLOVE RESEARCH INSTITUTE (360242)**,
460 West Tenth Avenue, Zip 43210–1240; tel. 614/293–3300, **A**1 2 3 5 10 **F**3
15 29 30 31 32 34 35 36 37 38 39 44 46 47 48 49 50 52 54 55 57 58 59 61
64 65 66 68 70 71 74 75 77 79 80 81 82 84 85 86 87 93 97 100 107 108
110 111 112 114 115 116 117 118 119 120 121 123 124 126 130 132 134
135 136 141 143 144 145 146 147 148 149 154 **P**6 **S** Ohio State University
Health System, Columbus, OH
Primary Contact: William Farrar, M.D., Interim Chief Executive Officer
CFO: Bell Julian, Associate Executive Director and Chief Financial Officer
CIO: Michael Townsend, Chief Information Officer
CHR: Jill Hannah, Director Human Resources
CNO: Kris M Kipp, Executive Director, Patient Services and Chief Nursing Officer
Web address: www.https://cancer.osu.edu/
Control: State, Government, nonfederal **Service**: Cancer

> **Staffed Beds**: 308 **Admissions**: 14392 **Census**: 261 **Outpatient Visits**:
> 415087 **Births**: 0 **Total Expense ($000)**: 967118 **Payroll Expense**
> **($000)**: 239792 **Personnel**: 4287

☒ **MOUNT CARMEL (360035)**, 793 West State Street, Zip 43222–1551;
tel. 614/234–5000, (Includes MOUNT CARMEL EAST HOSPITAL, 6001 East Broad
Street, Columbus, OH, Zip 43213; tel. 614/234–6000; Brinsley Lewis, FACHE,
President; MOUNT CARMEL WEST HOSPITAL, 793 West State Street, Columbus,
OH, Zip 43222; tel. 614/234–5000) **A**1 2 3 5 10 **F**3 11 12 15 17 18 20 22
24 26 28 29 30 31 34 35 37 40 43 44 45 46 47 48 49 50 51 54 55 57 58 59
61 63 64 65 66 68 70 72 74 75 76 77 78 79 81 82 83 84 85 86 87 90 93
97 98 100 101 102 103 104 107 108 109 110 111 114 115 116 117 118
119 120 121 123 126 130 131 132 146 147 148 149 **P**6 8 **S** Trinity Health,
Livonia, MI
Primary Contact: Sean McKibben, President and Chief Operating Officer
COO: Mary R Trimmer, Interim Chief Executive Officer
Web address: www.mountcarmelhealth.com
Control: Church operated, Nongovernment, not–for–profit **Service**: General
medical and surgical

> **Staffed Beds**: 685 **Admissions**: 37495 **Census**: 452 **Outpatient Visits**:
> 370714 **Births**: 3498 **Total Expense ($000)**: 740360 **Payroll Expense**
> **($000)**: 245831 **Personnel**: 3664

☒ △ **NATIONWIDE CHILDREN'S HOSPITAL (363305)**, 700 Children's Drive,
Zip 43205–2664; tel. 614/722–2000, **A**1 2 3 5 7 10 **F**3 5 7 8 12 16 17 18 19
20 21 22 23 24 25 26 27 28 29 30 31 32 34 35 36 38 39 40 41 43 44 45 47
48 50 51 52 53 54 55 57 59 61 62 63 64 65 66 68 71 72 74 75 77 78
79 81 82 83 84 85 86 87 88 89 90 92 93 94 96 97 98 99 100 101 102 104
105 107 108 111 112 114 115 116 117 118 119 126 127 129 130 131 132
133 134 135 136 137 138 139 140 141 143 144 145 146 148 149 150 153
154 **P**8
Primary Contact: Steve Allen, M.D., Chief Executive Officer
COO: Rick Miller, President and Chief Operating Officer
CFO: Tim Robinson, Executive Vice President, Chief Financial and Administrative
Officer and Treasurer
CMO: Richard Brilli, M.D., Chief Medical Officer
CIO: Denise Zabawski, Vice President Information Services and Chief Information
Officer
Web address: www.nationwidechildrens.org
Control: Other not–for–profit (including NFP Corporation) **Service**: Children's
general medical and surgical

> **Staffed Beds**: 625 **Admissions**: 17660 **Census**: 442 **Outpatient Visits**:
> 1327408 **Births**: 0 **Total Expense ($000)**: 1222735 **Payroll Expense**
> **($000)**: 560734 **Personnel**: 8887

☐ **OHIO HOSPITAL FOR PSYCHIATRY (364041)**, 880 Greenlawn Avenue,
Zip 43223–2616; tel. 614/449–9664, (Nonreporting) **A**1 10 **S** Acadia Healthcare
Company, Inc., Franklin, TN
Primary Contact: Stanley Frank, Chief Executive Officer
COO: Shannon Robbins, Chief Operating Officer
CFO: Steve Snyder, Chief Financial Officer
CMO: Richard Nockowitz, M.D., Medical Director
CNO: Jayne Zink, Director of Nursing
Web address: www.ohiohospitalforpsychiatry.com/
Control: Corporation, Investor–owned (for–profit) **Service**: Children's hospital
psychiatric

> **Staffed Beds**: 90

☒ △ **OHIO STATE UNIVERSITY WEXNER MEDICAL CENTER (360085)**,
410 West 10th Avenue, Zip 43210–1240; tel. 614/293–8000, (Includes OHIO
STATE UNIVERSITY HOSPITALS EAST, 1492 East Broad Street, Columbus, OH,
Zip 43205–1546; tel. 614/257–3000) **A**1 3 5 7 8 10 **F**3 4 5 6 8 9 11 12 13 15
16 17 18 20 22 24 26 28 29 30 31 33 34 35 36 37 38 39 40 43 44 45 46 47
48 49 50 51 52 53 54 55 56 57 58 59 60 61 64 65 66 68 70 72 73 74 75 76
77 78 79 80 81 82 84 85 86 87 90 91 92 93 95 96 97 98 99 100 101 102
103 104 105 107 108 110 111 112 113 114 115 118 119 126 129 130 131
132 134 135 137 138 139 140 141 142 143 144 145 146 147 148 149 152
153 154 **P**6 **S** Ohio State University Health System, Columbus, OH
Primary Contact: David P. McQuaid, FACHE, Chief Operating Officer
COO: David P McQuaid, FACHE, Chief Operating Officer
CMO: Andrew Thomas, M.D., Chief Medical Officer
CIO: Phyllis Teater, Chief Information Officer
CHR: Kim Shumate, Human Resources Officer
CNO: Mary G Nash, Ph.D., R.N., Chief Nursing Officer
Web address: www.medicalcenter.osu.edu
Control: State, Government, nonfederal **Service**: General medical and surgical

> **Staffed Beds**: 1057 **Admissions**: 47309 **Census**: 802 **Outpatient Visits**:
> 1348620 **Births**: 4989 **Total Expense ($000)**: 1531303 **Payroll Expense**
> **($000)**: 461747 **Personnel**: 10866

☒ **OHIOHEALTH DOCTORS HOSPITAL (360152)**, 5100 West Broad Street,
Zip 43228–1607; tel. 614/544–1000, **A**1 2 3 5 10 12 13 **F**3 13 15 17 18 20
22 26 28 29 30 31 34 35 36 40 45 46 47 48 49 50 57 58 59 64 65 66 68 70
72 74 75 76 77 78 79 81 82 84 85 87 90 92 93 97 100 107 109 110 111 114
115 116 117 119 120 121 123 126 130 131 135 145 146 147 148 154 **S**
OhioHealth, Columbus, OH
Primary Contact: Michael L. Reichfield, President
CMO: Dean Colwell, D.O., Vice President Medical Affairs
CIO: Michael Krouse, Chief Information Officer
CHR: David Sullivan, Director Human Resources
Web address: www.ohiohealth.com
Control: Church operated, Nongovernment, not–for–profit **Service**: General
medical and surgical

> **Staffed Beds**: 195 **Admissions**: 8362 **Census**: 93 **Births**: 1005 **Total**
> **Expense ($000)**: 215172 **Payroll Expense ($000)**: 94269 **Personnel**: 1138

☒ **OHIOHEALTH GRANT MEDICAL CENTER (360017)**, 111 South Grant Avenue,
Zip 43215–1898; tel. 614/566–9000, **A**1 2 3 5 8 10 **F**3 7 8 9 11 13 15 17 18
20 22 24 26 28 29 30 31 35 36 37 40 43 53 54 56 57 58 59 60 61 64 66 67
68 70 72 74 75 76 78 79 81 82 83 84 85 86 87 97 100 102 107 108 109 110
111 114 115 116 117 119 120 121 123 124 126 129 130 131 132 135 143
144 146 147 148 149 150 154 **S** OhioHealth, Columbus, OH
Primary Contact: Michael Lawson, President and Chief Operating Officer
COO: Kevin Lutz, DPM, Chief Operating Officer, Grant
CFO: Heather Brandon, Vice President of Finance, Grant
CMO: Michael Ezzie, Director of Medical Education and Interim Vice President of
Medical Affairs
CIO: Michael Krouse, Chief Information Officer
CHR: Qiana Williams, Director, Human Resource Business Partner, Grant
CNO: Sharon Neenan, R.N., Interim Chief Nursing Officer, Grant
Web address: www.ohiohealth.com
Control: Church operated, Nongovernment, not–for–profit **Service**: General
medical and surgical

> **Staffed Beds**: 425 **Admissions**: 19870 **Census**: 263 **Outpatient Visits**:
> 92405 **Births**: 2416 **Total Expense ($000)**: 537484 **Payroll Expense**
> **($000)**: 211914 **Personnel**: 2716

☒ **OHIOHEALTH REHABILITATION HOSPITAL (363037)**, 1087 Dennison Avenue,
4th Floor, Zip 43201–3201; tel. 614/484–9600, (Nonreporting) **A**1 10 **S** Select
Medical Corporation, Mechanicsburg, PA
Primary Contact: Eric Yap, Chief Executive Officer
CFO: Ted Bolcavage, Vice President Division Controller, Inpatient
CMO: Lisa Lombard, Chief Medical Officer
CHR: Josette Alexander, Director, Human Resources
CNO: Graydon Todd Auckerman, Chief Nursing Officer
Web address: www.ohiohealth–rehab.com
Control: Partnership, Investor–owned (for–profit) **Service**: Rehabilitation

> **Staffed Beds**: 44

Many Facility Codes have changed. Please refer to the AHA Guide Code Chart. © 2018 AHA Guide

⊠ **OHIOHEALTH RIVERSIDE METHODIST HOSPITAL (360006)**, 3535 Olentangy River Road, Zip 43214–3998; tel. 614/566–5000, **A**1 2 3 5 8 10 **F**3 5 7 8 12 13 14 15 17 18 20 22 24 26 28 29 30 31 34 35 36 37 38 39 40 43 44 45 46 47 48 49 50 51 53 54 55 56 57 58 59 60 61 62 63 64 65 66 67 68 69 70 71 72 73 74 75 76 77 78 79 80 81 82 83 84 85 86 87 90 91 92 93 94 96 97 98 100 102 103 104 105 106 107 108 110 111 114 115 116 117 118 119 120 121 122 123 124 126 130 131 132 141 143 144 145 146 147 148 152 153 154 **S** OhioHealth, Columbus, OH
Primary Contact: Brian Jepson, President
COO: Elizabeth Brill, M.D., Chief Operating Officer
CFO: Peter Bury, Vice President Finance
CMO: Thomas Harmon, M.D., Vice President Medical Affairs
CIO: Michael Krouse, Chief Information Officer
CHR: Shereen Solaiman, Vice President Human Resources
CNO: Lisa Gossett, MSN, R.N., Chief Nursing Officer
Web address: www.ohiohealth.com
Control: Church operated, Nongovernment, not–for–profit **Service**: General medical and surgical

Staffed Beds: 754 **Admissions**: 44544 **Census**: 545 **Outpatient Visits**: 871929 **Births**: 6660 **Total Expense ($000)**: 1092310 **Payroll Expense ($000)**: 423889 **Personnel**: 5429

⊠ **REGENCY HOSPITAL OF COLUMBUS (362037)**, 1430 South High Street, Zip 43207–1045; tel. 614/456–0300, (Includes SELECT SPECIALTY HOSPITAL – COLUMBUS EAST, 1492 East Broad Street, 6th Floor, Columbus, OH, Zip 43205–1546; tel. 614/685–1703; Lisa J. Pettrey, MSN, R.N., Interim Chief Executive Officer) (Nonreporting) **A**1 10 **S** Select Medical Corporation, Mechanicsburg, PA
Primary Contact: Kindra Marks, Chief Executive Officer
Web address: www.regencyhospital.com/
Control: Corporation, Investor–owned (for–profit) **Service**: Acute long–term care hospital

Staffed Beds: 66

⊠ **SELECT SPECIALTY HOSPITAL–COLUMBUS (362022)**, 1087 Dennison Avenue, Zip 43201–3201; tel. 614/458–9000, (Includes SELECT SPECIALTY HOSPITAL–COLUMBUS, MOUNT CARMEL CAMPUS, 793 West State Street, Columbus, OH, Zip 43222–1551; tel. 614/234–0950) (Nonreporting) **A**1 10 **S** Select Medical Corporation, Mechanicsburg, PA
Primary Contact: Lisa J. Pettrey, MSN, R.N., Chief Executive Officer
CMO: Victoria Ruff, M.D., Medical Director
CHR: Charles Pankowski, Manager Human Resources
Web address: www.selectspecialtyhospitals.com/company/locations/columbus.aspx
Control: Corporation, Investor–owned (for–profit) **Service**: Acute long–term care hospital

Staffed Beds: 186

SELECT SPECIALTY HOSPITAL–COLUMBUS, MOUNT CARMEL CAMPUS See Select Specialty Hospital–Columbus, Columbus

SEQUEL POMEGRANATE HEALTH SYSTEMS (364045), 765 Pierce Drive, Zip 43223, Mailing Address: 975 Pierce Avenue, Zip 43227; tel. 614/223–1650, (Nonreporting)
Primary Contact: Angela Nickell, Executive Director
Web address: www.pomegranatehealthsystems.com
Control: Other not–for–profit (including NFP Corporation) **Service**: Psychiatric

Staffed Beds: 90

SUN BEHAVIORAL COLUMBUS (364058), 900 Dublin Granville Road, Zip 43229–2452; tel. 614/706–2786, (Nonreporting)
Primary Contact: Lance Folske, Chief Executive Officer
Web address: www.suncolumbus.com
Control: Corporation, Investor–owned (for–profit) **Service**: Psychiatric

Staffed Beds: 72

☐ **TWIN VALLEY BEHAVIORAL HEALTHCARE (364007)**, 2200 West Broad Street, Zip 43223–1297; tel. 614/752–0333, **A**1 3 10 **F**29 30 54 59 98 104 130 **S** Ohio Department of Mental Health, Columbus, OH
Primary Contact: Veronica Lofton, Acting Chief Executive Officer
COO: David Blahnik, Chief Operating Officer
CFO: Tracy Gladen, Chief Financial Officer
CMO: R Alan Freeland, M.D., Chief Clinical Officer
CIO: Missy McGarvey, Chief Information Officer
CHR: Marcia McKeen, Director Human Resources
CNO: Michael Breakwell, R.N., Nurse Executive
Web address: www.mh.state.oh.us/ibhs/bhos/tvbh.html
Control: State, Government, nonfederal **Service**: Psychiatric

Staffed Beds: 178 **Admissions**: 1668 **Census**: 176 **Outpatient Visits**: 27838 **Births**: 0 **Total Expense ($000)**: 74044 **Payroll Expense ($000)**: 45681 **Personnel**: 450

CONCORD TOWNSHIP—Lake County

⊠ **LAKE HEALTH (360098)**, 7590 Auburn Road, Zip 44077–9176; tel. 440/953–9600, (Includes TRIPOINT MEDICAL CENTER, 7590 Auburn Road, Concord Township, OH, Zip 44077; tel. 614/234–0950; Cynthia Moore–Hardy, FACHE, President and Chief Executive Officer) **A**1 10 **F**3 5 11 12 13 15 18 20 22 24 26 28 29 30 34 35 36 40 44 45 50 51 53 54 56 57 58 59 60 62 63 64 65 68 70 75 76 77 79 81 82 85 86 87 90 93 97 98 103 107 108 110 111 112 113 114 115 116 117 119 120 121 122 123 124 126 129 130 131 132 133 135 143 144 146 147 148 **P**1
Primary Contact: Cynthia Moore–Hardy, FACHE, President and Chief Executive Officer
CFO: Robert B Tracz, CPA, Senior Vice President and Chief Financial Officer
CMO: John Baniewicz, M.D., Chief Medical Officer
CIO: Gerald Peters, Vice President Information Technologies and Chief Information Officer
CHR: Craig J Ghidotti, Vice President Human Resources
CNO: Mary L Ogrinc, R.N., MS, Chief Nursing Officer, Senior Vice President Patient Care Services
Web address: www.lakehealth.org
Control: Other not–for–profit (including NFP Corporation) **Service**: General medical and surgical

Staffed Beds: 352 **Admissions**: 17238 **Census**: 192 **Outpatient Visits**: 499392 **Births**: 1776 **Total Expense ($000)**: 391663 **Payroll Expense ($000)**: 127111 **Personnel**: 2330

CONNEAUT—Ashtabula County

⊠ **UNIVERSITY HOSPITALS CONNEAUT MEDICAL CENTER (361308)**, 158 West Main Road, Zip 44030–2039; tel. 440/593–1131, **A**1 3 10 18 **F**3 7 11 15 18 28 29 31 34 35 37 40 45 56 57 59 64 70 75 77 78 79 81 82 85 86 87 93 107 110 111 115 119 130 132 133 135 143 144 146 147 148 149 154 **S** University Hospitals, Cleveland, OH
Primary Contact: M Steven. Jones, President
COO: Jason Glowczewski, Chief Operating Officer
CFO: Lara Eggleston, Finance Manager
CMO: Abirammy Sundaramoorthy, M.D., Chief Medical Officer
CIO: Kirsten Hale, Coordinator Health Information Services
CHR: Danialle Lynce, Business Partner Human Resources
CNO: Ashley Fertig, Chief Nursing Officer
Web address: www.uhhospitals.org
Control: Other not–for–profit (including NFP Corporation) **Service**: General medical and surgical

Staffed Beds: 25 **Admissions**: 684 **Census**: 6 **Outpatient Visits**: 32809 **Births**: 0 **Total Expense ($000)**: 28258 **Payroll Expense ($000)**: 9291 **Personnel**: 153

COSHOCTON—Coshocton County

⊠ **COSHOCTON REGIONAL MEDICAL CENTER (360109)**, 1460 Orange Street, Zip 43812–2229, Mailing Address: P.O. Box 1330, Zip 43812–6330; tel. 740/622–6411, **A**1 5 10 20 **F**3 15 20 28 29 30 31 34 35 40 45 46 47 57 59 64 68 70 75 77 79 81 82 85 86 87 92 93 96 97 107 111 115 119 132 144 147 149 154 **P**3 **S** Prime Healthcare, Ontario, CA
Primary Contact: Stephanie Conn, Administrator and Chief Nursing Officer
CFO: Dennis Lockard, FACHE, Chief Financial Officer
CMO: Gary J. Carver, M.D., Chief Medical Officer
CIO: Seth Peterson, Director Information Services
CHR: Rick Davis, Chief Operating Officer and Support Services
Web address: www.coshoctonhospital.org
Control: Other not–for–profit (including NFP Corporation) **Service**: General medical and surgical

Staffed Beds: 44 **Admissions**: 1708 **Census**: 14 **Outpatient Visits**: 80168 **Births**: 0 **Total Expense ($000)**: 45517 **Payroll Expense ($000)**: 15411 **Personnel**: 295

OH

CUYAHOGA FALLS—Summit County

CUYAHOGA FALLS GENERAL HOSPITAL See Western Reserve Hospital

✉ △ EDWIN SHAW REHAB (360241), 330 Broadway Street East, Zip 44221–3312; tel. 330/436–0910, (Data for 311 days) **A**1 5 7 10 **F**5 29 34 35 57 90 93 96 130 132 135 146 **S** Cleveland Clinic Health System, Cleveland, OH
Primary Contact: Geoffrey Hall, Chief Executive Officer
CFO: Dave Frigo, Chief Financial Officer
CMO: Anthony Hayek, D.O., Medical Director
CHR: Heather Saus, Human Resource Generalist
Web address: www.edwinshaw.com
Control: Other not–for–profit (including NFP Corporation) **Service**: Rehabilitation

Staffed Beds: 35 Admissions: 550 Census: 25 Outpatient Visits: 16282
Births: 0 Total Expense ($000): 13267 Payroll Expense ($000): 1596
Personnel: 147

○ WESTERN RESERVE HOSPITAL (360150), 1900 23rd Street, Zip 44223–1499; tel. 330/971–7000, **A**3 10 11 13 **F**3 12 18 26 29 30 31 33 34 35 36 38 40 44 45 47 49 50 51 54 57 58 59 60 64 65 66 68 70 74 75 77 78 79 81 82 84 85 86 87 92 93 94 96 97 107 108 111 114 115 119 129 130 132 135 144 146 148 **P**6 8
Primary Contact: Robert Kent, D.O., President and Chief Executive Officer
CFO: Jill Hiner, Vice President and Chief Financial Officer
CMO: Charles Feunning, M.D., Chief Medical Officer
CIO: Pamela Banchy, Chief Information Officer
CHR: Heather Milicevic, Director Human Resources
CNO: Carrie Gallo, Chief Nursing Officer
Web address: www.westernreservehospital.org
Control: Partnership, Investor–owned (for–profit) **Service**: General medical and surgical

Staffed Beds: 83 Admissions: 3873 Census: 39 Outpatient Visits: 129923
Births: 0 Total Expense ($000): 122951 Payroll Expense ($000): 43834
Personnel: 768

DAYTON—Montgomery County

☐ ACCESS HOSPITAL DAYTON (364050), 2611 Wayne Avenue, Zip 45420–1833; tel. 937/256–7802, (Nonreporting) **A**1 10
Primary Contact: Belinda Stevens, Chief Executive Officer
Web address: www.accesshospital.com/
Control: Corporation, Investor–owned (for–profit) **Service**: Psychiatric

Staffed Beds: 28

☐ DAYTON CHILDREN'S HOSPITAL (363306), One Children's Plaza, Zip 45404–1815; tel. 937/641–3000, **A**1 2 3 5 10 **F**3 7 8 11 19 21 29 30 31 32 34 35 39 40 41 43 44 45 50 54 55 57 58 59 60 61 62 63 64 65 66 68 72 74 75 77 78 79 81 82 84 85 86 87 88 89 93 97 100 101 104 107 111 115 119 129 130 131 132 134 135 144 146 **P**6
Primary Contact: Deborah A. Feldman, President and Chief Executive Officer
COO: Matthew P Graybill, Vice President, Human Resources and Chief Administrative Officer
CFO: Chris Bergman, Chief Financial Officer
CMO: Adam Mezoff, M.D., Vice President and Chief Medical Officer
CIO: Beth Fredette, Chief Information Officer
Web address: www.childrensdayton.org
Control: Other not–for–profit (including NFP Corporation) **Service**: Children's general medical and surgical

Staffed Beds: 133 Admissions: 6728 Census: 78 Outpatient Visits: 349260 Births: 0 Total Expense ($000): 292806 Payroll Expense ($000): 120802 Personnel: 2463

✉ △ DAYTON VETERANS AFFAIRS MEDICAL CENTER, 4100 West Third Street, Zip 45428–9000; tel. 937/268–6511, (Nonreporting) **A**1 3 5 7 8 **S** Department of Veterans Affairs, Perry Point, MD
Primary Contact: James Hardy, D.O., Chief Executive Officer
CFO: Shannon Rappach, Chief Fiscal Services
CMO: James Hardy, D.O., Chief of Staff
CIO: Susan Sherer, Chief Information Resource Management
CHR: Rolanda Watkins, Chief Human Resources Management Service
CNO: Penelope Franklin Gorsuch, Associate Director Patient Care Services
Web address: www.dayton.va.gov/
Control: Veterans Affairs, Government, federal **Service**: General medical and surgical

Staffed Beds: 486

★ ○ GRANDVIEW MEDICAL CENTER (360133), 405 West Grand Avenue, Zip 45405–4796; tel. 937/723–3200, (Includes SOUTHVIEW MEDICAL CENTER, 1997 Miamisburg–Centerville Road, Dayton, OH, Zip 45459–3800; tel. 937/439–6000; Richard Manchur, President) **A**2 3 10 11 12 13 **F**3 11 12 13 15 18 20 22 24 28 29 30 31 34 35 36 38 40 43 44 45 47 48 49 50 51 53 54 56 57 58 59 60 61 64 65 66 68 70 73 74 75 76 77 78 79 81 82 85 86 87 93 96 97 98 100 101 102 103 104 106 107 108 110 111 114 115 116 117 118 119 120 121 123 124 129 130 131 132 135 141 144 145 146 147 148 149 **S** Kettering Health Network, Dayton, OH
Primary Contact: Rebecca Lewis, President
CFO: Luis Chanaga, Chief Financial Officer
CMO: Paul Martin, Chief Medical Officer
CIO: Andy Lehman, Senior Vice President Technology and Analytics
CHR: Keith Jenkins, Director, Human Resources
CNO: Ronda Brandstater, Vice President Patient Care
Web address: www.ketteringhealth.org/grandview/
Control: Church operated, Nongovernment, not–for–profit **Service**: General medical and surgical

Staffed Beds: 282 Admissions: 13715 Census: 166 Outpatient Visits: 418330 Births: 2098 Total Expense ($000): 414647 Payroll Expense ($000): 129284 Personnel: 1923

☐ HAVEN BEHAVIORAL SENIOR CARE OF DAYTON (364048), One Elizabeth Place, 4th Floor Southwest Tower, Zip 45417–3445; tel. 937/234–0100, (Nonreporting) **A**1 10 **S** Haven Behavioral Healthcare, Nashville, TN
Primary Contact: Keith Kuhn, Chief Executive Officer
CMO: Amita Patel, M.D., Medical Director
CNO: Cheryl Meyer, MSN, Director of Nursing
Web address: www.havenbehavioraldayton.com/
Control: Corporation, Investor–owned (for–profit) **Service**: Psychiatric

Staffed Beds: 32

✉ HEALTHSOUTH REHABILITATION HOSPITAL OF DAYTON (363033), One Elizabeth Place, Zip 45417–3445; tel. 937/424–8200, **A**1 10 **F**29 90 94 96 148 **P**5 **S** Encompass Health Corporation, Birmingham, AL
Primary Contact: Lynne Blinco, Chief Executive Officer
Web address: www.reliantdayton.com
Control: Corporation, Investor–owned (for–profit) **Service**: Rehabilitation

Staffed Beds: 50 Admissions: 545 Census: 20 Outpatient Visits: 0
Births: 0 Total Expense ($000): 8485 Payroll Expense ($000): 4598
Personnel: 81

✉ KINDRED HOSPITAL–DAYTON (362033), 707 South Edwin C Moses Boulevard, Zip 45417–3462; tel. 937/222–5963, (Nonreporting) **A**1 10 **S** Kindred Healthcare, Louisville, KY
Primary Contact: Phillip Underwood, Chief Executive Officer
CMO: Felipe Rubio, M.D., Medical Director
Web address: www.khdayton.com
Control: Corporation, Investor–owned (for–profit) **Service**: Acute long–term care hospital

Staffed Beds: 67

✉ △ MIAMI VALLEY HOSPITAL (360051), One Wyoming Street, Zip 45409–2793; tel. 937/208–8000, (Includes MIAMI VALLEY HOSPITAL SOUTH, 2400 Miami Valley Drive, Centerville, OH, Zip 45459–4774; tel. 937/438–2400) **A**1 2 3 5 7 10 **F**3 5 7 12 13 15 16 17 18 20 22 24 26 28 29 30 34 35 37 38 39 40 41 43 44 45 46 47 48 49 50 53 54 55 56 57 58 59 60 61 64 68 70 72 73 74 75 76 77 78 79 80 81 82 85 86 87 90 91 92 93 95 96 98 100 101 102 103 104 107 108 110 111 114 115 117 118 119 120 121 123 126 129 130 131 132 134 135 141 145 146 147 148 154 **P**6 8 **S** Premier Health, Dayton, OH
Primary Contact: Michael J. Maiberger, President
COO: Mikki Clancy, Chief Operating Officer
CFO: Thomas M Duncan, Executive Vice President and Chief Financial Officer
CMO: Marc Belcastro, D.O., Chief Medical Officer
CIO: Gary Ginter, System Vice President and Chief Information Officer
CNO: Jolyn M Angus, R.N., Chief Nursing Officer
Web address: www.miamivalleyhospital.org
Control: Other not–for–profit (including NFP Corporation) **Service**: General medical and surgical

Staffed Beds: 598 Admissions: 31016 Census: 413 Outpatient Visits: 510812 Births: 4466 Total Expense ($000): 788267 Payroll Expense ($000): 301739 Personnel: 5254

Many Facility Codes have changed. Please refer to the AHA Guide Code Chart.
© 2018 AHA Guide

THE MEDICAL CENTER AT ELIZABETH PLACE (360274), One Elizabeth Place, Zip 45417–3445; tel. 937/660–3100, (Nonreporting) **A**1 10
Primary Contact: Alexander M. Rintoul, Chief Executive Officer
Web address: www.regentsurgicalhealth.com/Partner+Centers/ Medical+Center+at+Elizabeth+Place
Control: Partnership, Investor–owned (for-profit) **Service**: General medical and surgical

Staffed Beds: 26

VETERANS AFFAIRS MEDICAL CENTER See Dayton Veterans Affairs Medical Center

DEFIANCE—Defiance County

MERCY HOSPITAL OF DEFIANCE (360270), 1404 East Second Street, Zip 43512–2440; tel. 419/782–8444, (Nonreporting) **A**1 10 **S** Mercy Health, Cincinnati, OH
Primary Contact: B Lynn. Detterman, President and Chief Executive Officer
COO: Kerry Knuth, Chief Operating Officer
CFO: James Puffenberger, Vice President and Chief Financial Officer
CMO: Jeffrey Pruitt, M.D., Chief of Staff
CHR: Susan Pscodna, Director Human Resources
CNO: Sonya Selhorst, R.N., Administrator and Chief Nursing Officer
Web address: www.ehealthconnection.com/regions/toledo/
Control: Partnership, Investor–owned (for-profit) **Service**: General medical and surgical

Staffed Beds: 23

PROMEDICA DEFIANCE REGIONAL HOSPITAL (361328), 1200 Ralston Avenue, Zip 43512–1396; tel. 419/783–6955, **A**1 5 10 18 **F**3 11 13 15 18 20 28 31 32 34 40 43 55 57 59 64 66 68 70 75 76 77 78 79 81 82 85 86 87 93 98 100 101 102 104 105 107 108 110 111 114 119 129 130 132 135 144 146 147 148 153 **S** ProMedica Health System, Toledo, OH
Primary Contact: Doug Bush, President
CFO: Ken Swint, Director Finance
CMO: Stanislaw Dajczak, M.D., Chief of Staff
CIO: Patricia Swint, Director Information Management Systems
CHR: Carrie Miller, Director Human Resources
Web address: www.promedica.org
Control: Other not–for–profit (including NFP Corporation) **Service**: General medical and surgical

Staffed Beds: 35 **Admissions**: 1881 **Census**: 17 **Outpatient Visits**: 93212 **Births**: 495 **Total Expense ($000)**: 54153 **Payroll Expense ($000)**: 15038 **Personnel**: 263

DELAWARE—Delaware County

OHIOHEALTH GRADY MEMORIAL HOSPITAL (360210), 561 West Central Avenue, Zip 43015–1410; tel. 740/615–1000, **A**1 2 10 **F**3 13 15 18 20 28 29 30 31 34 35 40 45 50 51 54 55 57 58 59 64 68 70 76 78 79 81 82 84 85 86 87 93 96 97 102 107 108 111 114 119 126 130 131 132 135 141 146 147 148 149 154 **S** OhioHealth, Columbus, OH
Primary Contact: Steve Bunyard, President
COO: Anna Hensley, Chief Operating Officer
CFO: David Hensel, Director Financial Operations
CMO: Barbara Evert, M.D., Vice President Medical Affairs
CIO: Michael Krouse, Chief Information Officer Information Services
CHR: Victoria L. Matlack, Director and Human Resources Business Partner
CNO: Elizabeth Anne Biegler, R.N., Chief Nursing Officer
Web address: www.ohiohealth.com
Control: Church operated, Nongovernment, not–for–profit **Service**: General medical and surgical

Staffed Beds: 59 **Admissions**: 1969 **Census**: 16 **Outpatient Visits**: 76832 **Births**: 289 **Total Expense ($000)**: 90106 **Payroll Expense ($000)**: 34146

DENNISON—Tuscarawas County

TEN LAKES CENTER (364042), 819 North First Street, 3rd Floor, Zip 44621–1003; tel. 740/922–7499, (Nonreporting) **A**1 10 **S** Acadia Healthcare Company, Inc., Franklin, TN
Primary Contact: Debra C. Gardner, R.N., MSN, Administrator
Web address: www.tenlakescenter.com/
Control: Corporation, Investor–owned (for-profit) **Service**: Psychiatric

Staffed Beds: 16

TRINITY HOSPITAL TWIN CITY (361302), 819 North First Street, Zip 44621–1098; tel. 740/922–2800, **A**1 10 18 **F**11 15 18 28 29 30 34 35 40 45 50 57 59 64 70 75 77 81 85 86 87 93 97 107 114 119 127 128 129 130 132 133 146 147 148 **P**4 **S** Catholic Health Initiatives, Englewood, CO
Primary Contact: Teresa Gagliardi, R.N., Vice President of Hospital Operations and Site Administrator
CMO: Tim McKnight, M.D., Chief of Staff
CHR: Bianca Love, Assistant Administrator Human Resources
CNO: Teresa Gagliardi, R.N., Chief Nursing Officer
Web address: www.trinitytwincity.org
Control: Church operated, Nongovernment, not–for–profit **Service**: General medical and surgical

Staffed Beds: 25 **Admissions**: 144 **Census**: 2 **Outpatient Visits**: 33172 **Births**: 0 **Total Expense ($000)**: 22685 **Payroll Expense ($000)**: 9974 **Personnel**: 208

DOVER—Tuscarawas County

★ △ ⇑ **CLEVELAND CLINIC UNION HOSPITAL (360010)**, 659 Boulevard, Zip 44622–2077; tel. 330/343–3311, **A**7 10 19 21 **F**3 8 11 13 15 18 28 29 34 35 40 48 50 53 54 57 59 62 64 70 74 75 76 77 79 80 81 82 85 86 90 93 100 102 104 105 107 108 110 111 115 119 124 129 130 131 132 135 144 146 148 149 150 **P**6 **S** Cleveland Clinic Health System, Cleveland, OH
Primary Contact: Bruce James, President and Chief Executive Officer
CFO: Eugene A Thorn III Vice President Finance and Chief Financial Officer
CMO: Todd Meyerhoefer, M.D., Vice President Medical Affairs
CIO: David Baumgardner, Director Information Management
CHR: Darwin K Smith, Vice President Human Resources
CNO: Diana Boyd, Vice President Nursing
Web address: www.unionhospital.org
Control: Other not–for–profit (including NFP Corporation) **Service**: General medical and surgical

Staffed Beds: 159 **Admissions**: 4724 **Census**: 51 **Outpatient Visits**: 272319 **Births**: 602 **Total Expense ($000)**: 117555 **Payroll Expense ($000)**: 49195 **Personnel**: 1003

DUBLIN—Franklin County

COLUMBUS DUBLIN SPRINGS (364049), 7625 Hospital Drive, Zip 43016–9649; tel. 614/717–1800, (Includes COLUMBUS SPRINGS EAST HOSPITAL, 2085 Citygate Drive, Columbus, OH, Zip 43219–3656; tel. 614/412–1772; Garry W Hoyes, Chief Executive Officer) (Nonreporting) **A**1 10 **S** Springstone, Louisville, KY
Primary Contact: Garry W. Hoyes, Chief Executive Officer
COO: Merissa McKinstry, Chief Operating Officer
CFO: Alexis Barbour, Director Finance
CMO: Mark Blair, M.D., Medical Director
CHR: Tam Wisler, Director Human Resources
CNO: Melissa Patton, MSN, Director of Nursing
Web address: www.dublinsprings.com
Control: Corporation, Investor–owned (for-profit) **Service**: Psychiatric

Staffed Beds: 144

OHIOHEALTH DUBLIN METHODIST HOSPITAL (360348), 7500 Hospital Drive, Zip 43016–8518; tel. 614/544–8000, **A**1 2 3 10 **F**3 13 15 18 20 28 29 30 34 40 45 50 51 57 58 59 68 70 76 79 81 84 85 87 97 100 102 107 108 110 111 115 119 126 130 131 132 135 141 146 147 148 149 154 **S** OhioHealth, Columbus, OH
Primary Contact: Steve Bunyard, President
COO: Anna Hensley, Chief Operating Officer
CFO: Keely Pummel, Director, Financial Operations
CMO: Barbara Evert, M.D., Vice President Medical Affairs
CIO: Michael Krouse, Senior Vice President Chief Information Officer
CHR: Victoria L. Matlack, Director and Human Resources Business Partner
CNO: Elizabeth Anne Biegler, R.N., Chief Nursing Officer
Web address: www.ohiohealth.com
Control: Church operated, Nongovernment, not–for–profit **Service**: General medical and surgical

Staffed Beds: 120 **Admissions**: 6439 **Census**: 45 **Births**: 2548 **Total Expense ($000)**: 161258 **Payroll Expense ($000)**: 56846 **Personnel**: 605

Hospital, Medicare Provider Number, Address, Telephone, Approval, Facility, and Physician Codes, Health Care System

★ American Hospital Association (AHA) membership   ○ Healthcare Facilities Accreditation Program   ⇑ Center for Improvement in Healthcare Quality Accreditation
□ The Joint Commission accreditation   ◇ DNV Healthcare Inc. accreditation   △ Commission on Accreditation of Rehabilitation Facilities (CARF) accreditation

OH

EAST LIVERPOOL—Columbiana County

✠ **EAST LIVERPOOL CITY HOSPITAL (360096)**, 425 West Fifth Street, Zip 43920–2498; tel. 330/385–7200, (Nonreporting) **A**1 10 13 **S** Prime Healthcare, Ontario, CA
Primary Contact: Keith Richardson, President and Chief Executive Officer
CFO: Kyle Johnson, Vice President Finance
CMO: Steve LaTulippe, President Medical Staff
CIO: Frank Mader, Director Information Services
CHR: Teri Pasco, Director Human Resources
CNO: Stacie Call, R.N., Vice President Patient Care and Chief Nursing Officer
Web address: www.elch.org
Control: Other not–for–profit (including NFP Corporation) **Service**: General medical and surgical

Staffed Beds: 120

ELYRIA—Lorain County

✠ **UNIVERSITY HOSPITALS ELYRIA MEDICAL CENTER (360145)**, 630 East River Street, Zip 44035–5902; tel. 440/329–7500, **A**1 2 10 13 **F**3 11 12 13 15 17 18 20 22 24 26 28 29 30 31 32 34 35 36 37 40 41 44 45 46 49 50 53 54 57 59 60 62 64 68 70 73 74 75 76 77 78 79 81 82 83 86 87 89 91 92 93 94 98 100 102 107 108 110 111 114 115 116 117 118 119 126 129 130 131 132 133 135 146 147 148 149 154 **S** University Hospitals, Cleveland, OH
Primary Contact: Kristi M. Sink, President
CFO: David A Cook, Vice President and Chief Financial Officer
CHR: Daniel Miller, Vice President Human Resources
CNO: Sandra Jean Kantelas, Chief Nursing Officer
Web address: www.uhhospitals.org/elyria
Control: Other not–for–profit (including NFP Corporation) **Service**: General medical and surgical

Staffed Beds: 202 Admissions: 9831 Census: 112 Outpatient Visits: 336810 Births: 643 Total Expense ($000): 199553 Payroll Expense ($000): 67479 Personnel: 1176

EUCLID—Cuyahoga County

✠ **EUCLID HOSPITAL (360082)**, 18901 Lake Shore Boulevard, Zip 44119–1090; tel. 216/531–9000, (Total facility includes 40 beds in nursing home–type unit) **A**1 3 10 **F**3 15 17 18 26 28 29 30 34 35 40 45 47 50 51 56 57 59 60 64 70 74 75 77 79 81 82 85 87 91 93 94 96 98 100 102 103 107 108 111 114 118 119 128 130 131 146 148 **S** Cleveland Clinic Health System, Cleveland, OH
Primary Contact: Daniel Napierkowski, M.D., President
COO: Rich Lea, Vice President Operations
CFO: Don Urbancsik, Director Finance
CMO: John Bertsch, M.D., Chief of Staff
CNO: Dawn A Bailey, R.N., Vice President Nursing and Chief Nursing Officer
Web address: www.euclidhospital.org
Control: Other not–for–profit (including NFP Corporation) **Service**: General medical and surgical

Staffed Beds: 165 Admissions: 7030 Census: 115 Outpatient Visits: 97264 Births: 0 Total Expense ($000): 116319 Payroll Expense ($000): 47582 Personnel: 679

FAIRFIELD—Butler County

✠ △ **MERCY HEALTH – FAIRFIELD HOSPITAL (360056)**, 3000 Mack Road, Zip 45014–5335; tel. 513/870–7000, (Nonreporting) **A**1 2 7 10 **S** Mercy Health, Cincinnati, OH
Primary Contact: Thomas S. Urban, FACHE, President and Chief Executive Officer
COO: Shane Knisley, Chief Operating Officer
CFO: Liz Mohr, Assistant Chief Financial Officer
CMO: John Kennedy, M.D., Vice President of Medical Affairs
CIO: Rebecca S Sykes, Chief Information Officer
CNO: Ramona Cheek, MS, R.N., Chief Nursing Officer
Web address: www.e–mercy.com
Control: Church operated, Nongovernment, not–for–profit **Service**: General medical and surgical

Staffed Beds: 236

FINDLAY—Hancock County

✠ **BLANCHARD VALLEY HOSPITAL (360095)**, 1900 South Main Street, Zip 45840–1214; tel. 419/423–4500, (Includes BLANCHARD VALLEY HOSPITAL, 1900 South Main Street, Findlay, OH, Zip 45840; tel. 419/423–4500) **A**1 2 5 10 19 **F**3 11 13 15 17 18 20 22 24 26 28 29 30 31 34 35 40 41 43 44 45 48 49 50 54 55 57 58 59 60 64 65 66 68 70 73 74 76 77 78 79 81 82 83 84 85 87 91 93 96 97 98 103 104 107 108 110 111 114 115 117 118 119 120 121 124 126 129 130 131 132 135 146 147 148 149 154 **S** Blanchard Valley Health System, Findlay, OH
Primary Contact: Scott C. Malaney, FACHE, President and Chief Executive Officer
CFO: David Cytlak, Chief Financial Officer
CMO: Michael Denike, D.O., Vice President, Medical Affairs
CIO: David Cytlak, Chief Financial Officer
CHR: Ryan Fisher, Director of Human Resources
CNO: Barbara J. Pasztor, R.N., Vice President Patient Care Services and Chief Nursing Officer
Web address: www.bvhealthsystem.org
Control: Other not–for–profit (including NFP Corporation) **Service**: General medical and surgical

Staffed Beds: 159 Admissions: 6785 Census: 63 Births: 1254 Total Expense ($000): 176879 Payroll Expense ($000): 77796 Personnel: 1289

FOSTORIA—Hancock County

✠ **PROMEDICA FOSTORIA COMMUNITY HOSPITAL (361318)**, 501 Van Buren Street, Zip 44830–1534, Mailing Address: P.O. Box 907, Zip 44830–0907; tel. 419/435–7734, **A**1 5 10 18 **F**3 11 15 28 29 31 34 35 40 45 46 55 57 59 60 64 66 68 70 75 77 78 79 81 82 85 86 87 89 93 94 96 97 107 108 110 111 115 116 117 118 119 128 129 130 131 132 133 135 146 147 148 149 **P**7 **S** ProMedica Health System, Toledo, OH
Primary Contact: Pamela M. Jensen, FACHE, President
COO: Tom Borer, Vice President Operations
CFO: Ken Swint, Vice President Finance and Chief Financial Officer
CMO: Terrence Fondessy, M.D., Vice President Medical Affairs
CIO: Rose Ann Laureto, Chief Information Officer
Web address: www.promedica.org
Control: Other not–for–profit (including NFP Corporation) **Service**: General medical and surgical

Staffed Beds: 25 Admissions: 386 Census: 2 Outpatient Visits: 64400 Births: 0 Total Expense ($000): 33143 Payroll Expense ($000): 8703 Personnel: 169

FREMONT—Sandusky County

✠ **PROMEDICA MEMORIAL HOSPITAL (360156)**, 715 South Taft Avenue, Zip 43420–3237; tel. 419/332–7321, **A**1 3 10 **F**3 7 11 13 14 15 18 19 28 29 30 31 34 35 38 40 44 45 46 47 48 50 51 53 56 57 59 61 64 65 70 74 75 76 77 78 79 80 81 82 84 85 86 87 89 91 92 93 96 97 107 108 110 111 114 115 119 123 129 130 131 132 135 141 142 146 147 148 149 **P**1 5 6 **S** ProMedica Health System, Toledo, OH
Primary Contact: Pamela M. Jensen, FACHE, President
CFO: David Brewer, Associate Vice President Finance and Operations
CMO: Scott Farrell, M.D., Vice President Medical Affairs
CHR: Warrenette Parthemore, Director Human Resources
CNO: Jodi Rucker, MSN, R.N., Vice President Patient Care Services and Chief Nursing Officer
Web address: www.promedica.org
Control: Other not–for–profit (including NFP Corporation) **Service**: General medical and surgical

Staffed Beds: 76 Admissions: 1057 Census: 8 Outpatient Visits: 79239 Births: 165 Total Expense ($000): 59856 Payroll Expense ($000): 14332 Personnel: 239

GAHANNA—Franklin County

THE WOODS AT PARKSIDE (360247), 349 Olde Ridenour Road, Zip 43230–2528; tel. 614/471–2552, (Nonreporting) **A**10
Primary Contact: Harry Nguyen, M.D., Medical Director
Web address: www.thewoodsatparkside.com
Control: Partnership, Investor–owned (for–profit) **Service**: Alcoholism and other chemical dependency

Staffed Beds: 50

GALION—Crawford County

★ ⇑ **GALION HOSPITAL (361325)**, 269 Portland Way South, Zip 44833–2399; tel. 419/468–4841, (Nonreporting) **A**10 18 21 **S** Avita Health System, Galion, OH
Primary Contact: Jerome Morasko, President and Chief Executive Officer
CFO: D. Eric Draime, Vice President and Chief Financial Officer
CIO: Alex Reed, Chief Information Officer
CHR: Traci L Oswald, Vice President of Human Resources
CNO: Kathy Durflinger, Vice President and Chief Nursing Officer
Web address: www.avitahs.org
Control: Other not–for–profit (including NFP Corporation) **Service**: General medical and surgical

Staffed Beds: 35

GALLIPOLIS—Gallia County

☐ △ **HOLZER MEDICAL CENTER (360054)**, 100 Jackson Pike, Zip 45631–1563; tel. 740/446–5000, **A**1 2 3 5 7 10 13 19 **F**3 12 13 15 18 20 22 26 28 29 30 31 33 34 35 37 40 45 49 55 57 59 60 62 63 64 70 74 76 77 78 79 81 82 85 87 89 90 93 96 97 98 103 107 108 110 111 114 115 118 119 120 121 123 126 129 130 131 132 144 146 149 **S** Holzer Health System, Jackson, OH
Primary Contact: Michael Canady, M.D., Interim Chief Executive Officer
CFO: Kenneth G Payne, Chief Financial Officer
CMO: John Viall, M.D., Vice President Medical Affairs
CIO: John Allen, Chief Information Officer
CHR: Lisa B Halley, Vice President Human Resources
Web address: www.holzer.org
Control: Other not–for–profit (including NFP Corporation) **Service**: General medical and surgical

Staffed Beds: 194 **Admissions:** 4796 **Census:** 58 **Outpatient Visits:** 784400 **Births:** 668 **Total Expense ($000):** 130463 **Payroll Expense ($000):** 47677 **Personnel:** 588

GARFIELD HEIGHTS—Cuyahoga County

⊞ **MARYMOUNT HOSPITAL (360143)**, 12300 McCracken Road, Zip 44125–2975; tel. 216/581–0500, **A**1 2 3 10 **F**3 7 8 11 15 18 28 29 30 31 34 35 38 40 44 50 51 53 54 56 57 59 60 62 63 64 65 68 70 74 75 77 78 79 81 82 85 86 87 92 93 96 97 98 100 102 103 104 107 108 110 111 114 115 116 118 119 124 129 130 131 132 135 143 144 146 147 148 153 154 **S** Cleveland Clinic Health System, Cleveland, OH
Primary Contact: Daniel Napierkowski, M.D., President
COO: Mark Nussbaum, Vice President Operations
CFO: Mike Stilgenbauer, Director Finance
CMO: Douglas Kohler, M.D., Vice President Medical Operations
CIO: Ralph A Cagna, Director Information Technology Operations, Cleveland Clinic Health System South Market
CHR: Judith Santora, Human Resources Business Partner
CNO: Barbara Zinner, Chief Nursing Officer
Web address: www.marymount.org
Control: Other not–for–profit (including NFP Corporation) **Service**: General medical and surgical

Staffed Beds: 277 **Admissions:** 8520 **Census:** 127 **Outpatient Visits:** 79598 **Births:** 0 **Total Expense ($000):** 156821 **Payroll Expense ($000):** 56776 **Personnel:** 868

GENEVA—Ashtabula County

⊞ **UNIVERSITY HOSPITALS GENEVA MEDICAL CENTER (361307)**, 870 West Main Street, Zip 44041–1295; tel. 440/466–1141, **A**1 3 10 18 **F**3 5 7 11 15 18 29 34 35 40 46 51 56 57 59 60 64 68 70 75 77 78 79 81 82 85 86 87 91 93 107 110 111 115 116 119 129 130 132 133 135 143 146 147 148 149 154 **S** University Hospitals, Cleveland, OH
Primary Contact: M Steven. Jones, President
COO: Jason Glowczewski, Chief Operating Officer
CFO: Lara Eggleston, Finance Manager
CMO: Amitabh Goel, M.D., Chief Medical Officer
CIO: Kirsten Hale, Coordinator Health Informations Systems and Coding
CHR: Danialle Lynce, Business Partner Human Resources
CNO: Ashley Fertig, Chief Nursing Officer
Web address: www.uhhs.com
Control: Other not–for–profit (including NFP Corporation) **Service**: General medical and surgical

Staffed Beds: 25 **Admissions:** 1410 **Census:** 15 **Outpatient Visits:** 55935 **Births:** 0 **Total Expense ($000):** 40564 **Payroll Expense ($000):** 13531 **Personnel:** 225

GREEN SPRINGS—Sandusky County

☐ **ELMWOOD HEALTHCARE CENTER AT THE SPRINGS (362007)**, 401 North Broadway, Zip 44836–9653; tel. 419/639–2626, (Nonreporting) **A**1 10
Primary Contact: Kathy Hunt, Chief Executive Officer
CFO: Douglas Morris, Chief Financial Officer
CMO: John Yuhas, D.O., Medical Director
CHR: Joan E Schmidt, Director Human Resources
Web address: www.sfhcc.org
Control: Church operated, Nongovernment, not–for–profit **Service**: Acute long–term care hospital

Staffed Beds: 186

GREENFIELD—Highland County

☐ △ **ADENA GREENFIELD MEDICAL CENTER (361304)**, 550 Mirabeau Street, Zip 45123–1617; tel. 937/981–9400, **A**1 7 10 18 **F**3 15 18 29 30 34 35 40 41 45 50 54 59 68 81 93 107 108 110 114 118 119 130 132 133 135 146 148 **P**6 **S** Adena Health System, Chillicothe, OH
Primary Contact: Josh McCoy, Administrator
CFO: Ralph W Sorrell Sr Chief Financial Officer
CIO: Marcus Bost, Director Information Services and Chief Information Officer
CHR: Brandt Lippert, Vice President Human Resources
Web address: www.adena.org
Control: Other not–for–profit (including NFP Corporation) **Service**: General medical and surgical

Staffed Beds: 25 **Admissions:** 339 **Census:** 8 **Outpatient Visits:** 40043 **Births:** 0 **Total Expense ($000):** 15564 **Payroll Expense ($000):** 6029 **Personnel:** 103

GREENVILLE—Darke County

★ ○ **WAYNE HEALTHCARE (360044)**, 835 Sweitzer Street, Zip 45331–1077; tel. 937/548–1141, **A**2 10 11 **F**3 8 11 13 15 28 29 30 31 34 35 39 40 41 45 57 59 64 65 70 75 76 77 78 79 81 82 84 85 86 89 93 98 103 107 108 110 111 114 117 118 119 124 129 130 131 132 135 141 146 147 148 149 **P**1
Primary Contact: Wayne G. Deschambeau, President and Chief Executive Officer
COO: Jeffrey R. Subler, Vice President Support Services
CMO: Tom Brown, M.D., President Medical Staff
CIO: Shelton Monger, Director Information Technology
CHR: Peggy Schwartz, Vice President Human Resources
CNO: Kimberlee Freeman, MS, R.N., Vice President Patient Care Services and Chief Nursing Officer
Web address: www.waynehealthcare.org
Control: Other not–for–profit (including NFP Corporation) **Service**: General medical and surgical

Staffed Beds: 53 **Admissions:** 1600 **Census:** 15 **Outpatient Visits:** 77560 **Births:** 282 **Total Expense ($000):** 53787 **Payroll Expense ($000):** 18539 **Personnel:** 337

HAMILTON—Butler County

★ ○ **FORT HAMILTON HOSPITAL (360132)**, 630 Eaton Avenue, Zip 45013–2770; tel. 513/867–2000, **A**2 10 11 **F**3 11 13 15 18 20 22 24 28 29 30 31 34 35 40 45 49 50 54 59 60 64 68 70 73 74 75 76 77 78 79 81 82 85 86 87 93 98 100 107 108 110 111 115 116 117 119 120 121 124 129 130 131 135 144 146 147 148 154 **S** Kettering Health Network, Dayton, OH
Primary Contact: Michael Mewhirter, President
CFO: William Villegas, Vice President Finance
CMO: Marcus Romanello, Chief Medical Officer
CIO: Andy Lehman, Senior Vice President Technology and Analytics
CHR: Joseph Geigle, Director Human Resources
CNO: Carol Applegeet, MSN, R.N., Vice President and Chief Nursing Officer
Web address: www.khnetwork.org/forthamilton
Control: Church operated, Nongovernment, not–for–profit **Service**: General medical and surgical

Staffed Beds: 164 **Admissions:** 7331 **Census:** 82 **Outpatient Visits:** 112666 **Births:** 613 **Total Expense ($000):** 162808 **Payroll Expense ($000):** 69297 **Personnel:** 959

OH

HICKSVILLE—Defiance County

☐ **COMMUNITY MEMORIAL HOSPITAL (361301)**, 208 North Columbus Street, Zip 43526–1299; tel. 419/542–6692, (Nonreporting) **A**1 10 18
Primary Contact: Michelle Waggoner, Chief Executive Officer
CFO: Steve Caryer, Chief Financial Officer
CNO: Betty Clevinger, Chief Nursing Officer
Web address: www.cmhosp.com
Control: Hospital district or authority, Government, nonfederal **Service:** General medical and surgical

Staffed Beds: 25

HIGHLAND HILLS—Cuyahoga County

HIGHLAND SPRINGS HOSPITAL (364053), 4199 Mill Pond Drive, Zip 44122–5731; tel. 602/314–7800, (Nonreporting) **S** Springstone, Louisville, KY
Primary Contact: Matthew Winchester, Chief Executive Officer
Web address: www.highlandspringshealth.com
Control: Corporation, Investor–owned (for–profit) **Service:** Psychiatric

Staffed Beds: 72

HILLSBORO—Highland County

⌘ **HIGHLAND DISTRICT HOSPITAL (361332)**, 1275 North High Street, Zip 45133–8273; tel. 937/393–6100, **A**1 10 18 **F**3 11 13 15 29 30 31 34 35 40 44 45 47 49 50 57 59 62 64 74 76 77 78 79 81 82 85 86 87 92 93 94 96 98 103 107 110 111 115 118 119 127 130 131 132 133 135 146 148 149 **P**3
Primary Contact: Randal P. Lennartz, CPA, President and Chief Executive Officer
COO: Timothy Parry, R.N., Chief Operating Officer
CMO: Ron Zile, M.D., Chief of Staff
CIO: Tim Bogard, Manager Information Technology
CHR: Melanie Wymer, Director Human Resources
CNO: Pam Barnett, R.N., Director of Nursing
Web address: www.hdh.org
Control: Hospital district or authority, Government, nonfederal **Service:** General medical and surgical

Staffed Beds: 35 Admissions: 1773 Census: 17 Outpatient Visits: 83874 Births: 247 Total Expense ($000): 42705 Payroll Expense ($000): 16574 Personnel: 330

JACKSON—Jackson County

⌘ **HOLZER MEDICAL CENTER – JACKSON (361320)**, 500 Burlington Road, Zip 45640–9360; tel. 740/288–4625, **A**1 10 18 **F**15 18 29 30 40 54 64 68 77 80 81 85 93 97 107 108 114 118 119 130 131 133 148 **S** Holzer Health System, Jackson, OH
Primary Contact: Michael Canady, M.D., Chief Executive Officer
CFO: Kevin Yeager, Vice President Fiscal Services
CMO: Nimal Dutla, M.D., Chief Medical Staff
CHR: Sandy Carlisle, Manager Human Resources
Web address: www.holzer.org
Control: Other not–for–profit (including NFP Corporation) **Service:** General medical and surgical

Staffed Beds: 24 Admissions: 760 Census: 6 Outpatient Visits: 64274 Births: 0 Total Expense ($000): 19909 Payroll Expense ($000): 7360 Personnel: 195

KENTON—Hardin County

⌘ **OHIOHEALTH HARDIN MEMORIAL HOSPITAL (361315)**, 921 East Franklin Street, Zip 43326–2099; tel. 419/673–0761, **A**1 10 18 **F**11 15 29 30 34 40 45 50 57 59 61 68 75 77 78 79 81 86 87 93 97 102 107 108 110 111 114 115 116 119 129 130 131 132 133 135 146 147 154 **S** OhioHealth, Columbus, OH
Primary Contact: Ron Snyder, Chief Operating Officer
Web address: www.hardinmemorial.org
Control: Other not–for–profit (including NFP Corporation) **Service:** General medical and surgical

Staffed Beds: 25 Admissions: 604 Census: 6 Outpatient Visits: 50602 Births: 0 Total Expense ($000): 24208 Payroll Expense ($000): 9764 Personnel: 180

KETTERING—Montgomery County

★ ○ △ **KETTERING MEDICAL CENTER (360079)**, 3535 Southern Boulevard, Zip 45429–1221; tel. 937/298–4331, **A**2 3 5 7 8 10 11 **F**3 8 11 13 17 18 20 22 24 26 28 29 30 31 34 35 36 37 38 39 40 43 44 45 46 47 48 49 50 51 52 53 54 55 56 57 58 59 60 61 62 64 65 66 68 70 71 72 74 75 76 77 78 79 81 82 84 85 86 87 90 91 92 93 96 97 102 107 108 110 111 114 115 116 117 118 119 120 121 123 124 126 129 130 131 132 135 141 145 146 147 148 149 **S** Kettering Health Network, Dayton, OH
Primary Contact: Terry M. Burns, President
CFO: Steven Chavez, Vice President Finance and Operations
CMO: Robert T. Smith, M.D., Chief Medical Officer
CIO: Andy Lehman, Senior Vice President Technology and Analytics
CHR: Derek Morgan, Vice President Human Resources
CNO: Brenda Kuhn, Ph.D., R.N., FACHE, Chief Nursing Officer
Web address: www.ketteringhealth.org/kettering
Control: Church operated, Nongovernment, not–for–profit **Service:** General medical and surgical

Staffed Beds: 391 Admissions: 22326 Census: 275 Outpatient Visits: 287369 Births: 2630 Total Expense ($000): 703133 Payroll Expense ($000): 278663 Personnel: 2827

LANCASTER—Fairfield County

☐ **FAIRFIELD MEDICAL CENTER (360072)**, 401 North Ewing Street, Zip 43130–3371; tel. 740/687–8000, **A**1 2 3 5 10 13 **F**3 8 11 12 13 15 18 20 22 24 26 28 29 30 31 34 35 38 40 44 45 48 49 50 53 54 57 59 64 70 74 75 76 77 78 79 81 82 83 84 85 87 89 93 96 97 98 102 104 105 107 108 110 111 114 115 118 119 129 130 131 132 135 144 145 146 147 148 149 152 154
Primary Contact: John R. Janoso, Chief Executive Officer
CFO: Sky Gettys, Chief Financial Officer
CMO: Renee Wagner, M.D., Chief Medical Officer
CIO: Martha Buckley, Chief Medical Informatics Officer
CHR: Debra L Palmer, MS, R.N., Chief Human Resources Officer and Corporate Compliance Officer
CNO: Helen Harding, Chief Nursing Officer
Web address: www.fmchealth.org
Control: Other not–for–profit (including NFP Corporation) **Service:** General medical and surgical

Staffed Beds: 222 Admissions: 11259 Census: 109 Outpatient Visits: 268382 Births: 962 Total Expense ($000): 244235 Payroll Expense ($000): 94593 Personnel: 1882

LIMA—Allen County

⌘ **INSTITUTE FOR ORTHOPAEDIC SURGERY (360263)**, 801 Medical Drive, Suite B, Zip 45804–4030; tel. 419/224–7586, (Nonreporting) **A**1 10 **S** Mercy Health, Cincinnati, OH
Primary Contact: Mark McDonald, M.D., President and Chief Executive Officer
CMO: Mark McDonald, M.D., President and Chief Executive Officer
CHR: Pat Farmer, Coordinator Human Resources and Safety Officer
Web address: www.ioshospital.com
Control: Partnership, Investor–owned (for–profit) **Service:** Orthopedic

Staffed Beds: 3

⌘ **KINDRED HOSPITAL LIMA (362020)**, 730 West Market Street, 6th Floor, Zip 45801–4602; tel. 419/224–1888, (Nonreporting) **A**1 10 **S** Kindred Healthcare, Louisville, KY
Primary Contact: Susan Krinke, Chief Executive Officer
Web address: www.khlima.com
Control: Corporation, Investor–owned (for–profit) **Service:** Acute long–term care hospital

Staffed Beds: 26

⌘ △ **LIMA MEMORIAL HEALTH SYSTEM (360009)**, 1001 Bellefontaine Avenue, Zip 45804–2899; tel. 419/228–3335, **A**1 2 7 10 **F**3 11 13 15 17 18 20 22 24 26 28 29 30 31 34 35 36 40 41 43 45 46 47 48 49 50 54 57 59 60 62 63 64 68 70 73 74 75 76 77 78 79 81 82 84 85 86 89 90 93 96 107 108 110 111 114 115 116 119 121 126 128 129 130 131 132 135 146 147 148 149 154 **P**8
Primary Contact: Michael D. Swick, President and Chief Executive Officer
COO: Robert E. Armstrong, Senior Vice President and Chief Operating Officer
CFO: John T. Fischbach, Vice President of Finance, Chief Financial Officer
CIO: Mathew P. Gaug, Executive Director of Information Techology
CHR: Denise G Kiraly, Director, Human Resources and Organization Development
CNO: Ann–Marie J Pohl, MSN, R.N., Vice President and Chief Nursing Officer
Web address: www.limamemorial.org
Control: Other not–for–profit (including NFP Corporation) **Service:** General medical and surgical

Staffed Beds: 200 Admissions: 6084 Census: 71 Outpatient Visits: 226518 Births: 569 Total Expense ($000): 167749 Payroll Expense ($000): 61994 Personnel: 1220

⊞ △ **ST. RITA'S MEDICAL CENTER (360066)**, 730 West Market Street, Zip 45801–4602; tel. 419/227–3361, **A**1 2 7 10 **F**3 5 7 8 11 12 13 15 17 18 20 22 24 26 28 29 30 31 34 35 36 38 40 43 45 46 47 48 49 50 53 54 57 58 59 60 61 62 63 64 65 67 68 70 73 74 75 76 77 78 79 81 82 84 85 86 87 89 90 92 93 94 96 98 100 102 104 105 107 108 110 111 114 117 118 119 120 121 123 126 128 129 130 132 135 143 144 146 147 148 149 153 154 **P**6 **S** Mercy Health, Cincinnati, OH
Primary Contact: Robert O. Baxter, Regional Chief Executive Officer, Lima
COO: Ronda Lehman, PharmD, Chief Operating Officer, SRPS
CFO: Tim Rieger, Chief Financial Officer
CMO: Kevin Casey, M.D., Chief Clinical Officer
CHR: Will Cason, Vice President Human Resources
CNO: Jodi Pahl, Chief Nurse Executive
Web address: www.stritas.org
Control: Other not–for–profit (including NFP Corporation) **Service:** General medical and surgical

Staffed Beds: 271 **Admissions:** 20594 **Census:** 219 **Outpatient Visits:** 459730 **Births:** 1526 **Total Expense ($000):** 367122 **Payroll Expense ($000):** 107939 **Personnel:** 2091

TRIUMPH HOSPITAL LIMA See Kindred Hospital Lima

LODI—Medina County

⊞ **CLEVELAND CLINIC AKRON GENERAL LODI HOSPITAL (361303)**, 225 Elyria Street, Zip 44254–1096; tel. 330/948–1222, **A**1 10 18 **F**3 15 18 28 29 30 34 35 40 45 51 57 59 64 65 75 81 90 93 96 97 107 111 114 119 128 129 130 133 135 146 147 154 **S** Cleveland Clinic Health System, Cleveland, OH
Primary Contact: Dana Kocsis, Vice President, Nursing and Operations
COO: Dana Kocsis, Vice President Nursing and Operations
CFO: Dave Frigo, Director Finance and Controller
CMO: David Peter, M.D., Senior Vice President Medical Affairs and Chief Medical Officer
CIO: Robb Baldauf, Coordinator Information Systems
CHR: Lynn Moraca, Director Human Resources
CNO: Dana Kocsis, Vice President, Nursing and Operations
Web address: www.lodihospital.org
Control: Other not–for–profit (including NFP Corporation) **Service:** General medical and surgical

Staffed Beds: 20 **Admissions:** 270 **Census:** 6 **Outpatient Visits:** 21769 **Births:** 0 **Total Expense ($000):** 15022 **Payroll Expense ($000):** 7099 **Personnel:** 98

LOGAN—Hocking County

⊞ **HOCKING VALLEY COMMUNITY HOSPITAL (361330)**, 601 State Route 664 North, Zip 43138–8541, Mailing Address: P.O. Box 966, Zip 43138–0966; tel. 740/380–8000, **A**1 10 18 **F**3 8 11 15 28 29 31 34 40 56 57 59 64 70 75 77 78 79 81 82 85 86 87 93 98 103 107 111 114 118 119 129 130 133 135 144 146 147 148 154 **P**1
Primary Contact: Stacey Gabriel, R.N., President and Chief Executive Officer
CFO: Julie E Grow, Chief Financial Officer
CMO: Duane Mast, M.D., Medical Director
CIO: John Burgess, Director Information Services
CHR: Robert F Schmidt, Director Human Resources
CNO: Janelle Hicks, R.N., Vice President Patient Services
Web address: www.hvch.org
Control: County, Government, nonfederal **Service:** General medical and surgical

Staffed Beds: 35 **Admissions:** 997 **Census:** 18 **Outpatient Visits:** 76888 **Births:** 0 **Total Expense ($000):** 39935 **Payroll Expense ($000):** 12954 **Personnel:** 279

LONDON—Madison County

⊞ **MADISON HEALTH (360189)**, 210 North Main Street, Zip 43140–1115; tel. 740/845–7000, **A**1 10 **F**3 11 13 15 18 29 30 31 34 40 45 50 53 57 59 64 68 70 75 76 77 78 79 81 85 87 89 93 97 107 108 110 111 114 118 119 129 130 132 135 146 **P**6
Primary Contact: Dana E. Engle, Chief Executive Officer
CFO: Michael Browning, Chief Financial Officer
CMO: Bernard Oppong, D.O., Chief of Staff
CIO: Dennis Vogt, Director Information Technology
CHR: Becky Rozell, Vice President, Human Resources
CNO: Jennifer Piccione, Chief Nursing and Clinical Services Officer
Web address: www.madison–health.com
Control: Other not–for–profit (including NFP Corporation) **Service:** General medical and surgical

Staffed Beds: 55 **Admissions:** 1109 **Census:** 10 **Outpatient Visits:** 55362 **Births:** 229 **Total Expense ($000):** 41144 **Payroll Expense ($000):** 16541 **Personnel:** 318

LORAIN—Lorain County

CLEARVISTA HEALTH AND WELLNESS (364052), 3364 Kolbe Road, Zip 44053–1628; tel. 440/960–7960, (Nonreporting)
Primary Contact: John Sannuto, Chief Executive Officer
Web address: www.clearvistahealth.com
Control: Corporation, Investor–owned (for–profit) **Service:** Psychiatric

Staffed Beds: 30

⊞ △ **MERCY REGIONAL MEDICAL CENTER (360172)**, 3700 Kolbe Road, Zip 44053–1697; tel. 440/960–4000, (Nonreporting) **A**1 2 7 10 **S** Mercy Health, Cincinnati, OH
Primary Contact: Edwin M. Oley, President and Chief Executive Officer
CMO: Sam El–Dalati, M.D., Chief Medical Officer
CHR: JC Fischer, Director Human Resources
CNO: Catherine Walsh, Interim Nursing Executive
Web address: www.community–health–partners.com
Control: Church operated, Nongovernment, not–for–profit **Service:** General medical and surgical

Staffed Beds: 259

MANSFIELD—Richland County

MEDCENTRAL – MANSFIELD HOSPITAL See Ohiohealth Medcentral Mansfield Hospital

⊞ **OHIOHEALTH MEDCENTRAL MANSFIELD HOSPITAL (360118)**, 335 Glessner Avenue, Zip 44903–2265; tel. 419/526–8000, (Includes MANSFIELD HOSPITAL, 335 Glessner Avenue, Mansfield, OH, Zip 44903–2265; tel. 419/526–8000) **A**1 2 3 5 10 **F**3 8 11 13 15 17 18 20 22 24 26 28 29 30 31 32 34 35 38 39 40 43 44 45 46 47 48 49 50 51 53 54 55 56 57 58 59 61 62 63 64 65 68 70 73 74 75 76 77 78 79 81 82 83 84 85 86 87 89 90 92 93 96 98 99 100 101 102 103 104 107 108 110 111 114 115 116 117 118 119 120 121 122 123 124 126 129 130 131 132 133 135 144 146 147 148 149 150 153 154 **S** OhioHealth, Columbus, OH
Primary Contact: Jean Halpin, President
CFO: Joseph Lyren, Chief Financial Officer
CMO: Terry Weston, M.D., Vice President Physician Services
CIO: Cindy Sheets, Vice President Information Systems and Chief Information Officer
CHR: Beth Hildreth, Vice President Human Resources
CNO: Pam Crawford, R.N., Ph.D., Vice President of Nursing and Chief Nursing Officer
Web address: www.medcentral.org
Control: Other not–for–profit (including NFP Corporation) **Service:** General medical and surgical

Staffed Beds: 253 **Admissions:** 11200 **Census:** 132 **Outpatient Visits:** 334573 **Births:** 848 **Total Expense ($000):** 236610 **Payroll Expense ($000):** 92747 **Personnel:** 1582

MARIETTA—Washington County

★ ○ **MARIETTA MEMORIAL HOSPITAL (360147)**, 401 Matthew Street, Zip 45750–1699; tel. 740/374–1400, **A**2 3 5 10 11 13 **F**3 8 11 12 13 15 18 20 22 26 28 29 30 31 34 35 36 38 40 41 43 44 45 46 47 48 49 50 51 53 54 56 57 58 59 60 62 63 64 66 68 70 74 75 76 77 78 79 81 82 84 85 86 87 89 92 93 96 97 98 100 102 103 104 107 109 110 111 114 115 116 117 119 120 121 123 124 126 129 130 131 132 144 146 148 149 154 **S** Memorial Health System, Marietta, OH
Primary Contact: J Scott. Cantley, President and Chief Executive Officer
CFO: Eric L Young, Vice President Finance and Chief Financial Officer
CMO: Matthew Macatol, M.D., President Medical Staff
CIO: Andy Altenburger, Chief Information Officer
CHR: Dee Ann Gehlauf, Senior Vice President Business and Organization Development
Web address: www.mhsystem.org
Control: Other not–for–profit (including NFP Corporation) **Service:** General medical and surgical

Staffed Beds: 218 **Admissions:** 12518 **Census:** 131 **Outpatient Visits:** 756489 **Total Expense ($000):** 409522 **Payroll Expense ($000):** 177048 **Personnel:** 2414

Hospital, Medicare Provider Number, Address, Telephone, Approval, Facility, and Physician Codes, Health Care System

★ American Hospital Association (AHA) membership   ○ Healthcare Facilities Accreditation Program   ⇑ Center for Improvement in Healthcare Quality Accreditation
□ The Joint Commission accreditation   ◇ DNV Healthcare Inc. accreditation   △ Commission on Accreditation of Rehabilitation Facilities (CARF) accreditation

© 2018 AHA Guide   *Many Facility Codes have changed. Please refer to the AHA Guide Code Chart.*   Hospitals **A485**

★ △ **SELBY GENERAL HOSPITAL (361319)**, 1106 Colegate Drive, Zip 45750–1323; tel. 740/568–2000, **A**7 10 18 **F**29 40 81 87 90 107 109 114 117 118 119 133 **S** Memorial Health System, Marietta, OH
Primary Contact: Stephen Smith, President
CFO: Eric L Young, Chief Financial Officer
CMO: David Spears, D.O., Chief of Staff
CHR: Tricia A Engfehr, Chief Human Resources
CNO: Misti Spencer, Director Inpatient Services
Web address: www.selbygeneral.org
Control: Other not–for–profit (including NFP Corporation) **Service:** General medical and surgical

Staffed Beds: 25 **Admissions:** 1507 **Census:** 18 **Outpatient Visits:** 21940 **Births:** 0 **Total Expense ($000):** 43868 **Payroll Expense ($000):** 12154 **Personnel:** 181

MARION—Marion County

⊞ **OHIOHEALTH MARION GENERAL HOSPITAL (360011)**, 1000 McKinley Park Drive, Zip 43302–6397; tel. 740/383–8400, **A**1 2 10 19 **F**3 8 13 15 18 20 22 24 26 28 29 30 31 35 40 53 54 57 59 60 63 64 68 70 72 73 74 75 76 77 78 79 81 82 83 87 89 91 94 95 98 104 105 107 111 114 116 119 126 129 130 132 135 146 147 148 149 153 154 **S** OhioHealth, Columbus, OH
Primary Contact: Bruce P. Hagen, President
CIO: Chris King, Director Information Services
CHR: Gianna Ferrarotti, Director Human Resources North Region
Web address: www.ohiohealth.com/mariongeneral
Control: Church operated, Nongovernment, not–for–profit **Service:** General medical and surgical

Staffed Beds: 174 **Admissions:** 7083 **Census:** 79 **Outpatient Visits:** 233553 **Births:** 894 **Total Expense ($000):** 183002 **Payroll Expense ($000):** 72439 **Personnel:** 1122

MARTINS FERRY—Belmont County

☐ **EAST OHIO REGIONAL HOSPITAL (360080)**, 90 North Fourth Street, Zip 43935–1648; tel. 740/633–1100, (Nonreporting) **A**1 3 10 **S** Alecto Healthcare, Irvine, CA
Primary Contact: Bernie Albertini, Chief Administrative Officer
COO: Bernie Albertini, Chief Administrative Officer
CFO: Lisa M. Simon, Senior Vice President Chief Financial Officer
CIO: Lisa M. Simon, Senior Vice President Chief Financial Officer
CHR: Robert Wright, Senior Human Resource Advisor
CNO: Christine Kerwood, Chief Nursing Officer
Web address: www.ovmc–eorh.com
Control: Corporation, Investor–owned (for–profit) **Service:** General medical and surgical

Staffed Beds: 139

MARYSVILLE—Union County

★ ⇑ **MEMORIAL HEALTH (360092)**, 500 London Avenue, Zip 43040–1594; tel. 937/644–6115, **A**5 10 21 **F**3 8 11 13 15 18 20 28 29 30 31 32 34 35 38 40 45 48 49 50 51 53 54 55 56 57 59 60 62 64 69 74 75 76 77 78 79 80 81 82 85 86 87 91 92 93 96 107 108 110 111 114 115 116 118 119 120 124 129 130 131 132 135 144 145 146 148 149 150 152 **P**6
Primary Contact: Olas A. Hubbs III, FACHE, President and Chief Executive Officer
COO: Laurie A Whittington, Chief Operating Officer
CFO: Jeffrey Ehlers, Chief Financial Officer
CMO: Matthew Hazelbaker, M.D., President Medical Staff
CIO: Carl Zani, Chief Technology Director
CHR: Larry C Schleeter, Chief Human Resources Officer
CNO: Robin Slattman, Chief Nursing Officer
Web address: www.memorialhosp.org
Control: County, Government, nonfederal **Service:** General medical and surgical

Staffed Beds: 74 **Admissions:** 1542 **Census:** 12 **Outpatient Visits:** 128319 **Births:** 576 **Total Expense ($000):** 105058 **Payroll Expense ($000):** 37665 **Personnel:** 573

MASON—Warren County

☐ **LINDNER CENTER OF HOPE (364044)**, 4075 Old Western Row Road, Zip 45040–3104; tel. 513/536–0311, (Nonreporting) **A**1 2 3 10
Primary Contact: Paul Keck, M.D., President and Chief Executive Officer
COO: Brian Owens, Chief Operating Officer
CFO: David McAdams, Chief Financial Officer
CIO: Cliff McClintick, Chief Information Officer
CHR: Debbie A Strawser, Director Human Resources
Web address: www.lindnercenterofhope.org
Control: Other not–for–profit (including NFP Corporation) **Service:** Psychiatric

Staffed Beds: 48

MASSILLON—Stark County

☐ **HEARTLAND BEHAVIORAL HEALTHCARE (364031)**, 3000 Erie Stree South, Zip 44646–7993, Mailing Address: 3000 Erie Street South, Zip 44646–7976; tel. 330/833–3135, (Nonreporting) **A**1 5 10 **S** Ohio Department of Mental Health, Columbus, OH
Primary Contact: Jeffrey Sims, Chief Executive Officer
CFO: Patricia Eddleman, Fiscal Officer
CMO: Steven Thomson, M.D., Medical Director
CIO: Robert Hobart, Director Management Information Systems
CHR: Jerald Wilhite, Administrator Human Resources
Web address: www.mh.state.oh.us/ibhs/bhos/hoh.html
Control: State, Government, nonfederal **Service:** Psychiatric

Staffed Beds: 152

MAUMEE—Lucas County

☐ **ARROWHEAD BEHAVIORAL HEALTH HOSPITAL (364036)**, 1725 Timber Line Road, Zip 43537–4015; tel. 419/891–9333, (Nonreporting) **A**1 10 **S** Universal Health Services, Inc., King of Prussia, PA
Primary Contact: Joseph Denicola, Chief Executive Officer and Managing Director
CFO: Allison Duncan, Chief Financial Officer
CMO: Kenneth Adler, M.D., Medical Director
CIO: Peggy Montgomery, Director Medical Records
CHR: Dawn Bosworth, Director Human Resources
CNO: Anita Zych, Director of Nursing
Web address: www.arrowheadbehavioral.com
Control: Corporation, Investor–owned (for–profit) **Service:** Psychiatric

Staffed Beds: 48

★ ⇑ **ST. LUKE'S HOSPITAL (360090)**, 5901 Monclova Road, Zip 43537–1899; tel. 419/893–5911, **A**3 5 10 21 **F**3 8 11 13 15 17 18 20 22 24 26 28 29 30 31 34 35 40 45 46 48 49 57 59 64 68 70 74 76 77 78 79 81 82 85 86 87 89 92 93 100 107 108 111 114 115 118 119 126 129 130 131 132 134 135 143 145 146 147 148 149 154
Primary Contact: Daniel L. Wakeman, President
CMO: Stephen Bazeley, M.D., Vice President Medical Affairs
CIO: Patricia Swint, Director Information Technology
CHR: Connie Sessler, Director Human Resources
CNO: Jill A. Trosin, R.N., MSN, Vice President Patient Care Services, Chief Nursing Officer
Web address: www.stlukeshospital.com
Control: Other not–for–profit (including NFP Corporation) **Service:** General medical and surgical

Staffed Beds: 170 **Admissions:** 9424 **Census:** 102 **Outpatient Visits:** 189053 **Births:** 675 **Total Expense ($000):** 185047 **Payroll Expense ($000):** 66309 **Personnel:** 1313

MEDINA—Medina County

⊞ **CLEVELAND CLINIC, MEDINA HOSPITAL (360091)**, 1000 East Washington Street, Zip 44256–2170; tel. 330/725–1000, **A**1 2 3 5 10 **F**3 7 8 15 18 20 28 29 30 31 34 35 40 47 49 50 51 57 59 60 64 70 74 75 77 78 79 81 82 85 86 93 96 107 111 114 117 119 129 130 131 132 133 135 146 148 154 **S** Cleveland Clinic Health System, Cleveland, OH
Primary Contact: Richard K. Shewbridge, President
COO: Vicky Snyder, Chief Operating Officer
CFO: Becky Molnar, Director of Finance
CMO: Matthew Vrobel, Vice President, Medical Operations
CIO: Frank Longley, Business Partner Information Technology
CHR: Tracie Curtis, Business Partner Human Resources
CNO: Julie Fetto, R.N., Chief Nursing Officer
Web address: www.medinahospital.org
Control: Other not–for–profit (including NFP Corporation) **Service:** General medical and surgical

Staffed Beds: 121 **Admissions:** 6552 **Census:** 71 **Outpatient Visits:** 85230 **Births:** 351 **Total Expense ($000):** 111172 **Payroll Expense ($000):** 40684 **Personnel:** 620

MIAMISBURG—Montgomery County

⊞ **LIFECARE HOSPITAL OF DAYTON (362028)**, 4000 Miamisburg–Centerville Road, Zip 45342–7615; tel. 937/384–8300, (Nonreporting) **A**1 10 **S** LifeCare Management Services, Plano, TX
Primary Contact: William Bryant, Chief Executive Officer
CMO: Richard Gregg, M.D., Medical Director
CHR: Pam Fannin, Coordinator Human Resources
Web address: www.lifecare–hospitals.com
Control: Corporation, Investor–owned (for–profit) **Service:** Acute long–term care hospital

Staffed Beds: 44

★ ○ **SYCAMORE MEDICAL CENTER (360239)**, 4000 Miamisburg–Centerville Road, Zip 45342–7615; tel. 937/866–0551, (Includes KETTERING BEHAVIORAL MEDICAL CENTER, 5350 Lamme Road, Dayton, OH, Zip 45439; tel. 937/534–4600; Jason Brown, Director) **A**10 11 **F**3 11 12 15 18 20 28 29 30 31 34 35 36 38 40 44 45 47 48 49 50 51 53 54 56 57 58 59 60 61 64 65 66 68 70 74 75 77 78 79 81 82 84 85 86 87 91 92 93 97 98 99 100 101 102 103 104 107 108 110 111 114 115 118 119 129 130 131 132 134 135 141 145 146 148 149 **S** Kettering Health Network, Dayton, OH
Primary Contact: Walter Sackett, President
CMO: Robert T. Smith, M.D., Chief Medical Officer
CIO: Andy Lehman, Senior Vice President Technology and Analytics
CHR: Derek Morgan, Vice President Human Resources
CNO: Julie S. Vincent, R.N., MSN, Chief Nursing Officer
Web address: www.khnetwork.org/sycamore
Control: Church operated, Nongovernment, not–for–profit **Service**: General medical and surgical

Staffed Beds: 202 **Admissions**: 9088 **Census**: 96 **Outpatient Visits**: 160160 **Births**: 0 **Total Expense ($000)**: 177063 **Payroll Expense ($000)**: 66771 **Personnel**: 683

MIDDLE POINT—Van Wert County

□ **RIDGEVIEW BEHAVIORAL HOSPITAL (364047)**, 17872 Lincoln Highway, Zip 45863–9700; tel. 419/968–2950, (Nonreporting) **A**1 10
Primary Contact: Pat Tracy, Administrator
Web address: www.ridgeviewhospital.net/
Control: Corporation, Investor–owned (for–profit) **Service**: Psychiatric

Staffed Beds: 40

MIDDLEBURG HEIGHTS—Cuyahoga County

□ **SOUTHWEST GENERAL HEALTH CENTER (360155)**, 18697 Bagley Road, Zip 44130–3497; tel. 440/816–8000, (Nonreporting) **A**1 2 3 5 10
Primary Contact: William A. Young Jr, President and Chief Executive Officer
COO: Bradley W. Rauh, Vice President, Chief Operating Officer
CFO: Mary Ann Freas, Senior Vice President and Chief Financial Officer
CMO: Marilyn McNamara, M.D., Chief Medical Officer
CIO: Alec Williams, Chief Information Officer
CHR: Dee Murphy, Vice President Human Resources
CNO: Martha F. Bauschka, R.N., Vice President and Chief Nursing Officer
Web address: www.swgeneral.com
Control: Other not–for–profit (including NFP Corporation) **Service**: General medical and surgical

Staffed Beds: 293

MIDDLETOWN—Warren County

✠ △ **ATRIUM MEDICAL CENTER (360076)**, One Medical Center Drive, Zip 45005–1066; tel. 513/424–2111, **A**1 2 3 7 10 **F**3 8 11 13 15 17 18 20 22 24 26 28 29 30 31 32 34 35 36 38 40 41 43 44 45 46 47 48 49 50 54 55 56 57 58 59 61 64 65 68 70 71 73 74 75 76 77 78 79 80 81 82 85 86 87 90 91 92 93 96 98 100 101 102 103 104 107 108 110 111 114 115 117 118 119 126 130 131 132 135 141 143 145 146 147 148 149 154 **S** Premier Health, Dayton, OH
Primary Contact: Michael Uhl, President
CMO: Matthew Reeves, D.O., Esq Chief Medical Officer
CHR: Ted Ripperger, Administrative Director Human Resources
CNO: Marquita Turner, Chief Operating Officer and Chief Nursing Officer
Web address: www.PremierHealth.com
Control: Other not–for–profit (including NFP Corporation) **Service**: General medical and surgical

Staffed Beds: 284 **Admissions**: 9402 **Census**: 100 **Outpatient Visits**: 259536 **Births**: 952 **Total Expense ($000)**: 229867 **Payroll Expense ($000)**: 88310 **Personnel**: 1331

MILLERSBURG—Holmes County

POMERENE HOSPITAL (360148), 981 Wooster Road, Zip 44654–1094; tel. 330/674–1015, **A**10 22 **F**3 11 13 15 18 28 29 30 34 35 40 50 53 55 57 59 70 75 76 77 79 81 85 86 87 89 93 107 108 110 115 119 130 131 132 135 143 144 146 147 149
Primary Contact: Tony Snyder, Administrator and Chief Executive Officer
CFO: Jason Justus, Vice President Finance and Chief Financial Officer
CMO: Yasser Omran, M.D., President Medical Staff
CIO: Brent Edington, Director Information Services
CHR: Kim Croft, R.N., Executive Director Human Resources
Web address: www.pomerenehospital.org
Control: Other not–for–profit (including NFP Corporation) **Service**: General medical and surgical

Staffed Beds: 41 **Admissions**: 1545 **Census**: 14 **Outpatient Visits**: 41944 **Births**: 570 **Total Expense ($000)**: 28113 **Payroll Expense ($000)**: 11255 **Personnel**: 280

MONTPELIER—Williams County

COMMUNITY HOSPITALS AND WELLNESS CENTERS–MONTPELIER (361327), 909 East Snyder Avenue, Zip 43543–1251; tel. 419/636–1131, (Nonreporting) **A**10 18
Primary Contact: Philip L. Ennen, President and Chief Executive Officer
Web address: www.chwchospital.com
Control: Corporation, Investor–owned (for–profit) **Service**: General medical and surgical

Staffed Beds: 35

MONTPELIER HOSPITAL See Community Hospitals and Wellness Centers, Bryan

MOUNT GILEAD—Morrow County

✠ **MORROW COUNTY HOSPITAL (361313)**, 651 West Marion Road, Zip 43338–1027; tel. 419/946–5015, **A**1 5 10 18 **F**15 18 28 29 30 35 39 40 45 50 59 64 70 75 79 81 93 96 107 110 111 119 127 129 130 131 133 135 144 146 154 **P**3 **S** OhioHealth, Columbus, OH
Primary Contact: Chad J. Miller, President and Chief Executive Officer
CFO: Joe Schueler, Chief Financial Officer
Web address: www.morrowcountyhospital.com
Control: County, Government, nonfederal **Service**: General medical and surgical

Staffed Beds: 22 **Admissions**: 485 **Census**: 4 **Outpatient Visits**: 58663 **Births**: 0 **Total Expense ($000)**: 33009 **Payroll Expense ($000)**: 11340 **Personnel**: 241

MOUNT VERNON—Knox County

✠ **KNOX COMMUNITY HOSPITAL (360040)**, 1330 Coshocton Road, Zip 43050–1495; tel. 740/393–9000, **A**1 2 10 20 **F**3 5 11 13 15 18 20 22 26 28 29 31 34 35 36 40 41 44 45 48 50 53 57 59 64 69 70 75 76 77 78 79 81 82 83 84 85 86 87 93 94 96 97 107 108 110 111 112 113 114 115 118 119 120 129 130 131 132 144 146 147 149 150 **P**6 **S** QHR, Brentwood, TN
Primary Contact: Bruce D. White, Chief Executive Officer
COO: Bruce M Behner, Chief Operating Officer
CFO: Michael Ambrosiani, Chief Financial Officer
CMO: Jeffrey Northup, D.O., Chief Medical Officer
CIO: Kwi Holland, Vice President Information Services
CHR: Lisa Bragg, Vice President Human Resources
CNO: James Middleton, MSN, R.N., Chief Nursing Officer
Web address: www.kch.org
Control: Other not–for–profit (including NFP Corporation) **Service**: General medical and surgical

Staffed Beds: 65 **Admissions**: 3393 **Census**: 30 **Outpatient Visits**: 142830 **Births**: 406 **Total Expense ($000)**: 148718 **Payroll Expense ($000)**: 66987 **Personnel**: 956

NAPOLEON—Henry County

★ ⇑ **HENRY COUNTY HOSPITAL (361309)**, 1600 East Riverview Avenue, Zip 43545–9399; tel. 419/592–4015, **A**5 10 18 21 **F**3 5 11 13 15 28 29 30 31 34 35 36 40 45 50 53 57 59 64 65 68 70 75 76 77 78 79 81 82 85 86 87 93 99 100 101 104 107 108 110 114 119 130 132 133 135 146 148 149
Primary Contact: Kimberly Hupp. Bordenkircher, Chief Executive Officer
CFO: Diane Walther, Controller
CIO: William Grimm, Chief Information Officer
CHR: Jennifer A Fisher, Manager Human Resources
CNO: Patricia Frank, Chief Nursing Officer
Web address: www.henrycountyhospital.org
Control: Other not–for–profit (including NFP Corporation) **Service**: General medical and surgical

Staffed Beds: 25 **Admissions**: 741 **Census**: 8 **Outpatient Visits**: 61372 **Births**: 152 **Total Expense ($000)**: 29760 **Payroll Expense ($000)**: 11996 **Personnel**: 213

NEW ALBANY—Franklin County

✠ **MOUNT CARMEL NEW ALBANY SURGICAL HOSPITAL (360266)**, 7333 Smith's Mill Road, Zip 43054–9291; tel. 614/775–6600, **A**1 5 10 **F**3 29 34 35 44 57 58 59 64 65 68 74 75 79 81 85 86 87 107 111 114 119 146 **P**6 8 **S** Trinity Health, Livonia, MI
Primary Contact: Diane Doucette, R.N., President
Web address: www.mountcarmelhealth.com
Control: Church operated, Nongovernment, not–for–profit **Service**: Surgical

Staffed Beds: 60 **Admissions**: 4708 **Census**: 20 **Outpatient Visits**: 15364 **Births**: 0 **Total Expense ($000)**: 85537 **Payroll Expense ($000)**: 15359 **Personnel**: 235

Hospital, Medicare Provider Number, Address, Telephone, Approval, Facility, and Physician Codes, Health Care System

★ American Hospital Association (AHA) membership
□ The Joint Commission accreditation
○ Healthcare Facilities Accreditation Program
◇ DNV Healthcare Inc. accreditation
⇑ Center for Improvement in Healthcare Quality Accreditation
△ Commission on Accreditation of Rehabilitation Facilities (CARF) accreditation

OH

NEWARK—Licking County

□ **LICKING MEMORIAL HOSPITAL (360218)**, 1320 West Main Street, Zip 43055–3699; tel. 740/348–4000, **A**1 2 10 **F**3 4 5 13 15 18 20 22 26 28 29 30 31 32 34 35 40 41 45 46 48 49 50 53 57 59 62 64 65 68 70 72 74 75 76 77 78 79 81 82 84 85 86 89 90 92 93 97 98 100 101 102 104 106 107 108 110 111 114 115 116 117 118 119 129 130 132 135 144 146 147 148 152 153 154 **P**6
Primary Contact: Robert A. Montagnese, President and Chief Executive Officer
CFO: Cindy Webster, Vice President Financial Services
CMO: Craig Cairns, M.D., Vice President Medical Affairs
CIO: Sallie Arnett, Vice President Information Systems
CHR: Anne Peterson, Vice President Human Resources and Support Services
Web address: www.lmhealth.org
Control: Other not–for–profit (including NFP Corporation) **Service**: General medical and surgical

Staffed Beds: 227 Admissions: 7838 Census: 77 Outpatient Visits: 312878 Births: 931 Total Expense ($000): 184607 Payroll Expense ($000): 75408 Personnel: 1464

⊞ **SELECT SPECIALTY HOSPITAL OF SOUTHEAST OHIO (362031)**, 2000 Tamarack Road, Zip 43055; tel. 740/588–7888, (Nonreporting) **A**1 10 **S** Select Medical Corporation, Mechanicsburg, PA
Primary Contact: Linda Supplee, Chief Executive Officer
CMO: Armand Bermudez, M.D., Medical Director
CHR: Jacqueline Nezbeth, Human Resources Officer
CNO: Taryn Vierling, Chief Nursing Officer
Web address: www.selectspecialtyhospitals.com/company/locations/zanesville.aspx
Control: Corporation, Investor–owned (for–profit) **Service**: Acute long–term care hospital

Staffed Beds: 35

NORTHFIELD—Summit County

□ **NORTHCOAST BEHAVIORAL HEALTHCARE (364011)**, 1756 Sagamore Road, Zip 44067–1086; tel. 330/467–7131, (Nonreporting) **A**1 10 **S** Ohio Department of Mental Health, Columbus, OH
Primary Contact: Douglas W. Kern, Chief Executive Officer
CIO: Karl Donenwirth, Vice President Information Services
Web address: www.mha.ohio.gov
Control: State, Government, nonfederal **Service**: Psychiatric

Staffed Beds: 260

NORWALK—Huron County

★ ○ **FISHER–TITUS MEDICAL CENTER (360065)**, 272 Benedict Avenue, Zip 44857–2374; tel. 419/668–8101, (Total facility includes 69 beds in nursing home–type unit) **A**2 3 5 10 11 19 **F**3 10 13 15 18 20 28 29 31 34 35 36 38 39 40 43 44 49 50 51 54 56 57 59 61 62 64 68 70 74 75 76 77 78 79 81 85 86 87 92 93 94 96 97 107 108 110 111 115 118 119 126 128 129 130 131 132 135 143 146 147 148 149 **P**6 8
Primary Contact: Matthew Gross, Chief Executive Officer
CFO: Duane L Woods Jr Chief Financial Officer
CMO: Shankar Kurra, M.D., Senior Vice President Medical Affairs
CIO: John Britton, Vice President Information Services
CHR: Phillip Annarino, Vice President Human Resources
CNO: Suzanne Inglis, MSN, FACHE, Senior Vice President Nursing Services
Web address: www.fisher–titus.org
Control: Other not–for–profit (including NFP Corporation) **Service**: General medical and surgical

Staffed Beds: 147 Admissions: 3842 Census: 95 Outpatient Visits: 175220 Births: 580 Total Expense ($000): 118369 Payroll Expense ($000): 46743 Personnel: 843

OBERLIN—Lorain County

⊞ **MERCY ALLEN HOSPITAL (361306)**, 200 West Lorain Street, Zip 44074–1077; tel. 440/775–1211, (Nonreporting) **A**1 10 18 **S** Mercy Health, Cincinnati, OH
Primary Contact: Ed Roth, President
COO: Ken Hale, Executive Director of Operations
CFO: Cynthia Dennison, Chief Financial Officer
CMO: Rafik Massouh, M.D., Chief of Staff
CHR: Kathy Dolbin, Director of Human Resources
CNO: Cheryl Rieves, Chief Nurse Executive Lorain Region
Web address: www.mercyonline.org/mercy_allen_hospital.aspx
Control: Other not–for–profit (including NFP Corporation) **Service**: General medical and surgical

Staffed Beds: 25

ONTARIO—Richland County

★ **AVITA ONTARIO HOSPITAL (360365)**, 715 Richland Mall, Zip 44906–3802; tel. 567/307–7666, (Nonreporting) **S** Avita Health System, Galion, OH
Primary Contact: Jerome Morasko, President and Chief Executive Officer
CFO: D. Eric Draime, Vice President and Chief Financial Officer
CIO: Alex Reed, Chief Information Officer
CHR: Traci L Oswald, Vice President, Chief Human Resources
CNO: Kathy Durflinger, Vice President and Chief Nursing Officer
Web address: www.avitahealth.org
Control: Other not–for–profit (including NFP Corporation) **Service**: General medical and surgical

Staffed Beds: 26

OREGON—Lucas County

⊞ △ **MERCY HEALTH – ST. CHARLES HOSPITAL (360081)**, 2600 Navarre Avenue, Zip 43616–3297; tel. 419/696–7200, **A**1 2 3 7 10 **F**3 11 13 15 18 28 29 30 31 34 35 40 43 44 46 47 48 49 51 56 57 59 60 64 66 68 70 74 75 76 77 78 79 81 82 85 86 87 90 91 92 93 97 98 100 101 102 103 104 107 108 110 111 114 115 118 119 120 121 123 126 129 130 132 135 146 147 148 149 154 **P**8 **S** Mercy Health, Cincinnati, OH
Primary Contact: Craig Albers, President and Chief Operating Officer
COO: Craig Albers, President and Chief Operating Officer
CFO: Mark Thompson, Market Chief Financial Officer Northern Region and Chief Financial Officer
CMO: Riaz Chaudhry, M.D., Chief Medical Officer
CIO: Rebecca S Sykes, Senior Vice President Resource Management, Chief Information Officer
Web address: www.mercyweb.org
Control: Church operated, Nongovernment, not–for–profit **Service**: General medical and surgical

Staffed Beds: 279 Admissions: 10949 Census: 151 Outpatient Visits: 120771 Births: 426 Personnel: 902

⊞ **PROMEDICA BAY PARK HOSPITAL (360259)**, 2801 Bay Park Drive, Zip 43616–4920; tel. 419/690–7900, **A**1 10 **F**3 11 13 15 18 28 29 30 31 34 35 40 45 49 50 54 57 59 64 68 70 74 75 76 77 78 79 81 82 85 86 92 93 97 107 108 110 111 114 118 119 124 126 129 130 131 132 134 135 143 146 147 148 149 154 **S** ProMedica Health System, Toledo, OH
Primary Contact: Arturo Polizzi, President
COO: Darrell Wachowiak, Associate Vice President Operations
CFO: Scott Fought, Vice President Finance
CMO: David Lindstrom, M.D., Vice President Medical Affairs
CIO: Rose Ann Laureto, Corporate Vice President Information Resources
CHR: Kara Zimmerly, Manager Human Resources
Web address: www.promedica.org
Control: Other not–for–profit (including NFP Corporation) **Service**: General medical and surgical

Staffed Beds: 44 Admissions: 3167 Census: 30 Outpatient Visits: 107070 Births: 555 Total Expense ($000): 72749 Payroll Expense ($000): 22780 Personnel: 337

ST. CHARLES MERCY HOSPITAL See Mercy Health – St. Charles Hospital

ORRVILLE—Wayne County

⊞ **AULTMAN ORRVILLE HOSPITAL (361323)**, 832 South Main Street, Zip 44667–2208; tel. 330/682–3010, **A**1 10 18 **F**3 8 11 12 13 14 15 28 29 30 34 35 40 45 50 51 53 55 57 59 68 70 75 76 77 79 81 82 85 86 87 93 108 110 111 115 118 119 127 129 130 131 132 133 135 143 146 147 149 150 152 **P**8 **S** Aultman Health Foundation, Canton, OH
Primary Contact: Jennifer Kessel, Chief Executive Officer
CFO: Adam Luntz, Chief Financial Officer
CIO: Vince Logozzo, Director Information Technology
CNO: Angela McGee, Vice President Nursing Services
Web address: www.aultmanorrville.org
Control: Other not–for–profit (including NFP Corporation) **Service**: General medical and surgical

Staffed Beds: 25 Admissions: 1072 Census: 7 Outpatient Visits: 37448 Births: 506 Total Expense ($000): 24158 Payroll Expense ($000): 10137 Personnel: 182

Many Facility Codes have changed. Please refer to the AHA Guide Code Chart. © 2018 AHA Guide

OXFORD—Butler County

★ ○ **MCCULLOUGH–HYDE MEMORIAL HOSPITAL/TRIHEALTH (360046)**, 110 North Poplar Street, Zip 45056–1292; tel. 513/523–2111, **A**2 10 11 **F**3 11 13 15 18 28 29 30 31 34 35 36 40 45 47 50 54 57 59 64 68 69 70 75 76 77 78 79 81 82 84 85 86 87 93 102 107 108 110 111 114 119 129 130 131 132 144 146 147 149 **P**6 8
Primary Contact: Brett Kirkpatrick, Executive Director
CFO: John R Clements, Chief Financial Officer
CMO: Amy Spivey, Chief Medical Officer
CHR: Sharon Hancock, Chief Human Resources Officer
CNO: Pamela Collins, Vice President Chief Patient Services Officer
Web address: www.mhmh.org
Control: Other not–for–profit (including NFP Corporation) **Service**: General medical and surgical

Staffed Beds: 48 **Admissions**: 1815 **Census**: 15 **Outpatient Visits**: 58039 **Births**: 429 **Total Expense ($000)**: 50466 **Payroll Expense ($000)**: 19547 **Personnel**: 308

PARMA—Cuyahoga County

⊞ △ **UNIVERSITY HOSPITALS PARMA MEDICAL CENTER (360041)**, 7007 Powers Boulevard, Zip 44129–5495; tel. 440/743–3000, **A**1 2 3 7 10 13 **F**2 3 11 12 13 15 17 18 20 22 24 26 28 29 30 34 35 36 40 44 45 49 50 51 53 56 57 58 59 60 62 63 64 65 68 69 70 71 74 75 76 77 78 79 81 82 84 85 86 87 90 93 96 97 98 100 101 103 107 108 111 114 115 116 117 119 120 121 126 130 131 132 135 143 146 147 148 149 154 **S** University Hospitals, Cleveland, OH
Primary Contact: Peter U. Bergmann, President
CMO: Christopher Loyke, Chief Medical Officer
CHR: Daniel Miller, Human Resources Business Partner
Web address: www.uhhospitals.org/parma
Control: Other not–for–profit (including NFP Corporation) **Service**: General medical and surgical

Staffed Beds: 266 **Admissions**: 9874 **Census**: 120 **Outpatient Visits**: 327680 **Births**: 384 **Total Expense ($000)**: 178688 **Payroll Expense ($000)**: 61092 **Personnel**: 1040

PAULDING—Paulding County

□ **PAULDING COUNTY HOSPITAL (361300)**, 1035 West Wayne Street, Zip 45879–1544; tel. 419/399–4080, (Nonreporting) **A**1 10 18
Primary Contact: Randy Ruge, Chief Executive Officer
COO: Randy Ruge, Chief Operating Officer
CFO: Rob Goshia, Chief Financial Officer
CMO: Wendell J Spangler, M.D., Chief of Staff
CIO: Dan Kaufman, Director Information Services
CHR: Melanie Rittenour, Director Human Resources
Web address: www.pauldingcountyhospital.com
Control: County, Government, nonfederal **Service**: General medical and surgical

Staffed Beds: 25

PORT CLINTON—Ottawa County

⊞ **MAGRUDER MEMORIAL HOSPITAL (361314)**, 615 Fulton Street, Zip 43452–2001; tel. 419/734–3131, **A**1 5 10 18 **F**3 11 15 18 28 29 31 34 35 40 44 45 46 48 50 53 57 59 64 65 70 75 77 78 79 81 82 85 86 87 89 93 107 108 110 115 118 119 129 130 131 132 133 135 144 146 147 148 149 **P**6 8
Primary Contact: J Todd. Almendinger, President and Chief Executive Officer
COO: Nick Marsico, Vice President and Chief Operating Officer
CFO: Julie Georgoff, Vice President of Finance and Chief Financial Officer
CHR: Jason Kraus, Director Human Resources
CNO: Lori Koethe, MS, Vice President of Nursing and Chief Nursing Officer
Web address: www.magruderhospital.com
Control: Other not–for–profit (including NFP Corporation) **Service**: General medical and surgical

Staffed Beds: 25 **Admissions**: 459 **Census**: 4 **Outpatient Visits**: 85327 **Births**: 0 **Total Expense ($000)**: 51715 **Payroll Expense ($000)**: 20287 **Personnel**: 365

PORTSMOUTH—Scioto County

KING'S DAUGHTERS MEDICAL CENTER OHIO (360361), 2001 Scioto Trail, Zip 45662–2845; tel. 740/991–4000, (Nonreporting)
Primary Contact: Kim Grooms, Administrator
Web address: www.kdmcohio.com/
Control: Other not–for–profit (including NFP Corporation) **Service**: General medical and surgical

Staffed Beds: 10

SOUTHERN OHIO MEDICAL CENTER (360008)

⊞ △ **SOUTHERN OHIO MEDICAL CENTER (360008)**, 1805 27th Street, Zip 45662–2640, Mailing Address: 1805 27th Street,Waller Building Suite B01, Zip 45662–2640; tel. 740/356–5000, **A**1 2 3 5 7 10 13 **F**3 11 13 15 17 18 20 22 24 26 28 29 30 31 34 35 37 38 40 41 44 45 46 47 48 49 50 53 54 57 59 62 63 64 65 70 74 75 76 77 78 79 81 82 84 85 86 87 89 90 92 97 98 100 101 102 103 104 105 107 108 109 110 111 114 115 116 117 118 119 120 121 122 123 124 129 130 131 132 135 144 145 146 147 149 152 154 **P**3
Primary Contact: Randal M. Arnett, President and Chief Executive Officer
CFO: Dean Wray, Vice President Finance
CMO: Kendall Stewart, M.D., Chief Medical Officer
CIO: Brent Richard, Administrative Director Information Systems
CHR: Vicki Noel, Vice President Human Resources
CNO: Claudia L Burchett, R.N., Vice President of Patient Services
Web address: www.somc.org
Control: Other not–for–profit (including NFP Corporation) **Service**: General medical and surgical

Staffed Beds: 248 **Admissions**: 12081 **Census**: 160 **Outpatient Visits**: 405601 **Births**: 1222 **Total Expense ($000)**: 294188 **Payroll Expense ($000)**: 116254 **Personnel**: 2461

PROCTORVILLE—Lawrence County

□ **THREE GABLES SURGERY CENTER (360261)**, 5897 County Road 107, Zip 45669–8852, Mailing Address: P.O. Box 490, Zip 45669–0490; tel. 740/886–9911, (Nonreporting) **A**1 10
Primary Contact: Tony Aluise, Chief Executive Officer
Web address: www.threegablessurgery.com
Control: Partnership, Investor–owned (for–profit) **Service**: Surgical

Staffed Beds: 8

RAVENNA—Portage County

⊞ **UH PORTAGE MEDICAL CENTER (360078)**, 6847 North Chestnut Street, Zip 44266–3929, Mailing Address: P.O. Box 1204, Zip 44266–1204; tel. 330/297–0811, **A**1 2 5 10 **F**3 11 13 15 18 20 22 26 28 29 30 34 35 39 40 43 44 45 46 47 48 49 50 51 54 56 57 58 59 60 63 64 65 68 70 74 75 76 77 78 79 81 82 84 85 87 92 93 100 107 108 109 110 111 115 117 119 129 130 131 132 135 143 144 145 146 147 148 149 152 154 **S** University Hospitals, Cleveland, OH
Primary Contact: M Steven. Jones, President
CFO: Jen Hahn, Finance Manager
CMO: Benjamin Prestegaard, Chief Medical Officer
CIO: Rhonda Smith, Applications Support Manager
CHR: Neil Everett, Vice President Human Resources
Web address: www.uhportage.org
Control: Other not–for–profit (including NFP Corporation) **Service**: General medical and surgical

Staffed Beds: 127 **Admissions**: 6457 **Census**: 72 **Outpatient Visits**: 203523 **Births**: 643 **Total Expense ($000)**: 121060 **Payroll Expense ($000)**: 39461 **Personnel**: 760

ROCK CREEK—Ashtabula County

GLENBEIGH HOSPITAL AND OUTPATIENT CENTERS (360245), 2863 Route 45, Zip 44084, Mailing Address: P.O. Box 298, Zip 44084–0298; tel. 440/563–3400, **A**10 **F**4 5 29 30 34 36 53 54 57 75 86 87 100 130 132 135 149 152
Primary Contact: Patricia Weston–Hall, Chief Executive Officer
CFO: Phil Pawlowski, Chief Financial Officer
CIO: Linda Advey, Manager Information Systems
CHR: Shirley Deary, Director Human Resources
Web address: www.glenbeigh.com
Control: Other not–for–profit (including NFP Corporation) **Service**: Alcoholism and other chemical dependency

Staffed Beds: 114 **Admissions**: 3191 **Census**: 113 **Outpatient Visits**: 81661 **Births**: 0 **Total Expense ($000)**: 22705 **Payroll Expense ($000)**: 10438 **Personnel**: 269

OH

SAINT MARYS—Auglaize County

⇑ **JOINT TOWNSHIP DISTRICT MEMORIAL HOSPITAL (360032)**, 200 St Clair Street, Zip 45885–2400; tel. 419/394–3335, (Total facility includes 16 beds in nursing home–type unit) **A**10 21 **F**3 7 8 12 13 15 28 29 30 32 34 35 36 40 41 45 46 47 51 53 56 57 59 62 63 64 67 70 74 75 76 77 79 81 82 83 84 85 87 90 93 107 108 110 115 119 124 128 129 130 131 132 143 144 146 147 148
Primary Contact: Kevin W. Harlan, President
CFO: Jeffrey W Vossler, Chief Financial Officer
CIO: Joshua Miller, Director Information Systems
CHR: Art Swain, Vice President Support Services
CNO: Debra McKee, R.N., Chief Clinical Officer and Chief Nursing Officer
Web address: www.grandlakehealth.org
Control: Other not–for–profit (including NFP Corporation) **Service**: General medical and surgical

Staffed Beds: 60 **Admissions**: 1383 **Census**: 12 **Outpatient Visits**: 72017 **Births**: 334 **Total Expense ($000)**: 68963 **Payroll Expense ($000)**: 20450 **Personnel**: 484

SALEM—Columbiana County

⊞ **SALEM REGIONAL MEDICAL CENTER (360185)**, 1995 East State Street, Zip 44460–2423; tel. 330/332–1551, (Nonreporting) **A**1 3 5 10
Primary Contact: Anita Hackstedde, M.D., President and Chief Executive Officer
COO: Keith Meredith, Chief Operating Officer
CFO: Mike Giangardella, Vice President Finance and Administration
CMO: Anita Hackstedde, M.D., Vice President Medical Affairs
CIO: Mark L'Italien, Director Information Services
CHR: Barb Hirst, R.N., Vice President Human Resources and Chief Nursing Officer
CNO: Barb Hirst, R.N., Vice President Human Resources and Chief Nursing Officer
Web address: www.salemregional.com
Control: Other not–for–profit (including NFP Corporation) **Service**: General medical and surgical

Staffed Beds: 116

SANDUSKY—Erie County

○ **FIRELANDS REGIONAL HEALTH SYSTEM (360025)**, 1111 Hayes Avenue, Zip 44870–3323; tel. 419/557–7400, (Includes FIRELANDS REGIONAL MEDICAL CENTER – MAIN CAMPUS, 1111 Hayes Avenue, Sandusky, OH, Zip 44870; tel. 419/557–7400; FIRELANDS REGIONAL MEDICAL CENTER SOUTH CAMPUS, 1912 Hayes Avenue, Sandusky, OH, Zip 44870–4736; tel. 419/557–7000) **A**2 3 10 11 12 13 19 **F**3 5 8 11 12 13 15 18 20 22 24 26 28 29 31 34 35 36 38 40 43 45 46 48 49 50 51 54 57 58 59 60 62 64 68 70 74 75 76 77 78 79 80 81 82 85 86 87 89 90 92 93 96 98 99 100 101 102 103 104 105 107 108 110 111 115 117 118 119 120 121 123 124 129 130 131 132 135 143 145 146 147 148 149 150 152 153 154 **P**8
Primary Contact: Daniel J. Moncher, Interim President and Chief Executive Officer
CFO: Daniel J Moncher, Vice President and Chief Financial Officer
CMO: Brenda Violette, M.D., Director Medical Staff
CIO: Robert Ayres, Director Information Systems
CHR: James Sennish, Vice President Human Resources
Web address: www.firelands.com
Control: Other not–for–profit (including NFP Corporation) **Service**: General medical and surgical

Staffed Beds: 239 **Admissions**: 9400 **Census**: 125 **Outpatient Visits**: 340210 **Births**: 800 **Total Expense ($000)**: 242319 **Payroll Expense ($000)**: 101734 **Personnel**: 1848

SEAMAN—Adams County

⊞ **ADAMS COUNTY REGIONAL MEDICAL CENTER (361326)**, 230 Medical Center Drive, Zip 45679–8002; tel. 937/386–3400, **A**1 10 18 **F**3 11 15 28 29 30 31 34 35 40 45 49 50 53 57 59 64 65 68 75 77 78 79 81 82 85 86 91 93 107 108 110 111 115 119 129 130 132 133 135 146 148 154
Primary Contact: Shawn Bright, Chief Executive Officer
CFO: Pete Dagenbach, Chief Financial Officer
CHR: Heather Hoop, Human Resources Generalist
CNO: Sharon Ashley, MSN, Chief Nursing Officer
Web address: www.acrmc.com
Control: County, Government, nonfederal **Service**: General medical and surgical

Staffed Beds: 25 **Admissions**: 790 **Census**: 8 **Births**: 0 **Personnel**: 191

SHELBY—Richland County

★ **OHIOHEALTH MEDCENTRAL SHELBY HOSPITAL (361324)**, 199 West Main Street, Zip 44875–1490; tel. 419/342–5015, **A**10 18 **F**3 11 13 15 18 29 30 31 34 35 40 57 59 64 68 69 70 75 76 78 79 81 93 107 108 110 115 118 119 130 133 146 149 154 **S** OhioHealth, Columbus, OH
Primary Contact: Jean Halpin, President
CNO: Trish DelGreco, Director of Nursing
Web address: www.medcentral.org/body.cfm?id=153
Control: Other not–for–profit (including NFP Corporation) **Service**: General medical and surgical

Staffed Beds: 25 **Admissions**: 1123 **Census**: 11 **Outpatient Visits**: 52049 **Births**: 209 **Total Expense ($000)**: 25424 **Payroll Expense ($000)**: 8686 **Personnel**: 143

SIDNEY—Shelby County

★ ○ **WILSON MEMORIAL HOSPITAL (360013)**, 915 West Michigan Street, Zip 45365–2491; tel. 937/498–2311, **A**10 11 **F**3 7 11 13 15 18 20 28 29 30 34 40 45 49 51 56 57 59 62 63 64 68 70 75 76 77 79 81 82 85 86 87 89 93 97 98 103 107 108 111 115 118 119 129 130 131 132 135 146 147 **P**6
Primary Contact: Duane Francis, Interim Chief Executive Officer
COO: Craig Lannoye, Vice President Operations
CFO: Julie Covault, Vice President Finance
CMO: Robert J McDevitt, M.D., Chief of Staff
CIO: Larry Meyers, Chief Information Officer
CHR: John Eve, Vice President Human Resources and Education
CNO: Linda Maurer, Vice President Patient Care Services
Web address: www.wilsonhospital.com
Control: Other not–for–profit (including NFP Corporation) **Service**: General medical and surgical

Staffed Beds: 71 **Admissions**: 2492 **Census**: 27 **Outpatient Visits**: 213190 **Births**: 708 **Total Expense ($000)**: 79035 **Payroll Expense ($000)**: 30020 **Personnel**: 583

SPRINGFIELD—Clark County

☐ **MENTAL HEALTH SERVICES FOR CLARK AND MADISON COUNTIES (364040)**, 474 North Yellow Springs Street, Zip 45504–2463; tel. 937/399–9500, (Nonreporting)
Primary Contact: Curt Gillespie, Chief Executive Officer
Web address: www.mhscc.org
Control: County, Government, nonfederal **Service**: Psychiatric

Staffed Beds: 16

☐ **OHIO VALLEY SURGICAL HOSPITAL (360355)**, 100 West Main Street, Zip 45502–1312; tel. 937/521–3900, (Nonreporting) **A**1 10
Primary Contact: Steve Eisentrager, President
CFO: Amanda martin, Manager Human Resources
CMO: Thales Pavlatos, Medical Director
CIO: Jonathan Bisdorf, Director Information Technology
CNO: Beth Lizza, Chief Nursing Officer
Web address: www.ovsurgical.com/
Control: Partnership, Investor–owned (for–profit) **Service**: Surgical

Staffed Beds: 24

⊞ **SPRINGFIELD REGIONAL MEDICAL CENTER (360086)**, 100 Medical Center Drive, Zip 45504–2687; tel. 937/523–1000, (Nonreporting) **A**1 2 3 10 **S** Mercy Health, Cincinnati, OH
Primary Contact: Matthew T. Caldwell, President and Chief Executive Officer
COO: Adam Groshans, Chief Operating Officer
CFO: William J. Kusnierz, Vice President and Chief Financial Officer
CNO: Elaine Storrs, Chief Nursing Officer
Web address: www.community–mercy.org
Control: Church operated, Nongovernment, not–for–profit **Service**: General medical and surgical

Staffed Beds: 259

STEUBENVILLE—Jefferson County

⊞ **ACUITY SPECIALTY HOSPITALS OHIO VALLEY (362035)**, 380 Summit Avenue, 3rd Floor, Zip 43952–2667; tel. 740/283–7600, (Includes ACUITY SPECIALTY HOSPITALS OHIO VALLEY AT BELMONT, 4697 Harrison Street, Bellaire, OH, Zip 43906–1338; tel. 740/671–2086) **A**1 10 **F**1 3 29 34 57 85 91 148 **S** AcuityHealthcare, LP, Charlotte, NC
Primary Contact: Judy K. Weaver, MS, Chief Executive Officer
Web address: www.acuityhealthcare.net
Control: Partnership, Investor–owned (for–profit) **Service**: Acute long–term care hospital

Staffed Beds: 52 **Admissions**: 564 **Census**: 45 **Outpatient Visits**: 0 **Births**: 0 **Total Expense ($000)**: 24884 **Payroll Expense ($000)**: 11153 **Personnel**: 171

LIFE LINE HOSPITAL (362039), 200 School Street, Zip 43953–9610; tel. 740/346–2600, (Nonreporting) **A**10
Primary Contact: Patricia Cross, Chief Executive Officer
Web address: www.llhospital.com
Control: Partnership, Investor–owned (for–profit) **Service**: Acute long–term care hospital

Staffed Beds: 30

Many Facility Codes have changed. Please refer to the AHA Guide Code Chart. © 2018 AHA Guide

⊞ **TRINITY HEALTH SYSTEM (360211)**, 380 Summit Avenue, Zip 43952–2699; tel. 740/283–7000, (Includes TRINITY MEDICAL CENTER EAST, 380 Summit Avenue, Steubenville, OH, Zip 43952–2699; tel. 740/283–7000; TRINITY MEDICAL CENTER WEST, 4000 Johnson Road, Steubenville, OH, Zip 43952–2393; tel. 740/264–8000) **A**1 2 10 13 **F**3 4 5 12 13 15 17 18 20 22 24 26 28 29 30 31 32 33 34 35 38 40 44 45 46 47 48 49 51 54 56 57 59 62 64 65 69 70 71 74 75 76 77 78 79 81 82 85 86 87 89 90 91 92 93 94 96 97 98 100 101 102 104 105 106 107 108 110 111 114 115 117 118 119 120 121 123 124 126 128 129 130 131 132 135 144 146 147 148 149 152 153 **P**6 **S** Catholic Health Initiatives, Englewood, CO
Primary Contact: Matthew Grimshaw, Market Chief Executive Officer
COO: JoAnn M Mulrooney, R.N., Chief Operating Officer
CFO: Dave Werkin, Vice President Finance and Chief Financial Officer
CMO: Gray Goncz, Vice President of Medical Affairs
CIO: Tom Kiger, Director Information Systems
CHR: Lewis C Musso, Vice President Human Resources
Web address: www.trinityhealth.com
Control: Other not–for–profit (including NFP Corporation) **Service**: General medical and surgical

Staffed Beds: 320 **Admissions**: 9440 **Census**: 138 **Outpatient Visits**: 285512 **Births**: 484 **Total Expense ($000)**: 226631 **Payroll Expense ($000)**: 82342 **Personnel**: 1626

SYLVANIA—Lucas County

⊞ △ **PROMEDICA FLOWER HOSPITAL (360074)**, 5200 Harroun Road, Zip 43560–2196; tel. 419/824–1444, **A**1 2 3 5 7 10 **F**3 11 12 13 15 18 28 29 30 31 34 35 36 38 40 45 47 48 49 50 53 54 57 59 64 65 67 68 70 75 76 77 78 79 81 82 84 85 86 87 90 91 92 93 96 97 98 100 101 102 103 107 108 109 110 111 114 116 117 118 119 120 121 123 124 126 129 130 131 132 143 146 147 149 150 154 **S** ProMedica Health System, Toledo, OH
Primary Contact: Arturo Polizzi, President
CFO: Michael Browning, Chief Financial Officer
CMO: John Evanoff, M.D., Vice President Medical Affairs
CIO: Lori Johnston, Chief Information Officer
CHR: Karen Strauss, Chief Human Resources Officer
CNO: Maurine Weis, MSN, R.N., Vice President Nursing and Chief Nursing Officer
Web address: www.promedica.org
Control: Other not–for–profit (including NFP Corporation) **Service**: General medical and surgical

Staffed Beds: 295 **Admissions**: 10392 **Census**: 147 **Outpatient Visits**: 186924 **Births**: 896 **Total Expense ($000)**: 210172 **Payroll Expense ($000)**: 66102 **Personnel**: 1174

⊞ **REGENCY HOSPITAL OF TOLEDO (362036)**, 5220 Alexis Road, Zip 43560–2504; tel. 419/318–5700, (Nonreporting) **A**1 5 10 **S** Select Medical Corporation, Mechanicsburg, PA
Primary Contact: Gary Zaciewski, Chief Executive Officer
Web address: www.regencyhospital.com
Control: Corporation, Investor–owned (for–profit) **Service**: Acute long–term care hospital

Staffed Beds: 45

TIFFIN—Seneca County

⊞ **MERCY TIFFIN HOSPITAL (360089)**, 45 St Lawrence Drive, Zip 44883–8310; tel. 419/455–7000, **A**1 2 10 **F**3 7 12 13 15 18 19 20 28 29 30 31 34 35 36 40 45 49 50 51 56 57 59 62 64 68 70 74 75 76 77 78 79 81 82 83 84 85 86 87 89 93 94 97 107 108 110 111 115 118 119 129 130 132 133 134 135 145 146 147 148 149 **S** Mercy Health, Cincinnati, OH
Primary Contact: B Lynn. Detterman, President and Chief Executive Officer
CMO: Steven Bruhl, Chief Medical Officer
CHR: Diana Olson, Director Human Resources
CNO: Anne Zimmerman, Senior Director Patient Care Services and Chief Nursing Officer
Web address: www.mercyweb.org
Control: Church operated, Nongovernment, not–for–profit **Service**: General medical and surgical

Staffed Beds: 45 **Admissions**: 2080 **Census**: 16 **Outpatient Visits**: 82599 **Births**: 434 **Total Expense ($000)**: 59001 **Payroll Expense ($000)**: 12602 **Personnel**: 330

TOLEDO—Lucas County

☐ **ADVANCED SPECIALTY HOSPITAL OF TOLEDO (362038)**, 1015 Garden Lake Parkway, Zip 43614–2779; tel. 419/381–0037, (Nonreporting) **A**1 3 10
Primary Contact: Kim Burkholder–McNutt, Chief Executive Officer
CFO: Troy Holmes, Director Finance
CMO: B Sarroui, M.D., Chief of Staff
CHR: Lauren Avigdor, Director Human Resources
CNO: Bridgett Mitchell, Chief Clinical Officer
Web address: www.advancedspecialtyhospitals.com
Control: Corporation, Investor–owned (for–profit) **Service**: Acute long–term care hospital

Staffed Beds: 25

⊞ **MERCY ST. ANNE HOSPITAL (360262)**, 3404 West Sylvania Avenue, Zip 43623–4467; tel. 419/407–2663, **A**1 2 3 10 **F**3 15 17 18 20 22 24 28 29 30 31 34 35 36 37 38 40 45 49 54 56 57 59 64 65 66 67 75 81 82 84 85 86 87 92 102 107 108 110 111 115 119 126 129 130 132 135 146 147 148 149 154 **P**8 **S** Mercy Health, Cincinnati, OH
Primary Contact: Bradley J. Bertke, President and Chief Operating Officer
CFO: Michael Whipple, Chief Financial Officer
CMO: Herbert Stockard, M.D., Chief Medical Officer
CIO: Rebecca S Sykes, Chief Information Officer
CNO: Barb Dianda–Martin, Chief Nursing Officer
Web address: www.mercyweb.org
Control: Church operated, Nongovernment, not–for–profit **Service**: General medical and surgical

Staffed Beds: 96 **Admissions**: 5534 **Census**: 54 **Outpatient Visits**: 124426 **Births**: 0 **Personnel**: 576

⊞ **MERCY ST. VINCENT MEDICAL CENTER (360112)**, 2213 Cherry Street, Zip 43608–2691; tel. 419/251–3232, (Includes MERCY CHILDREN'S HOSPITAL, 2213 Cherry Street, Toledo, OH, Zip 43608–2691; tel. 419/251–8000) **A**1 2 3 5 10 13 **F**3 7 8 11 12 13 15 16 18 19 20 21 22 23 24 26 29 30 31 32 34 35 37 38 39 40 41 43 44 45 46 47 48 49 50 51 53 54 55 56 57 58 59 60 61 64 65 66 68 70 72 74 75 76 77 78 79 81 82 83 84 85 86 87 88 89 92 93 97 107 108 110 111 114 115 118 119 126 129 130 131 132 134 135 146 147 154 **P**8 **S** Mercy Health, Cincinnati, OH
Primary Contact: Jeffrey Dempsey, President
CMO: Thomas Welch, M.D., Chief Medical Officer
CHR: Gary George, Senior Vice President Human Resources
CNO: Barbara Martin, Chief Nursing Officer
Web address: www.mercyweb.org
Control: Church operated, Nongovernment, not–for–profit **Service**: General medical and surgical

Staffed Beds: 350 **Admissions**: 17663 **Census**: 202 **Outpatient Visits**: 196559 **Births**: 1416 **Personnel**: 2387

☐ **NORTHWEST OHIO PSYCHIATRIC HOSPITAL (364014)**, 930 Detroit Avenue, Zip 43614–2701; tel. 419/381–1881, **A**1 3 10 **F**30 50 53 75 87 98 101 103 130 146 149 154 **S** Ohio Department of Mental Health, Columbus, OH
Primary Contact: Brett M. Johnson, Chief Executive Officer
COO: Kyle Hurst, Chief Operations Officer
CIO: Michael Carter, Administrator Information Technology
CHR: Ursula Barrera–Richards, Human Resource Director
CNO: Deb Duris, Director of Nursing
Web address: www.mh.state.oh.us/
Control: State, Government, nonfederal **Service**: Psychiatric

Staffed Beds: 114 **Admissions**: 679 **Census**: 75 **Outpatient Visits**: 0 **Births**: 0 **Total Expense ($000)**: 24209 **Personnel**: 209

⊞ **PROMEDICA TOLEDO HOSPITAL (360068)**, 2142 North Cove Boulevard, Zip 43606–3896; tel. 419/291–4000, (Includes PROMEDICA WILDWOOD ORTHOPAEDIC AND SPINE HOSPITAL, 2901 North Reynolds Road, Toledo, OH, Zip 43615; tel. 419/578–7700; Arturo Polizzi, President; TOLEDO CHILDREN'S HOSPITAL, 2142 North Cove Boulevard, Toledo, OH, Zip 43606; tel. 419/291–4000; Arturo Polizzi, President and Chief Executive Officer) (Total facility includes 35 beds in nursing home–type unit) **A**1 2 3 5 10 13 **F**3 7 8 11 12 13 15 17 18 20 22 24 26 29 30 31 34 35 38 39 40 41 43 45 46 47 48 49 50 51 53 54 55 57 58 59 60 64 65 67 68 70 72 74 75 76 77 78 79 81 82 84 85 86 87 88 89 91 92 93 94 96 97 98 99 100 101 102 104 105 107 108 109 110 111 113 114 115 118 119 126 128 129 130 131 132 134 135 143 144 146 147 148 150 153 154 **S** ProMedica Health System, Toledo, OH
Primary Contact: Arturo Polizzi, President
CMO: Khurram Kamran, M.D., Vice President Medical Affairs
CIO: Rose Ann Laureto, Chief Information Officer
CHR: Arturo Polizzi, Chief Human Resources Officer
Web address: www.promedica.org
Control: Other not–for–profit (including NFP Corporation) **Service**: General medical and surgical

Staffed Beds: 595 **Admissions**: 32624 **Census**: 437 **Outpatient Visits**: 723900 **Births**: 3626 **Total Expense ($000)**: 724283 **Payroll Expense ($000)**: 238179 **Personnel**: 3689

REHABILITATION HOSPITAL OF NORTHWEST OHIO (363040), 1455 West Medical Loop, Zip 43614; tel. 419/214–6600, (Nonreporting) **A**3 10 **S** Ernest Health, Inc., Albuquerque, NM
Primary Contact: Scott Williams, Chief Executive Officer
Control: Corporation, Investor–owned (for–profit) **Service**: Rehabilitation

Staffed Beds: 40

Hospital, Medicare Provider Number, Address, Telephone, Approval, Facility, and Physician Codes, Health Care System

★ American Hospital Association (AHA) membership
☐ The Joint Commission accreditation
○ Healthcare Facilities Accreditation Program
◇ DNV Healthcare Inc. accreditation
⇑ Center for Improvement in Healthcare Quality Accreditation
△ Commission on Accreditation of Rehabilitation Facilities (CARF) accreditation

OH

⊞ **THE UNIVERSITY OF TOLEDO MEDICAL CENTER (360048)**, 3000 Arlington Avenue, Zip 43614–2595; tel. 419/383–4000, **A**1 2 3 5 8 10 **F**3 4 8 11 15 17 18 20 22 24 26 28 29 30 31 32 34 35 36 37 38 39 40 43 44 45 46 47 48 49 50 51 53 54 55 56 57 58 59 60 61 64 65 67 68 70 74 75 77 78 79 81 82 84 85 86 87 91 92 93 94 96 97 98 99 100 101 102 103 104 105 107 108 110 111 114 115 116 117 118 119 120 121 123 124 126 129 130 131 132 134 135 138 146 147 148 149 151 152 153
Primary Contact: Daniel Barbee, Chief Executive Officer
CMO: Michael Ellis, M.D., Chief Medical Officer
CIO: William McCreary, Vice President and Chief Information Officer
CHR: Wendy Davis, Associate Vice President and Chief Human Resource Officer
CNO: Moneca Smith, Chief Nursing Officer
Web address: www.utoledo.edu
Control: State, Government, nonfederal **Service**: General medical and surgical

Staffed Beds: 246 **Admissions**: 11313 **Census**: 161 **Outpatient Visits**: 478922 **Births**: 0 **Total Expense ($000)**: 312203 **Payroll Expense ($000)**: 121771 **Personnel**: 2043

TROY—Miami County

⊞ △ **UPPER VALLEY MEDICAL CENTER (360174)**, 3130 North County Road 25A, Zip 45373–1309; tel. 937/440–4000, **A**1 2 3 5 7 10 **F**3 8 13 15 18 20 28 29 30 31 34 35 36 38 40 41 44 45 48 49 50 54 55 56 57 58 59 60 61 64 68 70 73 74 75 76 77 78 79 80 81 85 86 87 90 92 93 96 98 100 101 102 103 104 107 108 110 111 114 115 118 119 126 129 130 131 132 135 141 145 146 147 148 149 154 **P**6 8 **S** Premier Health, Dayton, OH
Primary Contact: Thomas Parker, President
CFO: Tim Snider, Senior Vice President for Finance
CMO: Jennifer Hauler, D.O., Chief Medical Officer
CIO: James Kaiser, Site Director Information Technology
CHR: Kathy Boerger, Director Human Resources
CNO: Terry Fry, R.N., Chief Nursing Officer
Web address: www.uvmc.com
Control: Other not–for–profit (including NFP Corporation) **Service**: General medical and surgical

Staffed Beds: 93 **Admissions**: 6266 **Census**: 58 **Births**: 675 **Total Expense ($000)**: 135665 **Payroll Expense ($000)**: 60151 **Personnel**: 969

UPPER SANDUSKY—Wyandot County

★ **WYANDOT MEMORIAL HOSPITAL (361329)**, 885 North Sandusky Avenue, Zip 43351–1098; tel. 419/294–4991, **A**10 18 **F**3 11 13 15 17 18 28 29 30 31 34 35 40 45 46 50 53 57 59 64 65 74 75 76 77 78 79 81 82 85 86 87 89 92 93 97 107 108 110 111 114 115 116 117 118 119 124 129 130 132 133 135 144 146 148 149 **P**6
Primary Contact: Ty Shaull, President and Chief Executive Officer
CFO: Alan H Yeates, Vice President Fiscal Services
CHR: Vickie Underwood, Director Human Resources
CNO: Marty Gray, R.N., Director of Nursing
Web address: www.wyandotmemorial.org
Control: Hospital district or authority, Government, nonfederal **Service**: General medical and surgical

Staffed Beds: 25 **Admissions**: 819 **Census**: 10 **Outpatient Visits**: 67579 **Births**: 113 **Total Expense ($000)**: 43681 **Payroll Expense ($000)**: 15560 **Personnel**: 230

URBANA—Champaign County

★ **MERCY MEMORIAL HOSPITAL (361312)**, 904 Scioto Street, Zip 43078–2200; tel. 937/653–5231, (Nonreporting) **A**10 18 **S** Mercy Health, Cincinnati, OH
Primary Contact: Matthew T. Caldwell, President and Chief Executive Officer
Web address: www.health–partners.org
Control: Church operated, Nongovernment, not–for–profit **Service**: General medical and surgical

Staffed Beds: 25

VAN WERT—Van Wert County

⊞ **VAN WERT COUNTY HOSPITAL (360071)**, 1250 South Washington Street, Zip 45891–2599; tel. 419/238–2390, **A**1 5 10 **F**8 13 15 28 29 34 35 40 48 50 53 54 57 59 62 64 70 76 77 79 81 85 87 89 93 107 108 113 119 127 129 130 135 146 154 **P**7 8
Primary Contact: James W. Pope, FACHE, President and Chief Executive Officer
CMO: Charles Hoehn, President, Medical Staff
CIO: Brett Taylor, Manager Information
CNO: Shelia Kay Brokenshire, Vice President of Nursing
Web address: www.vanwerthospital.org
Control: Other not–for–profit (including NFP Corporation) **Service**: General medical and surgical

Staffed Beds: 27 **Admissions**: 941 **Census**: 7 **Outpatient Visits**: 79992 **Births**: 160 **Total Expense ($000)**: 45109 **Payroll Expense ($000)**: 12419 **Personnel**: 354

WARREN—Trumbull County

⊞ △ **HILLSIDE REHABILITATION HOSPITAL (363026)**, 8747 Squires Lane NE, Zip 44484–1649; tel. 330/841–3700, (Nonreporting) **A**1 5 7 10 **S** Steward Health Care System, LLC, Dallas, TX
Primary Contact: Krista McFadden, Interim Chief Executive Officer
CMO: Joseph Cerimele, D.O., Medical Director
CIO: Barry Fitts, Chief Information Officer
CHR: Jody Roman, Chief Human Resource Officer
CNO: Susan Joy, Chief Nursing Officer
Web address: www.https://valleycareofohio.steward.org
Control: Corporation, Investor–owned (for–profit) **Service**: Rehabilitation

Staffed Beds: 65

⊞ **MERCY HEALTH – ST. JOSEPH WARREN HOSPITAL (360161)**, 667 Eastland Avenue SE, Zip 44484–4531, Mailing Address: 627 Eastland Avenue, Zip 44484–4531; tel. 330/841–4000, **A**1 2 3 10 13 **F**3 5 8 11 12 13 15 28 29 30 31 32 34 35 40 43 45 46 49 50 51 54 58 59 64 66 67 68 70 74 75 76 77 78 79 81 82 83 84 85 87 89 91 92 93 100 102 107 108 109 110 111 114 115 116 117 118 119 120 121 123 124 126 129 130 135 144 146 147 148 149 151 152 **S** Mercy Health, Cincinnati, OH
Primary Contact: Kathy Cook, FACHE, MSN, President
COO: Donald E. Koenig Jr Chief Operating Officer
CMO: Nicholas Kreatsoulas, Vice President Medical Affairs
Web address: www.hmpartners.org
Control: Church operated, Nongovernment, not–for–profit **Service**: General medical and surgical

Staffed Beds: 136 **Admissions**: 8792 **Census**: 95 **Outpatient Visits**: 177687 **Births**: 1079 **Total Expense ($000)**: 154944 **Payroll Expense ($000)**: 44764 **Personnel**: 704

⊞ **TRUMBULL MEMORIAL HOSPITAL (360055)**, 1350 East Market Street, Zip 44483–6628; tel. 330/841–9011, (Nonreporting) **A**1 2 3 5 10 **S** Steward Health Care System, LLC, Dallas, TX
Primary Contact: Ronald L. Bierman, Chief Executive Officer
CMO: Thomas L James, M.D., Chief Medical Officer
CIO: Barry Fitts, Chief Information Officer
CHR: Robert Sincich, Vice President Human Resources
CNO: Melissa Bennett, Chief Nursing Officer
Web address: www.https://trumbullmemorial.org/?_ga=2.209137234.1564767671.1497292183–315051339.1497292183
Control: Corporation, Investor–owned (for–profit) **Service**: General medical and surgical

Staffed Beds: 292

WARRENSVILLE HEIGHTS—Cuyahoga County

⊞ **REGENCY HOSPITAL CLEVELAND EAST (362029)**, 4200 Interchange Corporate Center Road, Zip 44128–5631; tel. 216/910–3800, (Includes REGENCY HOSPITAL OF CLEVELAND – WEST, 6990 Engle Road, Middleburg Heights, OH, Zip 44130–3420; tel. 440/202–4200; Timothy Rolsen, Chief Executive Officer) (Nonreporting) **A**1 10 **S** Select Medical Corporation, Mechanicsburg, PA
Primary Contact: Lisa Deering, Chief Executive Officer
Web address: www.regencyhospital.com/
Control: Corporation, Investor–owned (for–profit) **Service**: Acute long–term care hospital

Staffed Beds: 87

⊞ **SOUTH POINTE HOSPITAL (360144)**, 20000 Harvard Road, Zip 44122–6805; tel. 216/491–6000, **A**1 2 3 10 13 **F**3 15 18 26 28 29 30 31 34 35 36 38 39 40 44 50 54 55 56 57 58 59 60 61 64 65 66 68 70 74 75 77 78 79 81 82 84 85 86 87 93 97 100 102 107 108 110 111 114 117 119 130 131 132 135 143 144 146 148 154 **S** Cleveland Clinic Health System, Cleveland, OH
Primary Contact: Margaret McKenzie, M.D., President
COO: Andrea Jacobs, Chief Operating Officer
CFO: Lindsay Bird, Director Finance
CMO: Arun Gupta, M.D., Vice President Medical Affairs
CIO: Ralph A Cagna, Director Information Technology
CHR: Doris A. Zajec, Director Human Resources
Web address: www.southpointehospital.org
Control: Other not–for–profit (including NFP Corporation) **Service**: General medical and surgical

Staffed Beds: 139 **Admissions**: 6179 **Census**: 82 **Outpatient Visits**: 107564 **Births**: 0 **Total Expense ($000)**: 121819 **Payroll Expense ($000)**: 48337 **Personnel**: 751

Many Facility Codes have changed. Please refer to the AHA Guide Code Chart.

© 2018 AHA Guide

WASHINGTON COURT HOUSE—Fayette County

☒ **FAYETTE COUNTY MEMORIAL HOSPITAL (361331)**, 1430 Columbus Avenue, Zip 43160–1791; tel. 740/335–1210, **A**1 10 18 **F**3 7 8 11 18 29 34 35 40 57 59 64 70 75 77 81 89 91 97 107 108 110 114 119 127 128 130 131 132 133 135 144 146 147 148 149 154 **P**5
Primary Contact: D Michael. Diener, Chief Executive Officer
CFO: Trent Lemle, Chief Financial Officer
CNO: Tammie Wilson, R.N., MSN, Chief Nursing Officer
Web address: www.fcmh.org
Control: County, Government, nonfederal **Service**: General medical and surgical

Staffed Beds: 25 **Admissions**: 768 **Census**: 7 **Outpatient Visits**: 111676 **Births**: 0

WAUSEON—Fulton County

☒ **FULTON COUNTY HEALTH CENTER (361333)**, 725 South Shoop Avenue, Zip 43567–1701; tel. 419/335–2015, (Total facility includes 71 beds in nursing home–type unit) **A**1 2 5 10 18 **F**3 8 11 12 13 15 18 26 28 29 31 34 40 53 57 59 67 69 70 75 76 77 78 79 81 87 89 93 98 101 102 103 104 105 107 108 111 115 118 119 128 129 130 131 132 135 146 148 149 153
Primary Contact: Patricia Finn, Chief Executive Officer
COO: Kristine Snyder, Chief Operating Officer
CFO: Jenee Seibert, Chief Finance Officer
CIO: Larry Hefflinger, Chief Information Officer
CHR: Rachel Geckle, Chief Human Resource Officer
CNO: Tiffany Siegel, Chief Nursing Officer
Web address: www.fultoncountyhealthcenter.org
Control: Other not–for–profit (including NFP Corporation) **Service**: General medical and surgical

Staffed Beds: 106 **Admissions**: 1490 **Census**: 77 **Outpatient Visits**: 177665 **Births**: 208 **Total Expense ($000)**: 65255 **Payroll Expense ($000)**: 24337 **Personnel**: 667

WAVERLY—Pike County

ADENA PIKE MEDICAL CENTER (361334), 100 Dawn Lane, Zip 45690–9138; tel. 740/947–2186, **A**10 18 **F**3 11 18 29 30 34 35 40 41 43 44 45 50 57 59 62 63 64 65 78 79 81 82 85 86 91 97 104 107 111 114 118 130 131 133 135 146 148 149 154 **P**6 **S** Adena Health System, Chillicothe, OH
Primary Contact: David M. Zanni, Administrator
COO: Eric Cecava, Chief Operating Officer
CFO: Lisa Carlson, Chief Financial Officer
CMO: John Fortney, Chief Medical Officer
CIO: Tom Bialorucki, Chief Information Officer
CHR: Jay D. Justice, Chief Human Resources Officer
Web address: www.adena.org
Control: Other not–for–profit (including NFP Corporation) **Service**: General medical and surgical

Staffed Beds: 25 **Admissions**: 394 **Census**: 5 **Outpatient Visits**: 33581 **Births**: 0 **Total Expense ($000)**: 16976 **Payroll Expense ($000)**: 6352 **Personnel**: 103

WEST CHESTER—Butler County

☐ **BECKETT SPRINGS (364051)**, 8614 Shepherd Farm Drive, Zip 45069; tel. 513/942–9500, (Nonreporting) **A**1 10 **S** Springstone, Louisville, KY
Primary Contact: Phil Sheridan, Chief Executive Officer
Web address: www.springstone.com/hospitals.stmhl
Control: Corporation, Investor–owned (for–profit) **Service**: Psychiatric

Staffed Beds: 48

☒ **WEST CHESTER HOSPITAL (360354)**, 7700 University Drive, Zip 45069–2505; tel. 513/298–3000, (Includes WEST CHESTER HOSPITAL SURGICAL CENTER, 7750 University Court, West Chester, OH, Zip 45069; tel. 513/475–8300; Tom G Daskalakis, Chief Administrative Officer) **A**1 3 10 **F**3 9 12 13 15 18 20 22 26 29 30 31 34 35 37 38 40 41 43 44 45 46 47 48 49 50 51 54 57 58 59 60 61 63 64 70 73 74 75 76 77 78 79 80 81 82 84 85 86 87 91 92 100 107 108 110 111 114 115 119 126 129 130 131 132 134 135 141 145 146 147 148 149 150 154 **P**6 **S** UC Health, Cincinnati, OH
Primary Contact: Tom G. Daskalakis, Chief Administrative Officer
CFO: Karen Shadowens, Director Finance and Chief Financial Officer
CIO: Jay Brown, Senior Vice President, Chief Information Officer
CHR: Jack Talbot, Director, Human Resources
CNO: Kathie Hays, MSN, R.N., Chief Nursing Officer
Web address: www.uchealth.com/westchesterhospital
Control: Other not–for–profit (including NFP Corporation) **Service**: General medical and surgical

Staffed Beds: 182 **Admissions**: 8753 **Census**: 91 **Outpatient Visits**: 241882 **Births**: 785 **Total Expense ($000)**: 200133 **Payroll Expense ($000)**: 62508 **Personnel**: 1027

WESTERVILLE—Franklin County

☒ **MOUNT CARMEL ST. ANN'S (360012)**, 500 South Cleveland Avenue, Zip 43081–8998; tel. 614/898–4000, **A**1 2 3 5 10 **F**3 11 13 15 18 20 22 24 26 28 29 30 31 34 35 37 40 44 45 47 48 49 50 51 54 55 57 58 59 61 63 64 65 66 68 70 74 75 76 77 78 79 81 82 83 84 85 86 87 93 97 100 101 102 107 108 109 110 111 114 115 116 118 119 120 121 123 124 126 130 131 132 146 147 148 154 **P**6 8 **S** Trinity Health, Livonia, MI
Primary Contact: Kim Unhee, President
Web address: www.mountcarmelhealth.com
Control: Church operated, Nongovernment, not–for–profit **Service**: General medical and surgical

Staffed Beds: 305 **Admissions**: 21328 **Census**: 180 **Outpatient Visits**: 166081 **Births**: 4157 **Total Expense ($000)**: 311995 **Payroll Expense ($000)**: 101508 **Personnel**: 1579

WESTLAKE—Cuyahoga County

☒ **ST. JOHN MEDICAL CENTER (360123)**, 29000 Center Ridge Road, Zip 44145–5293; tel. 440/835–8000, **A**1 2 3 10 13 **F**3 8 13 15 17 18 19 20 22 24 26 28 29 30 31 34 35 36 39 40 41 43 44 45 47 49 50 51 54 56 57 58 59 60 63 64 65 67 68 70 71 74 75 76 78 79 81 82 83 84 85 86 87 92 93 100 102 107 108 110 111 114 115 119 130 131 132 135 143 144 146 147 148 149 154 **S** University Hospitals, Cleveland, OH
Primary Contact: Robert G. David, President
CFO: Allen R Tracy, Senior Vice President and Chief Financial Officer
CMO: Michael Dobrovich, M.D., Chief Medical Officer
CIO: James H Carroll, Chief Information Officer
CHR: Gary Lazroff, Vice President Human Resources
Web address: www.sjws.net
Control: Other not–for–profit (including NFP Corporation) **Service**: General medical and surgical

Staffed Beds: 176 **Admissions**: 9017 **Census**: 86 **Outpatient Visits**: 220447 **Births**: 853 **Total Expense ($000)**: 153082 **Payroll Expense ($000)**: 55569 **Personnel**: 885

ST. JOHN WEST SHORE HOSPITAL See St. John Medical Center

WILLARD—Huron County

☒ **MERCY HEALTH – WILLARD HOSPITAL (361310)**, 1100 Neal Zick Road, Zip 44890–9287; tel. 419/964–5000, **A**1 10 18 **F**3 5 7 15 18 28 29 30 31 34 35 40 45 46 57 59 68 70 74 75 77 78 79 81 84 85 87 89 93 97 107 111 114 119 129 130 131 132 133 135 143 145 146 147 149 154 **S** Mercy Health, Cincinnati, OH
Primary Contact: B Lynn. Detterman, President and Chief Executive Officer
CMO: Christopher Bohach, DPM, Chief of Staff
CHR: Diana Olson, Chief Human Resources Officer
Web address: www.mercyweb.org
Control: Church operated, Nongovernment, not–for–profit **Service**: General medical and surgical

Staffed Beds: 20 **Admissions**: 540 **Census**: 6 **Outpatient Visits**: 38994 **Births**: 0 **Total Expense ($000)**: 26320 **Payroll Expense ($000)**: 6944 **Personnel**: 146

WILLOUGHBY—Lake County

☐ **WINDSOR–LAURELWOOD CENTER FOR BEHAVIORAL MEDICINE (364029)**, 35900 Euclid Avenue, Zip 44094–4648; tel. 440/953–3000, (Nonreporting) **A**1 10 **S** Universal Health Services, Inc., King of Prussia, PA
Primary Contact: Ric McAllister, Chief Executive Officer
COO: Brenda Bailey, Assistant Administrator
CFO: Leanne Smith, Chief Financial Officer
CMO: Leonard Barley, M.D., Chief Medical Officer
CHR: Pam Connell, Manager Human Resources
CNO: Debra Schaefer, Chief Nursing Officer
Web address: www.windsorlaurelwood.com
Control: Individual, Investor–owned (for–profit) **Service**: Psychiatric

Staffed Beds: 159

Hospital, Medicare Provider Number, Address, Telephone, Approval, Facility, and Physician Codes, Health Care System

★ American Hospital Association (AHA) membership
☐ The Joint Commission accreditation
○ Healthcare Facilities Accreditation Program
◇ DNV Healthcare Inc. accreditation
⇑ Center for Improvement in Healthcare Quality Accreditation
△ Commission on Accreditation of Rehabilitation Facilities (CARF) accreditation

OH

WILMINGTON—Clinton County

☐ **CMH REGIONAL HEALTH SYSTEM (360175)**, 610 West Main Street, Zip 45177–2125; tel. 937/382–6611, (Nonreporting) **A**1 2 5 10 **S** RCCH HealthCare Partners, Brentwood, TN
Primary Contact: Lance Beus, Chief Executive Officer
CFO: Bradley Boggus, Chief Financial Officer
CIO: Ray Doherty, Director Information Technology
CHR: Jan Blair, Director Human Resources
CNO: Sheila Martin, Chief Nursing Officer
Web address: www.cmhregional.com
Control: Corporation, Investor–owned (for–profit) **Service**: General medical and surgical

Staffed Beds: 119

WOOSTER—Wayne County

△ ⇑ **WOOSTER COMMUNITY HOSPITAL (360036)**, 1761 Beall Avenue, Zip 44691–2342; tel. 330/263–8100, (Nonreporting) **A**2 5 7 10 19 21 **S** QHR, Brentwood, TN
Primary Contact: William E. Sheron, Chief Executive Officer
Web address: www.woosterhospital.org
Control: City, Government, nonfederal **Service**: General medical and surgical

Staffed Beds: 152

WRIGHT—PATTERSON AFB–Greene County

⊠ **WRIGHT PATTERSON MEDICAL CENTER**, 4881 Sugar Maple Drive, Zip 45433–5529; tel. 937/257–9144, (Nonreporting) **A**1 2 3 5 **S** Department of the Air Force, Washington, DC
Primary Contact: Colonel Brent J. Erickson, Administrator
COO: Colonel Brent J Erickson, Administrator
CFO: Major Kelly Lesnick, Resource Manager Flight Commander
CMO: Gregory Sweitzer, Chief Medical Officer
CIO: John Beighle, Flight Chief Medical Information Systems
CHR: Hubert Chatman, Chief Civilian Personnel
CNO: Colonel Daniel Gerke, Chief Nursing Officer
Web address: www.wpafb.af.mil/units/wpmc/
Control: Air Force, Government, federal **Service**: General medical and surgical

Staffed Beds: 62

XENIA—Greene County

★ ○ **GREENE MEMORIAL HOSPITAL (360026)**, 1141 North Monroe Drive, Zip 45385–1600; tel. 937/352–2000, **A**2 5 10 11 **F**3 11 15 18 28 29 30 31 34 35 36 38 40 43 44 45 46 48 50 51 53 54 56 57 59 60 61 64 68 70 74 75 77 78 79 81 82 85 86 87 91 93 96 102 107 108 110 111 114 118 119 127 129 130 132 135 146 147 148 154 **S** Kettering Health Network, Dayton, OH
Primary Contact: Rick A. Dodds, President
CFO: Ron D Connovich, Chief Financial Officer
CMO: Michael Caccamo, M.D., Chief Medical Officer
CIO: Andy Lehman, Senior Vice President Technology & Analytics
CHR: Jeff Jones, Director Human Resources
CNO: Brenda Kuhn, Ph.D., R.N., FACHE, Chief Nursing Officer
Web address: www.ketteringhealth.org/greene
Control: Church operated, Nongovernment, not–for–profit **Service**: General medical and surgical

Staffed Beds: 49 **Admissions**: 2199 **Census**: 23 **Outpatient Visits**: 104058 **Births**: 0 **Total Expense ($000)**: 96015 **Payroll Expense ($000)**: 47344 **Personnel**: 319

YOUNGSTOWN—Trumbull County

☐ **BELMONT PINES HOSPITAL (364038)**, 615 Churchill–Hubbard Road, Zip 44505–1379; tel. 330/759–2700, (Nonreporting) **A**1 10 **S** Universal Health Services, Inc., King of Prussia, PA
Primary Contact: Lisa Cocca, Chief Executive Officer
CFO: Sylvia Kuppler, Chief Financial Officer
CMO: Phillip G Maiden, M.D., Medical Director
CHR: Deidre L Watson, Director Human Resources
CNO: Tammy Shells, Chief Nursing Officer
Web address: www.belmontpines.com
Control: Corporation, Investor–owned (for–profit) **Service**: Psychiatric

Staffed Beds: 96

YOUNGSTOWN—Mahoning County

⊠ △ **MERCY HEALTH – ST. ELIZABETH YOUNGSTOWN HOSPITAL (360064)**, 1044 Belmont Avenue, Zip 44504–1096, Mailing Address: P.O. Box 1790, Zip 44501–1790; tel. 330/746–7211, **A**1 2 3 5 7 10 **F**3 7 8 11 15 17 18 20 22 24 26 28 29 30 31 33 34 35 37 39 40 43 44 45 46 50 51 53 54 56 57 58 59 60 61 64 66 68 70 71 74 75 77 78 79 81 84 85 86 87 88 89 90 91 92 93 96 97 98 99 100 101 102 103 104 105 107 110 111 114 115 116 117 118 119 120 121 123 126 130 131 132 135 143 146 147 148 149 153 154 **S** Mercy Health, Cincinnati, OH
Primary Contact: Donald E. Kline, President and Chief Executive Officer
COO: Donald E. Koenig Jr Executive Vice President and Regional Chief Operating Officer, President, St. Elizabeth Youngstown Hospital
CFO: Anthony J. Seminaro, Chief Financial Officer
CIO: Maureen Kordupel, Director Relationship Manager
CNO: Lori DeNiro, Regional Chief Nursing Officer
Web address: www.mercy.com
Control: Church operated, Nongovernment, not–for–profit **Service**: General medical and surgical

Staffed Beds: 396 **Admissions**: 19185 **Census**: 262 **Outpatient Visits**: 291772 **Births**: 0 **Total Expense ($000)**: 346830 **Payroll Expense ($000)**: 104019 **Personnel**: 2028

NORTHSIDE MEDICAL CENTER See Northside Medical Center, Youngstown

YOUNGSTOWN—Trumbull County

⊠ **NORTHSIDE MEDICAL CENTER (360141)**, 500 Gypsy Lane, Zip 44504–1315; tel. 330/884–1000, (Includes NORTHSIDE MEDICAL CENTER, 500 Gypsy Lane, Youngstown, OH, Zip 44501–0240; tel. 330/747–1444) (Nonreporting) **A**1 3 5 10 **S** Steward Health Care System, LLC, Dallas, TX
Primary Contact: Linda J. Grass, Chief Executive Officer
CMO: Jay Osborne, M.D., Senior Vice President Medical Affairs
CHR: Lavern H Carrera, Senior Vice President Human Resources
Web address: www.northsidemedicalcenter.net
Control: Corporation, Investor–owned (for–profit) **Service**: General medical and surgical

Staffed Beds: 373

YOUNGSTOWN—Mahoning County

⊠ **SELECT SPECIALTY HOSPITAL–YOUNGSTOWN (362024)**, 1044 Belmont Avenue, Zip 44504–1006; tel. 330/480–2349, (Includes SELECT SPECIALTY HOSPITAL–YOUNGSTOWN, BOARDMAN CAMPUS, 667 Eastland Avenue SE, Warren, OH, Zip 44484–4503; tel. 330/729–1700) (Nonreporting) **A**1 10 **S** Select Medical Corporation, Mechanicsburg, PA
Primary Contact: Jodi Costello, Chief Executive Officer
Web address: www.selectspecialtyhospitals.com/company/locations/youngstown.aspx
Control: Corporation, Investor–owned (for–profit) **Service**: Acute long–term care hospital

Staffed Beds: 56

☐ **SURGICAL HOSPITAL AT SOUTHWOODS (360352)**, 7630 Southern Boulevard, Zip 44512–5633; tel. 330/729–8000, (Nonreporting) **A**1 10
Primary Contact: Ed Muransky, Owner
Web address: www.surgeryatsouthwoods.com/
Control: Individual, Investor–owned (for–profit) **Service**: Surgical

Staffed Beds: 12

ZANESVILLE—Muskingum County

★ ○ **GENESIS HEALTHCARE SYSTEM (360039)**, 2951 Maple Avenue, Zip 43701–1406; tel. 740/454–5000, (Includes BETHESDA HOSPITAL, 2951 Maple Avenue, Zanesville, OH, Zip 43701–1465; tel. 614/454–4000; GOOD SAMARITAN MEDICAL AND REHABILITATION CENTER, 800 Forest Avenue, Zanesville, OH, Zip 43701–2881; tel. 614/454–5000) **A**2 3 5 10 11 **F**3 5 8 9 11 13 15 17 18 20 22 24 26 28 29 30 31 32 34 35 40 43 44 45 46 47 48 50 51 54 57 58 59 60 63 64 65 68 70 73 74 75 76 77 78 79 81 82 84 85 86 87 89 91 92 93 94 96 98 99 100 101 102 104 105 106 107 108 109 110 111 114 115 116 117 118 119 120 121 123 124 126 129 130 131 132 135 144 146 147 148 151 154 **P**6 8 **S** Franciscan Sisters of Christian Charity Sponsored Ministries, Inc., Manitowoc, WI
Primary Contact: Matthew J. Perry, President and Chief Executive Officer
COO: Richard S Helsper, Chief Operating Officer
CFO: Paul Masterson, Chief Financial Officer
CMO: Dan Scheerer, M.D., Chief Medical Officer
CIO: Edmund J Romito, Chief Information Officer
CHR: Dianna LeVeck, Chief Human Resources Officer
CNO: Abby Nguyen, R.N., Chief Nursing Officer
Web address: www.genesishcs.org
Control: Other not–for–profit (including NFP Corporation) **Service**: General medical and surgical

Staffed Beds: 321 **Admissions**: 13857 **Census**: 155 **Outpatient Visits**: 367298 **Births**: 1510 **Total Expense ($000)**: 359104 **Payroll Expense ($000)**: 122748 **Personnel**: 2786

OK

OKLAHOMA

ADA—Pontotoc County

✠ **CHICKASAW NATION MEDICAL CENTER (370180)**, 1921 Stonecipher Boulevard, Zip 74820–3439; tel. 580/436–3980, **A**1 3 10 13 **F**3 5 7 8 13 15 18 29 30 34 35 38 39 40 43 45 50 53 54 57 58 59 60 64 65 68 69 70 71 75 76 79 81 85 86 87 89 91 93 97 100 104 107 110 111 115 119 127 130 133 135 143 144 146 147 148 149 154
Primary Contact: Chris Anoatubby, Deputy Secretary of Health
CFO: Marty Wafford, Under Secretary of Support and Programs
CMO: Richard McClain, M.D., Chief Medical Officer
CIO: Desiree Traylor, Chief Information Officer
CHR: Jalinda Kelley, Secretary of Interior Services
CNO: Jerod Waters, Chief Nursing Officer
Web address: www.chickasaw.net
Control: PHS, Indian Service, Government, federal **Service**: General medical and surgical

Staffed Beds: 72 **Admissions**: 2853 **Census**: 27 **Outpatient Visits**: 353919 **Births**: 908 **Total Expense ($000)**: 224166 **Payroll Expense ($000)**: 97861 **Personnel**: 1241

✠ **MERCY HOSPITAL ADA (370020)**, 430 North Monte Vista, Zip 74820–4610; tel. 580/332–2323, **A**1 2 10 **F**3 7 11 13 15 18 29 30 31 34 35 40 43 44 45 49 50 59 64 68 69 70 72 75 76 77 78 79 81 85 86 87 89 90 93 98 100 101 102 103 107 108 110 111 114 116 117 119 120 121 124 127 129 130 131 132 133 146 148 149 **P**6 **S** Mercy, Chesterfield, MO
Primary Contact: Lori Wightman, R.N., MSN, FACHE, President
COO: Daniel J Coats, Vice President Operations
CFO: Mary Garber, Vice President Finance
CMO: Imtiaz Ahmed, Chief of Staff
CHR: Katrina Godfrey, Director Human Resources
CNO: Karen Sweeney, MSN, R.N., Vice President, Chief Nursing Officer
Web address: www.mercy.net/practice/mercy–hospital–ada/
Control: Church operated, Nongovernment, not–for–profit **Service**: General medical and surgical

Staffed Beds: 156 **Admissions**: 3365 **Census**: 48 **Outpatient Visits**: 126958 **Births**: 496 **Total Expense ($000)**: 87852 **Payroll Expense ($000)**: 35341 **Personnel**: 556

☐ **ROLLING HILLS HOSPITAL (374016)**, 1000 Rolling Hills Lane, Zip 74820–9415; tel. 580/436–3600, **A**1 10 **F**56 68 98 100 101 102 103 135 143 **P**6 **S** Acadia Healthcare Company, Inc., Franklin, TN
Primary Contact: Anthony Guild, Chief Executive Officer
CMO: Robert Morton, M.D., Medical Director
CIO: Sherry Barnes, Director Health Information and Quality Management
CHR: Timothy Blackwell, Manager Human Resources
Web address: www.rollinghillshospital.com
Control: Corporation, Investor–owned (for–profit) **Service**: Psychiatric

Staffed Beds: 108 **Admissions**: 1236 **Census**: 75 **Outpatient Visits**: 0 **Births**: 0 **Total Expense ($000)**: 14454 **Payroll Expense ($000)**: 7239 **Personnel**: 161

ALTUS—Jackson County

✠ **JACKSON COUNTY MEMORIAL HOSPITAL (370022)**, 1200 East Pecan Street, Zip 73521–6192, Mailing Address: P.O. Box 8190, Zip 73522–8190; tel. 580/379–5000, **A**1 3 10 **F**3 10 11 13 15 29 30 34 35 40 43 45 49 56 57 59 62 63 64 65 70 75 76 77 79 81 85 86 87 93 100 101 104 107 110 111 114 119 129 130 131 132 133 135 145 146 147 148 149 **P**6
Primary Contact: Steve L. Hartgraves, President and Chief Executive Officer
COO: Casey D. Miranda, Executive Vice President and Chief Operating Officer
CFO: Nancy Davidson, Senior Vice President and Chief Financial Officer
CMO: M. George Zakhary, M.D., Chief of Staff
CIO: Dena Daniel, Director Information Systems
CHR: Richard Pope, Vice President Human Resources
Web address: www.jcmh.com
Control: Hospital district or authority, Government, nonfederal **Service**: General medical and surgical

Staffed Beds: 49 **Admissions**: 2696 **Census**: 26 **Outpatient Visits**: 148669 **Births**: 358 **Total Expense ($000)**: 69324 **Payroll Expense ($000)**: 34358 **Personnel**: 630

ALVA—Woods County

SHARE MEDICAL CENTER (370080), 800 Share Drive, Zip 73717–3618, Mailing Address: P.O. Box 727, Zip 73717–0727; tel. 580/327–2800, (Nonreporting) **A**10 20
Primary Contact: Kandice K. Allen, R.N., Chief Executive Officer
CFO: Kevin O'Brien, Chief Financial Officer
CMO: Elizabeth Kinzic, M.D., Chief of Staff
CIO: Alan Vaughan, Director Information Technology
CHR: Mary Herold, Director Human Resources
CNO: Regina Wilson, R.N., Director of Nursing
Web address: www.smcok.com
Control: Hospital district or authority, Government, nonfederal **Service**: General medical and surgical

Staffed Beds: 90

ANADARKO—Caddo County

PHYSICIANS' HOSPITAL IN ANADARKO (371314), 1002 Central Boulevard East, Zip 73005–4496; tel. 405/247–2551, **A**10 18 **F**1 3 4 8 11 16 17 29 30 34 35 40 41 45 47 57 64 65 67 70 72 73 76 77 80 85 86 88 89 90 93 98 107 114 128 130 133 146 148 149 **S** First Physicians Capital Group, Inc., Oklahoma City, OK
Primary Contact: Travis A. Villani, FACHE, Chief Executive Officer and Administrator
Web address: www.anadarkohospital.com
Control: Other not–for–profit (including NFP Corporation) **Service**: General medical and surgical

Staffed Beds: 25 **Admissions**: 230 **Census**: 10 **Outpatient Visits**: 10524 **Births**: 5 **Personnel**: 97

ANTLERS—Pushmataha County

PUSHMATAHA HOSPITAL (370083), 510 East Main Street, Zip 74523–3262, Mailing Address: P.O. Box 518, Zip 74523–0518; tel. 580/298–3341, **A**10 **F**3 8 11 34 40 43 45 50 57 62 75 81 82 93 107 119 133 146
Primary Contact: Nick Rowland, Chief Executive Officer
COO: Nick Rowland, Chief Operating Officer
CFO: Rory Ward, Chief Financial Officer
CMO: G Wayne Flatt, D.O., Chief Medical Director
CHR: Paula Schalski, Director Human Resources
CNO: Marla Barnes, Director of Nursing
Web address: www.pushhospital.com
Control: City–county, Government, nonfederal **Service**: General medical and surgical

Staffed Beds: 23 **Admissions**: 585 **Census**: 7 **Outpatient Visits**: 5386 **Births**: 3

ARDMORE—Carter County

✠ **MERCY HOSPITAL ARDMORE (370047)**, 1011 14th Avenue NW, Zip 73401–1828; tel. 580/223–5400, **A**1 10 **F**3 11 13 15 18 20 22 28 29 30 31 34 35 40 43 45 47 48 49 50 57 59 62 64 67 68 70 74 75 76 77 78 79 81 82 84 85 87 89 90 93 98 103 107 108 110 111 114 117 118 119 120 121 123 126 129 130 146 148 149 **P**6 **S** Mercy, Chesterfield, MO
Primary Contact: Daryle Voss, FACHE, President and Chief Executive Officer
CMO: Pam Kimbrough, M.D., Vice President Medical Affairs
CHR: Melinda Sharum, Director Human Resources
CNO: Debra Pender, MS, R.N., Vice President Nursing
Web address: www.mercyok.net
Control: Church operated, Nongovernment, not–for–profit **Service**: General medical and surgical

Staffed Beds: 190 **Admissions**: 6332 **Census**: 78 **Outpatient Visits**: 198850 **Births**: 733 **Total Expense ($000)**: 136416 **Payroll Expense ($000)**: 51000 **Personnel**: 706

OK

ATOKA—Atoka County

ATOKA COUNTY MEDICAL CENTER (371300), 1590 West Liberty
Road, Zip 74525–1621, Mailing Address: PO Box 1107, Zip 74525–1621;
tel. 580/889–3333, **A**10 18 **F**3 29 34 40 45 46 53 56 57 59 64 81 91 93 107
119 128 133 146
Primary Contact: Shawn Howard, Interim Chief Executive Officer
CMO: Ted Rowland, Chief of Medical Staff
CHR: Stacy Sharp, Coordinator Human Resources
CNO: David Lively, Chief Nursing Officer
Web address: www.atokamedicalcenter.org
Control: Hospital district or authority, Government, nonfederal **Service**: General
medical and surgical

Staffed Beds: 25 **Admissions:** 469 **Census:** 6 **Outpatient Visits:** 62371
Births: 0 **Total Expense ($000):** 8734 **Payroll Expense ($000):** 3127
Personnel: 80

BARTLESVILLE—Washington County

★ ⇑ **JANE PHILLIPS MEDICAL CENTER (370018)**, 3500 East Frank Phillips
Boulevard, Zip 74006–2411; tel. 918/333–7200, **A**3 5 10 21 **F**8 11 13 15 17
18 20 22 24 28 29 30 31 34 35 40 46 49 50 51 53 57 58 59 60 61 64 68 74
75 77 78 79 81 82 84 85 86 87 90 92 93 96 98 102 105 107 111 114 115
116 117 118 119 121 123 127 129 130 131 135 143 145 146 147 148 154
P4 **S** Ascension Healthcare, Saint Louis, MO
Primary Contact: Mike Moore, President and Chief Operating Officer
CFO: James Brasel, Chief Financial Officer
CMO: Paul McQuillen, M.D., Chief Medical Officer
CNO: Angie Bidleman, Chief Nursing Officer
Web address: www.jpmc.org
Control: Church operated, Nongovernment, not-for-profit **Service**: General
medical and surgical

Staffed Beds: 114 **Admissions:** 4681 **Census:** 50 **Outpatient Visits:** 90886
Births: 540 **Total Expense ($000):** 102792 **Payroll Expense ($000):** 34024
Personnel: 563

BEAVER—Beaver County

BEAVER COUNTY MEMORIAL HOSPITAL (371322), 212 East Eighth Street,
Zip 73932, Mailing Address: P.O. Box 640, Zip 73932–0640; tel. 580/625–4551,
(Nonreporting) **A**10 18
Primary Contact: Alissa Schlessman, Administrator
CMO: Gary Mathews, M.D., Medical Doctor
CHR: Karla Leisher, Business Office Manager
Web address: www.beavercountyhospitalauthority.com
Control: Hospital district or authority, Government, nonfederal **Service**: General
medical and surgical

Staffed Beds: 24

BETHANY—Oklahoma County

△ **THE CHILDREN'S CENTER REHABILITATION HOSPITAL (373302)**, 6800 NW
39th Expressway, Zip 73008–2513; tel. 405/789–6711, **A**3 5 7 10 **F**1 29 30 34
35 39 53 58 59 68 74 75 79 84 87 90 91 93 96 107 130 132 146 148 149 **P**6
Primary Contact: Albert Gray, Chief Executive Officer
Web address: www.tccokc.org
Control: Other not-for-profit (including NFP Corporation) **Service**: Children's
general medical and surgical

Staffed Beds: 120 **Admissions:** 147 **Census:** 100 **Outpatient Visits:** 15867
Births: 0 **Total Expense ($000):** 40526 **Payroll Expense ($000):** 25104
Personnel: 532

BLACKWELL—Kay County

⊞ **BLACKWELL REGIONAL HOSPITAL (370030)**, 710 South 13th Street,
Zip 74631–3700; tel. 580/363–2311, (Nonreporting) **A**1 10
Primary Contact: Steven E. Taylor, Chief Executive Officer
CFO: Jacob Easson, Chief Financial Officer
CMO: Jeffery Shuart, M.D., Chief of Staff
CHR: Tonya Criner, Human Resource Lead
CNO: Joyce Daniel, Chief Nursing Officer
Web address: www.blackwellregional.org
Control: Partnership, Investor-owned (for-profit) **Service**: General medical and
surgical

Staffed Beds: 49

BOISE CITY—Cimarron County

CIMARRON MEMORIAL HOSPITAL (371307), 100 South Ellis
Street, Zip 73933, Mailing Address: P.O. Box 1059, Zip 73933–1059;
tel. 580/544–2501, **A**10 18 **F**3 29 34 40 57 59 65 66 97 107 119 127 133
154 **P**1
Primary Contact: Tim Beard, Chief Executive Officer
CFO: Jamie Jacoby, Chief Financial Officer
CIO: Tim Beard, Director, Information Technology
CNO: Barbara Carter, Chief Nursing Officer
Web address: www.cimarronmemorialhospital.org
Control: Hospital district or authority, Government, nonfederal **Service**: General
medical and surgical

Staffed Beds: 15 **Admissions:** 168 **Census:** 1 **Outpatient Visits:** 773
Births: 0

BRISTOW—Creek County

BRISTOW MEDICAL CENTER (370041), 700 West 7th Avenue, Suite 6,
Zip 74010–2302; tel. 918/367–2215, (Nonreporting) **A**10
Primary Contact: Jan Winter-Clark, Chief Executive Officer
CFO: Robin Van Vickle, Chief Financial Officer
Web address: www.bristowmedcenter.com
Control: Corporation, Investor-owned (for-profit) **Service**: General medical and
surgical

Staffed Beds: 30

BROKEN ARROW—Tulsa County

★ **ST. JOHN BROKEN ARROW (370235)**, 1000 West Boise Circle,
Zip 74012–4900; tel. 918/994–8100, **A**10 **F**3 11 14 15 18 29 30 34 35 37 40
43 45 50 57 59 64 65 68 74 79 81 84 85 87 94 107 108 110 111 114 115
119 130 132 135 143 146 **P**1 5 **S** Ascension Healthcare, Saint Louis, MO
Primary Contact: David L. Phillips, Chief Operating Officer
CFO: Katie Caughman, Chief Financial Officer
CMO: Jason Lepak, M.D., Medical Director
CNO: Dwan Borens, Chief Nursing Officer
Web address: www.stjohnbrokenarrow.com
Control: Church operated, Nongovernment, not-for-profit **Service**: General
medical and surgical

Staffed Beds: 44 **Admissions:** 2649 **Census:** 17 **Outpatient Visits:** 111350
Births: 0 **Total Expense ($000):** 58136 **Payroll Expense ($000):** 12924
Personnel: 227

☐ **ST. JOHN REHABILITATION HOSPITAL**, 1200 West Albany Drive,
Zip 74012–8146; tel. 918/744–2338, (Nonreporting) **A**1 **S** Encompass Health
Corporation, Birmingham, AL
Primary Contact: David Nicholas, Chief Executive Officer
Web address: www.stjohnrehab.com
Control: Corporation, Investor-owned (for-profit) **Service**: Rehabilitation

Staffed Beds: 22

BUFFALO—Harper County

★ **HARPER COUNTY COMMUNITY HOSPITAL (371324)**, Highway 64 North,
Zip 73834, Mailing Address: P.O. Box 60, Zip 73834–0060; tel. 580/735–2555,
(Nonreporting) **A**10 18
Primary Contact: Lana Shaffer, Chief Executive Officer
COO: Pam Dodd, Chief Operating Officer
CFO: Lisa Oakley, Chief Financial Officer
CNO: Melissa Madrid, R.N., Chief Nursing Officer
Web address: www.hcchospital.com/
Control: County, Government, nonfederal **Service**: General medical and surgical

Staffed Beds: 16

CARNEGIE—Caddo County

CARNEGIE TRI-COUNTY MUNICIPAL HOSPITAL (371334), 102 North
Broadway, Zip 73015, Mailing Address: P.O. Box 97, Zip 73015–0097;
tel. 580/654–1050, **A**10 18 **F**29 30 40 41 43 56 67 68 75 84 91 93 97 104
107 119 128 130 133 149 154 **S** First Physicians Capital Group, Inc., Oklahoma
City, OK
Primary Contact: Thomas Henton, Chief Executive Officer
Web address: www.carnegiehospital.org/
Control: Other not-for-profit (including NFP Corporation) **Service**: General
medical and surgical

Staffed Beds: 17 **Admissions:** 244 **Census:** 3 **Outpatient Visits:** 3995
Births: 0 **Personnel:** 83

OK

CHEYENNE—Roger Mills County

★ **ROGER MILLS MEMORIAL HOSPITAL (371303)**, 501 South L.L. Males, Zip 73628, Mailing Address: P.O. Box 219, Zip 73628; tel. 580/497–3336, **A**10 18 **F**3 7 34 40 57 59 64 65 93 107 115 119 133 **P**6
Primary Contact: Cynthia Duncan, Chief Executive Officer
Web address: www.rmmhonline.com
Control: Hospital district or authority, Government, nonfederal **Service**: General medical and surgical

Staffed Beds: 15 **Admissions**: 81 **Census**: 1 **Outpatient Visits**: 3536 **Births**: 0 **Total Expense ($000)**: 5916 **Payroll Expense ($000)**: 2601 **Personnel**: 40	

CHICKASHA—Grady County

★ **GRADY MEMORIAL HOSPITAL (370054)**, 2220 West Iowa Avenue, Zip 73018–2738; tel. 405/224–2300, **A**10 **F**3 8 11 15 17 29 30 34 35 40 43 45 57 59 65 66 70 76 79 81 82 85 87 89 91 93 107 110 111 114 115 119 127 128 130 131 132 133 144 146 147 148 149 **P**6
Primary Contact: Warren K. Spellman, Chief Executive Officer
CFO: Jackie McAdoo, Chief Financial Officer
CMO: Mitch Coppedge, M.D., Chief Medical Officer
CIO: Mike Townsend, Interim Director Health Information Systems
CHR: Rebel Rutledge, Director Human Resources
CNO: Cathy Groseclose, Vice President Patient Care Services
Web address: www.gradymem.org
Control: Hospital district or authority, Government, nonfederal **Service**: General medical and surgical

Staffed Beds: 39 **Admissions**: 962 **Census**: 9 **Outpatient Visits**: 66854 **Births**: 0 **Total Expense ($000)**: 32956 **Payroll Expense ($000)**: 17393 **Personnel**: 289	

CLAREMORE—Rogers County

☐ **CLAREMORE INDIAN HOSPITAL (370173)**, 101 South Moore Avenue, Zip 74017–5091; tel. 918/342–6200, (Nonreporting) **A**1 10 **S** U.S. Indian Health Service, Rockville, MD
Primary Contact: George Valliere, Chief Executive Officer
CFO: LaLana Spears, Supervisor Accounting
CMO: Gary Lang, M.D., Clinical Director
CIO: David Ponder, Information Technology Officer
CHR: Quinn Proctor, Director Human Resources
CNO: Alonna Adair–Triplett, Chief Nurse Executive
Web address: www.ihs.gov
Control: PHS, Indian Service, Government, federal **Service**: General medical and surgical

Staffed Beds: 44	

★ ⇑ **HILLCREST HOSPITAL CLAREMORE (370039)**, 1202 North Muskogee Place, Zip 74017–3036; tel. 918/341–2556, **A**10 21 **F**3 6 11 13 15 18 20 22 26 28 29 30 34 35 37 40 45 49 51 59 64 70 74 76 77 79 81 82 85 86 87 93 98 103 107 108 110 111 119 126 129 130 131 133 135 145 146 147 148 **P**6 **S** Ardent Health Services, Nashville, TN
Primary Contact: David Chaussard, Chief Executive Officer
CFO: Brandon Bullard, Chief Financial Officer
CIO: Celeste Rodden, Chief Information Officer
CHR: Pat Goad, Director Human Resources
CNO: Randy Walker, Chief Nursing Officer
Web address: www.hillcrestclaremore.com
Control: Corporation, Investor–owned (for–profit) **Service**: General medical and surgical

Staffed Beds: 67 **Admissions**: 2765 **Census**: 30 **Outpatient Visits**: 42050 **Births**: 705 **Total Expense ($000)**: 51141 **Payroll Expense ($000)**: 16672 **Personnel**: 296	

CLEVELAND—Pawnee County

CLEVELAND AREA HOSPITAL (371320), 1401 West Pawnee Street, Zip 74020–3019; tel. 918/358–2501, **A**10 18 **F**15 29 34 35 40 43 57 59 64 75 77 87 91 93 97 107 110 115 119 128 130 133 **P**6
Primary Contact: Edred Benton, Chief Executive Officer and Chief Operating Officer
COO: Edred Benton, Chief Executive Officer and Chief Operating Officer
CMO: Jason Sims, M.D., Chief Medical Officer
CHR: Sherry Brown, Director Human Resources
Web address: www.clevelandareahospital.com
Control: Hospital district or authority, Government, nonfederal **Service**: General medical and surgical

Staffed Beds: 14 **Admissions**: 164 **Census**: 6 **Outpatient Visits**: 13179 **Births**: 1 **Total Expense ($000)**: 12832 **Payroll Expense ($000)**: 7971 **Personnel**: 129	

CLINTON—Custer County

✉ **ALLIANCEHEALTH CLINTON (370029)**, 100 North 30th Street, Zip 73601–3117; tel. 580/323–2363, (Nonreporting) **A**1 10 **S** Community Health Systems, Inc., Franklin, TN
Primary Contact: Landon E. Hise, Chief Executive Officer
CFO: Jay Johnson, Chief Financial Officer
CHR: Julie Graumann, Director
CNO: Kimberly Todd, Chief Nursing Officer
Web address: www.alliancehealthclinton.com
Control: Partnership, Investor–owned (for–profit) **Service**: General medical and surgical

Staffed Beds: 49	

COALGATE—Coal County

★ **COAL COUNTY GENERAL HOSPITAL (371319)**, 6 North Covington Street, Zip 74538–2002, Mailing Address: P.O. Box 326, Zip 74538–0326; tel. 580/927–2327, (Total facility includes 75 beds in nursing home–type unit) **A**10 18 **F**34 35 40 54 56 57 64 104 107 114 119 128 133
Primary Contact: Billy Johnson, Chief Executive Officer
CFO: Diane Downard, Chief Financial Officer
CMO: R.J Helton, D.O., Chief of Staff
CIO: Matt Balliett, Chief Information Officer
CHR: Cyndie Martin, Director
CNO: Farra Ybarra, R.N., Chief Nursing Officer
Web address: www.hillcrest.com
Control: Hospital district or authority, Government, nonfederal **Service**: General medical and surgical

Staffed Beds: 95 **Admissions**: 665 **Census**: 73 **Outpatient Visits**: 4710 **Births**: 0 **Total Expense ($000)**: 5526 **Payroll Expense ($000)**: 2293	

CORDELL—Washita County

★ **CORDELL MEMORIAL HOSPITAL (371325)**, 1220 North Glenn English Street, Zip 73632–2010; tel. 580/832–3339, (Nonreporting) **A**10 18
Primary Contact: Kenny Downs, Chief Executive Officer
CFO: Sue Kelley, Chief Financial Officer
Web address: www.cordellmemorialhospital.com
Control: City, Government, nonfederal **Service**: General medical and surgical

Staffed Beds: 14	

CUSHING—Payne County

★ **HILLCREST HOSPITAL CUSHING (370099)**, 1027 East Cherry Street, Zip 74023–4101; tel. 918/225–2915, **A**10 **F**11 13 15 18 29 34 35 40 43 44 45 46 50 51 56 57 59 64 68 70 71 75 76 77 79 81 86 87 93 94 97 98 100 101 102 103 107 110 111 114 115 119 128 129 130 131 143 145 146 147 148 154 **S** Ardent Health Services, Nashville, TN
Primary Contact: Kevin Hawk, Chief Executive Officer
CFO: Joseph Mendoza, Chief Financial Officer
CHR: Bethany Leininger, Manager Human Resource
CNO: Tina Petersen, Chief Nursing Officer
Web address: www.hillcrestcushing.com/
Control: Corporation, Investor–owned (for–profit) **Service**: General medical and surgical

Staffed Beds: 99 **Admissions**: 1606 **Census**: 20 **Outpatient Visits**: 18951 **Births**: 167 **Total Expense ($000)**: 21935 **Payroll Expense ($000)**: 8436 **Personnel**: 156	

DRUMRIGHT—Creek County

DRUMRIGHT REGIONAL HOSPITAL (371331), 610 West Bypass, Zip 74030–5957; tel. 918/382–2300, **A**10 18 **F**3 11 18 29 40 45 56 59 64 65 68 77 81 85 93 104 107 114 119 127 128 130 132 133 146 **P**6 **S** Rural Community Hospitals of America, Kansas City, MO
Primary Contact: Tracy Byers, Chief Executive Officer
CFO: Mark Conrath, Chief Financial Officer
Web address: www.drumrighthospital.com/
Control: Corporation, Investor–owned (for–profit) **Service**: General medical and surgical

Staffed Beds: 15 **Admissions**: 322 **Census**: 4 **Outpatient Visits**: 17317 **Births**: 0	

Hospital, Medicare Provider Number, Address, Telephone, Approval, Facility, and Physician Codes, Health Care System

★ American Hospital Association (AHA) membership	○ Healthcare Facilities Accreditation Program	⇑ Center for Improvement in Healthcare Quality Accreditation
☐ The Joint Commission accreditation	◇ DNV Healthcare Inc. accreditation	△ Commission on Accreditation of Rehabilitation Facilities (CARF) accreditation

OK

DUNCAN—Stephens County

⊞ **DUNCAN REGIONAL HOSPITAL (370023)**, 1407 North Whisenant Drive, Zip 73533–1650, Mailing Address: P.O. Box 2000, Zip 73534–2000; tel. 580/252–5300, (Nonreporting) **A**1 3 5 10 20 **S** Duncan Regional Hospital, Duncan, OK
Primary Contact: Jay R. Johnson, FACHE, President and Chief Executive Officer
CFO: Douglas R Volinski, Vice President and Chief Financial Officer
CMO: Che' Miller, M.D., Chief of Staff
CIO: Roger Neal, Vice President Operations
CHR: Mark Rhoades, Vice President and Chief Human Resources Officer
CNO: Cindy Rauh, R.N., Vice President and Chief Nursing Officer
Web address: www.duncanregional.com
Control: Other not–for–profit (including NFP Corporation) **Service**: General medical and surgical

Staffed Beds: 117

DURANT—Bryan County

⊞ **ALLIANCEHEALTH DURANT (370014)**, 1800 University Boulevard, Zip 74701–3006, Mailing Address: P.O. Box 1207, Zip 74702–1207; tel. 580/924–3080, **A**1 5 10 13 19 **F**3 8 11 12 13 15 17 18 20 22 28 29 30 34 35 39 40 43 45 50 51 56 57 59 70 74 75 76 77 79 80 81 82 85 86 89 97 102 107 110 111 114 115 119 124 126 129 130 131 135 145 146 147 148 154 **P**8 **S** Community Health Systems, Inc., Franklin, TN
Primary Contact: Jeffrey S. Tarrant, FACHE, Chief Executive Officer
CFO: Cindy Rios, Chief Financial Officer
CMO: Kevin Gordon, M.D., Chief of Staff
CIO: Katy Stinson, Director Information Services
Web address: www.alliancehealthdurant.com/
Control: Corporation, Investor–owned (for–profit) **Service**: General medical and surgical

Staffed Beds: 140 **Admissions**: 4802 **Census**: 47 **Outpatient Visits**: 54869 **Births**: 902 **Total Expense ($000)**: 65059 **Payroll Expense ($000)**: 23336 **Personnel**: 343

EDMOND—Oklahoma County

⊞ **INTEGRIS HEALTH EDMOND (370236)**, 4801 Integris Parkway, Zip 73034–8864; tel. 405/657–3000, **A**1 10 **F**3 8 11 13 15 18 20 22 29 30 34 35 40 43 45 46 47 49 53 54 57 59 60 64 68 70 73 74 76 77 78 79 81 82 85 87 93 97 100 102 107 108 110 111 114 115 119 130 131 132 135 146 147 148 149 **P**6 7 **S** INTEGRIS Health, Oklahoma City, OK
Primary Contact: Avilla Williams, MS, President
CNO: Angela K Kamermayer, MS, Chief Nursing Officer
Web address: www.integrisok.com/edmond
Control: Other not–for–profit (including NFP Corporation) **Service**: General medical and surgical

Staffed Beds: 40 **Admissions**: 2700 **Census**: 25 **Outpatient Visits**: 50513 **Births**: 704 **Total Expense ($000)**: 58164 **Payroll Expense ($000)**: 16748 **Personnel**: 216

★ **SUMMIT MEDICAL CENTER (370225)**, 1800 S Renaissance Boulevard, Zip 73013–3023; tel. 405/359–2400, **A**10 **F**3 12 29 40 41 45 54 64 70 75 79 81 82 85 107 111 119 129 148 149
Primary Contact: Curtis Summers, Chief Executive Officer
Web address: www.summitmedcenter.com/
Control: Individual, Investor–owned (for–profit) **Service**: General medical and surgical

Staffed Beds: 9 **Admissions**: 261 **Census**: 1 **Outpatient Visits**: 24802 **Births**: 0

EL RENO—Canadian County

★ **MERCY HOSPITAL EL RENO (370011)**, 2115 Parkview Drive, Zip 73036–2199; tel. 405/262–2640, **A**10 **F**3 7 8 11 29 30 35 40 45 50 62 64 65 77 79 81 82 85 93 107 111 114 119 132 135 146 **P**6 **S** Mercy, Chesterfield, MO
Primary Contact: Cindy Carmichael, Administrator
CMO: Michael Dean Sullivan, M.D., Chief of Staff
CIO: Karen Heldreth, Director Data Processing
CHR: Wendy Ward, Director Human Resources
Web address: www.mercyok.net
Control: Church operated, Nongovernment, not–for–profit **Service**: General medical and surgical

Staffed Beds: 48 **Admissions**: 329 **Census**: 3 **Outpatient Visits**: 37049 **Births**: 0 **Total Expense ($000)**: 11969 **Payroll Expense ($000)**: 6755 **Personnel**: 94

PARKVIEW HOSPITAL See Mercy Hospital El Reno

ELK CITY—Beckham County

⊞ **GREAT PLAINS REGIONAL MEDICAL CENTER (370019)**, 1801 West Third Street, Zip 73644–5145, Mailing Address: P.O. Box 2339, Zip 73648–2339; tel. 580/225–2511, **A**1 3 10 **F**3 11 12 13 15 18 28 29 30 31 34 35 40 43 47 50 51 56 57 59 62 64 68 70 75 76 77 78 79 81 82 85 87 89 91 93 96 98 100 101 103 107 108 110 111 115 118 119 120 121 123 129 130 131 132 133 135 146 147 148 149
Primary Contact: Corey Lively, Chief Executive Officer
CFO: Monica Scott, Chief Financial Officer
CMO: Craig Phelps, M.D., Chief of Staff
CIO: Terry Price, Director Information Technology
CHR: Misty Carter, Vice President Human Resources and Ancillary Services
CNO: Debra D. Morris, R.N., MSN, Chief Nursing Officer
Web address: www.gprmc–ok.com
Control: Other not–for–profit (including NFP Corporation) **Service**: General medical and surgical

Staffed Beds: 50 **Admissions**: 1754 **Census**: 18 **Outpatient Visits**: 57265 **Births**: 330 **Total Expense ($000)**: 49942 **Payroll Expense ($000)**: 17928 **Personnel**: 371

ENID—Garfield County

INTEGRIS BASS BEHAVIORAL HEALTH SYSTEM See Integris Bass Meadowlake

⊞ **INTEGRIS BASS BAPTIST HEALTH CENTER (370016)**, 600 South Monroe Street, Zip 73701–7211, Mailing Address: P.O. Box 3168, Zip 73702–3168; tel. 580/233–2300, (Includes INTEGRIS BASS MEADOWLAKE, 2216 South Van Buren Street, Enid, OK, Zip 73703–8299; tel. 580/234–2220) **A**1 10 13 19 **F**3 11 13 15 17 18 20 22 24 28 29 30 31 35 40 43 45 49 57 62 68 70 74 75 76 77 78 79 81 85 98 99 103 107 108 110 111 114 118 119 120 121 126 127 128 129 132 144 146 147 148 **S** INTEGRIS Health, Oklahoma City, OK
Primary Contact: Finny Mathew, President
CFO: Duane Miller, Chief Financial Officer
CNO: Cynthia Leathers, R.N., Chief Nursing Officer
Web address: www.integris–health.com
Control: Other not–for–profit (including NFP Corporation) **Service**: General medical and surgical

Staffed Beds: 167 **Admissions**: 4184 **Census**: 79 **Outpatient Visits**: 59328 **Births**: 949 **Total Expense ($000)**: 102587 **Payroll Expense ($000)**: 29713 **Personnel**: 483

☐ **INTEGRIS BASS PAVILION (372016)**, 401 South Third Street, Zip 73701–5737; tel. 580/249–4260, **A**1 10 **F**11 29 30 43 68 75 77 82 85 93 132 146 148 154
Primary Contact: Finny Mathew, President
CHR: Kerri Johnson, Human Resources Operations Consultant
CNO: Sherry Dunlay, R.N., MSN, Vice President Chief Nursing Officer
Web address: www.integris–health.com/integris/en–us/locations/bass–enid
Control: Other not–for–profit (including NFP Corporation) **Service**: General medical and surgical

Staffed Beds: 24 **Admissions**: 114 **Census**: 8 **Outpatient Visits**: 5965 **Births**: 0 **Total Expense ($000)**: 7074 **Payroll Expense ($000)**: 2746 **Personnel**: 37

☐ △ **ST. MARY'S REGIONAL MEDICAL CENTER (370026)**, 305 South Fifth Street, Zip 73701–5899, Mailing Address: P.O. Box 232, Zip 73702–0232; tel. 580/233–6100, **A**1 7 10 **F**3 11 13 15 18 20 22 26 28 29 30 31 34 35 37 39 40 43 45 51 54 56 57 59 60 64 68 69 70 73 74 75 76 77 78 79 80 81 82 85 86 87 89 90 92 93 96 98 100 101 102 103 104 107 108 110 111 114 115 118 119 129 130 131 132 135 146 147 149 150 **P**6 **S** Universal Health Services, Inc., King of Prussia, PA
Primary Contact: Krista Roberts, Chief Executive Officer
COO: Anthony Rodebush, Chief Operating Officer
CFO: David Jamin, Chief Financial Officer
CMO: Michael Pontious, M.D., Chief of Staff
CIO: Tracy Andersen, Chief Information Officer
CHR: David Camp, Director Human Resources
CNO: Douglas W Coffey, R.N., MSN, Chief Nursing Officer
Web address: www.stmarysregional.com
Control: Corporation, Investor–owned (for–profit) **Service**: General medical and surgical

Staffed Beds: 154 **Admissions**: 4972 **Census**: 62 **Outpatient Visits**: 93425 **Births**: 344 **Total Expense ($000)**: 81139 **Payroll Expense ($000)**: 32859 **Personnel**: 519

Many Facility Codes have changed. Please refer to the AHA Guide Code Chart.   © 2018 AHA Guide

FAIRFAX—Osage County

FAIRFAX COMMUNITY HOSPITAL (371318), 40 Hospital Road, Zip 74637–5084; tel. 918/642–3291, **A**10 18 **F**3 29 40 45 57 77 93 107 117 119 133 **S** Rural Community Hospitals of America, Kansas City, MO
Primary Contact: Tina Steele, Chief Executive Officer and Chief Financial Officer
COO: Linda Thompson, Chief Operating Officer
CFO: Tina Steele, Chief Executive Officer and Chief Financial Officer
CMO: Arman Janloo, M.D., Chief Medical Staff
CIO: Lisa Drymon, Manager
CHR: Sharon Binkley, Director Human Resources
Control: Corporation, Investor–owned (for–profit) **Service:** General medical and surgical

Staffed Beds: 15 **Admissions:** 132 **Census:** 4 **Outpatient Visits:** 3776 **Births:** 0 **Total Expense ($000):** 5558 **Payroll Expense ($000):** 3092 **Personnel:** 62

FAIRFAX MEMORIAL HOSPITAL See Fairfax Community Hospital

FAIRVIEW—Major County

FAIRVIEW REGIONAL MEDICAL CENTER (371329), 523 East State Road, Zip 73737–1453, Mailing Address: P.O. Box 548, Zip 73737–0548; tel. 580/227–3721, **A**10 18 **F**3 28 34 35 40 43 45 57 59 64 65 68 69 75 77 81 84 85 91 93 107 114 127 128 130 131 132 133 135 146 149 154 **P**5 6
Primary Contact: Roger Knak, Administrator and Chief Executive Officer
CMO: John Stephen Price, M.D., Chief of Staff
CIO: Bob Maynard, Chief Information Officer
CHR: Elisabeth Hughes, Director Human Resources and Community Relations
CNO: Tamara Eitzen, Chief Nursing Officer
Web address: www.fairviewregionalmedicalcenter.com
Control: Hospital district or authority, Government, nonfederal **Service:** General medical and surgical

Staffed Beds: 25 **Admissions:** 229 **Census:** 3 **Outpatient Visits:** 10875 **Births:** 1 **Total Expense ($000):** 6161 **Payroll Expense ($000):** 3197 **Personnel:** 66

FORT SUPPLY—Major County

NORTHWEST CENTER FOR BEHAVIORAL HEALTH (374001), 1 Mi East Highway 270, Zip 73841, Mailing Address: 1222 10th Street, Suite 211, Woodward, Zip 73801–3156; tel. 580/766–2311, **A**3 10 **F**98 104 130 132 135 149 151 152 154 **P**6 **S** Oklahoma Department of Mental Health and Substance Abuse Services, Oklahoma City, OK
Primary Contact: Trudy Hoffman, Executive Director
Web address: www.ncbhok.org/
Control: State, Government, nonfederal **Service:** Psychiatric

Staffed Beds: 24 **Admissions:** 573 **Census:** 16 **Outpatient Visits:** 62332 **Births:** 0 **Total Expense ($000):** 12514 **Payroll Expense ($000):** 6195 **Personnel:** 180

GROVE—Delaware County

☒ **INTEGRIS GROVE HOSPITAL (370113)**, 1001 East 18th Street, Zip 74344–2907; tel. 918/786–2243, **A**1 10 20 **F**3 7 11 13 15 18 20 22 29 30 34 35 40 43 45 54 57 59 62 64 70 76 77 79 81 85 93 107 108 109 110 111 115 119 125 146 147 148 154 **S** INTEGRIS Health, Oklahoma City, OK
Primary Contact: Robert Rupp, President
CFO: Stacie Mason, Vice President and Chief Financial Officer
CMO: Kyle Schauf, M.D., President Medical Staff
CNO: Brandi Stewart, R.N., Vice President and Chief Nursing Officer
Web address: www.integris–health.com
Control: Other not–for–profit (including NFP Corporation) **Service:** General medical and surgical

Staffed Beds: 58 **Admissions:** 1911 **Census:** 16 **Outpatient Visits:** 46808 **Births:** 355 **Total Expense ($000):** 44435 **Payroll Expense ($000):** 12468 **Personnel:** 198

GUTHRIE—Logan County

★ **MERCY HOSPITAL LOGAN COUNTY (371317)**, 200 South Academy Road, Zip 73044–8727, Mailing Address: P.O. Box 1017, Zip 73044–1017; tel. 405/282–6700, **A**10 18 **F**3 15 29 30 34 35 40 44 50 57 59 68 75 77 87 93 107 110 111 114 119 127 129 130 131 133 144 146 148 149 **P**6 **S** Mercy, Chesterfield, MO
Primary Contact: Bobby Stitt, R.N., Administrator
CMO: Jignesh Veragiwala, Chief of Staff
CHR: Mary Jo Messelt, Senior Human Resources Manager
Web address: www.mercy.net
Control: Church operated, Nongovernment, not–for–profit **Service:** General medical and surgical

Staffed Beds: 25 **Admissions:** 692 **Census:** 9 **Outpatient Visits:** 84203 **Births:** 0 **Total Expense ($000):** 17530 **Payroll Expense ($000):** 10413 **Personnel:** 135

GUYMON—Texas County

MEMORIAL HOSPITAL OF TEXAS COUNTY (370138), 520 Medical Drive, Zip 73942–4438; tel. 580/338–6515, (Nonreporting) **A**10 20
Primary Contact: Doug Swim, Chief Executive Officer
CFO: Michele Reust, Controller
CIO: Sheldon Spence, Director of Revenue Cycle, IT
CHR: Sarah Wagner, Human Resources Officer
CNO: Dondie Rodgers, Interim Chief Nursing Officer
Web address: www.mhtcguymon.org
Control: County, Government, nonfederal **Service:** General medical and surgical

Staffed Beds: 14

HEALDTON—Carter County

★ **MERCY HOSPITAL HEALDTON (371310)**, 3462 Hospital Road, Zip 73438–6124, Mailing Address: P.O. Box 928, Zip 73438–0928; tel. 580/229–0701, **A**10 18 **F**3 29 34 35 40 43 44 57 64 68 107 114 127 133 146 149 **P**6 **S** Mercy, Chesterfield, MO
Primary Contact: Nichole Barrett, R.N., Interim Administrator
CMO: Mark Newey, D.O., Chief of Staff
CHR: Melinda Sharum, Director Human Resources
Web address: www.mercyok.com
Control: Church operated, Nongovernment, not–for–profit **Service:** General medical and surgical

Staffed Beds: 22 **Admissions:** 172 **Census:** 5 **Outpatient Visits:** 10863 **Births:** 0 **Total Expense ($000):** 5785 **Payroll Expense ($000):** 3291 **Personnel:** 41

HENRYETTA—Okmulgee County

★ **HILLCREST HOSPITAL HENRYETTA (370183)**, 2401 West Main Street, Zip 74437–3893, Mailing Address: P.O. Box 1269, Zip 74437–1269; tel. 918/650–1100, **A**10 **F**1 3 4 15 16 17 18 29 40 45 54 56 64 65 67 70 72 73 76 79 80 81 85 87 88 89 90 93 98 102 103 105 107 110 111 114 119 128 129 130 131 133 143 147 148 **P**6 **S** Ardent Health Services, Nashville, TN
Primary Contact: Dee Renshaw, Chief Executive Officer
CFO: Joseph Mendoza, Chief Financial Officer
CHR: Sheree Snyder, Manager Human Resources
CNO: April Secor, R.N., Chief Nursing Officer
Web address: www.hillcresthenryetta.com/
Control: Corporation, Investor–owned (for–profit) **Service:** General medical and surgical

Staffed Beds: 37 **Admissions:** 980 **Census:** 18 **Outpatient Visits:** 14039 **Births:** 0 **Total Expense ($000):** 17649 **Payroll Expense ($000):** 6576

HOBART—Kiowa County

★ **ELKVIEW GENERAL HOSPITAL (370153)**, 429 West Elm Street, Zip 73651–1615; tel. 580/726–1900, **A**10 20 **F**3 15 28 29 31 34 35 40 45 56 59 79 81 85 89 93 107 108 110 111 115 118 119 129 133 146 148 154 **P**6
Primary Contact: Lisa Hart, Chief Executive Officer
CFO: Amy Harmon, Chief Financial Officer
CMO: William Sims, M.D., Medical Director
CIO: Dennis Tarver, Director Information Technology
CHR: Sharon Moad, Human Resources Director Health Information Management
CNO: Debbie Norman, MSN, R.N., Chief Nursing Officer
Web address: www.elkviewhospital.com
Control: Hospital district or authority, Government, nonfederal **Service:** General medical and surgical

Staffed Beds: 38 **Admissions:** 803 **Census:** 7 **Outpatient Visits:** 17293 **Births:** 1 **Total Expense ($000):** 12332 **Payroll Expense ($000):** 6006 **Personnel:** 124

Hospital, Medicare Provider Number, Address, Telephone, Approval, Facility, and Physician Codes, Health Care System

★ American Hospital Association (AHA) membership
☐ The Joint Commission accreditation
◯ Healthcare Facilities Accreditation Program
◇ DNV Healthcare Inc. accreditation
⇑ Center for Improvement in Healthcare Quality Accreditation
△ Commission on Accreditation of Rehabilitation Facilities (CARF) accreditation

OK

HOLDENVILLE—Hughes County

★ **HOLDENVILLE GENERAL HOSPITAL (371321)**, 100 McDougal Drive, Zip 74848–2822; tel. 405/379–4200, **A**10 18 **F**3 11 29 30 34 40 45 57 59 64 65 79 81 97 107 111 115 119 127 133 146
Primary Contact: Daniel J. Coats, Interim Chief Executive Officer
CFO: Drew Johnson, Chief Financial Officer
CMO: Tom Osborn, D.O., Chief Medical Staff
CIO: Mike Combs, Manager Information Technology
CHR: Heather Heard, Director Human Resources
CNO: Jackie Smith, R.N., Chief Nursing Officer
Web address: www.holdenvillehospital.com/
Control: City, Government, nonfederal **Service**: General medical and surgical

Staffed Beds: 25 **Admissions**: 429 **Census**: 6 **Births**: 0 **Total Expense ($000)**: 12552 **Payroll Expense ($000)**: 6195 **Personnel**: 115

HOLLIS—Harmon County

HARMON MEMORIAL HOSPITAL (370036), 400 East Chestnut Street, Zip 73550–2030, Mailing Address: P.O. Box 791, Zip 73550–0791; tel. 580/688–3363, **A**10 18 **F**3 40 62 64 80 107 133
Primary Contact: Sheila Lewis, Administrator
CFO: Willie Mae Copeland, Chief Financial Officer
CMO: Akram Abraham, M.D., Chief of Staff
CHR: Abbey Welch, Director Human Resources
Control: Hospital district or authority, Government, nonfederal **Service**: General medical and surgical

Staffed Beds: 10 **Admissions**: 464 **Census**: 2 **Outpatient Visits**: 2423 **Births**: 0

HUGO—Choctaw County

CHOCTAW MEMORIAL HOSPITAL (370100), 1405 East Kirk Street, Zip 74743–3603; tel. 580/317–9500, (Nonreporting) **A**10
Primary Contact: Nick Rowland, Interim Chief Executive Officer
CIO: Andy Richmond, Director Information Technology
CHR: Darlene Galyon, Director Human Resources
Web address: www.choctawmemorial.com
Control: Hospital district or authority, Government, nonfederal **Service**: General medical and surgical

Staffed Beds: 32

IDABEL—Mccurtain County

MCCURTAIN MEMORIAL HOSPITAL (370048), 1301 Lincoln Road, Zip 74745–7341; tel. 580/286–7623, **A**10 20 **F**3 11 13 15 28 29 30 34 40 53 59 62 64 70 75 76 81 87 93 107 110 111 114 119 130 149 154 **P**6 8
Primary Contact: Rob Lake, Interim Chief Executive Officer
CFO: Ray B Whitmore, Chief Financial Officer
CMO: Michael C West, M.D., Chief of Staff
CIO: Dana A Stowell, Chief Information Officer
CNO: Pamela Johnson, R.N., Chief Nursing Officer
Web address: www.mmhok.com
Control: Other not-for-profit (including NFP Corporation) **Service**: General medical and surgical

Staffed Beds: 63 **Admissions**: 1066 **Census**: 10 **Outpatient Visits**: 31148 **Births**: 198 **Total Expense ($000)**: 28422 **Payroll Expense ($000)**: 8405 **Personnel**: 192

KINGFISHER—Kingfisher County

★ **MERCY HOSPITAL KINGFISHER (371313)**, 1000 Hospital Cirle, Zip 73750–5002, Mailing Address: P.O. Box 59, Zip 73750–0059; tel. 405/375–3141, **A**10 18 **F**3 11 15 29 30 34 35 40 41 43 45 50 59 64 68 75 77 79 81 82 85 87 89 93 107 110 111 114 119 128 129 132 133 146 148 149 **P**6 **S** Mercy, Chesterfield, MO
Primary Contact: Brian Denton, Administrator
CMO: Brett Krablin, M.D., Chief of Staff
CIO: Chad Kliewer, Information Technology Specialist
CHR: Carolyn Bjerke, Director Human Resources
CNO: Hannah Powell, Chief Nursing Officer
Web address: www.mercy.net/practice/mercy-hospital-kingfisher/
Control: Church operated, Nongovernment, not-for-profit **Service**: General medical and surgical

Staffed Beds: 25 **Admissions**: 306 **Census**: 4 **Outpatient Visits**: 19021 **Births**: 0 **Total Expense ($000)**: 11476 **Payroll Expense ($000)**: 5470 **Personnel**: 84

LAWTON—Comanche County

✠ △ **COMANCHE COUNTY MEMORIAL HOSPITAL (370056)**, 3401 West Gore Boulevard, Zip 73505–6332, Mailing Address: P.O. Box 129, Zip 73502–0129; tel. 580/355–8620, (Total facility includes 146 beds in nursing home–type unit) **A**1 2 3 5 7 10 13 **F**3 6 7 8 11 12 13 15 17 18 20 22 24 26 28 29 30 31 32 34 35 40 43 45 46 47 48 49 50 51 54 56 57 58 59 62 63 64 65 66 68 70 72 74 75 76 77 78 79 80 81 82 84 85 86 89 90 91 92 93 96 97 98 103 104 107 108 110 111 114 115 116 117 119 121 127 128 129 130 131 132 134 135 143 146 147 148 **P**6
Primary Contact: Brent Smith, Chief Executive Officer
CFO: George Kruger, CPA, Chief Financial Officer
CMO: Scott Michener, M.D., Chief Medical Officer
CIO: James Wellman, Senior Director Information Services
CHR: Donna Wade, Senior Director Human Resources
CNO: Chris Ward, Chief Nursing Officer
Web address: www.ccmhonline.com
Control: Hospital district or authority, Government, nonfederal **Service**: General medical and surgical

Staffed Beds: 370 **Admissions**: 9957 **Census**: 262 **Outpatient Visits**: 178985 **Births**: 1418 **Total Expense ($000)**: 262581 **Payroll Expense ($000)**: 108007 **Personnel**: 1567

JIM TALIAFERRO COMMUNITY MENTAL HEALTH (374008), 602 SW 38th Street, Zip 73505; tel. 580/248–5780, (Nonreporting) **A**3 10
Primary Contact: Brenda Ototivo, Executive Director
Web address: www.odmhsas.org
Control: State, Government, nonfederal **Service**: Psychiatric

Staffed Beds: 22

☐ **LAWTON INDIAN HOSPITAL (370170)**, 1515 Lawrie Tatum Road, Zip 73507–3099; tel. 580/353–0350, (Nonreporting) **A**1 10 **S** U.S. Indian Health Service, Rockville, MD
Primary Contact: Travis Scott, Chief Executive Officer
COO: John Bear, Hospital Administrator Officer and Supervisor Human Resources
CFO: Sarabeth Sahmaunt, Supervisory Accountant
CMO: Richard Chadek, M.D., Clinical Director
CIO: William R Harris, Chief Information Officer
CHR: John Bear, Hospital Administrator Officer and Supervisor Human Resources
CNO: Lenora Littledeer, R.N., Director of Nursing
Web address: www.ihs.gov
Control: PHS, Indian Service, Government, federal **Service**: General medical and surgical

Staffed Beds: 26

☐ ○ △ **SOUTHWESTERN MEDICAL CENTER (370097)**, 5602 SW Lee Boulevard, Zip 73505–9635; tel. 580/531–4700, **A**1 3 5 7 10 11 **F**3 8 13 29 30 34 38 40 41 45 47 49 50 51 57 59 60 64 65 67 68 70 74 76 77 79 81 85 87 89 90 91 92 93 98 99 100 101 102 104 106 107 108 111 114 118 119 129 130 131 133 135 146 147 148 **P**6 **S** RCCH HealthCare Partners, Brentwood, TN
Primary Contact: Larry Rodgers, Chief Executive Officer
CFO: Wayne Colson, Chief Financial Officer
CMO: Aryan Kadivar, M.D., Chief Medical Officer
CIO: Kent Lewis, Director Information Services
CHR: Danny Hale, Director Human Resources
CNO: Jayne Thomas, Chief Nursing Officer
Web address: www.swmconline.com
Control: Corporation, Investor-owned (for-profit) **Service**: General medical and surgical

Staffed Beds: 178 **Admissions**: 4607 **Census**: 82 **Outpatient Visits**: 60372 **Births**: 622 **Total Expense ($000)**: 80848 **Payroll Expense ($000)**: 36709 **Personnel**: 481

LINDSAY—Garvin County

LINDSAY MUNICIPAL HOSPITAL (370214), Highway 19 West, Zip 73052, Mailing Address: P.O. Box 888, Zip 73052–0888; tel. 405/756–1404, (Nonreporting) **A**10
Primary Contact: Jeff Walraven, Chief Executive Officer
Control: City, Government, nonfederal **Service**: General medical and surgical

Staffed Beds: 26

MADILL—Marshall County

✠ **ALLIANCEHEALTH MADILL (371326)**, 901 South Fifth Avenue, Zip 73446–3640, Mailing Address: P.O. Box 827, Zip 73446–0827; tel. 580/795–3384, (Nonreporting) **A**1 10 18 **S** Community Health Systems, Inc., Franklin, TN
Primary Contact: Jeffrey S. Tarrant, FACHE, Chief Executive Officer
CFO: Thomas Briggs, Chief Financial Officer
CMO: Heidi Haislip, M.D., Chief of Staff
CHR: D.J. Shawn, Director Human Resources
CNO: Carol Wright, Chief Nursing Officer
Web address: www.myalliancehealth.com
Control: Partnership, Investor-owned (for-profit) **Service**: General medical and surgical

Staffed Beds: 21

Many Facility Codes have changed. Please refer to the AHA Guide Code Chart.

OK

MANGUM—Greer County

MANGUM REGIONAL MEDICAL CENTER (371330), One Wickersham Drive, Zip 73554–9116, Mailing Address: P.O. Box 280, Zip 73554–0280; tel. 580/782–3353, (Nonreporting) **A**10 18
Primary Contact: Frank Avignone, Chief Executive Officer
COO: Danny Avery, Chief Financial Officer and Chief Operating Officer
CIO: Gregg Burnam, Chief Information Officer and Manager Business Office
Web address: www.qmhealth.org/
Control: City, Government, nonfederal **Service:** General medical and surgical

Staffed Beds: 25

MARIETTA—Love County

★ **MERCY HEALTH LOVE COUNTY (371306)**, 300 Wanda Street, Zip 73448–1200; tel. 580/276–3347, **A**10 18 **F**3 7 11 29 34 40 43 44 50 57 59 77 87 91 107 114 119 127 133 135 146 148 149 **S** Mercy, Chesterfield, MO
Primary Contact: Richard Barker, Administrator and Chief Executive Officer
CIO: Connie Graham, Public Information Officer
Web address: www.mercyhealthlovecounty.com
Control: Church operated, Nongovernment, not-for-profit **Service:** General medical and surgical

Staffed Beds: 25 **Admissions:** 300 **Census:** 7 **Outpatient Visits:** 30010
Births: 0 **Total Expense ($000):** 15513 **Payroll Expense ($000):** 8801
Personnel: 143

MCALESTER—Pittsburg County

CARL ALBERT COMMUNITY MENTAL HEALTH CENTER (374006), 1101 East Monroe Avenue, Zip 74501–4826; tel. 918/426–7800, (Nonreporting) **A**3 10
Primary Contact: Debbie Moran, Executive Director
CFO: Konnie Taylor, Chief Financial Officer
CMO: William Mings, M.D., Medical Director
CHR: Judy Allen, Human Resource Specialist
Web address: www.odmhsas.org
Control: State, Government, nonfederal **Service:** Psychiatric

Staffed Beds: 15

★ △ ⇑ **MCALESTER REGIONAL HEALTH CENTER (370034)**, One East Clark Bass Boulevard, Zip 74501–4267, Mailing Address: P.O. Box 1228, Zip 74502–1228; tel. 918/426–1800, **A**3 7 10 13 21 **F**3 10 11 13 15 18 20 22 26 29 30 34 35 40 43 45 49 50 51 53 54 56 57 59 61 62 63 64 66 68 69 70 75 76 77 79 81 82 85 86 87 90 91 92 93 98 101 102 104 107 108 109 110 111 114 115 116 117 118 119 125 129 130 131 132 135 144 146 147 148 152 154 **P**6
Primary Contact: David N. Keith, FACHE, President and Chief Executive Officer
CFO: Darryl Linnington, Chief Financial Officer
CIO: Jason Bray, Chief Information Officer
CHR: Scott Lowe, Director Human Resource
CNO: Kimberly Dawn Stout, CPHRM, Chief Nursing Officer and Chief Operating Officer
Web address: www.mrhcok.com
Control: City, Government, nonfederal **Service:** General medical and surgical

Staffed Beds: 209 **Admissions:** 4432 **Census:** 46 **Outpatient Visits:** 83526
Births: 511 **Total Expense ($000):** 89969 **Payroll Expense ($000):** 39904
Personnel: 682

MIAMI—Ottawa County

✠ **INTEGRIS MIAMI HOSPITAL (370004)**, 200 Second Avenue SW, Zip 74354–6830; tel. 918/542–6611, **A**1 10 20 **F**7 11 13 15 18 20 22 26 28 29 30 34 35 40 43 45 51 56 57 59 62 63 70 75 76 77 79 81 85 89 93 98 103 107 108 109 110 111 115 119 125 129 130 131 132 135 144 146 147 148 154 **S** INTEGRIS Health, Oklahoma City, OK
Primary Contact: Jonas Rabel, President
CFO: Valerie Reeves, Chief Financial Officer
CMO: Elaine Mader, M.D., Chief of Staff
CHR: Jamil Haynes, Regional Director Human Resources
CNO: Lisa Halstead, Chief Nursing Officer
Web address: www.integrisok.com/miami–hospital
Control: Other not-for-profit (including NFP Corporation) **Service:** General medical and surgical

Staffed Beds: 84 **Admissions:** 1941 **Census:** 21 **Outpatient Visits:** 56622
Births: 275 **Total Expense ($000):** 45829 **Payroll Expense ($000):** 14483
Personnel: 265

★ **WILLOW CREST HOSPITAL (374017)**, 130 'A' Street SW, Zip 74354–6800; tel. 918/542–1836, **A**10 **F**75 98 99 101 102 130 154 **P**6
Primary Contact: Shari Murphree, Chief Executive Officer
COO: Steven Goodman, Chief Operating Officer
CFO: Cindy Bell, Director Finance
CMO: Mark Elkington, M.D., Chief Medical Officer
CIO: Steven Goodman, Chief Operating Officer
CHR: Kathy Henderson, Director Human Resources
CNO: Kassi Davis, Director Patient Care Services
Web address: www.willowcresthospital.com
Control: Partnership, Investor–owned (for-profit) **Service:** Children's hospital psychiatric

Staffed Beds: 76 **Admissions:** 816 **Census:** 47 **Outpatient Visits:** 0
Births: 0 **Total Expense ($000):** 9548 **Payroll Expense ($000):** 5393

MIDWEST CITY—Oklahoma County

✠ **ALLIANCEHEALTH MIDWEST (370094)**, 2825 Parklawn Drive, Zip 73110–4258; tel. 405/610–4411, (Nonreporting) **A**1 3 5 10 **S** Community Health Systems, Inc., Franklin, TN
Primary Contact: Clay Franklin, Chief Executive Officer
COO: Lisa Ellis, Chief Operating Officer
CFO: Cynthia Gray, Interim Chief Financial Officer
CMO: Rockey Talley, M.D., Chief Medical Officer
CHR: Dana Leach, Director Human Resources
CNO: Jaconna Joni"" Tiller, Chief Nursing Officer
Web address: www.myalliancehealth.com
Control: Corporation, Investor–owned (for-profit) **Service:** General medical and surgical

Staffed Beds: 255

✠ **MIDWEST CITY SPECIALTY HOSPITAL (372012)**, 8210 National Avenue, Zip 73110–8518; tel. 405/739–0800, (Nonreporting) **A**1 10 **S** Concord Healthcare Group, Lakewood, NJ
Primary Contact: Bobby Snyder, Chief Executive Officer
CFO: Veronica Scott, Business Office Manager
CHR: Anna Emamghoraishi, Human Resources
CNO: Jason Farris, Chief Nursing Officer
Web address: www.midwestcityspecialtyhospital.com/
Control: Corporation, Investor–owned (for-profit) **Service:** Acute long–term care hospital

Staffed Beds: 31

MOORE—Cleveland County

NORMAN REGIONAL MOORE See Norman Regional Health System, Norman

MUSKOGEE—Muskogee County

CORNERSTONE HOSPITAL OF OKLAHOMA–MUSKOGEE (372022), 351 South 40th Street, Zip 74401–4916; tel. 918/682–6161, (Includes CORNERSTONE HOSPITAL OF OKLAHOMA–BROKEN ARROW, 1000 West Boise Circle, Third Floor, Broken Arrow, OK, Zip 74012–4900, Mailing Address: 1000 West Boise Circle, Zip 74012–4900, tel. 918/994–8300; Craig Koele, Chief Executive Officer) (Nonreporting) **A**10 22 **S** Cornerstone Healthcare Group, Dallas, TX
Primary Contact: Elizabeth Waytula, Chief Executive Officer
CMO: Jeremiah Rutherford, Chief Medical Officer
Web address: www.chghospitals.com/muskogee/
Control: Corporation, Investor–owned (for-profit) **Service:** Acute long–term care hospital

Staffed Beds: 41

EASTAR HEALTH SYSTEM, EAST CAMPUS See Saint Francis Hospital Muskogee, Muskogee

✠ △ **JACK C. MONTGOMERY VETERANS AFFAIRS MEDICAL CENTER**, 1011 Honor Heights Drive, Zip 74401–1318; tel. 918/577–3000, (Nonreporting) **A**1 2 3 5 7 **S** Department of Veterans Affairs, Perry Point, MD
Primary Contact: Mark E. Morgan, Medical Center Director
CFO: Dwight Beal, Chief Fiscal Services
CMO: Thomas D Schneider, D.O., Chief of Staff
CNO: Bonnie Pierce, MSN, R.N., Associate Director for Patient Care Services
Web address: www.muskogee.va.gov
Control: Veterans Affairs, Government, federal **Service:** General medical and surgical

Staffed Beds: 99

MUSKOGEE REGIONAL MEDICAL CENTER See Saint Francis Hospital Muskogee

Hospital, Medicare Provider Number, Address, Telephone, Approval, Facility, and Physician Codes, Health Care System

★ American Hospital Association (AHA) membership
□ The Joint Commission accreditation
○ Healthcare Facilities Accreditation Program
◇ DNV Healthcare Inc. accreditation
⇑ Center for Improvement in Healthcare Quality Accreditation
△ Commission on Accreditation of Rehabilitation Facilities (CARF) accreditation

OK

✠ **SAINT FRANCIS HOSPITAL MUSKOGEE (370025)**, 300 Rockefeller Drive, Zip 74401–5081; tel. 918/682–5501, (Includes EASTAR HEALTH SYSTEM, EAST CAMPUS, 2900 North Main Street, Muskogee, OK, Zip 74401–4078; tel. 918/687–7777) (Data for 91 days)**A**1 2 3 10 19 **F**3 8 11 13 15 18 20 22 28 29 30 31 35 37 40 43 45 53 54 56 57 60 64 68 70 74 75 78 79 81 82 85 86 87 90 92 96 98 100 102 103 107 108 110 111 114 115 119 120 121 123 124 126 129 130 131 141 143 146 147 148 **S** Saint Francis Health System, Tulsa, OK
Primary Contact: Anthony R. Young, Chief Executive Officer
COO: Tony Capuano, Chief Operating Officer
CFO: Scott Bailey, Chief Financial Officer
CMO: Jay Gregory, M.D., Chief Medical Officer
CIO: James Tolbert, Director Information Systems
CHR: Bill Peterson, Director Human Resources
CNO: James Wells, R.N., Chief Nursing Officer
Web address: www.saintfrancis.com/muskogee/Pages/default.aspx
Control: Church operated, Nongovernment, not–for–profit **Service:** General medical and surgical

Staffed Beds: 160 **Admissions:** 2189 **Census:** 127 **Outpatient Visits:** 16802 **Births:** 153 **Total Expense ($000):** 33136 **Payroll Expense ($000):** 12043 **Personnel:** 697

NORMAN—Cleveland County

☐ **GRIFFIN MEMORIAL HOSPITAL (374000)**, 900 East Main Street, Zip 73071–5305, Mailing Address: P.O. Box 151, Zip 73070–0151; tel. 405/573–6600, **A**1 3 5 10 **F**29 30 87 98 102 103 130 132 135 149 **P**6 **S** Oklahoma Department of Mental Health and Substance Abuse Services, Oklahoma City, OK
Primary Contact: Henry Hartsell, Ph.D., Executive Director
CFO: Cheryl Cupps, Director Finance
CMO: Clayton Morris, Medical Director
CNO: Mike Abla, Director of Nursing
Web address: www.odmhsas.org
Control: State, Government, nonfederal **Service:** Psychiatric

Staffed Beds: 120 **Admissions:** 1269 **Census:** 114 **Outpatient Visits:** 594 **Births:** 0 **Total Expense ($000):** 25727 **Payroll Expense ($000):** 11778 **Personnel:** 445

J. D. MCCARTY CENTER FOR CHILDREN WITH DEVELOPMENTAL DISABILITIES (373300), 2002 East Robinson, Zip 73071–7420; tel. 405/307–2800, **A**10 **F**3 29 35 64 65 75 77 87 90 91 93 119 130 134 135 146
Primary Contact: Vicki Kuerstersteffen, Director and Chief Executive Officer
CFO: Erik Paulson, Director of Finance
CMO: Thomas Thurston, M.D., Medical Director
CIO: Jeffery Setzer, Administrator Information Systems
CHR: Tina Martinez, Director Human Resources
Web address: www.jdmc.org
Control: State, Government, nonfederal **Service:** Children's rehabilitation

Staffed Beds: 36 **Admissions:** 188 **Census:** 32 **Outpatient Visits:** 8962 **Births:** 0 **Total Expense ($000):** 20728 **Payroll Expense ($000):** 8773 **Personnel:** 229

✠ △ **NORMAN REGIONAL HEALTH SYSTEM (370008)**, 901 North Porter Avenue, Zip 73071–6404, Mailing Address: P.O. Box 1308, Zip 73070–1308; tel. 405/515–1000, (Includes NORMAN REGIONAL HOSPITAL, 901 North Porter Street, Norman, OK, Zip 73071–6482, Mailing Address: P.O. Box 1308, Zip 73070–1308, tel. 405/307–1000; Richie Splitt, FACHE, President and Chief Executive Office; NORMAN REGIONAL MOORE, 700 South Telephone Road, Moore, OK, Zip 73160; tel. 405/793–9355; Richie Splitt, FACHE, President and Chief Executive Officer) **A**1 3 7 10 13 **F**3 7 11 12 13 15 17 18 20 22 24 28 29 30 31 32 34 35 36 37 39 40 43 44 45 47 48 50 53 54 55 56 57 58 59 63 64 65 69 70 72 74 75 76 77 78 79 80 81 82 83 84 85 86 87 89 90 93 94 96 97 98 100 101 102 103 104 107 110 111 114 115 117 118 119 120 123 126 127 129 130 131 132 135 143 145 146 147 148 **P**5 6 8
Primary Contact: Richie Splitt, FACHE, President and Chief Executive Officer
COO: John Manfredo, Chief Operating Officer
CFO: Ken Hopkins, Vice President Finance and Chief Financial Officer
CMO: Aaron Boyd, M.D., Chief Medical Officer
CIO: Danny Kelley, Administrative Director, Health Information Technology
CHR: Jim Beyer, Administrative Director Human Resources
CNO: Brittini McGill, MSN, R.N., Chief Nursing Officer
Web address: www.normanregional.com
Control: Hospital district or authority, Government, nonfederal **Service:** General medical and surgical

Staffed Beds: 387 **Admissions:** 15700 **Census:** 193 **Outpatient Visits:** 358704 **Births:** 2589 **Total Expense ($000):** 373932 **Payroll Expense ($000):** 172318 **Personnel:** 2878

NOWATA—Nowata County

★ **JANE PHILLIPS NOWATA HEALTH CENTER (371305)**, 237 South Locust Street, Zip 74048–3660; tel. 918/273–3102, **A**10 18 **F**3 29 30 34 35 40 50 57 64 68 107 114 119 128 133 146 **P**5 **S** Ascension Healthcare, Saint Louis, MO
Primary Contact: Jason McCauley, Administrator
CMO: David Caughell, M.D., Chief of Staff
Web address: www.jpmc.org
Control: Church operated, Nongovernment, not–for–profit **Service:** General medical and surgical

Staffed Beds: 15 **Admissions:** 166 **Census:** 4 **Outpatient Visits:** 9223 **Births:** 0 **Total Expense ($000):** 4990 **Payroll Expense ($000):** 2494 **Personnel:** 33

OKEENE—Blaine County

★ **OKEENE MUNICIPAL HOSPITAL (371327)**, 207 East 'F' Street, Zip 73763–9441, Mailing Address: P.O. Box 489, Zip 73763–0489; tel. 580/822–4417, **A**10 18 **F**3 29 34 40 59 64 65 68 85 93 97 107 130 133 135 148 149 154 **P**6
Primary Contact: Shelly Dunham, Chief Executive Officer
COO: Tammi Jantzen, Chief Operating Officer
CFO: Sandra Lamle, Chief Financial Officer
CMO: George S. Stenger, D.O., Chief of Staff
CHR: Barbara Creps, Director Human Resources and Accounting
CNO: Tamara Fischer, Chief Nursing Officer
Web address: www.okeenehospital.com
Control: Hospital district or authority, Government, nonfederal **Service:** General medical and surgical

Staffed Beds: 17 **Admissions:** 119 **Census:** 2 **Outpatient Visits:** 21417 **Births:** 0 **Total Expense ($000):** 6605 **Payroll Expense ($000):** 2802 **Personnel:** 54

OKEMAH—Okfuskee County

★ ⇑ **CREEK NATION COMMUNITY HOSPITAL (371333)**, 1800 East Coplin Street, Zip 74859–4642; tel. 918/623–1424, (Nonreporting) **A**10 18 21
Primary Contact: Sheryl Sharber–Howell, Administrator
COO: Rhonda Beaver, Chief Operating Officer
CFO: Tyler McIntosh, Chief Financial Officer
CMO: Lawrence Vark, M.D., Chief Medical Officer
CIO: Robert Coffee, Chief Information Officer
CHR: Russell B Torbett, Director Human Resources
CNO: Annette James, R.N., MSN, Chief Nursing Officer
Web address: www.creekhealth.org
Control: Other not–for–profit (including NFP Corporation) **Service:** General medical and surgical

Staffed Beds: 18

OKLAHOMA CITY—Oklahoma County

✠ △ **INTEGRIS DEACONESS (370032)**, 5501 North Portland Avenue, Zip 73112–2099; tel. 405/604–6000, **A**1 3 5 7 10 **F**3 13 15 17 18 20 22 24 28 29 30 34 39 40 45 46 47 48 49 50 51 54 56 57 59 60 64 68 70 72 74 75 77 78 79 81 82 84 86 87 90 93 97 107 108 109 110 111 112 114 115 119 120 121 124 126 129 130 131 135 146 147 148 154 **P**8 **S** Community Health Systems, Inc., Franklin, TN
Primary Contact: Rex Van Meter, President
COO: Brett Kirkham, Chief Operating Officer
CIO: Don Bandy, Director Information Technology
CHR: Ellen Gifford, Director Human Resources
CNO: Jayne Thomas, Chief Nursing Officer
Web address: www.deaconesskc.com
Control: Corporation, Investor–owned (for–profit) **Service:** General medical and surgical

Staffed Beds: 141 **Admissions:** 4671 **Census:** 63 **Outpatient Visits:** 56359 **Births:** 663 **Personnel:** 675

☐ **AMG SPECIALTY HOSPITAL AT MERCY (372005)**, 4300 West Memorial Road, 2nd Floor, Zip 73120–8304; tel. 405/936–5822, (Nonreporting) **A**1 **S** AMG Integrated Healthcare Management, Lafayette, LA
Primary Contact: Keith Carruth, Chief Executive Officer
Web address: www.https://amgmercy.com/
Service: Acute long–term care hospital

Staffed Beds: 30

☐ **CEDAR RIDGE HOSPITAL (374023)**, 6501 NE 50th Street, Zip 73141–9118; tel. 405/605–6111, (Includes BETHANY BEHAVIORAL HEALTH, 7600 NW 23rd Street, Bethany, OK, Zip 73008–4944; tel. 405/792–5360; Heather Joseph, Chief Executive Officer) **A**1 10 **F**98 99 103 105 106 130 149 153 **P**6 **S** Universal Health Services, Inc., King of Prussia, PA
Primary Contact: Heather Joseph, Chief Executive Officer
Web address: www.cedarridgebhs.com
Control: Corporation, Investor–owned (for–profit) **Service:** Psychiatric

Staffed Beds: 172 **Admissions:** 3549 **Census:** 105 **Outpatient Visits:** 594 **Births:** 0 **Total Expense ($000):** 20259 **Payroll Expense ($000):** 10890 **Personnel:** 233

CHILDREN'S HOSPITAL OF OKLAHOMA See Ou Medical Center, Oklahoma City

OKLAHOMA CITY—Cleveland County

⇧ **COMMUNITY HOSPITAL (370203)**, 3100 SW 89th Street, Zip 73159–7900, Mailing Address: 3125 SW 89th Street, Zip 73159–7900; tel. 405/602–8100, **A**10 21 **F**29 37 40 45 70 77 79 81 82 85 86 87 93 94 107 111 114 115 119 126 129 130 135 146 149 154 **P**2 6
Primary Contact: Debbie Kearns, Chief Executive Officer
Web address: www.communityhospitalokc.com
Control: Partnership, Investor–owned (for–profit) **Service:** Surgical

Staffed Beds: 45 **Admissions:** 2537 **Census:** 15 **Births:** 0

OKLAHOMA CITY—Oklahoma County

⊞ **CURAHEALTH HOSPITAL OKLAHOMA CITY (372004)**, 1407 North Robinson Avenue, Zip 73103–4823; tel. 405/232–8000, (Includes CURAHEALTH OKLAHOMA, 2129 SW 59th Street, Oklahoma City, OK, Zip 73119; tel. 405/713–5955; Brenda Hood, Chief Executive Officer) (Nonreporting) **A**1 5 10 **S** Curahealth Hospitals, Garland, TX
Primary Contact: Brenda Hood, Chief Executive Officer
Web address: www.curahealth.com
Control: Corporation, Investor–owned (for–profit) **Service:** Acute long–term care hospital

Staffed Beds: 93

EVERETT TOWER See Ou Medical Center, Oklahoma City

⊞ △ **INTEGRIS BAPTIST MEDICAL CENTER (370028)**, 3300 NW Expressway, Zip 73112–4418; tel. 405/949–3011, (Includes INTEGRIS MENTAL HEALTH SYSTEM–SPENCER, 2601 North Spencer Road, Spencer, OK, Zip 73084–3699, Mailing Address: P.O. Box 11137, Oklahoma City, Zip 73136–0137, tel. 405/717–9800) **A**1 2 3 5 7 10 **F**3 8 11 12 13 15 16 17 18 20 22 24 26 28 29 30 31 32 34 35 38 39 40 43 44 45 46 47 49 50 51 54 55 57 58 59 60 62 63 64 68 70 71 72 73 74 75 76 77 78 79 80 81 82 84 85 86 87 88 89 92 93 96 97 98 99 100 101 104 105 106 107 108 109 110 111 114 115 116 118 119 120 121 123 124 126 129 130 131 132 135 137 138 139 140 141 142 146 147 148 149 153 154 **P**6 7 **S** INTEGRIS Health, Oklahoma City, OK
Primary Contact: Timothy J. Johnsen, MS, President
CFO: Cheryl Perry, Chief Financial Officer
CIO: Mark Pasquale, Chief Information Officer
CHR: Jason L Eliot, Vice President Human Resources
Web address: www.integrisok.com
Control: Other not–for–profit (including NFP Corporation) **Service:** General medical and surgical

Staffed Beds: 597 **Admissions:** 23785 **Census:** 437 **Outpatient Visits:** 231030 **Births:** 2727 **Total Expense ($000):** 712826 **Payroll Expense ($000):** 201531 **Personnel:** 2115

⊞ △ **INTEGRIS SOUTHWEST MEDICAL CENTER (370106)**, 4401 South Western, Zip 73109–3413; tel. 405/636–7000, **A**1 2 3 7 10 13 **F**3 11 13 15 18 20 22 24 26 28 29 30 31 34 35 40 43 44 45 47 49 50 51 57 58 59 60 64 68 70 74 75 76 77 78 79 80 81 82 85 86 87 90 91 92 93 95 96 97 98 100 102 107 108 110 111 114 115 118 119 120 121 123 124 126 129 130 131 132 135 146 147 148 154 **S** INTEGRIS Health, Oklahoma City, OK
Primary Contact: Jordan Cash, President
CFO: Dan Davis, Managing Director and Chief Financial Officer
CMO: Philip Mosca, M.D., Medical Staff
CIO: Mark Pasquale, Chief Information Officer
CHR: Lynn Ketch, Regional Director Integris Southwest Medical Center
CNO: Marva Harrison, R.N., Vice President and Chief Nursing Officer
Web address: www.integrisok.com
Control: Other not–for–profit (including NFP Corporation) **Service:** General medical and surgical

Staffed Beds: 275 **Admissions:** 11587 **Census:** 183 **Outpatient Visits:** 171014 **Births:** 1182 **Total Expense ($000):** 231902 **Payroll Expense ($000):** 72210 **Personnel:** 1010

⊞ **LAKESIDE WOMEN'S HOSPITAL (370199)**, 11200 North Portland Avenue, Zip 73120–5045; tel. 405/936–1500, **A**1 10 **F**3 12 13 15 30 35 40 45 59 64 73 76 81 85 87 110 119 126 130 132 147 **P**6 **S** INTEGRIS Health, Oklahoma City, OK
Primary Contact: Kelley Brewer, R.N., MSN, President
CFO: Darla McCallister, Chief Financial Officer
CMO: Margaret Hall, M.D., Chief Medical Officer
Web address: www.lakeside-wh.net
Control: Corporation, Investor–owned (for–profit) **Service:** Obstetrics and gynecology

Staffed Beds: 23 **Admissions:** 1522 **Census:** 10 **Outpatient Visits:** 23123 **Births:** 1435 **Total Expense ($000):** 21639 **Payroll Expense ($000):** 8547 **Personnel:** 128

MCBRIDE ORTHOPEDIC HOSPITAL (370222), 9600 Broadway Extension, Zip 73114–7408; tel. 405/486–2100, **A**3 5 10 **F**3 29 34 40 64 68 77 79 81 82 85 86 87 93 97 107 111 114 119 126 130 131 146 149 **P**2 6
Primary Contact: Mark Galliart, Chief Executive Officer
CFO: Greg Gisler, Chief Financial Officer
CNO: Krista Reyna, Chief Nursing Officer
Web address: www.mcboh.com
Control: Corporation, Investor–owned (for–profit) **Service:** Orthopedic

Staffed Beds: 60 **Admissions:** 3580 **Census:** 28 **Outpatient Visits:** 157030 **Births:** 0 **Total Expense ($000):** 130813 **Payroll Expense ($000):** 52325 **Personnel:** 696

⊞ **MERCY HOSPITAL OKLAHOMA CITY (370013)**, 4300 West Memorial Road, Zip 73120–8362; tel. 405/755–1515, **A**1 2 3 5 10 **F**3 11 13 15 28 29 30 31 32 34 35 40 43 44 45 46 47 48 49 50 53 55 57 58 59 60 61 62 63 64 65 68 69 70 72 74 75 76 77 78 79 81 82 83 84 85 86 87 89 90 91 92 93 94 96 100 101 107 108 110 111 114 115 117 118 119 120 121 124 126 129 130 131 132 134 135 143 146 147 148 149 **P**6 **S** Mercy, Chesterfield, MO
Primary Contact: Jim Gebhart Jr, FACHE, President
COO: Aaron Steffens, Chief Operating Officer
CFO: Jon Vitiello, Senior Vice President, Finance Operations and Analytics
CIO: Ellen Stephens, Vice President Information Services
CHR: Becky J Payton, Vice President Human Resources
Web address: www.mercyok.net
Control: Church operated, Nongovernment, not–for–profit **Service:** General medical and surgical

Staffed Beds: 369 **Admissions:** 16292 **Census:** 212 **Outpatient Visits:** 493984 **Births:** 3864 **Total Expense ($000):** 442598 **Payroll Expense ($000):** 142372 **Personnel:** 2310

☐ △ **MERCY REHABILITATION HOSPITAL OKLAHOMA CITY (373033)**, 5401 West Memorial Rd, Zip 73142–2026; tel. 405/752–3935, (Nonreporting) **A**1 7 10
Primary Contact: Sharon Smeltzer, Chief Executive Officer
Control: Partnership, Investor–owned (for–profit) **Service:** Rehabilitation

Staffed Beds: 50

⇧ **NORTHWEST SURGICAL HOSPITAL (370192)**, 9204 North May Avenue, Zip 73120–4419; tel. 405/848–1918, **A**3 10 21 **F**3 29 40 75 77 79 81 82 85 107 111 119 130 135 149 **P**2
Primary Contact: Debbie Kearns, Chief Executive Officer
CFO: Cindy Thompson, Chief Financial Officer
CMO: Jimmy Conway, M.D., President Medical Staff
Web address: www.nwsurgicalokc.com/
Control: Partnership, Investor–owned (for–profit) **Service:** Surgical

Staffed Beds: 9 **Admissions:** 121 **Census:** 1 **Outpatient Visits:** 9297 **Births:** 0 **Total Expense ($000):** 11801 **Payroll Expense ($000):** 2359 **Personnel:** 38

OAKWOOD SPRINGS (374025), 13101 Memorial Springs Court, Zip 73114–2226; tel. 405/438–3000, (Data for 307 days) **A**10 **F**4 5 29 34 38 57 68 98 100 101 102 104 105 132 135 149 152 153 **P**6 **S** Springstone, Louisville, KY
Primary Contact: Karen Walker, Chief Executive Officer
Web address: www.oakwoodsprings.com/
Control: Corporation, Investor–owned (for–profit) **Service:** Psychiatric

Staffed Beds: 72 **Admissions:** 1126 **Census:** 27 **Outpatient Visits:** 3389 **Births:** 0 **Total Expense ($000):** 8452 **Payroll Expense ($000):** 4617

OK

☐ **OKLAHOMA CENTER FOR ORTHOPEDIC AND MULTI–SPECIALTY SURGERY (370212)**, 8100 South Walker, Suite C, Zip 73139–9402, Mailing Address: P.O. Box 890609, Zip 73189–0609; tel. 405/602–6500, **A**1 10 **F**3 12 29 34 35 37 39 40 45 47 48 54 57 59 64 74 79 81 82 85 86 93 94 97 107 111 131 148 149 **P**6 **S** United Surgical Partners International, Addison, TX
Primary Contact: Mike Kimzey, Chief Executive Officer and Administrator
COO: Jeff Bibb, Chief Operating Officer
CFO: Amy Taylor, Chief Financial Officer
CHR: Emily Phipps, Director Human Resources
CNO: Jolena Wyer, R.N., Chief Nursing Officer
Web address: www.ocomhospital.com
Control: Partnership, Investor–owned (for–profit) **Service:** General medical and surgical

Staffed Beds: 10 **Admissions:** 781 **Census:** 4 **Outpatient Visits:** 37096
Births: 0 **Total Expense ($000):** 50925 **Payroll Expense ($000):** 14152
Personnel: 241

☒ △ **OKLAHOMA CITY VETERANS AFFAIRS MEDICAL CENTER**, 921 NE 13th Street, Zip 73104–5028; tel. 405/456–1000, (Nonreporting) **A**1 2 3 5 7 8 **S** Department of Veterans Affairs, Perry Point, MD
Primary Contact: Kristopher Wade. Vlosich, Director
CFO: Michele Pipgrass, Chief Fiscal Service
CIO: David Buckley, Acting Chief Information Management Services
CHR: Kyle Inhofe, Chief Human Resources Officer
Web address: www.oklahoma.va.gov
Control: Veterans Affairs, Government, federal **Service:** General medical and surgical

Staffed Beds: 192

⇑ **OKLAHOMA HEART HOSPITAL (370215)**, 4050 West Memorial Road, Zip 73120–8382; tel. 405/608–3200, **A**10 21 **F**17 18 20 22 24 26 28 29 30 34 35 40 50 59 64 68 74 75 81 85 86 87 100 102 107 108 111 114 115 116 117 118 119 126 127 130 135 146 154 **P**3 6
Primary Contact: John Harvey, M.D., Chief Executive Officer
COO: Peggy Tipton, Chief Operating Officer and Chief Nursing Officer
CFO: Carol Walker, Chief Financial Officer
CMO: John Harvey, M.D., Chief Executive Officer
CIO: Michelle Mullins, Chief Information Officer
CHR: Katherine Wynn, Director Human Resource
Web address: www.okheart.com
Control: Corporation, Investor–owned (for–profit) **Service:** Heart

Staffed Beds: 94 **Admissions:** 6620 **Census:** 74 **Outpatient Visits:** 275735
Births: 0 **Total Expense ($000):** 220386 **Payroll Expense ($000):** 89168
Personnel: 1734

⇑ **OKLAHOMA HEART HOSPITAL SOUTH CAMPUS (370234)**, 5200 East I-240 Service Road, Zip 73135; tel. 405/628–6000, **A**10 **F**17 18 20 22 24 26 28 29 30 34 35 40 50 53 59 64 66 68 74 75 81 82 85 87 100 107 111 115 116 117 118 119 126 130 135 146 154 **P**3 6
Primary Contact: John Harvey, M.D., Chief Executive Officer
Web address: www.okheart.com
Control: Corporation, Investor–owned (for–profit) **Service:** Heart

Staffed Beds: 44 **Admissions:** 3862 **Census:** 39 **Outpatient Visits:** 58287
Births: 0 **Total Expense ($000):** 130028 **Payroll Expense ($000):** 47052
Personnel: 603

⇑ **OKLAHOMA SPINE HOSPITAL (370206)**, 14101 Parkway Commons Drive, Zip 73134–6012; tel. 405/749–2700, (Nonreporting) **A**10 21
Primary Contact: Kevin Blaylock, Chief Executive Officer
Web address: www.oklahomaspine.com
Control: Corporation, Investor–owned (for–profit) **Service:** Surgical

Staffed Beds: 12

ONECORE HEALTH (370220), 1044 SW 44th Street, Suite 350, Zip 73109–3609; tel. 405/631–3085, **A**10 **F**3 15 40 54 59 64 74 79 81 82 85 86 87 107 110 111 114 119 149
Primary Contact: Steve Hockert, Chief Executive Officer
CMO: Joel L Frazier, M.D., Medical Director
CNO: Teresa Carter, Vice President Patient Care Services
Web address: www.onecorehealth.com
Control: Corporation, Investor–owned (for–profit) **Service:** Orthopedic

Staffed Beds: 8 **Admissions:** 196 **Census:** 1 **Outpatient Visits:** 11222
Births: 0 **Total Expense ($000):** 13328 **Payroll Expense ($000):** 3585
Personnel: 65

☒ **OU MEDICAL CENTER (370093)**, 1200 Everett Drive, Zip 73104–5047, Mailing Address: P.O. Box 26307, Zip 73126–0307; tel. 405/271–3636, (Includes CHILDREN'S HOSPITAL OF OKLAHOMA, 940 NE 13th Street, Oklahoma City, OK, Zip 73104, Mailing Address: P.O. Box 26307, Zip 73126, tel. 405/271–6165; EVERETT TOWER, 1200 Everett Drive, Oklahoma City, OK, Zip 73104; tel. 405/271–4700; OU MEDICAL CENTER EDMOND, 1 South Bryant Avenue, Edmond, OK, Zip 73034–6309; tel. 405/341–6100; PRESBYTERIAN TOWER, 700 NE 13th Street, Oklahoma City, OK, Zip 73104–5070; tel. 405/271–5100) **A**1 2 3 5 8 10 **F**3 5 6 11 12 13 15 17 18 19 20 21 22 23 24 25 26 27 28 29 30 31 32 34 35 36 37 38 39 40 41 43 44 45 46 47 48 49 50 51 52 54 55 56 57 58 59 60 61 63 64 65 66 68 70 71 72 74 75 76 77 78 79 80 81 82 83 84 85 86 87 88 89 91 92 93 94 96 97 98 99 100 101 102 103 107 108 110 111 114 115 116 117 118 119 120 121 122 123 124 126 129 130 131 132 134 135 136 138 139 141 142 143 145 146 147 148 149 150 154
Primary Contact: Kristina Wallace, R.N., Chief Executive Officer
CFO: Mike Reese, Chief Financial Officer
CMO: Curt Steinhart, M.D., Chief Medical Officer
CIO: Larry Forsyth, Director Information Services
CHR: Jed M Liuzza, Chief Human Resources Officer
Web address: www.oumedicine.com/oumedicalcenter
Control: Other not–for–profit (including NFP Corporation) **Service:** General medical and surgical

Staffed Beds: 719 **Admissions:** 34281 **Census:** 581 **Outpatient Visits:** 378486 **Births:** 3613 **Total Expense ($000):** 865131 **Payroll Expense ($000):** 237686 **Personnel:** 3933

PRESBYTERIAN TOWER See Ou Medical Center, Oklahoma City

☒ **SELECT SPECIALTY HOSPITAL–OKLAHOMA CITY (372009)**, 3524 NW 56th Street, Zip 73112–4518; tel. 405/606–6700, **A**1 10 **F**1 3 12 29 74 75 79 87 107 119 130 148 **S** Select Medical Corporation, Mechanicsburg, PA
Primary Contact: Zackary L. Dawson, Chief Executive Officer
Web address: www.https://oklahomacity.selectspecialtyhospitals.com/
Control: Corporation, Investor–owned (for–profit) **Service:** Acute long–term care hospital

Staffed Beds: 72 **Admissions:** 723 **Census:** 50 **Outpatient Visits:** 0
Births: 0 **Total Expense ($000):** 27791 **Payroll Expense ($000):** 11976
Personnel: 198

☒ **SSM HEALTH ST. ANTHONY HOSPITAL – OKLAHOMA CITY (370037)**, 1000 North Lee Street, Zip 73102–1080, Mailing Address: P.O. Box 205, Zip 73101–0205; tel. 405/272–7000, (Includes SSM HEALTH BONE AND JOINT HOSPITAL AT ST. ANTHONY, 1111 North Dewey Avenue, Oklahoma City, OK, Zip 73103–2609; tel. 405/272–9671; Tammy Powell, FACHE, M.P.H., President; SSM HEALTH ST. ANTHONY SOUTH, 2129 SW 59th Street, Oklahoma City, OK, Zip 73119–7001; tel. 405/713–5700) **A**1 2 3 5 10 12 13 **F**3 4 5 7 8 11 12 13 15 17 18 20 22 24 26 28 29 30 31 34 35 36 37 40 43 45 46 47 48 49 50 54 56 57 58 59 64 67 70 71 72 74 76 77 78 79 81 82 84 85 86 87 89 90 91 92 93 96 97 98 99 100 101 102 103 104 105 106 107 108 110 111 114 115 117 118 119 120 121 122 124 126 127 129 130 131 132 136 144 146 147 148 149 152 153 154 **S** SSM Health, Saint Louis, MO
Primary Contact: Tammy Powell, FACHE, M.P.H., President
COO: Marti Jourden, FACHE, Chief Quality Officer
CFO: Shasta Manuel, Executive Director Finance
CMO: Kersey Winfree, M.D., Chief Medical Officer
CIO: Kevin Olson, Director Information Systems
CHR: Cynthia Brundise, Vice President Human Resources
Web address: www.saintsok.com
Control: Church operated, Nongovernment, not–for–profit **Service:** General medical and surgical

Staffed Beds: 625 **Admissions:** 23903 **Census:** 454 **Outpatient Visits:** 348159 **Births:** 1151 **Total Expense ($000):** 475731 **Payroll Expense ($000):** 149215 **Personnel:** 2594

☐ **SURGICAL HOSPITAL OF OKLAHOMA (370201)**, 100 SE 59th Street, Zip 73129–3616; tel. 405/634–9300, **A**1 10 **F**3 40 81 111 129
Primary Contact: Phil Ross, Chief Executive Officer
CNO: Cindy Ridge Braly, MAAL, R.N., Chief Nursing Officer
Web address: www.sh–ok.com/
Control: Partnership, Investor–owned (for–profit) **Service:** General medical and surgical

Staffed Beds: 12 **Admissions:** 197 **Census:** 1 **Outpatient Visits:** 4528
Births: 0 **Total Expense ($000):** 13746 **Payroll Expense ($000):** 3795
Personnel: 70

OK

☒ **VALIR REHABILITATION HOSPITAL (373025)**, 700 NW Seventh Street, Zip 73102–1212; tel. 405/236–3131, **A**1 10 **F**3 28 29 30 34 40 50 53 54 56 57 59 64 77 82 85 86 87 90 91 93 96 100 130 131 132 135 143 **P**1
Primary Contact: Tom Tucker, Chief Executive Officer
COO: Ginger Castleberry, Corporate Risk Manager, Quality and Patient Safety
CFO: Scott Brown, Chief Financial Officer
CMO: Tonya Washburn, M.D., Medical Director
CIO: Mark Dickey, Director Business Development
CHR: Bill Turner, Vice President Human Resources
Web address: www.valir.com
Control: Partnership, Investor–owned (for–profit) **Service**: Rehabilitation

Staffed Beds: 49 **Admissions**: 917 **Census**: 32 **Outpatient Visits**: 4479
Births: 0 **Total Expense ($000)**: 15836 **Payroll Expense ($000)**: 9256
Personnel: 186

VETERANS AFFAIRS MEDICAL CENTER See Oklahoma City Veterans Affairs Medical Center

OKMULGEE—Okmulgee County

★ **MUSCOGEE CREEK NATION MEDICAL CENTER (370057)**, 1401 Morris Drive, Zip 74447–6429, Mailing Address: P.O. Box 1038, Zip 74447–1038; tel. 918/756–4233, **A**10 **F**7 11 15 29 34 40 43 56 57 59 81 87 98 103 107 108 111 115 119 128 130 133 146
Primary Contact: Tim Hicks, Administrator
CFO: John W Crawford, Chief Financial Officer
CMO: Michael Sandlin, M.D., Chief of Staff
CHR: Stacey R. Burton, Director Human Resources
Web address: www.creekhealth.org/medical–center/
Control: PHS, Indian Service, Government, federal **Service**: General medical and surgical

Staffed Beds: 32 **Admissions**: 583 **Census**: 7 **Outpatient Visits**: 17008
Births: 1 **Total Expense ($000)**: 19549 **Payroll Expense ($000)**: 6796
Personnel: 179

MUSCOGEE CREEK NATION PHYSICAL REHABILITATION CENTER (372023), 1401 Morris Drive, Zip 74447–6429, Mailing Address: P.O. Box 1038, Zip 74447–1938; tel. 918/756–4233, (Nonreporting)
Primary Contact: Tim Hicks, Administrator
Control: Other not–for–profit (including NFP Corporation) **Service**: Acute long–term care hospital

Staffed Beds: 12

OWASSO—Tulsa County

★ **BAILEY MEDICAL CENTER (370228)**, 10502 North 110th East Avenue, Zip 74055–6655; tel. 918/376–8000, **A**10 **F**3 12 13 15 18 29 34 40 45 51 57 70 75 76 77 79 81 85 91 107 108 110 111 115 119 129 132 146 147 149 **S** Ardent Health Services, Nashville, TN
Primary Contact: Keith Mason, Chief Executive Officer
CFO: Brandon Bullard, Chief Financial Officer
CHR: Tandy Groves, Coordinator Human Resources
Web address: www.baileymedicalcenter.com
Control: Corporation, Investor–owned (for–profit) **Service**: General medical and surgical

Staffed Beds: 37 **Admissions**: 1535 **Census**: 9 **Outpatient Visits**: 34839
Births: 314 **Total Expense ($000)**: 37285 **Payroll Expense ($000)**: 12655
Personnel: 192

★ **ST. JOHN OWASSO (370227)**, 12451 East 100th Street North, Zip 74055–4600; tel. 918/274–5000, **A**10 **F**3 11 13 15 18 29 30 34 35 40 43 45 57 59 64 68 76 79 81 85 87 93 107 108 110 111 114 115 119 130 131 132 146 149 **P**5 6 **S** Ascension Healthcare, Saint Louis, MO
Primary Contact: David L. Phillips, President and Chief Operating Officer
CFO: Katie Caughman, Chief Financial Officer
CMO: Tim Hepner, M.D., Chief Medical Officer
CIO: Mike Reeves, Chief Information Officer
CNO: Dan Hall, R.N., Chief Operating Officer
Web address: www.stjohnowasso.com
Control: Church operated, Nongovernment, not–for–profit **Service**: General medical and surgical

Staffed Beds: 45 **Admissions**: 1780 **Census**: 12 **Outpatient Visits**: 107051
Births: 469 **Total Expense ($000)**: 30822 **Payroll Expense ($000)**: 10003
Personnel: 170

PAULS VALLEY—Garvin County

PAULS VALLEY GENERAL HOSPITAL (370156), 100 Valley Drive, Zip 73075–6613, Mailing Address: P.O. Box 368, Zip 73075–0368; tel. 405/238–5501, **A**10 20 **F**3 7 10 11 15 29 30 40 45 57 59 63 64 65 77 81 82 84 87 89 93 107 111 114 117 119 129 130 132 133 146 147 148 149 **P**3
Primary Contact: Nathan Staggs, Chief Executive Officer
CFO: Dale Semar, Controller
CIO: Rusty Weaver, Manager Information Technology
CHR: Stephanie Dancer, Manager Human Resources
CNO: Kari Howard, Interim Director of Nursing
Web address: www.pvgh.net
Control: City, Government, nonfederal **Service**: General medical and surgical

Staffed Beds: 53 **Admissions**: 476 **Census**: 4 **Outpatient Visits**: 17070
Births: 0 **Total Expense ($000)**: 16434 **Payroll Expense ($000)**: 7108
Personnel: 149

PAWHUSKA—Osage County

★ **PAWHUSKA HOSPITAL (371309)**, 1101 East 15th Street, Zip 74056–1920; tel. 918/287–3232, (Nonreporting) **A**10 18
Primary Contact: Godwin Feh, Interim Administrator
CMO: Mike Priest, M.D., Chief of Staff
Web address: www.https:/pawhuskahospital.com/
Control: City, Government, nonfederal **Service**: General medical and surgical

Staffed Beds: 15

PERRY—Noble County

★ ⇧ **PERRY MEMORIAL HOSPITAL (370139)**, 501 North 14th Street, Zip 73077–5099; tel. 580/336–3541, **A**10 20 21 **F**3 11 15 28 29 34 35 40 57 59 62 64 65 67 81 85 90 93 97 107 114 127 128 131 133 146 148 149 154 **P**6 **S** QHR, Brentwood, TN
Primary Contact: Steven E. Taylor, Chief Executive Officer
CFO: Courtney Kozikuski, Chief Financial Officer
CMO: Michael Hartwig, M.D., Chief of Staff
CIO: Randy Taylor, Chief Information Technology Officer
CHR: Deb Ellis, Director Human Resources
CNO: Jeannie Carey, R.N., Director Patient Care
Web address: www.pmh–ok.org
Control: Hospital district or authority, Government, nonfederal **Service**: General medical and surgical

Staffed Beds: 26 **Admissions**: 422 **Census**: 5 **Outpatient Visits**: 14029
Births: 0 **Total Expense ($000)**: 11788 **Payroll Expense ($000)**: 4100
Personnel: 64

PONCA CITY—Kay County

☒ **ALLIANCEHEALTH PONCA CITY (370006)**, 1900 North 14th Street, Zip 74601–2099; tel. 580/765–3321, **A**1 10 19 **F**3 13 15 18 28 29 30 34 35 40 43 45 46 50 51 53 57 59 64 65 66 68 69 70 75 76 77 79 81 82 85 89 90 93 97 107 108 110 111 115 119 127 130 131 132 133 145 146 147 148 149 154 **P**6 **S** Community Health Systems, Inc., Franklin, TN
Primary Contact: Christopher Mendoza, Chief Executive Officer
CFO: Sheryl Schmidtberger, Chief Financial Officer
CIO: William Gazaway, Information Technology Security Officer
CHR: Calvin Hodges, Director Human Resources
CNO: Jeanne Stara, R.N., MSN, Chief Nursing Officer
Web address: www.AllianceHealthPoncaCity.com
Control: Corporation, Investor–owned (for–profit) **Service**: General medical and surgical

Staffed Beds: 74 **Admissions**: 2480 **Census**: 23 **Outpatient Visits**: 56267
Births: 494 **Total Expense ($000)**: 52755 **Payroll Expense ($000)**: 21908
Personnel: 368

POTEAU—Le Flore County

★ ⇧ **EASTERN OKLAHOMA MEDICAL CENTER (371337)**, 105 Wall Street, Zip 74953–4433, Mailing Address: P.O. Box 1148, Zip 74953–1148; tel. 918/647–8161, **A**10 18 21 **F**3 11 13 15 29 30 34 35 40 45 46 50 56 57 59 65 68 70 76 81 83 93 97 98 102 103 107 108 111 119 127 129 133 144 148 154 **P**3 6
Primary Contact: Bob Carter, Interim Chief Executive Officer
CFO: Shaun Keef, Chief Financial Officer
CMO: Dennis Carter, M.D., Chief of Staff
CIO: Michael C Huggins, Administrator Network System
Web address: www.eomchospital.com
Control: County, Government, nonfederal **Service**: General medical and surgical

Staffed Beds: 43 **Admissions**: 1072 **Census**: 9 **Outpatient Visits**: 31877
Births: 253 **Total Expense ($000)**: 22735 **Payroll Expense ($000)**: 10328

Hospital, Medicare Provider Number, Address, Telephone, Approval, Facility, and Physician Codes, Health Care System

★ American Hospital Association (AHA) membership
□ The Joint Commission accreditation
○ Healthcare Facilities Accreditation Program
◇ DNV Healthcare Inc. accreditation
⇧ Center for Improvement in Healthcare Quality Accreditation
△ Commission on Accreditation of Rehabilitation Facilities (CARF) accreditation

OK

PRAGUE—Lincoln County

PRAGUE COMMUNITY HOSPITAL (371301), 1322 Klabzuba Avenue, Zip 74864–9005, Mailing Address: P.O. Box S, Zip 74864–1090; tel. 405/567–4922, **A**10 18 **F**3 29 34 40 43 45 55 57 59 64 65 68 79 81 93 97 107 111 114 119 127 128 130 133 148 **P**6 **S** Rural Community Hospitals of America, Kansas City, MO
Primary Contact: Shelly Dyer, Interim Chief Executive Officer
CFO: Doug Erickson, Chief Financial Officer
CMO: Darryl Jackson, D.O., Chief of Staff
CIO: Rhonda Whitnum, Director Health Improvement Management
CHR: Angie Brezny, Director Human Resources
Web address: www.praguehospital.com
Control: Corporation, Investor–owned (for–profit) **Service**: General medical and surgical

Staffed Beds: 15 **Admissions:** 110 **Census:** 3 **Outpatient Visits:** 18383 **Births:** 0 **Total Expense ($000):** 6019 **Payroll Expense ($000):** 3073 **Personnel:** 52

PRYOR—Mayes County

✠ **HILLCREST HOSPITAL PRYOR (370015)**, 111 North Bailey Street, Zip 74361–4201; tel. 918/825–1600, **A**1 10 **F**3 11 15 18 26 29 30 34 35 45 50 57 59 64 65 77 79 81 93 107 108 110 111 114 119 131 147 **S** Ardent Health Services, Nashville, TN
Primary Contact: Douglas K. Weaver, FACHE, Chief Executive Officer
CMO: Jason Joice, M.D., Chief Medical Staff
CHR: Pamela A Guthrie, Chief Human Resources Officer
CNO: Mary Ozment, Chief Nursing Officer
Web address: www.hillcrestpryor.com/
Control: Corporation, Investor–owned (for–profit) **Service**: General medical and surgical

Staffed Beds: 22 **Admissions:** 434 **Census:** 2 **Outpatient Visits:** 19005 **Births:** 0 **Total Expense ($000):** 11283 **Payroll Expense ($000):** 4164 **Personnel:** 115

PURCELL—McClain County

PURCELL MUNICIPAL HOSPITAL (370158), 1500 North Green Avenue, Zip 73080–1699, Mailing Address: P.O. Box 511, Zip 73080–0511; tel. 405/527–6524, **A**10 **F**3 11 18 29 30 34 35 40 45 48 57 59 64 65 75 79 81 82 86 87 89 114 119 130 132 133 144 154
Primary Contact: Kem Scully, Chief Executive Officer and Chief Nursing Officer
CFO: Mary Morris, Chief Financial Officer
CMO: David Bryan Dye, M.D., Chief Medical Officer
CIO: Jennifer Coates, Coordinator Information Technology
CHR: Tara Selfridge, Manager Human Resources
CNO: Kem Scully, Chief Executive Officer and Chief Nursing Officer
Web address: www.purcellhospital.com
Control: City, Government, nonfederal **Service**: General medical and surgical

Staffed Beds: 28 **Admissions:** 549 **Census:** 5 **Outpatient Visits:** 47816 **Births:** 0 **Total Expense ($000):** 10460 **Payroll Expense ($000):** 4701

SALLISAW—Sequoyah County

NORTHEASTERN HEALTH SYSTEM SEQUOYAH (370112), 213 East Redwood Street, Zip 74955–2811, Mailing Address: P.O. Box 505, Zip 74955–0505; tel. 918/774–1100, **A**10 **F**3 8 11 14 15 18 29 30 32 34 35 40 43 45 49 50 57 59 62 63 64 65 77 81 84 86 87 91 93 102 107 110 115 119 128 129 130 132 133 135 146 147 148 149 **P**5
Primary Contact: Stephanie Six, Chief Executive Officer
CMO: Jennifer Scoufos, M.D., Chief of Staff
CIO: Gary McClanahan, Chief Information Officer
CHR: Shayna Brooke Roberts, Director Human Resources
CNO: Ozalina Martinez, R.N., Director of Nursing
Web address: www.pmtc.ok.gov/sequoyah–memorial–hospital–sallisaw–ok
Control: Hospital district or authority, Government, nonfederal **Service**: General medical and surgical

Staffed Beds: 26 **Admissions:** 473 **Census:** 6 **Outpatient Visits:** 3025 **Births:** 0 **Total Expense ($000):** 12707 **Payroll Expense ($000):** 5571 **Personnel:** 155

SAPULPA—Creek County

★ **ST. JOHN SAPULPA (371312)**, 1004 East Bryan Avenue, Zip 74066–4513, Mailing Address: P.O. Box 1368, Zip 74067–1368; tel. 918/224–4280, **A**10 18 **F**3 8 11 14 29 30 34 35 40 45 57 59 64 68 79 81 85 86 87 107 111 119 130 132 133 135 143 149 154 **P**5 6 **S** Ascension Healthcare, Saint Louis, MO
Primary Contact: Michael Christian, Chief Operating Officer
COO: Michael Christian, Chief Operating Officer
CFO: John W Crawford, Chief Financial Officer
CMO: Jason Lepak, M.D., Medical Director
CNO: Kelly Johnson, R.N., Chief Nursing Officer
Web address: www.stjohnhealthsystem.com/sapulpa
Control: Church operated, Nongovernment, not–for–profit **Service**: General medical and surgical

Staffed Beds: 25 **Admissions:** 698 **Census:** 16 **Outpatient Visits:** 54468 **Births:** 0 **Total Expense ($000):** 22676 **Payroll Expense ($000):** 7561 **Personnel:** 118

SAYRE—Beckham County

SAYRE MEMORIAL HOSPITAL, 911 Hospital Drive, Zip 73662–1206; tel. 580/928–5541, (Nonreporting)
Primary Contact: , R.N.
Control: Other not–for–profit (including NFP Corporation) **Service**: General medical and surgical

Staffed Beds: 25

SEILING—Dewey County

★ **SEILING REGIONAL MEDICAL CENTER (371332)**, Highway 60 NE, Zip 73663, Mailing Address: P.O. Box 720, Zip 73663–0720; tel. 580/922–7361, (Nonreporting) **A**10 18
Primary Contact: Jennifer Coons, Chief Executive Officer
CFO: Nancy Freed, Chief Financial Officer
CMO: Kenneth Duffy, M.D., Medical Director
CHR: Sandy Landreth, Director Human Resources
Web address: www.seilingregional.org/
Control: City, Government, nonfederal **Service**: General medical and surgical

Staffed Beds: 18

SEMINOLE—Seminole County

✠ **ALLIANCEHEALTH SEMINOLE (370229)**, 2401 Wrangler Boulevard, Zip 74868–1917; tel. 405/303–4000, **A**1 10 **F**3 11 15 18 29 30 34 40 41 43 44 45 46 47 48 49 50 57 59 64 65 68 79 81 87 89 91 92 93 96 97 107 108 109 110 111 112 114 115 119 127 129 133 146 147 148 154 **P**5 **S** Community Health Systems, Inc., Franklin, TN
Primary Contact: Adam Bracks, Chief Executive Officer
CMO: Nikki Chawla, M.D., Medical Director
CHR: Lori Friend, Human Resources Director
CNO: Barbara Lewis, Chief Nursing Officer
Web address: www.alliancehealthseminole.com/
Control: Corporation, Investor–owned (for–profit) **Service**: General medical and surgical

Staffed Beds: 32 **Admissions:** 472 **Census:** 5 **Outpatient Visits:** 23511 **Births:** 4

SHATTUCK—Ellis County

★ **NEWMAN MEMORIAL HOSPITAL (371336)**, 905 South Main Street, Zip 73858–9205; tel. 580/938–2551, **A**10 18 **F**3 8 11 15 18 19 29 32 34 35 40 41 43 45 57 64 65 69 81 85 93 107 110 114 119 128 133 144
Primary Contact: Ed Majors, Chief Executive Officer
CFO: Kellcie Skinner, Controller
CMO: Danna Stuart, M.D., Chief Medical Officer
CIO: Robert Neal, Manager Information Technology Services
Web address: www.newmanmemorialhospital.org
Control: City, Government, nonfederal **Service**: General medical and surgical

Staffed Beds: 25 **Admissions:** 111 **Census:** 1 **Outpatient Visits:** 6254 **Births:** 0 **Total Expense ($000):** 30677 **Payroll Expense ($000):** 2336 **Personnel:** 62

SHAWNEE—Pottawatomie County

CORNERSTONE HOSPITAL OF OKLAHOMA–SHAWNEE (372019), 1900 Gordon Cooper Drive, 2nd Floor, Zip 74801–8603, Mailing Address: P.O. Box 1245, Zip 74802–1245; tel. 405/395–5800, **A**10 **F**1 40 60 68 75 77 91 148 **P**8 **S** Cornerstone Healthcare Group, Dallas, TX
Primary Contact: Jimmy D. Stuart, Chief Executive Officer
COO: Cindy Linck, Chief Nursing Officer
CMO: Rakesh Shrivastava, M.D., Chief Medical Officer
Web address: www.chghospitals.com/shawnee/
Control: Corporation, Investor–owned (for–profit) **Service**: Acute long–term care hospital

Staffed Beds: 34 **Admissions:** 433 **Census:** 29 **Outpatient Visits:** 0 **Births:** 0 **Total Expense ($000):** 13086 **Payroll Expense ($000):** 6423

✠ **SSM HEALTH ST. ANTHONY HOSPITAL – SHAWNEE (370149)**, 1102 West MacArthur Street, Zip 74804–1744; tel. 405/273–2270, **A**1 10 19 **F**3 11 13 15 18 20 22 29 30 31 34 35 40 43 45 50 57 59 60 64 65 68 69 70 75 76 77 78 79 81 82 84 87 94 107 110 111 114 115 116 117 119 120 121 123 129 130 131 132 135 146 147 148 **P**6 **S** SSM Health, Saint Louis, MO
Primary Contact: Charles E. Skillings, President and Chief Executive Officer
COO: Angela Mohr, R.N., MS, Vice President Nursing and Chief Operating Officer
CFO: Jennifer Pierce, Administrative Director of Finance
CMO: Gaynell Anderson, M.D., Medical Director
CHR: Michael Spears, Human Resource Leader
CNO: Angela Mohr, R.N., MS, Vice President Nursing and Chief Operating Officer
Web address: www.stanthonyshawnee.com
Control: Other not–for–profit (including NFP Corporation) **Service**: General medical and surgical

Staffed Beds: 70 **Admissions:** 3941 **Census:** 32 **Outpatient Visits:** 122318 **Births:** 836 **Total Expense ($000):** 78372 **Payroll Expense ($000):** 26040 **Personnel:** 521

UNITY HEALTH CENTER See Ssm Health St. Anthony Hospital – Shawnee

Many Facility Codes have changed. Please refer to the AHA Guide Code Chart. © 2018 AHA Guide

SPENCER—Oklahoma County

INTEGRIS MENTAL HEALTH SYSTEM–SPENCER See Integris Baptist Medical Center, Oklahoma City

STIGLER—Haskell County

HASKELL COUNTY COMMUNITY HOSPITAL (371335), 401 Northwest 'H' Street, Zip 74462–1625; tel. 918/967–4682, (Nonreporting) **A**10 18 **S** Rural Community Hospitals of America, Kansas City, MO
Primary Contact: Donald E. Buchanan, Chief Executive Officer
CMO: Stephen Woodson, D.O., Chief of Staff
CIO: Steve Hurst, Information Technology Specialist
Web address: www.haskellhospital.com
Control: Corporation, Investor–owned (for–profit) **Service**: General medical and surgical

Staffed Beds: 18

HASKELL COUNTY HEALTHCARE SYSTEM See Haskell County Community Hospital

STILLWATER—Payne County

★ ⇑ **STILLWATER MEDICAL CENTER (370049)**, 1323 West Sixth Avenue, Zip 74074–4399, Mailing Address: P.O. Box 2408, Zip 74076–2408; tel. 405/372–1480, **A**5 10 21 **F**3 13 15 18 20 22 28 29 31 34 35 40 43 45 50 51 53 54 57 59 62 63 64 65 68 70 76 78 79 81 82 85 87 90 93 94 97 107 108 110 111 115 119 120 121 124 126 129 130 131 132 144 146 147 148 149 154 **P**6
Primary Contact: Denise Webber, President and Chief Executive Officer
CFO: Alan Lovelace, Vice President and Chief Financial Officer
CMO: Steve Cummings, M.D., Chief of Medical Staff
CIO: Chris Roark, Chief Information Officer
CHR: Keith Hufnagel, Director Human Resources
CNO: Elizabeth Michael, R.N., MS, Vice President Patient Care Services and Chief Nursing Officer
Web address: www.stillwater–medical.org
Control: Hospital district or authority, Government, nonfederal **Service**: General medical and surgical

Staffed Beds: 100 **Admissions**: 3646 **Census**: 36 **Outpatient Visits**: 134279 **Births**: 817 **Total Expense ($000)**: 175838 **Payroll Expense ($000)**: 74873 **Personnel**: 1230

STILWELL—Adair County

MEMORIAL HOSPITAL OF STILWELL (370178), 1401 West Locust, Zip 74960–3275, Mailing Address: P.O. Box 272, Zip 74960–0272; tel. 918/696–3101, (Nonreporting) **A**10
Primary Contact: Alan L. Adams, Administrator
Web address: www.stilwellmemorialhospital.com
Control: Corporation, Investor–owned (for–profit) **Service**: General medical and surgical

Staffed Beds: 34

STROUD—Lincoln County

STROUD REGIONAL MEDICAL CENTER (371316), Highway 66 West, Zip 74079, Mailing Address: P.O. Box 530, Zip 74079–0530; tel. 918/968–3571, **A**10 18 **F**3 29 30 34 35 40 41 43 45 57 59 68 93 107 128 130 133 143 148 149 154 **P**5 **S** First Physicians Capital Group, Inc., Oklahoma City, OK
Primary Contact: Ed Dyer, Chief Executive Officer
CFO: Richard E Rentsch, President
CMO: Ken Darvin, M.D., Chief of Staff
CIO: Donna Buchanan, Director Nursing
CHR: Leannette Raffety, Administrative Generalist
Web address: www.stroudhospital.com/
Control: Other not–for–profit (including NFP Corporation) **Service**: General medical and surgical

Staffed Beds: 24 **Admissions**: 97 **Census**: 1 **Outpatient Visits**: 4048 **Births**: 0

SULPHUR—Murray County

★ **ARBUCKLE MEMORIAL HOSPITAL (371328)**, 2011 West Broadway Street, Zip 73086–4221, Mailing Address: P.O. Box 1109, Zip 73086–8109; tel. 580/622–2161, **A**10 18 **F**3 11 29 32 40 45 56 57 81 87 93 107 119 127 133 135 148 **P**6 **S** Mercy, Chesterfield, MO
Primary Contact: Jeremy A. Jones, Chief Executive Officer
CFO: Denise Welch, Chief Financial Officer
CMO: Ryan Oden, D.O., Chief of Staff
CIO: Tiffany Sands, Manager Health Information
CHR: Sallie Tomlinson, Manager Human Resources
CNO: Sarah Freehill, Chief Nursing Officer
Web address: www.arbucklehospital.com/
Control: County, Government, nonfederal **Service**: General medical and surgical

Staffed Beds: 15 **Admissions**: 618 **Census**: 15 **Outpatient Visits**: 27131 **Births**: 0 **Total Expense ($000)**: 15143 **Payroll Expense ($000)**: 8208 **Personnel**: 128

TAHLEQUAH—Cherokee County

★ ⇑ **CHEROKEE NATION W.W. HASTINGS INDIAN HOSPITAL (370171)**, 100 South Bliss Avenue, Zip 74464–2512; tel. 918/458–3100, (Nonreporting) **A**3 10 21
Primary Contact: Brian Hail, Chief Executive Officer
COO: Mitchell Thornbrugh, Administrative Officer
CMO: Douglas Nolan, M.D., Medical Director
CIO: Mitchell Thornbrugh, Acting Chief Information Officer
CNO: Valerie J Rogers, Director of Nursing
Web address: www.cherokee.org
Control: Public Health Service other than 47, Government, federal **Service**: General medical and surgical

Staffed Beds: 58

★ **NORTHEASTERN HEALTH SYSTEM (370089)**, 1400 East Downing Street, Zip 74464–3324, Mailing Address: P.O. Box 1008, Zip 74465–1008; tel. 918/456–0641, **A**3 10 13 20 **F**3 7 11 13 15 17 18 20 22 24 28 29 30 31 34 35 39 40 43 45 46 47 49 51 57 59 60 64 68 70 75 76 77 78 79 80 81 82 85 87 89 90 93 97 98 103 107 108 110 111 114 115 116 117 118 119 120 121 123 129 130 135 144 146 147 148 **P**6
Primary Contact: James T. Berry, FACHE, Executive Vice President and Administrator
COO: Mark McCroskey, Vice President Operations
CFO: Julie Ward, Vice President Finance
CIO: Julie Ward, Vice President Finance
CHR: Phyllis Smith, Vice President Human Resources
CNO: Donna Dallis, R.N., Vice President Patient Care
Web address: www.nhs–ok.org/
Control: City, Government, nonfederal **Service**: General medical and surgical

Staffed Beds: 90 **Admissions**: 4055 **Census**: 49 **Outpatient Visits**: 168385 **Births**: 264 **Total Expense ($000)**: 103879 **Payroll Expense ($000)**: 37051 **Personnel**: 944

TALIHINA—Latimer County

⊠ **CHOCTAW NATION HEALTH CARE CENTER (370172)**, One Choctaw Way, Zip 74571–2022; tel. 918/567–7000, **A**1 10 13 **F**3 5 7 12 13 15 18 29 34 35 38 39 40 45 50 53 54 56 57 58 59 64 65 68 71 74 75 76 79 81 87 89 93 97 100 101 102 104 107 110 111 119 127 129 130 135 141 142 143 147 148 149 154
Primary Contact: Todd Hallmark, Chief Executive Officer
COO: Todd Hallmark, Chief Operating Officer
CMO: Jason Hill, M.D., Chief Medical Officer
CIO: Dwane Sorrells, Chief Information Officer
CHR: Jami Beckwith, Director Human Resources
CNO: Lisa Isaac, Chief Nursing Officer
Web address: www.cnhsa.com
Control: PHS, Indian Service, Government, federal **Service**: General medical and surgical

Staffed Beds: 44 **Admissions**: 1232 **Census**: 9 **Outpatient Visits**: 121190 **Births**: 458 **Total Expense ($000)**: 198257 **Payroll Expense ($000)**: 83786 **Personnel**: 1826

TISHOMINGO—Johnston County

JOHNSTON MEMORIAL HOSPITAL See Mercy Hospital Tishomingo

Hospital, Medicare Provider Number, Address, Telephone, Approval, Facility, and Physician Codes, Health Care System

★ American Hospital Association (AHA) membership
□ The Joint Commission accreditation
○ Healthcare Facilities Accreditation Program
◇ DNV Healthcare Inc. accreditation
⇑ Center for Improvement in Healthcare Quality Accreditation
△ Commission on Accreditation of Rehabilitation Facilities (CARF) accreditation

★ **MERCY HOSPITAL TISHOMINGO (371304)**, 1000 South Byrd Street, Zip 73460–3299; tel. 580/371–2327, **A**10 18 **F**3 29 40 43 44 68 107 114 133 149 **P**6 **S** Mercy, Chesterfield, MO
Primary Contact: Lori McMillin, Administrator
CFO: Lisa Dowling, Manager Finance
CHR: Arlita Hummelke, Manager Human Resources
Web address: www.mercy.net/
Control: Church operated, Nongovernment, not–for–profit **Service**: General medical and surgical

Staffed Beds: 25 Admissions: 267 Census: 4 Outpatient Visits: 5308
Births: 0 Total Expense ($000): 6284 Payroll Expense ($000): 3437
Personnel: 52

TULSA—Tulsa County

△ **BROOKHAVEN HOSPITAL (374012)**, 201 South Garnett Road, Zip 74128–1805; tel. 918/438–4257, **A**7 10 **F**4 5 29 30 54 64 74 75 77 98 102 104 106 130 132 154 **P**5
Primary Contact: Rolf B. Gainer, Ph.D., Chief Executive Officer
CFO: Kenneth Pierce, Chief Financial Officer
CMO: Mark Gage, D.O., Medical Director
CHR: Heather Dudley, Director Administrative Services
CNO: Debbie Jones, Director of Nursing
Web address: www.brookhavenhospital.com
Control: Corporation, Investor–owned (for–profit) **Service**: Psychiatric

Staffed Beds: 64 Admissions: 839 Census: 49 Outpatient Visits: 1846
Births: 0 Total Expense ($000): 11475 Payroll Expense ($000): 7030
Personnel: 187

⊞ ⇑ **HILLCREST HOSPITAL – SOUTH (370202)**, 8801 South 101st East Avenue, Zip 74133–5716; tel. 918/294–4000, **A**1 10 21 **F**3 13 15 18 20 22 24 26 28 29 34 35 40 43 45 46 47 48 49 51 57 70 73 74 76 79 81 85 86 87 91 93 107 108 110 111 115 119 126 129 130 146 147 148 **S** Ardent Health Services, Nashville, TN
Primary Contact: Kevin Nowak, Interim Chief Executive Officer
COO: Matthew Morgan, Associate Administrator
CFO: James Washecka, Chief Financial Officer
CMO: David L. Pohl, M.D., Chief of Staff
CIO: David Graser, Vice President and Chief Information Officer
CHR: Rachel Steward, Director Human Resources
CNO: Dava Baldridge, R.N., Chief Nursing Officer
Web address: www.southcresthospital.com
Control: Corporation, Investor–owned (for–profit) **Service**: General medical and surgical

Staffed Beds: 161 Admissions: 8667 Census: 104 Outpatient Visits: 90485 Births: 1283 Total Expense ($000): 141002 Payroll Expense ($000): 45314 Personnel: 702

★ ⇑ **HILLCREST MEDICAL CENTER (370001)**, 1120 South Utica Avenue, Zip 74104–4090; tel. 918/579–1000, **A**3 5 10 21 **F**3 11 13 15 16 17 18 20 22 24 26 28 29 30 31 34 37 40 43 45 46 47 48 49 50 51 53 57 58 59 60 64 68 70 72 74 75 76 78 79 80 81 83 84 85 86 87 90 93 98 100 107 108 110 111 114 115 116 117 118 119 120 121 123 124 126 129 130 131 135 145 146 147 148 154 **S** Ardent Health Services, Nashville, TN
Primary Contact: Kevin J. Gross, FACHE, Chief Executive Officer
COO: Farron Sneed, Chief Operating Officer
CFO: Donald Baker, CPA, Chief Financial Officer
CIO: Richard Gomez, Assistant Vice President Information Technology Division
CHR: Donald Morris, Vice President Human Resources
CNO: Jodi Simmons, Chief Nursing Officer
Web address: www.hillcrestmedicalcenter.com
Control: Corporation, Investor–owned (for–profit) **Service**: General medical and surgical

Staffed Beds: 508 Admissions: 24515 Census: 345 Outpatient Visits: 85489 Births: 2866 Total Expense ($000): 435557 Payroll Expense ($000): 127584 Personnel: 2124

⊞ **LAUREATE PSYCHIATRIC CLINIC AND HOSPITAL (374020)**, 6655 South Yale Avenue, Zip 74136–3329; tel. 918/481–4000, **A**1 3 5 10 **F**4 5 98 99 100 101 102 103 104 105 106 146 151 152 153 **P**6 **S** Saint Francis Health System, Tulsa, OK
Primary Contact: Michele A. Keeling, Senior Vice President and Administrator
CFO: Eric Schick, Senior Vice President, Chief Administrative Officer and Chief Financial Officer
CMO: Mark I Frost, M.D., Senior Vice President Medical Affairs
CNO: Lynn A. Sund, Senior Vice President, Administrator and Chief Nursing Executive
Web address: www.laureate.com
Control: Other not–for–profit (including NFP Corporation) **Service**: Psychiatric

Staffed Beds: 106 Admissions: 3336 Census: 75 Outpatient Visits: 10222
Births: 0 Total Expense ($000): 35462 Payroll Expense ($000): 20381
Personnel: 383

MEADOWBROOK SPECIALTY HOSPITAL OF TULSA See Post Acute Medical Specialty Hospital of Tulsa

○ **OKLAHOMA STATE UNIVERSITY MEDICAL CENTER (370078)**, 744 West Ninth Street, Zip 74127–9020; tel. 918/599–1000, (Nonreporting) **A**3 10 11 12 13 **S** Saint Francis Health System, Tulsa, OK
Primary Contact: Matthew Adams, Administrator
COO: Jeff Stroup, Chief Operating Officer
CFO: Sara Bradley, Chief Financial Officer
CMO: Damon Baker, D.O., Chief Medical Officer
CIO: Heidi Holmes, Chief Information Officer
CNO: Joy Upshaw, Chief Nursing Officer
Web address: www.osumc.net
Control: City, Government, nonfederal **Service**: General medical and surgical

Staffed Beds: 191

○ **OKLAHOMA SURGICAL HOSPITAL (370210)**, 2408 East 81st Street, Suite 300, Zip 74137–4215; tel. 918/477–5000, **A**3 5 10 11 **F**3 12 18 20 22 24 26 29 30 34 37 40 41 44 45 46 50 51 57 58 64 65 68 70 74 75 77 79 81 82 85 86 87 93 94 107 108 111 115 119 126 129 130 131 148 149 **P**2
Primary Contact: Rick Ferguson, Chief Executive Officer
CFO: Dub Cleland, Chief Financial Officer
Web address: www.oklahomasurgicalhospital.com
Control: Partnership, Investor–owned (for–profit) **Service**: Surgical

Staffed Beds: 53 Admissions: 3833 Census: 22 Outpatient Visits: 29650
Births: 0 Total Expense ($000): 95845 Payroll Expense ($000): 21632
Personnel: 440

★ **PAM REHABILITATION HOSPITAL OF TULSA (373035)**, 10020 East 91st Street, Zip 74133; tel. 918/893–2400, (Nonreporting) **A**10 **S** Post Acute Medical, LLC, Enola, PA
Primary Contact: Thomas Biby, Chief Executive Officer
CNO: Angelia Sylsberry, Chief Nursing Officer
Web address: www.warmsprings.org/our–facilities/outpatient–rehabilitation
Control: Corporation, Investor–owned (for–profit) **Service**: Rehabilitation

Staffed Beds: 41

PARKSIDE PSYCHIATRIC HOSPITAL AND CLINIC (374021), 1619 East 13th Street, Zip 74120–5407; tel. 918/582–2131, **A**5 10 **F**3 4 5 29 34 35 38 40 41 44 50 56 57 59 64 87 98 99 100 101 102 103 104 106 130 132 143 146 149 151 153 154
Primary Contact: Debra Moore–Jones, Chief Executive Officer
CFO: Saunya Moore, Chief Financial Officer
CMO: Marvin Jin, M.D., Medical Director
CIO: Joe Vitali, Director Information Technology
CHR: David Patterson, Director Human Resources
Web address: www.parksideinc.org
Control: Other not–for–profit (including NFP Corporation) **Service**: Psychiatric

Staffed Beds: 71 Admissions: 1795 Census: 61 Outpatient Visits: 11168
Births: 0 Total Expense ($000): 15249 Payroll Expense ($000): 8417
Personnel: 184

○ **PINNACLE SPECIALTY HOSPITAL (370233)**, 2408 East 81st Street, Suite 600, Zip 74137–4200; tel. 918/392–2780, (Nonreporting) **A**10 11
Primary Contact: Marc Cravens, Interim Chief Executive Officer
CFO: Marc Cravens, Chief Financial Officer
CHR: Roberta Wagle, Director Human Resources
CNO: Jill Voelkel, Chief Nursing Officer
Web address: www.pinnaclespecialtyhospital.com/
Control: Partnership, Investor–owned (for–profit) **Service**: General medical and surgical

Staffed Beds: 4

⊞ **POST ACUTE MEDICAL SPECIALTY HOSPITAL OF TULSA (372018)**, 3219 South 79th East Avenue, Zip 74145–1343; tel. 918/663–8183, **A**1 10 **F**1 3 29 40 45 60 68 70 75 87 94 107 108 114 130 143 148 **S** Post Acute Medical, LLC, Enola, PA
Primary Contact: Kristopher Karns, Chief Executive Officer
Web address: www.postacutetulsa.com
Control: Corporation, Investor–owned (for–profit) **Service**: Acute long–term care hospital

Staffed Beds: 60 Admissions: 686 Census: 33 Outpatient Visits: 3
Births: 0 Total Expense ($000): 17461 Payroll Expense ($000): 8170
Personnel: 151

SAINT FRANCIS HEART HOSPITAL See Saint Francis Hospital, Tulsa

SAINT FRANCIS HOSPITAL (370091), 6161 South Yale Avenue, Zip 74136–1902; tel. 918/494–2200, (Includes CHILDREN'S HOSPITAL AT SAINT FRANCIS, 6161 South Yale Avenue, Tulsa, OK, Zip 74136–1902; tel. 918/502–6714; Shannon M. Filosa, Executive Director Women's and Children; SAINT FRANCIS HEART HOSPITAL, 6151 South Yale Avenue, Tulsa, OK, Zip 74136–1902; tel. 918/494–1817; Douglas Williams, Vice President, Saint Francis Heart Hospital) **A**1 2 3 5 10 **F**3 7 8 11 12 13 15 17 18 19 20 21 22 23 24 25 26 27 28 29 30 31 32 35 37 39 40 41 43 44 45 46 47 48 49 50 51 54 55 56 57 58 59 60 61 64 66 68 70 72 73 74 75 76 77 78 79 80 81 82 83 84 85 86 87 88 89 90 92 93 100 102 107 108 110 111 114 115 116 117 118 119 120 121 123 124 128 129 130 131 132 135 136 138 141 146 147 148 154 **P**6 **S** Saint Francis Health System, Tulsa, OK
Primary Contact: Lynn A. Sund, Chief Nurse Executive and Administrator
COO: Barry L Steichen, Executive Vice President and Chief Operating Officer, Saint Francis Health System
CFO: Eric Schick, Senior Vice President and Chief Financial Officer, Saint Francis Health System
CMO: Mark I Frost, M.D., Senior Vice President Medical Affairs, Saint Francis Health System
CIO: Meridith Coburn, Vice President Information Services
CHR: Maria E. Isquierdo, Executive Director, Human Resources
CNO: Lynn A. Sund, Senior Vice President, Chief Nurse Executive, Saint Francis Health System and Administrator, Saint Francis Hospital
Web address: www.saintfrancis.com
Control: Other not–for–profit (including NFP Corporation) **Service:** General medical and surgical

Staffed Beds: 842 **Admissions:** 45306 **Census:** 641 **Outpatient Visits:** 401992 **Births:** 4126 **Total Expense ($000):** 803626 **Payroll Expense ($000):** 312347 **Personnel:** 5058

SAINT FRANCIS HOSPITAL SOUTH (370218), 10501 East 91st Street, Zip 74133–5790; tel. 918/307–6010, **A**1 10 **F**11 13 15 18 20 22 26 29 30 34 35 37 39 40 44 48 49 50 51 57 58 60 61 64 68 70 72 75 76 79 80 81 82 85 87 107 108 110 111 114 115 118 119 130 146 148 **P**6 **S** Saint Francis Health System, Tulsa, OK
Primary Contact: David S. Weil, Senior Vice President and Administrator
COO: Barry L Steichen, Executive Vice President and Chief Operating Officer
CFO: Eric Schick, Chief Financial Officer
CMO: Mark I Frost, M.D., Senior Vice President Medical Affairs
CIO: Meridith Coburn, Vice President, Information Systems
CHR: Maria E. Isquierdo, Executive Director, Human Resources
CNO: Lynn A. Sund, Chief Nursing Executive
Web address: www.saintfrancis.com/south/
Control: Other not–for–profit (including NFP Corporation) **Service:** General medical and surgical

Staffed Beds: 90 **Admissions:** 5048 **Census:** 50 **Outpatient Visits:** 74662 **Births:** 942 **Total Expense ($000):** 72410 **Payroll Expense ($000):** 29481 **Personnel:** 444

SELECT SPECIALTY HOSPITAL–TULSA MIDTOWN (372007), 1125 South Trenton Avenue, 3rd Floor, Zip 74120–5418; tel. 918/579–7300, **A**1 10 **F**1 3 29 75 85 87 130 148 **S** Select Medical Corporation, Mechanicsburg, PA
Primary Contact: Raymond Carnevale, Interim Chief Executive Officer
CMO: E Joe Schelbar, M.D., Medical Director
CNO: Connie Ryan, Chief Nursing Officer
Web address: www.tulsa.selectspecialtyhospitals.com/
Control: Corporation, Investor–owned (for–profit) **Service:** Acute long–term care hospital

Staffed Beds: 56 **Admissions:** 348 **Census:** 25 **Outpatient Visits:** 0 **Births:** 0 **Total Expense ($000):** 13913 **Payroll Expense ($000):** 6119 **Personnel:** 92

SHADOW MOUNTAIN BEHAVIORAL HEALTH SYSTEM (374024), 6262 South Sheridan Road, Zip 74133–4055; tel. 918/492–8200, (Nonreporting) **A**1 5 **S** Universal Health Services, Inc., King of Prussia, PA
Primary Contact: Jeanne Wypyski, Chief Executive Officer
CFO: Kirt Penrod, Chief Financial Officer
CMO: K. Michael Saliba, M.D., Medical Director
CHR: Jordan Cooke, Director Human Resources
Web address: www.shadowmountainbhs.com
Control: Corporation, Investor–owned (for–profit) **Service:** Children's hospital psychiatric

Staffed Beds: 238

SOUTHWESTERN REGIONAL MEDICAL CENTER (370190), 10109 East 79th Street, Zip 74133–4564; tel. 918/286–5000, **A**1 2 3 5 10 **F**3 15 29 30 31 34 35 36 40 44 45 46 47 49 53 57 58 59 64 70 75 77 78 81 82 84 85 86 87 93 97 107 108 110 111 114 116 117 118 119 120 121 123 124 126 130 132 135 143 145 146 148 **P**6 **S** Cancer Treatment Centers of America, Schaumburg, IL
Primary Contact: Jay Foley, President and Chief Executive Officer
CFO: David Hedges, Chief Financial Officer
CMO: Daniel Nader, D.O., Chief of Staff
CIO: Craig Olson, Director Information Technology
CHR: Ryan Crawford, Director Talent
CNO: Denise Geuder, Vice President Patient Care Service and Chief Nursing Officer
Web address: www.cancercenter.com
Control: Corporation, Investor–owned (for–profit) **Service:** Cancer

Staffed Beds: 40 **Admissions:** 707 **Census:** 12 **Outpatient Visits:** 37737 **Births:** 0 **Personnel:** 430

ST. JOHN MEDICAL CENTER (370114), 1923 South Utica Avenue, Zip 74104–6502; tel. 918/744–2345, **A**1 2 3 5 10 **F**3 8 9 11 13 14 15 17 18 19 20 22 24 26 28 29 30 31 34 35 37 38 39 40 43 45 46 47 48 49 50 51 53 54 56 57 58 59 60 61 63 64 65 66 68 70 72 73 74 75 76 77 78 79 80 81 82 83 84 85 86 87 88 89 90 92 93 94 96 97 100 104 107 108 110 111 114 115 116 117 118 119 120 121 123 124 126 129 130 131 132 135 138 141 143 145 146 147 148 149 154 **P**1 5 **S** Ascension Healthcare, Saint Louis, MO
Primary Contact: Jeffrey D. Nowlin, President and Chief Operating Officer
COO: Jeffrey D Nowlin, President and Chief Operating Officer
CFO: Wayne Walthall, Vice President and Chief Financial Officer
CMO: William Allred, M.D., Vice President Medical Affairs
CIO: Mike Reeves, Vice President
CHR: John Page Bachman, Corporate Vice President
CNO: Pamela Kiser, R.N., MS, Chief Nursing Executive and Vice President of Nursing
Web address: www.sjmc.org
Control: Church operated, Nongovernment, not–for–profit **Service:** General medical and surgical

Staffed Beds: 523 **Admissions:** 29080 **Census:** 418 **Outpatient Visits:** 240380 **Births:** 2433 **Total Expense ($000):** 538673 **Payroll Expense ($000):** 149775 **Personnel:** 2273

TULSA SPINE AND SPECIALTY HOSPITAL (370216), 6901 South Olympia Avenue, Zip 74132–1843; tel. 918/388–5701, **A**1 10 **F**3 29 40 45 68 74 78 79 81 82 85 87 89 107 111 126 **S** Ardent Health Services, Nashville, TN
Primary Contact: Trent Gastineau, Chief Executive Officer
CMO: David Fell, M.D., Chief Medical Officer
Web address: www.tulsaspinehospital.com
Control: Partnership, Investor–owned (for–profit) **Service:** Surgical

Staffed Beds: 38 **Admissions:** 1145 **Census:** 8 **Births:** 0

VINITA—Craig County

OKLAHOMA FORENSIC CENTER, 24800 South 4420 Road, Zip 74301–5544, Mailing Address: P.O. Box 69, Zip 74301–0069; tel. 918/256–7841, (Nonreporting) **A**3 **S** Oklahoma Department of Mental Health and Substance Abuse Services, Oklahoma City, OK
Primary Contact: Kevan Finley, Chief Executive Officer
CFO: Miriam Harris, Director Finance
CMO: Satwant Tandon, M.D., Director of Clinical Services
CIO: Kevin Marble, Director Information Technology
CHR: Julie Jacobs, Director Human Resources
CNO: Glenda Satterwhite, Director of Nursing
Web address: www.odmhsas.org
Control: State, Government, nonfederal **Service:** Psychiatric

Staffed Beds: 200

SAINT FRANCIS HOSPITAL VINITA (370237), 735 North Foreman Street, Zip 74301–1418, Mailing Address: P.O. Box 326, Zip 74301–0326; tel. 918/256–7551, **A**10 20 **F**3 11 15 18 29 30 34 35 36 40 45 50 53 57 59 68 74 75 77 79 80 82 86 87 93 94 98 100 102 103 104 107 108 111 114 115 119 127 129 130 133 143 146 147 148 154 **P**6 **S** Saint Francis Health System, Tulsa, OK
Primary Contact: Todd Schuster, Administrator
CMO: Ed Allensworth, M.D., Medical Director
CHR: Darlene R Nolte, Chief Human Resource Officer
CNO: Ann Carr, R.N., Chief Nursing Officer
Web address: www.saintfrancis.com/vinita/Pages/default.aspx
Control: Other not–for–profit (including NFP Corporation) **Service:** General medical and surgical

Staffed Beds: 70 **Admissions:** 312 **Census:** 5 **Outpatient Visits:** 14107 **Births:** 0 **Total Expense ($000):** 10126 **Payroll Expense ($000):** 3532 **Personnel:** 122

Hospital, Medicare Provider Number, Address, Telephone, Approval, Facility, and Physician Codes, Health Care System

★ American Hospital Association (AHA) membership   ◯ Healthcare Facilities Accreditation Program   ⇑ Center for Improvement in Healthcare Quality Accreditation
☐ The Joint Commission accreditation   ◇ DNV Healthcare Inc. accreditation   △ Commission on Accreditation of Rehabilitation Facilities (CARF) accreditation

Hospitals, U.S. / OKLAHOMA

OK

WAGONER—Wagoner County

WAGONER COMMUNITY HOSPITAL (370166), 1200 West Cherokee Street, Zip 74467-4624, Mailing Address: P.O. Box 407, Zip 74477-0407; tel. 918/485-5514, **A**10 **F**3 11 15 18 28 29 30 34 39 40 41 45 50 51 57 59 64 65 68 70 75 79 81 82 85 87 98 102 107 108 110 111 115 118 119 129 130 131 132 135 146 147 148 149 154
Primary Contact: Jimmy Leopard, FACHE, Chief Executive Officer
COO: Louise Dodson, R.N., Chief Operating Officer and Chief Nursing Officer
CFO: Rebecca Sharp, Chief Financial Officer
CMO: Casey Hanna, M.D., Chief of Staff
CIO: Jim Riley, Director Information Technology
CHR: Barnetta Pofahl, Director Human Resources
CNO: Louise Dodson, R.N., Chief Nursing Officer
Web address: www.wagonerhospital.com
Control: Hospital district or authority, Government, nonfederal **Service**: General medical and surgical

Staffed Beds: 100 **Admissions**: 2308 **Census**: 35 **Outpatient Visits**: 31208
Births: 0 **Total Expense ($000)**: 22392 **Payroll Expense ($000)**: 9590
Personnel: 189

WATONGA—Blaine County

★ **MERCY HOSPITAL WATONGA (371302)**, 500 North Clarence Nash Boulevard, Zip 73772-2845, Mailing Address: P.O. Box 370, Zip 73772-0370; tel. 580/623-7211, **A**10 18 **F**3 11 29 30 34 40 43 50 57 59 64 68 75 85 87 93 107 114 119 128 130 132 133 135 149 **P**6 **S** Mercy, Chesterfield, MO
Primary Contact: Cindy Carmichael, Administrator
CHR: Mary Jo Messelt, Manager Human Resources
Web address: www.mercy.net/watongaok/practice/mercy-hospital-watonga
Control: Church operated, Nongovernment, not-for-profit **Service**: General medical and surgical

Staffed Beds: 25 **Admissions**: 224 **Census**: 3 **Outpatient Visits**: 9749
Births: 0 **Total Expense ($000)**: 6765 **Payroll Expense ($000)**: 3840
Personnel: 48

WAURIKA—Jefferson County

JEFFERSON COUNTY HOSPITAL (371311), Highway 70 and 81, Zip 73573-3075, Mailing Address: P.O. Box 90, Zip 73573-0090; tel. 580/228-2344, (Data for 150 days) **A**10 18 **F**40 43 64 68 93 107 114 127 133 148 154 **S** Duncan Regional Hospital, Duncan, OK
Primary Contact: Richard Gillespie, Chief Executive Officer
CFO: Richard Tallon, Chief Financial Officer
CMO: Rob Linzman, D.O., Chief of Staff
CIO: Nikki McGahey, Information Officer
Web address: www.jeffersoncountyhospital.net
Control: Other not-for-profit (including NFP Corporation) **Service**: General medical and surgical

Staffed Beds: 25 **Admissions**: 30 **Census**: 1 **Outpatient Visits**: 1851
Births: 0 **Total Expense ($000)**: 2120 **Payroll Expense ($000)**: 1305
Personnel: 30

WEATHERFORD—Custer County

★ **WEATHERFORD REGIONAL HOSPITAL (371323)**, 3701 East Main Street, Zip 73096-3309; tel. 580/772-5551, **A**10 18 **F**3 11 13 15 29 34 40 43 45 59 64 68 75 76 77 81 86 87 93 107 108 110 111 115 119 130 133 135 144 146 147 148 **P**6 7
Primary Contact: Debbie Howe, Chief Executive Officer
CFO: Stephanie Helton, Chief Financial Officer
CMO: Jonathan Ray Long, M.D., Chief of Staff
CIO: Amy Outhier, Director Health Information Management
CHR: Tawnya Paden, Director Human Resources
CNO: Delvin Mast, R.N., Director of Nursing
Web address: www.weatherfordhospital.com
Control: Hospital district or authority, Government, nonfederal **Service**: General medical and surgical

Staffed Beds: 22 **Admissions**: 585 **Census**: 5 **Outpatient Visits**: 54147
Births: 120 **Total Expense ($000)**: 18309 **Payroll Expense ($000)**: 6277
Personnel: 149

WILBURTON—Latimer County

LATIMER COUNTY GENERAL HOSPITAL (370072), 806 Highway 2 North, Zip 74578-3698; tel. 918/465-2391, (Nonreporting) **A**10
Primary Contact: Nikki Nix, Chief Executive Officer
CMO: Richard Valbuena, M.D., Medical Director
CHR: Rachel Chinnock, Chief Human Resources Officer
Web address: www.pmtc.ok.gov/latimer-county-general-hospital-wilburton-ok
Control: County, Government, nonfederal **Service**: General medical and surgical

Staffed Beds: 33

WOODWARD—Woodward County

✠ **ALLIANCEHEALTH WOODWARD (370002)**, 900 17th Street, Zip 73801-2448; tel. 580/256-5511, **A**1 10 20 **F**1 3 4 13 15 16 17 18 29 30 31 34 40 43 45 50 57 59 64 67 68 69 70 72 73 75 76 77 78 79 80 81 82 85 88 89 90 93 98 107 108 110 111 115 119 124 127 128 129 130 131 133 135 146 148 149 154 **S** Community Health Systems, Inc., Franklin, TN
Primary Contact: Ross Korkmas, Chief Executive Officer
CFO: Tom Earley, Chief Financial Officer
CIO: Larry Churchill, Director Information Services
CHR: Melinda Brock, Director Human Resources
CNO: Kimberly N Arnold, R.N., Chief Nursing Officer and Interim Chief Quality Officer
Web address: www.woodwardhospital.com
Control: Corporation, Investor-owned (for-profit) **Service**: General medical and surgical

Staffed Beds: 40 **Admissions**: 1429 **Census**: 13 **Outpatient Visits**: 94794
Births: 300

YUKON—Canadian County

✠ **INTEGRIS CANADIAN VALLEY HOSPITAL (370211)**, 1201 Health Center Parkway, Zip 73099-6381; tel. 405/717-6800, **A**1 3 10 **F**3 11 13 15 18 20 22 29 30 34 39 40 43 44 45 46 49 52 57 59 60 64 68 70 76 79 81 87 93 96 107 108 110 111 115 118 119 130 135 146 147 148 **P**6 7 **S** INTEGRIS Health, Oklahoma City, OK
Primary Contact: Teresa Gray, President
COO: Cindy White, CPA, Vice President of Operations
CFO: Errol Mitchell, Chief Financial Officer
CHR: Lynn Ketch, Human Resources Recruiter Generalist
CNO: Teresa Gray, Chief Nursing Officer and Assistant Vice President
Web address: www.integris-health.com
Control: Other not-for-profit (including NFP Corporation) **Service**: General medical and surgical

Staffed Beds: 58 **Admissions**: 2950 **Census**: 25 **Outpatient Visits**: 63944
Births: 820 **Total Expense ($000)**: 56505 **Payroll Expense ($000)**: 17633
Personnel: 233

Many Facility Codes have changed. Please refer to the AHA Guide Code Chart.

© 2018 AHA Guide

OR

OREGON

ALBANY—Linn County

★ ⇑ **SAMARITAN ALBANY GENERAL HOSPITAL (380022)**, 1046 Sixth Avenue, SW, Zip 97321–1999; tel. 541/812–4000, **A**3 10 21 **F**3 5 11 13 15 18 28 29 30 31 34 35 36 37 40 43 45 47 49 53 54 57 59 61 63 64 67 68 70 73 74 76 77 78 79 81 84 85 86 87 89 92 93 97 104 107 108 110 111 114 116 117 119 130 131 132 135 144 145 146 147 148 149 150 **P**6 **S** Samaritan Health Services, Corvallis, OR
Primary Contact: David G. Triebes, Chief Executive Officer
CFO: Daniel B Smith, Vice President Finance
Web address: www.samhealth.org
Control: Other not-for-profit (including NFP Corporation) **Service:** General medical and surgical

Staffed Beds: 70 **Admissions:** 2473 **Census:** 22 **Outpatient Visits:** 294187 **Births:** 541 **Total Expense ($000):** 188618 **Payroll Expense ($000):** 78590 **Personnel:** 841

ASHLAND—Jackson County

★ ⇑ **ASANTE ASHLAND COMMUNITY HOSPITAL (380005)**, 280 Maple Street, Zip 97520–1593; tel. 541/201–4000, **A**10 21 **F**3 11 13 15 29 30 34 35 36 40 45 46 48 50 57 59 62 64 65 70 75 76 79 81 85 86 87 107 110 114 119 130 131 132 143 145 146 147 148 **P**6 **S** Asante Health System, Medford, OR
Primary Contact: Sheila Clough, Chief Executive Officer
CFO: Patrick Hocking, Chief Financial Officer
CMO: Bill Steinsick, M.D., Chief Medical Staff
CIO: Mark Hetz, Chief Information Officer
CHR: Gregg Edwards, Vice President Human Resources
CNO: Susan Montgomery, Chief Nursing Officer
Web address: www.ashlandhospital.org
Control: Other not-for-profit (including NFP Corporation) **Service:** General medical and surgical

Staffed Beds: 36 **Admissions:** 1417 **Census:** 13 **Outpatient Visits:** 47460 **Births:** 271 **Total Expense ($000):** 52327 **Payroll Expense ($000):** 20464 **Personnel:** 265

ASTORIA—Clatsop County

★ **COLUMBIA MEMORIAL HOSPITAL (381320)**, 2111 Exchange Street, Zip 97103–3329; tel. 503/325–4321, **A**3 5 10 18 **F**3 11 13 15 18 26 28 29 30 31 32 34 35 36 40 41 43 44 45 50 51 57 58 59 63 64 65 68 70 75 76 77 78 79 81 85 86 87 89 91 93 97 107 108 110 114 115 116 117 119 127 130 131 132 133 134 135 142 146 147 148 149 154 **P**5 8
Primary Contact: Erik Thorsen, Chief Executive Officer
COO: Nicole Williams, Chief Operating Officer
CFO: Stephanie D Brenden, Vice President Finance
CMO: Bruce Bobek, President Professional Staff
CIO: Galina Gandy, Vice President Information Technology
CHR: Lucy G Dupree, Director Human Resources
CNO: Trece Gurrad, Vice President Patient Care Services
Web address: www.columbiamemorial.org
Control: Other not-for-profit (including NFP Corporation) **Service:** General medical and surgical

Staffed Beds: 25 **Admissions:** 1653 **Census:** 13 **Outpatient Visits:** 202854 **Births:** 302 **Total Expense ($000):** 102310 **Payroll Expense ($000):** 40994 **Personnel:** 533

BAKER CITY—Baker County

⊠ **SAINT ALPHONSUS MEDICAL CENTER – BAKER CITY (381315)**, 3325 Pocahontas Road, Zip 97814–1464; tel. 541/523–6461, **A**1 10 18 **F**3 11 13 15 29 31 34 35 36 37 40 43 44 45 50 59 64 68 70 75 76 77 79 81 82 83 85 91 93 97 107 110 111 115 119 127 128 129 131 133 143 146 147 148 154 **P**6 **S** Trinity Health, Livonia, MI
Primary Contact: Charles Davis, President
CFO: Robert D Wehling, Interim Chief Financial Officer
CHR: Jerry Nickell, Vice President Human Resource and Mission
Web address: www.saintalphonsus.org/bakercity
Control: Other not-for-profit (including NFP Corporation) **Service:** General medical and surgical

Staffed Beds: 25 **Admissions:** 793 **Census:** 7 **Outpatient Visits:** 43750 **Births:** 131 **Total Expense ($000):** 36381 **Payroll Expense ($000):** 13601 **Personnel:** 184

ST. ELIZABETH HEALTH SERVICES See Saint Alphonsus Medical Center – Baker City

BANDON—Coos County

★ **SOUTHERN COOS HOSPITAL AND HEALTH CENTER (381304)**, 900 11th Street SE, Zip 97411–9114; tel. 541/347–2426, **A**10 18 **F**3 11 15 29 34 35 40 45 50 57 59 64 65 75 81 82 85 87 97 107 110 115 119 130 132 133 135 146 148 149 154 **P**6
Primary Contact: JoDee Tittle, Chief Executive Officer
CFO: Robin Triplett, Chief Financial Officer
CMO: Megan Holland, Chief Medical Officer and Family Practitioner
CIO: Mandy Calvert, Director Information Systems
CHR: Kalen M Mills, Director Human Resources
CNO: Rachel Beissel, Chief Nursing Officer
Web address: www.southerncoos.org
Control: Hospital district or authority, Government, nonfederal **Service:** General medical and surgical

Staffed Beds: 19 **Admissions:** 275 **Census:** 3 **Outpatient Visits:** 67289 **Births:** 0 **Total Expense ($000):** 17846 **Payroll Expense ($000):** 7304 **Personnel:** 116

BEND—Deschutes County

⊠ **ST. CHARLES BEND (380047)**, 2500 NE Neff Road, Zip 97701–6015; tel. 541/382–4321, **A**1 2 3 5 10 19 **F**3 8 11 12 13 15 18 19 20 21 22 24 26 28 29 30 31 34 35 36 37 38 40 43 44 45 46 47 49 50 51 54 57 58 59 60 62 63 64 65 67 68 70 72 74 75 76 77 78 79 81 82 84 85 86 87 89 90 91 92 93 97 98 99 100 101 102 107 108 111 114 115 118 119 120 121 122 124 126 129 130 132 135 144 146 147 148 149 154 **P**6 **S** St. Charles Health System, Inc., Bend, OR
Primary Contact: Iman Simmons, Chief Operating Officer and Interim President
CFO: Jennifer Welander, CPA, Senior Vice President Finance and Chief Financial Officer
CMO: Jeffrey Absalon, M.D., Chief Physician Officer
CIO: Jerimiah Brickhouse, Chief Information Officer
CHR: Rebecca Berry, Vice President Human Resources
CNO: Karen Reed, R.N., MSN, Chief Nursing Officer
Web address: www.stcharleshealthcare.org
Control: Other not-for-profit (including NFP Corporation) **Service:** General medical and surgical

Staffed Beds: 259 **Admissions:** 16561 **Census:** 179 **Outpatient Visits:** 138126 **Births:** 1735 **Total Expense ($000):** 382446 **Payroll Expense ($000):** 157292 **Personnel:** 2891

BURNS—Harney County

★ **HARNEY DISTRICT HOSPITAL (381307)**, 557 West Washington Street, Zip 97720–1497; tel. 541/573–7281, **A**10 18 **F**3 7 13 15 29 31 34 35 40 43 45 50 53 57 59 64 65 70 75 76 78 81 82 85 93 97 107 111 114 119 127 129 131 132 133 146 149 **P**6
Primary Contact: Dan Grigg, Chief Executive Officer
CFO: Catherine White, Chief Financial Officer
CMO: Sarah Laiosa, M.D., Chief Medical Staff
CIO: Tanya Strong, Manager Information Technology
CHR: Sammie Masterson, Director Human Resources
CNO: Deana Altman, Interim Chief Nursing Officer
Web address: www.harneydh.com
Control: Hospital district or authority, Government, nonfederal **Service:** General medical and surgical

Staffed Beds: 21 **Admissions:** 383 **Census:** 4 **Outpatient Visits:** 39178 **Births:** 50 **Total Expense ($000):** 25161 **Payroll Expense ($000):** 10648 **Personnel:** 170

Hospital, Medicare Provider Number, Address, Telephone, Approval, Facility, and Physician Codes, Health Care System

★ American Hospital Association (AHA) membership
□ The Joint Commission accreditation
○ Healthcare Facilities Accreditation Program
◇ DNV Healthcare Inc. accreditation
⇑ Center for Improvement in Healthcare Quality Accreditation
△ Commission on Accreditation of Rehabilitation Facilities (CARF) accreditation

OR

CLACKAMAS—Clackamas County

✠ ⇑ **KAISER SUNNYSIDE MEDICAL CENTER (380091)**, 10180 SE Sunnyside Road, Zip 97015–8970; tel. 503/652–2880, **A**1 2 3 5 10 21 **F**3 11 12 13 15 17 18 20 22 24 26 29 30 31 34 35 40 45 46 47 49 51 60 61 64 65 68 70 72 74 75 76 77 78 79 81 84 85 86 87 93 94 97 102 107 108 110 111 114 115 118 119 130 135 141 146 147 148 149 154 **P**6 **S** Kaiser Foundation Hospitals, Oakland, CA
Primary Contact: Justin N. Evander, Administrator and Chief Operating Officer
CFO: Justin N. Evander, Chief Financial Officer
CMO: Richard Hunt, M.D., Chief Operating Officer
CIO: Mark A Burmester, Vice President Strategy and Communications
CHR: Rich Smith, Vice President Human Resources
CNO: Lauren M Bridge, R.N., Chief Nursing Officer
Web address: www.kaiserpermanente.org
Control: Other not–for–profit (including NFP Corporation) **Service**: General medical and surgical

Staffed Beds: 301 **Admissions**: 18861 **Census**: 205 **Outpatient Visits**: 70063 **Births**: 2397 **Total Expense ($000)**: 392190 **Payroll Expense ($000)**: 170874 **Personnel**: 2283	

COOS BAY—Coos County

✠ **BAY AREA HOSPITAL (380090)**, 1775 Thompson Road, Zip 97420–2198; tel. 541/269–8111, **A**1 2 3 5 10 **F**3 11 12 13 15 18 20 22 26 28 29 31 34 35 40 43 45 46 48 50 51 57 59 62 68 70 73 74 75 76 77 78 79 81 84 85 89 91 92 93 98 99 100 101 102 104 107 108 110 111 115 118 119 120 121 123 126 129 130 132 135 146 147 148 149 **P**6
Primary Contact: Paul Janke, FACHE, President and Chief Executive Officer
COO: Ben Pfau, Chief Facility and Information Officer
CFO: Sam Patterson, Chief Financial Officer
CIO: Bob Adams, Director Information Services
CHR: Suzie Q McDaniel, Chief Human Resource Officer
Web address: www.bayareahospital.org
Control: Hospital district or authority, Government, nonfederal **Service**: General medical and surgical

Staffed Beds: 130 **Admissions**: 6186 **Census**: 67 **Outpatient Visits**: 94555 **Births**: 648 **Total Expense ($000)**: 172711 **Payroll Expense ($000)**: 66516 **Personnel**: 885	

COQUILLE—Coos County

★ **COQUILLE VALLEY HOSPITAL (381312)**, 940 East Fifth Street, Zip 97423–1699; tel. 541/396–3101, **A**10 18 **F**3 8 11 15 29 34 35 40 43 45 50 57 59 62 64 75 79 81 82 85 86 87 97 107 110 111 115 118 119 132 133 135 146 148 149 **P**6
Primary Contact: Jeff Lang, Chief Executive Officer
CFO: Robert E Fisher, Chief Financial Officer
CMO: James Sinnott, M.D., Chief Medical Staff
CIO: Curt Carpenter, Manager Information Technology
CHR: Monte Johnston, Manager Human Resources
Web address: www.cvhospital.org
Control: Hospital district or authority, Government, nonfederal **Service**: General medical and surgical

Staffed Beds: 17 **Admissions**: 694 **Census**: 6 **Outpatient Visits**: 26004 **Births**: 0 **Total Expense ($000)**: 28296 **Payroll Expense ($000)**: 12026 **Personnel**: 183	

CORVALLIS—Benton County

★ ⇑ **GOOD SAMARITAN REGIONAL MEDICAL CENTER (380014)**, 3600 NW Samaritan Drive, Zip 97330–3737, Mailing Address: P.O. Box 1068, Zip 97339–1068; tel. 541/768–5111, **A**2 3 10 12 13 19 21 **F**3 11 12 13 15 17 18 20 22 24 26 28 29 30 31 34 35 36 37 40 43 53 54 56 57 58 59 61 62 64 68 70 73 74 76 77 78 79 81 82 85 86 87 89 92 93 97 98 100 101 102 104 107 108 110 111 114 115 116 117 118 119 120 121 123 124 126 130 131 132 135 144 146 147 148 149 153 154 **P**6 **S** Samaritan Health Services, Corvallis, OR
Primary Contact: Becky A. Pape, R.N., Chief Executive Officer
CFO: Daniel B Smith, Vice President Finance
CIO: Bob Power, Vice President Information Services
CHR: Doug Boysen, Chief Legal Counsel and Vice President Human Resources
CNO: William Howden, Vice President Nursing
Web address: www.samhealth.org
Control: Other not–for–profit (including NFP Corporation) **Service**: General medical and surgical

Staffed Beds: 182 **Admissions**: 8990 **Census**: 122 **Outpatient Visits**: 443536 **Births**: 1004 **Total Expense ($000)**: 428068 **Payroll Expense ($000)**: 168858 **Personnel**: 1755	

COTTAGE GROVE—Lane County

★ **PEACEHEALTH COTTAGE GROVE COMMUNITY MEDICAL CENTER (381301)**, 1515 Village Drive, Zip 97424–9700; tel. 541/942–0511, **A**10 18 **F**3 11 15 29 32 34 35 38 40 44 50 59 64 65 66 68 75 91 93 97 102 107 110 115 119 127 130 132 133 146 148 154 **P**6 **S** PeaceHealth, Vancouver, WA
Primary Contact: Tim Herrmann, R.N., Administrator
Control: Church operated, Nongovernment, not–for–profit **Service**: General medical and surgical

Staffed Beds: 14 **Admissions**: 449 **Census**: 3 **Outpatient Visits**: 36981 **Births**: 0 **Total Expense ($000)**: 36084 **Payroll Expense ($000)**: 12906 **Personnel**: 128	

DALLAS—Polk County

SALEM HEALTH WEST VALLEY (381308), 525 SE Washington Street, Zip 97338–2834, Mailing Address: P.O. Box 378, Zip 97338–0378; tel. 503/623–8301, **A**10 18 **F**3 15 35 40 50 59 64 75 79 81 85 93 97 107 108 110 111 114 119 131 132 133 143 146 148 **P**6 **S** Salem Health, Salem, OR
Primary Contact: Bruce C. Rodgers, Chief Administrative Officer
CFO: James Parr, Chief Financial Officer
CMO: Ralph Yates, D.O., Chief Medical Officer
CHR: Laurie C Barr, Vice President Human Resources
CNO: Sarah Horn, Chief Nursing Officer
Web address: www.salemhealth.org/wvh/
Control: Other not–for–profit (including NFP Corporation) **Service**: General medical and surgical

Staffed Beds: 6 **Admissions**: 137 **Census**: 1 **Outpatient Visits**: 68968 **Births**: 0 **Total Expense ($000)**: 24728 **Payroll Expense ($000)**: 11644 **Personnel**: 132	

ENTERPRISE—Wallowa County

★ **WALLOWA MEMORIAL HOSPITAL (381306)**, 601 Medical Parkway, Zip 97828–5124; tel. 541/426–3111, **A**3 5 10 18 **F**3 7 10 11 13 15 29 30 31 34 35 40 43 45 46 56 57 59 64 68 75 76 78 79 81 82 85 87 93 97 102 107 110 115 119 127 128 131 143 145 148 149 **P**6
Primary Contact: Larry Davy, Chief Executive Officer
CFO: Daniel Jessup, Chief Financial Officer
CMO: Keith DeYoung, M.D., Chief Medical Staff
CIO: John Straughan, Director Information Technology
CHR: Linda Childers, Director Human Resources
CNO: Jenni Word, R.N., Chief Nursing Officer
Web address: www.wchcd.org
Control: Hospital district or authority, Government, nonfederal **Service**: General medical and surgical

Staffed Beds: 25 **Admissions**: 621 **Census**: 7 **Outpatient Visits**: 22573 **Births**: 57 **Total Expense ($000)**: 21635 **Payroll Expense ($000)**: 9018 **Personnel**: 149	

EUGENE—Lane County

★ △ ⇑ **PEACEHEALTH SACRED HEART MEDICAL CENTER UNIVERSITY DISTRICT (380033)**, 1255 Hilyard Street, Zip 97401–3700, Mailing Address: P.O. Box 10905, Zip 97440–2905; tel. 541/686–7300, **A**7 10 21 **F**3 29 30 31 38 40 43 56 62 63 68 84 90 93 98 102 105 107 115 130 146 148 153 154 **P**6 **S** PeaceHealth, Vancouver, WA
Primary Contact: Mary Anne McMurren, R.N., Chief Administrative Officer
CFO: Wendy Apland, Interim Chief Financial Officer
CMO: Bill Moshofsky, M.D., Chief of Staff
CIO: Donn McMillan, Chief Information Officer
CHR: Craig Mills, Vice President Human Resources
Web address: www.peacehealth.org
Control: Church operated, Nongovernment, not–for–profit **Service**: General medical and surgical

Staffed Beds: 104 **Admissions**: 2636 **Census**: 61 **Outpatient Visits**: 117147 **Births**: 0 **Total Expense ($000)**: 112490 **Payroll Expense ($000)**: 47872 **Personnel**: 2288	

FLORENCE—Lane County

★ ⇑ **PEACEHEALTH PEACE HARBOR MEDICAL CENTER (381316)**, 400 Ninth Street, Zip 97439–7398; tel. 541/997–8412, **A**10 18 21 **F**3 8 11 13 15 28 29 30 34 38 40 43 45 50 54 57 59 62 63 65 66 68 70 75 76 77 79 81 84 85 87 93 97 99 100 102 104 107 108 110 111 115 119 130 132 133 135 144 147 148 149 **P**6 **S** PeaceHealth, Vancouver, WA
Primary Contact: Jason F. Hawkins, Chief Administrative Officer
CMO: Ron Shearer, M.D., Regional Medical Director
CIO: Ginni Boughal, Director Health Information and Information Technology
CHR: Don Bourland, Vice President Human Resources
Web address: www.peacehealth.org
Control: Church operated, Nongovernment, not–for–profit **Service**: General medical and surgical

Staffed Beds: 21 **Admissions**: 984 **Census**: 9 **Outpatient Visits**: 114828 **Births**: 66 **Total Expense ($000)**: 75087 **Payroll Expense ($000)**: 35196 **Personnel**: 159	

Many Facility Codes have changed. Please refer to the AHA Guide Code Chart.

FOREST GROVE—Washington County

TUALITY FOREST GROVE HOSPITAL See Tuality Healthcare, Hillsboro

GOLD BEACH—Curry County

★ ⇑ **CURRY GENERAL HOSPITAL (381322)**, 94220 Fourth Street,
Zip 97444–7756; tel. 541/247–3000, **A**10 18 21 **F**3 8 10 11 13 15 28 29 34
40 43 50 54 59 64 75 79 81 82 85 87 89 97 107 111 114 119 127 128 130
133 135 144 148 149 **P**6
Primary Contact: Virginia Razo, Chief Executive Officer
CFO: Carl Gerlach, Chief Financial Officer
CMO: Reginald Williams, M.D., Medical Staff President
CIO: Kristina Martin, Chief Information Officer
CNO: Barbara A Hannon, R.N., Interim Chief Nursing Officer and Chief Clinical
Officer
Web address: www.curryhealthnetwork.com
Control: Hospital district or authority, Government, nonfederal **Service**: General
medical and surgical

Staffed Beds: 18 Admissions: 476 Census: 5 Outpatient Visits: 88661
Births: 1 Total Expense ($000): 38530 **Payroll Expense ($000):** 19311
Personnel: 261

GRANTS PASS—Josephine County

★ ⇑ **ASANTE THREE RIVERS MEDICAL CENTER (380002)**, 500 SW Ramsey
Avenue, Zip 97527–5554; tel. 541/472–7000, **A**3 10 21 **F**3 11 13 15 28 29 30
31 34 35 36 40 43 45 46 48 49 50 53 54 57 59 64 65 70 75 76 78 81 85 86
87 93 94 107 110 111 114 118 119 129 130 132 143 144 145 146 147 148
P6 **S** Asante Health System, Medford, OR
Primary Contact: Win Howard, Chief Executive Officer
COO: David Kinyon, Vice President of Operations and Outpatient Services
CFO: Patrick Hocking, Chief Financial Officer
CMO: Eric Loeliger, Vice President of Medical Affairs
CIO: Mark Hetz, Chief Information Officer
CHR: Gregg Edwards, Chief People Officer
Web address: www.asante.org/trmc/
Control: Other not–for–profit (including NFP Corporation) **Service**: General
medical and surgical

**Staffed Beds: 111 Admissions: 7562 Census: 75 Outpatient
Visits:** 260452 **Births: 789 Total Expense ($000):** 165888 **Payroll Expense
($000):** 65207 **Personnel:** 966

GRESHAM—Multnomah County

⊠ **LEGACY MOUNT HOOD MEDICAL CENTER (380025)**, 24800 SE Stark,
Zip 97030–3378; tel. 503/667–1122, **A**1 2 10 **F**3 11 13 15 18 20 26 28 29 30
31 32 34 35 38 40 44 45 46 48 49 50 51 57 59 60 64 68 70 74 75 76 77 78
79 81 85 86 87 93 100 101 102 107 108 110 111 114 115 118 119 120 121
123 126 129 130 132 146 147 148 149 **P**6 **S** Legacy Health, Portland, OR
Primary Contact: Gretchen Nichols, R.N., President
COO: Michael Newcomb, D.O., Senior Vice President and Chief Operating Officer
CFO: Linda Hoff, Senior Vice President and Chief Financial Officer
CMO: Lewis Low, M.D., Chief Medical Officer
CIO: John Jay Kenagy, Ph.D., Senior Vice President and Chief Information Officer
CHR: Sonja Steves, Senior Vice President Human Resources
CNO: Marcia Soderling, R.N., Hospital Nurse Executive
Web address: www.legacyhealth.org
Control: Other not–for–profit (including NFP Corporation) **Service**: General
medical and surgical

Staffed Beds: 97 Admissions: 6400 Census: 67 Outpatient Visits: 135744
Births: 939 Total Expense ($000): 144410 **Payroll Expense ($000):** 56608
Personnel: 602

HEPPNER—Morrow County

PIONEER MEMORIAL HOSPITAL (381310), 564 East Pioneer Drive,
Zip 97836–7318, Mailing Address: P.O. Box 9, Zip 97836–0009;
tel. 541/676–9133, **A**10 18 **F**3 7 17 34 35 40 43 50 57 59 62 63 64 66 68
75 81 97 107 119 127 133 135 146 147 148 154 **P**6
Primary Contact: Robert Houser, FACHE, Chief Executive Officer
CFO: Nicole Mahoney, Chief Financial Officer
CIO: Shawn Cutsforth, Information Systems Officer
CHR: Patti Allstott, Administrative Coordinator Human Resources and Grant Writer
Web address: www.morrowcountyhealthdistrict.org
Control: Hospital district or authority, Government, nonfederal **Service**: General
medical and surgical

Staffed Beds: 21 Admissions: 100 Census: 7 Outpatient Visits: 5855
Births: 0 Total Expense ($000): 10891 **Payroll Expense ($000):** 5734
Personnel: 98

HERMISTON—Umatilla County

★ ⇑ **GOOD SHEPHERD HEALTH CARE SYSTEM (381325)**, 610 NW 11th Street,
Zip 97838–6601; tel. 541/667–3400, **A**10 18 21 **F**3 11 13 15 28 29 30 33 34
35 37 40 43 45 46 50 53 57 59 62 63 64 65 68 70 75 76 79 81 82 85 86 89
97 107 108 110 111 115 119 126 127 131 132 133 135 141 143 144 146
147 148 149 154
Primary Contact: Dennis E. Burke, President and Chief Executive Officer
COO: Jim Schlenker, Chief Operating Officer
CFO: Jan D Peter, Vice President Fiscal Services and Chief Financial Officer
CMO: Thomas Holt, M.D., Medical Staff President
CIO: Rob Rizk, Director Information Technology
CHR: Kelly B. Sanders, Vice President Human Resources
CNO: Theresa Brock, Vice President Nursing
Web address: www.gshealth.org
Control: Other not–for–profit (including NFP Corporation) **Service**: General
medical and surgical

Staffed Beds: 25 Admissions: 1566 Census: 10 Outpatient Visits: 68920
Births: 416 Total Expense ($000): 75534 **Payroll Expense ($000):** 32923
Personnel: 558

HILLSBORO—Washington County

⊠ **KAISER FOUNDATION HOSPITAL WESTSIDE MEDICAL CENTER (380103)**,
2875 NW Stucki Avenue, Zip 97124–5806; tel. 971/310–1000, **A**1 10 **F**3 13 15
29 30 31 34 35 40 45 46 47 49 51 59 60 61 64 65 68 70 74 75 77 79 81 84
85 86 87 93 94 96 97 102 107 108 110 111 114 115 118 119 126 130 135
141 146 147 148 149 154 **P**6 **S** Kaiser Foundation Hospitals, Oakland, CA
Primary Contact: Brantley Dettmer, Administrator and Chief Operating Officer
CMO: Carol Unitan, M.D., Chief Medical Officer
CIO: Charles Stearns, Area Information Officer
CHR: Rich Smith, Vice President Human Resources
CNO: Janet Lee Reeder, R.N., Chief Nurse Executive
Web address: www.kp.org
Control: Other not–for–profit (including NFP Corporation) **Service**: General
medical and surgical

Staffed Beds: 122 Admissions: 8654 Census: 69 Outpatient Visits: 42686
Births: 1536 Total Expense ($000): 162016 **Payroll Expense
($000):** 69263 **Personnel:** 1064

⊠ **TUALITY HEALTHCARE (380021)**, 335 SE Eighth Avenue, Zip 97123–4246;
tel. 503/681–1111, (Includes TUALITY COMMUNITY HOSPITAL, 335 SE Eighth
Avenue, Hillsboro, OR, Zip 97123, Mailing Address: P.O. Box 309, Zip 97123,
tel. 503/681–1111; Manuel S Berman, FACHE, President and Chief Executive
Officer; TUALITY FOREST GROVE HOSPITAL, 1809 Maple Street, Forest Grove, OR,
Zip 97116–1995; tel. 503/357–2173; Manuel S Berman, FACHE, President and
Chief Executive Officer) **A**1 5 10 **F**1 3 4 11 13 15 16 17 18 20 22 24 26 28 29
30 31 32 33 34 36 40 44 45 47 49 50 53 54 56 57 59 62 64 67 68 70 71 72
73 74 75 76 77 78 79 80 81 82 85 86 87 88 89 90 92 93 97 98 100 103 104
106 107 108 110 111 114 115 118 119 128 129 130 131 132 135 143 144
145 146 147 148 **P**1 6
Primary Contact: Lori James–Nielsen, President
COO: Steven P Krautscheid, Ancillary Services Administrator
CFO: Tim Fleischmann, Chief Financial Officer
CMO: Joe Hardman, M.D., Chief Medical Officer
CHR: Cheryl Gebhart, Chief Human Resources Officer
Web address: www.tuality.org
Control: Other not–for–profit (including NFP Corporation) **Service**: General
medical and surgical

**Staffed Beds: 148 Admissions: 4261 Census: 54 Outpatient
Visits:** 228656 **Births: 697 Total Expense ($000):** 190610 **Payroll Expense
($000):** 93761 **Personnel:** 1102

HOOD RIVER—Hood River County

⊠ **PROVIDENCE HOOD RIVER MEMORIAL HOSPITAL (381318)**, 810 12th
Street, Zip 97031–1587, Mailing Address: P.O. Box 149, Zip 97031–0055;
tel. 541/386–3911, **A**1 3 10 18 **F**3 5 9 10 11 12 13 15 18 28 29 30 31 34 35
36 40 43 45 47 48 53 54 56 57 59 60 64 65 68 70 74 75 76 77 78 79 81 82 84
85 86 89 92 97 100 101 102 104 107 108 110 111 114 118 119 125 130
131 132 133 134 135 143 146 147 148 149 154 **P**6 **S** Providence St. Joseph
Health, Renton, WA
Primary Contact: Jeanette Vieira, Chief Executive
CHR: Jami McCaslin, Director Human Resources
Web address: www.providence.org/hoodriver
Control: Church operated, Nongovernment, not–for–profit **Service**: General
medical and surgical

Staffed Beds: 25 Admissions: 1600 Census: 11 Outpatient Visits: 172052
Births: 451 Total Expense ($000): 91748 **Payroll Expense ($000):** 30920
Personnel: 409

OR

Hospital, Medicare Provider Number, Address, Telephone, Approval, Facility, and Physician Codes, Health Care System

★ American Hospital Association (AHA) membership ○ Healthcare Facilities Accreditation Program ⇑ Center for Improvement in Healthcare Quality Accreditation
□ The Joint Commission accreditation ◇ DNV Healthcare Inc. accreditation △ Commission on Accreditation of Rehabilitation Facilities (CARF) accreditation

OR

JOHN DAY—Grant County

★ **BLUE MOUNTAIN HOSPITAL (381305)**, 170 Ford Road, Zip 97845–2009;
tel. 541/575–1311, (Total facility includes 40 beds in nursing home–type unit)
A3 5 10 18 **F**3 7 8 11 13 15 29 30 34 35 36 40 41 43 45 50 57 59 62 63 64
65 67 68 70 75 76 77 81 82 85 86 87 89 93 97 107 110 111 114 119 127
130 132 133 134 135 143 145 146 148 149 **P**6 **S** HealthTech Management
Services, Brentwood, TN
Primary Contact: Derek Daly, Chief Executive Officer
CMO: Keith Thomas, M.D., Chief of Staff
CIO: Sean Tsao, Director Information Technology
CHR: Verlene Davis, Director Human Resources
CNO: Les McLeod, Director of Nursing Services
Web address: www.bluemountainhospital.org
Control: Hospital district or authority, Government, nonfederal **Service:** General
medical and surgical

> **Staffed Beds:** 62 **Admissions:** 489 **Census:** 23 **Outpatient Visits:** 21050
> **Births:** 48 **Total Expense ($000):** 23444 **Payroll Expense ($000):** 13606
> **Personnel:** 251

KLAMATH FALLS—Klamath County

★ ⭢ **SKY LAKES MEDICAL CENTER (380050)**, 2865 Daggett Avenue,
Zip 97601–1106; tel. 541/882–6311, **A**2 3 5 10 21 **F**3 8 11 13 15 18 20 22 29
30 31 34 35 37 40 43 44 45 46 47 48 50 51 53 54 56 57 59 61 62 64 68 70
71 75 76 77 78 79 81 83 85 86 87 92 93 94 96 97 100 102 107 108 110 111
114 115 116 117 118 119 120 121 123 130 131 132 134 135 141 142 143
144 145 146 147 148 149 154 **P**6
Primary Contact: Paul R. Stewart, President and Chief Executive Officer
CFO: Richard Rico, Vice President and Chief Financial Officer
CMO: Grant Niskanen, M.D., Vice President Medical Affairs
CHR: Don York, Vice President and Chief Human Resource Officer
CNO: Annette E. Cole, R.N., MSN, Vice President and Chief Nursing Officer
Web address: www.skylakes.org
Control: Other not–for–profit (including NFP Corporation) **Service:** General
medical and surgical

> **Staffed Beds:** 105 **Admissions:** 5220 **Census:** 54 **Outpatient**
> **Visits:** 269254 **Births:** 741 **Total Expense ($000):** 235722 **Payroll Expense**
> **($000):** 89182 **Personnel:** 1222

LA GRANDE—Union County

⊞ **GRANDE RONDE HOSPITAL (381321)**, 900 Sunset Drive, Zip 97850–1387,
Mailing Address: P.O. Box 3290, Zip 97850–7290; tel. 541/963–8421, **A**1 10 18
F3 8 11 13 15 17 18 29 30 31 34 35 37 39 40 41 44 45 46 50 54 59 62 63
64 66 70 74 75 76 78 79 81 82 84 85 86 87 89 91 92 93 96 97 107 108 110
111 114 118 119 127 128 129 130 131 132 133 135 144 146 147 148 149
154 **P**6
Primary Contact: James A. Mattes, President and Chief Executive Officer
CFO: Robert Seymour, Chief Financial Officer/Senior Director Finance
CMO: Mary Porter, M.D., Medical Staff President
CIO: Parhez Sattar, Senior Director Information Technology
CHR: Kristi Puckett, Director Human Resources
CNO: Douglas Romer, Executive Director Patient Care Services
Web address: www.grh.org
Control: Other not–for–profit (including NFP Corporation) **Service:** General
medical and surgical

> **Staffed Beds:** 25 **Admissions:** 1371 **Census:** 13 **Outpatient Visits:** 142375
> **Births:** 260 **Total Expense ($000):** 89714 **Payroll Expense ($000):** 49254
> **Personnel:** 662

LAKEVIEW—Lake County

★ **LAKE DISTRICT HOSPITAL (381309)**, 700 South 'J' Street, Zip 97630–1679;
tel. 541/947–2114, **A**5 10 18 **F**3 13 15 29 30 31 32 34 35 37 40 45 46 57 59
62 63 64 68 75 76 77 78 79 81 82 84 85 87 90 93 97 107 111 115 119 127
129 130 132 133 134 135 146 148 149 **P**6
Primary Contact: Charles B. Tveit, Chief Executive Officer
CFO: Cheryl J Cornwell, Chief Financial Officer
CMO: Stephen Hussey, M.D., Chief of Staff
CIO: Steven Vance, Information Technology Director
CHR: Lesley Hanson, Director Human Resources
CNO: Teresa Squires, R.N., Chief Nursing Officer
Web address: www.lakehealthdistrict.org
Control: Hospital district or authority, Government, nonfederal **Service:** General
medical and surgical

> **Staffed Beds:** 24 **Admissions:** 470 **Census:** 7 **Outpatient Visits:** 29540
> **Births:** 65 **Total Expense ($000):** 27973 **Payroll Expense ($000):** 12211
> **Personnel:** 211

LEBANON—Linn County

★ ⭢ **SAMARITAN LEBANON COMMUNITY HOSPITAL (381323)**, 525
North Santiam Highway, Zip 97355–4363, Mailing Address: P.O. Box 739,
Zip 97355–0739; tel. 541/258–2101, **A**3 10 18 21 **F**3 10 11 13 15 28 29 30
31 34 35 40 43 44 45 46 47 53 59 64 68 70 75 76 78 79 81 85 86 87 89 92
93 97 107 108 110 111 114 116 117 118 119 125 130 131 132 135 144 146
147 148 149 **P**6 **S** Samaritan Health Services, Corvallis, OR
Primary Contact: Marty Cahill, Chief Executive Officer
CFO: Daniel B Smith, Vice President Finance
CMO: Alan Blake, M.D., President Medical Staff
CIO: Robert Power, Vice President Information Services
CHR: Connie Erwin, Manager
CNO: Wendie Wunderwald, R.N., Vice President Patient Care Services
Web address: www.samhealth.org
Control: Other not–for–profit (including NFP Corporation) **Service:** General
medical and surgical

> **Staffed Beds:** 25 **Admissions:** 1624 **Census:** 16 **Outpatient Visits:** 231900
> **Births:** 290 **Total Expense ($000):** 122325 **Payroll Expense ($000):** 53696
> **Personnel:** 607

LINCOLN CITY—Lincoln County

★ ⭢ **SAMARITAN NORTH LINCOLN HOSPITAL (381302)**, 3043 NE 28th
Street, Zip 97367–4518, Mailing Address: P.O. Box 767, Zip 97367–0767;
tel. 541/994–3661, **A**3 10 18 21 **F**3 8 11 13 15 26 29 30 31 34 35 40 43 44
45 51 57 58 59 62 63 64 65 68 70 71 75 76 77 78 79 81 85 87 93 97 104
107 108 110 111 115 116 117 118 119 127 130 132 133 135 144 146 147
148 149 **P**6 **S** Samaritan Health Services, Corvallis, OR
Primary Contact: Lesley Ogden, M.D., Chief Executive Officer
CFO: Kathryn Doksum, Director Finance
CMO: Raj Baman, D.O., President Medical Staff
CHR: Gina Tapp, Director Human Resources
CNO: Virginia Riffle, Vice President Patient Care Services
Web address: www.samhealth.org
Control: Other not–for–profit (including NFP Corporation) **Service:** General
medical and surgical

> **Staffed Beds:** 25 **Admissions:** 1013 **Census:** 10 **Outpatient Visits:** 108145
> **Births:** 147 **Total Expense ($000):** 63075 **Payroll Expense ($000):** 30828
> **Personnel:** 304

MADRAS—Jefferson County

★ **ST. CHARLES MADRAS (381324)**, 470 NE 'A' Street, Zip 97741–1844;
tel. 541/475–3882, **A**10 18 **F**3 29 34 35 40 43 45 57 59 62 63 64 70
75 76 77 79 81 85 89 91 96 107 110 115 119 127 132 133 135 148 **P**6 **S** St.
Charles Health System, Inc., Bend, OR
Primary Contact: John Bishop, President
Web address: www.stcharleshealthcare.org/Our–Locations/Madras
Control: Other not–for–profit (including NFP Corporation) **Service:** General
medical and surgical

> **Staffed Beds:** 25 **Admissions:** 644 **Census:** 7 **Outpatient Visits:** 22477
> **Births:** 125 **Total Expense ($000):** 27679 **Payroll Expense ($000):** 14568
> **Personnel:** 150

MCMINNVILLE—Yamhill County

☐ **WILLAMETTE VALLEY MEDICAL CENTER (380071)**, 2700 SE Stratus Avenue,
Zip 97128–6255; tel. 503/472–6131, **A**1 2 10 **F**3 11 12 13 15 18 20 24 26 27
28 29 30 31 34 35 40 41 43 45 46 48 50 51 56 57 58 59 60 64 65 70 74 75
76 77 78 79 81 82 84 85 86 87 91 92 93 98 103 107 108 110 111 114 115
118 119 120 123 124 130 131 132 135 146 147 148 **P**6 **S** RCCH HealthCare
Partners, Brentwood, TN
Primary Contact: Peter A. Hofstetter, Chief Executive Officer
CFO: Meredith Nelson, Chief Financial Officer
CMO: Jeanne Savage, M.D., Chief Medical Officer
CIO: Diane Farrow, Manager Information Technology and Systems
CHR: Lisa Clark, Director Human Resources
CNO: Connie Pullen, R.N., Chief Nursing Officer
Web address: www.willamettevalleymedical.com/
Control: Corporation, Investor–owned (for–profit) **Service:** General medical and
surgical

> **Staffed Beds:** 88 **Admissions:** 3603 **Census:** 38 **Outpatient Visits:** 114846
> **Births:** 453 **Total Expense ($000):** 68633 **Payroll Expense ($000):** 32941
> **Personnel:** 528

MEDFORD—Jackson County

★ ⇑ **ASANTE ROGUE REGIONAL MEDICAL CENTER (380018)**, 2825 East Barnett Road, Zip 97504–8332; tel. 541/789–7000, **A**2 3 10 21 **F**3 11 12 13 15 17 18 20 22 24 26 28 29 30 31 32 34 35 36 37 40 43 45 46 48 49 50 54 57 58 59 60 63 64 65 70 72 74 75 76 78 79 81 85 86 87 89 90 93 94 96 98 100 101 102 107 108 110 111 112 115 119 120 121 122 126 129 130 132 143 145 146 147 148 154 **P**6 **S** Asante Health System, Medford, OR
Primary Contact: Mick Zdeblick, Chief Executive Officer
COO: Kristi Blackhurst, Interim Vice President Operations
CFO: Patrick Hocking, Chief Financial Officer
CMO: Jamie Grebosky, M.D., Vice President of Medical Affairs
CIO: Mark Hetz, Chief Information Officer
CHR: Gregg Edwards, Chief People Officer
Web address: www.asante.org
Control: Other not–for–profit (including NFP Corporation) **Service**: General medical and surgical

> **Staffed Beds:** 320 **Admissions:** 16081 **Census:** 231 **Outpatient Visits:** 520288 **Births:** 1570 **Total Expense ($000):** 462201 **Payroll Expense ($000):** 158435 **Personnel:** 2579

⊠ **PROVIDENCE MEDFORD MEDICAL CENTER (380075)**, 1111 Crater Lake Avenue, Zip 97504–6241; tel. 541/732–5000, **A**1 2 10 **F**3 11 13 15 17 18 19 20 21 22 28 29 30 31 32 34 35 40 43 45 49 50 55 56 57 59 61 64 68 70 74 75 76 77 78 79 81 82 84 85 86 87 90 91 92 93 96 97 102 107 110 114 115 118 119 120 121 123 124 126 129 130 131 132 146 147 148 154 **P**6 **S** Providence St. Joseph Health, Renton, WA
Primary Contact: Cindy Mayo, R.N., FACHE, Chief Executive
COO: Chris Pizzi, Chief Operating Officer and Chief Financial Officer
CFO: Chris Pizzi, Chief Operating Officer and Chief Financial Officer
CHR: Julie Levison, Director Human Resources
CNO: Sherri Steele, Chief Nursing Officer
Web address: www.providence.org
Control: Church operated, Nongovernment, not–for–profit **Service**: General medical and surgical

> **Staffed Beds:** 138 **Admissions:** 6745 **Census:** 76 **Outpatient Visits:** 375263 **Births:** 469 **Total Expense ($000):** 231397 **Payroll Expense ($000):** 65195 **Personnel:** 939

MILWAUKIE—Clackamas County

⊠ **PROVIDENCE MILWAUKIE HOSPITAL (380082)**, 10150 SE 32nd Avenue, Zip 97222–6516; tel. 503/513–8300, **A**1 3 5 10 **F**3 15 18 29 30 34 35 36 39 40 44 45 46 50 53 54 56 57 59 63 64 68 70 71 74 75 77 79 81 82 84 85 87 89 91 92 93 97 98 100 102 103 104 107 108 110 111 114 115 119 129 130 131 132 133 135 146 147 148 154 **P**6 **S** Providence St. Joseph Health, Renton, WA
Primary Contact: Keith Hyde, Chief Executive
COO: Sherri Paris, Chief Operating Officer
CFO: Sheila Waldron, Finance Manager
CHR: Julie Smith, Senior Human Resources Strategic Partner
CNO: Lisa Halvorsen, Chief Nurse Executive
Web address: www.providence.org
Control: Church operated, Nongovernment, not–for–profit **Service**: General medical and surgical

> **Staffed Beds:** 59 **Admissions:** 2797 **Census:** 37 **Outpatient Visits:** 265675 **Births:** 0 **Total Expense ($000):** 106705 **Payroll Expense ($000):** 37113 **Personnel:** 467

NEWBERG—Yamhill County

⊠ **PROVIDENCE NEWBERG MEDICAL CENTER (380037)**, 1001 Providence Drive, Zip 97132–7485; tel. 503/537–1555, **A**1 10 **F**3 11 13 15 18 20 29 30 34 35 40 45 46 47 49 50 51 57 59 60 64 68 70 74 75 76 77 79 81 84 85 87 93 100 107 108 110 111 114 118 119 129 130 132 135 146 147 148 154 **P**6 **S** Providence St. Joseph Health, Renton, WA
Primary Contact: Lorinda Van Zanten, MSN, Chief Executive
CFO: Jack R Sumner, Assistant Administrator Finance
CMO: George Weghorst, M.D., Chief Medical Officer
CIO: Laureen O'Brien, Chief Information Officer
CHR: Cheryl Gebhart, Director Human Resources Providence Health Plan and Providence Medical Group
Web address: www.phsor.org
Control: Church operated, Nongovernment, not–for–profit **Service**: General medical and surgical

> **Staffed Beds:** 40 **Admissions:** 2624 **Census:** 23 **Outpatient Visits:** 248455 **Births:** 561 **Total Expense ($000):** 105638 **Payroll Expense ($000):** 33366 **Personnel:** 407

NEWPORT—Lincoln County

★ ⇑ **SAMARITAN PACIFIC COMMUNITIES HOSPITAL (381314)**, 930 SW Abbey Street, Zip 97365–4820, Mailing Address: P.O. Box 945, Zip 97365–0072; tel. 541/265–2244, **A**10 18 21 **F**3 8 11 13 15 26 28 29 30 31 34 35 40 43 44 45 47 53 54 59 62 63 64 65 68 70 75 76 77 78 79 81 82 85 86 87 92 93 97 107 110 111 114 119 127 129 130 132 133 135 144 146 147 148 149 **P**6 **S** Samaritan Health Services, Corvallis, OR
Primary Contact: Lesley Ogden, M.D., Chief Executive Officer
CFO: Daniel B Smith, Chief Financial Officer
CIO: Robert Power, Chief Information Officer
CHR: Gina Tapp, Director Human Resources
CNO: Lorie Williams, R.N., Vice President Nursing
Web address: www.samhealth.org
Control: Other not–for–profit (including NFP Corporation) **Service**: General medical and surgical

> **Staffed Beds:** 25 **Admissions:** 1182 **Census:** 11 **Outpatient Visits:** 144058 **Births:** 170 **Total Expense ($000):** 92415 **Payroll Expense ($000):** 39847 **Personnel:** 373

ONTARIO—Malheur County

HOLY ROSARY MEDICAL CENTER See Saint Alphonsus Medical Center – Ontario

⊠ **SAINT ALPHONSUS MEDICAL CENTER – ONTARIO (380052)**, 351 SW Ninth Street, Zip 97914–2693; tel. 541/881–7000, **A**1 3 5 10 20 **F**3 11 13 15 28 29 30 31 34 35 39 40 43 44 45 46 50 54 56 57 59 64 65 68 70 75 76 77 78 79 81 83 85 87 93 97 107 108 110 111 114 118 119 127 129 130 131 132 135 144 146 147 148 149 154 **P**6 **S** Trinity Health, Livonia, MI
Primary Contact: Kenneth Hart, President
CFO: Lannie Checketts, Chief Financial Officer
CMO: Paul Gering, M.D., Vice President Medical Affairs
CHR: Stefanie Thiel, Senior Human Resources Business Partner
Web address: www.saintalphonsus.org/ontario
Control: Church operated, Nongovernment, not–for–profit **Service**: General medical and surgical

> **Staffed Beds:** 36 **Admissions:** 2141 **Census:** 17 **Outpatient Visits:** 71684 **Births:** 416 **Total Expense ($000):** 73446 **Payroll Expense ($000):** 26505 **Personnel:** 417

OREGON CITY—Clackamas County

⊠ **PROVIDENCE WILLAMETTE FALLS MEDICAL CENTER (380038)**, 1500 Division Street, Zip 97045–1597; tel. 503/656–1631, **A**1 10 **F**13 15 29 30 34 35 36 40 44 45 46 50 53 54 57 59 63 64 68 70 74 75 76 77 78 79 81 82 84 85 87 91 92 93 97 98 100 107 108 111 114 119 130 131 132 133 135 146 147 154 **P**6 **S** Providence St. Joseph Health, Renton, WA
Primary Contact: Russ Reinhard, Chief Executive
COO: Patricia A Markesino, FACHE, Chief Nurse Executive and Chief Operating Officer
CFO: Elizabeth Sublette, Director Finance
CMO: James Watkins, M.D., President Medical Staff
CHR: Joann M Pfister, Director Human Resources
CNO: Jessica Bailey–Oetker, Director Quality and Medical Staff
Web address: www.providence.org/pwfmc
Control: Church operated, Nongovernment, not–for–profit **Service**: General medical and surgical

> **Staffed Beds:** 111 **Admissions:** 4418 **Census:** 47 **Outpatient Visits:** 177731 **Births:** 953 **Total Expense ($000):** 127407 **Payroll Expense ($000):** 42302 **Personnel:** 506

PENDLETON—Umatilla County

⊠ **CHI ST. ANTHONY HOSPITAL (381319)**, 2801 St Anthony Way, Zip 97801–3800; tel. 541/276–5121, **A**1 10 18 **F**3 11 13 15 18 29 30 31 35 40 43 45 50 53 54 57 59 62 63 64 65 68 70 75 76 77 78 79 81 85 86 87 91 93 97 107 108 110 111 114 118 119 127 129 130 131 132 133 134 135 146 147 148 149 **P**6 **S** Catholic Health Initiatives, Englewood, CO
Primary Contact: Harold S. Geller, Chief Executive Officer
CFO: Scott Attridge, Chief Financial Officer
CMO: John McBee, Chief of Staff
CHR: Janeen K. Reding, Ed.D., Market Vice President of Human Resources
CNO: Joyce Bailey, Vice President Patient Care
Web address: www.sahpendleton.org
Control: Church operated, Nongovernment, not–for–profit **Service**: General medical and surgical

> **Staffed Beds:** 25 **Admissions:** 1538 **Census:** 13 **Outpatient Visits:** 79059 **Births:** 335 **Total Expense ($000):** 62774 **Payroll Expense ($000):** 24058 **Personnel:** 274

Hospital, Medicare Provider Number, Address, Telephone, Approval, Facility, and Physician Codes, Health Care System

★ American Hospital Association (AHA) membership   ○ Healthcare Facilities Accreditation Program   ⇑ Center for Improvement in Healthcare Quality Accreditation
□ The Joint Commission accreditation   ◇ DNV Healthcare Inc. accreditation   △ Commission on Accreditation of Rehabilitation Facilities (CARF) accreditation

PORTLAND—Multnomah County

✠ **ADVENTIST MEDICAL CENTER–PORTLAND (380060)**, 10123 SE Market Street, Zip 97216–2599; tel. 503/257–2500, **A**1 2 5 10 **F**3 9 11 13 15 17 18 20 22 24 26 28 29 30 31 34 35 36 37 40 44 45 46 49 53 54 57 58 59 64 70 71 74 75 76 77 78 79 81 82 84 85 86 93 97 100 102 104 105 107 108 110 111 114 115 118 119 120 121 123 126 129 130 131 132 135 143 144 146 147 148 149 153 154 **P**6 7 **S** Adventist Health, Roseville, CA
Primary Contact: David Russell, President and Chief Executive Officer
CFO: V Mark Perry, Chief Financial Officer
CMO: Wesley E Rippey, M.D., Chief Medical Officer
CHR: Shane Voshell, Director Human Resources
CNO: Ellen Tryon, R.N., Chief Nursing Officer
Web address: www.adventisthealthnw.com
Control: Church operated, Nongovernment, not–for–profit **Service**: General medical and surgical

Staffed Beds: 199 **Admissions**: 9410 **Census**: 84 **Outpatient Visits**: 462372 **Births**: 794 **Total Expense ($000)**: 365574 **Payroll Expense ($000)**: 122860 **Personnel**: 1571

PORTLAND—Washington County

☐ **CEDAR HILLS HOSPITAL (384012)**, 10300 SW Eastridge Street, Zip 97225–5004; tel. 503/944–5000, (Nonreporting) **A**1 10 **S** Universal Health Services, Inc., King of Prussia, PA
Primary Contact: Elizabeth Hutter, Chief Executive Officer
Web address: www.cedarhillshospital.com
Control: Corporation, Investor–owned (for–profit) **Service**: Psychiatric

Staffed Beds: 78

PORTLAND—Multnomah County

GOOD SAMARITAN HOSPITAL AND MEDICAL CENTER See Legacy Good Samaritan Medical Center, Portland

✠ △ ⇑ **LEGACY EMANUEL MEDICAL CENTER (380007)**, 2801 North Gantenbein Avenue, Zip 97227–1674; tel. 503/413–2200, (Includes RANDALL CHILDREN'S HOSPITAL, 2801 North Gantenbein Avenue, Portland, OR, Zip 97227–1623; tel. 503/413–2200) **A**1 2 3 5 7 10 21 **F**3 7 11 13 15 16 17 18 19 20 21 22 23 24 25 26 27 29 30 31 32 34 35 37 38 39 40 41 43 44 45 46 47 48 49 50 51 54 55 56 57 59 60 61 64 65 66 68 72 74 75 76 77 78 79 80 81 83 84 85 86 87 88 89 91 93 97 98 99 100 101 102 103 107 108 110 111 114 115 118 119 126 127 130 131 132 135 144 146 147 148 149 154 **P**6 **S** Legacy Health, Portland, OR
Primary Contact: Trent Green, President
CHR: Sonja Steves, Senior Vice President Human Resources and Marketing
Web address: www.legacyhealth.org
Control: Other not–for–profit (including NFP Corporation) **Service**: General medical and surgical

Staffed Beds: 518 **Admissions**: 19284 **Census**: 322 **Outpatient Visits**: 393148 **Births**: 1864 **Total Expense ($000)**: 846782 **Payroll Expense ($000)**: 407629 **Personnel**: 3056

✠ **LEGACY GOOD SAMARITAN MEDICAL CENTER (380017)**, 1015 NW 22nd Avenue, Zip 97210–3099; tel. 503/413–7711, (Includes GOOD SAMARITAN HOSPITAL AND MEDICAL CENTER, 1015 NW 22nd Avenue, Portland, OR, Zip 97210; tel. 503/229–7711; REHABILITATION INSTITUTE OF OREGON, 2010 NW Kearney Street, Portland, OR, Zip 97209; tel. 503/226–3774) **A**1 2 3 5 10 **F**3 8 11 12 15 18 20 22 26 38 40 44 45 46 47 43 44 50 51 55 56 57 58 59 60 61 64 65 68 70 74 75 76 77 78 79 80 81 82 83 84 85 86 87 90 91 93 94 95 96 97 107 108 110 111 114 115 116 117 118 119 120 121 123 124 126 129 130 132 135 138 142 143 144 145 146 147 148 149 154 **P**6 **S** Legacy Health, Portland, OR
Primary Contact: Jonathan Avery, Chief Administrative Officer
CIO: C Matthew Calais, Senior Vice President and Chief Information Officer
CHR: Sonja Steves, Vice President Marketing
CNO: Cindy Evans, R.N., MS, Chief Nursing Officer
Web address: www.legacyhealth.org
Control: Other not–for–profit (including NFP Corporation) **Service**: General medical and surgical

Staffed Beds: 222 **Admissions**: 10192 **Census**: 151 **Outpatient Visits**: 211088 **Births**: 1024 **Total Expense ($000)**: 314649 **Payroll Expense ($000)**: 122750 **Personnel**: 1304

✠ **OHSU HOSPITAL (380009)**, 3181 SW Sam Jackson Park Road, Zip 97239–3098; tel. 503/494–8311, (Includes DOERNBECHER CHILDREN'S HOSPITAL, 700 SW Campus Drive, Portland, OR, Zip 97239; tel. 503/494–8811; Timothy Goldfarb, Interim Chief Executive Officer) **A**1 2 3 5 8 10 **F**3 6 8 9 12 13 15 17 18 19 20 21 22 23 24 25 26 27 28 29 30 31 32 33 34 35 36 37 38 39 40 41 43 44 45 46 47 48 49 50 51 52 53 54 55 56 57 58 59 60 61 64 66 67 68 70 71 72 74 75 76 77 78 79 81 82 84 85 86 87 88 89 90 91 92 93 95 96 97 100 101 104 107 108 109 110 111 112 114 115 116 117 118 119 120 121 123 124 126 127 129 130 131 132 134 135 136 137 138 139 141 142 145 146 147 148 149 154 **P**6
Primary Contact: John G. Hunter, M.D., FACS, Chief Executive Officer
COO: Cynthia M Grueber, Senior Vice President and Chief Operating Officer
CFO: Diana Gernhart, Senior Vice President and Hospital Chief Financial Officer
CMO: Michael Bonazzola, M.D., Interim Chief Medical Officer
CIO: Bridget Barnes, Vice President and Chief Information Officer
CHR: Dan Forbes, Vice President Human Resources
CNO: Dana Bjarnason, Ph.D., R.N., Vice President and Chief Nursing Officer
Web address: www.ohsu.edu
Control: Hospital district or authority, Government, nonfederal **Service**: General medical and surgical

Staffed Beds: 556 **Admissions**: 29747 **Census**: 470 **Outpatient Visits**: 893999 **Births**: 2391 **Total Expense ($000)**: 1672671 **Payroll Expense ($000)**: 558654 **Personnel**: 7338

✠ **PROVIDENCE PORTLAND MEDICAL CENTER (380061)**, 4805 NE Glisan Street, Zip 97213–2933; tel. 503/215–5526, **A**1 2 3 5 10 **F**3 4 5 13 15 18 20 22 24 25 26 29 30 31 34 35 36 37 38 40 44 45 46 49 50 51 53 54 56 57 58 59 60 61 62 63 64 66 68 70 72 74 75 76 77 78 79 81 82 84 85 86 87 90 92 93 97 98 100 101 102 104 105 106 107 108 109 110 111 114 116 117 118 119 121 123 124 126 129 133 136 145 146 147 148 153 154 **P**6 **S** Providence St. Joseph Health, Renton, WA
Primary Contact: Krista Farnham, Chief Executive
CFO: Eric Olson, Chief Financial Officer
CMO: Robert Wells, M.D., Chief Medical Officer
CIO: Mark Premo, Senior Director HC Intelligence
CHR: Jeannie Mikulic, Director Human Resources
Web address: www.providence.org
Control: Church operated, Nongovernment, not–for–profit **Service**: General medical and surgical

Staffed Beds: 427 **Admissions**: 20092 **Census**: 297 **Outpatient Visits**: 1432027 **Births**: 2860 **Total Expense ($000)**: 734359 **Payroll Expense ($000)**: 237063 **Personnel**: 2870

PORTLAND—Washington County

✠ **PROVIDENCE ST. VINCENT MEDICAL CENTER (380004)**, 9205 SW Barnes Road, Zip 97225–6661; tel. 503/216–1234, (Includes CHILDREN AT PROVIDENCE ST. VINCENT, 9205 SW Barnes Road, Portland, OR, Zip 97225–6603; tel. 503/216–4400) **A**1 2 3 5 10 **F**3 5 13 15 17 18 20 22 24 26 28 29 30 31 34 35 36 37 38 40 41 44 45 46 47 48 49 50 53 54 56 57 58 59 60 61 64 65 70 72 74 75 76 77 78 79 81 82 84 85 86 87 88 89 91 92 93 97 98 100 102 104 105 106 107 108 109 110 111 112 114 115 116 117 118 120 121 123 126 129 130 131 132 135 146 147 148 149 153 154 **P**6 **S** Providence St. Joseph Health, Renton, WA
Primary Contact: Janice Burger, Chief Executive
COO: Nancy Roberts, Chief Operating Officer
CFO: Scott Pfister, Director Finance
Web address: www.providence.org/portland/hospitals
Control: Church operated, Nongovernment, not–for–profit **Service**: General medical and surgical

Staffed Beds: 487 **Admissions**: 25344 **Census**: 325 **Outpatient Visits**: 925599 **Births**: 3758 **Total Expense ($000)**: 811243 **Payroll Expense ($000)**: 238927 **Personnel**: 2918

PORTLAND—Multnomah County

REHABILITATION INSTITUTE OF OREGON See Legacy Good Samaritan Medical Center, Portland

☐ **SHRINERS HOSPITALS FOR CHILDREN–PORTLAND (383300)**, 3101 SW Sam Jackson Park Road, Zip 97239–3009; tel. 503/241–5090, **A**1 3 5 10 **F**3 29 34 35 37 50 53 58 64 68 75 77 79 81 85 86 87 91 93 94 130 131 132 134 146 148 **P**6 **S** Shriners Hospitals for Children, Tampa, FL
Primary Contact: Dereesa Reid, Administrator
CFO: Mark Knudsen, Director Fiscal Services
CMO: Michael Aiona, M.D., Chief of Staff
CIO: Carl Montante, Director Information Systems and Information Technology
CHR: Rhonda Smith, Director Human Resources
CNO: Suzanne Diers, R.N., Director Patient Care Services
Web address: www.shrinershospitalsforchildren.org/portland
Control: Other not–for–profit (including NFP Corporation) **Service**: Children's general medical and surgical

Staffed Beds: 12 **Admissions**: 337 **Census**: 5 **Outpatient Visits**: 12730 **Births**: 0 **Total Expense ($000)**: 41366 **Payroll Expense ($000)**: 22865 **Personnel**: 255

⊞ **VA PORTLAND HEALTHCARE SYSTEM**, 3710 SW US Veterans Hospital Road, Zip 97239–2964, Mailing Address: 3710 SW US Veterans Hospital Road, Zip 97207–1034; tel. 503/220–8262, (Nonreporting) **A**1 2 3 5 8 **S** Department of Veterans Affairs, Perry Point, MD
Primary Contact: Michael W. Fisher, Director
CFO: Josh Wiseman, Chief Financial Officer
CMO: Sahana Misra, Acting Chief of Staff
CHR: Karla Azcuy, Acting Chief Human Resources Officer
CNO: Kathleen Chapman Esq Deputy Director, Patient Care Services
Web address: www.portland.va.gov/
Control: Veterans Affairs, Government, federal **Service**: General medical and surgical

Staffed Beds: 303

VETERANS AFFAIRS MEDICAL CENTER See Va Portland Healthcare System

⊞ **VIBRA SPECIALTY HOSPITAL OF PORTLAND (382004)**, 10300 NE Hancock Street, Zip 97220–3831; tel. 503/257–5500, (Nonreporting) **A**1 10 **S** Vibra Healthcare, Mechanicsburg, PA
Primary Contact: Victor Jackson, Chief Executive Officer
CFO: Stephanie Lawrence, Chief Financial Officer
CMO: Cynthia Wallace, M.D., Medical Director
CIO: Marie Roof, Executive Vice President Information Systems
CHR: Kellie Bernert–Yap, Director Human Resources
CNO: Susan E Brooker, R.N., Chief Clinical Officer
Web address: www.vshportland.com
Control: Corporation, Investor–owned (for–profit) **Service**: Acute long–term care hospital

Staffed Beds: 68

PRINEVILLE—Crook County

★ **ST. CHARLES PRINEVILLE (381313)**, 384 SE Combs Flat Road, Zip 97754–1206; tel. 541/447–6254, **A**10 18 **F**3 11 15 29 30 34 35 40 43 45 50 59 64 65 75 77 79 81 82 84 85 86 87 89 93 97 100 107 110 115 119 127 128 130 132 133 **P**6 **S** St. Charles Health System, Inc., Bend, OR
Primary Contact: John Bishop, President
CFO: Karen Shepard, Senior Vice President and Chief Financial Officer
CMO: Michel Boileau, M.D., Chief Clinical Officer
CHR: Rebecca Berry, Senior Director Human Resources
Web address: www.stcharleshealthcare.org
Control: Other not–for–profit (including NFP Corporation) **Service**: General medical and surgical

Staffed Beds: 20 Admissions: 716 Census: 7 Outpatient Visits: 37489 Births: 0 Total Expense ($000): 28476 Payroll Expense ($000): 14125 Personnel: 148

REDMOND—Deschutes County

⊞ **ST. CHARLES REDMOND (380040)**, 1253 NW Canal Boulevard, Zip 97756–1395; tel. 541/548–8131, **A**1 10 20 **F**3 11 13 29 30 34 35 40 43 44 45 47 48 51 54 59 62 63 64 68 70 75 76 78 79 81 84 85 87 91 93 97 107 111 115 119 130 145 146 147 149 154 **P**6 **S** St. Charles Health System, Inc., Bend, OR
Primary Contact: Iman Simmons, Chief Operating Officer and Interim President
CFO: Jennifer Welander, CPA, Senior Vice President Finance and Chief Financial Officer
CMO: Jeffrey Absalon, M.D., Chief Physician Officer
CIO: Jerimiah Brickhouse, Chief Information Officer
CHR: Rebecca Berry, Vice President Human Resources
CNO: Karen Reed, R.N., MSN, Chief Nursing Officer
Web address: www.stcharleshealthcare.org
Control: Other not–for–profit (including NFP Corporation) **Service**: General medical and surgical

Staffed Beds: 48 Admissions: 2584 Census: 21 Outpatient Visits: 52231 Births: 507 Total Expense ($000): 67192 Payroll Expense ($000): 33922 Personnel: 394

REEDSPORT—Douglas County

LOWER UMPQUA HOSPITAL DISTRICT (381311), 600 Ranch Road, Zip 97467–1795; tel. 541/271–2171, **A**10 18 **F**3 7 11 15 29 34 35 40 43 45 46 50 57 59 64 70 75 77 79 81 82 85 87 93 97 107 108 115 119 127 130 131 132 133 143 144 148 153 **P**6
Primary Contact: Ryan Fowler, Chief Administrative Officer
CMO: Ronald Vail, M.D., Chief of Staff
CIO: Timothy Picou, Manager Information Technology
Web address: www.lowerumpquahospital.com
Control: Hospital district or authority, Government, nonfederal **Service**: General medical and surgical

Staffed Beds: 20 Admissions: 437 Census: 5 Outpatient Visits: 17993 Births: 0 Total Expense ($000): 25739 Payroll Expense ($000): 10371 Personnel: 147

ROSEBURG—Douglas County

⊞ **MERCY MEDICAL CENTER (380027)**, 2700 Stewart Parkway, Zip 97471–1281; tel. 541/673–0611, **A**1 3 10 **F**3 8 11 13 15 17 18 19 20 21 22 23 24 25 26 27 28 29 30 31 32 34 35 37 38 40 43 44 45 46 47 48 49 50 51 54 56 57 59 60 61 62 63 64 65 68 70 71 74 75 76 77 78 79 81 82 84 85 86 87 89 93 96 102 107 108 110 111 114 115 118 119 129 130 132 143 146 147 148 149 **S** Catholic Health Initiatives, Englewood, CO
Primary Contact: Kelly C. Morgan, President and Chief Executive Officer
COO: Debbie Boswell, Chief Operating Officer and Chief Nursing Officer
CFO: Grant L Glines, Vice President Operation Finance
CMO: Jason Gray, M.D., Chief Medical Officer
CIO: Kathleen Nickel, Director Communications
CHR: Debora Lightcap, Director Human Resources
CNO: Debbie Boswell, Chief Operating Officer and Chief Nursing Officer
Web address: www.mercyrose.org
Control: Church operated, Nongovernment, not–for–profit **Service**: General medical and surgical

Staffed Beds: 140 Admissions: 7188 Census: 77 Outpatient Visits: 404709 Births: 900 Total Expense ($000): 171475 Payroll Expense ($000): 64842 Personnel: 884

⊞ **VETERANS AFFAIRS ROSEBURG HEALTHCARE SYSTEM**, 913 NW Garden Valley Boulevard, Zip 97471–6513; tel. 541/440–1000, (Nonreporting) **A**1 3 **S** Department of Veterans Affairs, Perry Point, MD
Primary Contact: Douglas V. Paxton, Director
COO: Steven Broskey, Associate Director
CHR: Larry Mentzer, Chief Human Resources Officer
CNO: Tracy Weistreich, Ph.D., R.N., Associate Director Patient Care Services/ Nurse Executive
Web address: www.roseburg.va.gov/
Control: Veterans Affairs, Government, federal **Service**: General medical and surgical

Staffed Beds: 88

SALEM—Marion County

☐ **OREGON STATE HOSPITAL (384008)**, 2600 Center Street NE, Zip 97301–2682; tel. 503/945–2870, (Nonreporting) **A**1 3 5 10
Primary Contact: Greg Roberts, Superintendent
Web address: www.oregon.gov/OHA/amh/osh/
Control: State, Government, nonfederal **Service**: Psychiatric

Staffed Beds: 659

⊞ **SALEM HOSPITAL (380051)**, 890 Oak Street SE, Zip 97301–3959, Mailing Address: P.O. Box 14001, Zip 97309–5014; tel. 503/561–5200, (Includes PSYCHIATRIC MEDICINE CENTER, 1127 Oak Street SE, Salem, OR, Zip 97301, Mailing Address: P.O. Box 14001, Zip 97309–5014, tel. 503/561–5761; SALEM HEALTH REHABILITATION CENTER, 755 Mission St SE, Salem, OR, Zip 97301, Mailing Address: P.O. Box 14001, Zip 97309–5014, tel. 503/561–5986) **A**1 2 5 10 **F**3 11 12 13 15 17 18 20 22 24 26 28 29 30 31 34 35 36 37 38 40 43 45 46 47 48 49 50 53 54 55 56 57 58 59 64 67 68 70 72 74 75 76 77 78 79 81 82 84 85 86 87 89 90 91 92 93 94 95 96 97 98 102 105 106 107 108 109 110 111 112 113 114 115 116 117 118 119 120 121 122 123 124 126 129 130 131 132 135 145 146 147 148 **P**6 **S** Salem Health, Salem, OR
Primary Contact: Cheryl R. Nester Wolfe, President and Chief Executive Officer
COO: Bahaa Wanly, Interim Chief Operating Officer
CFO: James Parr, Chief Financial Officer
CMO: Ralph Yates, D.O., Chief Medical Officer
CIO: Leah Mitchell, R.N., Interim Chief Information Officer
CHR: Laurie C Barr, Vice President Human Resources
CNO: Sarah Horn, Chief Nursing Officer
Web address: www.salemhealth.org
Control: Other not–for–profit (including NFP Corporation) **Service**: General medical and surgical

Staffed Beds: 424 Admissions: 25907 Census: 314 Outpatient Visits: 416040 Births: 3498 Total Expense ($000): 681772 Payroll Expense ($000): 304826 Personnel: 3708

OR

Hospital, Medicare Provider Number, Address, Telephone, Approval, Facility, and Physician Codes, Health Care System

★ American Hospital Association (AHA) membership
☐ The Joint Commission accreditation
○ Healthcare Facilities Accreditation Program
◇ DNV Healthcare Inc. accreditation
⇑ Center for Improvement in Healthcare Quality Accreditation
△ Commission on Accreditation of Rehabilitation Facilities (CARF) accreditation

SEASIDE—Clatsop County

⊞ **PROVIDENCE SEASIDE HOSPITAL (381303)**, 725 South Wahanna Road, Zip 97138–7735; tel. 503/717–7000, **A**1 10 18 **F**3 12 13 15 18 29 30 31 32 34 35 40 45 46 56 57 59 61 64 65 66 70 75 76 78 79 81 82 83 84 85 86 87 91 92 93 97 107 108 110 111 114 119 127 130 132 133 135 143 146 147 148 149 154 **P**6 **S** Providence St. Joseph Health, Renton, WA
Primary Contact: Kendall Sawa, R.N., Chief Executive Officer
COO: Janiece Zauner, R.N., Chief Operating Officer
CFO: Pamela Cooper, Director Finance
CMO: Julie Paquette, M.D., Chief Medical Officer
CHR: John Anglim, Human Resources Client Manager
CNO: Janiece Zauner, R.N., Chief Nursing Officer
Web address: www.providence.org
Control: Church operated, Nongovernment, not–for–profit **Service**: General medical and surgical

Staffed Beds: 25 **Admissions**: 1026 **Census**: 10 **Outpatient Visits**: 158371 **Births**: 104 **Total Expense ($000)**: 68879 **Payroll Expense ($000)**: 28793 **Personnel**: 366

SILVERTON—Marion County

⊞ **LEGACY SILVERTON MEDICAL CENTER (380029)**, 342 Fairview Street, Zip 97381–1993; tel. 503/873–1500, **A**1 5 10 **F**3 11 13 15 20 28 29 30 34 35 40 43 47 50 54 59 64 65 70 75 76 77 79 81 85 86 87 107 108 110 111 114 115 116 119 124 127 130 131 132 135 143 144 146 147 148 149 154 **P**8 **S** Legacy Health, Portland, OR
Primary Contact: Sarah Fronza, President
COO: Karen Brady, Vice President, Chief Nursing Officer
CFO: Daniel Jessup, Chief Financial Officer
CMO: Joseph Huang, M.D., Chief Medical and Quality Officer
CIO: Karen Brady, Vice President, Chief Nursing Officer
CHR: Natalie Britton, Director Human Resources
CNO: Karen Brady, Vice President, Chief Nursing Officer
Web address: www.legacyhealth.org/locations/hospitals/legacy–silverton–medical–center.aspx
Control: Other not–for–profit (including NFP Corporation) **Service**: General medical and surgical

Staffed Beds: 48 **Admissions**: 2865 **Census**: 20 **Outpatient Visits**: 179502 **Births**: 1430 **Total Expense ($000)**: 119336 **Payroll Expense ($000)**: 47480 **Personnel**: 583

SPRINGFIELD—Lane County

⊞ **MCKENZIE–WILLAMETTE MEDICAL CENTER (380020)**, 1460 'G' Street, Zip 97477–4197; tel. 541/726–4400, **A**1 10 **F**3 11 13 17 18 20 22 24 26 28 29 30 31 34 35 39 40 41 43 45 46 47 49 50 57 59 70 72 73 76 79 81 82 85 87 89 107 108 111 115 118 119 126 129 130 132 146 147 148 154 **P**6 **S** Quorum Health, Brentwood, TN
Primary Contact: David Elgarico, Chief Executive Officer
CFO: Rosanne Devault, Chief Financial Officer
CIO: David Blomquist, Director Information Technology
CHR: Megan A O'Leary, Vice President Human Resources and Rehabilitation Services
Web address: www.mckweb.com
Control: Corporation, Investor–owned (for–profit) **Service**: General medical and surgical

Staffed Beds: 113 **Admissions**: 8309 **Census**: 76 **Outpatient Visits**: 91950 **Births**: 1301 **Total Expense ($000)**: 175124 **Payroll Expense ($000)**: 66544 **Personnel**: 740

★ ⇑ **PEACEHEALTH SACRED HEART MEDICAL CENTER AT RIVERBEND (380102)**, 3333 Riverbend Drive, Zip 97477–8800; tel. 541/222–7300, **A**10 21 **F**3 11 12 13 19 20 21 22 24 26 28 29 30 31 37 38 40 43 45 46 47 49 51 57 60 64 68 70 72 74 75 76 78 79 81 84 85 89 93 102 107 108 111 115 118 119 124 126 130 148 154 **P**6 **S** PeaceHealth, Vancouver, WA
Primary Contact: Mary E. Kingston, FACHE, R.N., Chief Executive
COO: Shannon Surber, Chief Operating Officer
CHR: Marie F Stehmer, Senior Director of Human Resources
CNO: Heather Wall, Chief Nursing Officer
Web address: www.peacehealth.org
Control: Church operated, Nongovernment, not–for–profit **Service**: General medical and surgical

Staffed Beds: 379 **Admissions**: 24695 **Census**: 318 **Outpatient Visits**: 99740 **Births**: 2624 **Total Expense ($000)**: 595195 **Payroll Expense ($000)**: 215974 **Personnel**: 2288

STAYTON—Marion County

⊞ **SANTIAM HOSPITAL (380056)**, 1401 North 10th Avenue, Zip 97383–1399; tel. 503/769–2175, **A**1 10 **F**3 7 11 13 15 16 17 29 30 40 41 43 50 65 70 72 73 76 80 81 85 87 88 89 90 98 107 111 115 119 128 130 133 135 143 154 **P**8
Primary Contact: Terry L. Fletchall, President and Chief Executive Officer
COO: Maggie Hudson, Chief Financial and Operations Officer
CFO: Rachael Seeder, Controller
CMO: Amy Sutkus, M.D., Medical Staff President
CIO: Trace Jacobs, Director Information Technology
CNO: Janet Dow, R.N., Chief Nursing Officer
Web address: www.santiamhospital.org
Control: Other not–for–profit (including NFP Corporation) **Service**: General medical and surgical

Staffed Beds: 40 **Admissions**: 993 **Census**: 10 **Outpatient Visits**: 46013 **Births**: 123 **Total Expense ($000)**: 49134 **Payroll Expense ($000)**: 23272 **Personnel**: 335

THE DALLES—Wasco County

⊞ △ **MID–COLUMBIA MEDICAL CENTER (380001)**, 1700 East 19th Street, Zip 97058–3317; tel. 541/296–1111, **A**1 2 7 10 **F**3 11 13 15 18 20 28 29 30 31 32 34 35 36 40 41 43 45 46 50 53 57 59 62 65 66 68 70 75 76 77 78 79 81 82 83 84 86 87 89 90 91 92 93 97 100 101 104 107 108 110 111 114 118 119 120 121 123 127 129 130 131 132 133 135 146 147 148 149 154 **P**6
Primary Contact: Dennis M. Knox, Chief Executive Officer
COO: Larry Kahl, Chief Operating Officer
CFO: Edwin J Bode, Chief Financial Officer
CMO: Judy Richardson, M.D., President Medical Staff
CIO: Erick Larson, Vice President and Chief Information Officer
CHR: Christine Espy, Division Director
CNO: Felicia M Adams, MS, Chief Nursing Officer
Web address: www.mcmc.net
Control: Other not–for–profit (including NFP Corporation) **Service**: General medical and surgical

Staffed Beds: 46 **Admissions**: 2196 **Census**: 19 **Outpatient Visits**: 114187 **Births**: 280 **Total Expense ($000)**: 99655 **Payroll Expense ($000)**: 46461 **Personnel**: 673

TILLAMOOK—Tillamook County

⊞ **TILLAMOOK REGIONAL MEDICAL CENTER (381317)**, 1000 Third Street, Zip 97141–3430; tel. 503/842–4444, **A**1 10 18 **F**2 3 7 13 15 17 18 29 30 31 33 34 35 37 40 43 45 50 57 59 64 65 68 75 76 77 78 79 81 82 85 87 93 94 97 102 107 108 110 111 115 119 127 129 130 131 132 133 134 135 144 146 147 148 149 **P**6 **S** Adventist Health, Roseville, CA
Primary Contact: David Butler, President and Chief Executive Officer
CFO: Walt Larson, Vice President Finance
CMO: Mark Bowman, M.D., Medical Staff President
CNO: Kathy Saxon, R.N., Vice President Patient Care Services
Web address: www.tillamookregionalmc.com
Control: Church operated, Nongovernment, not–for–profit **Service**: General medical and surgical

Staffed Beds: 25 **Admissions**: 1420 **Census**: 13 **Outpatient Visits**: 185138 **Births**: 151 **Total Expense ($000)**: 76659 **Payroll Expense ($000)**: 31251 **Personnel**: 384

TUALATIN—Clackamas County

⊞ **LEGACY MERIDIAN PARK MEDICAL CENTER (380089)**, 19300 SW 65th Avenue, Zip 97062–9741; tel. 503/692–1212, **A**1 2 10 **F**3 13 15 18 20 22 28 29 30 31 32 34 35 38 40 44 45 46 49 50 51 56 57 59 60 64 68 70 74 75 76 77 78 79 80 81 85 86 87 91 93 97 107 108 110 111 114 115 116 117 118 119 120 121 126 129 130 132 145 146 147 148 149 154 **P**6 **S** Legacy Health, Portland, OR
Primary Contact: Allyson Anderson, President
COO: Michael Newcomb, D.O., Senior Vice President and Chief Operating Officer
CMO: Lewis Low, M.D., Senior Vice President and Chief Medical Officer
CIO: John Jay Kenagy, Ph.D., Senior Vice President and Chief Information Officer
CHR: Sonja Steves, Vice President Human Resources and Marketing
CNO: Carol Bradley, MSN, R.N., Senior Vice President and Chief Nursing Officer
Web address: www.legacyhealth.org
Control: Other not–for–profit (including NFP Corporation) **Service**: General medical and surgical

Staffed Beds: 134 **Admissions**: 8823 **Census**: 86 **Outpatient Visits**: 244934 **Births**: 1043 **Total Expense ($000)**: 203610 **Payroll Expense ($000)**: 76290 **Personnel**: 817

PENNSYLVANIA

ABINGTON—Montgomery County

✠ **ABINGTON HOSPITAL (390231)**, 1200 Old York Road, Zip 19001–3720;
tel. 215/481–2000, **A**1 2 3 5 10 13 **F**3 6 8 9 11 12 13 15 17 18 20 22 24 26
28 29 30 31 34 35 36 37 38 39 40 43 44 45 46 47 48 49 50 52 53 54 55 56
57 58 59 61 62 63 64 65 66 68 70 72 73 74 75 76 77 78 79 80 81 82 84 85
86 87 89 90 91 92 93 94 96 97 98 100 101 102 103 104 107 108 110 111
114 115 118 119 120 121 123 124 126 129 130 131 132 135 144 145 146
147 148 149 150 154 **P**6 **S** Jefferson Health, Philadelphia, PA
Primary Contact: Margaret M. McGoldrick, President
COO: Eileen Jameson, Chief Operating Officer
CFO: Michael Walsh, Senior Vice President Finance and Chief Financial Officer
CMO: Gerard M. Cleary, M.D., Senior Vice President, Chief of Staff and Chief
Medical Officer
CIO: Daniel P. Walsh, Vice President, Information Systems and Technology Northern
Division
CHR: Meghan Patton, Vice President Human Resources
CNO: Theresa Reilly, MSN, R.N., Senior Vice President Patient Services and Chief
Nursing Officer
Web address: www.abingtonhealth.org
Control: Other not–for–profit (including NFP Corporation) **Service**: General
medical and surgical

Staffed Beds: 613 **Admissions**: 30044 **Census**: 379 **Outpatient Visits**:
580752 **Births**: 4573 **Total Expense ($000)**: 781648 **Payroll Expense
($000)**: 374672 **Personnel**: 4334

ALLENTOWN—Lehigh County

☐ △ **GOOD SHEPHERD REHABILITATION HOSPITAL (393035)**, 850 South
5th Street, Zip 18103–3308; tel. 610/776–3299, **A**1 3 5 7 10 **F**28 29 30 32 34
35 36 53 54 56 57 58 59 64 65 66 68 74 75 82 86 87 90 91 92 93 94 95 96
100 107 119 130 131 132 146 147 148 154 **P**1 **S** Good Shepherd Rehabilitation
Network, Allentown, PA
Primary Contact: John Kristel, President and Chief Executive Officer
CFO: Ronald J. Petula, Chief Financial Officer
Web address: www.goodshepherdrehab.org
Control: Other not–for–profit (including NFP Corporation) **Service**: Rehabilitation

Staffed Beds: 106 **Admissions**: 1494 **Census**: 81 **Outpatient Visits**:
228250 **Births**: 0 **Total Expense ($000)**: 84713 **Payroll Expense
($000)**: 34597 **Personnel**: 922

✠ **LEHIGH VALLEY HOSPITAL (390133)**, 1200 South Cedar Crest Boulevard,
Zip 18103–6248, Mailing Address: P.O. Box 689, Zip 18105–1556;
tel. 610/402–8000, (Includes LEHIGH VALLEY HEALTH NETWORK PEDITATRICS,
1200 South Cedar Crest Boulevard, Allentown, PA, Zip 18103–6202, Mailing
Address: P.O. Box 689, Zip 18105, tel. 484/862–3131) **A**1 2 3 5 8 10 **F**3 6 7 8
9 12 13 15 16 17 18 20 22 24 26 28 29 30 31 32 33 34 35 36 37 38 39 40
41 43 44 45 46 47 48 49 50 51 53 54 55 56 57 58 59 60 61 62 63 64 65 66
68 70 71 72 74 76 77 78 79 80 81 82 84 85 87 88 89 90 92 93 96 97 98 99
100 101 102 104 105 106 107 108 110 111 114 115 116 117 118 119 120
121 123 124 126 128 129 130 131 132 134 135 138 141 142 143 144 145
146 147 148 149 154 **P**5 6 8 **S** Lehigh Valley Health Network, Allentown, PA
Primary Contact: Brian A. Nester, D.O., President and Chief Executive Officer
COO: Terry Ann Capuano, R.N., MSN, FACHE, Executive Vice President and Chief
Operating Officer
CFO: Edward O'Dea, Executive Vice President and Chief Financial Officer
CMO: Thomas V. Whalen, M.D., Chief Medical Officer
CIO: Michael N. Minear, Senior Vice President and Chief Information Officer
CNO: Marie Kim Jordan, R.N., Senior Vice President and Chief Nursing Officer
Web address: www.lvhn.org
Control: Other not–for–profit (including NFP Corporation) **Service**: General
medical and surgical

Staffed Beds: 863 **Admissions**: 44386 **Census**: 695 **Outpatient Visits**:
516120 **Births**: 4370 **Total Expense ($000)**: 1425026 **Payroll Expense
($000)**: 475055 **Personnel**: 7781

ST LUKE'S HOSPITAL – ALLENTOWN CAMPUS See St. Luke's University
Hospital – Bethlehem Campus, Bethlehem

☐ △ **ST. LUKE'S SACRED HEART CAMPUS (390197)**, 421 West Chew Street,
Zip 18102–3490; tel. 610/776–4500, (Total facility includes 22 beds in nursing
home–type unit) **A**1 3 5 7 10 **F**3 11 12 13 15 18 20 22 24 29 30 31 32 34 35
38 39 40 43 46 47 49 50 56 57 59 61 64 66 68 74 75 76 77 78 79 80 81 82
84 85 87 91 92 93 97 98 101 102 103 107 108 110 111 114 115 117 118
119 121 128 129 130 132 135 143 146 147 148 **P**8 **S** St. Luke's University
Health Network, Bethlehem, PA
Primary Contact: John L. Nespoli, Chief Executive Officer
CMO: Farrokh Sadr, M.D., Chief Medical Officer
CIO: Tracy Burkhart, Vice President Information Services
CHR: Joseph Mikitka, Vice President Human Resources
Web address: www.shh.org
Control: Other not–for–profit (including NFP Corporation) **Service**: General
medical and surgical

Staffed Beds: 112 **Admissions**: 4386 **Census**: 96 **Outpatient Visits**:
156888 **Births**: 261 **Total Expense ($000)**: 100500 **Payroll Expense
($000)**: 36354 **Personnel**: 732

☐ **SURGICAL SPECIALTY CENTER AT COORDINATED HEALTH (390321)**,
1503 North Cedar Crest Boulevard, Zip 18104–2302; tel. 610/861–8080,
(Nonreporting) **A**1 10
Primary Contact: Emil Dilorio, M.D., Chief Executive Officer
Web address: www.coordinatedhealth.com
Control: Other not–for–profit (including NFP Corporation) **Service**: Surgical

Staffed Beds: 20

ALTOONA—Blair County

ALTOONA REGIONAL HEALTH SYSTEM See UPMC Altoona

✠ **HEALTHSOUTH REHABILITATION HOSPITAL OF ALTOONA (393040)**, 2005
Valley View Boulevard, Zip 16602–4598; tel. 814/944–3535, (Nonreporting) **A**1
10 **S** Encompass Health Corporation, Birmingham, AL
Primary Contact: Scott Filler, Chief Executive Officer
CFO: George Berger, Controller
CMO: Rakesh Patel, D.O., Medical Director
CIO: Kathleen Edwards, Manager Information Systems Operation
CHR: Christine Filer, Director Human Resources
CNO: Mary Gen Boyles, Chief Nursing Officer
Web address: www.healthsouthaltoona.com
Control: Corporation, Investor–owned (for–profit) **Service**: Rehabilitation

Staffed Beds: 80

✠ **JAMES E. VAN ZANDT VETERANS AFFAIRS MEDICAL CENTER**, 2907
Pleasant Valley Boulevard, Zip 16602–4305; tel. 877/626–2500, (Nonreporting)
A1 **S** Department of Veterans Affairs, Perry Point, MD
Primary Contact: Sigrid Andrew, Director
CFO: Carl Parrish, Chief Fiscal Service
CIO: Michael Hynoski, Chief Information Resource Management
CHR: Gina Dunio, Chief Human Resources
Web address: www.altoona.va.gov/
Control: Veterans Affairs, Government, federal **Service**: General medical and
surgical

Staffed Beds: 68

Hospital, Medicare Provider Number, Address, Telephone, Approval, Facility, and Physician Codes, Health Care System

★ American Hospital Association (AHA) membership   ○ Healthcare Facilities Accreditation Program   ⇑ Center for Improvement in Healthcare Quality Accreditation
☐ The Joint Commission accreditation   ◇ DNV Healthcare Inc. accreditation   △ Commission on Accreditation of Rehabilitation Facilities (CARF) accreditation

© 2018 AHA Guide   *Many Facility Codes have changed. Please refer to the AHA Guide Code Chart.*   Hospitals **A519**

PA

⊞ **UPMC ALTOONA (390073)**, 620 Howard Avenue, Zip 16601–4804;
tel. 814/889–2011, **A**1 2 3 5 10 12 13 **F**3 8 11 12 13 15 17 18 20 22 24 26
28 29 30 31 34 35 37 38 40 43 44 45 47 48 49 50 51 56 57 59 60 61 64
65 66 68 70 73 74 75 76 77 78 79 81 83 84 85 86 87 89 97 98 100 101 102
103 107 108 110 111 114 115 117 118 119 120 121 123 126 129 130 131
132 135 146 147 148 149 154 **P**6 **S** UPMC, Pittsburgh, PA
Primary Contact: Gerald Murray, President
COO: Ron McConnell, Chief Operating Officer
CFO: Betsy Kreuz, Chief Financial Officer
CMO: Linnane Batzel, M.D., Senior Vice President Quality and Medical Affairs and
Chief Medical Officer
CIO: Dale Fuller, Vice President and Chief Information Officer
CHR: Michelle A Speck, Vice President Human Resources
CNO: Chris Rickens, R.N., MS, Senior Vice President and Chief Nursing Officer
Web address: www.altoonaregional.org
Control: Other not–for–profit (including NFP Corporation) **Service**: General
medical and surgical

Staffed Beds: 346 Admissions: 18794 Census: 246 Outpatient Visits:
308042 Births: 810 Total Expense ($000): 408527 Payroll Expense
($000): 134947 Personnel: 1965

AMBLER—Montgomery County

☐ **HORSHAM CLINIC (394034)**, 722 East Butler Pike, Zip 19002–2310;
tel. 215/643–7800, (Nonreporting) **A**1 3 5 10 **S** Universal Health Services, Inc.,
King of Prussia, PA
Primary Contact: Phyllis Weisfield, Chief Executive Officer and Managing Director
CFO: Jeffrey Beiler, Chief Operating Officer
CMO: James B Congdon, M.D., Medical Director
CIO: Suzanne Scholz, Director Medical Records
CHR: Kathleen Nichelson, Director Human Resources
CNO: Calvin Litka, R.N., Director of Nursing
Web address: www.horshamclinic.com
Control: Individual, Investor–owned (for–profit) **Service**: Psychiatric

Staffed Beds: 138

BEAVER—Beaver County

⊞ **CURAHEALTH HERITAGE VALLEY (392043)**, 1000 Dutch Ridge Road,
Zip 15009–9727; tel. 724/773–8480, (Nonreporting) **A**1 10 **S** Curahealth
Hospitals, Garland, TX
Primary Contact: Janie Rosenberger–Slampack, Chief Executive Officer
CFO: Kevin Varley, Chief Financial Officer
CMO: Jeffrey Erukhimou, M.D., Medical Director
Web address: www.curahealth.com
Control: Corporation, Investor–owned (for–profit) **Service**: Acute long–term care
hospital

Staffed Beds: 35

☐ **HERITAGE VALLEY HEALTH SYSTEM (390036)**, 1000 Dutch Ridge Road,
Zip 15009–9727; tel. 724/728–7000, (Nonreporting) **A**1 3 10 13 **S** Heritage
Valley Health System, Beaver, PA
Primary Contact: Norman F. Mitry, President and Chief Executive Officer
COO: John Luellen, M.D., Chief Operating Officer
CFO: Bryan J Randall, Vice President Finance and Chief Financial Officer
CMO: Michael Cratty, M.D., Chief Medical Officer
CIO: David Carleton, Chief Information Officer
CHR: Bruce Edwards, Vice President Human Resources
CNO: Linda Homyk, Chief Nursing Officer
Web address: www.heritagevalley.org
Control: Other not–for–profit (including NFP Corporation) **Service**: General
medical and surgical

Staffed Beds: 271

BENSALEM—Bucks County

LIVENGRIN FOUNDATION, 4833 Hulmeville Road, Zip 19020–3099;
tel. 215/638–5200, (Nonreporting)
Primary Contact: Richard M. Pine, President and Chief Executive Officer
CFO: James D Flis, Chief Financial Officer
CMO: William J Lorman, Ph.D., Clinical Director
CIO: William Miller, Coordinator Management Information Systems
Web address: www.livengrin.org
Control: Other not–for–profit (including NFP Corporation) **Service**: Alcoholism and
other chemical dependency

Staffed Beds: 76

☐ **ROTHMAN SPECIALTY HOSPITAL (390322)**, 3300 Tillman Drive,
Zip 19020–2071; tel. 215/244–7400, (Nonreporting) **A**1 3 10
Primary Contact: Kelly Doyle, Chief Executive Officer
Web address: www.rothmanspecialtyhospital.com/
Control: Partnership, Investor–owned (for–profit) **Service**: Orthopedic

Staffed Beds: 24

BERWICK—Columbia County

⊞ **BERWICK HOSPITAL CENTER (390072)**, 701 East 16th Street,
Zip 18603–2397; tel. 570/759–5000, (Nonreporting) **A**1 10 **S** Community Health
Systems, Inc., Franklin, TN
Primary Contact: Thomas Neal, Chief Executive Officer
CFO: Whitney Holloway, Chief Financial Officer
CMO: John A. Guerriero, Chief of Staff
CIO: Kerry Yeager, Director Information Technology
CHR: Jackie Ridall, Director Human Resources
CNO: Maribeth Angeli, Chief Nursing Officer
Web address: www.berwick–hospital.com
Control: Corporation, Investor–owned (for–profit) **Service**: General medical and
surgical

Staffed Beds: 101

BETHLEHEM—Northampton County

☐ **COORDINATED HEALTH–BETHLEHEM (390314)**, 2310 Highland Avenue,
Zip 18020–8920, Mailing Address: 2300 Highland Avenue, Zip 18020;
tel. 610/861–8080, **A**1 3 10 **F**3 29 34 79 81 82 85 119 130 141 148 149
Primary Contact: Laurie H. Gombert, Administrator
Web address: www.coordinatedhealth.com
Control: Corporation, Investor–owned (for–profit) **Service**: Orthopedic

Staffed Beds: 20 Admissions: 1242 Census: 7 Outpatient Visits: 6328
Births: 0 Total Expense ($000): 28446 Payroll Expense ($000): 5348
Personnel: 109

BETHLEHEM—Lehigh County

⊞ △ **GOOD SHEPHERD SPECIALTY HOSPITAL (392033)**, 2545 Schoenersville
Road, 4th Floor, Zip 18017–7300; tel. 484/884–5051, **A**1 7 10 **F**1 3 29 30
36 77 85 87 91 95 130 148 **P**5 **S** Good Shepherd Rehabilitation Network,
Allentown, PA
Primary Contact: Andrew Shane. Martin, Administrator
CFO: Ronald J. Petula, Chief Financial Officer
CIO: Michael Cirba, Chief Information Officer
CHR: Kristen Melan, Director Human Resources Administration
CNO: Samuel Miranda Jr Chief Nursing Officer
Web address: www.goodshepherdrehab.org
Control: Other not–for–profit (including NFP Corporation) **Service**: Acute long–
term care hospital

Staffed Beds: 32 Admissions: 364 Census: 23 Outpatient Visits: 0
Births: 0 Total Expense ($000): 14723 Payroll Expense ($000): 5087
Personnel: 92

⊞ **LEHIGH VALLEY HOSPITAL–MUHLENBERG (390263)**, 2545 Schoenersville
Road, Zip 18017–7300; tel. 484/884–2200, **A**1 2 3 10 12 13 **F**3 7 8 11 12 13
15 17 18 20 22 24 26 28 29 30 31 33 34 35 36 37 38 39 40 44 45 46 47 48
49 50 51 53 54 57 58 59 60 61 62 63 64 65 68 70 72 74 76 77 78 79 80 81
82 84 85 86 87 90 92 93 96 97 100 102 104 105 107 108 110 111 115 118
119 126 129 130 131 132 134 135 141 143 145 146 148 149 150 154 **P**5 6
8 **S** Lehigh Valley Health Network, Allentown, PA
Primary Contact: Brian A. Nester, D.O., President and Chief Executive Officer
COO: Terry Ann Capuano, R.N., MSN, FACHE, Executive Vice President and Chief
Operating Officer
CFO: Edward O'Dea, Executive Vice President and Chief Financial Officer
CMO: Thomas V. Whalen, M.D., Executive Vice President and Chief Medical Officer
CIO: Michael N. Minear, Senior Vice President and Chief Information Officer
CHR: Deborah A. Patrick, Senior Vice President Human Resources
CNO: Marie Kim Jordan, R.N., Senior Vice President, Chief Nursing Officer
Web address: www.lvhn.org
Control: Other not–for–profit (including NFP Corporation) **Service**: General
medical and surgical

Staffed Beds: 186 Admissions: 9987 Census: 124 Outpatient Visits:
212381 Births: 27 Total Expense ($000): 229442 Payroll Expense
($000): 84993 Personnel: 1497

☐ △ **ST. LUKE'S UNIVERSITY HOSPITAL – BETHLEHEM CAMPUS (390049)**, 801 Ostrum Street, Zip 18015–1065; tel. 484/526–4000, (Includes ST LUKE'S HOSPITAL – ALLENTOWN CAMPUS, 1736 Hamilton Street, Allentown, PA, Zip 18104–5656; tel. 610/628–8300; William Moyer, President) **A**1 2 3 7 8 10 12 13 **F**3 9 11 12 13 15 17 18 19 20 22 24 26 27 28 29 30 31 32 34 35 36 37 38 39 40 43 44 45 46 47 48 49 50 51 52 53 54 55 56 57 58 59 60 61 63 64 65 66 68 70 71 72 73 74 75 76 77 78 79 81 82 84 85 86 87 89 90 92 93 96 97 98 100 101 102 103 104 105 107 108 109 110 111 115 117 118 119 120 121 123 124 126 129 130 131 132 134 135 144 145 146 147 148 149 153 154 **S** St. Luke's University Health Network, Bethlehem, PA
Primary Contact: Carol Kuplen, R.N., MSN, President and Chief Executive Officer
CFO: Tom Lichtenwalner, Vice President Finance
CMO: Jeffrey Jahre, M.D., Vice President Medical and Academic Affairs
CIO: Chad Brisendine, Chief Information Officer
CHR: Robert Zimmel, Senior Vice President Human Resources
Web address: www.slhn–lehighvalley.org
Control: Other not–for–profit (including NFP Corporation) **Service**: General medical and surgical

Staffed Beds: 540 **Admissions:** 28178 **Census:** 385 **Outpatient Visits:** 570822 **Births:** 4067 **Total Expense ($000):** 604312 **Payroll Expense ($000):** 257035 **Personnel:** 5285

BLOOMSBURG—Columbia County

★ **GEISINGER–BLOOMSBURG HOSPITAL (390003)**, 549 Fair Street, Zip 17815–1419; tel. 570/387–2100, **A**3 10 **F**3 8 11 13 15 20 26 27 28 29 30 32 34 35 36 38 39 40 41 44 45 46 50 51 53 55 56 57 59 62 63 65 68 70 74 75 76 79 81 85 86 87 91 92 93 97 98 100 101 102 103 104 107 108 110 111 115 119 130 131 132 144 145 146 147 148 149 150 153 154 **S** Geisinger, Danville, PA
Primary Contact: Lissa Bryan–Smith, Chief Administrative Officer
COO: Joseph M DeVito, Vice President Finance and Chief Operating Officer
CFO: Joseph M DeVito, Vice President Finance and Chief Operating Officer
CMO: James Joseph, M.D., President Medical Staff
CIO: Thomas Wray, Director Information
Web address: www.bloomhealth.net
Control: Other not–for–profit (including NFP Corporation) **Service**: General medical and surgical

Staffed Beds: 76 **Admissions:** 2371 **Census:** 25 **Outpatient Visits:** 80855 **Births:** 295 **Total Expense ($000):** 48017 **Payroll Expense ($000):** 16398 **Personnel:** 317

BRADFORD—Mckean County

☐ **BRADFORD REGIONAL MEDICAL CENTER (390118)**, 116 Interstate Parkway, Zip 16701–1036; tel. 814/368–4143, (Total facility includes 95 beds in nursing home–type unit) **A**1 10 **F**3 5 11 13 15 18 20 28 29 30 31 34 35 38 39 40 45 47 49 50 53 54 56 57 59 64 65 70 75 76 77 78 79 81 82 83 84 85 86 87 93 94 96 97 98 100 101 102 104 105 107 108 110 111 114 117 118 119 127 128 129 130 131 132 135 146 147 148 149 **P**6 8 **S** Upper Allegheny Health System, Olean, NY
Primary Contact: Timothy J. Finan, FACHE, President and Chief Executive Officer
COO: Jeff S Zewe, R.N., Chief Operating Officer
CFO: Richard G Braun, CPA, Jr Senior Vice President and Chief Financial Officer
CMO: William Mills, M.D., Senior Vice President Quality and Professional Affairs
CIO: Jason Yaworsky, Chief Information Officer
CHR: Timothy M McNamara, Senior Vice President Human Resources
Web address: www.brmc.com
Control: Other not–for–profit (including NFP Corporation) **Service**: General medical and surgical

Staffed Beds: 202 **Admissions:** 2911 **Census:** 125 **Outpatient Visits:** 150914 **Births:** 195 **Total Expense ($000):** 69718 **Payroll Expense ($000):** 28343 **Personnel:** 403

BRISTOL—Bucks County

⊞ **LOWER BUCKS HOSPITAL (390070)**, 501 Bath Road, Zip 19007–3190; tel. 215/785–9200, (Nonreporting) **A**1 10 13 **S** Prime Healthcare, Ontario, CA
Primary Contact: Kelly M. Lorah, FACHE, Chief Executive Officer
CMO: Sanjay Bhatia, Chief Medical Officer
CIO: Steve Kane, Director Information Technology
CNO: Pat Bain, Chief Nursing Officer
Web address: www.lowerbuckshosp.com
Control: Other not–for–profit (including NFP Corporation) **Service**: General medical and surgical

Staffed Beds: 104

BROOKVILLE—Jefferson County

PENN HIGHLANDS BROOKVILLE (391312), 100 Hospital Road, Zip 15825–1367; tel. 814/849–2312, (Nonreporting) **A**10 18
Primary Contact: Julianne Peer, President
CFO: Jessica Park, Director Accounting
CMO: Timothy Pendleton, M.D., President Medical Staff
CIO: Thomas Johnson, Director Information Systems
CHR: Rebecca Edwards, Chief Human Resources Officer
CNO: Debra A. Thomas, Vice President of Patient Care Services and Chief Nursing Officer
Web address: www.phhealthcare.org/
Control: Other not–for–profit (including NFP Corporation) **Service**: General medical and surgical

Staffed Beds: 35

BRYN MAWR—Montgomery County

⊞ **BRYN MAWR HOSPITAL (390139)**, 130 South Bryn Mawr Avenue, Zip 19010–3160; tel. 484/337–3000, **A**1 2 3 5 10 13 **F**3 5 11 12 13 15 17 18 20 22 24 26 28 29 30 31 34 35 36 37 38 39 40 41 44 45 46 48 49 50 54 55 56 57 58 59 63 64 65 70 72 74 75 76 78 79 80 81 82 84 85 86 87 89 92 97 98 100 102 103 104 107 108 110 111 114 115 118 119 120 124 126 129 130 131 134 135 141 146 147 148 149 154 **S** Main Line Health, Ontario, CA
Primary Contact: Andrea F. Gilbert, FACHE, President
CFO: Michael J Buongiorno, Executive Vice President Finance and Chief Financial Officer
CMO: Andrew J Norton, M.D., Chief Medical Officer
CIO: Kay Carr, Chief Information Officer
CHR: Terry Dougherty, Director Human Resources
CNO: Barbara A Wadsworth, MSN, R.N., FACHE, Chief Nursing Officer
Web address: www.brynmawrhospital.org
Control: Other not–for–profit (including NFP Corporation) **Service**: General medical and surgical

Staffed Beds: 287 **Admissions:** 14149 **Census:** 155 **Outpatient Visits:** 268704 **Births:** 1573 **Total Expense ($000):** 330544 **Payroll Expense ($000):** 107311 **Personnel:** 1552

BUTLER—Butler County

★ **BUTLER HEALTH SYSTEM (390168)**, 1 Hospital Way, Zip 16001–4697; tel. 724/283–6666, (Nonreporting) **A**2 10
Primary Contact: Ken DeFurio, President and Chief Executive Officer
COO: Stephanie Roskovski, Chief Operating Officer
CFO: Anne Krebs, Chief Financial Officer
CMO: John C Reefer, M.D., Director
CIO: Thomas McGill, M.D., Chief Information Officer
CHR: Thomas A Genevro, Vice President Human Resources
CNO: Karen A Allen, R.N., Chief Nursing Officer
Web address: www.butlerhealthsystem.org
Control: Other not–for–profit (including NFP Corporation) **Service**: General medical and surgical

Staffed Beds: 288

CAMP HILL—Cumberland County

⊞ **GEISINGER HOLY SPIRIT (390004)**, 503 North 21st Street, Zip 17011–2204; tel. 717/763–2100, **A**1 10 **F**3 8 11 13 14 15 17 18 20 22 24 26 28 29 30 31 34 35 37 38 40 43 44 45 46 48 49 50 54 55 57 58 59 60 64 65 70 71 72 74 75 76 77 78 79 81 82 84 85 86 87 89 93 98 100 101 102 104 105 107 108 110 111 114 115 117 119 120 121 124 126 129 130 132 134 135 146 147 148 149 153 154 **P**6 **S** Geisinger, Danville, PA
Primary Contact: Kyle C. Snyder, Chief Administrative Officer
CNO: Lisa F Torchia NEA–BC, MSN, R.N., Vice President and Chief Nursing Officer
Web address: www.hsh.org
Control: Other not–for–profit (including NFP Corporation) **Service**: General medical and surgical

Staffed Beds: 295 **Admissions:** 10828 **Census:** 152 **Outpatient Visits:** 208588 **Births:** 1138 **Total Expense ($000):** 315158 **Payroll Expense ($000):** 111949 **Personnel:** 1902

Hospital, Medicare Provider Number, Address, Telephone, Approval, Facility, and Physician Codes, Health Care System		
★ American Hospital Association (AHA) membership	○ Healthcare Facilities Accreditation Program	⇑ Center for Improvement in Healthcare Quality Accreditation
☐ The Joint Commission accreditation	◇ DNV Healthcare Inc. accreditation	△ Commission on Accreditation of Rehabilitation Facilities (CARF) accreditation

PA

☒ **SELECT SPECIALTY HOSPITAL–CAMP HILL (392039)**, 503 North 21st Street, 5th Floor, Zip 17011–2204; tel. 717/972–4575, (Includes SELECT SPECIALTY HOSPITAL–HARRISBURG, 111 South Front Street, Alex Grass Building, 5th Floor, Harrisburg, PA, Zip 17101; tel. 717/724–6610; John E Simodejka, Marketing Chief Executive Officer; SELECT SPECIALTY HOSPITAL–YORK, 1001 South George Street, York, PA, Zip 17403–3676; tel. 717/851–2661; Marcia Medlin, Chief Executive Officer) (Nonreporting) **A**1 10 **S** Select Medical Corporation, Mechanicsburg, PA
Primary Contact: Pat Alexander, Chief Executive Officer
Web address: www.camphill.selectspecialtyhospitals.com/
Control: Corporation, Investor–owned (for–profit) **Service**: Acute long–term care hospital

Staffed Beds: 92

STATE CORRECTIONAL INSTITUTION AT CAMP HILL, 2500 Lisburn Road, Zip 17011–8005, Mailing Address: P.O. Box 200, Zip 17001–0200; tel. 717/737–4531, (Nonreporting)
Primary Contact: Beth Herb, Administrator
Web address: www.cor.state.pa.us/
Control: State, Government, nonfederal **Service**: Hospital unit of an institution (prison hospital, college infirmary, etc.)

Staffed Beds: 34

CANONSBURG—Washington County

☒ **CANONSBURG HOSPITAL (390160)**, 100 Medical Boulevard, Zip 15317–9762; tel. 724/745–6100, **A**1 10 **F**3 7 11 15 18 28 29 30 34 35 38 40 44 45 46 47 49 50 54 57 64 70 74 75 77 79 81 84 85 86 87 90 92 93 96 101 102 107 108 110 111 114 118 119 129 130 131 132 135 143 146 148 149 **P**6 **S** Allegheny Health Network, Pittsburgh, PA
Primary Contact: Louise Urban, R.N., President and Chief Executive Officer
CMO: Thomas B Corkery, D.O., Chief Medical Officer
CIO: David Vincent, Director Information Systems
CHR: Martha L Clister, Director Human Resources
Web address: www.wpahs.org
Control: Other not–for–profit (including NFP Corporation) **Service**: General medical and surgical

Staffed Beds: 87 **Admissions**: 2213 **Census**: 26 **Outpatient Visits**: 63086 **Births**: 0 **Total Expense ($000)**: 47059 **Payroll Expense ($000)**: 17276 **Personnel**: 321

CARLISLE—Cumberland County

☒ **UPMC PINNACLE CARLISLE (390058)**, 361 Alexander Spring Road, Zip 17015–6940; tel. 717/249–1212, **A**1 10 **F**3 8 11 12 13 14 15 18 20 29 30 31 34 35 36 38 40 45 46 48 49 50 54 57 58 59 64 65 68 70 73 74 75 76 77 78 79 81 85 86 87 90 93 96 107 108 109 110 111 114 115 116 117 119 120 121 123 126 129 130 131 132 141 142 145 146 147 148 149 154 **P**5 6 **S** UPMC, Pittsburgh, PA
Primary Contact: Christian H. Caicedo, President
CFO: Mark Reyngoudt, Chief Financial Officer
CMO: Ivan' Sola', President Medical Staff
CIO: Sherry Aby, Director Information Management
CHR: Sylvia Rockwood, Director Human Resources
CNO: Ann M. Spade, Chief Nursing Executive
Web address: www.pinnaclehealth.org/carlisle/
Control: Other not–for–profit (including NFP Corporation) **Service**: General medical and surgical

Staffed Beds: 65 **Admissions**: 4076 **Census**: 41 **Outpatient Visits**: 110629 **Births**: 376 **Total Expense ($000)**: 116202 **Payroll Expense ($000)**: 40543 **Personnel**: 538

CENTRE HALL—Centre County

☒ **MEADOWS PSYCHIATRIC CENTER (394040)**, 132 The Meadows Drive, Zip 16828–9231; tel. 814/364–2161, **A**1 10 **F**29 38 40 59 98 99 100 103 130 135 **S** Universal Health Services, Inc., King of Prussia, PA
Primary Contact: Ann Wayne, Chief Executive Officer
CFO: David Witt, Chief Financial Officer
CMO: Craig Richman, M.D., Medical Director
CHR: Mary Jane Schreffler, Director Human Resources
CNO: Dana Thies, Director of Nursing
Web address: www.themeadows.net
Control: Corporation, Investor–owned (for–profit) **Service**: Psychiatric

Staffed Beds: 117 **Admissions**: 3014 **Census**: 106 **Outpatient Visits**: 145 **Births**: 0 **Personnel**: 203

CHAMBERSBURG—Franklin County

☒ **CHAMBERSBURG HOSPITAL (390151)**, 112 North Seventh Street, Zip 17201–1720; tel. 717/267–3000, **A**1 2 3 5 10 19 **F**3 11 12 13 15 17 18 20 22 26 28 29 30 31 34 35 39 40 44 45 49 50 54 56 57 58 59 64 65 68 70 72 74 75 76 77 79 81 84 85 86 87 90 93 98 100 101 102 103 104 107 108 110 111 114 115 119 129 130 131 132 135 144 146 147 148 149 154 **P**8 **S** Summit Health, Chambersburg, PA
Primary Contact: Patrick W. O'Donnell, CPA, President and Chief Executive Officer
COO: John P Massimilla, FACHE, Vice President and Chief Operating Officer
CFO: Kimberly Rzomp, Vice President and Chief Financial Officer
CMO: Thomas Anderson, M.D., Vice President Medical Affairs
CIO: Michele Zeigler, Vice President and Chief Information Officer
CHR: Cathy A. Puhl, Vice President Human Resources
CNO: Sherri Stahl, R.N., Senior Vice President Hospital Services
Web address: www.summithealth.org
Control: Other not–for–profit (including NFP Corporation) **Service**: General medical and surgical

Staffed Beds: 271 **Admissions**: 13481 **Census**: 156 **Outpatient Visits**: 380526 **Births**: 1353 **Total Expense ($000)**: 298931 **Payroll Expense ($000)**: 121132 **Personnel**: 1702

CLARION—Clarion County

★ ○ **CLARION HOSPITAL (390093)**, One Hospital Drive, Zip 16214–8501; tel. 814/226–9500, **A**10 11 12 13 **F**3 7 11 13 15 29 30 31 35 40 48 51 57 59 64 70 76 77 78 79 81 82 84 85 90 107 108 110 111 115 118 119 120 121 122 129 130 132 133 135 145 146 148 **S** QHR, Brentwood, TN
Primary Contact: Al Taylor, Interim Chief Executive Officer
CFO: Vincent M Lamorella, Chief Financial Officer
CMO: Janice Semeyn, D.O., President, Medical Staff
CIO: James Confer, Manager Information Systems
CNO: Leslie Walters, MSN, Chief Nursing Officer
Web address: www.clarionhospital.org
Control: Other not–for–profit (including NFP Corporation) **Service**: General medical and surgical

Staffed Beds: 66 **Admissions**: 1686 **Census**: 18 **Outpatient Visits**: 158724 **Births**: 111 **Total Expense ($000)**: 51914 **Payroll Expense ($000)**: 18977 **Personnel**: 421

☐ **CLARION PSYCHIATRIC CENTER (394043)**, 2 Hospital Drive, Zip 16214–8502; tel. 814/226–9545, (Nonreporting) **A**1 10 **S** Universal Health Services, Inc., King of Prussia, PA
Primary Contact: Michael Post, Chief Executive Officer
CFO: Shelly Rhoades, Chief Financial Officer
CMO: Jeffrey Moll, M.D., Medical Director
CHR: Dianne C Bilunka, Director Human Resources
CNO: Rhonda Massa, Director of Nursing
Web address: www.clarioncenter.com
Control: Corporation, Investor–owned (for–profit) **Service**: Psychiatric

Staffed Beds: 74

CLARKS SUMMIT—Lackawanna County

CLARKS SUMMIT STATE HOSPITAL (394012), 1451 Hillside Drive, Zip 18411–9504; tel. 570/586–2011, (Nonreporting) **A**10
Primary Contact: Monica Bradbury, Chief Executive Officer
COO: Gordon Weber, Chief Operating Officer
CMO: David Waibel, M.D., Medical Director
CHR: William Abda, Chief Human Resources Officer
Web address: www.dpw.state.pa.us/
Control: State, Government, nonfederal **Service**: Psychiatric

Staffed Beds: 210

CLEARFIELD—Clearfield County

PENN HIGHLANDS CLEARFIELD (390052), 809 Turnpike Avenue, Zip 16830–1232, Mailing Address: P.O. Box 992, Zip 16830–0992; tel. 814/765–5341, **A**10 **F**3 8 11 14 15 18 28 29 30 32 34 40 45 50 57 59 62 63 68 75 77 79 81 82 84 85 86 87 93 97 98 103 104 107 108 110 111 115 118 119 130 131 132 133 146 148
Primary Contact: Rhonda Halstead, President
CFO: William Cain, Controller
CMO: Kevin L Tyler, M.D., President Medical Staff
CNO: Kathy Bedger, Chief Nursing Officer
Web address: www.phhealthcare.org
Control: Other not–for–profit (including NFP Corporation) **Service**: General medical and surgical

Staffed Beds: 50 **Admissions**: 1733 **Census**: 22 **Outpatient Visits**: 114874 **Births**: 0 **Total Expense ($000)**: 47612 **Payroll Expense ($000)**: 17134 **Personnel**: 271

COALDALE—Schuylkill County

☐ **ST. LUKE'S HOSPITAL – MINERS CAMPUS (390183)**, 360 West Ruddle Street, Zip 18218–1027; tel. 570/645–2131, (Total facility includes 48 beds in nursing home–type unit) **A**1 2 10 **F**3 15 18 28 29 31 34 35 38 40 43 45 46 49 50 51 53 54 56 57 59 60 63 64 65 68 70 75 77 78 79 81 85 86 93 102 107 108 110 111 115 118 119 127 128 129 130 131 132 144 145 146 148 149 154 **S** St. Luke's University Health Network, Bethlehem, PA
Primary Contact: Wendy Lazo, President
COO: Joel Fagerstrom, Executive Vice President and Chief Operating Officer
CFO: Michele Levitz, Director Finance
CIO: Chad Brisendine, Vice President and Chief Information Officer
CHR: Susan Van Why, Director Human Resources
CNO: Kimberly Sargent, Vice President Patient Services
Web address: www.slhn.org
Control: Other not–for–profit (including NFP Corporation) **Service:** General medical and surgical

Staffed Beds: 92 **Admissions:** 2418 **Census:** 67 **Outpatient Visits:** 91765 **Births:** 0 **Total Expense ($000):** 53416 **Payroll Expense ($000):** 22910 **Personnel:** 324

COATESVILLE—Chester County

✠ **BRANDYWINE HOSPITAL (390076)**, 201 Reeceville Road, Zip 19320–1536; tel. 610/383–8000, (Nonreporting) **A**1 10 **S** Tower Health, West Reading, PA
Primary Contact: W. Jeffrey. Hunt, Chief Executive Officer
COO: Jill Tillman, Assistant Chief Executive Officer
CFO: Mark Reyngoudt, Chief Financial Officer
Web address: www.https://brandywine.towerhealth.org/
Control: Other not–for–profit (including NFP Corporation) **Service:** General medical and surgical

Staffed Beds: 169

✠ **COATESVILLE VETERANS AFFAIRS MEDICAL CENTER**, 1400 Black Horse Hill Road, Zip 19320–2040; tel. 610/384–7711, (Nonreporting) **A**1 3 5 **S** Department of Veterans Affairs, Perry Point, MD
Primary Contact: Carla Sivek, Director
CFO: Tony Wolfgang, Chief Financial Officer
CMO: Sheila Chellappa, M.D., Chief of Staff
CIO: Ryan McGettigan, Chief Information Officer
CHR: Andrew Sutton, Chief Human Resources Officer
CNO: Nancy A Schmid, R.N., MS, Associate Director Patient Care Services
Web address: www.coatesville.va.gov/
Control: Veterans Affairs, Government, federal **Service:** Alcoholism and other chemical dependency

Staffed Beds: 118

VETERANS AFFAIRS MEDICAL CENTER See Coatesville Veterans Affairs Medical Center

CONNELLSVILLE—Fayette County

HIGHLANDS HOSPITAL (390184), 401 East Murphy Avenue, Zip 15425–2700; tel. 724/628–1500, **A**10 **F**3 11 15 29 30 34 35 38 39 40 44 45 46 49 50 53 54 56 57 59 64 70 74 75 79 81 82 85 86 87 89 97 98 100 102 103 104 107 108 111 115 119 129 130 131 132 135 146
Primary Contact: Michelle P. Cunningham, Chief Executive Officer
CFO: John Andursky, Chief Financial Officer
CMO: Paul Means, M.D., President Medical Staff
CIO: John Andursky, Chief Financial Officer
CHR: Mary June Krosoff, Chief Human Resources Officer
CNO: Vicki Rough, Chief Nursing Officer
Web address: www.highlandshospital.org
Control: Other not–for–profit (including NFP Corporation) **Service:** General medical and surgical

Staffed Beds: 64 **Admissions:** 2137 **Census:** 25 **Outpatient Visits:** 64238 **Births:** 0 **Total Expense ($000):** 26461 **Payroll Expense ($000):** 11384 **Personnel:** 269

CORRY—Erie County

CORRY MEMORIAL HOSPITAL (391308), 965 Shamrock Lane, Zip 16407; tel. 814/664–4641, (Nonreporting) **A**10 18
Primary Contact: Barbara Nichols, R.N., President and Chief Executive Officer
CFO: Michael Heller, Chief Financial Officer
CMO: Paul McGeehan, M.D., Chief Medical Staff
CHR: Brenda Cooper, Director Quality and Human Resources
CNO: Patty White, R.N., Director Patient Care Services
Web address: www.corryhospital.com
Control: Other not–for–profit (including NFP Corporation) **Service:** General medical and surgical

Staffed Beds: 25

COUDERSPORT—Potter County

✠ **UPMC COLE (391313)**, 1001 East Second Street, Zip 16915–8161; tel. 814/274–9300, (Total facility includes 44 beds in nursing home–type unit) **A**1 10 18 **F**3 10 13 15 28 29 30 31 35 39 40 45 49 53 57 59 62 63 64 68 70 76 77 78 79 81 82 85 87 93 94 98 103 107 108 110 111 115 119 121 127 128 129 130 131 132 133 146 147 148 **P**6
Primary Contact: Edward C. Pitchford, President and Chief Executive Officer
CFO: Ron Rapp, Vice President Finance
CMO: Brenda Wahlers, M.D., Chief of Staff
CHR: James Evens, Executive Director, Human Resources and General Services
CNO: Emily Ann Bunnell, Chief Nurse Executive, Senior Director of Acute Care
Web address: www.colememorial.org/
Control: Other not–for–profit (including NFP Corporation) **Service:** General medical and surgical

Staffed Beds: 79 **Admissions:** 1998 **Census:** 60 **Outpatient Visits:** 253309 **Births:** 196 **Total Expense ($000):** 89520 **Payroll Expense ($000):** 30545 **Personnel:** 502

CRANBERRY—Butler County

UPMC PASSAVANT CRANBERRY See UPMC Passavant, Pittsburgh

DANVILLE—Montour County

DANVILLE STATE HOSPITAL (394004), 200 State Hospital Drive, Zip 17821–9198; tel. 570/271–4500, **A**3 10 **F**30 39 65 75 77 98 106 130 135 154 **P**6
Primary Contact: Theresa Long, Chief Executive Officer
COO: Thomas J Burk, Chief Operating Officer
CFO: Patricia Riegert, Director Fiscal Services
CMO: Vikrant Mittal, M.D., Chief Medical Officer
CHR: Thomas J Burk, Chief Operating Officer
CNO: Brenda Lahout, Chief Nurse Executive
Web address: www.dpw.state.pa.us/foradults/statehospitals/danvillestatehospital/index.htm
Control: State, Government, nonfederal **Service:** Psychiatric

Staffed Beds: 161 **Admissions:** 77 **Census:** 155 **Outpatient Visits:** 0 **Births:** 0 **Personnel:** 361

✠ **GEISINGER HEALTHSOUTH REHABILITATION HOSPITAL (393047)**, 2 Rehab Lane, Zip 17821–8498; tel. 570/271–6733, (Nonreporting) **A**1 10 **S** Encompass Health Corporation, Birmingham, AL
Primary Contact: Lorie Dillon, Chief Executive Officer
CMO: Greg Burke, M.D., Medical Director
CHR: Christian Shirley, Director Human Resources
Web address: www.geisingerhealthsouth.com
Control: Corporation, Investor–owned (for–profit) **Service:** Rehabilitation

Staffed Beds: 42

✠ **GEISINGER MEDICAL CENTER (390006)**, 100 North Academy Avenue, Zip 17822–2201; tel. 570/271–6211, (Includes GEISINGER–SHAMOKIN AREA COMMUNITY HOSPITAL, 4200 Hospital Road, Coal Township, PA, Zip 17866–9697; tel. 570/644–4200; Sam Balukoff, Interim Administrator) **A**1 2 3 5 8 10 13 19 **F**3 4 7 8 9 11 12 13 14 15 17 18 19 20 21 22 23 24 25 26 27 28 29 30 31 32 34 35 36 37 39 40 41 43 44 45 46 47 48 49 50 51 52 53 54 55 56 57 58 59 60 61 63 64 65 66 67 68 69 70 71 72 73 74 75 76 77 78 79 80 81 82 84 85 86 87 88 89 92 93 94 96 97 98 100 101 102 104 107 108 110 111 114 115 117 118 119 120 121 123 124 126 129 130 131 132 135 136 138 139 141 143 145 146 147 148 149 150 153 154 **P**6 **S** Geisinger, Danville, PA
Primary Contact: Thomas P. Sokola, Chief Administrative Officer
CFO: Kevin F Brennan, CPA, Executive Vice President and Chief Financial Officer
CMO: Albert Bothe, M.D., Jr Chief Medical Officer
CIO: Frank Richards, Chief Information Officer
CHR: Amy Brayford, Chief Human Resources Officer
CNO: Susan M Robel, R.N., Executive Vice President and Chief Nursing Officer
Web address: www.geisinger.org
Control: Other not–for–profit (including NFP Corporation) **Service:** General medical and surgical

Staffed Beds: 540 **Admissions:** 30766 **Census:** 418 **Outpatient Visits:** 1341986 **Births:** 1857 **Total Expense ($000):** 1049261 **Payroll Expense ($000):** 304710 **Personnel:** 7179

⊞ **SELECT SPECIALTY HOSPITAL–DANVILLE (392047)**, 100 North Academy Avenue, 3rd Floor, Zip 17822–3050; tel. 570/214–9653, (Nonreporting) **A**1 10 **S** Select Medical Corporation, Mechanicsburg, PA
Primary Contact: Brian Mann, Chief Executive Officer
Web address: www.selectspecialtyhospitals.com/company/locations/danville.aspx
Control: Corporation, Investor–owned (for–profit) **Service**: Acute long–term care hospital

Staffed Beds: 30

DARBY—Delaware County

⊞ △ **MERCY FITZGERALD HOSPITAL (390156)**, 1500 Lansdowne Avenue, Zip 19023–1200; tel. 610/237–4000, (Includes MERCY FITZGERALD HOSPITAL, 1500 South Lansdowne Avenue, Darby, PA, Zip 19023; tel. 610/237–4000; MERCY PHILADELPHIA HOSPITAL, 501 South 54th Street, Philadelphia, PA, Zip 19143; tel. 215/748–9000; Susan Cusack, Executive Director) **A**1 2 3 5 7 10 12 13 **F**3 4 11 12 15 18 20 22 24 26 28 29 30 31 34 35 38 40 45 46 49 50 51 54 55 57 58 59 61 64 66 70 75 77 78 79 81 82 85 86 87 90 91 92 93 97 98 100 101 102 107 108 110 111 114 115 118 119 120 121 123 124 130 132 135 145 146 147 148 149 150 154 **S** Trinity Health, Livonia, MI
Primary Contact: Susan Cusack, Executive Director
COO: Ruth Thomas, Chief Operating Officer
CFO: Don Snenk, Chief Financial Officer
CMO: Jeff Komins, M.D., Chief Medical Officer
CIO: Jeff Byda, Vice President Information Technology
Web address: www.mercyhealth.org
Control: Other not–for–profit (including NFP Corporation) **Service**: General medical and surgical

Staffed Beds: 340 Admissions: 15558 Census: 208 Births: 0
Personnel: 1985

DOWNINGTOWN—Chester County

★ **ST. JOHN VIANNEY HOSPITAL**, 151 Woodbine Road, Zip 19335–3057; tel. 610/269–2600, **F**4 29 30 98 **P**5
Primary Contact: David Shellenberger, President
CMO: James MacFadyen, M.D., Medical Director
CNO: Diana Karanja, R.N., Director of Nursing
Web address: www.sjvcenter.org
Control: Church operated, Nongovernment, not–for–profit **Service**: Psychiatric

Staffed Beds: 47 Admissions: 107 Census: 33 Outpatient Visits: 0
Births: 0 Total Expense ($000): 8222 Personnel: 61

DOYLESTOWN—Bucks County

⊞ △ **DOYLESTOWN HOSPITAL (390203)**, 595 West State Street, Zip 18901–2597; tel. 215/345–2200, **A**1 2 3 5 7 10 **F**3 8 13 15 17 18 20 22 24 26 28 29 30 31 32 34 35 40 45 46 49 50 51 54 55 56 57 58 59 62 63 64 70 73 74 75 76 77 78 79 81 85 86 87 89 92 93 94 96 107 108 110 111 114 115 118 119 124 126 130 131 132 141 146 147 149 **P**2 5 7 8
Primary Contact: James L. Brexler, President and Chief Executive Officer
COO: Eleanor Wilson, R.N., MSN, Vice President and Chief Operating Officer
CFO: Daniel Upton, Vice President and Chief Financial Officer
CMO: Scott S Levy, M.D., Vice President and Chief Medical Officer
CIO: Richard Lang, Ed.D., Vice President and Chief Information Officer
CHR: Barbara Hebel, Vice President Human Resources
CNO: Patricia A Stover, Administrator Nursing
Web address: www.doylestownhealth.org
Control: Other not–for–profit (including NFP Corporation) **Service**: General medical and surgical

Staffed Beds: 232 Admissions: 12511 Census: 133 Outpatient Visits:
305483 Births: 1171 Total Expense ($000): 258249 Payroll Expense
($000): 104894 Personnel: 1996

☐ **FOUNDATIONS BEHAVIORAL HEALTH (394038)**, 833 East Butler Avenue, Zip 18901–2280; tel. 215/345–0444, (Nonreporting) **A**1 10 **S** Universal Health Services, Inc., King of Prussia, PA
Primary Contact: Gina Fusco, Chief Executive Officer
Web address: www.fbh.com
Control: Other not–for–profit (including NFP Corporation) **Service**: Children's hospital psychiatric

Staffed Beds: 58

DREXEL HILL—Delaware County

☐ **DELAWARE COUNTY MEMORIAL HOSPITAL (390081)**, 501 North Lansdowne Avenue, Zip 19026–1114; tel. 610/284–8100, (Nonreporting) **A**1 2 3 5 10 **S** Prospect Medical Holdings, Los Angeles, CA
Primary Contact: Robert Haffey, R.N., President
CFO: Richard I Bennett, Senior Vice President and Chief Financial Officer
CMO: Seth Malin, M.D., President Medical and Dental Staff
CIO: Robert E Wilson, Vice President and Chief Information Officer
Web address: www.crozer.org
Control: Other not–for–profit (including NFP Corporation) **Service**: General medical and surgical

Staffed Beds: 168

DUBOIS—Clearfield County

☐ **PENN HIGHLANDS DUBOIS (390086)**, 100 Hospital Avenue, Zip 15801–1440, Mailing Address: P.O. Box 447, Zip 15801–0447; tel. 814/371–2200, (Nonreporting) **A**1 10 19
Primary Contact: John Sutika, President
CFO: Brian S Kline, Vice President and Chief Financial Officer
CMO: Gary Dugan, M.D., Vice President Medical Affairs
CHR: Robert J McKee, Vice President Human Resources
Web address: www.drmc.org
Control: Other not–for–profit (including NFP Corporation) **Service**: General medical and surgical

Staffed Beds: 219

EAGLEVILLE—Montgomery County

★ **EAGLEVILLE HOSPITAL (390278)**, 100 Eagleville Road, Zip 19403–1829, Mailing Address: P.O. Box 45, Zip 19408–0045; tel. 610/539–6000, (Nonreporting) **A**5 10
Primary Contact: Maureen King. Pollock, Chief Executive Officer
COO: Eugene J. Ott Jr Chief Operating Officer
CFO: Alfred P Salvitti, Chief Financial Officer
CMO: Robert Wilson, D.O., Director Medical Services
CIO: Richard R Mitchell, Director Information Technology
CHR: Zoe Yousaitis, Director Human Resources
Web address: www.eaglevillehospital.org
Control: Other not–for–profit (including NFP Corporation) **Service**: Alcoholism and other chemical dependency

Staffed Beds: 83

EAST NORRITON—Montgomery County

☐ **EINSTEIN MEDICAL CENTER MONTGOMERY (390329)**, 559 West Germantown Pike, Zip 19403–4250; tel. 484/622–1000, **A**1 2 3 10 **F**3 8 11 12 13 15 18 20 22 24 26 29 30 31 34 35 40 45 46 49 55 57 59 62 63 64 68 70 72 74 75 76 78 79 80 81 82 84 85 87 92 100 107 108 110 111 115 117 119 120 121 123 126 129 130 131 132 135 146 147 149 154 **S** Einstein Healthcare Network, Philadelphia, PA
Primary Contact: Beth Duffy, Chief Operating Officer
COO: Beth Duffy, Chief Operating Officer
CFO: Gerard Blaney, Vice President, Finance
CMO: Angela Nicholas, Vice President, Medical Affairs
CIO: Mary Carroll Ford, Chief Information Officer
CHR: Kenneth Levitan, Chief Administrative Officer
CNO: AnnMarie Papa, R.N., Vice President and Chief Nursing Officer
Control: Other not–for–profit (including NFP Corporation) **Service**: General medical and surgical

Staffed Beds: 171 Admissions: 9914 Census: 116 Outpatient Visits:
205911 Births: 1925 Total Expense ($000): 216220 Payroll Expense
($000): 75294 Personnel: 1120

EAST STROUDSBURG—Monroe County

⊞ △ **LEHIGH VALLEY HOSPITAL – POCONO (390201)**, 206 East Brown Street, Zip 18301–3006; tel. 570/421–4000, (Nonreporting) **A**1 2 7 10 **S** Lehigh Valley Health Network, Allentown, PA
Primary Contact: Elizabeth Wise, President and Chief Executive Officer
CMO: William K. Cors, M.D., Senior Medical Director
CIO: Ferd Feola, Chief Information Officer
CHR: Lynn M. Lansdowne, Administrator Human Resources
Web address: www.pmchealthsystem.org
Control: Other not–for–profit (including NFP Corporation) **Service**: General medical and surgical

Staffed Beds: 235

EASTON—Northampton County

⊞ **EASTON HOSPITAL (390162)**, 250 South 21st Street, Zip 18042–3892; tel. 610/250–4000, (Nonreporting) **A**1 2 3 5 10 **S** Steward Health Care System, LLC, Dallas, TX
Primary Contact: Jeffery Snyder, Chief Executive Officer
COO: Ron Ziobro, Chief Operating Officer
CFO: Steven Clark, Chief Financial Officer
CMO: Roman Tuma, Chief Medical Officer
CIO: Don Lutz, Director Information Technology
CHR: Tanya Segal, Director
CNO: Karen Vadyak, Chief Nursing Officer
Web address: www.easton–hospital.com
Control: Other not–for–profit (including NFP Corporation) **Service**: General medical and surgical

Staffed Beds: 196

PA

☐ **ST. LUKE'S HOSPITAL – ANDERSON CAMPUS (390326)**, 1872 Riverside Circle, Zip 18045–5669; tel. 484/503–3000, **A**1 2 3 10 **F**3 11 15 18 20 22 24 26 29 30 31 34 35 38 40 44 45 46 49 50 51 53 54 55 57 59 60 63 64 68 70 71 74 75 77 78 79 81 82 84 85 86 87 92 93 96 100 102 107 108 110 111 115 118 119 120 121 123 124 130 132 144 145 146 148 149 154 **S** St. Luke's University Health Network, Bethlehem, PA
Primary Contact: Edward Nawrocki, President
CMO: Justin P Psaila, M.D., Vice President Medical Affairs
CNO: Darla Frack, R.N., RN Vice President, Patient Services
Web address: www.mystlukesonline.org
Control: Other not–for–profit (including NFP Corporation) **Service**: General medical and surgical

Staffed Beds: 108 **Admissions**: 6720 **Census**: 73 **Outpatient Visits**: 209522 **Births**: 0 **Total Expense ($000)**: 148868 **Payroll Expense ($000)**: 51137 **Personnel**: 637

ELLWOOD CITY—Lawrence County

ELLWOOD CITY MEDICAL CENTER (390008), 724 Pershing Street, Zip 16117–1474; tel. 724/752–0081, (Nonreporting) **A**10
Primary Contact: Beverly Annarumo, R.N., MSN, President
CFO: Christopher M Little, Vice President and Chief Financial Officer
CIO: Connie Cunningham, Chief Information Officer
CHR: Paul Landman, Director Human Resources
CNO: Della Stabryla, Director of Nursing
Web address: www.TheEllwoodCityHospital.org
Control: Other not–for–profit (including NFP Corporation) **Service**: General medical and surgical

Staffed Beds: 95

EPHRATA—Lancaster County

☒ **WELLSPAN EPHRATA COMMUNITY HOSPITAL (390225)**, 169 Martin Avenue, Zip 17522–1724, Mailing Address: P.O. Box 1002, Zip 17522–1002; tel. 717/733–0311, **A**1 2 10 **F**3 13 15 18 20 22 26 28 29 30 31 34 35 40 44 45 46 49 50 51 54 57 59 60 61 64 70 72 74 75 76 77 78 79 80 81 82 85 87 89 90 97 98 100 101 102 107 108 110 111 114 115 116 117 118 119 120 121 123 129 130 132 135 144 146 147 148 **P**6 8 **S** WellSpan Health, York, PA
CFO: David Kreider, Controller
CMO: Mark Jacobson, D.O., Vice President Medical Affairs
CIO: Leon John Jabour, Regional Chief Information Officer
CHR: Jana Salaki, Regional Director Human Resources
CNO: Tina Citro, R.N., Chief Nursing Officer, Vice President, Patient Services
Web address: www.wellspan.org
Control: Other not–for–profit (including NFP Corporation) **Service**: General medical and surgical

Staffed Beds: 130 **Admissions**: 6209 **Census**: 75 **Outpatient Visits**: 359450 **Births**: 899 **Total Expense ($000)**: 198370 **Payroll Expense ($000)**: 58151 **Personnel**: 904

ERIE—Erie County

☒ **ERIE VETERANS AFFAIRS MEDICAL CENTER**, 135 East 38th Street, Zip 16504–1559; tel. 814/860–2576, (Total facility includes 45 beds in nursing home–type unit) **A**1 **F**3 5 8 29 30 31 33 34 35 36 38 39 45 54 55 56 57 59 61 62 63 64 65 68 74 75 77 78 79 81 82 83 84 85 86 87 91 93 94 97 100 101 102 104 107 114 119 127 128 130 132 135 143 144 146 147 148 149 153 154 **P**6 **S** Department of Veterans Affairs, Perry Point, MD
Primary Contact: John Gennaro, FACHE, Director
CFO: Joann Pritchard, Chief Financial Officer
CMO: Anthony Behm, D.O., Chief of Staff
CIO: Jonathan Seale, Chief Information Officer
CHR: Lynn Nies, Human Resources Officer
CNO: Dorene M. Sommers, Associate Director Patient Care Services
Web address: www.erie.va.gov/
Control: Veterans Affairs, Government, federal **Service**: General medical and surgical

Staffed Beds: 52 **Admissions**: 511 **Census**: 44 **Outpatient Visits**: 261243 **Births**: 0 **Total Expense ($000)**: 114706 **Personnel**: 794

HAMOT MEDICAL CENTER See UPMC Hamot

☒ **HEALTHSOUTH REHABILITATION HOSPITAL OF ERIE (393046)**, 143 East Second Street, Zip 16507–1501; tel. 814/878–1200, (Nonreporting) **A**1 10 **S** Encompass Health Corporation, Birmingham, AL
Primary Contact: John Papalia, Chief Executive Officer
CFO: Lori Gibbens, Controller
CMO: Douglas Grisier, D.O., Medical Director
CIO: Sharon Zielinski, Manager Health Information
CHR: William Robinson, Director Human Resources
Web address: www.healthsoutherie.com
Control: Corporation, Investor–owned (for–profit) **Service**: Rehabilitation

Staffed Beds: 100

○ **LECOM HEALTH MILLCREEK COMMUNITY HOSPITAL (390198)**, 5515 Peach Street, Zip 16509–2695; tel. 814/864–4031, (Nonreporting) **A**3 10 11 12 13
Primary Contact: Mary L. Eckert, President and Chief Executive Officer
CFO: Richard P Olinger, Chief Financial Officer
CMO: James Y Lin, D.O., Chief of Staff
CIO: Cheryl Girardier, Director Information Technology
CHR: Polly Momeyer, Manager Human Resources
CNO: Katie Agresti, R.N., Director Patient Care Services
Web address: www.millcreekcommunityhospital.com
Control: Other not–for–profit (including NFP Corporation) **Service**: General medical and surgical

Staffed Beds: 168

☒ **SAINT VINCENT HOSPITAL (390009)**, 232 West 25th Street, Zip 16544–0002; tel. 814/452–5000, **A**1 2 3 5 10 12 13 **F**3 8 11 12 13 15 17 18 20 22 24 26 28 29 30 31 34 35 37 38 39 40 44 46 47 48 49 50 51 54 56 57 58 59 60 61 64 65 68 70 71 72 74 75 76 77 78 79 80 81 82 84 85 86 87 89 90 92 93 94 96 98 101 102 103 107 108 110 111 115 118 119 121 123 124 126 129 130 132 135 141 146 147 149 154 **S** Allegheny Health Network, Pittsburgh, PA
Primary Contact: Christopher Clark, D.O., President and Chief Executive Officer
COO: Jason Roeback, Chief Operating Officer
CFO: Randolph Levis, Chief Financial Officer
CIO: Richard B Ong, Chief Information Officer
CHR: Johnie M Atkinson, Chief Human Resources Officer
CNO: Maureen C Chadwick, R.N., Chief Nursing Officer
Web address: www.svhs.org
Control: Other not–for–profit (including NFP Corporation) **Service**: General medical and surgical

Staffed Beds: 371 **Admissions**: 13785 **Census**: 179 **Outpatient Visits**: 171687 **Births**: 1005 **Total Expense ($000)**: 282277 **Payroll Expense ($000)**: 83135 **Personnel**: 1846

☒ **SELECT SPECIALTY HOSPITAL–ERIE (392037)**, 252 West 11th Street, Zip 16501–1702; tel. 814/874–5300, (Nonreporting) **A**1 10 **S** Select Medical Corporation, Mechanicsburg, PA
Primary Contact: Thomas Fucci, FACHE, Chief Executive Officer
CNO: Keith Christiansen, Chief Nursing Officer
Web address: www.erie.selectspecialtyhospitals.com/
Control: Corporation, Investor–owned (for–profit) **Service**: Acute long–term care hospital

Staffed Beds: 50

☐ **UPMC HAMOT (390063)**, 201 State Street, Zip 16550–0002; tel. 814/877–6000, **A**1 2 3 5 8 10 13 **F**3 5 9 12 13 15 17 18 20 22 24 26 28 29 30 31 34 35 36 37 38 39 40 43 44 45 46 47 48 49 50 51 56 57 58 59 60 61 62 63 64 65 66 68 70 72 74 75 76 77 78 79 80 81 82 84 85 86 87 89 92 93 96 97 100 101 102 104 106 107 108 109 110 111 114 115 118 119 124 126 129 130 131 132 134 135 138 141 147 148 149 150 154 **P**6 **S** UPMC, Pittsburgh, PA
Primary Contact: David Gibbons, President
CFO: Bradley Dinger, Chief Financial Offical
CMO: Richard Long, M.D., Chief Medical Officer
CIO: Lisa D McChesney, R.N., Senior Director Information Systems
CNO: James E Donnelly, Chief Nursing Officer and Vice President Patient Care Services
Web address: www.upmc.com/locations/hospitals/hamot
Control: Other not–for–profit (including NFP Corporation) **Service**: General medical and surgical

Staffed Beds: 327 **Admissions**: 20997 **Census**: 256 **Outpatient Visits**: 227582 **Births**: 2027 **Total Expense ($000)**: 364364 **Payroll Expense ($000)**: 103217 **Personnel**: 2017

VETERANS AFFAIRS MEDICAL CENTER See Erie Veterans Affairs Medical Center

---

Hospital, Medicare Provider Number, Address, Telephone, Approval, Facility, and Physician Codes, Health Care System

★ American Hospital Association (AHA) membership   ○ Healthcare Facilities Accreditation Program   ⇑ Center for Improvement in Healthcare Quality Accreditation
☐ The Joint Commission accreditation   ◇ DNV Healthcare Inc. accreditation   △ Commission on Accreditation of Rehabilitation Facilities (CARF) accreditation

PA

EVERETT—Bedford County

☐ **UPMC BEDFORD MEMORIAL (390117)**, 10455 Lincoln Highway, Zip 15537–7046; tel. 814/623–6161, **A**1 10 20 **F**3 8 11 13 15 18 28 29 30 31 34 35 36 40 41 45 50 51 56 57 59 61 64 65 68 70 74 75 76 77 78 79 81 85 86 87 89 102 104 107 108 110 111 114 119 129 130 131 132 133 135 146 147 149 154 **P**6 **S** UPMC, Pittsburgh, PA
Primary Contact: Gerald Murray, President
CFO: Mario Wilfong, Vice President Finance and Administration
CIO: Mark Wiley, Manager Information Systems Development
CHR: Michelle A Speck, Vice President Human Resources
CNO: Paula Thomas, R.N., MSN, Vice President Patient Services
Web address: www.upmcbedfordmemorial.com
Control: Other not–for–profit (including NFP Corporation) **Service:** General medical and surgical

> **Staffed Beds:** 27 **Admissions:** 1729 **Census:** 14 **Outpatient Visits:** 109991 **Births:** 284 **Total Expense ($000):** 58812 **Payroll Expense ($000):** 13937 **Personnel:** 242

FARRELL—Mercer County

SHENANGO VALLEY CAMPUS See UPMC Horizon, Farrell

☐ ○ **UPMC HORIZON (390178)**, 2200 Memorial Drive, Zip 16121–1357; tel. 724/588–2100, (Includes GREENVILLE CAMPUS, 110 North Main Street, Greenville, PA, Zip 16125–1795; tel. 724/588–2100; SHENANGO VALLEY CAMPUS, 2200 Memorial Drive, Farrell, PA, Zip 16121–1398; tel. 724/981–3500) **A**1 10 11 13 **F**3 11 12 13 15 18 26 28 29 30 31 32 34 35 39 40 43 44 45 46 49 50 53 54 56 57 59 61 64 65 68 70 73 74 75 76 77 78 79 81 82 85 86 87 90 92 97 107 110 111 114 115 118 119 120 129 130 131 132 133 135 146 147 148 149 **S** UPMC, Pittsburgh, PA
Primary Contact: Donald R. Owrey, President
CFO: David Shulik, Vice President and Chief Financial Officer
CMO: Samuel Daisley, D.O., Vice President Medical Affairs
CHR: Connie Mayle, Vice President Administrative Services
Web address: www.upmc.com
Control: Other not–for–profit (including NFP Corporation) **Service:** General medical and surgical

> **Staffed Beds:** 121 **Admissions:** 6076 **Census:** 67 **Outpatient Visits:** 219161 **Births:** 1016 **Total Expense ($000):** 150033 **Payroll Expense ($000):** 39452 **Personnel:** 654

FORT WASHINGTON—Montgomery County

☐ **BROOKE GLEN BEHAVIORAL HOSPITAL (394049)**, 7170 Lafayette Avenue, Zip 19034–2301; tel. 215/641–5300, (Nonreporting) **A**1 5 10 **S** Universal Health Services, Inc., King of Prussia, PA
Primary Contact: Neil Callahan, Chief Executive Officer
COO: William R Mason, Chief Operating Officer
CFO: Robert Zagerman, Chief Financial Officer
CMO: Chand Nair, M.D., Medical Director
CHR: Dawn Kownacki, Director Human Resources
Web address: www.brookeglenhospital.com
Control: Corporation, Investor–owned (for–profit) **Service:** Psychiatric

> **Staffed Beds:** 146

GETTYSBURG—Adams County

✠ **WELLSPAN GETTYSBURG HOSPITAL (390065)**, 147 Gettys Street, Zip 17325–2534; tel. 717/334–2121, **A**1 3 10 **F**3 8 11 13 15 18 20 26 28 29 30 31 35 40 46 49 50 51 54 56 59 64 68 70 74 75 76 77 78 79 81 82 84 85 87 91 93 94 95 96 102 107 108 110 111 114 119 120 121 123 129 130 131 132 134 135 146 147 148 149 154 **S** WellSpan Health, York, PA
Primary Contact: Jane E. Hyde, President
COO: Joseph H Edgar, Senior Vice President Operations
CMO: Charles Marley, D.O., Vice President Medical Affairs
CIO: Robin Kimple, Director Information Services
CHR: Kim Brister, Director Human Resources
Web address: www.wellspan.org
Control: Other not–for–profit (including NFP Corporation) **Service:** General medical and surgical

> **Staffed Beds:** 76 **Admissions:** 3944 **Census:** 42 **Outpatient Visits:** 197941 **Births:** 497 **Total Expense ($000):** 159812 **Payroll Expense ($000):** 41513 **Personnel:** 633

GREENSBURG—Westmoreland County

☐ **EXCELA HEALTH WESTMORELAND HOSPITAL (390145)**, 532 West Pittsburgh Street, Zip 15601–2282; tel. 724/832–4000, (Nonreporting) **A**1 3 10 **S** Excela Health, Greensburg, PA
Primary Contact: Ronald H. Ott, President
COO: Michael D Busch, Executive Vice President and Chief Operating Officer
CFO: Jeffrey T Curry, Executive Vice President and Chief Financial Officer
CMO: Jerome Granato, M.D., Senior Vice President and Chief Medical Officer
CIO: David Gawaluck, Vice President and Chief Information Officer
CHR: John Caverno, Chief Human Resources Officer
CNO: Helen K Burns, Ph.D., R.N., Senior Vice President and Chief Nursing Officer
Web address: www.excelahealth.org
Control: Other not–for–profit (including NFP Corporation) **Service:** General medical and surgical

> **Staffed Beds:** 270

GROVE CITY—Mercer County

GROVE CITY MEDICAL CENTER (390266), 631 North Broad Street Extension, Zip 16127–4603; tel. 724/450–7000, (Total facility includes 20 beds in nursing home–type unit) **A**10 **F**3 15 20 26 28 29 31 34 35 40 45 46 49 51 57 59 64 70 75 78 79 81 82 87 91 92 93 107 108 110 111 115 117 119 128 129 130 132 146 148 149 **P**6
Primary Contact: Robert Jackson Jr, Chief Executive Officer
CFO: David Poland, Chief Financial Officer
CMO: Daniel Ferguson, Chief of Staff
CIO: Philip Swartwood, Director Information Systems
CHR: Donald Henley, Vice President Human Resources
CNO: Anthony Bono Jr Chief Nursing Officer
Web address: www.gcmcpa.org
Control: Other not–for–profit (including NFP Corporation) **Service:** General medical and surgical

> **Staffed Beds:** 55 **Admissions:** 1887 **Census:** 27 **Outpatient Visits:** 101572 **Births:** 0 **Total Expense ($000):** 45440 **Payroll Expense ($000):** 17445 **Personnel:** 346

HANOVER—York County

✠ **UPMC PINNACLE HANOVER (390233)**, 300 Highland Avenue, Zip 17331–2297; tel. 717/316–3711, **A**1 10 **F**3 11 13 15 18 20 22 26 28 29 30 31 35 36 40 44 45 47 49 50 53 54 57 59 61 62 64 65 75 76 77 78 79 81 84 85 86 87 89 93 94 96 107 108 110 111 115 117 118 119 129 130 131 132 134 135 144 146 147 148 149 150 **S** UPMC, Pittsburgh, PA
Primary Contact: Michael W. Gaskins, President
COO: Michael A. Hockenberry, Senior Vice President and Chief Operating Officer
CFO: Donna L. Muller, Interim Chief Financial Officer
CMO: Michael H Ader, M.D., Vice President Medical Affairs
CIO: William C. Tandy, Chief Information Officer
CHR: Christine Miller, General Counsel and Vice President Human Resources
CNO: M Patricia Saunders, R.N., MS, Vice President Nursing
Web address: www.hanoverhospital.org
Control: Other not–for–profit (including NFP Corporation) **Service:** General medical and surgical

> **Staffed Beds:** 93 **Admissions:** 5440 **Census:** 56 **Outpatient Visits:** 220431 **Births:** 578 **Total Expense ($000):** 159597 **Payroll Expense ($000):** 59591 **Personnel:** 1010

HARRISBURG—Dauphin County

✠ **HELEN M. SIMPSON REHABILITATION HOSPITAL (393056)**, 4300 Londonderry Road, Zip 17109–5317; tel. 717/920–4300, (Nonreporting) **A**1 **S** Select Medical Corporation, Mechanicsburg, PA
Primary Contact: Mark Freeburn, Chief Executive Officer
Web address: www.simpson–rehab.com/
Control: Corporation, Investor–owned (for–profit) **Service:** Rehabilitation

> **Staffed Beds:** 55

✠ **PENNSYLVANIA PSYCHIATRIC INSTITUTE (394051)**, 2501 North Third Street, Zip 17110–1904; tel. 717/782–6420, (Nonreporting) **A**1 3 5 10
Primary Contact: William Daly, Chief Executive Officer
CFO: Robert Fotter, Chief Financial Officer
CMO: Elisabeth J. Kunkel, M.D., Professor, Pennsylvania State College of Medicine
CHR: Wanda Geesey, Director Human Resources
CNO: Teresa Terry–Williams, R.N., Chief Nursing Officer
Web address: www.ppimhs.org/
Control: Other not–for–profit (including NFP Corporation) **Service:** Psychiatric

> **Staffed Beds:** 80

PINNACLEHEALTH AT COMMUNITY GENERAL OSTEOPATHIC HOSPITAL See UPMC Pinnacle Harrisburg, Harrisburg

Many Facility Codes have changed. Please refer to the AHA Guide Code Chart.

© 2018 AHA Guide

SELECT SPECIALTY HOSPITAL–HARRISBURG See Select Specialty Hospital–Camp Hill, Camp Hill

☐ **UPMC PINNACLE HARRISBURG (390067)**, 111 South Front Street, Zip 17101–2010, Mailing Address: P.O. Box 8700, Zip 17105–8700; tel. 717/231–8900, (Includes PINNACLEHEALTH AT COMMUNITY GENERAL OSTEOPATHIC HOSPITAL, 4300 Londonderry Road, Harrisburg, PA, Zip 17109–5397, Mailing Address: P.O. Box 3000, Zip 17105–3000, tel. 717/652–3000; PINNACLEHEALTH AT HARRISBURG HOSPITAL, 111 South Front Street, Harrisburg, PA, Zip 17101–2099; tel. 717/782–3131; PINNACLEHEALTH WEST SHORE HOSPITAL, 1995 Technology Parkway, Mechanicsburg, PA, Zip 17050–8522; tel. 717/791–2600) **A**1 2 3 5 10 12 13 **F**3 7 8 11 12 13 14 15 17 18 19 20 22 24 26 27 28 29 30 31 32 34 35 36 37 38 40 44 45 46 47 48 49 50 52 53 54 55 56 57 58 59 60 61 64 65 66 68 70 72 74 75 76 77 78 79 81 82 84 85 86 87 89 93 97 100 107 108 110 111 114 115 116 117 118 119 120 121 123 124 126 129 130 131 132 134 138 141 142 143 144 145 146 147 148 149 154 **P**6 **S** UPMC, Pittsburgh, PA
Primary Contact: Philip Guarneschelli, Interim Chief Executive Officer
COO: Philip Guarneschelli, Senior Vice President and Chief Operating Officer
CFO: William H Pugh, Senior Vice President Corporate Finance and Chief Financial Officer
CMO: Nirmal Joshi, M.D., Senior Vice President Medical Affairs and Chief Medical Officer
CHR: Ann H Gormley, Senior Vice President Human Resources
CNO: Susan Comp, Senior Vice President and Chief Nursing Officer
Web address: www.pinnaclehealth.org
Control: Other not–for–profit (including NFP Corporation) **Service:** General medical and surgical

Staffed Beds: 659 **Admissions:** 35355 **Census:** 432 **Outpatient Visits:** 855193 **Births:** 3927 **Total Expense ($000):** 899784 **Payroll Expense ($000):** 289917 **Personnel:** 5057

HASTINGS—Cambria County

★ **CONEMAUGH MINERS MEDICAL CENTER (390130)**, 290 Haida Avenue, Zip 16646–5610, Mailing Address: P.O. Box 689, Zip 16646–0689; tel. 814/247–3100, **A**10 20 **F**3 15 18 29 30 31 35 36 40 45 48 50 56 59 64 70 75 78 79 81 86 92 93 96 97 102 107 108 110 119 129 130 133 144 148 **P**8 **S** Duke LifePoint Healthcare, Brentwood, TN
Primary Contact: Timothy Harclerode, Chief Executive Officer
COO: Debbie Spells–Wilson, R.N., Chief Operating Officer and Chief Nursing Officer
CFO: Linda Fanale, Chief Financial Officer
CMO: Susan Williams, M.D., Chief Medical Officer
CIO: Joe Dado, Chief Information Officer
CNO: Debbie Spells–Wilson, R.N., Chief Operating Officer and Chief Nursing Officer
Web address: www.conemaugh.org
Control: Corporation, Investor–owned (for–profit) **Service:** General medical and surgical

Staffed Beds: 30 **Admissions:** 397 **Census:** 5 **Outpatient Visits:** 37509 **Births:** 2 **Total Expense ($000):** 16685 **Payroll Expense ($000):** 5270 **Personnel:** 108

HAZLETON—Luzerne County

★ ○ **LEHIGH VALLEY HOSPITAL – HAZLETON (390185)**, 700 East Broad Street, Zip 18201–6897; tel. 570/501–4000, **A**10 11 **F**3 8 11 12 13 15 18 28 29 31 33 34 35 40 43 44 50 53 54 57 59 60 62 64 68 69 70 75 76 77 78 79 81 82 85 86 87 89 90 93 107 108 109 110 111 114 118 119 129 130 131 132 135 143 144 146 147 148 154 **P**5 6 8 **S** Lehigh Valley Health Network, Allentown, PA
Primary Contact: John R. Fletcher, President
CFO: William Bauer, Vice President Finance and Chief Financial Officer
CMO: Anthony Valente, M.D., Vice President Medical Affairs
CIO: Carl Shoener, Chief Information Officer
Web address: www.lvhn.org/hazleton/
Control: Other not–for–profit (including NFP Corporation) **Service:** General medical and surgical

Staffed Beds: 120 **Admissions:** 6437 **Census:** 82 **Outpatient Visits:** 162262 **Births:** 783 **Total Expense ($000):** 116279 **Payroll Expense ($000):** 45277 **Personnel:** 928

HERSHEY—Dauphin County

⊠ **PENN STATE MILTON S. HERSHEY MEDICAL CENTER (390256)**, 500 University Drive, Zip 17033–2360, Mailing Address: P.O. Box 850, Zip 17033–0850; tel. 717/531–8521, (Includes PENN STATE CHILDREN'S HOSPITAL, 500 University Drive, Hershey, PA, Zip 17033–2360; tel. 717/531–8521) **A**1 2 3 5 8 10 **F**3 5 6 7 8 9 11 12 13 14 15 17 18 19 20 21 22 23 24 25 26 27 28 29 30 31 32 34 35 36 37 38 40 41 43 44 45 46 47 48 49 50 51 52 53 54 55 56 57 58 59 60 61 64 65 66 68 70 71 72 73 74 75 76 77 78 79 80 81 82 84 85 86 87 88 89 91 92 93 95 96 97 100 101 102 104 105 107 108 110 111 114 115 116 117 118 119 121 123 124 126 129 130 131 132 134 135 136 137 138 139 141 142 143 144 145 146 147 148 149 150 153 154 **P**6 **S** Penn State Hershey Health System, Hershey, PA
Primary Contact: A. Craig. Hillemeier, M.D., Chief Executive Officer
COO: Stephen M. Massini, Chief Operating Officer
CFO: Stephen M. Massini, Chief Financial Officer
CMO: Thomas Tracy Jr Chief Medical Officer
CIO: Rod Dykehouse, Chief Information Officer
CHR: David Swift, Chief Human Resources Officer
CNO: Judy N. Himes, MSN, R.N., Chief Nursing Officer
Web address: www.pennstatehershey.org/
Control: Other not–for–profit (including NFP Corporation) **Service:** General medical and surgical

Staffed Beds: 530 **Admissions:** 27402 **Census:** 452 **Outpatient Visits:** 1077610 **Births:** 2055 **Total Expense ($000):** 1369071 **Payroll Expense ($000):** 469046 **Personnel:** 9794

HONESDALE—Wayne County

★ ⇑ **WAYNE MEMORIAL HOSPITAL (390125)**, 601 Park Street, Zip 18431–1498; tel. 570/253–8100, **A**10 20 21 **F**3 13 15 18 20 22 26 28 29 31 34 35 39 40 43 46 49 57 59 62 63 70 74 75 76 77 78 79 81 85 86 89 90 92 93 100 107 108 110 111 119 128 129 130 132 133 135 146 148 149 154
Primary Contact: David L. Hoff, Chief Executive Officer
COO: John Conte, Director Facility Services and Real Estate
CFO: Michael J Clifford, Director Finance
CMO: William Dewar, M.D., Chief of Staff
CIO: Tom Hoffman, Manager Information Systems
CHR: Elizabeth McDonald, Director Human Resources
CNO: Jim Pettinato, Director Patient Care Services
Web address: www.wmh.org
Control: Other not–for–profit (including NFP Corporation) **Service:** General medical and surgical

Staffed Beds: 87 **Admissions:** 3639 **Census:** 40 **Outpatient Visits:** 155806 **Births:** 472 **Total Expense ($000):** 87255 **Payroll Expense ($000):** 34448 **Personnel:** 658

HUMMELSTOWN—Dauphin County

⊠ △ **PENN STATE HERSHEY REHABILITATION HOSPITAL (393053)**, 1135 Old West Chocolate Avenue, Zip 17036; tel. 717/832–2600, (Nonreporting) **A**1 3 7 10 **S** Select Medical Corporation, Mechanicsburg, PA
Primary Contact: Michelle Von Arx, Chief Executive Officer
CMO: Brenda Mallory, M.D., Medical Director
Web address: www.psh–rehab.com
Control: Corporation, Investor–owned (for–profit) **Service:** Rehabilitation

Staffed Beds: 76

HUNTINGDON—Huntingdon County

⊠ **J. C. BLAIR MEMORIAL HOSPITAL (390056)**, 1225 Warm Springs Avenue, Zip 16652–2398; tel. 814/643–2290, **A**1 10 20 **F**3 11 13 15 18 20 22 26 28 29 34 35 40 45 50 53 55 56 59 64 68 70 75 76 77 79 81 84 85 86 87 89 96 98 100 102 103 107 108 110 111 115 118 119 129 130 132 133 135 146 148 154
Primary Contact: Joseph Myers, Interim Administrator
COO: Adam Dimm, Chief Executive Officer
CMO: James Hayden, M.D., Chief Medical Officer
CIO: Armen Arakelian, Chief Information Officer
CHR: Susan Hess, Director Human Resources
CNO: Joye Gingrich, Director Patient Care Services and Chief Nursing Officer
Web address: www.jcblair.org
Control: Other not–for–profit (including NFP Corporation) **Service:** General medical and surgical

Staffed Beds: 62 **Admissions:** 2278 **Census:** 30 **Outpatient Visits:** 106378 **Births:** 204 **Total Expense ($000):** 48751 **Payroll Expense ($000):** 22014 **Personnel:** 348

PA

Hospital, Medicare Provider Number, Address, Telephone, Approval, Facility, and Physician Codes, Health Care System

★ American Hospital Association (AHA) membership
☐ The Joint Commission accreditation
○ Healthcare Facilities Accreditation Program
◇ DNV Healthcare Inc. accreditation
⇑ Center for Improvement in Healthcare Quality Accreditation
△ Commission on Accreditation of Rehabilitation Facilities (CARF) accreditation

PA

INDIANA—Indiana County

★ **INDIANA REGIONAL MEDICAL CENTER (390173)**, 835 Hospital Road, Zip 15701–3629, Mailing Address: P.O. Box 788, Zip 15701–0788; tel. 724/357–7000, **A**2 10 20 22 **F**3 11 15 18 20 22 28 29 31 34 35 40 44 45 46 47 49 53 56 57 59 64 65 70 71 74 75 76 77 78 79 81 82 83 84 85 90 91 96 98 102 103 107 108 111 114 115 118 119 120 121 123 124 126 129 130 132 144 145 146 147 148 149
Primary Contact: Stephen A. Wolfe, President and Chief Executive Officer
COO: Dominic Paccapaniccia, Chief Operating Officer
CFO: Robert Gongaware, Senior Vice President Finance
CMO: Bruce A Bush, M.D., Senior Vice President Medical Affairs
CIO: Mark Volovic, Vice President and Chief Information Officer
CHR: James W Kinneer, Vice President Organizational Development
CNO: Cindy L Virgil, MSN, R.N., Senior Vice President Patient Care Services
Web address: www.indianarmc.org
Control: Other not–for–profit (including NFP Corporation) **Service:** General medical and surgical

Staffed Beds: 166 **Admissions:** 7404 **Census:** 83 **Outpatient Visits:** 263238 **Births:** 518 **Total Expense ($000):** 148839 **Payroll Expense ($000):** 63408 **Personnel:** 899

JEFFERSON HILLS—Allegheny County

✉ **JEFFERSON HOSPITAL (390265)**, 565 Coal Valley Road, Zip 15025–3703, Mailing Address: Box 18119, Pittsburgh, Zip 15236–0119; tel. 412/469–5000, **A**1 2 3 10 **F**3 8 11 12 13 15 18 20 22 24 26 28 29 30 31 34 35 36 38 40 44 45 46 47 48 49 50 51 54 57 59 60 64 70 73 74 75 76 77 78 79 81 82 84 85 86 87 89 90 96 98 101 102 104 107 108 110 111 114 115 117 118 119 126 129 130 131 132 135 146 147 148 149 153 154 **P**6 **S** Allegheny Health Network, Pittsburgh, PA
Primary Contact: Louise Urban, R.N., President and Chief Executive Officer
CMO: Richard F Collins, M.D., Executive Vice President and Chief Medical Officer
CIO: James Witenske, Chief Information Officer
CNO: Kimberley Finnerty, MSN, R.N., Chief Nursing Officer
Web address: www.jeffersonregional.com
Control: Other not–for–profit (including NFP Corporation) **Service:** General medical and surgical

Staffed Beds: 341 **Admissions:** 13558 **Census:** 190 **Outpatient Visits:** 286133 **Births:** 985 **Total Expense ($000):** 243111 **Payroll Expense ($000):** 81967 **Personnel:** 1544

JERSEY SHORE—Lycoming County

✉ **GEISINGER JERSEY SHORE HOSPITAL (391300)**, 1020 Thompson Street, Zip 17740–1794; tel. 570/398–0100, **A**1 10 18 **F**3 15 18 28 29 30 34 35 40 45 50 57 59 75 77 81 85 93 107 108 110 111 115 119 129 130 133 135 144 **S** Geisinger, Danville, PA
Primary Contact: Tammy Anderer, Acting President
CFO: Mark Rice, CPA, Chief Financial Officer
CMO: Stephen Goykovich, D.O., Chief Medical Officer
CIO: Christine Haas, Chief Information Officer
CHR: Joan Rounsley, Director Human Resources
CNO: Paulette Nish, Chief Nursing Officer
Web address: www.jsh.org
Control: Other not–for–profit (including NFP Corporation) **Service:** General medical and surgical

Staffed Beds: 25 **Admissions:** 602 **Census:** 6 **Outpatient Visits:** 60543 **Births:** 0 **Total Expense ($000):** 24497 **Payroll Expense ($000):** 9928 **Personnel:** 214

JOHNSTOWN—Cambria County

✉ △ **CONEMAUGH MEMORIAL MEDICAL CENTER (390110)**, 1086 Franklin Street, Zip 15905–4398; tel. 814/534–9000, (Includes MEMORIAL MEDICAL CENTER – LEE CAMPUS, 320 Main Street, Johnstown, PA, Zip 15901–1601; tel. 814/533–0123) **A**1 3 7 10 12 13 **F**3 5 8 12 13 15 17 18 20 22 24 26 27 28 29 30 31 34 35 36 37 39 40 43 45 46 49 50 53 54 55 56 57 58 59 60 61 64 65 68 70 72 74 75 76 77 78 79 81 82 83 84 85 86 87 89 90 91 92 93 96 97 98 100 101 102 103 104 107 108 109 110 111 114 115 118 119 126 127 128 129 130 131 132 134 144 145 146 147 148 149 150 154 **S** Duke LifePoint Healthcare, Brentwood, TN
Primary Contact: Steven E. Tucker, Chief Executive Officer
COO: Steven E Tucker, Chief Executive Officer
CMO: Susan Williams, M.D., Chief Medical Officer
CIO: Joe Dado, Chief Information Officer
CNO: Claudia Rager, R.N., Vice President Patient Care Services
Web address: www.conemaugh.org
Control: Corporation, Investor–owned (for–profit) **Service:** General medical and surgical

Staffed Beds: 539 **Admissions:** 19892 **Census:** 290 **Outpatient Visits:** 469285 **Births:** 1883 **Total Expense ($000):** 387457 **Payroll Expense ($000):** 152251 **Personnel:** 2664

MEMORIAL MEDICAL CENTER – LEE CAMPUS See Conemaugh Memorial Medical Center, Johnstown

✉ **SELECT SPECIALTY HOSPITAL–JOHNSTOWN (392031)**, 320 Main Street, 3rd Floor, Zip 15901–1601; tel. 814/534–7300, (Nonreporting) **A**1 10 **S** Select Medical Corporation, Mechanicsburg, PA
Primary Contact: Kelly Blake, Chief Executive Officer
CMO: Gary Davidson, M.D., Medical Director
Web address: www.selectspecialtyhospitals.com/company/locations/johnstown.aspx
Control: Corporation, Investor–owned (for–profit) **Service:** Acute long–term care hospital

Staffed Beds: 39

KANE—Mckean County

UPMC KANE (390104), 4372 Route 6, Zip 16735–3060; tel. 814/837–8585, (Nonreporting) **A**10 20 **S** UPMC, Pittsburgh, PA
Primary Contact: Mark Papalia, President
CFO: Angela Hadzega, Chief Financial Officer
CMO: Linda Rettger, M.D., President Medical Staff
CIO: Deano Cherry, Chief Information Officer
CHR: Marsha Keller, Director Human Resources
CNO: Pam Bray, Director of Nursing and Director Inpatient Services
Web address: www.kanehosp.com
Control: Other not–for–profit (including NFP Corporation) **Service:** General medical and surgical

Staffed Beds: 31

KINGSTON—Luzerne County

✉ **FIRST HOSPITAL WYOMING VALLEY (394039)**, 562 Wyoming Avenue, Zip 18704–3721; tel. 570/552–3900, (Nonreporting) **A**1 3 10 **S** Community Health Systems, Inc., Franklin, TN
Primary Contact: James Gallagher, Chief Executive Officer
CFO: Kelly Knorr, Chief Financial Officer
CMO: David Liskov, M.D., Medical Director
CNO: Rhonda Moffitt Sod, Chief Nursing Officer
Web address: www.commonwealthhealth.net/locations/first–hospital
Control: Corporation, Investor–owned (for–profit) **Service:** Psychiatric

Staffed Beds: 127

KITTANNING—Armstrong County

⇧ **ACMH HOSPITAL (390163)**, One Nolte Drive, Zip 16201–7111; tel. 724/543–8500, (Total facility includes 17 beds in nursing home–type unit) **A**2 10 19 21 **F**3 11 13 15 17 18 20 22 26 28 29 30 34 35 40 45 47 49 59 70 74 75 76 77 78 79 81 82 85 90 93 98 100 102 107 108 110 111 112 114 119 120 127 128 129 130 131 132 135 136 141 142 146 148 149
Primary Contact: John I. Lewis, President and Chief Executive Officer
CFO: Patrick Burns, Vice President Finance
CMO: Harold Altman, M.D., Chief Medical Officer
CIO: Dianne Emminger, Vice President Information Services
CHR: Anne Remaley, Vice President Human Resources
Web address: www.acmh.org
Control: Other not–for–profit (including NFP Corporation) **Service:** General medical and surgical

Staffed Beds: 157 **Admissions:** 5372 **Census:** 69 **Outpatient Visits:** 258890 **Births:** 418 **Total Expense ($000):** 100319 **Payroll Expense ($000):** 44293 **Personnel:** 831

LANCASTER—Lancaster County

☐ **LANCASTER REHABILITATION HOSPITAL (393054)**, 675 Good Drive, Zip 17601–2426; tel. 717/406–3000, (Nonreporting) **A**1 10
Primary Contact: Tammy Derk, Chief Executive Officer
CFO: David Stark, Chief Financial Officer
CHR: Lisa Andrews, Director Human Resources
Web address: www.lancastergeneral.org
Control: Corporation, Investor–owned (for–profit) **Service:** Rehabilitation

Staffed Beds: 10

Many Facility Codes have changed. Please refer to the AHA Guide Code Chart.

☒ **PENN MEDICINE LANCASTER GENERAL HOSPITAL (390100)**, 555 North Duke Street, Zip 17602–2250; tel. 717/544–5511, **A**1 2 3 5 10 **F**3 7 8 11 12 13 14 15 17 18 20 22 24 26 28 29 30 31 32 34 35 36 38 39 40 43 44 45 46 47 48 49 50 54 55 56 57 58 59 60 61 64 65 66 68 70 72 73 74 75 76 77 78 79 80 81 82 84 85 86 87 89 91 92 93 94 96 97 98 100 101 102 107 108 110 114 115 118 119 120 121 123 124 126 129 130 132 135 141 142 145 146 147 148 149 150 154 **P**6 **S** University of Pennsylvania Health System, Philadelphia, PA
Primary Contact: Jan L. Bergen, President and Chief Executive Officer
CFO: Joseph Byorick, Senior Vice President and Chief Financial Officer
CMO: Lee M Duke, M.D., II Senior Vice President and Chief Physician Executive
CIO: Gary Davidson, Senior Vice President and Chief Information Officer
CHR: Regina Mingle, Senior Vice President and Chief Leadership Officer
CNO: Lanyce Roldan, Chief Nursing Officer
Web address: www.lancastergeneralhealth.org
Control: Other not–for–profit (including NFP Corporation) **Service**: General medical and surgical

Staffed Beds: 604 **Admissions**: 33297 **Census**: 401 **Outpatient Visits**: 1598141 **Births**: 4228 **Total Expense ($000)**: 907896 **Payroll Expense ($000)**: 339653 **Personnel**: 4800

☒ **UPMC PINNACLE LANCASTER (390061)**, 250 College Avenue, Zip 17603–3363, Mailing Address: P.O. Box 3434, Zip 17604–3434; tel. 717/291–8211, **A**1 3 10 **F**3 15 18 20 22 24 26 28 29 30 31 34 35 37 40 45 46 47 48 49 50 51 56 57 59 64 68 70 74 75 77 78 79 81 82 84 85 87 90 91 92 93 96 98 100 101 102 103 107 108 110 111 114 119 121 126 129 130 131 132 135 146 **S** UPMC, Pittsburgh, PA
Primary Contact: Brooks Turkel, Chief Executive Officer
CFO: Mike Johnson, Chief Financial Officer
CMO: N. A. Mastropietro, M.D., Medical Director
CHR: Brian Hoffman, Director Human Resources
CNO: Michelle Reaser, R.N., Chief Nursing Executive
Web address: www.lancasterregional.com
Control: Other not–for–profit (including NFP Corporation) **Service**: General medical and surgical

Staffed Beds: 150 **Admissions**: 3513 **Census**: 54 **Outpatient Visits**: 63671 **Births**: 0 **Total Expense ($000)**: 109311 **Payroll Expense ($000)**: 31608 **Personnel**: 486

LANGHORNE—Bucks County

☐ **BARIX CLINICS OF PENNSYLVANIA (390302)**, 280 Middletown Boulevard, Zip 19047–1816; tel. 267/572–3100, (Nonreporting) **A**1 10
Primary Contact: Tony Adams, President
Web address: www.barixclinics.com
Control: Partnership, Investor–owned (for–profit) **Service**: Surgical

Staffed Beds: 40

BUCKS COUNTY CAMPUS See Jefferson Health Northeast, Philadelphia

☒ **ST. MARY MEDICAL CENTER (390258)**, 1201 Langhorne–Newtown Road, Zip 19047–1201; tel. 215/710–2000, **A**1 2 3 10 **F**7 12 15 17 18 20 22 24 26 28 29 30 31 32 34 35 36 37 40 43 44 46 49 50 53 54 56 57 58 59 63 64 70 72 74 76 77 78 79 80 81 82 84 85 86 87 89 91 92 93 94 96 107 108 110 111 114 115 117 118 119 120 121 123 124 126 129 130 131 132 135 146 147 149 154 **S** Trinity Health, Livonia, MI
Primary Contact: James L. Woodward, President and Chief Executive Officer
COO: Jeffrey N Yarmel, Chief Operating Officer
CFO: Daniel Confalone, Chief Financial Officer and Vice President Finance
CMO: Lawrence Brilliant, M.D., Vice President and Chief Medical Officer
CIO: Bonnie Buehler, Chief Information Officer
CNO: Sharon Brown, R.N., MSN, Vice President Patient Care and Chief Nursing Officer
Web address: www.stmaryhealthcare.org
Control: Church operated, Nongovernment, not–for–profit **Service**: General medical and surgical

Staffed Beds: 353 **Admissions**: 21136 **Census**: 228 **Outpatient Visits**: 305229 **Births**: 2256 **Total Expense ($000)**: 381880 **Payroll Expense ($000)**: 146237 **Personnel**: 2495

ST. MARY REHABILITATION HOSPITAL (393055), 1201 Langhorne Newtown Road, Zip 19047–1201, Mailing Address: 1208 Langhorne Newtown Road, Zip 19047–1234; tel. 267/560–1111, (Nonreporting) **S** Kindred Healthcare, Louisville, KY
Primary Contact: Lisa Haney, Chief Executive Officer
Web address: www.stmaryhealthcare.org
Control: Church operated, Nongovernment, not–for–profit **Service**: Rehabilitation

Staffed Beds: 50

LANSDALE—Montgomery County

☒ **ABINGTON–LANSDALE HOSPITAL JEFFERSON HEALTH (390012)**, 100 Medical Campus Drive, Zip 19446–1200; tel. 215/368–2100, **A**1 3 10 **F**2 3 11 15 18 28 29 30 32 34 35 36 37 40 44 45 49 50 53 56 57 59 63 64 65 66 68 70 74 75 77 79 81 82 84 85 86 87 93 96 97 107 108 110 111 114 115 119 129 130 131 132 135 146 147 148 149 150 **P**6 **S** Jefferson Health, Philadelphia, PA
Primary Contact: Kathleen Farrell, Chief Administrative Officer
CFO: Michael Walsh, Senior Vice President Finance and Chief Financial Officer
CMO: Michel Taupin, M.D., Chief Medical Officer
CIO: Alison Ferren, Vice President Information Technology and Chief Information Officer
CHR: Meghan Patton, Vice President Human Resources
CNO: Kelly Cummings, Chief Nursing Officer
Web address: www.abingtonhealth.org/find–a–location/abington–lansdale–hospital/#.V5dyVVL9yk4
Control: Other not–for–profit (including NFP Corporation) **Service**: General medical and surgical

Staffed Beds: 127 **Admissions**: 5958 **Census**: 52 **Outpatient Visits**: 79266 **Births**: 0 **Total Expense ($000)**: 85699 **Payroll Expense ($000)**: 33023 **Personnel**: 348

LATROBE—Westmoreland County

☐ **EXCELA LATROBE AREA HOSPITAL (390219)**, One Mellon Way, Zip 15650–1096; tel. 724/537–1000, (Nonreporting) **A**1 2 3 5 10 13 **S** Excela Health, Greensburg, PA
Primary Contact: Michael D. Busch, Executive Vice President and Chief Operating Officer
COO: Michael D Busch, Executive Vice President and Chief Operating Officer
CMO: Carol J. Fox, M.D., Senior Vice President and Chief Medical Officer
CIO: David Gawaluck, Vice President and Chief Information Officer
CHR: Laurie English, Senior Vice President and Chief Human Resource Officer
CNO: Helen K Burns, Ph.D., R.N., Senior Vice President and Chief Nursing Officer
Web address: www.excelahealth.org
Control: Other not–for–profit (including NFP Corporation) **Service**: General medical and surgical

Staffed Beds: 114

☒ **SELECT SPECIALTY HOSPITAL–LAUREL HIGHLANDS (392036)**, One Mellon Way, 3rd Floor, Zip 15650–1197; tel. 724/539–3870, (Nonreporting) **A**1 10 **S** Select Medical Corporation, Mechanicsburg, PA
Primary Contact: Eric Schwab, Chief Executive Officer
Web address: www.laurelhighlands.selectspecialtyhospitals.com/
Control: Corporation, Investor–owned (for–profit) **Service**: Acute long–term care hospital

Staffed Beds: 40

LEBANON—Lebanon County

☒ **LEBANON VETERANS AFFAIRS MEDICAL CENTER**, 1700 South Lincoln Avenue, Zip 17042–7529; tel. 717/272–6621, (Nonreporting) **A**1 3 5 **S** Department of Veterans Affairs, Perry Point, MD
Primary Contact: Margaret G. Wilson, R.N., MSN, Acting Director
CFO: Geoffrey Smith, Chief Financial Officer
CMO: Kanan Chatterjee, M.D., Chief of Staff
CIO: Andru Ditzler, Chief Information Officer
CHR: Cindy Shiner, Manager Human Resources
Web address: www.lebanon.va.gov
Control: Veterans Affairs, Government, federal **Service**: General medical and surgical

Staffed Beds: 213

VETERANS AFFAIRS MEDICAL CENTER See Lebanon Veterans Affairs Medical Center

☒ **WELLSPAN GOOD SAMARITAN HOSPITAL (390066)**, Fourth and Walnut Streets, Zip 17042–1281, Mailing Address: P.O. Box 1281, Zip 17042–1281; tel. 717/270–7500, (Total facility includes 19 beds in nursing home–type unit) **A**1 3 5 10 13 **F**3 8 11 13 14 15 17 18 20 22 24 26 28 29 30 31 34 35 40 45 49 50 55 57 58 59 62 63 64 68 70 74 75 76 77 78 79 80 81 82 85 87 89 90 91 92 93 94 96 97 107 110 111 114 115 116 117 118 119 120 121 124 126 129 130 132 135 145 146 148 149 **P**8 **S** WellSpan Health, York, PA
Primary Contact: Thomas R. Harlow, FACHE, President
COO: Kimberly Feeman, Senior Vice President and Chief Operating Officer
CMO: Robert D Shaver, M.D., Vice President Medical Affairs
CIO: Leon John Jabour, Regional Chief Information Officer
CHR: Denise M Garman, Director Human Resources
CNO: Jacquelyn M Gould, MS, R.N., Vice President Patient Care Services and Chief Nursing Officer
Web address: www.gshleb.org
Control: Other not–for–profit (including NFP Corporation) **Service**: General medical and surgical

Staffed Beds: 162 **Admissions**: 7392 **Census**: 97 **Outpatient Visits**: 251121 **Births**: 691 **Total Expense ($000)**: 201969 **Payroll Expense ($000)**: 62583 **Personnel**: 938

PA

☒ △ **ST. LUKE'S – GNADEN HUETTEN CAMPUS (390194)**, 211 North
12th Street, Zip 18235–1138; tel. 610/377–1300, (Includes ST. LUKE'S –
PALMERTON CAMPUS, 135 Lafayette Avenue, Palmerton, PA, Zip 18071–1596;
tel. 610/826–3141; Terrance J. Purcell, President) (Total facility includes 91 beds
in nursing home–type unit) **A**1 7 10 **F**2 3 11 12 15 28 29 30 34 35 40 46 47 49
50 51 56 57 59 62 64 65 68 70 74 75 77 79 81 82 85 87 90 93 94 97 98 102
107 108 110 111 114 116 117 119 124 128 129 130 132 133 135 146 147
148 **S** St. Luke's University Health Network, Bethlehem, PA
Primary Contact: Terrance J. Purcell, President
CFO: Andrea Andrae, Chief Financial Officer
CMO: Patrick Hanley, D.O., Interim Vice President Medical Affairs
CIO: Steve Kinkaid, Director Information Systems
Web address: www.blmtn.org
Control: Other not–for–profit (including NFP Corporation) **Service**: General
medical and surgical

Staffed Beds: 250 **Admissions**: 4549 **Census**: 158 **Outpatient Visits**:
104039 **Births**: 0 **Total Expense ($000)**: 87540 **Payroll Expense
($000)**: 38612 **Personnel**: 833

⇑ **EVANGELICAL COMMUNITY HOSPITAL (390013)**, One Hospital Drive,
Zip 17837–9350; tel. 570/522–2000, **A**10 19 21 **F**3 8 11 12 13 15 18 20 22
28 29 30 31 34 35 40 43 45 50 51 54 57 59 63 64 65 68 74 75 76 77 78 79
80 81 82 84 85 86 87 90 91 92 93 94 96 97 107 108 110 111 114 115 116
117 118 119 129 130 131 132 135 144 146 147 148 **P**7
Primary Contact: Kendra A. Aucker, President and Chief Executive Officer
COO: Kendra A. Aucker, Vice President Operations
CFO: Jim Stopper, CPA, Chief Financial Officer
CMO: J Lawrence Ginsburg, M.D., Vice President Medical Affairs
CIO: Dale Moyer, Vice President Information Systems
CHR: Angela Hummel, Vice President Human Resources
CNO: Tamara F. Persing MHA, BSN, Chief Nursing Officer
Web address: www.evanhospital.com
Control: Other not–for–profit (including NFP Corporation) **Service**: General
medical and surgical

Staffed Beds: 132 **Admissions**: 5978 **Census**: 53 **Outpatient Visits**:
244247 **Births**: 906 **Total Expense ($000)**: 158352 **Payroll Expense
($000)**: 64244 **Personnel**: 1365

U.S. PENITENTIARY INFIRMARY, Route 7, Zip 17837–9303;
tel. 570/523–1251, (Nonreporting)
Primary Contact: Steve Brown, Health Services Director
Control: Department of Justice, Government, federal **Service**: Hospital unit of an
institution (prison hospital, college infirmary, etc.)

Staffed Beds: 17

☒ **GEISINGER–LEWISTOWN HOSPITAL (390048)**, 400 Highland Avenue,
Zip 17044–1198; tel. 717/248–5411, **A**1 2 3 10 **F**3 11 13 15 17 18 28 29 30
31 34 35 40 41 45 46 49 50 51 57 59 64 70 71 74 75 76 78 79 81 82 84 85
86 87 98 100 101 102 107 108 110 111 114 115 116 117 118 119 120
121 123 124 129 130 132 135 146 147 148 149 154 **S** Geisinger, Danville, PA
Primary Contact: Kirk E Thomas, MHA, Chief Administrative Officer
COO: Kirk E Thomas, MHA, Chief Administrative Officer
CFO: Kristy Hine, Associate Vice President Finance
CMO: Michael T Hegstrom, M.D., Chief Medical Officer
CIO: Ronald M Cowan, Vice President Information Systems
CHR: N Sue Reinke, Vice President Human Resources
CNO: Christine Mathews, R.N., MSN, Vice President Nursing Services
Web address: www.geisinger.org
Control: Other not–for–profit (including NFP Corporation) **Service**: General
medical and surgical

Staffed Beds: 123 **Admissions**: 4773 **Census**: 52 **Outpatient Visits**:
148682 **Births**: 502 **Total Expense ($000)**: 107369 **Payroll Expense
($000)**: 40212 **Personnel**: 893

☒ **UPMC PINNACLE LITITZ (390068)**, 1500 Highlands Drive, Zip 17543–7694;
tel. 717/625–5000, **A**1 3 10 13 **F**3 12 13 15 18 29 30 31 34 35 44 45 47 49
50 57 59 60 64 68 70 72 74 75 76 77 79 81 82 85 87 89 107 108 110 111
115 119 126 130 146 147 148 **S** UPMC, Pittsburgh, PA
Primary Contact: Deborah J. Willwerth, R.N., MSN, Chief Executive Officer
CIO: David Fisher, Director Information Systems
Web address: www.heartoflancaster.com
Control: Other not–for–profit (including NFP Corporation) **Service**: General
medical and surgical

Staffed Beds: 90 **Admissions**: 2465 **Census**: 24 **Outpatient Visits**: 56500
Births: 1086

☒ **UPMC SUSQUEHANNA LOCK HAVEN (390071)**, 24 Cree Drive,
Zip 17745–2699; tel. 570/893–5000, (Total facility includes 65 beds in nursing
home–type unit) **A**1 10 **F**1 3 11 15 29 34 35 40 41 45 50 51 56 57 59 65 67
68 70 75 77 81 82 85 90 93 107 108 110 111 114 119 127 128 129 130 146
149 **S** UPMC Susquehanna, Williamsport, PA
Primary Contact: Ronald J. Reynolds, Vice President
CFO: Jennifer Lesher, Chief Financial Officer
CMO: Rajesh Patel, M.D., Chief of Staff
CIO: Judy Chapman, Interim Director Information Systems
CHR: Courtney Kunes, Director Human Resources
Web address: www.lockhavenhospital.com
Control: Corporation, Investor–owned (for–profit) **Service**: General medical and
surgical

Staffed Beds: 83 **Admissions**: 1126 **Census**: 84 **Outpatient Visits**: 35294
Births: 31 **Total Expense ($000)**: 35819 **Payroll Expense ($000)**: 13344
Personnel: 197

☒ △ **BRYN MAWR REHABILITATION HOSPITAL (393025)**, 414 Paoli
Pike, Zip 19355–3300, Mailing Address: P.O. Box 3007, Zip 19355–0707;
tel. 484/596–5400, **A**1 3 7 10 **F**3 11 28 29 30 34 35 36 44 50 65 71 75 82
86 87 90 91 92 93 95 96 119 130 131 132 143 146 **P**5 **S** Main Line Health,
Williamsport, PA
Primary Contact: Donna Phillips, President
CFO: Dave Schmotzer, Chief Financial Officer
CMO: John Kraus, M.D., Chief Medical Officer
CIO: Kay Carr, Chief Information Officer
Web address: www.brynmawrrehab.org
Control: Other not–for–profit (including NFP Corporation) **Service**: Rehabilitation

Staffed Beds: 148 **Admissions**: 1974 **Census**: 88 **Outpatient Visits**: 65136
Births: 0 **Total Expense ($000)**: 70718 **Payroll Expense ($000)**: 36908
Personnel: 560

DEVEREUX CHILDREN'S BEHAVIORAL HEALTH CENTER, 655 Sugartown
Road, Zip 19355–3303, Mailing Address: 655 Sugartown Rd, Zip 19355–3303;
tel. 800/345–1292, **F**29 32 34 35 38 44 59 75 86 97 98 99 100 106 128 130
132 135 149 150 154 **P**6 **S** Devereux, Villanova, PA
Primary Contact: David E. Woodward, Executive Director
CFO: Tim Evans, Assistant Financial Director
CMO: Jacquelyn Zavodnick, M.D., Medical Director
CIO: MaryLou Hettinger, Director Quality Management
CHR: Sean Maher, Director Human Resources
CNO: Deanna Reiss, Hospital Director of Nursing
Web address: www.devereux.org
Control: Other not–for–profit (including NFP Corporation) **Service**: Children's
hospital psychiatric

Staffed Beds: 49 **Admissions**: 434 **Census**: 33 **Outpatient Visits**: 0
Births: 0 **Total Expense ($000)**: 7957 **Payroll Expense ($000)**: 4203
Personnel: 103

MALVERN INSTITUTE, 940 King Road, Zip 19355–3166; tel. 610/647–0330,
(Nonreporting)
Primary Contact: Scott Weisenberger, Chief Executive Officer
CFO: Janet Corley, Accountant
Web address: www.malverninstitute.com
Control: Corporation, Investor–owned (for–profit) **Service**: Alcoholism and other
chemical dependency

Staffed Beds: 40

★ **FULTON COUNTY MEDICAL CENTER (391303)**, 214 Peach Orchard Road,
Zip 17233–8559, Mailing Address: McConnellsburg, tel. 717/485–3155, (Total
facility includes 67 beds in nursing home–type unit) **A**10 18 **F**3 11 15 18 28 29
30 34 35 40 46 50 57 59 62 64 70 75 77 78 79 81 87 91 93 97 107 108 110
111 115 118 119 128 129 130 132 133 135 146 147 148
Primary Contact: Michael D. Makosky, Chief Executive Officer
COO: Kim Slee, Chief Operating Officer
CFO: Deborah A Shughart, Chief Financial Officer
CMO: Sharon E Martin, M.D., Ph.D., President Medical Staff
CIO: Armen Arakelian, Chief Information Officer
CHR: Cheryl Rose, Human Resources Director
Web address: www.fcmcpa.org
Control: Other not–for–profit (including NFP Corporation) **Service**: General
medical and surgical

Staffed Beds: 88 **Admissions**: 698 **Census**: 74 **Outpatient Visits**: 65028
Births: 0 **Total Expense ($000)**: 46990 **Payroll Expense ($000)**: 22747
Personnel: 329

MCKEES ROCKS—Allegheny County

⊞ **OHIO VALLEY HOSPITAL (390157)**, 25 Heckel Road, Zip 15136–1694;
tel. 412/777–6161, **A**1 10 **F**3 7 10 15 18 20 29 30 40 45 46 49 51 59 65 70
74 75 77 79 81 82 85 87 90 92 93 98 103 104 107 108 111 118 119 126
129 130 143 146 148 149 154 **P**6
Primary Contact: David W. Scott, President and Chief Executive Officer
CFO: Jack Nelson, Vice President Finance and Chief Financial Officer
CHR: Erin J Frohnhofer, Vice President Human Resources
CNO: Paulette Bingham, Director Nursing Services
Web address: www.ohiovalleyhospital.org
Control: Other not–for–profit (including NFP Corporation) **Service:** General
medical and surgical

Staffed Beds: 124 **Admissions:** 3462 **Census:** 55 **Outpatient Visits:**
102176 **Births:** 0 **Total Expense ($000):** 64101 **Payroll Expense
($000):** 21781 **Personnel:** 489

MCKEESPORT—Allegheny County

⊞ **SELECT SPECIALTY HOSPITAL–MCKEESPORT (392045)**, 1500 Fifth Avenue,
6th Floor, Zip 15132–2422; tel. 412/664–2900, (Nonreporting) **A**1 10 **S** Select
Medical Corporation, Mechanicsburg, PA
Primary Contact: Angela Merryman, Chief Executive Officer
Web address: www.mckeesport.selectspecialtyhospitals.com/
Control: Corporation, Investor–owned (for–profit) **Service:** Acute long–term care
hospital

Staffed Beds: 30

☐ **UPMC MCKEESPORT (390002)**, 1500 Fifth Avenue, Zip 15132–2422;
tel. 412/664–2000, (Total facility includes 24 beds in nursing home–type unit) **A**1
3 5 10 13 **F**3 8 11 15 18 20 22 28 29 30 31 34 35 40 46 49 50 54 56 57 59
60 61 62 64 65 66 68 70 74 75 77 78 79 81 84 85 86 87 90 91 96 97 98 100
101 102 103 107 111 114 115 118 119 121 128 130 131 132 135 143 146
148 **S** UPMC, Pittsburgh, PA
Primary Contact: Mark Sevco, President
COO: Amy Bush, Vice President Operations
CFO: Christopher Stockhausen, Chief Financial Officer
CMO: R Curtis Waligura, D.O., Vice President Medical Affairs, Chief Medical Officer
CIO: Terri Keeling, Vice President Information Systems
CHR: Kelli Reale, Vice President Human Resources
CNO: Leeanna McKibben, R.N., MSN, Vice President Patient Services and Chief
Nursing Officer
Web address: www.mckeesport.upmc.com
Control: Other not–for–profit (including NFP Corporation) **Service:** General
medical and surgical

Staffed Beds: 181 **Admissions:** 7349 **Census:** 123 **Outpatient Visits:**
119482 **Births:** 0 **Total Expense ($000):** 133997 **Payroll Expense
($000):** 41098 **Personnel:** 639

MEADOWBROOK—Montgomery County

⇑ **HOLY REDEEMER HOSPITAL (390097)**, 1648 Huntingdon Pike,
Zip 19046–8001; tel. 215/947–3000, (Total facility includes 21 beds in nursing
home–type unit) **A**2 3 5 10 21 **F**3 13 15 17 18 20 22 29 30 31 32 34 35 36 39
40 41 44 45 46 49 50 51 54 55 56 57 58 59 61 62 63 64 68 69 70 72 74
75 76 77 78 79 81 82 84 85 86 87 92 93 96 98 100 103 104 107 108 109
110 114 115 116 117 118 119 120 121 123 128 129 130 131 132 135 141
143 146 147 148 149 154
Primary Contact: Michael B. Laign, President and Chief Executive Officer
CFO: Russell R Wagner, Executive Vice President and Chief Financial Officer
CMO: Henry D. Unger, M.D., Senior Vice President and Chief Medical Officer
CIO: Donald F. Friel, Executive Vice President
CHR: Joseph J Cassidy, Vice President
CNO: Anne Catino, MS, R.N., Vice President and Chief Nursing Officer
Web address: www.holyredeemer.com
Control: Other not–for–profit (including NFP Corporation) **Service:** General
medical and surgical

Staffed Beds: 263 **Admissions:** 10090 **Census:** 138 **Outpatient Visits:**
320329 **Births:** 2685 **Total Expense ($000):** 186550 **Payroll Expense
($000):** 75099 **Personnel:** 1324

MEADVILLE—Crawford County

★ ⇑ **MEADVILLE MEDICAL CENTER (390113)**, 751 Liberty Street,
Zip 16335–2559; tel. 814/333–5000, (Total facility includes 32 beds in nursing
home–type unit) **A**2 10 12 13 21 **F**3 4 5 8 11 13 15 18 20 22 28 29 30 31 35
36 38 39 40 43 45 46 49 53 57 59 63 64 66 68 70 74 75 76 77 78 79 81 82
84 85 86 87 89 90 91 93 96 98 100 102 103 104 107 110 111 114 115 118
119 120 121 127 128 129 130 131 132 135 144 146 147 148 149 154 **P**6 **S**
Meadville Medical Center, Meadville, PA
Primary Contact: Philip E. Pandolph, FACHE, Chief Executive Officer
CFO: Renato Suntay, Chief Financial Officer
CMO: Denise Johnson, M.D., Medical Director
CHR: Greg Maras, Vice President Human Resources
CNO: MaryAnn Hewston, R.N., Chief Nurse Executive
Web address: www.mmchs.org
Control: Other not–for–profit (including NFP Corporation) **Service:** General
medical and surgical

Staffed Beds: 234 **Admissions:** 7176 **Census:** 98 **Outpatient Visits:**
267053 **Births:** 547 **Total Expense ($000):** 164064 **Payroll Expense
($000):** 73585 **Personnel:** 1348

MECHANICSBURG—Cumberland County

HEALTHSOUTH REGIONAL SPECIALTY HOSPITAL See Lifecare Hospitals of
Mechanicsburg

⊞ **HEALTHSOUTH REHABILITATION HOSPITAL OF MECHANICSBURG
(393031)**, 175 Lancaster Boulevard, Zip 17055–3562; tel. 717/691–3700,
(Nonreporting) **A**1 10 **S** Encompass Health Corporation, Birmingham, AL
Primary Contact: Josette M. Myers, Chief Executive Officer
CMO: Michael Lupinacci, M.D., Medical Director
CHR: David Staskin, Director Human Resources
Web address: www.healthsouthpa.com
Control: Corporation, Investor–owned (for–profit) **Service:** Rehabilitation

Staffed Beds: 75

⊞ **LIFECARE HOSPITALS OF MECHANICSBURG (392038)**, 4950 Wilson
Lane, Zip 17055–4442; tel. 717/697–7706, (Nonreporting) **A**1 10 **S** LifeCare
Management Services, Plano, TX
Primary Contact: Jacob McGuirt, Chief Executive Officer
CMO: Michael Gluck, M.D., Medical Director
CHR: Jennifer Rashford, Manager Human Resources
CNO: Alicia Kuntz, Nurse Manager
Web address: www.lifecare–hospitals.com/hospital.php?id=20
Control: Corporation, Investor–owned (for–profit) **Service:** Acute long–term care
hospital

Staffed Beds: 68

MEDIA—Delaware County

⊞ **RIDDLE HOSPITAL (390222)**, 1068 West Baltimore Pike, Zip 19063–5177;
tel. 484/227–9400, (Total facility includes 23 beds in nursing home–type unit) **A**1
2 3 10 **F**3 7 11 13 15 18 20 22 26 28 29 30 31 34 35 36 37 38 40 41 44 45
46 49 50 51 53 54 55 56 57 58 59 63 64 65 70 72 74 75 76 78 79 80 81 82
84 85 86 87 92 97 100 102 107 108 110 111 114 115 118 119 120 124 126
128 129 130 131 132 135 141 143 145 146 147 148 149 **S** Main Line Health,
Plano, TX
Primary Contact: Gary L. Perecko, President
CFO: Ed McKillip, Vice President Finance
CMO: David Thomas, President Medical Staff
CHR: Mary Louise Ciciretti, Director Human Resources
Web address: www.riddlehospital.org
Control: Other not–for–profit (including NFP Corporation) **Service:** General
medical and surgical

Staffed Beds: 227 **Admissions:** 10461 **Census:** 130 **Outpatient Visits:**
99622 **Births:** 975 **Total Expense ($000):** 195047 **Payroll Expense
($000):** 69400 **Personnel:** 1033

RIDDLE MEMORIAL HOSPITAL See Riddle Hospital

PA

Hospital, Medicare Provider Number, Address, Telephone, Approval, Facility, and Physician Codes, Health Care System

★ American Hospital Association (AHA) membership
☐ The Joint Commission accreditation
○ Healthcare Facilities Accreditation Program
◇ DNV Healthcare Inc. accreditation
⇑ Center for Improvement in Healthcare Quality Accreditation
△ Commission on Accreditation of Rehabilitation Facilities (CARF) accreditation

PA

MEYERSDALE—Somerset County

★ **CONEMAUGH MEYERSDALE MEDICAL CENTER (391302)**, 200 Hospital Drive, Zip 15552–1249; tel. 814/634–5911, **A**10 18 **F**29 34 40 64 75 81 107 114 119 127 130 132 133 146 148 154 **S** Duke LifePoint Healthcare, Brentwood, TN
Primary Contact: Heather Smith, President
CMO: Dwayne Platt, M.D., Chief Medical Officer
Web address: www.conemaugh.org
Control: Corporation, Investor–owned (for–profit) **Service**: General medical and surgical

Staffed Beds: 20 Admissions: 284 Census: 5 Outpatient Visits: 46378 Births: 0 Total Expense ($000): 14295 Payroll Expense ($000): 4726 Personnel: 102

MONONGAHELA—Washington County

⊞ **MONONGAHELA VALLEY HOSPITAL (390147)**, 1163 Country Club Road, Zip 15063–1095; tel. 724/258–1000, **A**1 2 10 **F**3 8 9 11 12 15 17 18 20 22 28 29 30 31 32 34 35 40 45 48 49 51 54 55 56 57 59 61 64 68 70 74 75 77 78 79 80 81 82 85 86 87 89 90 92 93 96 98 100 101 102 103 107 108 110 111 114 115 118 119 120 121 123 124 129 130 131 132 134 135 146 147 148 149 154 **P**7 8
Primary Contact: Louis J. Panza Jr, President and Chief Executive Officer
COO: Patrick J Alberts, Senior Vice President and Chief Operating Officer
CFO: Daniel F Simmons, Senior Vice President and Treasurer
CMO: L. Douglas Pepper, M.D., President, Medical Staff
CIO: Matt Rashilla, Chief Information and Application Officer
CHR: Louis Goodman, Senior Vice President Human Resources
CNO: Mary Lou Murt, R.N., Senior Vice President Nursing
Web address: www.monvalleyhospital.com
Control: Other not–for–profit (including NFP Corporation) **Service**: General medical and surgical

Staffed Beds: 200 Admissions: 6853 Census: 99 Outpatient Visits: 297234 Births: 0 Total Expense ($000): 134164 Payroll Expense ($000): 55698 Personnel: 1024

MONROEVILLE—Allegheny County

⊞ **FORBES HOSPITAL (390267)**, 2570 Haymaker Road, Zip 15146–3513; tel. 412/858–2000, **A**1 2 3 5 10 **F**3 8 11 13 15 17 18 20 22 24 26 28 29 30 31 34 35 36 37 38 40 43 44 45 46 48 50 54 55 57 58 59 64 65 69 70 73 74 75 76 77 78 79 80 81 82 84 85 86 87 90 93 96 98 100 101 102 103 107 108 110 111 115 118 119 126 130 132 135 145 146 147 148 149 154 **P**6 **S** Allegheny Health Network, Pittsburgh, PA
Primary Contact: Mark Rubino, M.D., President
COO: Krista A. Bragg, MSN, Chief Operating Officer
CFO: Tom Hipkiss, Vice President Finance
CMO: Mark Rubino, M.D., Chief Medical Officer
CIO: Sharon Lewis, Director Information Systems
CHR: Georgia Redding, Director Human Resources
Web address: www.ahn.org
Control: Other not–for–profit (including NFP Corporation) **Service**: General medical and surgical

Staffed Beds: 315 Admissions: 13966 Census: 210 Outpatient Visits: 147494 Births: 1237 Total Expense ($000): 225288 Payroll Expense ($000): 76720 Personnel: 1422

UPMC EAST (390328), 2775 Mosside Boulevard, Zip 15146–2760; tel. 412/357–3000, **A**10 **F**3 18 20 22 26 29 30 31 34 35 40 45 46 49 50 57 59 60 62 64 68 70 74 75 77 78 79 81 84 85 87 90 91 92 96 100 107 108 111 115 119 120 121 122 123 130 132 135 146 148 **S** UPMC, Pittsburgh, PA
Primary Contact: Mark Sevco, President
CNO: Tamra Minton, R.N., MSN, Vice President Patient Care Services and Chief Nursing Officer
Web address: www.upmc.com/locations/hospitals/east/Pages/default.aspx
Control: Other not–for–profit (including NFP Corporation) **Service**: General medical and surgical

Staffed Beds: 155 Admissions: 8140 Census: 108 Outpatient Visits: 89238 Births: 0 Total Expense ($000): 141994 Payroll Expense ($000): 38962 Personnel: 593

WESTERN PENNSYLVANIA HOSPITAL – FORBES REGIONAL CAMPUS See Forbes Hospital

MONTROSE—Susquehanna County

ENDLESS MOUNTAIN HEALTH SYSTEMS (391306), 100 Hospital Drive, Zip 18801–6402; tel. 570/278–3801, (Nonreporting) **A**10 18
Primary Contact: Loren Stone, Chief Executive Officer
CIO: Gary Passmore, Chief Information Officer
CHR: Paula Anderson, Administrative Director Human Resources
Web address: www.endlesscare.org
Control: Other not–for–profit (including NFP Corporation) **Service**: General medical and surgical

Staffed Beds: 25

MOUNT GRETNA—Lebanon County

⊞ **WELLSPAN PHILHAVEN (394020)**, 283 South Butler Road, Zip 17064–6085, Mailing Address: P.O. Box 550, Zip 17064–0550; tel. 717/273–8871, (Nonreporting) **A**1 10 **S** WellSpan Health, York, PA
Primary Contact: Phil Hess, Chief Executive Officer
COO: Phil Hess, Chief Executive Officer
CFO: Matt Rogers, Chief Financial Officer
CMO: Francis D Sparrow, M.D., Medical Director
CIO: Lori Nolt, Director Information Technology
CHR: Denis Orthaus, Director Human Resources
CNO: Heidi McMullan, R.N., Chief Nursing Officer
Web address: www.philhaven.org
Control: Church operated, Nongovernment, not–for–profit **Service**: Psychiatric

Staffed Beds: 103

MOUNT PLEASANT—Westmoreland County

☐ **EXCELA FRICK HOSPITAL (390217)**, 508 South Church Street, Zip 15666–1790; tel. 724/547–1500, (Nonreporting) **A**1 10 **S** Excela Health, Greensburg, PA
Primary Contact: Michael D. Busch, Executive Vice President and Chief Operating Officer
COO: Michael D Busch, Executive Vice President and Chief Operating Officer
CFO: Jeffrey T Curry, Executive Vice President and Chief Financial Officer
CMO: Jerome Granato, M.D., Senior Vice President and Chief Medical Officer
CIO: David Gawaluck, Vice President and Chief Information Officer
CHR: John Caverno, Chief Human Resources Officer
CNO: Helen K Burns, Ph.D., R.N., Senior Vice President and Chief Nursing Officer
Web address: www.excelahealth.org/PatientsandVisitors/HospitalsFacilities/Hospitals/Frick.aspx
Control: Other not–for–profit (including NFP Corporation) **Service**: General medical and surgical

Staffed Beds: 33

MUNCY—Lycoming County

★ **UPMC SUSQUEHANNA MUNCY (391301)**, 215 East Water Street, Zip 17756–8700; tel. 570/546–8282, (Total facility includes 138 beds in nursing home–type unit) **A**3 10 18 **F**6 11 34 40 44 50 56 57 59 64 68 81 86 87 93 107 108 119 128 130 133 144 146 **P**1 4 5 **S** UPMC Susquehanna, Williamsport, PA
Primary Contact: Matthew McLaughlin, President and Chief Executive Officer
CFO: Eric Pohjala, Executive Vice President and Chief Financial Officer
CIO: Timothy E Schoener, Chief Information Officer
CHR: Donald Wilver Jr Vice President Human Resources
CNO: C Cynthia Whipple, Director of Nursing
Web address: www.susquehannahealth.org
Control: Other not–for–profit (including NFP Corporation) **Service**: General medical and surgical

Staffed Beds: 156 Admissions: 752 Census: 135 Outpatient Visits: 17819 Births: 0 Total Expense ($000): 43215 Payroll Expense ($000): 13883 Personnel: 258

NATRONA HEIGHTS—Allegheny County

⊞ **ALLEGHENY VALLEY HOSPITAL (390032)**, 1301 Carlisle Street, Zip 15065–1152; tel. 724/224–5100, **A**1 2 3 10 **F**3 11 15 17 18 24 28 29 30 31 34 35 38 39 40 44 45 47 50 54 56 57 58 59 64 65 70 74 75 77 78 79 80 81 84 85 86 87 90 92 93 96 98 101 102 103 107 108 110 111 114 115 118 119 121 123 124 126 129 130 132 135 144 146 147 148 149 154 **S** Allegheny Health Network, Pittsburgh, PA
Primary Contact: William Englert, Chief Executive Officer
CFO: James A Kanuch, Vice President Finance
CMO: Suzanne M. Labriola, D.O., Chief Medical Officer
CIO: Linda Fergus, Manager Information Technology
CHR: Cindy Moser, Director Human Resources
Web address: www.wpahs.org
Control: Other not–for–profit (including NFP Corporation) **Service**: General medical and surgical

Staffed Beds: 121 Admissions: 5463 Census: 72 Outpatient Visits: 181147 Births: 0 Total Expense ($000): 107247 Payroll Expense ($000): 39562 Personnel: 783

Many Facility Codes have changed. Please refer to the AHA Guide Code Chart. © 2018 AHA Guide

NEW CASTLE—Lawrence County

☐ **UPMC JAMESON (390016)**, 1211 Wilmington Avenue, Zip 16105–2516; tel. 724/658–9001, **A**1 10 19 **F**3 8 11 15 18 20 22 28 29 30 32 34 35 40 41 45 46 49 57 59 63 64 65 70 74 75 77 79 81 82 85 86 90 92 93 96 100 101 107 108 110 111 114 115 118 119 128 130 146 147 153 **S** UPMC, Pittsburgh, PA
Primary Contact: Donald R. Owrey, President
COO: Albert Boland, Vice President Operations
CMO: Elizabeth Piccione, M.D., Chief Medical Officer
CIO: Charles M. Rudek, Chief Information Officer
CHR: Eric D. McIntosh, Vice President Human Resources
CNO: Marianna Stoneburner, R.N., Chief Nursing Officer
Web address: www.upmcjameson.com
Control: Other not–for–profit (including NFP Corporation) **Service**: General medical and surgical

Staffed Beds: 102 **Admissions**: 5514 **Census**: 75 **Outpatient Visits**: 247470 **Births**: 0 **Total Expense ($000)**: 101037 **Payroll Expense ($000)**: 40679 **Personnel**: 711

NORRISTOWN—Montgomery County

☐ **MONTGOMERY COUNTY EMERGENCY SERVICE (394033)**, 50 Beech Drive, Zip 19403–5421; tel. 610/279–6100, **A**1 10 **F**4 7 29 35 38 50 64 98 100 101 102 103 104 130 151 **P**6
Primary Contact: William Myers, Chief Executive Officer
CFO: Wendy Wait, Chief Financial Officer
CMO: Marina Cooney, Medical Director
CHR: Byanka Meacham, Director Human Resources
CNO: Naomi Finkel, Nurse Executive
Web address: www.mces.org
Control: Other not–for–profit (including NFP Corporation) **Service**: Psychiatric

Staffed Beds: 81 **Admissions**: 1566 **Census**: 47 **Outpatient Visits**: 2236 **Births**: 0 **Total Expense ($000)**: 14935 **Payroll Expense ($000)**: 9277 **Personnel**: 187

NORRISTOWN STATE HOSPITAL (394001), 1001 Sterigere Street, Zip 19401–5300; tel. 610/270–1000, **A**10 **F**30 35 38 39 53 59 65 75 77 98 101 102 103 130 135 146 149 **P**6
Primary Contact: Edna I. McCutcheon, Chief Executive Officer
COO: Gary Raisner, Chief Operating Officer
CMO: Mia Marcovici, M.D., Chief Medical Officer
CHR: Richard Szczurowski, Director Human Resources
CNO: Taryn Mason–Jones, Chief Nurse Executive
Control: State, Government, nonfederal **Service**: Psychiatric

Staffed Beds: 259 **Admissions**: 136 **Census**: 250 **Outpatient Visits**: 135 **Births**: 0 **Total Expense ($000)**: 79766 **Payroll Expense ($000)**: 40116 **Personnel**: 546

✠ **SUBURBAN COMMUNITY HOSPITAL (390116)**, 2701 DeKalb Pike, Zip 19401–1820; tel. 610/278–2000, (Nonreporting) **A**1 2 3 10 12 13 **S** Prime Healthcare, Ontario, CA
Primary Contact: Mark McLoone, Chief Executive Officer
COO: Joseph Schofield, Chief Operating Officer
CFO: Joseph Marino, Chief Financial Officer
CMO: Andrea D Pedano, D.O., Chief Medical Officer
CIO: Jason Wayne, Network Administrator
CHR: Gretchen Pendleton, Director Human Resources
CNO: Mary Ellen Rauner, R.N., Chief Nursing Officer
Web address: www.suburbanhosp.org
Control: Corporation, Investor–owned (for–profit) **Service**: General medical and surgical

Staffed Beds: 126

☐ **VALLEY FORGE MEDICAL CENTER AND HOSPITAL (390272)**, 1033 West Germantown Pike, Zip 19403–3905; tel. 610/539–8500, (Nonreporting) **A**1 10
Primary Contact: Marian W. Colcher, President and Chief Executive Officer
CFO: Gregg Y Slocum, Chief Financial Officer
CMO: Robert E Colcher, M.D., Medical Director
CHR: Frederick D Jackes, Assistant Administrator and Director Human Resources
Web address: www.vfmc.net
Control: Corporation, Investor–owned (for–profit) **Service**: Alcoholism and other chemical dependency

Staffed Beds: 50

OAKDALE—Allegheny County

✠ **CURAHEALTH PITTSBURGH (392028)**, 7777 Steubenville Pike, Zip 15071–3409; tel. 412/494–5500, **A**1 10 **F**1 3 18 29 30 45 47 60 68 74 75 79 82 84 85 91 94 96 100 119 148 **P**5 **S** Curahealth Hospitals, Garland, TX
Primary Contact: Carol Falo, RN, BSN, MBA, Chief Executive Officer
CFO: Kevin Varley, Chief Financial Officer
CMO: Ravi Alagar, M.D., Medical Director
Web address: www.curahealth.com
Control: Corporation, Investor–owned (for–profit) **Service**: General medical and surgical

Staffed Beds: 31 **Admissions**: 240 **Census**: 17 **Outpatient Visits**: 0 **Births**: 0

OREFIELD—Lehigh County

KIDSPEACE CHILDREN'S HOSPITAL (394047), 5300 Kids Peace Drive, Zip 18069–2044; tel. 610/799–7900, **F**29 39 59 98 99 100 101 105 106 130 **P**7
Primary Contact: William R. Isemann, President and Chief Executive Officer
CFO: Michael Callan, Executive Vice President and Chief Financial Officer
CMO: Matthew Koval, M.D., Vice President Medical Affairs
CIO: Joan Lesko, Director Technical Support and Services
CHR: Sheila Rulli, Director Human Resources
CNO: Tamara Wasilick, Director Operations
Web address: www.kidspeace.org
Control: Other not–for–profit (including NFP Corporation) **Service**: Children's hospital psychiatric

Staffed Beds: 120 **Admissions**: 2163 **Census**: 73 **Outpatient Visits**: 0 **Births**: 0 **Personnel**: 232

PAOLI—Chester County

✠ **PAOLI HOSPITAL (390153)**, 255 West Lancaster Avenue, Zip 19301–1763; tel. 484/565–1000, **A**1 2 3 10 **F**3 11 13 15 18 20 22 24 26 28 29 30 31 32 34 35 36 38 39 40 41 43 44 45 46 47 48 49 50 55 56 57 59 63 64 65 70 72 74 75 76 78 79 80 81 82 84 85 86 87 92 97 102 107 108 110 111 114 115 118 119 120 121 123 124 126 129 130 131 132 134 135 141 146 147 148 149 150 154 **S** Main Line Health, Garland, TX
Primary Contact: James Paradis, President
CFO: John Doyle, Vice President Finance
CMO: Andrew J Norton, M.D., Chief Medical Officer
CIO: Kay Carr, Senior Vice President and Chief Information Officer
CHR: Deborah Fedora, Director Human Resources
Web address: www.mainlinehealth.org
Control: Other not–for–profit (including NFP Corporation) **Service**: General medical and surgical

Staffed Beds: 231 **Admissions**: 12888 **Census**: 136 **Outpatient Visits**: 298396 **Births**: 2114 **Total Expense ($000)**: 292151 **Payroll Expense ($000)**: 87473 **Personnel**: 1068

PHILADELPHIA—Philadelphia County

ALBERT EINSTEIN MEDICAL CENTER See Einstein Medical Center Philadelphia

☐ **BELMONT BEHAVIORAL HOSPITAL (394023)**, 4200 Monument Road, Zip 19131–1625; tel. 215/877–2000, **A**1 3 5 10 **F**4 5 29 77 86 87 98 99 103 104 130 146 149 **P**6 **S** Acadia Healthcare Company, Inc., Franklin, TN
Primary Contact: Mark Schor, Chief Executive Officer
CFO: Guy Romaniello, Director Fiscal Services
CMO: Richard Jaffe, M.D., Medical Director
CHR: Jenna Pacini, Human Resources Specialist
CNO: Nona Fain, Ph.D., R.N., Director of Nursing
Web address: www.einstein.edu/locations/belmont–behavioral–health/
Control: Individual, Investor–owned (for–profit) **Service**: Psychiatric

Staffed Beds: 171 **Admissions**: 4260 **Census**: 156 **Outpatient Visits**: 34012 **Births**: 0 **Total Expense ($000)**: 49384 **Payroll Expense ($000)**: 30952 **Personnel**: 294

PA

☐ **CANCER TREATMENT CENTERS OF AMERICA–EASTERN REGIONAL MEDICAL CENTER (390312)**, 1331 East Wyoming Avenue, Zip 19124–3808; tel. 215/537–7400, **A**1 2 3 10 **F**3 15 29 30 31 33 34 35 36 45 46 47 48 49 50 55 56 57 58 59 64 65 68 70 75 78 79 80 81 82 84 85 86 87 91 93 96 97 100 101 104 107 108 109 110 111 115 116 117 118 119 120 121 123 124 126 129 130 132 135 136 143 144 146 147 148 149 **P**6 **S** Cancer Treatment Centers of America, Schaumburg, IL
Primary Contact: Nancy Hesse, MSN, R.N., President and Chief Executive Officer
COO: Jeffrey Ryan, Chief Operating Officer
CFO: Jeffrey Ryan, Senior Vice President, Finance and Business Development
CMO: Steven B. Standiford, M.D., Chief of Staff
CIO: Kristin Darby, Chief Information Officer
CHR: Ronald Gilg, Assistant Vice President Talent
CNO: Joanne McGovern, MSN, R.N., Chief Nursing Officer
Web address: www.cancercenter.com
Control: Corporation, Investor–owned (for–profit) **Service**: Cancer

| **Staffed Beds**: 56 **Admissions**: 830 **Census**: 17 **Outpatient Visits**: 28162 **Births**: 0 **Personnel**: 540 |

☒ **CHESTNUT HILL HOSPITAL (390026)**, 8835 Germantown Avenue, Zip 19118–2718; tel. 215/248–8200, (Nonreporting) **A**1 3 5 10 **S** Tower Health, West Reading, PA
Primary Contact: John D. Cacciamani, M.D., Chief Executive Officer
CFO: Marc Costner, Chief Financial Officer
CMO: John Scanlon, DPM, Chief Medical Officer
CHR: Marilyn DiCicco, Director Human Resources
CNO: Teresa M Kelly, MSN, R.N., Chief Nursing Officer
Web address: www.chhealthsystem.com
Control: Other not–for–profit (including NFP Corporation) **Service**: General medical and surgical

| **Staffed Beds**: 212 |

☐ **CHILDREN'S HOSPITAL OF PHILADELPHIA (393303)**, 3401 Civic Center Boulevard, Zip 19104–4319; tel. 215/590–1000, **A**1 3 5 8 10 **F**3 7 8 11 12 13 17 18 19 20 21 22 23 24 25 26 27 28 29 30 31 32 33 34 35 36 37 38 39 40 41 43 44 45 46 48 49 50 53 54 55 57 58 59 60 61 62 64 65 66 68 71 72 74 75 76 77 78 79 81 82 83 84 85 86 87 88 89 90 91 92 93 95 96 97 99 100 101 102 104 107 108 111 112 113 114 115 116 117 118 119 126 129 130 131 132 134 136 137 138 139 140 141 142 143 144 146 148 149 150 154 **P**6
Primary Contact: Madeline Bell, President and Chief Executive Officer
COO: Douglas G Hock, Executive Vice President and Chief Operating Officer
CFO: Thomas Todorow, Chief Financial Officer and Executive Vice President
CMO: Jan Boswinkel, M.D., Vice President Medical Operations and Chief Safety Officer
CHR: Robert Croner, Senior Vice President and Chief Human Resources Officer
CNO: Paula M Agosto, R.N., MSN, Senior Vice President and Chief Nursing Officer
Web address: www.chop.edu
Control: Other not–for–profit (including NFP Corporation) **Service**: Children's general medical and surgical

| **Staffed Beds**: 546 **Admissions**: 28685 **Census**: 445 **Outpatient Visits**: 1316670 **Births**: 453 **Total Expense ($000)**: 2014584 **Payroll Expense ($000)**: 905395 **Personnel**: 11374 |

☐ **EINSTEIN MEDICAL CENTER PHILADELPHIA (390142)**, 5501 Old York Road, Zip 19141–3098; tel. 215/456–7890, (Includes EINSTEIN MEDICAL CENTER ELKINS PARK, 60 Township Line Road, Elkins Park, PA, Zip 19027–2220; tel. 215/663–6000; Barry R Freedman, President and Chief Executive Officer) (Total facility includes 38 beds in nursing home–type unit) **A**1 2 3 5 8 10 13 **F**3 8 11 12 13 15 17 18 20 22 24 26 28 29 30 31 32 34 35 36 37 38 39 40 41 43 44 45 46 47 48 49 54 55 56 57 58 59 61 64 65 66 68 70 72 73 74 75 76 77 78 79 81 82 84 85 86 87 90 91 92 93 95 97 98 99 100 101 102 103 104 106 107 108 110 111 114 115 119 120 121 123 124 126 128 129 130 131 132 138 139 142 143 145 146 147 148 149 150 **P**6 **S** Einstein Healthcare Network, Philadelphia, PA
Primary Contact: Barry R. Freedman, President and Chief Executive Officer
COO: Ruth Lefton, Chief Operating Officer
CFO: Gerard Blaney, Vice President Finance and Interim Chief Financial Officer
CMO: Steven Sivak, M.D., Chief Medical Officer, Einstein Physicians Philadelphia
CIO: Brenda West, Vice President, Information Services and Interim Chief Information Officer
CHR: Lynne R Kornblatt, Chief Human Resources Officer
CNO: Jill Stunkard, R.N., MSN, Associate Chief Nurse Executive and Interim Chief Nursing Officer
Web address: www.einstein.edu
Control: Other not–for–profit (including NFP Corporation) **Service**: General medical and surgical

| **Staffed Beds**: 472 **Admissions**: 25074 **Census**: 464 **Outpatient Visits**: 562384 **Births**: 2738 **Total Expense ($000)**: 796531 **Payroll Expense ($000)**: 351334 **Personnel**: 5031 |

☐ **FAIRMOUNT BEHAVIORAL HEALTH SYSTEM (394027)**, 561 Fairthorne Avenue, Zip 19128–2499; tel. 215/487–4000, (Nonreporting) **A**1 10 **S** Universal Health Services, Inc., King of Prussia, PA
Primary Contact: Lisa M. McConlogue, MSN, Ph.D., Chief Executive Officer and Managing Director
CFO: Anthony Tortella, Chief Financial Officer
CMO: Silvia Gratz, D.O., Chief Medical Officer
CIO: Anthony Tortella, Chief Financial Officer
CHR: Brendan Aurand, Director, Human Resources
CNO: Wanda Nolasco, Chief Nursing Officer
Web address: www.fairmountbhs.com
Control: Corporation, Investor–owned (for–profit) **Service**: Psychiatric

| **Staffed Beds**: 235 |

☒ **FOX CHASE CANCER CENTER–AMERICAN ONCOLOGIC HOSPITAL (390196)**, 333 Cottman Avenue, Zip 19111–2434; tel. 215/728–6900, **A**1 2 3 5 10 **F**11 15 29 30 31 34 35 46 45 46 47 49 50 55 57 58 59 60 61 63 64 68 70 71 75 77 78 79 81 82 84 85 86 87 93 100 104 107 108 109 110 111 114 115 116 117 118 119 120 121 123 124 130 133 136 145 146 147 148 149 **P**6 **S** Temple University Health System, Philadelphia, PA
Primary Contact: Richard Fisher, M.D., President and Chief Executive Officer
COO: Judith Lynn Bachman, Chief Operating Officer
CFO: Anthony J Diasio, Chief Financial Officer
CMO: James Helstrom, Chief Medical Officer
CIO: Michael Sweeney, Chief Information Officer
CNO: Anne Jadwin, R.N., MSN, Chief Nursing Officer
Web address: www.fccc.org
Control: Other not–for–profit (including NFP Corporation) **Service**: Cancer

| **Staffed Beds**: 67 **Admissions**: 4210 **Census**: 63 **Outpatient Visits**: 111468 **Births**: 0 **Total Expense ($000)**: 300474 **Payroll Expense ($000)**: 86347 **Personnel**: 1480 |

☐ **FRIENDS HOSPITAL (394008)**, 4641 Roosevelt Boulevard, Zip 19124–2343; tel. 215/831–4600, (Nonreporting) **A**1 3 5 10 **S** Universal Health Services, Inc., King of Prussia, PA
Primary Contact: Michael S. McDonald Jr, Chief Executive Officer
COO: Diane Carugati, Chief Operating Officer
CFO: Michael Terwilliger, Chief Financial Officer
CMO: Marc Rothman, M.D., Medical Director
CIO: John Healy, Manager Information Technology
CHR: Paul Cavanaugh, Director Human Resources
Web address: www.friendshospital.com
Control: Corporation, Investor–owned (for–profit) **Service**: Psychiatric

| **Staffed Beds**: 192 |

☒ **GOOD SHEPHERD PENN PARTNERS SPECIALTY HOSPITAL AT RITTENHOUSE (392050)**, 1800 Lombard Street, Zip 19146–1414; tel. 877/969–7342, **A**1 10 **F**1 3 28 29 30 34 35 44 50 55 56 57 58 59 60 64 68 75 77 79 82 84 85 86 87 90 91 93 94 95 96 100 130 131 132 143 146 148 149 154 **P**6
Primary Contact: Laura Porter, Executive Director
CFO: Ronald J. Petula, Vice President Finance
CMO: Michael Grippi, M.D., Chief Medical Officer
CHR: Mark Sneff, Vice President Human Resources
CNO: Jean Romano, Chief Nursing Officer
Web address: www.phillyrehab.com
Control: Other not–for–profit (including NFP Corporation) **Service**: Acute long–term care hospital

| **Staffed Beds**: 38 **Admissions**: 225 **Census**: 22 **Outpatient Visits**: 188188 **Births**: 0 **Total Expense ($000)**: 47449 **Payroll Expense ($000)**: 20684 **Personnel**: 388 |

☒ **HAHNEMANN UNIVERSITY HOSPITAL (390290)**, 230 North Broad Street, Zip 19102–1192; tel. 215/762–7000, **A**1 2 3 5 8 10 13 **F**3 12 13 14 15 17 18 20 22 24 26 29 31 34 35 40 43 45 46 47 48 49 50 51 58 59 60 61 65 70 72 74 75 76 78 79 80 81 82 85 87 92 94 96 97 98 100 101 102 105 107 108 109 110 111 112 113 114 115 116 117 118 119 120 121 123 124 126 130 132 135 136 138 139 147 148 149 154 **P**6
Primary Contact: David R. Small, FACHE, Interim Chief Executive Officer
COO: Barbara Boston, Interim Chief Operating Officer
CFO: Richard Imbimbo, Chief Financial Officer
CIO: Irvin Fisher, Director, Information Services
Web address: www.hahnemannhospital.com
Control: Corporation, Investor–owned (for–profit) **Service**: General medical and surgical

| **Staffed Beds**: 496 **Admissions**: 17179 **Census**: 254 **Outpatient Visits**: 108042 **Births**: 1759 **Personnel**: 2541 |

Many Facility Codes have changed. Please refer to the AHA Guide Code Chart.   © 2018 AHA Guide

HAVEN BEHAVIORAL HOSPITAL OF PHILADELPHIA (394053), Four Falls Building, Zip 19129–1121; tel. 215/791–6821, (Nonreporting) **S** Haven Behavioral Healthcare, Nashville, TN
Primary Contact: Abigail Halloran, Chief Executive Officer
Web address: www.https://philadelphia.havenbehavioral.com
Control: Corporation, Investor–owned (for–profit) **Service**: Psychiatric

Staffed Beds: 36

☒ △ **HOSPITAL OF THE UNIVERSITY OF PENNSYLVANIA (390111)**, 3400 Spruce Street, Zip 19104–4206; tel. 215/662–4000, (Includes SCHEIE EYE INSTITUTE OF THE HOSPITAL OF THE UNIVERSITY OF PENNSYLVANIA, 3400 Civic Center Blvd FL 3, West Pavilion, 3rd Floor, Philadelphia, PA, Zip 19104–5127; tel. 215/662–8100; Sheara Hollin, Chief Operating Officer) **A**1 2 5 7 8 10 **F**3 6 7 9 11 12 13 15 17 18 20 22 24 26 29 30 31 34 35 36 38 39 40 44 45 46 47 48 49 50 51 52 54 55 56 57 58 59 60 61 62 63 64 65 66 68 70 72 73 74 75 76 77 78 79 80 81 82 84 85 86 87 90 91 92 93 94 95 96 97 100 102 103 104 107 108 110 111 114 115 117 118 119 120 121 122 123 124 126 129 130 131 132 134 135 136 137 138 139 140 141 142 145 146 147 148 149 150 154 **P**6 **S** University of Pennsylvania Health System, Philadelphia, PA
Primary Contact: Regina Cunningham, Ph.D., R.N., Chief Executive Officer
COO: Carolyn Jackson, Chief Operating Officer
CFO: Joseph M Huber, Chief Financial Officer
CMO: Patrick J Brennan, M.D., Senior Vice President and Chief Medical Officer
CIO: Michael Restuccia, Chief Information Officer
CHR: Denise J. Mariotti, Chief Human Resource Officer
Web address: www.pennmedicine.org
Control: Other not–for–profit (including NFP Corporation) **Service**: General medical and surgical

Staffed Beds: 797 Admissions: 34531 Census: 687 Outpatient Visits: 1774597 Births: 4216 Total Expense ($000): 2565350 Payroll Expense ($000): 1006323 Personnel: 14169

☒ **JEANES HOSPITAL (390080)**, 7600 Central Avenue, Zip 19111–2499; tel. 215/728–2000, **A**1 3 5 10 **F**3 11 12 15 17 18 20 22 24 26 28 29 30 31 34 35 40 44 45 49 50 51 56 57 59 60 61 62 65 68 70 74 75 77 78 79 81 82 84 85 86 87 91 92 93 96 107 108 110 111 115 118 119 129 130 132 135 146 148 149 154 **S** Temple University Health System, Philadelphia, PA
Primary Contact: Marc P. Hurowitz, D.O., President and Chief Executive Officer
COO: Judith Lynn Bachman, Chief Operating Officer
CFO: Ray Lefton, Chief Financial Officer
CMO: Rebecca Armbruster, M.D., Chief Medical Officer
CIO: Michael Sweeney, Chief Informatics Officer
CHR: Beverly Sherbondy, Assistant Vice President, Human Resources
CNO: Denise Anne Lavery Frasca, MSN, R.N., Vice President Patient Care Services and Chief Nursing Officer
Web address: www.jeanes.com
Control: Other not–for–profit (including NFP Corporation) **Service**: General medical and surgical

Staffed Beds: 146 Admissions: 7096 Census: 81 Outpatient Visits: 127232 Births: 0 Total Expense ($000): 159648 Payroll Expense ($000): 63124 Personnel: 918

☒ △ **JEFFERSON HEALTH NORTHEAST (390115)**, 10800 Knights Road, Zip 19114–4200; tel. 215/612–4000, (Includes BUCKS COUNTY CAMPUS, 380 North Oxford Valley Road, Langhorne, PA, Zip 19047–8399; tel. 215/949–5000; FRANKFORD CAMPUS, Frankford Avenue and Wakeling Street, Philadelphia, PA, Zip 19124; tel. 215/831–2000) **A**1 3 5 7 10 13 **F**3 11 12 15 17 18 20 22 24 26 28 29 30 31 34 35 39 40 43 44 45 46 48 49 50 53 54 57 58 59 61 64 65 66 68 70 74 75 77 78 79 80 81 82 84 85 86 87 92 93 94 96 100 102 107 108 110 111 114 115 116 117 118 119 120 121 123 124 126 128 130 131 132 135 144 145 146 147 148 149 154 **P**6 7 **S** Jefferson Health, Philadelphia, PA
Primary Contact: Kathleen Kinslow, Ed.D., Chief Executive Officer
COO: Sandra Gomberg, Chief Operating Officer
CFO: William Degnan, Vice President Finance
CMO: Stanton Segal, M.D., Chief Medical Officer
CHR: Dorinda Carolina, Chief Human Resources Officer
CNO: Michelle E Conley, R.N., Chief Nursing Officer
Web address: www.ariahealth.org
Control: Other not–for–profit (including NFP Corporation) **Service**: General medical and surgical

Staffed Beds: 464 Admissions: 24529 Census: 304 Outpatient Visits: 229379 Births: 0 Total Expense ($000): 447312 Payroll Expense ($000): 202458 Personnel: 3603

JEFFERSON METHODIST HOSPITAL See Thomas Jefferson University Hospitals, Philadelphia

☐ **KENSINGTON HOSPITAL (390025)**, 136 West Diamond Street, Zip 19122–1721; tel. 215/426–8100, (Nonreporting) **A**1 10
Primary Contact: Eileen Hause, Chief Executive Officer
CFO: Kenneth Biddle, Controller
CMO: Luis F Vera, M.D., Medical Director
CHR: Maria Dimichele, Administrative Assistant
CNO: Aleyamma John, R.N., Director of Nursing
Control: State, Government, nonfederal **Service**: General medical and surgical

Staffed Beds: 33

☒ **KINDRED HOSPITAL SOUTH PHILADELPHIA (392046)**, 1930 South Broad Street, Zip 19145–2328; tel. 267/570–5200, (Nonreporting) **A**1 10 **S** Kindred Healthcare, Louisville, KY
Primary Contact: Michele S. Basile, Chief Executive Officer
COO: Diane K. White, MSN, R.N., Chief Clinical Officer
CFO: Kevin Varley, Chief Financial Officer
CMO: James Dovnarsky, M.D., Director Pulmonary Medical
CHR: Amy Cain, District Director Human Resources
CNO: Diane K. White, MSN, R.N., Chief Clinical Officer
Web address: www.khsouthphilly.com
Control: Corporation, Investor–owned (for–profit) **Service**: Acute long–term care hospital

Staffed Beds: 58

☒ **KINDRED HOSPITAL–PHILADELPHIA (392027)**, 6129 Palmetto Street, Zip 19111–5729; tel. 215/722–8555, (Includes KINDRED HOSPITAL PHILADELPHIA – HAVERTOWN, 2000 Old West Chester Pike, Havertown, PA, Zip 19083–2712; tel. 610/536–2100; Margaret M Murphy, Chief Executive Officer) **A**1 10 **F**1 3 18 28 29 30 35 45 50 60 62 63 65 68 70 74 75 77 84 85 86 87 90 96 98 130 143 145 148 149 151 **S** Kindred Healthcare, Louisville, KY
Primary Contact: Michael Bass, M.D., Chief Executive Officer
CFO: Kathy Andrews, Chief Financial Officer
CNO: Erin McCullough, Chief Clinical Officer
Web address: www.kindredphila.com/
Control: Corporation, Investor–owned (for–profit) **Service**: Acute long–term care hospital

Staffed Beds: 52 Admissions: 299 Census: 23 Outpatient Visits: 0 Births: 0 Total Expense ($000): 18037 Payroll Expense ($000): 7093

☐ **KIRKBRIDE CENTER (394007)**, 111 North 49th Street, Zip 19139–2718; tel. 215/471–2600, (Nonreporting) **A**1 10
Primary Contact: Marlene Douglas–Walsh, Chief Executive Officer
CFO: Robert Anthony, Chief Financial Officer
CMO: Mark Novitsky, M.D., Sr Corporate Medical Director
CHR: Arend Boersema, Director Human Resources
CNO: Abbie Lampie, Director of Nursing
Web address: www.kirkbridecenter.com
Control: Partnership, Investor–owned (for–profit) **Service**: Psychiatric

Staffed Beds: 205

☒ △ **MAGEE REHABILITATION HOSPITAL (393038)**, 1513 Race Street, Zip 19102–1177; tel. 215/587–3000, (Nonreporting) **A**1 3 5 7 10
Primary Contact: Jack A. Carroll, Ph.D., President and Chief Executive Officer
CFO: Stephen DeStefano, Chief Financial Officer
CMO: Guy Fried, M.D., Chief Medical Officer
CIO: Shawna White, Chief Information Officer
CHR: Cindy Tobin–Payne, Director
Web address: www.mageerehab.org
Control: Other not–for–profit (including NFP Corporation) **Service**: Rehabilitation

Staffed Beds: 96

MERCY PHILADELPHIA HOSPITAL See Mercy Fitzgerald Hospital, Darby

☒ △ **NAZARETH HOSPITAL (390204)**, 2601 Holme Avenue, Zip 19152–2096; tel. 215/335–6000, (Total facility includes 28 beds in nursing home–type unit) **A**1 3 7 10 **F**3 12 15 18 20 22 29 30 31 34 35 37 39 40 45 46 49 50 53 56 57 58 59 64 65 70 74 75 77 78 79 80 81 82 84 85 86 87 90 93 97 100 107 108 110 111 114 115 117 118 119 120 121 128 130 131 132 135 146 147 148 149 154 **P**7 **S** Trinity Health, Livonia, MI
Primary Contact: Nancy Cherone, Executive Director and Administrator
CFO: David Wajda, Chief Financial Officer
CMO: Mathew Matthew, M.D., Chief Medical Officer
CIO: Terry O'Neil, Chief Information Technology
CHR: Kathleen M Pries, Director Human Resources
CNO: Michael Beshel, R.N., Vice President Patient Care and Chief Nursing Officer
Web address: www.nazarethhospital.org
Control: Other not–for–profit (including NFP Corporation) **Service**: General medical and surgical

Staffed Beds: 162 Admissions: 7658 Census: 104 Outpatient Visits: 121984 Births: 0 Total Expense ($000): 142693 Payroll Expense ($000): 55578 Personnel: 910

PA

Hospital, Medicare Provider Number, Address, Telephone, Approval, Facility, and Physician Codes, Health Care System

★ American Hospital Association (AHA) membership
☐ The Joint Commission accreditation
◯ Healthcare Facilities Accreditation Program
◇ DNV Healthcare Inc. accreditation
⇧ Center for Improvement in Healthcare Quality Accreditation
△ Commission on Accreditation of Rehabilitation Facilities (CARF) accreditation

NORTH PHILADELPHIA HEALTH SYSTEM (390132), 801 West Girard Ave, Zip 19122–4212, Mailing Address: 801 West Girard Avenue, Zip 19122–4212; tel. 215/787–9000, (Includes GIRARD MEDICAL CENTER, Girard Avenue at Eighth Street, Philadelphia, PA, Zip 19122; tel. 215/787–2000; Gerri H. Walker, President and Chief Executive Officer) **A**10 **F**98 106
Primary Contact: Gerri H. Walker, President and Chief Executive Officer
CFO: Ronald Kaplan, Chief Financial Officer
CIO: Tony Iero, Director Management Information Systems
CHR: James Gloner, Senior Vice President
Web address: www.nphs.com
Control: Other not–for–profit (including NFP Corporation) **Service**: Psychiatric

Staffed Beds: 175 Admissions: 250 Census: 7 Births: 0

☒ **PENN PRESBYTERIAN MEDICAL CENTER (390223)**, 51 North 39th Street, Zip 19104–2699; tel. 215/662–8000, (Total facility includes 25 beds in nursing home–type unit) **A**1 2 3 5 10 **F**3 4 5 7 8 9 11 12 15 17 18 20 22 24 26 29 30 31 32 34 35 36 37 38 39 40 43 44 45 46 49 50 51 52 54 56 57 58 59 60 61 62 63 64 65 66 68 70 74 75 77 78 79 81 82 84 85 86 87 92 94 96 97 98 100 101 104 107 108 110 111 114 115 118 119 120 121 126 128 130 131 132 134 135 141 142 146 147 148 149 150 154 **P**6 **S** University of Pennsylvania Health System, Philadelphia, PA
Primary Contact: Michele M. Volpe, Chief Executive Officer
COO: Robert J Russell, Associate Executive Director Operations
CFO: Anthony Zumpano, Chief Financial Officer
CMO: Kevin Fosnocht, M.D., Chief Medical Officer and Associate Executive Director
CIO: Theresa Hiltunen, Entity Information Officer
CHR: Margorie Michele, Chief Human Resources Officer
CNO: James R Ballinghoff, MSN, R.N., Chief Nursing Officer and Associate Executive Director
Web address: www.pennmedicine.org/pmc/
Control: Other not–for–profit (including NFP Corporation) **Service**: General medical and surgical

Staffed Beds: 375 Admissions: 17405 Census: 269 Outpatient Visits: 277501 Births: 2 Total Expense ($000): 614120 Payroll Expense ($000): 226800 Personnel: 2442

☒ **PENNSYLVANIA HOSPITAL (390226)**, 800 Spruce Street, Zip 19107–6192; tel. 215/829–3000, **A**1 2 3 5 10 13 **F**3 7 8 11 12 13 15 17 18 20 22 24 26 29 30 31 34 35 36 37 38 39 40 44 45 46 49 50 51 52 54 55 56 57 58 59 60 61 62 63 64 65 66 68 70 72 73 74 75 76 77 78 79 80 81 82 84 85 86 87 92 96 97 98 100 101 102 103 104 107 108 110 111 114 115 116 117 118 119 120 121 123 124 126 129 130 131 132 135 141 142 145 146 147 148 149 150 154 **P**6 **S** University of Pennsylvania Health System, Philadelphia, PA
Primary Contact: Theresa M. Larivee, Chief Executive Officer
CFO: Frank Anastasi, Chief Financial Officer
CMO: Daniel Feinberg, M.D., Chief Medical Officer
CIO: Kwon Lee, Chief Information Officer
CNO: Mary Margaret Del Guidice, MSN, R.N., Chief Nursing Officer
Web address: www.pahosp.com
Control: Other not–for–profit (including NFP Corporation) **Service**: General medical and surgical

Staffed Beds: 475 Admissions: 18978 Census: 271 Outpatient Visits: 316216 Births: 5128 Total Expense ($000): 635896 Payroll Expense ($000): 208262 Personnel: 2514

☒ △ **PHILADELPHIA VETERANS AFFAIRS MEDICAL CENTER**, 3900 Woodland Avenue, Zip 19104–4594; tel. 215/823–5800, (Total facility includes 135 beds in nursing home–type unit) **A**1 2 3 5 7 8 **F**1 3 4 5 6 8 9 18 20 22 24 26 28 29 30 31 34 35 38 39 40 44 45 46 47 48 49 50 51 54 56 57 58 59 60 61 62 63 64 65 66 67 70 74 75 77 78 79 80 81 82 83 84 85 86 87 89 90 91 92 93 94 96 97 98 99 100 101 102 103 104 105 106 107 108 109 110 111 112 114 115 116 117 118 119 120 121 122 123 124 126 128 129 130 132 134 135 144 145 146 147 148 149 152 153 154 **S** Department of Veterans Affairs, Perry Point, MD
Primary Contact: Daniel Hendee, Director
CMO: Dave Oslin, M.D., Chief of Staff
CIO: Adrienne Ficchi, Vice President Information Management
CHR: Gerald Morelli, Director Human Resources
Web address: www.philadelphia.va.gov/
Control: Veterans Affairs, Government, federal **Service**: General medical and surgical

Staffed Beds: 317 Admissions: 6061 Census: 241 Outpatient Visits: 613433 Births: 0

☒ **ROXBOROUGH MEMORIAL HOSPITAL (390304)**, 5800 Ridge Avenue, Zip 19128–1737; tel. 215/483–9900, **A**1 3 10 **F**3 15 18 29 34 40 44 45 47 49 50 51 56 57 59 65 70 75 77 81 89 91 93 98 103 107 108 110 111 114 119 130 148 149 **S** Prime Healthcare, Ontario, CA
Primary Contact: Matt Shelak, Chief Executive Officer
CFO: Thomas Reinboth, Chief Financial Officer
CHR: Michael Henrici, Associate Administrator
Web address: www.roxboroughmemorial.com
Control: Corporation, Investor–owned (for–profit) **Service**: General medical and surgical

Staffed Beds: 131 Admissions: 4456 Census: 57 Outpatient Visits: 25489 Births: 0

☒ **SHRINERS HOSPITALS FOR CHILDREN–PHILADELPHIA (393309)**, 3551 North Broad Street, Zip 19140–4160; tel. 215/430–4000, (Nonreporting) **A**1 3 5 10 **S** Shriners Hospitals for Children, Tampa, FL
Primary Contact: Ed Myers, Administrator
CFO: Mario Salvati, Director Fiscal Services
CMO: Scott Kozin, M.D., Chief of Staff
CHR: Megan Hauser, Director Human Resources
CNO: Krista Miller, R.N., Chief Nursing Officer
Web address: www.shrinershospitalsforchildren.org/Hospitals/Locations/Philadelphia.aspx
Control: Other not–for–profit (including NFP Corporation) **Service**: Children's orthopedic

Staffed Beds: 39

☒ **ST. CHRISTOPHER'S HOSPITAL FOR CHILDREN (393307)**, 3601 A Street, Zip 19134–1043; tel. 215/427–5000, **A**1 3 5 8 10 **F**3 7 16 17 19 21 23 25 27 29 30 31 32 34 35 39 40 41 43 44 48 49 50 54 55 58 59 60 61 64 68 70 71 72 73 74 75 77 78 79 80 81 82 83 84 87 88 89 93 97 99 100 101 102 107 111 119 129 130 131 132 134 136 138 143 144 146 **P**6
Primary Contact: George Rizzuto, CPA, Interim Chief Executive Officer
COO: Thomas Runkle, MS, Ph.D., Chief Operating Officer
CMO: Mary Moran, M.D., Pediatrician In Chief
CIO: Robert Taylor, Director Information Services
CHR: Kellie T. Pearson, Chief Human Resource Officer
CNO: Joanna Horst, MSN, R.N., Chief Nursing Officer
Web address: www.stchristophershospital.com
Control: Corporation, Investor–owned (for–profit) **Service**: Children's general medical and surgical

Staffed Beds: 121 Admissions: 7828 Census: 93 Outpatient Visits: 134548 Births: 0

☒ **TEMPLE UNIVERSITY HOSPITAL (390027)**, 3401 North Broad Street, Zip 19140–5103; tel. 215/707–2000, (Includes TEMPLE UNIVERSITY HOSPITAL – EPISCOPAL DIVISION, 100 East Lehigh Avenue, Philadelphia, PA, Zip 19125–1098; tel. 215/427–7000; Kathleen Barron, Executive Director) **A**1 2 3 5 8 10 **F**3 4 8 12 13 14 15 16 17 18 20 22 24 26 28 29 30 31 34 35 37 38 40 41 43 44 45 46 47 48 49 50 53 54 55 56 57 58 59 60 61 64 68 70 72 73 74 75 76 77 78 79 80 81 82 83 84 85 86 87 90 92 93 94 96 97 98 100 101 102 104 107 108 109 110 111 112 114 115 118 119 120 121 123 124 126 129 130 131 132 134 135 136 137 138 139 140 141 142 145 146 147 148 149 154 **S** Temple University Health System, Philadelphia, PA
Primary Contact: Verdi Disesa, M.D., President and Chief Executive Officer
COO: Rosemary Nolan, R.N., MSN, JD, Chief Operating Officer
CFO: Gerald P Oetzel, Chief Financial Officer
CMO: Herbert Cushing, M.D., Chief Medical Officer
CIO: David Kamowski, Vice President and Chief Information Officer
CHR: John Lasky Jr Vice President, Chief Human Resources Officer
CNO: Elizabeth J Craig, MSN, Chief Nursing Officer and Vice President Patient Services
Web address: www.tuh.templehealth.org/content/default.htm
Control: Other not–for–profit (including NFP Corporation) **Service**: General medical and surgical

Staffed Beds: 732 Admissions: 34449 Census: 559 Outpatient Visits: 338717 Births: 2650 Total Expense ($000): 1122375 Payroll Expense ($000): 375828 Personnel: 4715

☒ △ **THOMAS JEFFERSON UNIVERSITY HOSPITALS (390174)**, 111 South 11th Street, Zip 19107–5084; tel. 215/955–6000, (Includes JEFFERSON METHODIST HOSPITAL, 2301 South Broad Street, Philadelphia, PA, Zip 19148; tel. 215/952–9000; Stephen K Klasko, M.D., President) **A**1 2 3 5 7 8 10 **F**3 5 6 7 8 9 11 12 13 14 15 17 18 20 22 24 26 28 29 30 31 34 35 36 37 38 39 40 43 44 45 46 47 48 49 50 53 54 55 56 57 58 59 61 64 65 66 68 70 72 74 75 76 77 78 79 80 81 82 84 85 86 87 89 90 92 93 94 96 97 98 100 101 102 103 104 107 108 110 111 114 115 116 117 118 119 120 121 123 124 126 129 130 131 132 134 135 136 137 138 139 141 142 144 145 146 147 148 149 150 153 154 **P**2 6 8 **S** Jefferson Health, Philadelphia, PA
Primary Contact: Richard Webster, R.N., President
CFO: Neil Lubarsky, Senior Vice President, Finance and Chief Financial Officer
CMO: Edmund A. Pribitkin, M.D., Chief Medical Officer
CIO: Nassar Nizami, Chief Information Officer
CHR: Jeffrey Stevens, Executive Vice President and Chief Human Resource Officer
CNO: Mary Ann McGinley, Ph.D., Senior Vice President, Patient Services and Chief Nursing Officer
Web address: www.jefferson.edu
Control: Other not–for–profit (including NFP Corporation) **Service**: General medical and surgical

Staffed Beds: 899 Admissions: 41368 Census: 627 Outpatient Visits: 472456 Births: 1857 Total Expense ($000): 1613171 Payroll Expense ($000): 504383 Personnel: 6825

TRIUMPH HOSPITAL PHILADELPHIA See Kindred Hospital South Philadelphia

VETERANS AFFAIRS MEDICAL CENTER See Philadelphia Veterans Affairs Medical Center

Many Facility Codes have changed. Please refer to the AHA Guide Code Chart. © 2018 AHA Guide

PHOENIXVILLE—Chester County

☒ △ **PHOENIXVILLE HOSPITAL (390127)**, 140 Nutt Road, Zip 19460–3900, Mailing Address: P.O. Box 3001, Zip 19460–0916; tel. 610/983–1000, **A**1 2 3 7 10 **F**3 8 13 15 18 20 22 24 26 28 29 31 32 34 35 36 38 39 40 45 49 50 51 55 56 57 59 61 64 68 69 70 72 74 75 76 77 78 79 81 82 85 86 87 93 102 107 108 111 114 115 117 118 119 126 130 132 134 135 146 147 154 **S** Tower Health, West Reading, PA
Primary Contact: Stephen M. Tullman, Chief Executive Officer
CFO: Edward Chabalowski, Chief Financial Officer
CMO: David Stepansky, M.D., Chief Medical Officer
CIO: Terry Murphy, Director Information Services
CHR: Denise Chiolo, Chief Human Resources Officer
CNO: Sarah Strzelecki, Ed.D., R.N., Chief Nursing Officer
Web address: www.https://phoenixville.towerhealth.org
Control: Other not-for-profit (including NFP Corporation) **Service:** General medical and surgical

Staffed Beds: 139 **Admissions:** 6879 **Census:** 84 **Outpatient Visits:** 91767 **Births:** 805 **Total Expense ($000):** 157069 **Payroll Expense ($000):** 48625 **Personnel:** 865

PITTSBURGH—Allegheny County

☒ **ALLEGHENY GENERAL HOSPITAL (390050)**, 320 East North Avenue, Zip 15212–4756; tel. 412/359–3131, **A**1 2 3 5 8 10 12 13 **F**3 6 8 11 12 15 17 18 20 22 24 26 28 29 30 31 32 33 34 35 36 37 38 39 40 44 45 46 47 48 49 50 53 54 57 58 59 61 64 65 70 74 75 77 78 79 80 81 82 84 85 86 87 89 92 93 96 100 101 102 104 105 107 108 110 111 114 115 117 118 119 121 123 124 126 130 131 132 135 137 138 139 146 147 148 149 153 154 **P**6 **S** Allegheny Health Network, Pittsburgh, PA
Primary Contact: Jeffrey Cohen, M.D., President
COO: Duke Rupert, Chief Operating Officer
CFO: Richard W Fries, Vice President Finance
CMO: Tony Farah, M.D., President Medical Staff
CIO: John Foley, Chief Information Officer
Web address: www.wpahs.org/locations/allegheny-general-hospital
Control: Other not-for-profit (including NFP Corporation) **Service:** General medical and surgical

Staffed Beds: 531 **Admissions:** 24526 **Census:** 357 **Outpatient Visits:** 332017 **Births:** 0 **Total Expense ($000):** 733876 **Payroll Expense ($000):** 202176 **Personnel:** 3785

☐ **CHILDREN'S HOSPITAL OF PITTSBURGH OF UPMC (393302)**, One Children's Hospital Drive, Zip 15224–1334; tel. 412/692–5325, **A**1 3 5 10 **F**3 8 12 17 19 21 22 23 24 25 27 28 29 30 31 32 34 35 36 38 39 40 41 43 45 46 48 49 50 53 54 55 57 58 59 60 61 64 65 66 68 71 72 74 75 77 78 79 81 82 84 86 87 88 89 90 91 92 93 94 97 100 107 108 109 111 112 114 115 116 117 118 119 120 121 123 124 126 127 129 130 131 132 134 135 136 137 138 139 140 141 142 143 144 146 148 150 154 **S** UPMC, Pittsburgh, PA
Primary Contact: Christopher A. Gessner, President
CFO: Nicholas J. Barcellona, Chief Financial Officer
CMO: Brian Martin, Vice President Medical Affairs
CIO: Srinivasan Suresh, M.D., Chief Medical Information Officer
CHR: Rhonda Larimore, Vice President, Human Resources
CNO: Diane Hupp, R.N., Vice President Support Services and Patient Care Services
Web address: www.chp.edu
Control: Other not-for-profit (including NFP Corporation) **Service:** Children's general medical and surgical

Staffed Beds: 305 **Admissions:** 12333 **Census:** 227 **Outpatient Visits:** 332295 **Births:** 0 **Total Expense ($000):** 654804 **Payroll Expense ($000):** 158232 **Personnel:** 2702

EYE AND EAR HOSPITAL OF PITTSBURGH See UPMC Presbyterian, Pittsburgh

☒ **HEALTHSOUTH HARMARVILLE REHABILITATION HOSPITAL (393027)**, 320 Guys Run Road, Zip 15238–0460, Mailing Address: P.O. Box 11460, Zip 15238–0460; tel. 412/828–1300, (Nonreporting) **A**1 10 **S** Encompass Health Corporation, Birmingham, AL
Primary Contact: Mark Van Volkenburg, Chief Executive Officer
CFO: Daniel A Vrana, Controller
CMO: James Kreshon, M.D., Medical Director
CHR: Kathy Grills, Director Human Resources
CNO: Eileen Skalski, Chief Nursing Officer
Web address: www.healthsouthharmarville.com
Control: Corporation, Investor-owned (for-profit) **Service:** Rehabilitation

Staffed Beds: 162

☒ **LIFECARE HOSPITALS OF PITTSBURGH (392024)**, 225 Penn Avenue, Zip 15221–2148; tel. 469/241–2100, (Includes LIFECARE HOSPITALS OF PITTSBURGH – SUBURBAN, 100 South Jackson Avenue, Pittsburgh, PA, Zip 15202–3428, Mailing Address: 100 South Jackson Avenue, 4th Floor, Zip 15202–3428, tel. 412/734–7600; Trisha Niemuth, Market Chief Executive Officer) (Nonreporting) **A**1 10 **S** LifeCare Management Services, Plano, TX
Primary Contact: Jennifer Malko, Market Chief Executive Officer
CFO: Asia Holyfield, Manager Business Office
CMO: Steven Sotos, M.D., President Medical Staff
CIO: Mike Wattenbarger, Chief Information Officer
CHR: Robin F. Arslanpay, Director Human Resources
CNO: Paula Pawloski, Chief Nursing Officer
Web address: www.lifecare-hospitals.com
Control: Corporation, Investor-owned (for-profit) **Service:** Acute long-term care hospital

Staffed Beds: 196

☒ **MAGEE–WOMENS HOSPITAL OF UPMC (390114)**, 300 Halket Street, Zip 15213–3108; tel. 412/641–1000, (Total facility includes 20 beds in nursing home–type unit) **A**1 2 3 5 10 **F**3 11 12 13 14 15 29 30 31 34 35 40 44 45 46 49 52 54 55 56 57 58 59 64 65 66 68 70 72 74 75 76 77 78 79 80 81 82 84 85 86 87 91 97 100 107 108 110 111 115 117 119 120 121 123 126 128 130 131 132 134 135 146 147 148 149 150 154 **S** UPMC, Pittsburgh, PA
Primary Contact: Leslie C. Davis, President
COO: Lou Baverso, Vice President Operations
CFO: Eileen Simmons, Chief Financial Officer
CMO: Dennis English, M.D., Vice President Medical Affairs
CHR: Rhonda Larimore, Vice President Human Resources
CNO: Maribeth McLaughlin, R.N., Vice President Patient Care Services
Web address: www.magee.edu
Control: Other not-for-profit (including NFP Corporation) **Service:** Obstetrics and gynecology

Staffed Beds: 321 **Admissions:** 18299 **Census:** 238 **Outpatient Visits:** 574274 **Births:** 8796 **Total Expense ($000):** 808942 **Payroll Expense ($000):** 136627 **Personnel:** 2161

☒ **SELECT SPECIALTY HOSPITAL–PITTSBURGH/UPMC (392044)**, 200 Lothrop Street, E824, Zip 15213–2536; tel. 412/586–9800, (Nonreporting) **A**1 10 **S** Select Medical Corporation, Mechanicsburg, PA
Primary Contact: Yvonne Kughn, Chief Executive Officer
CMO: Michael Donahue, M.D., Medical Director
CHR: Prudence Sloan, Coordinator Human Resources
CNO: Eli Babich, Chief Nursing Officer
Web address: www.pittsburghupmc.selectspecialtyhospitals.com/
Control: Corporation, Investor-owned (for-profit) **Service:** Acute long-term care hospital

Staffed Beds: 32

☐ **SOUTHWOOD PSYCHIATRIC HOSPITAL**, 2575 Boyce Plaza Road, Zip 15241–3925; tel. 412/257–2290, (Nonreporting) **A**1 **S** Acadia Healthcare Company, Inc., Franklin, TN
Primary Contact: Stephen J. Quigley, Chief Executive Officer
CFO: Frank Urban, Chief Financial Officer
CMO: Allan W Clark, M.D., Medical Director
CHR: Erin J Frohnhofer, Director Human Resources
Web address: www.southwoodhospital.com
Control: Corporation, Investor-owned (for-profit) **Service:** Children's hospital psychiatric

Staffed Beds: 156

☒ **ST. CLAIR HOSPITAL (390228)**, 1000 Bower Hill Road, Zip 15243–1873; tel. 412/942–4000, **A**1 2 3 10 **F**3 8 13 15 17 18 20 22 24 26 28 29 30 31 34 35 37 40 45 46 49 51 53 54 57 59 60 63 64 67 68 70 73 74 75 76 77 78 79 81 82 84 85 86 87 89 91 92 93 98 100 102 105 107 108 110 111 114 115 119 126 129 130 131 132 135 143 144 146 147 148 149 153 **P**6
Primary Contact: James M. Collins, President and Chief Executive Officer
COO: Michael J Flanagan, Senior Vice President and Chief Operating Officer
CFO: Richard C Chesnos, Senior Vice President Finance and Chief Financial Officer
CMO: John Sullivan, M.D., Chief Medical Officer
CIO: Richard Schaeffer, Vice President Information Systems and Chief Information Officer
CHR: Andrea Kalina, Vice President External Affairs and Chief Human Resources Officer
CNO: Joan Massella, Administrative Vice President and Chief Nursing Officer
Web address: www.stclair.org
Control: Other not-for-profit (including NFP Corporation) **Service:** General medical and surgical

Staffed Beds: 301 **Admissions:** 15988 **Census:** 184 **Outpatient Visits:** 321507 **Births:** 1512 **Total Expense ($000):** 266174 **Payroll Expense ($000):** 100422 **Personnel:** 1732

★ **THE CHILDREN'S HOME OF PITTSBURGH (393304)**, 5324 Penn Avenue, Zip 15224–1733; tel. 412/441–4884, (Nonreporting) **A**10
Primary Contact: Pamela R. Schanwald, Chief Executive Officer
COO: Kimberly Reblock, M.D., Chief Operating Officer
CFO: Kimberly A Phillips, Chief Financial Officer
CMO: Frederick C Sherman, M.D., Chief Medical Officer
Web address: www.childrenshomepgh.org
Control: Other not–for–profit (including NFP Corporation) **Service**: Children's general medical and surgical

Staffed Beds: 30

★ **THE CHILDREN'S INSTITUTE OF PITTSBURGH (393308)**, 1405 Shady Avenue, Zip 15217–1350; tel. 412/420–2400, (Nonreporting) **A**3 10
Primary Contact: Wendy Ann. Pardee, President and Chief Executive Officer
COO: Stacey Vaccaro, Chief Operating Officer
CFO: John Jubas, Vice President Finance
CMO: Matthew Masiello, M.D., Chief Medical Officer
CIO: Sharon Dorogy, Chief Information Officer
CHR: Linda M Allen, Vice President Human Resources
Web address: www.amazingkids.org
Control: Other not–for–profit (including NFP Corporation) **Service**: Children's rehabilitation

Staffed Beds: 62

☐ **UPMC MERCY (390028)**, 1400 Locust Street, Zip 15219–5166; tel. 412/232–8111, **A**1 3 5 10 12 13 **F**3 4 8 13 14 15 18 20 22 24 26 28 29 30 31 32 34 35 36 39 40 43 44 45 46 47 48 49 50 51 54 56 57 58 59 60 61 64 65 66 68 70 72 74 75 76 77 78 79 81 82 84 85 86 87 90 91 92 93 94 95 96 97 98 100 101 102 107 108 111 115 116 118 119 126 129 130 132 135 141 142 146 147 148 154 **P**6 **S** UPMC, Pittsburgh, PA
Primary Contact: Michael A. Grace, President
COO: Julie Hecker, Vice President, Operations
CFO: Eileen Simmons, Chief Financial Officer, UPMC Hospital Network
CIO: Kevin Conway, Chief Information Officer
CHR: Tracey Stange Kolo, Vice President, Human Resources
CNO: Leeanna McKibben, R.N., MSN, Vice President Patient Services and Chief Nursing Officer
Web address: www.upmc.com/HospitalsFacilities/HFHome/Hospitals/Mercy/
Control: Other not–for–profit (including NFP Corporation) **Service**: General medical and surgical

Staffed Beds: 453 **Admissions:** 18298 **Census:** 332 **Outpatient Visits:** 175129 **Births:** 989 **Total Expense ($000):** 402841 **Payroll Expense ($000):** 123867 **Personnel:** 2209

UPMC MONTEFIORE See UPMC Presbyterian, Pittsburgh

☐ **UPMC PASSAVANT (390107)**, 9100 Babcock Boulevard, Zip 15237–5815; tel. 412/748–6700, (Includes UPMC PASSAVANT CRANBERRY, One St Francis Way, Cranberry, PA, Zip 16066; tel. 724/772–5300; Teresa G Petrick, President) **A**1 2 3 5 10 **F**3 8 11 15 17 18 20 22 24 26 28 29 30 31 34 35 40 45 46 47 48 49 51 54 56 57 58 59 64 68 70 74 75 77 78 79 81 82 84 85 86 87 90 92 96 100 107 108 109 110 111 114 118 119 120 121 123 126 129 130 132 135 143 146 147 148 **S** UPMC, Pittsburgh, PA
Primary Contact: David T. Martin, President
CFO: Thomas M Newman, Chief Financial Officer
CMO: James W Boyle, M.D., Chief Medical Officer
CNO: Susan E Hoolahan, R.N., MSN, Vice President Patient Care Services and Chief Nursing Officer
Web address: www.upmc.edu/passavant
Control: Other not–for–profit (including NFP Corporation) **Service**: General medical and surgical

Staffed Beds: 286 **Admissions:** 15689 **Census:** 220 **Outpatient Visits:** 288195 **Births:** 0 **Total Expense ($000):** 353602 **Payroll Expense ($000):** 92215 **Personnel:** 1729

☐ **UPMC PRESBYTERIAN (390164)**, 200 Lothrop Street, Zip 15213–2536; tel. 412/647–2345, (Includes EYE AND EAR HOSPITAL OF PITTSBURGH, 200 Lothrop Street, Pittsburgh, PA, Zip 15213–2592; tel. 412/647–2345; UPMC MONTEFIORE, 3459 Fifth Avenue, Pittsburgh, PA, Zip 15213; tel. 412/647–2345; John Innocenti Sr, President and Chief Executive Officer; UPMC PRESBYTERIAN HOSPITAL, 200 Lothrop Street, Pittsburgh, PA, Zip 15213; tel. 412/647–2345; UPMC SHADYSIDE, 5230 Centre Avenue, Pittsburgh, PA, Zip 15232–1381; tel. 412/623–2121; WESTERN PSYCHIATRIC INSTITUTE AND CLINIC, 3811 O'Hara Street, Pittsburgh, PA, Zip 15213–2593; tel. 412/624–2100) **A**1 2 3 5 8 10 12 13 **F**3 5 6 8 9 11 12 14 17 18 20 22 24 26 28 29 30 31 35 36 37 38 39 40 43 44 45 46 47 48 49 50 51 54 55 56 58 59 60 61 64 65 66 68 70 71 74 75 77 78 79 81 82 84 85 86 87 90 91 92 93 94 95 96 97 98 99 100 101 102 103 104 105 106 107 108 111 113 114 115 116 117 118 119 120 121 123 124 126 129 130 134 137 138 139 140 141 142 145 146 148 149 152 153 154 **P**6 **S** UPMC, Pittsburgh, PA
Primary Contact: John Innocenti Sr, President and Chief Executive Officer
CFO: Eileen Simmons, Chief Financial Officer
CMO: Margaret Reidy, M.D., Vice President Medical Affairs
CHR: Kathryn Devine, Vice President Human Resources
Web address: www.upmc.edu
Control: Other not–for–profit (including NFP Corporation) **Service**: General medical and surgical

Staffed Beds: 1378 **Admissions:** 60423 **Census:** 1180 **Outpatient Visits:** 1008100 **Births:** 0 **Total Expense ($000):** 2033450 **Payroll Expense ($000):** 499688 **Personnel:** 9828

☐ **UPMC ST. MARGARET (390102)**, 815 Freeport Road, Zip 15215–3301; tel. 412/784–4000, **A**1 2 3 5 10 13 **F**3 6 7 8 9 11 15 18 20 29 30 31 34 35 40 44 45 49 50 51 54 56 57 58 59 60 61 63 64 65 68 70 74 75 77 78 79 81 82 84 85 86 87 90 96 97 102 104 107 108 111 114 115 119 120 121 123 129 130 131 132 134 135 144 146 148 **S** UPMC, Pittsburgh, PA
Primary Contact: David J. Patton, President
COO: Merle Taylor, Vice President Operations
CFO: Thomas M Newman, Vice President Finance
CMO: John Lagnese, M.D., Vice President Medical Affairs
CIO: Charles M. Rudek, Chief Information Officer
CHR: Tracey Stange Kolo, Vice President Human Resources
CNO: Mary C Barkhymer, R.N., MSN, Vice President Patient Care Services and Chief Nursing Officer
Web address: www.upmc.com/locations/hospitals/st-margaret/Pages/default.aspx
Control: Other not–for–profit (including NFP Corporation) **Service**: General medical and surgical

Staffed Beds: 208 **Admissions:** 11645 **Census:** 163 **Outpatient Visits:** 160269 **Births:** 0 **Total Expense ($000):** 233240 **Payroll Expense ($000):** 63694 **Personnel:** 1374

✠ △ **VETERANS AFFAIRS PITTSBURGH HEALTHCARE SYSTEM**, University Drive, Zip 15240–1001; tel. 866/482–7488, (Includes VETERANS AFFAIRS MEDICAL CENTER, 7180 Highland Drive, Pittsburgh, PA, Zip 15206–1297; tel. 412/365–4900; VETERANS AFFAIRS MEDICAL CENTER, University Drive 'C', Pittsburgh, PA, Zip 15240–1001; tel. 412/688–6000) (Nonreporting) **A**1 3 5 7 8 **S** Department of Veterans Affairs, Perry Point, MD
Primary Contact: Karin L. McGraw, MSN, FACHE, Director
CMO: Ali Sonel, M.D., Chief of Staff
CIO: John Kovac, Facility Chief Information Officer
CHR: Amber Mesoras, Chief Human Resources Officer
CNO: Ira Richmond, Associate Director Patient Care Services
Web address: www.pittsburgh.va.gov/
Control: Veterans Affairs, Government, federal **Service**: Psychiatric

Staffed Beds: 549

✠ **WEST PENN HOSPITAL (390090)**, 4800 Friendship Avenue, Zip 15224–1722; tel. 412/578–5000, **A**1 2 3 5 8 10 **F**3 11 12 13 15 16 17 18 20 22 24 26 29 30 31 34 35 37 38 39 40 44 45 46 47 48 49 50 51 54 57 58 59 64 65 66 70 72 74 75 76 77 78 79 80 81 82 84 85 86 87 89 90 97 101 102 107 108 110 111 115 118 119 120 124 126 129 130 132 135 136 141 142 145 146 147 148 149 154 **P**6 **S** Allegheny Health Network, Pittsburgh, PA
Primary Contact: Ronald J. Andro, R.N., MS, President and Chief Executive Officer
CFO: James A Kanuch, Vice President Finance
CMO: I William Goldfarb, Chief Medical Officer
CIO: Jacqueline Dailey, Chief Information Officer
CHR: Sally Carozza, Director Human Resources
CNO: Paula A Lacher, MSN, R.N., Chief Nursing Officer
Web address: www.wpahs.org
Control: Other not–for–profit (including NFP Corporation) **Service**: General medical and surgical

Staffed Beds: 309 **Admissions:** 13132 **Census:** 191 **Outpatient Visits:** 106611 **Births:** 4252 **Total Expense ($000):** 395610 **Payroll Expense ($000):** 95365 **Personnel:** 1716

WESTERN PSYCHIATRIC INSTITUTE AND CLINIC See UPMC Presbyterian, Pittsburgh

PLEASANT GAP—Centre County

✠ **HEALTHSOUTH NITTANY VALLEY REHABILITATION HOSPITAL (393039)**, 550 West College Avenue, Zip 16823–7401; tel. 814/359–3421, (Nonreporting) **A**1 10 **S** Encompass Health Corporation, Birmingham, AL
Primary Contact: Susan Hartman, Chief Executive Officer
CFO: Alan M Phillips, Controller
CMO: Richard Allatt, M.D., Medical Director
CHR: Michelle Katz, Director Human Resources
CNO: Penny Frownfelter, Chief Nursing Officer
Web address: www.nittanyvalleyrehab.com
Control: Corporation, Investor–owned (for–profit) **Service**: Rehabilitation

Staffed Beds: 73

Many Facility Codes have changed. Please refer to the AHA Guide Code Chart. © 2018 AHA Guide

POTTSTOWN—Montgomery County

POTTSTOWN HOSPITAL (390123), 1600 East High Street, Zip 19464–5093; tel. 610/327–7000, **A**1 2 10 **F**3 7 12 13 15 18 29 30 31 34 35 38 40 44 45 48 49 50 54 57 59 64 68 70 74 75 76 77 78 79 80 81 82 85 86 87 89 92 93 97 98 100 103 107 108 110 111 114 117 118 119 120 121 123 130 131 132 135 146 147 148 154 **S** Tower Health, West Reading, PA
Primary Contact: Richard Newell, Chief Executive Officer
CFO: Debbie Konarski, Interim Chief Financial Officer
CMO: Richard F Saylor, M.D., Chief Medical Officer
CIO: Ron Peterson, Chief Information Officer
CHR: Ruta Ore, Director Human Resources
COO: Bryce Sillyman, Chief Operating Officer
Web address: www.pottstownmemorial.com
Control: Other not–for–profit (including NFP Corporation) **Service**: General medical and surgical

Staffed Beds: 232 Admissions: 8704 Census: 109 Outpatient Visits: 110652 **Births: 428 Total Expense ($000): 151064 Payroll Expense ($000): 52826 Personnel: 921**

POTTSVILLE—Schuylkill County

△ **LEHIGH VALLEY HOSPITAL – SCHUYLKILL EAST NORWEGIAN STREET (390031)**, 700 East Norwegian Street, Zip 17901–2710; tel. 570/621–4000, **A**1 7 10 **F**3 5 11 15 18 29 30 31 34 40 45 49 56 57 59 64 70 74 75 77 78 79 81 85 86 90 93 98 100 103 107 108 109 110 115 117 118 119 126 130 132 135 146 147 148 149 **P**6 **S** Lehigh Valley Health Network, Allentown, PA
Primary Contact: William Reppy, President
CFO: Diane Boris, Vice President and Chief Financial Officer
CNO: Darnell F Furer, MS, R.N., Vice President of Patient Care Services
Web address: www.schuylkillhealth.com
Control: Other not–for–profit (including NFP Corporation) **Service**: General medical and surgical

Staffed Beds: 129 Admissions: 4973 Census: 71 Outpatient Visits: 112860 **Births: 0 Total Expense ($000): 63422 Payroll Expense ($000): 26384 Personnel: 583**

LEHIGH VALLEY HOSPITAL – SCHUYLKILL (390030), 420 South Jackson Street, Zip 17901–3625; tel. 570/621–5000, **A**1 10 19 **F**3 11 13 15 18 19 28 29 30 32 34 35 38 40 45 49 51 56 57 59 62 64 74 75 76 77 78 79 81 82 85 86 89 92 93 96 98 99 100 101 102 107 108 110 111 115 118 119 124 130 132 146 147 149 **P**6 **S** Lehigh Valley Health Network, Allentown, PA
Primary Contact: William Reppy, President
CFO: Diane Boris, Chief Financial Officer
CIO: Tina Zanis, Director Information Systems
CHR: Martin Treasure, Director Human Resources
CNO: Darnell F Furer, MS, R.N., Vice President Patient Care Services and Chief Nursing Officer
Web address: www.schuylkillhealth.com
Control: Other not–for–profit (including NFP Corporation) **Service**: General medical and surgical

Staffed Beds: 67 Admissions: 3052 Census: 56 Outpatient Visits: 70997 Births: 688 Total Expense ($000): 67858 Payroll Expense ($000): 32918 Personnel: 475

PUNXSUTAWNEY—Jefferson County

PUNXSUTAWNEY AREA HOSPITAL (390199), 81 Hillcrest Drive, Zip 15767–2616; tel. 814/938–1800, **A**10 20 **F**3 13 15 26 29 30 34 35 40 44 45 46 48 50 51 57 59 62 64 70 74 75 76 77 78 79 81 85 86 87 92 93 96 100 104 107 108 110 111 115 118 119 127 130 132 133 146 147 148 149 154 **P**6
Primary Contact: Daniel D. Blough Jr, Chief Executive Officer
CFO: Jack Sisk, Chief Financial Officer
CMO: Dajani Zuhd, M.D., President Medical Staff
CIO: Chuck States, Director Information Systems
CHR: Barbara Kostok, Manager Human Resources
CNO: Paula Spack, R.N., MSN, Vice President Nursing
Web address: www.pah.org
Control: Other not–for–profit (including NFP Corporation) **Service**: General medical and surgical

Staffed Beds: 49 Admissions: 1562 Census: 18 Outpatient Visits: 98679 Births: 118 Total Expense ($000): 36396 Payroll Expense ($000): 17981 Personnel: 348

QUAKERTOWN—Bucks County

☐ **ST. LUKE'S HOSPITAL – QUAKERTOWN CAMPUS (390035)**, 1021 Park Avenue, Zip 18951–1573; tel. 215/538–4500, **A**1 2 3 10 **F**3 15 18 28 29 30 31 34 35 38 40 43 44 45 49 50 51 54 56 57 59 60 63 64 65 68 70 71 74 75 77 78 79 81 82 85 86 87 92 93 98 100 102 107 108 109 110 111 115 118 119 129 130 131 132 135 144 146 148 149 154 **S** St. Luke's University Health Network, Bethlehem, PA
Primary Contact: Dennis Pfleiger, President and Chief Operating Officer
CFO: Theresa Corrado, Director Finance
CMO: Thomas Filipowicz, M.D., Medical Director
CIO: Chad Brisendine, Chief Information Officer
CHR: Shelley Maley, Director Human Resources
Web address: www.slhhn.org
Control: Other not–for–profit (including NFP Corporation) **Service**: General medical and surgical

Staffed Beds: 57 Admissions: 3102 Census: 40 Outpatient Visits: 84753 Births: 0 Total Expense ($000): 66394 Payroll Expense ($000): 25950 Personnel: 290

READING—Berks County

☐ **HAVEN BEHAVIORAL HOSPITAL OF EASTERN PENNSYLVANIA (394052)**, 145 North 6th Street, 3rd Floor, Zip 19601–3096; tel. 610/406–4340, (Nonreporting) **A**1 **S** Haven Behavioral Healthcare, Nashville, TN
Primary Contact: Bryan W. Lett, Chief Executive Officer
CMO: Mark Putnam, M.D., Medical Director
CHR: Kathy Copenhaver, Director Human Resources
Web address: www.https://havenbehavioral.com/
Control: Corporation, Investor–owned (for–profit) **Service**: Psychiatric

Staffed Beds: 48

HEALTHSOUTH READING REHABILITATION HOSPITAL (393026), 1623 Morgantown Road, Zip 19607–9455; tel. 610/796–6000, (Nonreporting) **A**1 10 **S** Encompass Health Corporation, Birmingham, AL
Primary Contact: Amy Teal, Chief Executive Officer
CFO: Jason Pulaski, Controller
CMO: Suzanne Adam, D.O., Medical Director
CHR: Kelly Kozik, Director Human Resources
Web address: www.healthsouthreading.com
Control: Corporation, Investor–owned (for–profit) **Service**: Rehabilitation

Staffed Beds: 60

PENN STATE HEALTH ST. JOSEPH (390096), 2500 Bernville Road, Zip 19605–9453, Mailing Address: P.O. Box 316, Zip 19603–0316; tel. 610/378–2000, (Includes PENN STATE HEALTH ST. JOSEPH – DOWNTOWN CAMPUS, 145 North Sixth Street, Reading, PA, Zip 19601, Mailing Address: P.O. Box 316, Zip 19603–0316, tel. 610/378–2000; John R Morahan, President and Chief Executive Officer) **A**1 2 10 12 13 **F**3 13 15 18 20 22 24 26 28 29 30 31 32 34 35 39 40 44 45 46 48 54 57 58 59 64 66 68 70 72 74 75 76 77 78 79 81 82 84 85 87 89 93 97 107 108 111 113 114 115 116 117 118 119 120 121 130 131 132 135 144 146 147 148 149 **P**1 6 **S** Penn State Hershey Health System, Hershey, PA
Primary Contact: John R. Morahan, President and Chief Executive Officer
CFO: Courtney Coffman, Vice President, Finance and Chief Financial Officer
CMO: Christopher Newman, M.D., Vice President Medical Affairs and Chief Medical Officer
CIO: Amanda Klopp, Director, Innovation and Clinical Integration
CHR: Scott Mengle, Vice President Human Resources
CNO: Sharon Strohecker, R.N., MSN, Vice President Clinical Operations and Chief Nursing Officer
Web address: www.thefutureofhealthcare.org
Control: Other not–for–profit (including NFP Corporation) **Service**: General medical and surgical

Staffed Beds: 144 Admissions: 7335 Census: 88 Outpatient Visits: 251612 **Births: 670 Total Expense ($000): 209051 Payroll Expense ($000): 67772 Personnel: 1394**

PA

Hospital, Medicare Provider Number, Address, Telephone, Approval, Facility, and Physician Codes, Health Care System

★ American Hospital Association (AHA) membership
☐ The Joint Commission accreditation
○ Healthcare Facilities Accreditation Program
◇ DNV Healthcare Inc. accreditation
⇑ Center for Improvement in Healthcare Quality Accreditation
△ Commission on Accreditation of Rehabilitation Facilities (CARF) accreditation

© 2018 AHA Guide   *Many Facility Codes have changed. Please refer to the AHA Guide Code Chart.*   Hospitals **A539**

PA

RENOVO—Clinton County

BUCKTAIL MEDICAL CENTER (391304), 1001 Pine Street, Zip 17764–1620; tel. 570/923–1000, (Nonreporting) **A**10 18
Primary Contact: Timothy Reeves, Administrator
CFO: Wendy Janerella, Controller
CMO: Alvin Berlot, M.D., Medical Director
Web address: www.bucktailmed.org
Control: Other not–for–profit (including NFP Corporation) **Service**: General medical and surgical

Staffed Beds: 64

RIDLEY PARK—Delaware County

TAYLOR HOSPITAL See Crozer–Chester Medical Center, Upland

ROARING SPRING—Blair County

⊞ **CONEMAUGH NASON MEDICAL CENTER (390062)**, 105 Nason Drive, Zip 16673–1202; tel. 814/224–2141, **A**1 10 **F**3 11 13 15 18 19 26 29 30 34 35 40 45 50 56 57 59 64 65 70 74 75 76 77 79 81 85 87 91 107 108 110 111 114 119 124 130 141 146 147 148 149 154 **S** LifePoint Health, Brentwood, TN
Primary Contact: Timothy Harclerode, Chief Executive Officer
CFO: Kimberly Semelsberger, CPA, Chief Financial Officer
CHR: Lorie Smith, Director Human Resources
Web address: www.nasonhospital.com
Control: Corporation, Investor–owned (for–profit) **Service**: General medical and surgical

Staffed Beds: 45 Admissions: 1792 Census: 14 Outpatient Visits: 73676 Births: 328 Total Expense ($000): 33457 Payroll Expense ($000): 13249 Personnel: 240

ROYERSFORD—Montgomery County

⇑ **PHYSICIANS CARE SURGICAL HOSPITAL (390324)**, 454 Enterprise Drive, Zip 19468–1200; tel. 610/495–3330, (Nonreporting) **A**10 21
Primary Contact: Christopher Doyle, Chief Executive Officer
Web address: www.phycarehospital.com
Control: Partnership, Investor–owned (for–profit) **Service**: Surgical

Staffed Beds: 12

SAINT MARYS—Elk County

PENN HIGHLANDS ELK (391315), 763 Johnsonburg Road, Zip 15857–3498; tel. 814/788–8000, (Total facility includes 138 beds in nursing home–type unit) **A**10 18 **F**2 3 6 8 11 13 15 28 29 30 34 35 40 45 56 57 59 62 63 64 65 75 76 77 79 80 81 82 84 85 86 87 93 98 100 103 107 108 110 111 115 118 119 124 128 129 130 131 132 133 135 146 147 148 154
Primary Contact: Bradley Chapman, President
CFO: Laurie MacDonald, Vice President Finance
CMO: David Johe, M.D., President Medical Staff
CIO: Mary Ann Schwabenbauer, Director Information Technology
CHR: Seanna D'Amore, Director Human Resources
Web address: www.phhealthcare.org
Control: Other not–for–profit (including NFP Corporation) **Service**: General medical and surgical

Staffed Beds: 173 Admissions: 2089 Census: 145 Outpatient Visits: 139797 Births: 213 Total Expense ($000): 56949 Payroll Expense ($000): 22096 Personnel: 497

SAYRE—Bradford County

⊞ **GUTHRIE ROBERT PACKER HOSPITAL (390079)**, 1 Guthrie Square, Zip 18840–1698; tel. 570/888–6666, **A**1 2 3 5 10 12 13 19 **F**3 11 12 13 15 18 20 22 24 26 28 29 30 31 34 37 38 40 43 45 46 47 48 49 50 57 58 59 61 64 70 73 74 75 76 78 79 81 82 84 85 86 87 89 91 92 93 96 98 100 102 105 107 108 110 111 114 115 116 117 119 120 121 123 126 129 130 132 141 142 145 146 148 149 150 154 **S** Guthrie Clinic, Sayre, PA
Primary Contact: Joseph T. Sawyer Jr, President
CFO: Scott Silvestri, Chief Financial Officer, Hospital Financial Operations
CMO: Brian Fillipo, M.D., Chief Medical Officer
CIO: Burt Robles, Vice President Information Services
CHR: Frank Pinkosky, Senior Vice President
CNO: Catherine Mohr, R.N., MSN, Chief Nursing Officer
Web address: www.guthrie.org/location/robert–packer–hospital
Control: Other not–for–profit (including NFP Corporation) **Service**: General medical and surgical

Staffed Beds: 254 Admissions: 13462 Census: 166 Outpatient Visits: 127652 Births: 850 Total Expense ($000): 290977 Payroll Expense ($000): 84680 Personnel: 1293

SCRANTON—Lackawanna County

☐ △ **ALLIED SERVICES REHABILITATION HOSPITAL (393030)**, 475 Morgan Highway, Zip 18508–2605, Mailing Address: P.O. Box 1103, Zip 18501–1103; tel. 570/348–1300, (Nonreporting) **A**1 7 10
Primary Contact: Karen Kearney, Vice President Inpatient Rehabilitation Services
CFO: Michael Avvisato, Senior Vice President and Chief Financial Officer
CMO: Gregory Basting, M.D., Vice President Medical Affairs
CIO: John Regula, Chief Information Officer
CHR: Judy P Oprisko, Vice President
CNO: Jeana Sluck, R.N., Executive Director Nursing Clinical Inpatient Departments
Web address: www.allied-services.org
Control: Other not–for–profit (including NFP Corporation) **Service**: Rehabilitation

Staffed Beds: 117

COMMUNITY MEDICAL CENTER HEALTHCARE SYSTEM See Geisinger–Community Medical Center

⊞ **GEISINGER–COMMUNITY MEDICAL CENTER (390001)**, 1800 Mulberry Street, Zip 18510–2369; tel. 570/703–8000, **A**1 2 3 5 10 **F**3 11 15 18 20 22 24 26 28 29 30 31 34 35 39 40 43 44 45 46 47 49 54 56 57 58 59 61 64 65 68 70 74 75 77 78 79 80 81 82 84 85 86 87 89 91 92 93 94 98 100 102 107 108 110 111 114 115 117 118 119 126 129 130 131 132 135 145 146 147 148 149 154 **P**6 **S** Geisinger, Danville, PA
Primary Contact: Ronald R Beer, FACHE, Chief Administrative Officer
CMO: Anthony Aquilina, D.O., Chief Medical Officer
CHR: Lois Wolfe, Director Human Resources
Web address: www.geisinger.org/for-patients/locations–directions/gcmc/
Control: Other not–for–profit (including NFP Corporation) **Service**: General medical and surgical

Staffed Beds: 182 Admissions: 12605 Census: 160 Outpatient Visits: 345405 Births: 0 Total Expense ($000): 265595 Payroll Expense ($000): 97521 Personnel: 1581

MERCY HOSPITAL OF SCRANTON See Regional Hospital of Scranton

⊞ △ **MOSES TAYLOR HOSPITAL (390119)**, 700 Quincy Avenue, Zip 18510–1724; tel. 570/770–5000, **A**1 3 5 7 10 **F**3 7 13 15 18 29 30 31 34 40 44 45 49 50 51 54 56 57 59 60 61 64 65 66 68 70 72 74 75 77 78 79 81 85 86 87 92 93 98 103 107 108 110 114 115 116 117 119 124 129 130 132 135 146 147 154 **P**6 **S** Community Health Systems, Inc., Franklin, TN
CFO: Thomas Bisignani, Chief Financial Officer
CMO: Mary Sewatsky, M.D., Chief Medical Officer
CHR: Elizabeth Leo, Chief Human Resources Officer
CNO: Patricia Seliga, R.N., Chief Nursing Officer
Web address: www.mth.org
Control: Corporation, Investor–owned (for–profit) **Service**: General medical and surgical

Staffed Beds: 213 Admissions: 8689 Census: 116 Outpatient Visits: 191107 Births: 2363 Total Expense ($000): 145547 Payroll Expense ($000): 44723 Personnel: 790

⊞ △ **REGIONAL HOSPITAL OF SCRANTON (390237)**, 746 Jefferson Avenue, Zip 18510–1624; tel. 570/348–7100, **A**1 2 3 5 7 10 12 **F**7 8 11 12 15 17 18 20 22 24 26 28 29 30 31 34 35 39 40 44 45 46 47 48 49 50 51 53 54 57 58 59 60 61 64 65 66 68 70 74 75 77 78 79 81 85 86 87 91 92 93 97 107 108 109 110 111 112 113 114 115 116 117 118 119 120 121 122 123 124 126 130 132 143 144 145 146 147 148 149 **P**6 **S** Community Health Systems, Inc., Franklin, TN
Primary Contact: Ronald Ziobro, Interim Chief Executive Officer
CFO: Stephen Franko, Vice President Finance and Chief Financial Officer
CMO: Anthony Yanni, M.D., Vice President Medical Affairs
CIO: Jorge Coronel, Chief Information Officer
Web address: www.regionalhospitalofscranton.net
Control: Corporation, Investor–owned (for–profit) **Service**: General medical and surgical

Staffed Beds: 186 Admissions: 8240 Census: 110 Outpatient Visits: 98949 Births: 0 Total Expense ($000): 163081 Payroll Expense ($000): 50285 Personnel: 787

Many Facility Codes have changed. Please refer to the AHA Guide Code Chart.   © 2018 AHA Guide

SELLERSVILLE—Bucks County

☒ **GRAND VIEW HEALTH (390057)**, 700 Lawn Avenue, Zip 18960–1548, Mailing Address: P.O. Box 902, Zip 18960–0902; tel. 215/453–4000, **A**1 2 10 **F**3 7 11 12 13 15 18 28 29 31 34 35 40 44 45 46 47 48 49 50 51 54 56 57 59 61 62 63 64 65 66 68 70 71 72 74 75 76 77 78 79 81 84 85 86 87 89 90 93 96 97 107 108 110 111 114 115 117 118 119 120 121 123 130 131 132 135 143 144 146 147 148 149 **P**6
Primary Contact: Jean M. Keeler, President and Chief Executive Officer
COO: J Mark Horne, Senior Vice President, Ambulatory Services and Chief Operating Officer
CFO: Michael Keen, Senior Vice President and Chief Financial Officer
CMO: Jane Ferry, M.D., Vice President Medical Affairs
CIO: Jane Doll Loveless, Vice President, Chief Information Officer
CNO: Kathleen Burkey, R.N., MSN, Vice President, Patient Care Service and Chief Nursing Officer
Web address: www.gvh.org
Control: Other not–for–profit (including NFP Corporation) **Service**: General medical and surgical

Staffed Beds: 194 **Admissions**: 8131 **Census**: 96 **Outpatient Visits**: 330578 **Births**: 1173 **Total Expense ($000)**: 197845 **Payroll Expense ($000)**: 102929 **Personnel**: 1394

SENECA—Venango County

☐ **UPMC NORTHWEST (390091)**, 100 Fairfield Drive, Zip 16346–2130; tel. 814/676–7600, (Total facility includes 16 beds in nursing home–type unit) **A**1 2 3 10 19 **F**3 11 13 15 18 20 28 29 31 34 35 40 44 45 46 47 50 51 56 57 59 63 64 65 68 70 74 75 76 77 78 79 81 82 84 85 86 87 90 93 96 98 100 101 102 103 107 108 110 111 115 119 121 123 128 130 131 132 135 141 142 146 147 148 149 154 **S** UPMC, Pittsburgh, PA
Primary Contact: Brian Durniok, President
COO: Brian Durniok, Vice President Operations
CFO: Bradley Dinger, Financial Representative
CMO: David McCandless, Vice President Medical Affairs
CHR: Brian Durniok, President
CNO: Joanne L. Sorensen, R.N., FACHE, MS, Vice President Patient Care Services
Web address: www.upmc.com/locations/hospitals/northwest/Pages/default.aspx
Control: Other not–for–profit (including NFP Corporation) **Service**: General medical and surgical

Staffed Beds: 128 **Admissions**: 6095 **Census**: 86 **Outpatient Visits**: 136995 **Births**: 580 **Total Expense ($000)**: 101329 **Payroll Expense ($000)**: 28397 **Personnel**: 754

SEWICKLEY—Allegheny County

☒ **HEALTHSOUTH REHABILITATION HOSPITAL OF SEWICKLEY (393045)**, 303 Camp Meeting Road, Zip 15143–8322; tel. 412/741–9500, (Nonreporting) **A**1 10 **S** Encompass Health Corporation, Birmingham, AL
Primary Contact: Leah Laffey, R.N., Chief Executive Officer
CFO: Daniel A Vrana, Area Controller
CMO: Shelana Gibbs–McElvy, M.D., Medical Director
CIO: Jamie Smith, Supervisor Health Information Management Systems
CHR: Melissa Coleman, Director Human Resources
CNO: Christie Ryan, Chief Nursing Officer
Web address: www.healthsouthsewickley.com
Control: Corporation, Investor–owned (for–profit) **Service**: Rehabilitation

Staffed Beds: 44

☐ **SEWICKLEY VALLEY HOSPITAL, (A DIVISION OF VALLEY MEDICAL FACILITIES) (390037)**, 720 Blackburn Road, Zip 15143–1459; tel. 412/741–6600, (Nonreporting) **A**1 10 **S** Heritage Valley Health System, Beaver, PA
Primary Contact: Norman F. Mitry, President and Chief Executive Officer
COO: John Luellen, M.D., Chief Operating Officer
CFO: Bryan J Randall, Vice President Finance and Chief Financial Officer
CMO: Michael Cratty, M.D., Chief Medical Officer
CIO: David Carleton, Chief Information Officer
CHR: Bruce Edwards, Vice President Human Resources
CNO: Linda Homyk, Chief Nursing Officer
Web address: www.heritagevalley.org
Control: Other not–for–profit (including NFP Corporation) **Service**: General medical and surgical

Staffed Beds: 179

SHARON—Mercer County

☒ **SHARON REGIONAL MEDICAL CENTER (390211)**, 740 East State Street, Zip 16146–3395; tel. 724/983–3911, (Nonreporting) **A**1 3 10 19 **S** Steward Health Care System, LLC, Dallas, TX
Primary Contact: Joseph G. Hugar, President
Web address: www.sharonregionalmedical.org
Control: Corporation, Investor–owned (for–profit) **Service**: General medical and surgical

Staffed Beds: 218

SHICKSHINNY—Luzerne County

HUNTINGTON CREEK RECOVERY CENTER, 890 Bethel Road, Zip 18655; tel. 570/864–3116, (Nonreporting)
Primary Contact: Robert Norris, Chief Executive Officer
Web address: www.clearbrookinc.com
Control: Other not–for–profit (including NFP Corporation) **Service**: Alcoholism and other chemical dependency

Staffed Beds: 65

SHIPPENSBURG—Franklin County

☐ **ROXBURY TREATMENT CENTER (394050)**, 601 Roxbury Road, Zip 17257–9302; tel. 800/648–4673, (Nonreporting) **A**1 10 **S** Universal Health Services, Inc., King of Prussia, PA
Primary Contact: Shauna Mogerner, Chief Executive Officer
Web address: www.roxburyhospital.com
Control: Corporation, Investor–owned (for–profit) **Service**: Psychiatric

Staffed Beds: 94

SOMERSET—Somerset County

★ **SOMERSET HOSPITAL (390039)**, 225 South Center Avenue, Zip 15501–2088; tel. 814/443–5000, **A**10 20 **F**3 8 11 15 17 18 20 22 26 28 29 30 32 34 35 40 45 47 49 50 53 57 59 62 63 64 68 77 79 80 81 82 84 85 86 87 89 93 97 98 100 103 104 107 108 110 111 115 119 129 130 131 132 133 135 141 146 148 149 154
Primary Contact: Andrew G. Rush, Chief Executive Officer
CFO: Matthew Kociola, Senior Vice President and Chief Financial Officer
CIO: Jonathan Bauer, Director Information Systems
CHR: Mark P Frick, Senior Vice President Human Resources
CNO: Suellen Lichtenfels, Vice President and Chief Nursing Officer
Web address: www.somersethospital.com
Control: Other not–for–profit (including NFP Corporation) **Service**: General medical and surgical

Staffed Beds: 102 **Admissions**: 2887 **Census**: 35 **Outpatient Visits**: 136786 **Births**: 75 **Total Expense ($000)**: 62902 **Payroll Expense ($000)**: 25126 **Personnel**: 563

SPRINGFIELD—Delaware County

SPRINGFIELD HOSPITAL See Crozer–Chester Medical Center, Upland

STATE COLLEGE—Centre County

☒ **MOUNT NITTANY MEDICAL CENTER (390268)**, 1800 East Park Avenue, Zip 16803–6797; tel. 814/231–7000, **A**1 2 3 5 10 **F**3 7 8 13 15 17 20 22 26 28 29 30 31 35 40 46 49 51 57 59 64 68 70 73 74 75 76 77 78 79 80 81 82 84 85 87 89 93 98 100 101 102 107 108 111 114 115 118 119 121 126 129 130 132 135 143 146 148 149 154
Primary Contact: Kathleen Rhine, President and Chief Executive Officer
CFO: Randy E Tewksbury, Senior Vice President Finance and Chief Financial Officer
CIO: Wayne Thompson, Executive Vice President and Chief Information Officer
CHR: Gerald P Dittmann, Vice President Human Resources
Web address: www.mountnittany.org
Control: Other not–for–profit (including NFP Corporation) **Service**: General medical and surgical

Staffed Beds: 260 **Admissions**: 14151 **Census**: 141 **Outpatient Visits**: 311376 **Births**: 1368 **Total Expense ($000)**: 391000 **Payroll Expense ($000)**: 173673 **Personnel**: 1602

PA

STROUDSBURG—Centre County

ST. LUKE'S MONROE (390330), 100 St. Luke's Lane, Zip 18360;
tel. 484/526–2116, (Data for 271 days) **A**10 **F**3 7 11 12 15 18 20 22 26 29 30
31 34 35 38 40 44 45 46 47 49 50 51 57 59 60 63 64 68 70 74 75 78 79 81
85 86 87 96 100 102 107 108 109 110 111 115 118 119 130 132 145 146
149 154
Primary Contact: Donald Seiple, President
Web address: www.slhn.org/Choose/choose–monroe
Control: Other not–for–profit (including NFP Corporation) **Service:** General
medical and surgical

Staffed Beds: 72 **Admissions:** 3191 **Census:** 48 **Outpatient Visits:** 35707 **Births:** 0 **Total Expense ($000):** 47854 **Payroll Expense ($000):** 19469 **Personnel:** 285	

SUNBURY—Northumberland County

✠ **UPMC SUSQUEHANNA SUNBURY (390084)**, 350 North Eleventh Street,
Zip 17801–1611; tel. 570/286–3333, **A**1 10 **F**11 18 28 29 30 34 35 40 50 51
57 59 68 69 75 77 79 81 85 93 98 102 107 108 110 111 114 119 130 146 **S**
UPMC Susquehanna, Williamsport, PA
Primary Contact: Robert D. Williams, Chief Executive Officer
CFO: James J. Pachucki Jr Chief Financial Officer
CMO: Charles C Pagana, M.D., Chief Medical Officer
CIO: Fax Rector III Director Information Technology
CHR: Talia Beatty, Director Human Resources
CNO: Catharine L Keister, Chief Nursing Officer
Web address: www.sunburyhospital.com
Control: Other not–for–profit (including NFP Corporation) **Service:** General
medical and surgical

Staffed Beds: 70 **Admissions:** 1005 **Census:** 15 **Outpatient Visits:** 11632 **Births:** 0 **Total Expense ($000):** 19364 **Payroll Expense ($000):** 8152 **Personnel:** 130	

SUSQUEHANNA—Susquehanna County

BARNES–KASSON COUNTY HOSPITAL (391309), 2872 Turnpike Street,
Zip 18847–2771; tel. 570/853–3135, (Nonreporting) **A**10 18
Primary Contact: Sara F. Adornato, Executive Director
CFO: Kelli R Kane, Director of Finance
CMO: Pravinchandra Patel, M.D., Chief Medical Officer
CIO: Eric Detwiler, Director Information Technology
Web address: www.barnes–kasson.org
Control: Other not–for–profit (including NFP Corporation) **Service:** General
medical and surgical

Staffed Beds: 83	

TITUSVILLE—Crawford County

★ **TITUSVILLE AREA HOSPITAL (391314)**, 406 West Oak Street,
Zip 16354–1404; tel. 814/827–1851, (Nonreporting) **A**10 18 **S** Meadville Medical
Center, Meadville, PA
Primary Contact: Lee Clinton, FACHE, Chief Executive Officer
CFO: Jill Neely, Chief Financial Officer
CMO: William Sonnenberg, M.D., President Medical Staff
CIO: Karen Humes, Chief Information Officer
CHR: Jeffrey Saintz, Vice President Human Resources
CNO: Brenda Burnett, R.N., Vice President Patient Care Services and Chief Nursing
Officer
Web address: www.titusvillehospital.org
Control: Other not–for–profit (including NFP Corporation) **Service:** General
medical and surgical

Staffed Beds: 25	

TORRANCE—Westmoreland County

TORRANCE STATE HOSPITAL (394026), Torrance Road, Zip 15779–0111,
Mailing Address: P.O. Box 111, Zip 15779–0111; tel. 724/459–8000, **A**10 **F**39
65 75 77 97 98 100 101 130 135 143 146 147 148
Primary Contact: Edna I. McCutcheon, Chief Executive Officer
COO: R Brad Snyder, Chief Operating Officer
CFO: Michael Yahner, Chief Financial Officer
CMO: Herbert G Chissell, M.D., Chief Medical Officer
Web address: www.dpw.state.pa.us
Control: State, Government, nonfederal **Service:** Psychiatric

Staffed Beds: 353 **Admissions:** 238 **Census:** 327 **Outpatient Visits:** 0 **Births:** 0 **Total Expense ($000):** 75555 **Payroll Expense ($000):** 33881 **Personnel:** 699	

TOWANDA—Bradford County

★ **GUTHRIE TOWANDA MEMORIAL HOSPITAL (390236)**, 91 Hospital Drive,
Zip 18848–9702; tel. 570/265–2191, (Total facility includes 160 beds in nursing
home–type unit) **A**10 **F**3 7 10 11 28 29 34 35 36 40 50 57 59 64 70 75 77 79
81 82 84 85 87 93 107 108 111 115 119 128 129 130 133 135 143 146 **S**
Guthrie Clinic, Sayre, PA
Primary Contact: Staci Covey, R.N., MS, President
CIO: Karen Brown, Manager Information Technology
CHR: Linda Berry, Vice President Human Resources
CNO: Lynn Dibble, Vice President Patient Care Services
Web address: www.memorialhospital.org
Control: Other not–for–profit (including NFP Corporation) **Service:** General
medical and surgical

Staffed Beds: 195 **Admissions:** 939 **Census:** 155 **Outpatient Visits:** 53617 **Births:** 0 **Total Expense ($000):** 32991 **Payroll Expense ($000):** 13833 **Personnel:** 292	

TRANSFER—Mercer County

EDGEWOOD SURGICAL HOSPITAL (390307), 239 Edgewood Drive Extension,
Zip 16154–1817; tel. 724/646–0400, (Nonreporting) **A**10
Primary Contact: Lloyd Scarrow, FACHE, Chief Executive Officer
Web address: www.edgewoodsurgical.com
Control: Corporation, Investor–owned (for–profit) **Service:** Surgical

Staffed Beds: 10	

TROY—Bradford County

★ **TROY COMMUNITY HOSPITAL (391305)**, 275 Guthrie Drive, Zip 16947;
tel. 570/297–2121, **A**10 18 **F**3 11 15 28 29 30 34 40 43 45 50 57 64 75 81
82 85 87 93 96 107 110 111 119 129 130 133 135 146 148 **S** Guthrie Clinic,
Sayre, PA
Primary Contact: Staci Covey, R.N., MS, President
CFO: Bernie Smith, Chief Financial Officer
CMO: Vance A Good, M.D., Chief Medical Staff
CIO: Dale Swingle, Vice President Information Services
CHR: Frank Pinkosky, Executive Vice President
CNO: Lori Barnett, R.N., MSN, Chief Nursing Officer
Web address: www.guthrie.org
Control: Other not–for–profit (including NFP Corporation) **Service:** General
medical and surgical

Staffed Beds: 25 **Admissions:** 902 **Census:** 17 **Outpatient Visits:** 34648 **Births:** 0 **Total Expense ($000):** 20658 **Payroll Expense ($000):** 6063 **Personnel:** 129	

TUNKHANNOCK—Bradford County

✠ **TYLER MEMORIAL HOSPITAL (390192)**, 5950 State Route 6,
Zip 18657–7905; tel. 570/836–2161, (Nonreporting) **A**1 10 **S** Community Health
Systems, Inc., Franklin, TN
Primary Contact: Ann Marie. Stevens, R.N., Chief Executive Officer
CMO: Terrance Chilson, Chief of Staff
CNO: Judith Ragukas, Interim Chief Nursing Officer
Web address: www.tylermemorialhospital.net
Control: Corporation, Investor–owned (for–profit) **Service:** General medical and
surgical

Staffed Beds: 44	

TYRONE—Blair County

TYRONE HOSPITAL (391307), 187 Hospital Drive, Zip 16686–1808;
tel. 814/684–1255, (Nonreporting) **A**10 18
Primary Contact: Joseph J. Peluso, Chief Executive Officer
CMO: Kelly Biggs, M.D., Chief Medical Officer
CHR: Rosemary Jorden Best, Director Human Resources
CNO: Sharon Fisher, R.N., Chief Nursing Officer
Web address: www.tyronehospital.org
Control: Other not–for–profit (including NFP Corporation) **Service:** General
medical and surgical

Staffed Beds: 25	

UNIONTOWN—Fayette County

✠ **UNIONTOWN HOSPITAL (390041)**, 500 West Berkeley Street,
Zip 15401–5596; tel. 724/430–5000, **A**1 10 **F**3 11 13 15 18 20 22 28 29 30
34 35 40 45 49 51 54 57 59 64 70 73 74 75 76 77 78 79 81 89 90 92 96 102
107 108 110 111 114 115 118 119 130 132 146 148 149 154
Primary Contact: Steven P. Handy, CPA, Chief Executive Officer
CHR: James Proud, Vice President Human Resources and Marketing
CNO: Betty Ann Rock, Vice President Nursing and Chief Nursing Officer
Web address: www.uniontownhospital.com
Control: Other not–for–profit (including NFP Corporation) **Service:** General
medical and surgical

Staffed Beds: 142 **Admissions:** 8491 **Census:** 94 **Outpatient Visits:** 219097 **Births:** 877 **Total Expense ($000):** 132310 **Payroll Expense ($000):** 45832 **Personnel:** 1023	

PA

UPLAND—Delaware County

☐ **CROZER–CHESTER MEDICAL CENTER (390180)**, One Medical Center Boulevard, Zip 19013–3995; tel. 610/447–2000, (Includes SPRINGFIELD HOSPITAL, 190 West Sproul Road, Springfield, PA, Zip 19064–2097; tel. 610/328–8700; TAYLOR HOSPITAL, 175 East Chester Pike, Ridley Park, PA, Zip 19078–2212; tel. 610/595–6000) (Nonreporting) **A**1 2 3 5 10 12 13 **S** Prospect Medical Holdings, Los Angeles, CA
Primary Contact: Michael Curran, President
CMO: Sat Arora, M.D., President Medical and Dental Staff
CIO: Robert E Wilson, Vice President and Chief Information Officer
Web address: www.crozer.org
Control: Other not–for–profit (including NFP Corporation) **Service**: General medical and surgical

Staffed Beds: 384

WARREN—Warren County

WARREN GENERAL HOSPITAL (390146), Two Crescent Park West, Zip 16365–0068, Mailing Address: P.O. Box 68, Zip 16365–0068; tel. 814/723–4973, **A**10 **F**3 4 11 13 15 28 29 31 34 35 40 44 45 47 50 57 59 62 63 64 70 75 76 77 78 79 81 84 85 86 87 89 92 93 96 97 98 100 107 108 110 111 114 117 119 120 121 130 131 133 145 146 154 **P**6
Primary Contact: Richard Allen, Chief Executive Officer
COO: Randy California, Chief Operating Officer
CFO: Julie Jacobs, Chief Financial Officer
CMO: John Maljovec, M.D., Medical Director
CIO: Helen Rosequist, Manager Information Systems
CHR: Matthew Franklin, Director Human Resources
CNO: Joe Akif, Chief Clinical Officer and Chief Nursing Officer
Web address: www.wgh.org
Control: Other not–for–profit (including NFP Corporation) **Service**: General medical and surgical

Staffed Beds: 87 Admissions: 2861 Census: 32 Outpatient Visits: 150617 Births: 316 Total Expense ($000): 76377 Payroll Expense ($000): 31947

WARREN STATE HOSPITAL (394016), 33 Main Drive, Zip 16365–5001; tel. 814/723–5500, **A**10 **F**4 39 50 56 75 77 82 98 100 101 103 128 130 132 135 143 146 149 **P**6
Primary Contact: Charlotte M. Uber, Chief Executive Officer
COO: Ronnie Cropper, Chief Operating Officer
CFO: Terry Crambes, Manager Finance
CMO: Andrea J. Richard, M.D., Chief Medical Officer
CIO: Karen Byler, Information Technology Generalist
CNO: Sara Flasher, Chief Nurse Executive
Web address: www.dpw.pa.gov
Control: State, Government, nonfederal **Service**: Psychiatric

Staffed Beds: 152 Admissions: 83 Census: 140 Outpatient Visits: 0 Births: 0 Total Expense ($000): 47160 Payroll Expense ($000): 20870 Personnel: 386

WASHINGTON—Washington County

☐ **ADVANCED SURGICAL HOSPITAL (390323)**, 100 Trich Drive Suite 1, Zip 15301–5990; tel. 724/884–0710, (Nonreporting) **A**1 10
Primary Contact: Anne S. Hast, R.N., Chief Executive Officer
CFO: Diane Hritz, Chief Financial Officer
CNO: Anne S Hast, R.N., Director of Nursing
Web address: www.ashospital.net
Control: Partnership, Investor–owned (for–profit) **Service**: Orthopedic

Staffed Beds: 14

⊞ **WASHINGTON HOSPITAL (390042)**, 155 Wilson Avenue, Zip 15301–3398; tel. 724/225–7000, **A**1 3 5 10 13 **F**3 5 11 12 13 15 18 20 22 24 26 28 29 30 31 32 34 35 36 38 39 40 45 46 49 50 53 54 56 57 59 60 61 64 65 70 74 75 76 77 78 79 81 82 84 85 86 87 89 90 91 92 93 94 96 97 98 100 101 102 103 107 108 110 111 114 115 118 119 126 127 130 131 132 134 135 146 147 148 154 **P**1 7 **S** Washington Health System, Washington, PA
Primary Contact: Gary B. Weinstein, President and Chief Executive Officer
COO: Brook Ward, Executive Vice President
CFO: Alisa Rucker, Vice President Finance and Chief Financial Officer
CMO: Paul T Cullen, M.D., Vice President Medical Affairs
CIO: Rodney Louk, Vice President Information Systems
CHR: Barbara A McCullough, Vice President Human Resources
CNO: Karen A Bray, R.N., MSN, Vice President Patient Care Services
Web address: www.washingtonhospital.org
Control: Other not–for–profit (including NFP Corporation) **Service**: General medical and surgical

Staffed Beds: 206 Admissions: 11599 Census: 143 Outpatient Visits: 737457 Births: 898 Total Expense ($000): 233557 Payroll Expense ($000): 104000 Personnel: 1611

WAYNESBORO—Franklin County

⊞ **WAYNESBORO HOSPITAL (390138)**, 501 East Main Street, Zip 17268–2394; tel. 717/765–4000, **A**1 10 **F**3 11 15 29 30 34 40 44 45 49 50 54 56 57 59 61 64 65 68 74 75 76 77 79 81 85 86 87 93 94 100 107 108 110 111 115 118 119 130 131 132 133 135 146 147 148 149 150 154 **P**8 **S** Summit Health, Chambersburg, PA
Primary Contact: Melissa Dubrow, Chief Operating Officer
COO: Melissa Dubrow, Vice President and Chief Operating Officer
CFO: Kimberly Rzomp, Vice President Finance
CMO: Thomas Anderson, M.D., Vice President Medical Affairs
CIO: Michele Zeigler, Vice President Information Services
CHR: Jennifer Knight, Manager Human Resources
CNO: Jill Keller, R.N., MSN, Vice President for Nursing Services, Quality and Risk Management
Web address: www.summithealth.org
Control: Other not–for–profit (including NFP Corporation) **Service**: General medical and surgical

Staffed Beds: 56 Admissions: 2511 Census: 22 Outpatient Visits: 100968 Births: 420 Total Expense ($000): 59834 Payroll Expense ($000): 28299 Personnel: 425

WAYNESBURG—Greene County

⊞ **WASHINGTON HEALTH SYSTEM GREENE (390150)**, 350 Bonar Avenue, Zip 15370–1608; tel. 724/627–3101, **A**1 3 10 **F**3 11 15 29 30 34 35 40 44 45 51 57 59 64 81 85 87 98 103 104 107 108 110 111 114 119 130 133 135 146 **S** Washington Health System, Washington, PA
Primary Contact: Terry Wiltrout, President
COO: Janel Mudry, Chief Operating Officer
CMO: Jamie Boris, M.D., President Medical Staff
CIO: Leslie Hayhurst, Director Information Systems
CHR: Patricia Marshall, Assistant Administrator Human Resources
Web address: www.southwestregionalmed.com/
Control: Other not–for–profit (including NFP Corporation) **Service**: General medical and surgical

Staffed Beds: 49 Admissions: 1598 Census: 22 Outpatient Visits: 53827 Births: 0 Total Expense ($000): 25165 Payroll Expense ($000): 12372 Personnel: 206

WELLSBORO—Tioga County

⊞ **UPMC SUSQUEHANNA SOLDIERS + SAILORS (390043)**, 32–36 Central Avenue, Zip 16901–1899; tel. 570/724–1631, **A**1 10 **F**3 7 8 11 13 15 28 29 30 31 34 35 40 44 45 48 49 60 64 65 70 75 76 78 79 81 85 93 104 107 108 110 111 115 119 129 130 146 **P**6 **S** UPMC Susquehanna, Williamsport, PA
Primary Contact: Janie Hilfiger, Chief Administrative Officer
CFO: Eric Pohjala, Chief Financial Officer
CMO: Walter Laibinis, M.D., Chief Medical Officer
CIO: Timothy E Schoener, Senior Vice President and Chief Information Officer
CHR: Christine Ballard, Vice President Human Resources
CNO: Matt Romania, Director of Nursing
Web address: www.susquehannahealth.org
Control: Other not–for–profit (including NFP Corporation) **Service**: General medical and surgical

Staffed Beds: 25 Admissions: 1760 Census: 18 Outpatient Visits: 98431 Births: 215 Total Expense ($000): 56491 Payroll Expense ($000): 20439 Personnel: 470

WERNERSVILLE—Berks County

WERNERSVILLE STATE HOSPITAL (394014), 160 Main Street, Zip 19565–9490; tel. 610/678–3411, **A**10 **F**30 39 75 77 98 103 130 135 146
Primary Contact: Shirley Sowizral, Chief Executive Officer
COO: Cheryl Benson, Chief Operating Officer
CMO: Dale K Adair, M.D., Chief Medical Officer
CIO: William Edwards, Information Technology Generalist
CHR: Melvin McMinn, Director Human Resources
Web address: www.dhs.pa.gov/citizens/statehospitals/wernersvillestatehospital/
Control: State, Government, nonfederal **Service**: Psychiatric

Staffed Beds: 266 Admissions: 65 Census: 270 Outpatient Visits: 0 Births: 0 Total Expense ($000): 67359 Payroll Expense ($000): 30638 Personnel: 558

Hospital, Medicare Provider Number, Address, Telephone, Approval, Facility, and Physician Codes, Health Care System
★ American Hospital Association (AHA) membership ☐ The Joint Commission accreditation ◯ Healthcare Facilities Accreditation Program ◇ DNV Healthcare Inc. accreditation ⇑ Center for Improvement in Healthcare Quality Accreditation △ Commission on Accreditation of Rehabilitation Facilities (CARF) accreditation

PA

WEST CHESTER—Chester County

✠ **CHESTER COUNTY HOSPITAL (390179)**, 701 East Marshall Street,
Zip 19380–4412; tel. 610/431–5000, **A**1 2 3 5 10 **F**1 3 4 11 13 15 17 18 20
22 24 26 28 29 30 31 34 35 36 39 40 44 45 46 49 50 51 54 55 57 58 59
60 62 63 64 68 70 72 73 74 75 76 77 78 79 80 81 82 84 85 86 87 89 90 91
92 93 96 98 107 108 110 111 114 115 116 117 119 120 121 126 128 130
131 132 135 146 147 148 149 154 **S** University of Pennsylvania Health System,
Philadelphia, PA
Primary Contact: Michael J. Duncan, President and Chief Executive Officer
COO: Michael Barber, Chief Operating Officer
CFO: Kenneth E Flickinger, Chief Financial Officer
CMO: Richard D Donze, D.O., Senior Vice President Medical Affairs
CIO: Karen Pinsky, M.D., Chief Medical Information Officer
CHR: Jacqueline Felicetti, Chief Human Resource Officer
CNO: Angela R. Coladonato, R.N., MSN, Chief Nursing Officer
Web address: www.chestercountyhospital.org
Control: Other not–for–profit (including NFP Corporation) **Service**: General
medical and surgical

Staffed Beds: 248 Admissions: 14530 Census: 154 Outpatient Visits:
256594 Births: 2877 Total Expense ($000): 327693 Payroll Expense
($000): 121483 Personnel: 1824

✠ **LIFECARE HOSPITALS OF CHESTER COUNTY (392048)**, 400 East Marshall
Street, Zip 19380–5412; tel. 484/826–0400, (Nonreporting) **A**1 10 **S** LifeCare
Management Services, Plano, TX
Primary Contact: Janet Biedron, R.N., Chief Executive Officer
CMO: Raj Patel, M.D., Medical Director
CHR: Evan Ganley, Manager Human Resources
CNO: Bonnie Barclay, Chief Nursing Officer
Web address: www.lifecare–hospitals.com
Control: Corporation, Investor–owned (for–profit) **Service**: Acute long–term care
hospital

Staffed Beds: 39

WEST GROVE—Chester County

✠ **JENNERSVILLE HOSPITAL (390220)**, 1015 West Baltimore Pike,
Zip 19390–9459; tel. 610/869–1000, (Data for 181 days) **A**1 2 10 **F**3 15 18 29
40 45 49 50 51 57 59 70 74 75 79 81 85 87 92 93 107 108 110 111 115 119
129 130 132 146 147 149 154 **P**6 **S** Tower Health, West Reading, PA
Primary Contact: Ronnie Ursin, FACHE, President and Chief Executive Officer
CFO: Tracey Claxton, Chief Financial Officer
CMO: Tracy Carmellini, M.D., Chief of Staff
CHR: Debra Basquill, Director Human Resources
CNO: Claire Bradley Mooney, Vice President and Chief Nursing Officer
Web address: www.jennersville.com
Control: Individual, Investor–owned (for–profit) **Service**: General medical and
surgical

Staffed Beds: 63 Admissions: 1143 Census: 20 Outpatient Visits: 61171
Births: 0 Total Expense ($000): 24113 Payroll Expense ($000): 6712
Personnel: 236

WEST READING—Berks County

✠ **READING HOSPITAL (390044)**, Sixth Avenue and Spruce Street,
Zip 19611–1428, Mailing Address: P.O. Box 16052, Zip 19612–6052;
tel. 610/988–8000, **A**1 2 3 5 8 10 12 13 **F**3 5 7 11 12 13 15 18 20 22 24 26
28 29 30 31 32 34 35 40 41 43 44 45 46 47 48 49 50 52 54 55 56 57 58 59
60 61 64 65 66 68 70 71 72 73 74 75 76 77 78 79 80 81 82 84 85 87 88 89
92 93 96 97 98 100 101 102 103 104 105 107 108 110 111 114 115 116
117 118 119 120 121 123 124 126 128 129 130 131 132 135 144 146 147
148 149 150 154 **P**5 8 **S** Tower Health, West Reading, PA
Primary Contact: Clinton Matthews, President and Chief Executive Officer
CFO: Richard W Jones, Chief Financial Officer
CMO: M. Joseph Grennan, M.D., Jr Senior Vice President and Chief Medical Officer
CIO: Jayashree Raman, Vice President and Chief Information Officer
CNO: Mary Christine Agnew, R.N., Senior Vice President and Chief Nursing Officer
Web address: www.readinghospital.org
Control: Other not–for–profit (including NFP Corporation) **Service**: General
medical and surgical

Staffed Beds: 732 Admissions: 33627 Census: 404 Outpatient Visits:
1113411 Births: 3609 Total Expense ($000): 851413 Payroll Expense
($000): 351823 Personnel: 5047

WILKES BARRE—Luzerne County

✠ **GEISINGER WYOMING VALLEY MEDICAL CENTER (390270)**, 1000 East
Mountain Boulevard, Zip 18711–0027; tel. 570/808–7300, **A**1 2 3 5 10 13 **F**3 6
9 11 12 13 15 18 19 20 22 24 26 28 29 30 31 32 34 35 37 39 40 43 44 45
46 47 48 49 52 53 54 56 57 58 59 61 64 65 68 70 71 72 74 75 76 77 78 79
80 81 82 84 85 86 87 89 90 91 92 93 94 96 97 100 102 107 108 110 111
114 115 116 117 118 119 120 121 123 124 126 129 130 131 132 135 143
144 145 146 147 148 149 154 **P**6 **S** Geisinger, Danville, PA
Primary Contact: Ronald R Beer, FACHE, Chief Administrative Officer
CFO: Thomas A Bielecki, Chief Financial Officer
CMO: Steven Pierdon, M.D., Executive Vice President and Chief Medical Officer
CIO: Frank Richards, Chief Information Officer
CHR: Margaret Heffers, Assistant Vice President Human Resources
Web address: www.geisinger.org
Control: Other not–for–profit (including NFP Corporation) **Service**: General
medical and surgical

Staffed Beds: 268 Admissions: 16663 Census: 208 Outpatient Visits:
825264 Births: 1580 Total Expense ($000): 465484 Payroll Expense
($000): 117463 Personnel: 2846

★ **PAM SPECIALTY HOSPITAL OF WILKES–BARRE (392025)**, 575 North River
Street, 7th Floor, Zip 18702–2634; tel. 570/208–3310, (Nonreporting) **S** Post
Acute Medical, LLC, Enola, PA
Primary Contact: Salvatore Aquilina, Chief Executive Officer
Web address: www.warmsprings.org/our–facilities/hospitals/post–acute–medical–
specialty–hospital–wilkes–barre/
Control: Corporation, Investor–owned (for–profit) **Service**: Acute long–term care
hospital

Staffed Beds: 36

WILKES—BARRE—Luzerne County

☐ △ **JOHN HEINZ INSTITUTE OF REHABILITATION MEDICINE (393036)**, 150
Mundy Street, Zip 18702–6830; tel. 570/826–3800, (Nonreporting) **A**1 7 10
Primary Contact: Karen Kearney, Vice President Inpatient Rehabilitation Services
CFO: Mike Avvisato, Vice President and Chief Financial Officer
CMO: Gregory Basting, M.D., Vice President Medical Affairs
CIO: John Regula, Chief Information Officer
CHR: Judy P Oprisko, Vice President Human Resources
CNO: Maria Berlyn, Assistant Vice President Nursing Services
Web address: www.allied–services.org
Control: Other not–for–profit (including NFP Corporation) **Service**: Rehabilitation

Staffed Beds: 71

VETERANS AFFAIRS MEDICAL CENTER See Wilkes–Barre Veterans Affairs
Medical Center

★ △ **WILKES–BARRE GENERAL HOSPITAL (390137)**, 575 North River
Street, Zip 18764–0001; tel. 570/829–8111, (Includes WILKES–BARRE
GENERAL HOSPITAL, 575 North River Street, Wilkes–Barre, PA, Zip 18764;
tel. 570/829–8111) **A**2 3 5 7 10 **F**3 8 12 13 15 17 18 20 22 24 26 28 29 30
31 34 37 40 43 44 45 46 47 48 49 50 51 54 56 57 59 61 64 66 70 73 74 75
76 78 79 81 82 83 84 85 86 87 89 90 92 93 96 107 108 110 111 112 114
115 116 117 118 119 120 121 123 124 126 129 130 132 145 146 147 148
149 154 **S** Community Health Systems, Inc., Franklin, TN
Primary Contact: Cornelio R. Catena, President and Chief Executive Officer
COO: Robert Stiekes, Chief Operating Officer
CFO: Roy Boyd, Chief Financial Officer
CIO: Denis Tucker, Chief Information Officer
CHR: James Carmody, Vice President Human Resources
CNO: Robert P Hoffman, Chief Nursing Officer
Web address: www.wvhc.org
Control: Corporation, Investor–owned (for–profit) **Service**: General medical and
surgical

Staffed Beds: 374 Admissions: 13603 Census: 186 Outpatient Visits:
526519 Births: 1083 Total Expense ($000): 293514 Payroll Expense
($000): 81401 Personnel: 1364

✠ **WILKES–BARRE VETERANS AFFAIRS MEDICAL CENTER**, 1111 East End
Boulevard, Zip 18711–0030; tel. 570/824–3521, (Total facility includes 64 beds
in nursing home–type unit) **A**1 2 3 5 **F**3 4 5 18 20 26 29 30 31 34 35 36 38 39
40 44 50 54 55 56 57 58 59 60 61 62 63 64 65 70 74 75 77 78 79 81 82 83
84 85 86 87 90 93 94 97 98 100 101 102 103 104 105 106 107 111 115 116
117 119 127 128 129 130 132 135 143 145 147 148 149 150 152 153
154 **S** Department of Veterans Affairs, Perry Point, MD
Primary Contact: Russell E. Lloyd, Director
COO: Joesph P. Sharon, Associate Director
CFO: Donald E Foote, Fiscal Officer
CMO: Mirza Z Ali, M.D., Chief of Staff
CIO: David Longmore, Chief Information Officer
CHR: Dawn P DeMorrow, Chief Human Resources Service
Web address: www.va.gov/vamcwb
Control: Veterans Affairs, Government, federal **Service**: General medical and
surgical

Staffed Beds: 146 Admissions: 3264 Census: 121 Outpatient Visits:
407073 Births: 0 Total Expense ($000): 287308 Payroll Expense
($000): 100010 Personnel: 1327

Many Facility Codes have changed. Please refer to the AHA Guide Code Chart. © 2018 AHA Guide

WYOMING VALLEY HEALTH CARE SYSTEM See Wilkes–Barre General Hospital

WILLIAMSPORT—Lycoming County

★ **DIVINE PROVIDENCE HOSPITAL (394048)**, 1100 Grampian Boulevard, Zip 17701–1995; tel. 570/326–8000, **A**3 10 **F**11 12 15 31 35 38 44 50 51 53 54 55 56 59 62 63 64 68 75 77 78 79 81 82 83 84 86 87 91 93 98 99 100 103 104 107 108 110 115 120 121 129 130 131 132 134 146 147 148 149 150 **P**7 **S** UPMC Susquehanna, Williamsport, PA
Primary Contact: Robert E. Kane, Chief Administrative Officer
COO: Neil G Armstrong, FACHE, Vice President and Chief Operating Officer
Web address: www.susquehannahealth.org
Control: Other not–for–profit (including NFP Corporation) **Service:** Psychiatric

Staffed Beds: 31 **Admissions:** 656 **Census:** 14 **Outpatient Visits:** 131156 **Births:** 0 **Total Expense ($000):** 91593 **Payroll Expense ($000):** 24480 **Personnel:** 360	

✠ **UPMC SUSQUEHANNA WILLIAMSPORT REGIONAL MEDICAL CENTER (390045)**, 700 High Street, Zip 17701–3100; tel. 570/321–1000, **A**1 2 5 10 13 **F**3 7 11 13 15 18 20 22 24 26 28 29 30 31 32 34 35 37 38 40 44 45 46 47 48 49 50 51 52 53 54 56 57 58 59 60 61 68 70 73 74 75 76 77 79 81 82 85 86 87 89 90 91 92 93 94 96 97 107 108 110 111 114 115 116 117 118 119 120 121 123 124 126 130 132 134 135 143 146 147 **P**7 **S** UPMC Susquehanna, Williamsport, PA
Primary Contact: Steven P. Johnson, FACHE, President
COO: Jan E Fisher, Executive Vice President, Chief Operating Officer and Chief Administrative Officer
CFO: Eric Pohjala, Executive Vice President and Chief Financial Officer
CIO: Timothy E Schoener, Vice President and Chief Information Officer
CHR: Donald Wilver Jr Vice President Human Resources
CNO: Lori A Beucler, MSN, RN, BS–NE, FACHE, R.N., Vice President and Chief Nursing Officer
Web address: www.susquehannahealth.org
Control: Other not–for–profit (including NFP Corporation) **Service:** General medical and surgical

Staffed Beds: 220 **Admissions:** 11495 **Census:** 137 **Outpatient Visits:** 227376 **Births:** 1015 **Total Expense ($000):** 293153 **Payroll Expense ($000):** 106214 **Personnel:** 1551	

WILLIAMSPORT HOSPITAL AND MEDICAL CENTER See UPMC Susquehanna Williamsport Regional Medical Center

WINDBER—Somerset County

★ **CHAN SOON–SHIONG MEDICAL CENTER (390112)**, 600 Somerset Avenue, Zip 15963–1331; tel. 814/467–3000, **A**10 **F**3 11 12 15 18 28 29 30 34 35 36 40 45 48 53 55 56 57 58 59 62 63 70 75 79 81 83 84 85 93 107 108 110 111 114 118 119 129 130 131 132 135 146 147
Primary Contact: Thomas M. Kurtz, President and Chief Executive Officer
CFO: Richard Sukenik, CPA, Vice President Finance and Chief Financial Officer
CIO: Renee Adams, Director Information Technology
CHR: Jamie Brock, Vice President Human Resources
CNO: Michelle Hamula, Director of Nursing and Quality
Web address: www.windbercare.org
Control: Other not–for–profit (including NFP Corporation) **Service:** General medical and surgical

Staffed Beds: 54 **Admissions:** 1389 **Census:** 9 **Outpatient Visits:** 101431 **Births:** 0 **Total Expense ($000):** 46923 **Payroll Expense ($000):** 18836 **Personnel:** 326	

WYNNEWOOD—Montgomery County

LANKENAU HOSPITAL See Lankenau Medical Center

✠ **LANKENAU MEDICAL CENTER (390195)**, 100 Lancaster Avenue West, Zip 19096–3411; tel. 484/476–2000, (Total facility includes 22 beds in nursing home–type unit) **A**1 2 3 5 8 10 12 13 **F**3 11 13 15 17 18 20 22 24 26 28 29 30 31 34 35 36 37 38 39 40 41 43 44 45 46 47 48 49 50 54 55 56 57 58 59 63 64 65 66 70 72 73 74 75 76 78 79 80 81 82 84 85 86 87 89 92 97 100 102 107 108 110 111 114 115 119 120 121 124 126 128 129 130 131 132 135 138 146 148 149 154 **S** Main Line Health, Williamsport, PA
Primary Contact: Phillip D. Robinson, President
COO: John Schwarz, Vice President Administration
CFO: Michael J Buongiorno, Vice President Finance
CMO: Robert Benz, M.D., Chief Medical Officer
CIO: Kay Carr, Chief Information Officer
CHR: Paul Yakulis, MS, R.N., Senior Vice President Human Resources
CNO: Margaret Iacobacci, Vice President Patient Care
Web address: www.mainlinehealth.org
Control: Other not–for–profit (including NFP Corporation) **Service:** General medical and surgical

Staffed Beds: 392 **Admissions:** 18483 **Census:** 257 **Outpatient Visits:** 337448 **Births:** 2929 **Total Expense ($000):** 517173 **Payroll Expense ($000):** 149781 **Personnel:** 2214	

WYOMISSING—Berks County

☐ **READING HOSPITAL REHABILITATION AT WYOMISSING**, 2802 Papermill Road, Zip 19610–1065; tel. 484/628–2388, (Nonreporting) **A**1
Primary Contact: Clinton Matthews, President and Chief Executive Officer
Web address: www.readinghealth.org/locations/locations–module/reading–health–rehabilitation–hospital–2802–papermill–road–wyomissing–pa–19610–889615952/
Control: Other not–for–profit (including NFP Corporation) **Service:** Rehabilitation

Staffed Beds: 112	

✠ **SURGICAL INSTITUTE OF READING (390316)**, 2752 Century Boulevard, Zip 19610–3345; tel. 610/378–8800, (Nonreporting) **A**1 10
Primary Contact: James Bennett, Chief Executive Officer
CFO: Cheryl Peterson, Business Office Manager
CHR: Megan Schaffer, Administrative Assistant
Web address: www.sireading.com
Control: Partnership, Investor–owned (for–profit) **Service:** Surgical

Staffed Beds: 15	

YORK—York County

✠ **HEALTHSOUTH REHABILITATION HOSPITAL OF YORK (393037)**, 1850 Normandie Drive, Zip 17408–1534; tel. 717/767–6941, (Nonreporting) **A**1 10 **S** Encompass Health Corporation, Birmingham, AL
Primary Contact: Steven Alwine, Chief Executive Officer
CFO: Joyce Henry, Controller
CMO: Bruce Sicilia, M.D., Medical Director
CIO: Laura Emig, Director Marketing Operations
CHR: Bradley Teahl, Director Human Resources
CNO: Julie Scott, Chief Nursing Officer
Web address: www.healthsouthyork.com
Control: Corporation, Investor–owned (for–profit) **Service:** Rehabilitation

Staffed Beds: 90	

✠ **OSS ORTHOPAEDIC HOSPITAL (390325)**, 1861 Powder Mill Road, Zip 17402–4723; tel. 717/718–2000, (Nonreporting) **A**1 10
Primary Contact: Joseph Alhadeff, M.D., President
COO: Cynthia Page, FACHE, Chief Operating Officer
CFO: Dale Bushey, Chief Financial Officer
CMO: Todd A. Curran, M.D., President Medical Staff
CIO: Tricia Wolf, Director Information Technology
CHR: Maureen M Putnam, Director Human Resources
CNO: Debra Garton, R.N., Chief Nursing Officer
Web address: www.osshealth.com
Control: Partnership, Investor–owned (for–profit) **Service:** Orthopedic

Staffed Beds: 30	

SELECT SPECIALTY HOSPITAL–YORK See Select Specialty Hospital–Camp Hill, Camp Hill

PA

Hospital, Medicare Provider Number, Address, Telephone, Approval, Facility, and Physician Codes, Health Care System

★ American Hospital Association (AHA) membership
☐ The Joint Commission accreditation
○ Healthcare Facilities Accreditation Program
◇ DNV Healthcare Inc. accreditation
⇑ Center for Improvement in Healthcare Quality Accreditation
△ Commission on Accreditation of Rehabilitation Facilities (CARF) accreditation

★ ○ **UPMC PINNACLE MEMORIAL (390101)**, 325 South Belmont Street,
Zip 17403–2609, Mailing Address: P.O. Box 15118, Zip 17405–7118;
tel. 717/843–8623, **A**10 11 13 **F**3 7 8 13 15 18 20 22 26 29 30 31 34 35 40
45 47 48 49 50 51 54 56 57 58 59 60 64 65 66 68 70 75 76 77 78 79 81 84
85 93 97 107 108 111 116 117 118 119 126 129 130 132 135 146 147 154
P6 **S** UPMC, Pittsburgh, PA
Primary Contact: Curtis Herrin, Chief Financial Officer
CIO: James Mahoney, Chief Information Officer
CHR: Corey Hudak, Director Human Resources
CNO: Susan Gordon, R.N., Chief Nursing Officer
Web address: www.mhyork.org
Control: Other not–for–profit (including NFP Corporation) **Service**: General
medical and surgical

Staffed Beds: 100 **Admissions:** 3928 **Census:** 40 **Outpatient Visits:** 97823
Births: 509 **Total Expense ($000):** 87007 **Payroll Expense ($000):** 34910
Personnel: 530

⇑ **WELLSPAN SURGERY AND REHABILLITATION HOSPITAL (390327)**, 55
Monument Road, Zip 17403–5023; tel. 717/812–6100, (Nonreporting) **A**3 21 **S**
WellSpan Health, York, PA
Primary Contact: Barbara Yarrish, R.N., President
Web address: www.wellspan.org
Control: Other not–for–profit (including NFP Corporation) **Service**: Rehabilitation

Staffed Beds: 73

⊞ △ **WELLSPAN YORK HOSPITAL (390046)**, 1001 South George Street,
Zip 17403–3645; tel. 717/851–2345, **A**1 2 3 5 7 8 10 12 13 **F**3 7 11 12 13 14
15 17 18 20 22 24 26 28 29 30 31 34 35 39 40 43 44 45 46 47 48 49 50 54
55 56 57 58 59 60 61 64 65 66 68 70 72 74 75 76 77 78 79 81 82 84 85 86
87 89 92 93 96 97 98 100 101 102 103 104 105 107 108 110 111 114 115
117 118 119 120 121 123 124 126 129 130 131 132 135 146 147 148 154 **S**
WellSpan Health, York, PA
Primary Contact: Keith D. Noll, President
COO: Raymond Rosen, FACHE, Vice President Operations
CFO: Michael F O'Connor, Senior Vice President Finance
CMO: Peter M Hartmann, M.D., Vice President Medical Affairs
CIO: R Hal Baker, M.D., Vice President and Chief Information Officer
CHR: Robert J Batory, Vice President Human Resources
CNO: Astrid Davis, R.N., Chief Nursing Officer
Web address: www.wellspan.org
Control: Other not–for–profit (including NFP Corporation) **Service**: General
medical and surgical

Staffed Beds: 564 **Admissions:** 30719 **Census:** 451 **Outpatient Visits:**
888888 **Births:** 3057 **Total Expense ($000):** 907579 **Payroll Expense
($000):** 253992 **Personnel:** 4023

PA

RHODE ISLAND

RI

CRANSTON—Providence County

☐ **ELEANOR SLATER HOSPITAL (412001)**, 111 Howard Avenue, Zip 02920–0269, Mailing Address: P.O. Box 8269, Zip 02920–0269; tel. 401/462–3085, (Nonreporting) **A**1 3 10
Primary Contact: Paul J. Despres, Chief Executive Officer
CMO: Charlene Tate, M.D., Chief Medical Staff and Clinical Services
Web address: www.bhddh.ri.gov/esh/
Control: State, Government, nonfederal **Service**: Acute long–term care hospital

Staffed Beds: 495

EAST PROVIDENCE—Providence County

☐ **EMMA PENDLETON BRADLEY HOSPITAL (414003)**, 1011 Veterans Memorial Parkway, Zip 02915–5099; tel. 401/432–1000, **A**1 3 5 10 **F**5 29 30 35 55 75 98 99 101 104 105 106 130 132 153 **P**1 **S** Lifespan Corporation, Providence, RI
Primary Contact: Daniel J. Wall, President and Chief Executive Officer
CFO: Mamie Wakefield, Vice President Finance and Chief Financial Officer
CMO: Henry T Sachs, M.D., III Medical Director
CIO: Carole Cotter, Senior Vice President and Chief Information Officer
CHR: Rob Duval, Chief Human Resources Officer
CNO: Vareen O'Keefe Domaleski, MS, R.N., Vice Patient Care Services and Chief Nursing Officer
Web address: www.lifespan.org
Control: Other not–for–profit (including NFP Corporation) **Service**: Children's hospital psychiatric

Staffed Beds: 70 **Admissions**: 1168 **Census**: 66 **Outpatient Visits**: 2872 **Births**: 0 **Total Expense ($000)**: 70675 **Payroll Expense ($000)**: 41563 **Personnel**: 628

NEWPORT—Newport County

☐ △ **NEWPORT HOSPITAL (410006)**, 11 Friendship Street, Zip 02840–2299; tel. 401/846–6400, **A**1 2 3 7 10 **F**3 8 11 13 15 18 28 29 30 31 34 35 40 45 49 50 51 53 54 56 57 59 60 64 68 70 74 75 76 77 78 79 81 82 85 86 87 89 90 91 92 93 94 96 97 98 100 102 104 105 107 108 110 111 114 118 119 129 130 132 135 141 143 146 147 148 **S** Lifespan Corporation, Providence, RI
Primary Contact: Crista F. Durand, President
CFO: Frank J Byrne, Vice President Finance
CMO: Thomas E. McGue, M.D., Vice President Medical Affairs and Chief Medical Officer
CHR: Barbara J. Arcangeli, Vice President Human Resources
CNO: Orla Brandos, MSN, R.N., Vice President of Patient Care Services and Chief Nursing Officer
Web address: www.newporthospital.org
Control: Other not–for–profit (including NFP Corporation) **Service**: General medical and surgical

Staffed Beds: 119 **Admissions**: 4869 **Census**: 68 **Outpatient Visits**: 82545 **Births**: 456 **Total Expense ($000)**: 106548 **Payroll Expense ($000)**: 47302 **Personnel**: 626

NORTH PROVIDENCE—Providence County

☐ △ **ST. JOSEPH HEALTH SERVICES OF RHODE ISLAND (410005)**, 200 High Service Avenue, Zip 02904–5199; tel. 401/456–3000, (Includes OUR LADY OF FATIMA HOSPITAL, 200 High Service Avenue, North Providence, RI, Zip 2904; tel. 401/456–3000; Thomas Hughes, President; ST. JOSEPH HOSPITAL FOR SPECIALTY CARE, 21 Peace Street, Providence, RI, Zip 2907; tel. 401/456–3000) (Nonreporting) **A**1 7 10 **S** Prospect Medical Holdings, Los Angeles, CA
Primary Contact: John J. Holiver, Chief Executive Officer
CFO: Michael E Conklin Jr Chief Financial Officer
CIO: Susan Cerrone Abely, Chief Information Officer
CHR: Darlene Souza, Vice President
CNO: Patricia A Nadle, R.N., Chief Nursing Officer
Web address: www.saintjosephri.com
Control: Other not–for–profit (including NFP Corporation) **Service**: General medical and surgical

Staffed Beds: 125

NORTH SMITHFIELD—Providence County

LANDMARK MEDICAL CENTER–FOGARTY UNIT See Landmark Medical Center, Woonsocket

✠ **REHABILITATION HOSPITAL OF RHODE ISLAND (413025)**, 116 Eddie Dowling Highway, Zip 02896–7327; tel. 401/766–0800, (Nonreporting) **A**1 10 **S** Prime Healthcare, Ontario, CA
Primary Contact: Michael Souza, Chief Executive Officer
COO: Demetra Ouellette, Chief Operating Officer
CFO: Thomas Klessens, Chief Financial Officer
CMO: Khin Yin, Medical Director
CIO: Vincent Larosa, Director of Information Technology Services
CHR: Gail Gosselin, Director Human Resources
CNO: Kathy Keeling, Director of Nursing
Web address: www.rhri.net
Control: Corporation, Investor–owned (for–profit) **Service**: Rehabilitation

Staffed Beds: 70

PROVIDENCE—Providence County

✠ **BUTLER HOSPITAL (414000)**, 345 Blackstone Boulevard, Zip 02906–4829; tel. 401/455–6200, (Nonreporting) **A**1 3 5 10 **S** Care New England Health System, Providence, RI
Primary Contact: Mary Marran, MS, President and Chief Operating Officer
CFO: Bonnie Baker, Vice President Finance and Chief Financial Officer
CMO: James Sullivan, M.D., Chief Medical Officer
CIO: Summa Gaddam, Chief Information Officer
CHR: Timothy Bigelow, Director Human Resources
CNO: Mary Leveillee, Senior Vice President Patient Care Services and Chief Nursing Officer
Web address: www.butler.org
Control: Other not–for–profit (including NFP Corporation) **Service**: Psychiatric

Staffed Beds: 143

☐ **MIRIAM HOSPITAL (410012)**, 164 Summit Avenue, Zip 02906–2853; tel. 401/793–2500, **A**1 2 3 5 8 10 **F**3 8 11 12 15 18 20 22 26 28 29 30 31 34 35 40 44 45 46 49 50 53 54 56 57 58 59 60 61 64 65 66 67 68 70 74 75 77 78 79 81 82 84 85 87 92 93 97 100 107 108 110 111 114 115 118 119 126 130 132 135 143 146 147 148 **S** Lifespan Corporation, Providence, RI
Primary Contact: Arthur J. Sampson, FACHE, President
COO: Maria Ducharme, R.N., Senior Vice President Patient Care Services and Chief Nursing Officer
CFO: Mamie Wakefield, Chief Financial Officer
CMO: G. Dean Roye, M.D., Senior Vice President of Medical Affairs and Chief Medical Officer
CIO: Carole Cotter, Vice President and Chief Information Officer
CHR: Nancy McMahon, Vice President Human Resources
Web address: www.lifespan.org
Control: Other not–for–profit (including NFP Corporation) **Service**: General medical and surgical

Staffed Beds: 247 **Admissions**: 18572 **Census**: 199 **Outpatient Visits**: 211756 **Births**: 0 **Total Expense ($000)**: 447383 **Payroll Expense ($000)**: 190507 **Personnel**: 2411

✠ **PROVIDENCE VETERANS AFFAIRS MEDICAL CENTER**, 830 Chalkstone Avenue, Zip 02908–4799; tel. 401/273–7100, **A**1 2 3 5 **F**3 5 8 12 18 29 30 31 34 35 36 37 38 39 40 44 45 46 47 48 49 50 51 53 54 55 56 57 58 59 60 61 62 63 64 65 68 70 74 75 77 78 79 81 82 84 85 86 87 91 92 93 94 97 98 100 101 102 103 104 107 108 111 114 115 118 119 126 130 132 135 143 144 145 146 147 148 149 150 152 153 154 **S** Department of Veterans Affairs, Perry Point, MD
Primary Contact: Susan Mackenzie, Ph.D., Medical Center Director
COO: Erin Clare Sears, Associate Director of Operations
CMO: Satish C Sharma, M.D., Chief of Staff
Web address: www.providence.va.gov/
Control: Veterans Affairs, Government, federal **Service**: General medical and surgical

Staffed Beds: 73 **Admissions**: 3312 **Census**: 45 **Outpatient Visits**: 474449 **Births**: 0 **Total Expense ($000)**: 292951

Hospital, Medicare Provider Number, Address, Telephone, Approval, Facility, and Physician Codes, Health Care System

★ American Hospital Association (AHA) membership
☐ The Joint Commission accreditation
○ Healthcare Facilities Accreditation Program
◇ DNV Healthcare Inc. accreditation
⇧ Center for Improvement in Healthcare Quality Accreditation
△ Commission on Accreditation of Rehabilitation Facilities (CARF) accreditation

☐ **RHODE ISLAND HOSPITAL (410007)**, 593 Eddy Street, Zip 02903–4900; tel. 401/444–4000, (Includes HASBRO CHILDREN'S HOSPITAL, 593 Eddy Street, Providence, RI, Zip 02903–4923; tel. 401/444–4000) **A**1 2 3 5 8 10 **F**3 6 7 8 11 15 16 17 18 19 20 21 22 23 24 26 27 30 31 32 34 35 38 39 40 41 43 44 45 46 47 48 49 50 51 53 54 55 56 57 58 59 60 61 64 65 66 67 68 70 74 75 77 78 79 81 82 84 85 86 87 88 89 90 92 93 94 97 98 99 100 101 102 103 104 105 107 108 110 111 114 115 116 117 118 119 120 121 122 123 124 126 129 130 131 132 133 134 135 138 142 143 145 146 147 148 **S** Lifespan Corporation, Providence, RI
Primary Contact: Margaret M. Van Bree, Dr.PH, President
COO: Fredrick Macri, Executive Vice President
CFO: Mamie Wakefield, Senior Vice President and Chief Financial Officer
CMO: John B Murphy, M.D., Vice President Medical Affairs and Chief Medical Officer
CIO: Carole Cotter, Senior Vice President and Chief Information Officer
CHR: Louis J Sperling, Vice President Human Resources
Web address: www.rhodeislandhospital.org/
Control: Other not–for–profit (including NFP Corporation) **Service**: General medical and surgical

Staffed Beds: 679 **Admissions**: 37491 **Census**: 555 **Outpatient Visits**: 495813 **Births**: 0 **Total Expense ($000)**: 1305316 **Payroll Expense ($000)**: 550935 **Personnel**: 6128

✠ **ROGER WILLIAMS MEDICAL CENTER (410004)**, 825 Chalkstone Avenue, Zip 02908–4735; tel. 401/456–2000, (Nonreporting) **A**1 2 3 5 10 **S** Prospect Medical Holdings, Los Angeles, CA
Primary Contact: Demetra Ouellette, President
CFO: Addy Kane, Chief Financial Officer
CMO: Elaine Jones, M.D., President Medical Staff
CIO: Susan Cerrone Abely, Vice President and Chief Information Officer
Web address: www.rwmc.org/
Control: Other not–for–profit (including NFP Corporation) **Service**: General medical and surgical

Staffed Beds: 86

ST. JOSEPH HOSPITAL FOR SPECIALTY CARE See St. Joseph Health Services of Rhode Island, North Providence

VETERANS AFFAIRS MEDICAL CENTER See Providence Veterans Affairs Medical Center

✠ **WOMEN & INFANTS HOSPITAL OF RHODE ISLAND (410010)**, 101 Dudley Street, Zip 02905–2499; tel. 401/274–1100, **A**1 2 3 5 8 10 **F**3 5 11 15 29 30 31 33 34 35 36 38 40 44 45 50 52 54 55 57 58 59 63 64 65 66 68 72 74 75 77 78 81 82 84 85 86 87 93 97 100 101 102 104 107 110 111 114 119 126 130 132 134 135 143 146 147 149 150 **P**6 **S** Care New England Health System, Providence, RI
Primary Contact: Rick Majzun, FACHE, President and Chief Operating Officer
CFO: Robert W Pacheco, Vice President Finance
CMO: Raymond Powrie, M.D., Senior Vice President Quality and Clinical Effectiveness
CHR: Paul F Heffernan, Vice President Human Resources
Web address: www.womenandinfants.org
Control: Other not–for–profit (including NFP Corporation) **Service**: Obstetrics and gynecology

Staffed Beds: 247 **Admissions**: 11499 **Census**: 151 **Outpatient Visits**: 310733 **Births**: 8823 **Total Expense ($000)**: 467390 **Payroll Expense ($000)**: 167961 **Personnel**: 1730

WAKEFIELD—Washington County

☐ **SOUTH COUNTY HOSPITAL (410008)**, 100 Kenyon Avenue, Zip 02879–4299; tel. 401/782–8000, **A**1 2 10 **F**3 11 13 15 18 20 26 28 29 30 31 34 35 36 37 39 40 44 45 46 47 49 50 51 53 54 56 57 59 60 61 64 65 68 70 74 76 77 78 79 81 85 86 87 89 107 108 110 111 114 119 126 129 130 131 135 141 145 146 149 154 **P**6
Primary Contact: Louis R. Giancola, President and Chief Executive Officer
CFO: Thomas Breen, Vice President and Chief Financial Officer
CMO: John Russell Corcoran, Vice President Medical Affairs
CIO: Gary Croteau, Assistant Vice President and Chief Information Officer
CHR: Maggie Thomas, Vice President Human Resources and Practice Management
CNO: Anne Schmidt, Vice President of Patient Care Services and Chief Nursing Officer
Web address: www.schospital.com
Control: Other not–for–profit (including NFP Corporation) **Service**: General medical and surgical

Staffed Beds: 85 **Admissions**: 5174 **Census**: 49 **Outpatient Visits**: 219761 **Births**: 660 **Total Expense ($000)**: 164730 **Payroll Expense ($000)**: 72579 **Personnel**: 990

WARWICK—Kent County

✠ △ **KENT COUNTY MEMORIAL HOSPITAL (410009)**, 455 Tollgate Road, Zip 02886–2770; tel. 401/737–7000, **A**1 3 5 7 10 13 **F**3 4 8 11 12 13 15 18 20 22 26 29 30 31 34 35 36 40 44 45 46 47 48 49 50 51 55 56 57 58 59 60 61 63 64 65 68 70 73 74 75 77 78 79 80 81 82 84 85 86 87 90 93 94 96 97 100 102 107 108 110 111 114 115 116 118 119 126 129 130 131 132 143 146 147 148 149 154 **S** Care New England Health System, Providence, RI
Primary Contact: Robert Haffey, R.N., President and Chief Operating Officer
CFO: James M. Burke, Vice President Finance, Chief Nursing Executive Medical Surgical Hospitals
CMO: Paari Gopalakrishnan, M.D., Chief Medical Officer
CIO: Sumalatha Gaddam, Senior Vice President and Chief Information Officer
CHR: Marilyn J Walsh, Vice President Human Resources
CNO: Rebecca Burke, R.N., MS, Senior Vice President and Chief Nursing Officer
Web address: www.kentri.org
Control: Other not–for–profit (including NFP Corporation) **Service**: General medical and surgical

Staffed Beds: 317 **Admissions**: 13784 **Census**: 182 **Outpatient Visits**: 268686 **Births**: 744 **Total Expense ($000)**: 426787 **Payroll Expense ($000)**: 197980 **Personnel**: 1952

WESTERLY—Washington County

✠ **WESTERLY HOSPITAL (410013)**, 25 Wells Street, Zip 02891–2934; tel. 401/596–6000, **A**1 2 10 **F**3 11 15 18 20 26 34 35 40 44 49 51 57 59 64 68 70 75 79 81 85 86 87 93 94 101 107 108 110 111 115 118 119 130 132 135 146 149 **P**3 **S** Yale New Haven Health, New Haven, CT
Primary Contact: Patrick Green, FACHE, President and Chief Executive Officer
CFO: Seth Van Essendelft, Vice President and Chief Financial Officer
CMO: Oliver Mayorga, M.D., Chief Medical Officer
CIO: Kimberly Kalajainen, Vice President, Operations and Information Technology, Chief Information Officer
CHR: Donna Epps, Vice President, Chief Human Resource Officer
Web address: www.westerlyhospital.org
Control: Other not–for–profit (including NFP Corporation) **Service**: General medical and surgical

Staffed Beds: 41 **Admissions**: 2518 **Census**: 29 **Outpatient Visits**: 102682 **Births**: 0 **Total Expense ($000)**: 70580 **Payroll Expense ($000)**: 27784 **Personnel**: 370

WOONSOCKET—Providence County

✠ **LANDMARK MEDICAL CENTER (410011)**, 115 Cass Avenue, Zip 02895–4731; tel. 401/769–4100, (Includes LANDMARK MEDICAL CENTER–FOGARTY UNIT, 116 Eddie Dowling Highway, North Smithfield, RI, Zip 02896–7327; tel. 401/766–0800; LANDMARK MEDICAL CENTER–WOONSOCKET UNIT, 115 Cass Avenue, Woonsocket, RI, Zip 2895; tel. 401/769–4100) (Nonreporting) **A**1 2 10 **S** Prime Healthcare, Ontario, CA
Primary Contact: Michael Souza, Chief Executive Officer
CFO: Thomas Klessens, Chief Financial Officer
CMO: Glenn Fort, Chief Medical Officer
CIO: Vincent Larosa, Director of Information Systems
CHR: Gail Gosselin, Director Human Resources
Web address: www.landmarkmedcenter.com
Control: Corporation, Investor–owned (for–profit) **Service**: General medical and surgical

Staffed Beds: 140

RI

Many Facility Codes have changed. Please refer to the AHA Guide Code Chart. © 2018 AHA Guide

SOUTH CAROLINA

ABBEVILLE—Abbeville County

★ ⇧ **ABBEVILLE AREA MEDICAL CENTER (421301)**, 420 Thomson Circle, Zip 29620–5656, Mailing Address: P.O. Box 887, Zip 29620–0887; tel. 864/366–5011, **A**10 18 21 **F**3 15 29 30 35 40 51 53 56 57 59 62 67 70 74 75 77 81 85 87 89 90 94 103 107 108 110 114 119 127 128 129 130 132 133 135 146 147 148 **S** Quorum Health, Brentwood, TN
Primary Contact: Howard D. Turner, Chief Executive Officer
CFO: Timothy Wren, Chief Financial Officer
CMO: Christopher Ceraldi, M.D., Chief of Staff
CIO: Tim Stewart, Chief Information Officer
CHR: Alice Rigney, Chief Human Resources Officer
CNO: Ernest Shock, Chief Nursing Officer
Web address: www.abbevilleareamc.com
Control: County, Government, nonfederal **Service**: General medical and surgical

Staffed Beds: 25 **Admissions**: 517 **Census**: 7 **Outpatient Visits**: 28479
Births: 0 **Total Expense ($000)**: 42771 **Payroll Expense ($000)**: 20952
Personnel: 406

AIKEN—Aiken County

☐ **AIKEN REGIONAL MEDICAL CENTERS (420082)**, 302 University Parkway, Zip 29801–6302; tel. 803/641–5000, (Includes AURORA PAVILION, 655 Medical Park Drive, Aiken, SC, Zip 29801; tel. 803/641–5900) **A**1 3 5 10 **F**3 4 11 15 18 20 22 24 29 30 31 34 35 40 46 49 56 57 58 59 64 70 73 74 76 77 78 79 80 81 85 86 87 89 90 94 98 99 100 101 102 103 104 107 108 110 111 114 115 119 121 123 126 129 130 131 132 135 146 147 148 149 **S** Universal Health Services, Inc., King of Prussia, PA
Primary Contact: Matt Merrifield, Interim Chief Executive Officer
COO: Matt Merrifield, Chief Operating Officer
Web address: www.aikenregional.com
Control: Corporation, Investor–owned (for–profit) **Service**: General medical and surgical

Staffed Beds: 285 **Admissions**: 12339 **Census**: 162 **Outpatient Visits**: 144637 **Births**: 1023 **Total Expense ($000)**: 162803 **Payroll Expense ($000)**: 57322 **Personnel**: 848

ANDERSON—Anderson County

⊞ **ANMED HEALTH MEDICAL CENTER (420027)**, 800 North Fant Street, Zip 29621–5793; tel. 864/512–1000, (Includes ANMED HEALTH WOMEN'S AND CHILDREN'S HOSPITAL, 2000 East Greenville Street, Anderson, SC, Zip 29621; tel. 864/512–1000; William T Manson III, FACHE, Chief Executive Officer) **A**1 2 3 5 10 **F**3 4 5 8 11 12 13 14 15 17 18 20 22 24 26 28 29 30 31 34 35 37 39 40 43 45 46 48 49 50 51 53 54 56 57 58 59 60 61 62 64 65 68 70 71 73 74 75 76 77 78 79 80 81 84 85 86 87 89 90 91 97 98 100 101 102 103 104 107 108 110 111 114 115 117 118 119 121 123 126 127 129 130 131 132 135 144 146 147 148 149 153 **P**2 6 **S** AnMed Health, Anderson, SC
Primary Contact: William T. Manson III, FACHE, Chief Executive Officer
CFO: Christine Pearson, Chief Financial Officer
CMO: Thomas Kayrouz, M.D., Chief Medical Officer
CIO: Marty Stewart, Chief Information Officer
CHR: Richard Walter Grooms Jr Chief Human Resources Officer
CNO: Tina M. Jury, MSN, Chief Nursing Officer
Web address: www.anmedhealth.org
Control: Other not–for–profit (including NFP Corporation) **Service**: General medical and surgical

Staffed Beds: 394 **Admissions**: 21633 **Census**: 267 **Outpatient Visits**: 791540 **Births**: 1784 **Total Expense ($000)**: 531032 **Payroll Expense ($000)**: 217818 **Personnel**: 3812

⊞ **ANMED HEALTH REHABILITATION HOSPITAL (423029)**, 1 Spring Back Way, Zip 29621–2676; tel. 864/716–2600, **A**1 10 **F**3 29 30 56 57 60 68 74 75 79 90 91 93 94 95 96 **S** Encompass Health Corporation, Birmingham, AL
Primary Contact: Denise R. Murray, Chief Executive Officer
CFO: Julie Harris, Controller
CMO: William Vogentz, M.D., Medical Director
CHR: Morgan Clements, Director of Human Resources
CNO: Kelly Davis, Chief Nursing Officer
Web address: www.anmedrehab.com
Control: Corporation, Investor–owned (for–profit) **Service**: Rehabilitation

Staffed Beds: 60 **Admissions**: 1422 **Census**: 49 **Births**: 0 **Total Expense ($000)**: 15970 **Payroll Expense ($000)**: 9068 **Personnel**: 188

☐ **PATRICK B. HARRIS PSYCHIATRIC HOSPITAL (424011)**, 130 Highway 252, Zip 29621–5054; tel. 864/231–2600, **A**1 3 5 10 **F**98 100 101 102 103 106 130 143 146
Primary Contact: John Fletcher, Chief Executive Officer
Web address: www.patrickbharris.com/
Control: State, Government, nonfederal **Service**: Psychiatric

Staffed Beds: 131 **Admissions**: 480 **Census**: 113 **Outpatient Visits**: 0
Births: 0 **Personnel**: 292

BEAUFORT—Beaufort County

⊞ **BEAUFORT MEMORIAL HOSPITAL (420067)**, 955 Ribaut Road, Zip 29902–5441; tel. 843/522–5200, **A**1 2 10 **F**3 11 12 13 15 18 20 22 28 29 30 31 32 34 35 40 45 46 49 50 51 53 54 57 59 60 64 65 69 70 71 73 74 75 76 77 78 79 81 85 86 87 89 90 91 93 94 96 97 98 100 101 102 103 104 107 108 110 111 114 115 118 119 120 121 126 127 130 132 134 135 145 146 147 148 149 154 **P**6
Primary Contact: Edmond Russell. Baxley III, President and Chief Executive Officer
CFO: Ken Miller, Chief Financial Officer
CMO: Kurt Gambla, D.O., Chief Medical Officer
CIO: Edward Ricks, Vice President and Chief Information Officer
CHR: Doug Douglas, Interim Vice President Human Resources
CNO: Karen Manuel Carroll, R.N., Vice President Patient Care Services
Web address: www.bmhsc.org
Control: County, Government, nonfederal **Service**: General medical and surgical

Staffed Beds: 203 **Admissions**: 8787 **Census**: 120 **Outpatient Visits**: 154510 **Births**: 973

⊞ **NAVAL HOSPITAL BEAUFORT**, 1 Pinckney Boulevard, Zip 29902–6122; tel. 843/228–5301, (Nonreporting) **A**1 5 **S** Bureau of Medicine and Surgery, Department of the Navy, Falls Church, VA
Primary Contact: Lieutenant Commander Willie Brown, Director Administration
Web address: www.med.navy.mil/sites/nhbeaufort/Pages/Welcome_Page.aspx
Control: Navy, Government, federal **Service**: General medical and surgical

Staffed Beds: 20

CAMDEN—Kershaw County

⊞ **KERSHAWHEALTH (420048)**, 1315 Roberts Street, Zip 29020–3737, Mailing Address: P.O. Box 7003, Zip 29021–7003; tel. 803/432–4311, **A**1 10 **F**3 11 13 15 18 20 24 28 29 30 31 32 34 35 40 44 45 49 50 51 54 57 59 61 62 63 64 66 68 70 75 76 77 78 79 81 85 86 87 89 90 94 97 107 108 110 111 114 115 118 119 127 129 130 132 144 146 147 148 **S** RCCH HealthCare Partners, Brentwood, TN
Primary Contact: Terry Gunn, FACHE, Chief Executive Officer
COO: Susan R Burroughs, FACHE, Chief Operating Officer
CFO: Mike Bunch, Executive Vice President, Chief Operating Officer and Chief Financial Officer
CMO: Tallulah Holmstrom, M.D., Chief Medical Officer
CIO: Diane Arrants, Chief Information Officer
CHR: Angela F Nettles, Vice President, Human Resources and Support Services
Web address: www.kershawhealth.com
Control: Corporation, Investor–owned (for–profit) **Service**: General medical and surgical

Staffed Beds: 119 **Admissions**: 3907 **Census**: 45 **Outpatient Visits**: 109689 **Births**: 284 **Personnel**: 736

CHARLESTON—Charleston County

⊞ **BON SECOURS ST. FRANCIS HOSPITAL (420065)**, 2095 Henry Tecklenburg Drive, Zip 29414–5733; tel. 843/402–1000, **A**1 10 **F**3 7 12 13 14 15 28 29 30 31 34 35 40 45 46 47 48 49 50 51 56 57 59 64 68 70 73 74 75 76 77 78 79 80 81 82 84 85 86 87 89 93 94 100 102 107 108 110 111 114 115 117 118 119 120 121 123 130 131 132 145 146 147 148 149 154 **S** Atrium Health, Charlotte, NC
Primary Contact: Anthony Jackson, Chief Executive Officer
CFO: Bret Johnson, Chief Financial Officer
CMO: Steven D Shapiro, M.D., Chief Medical Officer
CIO: Michael Taylor, Chief Information Officer
CNO: Pennie Peralta, R.N., VP, Nursing & Chief Nursing Officer
Web address: www.rsfh.com/
Control: Other not–for–profit (including NFP Corporation) **Service**: General medical and surgical

Staffed Beds: 160 **Admissions**: 9335 **Census**: 96 **Outpatient Visits**: 163355 **Births**: 2448 **Total Expense ($000)**: 191181 **Payroll Expense ($000)**: 58291 **Personnel**: 1059

Hospital, Medicare Provider Number, Address, Telephone, Approval, Facility, and Physician Codes, Health Care System

★ American Hospital Association (AHA) membership ○ Healthcare Facilities Accreditation Program ⇧ Center for Improvement in Healthcare Quality Accreditation
☐ The Joint Commission accreditation ◇ DNV Healthcare Inc. accreditation △ Commission on Accreditation of Rehabilitation Facilities (CARF) accreditation

© 2018 AHA Guide *Many Facility Codes have changed. Please refer to the AHA Guide Code Chart.* Hospitals **A549**

⊞ **ENCOMPASS HEALTH REHABILITATION HOSPITAL OF CHARLESTON
(423027)**, 9181 Medcom Street, Zip 29406–9168; tel. 843/820–7777, **A**1 10
F90 94 96 **S** Encompass Health Corporation, Birmingham, AL
Primary Contact: Michele M. Skripps, R.N., Chief Executive Officer
CFO: Beckye Lariviere, Controller
CMO: William Livesay, D.O., Jr Medical Director
CHR: Traxler Littlejohn, Human Resources Director
CNO: Patricia Simon, Chief Nursing Officer
Web address: www.healthsouthcharleston.com
Control: Corporation, Investor–owned (for–profit) **Service**: Rehabilitation

Staffed Beds: 49 **Admissions**: 963 **Census**: 38 **Births**: 0 **Total Expense
($000)**: 17138 **Payroll Expense ($000)**: 7719 **Personnel**: 110

⊞ **MUSC HEALTH OF MEDICAL UNIVERSITY OF SOUTH CAROLINA (420004)**,
169 Ashley Avenue, Zip 29425–8905; tel. 843/792–2300, (Includes CHILDREN'S
HOSPITAL OF SOUTH CAROLINA AT MUSC, 171 Ashley Avenue, Charleston, SC,
Zip 29425–8908; tel. 843/792–1414; Patrick J Cawley, Chief Executive Officer,
MUSC Health and Vice President for Health Affairs, University) **A**1 2 3 5 8 10 **F**3 4
5 6 7 8 9 11 12 13 14 15 16 17 18 19 20 21 22 23 24 25 26 27 28 29 30 31
32 34 35 36 37 38 39 40 41 43 44 45 46 47 48 49 50 51 52 53 54 55 56 57
58 59 60 61 64 65 66 67 68 70 71 72 73 74 75 76 77 78 79 80 81 82 84 85
86 87 88 89 91 92 93 94 97 98 99 100 101 102 103 104 107 108 109 110
111 114 115 116 117 118 119 120 121 123 124 126 129 130 131 132 134
135 136 137 138 139 140 141 142 144 145 146 147 148 149 150 151 153
154
Primary Contact: Patrick J. Cawley, Chief Executive Officer, MUSC Health and Vice
President for Health Affairs, University
COO: Matthew Wain, Chief Operating Officer
CFO: Lisa Goodlett, Administrator Finance and Support Services
CMO: Daniel Handel, M.D., Chief Medical Officer
CIO: Michael Caputo, Chief Information Officer
CHR: Darrick Paul, Chief People Officer
CNO: Jerry A Mansfield, Ph.D., R.N., Executive Chief Nursing Officer & Chief Patient
Experience Officer
Web address: www.muschealth.com
Control: State, Government, nonfederal **Service**: General medical and surgical

Staffed Beds: 779 **Admissions**: 36394 **Census**: 697 **Outpatient
Visits**: 1079453 **Births**: 2668 **Total Expense ($000)**: 1395239 **Payroll
Expense ($000)**: 472824 **Personnel**: 7103

☐ **PALMETTO LOWCOUNTRY BEHAVIORAL HEALTH (424006)**, 2777
Speissegger Drive, Zip 29405–8229; tel. 843/747–5830, **A**1 10 **F**4 5 98 99 102
103 104 105 152 153 **S** Universal Health Services, Inc., King of Prussia, PA
Primary Contact: Clint Hauger, Chief Executive Officer
CFO: Stan Markowski, Chief Financial Officer
CMO: Steven Lopez, M.D., Chief Medical Officer
CHR: Sheila Simpson, Vice President Human Resources
CNO: Jo Good, Director of Nursing
Web address: www.palmettobehavioralhealth.com
Control: Corporation, Investor–owned (for–profit) **Service**: Psychiatric

Staffed Beds: 100 **Admissions**: 3084 **Census**: 65 **Outpatient Visits**: 3777
Births: 0 **Total Expense ($000)**: 16569 **Payroll Expense ($000)**: 8555
Personnel: 132

⊞ **RALPH H. JOHNSON VETERANS AFFAIRS MEDICAL CENTER**, 109 Bee
Street, Zip 29401–5799; tel. 843/577–5011, (Nonreporting) **A**1 2 3 5 8 **S**
Department of Veterans Affairs, Perry Point, MD
Primary Contact: Scott R. Isaacks, FACHE, Director and Chief Executive Officer
CFO: Cassandra Helfer, Chief Financial Officer
CMO: Florence N. Hutchison, M.D., Chief of Staff
CIO: LaBon Hardy, Chief Information Officer
CHR: Renae A. Jacobson, Human Resources Officer
CNO: Garett E. Schreier, R.N., Associate Director, Nursing and Patient Care
Services
Web address: www.charleston.va.gov/
Control: Veterans Affairs, Government, federal **Service**: General medical and
surgical

Staffed Beds: 98

⊞ △ **ROPER ST. FRANCIS (420087)**, 316 Calhoun Street, Zip 29401–1125;
tel. 843/724–2000, **A**1 2 3 5 7 10 **F**3 7 8 9 14 15 17 18 20 22 24 26 28 29 30
31 34 35 37 40 45 49 50 51 53 54 55 56 57 58 59 60 61 62 63 64 65 67 68
69 70 74 75 77 78 79 80 81 82 84 85 86 87 90 92 93 94 95 96 102 107 108
110 111 114 115 118 119 120 121 123 124 126 130 131 132 135 136
143 146 147 148 149 154 **S** Atrium Health, Charlotte, NC
Primary Contact: Stephen D. Porter, Chief Executive Officer
CFO: Bret Johnson, Chief Financial Officer
CMO: Steven D Shapiro, M.D., Vice President Medical Affairs
CIO: Melinda H. Cardell, Interim Vice President and Chief Information Officer
CHR: Melanie Stith, Vice President Human Resources
Web address: www.rsfh.com/
Control: Other not–for–profit (including NFP Corporation) **Service**: General
medical and surgical

Staffed Beds: 292 **Admissions**: 13601 **Census**: 192 **Outpatient
Visits**: 209340 **Births**: 0 **Total Expense ($000)**: 349429 **Payroll Expense
($000)**: 98540 **Personnel**: 1967

⊞ **TRIDENT MEDICAL CENTER (420079)**, 9330 Medical Plaza Drive,
Zip 29406–9195; tel. 843/797–7000, (Includes MONCKS CORNER MEDICAL
CENTER, 401 North Live Oak Drive, Highway 17A, Moncks Corner, SC,
Zip 29461–5603; tel. 843/761–8721; SUMMERVILLE MEDICAL CENTER, 295
Midland Parkway, Summerville, SC, Zip 29485–8104; tel. 843/832–5000) **A**1 2 3
5 10 **F**3 8 12 13 15 16 18 20 22 24 26 28 29 30 31 34 35 40 41 43 45 46 47
48 49 50 54 55 56 57 59 60 61 64 70 72 73 74 75 76 77 78 79 80 81 84 85
86 87 89 90 93 94 98 100 102 107 108 110 111 114 115 116 117 118 119
120 121 123 126 129 130 131 132 135 145 146 147 148 **S** HCA Healthcare,
Nashville, TN
Primary Contact: Todd Gallati, FACHE, President and Chief Executive Officer
COO: Scott Weiskittel, Chief Operating Officer
CFO: Teresa Finch, Chief Financial Officer
CIO: Susan Murray, Director Information Services
CHR: Joe B Hill Jr Vice President Human Resources
Web address: www.tridenthealthsystem.com
Control: Corporation, Investor–owned (for–profit) **Service**: General medical and
surgical

Staffed Beds: 421 **Admissions**: 24665 **Census**: 291 **Outpatient
Visits**: 355866 **Births**: 2730 **Personnel**: 1558

CHERAW—Chesterfield County

⇑ **MCLEOD HEALTH CHERAW (420107)**, 711 Chesterfield Highway,
Zip 29520–7002; tel. 843/537–7881, **A**10 21 **F**3 13 15 18 28 29 30 34 35 40
45 56 57 59 68 70 76 79 81 85 86 87 89 102 107 108 111 114 118 119 130
132 133 135 **P**3 **S** McLeod Health, Florence, SC
Primary Contact: Mib Scoggins, Chief Executive Officer
CFO: Louis Anderson, Chief Financial Officer
CMO: David Bersinger, M.D., Chief of Staff
CIO: Jim Spencer, Director Information System
Web address: www.chesterfieldgeneral.com
Control: Other not–for–profit (including NFP Corporation) **Service**: General
medical and surgical

Staffed Beds: 52 **Admissions**: 2063 **Census**: 20 **Outpatient Visits**: 36803
Births: 204 **Total Expense ($000)**: 36094 **Payroll Expense ($000)**: 13413
Personnel: 195

CHESTER—Chester County

⊞ **CHESTER REGIONAL MEDICAL CENTER (420019)**, 1 Medical Park Drive,
Zip 29706–9769; tel. 803/581–3151, **A**1 10 **F**15 28 29 34 35 40 50 56 57 59
70 75 77 79 81 85 86 87 89 90 94 107 108 110 111 119 128 130 131 132
135 **S** Community Health Systems, Inc., Franklin, TN
Primary Contact: Page H. Vaughan, Chief Executive Officer
CFO: Tracey Claxton, Chief Financial Officer
CMO: Terry Dodge, M.D., Chief of Staff
CIO: Shaw Laird, Chief Information Officer
CHR: Karen Chapman, Director Human Resources
CNO: Betty Griffin, Interim Chief Nursing Officer
Web address: www.chesterregional.com
Control: Corporation, Investor–owned (for–profit) **Service**: General medical and
surgical

Staffed Beds: 36 **Admissions**: 816 **Census**: 7 **Outpatient Visits**: 47290
Births: 0

CLINTON—Laurens County

⊞ **GREENVILLE HEALTH SYSTEM – LAURENS COUNTY MEMORIAL HOSPITAL
(420038)**, 22725 Highway 76 East, Zip 29325–7527, Mailing Address: P O
Drawer 976, Zip 29325–0976; tel. 864/833–9100, (Includes GHS – LAURENS
COUNTY MEMORIAL HOSPITAL, 22725 Highway 76 E, PO Drawer 976, Clinton,
SC, Zip 29325–7527, Mailing Address: PO Box 976, Zip 29325–0976,
tel. 803/833–9100; Justin Benfield, Southern Region Chief Operating Officer)
(Total facility includes 14 beds in nursing home–type unit) **A**1 5 10 20 **F**1 3 13 15
18 28 30 40 45 46 59 70 76 79 80 81 87 89 107 110 111 114 115 119 127
128 132 146 147 **P**6 **S** Greenville Health System, Greenville, SC
Primary Contact: Justin Benfield, Southern Region Chief Operating Officer
CFO: Michael Norrick, Director of Campus Operations
CMO: Vincent Green, Medical Director
CIO: Kathleen Anderson, Director, Acute Clinical Systems
CHR: Cathy M Rogers, Manager Human Resources
CNO: Kay Swisher, Chief Nursing Officer
Web address: www.ghs.org/laurens
Control: Other not–for–profit (including NFP Corporation) **Service**: General
medical and surgical

Staffed Beds: 71 **Admissions**: 2601 **Census**: 34 **Outpatient Visits**: 78861
Births: 328 **Total Expense ($000)**: 65230 **Payroll Expense ($000)**: 16852
Personnel: 289

WHITTEN CENTER, Highway 76 East, Zip 29325, Mailing Address: P.O. Box 239, Zip 29325–0239; tel. 864/833–2733, (Nonreporting)
Primary Contact: Wes Leonard, Chief Executive Officer
Control: State, Government, nonfederal **Service**: Intellectual disabilities

Staffed Beds: 22

COLUMBIA—Laurens County

★ **CONTINUECARE HOSPITAL AT PALMETTO HEALTH BAPTIST (422006)**, Taylor at Marion Street, Zip 29220, Mailing Address: PO BOX 11069, Zip 29211–1069; tel. 803/296–3757, **A**10 22 **F**1 3 29 35 85 **S** Community Hospital Corporation, Plano, TX
Primary Contact: Thomas P. Harlan, Chief Executive Officer
Web address: www.continuecare.org/palmetto//
Control: Other not–for–profit (including NFP Corporation) **Service**: Acute long–term care hospital

Staffed Beds: 35 **Admissions**: 227 **Census**: 23 **Outpatient Visits**: 0 **Births**: 0 **Total Expense ($000)**: 7562 **Payroll Expense ($000)**: 3220

COLUMBIA—Richland County

☐ **EARLE E. MORRIS ALCOHOL AND DRUG TREATMENT CENTER**, 610 Faison Drive, Zip 29203–3218; tel. 803/935–7100, **A**1 **F**4 29 39 53 61 67 74 75 87 98 130 132 146
Primary Contact: George McConnell, Director
Web address: www.state.sc.us/dmh/morris_village/
Control: State, Government, nonfederal **Service**: Alcoholism and other chemical dependency

Staffed Beds: 103 **Admissions**: 1447 **Census**: 98 **Outpatient Visits**: 0 **Births**: 0 **Personnel**: 168

⊞ **ENCOMPASS HEALTH REHABILITATION HOSPITAL OF COLUMBIA (423025)**, 2935 Colonial Drive, Zip 29203–6811; tel. 803/254–7777, **A**1 10 **F**29 50 53 60 64 77 90 91 92 93 94 95 96 97 119 149 **S** Encompass Health Corporation, Birmingham, AL
Primary Contact: Chris Daughtry, Chief Executive Officer
CFO: Jessica Burriss, Chief Financial Officer
CMO: Devin Troyer, M.D., Medical Director
CHR: Luanne Burton, Director Human Resources
CNO: April Brooks, Chief Nursing Officer
Web address: www.healthsouthcolumbia.com
Control: Corporation, Investor–owned (for–profit) **Service**: Rehabilitation

Staffed Beds: 96 **Admissions**: 1846 **Census**: 66 **Outpatient Visits**: 13265 **Births**: 0 **Total Expense ($000)**: 21308 **Payroll Expense ($000)**: 11506

☐ **G. WERBER BRYAN PSYCHIATRIC HOSPITAL (424005)**, 220 Faison Drive, Zip 29203–3210; tel. 803/935–7140, **A**1 3 10 **F**4 30 50 74 75 97 98 99 101 103 130 132 135 146
Primary Contact: Stuart Shields, Director
COO: Jaclyn Upfield, Chief Operating Officer
CIO: Sam Livingston, Information Resource Consultant
CHR: Kim Church, Manager Human Resources
Web address: www.scdmh.org
Control: State, Government, nonfederal **Service**: Psychiatric

Staffed Beds: 227 **Admissions**: 687 **Census**: 187 **Outpatient Visits**: 0 **Births**: 0 **Personnel**: 588

⊞ **PALMETTO HEALTH BAPTIST (420086)**, Taylor at Marion Street, Zip 29220–0001; tel. 803/296–5010, (Total facility includes 22 beds in nursing home–type unit) **A**1 2 3 5 10 **F**1 3 4 5 11 12 13 15 18 20 29 30 31 34 35 38 40 45 47 48 49 51 53 54 57 59 61 62 63 64 65 66 67 70 72 73 74 75 76 77 78 79 80 81 82 84 85 86 87 89 90 93 94 97 98 99 100 101 102 103 104 105 107 108 110 111 114 115 117 118 119 126 130 132 146 147 148 151 153 **S** Palmetto Health, Columbia, SC
Primary Contact: Gregory B. Gattman, Chief Operating Officer
COO: James M Bridges, Executive Vice President and Chief Operating Officer
CFO: Paul K Duane, Chief Financial Officer and Office of Health Reform
CMO: Mark J Mayson, M.D., Medical Director
CIO: Michelle Edwards, Executive Vice President Information Technology
CHR: Trip Gregory, Senior Vice President Human Resources
Web address: www.palmettohealth.org
Control: Other not–for–profit (including NFP Corporation) **Service**: General medical and surgical

Staffed Beds: 400 **Admissions**: 20576 **Census**: 269 **Outpatient Visits**: 206451 **Births**: 3001 **Total Expense ($000)**: 354201 **Payroll Expense ($000)**: 142678 **Personnel**: 2291

COLUMBIA—Lexington County

⊞ **PALMETTO HEALTH BAPTIST PARKRIDGE (420106)**, 400 Palmetto Health Parkway, Zip 29212–1760, Mailing Address: P.O. Box 2266, Zip 29202–2266; tel. 803/907–7000, **A**1 3 10 **F**3 8 11 13 15 29 30 34 35 40 45 46 50 57 59 64 70 75 76 77 79 81 85 86 87 90 93 94 97 107 110 111 115 119 130 132 144 146 147 **S** Palmetto Health, Columbia, SC
Primary Contact: Emilie Keene, Interim Chief Operating Officer
COO: Emilie Keene, Interim Chief Operating Officer
Web address: www.palmettohealth.org
Control: Other not–for–profit (including NFP Corporation) **Service**: General medical and surgical

Staffed Beds: 76 **Admissions**: 4778 **Census**: 52 **Outpatient Visits**: 109657 **Births**: 722 **Total Expense ($000)**: 129654 **Payroll Expense ($000)**: 45349 **Personnel**: 865

COLUMBIA—Richland County

⊞ **PALMETTO HEALTH RICHLAND (420018)**, Five Richland Medical Park Drive, Zip 29203–6897; tel. 803/434–7000, (Includes PALMETTO HEALTH CHILDREN'S HOSPITAL, Five Richland Medical Park Dr, Columbia, SC, Zip 29203–6863; tel. 803/434–6882) **A**1 2 3 5 8 10 **F**3 4 7 11 13 15 17 18 19 20 22 24 26 28 29 30 31 32 34 35 38 39 40 41 43 45 46 50 53 54 56 57 59 61 64 65 66 68 70 72 73 74 75 76 77 78 79 81 86 87 88 89 90 93 94 97 98 100 101 102 103 104 107 110 111 114 115 119 124 126 129 130 132 146 147 148 154 **S** Palmetto Health, Columbia, SC
Primary Contact: Jay Hamm, R.N., FACHE, Chief Operating Officer
CFO: Paul K Duane, Chief Financial Officer and Office of Health Reform
CMO: Eric Brown, M.D., Physician Executive
CNO: Carole A Siegfried, MSN, R.N., Campus Nurse Executive
Web address: www.palmettohealth.org
Control: Other not–for–profit (including NFP Corporation) **Service**: General medical and surgical

Staffed Beds: 671 **Admissions**: 32788 **Census**: 567 **Outpatient Visits**: 602812 **Births**: 2272 **Total Expense ($000)**: 812732 **Payroll Expense ($000)**: 318824 **Personnel**: 5103

★ ⇑ **PROVIDENCE HOSPITAL (420026)**, 2435 Forest Drive, Zip 29204–2098; tel. 803/865–4500, (Includes PROVIDENCE HOSPITAL NORTHEAST, 120 Gateway Corporate Boulevard, Columbia, SC, Zip 29203–9611; tel. 803/865–4500; Ryan Hall, Vice President) (Nonreporting) **A**10 21 **S** LifePoint Health, Brentwood, TN
Primary Contact: Stephen R. Selzer, Market Chief Executive Officer
COO: W. Carl Martin, Chief Operating Officer
CFO: Pamela Gallagher, Chief Financial Officer
CMO: Wayne Sribnick, M.D., Senior Vice President and Chief Medical Officer
CIO: Lib Cumbee, Director Information Systems
CHR: Justin A Lofurno, Director Human Resources
Web address: www.sistersofcharityhealth.org/health–care/providence–hospitals/
Control: Church operated, Nongovernment, not–for–profit **Service**: General medical and surgical

Staffed Beds: 247

PROVIDENCE HOSPITAL NORTHEAST See Providence Hospital, Columbia

SOUTH CAROLINA DEPARTMENT OF CORRECTIONS HOSPITAL, 4344 Broad River Road, Zip 29210–4098; tel. 803/896–8567, (Nonreporting) **A**3
Primary Contact: John Solomon, M.D., Director
Web address: www.doc.sc.gov/
Control: State, Government, nonfederal **Service**: Hospital unit of an institution (prison hospital, college infirmary, etc.)

Staffed Beds: 70

☐ **WILLIAM S. HALL PSYCHIATRIC INSTITUTE (424003)**, 1800 Colonial Drive, Zip 29203–6827; tel. 803/898–1693, (Nonreporting) **A**1 3 5 10
Primary Contact: Angela Forand, Director
COO: Doug Glover, Controller
CFO: Doug Glover, Controller
CMO: Phyllis Bryant–Mobley, M.D., Director Medical Services
CIO: Mesa Foard, Director Information technology
CHR: Kim Church, Manager Human Resources
Web address: www.scdmh.org
Control: State, Government, nonfederal **Service**: Psychiatric

Staffed Beds: 38

SC

Hospital, Medicare Provider Number, Address, Telephone, Approval, Facility, and Physician Codes, Health Care System

★ American Hospital Association (AHA) membership
☐ The Joint Commission accreditation
○ Healthcare Facilities Accreditation Program
◇ DNV Healthcare Inc. accreditation
⇑ Center for Improvement in Healthcare Quality Accreditation
△ Commission on Accreditation of Rehabilitation Facilities (CARF) accreditation

✠ △ **WM. JENNINGS BRYAN DORN VETERANS AFFAIRS MEDICAL CENTER,**
6439 Garners Ferry Road, Zip 29209–1639; tel. 803/776–4000, (Nonreporting)
A1 2 3 5 7 8 **S** Department of Veterans Affairs, Perry Point, MD
Primary Contact: David Omura, Interim Director
COO: David Omura, Associate Director
CMO: Bernard L. DeKoning, M.D., Chief of Staff
CIO: Steve Chalphant, Director Information Management Service Line
CHR: Phyllis Jones, Chief Human Resources
CNO: Ruth W. Mustard, R.N., MSN, Associate Director Nursing and Patient Services
Web address: www.columbiasc.va.gov/
Control: Veterans Affairs, Government, federal **Service:** General medical and
surgical

Staffed Beds: 216

CONWAY—Horry County

★ ⇑ **CONWAY MEDICAL CENTER (420049)**, 300 Singleton Ridge Road,
Zip 29526–9142, Mailing Address: P.O. Box 829, Zip 29528–0829;
tel. 843/347–7111, (Total facility includes 88 beds in nursing home–type unit) **A**10
21 **F**1 3 8 11 12 13 15 18 20 26 28 29 30 34 35 37 40 43 45 46 49 50 51 57
59 60 61 68 70 71 73 74 75 76 77 79 81 84 85 86 87 89 90 93 94 100 102
107 108 110 111 114 115 118 119 128 129 130 132 135 145 146 147 148
149 150 **P**6
Primary Contact: Bret A. Barr, President and Chief Executive Officer
CMO: Paul McKinley Richardson Jr Vice President, Medical Affairs
CIO: David Crutchfield, Vice President, Information Services & Chief Information
Officer
CHR: Matthew J. Securro, Vice President, Human Resources
CNO: Tony L. Minshew, Vice President, Patient Care Services
Web address: www.conwaymedicalcenter.com
Control: Other not–for–profit (including NFP Corporation) **Service:** General
medical and surgical

Staffed Beds: 266 **Admissions:** 9471 **Census:** 187 **Outpatient
Visits:** 176902 **Births:** 1527 **Total Expense ($000):** 167388 **Payroll
Expense ($000):** 57396 **Personnel:** 1179

☐ **LIGHTHOUSE BEHAVIORAL HEALTH HOSPITAL (424002)**, 152 Waccamaw
Medical Park Drive, Zip 29526–8901; tel. 843/347–8871, **A**1 10 **F**4 98 99 101
102 103 130 **S** Universal Health Services, Inc., King of Prussia, PA
Primary Contact: Thomas L. Ryba, Chief Executive Officer
CFO: Gabrielle Gale, Chief Financial Officer
CMO: Adedapo Oduwole, M.D., Medical Director
CIO: Gabrielle Gale, Chief Financial Officer
CHR: Lois Woodall, Director Human Resources
Web address: www.lighthousecarecenterofconway.com/
Control: Corporation, Investor–owned (for–profit) **Service:** Psychiatric

Staffed Beds: 87 **Admissions:** 3199 **Census:** 81 **Outpatient Visits:** 0
Births: 0 **Personnel:** 163

DARLINGTON—Darlington County

⇑ **MCLEOD MEDICAL CENTER DARLINGTON (420057)**, 701 Cashua
Ferry Road, Zip 29532–8488, Mailing Address: P.O. Box 1859, Zip 29540;
tel. 843/395–1100, **A**10 21 **F**3 4 15 34 35 38 56 57 59 61 64 68 77 85 94 97
98 100 101 103 104 107 110 119 127 128 130 133 147 148 153 **P**3 **S**
McLeod Health, Florence, SC
Primary Contact: Tim Smoak, Administrator
Web address: www.mcleodhealth.org
Control: Other not–for–profit (including NFP Corporation) **Service:** General
medical and surgical

Staffed Beds: 40 **Admissions:** 1156 **Census:** 39 **Outpatient Visits:** 8487
Births: 0 **Total Expense ($000):** 12810 **Payroll Expense ($000):** 6645
Personnel: 104

DILLON—Dillon County

⇑ **MCLEOD MEDICAL CENTER DILLON (420005)**, 301 East Jackson
Street, Zip 29536–2509, Mailing Address: P.O. Box 1327, Zip 29536–1327;
tel. 843/774–4111, **A**10 21 **F**3 11 13 15 28 29 30 34 35 40 50 57 59 64 68
70 75 76 79 81 85 87 89 90 94 107 111 114 119 130 132 133 134 135 146
147 148 149 154 **P**8 **S** McLeod Health, Florence, SC
Primary Contact: Joan Ervin, Administrator
CFO: Fulton Ervin, Senior Vice President and Chief Financial Officer
CMO: Walter B Blum, M.D., Chief of Staff
CIO: Jenean Blackmon, Assistant Vice President and Chief Information Officer
CHR: Cynthia Causey, Associate Administrator Human and Mission Services
Web address: www.mcleodhealth.org
Control: Other not–for–profit (including NFP Corporation) **Service:** General
medical and surgical

Staffed Beds: 34 **Admissions:** 2376 **Census:** 26 **Outpatient Visits:** 80275
Births: 286 **Total Expense ($000):** 40654 **Payroll Expense ($000):** 17859
Personnel: 262

EASLEY—Pickens County

✠ **BAPTIST EASLEY HOSPITAL (420015)**, 200 Fleetwood Drive, Zip 29640–2022,
Mailing Address: P.O. Box 2129, Zip 29641–2129; tel. 864/442–7200, **A**1 5 10
F3 11 13 15 28 29 30 34 35 39 40 56 57 59 64 70 76 79 81 85 86 87 89 107
108 111 114 115 119 124 130 132 146 147
Primary Contact: Todd Walker, President
CFO: Kathleen Stapleton, Chief Financial Officer
CIO: Cynthia Ellenburg, Director Health Information Services
CHR: Richard B Posey, Director Human Resources
CNO: Mary Ann Hunter, Director Nursing Services
Web address: www.baptisteasley.org
Control: Other not–for–profit (including NFP Corporation) **Service:** General
medical and surgical

Staffed Beds: 89 **Admissions:** 3237 **Census:** 38 **Outpatient Visits:** 102118
Total Expense ($000): 74798 **Payroll Expense ($000):** 25018
Personnel: 648

EDGEFIELD—Edgefield County

★ **EDGEFIELD COUNTY HOSPITAL (421304)**, 300 Ridge Medical Plaza,
Zip 29824–4525, Mailing Address: PO Box 590, Zip 29824–4525;
tel. 803/637–3174, **A**10 18 **F**3 28 29 34 35 40 45 59 65 68 77 79 81 84 93
94 107 119 127 130 133 146
Primary Contact: Carlos Milanes, Chief Executive Officer
CFO: Lori Jacobs, Chief Financial Officer
CMO: Tami Massey, M.D., Chief of Medical Staff
CIO: Juli Corley, Chief Information Officer
CHR: Theresa Stover, Chief Human Resource Officer
CNO: Cheryl Faust, Chief Nursing Officer
Web address: www.myech.org
Control: County, Government, nonfederal **Service:** General medical and surgical

Staffed Beds: 25 **Admissions:** 248 **Census:** 8 **Outpatient Visits:** 14059
Births: 0 **Personnel:** 161

FAIRFAX—Allendale County

★ **ALLENDALE COUNTY HOSPITAL (421300)**, 1787 Allendale Fairfax
Highway, Zip 29827–9133, Mailing Address: P.O. Box 218, Zip 29827–0218;
tel. 803/632–3311, (Total facility includes 44 beds in nursing home–type unit) **A**10
18 **F**3 15 34 35 40 56 57 59 61 64 67 68 90 97 107 110 114 119 127 128
133 147 **P**6
Primary Contact: Lari Gooding, Chief Executive Officer
Web address: www.achospital.org
Control: County, Government, nonfederal **Service:** General medical and surgical

Staffed Beds: 69 **Admissions:** 233 **Census:** 36 **Outpatient Visits:** 28345
Births: 0 **Personnel:** 150

FLORENCE—Florence County

✠ △ **CAROLINAS HOSPITAL SYSTEM (420091)**, 805 Pamplico Highway,
Zip 29505–6050, Mailing Address: P.O. Box 100550, Zip 29502–0550;
tel. 843/674–5000, **A**1 7 10 **F**4 5 6 8 13 15 17 18 20 22 24 26 28 29 30 31
34 35 40 41 43 45 53 56 57 59 60 63 64 67 70 72 73 74 75 76 77 78 79 81
87 88 89 90 94 107 110 111 114 115 116 117 119 121 128 129 132 135
145 146 147 148 **S** Community Health Systems, Inc., Franklin, TN
Primary Contact: Vance V. Reynolds, FACHE, CPA, Chief Executive Officer
COO: Kyle Baxter, Chief Operating Officer
CFO: Loren Rials, Chief Financial Officer
CIO: Lynn Northcutt, Chief Information Officer
CHR: Kay Douglas, Human Resources Director
CNO: Costa Cockfield, Chief Nursing Officer
Web address: www.carolinashospital.com
Control: Corporation, Investor–owned (for–profit) **Service:** General medical and
surgical

Staffed Beds: 416 **Admissions:** 10370 **Census:** 148 **Outpatient
Visits:** 119163

✠ **ENCOMPASS HEALTH REHABILITATION HOSPITAL OF FLORENCE (423026)**,
900 East Cheves Street, Zip 29506–2704; tel. 843/679–9000, **A**1 10 **F**9 28 29
34 35 56 57 59 75 77 82 86 87 90 91 92 93 94 95 96 130 131 132 148 **S**
Encompass Health Corporation, Birmingham, AL
Primary Contact: Brian Nunn, R.N., Chief Executive Officer
CFO: Robert Wheeler, Controller
CMO: Adora Matthews, M.D., Medical Director
CHR: Susan Trantham, Director Human Resources
Web address: www.healthsouthflorence.com
Control: Corporation, Investor–owned (for–profit) **Service:** Rehabilitation

Staffed Beds: 88 **Admissions:** 1180 **Census:** 44 **Outpatient Visits:** 0
Births: 0

★ ⇑ **MCLEOD REGIONAL MEDICAL CENTER (420051)**, 555 East Cheves Street, Zip 29506–2617, Mailing Address: P.O. Box 100551, Zip 29502–0551; tel. 843/777–2000, **A**2 3 5 10 21 **F**1 3 7 8 11 13 15 17 18 19 20 22 24 26 28 29 30 31 32 34 35 37 40 43 44 45 46 47 48 49 50 51 53 54 56 57 58 59 60 61 62 63 64 65 66 68 70 71 72 73 74 75 76 77 78 79 80 81 82 84 85 86 87 88 89 92 94 96 97 100 102 107 108 110 111 115 117 118 119 120 121 123 124 126 128 129 130 131 132 135 143 145 146 147 148 149 150 **P**8 **S** McLeod Health, Florence, SC
Primary Contact: Robert L. Colones, President and Chief Executive Officer
COO: Ron Boring, Senior Vice President and Chief Operating Officer
CFO: Fulton Ervin, Chief Financial Officer
CMO: Alva W Whitehead, M.D., Vice President Medical Services
CIO: Jenean Blackmon, Associate Vice President and Chief Information Officer
CHR: Jeannette Glenn, Vice President Human Resources, Education and Training
Web address: www.mcleodhealth.org
Control: Other not–for–profit (including NFP Corporation) **Service:** General medical and surgical

Staffed Beds: 466 **Admissions:** 26875 **Census:** 356 **Outpatient Visits:** 231346 **Births:** 2009 **Total Expense ($000):** 598991 **Payroll Expense ($000):** 210272 **Personnel:** 3003	

⊞ **REGENCY HOSPITAL OF FLORENCE (422007)**, 121 East Cedar Street, 4th Floor, Zip 29506–2576; tel. 843/661–3471, **A**1 10 **F**1 3 29 34 35 57 58 77 80 85 90 100 130 148 **S** Select Medical Corporation, Mechanicsburg, PA
Primary Contact: Amy Metz, Chief Executive Officer
CMO: Stephen Dersch, M.D., President Medical Staff
CHR: Tina Stokes, Manager Human Resources
Web address: www.regencyhospital.com
Control: Corporation, Investor–owned (for–profit) **Service:** Acute long–term care hospital

Staffed Beds: 40 **Admissions:** 460 **Census:** 34 **Outpatient Visits:** 0 **Births:** 0 **Personnel:** 110	

FORT JACKSON—Richland County

⊞ **MONCRIEF ARMY COMMUNITY HOSPITAL**, 4500 Stuart Street, Zip 29207–5700; tel. 803/751–2160, (Nonreporting) **A**1 5 **S** Department of the Army, Office of the Surgeon General, Falls Church, VA
Primary Contact: Colonel Traci Crawford, R.N., Commander
Web address: www.moncrief.amedd.army.mil
Control: Army, Government, federal **Service:** General medical and surgical

Staffed Beds: 60	

GAFFNEY—Cherokee County

⊞ **MARY BLACK HEALTH SYSTEM – GAFFNEY (420043)**, 1530 North Limestone Street, Zip 29340–4738; tel. 864/487–4271, **A**1 10 **F**3 11 13 15 18 19 29 34 35 40 45 46 51 57 59 64 65 67 70 75 76 79 81 82 85 86 87 89 107 108 110 111 113 119 129 130 131 132 135 145 146 147 148 **S** Community Health Systems, Inc., Franklin, TN
Primary Contact: Joshua Self, Chief Executive Officer
COO: Leslie Glover, Director Operations
CFO: Christine Poplawski, Chief Financial Officer
CMO: Frank Phillips, M.D., Chief of Staff
CIO: Richard Bledsoe, Director Information Systems
CHR: Connie Gibson, R.N., Director Human Resources
Web address: www.maryblackgaffney.com/mary-black-gaffney/home.aspx
Control: Corporation, Investor–owned (for–profit) **Service:** General medical and surgical

Staffed Beds: 125 **Admissions:** 2219 **Census:** 25	

GEORGETOWN—Georgetown County

⊞ **TIDELANDS GEORGETOWN MEMORIAL HOSPITAL (420020)**, 606 Black River Road, Zip 29440–3368, Mailing Address: Drawer 421718, Zip 29442–4203; tel. 843/527–7000, **A**1 3 5 10 19 **F**3 8 11 12 13 15 17 18 20 22 26 28 29 30 31 32 34 35 39 40 45 50 51 53 54 56 57 59 60 61 64 65 68 70 73 74 75 76 77 78 79 80 81 82 84 85 86 90 94 97 100 102 107 108 110 111 115 118 119 130 131 132 135 146 147 148 **S** QHR, Brentwood, TN
Primary Contact: Bruce P. Bailey, Chief Executive Officer
COO: Gayle L Resetar, Vice President and Chief Operating Officer
CFO: Elizabeth S. Ward, Chief Financial Officer
CHR: James F Harper, Senior Vice President and Chief Human Resources Officer
Web address: www.tidelandshealth.org
Control: Other not–for–profit (including NFP Corporation) **Service:** General medical and surgical

Staffed Beds: 136 **Admissions:** 4068 **Census:** 43 **Outpatient Visits:** 187962 **Births:** 269 **Total Expense ($000):** 132159 **Payroll Expense ($000):** 52451 **Personnel:** 844	

GREENVILLE—Greenville County

⊞ △ **BON SECOURS ST. FRANCIS HEALTH SYSTEM (420023)**, One St Francis Drive, Zip 29601–3207; tel. 864/255–1000, (Includes ST. FRANCIS EASTSIDE, 125 Commonwealth Drive, Greenville, SC, Zip 29615–4812; tel. 864/675–4000) **A**1 2 7 10 **F**3 8 11 12 13 15 17 18 20 22 24 26 28 29 30 31 34 35 36 39 40 44 45 46 47 48 49 50 51 53 54 55 57 58 59 60 61 62 63 64 66 68 69 70 71 73 74 75 76 77 78 79 80 81 82 83 84 85 86 87 89 90 94 96 97 107 108 110 111 114 115 118 119 124 126 129 130 132 135 136 141 146 147 **S** Bon Secours Health System, Inc., Marriottsville, MD
Primary Contact: Craig McCoy, Chief Executive Officer
CFO: Ronnie Hyatt, Senior Vice President Finance and Chief Financial Officer
CMO: Thomas H. Cummins, M.D., Chief Medical Officer
CIO: Rita Hooker, Administrative Director Information Services
CHR: Fernando Fleites, Senior Vice President Human Resources
CNO: Teri Ficicchy, R.N., MSN, Chief Nursing Officer
Web address: www.stfrancishealth.org
Control: Other not–for–profit (including NFP Corporation) **Service:** General medical and surgical

Staffed Beds: 352 **Admissions:** 19893 **Census:** 233 **Outpatient Visits:** 197705 **Births:** 2207 **Total Expense ($000):** 412670 **Payroll Expense ($000):** 132619 **Personnel:** 2770	

⊞ △ **GHS GREENVILLE MEMORIAL HOSPITAL (420078)**, 701 Grove Road, Zip 29605–4295; tel. 864/455–7000, (Includes GHS CHILDREN'S HOSPITAL, 701 Grove Road, Greenville, SC, Zip 29605–5611; tel. 864/455–7000; MARSHALL I. PICKENS HOSPITAL, 701 Grove Road, Greenville, SC, Zip 29605–5601; tel. 864/455–8988; ROGER C. PEACE REHABILITATION HOSPITAL, 701 Grove Road, Greenville, SC, Zip 29605–4295; tel. 864/455–7000) (Total facility includes 15 beds in nursing home–type unit) **A**1 2 3 5 7 8 10 **F**3 4 11 13 15 17 18 19 20 22 24 26 27 28 29 30 31 34 35 36 38 39 40 41 43 44 45 46 47 48 49 50 51 52 53 54 56 57 58 59 61 64 65 66 68 70 72 73 74 75 76 77 78 79 80 81 82 83 84 85 86 87 88 89 90 92 93 94 96 97 98 99 100 101 102 103 104 105 106 107 108 110 111 114 115 116 117 118 119 120 121 123 124 126 128 129 130 132 134 135 136 141 142 145 146 147 148 153 154 **P**6 **S** Greenville Health System, Greenville, SC
Primary Contact: Ric A. Ransom, Chief Operating Officer
COO: Greg Rusnak, Executive Vice President and Chief Operating Officer
CFO: Terri T. Newsom, Vice President of Finance and Chief Financial Officer
CMO: Angelo Sinopoli, M.D., Vice President Clinical Integration and Chief Medical Officer
CIO: Rich Rogers, Vice President Information Services
CHR: Doug Dorman, Vice President Human Resources
CNO: Michelle T Smith, R.N., MSN, FACHE, Vice President Nursing Chief Nursing Officer Chief Experience Officer
Web address: www.ghs.org
Control: Other not–for–profit (including NFP Corporation) **Service:** General medical and surgical

Staffed Beds: 822 **Admissions:** 38512 **Census:** 596 **Outpatient Visits:** 669335 **Births:** 5642 **Total Expense ($000):** 1020586 **Payroll Expense ($000):** 271133 **Personnel:** 5793	

⊞ **PATEWOOD MEMORIAL HOSPITAL (420102)**, 175 Patewood Drive, Zip 29615–3570; tel. 864/797–1000, **A**1 5 10 **F**3 11 13 29 30 37 45 50 64 74 76 77 79 80 81 85 86 130 146 147 **P**6 **S** Greenville Health System, Greenville, SC
Primary Contact: Tim Brookshire, Chief Operating Officer
Web address: www.ghs.org/patewood
Control: Other not–for–profit (including NFP Corporation) **Service:** Surgical

Staffed Beds: 72 **Admissions:** 1464 **Census:** 7 **Outpatient Visits:** 6504 **Births:** 37 **Total Expense ($000):** 82930 **Payroll Expense ($000):** 22035 **Personnel:** 250	

⊞ **REGENCY HOSPITAL OF GREENVILLE (422009)**, One St Francis Drive, 4th Floor, Zip 29601–3955; tel. 864/255–1438, (Nonreporting) **A**1 10 **S** Select Medical Corporation, Mechanicsburg, PA
Primary Contact: Paige Beauregard, Chief Executive Officer
Web address: www.regencyhospital.com
Control: Corporation, Investor–owned (for–profit) **Service:** Acute long–term care hospital

Staffed Beds: 32	

SC

Hospital, Medicare Provider Number, Address, Telephone, Approval, Facility, and Physician Codes, Health Care System			
★ American Hospital Association (AHA) membership	○ Healthcare Facilities Accreditation Program	⇑ Center for Improvement in Healthcare Quality Accreditation	
□ The Joint Commission accreditation	◇ DNV Healthcare Inc. accreditation	△ Commission on Accreditation of Rehabilitation Facilities (CARF) accreditation	

☐ **SHRINERS HOSPITALS FOR CHILDREN–GREENVILLE (423300)**, 950 West Faris Road, Zip 29605–4277; tel. 864/271–3444, **A**1 3 5 10 **F**29 59 64 68 75 77 79 81 85 87 89 90 93 94 130 131 146 148 **P**6 **S** Shriners Hospitals for Children, Tampa, FL
Primary Contact: Bill Munley, Administrator
CFO: John Conti, Director Finance
CMO: J. Michael Wattenbarger, M.D., Chief of Staff
CHR: Willis E Tisdale, Director Human Resources
CNO: Allison Leigh Windas, Director of Patient Care Services–Nurse Executive
Web address: www.greenvilleshrinershospital.org
Control: Other not–for–profit (including NFP Corporation) **Service**: Children's orthopedic

> **Staffed Beds**: 15 **Admissions**: 215 **Census**: 1 **Outpatient Visits**: 19915
> **Births**: 0 **Total Expense ($000)**: 27026 **Payroll Expense ($000)**: 13818
> **Personnel**: 180

GREENWOOD—Greenwood County

☐ **GREENWOOD REGIONAL REHABILITATION HOSPITAL (423030)**, 1530 Parkway, Zip 29646–4027; tel. 864/330–1800, (Total facility includes 12 beds in nursing home–type unit) **A**1 10 **F**3 29 75 77 90 128 130 132 143 148 **S** Ernest Health, Inc., Albuquerque, NM
Primary Contact: Kristin Manske, Chief Executive Officer
CFO: Charity Martin, Controller and Regional Business Officer Manager
CMO: Cam Monda, D.O., Medical Director
CHR: Michelle Watkins, Human Resources Manager
CNO: Jessica Lawson, Director of Nursing
Web address: www.grrh.ernesthealth.com
Control: Corporation, Investor–owned (for–profit) **Service**: Rehabilitation

> **Staffed Beds**: 54 **Admissions**: 1082 **Census**: 40 **Outpatient Visits**: 0
> **Births**: 0 **Total Expense ($000)**: 17285 **Payroll Expense ($000)**: 6821
> **Personnel**: 214

★ ⇑ **SELF REGIONAL HEALTHCARE (420071)**, 1325 Spring Street, Zip 29646–3860; tel. 864/725–4111, **A**2 3 5 10 21 **F**3 8 11 13 15 17 18 20 22 24 26 28 29 30 31 32 34 35 43 44 45 46 48 49 50 51 53 55 57 58 59 60 61 62 64 68 70 71 72 73 74 75 76 77 78 79 80 81 82 85 86 87 89 90 91 94 96 97 98 102 103 107 108 110 111 114 115 119 120 121 123 124 129 130 131 132 134 135 146 147 148 149 **P**6
Primary Contact: James A. Pfeiffer, FACHE, President and Chief Executive Officer
CFO: Timothy Evans, Vice President and Chief Financial Officer
CMO: F Gregory Mappin, M.D., Vice President Medical Affairs and Chief Medical Officer
CIO: Andy Hartung, Director Information Systems
CHR: Michael Dixon, Director Human Resources
CNO: Linda Russell, Vice President and Chief Nursing Officer
Web address: www.selfregional.org
Control: County, Government, nonfederal **Service**: General medical and surgical

> **Staffed Beds**: 322 **Admissions**: 11552 **Census**: 153 **Outpatient Visits**: 346313 **Births**: 1384 **Total Expense ($000)**: 329315 **Payroll Expense ($000)**: 109309 **Personnel**: 1915

GREER—Greenville County

☐ **CAROLINA CENTER FOR BEHAVIORAL HEALTH (424010)**, 2700 East Phillips Road, Zip 29650–4816; tel. 864/235–2335, **A**1 10 **F**4 5 98 99 100 101 102 103 104 105 153 **S** Universal Health Services, Inc., King of Prussia, PA
Primary Contact: John Willingham, Chief Executive Officer and Managing Director
COO: Greg Schlangen, R.N., Chief Operating Officer
CFO: James P Boynton Jr Chief Financial Officer
CMO: Gergana Dimitrova, M.D., Medical Director
CHR: Ginny Savage, Director of Human Resources
CNO: Jennifer Daigle, R.N., Director of Nursing and Utilization Review
Web address: www.thecarolinacenter.com
Control: Corporation, Investor–owned (for–profit) **Service**: Psychiatric

> **Staffed Beds**: 130 **Admissions**: 4018 **Census**: 110 **Outpatient Visits**: 15859 **Births**: 0 **Personnel**: 271

⊞ **GHS GREER MEMORIAL HOSPITAL (420033)**, 830 South Buncombe Road, Zip 29650–2400; tel. 864/797–8000, **A**1 5 10 **F**3 11 13 15 18 28 29 30 34 35 40 44 45 49 50 51 57 59 64 65 68 70 76 77 79 81 85 86 87 89 94 107 110 111 114 119 129 130 146 147 148 **P**6 **S** Greenville Health System, Greenville, SC
Primary Contact: John F. Mansure, FACHE, President
Web address: www.ghs.org
Control: Other not–for–profit (including NFP Corporation) **Service**: General medical and surgical

> **Staffed Beds**: 70 **Admissions**: 3311 **Census**: 24 **Outpatient Visits**: 113669
> **Births**: 736 **Total Expense ($000)**: 80518 **Payroll Expense ($000)**: 23790
> **Personnel**: 380

GREER—Spartanburg County

★ ⇑ **PELHAM MEDICAL CENTER (420103)**, 250 Westmoreland Road, Zip 29651–9013; tel. 864/530–6000, **A**10 21 **F**3 11 15 18 20 26 29 30 34 35 37 40 45 49 50 54 57 59 64 68 70 74 75 77 79 81 82 84 85 86 87 90 94 107 108 110 111 114 115 118 119 130 146 148 149 154 **S** Spartanburg Regional Healthcare System, Spartanburg, SC
Primary Contact: Anthony Kouskolekas, FACHE, President
CNO: Connie Spykerman, Chief Nursing Officer
Web address: www.pelhammedicalcenter.com
Control: Hospital district or authority, Government, nonfederal **Service**: General medical and surgical

> **Staffed Beds**: 48 **Admissions**: 3143 **Census**: 37 **Outpatient Visits**: 53281
> **Births**: 0 **Total Expense ($000)**: 73476 **Payroll Expense ($000)**: 22079
> **Personnel**: 603

HARDEEVILLE—Jasper County

⊞ **COASTAL CAROLINA HOSPITAL (420101)**, 1000 Medical Center Drive, Zip 29927–3446; tel. 843/784–8000, **A**1 10 **F**3 11 13 15 28 29 34 35 40 45 46 47 48 49 57 59 64 70 74 75 76 77 79 81 85 90 93 94 107 108 110 111 115 117 119 126 127 132 135 146 147 148 **S** TENET Healthcare Corporation, Dallas, TX
Primary Contact: Joel Taylor, Chief Executive Officer
COO: Christopher Borgstrom, Associate Administrator
CFO: Ronald J. Groteluschen, Chief Financial Officer
CIO: Cheryl Grant, Director Information Systems
CHR: Darlene E. Nester, Market Chief Human Resources Officer
CNO: Jennifer LeBlanc, Chief Nursing Officer
Web address: www.coastalhospital.com
Control: Corporation, Investor–owned (for–profit) **Service**: General medical and surgical

> **Staffed Beds**: 35 **Admissions**: 2992 **Census**: 27 **Outpatient Visits**: 47181
> **Births**: 694 **Total Expense ($000)**: 50747 **Payroll Expense ($000)**: 16556
> **Personnel**: 359

HARTSVILLE—Darlington County

☐ ○ **CAROLINA PINES REGIONAL MEDICAL CENTER (420010)**, 1304 West Bobo Newsom Highway, Zip 29550–4710; tel. 843/339–2100, **A**1 10 11 **F**3 11 13 15 20 28 29 30 34 35 40 43 46 49 57 64 70 73 75 76 79 81 82 85 86 87 89 90 93 107 108 110 111 114 115 118 119 129 130 131 132 135 146 147 148 **S** RCCH HealthCare Partners, Brentwood, TN
Primary Contact: William Little, Chief Executive Officer
COO: Susan C Shugart, Chief Operating Officer
CFO: Rodney VanDonkelaar, Chief Financial Officer
CMO: Tallulah Holmstrom, M.D., Chief Medical Officer
CIO: Denise Barefoot, Director of Information Technology
CHR: Charlotte Adams, Director of Human Resources
CNO: Christy Moody, R.N., Chief Nursing Officer
Web address: www.cprmc.com
Control: Corporation, Investor–owned (for–profit) **Service**: General medical and surgical

> **Staffed Beds**: 105 **Admissions**: 4022 **Census**: 36 **Outpatient Visits**: 95064
> **Births**: 563 **Personnel**: 410

HILTON HEAD ISLAND—Beaufort County

⊞ **HILTON HEAD HOSPITAL (420080)**, 25 Hospital Center Boulevard, Zip 29926–2738; tel. 843/681–6122, **A**1 10 20 **F**3 11 13 15 17 18 20 22 24 28 29 30 34 35 37 40 45 46 48 49 50 51 54 57 59 60 61 64 65 68 70 74 76 77 78 79 81 85 86 89 94 96 107 108 110 111 114 115 119 126 130 131 132 135 146 147 148 **S** TENET Healthcare Corporation, Dallas, TX
Primary Contact: Jeremy L. Clark, Market Chief Executive Officer
CMO: Glenn Neil Love, M.D., Medical Director
CIO: Stephen Brendler, Director Information Systems
CHR: Darlene E. Nester, Chief Human Resources Officer
Web address: www.hiltonheadregional.com
Control: Partnership, Investor–owned (for–profit) **Service**: General medical and surgical

> **Staffed Beds**: 93 **Admissions**: 5898 **Census**: 59 **Outpatient Visits**: 85024
> **Births**: 488 **Total Expense ($000)**: 102086 **Payroll Expense ($000)**: 26927
> **Personnel**: 463

SC

Many Facility Codes have changed. Please refer to the AHA Guide Code Chart. © 2018 AHA Guide

LAKE CITY—Florence County

★ **LAKE CITY COMMUNITY HOSPITAL (420066)**, 258 N Ron McNair Boulevard, Zip 29560–2462, Mailing Address: P.O. Box 1479, Zip 29560–1479; tel. 843/374–2036, **A**10 **F**3 11 15 28 29 34 35 40 50 53 56 57 59 64 65 69 75 77 79 81 85 86 87 93 94 107 108 110 111 113 114 119 127 130 132 146
Primary Contact: Michael Faucett, Chief Operating Officer
COO: Michael Faucett, Chief Operating Officer
CMO: Stephen Askins, M.D., Chief of Staff
CIO: David Moon Jr Director Information Systems
CHR: Anne Poston, Director of Human Resources/Compliance
CNO: Renate Browder, R.N., Director of Nursing
Web address: www.lcchospital.org
Control: Hospital district or authority, Government, nonfederal **Service**: General medical and surgical

Staffed Beds: 26 **Admissions**: 744 **Census**: 8 **Outpatient Visits**: 41364 **Births**: 0 **Total Expense ($000)**: 15619 **Payroll Expense ($000)**: 7695 **Personnel**: 220

LANCASTER—Lancaster County

☐ **REBOUND BEHAVIORAL HEALTH (044014)**, 134 East Rebound Road, Zip 29720–7712; tel. 877/959–5063, (Nonreporting) **A**1 **S** Acadia Healthcare Company, Inc., Franklin, TN
Primary Contact: Patricia Hamilton, Chief Executive Officer
Web address: www.reboundbehavioralhealth.com
Control: Corporation, Investor–owned (for–profit) **Service**: Psychiatric

Staffed Beds: 42

⊞ **SPRINGS MEMORIAL HOSPITAL (420036)**, 800 West Meeting Street, Zip 29720–2298; tel. 803/286–1214, (Nonreporting) **A**1 5 10 **S** Community Health Systems, Inc., Franklin, TN
Primary Contact: Page H. Vaughan, Chief Executive Officer
COO: Richard Warrin, Chief Operating Officer
CFO: Holt Smith, Chief Financial Officer
CMO: Douglas Tiedt, M.D., Chief of Staff
CIO: Chrys Steele, Director Information Systems
CHR: Karen Chapman, Human Resources Director
CNO: Karen Martin, Chief Nursing Officer
Web address: www.springsmemorial.com
Control: Corporation, Investor–owned (for–profit) **Service**: General medical and surgical

Staffed Beds: 162

LORIS—Horry County

⇑ **MCLEOD LORIS SEACOAST HOSPITAL (420105)**, 3655 Mitchell Street, Zip 29569–2827; tel. 843/716–7000, (Includes MCLEOD SEACOAST, 4000 Highway 9 East, Little River, SC, Zip 29566–7833; tel. 843/390–8100) **A**10 21 **F**3 11 13 15 17 18 20 28 29 30 31 32 34 35 40 44 50 53 57 58 59 60 63 64 68 70 74 75 76 77 78 79 81 82 85 86 87 89 90 94 96 102 107 108 110 111 114 115 116 118 119 130 131 132 134 135 143 146 148 149 154 **P**3 **S** McLeod Health, Florence, SC
Primary Contact: Edward D. Tinsley III, Regional Administrator
CMO: John Charles, M.D., Chief Medical Officer
CNO: Amanda Mills, Chief Nursing Officer
Web address: www.mcleodhealth.org
Control: Other not–for–profit (including NFP Corporation) **Service**: General medical and surgical

Staffed Beds: 155 **Admissions**: 5626 **Census**: 58 **Outpatient Visits**: 111423 **Births**: 435 **Total Expense ($000)**: 124765 **Payroll Expense ($000)**: 45251 **Personnel**: 321

MANNING—Clarendon County

★ ⇑ **MCLEOD HEALTH CLARENDON (420109)**, 10 Hospital Street, Zip 29102–3153, Mailing Address: P.O. Box 550, Zip 29102–0550; tel. 803/433–3000, **A**10 21 **F**3 7 13 15 17 28 29 34 35 40 45 51 53 59 62 63 64 65 68 70 75 76 77 79 81 85 87 90 93 94 96 97 107 108 110 111 114 119 127 128 130 133 135 143 146 147 148 149 **P**3 **S** McLeod Health, Florence, SC
Primary Contact: Rachel Gainey, Administrator
COO: Paul Schumacher, Chief Operating Officer
CFO: John Shaughnessy, Chief Financial Officer
CMO: Catherine Rabon, M.D., Chief Medical Officer
CIO: Pat Kolb, Manager Information Technology
CHR: Gail A Richbourg, Director Human Resources
CNO: Natalie Davis, R.N., Interim Chief Nursing Officer
Web address: www.clarendonhealth.org
Control: Other not–for–profit (including NFP Corporation) **Service**: General medical and surgical

Staffed Beds: 64 **Admissions**: 2140 **Census**: 26 **Outpatient Visits**: 86843 **Births**: 348 **Total Expense ($000)**: 45835 **Payroll Expense ($000)**: 16017

MOUNT PLEASANT—Charleston County

⊞ **EAST COOPER MEDICAL CENTER (420089)**, 2000 Hospital Drive, Zip 29464–3764; tel. 843/881–0100, **A**1 3 5 10 **F**3 13 15 18 29 31 34 35 40 43 46 51 57 59 60 64 68 70 73 74 75 76 77 78 79 80 81 82 84 85 86 90 92 93 94 100 102 107 108 110 111 114 115 119 126 129 130 131 132 135 147 148 **S** TENET Healthcare Corporation, Dallas, TX
Primary Contact: Patrick Downes, Chief Executive Officer
COO: Ramona Pickens, Chief Operating Officer
CFO: Patrick C Bolander, Chief Financial Officer
CMO: Kevin Keenan, M.D., Physician Advisor
CIO: Michael Foster, Director Information Systems
CHR: Tracy Hunter, Chief Human Resources Officer
CNO: Patrick Beaver, MSN, R.N., Chief Nursing Officer
Web address: www.eastcoopermedctr.com
Control: Corporation, Investor–owned (for–profit) **Service**: General medical and surgical

Staffed Beds: 140 **Admissions**: 4878 **Census**: 40 **Outpatient Visits**: 52371 **Births**: 1435 **Total Expense ($000)**: 123558 **Payroll Expense ($000)**: 33190 **Personnel**: 494

EAST COOPER REGIONAL MEDICAL CENTER See East Cooper Medical Center

⊞ **ROPER ST. FRANCIS MOUNT PLEASANT HOSPITAL (420104)**, 3500 Highway 17 North, Zip 29466–9123, Mailing Address: 3500 North Highway 17, Zip 29466–9123; tel. 843/606–7000, **A**1 10 **F**3 7 13 15 29 30 34 40 45 54 59 67 68 70 75 76 79 81 84 85 86 87 89 94 102 107 108 110 111 115 118 119 129 143 146 147 148 149 **S** Atrium Health, Charlotte, NC
Primary Contact: Anthony Jackson, Chief Executive Officer
CFO: Bret Johnson, Chief Financial Officer
CMO: Steven D Shapiro, M.D., Chief Medical Officer
CIO: Melinda H. Cardell, Interim Chief Information Officer
CHR: Melanie Stith, Vice President Human Resources
CNO: Tavia Buck, Chief Nursing Officer
Web address: www.rsfh.com/mount–pleasant–hospital
Control: Other not–for–profit (including NFP Corporation) **Service**: General medical and surgical

Staffed Beds: 73 **Admissions**: 2314 **Census**: 19 **Outpatient Visits**: 45629 **Births**: 535 **Total Expense ($000)**: 65979 **Payroll Expense ($000)**: 17095 **Personnel**: 338

MT. PLEASANT—Mt. Pleasant County

KINDRED HOSPITAL–CHARLESTON See Vibra Hospital of Charleston

⊞ **VIBRA HOSPITAL OF CHARLESTON (422005)**, 1200 Hospital Drive, Zip 29464; tel. 843/375–4000, (Nonreporting) **A**1 10 **S** Vibra Healthcare, Mechanicsburg, PA
Primary Contact: J. Scott Broome, Chief Executive Officer
CFO: Julia Smith, Chief Financial Officer
CMO: Athena Beldecos, M.D., Medical Director
CHR: Julia Taylor, Area Director Human Resources
Web address: www.vhcharleston.com
Control: Corporation, Investor–owned (for–profit) **Service**: Acute long–term care hospital

Staffed Beds: 94

MULLINS—Marion County

⊞ **CAROLINAS HOSPITAL SYSTEM MARION (420055)**, 2829 East Highway 76, Zip 29574–6035, Mailing Address: P O Drawer 1150, Marion, Zip 29571–1150; tel. 843/431–2000, (Total facility includes 92 beds in nursing home–type unit) **A**1 10 **F**3 13 15 28 29 34 40 45 46 53 57 59 60 67 70 72 75 76 77 79 81 82 85 86 89 90 94 107 111 119 128 129 130 131 133 146 148 **S** Community Health Systems, Inc., Franklin, TN
CFO: Loren Rials, Chief Financial Officer
CMO: Robert DeGrood, M.D., Chief Medical Staff
CIO: Charlie Grantham, Manager Information Systems
CHR: Christi Meggs, Director
CNO: Linda Parnell, Chief Nursing Officer
Web address: www.carolinashospitalmarion.com
Control: Corporation, Investor–owned (for–profit) **Service**: General medical and surgical

Staffed Beds: 216 **Admissions**: 2058 **Census**: 103 **Outpatient Visits**: 48820 **Births**: 233 **Total Expense ($000)**: 72841 **Payroll Expense ($000)**: 15707 **Personnel**: 263

SC

Hospital, Medicare Provider Number, Address, Telephone, Approval, Facility, and Physician Codes, Health Care System

★ American Hospital Association (AHA) membership
☐ The Joint Commission accreditation
○ Healthcare Facilities Accreditation Program
◇ DNV Healthcare Inc. accreditation
⇑ Center for Improvement in Healthcare Quality Accreditation
△ Commission on Accreditation of Rehabilitation Facilities (CARF) accreditation

© 2018 AHA Guide   *Many Facility Codes have changed. Please refer to the AHA Guide Code Chart.*   Hospitals **A555**

MARION COUNTY MEDICAL CENTER See Carolinas Hospital System Marion

MURRELLS INLET—Georgetown County

☒ △ **TIDELANDS WACCAMAW COMMUNITY HOSPITAL (420098)**, 4070 Highway 17 Bypass, Zip 29576–5033, Mailing Address: P O Drawer 3350, Zip 29576–2673; tel. 843/652–1000, **A**1 2 3 7 10 **F**3 8 11 13 15 17 18 28 29 30 31 32 35 37 39 40 45 50 51 56 60 61 64 65 68 70 73 74 75 76 77 78 79 81 82 84 85 86 87 89 90 93 94 96 97 100 102 107 108 110 111 114 115 118 119 130 131 146 147 148 **S** QHR, Brentwood, TN
Primary Contact: Bruce P. Bailey, Chief Executive Officer
CFO: Elizabeth S. Ward, Chief Financial Officer
Web address: www.tidelandswaccamawcommunity.org
Control: Other not–for–profit (including NFP Corporation) **Service**: General medical and surgical

> **Staffed Beds**: 169 **Admissions**: 7653 **Census**: 93 **Outpatient Visits**: 122116 **Births**: 490 **Total Expense ($000)**: 151673 **Payroll Expense ($000)**: 33640 **Personnel**: 612

MYRTLE BEACH—Horry County

☒ **GRAND STRAND REGIONAL MEDICAL CENTER (420085)**, 809 82nd Parkway, Zip 29572–4607; tel. 843/692–1000, (Nonreporting) **A**1 2 3 5 10 19 **S** HCA Healthcare, Nashville, TN
Primary Contact: Mark E. Sims, Chief Executive Officer
COO: Mark Miller, FACHE, Chief Operating Officer
CFO: Turner Wortham, Chief Financial Officer
Web address: www.grandstrandmed.com
Control: Corporation, Investor–owned (for–profit) **Service**: General medical and surgical

> **Staffed Beds**: 303

NEWBERRY—Newberry County

☒ **NEWBERRY COUNTY MEMORIAL HOSPITAL (420053)**, 2669 Kinard Street, Zip 29108–2911, Mailing Address: P.O. Box 497, Zip 29108–0497; tel. 803/276–7570, **A**1 10 20 **F**3 7 11 13 15 17 28 29 30 31 32 34 35 40 45 47 53 56 57 59 64 68 70 75 76 77 78 79 81 82 85 86 87 89 90 93 94 107 108 109 110 111 115 119 130 133 135 143 146 147 148 149 **P**6 **S** QHR, Brentwood, TN
Primary Contact: Bruce A. Baldwin, Chief Executive Officer
CFO: Mike Reynolds, Chief Financial Officer
CMO: Mark Davis, M.D., Chief of Staff
CIO: David Wolff, Director Information Technology
CHR: Dyan Bowman, Director Human Resources
Web address: www.newberryhospital.org
Control: County, Government, nonfederal **Service**: General medical and surgical

> **Staffed Beds**: 54 **Admissions**: 1885 **Census**: 19 **Outpatient Visits**: 41586 **Births**: 277 **Total Expense ($000)**: 45161 **Payroll Expense ($000)**: 15644 **Personnel**: 353

ORANGEBURG—Orangeburg County

☒ **REGIONAL MEDICAL CENTER (420068)**, 3000 St Matthews Road, Zip 29118–1442; tel. 803/395–2200, **A**1 10 13 **F**3 11 12 13 14 15 17 18 20 28 29 30 31 34 35 40 43 44 45 46 47 48 49 50 53 57 58 59 60 61 62 64 65 66 68 70 71 73 76 77 78 79 81 82 84 85 86 87 89 90 93 94 97 98 100 101 102 103 104 107 108 110 111 115 119 121 127 129 130 131 132 135 144 146 147 149 **S** QHR, Brentwood, TN
Primary Contact: Charles E. Williams, FACHE, President and Chief Executive Officer
CFO: Liza Porterfield, Chief Financial Officer
CIO: James Albin, Chief Information Officer
CHR: Howard Harris, Vice President Human Resources
CNO: Mickey Whisenhunt, Interim Chief Nursing Officer
Web address: www.trmchealth.org
Control: County, Government, nonfederal **Service**: General medical and surgical

> **Staffed Beds**: 283 **Admissions**: 10382 **Census**: 133 **Outpatient Visits**: 202663 **Births**: 890 **Total Expense ($000)**: 216837 **Payroll Expense ($000)**: 93374 **Personnel**: 1020

☐ **WILLIAM J. MCCORD ADOLESCENT TREATMENT FACILITY (424013)**, 910 Cook Road, Zip 29118–2124, Mailing Address: P.O. Box 1166, Zip 29116–1166; tel. 803/534–2328, **A**1 10 **F**4 29 34 38 57 61 98 99 130 132 134 135 151
Primary Contact: Michael Dennis, Director
CFO: Laura Murdaugh, Finance Director
CMO: Dorothy Kendall, Medical Director
CNO: Linda Mitchum, Director of Nursing
Web address: www.tccada.com
Control: Other not–for–profit (including NFP Corporation) **Service**: Children's hospital psychiatric

> **Staffed Beds**: 15 **Admissions**: 120 **Census**: 14 **Outpatient Visits**: 0 **Births**: 0 **Total Expense ($000)**: 2262 **Payroll Expense ($000)**: 1199 **Personnel**: 29

PICKENS—Pickens County

★ ⇑ **ANMED HEALTH CANNON (420011)**, 123 W G Acker Drive, Zip 29671–2739, Mailing Address: P.O. Box 188, Zip 29671–0188; tel. 864/878–4791, **A**10 21 **F**3 11 15 29 34 40 45 50 56 57 59 64 70 75 79 81 85 94 97 107 108 110 111 114 119 127 135 146 149 **P**8 **S** AnMed Health, Anderson, SC
Primary Contact: Brandon Clary, President and Chief Executive Officer
CFO: Will Grant, Chief Financial Officer
CMO: Daniel J Dahlhausen, M.D., President of Medical Staff/Chief Medical Officer
CIO: Robert Furr, Director Information Services
CHR: Lisa G Bryant, Director Human Resources
CNO: Donna K Anderson, R.N., Chief Nursing Officer
Web address: www.cannonhospital.org
Control: Other not–for–profit (including NFP Corporation) **Service**: General medical and surgical

> **Staffed Beds**: 24 **Admissions**: 759 **Census**: 8 **Outpatient Visits**: 55558 **Births**: 0 **Personnel**: 180

ROCK HILL—York County

☒ **ENCOMPASS HEALTH REHABILITATION HOSPITAL OF ROCK HILL (423028)**, 1795 Dr. Frank Gaston Boulevard, Zip 29732–1190; tel. 803/326–3500, **A**1 10 **F**29 90 95 96 146 148 **S** Encompass Health Corporation, Birmingham, AL
Primary Contact: Deanna Martin, Chief Executive Officer
Web address: www.healthsouthrockhill.com
Control: Corporation, Investor–owned (for–profit) **Service**: Rehabilitation

> **Staffed Beds**: 50 **Admissions**: 1389 **Census**: 44 **Outpatient Visits**: 0 **Births**: 0 **Personnel**: 83

☒ **PIEDMONT MEDICAL CENTER (420002)**, 222 Herlong Avenue, Zip 29732; tel. 803/329–1234, **A**1 2 10 **F**3 7 11 17 18 20 22 24 26 28 29 30 31 34 35 40 43 45 49 50 57 59 60 64 70 72 73 74 75 76 77 78 79 81 82 85 86 89 90 91 93 98 100 102 107 108 110 111 114 115 118 119 126 130 132 135 146 147 148 154 **S** TENET Healthcare Corporation, Dallas, TX
Primary Contact: Mark Nosacka, Chief Executive Officer
COO: James Riley, Chief Operating Officer
CFO: Stephen Gilmore, Chief Financial Officer
CIO: Joel Dean, Director Information Services
CHR: Elizabeth Elich, Chief Human Resources Officer
CNO: Patricia A. Feilmeier, R.N., Chief Nursing Officer
Web address: www.piedmontmedicalcenter.com
Control: Corporation, Investor–owned (for–profit) **Service**: General medical and surgical

> **Staffed Beds**: 276 **Admissions**: 14011 **Census**: 191 **Outpatient Visits**: 139583 **Births**: 1708 **Total Expense ($000)**: 228018 **Payroll Expense ($000)**: 78930 **Personnel**: 1531

SENECA—Oconee County

☒ **OCONEE MEMORIAL HOSPITAL (420009)**, 298 Memorial Drive, Zip 29672–9499; tel. 864/882–3351, (Total facility includes 120 beds in nursing home–type unit) **A**1 3 5 10 20 **F**3 7 11 13 15 17 18 20 28 29 30 31 34 35 39 40 51 54 56 57 59 62 63 64 67 70 75 76 77 78 79 81 82 84 85 86 87 89 90 94 97 107 108 111 114 119 128 130 132 143 146 **P**2 **S** Greenville Health System, Greenville, SC
Primary Contact: Hunter Kome, Campus President
CMO: Conrad K Shuler, M.D., Chief Medical Officer
CIO: Jay Hansen, Director Information Services
CNO: Patricia Smith, Chief Nursing Officer
Web address: www.oconeemed.org
Control: Other not–for–profit (including NFP Corporation) **Service**: General medical and surgical

> **Staffed Beds**: 252 **Admissions**: 6371 **Census**: 165 **Outpatient Visits**: 110965 **Births**: 436 **Total Expense ($000)**: 110182 **Payroll Expense ($000)**: 35820 **Personnel**: 757

SIMPSONVILLE—Greenville County

☒ **GHS HILLCREST MEMORIAL HOSPITAL (420037)**, 729 SE Main Street, Zip 29681–3280; tel. 864/454–6100, **A**1 5 10 **F**3 11 12 15 18 29 34 35 40 44 45 50 57 59 64 68 70 79 81 85 86 90 107 110 111 114 119 129 130 132 146 **P**6 **S** Greenville Health System, Greenville, SC
Primary Contact: Scott R. Jones, FACHE, Chief Operating Officer
Web address: www.ghs.org
Control: Other not–for–profit (including NFP Corporation) **Service**: General medical and surgical

> **Staffed Beds**: 43 **Admissions**: 1920 **Census**: 13 **Outpatient Visits**: 70491 **Births**: 0 **Total Expense ($000)**: 58384 **Payroll Expense ($000)**: 16517 **Personnel**: 252

SC

Many Facility Codes have changed. Please refer to the AHA Guide Code Chart.
© 2018 AHA Guide

SPARTANBURG—Spartanburg County

☒ △ **MARY BLACK HEALTH SYSTEM–SPARTANBURG (420083)**, 1700 Skylyn Drive, Zip 29307–1061, Mailing Address: P.O. Box 3217, Zip 29304–3217; tel. 864/573–3000, **A**1 5 7 10 **F**3 11 13 15 18 20 29 30 31 34 35 40 45 47 49 50 51 56 57 59 60 64 68 70 73 74 76 77 78 79 81 85 89 90 93 94 96 98 102 103 107 108 110 111 114 115 119 126 129 130 135 145 146 147 148 **S** Community Health Systems, Inc., Franklin, TN
Primary Contact: Parkes Coggins, Chief Executive Officer
CFO: Brett English, Chief Financial Officer
CMO: Howard Bean, M.D., Chief Medical Officer
CIO: John O'Donnell, Director of Information Technology Services
CHR: Lee Ann Roque, Director of Human Resources
CNO: Chanda Flynn, R.N., MSN, Chief Nursing Officer
Web address: www.maryblackhealthsystem.com
Control: Corporation, Investor–owned (for–profit) **Service**: General medical and surgical

Staffed Beds: 176 Admissions: 6034 Census: 75 Outpatient Visits: 110968 Births: 1016 Total Expense ($000): 108127 Payroll Expense ($000): 37735 Personnel: 852

☒ **SPARTANBURG HOSPITAL FOR RESTORATIVE CARE (422004)**, 389 Serpentine Drive, Zip 29303–3026; tel. 864/560–3280, (Total facility includes 25 beds in nursing home–type unit) **A**1 10 **F**1 29 30 31 35 57 59 60 68 70 75 77 79 82 84 85 87 90 119 128 130 148 149 **S** Spartanburg Regional Healthcare System, Spartanburg, SC
Primary Contact: Anita M. Butler, Chief Executive Officer
Web address: www.srhs.com
Control: Hospital district or authority, Government, nonfederal **Service**: Acute long–term care hospital

Staffed Beds: 116 Admissions: 851 Census: 42 Outpatient Visits: 0 Births: 0 Total Expense ($000): 23517 Payroll Expense ($000): 11591 Personnel: 196

★ ⇑ **SPARTANBURG MEDICAL CENTER (420007)**, 101 East Wood Street, Zip 29303–3040; tel. 864/560–6000, **A**2 3 5 10 13 21 **F**3 7 11 12 13 15 17 18 20 22 24 26 28 29 30 31 34 35 36 37 38 39 40 43 45 46 47 48 49 50 53 54 56 57 58 59 60 61 62 63 64 65 66 68 70 71 72 73 74 75 76 77 78 79 81 82 83 84 85 86 87 88 89 90 94 97 98 99 100 101 102 103 104 107 108 110 111 114 115 117 118 119 120 123 124 126 129 130 131 132 135 143 144 145 146 147 148 149 **S** Spartanburg Regional Healthcare System, Spartanburg, SC
Primary Contact: J Philip. Feisal, President and Chief Executive Officer
COO: Mark Aycock, Chief Operating Officer
CFO: Kenneth Meinke, Senior Vice President Administrative Services, Finance and Chief Financial Officer
CMO: Charles Morrow, M.D., Chief Medical Officer
CIO: Harold Moore, Chief Information Technology Officer
CHR: Kathy Sinclair, Vice President Human Resources
CNO: Susan Duggar, R.N., MSN, Vice President Nursing
Web address: www.spartanburgregional.com
Control: Hospital district or authority, Government, nonfederal **Service**: General medical and surgical

Staffed Beds: 514 Admissions: 26660 Census: 420 Outpatient Visits: 416690 Births: 2936 Total Expense ($000): 708051 Payroll Expense ($000): 231343 Personnel: 6312

SUMTER—Sumter County

☒ **PALMETTO HEALTH TUOMEY (420070)**, 129 North Washington Street, Zip 29150–4983; tel. 803/774–9000, (Total facility includes 18 beds in nursing home–type unit) **A**1 3 10 19 **F**1 3 11 13 15 20 28 29 30 31 32 34 35 40 48 49 50 51 54 56 59 62 63 64 68 70 71 73 75 76 77 78 79 80 81 84 85 86 87 89 90 94 102 107 108 110 111 114 119 120 121 128 129 130 131 132 135 146 147 148 **S** Palmetto Health, Columbia, SC
Primary Contact: Michelle Logan–Owens, Ph.D., R.N., Chief Operating Officer
CFO: Mark Lovell, Vice President and Chief Financial Officer
CMO: Gene Dickerson, M.D., Vice President Medical Affairs
CIO: Cheryl Martin, Chief Information Officer
CHR: Letitia Pringle–Miller, Administrative Director
CNO: Terrie Carlton, R.N., Vice President & Chief Nursing Officer
Web address: www.tuomey.com
Control: Other not–for–profit (including NFP Corporation) **Service**: General medical and surgical

Staffed Beds: 238 Admissions: 8349 Census: 180 Outpatient Visits: 146414 Births: 1306 Total Expense ($000): 173654 Payroll Expense ($000): 70381 Personnel: 1449

TRAVELERS REST—Greenville County

☒ △ **NORTH GREENVILLE HOSPITAL (422008)**, 807 North Main Street, Zip 29690–1551; tel. 864/455–9206, **A**1 5 7 10 **F**1 3 15 29 30 34 35 40 44 50 64 68 75 79 85 86 87 107 110 111 114 119 130 146 148 **P**6
Primary Contact: Adrienne Talbert, Interim Administrator
CMO: Amy Treece, M.D., Medical Director
CHR: Carol Bish, Human Resources Coordinator
CNO: Marian Lorraine McVey, Chief Nursing Officer
Web address: www.ghs.org
Control: Other not–for–profit (including NFP Corporation) **Service**: Acute long–term care hospital

Staffed Beds: 28 Admissions: 228 Census: 19 Outpatient Visits: 26678 Births: 0 Total Expense ($000): 28881 Payroll Expense ($000): 8197 Personnel: 138

☐ **SPRINGBROOK BEHAVIORAL HEALTH SYSTEM (424007)**, One Havenwood Lane, Zip 29690–9447, Mailing Address: P.O. Box 1005, Zip 29690–1005; tel. 864/834–8013, (Total facility includes 68 beds in nursing home–type unit) **A**1 10 **F**4 98 99 103 104
Primary Contact: Mike Rowley, Chief Executive Officer
COO: Mary Ann Bennett, R.N., Chief Operating Officer and Chief Nursing Officer
CFO: Bart Bennett, Chief Financial Officer
CMO: Mathew Fisher, M.D., Medical Director
CIO: Bart Bennett, Chief Information Technology Officer
CHR: Teresa Lipscomb, Director Human Resources
CNO: Marylynn Johnson, Director of Nursing
Web address: www.springbrookbehavioral.com
Control: Corporation, Investor–owned (for–profit) **Service**: Psychiatric

Staffed Beds: 112 Admissions: 1121 Census: 93 Outpatient Visits: 0 Births: 0 Personnel: 261

UNION—Union County

⇑ **UNION MEDICAL CENTER (420108)**, 322 West South Street, Zip 29379–2857, Mailing Address: P.O. Box 789, Zip 29379–0789; tel. 864/301–2000, **A**10 21 **F**3 7 11 15 29 30 34 35 40 57 59 64 69 75 89 107 111 115 119 129 130 133 135 146 147 149 **S** Spartanburg Regional Healthcare System, Spartanburg, SC
Primary Contact: Paul R. Newhouse, President
CFO: Cindy L. Gault, Chief Financial Officer
CHR: Angie Benfield, Human Resources Generalist
CNO: Beth Lawson, Chief Nursing Officer
Web address: www.spartanburgregional.com/locations/union–medical–center/
Control: Hospital district or authority, Government, nonfederal **Service**: General medical and surgical

Staffed Beds: 50 Admissions: 682 Census: 11 Births: 0 Total Expense ($000): 22412 Payroll Expense ($000): 9043 Personnel: 161

VARNVILLE—Hampton County

★ **HAMPTON REGIONAL MEDICAL CENTER (420072)**, 503 West Carolina Avenue, Zip 29944–4735, Mailing Address: P.O. Box 338, Zip 29944–0338; tel. 803/943–2771, **A**10 20 **F**15 17 18 24 28 29 31 34 40 57 59 65 67 70 75 78 79 81 90 93 94 102 107 108 110 111 115 119 127 128 129 133 146
Primary Contact: Dave H. Hamill, President and Chief Executive Officer
Web address: www.hamptonregional.com
Control: Other not–for–profit (including NFP Corporation) **Service**: General medical and surgical

Staffed Beds: 32 Admissions: 575 Census: 9 Outpatient Visits: 26737 Births: 1 Total Expense ($000): 21395 Payroll Expense ($000): 9676 Personnel: 184

WALTERBORO—Colleton County

☒ **COLLETON MEDICAL CENTER (420030)**, 501 Robertson Boulevard, Zip 29488–5714; tel. 843/782–2000, **A**1 10 20 **F**3 11 13 15 26 29 30 32 34 35 36 40 41 45 47 49 56 57 59 60 64 65 68 70 75 76 77 79 81 82 85 86 87 89 90 93 94 96 98 102 107 108 110 111 114 115 119 129 130 131 132 146 147 148 149 **S** HCA Healthcare, Nashville, TN
Primary Contact: Jimmy O. Hiott III, Chief Executive Officer
CFO: Cassie Ball, Chief Financial Officer
CMO: Kim Rakes–Stephens, M.D., Chief Medical Staff
CIO: Damien Noble, Director Information Technology and System
CHR: Wendy Glass, Director Human Resources
CNO: Anna Jonason, Ph.D., R.N., Chief Nursing Officer
Web address: www.colletonmedical.com
Control: Corporation, Investor–owned (for–profit) **Service**: General medical and surgical

Staffed Beds: 131 Admissions: 4448 Census: 58 Outpatient Visits: 74694 Births: 320 Total Expense ($000): 70690 Payroll Expense ($000): 22099 Personnel: 412

SC

Hospital, Medicare Provider Number, Address, Telephone, Approval, Facility, and Physician Codes, Health Care System

★ American Hospital Association (AHA) membership ◯ Healthcare Facilities Accreditation Program ⇑ Center for Improvement in Healthcare Quality Accreditation
☐ The Joint Commission accreditation ◇ DNV Healthcare Inc. accreditation △ Commission on Accreditation of Rehabilitation Facilities (CARF) accreditation

WEST COLUMBIA—Lexington County

★ ⬆ **LEXINGTON MEDICAL CENTER (420073)**, 2720 Sunset Boulevard,
Zip 29169–4810; tel. 803/791–2000, **A**2 3 10 21 **F**3 8 11 12 13 15 18 20 22
24 26 28 29 30 31 32 34 35 38 39 40 43 44 45 46 48 49 50 53 54 57 58 59
60 61 64 68 70 72 73 74 75 76 77 78 79 80 81 82 84 85 86 87 90 92 93 94
107 108 110 111 114 115 118 119 120 121 123 124 126 127 129 130 131
132 135 141 142 144 145 146 147 148 **P**6
Primary Contact: Tod Augsburger, FACHE, President and Chief Executive Officer
COO: Tod Augsburger, FACHE, Senior Vice President and Chief Operating Officer
CFO: Melinda Kruzner, Chief Financial Officer
CMO: Brent Powers, M.D., Vice President/Chief Medical Officer
CIO: Kathleen R Herald, Vice President and Chief Information Officer
CHR: Kathy A Howell, Vice President Human Resources
CNO: Cindy Rohman, R.N., MS, Vice President/Chief Nursing Officer
Web address: www.lexmed.com
Control: Hospital district or authority, Government, nonfederal **Service**: General
medical and surgical

Staffed Beds: 458 **Admissions**: 28095 **Census**: 328 **Outpatient
Visits**: 312141 **Births**: 3263 **Total Expense ($000)**: 655526 **Payroll
Expense ($000)**: 232055 **Personnel**: 3667

☐ **THREE RIVERS BEHAVIORAL HEALTH (424008)**, 2900 Sunset Boulevard,
Zip 29169–3422; tel. 803/796–9911, **A**1 10 **F**4 5 35 98 99 100 101 103 104
105 152 153 **S** Universal Health Services, Inc., King of Prussia, PA
Primary Contact: Nannette M. Lewis, Chief Executive Officer
CFO: Christopher Jensen, Chief Financial Officer
CMO: Christina Lynn, M.D., Medical Director
CHR: Nita Sundberg, Director Human Resources
CNO: Lilly Wing, Chief Nursing Officer
Web address: www.threeriversbehavioral.org
Control: Corporation, Investor–owned (for–profit) **Service**: Psychiatric

Staffed Beds: 122 **Admissions**: 3156 **Census**: 79 **Births**: 0 **Total Expense
($000)**: 21448 **Payroll Expense ($000)**: 9532 **Personnel**: 176

WINNSBORO—Fairfield County

☐ **FAIRFIELD MEMORIAL HOSPITAL (421302)**, 102 US Hwy 321 By–Pass
N, Zip 29180–9251, Mailing Address: P.O. Box 620, Zip 29180–0620;
tel. 803/635–5548, **A**1 5 10 18 **F**3 11 15 28 29 30 34 35 40 50 56 57 59 62
63 64 65 68 75 77 86 87 90 94 102 107 110 111 114 119 127 128 129 130
132 133 146 148 154
Primary Contact: Suzanne C. Doscher, Chief Executive Officer
COO: Darlene Hines
CFO: Timothy Mitchell, Chief Financial Officer
CMO: Roger A Gaddy Jr Chief Medical Officer
CIO: Donnie Doherty, Director Information Systems
CHR: Kristi Godwin, Interim Human Resource Director
CNO: Starr Connor, Chief Nursing Officer
Web address: www.fairfieldmemorial.com
Control: County, Government, nonfederal **Service**: General medical and surgical

Staffed Beds: 25 **Admissions**: 67 **Census**: 1 **Outpatient Visits**: 14407
Births: 0 **Personnel**: 102

SC

SOUTH DAKOTA

ABERDEEN—Brown County

★ **AVERA ST. LUKE'S HOSPITAL (430014)**, 305 South State Street, Zip 57401–4527; tel. 605/622–5000, (Nonreporting) **A**2 10 19 **S** Avera Health, Sioux Falls, SD
Primary Contact: Todd Forkel, President and Chief Executive Officer
CFO: Geoff Durst, Vice President Finance
CMO: Shahid Chaudhary, M.D., Chief Medical Officer
CIO: Julie Kusler, Manager Information Services
CHR: Tracy L Olson, Human Resource Officer
CNO: Jan Patterson, Chief Nursing Officer
Web address: www.avera.org/st–lukes–hospital/
Control: Church operated, Nongovernment, not–for–profit **Service:** General medical and surgical

Staffed Beds: 222

DAKOTA PLAINS SURGICAL CENTER (430092), 701 8th Avenue NW, Suite C, Zip 57401–1865; tel. 605/225–3300, (Nonreporting) **A**10
Primary Contact: Charles Livingston, Administrator
Control: Corporation, Investor–owned (for–profit) **Service:** Surgical

Staffed Beds: 15

★ **SANFORD ABERDEEN MEDICAL CENTER (430097)**, 2905 3rd Avenue SE, Zip 57401–5420; tel. 605/626–4200, (Nonreporting) **A**10 **S** Sanford Health, Sioux Falls, SD
Primary Contact: Ashley M. Erickson, Chief Executive Officer
CFO: Jeffrey Poppen, Chief Financial Officer
CMO: Samuel Nyamu, M.D., Chief Medical Officer
CHR: Katie Palmer, Manager Human Resources
CNO: Kila Legrand, Chief Nursing Officer
Web address: www.sanfordaberdeen.org/
Control: Other not–for–profit (including NFP Corporation) **Service:** General medical and surgical

Staffed Beds: 16

ARMOUR—Douglas County

DOUGLAS COUNTY MEMORIAL HOSPITAL (431305), 708 Eighth Street, Zip 57313–2102; tel. 605/724–2159, **A**10 18 **F**3 8 10 28 31 34 40 43 45 46 47 49 53 57 59 62 64 65 68 69 77 81 93 107 114 119 127 133 154 **P**6
Primary Contact: Heath Brouwer, Administrator
CFO: Dorothy Spease, Manager Business Office
Web address: www.dcmhsd.org
Control: Other not–for–profit (including NFP Corporation) **Service:** General medical and surgical

Staffed Beds: 11 Admissions: 148 Census: 3 Outpatient Visits: 9923 Births: 0 Total Expense ($000): 9319 Payroll Expense ($000): 4010 Personnel: 79

BOWDLE—Douglas County

★ **BOWDLE HOSPITAL (431318)**, 8001 West Fifth Street, Zip 57428, Mailing Address: P.O. Box 556, Zip 57428–0556; tel. 605/285–6146, (Total facility includes 38 beds in nursing home–type unit) **A**10 18 **F**2 3 7 10 28 40 53 59 62 65 81 107 119 127 128 133 148 149
Primary Contact: Sandy Schlechter, Chief Executive Officer
CFO: Brooke Heilman, Chief Financial Officer
CMO: John Ottenbacher, Chief of Staff
CNO: Bobbi Noess, Director of Nursing
Web address: www.bowdlehc.com
Control: City, Government, nonfederal **Service:** General medical and surgical

Staffed Beds: 50 Admissions: 182 Census: 35 Outpatient Visits: 4595 Births: 0 Total Expense ($000): 7286 Payroll Expense ($000): 3660 Personnel: 99

BRITTON—Marshall County

★ **MARSHALL COUNTY HEALTHCARE CENTER AVERA (431312)**, 413 Ninth Street, Zip 57430–2274; tel. 605/448–2253, (Nonreporting) **A**10 18 **S** Avera Health, Sioux Falls, SD
Primary Contact: Nick Fosness, Chief Executive Officer
Web address: www.avera.org
Control: Other not–for–profit (including NFP Corporation) **Service:** General medical and surgical

Staffed Beds: 18

BROOKINGS—Brookings County

★ **BROOKINGS HEALTH SYSTEM (430008)**, 300 22nd Avenue, Zip 57006–2496; tel. 605/696–9000, (Total facility includes 79 beds in nursing home–type unit) **A**10 20 **F**3 7 8 11 13 28 29 30 31 32 34 37 40 41 45 51 53 57 59 62 63 64 65 70 74 75 76 77 79 81 82 85 86 87 92 93 102 107 108 111 114 118 119 125 126 127 128 129 130 133 135 146 147 148 149 154
Primary Contact: Jason R. Merkley, Chief Executive Officer
CFO: Steve Lindemann, Chief Financial Officer
CMO: Shelby Eischens, Chief Medical Officer
CHR: September Bessler, Director, Human Resources
CNO: Tammy Hillestad, Chief Nursing Officer
Web address: www.brookingshealth.org
Control: City, Government, nonfederal **Service:** General medical and surgical

Staffed Beds: 128 Admissions: 1374 Census: 88 Outpatient Visits: 75549 Births: 372 Total Expense ($000): 60235 Payroll Expense ($000): 30217 Personnel: 356

BURKE—Gregory County

★ **COMMUNITY MEMORIAL HOSPITAL (431309)**, 809 Jackson Street, Zip 57523–2065, Mailing Address: P.O. Box 319, Zip 57523–0319; tel. 605/775–2621, **A**10 18 **F**3 28 31 34 40 41 43 57 62 64 65 68 85 87 97 107 115 127 128 133 148 154 **P**6 **S** Sanford Health, Sioux Falls, SD
Primary Contact: Mistie Sachtjen, Chief Executive Officer
CMO: Megan Smith, M.D., Chief Medical Staff
CHR: Tami Lyon, Director Human Resources
Web address: www.sanfordhealth.org
Control: Other not–for–profit (including NFP Corporation) **Service:** General medical and surgical

Staffed Beds: 16 Admissions: 196 Census: 4 Outpatient Visits: 3115 Births: 1 Total Expense ($000): 3352 Payroll Expense ($000): 2027 Personnel: 43

CANTON—Lincoln County

★ **SANFORD CANTON–INWOOD MEDICAL CENTER (431333)**, 440 North Hiawatha Drive, Zip 57013–5800; tel. 605/764–1400, **A**10 18 **F**7 10 15 28 34 40 45 59 65 71 75 77 81 93 97 104 107 114 119 128 130 133 143 149 150 **P**6 **S** Sanford Health, Sioux Falls, SD
Primary Contact: Scott C. Larson, Chief Executive Officer
CFO: Paul Gerhart, Chief Financial Officer
Web address: www.sanfordcantoninwood.org
Control: Other not–for–profit (including NFP Corporation) **Service:** General medical and surgical

Staffed Beds: 11 Admissions: 186 Census: 4 Outpatient Visits: 19277 Births: 0 Total Expense ($000): 6752 Payroll Expense ($000): 3125 Personnel: 77

SD

Hospital, Medicare Provider Number, Address, Telephone, Approval, Facility, and Physician Codes, Health Care System

★ American Hospital Association (AHA) membership
☐ The Joint Commission accreditation
○ Healthcare Facilities Accreditation Program
◇ DNV Healthcare Inc. accreditation
⇑ Center for Improvement in Healthcare Quality Accreditation
△ Commission on Accreditation of Rehabilitation Facilities (CARF) accreditation

CHAMBERLAIN—Brule County

★ **SANFORD CHAMBERLAIN MEDICAL CENTER (431329)**, 300 South Byron Boulevard, Zip 57325–9741; tel. 605/234–5511, (Total facility includes 44 beds in nursing home–type unit) **A**10 18 **F**3 8 13 15 18 19 28 29 31 34 35 40 43 50 57 59 68 70 75 76 77 78 81 85 86 87 89 93 100 101 102 104 107 110 114 119 130 131 132 133 148 149 154 **P**6 **S** Sanford Health, Sioux Falls, SD
Primary Contact: Erica Peterson, Chief Executive Officer
COO: Paul Miller, Director of Operations
CFO: Erica Peterson, Chief Executive Officer and Chief Financial Officer
CMO: Lacey Olson, M.D., Chief Medical Staff
CHR: Dorothy Hieb, Director Human Resources
CNO: Sarah Talbott, Chief Nursing Officer
Web address: www.sanfordchamberlain.org
Control: Other not–for–profit (including NFP Corporation) **Service**: General medical and surgical

Staffed Beds: 69 **Admissions:** 401 **Census:** 47 **Outpatient Visits:** 27705 **Births:** 50 **Total Expense ($000):** 21447 **Payroll Expense ($000):** 10267 **Personnel:** 146

SANFORD MID DAKOTA MEDICAL CENTER See Sanford Chamberlain Medical Center

CLEAR LAKE—Deuel County

★ **SANFORD CLEAR LAKE MEDICAL CENTER (431307)**, 701 Third Avenue South, Zip 57226–2016; tel. 605/874–2141, **A**10 18 **F**3 28 29 34 35 40 43 45 50 53 57 59 62 64 65 68 93 92 93 97 107 115 119 127 128 133 135 144 149 **P**6 **S** Sanford Health, Sioux Falls, SD
Primary Contact: Lori Sisk, R.N., Chief Executive Officer
CFO: Allison Nelson, Chief Financial Officer
CMO: Terrance Smith, M.D., Chairman Medical Staff
CNO: Stephanie Dobbs, Chief Nursing Officer
Web address: www.sanforddeuelcounty.org
Control: Other not–for–profit (including NFP Corporation) **Service**: General medical and surgical

Staffed Beds: 10 **Admissions:** 180 **Census:** 4 **Outpatient Visits:** 17684 **Births:** 0 **Total Expense ($000):** 6370 **Payroll Expense ($000):** 3158 **Personnel:** 72

CUSTER—Custer County

★ **CUSTER REGIONAL HOSPITAL (431323)**, 1039 Montgomery Street, Zip 57730–1397; tel. 605/673–2229, (Nonreporting) **A**10 18 **S** Regional Health, Rapid City, SD
Primary Contact: Mark C. Schmidt, President
Web address: www.regionalhealth.com
Control: Other not–for–profit (including NFP Corporation) **Service**: General medical and surgical

Staffed Beds: 87

DAKOTA DUNES—Union County

SIOUXLAND SURGERY CENTER (430089), 600 North Sioux Point Road, Zip 57049–5000; tel. 605/232–3332, (Nonreporting) **A**10
Primary Contact: Greg Miner, Administrator
Web address: www.siouxlandsurg.com/
Control: Corporation, Investor–owned (for–profit) **Service**: Surgical

Staffed Beds: 40

DE SMET—Kingsbury County

★ **AVERA DE SMET MEMORIAL HOSPITAL (431332)**, 306 Prairie Avenue SW, Zip 57231–2285, Mailing Address: P.O. Box 160, Zip 57231–0160; tel. 605/854–6100, **A**10 18 **F**3 15 28 34 35 40 59 68 93 107 133 154 **P**6 **S** Avera Health, Sioux Falls, SD
Primary Contact: Stephanie Reasy, Administrator and Chief Executive Officer
Web address: www.avera.org
Control: Other not–for–profit (including NFP Corporation) **Service**: General medical and surgical

Staffed Beds: 6 **Admissions:** 39 **Census:** 1 **Outpatient Visits:** 12150 **Births:** 0 **Total Expense ($000):** 4105 **Payroll Expense ($000):** 1880 **Personnel:** 23

DEADWOOD—Lawrence County

★ **LEAD–DEADWOOD REGIONAL HOSPITAL (431320)**, 61 Charles Street, Zip 57732–1303; tel. 605/717–6000, **A**10 18 **F**3 7 15 28 29 30 34 40 43 45 59 64 68 69 70 75 77 78 81 85 87 93 97 107 114 119 132 133 **S** Regional Health, Rapid City, SD
Primary Contact: Mark C. Schmidt, President
CMO: Elizabeth Sayler, M.D., Chief of Staff
CHR: Kathryn L Shockey, Director Human Resources
Web address: www.regionalhealth.com
Control: State, Government, nonfederal **Service**: General medical and surgical

Staffed Beds: 9 **Admissions:** 314 **Census:** 6 **Outpatient Visits:** 10501 **Births:** 0 **Total Expense ($000):** 12419 **Payroll Expense ($000):** 6800 **Personnel:** 114

DELL RAPIDS—Minnehaha County

AVERA DELLS AREA HEALTH CENTER See Avera Dells Area Hospital

★ **AVERA DELLS AREA HOSPITAL (431331)**, 909 North Iowa Avenue, Zip 57022–1231; tel. 605/428–5431, **A**10 18 **F**3 15 28 34 35 40 41 45 53 57 59 64 65 75 81 86 92 93 94 97 107 110 128 132 133 144 148 154 **P**6 **S** Avera Health, Sioux Falls, SD
Primary Contact: Scott James. Hargens, Administrator and Chief Executive Officer
CFO: Kory Holt, Division Controller Network Operations
CMO: Demetre Skliris, Chief Medical Officer
CIO: Val Witham, Director of Health Information
CHR: Amy Aukes, Regional Manager of Human Resources
CNO: Karla Carstensen, Director Patient Care
Web address: www.avera.org/dell–rapids/
Control: Other not–for–profit (including NFP Corporation) **Service**: General medical and surgical

Staffed Beds: 23 **Admissions:** 241 **Census:** 3 **Outpatient Visits:** 17237 **Births:** 0 **Total Expense ($000):** 5485 **Payroll Expense ($000):** 2342 **Personnel:** 53

EAGLE BUTTE—Dewey County

⇑ **U.S. PUBLIC HEALTH SERVICE INDIAN HOSPITAL (430083)**, 317 Main Street, Zip 57625–1012, Mailing Address: P.O. Box 1012, Zip 57625–1012; tel. 605/964–7724, (Nonreporting) **A**10 21 **S** U.S. Indian Health Service, Rockville, MD
Primary Contact: Charles Fisher, Chief Executive Officer
CFO: Lisa Deal, Budget Analyst
Web address: www.ihs.gov
Control: PHS, Indian Service, Government, federal **Service**: General medical and surgical

Staffed Beds: 8

EUREKA—Mcpherson County

★ **EUREKA COMMUNITY HEALTH SERVICES AVERA (431308)**, 410 Ninth Street, Zip 57437–2182, Mailing Address: P.O. Box 517, Zip 57437–0517; tel. 605/284–2661, **A**10 18 **F**10 28 34 35 40 41 45 59 62 65 81 93 133 154 **P**4 5 **S** Avera Health, Sioux Falls, SD
Primary Contact: Carmen Weber, Administrator
CFO: Joyce Schwingler, Chief Financial Officer
Web address: www.avera.org
Control: Other not–for–profit (including NFP Corporation) **Service**: General medical and surgical

Staffed Beds: 6 **Admissions:** 94 **Census:** 1 **Outpatient Visits:** 6487 **Births:** 0 **Total Expense ($000):** 2873 **Payroll Expense ($000):** 1241 **Personnel:** 32

FAULKTON—Faulk County

FAULKTON AREA MEDICAL CENTER (431301), 1300 Oak Street, Zip 57438–2149, Mailing Address: P.O. Box 100, Zip 57438–0100; tel. 605/598–6262, **A**10 18 **F**3 17 28 29 31 40 45 59 64 77 93 97 107 115 127 128 133
Primary Contact: Dirkland T. Smith, Chief Executive Officer
COO: Jay A Jahnig, Chief Executive Officer
CFO: Susan Miller, Financial Administrator
CMO: K A Bartholomew, M.D., Medical Director
CIO: Cheryl Bue, Health Information Transcriptionist
CHR: Blythe Smith, Administrative Assistant
CNO: Shannon Stuwe, Director of Nursing
Web address: www.faulktonmedical.org
Control: Other not–for–profit (including NFP Corporation) **Service**: General medical and surgical

Staffed Beds: 12 **Admissions:** 162 **Census:** 1 **Outpatient Visits:** 12191 **Births:** 0 **Total Expense ($000):** 9551 **Payroll Expense ($000):** 4421 **Personnel:** 77

SD

Many Facility Codes have changed. Please refer to the AHA Guide Code Chart. © 2018 AHA Guide

FLANDREAU—Moody County

★ **AVERA FLANDREAU HOSPITAL (431310)**, 214 North Prairie Street, Zip 57028–1243; tel. 605/997–2433, **A**10 18 **F**3 28 34 35 40 41 45 57 59 64 65 75 81 86 92 93 97 107 127 128 132 133 144 146 148 154 **P**6 **S** Avera Health, Sioux Falls, SD
Primary Contact: Scott James. Hargens, Administrator and Chief Executive Officer
CFO: Kory Holt, Assistant Vice President for Financial Integration
CMO: Scott Peterson, M.D., President Medical Staff
CIO: Val Witham, Director Health Information
CHR: Amy Aukes, Human Resources Analyst
Web address: www.avera.org/flandreau–medical/
Control: Other not–for–profit (including NFP Corporation) **Service**: General medical and surgical

Staffed Beds: 18 Admissions: 147 Census: 2 Outpatient Visits: 14063 Births: 0 Total Expense ($000): 5849 Payroll Expense ($000): 2318 Personnel: 47

AVERA FLANDREAU MEDICAL CENTER See Avera Flandreau Hospital

FORT MEADE—Meade County

☒ **VETERANS AFFAIRS BLACK HILLS HEALTH CARE SYSTEM**, 113 Comanche Road, Zip 57741–1099; tel. 605/347–2511, (Includes VETERANS AFFAIRS MEDICAL CENTER HOT SPRINGS CAMPUS, 500 North Fifth Street, Hot Springs, SD, Zip 57747; tel. 605/745–2052) (Total facility includes 64 beds in nursing home–type unit) **A**1 5 **F**3 4 5 8 12 29 30 31 33 34 35 36 37 38 39 40 44 45 53 54 56 57 59 60 61 62 63 64 65 66 68 70 74 75 77 78 79 81 82 83 84 85 86 87 91 92 93 94 96 97 98 100 101 102 104 106 107 108 111 115 118 119 127 129 130 132 135 143 144 146 147 148 149 152 154 **S** Department of Veterans Affairs, Perry Point, MD
Primary Contact: Sandra Horsman, Director
CFO: Joseph Ferris, Chief Financial Officer
CHR: Denis Sullivan, Chief Human Resources Management
Web address: www.blackhills.va.gov/
Control: Veterans Affairs, Government, federal **Service**: General medical and surgical

Staffed Beds: 247 Admissions: 1239 Census: 178 Outpatient Visits: 239096 Births: 0 Total Expense ($000): 170022 Payroll Expense ($000): 68622 Personnel: 568

FREEMAN—Hutchinson County

★ **FREEMAN REGIONAL HEALTH SERVICES (431313)**, 510 East Eighth Street, Zip 57029–2086, Mailing Address: P.O. Box 370, Zip 57029–0370; tel. 605/925–4000, (Total facility includes 56 beds in nursing home–type unit) **A**10 18 **F**2 3 6 11 15 28 30 34 35 40 43 45 49 54 56 57 59 64 65 68 69 70 75 77 79 81 82 86 89 90 93 97 107 115 119 125 127 128 130 132 133 146 154 **P**6
Primary Contact: Nicholas R. Brandner, Chief Executive Officer
CFO: Mark Miller, Chief Financial Officer
Web address: www.freemanregional.com
Control: Other not–for–profit (including NFP Corporation) **Service**: General medical and surgical

Staffed Beds: 81 Admissions: 167 Census: 53 Outpatient Visits: 11391 Births: 0 Total Expense ($000): 11386 Payroll Expense ($000): 4890 Personnel: 127

GETTYSBURG—Potter County

★ **AVERA GETTYSBURG HOSPITAL (431302)**, 606 East Garfield Avenue, Zip 57442–1398; tel. 605/765–2480, (Nonreporting) **A**10 18 **S** Avera Health, Sioux Falls, SD
Primary Contact: Robert L. Sheckler, Administrator
Web address: www.avera.org/st–marys–pierre/gettysburg–hospital/
Control: Church operated, Nongovernment, not–for–profit **Service**: General medical and surgical

Staffed Beds: 55

GREGORY—Gregory County

★ **AVERA GREGORY HOSPITAL (431338)**, 400 Park Avenue, Zip 57533–1302, Mailing Address: P.O. Box 408, Zip 57533–0408; tel. 605/835–8394, (Total facility includes 40 beds in nursing home–type unit) **A**10 18 **F**1 8 15 28 29 31 34 35 38 40 45 59 60 64 75 77 81 84 85 91 93 97 107 110 114 127 128 132 133 135 154 **P**6 **S** Avera Health, Sioux Falls, SD
Primary Contact: Anthony Timanus, Chief Executive Officer
CFO: Trish Keiser, Comptroller
CMO: Rich Kafka, M.D., Chief Medical Officer
CIO: Justin Keegan, Director Support Services
CHR: Carol Postulka, Administrative Coordinator
Web address: www.gregoryhealthcare.org
Control: Other not–for–profit (including NFP Corporation) **Service**: General medical and surgical

Staffed Beds: 65 Admissions: 598 Census: 44 Outpatient Visits: 13012 Births: 0 Total Expense ($000): 15039 Payroll Expense ($000): 7210 Personnel: 106

HOT SPRINGS—Fall River County

★ **FALL RIVER HOSPITAL (431322)**, 1201 Highway 71 South, Zip 57747–8800; tel. 605/745–3159, (Total facility includes 48 beds in nursing home–type unit) **A**10 18 **F**3 28 29 34 40 56 57 59 64 65 74 77 81 89 93 104 107 119 127 128 129 132 133 146 148 154
Primary Contact: Tricia Uhlir, Chief Executive Officer
CFO: Jesse Naze, Chief Financial Officer
CMO: Rodney Larson, M.D., Medical Director
CIO: Dustin Kleinsasser, Information Technology and BioMed
CHR: Cindy Trent, Manager Personnel
Web address: www.frhssd.org
Control: Other not–for–profit (including NFP Corporation) **Service**: General medical and surgical

Staffed Beds: 73 Admissions: 318 Census: 55 Outpatient Visits: 13261 Births: 0 Total Expense ($000): 19432 Payroll Expense ($000): 9217 Personnel: 117

VETERANS AFFAIRS MEDICAL CENTER HOT SPRINGS CAMPUS See Veterans Affairs Black Hills Health Care System, Fort Meade

HURON—Beadle County

★ **HURON REGIONAL MEDICAL CENTER (431335)**, 172 Fourth Street SE, Zip 57350–2590; tel. 605/353–6200, **A**10 18 **F**3 11 13 14 15 28 29 31 34 35 40 43 45 57 59 60 62 63 64 68 70 75 76 77 78 79 81 85 86 93 102 107 108 110 111 115 118 119 130 132 133 146 148 **P**6 **S** QHR, Brentwood, TN
Primary Contact: David Dick, Chief Executive Officer
CFO: Marcia Zwanziger, Vice President Finance
CMO: Bill Miner, M.D., Chief of Staff
CHR: Rhonda Hanson, Director Human Resources
CNO: Gail Robeson, Vice President Patient Services
Web address: www.huronregional.org
Control: Other not–for–profit (including NFP Corporation) **Service**: General medical and surgical

Staffed Beds: 30 Admissions: 1376 Census: 14 Outpatient Visits: 58119 Births: 320 Total Expense ($000): 34166 Payroll Expense ($000): 15095 Personnel: 252

MADISON—Lake County

★ **MADISON REGIONAL HEALTH SYSTEM (431300)**, 323 SW 10th Street, Zip 57042–3200; tel. 605/256–6551, **A**10 18 **F**7 13 15 28 31 34 35 40 41 43 50 57 59 62 64 65 70 75 76 77 81 82 85 87 89 93 97 107 110 111 114 119 129 132 133 135 143 144 145 146 148 **P**6
Primary Contact: Tamara Miller, FACHE, Chief Executive Officer and Administrator
CFO: Teresa Mallett, Chief Financial Officer
CNO: Charlotte Charles, Director Acute Patient Services
Web address: www.madisonregionalhealth.org
Control: Other not–for–profit (including NFP Corporation) **Service**: General medical and surgical

Staffed Beds: 22 Admissions: 634 Census: 11 Outpatient Visits: 25690 Births: 41 Total Expense ($000): 25502 Payroll Expense ($000): 11936 Personnel: 235

SD

Hospital, Medicare Provider Number, Address, Telephone, Approval, Facility, and Physician Codes, Health Care System

★ American Hospital Association (AHA) membership ○ Healthcare Facilities Accreditation Program ⇑ Center for Improvement in Healthcare Quality Accreditation
☐ The Joint Commission accreditation ◇ DNV Healthcare Inc. accreditation △ Commission on Accreditation of Rehabilitation Facilities (CARF) accreditation

MARTIN—Bennett County

★ **BENNETT COUNTY HOSPITAL AND NURSING HOME (431314)**, 102 Major Allen Street, Zip 57551–6005, Mailing Address: P.O. Box 70, Zip 57551–0070; tel. 605/685–6622, (Total facility includes 48 beds in nursing home–type unit) **A**10 18 **F**7 34 40 50 53 57 59 62 65 66 67 68 77 84 93 107 119 130 133 143
Primary Contact: Andrew Riggin, Chief Executive Officer
CFO: Jean Kirk, Chief Financial Officer
CMO: Peter Knowles–Smith, M.D., Medical Director
CIO: Jean Kirk, Chief Financial Officer
CHR: T J Porter, Director Human Resources
Web address: www.bennettcountyhospital.com/
Control: Other not–for–profit (including NFP Corporation) **Service**: General medical and surgical

Staffed Beds: 62 **Admissions**: 238 **Census**: 38 **Outpatient Visits**: 46566 **Births**: 2 **Total Expense ($000)**: 8428 **Payroll Expense ($000)**: 4534 **Personnel**: 94	

MILBANK—Grant County

★ **MILBANK AREA HOSPITAL AVERA (431326)**, 301 Flynn Drive, Zip 57252–1508; tel. 605/432–4538, (Nonreporting) **A**10 18 **S** Avera Health, Sioux Falls, SD
Primary Contact: Natalie Gauer, Administrator
CMO: Kevin Bjordahl, M.D., Chief Medical Officer
CHR: Mona Schafer, Regional Manager Human Resources
Web address: www.averamilbank.org
Control: Other not–for–profit (including NFP Corporation) **Service**: General medical and surgical

Staffed Beds: 25	

MILLER—Hand County

★ **AVERA HAND COUNTY MEMORIAL HOSPITAL (431337)**, 300 West Fifth Street, Zip 57362–1238; tel. 605/853–2421, **A**10 18 **F**3 8 11 15 17 28 29 34 35 40 43 45 46 50 53 57 59 64 77 79 81 86 87 93 107 115 119 128 129 132 133 146 148 154 **S** Avera Health, Sioux Falls, SD
Primary Contact: Bryan Breitling, Administrator
CFO: Debbie Pullman, Director Finance
CMO: John Hopkins, M.D., Chief of Staff
CIO: Janice Purrington, Coordinator Medical Records
CNO: Sarah DeHaai, R.N., Director of Nursing
Web address: www.avera.org
Control: Other not–for–profit (including NFP Corporation) **Service**: General medical and surgical

Staffed Beds: 9 **Admissions**: 312 **Census**: 4 **Outpatient Visits**: 18616 **Births**: 0 **Total Expense ($000)**: 7425 **Payroll Expense ($000)**: 3413 **Personnel**: 65	

MITCHELL—Davison County

⊞ **AVERA QUEEN OF PEACE HOSPITAL (430013)**, 525 North Foster, Zip 57301–2999; tel. 605/995–2000, (Total facility includes 109 beds in nursing home–type unit) **A**1 2 10 **F**3 10 13 15 28 29 30 31 34 40 43 45 48 50 51 53 54 57 59 64 69 70 71 75 76 77 78 79 81 82 84 85 86 89 93 94 96 104 107 108 110 111 114 117 118 119 121 123 127 128 129 130 131 132 133 135 146 147 148 154 **P**6 **S** Avera Health, Sioux Falls, SD
Primary Contact: Thomas A. Clark, Regional President and Chief Executive Officer
CFO: Will Flett, Vice President Finance and Chief Financial Officer
CMO: David Balt, D.O., Chief Medical Officer
CIO: Jim Hanson, Director Information Systems
CHR: Rita Lemon, Director Human Resources
CNO: Rochelle Reider, Vice President Patient Care
Web address: www.averaqueenofpeace.org
Control: Church operated, Nongovernment, not–for–profit **Service**: General medical and surgical

Staffed Beds: 159 **Admissions**: 2287 **Census**: 121 **Outpatient Visits**: 130197 **Births**: 521 **Total Expense ($000)**: 98720 **Payroll Expense ($000)**: 44853 **Personnel**: 476	

MOBRIDGE—Walworth County

★ **MOBRIDGE REGIONAL HOSPITAL (431325)**, 1401 Tenth Avenue West, Zip 57601–1106, Mailing Address: P.O. Box 580, Zip 57601–0580; tel. 605/845–3692, **A**10 18 **F**3 7 10 11 13 15 17 28 29 32 34 35 40 43 45 50 56 57 59 62 64 65 70 76 77 81 84 85 93 97 107 110 114 119 125 127 128 129 131 132 133 147 148 154 **P**6
Primary Contact: John J. Ayoub, FACHE, Chief Executive Officer
COO: Beth Jensen, Director Clinic Operations
CFO: Renae Tisdall, Chief Financial Officer
CMO: Travis Henderson, M.D., Chief of Staff
CIO: Josiah Barton, Director Information Technology
CHR: Keri Wientjes, Director Human Resources
CNO: Kristi Voller, Director of Nursing
Web address: www.mobridgehospital.org
Control: Other not–for–profit (including NFP Corporation) **Service**: General medical and surgical

Staffed Beds: 25 **Admissions**: 925 **Census**: 8 **Outpatient Visits**: 57003 **Births**: 68 **Total Expense ($000)**: 19942 **Payroll Expense ($000)**: 9252 **Personnel**: 159	

PARKSTON—Hutchinson County

★ **AVERA ST. BENEDICT HEALTH CENTER (431330)**, 401 West Glynn Drive, Zip 57366–9605; tel. 605/928–3311, (Total facility includes 74 beds in nursing home–type unit) **A**10 18 **F**2 3 8 10 13 15 28 29 30 31 32 34 35 38 40 45 53 56 57 59 62 64 65 69 71 75 76 81 82 83 85 86 87 89 107 110 111 115 116 119 127 128 129 130 131 132 133 135 146 147 148 154 **P**6 **S** Avera Health, Sioux Falls, SD
Primary Contact: Rita Blasius, President and Chief Executive Officer
CFO: Rita Blasius, Assistant Administrator and Chief Financial Officer
CMO: Antoinette VanderPol, Chief of Staff
CIO: Adam Popp, Director Information Systems
CHR: Phyllis Ehler, Director Human Resources
CNO: Denise Muntefering, Vice President Patient Care Services
Web address: www.averastbenedict.org
Control: Church operated, Nongovernment, not–for–profit **Service**: General medical and surgical

Staffed Beds: 99 **Admissions**: 646 **Census**: 79 **Outpatient Visits**: 20206 **Births**: 52 **Total Expense ($000)**: 21535 **Payroll Expense ($000)**: 10698 **Personnel**: 169	

PHILIP—Haakon County

HANS P. PETERSON MEMORIAL HOSPITAL See Philip Health Services

★ **PHILIP HEALTH SERVICES (431319)**, 503 West Pine Street, Zip 57567–3300, Mailing Address: P.O. Box 790, Zip 57567–0790; tel. 605/859–2511, (Total facility includes 30 beds in nursing home–type unit) **A**10 18 **F**10 11 40 43 57 59 62 85 93 107 114 125 127 128 130 131 133 145 148 150 **P**6 **S** Regional Health, Rapid City, SD
Primary Contact: Jeremy Schultes, Administrator and Chief Executive Officer
Web address: www.philiphealthservices.com/
Control: Other not–for–profit (including NFP Corporation) **Service**: General medical and surgical

Staffed Beds: 48 **Admissions**: 210 **Census**: 31 **Outpatient Visits**: 16818 **Births**: 0 **Total Expense ($000)**: 11495 **Payroll Expense ($000)**: 6556 **Personnel**: 179	

PIERRE—Hughes County

⊞ **AVERA ST. MARY'S HOSPITAL (430015)**, 801 East Sioux Avenue, Zip 57501–3323; tel. 605/224–3100, (Nonreporting) **A**1 3 10 20 **S** Avera Health, Sioux Falls, SD
Primary Contact: Todd Forkel, Interim Chief Executive Officer
CFO: Tom Wagner, Interim Vice President Finance
CMO: Denise Hanisch, M.D., Chief of Staff
CIO: Jamie Raske, Information Technology Lead
CHR: Paul Marso, Vice President Human Resources
Web address: www.avera.org/st-marys-pierre/
Control: Other not–for–profit (including NFP Corporation) **Service**: General medical and surgical

Staffed Beds: 110	

PINE RIDGE—Shannon County

⇑ **U.S. PUBLIC HEALTH SERVICE INDIAN HOSPITAL (430081)**, East Highway 18, Zip 57770, Mailing Address: P.O. Box 1201, Zip 57770–1201; tel. 605/867–5131, (Nonreporting) **A**10 21 **S** U.S. Indian Health Service, Rockville, MD
Primary Contact: Travis Scott, Service Unit Director
CFO: Sophia Conny, Deputy Administrative Officer
CMO: Jan Colton, M.D., Acting Clinical Director
CHR: Annabelle Blackbear, Human Resources Specialist
Web address: www.ihs.gov
Control: PHS, Indian Service, Government, federal **Service**: General medical and surgical

Staffed Beds: 45	

PLATTE—Charles Mix County

★ **PLATTE HEALTH CENTER AVERA (431306)**, 601 East Seventh, Zip 57369–2123, Mailing Address: P.O. Box 200, Zip 57369–0200; tel. 605/337–3364, (Total facility includes 42 beds in nursing home–type unit) **A**10 18 **F**3 11 15 28 29 30 31 34 35 40 41 45 56 57 59 62 64 65 66 67 68 69 75 77 78 79 81 87 91 93 97 107 110 115 119 127 128 129 130 131 132 133 146 148 154 **S** Avera Health, Sioux Falls, SD
Primary Contact: Mark Burket, Chief Executive Officer
CFO: Jerry Hoffman, Chief Financial Officer
Web address: www.phcavera.org
Control: Other not–for–profit (including NFP Corporation) **Service**: General medical and surgical

Staffed Beds: 59 **Admissions**: 161 **Census**: 47 **Outpatient Visits**: 12288 **Births**: 1 **Total Expense ($000)**: 13611 **Payroll Expense ($000)**: 7349 **Personnel**: 124	

RAPID CITY—Pennington County

BLACK HILLS SURGICAL HOSPITAL (430091), 216 Anamaria Drive, Zip 57701–7366, Mailing Address: 1868 Lombardy Drive, Zip 57703–4130; tel. 605/721–4900, (Nonreporting) **A**10
Primary Contact: Franklin Shobe, Administrator and Chief Executive Officer
Web address: www.bhsc.com
Control: Partnership, Investor–owned (for–profit) **Service:** Surgical

Staffed Beds: 26

⇑ **INDIAN HEALTH SERVICE HOSPITAL (430082)**, 3200 Canyon Lake Drive, Zip 57702–8197; tel. 605/355–2280, (Nonreporting) **A**10 21 **S** U.S. Indian Health Service, Rockville, MD
Primary Contact: Kevin J. Stiffarm, Chief Executive Officer
Web address: www.ihs.gov
Control: PHS, Indian Service, Government, federal **Service:** General medical and surgical

Staffed Beds: 9

⊞ **RAPID CITY REGIONAL HOSPITAL (430077)**, 353 Fairmont Boulevard, Zip 57701–7393, Mailing Address: P.O. Box 6000, Zip 57709–6000; tel. 605/755–1000, **A**1 3 5 10 **F**3 12 13 15 17 18 20 22 24 26 28 29 30 31 34 40 43 45 46 48 49 51 56 58 59 60 64 70 72 74 77 78 79 81 82 83 84 85 87 90 92 93 97 98 99 102 104 107 108 111 115 118 119 120 121 124 126 129 130 131 144 146 148 149 154 **P**8 **S** Regional Health, Rapid City, SD
Primary Contact: John Pierce, Acting President
CFO: Mark Thompson, Vice President Financial Services
CMO: David Houser, M.D., Vice President Medical Affairs
CIO: Richard Latuchie, Vice President Business Development
CHR: Maureen Henson, Vice President Human Resources
Web address: www.regionalhealth.com
Control: Other not–for–profit (including NFP Corporation) **Service:** General medical and surgical

Staffed Beds: 366 Admissions: 20395 Census: 271 Outpatient Visits: 215785 Births: 2108 Total Expense ($000): 536557 Payroll Expense ($000): 206056 Personnel: 3190

SAME DAY SURGERY CENTER (430093), 651 Cathedral Drive, Zip 57701–7368; tel. 605/755–9900, (Nonreporting) **A**10
Primary Contact: Doris Fritts, R.N., Executive Director
Web address: www.samedaysurgerycenter.org
Control: Corporation, Investor–owned (for–profit) **Service:** Surgical

Staffed Beds: 8

REDFIELD—Spink County

COMMUNITY MEMORIAL HOSPITAL (431316), 110 West Tenth Avenue, Zip 57469–1520, Mailing Address: P.O. Box 420, Zip 57469–0420; tel. 605/472–1110, (Nonreporting) **A**10 18
Primary Contact: Michael O'Keefe, Interim Chief Executive Officer
CFO: William Boyer, Chief Financial Officer
CHR: Rhonda Stroh, Chief Human Resources Officer
CNO: Julene J Cass, R.N., Director of Nursing
Web address: www.redfield-sd.com/hospital.html
Control: City, Government, nonfederal **Service:** General medical and surgical

Staffed Beds: 18

ROSEBUD—Todd County

⇑ **U.S. PUBLIC HEALTH SERVICE INDIAN HOSPITAL (430084)**, Highway 18, Soldier Creek Road, Zip 57570; tel. 605/747–2231, (Nonreporting) **A**10 21 **S** U.S. Indian Health Service, Rockville, MD
Primary Contact: Kathey Wilson, Acting Chief Executive Officer
COO: Romeo Vivit, Chief Surgeon
CMO: Valerie Parker, M.D., Clinical Director
CHR: Michelle Zephier, Human Resource Specialist
Web address: www.ihs.gov
Control: PHS, Indian Service, Government, federal **Service:** General medical and surgical

Staffed Beds: 35

SCOTLAND—Bon Homme County

★ **LANDMANN–JUNGMAN MEMORIAL HOSPITAL AVERA (431317)**, 600 Billars Street, Zip 57059–2026; tel. 605/583–2226, **A**10 18 **F**28 29 34 35 40 43 53 55 56 57 59 64 65 67 68 81 93 97 107 114 119 125 128 131 132 133 147 148 154 **S** Avera Health, Sioux Falls, SD
Primary Contact: Melissa Gale, Chief Executive Officer
CFO: Darcy Permann, Manager Business Office
Web address: www.ljmh.org
Control: Other not–for–profit (including NFP Corporation) **Service:** General medical and surgical

Staffed Beds: 25 Admissions: 54 Census: 1 Outpatient Visits: 11075 Births: 0 Total Expense ($000): 4331 Payroll Expense ($000): 1907 Personnel: 35

SIOUX FALLS—Lincoln County

☐ **AVERA HEART HOSPITAL OF SOUTH DAKOTA (430095)**, 4500 West 69th Street, Zip 57108–8148; tel. 605/977–7000, **A**1 3 5 10 **F**3 17 18 19 20 21 22 23 24 26 28 29 30 34 35 40 41 43 50 57 58 59 60 64 68 74 75 81 84 85 87 102 107 108 114 119 130 146 154 **P**2 **S** Avera Health, Sioux Falls, SD
Primary Contact: Michael Gibbs, President
CFO: Jean White, Vice President Finance
Web address: www.avera.org/heart-hospital
Control: Corporation, Investor–owned (for–profit) **Service:** Heart

Staffed Beds: 53 Admissions: 2158 Census: 22 Outpatient Visits: 55811 Births: 0 Total Expense ($000): 90049 Payroll Expense ($000): 28921 Personnel: 472

SIOUX FALLS—Minnehaha County

⊞ △ **AVERA McKENNAN HOSPITAL AND UNIVERSITY HEALTH CENTER (430016)**, 1325 South Cliff Avenue, Zip 57105–1007, Mailing Address: P.O. Box 5045, Zip 57117–5045; tel. 605/322–8000, (Includes AVERA BEHAVIORAL HEALTH CENTER, 440 West 69th Street, Sioux Falls, SD, Zip 57108; tel. 605/322–4065; Steve Lindquist, Assistant Vice President, Behavioral Health; AVERA CHILDREN'S HOSPITAL, 1325 South Cliff Avenue, Sioux Falls, SD, Zip 57105–1016, Mailing Address: PO Box 5045, Zip 57117–5045; tel. 605/322–5437) (Total facility includes 114 beds in nursing home–type unit) **A**1 2 3 5 7 10 **F**3 5 7 10 11 12 13 15 18 19 20 21 22 23 24 29 30 31 32 34 35 36 38 39 40 41 43 44 45 46 47 48 49 50 53 54 55 56 57 58 59 60 61 62 63 64 65 66 68 70 71 72 74 75 76 77 78 79 81 82 83 84 85 86 87 88 89 90 91 92 93 94 95 96 97 98 99 100 101 102 103 104 105 107 108 109 110 111 112 114 115 116 117 118 119 120 121 122 123 124 125 126 127 128 129 130 131 132 134 135 136 138 139 141 142 143 144 145 146 147 148 149 152 153 154 **P**6 **S** Avera Health, Sioux Falls, SD
Primary Contact: David Flicek, President and Chief Executive Officer
COO: Judy Blauwet, M.P.H., R.N., Senior Vice President Operations and Chief Nursing Officer
CFO: Julie Norton, Vice President, Operational Finance
CMO: Michael Elliott, M.D., Chief Medical Officer and Senior Vice President of Medical Affairs
CIO: Kristin Gross, Director Information Technology Center
CHR: Lynne D Hagen, Human Resources Officer
CNO: Judy Blauwet, M.P.H., R.N., Senior Vice President of Hospital Operations and Chief Nursing Officer
Web address: www.averamckennan.org
Control: Church operated, Nongovernment, not–for–profit **Service:** General medical and surgical

Staffed Beds: 485 Admissions: 22422 Census: 336 Outpatient Visits: 309886 Births: 2154 Total Expense ($000): 899278 Payroll Expense ($000): 376429 Personnel: 6523

LIFESCAPE (433300), 2501 West 26th Street, Zip 57105–2498; tel. 605/444–9500, (Nonreporting) **A**10
Primary Contact: Anne Rieck McFarland, President and Chief Executive Officer
CFO: Stephan A. Wilson, Chief Financial Officer
CMO: Christiane Maroun, M.D., Chief of Staff
CHR: Tiffany Reilly, Director Human Resources
Web address: www.cchs.org
Control: Other not–for–profit (including NFP Corporation) **Service:** Children's rehabilitation

Staffed Beds: 114

SD

Hospital, Medicare Provider Number, Address, Telephone, Approval, Facility, and Physician Codes, Health Care System

★ American Hospital Association (AHA) membership
☐ The Joint Commission accreditation
○ Healthcare Facilities Accreditation Program
◇ DNV Healthcare Inc. accreditation
⇑ Center for Improvement in Healthcare Quality Accreditation
△ Commission on Accreditation of Rehabilitation Facilities (CARF) accreditation

✈ △ **SANFORD USD MEDICAL CENTER (430027)**, 1305 West 18th Street, Zip 57105–0496, Mailing Address: P.O. Box 5039, Zip 57117–5039; tel. 605/333–1000, (Includes SANFORD CHILDREN'S HOSPITAL, 1600 West 22nd Street, Sioux Falls, SD, Zip 57105, Mailing Address: PO Box 5039, Zip 57117–5039, tel. 605/333–1000) **A**1 2 3 5 7 8 10 **F**3 7 8 9 11 12 13 14 15 17 18 19 20 21 22 23 24 25 26 27 28 29 30 31 32 34 35 36 37 38 40 43 44 45 46 47 48 49 50 51 52 53 54 55 56 57 58 59 60 61 62 63 64 65 66 67 68 69 70 71 72 73 74 75 76 77 78 79 80 81 82 83 84 85 86 87 88 89 90 91 92 93 94 96 97 99 100 101 102 103 104 105 106 107 108 110 111 114 115 116 117 118 119 120 121 123 124 125 126 129 130 131 132 134 135 138 141 142 143 144 146 147 148 149 150 153 154 **P**6 **S** Sanford Health, Sioux Falls, SD
Primary Contact: Paul A. Hanson, FACHE, President
COO: Brad J. Schipper, Chief Operating Officer
CFO: Merrilee Schultz, Chief Finance
CIO: Arlyn Broekhuis, Vice President and Chief Information Officer
CHR: Evan Burkett, Chief Human Resource Officer
Web address: www.sanfordhealth.org
Control: Other not–for–profit (including NFP Corporation) **Service**: General medical and surgical

Staffed Beds: 500 Admissions: 23872 Census: 297 Outpatient Visits: 516829 Births: 3194 Total Expense ($000): 830428 Payroll Expense ($000): 368301 Personnel: 5183

✈ **SELECT SPECIALTY HOSPITAL–SIOUX FALLS (432002)**, 1305 West 18th Street, Zip 57105–0401; tel. 605/312–9500, (Nonreporting) **A**1 10 **S** Select Medical Corporation, Mechanicsburg, PA
Primary Contact: Carol Ulmer, Chief Executive Officer
CNO: Alison Anderson, Chief Nursing Officer
Web address: www.selectspecialtyhospitals.com/company/locations/siouxfalls.aspx
Control: Corporation, Investor–owned (for–profit) **Service**: Acute long–term care hospital

Staffed Beds: 24

SIOUX FALLS SPECIALTY HOSPITAL (430090), 910 East 20th Street, Zip 57105–1012; tel. 605/334–6730, (Nonreporting) **A**10
Primary Contact: R Blake. Curd, M.D., Chief Executive Officer
CFO: Kyle Goldammer, Chief Financial Officer
Web address: www.sfsurgical.com
Control: Partnership, Investor–owned (for–profit) **Service**: Surgical

Staffed Beds: 35

✈ **SIOUX FALLS VETERANS AFFAIRS HEALTH CARE SYSTEM**, 2501 West 22nd Street, Zip 57105–1305, Mailing Address: P.O. Box 5046, Zip 57117–5046; tel. 605/336–3230, (Total facility includes 58 beds in nursing home–type unit) **A**1 3 5 **F**3 5 12 18 24 26 28 29 30 31 33 34 35 36 38 39 40 44 45 50 51 53 54 55 56 57 58 59 60 61 62 63 64 65 68 70 71 74 75 77 78 79 81 82 83 84 85 86 87 91 92 93 94 97 98 100 101 102 103 104 106 107 108 111 115 118 119 127 130 132 135 143 146 147 148 149 152 153 154 **P**6 **S** Department of Veterans Affairs, Perry Point, MD
Primary Contact: Darwin Goodspeed, Director
COO: Sara Ackert, Associate Director
CFO: Daniel Hubbard, Chief Financial Officer
CMO: John M Wempe, M.D., Chief of Staff
CIO: Eric Heiser, Chief Information Resource Management
CHR: Betsy Geiver, Chief Human Resources Officer
CNO: Barbara Teal, R.N., Associate Director Patient Care Services and Nurse Executive
Web address: www.siouxfalls.va.gov
Control: Veterans Affairs, Government, federal **Service**: General medical and surgical

Staffed Beds: 92 Admissions: 2891 Census: 76 Outpatient Visits: 280207 Births: 0 Total Expense ($000): 212652 Payroll Expense ($000): 76794 Personnel: 953

SISSETON—Roberts County

★ **COTEAU DES PRAIRIES HOSPITAL (431339)**, 205 Orchard Drive, Zip 57262–2398; tel. 605/698–7647, **A**10 18 **F**13 15 29 40 43 45 62 65 81 97 107 108 119 127 133
Primary Contact: Greg Weaver, Interim Chief Executive Officer and Chief Operating Officer
COO: Greg Weaver, Chief Operating Officer
CFO: Larry Moen, Chief Financial Officer
CMO: David Staub, M.D., Chief of Staff
CIO: Cheryl Kaufman, Information Technology Technician
CHR: Leslie Hendrickson, Director Human Resources
CNO: Brenda Bostrom, Director of Nursing
Web address: www.cdphospital.com
Control: Other not–for–profit (including NFP Corporation) **Service**: General medical and surgical

Staffed Beds: 25 Admissions: 488 Census: 4 Outpatient Visits: 42734 Births: 146 Total Expense ($000): 18263 Payroll Expense ($000): 8172 Personnel: 157

SPEARFISH—Lawrence County

★ **SPEARFISH REGIONAL HOSPITAL (430048)**, 1440 North Main Street, Zip 57783–1504; tel. 605/644–4000, (Includes SPEARFISH REGIONAL SURGERY CENTER, 1316 N 10th St, Spearfish, SD, Zip 57783–1530, Mailing Address: 1316 North 10th Street, Zip 57783–1530, tel. 605/642–3113) **A**10 20 **F**3 12 13 15 18 28 29 34 40 57 59 70 75 76 79 81 82 85 89 93 97 107 108 110 111 115 119 127 129 130 131 132 144 147 148 154 **P**6 **S** Regional Health, Rapid City, SD
Primary Contact: Thomas Worsley, Chief Executive Officer
CFO: Marcia Olson, Director Finance and Controller
CMO: Christopher Gasbarre, D.O., Community Medical Director
CIO: Richard Latuchie, Chief Information Officer
CHR: Patsy Aiken, Coordinator Human Resource
CNO: Suzanne Campbell, Director Patient Services
Web address: www.regionalhealth.com/Our–Locations/Regional–Hospitals/Spearfish–Regional–Hospital.aspx
Control: Other not–for–profit (including NFP Corporation) **Service**: General medical and surgical

Staffed Beds: 35 Admissions: 1557 Census: 9 Outpatient Visits: 183465 Births: 465 Total Expense ($000): 83904 Payroll Expense ($000): 36896 Personnel: 436

STURGIS—Meade County

★ **STURGIS REGIONAL HOSPITAL (431321)**, 949 Harmon Street, Zip 57785–2452; tel. 605/720–2400, (Total facility includes 84 beds in nursing home–type unit) **A**10 18 **F**11 15 28 29 40 43 70 77 81 82 93 107 108 110 114 119 128 130 132 133 148 **S** Regional Health, Rapid City, SD
Primary Contact: Mark Schulte, FACHE, President
CFO: Jodie Mitchell, Facility Financial Director
CMO: Constance Stock, M.D., Chief Medical Officer
CHR: Ginger Chord, Coordinator Human Resources
CNO: Rikki Plaggemeyer, Director Acute Care Nursing
Web address: www.regionalhealth.org/Our–Locations/Regional–Hospitals/Sturgis–Regional–Hospital.aspx
Control: Other not–for–profit (including NFP Corporation) **Service**: General medical and surgical

Staffed Beds: 109 Admissions: 662 Census: 92 Outpatient Visits: 13646 Births: 0 Total Expense ($000): 23468 Payroll Expense ($000): 11065 Personnel: 152

TYNDALL—Bon Homme County

★ **ST. MICHAEL'S HOSPITAL AVERA (431327)**, 410 West 16th Avenue, Zip 57066–2318; tel. 605/589–2152, **A**10 18 **F**3 15 28 31 34 40 43 45 53 57 59 64 65 67 70 75 77 81 86 89 92 93 94 107 110 114 119 127 128 129 131 133 148 154 **P**6 **S** Avera Health, Sioux Falls, SD
Primary Contact: Carol Deurmier, Chief Executive Officer
CFO: Lisa Ronke, Director Finance
CMO: Melvin Wallinga, M.D., Medical Director
Web address: www.stmichaels–bhfp.org
Control: Church operated, Nongovernment, not–for–profit **Service**: General medical and surgical

Staffed Beds: 25 Admissions: 222 Census: 4 Outpatient Visits: 10931 Births: 0 Total Expense ($000): 8418 Payroll Expense ($000): 3375 Personnel: 71

VERMILLION—Clay County

★ **SANFORD VERMILLION MEDICAL CENTER (431336)**, 20 South Plum Street, Zip 57069–3346; tel. 605/677–3500, (Total facility includes 66 beds in nursing home–type unit) **A**10 18 **F**10 15 28 29 31 34 35 40 43 45 57 59 67 81 91 92 93 97 107 110 111 114 116 119 129 130 131 132 133 135 148 149 **P**8 **S** Sanford Health, Sioux Falls, SD
Primary Contact: Timothy J. Tracy, Senior Director
CFO: Valerie Osterberg, Chief Financial Officer
CMO: Roy Mortinsen, M.D., Chief of Staff
CIO: Mary C Merrigan, Manager Public Relations
CHR: Cindy Benzel, Manager Human Resources
CNO: Jeff Berens, MS, Chief Nursing Officer
Web address: www.sanfordvermillion.org
Control: Other not–for–profit (including NFP Corporation) **Service**: General medical and surgical

Staffed Beds: 120 Admissions: 386 Census: 63 Outpatient Visits: 39006 Births: 102 Total Expense ($000): 21813 Payroll Expense ($000): 8540 Personnel: 173

SD

Many Facility Codes have changed. Please refer to the AHA Guide Code Chart. © 2018 AHA Guide

VIBORG—Turner County

★ **PIONEER MEMORIAL HOSPITAL AND HEALTH SERVICES (431328)**, 315 North Washington Street, Zip 57070–2002, Mailing Address: P.O. Box 368, Zip 57070–0368; tel. 605/326–5161, (Total facility includes 52 beds in nursing home–type unit) **A**10 18 **F**6 10 15 28 30 34 40 43 45 53 56 57 59 63 65 69 75 79 81 87 97 107 111 119 125 127 128 130 132 133 154 **P**6 **S** Sanford Health, Sioux Falls, SD
Primary Contact: Thomas V. Richter, Chief Executive Officer
CFO: Anne Christiansen, Chief Financial Officer
CMO: Syed Shah, M.D., Chief of Staff
Web address: www.pioneermemorial.org
Control: Other not–for–profit (including NFP Corporation) **Service:** General medical and surgical

Staffed Beds: 64 **Admissions:** 149 **Census:** 50 **Outpatient Visits:** 26854 **Births:** 0 **Total Expense ($000):** 11472 **Payroll Expense ($000):** 6424 **Personnel:** 142	

WAGNER—Charles Mix County

★ **WAGNER COMMUNITY MEMORIAL HOSPITAL AVERA (431315)**, 513 Third Street SW, Zip 57380–9675, Mailing Address: P.O. Box 280, Zip 57380–0280; tel. 605/384–3611, **A**10 18 **F**3 11 15 18 28 31 34 40 43 45 57 59 64 67 70 75 77 81 93 97 107 110 114 119 128 130 133 148 154 **P**6 **S** Avera Health, Sioux Falls, SD
Primary Contact: Bryan Slaba, Chief Executive Officer
CFO: Lisa Weisser, Supervisor Finance
CHR: Marcia Podzimek, Chief Human Resources Officer
Web address: www.avera.org/wagnerhospital
Control: Other not–for–profit (including NFP Corporation) **Service:** General medical and surgical

Staffed Beds: 20 **Admissions:** 129 **Census:** 1 **Outpatient Visits:** 8044 **Births:** 0 **Total Expense ($000):** 8306 **Payroll Expense ($000):** 3724 **Personnel:** 64	

WATERTOWN—Codington County

★ **PRAIRIE LAKES HEALTHCARE SYSTEM (430005)**, 401 9th Avenue NW, Zip 57201–1548, Mailing Address: P.O. Box 1210, Zip 57201–6210; tel. 605/882–7000, **A**10 20 **F**3 8 12 13 18 20 22 28 29 30 31 34 35 38 40 43 48 50 57 58 59 60 62 63 64 75 76 77 78 79 80 81 82 83 84 85 87 89 93 107 111 114 115 118 119 120 121 123 130 132 133 146 148 154
Primary Contact: K. C. DeBoer, President and Chief Executive Officer
COO: Traci Rabine, Vice President Clinic Operations
CFO: Adam Paul, Chief Financial Officer
CMO: Henri Lanctin, M.D., Chief of Staff
CIO: Grant Tillett, Chief Information Officer
CHR: Nathan Lake, Vice President Human Resources
CNO: Shelly Turbak, R.N., Chief Nursing Officer
Web address: www.prairielakes.com
Control: Other not–for–profit (including NFP Corporation) **Service:** General medical and surgical

Staffed Beds: 79 **Admissions:** 2993 **Census:** 27 **Outpatient Visits:** 98165 **Births:** 675 **Total Expense ($000):** 89290 **Payroll Expense ($000):** 38490 **Personnel:** 488	

WEBSTER—Day County

SANFORD WEBSTER MEDICAL CENTER See Sanford Webster Medical Center

★ **SANFORD WEBSTER MEDICAL CENTER (431311)**, 1401 West 1st Street, Zip 57274–1054, Mailing Address: P.O. Box 489, Zip 57274–0489; tel. 605/345–3336, **A**10 18 **F**3 15 28 29 34 35 40 43 57 59 63 64 71 77 81 86 87 91 93 97 107 111 114 119 127 128 130 131 133 148 149 150 154 **P**6 **S** Sanford Health, Sioux Falls, SD
Primary Contact: Isaac Gerdes, Chief Executive Officer
CFO: Sheryl L Pappas, Chief Financial Officer
Web address: www.sanfordhealth.org
Control: Other not–for–profit (including NFP Corporation) **Service:** General medical and surgical

Staffed Beds: 20 **Admissions:** 164 **Census:** 2 **Outpatient Visits:** 15715 **Births:** 0 **Total Expense ($000):** 7470 **Payroll Expense ($000):** 3410 **Personnel:** 64	

WESSINGTON SPRINGS—Jerauld County

★ **AVERA WESKOTA MEMORIAL HOSPITAL (431324)**, 604 First Street NE, Zip 57382–2166; tel. 605/539–1201, **A**10 18 **F**3 15 28 31 34 35 40 53 57 59 64 75 77 81 85 93 107 114 119 128 130 131 132 133 **P**5 **S** Avera Health, Sioux Falls, SD
Primary Contact: Stephanie Reasy, Administrator and Chief Executive Officer
CFO: Linda Jager, Director Finance
CMO: Thomas Dean, M.D., Chief of Staff
CNO: JoAnn Hettinger, R.N., Director of Patient Care Services
Web address: www.averaweskota.org
Control: Other not–for–profit (including NFP Corporation) **Service:** General medical and surgical

Staffed Beds: 23 **Admissions:** 118 **Census:** 2 **Outpatient Visits:** 4914 **Births:** 0 **Total Expense ($000):** 4045 **Payroll Expense ($000):** 1747 **Personnel:** 21	

WINNER—Tripp County

★ **WINNER REGIONAL HEALTHCARE CENTER (431334)**, 745 East Eighth Street, Zip 57580–2631; tel. 605/842–7100, (Total facility includes 79 beds in nursing home–type unit) **A**10 18 **F**6 11 13 15 28 29 31 34 35 40 43 47 56 57 59 62 64 65 68 70 77 79 81 85 91 93 96 97 107 108 127 128 129 130 131 132 133 148 154 **P**3 **S** Sanford Health, Sioux Falls, SD
Primary Contact: Kevin Coffey, Chief Executive Officer
COO: Debra K. Davis, Director of Operations
CFO: Phil Husher, Chief Financial Officer
CMO: Tony L. Berg, M.D., Chief of Staff
CIO: Gary Burrus, Director Information Technology
CHR: Susan Hughes, Interim Director Human Resources
CNO: Julie Hennebold, R.N., Interim Chief Nursing Officer
Web address: www.winnerregional.org
Control: Other not–for–profit (including NFP Corporation) **Service:** General medical and surgical

Staffed Beds: 104 **Admissions:** 759 **Census:** 80 **Outpatient Visits:** 8018 **Births:** 231 **Total Expense ($000):** 20042 **Payroll Expense ($000):** 6341 **Personnel:** 159	

YANKTON—Yankton County

⊞ **AVERA SACRED HEART HOSPITAL (430012)**, 501 Summit Avenue, Zip 57078–3855; tel. 605/668–8000, (Total facility includes 187 beds in nursing home–type unit) **A**1 2 3 5 10 **F**2 3 6 8 10 13 15 18 20 28 29 30 31 34 35 39 40 43 45 46 47 48 53 57 59 60 62 63 64 71 75 77 78 79 81 82 84 85 86 87 91 93 96 97 100 104 107 108 110 111 114 115 118 119 120 121 125 127 129 130 132 133 146 147 148 **P**6 **S** Avera Health, Sioux Falls, SD
Primary Contact: Douglas R. Ekeren, Regional President and Chief Executive Officer
CFO: Jamie Schaefer, Vice President Finance
CIO: Kathy Quinlivan, Director Management Information Systems
CHR: Jane E. Miller, Human Resources Officer
CNO: Lindsay Flannery, R.N., Vice President Patient Care Services
Web address: www.averasacredheart.com
Control: Church operated, Nongovernment, not–for–profit **Service:** General medical and surgical

Staffed Beds: 286 **Admissions:** 3678 **Census:** 214 **Outpatient Visits:** 87615 **Births:** 644 **Total Expense ($000):** 102874 **Payroll Expense ($000):** 40212 **Personnel:** 681	

LEWIS AND CLARK SPECIALTY HOSPITAL (430096), 2601 Fox Run Parkway, Zip 57078–5341; tel. 605/665–5100, (Nonreporting) **A**10
Primary Contact: Douglas Doorn, Chief Executive Officer
CFO: Terry Steichen, Business Officer
CHR: Elizabeth Steichen, Human Resources
Web address: www.lewisandclarkspecialty.com
Control: Corporation, Investor–owned (for–profit) **Service:** Surgical

Staffed Beds: 6	

SD

Hospital, Medicare Provider Number, Address, Telephone, Approval, Facility, and Physician Codes, Health Care System

★ American Hospital Association (AHA) membership
□ The Joint Commission accreditation
○ Healthcare Facilities Accreditation Program
◇ DNV Healthcare Inc. accreditation
⇑ Center for Improvement in Healthcare Quality Accreditation
△ Commission on Accreditation of Rehabilitation Facilities (CARF) accreditation

TENNESSEE

ASHLAND CITY—Cheatham County

★ **TRISTAR ASHLAND CITY MEDICAL CENTER (441311)**, 313 North Main Street, Zip 37015–1347; tel. 615/792–3030, **A**10 18 **F**3 29 34 40 45 77 91 93 107 111 114 119 128 133 134 135 148 154 **S** HCA Healthcare, Nashville, TN
Primary Contact: Darrell White, R.N., Administrator and Chief Nursing Officer
CFO: Joe Bowman, Chief Financial Officer
CMO: Divya Shroff, Chief Medical Officer
CIO: David Archer, Director Information Systems
CNO: Darrell White, R.N., Administrator and Chief Nursing Officer
Web address: www.tristarashlandcity.com/
Control: Corporation, Investor–owned (for–profit) **Service**: General medical and surgical

Staffed Beds: 12 **Admissions**: 121 **Census**: 1 **Outpatient Visits**: 17370
Births: 0

ATHENS—Mcminn County

⊞ **STARR REGIONAL MEDICAL CENTER (440068)**, 1114 West Madison Avenue, Zip 37303–4150, Mailing Address: P.O. Box 250, Zip 37371–0250; tel. 423/745–1411, (Nonreporting) **A**1 3 5 10 **S** LifePoint Health, Brentwood, TN
Primary Contact: Mark Nichols, FACHE, Chief Executive Officer
COO: Michael Herr, Chief Operating Officer
CFO: David Alley, Chief Financial Officer
Web address: www.starrregional.com
Control: Corporation, Investor–owned (for–profit) **Service**: General medical and surgical

Staffed Beds: 63

BARTLETT—Shelby County

⊞ **SAINT FRANCIS HOSPITAL–BARTLETT (440228)**, 2986 Kate Bond Road, Zip 38133–4003; tel. 901/820–7000, **A**1 10 **F**3 11 13 15 18 20 22 29 30 31 34 35 38 40 45 46 49 50 54 57 59 64 70 72 74 75 76 77 78 79 81 85 86 87 93 102 107 108 110 111 115 118 119 126 130 131 132 142 146 147 148 149 **S** TENET Healthcare Corporation, Dallas, TX
Primary Contact: Christopher Locke, Chief Executive Officer
COO: Gwen Bonner, Chief Operating Officer
CFO: Tina Kovacs, Chief Financial Officer
CMO: David Schwartz, M.D., Chief Medical Officer
CIO: Mark Lawrence, Director Information Systems
CHR: Adrienne Huntley, Chief Human Resources Officer
CNO: Kris Cherry, Ph.D., R.N., Chief Nursing Officer
Web address: www.saintfrancisbartlett.com
Control: Corporation, Investor–owned (for–profit) **Service**: General medical and surgical

Staffed Beds: 156 **Admissions**: 7789 **Census**: 99 **Outpatient Visits**: 66135
Births: 408 **Total Expense ($000)**: 108528 **Payroll Expense ($000)**: 36551
Personnel: 553

BOLIVAR—Hardeman County

⊞ **BOLIVAR GENERAL HOSPITAL (440181)**, 650 Nuckolls Road, Zip 38008–1532, Mailing Address: PO Box 509, Zip 38008–0509; tel. 731/658–3100, **A**1 10 **F**3 15 29 30 35 40 44 45 57 59 64 75 81 87 93 107 119 130 132 133 146 149 **S** West Tennessee Healthcare, Jackson, TN
Primary Contact: Ruby Kirby, Administrator
CFO: Terry Swindell, Controller
CMO: Felix Nnaji, Chief Medical Staff
CNO: Angela Lacy, Director of Nursing
Web address: www.wth.net
Control: Hospital district or authority, Government, nonfederal **Service**: General medical and surgical

Staffed Beds: 21 **Admissions**: 260 **Census**: 2 **Outpatient Visits**: 15151 **Births**: 0
Total Expense ($000): 6932 **Payroll Expense ($000)**: 2856 **Personnel**: 59

☐ **WESTERN MENTAL HEALTH INSTITUTE (444008)**, 11100 Old Highway 64, West, Zip 38008–1554; tel. 731/228–2000, **A**1 10 **F**75 98 101 130 154 **P**6
Primary Contact: Roger Pursley, Chief Executive Officer
CFO: Richard Taylor, Chief Financial Officer
CMO: Doug King, M.D., Director Clinical Services
CIO: Earl Bates, Director Information Technology
CHR: Barry Young, Director Human Resources
Control: State, Government, nonfederal **Service**: Psychiatric

Staffed Beds: 150 **Admissions**: 959 **Census**: 141 **Outpatient Visits**: 0
Births: 0 **Total Expense ($000)**: 35243 **Payroll Expense ($000)**: 19378
Personnel: 413

BRISTOL—Sullivan County

⊞ **BRISTOL REGIONAL MEDICAL CENTER (440012)**, 1 Medical Park Boulevard, Zip 37620–7430; tel. 423/844–1121, **A**1 2 5 10 **F**3 8 11 13 15 17 18 20 22 24 28 29 30 31 34 35 37 38 39 40 43 44 45 46 47 48 49 51 54 56 57 58 59 60 61 62 63 64 70 73 74 75 76 77 78 79 81 82 83 84 85 86 87 91 92 93 94 96 97 98 100 102 103 107 108 110 111 114 115 118 119 120 121 123 124 126 129 130 131 132 135 144 145 146 147 148 149 **P**1 5 **S** Ballad Health, Johnson City, TN
Primary Contact: Greg Neal, FACHE, President
COO: Christopher Brian Hobson, Chief Operating Officer
CFO: Bob Bender, Vice–President Hospital Finance and Operations
CMO: Chad Couch, Chief Medical Officer
CIO: Martha O'Regan Chill, Chief Information Officer
CHR: Hamlin J Wilson, Senior Vice President Human Resources
CNO: Timothy Craig Anderson Jr Chief Nursing Officer
Web address: www.wellmont.org
Control: Other not–for–profit (including NFP Corporation) **Service**: General medical and surgical

Staffed Beds: 314 **Admissions**: 14821 **Census**: 180 **Outpatient Visits**: 128811 **Births**: 871 **Total Expense ($000)**: 226858 **Payroll Expense ($000)**: 68226 **Personnel**: 1592

⊞ **SELECT SPECIALTY HOSPITAL–TRI CITIES (442016)**, One Medical Park Boulevard, 5th Floor, Zip 37620–8964; tel. 423/844–5900, (Nonreporting) **A**1 10 **S** Select Medical Corporation, Mechanicsburg, PA
Primary Contact: Jeffrey Radford, Chief Executive Officer
CMO: John Byers, M.D., Medical Director
CHR: William G Ison, Human Resources Manager
CNO: Valerie Anderson, Chief Nursing Officer
Web address: www.tricities.selectspecialtyhospitals.com/
Control: Corporation, Investor–owned (for–profit) **Service**: Acute long–term care hospital

Staffed Beds: 33

CAMDEN—Benton County

⊞ **CAMDEN GENERAL HOSPITAL (441316)**, 175 Hospital Drive, Zip 38320–1617; tel. 731/593–6300, **A**1 10 18 **F**3 15 29 30 35 40 44 57 59 64 75 79 81 85 87 93 107 111 119 130 132 133 146 149 **S** West Tennessee Healthcare, Jackson, TN
Primary Contact: Scott Barber, Vice President
CFO: Terry Swindell, Chief Financial Officer
CMO: Jon R. Winter, D.O., Chief of Staff
CIO: Jeff Frieling, Vice President Information Systems
CHR: Barry Phillips, Executive Director Human Resources
Web address: www.wth.net
Control: Hospital district or authority, Government, nonfederal **Service**: General medical and surgical

Staffed Beds: 25 **Admissions**: 277 **Census**: 3 **Outpatient Visits**: 12074 **Births**: 0
Total Expense ($000): 7392 **Payroll Expense ($000)**: 3009 **Personnel**: 70

CARTHAGE—Smith County

⊞ **RIVERVIEW REGIONAL MEDICAL CENTER (441307)**, 158 Hospital Drive, Zip 37030–1096; tel. 615/735–1560, (Nonreporting) **A**1 10 18 **S** LifePoint Health, Brentwood, TN
Primary Contact: Michael Herman, Chief Executive Officer
CHR: Gina Anderson, Human Resources Officer
CNO: Patricia Anderson, Chief Nursing Officer
Web address: www.myriverviewmedical.com/
Control: Corporation, Investor–owned (for–profit) **Service**: General medical and surgical

Staffed Beds: 35

CELINA—Clay County

☐ **CUMBERLAND RIVER HOSPITAL (441319)**, 100 Old Jefferson Street, Zip 38551–4040, Mailing Address: P.O. Box 427, Zip 38551–0427; tel. 931/243–3581, (Nonreporting) **A**1 10 18
Primary Contact: Patsy Marinich, Chief Administrative Officer and Chief Nursing Officer
CFO: Patricia Strong, Chief Financial Officer
CMO: Harry Horne, D.O., Chief of Staff
CIO: Margie Boone, Registered Health Information Technician
CHR: Angel Lewis, Senior Vice President
CNO: Patsy Marinich, Chief Adminstrative Officer and Chief Nursing Officer
Web address: www.cumberlandriverhospital.com
Control: Corporation, Investor–owned (for–profit) **Service**: General medical and surgical

Staffed Beds: 34

TN

CENTERVILLE—Hickman County

SAINT THOMAS HICKMAN HOSPITAL (441300), 135 East Swan Street, Zip 37033–1417; tel. 931/729–4271, (Nonreporting) **A**1 10 18 **S** Ascension Healthcare, Saint Louis, MO
Primary Contact: Kevin Campbell, Chief Executive Officer
COO: Robin Crowell, Chief Nursing Officer and Chief Operating Officer
CMO: Zachary Hutchens, M.D., Chief Medical Officer
CHR: Patty Matney, Human Resources Consultant
CNO: Robin Crowell, Chief Nursing Officer and Chief Operating Officer
Web address: www.sths.com/hickman
Control: Other not-for-profit (including NFP Corporation) **Service:** General medical and surgical

Staffed Beds: 65

CHATTANOOGA—Hamilton County

CHI MEMORIAL (440091), 2525 De Sales Avenue, Zip 37404–1161; tel. 423/495–2525, (Includes MEMORIAL HOSPITAL HIXSON, 2051 Hamill Road, Hixson, TN, Zip 37343–4026; tel. 423/495–7100; Larry P Schumacher, R.N., MSN, Chief Executive Officer) **A**1 2 3 10 **F**3 7 8 11 12 15 17 18 20 22 24 26 28 29 30 31 34 35 36 40 44 45 46 47 48 49 50 53 54 55 56 57 58 59 60 61 64 67 68 70 71 74 75 77 78 79 81 82 84 85 86 87 93 107 108 110 111 114 115 116 117 118 119 120 121 124 126 129 130 132 135 145 146 147 148 149 150 154 **P**3 6 7 8 **S** Catholic Health Initiatives, Englewood, CO
Primary Contact: Janelle Reilly, Chief Executive Officer
COO: Janelle Reilly, Chief Operating Officer
CFO: Troy Hammett, Senior Vice President and Chief Financial Officer South Eastern Division
CMO: Helen Kuroki, Senior Vice President and Chief Medical Officer
CHR: Brad W Pope, Vice President Human Resources
CNO: Rhonda Poulson, Chief Nursing Officer and Vice President of Clinical Operations
Web address: www.memorial.org
Control: Church operated, Nongovernment, not-for-profit **Service:** General medical and surgical

Staffed Beds: 405 **Admissions:** 23789 **Census:** 315 **Outpatient Visits:** 385397 **Births:** 9 **Total Expense ($000):** 501421 **Payroll Expense ($000):** 144680 **Personnel:** 2527

ERLANGER MEDICAL CENTER (440104), 975 East Third Street, Zip 37403–2147; tel. 423/778–7000, (Includes ERLANGER EAST HOSPITAL, 1755 Gunbarrel Road, Chattanooga, TN, Zip 37421; tel. 423/778–8700; Phillip E. Jackson, Vice President & CEO; ERLANGER NORTH HOSPITAL, 632 Morrison Springs Road, Chattanooga, TN, Zip 37415; tel. 615/778–3300; Phillip E. Jackson, Vice President and CEO; T. C. THOMPSON CHILDREN'S HOSPITAL, 910 Blackford Street, Chattanooga, TN, Zip 37403; tel. 615/778–6011; Donald Mueller, Vice President and CEO; WILLIE D. MILLER EYE CENTER, 975 East Third Street, Chattanooga, TN, Zip 37403; tel. 615/778–6011) **A**1 2 5 8 10 **F**3 5 6 7 8 9 11 12 13 14 15 17 18 19 20 21 22 23 24 25 26 27 28 29 30 31 32 34 35 36 37 38 39 40 41 43 44 45 46 47 48 49 50 51 52 53 54 55 56 57 58 59 60 61 62 63 65 66 68 70 71 72 73 74 75 77 78 79 80 81 82 83 84 85 86 87 88 91 92 93 94 96 97 98 99 100 101 102 103 104 105 107 108 109 110 111 112 114 115 116 117 118 119 120 121 123 124 126 127 129 130 131 132 133 134 135 138 141 142 143 144 145 146 147 148 149 150 153 154 **P**2 4 6 7 **S** Erlanger Health System, Chattanooga, TN
Primary Contact: Kevin M. Spiegel, Chief Executive Officer
COO: Robert M. Brooks, FACHE, Executive Vice President, Chief Operating Officer
CFO: J. Britton Tabor, Executive Vice President, Chief Financial Officer
CMO: William L. Jackson, M.D., Jr Executive Vice President, Chief Medical Officer
CIO: David Peterson, Senior Vice President, Chief Technology Officer
CHR: Floyd Chasse, Vice President Human Resources
CNO: Janice C. Keys, FACHE, Senior Vice President, Chief Nurse Executive
Web address: www.erlanger.org
Control: Hospital district or authority, Government, nonfederal **Service:** General medical and surgical

Staffed Beds: 688 **Admissions:** 38626 **Census:** 497 **Outpatient Visits:** 592460 **Births:** 5480 **Total Expense ($000):** 827219 **Payroll Expense ($000):** 340513 **Personnel:** 5215

ERLANGER WOMEN'S EAST HOSPITAL See Erlanger East Hospital

HEALTHSOUTH CHATTANOOGA REHABILITATION HOSPITAL (443032), 2412 McCallie Avenue, Zip 37404–3398; tel. 423/698–0221, (Nonreporting) **A**1 10 **S** Encompass Health Corporation, Birmingham, AL
Primary Contact: Scott Rowe, Chief Executive Officer
COO: Scott Rowe, Chief Executive Officer
CFO: Karen Klassen, Controller
CMO: Amjad Munir, M.D., Medical Director
CIO: Denise Smith, Director Health Information
CHR: Rebekah McNair, Director Human Resources
CNO: Cinthia Campbell, Chief Nursing Officer
Web address: www.healthsouthchattanooga.com
Control: Corporation, Investor-owned (for-profit) **Service:** Rehabilitation

Staffed Beds: 69

KINDRED HOSPITAL–CHATTANOOGA (442007), 709 Walnut Street, Zip 37402–1916; tel. 423/266–7721, (Nonreporting) **A**1 10 **S** Kindred Healthcare, Louisville, KY
Primary Contact: Andrea White, Chief Executive Officer
COO: Rick Rheinheimer, Chief Clinical Officer
CFO: Julia Smith, Chief Financial Officer
CMO: Randy Heisser, M.D., Medical Director
CHR: Kellie McCampbell, Coordinator Human Resources
CNO: Gigi Johnson, Chief Nursing Officer
Web address: www.kindredchattanooga.com/
Control: Corporation, Investor-owned (for-profit) **Service:** Acute long-term care hospital

Staffed Beds: 44

MOCCASIN BEND MENTAL HEALTH INSTITUTE (444002), 100 Moccasin Bend Road, Zip 37405–4415; tel. 423/265–2271, (Nonreporting) **A**1 10
Primary Contact: Mary C. Young, Chief Executive Officer
CFO: Sylvia Harris, Fiscal Director
CMO: Terry R Holmes, M.D., Clinical Director
CIO: Mickey Williams, Manager Information Technology
CHR: Cynthia Honeycutt, Director Human Resources
CNO: Charlynne Parson, Nurse Executive
Web address: www.state.tn.us/mental/mhs/mbhmhi/moc.htm
Control: State, Government, nonfederal **Service:** Psychiatric

Staffed Beds: 150

PARKRIDGE MEDICAL CENTER (440156), 2333 McCallie Avenue, Zip 37404–3258; tel. 423/698–6061, (Includes EAST RIDGE HOSPITAL, 941 Spring Creek Road, East Ridge, TN, Zip 37412, Mailing Address: P.O. Box 91229, Zip 37412–6229, tel. 423/855–3500; Jarrett B. Millsaps Jr, FACHE, Chief Executive Officer; PARKRIDGE EAST HOSPITAL, 941 Spring Creek Road, Chattanooga, TN, Zip 37412–3909; tel. 423/894–7870; Jarrett B. Millsaps Jr, FACHE, Chief Executive Officer; PARKRIDGE VALLEY CHILD AND ADOLESCENT CAMPUS, 2200 Morris Hill Road, Chattanooga, TN, Zip 37421; tel. 423/894–4220; Melissa Arkin, Chief Executive Officer; PARKRIDGE WEST HOSPITAL, 1000 Highway 28, Jasper, TN, Zip 37347–3638; tel. 423/837–9500; Shirley K Scarlatti, Associate Chief Nursing Officer) (Nonreporting) **A**1 2 3 5 10 **S** HCA Healthcare, Nashville, TN
Primary Contact: Thomas H. Ozburn, Chief Executive Officer
COO: Jim L Coleman Jr Chief Operating Officer
CFO: Tom Jackson, Chief Financial Officer
CMO: Timothy M. Grant, M.D., Chief Medical Officer
CIO: David Cornelius, Director Information Systems
CHR: Carole Hoffman, Vice President
CNO: Jerri C Underwood, R.N., Chief Nursing Officer
Web address: www.parkridgemedicalcenter.com
Control: Corporation, Investor-owned (for-profit) **Service:** General medical and surgical

Staffed Beds: 472

SISKIN HOSPITAL FOR PHYSICAL REHABILITATION (443025), One Siskin Plaza, Zip 37403–1306; tel. 423/634–1200, (Nonreporting) **A**1 7 10
Primary Contact: Carol Sim, President and Chief Executive Officer
CFO: Carol Arnhart, Vice President Finance and Chief Financial Officer
CMO: David N Bowers, M.D., Medical Director
CIO: Shane Pilcher, Administrative Director Information Systems
CHR: Kristi Delaney, Director, Human Resources
CNO: Tracy Collings Reed, Vice President Patient Care Services, Chief Nursing Officer
Web address: www.siskinrehab.org
Control: Other not-for-profit (including NFP Corporation) **Service:** Rehabilitation

Staffed Beds: 195

TN

T. C. THOMPSON CHILDREN'S HOSPITAL See Erlanger Medical Center, Chattanooga

CLARKSVILLE—Montgomery County

✠ **TENNOVA HEALTHCARE–CLARKSVILLE (440035)**, 651 Dunlop Lane, Zip 37040–5015, Mailing Address: P.O. Box 31629, Zip 37040–0028; tel. 931/502–1000, (Nonreporting) **A**1 10 **S** Community Health Systems, Inc., Franklin, TN
Primary Contact: Alex Villa, Chief Executive Officer
CFO: George Sprinkel, Chief Financial Officer
CMO: Thomas L Ely, D.O., Chief Medical Officer
CIO: Scott Greene, Chief Information Officer
CHR: Liza Edmunds, Director Human Resources
CNO: Faye Perry, Chief Nursing Officer
Web address: www.tennova.com/
Control: Partnership, Investor–owned (for–profit) **Service**: General medical and surgical

Staffed Beds: 247

UNITY PSYCHIATRIC CARE–CLARKSVILLE (444019), 930 Professional Park Drive, Zip 37040–5136; tel. 931/538–6420, (Nonreporting) **A**10 **S** Tennessee Health Management, Parsons, TN
Primary Contact: Jennifer Robinson, Administrator
CMO: Michael McGhee, M.D., Medical Director
CNO: Chrissy Myers, R.N., Director of Nursing
Web address: www.unitypsych.com
Control: Partnership, Investor–owned (for–profit) **Service**: Psychiatric

Staffed Beds: 26

CLEVELAND—Bradley County

✠ **TENNOVA HEALTHCARE – CLEVELAND (440185)**, 2305 Chambliss Avenue NW, Zip 37311–3847, Mailing Address: P.O. Box 3060, Zip 37320–3060; tel. 423/559–6000, (Includes SKYRIDGE MEDICAL CENTER – WESTSIDE CAMPUS, 2800 Westside Drive NW, Cleveland, TN, Zip 37312–3599; tel. 423/339–4100; R Coleman Foss, Chief Executive Officer) **A**1 3 5 10 **F**3 5 13 15 18 20 22 28 29 30 31 32 34 35 39 40 41 44 45 49 50 51 57 58 59 60 68 70 73 74 75 76 77 78 79 81 82 85 87 89 93 98 100 101 102 104 107 108 110 111 114 115 119 124 126 129 135 136 141 146 148 149 153 **S** Community Health Systems, Inc., Franklin, TN
Primary Contact: R Coleman. Foss, Chief Executive Officer
CFO: H. Wes Griffith, Chief Financial Officer
CMO: William F Johnson, Chief Medical Officer
CHR: Kristine Godfrey, Director Human Resources
Web address: www.skyridgemedicalcenter.net
Control: Corporation, Investor–owned (for–profit) **Service**: General medical and surgical

Staffed Beds: 187 Admissions: 8886 Census: 106 Outpatient Visits: 91543 Births: 1068 Total Expense ($000): 127472 Payroll Expense ($000): 45463 Personnel: 867

COLLIERVILLE—Shelby County

★ **BAPTIST MEMORIAL HOSPITAL–COLLIERVILLE (440217)**, 1500 West Poplar Avenue, Zip 38017–0601; tel. 901/861–9400, **A**5 **F**3 7 8 12 15 18 29 30 34 35 36 38 40 41 45 46 47 48 49 50 53 57 58 59 60 61 64 65 68 70 74 75 77 79 80 81 84 85 87 91 92 93 96 107 108 109 110 111 114 115 119 120 129 130 132 135 146 147 148 149 154 **S** Baptist Memorial Health Care Corporation, Memphis, TN
Primary Contact: Lindsay Stencel, Chief Administrative Officer
CFO: Terri Seago, Chief Financial Officer
CIO: Doug Reiselt, Vice President and Chief Information Officer
CHR: Brenda Johnson, Director Human Resources
CNO: Denise Ferguson, Chief Nursing Officer
Web address: www.baptistonline.org/collierville/
Control: Other not–for–profit (including NFP Corporation) **Service**: General medical and surgical

Staffed Beds: 51 Admissions: 2766 Census: 21 Outpatient Visits: 35274 Births: 0 Total Expense ($000): 54718 Payroll Expense ($000): 17650 Personnel: 263

COLUMBIA—Maury County

✠ **MAURY REGIONAL HOSPITAL (440073)**, 1224 Trotwood Avenue, Zip 38401–4802; tel. 931/381–1111, **A**1 2 10 19 **F**3 7 8 11 13 15 18 20 22 24 26 28 29 30 31 34 35 37 38 40 41 44 45 46 47 48 49 50 51 53 54 55 57 58 59 60 62 64 66 68 70 73 74 75 76 77 78 79 80 81 82 84 85 86 87 89 91 92 93 96 102 107 108 110 111 114 115 116 117 118 119 120 121 123 124 126 127 129 130 131 132 135 146 147 149 154 **S** Maury Regional Health System, Columbia, TN
Primary Contact: H Alan. Watson, FACHE, Chief Executive Officer
COO: Kenneth Boyd, Chief Operating Officer
CFO: Nick Swift, Chief Financial Officer
CMO: Chris Edwards, M.D., Chief Medical Officer
CIO: Jim Parcel, Director Information Technology
CHR: Kaye Brewer, Vice President Human Resources
CNO: Deborah Lumpkins, MSN, Chief Nursing Officer
Web address: www.mauryregional.com
Control: County, Government, nonfederal **Service**: General medical and surgical

Staffed Beds: 209 Admissions: 11804 Census: 124 Outpatient Visits: 251359 Births: 1452 Total Expense ($000): 274324 Payroll Expense ($000): 103181 Personnel: 2011

UNITY PSYCHIATRIC CARE–COLUMBIA (440230), 1400 Rosewood Drive, Zip 38401–4878; tel. 931/388–6573, (Nonreporting) **A**10 **S** Tennessee Health Management, Parsons, TN
Primary Contact: Paula Chennault, Administrator
CMO: Rodney Poling, M.D., Medical Director
CHR: Pam Brown, Human Resources Manager
CNO: Sheila Ridner, R.N., Director of Nursing
Web address: www.unitypsych.com
Control: Partnership, Investor–owned (for–profit) **Service**: Psychiatric

Staffed Beds: 16

COOKEVILLE—Putnam County

✠ **COOKEVILLE REGIONAL MEDICAL CENTER (440059)**, 1 Medical Center Boulevard, Zip 38501–4294; tel. 931/783–2000, **A**1 2 10 19 **F**3 8 11 12 13 15 17 18 20 22 24 26 28 29 30 31 34 35 40 44 45 49 50 51 54 57 59 62 64 65 68 70 73 74 75 76 77 78 79 81 85 86 87 89 90 93 96 107 108 110 111 114 115 117 118 119 120 121 123 126 129 130 132 133 135 146 147 148
Primary Contact: Paul Korth, Chief Executive Officer
COO: Scott Williams, Chief Operating Officer
CFO: Paul Korth, Chief Financial Officer
CMO: Jeffrey J Gleason, M.D., Chief Medical Officer
CIO: Les Bernstein, Chief Information Officer
CHR: Angel Lewis, Senior Vice President Administration
CNO: Linda Crawford, R.N., MSN, Chief Nursing Officer
Web address: www.crmchealth.org
Control: Hospital district or authority, Government, nonfederal **Service**: General medical and surgical

Staffed Beds: 243 Admissions: 12888 Census: 152 Outpatient Visits: 218615 Births: 1576 Total Expense ($000): 247597 Payroll Expense ($000): 97698 Personnel: 2327

⇑ **TEN BROECK TENNESSEE TREATMENT FACILITY (444022)**, 1 Medical Center Boulevard, 5 West, Zip 38501; tel. 931/783–2570, **A**10 21 **F**4 5 98 101 103 104 105 151 152 153 **S** United Medical Corporation, Windermere, FL
Primary Contact: Kelly Tripp, Chief Executive Officer
CFO: David Corddry, Chief Financial Officer
CMO: Glenn T. Webb, M.D., Medical Director
CHR: Glenda Guy, Director, Health Information Management
CNO: Annasue Collins, Chief Nursing Officer
Web address: www.tenbroeck.com
Control: Corporation, Investor–owned (for–profit) **Service**: Psychiatric

Staffed Beds: 38 Admissions: 1801 Census: 27 Outpatient Visits: 215 Births: 0 Personnel: 80

COVINGTON—Tipton County

✠ **BAPTIST MEMORIAL HOSPITAL–TIPTON (440131)**, 1995 Highway 51 South, Zip 38019–3635; tel. 901/476–2621, **A**1 10 **F**3 11 15 29 30 31 34 35 40 45 55 57 58 59 65 70 74 75 76 78 79 81 85 87 89 93 100 107 108 110 111 114 115 119 120 121 130 146 148 154 **S** Baptist Memorial Health Care Corporation, Memphis, TN
Primary Contact: Samuel Lynd, Administrator and Chief Executive Officer
CFO: Monique Hart, Chief Financial Officer
CMO: Kenneth Afenya, M.D., Chief of Staff
CHR: Myra Cousar, Director Human Resources
Web address: www.baptistonline.org/tipton/
Control: Other not–for–profit (including NFP Corporation) **Service**: General medical and surgical

Staffed Beds: 50 Admissions: 1190 Census: 8 Outpatient Visits: 56002 Births: 404 Total Expense ($000): 84395 Payroll Expense ($000): 16120 Personnel: 242

TN

CROSSVILLE—Cumberland County

☒ **CUMBERLAND MEDICAL CENTER (440009)**, 421 South Main Street, Zip 38555–5031; tel. 931/484–9511, **A**1 2 10 20 **F**3 11 13 15 18 20 22 28 29 30 31 34 35 40 44 45 47 48 51 53 57 59 68 70 74 75 76 77 78 79 81 82 85 86 87 93 107 108 110 111 114 115 119 120 121 129 130 132 135 146 147 148 **P**6 **S** Covenant Health, Knoxville, TN
Primary Contact: David V. Bunch, President and Chief Administrative Officer
CFO: April VonAchen, Chief Financial Officer and Vice President Financial Services
CIO: Joe Lowe, Director Management Information Systems
CHR: Charles Sexton, Manager Human Resources
CNO: Rebecca Foster, MSN, R.N., Chief Nursing Officer
Web address: www.cmchealthcare.org
Control: Other not–for–profit (including NFP Corporation) **Service:** General medical and surgical

Staffed Beds: 85 **Admissions:** 4766 **Census:** 47 **Outpatient Visits:** 81617 **Births:** 647 **Total Expense ($000):** 72049 **Payroll Expense ($000):** 28366 **Personnel:** 748

DAYTON—Rhea County

☒ **RHEA MEDICAL CENTER (441310)**, 9400 Rhea County Highway, Zip 37321–7922; tel. 423/775–1121, (Nonreporting) **A**1 10 18 **S** QHR, Brentwood, TN
Primary Contact: David Bixler, Chief Executive Officer
CFO: Harv Sanders, Chief Financial Officer
CMO: Benjamin Kellogg, M.D., Chief of Staff
CNO: Samantha Bryant, Chief Nursing Officer
Web address: www.rheamedical.org
Control: County, Government, nonfederal **Service:** General medical and surgical

Staffed Beds: 25

DICKSON—Dickson County

☒ **TRISTAR HORIZON MEDICAL CENTER (440046)**, 111 Highway 70 East, Zip 37055–2080; tel. 615/446–0446, (Nonreporting) **A**1 2 10 **S** HCA Healthcare, Nashville, TN
Primary Contact: Dustin Greene, Chief Executive Officer
CFO: Clarence Gray, Chief Financial Officer
CIO: Rick Stoker, Director Management Information Systems
CHR: Sheila Kight, Director Human Resources
CNO: Gina Bullington, Chief Nursing Officer
Web address: www.horizonmedicalcenter.com
Control: Corporation, Investor–owned (for–profit) **Service:** General medical and surgical

Staffed Beds: 130

DYERSBURG—Dyer County

☒ **WEST TENNESSEE HEALTHCARE DYERSBURG HOSPITAL (440072)**, 400 East Tickle Street, Zip 38024–3120; tel. 731/285–2410, (Nonreporting) **A**1 10 20 **S** West Tennessee Healthcare, Jackson, TN
Primary Contact: Reba Celsor, Chief Executive Officer
CFO: Meredith Malone, Chief Financial Officer
CMO: Darren Johnson, M.D., Chief of Staff
CIO: Russ Shephard, Senior Systems Analyst
CHR: Beverly Ray, Director Human Resources
CNO: Jan Zimmer, R.N., MSN, R.N., MS, Chief Nursing Officer
Web address: www.wth.org/locations/west–tennessee–healthcare–dyersburg–hospital
Control: Other not–for–profit (including NFP Corporation) **Service:** General medical and surgical

Staffed Beds: 120

EAST RIDGE—Hamilton County

EAST RIDGE HOSPITAL See Parkridge Medical Center, Chattanooga

ELIZABETHTON—Carter County

☐ **SYCAMORE SHOALS HOSPITAL (440018)**, 1501 West Elk Avenue, Zip 37643–2874; tel. 423/542–1300, **A**1 10 **F**3 11 15 18 29 30 34 35 40 41 44 45 48 50 53 54 56 57 59 62 63 64 68 70 75 77 79 81 84 85 87 93 97 98 103 107 110 111 115 118 119 130 135 144 146 147 148 154 **S** Ballad Health, Johnson City, TN
Primary Contact: Dwayne Taylor, Chief Executive Officer
COO: Melanie Stanton, R.N., Chief Nursing Officer
CFO: Chase Wilson, Chief Financial Officer
CMO: Morris H Seligman, M.D., Chief Medical Officer and Chief Medical Information Officer
CIO: Paul Merrywell, Chief Information Officer
CHR: Sharon Sheppard, Manager Human Resources
Web address: www.msha.com
Control: Other not–for–profit (including NFP Corporation) **Service:** General medical and surgical

Staffed Beds: 74 **Admissions:** 3686 **Census:** 43 **Outpatient Visits:** 66594 **Births:** 0 **Total Expense ($000):** 41722 **Payroll Expense ($000):** 17335 **Personnel:** 327

ERIN—Houston County

☒ **HOUSTON COUNTY COMMUNITY HOSPITAL (440232)**, 5001 East Main Street, Zip 37061–4115, Mailing Address: P.O. Box 489, Zip 37061–0489; tel. 931/289–4211, (Nonreporting) **A**1 10
Primary Contact: Randy Davis, Chief Executive Officer
CFO: Kim Pridgen, Chief Financial Officer
CMO: Michael Carter, M.D., Chief Medical Officer
CNO: Angie Beard, R.N.
Control: County, Government, nonfederal **Service:** General medical and surgical

Staffed Beds: 25

ERWIN—Unicoi County

☒ **UNICOI COUNTY MEMORIAL HOSPITAL (440001)**, 100 Greenway Circle, Zip 37650–2196, Mailing Address: P.O. Box 802, Zip 37650–0802; tel. 423/743–3141, (Total facility includes 1 beds in nursing home–type unit) **A**1 10 **F**11 15 29 30 34 35 40 64 67 68 75 77 85 107 110 111 115 119 130 131 146 154 **S** Ballad Health, Johnson City, TN
Primary Contact: Eric Carroll, Chief Executive Officer
CFO: Toni Buchanan, Chief Financial Officer
CMO: Jose Picaza, M.D., Chief of Staff
CIO: Maggie Tipton, Chief Information Officer
CHR: Susan Broyles, Director Human Resources and Safety
CNO: Melanie Stanton, R.N., Chief Nursing Officer
Web address: www.msha.com
Control: Other not–for–profit (including NFP Corporation) **Service:** General medical and surgical

Staffed Beds: 94 **Admissions:** 509 **Census:** 47 **Outpatient Visits:** 23548 **Births:** 0 **Total Expense ($000):** 11381 **Payroll Expense ($000):** 4857 **Personnel:** 71

FAYETTEVILLE—Lincoln County

☐ **LINCOLN COUNTY HEALTH SYSTEM (440102)**, 106 Medical Center Boulevard, Zip 37334–2684, Mailing Address: PO Box 637, Zip 37334–2684; tel. 931/438–1100, (Nonreporting) **A**1 10
Primary Contact: Candie Starr, Chief Executive Officer
CFO: Robert M Lonis, CPA, Chief Financial Officer
CIO: John Kenneth Lavender, Chief Information Officer
CHR: Wendy Nogler, Director Human Resources
CNO: Vicky Groce, Chief Nursing Officer
Web address: www.lchealthsystem.com
Control: County, Government, nonfederal **Service:** General medical and surgical

Staffed Beds: 577

FRANKLIN—Williamson County

★ **HEALTHSOUTH REHABILITATION HOSPITAL OF FRANKLIN (443035)**, 1000 Physicians Way, Zip 37067–1471; tel. 615/721–4000, **F**28 29 34 35 68 75 90 91 96 148 154 **P**5 **S** Encompass Health Corporation, Birmingham, AL
Primary Contact: Scott J. Peterson, Chief Executive Officer
CMO: Scott Craig, M.D., Medical Director
Web address: www.healthsouthfranklin.com
Control: Corporation, Investor–owned (for–profit) **Service:** Rehabilitation

Staffed Beds: 40 **Admissions:** 591 **Census:** 20 **Outpatient Visits:** 0 **Births:** 0 **Total Expense ($000):** 9672 **Payroll Expense ($000):** 4622 **Personnel:** 75

TN

Hospital, Medicare Provider Number, Address, Telephone, Approval, Facility, and Physician Codes, Health Care System

★ American Hospital Association (AHA) membership
☐ The Joint Commission accreditation
○ Healthcare Facilities Accreditation Program
◇ DNV Healthcare Inc. accreditation
⇑ Center for Improvement in Healthcare Quality Accreditation
△ Commission on Accreditation of Rehabilitation Facilities (CARF) accreditation

☐ **ROLLING HILLS HOSPITAL (444007)**, 2014 Quail Hollow Circle,
Zip 37067-5967; tel. 615/628-5700, **A**1 10 **F**4 5 34 44 50 54 56 64 68 75 98
99 100 101 102 103 104 130 132 135 149 154 **S** Universal Health Services,
Inc., King of Prussia, PA
Primary Contact: Jim Spruyt, Chief Executive Officer
CFO: Ray Brocato, Chief Financial Officer
CMO: James Hart, M.D., Medical Director
CHR: Lisa Hodge, Director, Human Resources
CNO: Laurel Roberts, R.N., MSN, Chief Nursing Officer
Web address: www.RollingHillsHospital.org/
Control: Corporation, Investor-owned (for-profit) **Service**: Psychiatric

Staffed Beds: 130 **Admissions**: 4333 **Census**: 92 **Outpatient Visits**: 0
Births: 0

☐ **WILLIAMSON MEDICAL CENTER (440029)**, 4321 Carothers Parkway,
Zip 37067-8542; tel. 615/435-5000, **A**1 2 3 10 **F**3 7 11 13 15 18 20 22 28 29
30 31 34 35 40 41 43 45 46 49 50 54 57 59 64 68 70 72 74 75 76 77 78 79
81 82 84 85 86 87 89 93 96 97 102 107 108 110 111 114 115 118 119 124
126 129 130 132 135 146 148 149
Primary Contact: Donald Webb, Chief Executive Officer
COO: Julie Miller, Chief Operating Officer
CMO: Starling C Evins, M.D., Chief of Staff
CIO: Steve Dycus, Director Marketing and Public Relations
CHR: Phyllis Molyneux, Associate Administrator Human Resources and Education
Web address: www.williamsonmedicalcenter.org
Control: County, Government, nonfederal **Service**: General medical and surgical

Staffed Beds: 185 **Admissions**: 8886 **Census**: 89 **Outpatient Visits**:
124762 **Births**: 1865 **Total Expense ($000)**: 195698 **Payroll Expense**
($000): 79571 **Personnel**: 1187

GALLATIN—Sumner County

☒ **SUMNER REGIONAL MEDICAL CENTER (440003)**, 555 Hartsville Pike,
Zip 37066-2400, Mailing Address: P.O. Box 1558, Zip 37066-1558;
tel. 615/452-4210, (Nonreporting) **A**1 2 3 10 **S** LifePoint Health, Brentwood, TN
Primary Contact: Susan M. Peach, R.N., Chief Executive Officer
CMO: Geoffrey Lifferth, M.D., Chief Medical Officer
CIO: Vickie Carter, Information Systems Director
CNO: Anne Melton, Chief Nursing Officer
Web address: www.mysumnermedical.com
Control: Corporation, Investor-owned (for-profit) **Service**: General medical and surgical

Staffed Beds: 155

GERMANTOWN—Shelby County

☐ **BAPTIST MEMORIAL REHABILITATION HOSPITAL (443034)**, 1240 South
Germantown Road, Zip 38138-2226; tel. 901/275-3300, **A**1 10 **F**3 90 **S** Baptist
Memorial Health Care Corporation, Memphis, TN
Primary Contact: Christopher L. Bariola, Chief Executive Officer
CFO: Carlos Mendoza, Controller
CHR: Stacie Schroeppel, Director of Human Resources
CNO: Donna Hale, Director of Nursing
Web address: www.baptistrehab.com
Control: Corporation, Investor-owned (for-profit) **Service**: Rehabilitation

Staffed Beds: 49 **Admissions**: 1120 **Census**: 38 **Outpatient Visits**: 0
Births: 0 **Total Expense ($000)**: 16235 **Payroll Expense ($000)**: 8430
Personnel: 194

METHODIST LE BONHEUR GERMANTOWN HOSPITAL See Methodist
Healthcare Memphis Hospitals, Memphis

GREENEVILLE—Greene County

☒ **LAUGHLIN MEMORIAL HOSPITAL (440025)**, 1420 Tusculum Boulevard,
Zip 37745-5825; tel. 423/787-5000, (Nonreporting) **A**1 2 10 19 **S** Ballad Health,
Johnson City, TN
Primary Contact: Charles H. Whitfield Jr, President and Chief Executive Officer
CFO: Mark Compton, Chief Financial Officer
CMO: Mark Patterson, M.D., Chief Medical Officer
CIO: Eric L Garrison, Chief Information Officer
CHR: Robert R Roark, Director Human Resources
CNO: Brenda Cannon, R.N., Director of Nursing
Web address: www.laughlinmemorial.org
Control: Other not-for-profit (including NFP Corporation) **Service**: General
medical and surgical

Staffed Beds: 143

☒ **TAKOMA REGIONAL HOSPITAL (440050)**, 401 Takoma Avenue,
Zip 37743-4647; tel. 423/639-3151, **A**1 10 **F**3 6 12 13 15 29 30 32 34 35 40
44 45 49 50 54 56 57 59 64 65 68 70 74 75 76 77 79 81 85 87 90 93 97 98
100 102 103 104 107 108 110 111 115 119 129 130 131 135 144 146 147
148 149 154 **S** Ballad Health, Johnson City, TN
Primary Contact: Tammy Albright, President
CFO: Judith Clark, Chief Financial Officer
CMO: Daniel Lewis, Chief Medical Officer
CHR: Jack Lister, Director Human Resources
CNO: Robin Roberts, Executive Director of Patient Services
Web address: www.takoma.org
Control: Other not-for-profit (including NFP Corporation) **Service**: General
medical and surgical

Staffed Beds: 92 **Admissions**: 2348 **Census**: 25 **Outpatient Visits**: 85947
Births: 313 **Total Expense ($000)**: 68438 **Payroll Expense ($000)**: 31787
Personnel: 504

HARRIMAN—Roane County

☒ **ROANE MEDICAL CENTER (440031)**, 8045 Roane Medical Center Dr,
Zip 37748-8333; tel. 865/316-1000, **A**1 3 10 **F**3 11 15 18 20 28 29 30 34
40 45 50 57 59 68 70 75 79 81 85 87 93 107 108 110 111 114 118 119 129
130 146 154 **S** Covenant Health, Knoxville, TN
Primary Contact: Jason B. Pilant, President and Chief Administrative Officer
CFO: Julie Utterback, Chief Financial Officer
CMO: Mark Browne, M.D., Chief Medical Officer
CIO: Mike Ward, Senior Vice President Chief Information Officer
CHR: Randall Carr, Director Human Resources
CNO: Carolyn Shipley, Chief Nursing Officer
Web address: www.roanemedical.com
Control: Other not-for-profit (including NFP Corporation) **Service**: General
medical and surgical

Staffed Beds: 52 **Admissions**: 2344 **Census**: 23 **Outpatient Visits**: 65279
Births: 0 **Total Expense ($000)**: 34107 **Payroll Expense ($000)**: 12734
Personnel: 252

HARTSVILLE—Trousdale County

☒ **TROUSDALE MEDICAL CENTER (441301)**, 500 Church Street,
Zip 37074-1744; tel. 615/374-2221, (Nonreporting) **A**1 10 18 **S** LifePoint
Health, Brentwood, TN
Primary Contact: Michael Herman, Chief Executive Officer
COO: William D Mize, Chief Operating Officer
CFO: David Wilhoite, CPA, Senior Vice President Finance and Chief Financial Officer
CIO: David Young, Senior Vice President Planning and Technology
CHR: Amy Overstreet, Director Human Resources
CNO: Jennifer Holder, Chief Nursing Officer
Web address: www.mytrousdalemedical.com
Control: Corporation, Investor-owned (for-profit) **Service**: General medical and surgical

Staffed Beds: 25

HENDERSONVILLE—Sumner County

☒ **TRISTAR HENDERSONVILLE MEDICAL CENTER (440194)**, 355 New Shackle
Island Road, Zip 37075-2479; tel. 615/338-1000, (Nonreporting) **A**1 10 **S** HCA
Healthcare, Nashville, TN
Primary Contact: Regina Bartlett, Chief Executive Officer
CFO: Jon Baker, Chief Financial Officer
CMO: Brett Branson, M.D., Chief Medical Officer
CIO: Hal Schultheis, Director Information Systems
CHR: Matt Gilday, Vice President of Human Resources
CNO: Lisa Gann, R.N., Chief Nursing Officer
Web address: www.hendersonvillemedicalcenter.com
Control: Corporation, Investor-owned (for-profit) **Service**: General medical and
surgical

Staffed Beds: 96

HERMITAGE—Davidson County

☒ **TRISTAR SUMMIT MEDICAL CENTER (440150)**, 5655 Frist Boulevard,
Zip 37076-2053; tel. 615/316-3000, **A**1 2 10 **F**3 11 13 15 18 20 22 26 28 29
30 31 34 35 37 38 39 40 43 45 46 47 48 49 50 56 57 61 64 70 72 74 75 76 77
78 79 80 81 82 85 87 90 93 96 107 108 110 111 114 115 119 120 121 122
124 126 129 130 131 135 145 146 147 148 **S** HCA Healthcare, Nashville, TN
Primary Contact: Brian Marger, Chief Executive Officer
CFO: Bryan Shephard, Chief Financial Officer
CMO: Kevin M. Hamilton, M.D., Chief Medical Officer
CIO: Joel Bain, Director Information Services
CHR: Emily Dye, Vice President Human Resources
CNO: Mary Ann Angle, R.N., FACHE, Chief Nursing Officer
Web address: www.summitmedctr.com
Control: Corporation, Investor-owned (for-profit) **Service**: General medical and
surgical

Staffed Beds: 200 **Admissions**: 12254 **Census**: 139 **Outpatient Visits**: 129769
Births: 1135 **Total Expense ($000)**: 145593 **Payroll Expense ($000)**: 54671

HUNTINGDON—Carroll County

✉ **BAPTIST MEMORIAL HOSPITAL–HUNTINGDON (440016)**, 631 R.B. Wilson Drive, Zip 38344–1727; tel. 731/986–4461, **A**1 10 **F**3 11 15 18 28 29 30 34 35 38 40 44 50 56 57 59 61 64 65 66 70 75 77 79 81 85 86 87 91 93 97 98 101 102 103 107 108 111 115 118 119 130 132 133 134 135 145 146 148 149 154 **S** Baptist Memorial Health Care Corporation, Memphis, TN
Primary Contact: Susan M. Breeden, Administrator and Chief Executive Officer
CFO: Sharron Holland, Chief Financial Officer
CHR: Kim King, Director Human Resources and Public Relations
CNO: Kimberly Sanders, Chief Nursing Officer
Web address: www.baptistonline.org/huntingdon/
Control: Other not–for–profit (including NFP Corporation) **Service:** General medical and surgical

Staffed Beds: 35 **Admissions:** 851 **Census:** 14 **Outpatient Visits:** 16446
Births: 0 **Total Expense ($000):** 18189 **Payroll Expense ($000):** 6598
Personnel: 145

JACKSON—Madison County

✉ △ **JACKSON–MADISON COUNTY GENERAL HOSPITAL (440002)**, 620 Skyline Drive, Zip 38301–3923; tel. 731/541–5000, (Includes WEST TENNESSEE HEALTHCARE NORTH HOSPITAL, 367 Hospital Boulevard, Jackson, TN, Zip 38305–2080; tel. 731/661–2000; Kevin Rinks, Chief Executive Officer) **A**1 2 3 5 7 10 19 **F**3 7 8 11 13 15 17 18 20 22 24 26 28 29 30 31 34 35 40 44 45 46 47 48 49 51 53 55 56 57 58 59 60 63 64 65 68 70 72 74 75 76 77 78 79 80 81 82 83 84 85 86 87 89 90 92 93 94 96 97 107 108 109 110 111 112 114 115 116 117 118 119 120 121 124 126 129 130 131 132 135 145 146 147 148 149 **P**1 5 **S** West Tennessee Healthcare, Jackson, TN
Primary Contact: James E. Ross, President and Chief Executive Officer
CFO: Jeff Blankenship, CPA, Vice President and Chief Financial Officer
CMO: David Roberts, M.D., Chief Medical Officer
CIO: Jeff Frieling, Vice President and Chief Information Officer
CHR: Wendie Carlson, Chief Human Resources Officer
CNO: Tina Prescott, Vice President, Hospital Services
Web address: www.wth.org
Control: Hospital district or authority, Government, nonfederal **Service:** General medical and surgical

Staffed Beds: 690 **Admissions:** 29961 **Census:** 477 **Outpatient Visits:** 215041 **Births:** 3041 **Total Expense ($000):** 629608 **Payroll Expense ($000):** 235323 **Personnel:** 4386

★ **PATHWAYS OF TENNESSEE (444010)**, 238 Summar Drive, Zip 38301–3906; tel. 731/541–8200, **A**10 **F**4 5 29 35 38 44 57 59 98 99 100 101 102 103 104 132 134 149 150 153 154 **S** West Tennessee Healthcare, Jackson, TN
Primary Contact: Pam Henson, Executive Director
CFO: Jeff Blankenship, CPA, Chief Financial Officer
CMO: Kevin Turner, M.D., Medical Director
CIO: Jeff Frieling, Chief Information Officer
CHR: Wendy Carlson, Director Human Resources
CNO: Angela Hensley, Director of Nursing
Web address: www.wth.net/pathways
Control: Hospital district or authority, Government, nonfederal **Service:** Psychiatric

Staffed Beds: 25 **Admissions:** 904 **Census:** 10 **Outpatient Visits:** 102343
Births: 0 **Total Expense ($000):** 16121 **Payroll Expense ($000):** 9064
Personnel: 200

JAMESTOWN—Fentress County

✉ **JAMESTOWN REGIONAL MEDICAL CENTER (440083)**, 436 Central Ave W, Zip 38556–3031, Mailing Address: P.O. Box 1500, Zip 38556–1500; tel. 931/879–8171, (Nonreporting) **A**1 10 20
Primary Contact: Lynette Pritchett, Chief Executive Officer
CMO: Mark Hendrixson, M.D., Chief Medical Officer
CIO: Rick Smith, Director Information Systems
CHR: Shelia Russell, Director Human Resources
Web address: www.jamestownregional.org
Control: Corporation, Investor–owned (for–profit) **Service:** General medical and surgical

Staffed Beds: 85

JEFFERSON CITY—Jefferson County

ST. MARY'S JEFFERSON MEMORIAL HOSPITAL See Tennova Healthcare–Jefferson Memorial Hospital

✉ **TENNOVA HEALTHCARE–JEFFERSON MEMORIAL HOSPITAL (440056)**, 110 Hospital Drive, Zip 37760–5281; tel. 865/471–2500, (Nonreporting) **A**1 10 **S** Community Health Systems, Inc., Franklin, TN
Primary Contact: Colin McRae, Chief Executive Officer
CFO: Roseann M Devault, Chief Financial Officer
CMO: Richard Carter, M.D., Chief of Staff
Web address: www.tennova.com/
Control: Corporation, Investor–owned (for–profit) **Service:** General medical and surgical

Staffed Beds: 54

JELLICO—Campbell County

✉ **JELLICO COMMUNITY HOSPITAL (440180)**, 188 Hospital Lane, Zip 37762–4400; tel. 423/784–7252, **A**1 10 **F**3 13 29 30 34 40 41 43 45 47 48 57 59 64 65 67 76 77 81 85 86 87 89 107 108 110 111 114 115 119 133 135 **S** Community Hospital Corporation, Plano, TX
Primary Contact: Gene Miller, Interim Chief Executive Officer
COO: Pamela Hodge, R.N., Chief Nursing Officer and Coordinator Performance Improvement
CFO: Evelyn Ghulum, Chief Financial Officer
CMO: Gregory Wilkens, M.D., Chief of Staff
CIO: Derek Brown, Chief Information Officer
CHR: Vince Vannett, Director Human Resources
Web address: www.jellicohospital.com
Control: Other not–for–profit (including NFP Corporation) **Service:** General medical and surgical

Staffed Beds: 47 **Admissions:** 796 **Census:** 4 **Outpatient Visits:** 14512
Births: 130

JOHNSON CITY—Washington County

✉ **FRANKLIN WOODS COMMUNITY HOSPITAL (440184)**, 300 MedTech Parkway, Zip 37604–2277; tel. 423/302–1000, (Total facility includes 1 beds in nursing home–type unit) **A**1 10 **F**3 11 13 29 30 34 35 36 38 40 44 45 50 51 56 57 63 65 68 70 74 75 76 77 81 85 87 97 100 107 108 111 114 115 118 119 126 128 130 146 147 148 149 154 **S** Ballad Health, Johnson City, TN
Primary Contact: Patricia Baise, R.N., FACHE, Chief Executive Officer
CFO: Andrew Wampler, Chief Financial Officer
CHR: Brooke Graham, Human Resources Manager
CNO: Rhonda Mann, Chief Nursing Officer
Web address: www.msha.com
Control: Other not–for–profit (including NFP Corporation) **Service:** General medical and surgical

Staffed Beds: 80 **Admissions:** 5319 **Census:** 79 **Outpatient Visits:** 51092
Births: 1205 **Total Expense ($000):** 63035 **Payroll Expense ($000):** 22426
Personnel: 275

✉ **JOHNSON CITY MEDICAL CENTER (440063)**, 400 North State of Franklin Road, Zip 37604–6094; tel. 423/431–6111, (Includes NISWONGER CHILDREN'S HOSPITAL, 400 North State Of Franklin Road, Johnson City, TN, Zip 37604–6035; tel. 423/431–6111; Lisa Carter, Chief Executive Officer; WOODRIDGE HOSPITAL, 403 State of Franklin Road, Johnson City, TN, Zip 37604–6034; tel. 423/431–7111; Patricia Baise, R.N., FACHE, Chief Executive Officer) **A**1 2 3 5 8 10 **F**3 4 5 7 11 12 13 15 17 18 19 20 21 22 24 26 28 29 30 31 32 34 35 38 39 40 41 43 44 45 46 47 48 49 50 51 52 53 54 55 56 57 58 59 60 61 62 63 64 68 70 72 74 75 76 77 78 79 81 82 84 85 86 87 88 89 91 93 97 98 99 100 101 102 103 104 107 108 110 111 114 115 117 118 119 120 121 123 124 129 130 131 132 134 135 143 146 147 148 153 154 **S** Ballad Health, Johnson City, TN
Primary Contact: Stan Hickson, FACHE, Chief Executive Officer
COO: Kenny Shafer, Chief Operating Officer
CFO: Richard Boone, Chief Financial Officer
CMO: Clay Runnels, Vice President Chief Medical Officer Washington County
CHR: Barry Tourigny, Human Resources Director
CNO: Dru Malcolm, Vice President and Chief Nursing Officer
Web address: www.msha.com
Control: Other not–for–profit (including NFP Corporation) **Service:** General medical and surgical

Staffed Beds: 585 **Admissions:** 30469 **Census:** 417 **Outpatient Visits:** 263535 **Births:** 1412 **Total Expense ($000):** 403596 **Payroll Expense ($000):** 128045 **Personnel:** 2161

NORTH SIDE HOSPITAL See Franklin Woods Community Hospital

TN

✠ △ **QUILLEN REHABILITATION HOSPITAL (443033)**, 2511 Wesley Street,
Zip 37601–1723; tel. 423/952–1700, **A**1 7 10 **F**29 75 90 132 148 154 **S**
Encompass Health Corporation, Birmingham, AL
Primary Contact: Brian Luff, Chief Executive Officer
CFO: Debbie Wyse, Controller
CHR: Penny Lawson, Human Resource Director
CNO: Lynn Langan, Chief Nursing Officer
Web address: www.quillenrehabilitationhospital.com/
Control: Corporation, Investor–owned (for–profit) **Service**: Rehabilitation

> **Staffed Beds**: 31 **Admissions**: 632 **Census**: 25 **Outpatient Visits**: 0
> **Births**: 0 **Total Expense ($000)**: 9830 **Payroll Expense ($000)**: 4996
> **Personnel**: 87

KINGSPORT—Sullivan County

✠ **HEALTHSOUTH REHABILITATION HOSPITAL (443027)**, 113 Cassel Drive,
Zip 37660–3775; tel. 423/246–7240, (Nonreporting) **A**1 10 **S** Encompass Health
Corporation, Birmingham, AL
Primary Contact: Troy Clark, Chief Executive Officer
CFO: Natalie Tilson, Controller
CMO: James P Little, M.D., Medical Director
CIO: Natalie Tilson, Controller
CHR: Joyce Jones, Director Human Resources
CNO: Debra Smith, Chief Nursing Officer
Web address: www.healthsouthkingsport.com
Control: Corporation, Investor–owned (for–profit) **Service**: Rehabilitation

> **Staffed Beds**: 50

✠ **HOLSTON VALLEY MEDICAL CENTER (440017)**, 130 West Ravine
Street, Zip 37660–3837, Mailing Address: P.O. Box 238, Zip 37662–0238;
tel. 423/224–4000, (Nonreporting) **A**1 2 3 5 10 13 19 **S** Ballad Health, Johnson
City, TN
Primary Contact: Monty E. McLaurin, Interim Chief Executive Officer
COO: Dale Clark, Chief Operating Officer
CFO: Dale Poe, Vice President Finance and Operations
CMO: Daniel Carlson, M.D., Chief Medical Officer
CIO: Will Showalter, Senior Vice President Information Technology
CHR: Hamlin J Wilson, Senior Vice President Human Resources
CNO: Kathy Campbell, Interim Chief Nursing Officer
Web address: www.wellmont.org
Control: Other not–for–profit (including NFP Corporation) **Service**: General
medical and surgical

> **Staffed Beds**: 345

☐ **INDIAN PATH MEDICAL CENTER (440176)**, 2000 Brookside Drive,
Zip 37660–4627; tel. 423/857–7000, **A**1 10 **F**8 11 13 15 18 20 22 26 28 29
30 31 34 40 45 46 47 49 50 51 57 59 60 64 65 68 70 73 74 75 76 77 78
79 81 84 85 86 87 93 97 107 108 110 111 114 115 116 117 118 119 121
123 129 130 132 135 146 147 149 154 **S** Ballad Health, Johnson City, TN
Primary Contact: Monty E. McLaurin, Chief Executive Officer, Northwest Market
CFO: Steve Sawyer, Chief Financial Officer
CMO: Mark Wilkinson, M.D., Chief Medical Officer
CIO: Jackson Dale, Site Manager Information Systems
CHR: Kevin M Smith, Director Human Resources
CNO: Susan Fannon, Chief Nursing Officer
Web address: www.msha.com
Control: Other not–for–profit (including NFP Corporation) **Service**: General
medical and surgical

> **Staffed Beds**: 160 **Admissions**: 5358 **Census**: 59 **Outpatient Visits**:
> 125128 **Births**: 865 **Total Expense ($000)**: 89919 **Payroll Expense**
> **($000)**: 30455 **Personnel**: 550

KNOXVILLE—Knox County

☐ **EAST TENNESSEE CHILDREN'S HOSPITAL (443303)**, 2018 Clinch Avenue,
Zip 37916–2393, Mailing Address: P.O. Box 15010, Zip 37901–5010;
tel. 865/541–8000, **A**1 3 5 10 **F**7 11 19 29 30 31 32 34 35 39 40 41 43 50 55
57 58 59 61 62 64 68 72 74 75 77 78 79 81 82 84 85 86 87 88 89 91 93 97
102 107 111 115 119 129 130 135 146 148 154
Primary Contact: Keith D. Goodwin, President and Chief Executive Officer
COO: Steven Godbold, Vice President Operations and Chief Operating Officer
CFO: Caryn Hawthorne, Vice President Finance and Chief Finance Officer
CMO: Joe Childs, M.D., Vice President Medical Services
CIO: John Hanks, Director Information Systems
CHR: Sue Wilburn, Vice President Human Resources and Organizational Development
CNO: Hella Ewing, Vice President Patient Care Services and Chief Nursing Officer
Web address: www.etch.com
Control: Other not–for–profit (including NFP Corporation) **Service**: Children's
general medical and surgical

> **Staffed Beds**: 152 **Admissions**: 5420 **Census**: 90 **Outpatient Visits**:
> 167651 **Births**: 0 **Total Expense ($000)**: 217890 **Payroll Expense**
> **($000)**: 87718 **Personnel**: 1311

✠ △ **FORT SANDERS REGIONAL MEDICAL CENTER (440125)**, 1901 West
Clinch Avenue, Zip 37916–2307; tel. 865/541–1111, (Total facility includes 24
beds in nursing home–type unit) **A**1 2 7 10 19 **F**3 11 12 13 15 17 18 20 22 24
26 28 29 30 31 34 35 40 45 47 49 50 51 54 55 57 59 60 61 64 68 74 75 76
77 78 79 80 81 84 85 87 90 93 94 100 107 108 110 111 114 115 116 117
118 119 120 121 123 124 126 128 129 130 131 132 135 146 147 148 154 **S**
Covenant Health, Knoxville, TN
Primary Contact: Keith Altshuler, President and Chief Administrative Officer
CNO: Lynda Watts, R.N., Vice President, Chief Nursing Officer
Web address: www.covenanthealth.com
Control: Other not–for–profit (including NFP Corporation) **Service**: General
medical and surgical

> **Staffed Beds**: 384 **Admissions**: 17712 **Census**: 273 **Outpatient Visits**:
> 225713 **Births**: 2539 **Total Expense ($000)**: 277750 **Payroll Expense**
> **($000)**: 94560 **Personnel**: 1631

MERCY MEDICAL CENTER WEST See Tennova Turkey Creek Medical Center

✠ **PARKWEST MEDICAL CENTER (440173)**, 9352 Park West Boulevard,
Zip 37923–4325, Mailing Address: P.O. Box 22993, Zip 37933–0993;
tel. 865/373–1000, (Includes PENINSULA HOSPITAL, 2347 Jones Bend
Road, Louisville, TN, Zip 37777–5213, Mailing Address: P.O. Box 2000,
Zip 37777–2000, tel. 865/970–9800; Elizabeth P Clary, R.N., Vice President
Behavioral Services) **A**1 2 10 **F**3 13 15 17 18 20 22 24 26 28 29 30 31 34 35 37
40 45 50 51 56 60 64 68 70 74 75 76 77 78 79 80 81 84 85 87 93 98 103
107 108 110 111 114 115 116 117 118 119 120 121 123 126 130 131 132
135 146 147 148 **S** Covenant Health, Knoxville, TN
Primary Contact: Neil Heatherly, President and Chief Administrative Officer
COO: Emlyn Cobble, Vice President and Chief Support Officer
CFO: Scott Hamilton, Vice President and Chief Financial Officer
CHR: Randall Carr, Director Human Resources
CNO: Diane Oliver, R.N., MSN, Chief Nursing Officer
Web address: www.treatedwell.com/
Control: Other not–for–profit (including NFP Corporation) **Service**: General
medical and surgical

> **Staffed Beds**: 434 **Admissions**: 22334 **Census**: 297 **Outpatient Visits**:
> 245982 **Births**: 1404 **Total Expense ($000)**: 300100 **Payroll Expense**
> **($000)**: 101517 **Personnel**: 1891

✠ △ **TENNOVA PHYSICIANS REGIONAL MEDICAL CENTER (440120)**,
900 East Oak Hill Avenue, Zip 37917–4556; tel. 865/545–8000, (Includes
TENNOVA NORTH KNOXVILLE MEDICAL CENTER, 7565 Dannaher Way, Powell,
TN, Zip 37849–4029; tel. 865/859–7000; Clyde Wood, Chief Executive
Officer; TENNOVA TURKEY CREEK MEDICAL CENTER, 10800 Parkside Drive,
Knoxville, TN, Zip 37922–1956; tel. 865/218–7090; TENNOVA TURKEY CREEK
MEDICAL CENTER, 10820 Parkside Drive, Knoxville, TN, Zip 37934–1956;
tel. 865/218–7092; Ben Youree, Chief Executive Officer) (Nonreporting) **A**1 2 7 10
S Community Health Systems, Inc., Franklin, TN
Primary Contact: Pamela Beck, Interim Chief Executive Officer
CFO: Rhonda Maynard, Chief Financial Officer
CIO: Tom Lakins, Director Information Systems
CHR: Sarah M Laboranti, Interim Director Human Resources
Web address: www.hma.com/content/physicians–regional–medical–center
Control: Corporation, Investor–owned (for–profit) **Service**: General medical and
surgical

> **Staffed Beds**: 220

✠ **UNIVERSITY OF TENNESSEE MEDICAL CENTER (440015)**, 1924 Alcoa
Highway, Zip 37920–6900; tel. 865/305–9000, **A**1 2 3 5 8 10 **F**3 6 8 9 11 12
13 15 17 18 20 22 24 26 28 29 30 31 34 35 36 39 40 41 43 44 45 46 47 48
49 50 51 52 53 54 55 56 57 58 59 60 61 64 65 70 71 72 74 75 76 77 78 79
81 82 84 85 86 87 88 91 92 93 94 96 97 100 102 103 105 107 108 109 110
111 114 115 116 117 118 119 120 121 123 124 126 129 130 131 132 135
138 141 142 144 145 146 147 148 149 150 153 154 **P**1 5 6
Primary Contact: Joseph Landsman, President and Chief Executive Officer
COO: David Hall, Senior Vice President and Chief Operating Officer
CFO: Thomas Fisher, Senior Vice President and Chief Financial Officer
CMO: Jerry Epps, M.D., Senior Vice President and Chief Medical Officer
CIO: Michael Saad, Vice President and Chief Information Officer
CHR: Julie Simpson, Vice President Human Resources
CNO: Janell Cecil, R.N., MSN, Senior Vice President and Chief Nursing Officer
Web address: www.utmedicalcenter.org
Control: Other not–for–profit (including NFP Corporation) **Service**: General
medical and surgical

> **Staffed Beds**: 609 **Admissions**: 29331 **Census**: 449 **Outpatient Visits**:
> 291787 **Births**: 3091 **Total Expense ($000)**: 835165 **Payroll Expense**
> **($000)**: 294514 **Personnel**: 3897

TN

LA FOLLETTE—Campbell County

☒ **TENNOVA HEALTHCARE–LAFOLLETTE MEDICAL CENTER (440033)**, 923 East Central Avenue, Zip 37766–2768, Mailing Address: P.O. Box 1301, Zip 37766–1301; tel. 423/907–1200, **A**1 10 20 **F**1 3 11 15 18 29 30 34 35 40 41 45 47 48 50 51 56 64 68 70 77 78 79 81 85 97 98 100 103 107 110 111 119 120 121 123 127 129 131 146 148 154 **S** Community Health Systems, Inc., Franklin, TN
Primary Contact: Mark Cain, Chief Executive Officer
COO: Sara Heatherly–Lloyd, Chief Operating Officer
CFO: Michael Cherry, Chief Financial Officer
CMO: George O'Neal Vinsant, M.D., Chief Medical Officer
CIO: Dillon Ward, Management Information Systems Specialist
CHR: Bess Stout, Director Human Resources
CNO: Kathy R Myers, MS, R.N., Chief Nursing Officer
Web address: www.tennova.com
Control: Corporation, Investor–owned (for–profit) **Service:** General medical and surgical

Staffed Beds: 164 **Admissions:** 2438 **Census:** 48

LAFAYETTE—Macon County

★ ⇑ **MACON COMMUNITY HOSPITAL (441305)**, 204 Medical Drive, Zip 37083–1799, Mailing Address: P.O. Box 378, Zip 37083–0378; tel. 615/666–2147, **A**10 18 21 **F**3 15 29 30 34 35 40 45 57 59 68 77 81 87 93 107 110 111 119 128 130 132 133 141 142 146 **S** QHR, Brentwood, TN
Primary Contact: Thomas J. Kidd, CPA, Chief Executive Officer
CFO: Scott A. Tongate, Chief Financial Officer
Web address: www.mcgh.net
Control: Other not–for–profit (including NFP Corporation) **Service:** General medical and surgical

Staffed Beds: 25 **Admissions:** 689 **Census:** 7 **Outpatient Visits:** 26609
Births: 0 **Total Expense ($000):** 11624 **Payroll Expense ($000):** 5428

LAWRENCEBURG—Lawrence County

☒ **SOUTHERN TENNESSEE REGIONAL HEALTH SYSTEM–LAWRENCEBURG (440175)**, 1607 South Locust Avenue, Zip 38464–4011, Mailing Address: P.O. Box 847, Zip 38464–0847; tel. 931/762–6571, **A**1 10 **F**3 13 15 18 28 29 30 34 35 39 40 41 46 48 50 51 57 59 64 68 70 74 75 76 77 79 81 82 85 86 87 89 90 93 96 97 107 108 110 111 115 119 124 128 129 130 131 132 133 147 148 154 **S** LifePoint Health, Brentwood, TN
Primary Contact: Jeff Noblin, FACHE, Chief Executive Officer
CFO: Kristie Taylor, Chief Financial Officer
CIO: Jason Weaver, Director Information Systems
CHR: Robert Augustin, Director Human Resources
CNO: Carrie Rogers, Chief Nursing Officer
Web address: www.crocketthospital.com
Control: Corporation, Investor–owned (for–profit) **Service:** General medical and surgical

Staffed Beds: 99 **Admissions:** 2231 **Census:** 23 **Outpatient Visits:** 50136
Births: 415 **Total Expense ($000):** 34827 **Payroll Expense ($000):** 12388
Personnel: 223

LEBANON—Wilson County

☒ **TENNOVA HEALTHCARE–LEBANON (440193)**, 1411 Baddour Parkway, Zip 37087–2513; tel. 615/444–8262, (Includes TENNOVA HEALTHCARE–LEBANON MCFARLAND CAMPUS, 500 Park Avenue, Lebanon, TN, Zip 37087–3720; tel. 615/449–0500) (Nonreporting) **A**1 5 10 **S** Community Health Systems, Inc., Franklin, TN
Primary Contact: Jay Hinesley, FACHE, Chief Executive Officer
CMO: Andrew Jordan, M.D., Chief of Staff
CIO: Adrian Fung, Director Information Systems
Web address: www.universitymedicalcenter.com
Control: Corporation, Investor–owned (for–profit) **Service:** General medical and surgical

Staffed Beds: 245

LENOIR CITY—Loudon County

☒ **FORT LOUDOUN MEDICAL CENTER (440110)**, 550 Fort Loudoun Medical Center Drive, Zip 37772–5673; tel. 865/271–6000, **A**1 10 **F**3 15 18 28 29 30 34 35 40 50 57 59 68 70 75 77 79 81 85 87 107 108 110 111 114 118 119 130 135 146 154 **S** Covenant Health, Knoxville, TN
Primary Contact: Jeffrey Feike, President and Chief Administrative Officer
CNO: Teresa Fisher, R.N., Chief Nursing Officer
Web address: www.covenanthealth.com
Control: Other not–for–profit (including NFP Corporation) **Service:** General medical and surgical

Staffed Beds: 30 **Admissions:** 2102 **Census:** 24 **Outpatient Visits:** 67867
Births: 0 **Total Expense ($000):** 29747 **Payroll Expense ($000):** 12366
Personnel: 232

LEWISBURG—Marshall County

☒ **MARSHALL MEDICAL CENTER (441309)**, 1080 North Ellington Parkway, Zip 37091–2227, Mailing Address: P.O. Box 1609, Zip 37091–1609; tel. 931/359–6241, **A**1 10 18 **F**3 11 15 29 30 34 40 45 50 56 57 59 68 75 77 81 85 86 92 93 102 104 107 108 110 111 114 119 129 131 132 133 135 146 149 **S** Maury Regional Health System, Columbia, TN
Primary Contact: Phyllis Brown, Chief Executive Officer
CFO: Kyle Jones, Chief Financial Officer
CMO: Tim Nash, M.D., Chief of Staff, Board Vice Chairman
CHR: Jeff M Pierce, Chief Human Resource Officer
CNO: Karen Martin, R.N., MSN, Chief Nursing Officer
Web address: www.mauryregional.com
Control: County, Government, nonfederal **Service:** General medical and surgical

Staffed Beds: 12 **Admissions:** 245 **Census:** 2 **Outpatient Visits:** 34387
Births: 0 **Total Expense ($000):** 14229 **Payroll Expense ($000):** 6914
Personnel: 137

LEXINGTON—Henderson County

☒ **HENDERSON COUNTY COMMUNITY HOSPITAL (440008)**, 200 West Church Street, Zip 38351–2038; tel. 731/968–3646, (Nonreporting) **A**1 10 **S** Quorum Health, Brentwood, TN
Primary Contact: Pamela W. Roberts, Chief Executive Officer
CFO: John Bostwick, Interim Chief Financial Officer
CHR: Linda Durham, Director Human Resources
CNO: Charlene Morgan, Chief Nursing Officer
Web address: www.hendersoncchospital.com
Control: Corporation, Investor–owned (for–profit) **Service:** General medical and surgical

Staffed Beds: 45

LINDEN—Perry County

PERRY COMMUNITY HOSPITAL (440040), 2718 Squirrel Hollow Drive, Zip 37096–3526; tel. 931/589–2121, (Nonreporting) **A**10
Primary Contact: John B. Avery III, Administrator
Control: Other not–for–profit (including NFP Corporation) **Service:** General medical and surgical

Staffed Beds: 53

LIVINGSTON—Overton County

☒ **LIVINGSTON REGIONAL HOSPITAL (440187)**, 315 Oak Street, Zip 38570–1728, Mailing Address: P.O. Box 550, Zip 38570–0550; tel. 931/823–5611, (Nonreporting) **A**1 10 **S** LifePoint Health, Brentwood, TN
Primary Contact: Timothy W. McGill, Chief Executive Officer
CMO: Christopher Nahm, M.D., Chief Medical Officer
CIO: Mark Hambridge, Director Information Systems
CNO: Penny V Kirby, MSN, Chief Nursing Officer
Web address: www.MyLivingstonHospital.com
Control: Corporation, Investor–owned (for–profit) **Service:** General medical and surgical

Staffed Beds: 114

Hospital, Medicare Provider Number, Address, Telephone, Approval, Facility, and Physician Codes, Health Care System

★ American Hospital Association (AHA) membership ◯ Healthcare Facilities Accreditation Program ⇑ Center for Improvement in Healthcare Quality Accreditation
☐ The Joint Commission accreditation ◇ DNV Healthcare Inc. accreditation △ Commission on Accreditation of Rehabilitation Facilities (CARF) accreditation

MANCHESTER—Coffee County

UNITY MEDICAL CENTER (440007), 1001 McArthur Drive, Zip 37355–2455, Mailing Address: P.O. Box 1079, Zip 37349–1079; tel. 931/728–3586, (Nonreporting) **A**10
Primary Contact: Martha McCormick, Chief Executive Officer
CFO: Pam Jernigan, Chief Financial Officer
CMO: James Van Winkle, M.D., Chief of Staff
CIO: Matt Burks, Director Information Technology
CHR: Sherry Holt, Director Human Resources
CNO: Stephanie Byars, Chief Nursing Officer
Web address: www.urmchealthcare.com
Control: Corporation, Investor–owned (for–profit) **Service**: General medical and surgical

Staffed Beds: 36

MARTIN—Weakley County

✠ **SPIRE CANE CREEK REHABILITATION HOSPITAL (443030)**, 180 Mount Pelia Road, Zip 38237–3812; tel. 731/587–4231, (Nonreporting) **A**1 10 **S** Encompass Health Corporation, Birmingham, AL
Primary Contact: Rick Johnson, Chief Executive Officer
CFO: Bethany Smith, Controller
CMO: Belinda Merritt, M.D., Medical Director
CIO: Jan Trowhill, Director Health Information Management Systems
CHR: Sharon Shihady, Director Human Resources
CNO: Lindsey Rotger, Chief Nursing Officer
Web address: www.healthsouthcanecreek.com
Control: Corporation, Investor–owned (for–profit) **Service**: Rehabilitation

Staffed Beds: 40

UNITY PSYCHIATRIC CARE–MARTIN (444005), 458 Hannings Lane, Zip 38237–3308; tel. 731/588–2830, (Nonreporting) **A**10 **S** Tennessee Health Management, Parsons, TN
Primary Contact: Carrie Brawley, Administrator
Web address: www.unitypsych.com
Control: Partnership, Investor–owned (for–profit) **Service**: Psychiatric

Staffed Beds: 16

✠ **WEST TENNESSEE HEALTHCARE VOLUNTEER HOSPITAL (440061)**, 161 Mount Pelia Road, Zip 38237–3811; tel. 731/587–4261, (Nonreporting) **A**1 10 **S** West Tennessee Healthcare, Jackson, TN
Primary Contact: Darrell Blaylock, Chief Executive Officer
CFO: Jason Draper, Chief Financial Officer
CMO: Elizabeth Lund, M.D., Chief of Staff
CHR: Tammie Bell, Director Human Resources
CNO: Donna Barfield, Chief Nursing Officer
Web address: www.wth.org/locations/west–tennessee–healthcare–volunteer–hospital
Control: Other not–for–profit (including NFP Corporation) **Service**: General medical and surgical

Staffed Beds: 65

MARYVILLE—Blount County

✠ **BLOUNT MEMORIAL HOSPITAL (440011)**, 907 East Lamar Alexander Parkway, Zip 37804–5016; tel. 865/983–7211, (Total facility includes 76 beds in nursing home–type unit) **A**1 2 10 **F**3 4 10 11 12 13 15 17 18 20 22 26 28 29 30 31 35 38 40 43 45 46 48 49 53 54 56 57 59 62 63 64 67 70 74 75 76 77 78 79 80 81 84 85 86 87 90 93 96 97 98 100 101 102 103 104 105 107 108 110 111 115 116 119 120 121 123 125 126 128 129 130 131 132 135 144 146 147 148 153 **P**6
Primary Contact: Don Heinemann, Administrator and Chief Executive Officer
CFO: Jonathan Smith, Assistant Administrator and Chief Financial Officer
CMO: G Harold Naramore, M.D., Chief Medical Officer and In house Legal Counsel
CIO: Clay Puckett, Assistant Administrator and Chief Information Officer
CHR: Chris Wilkes, MS, Director Human Resources
CNO: Sonya Newman, R.N., Chief Nursing Officer
Web address: www.blountmemorial.org
Control: County, Government, nonfederal **Service**: General medical and surgical

Staffed Beds: 275 **Admissions**: 12360 **Census**: 205 **Outpatient Visits**: 368396 **Births**: 715 **Total Expense ($000)**: 266803 **Payroll Expense ($000)**: 129184 **Personnel**: 1823

MC MINNVILLE—Warren County

✠ **SAINT THOMAS RIVER PARK HOSPITAL (440151)**, 1559 Sparta Street, Zip 37110–1316; tel. 931/815–4000, (Nonreporting) **A**1 10 **S** Ascension Healthcare, Saint Louis, MO
Primary Contact: Dale Humphrey, Chief Executive Officer
CFO: Christina Patterson, Chief Financial Officer
CMO: Randal D Rampp, M.D., Chief Medical Officer
CIO: Jeff Johnson, Director Information Systems
CHR: Deeann Johnson, Director Human Resources
Web address: www.riverparkhospital.com
Control: Church operated, Nongovernment, not–for–profit **Service**: General medical and surgical

Staffed Beds: 85

MCKENZIE—Carroll County

✠ **MCKENZIE REGIONAL HOSPITAL (440182)**, 161 Hospital Drive, Zip 38201–1636; tel. 731/352–5344, **A**1 10 **F**13 29 34 40 45 53 57 59 64 79 81 85 93 107 110 111 114 115 119 131 133 146 **S** Quorum Health, Brentwood, TN
Primary Contact: Michael Morrical, Chief Executive Officer
CFO: Kevin Harvey, Chief Financial Officer
CHR: Keri Stepp, Human Resources Director
CNO: Shelley McArthur, R.N., Chief Nursing Officer
Web address: www.mckenzieregionalhospital.com
Control: Corporation, Investor–owned (for–profit) **Service**: General medical and surgical

Staffed Beds: 35 **Admissions**: 1019 **Census**: 8 **Outpatient Visits**: 24690 **Births**: 342 **Total Expense ($000)**: 18058 **Payroll Expense ($000)**: 6308

MEMPHIS—Shelby County

✠ **BAPTIST MEMORIAL HOSPITAL – MEMPHIS (440048)**, 6019 Walnut Grove Road, Zip 38120–2173; tel. 901/226–5000, **A**1 2 5 10 **F**3 6 8 12 17 18 20 22 26 27 28 29 30 31 34 35 36 40 41 45 46 47 48 49 50 53 54 56 57 58 59 60 63 64 65 68 70 74 75 77 78 79 80 81 82 84 85 86 87 91 92 93 102 107 108 109 111 112 114 115 116 118 119 120 121 122 123 124 126 130 132 135 136 137 143 146 148 154 **P**8 **S** Baptist Memorial Health Care Corporation, Memphis, TN
Primary Contact: Dana Dye, R.N., Vice President, Administrator and Chief Executive Officer
CFO: Cyndi Pittman, Chief Financial Officer
CMO: Christian C Patrick, M.D., Chief Medical Officer
CIO: Doug Reiselt, Vice President and Chief Information Officer
CHR: Jerry Barbaree, Director Human Resources
Web address: www.baptistonline.org/memphis/
Control: Other not–for–profit (including NFP Corporation) **Service**: General medical and surgical

Staffed Beds: 563 **Admissions**: 26215 **Census**: 432 **Outpatient Visits**: 136549 **Births**: 0 **Total Expense ($000)**: 503778 **Payroll Expense ($000)**: 157639 **Personnel**: 2723

★ **BAPTIST MEMORIAL HOSPITAL FOR WOMEN (440222)**, 6225 Humphreys Boulevard, Zip 38120–2373; tel. 901/227–9000, **A**3 **F**3 7 8 12 13 15 19 25 29 30 32 34 35 38 41 45 46 47 48 49 54 55 56 57 58 59 64 65 68 70 71 72 73 74 75 76 77 78 79 81 82 85 86 87 88 89 107 108 109 110 111 112 114 115 119 124 126 130 132 135 146 147 148 154 **S** Baptist Memorial Health Care Corporation, Memphis, TN
Primary Contact: Kevin R. Hammeran, Chief Executive Officer and Administrator
CFO: Margaret Williams, Chief Financial Officer
CMO: Judi Carney, M.D., President Medical Staff
CIO: Melissa Nelson, Assistant Administrator
CHR: Karen Ingram, Director Human Resources
CNO: Carol Thetford, Chief Nursing Officer
Web address: www.baptistonline.org/womens/
Control: Other not–for–profit (including NFP Corporation) **Service**: Obstetrics and gynecology

Staffed Beds: 140 **Admissions**: 7065 **Census**: 65 **Outpatient Visits**: 64469 **Births**: 5314 **Total Expense ($000)**: 97988 **Payroll Expense ($000)**: 38253 **Personnel**: 586

✠ **BAPTIST MEMORIAL RESTORATIVE CARE HOSPITAL (442010)**, 6019 Walnut Grove Road, Zip 38120–2113; tel. 901/226–4200, **A**1 10 **F**1 3 29 68 75 77 130 148 **S** Baptist Memorial Health Care Corporation, Memphis, TN
Primary Contact: Janice Hill, R.N., Administrator
Web address: www.baptistonline.org/restorative–care/
Control: Other not–for–profit (including NFP Corporation) **Service**: Acute long–term care hospital

Staffed Beds: 30 **Admissions**: 213 **Census**: 20 **Outpatient Visits**: 0 **Births**: 0 **Total Expense ($000)**: 13423 **Payroll Expense ($000)**: 4970 **Personnel**: 71

Many Facility Codes have changed. Please refer to the AHA Guide Code Chart.

TN

CRESTWYN BEHAVIORAL HEALTH (444025), 9485 Crestwyn Hills Cove, Zip 38125–8515; tel. 901/248–1500, (Nonreporting) **A**10 **S** Acadia Healthcare Company, Inc., Franklin, TN
Primary Contact: Jeb Stokes, Chief Executive Officer
Web address: www.crestwynbh.com
Control: Corporation, Investor–owned (for–profit) **Service:** Psychiatric

Staffed Beds: 60

DELTA MEDICAL CENTER (440159), 3000 Getwell Road, Zip 38118–2299; tel. 901/369–8100, (Nonreporting) **A**1 10 **S** Acadia Healthcare Company, Inc., Franklin, TN
Primary Contact: Phil Willcoxon, Chief Executive Officer
CFO: Mike Reynolds, Chief Financial Officer
CMO: David Richardson, M.D., Chief of Staff
CIO: Patrick Duffee, Director Medical Information Systems
CHR: Karyn Erickson, Director Human Resources
CNO: Donna Lanier, R.N., Chief Nursing Officer
Web address: www.deltamedcenter.com
Control: Corporation, Investor–owned (for–profit) **Service:** General medical and surgical

Staffed Beds: 179

✠ **HEALTHSOUTH REHABILITATION HOSPITAL MEMPHIS–NORTH (443031)**, 4100 Austin Peay Highway, Zip 38128–2502; tel. 901/213–5400, **A**1 10 **F**3 28 29 34 35 57 59 75 77 82 87 90 91 95 96 130 132 135 148 **S** Encompass Health Corporation, Birmingham, AL
Primary Contact: Adam Yoe, Chief Executive Officer
CFO: Thaddeus Williams, Controller
CMO: Donald Sullivan, M.D., Medical Director
CHR: Adrienne Huntley, Director Human Resources
CNO: Charlotte Boyce, Chief Nursing Officer
Web address: www.healthsouthnorthmemphis.com
Control: Corporation, Investor–owned (for–profit) **Service:** Rehabilitation

Staffed Beds: 50 Admissions: 1191 Census: 39 Outpatient Visits: 0 Births: 0 Total Expense ($000): 13411 Payroll Expense ($000): 7359 Personnel: 102

✠ **HEALTHSOUTH REHABILITATION HOSPITAL OF MEMPHIS (443029)**, 1282 Union Avenue, Zip 38104–3414; tel. 901/722–2000, **A**1 3 5 10 **F**3 28 29 30 34 60 68 75 90 91 93 96 130 148 149 **S** Encompass Health Corporation, Birmingham, AL
Primary Contact: Stephanie Bridges, Chief Executive Officer
CFO: Eric Gray, Chief Financial Officer
CMO: Jonathan D Ellen, M.D., Medical Director
CHR: Sandra Milburn, Director Human Resources
CNO: Jennifer Ferrell, Chief Nursing Officer
Web address: www.healthsouthmemphis.com
Control: Partnership, Investor–owned (for–profit) **Service:** Rehabilitation

Staffed Beds: 72 Admissions: 1496 Census: 46 Outpatient Visits: 6253 Births: 0 Total Expense ($000): 17887 Payroll Expense ($000): 8585 Personnel: 161

✠ **LAKESIDE BEHAVIORAL HEALTH SYSTEM (444004)**, 2911 Brunswick Road, Zip 38133–4199; tel. 901/377–4700, **A**1 3 5 10 **F**4 5 34 38 54 56 98 99 100 101 102 103 104 105 106 130 132 149 152 153 154 **S** Universal Health Services, Inc., King of Prussia, PA
Primary Contact: Joy Golden, Chief Executive Officer
CFO: Thomas Joyner, Chief Financial Officer
CMO: C Hal Brunt, M.D., Medical Director
CIO: Jacob Arnett, Chief Information Technology Officer
CHR: Lori Deason, Director
CNO: Scott Thomason, Chief Nursing Officer
Web address: www.lakesidebhs.com
Control: Corporation, Investor–owned (for–profit) **Service:** Psychiatric

Staffed Beds: 345 Admissions: 8986 Census: 246 Outpatient Visits: 23856 Births: 0 Total Expense ($000): 44630 Payroll Expense ($000): 22849 Personnel: 499

LE BONHEUR CHILDREN'S HOSPITAL See Methodist Healthcare Memphis Hospitals, Memphis

MEMPHIS MENTAL HEALTH INSTITUTE (444001), 951 Court Ave, Zip 38103–2813, Mailing Address: P.O. Box 63656, Zip 38163–3656; tel. 901/577–1800, **A**1 3 5 10 **F**98 130 154 **P**6
Primary Contact: Josh Carter, Chief Executive Officer
CFO: Donny Hornsby, Director Fiscal Services
CHR: Claudette Seymour, Director Personnel
Web address: www.tn.gov/mental/mhs/mhs2.html
Control: State, Government, nonfederal **Service:** Psychiatric

Staffed Beds: 55 Admissions: 1527 Census: 52 Outpatient Visits: 0 Births: 0 Total Expense ($000): 18519 Payroll Expense ($000): 9211 Personnel: 179

✠ △ **MEMPHIS VETERANS AFFAIRS MEDICAL CENTER**, 1030 Jefferson Avenue, Zip 38104–2193; tel. 901/523–8990, (Nonreporting) **A**1 3 5 7 **S** Department of Veterans Affairs, Perry Point, MD
Primary Contact: David K. Dunning, Medical Center Director and Chief Executive Officer
CFO: Kristi Depperman, Chief Financial Officer
CMO: Christopher Marino, M.D., Chief of Staff
CIO: Robert Page III Chief Information and Technology Officer
CHR: Natalie Brown, Chief Human Resources Management Services
CNO: Karen Gillette, Associate Director Patient Care Services
Web address: www.memphis.va.gov/
Control: Veterans Affairs, Government, federal **Service:** General medical and surgical

Staffed Beds: 251

✠ **METHODIST HEALTHCARE MEMPHIS HOSPITALS (440049)**, 1265 Union Avenue, Zip 38104–3415; tel. 901/516–7000, (Includes LE BONHEUR CHILDREN'S HOSPITAL, 848 Adams Avenue, Memphis, TN, Zip 38103; tel. 901/287–5437; Meri Armour, President; METHODIST HEALTHCARE–NORTH HOSPITAL, 3960 New Covington Pike, Memphis, TN, Zip 38128; tel. 901/516–5200; Florence Jones, President; METHODIST HEALTHCARE–SOUTH HOSPITAL, 1300 Wesley Drive, Memphis, TN, Zip 38116; tel. 901/516–3700; David G Baytos, Interim President; METHODIST LE BONHEUR GERMANTOWN HOSPITAL, 7691 Poplar Avenue, Germantown, TN, Zip 38138; tel. 901/516–6000; Diane Ridgway, President) **A**1 2 3 5 8 10 **F**3 7 8 9 11 12 13 15 17 18 19 20 21 22 23 24 25 26 27 28 29 30 31 32 34 35 37 38 39 40 41 43 44 45 46 47 48 49 50 54 55 56 57 58 59 60 61 64 65 68 70 71 72 73 74 75 76 78 79 80 81 82 84 85 86 87 88 89 91 92 93 94 96 97 98 100 101 102 103 104 107 108 110 111 112 113 114 115 116 117 118 119 120 121 123 126 129 130 132 134 135 136 137 138 139 141 142 143 144 146 147 148 149 150 154 **P**5 6 8 **S** Methodist Le Bonheur Healthcare, Memphis, TN
Primary Contact: Michael Ugwueke, President and Chief Executive Officer
CFO: Chris McLean, Chief Administrative Officer
CIO: Mark W McMath, Chief Information Officer
CHR: Carol Ross–Spang, Chief Human Resources Officer
CNO: Nikki S Polis, Ph.D., Chief Nurse Executive
Web address: www.methodisthealth.org
Control: Other not–for–profit (including NFP Corporation) **Service:** General medical and surgical

Staffed Beds: 1384 Admissions: 63476 Census: 963 Outpatient Visits: 1069096 Births: 5342 Total Expense ($000): 1647422 Payroll Expense ($000): 513713 Personnel: 7696

✠ **REGIONAL ONE HEALTH (440152)**, 877 Jefferson Avenue, Zip 38103–2897; tel. 901/545–7100, (Nonreporting) **A**1 3 5 10
Primary Contact: Reginald W. Coopwood, M.D., President and Chief Executive Officer
COO: Rob Sumter, Executive Vice President and Chief Operating Officer
CFO: Rick Wagers, Senior Executive Vice President and Chief Financial Officer
CIO: Rob Sumter, Executive Vice President and Chief Operation Officer
CHR: Sarah Colley, Senior Vice President Human Resources
CNO: Pam Castleman, MSN, Chief Nursing Officer
CMO: Martin Croce, MD, Senior Vice President and Chief Medical Officer
Web address: www.regionalonehealth.org
Control: Other not–for–profit (including NFP Corporation) **Service:** General medical and surgical

Staffed Beds: 353

REGIONAL ONE HEALTH EXTENDED CARE HOSPITAL (442017), 890 Madison Avenue, Turner Tower, Zip 38103–3409; tel. 901/515–3000, (Nonreporting)
Primary Contact: Mark Kelly, Administrator
CNO: Paula Harrell, Chief Nursing Officer
Web address: www.regionalonehealth.org/extended–care–hospital/
Control: Other not–for–profit (including NFP Corporation) **Service:** Acute long–term care hospital

Staffed Beds: 21

Hospital, Medicare Provider Number, Address, Telephone, Approval, Facility, and Physician Codes, Health Care System

★ American Hospital Association (AHA) membership ○ Healthcare Facilities Accreditation Program ⇑ Center for Improvement in Healthcare Quality Accreditation
□ The Joint Commission accreditation ◇ DNV Healthcare Inc. accreditation △ Commission on Accreditation of Rehabilitation Facilities (CARF) accreditation

✠ **SAINT FRANCIS HOSPITAL (440183)**, 5959 Park Avenue, Zip 38119–5198; tel. 901/765–1000, **A**1 3 5 10 **F**3 8 11 12 13 15 17 18 20 22 24 26 28 29 30 31 34 35 37 38 40 45 46 47 48 49 50 54 57 58 59 64 70 72 74 75 76 77 78 79 81 85 86 87 90 93 98 99 100 101 102 103 106 107 108 110 111 114 115 118 119 121 123 124 126 130 131 132 142 146 147 148 149 **S** TENET Healthcare Corporation, Dallas, TX
Primary Contact: Audrey Gregory, R.N., MSN, Chief Executive Officer
COO: Samuel Pieh, Chief Operating Officer
CFO: Steven Frantz, Chief Financial Officer
CMO: David Schwartz, M.D., Chief Medical Officer
CIO: Keith Scarbrough, Director, Information Systems
CHR: Keith Stanhill, Chief Human Resources Officer
CNO: Jennifer Chiusano, R.N., Chief Nursing Officer
Web address: www.saintfrancishosp.com
Control: Corporation, Investor–owned (for–profit) **Service**: General medical and surgical

Staffed Beds: 415 **Admissions:** 15314 **Census:** 212 **Outpatient Visits:** 119509 **Births:** 1291 **Total Expense ($000):** 246839 **Payroll Expense ($000):** 82947 **Personnel:** 1194	

✠ **SELECT SPECIALTY HOSPITAL–MEMPHIS (442014)**, 5959 Park Avenue, 12th Floor, Zip 38119–5200; tel. 901/765–1245, (Nonreporting) **A**1 10 **S** Select Medical Corporation, Mechanicsburg, PA
Primary Contact: Marcia Taylor, Chief Executive Officer
Web address: www.selectspecialtyhospitals.com/company/locations/memphis.aspx
Control: Corporation, Investor–owned (for–profit) **Service**: Acute long–term care hospital

Staffed Beds: 39

✠ **ST. JUDE CHILDREN'S RESEARCH HOSPITAL (443302)**, 262 Danny Thomas Place, Zip 38105–3678; tel. 901/595–3300, **A**1 3 5 10 **F**31 39 53 78 81 86 88 89 100 104 120 121 122 124
Primary Contact: James R. Downing, M.D., Chief Executive Officer
COO: Mary Anna Quinn, Executive Vice President, Chief Administrative Officer
CFO: Patricia Keel, Senior Vice President and Chief Financial Officer
CMO: Ellis Neufeld, M.D., Chief Medical Officer
CIO: Darrin Keith Perry, Chief Information Officer and Senior Vice President
CHR: Dana Bottenfield, Vice President Human Resources
CNO: Tiffany Rooks, Interim Chief Nursing Officer
Web address: www.stjude.org
Control: Other not–for–profit (including NFP Corporation)

Staffed Beds: 68 **Admissions:** 3440 **Census:** 54 **Outpatient Visits:** 78587 **Births:** 0 **Total Expense ($000):** 857022 **Payroll Expense ($000):** 361994

VETERANS AFFAIRS MEDICAL CENTER See Memphis Veterans Affairs Medical Center

MILAN—Gibson County

✠ **MILAN GENERAL HOSPITAL (440060)**, 4039 Highland Street, Zip 38358–3483; tel. 731/686–1591, **A**1 10 **F**3 15 29 30 35 40 44 45 57 59 64 68 70 81 87 107 110 114 119 130 132 133 135 146 149 **S** West Tennessee Healthcare, Jackson, TN
Primary Contact: Sherry Scruggs, Administrator
CMO: Joe Appleton, M.D., Chief of Surgery
CNO: Carolyn Drake, Director of Nursing
Web address: www.wth.org
Control: Hospital district or authority, Government, nonfederal **Service**: General medical and surgical

Staffed Beds: 28 **Admissions:** 443 **Census:** 4 **Outpatient Visits:** 13944 **Births:** 0 **Total Expense ($000):** 9623 **Payroll Expense ($000):** 3877 **Personnel:** 70

MORRISTOWN—Hamblen County

✠ **LAKEWAY REGIONAL HOSPITAL (440067)**, 726 McFarland Street, Zip 37814–3990; tel. 423/586–2302, (Nonreporting) **A**1 10 19 **S** Community Health Systems, Inc., Franklin, TN
Primary Contact: Tammy White, Interim Chief Executive Officer
CMO: Paul Cardali, M.D., Chief of Staff
CHR: Deirdre Helton, Director Human Resources
Web address: www.tennova.com
Control: Corporation, Investor–owned (for–profit) **Service**: General medical and surgical

Staffed Beds: 135

✠ **MORRISTOWN–HAMBLEN HEALTHCARE SYSTEM (440030)**, 908 West Fourth North Street, Zip 37814–3894, Mailing Address: P.O. Box 1178, Zip 37816–1178; tel. 423/492–9000, **A**1 2 3 5 10 **F**3 11 13 15 18 20 22 26 28 29 30 31 34 35 40 41 45 46 47 49 50 51 56 57 59 60 64 68 74 75 76 78 79 80 81 85 98 103 107 108 110 114 115 117 118 119 120 121 123 129 146 147 **S** Covenant Health, Knoxville, TN
Primary Contact: Gordon Lintz, President and Chief Administrative Officer
CFO: Amy Herndon, Chief Finance Officer
CIO: Mike Ward, Chief Information Officer
CNO: Wilma Hart–Flynn, MSN, Ph.D., R.N., Chief Nursing Officer
Web address: www.morristownhamblen.com
Control: Other not–for–profit (including NFP Corporation) **Service**: General medical and surgical

Staffed Beds: 131 **Admissions:** 6000 **Census:** 68 **Outpatient Visits:** 102677 **Births:** 827 **Total Expense ($000):** 78093 **Payroll Expense ($000):** 29683 **Personnel:** 574

MOUNTAIN CITY—Johnson County

JOHNSON COUNTY COMMUNITY HOSPITAL (441304), 1901 South Shady Street, Zip 37683–2271; tel. 423/727–1100, **A**5 10 18 **F**3 15 18 28 30 34 35 40 44 50 57 62 64 68 87 93 97 104 107 108 110 111 114 119 127 153 154 **S** Ballad Health, Johnson City, TN
Primary Contact: Chastity Trivette, Chief Executive Officer
CNO: Helen Pardue, Interim Chief Nursing Officer
Web address: www.msha.com
Control: Other not–for–profit (including NFP Corporation) **Service**: General medical and surgical

Staffed Beds: 2 **Admissions:** 31 **Census:** 1 **Outpatient Visits:** 42616 **Births:** 0 **Total Expense ($000):** 9082 **Payroll Expense ($000):** 4181 **Personnel:** 68

MOUNTAIN HOME—Johnson County

✠ **JAMES H. QUILLEN VETERANS AFFAIRS MEDICAL CENTER**, Corner of Lamont & Veterans Way, Zip 37684, Mailing Address: P.O. Box 4000, Zip 37684–4000; tel. 423/926–1171, (Nonreporting) **A**1 3 5 **S** Department of Veterans Affairs, Perry Point, MD
Primary Contact: Dean B. Borsos, Medical Center Director
CFO: Sandra Nash, Chief Fiscal Service
CMO: David Hecht, M.D., Chief of Staff
CIO: Karen Perry, Chief Information Resource Management Services
CHR: John Henderson, Chief Human Resources Management
CNO: Linda M McConnell, R.N., MSN, FACHE, Associate Medical Center Director Patient Care Services
Web address: www.mountainhome.va.gov/
Control: Veterans Affairs, Government, federal **Service**: General medical and surgical

Staffed Beds: 98

MURFREESBORO—Rutherford County

ALVIN C. YORK CAMPUS See Tennessee Valley Healthcare System, Nashville

✠ **SAINT THOMAS RUTHERFORD HOSPITAL (440053)**, 1700 Medical Center Parkway, Zip 37129–2245; tel. 615/396–4100, (Nonreporting) **A**1 2 3 5 10 **S** Ascension Healthcare, Saint Louis, MO
Primary Contact: Gordon B. Ferguson, President and Chief Executive Officer
COO: Thomas Roddy, Chief Operating Officer
CFO: Bailey Pratt, Chief Financial Officer
CMO: Scott Corlew, M.D., Chief Medical Officer
CHR: Carol Bragdon, Director Human Resources
CNO: Stacey Beaven, R.N., Chief Nursing Officer
Web address: www.mtmc.org
Control: Church operated, Nongovernment, not–for–profit **Service**: General medical and surgical

Staffed Beds: 286

☐ **TRUSTPOINT HOSPITAL (440231)**, 1009 North Thompson Lane, Zip 37129–4351; tel. 615/867–1111, (Nonreporting) **A**1 10 **S** Acadia Healthcare Company, Inc., Franklin, TN
Primary Contact: Beth Goodner, Chief Executive Officer
Web address: www.trustpointhospital.com
Control: Corporation, Investor–owned (for–profit) **Service**: Rehabilitation

Staffed Beds: 101

TN

NASHVILLE—Davidson County

CENTENNIAL MEDICAL CENTER See Tristar Centennial Medical Center

☐ **CURAHEALTH NASHVILLE (442006)**, 1412 County Hospital Road, Zip 37218–3007; tel. 615/687–2600, (Nonreporting) **A**1 10 **S** Curahealth Hospitals, Garland, TX
Primary Contact: Timothy C. Deaton, Chief Executive Officer
CFO: Philip L Jones, Chief Financial Officer
CMO: Clyde Heflin, M.D., Chief Medical Officer
Web address: www.curahealth.com
Control: Corporation, Investor–owned (for–profit) **Service:** Acute long–term care hospital

Staffed Beds: 58

☐ **MIDDLE TENNESSEE MENTAL HEALTH INSTITUTE (444014)**, 221 Stewarts Ferry Pike, Zip 37214–3325; tel. 615/902–7535, **A**1 3 5 10 **F**3 29 30 75 98 101 102 103 130
Primary Contact: Rob Cotterman, Chief Executive Officer
CFO: Mark Stanley, Director Fiscal Services
CMO: Mohammad S Jahan, M.D., Clinical Director
CHR: Margie Dunn, Director Human Resources
Web address: www.tn.gov/mental/mhs/mhs2.html
Control: State, Government, nonfederal **Service:** Psychiatric

Staffed Beds: 207 **Admissions:** 3786 **Census:** 175 **Outpatient Visits:** 0 **Births:** 0 **Total Expense ($000):** 50695 **Payroll Expense ($000):** 26988 **Personnel:** 579

MONROE CARELL JR. CHILDREN'S HOSPITAL AT VANDERBILT See Vanderbilt University Medical Center, Nashville

☐ **NASHVILLE GENERAL HOSPITAL (440111)**, 1818 Albion Street, Zip 37208–2918; tel. 615/341–4000, (Nonreporting) **A**1 2 3 5 10
Primary Contact: Joseph Webb, Chief Executive Officer
CMO: Chike Nzerue, M.D., Chief Medical Officer
CIO: Chris Whorley, Chief Information Officer
CHR: Diana Wohlfardt, Director Human Resources
CNO: Leonora Collins, Chief Nursing Officer
Web address: www.nashvillegeneral.org/
Control: City–county, Government, nonfederal **Service:** General medical and surgical

Staffed Beds: 116

⊞ **SAINT THOMAS HOSPITAL FOR SPINAL SURGERY (440218)**, 2011 Murphy Avenue, Suite 400, Zip 37203–2065; tel. 615/341–7500, (Nonreporting) **A**1 10 **S** Ascension Healthcare, Saint Louis, MO
Primary Contact: Kathy Watson, R.N., Administrator and Chief Nursing Officer
CFO: Angie Crow, Director Finance
CMO: Carl Hampf, M.D., Chief Medical Officer
Web address: www.hospitalforspinalsurgery.com
Control: Partnership, Investor–owned (for–profit) **Service:** General medical and surgical

Staffed Beds: 23

⊞ **SAINT THOMAS MIDTOWN HOSPITAL (440133)**, 2000 Church Street, Zip 37236–0002; tel. 615/284–5555, (Nonreporting) **A**1 2 3 5 10 **S** Ascension Healthcare, Saint Louis, MO
Primary Contact: Fahad Tahir, Chief Executive Officer
COO: Jeremy Gray, Chief Operating Officer
CFO: Pamela Hess, Chief Financial Officer
CMO: William Thompson, M.D., Chief Medical Officer
CIO: Jim Drew, Chief Information Officer
CHR: Martha Underwood, Chief Human Resources Officer
CNO: Marco Fernandez, R.N., MSN, Chief Nursing Officer
Web address: www.sths.com
Control: Other not–for–profit (including NFP Corporation) **Service:** General medical and surgical

Staffed Beds: 425

⊞ **SAINT THOMAS WEST HOSPITAL (440082)**, 4220 Harding Road, Zip 37205–2095, Mailing Address: P.O. Box 380, Zip 37202–0380; tel. 615/222–2111, (Nonreporting) **A**1 2 3 5 10 **S** Ascension Healthcare, Saint Louis, MO
Primary Contact: Fahad Tahir, Chief Executive Officer
COO: Harrison Kiser, Chief Operating Officer
CFO: Pamela Hess, Chief Financial Officer
CMO: Dale Batchelor, M.D., Chief Medical Officer
CHR: Bud Wood, Chief Human Resources Officer
CNO: Sam Straton, Chief Nursing Officer
Web address: www.stthomas.org
Control: Church operated, Nongovernment, not–for–profit **Service:** General medical and surgical

Staffed Beds: 395

⊞ **SELECT SPECIALTY HOSPITAL–NASHVILLE (442011)**, 2000 Hayes Street, Zip 37203–2318; tel. 615/284–4599, (Nonreporting) **A**1 10 **S** Select Medical Corporation, Mechanicsburg, PA
Primary Contact: Jennifer Causey, Chief Executive Officer
CNO: Karen Cagle, Chief Nursing Officer
Web address: www.selectspecialtyhospitals.com/company/locations/nashville.aspx
Control: Corporation, Investor–owned (for–profit) **Service:** Acute long–term care hospital

Staffed Beds: 70

⊞ **TENNESSEE VALLEY HEALTHCARE SYSTEM**, 1310 24th Avenue South, Zip 37212–2637; tel. 615/327–4751, (Includes ALVIN C. YORK CAMPUS, 3400 Lebanon Pike, Murfreesboro, TN, Zip 37129–1236; tel. 615/867–6000; NASHVILLE CAMPUS, 1310 24th Avenue South, Nashville, TN, Zip 37212–2637; tel. 615/327–4751) (Total facility includes 178 beds in nursing home–type unit) **A**1 3 5 **F**1 2 3 4 5 6 7 8 9 10 12 15 18 20 22 24 26 28 29 30 31 33 34 35 36 38 39 40 44 45 46 47 48 49 50 51 53 54 55 56 57 58 59 60 61 62 63 64 65 66 67 70 74 75 77 78 79 80 81 82 83 84 85 86 87 91 92 93 94 95 96 97 98 100 101 102 103 104 105 106 107 109 111 113 114 115 116 118 119 120 121 125 126 127 128 129 130 131 132 133 135 136 137 138 139 140 143 144 145 146 147 148 149 150 152 153 154 **P**6 **S** Department of Veterans Affairs, Perry Point, MD
Primary Contact: Captain Jennifer Vedral–Baron, Health System Director
COO: Suzanne L. Jene, Chief Operating Officer
CFO: Lynn Menthcoast, Chief Fiscal Service
CMO: Roger Jones, M.D., Interim Chief of Staff
CIO: Paul Mardy, Chief Information Technology Officer
CHR: Shirley F Pettite, Chief Human Resources Officer
CNO: Janice M Cobb, R.N., Chief Nursing Officer
Web address: www.tennesseevalley.va.gov
Control: Veterans Affairs, Government, federal **Service:** General medical and surgical

Staffed Beds: 437 **Admissions:** 9533 **Census:** 308 **Outpatient Visits:** 1161685 **Births:** 0 **Total Expense ($000):** 829720 **Payroll Expense ($000):** 325000

⊞ **TRISTAR CENTENNIAL MEDICAL CENTER (440161)**, 2300 Patterson Street, Zip 37203–1528; tel. 615/342–1000, (Includes TRISTAR CENTENNIAL WOMEN'S & CHILDREN'S, 2221 Murphy Avenue, Nashville, TN, Zip 37203; tel. 615/342–1000) (Nonreporting) **A**1 2 3 5 10 **S** HCA Healthcare, Nashville, TN
Primary Contact: Scott A. Cihak, President and Chief Executive Officer
COO: Justin Coury, Chief Operating Officer
CFO: David A Summers, Chief Financial Officer
CHR: Jennifer Burden, Human Resources Director
Web address: www.tristarcentennial.com
Control: Corporation, Investor–owned (for–profit) **Service:** General medical and surgical

Staffed Beds: 650

⊞ △ **TRISTAR SKYLINE MEDICAL CENTER (440006)**, 3441 Dickerson Pike, Zip 37207–2539; tel. 615/769–2000, (Includes TRISTAR SKYLINE MADISON CAMPUS, 500 Hospital Drive, Madison, TN, Zip 37115–5032; tel. 615/769–5000; Steve Otto, Chief Executive Officer) (Nonreporting) **A**1 2 5 7 10 **S** HCA Healthcare, Nashville, TN
Primary Contact: Steve Otto, Chief Executive Officer
COO: Jason E Boyd, Chief Operating Officer
CFO: Michael Morrison, Chief Financial Officer
CMO: Christopher Conley, M.D., President of the Medical Staff
CIO: Troy Sypien, Director Information Technology and Systems
CHR: Robert A Hooper, Director Human Resources
CNO: Laurie Turner, Chief Nursing Officer
Web address: www.tristarskyline.com
Control: Corporation, Investor–owned (for–profit) **Service:** General medical and surgical

Staffed Beds: 579

TN

Hospital, Medicare Provider Number, Address, Telephone, Approval, Facility, and Physician Codes, Health Care System

★ American Hospital Association (AHA) membership ☐ The Joint Commission accreditation ○ Healthcare Facilities Accreditation Program ◇ DNV Healthcare Inc. accreditation ⇑ Center for Improvement in Healthcare Quality Accreditation △ Commission on Accreditation of Rehabilitation Facilities (CARF) accreditation

✠ **TRISTAR SOUTHERN HILLS MEDICAL CENTER (440197)**, 391 Wallace Road, Zip 37211–4859; tel. 615/781–4000, (Nonreporting) **A**1 2 10 **S** HCA Healthcare, Nashville, TN
Primary Contact: Joanna J. Conley, FACHE, Chief Executive Officer
CFO: John Porada, Chief Financial Officer
CMO: Eric Schuck, M.D., Chief Medical Officer
CIO: Ronnie Gannon, Director Information Services
CHR: Gary Briggs, Vice President Human Resources
CNO: Chris Staigl, Chief Nursing Officer
Web address: www.tristarsouthernhills.com
Control: Corporation, Investor–owned (for–profit) **Service**: General medical and surgical

Staffed Beds: 87

VANDERBILT PSYCHIATRIC HOSPITAL See Vanderbilt University Medical Center, Nashville

✠ **VANDERBILT STALLWORTH REHABILITATION HOSPITAL (443028)**, 2201 Childrens Way, Zip 37212–3165; tel. 615/320–7600, **A**1 3 5 10 **F**29 34 35 50 57 59 75 86 87 90 91 96 132 143 148 149 **S** Encompass Health Corporation, Birmingham, AL
Primary Contact: Jeffrey Palmucci, Chief Executive Officer
CFO: Christine Campbell, Controller
CMO: Jeffery Johns, M.D., Medical Director
CHR: Ruth Beasley, Director Human Resources
CNO: Karen Lasher, Chief Nursing Officer
Web address: www.vanderbiltstallworthrehab.com
Control: Partnership, Investor–owned (for–profit) **Service**: Rehabilitation

Staffed Beds: 70 **Admissions**: 1367 **Census**: 52 **Outpatient Visits**: 0 **Births**: 0

✠ **VANDERBILT UNIVERSITY MEDICAL CENTER (440039)**, 1211 Medical Center Drive, Zip 37232–2102; tel. 615/322–5000, (Includes MONROE CARELL JR. CHILDREN'S HOSPITAL AT VANDERBILT, 2200 Children's Way, Nashville, TN, Zip 37232; tel. 615/936–1000; Luke Gregory, Chief Executive Officer; VANDERBILT PSYCHIATRIC HOSPITAL, 1601 23rd Avenue South, Nashville, TN, Zip 37212–3198; tel. 615/320–7770) **A**1 2 3 5 8 10 **F**3 4 5 6 7 8 9 12 13 15 16 17 18 19 20 21 22 23 24 25 26 27 28 29 30 31 32 34 35 36 37 38 39 40 41 43 44 45 46 47 48 49 50 51 52 53 54 55 56 57 58 59 60 61 62 63 64 65 66 68 70 71 72 74 75 76 77 78 79 80 81 82 83 84 85 86 87 88 89 91 92 93 94 96 97 98 99 100 101 102 103 104 105 107 108 110 111 114 115 116 117 118 119 120 121 123 124 126 129 130 131 132 134 135 136 137 138 139 140 141 142 143 144 146 147 148 149 150 151 154 **P**2 5 6 **S** Vanderbilt Health, Nashville, TN
Primary Contact: Jeffrey R. Balsar, President and Chief Executive Officer Vanderbilt Medical Center and Dean, Vanderbilt University Scho
CFO: Cecelia B Moore, CPA, Associate Vice Chancellor Finance
CMO: Paul Sternberg, M.D., Professor and Chairman
CIO: William Stead, Associate Vice Chancellor Health Affairs, Director Informatics Center and Chief Strategy and Information Officer
CHR: Traci Nordberg, Chief Human Resources Officer
CNO: Pam Jones, MSN, R.N., Associate Hospital Director and Chief Nursing Officer
Web address: www.mc.vanderbilt.edu
Control: Other not–for–profit (including NFP Corporation) **Service**: General medical and surgical

Staffed Beds: 1011 **Admissions**: 57526 **Census**: 861 **Outpatient Visits**: 2210307 **Births**: 4509 **Total Expense ($000)**: 3000926 **Payroll Expense ($000)**: 1159041 **Personnel**: 24736

VETERANS AFFAIRS TENNESSEE VALLEY HEALTHCARE SYSTEM See Tennessee Valley Healthcare System

NEWPORT—Cocke County

BAPTIST HOSPITAL OF COCKE COUNTY See Tennova Newport Medical Center

✠ **TENNOVA NEWPORT MEDICAL CENTER (440153)**, 435 Second Street, Zip 37821–3799; tel. 423/625–2200, (Nonreporting) **A**1 10 **S** Community Health Systems, Inc., Franklin, TN
Primary Contact: Pamela Beck, Interim Chief Executive Officer
CFO: Jon Richards, Chief Financial Officer
CMO: Larry Mathers, M.D., Chief of Staff
CNO: Tonia Hale, Chief Nursing Officer
Web address: www.tennova.com
Control: Corporation, Investor–owned (for–profit) **Service**: General medical and surgical

Staffed Beds: 47

OAK RIDGE—Anderson County

✠ **METHODIST MEDICAL CENTER OF OAK RIDGE (440034)**, 990 Oak Ridge Turnpike, Zip 37830–6976, Mailing Address: P.O. Box 2529, Zip 37831–2529; tel. 865/835–1000, **A**1 2 3 10 **F**3 11 13 15 17 18 20 22 24 26 28 29 30 31 34 35 40 45 47 49 50 51 54 57 59 60 61 64 68 70 74 75 76 78 79 80 81 84 85 86 87 107 108 110 111 114 115 118 119 120 121 123 126 129 130 132 135 146 148 154 **S** Covenant Health, Knoxville, TN
Primary Contact: Jeremy Biggs, President and Chief Administrative Officer
COO: Connie Martin, Vice President and Chief Support Officer
CFO: Rick Carringer, Vice President and Chief Financial Officer
CMO: Mark Browne, M.D., Covenant Health, Senior Vice President and Chief Medical Officer
CIO: Mike Ward, Covenant Health, Senior Vice President and Chief Information Officer
CHR: Rick Akens, Director Human Resources and Labor Relations
CNO: Sue Harris, Vice President and Chief Nursing Officer
Web address: www.mmcoakridge.com
Control: Other not–for–profit (including NFP Corporation) **Service**: General medical and surgical

Staffed Beds: 210 **Admissions**: 10364 **Census**: 128 **Outpatient Visits**: 163645 **Births**: 460 **Total Expense ($000)**: 155378 **Payroll Expense ($000)**: 55853 **Personnel**: 900

RIDGEVIEW PSYCHIATRIC HOSPITAL AND CENTER (444003), 240 West Tyrone Road, Zip 37830–6571; tel. 865/482–1076, (Nonreporting) **A**10
Primary Contact: Brian Buuck, Chief Executive Officer
CFO: Mary Claire Duff, CPA, Chief Financial Officer
CMO: Renu Bhateja, M.D., President Medical Staff
CHR: Julie M Wright, Director Human Resources
Web address: www.ridgeviewresources.com
Control: Other not–for–profit (including NFP Corporation) **Service**: Psychiatric

Staffed Beds: 20

ONEIDA—Scott County

BIG SOUTH FORK MEDICAL CENTER (440235), 18797 Alberta Street, Zip 37841–2127; tel. 423/286–5500, (Data for 146 days) **F**3 29 34 40 107 114 135 149 154
Primary Contact: Hal W. Leftwich, FACHE, Chief Executive Officer
Web address: www.bsfmedical.com
Control: Corporation, Investor–owned (for–profit) **Service**: General medical and surgical

Staffed Beds: 25 **Admissions**: 182 **Census**: 5

PARIS—Henry County

✠ **HENRY COUNTY MEDICAL CENTER (440132)**, 301 Tyson Avenue, Zip 38242–4544, Mailing Address: P.O. Box 1030, Zip 38242–1030; tel. 731/642–1220, (Total facility includes 122 beds in nursing home–type unit) **A**1 10 **F**3 7 8 11 13 15 18 20 28 29 30 32 34 35 37 40 44 50 51 53 56 57 59 62 63 64 65 67 68 70 71 76 77 79 81 85 86 87 89 93 98 100 102 103 107 108 110 111 114 115 118 119 126 127 128 129 130 131 132 133 135 143 146 147 148 154 **P**6
Primary Contact: Lisa Casteel, Chief Executive Officer
CIO: Pam Ridley, Director Information Systems
CHR: Edwin L Ledden, Assistant Administrator and Director Human Resources
CNO: Cynthia Whitaker, Chief Nursing Officer
Web address: www.hcmc–tn.org
Control: Hospital district or authority, Government, nonfederal **Service**: General medical and surgical

Staffed Beds: 251 **Admissions**: 4018 **Census**: 119 **Outpatient Visits**: 160614 **Births**: 324 **Total Expense ($000)**: 90508 **Payroll Expense ($000)**: 40569 **Personnel**: 717

PARSONS—Decatur County

☐ **DECATUR COUNTY GENERAL HOSPITAL (440070)**, 969 Tennessee Avenue South, Zip 38363–3700, Mailing Address: P.O. Box 250, Zip 38363–0250; tel. 731/847–3031, (Nonreporting) **A**1 10
Primary Contact: Scott Barber, Chief Executive Officer
CFO: Donna Hayes, Controller
CMO: Tom Hamilton, M.D., Chief of Staff
CHR: Shelley Bartholomew, Director Human Resources
Web address: www.dcgh.org
Control: County, Government, nonfederal **Service**: General medical and surgical

Staffed Beds: 40

Many Facility Codes have changed. Please refer to the AHA Guide Code Chart.

TN

PIKEVILLE—Bledsoe County

ERLANGER BLEDSOE HOSPITAL (441306), 71 Wheeler Avenue, Zip 37367, Mailing Address: P.O. Box 699, Zip 37367–0699; tel. 423/447–2112, **A**10 18 **F**3 11 15 18 28 29 30 34 35 38 40 41 43 44 50 54 56 57 59 61 63 64 65 66 68 75 82 84 86 87 92 93 96 97 102 103 107 110 114 119 127 130 131 133 135 144 146 147 148 **P**2 4 6 7 **S** Erlanger Health System, Chattanooga, TN
Primary Contact: Stephanie Boynton, Administrator
CMO: Arturo L Quito, M.D., Chief of Staff
CIO: Debbie Rains, Coordinator Health Information Management
CHR: Patsy Brown, Site Coordinator Human Resources
Web address: www.erlanger.org
Control: Hospital district or authority, Government, nonfederal **Service**: General medical and surgical

Staffed Beds: 25 **Admissions**: 373 **Census**: 8 **Outpatient Visits**: 28642
Births: 0 **Total Expense ($000)**: 14643 **Payroll Expense ($000)**: 5998
Personnel: 94

POWELL—Knox County

MERCY MEDICAL CENTER NORTH See Tennova North Knoxville Medical Center

SELECT SPECIALTY HOSPITAL–NORTH KNOXVILLE (442015), 7557B Dannaher Drive, Suite 145, Zip 37849–3568; tel. 865/512–2450, (Includes SELECT SPECIALTY HOSPITAL–KNOXVILLE, 1901 Clinch Avenue, 4th Floor North, Knoxville, TN, Zip 37916–2307; tel. 865/541–2615; Andrew Howard, Chief Executive Officer) (Nonreporting) **A**1 10 **S** Select Medical Corporation, Mechanicsburg, PA
Primary Contact: Steve Plumlee, Chief Executive Officer
CFO: David Elledge, Controller
CMO: Jeff Summers, M.D., Medical Director
CIO: Steve Plumlee, Chief Executive Officer
CHR: Mallory Wilson, Administrative Assistant and Human Resources Coordinator
CNO: Nancy Johnson, Chief Nursing Officer
Web address: www.northknoxville.selectspecialtyhospitals.com/
Control: Corporation, Investor–owned (for–profit) **Service**: Acute long–term care hospital

Staffed Beds: 68

PULASKI—Giles County

SOUTHERN TENNESSEE REGIONAL HEALTH SYSTEM–PULASKI (440020), 1265 East College Street, Zip 38478–4541; tel. 931/363–7531, **A**1 10 **F**3 4 13 15 17 28 29 30 34 39 40 41 45 50 56 57 59 63 68 70 74 75 76 77 79 81 83 85 89 91 93 98 103 107 111 115 116 117 119 129 130 133 146 147 148 154 **S** LifePoint Health, Brentwood, TN
Primary Contact: James H. Edmondson, Chief Executive Officer
CFO: Donald Gavin, Chief Financial Officer
CMO: J Michael Windland, M.D., Chief of Staff
CIO: Mitzi Foster, Director Information Services
CHR: Jane Petty, Director Human Resources
CNO: Sherry Sands, R.N., Chief Nursing Officer
Web address: www.southerntnpulaski.com/
Control: Corporation, Investor–owned (for–profit) **Service**: General medical and surgical

Staffed Beds: 59 **Admissions**: 1831 **Census**: 23 **Outpatient Visits**: 34703
Births: 121 **Total Expense ($000)**: 30944 **Payroll Expense ($000)**: 11523
Personnel: 195

RIPLEY—Lauderdale County

⇧ **LAUDERDALE COMMUNITY HOSPITAL (441314)**, 326 Asbury Avenue, Zip 38063–5577; tel. 731/221–2200, (Nonreporting) **A**10 18 21 **S** Rural Community Hospitals of America, Kansas City, MO
Primary Contact: Michael G. Layfield, Interim Chief Executive Officer
CFO: T J Sheehan, Chief Financial Officer
CMO: Syed A. Zaidi, M.D., Chief of Staff
CIO: Jim Vaden, Director Information Systems
CHR: Joan W. Simpson, Manager Human Resources
CNO: Michelle Simpson, Chief Nursing Officer and Quality Leader
Web address: www.lauderdalehospital.com/
Control: Corporation, Investor–owned (for–profit) **Service**: General medical and surgical

Staffed Beds: 25

ROGERSVILLE—Hawkins County

HAWKINS COUNTY MEMORIAL HOSPITAL (440032), 851 Locust Street, Zip 37857–2407, Mailing Address: P.O. Box 130, Zip 37857–0130; tel. 423/921–7000, **A**1 5 10 **F**3 11 15 29 30 34 40 45 50 57 59 64 70 75 77 79 80 81 82 85 87 93 97 107 108 110 114 119 129 130 133 135 146 **S** Ballad Health, Johnson City, TN
Primary Contact: Regina Day, Chief Executive Officer
CFO: Dale Poe, Vice President and Chief Financial Officer
CHR: Robin Poteete, Manager Human Resources
Web address: www.wellmont.org
Control: Other not–for–profit (including NFP Corporation) **Service**: General medical and surgical

Staffed Beds: 22 **Admissions**: 990 **Census**: 8 **Outpatient Visits**: 30607
Births: 0 **Total Expense ($000)**: 44164 **Payroll Expense ($000)**: 6213
Personnel: 141

SAVANNAH—Hardin County

★ ⇧ **HARDIN MEDICAL CENTER (440109)**, 935 Wayne Road, Zip 38372–1904; tel. 731/926–8000, (Total facility includes 73 beds in nursing home–type unit) **A**10 21 **F**2 3 7 11 13 15 18 19 28 29 31 34 40 45 57 59 62 65 68 69 75 76 77 78 79 80 81 89 93 107 110 111 115 119 124 128 129 130 133 144 148 **P**6
Primary Contact: Nicholas P. Lewis, Chief Executive Officer
CFO: Leigh Ann Hughes, Chief Financial Officer
CMO: Gilbert M. Thayer, M.D., Chief Medical Staff
CIO: Jacob Bomar, Director Information Technology
CNO: Jesse Wint, Director of Nursing
Web address: www.hardinmedicalcenter.org
Control: County, Government, nonfederal **Service**: General medical and surgical

Staffed Beds: 122 **Admissions**: 1589 **Census**: 84 **Outpatient Visits**: 66400
Births: 367 **Total Expense ($000)**: 34089 **Payroll Expense ($000)**: 14936
Personnel: 406

SEVIERVILLE—Sevier County

LECONTE MEDICAL CENTER (440081), 742 Middle Creek Road, Zip 37862–5019, Mailing Address: P.O. Box 8005, Zip 37864–8005; tel. 865/446–7000, (Total facility includes 54 beds in nursing home–type unit) **A**1 5 10 **F**3 11 13 15 18 20 28 29 30 31 34 35 40 45 50 51 53 57 59 61 64 67 68 70 75 76 77 78 79 80 81 85 87 90 107 110 111 112 114 115 119 120 121 123 124 128 129 130 131 135 146 147 154 **S** Covenant Health, Knoxville, TN
Primary Contact: Gaye Jolly, FACHE, President and Chief Administrative Officer
COO: Michael Hatmaker, Vice President Support Services and Admin Nursing Home
CFO: Jacqueline Hounshell, Chief Financial Officer
CMO: William Clifford Cole, M.D., Chief of Staff
CHR: Tami McClain, Human Resources Operations Specialist
CNO: Carol Pahde, R.N., Chief Nursing Officer
Web address: www.lecontemedicalcenter.com
Control: Other not–for–profit (including NFP Corporation) **Service**: General medical and surgical

Staffed Beds: 131 **Admissions**: 5178 **Census**: 90 **Outpatient Visits**: 141111 **Births**: 1100 **Total Expense ($000)**: 95925 **Payroll Expense ($000)**: 30897 **Personnel**: 520

SEWANEE—Franklin County

SOUTHERN TENNESSEE REGIONAL HEALTH SYSTEM–SEWANEE See Southern Tennessee Regional Health System–Winchester, Winchester

SHELBYVILLE—Bedford County

TENNOVA HEALTHCARE–SHELBYVILLE (440137), 2835 Highway 231 North, Zip 37160–7327; tel. 931/685–5433, **A**1 10 **F**3 12 13 15 18 29 34 40 45 57 59 60 64 68 70 76 79 81 85 87 89 93 96 102 107 108 111 115 119 124 129 130 131 132 148 154 **S** Community Health Systems, Inc., Franklin, TN
Primary Contact: Bill Rich, Chief Executive Officer
CFO: Tammy Cobb, Chief Financial Officer
CIO: Jonathon Willis, Director Information Services
CHR: Charisse Parker, Director Human Resources
CNO: Vickie Vaughn, Chief Nursing Officer
Web address: www.Tennova.com
Control: Corporation, Investor–owned (for–profit) **Service**: General medical and surgical

Staffed Beds: 49 **Admissions**: 1484 **Census**: 13 **Outpatient Visits**: 40926
Births: 1 **Total Expense ($000)**: 34831 **Payroll Expense ($000)**: 9970
Personnel: 185

TN

Hospital, Medicare Provider Number, Address, Telephone, Approval, Facility, and Physician Codes, Health Care System

★ American Hospital Association (AHA) membership   ○ Healthcare Facilities Accreditation Program   ⇧ Center for Improvement in Healthcare Quality Accreditation
□ The Joint Commission accreditation   ◇ DNV Healthcare Inc. accreditation   △ Commission on Accreditation of Rehabilitation Facilities (CARF) accreditation

SMITHVILLE—Dekalb County

✠ **SAINT THOMAS DEKALB HOSPITAL (440148)**, 520 West Main Street,
Zip 37166–1138, Mailing Address: P.O. Box 640, Zip 37166–0640;
tel. 615/215–5000, (Nonreporting) **A**1 10 **S** Ascension Healthcare, Saint Louis, MO
Primary Contact: Bradley Mullinax, Chief Administrative Officer
CFO: Alan Sharp, Chief Financial Officer
CMO: Kimberly Collins, M.D., Chief of Staff
CNO: Emily Elrod, R.N., Chief Nursing Officer
Web address: www.dekalbcommunityhospital.com
Control: Church operated, Nongovernment, not–for–profit **Service:** General medical and surgical

Staffed Beds: 56

SMYRNA—Rutherford County

✠ **TRISTAR STONECREST MEDICAL CENTER (440227)**, 200 StoneCrest
Boulevard, Zip 37167–6810; tel. 615/768–2000, (Nonreporting) **A**1 2 10 **S** HCA
Healthcare, Nashville, TN
Primary Contact: Louis Caputo, Chief Executive Officer
COO: Andrew Tyrer, Chief Operating Officer
CFO: Joseph E Bowman, Chief Financial Officer
CMO: William Mayfield, M.D., Chief of Staff
CHR: Cynthia Adams, Vice President Human Resources
CNO: Amy Cason, MSN, Chief Nursing Officer
Web address: www.stonecrestmedical.com
Control: Corporation, Investor–owned (for–profit) **Service:** General medical and surgical

Staffed Beds: 101

SNEEDVILLE—Hancock County

★ **HANCOCK COUNTY HOSPITAL (441313)**, 1519 Main Street, Zip 37869–3657;
tel. 423/733–5000, **A**10 18 **F**3 29 30 34 40 50 57 59 85 87 107 108 118 119
127 133 135 **P**6 **S** Ballad Health, Johnson City, TN
Primary Contact: Rebecca Beck, President
COO: Eric Deaton, Executive Vice President, Chief Operating Officer and Corporate Operating
CFO: Regina Day, Director of Finance
CIO: Martha O'Regan Chill, Interim Chief Information Officer
CHR: Denise Adams, Human Resources Generalist
CNO: Phyllis Dossett, Director of Clinical Services
Web address: www.wellmont.org/Hospitals/Hancock–County–Hospital.aspx
Control: Other not–for–profit (including NFP Corporation) **Service:** General medical and surgical

Staffed Beds: 10 Admissions: 179 Census: 2 Outpatient Visits: 7357
Births: 0 Total Expense ($000): 6249 Payroll Expense ($000): 1691
Personnel: 37

SPARTA—White County

✠ **SAINT THOMAS HIGHLANDS HOSPITAL (440192)**, 401 Sewell Road,
Zip 38583–1299; tel. 931/738–9211, (Nonreporting) **A**1 10 **S** Ascension
Healthcare, Saint Louis, MO
Primary Contact: Richard Tumlin, Chief Administrative Officer
CFO: Rodney VanDonkelaar, Chief Financial Officer
CMO: Robert Knowles, M.D., Chief of Staff
CIO: Glenn Wade, Director Information Systems
CHR: Kent Frisbee, Director Human Resources
CNO: Gearline Copeland, R.N., Chief Nursing Officer
Web address: www.whitecountyhospital.com
Control: Church operated, Nongovernment, not–for–profit **Service:** General medical and surgical

Staffed Beds: 60

SPRINGFIELD—Robertson County

✠ **NORTHCREST MEDICAL CENTER (440065)**, 100 North Crest Drive,
Zip 37172–3961; tel. 615/384–2411, **A**1 10 **F**3 13 18 20 22 28 29 30 40 46
63 70 76 89 107 111 115 117 119 129 130
Primary Contact: Randy Davis, Chief Executive Officer
CFO: Kim Pridgen, Chief Financial Officer
CHR: Kimberly Walker, Director of Human Resources
CNO: Angie Beard, R.N., Chief Nursing Officer
Web address: www.northcrest.com
Control: Other not–for–profit (including NFP Corporation) **Service:** General medical and surgical

Staffed Beds: 80 Admissions: 2751 Census: 31

SWEETWATER—Monroe County

✠ **SWEETWATER HOSPITAL (440084)**, 304 Wright Street, Zip 37874–2823;
tel. 865/213–8200, (Nonreporting) **A**1 10
Primary Contact: Scott Bowman, Administrator
CFO: Debbie Thompson, Chief Financial Officer
CMO: David Norris, Chief Medical Staff
CIO: Tony Sharp, Supervisor Information System
CHR: Lucretia Allen, Director Human Resources
CNO: Andrea Henry, Director of Nursing
Web address: www.sweetwaterhospital.org
Control: Other not–for–profit (including NFP Corporation) **Service:** General medical and surgical

Staffed Beds: 59

TAZEWELL—Claiborne County

✠ **CLAIBORNE MEDICAL CENTER (440057)**, 1850 Old Knoxville Road,
Zip 37879–3625; tel. 423/626–4211, (Total facility includes 99 beds in nursing
home–type unit) **A**1 10 **F**7 15 18 28 29 30 34 40 57 70 77 81 93 107 110 111
115 119 128 130 146 147 **S** Covenant Health, Knoxville, TN
Primary Contact: Patricia P. Ketterman, R.N., President and Chief Administrative Officer
CFO: Tracee McFarland, Chief Financial Officer
CHR: Susan Stone, Director Human Resources
Web address: www.claibornehospital.org
Control: Other not–for–profit (including NFP Corporation) **Service:** General medical and surgical

Staffed Beds: 132 Admissions: 1384 Census: 78 Outpatient Visits: 40105
Births: 0 Total Expense ($000): 28892 Payroll Expense ($000): 13115
Personnel: 322

TULLAHOMA—Coffee County

✠ **TENNOVA HEALTHCARE–HARTON (440144)**, 1801 North Jackson Street,
Zip 37388–8259; tel. 931/393–3000, (Nonreporting) **A**1 10 19 **S** Community
Health Systems, Inc., Franklin, TN
Primary Contact: Richard Ellis, Chief Executive Officer
CFO: Shaun Adams, Chief Financial Officer
CMO: John D Crabtree, M.D., Chief of Staff
CIO: Donald Cooper, Director Information Systems
CHR: Lenore Blackwell, Director Human Resources
Web address: www.hartonmedicalcenter.com
Control: Corporation, Investor–owned (for–profit) **Service:** General medical and surgical

Staffed Beds: 135

UNION CITY—Obion County

✠ **BAPTIST MEMORIAL HOSPITAL–UNION CITY (440130)**, 1201 Bishop
Street, Zip 38261–5403, Mailing Address: P.O. Box 310, Zip 38281–0310;
tel. 731/885–2410, **A**1 10 **F**7 11 13 15 18 20 26 28 29 30 34 35 40 45 48 50
51 53 57 59 63 64 70 75 76 79 81 82 84 85 86 87 89 91 93 107 108 109
110 111 115 118 119 124 130 132 135 146 **P**3 **S** Baptist Memorial Health Care
Corporation, Memphis, TN
Primary Contact: Barry Bondurant, Administrator and Chief Executive Officer
CFO: Mike Perryman, Chief Financial Officer
CMO: Kofi Nuako, M.D., President Medical Staff
CIO: David Mercer, Coordinator Information Systems
CHR: Nicky Thomas, Director Human Resources
CNO: Lori Brown, Chief Nursing Officer
Web address: www.baptistonline.org/union–city/
Control: Other not–for–profit (including NFP Corporation) **Service:** General medical and surgical

Staffed Beds: 63 Admissions: 2563 Census: 22 Outpatient Visits: 51343
Births: 293 Total Expense ($000): 44794 Payroll Expense ($000): 14919
Personnel: 259

WAVERLY—Humphreys County

THREE RIVERS HOSPITAL (441303), 451 Highway 13 South, Zip 37185–2109,
Mailing Address: P.O. Box 437, Zip 37185–0437; tel. 931/296–4203,
(Nonreporting) **A**10 18
Primary Contact: Freda Russell, R.N., Chief Executive Officer and Chief Nursing Officer
CFO: Sandra Patrick, Chief Financial Officer
CMO: George Mathai, M.D., Chief of Staff
CIO: Joe Hildreth, Director Information Technology
CHR: Linda Rawlings, Director Human Resources and Personnel
CNO: Freda Russell, R.N., Chief Executive Officer and Chief Nursing Officer
Web address: www.threerivershospital.org
Control: Other not–for–profit (including NFP Corporation) **Service:** General medical and surgical

Staffed Beds: 25

TN

Many Facility Codes have changed. Please refer to the AHA Guide Code Chart. © 2018 AHA Guide

WAYNESBORO—Wayne County

✠ **WAYNE MEDICAL CENTER (440010)**, 103 J V Mangubat Drive,
Zip 38485–2440, Mailing Address: P.O. Box 580, Zip 38485–0580;
tel. 931/722–5411, **A**1 10 20 **F**7 15 29 34 35 40 45 57 59 68 75 77 81 82
85 86 93 102 107 110 111 114 119 129 130 133 135 149 **S** Maury Regional
Health System, Columbia, TN
Primary Contact: Tyler Taylor, Chief Executive Officer
CMO: Harish Veeramachaneni, M.D., Chief of Staff
CHR: Jeff M Pierce, Manager Human Resources
Web address: www.mauryregional.com
Control: County, Government, nonfederal **Service**: General medical and surgical

Staffed Beds: 25 **Admissions:** 369 **Census:** 4 **Outpatient Visits:** 28806 **Births:** 0 **Total Expense ($000):** 12275 **Payroll Expense ($000):** 5701 **Personnel:** 148

WINCHESTER—Franklin County

✠ **SOUTHERN TENNESSEE REGIONAL HEALTH SYSTEM–WINCHESTER**
(440058), 185 Hospital Road, Zip 37398–2404; tel. 931/967–8200, (Includes
SOUTHERN TENNESSEE REGIONAL HEALTH SYSTEM–SEWANEE, 1260 University
Avenue, Sewanee, TN, Zip 37375–2303; tel. 931/598–5691; William R Spray,
Interim Chief Executive Officer) (Nonreporting) **A**1 10 **S** LifePoint Health,
Brentwood, TN
Primary Contact: William R. Spray, Chief Executive Officer
COO: Clifford Wilson, Chief Operating Officer
CFO: Steve Moore, Chief Financial Officer
CIO: James Payne, Director Information Systems
CHR: Linda Tipps, Director Human Resources
CNO: Jean Ann McMurrey, R.N., MSN, Chief Nursing Officer
Web address: www.southerntennessee.com
Control: Corporation, Investor–owned (for–profit) **Service**: General medical and
surgical

Staffed Beds: 142

WOODBURY—Cannon County

✠ **SAINT THOMAS STONES RIVER HOSPITAL (440200)**, 324 Doolittle Road,
Zip 37190–1139; tel. 615/563–4001, (Nonreporting) **A**1 10 **S** Ascension
Healthcare, Saint Louis, MO
Primary Contact: Brian Gill, Chief Administrative Officer
CFO: Alan Sharp, Chief Financial Officer
CMO: James Spurlock, D.O., Chief of Staff
CNO: Emily Elrod, R.N., Director of Nursing
Web address: www.stonesriverhospital.com
Control: Church operated, Nongovernment, not–for–profit **Service**: General
medical and surgical

Staffed Beds: 60

Hospital, Medicare Provider Number, Address, Telephone, Approval, Facility, and Physician Codes, Health Care System

★ American Hospital Association (AHA) membership
□ The Joint Commission accreditation
○ Healthcare Facilities Accreditation Program
◇ DNV Healthcare Inc. accreditation
⇑ Center for Improvement in Healthcare Quality Accreditation
△ Commission on Accreditation of Rehabilitation Facilities (CARF) accreditation

TEXAS

TX

ABILENE—Taylor County

✠ **ABILENE REGIONAL MEDICAL CENTER (450558)**, 6250 US Highway 83, Zip 79606–5299; tel. 325/428–1000, (Total facility includes 25 beds in nursing home–type unit) **A**1 10 **F**8 11 13 15 17 18 20 22 24 26 28 29 30 31 34 35 40 41 43 45 46 49 50 53 56 57 59 64 68 70 72 75 76 77 78 79 81 85 86 87 89 91 93 107 108 110 111 114 115 118 119 126 128 130 132 135 146 147 148 149 154 **S** Community Health Systems, Inc., Franklin, TN
Primary Contact: Michael D. Murphy, FACHE, Chief Executive Officer
COO: Matthew van Leeuwe, Chief Operating Officer
CFO: Ron Bennett, Chief Financial Officer
CMO: Tim Bumann, D.O., Chief of Staff
CIO: Dennis Newquist, Director Information Systems
CHR: John J Jeziorske, Director Human Resources
CNO: Jessica Kiehle, R.N., Chief Nursing Officer
Web address: www.abileneregional.com
Control: Partnership, Investor–owned (for–profit) **Service:** General medical and surgical

Staffed Beds: 205 **Admissions:** 6199 **Census:** 71 **Outpatient Visits:** 79502 **Births:** 1276 **Total Expense ($000):** 106809 **Payroll Expense ($000):** 36052 **Personnel:** 595

★ **CONTINUECARE HOSPITAL AT HENDRICK MEDICAL CENTER (452029)**, 1900 Pine Street, Zip 79601–2432; tel. 325/670–6251, **A**10 **F**1 3 29 34 35 68 85 87 148 149 **S** Community Hospital Corporation, Plano, TX
Primary Contact: Billy Blasingame, Chief Executive Officer
CFO: Lisa Young, CPA, Chief Financial Officer
CHR: Trisha Kane, Director Human Resources
CNO: Sherry Hendricksen, R.N., MSN, Chief Nursing Officer
Web address: www.continuecare.org/hendrick/
Control: Other not–for–profit (including NFP Corporation) **Service:** Acute long–term care hospital

Staffed Beds: 23 **Admissions:** 172 **Census:** 10 **Outpatient Visits:** 0 **Births:** 0 **Total Expense ($000):** 5954 **Payroll Expense ($000):** 2957 **Personnel:** 37

✠ **ENCOMPASS HEALTH REHABILITATION HOSPITAL OF ABILENE (673039)**, 6401 Directors Parkway, Zip 79606–5869; tel. 325/691–1600, **A**1 10 **F**3 29 57 59 74 75 77 90 96 130 143 148 **S** Encompass Health Corporation, Birmingham, AL
Primary Contact: Joe Roberson, Chief Executive Officer
Web address: www.reliantabilene.com
Control: Corporation, Investor–owned (for–profit) **Service:** Rehabilitation

Staffed Beds: 60 **Admissions:** 842 **Census:** 28 **Outpatient Visits:** 0 **Births:** 0 **Total Expense ($000):** 14191 **Payroll Expense ($000):** 6646 **Personnel:** 132

✠ **HENDRICK HEALTH SYSTEM (450229)**, 1900 Pine Street, Zip 79601–2432; tel. 325/670–2000, (Total facility includes 20 beds in nursing home–type unit) **A**1 10 **F**3 11 12 13 14 15 17 18 20 22 24 26 28 29 30 31 32 34 35 36 39 40 43 44 45 48 49 50 51 53 54 56 57 59 60 61 62 64 68 70 72 73 74 75 76 77 78 79 80 81 84 85 86 87 88 89 90 92 93 96 97 102 107 108 110 111 114 115 118 119 121 123 128 129 130 131 132 135 143 146 147 148 149 **P**6 8
Primary Contact: Tim Lancaster, FACHE, President and Chief Executive Officer
CFO: Jeremy Tyler Walker, Vice President and Chief Financial Officer
CIO: Duane Donaway, Director Information Technology
CHR: Susan Wade, Vice President
CNO: Susie Cassle, R.N., MSN, Vice President Nursing Services
Web address: www.ehendrick.org
Control: Church operated, Nongovernment, not–for–profit **Service:** General medical and surgical

Staffed Beds: 407 **Admissions:** 16917 **Census:** 243 **Outpatient Visits:** 308418 **Births:** 1393 **Total Expense ($000):** 365573 **Payroll Expense ($000):** 127269 **Personnel:** 2794

✠ **OCEANS BEHAVIORAL HOSPITAL ABILENE (454122)**, 4225 Woods Place, Zip 79602–7991; tel. 325/691–0030, **A**1 10 **F**29 34 35 98 99 100 101 103 104 130 132 149 153 154 **P**6 **S** Oceans Healthcare, Lake Charles, LA
Primary Contact: Stacy Sanford, Chief Executive Officer
Web address: www.oceansabilene.com
Control: Corporation, Investor–owned (for–profit) **Service:** Psychiatric

Staffed Beds: 90 **Admissions:** 2242 **Census:** 63 **Outpatient Visits:** 22928 **Births:** 0 **Total Expense ($000):** 13919 **Payroll Expense ($000):** 7075 **Personnel:** 268

ADDISON—Dallas County

⇑ **METHODIST HOSPITAL FOR SURGERY (670073)**, 17101 North Dallas Parkway, Zip 75001–7103; tel. 469/248–3900, **A**10 21 **F**3 29 30 35 40 64 68 70 75 81 85 93 107 111 119 129 146 148
Primary Contact: Lynn Warren, Interim Chief Executive Officer, Group Vice President NueHealth
CFO: Kelly Hayes, Chief Financial Officer
CMO: Robert Fischer, M.D., Medical Director
CHR: Erik Leopard, Manager Human Resource
CNO: Patti Griffith, R.N., MS, Chief Nursing Officer
Web address: www.methodisthospitalforsurgery.com/
Control: Partnership, Investor–owned (for–profit) **Service:** Surgical

Staffed Beds: 32 **Admissions:** 2585 **Census:** 19 **Outpatient Visits:** 21202 **Births:** 1 **Total Expense ($000):** 124710 **Payroll Expense ($000):** 16836 **Personnel:** 207

ALICE—Jim Wells County

✠ **CHRISTUS SPOHN HOSPITAL ALICE (450828)**, 2500 East Main Street, Zip 78332–4169; tel. 361/661–8000, **A**1 10 20 **F**3 13 18 20 24 26 28 29 30 40 43 70 76 81 93 98 107 111 115 119 127 146 147 148 **P**8 **S** CHRISTUS Health, Irving, TX
Primary Contact: Thomas McKinney, President
CFO: Michael Guajardo, Director Finance
CMO: Jerry Liles, D.O.
CHR: Mindy Soliz, Director Human Resources
CNO: Margot Rios, R.N., Chief Nursing Officer
Web address: www.christusspohn.org/locations_alice.htm
Control: Church operated, Nongovernment, not–for–profit **Service:** General medical and surgical

Staffed Beds: 74 **Admissions:** 2734 **Census:** 28 **Outpatient Visits:** 52327 **Births:** 323 **Total Expense ($000):** 46449 **Payroll Expense ($000):** 15013 **Personnel:** 215

ALLEN—Collin County

✠ **POST ACUTE/WARM SPRINGS REHABILITATION HOSPITAL OF ALLEN (673025)**, 1001 Raintree Circle, Zip 75013–4912; tel. 972/908–2015, **A**1 10 **F**3 29 30 34 40 56 59 60 74 75 79 87 90 91 94 96 100 130 132 148 **S** Post Acute Medical, LLC, Enola, PA
Primary Contact: Bill Kaupas, Chief Executive Officer
Web address: www.warmsprings.org
Control: Partnership, Investor–owned (for–profit) **Service:** Rehabilitation

Staffed Beds: 39 **Admissions:** 939 **Census:** 30 **Outpatient Visits:** 0 **Births:** 0 **Total Expense ($000):** 14485 **Payroll Expense ($000):** 7025 **Personnel:** 159

✠ **TEXAS HEALTH PRESBYTERIAN HOSPITAL ALLEN (450840)**, 1105 Central Expressway North, Suite 140, Zip 75013–6103; tel. 972/747–1000, **A**1 10 **F**3 13 15 18 20 22 28 29 30 34 35 38 40 43 44 45 47 49 51 55 57 59 64 65 70 72 73 74 75 76 78 79 81 85 89 90 91 93 98 102 104 105 107 108 110 111 115 118 119 126 130 132 135 146 147 148 149 153 154 **S** Texas Health Resources, Arlington, TX
Primary Contact: Jared Shelton, Chief Executive Officer
COO: Crispin P Hocate, Professional and Support Services Officer
CFO: Lisa Gildon, Group Financial Officer
CMO: Bob Schwab, M.D., Chief Medical Officer
CHR: Sharon Chisholm, Entity Human Resource Officer
Web address: www.texashealth.org
Control: Other not–for–profit (including NFP Corporation) **Service:** General medical and surgical

Staffed Beds: 68 **Admissions:** 3824 **Census:** 34 **Outpatient Visits:** 42813 **Births:** 757 **Total Expense ($000):** 88268 **Payroll Expense ($000):** 32142 **Personnel:** 340

ALPINE—Brewster County

✠ **BIG BEND REGIONAL MEDICAL CENTER (451378)**, 2600 Highway 118 North, Zip 79830–2002; tel. 432/837–3447, **A**1 3 10 18 **F**3 13 29 30 34 35 40 43 45 49 57 59 64 68 70 75 77 81 85 93 107 119 132 133 146 147 148 **P**6 **S** Quorum Health, Brentwood, TN
Primary Contact: Rick Flores, Interim Chief Executive Officer
CNO: Keith Ellison, Chief Nursing Officer
Web address: www.bigbendhealthcare.com
Control: Corporation, Investor–owned (for–profit) **Service:** General medical and surgical

Staffed Beds: 25 **Admissions:** 818 **Census:** 7 **Outpatient Visits:** 15489 **Births:** 193 **Total Expense ($000):** 16777 **Payroll Expense ($000):** 7200 **Personnel:** 130

Many Facility Codes have changed. Please refer to the AHA Guide Code Chart. © 2018 AHA Guide

ALVIN—Brazoria County

ALVIN DIAGNOSTIC AND URGENT CARE CENTER See Clear Lake Regional Medical Center, Webster

AMARILLO—Potter County

☒ **AMARILLO VETERANS AFFAIRS HEALTH CARE SYSTEM**, 6010 West Amarillo Boulevard, Zip 79106–1992; tel. 806/355–9703, (Nonreporting) **A**1 2 3 5 **S** Department of Veterans Affairs, Perry Point, MD
Primary Contact: Elizabeth Lowery, Interim Director
CIO: Modesto Baca, Chief Information Officer
CHR: Ken Creamer, Chief Human Resource
Web address: www.amarillo.va.gov/
Control: Veterans Affairs, Government, federal **Service:** General medical and surgical

Staffed Beds: 55

★ ⇑ **BSA HOSPITAL, LLC (450231)**, 1600 Wallace Boulevard, Zip 79106–1799; tel. 806/212–2000, **A**2 3 5 10 21 **F**3 7 8 11 12 13 15 17 18 20 22 24 26 28 29 30 31 34 35 40 45 46 48 49 53 54 56 57 58 59 64 70 71 72 74 75 76 77 78 79 81 82 84 85 86 87 88 89 90 91 92 93 96 107 108 109 110 111 114 115 116 117 118 119 121 123 124 126 129 130 135 143 145 146 147 148 **S** Ardent Health Services, Nashville, TN
Primary Contact: Bob Williams, President and Chief Executive Officer
COO: Michael Cruz, Senior Vice President Operations
CFO: Lorenzo Olivarez, Senior Vice President and Chief Financial Officer
CMO: Mike Lamanteer, M.D., Senior Vice President Medical Affairs
CIO: Lewis Brown, Director Information Technology
CHR: Cheryl L Jones, Vice President Human Resources and Organizational Development
CNO: Belinda D Gibson, R.N., Senior Vice President Patient Services
Web address: www.bsahs.org
Control: Corporation, Investor–owned (for–profit) **Service:** General medical and surgical

Staffed Beds: 355 **Admissions:** 20236 **Census:** 241 **Outpatient Visits:** 164831 **Births:** 1994 **Total Expense ($000):** 325845 **Payroll Expense ($000):** 128190 **Personnel:** 2147

KINDRED HOSPITAL–AMARILLO See Vibra Hospital of Amarillo

KINDRED REHABILITATION HOSPITAL AMARILLO See Vibra Rehabilitation Hospital of Amarillo

☐ **NORTHWEST TEXAS HEALTHCARE SYSTEM (450209)**, 1501 South Coulter Avenue, Zip 79106–1770, Mailing Address: P.O. Box 1110, Zip 79105–1110; tel. 806/354–1000, (Includes NORTHWEST CHILDREN'S HOSPITAL, 1501 South Coulter Street, Amarillo, TX, Zip 79106–1770; tel. 806/354–1000; NORTHWEST PAVILION, 7201 Evans, Amarillo, TX, Zip 79106, Mailing Address: P.O. Box 1110, Zip 79105–1110, tel. 806/354–1000; NORTHWEST TEXAS SURGERY CENTER, 3501 South Soncy Road Suite 118, Amarillo, TX, Zip 79119–6405; tel. 806/359–7999; Ryan Chandler, Chief Executive Officer) **A**1 2 3 5 10 **F**3 4 5 8 11 12 13 15 17 18 20 22 24 26 28 29 30 31 32 34 35 37 38 39 40 43 44 45 46 48 49 50 54 56 57 59 60 61 64 65 66 68 70 72 74 75 76 77 78 79 80 81 82 84 85 86 87 88 89 90 92 93 94 96 97 98 99 100 101 102 103 104 105 107 108 110 111 115 118 119 126 130 132 135 144 146 147 148 152 153 154 **S** Universal Health Services, Inc., King of Prussia, PA
Primary Contact: Ryan Chandler, Chief Executive Officer
COO: John McDonald, Chief Operating Officer
CFO: Gene Winters, Chief Financial Officer
CMO: Brian Weis, M.D., Chief Medical Officer
CIO: Bach Nguyen, Director Information Systems
CHR: Samuel Lynn, Director Human Resources
Web address: www.nwtexashealthcare.com
Control: Corporation, Investor–owned (for–profit) **Service:** General medical and surgical

Staffed Beds: 424 **Admissions:** 17864 **Census:** 227 **Outpatient Visits:** 219427 **Births:** 2315 **Total Expense ($000):** 285186 **Payroll Expense ($000):** 95035 **Personnel:** 1617

★ **PHYSICIANS SURGICAL HOSPITAL – QUAIL CREEK (450875)**, 6819 Plum Creek, Zip 79124–1602; tel. 806/354–6100, (Includes PHYSICIANS SURGICAL HOSPITAL – PANHANDLE CAMPUS, 7100 West 9th Avenue, Amarillo, TX, Zip 79106–1704; tel. 806/212–0247; Todd Greene, Chief Executive Officer) **A**10 **F**3 29 30 40 44 68 75 79 81 82 85 130 135 **S** Ardent Health Services, Nashville, TN
Primary Contact: Todd Greene, Chief Executive Officer
CFO: Austin Jones, CPA, Chief Financial Officer
CMO: Robert Crabtree, M.D., Chief of Staff and Medical Director
CNO: Debbie Inman, Chief Nursing Officer
Web address: www.physurg.com
Control: Partnership, Investor–owned (for–profit) **Service:** Surgical

Staffed Beds: 41 **Admissions:** 2100 **Census:** 12 **Outpatient Visits:** 11807 **Births:** 0 **Total Expense ($000):** 49771 **Payroll Expense ($000):** 12469 **Personnel:** 191

☒ **VIBRA HOSPITAL OF AMARILLO (452060)**, 7501 Wallace Boulevard, Zip 79124–2150; tel. 806/467–7000, (Nonreporting) **A**1 10 **S** Vibra Healthcare, Mechanicsburg, PA
Primary Contact: Becky Burton, R.N., Chief Executive Officer and Market Chief Executive Officer
CFO: Carlene Wright, Chief Financial Officer
CMO: Pablo Rodrigues, M.D., Medical Director
CNO: Melany McCarty, R.N., Chief Clinical Officer
Web address: www.vhamarillo.com
Control: Corporation, Investor–owned (for–profit) **Service:** Acute long–term care hospital

Staffed Beds: 72

☒ △ **VIBRA REHABILITATION HOSPITAL OF AMARILLO (453096)**, 7200 West 9th Avenue, Zip 79106–1703; tel. 806/468–2900, **A**1 7 10 **F**3 28 29 34 56 57 75 77 79 82 87 90 91 96 130 132 143 148 154 **S** Vibra Healthcare, Mechanicsburg, PA
Primary Contact: Tammie Tabor, Chief Executive Officer
Web address: www.vrhamarillo.com
Control: Corporation, Investor–owned (for–profit) **Service:** Rehabilitation

Staffed Beds: 44 **Admissions:** 663 **Census:** 21 **Outpatient Visits:** 0 **Births:** 0 **Total Expense ($000):** 8307 **Payroll Expense ($000):** 5736 **Personnel:** 124

ANAHUAC—Chambers County

★ **BAYSIDE COMMUNITY HOSPITAL (451320)**, 200 Hospital Drive, Zip 77514, Mailing Address: P.O. Box 398, Zip 77514–0398; tel. 409/267–3143, **A**10 18 **F**3 11 29 34 35 40 41 43 45 50 53 54 56 57 59 64 81 86 107 111 114 119 130 133 **P**3
Primary Contact: Steven Gularte, Chief Executive Officer
CFO: Peggy Hamilton, Chief Financial Officer
CMO: Anthony Capili, M.D., Chief of Staff
CNO: Christi Morris, Director of Nursing
Web address: www.chambershealth.org/html/bayside_hospital.html
Control: Hospital district or authority, Government, nonfederal **Service:** General medical and surgical

Staffed Beds: 10 **Admissions:** 126 **Census:** 1 **Outpatient Visits:** 15537 **Births:** 0 **Total Expense ($000):** 21728 **Payroll Expense ($000):** 6303 **Personnel:** 102

ANDREWS—Andrews County

★ ⇑ **PERMIAN REGIONAL MEDICAL CENTER (450144)**, Northeast By–Pass, Zip 79714, Mailing Address: P.O. Box 2108, Zip 79714–2108; tel. 432/523–2200, **A**3 10 20 21 **F**3 11 13 15 29 34 35 36 38 40 43 44 50 53 56 57 59 62 63 64 65 68 70 75 76 77 81 82 84 85 86 87 93 97 107 108 110 111 115 119 127 129 130 131 132 133 135 145 146 148 **P**6
Primary Contact: Russell Tippin, Chief Executive Officer and Administrator
CFO: Sandra Cox, Controller
CIO: Dan Smart, Chief Information Management Officer
CHR: Pam McCormick, Director Human Resources
Web address: www.permianregional.com
Control: Hospital district or authority, Government, nonfederal **Service:** General medical and surgical

Staffed Beds: 34 **Admissions:** 860 **Census:** 5 **Outpatient Visits:** 27985 **Births:** 310 **Total Expense ($000):** 50703 **Payroll Expense ($000):** 21636 **Personnel:** 248

TX

ANSON—Jones County

★ **ANSON GENERAL HOSPITAL (450078)**, 101 Avenue 'J', Zip 79501–2198; tel. 325/823–3231, **A**10 **F**7 11 29 40 75 77 81 93 107 127 133 **P**8
Primary Contact: Terry L. Amstutz, FACHE, Chief Executive Officer
CIO: Lynna B Cox, Director Health Information Services
Control: Hospital district or authority, Government, nonfederal **Service**: General medical and surgical

Staffed Beds: 13 **Admissions**: 319 **Census**: 6 **Outpatient Visits**: 9100
Births: 0 **Total Expense ($000)**: 5714 **Payroll Expense ($000)**: 2946
Personnel: 54

ARLINGTON—Tarrant County

☐ **BAYLOR ORTHOPEDIC AND SPINE HOSPITAL AT ARLINGTON (670067)**, 707 Highlander Boulevard, Zip 76015–4319; tel. 817/583–7100, **A**1 10 **F**3 29 40 75 79 81 82 107 111 114 119
Primary Contact: Allan Beck, Chief Executive Officer
Web address: www.baylorarlington.com/
Control: Partnership, Investor–owned (for–profit) **Service**: Orthopedic

Staffed Beds: 20 **Admissions**: 1677 **Census**: 9 **Outpatient Visits**: 12178
Births: 0 **Total Expense ($000)**: 61084 **Payroll Expense ($000)**: 10594
Personnel: 145

⊞ **ENCOMPASS HEALTH REHABILITATION HOSPITAL OF ARLINGTON (453040)**, 3200 Matlock Road, Zip 76015–2911; tel. 817/468–4000, **A**1 10 **F**3 29 74 75 77 79 90 91 95 96 130 148 154 **S** Encompass Health Corporation, Birmingham, AL
Primary Contact: Tyrrell Taplin, Chief Executive Officer
CFO: Kathy Dickerson, Chief Financial Officer
CMO: Todd Daniels, M.D., Medical Director
CHR: Nancy Rosiles, Director Human Resources
CNO: David Jones, Chief Nursing Officer
Web address: www.healthsoutharlington.com
Control: Corporation, Investor–owned (for–profit) **Service**: Rehabilitation

Staffed Beds: 85 **Admissions**: 1597 **Census**: 52 **Outpatient Visits**: 0
Births: 0 **Total Expense ($000)**: 25264 **Payroll Expense ($000)**: 11475
Personnel: 146

⊞ **KINDRED HOSPITAL TARRANT COUNTY–ARLINGTON (452028)**, 1000 North Cooper Street, Zip 76011–5540; tel. 817/548–3400, **A**1 10 **F**1 3 29 30 40 56 57 77 80 82 93 130 148 **S** Kindred Healthcare, Louisville, KY
Primary Contact: Christina Richard, Market Chief Executive Officer
CFO: Jennifer Penland, Controller
CMO: Bernard A McGowen, M.D., Medical Director
Web address: www.kindredhospitalarl.com/
Control: Corporation, Investor–owned (for–profit) **Service**: Acute long–term care hospital

Staffed Beds: 55 **Admissions**: 440 **Census**: 32 **Outpatient Visits**: 1929
Births: 0 **Total Expense ($000)**: 15571 **Payroll Expense ($000)**: 7784
Personnel: 123

⊞ **MEDICAL CITY ARLINGTON (450675)**, 3301 Matlock Road, Zip 76015–2908; tel. 817/465–3241, **A**1 2 3 10 **F**3 11 12 13 17 18 20 22 24 26 28 29 31 34 35 39 40 41 43 45 47 49 50 57 59 64 70 72 73 74 75 76 78 79 81 82 85 86 87 90 93 96 107 108 111 114 115 118 119 126 130 131 132 135 146 147 148 149 **S** HCA Healthcare, Nashville, TN
Primary Contact: Keith Zimmerman, Chief Executive Officer
COO: Ben Coogan, Chief Operating Officer
CFO: Jeff Ardemagni, Chief Financial Officer
CMO: Eric Benink, M.D., Chief Medical Officer
CIO: Craig Santangelo, Director Information Services
CNO: Cathy McLaughlin, R.N., MSN, Chief Nursing Officer
Web address: www.medicalcenterarlington.com
Control: Partnership, Investor–owned (for–profit) **Service**: General medical and surgical

Staffed Beds: 309 **Admissions**: 16912 **Census**: 229 **Outpatient Visits**: 139054 **Births**: 4205 **Total Expense ($000)**: 221495 **Payroll Expense ($000)**: 93390 **Personnel**: 1215

☐ **MILLWOOD HOSPITAL (454012)**, 1011 North Cooper Street, Zip 76011–5517; tel. 817/261–3121, **A**1 10 **F**4 5 29 30 35 54 56 71 75 87 98 99 100 101 102 103 104 105 130 132 135 143 148 152 153 154 **S** Universal Health Services, Inc., King of Prussia, PA
Primary Contact: Dwight A. Lacy, Chief Executive Officer
CFO: Jeff Epperson, Chief Financial Officer
CMO: Robert Bennett, M.D., Medical Director
CIO: William Jackson, Director Medical Records
CHR: Betty Nuru, Director Human Resources
Web address: www.millwoodhospital.com
Control: Partnership, Investor–owned (for–profit) **Service**: Psychiatric

Staffed Beds: 128 **Admissions**: 4046 **Census**: 107 **Outpatient Visits**: 24755 **Births**: 0 **Total Expense ($000)**: 29852 **Payroll Expense ($000)**: 14151 **Personnel**: 286

☐ **SUNDANCE HOSPITAL ARLINGTON (454113)**, 7000 US Highway 287 South, Zip 76001; tel. 817/583–8080, (Includes SUNDANCE HOSPITAL DALLAS, 2696 West Walnut Street, Garland, TX, Zip 75042–6441; tel. 469/440–5566; Scott Blakeley, Chief Executive Officer) **A**1 10 **F**4 5 40 56 98 99 101 102 103 104 105 106 151 152 153 154
Primary Contact: Scott Blakeley, Chief Executive Officer
Web address: www.sunbhc.com/
Control: Corporation, Investor–owned (for–profit) **Service**: Psychiatric

Staffed Beds: 232 **Admissions**: 6840 **Census**: 139 **Outpatient Visits**: 4403
Births: 0 **Total Expense ($000)**: 27469 **Payroll Expense ($000)**: 16961
Personnel: 852

⊞ **TEXAS HEALTH ARLINGTON MEMORIAL HOSPITAL (450064)**, 800 West Randol Mill Road, Zip 76012–2503; tel. 817/548–6100, **A**1 2 10 **F**3 11 12 13 15 18 26 28 29 30 31 34 35 37 40 43 45 46 47 48 49 51 53 54 57 59 60 63 64 65 66 68 70 72 74 75 76 77 78 79 80 81 82 85 86 87 93 98 100 101 102 103 104 105 106 107 108 110 111 114 115 118 119 120 123 124 126 130 131 132 135 145 146 147 148 149 153 **S** Texas Health Resources, Arlington, TX
Primary Contact: Blake Kretz, FACHE, President
CMO: Robert N Cluck, M.D., Vice President and Medical Director
CHR: Yvonne Kyler, Director Human Resources
Web address: www.arlingtonmemorial.org
Control: Other not–for–profit (including NFP Corporation) **Service**: General medical and surgical

Staffed Beds: 269 **Admissions**: 13100 **Census**: 188 **Outpatient Visits**: 109642 **Births**: 1925 **Total Expense ($000)**: 285122 **Payroll Expense ($000)**: 109269 **Personnel**: 1432

☐ **TEXAS HEALTH HEART & VASCULAR HOSPITAL ARLINGTON (670071)**, 811 Wright Street, Zip 76012–4708; tel. 817/960–3500, **A**1 10 **F**3 17 18 20 22 24 26 29 30 34 60 64 65 68 81 85
Primary Contact: William Nesbitt, M.D., President
COO: Sherri Leigh Emerson, Chief Operating Officer
CFO: Kay Mason, Chief Financial Officer
CMO: Baron L Hamman, M.D., Chief Medical Officer
CHR: Yvonne Kyler, Director Human Resources
Web address: www.texashealthheartandvascular.org/
Control: Partnership, Investor–owned (for–profit) **Service**: Heart

Staffed Beds: 32 **Admissions**: 1100 **Census**: 15 **Outpatient Visits**: 2796
Births: 0 **Total Expense ($000)**: 43209 **Payroll Expense ($000)**: 9321
Personnel: 126

TEXAS REHABILITATION HOSPITAL OF ARLINGTON (673060), 900 W Arbrook Blvd, Zip 76015; tel. 682/304–6000, (Nonreporting)
Primary Contact: Teresa Huffman, Chief Executive Officer
CFO: Debbie Horn, Controller
CMO: Camelia Mitchell, M.D., Medical Director
CHR: Stanley Coleman, Director Human Resources
Web address: www.texasrehabarlington.com
Control: Partnership, Investor–owned (for–profit) **Service**: Rehabilitation

Staffed Beds: 40

⊞ **USMD HOSPITAL AT ARLINGTON (450872)**, 801 West Interstate 20, Zip 76017–5851; tel. 817/472–3400, **A**1 10 **F**3 12 29 34 35 36 39 40 45 46 49 50 51 57 59 64 70 74 75 78 79 81 82 85 87 107 108 111 114 115 119 124 126 132 **S** USMD Health System, Irving, TX
Primary Contact: Marcia Crim, R.N., MSN, Chief Executive Officer
CFO: Tonya Smith, Chief Financial Officer
CMO: M. Patrick Collini, M.D., President Medical Staff
CIO: Bob Rick, Vice President Information Technology
CHR: Bernardo Valle, Vice President Human Resources
CNO: Marcia Crim, R.N., MSN, Chief Nursing Officer and Chief Executive Officer
Web address: www.usmdarlington.com
Control: Partnership, Investor–owned (for–profit) **Service**: General medical and surgical

Staffed Beds: 34 **Admissions**: 1600 **Census**: 14 **Outpatient Visits**: 26696
Births: 0 **Total Expense ($000)**: 76443 **Payroll Expense ($000)**: 18609
Personnel: 318

ASPERMONT—Stonewall County

STONEWALL MEMORIAL HOSPITAL (451318), 821 North Broadway, Zip 79502–2029, Mailing Address: P.O. Box 'C', Zip 79502–0902; tel. 940/989–3551, **A**10 18 **F**3 29 34 35 40 41 56 57 59 64 93 97 103 107 114 119 127 128 133 148 **P**5
Primary Contact: Andy Kolb, Chief Executive Officer
COO: Billie Carter, Chief Operating Officer and Assistant Administrator
CFO: Andy Kolb, Chief Executive Officer
CMO: Frederic K Passmann, M.D., Chief of Staff
CIO: Billie Carter, Chief Operating Officer and Assistant Administrator
CHR: Andy Kolb, Chief Executive Officer
CNO: Jan Harris, R.N., Director of Nursing
Web address: www.smhdhealth.org/
Control: Hospital district or authority, Government, nonfederal **Service**: General medical and surgical

Staffed Beds: 12 **Admissions**: 82 **Census**: 2 **Outpatient Visits**: 4174
Births: 0 **Total Expense ($000)**: 10180 **Payroll Expense ($000)**: 4659
Personnel: 54

TX

Many Facility Codes have changed. Please refer to the AHA Guide Code Chart.

© 2018 AHA Guide

ATHENS—Henderson County

☒ **UT HEALTH ATHENS (450389)**, 2000 South Palestine Street, Zip 75751–5610; tel. 903/676–1000, **A**1 10 **F**3 11 13 15 18 20 29 34 40 43 45 49 50 70 74 76 78 79 81 85 89 107 108 110 111 114 115 118 119 127 130 132 146 **S** Ardent Health Services, Nashville, TN
Primary Contact: Jack A. Endres, FACHE, JD, Administrator
CFO: David A Travis, Chief Financial Officer
CHR: Jennifer Rummel, Director Human Resources
CNO: Kevin M Jablonski, Chief Nursing Officer
Web address: www.https://uthealthathens.com/
Control: Other not–for–profit (including NFP Corporation) **Service**: General medical and surgical

Staffed Beds: 127 **Admissions**: 4921 **Census**: 48 **Outpatient Visits**: 90288
Births: 931 **Total Expense ($000)**: 80363 **Payroll Expense ($000)**: 26073
Personnel: 436

AUBREY—Denton County

★ ⇧ **BAYLOR EMERGENCY MEDICAL CENTER AT AUBREY (670062)**, 26791 Highway 380, Zip 76227; tel. 972/347–2525, (Includes BAYLOR EMERGENCY MEDICAL CENTER MURPHY, 511 FM 544, Suite 100, Plano, TX, Zip 75094; tel. 214/294–6150; Kyle Kirkpatrick, Chief Executive Officer; BAYLOR EMERGENCY MEDICAL CENTERS – COLLEYVILLE, 5500 Colleyville Boulevard, Colleyville, TX, Zip 76034–5835; tel. 214/294–6350; Kyle Kirkpatrick, Chief Executive Officer; BAYLOR EMERGENCY MEDICAL CENTERS – KELLER, 620 S Main Street, Suite 100, Keller, TX, Zip 76248–4960; tel. 214/294–6100; Kyle Kirkpatrick, Chief Executive Officer) **A**10 21 **F**3 29 40 75 87 107 119 149 **P**5 **S** Emerus, The Woodlands, TX
Primary Contact: Kyle Kirkpatrick, Chief Executive Officer
CMO: Amynah Kara, M.D., Chief Medical Officer
CIO: Trang Dawson, Chief Information Officer
CHR: Larry Guillory, Chief Human Resources Officer
Web address: www.bemcataubrey.com
Control: Corporation, Investor–owned (for–profit) **Service**: General medical and surgical

Staffed Beds: 32 **Admissions**: 340 **Census**: 2 **Outpatient Visits**: 31794
Births: 0 **Total Expense ($000)**: 28652 **Payroll Expense ($000)**: 8333
Personnel: 129

AUSTIN—Travis County

☐ **ARISE AUSTIN MEDICAL CENTER (450871)**, 3003 Bee Caves Road, Zip 78746–5542; tel. 512/314–3800, **A**1 10 **F**29 40 59 64 68 70 75 79 81 82 85 91 107 111 114 119 126 148
Primary Contact: Shawn G. Strash, Chief Executive Officer
CFO: Lawrence Oldham, Chief Financial Officer
CMO: Robert Wills, M.D., Chief Medical Officer
CHR: Marilyn Jennings, Director Human Resources
Web address: www.austinsurgicalhospital.com
Control: Corporation, Investor–owned (for–profit) **Service**: Orthopedic

Staffed Beds: 23 **Admissions**: 909 **Census**: 5 **Outpatient Visits**: 7858
Births: 0 **Total Expense ($000)**: 29964 **Payroll Expense ($000)**: 7668
Personnel: 108

☐ **AUSTIN LAKES HOSPITAL (454069)**, 1025 East 32nd Street, Zip 78705–2714; tel. 512/544–5253, **A**1 5 10 **F**98 103 104 105 130 153 154 **S** Universal Health Services, Inc., King of Prussia, PA
Primary Contact: Robert J. Lerma, MS, Chief Executive Officer
CFO: Greg Wysocki, Chief Financial Officer
CMO: Shiva Lam, M.D., Executive Medical Director
CHR: Dan Smith, Director Human Resources
CNO: Barbara Powers, R.N., Chief Nursing Officer
Web address: www.austinlakeshospital.com
Control: Corporation, Investor–owned (for–profit) **Service**: Psychiatric

Staffed Beds: 58 **Admissions**: 2610 **Census**: 47 **Outpatient Visits**: 6437
Births: 0 **Total Expense ($000)**: 12444 **Payroll Expense ($000)**: 6691
Personnel: 122

☐ **AUSTIN OAKS HOSPITAL (454121)**, 1407 West Stassney Lane, Zip 78745–2947; tel. 512/440–4800, (Nonreporting) **A**1 10 **S** Universal Health Services, Inc., King of Prussia, PA
Primary Contact: Steve Kelly, Interim Chief Executive Officer
Web address: www.austinoakshospital.com
Control: Corporation, Investor–owned (for–profit) **Service**: Psychiatric

Staffed Beds: 80

☐ **AUSTIN STATE HOSPITAL (454084)**, 4110 Guadalupe Street, Zip 78751–4296; tel. 512/452–0381, **A**1 3 5 10 **F**29 30 39 50 56 59 65 68 75 86 98 99 101 103 106 130 132 143 146 **P**1 **S** Texas Department of State Health Services, Austin, TX
Primary Contact: Alan Isaacson, Superintendent
CMO: Ross Taylor, M.D., Clinical Director
CIO: Cindy Reed, Director Community Relations
Web address: www.dshs.state.tx.us/mhhospitals/austinsh/default.shtm
Control: State, Government, nonfederal **Service**: Psychiatric

Staffed Beds: 252 **Admissions**: 913 **Census**: 257 **Outpatient Visits**: 0
Births: 0 **Total Expense ($000)**: 93255 **Payroll Expense ($000)**: 40838
Personnel: 909

☐ **CENTRAL TEXAS REHABILITATION HOSPITAL (673027)**, 700 West 45th Street, Zip 78751–2800; tel. 512/407–2111, **A**1 3 5 10 **F**3 29 59 74 79 90 91 95 96 130 132 148
Primary Contact: A. Jay. Rimovsky, Chief Executive Officer
CFO: Lisa Donnely, Controller II
CMO: Christopher Garrison, M.D., Medical Director
CHR: Trena Robinson, Director, Human Resources
CNO: Lauren Brandt, Chief Clinical Officer
Web address: www.khrehabcentraltexas.com/
Control: Partnership, Investor–owned (for–profit) **Service**: Rehabilitation

Staffed Beds: 50 **Admissions**: 1031 **Census**: 36 **Outpatient Visits**: 0
Births: 0 **Total Expense ($000)**: 14462 **Payroll Expense ($000)**: 7309
Personnel: 101

CORNERSTONE HOSPITAL OF AUSTIN (452034), 4207 Burnet Road, Zip 78756–3396; tel. 512/706–1900, (Includes CORNERSTONE HOSPITAL OF AUSTIN, 1005 East 32nd Street, Austin, TX, Zip 78705; tel. 512/867–5822; Edward J Sherwood, M.D., Chief Executive Officer; CORNERSTONE HOSPITAL OF ROUND ROCK, 4681 College Park Drive, Round Rock, TX, Zip 78665; tel. 512/533–2525; Edward L Dyer, Chief Executive Officer) **A**10 22 **F**1 3 29 30 45 64 70 75 77 87 107 148 **S** Cornerstone Healthcare Group, Dallas, TX
Primary Contact: Curt L. Roberts, Chief Executive Officer
CMO: David F. Pohl, M.D., Chief of Staff
Web address: www.chghospitals.com/austin/
Control: Corporation, Investor–owned (for–profit) **Service**: Acute long–term care hospital

Staffed Beds: 86 **Admissions**: 928 **Census**: 58 **Outpatient Visits**: 2358
Births: 0 **Total Expense ($000)**: 27460 **Payroll Expense ($000)**: 12836
Personnel: 198

CROSS CREEK HOSPITAL (454133), 8402 Cross Park Drive, Zip 78754; tel. 512/215–3900, (Nonreporting) **S** Acadia Healthcare Company, Inc., Franklin, TN
Primary Contact: Coleby Wright, Chief Executive Officer
Web address: www.cornerstonehealthcaregroup.com
Control: Corporation, Investor–owned (for–profit) **Service**: Psychiatric

Staffed Beds: 90

☒ **DELL CHILDREN'S MEDICAL CENTER OF CENTRAL TEXAS (453310)**, 4900 Mueller Boulevard, Zip 78723–3079; tel. 512/324–0000, **A**1 2 3 5 10 **F**3 11 12 21 23 25 27 29 30 31 34 35 39 40 41 43 44 46 49 50 53 54 55 57 58 59 60 64 68 71 72 74 75 78 79 81 82 84 85 86 87 88 89 90 92 93 94 96 99 100 102 104 107 108 111 112 113 114 115 119 129 130 131 132 133 143 146 148 154 **P**3 8 **S** Ascension Healthcare, Saint Louis, MO
Primary Contact: Debra M. Brown, Vice President, Chief Nursing Officer and Chief Operating Officer
CNO: Elizabeth E. Fredeboelling, MSN, R.N., Chief Nursing Officer
Web address: www.dellchildrens.net
Control: Church operated, Nongovernment, not–for–profit **Service**: Children's general medical and surgical

Staffed Beds: 189 **Admissions**: 8822 **Census**: 103 **Outpatient Visits**: 289079 **Births**: 0 **Total Expense ($000)**: 410783 **Payroll Expense ($000)**: 138122 **Personnel**: 2102

TX

☒ **DELL SETON MEDICAL CENTER AT THE UNIVERSITY OF TEXAS**, 1500 Red River Street, Zip 78701; tel. 512/324–7000, (Nonreporting) **A**1 **S** Ascension Healthcare, Saint Louis, MO
Primary Contact: Christann Vasquez, President
COO: Debra T. Hernandez, Vice President, Chief Operation Officer and Chief Nursing Officer
CFO: Scott Herndon, FACHE, Chief Financial Officer, Ministry Market Texas
CMO: Tom Caven, M.D., Vice President, Medical Director
CIO: Michael H. Minks, Chief Information Officer VI
CHR: Joe Canales, Vice President Human Resources, Ministry Market Texas
CNO: Debra T. Hernandez, Vice President, Chief Operating Officer and Chief Nursing Officer
Web address: www.seton.net/locations/dell–seton/
Control: Church operated, Nongovernment, not–for–profit **Service**: General medical and surgical

Staffed Beds: 211

☒ **ENCOMPASS HEALTH REHABILITATION HOSPITAL OF AUSTIN (673054)**, 330 West Ben White Boulevard, Zip 78704; tel. 512/730–4800, (Nonreporting) **A**1 10 **S** Encompass Health Corporation, Birmingham, AL
Primary Contact: Brad Dinsmore, Chief Executive Officer
CFO: Pamela McLaughlin, Chief Financial Officer
CMO: Johnny Shane Ross, Executive Medical Director
Web address: www.healthsouthaustin.com
Control: Corporation, Investor–owned (for–profit) **Service**: Rehabilitation

Staffed Beds: 40

☐ **NORTHWEST HILLS SURGICAL HOSPITAL (450808)**, 6818 Austin Center Boulevard, Suite 100, Zip 78731–3199; tel. 512/346–1994, **A**1 5 10 **F**3 18 40 45 64 74 75 79 81
Primary Contact: Cullen Scott, Chief Executive Officer
CFO: Jenny Salome, Chief Financial Officer and Assistant Administrator
Web address: www.northwesthillssurgical.com
Control: Partnership, Investor–owned (for–profit) **Service**: General medical and surgical

Staffed Beds: 8 Admissions: 507 Census: 2 Outpatient Visits: 6218 Births: 0 Total Expense ($000): 31241 Payroll Expense ($000): 6806 Personnel: 116

☒ ⇑ **SETON MEDICAL CENTER AUSTIN (450056)**, 1201 West 38th Street, Zip 78705–1006; tel. 512/324–1000, **A**1 2 3 5 10 21 **F**3 11 12 13 15 18 20 22 24 26 28 29 30 31 34 40 43 44 45 46 49 50 51 57 58 59 60 61 64 68 70 72 74 75 76 77 78 79 80 81 82 84 85 86 87 93 107 108 110 111 114 115 118 119 124 126 130 131 132 135 137 145 146 147 148 149 154 **P**3 8 **S** Ascension Healthcare, Saint Louis, MO
Primary Contact: Christann Vasquez, President and Chief Executive Officer
COO: Tad Hatton, Vice President Chief Operating Officer
CFO: Robert Scott Herndon, Vice President Chief Financial Officer
CMO: David W Martin, M.D., Vice President Chief Medical Officer
CIO: Michael H. Minks, Chief Information Officer VI
CHR: Joe Canales, Vice President Human Resources
CNO: Elizabeth Steger, FACHE, R.N., Chief Nursing Officer
Web address: www.seton.net/locations/smc/
Control: Church operated, Nongovernment, not–for–profit **Service**: General medical and surgical

Staffed Beds: 382 Admissions: 19762 Census: 262 Outpatient Visits: 298668 Births: 4805 Total Expense ($000): 465265 Payroll Expense ($000): 109807 Personnel: 1973

☒ **SETON NORTHWEST HOSPITAL (450867)**, 11113 Research Boulevard, Zip 78759–5236; tel. 512/324–6000, **A**1 2 3 5 10 **F**3 11 12 13 15 29 30 34 35 40 41 43 45 47 49 57 59 60 70 72 76 77 79 81 85 87 107 109 110 111 115 119 126 130 146 147 **P**3 8 **S** Ascension Healthcare, Saint Louis, MO
Primary Contact: Katherine Henderson, President and Chief Executive Officer
COO: Margaret E Butler, Vice President Chief Operating Officer, Seton Northwest Hospital
CFO: Scott Herndon, FACHE, Chief Financial Officer, Texas Market
CMO: Jason Martin, M.D., Medical Director
CIO: Michael H. Minks, Chief Information Officer
CHR: Joe Canales, Vice President, Ascension and Human Resources Officer, Texas Market
CNO: Yvonne VanDyke, R.N., MSN, Chief Nursing Officer, Texas Market
Web address: www.seton.net
Control: Church operated, Nongovernment, not–for–profit **Service**: General medical and surgical

Staffed Beds: 117 Admissions: 4559 Census: 40 Outpatient Visits: 45739 Births: 1276 Total Expense ($000): 85503 Payroll Expense ($000): 24612 Personnel: 394

☒ **SETON SHOAL CREEK HOSPITAL (454029)**, 3501 Mills Avenue, Zip 78731–6391; tel. 512/324–2000, **A**1 3 5 10 **F**4 5 29 30 68 98 99 100 101 130 132 135 154 **P**3 8 **S** Ascension Healthcare, Saint Louis, MO
Primary Contact: Christann Vasquez, President and Chief Executive Officer
COO: William Henricks, Ph.D., Vice President and Chief Operating Officer
CFO: Robert Scott Herndon, Chief Financial Officer
CMO: Amy E. Walton, M.D., Chief Medical Officer
CIO: Michael H. Minks, Chief Information Officer
CHR: Joe Canales, Director Human Resources
Web address: www.seton.net
Control: Church operated, Nongovernment, not–for–profit **Service**: Psychiatric

Staffed Beds: 94 Admissions: 3975 Census: 62 Outpatient Visits: 23135 Births: 0 Total Expense ($000): 29359 Payroll Expense ($000): 12961 Personnel: 223

☒ **SETON SOUTHWEST HOSPITAL (450865)**, 7900 F M 1826, Building 1, Zip 78737–1407; tel. 512/324–9000, **A**1 10 **F**11 28 29 30 40 41 45 46 50 57 64 68 79 81 85 87 107 110 111 119 126 130 135 146 **P**3 8 **S** Ascension Healthcare, Saint Louis, MO
Primary Contact: Katherine Henderson, President and Chief Executive Officer
Web address: www.seton.net
Control: Church operated, Nongovernment, not–for–profit **Service**: General medical and surgical

Staffed Beds: 11 Admissions: 503 Census: 4 Outpatient Visits: 26896 Births: 322 Total Expense ($000): 26375 Payroll Expense ($000): 8409 Personnel: 111

☒ ⇑ **ST. DAVID'S MEDICAL CENTER (450431)**, 919 East 32nd Street, Zip 78705–2709, Mailing Address: P.O. Box 4039, Zip 78765–4039; tel. 512/476–7111, (Includes HEART HOSPITAL OF AUSTIN, 3801 North Lamar Boulevard, Austin, TX, Zip 78756–4080; tel. 512/407–7000; David Laird, Chief Executive Officer; ST. DAVID'S GEORGETOWN HOSPITAL, 2000 Scenic Drive, Georgetown, TX, Zip 78626–7726; tel. 512/943–3000; Hugh Brown, Chief Executive Officer; ST. DAVID'S REHABILITATION CENTER, 1005 East 32nd Street, Austin, TX, Zip 78705–2713, Mailing Address: P.O. Box 4270, Zip 78765–4270, tel. 512/544–5100; Diane Owens, Assistant Administrator) **A**1 2 3 5 10 21 **F**3 8 11 12 13 15 17 18 20 22 24 26 28 29 30 31 34 35 36 37 39 40 43 45 46 47 48 49 53 59 60 61 64 70 72 73 74 75 76 77 78 79 81 82 84 85 86 87 90 93 95 96 107 108 110 111 114 115 116 119 126 129 130 131 132 135 146 147 148 149 154 **P**3 6 **S** HCA Healthcare, Nashville, TN
Primary Contact: Donald H. Wilkerson, FACHE, Chief Executive Officer
COO: Esther Chung, Chief Operating Officer
CFO: Daniel Huffine, Chief Financial Officer
CMO: John Marietta, M.D., Chief Medical Officer
CIO: Richard Lear, Director Information Systems
CHR: Julie Hajek, Director Human Resources
Web address: www.stdavids.com
Control: Other not–for–profit (including NFP Corporation) **Service**: General medical and surgical

Staffed Beds: 595 Admissions: 26837 Census: 399 Outpatient Visits: 196245 Births: 5186 Total Expense ($000): 520248 Payroll Expense ($000): 164509 Personnel: 2597

☒ **ST. DAVID'S NORTH AUSTIN MEDICAL CENTER (450809)**, 12221 North MoPac Expressway, Zip 78758–2496; tel. 512/901–1000, **A**1 2 3 5 10 **F**3 12 13 15 18 20 22 24 28 29 30 31 34 35 37 40 41 45 46 47 49 53 54 58 59 64 70 72 73 74 75 76 77 78 79 80 81 85 86 87 88 89 90 92 93 96 107 108 110 111 114 115 118 119 124 126 129 130 132 138 141 145 146 147 148 149 154 **P**3 6 **S** HCA Healthcare, Nashville, TN
Primary Contact: Thomas W. Jackson, Chief Executive Officer
COO: Becky Barnes, Chief Operating Officer
CFO: Natalie Pack, Chief Financial Officer
CMO: Ryan Charbeneau, M.D., Chief Medical Officer
CIO: Marshall Pearson, Director Management Information Systems
CHR: Laura Light, Director Human Resources
Web address: www.northaustin.com
Control: Other not–for–profit (including NFP Corporation) **Service**: General medical and surgical

Staffed Beds: 398 Admissions: 20301 Census: 278 Outpatient Visits: 156793 Births: 6911 Total Expense ($000): 311867 Payroll Expense ($000): 106696 Personnel: 1667

Many Facility Codes have changed. Please refer to the AHA Guide Code Chart. © 2018 AHA Guide

⊠ **ST. DAVID'S SOUTH AUSTIN MEDICAL CENTER (450713)**, 901 West Ben White Boulevard, Zip 78704–6903; tel. 512/447–2211, **A**1 2 3 5 10 **F**3 11 12 13 15 17 18 20 22 24 26 28 29 30 31 34 35 37 40 43 45 46 48 49 54 56 59 64 70 73 74 75 76 77 78 79 80 81 82 84 85 87 93 107 108 110 111 114 115 119 124 126 129 130 132 136 145 146 147 **P**1 3 6 8 **S** HCA Healthcare, Nashville, TN
Primary Contact: Todd E. Steward, FACHE, Chief Executive Officer
CFO: Wesley D Fountain, Chief Financial Officer
CMO: Albert Gros, M.D., Chief Medical Officer
CIO: Richard Lear, Director Information Systems
CHR: Lisa Talbot, Director Human Resources
CNO: Sally A Gillam, R.N., Chief Nursing Officer
Web address: www.southaustinmc.com
Control: Other not–for–profit (including NFP Corporation) **Service:** General medical and surgical

Staffed Beds: 290 **Admissions:** 19176 **Census:** 245 **Outpatient Visits:** 148054 **Births:** 2439 **Total Expense ($000):** 276203 **Payroll Expense ($000):** 91238 **Personnel:** 1423

⊠ **TEXAS NEUROREHAB CENTER (452038)**, 1106 West Dittmar Road, Building 9, Zip 78745–6328, Mailing Address: P.O. Box 150459, Zip 78715–0459; tel. 512/444–4835, **A**1 10 **F**1 3 29 54 74 75 77 79 93 108 130 148 154 **P**5 **S** Universal Health Services, Inc., King of Prussia, PA
Primary Contact: Edgar E. Prettyman, PsyD, Chief Executive Officer
COO: Janet Bitner, Chief Operating Officer
CFO: Omar Correa, Chief Financial Officer
CMO: James Boysen, M.D., Executive Medical Director
CHR: Colleen Lewis, Director Human Resources
Web address: www.texasneurorehab.com
Control: Partnership, Investor–owned (for–profit) **Service:** Acute long–term care hospital

Staffed Beds: 47 **Admissions:** 475 **Census:** 40 **Outpatient Visits:** 5578 **Births:** 0 **Total Expense ($000):** 15434 **Payroll Expense ($000):** 9056 **Personnel:** 311

☐ **TEXAS STAR RECOVERY (454111)**, 1106 West Dittmar Road, Zip 78745–6328; tel. 512/462–6729, (Nonreporting) **A**1 10
Primary Contact: Craig Franke, M.D., Medical Director
Web address: www.texasstarrecovery.com
Control: Partnership, Investor–owned (for–profit) **Service:** Psychiatric

Staffed Beds: 28

THE HOSPITAL AT WESTLAKE MEDICAL CENTER (670006), 5656 Bee Caves Road, Suite M302, Zip 78746–5280; tel. 512/327–0000, **A**10 **F**3 18 20 22 26 29 37 39 40 45 51 53 58 59 64 70 75 77 79 81 82 85 93 96 107 108 111 114 119 130 131 148
Primary Contact: Tammy Smittle, R.N., Chief Executive Officer
CFO: Devon Culbert, Controller
CMO: Tom Burns, M.D., Chief of Staff
CHR: Kellie Bryson, Director Human Resources
Web address: www.westlakemedical.com
Control: Partnership, Investor–owned (for–profit) **Service:** General medical and surgical

Staffed Beds: 23 **Admissions:** 877 **Census:** 5 **Outpatient Visits:** 6842 **Births:** 0 **Total Expense ($000):** 35679 **Payroll Expense ($000):** 8391 **Personnel:** 161

AZLE—Tarrant County

⊠ **TEXAS HEALTH HARRIS METHODIST HOSPITAL AZLE (450419)**, 108 Denver Trail, Zip 76020–3614; tel. 817/444–8600, **A**1 10 **F**3 11 15 18 29 30 34 35 40 43 45 56 57 59 64 70 75 77 79 81 85 93 107 110 114 119 130 135 146 147 148 149 **S** Texas Health Resources, Arlington, TX
Primary Contact: Bob S. Ellzey, FACHE, President
CFO: Brian Blessing, Chief Financial Officer
CMO: Judy Laviolette, M.D., Chief Medical Officer
CIO: Patricia Johnston, Vice President Information Services
CHR: Lance Waring, Director Human Resources
CNO: Valarie Gilbert, R.N., Chief Nursing Officer
Web address: www.texashealth.org/Azle
Control: Other not–for–profit (including NFP Corporation) **Service:** General medical and surgical

Staffed Beds: 31 **Admissions:** 1447 **Census:** 13 **Outpatient Visits:** 31940 **Births:** 0 **Total Expense ($000):** 37499 **Payroll Expense ($000):** 15575 **Personnel:** 202

BALLINGER—Runnels County

★ **BALLINGER MEMORIAL HOSPITAL (451310)**, 608 Avenue 'B', Zip 76821–2499, Mailing Address: P.O. Box 617, Zip 76821–0617; tel. 325/365–2531, **A**10 18 **F**3 7 11 29 34 40 43 53 64 65 68 77 93 107 114 119 127 130 133 154 **P**5
Primary Contact: Rhett D. Fricke, Chief Executive Officer
CFO: Josilyn Peterson, Chief Financial Officer
CHR: Roselyn Hudgens, Director Human Resources
Web address: www.ballingerhospital.org
Control: Hospital district or authority, Government, nonfederal **Service:** General medical and surgical

Staffed Beds: 16 **Admissions:** 84 **Census:** 1 **Outpatient Visits:** 18805 **Births:** 0 **Total Expense ($000):** 9873 **Payroll Expense ($000):** 4287 **Personnel:** 87

BAY CITY—Matagorda County

⊠ **MATAGORDA REGIONAL MEDICAL CENTER (450465)**, 104 7th Street, Zip 77414–4853; tel. 979/245–6383, (Data for 360 days) **A**1 10 20 **F**3 11 13 15 18 20 22 28 29 30 32 34 38 39 40 43 45 46 47 50 51 53 56 57 59 64 65 66 68 70 75 76 77 79 81 82 85 86 89 93 98 103 107 108 110 111 114 119 130 132 135 146 147 148 154 **S** QHR, Brentwood, TN
Primary Contact: Bryan Prochnow, Interim Chief Executive Officer
CFO: Bryan Prochnow, Chief Financial Officer
CIO: Beverly Trombatore, R.N., Director Managed Information Systems
CHR: Cindy Krebs, District Director Human Resources
CNO: Mike Lee, R.N., Chief Nursing Officer
Web address: www.matagordaregional.org
Control: Hospital district or authority, Government, nonfederal **Service:** General medical and surgical

Staffed Beds: 58 **Admissions:** 2158 **Census:** 23 **Outpatient Visits:** 65315 **Births:** 532 **Total Expense ($000):** 60468 **Payroll Expense ($000):** 21611 **Personnel:** 314

BAYTOWN—Harris County

ALTUS BAYTOWN HOSPITAL (670109), 1626 West Baker Road, Zip 77521–2271; tel. 281/837–7600, **F**3 12 29 40 44 45 49 74 77 79 81 82 85 87 107 108 111 114 116 117 119 124 149
Primary Contact: Sourabh Sanduja, Administrator
Web address: www.altusbaytownhospital.org
Control: Partnership, Investor–owned (for–profit) **Service:** General medical and surgical

Staffed Beds: 10 **Admissions:** 238 **Census:** 2 **Outpatient Visits:** 8978 **Births:** 0 **Total Expense ($000):** 25318 **Payroll Expense ($000):** 8272 **Personnel:** 81

★ ⇧ **HOUSTON METHODIST BAYTOWN HOSPITAL (450424)**, 4401 Garth Road, Zip 77521–2122; tel. 281/420–8600, (Includes HOUSTON METHODIST SAN JACINTO HOSPITAL – ALEXANDER, 1700 James Bowie Drive, Baytown, TX, Zip 77520–3386, Mailing Address: 4401 Garth Road, Zip 77520–1451, tel. 281/420–6100; David P. Bernard, FACHE, Chief Executive Officer) (Total facility includes 30 beds in nursing home–type unit) **A**2 3 10 21 **F**3 8 11 12 13 15 18 20 22 24 26 28 29 30 31 34 35 38 40 41 44 45 49 50 51 53 57 59 61 64 65 68 70 73 74 75 76 77 78 79 81 82 84 85 86 87 90 91 93 96 97 102 107 108 110 111 115 116 117 118 119 120 121 123 126 128 129 130 131 132 145 146 147 148 149 154 **P**5 6 **S** Houston Methodist, Houston, TX
Primary Contact: David P. Bernard, FACHE, Chief Executive Officer
CFO: Jonathan Sturgis, Chief Financial Officer
CMO: Klaus Thaler, FACS, M.D., Chief Medical Officer
CHR: Courtney Lewis, Director Human Resources
CNO: Rebecca Chalupa, MSN, R.N., Chief Nursing Officer
Web address: www.houstonmethodist.org
Control: Other not–for–profit (including NFP Corporation) **Service:** General medical and surgical

Staffed Beds: 257 **Admissions:** 12778 **Census:** 188 **Outpatient Visits:** 163291 **Births:** 1578 **Total Expense ($000):** 239760 **Payroll Expense ($000):** 97694 **Personnel:** 1398

TX

BEAUMONT—Jefferson County

★ **BAPTIST HOSPITALS OF SOUTHEAST TEXAS (450346)**, 3080 College Street, Zip 77701–4689, Mailing Address: P.O. Box 1591, Zip 77704–1591; tel. 409/212–5000, (Includes BAPTIST HOSPITALS OF SOUTHEAST TEXAS FANNIN BEHAVIORAL HEALTH CENTER, 3250 Fannin Street, Beaumont, TX, Zip 77701; tel. 409/212–7000; David N Parmer, FACHE, Chief Executive Officer) **A**2 10 22 **F**3 4 5 11 12 13 15 17 18 20 22 24 26 28 29 30 31 34 35 40 41 43 45 46 49 50 51 55 57 59 60 61 64 70 72 73 74 75 76 77 78 79 81 85 86 87 88 89 90 93 98 101 102 103 104 105 107 108 110 111 114 115 116 117 118 119 120 121 123 124 129 130 131 132 135 144 145 146 147 148 153 154 **P**6 **S** Community Hospital Corporation, Plano, TX
Primary Contact: David N. Parmer, FACHE, Chief Executive Officer
COO: Patrick Shannon, Chief Operating Officer
CFO: Gary Troutman, CPA, Chief Financial Officer
CMO: Shariq Ahmad, M.D., Chief of Staff
CIO: William Toon, Chief Information Officer
CHR: Hannah Schiesler, Interim Assistant Director Human Resources
CNO: Karen Tomsu, MSN, R.N., Chief Nursing Officer
Web address: www.bhset.net
Control: Other not–for–profit (including NFP Corporation) **Service:** General medical and surgical

Staffed Beds: 323 **Admissions:** 16839 **Census:** 192 **Outpatient Visits:** 171133 **Births:** 1456 **Total Expense ($000):** 246889 **Payroll Expense ($000):** 92435 **Personnel:** 1615

☒ **CHRISTUS DUBUIS HOSPITAL OF BEAUMONT (452042)**, 2830 Calder Avenue, 4th Floor, Zip 77702–1809; tel. 409/899–7680, (Includes CHRISTUS DUBUIS HOSPITAL OF PORT ARTHUR, 3600 Gates Boulevard, 3rd Floor West, Port Arthur, TX, Zip 77642–3858; tel. 409/989–5300; Tuan Le, Chief Executive Officer) (Nonreporting) **A**1 10 **S** LHC Group, Lafayette, LA
Primary Contact: William E. Klamfoth, Administrator
Web address: www.christusdubuis.org/BeaumontandPortArthurSystem–CHRISTUSDubuisHospitalofBeaumont
Control: Church operated, Nongovernment, not–for–profit **Service:** Acute long–term care hospital

Staffed Beds: 51

☒ **CHRISTUS SOUTHEAST TEXAS HOSPITAL – ST. ELIZABETH (450034)**, 2830 Calder Avenue, Zip 77702–1809, Mailing Address: P.O. Box 5405, Zip 77726–5405; tel. 409/892–7171, (Includes CHRISTUS SOUTHEAST TEXAS HOSPITAL–ST. MARY, 3600 Gates Boulevard, Port Arthur, TX, Zip 77642–3601, Mailing Address: P.O. Box 3696, Zip 77643–3696, tel. 409/985–7431; Ryan Miller, FACHE, Administrator) **A**1 2 3 10 **F**3 11 12 13 15 17 18 20 22 24 26 28 29 30 31 34 35 36 38 40 43 44 45 46 49 50 51 54 57 59 60 63 64 70 72 74 75 76 77 78 79 81 82 84 85 86 87 89 93 94 107 108 110 111 114 118 119 126 130 131 132 144 146 147 148 149 **P**8 **S** CHRISTUS Health, Irving, TX
Primary Contact: Paul Trevino, Chief Executive Officer
CFO: Shawn Adams, Chief Financial Officer
CMO: Rick Tyler, M.D., Vice President Medical Affairs
CIO: Robert Jacobs, Regional Director Information Management
CHR: Charles Foster, Regional Director Human Resources
Web address: www.christushospital.org
Control: Church operated, Nongovernment, not–for–profit **Service:** General medical and surgical

Staffed Beds: 370 **Admissions:** 15589 **Census:** 178 **Outpatient Visits:** 279293 **Births:** 1980 **Total Expense ($000):** 318648 **Payroll Expense ($000):** 99669 **Personnel:** 1578

CHRISTUS SOUTHEAST TEXAS ORTHOPEDIC SPECIALTY CENTER (670007), 3650 Laurel Street, Zip 77707–2216; tel. 409/838–0346, (Nonreporting) **A**10
Primary Contact: Ryan Miller, FACHE, Administrator and Executive Director
Web address: www.orthodoc.aaos.org/bbji/
Control: Partnership, Investor–owned (for–profit) **Service:** General medical and surgical

Staffed Beds: 6

KATE DISHMAN REHABILITATION HOSPITAL (673030), 2830 Calder Street, 6th Floor, Zip 77702–1809; tel. 409/899–8380, (Nonreporting) **S** CHRISTUS Health, Irving, TX
Primary Contact: David Pipkins, Chief Executive Officer and Administrator
Web address: www.christushospital.org
Control: Other not–for–profit (including NFP Corporation) **Service:** Rehabilitation

Staffed Beds: 27

☐ **MEDICAL CENTER OF SOUTHEAST TEXAS**, 6025 Metropolitan Drive, Zip 77706–2407; tel. 409/617–7700, (Nonreporting) **A**1 **S** Steward Health Care System, LLC, Dallas, TX
Primary Contact: Becky Ames, Chief Executive Officer
Web address: www.medicalcentersetexas.com/
Control: Other not–for–profit (including NFP Corporation) **Service:** Surgical

Staffed Beds: 17

MEMORIAL HERMANN BAPTIST FANNIN BEHAVIORAL HEALTH CENTER See Baptist Hospitals of Southeast Texas Fannin Behavioral Health Center

☒ **PAM REHABILITATION HOSPITAL OF BEAUMONT (453048)**, 3340 Plaza 10 Boulevard, Zip 77707–2551; tel. 409/835–0835, **A**1 10 **F**3 29 35 57 90 93 96 148 **S** Post Acute Medical, LLC, Enola, PA
Primary Contact: Todd Lorenz, Chief Executive Officer
CMO: Linda C Smith, M.D., Medical Director
CHR: Joanna Donica, Director Human Resource
CNO: Barbara Morris, R.N., Chief Nursing Officer
Web address: www.postacutemedical.com/our–facilities/outpatient–rehabilitation/rehabilitation–hospital–beaumont/
Control: Partnership, Investor–owned (for–profit) **Service:** Rehabilitation

Staffed Beds: 61 **Admissions:** 557 **Census:** 18 **Outpatient Visits:** 0 **Births:** 0 **Total Expense ($000):** 9811 **Payroll Expense ($000):** 6881 **Personnel:** 107

BEDFORD—Tarrant County

☒ **ENCOMPASS HEALTH REHABILITATION HOSPITAL OF THE MID–CITIES (673044)**, 2304 State Highway 121, Zip 76021–5985; tel. 817/684–2000, **A**1 10 **F**3 29 90 96 148 **S** Encompass Health Corporation, Birmingham, AL
Primary Contact: Robert M. Smart, Chief Executive Officer
CFO: Mary Mwaniki, Chief Financial Officer
CMO: Toni Willis, M.D., Medical Director
CHR: Christie Moore, Director Human Resources
Web address: www.relianthcp.com
Control: Partnership, Investor–owned (for–profit) **Service:** Rehabilitation

Staffed Beds: 60 **Admissions:** 1270 **Census:** 41 **Outpatient Visits:** 0 **Births:** 0 **Total Expense ($000):** 18378 **Payroll Expense ($000):** 8990 **Personnel:** 165

☒ **TEXAS HEALTH HARRIS METHODIST HOSPITAL HURST–EULESS–BEDFORD (450639)**, 1600 Hospital Parkway, Zip 76022–6913; tel. 817/685–4000, (Includes TEXAS HEALTH SPRINGWOOD, 1608 Hospital Parkway, Bedford, TX, Zip 76022; tel. 817/355–7700) **A**1 2 10 **F**9 11 12 13 15 18 20 22 24 26 28 29 30 31 34 35 40 43 45 46 47 48 49 50 53 57 59 64 70 72 74 75 76 78 79 80 81 82 84 86 87 93 107 108 111 114 118 119 126 130 131 132 134 135 146 147 148 **S** Texas Health Resources, Arlington, TX
Primary Contact: Fraser Hay, President
COO: Alice Landers, Administrative Director Operations
CFO: Jaime James, Entity Finance Officer
CMO: Susann Land, M.D., Chief Medical Officer
CHR: Lee Mulvey, Human Resource Officer
CNO: Ray Kelly, R.N., MSN, Vice President Chief Nursing Officer
Web address: www.texashealth.org
Control: Other not–for–profit (including NFP Corporation) **Service:** General medical and surgical

Staffed Beds: 285 **Admissions:** 16206 **Census:** 202 **Outpatient Visits:** 82593 **Births:** 2098 **Total Expense ($000):** 248270 **Payroll Expense ($000):** 97942 **Personnel:** 1247

BEEVILLE—Bee County

☒ **CHRISTUS SPOHN HOSPITAL BEEVILLE (450082)**, 1500 East Houston Street, Zip 78102–5312; tel. 361/354–2000, **A**1 10 20 **F**3 11 13 29 30 32 34 35 40 43 45 50 53 57 59 63 64 70 75 76 79 81 85 87 93 97 107 108 111 114 115 119 127 130 146 147 148 **P**8 **S** CHRISTUS Health, Irving, TX
Primary Contact: Genifer Rucker, President
Web address: www.christusspohn.org
Control: Church operated, Nongovernment, not–for–profit **Service:** General medical and surgical

Staffed Beds: 49 **Admissions:** 1839 **Census:** 15 **Outpatient Visits:** 41395 **Births:** 240 **Total Expense ($000):** 29002 **Payroll Expense ($000):** 10177 **Personnel:** 153

Many Facility Codes have changed. Please refer to the AHA Guide Code Chart.   © 2018 AHA Guide

BELLAIRE—Harris County

⇧ **FIRST SURGICAL HOSPITAL (670029)**, 4801 Bissonnet, Zip 77401–4028; tel. 713/275–1111, (Nonreporting) **A**10 21 **S** Nobilis Health Corporation, Houston, TX
Primary Contact: Susan Bosnick–Sinift, Chief Executive Officer
Web address: www.firststreethospital.com
Control: Corporation, Investor–owned (for–profit) **Service:** Surgical

Staffed Beds: 19

BELLVILLE—Austin County

BELLVILLE GENERAL HOSPITAL See Chi St. Joseph Health Bellville Hospital

✠ **CHI ST. JOSEPH HEALTH BELLVILLE HOSPITAL (450253)**, 44 North Cummings Street, Zip 77418–1347, Mailing Address: P.O. Box 977, Zip 77418–0977; tel. 979/413–7400, **A**1 10 **F**3 11 15 29 34 35 40 43 45 50 53 57 59 64 65 68 75 81 87 93 107 110 111 114 119 133 146 **S** Catholic Health Initiatives, Englewood, CO
Primary Contact: Theron Park, Chief Executive Officer
CMO: Christophe Gay, M.D., Chief of Staff
CHR: Jacqueline McEuen, Coordinator Human Resources
Web address: www.chistjoseph.org/
Control: Other not-for-profit (including NFP Corporation) **Service:** General medical and surgical

Staffed Beds: 10 **Admissions:** 74 **Census:** 2 **Outpatient Visits:** 16926
Births: 0 **Total Expense ($000):** 12903 **Payroll Expense ($000):** 4047
Personnel: 82

BELTON—Bell County

☐ **CEDAR CREST HOSPITAL AND RESIDENTIAL TREATMENT CENTER (454114)**, 3500 I–35 South, Zip 76513; tel. 254/939–2100, **A**1 10 **F**4 29 34 35 59 68 86 87 98 99 100 101 102 103 104 105 106 130 143 151 152 153 **P**4
Primary Contact: Joshua Woodson, Chief Executive Officer
CFO: Melissa West, Chief Financial Officer
CMO: Alejandro Munoz, M.D., Chief Medical Officer
CIO: Cesar Osario, Specialist Information Technology
CHR: Allison Liston, Director, Human Resources
CNO: Catherine Reed, MSN, R.N., Chief Nursing Officer
Web address: www.cedarcresthospital.com
Control: Corporation, Investor–owned (for–profit) **Service:** Psychiatric

Staffed Beds: 88 **Admissions:** 2870 **Census:** 62 **Outpatient Visits:** 4596
Births: 0 **Total Expense ($000):** 10418 **Payroll Expense ($000):** 6249
Personnel: 166

BIG LAKE—Reagan County

★ **REAGAN MEMORIAL HOSPITAL (451301)**, 805 North Main Avenue, Zip 76932–3938; tel. 325/884–2561, **A**10 18 **F**3 40 43 53 57 89 93 107 114 115 128 130 133 143 **P**5
Primary Contact: William A. Rohloff, FACHE, Interim Chief Executive Officer
CMO: Joseph Sudolcan, M.D., Medical Director
Web address: www.reaganhealth.com/getpage.php?name=index
Control: Hospital district or authority, Government, nonfederal **Service:** General medical and surgical

Staffed Beds: 7 **Admissions:** 40 **Census:** 1 **Outpatient Visits:** 4741
Births: 0 **Total Expense ($000):** 13746 **Payroll Expense ($000):** 5361
Personnel: 40

BIG SPRING—Howard County

☐ **BIG SPRING STATE HOSPITAL (454000)**, 1901 North Highway 87, Zip 79720–0283; tel. 432/267–8216, **A**1 3 5 10 **F**30 39 50 56 59 61 68 74 75 77 86 87 97 98 101 103 106 130 132 135 146 154 **P**6 **S** Texas Department of State Health Services, Austin, TX
Primary Contact: Traci Phillips, Superintendent
CFO: Adrienne Bides, Assistant Chief Financial Officer and Budget Analyst
CMO: Guido Spangher, M.D., Clinical Director
CIO: Elizabeth Correa, Director Information Management
CNO: Stormy Ward, Chief Nurse Executive
Web address: www.dshs.state.tx.us/mhhospitals/BigSpringSH/default.shtm
Control: State, Government, nonfederal **Service:** Psychiatric

Staffed Beds: 200 **Admissions:** 175 **Census:** 171 **Outpatient Visits:** 0
Births: 0 **Total Expense ($000):** 52898 **Payroll Expense ($000):** 24919
Personnel: 520

✠ **SCENIC MOUNTAIN MEDICAL CENTER (450653)**, 1601 West 11th Place, Zip 79720–4198; tel. 432/263–1211, **A**1 3 10 20 **F**3 13 15 18 20 29 30 34 35 40 43 47 50 57 59 64 65 69 70 75 77 79 80 81 85 86 87 93 100 105 107 108 110 111 115 119 129 130 146 147 148 **P**7 **S** Quorum Health, Brentwood, TN
Primary Contact: Emma Krabill, Chief Executive Officer
CFO: Rodger W Bowen, M.P.H., Chief Financial Officer
CMO: Keith Ledford, M.D., Chief of Staff
CIO: Gene Mills, Director Information Technology
CHR: Deborah Elder, Director Human Resources
CNO: Judy Roever, MSN, R.N., Chief Nursing Officer
Web address: www.smmccares.com
Control: Corporation, Investor–owned (for–profit) **Service:** General medical and surgical

Staffed Beds: 82 **Admissions:** 2383 **Census:** 22 **Outpatient Visits:** 33835
Births: 204 **Total Expense ($000):** 38659 **Payroll Expense ($000):** 15298
Personnel: 212

★ **WEST TEXAS VETERANS AFFAIRS HEALTH CARE SYSTEM**, 300 Veterans Boulevard, Zip 79720–5500, Mailing Address: Big Springs, tel. 432/263–7361, (Nonreporting) **A**3 5 **S** Department of Veterans Affairs, Perry Point, MD
Primary Contact: Kalautie JangDhari, Director
CFO: Ray Olivas, Chief Fiscal Service
CMO: Martin Schnier, D.O., Chief of Staff
CIO: Mike McKinley, Information Security Officer
CHR: Anna Osborne, Chief Human Resources Management Service
Web address: www.bigspring.va.gov/about/
Control: Veterans Affairs, Government, federal **Service:** General medical and surgical

Staffed Beds: 149

BONHAM—Fannin County

SAM RAYBURN MEMORIAL VETERANS CENTER See Veterans Affairs North Texas Health Care System, Dallas

TMC BONHAM HOSPITAL (451370), 504 Lipscomb Street, Zip 75418–4028; tel. 903/583–8585, **A**10 18 **F**3 11 15 29 30 34 35 40 46 50 57 59 64 65 70 75 81 87 93 107 108 110 111 118 119 130 133 135 154
Primary Contact: Harley Smith, Chief Executive Officer
CFO: Jay Hodges, Chief Financial Officer
CMO: Michael Brown, D.O., Chief of Staff
CIO: Jack Farguson, Director Information Technology
CHR: Brenda Bagley, Director Human Resources
CNO: William Kiefer, Chief Nursing Officer
Web address: www.redriverregional.com/
Control: Hospital district or authority, Government, nonfederal **Service:** General medical and surgical

Staffed Beds: 25 **Admissions:** 758 **Census:** 13 **Outpatient Visits:** 20297
Births: 0 **Total Expense ($000):** 18809 **Payroll Expense ($000):** 8587
Personnel: 142

BORGER—Hutchinson County

GOLDEN PLAINS COMMUNITY HOSPITAL (451369), 100 Medical Drive, Zip 79007–7579; tel. 806/467–5700, **A**10 18 **F**11 13 15 29 30 34 35 40 43 45 50 54 56 57 59 62 64 65 66 68 70 75 76 77 79 81 85 86 87 89 93 107 108 110 115 119 127 130 131 132 133 143 146 147 148 153 154 **P**6
Primary Contact: Don Bates, Chief Executive Officer
COO: Melody Henderson, Ph.D., R.N., Chief Operating Officer and Chief Nursing Officer
CFO: Dina Hermes, Chief Financial Officer
CMO: Tanay M. Patel, M.D., Chief of Staff
CHR: Jennifer Harvey, Director Human Resources
Web address: www.goldenplains.org
Control: Corporation, Investor–owned (for–profit) **Service:** General medical and surgical

Staffed Beds: 17 **Admissions:** 766 **Census:** 6 **Outpatient Visits:** 36970
Births: 280 **Total Expense ($000):** 28212 **Payroll Expense ($000):** 8481
Personnel: 195

TX

BOWIE—Montague County

CENTRAL HOSPITAL OF BOWIE (450497), 705 East Greenwood Avenue,
Zip 76230–3135; tel. 940/872–1126, (Nonreporting) **A**5
Primary Contact: Faraz Hashmi, Chief Executive Officer
CNO: Jeannia Case, Chief Nursing Officer
Web address: www.bowiehospital.com
Control: Individual, Investor–owned (for–profit) **Service:** General medical and
surgical

Staffed Beds: 49

BRADY—Mcculloch County

HEART OF TEXAS MEMORIAL HOSPITAL (451348), 2008 Nine Road,
Zip 76825–7210, Mailing Address: P.O. Box 1150, Zip 76825–1150;
tel. 325/597–2901, **A**10 18 **F**15 28 40 43 45 64 81 93 107 111 114 119 127
133 152 **P**4
Primary Contact: Tim Jones, Chief Executive Officer
CFO: Brad Burnett, Chief Financial Officer
CMO: Pete Castro, D.O., Chief of Staff
Web address: www.bradyhospital.com/
Control: Other not–for–profit (including NFP Corporation) **Service:** General
medical and surgical

Staffed Beds: 25 **Admissions:** 204 **Census:** 2 **Outpatient Visits:** 10405
Births: 0 **Total Expense ($000):** 14484 **Payroll Expense ($000):** 3480
Personnel: 99

BRECKENRIDGE—Stephens County

STEPHENS MEMORIAL HOSPITAL (450498), 200 South Geneva Street,
Zip 76424–4799; tel. 254/559–2242, **A**10 20 **F**3 7 8 11 15 28 30 34 35 40 43
45 50 53 54 56 57 59 63 64 68 69 81 85 87 89 93 97 107 114 127 130 133
146 **P**6
Primary Contact: Matthew Kempton, Chief Executive Officer and Administrator
CFO: Samuel Grant, Chief Financial Officer
CMO: Cynthia Perry, M.D., Chief of Staff
CIO: Bobby Thompson, Director Information Technology
CHR: Michelle Funderburg, Director Human Resources
CNO: Alicia Whitt, R.N., Chief Nursing Officer
Web address: www.smhtx.com
Control: County, Government, nonfederal **Service:** General medical and surgical

Staffed Beds: 14 **Admissions:** 258 **Census:** 3 **Outpatient Visits:** 15622
Births: 0 **Total Expense ($000):** 11976 **Payroll Expense ($000):** 5427
Personnel: 128

BRENHAM—Washington County

SCOTT & WHITE HOSPITAL – BRENHAM (450187), 700 Medical Parkway,
Zip 77833–5498; tel. 979/337–5000, **A**1 10 **F**3 11 13 15 18 29 30 34 35 38
40 43 50 57 59 64 65 70 75 76 77 79 80 81 82 85 86 87 89 93 97 107 119
130 132 133 135 146 147 148 149 **S** Baylor Scott & White Health, Dallas, TX
Primary Contact: Jason Jennings, FACHE, President
CFO: Jane Wellmann, Chief Financial Officer
CMO: Michael Schlabach, M.D., Chief Medical Officer
CIO: Sharon Schwartz, Director Medical Records
CHR: Virginia Counts, Manager Human Resources
Web address: www.swbrenham.org
Control: Other not–for–profit (including NFP Corporation) **Service:** General
medical and surgical

Staffed Beds: 56 **Admissions:** 1354 **Census:** 13 **Outpatient Visits:** 39894
Births: 331 **Total Expense ($000):** 34221 **Payroll Expense ($000):** 13557
Personnel: 366

BROWNFIELD—Terry County

★ **BROWNFIELD REGIONAL MEDICAL CENTER (450399)**, 705 East Felt Street,
Zip 79316–3439; tel. 806/637–3551, **A**10 20 **F**3 7 13 28 29 30 34 40 43 45
50 53 57 59 62 64 65 68 75 76 80 81 85 86 87 93 97 102 107 119 127 129
130 133 135 148 149 **P**4
Primary Contact: Jerry Jasper, Chief Executive Officer
CFO: Grady Paul Gafford, Chief Financial Officer
CIO: Edgar Rivera, Chief Information Officer
CHR: Kelly Barnett, Human Resource Officer
CNO: Chris Beard, Chief Nursing Officer
Web address: www.brownfield–rmc.org
Control: Hospital district or authority, Government, nonfederal **Service:** General
medical and surgical

Staffed Beds: 26 **Admissions:** 671 **Census:** 5 **Outpatient Visits:** 45118
Births: 122 **Total Expense ($000):** 16033 **Payroll Expense ($000):** 7678
Personnel: 176

BROWNSVILLE—Cameron County

☐ **SOUTH TEXAS REHABILITATION HOSPITAL (453092)**, 425 East Alton
Gloor Boulevard, Zip 78526–3361; tel. 956/554–6000, **A**1 10 **F**3 28 29 34
35 59 64 75 77 86 87 90 93 94 96 130 132 148 149 **S** Ernest Health, Inc.,
Albuquerque, NM
Primary Contact: Leo Garza, Chief Executive Officer
CFO: Ernest Nash, Chief Financial Officer
CMO: Christopher Wilson, M.D., Inpatient Medical Director
CIO: Deborah Alcocer, Chief Information Officer
CHR: Tony Rodriguez, Director Human Resources
CNO: Aaron Cepeda, Director Nursing Operations
Web address: www.strh.ernesthealth.com
Control: Partnership, Investor–owned (for–profit) **Service:** Rehabilitation

Staffed Beds: 40 **Admissions:** 797 **Census:** 32 **Outpatient Visits:** 5099
Births: 0 **Total Expense ($000):** 15283 **Payroll Expense ($000):** 6633
Personnel: 138

★ **VALLEY BAPTIST MEDICAL CENTER–BROWNSVILLE (450028)**, 1040
West Jefferson Street, Zip 78520–6338, Mailing Address: P.O. Box 3590,
Zip 78523–3590; tel. 956/698–5400, **A**5 10 **F**3 11 12 13 15 18 20 22 24 26
29 30 34 35 37 40 43 44 45 49 50 53 57 59 60 63 64 65 68 70 72 74
75 76 77 79 81 82 84 85 87 89 93 98 101 102 103 104 107 108 110 111
112 114 115 119 126 129 130 132 146 147 148 149 153 **S** TENET Healthcare
Corporation, Dallas, TX
Primary Contact: Leslie Bingham, Senior Vice President and Chief Executive Officer
COO: Marisa Aguilar, Chief Operating Officer
CFO: Edwin Cordero, Chief Financial Officer
CMO: Jose L Ayala, M.D., Chief Medical Officer
CNO: Marisa Aguilar, Interim Chief Nursing Officer
Web address: www.valleybaptist.net/brownsville/index.htm
Control: Corporation, Investor–owned (for–profit) **Service:** General medical and
surgical

Staffed Beds: 262 **Admissions:** 10057 **Census:** 121 **Outpatient
Visits:** 73550 **Births:** 1908 **Total Expense ($000):** 130536 **Payroll Expense
($000):** 50521 **Personnel:** 675

⊞ **VALLEY REGIONAL MEDICAL CENTER (450662)**, 100A Alton Gloor Boulevard,
Zip 78526–3354; tel. 956/350–7101, **A**1 10 **F**3 11 12 13 15 18 20 22 24
26 29 30 31 32 34 35 40 43 44 45 47 49 50 53 57 59 60 61 64 65 68 70
72 73 74 75 76 77 78 79 81 82 84 85 86 87 89 93 107 108 110 111 114
115 118 119 124 126 130 132 135 146 147 148 149 **P**7 **S** HCA Healthcare,
Nashville, TN
Primary Contact: Art Garza, FACHE, Chief Executive Officer
COO: Steven C Hoelscher, Chief Operating Officer
CFO: Marcia Patterson, Chief Financial Officer
CIO: Carlos Leal, Director Information Technology
CHR: Vicky Kahl, Director Human Resources
Web address: www.valleyregionalmedicalcenter.com
Control: Partnership, Investor–owned (for–profit) **Service:** General medical and
surgical

Staffed Beds: 214 **Admissions:** 8673 **Census:** 128 **Outpatient
Visits:** 68528 **Births:** 2170 **Total Expense ($000):** 120546 **Payroll Expense
($000):** 56170 **Personnel:** 667

BROWNWOOD—Brown County

⊞ **BROWNWOOD REGIONAL MEDICAL CENTER (450587)**, 1501 Burnet
Road, Zip 76801–8520, Mailing Address: P.O. Box 760, Zip 76804–0760;
tel. 325/646–8541, (Total facility includes 20 beds in nursing home–type unit) **A**1
10 20 **F**3 11 13 15 18 28 29 30 31 34 35 39 40 45 48 49 50 51 53 54 56 57
59 63 64 68 70 74 75 76 77 79 81 82 85 86 87 93 97 98 103 107 108
111 114 119 120 121 123 128 129 130 132 146 147 148 **P**3 8 **S** Community
Health Systems, Inc., Franklin, TN
Primary Contact: Claude E Chip"". Camp III, FACHE, Chief Executive Officer
CFO: Joseph Wooldridge, Chief Financial Officer
CMO: Sammy Horton, Chief of Staff
CIO: Jay Smith, Director Information Systems
CHR: Mikeana Bailey, Director Human Resources
CNO: Alicia R. Kayga, R.N., Chief Nursing Officer
Web address: www.brmc–cares.com
Control: Partnership, Investor–owned (for–profit) **Service:** General medical and
surgical

Staffed Beds: 188 **Admissions:** 2982 **Census:** 36 **Outpatient Visits:** 64688
Births: 587 **Total Expense ($000):** 70289 **Payroll Expense ($000):** 22011
Personnel: 356

Many Facility Codes have changed. Please refer to the AHA Guide Code Chart.
© 2018 AHA Guide

BRYAN—Brazos County

CHI ST. JOSEPH HEALTH REHABILITATION HOSPITAL, AN AFFILIATE OF ENCOMPASS HEALTH (673065), 1600 Joseph Drive, Suite 2000, Zip 77802–1502; tel. 979/213–4300, (Nonreporting) **S** Encompass Health Corporation, Birmingham, AL
Primary Contact: Amy Gray, Chief Executive Officer
CFO: Kris Smith, Controller
Web address: www.encompasshealth.com/locations/stjrehab
Control: Corporation, Investor–owned (for–profit) **Service:** Rehabilitation

Staffed Beds: 49

☒ **CHI ST. JOSEPH REGIONAL HEALTH CENTER (450011)**, 2801 Franciscan Drive, Zip 77802–2599; tel. 979/776–3777, **A**1 2 3 5 10 **F**3 7 11 12 13 15 17 18 20 22 24 28 29 30 31 32 34 35 37 40 43 44 45 46 48 49 50 53 54 57 59 64 65 67 68 70 72 74 75 76 77 78 79 80 81 82 84 85 86 87 89 93 96 107 110 111 114 118 119 121 123 124 126 127 129 130 131 132 135 143 144 146 148 **S** Catholic Health Initiatives, Englewood, CO
Primary Contact: Theron Park, Chief Executive Officer
CFO: Lisa McNair, CPA, Senior Vice President and Chief Financial Officer
CMO: Kia Parsi, M.D., Chief Medical Officer
CIO: John Phillips, Vice President Information Services
CHR: Michael G Costa, Vice President Human Resources
Web address: www.st–joseph.org
Control: Church operated, Nongovernment, not–for–profit **Service:** General medical and surgical

Staffed Beds: 222 **Admissions:** 13737 **Census:** 152 **Outpatient Visits:** 238150 **Births:** 1553 **Total Expense ($000):** 253100 **Payroll Expense ($000):** 89021 **Personnel:** 1417

☐ **THE PHYSICIANS CENTRE HOSPITAL (450834)**, 3131 University Drive East, Zip 77802–3473; tel. 979/731–3100, **A**1 3 10 **F**3 12 15 29 34 35 40 44 45 51 59 64 74 75 77 79 81 82 85 86 87 89 107 111 114 119 126 130 131 135
Primary Contact: Kori Rich, Chief Executive Officer
CFO: Paul Tannos, Chief Financial Officer
CMO: Barry Solcher, M.D., Chief of Staff
CIO: Shawn Clark, Director Information Systems
CHR: LeeAnn Ford, Director Human Resources and Imaging
CNO: Robert Raymond Lemay, R.N., Chief Nursing Officer
Web address: www.thephysicianscentre.com
Control: Corporation, Investor–owned (for–profit) **Service:** Surgical

Staffed Beds: 16 **Admissions:** 311 **Census:** 2 **Outpatient Visits:** 10019 **Births:** 0 **Total Expense ($000):** 15978 **Payroll Expense ($000):** 4088 **Personnel:** 112

BURLESON—Tarrant County

⇧ **BAYLOR EMERGENCY MEDICAL CENTERS – BURLESON (670107)**, 12500 South Freeway Suite 100, Zip 76028–7128; tel. 214/294–6250, (Includes BAYLOR EMERGENCY MEDICAL CENTERS – MANSFIELD, 1776 US 287, Suite 100, Mansfield, TX, Zip 76063; tel. 214/294–6300; Kyle Kirkpatrick, Chief Executive Officer) **A**10 21 **F**3 40 107 119 149 **P**5 **S** Emerus, The Woodlands, TX
Primary Contact: Kyle Kirkpatrick, Chief Executive Officer
Web address: www.bayloremc.com/burleson
Control: Corporation, Investor–owned (for–profit) **Service:** General medical and surgical

Staffed Beds: 24 **Admissions:** 207 **Census:** 1 **Outpatient Visits:** 24979 **Births:** 0 **Total Expense ($000):** 18744 **Payroll Expense ($000):** 5468 **Personnel:** 77

☒ **TEXAS HEALTH HUGULEY HOSPITAL FORT WORTH SOUTH (450677)**, 11801 South Freeway, Zip 76028–7021, Mailing Address: P.O. Box 6337, Fort Worth, Zip 76115–0337; tel. 817/293–9110, **A**1 10 **F**3 5 8 11 13 15 17 18 20 22 24 26 28 29 30 31 34 35 37 38 40 41 43 45 46 48 49 51 53 54 56 57 59 60 64 65 68 70 71 73 74 75 76 77 78 79 80 81 84 85 86 87 91 93 98 100 101 102 103 104 105 107 108 118 115 118 119 126 130 131 132 135 146 147 148 152 153 **S** Adventist Health System Sunbelt Health Care Corporation, Altamonte Springs, FL
Primary Contact: Kenneth A. Finch, President and Chief Executive Officer
CFO: Jesse Sutton, Senior Vice President and Chief Financial Officer
CMO: Edward Laue, M.D., Chief Medical Officer
CIO: Thomas Schoenig, Regional Chief Information Officer
CHR: Laura Shepherd, Director Human Resources
CNO: Tammy Ellis, FACHE, R.N., Vice President Patient Services
Web address: www.TexasHealthHuguley.org
Control: Church operated, Nongovernment, not–for–profit **Service:** General medical and surgical

Staffed Beds: 193 **Admissions:** 10447 **Census:** 120 **Outpatient Visits:** 125882 **Births:** 1366 **Total Expense ($000):** 181048 **Payroll Expense ($000):** 69693 **Personnel:** 1138

BURNET—Burnet County

☒ **SETON HIGHLAND LAKES (451365)**, 3201 South Water Street, Zip 78611–4510, Mailing Address: P.O. Box 1219, Zip 78611–7219; tel. 512/715–3000, **A**1 3 10 18 **F**3 11 15 28 29 34 35 40 43 45 50 51 57 59 64 67 68 71 74 79 81 85 87 92 93 97 107 108 110 111 115 119 126 127 130 132 133 146 154 **P**3 8 **S** Ascension Healthcare, Saint Louis, MO
Primary Contact: Scott O. Fuller, President and Chief Executive Officer
COO: Karen Litterer, R.N., MSN, Administrator and Chief Operating Officer
CFO: Douglas D Waite, Senior Vice President and Chief Financial Officer
CIO: Gerry Lewis, Chief Information Officer
Web address: www.seton.net
Control: Church operated, Nongovernment, not–for–profit **Service:** General medical and surgical

Staffed Beds: 19 **Admissions:** 769 **Census:** 7 **Outpatient Visits:** 98629 **Births:** 0 **Total Expense ($000):** 44993 **Payroll Expense ($000):** 13025 **Personnel:** 240

CALDWELL—Burleson County

☒ **CHI ST. JOSEPH HEALTH BURLESON HOSPITAL (451305)**, 1101 Woodson Drive, Zip 77836–1052, Mailing Address: P.O. Box 360, Zip 77836–0360; tel. 979/567–3245, **A**1 10 18 **F**3 7 11 28 29 30 34 35 40 43 57 59 64 93 119 130 133 135 143 **S** Catholic Health Initiatives, Englewood, CO
Primary Contact: Theron Park, Chief Executive Officer
CFO: Daniel Goggin, Senior Vice President and Chief Financial Officer
CMO: Kristel Leubner, D.O., Chief of Staff
CHR: Jackie Stradman, Director Human Resources
CNO: Heather Page, MSN, Director of Nursing
Web address: www.chistjoseph.org/
Control: Church operated, Nongovernment, not–for–profit **Service:** General medical and surgical

Staffed Beds: 12 **Admissions:** 165 **Census:** 4 **Outpatient Visits:** 14267 **Births:** 0 **Total Expense ($000):** 10307 **Payroll Expense ($000):** 4043 **Personnel:** 73

CAMERON—Milam County

⇧ **CAMERON HOSPITAL (670094)**, 806 North Crockett Avenue, Zip 76520–2553; tel. 254/605–1300, **A**21 **F**3 8 40 41 81 107 114 149
Primary Contact: Troy Zinn, Chief Executive Officer
Web address: www.lrhealthcare.com/cameronhospital
Control: Partnership, Investor–owned (for–profit) **Service:** General medical and surgical

Staffed Beds: 6 **Admissions:** 29 **Census:** 1 **Outpatient Visits:** 12642 **Births:** 0 **Total Expense ($000):** 10267 **Payroll Expense ($000):** 3183 **Personnel:** 56

CANADIAN—Hemphill County

HEMPHILL COUNTY HOSPITAL (450578), 1020 South Fourth Street, Zip 79014–3315; tel. 806/323–6422, (Total facility includes 42 beds in nursing home–type unit) **A**10 20 **F**2 7 29 35 40 45 56 57 62 63 64 68 69 87 89 93 97 102 107 108 130 133 146 148
Primary Contact: Christy Francis, Chief Executive Officer
CFO: Bob Ericson, Chief Financial Officer
CMO: G. Anthony Cook, M.D., Medical Director
CIO: Brian Goza, Chief Information Officer
CHR: David Troublefield, Chief Communications Officer
CNO: Debra Sappenfield, R.N., Chief Nursing Officer
Web address: www.hchdst.org
Control: Hospital district or authority, Government, nonfederal **Service:** General medical and surgical

Staffed Beds: 61 **Admissions:** 260 **Census:** 36 **Outpatient Visits:** 14522 **Births:** 0 **Total Expense ($000):** 13885 **Payroll Expense ($000):** 7626 **Personnel:** 91

CARRIZO SPRINGS—Dimmit County

★ **DIMMIT REGIONAL HOSPITAL (450620)**, 704 Hospital Drive, Zip 78834–3836, Mailing Address: P.O. Box 1016, Zip 78834–7016; tel. 830/876–2424, **A**10 20 **F**11 13 40 43 45 57 64 70 76 81 89 93 107 115 119 154
Primary Contact: John A. Graves, Chief Executive Officer
CFO: Alma Melendez, Controller
Web address: www.dcmhospital.org
Control: Other not–for–profit (including NFP Corporation) **Service:** General medical and surgical

Staffed Beds: 35 **Admissions:** 501 **Census:** 5 **Outpatient Visits:** 21662 **Births:** 155 **Total Expense ($000):** 17620 **Payroll Expense ($000):** 7999 **Personnel:** 162

TX

CARROLLTON—Denton County

✠ **BAYLOR SCOTT & WHITE MEDICAL CENTER – CARROLLTON (450730)**, 4343 North Josey Lane, Zip 75010–4691; tel. 972/394–1010, **A**1 2 10 **F**3 11 12 13 15 18 20 22 26 29 30 31 35 40 45 46 47 48 50 51 66 70 72 74 76 78 79 81 84 85 107 108 109 110 111 112 114 115 116 117 118 119 126 129 130 131 132 135 146 147 148 154 **S** Baylor Scott & White Health, Dallas, TX
Primary Contact: Jerri Garison, R.N., Interim Chief Executive Officer and Chief Operating Officer
COO: Jerri Garison, R.N., Interim Chief Executve Officer and Chief Operating Officer
CFO: James McNatt, Chief Financial Officer
CMO: Matthew Smith, M.D., Vice President Medical Affairs and Chief Medical Officer
CIO: Paul Ratcliff, Director Information Services
CHR: Erica Calime, Director Human Resources
CNO: Barbara Vaughn, R.N., Chief Nursing Officer
Web address: www.baylorhealth.com
Control: Other not-for-profit (including NFP Corporation) **Service:** General medical and surgical

Staffed Beds: 120 **Admissions:** 6200 **Census:** 74 **Outpatient Visits:** 51853 **Births:** 698 **Total Expense ($000):** 167284 **Payroll Expense ($000):** 48851 **Personnel:** 472

☐ **CARROLLTON SPRINGS (454119)**, 2225 Parker Road, Zip 75010–4711; tel. 972/242–4114, **A**1 10 **F**4 98 102 103 104 105 151 152 153 154 **S** Springstone, Louisville, KY
Primary Contact: Samantha Castle, Chief Executive Officer
Web address: www.carrolltonsprings.com
Control: Corporation, Investor-owned (for-profit) **Service:** Psychiatric

Staffed Beds: 53 **Admissions:** 1750 **Census:** 46 **Outpatient Visits:** 23278 **Births:** 0 **Total Expense ($000):** 14791 **Payroll Expense ($000):** 9192 **Personnel:** 202

✠ **SELECT SPECIALTY HOSPITAL–DALLAS (452022)**, 2329 West Parker Road, Zip 75010–4713; **A**1 10 **F**1 3 29 56 74 75 77 85 91 107 114 119 130 135 148 **S** Select Medical Corporation, Mechanicsburg, PA
Primary Contact: Ty Burgess, Chief Executive Officer
Web address: www.firsttexashospital.com/
Control: Corporation, Investor-owned (for-profit) **Service:** Acute long-term care hospital

Staffed Beds: 60 **Admissions:** 360 **Census:** 29 **Outpatient Visits:** 0 **Births:** 0 **Total Expense ($000):** 17912 **Payroll Expense ($000):** 8771 **Personnel:** 132

TEXAS HEALTH HOSPITAL (670110), 1401 East Trinity Mills Road, Zip 75006; tel. 972/810–0700, **A**10 **F**3 29 40 45 46 49 50 68 70 75 79 81 82 85 87 102 107 114 119 130 148 149
Primary Contact: Ashley Anson, Chief Executive Officer
Web address: www.firsttexashospital.com/
Control: Corporation, Investor-owned (for-profit) **Service:** General medical and surgical

Staffed Beds: 50 **Admissions:** 655 **Census:** 6 **Outpatient Visits:** 167977 **Births:** 0 **Total Expense ($000):** 183799 **Payroll Expense ($000):** 99574 **Personnel:** 958

CARTHAGE—Panola County

✠ **UT HEALTH CARTHAGE (450210)**, 409 Cottage Road, Zip 75633–1466; tel. 903/693–3841, **A**1 10 20 **F**3 8 11 15 28 29 30 34 35 40 43 45 50 57 59 64 65 75 81 85 107 108 110 111 115 119 127 129 145 146 149 150 **S** Ardent Health Services, Nashville, TN
Primary Contact: Gary Mikeal. Hudson, Administrator
COO: Gary Mikeal Hudson, Administrator
CMO: Salah Almohammed, Chief of Staff
CIO: Renee Lawhorn, Director Medical Records
CHR: Amber Cox, Director Human Resources
CNO: Judy Peterson, R.N., Chief Nursing Officer
Web address: www.https://uthealthcarthage.com/
Control: Other not-for-profit (including NFP Corporation) **Service:** General medical and surgical

Staffed Beds: 23 **Admissions:** 630 **Census:** 5 **Outpatient Visits:** 69398 **Births:** 0 **Total Expense ($000):** 19484 **Payroll Expense ($000):** 6912 **Personnel:** 125

CEDAR PARK—Williamson County

★ ⇑ **BAYLOR SCOTT & WHITE EMERGENCY MEDICAL CENTER– CEDAR PARK (670087)**, 900 East Whitestone Boulevard, Zip 78613–9093; tel. 512/684–4911, **A**10 21 **F**3 29 40 75 87 107 119 149 **P**5
Primary Contact: Kyle Kirkpatrick, Chief Executive Officer
Web address: www.sweh.org
Control: Corporation, Investor-owned (for-profit) **Service:** General medical and surgical

Staffed Beds: 8 **Admissions:** 16 **Census:** 1 **Outpatient Visits:** 7664 **Births:** 0 **Total Expense ($000):** 5784 **Payroll Expense ($000):** 1948 **Personnel:** 38

✠ **CEDAR PARK REGIONAL MEDICAL CENTER (670043)**, 1401 Medical Parkway, Zip 78613–7763; tel. 512/528–7000, **A**1 5 10 **F**3 12 13 15 18 20 22 28 29 34 35 37 39 40 43 45 46 47 49 50 54 57 59 64 70 73 74 75 76 77 78 79 81 82 85 87 89 93 107 108 110 111 114 115 118 119 126 129 130 132 135 146 147 148 **S** Community Health Systems, Inc., Franklin, TN
Primary Contact: Brad D. Holland, Chief Executive Officer
COO: Curt M. Junkins, Chief Operating Officer
CFO: Erich Wallschlaeger, Chief Financial Officer
CIO: Brad Hoar, Director Information and Technology
CHR: Jeffery Ward, Director Human Resources
CNO: Krista Baty, R.N., Chief Nursing Officer
Web address: www.cedarparkregional.com
Control: Corporation, Investor-owned (for-profit) **Service:** General medical and surgical

Staffed Beds: 108 **Admissions:** 4778 **Census:** 43 **Outpatient Visits:** 49722 **Births:** 914 **Total Expense ($000):** 92264 **Payroll Expense ($000):** 32293 **Personnel:** 527

CHILDRESS—Childress County

★ **CHILDRESS REGIONAL MEDICAL CENTER (450369)**, Highway 83 North, Zip 79201–5800, Mailing Address: P.O. Box 1030, Zip 79201–1030; tel. 940/937–6371, **A**10 20 **F**3 7 8 13 15 29 31 32 34 35 40 43 45 50 56 57 59 60 61 62 63 64 65 66 68 76 77 78 79 81 84 91 92 93 107 108 111 114 119 127 129 130 133 154 **P**6
Primary Contact: Kevin Latimer, Chief Executive Officer
COO: Holly Holcomb, R.N., Chief Operating Officer
CMO: Dustin Pratt, M.D., Chief of Staff
CIO: Holly Holcomb, R.N., Chie Operating Officer
CHR: Gayle Cannon, Director Human Resources
CNO: Sulynn Mester, R.N., Chief Nursing Officer
Web address: www.childresshospital.com
Control: Hospital district or authority, Government, nonfederal **Service:** General medical and surgical

Staffed Beds: 35 **Admissions:** 895 **Census:** 7 **Outpatient Visits:** 178573 **Births:** 197 **Total Expense ($000):** 29763 **Payroll Expense ($000):** 14446 **Personnel:** 244

CHILLICOTHE—Hardeman County

CHILLICOTHE HOSPITAL DISTRICT (451326), 303 Avenue 'I', Zip 79225, Mailing Address: P.O. Box 370, Zip 79225–0370; tel. 940/852–5131, **A**10 18 **F**29 34 40 43 57 59 69 89 132 133 148 **P**5
Primary Contact: Linda Hall, Administrator and Chief Executive Officer
COO: Linda Hall, Administrator and Chief Executive Officer
CFO: Linda Hall, Administrator and Chief Executive Officer
CMO: Sherry L Wolf, M.D., Chief of Medical Staff
CIO: Kathy Busby, Medical Record Technician
CHR: Linda Hall, Administrator and Chief Executive Officer
CNO: Stormy Smith, Chief Nursing Officer
Web address: www.chillhd.org
Control: Hospital district or authority, Government, nonfederal **Service:** General medical and surgical

Staffed Beds: 13 **Admissions:** 38 **Census:** 1 **Outpatient Visits:** 6709 **Births:** 0 **Total Expense ($000):** 2356 **Payroll Expense ($000):** 1061 **Personnel:** 23

CLEBURNE—Johnson County

✠ **TEXAS HEALTH HARRIS METHODIST HOSPITAL CLEBURNE (450148)**, 201 Walls Drive, Zip 76033–4007; tel. 817/641–2551, **A**1 10 **F**3 11 13 15 18 29 30 34 35 39 40 43 44 47 48 57 59 64 65 68 70 75 76 77 79 81 85 87 89 93 107 108 110 111 114 119 124 126 132 146 147 148 154 **S** Texas Health Resources, Arlington, TX
Primary Contact: Ajith Pai, PharmD, FACHE, President
CFO: Shelly Miland, Group Finance Officer
CMO: Judy Laviolette, M.D., Chief Medical Officer
CIO: Brenda Taylor, Director Information Systems
CHR: Marsha Adams, Interim Director Human Resources
CNO: Vicki Brockman, R.N., Chief Nursing Officer
Web address: www.texashealth.org
Control: Other not-for-profit (including NFP Corporation) **Service:** General medical and surgical

Staffed Beds: 92 **Admissions:** 3278 **Census:** 32 **Outpatient Visits:** 45056 **Births:** 324 **Total Expense ($000):** 70319 **Payroll Expense ($000):** 25998 **Personnel:** 328

CLEVELAND—Liberty County

CLEVELAND EMERGENCY HOSPITAL (670115), 1017 South Travis Avenue, Zip 77327–5152; tel. 281/592–5400, (Nonreporting) **A**10
Primary Contact: Don Vickers, Chief Executive Officer
Control: Other not-for-profit (including NFP Corporation) **Service:** General medical and surgical

Staffed Beds: 40

Many Facility Codes have changed. Please refer to the AHA Guide Code Chart. © 2018 AHA Guide

CLIFTON—Bosque County

★ ⇑ **GOODALL–WITCHER HOSPITAL AUTHORITY (450052)**, 101 South Avenue 'T', Zip 76634–1897, Mailing Address: P.O. Box 549, Zip 76634–0549; tel. 254/675–8322, **A**10 18 21 **F**3 11 13 15 28 29 30 34 35 36 40 43 45 50 53 57 59 62 64 65 68 76 77 81 93 107 108 114 119 127 130 133 146 147 148 **P**3
Primary Contact: Adam Willmann, President and Chief Executive Officer
CFO: Vicki Gloff, Chief Financial Officer
CMO: Kevin Blanton, D.O., Chief of Staff
CHR: Jennie Oldham, Director Human Resources
CNO: Donna Nichols, R.N., Chief Nursing Officer
Web address: www.gwhf.org
Control: Hospital district or authority, Government, nonfederal **Service:** General medical and surgical

Staffed Beds: 25 **Admissions:** 474 **Census:** 7 **Outpatient Visits:** 47563 **Births:** 67 **Total Expense ($000):** 17974 **Payroll Expense ($000):** 7782 **Personnel:** 175

COLEMAN—Coleman County

COLEMAN COUNTY MEDICAL CENTER (451347), 310 South Pecos Street, Zip 76834–4159; tel. 325/625–2135, **A**10 18 **F**3 11 13 28 29 32 34 40 41 43 44 45 50 54 56 57 59 62 63 64 65 68 81 83 84 86 87 93 97 107 114 127 130 132 133 147 148 149 150 **S** Preferred Management Corporation, Shawnee, OK
Primary Contact: Clay Vogel, Administrator and Chief Executive Officer
CMO: Paul Reynolds, M.D., Medical Director
CIO: Harvey Ramirez, Chief Information Officer
CHR: Sue Titsworth, Director Human Resources
CNO: Melissa Ereman, R.N., Chief Nursing Officer
Web address: www.colemantexas.org/hospital.html
Control: Corporation, Investor–owned (for–profit) **Service:** General medical and surgical

Staffed Beds: 25 **Admissions:** 717 **Census:** 9 **Outpatient Visits:** 25350 **Births:** 21 **Total Expense ($000):** 11038 **Payroll Expense ($000):** 5031 **Personnel:** 115

COLLEGE STATION—Brazos County

⊞ **COLLEGE STATION MEDICAL CENTER (450299)**, 1604 Rock Prairie Road, Zip 77845–8345; tel. 979/764–5100, **A**1 3 5 10 **F**3 11 12 13 15 18 20 22 24 26 28 29 30 31 34 40 43 45 46 49 53 57 70 72 74 76 77 78 79 81 82 84 85 87 89 93 107 108 110 111 113 115 118 119 126 127 129 130 131 132 135 146 147 148 154 **P**7 **S** Community Health Systems, Inc., Franklin, TN
Primary Contact: America S. Farrell, FACHE, Chief Executive Officer
COO: Vicky Cha Bridier, Chief Operating Officer
CFO: Kenneth Pannell, Chief Financial Officer
CIO: Daphane Hartman, Director Information Systems
CHR: Sharon Bond, Director Human Resources
CNO: Sherri Welch, R.N., Chief Nursing Officer
Web address: www.csmedcenter.com
Control: Corporation, Investor–owned (for–profit) **Service:** General medical and surgical

Staffed Beds: 160 **Admissions:** 3796 **Census:** 37 **Outpatient Visits:** 45177 **Births:** 1104 **Total Expense ($000):** 82014 **Payroll Expense ($000):** 26282 **Personnel:** 357

☐ **ROCK PRAIRIE BEHAVIORAL HEALTH (454125)**, 3550 Normand Drive, Zip 77845–6399; tel. 979/703–8848, **A**1 10 **F**5 29 30 34 35 38 40 57 98 99 101 102 103 105 130 135 152 153 **S** Strategic Behavioral Health, LLC, Memphis, TN
Primary Contact: Jackie St. Germain, Chief Executive Officer
CMO: Jason Boley, M.D., Medical Director
CHR: MaxAnne Jones, Director Human Resources
Control: Partnership, Investor–owned (for–profit) **Service:** Psychiatric

Staffed Beds: 72 **Admissions:** 1972 **Census:** 47 **Outpatient Visits:** 4282 **Births:** 0 **Total Expense ($000):** 11984 **Payroll Expense ($000):** 6598 **Personnel:** 121

⊞ **SCOTT & WHITE HOSPITAL – COLLEGE STATION (670088)**, 700 Scott & White Drive, Zip 77845; tel. 979/207–0100, **A**1 5 10 **F**3 7 11 12 13 14 15 18 20 22 24 26 28 29 30 31 34 35 40 43 45 46 47 48 49 50 51 56 57 59 61 64 65 67 68 70 72 73 74 75 76 77 78 79 81 82 83 84 85 87 89 93 94 97 101 102 103 104 107 108 110 111 114 115 118 119 120 121 122 123 124 126 129 130 131 145 146 147 148 154 **S** Baylor Scott & White Health, Dallas, TX
Primary Contact: Jason Jennings, FACHE, President
Web address: www.sw.org/location/college–station–hospital
Control: Other not–for–profit (including NFP Corporation) **Service:** General medical and surgical

Staffed Beds: 119 **Admissions:** 6137 **Census:** 57 **Outpatient Visits:** 242092 **Births:** 1182 **Total Expense ($000):** 144008 **Payroll Expense ($000):** 44389 **Personnel:** 918

COLORADO CITY—Mitchell County

★ **MITCHELL COUNTY HOSPITAL (451342)**, 997 West Interstate 20, Zip 79512–2685; tel. 325/728–3431, **A**10 18 **F**3 7 11 28 29 34 35 40 43 45 50 53 57 59 64 65 68 71 81 86 87 93 107 108 109 114 119 127 133 135 146 **P**6
Primary Contact: Robbie Dewberry, Chief Executive Officer
CFO: Joe Wright, Chief Financial Officer
CMO: Dee A Roach, M.D., Chief of Staff
CHR: Deana Overton, Director Human Resources
CNO: Donna Goebel, M.D., Chief Nursing Officer
Web address: www.mitchellcountyhospital.com
Control: Hospital district or authority, Government, nonfederal **Service:** General medical and surgical

Staffed Beds: 17 **Admissions:** 480 **Census:** 8 **Outpatient Visits:** 13633 **Births:** 0 **Total Expense ($000):** 17514 **Payroll Expense ($000):** 8485 **Personnel:** 171

COLUMBUS—Colorado County

COLUMBUS COMMUNITY HOSPITAL (450370), 110 Shult Drive, Zip 78934–3010; tel. 979/732–2371, **A**5 10 20 **F**11 13 15 29 35 40 43 57 68 76 79 81 89 107 110 111 114 119 127 130 133 135 149 154
Primary Contact: James Vanek, Chief Executive Officer
CFO: Regina Wicke, Chief Financial Officer
CMO: Robert Katz, M.D., Chief of Staff
CIO: Ashley Mathis, Privacy Officer
CHR: Janie Hammonds, Human Resources Officer
CNO: Jeno Hargrove, R.N., Director of Nursing
Web address: www.columbusch.com
Control: Other not–for–profit (including NFP Corporation) **Service:** General medical and surgical

Staffed Beds: 40 **Admissions:** 1064 **Census:** 11 **Outpatient Visits:** 83989 **Births:** 264 **Total Expense ($000):** 27263 **Payroll Expense ($000):** 8873 **Personnel:** 157

COMANCHE—Comanche County

★ **COMANCHE COUNTY MEDICAL CENTER (451382)**, 10201 Highway 16 North, Zip 76442–4462; tel. 254/879–4900, **A**10 18 **F**3 11 15 28 29 30 34 35 40 43 45 50 53 57 59 64 65 75 77 79 81 85 86 87 93 97 107 108 110 111 115 119 127 129 130 131 133 145 146 147 148
Primary Contact: Larry Troxell, Chief Executive Officer
CMO: Guyle Donham, M.D., Chief of Staff
CIO: Ismelda Garza, Director Information Systems
CHR: Karen DeLavan, Interim Director Human Resources
CNO: Colleen Jedlicka, R.N., JD, Chief Nursing Officer
Web address: www.comanchecmc.com
Control: Other not–for–profit (including NFP Corporation) **Service:** General medical and surgical

Staffed Beds: 23 **Admissions:** 558 **Census:** 7 **Outpatient Visits:** 30855 **Births:** 0 **Total Expense ($000):** 21647 **Payroll Expense ($000):** 7206 **Personnel:** 139

CONROE—Montgomery County

⊞ **ASPIRE HOSPITAL (670093)**, 2006 South Loop 336 West, Suite 500, Zip 77304–3315; tel. 936/647–3500, **A**1 10 **F**3 34 54 56 57 59 78 79 87 93 96 98 101 103 105 107 108 111 112 113 114 115 118 119 120 121 123 124 129 130 131 149 153 **P**6
Primary Contact: Kostas Gotsoulias, Interim Chief Executive Officer
CFO: Bob Gray, Chief Financial Officer
CIO: John Heemann, Vice President and Chief Information Officer
CHR: Angela Walker, Manager Human Resources
Web address: www.aspirehospital.com
Control: Partnership, Investor–owned (for–profit) **Service:** Psychiatric

Staffed Beds: 28 **Admissions:** 760 **Census:** 20 **Outpatient Visits:** 28577 **Births:** 0 **Total Expense ($000):** 12278 **Payroll Expense ($000):** 4863 **Personnel:** 136

☐ **CHG CORNERSTONE HOSPITAL CONROE (452107)**, 1500 Grand Lake Drive, Zip 77304–2891; tel. 936/523–1800, **A**1 10 **F**1 3 29 40 70 74 75 77 79 85 86 87 91 119 130 148 149 **S** Cornerstone Healthcare Group, Dallas, TX
Primary Contact: Suzanne Kretschmer, Chief Executive Officer
Web address: www.chghospitals.com/conroe/
Control: Partnership, Investor–owned (for–profit) **Service:** Acute long–term care hospital

Staffed Beds: 41 **Admissions:** 564 **Census:** 34 **Outpatient Visits:** 0 **Births:** 0 **Total Expense ($000):** 15292 **Payroll Expense ($000):** 6792 **Personnel:** 91

TX

✠ **CONROE REGIONAL MEDICAL CENTER (450222)**, 504 Medical Boulevard, Zip 77304, Mailing Address: P.O. Box 1538, Zip 77305–1538; tel. 936/539–1111, **A**1 3 10 13 **F**3 11 12 13 15 17 18 20 22 24 26 28 29 31 34 35 40 41 43 45 46 53 54 57 59 64 68 70 72 73 74 75 76 78 79 81 82 85 86 89 90 91 93 107 108 111 114 115 118 119 121 124 129 130 132 135 137 138 139 140 141 142 146 147 148 152 **S** HCA Healthcare, Nashville, TN
Primary Contact: Matt Davis, FACHE, Chief Executive Officer
COO: Reed Hammond, Chief Operating Officer
CFO: Thomas A Holt, Chief Financial Officer
CMO: Mujtaba Ali–Khan, D.O., Chief Medical Officer
CIO: Jeremy Fuller, Director Information Systems
CHR: Diana Howell, Director Human Resources
Web address: www.conroeregional.com/
Control: Partnership, Investor–owned (for–profit) **Service**: General medical and surgical

> **Staffed Beds: 301 Admissions: 15753 Census: 202 Outpatient Visits: 122628 Births: 1364 Total Expense ($000): 219104 Payroll Expense ($000): 78655 Personnel: 1017**

✠ **ENCOMPASS HEALTH REHABILITATION HOSPITAL THE WOODLANDS (453059)**, 18550 'IH' 45 South, Zip 77384; tel. 281/364–2000, **A**1 10 **F**3 28 29 34 44 57 59 65 68 74 75 77 79 82 86 87 90 91 95 96 130 148 149 **S** Encompass Health Corporation, Birmingham, AL
Primary Contact: Jennifer Brewer, Chief Executive Officer
CMO: Ben Agana, M.D., Medical Director
CHR: Valerie Wells, Manager Human Resources
Web address: www.healthsouththewoodlands.com
Control: Corporation, Investor–owned (for–profit) **Service**: Rehabilitation

> **Staffed Beds: 84 Admissions: 770 Census: 26 Outpatient Visits: 0 Births: 0 Total Expense ($000): 14938 Payroll Expense ($000): 6840 Personnel: 102**

WOODLAND SPRINGS HOSPITAL, 15680 Old Conroe Road, Zip 77384; tel. 936/270–7520, (Nonreporting) **S** Springstone, Louisville, KY
Primary Contact: Dustin Davis, Chief Executive Officer
Web address: www.woodlandspringshealth.com/
Control: Corporation, Investor–owned (for–profit) **Service**: Psychiatric

> **Staffed Beds: 96**

CORINTH—Denton County

ATRIUM MEDICAL CENTER OF CORINTH (452111), 3305 Corinth Parkway, Zip 76208–5380; tel. 940/270–4100, **A**10 **F**1 3 8 29 64 75 81 129 148 **P**2
Primary Contact: Andrew Carlton, Administrator
COO: Kathy Mason, Chief Operating Officer
CFO: Anbu Nachimuthu, Chief Financial Officer
CMO: Jalil Kahn, M.D., Chief of Staff
CIO: Wendy Keller, Director Health Information Management
CHR: Melissa Dovel, Manager Human Resources
CNO: Michelle Gray, Nurse Executive
Web address: www.atriumhealthcare.net
Control: Partnership, Investor–owned (for–profit) **Service**: Acute long–term care hospital

> **Staffed Beds: 13 Admissions: 103 Census: 7 Outpatient Visits: 1850 Births: 0 Total Expense ($000): 9058 Payroll Expense ($000): 2722 Personnel: 65**

CORPUS CHRISTI—Nueces County

✠ **CHRISTUS SPOHN HOSPITAL CORPUS CHRISTI MEMORIAL (450046)**, 2606 Hospital Boulevard, Zip 78405–1804, Mailing Address: P.O. Box 5280, Zip 78405; tel. 361/902–4000, (Includes CHRISTUS SPOHN HOSPITAL CORPUS CHRISTI SHORELINE, 600 Elizabeth Street, Corpus Christi, TX, Zip 78404–2235; tel. 361/881–3000; Brian Connor, FACHE, President; CHRISTUS SPOHN HOSPITAL CORPUS CHRISTUS SOUTH, 5950 Saratoga, Corpus Christi, TX, Zip 78414–4100; tel. 361/985–5000) (Total facility includes 22 beds in nursing home–type unit) **A**1 2 3 5 10 **F**3 11 12 16 17 18 20 22 24 26 28 29 30 31 34 35 37 38 39 40 43 45 46 47 48 49 50 51 53 54 56 57 59 60 64 65 68 70 71 72 74 75 76 77 78 79 81 84 85 87 90 91 92 93 94 96 98 102 103 107 108 111 114 115 118 119 120 121 123 124 126 127 128 130 131 141 142 145 146 147 148 154 **P**8 **S** CHRISTUS Health, Irving, TX
Primary Contact: Brian Connor, FACHE, President
CFO: Brower Pam, Chief Financial Officer
CMO: Charles T. Volk, M.D., Regional Chief Medical Officer
CHR: Mary LaFrancois, Vice President Human Resources
CNO: Jennifer Gentry, R.N., Chief Nursing Officer
Web address: www.christusspohn.org
Control: Church operated, Nongovernment, not–for–profit **Service**: General medical and surgical

> **Staffed Beds: 572 Admissions: 28736 Census: 420 Outpatient Visits: 264278 Births: 2417 Total Expense ($000): 606224 Payroll Expense ($000): 173127 Personnel: 2689**

✠ **CORPUS CHRISTI MEDICAL CENTER (450788)**, 3315 South Alameda Street, Zip 78411–1883, Mailing Address: P.O. Box 8991, Zip 78468–8991; tel. 361/761–1400, (Includes BAYVIEW BEHAVIORAL HOSPITAL, 6629 Wooldridge Road, Corpus Christi, TX, Zip 78414; tel. 361/986–9444; CORPUS CHRISTI MEDICAL CENTER BAY AREA, 7101 South Padre Island Drive, Corpus Christi, TX, Zip 78412–4999; tel. 361/985–1200) **A**1 10 13 **F**3 4 5 11 12 13 15 17 18 20 22 24 26 28 29 31 34 35 37 38 40 44 47 49 50 53 57 58 59 64 68 70 72 73 74 75 76 77 78 79 81 82 85 86 87 90 93 97 98 99 101 102 103 104 105 107 108 110 111 114 115 118 119 120 121 123 124 126 130 131 132 146 147 148 149 150 152 153 154 **P**3 8 **S** HCA Healthcare, Nashville, TN
Primary Contact: Jay Woodall, FACHE, Chief Executive Officer
CFO: Chris Nicosia, Chief Financial Officer
CHR: Michael Conwill, Director Human Resources
CNO: Kathleen A Rubano, MSN, R.N., Chief Nursing Officer
Web address: www.ccmedicalcenter.com
Control: Partnership, Investor–owned (for–profit) **Service**: General medical and surgical

> **Staffed Beds: 416 Admissions: 20186 Census: 255 Outpatient Visits: 132820 Births: 4081 Total Expense ($000): 293886 Payroll Expense ($000): 92541 Personnel: 1583**

✠ △ **DRISCOLL CHILDREN'S HOSPITAL (453301)**, 3533 South Alameda Street, Zip 78411–1785, Mailing Address: P.O. Box 6530, Zip 78466–6530; tel. 361/694–5000, **A**1 3 5 7 10 **F**3 7 11 12 19 21 23 25 27 29 30 31 32 34 35 38 39 40 41 43 49 50 54 55 57 58 59 60 61 64 65 68 72 74 75 77 78 79 81 82 85 86 87 88 89 92 93 97 104 107 108 111 115 118 119 130 132 134 138 143 144 146 148 149 150 153
Primary Contact: Eric Hamon, Interim President and Chief Executive Officer
COO: Donna Quinn, Vice President Operations
CFO: Eric Hamon, Executive Vice President and Chief Financial Officer
CIO: Miguel Perez, III, Chief Information Officer
CHR: Bill Larsen, Vice President Human Resources
CNO: Julie A. Pina, Assistant Vice President Patient Care Services and Chief Nursing Officer
Web address: www.driscollchildrens.org
Control: Other not–for–profit (including NFP Corporation) **Service**: Children's general medical and surgical

> **Staffed Beds: 162 Admissions: 3196 Census: 74 Outpatient Visits: 181168 Births: 0 Total Expense ($000): 269697 Payroll Expense ($000): 105427 Personnel: 2004**

KINDRED HOSPITAL–CORPUS CHRISTI See Pam Specialty Hospital of Corpus Christi South

✠ **PAM SPECIALTY HOSPITAL OF CORPUS CHRISTI SOUTH (452092)**, 6226 Saratoga Boulevard, Zip 78414–3421; tel. 361/986–1600, **A**1 10 **F**1 3 29 34 35 45 59 74 75 77 79 82 86 87 107 130 148 **S** Post Acute Medical, LLC, Enola, PA
Primary Contact: Hector Bernal, Chief Executive Officer
CHR: Kasey Parkey, Coordinator Payroll and Benefits
Web address: www.postacutemedical.com
Control: Corporation, Investor–owned (for–profit) **Service**: Acute long–term care hospital

> **Staffed Beds: 74 Admissions: 717 Census: 37 Outpatient Visits: 0 Births: 0 Total Expense ($000): 18406 Payroll Expense ($000): 7937 Personnel: 132**

✠ **POST ACUTE MEDICAL SPECIALTY HOSPITAL OF CORPUS CHRISTI – NORTH (452086)**, 600 Elizabeth Street, 3rd Floor, Zip 78404–2235; tel. 361/881–3223, **A**1 10 **F**1 3 29 75 85 87 91 148 **P**5 **S** Post Acute Medical, LLC, Enola, PA
Primary Contact: Hector Bernal, Chief Executive Officer
Web address: www.postacutemedical.com/our-facilities/hospitals/post-acute-medical-specialty-hospital-corpus-christi/
Control: Corporation, Investor–owned (for–profit) **Service**: Acute long–term care hospital

> **Staffed Beds: 22 Admissions: 316 Census: 20 Outpatient Visits: 0 Births: 0 Total Expense ($000): 9892 Payroll Expense ($000): 3751 Personnel: 66**

☐ **SOUTH TEXAS SURGICAL HOSPITAL (670061)**, 6130 Parkway Drive, Zip 78414–2455; tel. 361/993–2000, **A**1 3 10 **F**3 29 40 45 54 64 68 75 79 81 82 85 119 126 130 149 **S** National Surgical Healthcare, Chicago, IL
Primary Contact: David G. Covert, Chief Executive Officer
CFO: Julie Wittwer, Chief Financial Officer
CMO: Michael Mintz, M.D., Chief Medical Officer
CHR: Lory Beth Smith, Manager Human Resource
CNO: Jan O'Donnell, Chief Nursing Officer
Web address: www.southtexassurgicalhospital.com
Control: Partnership, Investor–owned (for–profit) **Service**: Surgical

> **Staffed Beds: 20 Admissions: 757 Census: 6 Outpatient Visits: 16138 Births: 0 Total Expense ($000): 34099 Payroll Expense ($000): 9059 Personnel: 183**

CORSICANA—Navarro County

⊞ **NAVARRO REGIONAL HOSPITAL (450447)**, 3201 West State Highway 22, Zip 75110-2469; tel. 903/654-6800, **A**1 3 10 19 **F**3 11 13 15 18 28 29 30 34 35 39 40 43 45 49 50 51 54 57 60 64 68 70 75 76 79 81 82 85 93 107 108 110 111 114 115 119 129 132 135 146 148 **S** Community Health Systems, Inc., Franklin, TN
Primary Contact: Michael K. Stewart, Chief Executive Officer
CFO: Shea C. Brock, Chief Financial Officer
CIO: Bryan Chilton, Director Information Systems
CHR: Melodee Pugh, Director Human Resources
CNO: Dona E Townsend, Chief Nursing Officer
Web address: www.navarrohospital.com
Control: Partnership, Investor-owned (for-profit) **Service:** General medical and surgical

Staffed Beds: 49 **Admissions:** 2532 **Census:** 22 **Outpatient Visits:** 45158 **Births:** 615 **Total Expense ($000):** 42712 **Payroll Expense ($000):** 14449 **Personnel:** 304

CRANE—Crane County

★ **CRANE MEMORIAL HOSPITAL (451353)**, 1310 South Alford Street, Zip 79731-3899; tel. 432/558-3555, **A**10 18 **F**3 29 32 34 40 57 59 64 65 68 75 81 86 97 107 114 119 127 133 145 147 148 **P**2 6
Primary Contact: Dianne Yeager, Chief Executive Officer
CFO: Daniel Ibarra, Chief Financial Officer
CMO: Sixta Gumato, M.D., Chief Medical Officer
CHR: Becky Esparza, Human Resources
CNO: Pat Touchstone, Chief Nursing Officer
Web address: www.cranememorial.org
Control: Hospital district or authority, Government, nonfederal **Service:** General medical and surgical

Staffed Beds: 10 **Admissions:** 135 **Census:** 2 **Outpatient Visits:** 11155 **Births:** 0 **Total Expense ($000):** 7279 **Payroll Expense ($000):** 3281 **Personnel:** 53

CROSBYTON—Crosby County

CROSBYTON CLINIC HOSPITAL (451345), 710 West Main Street, Zip 79322-2143; tel. 806/675-2382, **A**10 18 **F**7 10 29 34 40 50 57 59 63 64 68 87 93 119 127 130 133 148 **P**6
Primary Contact: Debra Miller, Administrator
CFO: Cherie Parkhill, Chief Financial Officer
CMO: Steve B Alley, M.D., Chief of Staff
CHR: Janie Cantu, Director Human Resources
CNO: Freda Bartlett, Director of Nursing
Web address: www.crosbytonclinichospital.com
Control: Other not-for-profit (including NFP Corporation) **Service:** General medical and surgical

Staffed Beds: 7 **Admissions:** 118 **Census:** 2 **Outpatient Visits:** 17116 **Births:** 0 **Total Expense ($000):** 6151 **Payroll Expense ($000):** 2746 **Personnel:** 78

CUERO—Dewitt County

★ **CUERO COMMUNITY HOSPITAL (450597)**, 2550 North Esplanade Street, Zip 77954-4716; tel. 361/275-6191, **A**10 **F**3 7 11 13 15 29 34 40 43 45 53 57 59 62 64 68 70 75 76 77 79 81 85 86 93 107 108 110 111 115 118 119 127 129 130 131 154 **P**6
Primary Contact: Lynn Falcone, Chief Executive Officer
CFO: Greg Pritchett, Chief Financial Officer
CMO: Michael McLeod, M.D., Chief Medical Officer
CIO: Arthur Mueller, Director Management Information Systems
CHR: Wanda S Kolodziejcyk, Director Human Resources
CNO: Judith Krupala, R.N., Chief Nursing Officer
Web address: www.cuerohospital.org
Control: Hospital district or authority, Government, nonfederal **Service:** General medical and surgical

Staffed Beds: 24 **Admissions:** 909 **Census:** 9 **Outpatient Visits:** 115636 **Births:** 105 **Total Expense ($000):** 36272 **Payroll Expense ($000):** 16322 **Personnel:** 343

CYPRESS—Harris County

☐ **LONE STAR BEHAVIORAL HEALTH (454118)**, 16303 Grant Road, Zip 77429-1253; tel. 281/516-6200, **A**1 10 **F**98 105 149 153 **P**5
Primary Contact: Nathan Daniel. Ingram, Chief Executive Officer and Owner
Web address: www.lonestarbehavioralhealth.com
Control: Corporation, Investor-owned (for-profit) **Service:** Psychiatric

Staffed Beds: 24 **Admissions:** 428 **Census:** 14 **Outpatient Visits:** 35402 **Births:** 0 **Total Expense ($000):** 5990 **Payroll Expense ($000):** 3684 **Personnel:** 78

☐ **NORTH CYPRESS MEDICAL CENTER (670024)**, 21214 Northwest Freeway, Zip 77429-3373; tel. 832/912-3500, **A**1 10 **F**3 4 5 8 11 12 15 17 18 19 20 22 24 26 28 29 31 34 35 37 39 40 41 44 45 46 47 48 49 50 51 53 54 55 56 57 58 59 60 61 64 65 67 70 74 75 77 78 79 80 81 82 84 85 86 87 89 90 91 92 93 96 97 107 108 109 110 111 114 115 116 117 118 119 120 121 123 124 126 129 130 131 132 135 141 142 144 146 148 149 151 **S** HCA Healthcare, Nashville, TN
Primary Contact: Jim Brown, Chief Executive Officer
Web address: www.ncmc-hospital.com
Control: Partnership, Investor-owned (for-profit) **Service:** General medical and surgical

Staffed Beds: 139 **Admissions:** 8556 **Census:** 106 **Outpatient Visits:** 193703 **Births:** 0 **Total Expense ($000):** 217267 **Payroll Expense ($000):** 75289 **Personnel:** 1208

DALHART—Hartley County

COON MEMORIAL HOSPITAL (451331), 1411 Denver Avenue, Zip 79022-4809, Mailing Address: P.O. Box 2014, Zip 79022-6014; tel. 806/244-4571, **A**10 18 **F**3 7 10 11 13 30 34 35 40 43 45 50 53 57 59 62 63 64 65 68 69 71 76 77 79 81 82 83 85 87 93 97 103 107 114 119 125 127 131 133 143 144 146 148 **P**5
Primary Contact: Loree Tamayo, Chief Executive Officer
CFO: Donny Pettit, Chief Financial Officer
CMO: Randy Herring, M.D., Chief of Staff
CIO: Anthony Lovato, Director Information Technology
CHR: Dee Dawn McCormick, Director Personnel and Human Resources
Web address: www.coonmemorial.org
Control: Hospital district or authority, Government, nonfederal **Service:** General medical and surgical

Staffed Beds: 21 **Admissions:** 359 **Census:** 5 **Outpatient Visits:** 20978 **Births:** 115 **Total Expense ($000):** 26895 **Payroll Expense ($000):** 10215 **Personnel:** 201

DALLAS—Dallas County

⊞ **BAYLOR INSTITUTE FOR REHABILITATION (453036)**, 909 North Washington Avenue, Zip 75246-1520; tel. 214/820-9300, **A**1 3 10 **F**3 29 30 34 35 44 62 64 65 68 74 75 77 85 86 87 90 92 93 94 95 96 130 131 132 135 143 148 149
Primary Contact: David Smith, Chief Executive Officer
CMO: Amy Wilson, M.D., Medical Director
CHR: Karen Hill, Director Human Resources
CNO: Beth Hudson, Chief Nursing Officer
Web address: www.baylorhealth.com/PhysiciansLocations/BIR/Pages/Default.aspx
Control: Partnership, Investor-owned (for-profit) **Service:** Rehabilitation

Staffed Beds: 89 **Admissions:** 1492 **Census:** 78 **Outpatient Visits:** 234 **Births:** 0 **Total Expense ($000):** 72757 **Payroll Expense ($000):** 46529 **Personnel:** 308

⊞ **BAYLOR JACK AND JANE HAMILTON HEART AND VASCULAR HOSPITAL (450851)**, 621 North Hall Street, Suite 150, Zip 75226-1339; tel. 214/820-0600, **A**1 5 10 **F**3 18 20 22 26 28 29 30 34 35 44 50 57 58 59 60 64 68 75 77 81 85 86 87 93 96 107 109 115 119 130 131 132 135 146 149
Primary Contact: Nancy Vish, Ph.D., FACHE, R.N., President
CFO: Julius Wicke III Vice President Finance and Hospital Financial Officer
CMO: Kevin Wheelan, M.D., Medical Director
CHR: Kim Krause, Director Human Resources
Web address: www.baylorhearthospital.com
Control: Partnership, Investor-owned (for-profit) **Service:** Heart

Staffed Beds: 54 **Admissions:** 2480 **Census:** 23 **Outpatient Visits:** 37843 **Births:** 0 **Total Expense ($000):** 131035 **Payroll Expense ($000):** 34672 **Personnel:** 366

⊞ **BAYLOR MEDICAL CENTER AT UPTOWN (450422)**, 2727 East Lemmon Avenue, Zip 75204-2895; tel. 214/443-3000, **A**1 3 5 10 **F**29 40 68 77 79 81 82 85 107 111 **P**4 **S** United Surgical Partners International, Addison, TX
Primary Contact: Nick Taylor, Chief Executive Officer
CFO: Colene Fielding, Manager Business Office
CMO: Mark Armstrong, M.D., Medical Director
CIO: Javier Vela, Director Information Technology
CHR: Emalie Sanchez, Director Human Resources
CNO: Verette Neeb, R.N., MSN, Chief Nursing Officer
Web address: www.bmcuptown.com
Control: Partnership, Investor-owned (for-profit) **Service:** Surgical

Staffed Beds: 24 **Admissions:** 1114 **Census:** 5 **Outpatient Visits:** 10309 **Births:** 0 **Total Expense ($000):** 55046 **Payroll Expense ($000):** 12290 **Personnel:** 177

TX

⊞ ⇑ **BAYLOR UNIVERSITY MEDICAL CENTER (450021)**, 3500 Gaston Avenue, Zip 75246–2088; tel. 214/820–0111, (Includes A. WEBB ROBERTS HOSPITAL, 3500 Gaston Avenue, Dallas, TX, Zip 75246–2017; tel. 361/986–9444; ERIK AND MARGARET JONSSON HOSPITAL, 3500 Gaston Avenue, Dallas, TX, Zip 75246–2017; tel. 361/986–9444; GEORGE W. TRUETT MEMORIAL HOSPITAL, 3500 Gaston Avenue, Dallas, TX, Zip 75246; tel. 361/986–9444; KARL AND ESTHER HOBLITZELLE MEMORIAL HOSPITAL, 3500 Gaston Avenue, Dallas, TX, Zip 75246; tel. 361/986–9444) **A**1 2 3 5 8 10 21 **F**3 8 12 13 14 15 17 18 20 22 24 26 29 30 31 34 35 37 38 40 41 43 45 46 47 48 49 50 51 54 55 56 57 58 59 60 61 68 70 71 72 74 75 76 77 78 79 80 81 82 84 85 86 87 100 101 102 107 108 110 111 114 115 116 117 118 119 121 126 129 130 131 132 135 136 137 138 139 140 141 142 146 147 148 149 154 **S** Baylor Scott & White Health, Dallas, TX
Primary Contact: Steven R. Newton, FACHE, President
COO: Scott Peek, FACHE, Chief Operating Officer
CFO: Jay Whitfield, Chief Financial Officer
CMO: Brad Lembcke, M.D., Vice President Medical Staff Affairs
CHR: Julie Strittmatter, Director Human Resources
CNO: Beth P Beckman, R.N., Ph.D., Chief Nursing Officer and Vice President
Web address: www.baylorhealth.com/PhysiciansLocations/Dallas/Pages/Default.aspx
Control: Other not–for–profit (including NFP Corporation) **Service**: General medical and surgical

Staffed Beds: 863 **Admissions**: 37840 **Census**: 654 **Outpatient Visits**: 232420 **Births**: 4370 **Total Expense ($000)**: 1067349 **Payroll Expense ($000)**: 344950 **Personnel**: 3712

⊞ **CHILDREN'S MEDICAL CENTER DALLAS (453302)**, 1935 Medical District Drive, Zip 75235–7701; tel. 214/456–7000, **A**1 3 5 8 10 **F**3 7 8 11 12 17 19 21 23 25 27 29 30 31 32 34 35 38 39 40 41 43 44 45 46 47 48 49 50 51 54 55 57 58 59 60 61 62 64 65 66 68 72 74 75 77 78 79 81 82 84 85 86 87 88 89 91 92 93 94 97 98 99 100 101 102 104 105 107 108 111 114 116 117 118 119 126 127 129 130 131 132 134 136 137 138 139 140 141 142 143 144 145 146 148 153 154 **S** Children's Health, Dallas, TX
Primary Contact: Christopher J. Durovich, President and Chief Executive Officer
COO: David T. Berry, President, System Clinical Operations
CFO: Richard P. Goode, Executive Vice President and Chief Financial Officer
CMO: W. Robert Morrow, M.D., Executive Vice President and Chief Medical Officer
CIO: Pamela Arora, Senior Vice President Information Systems
CHR: Kim Besse, Executive Vice President and Chief Human Resource Officer
CNO: Mary Stowe, Senior Vice President and Chief Nursing Officer
Web address: www.childrens.com
Control: Other not–for–profit (including NFP Corporation) **Service**: Children's general medical and surgical

Staffed Beds: 362 **Admissions**: 29242 **Census**: 241 **Outpatient Visits**: 498771 **Births**: 0 **Total Expense ($000)**: 968927 **Payroll Expense ($000)**: 312324 **Personnel**: 4226

⊞ **CITY HOSPITAL AT WHITE ROCK (450678)**, 9440 Poppy Drive, Zip 75218–3694; tel. 214/324–6100, **A**1 10 **F**3 11 12 13 15 17 18 20 22 24 26 28 29 30 31 34 35 37 40 45 47 49 50 51 53 56 57 59 64 70 72 74 75 76 77 78 79 81 85 93 107 108 110 111 114 115 119 120 124 126 129 130 132 135 144 146 147 148
Primary Contact: Jorge Trevino, Chief Executive Officer
COO: Jorge Trevino, Chief Executive Officer
CFO: Drew Shea, Chief Financial Officer
CMO: William Jones, M.D., II Chief Medical Officer
CHR: David Olmstead, Director, Human Resources
CNO: Cheryl Nail, R.N., Chief Nursing Officer
Web address: www.BaylorScottandWhite.com/WhiteRock
Control: Partnership, Investor–owned (for–profit) **Service**: General medical and surgical

Staffed Beds: 151 **Admissions**: 7503 **Census**: 83 **Outpatient Visits**: 71163 **Births**: 1210 **Total Expense ($000)**: 120249 **Payroll Expense ($000)**: 43361 **Personnel**: 649

⊞ **DALLAS MEDICAL CENTER (450379)**, Seven Medical Parkway, Zip 75234–7823, Mailing Address: P.O. Box 819094, Zip 75381–9094; tel. 972/247–1000, **A**1 10 **F**3 12 13 15 18 20 22 26 29 34 40 44 45 49 50 51 56 57 59 64 68 70 74 75 77 78 79 81 82 84 85 86 93 97 107 108 111 114 116 119 130 131 132 141 142 146 147 148 149 **S** Prime Healthcare, Ontario, CA
Primary Contact: J. T. Barnhart, Chief Executive Officer
CFO: Nicholas Geer, Chief Financial Officer
CHR: Sheila K Richards, Human Resources Director
Web address: www.dallasmedcenter.com
Control: Corporation, Investor–owned (for–profit) **Service**: General medical and surgical

Staffed Beds: 71 **Admissions**: 3027 **Census**: 30 **Outpatient Visits**: 34177 **Births**: 351 **Total Expense ($000)**: 72688 **Payroll Expense ($000)**: 24297 **Personnel**: 473

⊞ **ENCOMPASS HEALTH REHABILITATION HOSPITAL OF DALLAS (673043)**, 7930 Northaven Road, Zip 75230–3331; tel. 214/706–8200, **A**1 10 **F**3 29 90 96 128 130 148 **S** Encompass Health Corporation, Birmingham, AL
Primary Contact: Daniel MacNicol, Chief Executive Officer
CFO: Elizabeth Robertson, Area Controller
CMO: Anna Freed–Sigurdsson, M.D., Medical Director
CHR: Lindsay Battles, Director Human Resources
CNO: Elysia Clay, Chief Nursing Officer
Web address: www.healthsouthdallas.com
Control: Corporation, Investor–owned (for–profit) **Service**: Rehabilitation

Staffed Beds: 60 **Admissions**: 1075 **Census**: 38 **Outpatient Visits**: 0 **Births**: 0 **Total Expense ($000)**: 19825 **Payroll Expense ($000)**: 8240 **Personnel**: 125

★ ⇑ **FIRST BAPTIST MEDICAL CENTER**, 8111 Meadow Road, Zip 75231; tel. 469/329–3700, **A**21 **F**3 12 29 37 40 45 49 64 70 79 81 82 85 86 87 107 114 119 126 130 149 **S** QHR, Brentwood, TN
Primary Contact: Harold Gaskill III, M.D., Chief Executive Officer
Web address: www.fbmcdallas.com
Control: Corporation, Investor–owned (for–profit) **Service**: Surgical

Staffed Beds: 18 **Admissions**: 415 **Census**: 4 **Outpatient Visits**: 2279 **Births**: 0 **Total Expense ($000)**: 34653 **Payroll Expense ($000)**: 8012 **Personnel**: 113

⊞ **KINDRED HOSPITAL DALLAS CENTRAL (452108)**, 8050 Meadow Road, Zip 75231–3406; tel. 469/232–6500, **A**1 10 **F**1 3 29 75 77 85 87 96 107 114 148 **P**8 **S** Kindred Healthcare, Louisville, KY
Primary Contact: Kyron J. Kooken, MS, Chief Executive Officer
CFO: Robin Fry, CPA, Market Controller
CNO: Traci Brewer, R.N., Chief Clinical Officer
Web address: www.khdallascentral.com/
Control: Partnership, Investor–owned (for–profit) **Service**: Acute long–term care hospital

Staffed Beds: 60 **Admissions**: 605 **Census**: 42 **Outpatient Visits**: 0 **Births**: 0 **Total Expense ($000)**: 25658 **Payroll Expense ($000)**: 9042 **Personnel**: 147

⊞ **KINDRED HOSPITAL–DALLAS (452015)**, 9525 Greenville Avenue, Zip 75243–4116; tel. 214/355–2600, **A**1 10 **F**1 3 16 17 29 67 70 80 89 90 107 114 130 148 152 **S** Kindred Healthcare, Louisville, KY
Primary Contact: Kyron J. Kooken, MS, Chief Executive Officer
CFO: Jean McDowell, Chief Financial Officer
Web address: www.khdallas.com
Control: Corporation, Investor–owned (for–profit) **Service**: Acute long–term care hospital

Staffed Beds: 50 **Admissions**: 503 **Census**: 41 **Outpatient Visits**: 1215 **Births**: 0 **Total Expense ($000)**: 23155 **Payroll Expense ($000)**: 8372 **Personnel**: 137

⊞ **LIFECARE HOSPITALS OF DALLAS (452044)**, 1950 Record Crossing Road, Zip 75235–6223; tel. 214/640–9600, (Includes LIFECARE HOSPITALS OF NORTH TEXAS–FORT WORTH, 6201 Overton Ridge Boulevard, Fort Worth, TX, Zip 76132–3613; tel. 817/370–6078; Phillip B Douglas, Chairman and Chief Executive Officer; LIFECARE HOSPITALS OF NORTH TEXAS–PLANO, 6800 Preston Road, Plano, TX, Zip 75024–2505; tel. 214/473–8822; Kathleen Wallace, R.N., MSN, Administrator and Chief Executive Officer) **A**1 10 **F**1 3 29 75 91 107 114 119 130 148 **S** LifeCare Management Services, Plano, TX
Primary Contact: Deborah Paganelli, FACHE, Chief Executive Officer
CFO: Amie Gratch, Director Financial Services
CMO: Jonathan Weissler, M.D., Chief Medical Officer
CHR: Linzie Riley, Interim Human Resource Manager
CNO: Kathy Mason, R.N., MSN, Chief Nursing Officer
Web address: www.lifecare–hospitals.com/hospital/dallas
Control: Corporation, Investor–owned (for–profit) **Service**: Acute long–term care hospital

Staffed Beds: 113 **Admissions**: 1158 **Census**: 84 **Outpatient Visits**: 6034 **Births**: 0 **Total Expense ($000)**: 49906 **Payroll Expense ($000)**: 21166 **Personnel**: 394

LIFECARE HOSPITALS OF NORTH TEXAS See Lifecare Hospitals of Dallas

MARY SHIELS HOSPITAL See Baylor Medical Center At Uptown

Many Facility Codes have changed. Please refer to the AHA Guide Code Chart. © 2018 AHA Guide

☒ ⇑ **MEDICAL CITY DALLAS (450647)**, 7777 Forest Lane, Zip 75230–2598; tel. 972/566–7000, (Includes MEDICAL CITY CHILDREN'S HOSPITAL, 7777 Forest Lane, Dallas, TX, Zip 75230–2505; tel. 972/566–7000; Bill Lee, Chief Executive Officer) **A**1 2 3 5 10 21 **F**3 8 11 12 13 17 18 19 20 21 22 23 24 25 26 27 28 29 31 35 37 40 41 43 44 45 46 47 49 50 51 55 56 57 58 59 60 64 65 68 70 72 73 74 75 76 77 78 79 81 82 84 85 86 87 88 89 90 91 93 96 107 108 111 114 115 116 117 118 119 124 126 130 132 135 136 137 138 141 142 143 146 147 148 149 **S** HCA Healthcare, Nashville, TN
Primary Contact: Chris Mowan, Chief Executive Officer
CFO: Mark Atchley, Vice President and Chief Financial Officer
CMO: Kenneth Rothfield, M.D., Chief Medical Officer
CIO: Troy Sypien, Director Information Technology and Systems
CHR: Jenifer K Tertel, Director Human Resources
CNO: Joyce M Soule, R.N., MSN, Chief Nursing Officer
Web address: www.medicalcityhospital.com
Control: Corporation, Investor–owned (for–profit) **Service:** General medical and surgical

Staffed Beds: 607 **Admissions:** 26331 **Census:** 466 **Outpatient Visits:** 184431 **Births:** 3551 **Total Expense ($000):** 582923 **Payroll Expense ($000):** 194861 **Personnel:** 1888

☒ **MEDICAL CITY GREEN OAKS HOSPITAL (454094)**, 7808 Clodus Fields Drive, Zip 75251–2206; tel. 972/991–9504, **A**1 5 10 **F**4 5 29 87 98 99 102 104 105 130 132 151 152 153 154 **P**7 **S** HCA Healthcare, Nashville, TN
Primary Contact: Thomas M. Collins, President, Chairman and Chief Executive Officer
COO: Pam Whitley, R.N., Chief Operating Officer and Chief Nursing Officer
CMO: Joel Holiner, M.D., Executive Medical Director
CIO: Richard Fontenault, Director Information Systems
CHR: Kevin Adkins, Director Human Resources
CNO: Pam Whitley, R.N., Chief Nursing Officer and Chief Operating Officer
Web address: www.greenoakspsych.com
Control: Corporation, Investor–owned (for–profit) **Service:** Psychiatric

Staffed Beds: 124 **Admissions:** 5207 **Census:** 119 **Outpatient Visits:** 26323 **Births:** 0 **Total Expense ($000):** 43257 **Payroll Expense ($000):** 20386 **Personnel:** 297

☒ **METHODIST CHARLTON MEDICAL CENTER (450723)**, 3500 West Wheatland Road, Zip 75237–3460, Mailing Address: P.O. Box 225357, Zip 75222–5357; tel. 214/947–7777, **A**1 3 10 13 **F**3 11 13 15 18 20 22 24 28 29 30 31 34 35 40 45 46 47 49 50 53 58 59 60 64 66 68 70 74 76 78 79 81 82 84 85 86 87 97 107 108 110 111 114 115 118 119 126 130 131 132 146 148 **P**5 **S** Methodist Health System, Dallas, TX
Primary Contact: Fran Laukaitis, R.N., FACHE, President
COO: Pamela Stoyanoff, Executive Vice President and Chief Operating Officer
CFO: Michael J Schaefer, Executive Vice President and Chief Financial Officer
CIO: Pamela McNutt, Vice President Information Systems
CHR: Cheryl Flynn, Senior Vice President Chief Human Resources Officer
Web address: www.methodisthealthsystem.org/charlton
Control: Other not–for–profit (including NFP Corporation) **Service:** General medical and surgical

Staffed Beds: 292 **Admissions:** 13034 **Census:** 179 **Outpatient Visits:** 146079 **Births:** 1915 **Total Expense ($000):** 254613 **Payroll Expense ($000):** 117701 **Personnel:** 1618

☒ **METHODIST DALLAS MEDICAL CENTER (450051)**, 1441 North Beckley Avenue, Zip 75203–1201, Mailing Address: P.O. Box 655999, Zip 75265–5999; tel. 214/947–8181, **A**1 2 5 10 **F**3 11 12 13 15 18 20 22 24 26 28 29 30 31 34 35 37 40 43 45 46 47 48 49 50 53 54 58 59 60 64 66 68 70 72 74 76 78 79 81 82 84 85 87 92 93 97 107 108 110 111 114 115 118 119 126 130 132 138 139 142 146 148 149 **P**5 **S** Methodist Health System, Dallas, TX
Primary Contact: John E. Phillips, FACHE, President
COO: Pamela Stoyanoff, Executive Vice President and Chief Operating Officer
CFO: Randy Walker, Vice President
CMO: Leslie Cler, M.D., Chief Medical Officer
CIO: Pamela McNutt, Senior Vice President and Chief Information Officer
CHR: Jackie Middleton, Vice President Human Resources
Web address: www.methodisthealthsystem.org/Dallas
Control: Other not–for–profit (including NFP Corporation) **Service:** General medical and surgical

Staffed Beds: 390 **Admissions:** 15379 **Census:** 241 **Outpatient Visits:** 153357 **Births:** 2791 **Total Expense ($000):** 465761 **Payroll Expense ($000):** 172735 **Personnel:** 2317

☐ **METHODIST REHABILITATION HOSPITAL (673031)**, 3020 West Wheatland Road, Zip 75237–3537; tel. 972/708–8600, (Nonreporting) **A**1 10
Primary Contact: Shari Moore, Chief Executive Officer
CFO: Darline Kennemer, Controller
Web address: www.methodist-rehab.com
Control: Partnership, Investor–owned (for–profit) **Service:** Rehabilitation

Staffed Beds: 40

☐ **NORTH CENTRAL SURGICAL CENTER (670049)**, 9301 North Central Expressway, Suite 100, Zip 75231–0802; tel. 214/265–2810, **A**1 10 **F**3 40 45 79 81 82 85 93 96 107 111 115 119
Primary Contact: Thanh Tran, FACHE, Chief Executive Officer
COO: Ben Magestro, Chief Operating Officer
CFO: Mike Quaglieri, Chief Financial Officer
CMO: Stuart Simon, M.D., Medical Director
CNO: Katherine Martinez, Chief Nursing Officer
Web address: www.northcentralsurgical.com
Control: Partnership, Investor–owned (for–profit) **Service:** Surgical

Staffed Beds: 24 **Admissions:** 1459 **Census:** 8 **Outpatient Visits:** 20130 **Births:** 0 **Total Expense ($000):** 69635 **Payroll Expense ($000):** 16562 **Personnel:** 274

★ **OUR CHILDREN'S HOUSE (453308)**, 1340 Empire Central Drive, Zip 75247–4022; tel. 214/867–6700, **A**3 5 10 **F**3 29 30 35 39 81 89 93 105 129 130 132 146 153 154 **S** Children's Health, Dallas, TX
Primary Contact: David T. Berry, President, Children's Health Clinical Operations
CMO: Andrew Gelfand, M.D., Medical Director
CNO: Kelli Terpstra, R.N., Senior Director
Web address: www.childrens.com/och
Control: Other not–for–profit (including NFP Corporation) **Service:** Children's general medical and surgical

Staffed Beds: 39 **Admissions:** 359 **Census:** 23 **Outpatient Visits:** 76625 **Births:** 0 **Total Expense ($000):** 38091 **Payroll Expense ($000):** 17619 **Personnel:** 169

☒ **PARKLAND HEALTH & HOSPITAL SYSTEM (450015)**, 5200 Harry Hines Boulevard, Zip 75235–7708; tel. 214/590–8000, **A**1 2 3 5 8 10 **F**3 6 8 9 11 12 13 15 16 17 18 20 22 26 28 29 30 31 34 35 37 38 39 40 43 46 47 48 49 50 51 54 55 56 57 58 59 60 61 64 65 66 68 70 71 72 74 75 76 77 78 79 81 82 83 84 85 86 87 90 91 92 93 94 97 98 100 101 102 104 105 107 108 110 111 115 116 117 118 119 129 130 131 132 134 135 138 141 144 146 147 148 149 150 152 154 **P**1
Primary Contact: Fred Cerise, M.D., Chief Executive Officer
COO: David S Lopez, FACHE, Executive Vice President and Chief Operating Officer
CFO: Richard Humphrey, Executive Vice President and Chief Financial Officer
CIO: Fernando Martinez, Senior Vice President and Chief Information Officer
CHR: Corey D. Jackson, Executive Vice President and Chief Talent Officer
CNO: Mary K Eagen, R.N., MS, Executive Vice President, Chief Nursing Officer
Web address: www.parklandhospital.com
Control: Hospital district or authority, Government, nonfederal **Service:** General medical and surgical

Staffed Beds: 844 **Admissions:** 41728 **Census:** 666 **Outpatient Visits:** 1336434 **Births:** 12527 **Total Expense ($000):** 1649217 **Payroll Expense ($000):** 781058 **Personnel:** 11506

☐ **PINE CREEK MEDICAL CENTER (450894)**, 9032 Harry Hines Boulevard, Zip 75235–1720; tel. 214/231–2273, **A**1 10 **F**3 12 18 24 29 30 40 45 49 51 64 79 81 82 85 93 107 111 114 149
Primary Contact: Daniel L. Gideon, FACHE, Chief Executive Officer
CFO: Michael Conroy, Chief Financial Officer
CIO: Kevin Carney, Senior Information Systems Analyst
Web address: www.pinecreekmedicalcenter.com
Control: Partnership, Investor–owned (for–profit) **Service:** Surgical

Staffed Beds: 15 **Admissions:** 1426 **Census:** 8 **Outpatient Visits:** 5855 **Births:** 0 **Total Expense ($000):** 78356 **Payroll Expense ($000):** 13161 **Personnel:** 141

☐ **PROMISE HOSPITAL OF DALLAS (452067)**, 7955 Harry Hines Boulevard, Zip 75235–3305; tel. 214/637–0000, (Nonreporting) **A**1 10 **S** Promise Healthcare, Boca Raton, FL
Primary Contact: Louis P. Bradley Jr, Chief Executive Officer
CFO: Diana B Smith, Chief Financial Officer
CMO: Gary E. Goff, M.D., Medical Director
CHR: Ginger Davenport, Director Human Resources
Web address: www.promise-dallas.com/
Control: Corporation, Investor–owned (for–profit) **Service:** Acute long–term care hospital

Staffed Beds: 62

TX

Hospital, Medicare Provider Number, Address, Telephone, Approval, Facility, and Physician Codes, Health Care System

★ American Hospital Association (AHA) membership
☐ The Joint Commission accreditation
○ Healthcare Facilities Accreditation Program
◇ DNV Healthcare Inc. accreditation
⇑ Center for Improvement in Healthcare Quality Accreditation
△ Commission on Accreditation of Rehabilitation Facilities (CARF) accreditation

© 2018 AHA Guide   *Many Facility Codes have changed. Please refer to the AHA Guide Code Chart.*   Hospitals **A597**

★ **SELECT SPECIALTY HOSPITAL – DALLAS DOWNTOWN (452119)**, 3500 Gaston Avenue, Floors 3&4 Jonsson, Zip 75246–2017; tel. 469/801–4500, **F1** 3 29 74 77 85 86 87 91 96 148 **S** Select Medical Corporation, Mechanicsburg, PA
Primary Contact: Michael McAlister, Chief Executive Officer
Web address: www.dallasdowntown.selectspecialtyhospitals.com/
Control: Corporation, Investor–owned (for–profit) **Service:** Acute long–term care hospital

Staffed Beds: 26 **Admissions:** 295 **Census:** 22 **Outpatient Visits:** 0
Births: 0 **Total Expense ($000):** 15239 **Payroll Expense ($000):** 6324
Personnel: 85

⊠ △ ⇑ **TEXAS HEALTH PRESBYTERIAN HOSPITAL DALLAS (450462)**, 8200 Walnut Hill Lane, Zip 75231–4426; tel. 214/345–6789, **A1** 2 3 5 7 10 21 **F3** 5 11 12 13 15 17 18 20 22 24 26 28 29 30 31 32 34 35 37 38 40 44 45 46 47 49 50 51 53 54 56 57 58 59 60 61 64 65 66 68 70 72 73 74 75 76 77 78 79 81 84 85 86 87 90 91 92 93 94 95 96 97 98 100 101 102 104 105 106 107 108 110 111 112 114 115 118 119 124 126 129 131 132 135 141 143 144 146 147 148 151 152 153 **P6** 5 **S** Texas Health Resources, Arlington, TX
Primary Contact: James Berg, FACHE, President
CFO: Brian Craft, Group Finance Officer
CMO: Aurora Estevez, M.D., Chief Medical Officer
CIO: Tammy Phillips, Director, Information Systems
CHR: Stacy Miller, Entity Human Resources Officer
CNO: Cole Edmonson, R.N., MS, FACHE, Vice President and Chief Nursing Officer
Web address: www.texashealth.org
Control: Other not–for–profit (including NFP Corporation) **Service:** General medical and surgical

Staffed Beds: 611 **Admissions:** 27263 **Census:** 399 **Outpatient Visits:** 145360 **Births:** 5145 **Total Expense ($000):** 606919 **Payroll Expense ($000):** 217193 **Personnel:** 2420

TEXAS HOSPITAL FOR ADVANCED MEDICINE See Dallas Medical Center

☐ **TEXAS INSTITUTE FOR SURGERY AT TEXAS HEALTH PRESBYTERIAN DALLAS (450889)**, 7115 Greenville Avenue, Suite 100, Zip 75231–5100; tel. 214/647–5300, **A1** 10 **F40** 51 64 79 81 82 107 114 115 119
Primary Contact: David Helfer, FACHE, President
CFO: John S Croley, Vice President Business Operations
CMO: Presley Mock, M.D., Chief of Staff
CHR: Jennifer C. Levy, Director Human Resources
CNO: Tammy Jarvis, Vice President Clinical Services and Chief Nursing Officer
Web address: www.texasinstituteforsurgery.com
Control: Partnership, Investor–owned (for–profit) **Service:** General medical and surgical

Staffed Beds: 9 **Admissions:** 420 **Census:** 2 **Outpatient Visits:** 10852 **Births:** 0 **Total Expense ($000):** 52128 **Payroll Expense ($000):** 12152 **Personnel:** 189

⊠ **TEXAS SCOTTISH RITE HOSPITAL FOR CHILDREN (453314)**, 2222 Welborn Street, Zip 75219–3924, Mailing Address: P.O. Box 190567, Zip 75219–0567; tel. 214/559–5000, **A1** 3 5 10 **F3** 9 11 29 34 35 50 53 54 57 58 64 68 74 75 77 79 81 82 85 86 87 89 92 94 107 111 115 119 130 131 132 146 148 **P6**
Primary Contact: Robert L. Walker, FACHE, President and Chief Executive Officer
CFO: William R Huston, Senior Vice President and Chief Financial Officer
CMO: Daniel J Sucato, M.D., MS, Chief of Staff
CIO: Les Clonch, Chief Information Officer
CHR: Connie Wright, Vice President Human Resources
CNO: Debbie A Sayles, R.N., Vice President and Chief Nursing Officer
Web address: www.tsrhc.org
Control: Other not–for–profit (including NFP Corporation) **Service:** Children's orthopedic

Staffed Beds: 52 **Admissions:** 577 **Census:** 12 **Outpatient Visits:** 51947 **Births:** 0 **Total Expense ($000):** 173406 **Payroll Expense ($000):** 79766 **Personnel:** 959

☐ **TIMBERLAWN MENTAL HEALTH SYSTEM (454081)**, 4600 Samuell Boulevard, Zip 75228–6800; tel. 214/381–7181, **A1** 5 10 **F56** 59 98 100 101 103 130 **S** Universal Health Services, Inc., King of Prussia, PA
Primary Contact: Shelah Adams, Chief Executive Officer
COO: Rick Paczkowski, Chief Operating Officer
CFO: Lori Verbeke, Chief Financial Officer
CMO: John Pascoe, M.D., Executive Medical Director
CIO: Twila Ragar–Thomas, Director Health Information Management and Quality Improvement
CHR: Winnie Boehnke, Director Human Resources
CNO: Paula Hirschberg, R.N., Director of Nursing
Web address: www.timberlawn.com
Control: Corporation, Investor–owned (for–profit) **Service:** Psychiatric

Staffed Beds: 57 **Admissions:** 1571 **Census:** 28 **Outpatient Visits:** 0
Births: 0 **Total Expense ($000):** 11539 **Payroll Expense ($000):** 5746
Personnel: 70

⊠ △ **UNIVERSITY OF TEXAS SOUTHWESTERN MEDICAL CENTER (450766)**, 5323 Harry Hines Boulevard, Zip 75390–9265; tel. 214/648–3111, (Includes UNIVERSITY OF TEXAS SOUTHWESTERN MEDICAL CENTER – ZALE LIPSHY, 5151 Harry Hines Boulevard, Dallas, TX, Zip 75390–9265; tel. 214/645–8300; Daniel Podolsky, M.D., President) **A1** 2 5 7 8 10 **F3** 7 8 11 12 13 15 17 18 20 22 24 26 28 29 30 31 34 35 36 38 39 40 44 45 46 47 48 49 50 52 53 54 55 56 57 58 59 60 61 62 64 65 68 70 71 72 74 75 76 77 78 79 80 81 82 84 85 86 87 90 91 92 93 94 95 96 97 98 99 100 101 102 103 104 107 108 109 110 111 114 115 116 117 118 119 120 121 123 124 126 129 130 131 132 135 136 137 138 139 140 141 142 143 145 146 147 148 149 150 153 154 **P4** 6
Primary Contact: John Warner, M.D., Chief Executive Officer
COO: Becky McCulley, Chief Operations Officer
CMO: John Warner, M.D., Chief Executive Officer, Interim Chief Medical Officer
CIO: Marc E. Milstein, Vice President Information Resources
CHR: Ivan Thompson, Vice President, Chief Human Resource Officer
CNO: Susan Hernandez, R.N., Chief Nurse Executive
Web address: www.utsouthwestern.edu
Control: State, Government, nonfederal **Service:** General medical and surgical

Staffed Beds: 608 **Admissions:** 27152 **Census:** 431 **Outpatient Visits:** 439615 **Births:** 2001 **Total Expense ($000):** 1158482 **Payroll Expense ($000):** 444700 **Personnel:** 5989

⊠ △ **VETERANS AFFAIRS NORTH TEXAS HEALTH CARE SYSTEM**, 4500 South Lancaster Road, Zip 75216–7167; tel. 214/742–8387, (Includes SAM RAYBURN MEMORIAL VETERANS CENTER, 1201 East Ninth Street, Bonham, TX, Zip 75418–4091; tel. 903/583–2111; Angela Nix, Administrator) (Nonreporting) **A1** 2 3 5 7 **S** Department of Veterans Affairs, Perry Point, MD
Primary Contact: Stephen R. Holt, M.D., Director
CFO: Alton McKinley, Chief Financial Officer
CIO: Lucy Rogers, Chief Information Resource Management Systems
Web address: www.northtexas.va.gov/
Control: Veterans Affairs, Government, federal **Service:** General medical and surgical

Staffed Beds: 875

WILLIAM P. CLEMENTS, JR. UNIVERSITY HOSPITAL (450044), 6201 Harry Hines Boulevard, Zip 75235–5202; tel. 214/633–5555, (Nonreporting) **A3** 5
Primary Contact: Daniel Podolsky, M.D., President
Web address: www.utswmedicine.org/hospitals–clinics/clements/about/faqs/
Control: State, Government, nonfederal **Service:** General medical and surgical

Staffed Beds: 460

DECATUR—Wise County

⊠ **WISE HEALTH SYSTEM (450271)**, 609 Medical Center Drive, Zip 76234–3836; tel. 940/627–5921, (Includes WISE HEALTH SURGICAL HOSPITAL AT ARGYLE, 7218 Crawford Road, Argyle, TX, Zip 76226; tel. 940/293–2885; Jason Wren, President and Chief Executive Officer; WISE HEALTH SURGICAL HOSPITAL AT PARKWAY, 3200 North Tarrant Parkway, Fort Worth, TX, Zip 76177–8611; tel. 817/502–7300; Jason Wren, President and Chief Executive Officer; WISE REGIONAL HEALTH SYSTEM, EAST CAMPUS DECATUR, 609 Medical Center Drive, Decatur, TX, Zip 76234–3836; tel. 940/627–5921; WISE REGIONAL HEALTH SYSTEM, WEST CAMPUS DECATUR, 2000 South Fm 51, Decatur, TX, Zip 76234–3702; tel. 940/627–5921; Jason Wren, Chief Executive Officer) **A1** 2 10 **F3** 11 12 13 15 17 18 20 22 24 26 28 29 30 31 32 34 40 43 45 47 49 51 53 54 56 57 59 60 64 70 74 75 76 77 78 79 81 85 87 89 90 93 96 97 98 103 104 107 108 110 111 114 115 117 119 129 130 131 132 135 144 147 148 149 154
Primary Contact: Jason Wren, President and Chief Executive Officer
COO: Leon Fuqua, Chief Operating Officer
CFO: Todd Scroggins, Chief Financial Officer
CMO: Jon W. Walker, M.D., Chief Medical Officer
CIO: Joe Arispe, Director Information Systems
CHR: Mike McQuiston, Administrative Director Human Resources
CNO: Lee Ann Jennings, R.N., Vice President, Nursing Services
Web address: www.wiseregional.com
Control: Hospital district or authority, Government, nonfederal **Service:** General medical and surgical

Staffed Beds: 157 **Admissions:** 5352 **Census:** 74 **Outpatient Visits:** 367366 **Births:** 566 **Total Expense ($000):** 386807 **Payroll Expense ($000):** 89207 **Personnel:** 1445

DEL RIO—Val Verde County

⊠ **VAL VERDE REGIONAL MEDICAL CENTER (450154)**, 801 Bedell Avenue, Zip 78840–4112, Mailing Address: 801 North Bedell Avenue, Zip 78840–4112; tel. 830/775–8566, **A1** 10 20 22 **F3** 7 11 13 15 18 20 29 30 34 35 40 43 46 48 54 56 57 59 63 73 75 76 77 79 81 82 84 85 87 89 93 96 101 104 107 108 110 111 114 119 129 131 132 133 146 147 149 153 154
Primary Contact: Xochy Hurtado, FACHE, Chief Executive Officer
CFO: Eddie Read, Interim Chief Financial Officer
CMO: Mohamed Shafiu, M.D., Chief of Staff
CIO: Val King, Chief Information Officer
CNO: Kathy Fletcher, R.N., MSN, Interim Chief Nursing Officer
Web address: www.vvrmc.org
Control: Hospital district or authority, Government, nonfederal **Service:** General medical and surgical

Staffed Beds: 80 **Admissions:** 2537 **Census:** 21 **Outpatient Visits:** 80596 **Births:** 886 **Total Expense ($000):** 65234 **Payroll Expense ($000):** 21862 **Personnel:** 454

Many Facility Codes have changed. Please refer to the AHA Guide Code Chart. © 2018 AHA Guide

TX

DENISON—Grayson County

☐ **TEXOMA MEDICAL CENTER (450324)**, 5016 South US Highway 75, Zip 75020–4584, Mailing Address: P.O. Box 890, Zip 75021–0890; tel. 903/416–4000, (Includes TMC BEHAVIORAL HEALTH CENTER, 2601 North Cornerstone Drive, Sherman, TX, Zip 75092–2551; tel. 903/416–3000; Ryan Tatu, Chief Executive Officer) **A**1 10 13 **F**3 11 12 13 15 17 18 20 22 24 28 29 30 31 34 35 40 43 45 46 47 48 49 50 53 54 57 59 62 64 70 74 75 76 77 78 79 80 81 82 85 86 87 89 90 91 93 96 98 99 100 101 102 103 104 107 108 110 111 115 118 119 126 129 130 132 144 145 146 147 148 149 150 153 **P**5 **S** Universal Health Services, Inc., King of Prussia, PA
Primary Contact: Ronald T. Seal, Chief Executive Officer
CFO: Gerard Hebert, Chief Financial Officer
CMO: Robert Sanders, M.D., Chief Medical Officer
CIO: Lisa Engle, Director Information Technology
CHR: Bill Heinzmann, Director Human Resources
CNO: Andrea Brenn, R.N., Chief Nursing Officer
Web address: www.texomamedicalcenter.net
Control: Corporation, Investor–owned (for–profit) **Service**: General medical and surgical

Staffed Beds: 326 Admissions: 18139 Census: 240 Outpatient Visits: 132616 Births: 1086 Total Expense ($000): 234504 Payroll Expense ($000): 98495 Personnel: 2050

DENTON—Denton County

☐ **INTEGRITY TRANSITIONAL HOSPITAL (452109)**, 2813 South Mayhill Road, Zip 76208–5910; tel. 940/320–2300, (Nonreporting) **A**1 10
Primary Contact: Israel Navarro, Chief Executive Officer
CNO: Michele Andrews, Chief Clinical Officer
Web address: www.ithcare.com
Control: Partnership, Investor–owned (for–profit) **Service**: Acute long–term care hospital

Staffed Beds: 44

☒ **MAYHILL HOSPITAL (670010)**, 2809 South Mayhill Road, Zip 76208–5910; tel. 940/239–3000, (Nonreporting) **A**1 10 **S** Universal Health Services, Inc., King of Prussia, PA
Primary Contact: Nichol Attar, Chief Executive Officer
CFO: Emmy Adams, Chief Financial Officer
CMO: Asad Islam, M.D., Chief Medical Officer
CIO: Kyle Murphy, Director Information Technology
CHR: Patricia Gloria–Barraza, Coordinator Human Resources
Web address: www.mayhillhospital.com
Control: Partnership, Investor–owned (for–profit) **Service**: Psychiatric

Staffed Beds: 59

☒ **MEDICAL CITY DENTON (450634)**, 3535 South I–35 East, Zip 76210; tel. 940/384–3535, **A**1 10 **F**3 15 18 20 22 24 26 28 29 30 34 35 40 43 45 46 47 49 50 57 59 64 70 74 75 77 79 80 81 82 84 85 86 87 93 107 108 110 111 114 115 118 119 126 130 132 144 146 148 154 **S** HCA Healthcare, Nashville, TN
Primary Contact: Steven Edgar, FACHE, President and Chief Executive Officer
COO: John Walker, Chief Operating Officer
CFO: Todd Gibson, Chief Financial Officer
CMO: Howard Shaw, M.D., Chief Medical Officer
CHR: Stacey Bravo, Vice President Human Resources
CNO: Nicki Roderman, Chief Nursing Officer
Web address: www.dentonregional.com
Control: Partnership, Investor–owned (for–profit) **Service**: General medical and surgical

Staffed Beds: 185 Admissions: 9271 Census: 126 Outpatient Visits: 74662 Births: 0 Total Expense ($000): 155526 Payroll Expense ($000): 52448 Personnel: 799

☒ **SELECT REHABILITATION HOSPITAL OF DENTON (673036)**, 2620 Scripture Street, Zip 76201–4315; tel. 940/297–6500, **A**1 10 **F**3 29 60 64 68 74 75 77 79 86 87 90 93 96 132 135 148 149 **P**6 **S** Select Medical Corporation, Mechanicsburg, PA
Primary Contact: Michelle Powell, Chief Executive Officer
CFO: Doug Selsor, Director Finance
CHR: Patsy Martin, Manager Human Resources
CNO: Lee Ann Elliott, R.N., Director of Nursing
Web address: www.selectrehab–denton.com/
Control: Partnership, Investor–owned (for–profit) **Service**: Rehabilitation

Staffed Beds: 44 Admissions: 711 Census: 23 Outpatient Visits: 12439 Births: 0 Total Expense ($000): 14475 Payroll Expense ($000): 7900 Personnel: 110

☒ **TEXAS HEALTH PRESBYTERIAN HOSPITAL DENTON (450743)**, 3000 North I–35, Zip 76201–5119; tel. 940/898–7000, **A**1 10 **F**3 12 13 15 18 20 22 24 26 28 29 30 31 34 35 39 40 45 46 47 48 49 57 59 65 66 68 70 72 74 75 76 78 79 81 82 83 84 85 86 87 93 107 108 110 111 115 118 119 126 129 130 132 135 146 147 148 149 **S** Texas Health Resources, Arlington, TX
Primary Contact: Jeff Reecer, FACHE, Chief Executive Officer
CFO: David B Meltzer, Chief Financial Officer
CMO: Timothy Harris, M.D., Chief Quality Officer
CIO: Melissa Smart, Communication ad Public Relations Specialist
CHR: Kathy Hardcastle, Director Human Resources
CNO: Deborah Bostic, R.N., Chief Nursing Officer
Web address: www.dentonhospital.com
Control: Other not–for–profit (including NFP Corporation) **Service**: General medical and surgical

Staffed Beds: 197 Admissions: 10507 Census: 127 Outpatient Visits: 73219 Births: 2268 Total Expense ($000): 194536 Payroll Expense ($000): 72653 Personnel: 945

★ ⇑ **THE HEART HOSPITAL BAYLOR DENTON (450893)**, 2801 South Mayhill Road, Zip 76208–5910, Mailing Address: 1100 Allied Drive, Plano, Zip 76208–5910; tel. 940/220–0600, **A**10 21 **F**3 17 18 20 22 24 26 28 29 30 34 35 40 54 57 59 60 64 68 74 75 77 81 82 84 85 87 90 107 111 115 119 130 132 135 146 148 149 154
Primary Contact: Mark Valentine, President
COO: Bradley Morgan, Vice President of Operations
CFO: Bryan Nichols, Chief Financial Officer
CMO: Trent Pettijohn, M.D., Esq Chief Medical Officer
CHR: Tracy Stanford, Director Human Resources
CNO: Susan K. Moats, R.N., Vice President Patient Care Services and Chief Nursing Officer
Web address: www.https://denton.thehearthospitalbaylor.com
Control: Partnership, Investor–owned (for–profit) **Service**: Heart

Staffed Beds: 22 Admissions: 646 Census: 8 Outpatient Visits: 6237 Births: 0 Total Expense ($000): 38211 Payroll Expense ($000): 12575 Personnel: 117

☒ **UNIVERSITY BEHAVIORAL HEALTH OF DENTON (454104)**, 2026 West University Drive, Zip 76201–0644; tel. 940/320–8100, (Nonreporting) **A**1 10 **S** Universal Health Services, Inc., King of Prussia, PA
Primary Contact: Ronald Rains, Chief Executive Officer
CFO: Ed Sopiarz, Chief Financial Officer
CMO: Atique Khan, M.D., Medical Director
CIO: Marsh Smith, Manager Health Information
CHR: Dorie Atherton, Manager Human Resources
CNO: Vicki Stoker, Chief Nursing Officer
Web address: www.ubhdenton.com
Control: Partnership, Investor–owned (for–profit) **Service**: Psychiatric

Staffed Beds: 104

DENVER CITY—Yoakum County

★ **YOAKUM COUNTY HOSPITAL (451308)**, 412 Mustang Avenue, Zip 79323–2762, Mailing Address: P.O. Box 1130, Zip 79323–1130; tel. 806/592–2121, **A**10 18 **F**3 11 13 28 34 35 40 41 43 50 53 57 59 60 62 64 76 81 87 89 93 107 114 119 127 129 133 149 154 **P**6
Primary Contact: Jerry Osburn, Chief Executive Officer
CFO: Suann Parrish, Chief Financial Officer
CMO: Dan Khan, M.D., Chief Medical Officer
CIO: Todd Carrillo, Chief Information Officer
CHR: Teresa Howard, Manager Human Resources
Web address: www.ych.us
Control: County, Government, nonfederal **Service**: General medical and surgical

Staffed Beds: 22 Admissions: 584 Census: 6 Outpatient Visits: 55609 Births: 260 Total Expense ($000): 26329 Payroll Expense ($000): 8700 Personnel: 181

DESOTO—Dallas County

☐ **DALLAS BEHAVIORAL HEALTHCARE HOSPITAL (454126)**, 800 Kirnwood Drive, Zip 75115–2000; tel. 855/982–0897, **A**1 **F**4 5 56 87 98 99 100 101 103 104 105 130 151 152 153 154 **S** Signature Healthcare Services, Corona, CA
Primary Contact: Selene Q. Hammon, Chief Executive Officer
CMO: Rahim Haqqani, M.D., Medical Director
CHR: Henry In, Director Human Resources
CNO: Susie Edler, R.N., Chief Nursing Officer
Web address: www.dallasbehavioral.com
Control: Individual, Investor–owned (for–profit) **Service**: Psychiatric

Staffed Beds: 116 Admissions: 4530 Census: 99 Outpatient Visits: 8337 Births: 0 Total Expense ($000): 20489 Payroll Expense ($000): 11680 Personnel: 259

TX

Hospital, Medicare Provider Number, Address, Telephone, Approval, Facility, and Physician Codes, Health Care System

★ American Hospital Association (AHA) membership ○ Healthcare Facilities Accreditation Program ⇑ Center for Improvement in Healthcare Quality Accreditation
☐ The Joint Commission accreditation ◇ DNV Healthcare Inc. accreditation △ Commission on Accreditation of Rehabilitation Facilities (CARF) accreditation

☐ **HICKORY TRAIL HOSPITAL (454065)**, 2000 Old Hickory Trail,
Zip 75115–2242; tel. 972/298–7323, **A**1 10 **F**4 5 29 38 98 99 100 101 103
104 105 130 152 153 **S** Universal Health Services, Inc., King of Prussia, PA
Primary Contact: Kay McKennery, Interim Chief Executive Officer
CFO: Terri Logsdon, Chief Financial Officer
CMO: Manoochehr Khatami, M.D., Medical Director
CHR: Sarah Warren, Coordinator Human Resources
Web address: www.hickorytrail.com
Control: Corporation, Investor–owned (for–profit) **Service**: Psychiatric

Staffed Beds: 86 **Admissions**: 2876 **Census**: 59 **Outpatient Visits**: 7483
Births: 0 **Total Expense ($000)**: 16663 **Payroll Expense ($000)**: 8131
Personnel: 161

⊠ **VIBRA SPECIALTY HOSPITAL AT DESOTO (452097)**, 2700 Walker Way,
Zip 75115–2088; tel. 972/298–1100, (Nonreporting) **A**1 10 **S** Vibra Healthcare,
Mechanicsburg, PA
Primary Contact: Thomas Alexander, Chief Executive Officer
CFO: Donald Trimble, CPA, Chief Financial Officer
CMO: Ed Dominguez, President Medical Staff
CHR: Tim Lozier, Director Human Resources
CNO: Mae C Weathersby, R.N., Chief Clinical Officer
Web address: www.vshdesoto.com
Control: Corporation, Investor–owned (for–profit) **Service**: Acute long–term care
hospital

Staffed Beds: 40

DIMMITT—Castro County

★ **PLAINS MEMORIAL HOSPITAL (451350)**, 310 West Halsell Street,
Zip 79027–1846, Mailing Address: P.O. Box 278, Zip 79027–0278;
tel. 806/647–2191, **A**10 18 **F**3 7 32 34 35 40 43 53 57 59 64 65 69 75 77 85
86 87 93 97 107 114 115 119 127 130 133 135 149 **P**6
Primary Contact: Linda Rasor, R.N., Chief Executive Officer
CFO: Terri Martinez, Chief Financial Officer
CMO: Gary R Hardee, M.D., Medical Director
CIO: Terry Young, Chief Information Officer
CHR: Debbie Underwood, Manager Human Resources
CNO: Renee Castillo, Chief Nursing Officer
Web address: www.plainsmemorial.com
Control: Hospital district or authority, Government, nonfederal **Service**: General
medical and surgical

Staffed Beds: 17 **Admissions**: 170 **Census**: 3 **Outpatient Visits**: 14598
Births: 0 **Total Expense ($000)**: 11534 **Payroll Expense ($000)**: 4820
Personnel: 106

DUMAS—Moore County

☐ **MOORE COUNTY HOSPITAL DISTRICT (450221)**, 224 East Second Street,
Zip 79029–3808; tel. 806/935–7171, **A**1 10 **F**3 7 11 13 15 28 34 35 40 43 46
50 51 57 59 62 63 70 75 79 81 85 86 91 93 107 110 111 115 119 130 131
132 133 135 146 147 148 154
Primary Contact: Jeff Turner, FACHE, Chief Executive Officer
COO: Ashleigh Wiswell, Chief Operations Officer
CFO: John E. Bailey, Chief Financial Officer
CHR: Kathie Fuston, Director Human Resources
CNO: Ronda Crow, Chief Nursing Officer
Web address: www.mchd.net
Control: Hospital district or authority, Government, nonfederal **Service**: General
medical and surgical

Staffed Beds: 25 **Admissions**: 928 **Census**: 7 **Outpatient Visits**: 46462
Births: 353 **Total Expense ($000)**: 36147 **Payroll Expense ($000)**: 16618
Personnel: 341

EAGLE LAKE—Colorado County

RICE MEDICAL CENTER (451312), 600 South Austin Road, Zip 77434–3298,
Mailing Address: P.O. Box 277, Zip 77434–0277; tel. 979/234–5571, **A**10 18
F3 11 13 15 29 34 35 40 43 56 59 64 65 75 76 77 79 80 81 85 101 104 107
114 119 127 133 153 154 **P**6
Primary Contact: James D. Janek, Chief Executive Officer
CMO: Russell Thomas, M.D., Chief of Staff
CHR: Velma Loya, Administrative Human Resource Coordinator
CNO: Susan Hernandez, R.N., Chief Nursing Officer
Web address: www.ricemedicalcenter.net/
Control: Corporation, Investor–owned (for–profit) **Service**: General medical and
surgical

Staffed Beds: 13 **Admissions**: 218 **Census**: 3 **Outpatient Visits**: 25125
Births: 28 **Total Expense ($000)**: 13885 **Payroll Expense ($000)**: 3398
Personnel: 97

EAGLE PASS—Maverick County

☐ **FORT DUNCAN REGIONAL MEDICAL CENTER (450092)**, 3333 North Foster
Maldonado Boulevard, Zip 78852–5893; tel. 830/773–5321, **A**1 10 20 **F**11 13
15 29 40 43 45 57 60 65 68 70 75 76 77 79 81 85 89 90 91 93 107 108 110
111 114 118 119 129 130 146 147 148 **S** Universal Health Services, Inc., King
of Prussia, PA
Primary Contact: Eladio Montalvo, Chief Executive Officer
COO: Alan Gonzalez, Chief Operating Officer
CFO: Joel Morales, Chief Financial Officer
CMO: Ruben de los Santos, M.D., Chief Medical Officer
CIO: Jose Elias, Director Information Technology
CHR: Daisy Rodriquez, Director Human Resources
CNO: Scott Lethi, R.N., FACHE, Chief Nursing Officer
Web address: www.fortduncanmedicalcenter.com
Control: Partnership, Investor–owned (for–profit) **Service**: General medical and surgical

Staffed Beds: 101 **Admissions**: 4365 **Census**: 49 **Outpatient Visits**: 47314
Births: 1088 **Total Expense ($000)**: 53627 **Payroll Expense ($000)**: 21555
Personnel: 357

EASTLAND—Eastland County

EASTLAND MEMORIAL HOSPITAL (450411), 304 South Daugherty
Street, Zip 76448–2609, Mailing Address: P.O. Box 897, Zip 76448–0897;
tel. 254/629–2601, **A**10 20 **F**7 11 12 15 28 29 30 34 35 40 43 45 50 53 57 59
64 68 77 81 85 86 87 89 93 107 108 110 114 128 130 131 133 135 146 148
Primary Contact: Ted Matthews, Chief Executive Officer
CFO: Jamie Hayden, Chief Financial Officer
CHR: Leisha Hodges, Human Resources Officer
Web address: www.eastlandmemorial.com
Control: Hospital district or authority, Government, nonfederal **Service**: General
medical and surgical

Staffed Beds: 36 **Admissions**: 499 **Census**: 7 **Outpatient Visits**: 21983
Births: 0 **Total Expense ($000)**: 13776 **Payroll Expense ($000)**: 5677
Personnel: 146

EDEN—Concho County

CONCHO COUNTY HOSPITAL (451325), 614 Eaker Street, Zip 76837–0359,
Mailing Address: P.O. Box 987, Zip 76837–0987; tel. 325/869–5911, **A**10 18 **F**3
34 40 43 50 53 59 77 87 107 133 146
Primary Contact: Brian Lady, Administrator and Chief Executive Officer
CFO: Melanie Lozano, Chief Financial Officer
CNO: Toby Lehn, Director of Nurses
Web address: www.conchocountyhospital.com/
Control: Hospital district or authority, Government, nonfederal **Service**: General
medical and surgical

Staffed Beds: 16 **Admissions**: 125 **Census**: 2 **Outpatient Visits**: 3874
Births: 0 **Total Expense ($000)**: 8484 **Payroll Expense ($000)**: 3162
Personnel: 49

EDINBURG—Hidalgo County

⊠ **CORNERSTONE REGIONAL HOSPITAL (450825)**, 2302 Cornerstone
Boulevard, Zip 78539–8471; tel. 956/618–4444, **A**1 10 **F**3 8 29 34 35 37 39
40 45 46 47 51 57 59 68 74 79 81 82 85 119 126 145 **S** Universal Health
Services, Inc., King of Prussia, PA
Primary Contact: Roxanna M. Godinez, Chief Executive Officer
CFO: Janie Alvarez, Accounting Director
CMO: Omar Gomez, M.D., Chief of Staff
CHR: Erika Betancourt, Coordinator Human Resources
CNO: Roxanne Reyes, Director of Nursing
Web address: www.cornerstoneregional.com
Control: Partnership, Investor–owned (for–profit) **Service**: Surgical

Staffed Beds: 14 **Admissions**: 652 **Census**: 4 **Outpatient Visits**: 2960
Births: 0 **Total Expense ($000)**: 14568 **Payroll Expense ($000)**: 4016
Personnel: 80

☐ △ **DOCTOR'S HOSPITAL AT RENAISSANCE (450869)**, 5501 South McColl
Road, Zip 78539–9152; tel. 956/362–7360, **A**1 2 3 5 7 10 **F**1 3 4 5 8 9 12 13
15 17 18 19 20 22 24 26 28 29 30 31 34 35 38 39 40 41 43 45 46 47 48 49
50 51 53 54 55 57 58 59 60 63 64 65 66 67 68 70 71 72 73 74 75 76 77
78 79 80 81 82 83 84 85 86 87 88 89 90 91 92 93 95 96 97 98 99 100 101
102 103 104 107 108 109 110 111 112 113 114 115 116 117 118 119 120
121 123 124 126 127 128 130 131 132 135 138 139 144 145 146 147 148
149 151 154 **P**1 3
Primary Contact: Susan S. Turley, President
COO: Marissa Castaneda, Chief Operating Officer and Director Marketing
CFO: Susan S. Turley, Chief Financial Officer
Web address: www.dhr–rgv.com
Control: Partnership, Investor–owned (for–profit) **Service**: General medical and surgical

Staffed Beds: 519 **Admissions**: 30302 **Census**: 401 **Outpatient
Visits**: 375793 **Births**: 8123 **Total Expense ($000)**: 457699 **Payroll
Expense ($000)**: 195038 **Personnel**: 4439

Many Facility Codes have changed. Please refer to the AHA Guide Code Chart.   © 2018 AHA Guide

☐ **SOUTH TEXAS HEALTH SYSTEM (450119)**, 1400 West Trenton Road,
Zip 78539–9105, Mailing Address: 1102 West Trenton Road, Zip 78539–9105;
tel. 956/388–6000, (Includes EDINBURG CHILDREN'S HOSPITAL, 1400 West
Trenton Road, Edinburg, TX, Zip 78539; tel. 956/388–8000, EDINBURG
REGIONAL MEDICAL CENTER, 1102 West Trenton Road, Edinburg, TX,
Zip 78539–6199; tel. 956/388–6000; Lance Ames, Interim Chief Executive
Officer; MCALLEN HEART HOSPITAL, 1900 South D Street, McAllen, TX,
Zip 78503; tel. 956/994–2000; Dan Caldwell, Chief Executive Officer; MCALLEN
MEDICAL CENTER, 301 West Expressway 83, McAllen, TX, Zip 78503–3045;
tel. 956/632–4000; Todd Mann, Chief Executive Officer; SOUTH TEXAS
BEHAVIORAL HEALTH CENTER, 2101 West Trenton Road, Edinburg, TX, Zip 78539;
tel. 956/388–1300; Joe Rodriguez, Chief Executive Officer) **A**1 10 **F**3 4 5 11 12
13 15 17 18 19 20 22 24 26 29 30 31 34 35 38 40 41 43 45 46 47 48 49 50
56 57 58 59 60 64 68 70 72 74 75 76 77 78 79 81 85 86 87 88 89 90 93 96
97 98 99 100 101 102 103 104 107 108 110 111 114 115 119 126 129 130
132 135 146 148 149 150 154 **P**6 **S** Universal Health Services, Inc., King of
Prussia, PA
Primary Contact: Lance Ames, Interim Chief Executive Officer
COO: Jerome M Brooks, Chief Operating Officer
CFO: Carlos Guajardo, Chief Financial Officer
CMO: Yuri Bermudez, M.D., Chief of Staff
CIO: Rosie L Mendiola-Balderas, Director Information Systems
CHR: Patricia Mcclelland, Director Human Resources
CNO: Candida Constantine-Castillo, MSN, R.N., Chief Nursing Officer
Web address: www.southtexashealthsystem.com
Control: Partnership, Investor–owned (for–profit) **Service:** General medical and
surgical

Staffed Beds: 810 **Admissions:** 26035 **Census:** 351 **Outpatient
Visits:** 203475 **Births:** 1665 **Total Expense ($000):** 345270 **Payroll
Expense ($000):** 121266 **Personnel:** 2294

EDNA—Jackson County

★ **JACKSON COUNTY HOSPITAL DISTRICT (451363)**, 1013 South Wells Street,
Zip 77957–4098; tel. 361/782–7800, **A**10 18 **F**3 7 15 29 34 35 40 43 44 45
50 53 57 59 62 64 65 68 75 81 87 97 102 107 110 114 119 127 130 133
143 146 **P**8
Primary Contact: Bill Jones, Chief Executive Officer
CFO: Lance Smiga, Chief Financial Officer
CMO: Francisco Ortiz, M.D., Chief of Staff
CIO: Jeff Prukop, Director Professional Services
CHR: Donna Coleman, Coordinator Human Resources
CNO: Tammy Zajicek, Director of Nursing
Web address: www.jchd.org
Control: Hospital district or authority, Government, nonfederal **Service:** General
medical and surgical

Staffed Beds: 17 **Admissions:** 192 **Census:** 3 **Outpatient Visits:** 16760
Births: 0 **Total Expense ($000):** 19537 **Payroll Expense ($000):** 7829
Personnel: 124

EL CAMPO—Wharton County

EL CAMPO MEMORIAL HOSPITAL (450694), 303 Sandy Corner Road,
Zip 77437–9535; tel. 979/543–6251, **A**10 **F**3 11 15 18 28 29 30 34 35 40 45
54 57 59 60 64 65 66 68 70 77 79 81 85 86 91 92 93 97 107 108 110 111
112 114 119 127 129 130 133 135 148 154 **P**6
Primary Contact: Nathan Tudor, Chief Executive Officer
CFO: David Mak, Chief Financial Officer
CMO: Thai Huynh, M.D., Chief of Medical Staff
CIO: Bill Eller, Director Information Technology
CHR: Ginger Andreas, Coordinator Personnel and Credentialing
CNO: Desiree Cernoch, Director of Nurses
Web address: www.ecmh.org
Control: Other not–for–profit (including NFP Corporation) **Service:** General
medical and surgical

Staffed Beds: 26 **Admissions:** 918 **Census:** 9 **Outpatient Visits:** 66010
Births: 0 **Total Expense ($000):** 24286 **Payroll Expense ($000):** 9246
Personnel: 157

EL PASO—El Paso County

EAST EL PASO PHYSICIANS MEDICAL CENTER See Foundation Surgical
Hospital of El Paso

☐ **EL PASO BEHAVIORAL HEALTH SYSTEM (454109)**, 1900 Denver Avenue,
Zip 79902–3008; tel. 915/544–4000, (Nonreporting) **A**1 5 10 **S** Universal Health
Services, Inc., King of Prussia, PA
Primary Contact: Phillip Sosa, Interim Chief Executive Officer
CFO: Phillip Sosa, Chief Financial Officer
CMO: Arthur L. Ramirez, M.D., Medical Director
CIO: Victor Torres, Information Technology Specialist Administrator
CHR: Brenda Holguin, Manager Human Resources
CNO: Susan Brown, Chief Nursing Officer
Web address: www.ubhelpaso.com/
Control: Corporation, Investor–owned (for–profit) **Service:** Psychiatric

Staffed Beds: 163

☐ **EL PASO CHILDREN'S HOSPITAL (453313)**, 4845 Alameda Avenue,
Zip 79905–2705; tel. 915/242–8614, **A**1 3 5 10 **F**3 19 29 30 31 34 35 38 39
40 41 44 45 48 49 50 57 58 59 61 64 68 72 73 74 75 78 79 81 82 85 86 87
88 89 93 96 99 100 111 119 130 132 134 146 148 149 150 **P**6
Primary Contact: Cindy Stout, R.N., Chief Executive Officer
COO: Ellen Pitcher, Chief Nursing Officer and Chief Operating Officer
CFO: Andrew Rybolt, Chief Financial Officer
CMO: Bradley Fuhrman, M.D., Physician in Chief
CIO: Janina Prada, Director Information Technology
CHR: Marina Estrada, Director Human Resources
CNO: Ellen Pitcher, Chief Nursing Officer and Chief Operating Officer
Web address: www.elpasochildrens.org
Control: Other not–for–profit (including NFP Corporation) **Service:** Children's
general medical and surgical

Staffed Beds: 122 **Admissions:** 3556 **Census:** 57 **Outpatient Visits:** 44568
Births: 0 **Total Expense ($000):** 101456 **Payroll Expense ($000):** 31519
Personnel: 478

EL PASO LTAC HOSPITAL (452103), 1221 North Cotton Street,
Zip 79902–3015; tel. 915/546–5822, **A**10 **F**1 3 7 29 30 34 57 60 75 77 82 84
85 86 87 100 103 119 130 148
Primary Contact: Skylier Blake, R.N., Chief Executive Officer
CFO: Eddie Martinez, Chief Financial Officer
Control: Partnership, Investor–owned (for–profit) **Service:** Acute long–term care
hospital

Staffed Beds: 33 **Admissions:** 219 **Census:** 14 **Outpatient Visits:** 0
Births: 0 **Total Expense ($000):** 6499 **Payroll Expense ($000):** 2747
Personnel: 53

☐ **EL PASO PSYCHIATRIC CENTER (454100)**, 4615 Alameda Avenue,
Zip 79905–2702; tel. 915/532–2202, **A**1 3 5 10 **F**29 98 99 103 130 135 **P**6 **S**
Texas Department of State Health Services, Austin, TX
Primary Contact: Zulema Carrillo, Superintendent
CFO: David Osterhout, Assistant Superintendent and Chief Financial Officer
CNO: Raul D. Luna, Chief Nurse Executive
Web address: www.dshs.state.tx.us/mhhospitals/ElPasoPC/default.shtm
Control: State, Government, nonfederal **Service:** Psychiatric

Staffed Beds: 74 **Admissions:** 900 **Census:** 65 **Outpatient Visits:** 0
Births: 0 **Total Expense ($000):** 25898 **Payroll Expense ($000):** 10871
Personnel: 230

☐ **EL PASO SPECIALTY HOSPITAL (450845)**, 1755 Curie Drive, Zip 79902–2919;
tel. 915/544–3636, **A**1 3 10 **F**3 12 29 34 35 40 51 59 64 68 75 79 81 82 85
86 87 107 111 115 130 131 148 **S** National Surgical Healthcare, Chicago, IL
Primary Contact: James Wilcox, Chief Executive Officer
CFO: Greg Watters, Chief Financial Officer
CMO: David Mansfield, M.D., Chief of Staff
CNO: Anne Harvey, MSN, Chief Nursing Officer
Web address: www.elpasospecialtyhospital.com
Control: Partnership, Investor–owned (for–profit) **Service:** Orthopedic

Staffed Beds: 20 **Admissions:** 703 **Census:** 4 **Outpatient Visits:** 20706
Births: 0 **Total Expense ($000):** 27890 **Payroll Expense ($000):** 8544
Personnel: 153

TX

Hospital, Medicare Provider Number, Address, Telephone, Approval, Facility, and Physician Codes, Health Care System

★ American Hospital Association (AHA) membership ○ Healthcare Facilities Accreditation Program ⇧ Center for Improvement in Healthcare Quality Accreditation
☐ The Joint Commission accreditation ◇ DNV Healthcare Inc. accreditation △ Commission on Accreditation of Rehabilitation Facilities (CARF) accreditation

© 2018 AHA Guide   *Many Facility Codes have changed. Please refer to the AHA Guide Code Chart.*   Hospitals **A601**

○ **FOUNDATION SURGICAL HOSPITAL OF EL PASO (450877)**, 1416 George Dieter Drive, Zip 79936–7601; tel. 915/598–4240, **A**3 10 11 **F**3 29 40 45 49 79 81 82 85 86 93 107 111 114 119 126 **S** Foundation Surgical Hospital Affiliates, Oklahoma City, OK
Primary Contact: Don Burris, Chief Executive Officer
COO: Marta Contreras, Chief Nursing Officer and Chief Operating Officer
CIO: Louie Aguilera, Director Information Technology
CHR: Grace Beltran, Director Human Resources
CNO: Marta Contreras, Chief Nursing Officer and Chief Operating Officer
Web address: www.foundationhospitals.com/elpaso/
Control: Partnership, Investor–owned (for–profit) **Service**: Surgical

Staffed Beds: 20 **Admissions**: 718 **Census**: 5 **Outpatient Visits**: 51422 **Births**: 0 **Total Expense ($000)**: 41331 **Payroll Expense ($000)**: 8760 **Personnel**: 251

⊠ **HIGHLANDS REHABILITATION HOSPITAL (453086)**, 1395 George Dieter Drive, Zip 79936–7410; tel. 915/298–7222, **A**1 10 **F**3 29 30 34 57 59 64 74 75 79 86 87 90 93 96 100 130 132 143 146 148 149 **S** Vibra Healthcare, Mechanicsburg, PA
Primary Contact: Travis Rich, Chief Executive Officer
CHR: Janet Straughan, Manager Human Resources
CNO: Oscar Mendizabal, Chief Nursing Officer
Web address: www.vrhhighlands.com/
Control: Partnership, Investor–owned (for–profit) **Service**: Rehabilitation

Staffed Beds: 41 **Admissions**: 856 **Census**: 25 **Outpatient Visits**: 4533 **Births**: 0 **Total Expense ($000)**: 12547 **Payroll Expense ($000)**: 7062 **Personnel**: 121

⊠ **KINDRED HOSPITAL EL PASO (452079)**, 1740 Curie Drive, Zip 79902–2901; tel. 915/351–9044, **A**1 10 **F**1 3 29 45 46 70 75 148 149 **S** Kindred Healthcare, Louisville, KY
Primary Contact: America Jones, R.N., Chief Executive Officer
CFO: Melissa Campa, Controller
CMO: Edward Juarez, M.D., Chief Medical Officer
CHR: Laura Anchondo, Administrator Human Resources
Web address: www.khelpaso.com
Control: Corporation, Investor–owned (for–profit) **Service**: Acute long–term care hospital

Staffed Beds: 57 **Admissions**: 572 **Census**: 39 **Outpatient Visits**: 256 **Births**: 0 **Total Expense ($000)**: 18920 **Payroll Expense ($000)**: 7777 **Personnel**: 138

⊠ △ **LAS PALMAS MEDICAL CENTER (450107)**, 1801 North Oregon Street, Zip 79902–3591; tel. 915/521–1200, (Includes DEL SOL MEDICAL CENTER, 10301 West Gateway Boulevard, El Paso, TX, Zip 79925–7798; tel. 915/595–9000; David Shimp, Chief Executive Officer; LAS PALMAS REHABILITATION HOSPITAL, 300 Waymore Drive, El Paso, TX, Zip 79902–1628; tel. 915/577–2600; Don Karl, Interim Chief Executive Officer) **A**1 3 5 7 10 **F**3 8 9 10 11 12 13 15 17 18 19 20 22 24 26 27 28 29 30 31 34 35 37 38 39 40 41 43 45 46 47 48 49 50 51 53 54 56 57 58 59 60 64 68 70 72 73 74 75 76 77 78 79 81 82 85 86 87 88 89 91 92 93 96 102 107 108 110 111 112 114 115 119 120 121 122 124 126 127 129 130 132 134 135 136 138 143 144 145 146 147 148 149 150 **S** HCA Healthcare, Nashville, TN
Primary Contact: Don Karl, Interim Chief Executive Officer
COO: Don Karl, Chief Operating Officer
CMO: Oscar Vega, M.D., Chief Medical Officer
CNO: Jerry Gonzalez, Interim Chief Nursing Officer
Web address: www.laspalmashealth.com
Control: Partnership, Investor–owned (for–profit) **Service**: General medical and surgical

Staffed Beds: 509 **Admissions**: 26453 **Census**: 371 **Outpatient Visits**: 144325 **Births**: 4532 **Total Expense ($000)**: 440788 **Payroll Expense ($000)**: 154876 **Personnel**: 2184

☐ **MESA HILLS SPECIALTY HOSPITAL (452035)**, 2311 North Oregon Street, 5th Floor, Zip 79902–3216; tel. 915/545–1823, **A**1 10 **F**1 3 29 64 75 81 148 **S** Concord Healthcare Group, Lakewood, NJ
Primary Contact: Jose Huerta, Chief Executive Officer
COO: Elena Pino, Chief Operating Officer and Chief Nursing Officer
CFO: Priscilla Carter, Chief Financial Officer
Web address: www.specialtyhospitalmesahills.com/
Control: Corporation, Investor–owned (for–profit) **Service**: Acute long–term care hospital

Staffed Beds: 32 **Admissions**: 251 **Census**: 13 **Outpatient Visits**: 62 **Births**: 0 **Total Expense ($000)**: 7543 **Payroll Expense ($000)**: 3786 **Personnel**: 63

⊠ **THE HOSPITALS OF PROVIDENCE EAST CAMPUS (670047)**, 3280 Joe Battle Boulevard, Zip 79938–2622; tel. 915/832–2000, **A**1 5 10 **F**3 13 15 18 20 22 26 29 30 31 34 35 37 39 40 41 45 49 50 51 57 59 60 63 64 68 70 72 73 74 75 76 77 78 79 81 83 84 85 86 87 89 93 107 108 110 111 115 119 126 130 134 146 147 148 149 154 **P**4 **S** TENET Healthcare Corporation, Dallas, TX
Primary Contact: Monica Vargas–Mahar, FACHE, Chief Executive Officer
COO: Brandon May, Chief Operating Officer
Web address: www.sphn.com
Control: Individual, Investor–owned (for–profit) **Service**: General medical and surgical

Staffed Beds: 182 **Admissions**: 12241 **Census**: 143 **Outpatient Visits**: 96988 **Births**: 2252 **Total Expense ($000)**: 171932 **Payroll Expense ($000)**: 53246 **Personnel**: 908

⊠ **THE HOSPITALS OF PROVIDENCE MEMORIAL CAMPUS (450002)**, 2001 North Oregon Street, Zip 79902–3368; tel. 915/577–6625, (Includes PROVIDENCE CHILDREN'S HOSPITAL, 2001 North Oregon Street, El Paso, TX, Zip 79902–3320; tel. 915/577–7746; Nicholas R Tejeda, FACHE, Market Chief Executive Officer) **A**1 10 **F**3 8 11 12 13 14 15 17 18 19 20 21 22 23 26 29 30 31 32 34 35 37 40 41 43 45 46 48 49 50 54 55 56 57 58 59 60 63 64 65 67 70 71 72 74 75 76 77 78 79 81 84 85 86 88 89 93 97 98 100 101 102 103 105 107 110 111 115 119 126 130 133 134 141 143 145 146 147 148 149 150 154 **S** TENET Healthcare Corporation, Dallas, TX
Primary Contact: Nicholas R. Tejeda, FACHE, Market Chief Executive Officer
COO: Roddex Barlow, Chief Operating Officer
CFO: Charles Handley, Chief Financial Officer
CIO: Ray Davis, Administrative Director
CHR: Stephanie S. Talley, Market Chief Human Resource Officer
CNO: Barbara Vazquez, Chief Nursing Officer
Web address: www.thehospitalsofprovidence.com
Control: Partnership, Investor–owned (for–profit) **Service**: General medical and surgical

Staffed Beds: 382 **Admissions**: 15910 **Census**: 187 **Outpatient Visits**: 139340 **Births**: 3015 **Total Expense ($000)**: 250799 **Payroll Expense ($000)**: 80310 **Personnel**: 1335

⊠ **THE HOSPITALS OF PROVIDENCE SIERRA CAMPUS (450668)**, 1625 Medical Center Drive, Zip 79902–5005; tel. 915/747–4000, **A**1 5 10 **F**3 17 18 20 22 24 26 28 29 30 34 37 40 43 45 46 48 49 50 54 57 58 59 60 61 64 65 68 69 70 72 74 75 76 77 78 79 81 82 85 86 90 96 97 107 108 110 111 114 115 119 124 126 130 132 135 143 145 146 147 148 149 154 **S** TENET Healthcare Corporation, Dallas, TX
Primary Contact: Nicholas R. Tejeda, FACHE, Chief Executive Officer
COO: Benson Chacko, Chief Operating Officer
CFO: Victoria Gonzalez, Chief Financial Officer
CIO: Ray Davis, Administrative Director Information Systems
CHR: Stephanie S. Talley, Chief Human Resource Officer
CNO: Erik Cazares, Chief Nursing Officer
Web address: www.thehospitalsofprovidence.com
Control: Partnership, Investor–owned (for–profit) **Service**: General medical and surgical

Staffed Beds: 297 **Admissions**: 9744 **Census**: 126 **Outpatient Visits**: 96952 **Births**: 950 **Total Expense ($000)**: 170727 **Payroll Expense ($000)**: 54545 **Personnel**: 820

★ **THE HOSPITALS OF PROVIDENCE TRANSMOUNTAIN CAMPUS (670120)**, 2000 Transmountain Road, Zip 79911; tel. 915/877–8300, (Data for 349 days) **A**10 **F**3 11 13 15 18 20 22 29 30 31 34 35 40 41 43 44 45 46 48 49 50 57 58 59 60 64 68 70 73 74 75 76 77 78 79 81 85 100 107 108 111 115 118 119 126 130 131 134 146 147 148 154 **S** TENET Healthcare Corporation, Dallas, TX
Primary Contact: Tasha Hopper, Chief Executive Officer
COO: Tasha Hopper, Chief Operating Officer
CFO: David Byrd, Chief Financial Officer
CMO: Gustavo Martell, M.D., Chief Medical Officer
CIO: Ray Davis, Chief Information Officer
CHR: Stephanie S. Talley, Chief Human Resource Officer
CNO: Linda B. Lawson, Chief Nursing Officer
Web address: www.thehospitalsofprovidence.com/our-locations/transmountain
Control: Corporation, Investor–owned (for–profit) **Service**: General medical and surgical

Staffed Beds: 106 **Admissions**: 2937 **Census**: 33 **Outpatient Visits**: 22295 **Births**: 222 **Total Expense ($000)**: 68292 **Payroll Expense ($000)**: 23930 **Personnel**: 342

TRIUMPH HOSPITAL EL PASO See Kindred Hospital El Paso

TX

Many Facility Codes have changed. Please refer to the AHA Guide Code Chart. © 2018 AHA Guide

⊞ **UNIVERSITY MEDICAL CENTER OF EL PASO (450024)**, 4815 Alameda Avenue, Zip 79905-2794, Mailing Address: P.O. Box 20009, Zip 79998-0009; tel. 915/544-1200, **A**1 2 3 5 10 **F**3 8 11 13 15 17 18 20 22 24 26 28 29 30 31 34 35 37 40 43 45 46 47 48 49 50 51 53 54 56 57 59 60 61 64 65 68 70 74 75 76 77 78 79 81 82 85 86 87 91 92 93 94 96 97 100 102 107 108 110 111 112 113 114 115 118 119 126 127 130 131 134 143 144 145 146 147 148 149 150 **P**6
Primary Contact: Jacob Cintron, FACHE, President and Chief Executive Officer
COO: Maria Zampini, Chief Operating Officer
CFO: Michael Nunez, Chief Financial Officer
CMO: Joel Hendryx, M.D., Chief Medical Officer
CIO: Janina Prada, Director Information Services
CHR: Janice M Harris, Director Human Resources
Web address: www.thomasoncares.org
Control: Hospital district or authority, Government, nonfederal **Service**: General medical and surgical

Staffed Beds: 251 **Admissions:** 14824 **Census:** 185 **Outpatient Visits:** 809927 **Births:** 2968 **Total Expense ($000):** 628646 **Payroll Expense ($000):** 159359 **Personnel:** 2619	

⊞ **WILLIAM BEAUMONT ARMY MEDICAL CENTER**, 5005 North Piedras Street, Zip 79920-5001; tel. 915/742-2121, (Nonreporting) **A**1 2 5 **S** Department of the Army, Office of the Surgeon General, Falls Church, VA
Primary Contact: Colonel Erik G. Rude, Commander
CIO: Major Rion Koon, Chief Information Management Division
Web address: www.wbamc.amedd.army.mil/NewPersonnel/CDR.aspx
Control: Army, Government, federal **Service**: General medical and surgical

Staffed Beds: 209

ELDORADO—Schleicher County

★ **SCHLEICHER COUNTY MEDICAL CENTER (451304)**, 102 North US Highway 277, Zip 76936-4010; tel. 325/853-2507, **A**10 18 **F**34 40 57 59 64 65 66 68 87 93 107 127 133 **S** Preferred Management Corporation, Shawnee, OK
Primary Contact: Paul Burke, Administrator
CFO: Larry Stephens, Chief Financial Officer
CMO: Gordy Day, M.D., Medical Director
CHR: Beverly Minor, Chief Human Resources
Web address: www.scmc.us
Control: Corporation, Investor-owned (for-profit) **Service**: General medical and surgical

Staffed Beds: 14 **Admissions:** 90 **Census:** 1 **Outpatient Visits:** 8608 **Births:** 0 **Total Expense ($000):** 5116 **Payroll Expense ($000):** 2287 **Personnel:** 53

ELECTRA—Wichita County

★ **ELECTRA MEMORIAL HOSPITAL (451343)**, 1207 South Bailey Street, Zip 76360-3221, Mailing Address: P.O. Box 1112, Zip 76360-1112; tel. 940/495-3981, **A**10 18 **F**3 7 11 28 29 32 34 35 40 43 53 57 59 62 64 65 66 75 77 86 93 97 107 114 119 127 129 130 131 133 148
Primary Contact: Rebecca J. McCain, Chief Executive Officer
CFO: Ginnie Holmes, Chief Financial Officer
CIO: Brandon Huffstutler, Chief Information Officer
CNO: Kim Gilbert, R.N., Chief Nursing Officer
Web address: www.electrahospital.com
Control: Hospital district or authority, Government, nonfederal **Service**: General medical and surgical

Staffed Beds: 19 **Admissions:** 402 **Census:** 5 **Outpatient Visits:** 28335 **Births:** 0 **Total Expense ($000):** 16725 **Payroll Expense ($000):** 8556 **Personnel:** 115

ENNIS—Ellis County

⊞ **ENNIS REGIONAL MEDICAL CENTER (450833)**, 2201 West Lampasas Street, Zip 75119-5644; tel. 972/875-0900, **A**1 10 **F**3 11 15 18 29 30 34 35 40 43 45 50 51 57 59 64 65 70 75 77 79 81 82 85 91 93 107 108 110 111 115 119 146 147 149 **S** LifePoint Health, Brentwood, TN
Primary Contact: Robert C. Honeycutt, Chief Executive Officer
CFO: Jack Wilcox, Chief Financial Officer
CMO: Raymond W Blair, M.D., Jr Chief of Staff
CHR: Selena Cryer, Director Human Resources
CNO: Edwina A Miner, R.N., Chief Nursing Officer
Web address: www.ennisregional.com
Control: Partnership, Investor-owned (for-profit) **Service**: General medical and surgical

Staffed Beds: 58 **Admissions:** 595 **Census:** 5 **Outpatient Visits:** 29418 **Births:** 0 **Total Expense ($000):** 23123 **Payroll Expense ($000):** 8037 **Personnel:** 142

FAIRFIELD—Freestone County

★ **FREESTONE MEDICAL CENTER (450658)**, 125 Newman Street, Zip 75840-1499; tel. 903/389-2121, **A**10 **F**3 11 15 28 29 34 40 43 45 50 57 59 64 65 75 81 97 107 108 110 115 119 127 130 132 **S** Community Hospital Corporation, Plano, TX
Primary Contact: John M. Yeary, FACHE, Chief Executive Officer
CFO: David A Travis, Chief Financial Officer
CMO: Darryl White, M.D., Chief of Staff
CHR: Jennifer Rummel, Director Human Resources
CNO: Tonya Basque, Chief Nursing Officer
Web address: www.freestonemc.com/
Control: County, Government, nonfederal **Service**: General medical and surgical

Staffed Beds: 37 **Admissions:** 304 **Census:** 2 **Outpatient Visits:** 28857 **Births:** 0 **Total Expense ($000):** 10675 **Payroll Expense ($000):** 4619 **Personnel:** 88

FLORESVILLE—Wilson County

CONNALLY MEMORIAL MEDICAL CENTER (450108), 499 10th Street, Zip 78114-3175; tel. 830/393-1300, **A**10 **F**3 15 18 29 34 35 40 43 45 47 49 54 57 59 62 64 70 75 81 82 85 86 87 107 108 110 111 114 119 130 132 133 144 146 148 154 **P**6
Primary Contact: Jeremy Riney, Chief Executive Officer
COO: Bob Gillespie, Chief Operating Officer
CFO: Curtis Rojas, Interim Chief Financial Officer
CMO: Wade Krause, M.D., Chief Medical Officer
CIO: Bob Gillespie, Chief Information Technology Officer
CHR: Loretta Y Morgan, Director Human Resources
CNO: Sue Tackitt, Chief Nursing Officer
Web address: www.connallymmc.org
Control: Hospital district or authority, Government, nonfederal **Service**: General medical and surgical

Staffed Beds: 26 **Admissions:** 985 **Census:** 10 **Outpatient Visits:** 125762 **Births:** 0 **Total Expense ($000):** 38795 **Payroll Expense ($000):** 15550 **Personnel:** 333

FLOWER MOUND—Denton County

ICARE REHABILITATION HOSPITAL (673064), 3100 Peters Colony Road, Zip 75022-2949; tel. 214/513-0310, (Nonreporting) **A**10 22
Primary Contact: Gina Tomaseski, Chief Executive Officer
Web address: www.icarerehabilitation.com/
Control: Corporation, Investor-owned (for-profit) **Service**: Rehabilitation

Staffed Beds: 41

☐ **TEXAS HEALTH PRESBYTERIAN HOSPITAL FLOWER MOUND (670068)**, 4400 Long Prairie Road, Zip 75028-1892; tel. 469/322-7000, **A**1 10 **F**3 12 13 15 18 20 29 30 31 34 40 45 49 57 59 70 73 74 75 76 77 78 79 81 82 85 87 91 107 108 110 111 114 115 119 126 130 146 147 149
Primary Contact: Spencer Turner, FACHE, President
COO: Shelley R Tobey, R.N., MS, Chief Operating Officer and Chief Nursing Officer
CFO: Tom Howard, Chief Financial Officer
CHR: Nicole Schweigert, Director Human Resources
CNO: Shelley R Tobey, R.N., MS, Chief Operating Officer and Chief Nursing Officer
Web address: www.texashealthflowermound.com/
Control: Partnership, Investor-owned (for-profit) **Service**: General medical and surgical

Staffed Beds: 92 **Admissions:** 6187 **Census:** 51 **Outpatient Visits:** 37401 **Births:** 1846 **Total Expense ($000):** 117303 **Payroll Expense ($000):** 42785 **Personnel:** 646

FORT HOOD—Bell County

⊞ **CARL R. DARNALL ARMY MEDICAL CENTER**, 36000 Darnall Loop, Zip 76544-5095; tel. 254/288-8000, (Nonreporting) **A**1 2 3 5 **S** Department of the Army, Office of the Surgeon General, Falls Church, VA
Primary Contact: Colonel David R. Gibson, Chief Executive Officer
CHR: Charles Burton, Chief Human Resources
Web address: www.crdamc.amedd.army.mil
Control: Army, Government, federal **Service**: General medical and surgical

Staffed Beds: 109

TX

Hospital, Medicare Provider Number, Address, Telephone, Approval, Facility, and Physician Codes, Health Care System
★ American Hospital Association (AHA) membership   ○ Healthcare Facilities Accreditation Program   ⇑ Center for Improvement in Healthcare Quality Accreditation ☐ The Joint Commission accreditation   ◇ DNV Healthcare Inc. accreditation   △ Commission on Accreditation of Rehabilitation Facilities (CARF) accreditation

FORT SAM HOUSTON—Bexar County

☒ **BROOKE ARMY MEDICAL CENTER**, 3851 Roger Brookes Drive,
Zip 78234–4501; tel. 210/916–4141, (Nonreporting) **A**1 2 3 5 **S** Department of
the Army, Office of the Surgeon General, Falls Church, VA
Primary Contact: Brigadier General Jeffrey Johnson, Commander
CMO: Colonel Joseph P Chozinski, M.D., Deputy Commander Clinical Services
CHR: Rose Juarez, Chief Civilian Personnel Branch
CNO: Colonel Sheri Howell, Deputy Commander Nursing
Web address: www.bamc.amedd.army.mil
Control: Army, Government, federal **Service**: General medical and surgical

Staffed Beds: 226

BROOKE ARMY MEDICAL CENTER See Brooke Army Medical Center

FORT STOCKTON—Pecos County

PECOS COUNTY MEMORIAL HOSPITAL (450178), 387 West I H–10,
Zip 79735–8912, Mailing Address: P.O. Box 1648, Zip 79735–1648;
tel. 432/336–2004, **A**3 10 20 **F**3 11 13 28 29 30 32 34 35 40 43 45 46 50 53
57 59 62 63 64 65 75 76 81 93 107 111 119 127 130 133 144 146 148 **P**6
Primary Contact: Betsy Briscoe, Chief Executive Officer
COO: Margaret Davis, Chief Operating Officer
CFO: Sharon Hunt, Interim Chief Financial Officer
CMO: Subodh Mallik, M.D., Chief of Staff
CHR: Malissa Trevino, Director Human Resources
CNO: Gina Kalka, R.N., Chief Nursing Officer
Web address: www.pcmhfs.com
Control: County, Government, nonfederal **Service**: General medical and surgical

Staffed Beds: 25 **Admissions**: 551 **Census**: 5 **Outpatient Visits**: 59830
Births: 110 **Total Expense ($000)**: 26887 **Payroll Expense ($000)**: 13110
Personnel: 254

FORT WORTH—Tarrant County

☒ **BAYLOR ALL SAINTS MEDICAL CENTER AT FORT WORTH (450137)**, 1400
Eighth Avenue, Zip 76104–4192; tel. 817/926–2544, **A**1 2 3 5 10 **F**3 11 12 13
17 18 24 26 28 29 30 31 34 35 38 40 43 45 46 47 49 53 55 59 64 70 72 73
74 75 76 77 78 79 80 81 84 86 87 96 97 102 107 108 111 114 115 119 124
126 130 131 132 138 139 142 146 147 148 149 154 **S** Baylor Scott & White
Health, Dallas, TX
Primary Contact: Michael Sanborn, FACHE, MS, President
COO: Janice L Walker, R.N., Chief Operating Officer
CFO: Lucy Catala, Vice President Finance
CMO: Dahlia Hassani, Vice President of Medical Affairs
CIO: Sandy Vaughn, Director Information Services
CHR: Tracy Stanford, Director Human Resources
Web address: www.baylorhealth.com/PhysiciansLocations/AllSaints/Pages/
Default.aspx
Control: Other not–for–profit (including NFP Corporation) **Service**: General
medical and surgical

Staffed Beds: 360 **Admissions**: 18065 **Census**: 241 **Outpatient
Visits**: 63696 **Births**: 5398 **Total Expense ($000)**: 347696 **Payroll Expense
($000)**: 129936 **Personnel**: 1348

☒ **BAYLOR INSTITUTE FOR REHABILITATION AT FORT WORTH (673035)**, 6601
Harris Parkway, Zip 76132–6108; **A**1 10 **F**3 28 29 30 64 75 90 93 130 149 **S**
Select Medical Corporation, Mechanicsburg, PA
Primary Contact: Victoria Odom. Sanders, FACHE, Chief Executive Officer
CMO: Asher Light, M.D., Medical Director
CHR: Nissi Dalton, Manager Human Resources
CNO: Catherine Ewing, M.D., Chief Nursing Officer
Web address: www.baylorhealth.com/PhysiciansLocations/BIR/Pages/Default.aspx
Control: Partnership, Investor–owned (for–profit) **Service**: Rehabilitation

Staffed Beds: 42 **Admissions**: 569 **Census**: 19 **Outpatient Visits**: 5033
Births: 0 **Total Expense ($000)**: 14758 **Payroll Expense ($000)**: 7755
Personnel: 107

☐ **BAYLOR SURGICAL HOSPITAL AT FORT WORTH (450880)**, 1800 Park Place
Avenue, Zip 76110–1302; tel. 682/703–5600, **A**1 10 **F**3 8 12 40 51 64 70 79
81 82 85 87 107 111 119 131
Primary Contact: Paul Debona, Chief Executive Officer
CFO: Jane Mathis, Chief Financial Officer
CMO: Bruce Bollinger, M.D., Medical Director
CNO: Stacie Merrill, Chief Nursing Officer
Web address: www.mcsh–hospital.com
Control: Partnership, Investor–owned (for–profit) **Service**: General medical and
surgical

Staffed Beds: 30 **Admissions**: 1926 **Census**: 12 **Outpatient Visits**: 10682
Births: 0 **Total Expense ($000)**: 91080 **Payroll Expense ($000)**: 15815
Personnel: 234

☒ **COOK CHILDREN'S MEDICAL CENTER (453300)**, 801 Seventh Avenue,
Zip 76104–2796; tel. 682/885–4000, **A**1 3 5 10 **F**3 7 8 9 17 19 21 23 25 27
29 30 31 32 34 35 37 38 39 40 41 43 44 45 46 47 48 49 54 55 57 59 60 61
62 63 64 65 68 72 74 75 77 78 79 80 81 82 83 84 85 86 87 88 89 90 91 92
93 97 98 99 100 101 105 107 108 111 112 113 114 115 118 119 126 129
130 132 133 136 138 144 146 148 149 150 154 **P**6
Primary Contact: Rick W. Merrill, System President and Chief Executive Officer
CFO: Stephen Kimmel, Chief Financial Officer
CMO: James C Cunningham, M.D., Chief Medical Officer
CIO: Theresa Meadows, Chief Information Officer
CNO: Teresa J Clark, R.N., MS, Chief Nursing Officer
Web address: www.cookchildrens.org
Control: Other not–for–profit (including NFP Corporation) **Service**: Children's
general medical and surgical

Staffed Beds: 372 **Admissions**: 11206 **Census**: 221 **Outpatient
Visits**: 380432 **Births**: 0 **Total Expense ($000)**: 829900 **Payroll Expense
($000)**: 263304 **Personnel**: 4066

☒ **ENCOMPASS HEALTH REHABILITATION HOSPITAL OF CITY VIEW (453042)**,
6701 Oakmont Boulevard, Zip 76132–2957; tel. 817/370–4700, **A**1 10 **F**3
29 75 77 90 91 94 95 96 130 148 154 **S** Encompass Health Corporation,
Birmingham, AL
Primary Contact: Janell Briscoe, Chief Executive Officer
Web address: www.healthsouthcityview.com
Control: Corporation, Investor–owned (for–profit) **Service**: Rehabilitation

Staffed Beds: 62 **Admissions**: 1159 **Census**: 40 **Outpatient Visits**: 0
Births: 0 **Total Expense ($000)**: 14541 **Payroll Expense ($000)**: 8592
Personnel: 145

☒ **ENCOMPASS HEALTH REHABILITATION HOSPITAL OF FORT WORTH
(453041)**, 1212 West Lancaster Avenue, Zip 76102–4510; tel. 817/870–2336,
A1 10 **F**3 29 60 74 75 77 79 86 90 91 95 96 130 131 148 154 **S** Encompass
Health Corporation, Birmingham, AL
Primary Contact: Janell Briscoe, Chief Executive Officer
CFO: Sherry Hapney, Chief Financial Officer
CMO: Patrick Donovan, M.D., Director Medical Staff
CHR: Tara Kleas, Area Director Human Resources
Web address: www.healthsouthfortworth.com
Control: Corporation, Investor–owned (for–profit) **Service**: Rehabilitation

Staffed Beds: 60 **Admissions**: 990 **Census**: 34 **Outpatient Visits**: 0
Births: 0 **Total Expense ($000)**: 13646 **Payroll Expense ($000)**: 7659
Personnel: 141

JOHN PETER SMITH HOSPITAL See JPS Health Network, Fort Worth

★ ⇑ **JPS HEALTH NETWORK (450039)**, 1500 South Main Street,
Zip 76104–4917; tel. 817/921–3431, (Includes JOHN PETER SMITH HOSPITAL,
1500 South Main Street, Fort Worth, TX, Zip 76104; tel. 817/921–3431; TRINITY
SPRINGS PAVILION, 1500 South Main Street, Fort Worth, TX, Zip 76104–4917;
tel. 817/927–3636; Lily Wong, Director Psychiatry) **A**2 3 5 8 10 21 **F**3 8 11 13
15 18 20 22 24 26 28 29 30 31 32 34 35 36 38 39 40 43 44 45 47 49 50 54
56 57 58 59 60 61 64 65 66 68 70 72 74 75 76 77 78 79 80 81 82 84 85 86
87 91 92 93 97 98 100 101 102 104 105 107 108 110 111 115 119 123 124
126 130 131 132 134 142 143 144 146 147 148 149 153 **P**8
Primary Contact: Robert Earley, President and Chief Executive Officer
CFO: Alan Townsend, Interim Chief Financial Officer
CIO: Melinda Custin, Chief Information Officer
CHR: Nikki Sumpter, Senior Vice President Human Resources
CNO: Wanda V. Peebles, Chief Nursing Officer
Web address: www.jpshealthnet.org
Control: Hospital district or authority, Government, nonfederal **Service**: General
medical and surgical

Staffed Beds: 556 **Admissions**: 30274 **Census**: 452 **Outpatient
Visits**: 1010105 **Births**: 4561 **Total Expense ($000)**: 902946 **Payroll
Expense ($000)**: 378285 **Personnel**: 5784

☒ **KINDRED HOSPITAL–FORT WORTH (452088)**, 815 Eighth Avenue,
Zip 76104–2609; tel. 817/332–4812, (Includes KINDRED HOSPITAL TARRANT
COUNTY–FORT WORTH SOUTHWEST, 7800 Oakmont Boulevard, Fort Worth, TX,
Zip 76132–4299; tel. 817/346–0094; Anna Rojas, Chief Executive Officer) **A**1 10
F3 29 46 48 70 77 79 82 85 107 114 119 130 148 154 **S** Kindred Healthcare,
Louisville, KY
Primary Contact: Susan Schaetti, Chief Executive Officer
CFO: Susan Popp, Controller
CMO: Stuart McDonald, M.D., President Medical Staff
CIO: Norma Warner, Area Director Health Information Management
CHR: Nicole Newpower, Coordinator Human Resources
Web address: www.kindredfortworth.com/
Control: Corporation, Investor–owned (for–profit) **Service**: Acute long–term care hospital

Staffed Beds: 156 **Admissions**: 1718 **Census**: 116 **Outpatient Visits**: 5805
Births: 0 **Total Expense ($000)**: 56729 **Payroll Expense ($000)**: 24214
Personnel: 369

TX

Many Facility Codes have changed. Please refer to the AHA Guide Code Chart. © 2018 AHA Guide

★ **MEDICAL CITY ALLIANCE (670103)**, 3101 North Tarrant Parkway, Zip 76177; tel. 817/639-1000, **F**3 11 12 13 15 18 20 22 24 26 29 30 34 35 40 45 46 47 48 49 50 54 56 57 59 64 70 72 74 75 76 79 81 82 85 86 87 92 107 108 110 111 114 119 126 130 132 135 145 146 147 148 149 154 **S** HCA Healthcare, Nashville, TN
Primary Contact: Glenn Wallace, Chief Executive Officer
Web address: www.baylorhealth.com/PhysiciansLocations/BIR/Pages/Default.aspx
Control: Corporation, Investor-owned (for-profit) **Service:** General medical and surgical

**Staffed Beds: 75 Admissions: 2836 Census: 30 Outpatient Visits: 45728
Births: 741 Total Expense ($000): 74551 Payroll Expense ($000): 23281
Personnel: 361**

⊞ **MEDICAL CITY FORT WORTH (450672)**, 900 Eighth Avenue, Zip 76104-3902; tel. 817/336-2100, **A**1 2 3 10 13 **F**3 11 12 17 18 20 22 24 26 28 29 30 31 34 35 40 45 46 48 49 53 56 58 64 67 70 74 77 78 79 81 85 87 91 93 107 108 111 114 115 119 126 130 138 139 145 146 148 **P**8 **S** HCA Healthcare, Nashville, TN
Primary Contact: Jyric Sims, FACHE, Chief Executive Officer
COO: John Corbeil, Chief Operating Officer
CFO: Elia Stokes, Chief Financial Officer
CMO: Terry Loftus, M.D., Chief Medical Officer
CIO: Kelley Fredrickson, Director Information Services
CHR: Cyndi Roberts, Director Human Resources
CNO: Damita Williams, Ed.D., R.N., MSN, Chief Nursing Officer
Web address: www.medicalcityfortworth.com/about/
Control: Partnership, Investor-owned (for-profit) **Service:** General medical and surgical

**Staffed Beds: 212 Admissions: 9553 Census: 143 Outpatient
Visits: 44019 Births: 0 Total Expense ($000): 206422 Payroll Expense
($000): 63894 Personnel: 867**

☐ **MESA SPRINGS (454124)**, 5560 Mesa Springs Drive, Zip 76123; tel. 817/292-4600, **A**1 10 **F**5 29 54 98 99 101 103 104 105 135 153 **S** Springstone, Louisville, KY
Primary Contact: Barbara Schmidt, Chief Executive Officer
CFO: Kent Ashley, Chief Financial Officer
CMO: Stewart Keller, M.D., Medical Director
CHR: Jill Housand, Director Human Resources
CNO: Ana Ramirez, Director of Nursing
Web address: www.springstone.com/hospitals.stmhl
Control: Corporation, Investor-owned (for-profit) **Service:** Psychiatric

**Staffed Beds: 72 Admissions: 3009 Census: 63 Outpatient Visits: 35164
Births: 0 Total Expense ($000): 20188 Payroll Expense ($000): 12163
Personnel: 239**

⊞ **TEXAS HEALTH HARRIS METHODIST HOSPITAL ALLIANCE (670085)**, 10864 Texas Health Trail, Zip 76244-4897; tel. 682/212-2000, **A**1 10 **F**3 11 12 13 15 18 20 22 24 26 28 29 30 34 35 40 45 48 49 50 57 59 64 70 72 74 75 76 77 79 80 81 82 85 86 91 93 107 108 110 111 113 114 115 118 119 126 130 131 132 135 146 147 148 **S** Texas Health Resources, Arlington, TX
Primary Contact: Clint Abernathy, President and Chief Operating Officer
Web address: www.texashealth.org/alliance/Pages/default.aspx
Control: Other not-for-profit (including NFP Corporation) **Service:** General medical and surgical

**Staffed Beds: 101 Admissions: 6252 Census: 63 Outpatient Visits: 38180
Births: 1871 Total Expense ($000): 102663 Payroll Expense
($000): 39348 Personnel: 544**

⊞ △ ⇧ **TEXAS HEALTH HARRIS METHODIST HOSPITAL FORT WORTH (450135)**, 1301 Pennsylvania Avenue, Zip 76104-2122; tel. 817/250-2000, **A**1 2 3 5 7 10 21 **F**3 8 11 12 13 15 17 18 20 22 24 26 28 29 30 31 34 35 36 43 45 46 47 48 49 53 54 56 57 58 59 60 61 62 64 65 66 67 68 70 71 72 74 75 76 77 78 79 81 82 83 84 85 86 87 91 92 93 94 95 96 107 108 110 111 112 114 115 116 117 118 119 120 126 129 130 131 132 135 138 145 146 147 148 149 150 154 **S** Texas Health Resources, Arlington, TX
Primary Contact: Joseph DeLeon, President
CFO: Shelly Miland, Group Financial Officer
CMO: Joseph Prosser, M.D., Chief Medical Officer
CHR: Joseph Condon, Entity Human Resources Officer
CNO: Elaine Nelson, R.N., MSN, Chief Nursing Officer
Web address: www.texashealth.org
Control: Other not-for-profit (including NFP Corporation) **Service:** General medical and surgical

**Staffed Beds: 639 Admissions: 35465 Census: 550 Outpatient
Visits: 206220 Births: 3254 Total Expense ($000): 789164 Payroll
Expense ($000): 291438 Personnel: 4348**

⊞ **TEXAS HEALTH HARRIS METHODIST HOSPITAL SOUTHWEST FORT WORTH (450779)**, 6100 Harris Parkway, Zip 76132-4199; tel. 817/433-5000, (Includes TEXAS HEALTH HOSPITAL CLEARFORK, 5400 Clearfork Main Street, Fort Worth, TX, Zip 76109-3553; tel. 682/703-5000; Rebecca Tucker, President) **A**1 2 10 **F**3 8 11 13 15 18 20 28 29 30 34 35 36 37 40 45 46 47 48 49 50 53 57 59 60 64 68 70 72 75 76 77 78 79 80 81 84 85 86 87 93 102 107 110 111 114 115 119 126 130 131 146 147 148 149 **S** Texas Health Resources, Arlington, TX
Primary Contact: Rebecca Tucker, President
CFO: Charlotte Ward, Entity Financial Officer
CMO: Mark Montgomery, M.D., Chief Medical Officer
CHR: Leanna W Nalley, Director Human Resources
CNO: Mary Robinson, Chief Nursing Officer and Vice President Patient Care Services
Web address: www.texashealth.org
Control: Other not-for-profit (including NFP Corporation) **Service:** General medical and surgical

**Staffed Beds: 247 Admissions: 14810 Census: 144 Outpatient
Visits: 96412 Births: 2991 Total Expense ($000): 283326 Payroll Expense
($000): 88996 Personnel: 1098**

⊞ **TEXAS HEALTH SPECIALTY HOSPITAL (452018)**, 1301 Pennsylvania Avenue, 4th Floor, Zip 76104-2190; tel. 817/250-5500, **A**1 10 **F**1 3 87 130 148 **S** Texas Health Resources, Arlington, TX
Primary Contact: Pam Duffey, MSN, R.N., Interim Chief Executive Officer
CFO: Shelly Miland, Chief Financial Officer
CMO: Michael Thornsberry, M.D., Chief Medical Officer
CHR: Joseph Condon, Director Human Resources
CNO: Pam Duffey, MSN, R.N., Chief Nursing Officer
Web address: www.texashealth.org
Control: Church operated, Nongovernment, not-for-profit **Service:** Acute long-term care hospital

**Staffed Beds: 10 Admissions: 101 Census: 9 Outpatient Visits: 0 Births: 0
Total Expense ($000): 7244 Payroll Expense ($000): 3490 Personnel: 33**

☐ △ **TEXAS REHABILITATION HOSPITAL OF FORT WORTH (673048)**, 425 Alabama Avenue, Zip 76104-1022; tel. 817/820-3400, **A**1 7 10 **F**3 29 34 57 74 79 90 91 96 130 132 148 **S** Kindred Healthcare, Louisville, KY
Primary Contact: Jake Daggett, Chief Executive Officer
Web address: www.texasrehabhospital.com/
Control: Corporation, Investor-owned (for-profit) **Service:** Rehabilitation

**Staffed Beds: 66 Admissions: 1271 Census: 46 Outpatient Visits: 0
Births: 0 Total Expense ($000): 15732 Payroll Expense ($000): 8819
Personnel: 183**

☐ **USMD HOSPITAL AT FORT WORTH (670046)**, 5900 Altamesa Boulevard, Zip 76132-5473; tel. 817/433-9100, **A**1 10 **F**3 29 39 40 51 64 68 81 85 89 107 114 119 130 **S** USMD Health System, Irving, TX
Primary Contact: Kathy L Early, CPHRM, Chief Executive Officer and Chief Nursing Officer
CHR: Michelle Speck, Senior Vice President Human Resources
Web address: www.usmdfortworth.com/
Control: Partnership, Investor-owned (for-profit) **Service:** General medical and surgical

**Staffed Beds: 8 Admissions: 218 Census: 1 Outpatient Visits: 4559
Births: 0 Total Expense ($000): 22861 Payroll Expense ($000): 4872
Personnel: 81**

WELLBRIDGE HEALTHCARE OF FORT WORTH (454128), 6200 Overton Ridge Boulevard, Zip 76132-3614; tel. 817/361-1991, **F**34 38 44 56 57 68 87 98 100 101 102 103 130 149 153 154
Primary Contact: Soni Helmicki, Chief Executive Officer
Web address: www.oceanshealthcare.com
Control: Corporation, Investor-owned (for-profit) **Service:** Psychiatric

**Staffed Beds: 48 Admissions: 851 Census: 33 Outpatient Visits: 8715
Births: 0 Total Expense ($000): 9952 Payroll Expense ($000): 4262
Personnel: 79**

TX

FREDERICKSBURG—Gillespie County

✠ **HILL COUNTRY MEMORIAL HOSPITAL (450604)**, 1020 South State Highway
16, Zip 78624–4471, Mailing Address: P.O. Box 835, Zip 78624–0835;
tel. 830/997–4353, **A**1 10 **F**3 11 13 15 18 20 28 29 30 31 32 34 35 37 40 43
45 49 50 51 53 57 59 62 63 64 68 70 74 75 76 77 78 79 81 82 84 85 86 87
93 96 97 107 108 110 111 114 115 119 124 129 130 132 135 144 146
148 149 **P**6 8
Primary Contact: Jayne E. Pope, R.N., FACHE, Chief Executive Officer
COO: Mike Reno, Chief Operating Officer
CFO: Mark Jones, Chief Financial Officer
CMO: James R Partin, M.D., Chief Medical Director
CIO: John Mason, Chief Information Officer
CHR: Alysha Metzger, Director Human Resources
CNO: Maureen Polivka, Chief Nursing Officer
Web address: www.hillcountrymemorial.org
Control: Other not–for–profit (including NFP Corporation) **Service:** General
medical and surgical

Staffed Beds: 57 **Admissions:** 2398 **Census:** 19 **Outpatient Visits:** 96920
Births: 464 **Total Expense ($000):** 78204 **Payroll Expense ($000):** 29700
Personnel: 484

FRIONA—Parmer County

PARMER COUNTY COMMUNITY HOSPITAL See Parmer Medical Center

★ **PARMER MEDICAL CENTER (451300)**, 1307 Cleveland Street,
Zip 79035–1121; tel. 806/250–2754, **A**10 18 **F**11 30 34 35 40 43 57 64 75
77 89 93 107 119 127 130 133 148 **S** Preferred Management Corporation,
Shawnee, OK
Primary Contact: Gayla Quillin, Administrator
Web address: www.parmermedicalcenter.com
Control: Other not–for–profit (including NFP Corporation) **Service:** General
medical and surgical

Staffed Beds: 15 **Admissions:** 151 **Census:** 3 **Outpatient Visits:** 8563
Births: 1 **Total Expense ($000):** 11009 **Payroll Expense ($000):** 4636
Personnel: 92

FRISCO—Collin County

✠ **BAYLOR INSTITUTE FOR REHABILITATION AT FRISCO (673046)**, 2990
Legacy Drive, Zip 75034–6066; tel. 469/888–5100, **A**1 10 **F**3 29 30 34 35 36
64 75 90 91 92 93 96 130 132 148 149 154 **S** Select Medical Corporation,
Mechanicsburg, PA
Primary Contact: Ryan Seymour, Chief Executive Officer
Web address: www.baylorhealth.com/bir
Control: Partnership, Investor–owned (for–profit) **Service:** Rehabilitation

Staffed Beds: 44 **Admissions:** 863 **Census:** 32 **Outpatient Visits:** 13660
Births: 0 **Total Expense ($000):** 20979 **Payroll Expense ($000):** 10843
Personnel: 104

☐ **BAYLOR MEDICAL CENTER AT FRISCO (450853)**, 5601 Warren Parkway,
Zip 75034–4069; tel. 214/407–5000, **A**1 3 5 10 **F**3 13 29 34 40 45 51 54 57
64 68 72 75 76 79 81 85 86 87 107 111 115 119 126 129 130 131 144 **S**
United Surgical Partners International, Addison, TX
Primary Contact: Trevor Castaneda, Chief Executive Officer
COO: Kevin Coats, Chief Operating Officer and Chief Financial Officer
CFO: Kevin Coats, Chief Financial Officer
CMO: Jimmy Laferney, M.D., Vice President Medical Staff Affairs
CIO: Rick Barry, Director Information Systems
CHR: Margaret Garcia, Manager Human Resources
CNO: Randi Elliott, MSN, Chief Nursing Officer
Web address: www.bmcf.com
Control: Partnership, Investor–owned (for–profit) **Service:** Surgical

Staffed Beds: 68 **Admissions:** 4408 **Census:** 34 **Outpatient Visits:** 25448
Births: 2360 **Total Expense ($000):** 127243 **Payroll Expense
($000):** 45036 **Personnel:** 543

✠ **BAYLOR SCOTT & WHITE MEDICAL CENTER – CENTENNIAL (450885)**,
12505 Lebanon Road, Zip 75035–8298; tel. 972/963–3333, **A**1 10 **F**3 13 15
17 18 20 22 26 29 30 34 35 40 41 45 46 47 48 49 50 51 57 59 64 65 70 72
74 75 76 77 78 79 81 82 85 89 93 107 110 111 114 115 119 126 132 146 **S**
Baylor Scott & White Health, Dallas, TX
Primary Contact: Jaikumar Krishnaswamy, President
CFO: Blaise Bondi, Chief Financial Officer
CIO: Dianne Yarborough, Director of Information Technology
CHR: Stephanie S. Talley, Director Human Resources
CNO: Calee Travis, R.N., Chief Nursing Officer
Web address: www.centennialmedcenter.com
Control: Partnership, Investor–owned (for–profit) **Service:** General medical and surgical

Staffed Beds: 106 **Admissions:** 3834 **Census:** 42 **Outpatient Visits:** 31179
Births: 703 **Total Expense ($000):** 92727 **Payroll Expense ($000):** 29381
Personnel: 350

☐ **HAVEN BEHAVIORAL HOSPITAL OF FRISCO (454134)**, 5680 Frisco Square
Boulevard, Suite 3000, Zip 75034–3300; tel. 469/353–2219, **A**1 **F**98 130
Primary Contact: William W. Brattvet, Chief Executive Officer
Web address: www.frisco.havenbehavioral.com/
Control: Corporation, Investor–owned (for–profit) **Service:** Psychiatric

Staffed Beds: 36 **Admissions:** 655 **Census:** 26 **Outpatient Visits:** 0
Births: 0 **Total Expense ($000):** 9456 **Payroll Expense ($000):** 4259
Personnel: 55

GAINESVILLE—Cooke County

NORTH TEXAS MEDICAL CENTER (450090), 1900 Hospital Boulevard,
Zip 76240–2002; tel. 940/665–1751, **A**10 20 **F**3 11 13 15 28 29 34 35 40 43
45 50 59 62 64 65 68 70 75 76 77 79 81 82 85 86 87 93 107 108 110 111
115 118 119 127 129 130 132 133 135 146 147 149 154 **P**6
Primary Contact: Thomas Sledge, Chief Executive Officer
CFO: Melissa Walker, CPA, Chief Financial Officer
CHR: Teresa Westover, Director Human Resources
CNO: Becky Small, Chief Nursing Officer
Web address: www.ntmconline.net
Control: Hospital district or authority, Government, nonfederal **Service:** General
medical and surgical

Staffed Beds: 48 **Admissions:** 1156 **Census:** 10 **Outpatient Visits:** 71048
Births: 303 **Total Expense ($000):** 39388 **Payroll Expense ($000):** 14023
Personnel: 244

GALVESTON—Galveston County

☐ **SHRINERS HOSPITALS FOR CHILDREN–GALVESTON (453311)**, 815 Market
Street, Zip 77550–2725; tel. 409/770–6600, **A**1 3 5 10 **F**3 11 16 29 30 32
34 35 50 64 68 75 77 81 82 85 86 93 100 104 119 130 132 146 148 154 **S**
Shriners Hospitals for Children, Tampa, FL
Primary Contact: Mary Jaco, Administrator
CFO: Michael B Schimming, Director Financial Services
CMO: David N Herndon, M.D., Chief of Staff
CIO: Michael Lyons, Regional Director Information Services
CHR: Robert A Magee, Director Human Resources
CNO: Angel Martinez, R.N., RN, BSN, Director Patient Care Services
Web address: www.shrinershospitalsforchildren.org/Hospitals/Locations/
Galveston.aspx
Control: Other not–for–profit (including NFP Corporation) **Service:** Children's other
specialty

Staffed Beds: 15 **Admissions:** 174 **Census:** 10 **Outpatient Visits:** 6010
Births: 0 **Total Expense ($000):** 36106 **Payroll Expense ($000):** 15222
Personnel: 233

✠ **UNIVERSITY OF TEXAS MEDICAL BRANCH (450018)**, 301 University
Boulevard, Zip 77555–0128; tel. 409/772–1011, (Includes ANGLETON
DANBURY CAMPUS, 132 East Hospital Drive, Angleton, TX, Zip 77515–4112;
tel. 979/849–7721; Donna K Sollenberger, Executive Vice President and Chief
Executive Officer) **A**1 2 3 5 10 **F**3 11 12 13 15 16 17 18 19 20 22 24 26 28
29 30 31 34 35 36 38 39 40 41 43 44 45 46 49 50 51 53 54 55 56 57 58 59
60 61 63 64 65 66 68 70 71 72 73 74 75 76 77 78 79 81 82 84 85 86 87
88 89 92 93 94 96 97 100 101 102 104 107 108 110 111 112 114 115 116
117 118 119 120 121 123 124 126 129 130 131 132 134 135 137 138 139
141 142 144 145 146 147 148 149 150 154 **P**6 **S** University of Texas System,
Austin, TX
Primary Contact: Donna K. Sollenberger, Executive Vice President and Chief
Executive Officer
COO: Deborah A McGrew, Vice President and Chief Operating Officer
CFO: Cheryl A Sadro, Executive Vice President Chief Business and Finance Officer
CIO: Todd Leach, Vice President and Chief Information Officer
CHR: Ronald McKinley, Ph.D., Vice President Human Resources and Employee
Services
CNO: Macias, R.N., Chief Nursing Officer
Web address: www.utmb.edu
Control: State, Government, nonfederal **Service:** General medical and surgical

Staffed Beds: 456 **Admissions:** 29220 **Census:** 384 **Outpatient
Visits:** 1073637 **Births:** 6364 **Total Expense ($000):** 981891 **Payroll
Expense ($000):** 340928 **Personnel:** 4854

GARLAND—Dallas County

GARLAND BEHAVIORAL HOSPITAL (454138), 2300 Marie Curie Boulevard,
5th Floor, Zip 75402; tel. 972/487–5309, **A**3 **F**98 101 103 **S** Universal Health
Services, Inc., King of Prussia, PA
Primary Contact: Kristin Harris, Chief Executive Officer
CFO: Scott Cook, Chief Financial Officer
Web address: www.garlandbehavioralhospital.com/
Control: Corporation, Investor–owned (for–profit) **Service:** Psychiatric

Staffed Beds: 72 **Admissions:** 1619 **Census:** 35 **Outpatient Visits:** 0
Births: 0 **Total Expense ($000):** 10361 **Payroll Expense ($000):** 5401
Personnel: 169

TX

GATESVILLE—Coryell County

☐ **CORYELL MEMORIAL HOSPITAL (451379)**, 1507 West Main Street, Zip 76528–1098; tel. 254/865–8251, **A**1 10 18 **F**3 7 10 11 15 18 20 28 34 40 43 45 50 57 58 59 61 62 64 65 70 74 79 81 82 84 87 93 97 102 104 107 108 110 111 115 119 125 127 129 130 131 133 146 154 **P**6
Primary Contact: David Byrom, Chief Executive Officer
COO: David Byrom, Chief Executive Officer
CFO: Carol Jones, Controller and Manager Business Office
CMO: Diedra Wuenschel, D.O., President Medical Staff
CIO: Mike Huckabee, Network Administrator
CHR: Paula Smithhart, Director Human Resources
CNO: Jeanne Griffith, Chief Nursing Officer
Web address: www.cmhos.org
Control: Hospital district or authority, Government, nonfederal **Service**: General medical and surgical

Staffed Beds: 25 **Admissions**: 925 **Census**: 10 **Outpatient Visits**: 73789 **Births**: 0 **Total Expense ($000)**: 46596 **Payroll Expense ($000)**: 15993 **Personnel**: 394

GEORGETOWN—Williamson County

☐ **GEORGETOWN BEHAVIORAL HEALTH INSTITUTE (454129)**, 3101 South Austin Avenue, Zip 78626–7541; tel. 512/819–1100, **A**1 **F**4 5 56 98 99 100 102 103 104 105 130 132 135 151 152 153 154 **S** Signature Healthcare Services, Corona, CA
Primary Contact: Lisa Salter, Chief Executive Officer
COO: Ellen Payne, Chief Operating Officer
CFO: Shelli Surcouf, Chief Financial Officer
CHR: Kristi Hynes, Director Human Resources
CNO: Nini Perry, Chief Nursing Officer
Web address: www.georgetownbehavioral.com
Control: Corporation, Investor-owned (for-profit) **Service**: Psychiatric

Staffed Beds: 118 **Admissions**: 3158 **Census**: 71 **Outpatient Visits**: 8420 **Births**: 0 **Total Expense ($000)**: 20446 **Payroll Expense ($000)**: 9951 **Personnel**: 272

★ **ROCK SPRINGS (454127)**, 700 Southeast Inner Loop, Zip 78626; tel. 512/819–9400, **F**5 98 100 102 104 105 152 153 **S** Springstone, Louisville, KY
Primary Contact: Jason McPherson, Chief Executive Officer
CFO: Jason Guzak, Chief Financial Officer
CHR: Sharon McMurray, Director, Human Resources
CNO: Randall Luce, R.N., Director of Nursing
Web address: www.rockspringshealth.com/
Control: Corporation, Investor-owned (for-profit) **Service**: Psychiatric

Staffed Beds: 72 **Admissions**: 2305 **Census**: 55 **Outpatient Visits**: 9153 **Births**: 0 **Total Expense ($000)**: 16951 **Payroll Expense ($000)**: 8813 **Personnel**: 161

GLEN ROSE—Somervell County

☐ **GLEN ROSE MEDICAL CENTER (450451)**, 1021 Holden Street, Zip 76043–4937, Mailing Address: P.O. Box 2099, Zip 76043–2099; tel. 254/897–2215, **A**1 **F**2 3 15 29 34 40 43 48 51 56 57 59 65 68 81 93 97 100 103 104 107 110 114 119 129 130 141 143 146 148 153 **P**7
Primary Contact: Ray Reynolds, Chief Executive Officer
CFO: Michael Honea, Chief Financial Officer
CHR: Ladonna Green, Director Human Resources
CNO: Laura Hodnett, Interim Chief Nursing Officer
Web address: www.glenrosemedicalcenter.com
Control: Hospital district or authority, Government, nonfederal **Service**: General medical and surgical

Staffed Beds: 10 **Admissions**: 272 **Census**: 2 **Outpatient Visits**: 18083 **Births**: 0 **Total Expense ($000)**: 15062 **Payroll Expense ($000)**: 5699 **Personnel**: 169

GONZALES—Gonzales County

★ **GONZALES HEALTHCARE SYSTEMS (450235)**, 1110 Sarah Dewitt Drive, Zip 78629–3311, Mailing Address: P.O. Box 587, Zip 78629–0587; tel. 830/672–7581, **A**10 20 **F**3 11 13 15 29 34 35 38 40 43 53 57 59 62 64 65 68 70 75 77 79 81 85 87 93 97 107 110 111 115 119 127 129 130 132 148 **S** QHR, Brentwood, TN
Primary Contact: John R. Hughson, Chief Executive Officer
CFO: Patty Stewart, Chief Financial Officer
CMO: Commie Hisey, D.O., Chief of Staff
CHR: Joni Leland, Director Human Resources
CNO: Valerie Hohenshell, Director of Clinical Services
Web address: www.gonzaleshealthcare.com
Control: Hospital district or authority, Government, nonfederal **Service**: General medical and surgical

Staffed Beds: 33 **Admissions**: 1131 **Census**: 6 **Outpatient Visits**: 76824 **Births**: 146 **Total Expense ($000)**: 49215 **Payroll Expense ($000)**: 11892 **Personnel**: 304

GRAHAM—Young County

★ **GRAHAM REGIONAL MEDICAL CENTER (450085)**, 1301 Montgomery Road, Zip 76450–4240, Mailing Address: P.O. Box 1390, Zip 76450–1390; tel. 940/549–3400, **A**10 20 **F**3 7 11 15 28 29 40 43 45 50 53 57 59 62 63 75 77 79 81 85 89 93 104 107 111 115 119 127 130 133 135
Primary Contact: Shane Kernell, Chief Executive Officer
CIO: Jeff Clark, Director Information Systems
Web address: www.grahamrmc.com
Control: Hospital district or authority, Government, nonfederal **Service**: General medical and surgical

Staffed Beds: 17 **Admissions**: 654 **Census**: 7 **Outpatient Visits**: 40986 **Births**: 0 **Total Expense ($000)**: 21905 **Payroll Expense ($000)**: 8041 **Personnel**: 171

GRANBURY—Hood County

⊞ **LAKE GRANBURY MEDICAL CENTER (450596)**, 1310 Paluxy Road, Zip 76048–5655; tel. 817/573–2273, **A**1 10 **F**3 8 11 12 13 15 18 20 22 26 28 29 30 34 37 40 43 45 49 53 57 59 64 68 70 74 75 76 77 79 81 82 85 86 93 107 108 110 111 114 118 119 126 129 146 147 149 154 **S** Community Health Systems, Inc., Franklin, TN
Primary Contact: David Orcutt, Chief Executive Officer
CFO: Noe Gutierrez, Chief Financial Officer
CIO: Kevin Myers, Director Information Systems
CHR: Brooke Montoya, Director Human Resources
CNO: Abigail Kendall, Chief Nursing Officer
Web address: www.lakegranburymedicalcenter.com
Control: Corporation, Investor-owned (for-profit) **Service**: General medical and surgical

Staffed Beds: 73 **Admissions**: 3021 **Census**: 26 **Outpatient Visits**: 74478 **Births**: 559 **Total Expense ($000)**: 71848 **Payroll Expense ($000)**: 22805 **Personnel**: 364

GRAND PRAIRIE—Dallas County

⇑ **TEXAS GENERAL HOSPITAL (670083)**, 2709 Hospital Boulevard, Zip 75051–1017; tel. 469/557–9430, (Nonreporting) **A**10 21
Primary Contact: Suleman Hashmi, President and Chief Executive Officer
Web address: www.texasgeneralhospital.com
Control: Partnership, Investor-owned (for-profit) **Service**: General medical and surgical

Staffed Beds: 41

GRAND SALINE—Van Zandt County

⇑ **TEXAS GENERAL HOSPITAL – VAN ZANDT REGIONAL MEDICAL CENTER (670117)**, 707 North Waldrip Street, Zip 75140–1555; tel. 903/717–3300, (Nonreporting) **A**21
Primary Contact: Faraz Hashmi, Chief Executive Officer
Control: Individual, Investor-owned (for-profit) **Service**: General medical and surgical

Staffed Beds: 52

GRAPEVINE—Tarrant County

⊞ **BAYLOR REGIONAL MEDICAL CENTER AT GRAPEVINE (450563)**, 1650 West College Street, Zip 76051–3565; tel. 817/481–1588, **A**1 2 3 10 **F**3 8 12 13 15 18 20 22 24 26 28 29 30 31 34 35 40 43 45 46 47 48 49 56 57 59 64 65 70 72 74 75 76 77 78 79 80 81 82 84 86 87 90 93 107 108 110 111 114 115 119 126 130 131 132 135 145 146 147 148 149 **S** Baylor Scott & White Health, Dallas, TX
Primary Contact: Christopher York, FACHE, President
CFO: Terri Foster, Hospital Finance Officer
CMO: Ron Jensen, D.O., Chief Medical Officer and Vice President
CIO: Sandy Vaughn, Director Information Systems
CHR: Donna Stark, Director Human Resources
CNO: Beth P Beckman, R.N., Ph.D., Chief Nursing Officer
Web address: www.baylorhealth.com/PhysiciansLocations/Grapevine/Pages/Default.aspx
Control: Other not-for-profit (including NFP Corporation) **Service**: General medical and surgical

Staffed Beds: 270 **Admissions**: 13957 **Census**: 178 **Outpatient Visits**: 61264 **Births**: 2432 **Total Expense ($000)**: 219829 **Payroll Expense ($000)**: 82886 **Personnel**: 832

Hospital, Medicare Provider Number, Address, Telephone, Approval, Facility, and Physician Codes, Health Care System

★ American Hospital Association (AHA) membership
☐ The Joint Commission accreditation
○ Healthcare Facilities Accreditation Program
◇ DNV Healthcare Inc. accreditation
⇑ Center for Improvement in Healthcare Quality Accreditation
△ Commission on Accreditation of Rehabilitation Facilities (CARF) accreditation

☐ **ETHICUS HOSPITAL – GRAPEVINE (452110)**, 4201 William D Tate Avenue, Zip 76051–5736; tel. 817/288–1300, **A**1 10 **F**1 3 29 64 75 77 82 85 93 96 107 114 119 130 135 148
Primary Contact: Roger T. Jenkins, Chief Executive Officer
Web address: www.ethicusgrapevine.com
Control: Partnership, Investor–owned (for–profit) **Service**: Acute long–term care hospital

Staffed Beds: 60 **Admissions:** 117 **Census:** 8 **Outpatient Visits:** 3042 **Births:** 0 **Total Expense ($000):** 27622 **Payroll Expense ($000):** 6444 **Personnel:** 95

GREENVILLE—Hunt County

✠ **GLEN OAKS HOSPITAL (454050)**, 301 Division Street, Zip 75401–4101; tel. 903/454–6000, **A**1 10 **F**4 5 29 34 35 50 75 86 87 98 99 100 101 102 103 104 105 132 135 149 151 152 153 **S** Universal Health Services, Inc., King of Prussia, PA
Primary Contact: Jonathon Gammon, Interim Chief Executive Officer
Web address: www.glenoakshospital.com
Control: Corporation, Investor–owned (for–profit) **Service**: Psychiatric

Staffed Beds: 54 **Admissions:** 1818 **Census:** 38 **Outpatient Visits:** 2459 **Births:** 0 **Total Expense ($000):** 11495 **Payroll Expense ($000):** 5636 **Personnel:** 106

✠ **HUNT REGIONAL MEDICAL CENTER (450352)**, 4215 Joe Ramsey Boulevard, Zip 75401–7899, Mailing Address: P.O. Box 1059, Zip 75403–1059; tel. 903/408–5000, **A**1 10 **F**3 11 12 13 15 28 29 30 34 37 40 43 44 45 46 49 50 53 56 57 59 62 64 65 68 70 71 72 73 74 75 76 77 78 79 81 82 84 85 86 87 90 91 92 93 94 96 98 102 103 104 107 108 110 111 114 115 118 119 120 121 123 129 130 132 135 141 143 144 146 147 148 149 154 **P**1 6 **S** Hunt Regional Healthcare, Greenville, TX
Primary Contact: Richard Carter, District Chief Executive Officer
COO: Michael R Klepin, Administrator
CFO: Lee Boles, Assistant Administrator and Chief Financial Officer
CMO: James H Sandin, M.D., Assistant Administrator Medical Affairs
CIO: Richard Montanye, Director Information Systems
CNO: Deborah Clack, Chief Nursing Officer
Web address: www.huntregional.org
Control: Hospital district or authority, Government, nonfederal **Service**: General medical and surgical

Staffed Beds: 167 **Admissions:** 6808 **Census:** 88 **Outpatient Visits:** 139284 **Births:** 1161 **Total Expense ($000):** 145549 **Payroll Expense ($000):** 60411 **Personnel:** 1032

GROESBECK—Limestone County

LIMESTONE MEDICAL CENTER (451303), 701 McClintic Drive, Zip 76642–2128; tel. 254/729–3281, **A**10 18 **F**3 7 11 28 29 30 32 34 35 40 41 43 45 57 64 65 68 75 77 84 85 90 93 96 97 104 107 111 115 119 127 129 130 133 135 146 148 153
Primary Contact: Larry Price, Chief Executive Officer
CFO: Michael F. Williams, Chief Financial Officer
CMO: Jeffrey Rettig, D.O., Chief of Staff
CIO: Byong Lee, Chief Information Officer
CHR: Jean Koester, Manager Human Resources
CNO: Jean Wragge, Chief Nursing Officer
Web address: www.lmchospital.com
Control: Hospital district or authority, Government, nonfederal **Service**: General medical and surgical

Staffed Beds: 14 **Admissions:** 202 **Census:** 5 **Outpatient Visits:** 14128 **Births:** 0 **Total Expense ($000):** 18905 **Payroll Expense ($000):** 9027 **Personnel:** 191

HALLETTSVILLE—Lavaca County

LAVACA MEDICAL CENTER (451376), 1400 North Texana Street, Zip 77964–2099; tel. 361/798–3671, **A**10 18 **F**3 11 15 18 29 34 40 41 43 45 47 53 56 57 59 64 65 68 75 77 81 85 86 87 93 107 108 110 111 114 118 119 127 133 135 146 148 149
Primary Contact: Stephen Bowen, Administrator
Control: Hospital district or authority, Government, nonfederal **Service**: General medical and surgical

Staffed Beds: 25 **Admissions:** 534 **Census:** 7 **Outpatient Visits:** 43985 **Births:** 0 **Total Expense ($000):** 18421 **Payroll Expense ($000):** 6253 **Personnel:** 156

HAMILTON—Hamilton County

★ ⬆ **HAMILTON GENERAL HOSPITAL (450754)**, 400 North Brown Street, Zip 76531–1518; tel. 254/386–1600, **A**10 20 21 **F**3 7 11 15 28 29 34 35 40 43 44 45 50 53 56 57 59 64 65 68 75 79 80 81 82 85 86 93 97 100 104 107 108 110 114 119 127 129 130 132 133 135
Primary Contact: Grady A. Hooper, Chief Executive Officer
CMO: James R Lee, M.D., Chief of Staff
CIO: Chad Reinert, Chief Information Officer
CHR: Keela Payne, Director Human Resources
CNO: Debra Martin, Chief Nursing Officer
Web address: www.hamiltonhospital.org
Control: Hospital district or authority, Government, nonfederal **Service**: General medical and surgical

Staffed Beds: 42 **Admissions:** 877 **Census:** 9 **Outpatient Visits:** 70507 **Births:** 0 **Total Expense ($000):** 25612 **Payroll Expense ($000):** 11444 **Personnel:** 240

HAMLIN—Jones County

HAMLIN MEMORIAL HOSPITAL (450243), 632 Northwest Second Street, Zip 79520–3831, Mailing Address: P.O. Box 400, Zip 79520–0400; tel. 325/576–3646, **A**10 **F**7 11 28 29 35 40 43 64 68 69 89 93 107 114 127 133 135 146 148 149 **P**5
Primary Contact: Angela Jaco, Chief Executive Officer
CMO: Krishna Sunkavalle, M.D., Chief Medical Officer
Control: Hospital district or authority, Government, nonfederal **Service**: General medical and surgical

Staffed Beds: 23 **Admissions:** 89 **Census:** 1 **Outpatient Visits:** 3637 **Births:** 0 **Total Expense ($000):** 4427 **Payroll Expense ($000):** 2127 **Personnel:** 53

HARKER HEIGHTS—Bell County

✠ **SETON MEDICAL CENTER HARKER HEIGHTS (670080)**, 850 West Central Texas Expressway, Zip 76548–1890; tel. 254/690–0900, **A**1 10 **F**3 13 15 18 20 22 26 28 29 30 34 35 40 43 45 49 50 51 57 59 60 66 70 74 75 76 79 81 91 93 107 108 110 111 115 119 129 130 146 147 148 **P**3 **S** Ardent Health Services, Nashville, TN
Primary Contact: Zachary K. Dietze, Chief Executive Officer
CFO: John K Sharp, Chief Financial Officer
CHR: Mona Tucker, Director Human Resources
CNO: Pamela Craig, R.N., Chief Nursing Officer
Web address: www.setonharkerheights.net
Control: Partnership, Investor–owned (for–profit) **Service**: General medical and surgical

Staffed Beds: 83 **Admissions:** 3943 **Census:** 26 **Outpatient Visits:** 79342 **Births:** 990 **Total Expense ($000):** 72532 **Payroll Expense ($000):** 23184 **Personnel:** 355

HARLINGEN—Cameron County

✠ **HARLINGEN MEDICAL CENTER (450855)**, 5501 South Expressway 77, Zip 78550–3213; tel. 956/365–1000, **A**1 3 5 10 **F**3 12 13 15 17 18 20 22 24 29 30 40 43 49 50 51 57 59 64 68 70 74 75 76 79 81 85 86 107 108 110 111 114 115 118 119 129 130 146 147 148 **S** Prime Healthcare, Ontario, CA
Primary Contact: Brenda Ivory, Chief Executive Officer
CFO: David Glassburn, Vice President Finance and Chief Financial Officer
CMO: Elizabeth Juarez, M.D., Chief Medical Officer
CHR: Emmett Craig, Director Human Resources
CNO: Deborah Meeks, Chief Nursing Officer
Web address: www.harlingenmedicalcenter.com
Control: Partnership, Investor–owned (for–profit) **Service**: General medical and surgical

Staffed Beds: 88 **Admissions:** 5603 **Census:** 57 **Outpatient Visits:** 60076 **Births:** 994 **Total Expense ($000):** 93943 **Payroll Expense ($000):** 32960 **Personnel:** 570

☐ **RIO GRANDE STATE CENTER/SOUTH TEXAS HEALTH CARE SYSTEM (454088)**, 1401 South Rangerville Road, Zip 78552–7638; tel. 956/364–8000, (Includes RIO GRANDE STATE CENTER, 1401 South Rangerville Road, Harlingen, TX, Zip 78552–7638; tel. 956/364–8000; SOUTH TEXAS HEALTH CARE SYSTEM, 1401 Rangerville Road, Harlingen, TX, Zip 78552–7609; tel. 956/364–8000) **A**1 3 5 10 **F**30 53 57 65 66 68 75 87 97 101 107 119 130 132 135 143 146 147 154 **P**6 **S** Texas Department of State Health Services, Austin, TX
Primary Contact: Sonia Hernandez–Keeble, Superintendent
CFO: Tom Garza, Director Fiscal and Support
CMO: David Moron, M.D., Clinical Director
CIO: Blas Ortiz Jr Assistant Superintendent and Public Information Officer
CHR: Irma Garcia, Job Coordinator
CNO: Maia Baker, MSN, Chief Nurse Executive
Web address: www.dshs.state.tx.us/mhhospitals/RioGrandeSC/default.shtm
Control: State, Government, nonfederal **Service**: Psychiatric

Staffed Beds: 55 **Admissions:** 734 **Census:** 53 **Outpatient Visits:** 0 **Births:** 0 **Total Expense ($000):** 26988 **Payroll Expense ($000):** 9903 **Personnel:** 264

Many Facility Codes have changed. Please refer to the AHA Guide Code Chart.

TX

SOLARA HOSPITAL HARLINGEN (452101), 508 Victoria Lane, Zip 78550–3225; tel. 956/425–9600, (Includes SOLARA HOSPITAL – BROWNSVILLE CAMPUS, 333 Lorenaly Drive, Brownsville, TX, Zip 78526–4333; tel. 956/546–0808) **A**10 22 **F**1 29 35 40 57 70 85 86 130 148 **S** Cornerstone Healthcare Group, Dallas, TX
Primary Contact: Cary L. Montalvo, Chief Executive Officer
CFO: Kurt Schultz, Chief Financial Officer
CHR: Dan Perkins, Vice President of Human Resources
CNO: Nesa Caldwell, Chief Nursing Officer
Web address: www.chghospitals.com/harlingen/
Control: Partnership, Investor–owned (for–profit) **Service**: Acute long–term care hospital

Staffed Beds: 82 **Admissions**: 956 **Census**: 62 **Outpatient Visits**: 0 **Births**: 0
Total Expense ($000): 21793 **Payroll Expense ($000)**: 10723 **Personnel**: 157

⊞ ⇑ **VALLEY BAPTIST MEDICAL CENTER–HARLINGEN (450033)**, 2101 Pease Street, Zip 78550–8307, Mailing Address: P O Drawer 2588, Zip 78551–2588; tel. 956/389–1100, **A**1 3 5 10 21 **F**3 11 12 13 14 15 17 18 20 22 24 26 28 29 30 31 34 35 39 40 41 43 44 45 46 47 48 49 50 53 54 56 57 58 59 60 63 64 65 68 70 71 72 73 74 75 76 77 78 79 80 81 82 84 85 86 87 88 89 90 92 93 94 98 100 101 102 103 104 105 107 108 110 111 112 114 115 119 126 129 130 132 144 146 147 148 153 **S** TENET Healthcare Corporation, Dallas, TX
Primary Contact: Manuel Vela, President and Chief Executive Officer
CFO: Marco Rodriguez, Chief Financial Officer
CNO: Stephen Hill, Vice President and Chief Nursing Officer
Web address: www.valleybaptist.net/harlingen/index.htm
Control: Corporation, Investor–owned (for–profit) **Service**: General medical and surgical

Staffed Beds: 428 **Admissions**: 16592 **Census**: 215 **Outpatient Visits**: 120797 **Births**: 1737 **Total Expense ($000)**: 252143 **Payroll Expense ($000)**: 85185 **Personnel**: 1139

HASKELL—Haskell County

HASKELL MEMORIAL HOSPITAL (451341), 1 North Avenue 'N', Zip 79521–5499, Mailing Address: P.O. Box 1117, Zip 79521–1117; tel. 940/864–2621, **A**10 18 **F**11 28 29 34 35 40 53 54 57 59 64 68 75 77 86 87 93 97 107 119 130 131 133 146 **P**1
Primary Contact: Fran McCown, Administrator
CHR: Emily Moore, Director Human Resources and Information Technology
CNO: Teri Turner, Chief Nursing Officer
Web address: www.haskellmemorialhospital.com/
Control: Hospital district or authority, Government, nonfederal **Service**: General medical and surgical

Staffed Beds: 15 **Admissions**: 216 **Census**: 3 **Outpatient Visits**: 17540 **Births**: 0 **Total Expense ($000)**: 7476 **Payroll Expense ($000)**: 3329 **Personnel**: 102

HEMPHILL—Sabine County

☐ **SABINE COUNTY HOSPITAL (451361)**, 2301 Worth Street, Zip 75948–7216, Mailing Address: P.O. Box 750, Zip 75948–0750; tel. 409/787–3300, **A**1 10 18 **F**3 29 40 43 93 97 107 108 110 114 119 127 133 **S** Preferred Management Corporation, Shawnee, OK
Primary Contact: Jerry Howell, Administrator
COO: Mike Easley, Vice President and Chief Operating Officer
CFO: Larry Stephens, Chief Financial Officer
CMO: Vera Luther, M.D., Chief of Staff
CIO: Margaret Moore, Director Business Office
CHR: Laura Simpson, Director Human Resources
CNO: Margie Watson MSN, RN–B Chief Nursing Officer
Web address: www.sabinecountyhospital.com
Control: Corporation, Investor–owned (for–profit) **Service**: General medical and surgical

Staffed Beds: 25 **Admissions**: 237 **Census**: 4 **Outpatient Visits**: 18889 **Births**: 0 **Total Expense ($000)**: 8667 **Payroll Expense ($000)**: 3727 **Personnel**: 81

HENDERSON—Rusk County

⊞ **UT HEALTH HENDERSON (450475)**, 300 Wilson Street, Zip 75652–5956; tel. 903/657–7541, **A**1 10 **F**3 8 11 13 15 18 28 29 30 34 35 37 40 43 45 50 57 59 64 65 75 76 77 107 108 110 111 115 119 127 129 133 135 145 146 147 148 149 **S** Ardent Health Services, Nashville, TN
Primary Contact: Mark Leitner, FACHE, Administrator
CFO: Wesley Knight, Chief Financial Officer
CHR: William Henry, Director Human Resources
CNO: Donna K Stanley, R.N., Chief Nursing Officer
Web address: www.https://uthealthhenderson.com/
Control: Other not–for–profit (including NFP Corporation) **Service**: General medical and surgical

Staffed Beds: 41 **Admissions**: 1448 **Census**: 11 **Outpatient Visits**: 54142 **Births**: 238 **Total Expense ($000)**: 35792 **Payroll Expense ($000)**: 8546 **Personnel**: 141

HENRIETTA—Clay County

CLAY COUNTY MEMORIAL HOSPITAL (451362), 310 West South Street, Zip 76365–3346; tel. 940/538–5621, **A**10 18 **F**7 8 11 28 34 35 40 50 53 57 62 68 80 81 90 93 107 111 119 130 132 133 144 146 148 **P**5
Primary Contact: Jeff Huskey, Chief Executive Officer and Administrator
CFO: Debra Haehn, Chief Financial Officer
CMO: Lexi Mitchell Sanchez, D.O., Chief of Staff
CHR: Linda Burleson, Administrative Secretary
CNO: Kelley McMillion, Chief Nursing Officer
Web address: www.ccmhospital.com
Control: County, Government, nonfederal **Service**: General medical and surgical

Staffed Beds: 25 **Admissions**: 117 **Census**: 1 **Outpatient Visits**: 8106 **Births**: 0 **Total Expense ($000)**: 8000 **Payroll Expense ($000)**: 3251 **Personnel**: 83

HEREFORD—Deaf Smith County

HEREFORD REGIONAL MEDICAL CENTER (450155), 540 West 15th Street, Zip 79045–2820; tel. 806/364–2141, **A**10 **F**3 7 11 13 15 29 35 40 43 50 57 59 62 65 70 76 77 81 85 93 107 111 114 119 127 130 133 147 154 **P**5
Primary Contact: Jeff Barnhart, Chief Executive Officer
COO: Meri Killingsworth, Chief Operating Officer
CNO: Anthony T. Jerina, Chief Nursing Officer
Web address: www.dschd.org/
Control: Hospital district or authority, Government, nonfederal **Service**: General medical and surgical

Staffed Beds: 39 **Admissions**: 644 **Census**: 6 **Outpatient Visits**: 72410 **Births**: 317 **Total Expense ($000)**: 26342 **Payroll Expense ($000)**: 9618 **Personnel**: 195

HILLSBORO—Hill County

⊞ **HILL REGIONAL HOSPITAL (450192)**, 101 Circle Drive, Zip 76645–2670; tel. 254/580–8500, **A**1 10 20 **F**3 13 15 17 18 19 29 34 35 40 43 45 50 57 59 64 65 68 70 75 76 77 78 79 81 86 87 88 89 93 107 114 118 119 133 146 147 149 152 **S** Community Health Systems, Inc., Franklin, TN
Primary Contact: Michael J. Ellis, FACHE, Chief Executive Officer
CFO: Judy Culp, Chief Financial Officer
CHR: Becky Hale, Director Human Resources
Web address: www.chs.net
Control: Corporation, Investor–owned (for–profit) **Service**: General medical and surgical

Staffed Beds: 66 **Admissions**: 937 **Census**: 8 **Outpatient Visits**: 23556 **Births**: 185 **Total Expense ($000)**: 32012 **Payroll Expense ($000)**: 8533 **Personnel**: 132

HONDO—Medina County

MEDINA COMMUNITY HOSPITAL See Medina Regional Hospital

MEDINA REGIONAL HOSPITAL (451330), 3100 Avenue E, Zip 78861–3599; tel. 830/426–7700, **A**10 18 **F**3 11 13 15 28 29 34 35 40 41 43 45 57 59 64 66 75 76 77 81 82 85 87 93 107 110 111 115 119 127 133 135 145 146 148 154 **P**4
Primary Contact: Janice Simons, FACHE, Chief Executive Officer
CFO: Kevin Frosch, Chief Financial Officer
CMO: Matthew Windrow, M.D., Chief of Staff
CIO: Ken Gallegos, Director Support Services and Information Technology
CHR: Sharon Garcia, Human Resources Representative
CNO: Billie Bell, Chief Nursing Officer
Web address: www.medinahospital.net
Control: Hospital district or authority, Government, nonfederal **Service**: General medical and surgical

Staffed Beds: 25 **Admissions**: 706 **Census**: 9 **Outpatient Visits**: 110195 **Births**: 151 **Total Expense ($000)**: 26782 **Payroll Expense ($000)**: 10407 **Personnel**: 236

HOUSTON—Harris County

AD HOSPITAL EAST (670102), 12950 East Freeway, Zip 77015–5710; tel. 713/330–3887, (Nonreporting)
Primary Contact: Robert A. Turner, Chief Executive Officer
Control: Other not–for–profit (including NFP Corporation) **Service**: General medical and surgical

Staffed Beds: 25

TX

Hospital, Medicare Provider Number, Address, Telephone, Approval, Facility, and Physician Codes, Health Care System

★ American Hospital Association (AHA) membership
☐ The Joint Commission accreditation
○ Healthcare Facilities Accreditation Program
◇ DNV Healthcare Inc. accreditation
⇑ Center for Improvement in Healthcare Quality Accreditation
△ Commission on Accreditation of Rehabilitation Facilities (CARF) accreditation

☐ **ADVANCED DIAGNOSTICS HOSPITAL (670203)**, 12950 East Freeway, Zip 77015–5710; tel. 713/330–3887, **A**1 **F**3 12 29 40 44 45 54 64 68 75 79 81 82 85 92 107 111 114 115 119 131 149
Primary Contact: Steve Winnett, Chief Executive Officer
CFO: Carol Files, Chief Financial Officer
CMO: Ian Reynolds, Chief Medical Officer
CIO: Yobi Kasper, Chief Information Officer
CHR: Gabby Myers, Human Resources Director
CNO: David Gonzalez, Chief Clinical Officer
Control: Individual, Investor–owned (for–profit) **Service**: General medical and surgical

Staffed Beds: 4 **Admissions**: 237 **Census**: 2 **Outpatient Visits**: 5674 **Births**: 0 **Total Expense ($000)**: 16516 **Payroll Expense ($000)**: 4307 **Personnel**: 71

★ ⇑ **BAYLOR ST. LUKE'S MEDICAL CENTER (450193)**, 6720 Bertner Avenue, Zip 77030–2697, Mailing Address: P.O. Box 20269, Zip 77225–0269; tel. 832/355–1000, **A**2 3 5 8 10 21 **F**3 8 11 12 14 15 17 18 20 22 24 26 28 29 30 31 34 35 36 37 39 40 43 45 46 47 48 49 50 51 54 55 56 57 58 59 60 61 63 64 65 66 68 70 74 75 77 78 79 81 82 84 85 86 87 90 91 92 93 100 107 108 109 110 111 112 113 114 115 116 117 118 119 120 121 122 123 124 126 129 130 131 132 137 138 139 140 142 146 148 149 154 **P**6 **S** Catholic Health Initiatives, Englewood, CO
Primary Contact: Gay Nord, President
CIO: James Albin, Chief Information Officer
CHR: Susan Bailey–Newell, Vice President Human Resources
Web address: www.stlukestexas.com
Control: Church operated, Nongovernment, not–for–profit **Service**: General medical and surgical

Staffed Beds: 615 **Admissions**: 23893 **Census**: 435 **Outpatient Visits**: 169828 **Births**: 0 **Total Expense ($000)**: 890465 **Payroll Expense ($000)**: 315065 **Personnel**: 3357

✠ **BAYLOR ST. LUKE'S MEDICAL CENTER MCNAIR CAMPUS**, One Baylor Plaza, BCM 100, Zip 77030–3411; tel. 713/798–4951, (Nonreporting) **A**1 **S** Catholic Health Initiatives, Englewood, CO
Primary Contact: Gay Nord, President
Web address: www.bcm.edu
Control: Other not–for–profit (including NFP Corporation) **Service**: General medical and surgical

Staffed Beds: 256

☐ **BEHAVIORAL HOSPITAL OF BELLAIRE (454107)**, 5314 Dashwood Drive, Zip 77081–4603; tel. 713/600–9500, **A**1 10 **F**4 5 29 98 99 100 101 104 105 130 152 153 **S** Universal Health Services, Inc., King of Prussia, PA
Primary Contact: Dhruv Narielwala, Interim Chief Executive Officer
Web address: www.bhbhospital.com
Control: Corporation, Investor–owned (for–profit) **Service**: Psychiatric

Staffed Beds: 122 **Admissions**: 3303 **Census**: 87 **Outpatient Visits**: 4729 **Births**: 0 **Total Expense ($000)**: 19559 **Payroll Expense ($000)**: 10772 **Personnel**: 201

★ ⇑ **CHI ST. LUKE'S HOSPITAL – THE VINTAGE HOSPITAL (670075)**, 20171 Chasewood Park Drive, Zip 77070–1437; tel. 832/534–5000, **A**10 21 **F**3 11 13 15 18 20 22 24 26 29 30 34 35 40 45 49 50 57 59 64 68 70 72 75 76 77 79 81 85 87 107 108 110 111 114 115 118 119 130 146 147 149 **P**5 **S** Catholic Health Initiatives, Englewood, CO
Primary Contact: Roland Cruickshank, President
Web address: www.stlukesvintage.com/
Control: Church operated, Nongovernment, not–for–profit **Service**: General medical and surgical

Staffed Beds: 78 **Admissions**: 3861 **Census**: 41 **Outpatient Visits**: 26734 **Births**: 1158 **Total Expense ($000)**: 71898 **Payroll Expense ($000)**: 31572 **Personnel**: 335

CORNERSTONE HOSPITAL–MEDICAL CENTER OF HOUSTON (452055), 2001 Hermann Drive, Zip 77004; tel. 832/649–6200, **A**10 22 **F**1 3 29 70 85 86 87 91 119 130 148 149 **S** Cornerstone Healthcare Group, Dallas, TX
Primary Contact: Michael Higginbotham, Chief Executive Officer
Web address: www.chghospitals.com
Control: Corporation, Investor–owned (for–profit) **Service**: Acute long–term care hospital

Staffed Beds: 35 **Admissions**: 484 **Census**: 30 **Outpatient Visits**: 0 **Births**: 0 **Total Expense ($000)**: 18297 **Payroll Expense ($000)**: 7544 **Personnel**: 98

☐ **CYPRESS CREEK HOSPITAL (454108)**, 17750 Cali Drive, Zip 77090–2700; tel. 281/586–7600, **A**1 10 **F**4 5 29 30 64 75 87 98 100 102 104 105 130 132 153 154 **S** Universal Health Services, Inc., King of Prussia, PA
Primary Contact: Phuong Cardoza, Interim Chief Executive Officer
CFO: Stephen Copeland, Chief Financial Officer
CMO: Marshall Lucas, M.D., Medical Director
CIO: James Harmon, Information Technology
CHR: Brenda Dominguez, Director Human Resources
CNO: Michael Smith, Director of Nursing
Web address: www.cypresscreekhospital.com
Control: Corporation, Investor–owned (for–profit) **Service**: Psychiatric

Staffed Beds: 96 **Admissions**: 3599 **Census**: 84 **Outpatient Visits**: 8915 **Births**: 0 **Total Expense ($000)**: 22807 **Payroll Expense ($000)**: 11002 **Personnel**: 204

✠ **CYPRESS FAIRBANKS MEDICAL CENTER (450716)**, 10655 Steepletop Drive, Zip 77065–4297; tel. 281/890–4285, **A**1 10 **F**3 12 13 15 18 20 22 24 29 30 31 34 35 40 43 45 46 47 49 50 57 59 64 65 70 72 74 75 76 77 78 79 81 82 85 87 89 93 107 108 110 111 114 115 119 120 121 124 129 130 132 144 145 146 147 148 **S** HCA Healthcare, Nashville, TN
Primary Contact: Naman Mahajan, Chief Executive Officer
COO: Hannah Gelbs, Chief Operating Officer
CFO: James Wright, M.D., Chief Financial Officer
CMO: Arturo Bravo, M.D., Chief of Staff
CIO: Donna Cain, Director Information Systems Department
CHR: Linda Creswell, Director Human Resource
CNO: Lisa D. Cox, R.N., MSN, Chief Nursing Officer
Web address: www.cyfairhospital.com
Control: Corporation, Investor–owned (for–profit) **Service**: General medical and surgical

Staffed Beds: 155 **Admissions**: 8626 **Census**: 90 **Outpatient Visits**: 117020 **Births**: 2925 **Total Expense ($000)**: 151019 **Payroll Expense ($000)**: 68478 **Personnel**: 825

DUBUIS HOSPITAL OF HOUSTON See Cornerstone Hospital–Medical Center of Houston

✠ **ENCOMPASS HEALTH REHABILITATION HOSPITAL OF CYPRESS (673050)**, 13031 Wortham Center Drive, Zip 77065–5662; tel. 832/280–2500, **A**1 10 **F**3 29 34 57 62 64 75 77 87 90 91 93 95 96 130 132 148 149 **S** Encompass Health Corporation, Birmingham, AL
Primary Contact: Sheila A. Bollier, Chief Executive Officer
CFO: Melissa Haddox, Controller
CMO: Ignazio LaChina, M.D., Medical Director
CNO: Roshonda Henry, Chief Nursing Officer
Web address: www.healthsouthcypress.com
Control: Corporation, Investor–owned (for–profit) **Service**: Rehabilitation

Staffed Beds: 60 **Admissions**: 1428 **Census**: 50 **Outpatient Visits**: 4917 **Births**: 0 **Total Expense ($000)**: 19590 **Payroll Expense ($000)**: 10550 **Personnel**: 165

✠ **ENCOMPASS HEALTH REHABILITATION HOSPITAL THE VINTAGE (673052)**, 20180 Chasewood Park Drive, Zip 77070–1436; tel. 281/205–5100, **A**1 10 **F**3 29 65 90 91 96 130 148 149 **S** Encompass Health Corporation, Birmingham, AL
Primary Contact: Krista Uselman, Chief Executive Officer
CNO: Stanley F Kiebzak, R.N., Chief Nursing Officer
Web address: www.reliantnwhouston.com
Control: Corporation, Investor–owned (for–profit) **Service**: Rehabilitation

Staffed Beds: 39 **Admissions**: 1073 **Census**: 31 **Outpatient Visits**: 3455 **Births**: 0 **Total Expense ($000)**: 21857 **Payroll Expense ($000)**: 8701 **Personnel**: 133

☐ **FIRST TEXAS HOSPITAL (670118)**, 9922 Louetta Road, Zip 77070–1468, Mailing Address: 2941 Lake Vista Drive, Lewisville, Zip 75067–3801; tel. 346/206–2300, (Nonreporting) **A**1
Primary Contact: Maridel Acosta–Cruz, Chief Executive Officer
Control: Corporation, Investor–owned (for–profit) **Service**: General medical and surgical

Staffed Beds: 50

TX

△ ⇑ **HARRIS HEALTH SYSTEM (450289)**, 2525 Holly Hall Street, Zip 77054–4108, Mailing Address: P.O. Box 66769, Zip 77266–6769; tel. 713/566–6403, (Includes BEN TAUB GENERAL HOSPITAL, 1504 Taub Loop, Houston, TX, Zip 77030; tel. 713/873–2300; LYNDON B JOHNSON GENERAL HOSPITAL, 5656 Kelley, Houston, TX, Zip 77026; tel. 713/566–5000; QUENTIN MEASE HOSPITAL, 3601 North MacGregor, Houston, TX, Zip 77004; tel. 713/873–3700; Jeffrey Webster, Administrator) (Total facility includes 24 beds in nursing home–type unit) **A**2 5 7 10 21 **F**3 5 7 8 13 15 17 18 20 22 24 26 29 30 31 32 34 35 39 40 41 43 45 46 49 50 51 54 55 56 57 58 59 60 61 64 65 68 70 71 72 73 74 75 76 77 78 79 81 82 84 87 89 90 91 92 93 94 97 98 100 101 102 104 107 110 111 112 114 115 118 119 120 121 124 128 129 130 132 134 135 143 144 146 147 148 149 150 153 **P**6
Primary Contact: George V. Masi, Chief Executive Officer
CFO: Michael Norby, Chief Financial Officer
CMO: Fred Sutton, M.D., Chief Medical Officer
CIO: Tim Tindle, Chief Information Officer
CHR: Diane Poirot, Vice President Human Resources
CNO: Elizabeth Cloyd, R.N., Chief Nurse Executive and Executive Vice President
Web address: www.hchdonline.com
Control: Hospital district or authority, Government, nonfederal **Service:** General medical and surgical

Staffed Beds: 741 **Admissions:** 33510 **Census:** 508 **Outpatient Visits:** 1898600 **Births:** 5988 **Total Expense ($000):** 1338543 **Payroll Expense ($000):** 519627 **Personnel:** 8729

⇑ **HEALTHBRIDGE CHILDREN'S HOSPITAL OF HOUSTON (453309)**, 2929 Woodland Park Drive, Zip 77082–2687; tel. 281/293–7774, **A**3 10 21 **F**3 29 74 75 79 85 87 89 91 93 100 130 146 148 **S** Nexus Health Systems, Houston, TX
Primary Contact: Joel Telly, Chief Executive Officer
CMO: Robert Yetman, M.D., Medical Director
CHR: Guy Murdock, Vice President Human Resources
Web address: www.healthbridgehouston.com/
Control: Partnership, Investor–owned (for–profit) **Service:** Children's general medical and surgical

Staffed Beds: 40 **Admissions:** 150 **Census:** 18 **Outpatient Visits:** 310 **Births:** 0 **Total Expense ($000):** 12024 **Payroll Expense ($000):** 4938 **Personnel:** 103

□ **HERMANN DRIVE SURGICAL HOSPITAL**, 2001 Hermann Drive, Zip 77004–7643; tel. 713/285–5500, **A**1 **F**3 12 29 40 45 46 64 68 74 75 77 81 85 86 107 114 119 **S** Nobilis Health Corporation, Houston, TX
Primary Contact: Nicole Walker, Chief Executive Officer
Web address: www.nobilishealth.com/our-facilities/houston/
Control: Corporation, Investor–owned (for–profit) **Service:** Surgical

Staffed Beds: 25 **Admissions:** 765 **Census:** 5 **Outpatient Visits:** 2743 **Births:** 0 **Total Expense ($000):** 40099 **Payroll Expense ($000):** 6597 **Personnel:** 39

HOUSTON BEHAVIORAL HEALTHCARE HOSPITAL (454135), 2801 Gessner Road, Zip 77080–2503; tel. 832/834–7710, (Nonreporting) **S** Signature Healthcare Services, Corona, CA
Primary Contact: Roy Hollis, Chief Executive Officer
Web address: www.houstonbehavioralhealth.com/
Control: Individual, Investor–owned (for–profit) **Service:** Psychiatric

Staffed Beds: 25

★ △ ⇑ **HOUSTON METHODIST HOSPITAL (450358)**, 6565 Fannin Street, D200, Zip 77030–2707; tel. 713/790–3311, (Total facility includes 18 beds in nursing home–type unit) **A**2 3 5 7 8 10 21 **F**3 5 6 8 9 11 12 13 17 18 20 22 24 26 28 29 30 31 33 36 39 40 41 44 45 46 47 48 49 50 51 53 54 55 56 57 58 59 60 61 62 63 64 65 66 67 68 70 73 74 75 76 77 78 79 81 82 84 85 86 87 90 91 92 93 95 96 97 98 100 101 103 104 107 108 110 111 114 115 117 118 119 120 121 123 124 126 128 129 130 131 132 135 136 137 138 139 140 141 142 145 146 147 148 149 150 154 **P**5 6 **S** Houston Methodist, Houston, TX
Primary Contact: Roberta Schwartz, Ph.D., Executive Vice President
CMO: Robert Phillips, M.D., Ph.D., FACC, Executive Vice President and Chief Medical Officer
CIO: Robert K Eardley, Senior Vice President and Chief Information Officer
CNO: Katherine Walsh, MS, R.N., Dr.PH, Vice President and Chief Nursing Officer
Web address: www.methodisthealth.com
Control: Other not–for–profit (including NFP Corporation) **Service:** General medical and surgical

Staffed Beds: 933 **Admissions:** 38465 **Census:** 718 **Outpatient Visits:** 383780 **Births:** 998 **Total Expense ($000):** 1673707 **Payroll Expense ($000):** 468008 **Personnel:** 9351

★ ⇑ **HOUSTON METHODIST WEST HOSPITAL (670077)**, 18500 Katy Freeway, Zip 77094–1110; tel. 832/522–1000, **A**3 10 21 **F**3 11 13 15 18 20 22 24 26 28 29 30 31 34 35 36 39 40 44 45 49 50 51 53 54 57 59 60 61 63 64 68 70 72 74 75 76 77 78 79 81 82 84 85 86 87 93 107 108 109 110 111 114 115 116 117 118 119 120 121 123 124 126 130 131 132 135 146 147 148 149 **P**6 **S** Houston Methodist, Houston, TX
Primary Contact: Wayne M. Voss, Chief Executive Officer
CNO: Victoria Brownewell, Chief Nursing Officer
Web address: www.methodisthealth.com
Control: Other not–for–profit (including NFP Corporation) **Service:** General medical and surgical

Staffed Beds: 193 **Admissions:** 11639 **Census:** 119 **Outpatient Visits:** 125183 **Births:** 2360 **Total Expense ($000):** 249577 **Payroll Expense ($000):** 90145 **Personnel:** 1297

★ ⇑ **HOUSTON METHODIST WILLOWBROOK HOSPITAL (450844)**, 18220 State Highway 249, Zip 77070–4347; tel. 281/477–1000, **A**3 10 21 **F**3 8 11 12 13 15 17 18 20 22 24 26 28 29 30 34 36 37 40 44 45 49 50 53 54 57 59 64 65 70 72 73 74 75 76 77 78 79 81 85 86 87 93 97 102 107 108 110 111 112 115 119 120 121 123 126 129 130 131 132 135 146 147 149 **P**6 **S** Houston Methodist, Houston, TX
Primary Contact: Keith Barber, CPA, Chief Executive Officer
CHR: Elizabeth Acevedo, Director Human Resources
CNO: Nancy C Keenan, R.N., Senior Vice President and Chief Nursing Officer
Web address: www.houstonmethodist.org/locations/willowbrook/
Control: Other not–for–profit (including NFP Corporation) **Service:** General medical and surgical

Staffed Beds: 312 **Admissions:** 18302 **Census:** 222 **Outpatient Visits:** 203245 **Births:** 3640 **Total Expense ($000):** 360325 **Payroll Expense ($000):** 136440 **Personnel:** 1871

⊞ **HOUSTON NORTHWEST MEDICAL CENTER (450638)**, 710 Cypress Creek Parkway, Zip 77090–3402; tel. 281/440–1000, **A**1 3 5 10 **F**3 11 12 13 15 18 20 22 24 26 28 29 30 31 34 35 40 45 46 49 50 57 59 64 65 70 72 74 75 76 77 78 79 81 82 84 85 86 87 90 91 92 93 96 102 107 108 109 110 111 114 115 117 118 119 126 129 130 132 135 144 145 146 147 148 149 **S** HCA Healthcare, Nashville, TN
Primary Contact: Timothy Puthoff, Chief Executive Officer
COO: Michael Adkins, Chief Operating Officer
CFO: Cameron Pophan, CPA, Chief Financial Officer
CIO: Ed Roberson, Director Information Systems
CHR: Melanie R Webb, Vice President Human Resources
CNO: Cindy Henning, R.N., Chief Nursing Officer
Web address: www.hnmc.com
Control: Partnership, Investor–owned (for–profit) **Service:** General medical and surgical

Staffed Beds: 339 **Admissions:** 16070 **Census:** 194 **Outpatient Visits:** 144635 **Births:** 3963 **Total Expense ($000):** 251689 **Payroll Expense ($000):** 100972 **Personnel:** 1300

□ **INTRACARE NORTH HOSPITAL (454083)**, 1120 Cypress Station Drive, Zip 77090–3031; tel. 281/893–7200, **A**1 10 **F**98 99 100 101 103 104 153
Primary Contact: Terry Scovill, Chief Executive Officer
CFO: Fred Chan, Chief Financial Officer
CMO: Javier Ruiz, M.D., Medical Director
Web address: www.intracare.org
Control: Other not–for–profit (including NFP Corporation) **Service:** Psychiatric

Staffed Beds: 90 **Admissions:** 2366 **Census:** 56 **Outpatient Visits:** 30787 **Births:** 0 **Total Expense ($000):** 17096 **Payroll Expense ($000):** 7944 **Personnel:** 194

⊞ **KINDRED HOSPITAL HOUSTON MEDICAL CENTER (452023)**, 6441 Main Street, Zip 77030–1596; tel. 713/790–0500, **A**1 3 5 10 **F**1 29 30 70 75 77 85 107 130 148 **S** Kindred Healthcare, Louisville, KY
Primary Contact: Robert Stein, Chief Executive Officer
CFO: Sara Langlitz, Controller
Web address: www.khhouston.com/
Control: Corporation, Investor–owned (for–profit) **Service:** Acute long–term care hospital

Staffed Beds: 105 **Admissions:** 958 **Census:** 83 **Outpatient Visits:** 0 **Births:** 0 **Total Expense ($000):** 45239 **Payroll Expense ($000):** 21721 **Personnel:** 313

TX

⊠ **KINDRED HOSPITAL–HOUSTON NORTHWEST (452039)**, 11297 Fallbrook Drive, Zip 77065–4292; tel. 281/897–8114, (Includes KINDRED HOSPITAL–BAY AREA, 4801 East Sam Houston Parkway South, Pasadena, TX, Zip 77505–3955; tel. 281/991–5463) **A**1 10 **F**1 3 29 49 57 64 70 77 85 87 107 114 130 148 **P**5 **S** Kindred Healthcare, Louisville, KY
Primary Contact: Tracy Kohler, Chief Executive Officer
Web address: www.khhoustonnw.com/
Control: Corporation, Investor–owned (for–profit) **Service**: Acute long–term care hospital

Staffed Beds: 84 Admissions: 697 Census: 45 Outpatient Visits: 277
Births: 0 Total Expense ($000): 27880 Payroll Expense ($000): 10510
Personnel: 152

LYNDON B JOHNSON GENERAL HOSPITAL See Harris Health System, Houston

⊠ **MEMORIAL HERMANN – TEXAS MEDICAL CENTER (450068)**, 6411 Fannin Street, Zip 77030–1501; tel. 713/704–4000, (Includes CHILDREN'S MEMORIAL HERMANN HOSPITAL, 6411 Fannin, Houston, TX, Zip 77030; tel. 713/704–5437; MEMORIAL HERMANN CYPRESS, 27700 NW Freeway, Suite 380, Cypress, TX, Zip 77433; tel. 832/658–3102; Heath Rushing, Senior Vice President and Chief Executive Officer; MEMORIAL HERMANN ORTHOPEDIC AND SPINE HOSPITAL, 5410 West Loop South, Bellaire, TX, Zip 77401–2103; tel. 713/314–4500; Gregory Haralson, FACHE, Senior Vice President and Chief Executive Officer) (Total facility includes 8 beds in nursing home–type unit) **A**1 2 3 5 8 10 **F**3 7 8 11 12 13 15 16 17 18 19 20 21 22 23 24 25 26 27 28 29 30 31 32 34 35 36 37 39 40 41 43 44 45 46 47 48 49 50 53 54 55 56 57 58 59 60 61 63 64 65 68 70 71 72 73 74 75 76 77 78 80 81 82 83 84 85 86 87 88 89 90 92 93 97 102 107 108 109 110 111 113 114 115 116 117 118 119 120 121 123 124 126 128 129 130 131 132 135 136 137 138 139 140 141 142 144 146 147 148 149 150 154 **P**5 6 **S** Memorial Hermann Health System, Houston, TX
Primary Contact: Gregory Haralson, FACHE, Senior Vice President and Chief Executive Officer
COO: Shawn Cloonan, Executive Vice President and Chief Operating Officer
CFO: William Pack, Chief Financial Officer
CMO: Jeffrey Katz, M.D., Chief Medical Officer
CIO: David Bradshaw, Chief Information Officer
CHR: Vivian Kardow, Chief Human Resources Officer
Web address: www.mhhs.org
Control: Other not–for–profit (including NFP Corporation) **Service**: General medical and surgical

Staffed Beds: 1042 Admissions: 40827 Census: 728 Outpatient
Visits: 252397 Births: 5004 Total Expense ($000): 1525891 Payroll
Expense ($000): 451437 Personnel: 5381

⊠ △ **MEMORIAL HERMANN GREATER HEIGHTS HOSPITAL (450184)**, 1635 North Loop West, Zip 77008–1532; tel. 713/867–3380, (Includes MEMORIAL HERMANN PEARLAND MEDICAL CENTER, 16100 South Freeway, Pearland, TX, Zip 77584–1895; tel. 713/413–5000; Kyle Price, Chief Executive Officer; MEMORIAL HERMANN SOUTHEAST HOSPITAL, 11800 Astoria Boulevard, Houston, TX, Zip 77089–6041; tel. 281/929–6100; Kyle Price, Chief Executive Officer; MEMORIAL HERMANN SOUTHWEST HOSPITAL, 7600 Beechnut, Houston, TX, Zip 77074–1850; tel. 713/456–5000; Malisha Patel, Senior Vice President and Chief Executive Officer; MEMORIAL HERMANN THE WOODLANDS HOSPITAL, 9250 Pinecroft Drive, The Woodlands, TX, Zip 77380–3225; tel. 281/364–2300) **A**1 2 3 5 7 10 **F**3 8 11 12 13 15 17 18 20 22 24 26 28 29 30 31 34 35 36 37 40 41 43 44 45 46 47 48 49 50 51 54 55 56 57 58 59 60 62 64 65 68 69 70 72 73 74 75 76 77 78 79 80 81 82 84 85 86 87 89 90 91 92 93 94 96 100 102 107 108 109 110 111 112 114 115 116 117 119 120 122 123 124 126 129 130 131 132 135 143 144 146 147 148 149 154 **P**5 6 **S** Memorial Hermann Health System, Houston, TX
Primary Contact: Paul O'Sullivan, FACHE, Chief Executive Officer
COO: Wesley Tidwell, Chief Operating Officer
CFO: James R Shallock, Chief Financial Officer
CMO: Maurice Leibman, M.D., Chief Medical Officer
CIO: David Bradshaw, Chief Information Officer
CNO: Ann Szapor, Vice President and Chief Nursing Officer
Web address: www.memorialhermann.org
Control: Other not–for–profit (including NFP Corporation) **Service**: General medical and surgical

Staffed Beds: 1379 Admissions: 67257 Census: 892 Outpatient
Visits: 623226 Births: 10709 Total Expense ($000): 1360499 Payroll
Expense ($000): 452660 Personnel: 5513

⊠ **MEMORIAL HERMANN MEMORIAL CITY MEDICAL CENTER (450610)**, 921 Gessner Road, Zip 77024–2501; tel. 713/242–3000, **A**1 2 3 5 10 **F**3 12 13 15 17 18 20 22 24 26 28 29 30 31 34 35 37 40 41 43 45 46 47 49 51 56 57 59 60 65 70 72 74 75 76 77 78 79 80 81 82 84 85 87 89 107 108 110 111 114 115 117 118 119 120 121 123 124 126 129 130 131 132 135 146 147 148 149 **P**5 6 **S** Memorial Hermann Health System, Houston, TX
Primary Contact: Paul O'Sullivan, FACHE, Chief Executive Officer
COO: Allen Tseng, Chief Operations Officer
CFO: Lisa Kendler, Chief Financial Officer
CMO: Harold Gottlieb, M.D., Chief Medical Officer
CIO: David Bradshaw, Chief Information, Planning and Marketing Officer
CHR: Suzanne S Meier, System Director, Compensation and Human Resources Technology
CNO: Dan Kelly, R.N., Chief Nursing Officer
Web address: www.memorialhermann.org
Control: Other not–for–profit (including NFP Corporation) **Service**: General medical and surgical

Staffed Beds: 421 Admissions: 21110 Census: 236 Outpatient
Visits: 207798 Births: 3664 Total Expense ($000): 497237 Payroll
Expense ($000): 127299 Personnel: 1616

MEMORIAL HERMANN SOUTHEAST HOSPITAL See Memorial Hermann Greater Heights Hospital, Houston

MEMORIAL HERMANN SOUTHWEST HOSPITAL See Memorial Hermann Greater Heights Hospital, Houston

☐ **MENNINGER CLINIC**, 12301 Main Street, Zip 77035–6207; tel. 713/275–5000, **A**1 3 5 **F**30 35 74 98 101 104 106 130 132 154
Primary Contact: Anthony Gaglio, CPA, Interim President and Chief Executive Officer
CFO: Anthony Gaglio, CPA, Senior Vice President and Chief Financial Officer
CIO: M. Justin Coffey, Vice President and Chief Information Officer, Medical Director Center for Brain Stimulation
CHR: Andrea Preisinger, Director Human Resources
CNO: Avni Cirpili, Senior Vice President, Chief Nursing Officer
Web address: www.menningerclinic.com
Control: Other not–for–profit (including NFP Corporation) **Service**: Psychiatric

Staffed Beds: 102 Admissions: 712 Census: 67 Outpatient Visits: 4566
Births: 0 Total Expense ($000): 58484 Payroll Expense ($000): 25490
Personnel: 396

⇑ **METHODIST WEST HOUSTON HOSPITAL** See Houston Methodist West Hospital

⇑ **METHODIST WILLOWBROOK HOSPITAL** See Houston Methodist Willowbrook Hospital

⊠ △ **MICHAEL E. DEBAKEY VETERANS AFFAIRS MEDICAL CENTER**, 2002 Holcombe Boulevard, Zip 77030–4298; tel. 713/791–1414, (Nonreporting) **A**1 3 5 7 8 **S** Department of Veterans Affairs, Perry Point, MD
Primary Contact: Francisco Vazquez, Director
CFO: Alisa Cooper, Manager Financial Resources
CMO: Jagadeesh S Kalavar, M.D., Chief of Staff
CIO: Kevin Lenamond, Information Management Service Line Executive
CHR: Mark Muhammad, Manager Human Resources
CNO: Kelly Ann Irving MSN, RN–B Associate Director for Patient Care Services
Web address: www.houston.va.gov
Control: Veterans Affairs, Government, federal **Service**: General medical and surgical

Staffed Beds: 479

⊠ **PARK PLAZA HOSPITAL (450659)**, 1313 Hermann Drive, Zip 77004–7092; tel. 713/527–5000, **A**1 2 10 **F**3 12 15 18 20 22 29 31 34 35 40 45 49 50 56 57 59 70 74 78 79 81 85 92 107 108 110 111 114 115 118 119 120 121 123 129 130 132 146 147 148 **S** HCA Healthcare, Nashville, TN
Primary Contact: Peyton Elliott, Chief Executive Officer
COO: Mary Jo Goodman, Chief Operating Officer
CIO: Terry Janis, Assistant Vice President
CHR: Melanie R Webb, Vice President Human Resources
Web address: www.parkplazahospital.com
Control: Corporation, Investor–owned (for–profit) **Service**: General medical and surgical

Staffed Beds: 139 Admissions: 3660 Census: 60 Outpatient Visits: 31834
Births: 0 Total Expense ($000): 78819 Payroll Expense ($000): 30369
Personnel: 416

TX

☐ **PINE VALLEY SPECIALTY HOSPITAL (452043)**, 6160 South Loop East, Zip 77087–1010; tel. 713/640–2400, (Nonreporting) **A**1 10 **S** Concord Healthcare Group, Lakewood, NJ
CFO: Betty Priestley, Manager Business Office
CMO: Alfred Louis, M.D., Chief Medical Staff
CHR: Laura Garza, Director Human Resources
Web address: www.pinevalleyspecialtyhospital.com/wp-pine/
Control: Corporation, Investor–owned (for–profit) **Service:** Acute long–term care hospital

Staffed Beds: 35

⊠ **PLAZA SPECIALTY HOSPITAL (452046)**, 1300 Binz Street, Zip 77004–7016; tel. 713/285–1000, **A**1 10 **F**1 3 70 85 87 **P**8 **S** HCA Healthcare, Nashville, TN
Primary Contact: Richard Andrew. Pletz, Chief Executive Officer
CFO: Charles Handley, Chief Financial Officer
CMO: Wasae S Tabibi, M.D., President Medical Staff
CIO: Michael Turner, Chief Information Officer
Web address: www.plazaspecialtyhospital.com
Control: Corporation, Investor–owned (for–profit) **Service:** Acute long–term care hospital

Staffed Beds: 46 **Admissions:** 366 **Census:** 26 **Outpatient Visits:** 0 **Births:** 0 **Total Expense ($000):** 22252 **Payroll Expense ($000):** 7282 **Personnel:** 75

PROVIDENCE HOSPITAL OF NORTH HOUSTON (670119), 16750 Red Oak Drive, Zip 77090; tel. 281/453–7110, **A**10 22 **F**3 15 18 20 22 26 29 37 40 45 48 49 51 64 68 70 81 82 85 91 107 108 110 111 115 119 129 148 **P**8
Primary Contact: Stephen Myers, Chief Executive Officer
Control: Partnership, Investor–owned (for–profit) **Service:** General medical and surgical

Staffed Beds: 16 **Admissions:** 226 **Census:** 1 **Outpatient Visits:** 4894 **Births:** 0 **Total Expense ($000):** 22599 **Payroll Expense ($000):** 5808 **Personnel:** 121

SACRED OAK MEDICAL CENTER (454142), 11500 Space Center Boulevard, Zip 77059–3603; tel. 281/241–6460, (Nonreporting) **A**10
Primary Contact: Raquel Diati, Chief Executive Officer
Web address: sacredoakmedical.com/
Control: Other not–for–profit (including NFP Corporation) **Service:** General medical and surgical

Staffed Beds: 25

☐ **SCA HOUSTON HOSPITAL FOR SPECIALIZED SURGERY (450797)**, 5445 La Branch Street, Zip 77004–6835; tel. 713/528–6800, **A**1 10 **F**3 8 40 54 64 79 81 82 85 107 111 114 119 149
Primary Contact: Mary Whitmeyer, Chief Executive Officer
CFO: Deborah Jones, Controller
Web address: www.scasurgery.com
Control: Partnership, Investor–owned (for–profit) **Service:** Surgical

Staffed Beds: 7 **Admissions:** 218 **Census:** 2 **Outpatient Visits:** 40506 **Births:** 0 **Total Expense ($000):** 25937 **Payroll Expense ($000):** 8290 **Personnel:** 175

☐ **SHRINERS HOSPITALS FOR CHILDREN–HOUSTON (453312)**, 6977 Main Street, Zip 77030–3701; tel. 713/797–1616, **A**1 3 5 10 **F**3 29 30 35 50 59 64 68 74 75 77 79 81 86 87 89 93 94 96 130 131 132 134 143 146 148 154 **P**6 **S** Shriners Hospitals for Children, Tampa, FL
Primary Contact: Cathy Moniaci, R.N., MS, Administrator
COO: Cathy Moniaci, R.N., MS, Administrator
CFO: Michael B Schimming, Director Fiscal Services
CMO: Douglas A Barnes, M.D., Chief of Staff
CHR: Robert A Magee, Director Human Resources
CNO: Jeannie Keith, Director Patient Care Services and Nurse Executive
Web address: www.shrinershospitalsforchildren.org/Locations/houston
Control: Other not–for–profit (including NFP Corporation) **Service:** Children's orthopedic

Staffed Beds: 40 **Admissions:** 488 **Census:** 11 **Outpatient Visits:** 7169 **Births:** 0 **Total Expense ($000):** 29871 **Payroll Expense ($000):** 15960 **Personnel:** 173

⇑ **ST. JOSEPH MEDICAL CENTER (450035)**, 1401 St Joseph Parkway, Zip 77002–8301; tel. 713/757–1000, (Includes ST. JOSEPH MEDICAL CENTER IN THE HEIGHTS, 1917 Ashland Street, Houston, TX, Zip 77008–3907; tel. 713/969–5400; Kirsten M. Benjamin, Administrative Director) (Total facility includes 16 beds in nursing home–type unit) **A**3 5 10 21 **F**3 11 12 13 15 18 20 22 24 26 29 30 31 34 35 40 43 45 49 50 51 53 55 57 58 59 60 64 68 70 72 74 75 76 77 78 79 81 82 84 85 86 87 90 93 94 97 98 101 102 104 107 108 110 111 114 115 116 117 118 119 121 123 124 126 128 129 130 131 132 135 143 144 146 147 148 149 153 **P**8 **S** Steward Health Care System, LLC, Dallas, TX
Primary Contact: Kimberly S. Bassett, R.N., President
COO: Laura Fortin, R.N., Chief Operating Officer
CFO: Mark Hartman, Interim Chief Financial Officer
CIO: Robin Brown, Chief Information Officer and Compliance Officer
CHR: Kris Clatanoff, Director Human Resources
Web address: www.sjmctx.com
Control: Partnership, Investor–owned (for–profit) **Service:** General medical and surgical

Staffed Beds: 463 **Admissions:** 14791 **Census:** 213 **Outpatient Visits:** 111491 **Births:** 4182 **Total Expense ($000):** 208543 **Payroll Expense ($000):** 98435 **Personnel:** 1639

SUN BEHAVIORAL HOUSTON (454139), 7601 Fannin Street, Zip 77054–1905; tel. 713/796–2273, (Nonreporting) **A**3
Primary Contact: Rick Harding, Chief Executive Officer
CFO: Doug Smith, Chief Financial Officer
CMO: Vernon Walling, M.D., Chief Medical Officer
Web address: www.sunhouston.com
Control: Other not–for–profit (including NFP Corporation) **Service:** Psychiatric

Staffed Beds: 148

☐ △ **TEXAS CHILDREN'S HOSPITAL (453304)**, 6621 Fannin Street, Zip 77030–2399, Mailing Address: Box 300630, Zip 77230–0630; tel. 832/824–1000, (Includes TEXAS CHILDREN'S HOSPITAL THE WOODLANDS, 17600 Interstate 45 South, The Woodlands, TX, Zip 77384–5148; tel. 936/267–5000; Michelle Riley–Brown, President; TEXAS CHILDREN'S HOSPITAL WEST CAMPUS, 18200 Katy Freeway, Houston, TX, Zip 77094–1285; tel. 832/227–1000; Michelle Riley–Brown, President) **A**1 3 5 7 8 10 **F**3 7 11 12 13 17 19 21 23 25 27 29 30 31 32 34 35 38 39 40 41 43 46 48 49 50 52 54 55 57 58 59 60 61 64 65 66 68 71 72 73 74 75 76 77 78 79 80 81 82 84 85 86 87 88 89 90 92 93 94 95 96 97 100 101 102 104 107 108 111 113 114 115 116 117 118 119 126 129 130 131 132 134 136 137 138 139 140 143 146 147 148 149 150
Primary Contact: Mark A. Wallace, FACHE, President and Chief Executive Officer
CMO: Mark W Kline, M.D., Physician in Chief
CIO: Myra Davis, Senior Vice President and Chief Information Officer
CHR: Linda W Aldred, Senior Vice President
Web address: www.texaschildrens.org
Control: Other not–for–profit (including NFP Corporation) **Service:** Children's general medical and surgical

Staffed Beds: 743 **Admissions:** 33366 **Census:** 566 **Outpatient Visits:** 1150717 **Births:** 5719 **Total Expense ($000):** 1939329 **Payroll Expense ($000):** 762323 **Personnel:** 8432

⊠ **TEXAS ORTHOPEDIC HOSPITAL (450804)**, 7401 South Main Street, Zip 77030–4509; tel. 713/799–8600, **A**1 3 5 10 **F**3 29 30 40 59 64 68 70 79 81 82 85 86 87 93 94 97 107 111 119 146 149 **S** HCA Healthcare, Nashville, TN
Primary Contact: Eric Becker, Chief Executive Officer
CFO: Blair Callaway, Chief Financial Officer
CMO: Gregory Stocks, M.D., Chief of Staff
CNO: Troy Sarver, R.N., Chief Nursing Officer
Web address: www.texasorthopedic.com
Control: Partnership, Investor–owned (for–profit) **Service:** Orthopedic

Staffed Beds: 49 **Admissions:** 3586 **Census:** 21 **Outpatient Visits:** 35061 **Births:** 0 **Total Expense ($000):** 87896 **Payroll Expense ($000):** 24889 **Personnel:** 350

⇑ **THE METHODIST HOSPITAL** See Houston Methodist Hospital

Hospital, Medicare Provider Number, Address, Telephone, Approval, Facility, and Physician Codes, Health Care System

★ American Hospital Association (AHA) membership
☐ The Joint Commission accreditation
○ Healthcare Facilities Accreditation Program
◇ DNV Healthcare Inc. accreditation
⇑ Center for Improvement in Healthcare Quality Accreditation
△ Commission on Accreditation of Rehabilitation Facilities (CARF) accreditation

⊠ △ **TIRR MEMORIAL HERMANN (453025)**, 1333 Moursund Street,
Zip 77030–3405; tel. 713/799–5000, **A**1 3 5 7 10 **F**3 11 29 30 34 35 44 50 54
58 59 60 64 68 74 75 77 79 82 86 87 90 91 93 95 96 97 100 104 107 114
119 129 130 131 132 146 148 149 **P**5 6 **S** Memorial Hermann Health System,
Houston, TX
Primary Contact: Jerry Ashworth, Interim Chief Executive Officer
COO: Jerry Ashworth, Chief Operating Officer
CFO: Wayne Gordon, Chief Financial Officer
CMO: Gerard E Francisco, M.D., Chief Medical Officer
CIO: Gina Tripp, Director Information Systems
CHR: Vivian Kardow, Chief Human Resources Officer
Web address: www.memorialhermann.org/locations/tirr.html
Control: Other not–for–profit (including NFP Corporation) **Service**: Rehabilitation

Staffed Beds: 134 **Admissions**: 1296 **Census**: 97 **Outpatient Visits**: 34281
Births: 0 **Total Expense ($000)**: 125820 **Payroll Expense ($000)**: 60501
Personnel: 808

□ **TOPS SURGICAL SPECIALTY HOSPITAL (450774)**, 17080 Red Oak Drive,
Zip 77090–2602; tel. 281/539–2900, **A**1 10 **F**3 15 29 40 45 64 78 79 81 82
86 87 107 119 148 **P**2 **S** United Surgical Partners International, Addison, TX
Primary Contact: Samuel H. Rossmann, Chief Executive Officer
CFO: Daniel Smith, Chief Financial Officer
CMO: Thomas Barton, M.D., Medical Director
CIO: Maud Jones, Manager Medical Records
CHR: Ashley Monzingo, Human Resources, Accounts Payable and Payroll
CNO: Andrea Wappelhorst, Chief Nursing Officer
Web address: www.tops–hospital.com
Control: Partnership, Investor–owned (for–profit) **Service**: Surgical

Staffed Beds: 15 **Admissions**: 688 **Census**: 4 **Outpatient Visits**: 44791
Births: 0 **Total Expense ($000)**: 33866 **Payroll Expense ($000)**: 8922
Personnel: 175

TRIUMPH HOSPITAL NORTHWEST See Kindred Hospital Spring

UNITED MEMORIAL MEDICAL CARE (450803), 510 West Tidwell Road,
Zip 77091–4399; tel. 281/618–8500, (Includes DOCTORS HOSPITAL PARKWAY,
233 West Parker Road, Houston, TX, Zip 77076–2999; tel. 281/765–2600)
(Nonreporting) **A**10 22
Primary Contact: Farida Moeen, M.D., Chief Executive Officer
COO: Farida Moeen, M.D., Chief Executive Officer
CFO: Theresa Eatherly, Chief Financial Officer
CMO: Cesar Ortega, M.D., Chief of Staff
CIO: Dell Davis, Director Information Systems
CHR: Carolyn Washington, Director of Human Resources
Web address: www.ummc.care/
Control: Partnership, Investor–owned (for–profit) **Service**: General medical and surgical

Staffed Beds: 42

★ **UNIVERSITY OF TEXAS HARRIS COUNTY PSYCHIATRIC CENTER (454076)**,
2800 South MacGregor Way, Zip 77021–1000, Mailing Address: P.O. Box 20249,
Zip 77225–0249; tel. 713/741–7870, **A**5 10 **F**29 30 34 35 57 58 68 75 86 87
98 99 100 101 103 104 130 146 **P**6 **S** University of Texas System, Austin, TX
Primary Contact: Jair C. Soares, M.D., Executive Director
COO: Stephen Glazier, Chief Operating Officer
CFO: Lois K. Pierson, Chief Financial Officer
CMO: R Andrew Harper, M.D., Medical Director
CNO: Margaret Pung, R.N., Chief Nursing Officer
Web address: www.hcpc.uth.tmc.edu
Control: State, Government, nonfederal **Service**: Psychiatric

Staffed Beds: 206 **Admissions**: 8415 **Census**: 182 **Outpatient Visits**: 543
Births: 0 **Total Expense ($000)**: 50205 **Payroll Expense ($000)**: 33405
Personnel: 454

⊠ **UNIVERSITY OF TEXAS M.D. ANDERSON CANCER CENTER (450076)**, 1515
Holcombe Boulevard, Unit 1491, Zip 77030–4000; tel. 713/792–2121, **A**1 2 3 5 8
10 **F**3 8 11 14 15 18 20 22 26 29 30 31 32 34 35 36 37 38 39 40 41 44 45 46
47 49 50 54 55 56 57 58 59 64 66 68 70 71 74 75 77 78 79 80 81 82 83 84
85 86 87 88 89 91 92 93 96 97 100 101 102 104 107 108 110 111 112 114
115 116 117 118 119 120 121 122 123 124 126 129 130 132 134 135 136
141 142 145 146 147 148 149 150 **P**6 **S** University of Texas System, Austin, TX
Primary Contact: Peter Pisters, M.D., President
COO: Stephen Hahn, Deputy to the President and Chief Operating Officer
CFO: Weldon Gage, Chief Financial Officer
CIO: Chris Belmont, Chief Information Officer and Vice President
CHR: Shibu Varghese, Vice President Human Resources
CNO: Barbara L. Summers, Ph.D., R.N., Vice President Nursing Practice and Chief
Nursing Officer
Web address: www.mdanderson.org
Control: State, Government, nonfederal **Service**: Cancer

Staffed Beds: 658 **Admissions**: 28793 **Census**: 555 **Outpatient Visits**: 1453277 **Births**: 0 **Total Expense ($000)**: 4332225 **Payroll Expense ($000)**: 1893948 **Personnel**: 19096

⊠ **WEST HOUSTON MEDICAL CENTER (450644)**, 12141 Richmond Avenue,
Zip 77082–2499; tel. 281/558–3444, **A**1 10 **F**3 11 12 13 15 18 20 22 24 26
28 29 31 39 40 45 46 47 48 49 50 51 56 57 59 60 64 70 73 74 75 76 77 78
79 80 81 82 85 90 93 96 98 102 103 107 110 111 115 116 117 118 119 121
124 126 129 130 132 145 146 147 148 149 **S** HCA Healthcare, Nashville, TN
Primary Contact: Megan Marietta, Chief Executive Officer
COO: Philip Morris, Chief Operating Officer
CFO: Stanley K Nord, Chief Financial Officer
CMO: Magdy Rizk, M.D., Chief of Staff
CIO: Sergio Almeida, Director Information Systems
CHR: Carol Melville, Director Human Resources
Web address: www.westhoustonmedical.com
Control: Partnership, Investor–owned (for–profit) **Service**: General medical and surgical

Staffed Beds: 264 **Admissions**: 12375 **Census**: 174 **Outpatient Visits**: 106620 **Births**: 2695 **Total Expense ($000)**: 201618 **Payroll Expense ($000)**: 80327 **Personnel**: 975

□ **WEST OAKS HOSPITAL (454026)**, 6500 Hornwood Drive, Zip 77074–5095;
tel. 713/995–0909, **A**1 5 10 **F**5 29 54 56 64 68 98 99 101 104 105 132 152
153 **S** Universal Health Services, Inc., King of Prussia, PA
Primary Contact: Mandy Westerman, Chief Executive Officer
CFO: Rob Tyler, Chief Financial Officer
CMO: Vernon Walling, M.D., Executive Medical Director
CIO: James Harmon, Network Administrator
CHR: Janice Webster, Director Human Resources
CNO: Israel Ahaine, Chief Nursing Officer
Web address: www.westoakshospital.com
Control: Corporation, Investor–owned (for–profit) **Service**: Psychiatric

Staffed Beds: 144 **Admissions**: 5827 **Census**: 141 **Outpatient Visits**: 14490 **Births**: 0 **Total Expense ($000)**: 27941 **Payroll Expense ($000)**: 17002 **Personnel**: 297

⇑ **WESTSIDE SURGICAL HOSPITAL**, 4200 Twelve Oaks Drive, Zip 77027;
tel. 713/621–5010, **A**21 **F**3 15 29 34 35 37 40 45 79 81 82 85 86 107 110
114 126 149
Primary Contact: Chad Baldwin, Interim Chief Executive Officer
CNO: Jimmy Wells, Chief Nursing and Administrative Officer
Web address: www.westsidesurgical.net
Control: Corporation, Investor–owned (for–profit) **Service**: Surgical

Staffed Beds: 12 **Admissions**: 275 **Census**: 2 **Outpatient Visits**: 443
Births: 0 **Total Expense ($000)**: 32035 **Payroll Expense ($000)**: 5703
Personnel: 75

⊠ **WOMAN'S HOSPITAL OF TEXAS (450674)**, 7600 Fannin Street,
Zip 77054–1906; tel. 713/790–1234, **A**1 3 5 10 **F**3 7 8 13 15 19 29 30 34
35 40 41 45 46 50 53 54 55 58 64 65 68 70 71 72 73 75 76 77 78 81 85 86
87 88 89 90 93 100 107 108 110 111 114 119 126 130 132 146 147 **S** HCA
Healthcare, Nashville, TN
Primary Contact: Ashley McClellan, FACHE, Chief Executive Officer
CFO: Scott Bentley, Chief Financial Officer
CMO: Eberhard Lotze, M.D., Chief Medical Officer
CIO: Emily Le, Director Information Technology and Services
CHR: Arnita Crawford, Director Human Resources
CNO: Holley Tyler, R.N., Chief Nursing Officer
Web address: www.womanshospital.com
Control: Partnership, Investor–owned (for–profit) **Service**: Obstetrics and gynecology

Staffed Beds: 367 **Admissions**: 16458 **Census**: 256 **Outpatient Visits**: 58301 **Births**: 10697 **Total Expense ($000)**: 238125 **Payroll Expense ($000)**: 117914 **Personnel**: 1271

HUMBLE—Harris County

⊠ **ENCOMPASS HEALTH REHABILITATION HOSPITAL OF HUMBLE (453029)**,
19002 McKay Drive, Zip 77338–5701; tel. 281/446–6148, **A**1 10 **F**29 56 75
77 82 86 87 90 91 92 95 96 130 132 143 148 149 **P**5 **S** Encompass Health
Corporation, Birmingham, AL
Primary Contact: Angela L. Simmons, Chief Executive Officer
CFO: Sheila Shepard, Controller
CMO: Emile Mathurin, M.D., Jr Medical Director
CHR: Christy Dixon, Chief Human Resources Officer
CNO: Christie Griffin-Jones, R.N., Chief Nursing Officer
Web address: www.healthsouthhumble.com
Control: Corporation, Investor–owned (for–profit) **Service**: Rehabilitation

Staffed Beds: 60 **Admissions**: 1066 **Census**: 38 **Outpatient Visits**: 0
Births: 0 **Total Expense ($000)**: 15044 **Payroll Expense ($000)**: 9351
Personnel: 161

TX

Many Facility Codes have changed. Please refer to the AHA Guide Code Chart. © 2018 AHA Guide

★ **ICON HOSPITAL (452112)**, 19211 McKay Boulevard, Zip 77338–5502; tel. 281/883–5500, (Nonreporting) **A**10 22
Primary Contact: Stephen Myers, Interim Chief Executive Officer
Web address: www.iconhospitalonline.com/
Control: Partnership, Investor–owned (for–profit) **Service**: Acute long–term care hospital

> **Staffed Beds**: 32

☐ **KINDRED REHABILITATION HOSPITAL NORTHEAST HOUSTON (673051)**, 18839 McKay Boulevard, Zip 77338–5721; tel. 281/964–6600, **A**1 10 **F**3 29 77 90 91 93 130 148 149
Primary Contact: Tracy Wilson, Chief Executive Officer
CFO: Cheryl Csepke, Controller
CMO: Helen Schilling, M.D., Medical Director
CHR: Stephanie Williams, Coordinator Human Resources
CNO: Albert J. Chapple, R.N., Chief Clinical Officer
Web address: www.khrehabnortheasthouston.com
Control: Corporation, Investor–owned (for–profit) **Service**: Rehabilitation

> **Staffed Beds**: 46 **Admissions**: 468 **Census**: 16 **Outpatient Visits**: 4197
> **Births**: 0 **Total Expense ($000)**: 12026 **Payroll Expense ($000)**: 4607
> **Personnel**: 89

⊞ **MEMORIAL HERMANN NORTHEAST (450684)**, 18951 North Memorial Drive, Zip 77338–4297; tel. 281/540–7700, **A**1 2 3 5 10 **F**3 11 13 15 18 20 22 24 26 29 30 31 34 35 40 44 45 46 49 53 54 57 59 64 65 68 70 72 73 74 75 76 77 78 79 80 81 84 85 87 91 93 100 107 108 109 111 114 115 119 120 121 126 129 130 131 132 135 146 147 148 **P**5 6 **S** Memorial Hermann Health System, Houston, TX
Primary Contact: Josh Urban, Chief Executive Officer
CFO: Rebecca Tucker, Chief Financial Officer
CMO: Susan Curling, M.D., Chief Medical Officer
CHR: Monica Baisden, Director Human Resources
CNO: Linda Stephens, R.N., Chief Nursing Officer
Web address: www.memorialhermann.org/locations/northeast/
Control: Other not–for–profit (including NFP Corporation) **Service**: General medical and surgical

> **Staffed Beds**: 217 **Admissions**: 12603 **Census**: 152 **Outpatient Visits**: 132785 **Births**: 1293 **Total Expense ($000)**: 228052 **Payroll Expense ($000)**: 78659 **Personnel**: 926

HUNTSVILLE—Walker County

⊞ **HUNTSVILLE MEMORIAL HOSPITAL (450347)**, 110 Memorial Hospital Drive, Zip 77340–4940, Mailing Address: P.O. Box 4001, Zip 77342–4001; tel. 936/291–3411, **A**1 10 **F**3 8 11 12 13 15 18 20 22 26 28 29 32 34 35 40 43 45 46 47 49 50 53 54 57 59 60 64 65 66 67 68 70 74 75 76 77 79 81 82 85 86 87 89 90 91 92 93 96 97 100 107 108 110 111 114 115 119 126 127 130 131 132 135 146 147 148 149 150 154
Primary Contact: Michael Morgan, Interim Chief Executive Officer
CFO: Maxwell Owens, FACHE, Chief Financial Officer
CIO: Raul Velez, Director Information Systems
CHR: Brenda Ray, Director Human Resources
CNO: Sheila Ard, Chief Nursing Officer
Web address: www.huntsvillememorial.com
Control: Other not–for–profit (including NFP Corporation) **Service**: General medical and surgical

> **Staffed Beds**: 98 **Admissions**: 4610 **Census**: 56 **Outpatient Visits**: 121469 **Births**: 384 **Total Expense ($000)**: 106358 **Payroll Expense ($000)**: 36987 **Personnel**: 524

HURST—Tarrant County

SAINT CAMILLUS MEDICAL CENTER (670121), 1612 Hurst Town Center Drive, Zip 76054–6236; tel. 817/519–3700, (Nonreporting)
COO: Karen Sperduti, Chief Operating Officer
Web address: www.https://saintcamillusmedicalcenter.com/
Control: Other not–for–profit (including NFP Corporation) **Service**: General medical and surgical

> **Staffed Beds**: 23

IRAAN—Pecos County

IRAAN GENERAL HOSPITAL (451307), 600 349 North, Zip 79744, Mailing Address: P.O. Box 665, Zip 79744–0665; tel. 432/639–2871, **A**10 18 **F**28 40 43 56 57 59 64 65 75 86 93 104 107 119 127 130 133
Primary Contact: Keith L. Butler, Chief Executive Officer
CFO: Tami Burks, Chief Fiscal Services
CMO: Robert W Garcia, M.D., Chief Medical Officer
CHR: Cathy Tucker, Director Human Resources
Web address: www.igh–hospital.com
Control: Hospital district or authority, Government, nonfederal **Service**: General medical and surgical

> **Staffed Beds**: 14 **Admissions**: 135 **Census**: 3 **Outpatient Visits**: 8401
> **Births**: 0 **Total Expense ($000)**: 9802 **Payroll Expense ($000)**: 4035
> **Personnel**: 60

IRVING—Dallas County

⊞ **BAYLOR SCOTT & WHITE MEDICAL CENTER–IRVING (450079)**, 1901 North MacArthur Boulevard, Zip 75061–2220, tel. 972/579–8100, **A**1 2 3 5 10 **F**3 8 11 13 15 17 18 20 22 24 26 28 29 30 31 34 35 40 45 46 47 49 54 55 57 58 59 64 65 66 70 73 74 75 76 77 78 79 80 81 82 84 85 86 87 90 93 94 100 107 108 110 111 114 115 116 117 118 119 120 121 122 126 129 130 141 143 146 147 148 149 150 **S** Baylor Scott & White Health, Dallas, TX
Primary Contact: Cindy K. Schamp, FACHE, President
CFO: Steve Roussel, Vice President Finance
CMO: Jeffrey Embrey, M.D., Chief Medical Officer
CIO: Tim Huffman, Western Region Director, Information Systems Business Relationships
CHR: Vonetta Fuller–Williams, Director Human Resources Strategic and Business Services
Web address: www.bswhealth.com
Control: Other not–for–profit (including NFP Corporation) **Service**: General medical and surgical

> **Staffed Beds**: 233 **Admissions**: 11490 **Census**: 147 **Outpatient Visits**: 95843 **Births**: 1592 **Total Expense ($000)**: 220409 **Payroll Expense ($000)**: 78434 **Personnel**: 804

☐ **BAYLOR SURGICAL HOSPITAL AT LAS COLINAS (450874)**, 400 West Interstate 635, Zip 75063; tel. 972/868–4000, **A**1 10 **F**3 29 30 40 51 68 79 81 107 111 119 130 **S** United Surgical Partners International, Addison, TX
Primary Contact: Deonna Unell, Chief Executive Officer
CFO: Gabrielle Holland, Chief Financial Officer
CMO: Scott McGraw, M.D., Medical Director
Web address: www.baylorhealth.com/About/Community/Assessments/West/ICSH/Pages/Default.aspx
Control: Partnership, Investor–owned (for–profit) **Service**: General medical and surgical

> **Staffed Beds**: 12 **Admissions**: 804 **Census**: 4 **Outpatient Visits**: 8561
> **Births**: 0 **Total Expense ($000)**: 44845 **Payroll Expense ($000)**: 8998
> **Personnel**: 178

⊞ **MEDICAL CITY LAS COLINAS (450822)**, 6800 North MacArthur Boulevard, Zip 75039–2422; tel. 972/969–2000, **A**1 10 **F**3 8 12 13 15 18 20 22 24 29 30 34 35 37 40 45 46 47 48 49 50 57 59 60 63 64 68 70 72 74 75 76 77 78 79 81 87 93 100 102 107 108 110 111 114 118 119 126 130 147 148 149 **S** HCA Healthcare, Nashville, TN
Primary Contact: Daniela Decell, Chief Executive Officer
COO: Chip Zahn, Chief Operating Officer
CFO: Nick Galt, Chief Financial Officer
CMO: Miguel Benet, M.D., Chief Medical Officer
Web address: www.lascolinasmedical.com
Control: Corporation, Investor–owned (for–profit) **Service**: General medical and surgical

> **Staffed Beds**: 90 **Admissions**: 5258 **Census**: 50 **Outpatient Visits**: 55685 **Births**: 1855 **Total Expense ($000)**: 80434 **Payroll Expense ($000)**: 27093 **Personnel**: 348

TX

Hospital, Medicare Provider Number, Address, Telephone, Approval, Facility, and Physician Codes, Health Care System

★ American Hospital Association (AHA) membership   ○ Healthcare Facilities Accreditation Program   ⇑ Center for Improvement in Healthcare Quality Accreditation
☐ The Joint Commission accreditation   ◇ DNV Healthcare Inc. accreditation   △ Commission on Accreditation of Rehabilitation Facilities (CARF) accreditation

© 2018 AHA Guide   *Many Facility Codes have changed. Please refer to the AHA Guide Code Chart.*   Hospitals **A615**

JACKSBORO—Jack County

FAITH COMMUNITY HOSPITAL (450241), 215 Chisholm Trail,
Zip 76458–1111; tel. 940/567–6633, **A**10 20 **F**7 11 13 15 28 34 35 40 43 45
57 59 75 76 77 81 93 97 107 110 114 119 127 130 133 135 149 **P**6
Primary Contact: Frank Beaman, Chief Executive Officer
COO: Kim Lee, Chief Operating Officer
CFO: Bonnie Blevins, R.N., Chief Financial Officer
CMO: Sushil Chokshi, M.D., Chief Medical Officer
CIO: Troy McKenzie, Chief information Officer
CHR: Deborah White, Human Resource Coordinator
CNO: Joy Henry, R.N., Chief of Nursing
Web address: www.fchtexas.com
Control: Hospital district or authority, Government, nonfederal **Service**: General
medical and surgical

Staffed Beds: 17 Admissions: 277 Census: 2 Outpatient Visits: 55298
Births: 94 Total Expense ($000): 108785 Payroll Expense ($000): 6793
Personnel: 180

JACKSONVILLE—Cherokee County

⊞ **CHRISTUS MOTHER FRANCES HOSPITAL – JACKSONVILLE (451319)**, 2026
South Jackson, Zip 75766–5822; tel. 903/541–4500, **A**1 10 18 **F**3 15 18 29 30
32 34 35 40 41 43 45 50 53 56 57 59 64 65 68 79 81 82 85 93 97 107 108
110 111 114 119 129 130 133 145 147 **P**5 6 7 8 **S** CHRISTUS Health, Irving, TX
Primary Contact: Anne Pileggi, Administrator and Associate Vice President
CFO: Elizabeth Pulliam, Chief Financial Officer
CMO: Jane Ragland, President Medical Staff
CIO: Jeff Pearson, Chief Information Officer
CHR: Marsha Ballard, Human Resources
CNO: Jamie Maddox, Chief Nursing Officer
Web address: www.tmfhs.org/jacksonville
Control: Other not–for–profit (including NFP Corporation) **Service**: General
medical and surgical

Staffed Beds: 23 Admissions: 759 Census: 10 Outpatient Visits: 69516
Births: 0 Total Expense ($000): 30830 Payroll Expense ($000): 9109
Personnel: 174

⊞ **UT HEALTH JACKSONVILLE (450194)**, 501 South Ragsdale Street,
Zip 75766–2413; tel. 903/541–5000, **A**1 10 20 **F**3 8 11 13 15 18 26 29 34 35
39 40 43 45 50 57 59 64 65 70 75 76 79 81 82 85 97 107 108 110 111 115
119 127 129 145 146 147 148 **S** Ardent Health Services, Nashville, TN
Primary Contact: DeLeigh Haley, Chief Executive Officer
CMO: Todd Parrish, M.D., Chief of Staff
CHR: Elysia Epperson, Director Human Resources
CNO: Jana Bateman, R.N., Chief Nursing Officer
Web address: www.https://uthealthjacksonville.com/
Control: Other not–for–profit (including NFP Corporation) **Service**: General
medical and surgical

Staffed Beds: 38 Admissions: 1342 Census: 10 Outpatient Visits: 86791
Births: 435 Total Expense ($000): 34337 Payroll Expense ($000): 9949
Personnel: 175

JASPER—Jasper County

⊞ **CHRISTUS SOUTHEAST TEXAS JASPER MEMORIAL (450573)**, 1275 Marvin
Hancock Drive, Zip 75951–4995; tel. 409/384–5461, **A**1 10 **F**3 11 13 15 29 30
34 40 43 50 51 57 59 64 70 76 77 79 81 82 107 110 111 114 119 127 130
135 146 149 **P**8 **S** CHRISTUS Health, Irving, TX
Primary Contact: Wayne Moore, Interim Administrator
COO: Mark Durand, Assistant Administrator Operations
CFO: Nikki Martin, Chief Financial Officer
CIO: Robert Jacobs, Regional Information Management Executive
CHR: Kay Powell, Director Human Resources
Web address: www.christusjasper.org
Control: Hospital district or authority, Government, nonfederal **Service**: General
medical and surgical

Staffed Beds: 40 Admissions: 1246 Census: 9 Outpatient Visits: 56639
Births: 232 Total Expense ($000): 28393 Payroll Expense ($000): 9980
Personnel: 141

JOURDANTON—Atascosa County

⊞ **METHODIST HOSPITAL SOUTH (450165)**, 1905 Highway 97 East,
Zip 78026–1504; tel. 830/769–3515, **A**1 10 20 **F**3 11 13 15 18 29 30 34 35
39 40 43 45 49 57 59 63 64 68 70 75 76 77 81 85 93 107 108 110 111 114
119 129 130 132 133 146 147 148 **P**3 **S** HCA Healthcare, Nashville, TN
Primary Contact: Pamela Guillory, Interim Chief Executive Officer
CFO: Gary Redmon, Chief Financial Officer
CIO: Rita S Castillo, R.N., Vice President, Quality, Risk and Safety
CNO: Pamela Guillory, Chief Nursing Officer
Web address: www.https://sahealth.com/locations/methodisthospitalsouth/
Control: Partnership, Investor–owned (for–profit) **Service**: General medical and
surgical

Staffed Beds: 67 Admissions: 1634 Census: 14 Outpatient Visits: 37254
Births: 257 Total Expense ($000): 35935 Payroll Expense ($000): 12402
Personnel: 166

JUNCTION—Kimble County

KIMBLE HOSPITAL (451306), 349 Reid Road, Zip 76849–3049;
tel. 325/446–3321, **A**10 18 **F**3 34 40 41 43 45 57 59 65 66 68 84 93 97 107
119 127 133 146 148 154 **S** Preferred Management Corporation, Shawnee, OK
Primary Contact: William Barnes, FACHE, Administrator
COO: Teena Hagood, Chief Nursing Officer
CFO: Larry Stephens, Chief Financial Officer
CMO: Ben Udall, M.D., Chief of Staff
CIO: Anna Henry, Chief Information Officer
CHR: Hope Lamb, Manager Human Resources
Web address: www.kimblehospital.org/
Control: Corporation, Investor–owned (for–profit) **Service**: General medical and
surgical

Staffed Beds: 15 Admissions: 96 Census: 1 Outpatient Visits: 14096
Births: 1 Total Expense ($000): 7207 Payroll Expense ($000): 2996
Personnel: 73

KATY—Harris County

⇧ **CHRISTUS ST. CATHERINE HOSPITAL** See Houston Methodist Continuing Care
Hospital

★ ⇧ **HOUSTON METHODIST CONTINUING CARE HOSPITAL (452118)**, 701 Fry
Road, Zip 77450–2255; tel. 281/599–5700, **A**10 21 **F**1 68 75 82 84 86 87 130
132 149 150 **S** Houston Methodist, Houston, TX
Primary Contact: Gary L. Kempf, R.N., Administrator
CFO: Nancy Brock, Chief Financial Officer
CHR: James A Fitch, Director Human Resources
Web address: www.houstonmethodist.org/katy–st–catherine–hospital
Control: Other not–for–profit (including NFP Corporation) **Service**: Acute long–
term care hospital

Staffed Beds: 58 Admissions: 466 Census: 39 Outpatient Visits: 0
Births: 0 Total Expense ($000): 34352 Payroll Expense ($000): 14204
Personnel: 211

⊞ **MEMORIAL HERMANN KATY HOSPITAL (450847)**, 23900 Katy Freeway,
Zip 77494–1323; tel. 281/644–7000, **A**1 2 3 5 10 **F**3 8 11 13 15 18 20 22 26
29 30 34 35 37 39 40 43 45 46 49 50 51 54 57 59 61 64 65 68 70 72 73 74
75 76 77 78 79 80 81 85 87 89 93 102 107 108 110 111 114 119 126 130
131 132 144 145 146 147 149 154 **P**5 6 **S** Memorial Hermann Health System,
Houston, TX
Primary Contact: Heath Rushing, Senior Vice President and Chief Executive Officer
CFO: Linda Kulhanek, Chief Financial Officer
Web address: www.memorialhermann.org/locations/katy/
Control: Other not–for–profit (including NFP Corporation) **Service**: General
medical and surgical

Staffed Beds: 208 Admissions: 10382 Census: 105 Outpatient
Visits: 111717 Births: 2359 Total Expense ($000): 212894 Payroll
Expense ($000): 71400 Personnel: 845

⊞ **MEMORIAL HERMANN REHABILITATION HOSPITAL – KATY (673038)**,
21720 Kingsland Boulevard, 2nd Floor, Zip 77450–2550; **A**1 2 10 **F**3 29 30 64
79 90 92 93 107 111 114 119 129 130 131 148 **P**5 6 **S** Memorial Hermann
Health System, Houston, TX
Primary Contact: Jerry Ashworth, Interim Chief Executive Officer
COO: Mary Ann Euliarte, R.N., Chief Operating Officer
CFO: Wayne Gordon, Chief Financial Officer
CMO: Shalin Patel, M.D., Chief Medical Officer
CHR: Joyce Williams, Consultant Human Resources and Organizational
Development
CNO: Mary Ann Euliarte, R.N., Chief Nursing Officer
Web address: www.memorialhermann.org/locations/katy–rehab/
Control: Partnership, Investor–owned (for–profit) **Service**: Rehabilitation

Staffed Beds: 35 Admissions: 634 Census: 26 Outpatient Visits: 13273
Births: 0 Total Expense ($000): 22489 Payroll Expense ($000): 10292
Personnel: 117

OCEANS BEHAVIORAL HOSPITAL KATY (454136), 455 Park Grove Lane,
Zip 77450–1572; tel. 281/492–8888, **F**29 34 35 64 98 100 101 103 104 149
153 154 **S** Oceans Healthcare, Lake Charles, LA
Primary Contact: Stuart Archer, Chief Executive Officer
Web address: www.memorialhermann.org/locations/katy–rehab/
Control: Corporation, Investor–owned (for–profit) **Service**: Psychiatric

Staffed Beds: 48 Admissions: 943 Census: 36 Outpatient Visits: 11742
Births: 0 Total Expense ($000): 9105 Payroll Expense ($000): 4161
Personnel: 138

TX

KAUFMAN—Kaufman County

⊠ **TEXAS HEALTH PRESBYTERIAN HOSPITAL KAUFMAN (450292)**, 850 Ed Hall Drive, Zip 75142–1861, Mailing Address: P.O. Box 1108, Zip 75142–5401; tel. 972/932–7200, **A**1 10 **F**3 11 15 18 29 30 34 35 40 43 45 53 57 59 64 65 70 75 79 81 82 85 86 87 93 102 107 108 111 115 118 119 130 132 146 149 **S** Texas Health Resources, Arlington, TX
Primary Contact: Patsy Youngs, President
CMO: Benjamin Bradshaw, M.D., President Medical Staff
CHR: Mark J Rainey, Director Human Resources
CNO: Denise Claussen, R.N., MSN, Chief Nursing Officer
Web address: www.texashealth.org/Kaufman
Control: Other not–for–profit (including NFP Corporation) **Service**: General medical and surgical

Staffed Beds: 37 **Admissions:** 1444 **Census:** 13 **Outpatient Visits:** 33420 **Births:** 0 **Total Expense ($000):** 35721 **Payroll Expense ($000):** 13497 **Personnel:** 200

KENEDY—Karnes County

★ **OTTO KAISER MEMORIAL HOSPITAL (451364)**, 3349 South Highway 181, Zip 78119–5247; tel. 830/583–3401, **A**10 18 **F**3 11 15 29 30 34 40 43 45 46 53 57 59 62 64 68 77 81 93 107 111 115 119 132 133 135 148 154 **P**3 8
Primary Contact: David Lee, Chief Executive Officer
CIO: Joseph Wiatrek, Director Information Technology
CHR: Christina Benavides, Director Employee Services
CNO: Vincent Sowell, Chief Nursing Officer
Web address: www.okmh.org/
Control: Hospital district or authority, Government, nonfederal **Service**: General medical and surgical

Staffed Beds: 25 **Admissions:** 298 **Census:** 5 **Outpatient Visits:** 22115 **Births:** 0 **Total Expense ($000):** 22079 **Payroll Expense ($000):** 8590 **Personnel:** 135

KERMIT—Winkler County

WINKLER COUNTY MEMORIAL HOSPITAL (451314), 821 Jeffee Drive, Zip 79745–4696, Mailing Address: P.O. Box H, Zip 79745–6008; tel. 432/586–5864, (Data for 273 days) **A**10 18 **F**3 32 34 36 40 57 59 64 65 69 93 97 107 114 119 127 133
Primary Contact: Lorenzo Serrano, Chief Executive Officer
CFO: Wannah Hartley, Controller
CMO: K Pham, M.D., Chief of Staff
CIO: Keith Palmer, Assistant Administrator
Control: County, Government, nonfederal **Service**: General medical and surgical

Staffed Beds: 19 **Admissions:** 101 **Census:** 2 **Outpatient Visits:** 6876 **Births:** 0 **Total Expense ($000):** 6127 **Payroll Expense ($000):** 2503 **Personnel:** 72

KERRVILLE—Kerr County

KERRVILLE DIVISION See South Texas Veterans Health Care System, San Antonio

☐ **KERRVILLE STATE HOSPITAL (454014)**, 721 Thompson Drive, Zip 78028–5154; tel. 830/896–2211, **A**1 5 10 **F**11 30 34 39 44 50 56 65 68 75 86 87 97 98 101 103 130 132 135 146 149 **S** Texas Department of State Health Services, Austin, TX
Primary Contact: Leigh Ann Fitzpatrick, Superintendent
CFO: Laurie Harris, Chief Accountant
CMO: Matthew Faubion, M.D., Clinical Director
CNO: Amanda McDonald, MSN, Chief Nurse Executive
Web address: www.dshs.state.tx.us/mhhospitals/KerrvilleSH/default.shtm
Control: State, Government, nonfederal **Service**: Psychiatric

Staffed Beds: 202 **Admissions:** 80 **Census:** 197 **Outpatient Visits:** 0 **Births:** 0 **Total Expense ($000):** 52086 **Payroll Expense ($000):** 23076 **Personnel:** 539

PETERSON REGIONAL MEDICAL CENTER (450007), 551 Hill Country Drive, Zip 78028–6085; tel. 830/896–4200, **A**1 10 **F**3 8 11 13 15 18 20 22 28 29 30 31 34 35 39 40 44 45 49 51 54 57 59 64 65 68 70 74 75 76 77 78 79 81 82 85 86 87 90 93 95 96 97 100 107 108 109 110 111 114 115 118 119 126 130 131 132 135 145 146 147 148 **P**8
Primary Contact: J. Patrick. Murray, FACHE, President and Chief Executive Officer
COO: J. Stephen Pautler, FACHE, Chief Operating Officer
CFO: Lisa Medovich, Chief Financial Officer
CMO: Thomas Ducker, M.D., Chief of Staff
CIO: Richard Cruthirds, Director Information Systems
CHR: Buddy Volpe, Director Human Resources
CNO: Kaeli Dressler, R.N., MSN, Chief Nursing Officer
Web address: www.petersonhealth.com
Control: Other not–for–profit (including NFP Corporation) **Service**: General medical and surgical

Staffed Beds: 124 **Admissions:** 4860 **Census:** 57 **Outpatient Visits:** 151736 **Births:** 510 **Total Expense ($000):** 122026 **Payroll Expense ($000):** 52928 **Personnel:** 907

KILGORE—Gregg County

★ ⇑ **ALLEGIANCE SPECIALTY HOSPITAL OF KILGORE (450488)**, 1612 South Henderson Boulevard, Zip 75662–3594; tel. 903/984–3505, (Nonreporting) **A**10 21 **S** Allegiance Health Management, Shreveport, LA
Primary Contact: Karen Ross, Chief Executive Officer
CHR: Michelle Yarbrough, Coordinator Human Resources
Web address: www.ahmgt.com
Control: Corporation, Investor–owned (for–profit) **Service**: Psychiatric

Staffed Beds: 60

KILLEEN—Bell County

⊠ **METROPLEX ADVENTIST HOSPITAL (450152)**, 2201 South Clear Creek Road, Zip 76549–4110; tel. 254/526–7523, (Includes METROPLEX BEHAVIORAL HEALTH CENTER, 2201 South Clear Creek Road, Killeen, TX, Zip 76549–4110; tel. 254/628–1000; Dennis Kiley, Interim President and Chief Executive Officer) **A**1 3 10 **F**3 8 11 12 13 15 18 20 22 26 28 29 30 34 35 39 40 43 45 46 48 49 54 57 59 62 65 68 70 71 74 75 76 77 78 79 81 82 83 85 86 87 89 91 93 98 100 101 102 104 107 108 110 111 114 115 118 119 129 130 131 132 135 146 147 148 154 **P**8 **S** Adventist Health System Sunbelt Health Care Corporation, Altamonte Springs, FL
Primary Contact: Kevin A. Roberts, FACHE, President and Chief Executive Officer
CFO: Penny Johnson, Chief Financial Officer
CMO: Frederick Barnett, M.D., Chief of Staff
CHR: Brenda Coley, Executive Director
Web address: www.mplex.org
Control: Church operated, Nongovernment, not–for–profit **Service**: General medical and surgical

Staffed Beds: 177 **Admissions:** 6503 **Census:** 66 **Outpatient Visits:** 92262 **Births:** 1215 **Total Expense ($000):** 106660 **Payroll Expense ($000):** 44970 **Personnel:** 845

KINGSVILLE—Kleberg County

⊠ **CHRISTUS SPOHN HOSPITAL KLEBERG (450163)**, 1311 General Cavazos Boulevard, Zip 78363–7130; tel. 361/595–1661, **A**1 10 20 **F**3 11 13 15 28 29 30 34 35 40 43 53 54 57 59 64 65 76 77 79 81 85 86 87 89 93 102 107 108 110 111 115 119 130 146 **P**8 **S** CHRISTUS Health, Irving, TX
Primary Contact: Thomas McKinney, President
COO: David LeMonte, Vice President and Chief Operating Officer
CFO: Jessica Pena, Manager Finance
CHR: Mindy Soliz, Director Human Resource Strategy
CNO: Lieutenant Laci Lasater, R.N., Chief Nursing Officer
Web address: www.christusspohn.org
Control: Church operated, Nongovernment, not–for–profit **Service**: General medical and surgical

Staffed Beds: 50 **Admissions:** 2976 **Census:** 36 **Outpatient Visits:** 37293 **Births:** 276 **Total Expense ($000):** 38309 **Payroll Expense ($000):** 14601 **Personnel:** 207

TX

KINGWOOD—Montgomery County

⊠ ⇧ **KINGWOOD MEDICAL CENTER (450775)**, 22999 US Highway 59 North, Zip 77339; tel. 281/348-8000, **A**1 10 21 **F**3 13 15 18 19 20 21 22 24 26 28 29 34 35 40 41 45 46 49 57 58 59 70 72 74 76 79 81 84 85 86 87 89 90 96 107 108 110 111 114 115 119 126 130 132 146 147 148 **S** HCA Healthcare, Nashville, TN
Primary Contact: Melinda Stephenson, Chief Executive Officer
CFO: Daniel E Davis, Chief Financial Officer
CMO: Eugene Ogrod, M.D., Chief Medical Officer
CNO: Kevin Manning, Chief Nursing Officer
Web address: www.kingwoodmedical.com
Control: Corporation, Investor-owned (for-profit) **Service**: General medical and surgical

Staffed Beds: 358 **Admissions**: 18409 **Census**: 261 **Outpatient Visits**: 122265 **Births**: 2655 **Total Expense ($000)**: 236189 **Payroll Expense ($000)**: 96567 **Personnel**: 1194

KINGWOOD—Harris County

☐ **KINGWOOD PINES HOSPITAL (454103)**, 2001 Ladbrook Drive, Zip 77339-3004; tel. 281/404-1001, **A**1 10 **F**4 5 75 86 87 98 99 101 102 103 105 130 132 149 153 **S** Universal Health Services, Inc., King of Prussia, PA
Primary Contact: Shanti Carter, Chief Executive Officer
COO: Grey Mc Kellar, Chief Operating Officer and Director of Performance Improvement and Risk
CFO: Sharon Corum, Chief Financial Officer
CMO: Javier Ruiz, M.D., Medical Director
CNO: Kim Wheeler, R.N., Director of Nursing
Web address: www.kingwoodpines.com
Control: Corporation, Investor-owned (for-profit) **Service**: Psychiatric

Staffed Beds: 65 **Admissions**: 3979 **Census**: 94 **Outpatient Visits**: 4054 **Births**: 0 **Total Expense ($000)**: 21615 **Payroll Expense ($000)**: 11245 **Personnel**: 198

KINGWOOD—Montgomery County

KINGWOOD SPECIALTY HOSPITAL See Memorial Hermann Surgical Hospital Kingwood

☐ **MEMORIAL HERMANN SURGICAL HOSPITAL KINGWOOD (670005)**, 300 Kingwood Medical Drive, Zip 77339-6400; tel. 281/312-4000, **A**1 10 **F**3 29 40 45 64 79 81 82 85 86 87 111 119
Primary Contact: Teal A. Holden, Chief Executive Officer
CFO: Jay Michael Gomez, Chief Financial Officer
CNO: Shawna Fugler, R.N., Chief Nursing Officer
Web address: www.memorialhermannkingwood.com
Control: Partnership, Investor-owned (for-profit) **Service**: Surgical

Staffed Beds: 10 **Admissions**: 294 **Census**: 2 **Outpatient Visits**: 8668 **Births**: 0 **Total Expense ($000)**: 25142 **Payroll Expense ($000)**: 5416 **Personnel**: 100

KNOX CITY—Knox County

KNOX COUNTY HOSPITAL (450746), 701 South Fifth Street, Zip 79529-2107, Mailing Address: P.O. Box 608, Zip 79529-0608; tel. 940/657-3535, **A**10 20 **F**7 11 28 33 34 35 40 43 57 59 62 127 130 133 149 **P**6
Primary Contact: Stephen A. Kuehler, Administrator
CFO: Dan Offutt, Manager Finance
CMO: Ezekiel Duke, M.D., Chief of Staff
CNO: Sheila Kuehler, R.N., Director of Nursing
Web address: www.knoxcountyhospital-texas.com
Control: Hospital district or authority, Government, nonfederal **Service**: General medical and surgical

Staffed Beds: 14 **Admissions**: 61 **Census**: 1 **Outpatient Visits**: 27976 **Births**: 0 **Total Expense ($000)**: 13111 **Payroll Expense ($000)**: 4851 **Personnel**: 82

KYLE—Hays County

⊠ **SETON MEDICAL CENTER HAYS (670056)**, 6001 Kyle Parkway, Zip 78640-6112; tel. 512/504-5000, **A**1 3 5 10 **F**3 11 13 15 17 18 20 22 24 28 29 30 31 34 40 41 43 45 46 47 48 49 50 57 59 64 68 70 72 76 78 79 81 82 84 85 93 107 108 110 111 115 119 126 129 130 131 132 135 146 147 148 154 **P**3 8 **S** Ascension Healthcare, Saint Louis, MO
Primary Contact: Katherine Henderson, President and Chief Executive Officer
COO: Neal Kelley, Vice President and Chief Operating Officer
Web address: www.seton.net/locations/seton_medical_center_hays/
Control: Church operated, Nongovernment, not-for-profit **Service**: General medical and surgical

Staffed Beds: 142 **Admissions**: 6796 **Census**: 79 **Outpatient Visits**: 61571 **Births**: 1104 **Total Expense ($000)**: 131725 **Payroll Expense ($000)**: 35094 **Personnel**: 629

★ **WARM SPRINGS REHABILITATION HOSPITAL OF KYLE (673057)**, 5980 Kyle Parkway, Zip 78640-2400; tel. 512/262-0821, (Nonreporting) **S** Post Acute Medical, LLC, Enola, PA
Primary Contact: Duke Saldivar, FACHE, Chief Executive Officer
Web address: www.warmsprings.org/our-facilities/outpatient-rehabilitation/warm-springs-rehabilitation-center-kyle/
Control: Corporation, Investor-owned (for-profit) **Service**: Rehabilitation

Staffed Beds: 40

LA GRANGE—Fayette County

★ **ST. MARK'S MEDICAL CENTER (670004)**, One St Mark's Place, Zip 78945; tel. 979/242-2200, **A**5 10 **F**3 8 11 12 13 15 29 30 34 40 43 45 50 56 57 59 68 70 74 75 76 79 81 82 84 85 87 93 107 110 111 114 119 128 129 130 133 145 146 147 **P**6 **S** Community Hospital Corporation, Plano, TX
Primary Contact: Rick J. Montelongo, Chief Executive Officer
COO: Carol Drozd, Chief Operating Officer
CFO: Barbara Brooks, Interim Chief Financial Officer
CMO: Russell Juno, M.D., Chief of Staff
CHR: Tammy Oehlke, Director Human Resources
Web address: www.smmctx.org
Control: Other not-for-profit (including NFP Corporation) **Service**: General medical and surgical

Staffed Beds: 65 **Admissions**: 1411 **Census**: 14 **Outpatient Visits**: 48431 **Births**: 194 **Total Expense ($000)**: 33112 **Payroll Expense ($000)**: 11309 **Personnel**: 168

LAKE JACKSON—Brazoria County

⊠ **CHI ST. LUKE'S HEALTH BRAZOSPORT (450072)**, 100 Medical Drive, Zip 77566-5674; tel. 979/297-4411, (Data for 181 days) **A**1 10 **F**3 11 13 15 18 20 22 28 29 30 31 34 37 40 41 43 47 48 49 51 54 57 59 60 62 64 65 70 74 75 76 78 79 81 82 85 86 87 89 90 91 93 94 107 108 110 111 114 115 117 118 119 120 121 123 129 130 131 132 146 147 148 149 154 **P**8 **S** Catholic Health Initiatives, Englewood, CO
Primary Contact: Al Guevara Jr, FACHE, President
CFO: Chuck Jeffress, Vice President Fiscal Services
CMO: Michael Gilliand, M.D., Chief of Staff
CIO: Todd Edwards, Director Information Management Systems
CHR: Christopher Calia, Vice President Human Resources
CNO: Shannon Haltom, Vice President, Patient Care Services
Web address: www.chistlukesbrazosport.org
Control: Other not-for-profit (including NFP Corporation) **Service**: General medical and surgical

Staffed Beds: 103 **Admissions**: 2333 **Census**: 49 **Outpatient Visits**: 50657 **Births**: 198 **Total Expense ($000)**: 38753 **Payroll Expense ($000)**: 16806 **Personnel**: 591

LAKEWAY—Travis County

⊠ △ **VIBRA REHABILITATION HOSPITAL LAKE TRAVIS (673058)**, 2000 Medical Drive, Zip 78734-4200; tel. 512/263-4500, **A**1 7 **F**3 29 68 90 91 96 119 148 **S** Vibra Healthcare, Mechanicsburg, PA
Primary Contact: Deborah Hopps, R.N., FACHE, Chief Executive Officer
CMO: Maria Elena Arizmendez, M.D., Medical Director
CHR: Debbie Belcher, Director Human Resource
CNO: Ramon Austria, R.N., Chief Nursing Officer
Web address: www.vrhlaketravis.com
Control: Corporation, Investor-owned (for-profit) **Service**: Rehabilitation

Staffed Beds: 36 **Admissions**: 693 **Census**: 21 **Outpatient Visits**: 2835 **Births**: 0 **Total Expense ($000)**: 13696 **Payroll Expense ($000)**: 6837 **Personnel**: 115

LAMESA—Dawson County

MEDICAL ARTS HOSPITAL (450489), 2200 North Bryan Avenue, Zip 79331-2451; tel. 806/872-2183, **A**3 10 20 **F**3 7 11 13 29 30 35 40 43 45 50 57 59 62 63 64 75 76 81 87 97 107 111 115 119 127 128 130 133 146 148 **P**6
Primary Contact: Letha Stokes, Chief Executive Officer
COO: Jo Beth Smith, Chief Operating Officer
CFO: Jeff Weaver, Chief Financial Officer
CMO: Michael Sprys, D.O., Chief of Staff
CHR: Traci Brown, Human Resources Generalist
CNO: Heidi Cobb, R.N., Chief Nursing Officer
Web address: www.medicalartshospital.org
Control: Hospital district or authority, Government, nonfederal **Service**: General medical and surgical

Staffed Beds: 22 **Admissions**: 308 **Census**: 3 **Outpatient Visits**: 79045 **Births**: 112 **Total Expense ($000)**: 21968 **Payroll Expense ($000)**: 8973 **Personnel**: 191

TX

LAMPASAS—Lampasas County

⊠ **ROLLINS BROOK COMMUNITY HOSPITAL (451323)**, 608 North Key Avenue, Zip 76550–1106, Mailing Address: P.O. Box 589, Zip 76550–0032; tel. 512/556–3682, **A**1 10 18 **F**3 8 15 29 35 40 43 45 46 61 81 85 87 93 97 107 110 111 114 119 130 131 133 146 **P**4 8 **S** Adventist Health System Sunbelt Health Care Corporation, Altamonte Springs, FL
Primary Contact: Kevin A. Roberts, FACHE, President and Chief Executive Officer
CFO: Robert Brock, Chief Financial Officer and Vice President
CMO: Don Daniels, M.D., Chief Medical Officer
CIO: Carl Elkins, Director Information Technology
CHR: Brenda Coley, Executive Director
CNO: Tammy Rodriguez, Vice President of Patient Care Services
Web address: www.mplex.org
Control: Church operated, Nongovernment, not–for–profit **Service**: General medical and surgical

Staffed Beds: 35 **Admissions**: 562 **Census**: 8 **Outpatient Visits**: 13437 **Births**: 0 **Total Expense ($000)**: 13958 **Payroll Expense ($000)**: 4623 **Personnel**: 40

LANCASTER—Dallas County

⇑ **CRESCENT MEDICAL CENTER LANCASTER (670090)**, 2600 West Pleasant Run Road, Zip 75146–1114; tel. 972/230–8888, **A**10 21 **F**3 29 30 34 40 51 57 59 60 64 68 70 77 79 81 82 85 107 108 111 114 119 129 130 143 148
Primary Contact: Khalid Mahmood, M.D., President and Chairman
Web address: www.cmcl.us/
Control: Partnership, Investor–owned (for–profit) **Service**: General medical and surgical

Staffed Beds: 23 **Admissions**: 456 **Census**: 5 **Outpatient Visits**: 18825 **Births**: 0 **Total Expense ($000)**: 31502 **Payroll Expense ($000)**: 10839 **Personnel**: 242

LAREDO—Webb County

☐ **DOCTORS HOSPITAL OF LAREDO (450643)**, 10700 McPherson Road, Zip 78045–6268; tel. 956/523–2000, **A**1 2 10 **F**3 11 12 13 15 18 20 22 24 26 28 29 31 32 34 35 37 39 40 43 45 48 49 50 54 57 59 60 63 64 70 71 72 74 75 76 77 78 79 81 85 87 89 90 91 93 107 108 111 115 119 126 129 130 132 146 147 148 **P**5 7 **S** Universal Health Services, Inc., King of Prussia, PA
Primary Contact: James R. Resendez, Chief Executive Officer
COO: Raymond Ramos, FACHE, Chief Operating Officer
CFO: Faraz Khan, Chief Financial Officer
CMO: Santiago Gutierrez, M.D., Chief Medical Officer
CIO: Maribel Mata, Director Information Services
CHR: Roseann Figueroa, Director Human Resources
CNO: Daman Mott, MSN, Chief Nursing Officer
Web address: www.doctorshosplaredo.com
Control: Partnership, Investor–owned (for–profit) **Service**: General medical and surgical

Staffed Beds: 183 **Admissions**: 8192 **Census**: 102 **Outpatient Visits**: 127226 **Births**: 1984 **Total Expense ($000)**: 117778 **Payroll Expense ($000)**: 46573 **Personnel**: 722

⊠ **LAREDO MEDICAL CENTER (450029)**, 1700 East Saunders Avenue, Zip 78041–5474, Mailing Address: P.O. Box 2068, Zip 78044–2068; tel. 956/796–5000, (Total facility includes 18 beds in nursing home–type unit) **A**1 10 13 **F**3 8 11 12 13 15 18 20 24 26 28 29 30 31 34 35 40 43 45 46 49 50 51 53 54 57 59 60 64 65 68 70 72 74 75 76 77 78 79 81 85 86 87 89 91 92 93 107 108 110 111 114 119 120 121 123 128 132 135 144 146 147 148 149 **S** Community Health Systems, Inc., Franklin, TN
Primary Contact: Enrique Gallegos, Chief Executive Officer
CIO: Joe Rivera, Chief Information Technology Officer
Web address: www.laredomedical.com
Control: Corporation, Investor–owned (for–profit) **Service**: General medical and surgical

Staffed Beds: 326 **Admissions**: 13179 **Census**: 192 **Outpatient Visits**: 132793 **Births**: 3456 **Total Expense ($000)**: 173390 **Payroll Expense ($000)**: 57053 **Personnel**: 1069

LAREDO REHABILITATION HOSPITAL (673059), 2005a East Bustamante Street, Zip 78041; tel. 956/764–8555, **F**3 29 75 90 91 96 **S** Ernest Health, Inc., Albuquerque, NM
Primary Contact: Larisa Higgins, Administrator and Chief Operating Officer
Web address: www.lrh.ernesthealth.com
Control: Corporation, Investor–owned (for–profit) **Service**: Rehabilitation

Staffed Beds: 20 **Admissions**: 434 **Census**: 18 **Outpatient Visits**: 0 **Births**: 0 **Total Expense ($000)**: 6244 **Payroll Expense ($000)**: 3331 **Personnel**: 56

☐ **LAREDO SPECIALTY HOSPITAL (452096)**, 2005 Bustamante Street, Zip 78041–5470; tel. 956/753–5353, (Nonreporting) **A**1 10 **S** Ernest Health, Inc., Albuquerque, NM
Primary Contact: Hanna Huang, Chief Executive Officer
CFO: Robert Voss, Chief Financial Officer
CMO: Marisa Guerrero, Director Human Resources
Web address: www.lsh.ernesthealth.com
Control: Partnership, Investor–owned (for–profit) **Service**: Acute long–term care hospital

Staffed Beds: 40

LEAGUE CITY—Galveston County

☐ **DEVEREUX TEXAS TREATMENT NETWORK (454085)**, 1150 Devereux Drive, Zip 77573–2043; tel. 281/335–1000, **A**1 3 10 **F**4 29 32 35 38 53 59 75 86 87 98 101 106 130 132 134 **S** Devereux, Villanova, PA
Primary Contact: Pamela E. Helm, Executive Director
Web address: www.devereux.org
Control: Other not–for–profit (including NFP Corporation) **Service**: Children's hospital psychiatric

Staffed Beds: 47 **Admissions**: 38 **Census**: 46 **Outpatient Visits**: 0 **Births**: 0 **Total Expense ($000)**: 8458 **Payroll Expense ($000)**: 3051 **Personnel**: 71

LEVELLAND—Hockley County

★ **COVENANT HOSPITAL–LEVELLAND (450755)**, 1900 South College Avenue, Zip 79336–6508; tel. 806/894–4963, **A**10 **F**11 13 15 29 30 34 40 43 45 50 57 59 64 65 68 75 76 77 81 85 87 93 97 107 110 111 114 115 119 127 133 149 **P**6 **S** Providence St. Joseph Health, Renton, WA
Primary Contact: Bruce White, Administrator
CFO: Newman Wheeler, Chief Financial Officer and Chief Operating Officer
CMO: Harry Weaver, M.D., Chief of Staff
CIO: Kevin Elmore, Chief Information Officer
CHR: Tammy Franklin, Manager Personnel and Marketing
CNO: Connie Thomman, Director of Nursing
Web address: www.covenanthospitallevelland.com/
Control: Church operated, Nongovernment, not–for–profit **Service**: General medical and surgical

Staffed Beds: 26 **Admissions**: 683 **Census**: 5 **Outpatient Visits**: 32328 **Births**: 229 **Total Expense ($000)**: 20774 **Payroll Expense ($000)**: 8611 **Personnel**: 183

LEWISVILLE—Denton County

⊠ **MEDICAL CITY LEWISVILLE (450669)**, 500 West Main, Zip 75057–3699; tel. 972/420–1000, **A**1 2 10 **F**3 12 13 15 18 20 22 24 26 28 29 30 31 34 35 40 41 43 46 49 50 56 57 59 68 70 72 74 75 76 78 79 81 85 87 89 90 93 96 107 108 110 111 114 118 119 126 129 130 131 132 133 135 146 147 148 149 154 **S** HCA Healthcare, Nashville, TN
Primary Contact: LaSharndra Barbarin, Chief Executive Officer
CFO: Lisa Brodbeck, Chief Financial Officer
CIO: Shirley Archambeault, Chief Information Officer
CHR: Dara Biegert, Vice President Human Resources
CNO: Lynn O'Neill, R.N., Chief Nursing Officer
Web address: www.lewisvillemedical.com
Control: Corporation, Investor–owned (for–profit) **Service**: General medical and surgical

Staffed Beds: 166 **Admissions**: 6567 **Census**: 86 **Outpatient Visits**: 87782 **Births**: 1420 **Total Expense ($000)**: 132335 **Payroll Expense ($000)**: 52039 **Personnel**: 651

LIBERTY—Liberty County

☐ **LIBERTY DAYTON REGIONAL MEDICAL CENTER (451375)**, 1353 North Travis, Zip 77575–3549; tel. 936/336–7316, **A**1 10 18 **F**3 29 40 45 59 64 89 107 114 119 127 128 130 133
Primary Contact: Matt Thornton, Chief Executive Officer
CFO: Hal Mayo, Chief Financial Officer
CMO: Don Callens, M.D., Chief Medical Officer
CNO: Cindy Griffin, Chief Nursing Officer
Web address: www.libertydaytonrmc.com
Control: Hospital district or authority, Government, nonfederal **Service**: General medical and surgical

Staffed Beds: 15 **Admissions**: 121 **Census**: 1 **Outpatient Visits**: 22262 **Births**: 0 **Total Expense ($000)**: 6202 **Payroll Expense ($000)**: 4496 **Personnel**: 104

TX

Hospital, Medicare Provider Number, Address, Telephone, Approval, Facility, and Physician Codes, Health Care System

★ American Hospital Association (AHA) membership
☐ The Joint Commission accreditation
○ Healthcare Facilities Accreditation Program
◇ DNV Healthcare Inc. accreditation
⇑ Center for Improvement in Healthcare Quality Accreditation
△ Commission on Accreditation of Rehabilitation Facilities (CARF) accreditation

LITTLEFIELD—Lamb County

★ **LAMB HEALTHCARE CENTER (450698)**, 1500 South Sunset, Zip 79339–4899; tel. 806/385–6411, **A**10 20 **F**13 35 40 43 50 57 59 64 66 75 76 81 86 87 89 107 114 119 127 132 133 134 146 147 149 **P**6
Primary Contact: Cindy Klein, Chief Executive Officer
CMO: Isabel Molina, M.D., Chief Medical Officer
CHR: Joan Williams, Administrative Assistant/Human Resources
CNO: Stacie Styron, Chief Nursing Officer
Web address: www.littlefieldtexas.net/index.php/our–community/lamb–healthcare–center
Control: County, Government, nonfederal **Service**: General medical and surgical

Staffed Beds: 41 **Admissions**: 335 **Census**: 4 **Outpatient Visits**: 32288 **Births**: 96 **Total Expense ($000)**: 11374 **Payroll Expense ($000)**: 4675 **Personnel**: 116

LIVINGSTON—Polk County

☒ **CHI ST. LUKE'S HEALTH MEMORIAL LIVINGSTON (450395)**, 1717 Highway 59 Bypass, Zip 77351–1257, Mailing Address: P.O. Box 1257, Zip 77351–0022; tel. 936/329–8700, **A**1 10 **F**3 11 13 15 29 34 35 40 45 46 50 57 59 62 64 68 70 74 75 76 79 81 85 87 89 107 108 110 111 114 119 129 130 132 146 149 **S** Catholic Health Initiatives, Englewood, CO
Primary Contact: Kristi Froese, R.N., Vice President Clinical Operations
CFO: Duane Miller, Chief Financial Officer
CMO: Verner Nellsch, M.D., Chief of Staff
CIO: Kathy DeFiguieredo, Director, Information Technology
CHR: Heather Jordan, Director Human Resources
CNO: Kristi Froese, R.N., Chief Nursing Officer
Web address: www.memorialhealth.org
Control: Other not–for–profit (including NFP Corporation) **Service**: General medical and surgical

Staffed Beds: 66 **Admissions**: 1794 **Census**: 15 **Outpatient Visits**: 53079 **Births**: 391 **Total Expense ($000)**: 38457 **Payroll Expense ($000)**: 13454 **Personnel**: 178

LLANO—Llano County

★ **BAYLOR SCOTT & WHITE MEDICAL CENTER – LLANO (450219)**, 200 West Ollie Street, Zip 78643–2628; tel. 325/247–5040, **A**10 20 **F**3 29 40 45 57 64 85 93 107 115 129 130 149 **S** Baylor Scott & White Health, Dallas, TX
Primary Contact: Timothy A. Ols, FACHE, Chief Executive Officer
COO: Royce Bramer Owens, Chief Operating Officer
CFO: Jennie Campbell, Chief Financial Officer
CMO: Paul Cook, M.D., Chief Medical Officer
CIO: Rodney Lott, Director Management Information Systems and Facility Operations
CHR: Jane Frasure, Human Resources
CNO: Betsy B Patterson, MSN, R.N., Chief Nursing Officer
Web address: www.bswhealth.com
Control: Other not–for–profit (including NFP Corporation) **Service**: General medical and surgical

Staffed Beds: 10 **Admissions**: 209 **Census**: 1 **Outpatient Visits**: 8179 **Births**: 0 **Total Expense ($000)**: 24891 **Payroll Expense ($000)**: 13525 **Personnel**: 130

LOCKNEY—Floyd County

★ **W. J. MANGOLD MEMORIAL HOSPITAL (451337)**, 320 North Main Street, Zip 79241–0037, Mailing Address: Box 37, Zip 79241–0037; tel. 806/652–3373, **A**10 18 **F**3 35 40 43 45 53 57 59 62 64 65 81 85 93 97 107 111 119 127 130 133 148 **P**4
Primary Contact: James F. Heitzenrater, FACHE, Chief Executive Officer
CFO: Alyssa McCarter, Chief Financial Officer
CMO: Kevin T Stennett, M.D., Chief of Staff
CIO: Sam Vanderbeek, Chief Information Officer
CNO: Billie Hendrix, R.N., Director of Nursing
Web address: www.mangoldmemorial.org
Control: Hospital district or authority, Government, nonfederal **Service**: General medical and surgical

Staffed Beds: 25 **Admissions**: 380 **Census**: 5 **Outpatient Visits**: 23757 **Births**: 0 **Total Expense ($000)**: 10370 **Payroll Expense ($000)**: 4360 **Personnel**: 108

LONGVIEW—Gregg County

☒ **LONGVIEW REGIONAL MEDICAL CENTER (450702)**, 2901 North Fourth Street, Zip 75605–5191, Mailing Address: P.O. Box 14000, Zip 75607–4000; tel. 903/758–1818, (Total facility includes 15 beds in nursing home–type unit) **A**1 3 10 **F**3 8 11 12 13 15 18 20 22 24 26 28 29 30 31 34 35 37 39 40 43 45 46 47 49 50 57 59 61 64 65 67 70 72 74 75 76 77 78 79 81 85 86 87 89 91 93 107 108 110 111 114 115 118 119 120 126 130 146 148 **P**8 **S** Community Health Systems, Inc., Franklin, TN
Primary Contact: Casey Robertson, Chief Executive Officer
COO: Roy Finch, Chief Operating Officer
CFO: Todd Johnson, Chief Financial Officer
CMO: Kenneth McClure, M.D., Chief of Staff
CIO: Keith Jarvis, Director Information Systems
CHR: Terry Hardan, Director Human Resources
CNO: Stephanie Foster, MSN, R.N., Chief Nursing Officer
Web address: www.longviewregional.com
Control: Partnership, Investor–owned (for–profit) **Service**: General medical and surgical

Staffed Beds: 224 **Admissions**: 10181 **Census**: 124 **Outpatient Visits**: 94930 **Births**: 1833 **Total Expense ($000)**: 164939 **Payroll Expense ($000)**: 58132 **Personnel**: 912

☐ **MAGNOLIA BEHAVIORAL HOSPITAL OF EAST TEXAS**, 22 Bermuda Lane, Zip 75605–2902; tel. 903/291–3456, (Data for 334 days) **A**1 **F**29 98 100 105 130 152 153
Primary Contact: Allison Debruycker, Administrator
Web address: www.magnoliabehavioralhospital.com/
Control: Corporation, Investor–owned (for–profit) **Service**: Psychiatric

Staffed Beds: 20 **Admissions**: 243 **Census**: 5 **Outpatient Visits**: 537 **Births**: 0 **Total Expense ($000)**: 4602 **Payroll Expense ($000)**: 2293 **Personnel**: 46

☐ **OCEANS BEHAVIORAL HOSPITAL LONGVIEW (454117)**, 615 Clinic Drive, Zip 75605–5172; tel. 903/212–3105, **A**1 10 **F**29 64 98 100 101 103 104 130 132 149 153 154 **S** Oceans Healthcare, Lake Charles, LA
Primary Contact: Lauren Weber, Administrator
Web address: www.oceanslongview.com/
Control: Corporation, Investor–owned (for–profit) **Service**: Psychiatric

Staffed Beds: 24 **Admissions**: 590 **Census**: 20 **Outpatient Visits**: 20289 **Births**: 0 **Total Expense ($000)**: 5555 **Payroll Expense ($000)**: 2520 **Personnel**: 92

☒ **SELECT SPECIALTY HOSPITAL–LONGVIEW (452087)**, 700 East Marshall Avenue, 1st Floor, Zip 75601–5580; tel. 903/315–1100, **A**1 10 **F**1 3 28 29 75 77 85 91 92 130 148 **S** Select Medical Corporation, Mechanicsburg, PA
Primary Contact: Andrew Meade, Chief Executive Officer
Web address: www.longview.selectspecialtyhospitals.com/
Control: Corporation, Investor–owned (for–profit) **Service**: Acute long–term care hospital

Staffed Beds: 32 **Admissions**: 318 **Census**: 22 **Outpatient Visits**: 0 **Births**: 0 **Total Expense ($000)**: 11223 **Payroll Expense ($000)**: 5540 **Personnel**: 84

LUBBOCK—Lubbock County

☒ **COVENANT CHILDREN'S HOSPITAL (453306)**, 4015 22nd Place, Zip 79410; tel. 806/725–1011, **A**1 3 5 10 **F**3 4 19 21 23 25 27 30 31 32 40 41 43 50 59 70 72 73 76 81 88 89 98 102 104 154 **P**8 **S** Providence St. Joseph Health, Renton, WA
Primary Contact: Amy Thompson, M.D., Chief Executive Officer
COO: Clay Thomas, Chief Operating Officer
CMO: Craig Rhyne, M.D., FACS, Chief Medical Officer
CIO: Jim Reid, Vice President and Chief Information Officer
CHR: Chris Shaver, Vice President Human Resources
Web address: www.covenanthealth.org/About–Us/Facilities/Childrens–Hospital.aspx
Control: Other not–for–profit (including NFP Corporation) **Service**: Children's general medical and surgical

Staffed Beds: 269 **Admissions**: 3338 **Census**: 55 **Outpatient Visits**: 34847 **Births**: 848 **Total Expense ($000)**: 103022 **Payroll Expense ($000)**: 28927 **Personnel**: 819

Many Facility Codes have changed. Please refer to the AHA Guide Code Chart.

© 2018 AHA Guide

✠ **COVENANT MEDICAL CENTER (450040)**, 3615 19th Street, Zip 79410–1203, Mailing Address: P.O. Box 1201, Zip 79408–1201; tel. 806/725–0000, (Includes COVENANT MEDICAL CENTER–LAKESIDE, 4000 24th Street, Lubbock, TX, Zip 79410–1894; tel. 806/725–0000) **A**1 3 10 **F**7 8 15 17 18 19 20 22 23 26 27 28 30 34 35 37 39 40 43 46 47 48 49 50 51 53 54 55 57 58 59 60 61 63 64 65 68 70 71 74 75 77 78 79 80 81 82 83 84 85 86 87 91 92 93 94 107 108 109 111 114 115 116 117 118 120 121 123 129 130 131 132 135 143 144 146 147 148 **P**6 8 **S** Providence St. Joseph Health, Renton, WA
Primary Contact: Walt Cathey, Chief Executive Officer
CFO: John A Grigson, Vice President and Chief Financial Officer
CMO: Craig Rhyne, M.D., FACS, Chief Medical Officer
CIO: Troy Pratt, Information Technology Site Director
CHR: Chris Shaver, Vice President Human Resources
CNO: Karen Baggerly, Chief Nursing Officer and Vice President
Web address: www.covenanthealth.org
Control: Other not–for–profit (including NFP Corporation) **Service:** General medical and surgical

Staffed Beds: 394 **Admissions:** 19700 **Census:** 278 **Outpatient Visits:** 314327 **Births:** 1402 **Total Expense ($000):** 532803 **Payroll Expense ($000):** 134076 **Personnel:** 2376

★ **COVENANT SPECIALTY HOSPITAL (452102)**, 3815 20th Street, Zip 79410–1235; tel. 806/725–9200, **A**10 **F**1 3 29 30 31 60 63 68 75 77 78 79 87 119 130 143 148 **S** Providence St. Joseph Health, Renton, WA
Primary Contact: Ely Perea, Director and Chief Executive Officer
CFO: John Carigson, Chief Financial Officer
CMO: Naidu Chekuru, M.D., Chief Medical Officer
CHR: Chris Shaver, Vice President Human Resources
Web address: www.covenanthealth.org/view/Facilities/Specialty_Hospital
Control: Partnership, Investor–owned (for–profit) **Service:** Acute long–term care hospital

Staffed Beds: 56 **Admissions:** 431 **Census:** 31 **Outpatient Visits:** 0 **Births:** 0 **Total Expense ($000):** 18207 **Payroll Expense ($000):** 7316 **Personnel:** 124

✠ **GRACE MEDICAL CENTER (450162)**, 2412 50th Street, Zip 79412–2494; tel. 806/788–4100, **A**1 10 **F**3 8 11 12 15 29 34 35 37 40 44 45 47 49 50 51 59 64 66 70 75 79 81 82 85 87 107 108 110 111 114 115 118 119 135 146 **S** Providence St. Joseph Health, Renton, WA
Primary Contact: Vanessa Reasoner, Chief Executive Officer
CMO: Howard Beck, M.D., Chief of Staff
CIO: Jason Derouen, Director Management Information Systems
CHR: Sally Charles, Coordinator Human Resources
Web address: www.gracehealthsystem.com
Control: Partnership, Investor–owned (for–profit) **Service:** General medical and surgical

Staffed Beds: 43 **Admissions:** 1064 **Census:** 8 **Outpatient Visits:** 105446 **Births:** 0 **Total Expense ($000):** 66312 **Payroll Expense ($000):** 12501 **Personnel:** 251

LUBBOCK HEART & SURGICAL HOSPITAL (450876), 4810 North Loop 289, Zip 79416–3025; tel. 806/687–7777, **A**3 5 10 **F**3 17 18 20 22 24 26 29 34 40 45 57 59 79 81 82 85 107 108 115 119 130 131 148
Primary Contact: Charles Powell, Interim Chief Executive Officer
Web address: www.lubbockhsns.com/lubbock–heart/
Control: Partnership, Investor–owned (for–profit) **Service:** Heart

Staffed Beds: 73 **Admissions:** 2768 **Census:** 26 **Outpatient Visits:** 70485 **Births:** 0 **Total Expense ($000):** 79223 **Payroll Expense ($000):** 23417 **Personnel:** 373

☐ **SUNRISE CANYON HOSPITAL (454093)**, 1950 Aspen Ave, Zip 79404–1211, Mailing Address: P.O. Box 2828, Zip 79408–2828; tel. 806/740–1420, **A**1 10 **F**35 38 98 101 130 135 154
Primary Contact: Leonard Valderaz, Administrator
CFO: Jerome Flores, Chief Financial Officer
CMO: Dana Butler, M.D., Medical Director
CIO: Wendy Potitadkul, Chief Information Officer
CHR: Barbara McCann, Director Human Resources
Web address: www.starcarelubbock.org
Control: Other not–for–profit (including NFP Corporation) **Service:** Psychiatric

Staffed Beds: 30 **Admissions:** 502 **Census:** 28 **Outpatient Visits:** 0 **Births:** 0 **Total Expense ($000):** 5856 **Payroll Expense ($000):** 2099 **Personnel:** 50

☐ **TRUSTPOINT REHABILITATION HOSPITAL OF LUBBOCK (670050)**, 4302A Princeton Street, Zip 79415–1304; tel. 806/749–2222, **A**1 5 10 **F**3 29 34 35 56 57 74 75 77 79 85 86 87 90 91 96 130 132 154 **S** Ernest Health, Inc., Albuquerque, NM
Primary Contact: Craig Bragg, Chief Executive Officer
CFO: Crystal Roach, Chief Financial Officer
CNO: John Parsons, R.N., Chief Nursing Officer
Web address: www.trustpointhospital.com/
Control: Partnership, Investor–owned (for–profit) **Service:** Rehabilitation

Staffed Beds: 66 **Admissions:** 1351 **Census:** 59 **Outpatient Visits:** 0 **Births:** 0 **Total Expense ($000):** 24466 **Payroll Expense ($000):** 10968 **Personnel:** 217

⇑ **UNIVERSITY MEDICAL CENTER (450686)**, 602 Indiana Avenue, Zip 79415–3364, Mailing Address: P.O. Box 5980, Zip 79408–5980; tel. 806/775–8200, **A**2 3 5 10 21 **F**3 7 11 12 13 15 16 17 18 19 20 22 24 26 28 29 30 31 34 35 38 40 41 43 45 49 50 54 55 57 58 59 60 61 62 64 65 66 68 70 72 74 75 76 77 78 79 81 82 83 84 85 86 87 88 89 92 93 94 96 97 107 108 110 111 114 115 116 117 118 119 120 121 122 123 124 126 127 130 131 132 135 141 142 143 144 146 147 148 149 150
Primary Contact: Mark Funderburk, President and Chief Executive Officer
CFO: Jeff Dane, Executive Vice President and Chief Financial Officer
CMO: Michael Ragain, M.D., Chief Medical Officer and Senior Vice President
CIO: Bill Eubanks, Senior Vice President and Chief Information Officer
CHR: Adrienne Cozart, Senior Vice President Human Resources
CNO: Timothy W. Howell, R.N., Senior Vice President and Chief Nursing Officer
Web address: www.umchealthsystem.com
Control: Hospital district or authority, Government, nonfederal **Service:** General medical and surgical

Staffed Beds: 449 **Admissions:** 30748 **Census:** 383 **Outpatient Visits:** 191265 **Births:** 3111 **Total Expense ($000):** 571613 **Payroll Expense ($000):** 214622 **Personnel:** 3274

LUFKIN—Angelina County

★ **CHI ST. LUKE'S HEALTH MEMORIAL LUFKIN (450211)**, 1201 West Frank Avenue, Zip 75904–3357, Mailing Address: P.O. Box 1447, Zip 75902–1447; tel. 936/634–8111, **A**2 10 19 **F**3 11 12 13 14 15 17 18 20 21 22 23 24 26 28 29 30 31 34 35 37 38 40 44 45 46 47 48 49 50 51 56 57 59 60 61 62 63 64 68 70 71 74 75 76 77 78 79 81 82 83 84 85 86 87 90 91 92 93 97 100 101 102 107 108 110 111 112 114 115 116 117 119 121 126 129 130 132 135 143 144 146 147 148 149 **S** Catholic Health Initiatives, Englewood, CO
Primary Contact: Monte J. Bostwick, Market Chief Executive Officer
CFO: Kristi Gay, Chief Financial Officer
CHR: Tanya Tyler, Vice President Human Resources
Web address: www.memorialhealth.us/centers/lufkin
Control: Other not–for–profit (including NFP Corporation) **Service:** General medical and surgical

Staffed Beds: 194 **Admissions:** 6254 **Census:** 82 **Outpatient Visits:** 91398 **Births:** 291 **Total Expense ($000):** 141874 **Payroll Expense ($000):** 45210 **Personnel:** 679

★ **CHI ST. LUKE'S HEALTH MEMORIAL SPECIALTY HOSPITAL (452031)**, 1201 West Frank Avenue, D5, Zip 75904–3357, Mailing Address: P.O. Box 1447, Zip 75902–1447; tel. 936/639–7530, **A**10 **F**1 3 29 31 50 61 68 74 75 86 149 **S** Catholic Health Initiatives, Englewood, CO
Primary Contact: Darlene Williams, R.N., Administrator
CFO: Duane Miller, Chief Financial Officer
CMO: David Todd, M.D., President Medical Staff
CNO: Deborah Burgess, R.N., Chief Nursing Officer
Web address: www.memorialhealth.org
Control: Other not–for–profit (including NFP Corporation) **Service:** Acute long–term care hospital

Staffed Beds: 20 **Admissions:** 178 **Census:** 10 **Outpatient Visits:** 0 **Births:** 0 **Total Expense ($000):** 8569 **Payroll Expense ($000):** 2400 **Personnel:** 43

☐ **OCEANS BEHAVIORAL HOSPITAL LUFKIN (454123)**, 302 Gobblers Knob Road, Zip 75904–5419; tel. 936/632–2276, **A**1 10 **F**29 35 64 98 100 101 103 104 130 153 154 **S** Oceans Healthcare, Lake Charles, LA
Primary Contact: Laci Laird, Chief Executive Officer
Web address: www.oceanslufkin.com/
Control: Corporation, Investor–owned (for–profit) **Service:** Psychiatric

Staffed Beds: 24 **Admissions:** 472 **Census:** 19 **Outpatient Visits:** 21057 **Births:** 0 **Total Expense ($000):** 5028 **Payroll Expense ($000):** 2393 **Personnel:** 93

TX

Hospital, Medicare Provider Number, Address, Telephone, Approval, Facility, and Physician Codes, Health Care System

★ American Hospital Association (AHA) membership
☐ The Joint Commission accreditation
◯ Healthcare Facilities Accreditation Program
◇ DNV Healthcare Inc. accreditation
⇑ Center for Improvement in Healthcare Quality Accreditation
△ Commission on Accreditation of Rehabilitation Facilities (CARF) accreditation

✠ **WOODLAND HEIGHTS MEDICAL CENTER (450484)**, 505 South John Redditt Drive, Zip 75904–3157, Mailing Address: P.O. Box 150610, Zip 75904; tel. 936/634–8311, **A**1 10 19 **F**8 11 12 13 15 18 20 22 24 26 28 29 30 34 35 40 41 46 49 50 51 53 57 59 64 68 70 72 74 75 76 77 78 79 81 82 85 86 87 93 102 107 108 111 114 115 118 119 126 129 130 131 146 147 148 **S** Community Health Systems, Inc., Franklin, TN
Primary Contact: Kyle Swift, Chief Executive Officer
COO: Conner Hickey, Chief Operating Officer
CFO: William Whiddon, Chief Financial Officer
CMO: Imran Nazeer, M.D., Chief of Staff
CIO: Kalvin Buckley, Director Information Systems
CHR: Emilie Hobbs, Director Human Resources
Web address: www.woodlandheights.net
Control: Partnership, Investor–owned (for–profit) **Service**: General medical and surgical

Staffed Beds: 124 **Admissions**: 5117 **Census**: 56 **Outpatient Visits**: 51164 **Births**: 1080 **Total Expense ($000)**: 84421 **Payroll Expense ($000)**: 30808 **Personnel**: 503

LULING—Caldwell County

✠ **POST ACUTE/WARM SPRINGS SPECIALTY HOSPITAL OF LULING (452062)**, 200 Memorial Drive, Zip 78648–3213; tel. 830/875–8400, **A**1 10 **F**1 3 29 53 64 93 96 130 133 148 **S** Post Acute Medical, LLC, Enola, PA
Primary Contact: Jana Kuykendall, Chief Executive Officer
Web address: www.warmsprings.org
Control: Partnership, Investor–owned (for–profit) **Service**: Acute long–term care hospital

Staffed Beds: 34 **Admissions**: 592 **Census**: 29 **Outpatient Visits**: 11818 **Births**: 0 **Total Expense ($000)**: 14892 **Payroll Expense ($000)**: 6643 **Personnel**: 135

✠ **SETON EDGAR B. DAVIS HOSPITAL (451371)**, 130 Hays Street, Zip 78648–3207; tel. 830/875–7000, **A**1 10 18 **F**3 7 11 29 30 31 35 40 45 46 50 56 57 59 64 65 66 68 71 81 85 97 104 107 110 115 119 127 130 133 135 146 150 **P**3 8 **S** Ascension Healthcare, Saint Louis, MO
Primary Contact: Scott O. Fuller, President and Chief Executive Officer
CMO: Arjun Mohandas, M.D., Chief of Staff
CIO: Michael H. Minks, Chief Information Officer
CHR: Joe Canales, Director Human Resources
CNO: Nikki Rivers, R.N., Regional Chief Nursing Officer, South Market
Web address: www.seton.net/locations/edgar_davis/
Control: Church operated, Nongovernment, not–for–profit **Service**: General medical and surgical

Staffed Beds: 25 **Admissions**: 568 **Census**: 6 **Outpatient Visits**: 61140 **Births**: 0 **Total Expense ($000)**: 23767 **Payroll Expense ($000)**: 8310 **Personnel**: 160

WARM SPRINGS SPECIALTY HOSPITAL OF LULING See Post Acute/Warm Springs Specialty Hospital of Luling

MADISONVILLE—Madison County

✠ **CHI ST. JOSEPH HEALTH MADISON HOSPITAL (451316)**, 100 West Cross Street, Zip 77864–2432, Mailing Address: Box 698, Zip 77864–0698; tel. 936/348–2631, **A**1 10 18 **F**3 7 11 15 30 34 40 43 50 56 57 59 64 68 75 77 93 103 107 110 119 130 133 146 148 **S** Catholic Health Initiatives, Englewood, CO
Primary Contact: Theron Park, Chief Executive Officer
CMO: Grover Hubley, M.D., President Medical Staff
CIO: Maurita Turner, Team Leader Health Information Systems Services
CNO: Roxanne Hass, Director of Nursing
Web address: www.st-joseph.org
Control: Church operated, Nongovernment, not–for–profit **Service**: General medical and surgical

Staffed Beds: 25 **Admissions**: 201 **Census**: 7 **Outpatient Visits**: 11702 **Births**: 0 **Total Expense ($000)**: 10172 **Payroll Expense ($000)**: 4274 **Personnel**: 84

MANSFIELD—Tarrant County

✠ **KINDRED HOSPITAL–MANSFIELD (452019)**, 1802 Highway 157 North, Zip 76063–3923; tel. 817/473–6101, **A**1 10 **F**1 3 29 30 45 46 64 70 75 82 85 107 130 132 148 **S** Kindred Healthcare, Louisville, KY
Primary Contact: Blake Peart, Administrator
CFO: Judy Baker, Chief Financial Officer
Web address: www.kindredmansfield.com
Control: Corporation, Investor–owned (for–profit) **Service**: Acute long–term care hospital

Staffed Beds: 55 **Admissions**: 470 **Census**: 31 **Outpatient Visits**: 440 **Births**: 0

✠ **METHODIST MANSFIELD MEDICAL CENTER (670023)**, 2700 East Broad Street, Zip 76063–5899; tel. 682/622–2000, **A**1 10 **F**3 11 13 15 18 20 22 24 29 30 31 34 35 37 40 45 46 48 49 50 58 59 60 64 68 70 74 76 78 79 81 82 85 87 93 97 107 108 110 111 115 118 119 126 130 132 146 148 **P**5 **S** Methodist Health System, Dallas, TX
Primary Contact: John E. Phillips, FACHE, President
CFO: Jary Ganske, Chief Financial Officer
CIO: Pamela McNutt, Senior Vice President and Chief Information Officer
CHR: Judy K Laister, Director, Human Resources
CNO: Nora Frasier, R.N., FACHE, Chief Nursing Officer
Web address: www.methodisthealthsystem.org/mansfield
Control: Other not–for–profit (including NFP Corporation) **Service**: General medical and surgical

Staffed Beds: 221 **Admissions**: 9825 **Census**: 131 **Outpatient Visits**: 86086 **Births**: 2028 **Total Expense ($000)**: 185486 **Payroll Expense ($000)**: 79593 **Personnel**: 956

MARBLE FALLS—Burnet County

★ **BAYLOR SCOTT & WHITE MEDICAL CENTER – MARBLE FALLS (670108)**, 800 West Highway 71, Zip 78654; tel. 830/201–8000, **F**3 13 15 18 20 29 31 34 40 45 50 59 64 70 74 75 76 78 79 81 82 85 93 107 110 111 115 119 130 132 146 147 149 154 **S** Baylor Scott & White Health, Dallas, TX
Primary Contact: Timothy A. Ols, FACHE, President
Web address: www.sw.org/location/marble–falls–hospital
Control: Other not–for–profit (including NFP Corporation) **Service**: General medical and surgical

Staffed Beds: 46 **Admissions**: 2504 **Census**: 19 **Outpatient Visits**: 100925 **Births**: 372 **Total Expense ($000)**: 65489 **Payroll Expense ($000)**: 23256 **Personnel**: 313

MARLIN—Falls County

★ **FALLS COMMUNITY HOSPITAL AND CLINIC (450348)**, 322 Coleman Street, Zip 76661–2358, Mailing Address: P.O. Box 60, Zip 76661–0060; tel. 254/803–3561, **A**10 20 **F**3 11 32 33 34 35 36 40 43 53 56 57 59 64 65 66 68 75 82 87 91 93 97 99 103 104 107 114 119 127 129 131 135 146 148 Primary Contact: Jeffrey Lyle, Chief Executive Officer
COO: Becca Brewer, Chief Operations Officer
CMO: James Scott Crockett, M.D., Chief of Staff
CIO: Chris Smith, Chief Information Officer
CHR: Peggy Polster, Manager Personnel and Administrative Assistant
CNO: Tasha Burnett, Director of Nursing
Web address: www.fallshospital.com
Control: Other not–for–profit (including NFP Corporation) **Service**: General medical and surgical

Staffed Beds: 32 **Admissions**: 463 **Census**: 4 **Outpatient Visits**: 68372 **Births**: 2 **Total Expense ($000)**: 19706 **Payroll Expense ($000)**: 6259 **Personnel**: 155

MARSHALL—Harrison County

✠ **CHRISTUS GOOD SHEPHERD MEDICAL CENTER–MARSHALL (450032)**, 811 South Washington Avenue, Zip 75670–5336, Mailing Address: P.O. Box 1599, Zip 75671–1599; tel. 903/927–6000, (Includes CHRISTUS GOOD SHEPHERD MEDICAL CENTER, 700 East Marshall Avenue, Longview, TX, Zip 75601–5580; tel. 903/315–1800; Todd Hancock, President and Chief Executive Officer) **A**1 3 10 **F**3 8 11 13 15 18 20 22 24 28 29 30 31 34 35 38 40 43 45 46 49 50 51 53 54 56 57 59 60 61 64 65 68 70 71 72 73 74 75 76 77 78 79 80 81 82 85 86 87 89 90 93 97 102 103 107 110 111 114 115 117 119 127 129 130 131 132 135 143 144 145 146 147 148 149 150 154 **P**7 8 **S** CHRISTUS Health, Irving, TX
Primary Contact: Todd Hancock, President and Chief Executive Officer
COO: Keith Creel, Vice President Operations
CFO: Michael Cheek, Chief Financial Officer
CMO: Larry Verfurth, D.O., Executive Vice President and Chief Medical Officer
CIO: Walter Grimes, Director Information Technology
CHR: Ginger Morrow, Executive Vice President Human Resources
CNO: Keith Kirbow, R.N., Vice President and Chief Nursing Officer
Web address: www.christushealth.org/good–shepherd/marshall
Control: Church operated, Nongovernment, not–for–profit **Service**: General medical and surgical

Staffed Beds: 891 **Admissions**: 17304 **Census**: 206 **Outpatient Visits**: 275912 **Births**: 2152 **Total Expense ($000)**: 323420 **Payroll Expense ($000)**: 117726 **Personnel**: 2625

Many Facility Codes have changed. Please refer to the AHA Guide Code Chart.   © 2018 AHA Guide

TX

MCALLEN—Hidalgo County

✠ **RIO GRANDE REGIONAL HOSPITAL (450711)**, 101 East Ridge Road, Zip 78503–1299; tel. 956/632–6000, **A**1 10 **F**3 8 11 12 13 15 18 19 20 21 22 23 24 25 26 27 29 30 31 34 35 39 40 43 45 46 49 50 54 56 57 59 60 64 66 68 70 71 72 73 74 75 76 78 79 81 85 87 88 89 93 107 108 110 111 114 118 119 126 130 132 146 147 148 149 **P**7 **S** HCA Healthcare, Nashville, TN
Primary Contact: Cristina Rivera, Chief Executive Officer
CFO: William Saller, Chief Financial Officer
CHR: Marjorie Whittemore, Director Human Resources
Web address: www.riohealth.com
Control: Partnership, Investor–owned (for–profit) **Service**: General medical and surgical

Staffed Beds: 320 Admissions: 14186 Census: 175 Outpatient Visits: 127466 Births: 2236 Total Expense ($000): 163108 Payroll Expense ($000): 66469 Personnel: 838

SOLARA HOSPITAL MCALLEN (452095), 301 West Expressway 83, 8th Floor, Zip 78503–3045; tel. 956/632–4880, **A**10 22 **F**1 3 29 30 56 57 70 75 77 85 86 87 91 130 148 **S** Cornerstone Healthcare Group, Dallas, TX
Primary Contact: Austin B. Cleveland, Chief Executive Officer
Web address: www.chghospitals.com/mcallen/
Control: Corporation, Investor–owned (for–profit) **Service**: Acute long–term care hospital

Staffed Beds: 78 Admissions: 601 Census: 44 Outpatient Visits: 0 Births: 0 Total Expense ($000): 16298 Payroll Expense ($000): 8941 Personnel: 126

MCCAMEY—Upton County

★ **MCCAMEY COUNTY HOSPITAL DISTRICT (451309)**, 2500 Highway 305 South, Zip 79752, Mailing Address: P.O. Box 1200, Zip 79752–1200; tel. 432/652–8626, (Total facility includes 30 beds in nursing home–type unit) **A**10 18 **F**3 40 53 59 64 65 66 93 127 128 133
Primary Contact: Jaime Ramirez, Chief Executive Officer
CFO: Jason J Menefee, Chief Financial Officer
CMO: John Bruce Addison, D.O., Chief Medical Officer
CIO: Larry Rollins, Supervisor Information Technology
CHR: Ashley Johnson, Director Human Resource
CNO: Erin Mann, R.N., Chief Nursing Officer
Web address: www.mccameyhospitaldistrict.org
Control: Hospital district or authority, Government, nonfederal **Service**: General medical and surgical

Staffed Beds: 44 Admissions: 99 Census: 27 Outpatient Visits: 6709 Births: 0 Total Expense ($000): 13121 Payroll Expense ($000): 4276 Personnel: 71

MCKINNEY—Collin County

✠ **BAYLOR MEDICAL CENTER AT MCKINNEY (670082)**, 5252 West University Drive, Zip 75071–7822; tel. 469/764–1000, **A**1 2 5 10 **F**3 13 15 18 20 22 26 29 30 31 34 35 40 43 45 46 47 49 50 51 57 59 60 67 70 72 73 74 75 76 77 78 79 81 84 85 87 107 110 111 114 115 116 119 126 130 131 132 146 147 148 **S** Baylor Scott & White Health, Dallas, TX
Primary Contact: Kyle Armstrong, President
COO: Melissa Winter, R.N., MSN, Chief Operating Officer and Chief Nursing Officer
CFO: Steve Roussel, Chief Financial Officer
CMO: Jeff Kerr, M.D., Chief Medical Officer
CNO: Melissa Winter, R.N., MSN, Chief Operating Officer and Chief Nursing Officer
Web address: www.baylorhealth.com/PhysiciansLocations/McKinney/Pages/Default.aspx
Control: Other not–for–profit (including NFP Corporation) **Service**: General medical and surgical

Staffed Beds: 143 Admissions: 8105 Census: 83 Outpatient Visits: 54513 Births: 1914 Total Expense ($000): 148904 Payroll Expense ($000): 51831 Personnel: 526

✠ **MEDICAL CITY MCKINNEY (450403)**, 4500 Medical Center Drive, Zip 75069–1650; tel. 972/547–8000, (Includes WYSONG CAMPUS, 130 South Central Expressway, McKinney, TX, Zip 75070; tel. 972/548–5300) **A**1 10 **F**3 4 11 13 18 20 22 24 25 26 28 29 30 34 37 40 43 45 49 50 56 57 59 60 64 68 70 72 74 75 76 77 78 79 81 82 85 87 90 91 92 93 94 96 97 98 102 103 107 108 109 111 114 115 119 126 130 131 132 146 147 148 149 **S** HCA Healthcare, Nashville, TN
Primary Contact: Ernest C. Lynch III, FACHE, President and Chief Executive Officer
COO: Andrew Nice, Chief Operating Officer
CFO: Brad Stein, Chief Financial Officer
CMO: Steven Kaster, M.D., Chief Medical Officer
CIO: Kevin Fletcher, Director Information Systems
CHR: Alayne Sewick, Vice President Human Resources
CNO: Cassidi Roberts, R.N., Chief Nursing Officer
Web address: www.medicalcenterofmckinney.com
Control: Partnership, Investor–owned (for–profit) **Service**: General medical and surgical

Staffed Beds: 222 Admissions: 11756 Census: 169 Outpatient Visits: 79180 Births: 1095 Total Expense ($000): 141084 Payroll Expense ($000): 61426 Personnel: 843

☐ **METHODIST MCKINNEY HOSPITAL (670069)**, 8000 West Eldorado Parkway, Zip 75070–5940; tel. 972/569–2700, **A**1 10 **F**3 8 29 34 37 40 45 51 75 79 81 82 85 93 107 111 119 126 129 130 131
Primary Contact: Joseph Minissale, President
CFO: Mike Conroy, Chief Financial Officer
CIO: Sharon Stark, R.N., Manager Clinical Information Systems
CHR: Diana Hume, Manager Human Resources
CNO: Staci Jones, R.N., Chief Nursing Officer
Web address: www.methodistmckinneyhospital.com
Control: Partnership, Investor–owned (for–profit) **Service**: Surgical

Staffed Beds: 21 Admissions: 1285 Census: 9 Outpatient Visits: 47209 Births: 0 Total Expense ($000): 60473 Payroll Expense ($000): 12149 Personnel: 183

MESQUITE—Dallas County

✠ **DALLAS REGIONAL MEDICAL CENTER (450688)**, 1011 North Galloway Avenue, Zip 75149–2433; tel. 214/320–7000, **A**1 10 **F**3 12 13 15 18 20 22 24 26 29 30 34 35 37 39 40 41 43 45 46 49 50 56 57 59 65 67 70 74 75 76 78 79 81 85 86 87 102 105 107 108 110 111 115 118 119 126 129 130 134 135 146 147 148 149 154 **S** Prime Healthcare, Ontario, CA
Primary Contact: Glenda Newby, Chief Executive Officer
CMO: Srinivas Gunukula, M.D., Chief of Staff
Web address: www.dallasregionalmedicalcenter.com
Control: Individual, Investor–owned (for–profit) **Service**: General medical and surgical

Staffed Beds: 127 Admissions: 6422 Census: 67 Outpatient Visits: 49452 Births: 845 Total Expense ($000): 80015 Payroll Expense ($000): 36240 Personnel: 451

☐ **MESQUITE REHABILITATION INSTITUTE (673045)**, 1023 North Belt Line Road, Zip 75149–1788; tel. 972/216–2400, (Nonreporting) **A**1 10 **S** Ernest Health, Inc., Albuquerque, NM
Primary Contact: Brian Abraham, Chief Executive Officer
Web address: www.mesquiterehab.ernesthealth.com/
Control: Corporation, Investor–owned (for–profit) **Service**: Rehabilitation

Staffed Beds: 20

☐ **MESQUITE SPECIALTY HOSPITAL (452100)**, 1024 North Galloway Avenue, Zip 75149–2434; tel. 972/216–2300, **A**1 10 **F**1 3 29 74 75 148 149 **S** Ernest Health, Inc., Albuquerque, NM
Primary Contact: Louis Bradley, Chief Executive Officer
Web address: www.msh.ernesthealth.com
Control: Partnership, Investor–owned (for–profit) **Service**: Acute long–term care hospital

Staffed Beds: 40 Admissions: 390 Census: 26 Outpatient Visits: 0 Births: 0 Total Expense ($000): 16817 Payroll Expense ($000): 5763 Personnel: 126

TX

Hospital, Medicare Provider Number, Address, Telephone, Approval, Facility, and Physician Codes, Health Care System

★ American Hospital Association (AHA) membership
☐ The Joint Commission accreditation
○ Healthcare Facilities Accreditation Program
◇ DNV Healthcare Inc. accreditation
⇑ Center for Improvement in Healthcare Quality Accreditation
△ Commission on Accreditation of Rehabilitation Facilities (CARF) accreditation

MEXIA—Limestone County

PARKVIEW REGIONAL HOSPITAL (450400), 600 South Bonham, Zip 76667–3603; tel. 254/562–5332, **A**1 10 **F**3 11 15 29 30 34 35 40 43 45 51 53 56 57 59 64 65 70 75 77 78 79 81 85 86 87 90 93 97 98 103 107 108 110 111 114 119 127 130 132 133 146 **P**5 6 **S** LifePoint Health, Brentwood, TN
Primary Contact: Robert C. Honeycutt, Chief Executive Officer
COO: R. Austin Wratchford, Chief Operating Officer
CFO: Jack Wilcox, Chief Financial Officer
CNO: Edwina J Henry, Assistant Chief Nursing Officer
Web address: www.parkviewregional.com
Control: Partnership, Investor–owned (for–profit) **Service**: General medical and surgical

Staffed Beds: 58 **Admissions**: 507 **Census**: 6 **Outpatient Visits**: 21980
Births: 0 **Total Expense ($000)**: 17920 **Payroll Expense ($000)**: 6878
Personnel: 136

MIDLAND—Midland County

★ **CONTINUECARE HOSPITAL AT MIDLAND MEMORIAL (452117)**, 4214 Andrews Highway, 3rd Floor, Zip 79703–4822; tel. 432/221–3044, **A**10 22 **F**1 3 29 34 35 79 85 87 148 **S** Community Hospital Corporation, Plano, TX
Primary Contact: Cynthia Rodgers, Chief Executive Officer
Web address: www.continuecare.org/midland/
Control: Other not–for–profit (including NFP Corporation) **Service**: Acute long–term care hospital

Staffed Beds: 29 **Admissions**: 215 **Census**: 16 **Outpatient Visits**: 0
Births: 0 **Total Expense ($000)**: 9477 **Payroll Expense ($000)**: 4239
Personnel: 52

ENCOMPASS HEALTH REHABILITATION HOSPITAL MIDLAND ODESSA (453057), 1800 Heritage Boulevard, Zip 79707–9750; tel. 432/520–1600, **A**1 10 **F**3 29 57 59 74 75 77 90 91 96 130 143 148 154 **S** Encompass Health Corporation, Birmingham, AL
Primary Contact: Christopher Wortham, Chief Executive Officer
CFO: Vivian Irwin, Chief Financial Officer and Controller
CMO: Mark A Fredrickson, M.D., Medical Director
CHR: Tina Parker, Director Human Resources
Web address: www.healthsouthmidland.com
Control: Corporation, Investor–owned (for–profit) **Service**: Rehabilitation

Staffed Beds: 80 **Admissions**: 1466 **Census**: 54 **Outpatient Visits**: 0
Births: 0 **Total Expense ($000)**: 22902 **Payroll Expense ($000)**: 12137
Personnel: 174

★ ⇑ **MIDLAND MEMORIAL HOSPITAL (450133)**, 400 Rosalind Redfern Grover Parkway, Zip 79701–6499; tel. 432/221–1111, (Includes MIDLAND MEMORIAL HOSPITAL, 400 Rosalind Redfern Grover Pkwy, Midland, TX, Zip 79701–5846; tel. 432/221–1111) **A**3 5 10 21 **F**3 8 11 12 13 15 17 18 20 22 24 26 28 29 30 32 34 35 37 40 43 45 49 50 56 57 59 61 64 68 70 73 74 75 76 77 78 79 81 82 83 84 85 86 87 88 89 93 97 107 108 111 114 115 116 117 118 119 124 126 129 130 131 132 135 145 146 147 148 154 **P**8
Primary Contact: Russell Meyers, FACHE, President and Chief Executive Officer
COO: Bob Dent, R.N., Senior Vice President, Chief Operating Officer and Chief Nursing Officer
CFO: Stephen Bowerman, Senior Vice President, Chief Financial Officer
CMO: Lawrence Wilson, M.D., Vice President, Chief Medical Officer
CIO: Taylor Weems, Vice President, Chief Information Officer
CHR: Roberta SoloRio, Vice President, Chief Human Resource Officer
Web address: www.midland–memorial.com
Control: Hospital district or authority, Government, nonfederal **Service**: General medical and surgical

Staffed Beds: 245 **Admissions**: 11115 **Census**: 131 **Outpatient Visits**: 151921 **Births**: 2380 **Total Expense ($000)**: 252309 **Payroll Expense ($000)**: 102622 **Personnel**: 1683

☐ **OCEANS BEHAVIORAL HEALTH CENTER PERMIAN BASIN (454110)**, 3300 South FM 1788, Zip 79706–2601; tel. 432/561–5915, **A**1 3 10 **F**29 34 35 64 68 98 99 100 101 103 104 130 132 153 154 **P**6 **S** Oceans Healthcare, Lake Charles, LA
Primary Contact: Lorie Dunnam, Chief Executive Officer
Web address: www.oceanspermianbasin.com/
Control: Corporation, Investor–owned (for–profit) **Service**: Psychiatric

Staffed Beds: 58 **Admissions**: 2027 **Census**: 48 **Outpatient Visits**: 10229
Births: 0 **Total Expense ($000)**: 10472 **Payroll Expense ($000)**: 5014
Personnel: 193

MINERAL WELLS—Palo Pinto County

PALO PINTO GENERAL HOSPITAL (450565), 400 SW 25th Avenue, Zip 76067–8246; tel. 940/325–7891, **A**1 10 **F**11 13 15 17 18 28 29 34 40 43 45 46 51 53 54 57 59 64 65 66 68 69 71 74 75 76 77 79 81 82 86 87 91 93 107 108 110 111 114 119 127 129 130 131 133 135 146 147 **P**1
Primary Contact: Daniel Smith, Interim Chief Executive Officer
CFO: Daniel Smith, Chief Financial Officer
CMO: George Thomas, M.D., Chief of Staff
CIO: Shane Coleman, Chief Information Officer
CHR: Mary B Braddock, Director Human Resources
CNO: James Fesser, Chief Nursing Officer
Web address: www.ppgh.com
Control: Hospital district or authority, Government, nonfederal **Service**: General medical and surgical

Staffed Beds: 48 **Admissions**: 1538 **Census**: 16 **Outpatient Visits**: 96934
Births: 305 **Total Expense ($000)**: 40787 **Payroll Expense ($000)**: 17489
Personnel: 350

MISSION—Hidalgo County

△ **MISSION REGIONAL MEDICAL CENTER (450176)**, 900 South Bryan Road, Zip 78572–6613; tel. 956/323–9103, (Data for 92 days) **A**1 7 10 **F**3 11 12 13 15 18 20 22 29 34 35 40 43 45 46 49 50 51 57 59 60 64 65 66 68 70 72 74 75 76 77 79 81 85 87 89 90 93 96 107 108 110 111 115 119 130 132 146 147 148 149 154 **P**8 **S** Prime Healthcare, Ontario, CA
Primary Contact: Kane A. Dawson, Chief Executive Officer
CFO: Lester Surrock, Chief Financial Officer
CMO: Humberto F. Nunez, M.D., Chief Medical Officer
CNO: Kennetha Foster, Chief Nursing Officer
Web address: www.missionrmc.org
Control: Other not–for–profit (including NFP Corporation) **Service**: General medical and surgical

Staffed Beds: 228 **Admissions**: 2493 **Census**: 127 **Outpatient Visits**: 16267 **Births**: 454 **Total Expense ($000)**: 24613 **Payroll Expense ($000)**: 10955 **Personnel**: 762

MONAHANS—Ward County

WARD MEMORIAL HOSPITAL (451373), 406 South Gary Street, Zip 79756–4798, Mailing Address: P.O. Box 40, Zip 79756–0040; tel. 432/943–2511, **A**10 18 **F**3 40 43 45 64 65 66 81 82 89 93 107 114 119 127 131 133 148 **P**6
Primary Contact: Leticia Rodriguez, Chief Executive Officer
CFO: Alison Cooper, Chief Financial Officer
CMO: Htin Thaung, M.D., Chief Medical Officer
CIO: David Hargrave, Chief Information Officer
CHR: Corina Subia, Director Human Resources
CNO: Jason Harbin, Director of Nursing
Web address: www.wardmemorial.com
Control: County, Government, nonfederal **Service**: General medical and surgical

Staffed Beds: 25 **Admissions**: 275 **Census**: 2 **Outpatient Visits**: 59743
Births: 0 **Total Expense ($000)**: 14066 **Payroll Expense ($000)**: 6635
Personnel: 130

MORTON—Cochran County

COCHRAN MEMORIAL HOSPITAL (451366), 201 East Grant Street, Zip 79346–3444; tel. 806/266–5565, **A**10 18 **F**34 40 57 59 65 127 149 **P**6
Primary Contact: Larry Turney, Administrator
CFO: Maggie Ramon, Chief Financial Officer
CIO: David Turney, Chief Information Officer
CHR: Amanda Turney, Director Human Resources
CNO: Rosemary Franco, Chief Nursing Officer
Control: Hospital district or authority, Government, nonfederal **Service**: General medical and surgical

Staffed Beds: 13 **Admissions**: 18 **Census**: 1 **Outpatient Visits**: 3523
Births: 0 **Total Expense ($000)**: 4107 **Payroll Expense ($000)**: 1956
Personnel: 49

MOUNT PLEASANT—Titus County

☐ **TITUS REGIONAL MEDICAL CENTER (450080)**, 2001 North Jefferson Avenue, Zip 75455–2398; tel. 903/577–6000, **A**1 10 **F**3 7 11 12 13 15 18 20 22 24 28 29 30 34 35 39 40 43 45 47 50 51 53 54 56 57 58 59 64 68 70 72 73 74 75 76 77 78 79 81 82 85 87 89 90 93 97 98 103 107 108 110 111 114 115 117 118 119 121 123 127 129 130 132 135 144 147 148 154
Primary Contact: Terry Scoggin, Interim Chief Executive Officer
CFO: Terry Scoggin, Chief Financial Officer
CMO: Chris Burling, M.D., Chief of Staff
CIO: Kevin Harris, Director Information Systems
CHR: Tony Piazza, Director Human Resources
CNO: Carol Slider, Chief Nursing Officer
Web address: www.titusregional.com
Control: Hospital district or authority, Government, nonfederal **Service**: General medical and surgical

Staffed Beds: 64 **Admissions**: 4669 **Census**: 47 **Outpatient Visits**: 231017
Births: 1021 **Total Expense ($000)**: 85791 **Payroll Expense ($000)**: 26925
Personnel: 566

TX

MUENSTER—Cooke County

MUENSTER MEMORIAL HOSPITAL (451335), 605 North Maple Street,
Zip 76252–2424, Mailing Address: P.O. Box 370, Zip 76252–0370;
tel. 940/759–2271, **A**10 18 **F**11 35 40 43 45 53 57 59 62 64 65 75 77 81 93
107 114 119 127 130 133 146 **P**8
Primary Contact: Brian Roland, Chief Executive Officer
CFO: Julie Williams, Chief Financial Officer
CNO: Tiffany Lutkenhaus, Chief Nursing Officer
Web address: www.muensterhospital.com
Control: Hospital district or authority, Government, nonfederal **Service:** General
medical and surgical

Staffed Beds: 18 **Admissions:** 43 **Census:** 8 **Outpatient Visits:** 4163
Births: 0 **Total Expense ($000):** 11363 **Payroll Expense ($000):** 5009
Personnel: 94

MULESHOE—Bailey County

MULESHOE AREA MEDICAL CENTER (451372), 708 South First Street,
Zip 79347–3627; tel. 806/272–4524, **A**10 18 **F**34 40 57 59 64 93 97 107 119
127 133 135 154 **S** Preferred Management Corporation, Shawnee, OK
Primary Contact: Dennis Fleenor, R.N., Administrator
CMO: Bruce Purdy, M.D., Chief of Staff
CHR: Suzanne Nichols, Director Human Resources
Web address: www.mahdtx.org
Control: Corporation, Investor–owned (for–profit) **Service:** General medical and
surgical

Staffed Beds: 25 **Admissions:** 276 **Census:** 5 **Outpatient Visits:** 18388
Births: 1 **Total Expense ($000):** 9304 **Payroll Expense ($000):** 3591
Personnel: 83

NACOGDOCHES—Nacogdoches County

⊞ **NACOGDOCHES MEDICAL CENTER (450656)**, 4920 NE Stallings Drive,
Zip 75965–1200; tel. 936/569–9481, (Nonreporting) **A**1 2 10 19 **S** TENET
Healthcare Corporation, Dallas, TX
Primary Contact: Philip Koovakada, Chief Executive Officer
CFO: Randy Slack, Chief Financial Officer
CMO: Charles Thompson, M.D., Chief Medical Officer
CIO: Teresa Simon, Director Information Systems
CHR: Teresa Farrell, Chief Human Resources Officer
CNO: Mario B Estrella, Chief Nursing Officer
Web address: www.nacmedicalcenter.com
Control: Partnership, Investor–owned (for–profit) **Service:** General medical and
surgical

Staffed Beds: 109

☐ **NACOGDOCHES MEMORIAL HOSPITAL (450508)**, 1204 North Mound Street,
Zip 75961–4061; tel. 936/564–4611, **A**1 10 19 **F**3 7 11 13 15 18 20 22 26 28
29 30 31 38 40 43 45 50 59 64 65 66 70 72 74 75 76 77 78 79 80 81 85 90
97 107 108 110 111 115 118 119 130 135 146 147 148 149 **P**5 6
Primary Contact: Gary G. Kendrick, FACHE, Interim Chief Executive Officer
CFO: Jane Ann Bridges, Chief Financial Officer
CNO: Beth Knight, Chief Nursing Officer
Web address: www.nacmem.org
Control: Hospital district or authority, Government, nonfederal **Service:** General
medical and surgical

Staffed Beds: 118 **Admissions:** 4527 **Census:** 64 **Outpatient
Visits:** 102763 **Births:** 902 **Total Expense ($000):** 94478 **Payroll Expense
($000):** 34416 **Personnel:** 862

NASSAU BAY—Harris County

★ ⇑ **HOUSTON METHODIST CLEAR LAKE HOSPITAL (450709)**, 18300 St John
Drive, Zip 77058–6302; tel. 281/333–5503, **A**3 5 10 21 **F**3 8 11 12 13 15 18
20 22 24 26 28 29 30 31 34 35 39 40 41 44 45 47 49 50 51 53 54 57 59 60
63 64 65 68 70 73 74 75 76 77 78 79 81 82 84 85 86 87 93 94 96 102 107
108 110 111 115 118 119 126 130 131 132 135 146 147 148 149 150 **S**
Houston Methodist, Houston, TX
Primary Contact: Dan Newman, Chief Executive Officer
CFO: David A Witt, Vice President Finances
CHR: Becky A Merritt, Director Human Resources
Web address: www.houstonmethodist.org/st–john–clear–lake
Control: Other not–for–profit (including NFP Corporation) **Service:** General
medical and surgical

Staffed Beds: 113 **Admissions:** 5756 **Census:** 62 **Outpatient Visits:** 79690
Births: 338 **Total Expense ($000):** 131485 **Payroll Expense ($000):** 52838
Personnel: 855

NAVASOTA—Grimes County

⊞ **CHI ST. JOSEPH HEALTH GRIMES HOSPITAL (451322)**, 210 South Judson
Street, Zip 77868–3704; tel. 936/825–6585, **A**1 10 18 **F**3 28 29 34 40 43 56
57 59 75 77 93 104 107 111 119 130 132 133 135 146 **S** Catholic Health
Initiatives, Englewood, CO
Primary Contact: Theron Park, Chief Executive Officer
CFO: Daniel Goggin, Senior Vice President and Chief Financial Officer
CMO: Luke P Scamardo, M.D., II Chief of Staff
CIO: Mike Russo, Vice President Information Systems
CHR: Kristina Lee, Director Human Resources
CNO: Cesar Lopez, R.N., Director of Nurses
Web address: www.st–joseph.org
Control: Church operated, Nongovernment, not–for–profit **Service:** General
medical and surgical

Staffed Beds: 18 **Admissions:** 164 **Census:** 5 **Outpatient Visits:** 18687
Births: 0 **Total Expense ($000):** 10081 **Payroll Expense ($000):** 4307
Personnel: 85

NEDERLAND—Jefferson County

MID–JEFFERSON EXTENDED CARE HOSPITAL (452083), 2600 Highway 365,
Zip 77627–6237; tel. 409/726–8700, (Nonreporting) **A**10
Primary Contact: Wade K. Lester, Administrator
Web address: www.midjeffextendedcare.com/index.php
Control: Corporation, Investor–owned (for–profit) **Service:** Acute long–term care
hospital

Staffed Beds: 48

NEW BRAUNFELS—Comal County

GULF STATES LONG TERM ACUTE CARE OF NEW BRAUNFELS See Post
Acute/Warm Springs Specialty Hospital of New Braunfels

☐ **NEW BRAUNFELS REGIONAL REHABILITATION HOSPITAL (673049)**, 2041
Sundance Parkway, Zip 78130–2779; tel. 830/625–6700, **A**1 10 **F**3 29 34 57
64 90 93 96 130 132 148 **S** Ernest Health, Inc., Albuquerque, NM
Primary Contact: Mario Rodriguez, Chief Executive Officer
CFO: Sue Thomsen, Chief Financial Officer
CMO: Maria R Lomba, Medical Director
CHR: Cheryl Smith, Manager Human Resources
CNO: Peggy Schmits, Director, Nursing Operations
Web address: www.nbrrh.ernesthealth.com
Control: Corporation, Investor–owned (for–profit) **Service:** Rehabilitation

Staffed Beds: 40 **Admissions:** 811 **Census:** 32 **Outpatient Visits:** 7146
Births: 0 **Total Expense ($000):** 13775 **Payroll Expense ($000):** 6913
Personnel: 141

⊞ **POST ACUTE/WARM SPRINGS SPECIALTY HOSPITAL OF NEW BRAUNFELS
(452106)**, 1445 Hanz Drive, Zip 78130–2567; tel. 830/627–7600, **A**1 10 **F**1 3
29 30 34 85 130 148 **S** Post Acute Medical, LLC, Enola, PA
Primary Contact: Ashley Ondrusek, Chief Executive Officer
Web address: www.warmsprings.org/locations/hos/h1/
Control: Partnership, Investor–owned (for–profit) **Service:** Acute long–term care
hospital

Staffed Beds: 40 **Admissions:** 755 **Census:** 28 **Outpatient Visits:** 0
Births: 0 **Total Expense ($000):** 13958 **Payroll Expense ($000):** 5592
Personnel: 98

⊞ **RESOLUTE HEALTH (670098)**, 555 Creekside Crossing, Zip 78130–2594;
tel. 830/500–6000, **A**1 10 **F**3 13 15 18 20 22 29 30 34 35 40 45 48 49 50 53
60 64 65 70 72 74 75 76 77 79 81 85 87 107 108 111 114 115 119 126 130
146 147 149 150 **P**8 **S** TENET Healthcare Corporation, Dallas, TX
Primary Contact: Mark L. Bernard, Chief Executive Officer
Web address: www.resolutehealth.com
Control: Corporation, Investor–owned (for–profit) **Service:** General medical and
surgical

Staffed Beds: 70 **Admissions:** 4017 **Census:** 37 **Outpatient Visits:** 33146
Births: 647 **Total Expense ($000):** 83301 **Payroll Expense ($000):** 22662
Personnel: 361

TX

NOCONA—Montague County

NOCONA GENERAL HOSPITAL (450641), 100 Park Road, Zip 76255–3616;
tel. 940/825–3235, **A**10 **F**3 7 11 28 29 30 34 35 40 43 45 50 53 57 59 62 64
68 75 81 82 86 87 93 107 108 114 119 130 133 146 148 **P**5
Primary Contact: Lance Meekins, Chief Executive Officer
CFO: Lance Meekins, Chief Executive Officer
CMO: Chance Dingler, M.D., Chief Medical Officer
CHR: Paula Monkres, Administrative Assistant and Director Human Resources
Web address: www.noconageneral.com/
Control: Hospital district or authority, Government, nonfederal **Service**: General
medical and surgical

Staffed Beds: 25 **Admissions**: 511 **Census**: 7 **Outpatient Visits**: 7706
Births: 0 **Total Expense ($000)**: 8154 **Payroll Expense ($000)**: 4155
Personnel: 92

NORTH RICHLAND HILLS—Tarrant County

✠ **MEDICAL CITY NORTH HILLS (450087)**, 4401 Booth Calloway Road,
Zip 76180–7399; tel. 817/255–1000, **A**1 10 **F**3 8 12 15 17 18 20 22 24 28 29
31 34 37 39 40 41 43 45 49 53 56 57 64 70 74 75 77 78 79 81 84 85 86 87
93 98 103 107 108 110 111 115 118 119 126 130 132 135 146 148 149 **S**
HCA Healthcare, Nashville, TN
Primary Contact: Xavier Villarreal, FACHE, Chief Executive Officer
COO: Nancy L Hill, R.N., MSN, Chief Operating Officer
CFO: Nick Galt, Chief Financial Officer
CMO: John McDonald, M.D., Chief Medical Officer
CIO: Jason Sims, Facility Information Security Officer
CHR: Cynthia Dang, Vice President Human Resources
CNO: John Marker, MSN, R.N., Chief Nursing Officer
Web address: www.northhillshospital.com
Control: Partnership, Investor–owned (for–profit) **Service**: General medical and
surgical

Staffed Beds: 137 **Admissions**: 6859 **Census**: 92 **Outpatient Visits**: 56852
Births: 0 **Total Expense ($000)**: 117231 **Payroll Expense ($000)**: 45570
Personnel: 593

ODESSA—Ector County

★ **CONTINUECARE HOSPITAL AT MEDICAL CENTER (ODESSA) (452121)**,
500 West Fourth Street, 4th Floor, Zip 79761–5001; tel. 432/640–4380,
(Nonreporting) **A**10 22 **S** Community Hospital Corporation, Plano, TX
Primary Contact: Holly Powell, Administrator
Web address: www.continuecare.org/odessa//
Control: Other not–for–profit (including NFP Corporation) **Service**: Acute long–
term care hospital

Staffed Beds: 25

✠ **MEDICAL CENTER HEALTH SYSTEM (450132)**, 500 West Fourth Street,
Zip 79761–5059, Mailing Address: P O Drawer 7239, Zip 79760–7239;
tel. 432/640–4000, **A**1 2 3 5 10 **F**3 8 11 12 13 15 17 18 20 22 24 26 28 29
30 31 34 35 40 43 45 46 47 48 49 50 53 54 57 59 64 65 66 68 70 71 72 74
75 76 77 78 79 81 85 87 89 90 93 107 111 114 115 116 117 118 119 126
129 130 131 132 135 144 146 147 148 **P**6 8
Primary Contact: Rick D. Napper, Chief Executive Officer
COO: Tony Ruiz, Senior Vice President, Chief Operating Officer
CFO: Robert Abernethy, Interim Chief Financial Officer
CMO: Arun Mathews, M.D., Chief Medical Officer (Acute)
CIO: Gary Barnes, Senior Vice President, Chief Information Officer
CHR: Robbi Banks, Vice President, Human Resources
CNO: Chad Dunavan, R.N., Vice President, Chief Nursing Officer
Web address: www.mchodessa.com
Control: Hospital district or authority, Government, nonfederal **Service**: General
medical and surgical

Staffed Beds: 368 **Admissions**: 12850 **Census**: 198 **Outpatient
Visits**: 314579 **Births**: 1687 **Total Expense ($000)**: 281702 **Payroll
Expense ($000)**: 105810 **Personnel**: 1627

MEDICAL CENTER HOSPITAL See Medical Center Health System

⇑ **ODESSA REGIONAL MEDICAL CENTER (450661)**, 520 East Sixth
Street, Zip 79761–4565, Mailing Address: P.O. Box 4859, Zip 79760–4859;
tel. 432/582–8000, **A**3 5 10 21 **F**3 12 13 15 17 18 20 22 23 24 25 29 34 35
40 43 46 49 50 51 52 55 57 59 60 64 66 72 74 75 76 79 81 82 85 86 87 89
90 91 107 108 111 115 119 124 130 132 146 147 148 154 **P**8 **S** Steward
Health Care System, LLC, Dallas, TX
Primary Contact: Stacey L. Gerig, Chief Executive Officer
CIO: Jimmy Diaz, Director Information Technology
CHR: Jill Sparkman, Director Human Resources
CNO: Levi Ross Stone, R.N., Chief Nursing Officer and Chief Operating Officer
Web address: www.odessaregionalmedicalcenter.com
Control: Partnership, Investor–owned (for–profit) **Service**: General medical and
surgical

Staffed Beds: 213 **Admissions**: 6288 **Census**: 86 **Outpatient Visits**: 47716
Births: 2323 **Total Expense ($000)**: 136284 **Payroll Expense
($000)**: 42192 **Personnel**: 682

☐ **ODESSA REGIONAL MEDICAL CENTER SOUTH CAMPUS (670066)**, 900 East
4th Street, Zip 79761–5255; tel. 432/362–9900, (Nonreporting) **A**1 10
Primary Contact: Stacey L. Gerig, Chief Executive Officer
CMO: Richard Bartlett, M.D., Chief Medical Officer
Web address: www.bhcodessa.com/
Control: Partnership, Investor–owned (for–profit) **Service**: General medical and
surgical

Staffed Beds: 14

OLNEY—Young County

★ **HAMILTON HOSPITAL (451354)**, 901 West Hamilton Street, Zip 76374–1725,
Mailing Address: P.O. Box 158, Zip 76374–0158; tel. 940/564–5521, **A**10 18 **F**7
11 13 28 29 30 34 40 43 53 57 76 77 81 86 89 93 107 114 127 129 130 133
146 148
Primary Contact: Michael H. Huff, Chief Executive Officer
CFO: Coy Noles, Chief Financial Officer Consultant
CMO: Mark L Mankins, M.D., Chief of Staff
CIO: Rick Oliver, Information Technology
CHR: Amy Moore, Human Resources
CNO: Samantha Isbell, R.N., Chief Nursing Officer
Web address: www.olneyhamiltonhospital.com
Control: Hospital district or authority, Government, nonfederal **Service**: General
medical and surgical

Staffed Beds: 25 **Admissions**: 405 **Census**: 9 **Outpatient Visits**: 17172
Births: 46 **Total Expense ($000)**: 17068 **Payroll Expense ($000)**: 5369
Personnel: 135

PALACIOS—Matagorda County

PALACIOS COMMUNITY MEDICAL CENTER (451332), 311 Green Street,
Zip 77465–3213; tel. 361/972–2511, **A**10 18 **F**29 34 40 41 50 54 57 59 64 65
87 91 93 97 107 119 127 133 146 148 **P**6
Primary Contact: Barbara Hayes, Chief Executive Officer
COO: Lisa Henderson, Chief Operating Officer
CFO: Claude Manning, Chief Financial Officer
CIO: Angela Yeager, Director Information Technology
CHR: Lisa Henderson, Chief Operations Officer
CNO: Susan Easter, Chief Nursing Officer
Web address: www.palacioshospital.net/
Control: Other not–for–profit (including NFP Corporation) **Service**: General
medical and surgical

Staffed Beds: 17 **Admissions**: 107 **Census**: 1 **Outpatient Visits**: 12154
Births: 0 **Total Expense ($000)**: 4982 **Payroll Expense ($000)**: 2564
Personnel: 45

PALESTINE—Anderson County

✠ **PALESTINE REGIONAL MEDICAL CENTER (453089)**, 2900 S Loop 256,
Zip 75801–6958; tel. 903/731–1000, (Nonreporting) **A**1 **S** LifePoint Health,
Brentwood, TN
Primary Contact: Roy Finch, Chief Executive Officer
CFO: Celena Brim, Chief Financial Officer
CIO: Rebecca Chou, Directory Information Systems
CHR: Rhonda Beard, Director Human Resources
Web address: www.palestineregional.com
Control: Corporation, Investor–owned (for–profit) **Service**: Rehabilitation

Staffed Beds: 12

✠ **PALESTINE REGIONAL MEDICAL CENTER–EAST (450747)**, 2900 South Loop
256, Zip 75801–6958; tel. 903/731–1000, **A**1 10 **F**3 4 7 11 13 15 18 20 22
26 28 29 30 34 40 43 44 47 48 49 50 51 56 57 59 60 62 63 70 76 79 81 82
85 86 87 89 90 93 96 97 98 100 101 102 103 104 107 108 110 111 114 118
119 129 130 131 146 147 148 154 **S** LifePoint Health, Brentwood, TN
Primary Contact: Roy Finch, Chief Executive Officer
CFO: Celena Brim, Chief Financial Officer
CIO: Rebecca Chou, Director Information Systems
CHR: Rhonda Beard, Director Human Resources
Web address: www.palestineregional.com
Control: Partnership, Investor–owned (for–profit) **Service**: General medical and
surgical

Staffed Beds: 120 **Admissions**: 3624 **Census**: 57 **Outpatient Visits**: 65964
Births: 631 **Total Expense ($000)**: 56460 **Payroll Expense ($000)**: 27658
Personnel: 490

TX

Many Facility Codes have changed. Please refer to the AHA Guide Code Chart. © 2018 AHA Guide

PAMPA—Gray County

☒ **PAMPA REGIONAL MEDICAL CENTER (450099)**, One Medical Plaza, Zip 79065; tel. 806/665–3721, **A**1 10 20 **F**3 11 12 13 15 18 20 22 29 30 34 40 43 45 46 47 48 49 50 51 52 54 56 57 58 59 60 61 63 64 65 66 68 70 75 76 77 79 81 83 84 85 86 87 91 92 93 96 97 98 100 101 103 104 105 107 108 110 111 114 115 119 130 132 134 135 146 147 148 153 154 **P**7 **S** Prime Healthcare, Ontario, CA
Primary Contact: Edwin Leon, Chief Executive Officer
CFO: Ronald Collins, Chief Financial Officer
CMO: James Hall, M.D., Chief Medical Officer
CIO: Joy Patton, Director Information Technology
CHR: Debbie Dixon, Director Human Resources
CNO: Twilla Thomas, Chief Nursing Officer
Web address: www.prmctx.com
Control: Other not–for–profit (including NFP Corporation) **Service**: General medical and surgical

Staffed Beds: 72 Admissions: 2126 Census: 21 Outpatient Visits: 41215 Births: 182 Total Expense ($000): 40719 Payroll Expense ($000): 13202 Personnel: 256

PARIS—Lamar County

★ **CHRISTUS DUBUIS HOSPITAL OF PARIS (452082)**, 820 Clarksville Street, 6th Floor, Zip 75460–6027; tel. 903/737–3600, (Nonreporting) **A**10 **S** LHC Group, Lafayette, LA
Primary Contact: Kathie Reese, R.N., Regional Administrator and Chief Executive Officer
CFO: Michael Murray, Chief Financial Officer
CMO: Devabrata Ganguly, M.D., Medical Director
CNO: Janice Cochran, R.N., Director Patient Care
Web address: www.christusdubuis.org
Control: Church operated, Nongovernment, not–for–profit **Service**: Acute long–term care hospital

Staffed Beds: 25

☐ **PARIS REGIONAL MEDICAL CENTER (450196)**, 865 Deshong Drive, Zip 75460–9313, Mailing Address: P.O. Box 9070, Zip 75461–9070; tel. 903/785–4521, (Includes PARIS REGIONAL MEDICAL CENTER, 865 Deshong Drive, Paris, TX, Zip 75462–2097; tel. 903/785–4521) **A**1 10 19 **F**3 8 11 13 15 17 18 20 22 24 26 28 29 30 34 35 36 39 40 45 49 50 51 55 57 59 60 64 65 66 68 70 74 75 76 77 78 79 81 82 85 86 87 89 90 91 93 97 102 107 108 111 115 119 126 127 129 130 132 135 145 146 147 148 149 **P**5 **S** RCCH HealthCare Partners, Brentwood, TN
Primary Contact: Steve Hyde, Chief Executive Officer
COO: Scott B. Avery, Chief Operating Officer
CFO: Donald E McDaniel III Chief Financial Officer
CMO: Richard Bercher, M.D., Chief Medical Officer
CHR: Cheryl Perry, Executive Director Human Resources
CNO: Debra Taylor, Chief Nursing Officer
Web address: www.https://parisregionalmedical.com/
Control: Partnership, Investor–owned (for–profit) **Service**: General medical and surgical

Staffed Beds: 165 Admissions: 7264 Census: 89 Outpatient Visits: 79153 Births: 749 Total Expense ($000): 110945 Payroll Expense ($000): 39968 Personnel: 664

PASADENA—Harris County

☒ **BAYSHORE MEDICAL CENTER (450097)**, 4000 Spencer Highway, Zip 77504–1202; tel. 713/359–2000, **A**1 2 10 **F**3 8 11 12 13 15 17 18 20 22 24 26 28 29 31 34 35 40 43 45 46 49 50 51 54 56 57 59 60 64 67 70 72 74 75 76 77 78 79 81 82 84 85 90 93 96 98 100 102 103 107 108 110 111 114 115 118 119 121 123 124 126 129 130 131 132 146 147 154 **S** HCA Healthcare, Nashville, TN
Primary Contact: Jeanna Barnard, FACHE, Chief Executive Officer
CFO: John Armour, Chief Financial Officer
CIO: Clifford Ferguson, Director Information Technology and Systems
Web address: www.bayshoremedical.com
Control: Partnership, Investor–owned (for–profit) **Service**: General medical and surgical

Staffed Beds: 286 Admissions: 17133 Census: 240 Outpatient Visits: 162106 Births: 2325 Total Expense ($000): 277637 Payroll Expense ($000): 104004 Personnel: 1011

★ ⇧ **CHI ST. LUKE'S HEALTH – PATIENTS MEDICAL CENTER (670031)**, 4600 East Sam Houston Parkway South, Zip 77505–3948; tel. 713/948–7000, **A**10 21 **F**15 17 18 20 22 24 26 28 29 30 35 40 45 46 54 64 70 74 77 79 81 82 86 87 91 93 94 107 111 114 115 116 117 119 129 130 146 147 148 **S** Catholic Health Initiatives, Englewood, CO
Primary Contact: Steven Foster, Chief Executive Officer
Web address: www.stlukestexas.com
Control: Partnership, Investor–owned (for–profit) **Service**: General medical and surgical

Staffed Beds: 61 Admissions: 3814 Census: 52 Outpatient Visits: 32822 Births: 0 Total Expense ($000): 67786 Payroll Expense ($000): 25877 Personnel: 387

⇧ **PATIENTS MEDICAL CENTER** See Chi St. Luke's Health – Patients Medical Center

○ **SURGERY SPECIALTY HOSPITALS OF AMERICA (450831)**, 4301B Vista Road, Zip 77504; tel. 713/378–3000, **A**10 11 **F**3 12 29 40 68 70 75 79 81 85 107 111 119 132
Primary Contact: Eric Chan, M.D., Chief Executive Officer
COO: Hemant Khemka, Chief Operating Officer
CFO: Hemant Khemka, Chief Financial Officer
CMO: Xiao H. Li, M.D., Chief of Staff
CIO: Ringo Cheng, Director Information Technology
Web address: www.surgeryspecialty.com/
Control: Partnership, Investor–owned (for–profit) **Service**: General medical and surgical

Staffed Beds: 37 Admissions: 37 Census: 1 Outpatient Visits: 567 Births: 0 Total Expense ($000): 12165 Payroll Expense ($000): 3041 Personnel: 78

PEARLAND—Brazoria County

ENCOMPASS HEALTH REHABILITATION HOSPITAL OF PEARLAND (673066), 2121 Business Center Drive, Zip 77584–2153; tel. 346/907–3000, (Nonreporting) **A**10 **S** Encompass Health Corporation, Birmingham, AL
Primary Contact: Michael Cabiro, Chief Executive Officer
Web address: www.encompasshealth.com/locations/pearlandrehab
Control: Corporation, Investor–owned (for–profit) **Service**: Rehabilitation

Staffed Beds: 40

☒ **PEARLAND MEDICAL CENTER (670106)**, 11100 Shadow Creek Parkway, Zip 77584–7285; tel. 713/770–7000, **A**1 **F**3 15 18 20 22 26 29 31 34 35 37 40 41 45 49 50 51 57 59 68 74 75 77 78 79 81 82 85 86 87 107 108 110 111 114 119 126 130 143 146 148 **S** HCA Healthcare, Nashville, TN
Primary Contact: David S. Wagner, FACHE, Chief Executive Officer
Web address: www.pearlandmc.com
Control: Partnership, Investor–owned (for–profit) **Service**: General medical and surgical

Staffed Beds: 30 Admissions: 1987 Census: 17 Outpatient Visits: 25024 Births: 141 Total Expense ($000): 54529 Payroll Expense ($000): 15541 Personnel: 190

PEARSALL—Frio County

★ **FRIO REGIONAL HOSPITAL (450293)**, 200 South I H 35, Zip 78061–3998; tel. 830/334–3617, **A**10 **F**3 13 15 29 34 35 40 43 45 57 59 62 64 68 76 77 81 87 96 107 110 114 115 119 130 133 146 148 154 **P**5 6
Primary Contact: Andrew G. Williams, Chief Executive Officer
CMO: Oscar Garza, M.D., Chief Medical Staff
CIO: Jacob Flores, Chief Information Officer
CHR: Nancy Ortiz, Director Human Resource and Marketing
CNO: Louisa Martinez, Director of Nursing
Web address: www.frioregionalhospital.com
Control: Other not–for–profit (including NFP Corporation) **Service**: General medical and surgical

Staffed Beds: 22 Admissions: 403 Census: 4 Outpatient Visits: 25305 Births: 108 Total Expense ($000): 16785 Payroll Expense ($000): 6839 Personnel: 126

TX

Hospital, Medicare Provider Number, Address, Telephone, Approval, Facility, and Physician Codes, Health Care System

★ American Hospital Association (AHA) membership
☐ The Joint Commission accreditation
○ Healthcare Facilities Accreditation Program
◇ DNV Healthcare Inc. accreditation
⇧ Center for Improvement in Healthcare Quality Accreditation
△ Commission on Accreditation of Rehabilitation Facilities (CARF) accreditation

PECOS—Reeves County

REEVES COUNTY HOSPITAL (451377), 2323 Texas Street, Zip 79772–7338; tel. 432/447–3551, **A**10 18 **F**3 11 13 15 35 40 43 57 60 64 68 70 81 87 93 107 110 114 119 127 130 131 133 146 147 148
Primary Contact: Brenda McKinney, Chief Executive Officer
CFO: Bomi Bharucha, Chief Financial Officer
CMO: W J Bang, M.D., Chief of Staff
CHR: Nadine Smith, Director Human Resources
CNO: Faye Lease, Director of Nursing
Web address: www.reevescountyhospital.com
Control: Hospital district or authority, Government, nonfederal **Service**: General medical and surgical

Staffed Beds: 25 **Admissions**: 802 **Census**: 9 **Outpatient Visits**: 62489
Births: 135 **Total Expense ($000)**: 27666 **Payroll Expense ($000)**: 14296
Personnel: 266

PERRYTON—Ochiltree County

★ **OCHILTREE GENERAL HOSPITAL (451359)**, 3101 Garrett Drive, Zip 79070–5323; tel. 806/435–3606, **A**10 18 **F**10 11 13 15 30 35 40 43 57 59 62 63 64 69 81 85 93 107 108 114 119 127 130 133 143 146 147 **P**1
Primary Contact: Robert A. Pascasio, FACHE, Administrator and Chief Executive Officer
CFO: Debbie Blodgett, Director Fiscal Services
CMO: Rex Mann, M.D., Chief Medical Officer
CIO: Dyan Harrison, Manager Health Information
CHR: Debbie Beck, Manager Human Resource and Payroll
Web address: www.ochiltreehospital.com
Control: Hospital district or authority, Government, nonfederal **Service**: General medical and surgical

Staffed Beds: 25 **Admissions**: 460 **Census**: 7 **Outpatient Visits**: 39319
Births: 143 **Total Expense ($000)**: 16824 **Payroll Expense ($000)**: 8143
Personnel: 157

PITTSBURG—Camp County

★ **UT HEALTH PITTSBURG (451367)**, 2701 Highway 271 North, Zip 75686–1032; tel. 903/946–5000, **A**10 18 **F**3 11 12 28 29 35 40 43 45 50 53 57 59 64 68 70 75 77 81 85 87 89 92 93 97 107 108 111 115 119 127 129 130 133 **P**6 **S** Ardent Health Services, Nashville, TN
Primary Contact: James Warren. Robicheaux, FACHE, Senior Administrator
CFO: Janet Andersen, Chief Financial Officer
CMO: W R Christensen, M.D., Chief of Staff
CIO: Paula Anthony, Vice President Information Services
CHR: Kathy Shelton, Director Human Resources
CNO: Casey Mayben, Chief Nursing Officer
Web address: www.https://uthealthpittsburg.com/
Control: Other not–for–profit (including NFP Corporation) **Service**: General medical and surgical

Staffed Beds: 25 **Admissions**: 908 **Census**: 11 **Outpatient Visits**: 79014
Births: 0 **Total Expense ($000)**: 25311 **Payroll Expense ($000)**: 9601
Personnel: 203

PLAINVIEW—Hale County

ALLEGIANCE BEHAVIORAL HEALTH CENTER OF PLAINVIEW (454101), 2601 Dimmit Road, Suite 400, Zip 79072–1833; tel. 806/296–9191, **A**10 **F**29 35 56 64 98 101 103 104 149 **S** Allegiance Health Management, Shreveport, LA
Primary Contact: Angie Alexander, Chief Executive Officer
COO: Don Cameron, Chief Operating Officer
CMO: Victor A Gutierrez, M.D., Medical Director
CIO: Richard Merk, Executive Vice President
CHR: Richard Merk, Director Human Resources
Web address: www.ahmgt.com
Control: Corporation, Investor–owned (for–profit) **Service**: Psychiatric

Staffed Beds: 20 **Admissions**: 302 **Census**: 11 **Outpatient Visits**: 29798
Births: 0 **Total Expense ($000)**: 7305 **Payroll Expense ($000)**: 2081
Personnel: 68

⊠ **COVENANT HOSPITAL PLAINVIEW (450539)**, 2601 Dimmit Road, Zip 79072–1833; tel. 806/296–5531, **A**1 3 10 20 **F**3 11 12 13 15 18 29 30 32 34 35 38 40 41 43 44 45 46 48 50 51 54 56 57 59 61 64 65 68 70 75 76 77 79 80 81 85 86 87 97 107 108 110 111 114 119 127 130 131 132 135 146 147 148 149 **S** Providence St. Joseph Health, Renton, WA
Primary Contact: Robert Copeland, Interim Chief Executive Officer
COO: Mike McNutt, Assistant Administrator
CFO: Cassie Mogg, Chief Financial Officer
CMO: Sergio Lara, M.D., Chief Medical Officer
CNO: Leslie Hackett, Chief Nursing Officer
Web address: www.covenantplainview.org
Control: Other not–for–profit (including NFP Corporation) **Service**: General medical and surgical

Staffed Beds: 68 **Admissions**: 1897 **Census**: 16 **Outpatient Visits**: 83965
Births: 449 **Total Expense ($000)**: 44895 **Payroll Expense ($000)**: 13968
Personnel: 312

PLANO—Denton County

ACCEL REHABILITATION HOSPITAL OF PLANO (673055), 2301 Marsh Lane, #200, Zip 75093–8497; tel. 972/899–5510, (Nonreporting)
Primary Contact: Rick Tichenor, Chief Executive Officer
Web address: www.accelrehab.com
Control: Corporation, Investor–owned (for–profit) **Service**: Rehabilitation

Staffed Beds: 48

PLANO—Collin County

⊠ **BAYLOR REGIONAL MEDICAL CENTER AT PLANO (450890)**, 4700 Alliance Boulevard, Zip 75093–5323; tel. 469/814–2000, **A**1 2 3 5 10 **F**3 12 15 29 30 31 34 35 40 45 46 47 48 49 51 54 55 57 58 59 60 64 70 74 75 77 78 79 80 81 82 84 85 86 87 107 108 110 111 114 118 119 126 130 131 132 135 145 146 147 148 149 154 **S** Baylor Scott & White Health, Dallas, TX
Primary Contact: Jerri Garison, R.N., President
COO: Joseph C. Brown, Vice President Operations
CFO: Deanne Kindred, Vice President Finance
CMO: John Marcucci, M.D., Vice President Medical Affairs
CHR: Kriss Gamez, Director Human Resources
Web address: www.baylorhealth.com/PhysiciansLocations/Plano/Pages/Default.aspx
Control: Other not–for–profit (including NFP Corporation) **Service**: General medical and surgical

Staffed Beds: 124 **Admissions**: 6987 **Census**: 94 **Outpatient Visits**: 53128
Births: 0 **Total Expense ($000)**: 179593 **Payroll Expense ($000)**: 60961
Personnel: 644

CHILDREN'S MEDICAL CENTER PLANO (453316), 7601 Preston Road, Zip 75024–3214; tel. 469/303–7000, **A**3 5 **F**3 88 89 98 154 **S** Children's Health, Dallas, TX
Primary Contact: Jeremiah Radandt, President
CIO: Pamela Arora, Senior Vice President and Chief Information Officer
CHR: Kim Besse, Executive Vice President and Chief Human Resource Officer
CNO: Mary Stowe, Senior Vice President and Chief Nursing Officer
Web address: www.childrens.com/location–landing/locations–and–directions/childrens–health–plano
Control: Other not–for–profit (including NFP Corporation) **Service**: Children's general medical and surgical

Staffed Beds: 72 **Admissions**: 7095 **Census**: 26 **Outpatient Visits**: 171317
Births: 0 **Total Expense ($000)**: 163966 **Payroll Expense ($000)**: 48126
Personnel: 707

⊠ **ENCOMPASS HEALTH REHABILITATION HOSPITAL OF PLANO (453047)**, 2800 West 15th Street, Zip 75075–7526; tel. 972/612–9000, **A**1 10 **F**34 57 59 90 93 95 96 130 132 148 **S** Encompass Health Corporation, Birmingham, AL
Primary Contact: Brandon Tudor, Chief Executive Officer
CFO: Catrina Madkins, Controller and Chief Financial Officer
CMO: Omar Colon, M.D., Medical Director
Web address: www.healthsouthplano.com
Control: Corporation, Investor–owned (for–profit) **Service**: Rehabilitation

Staffed Beds: 83 **Admissions**: 1634 **Census**: 51 **Outpatient Visits**: 6529
Births: 0 **Total Expense ($000)**: 20518 **Payroll Expense ($000)**: 11836
Personnel: 210

⊠ ⇑ **MEDICAL CITY PLANO (450651)**, 3901 West 15th Street, Zip 75075–7738; tel. 972/596–6800, (Includes MEDICAL CITY FRISCO, 5500 Frisco Square Boulevard, Frisco, TX, Zip 75034–3305; tel. 214/618–0500; Charles Gressle, Chief Executive Officer) **A**1 2 3 10 13 21 **F**3 12 13 15 16 18 19 20 22 24 26 28 29 30 31 34 35 40 41 43 45 46 47 48 49 51 54 55 57 58 59 60 64 70 72 74 75 76 78 79 81 82 84 85 86 87 90 93 107 108 110 111 112 114 115 117 118 119 124 126 130 132 135 145 146 147 148 **P**5 **S** HCA Healthcare, Nashville, TN
Primary Contact: Charles Gressle, Chief Executive Officer
CFO: Jon Alford, Chief Financial Officer
CMO: Ann Arnold, M.D., Medical Director
CIO: Michael Gfeller, Director Information Systems
CHR: Shanna Warren, Director Human Resources
Web address: www.medicalcenterplano.com
Control: Partnership, Investor–owned (for–profit) **Service**: General medical and surgical

Staffed Beds: 442 **Admissions**: 20916 **Census**: 333 **Outpatient Visits**: 152432 **Births**: 2623 **Total Expense ($000)**: 395536 **Payroll Expense ($000)**: 129834 **Personnel**: 2014

☐ **PLANO SPECIALTY HOSPITAL (452054)**, 1621 Coit Road, Zip 75075–6141; tel. 972/758–5200, (Nonreporting) **A**1 10 **S** Concord Healthcare Group, Lakewood, NJ
Primary Contact: Wayne Cook, Chief Executive Officer
CFO: Deanna Lankford, Business Office Manager
CHR: Robbie McCranie, Director Human Resources
Web address: www.specialtyhospital–plano.com
Control: Corporation, Investor–owned (for–profit) **Service**: Acute long–term care hospital

Staffed Beds: 43

Many Facility Codes have changed. Please refer to the AHA Guide Code Chart.
© 2018 AHA Guide

PLANO—Denton County

☐ ⇑ **PLANO SURGICAL HOSPITAL**, 2301 Marsh Lane, Zip 75093–8497; tel. 972/820–2600, **A**1 21 **F**3 29 40 45 46 49 79 81 82 85 87 107 114 149 **S** Nobilis Health Corporation, Houston, TX
Primary Contact: Jay Lindsey, Chief Executive Officer
Web address: www.nobilishealth.com/our–facilities/dallas/
Control: Corporation, Investor–owned (for–profit) **Service**: Surgical

Staffed Beds: 26 **Admissions**: 194 **Census**: 1 **Outpatient Visits**: 2114
Births: 0 **Total Expense ($000)**: 46530 **Payroll Expense ($000)**: 6344
Personnel: 61

PLANO—Collin County

STAR MEDICAL CENTER, 4100 Mapleshade Lane, Zip 75093–0012; tel. 972/265–1050, (Nonreporting)
Primary Contact: Jeffrey VanHorn, Chief Executive Officer
CNO: Joyce O. Winbush, Chief Nursing Officer
Web address: www.https://starmedicalcenter.com/
Control: Partnership, Investor–owned (for–profit) **Service**: Surgical

Staffed Beds: 7

☐ **TEXAS HEALTH CENTER FOR DIAGNOSTIC & SURGERY (450891)**, 6020 West Parker Road, Suite 100, Zip 75093–8171; tel. 972/403–2700, **A**1 2 10 **F**3 29 40 45 54 64 79 81 82 85 87 107 111 115 119 126 129 149
Primary Contact: Larry Robertson, President
CFO: Douglas Browning, Chief Financial Officer
CHR: Cookie Tedder, Human Resources Manager
CNO: Ellen Baldwin, R.N., Chief Nursing Officer
Web address: www.thcds.com
Control: Partnership, Investor–owned (for–profit) **Service**: General medical and surgical

Staffed Beds: 18 **Admissions**: 706 **Census**: 4 **Outpatient Visits**: 15004
Births: 0 **Total Expense ($000)**: 58244 **Payroll Expense ($000)**: 14065
Personnel: 174

☒ **TEXAS HEALTH PRESBYTERIAN HOSPITAL PLANO (450771)**, 6200 West Parker Road, Zip 75093–8185; tel. 972/981–8000, **A**1 3 10 **F**3 12 13 15 18 20 22 24 26 28 29 30 31 34 35 37 38 40 43 44 45 46 49 50 52 53 54 55 57 58 59 60 64 65 68 70 72 74 75 76 77 78 79 81 84 85 86 87 89 93 98 104 105 107 108 110 111 114 115 118 119 126 130 131 132 134 135 141 145 146 147 148 149 150 153 **S** Texas Health Resources, Arlington, TX
Primary Contact: Joshua Floren, President
CFO: Lisa Gildon, Vice President and Chief Financial Officer
CMO: Gwen Webster, M.D., President Medical Staff
CIO: Susan Anderson, Director Information Systems
CHR: Kelly K Martin, Human Resource Officer
Web address: www.texashealth.org
Control: Other not–for–profit (including NFP Corporation) **Service**: General medical and surgical

Staffed Beds: 361 **Admissions**: 17359 **Census**: 222 **Outpatient Visits**: 98592 **Births**: 4173 **Total Expense ($000)**: 347988 **Payroll Expense ($000)**: 120480 **Personnel**: 1633

☒ **THE HEART HOSPITAL BAYLOR PLANO (670025)**, 1100 Allied Drive, Zip 75093–5348; tel. 469/814–3278, **A**1 3 5 10 **F**3 17 18 20 22 24 26 28 29 30 34 35 40 46 49 53 54 57 58 59 60 64 68 74 75 77 81 82 84 85 86 87 90 107 108 111 114 115 119 126 130 132 135 146 148 149 154
Primary Contact: Mark Valentine, President
CFO: Bryan Nichols, Chief Financial Officer
CMO: Trent Pettijohn, M.D., Esq Chief Medical Officer
CHR: Tracy Stanford, Director Human Resources
CNO: Susan K. Moats, R.N., Vice President Patient Care Services and Chief Nursing Officer
Web address: www.thehearthospitalbaylor.com
Control: Partnership, Investor–owned (for–profit) **Service**: Heart

Staffed Beds: 116 **Admissions**: 4924 **Census**: 80 **Outpatient Visits**: 29090
Births: 0 **Total Expense ($000)**: 228097 **Payroll Expense ($000)**: 72149
Personnel: 748

WELLBRIDGE HEALTHCARE GREATER DALLAS (454130), 4301 Mapleshade Lane, Zip 75093–0010; tel. 972/596–5445, **F**98 103
Primary Contact: John Sannuto, Chief Executive Officer
Web address: www.wellbridgedallas.com/
Control: Partnership, Investor–owned (for–profit) **Service**: Psychiatric

Staffed Beds: 48 **Admissions**: 467 **Census**: 23 **Outpatient Visits**: 0
Births: 0 **Total Expense ($000)**: 4621 **Payroll Expense ($000)**: 3557
Personnel: 78

PORT ARTHUR—Jefferson County

DUBUIS HOSPITAL OF PORT ARTHUR See Christus Dubuis Hospital of Port Arthur

⇑ **THE MEDICAL CENTER OF SOUTHEAST TEXAS (450518)**, 2555 Jimmy Johnson Boulevard, Zip 77640–2007; tel. 409/724–7389, **A**10 21 **F**3 8 11 12 13 15 17 18 20 22 24 26 28 29 30 34 35 40 43 44 45 47 49 50 56 57 59 64 70 72 74 76 77 78 79 81 82 85 86 87 89 90 91 92 93 94 98 101 102 103 104 105 107 108 110 111 114 115 119 121 129 130 132 135 146 147 148 153 154 **P**2 **S** Steward Health Care System, LLC, Dallas, TX
Primary Contact: Carl Bo"". Beaudry, President
COO: Chris McMahon, Chief Operating Officer
CFO: Jason R. Miller, Chief Financial Officer
CMO: Ryan McHugh, M.D., Chief of Staff
CIO: Bryan Hebert, Director Information Systems
CHR: Carol Hebert, Director Human Resources
CNO: Debbie Vaughn, Chief Nursing Officer
Web address: www.medicalcentersetexas.com
Control: Partnership, Investor–owned (for–profit) **Service**: General medical and surgical

Staffed Beds: 172 **Admissions**: 8744 **Census**: 115 **Outpatient Visits**: 79161 **Births**: 1411 **Total Expense ($000)**: 134559 **Payroll Expense ($000)**: 51562 **Personnel**: 814

PORT LAVACA—Calhoun County

★ **MEMORIAL MEDICAL CENTER (451356)**, 815 North Virginia Street, Zip 77979–3025, Mailing Address: P.O. Box 25, Zip 77979–0025; tel. 361/552–6713, **A**10 18 **F**3 11 13 15 18 29 30 32 34 35 40 43 44 45 46 49 50 57 59 64 65 68 70 75 76 77 78 79 81 84 85 86 87 93 107 108 111 115 118 119 127 129 130 132 133 134 135 146 147 148
Primary Contact: Jason Anglin, Chief Executive Officer
COO: Roshanda Gray, Assistant Administrator
CFO: Diane C. Moore, Chief Financial Officer
CMO: Jeannine Griffin, M.D., Chief of Staff
CIO: Adam Besio, Chief Information Officer
CNO: Erin R Clevenger, Chief Nursing Officer and Director of Quality
Web address: www.mmcportlavaca.com
Control: County, Government, nonfederal **Service**: General medical and surgical

Staffed Beds: 25 **Admissions**: 932 **Census**: 10 **Outpatient Visits**: 65741
Births: 96 **Total Expense ($000)**: 26306 **Payroll Expense ($000)**: 9783
Personnel: 198

QUANAH—Hardeman County

HARDEMAN COUNTY MEMORIAL HOSPITAL (451352), 402 Mercer Street, Zip 79252–4026, Mailing Address: P.O. Box 90, Zip 79252–0090; tel. 940/663–2795, **A**10 18 **F**28 29 34 40 43 50 56 59 64 75 77 93 100 101 104 107 127 130 133 149 153 **P**5
Primary Contact: Dave Clark, FACHE, Interim Chief Executive Officer
CFO: Tracy Betts, Chief Financial Officer
CMO: Kevin Lane, D.O., Chief of Staff
CNO: Dennis Thomas, Chief Nursing Officer
Web address: www.hcmhosp.com/
Control: Hospital district or authority, Government, nonfederal **Service**: General medical and surgical

Staffed Beds: 18 **Admissions**: 222 **Census**: 3 **Outpatient Visits**: 18403
Births: 0 **Total Expense ($000)**: 8767 **Payroll Expense ($000)**: 3582
Personnel: 96

QUITMAN—Wood County

★ **UT HEALTH QUITMAN (451380)**, 117 Winnsboro Street, Zip 75783–2144, Mailing Address: P.O. Box 1000, Zip 75783–1000; tel. 903/763–6300, **A**10 18 **F**3 11 15 29 30 35 40 43 45 50 57 59 64 65 68 79 81 85 87 107 108 110 111 115 119 127 129 130 133 **P**7 **S** Ardent Health Services, Nashville, TN
Primary Contact: Patrick Swindle, Administrator
CFO: Janet Andersen, Chief Financial Officer
CHR: William Henry, Director Human Resources
CNO: Allicia Settles, Chief Nursing Officer
Web address: www.https://uthealthquitman.com/
Control: Other not–for–profit (including NFP Corporation) **Service**: General medical and surgical

Staffed Beds: 25 **Admissions**: 955 **Census**: 12 **Outpatient Visits**: 55098
Births: 0 **Total Expense ($000)**: 27382 **Payroll Expense ($000)**: 8052
Personnel: 134

TX

RANKIN—Upton County

★ **RANKIN COUNTY HOSPITAL DISTRICT (451329)**, 1105 Elizabeth Street,
Zip 79778, Mailing Address: P.O. Box 327, Zip 79778–0327; tel. 432/693–2443,
A10 18 **F**3 7 34 35 40 50 53 54 55 56 57 59 64 65 66 68 75 86 87 93 97 102
107 119 130 131 133 135 147 148 **P**6
Primary Contact: Jim Horton, Chief Executive Officer
CFO: Tami Burks, Comptroller
CMO: Thomas J Curvin, M.D., Chief of Staff
Web address: www.rankincountyhospital.com/
Control: Hospital district or authority, Government, nonfederal **Service**: General
medical and surgical

Staffed Beds: 14 **Admissions**: 32 **Census**: 1 **Outpatient Visits**: 9195
Births: 0 **Total Expense ($000)**: 11905 **Payroll Expense ($000)**: 5408
Personnel: 75

REFUGIO—Refugio County

REFUGIO COUNTY MEMORIAL HOSPITAL (451317), 107 Swift Street,
Zip 78377–2425; tel. 361/526–2321, **A**10 18 **F**3 7 29 40 43 57 61 64 75 81
86 87 93 97 107 119 127 133 **P**6
Primary Contact: Horace Whitt, Chief Executive Officer and Chief Operating Officer
Web address: www.refugiohospital.com/
Control: Hospital district or authority, Government, nonfederal **Service**: General
medical and surgical

Staffed Beds: 20 **Admissions**: 93 **Census**: 1 **Outpatient Visits**: 20812
Births: 0 **Total Expense ($000)**: 13562 **Payroll Expense ($000)**: 5469
Personnel: 126

RICHARDSON—Collin County

⇑ **EMINENT MEDICAL CENTER**, 1351 West President George Bush Hwy,
Zip 75080; tel. 469/910–8800, **A**21 **F**3 29 40 75 77 79 81 85 92 149 **P**2
Primary Contact: Ryan Gehrke, Chief Executive Officer
CNO: Erin Baker, Chief Nursing Officer
Web address: www.eminentmedicalcenter.com
Control: Partnership, Investor–owned (for–profit) **Service**: Surgical

Staffed Beds: 5 **Admissions**: 74 **Census**: 1 **Outpatient Visits**: 517 **Births**: 0
Total Expense ($000): 8267 **Payroll Expense ($000)**: 2587 **Personnel**: 35

⊠ **ENCOMPASS HEALTH REHABILITATION HOSPITAL OF RICHARDSON
(673029)**, 3351 Waterview Parkway, Zip 75080–1449; tel. 972/398–5700, **A**1
10 **F**3 29 90 93 96 148 149 **S** Encompass Health Corporation, Birmingham, AL
Primary Contact: Brent Yates, Chief Executive Officer
CMO: Richard Jones, M.D., Medical Director
CNO: Pam Smith, Chief Nursing Officer
Web address: www.relianthcp.com
Control: Corporation, Investor–owned (for–profit) **Service**: Rehabilitation

Staffed Beds: 50 **Admissions**: 1288 **Census**: 42 **Outpatient Visits**: 0
Births: 0 **Total Expense ($000)**: 18855 **Payroll Expense ($000)**: 9546
Personnel: 139

⊠ **METHODIST RICHARDSON MEDICAL CENTER (450537)**, 2831 East President
George Bush Highway, Zip 75082–3561; tel. 469/204–1000, **A**1 2 10 **F**3 5 11
13 15 18 20 22 24 29 30 31 34 35 38 40 45 46 49 54 55 56 57 59 64 65 68
70 72 74 75 76 77 78 79 81 82 85 86 87 93 97 98 100 101 102 103 104 105
107 108 109 110 111 112 115 116 117 119 120 121 123 124 126 129 130
131 132 135 146 147 148 153 **P**5 **S** Methodist Health System, Dallas, TX
Primary Contact: E. Kenneth. Hutchenrider Jr, FACHE, President
COO: Robert Simpson, Vice President Operations
CFO: Amy Bodwell, Vice President Finance
CMO: Mark Smith, M.D., Chief Medical Officer
CIO: Pamela McNutt, Senior Vice President and Chief Information Officer
CHR: Chris Loyd, Director Human Resources
CNO: Irene T Strejc, M.P.H., R.N., Vice President, Nursing
Web address: www.methodisthealthsystem.org/richardson
Control: Other not–for–profit (including NFP Corporation) **Service**: General
medical and surgical

Staffed Beds: 266 **Admissions**: 11040 **Census**: 157 **Outpatient
Visits**: 87443 **Births**: 1675 **Total Expense ($000)**: 222326 **Payroll Expense
($000)**: 90551 **Personnel**: 1059

RICHMOND—Fort Bend County

☐ **OAKBEND MEDICAL CENTER (450330)**, 1705 Jackson Street,
Zip 77469–3289; tel. 281/341–3000, (Includes HOSPITAL FOR SURGICAL
EXCELLENCE, 1211 Highway 6, Suite 70, Sugar Land, TX, Zip 77478–4940;
tel. 281/238–3900; Joe Freudenberger, Chief Executive Officer; OAKBEND
MEDICAL CENTER WILLIAMS WAY CAMPUS, 22003 Southwest Freeway, Richmond,
TX, Zip 77469–7003; tel. 281/341–2000; Joe Freudenberger, Chief Executive
Officer) (Total facility includes 36 beds in nursing home–type unit) **A**1 10 **F**3 8 13
15 18 20 22 24 26 28 29 30 34 35 40 43 45 46 48 49 50 51 53 56 57 59 60
70 72 74 75 76 77 78 79 81 85 87 93 97 98 103 107 108 110 111 114 115
119 128 129 130 131 146 147 148 **P**6
Primary Contact: Joe Freudenberger, Chief Executive Officer
CFO: Rodney Lenfant, Chief Financial Officer
CMO: Douglas Thibodeaux, M.D., Chief Medical Officer
CIO: Tim McCarty, Chief Information Officer
CHR: Eileen Gamboa, Director Human Resources
Web address: www.oakbendmedcenter.org
Control: Hospital district or authority, Government, nonfederal **Service**: General
medical and surgical

Staffed Beds: 200 **Admissions**: 6570 **Census**: 84 **Outpatient Visits**: 82618
Births: 1603 **Total Expense ($000)**: 191728 **Payroll Expense
($000)**: 53736 **Personnel**: 775

WESTPARK SPRINGS (454131), 6902 South Peek Road, Zip 77407;
tel. 832/532–8107, (Nonreporting) **S** Springstone, Louisville, KY
Primary Contact: Colleen McCammon, Chief Executive Officer
Web address: www.westparksprings.com/why–westpark–springs/
Control: Other not–for–profit (including NFP Corporation) **Service**: Psychiatric

Staffed Beds: 72

RIO GRANDE CITY—Starr County

★ **STARR COUNTY MEMORIAL HOSPITAL (450654)**, 2753 Hospital
Court, Zip 78582–6859, Mailing Address: P.O. Box 78, Zip 78582–0078;
tel. 956/487–5561, **A**10 20 **F**7 11 13 15 29 34 35 40 43 45 46 50 57 59 64
65 66 68 75 76 81 89 107 111 115 119 121 130 135 145 148 **P**5
Primary Contact: Thalia H. Munoz, R.N., MS, Chief Executive Officer
CFO: Rafael Olivares, Controller
CHR: Amaro Salinas, Assistant Administrator and Human Resource Officer
CNO: Mario Segura, Director of Nursing
Web address: www.starrcountyhospital.com
Control: Hospital district or authority, Government, nonfederal **Service**: General
medical and surgical

Staffed Beds: 47 **Admissions**: 1202 **Census**: 11 **Outpatient Visits**: 43003
Births: 173 **Total Expense ($000)**: 30064 **Payroll Expense ($000)**: 13947
Personnel: 267

ROCKDALE—Milam County

⇑ **ROCKDALE HOSPITAL (451357)**, 1700 Brazos Street, Zip 76567–2517,
Mailing Address: Drawer 1010, Zip 76567–1010; tel. 512/446–4500, **A**10 18
21 **F**3 15 18 20 22 26 29 33 34 40 43 45 46 47 50 54 56 57 59 64 65 68 74
75 77 78 79 81 82 84 85 87 91 92 93 97 107 108 110 111 114 116 117 119
127 128 129 130 131 133 135 146 147 148 149
Primary Contact: Jeffrey Madison, FACHE, Chief Executive Officer
CMO: John Weed, M.D., III Medical Director
CHR: Crystal Foley, Director Human Resources
Web address: www.lrhealthcare.com
Control: Partnership, Investor–owned (for–profit) **Service**: General medical and
surgical

Staffed Beds: 21 **Admissions**: 231 **Census**: 3 **Outpatient Visits**: 144029
Births: 0 **Total Expense ($000)**: 158908 **Payroll Expense ($000)**: 35794
Personnel: 306

ROCKWALL—Rockwall County

⇑ **BAYLOR EMERGENCY MEDICAL CENTERS – ROCKWALL (670097)**, 1975
Alpha Drive Suite 100, Zip 75087–4951; tel. 214/294–6200, **A**10 21 **F**3 40 107
119 149 **P**5 **S** Emerus, The Woodlands, TX
Primary Contact: Kyle Kirkpatrick, Chief Executive Officer
Web address: www.bayloremc.com/rockwall
Control: Corporation, Investor–owned (for–profit) **Service**: General medical and
surgical

Staffed Beds: 8 **Admissions**: 80 **Census**: 1 **Outpatient Visits**: 11589
Births: 0 **Total Expense ($000)**: 8398 **Payroll Expense ($000)**: 2380
Personnel: 42

TEXAS HEALTH PRESBYTERIAN HOSPITAL OF ROCKWALL (670044), 3150 Horizon Road, Zip 75032–7805; tel. 469/698–1000, **A**1 3 10 **F**3 12 13 15 29 30 34 35 40 45 46 47 49 50 54 68 70 75 76 77 79 81 82 84 85 87 107 108 110 111 115 119 126 130 131 146 147
Primary Contact: Cynthia K. Perrin, FACHE, R.N., President and Chief Executive Officer
CFO: Jason Linscott, CPA, Chief Financial Officer
CMO: Gary Bonacquisti, M.D., Chief Medical Officer
CNO: Tami Hawkins, R.N., MSN, Vice President Patient Care and Chief Nursing Officer
Web address: www.phrtexas.com
Control: Corporation, Investor–owned (for–profit) **Service**: General medical and surgical

Staffed Beds: 61 **Admissions:** 4080 **Census:** 36 **Outpatient Visits:** 52783 **Births:** 749 **Total Expense ($000):** 100019 **Payroll Expense ($000):** 35053 **Personnel:** 500

ROTAN—Fisher County

FISHER COUNTY HOSPITAL DISTRICT (451313), 774 State Highway 70 North, Zip 79546–6918, Mailing Address: P O Drawer 'F', Zip 79546–4019; tel. 325/735–2256, **A**10 18 **F**7 28 32 34 35 40 43 50 53 56 57 59 64 66 75 93 97 107 119 127 133 **P**6
Primary Contact: Leanne Martinez, Chief Executive Officer and Administrator
CFO: Debbie Hull, Chief Financial Officer
CMO: Joseph Lampley, D.O., Chief of Staff
CHR: Teresa Terry, Director Human Resource, Payroll
CNO: D'Linda Benham, Director of Nursing
Web address: www.fishercountyhospital.com
Control: Hospital district or authority, Government, nonfederal **Service**: General medical and surgical

Staffed Beds: 14 **Admissions:** 138 **Census:** 2 **Outpatient Visits:** 16950 **Births:** 0 **Total Expense ($000):** 9372 **Payroll Expense ($000):** 4246 **Personnel:** 70

ROUND ROCK—Williamson County

BAYLOR SCOTT & WHITE MEDICAL CENTER – ROUND ROCK (670034), 300 University Boulevard, Zip 78665–1032; tel. 512/509–0100, (Includes BAYLOR SCOTT & WHITE MEDICAL CENTER – LAKEWAY, 100 Medical Parkway, Lakeway, TX, Zip 78738–5621; tel. 512/571–5000; Philippe Bochaton, President) **A**1 3 10 **F**3 11 13 15 18 20 22 24 28 29 30 34 35 36 40 45 46 47 49 50 51 54 56 58 60 62 63 65 68 72 74 75 76 78 79 81 82 84 85 87 89 91 92 93 97 100 107 108 110 111 114 115 116 117 119 126 129 130 132 133 135 143 146 147 148 149 154 **S** Baylor Scott & White Health, Dallas, TX
Primary Contact: Jay Fox, President
COO: Joseph C. Brown, Vice President Operations
CFO: Jason Cole, Regional Chief Financial Officer
CMO: Rob Watson, M.D., Chief Medical Officer
CIO: Matthew Chambers, Chief Information Officer
CHR: Mark A. Sherry, Regional Director Human Resource Strategic Services, Austin/Round Rock Region
CNO: Leslie Gembol, MSN, R.N., Chief Nursing Officer
Web address: www.sw.org
Control: Other not–for–profit (including NFP Corporation) **Service**: General medical and surgical

Staffed Beds: 173 **Admissions:** 9082 **Census:** 87 **Outpatient Visits:** 605954 **Births:** 751 **Total Expense ($000):** 273103 **Payroll Expense ($000):** 75408 **Personnel:** 1328

ENCOMPASS HEALTH REHABILITATION HOSPITAL OF ROUND ROCK (673032), 1400 Hester's Crossing, Zip 78681–8025; tel. 512/244–4400, (Total facility includes 25 beds in nursing home–type unit) **A**1 10 **F**3 29 90 96 128 130 148 149 150 **S** Encompass Health Corporation, Birmingham, AL
Primary Contact: Jack Boggess, Chief Executive Officer
CFO: Joe Griffin, Controller
CHR: Amelia Leudecke, Director Human Resources
CNO: Stephanie Guerin, Chief Nursing Officer
Web address: www.healthsouthroundrock.com/
Control: Corporation, Investor–owned (for–profit) **Service**: Rehabilitation

Staffed Beds: 75 **Admissions:** 1925 **Census:** 69 **Outpatient Visits:** 1285 **Births:** 0 **Total Expense ($000):** 22407 **Payroll Expense ($000):** 12289 **Personnel:** 171

SETON MEDICAL CENTER WILLIAMSON (670041), 201 Seton Parkway, Zip 78665–8000; tel. 512/324–4000, **A**1 2 3 10 **F**3 11 12 13 18 20 22 24 26 28 29 30 35 37 40 41 43 45 46 47 48 49 60 64 68 70 74 76 77 79 81 85 87 92 100 107 108 109 111 114 115 116 117 118 119 120 126 130 131 132 146 147 148 149 154 **P**3 8 **S** Ascension Healthcare, Saint Louis, MO
Primary Contact: Katherine Henderson, President and Chief Executive Officer
CFO: Douglas D Waite, Senior Vice President and Chief Financial Officer
CMO: Hugh V Gilmore, M.D., Vice President Medical Affairs
CIO: Gerry Lewis, Chief Information Officer
CHR: Thomas Wilken, Vice President Human Resources
Web address: www.seton.net/williamson
Control: Church operated, Nongovernment, not–for–profit **Service**: General medical and surgical

Staffed Beds: 126 **Admissions:** 7342 **Census:** 87 **Outpatient Visits:** 57070 **Births:** 347 **Total Expense ($000):** 155230 **Payroll Expense ($000):** 40680 **Personnel:** 677

ST. DAVID'S ROUND ROCK MEDICAL CENTER (450718), 2400 Round Rock Avenue, Zip 78681–4097; tel. 512/341–1000, **A**1 2 5 10 **F**3 12 13 15 18 20 22 24 26 28 29 30 31 34 35 37 40 43 45 49 54 64 70 72 74 76 77 78 79 80 81 85 87 90 93 102 107 108 110 111 115 116 117 119 124 126 130 132 135 146 147 149 152 154 **P**3 6 **S** HCA Healthcare, Nashville, TN
Primary Contact: Jeremy Barclay, Chief Executive Officer
COO: Tad Hatton, Chief Operating Officer
CFO: Cindy Sexton, Chief Financial Officer
CHR: Amy Noak, Director Human Resources
Web address: www.stdavids.com
Control: Other not–for–profit (including NFP Corporation) **Service**: General medical and surgical

Staffed Beds: 171 **Admissions:** 8772 **Census:** 112 **Outpatient Visits:** 64824 **Births:** 1694 **Total Expense ($000):** 163833 **Payroll Expense ($000):** 51570 **Personnel:** 789

ROWLETT—Rockwall County

BAYLOR SCOTT & WHITE MEDICAL CENTER – LAKE POINTE (450742), 6800 Scenic Drive, Zip 75088–4552, Mailing Address: P.O. Box 1550, Zip 75030–1550; tel. 972/412–2273, **A**1 10 **F**3 12 13 15 18 20 22 24 28 29 30 34 35 40 43 45 46 49 50 53 54 57 59 64 65 70 72 73 74 75 76 77 78 79 81 82 84 85 86 87 93 107 108 110 111 114 115 118 119 120 121 124 126 129 130 131 132 146 147 148 149 154 **S** Baylor Scott & White Health, Dallas, TX
Primary Contact: Donas Cole, FACHE, President
COO: Benson Chacko, Vice President, Operations
CMO: Larry Dencklau, D.O., Chief of Staff
CIO: Mark Slater, Director Information Systems
Web address: www.lakepointemedical.com
Control: Corporation, Investor–owned (for–profit) **Service**: General medical and surgical

Staffed Beds: 112 **Admissions:** 8071 **Census:** 81 **Outpatient Visits:** 106079 **Births:** 1771 **Total Expense ($000):** 138528 **Payroll Expense ($000):** 42019 **Personnel:** 701

RUSK—Cherokee County

RUSK STATE HOSPITAL (454009), 805 North Dickinson, Zip 75785–2333, Mailing Address: P.O. Box 318, Zip 75785–0318; tel. 903/683–3421, **A**1 3 10 **F**3 30 39 44 50 68 75 77 86 87 96 98 103 106 130 135 146 148 149 **P**6 **S** Texas Department of State Health Services, Austin, TX
Primary Contact: Brenda Slaton, Superintendent
COO: Lynda Roberson, Senior Program Director
CFO: Rhonda Transier, Financial Officer
CMO: Joe Bates, M.D., Clinical Director
CHR: Kendra Brown, Job Requisition Coordinator
Web address: www.dshs.state.tx.us/mhhospitals/RuskSH/default.shtm
Control: State, Government, nonfederal **Service**: Psychiatric

Staffed Beds: 262 **Admissions:** 283 **Census:** 245 **Outpatient Visits:** 0 **Births:** 0 **Total Expense ($000):** 126915 **Payroll Expense ($000):** 37465 **Personnel:** 946

TX

Hospital, Medicare Provider Number, Address, Telephone, Approval, Facility, and Physician Codes, Health Care System

★ American Hospital Association (AHA) membership ○ Healthcare Facilities Accreditation Program ⇑ Center for Improvement in Healthcare Quality Accreditation
☐ The Joint Commission accreditation ◇ DNV Healthcare Inc. accreditation △ Commission on Accreditation of Rehabilitation Facilities (CARF) accreditation

SAN ANGELO—Tom Green County

☐ **RIVER CREST HOSPITAL (454064)**, 1636 Hunters Glen Road, Zip 76901–5016; tel. 325/949–5722, **A**1 10 **F**4 5 29 64 87 98 99 100 101 102 103 104 105 130 132 151 152 153 **S** Universal Health Services, Inc., King of Prussia, PA
Primary Contact: Juana Giralt, Interim Chief Executive Officer
CFO: Juana Giralt, Chief Financial Officer
CMO: Raymond Mays, M.D., Medical Director
CHR: Lydia Cardenas, Director Human Resources
CNO: Debra Millsap, Director of Nursing
Web address: www.rivercresthospital.com
Control: Corporation, Investor–owned (for–profit) **Service**: Psychiatric

Staffed Beds: 80 **Admissions**: 3193 **Census**: 52 **Outpatient Visits**: 2575
Births: 0 **Total Expense ($000)**: 12953 **Payroll Expense ($000)**: 6441
Personnel: 141

☒ **SAN ANGELO COMMUNITY MEDICAL CENTER (450340)**, 3501 Knickerbocker Road, Zip 76904–7698; tel. 325/949–9511, **A**1 10 **F**3 8 11 13 15 18 20 22 24 26 28 29 30 31 34 35 37 40 43 45 49 51 53 54 57 59 60 63 64 68 70 72 74 75 76 77 78 79 81 82 85 89 93 107 108 110 111 115 118 119 126 129 130 131 135 144 145 146 147 148 **P**8 **S** Community Health Systems, Inc., Franklin, TN
Primary Contact: Buddy Daniels, Chief Executive Officer
CFO: Steven Ewing, Chief Financial Officer
CHR: Lisa Bibb, Director Human Resources
Web address: www.sacmc.com
Control: Partnership, Investor–owned (for–profit) **Service**: General medical and surgical

Staffed Beds: 131 **Admissions**: 4569 **Census**: 50 **Outpatient Visits**: 72886
Births: 953 **Total Expense ($000)**: 97717 **Payroll Expense ($000)**: 30983
Personnel: 605

★ **SHANNON MEDICAL CENTER (450571)**, 120 East Harris Street, Zip 76903–5976, Mailing Address: P.O. Box 1879, Zip 76902–1879; tel. 325/653–6741, (Includes SHANNON MEDICAL CENTER– ST. JOHN'S CAMPUS, 2018 Pulliam Street, San Angelo, TX, Zip 76905–5197; tel. 325/659–7100; Bryan Horner, President and Chief Executive Officer) (Total facility includes 21 beds in nursing home–type unit) **A**3 5 10 22 **F**3 7 8 11 13 15 18 20 22 24 26 28 29 30 31 32 34 35 37 38 40 43 44 45 47 48 49 50 51 53 54 56 57 58 59 60 61 62 64 68 70 71 72 73 74 75 76 77 78 79 80 81 82 84 85 86 87 89 90 92 93 94 96 98 100 101 102 107 108 110 111 114 115 117 119 126 128 130 132 145 146 147 148 149 **P**6
Primary Contact: Shane Plymell, Chief Executive Officer
COO: Pamela Bradshaw, Vice President, Chief Operating Officer and Chief Nursing Officer
CFO: Staci Wetz, Chief Financial Officer
CMO: Irvin Zeitler, D.O., Vice President Medical Affairs
CIO: Tom Perkins, Chief Information Officer
CHR: Teresa Morgan, Assistant Vice President Human Resources
CNO: Pamela Bradshaw, Vice President, Chief Operating Officer and Chief Nursing Officer
Web address: www.shannonhealth.com
Control: Other not–for–profit (including NFP Corporation) **Service**: General medical and surgical

Staffed Beds: 310 **Admissions**: 13047 **Census**: 182 **Outpatient Visits**: 113128 **Births**: 1060 **Total Expense ($000)**: 277495 **Payroll Expense ($000)**: 100596 **Personnel**: 1642

SAN ANTONIO—Bexar County

☐ **ACUITY HOSPITAL OF SOUTH TEXAS (452040)**, 718 Lexington Avenue, Zip 78212–4768; tel. 210/572–4600, **A**1 10 **F**1 3 29 40 45 75 85 87 91 107 119 148 149 **S** AcuityHealthcare, LP, Charlotte, NC
CFO: Merald Manigault, Chief Financial Officer
CMO: Aamir Malik, M.D., Chief Medical Officer
CHR: Barbie Gordner, Director Human Resources
Web address: www.southtexas.acuityhealthcare.net/
Control: Corporation, Investor–owned (for–profit) **Service**: Acute long–term care hospital

Staffed Beds: 30 **Admissions**: 319 **Census**: 19 **Outpatient Visits**: 3
Births: 0 **Total Expense ($000)**: 15377 **Payroll Expense ($000)**: 6596
Personnel: 114

AMG SPECIALTY HOSPITAL, 718 Lexington Avenue, Zip 78212–4768; tel. 210/572–4600, (Nonreporting) **S** AMG Integrated Healthcare Management, Lafayette, LA
Primary Contact: Melissa Low, Chief Executive Officer
Control: Partnership, Investor–owned (for–profit) **Service**: Acute long–term care hospital

Staffed Beds: 30

⇑ **BAPTIST EMERGENCY HOSPITAL (670078)**, 16088 San Pedro, Zip 78232–2249; tel. 210/402–4092, (Includes BAPTIST EMERGENCY HOSPITAL – HAUSMAN, 8230 North 1604 West, San Antonio, TX, Zip 78249; tel. 210/572–8885; David Mitchell, Chief Executive Officer; BAPTIST EMERGENCY HOSPITAL – OVERLOOK, 25615 US Highway 281 North, San Antonio, TX, Zip 78258–7135; tel. 210/572–2911; David Mitchell, Chief Executive Officer; BAPTIST EMERGENCY HOSPITAL – SCHERTZ, 16977 Interstate 35 North, Schertz, TX, Zip 78154–1466; tel. 210/572–8400; Sandra Diaz, Administrator; BAPTIST EMERGENCY HOSPITAL – WESTOVER HILLS, 10811 Town Center Drive, San Antonio, TX, Zip 78251–4585; tel. 210/572–0911; David Mitchell, Chief Executive Officer) **A**10 21 **F**3 40 41 75 87 107 119 149 **P**5 **S** Emerus, The Woodlands, TX
Primary Contact: David Mitchell, Interim Chief Executive Officer
Web address: www.baptistemergencyhospital.com
Control: Corporation, Investor–owned (for–profit) **Service**: General medical and surgical

Staffed Beds: 30 **Admissions**: 964 **Census**: 6 **Outpatient Visits**: 109500
Births: 0 **Total Expense ($000)**: 45081 **Payroll Expense ($000)**: 12839
Personnel: 323

★ △ ⇑ **BAPTIST MEDICAL CENTER (450058)**, 111 Dallas Street, Zip 78205–1230; tel. 210/297–7000, (Includes MISSION TRAIL BAPTIST HOSPITAL, 3333 Research Plaza, San Antonio, TX, Zip 78235–5154; tel. 210/297–3000; Eric Schmacker, President; NORTH CENTRAL BAPTIST HOSPITAL, 520 Madison Oak Drive, San Antonio, TX, Zip 78258–3912; tel. 210/297–4000; NORTHEAST BAPTIST HOSPITAL, 8811 Village Drive, San Antonio, TX, Zip 78217–5440; tel. 210/297–2000; J Phillip Young, FACHE, Chief Executive Officer; ST. LUKE'S BAPTIST HOSPITAL, 7930 Floyd Curl Drive, San Antonio, TX, Zip 78229–0100; tel. 210/297–5000; John E Knox, FACHE, Chief Executive Officer) **A**2 3 5 7 10 21 **F**3 11 12 13 14 15 17 18 19 20 22 24 26 28 29 30 31 35 37 38 40 41 43 44 45 47 50 54 55 56 57 59 60 64 65 68 70 72 73 74 75 77 78 79 80 81 82 85 86 87 88 90 91 92 93 95 96 98 101 102 103 107 108 111 114 115 116 117 119 124 126 129 130 132 135 145 146 147 148 149 **P**8 **S** TENET Healthcare Corporation, Dallas, TX
Primary Contact: Matt Stone, President and Chief Executive Officer
COO: Sandy Ethridge, Interim Chief Operating Officer
CIO: Gary Davis, Vice President Information Systems
CNO: Nelson Tuazon, R.N., Chief Nursing Officer
Web address: www.baptisthealthsystem.com
Control: Partnership, Investor–owned (for–profit) **Service**: General medical and surgical

Staffed Beds: 1580 **Admissions**: 64229 **Census**: 785 **Outpatient Visits**: 437892 **Births**: 10731 **Total Expense ($000)**: 896454 **Payroll Expense ($000)**: 323842 **Personnel**: 5384

☒ **CHRISTUS SANTA ROSA HEALTH SYSTEM (450237)**, 333 North Santa Rosa Street, Zip 78207–3108, Mailing Address: 100 NE Loop 410 Suite 800, Zip 78216–4749; tel. 210/704–2000, (Includes CHILDREN'S HOSPITAL OF SAN ANTONIO, 333 North Santa Rosa Street, San Antonio, TX, Zip 78207; tel. 210/704–2011; Cris Daskevich, Chief Executive Officer; CHRISTUS SANTA ROSA HOSPITAL – ALAMO HEIGHTS, 403 Treeline Park Building, San Antonio, TX, Zip 78209–2042; tel. 216/704–2011; Julie Seale, Administrator; CHRISTUS SANTA ROSA HOSPITAL – NEW BRAUNFELS, 600 North Union Avenue, New Braunfels, TX, Zip 78130–4191; tel. 830/606–9111; Jim D Wesson, President and Administrator; CHRISTUS SANTA ROSA–MEDICAL CENTER, 2827 Babcock Road, San Antonio, TX, Zip 78229–4813; tel. 210/705–6300; Ian Thompson Jr, M.D., President) (Nonreporting) **A**1 3 5 10 **S** CHRISTUS Health, Irving, TX
Primary Contact: Dean Alexander, President and Chief Executive Officer
CFO: Linda Kirks, Vice President and Chief Financial Officer
CMO: Kenneth Davis, M.D., Chief Medical Officer
CHR: Crystal H Kohanke, Group Vice President, Human Resources
CNO: Patty Toney, R.N., MSN, Chief Nurse Executive
Web address: www.christussantarosa.org
Control: Church operated, Nongovernment, not–for–profit **Service**: General medical and surgical

Staffed Beds: 766

☐ **CLARITY CHILD GUIDANCE CENTER**, 8535 Tom Slick, Zip 78229–3363; tel. 210/616–0300, **A**1 3 5 **F**29 98 99 101 102 104 105 106 130
Primary Contact: Frederick W. Hines, President and Chief Executive Officer
CFO: Michael Bernick, Executive Vice President and Chief Financial Officer
CMO: Soad Michelson, M.D., Senior Medical Director
CHR: Gina Massey, Vice President Human Resources
CNO: Carol Carver, MSN, R.N., Vice President Patient Services
Web address: www.claritycgc.org
Control: Other not–for–profit (including NFP Corporation) **Service**: Children's hospital psychiatric

Staffed Beds: 66 **Admissions**: 2931 **Census**: 63 **Outpatient Visits**: 22739
Births: 0 **Total Expense ($000)**: 27274 **Payroll Expense ($000)**: 15575
Personnel: 281

Many Facility Codes have changed. Please refer to the AHA Guide Code Chart. © 2018 AHA Guide

TX

☐ **CUMBERLAND SURGICAL HOSPITAL (670112)**, 5330 N. Loop 1604 W, Zip 78249; tel. 210/877–8000, **A**1 10 **F**3 12 29 30 40 45 47 51 70 75 79 81 82 85 107 **S** Post Acute Medical, LLC, Enola, PA
Primary Contact: Paul B. Abraham, FACHE, Chief Executive Officer
CNO: Lisa Kuopus, Chief Nursing Officer
Web address: www.cumberlandsh.com/
Control: Partnership, Investor–owned (for–profit) **Service:** General medical and surgical

Staffed Beds: 25 **Admissions:** 369 **Census:** 2 **Outpatient Visits:** 2893 **Births:** 0 **Total Expense ($000):** 27956 **Payroll Expense ($000):** 5307 **Personnel:** 69	

☒ **ENCOMPASS HEALTH REHABILITATION HOSPITAL OF SAN ANTONIO (453031)**, 9119 Cinnamon Hill, Zip 78240–5401; tel. 210/691–0737, **A**1 10 **F**29 90 91 96 130 132 148 **P**5 **S** Encompass Health Corporation, Birmingham, AL
Primary Contact: Michael Thomas, Chief Executive Officer
CFO: Larry Floyd Spriggs, CPA, Controller
CMO: Chaula Rana, M.D., Medical Director
CHR: Vanessa Tejada, Director Human Resources
CNO: Matthew D'Ambrosio, MSN, R.N., Chief Nursing Officer
Web address: www.hsriosa.com
Control: Corporation, Investor–owned (for–profit) **Service:** Rehabilitation

Staffed Beds: 96 **Admissions:** 1175 **Census:** 47 **Outpatient Visits:** 0 **Births:** 0 **Total Expense ($000):** 19962 **Payroll Expense ($000):** 10785 **Personnel:** 180	

⇑ **FOUNDATION SURGICAL HOSPITAL OF SAN ANTONIO (670054)**, 9522 Huebner Road, Zip 78240–1548; tel. 210/478–5400, (Nonreporting) **A**3 5 10 21
Primary Contact: Blake W. Hubbard, FACHE, Chief Executive Officer
CNO: Beckie Leonard, R.N., Chief Nursing Officer
Web address: www.fshsanantonio.com/
Control: Corporation, Investor–owned (for–profit) **Service:** General medical and surgical

Staffed Beds: 20	

☒ **KINDRED HOSPITAL SAN ANTONIO CENTRAL (452073)**, 111 Dallas Street, 4th Floor, Zip 78205–1201; tel. 210/297–7185, **A**1 10 **F**1 29 75 77 87 91 130 148 **S** Kindred Healthcare, Louisville, KY
Primary Contact: Abiola Anyebe, Interim Chief Executive Officer
Web address: www.kindredsanantoniocentral.com/
Control: Corporation, Investor–owned (for–profit) **Service:** Acute long–term care hospital

Staffed Beds: 44 **Admissions:** 375 **Census:** 27 **Outpatient Visits:** 0 **Births:** 0 **Total Expense ($000):** 15951 **Payroll Expense ($000):** 5866 **Personnel:** 76	

☒ **KINDRED HOSPITAL–SAN ANTONIO (452016)**, 3636 Medical Drive, Zip 78229–2183; tel. 210/616–0616, **A**1 10 **F**1 3 29 30 70 75 77 85 87 91 107 130 148 **S** Kindred Healthcare, Louisville, KY
Primary Contact: Abiola Anyebe, Interim Chief Executive Officer
CFO: Erin Russell, Controller
CMO: Charles Duncan, M.D., Medical Director
CHR: Stanley Richardson, Coordinator Human Resources and Payroll Benefits
Web address: www.khsanantonio.com/
Control: Corporation, Investor–owned (for–profit) **Service:** Acute long–term care hospital

Staffed Beds: 59 **Admissions:** 370 **Census:** 25 **Outpatient Visits:** 0 **Births:** 0 **Total Expense ($000):** 17224 **Payroll Expense ($000):** 6247 **Personnel:** 89	

☒ **LAUREL RIDGE TREATMENT CENTER (454060)**, 17720 Corporate Woods Drive, Zip 78259–3500; tel. 210/491–9400, **A**1 3 10 **F**4 5 29 35 38 75 77 98 99 100 101 103 105 106 130 132 135 151 152 153 **S** Universal Health Services, Inc., King of Prussia, PA
Primary Contact: Jacob Cuellar, M.D., Chief Executive Officer
CFO: Linda Maenius, Chief Financial Officer
CMO: Benigno J Fernandez, M.D., Executive Medical Director
CHR: Brenda Frederick, Director Human Resources
CNO: Kathy Rosetta, Chief Nursing Officer
Web address: www.laurelridgetc.com
Control: Partnership, Investor–owned (for–profit) **Service:** Psychiatric

Staffed Beds: 208 **Admissions:** 7493 **Census:** 181 **Outpatient Visits:** 20556 **Births:** 0 **Total Expense ($000):** 54427 **Payroll Expense ($000):** 22783 **Personnel:** 363	

☒ **LIFECARE HOSPITALS OF SAN ANTONIO (452059)**, 8902 Floyd Curl Drive, Zip 78240–1681; tel. 210/690–7000, **A**1 10 **F**1 3 29 45 70 75 77 85 86 87 96 97 107 114 130 148 149 **S** LifeCare Management Services, Plano, TX
Primary Contact: Michelle Lozano, Chief Executive Officer
CMO: Randall C Bell, M.D., Medical Director
CIO: Mike Wattenbarger, Chief Information Officer
Web address: www.lifecare–hospitals.com
Control: Corporation, Investor–owned (for–profit) **Service:** Acute long–term care hospital

Staffed Beds: 62 **Admissions:** 610 **Census:** 49 **Outpatient Visits:** 0 **Births:** 0 **Total Expense ($000):** 29191 **Payroll Expense ($000):** 12710 **Personnel:** 251	

☒ **METHODIST AMBULATORY SURGERY HOSPITAL – NORTHWEST (450780)**, 9150 Huebner Road, Suite 100, Zip 78240–1545; tel. 210/575–5000, **A**1 3 10 **F**3 29 40 65 68 79 81 85 87 **P**8 **S** HCA Healthcare, Nashville, TN
Primary Contact: Scott Davis, Chief Executive Officer
CFO: Tim Carr, Chief Financial Officer
CHR: Barry Burns, Vice President
CNO: Cathy Bump, R.N., Chief Nursing Officer
Web address: www.sahealth.com
Control: Partnership, Investor–owned (for–profit) **Service:** Surgical

Staffed Beds: 21 **Admissions:** 447 **Census:** 3 **Outpatient Visits:** 5947 **Births:** 0 **Total Expense ($000):** 20646 **Payroll Expense ($000):** 6291 **Personnel:** 95	

★ ⇑ **METHODIST HOSPITAL (450388)**, 7700 Floyd Curl Drive, Zip 78229–3993; tel. 210/575–4000, (Includes METHODIST CHILDREN'S HOSPITAL, 7700 Floyd Curl Drive, San Antonio, TX, Zip 78229–3383; tel. 210/575–7000; Robert Lenza, Chief Executive Officer; METHODIST SPECIALTY AND TRANSPLANT HOSPITAL, 8026 Floyd Curl Drive, San Antonio, TX, Zip 78229–3915; tel. 210/575–8090; Jeffrey Wilson, Chief Executive Officer; METHODIST TEXSAN HOSPITAL, 6700 IH–10 West, San Antonio, TX, Zip 78201; tel. 210/736–6700; Scott Davis, Chief Executive Officer; METROPOLITAN METHODIST HOSPITAL, 1310 McCullough Avenue, San Antonio, TX, Zip 78212–2617; tel. 210/757–2909; Gregory A Seiler, Chief Executive Officer; NORTHEAST METHODIST HOSPITAL, 12412 Judson Road, Live Oak, TX, Zip 78233–3255; tel. 210/757–5000; Michael D Beaver, Chief Executive Officer) **A**2 3 5 10 21 **F**3 5 8 11 12 13 15 17 18 19 20 21 22 23 24 25 26 27 28 29 30 31 34 35 38 40 41 43 44 45 46 47 48 49 51 53 54 56 57 58 59 60 64 65 68 70 72 74 75 76 77 78 79 80 81 82 84 85 86 87 88 89 90 93 95 96 98 100 101 102 103 104 105 107 108 111 114 115 119 120 121 124 126 127 129 130 132 135 136 137 138 139 142 143 145 146 147 148 152 153 154 **P**7 **S** HCA Healthcare, Nashville, TN
Primary Contact: Allen Harrison, Chief Executive Officer
CFO: Nancy Meadows, Chief Financial Officer
CMO: Russell Woodward, M.D., Chief Medical Officer
CIO: Eddie Cuellar, Vice President Information Systems
CHR: Nancy Edgar, Vice President Human Resources
Web address: www.sahealth.com
Control: Partnership, Investor–owned (for–profit) **Service:** General medical and surgical

Staffed Beds: 1599 **Admissions:** 81129 **Census:** 1198 **Outpatient Visits:** 480949 **Births:** 9175 **Total Expense ($000):** 1267219 **Payroll Expense ($000):** 455299 **Personnel:** 5975	

☒ **METHODIST STONE OAK HOSPITAL (670055)**, 1139 E Sonterra Boulevard, Zip 78258–4347, Mailing Address: 1139 East Sonterra Boulevard, Zip 78258–4347; tel. 210/638–2100, **A**1 3 5 10 **F**3 13 15 18 20 22 24 28 29 30 31 34 35 38 40 41 44 45 46 47 49 52 56 57 59 60 65 68 70 72 74 75 76 77 78 79 80 81 82 85 87 90 102 107 108 114 119 126 130 145 146 147 148 149 154 **S** HCA Healthcare, Nashville, TN
Primary Contact: Marc Strode, Chief Executive Officer
CFO: Gabriel Marrufo, Chief Financial Officer
CNO: Ann M Winn, M.D., R.N., FACHE, Chief Nursing Officer
Web address: www.sahealth.com/locations/methodist–stone–oak–hospital/
Control: Partnership, Investor–owned (for–profit) **Service:** General medical and surgical

Staffed Beds: 242 **Admissions:** 11592 **Census:** 133 **Outpatient Visits:** 49848 **Births:** 1795 **Total Expense ($000):** 172357 **Payroll Expense ($000):** 49270 **Personnel:** 800	

⇑ **NIX HEALTH CARE SYSTEM (450130)**, 414 Navarro Street, Zip 78205–2516; tel. 210/271–1800, (Nonreporting) **A**3 5 10 21 **S** Prospect Medical Holdings, Los Angeles, CA
Primary Contact: James A. Summersett III, FACHE, Interim Chief Executive Officer
CMO: Dina Goytia–Leos, M.D., Chief of Staff
CIO: Adrian Dickreiter, Vice President Technology
CNO: Maria Rose Lopez, R.N., Chief of Nursing
Web address: www.nixhealth.com
Control: Partnership, Investor–owned (for–profit) **Service:** General medical and surgical

Staffed Beds: 246	

TX

⊞ **POST ACUTE/WARM SPRINGS SPECIALTY HOSPITAL OF SAN ANTONIO (452090)**, 5418 N Loop 1604 W, Zip 78247; tel. 210/921-3550, **A**1 10 **F**1 3 29 30 148 **S** Post Acute Medical, LLC, Enola, PA
Primary Contact: Kristen Lowe, Chief Executive Officer
CNO: Carrie Nims, Director of Nursing
Web address: www.postacutemedical.com
Control: Partnership, Investor-owned (for-profit) **Service:** Acute long-term care hospital

Staffed Beds: 26 **Admissions:** 362 **Census:** 21 **Outpatient Visits:** 0 **Births:** 0 **Total Expense ($000):** 12518 **Payroll Expense ($000):** 4507 **Personnel:** 75

SAN ANTONIO BEHAVIORAL HEALTHCARE HOSPITAL (454132), 8550 Huebner Road, Zip 78240-1803; tel. 877/514-0010, (Nonreporting) **S** Signature Healthcare Services, Corona, CA
Primary Contact: Aleen D. Arabit, Chief Executive Officer
Web address: www.sanantoniobehavioral.com
Control: Other not-for-profit (including NFP Corporation) **Service:** Psychiatric

Staffed Beds: 108

☐ **SAN ANTONIO STATE HOSPITAL (454011)**, 6711 South New Braunfels, Suite 100, Zip 78223-3006; tel. 210/531-7711, **A**1 3 5 10 **F**30 39 53 56 57 59 68 75 77 86 87 91 98 99 100 101 103 130 132 135 146 **P**1 **S** Texas Department of State Health Services, Austin, TX
Primary Contact: Robert C. Arizpe, Superintendent
CFO: Janie Rabago, Chief Accountant
CMO: Terresa Stallworth, M.D., Clinical Director
CIO: Chris Stanush, Director Information Management
CHR: Renee Bourland, Human Resources Specialist
CNO: Maria DC Ostrander, R.N., MSN, Chief Nurse Executive
Web address: www.dshs.state.tx.us/mhhospitals/SanAntonioSH/default.shtm
Control: State, Government, nonfederal **Service:** Psychiatric

Staffed Beds: 278 **Admissions:** 898 **Census:** 251 **Outpatient Visits:** 0 **Births:** 0 **Total Expense ($000):** 76761 **Payroll Expense ($000):** 36850 **Personnel:** 821

★ **SELECT REHABILITATION HOSPITAL OF SAN ANTONIO (673040)**, 19126 Stonehue Road, Zip 78258-3490; tel. 210/482-3400, **A**10 **F**3 29 30 75 90 91 96 130 148 149 **S** Select Medical Corporation, Mechanicsburg, PA
Primary Contact: Robert Ward, Chief Executive Officer
Web address: www.sanantonio-rehab.com/
Control: Partnership, Investor-owned (for-profit) **Service:** Rehabilitation

Staffed Beds: 42 **Admissions:** 1073 **Census:** 41 **Outpatient Visits:** 0 **Births:** 0 **Total Expense ($000):** 16869 **Payroll Expense ($000):** 9033 **Personnel:** 168

☐ **SOUTH TEXAS SPINE AND SURGICAL HOSPITAL (450856)**, 18600 Hardy Oak Boulevard, Zip 78258-4206; tel. 210/507-4090, **A**1 3 5 10 **F**3 29 40 41 70 75 77 79 81 82 85 86 87 89 126 **P**3 6 **S** National Surgical Healthcare, Chicago, IL
Primary Contact: Angie Kauffman, Chief Executive Officer
CFO: Sylvia Garcia, Chief Accounting Officer
CHR: Sally Hall, Manager Human Resources
CNO: Jennifer West, R.N., Chief Nursing Officer
Web address: www.southtexassurgical.com
Control: Partnership, Investor-owned (for-profit) **Service:** Orthopedic

Staffed Beds: 30 **Admissions:** 1429 **Census:** 9 **Outpatient Visits:** 3874 **Births:** 0 **Total Expense ($000):** 40234 **Payroll Expense ($000):** 7687 **Personnel:** 118

⊞ △ **SOUTH TEXAS VETERANS HEALTH CARE SYSTEM**, 7400 Merton Minter Boulevard, Zip 78229-4404; tel. 210/617-5300, (Includes KERRVILLE DIVISION, 3600 Memorial Boulevard, Kerrville, TX, Zip 78028; tel. 210/896-2020; SAN ANTONIO DIVISION, 7400 Merton Minter Boulevard, San Antonio, TX, Zip 78284-5799; tel. 210/617-5300) (Nonreporting) **A**1 3 5 7 8 **S** Department of Veterans Affairs, Perry Point, MD
Primary Contact: Robert M. Walton, Healthcare System Director
COO: Joe Perez, Associate Director
CFO: Eloisa Salazar, Chief Financial Officer
CMO: Julianne Flynn, M.D., Chief of Staff
CIO: Simon Willett, Director Administrative Operations
CHR: Jeffrey Young, Chief Human Resource Officer
CNO: Sharon Millican, Associate Director, Patient Care Services
Web address: www.southtexas.va.gov/
Control: Veterans Affairs, Government, federal **Service:** General medical and surgical

Staffed Beds: 838

⇧ **SOUTHWEST GENERAL HOSPITAL (450697)**, 7400 Barlite Boulevard, Zip 78224-1399; tel. 210/921-2000, **A**10 21 **F**3 12 13 18 20 22 24 26 29 30 35 37 40 43 44 45 49 50 51 56 57 59 60 64 65 70 71 72 74 75 76 77 79 80 81 85 87 90 96 98 100 102 103 104 107 108 111 114 115 119 129 130 132 135 146 147 148 149 153 **P**6 **S** Steward Health Care System, LLC, Dallas, TX
Primary Contact: P Craig. Desmond, Chief Executive Officer
COO: Sarah Humme, MSN, R.N., Chief Operating Officer
CFO: Colin B. Brooks, Chief Financial Officer
CIO: Debbie Mora, Director
CHR: Christina Rivera, Director Human Resources
CNO: Sarah Humme, MSN, R.N., Chief Nursing Officer
Web address: www.swgeneralhospital.com
Control: Corporation, Investor-owned (for-profit) **Service:** General medical and surgical

Staffed Beds: 253 **Admissions:** 9798 **Census:** 134 **Outpatient Visits:** 54339 **Births:** 1553 **Total Expense ($000):** 119722 **Payroll Expense ($000):** 48934 **Personnel:** 727

ST. LUKE'S BAPTIST HOSPITAL See Baptist Medical Center, San Antonio

☐ **TEXAS CENTER FOR INFECTIOUS DISEASE (452033)**, 2303 SE Military Drive, Zip 78223-3597; tel. 210/534-8857, **A**1 3 10 **F**3 29 30 50 53 54 58 59 61 65 68 75 77 80 86 87 130 132 135 143 146 149 **S** Texas Department of State Health Services, Austin, TX
Primary Contact: James N. Elkins, FACHE, Director
CFO: Glenda Armstrong-Huff, Assistant Superintendent
CMO: David Griffith, M.D., Medical Director
CIO: Andre Avant, Facility Automation Manager
CHR: Gerald Shackelford, Staff Support Specialist
CNO: Rebecca Sanchez, R.N., M.P.H., Director of Nursing
Web address: www.dshs.state.tx.us/tcid/default.shtm
Control: State, Government, nonfederal **Service:** Tuberculosis and other respiratory diseases

Staffed Beds: 31 **Admissions:** 52 **Census:** 31 **Outpatient Visits:** 0 **Births:** 0 **Total Expense ($000):** 14069 **Payroll Expense ($000):** 6233 **Personnel:** 161

⊞ **UNIVERSITY HEALTH SYSTEM (450213)**, 4502 Medical Drive, Zip 78229-4493; tel. 210/358-2000, (Includes UNIVERSITY HEALTH CENTER – DOWNTOWN, 4502 Medical Drive, San Antonio, TX, Zip 78229-4493; tel. 210/358-3300; UNIVERSITY HOSPITAL, 4502 Medical Drive, San Antonio, TX, Zip 78229-4493; tel. 210/358-4000; Michael Roussos, Administrator) **A**1 2 3 5 8 10 **F**3 4 7 11 12 13 14 15 16 17 18 19 20 21 22 23 24 25 26 27 28 29 30 31 32 34 35 38 40 41 43 44 45 46 47 48 49 50 51 52 54 55 56 57 58 59 60 61 64 65 66 68 70 72 73 74 75 76 77 78 79 81 82 84 85 86 87 88 89 90 92 93 95 98 100 101 102 107 108 110 111 115 118 119 126 129 130 132 135 138 139 140 141 142 143 144 145 146 147 148 149 **P**6
Primary Contact: George B. Hernandez Jr, President and Chief Executive Officer
COO: Christann Vasquez, Executive Vice President and Chief Operating Officer
CFO: Peggy Deming, Executive Vice President and Chief Financial Officer
CMO: Bryan Alsip, M.D., Executive Vice President, Chief Medical Officer
CIO: Bill Phillips, Vice President Information Services
CHR: Theresa Scepanski, Vice President People and Organizational Development
CNO: Nancy L Ray, R.N., Executive Vice President, Chief Nursing Executive
Web address: www.universityhealthsystem.com
Control: Hospital district or authority, Government, nonfederal **Service:** General medical and surgical

Staffed Beds: 639 **Admissions:** 29284 **Census:** 467 **Outpatient Visits:** 1603953 **Births:** 2911 **Total Expense ($000):** 1192495 **Payroll Expense ($000):** 447259 **Personnel:** 7139

⊞ **WARM SPRINGS REHABILITATION HOSPITAL OF SAN ANTONIO (453035)**, 5101 Medical Drive, Zip 78229-4801; tel. 210/616-0100, (Includes WARM SPRINGS REHABILITATION HOSPITAL OF THOUSAND OAKS, 14747 Jones Maltsberger Road, San Antonio, TX, Zip 78247-3713; tel. 210/581-5300; Kasondra Kistner, R.N., Chief Executive Officer; WARM SPRINGS REHABILITATION HOSPITAL OF WESTOVER HILLS, 10323 State Highway 151, San Antonio, TX, Zip 78251-4557; tel. 210/581-5306; Steve Flaherty, Chief Executive Officer) (Total facility includes 10 beds in nursing home–type unit) **A**1 3 5 10 **F**3 11 29 30 57 64 68 74 75 79 82 90 93 94 96 128 130 132 146 148 **S** Post Acute Medical, LLC, Enola, PA
Primary Contact: Debra Bornmann, Chief Executive Officer
CIO: Rick Marek, Vice President Medical Information Systems
CHR: Waynea Finley, System Director Human Resources
Web address: www.postacutemedical.com/our-facilities/hospitals/warm-springs-rehabilitation-hospital-san-antonio/
Control: Partnership, Investor-owned (for-profit) **Service:** Rehabilitation

Staffed Beds: 139 **Admissions:** 2674 **Census:** 94 **Outpatient Visits:** 29839 **Births:** 0 **Total Expense ($000):** 47520 **Payroll Expense ($000):** 22834 **Personnel:** 535

Many Facility Codes have changed. Please refer to the AHA Guide Code Chart. © 2018 AHA Guide

SAN AUGUSTINE—San Augustine County

★ **CHI ST. LUKE'S HEALTH MEMORIAL SAN AUGUSTINE (451360)**, 511 East Hospital Street, Zip 75972-2121, Mailing Address: P.O. Box 658, Zip 75972-0658; tel. 936/275-3446, **A**10 18 **F**29 35 40 57 59 64 102 107 119 133 143 149 **S** Catholic Health Initiatives, Englewood, CO
Primary Contact: Darlene Williams, R.N., Administrator
CFO: Kristi Gay, Chief Financial Officer
Web address: www.memorialhealth.org
Control: Other not-for-profit (including NFP Corporation) **Service:** General medical and surgical

Staffed Beds: 9 **Admissions:** 215 **Census:** 2 **Outpatient Visits:** 10640
Births: 0 **Total Expense ($000):** 6427 **Payroll Expense ($000):** 2630
Personnel: 43

SAN MARCOS—Hays County

⊞ **CENTRAL TEXAS MEDICAL CENTER (450272)**, 1301 Wonder World Drive, Zip 78666-7544; tel. 512/353-8979, **A**1 10 **F**3 11 13 15 18 20 29 30 32 34 35 39 40 43 44 45 49 50 51 56 57 59 60 62 63 64 65 66 68 70 72 75 76 77 79 80 81 82 85 86 87 92 93 94 98 107 108 109 110 111 114 116 117 118 119 126 129 130 131 132 146 147 148 152 **P**6 8 **S** Adventist Health System Sunbelt Health Care Corporation, Altamonte Springs, FL
Primary Contact: Anthony Stahl, Ph.D., FACHE, Chief Executive Officer
CFO: Parker Pridgen, Chief Financial Officer
CMO: Lee Johannsen, M.D., Chief Medical Officer
CHR: Debbie D Cox, Administrative Director Human Resources
CNO: Elsie Graves, Chief Nursing Officer
Web address: www.ctmc.org
Control: Church operated, Nongovernment, not-for-profit **Service:** General medical and surgical

Staffed Beds: 111 **Admissions:** 3966 **Census:** 41 **Outpatient Visits:** 77454
Births: 814 **Total Expense ($000):** 90973 **Payroll Expense ($000):** 31578
Personnel: 498

WELLBRIDGE HEATLHCARE OF SAN MARCOS (454137), 1106 North Interstate 35, Zip 78666-7030; tel. 512/353-0194, **F**29 30 35 38 56 75 86 87 98 100 101 103 106 130 135 149 154 **P**7
Primary Contact: Gregory Drummond, Chief Executive Officer
Web address: www.oceanssanmarcos.com
Control: Partnership, Investor-owned (for-profit) **Service:** Psychiatric

Staffed Beds: 24 **Admissions:** 250 **Census:** 14 **Outpatient Visits:** 0
Births: 0 **Total Expense ($000):** 5516 **Payroll Expense ($000):** 2504
Personnel: 52

SEGUIN—Guadalupe County

⊞ **GUADALUPE REGIONAL MEDICAL CENTER (450104)**, 1215 East Court Street, Zip 78155-5189; tel. 830/379-2411, **A**1 10 **F**3 5 11 13 15 18 20 22 28 29 30 31 34 35 38 40 43 44 45 46 49 50 53 56 57 58 60 63 66 68 70 74 75 76 77 78 79 81 82 84 85 90 93 96 104 107 108 110 111 114 115 118 119 126 129 130 132 135 146 148 149 150 154 **P**8
Primary Contact: Robert Gerard. Haynes, FACHE, Chief Executive Officer
COO: Sheri Williams, Chief Operating Officer
CFO: Penny Wallace, Chief Financial Officer
CMO: Robert Ryan, M.D., Chief Medical Officer
CIO: Steve Ratliff, Director Information Technology
CHR: Fay Bennett, Vice President Employee Services
CNO: Daphne Blake, R.N., MSN, Chief Nursing Officer
Web address: www.grmedcenter.com
Control: City-county, Government, nonfederal **Service:** General medical and surgical

Staffed Beds: 92 **Admissions:** 3934 **Census:** 42 **Outpatient Visits:** 136577
Births: 747 **Total Expense ($000):** 92971 **Payroll Expense ($000):** 34072
Personnel: 671

SEMINOLE—Gaines County

★ **MEMORIAL HOSPITAL (451358)**, 209 NW Eighth Street, Zip 79360-3447; tel. 432/758-5811, **A**10 18 **F**3 10 11 13 28 29 30 32 34 35 40 43 45 53 56 57 59 62 63 64 65 75 76 81 87 93 97 102 107 114 119 129 130 131 132 133 143 146 147 148 **P**6
Primary Contact: James G. Parrish, FACHE, Chief Executive Officer
COO: Heath Mitchell, Chief Operating Officer
CFO: Traci Anderson, Chief Financial Officer
CMO: Michael Watson, M.D., Chief of Staff
Web address: www.seminolehospitaldistrict.com
Control: Hospital district or authority, Government, nonfederal **Service:** General medical and surgical

Staffed Beds: 25 **Admissions:** 785 **Census:** 8 **Outpatient Visits:** 86048
Births: 421 **Total Expense ($000):** 37974 **Payroll Expense ($000):** 10963
Personnel: 202

SEYMOUR—Baylor County

SEYMOUR HOSPITAL (450586), 200 Stadium Drive, Zip 76380-2344; tel. 940/889-5572, **A**10 20 **F**3 7 8 11 13 14 28 29 34 36 40 43 45 50 53 56 57 59 62 64 65 66 68 70 75 76 81 85 86 87 89 93 94 100 102 103 104 107 119 127 130 133 135 146 147 148 154 **P**1
Primary Contact: Leslie Hardin, Chief Executive Officer and Chief Financial Officer
CFO: Leslie Hardin, Chief Executive Officer and Chief Financial Officer
CMO: Kory Lann Martin, M.D., Chief of Staff
CHR: Linda Moore, Manager Human Resources
CNO: Julie Smajstrla, Director Nursing
Web address: www.seymourhospital.com/
Control: Hospital district or authority, Government, nonfederal **Service:** General medical and surgical

Staffed Beds: 40 **Admissions:** 456 **Census:** 5 **Outpatient Visits:** 36285
Births: 26 **Total Expense ($000):** 36004 **Payroll Expense ($000):** 5432
Personnel: 114

SHAMROCK—Wheeler County

SHAMROCK GENERAL HOSPITAL (451340), 1000 South Main Street, Zip 79079-2896, Mailing Address: P.O. Box 511, Zip 79079-0511; tel. 806/256-2114, **A**10 18 **F**7 11 29 32 34 35 40 43 63 65 68 93 107 119 127 130 133 **P**4
Primary Contact: Wiley M. Fires, Administrator
CFO: Wiley M Fires, Administrator
CHR: Cecille Williams, Assistant Administrator
CNO: Jeanne Crossland, Director of Nursing
Control: Hospital district or authority, Government, nonfederal **Service:** General medical and surgical

Staffed Beds: 13 **Admissions:** 87 **Census:** 1 **Outpatient Visits:** 10311
Births: 0 **Total Expense ($000):** 5974 **Payroll Expense ($000):** 3202
Personnel: 71

SHENANDOAH—Montgomery County

⊞ **ENCOMPASS HEALTH REHABILITATION HOSPITAL VISION PARK (673034)**, 117 Vision Park Boulevard, Zip 77384-3001; tel. 936/444-1700, **A**1 10 **F**3 29 65 77 90 91 93 96 130 148 **S** Encompass Health Corporation, Birmingham, AL
Primary Contact: Jennifer Brewer, Chief Executive Officer
CFO: Terri Weiss, Chief Financial Officer
Web address: www.healthsouthvisionpark.com/
Control: Corporation, Investor-owned (for-profit) **Service:** Rehabilitation

Staffed Beds: 60 **Admissions:** 1293 **Census:** 41 **Outpatient Visits:** 3686
Births: 0 **Total Expense ($000):** 19068 **Payroll Expense ($000):** 9380
Personnel: 156

⇑ **NEXUS SPECIALTY HOSPITAL**, 123 Vision Park Boulevard, Zip 77384-3001; tel. 281/364-0317, **A**21 **F**1 3 70 74 75 77 82 84 85 91 92 93 100 101 107 119 130 132 135 148 **S** Nexus Health Systems, Houston, TX
Primary Contact: Eric Cantrell, Chief Executive Officer
CFO: David Strickler, Chief Financial Officer
CMO: Ather Siddiqi, M.D., Medical Director
CIO: Noe Salinas, Vice President Information Technology
CHR: Kevin McAndrews, Vice President Human Resources
CNO: Rhena Anderson, Chief Nursing Officer
Web address: www.nexusspecialty.com
Control: Partnership, Investor-owned (for-profit) **Service:** Acute long-term care hospital

Staffed Beds: 76 **Admissions:** 536 **Census:** 38 **Outpatient Visits:** 37
Births: 0 **Total Expense ($000):** 22239 **Payroll Expense ($000):** 9134
Personnel: 121

SHERMAN—Grayson County

⇑ **BAYLOR SCOTT & WHITE SURGICAL HOSPITAL AT SHERMAN (670076)**, 3601 North Calais Street, Zip 75090-1785; tel. 903/870-0999, **A**10 21 **F**3 29 37 40 45 47 77 81 85 107 111 119 126 131 145 **S** Foundation Surgical Hospital Affiliates, Oklahoma City, OK
Primary Contact: Marc Devorsetz, Chief Executive Officer
CMO: Curtis Holbrook, M.D., Chief Medical Officer
CIO: Grant Hulsey, Director Information Technology
CHR: Terrie Langford, Director Human Resources
CNO: Teresa Dutton, R.N., Chief Nursing Officer
Web address: www.heritageparksurgicalhospital.com
Control: Partnership, Investor-owned (for-profit) **Service:** General medical and surgical

Staffed Beds: 12 **Admissions:** 485 **Census:** 3 **Outpatient Visits:** 23600
Births: 0 **Total Expense ($000):** 40796 **Payroll Expense ($000):** 10653
Personnel: 205

TX

Hospital, Medicare Provider Number, Address, Telephone, Approval, Facility, and Physician Codes, Health Care System

★ American Hospital Association (AHA) membership
☐ The Joint Commission accreditation
○ Healthcare Facilities Accreditation Program
◇ DNV Healthcare Inc. accreditation
⇑ Center for Improvement in Healthcare Quality Accreditation
△ Commission on Accreditation of Rehabilitation Facilities (CARF) accreditation

☐ **CARRUS REHABILITATION HOSPITAL (673041)**, 1810 West US Highway 82, Suite 100, Zip 75092–7069; tel. 903/870–2600, **A**1 10 **F**3 29 40 41 44 65 74 75 77 79 85 86 87 90 91 96 130 **S** Carrus Hospitals, Sherman, TX
Primary Contact: Jon–Michael Rains, Chief Executive Officer
CFO: Michael Exline, Chief Financial Officer
CMO: Jose Matus, M.D., Director Medical
CIO: Gary Glenn, Director Information Technology
CHR: Charlene Shupert, Director Staff Services
CNO: Marie Johnson, Chief Nursing Officer
Web address: www.carrushospital.com
Control: Corporation, Investor–owned (for–profit) **Service**: Rehabilitation

Staffed Beds: 24 **Admissions**: 615 **Census**: 24 **Outpatient Visits**: 0
Births: 0 **Total Expense ($000)**: 9742 **Payroll Expense ($000)**: 4437
Personnel: 83

CARRUS SPECIALTY HOSPITAL (452041), 1810 West US Highway 82, Zip 75092–7069; tel. 903/870–2600, **A**10 **F**1 3 29 40 41 44 56 65 74 75 77 78 79 82 83 85 86 87 91 107 114 119 129 130 148 **S** Carrus Hospitals, Sherman, TX
Primary Contact: Jon–Michael Rains, Chief Executive Officer
CFO: Michael Exline, Chief Financial Officer
CMO: Nathan Watson, M.D., Jr Chief of Staff
CIO: Gary Glenn, Director Information Technology
CHR: Charlene Shupert, Director Staff Services
CNO: Marie Johnson, Chief Nursing Officer
Web address: www.carrushospital.com
Control: Corporation, Investor–owned (for–profit) **Service**: Acute long–term care hospital

Staffed Beds: 16 **Admissions**: 246 **Census**: 15 **Outpatient Visits**: 1497
Births: 0 **Total Expense ($000)**: 12659 **Payroll Expense ($000)**: 5899
Personnel: 109

WILSON N. JONES MEDICAL CENTER See Wilson N. Jones Regional Medical Center

☐ **WILSON N. JONES REGIONAL MEDICAL CENTER (450469)**, 500 North Highland Avenue, Zip 75092–7354; tel. 903/870–4611, **A**1 10 **F**3 11 12 13 15 18 20 22 24 26 28 29 30 35 35 40 41 43 45 53 54 56 57 58 59 61 64 70 74 76 77 78 79 81 84 86 87 93 96 98 100 103 105 107 108 111 118 119 129 130 132 146 147 148 149 154 **S** Alecto Healthcare, Irvine, CA
Primary Contact: John Rossfeld, Administrator
CFO: Chuck Cave, CPA, Chief Financial Officer
CMO: Kenton Schrank, M.D., President Medical Staff
CIO: Prabhu Bollu, Director Information Technology
CHR: Bill Barrett, Manager Human Resources
CNO: Tonya Price, Chief Nursing Officer
Web address: www.wnj.org
Control: Corporation, Investor–owned (for–profit) **Service**: General medical and surgical

Staffed Beds: 108 **Admissions**: 5578 **Census**: 66 **Outpatient Visits**: 38626
Births: 487 **Total Expense ($000)**: 77725 **Payroll Expense ($000)**: 29287
Personnel: 524

SMITHVILLE—Bastrop County

⊠ **SETON SMITHVILLE REGIONAL HOSPITAL (450143)**, 1201 Hill Road, Zip 78957; tel. 512/237–3214, **A**1 10 **F**11 15 29 30 35 40 45 46 47 50 53 57 77 79 81 82 85 87 92 93 97 107 110 111 119 130 146 147 148 149 **P**3 8 **S** Ascension Healthcare, Saint Louis, MO
Primary Contact: Scott O. Fuller, President and Chief Executive Officer
CFO: Melissa Nordyke, Chief Financial Officer
CHR: Sara Rodriguez, Human Resources
CNO: Christine Laflamme, R.N., MSN, Chief Nursing Officer
Web address: www.seton.org
Control: Church operated, Nongovernment, not–for–profit **Service**: General medical and surgical

Staffed Beds: 5 **Admissions**: 163 **Census**: 1 **Outpatient Visits**: 26515
Births: 0 **Total Expense ($000)**: 14887 **Payroll Expense ($000)**: 5415
Personnel: 86

SNYDER—Scurry County

⇑ **COGDELL MEMORIAL HOSPITAL (451384)**, 1700 Cogdell Boulevard, Zip 79549–6198; tel. 325/573–6374, **A**10 18 21 **F**8 11 12 13 15 18 19 29 30 34 35 40 43 45 46 47 48 49 50 53 56 57 59 62 63 64 65 66 68 75 76 77 79 81 83 84 85 86 87 91 92 93 97 107 110 111 115 119 127 130 131 132 133 145 146 147 148 149 154 **P**6
Primary Contact: Ella Raye. Helms, Chief Executive Officer
CFO: John Everett, Chief Financial Officer
CMO: Robert Rakov, M.D., Chief Medical Officer
CHR: Linda Warren, Director Human Resources
Web address: www.cogdellhospital.com
Control: Hospital district or authority, Government, nonfederal **Service**: General medical and surgical

Staffed Beds: 25 **Admissions**: 721 **Census**: 7 **Outpatient Visits**: 84470
Births: 167 **Total Expense ($000)**: 47428 **Payroll Expense ($000)**: 15355
Personnel: 245

SONORA—Sutton County

★ **LILLIAN M. HUDSPETH MEMORIAL HOSPITAL (451324)**, 308 Hudspeth Avenue, Zip 76950–8003, Mailing Address: P.O. Box 455, Zip 76950–0455; tel. 325/387–2521, **A**10 18 **F**3 7 15 26 28 29 30 34 35 40 41 43 50 53 57 59 63 64 65 66 68 75 79 86 87 90 93 96 97 107 110 111 115 119 127 128 131 133 135 154
Primary Contact: Michelle Schaefer, Chief Executive Officer
COO: Joe Marshall, Chief Operating Officer
CFO: Michelle Schaefer, Chief Financial Officer
CNO: Lara Ellen Teague, R.N., Chief Nursing Officer
Web address: www.sonora–hospital.org
Control: Hospital district or authority, Government, nonfederal **Service**: General medical and surgical

Staffed Beds: 12 **Admissions**: 105 **Census**: 1 **Outpatient Visits**: 8252
Births: 0 **Total Expense ($000)**: 8898 **Payroll Expense ($000)**: 3705
Personnel: 87

SOUTHLAKE—Tarrant County

★ **METHODIST SOUTHLAKE HOSPITAL**, 421 East State Highway 114, Zip 76092; tel. 817/865–4400, **F**3 12 29 40 45 49 50 51 68 70 75 79 81 82 85 107 111 115 119 124 126 130 132 135 149 **S** Methodist Health System, Dallas, TX
Primary Contact: John McGreevy, FACHE, President
Web address: www.https://methodistsouthlake.com/
Control: Partnership, Investor–owned (for–profit) **Service**: General medical and surgical

Staffed Beds: 12 **Admissions**: 533 **Census**: 3 **Outpatient Visits**: 5901
Births: 0 **Total Expense ($000)**: 53668 **Payroll Expense ($000)**: 11513
Personnel: 168

☐ **TEXAS HEALTH HARRIS METHODIST HOSPITAL SOUTHLAKE (450888)**, 1545 East Southlake Boulevard, Zip 76092–6422; tel. 817/748–8700, **A**1 10 **F**3 29 30 40 64 74 79 81 85 107 111 113 114 119 130 **P**2
Primary Contact: Traci Bernard, R.N., President, Chief Executive Officer and Chief Operating Officer
CFO: Mitchell Mulvehill, Group Financial Officer
CMO: David Taunton, M.D., Chief of Staff
CHR: Tasha Sledge, Director Human Resources
CNO: Debra Ennis, R.N., Vice President and Chief Nursing Officer
Web address: www.texashealthsouthlake.com
Control: Corporation, Investor–owned (for–profit) **Service**: Surgical

Staffed Beds: 23 **Admissions**: 1004 **Census**: 6 **Outpatient Visits**: 13363
Births: 0 **Total Expense ($000)**: 55988 **Payroll Expense ($000)**: 11544
Personnel: 134

SPEARMAN—Hansford County

★ **HANSFORD HOSPITAL (451344)**, 707 South Roland Street, Zip 79081–3441; tel. 806/659–2535, **A**10 18 **F**3 7 11 32 34 35 40 43 56 57 59 62 63 64 65 68 69 77 78 93 107 114 127 130 133 148 **P**6
Primary Contact: Jonathan D. Bailey, Chief Executive Officer and Administrator
CFO: Scott Beedy, Chief Financial Officer
CMO: Mark Garnett, M.D., Chief of Staff
CHR: Jackie Nelson, Director Human Resources
Web address: www.hchd.net
Control: Hospital district or authority, Government, nonfederal **Service**: General medical and surgical

Staffed Beds: 14 **Admissions**: 110 **Census**: 2 **Outpatient Visits**: 29258
Births: 0 **Total Expense ($000)**: 11369 **Payroll Expense ($000)**: 4693
Personnel: 100

STAFFORD—Fort Bend County

ATRIUM MEDICAL CENTER (452114), 11929 West Airport Boulevard, Zip 77477–2451; tel. 281/207–8200, **A**10 22 **F**1 3 18 28 29 45 46 56 59 60 64 65 68 70 74 77 82 83 85 90 91 107 114 119 130 148
Primary Contact: Ahmad Zaid, Chief Executive Officer
CFO: Ana Urbina, Chief Financial Officer
CMO: Shatish Patel, M.D., Chief Medical Officer
CNO: Ava Hearing, Chief Nursing Officer
Web address: www.atriummedicalcenter.com
Control: Partnership, Investor–owned (for–profit) **Service**: Acute long–term care hospital

Staffed Beds: 68 **Admissions**: 335 **Census**: 21 **Outpatient Visits**: 137
Births: 0 **Total Expense ($000)**: 11652 **Payroll Expense ($000)**: 4753
Personnel: 98

Many Facility Codes have changed. Please refer to the AHA Guide Code Chart.

TX

STANTON—Martin County

MARTIN COUNTY HOSPITAL DISTRICT (451333), 600 Interstate 20E, Zip 79782, Mailing Address: P.O. Box 640, Zip 79782–0640; tel. 432/607–3200, **A**10 18 **F**3 7 29 34 35 39 40 45 57 59 64 65 75 81 87 93 107 114 119 127 133 **P**6
Primary Contact: Rance Ramsey, Chief Executive Officer
CFO: Michele Cathey, Interim Chief Financial officer
CIO: Freddy Oliveras, Chief Information Officer
CHR: Paula Dority, Director Human Resources
CNO: Brandi Avila, Chief Nursing Officer
Web address: www.martincountyhospital.org/
Control: Hospital district or authority, Government, nonfederal **Service**: General medical and surgical

Staffed Beds: 18 **Admissions**: 200 **Census**: 5 **Outpatient Visits**: 7183
Births: 0 **Total Expense ($000)**: 23027 **Payroll Expense ($000)**: 10184
Personnel: 171

STEPHENVILLE—Erath County

☒ **TEXAS HEALTH HARRIS METHODIST HOSPITAL STEPHENVILLE (450351)**, 411 North Belknap Street, Zip 76401–3415; tel. 254/965–1500, **A**1 10 20 **F**3 13 15 28 29 30 34 35 39 40 41 43 45 50 51 57 59 64 65 68 70 75 76 77 79 81 85 86 89 107 108 110 111 114 118 119 130 146 147 148 149 154 **P**6 **S** Texas Health Resources, Arlington, TX
Primary Contact: Christopher Leu, President
CMO: Marilyn Brister, M.D., Chief of Staff
CHR: Kimberly Leondar, Director Human Resources
CNO: Cynthia L McCarthy, MS, R.N., Chief Nursing Officer
Web address: www.texashealth.org/landing.cfm?id=108
Control: Other not–for–profit (including NFP Corporation) **Service**: General medical and surgical

Staffed Beds: 54 **Admissions**: 1888 **Census**: 16 **Outpatient Visits**: 28827
Births: 398 **Total Expense ($000)**: 45064 **Payroll Expense ($000)**: 16743
Personnel: 187

SUGAR LAND—Fort Bend County

⇑ **MEMORIAL HERMANN FIRST COLONY HOSPITAL (670058)**, 16000 Southwest Freeway, Suite 100, Zip 77479–2674; tel. 281/277–0911, **A**10 21 **F**3 40 75 107 114 119 149 152 **P**5 **S** Emerus, The Woodlands, TX
Primary Contact: Brenda Villafranco, Administrator
Web address: www.emerus.com
Control: Corporation, Investor–owned (for–profit) **Service**: General medical and surgical

Staffed Beds: 7 **Admissions**: 83 **Census**: 1 **Outpatient Visits**: 4975 **Births**: 0
Total Expense ($000): 5530 **Payroll Expense ($000)**: 1639 **Personnel**: 27

☒ **ENCOMPASS HEALTH REHABILITATION HOSPITAL OF SUGAR LAND (673042)**, 1325 Highway 6, Zip 77478–4906; tel. 281/276–7574, **A**1 10 **F**3 29 30 34 75 87 90 95 96 130 132 146 148 154 **S** Encompass Health Corporation, Birmingham, AL
Primary Contact: Nicholas Hardin, FACHE, Chief Executive Officer
CFO: Carol Neilson, CPA, Controller
CNO: Steve Midgett, R.N., Chief Nursing Officer
Web address: www.healthsouthsugarland.com
Control: Corporation, Investor–owned (for–profit) **Service**: Rehabilitation

Staffed Beds: 50 **Admissions**: 1359 **Census**: 45 **Outpatient Visits**: 0
Births: 0 **Total Expense ($000)**: 20061 **Payroll Expense ($000)**: 10241
Personnel: 182

★ ⇑ **HOUSTON METHODIST SUGAR LAND HOSPITAL (450820)**, 16655 SW Freeway, Zip 77479–2329; tel. 281/274–7000, **A**2 3 10 21 **F**3 12 13 15 18 20 22 24 26 29 30 31 33 34 35 36 37 38 39 40 41 44 45 46 47 49 50 51 53 54 55 57 58 59 60 61 64 65 68 70 73 74 75 76 77 78 79 81 82 84 85 86 87 92 93 94 96 100 102 107 108 110 111 114 115 118 119 121 123 124 126 130 131 132 135 145 146 147 148 149 150 **P**6 **S** Houston Methodist, Houston, TX
Primary Contact: Christopher Siebenaler, Regional Senior Vice President and Chief Executive Officer
CFO: Lowell Stanton, Chief Financial Officer
CMO: Jeffrey Jackson, M.D., Medical Director
CHR: Luis Mario Garcia Jr Director Human Resources
Web address: www.methodisthealth.com
Control: Other not–for–profit (including NFP Corporation) **Service**: General medical and surgical

Staffed Beds: 305 **Admissions**: 16947 **Census**: 212 **Outpatient Visits**: 211144 **Births**: 2913 **Total Expense ($000)**: 384688 **Payroll Expense ($000)**: 135632 **Personnel**: 2323

☒ **KINDRED HOSPITAL SUGAR LAND (452080)**, 1550 First Colony Boulevard, Zip 77479–4000; tel. 281/275–6000, **A**1 10 **F**1 3 29 30 35 64 65 75 77 84 87 107 130 148 149 154 **S** Kindred Healthcare, Louisville, KY
Primary Contact: John D. Cross, Chief Executive Officer
CFO: Sara Rodriguez, Chief Financial Officer
CMO: Subodh Bhuchar, M.D., Chief of Staff
CIO: Feisal Ndomea, Director Case Management
CHR: Lupe Delgado, Coordinator Human Resources
CNO: Hala Alameddine, Chief Nursing Executive
Web address: www.kindred.com
Control: Corporation, Investor–owned (for–profit) **Service**: Acute long–term care hospital

Staffed Beds: 105 **Admissions**: 992 **Census**: 72 **Outpatient Visits**: 89
Births: 0 **Total Expense ($000)**: 39871 **Payroll Expense ($000)**: 14986
Personnel: 271

☒ **MEMORIAL HERMANN SUGAR LAND HOSPITAL (450848)**, 17500 West Grand Parkway South, Zip 77479–2562; tel. 281/725–5000, **A**1 3 5 10 **F**3 8 11 12 13 15 18 20 22 26 29 30 34 35 37 40 41 43 44 45 46 47 48 49 50 51 55 56 57 58 59 64 68 70 72 74 75 76 77 78 79 80 81 82 85 86 87 89 91 107 108 109 110 111 112 114 119 126 129 130 146 147 148 154 **P**5 6 **S** Memorial Hermann Health System, Houston, TX
Primary Contact: Malisha Patel, Senior Vice President and Chief Executive Officer
CFO: Lisa Kendler, Chief Financial Officer
CMO: William Riley, M.D., Jr Chief of Staff
CHR: Robert Blake, Chief Human Resources Officer Southwest Market
Web address: www.memorialhermann.org
Control: Other not–for–profit (including NFP Corporation) **Service**: General medical and surgical

Staffed Beds: 149 **Admissions**: 7123 **Census**: 67 **Outpatient Visits**: 103482 **Births**: 1904 **Total Expense ($000)**: 159683 **Payroll Expense ($000)**: 53141 **Personnel**: 687

⇑ **METHODIST SUGAR LAND HOSPITAL** See Houston Methodist Sugar Land Hospital

★ ⇑ **ST. LUKE'S SUGAR LAND HOSPITAL (670053)**, 1317 Lake Pointe Parkway, Zip 77478–3997; tel. 281/637–7000, **A**10 21 **F**3 15 18 20 22 26 29 30 34 35 37 39 40 41 44 45 46 49 50 57 60 64 68 70 72 74 75 79 81 82 85 107 108 110 111 115 119 126 130 146 147 148 **P**5 **S** Catholic Health Initiatives, Englewood, CO
Primary Contact: Robert A. Heifner, FACHE, Chief Executive Officer
CFO: Bill Beauchamp, Chief Financial Officer
CNO: Wes Garrison
Web address: www.stlukessugarland.com
Control: Church operated, Nongovernment, not–for–profit **Service**: General medical and surgical

Staffed Beds: 96 **Admissions**: 4363 **Census**: 50 **Outpatient Visits**: 24783
Births: 1196 **Total Expense ($000)**: 79151 **Payroll Expense ($000)**: 34192
Personnel: 370

SUGAR LAND REHABILITATION HOSPITAL See Encompass Health Rehabilitation Hospital of Sugar Land

TRIUMPH HOSPITAL SOUTHWEST See Kindred Hospital Sugar Land

SULPHUR SPRINGS—Hopkins County

★ **CHRISTUS MOTHER FRANCES HOSPITAL – SULPHUR SPRINGS (450236)**, 115 Airport Road, Zip 75482–2105; tel. 903/885–7671, **A**3 10 **F**1 3 11 13 15 29 30 34 35 40 43 45 57 59 64 66 70 73 76 80 81 93 96 107 110 111 115 119 130 146 148 **S** CHRISTUS Health, Irving, TX
Primary Contact: Paul Harvey, President and Chief Executive Officer
COO: Donna Geiken Wallace, Chief Operating Officer and Chief Financial Officer
CFO: Donna Geiken Wallace, Chief Operating Officer and Chief Financial Officer
CMO: Chris Gallagher, M.D., Chief Medical Officer
CHR: Donna Rudzik, Director Human Resources
Web address: www.tmfhc.org/maps–and–locations/locations–profile/?id=72&searchId=8bcb329f–a152–e611–b37f–2c768a4e1b84&sort=11&page=1&pageSize=10
Control: Other not–for–profit (including NFP Corporation) **Service**: General medical and surgical

Staffed Beds: 56 **Admissions**: 2955 **Census**: 27 **Outpatient Visits**: 55831
Births: 694 **Total Expense ($000)**: 57047 **Payroll Expense ($000)**: 20415
Personnel: 315

TX

SUNNYVALE—Dallas County

✠ **BAYLOR SCOTT & WHITE MEDICAL CENTER – SUNNYVALE (670060)**, 231 South Collins Road, Zip 75182–4624; tel. 972/892–3000, (Nonreporting) **A**1 10 **S** TENET Healthcare Corporation, Dallas, TX
Primary Contact: Jon Duckert, FACHE, Chief Executive Officer
COO: Josiah De La Garza, Chief Operating Officer
CMO: William G. Jones, M.D., Chief Medical Officer
CNO: Deborah A Moeller, R.N., MS, Interim Chief Nursing Officer
Web address: www.BaylorScottandWhite.com/Sunnyvale
Control: Partnership, Investor–owned (for–profit) **Service**: General medical and surgical

Staffed Beds: 70

SWEENY—Brazoria County

★ **SWEENY COMMUNITY HOSPITAL (451311)**, 305 North McKinney Street, Zip 77480–2895; tel. 979/548–1500, (Data for 354 days) **A**10 18 **F**3 7 10 11 15 29 34 35 40 43 45 53 56 57 59 64 65 69 70 75 81 85 93 104 107 110 114 119 130 132 133 143 145 148 149 153
Primary Contact: Scott Briner, Chief Executive Officer
CFO: Hong Wade, Chief Financial Officer
CMO: Enrique A Leal, M.D., III Chief of Staff
CIO: Stuart Butler, Director Information Technology
CHR: Rebecca McKay, Director Human Resources
CNO: Sherri Pierce, R.N., Chief Nursing Officer
Web address: www.sweenyhospital.org
Control: Hospital district or authority, Government, nonfederal **Service**: General medical and surgical

Staffed Beds: 14 Admissions: 238 Census: 2 Outpatient Visits: 15310 Births: 0 Total Expense ($000): 47571 Payroll Expense ($000): 7917 Personnel: 176

SWEETWATER—Nolan County

★ ⇑ **ROLLING PLAINS MEMORIAL HOSPITAL (450055)**, 200 East Arizona Street, Zip 79556–7199, Mailing Address: P.O. Box 690, Zip 79556–0690; tel. 325/235–1701, **A**10 20 21 **F**3 11 13 15 28 29 34 40 43 45 53 57 59 62 70 76 77 79 81 85 89 93 107 108 114 119 127 130 133 135 146 148
Primary Contact: Donna Boatright, R.N., MSN, Chief Executive Officer
COO: Rhonda Guelker, Senior Director Finance
CFO: Rhonda Guelker, Senior Director Finance
CIO: Rhonda Guelker, Senior Director Finance
CHR: Ame Monroe, Director Human Resources
CNO: Maxine Montano, R.N., Chief Nursing Officer
Web address: www.rpmh.net
Control: Hospital district or authority, Government, nonfederal **Service**: General medical and surgical

Staffed Beds: 57 Admissions: 994 Census: 10 Outpatient Visits: 64110 Births: 200 Total Expense ($000): 36205 Payroll Expense ($000): 16215 Personnel: 299

TAHOKA—Lynn County

★ **LYNN COUNTY HOSPITAL DISTRICT (451351)**, 2600 Lockwood, Zip 79373–4118; tel. 806/998–4533, **A**10 18 **F**3 7 10 13 29 32 34 35 40 43 44 53 54 56 57 59 64 65 66 75 86 93 97 107 133 147 148 149 **P**5
Primary Contact: Melanie Richburg, Chief Executive Officer
CFO: Steve Brock, Chief Financial Officer
CMO: Donald Freitag, M.D., Chief Medical Officer
CIO: Jim Brown, Director Information Technology
CHR: Jill Stone, Manager Human Resources
CNO: Angie Jalomo, Chief Nursing Officer
Web address: www.lchdhealthcare.org
Control: Hospital district or authority, Government, nonfederal **Service**: General medical and surgical

Staffed Beds: 16 Admissions: 207 Census: 6 Outpatient Visits: 7093 Births: 0 Total Expense ($000): 13599 Payroll Expense ($000): 4989 Personnel: 135

TAYLOR—Williamson County

✠ **BAYLOR SCOTT & WHITE MEDICAL CENTER – TAYLOR (451374)**, 305 Mallard Lane, Zip 76574–1208; tel. 512/352–7611, **A**1 10 18 **F**3 18 29 34 35 40 45 50 56 57 59 62 64 65 68 75 77 81 82 85 87 91 92 93 97 107 108 111 119 127 129 130 132 133 135 146 148 149 **S** Baylor Scott & White Health, Dallas, TX
Primary Contact: Jay Fox, Director Operations
Web address: www.swtaylor.org
Control: Other not–for–profit (including NFP Corporation) **Service**: General medical and surgical

Staffed Beds: 25 Admissions: 344 Census: 5 Outpatient Visits: 55558 Births: 0 Total Expense ($000): 21835 Payroll Expense ($000): 11650 Personnel: 145

JOHNS COMMUNITY HOSPITAL See Baylor Scott & White Medical Center – Taylor

TEMPLE—Bell County

★ **BAYLOR SCOTT AND WHITE CONTINUING CARE HOSPITAL (452105)**, 546 North Kegley Road, Zip 76502–4069; tel. 254/215–0900, **A**10 **F**1 3 29 30 60 85 107 119 128 148 **S** Baylor Scott & White Health, Dallas, TX
Primary Contact: Shahin Motakef, FACHE, President
CMO: David P Ciceri, M.D., Chief Medical Officer
CNO: Robert Pisicotta, Chief Nursing Officer
Web address: www.sw.org/location/temple–cch
Control: Other not–for–profit (including NFP Corporation) **Service**: Acute long–term care hospital

Staffed Beds: 48 Admissions: 374 Census: 32 Outpatient Visits: 2 Births: 0 Total Expense ($000): 19398 Payroll Expense ($000): 8655 Personnel: 104

CENTRAL TEXAS VETERANS AFFAIRS HEALTH CARE SYSTEM, OLIN E. TEAGUE VETERANS MEDICAL CENTER See Central Texas Veterans Health Care System, Temple

✠ △ **CENTRAL TEXAS VETERANS HEALTH CARE SYSTEM**, 1901 Veterans Memorial Drive, Zip 76504–7493; tel. 254/778–4811, (Includes CENTRAL TEXAS VETERANS AFFAIRS HEALTH CARE SYSTEM, OLIN E. TEAGUE VETERANS MEDICAL CENTER, 1901 Veterans Memorial Drive, Temple, TX, Zip 76504; tel. 254/778–4811; Christopher R. Sandles, FACHE, Director; CENTRAL TEXAS VETERANS HEALTH CARE SYSTEM, DORIS MILLER VETERANS MEDICAL CENTER, 4800 Memorial Drive, Waco, TX, Zip 76711–1397; tel. 254/752–6581; Christopher R. Sandles, FACHE, Director) (Nonreporting) **A**1 3 5 7 8 **S** Department of Veterans Affairs, Perry Point, MD
Primary Contact: Christopher R. Sandles, FACHE, Medical Center Director and Chief Executive Officer
COO: Andrew T. Garcia, Acting Associate Director
CFO: Rosey Anzures, Acting Chief Financial Officer
CMO: Olawale Fashina, M.D., Chief of Staff
CIO: Victor Vitolas, Acting Chief Information Technology Services
CHR: Mary P. Doerfler, Chief Human Resources Officer
CNO: Bryan W. Sisk, Associate Director Patient and Nursing Services
Web address: www.centraltexas.va.gov/
Control: Veterans Affairs, Government, federal **Service**: General medical and surgical

Staffed Beds: 1532

MCLANE CHILDREN'S HOSPITAL SCOTT & WHITE See Scott & White Medical Center – Temple, Temple

✠ **SCOTT & WHITE MEDICAL CENTER – TEMPLE (450054)**, 2401 South 31st Street, Zip 76508–0002; tel. 254/724–2111, (Includes MCLANE CHILDREN'S HOSPITAL SCOTT & WHITE, 1901 SW H K Dodgen Loop, Temple, TX, Zip 76502–1896; tel. 254/771–8600; John Boyd III, M.D., Chief Executive Officer; MCLANE CHILDREN'S HOSPITAL SCOTT & WHITE, 2401 South 31st Street, Temple, TX, Zip 76508–0001; tel. 877/724–5437; John Boyd III, M.D., Chief Executive Officer and Chief Medical Officer) (Total facility includes 29 beds in nursing home–type unit) **A**1 2 3 5 8 10 **F**3 5 8 9 11 12 13 14 15 17 18 19 20 22 24 25 26 27 28 29 30 31 32 34 35 36 37 38 39 40 41 43 45 46 47 48 49 50 51 52 53 56 57 58 59 60 61 63 64 65 66 67 68 70 72 73 74 75 76 77 78 79 81 82 83 84 85 86 87 88 89 91 92 93 94 95 97 98 99 100 101 102 103 104 107 108 109 110 111 112 113 114 115 116 117 118 119 120 121 124 126 127 129 130 131 132 133 134 135 137 138 141 142 144 146 147 148 149 150 154 **S** Baylor Scott & White Health, Dallas, TX
Primary Contact: Shahin Motakef, FACHE, President
CFO: Alita Prosser, Chief Financial Officer
CMO: Stephen Sibbitt, M.D., Chief Medical Officer
CIO: Matthew Chambers, Chief Information Officer
CHR: Pat Balz, Vice President Operations Human Resources
CNO: Gerald W Bryant, R.N., Chief Nursing Officer
Web address: www.sw.org/location/temple–hospital
Control: Other not–for–profit (including NFP Corporation) **Service**: General medical and surgical

Staffed Beds: 647 Admissions: 35063 Census: 452 Outpatient Visits: 1775803 Births: 2469 Total Expense ($000): 997965 Payroll Expense ($000): 318216 Personnel: 6040

Many Facility Codes have changed. Please refer to the AHA Guide Code Chart. © 2018 AHA Guide

TERRELL—Kaufman County

☐ **TERRELL STATE HOSPITAL (454006)**, 1200 East Brin Street, Zip 75160–2938, Mailing Address: P.O. Box 70, Zip 75160–9000; tel. 972/524–6452, **A1** 3 10 **F**30 34 39 57 68 75 86 87 98 99 100 101 103 130 132 135 146 **P**6 **S** Texas Department of State Health Services, Austin, TX
Primary Contact: Dorothy Floyd, Ph.D., Superintendent
CFO: David R. Teel, Financial Officer
CMO: Mark Messer, D.O., Clinical Director
CIO: Sims Anderson, Manager Facility Automation
CNO: Kathryn Griffin, Chief Nurse Executive
Web address: www.dshs.state.tx.us/mhhospitals/terrellsh
Control: State, Government, nonfederal **Service**: Psychiatric

Staffed Beds: 288 Admissions: 1502 Census: 261 Outpatient Visits: 0
Births: 0 Total Expense ($000): 89452 Payroll Expense ($000): 38916
Personnel: 869

TEXARKANA—Bowie County

⊞ **CHRISTUS ST. MICHAEL HEALTH SYSTEM (450801)**, 2600 St Michael Drive, Zip 75503–5220; tel. 903/614–1000, (Includes CHRISTUS ST. MICHAEL HOSPITAL–ATLANTA, 1007 South William Street, Atlanta, TX, Zip 75551–3245; tel. 903/799–3000; William Micah Johnson, Administrator and Chief Nursing Officer) **A1** 2 3 10 **F**3 11 13 15 17 18 20 22 24 26 28 29 30 31 34 35 37 40 41 43 45 48 49 51 53 55 56 57 59 60 64 65 68 70 71 72 73 74 75 76 77 78 79 80 81 82 84 85 86 87 89 92 97 102 107 108 109 110 111 114 115 118 119 120 121 122 123 124 126 129 130 131 132 135 143 144 146 147 148 149 154 **P**8 **S** CHRISTUS Health, Irving, TX
Primary Contact: Jason Rounds, Interim Chief Executive Officer
COO: Jason Rounds, Chief Operating Officer and Administrator
CFO: Glen Boles, Vice President and Chief Financial Officer
CMO: Mike Finley, M.D., Chief Medical Officer
CIO: Alana Higgins, Regional Information Management Executive
CHR: Jennifer Wright, Vice President Regional Human Resources
CNO: Louise Thornell, Chief Nursing Officer
Web address: www.christusstmichael.org
Control: Church operated, Nongovernment, not–for–profit **Service**: General medical and surgical

Staffed Beds: 354 Admissions: 13364 Census: 156 Outpatient Visits: 144704 Births: 1601 Total Expense ($000): 249774 Payroll Expense ($000): 75250 Personnel: 1359

⊞ △ **CHRISTUS ST. MICHAEL REHABILITATION HOSPITAL (453065)**, 2400 St Michael Drive, Zip 75503–2374; tel. 903/614–4000, **A1** 7 10 **F**3 11 18 28 29 30 34 35 57 59 65 68 75 77 79 82 87 90 93 96 132 135 143 148 149 154 **S** CHRISTUS Health, Irving, TX
Primary Contact: Patrick Flannery, Administrator
CFO: Glen Boles, Vice President and Chief Financial Officer
CMO: Richard Sharp, M.D., Medical Director
CIO: Alana Higgins, Regional Information Management Executive
CHR: Jennifer Wright, Vice President Human Resources
CNO: Stacey Breedlove, Chief Nursing Officer
Web address: www.christusstmichael.org/rehab
Control: Church operated, Nongovernment, not–for–profit **Service**: Rehabilitation

Staffed Beds: 50 Admissions: 1130 Census: 34 Outpatient Visits: 11431
Births: 0 Total Expense ($000): 22882 Payroll Expense ($000): 10783
Personnel: 163

⊞ **ENCOMPASS HEALTH REHABILITATION HOSPITAL OF TEXARKANA (453053)**, 515 West 12th Street, Zip 75501–4416; tel. 903/735–5000, **A1** 10 **F**3 28 29 64 74 77 79 90 91 93 95 96 130 131 132 143 148 154 **P**5 **S** Encompass Health Corporation, Birmingham, AL
Primary Contact: Harlo McCall, Chief Executive Officer
CFO: Phylis Buck, Controller
CMO: Mark A Wren, M.D., Medical Director
CHR: Ann R Clapp, Director Human Resources
CNO: Lorri Oglesby, Chief Nursing Officer
Web address: www.healthsouthtexarkana.com
Control: Corporation, Investor–owned (for–profit) **Service**: Rehabilitation

Staffed Beds: 60 Admissions: 1285 Census: 46 Outpatient Visits: 7175
Births: 0 Total Expense ($000): 19118 Payroll Expense ($000): 10309
Personnel: 203

⊞ **POST ACUTE MEDICAL SPECIALTY HOSPITAL OF TEXARKANA – NORTH (452061)**, 2400 St Michael Drive, 2nd Floor, Zip 75503–2372; tel. 903/614–7600, **A1** 10 **F**1 3 29 148 **S** Post Acute Medical, LLC, Enola, PA
Primary Contact: Lorraine Murray, Chief Executive Officer
Web address: www.postacutemedical.com
Control: Corporation, Investor–owned (for–profit) **Service**: Acute long–term care hospital

Staffed Beds: 49 Admissions: 717 Census: 34 Outpatient Visits: 0
Births: 0 Total Expense ($000): 16961 Payroll Expense ($000): 6168
Personnel: 100

☐ **WADLEY REGIONAL MEDICAL CENTER (450200)**, 1000 Pine Street, Zip 75501–5170; tel. 903/798–8000, **A1** 3 10 **F**3 11 13 15 18 20 22 24 28 29 30 31 34 35 40 43 45 49 50 56 57 59 60 64 65 70 71 73 74 75 77 78 79 81 85 86 87 98 103 107 108 110 111 114 115 119 120 121 123 126 130 146 147 148 149 154 **S** Steward Health Care System, LLC, Dallas, TX
Primary Contact: Thomas D. Gilbert, FACHE, Chief Executive Officer
CFO: Bonny Sorensen, Chief Financial Officer
CIO: Matt Kesterson, Director Information Services
CHR: Debby Butler, Director Human Resources
CNO: Shelly Strayhorn, R.N., Chief Nursing Officer
Web address: www.wadleyhealth.com
Control: Corporation, Investor–owned (for–profit) **Service**: General medical and surgical

Staffed Beds: 179 Admissions: 6736 Census: 82 Outpatient Visits: 87315
Births: 1034 Total Expense ($000): 94310 Payroll Expense ($000): 42421
Personnel: 725

THE COLONY—Denton County

THE COLONY ER HOSPITAL, 4780 State Highway 121, Zip 75056–2913; tel. 214/469–1119, (Nonreporting)
Primary Contact: Russell Kaiser, Interim Chief Executive Officer and Chief Nursing Officer
Web address: www.https://thecolonyer.com/
Control: Individual, Investor–owned (for–profit) **Service**: General medical and surgical

Staffed Beds: 13

THE WOODLANDS—Montgomery County

★ ⇑ **CHI ST. LUKE'S HEALTH–LAKESIDE HOSPITAL (670059)**, 17400 St. Luke's Way, Zip 77384–8036; tel. 936/266–9000, **A**10 21 **F**3 18 20 22 26 29 30 34 35 40 50 57 59 64 68 75 79 81 92 94 107 111 115 119 130 131 135 **P**5 **S** Catholic Health Initiatives, Englewood, CO
Primary Contact: James Parisi, Chief Executive Officer
CHR: Debra Roberts, Director of Human Resources
CNO: Diane Freeman, R.N., Assistant Vice President and Chief Nursing Officer
Web address: www.stlukeslakeside.com/
Control: Corporation, Investor–owned (for–profit) **Service**: Surgical

Staffed Beds: 30 Admissions: 759 Census: 5 Outpatient Visits: 17393
Births: 0 Total Expense ($000): 38325 Payroll Expense ($000): 7920
Personnel: 119

⊞ **CHI ST. LUKE'S HEALTH–THE WOODLANDS HOSPITAL (450862)**, 17200 St. Luke's Way, Zip 77384–8007; tel. 936/266–2000, **A1** 10 **F**3 11 12 13 15 18 20 22 24 26 28 29 30 34 35 38 40 41 45 49 50 57 58 59 64 68 70 72 74 75 76 78 79 81 82 85 86 87 89 90 93 107 108 109 110 111 114 118 119 124 126 129 130 131 135 145 146 147 148 **P**5 **S** Catholic Health Initiatives, Englewood, CO
Primary Contact: James Parisi, Chief Executive Officer
CMO: Charles Sims, M.D., Chief of Staff
Web address: www.stlukeswoodlands.com
Control: Church operated, Nongovernment, not–for–profit **Service**: General medical and surgical

Staffed Beds: 207 Admissions: 11003 Census: 128 Outpatient Visits: 79944 Births: 1909 Total Expense ($000): 205181 Payroll Expense ($000): 77631 Personnel: 1080

TX

★ **HOUSTON METHODIST THE WOODLANDS HOSPITAL (670122)**, 17201 Interstate 45 South, Zip 77385; tel. 713/790-3333, (Data for 189 days) **A**10 **F**3 11 12 13 15 18 20 22 24 26 28 29 30 31 34 35 36 37 40 41 44 45 49 50 51 53 57 59 64 68 70 72 74 75 76 77 78 79 81 85 86 87 93 96 97 102 107 108 110 111 115 116 117 119 120 121 122 124 126 130 131 132 135 146 147 154 **P**5 6 **S** Houston Methodist, Houston, TX
Primary Contact: Debra F. Sukin, Ph.D., Regional Senior Vice President and Chief Executive Officer
CNO: Kerrie Guerrero, R.N., MSN, Vice President and Chief Nursing Officer
Web address: www.houstonmethodist.org/locations/the-woodlands/
Control: Other not-for-profit (including NFP Corporation) **Service:** General medical and surgical

Staffed Beds: 101 **Admissions:** 2875 **Census:** 47 **Outpatient Visits:** 32136 **Births:** 700 **Total Expense ($000):** 95387 **Payroll Expense ($000):** 34320 **Personnel:** 780	

MEMORIAL HERMANN THE WOODLANDS HOSPITAL See Memorial Hermann Greater Heights Hospital, Houston

NEXUS SPECIALTY HOSPITAL THE WOODLANDS (452057), 9182 Six Pines Drive, Zip 77380-3670; tel. 281/364-0317, (Nonreporting) **A**10
Primary Contact: Eric Cantrell, Chief Executive Officer
CFO: David Strickler, Chief Financial Officer
CMO: Ather Siddiqi, M.D., Medical Director
CIO: Noe Salinas, Vice President Information Technology
CHR: Kevin McAndrews, Vice President, Human Resources
CNO: Rhena Anderson, Chief Nursing Officer
Web address: www.nexusspecialty.com
Control: Partnership, Investor-owned (for-profit) **Service:** Acute long-term care hospital

Staffed Beds: 21

★ **WOODLANDS SPECIALTY HOSPITAL**, 9182 Six Pines Drive, Zip 77380-3670, Mailing Address: 25540 I-45 North, Suite 100, Spring, Zip 77380-3670; tel. 281/602-8160, (Nonreporting)
Primary Contact: Don Vickers, Chief Executive Officer
CFO: Virginia de Bond, Chief Financial Officer
Web address: www.woodlandsspecialtyhospital.com/
Control: Partnership, Investor-owned (for-profit) **Service:** General medical and surgical

Staffed Beds: 6

THROCKMORTON—Throckmorton County

THROCKMORTON COUNTY MEMORIAL HOSPITAL (451339), 802 North Minter Street, Zip 76483-5357, Mailing Address: P.O. Box 729, Zip 76483-0729; tel. 940/849-2151, **A**10 18 **F**1 4 7 40 41 43 44 50 59 61 64 65 67 68 79 87 97 102 127 128 130 133 148 **P**5 6
Primary Contact: Kirby Gober, Chief Executive Officer
CFO: Cindy Parker, Chief Financial Officer and Director Human Resources
CMO: Ruth Ebangit, M.D., Chief of Staff and Medical Officer
CIO: Amber Myer, Director Medical Technology
CHR: Cindy Parker, Chief Financial Officer and Director Human Resources
CNO: Pam Stamm, Chief Nursing Officer
Web address: www.throckmortonhospital.com/index.html
Control: County, Government, nonfederal **Service:** General medical and surgical

Staffed Beds: 14 **Admissions:** 76 **Census:** 1 **Outpatient Visits:** 8069 **Births:** 0 **Total Expense ($000):** 4153 **Payroll Expense ($000):** 1679 **Personnel:** 48

TOMBALL—Harris County

✠ **KINDRED HOSPITAL TOMBALL (452074)**, 505 Graham Drive, Zip 77375-3368; tel. 281/255-5600, (Includes KINDRED HOSPITAL SPRING, 205 Hollow Tree Lane, Houston, TX, Zip 77090; tel. 832/249-2700; Randy Briones, Chief Executive Officer) **A**1 10 **F**1 3 18 29 30 31 44 70 74 75 78 79 84 85 86 87 93 94 107 119 130 **S** Kindred Healthcare, Louisville, KY
Primary Contact: Tracy Kohler, Chief Executive Officer
Web address: www.khtomball.com/
Control: Partnership, Investor-owned (for-profit) **Service:** Acute long-term care hospital

Staffed Beds: 258 **Admissions:** 2000 **Census:** 145 **Outpatient Visits:** 6838 **Births:** 0 **Total Expense ($000):** 86436 **Payroll Expense ($000):** 32063 **Personnel:** 446

⇑ **MEMORIAL HERMANN TOMBALL HOSPITAL (670095)**, 24429 State Highway 249, Zip 77375-8214; tel. 281/516-0911, **A**21 **F**3 40 68 75 107 114 119 149 **P**5 **S** Emerus, The Woodlands, TX
Primary Contact: Brenda Villafranco, Administrator
Web address: www.emerus.com/tomball/
Control: Corporation, Investor-owned (for-profit) **Service:** General medical and surgical

Staffed Beds: 8 **Admissions:** 66 **Census:** 1 **Outpatient Visits:** 5435 **Births:** 0 **Total Expense ($000):** 6700 **Payroll Expense ($000):** 1960 **Personnel:** 35

✠ **TOMBALL REGIONAL MEDICAL CENTER (450670)**, 605 Holderrieth Street, Zip 77375-6445; tel. 281/401-7500, (Includes KINDRED HOSPITAL THE HEIGHTS, 1800 West 26th Street, Houston, TX, Zip 77008-1450; tel. 832/673-4200; William Elsesser, Chief Executive Officer) **A**1 10 **F**3 8 12 13 15 18 20 22 24 26 28 29 30 34 40 44 45 46 47 48 49 50 51 53 54 57 59 64 70 72 74 75 76 79 80 81 82 85 86 87 90 91 94 96 98 102 103 107 108 110 111 114 115 119 124 126 129 130 131 132 146 149 **P**6 **S** HCA Healthcare, Nashville, TN
Primary Contact: Eric Evans, Chief Executive Officer
COO: Ryan Henry, Chief Operating Officer
CFO: Richard Ervin, Chief Financial Officer
CMO: Ian Glass, M.D., Chief Medical Officer
CIO: Marisa Smith, Director
CHR: Vanessa Anyaso, Chief Human Resources
Web address: www.tomballregionalmedicalcenter.com
Control: Corporation, Investor-owned (for-profit) **Service:** General medical and surgical

Staffed Beds: 191 **Admissions:** 9356 **Census:** 132 **Outpatient Visits:** 63320 **Births:** 974 **Total Expense ($000):** 175461 **Payroll Expense ($000):** 58102 **Personnel:** 708

TROPHY CLUB—Denton County

☐ **BAYLOR MEDICAL CENTER AT TROPHY CLUB (450883)**, 2850 East State Highway 114, Zip 76262-5302; tel. 817/837-4600, **A**1 10 **F**3 29 40 70 75 79 81 85 87 107 108 111 114 118 121 123 141
Primary Contact: Melanie Chick, Chief Executive Officer
CFO: Jonathan Saunders, Chief Financial Officer
CMO: Mike Stanton, D.O., Medical Director
CIO: Scot Bradford, Chief Information Officer
CHR: Donna Irvin, Director Human Resources
CNO: Tina Huddleston, R.N., Chief Nursing Officer
Web address: www.baylortrophyclub.com
Control: Partnership, Investor-owned (for-profit) **Service:** General medical and surgical

Staffed Beds: 22 **Admissions:** 1243 **Census:** 7 **Outpatient Visits:** 8570 **Births:** 0 **Total Expense ($000):** 64518 **Payroll Expense ($000):** 11805 **Personnel:** 209

TULIA—Swisher County

★ **SWISHER MEMORIAL HOSPITAL DISTRICT (451349)**, 539 Southeast Second, Zip 79088-2400, Mailing Address: P.O. Box 808, Zip 79088-0808; tel. 806/995-3581, **A**3 10 18 **F**3 7 10 11 29 33 34 35 36 40 43 50 53 57 59 64 65 68 75 77 93 104 107 114 127 130 132 133 **P**4
Primary Contact: Luke Brewer, Acting Chief Executive Officer
CFO: Connie Wilhelm, Chief Financial Officer
CIO: Brad Roberts, Network Administrator
Web address: www.swisherhospital.com
Control: Other not-for-profit (including NFP Corporation) **Service:** General medical and surgical

Staffed Beds: 20 **Admissions:** 273 **Census:** 5 **Outpatient Visits:** 21180 **Births:** 0 **Total Expense ($000):** 11625 **Payroll Expense ($000):** 4457 **Personnel:** 83

TYLER—Smith County

✠ **CHRISTUS MOTHER FRANCES HOSPITAL – TYLER (450102)**, 800 East Dawson Street, Zip 75701-2036; tel. 903/593-8441, (Includes LOUIS & PEACHES OWEN HEART HOSPITAL, 703 South Fleishel Avenue, Tyler, TX, Zip 75701-2015; tel. 903/606-3000; John McGreevy, FACHE, Chief Executive Officer) **A**1 2 3 10 **F**3 7 8 11 12 13 15 17 18 20 22 24 26 28 29 30 31 34 35 37 40 41 43 45 46 47 49 53 57 58 59 60 64 68 70 72 73 74 75 76 78 79 80 81 82 84 85 86 87 89 93 107 108 109 110 111 112 114 115 118 119 126 129 130 131 132 133 144 146 147 148 **P**5 6 7 8 **S** CHRISTUS Health, Irving, TX
Primary Contact: Jason J. Proctor, Chief Operating Officer
CFO: Joyce Hester, CPA, Senior Vice President and Chief Financial Officer
CMO: Fadi Nasrallah, M.D., Vice President Medical Affairs
CIO: Jeff Pearson, Vice President and Chief Information Officer
CHR: Thomas Wilken, Senior Vice President and Chief Human Resources Officer
Web address: www.tmfhc.org
Control: Other not-for-profit (including NFP Corporation) **Service:** General medical and surgical

Staffed Beds: 466 **Admissions:** 25008 **Census:** 310 **Outpatient Visits:** 630202 **Births:** 2694 **Total Expense ($000):** 559211 **Payroll Expense ($000):** 206045 **Personnel:** 3423

TX

Many Facility Codes have changed. Please refer to the AHA Guide Code Chart. © 2018 AHA Guide

⊞ **CHRISTUS TRINITY MOTHER FRANCES REHABILITATION HOSPITAL, A PARTNER OF ENCOMPASS HEALTH (453056)**, 3131 Troup Highway, Zip 75701–8352; tel. 903/510–7000, **A**1 10 **F**3 9 28 29 56 60 74 75 77 79 82 87 90 91 95 96 130 132 143 148 154 **S** Encompass Health Corporation, Birmingham, AL
Primary Contact: Sharla Anderson, Chief Executive Officer
CFO: Michael G Treadway, Controller
CMO: Bradley Merritt, M.D., Medical Director
Web address: www.tmfrehabhospital.com
Control: Partnership, Investor–owned (for–profit) **Service**: Rehabilitation

Staffed Beds: 94 Admissions: 1876 Census: 64 Outpatient Visits: 300 Births: 0 Total Expense ($000): 21868 Payroll Expense ($000): 11047 Personnel: 190

⊞ **BAYLOR SCOTT & WHITE TEXAS SPINE & JOINT HOSPITAL (450864)**, 1814 Roseland Boulevard, Suite 100, Zip 75701–4262; tel. 903/525–3300, **A**1 3 10 **F**8 29 39 40 53 77 79 81 82 107 111 114 119 131 144
Primary Contact: Tony Wahl, Chief Executive Officer
CFO: Greg Cummings, Chief Financial Officer
CMO: Kim Foreman, M.D., Chief of Staff
CNO: Aaron Fleet, R.N., Chief Nursing Officer
Web address: www.tsjh.org
Control: Partnership, Investor–owned (for–profit) **Service**: Orthopedic

Staffed Beds: 20 Admissions: 2035 Census: 13 Outpatient Visits: 42335 Births: 0 Total Expense ($000): 93600 Payroll Expense ($000): 18502 Personnel: 416

★ **TYLER CONTINUECARE HOSPITAL (452091)**, 800 East Dawson, 4th Floor, Zip 75701–2036; tel. 903/531–4080, **A**10 22 **F**1 3 29 34 40 57 59 85 86 130 148 **P**4 **S** Community Hospital Corporation, Plano, TX
Primary Contact: Stephanie Hyde, R.N., MSN, Chief Executive Officer
Web address: www.continuecare.org
Control: Other not–for–profit (including NFP Corporation) **Service**: Acute long–term care hospital

Staffed Beds: 51 Admissions: 486 Census: 42 Outpatient Visits: 0 Births: 0 Total Expense ($000): 23184 Payroll Expense ($000): 8505 Personnel: 117

⊞ **UT HEALTH NORTH CAMPUS TYLER (450690)**, 11937 Highway 271, Zip 75708–3154; tel. 903/877–7777, **A**1 2 8 10 **F**3 8 11 15 18 20 22 24 26 28 29 30 31 32 34 35 40 45 47 49 50 53 54 55 56 57 58 59 64 65 70 71 75 77 78 79 81 84 85 86 87 93 97 98 101 102 103 104 107 108 110 111 114 115 116 117 118 119 120 121 123 124 129 130 132 135 143 146 147 148 153 **P**6 **S** University of Texas System, Austin, TX
Primary Contact: Kirk A. Calhoun, M.D., President
COO: Joe Woelkers, Executive Vice President and Chief Staff
CFO: Vernon Moore, Senior Vice President Chief Business and Finance
CMO: Steven Cox, M.D., Chief Medical Officer
CIO: Vernon Moore, Senior Vice President Chief Business and Finance
CHR: Jesse Gomez, Vice President Human Resources
CNO: Don Hunt, M.D., Vice President Patient Centered Care and Chief Nursing Officer
Web address: www.https://uthealthnorth.com/
Control: State, Government, nonfederal **Service**: General medical and surgical

Staffed Beds: 130 Admissions: 1684 Census: 30 Outpatient Visits: 283981 Births: 0 Total Expense ($000): 211951 Payroll Expense ($000): 75061 Personnel: 1443

⊞ **UT HEALTH REHABILITATION HOSPITAL (453072)**, 701 Olympic Plaza Circle, Zip 75701–1950, Mailing Address: P.O. Box 7530, Zip 75711–7530; tel. 903/596–3000, **A**1 10 **F**3 28 29 30 34 53 57 75 86 90 91 93 96 130 131 132 148 149 **S** Ardent Health Services, Nashville, TN
Primary Contact: Laurie Lehnhof–Watts, Administrator and Chief Nursing Officer
COO: Eddie L Howard, Chief Operating Officer
CFO: James Blanton, Chief Financial Officer
CMO: Jerry Schwarzbach, M.D., Medical Director
CIO: Paula Anthony, Vice President Information Services
CHR: David L Langston, Corporate Vice President Human Resources
CNO: Laurie Lehnhof–Watts, Assistant Administrator Patient Services
Web address: www.https://uthealthrehab.com/
Control: Other not–for–profit (including NFP Corporation) **Service**: Rehabilitation

Staffed Beds: 49 Admissions: 963 Census: 35 Outpatient Visits: 85048 Births: 0 Total Expense ($000): 28005 Payroll Expense ($000): 13500 Personnel: 174

⊞ **UT HEALTH SPECIALTY HOSPITAL (452051)**, 1000 South Beckham, 5th Floor, Zip 75701–1908, Mailing Address: P.O. Box 7018, Zip 75711–7018; tel. 903/596–3600, **A**1 10 **F**1 3 29 30 75 84 130 148 149 **S** Ardent Health Services, Nashville, TN
Primary Contact: Laurie Lehnhof–Watts, Administrator and Chief Nursing Officer
CFO: James Blanton, Chief Financial Officer
CMO: J David Johnson, M.D., Chief of Staff
CIO: Paula Anthony, Vice President Information Services
CHR: David L Langston, Corporate Vice President Human Resources
CNO: Laurie Lehnhof–Watts, Assistant Administrator Risk Management Performance Improvement and Education
Web address: www.https://uthealtheasttexas.com/locations/ut–health–east–texas–specialty–hospital
Control: Other not–for–profit (including NFP Corporation) **Service**: Acute long–term care hospital

Staffed Beds: 36 Admissions: 311 Census: 25 Outpatient Visits: 0 Births: 0 Total Expense ($000): 14758 Payroll Expense ($000): 4621 Personnel: 72

⊞ **UT HEALTH TYLER (450083)**, 1000 South Beckham Street, Zip 75701–1908, Mailing Address: Box 6400, Zip 75711–6400; tel. 903/597–0351, (Includes UT HEALTH BEHAVIORAL HEALTH CENTER, 4101 University Boulevard, Tyler, TX, Zip 75701–6600; tel. 903/566–8668; Cecile Hunt, Interim Chief Executive Officer) **A**1 2 3 5 10 **F**3 5 8 11 12 13 15 17 18 20 22 24 26 28 29 30 31 34 35 37 38 40 43 44 45 46 47 48 49 51 56 58 59 60 61 64 65 68 70 71 73 74 75 76 78 79 80 81 82 84 85 86 87 89 93 98 99 100 101 102 104 107 110 111 115 117 118 119 126 129 130 132 138 141 145 146 147 148 149 150 152 153 **S** Ardent Health Services, Nashville, TN
Primary Contact: Vicki R. Briggs, Chief Executive Officer
CFO: Byron Hale, Chief Financial Officer
CMO: John Andrews, M.D., Chief of Staff
CIO: Paula Anthony, Vice President Information Services
CHR: Mike Gray, Corporate Vice President Human Resources
CNO: Mariarose Kulma, R.N., Vice President Patient Services
Web address: www.https://uthealthtylerhospital.com/
Control: Other not–for–profit (including NFP Corporation) **Service**: General medical and surgical

Staffed Beds: 399 Admissions: 20691 Census: 280 Outpatient Visits: 114198 Births: 762 Total Expense ($000): 357522 Payroll Expense ($000): 120402 Personnel: 2177

UVALDE—Uvalde County

⊞ **UVALDE MEMORIAL HOSPITAL (450177)**, 1025 Garner Field Road, Zip 78801–4809; tel. 830/278–6251, **A**1 10 18 **F**3 11 13 15 18 29 30 34 39 40 43 45 50 57 59 63 64 70 76 79 81 84 85 86 87 88 89 93 104 107 108 110 111 115 118 119 127 130 132 133 146 147 148 149 **P**3
Primary Contact: Thomas Nordwick, FACHE, Chief Executive Officer
CFO: Valerie Lopez, CPA, Chief Financial Officer
CMO: Jared Reading, M.D., Chief of Staff
CIO: Blake Eaker, Interim Director Information Services
CHR: Charla Carter, Human Resource Officer
CNO: Adam Apolinar, Chief Nursing Officer
Web address: www.umhtx.org
Control: Hospital district or authority, Government, nonfederal **Service**: General medical and surgical

Staffed Beds: 44 Admissions: 1484 Census: 13 Outpatient Visits: 71205 Births: 407 Total Expense ($000): 56964 Payroll Expense ($000): 23166 Personnel: 436

VAN HORN—Culberson County

CULBERSON HOSPITAL (451338), Eisenhower–Farm Market Road 2185, Zip 79855, Mailing Address: P.O. Box 609, Zip 79855–0609; tel. 432/283–2760, **A**10 18 **F**3 7 34 40 43 50 57 59 64 65 66 68 74 75 93 107 114 119 127 133 154 **P**5 **S** Preferred Management Corporation, Shawnee, OK
Primary Contact: Jonathon Voelkel, Administrator
CMO: John A. Thomas, M.D., Chief Medical Staff
Web address: www.culbersonhospital.org
Control: Corporation, Investor–owned (for–profit) **Service**: General medical and surgical

Staffed Beds: 14 Admissions: 139 Census: 3 Outpatient Visits: 10582 Births: 0 Total Expense ($000): 6725 Payroll Expense ($000): 3059 Personnel: 63

TX

Hospital, Medicare Provider Number, Address, Telephone, Approval, Facility, and Physician Codes, Health Care System

★ American Hospital Association (AHA) membership
□ The Joint Commission accreditation
○ Healthcare Facilities Accreditation Program
◇ DNV Healthcare Inc. accreditation
⇑ Center for Improvement in Healthcare Quality Accreditation
△ Commission on Accreditation of Rehabilitation Facilities (CARF) accreditation

VERNON—Wilbarger County

☐ **NORTH TEXAS STATE HOSPITAL**, Highway 70 Northwest, Zip 76384, Mailing Address: P.O. Box 2231, Zip 76385–2231; tel. 940/552–9901, **A**1 **F**30 39 50 56 57 68 87 96 97 98 99 100 101 103 130 132 135 143 145 146 149 154 **P**6 **S** Texas Department of State Health Services, Austin, TX
Primary Contact: James E. Smith, Superintendent
CFO: Robin Moreno, Financial Officer
CIO: Chad Hughes, Information Officer
Web address: www.online.dshs.state.tx.us/northtexassh/default.htm
Control: State, Government, nonfederal **Service:** Psychiatric

Staffed Beds: 641 **Admissions:** 1549 **Census:** 512 **Outpatient Visits:** 0 **Births:** 0 **Total Expense ($000):** 206737 **Payroll Expense ($000):** 73287 **Personnel:** 2016	

WILBARGER GENERAL HOSPITAL (450584), 920 Hillcrest Drive, Zip 76384–3196; tel. 940/552–9351, (Nonreporting) **A**10 20
Primary Contact: Scott M. Landrum, Interim Chief Executive Officer
CMO: Travis Lehman, M.D., Medical Director
CIO: Ken Mikos, Director Information Technology
CHR: Alisha Nix, Director Human Resources
CNO: Kim Pierson, R.N., Chief Nursing Officer
Web address: www.wghospital.com
Control: Hospital district or authority, Government, nonfederal **Service:** General medical and surgical

Staffed Beds: 27	

VICTORIA—Victoria County

★ ⇑ **CITIZENS MEDICAL CENTER (450023)**, 2701 Hospital Drive, Zip 77901–5749; tel. 361/573–9181, (Total facility includes 20 beds in nursing home–type unit) **A**2 10 21 **F**3 11 12 13 15 18 20 22 24 28 29 30 31 34 35 40 41 43 45 46 49 50 53 54 56 57 59 62 64 65 70 72 74 75 76 78 79 81 82 85 86 87 89 93 97 107 108 109 110 111 113 114 115 116 117 118 119 120 121 123 126 128 129 130 131 132 135 146 147 148 149 154 **P**4
Primary Contact: Michael R. Olson, Chief Executive Officer
CFO: Carolyn Zafereo, Chief Accounting Officer
CMO: Daniel Cano, M.D., Chief Medical Officer
CIO: Russell Witte, Director Information Technology
CHR: Kathleen C Mosmeyer, Director Human Resources
Web address: www.citizensmedicalcenter.org
Control: County, Government, nonfederal **Service:** General medical and surgical

Staffed Beds: 265 **Admissions:** 7410 **Census:** 104 **Outpatient Visits:** 127213 **Births:** 773 **Total Expense ($000):** 165203 **Payroll Expense ($000):** 72766 **Personnel:** 1120	

✠ **DETAR HEALTHCARE SYSTEM (450147)**, 506 East San Antonio Street, Zip 77901–6060, Mailing Address: P.O. Box 2089, Zip 77902–2089; tel. 361/575–7441, (Includes DETAR HOSPITAL NORTH, 101 Medical Drive, Victoria, TX, Zip 77904–3198; tel. 361/573–6100; Gary Malaer, Chief Executive Officer) (Nonreporting) **A**1 3 10 **F**3 12 13 15 18 20 22 24 26 28 29 30 31 34 39 40 41 43 45 47 49 50 51 53 54 56 64 70 72 74 75 76 77 78 79 81 82 85 86 87 89 90 93 107 108 110 111 114 118 119 126 130 132 146 147 148 **P**3 5 **S** Community Health Systems, Inc., Franklin, TN
Primary Contact: Gary Malaer, Chief Executive Officer
COO: George N Parsley, Chief Operating Officer
CFO: Donald E Hagan, Chief Financial Officer
CMO: Conde Nevin Anderson, M.D., Chief of Staff
CIO: Kim Tompkins, Director Information Services
CHR: Dwight Linton, Director Human Resources
CNO: Sammie Drehr, Chief Nursing Officer
Web address: www.detar.com
Control: Corporation, Investor–owned (for–profit) **Service:** General medical and surgical

Staffed Beds: 225 **Admissions:** 8910 **Census:** 108 **Outpatient Visits:** 95936 **Births:** 1213 **Total Expense ($000):** 152195 **Payroll Expense ($000):** 54432 **Personnel:** 949	

★ **PAM REHABILITATION HOSPITAL OF VICTORIA (673056)**, 101 James Coleman Drive, Zip 77904–3147; **S** Post Acute Medical, LLC, Enola, PA
Primary Contact: Shawn Todd, Chief Executive Officer
Web address: www.warmsprings.org/our–facilities/outpatient–rehabilitation/warm–springs–rehabilitation–center–victoria/
Control: Partnership, Investor–owned (for–profit) **Service:** Rehabilitation

Staffed Beds: 26	

✠ **PAM SPECIALTY HOSPITAL OF VICTORIA NORTH (452094)**, 102 Medical Drive, Zip 77904–3101; tel. 361/576–6200, **A**1 10 **F**1 3 29 64 75 77 85 93 94 96 148 **S** Post Acute Medical, LLC, Enola, PA
Primary Contact: Christina Adrean, Chief Executive Officer
CMO: Adam Burick, M.D., Chief Medical Officer
CHR: Waynea Finley, Corporate Director Human Resources
CNO: Chris Reed, Director of Nursing
Web address: www.warmsprings.org
Control: Partnership, Investor–owned (for–profit) **Service:** Acute long–term care hospital

Staffed Beds: 26 **Admissions:** 496 **Census:** 24 **Outpatient Visits:** 8609 **Births:** 0 **Total Expense ($000):** 13577 **Payroll Expense ($000):** 5308 **Personnel:** 110	

✠ **PAM SPECIALTY HOSPITAL OF VICTORIA SOUTH (452056)**, 506 East San Antonio Street, 3rd Floor, Zip 77901–6060; tel. 361/575–1445, **A**1 10 **F**1 3 29 82 85 86 87 97 130 148 **S** Post Acute Medical, LLC, Enola, PA
Primary Contact: Christina Adrean, Chief Executive Officer
CMO: Adam Burick, M.D., Chief Medical Officer
CHR: Waynea Finley, Manager Human Resources
CNO: Pamella Barrett, Director of Nursing
Web address: www.warmsprings.org/our–facilities/hospitals/post–acute–medical–specialty–hospital–victoria/
Control: Partnership, Investor–owned (for–profit) **Service:** Acute long–term care hospital

Staffed Beds: 23 **Admissions:** 313 **Census:** 22 **Outpatient Visits:** 0 **Births:** 0 **Total Expense ($000):** 11145 **Payroll Expense ($000):** 4297 **Personnel:** 73	

WACO—Mclennan County

✠ **BAYLOR SCOTT & WHITE MEDICAL CENTER – HILLCREST (450101)**, 100 Hillcrest Medical Boulevard, Zip 76712–8897; tel. 254/202–2000, **A**1 2 3 10 **F**3 8 11 13 15 18 20 22 24 26 28 29 30 31 34 40 43 45 46 49 50 53 54 56 57 59 60 63 64 68 70 72 74 75 76 77 78 79 81 82 84 85 86 87 89 90 93 96 107 108 110 111 115 118 119 120 121 123 129 130 131 132 135 145 146 148 149 **S** Baylor Scott & White Health, Dallas, TX
Primary Contact: Glenn A. Robinson, FACHE, President
COO: David Blackwell, Vice President Operations
CFO: Richard Perkins, Chief Financial Officer
CMO: J. E. Morrison, M.D., M.P.H., Chief Medical Officer
CNO: Rebecca Kay Hardie, Chief Nursing Officer
Web address: www.sw.org/hillcrest–medical–center
Control: Other not–for–profit (including NFP Corporation) **Service:** General medical and surgical

Staffed Beds: 226 **Admissions:** 13757 **Census:** 171 **Outpatient Visits:** 169411 **Births:** 2934 **Total Expense ($000):** 254952 **Payroll Expense ($000):** 80720 **Personnel:** 1280	

WACO—McLennan County

CENTRAL TEXAS VETERANS HEALTH CARE SYSTEM, DORIS MILLER VETERANS MEDICAL CENTER See Central Texas Veterans Health Care System, Temple

✠ **PROVIDENCE HEALTHCARE NETWORK (450042)**, 6901 Medical Parkway, Zip 76712–7998, Mailing Address: P.O. Box 2589, Zip 76702–2589; tel. 254/751–4000, (Includes DEPAUL CENTER, 301 Londonderry Drive, Waco, TX, Zip 76712; tel. 254/776–5970; Vicky Campbell, Vice President Mental Health and Support Services) (Nonreporting) **A**1 2 3 10 **S** Ascension Healthcare, Saint Louis, MO
Primary Contact: Philip A. Patterson, President
CFO: Karen K. Richardson, Senior Vice President and Chief Financial Officer
CMO: Brian Becker, Vice Presdient Medical Affairs and Chief Medical Officer
CIO: Jay Scherler, Vice President Finance and Chief Information Officer
CNO: Cyndy Dunlap, R.N., FACHE, Chief Nursing Officer
Web address: www.providence.net
Control: Church operated, Nongovernment, not–for–profit **Service:** General medical and surgical

Staffed Beds: 284	

WAXAHACHIE—Ellis County

✠ **BAYLOR SCOTT & WHITE MEDICAL CENTER AT WAXAHACHIE (450372)**, 2400 North I–35E, Zip 75165; tel. 469/843–4000, **A**1 2 3 10 **F**3 8 11 12 13 15 18 28 29 30 31 34 35 37 39 40 41 45 47 48 49 50 51 54 55 57 58 59 64 68 70 74 75 76 78 79 80 81 82 84 85 86 87 97 100 107 108 109 110 111 114 115 116 117 118 119 120 121 129 130 131 132 135 145 146 147 148 149 154 **S** Baylor Scott & White Health, Dallas, TX
Primary Contact: Christopher York, FACHE, President
COO: Cindy Murray, R.N., Chief Nursing Officer and Chief Operating Officer
CFO: Cheryl McMullan, Chief Financial Officer
CMO: Thomas Glenn Ledbetter, M.D., Chief Medical Officer
CNO: Cindy Murray, R.N., Chief Nursing Officer and Chief Operating Officer
Web address: www.baylorhealth.com/PhysiciansLocations/Waxahachie/Pages/Default.aspx
Control: Other not–for–profit (including NFP Corporation) **Service:** General medical and surgical

Staffed Beds: 104 **Admissions:** 7212 **Census:** 68 **Outpatient Visits:** 91853 **Births:** 969 **Total Expense ($000):** 138067 **Payroll Expense ($000):** 49597 **Personnel:** 580	

TX

Many Facility Codes have changed. Please refer to the AHA Guide Code Chart. © 2018 AHA Guide

WEATHERFORD—Parker County

✠ **MEDICAL CITY WEATHERFORD (450203)**, 713 East Anderson Street, Zip 76086–5705; tel. 682/582–1000, **A**1 3 10 12 13 **F**3 8 13 15 17 18 20 22 28 29 34 35 40 43 48 49 51 57 59 60 68 70 74 75 76 79 81 82 85 93 98 107 110 111 114 115 119 130 133 135 146 148 **S** HCA Healthcare, Nashville, TN
Primary Contact: Sean Kamber, Chief Executive Officer
CFO: Nancy Cooke, Chief Financial Officer
CMO: Sanjeeb Shrestha, M.D., Chief Medical Staff
CIO: Brett Cates, Director Information Services
CNO: Donna Boone, MS, R.N., Chief Nursing Officer
Web address: www.weatherfordregional.com
Control: Corporation, Investor–owned (for–profit) **Service**: General medical and surgical

Staffed Beds: 92 **Admissions:** 5543 **Census:** 56 **Outpatient Visits:** 79092
Births: 778 **Total Expense ($000):** 95524 **Payroll Expense ($000):** 29006
Personnel: 401

WEATHERFORD REHABILITATION HOSPITAL (673062), 703 Eureka Street, Zip 76086–6547; tel. 682/803–0100, (Nonreporting)
Primary Contact: Tina Densley, R.N., Chief Executive Officer
Web address: www.weatherfordrehab.com
Control: Corporation, Investor–owned (for–profit) **Service**: Rehabilitation

Staffed Beds: 26

WEBSTER—Harris County

✠ **CLEAR LAKE REGIONAL MEDICAL CENTER (450617)**, 500 Medical Center Boulevard, Zip 77598–4220; tel. 281/332–2511, (Includes ALVIN DIAGNOSTIC AND URGENT CARE CENTER, 301 Medic Lane, Alvin, TX, Zip 77511–5597; tel. 281/331–6141; MAINLAND MEDICAL CENTER, 6801 'E' 'F' Lowry Expressway, Texas City, TX, Zip 77591; tel. 409/938–5000; Tripp Montalbo, Chief Executive Officer) **A**1 2 3 5 10 **F**3 11 12 13 15 17 18 19 20 22 24 26 28 29 31 34 35 40 41 43 44 45 46 47 49 50 51 56 57 59 60 64 70 72 74 75 76 78 79 81 85 86 87 88 89 90 91 93 94 96 98 100 103 105 107 108 110 111 114 115 119 124 126 130 132 135 146 147 148 149 153 **S** HCA Healthcare, Nashville, TN
Primary Contact: Todd Caliva, FACHE, Chief Executive Officer
CFO: Jeff Sliwinski, Chief Financial Officer
CMO: Richard Marietta, M.D., Medical Director
CIO: Ley Samson, Director Management Information Systems
CHR: Brad Horst, Director Human Resources
Web address: www.clearlakermc.com
Control: Partnership, Investor–owned (for–profit) **Service**: General medical and surgical

Staffed Beds: 589 **Admissions:** 30074 **Census:** 445 **Outpatient Visits:** 185514 **Births:** 3511 **Total Expense ($000):** 418036 **Payroll Expense ($000):** 183227 **Personnel:** 2255

CLEAR LAKE REHABILITATION HOSPITAL See Kindred Rehabilitation Hospital Clear Lake

CORNERSTONE HOSPITAL OF HOUSTON AT CLEARLAKE (452032), 709 Medical Center Boulevard, Zip 77598; tel. 281/332–3322, (Includes CORNERSTONE HOSPITAL OF HOUSTON – BELLAIRE, 5314 Dashwood, Houston, TX, Zip 77081–4603; tel. 713/295–5300; Colin O'Sullivan, Interim Chief Executive Officer) **A**10 22 **F**1 3 29 30 44 50 56 75 82 85 86 87 130 148 149 **S** Cornerstone Healthcare Group, Dallas, TX
Primary Contact: Amy Stasney, R.N., Chief Executive Officer
COO: Brenda Lucero, Chief Clinical Officer
CFO: A Shane Wells, Chief Financial Officer
CMO: Mark Barlow, M.D., Chief Medical Officer and President Medical Staff
CIO: Jerald Harris, Chief Information Officer
CHR: Yolanda Jacobs, Coordinator Human Resources
Web address: www.cornerstonehealthcaregroup.com
Control: Partnership, Investor–owned (for–profit) **Service**: Acute long–term care hospital

Staffed Beds: 148 **Admissions:** 1318 **Census:** 88 **Outpatient Visits:** 0
Births: 0 **Total Expense ($000):** 46187 **Payroll Expense ($000):** 18655
Personnel: 268

⇑ **HOUSTON PHYSICIANS HOSPITAL (670008)**, 333 North Texas Avenue, Suite 100, Zip 77598–4966; tel. 281/557–5620, **A**10 21 **F**3 29 37 40 51 64 74 79 81 82 85 86 91 93 107 111 114 141 149
Primary Contact: Nicholas Crafts, Chief Executive Officer
Web address: www.houstonphysicianshospital.com
Control: Corporation, Investor–owned (for–profit) **Service**: Surgical

Staffed Beds: 21 **Admissions:** 662 **Census:** 3 **Outpatient Visits:** 58690
Births: 0 **Total Expense ($000):** 49114 **Payroll Expense ($000):** 14229
Personnel: 194

✠ **KINDRED HOSPITAL CLEAR LAKE (452075)**, 350 Blossom Street, Zip 77598; tel. 281/316–7800, **A**1 **F**1 3 29 45 57 60 64 75 77 85 91 93 96 107 130 148 **S** Kindred Healthcare, Louisville, KY
Primary Contact: Angel Gradney, Chief Executive Officer
Web address: www.khclearlake.com
Control: Corporation, Investor–owned (for–profit) **Service**: Acute long–term care hospital

Staffed Beds: 110 **Admissions:** 873 **Census:** 61 **Outpatient Visits:** 3483
Births: 0 **Total Expense ($000):** 42740 **Payroll Expense ($000):** 14008
Personnel: 221

☐ **KINDRED REHABILITATION HOSPITAL CLEAR LAKE (453052)**, 655 East Medical Center Boulevard, Zip 77598–4328; tel. 281/286–1500, (Nonreporting) **A**1 10
Primary Contact: Sandra Hegland, Chief Executive Officer
CFO: Michael McFall, Chief Financial Officer
CMO: Michael Rosenblatt, M.D., Medical Director
CHR: Monica Little, Coordinator Human Resources
CNO: Kathy Hutchins–Otero, Chief Clinical Officer
Web address: www.khrehabclearlake.com/
Control: Corporation, Investor–owned (for–profit) **Service**: Rehabilitation

Staffed Beds: 60

WELLINGTON—Collingsworth County

COLLINGSWORTH GENERAL HOSPITAL (451355), 1013 15th Street, Zip 79095–3703, Mailing Address: P.O. Box 1112, Zip 79095–1112; tel. 806/447–2521, **A**10 18 **F**3 40 43 57 59 64 65 66 68 93 97 107 114 127 130 133 **S** Preferred Management Corporation, Shawnee, OK
Primary Contact: Candy Powell, Administrator
CFO: Larry Stephens, Chief Financial Officer
CMO: Wesley Nickens, M.D., Chief of Staff
CIO: Thomas T. Ng, Chief Information Officer
CHR: April Wright, Human Resources Officer
CNO: Vikki Barton, R.N., Chief Nursing Officer
Web address: www.collingsworthgeneral.net
Control: Corporation, Investor–owned (for–profit) **Service**: General medical and surgical

Staffed Beds: 13 **Admissions:** 193 **Census:** 4 **Outpatient Visits:** 12182
Births: 0 **Total Expense ($000):** 6876 **Payroll Expense ($000):** 2914
Personnel: 64

WESLACO—Hidalgo County

✠ **KNAPP MEDICAL CENTER (450128)**, 1401 East Eighth Street, Zip 78596–6640, Mailing Address: P.O. Box 1110, Zip 78599–1110; tel. 956/968–8567, **A**1 3 5 10 **F**3 8 11 12 13 15 20 22 29 30 31 34 35 39 40 43 44 46 49 50 51 56 57 59 60 63 64 70 73 74 75 76 77 78 79 81 82 84 85 86 87 89 93 107 108 110 111 114 115 119 130 131 132 134 135 143 146 147 148 149 154 **P**8 **S** Prime Healthcare, Ontario, CA
Primary Contact: Rene Lopez, Chief Executive Officer
CFO: Dinah L. Gonzalez, Chief Financial Officer
CIO: Teri Garza, Director Health Information Services
CHR: Emmett Craig, Chief Human Resources Officer
CNO: Anna Hinojosa, MSN, R.N., Interim Chief Nursing Officer
Web address: www.knappmed.org
Control: Other not–for–profit (including NFP Corporation) **Service**: General medical and surgical

Staffed Beds: 196 **Admissions:** 8703 **Census:** 90 **Outpatient Visits:** 83632
Births: 1503 **Total Expense ($000):** 98586 **Payroll Expense ($000):** 41892
Personnel: 595

WESLACO REGIONAL REHABILITATION HOSPITAL (453091), 906 South James Street, Zip 78596–9840; tel. 956/969–2222, **A**10 **F**3 29 34 68 75 77 86 87 90 94 96 130 132 148 149 154 **P**6
Primary Contact: Corina Humphreys, Chief Executive Officer
COO: Corina Humphreys, Chief Operating Officer
CFO: Ernest Nash, Chief Financial Officer
CMO: Daisy Arce, President Medical Staff
CHR: Debbie Pemelton, Director Human Resources
CNO: Rita Mata–Guerrero, Director of Nursing
Web address: www.wrrh.ernesthealth.com
Control: Partnership, Investor–owned (for–profit) **Service**: Rehabilitation

Staffed Beds: 32 **Admissions:** 547 **Census:** 20 **Outpatient Visits:** 0
Births: 0 **Total Expense ($000):** 10539 **Payroll Expense ($000):** 4661
Personnel: 94

Hospital, Medicare Provider Number, Address, Telephone, Approval, Facility, and Physician Codes, Health Care System

★ American Hospital Association (AHA) membership
☐ The Joint Commission accreditation
○ Healthcare Facilities Accreditation Program
◇ DNV Healthcare Inc. accreditation
⇑ Center for Improvement in Healthcare Quality Accreditation
△ Commission on Accreditation of Rehabilitation Facilities (CARF) accreditation

WHEELER—Wheeler County

PARKVIEW HOSPITAL (451334), 901 Sweetwater Street, Zip 79096–2421, Mailing Address: P.O. Box 1030, Zip 79096–1030; tel. 806/826–5581, **A**10 18 **F**3 7 10 40 43 59 62 64 65 68 91 93 107 114 127 128 130 133 148
Primary Contact: Monica Kidd, R.N., MSN, Administrator
CFO: Jace Henderson, Chief Financial Officer
CMO: John P. Lavelle, M.D., Chief Medical Officer
CNO: Melisa Scales, Director of Nursing
Web address: www.parkviewhosp.org
Control: Hospital district or authority, Government, nonfederal **Service:** General medical and surgical

Staffed Beds: 15 **Admissions:** 121 **Census:** 3 **Outpatient Visits:** 3666
Births: 0 **Total Expense ($000):** 8034 **Payroll Expense ($000):** 3827
Personnel: 112

WICHITA FALLS—Wichita County

☒ **ENCOMPASS HEALTH REHABILITATION HOSPITAL OF WICHITA FALLS (453054)**, 3901 Armory Road, Zip 76302–2204; tel. 940/720–5700, **A**1 10 **F**3 28 29 68 74 75 77 79 86 87 90 91 94 95 96 130 132 **S** Encompass Health Corporation, Birmingham, AL
Primary Contact: Robbi Hudson, Chief Executive Officer
CMO: Virgil Frardo, M.D., Medical Director
CIO: Mary Walker, Manager Information Technology
CHR: Kathleen Pirtle, Director Human Resources
CNO: Jody S Gregory, R.N., Chief Nursing Officer
Web address: www.healthsouthwichitafalls.com
Control: Partnership, Investor–owned (for–profit) **Service:** Rehabilitation

Staffed Beds: 63 **Admissions:** 1439 **Census:** 49 **Outpatient Visits:** 1652
Births: 0 **Total Expense ($000):** 15721 **Payroll Expense ($000):** 9582
Personnel: 169

☐ **KELL WEST REGIONAL HOSPITAL (450827)**, 5420 Kell West Boulevard, Zip 76310–1610; tel. 940/692–5888, **A**1 10 **F**3 39 40 49 51 54 59 65 74 75 78 79 81 85 91 107 108 114 119 126 129 130 135
Primary Contact: Jerry Myers, M.D., Chief Executive Officer and Medical Director
CFO: Fran Lindemann, Director Finance
Web address: www.kellwest.com
Control: Partnership, Investor–owned (for–profit) **Service:** General medical and surgical

Staffed Beds: 41 **Admissions:** 1175 **Census:** 10 **Outpatient Visits:** 24042
Births: 0 **Total Expense ($000):** 33358 **Payroll Expense ($000):** 10356
Personnel: 253

☐ **NORTH TEXAS STATE HOSPITAL, WICHITA FALLS CAMPUS (454008)**, 6515 Lake Road, Zip 76308–5419, Mailing Address: Box 300, Zip 76307–0300; tel. 940/692–1220, (Nonreporting) **A**1 3 10
Primary Contact: James E. Smith, Superintendent
CFO: Robin Moreno, Chief Financial Officer
CMO: Eulon Ross Taylor, Clinical Director
CIO: Chad Hughes, Chief Information Officer
Web address: www.online.dshs.state.tx.us/northtexassh/default.htm
Control: State, Government, nonfederal **Service:** Psychiatric

Staffed Beds: 381

☐ **PROMISE HOSPITAL OF WICHITA FALLS (452068)**, 1103 Grace Street, Zip 76301–4414; tel. 940/720–6633, (Nonreporting) **A**1 10 **S** Promise Healthcare, Boca Raton, FL
Primary Contact: Louis P. Bradley Jr, Chief Executive Officer
CFO: Debbie Herder, Controller
CMO: Robert McBroom, M.D., Medical Director
CIO: Gail McIlroy, Director Medical Records
CNO: Deanna Dowling, R.N., Chief Nursing Officer
Web address: www.promise-wichitafalls.com
Control: Corporation, Investor–owned (for–profit) **Service:** Acute long–term care hospital

Staffed Beds: 31

☐ **RED RIVER HOSPITAL, LLC (454018)**, 1505 Eighth Street, Zip 76301–3106; tel. 940/322–3171, **A**1 10 **F**4 5 29 38 50 86 87 98 99 100 101 102 103 104 105 130 135 143 152 153 **P**5 **S** Acadia Healthcare Company, Inc., Franklin, TN
Primary Contact: James Wilfer, Chief Executive Officer
CFO: Bruce Porter, Chief Financial Officer
CMO: Harvey C Martin, M.D., Medical Director
CIO: Fay Helton, Director Medical Records
CHR: Kimberley Pellegrin, Director, Human Resources
CNO: Glenda Lawrence, R.N., Chief Nursing Officer
Web address: www.redriverhospital.com
Control: Corporation, Investor–owned (for–profit) **Service:** Psychiatric

Staffed Beds: 96 **Admissions:** 2220 **Census:** 66 **Outpatient Visits:** 4723
Births: 0 **Total Expense ($000):** 12623 **Payroll Expense ($000):** 6923
Personnel: 224

☒ **UNITED REGIONAL HEALTH CARE SYSTEM (450010)**, 1600 11th Street, Zip 76301–4300; tel. 940/764–7000, (Includes UNITED REGIONAL HEALTH CARE SYSTEM–ELEVENTH STREET CAMPUS, 1600 11th Street, Wichita Falls, TX, Zip 76301–9988; tel. 940/764–7000) **A**1 3 10 20 **F**3 11 12 13 15 17 18 20 21 22 24 26 28 29 30 31 32 34 35 37 39 40 43 44 45 46 47 48 49 50 51 53 57 59 60 61 64 65 68 70 73 74 75 76 77 78 79 80 81 82 84 85 86 87 89 92 93 102 107 110 111 114 115 116 117 118 119 126 130 131 132 134 146 147 148 149 **P**3
Primary Contact: Phyllis A. Cowling, CPA, President and Chief Executive Officer
COO: Nancy Townley, R.N., Senior Vice President Operations
CFO: Robert M Pert, Vice President Finance and Chief Financial Officer
CMO: Lee Rodgers, M.D., Vice President Quality
CIO: Jerry Marshall, Director Information Services, Information Technology Security Officer
CHR: Kristi Faulkner, Vice President Organizational Growth
CNO: Jane Ritter, R.N., Vice President, Patient Care and Clinical Services
Web address: www.unitedregional.org
Control: Other not–for–profit (including NFP Corporation) **Service:** General medical and surgical

Staffed Beds: 277 **Admissions:** 14899 **Census:** 175 **Outpatient Visits:** 132431 **Births:** 1944 **Total Expense ($000):** 290099 **Payroll Expense ($000):** 116011 **Personnel:** 1989

WINNIE—Chambers County

RICELAND MEDICAL CENTER (451328), 538 Broadway, Zip 77665–7600; tel. 409/296–6000, **A**10 18 **F**3 8 29 34 40 59 65 81 105 107 119 127 133 146
Primary Contact: Daniel Yancy, Chief Executive Officer
CFO: Julie Harris, Chief Financial Officer
CMO: Leonidas Andres, M.D., Chief of Staff
CHR: Anha Simon, Director Human Resources
Web address: www.energis.in/index.html
Control: Partnership, Investor–owned (for–profit) **Service:** General medical and surgical

Staffed Beds: 25 **Admissions:** 312 **Census:** 4 **Outpatient Visits:** 59045
Births: 0 **Total Expense ($000):** 26307 **Payroll Expense ($000):** 10579
Personnel: 218

WINNSBORO—Wood County

☒ **CHRISTUS MOTHER FRANCES HOSPITAL – WINNSBORO (451381)**, 719 West Coke Road, Zip 75494–3011; tel. 903/342–5227, **A**1 10 18 **F**3 18 29 30 34 35 40 43 45 57 59 64 68 70 75 79 81 82 85 87 93 102 107 108 111 115 119 127 129 130 131 132 133 146 148 **P**5 6 7 8 **S** CHRISTUS Health, Irving, TX
Primary Contact: Paul Harvey, Chief Executive Officer
CFO: Glenn Peltier, Chief Financial Officer
CNO: Kevin Jablonski, Chief Nursing Officer
Web address: www.tmfhs.org
Control: Other not–for–profit (including NFP Corporation) **Service:** General medical and surgical

Staffed Beds: 25 **Admissions:** 457 **Census:** 6 **Outpatient Visits:** 22913
Births: 0 **Total Expense ($000):** 17942 **Payroll Expense ($000):** 5414
Personnel: 104

TEXAS HEALTH PRESBYTERIAN HOSPITAL WINNSBORO See Christus Mother Frances Hospital – Winnsboro

WINTERS—Runnels County

★ **NORTH RUNNELS HOSPITAL (451315)**, 7821 State Highway 153, Zip 79567–7345, Mailing Address: P.O. Box 185, Zip 79567–0185; tel. 325/754–1317, **A**10 18 **F**7 11 40 57 59 62 65 66 68 97 107 119 127 133 **P**5
Primary Contact: Richard C. Mathis, Chief Executive Officer
CMO: Mark McKinnon, M.D., Chief of Staff
CNO: Bobbie Collom, Nursing Director
Control: Hospital district or authority, Government, nonfederal **Service:** General medical and surgical

Staffed Beds: 21 **Admissions:** 109 **Census:** 1 **Outpatient Visits:** 4632
Births: 0 **Total Expense ($000):** 5643 **Payroll Expense ($000):** 2852
Personnel: 61

Many Facility Codes have changed. Please refer to the AHA Guide Code Chart.   © 2018 AHA Guide

WOODVILLE—Tyler County

★ **TYLER COUNTY HOSPITAL (450460)**, 1100 West Bluff Street,
Zip 75979–4799, Mailing Address: P.O. Box 549, Zip 75979–0549;
tel. 409/283–8141, **A**10 20 **F**3 11 30 35 40 43 57 59 64 75 107 114 119 127
146
Primary Contact: Sondra Dianne Wilson, Chief Executive Officer
CFO: Scott Elton McCluskey, Chief Financial Officer
CMO: Paula Lajean Denson, M.D., President
CIO: Rachel Joy Haygood, Director Information Technology
CHR: Kenneth Lynn Jobe, Director Human Resources
CNO: Sondra Dianne Wilson RN, MSN,CEN, R.N., MSN, Assistant Administrator and
Chief Nursing Officer
Web address: www.tchospital.us
Control: County, Government, nonfederal **Service**: General medical and surgical

Staffed Beds: 25 **Admissions:** 404 **Census:** 4 **Outpatient Visits:** 25684
Births: 1 **Total Expense ($000):** 11788 **Payroll Expense ($000):** 4763
Personnel: 109

YOAKUM—Lavaca County

★ **YOAKUM COMMUNITY HOSPITAL (451346)**, 1200 Carl Ramert Drive,
Zip 77995–4868; tel. 361/293–2321, **A**10 18 **F**3 11 13 15 29 34 35 40 43 56
57 59 64 70 76 79 81 85 86 93 104 107 108 111 114 119 129 132 133 134
146 148 153 **S** Community Hospital Corporation, Plano, TX
Primary Contact: Karen Barber, R.N., Chief Executive Officer
CFO: Robert Foret, Chief Financial Officer
CMO: Timothy Wagner, M.D., Chief Medical Staff
CIO: Barbara Vasek, Director Information Technology
CHR: Karen Roznovsky, Director Human Resources
CNO: Jennifer Franklin, R.N., Chief Clinical Officer
Web address: www.yoakumhospital.org
Control: Other not-for-profit (including NFP Corporation) **Service**: General
medical and surgical

Staffed Beds: 25 **Admissions:** 819 **Census:** 10 **Outpatient Visits:** 22073
Births: 74 **Total Expense ($000):** 18236 **Payroll Expense ($000):** 7578
Personnel: 118

TX

Hospital, Medicare Provider Number, Address, Telephone, Approval, Facility, and Physician Codes, Health Care System

★ American Hospital Association (AHA) membership ○ Healthcare Facilities Accreditation Program ⇑ Center for Improvement in Healthcare Quality Accreditation
□ The Joint Commission accreditation ◇ DNV Healthcare Inc. accreditation △ Commission on Accreditation of Rehabilitation Facilities (CARF) accreditation

UTAH

AMERICAN FORK—Utah County

✠ **AMERICAN FORK HOSPITAL (460023)**, 170 North 1100 East,
Zip 84003-2096; tel. 801/855-3300, **A**1 10 **F**3 13 15 29 30 31 34 35 38 40
41 43 44 45 46 47 48 49 50 53 57 60 68 70 73 75 76 77 78 79 81 85 87 89
97 102 107 108 110 111 115 118 119 120 121 123 124 129 130 132 141
145 146 147 148 149 154 **S** Intermountain Healthcare, Inc., Salt Lake City, UT
Primary Contact: Jason Wilson, Administrator and Chief Executive Officer
CMO: Paul H Robinson, M.D., Medical Director
CIO: Mary Gathers, Manager Information Systems
CHR: Luke P Morris, Assistant Vice President Talent
CNO: Terri Lynn Hunter, R.N., Nurse Administrator
Web address: www.intermountainhealthcare.org
Control: Other not-for-profit (including NFP Corporation) **Service**: General
medical and surgical

Staffed Beds: 89 **Admissions**: 5570 **Census**: 39 **Outpatient Visits**: 288713
Births: 2867 **Total Expense ($000)**: 118151 **Payroll Expense
($000)**: 36810 **Personnel**: 609

BEAVER—Beaver County

BEAVER VALLEY HOSPITAL (461335), 1109 North 100 West, Zip 84713,
Mailing Address: P.O. Box 1670, Zip 84713-1670; tel. 435/438-7100, (Total
facility includes 17 beds in nursing home–type unit) **A**10 18 **F**13 34 40 41 43 44
45 50 56 57 59 62 63 64 68 75 76 77 79 81 84 87 89 90 91 101 102 104
107 111 119 128 130 133 146 147 148 149 150 154 **P**5
Primary Contact: Scott Langford, Administrator
Web address: www.bvhospital.com/
Control: City–county, Government, nonfederal **Service**: General medical and
surgical

Staffed Beds: 27 **Admissions**: 303 **Census**: 16 **Outpatient Visits**: 8634
Births: 71

BLANDING—San Juan County

✠ **BLUE MOUNTAIN HOSPITAL (461310)**, 802 South 200 West, Suite A,
Zip 84511-3910; tel. 435/678-3993, **A**1 10 18 **F**3 8 15 29 34 35 40 41 45 50
59 60 65 68 70 75 79 81 83 87 107 111 119 133 145 146 154 **P**8
Primary Contact: Jeremy Lyman, Chief Executive Officer
CFO: Jimmy Johnson, Chief Financial Officer
CMO: Mahana Fisher, M.D., Medical Director
CIO: Anthony Torres, Manager Information Technology
CHR: Gail M. Northern, Director Human Resources
CNO: Derrill Kent Turek, R.N., Chief Nursing Officer
Web address: www.bmhutah.org/
Control: Other not-for-profit (including NFP Corporation) **Service**: General
medical and surgical

Staffed Beds: 11 **Admissions**: 246 **Census**: 3 **Outpatient Visits**: 7365
Births: 100 **Total Expense ($000)**: 11687 **Payroll Expense ($000)**: 4085

BOUNTIFUL—Davis County

✠ **LAKEVIEW HOSPITAL (460042)**, 630 East Medical Drive, Zip 84010-4908;
tel. 801/299-2200, (Nonreporting) **A**1 10 13 **S** HCA Healthcare, Nashville, TN
Primary Contact: Troy Wood, Chief Executive Officer
CFO: Wayne Dalton, Chief Financial Officer
CMO: Michael Hess, M.D., Chief Medical Officer
CIO: Mark Ellis, Director Information Technology
CHR: Julie Isom, Director Human Resources
CNO: Marilyn Mariani, R.N., Chief Nursing Officer
Web address: www.lakeviewhospital.com
Control: Corporation, Investor–owned (for-profit) **Service**: General medical and
surgical

Staffed Beds: 119

SOUTH DAVIS COMMUNITY HOSPITAL (462003), 401 South 400 East,
Zip 84010-4933; tel. 801/295-2361, (Nonreporting) **A**10
Primary Contact: David Bland, Chief Executive Officer
CMO: Scott Southworth, M.D., Medical Director
CHR: Jamey Sulser, Director Human Resources
Web address: www.sdch.com
Control: Other not-for-profit (including NFP Corporation) **Service**: Acute long-
term care hospital

Staffed Beds: 176

BRIGHAM CITY—Box Elder County

✠ **BRIGHAM CITY COMMUNITY HOSPITAL (460017)**, 950 South Medical Drive,
Zip 84302-4724; tel. 435/734-9471, (Nonreporting) **A**1 10 **S** HCA Healthcare,
Nashville, TN
Primary Contact: Richard Spuhler, Chief Executive Officer
CMO: Joel Gardner, D.O., Chief Medical Officer
CIO: Steve Reichard, Manager Information Systems
CHR: Tracie Greene, Director Human Resources
CNO: Jerry Bushman, Chief Nursing Officer
Web address: www.brighamcityhospital.com
Control: Corporation, Investor–owned (for-profit) **Service**: General medical and
surgical

Staffed Beds: 39

CEDAR CITY—Iron County

✠ **CEDAR CITY HOSPITAL (460007)**, 1303 North Main Street, Zip 84721-9746;
tel. 435/868-5000, **A**1 10 20 **F**3 13 15 29 34 35 38 39 40 43 50 64 68 70
75 76 77 79 81 85 86 87 97 102 107 108 110 111 115 118 119 120 121
123 124 130 132 141 146 147 149 **S** Intermountain Healthcare, Inc., Salt Lake
City, UT
Primary Contact: Eric Packer, Chief Executive Officer
CFO: Reed Sargent, Assistant Administrator Finance
Web address: www.https://intermountainhealthcare.org/locations/cedar–city-
hospital/
Control: Other not-for-profit (including NFP Corporation) **Service**: General
medical and surgical

Staffed Beds: 48 **Admissions**: 2518 **Census**: 17 **Outpatient Visits**: 283457
Births: 852 **Total Expense ($000)**: 73049 **Payroll Expense ($000)**: 21388
Personnel: 387

DELTA—Millard County

★ **DELTA COMMUNITY MEDICAL CENTER (461300)**, 126 South White Sage
Avenue, Zip 84624-8937; tel. 435/864-5591, **A**10 18 **F**3 13 15 29 34 35 40
41 43 44 45 50 59 64 68 75 76 77 81 86 87 97 107 110 111 114 119 128
130 133 146 148 149 **S** Intermountain Healthcare, Inc., Salt Lake City, UT
Primary Contact: Lenny Lyons, Administrator
CFO: Chris Thompson, Chief Financial Officer
Web address: www.ihc.com
Control: Other not-for-profit (including NFP Corporation) **Service**: General
medical and surgical

Staffed Beds: 15 **Admissions**: 244 **Census**: 2 **Outpatient Visits**: 38536
Births: 101 **Total Expense ($000)**: 9883 **Payroll Expense ($000)**: 3292
Personnel: 36

DRAPER—Salt Lake County

✠ **LONE PEAK HOSPITAL (460060)**, 1925 South State Street, Zip 84020;
tel. 801/545-8000, (Nonreporting) **A**1 10 **S** HCA Healthcare, Nashville, TN
Primary Contact: Mark Meadows, Chief Executive Officer
Web address: www.lonepeakhospital.com
Control: Corporation, Investor–owned (for-profit) **Service**: General medical and
surgical

Staffed Beds: 32

FILLMORE—Millard County

★ **FILLMORE COMMUNITY HOSPITAL (461301)**, 674 South Highway 99,
Zip 84631-5013; tel. 435/743-5591, **A**10 18 **F**3 15 29 34 35 40 41 43 44 50
68 75 76 77 81 85 86 87 97 107 110 111 119 127 128 130 132 133 146 147
148 149 **S** Intermountain Healthcare, Inc., Salt Lake City, UT
Primary Contact: Lenny Lyons, Administrator
CFO: Chris Thompson, Chief Financial Officer
Web address: www.ihc.com
Control: Other not-for-profit (including NFP Corporation) **Service**: General
medical and surgical

Staffed Beds: 19 **Admissions**: 181 **Census**: 1 **Outpatient Visits**: 23516
Births: 49 **Total Expense ($000)**: 9449 **Payroll Expense ($000)**: 3694
Personnel: 39

GUNNISON—Sanpete County

★ **GUNNISON VALLEY HOSPITAL (461306)**, 64 East 100 North, Zip 84634, Mailing Address: P.O. Box 759, Zip 84634–0759; tel. 435/528–7246, (Total facility includes 84 beds in nursing home–type unit) **A**10 18 **F**7 11 13 15 18 30 34 35 39 40 45 56 57 59 62 63 64 65 68 75 77 79 81 82 84 85 97 102 107 110 115 119 130 132 133 135 146 147 148 149
Primary Contact: Mark F. Dalley, Administrator
CFO: Brian Murray, Chief Financial Officer
CIO: Mike Ryan, Director of Information Services
CHR: Liz Brown, Manager Human Resources
CNO: Brenda Bartholomew, Chief Nursing Officer
Web address: www.gvhospital.org
Control: County, Government, nonfederal **Service**: General medical and surgical

Staffed Beds: 119 **Admissions**: 941 **Census**: 96 **Outpatient Visits**: 29141 **Births**: 171 **Total Expense ($000)**: 26568 **Payroll Expense ($000)**: 6497 **Personnel**: 157

HEBER CITY—Wasatch County

★ **HEBER VALLEY MEDICAL CENTER (461307)**, 1485 South Highway 40, Zip 84032–3522; tel. 435/654–2500, **A**10 18 **F**3 13 15 29 34 35 38 40 43 44 45 50 57 59 64 68 75 76 77 79 81 85 86 87 97 102 107 110 111 115 119 127 128 130 132 133 141 144 146 147 149 **S** Intermountain Healthcare, Inc., Salt Lake City, UT
Primary Contact: Shawn Morrow, Administrator
CFO: Craig Mills, Chief Financial Officer
CMO: Stanton B McDonald, M.D., Medical Director
CHR: Bruce Dent, Human Resources Director
CNO: Gayle Sturgis, R.N., Nurse Administrator
Web address: www.intermountainhealthcare.org
Control: Other not–for–profit (including NFP Corporation) **Service**: General medical and surgical

Staffed Beds: 19 **Admissions**: 574 **Census**: 4 **Outpatient Visits**: 98254 **Births**: 188 **Total Expense ($000)**: 30173 **Payroll Expense ($000)**: 11391 **Personnel**: 154

KANAB—Kane County

KANE COUNTY HOSPITAL (461309), 355 North Main Street, Zip 84741–3260; tel. 435/644–5811, (Nonreporting) **A**10 18
Primary Contact: Sherrie Pandya, Administrator
CFO: Stephen Howells, Chief Financial Officer
CMO: Darin Ott, D.O., Chief of Staff
CHR: Laurali Noteman, Director Human Resources
CNO: Charlene Kelly, Chief Nursing Officer
Web address: www.kanecountyhospital.net
Control: Hospital district or authority, Government, nonfederal **Service**: General medical and surgical

Staffed Beds: 25

LAYTON—Davis County

★ ⇑ **DAVIS HOSPITAL AND MEDICAL CENTER (460041)**, 1600 West Antelope Drive, Zip 84041–1142; tel. 801/807–1000, **A**3 10 21 **F**3 8 11 12 13 15 17 18 20 22 26 28 29 31 34 35 38 40 43 45 46 47 48 49 55 57 59 64 65 68 70 72 74 75 76 77 78 79 81 82 85 86 87 89 90 93 94 98 102 105 107 108 109 110 111 114 115 116 117 119 120 126 129 130 146 147 148 149 **S** Steward Health Care System, LLC, Dallas, TX
Primary Contact: Michael Jensen, Chief Executive Officer
COO: Jared Spackman, Chief Operating Officer
CFO: Jared Spackman, Chief Financial Officer
CMO: Les Greenwood, M.D., President, Medical Staff
CIO: Shane Williams, Director Information Systems
CHR: Tara Figgins, Director Human Resources
CNO: Chris Johnson, R.N., MSN, Chief Nursing Officer
Web address: www.davishospital.com
Control: Corporation, Investor–owned (for–profit) **Service**: General medical and surgical

Staffed Beds: 221 **Admissions**: 5824 **Census**: 64 **Outpatient Visits**: 178238 **Births**: 1580 **Personnel**: 755

LOGAN—Cache County

⊞ **LOGAN REGIONAL HOSPITAL (460015)**, 1400 North 500 East, Zip 84341–2455; tel. 435/716–1000, (Total facility includes 11 beds in nursing home–type unit) **A**1 10 **F**3 13 15 29 34 35 38 39 40 43 44 45 46 48 49 50 56 57 59 64 68 70 73 75 76 77 78 79 81 85 86 87 97 102 103 107 108 110 111 115 116 117 118 119 120 121 123 124 128 130 132 141 146 147 148 149 **S** Intermountain Healthcare, Inc., Salt Lake City, UT
Primary Contact: Kyle A. Hansen, Chief Executive Officer
COO: Brandon McBride, Operations Officer
CFO: Alan Robinson, Chief Financial Officer
CMO: Todd A Brown, M.D., Medical Director
CIO: Dave Felts, Chief Information Systems
CHR: Jolene Clonts, Director Human Resources
CNO: Neil C Perkes, Operations Officer
Web address: www.loganregionalhospital.org
Control: Other not–for–profit (including NFP Corporation) **Service**: General medical and surgical

Staffed Beds: 128 **Admissions**: 6549 **Census**: 49 **Births**: 2417 **Total Expense ($000)**: 167000 **Payroll Expense ($000)**: 50362 **Personnel**: 919

MIDVALE—Salt Lake County

☐ **HIGHLAND RIDGE HOSPITAL (464015)**, 7309 South 180 West, Zip 84047–3769; tel. 801/569–2153, (Nonreporting) **A**1 **S** Acadia Healthcare Company, Inc., Franklin, TN
Primary Contact: Matt Wilburn, Chief Executive Officer
COO: Robert Beatty, Chief Operating Officer
CFO: Sheri Sorenson, Manager Business Office
CHR: Carol Cunningham, Administrative Assistant
Web address: www.highlandridgehospital.com
Control: Corporation, Investor–owned (for–profit) **Service**: Psychiatric

Staffed Beds: 83

MILFORD—Beaver County

★ **MILFORD VALLEY MEMORIAL HOSPITAL (461305)**, 850 North Main Street, Zip 84751–0640, Mailing Address: P.O. Box 640, Zip 84751–0640; tel. 435/387–2411, (Nonreporting) **A**10 18
Primary Contact: Scott Langford, Administrator
COO: Michelle Barton, Chief Operating Officer
CFO: Tyler Moss, Chief Financial Officer
CNO: Amy Contreras Esq Chief Nursing Officer
Web address: www.milfordmemorialhospital.org
Control: Hospital district or authority, Government, nonfederal **Service**: General medical and surgical

Staffed Beds: 25

MOAB—Grand County

★ **MOAB REGIONAL HOSPITAL (461302)**, 450 West Williams Way, Zip 84532–2065, Mailing Address: P.O. Box 998, Zip 84532–0998; tel. 435/719–3500, **A**10 18 **F**3 4 5 11 13 15 29 30 31 34 35 40 43 45 57 59 63 64 65 66 67 68 75 76 79 81 82 85 86 89 90 97 107 110 111 114 115 119 128 130 131 132 133 144 148 151 **P**6
Primary Contact: Jennifer Sadoff, Chief Executive Officer
COO: Vicki Gigliotti, Chief Clinical Officer
CFO: Craig M Daniels, Chief Financial Officer
CMO: Dylan Cole, Chief Medical Officer
CIO: Mike Foster, Manager Information Systems
CHR: Katherine Sullivan, Director, Human Resources
Web address: www.mrhmoab.org
Control: Other not–for–profit (including NFP Corporation) **Service**: General medical and surgical

Staffed Beds: 17 **Admissions**: 859 **Census**: 5 **Outpatient Visits**: 14467 **Births**: 87 **Total Expense ($000)**: 27910 **Payroll Expense ($000)**: 12002 **Personnel**: 223

UT

Hospital, Medicare Provider Number, Address, Telephone, Approval, Facility, and Physician Codes, Health Care System

★ American Hospital Association (AHA) membership
☐ The Joint Commission accreditation
○ Healthcare Facilities Accreditation Program
◇ DNV Healthcare Inc. accreditation
⇑ Center for Improvement in Healthcare Quality Accreditation
△ Commission on Accreditation of Rehabilitation Facilities (CARF) accreditation

MONTICELLO—San Juan County

SAN JUAN HEALTH SERVICE DISTRICT (461308), 380 West 100 North, Zip 84535, Mailing Address: P.O. Box 308, Zip 84535–0308; tel. 435/587–2116, **A**10 18 **F**3 13 15 29 31 32 34 35 38 39 40 41 44 45 47 50 56 57 59 64 65 66 68 76 79 80 81 82 87 107 110 114 119 127 128 133 145 148 **P**6
Primary Contact: Clayton Holt, Chief Executive Officer
CFO: Lyman Duncan, Chief Financial Officer
CMO: Kelly Jeppesen, Chief Medical Officer
CIO: Julie Bingham, IT Supervisor
CHR: Deana Dalton, Human Resources
CNO: Laurie Schafer, Chief Nursing Officer
Web address: www.sanjuanhealthservices.org/
Control: Hospital district or authority, Government, nonfederal **Service**: General medical and surgical

Staffed Beds: 25 **Admissions**: 220 **Census**: 2 **Outpatient Visits**: 4500
Births: 46 **Total Expense ($000)**: 14444 **Payroll Expense ($000)**: 6160
Personnel: 110

MOUNT PLEASANT—Sanpete County

★ **SANPETE VALLEY HOSPITAL (461303)**, 1100 South Medical Drive, Zip 84647–2222; tel. 435/462–2441, **A**10 18 **F**8 13 15 29 30 32 34 35 39 40 41 43 45 46 50 54 56 57 59 64 65 67 68 75 76 78 79 81 82 84 89 90 93 97 102 105 107 110 111 115 119 128 129 130 131 132 133 148 154 **P**4 5 **S** Intermountain Healthcare, Inc., Salt Lake City, UT
Primary Contact: Aaron C. Wood, Chief Executive Officer and Administrator
COO: Kristina Skinner, Director Quality
CFO: Chris Thompson, Chief Financial Officer
CMO: David Krzymowski, M.D., Chief of Staff
CIO: Michael Ence, Computer Specialist
CHR: Brett Gray, Director Human Resource
CNO: Ryan Robison, Chief Nursing Officer
Web address: www.intermountainhealthcare.com
Control: Other not-for-profit (including NFP Corporation) **Service**: General medical and surgical

Staffed Beds: 18 **Admissions**: 454 **Census**: 3 **Outpatient Visits**: 9700
Births: 122

MURRAY—Salt Lake County

☐ △ **INTERMOUNTAIN MEDICAL CENTER (460010)**, 5121 South Cottonwood Street, Zip 84107–5701; tel. 801/507–7000, **A**1 2 5 7 10 **F**3 8 13 15 17 18 20 22 24 26 28 29 30 31 34 35 37 38 39 40 43 44 45 46 47 48 49 50 51 53 54 55 56 57 59 60 61 64 66 68 70 71 72 74 75 76 77 78 79 81 82 84 85 86 87 90 91 92 93 94 96 97 100 102 107 108 110 111 115 116 117 118 119 120 121 123 124 126 129 130 131 132 135 137 138 139 141 142 145 146 147 148 149 154 **S** Intermountain Healthcare, Inc., Salt Lake City, UT
Primary Contact: Joseph Mott, Chief Executive Officer
COO: Kelly L Duffin, Operations Officer
CFO: Royce Stephens, Director Finance
CMO: Mark Ott, M.D., Regional Chief Medical Director
CIO: David Baird, Director of Information Systems
CHR: Tiffiny J Lipscomb, Manager Human Resources
CNO: Suzanne P. Anderson, Nurse Administrator
Web address: www.intermountainhealthcare.org
Control: Other not-for-profit (including NFP Corporation) **Service**: General medical and surgical

Staffed Beds: 510 **Admissions**: 26198 **Census**: 330 **Outpatient Visits**: 1095558 **Births**: 4362 **Total Expense ($000)**: 846609 **Payroll Expense ($000)**: 263325 **Personnel**: 4013

LANDMARK HOSPITAL OF SALT LAKE CITY (462006), 4252 South Birkhill Boulevard, Zip 84107–5715; tel. 801/268–5400, (Nonreporting) **A**10 22 **S** Landmark Hospitals, Cape Girardeau, MO
Primary Contact: Ted Paarlberg, Chief Executive Officer
Web address: www.landmarkhospitals.com/utah.aspx
Control: Partnership, Investor–owned (for–profit) **Service**: Acute long–term care hospital

Staffed Beds: 38

⊞ **THE ORTHOPEDIC SPECIALTY HOSPITAL (460049)**, 5848 South 300 East, Zip 84107–6121; tel. 801/314–4100, **A**1 10 **F**3 9 29 34 35 37 44 50 53 54 57 58 59 64 68 75 77 79 81 82 85 86 87 93 94 97 107 111 115 119 129 130 131 132 141 144 146 149 **S** Intermountain Healthcare, Inc., Salt Lake City, UT
Primary Contact: Lisa Bagley, Nurse Administrator
CFO: Sherlyn Lewis, Manager Finance
CMO: Jon Sundin, M.D., Medical Director
CIO: David Baird, Chief Information Officer
CHR: Tina Tasso, Manager Human Resources
Web address: www.intermountainhealthcare.org
Control: Other not-for-profit (including NFP Corporation) **Service**: Orthopedic

Staffed Beds: 40 **Admissions**: 2001 **Census**: 11 **Outpatient Visits**: 209874
Births: 0 **Total Expense ($000)**: 71087 **Payroll Expense ($000)**: 20712
Personnel: 341

NEPHI—Juab County

★ **CENTRAL VALLEY MEDICAL CENTER (461304)**, 48 West 1500 North, Zip 84648–8900; tel. 435/623–3000, (Nonreporting) **A**10 18 **S** Rural Health Group, Nephi, UT
Primary Contact: Mark R. Stoddard, Chief Executive Officer
COO: Randy Cuff, Chief Operating Officer
CFO: Brent Davis, Chief Financial Officer
CMO: Mark Oveson, M.D., Chief Medical Staff
CIO: Ken Richens, Chief Information Officer
CHR: Brian Allsop, Director Human Resources
CNO: Randy Allinson, R.N., Chief Nursing Officer
Web address: www.cvmed.net
Control: Other not-for-profit (including NFP Corporation) **Service**: General medical and surgical

Staffed Beds: 27

NORTH LOGAN—Cache County

⊠ **CACHE VALLEY HOSPITAL (460054)**, 2380 North 400 East, Zip 84341–6000; tel. 435/713–9700, (Nonreporting) **A**1 10 **S** HCA Healthcare, Nashville, TN
Primary Contact: John C. Worley III, Chief Executive Officer
CFO: David S Geary, Chief Financial Officer
CMO: Matt Welter, Chief Medical Officer
Web address: www.cachevalleyhospital.com/
Control: Corporation, Investor–owned (for–profit) **Service**: General medical and surgical

Staffed Beds: 22

OGDEN—Weber County

⊠ **MCKAY–DEE HOSPITAL (460004)**, 4401 Harrison Boulevard, Zip 84403–3195; tel. 801/387–2800, **A**1 2 3 10 **F**3 8 11 13 15 18 20 22 24 26 28 29 30 31 34 35 38 39 40 43 44 45 46 49 50 51 53 54 57 58 59 60 64 68 70 72 74 75 76 77 78 79 80 81 82 84 85 86 87 89 90 91 92 93 94 96 97 98 99 100 101 102 103 104 105 107 108 110 111 115 116 117 118 119 120 121 123 126 129 130 131 132 134 135 141 146 147 148 149 153 **S** Intermountain Healthcare, Inc., Salt Lake City, UT
Primary Contact: Michael A. Clark, Administrator
COO: Michael A Clark, Chief Operating Officer
CFO: Doug Smith, Chief Financial Officer
CMO: Christine Nefcy, Chief Medical Officer
CIO: Mary Gathers, Director Information Systems
CHR: Lee Lorimer IV Regional Director Human Resources
CNO: Bonnie Jacklin, R.N., MSN, Chief Nursing Officer
Web address: www.mckay–dee.org
Control: Other not-for-profit (including NFP Corporation) **Service**: General medical and surgical

Staffed Beds: 312 **Admissions**: 18185 **Census**: 182 **Births**: 3751
Total Expense ($000): 426258 **Payroll Expense ($000)**: 131777
Personnel: 2285

⊠ **OGDEN REGIONAL MEDICAL CENTER (460005)**, 5475 South 500 East, Zip 84405–6905; tel. 801/479–2111, (Nonreporting) **A**1 3 10 13 **S** HCA Healthcare, Nashville, TN
Primary Contact: Mark B. Adams, Chief Executive Officer
COO: Brian Lines, Chief Operating Officer
CFO: Judd Taylor, Chief Financial Officer
CMO: Jeffrey Abel, M.D., Chief Medical Officer
CIO: Eric Peterson, Director
CHR: Chris Bissenden, Director Human Resources
CNO: Elizabeth B. Later, R.N., Chief Nursing Officer
Web address: www.ogdenregional.com
Control: Corporation, Investor–owned (for–profit) **Service**: General medical and surgical

Staffed Beds: 167

OREM—Utah County

⊠ **OREM COMMUNITY HOSPITAL (460043)**, 331 North 400 West, Zip 84057–1999; tel. 801/224–4080, **A**1 10 **F**3 13 29 34 35 40 44 50 64 68 75 76 77 81 85 86 87 97 102 107 111 115 119 130 132 141 146 147 149 **S** Intermountain Healthcare, Inc., Salt Lake City, UT
Primary Contact: J. Francis. Gibson, Administrator and Chief Executive Officer
CMO: Neil Whitaker, M.D., Chief Medical Director
CIO: Diane Rindlisbacher, Manager Information Systems
CHR: Pamela S Niece, Director Human Resources
Web address: www.intermountainhealthcare.org
Control: Other not-for-profit (including NFP Corporation) **Service**: General medical and surgical

Staffed Beds: 18 **Admissions**: 1022 **Census**: 5 **Births**: 1003 **Total Expense ($000)**: 27897 **Payroll Expense ($000)**: 9767 **Personnel**: 159

UT

☐ **PROVO CANYON BEHAVIORAL HOSPITAL (464014)**, 1350 East 750 North, Zip 84097–4345; tel. 801/852–2273, **A**1 10 **F**4 5 29 35 36 38 56 57 59 75 82 86 87 97 98 99 101 103 104 106 153 **P**4 6 **S** Universal Health Services, Inc., King of Prussia, PA
Primary Contact: Jeremy Cottle, Ph.D., Chief Executive Officer
CFO: Emmy Adams, Chief Financial Officer
CHR: Diann Decker, Chief Human Resource Officer
Web address: www.pcbh.com
Control: Corporation, Investor–owned (for–profit) **Service:** Psychiatric

Staffed Beds: 80 **Admissions:** 2460 **Census:** 57 **Outpatient Visits:** 2244 **Births:** 0 **Total Expense ($000):** 12322 **Payroll Expense ($000):** 6732 **Personnel:** 138

☒ **TIMPANOGOS REGIONAL HOSPITAL (460052)**, 750 West 800 North, Zip 84057–3660; tel. 801/714–6000, (Nonreporting) **A**1 10 **S** HCA Healthcare, Nashville, TN
Primary Contact: Kimball S. Anderson, FACHE, Chief Executive Officer
COO: Austin Lane Manning, Chief Operating Officer
CFO: Jody S Dial, Chief Financial Officer
CMO: Randle L Likes, M.D., Chief Medical Officer
CIO: Richard Neilson, Director of Information Services
CHR: Tim Black, Director Human Resources
CNO: Sandy Ewell, Chief Nursing Officer
Web address: www.timpanogosregionalhospital.com
Control: Corporation, Investor–owned (for–profit) **Service:** General medical and surgical

Staffed Beds: 105

PANGUITCH—Garfield County

★ **GARFIELD MEMORIAL HOSPITAL (460033)**, 200 North 400 East, Zip 84759, Mailing Address: P.O. Box 389, Zip 84759–0389; tel. 435/676–8811, **A**10 18 **F**3 13 15 29 34 40 44 50 68 71 75 77 81 85 87 107 110 115 119 127 128 130 131 132 133 149 **S** Intermountain Healthcare, Inc., Salt Lake City, UT
Primary Contact: Alberto Vasquez, Administrator
CFO: Reed Sargent, Assistant Administrator Finance
Web address: www.ihc.com/hospitals/garfield
Control: County, Government, nonfederal **Service:** General medical and surgical

Staffed Beds: 15 **Admissions:** 293 **Census:** 4 **Births:** 36 **Total Expense ($000):** 10964 **Payroll Expense ($000):** 5737 **Personnel:** 97

PARK CITY—Summit County

☒ **PARK CITY HOSPITAL (460057)**, 900 Round Valley Drive, Zip 84060–7552; tel. 435/658–7000, **A**1 10 **F**3 13 15 18 29 34 35 36 38 40 43 44 45 49 50 53 57 59 64 68 70 75 76 77 79 81 85 86 87 93 97 102 107 108 110 111 115 118 119 129 130 131 132 141 146 147 149 154 **S** Intermountain Healthcare, Inc., Salt Lake City, UT
Primary Contact: Si William. Hutt, Administrator
CFO: Lori Nielson, Regional Finance Director
CMO: Wain Allen, M.D., Medical Director
CHR: Christopher Saling, Manager Human Resources
CNO: Dan Davis, MSN, R.N., Nurse Administrator
Web address: www.intermountainhealthcare.org
Control: Other not–for–profit (including NFP Corporation) **Service:** General medical and surgical

Staffed Beds: 37 **Admissions:** 1810 **Census:** 11 **Births:** 358 **Total Expense ($000):** 83177 **Payroll Expense ($000):** 24587 **Personnel:** 390

PAYSON—Utah County

☒ **MOUNTAIN VIEW HOSPITAL (460013)**, 1000 East 100 North, Zip 84651–1600; tel. 801/465–7000, (Nonreporting) **A**1 10 **S** HCA Healthcare, Nashville, TN
Primary Contact: Kevin Johnson, Chief Executive Officer
COO: Ric Johnson, Associate Administrator
CFO: Steven R Schramm, Chief Financial Officer
CMO: Jeffrey Wallentine, Chief of Staff
CIO: Cindy Mecham, Health Information Director
CHR: Wally Trotter, Director Human Resources
CNO: Katie King, R.N., Chief Nursing Officer
Web address: www.mvhpayson.com
Control: Corporation, Investor–owned (for–profit) **Service:** General medical and surgical

Staffed Beds: 114

PRICE—Carbon County

☒ **CASTLEVIEW HOSPITAL (460011)**, 300 North Hospital Drive, Zip 84501–4200; tel. 435/637–4800, **A**1 10 20 **F**3 8 11 12 13 15 18 29 31 34 39 40 41 45 47 48 50 51 56 57 59 68 70 75 76 77 78 79 81 82 85 86 87 89 92 93 107 108 110 111 115 119 127 130 131 146 147 148 149 **S** LifePoint Health, Brentwood, TN
Primary Contact: Jerry Dooley, Interim Chief Executive Officer
CFO: Greg Cook, Chief Financial Officer
CMO: Glen T. Etzel, M.D., Chief of Staff
CIO: Fiore Wilson, Director Information Systems
CHR: Misty Birch, Director Human Resources
CNO: Grant Barraclough, R.N., Chief Nursing Officer
Web address: www.castleviewhospital.net
Control: Corporation, Investor–owned (for–profit) **Service:** General medical and surgical

Staffed Beds: 49 **Admissions:** 1640 **Census:** 12 **Outpatient Visits:** 41209 **Births:** 250 **Total Expense ($000):** 37012 **Payroll Expense ($000):** 13802 **Personnel:** 357

PROVO—Utah County

☐ **UTAH STATE HOSPITAL (464001)**, 1300 East Center Street, Zip 84606–3554, Mailing Address: P.O. Box 270, Zip 84603–0270; tel. 801/344–4400, **A**1 3 10 **F**30 34 56 75 77 86 87 91 98 99 100 101 103 106 130 135 143 146 149 150 **P**6
Primary Contact: Dallas Earnshaw, Superintendent
COO: Dallas Earnshaw, Superintendent
CFO: Robert Burton, Manager Finance
CMO: Madhu Gundlapalli, M.D., Clinical Director
CIO: Jill Hill, Director Information Technology
CHR: Devin Patrick, Manager Human Resources
CNO: Chris Metcalf, Director of Nursing
Web address: www.ush.utah.gov
Control: State, Government, nonfederal **Service:** Psychiatric

Staffed Beds: 324 **Admissions:** 291 **Census:** 315 **Outpatient Visits:** 0 **Births:** 0 **Total Expense ($000):** 61205 **Payroll Expense ($000):** 35302 **Personnel:** 789

☒ △ **UTAH VALLEY HOSPITAL (460001)**, 1034 North 500 West, Zip 84604–3337; tel. 801/357–7850, **A**1 2 3 7 10 **F**3 13 15 17 18 20 22 24 26 28 29 30 31 32 34 35 37 38 39 40 43 44 45 46 48 49 50 51 53 54 56 57 59 60 64 68 70 72 74 75 76 77 78 79 81 82 84 85 86 87 89 90 93 94 97 98 102 103 107 108 110 111 115 116 117 118 119 120 121 123 124 126 129 130 131 132 141 146 147 148 149 **S** Intermountain Healthcare, Inc., Salt Lake City, UT
Primary Contact: Kevin Brooks, Hospital Administrator
CFO: Rod Lisonbee, Chief Financial Officer
CIO: Mary Gathers, Director Information Systems
CHR: Luke P Morris, Assistant Vice President Talent
CNO: Lisa A. Paletta, R.N., FACHE, Chief Nursing Officer
Web address: www.utahvalleyregional.org
Control: Other not–for–profit (including NFP Corporation) **Service:** General medical and surgical

Staffed Beds: 359 **Admissions:** 18997 **Census:** 226 **Outpatient Visits:** 703364 **Births:** 4069 **Total Expense ($000):** 485394 **Payroll Expense ($000):** 154213 **Personnel:** 2692

☐ **UTAH VALLEY SPECIALTY HOSPITAL (462005)**, 306 River Bend Lane, Zip 84604–5625; tel. 801/226–8880, (Nonreporting) **A**1 10 **S** Ernest Health, Inc., Albuquerque, NM
Primary Contact: Ezra Segura, Chief Executive Officer
Web address: www.uvsh.ernesthealth.com
Control: Corporation, Investor–owned (for–profit) **Service:** Acute long–term care hospital

Staffed Beds: 40

RICHFIELD—Sevier County

☒ **SEVIER VALLEY HOSPITAL (460026)**, 1000 North Main Street, Zip 84701–1857; tel. 435/893–4100, **A**1 10 20 **F**3 15 29 34 35 38 40 44 50 64 68 75 76 77 79 81 85 86 87 97 102 107 108 110 111 115 118 119 127 130 132 141 149 **S** Intermountain Healthcare, Inc., Salt Lake City, UT
Primary Contact: Gary E. Beck, Administrator
CFO: Chris Thompson, Chief Financial Officer
CMO: Justin Abbott, M.D., Medical Director
CHR: Katey Nelson, Director Human Resources
CNO: Cami Blackham, R.N., Nurse Administrator
Web address: www.sevierhospital.org
Control: Other not–for–profit (including NFP Corporation) **Service:** General medical and surgical

Staffed Beds: 29 **Admissions:** 999 **Census:** 7 **Births:** 269 **Total Expense ($000):** 37358 **Payroll Expense ($000):** 9764 **Personnel:** 170

UT

Hospital, Medicare Provider Number, Address, Telephone, Approval, Facility, and Physician Codes, Health Care System

★ American Hospital Association (AHA) membership ☐ The Joint Commission accreditation
○ Healthcare Facilities Accreditation Program ◇ DNV Healthcare Inc. accreditation
⇑ Center for Improvement in Healthcare Quality Accreditation △ Commission on Accreditation of Rehabilitation Facilities (CARF) accreditation

RIVERTON—Salt Lake County

⊞ **RIVERTON HOSPITAL (460058)**, 3741 West 12600 South, Zip 84065–7215; tel. 801/285–4000, **A**1 3 10 **F**3 13 15 29 31 34 35 38 39 40 44 45 49 50 51 54 57 59 64 68 70 73 75 76 77 79 81 85 86 87 89 93 97 102 107 108 110 111 115 118 119 120 121 123 124 129 131 132 141 146 147 148 149 **S** Intermountain Healthcare, Inc., Salt Lake City, UT
Primary Contact: Todd Neubert, Chief Executive Officer
CFO: Royce Stephens, Chief Financial Officer
CMO: David Haselton, Chief Medical Officer
CIO: Susan Hanks, Chief Information Officer
Web address: www.intermountainhealthcare.org/
Control: Other not–for–profit (including NFP Corporation) **Service:** General medical and surgical

Staffed Beds: 88 **Admissions:** 5563 **Census:** 36 **Outpatient Visits:** 318338 **Births:** 2300 **Total Expense ($000):** 122117 **Payroll Expense ($000):** 35104 **Personnel:** 554

ROOSEVELT—Duchesne County

★ **UINTAH BASIN MEDICAL CENTER (460019)**, 250 West 300 North, 75–2, Zip 84066–2336; tel. 435/722–6163, (Total facility includes 75 beds in nursing home–type unit) **A**10 20 **F**6 7 11 13 15 17 35 40 43 45 50 52 53 54 57 59 60 62 63 70 73 76 77 79 81 82 84 85 87 89 93 107 108 110 111 115 119 127 128 129 130 131 132 135 146 147 148 154 **P**3
Primary Contact: James I. Marshall, President and Chief Executive Officer
CFO: Brent Hales, Chief Financial Officer
CMO: Gary B White, M.D., Chief Medical Staff
CHR: Randall Bennett, Assistant Administrator
Web address: www.ubmc.org
Control: Other not–for–profit (including NFP Corporation) **Service:** General medical and surgical

Staffed Beds: 124 **Admissions:** 1828 **Census:** 74 **Outpatient Visits:** 66293 **Births:** 561 **Total Expense ($000):** 79964 **Payroll Expense ($000):** 26032 **Personnel:** 573

SAINT GEORGE—Washington County

⊞ △ **DIXIE REGIONAL MEDICAL CENTER (460021)**, 1380 East Medical Center Drive, Zip 84790–2123; tel. 435/251–1000, (Includes DIXIE REGIONAL MEDICAL CENTER, 544 South 400 East, St George, UT, Zip 84770; tel. 940/764–7000) **A**1 7 10 **F**3 11 12 13 15 18 20 22 24 26 28 29 30 31 34 35 38 39 40 43 44 45 46 47 48 49 50 51 53 54 55 56 57 58 59 64 65 68 70 71 72 74 75 76 77 78 79 80 81 82 84 85 86 87 89 90 92 93 96 97 102 107 108 110 111 114 115 116 117 118 119 120 121 123 124 129 130 131 132 141 146 147 148 149 **S** Intermountain Healthcare, Inc., Salt Lake City, UT
Primary Contact: Mitchell Cloward, Administrator
CFO: Steven Vance, Chief Financial Officer
CMO: Steven Van Norman, M.D., Medical Director
CIO: Lance Bedingfield, Director Information Services
CHR: Vicki Wilson, Human Resources Director
CNO: Gary Cunningham, Chief Nursing Officer
Web address: www.intermountainhealthcare.org
Control: Other not–for–profit (including NFP Corporation) **Service:** General medical and surgical

Staffed Beds: 245 **Admissions:** 17301 **Census:** 174 **Outpatient Visits:** 580656 **Births:** 2386 **Total Expense ($000):** 487504 **Payroll Expense ($000):** 143040 **Personnel:** 2308

SALT LAKE CITY—Salt Lake County

⊞ **LDS HOSPITAL (460006)**, Eighth Avenue and 'C' Street, Zip 84143–0001; tel. 801/408–1100, **A**1 2 3 5 10 **F**3 4 5 12 13 15 29 31 34 35 37 38 39 40 44 45 46 48 49 50 51 53 54 55 56 57 58 59 60 64 66 68 70 74 75 76 77 78 79 81 82 84 85 86 87 97 98 100 101 102 103 104 105 106 107 108 110 111 115 118 119 120 121 123 124 129 130 131 132 135 136 141 146 147 148 149 152 153 154 **S** Intermountain Healthcare, Inc., Salt Lake City, UT
Primary Contact: Jim Sheets, Chief Executive Officer and Administrator
CFO: Dan Brady, Chief Financial Officer
CMO: Kerry Fisher, M.D., Medical Director
CIO: David Baird, Chief Information Officer
CHR: Mollee Lamb, Manager Human Resources
CNO: Brandon Vonk, Nurse Administrator
Web address: www.intermountainhealthcare.org
Control: Other not–for–profit (including NFP Corporation) **Service:** General medical and surgical

Staffed Beds: 243 **Admissions:** 10810 **Census:** 121 **Births:** 2193 **Total Expense ($000):** 249854 **Payroll Expense ($000):** 74179 **Personnel:** 1195

⊞ **MARIAN CENTER (464012)**, 451 East Bishop Federal Lane, Zip 84115–2357; tel. 801/487–7557, **A**1 10 **F**29 34 98 100 101 103 130 **P**8
Primary Contact: Brent Wilson, Chief Executive Officer
Web address: www.stjosephvilla.com
Control: Corporation, Investor–owned (for–profit) **Service:** Psychiatric

Staffed Beds: 14 **Admissions:** 271 **Census:** 9 **Births:** 0 **Total Expense ($000):** 2275 **Personnel:** 32

☐ **PRIMARY CHILDREN'S HOSPITAL (463301)**, 100 North Mario Capecchi Drive, Zip 84113–1100; tel. 801/662–1000, **A**1 3 5 10 **F**3 17 19 21 23 25 27 28 29 30 31 32 34 35 36 37 38 39 40 41 43 44 45 46 47 48 49 50 51 53 54 55 57 58 59 60 64 68 71 72 73 74 75 77 78 79 80 81 82 84 85 86 87 88 89 91 92 93 94 96 97 98 99 100 101 102 104 105 106 107 108 111 115 116 117 118 119 129 130 131 132 134 135 136 137 138 139 141 146 148 149 151 153 154 **S** Intermountain Healthcare, Inc., Salt Lake City, UT
Primary Contact: Katy Welkie MBA, R.N., Chief Executive Officer
CFO: Jeremiah Radandt, Chief Financial Officer
CMO: Ed Clark, M.D., Chief Medical Officer
CIO: Joe Hales, Chief Information Officer
CHR: Albert Bennett Buckworth, Human Resources Administrative Director
CNO: Judy Geiger, R.N., Chief Nursing Officer
Web address: www.intermountainhealthcare.org
Control: Other not–for–profit (including NFP Corporation) **Service:** Children's general medical and surgical

Staffed Beds: 289 **Admissions:** 13216 **Census:** 194 **Births:** 0 **Total Expense ($000):** 524626 **Payroll Expense ($000):** 187757 **Personnel:** 2815

PROMISE HOSPITAL OF SALT LAKE (462004), 8 Avenue, C Street, Zip 84143; tel. 801/408–7110, **A**10 **F**1 3 29 34 75 77 84 85 87 130 148 149 **S** Promise Healthcare, Boca Raton, FL
Primary Contact: Wayne Kinsey, Chief Executive Officer
CMO: Geoff Harding, Chief Clinical Officer
Web address: www.promise–saltlake.com
Control: Corporation, Investor–owned (for–profit) **Service:** Acute long–term care hospital

Staffed Beds: 41 **Admissions:** 437 **Census:** 33 **Outpatient Visits:** 0 **Births:** 0 **Total Expense ($000):** 16462 **Payroll Expense ($000):** 9211 **Personnel:** 161

☐ **SALT LAKE BEHAVIORAL HEALTH (464013)**, 3802 South 700 East, Zip 84106–1182; tel. 801/264–6000, **A**1 10 **F**4 5 29 38 75 98 102 104 130 135 143 152 153 **S** Universal Health Services, Inc., King of Prussia, PA
Primary Contact: Kreg Gillman, Chief Executive Officer
COO: Jim Hess, Chief Operations Officer
CFO: Daren Woolstenhulme, Chief Financial Officer
CMO: Monica Polk, M.D., Chief Medical Officer
CHR: Robyn Holsten, Human Resources Director
CNO: Suzanne Nelson, R.N., Director of Nursing
Web address: www.saltlakebehavioralhealth.com
Control: Corporation, Investor–owned (for–profit) **Service:** Psychiatric

Staffed Beds: 118 **Admissions:** 2408 **Census:** 61 **Outpatient Visits:** 6308 **Births:** 0 **Total Expense ($000):** 19518 **Payroll Expense ($000):** 9616 **Personnel:** 162

★ ⇑ **SALT LAKE REGIONAL MEDICAL CENTER (460003)**, 1050 East South Temple, Zip 84102–1507; tel. 801/350–4111, (Nonreporting) **A**3 5 10 21 **S** Steward Health Care System, LLC, Dallas, TX
Primary Contact: Dale Johns, FACHE, Chief Executive Officer
COO: Scot Stevens, Assistant Administrator
CFO: Brian Ebright, Chief Financial Officer
CMO: Blake Johnson, M.D., Chief of Staff
CIO: Mark Runyan, Director Information Services
CHR: Carolyn Livingston, Director Human Resources
CNO: Terron Arbon, R.N., Chief Nursing Officer
Web address: www.saltlakeregional.com
Control: Corporation, Investor–owned (for–profit) **Service:** General medical and surgical

Staffed Beds: 132

☐ **SHRINERS HOSPITALS FOR CHILDREN–SALT LAKE CITY (463302)**, 1275 East Fairfax Road, Zip 84103–4399; tel. 801/536–3500, (Nonreporting) **A**1 3 5 10 **S** Shriners Hospitals for Children, Tampa, FL
Primary Contact: Kevin Martin, M.P.H., R.N., FACHE, Administrator
CFO: Heath Braby, Director Fiscal Services
CMO: Kristen Carroll, M.D., Chief of Staff
CIO: Mike Allen, Director Information Technology
CHR: Kris Goldman, Director Human Resources
CNO: Gail McGuill, R.N., MSN, Chief Nursing Officer and Administrative Director of Patient Care Services
Web address: www.shrinershospitalsforchildren.org/Hospitals/Locations/SaltLakeCity.aspx
Control: Other not–for–profit (including NFP Corporation) **Service:** Children's orthopedic

Staffed Beds: 45

⊞ **ST. MARK'S HOSPITAL (460047)**, 1200 East 3900 South, Zip 84124–1390; tel. 801/268–7111, (Nonreporting) **A**1 3 10 **S** HCA Healthcare, Nashville, TN
Primary Contact: Mark Robinson, FACHE, Chief Executive Officer
CFO: Bryan McKinley, Chief Financial Officer
CMO: J Eric Vanderhooft, M.D., President Medical Staff
CIO: Jesse Trujillo, Chief Information Officer
CHR: Robyn Opheikens, Assistant Administrator Human Resources
Web address: www.stmarkshospital.com
Control: Corporation, Investor–owned (for–profit) **Service:** General medical and surgical

Staffed Beds: 277

★ △ ⇑ **UNIVERSITY OF UTAH HEALTH (460009)**, 50 North Medical Drive, Zip 84132–0002; tel. 801/587–3572, **A**3 5 7 8 10 21 **F**3 5 6 7 8 9 11 12 13 15 16 17 18 20 22 24 26 28 29 30 31 34 35 36 37 38 39 40 43 44 45 46 47 48 49 50 51 52 53 54 55 56 57 58 59 60 61 64 65 68 70 71 72 73 74 75 76 77 78 79 80 81 82 83 84 85 86 87 90 91 92 93 94 95 96 97 98 100 101 102 107 108 109 110 111 112 113 114 115 116 117 118 119 120 121 123 124 126 129 130 131 132 134 135 136 137 138 139 140 141 142 143 144 146 147 148 149 152 154 **P**1
Primary Contact: Gordon Crabtree, Interim Chief Executive Officer
CFO: Gordon Crabtree, Chief Financial Officer
CMO: Thomas Miller, M.D., Medical Director
CIO: James Turnbull, Chief Information Officer
CHR: Dale A Spartz, Chief Human Resources Officer
CNO: Margaret Pearce, R.N., Ph.D., Chief Nursing Officer
Web address: www.uuhsc.utah.edu
Control: State, Government, nonfederal **Service:** General medical and surgical

Staffed Beds: 602 **Admissions:** 27836 **Census:** 435 **Outpatient Visits:** 2176744 **Births:** 4168 **Total Expense ($000):** 1491529 **Payroll Expense ($000):** 511532 **Personnel:** 10217

⇑ **UNIVERSITY OF UTAH NEUROPSYCHIATRIC INSTITUTE (464009)**, 501 South Chipeta Way, Zip 84108–1222; tel. 801/583–2500, **A**3 5 10 21 **F**4 5 34 35 38 58 98 99 100 101 102 103 104 105 106 130 149 153 154
Primary Contact: Ross Van Vranken, Executive Director
CFO: Becky Schaefer, Chief Financial Officer
CMO: James Ashworth, M.D., Medical Director
Web address: www.med.utah.edu/uni
Control: State, Government, nonfederal **Service:** Psychiatric

Staffed Beds: 157 **Admissions:** 4732 **Census:** 121 **Outpatient Visits:** 43887 **Births:** 0 **Total Expense ($000):** 94294 **Payroll Expense ($000):** 35933 **Personnel:** 740

⊞ △ **VETERANS AFFAIRS SALT LAKE CITY HEALTH CARE SYSTEM**, 500 Foothill Drive, Zip 84148–0002; tel. 801/582–1565, **A**1 3 5 7 **F**3 4 5 8 12 18 20 22 24 28 29 30 34 35 36 38 39 40 44 45 46 47 48 49 50 53 54 55 56 57 58 59 60 61 62 63 64 65 70 71 74 75 77 78 79 81 82 83 84 85 86 87 90 92 93 94 96 97 98 100 101 102 103 104 105 106 107 108 109 111 114 115 116 117 118 119 126 127 129 130 132 133 135 137 143 144 146 147 148 149 151 152 153 154 **P**6 **S** Department of Veterans Affairs, Perry Point, MD
Primary Contact: Shella D. Stovall, R.N., Acting Director
CFO: Val Martin, Director Financial Management Services Center
CMO: Ronald J Gebhart, M.D., Chief of Staff
CIO: Lisa Leonelis, Chief Information Officer
CHR: Lisa Porter, Director Human Resources, Leadership and Education
Web address: www.saltlakecity.va.gov/
Control: Veterans Affairs, Government, federal **Service:** General medical and surgical

Staffed Beds: 130 **Admissions:** 4561 **Census:** 81 **Outpatient Visits:** 687572 **Births:** 0 **Personnel:** 2553

SANDY—Salt Lake County

⊞ △ **ALTA VIEW HOSPITAL (460044)**, 9660 South 1300 East, Zip 84094–3793; tel. 801/501–2600, **A**1 2 10 **F**3 12 13 15 29 34 35 38 39 40 43 44 45 46 47 48 49 50 51 54 56 57 59 64 68 70 75 76 77 78 79 81 85 86 87 97 102 107 108 110 111 115 118 119 129 130 132 141 146 147 149 **S** Intermountain Healthcare, Inc., Salt Lake City, UT
Primary Contact: Lisa A. Paletta, RN, MPA, NEA–BC, Chief Executive Officer
CFO: Chris Hargis, Manager Finance
CHR: Leslie Bates, Manager Human Resources
Web address: www.intermountainhealthcare.org
Control: Other not–for–profit (including NFP Corporation) **Service:** General medical and surgical

Staffed Beds: 66 **Admissions:** 2783 **Census:** 19 **Outpatient Visits:** 234812 **Births:** 946 **Total Expense ($000):** 96851 **Payroll Expense ($000):** 27543 **Personnel:** 440

⊞ **HEALTHSOUTH REHABILITATION HOSPITAL OF UTAH (463025)**, 8074 South 1300 East, Zip 84094–0743; tel. 801/561–3400, (Nonreporting) **A**1 10 **S** Encompass Health Corporation, Birmingham, AL
Primary Contact: Jeff Frandsen, Chief Executive Officer
CMO: Joseph VickRoy, M.D., Medical Director
CHR: Troy Jensen, Director Human Resources
Web address: www.healthsouthutah.com
Control: Corporation, Investor–owned (for–profit) **Service:** Rehabilitation

Staffed Beds: 105

SOUTH OGDEN—Weber County

NORTHERN UTAH REHABILITATION HOSPITAL (463027), 5825 Harrison Boulevard, Zip 84403–4316; tel. 801/475–5254, (Nonreporting) **S** Ernest Health, Inc., Albuquerque, NM
Primary Contact: Ryan Keele, Chief Executive Officer
COO: Reuben Jessop, Chief Operating Officer
CFO: Daniel J Foster, Chief Financial Officer
CNO: Terina Chapman, Director of Nursing
Web address: www.ernesthealth.com/gallery–item/northern–utah–rehabilitation–hospital/
Control: Other not–for–profit (including NFP Corporation) **Service:** Rehabilitation

Staffed Beds: 40

TOOELE—Tooele County

⊞ **MOUNTAIN WEST MEDICAL CENTER (460014)**, 2055 North Main Street, Zip 84074–9819; tel. 435/843–3600, **A**1 10 **F**3 7 13 15 18 29 30 34 40 49 50 51 57 64 67 68 70 74 75 76 77 79 81 85 87 89 93 97 102 107 110 111 114 115 118 119 126 130 132 135 146 147 148 **S** Quorum Health, Brentwood, TN
Primary Contact: Philip Eaton, Interim Chief Executive Officer
CMO: James Antinori, M.D., Chief of Staff
CIO: Marc Taylor, IS Director
CHR: Matthew Flygare, Director Human Resources
CNO: Yvonne Nielson, Chief Nursing Officer, Director Quality Management and Regulatory Compliance
Web address: www.mountainwestmc.com
Control: Corporation, Investor–owned (for–profit) **Service:** General medical and surgical

Staffed Beds: 44 **Admissions:** 1827 **Census:** 11 **Outpatient Visits:** 87137 **Births:** 482 **Total Expense ($000):** 38755 **Payroll Expense ($000):** 14067 **Personnel:** 258

TREMONTON—Box Elder County

★ **BEAR RIVER VALLEY HOSPITAL (460039)**, 905 North 1000 West, Zip 84337–2497; tel. 435/207–4500, **A**10 **F**3 13 15 29 34 35 40 44 50 68 75 76 77 81 85 87 97 107 108 110 111 115 118 119 127 129 140 146 149 **S** Intermountain Healthcare, Inc., Salt Lake City, UT
Primary Contact: James Montgomery, Interim Chief Executive Officer
CHR: Joy Sadler, Director Human Resources
CNO: Penny Marshall, Chief Nursing Officer
Web address: www.https://intermountainhealthcare.org/locations/bear–river–valley–hospital/
Control: Other not–for–profit (including NFP Corporation) **Service:** General medical and surgical

Staffed Beds: 14 **Admissions:** 322 **Census:** 2 **Outpatient Visits:** 46536 **Births:** 123 **Total Expense ($000):** 22910 **Payroll Expense ($000):** 7781 **Personnel:** 113

VERNAL—Uintah County

⊞ **ASHLEY REGIONAL MEDICAL CENTER (460030)**, 150 West 100 North, Zip 84078–2036; tel. 435/789–3342, (Nonreporting) **A**1 10 20 **S** LifePoint Health, Brentwood, TN
Primary Contact: Ben Cluff, Chief Executive Officer
CFO: Chad Labrum, Chief Financial Officer
CMO: Dennis Lewis, M.D., Chief of Staff
CIO: Cameron Winn, Director Information Services
CHR: Deena Mansfield, Director Human Resources
CNO: Greg Gardiner, Chief Clinical Officer
Web address: www.ashleyregional.com
Control: Corporation, Investor–owned (for–profit) **Service:** General medical and surgical

Staffed Beds: 39

UT

Hospital, Medicare Provider Number, Address, Telephone, Approval, Facility, and Physician Codes, Health Care System

★ American Hospital Association (AHA) membership
☐ The Joint Commission accreditation
○ Healthcare Facilities Accreditation Program
◇ DNV Healthcare Inc. accreditation
⇑ Center for Improvement in Healthcare Quality Accreditation
△ Commission on Accreditation of Rehabilitation Facilities (CARF) accreditation

WEST JORDAN—Salt Lake County

★ ⇑ **JORDAN VALLEY MEDICAL CENTER (460051)**, 3580 West 9000 South, Zip 84088–8812; tel. 801/561–8888, (Includes MOUNTAIN POINT MEDICAL CENTER, 3000 North Triumph Boulevard, Lehii, UT, Zip 84043, Lehi, tel. 385/345–3000) (Nonreporting) **A**10 21 **S** Steward Health Care System, LLC, Dallas, TX
COO: Jon Butterfield, Chief Operating Officer
CFO: Kurt Shipley, Chief Financial Officer
CMO: B Dee Allred, M.D., President Medical Staff
Web address: www.jordanvalleymc.com
Control: Partnership, Investor–owned (for–profit) **Service**: General medical and surgical

Staffed Beds: 183

WEST VALLEY CITY—Salt Lake County

★ **JORDAN VALLEY MEDICAL CENTER WEST VALLEY CAMPUS**, 3460 South Pioneer Parkway, Zip 84120–2049; tel. 801/561–8888, (Nonreporting) **S** Steward Health Care System, LLC, Dallas, TX
Primary Contact: Jon R. Butterfield, Administrator and Chief Executive Officer
COO: Jon Butterfield, Administrator and Chief Operating Officer
CFO: Steven Payne, Chief Financial Officer
CMO: Justin Parkinson, M.D., President Medical Staff
CIO: Mark Runyan, Director Information Systems
CHR: Rob Burnett, Director Human Resources
Web address: www.jordanwestvalley.org
Control: Corporation, Investor–owned (for–profit) **Service**: General medical and surgical

Staffed Beds: 101

UT

Many Facility Codes have changed. Please refer to the AHA Guide Code Chart. © 2018 AHA Guide

VERMONT

BENNINGTON—Bennington County

⊞ **SOUTHWESTERN VERMONT MEDICAL CENTER (470012)**, 100 Hospital Drive, Zip 05201–5004; tel. 802/442–6361, (Nonreporting) **A**1 2 10
Primary Contact: Thomas A. Dee, President and Chief Executive Officer
CFO: Stephen D Majetich, CPA, Chief Financial Officer
CMO: Trey Dobson, M.D., Chief Medical Officer
CIO: Richard Ogilvie, Chief Information Officer
CHR: Rudolph D Weaver, Vice President Human Resources
Web address: www.svhealthcare.org
Control: Other not–for–profit (including NFP Corporation) **Service**: General medical and surgical

Staffed Beds: 77

BERLIN—Washington County

⊞ **THE UNIVERSITY OF VERMONT HEALTH NETWORK CENTRAL VERMONT MEDICAL CENTER (470001)**, 130 Fisher Road, Zip 05602–9516, Mailing Address: P.O. Box 547, Barre, Zip 05641–0547; tel. 802/371–4100, (Total facility includes 153 beds in nursing home–type unit) **A**1 2 3 10 **F**3 5 11 13 15 18 28 29 30 31 34 35 36 40 44 45 48 49 50 51 53 54 59 63 64 65 68 70 74 75 76 77 78 79 81 82 84 85 86 87 92 93 94 96 97 98 99 100 102 103 104 107 108 110 111 114 118 119 120 121 123 128 130 131 132 135 141 143 146 147 148 149 **P**6
Primary Contact: Anna T. Noonan, President and Chief Operating Officer
CFO: Cheyenne Holland, Chief Financial Officer
CMO: Philip Brown, D.O., Vice President Medical Affairs
CHR: Robert Patterson, Vice President Human Resources and Rehabilitation Services
CNO: Matthew Choate, Chief Nursing Officer
Web address: www.cvmc.org/
Control: Other not–for–profit (including NFP Corporation) **Service**: General medical and surgical

Staffed Beds: 245 **Admissions**: 4470 **Census**: 174 **Outpatient Visits**: 434124 **Births**: 339 **Total Expense ($000)**: 154899 **Payroll Expense ($000)**: 73544 **Personnel**: 1293

VERMONT PSYCHIATRIC CARE HOSPITAL (474004), 350 Fisher Road, Zip 5602; tel. 802/828–3300, **F**98 130 135 143 146 149 154
Primary Contact: Melissa Bailey, Commissioner, Department of Mental Health
Web address: www.mentalhealth.vermont.gov/Vermont–psychiatric–care–hospital
Control: State, Government, nonfederal **Service**: Psychiatric

Staffed Beds: 25 **Admissions**: 64 **Census**: 24 **Outpatient Visits**: 0 **Births**: 0 **Total Expense ($000)**: 21742 **Payroll Expense ($000)**: 10107 **Personnel**: 188

BRATTLEBORO—Windham County

★ **BRATTLEBORO MEMORIAL HOSPITAL (470011)**, 17 Belmont Avenue, Zip 05301–3498; tel. 802/257–0341, **A**10 **F**3 11 13 15 18 28 29 30 31 34 35 37 39 40 45 49 50 51 53 55 57 59 64 68 70 74 75 76 77 78 79 81 85 87 93 107 108 110 111 115 118 119 130 131 132 135 146 147 148 149
Primary Contact: Steven R. Gordon, President and Chief Executive Officer
CFO: Michael Rogers, Vice President Fiscal Services
CMO: Kathleen McGraw, M.D., Chief Medical Officer
CIO: Jonathan Farina, Chief Information Officer
CHR: William Norwood, Vice President, Human Resources
CNO: Mary Urquhart, R.N., Vice President Patient Care
Web address: www.bmhvt.org
Control: Other not–for–profit (including NFP Corporation) **Service**: General medical and surgical

Staffed Beds: 42 **Admissions**: 1618 **Census**: 15 **Outpatient Visits**: 167953 **Births**: 325 **Total Expense ($000)**: 81303 **Payroll Expense ($000)**: 34333 **Personnel**: 409

⊞ **BRATTLEBORO RETREAT (474001)**, Anna Marsh Lane, Zip 5301, Mailing Address: P.O. Box 803, Zip 05302–0803; tel. 802/257–7785, **A**1 5 10 **F**5 29 34 35 44 50 68 75 82 87 98 99 100 101 102 103 104 105 106 135 149 152 153 154 **P**6 7
Primary Contact: Louis Josephson, Ph.D., President and Chief Executive Officer
COO: Gerri Cote, Chief Operating Officer
CFO: Steven Monette, Chief Financial Officer
CMO: Frederick Engstrom, M.D., Chief Medical Officer
CHR: Jeffrey T. Corrigan, Vice President Human Resources
CNO: Linda J. Nagy, MSN, R.N., Chief Nursing Officer
Web address: www.brattlebororetreat.org
Control: Other not–for–profit (including NFP Corporation) **Service**: Psychiatric

Staffed Beds: 114 **Admissions**: 3803 **Census**: 100 **Outpatient Visits**: 30211 **Births**: 0 **Total Expense ($000)**: 69581 **Payroll Expense ($000)**: 42596 **Personnel**: 563

BURLINGTON—Chittenden County

⊞ **UNIVERSITY OF VERMONT MEDICAL CENTER (470003)**, 111 Colchester Avenue, Zip 05401–1473; tel. 802/847–0000, (Includes FANNY ALLEN CAMPUS, 101 College Parkway, Colchester, VT, Zip 05446–3035; tel. 802/655–1234; MEDICAL CENTER HOSPITAL CAMPUS, 111 Colchester Avenue, Burlington, VT, Zip 5401; tel. 802/847–2345; VERMONT CHILDREN'S HOSPITAL, 111 Colchester Avenue, Burlington, VT, Zip 05401–1473; tel. 802/847–0000) **A**1 2 3 5 8 10 **F**3 4 5 6 7 9 11 12 13 15 17 18 19 20 21 22 23 24 25 26 28 29 30 31 32 34 35 36 37 39 40 43 44 45 46 47 48 49 50 51 52 54 55 56 57 58 59 60 61 63 64 65 66 68 70 72 73 74 75 76 77 78 79 81 82 84 85 86 87 88 89 90 91 92 93 94 96 97 98 99 100 101 102 103 104 105 107 108 110 111 114 115 116 117 118 119 120 121 123 124 126 128 129 130 131 132 135 136 138 141 142 143 144 145 146 147 148 151 152 153 154 **P**6
Primary Contact: Eileen Whalen, R.N., President and Chief Operating Officer
CFO: Todd Keating, Chief Financial Officer
CMO: Isabelle Desjardins, M.D., Chief Medical Officer
CHR: Jerald Novak, Chief People Officer
Web address: www.uvmhealth.org/medcenter/Pages/default.aspx
Control: Other not–for–profit (including NFP Corporation) **Service**: General medical and surgical

Staffed Beds: 495 **Admissions**: 20028 **Census**: 328 **Outpatient Visits**: 1094400 **Births**: 2246 **Total Expense ($000)**: 1178350 **Payroll Expense ($000)**: 574530 **Personnel**: 7085

COLCHESTER—Chittenden County

FANNY ALLEN CAMPUS See University of Vermont Medical Center, Burlington

FANNY ALLEN CAMPUS

MIDDLEBURY—Addison County

★ **PORTER MEDICAL CENTER (471307)**, 115 Porter Drive, Zip 05753–8423; tel. 802/388–4701, **A**10 18 **F**8 11 13 15 29 30 34 35 37 40 45 50 59 64 68 75 76 79 81 82 84 85 86 93 97 107 108 110 111 114 119 130 132 133 135 144 146 147 149 154
Primary Contact: Fred Kniffin, M.D., Chief Executive Officer
CFO: Steve Ciampa, Vice President Finance
CMO: Fred Kniffin, M.D., Chief Medical Officer
CIO: Rebecca Woods, Chief Information Officer
CHR: David Fuller, Vice President of Human Resources
CNO: Lorraina Smith–Zuba, R.N., MSN, Chief Nursing Officer
Web address: www.portermedical.org
Control: Other not–for–profit (including NFP Corporation) **Service**: General medical and surgical

Staffed Beds: 25 **Admissions**: 1438 **Census**: 13 **Outpatient Visits**: 180230 **Births**: 367 **Total Expense ($000)**: 78875 **Payroll Expense ($000)**: 37499 **Personnel**: 480

VT

Hospital, Medicare Provider Number, Address, Telephone, Approval, Facility, and Physician Codes, Health Care System

★ American Hospital Association (AHA) membership ○ Healthcare Facilities Accreditation Program ⇑ Center for Improvement in Healthcare Quality Accreditation
☐ The Joint Commission accreditation ◇ DNV Healthcare Inc. accreditation △ Commission on Accreditation of Rehabilitation Facilities (CARF) accreditation

© 2018 AHA Guide   *Many Facility Codes have changed. Please refer to the AHA Guide Code Chart.*   Hospitals **A653**

MORRISVILLE—Lamoille County

★ **COPLEY HOSPITAL (471305)**, 528 Washington Highway, Zip 05661–8973; tel. 802/888–8888, **A**10 18 **F**1 3 4 8 11 13 15 28 29 30 31 34 35 38 39 40 44 45 57 58 59 64 65 67 70 74 75 76 77 78 79 81 82 85 86 87 91 93 98 107 108 110 111 114 118 119 128 129 130 131 133 135 146 147 148 149 154
Primary Contact: Arthur Mathisen, FACHE, President and Chief Executive Officer
COO: Vera A. Jones, Chief Operating Officer
CFO: Rassoul Rangaviz, Chief Financial Officer
CMO: Joel Silverstein, M.D., Chief Medical Officer
CIO: Randy Chesley, Director Information Technology
CHR: Amy Fitzgerald, Human Resources Manager
CNO: Lori Profota, R.N., Chief Nursing Officer
Web address: www.copleyvt.org
Control: Other not–for–profit (including NFP Corporation) **Service**: General medical and surgical

Staffed Beds: 25 Admissions: 1788 **Census:** 12 **Outpatient Visits:** 93834 **Births:** 194 **Total Expense ($000):** 66780 **Payroll Expense ($000):** 30151 **Personnel:** 333

NEWPORT—Orleans County

★ **NORTH COUNTRY HOSPITAL AND HEALTH CENTER (471304)**, 189 Prouty Drive, Zip 05855–9326; tel. 802/334–7331, **A**10 18 **F**11 13 15 28 29 30 34 35 40 43 45 50 53 70 74 75 76 77 79 81 82 84 85 89 91 93 107 108 110 111 114 118 119 127 129 130 131 133 135 146 148 149
Primary Contact: Thomas Frank, Interim Chief Executive Officer
COO: Thomas Frank, Chief Operating Officer
CFO: Andre Bissonnette, Chief Financial Officer
CHR: William Perket, Vice President Human Resources
CNO: Avril Cochran, R.N., Vice President Patient Care Services
Web address: www.nchsi.org
Control: Other not–for–profit (including NFP Corporation) **Service**: General medical and surgical

Staffed Beds: 25 Admissions: 1371 **Census:** 17 **Outpatient Visits:** 65830 **Births:** 201 **Total Expense ($000):** 84161 **Payroll Expense ($000):** 38757 **Personnel:** 470

RANDOLPH—Orange County

★ **GIFFORD MEDICAL CENTER (471301)**, 44 South Main Street, Zip 05060–1381, Mailing Address: P.O. Box 2000, Zip 05060–2000; tel. 802/728–7000, (Nonreporting) **A**2 10 18
Primary Contact: Dan Bennett, President and Chief Executive Officer
CFO: Jeff Hebert, Interim Vice President Finance
CMO: Joshua Plavin, M.D., Medical Director Medicine Division
CIO: Sean Patrick, Director Information Systems
CHR: Janice Davis, Interim Director Human Resources
CNO: Linda Minsinger, Vice President Hospital Division
Web address: www.giffordmed.org
Control: Other not–for–profit (including NFP Corporation) **Service**: General medical and surgical

Staffed Beds: 52

RUTLAND—Rutland County

⊞ **RUTLAND REGIONAL MEDICAL CENTER (470005)**, 160 Allen Street, Zip 05701–4595; tel. 802/775–7111, **A**1 2 10 **F**3 5 13 15 18 28 29 31 34 37 40 44 45 50 55 57 59 64 65 70 74 76 78 79 81 82 83 84 85 87 92 93 98 100 101 102 104 107 108 109 110 111 115 117 118 119 120 121 123 124 129 130 133 135 146 147 148 149 154
Primary Contact: Claudio D. Fort, President and Chief Executive Officer
CFO: Ed Ogorzalek, Chief Financial Officer
CMO: Baxter C Holland, M.D., Chief Medical Officer
CNO: Carol Egan, R.N., MSN, Chief Nursing Officer
Web address: www.rrmc.org
Control: Other not–for–profit (including NFP Corporation) **Service**: General medical and surgical

Staffed Beds: 121 Admissions: 5734 **Census:** 85 **Outpatient Visits:** 247908 **Births:** 361 **Total Expense ($000):** 250112 **Payroll Expense ($000):** 124899 **Personnel:** 1381

SAINT ALBANS—Franklin County

⊞ **NORTHWESTERN MEDICAL CENTER (470024)**, 133 Fairfield Street, Zip 05478–1726; tel. 802/524–5911, (Nonreporting) **A**1 2 10 20 **S** QHR, Brentwood, TN
Primary Contact: Jill Berry. Bowen, Chief Executive Officer
COO: Jane Catton, R.N., Chief Operating Officer and Chief Nursing Officer
CFO: Christopher Hickey, Chief Financial Officer
CMO: Lowery Sullivan, M.D., Chief Medical Officer
CIO: Joel Benware, Vice President Information Technology and Compliance
CHR: Thomas C Conley, Vice President, Human Resources and Organizational Development
CNO: Jane Catton, R.N., Chief Operating Officer and Chief Nursing Officer
Web address: www.northwesternmedicalcenter.org
Control: Other not–for–profit (including NFP Corporation) **Service**: General medical and surgical

Staffed Beds: 70

SAINT JOHNSBURY—Caledonia County

★ **NORTHEASTERN VERMONT REGIONAL HOSPITAL (471303)**, 1315 Hospital Drive, Zip 05819–9210, Mailing Address: PO Box 905, Zip 05819–0905; tel. 802/748–8141, (Nonreporting) **A**10 18
Primary Contact: Paul R. Bengtson, Chief Executive Officer
CFO: Robert Hersey, Chief Financial Officer
CMO: Michael Rousse, M.D., Vice President of Medical Affairs
CIO: Shawn Burroughs, Director of Information Services
CHR: Elizabeth Gwatkin, Vice President Human Resources
CNO: Seleem Choudhury, R.N., MSN, Chief Nursing Officer
Web address: www.nvrh.org
Control: Other not–for–profit (including NFP Corporation) **Service**: General medical and surgical

Staffed Beds: 25

SPRINGFIELD—Windsor County

★ **SPRINGFIELD HOSPITAL (471306)**, 25 Ridgewood Road, Zip 05156–3050, Mailing Address: 25 Ridgewood Rd, Zip 05156–3050; tel. 802/885–2151, (Nonreporting) **A**10 18
Primary Contact: Timothy R. Ford, President and Chief Executive Officer
CFO: Scott Whittemore, Chief Financial Officer and Chief of Ancillary Services
CMO: Richard Marasa, M.D., President Medical Staff
CIO: Kyle Peoples, Director Technology Management Services
CHR: Janet Lyle, Chief Human Resources and Allied Health Services
CNO: Janet Sherer, Chief of Patient Care Services
Web address: www.springfieldmed.org
Control: Other not–for–profit (including NFP Corporation) **Service**: General medical and surgical

Staffed Beds: 35

TOWNSHEND—Windham County

★ **GRACE COTTAGE HOSPITAL (471300)**, 185 Grafton Road, Zip 05353–0216, Mailing Address: P.O. Box 216, Zip 05353–0216; tel. 802/365–7357, **A**10 18 **F**3 29 30 34 35 40 50 57 59 64 65 66 68 85 93 96 97 104 107 115 119 127 130 132 133 135 146 147
Primary Contact: Douglas F. DiVello, President and Chief Executive Officer
COO: Jeanne M Fortier, R.N., Chief Nursing Officer and Interim Chief Operating Officer
CFO: Stephen A Brown, Chief Financial Officer
CMO: Timothy Shafer, M.D., Medical Director
CIO: Tony Marques, Director Information Systems
CHR: Christopher J Lackney, Director Human Resources
CNO: Jeanne M Fortier, R.N., Chief Nursing Officer and Interim Chief Operating Officer
Web address: www.gracecottage.org
Control: Other not–for–profit (including NFP Corporation) **Service**: General medical and surgical

Staffed Beds: 38 Admissions: 352 **Census:** 10 **Births:** 0

WHITE RIVER JUNCTION—Windsor County

⊞ **WHITE RIVER JUNCTION VETERANS AFFAIRS MEDICAL CENTER**, 215 North Main Street, Zip 05009–0001; tel. 802/295–9363, **A**1 3 5 8 **F**3 4 5 12 18 29 30 31 33 35 36 38 40 45 46 47 48 49 50 53 56 58 59 60 61 63 64 65 70 74 75 77 78 79 81 82 84 85 86 87 92 93 97 98 100 101 102 103 104 107 108 111 114 115 118 119 127 130 132 135 141 143 146 147 148 149 154 **S** Department of Veterans Affairs, Perry Point, MD
Primary Contact: Brett Rusch, M.D., Acting Director
CFO: Joan Wilmot, Chief Finance Officer
CMO: M. Ganga Hematillake, M.D., Chief of Staff
CIO: Matthew Rafus, Chief Information Officer
CHR: Barbara Nadeau, Chief Human Resources Management Service
Web address: www.whiteriver.va.gov/
Control: Veterans Affairs, Government, federal **Service**: General medical and surgical

Staffed Beds: 74 Admissions: 2449 **Census:** 45 **Outpatient Visits:** 298857 **Births:** 0 **Total Expense ($000):** 130713 **Payroll Expense ($000):** 97350 **Personnel:** 1163

WINDSOR—Windsor County

★ △ **MT. ASCUTNEY HOSPITAL AND HEALTH CENTER (471302)**, 289 County Road, Zip 05089–9000; tel. 802/674–6711, **A**7 10 18 **F**3 8 10 11 15 28 29 30 31 32 34 35 40 41 44 45 49 50 53 54 56 57 59 63 64 65 66 68 69 70 71 75 77 78 81 82 85 86 87 90 91 92 93 94 95 96 97 100 104 107 110 111 114 119 125 129 130 132 133 134 135 143 146 148 149 154 **P**6
Primary Contact: Joseph L. Perras, President and Chief Executive Officer
COO: Paul Calandrella, Chief Operating Officer
CFO: David Sanville, Chief Financial Officer
CHR: Jean Martaniuk, Director Human Resources
CNO: Deanna Orfanidis, MS, R.N., Chief Nursing Officer
Web address: www.mtascutneyhospital.org
Control: Other not–for–profit (including NFP Corporation) **Service**: General medical and surgical

Staffed Beds: 35 Admissions: 1016 **Census:** 28 **Outpatient Visits:** 69935 **Births:** 0 **Total Expense ($000):** 50393 **Payroll Expense ($000):** 23997 **Personnel:** 391

Many Facility Codes have changed. Please refer to the AHA Guide Code Chart. © 2018 AHA Guide

VT

VIRGINIA

ABINGDON—Washington County

✠ **JOHNSTON MEMORIAL HOSPITAL (490053)**, 16000 Johnston Memorial Drive, Zip 24211–7659; tel. 276/258–1000, **A**1 2 3 10 13 **F**3 8 11 13 15 18 20 22 24 26 28 29 30 31 34 35 36 39 40 44 45 46 47 48 49 51 54 55 57 58 59 60 62 63 64 68 70 74 75 76 77 78 79 81 82 84 85 87 92 93 97 100 107 110 111 114 115 118 119 120 121 122 123 124 129 130 132 135 136 141 144 145 146 147 148 149 154 **S** Ballad Health, Johnson City, TN
Primary Contact: John Jeter, Chief Executive Officer
COO: Bryan Mullins, Chief Operating Officer
CMO: Brian Condit, M.D., Chief Medical Officer
CIO: Jackson Dale, Director Management Information Services
CHR: Jackie G Phipps, Director Human Resources
CNO: Linda M. Shepherd, Chief Nursing Officer
Web address: www.jmh.org
Control: Other not–for–profit (including NFP Corporation) **Service**: General medical and surgical

Staffed Beds: 116 **Admissions:** 8656 **Census:** 88 **Outpatient Visits:** 159772 **Births:** 624 **Total Expense ($000):** 133783 **Payroll Expense ($000):** 40355 **Personnel:** 733

ALDIE—Loudoun County

✠ **ENCOMPASS HEALTH REHABILITATION HOSPITAL OF NORTHERN VIRGINIA (493033)**, 24430 Millstream Drive, Zip 20105–3098; tel. 703/957–2000, **A**1 10 **F**29 75 90 95 135 **P**5 **S** Encompass Health Corporation, Birmingham, AL
Primary Contact: Alfred Santos, Chief Executive Officer
Web address: www.healthsouthnorthernvirginia.com
Control: Corporation, Investor–owned (for–profit) **Service**: Rehabilitation

Staffed Beds: 60 **Admissions:** 1541 **Census:** 51 **Outpatient Visits:** 0 **Births:** 0 **Total Expense ($000):** 17948 **Payroll Expense ($000):** 11951 **Personnel:** 197

ALEXANDRIA—Alexandria City County

✠ **INOVA ALEXANDRIA HOSPITAL (490040)**, 4320 Seminary Road, Zip 22304–1535; tel. 703/504–3167, **A**1 2 5 10 **F**3 11 13 14 15 17 18 20 22 24 26 28 29 30 31 34 35 38 40 44 45 46 48 49 50 51 54 55 56 57 58 59 60 61 63 64 65 66 68 70 72 74 75 76 77 78 79 81 82 84 85 86 87 91 92 93 100 101 102 107 108 110 111 114 115 118 119 120 121 123 124 126 129 130 131 132 135 145 146 147 148 149 154 **P**6 **S** Inova Health System, Falls Church, VA
Primary Contact: Susan Carroll, Chief Executive Officer
CFO: Todd Lockcuff, Chief Financial Officer
CMO: William L Jackson, Chief Medical Officer
CHR: Hugo Aguas, Vice President Human Resources
Web address: www.inova.org
Control: Other not–for–profit (including NFP Corporation) **Service**: General medical and surgical

Staffed Beds: 334 **Admissions:** 15951 **Census:** 182 **Outpatient Visits:** 177423 **Births:** 3438 **Total Expense ($000):** 307524 **Payroll Expense ($000):** 109322 **Personnel:** 1391

ALEXANDRIA—Fairfax County

✠ **INOVA MOUNT VERNON HOSPITAL (490122)**, 2501 Parker's Lane, Zip 22306–3209; tel. 703/664–7000, **A**1 2 3 5 10 **F**3 5 11 14 15 18 26 28 29 30 31 34 35 38 40 44 45 48 49 50 51 53 54 55 57 58 59 60 61 63 64 65 68 70 74 75 77 78 79 81 82 84 85 86 87 90 91 92 93 94 95 96 98 100 101 102 103 104 105 107 110 111 114 115 118 119 130 131 132 135 145 146 147 148 149 **P**6 **S** Inova Health System, Falls Church, VA
Primary Contact: Donald Brideau, Chief Executive Officer
CFO: Tammy Razmic, Associate Administrator Finance and Chief Financial Officer
CMO: Donald Brideau, M.D., Chief Medical Officer
CHR: Bev Sugar, Associate Administrator and Director Human Resources
Web address: www.inova.org
Control: Other not–for–profit (including NFP Corporation) **Service**: General medical and surgical

Staffed Beds: 237 **Admissions:** 8505 **Census:** 141 **Outpatient Visits:** 98231 **Births:** 0 **Total Expense ($000):** 196921 **Payroll Expense ($000):** 71221 **Personnel:** 973

ARLINGTON—Arlington County

✠ **CAPITAL HOSPICE (490129)**, 4715 15th Street North, Zip 22205–2640; tel. 703/538–2065, (Nonreporting) **A**3 10
Primary Contact: Malene S. Davis, R.N., President and Chief Executive Officer
CFO: David Schwind, Chief Financial Officer
CIO: Diane Rigsby, Chief Information Officer
Web address: www.capitalhospice.org
Control: Other not–for–profit (including NFP Corporation) **Service**: Other specialty treatment

Staffed Beds: 15

✠ △ **VIRGINIA HOSPITAL CENTER (490050)**, 1701 North George Mason Drive, Zip 22205–3698; tel. 703/558–5000, (Nonreporting) **A**1 2 3 5 7 10
Primary Contact: James B. Cole, President and Chief Executive Officer
COO: Carl Bahnlein, Executive Vice President and Chief Operating Officer
CFO: Robin Norman, Senior Vice President and Chief Financial Officer
CMO: Jeffrey P DiLisi, Vice President and Chief Medical Officer
CIO: Russ McWey, M.D., Vice President and Chief Information Officer
CHR: Michael Malone, Vice President and Chief Human Resources Officer
CNO: Darlene Vrotsos, R.N., Senior Vice President and Chief Nursing Officer
Web address: www.virginiahospitalcenter.com
Control: Other not–for–profit (including NFP Corporation) **Service**: General medical and surgical

Staffed Beds: 357

BEDFORD—Bedford City County

✠ **CENTRA BEDFORD MEMORIAL HOSPITAL (490088)**, 1613 Oakwood Street, Zip 24523–1213; tel. 540/586–2441, (Total facility includes 111 beds in nursing home–type unit) **A**1 10 **F**2 3 11 15 28 29 30 34 35 40 46 53 57 59 63 67 70 81 84 85 86 87 97 107 110 115 119 128 130 143 146 148 **S** Centra Health, Inc., Lynchburg, VA
Primary Contact: Patti Jurkus, Vice President and Chief Executive Officer
CFO: Donald E Lorton, Executive Vice President
CMO: E Allen Joslyn, M.D., Chief Medical Officer
Web address: www.bmhva.com
Control: Other not–for–profit (including NFP Corporation) **Service**: General medical and surgical

Staffed Beds: 145 **Admissions:** 2045 **Census:** 106 **Outpatient Visits:** 46061 **Births:** 0 **Total Expense ($000):** 40550 **Payroll Expense ($000):** 16900 **Personnel:** 329

BIG STONE GAP—Wise County

✠ **LONESOME PINE HOSPITAL (490114)**, 1990 Holton Avenue East, Zip 24219–3350; tel. 276/523–3111, **A**1 10 13 **F**3 11 15 29 30 31 34 40 45 50 57 59 63 70 76 77 78 79 81 82 85 87 89 93 107 108 110 111 114 118 119 120 121 129 130 135 146 148 **S** Ballad Health, Johnson City, TN
Primary Contact: Mark T. Leonard, Interim Chief Executive Officer
CFO: Regina Day, Executive Vice President of Finance
CMO: Michael Ketcham, President, Medical Staff
CHR: Bobby Collins, Director Human Resources
Web address: www.wellmont.org
Control: Other not–for–profit (including NFP Corporation) **Service**: General medical and surgical

Staffed Beds: 32 **Admissions:** 1345 **Census:** 10 **Outpatient Visits:** 84567 **Births:** 299 **Total Expense ($000):** 53440 **Payroll Expense ($000):** 9742 **Personnel:** 193

BLACKSBURG—Montgomery County

✠ **LEWISGALE HOSPITAL MONTGOMERY (490110)**, 3700 South Main Street, Zip 24060–7081, Mailing Address: P.O. Box 90004, Zip 24062–9004; tel. 540/951–1111, (Nonreporting) **A**1 3 10 12 13 **S** HCA Healthcare, Nashville, TN
Primary Contact: Alan J. Fabian, Chief Executive Officer
COO: Matt Mathias, Chief Operating Officer
CFO: Timothy W Haasken, Chief Financial Officer
CIO: Diron Lane, Director Information Systems
CNO: Ellen Y Linkenhoker, Chief Nursing Officer
Web address: www.lewisgale.com
Control: Corporation, Investor–owned (for–profit) **Service**: General medical and surgical

Staffed Beds: 89

VA

Hospital, Medicare Provider Number, Address, Telephone, Approval, Facility, and Physician Codes, Health Care System

★ American Hospital Association (AHA) membership
☐ The Joint Commission accreditation
○ Healthcare Facilities Accreditation Program
◇ DNV Healthcare Inc. accreditation
⇑ Center for Improvement in Healthcare Quality Accreditation
△ Commission on Accreditation of Rehabilitation Facilities (CARF) accreditation

BRISTOL—Bristol City County

☒ **REHABILITATION HOSPITAL OF SOUTHWEST VIRGINIA (493034)**, 103 North Street, Zip 24201–3201; tel. 276/642–7900, (Nonreporting) **A**1 10 **S** Encompass Health Corporation, Birmingham, AL
Primary Contact: Georgeanne Cole, Chief Executive Officer
Web address: www.rehabilitationhospitalswvirginia.com
Control: Corporation, Investor–owned (for–profit) **Service**: Rehabilitation

Staffed Beds: 25

BURKEVILLE—Nottoway County

PIEDMONT GERIATRIC HOSPITAL (490134), 5001 East Patrick Henry Hwy, Zip 23922–3460, Mailing Address: P.O. Box 427, Zip 23922–0427; tel. 434/767–4401, (Nonreporting) **S** Virginia Department of Mental Health, Richmond, VA
Primary Contact: Hilton McDaniel, President
CFO: James G Ayers, Chief Financial Officer
CMO: Hugo Falcon, M.D., Director Medical Services
CHR: Michael Wimsatt, Director Human Resources
Web address: www.pgh.dmhmrsas.virginia.gov
Control: State, Government, nonfederal **Service**: Other specialty treatment

Staffed Beds: 135

CATAWBA—Roanoke County

☐ **CATAWBA HOSPITAL (490135)**, 5525 Catawba Hospital Drive, Zip 24070–2115, Mailing Address: P.O. Box 200, Zip 24070–0200; tel. 540/375–4200, **A**1 3 10 **F**29 30 35 39 44 50 68 75 77 98 103 130 146 149 **P**6 **S** Virginia Department of Mental Health, Richmond, VA
Primary Contact: Walton F. Mitchell III, Director
COO: Charles Law, Ph.D., Chief Operating Officer
CFO: Cecil Hardin, CPA, Chief Financial Officer
CMO: Yad Jabbarpour, M.D., Chief of Staff
CIO: Charles Law, Ph.D., Chief Operating Officer
CHR: Patricia Ebbett, Chief Human Resources Officer
CNO: Vicky Fisher, Ph.D., R.N., Chief Nurse Executive
Web address: www.catawba.dbhds.virginia.gov
Control: State, Government, nonfederal **Service**: Psychiatric

Staffed Beds: 110 Admissions: 515 Census: 102 Outpatient Visits: 0 Births: 0 Total Expense ($000): 24036 Payroll Expense ($000): 12920 Personnel: 262

CHARLOTTESVILLE—Charlottesville City County

★ ⇑ **SENTARA MARTHA JEFFERSON HOSPITAL (490077)**, 500 Martha Jefferson Drive, Zip 22911–4668; tel. 434/654–7000, **A**2 5 10 21 **F**3 5 8 11 12 13 15 18 20 22 26 28 29 30 35 36 40 41 44 45 46 47 48 49 50 53 54 55 56 57 58 59 61 64 65 68 70 74 75 76 77 78 79 81 82 84 85 86 87 89 91 92 93 94 96 97 107 108 110 111 114 115 116 117 118 119 120 121 123 124 129 130 131 132 134 135 141 145 146 147 149 154 **P**1 **S** Sentara Healthcare, Norfolk, VA
Primary Contact: Jonathan S. Davis, FACHE, President
COO: Amy Black, R.N., MSN, Chief Operating Officer
CFO: Stewart R Nelson, Vice President and Chief Financial Officer
CMO: F Michael Ashby, M.D., Vice President and Medical Director
CIO: Marijo Lecker, Vice President
CHR: Debbie Desmond, Director Human Resources
Web address: www.marthajefferson.org
Control: Other not–for–profit (including NFP Corporation) **Service**: General medical and surgical

Staffed Beds: 144 Admissions: 9973 Census: 94 Outpatient Visits: 649963 Births: 1510 Total Expense ($000): 285179 Payroll Expense ($000): 117708 Personnel: 1595

☒ △ **UNIVERSITY OF VIRGINIA MEDICAL CENTER (490009)**, 1215 Lee Street, Zip 22908–0001, Mailing Address: P.O. Box 800809, Zip 22908–0809; tel. 434/924–0211, (Includes UNIVERSITY OF VIRGINIA CHILDREN'S HOSPITAL, 1215 Lee Street, Charlottesville, VA, Zip 22908, Mailing Address: PO Box 800566, Zip 22908, tel. 434/243–5500) **A**1 2 3 5 7 8 10 **F**3 4 5 6 7 8 9 11 12 13 15 16 17 18 19 20 21 22 23 24 25 26 27 28 29 30 31 32 34 35 36 37 38 39 40 41 43 44 45 46 47 48 49 50 51 52 54 55 56 57 58 59 60 61 62 63 64 65 66 68 69 70 71 72 73 74 75 76 77 78 79 80 81 82 83 84 85 86 87 88 89 90 91 92 93 94 97 98 100 101 102 103 104 107 108 110 111 112 114 115 116 117 118 119 120 121 123 124 126 129 130 131 132 134 135 136 137 138 139 140 141 142 143 145 146 147 148 149 153 **P**3 4 **S** UVA Health System, Charlottesville, VA
Primary Contact: Pamela Sutton–Wallace, Chief Executive Officer
COO: William T. Fulkerson, Chief Operating Officer
CFO: Nick Mendyka, Chief Financial Officer
CMO: Chris A. Ghaemmaghami, M.D., Chief Medical Officer
CIO: Richard Skinner, Chief Information Technology Officer
CHR: John Boswell, Chief Human Resources Officer
CNO: Mary E. Dixon, MSN, R.N., Interim Chief Nursing Officer
Web address: www.healthsystem.virginia.edu
Control: State, Government, nonfederal **Service**: General medical and surgical

Staffed Beds: 596 Admissions: 28597 Census: 468 Outpatient Visits: 2008891 Births: 1784 Total Expense ($000): 1506938 Payroll Expense ($000): 519364 Personnel: 7769

CHARLOTTESVILLE—Albemarle County

☒ **UVA TRANSITIONAL CARE HOSPITAL (492011)**, 2965 Ivy Rd (250 West), Zip 22903–9330; tel. 434/924–8245, **A**1 10 **F**1 3 29 30 60 77 85 94 114 129 130 146 148 149 **P**3 4 **S** UVA Health System, Charlottesville, VA
Primary Contact: Christine K. Matt, Interim Associate Chief
Web address: www.uvahealth.com/services/transitional–care–hospital
Control: State, Government, nonfederal **Service**: Acute long–term care hospital

Staffed Beds: 40 Admissions: 405 Census: 30 Outpatient Visits: 0 Births: 0 Total Expense ($000): 18652 Payroll Expense ($000): 7884 Personnel: 120

☒ **UVA–HEALTHSOUTH REHABILITATION HOSPITAL (493029)**, 515 Ray C Hunt Drive, Zip 22903–2981; tel. 434/244–2000, **A**1 3 5 10 **F**3 28 29 34 35 54 57 59 64 74 75 77 90 91 93 131 132 148 **P**5 **S** Encompass Health Corporation, Birmingham, AL
Primary Contact: Barbara Adcock Mohr, Chief Executive Officer
CFO: Dianna Gomez, Controller
CMO: Alan Alfano, M.D., Medical Director
CIO: Michael Vanhoy, Director of Quality
CHR: Tonya Loving, Director of Human Resources
CNO: Sherry Herring, Chief Nursing Officer
Web address: www.uvahealthsouth.com
Control: Corporation, Investor–owned (for–profit) **Service**: Rehabilitation

Staffed Beds: 50 Admissions: 1182 Census: 42 Outpatient Visits: 30845 Births: 0 Total Expense ($000): 23453 Payroll Expense ($000): 14768 Personnel: 228

CHESAPEAKE—Chesapeake City County

★ ○ **CHESAPEAKE REGIONAL MEDICAL CENTER (490120)**, 736 Battlefield Boulevard North, Zip 23320–4941, Mailing Address: P.O. Box 2028, Zip 23327–2028; tel. 757/312–8121, **A**2 3 10 11 **F**3 11 12 13 15 18 20 22 26 28 29 30 31 34 35 37 38 40 44 45 46 49 50 53 54 57 58 59 62 63 64 65 66 68 69 70 71 73 74 75 76 77 78 79 81 83 84 85 86 87 89 91 93 100 101 102 107 108 110 111 114 115 118 119 120 121 123 126 129 130 132 135 143 146 147 148 149 154 **P**6
Primary Contact: Reese Jackson, President and Chief Executive Officer
COO: Amber Egyud, R.N., Chief Nursing Officer and Chief Operating Officer
CFO: Stephen C McDonnell, Chief Financial Officer
CMO: Raymond McCue, M.D., Vice President, Medical Affairs and Chief Medical Officer
CIO: Maurice Bastarache, Chief Information Officer
CHR: Deborah L Rosenburg, Vice President Human Resources
CNO: Amber Egyud, R.N., Chief Nursing Officer and Chief Operating Officer
Web address: www.chesapeakeregional.com
Control: Hospital district or authority, Government, nonfederal **Service**: General medical and surgical

Staffed Beds: 310 Admissions: 15022 Census: 179 Outpatient Visits: 167838 Births: 2190 Total Expense ($000): 290866 Payroll Expense ($000): 104159 Personnel: 1925

CHRISTIANSBURG—Montgomery County

☒ **CARILION NEW RIVER VALLEY MEDICAL CENTER (490042)**, 2900 Lamb Circle, Zip 24073–6344, Mailing Address: P.O. Box 5, Radford, Zip 24143–0005; tel. 540/731–2000, (Includes CARILION CLINIC SAINT ALBANS HOSPITAL, 2900 Lamb Circle, Christiansburg, VA, Zip 24073–6344; tel. 540/731–2000) **A**1 3 10 13 19 **F**3 5 8 12 13 15 18 20 22 24 26 28 29 30 34 35 36 40 43 45 47 48 49 50 51 53 57 59 60 62 63 64 65 68 70 74 75 76 77 79 81 82 84 85 86 87 89 91 92 93 96 98 99 102 103 104 105 107 108 110 111 114 115 118 119 126 129 130 131 135 146 147 148 149 154 **P**6 **S** Carilion Clinic, Roanoke, VA
Primary Contact: William Flattery, Vice President and Administrator Western Division
CFO: Rob Vaughan, Chief Financial Officer
CMO: Dennis Means, M.D., Vice President Medical Affairs
CIO: Daniel Borchi, Chief Information Officer
CHR: Patti Jurkus, Director Human Resources
Web address: www.carilionclinic.org/Carilion/cnrv
Control: Other not–for–profit (including NFP Corporation) **Service**: General medical and surgical

Staffed Beds: 88 Admissions: 8488 Census: 92 Outpatient Visits: 101549 Births: 1096 Total Expense ($000): 174082 Payroll Expense ($000): 63399 Personnel: 977

VA

CLINTWOOD—Dickenson County

DICKENSON COMMUNITY HOSPITAL (491303), 312 Hospital Drive, Zip 24228, Mailing Address: P.O. Box 1440, Zip 24228–1440; tel. 276/926–0300, **A**10 18 **F**3 29 40 44 64 97 98 103 104 107 119 130 148 153 154 **S** Ballad Health, Johnson City, TN
Primary Contact: Mark T. Leonard, Chief Executive Officer
CFO: Kevin Morrison, Chief Financial Officer
CMO: Erin Mullins, D.O., Chief Medical Staff
CHR: Valeri J Colyer, Director Human Resources
CNO: Terri Roop, Director Patient Care Services
Web address: www.msha.com/dch
Control: Other not–for–profit (including NFP Corporation) **Service**: General medical and surgical

Staffed Beds: 11 **Admissions:** 232 **Census:** 6 **Outpatient Visits:** 26032 **Births:** 0 **Total Expense ($000):** 8834 **Payroll Expense ($000):** 3590 **Personnel:** 59

CULPEPER—Culpeper County

NOVANT HEALTH UVA HEALTH SYSTEM CULPEPER MEDICAL CENTER (490019), 501 Sunset Lane, Zip 22701–3917, Mailing Address: P.O. Box 592, Zip 22701–0500; tel. 540/829–4100, (Nonreporting) **A**1 3 5 10 **S** Novant Health, Winston Salem, NC
Primary Contact: Jeff Hetmanski, President and Chief Operating Officer
CFO: David J Plaviak, Interim Chief Financial Officer
CMO: Morton Chiles, M.D., Chief Medical Officer
CIO: Steven Speelman, Director Information Systems
CHR: Susan Edwards, Vice President Human Resources
Web address: www.culpeperhealth.org
Control: Other not–for–profit (including NFP Corporation) **Service**: General medical and surgical

Staffed Beds: 68

DANVILLE—Danville City County

SOUTHERN VIRGINIA MENTAL HEALTH INSTITUTE (494017), 382 Taylor Drive, Zip 24541–4023; tel. 434/799–6220, (Nonreporting) **A**1 10 **S** Virginia Department of Mental Health, Richmond, VA
Primary Contact: William Cook, Director
CFO: Wayne Peters, Administrator
CMO: Pravin Patel, M.D., Acting President and Chief Executive Officer
CIO: Larry Hays, Director Information Technology
CHR: Stephanie Haywood, Director Human Resources
CNO: Kathy M Dodd, Director of Nursing
Web address: www.svmhi.dbhds.virginia.gov
Control: State, Government, nonfederal **Service**: Psychiatric

Staffed Beds: 72

SOVAH HEALTH–DANVILLE (490075), 142 South Main Street, Zip 24541–2922; tel. 434/799–2100, (Nonreporting) **A**1 2 3 10 12 13 **S** LifePoint Health, Brentwood, TN
Primary Contact: Alan Larson, Chief Executive Officer
CFO: Mark T Anderson, Chief Financial Officer
CMO: James F Starling, M.D., Chief Medical Officer
CIO: David Cartwright, Director Management Information Systems
CNO: Aundrea Mills, Chief Nursing Officer
Web address: www.danvilleregional.com/
Control: Other not–for–profit (including NFP Corporation) **Service**: General medical and surgical

Staffed Beds: 250

DULLES—Loudoun County

★ **STONESPRINGS HOSPITAL CENTER (490145)**, 24440 Stone Spring Boulevard, Zip 20166–2247; tel. 571/349–4000, (Nonreporting) **S** HCA Healthcare, Nashville, TN
Primary Contact: Lance Jones, Chief Executive Officer
COO: Benjamin Brown, Chief Operating Officer
CFO: Candi Christopher, CPA, Chief Financial Officer
CMO: Walter R Zolkiwsky, M.D., Chief Medical Officer
CHR: Tiffani Smith, Chief Human Resources Officer
CNO: Michelle L. Epps, MSN, R.N., Chief Nursing Officer
Web address: www.stonespringshospital.com
Control: Corporation, Investor–owned (for–profit) **Service**: General medical and surgical

Staffed Beds: 124

EMPORIA—Emporia City County

SOUTHERN VIRGINIA REGIONAL MEDICAL CENTER (490097), 727 North Main Street, Zip 23847–1274; tel. 434/348–4400, **A**1 10 **F**3 11 15 26 28 29 30 31 40 45 49 50 57 59 64 70 77 78 79 81 85 93 98 103 107 115 119 124 129 130 133 146 148 **S** Community Health Systems, Inc., Franklin, TN
Primary Contact: Wilson A. Thomas, Chief Executive Officer
CFO: Jim Porter, Chief Financial Officer
CMO: Fitzgerald Marcelin, M.D., Chief of Staff
CIO: Larry Gold, Vice President, Information Services
CHR: Becky Parrish, Director Human Resources
CNO: Linda Burnette, R.N., Chief Nursing Officer
Web address: www.svrmc.com
Control: Corporation, Investor–owned (for–profit) **Service**: General medical and surgical

Staffed Beds: 80 **Admissions:** 1255 **Census:** 16 **Outpatient Visits:** 21397 **Births:** 0 **Total Expense ($000):** 31763 **Payroll Expense ($000):** 9688 **Personnel:** 178

FAIRFAX—Fairfax County

INOVA FAIR OAKS HOSPITAL (490101), 3600 Joseph Siewick Drive, Zip 22033–1798; tel. 703/391–3600, **A**1 2 3 5 10 **F**3 11 12 13 14 15 18 29 30 31 34 35 37 38 39 40 41 44 45 47 48 49 50 51 54 55 57 58 59 60 61 63 64 65 66 70 72 74 75 76 77 78 79 80 81 82 84 85 86 87 89 91 92 93 100 101 102 107 108 110 111 114 115 118 119 120 121 123 124 126 129 130 131 132 135 145 146 147 148 149 154 **P6 S** Inova Health System, Falls Church, VA
Primary Contact: John L. Fitzgerald, Chief Executive Officer
CFO: Jerry Seager, Assistant Vice President and Chief Financial Officer
CMO: G Michael Lynch, M.D., Chief Medical Officer
CIO: Marshall Ruffin, Chief Information Officer
CHR: Jeanne Robinson, Director Human Resources
Web address: www.inova.org
Control: Other not–for–profit (including NFP Corporation) **Service**: General medical and surgical

Staffed Beds: 201 **Admissions:** 11814 **Census:** 109 **Outpatient Visits:** 97780 **Births:** 3224 **Total Expense ($000):** 245934 **Payroll Expense ($000):** 73259 **Personnel:** 993

FALLS CHURCH—Fairfax County

DOMINION HOSPITAL (494023), 2960 Sleepy Hollow Road, Zip 22044–2030; tel. 703/536–2000, (Nonreporting) **A**1 10 **S** HCA Healthcare, Nashville, TN
Primary Contact: Lee Higginbotham, Chief Executive Officer
CFO: Edward R Stojakovich, Chief Financial Officer
CMO: Gary Litovitz, M.D., Medical Director
CIO: Leslie Gilliam, Director Health Information Management
CHR: Lesley Channell, Vice President Human Resources
Web address: www.dominionhospital.com
Control: Corporation, Investor–owned (for–profit) **Service**: Psychiatric

Staffed Beds: 100

INOVA FAIRFAX HOSPITAL (490063), 3300 Gallows Road, Zip 22042–3300; tel. 703/776–4001, (Includes INOVA FAIRFAX HOSPITAL FOR CHILDREN, 3300 Gallows Road, Falls Church, VA, Zip 22042–3307; tel. 703/776–4002) **A**1 2 3 5 8 10 **F**3 4 5 6 8 9 11 12 13 14 15 17 18 19 20 21 22 23 24 25 26 27 28 29 30 31 32 34 35 36 37 38 39 40 41 43 44 45 46 47 48 49 50 51 53 54 55 56 57 58 59 60 61 63 64 65 66 68 70 71 72 74 75 76 77 78 79 80 81 82 83 84 85 86 87 88 89 91 92 93 94 96 97 98 99 100 101 102 103 104 105 107 108 109 110 111 114 115 118 119 120 121 123 124 126 129 130 131 132 134 135 136 137 138 140 141 142 145 146 147 148 149 150 152 154 **P6 S** Inova Health System, Falls Church, VA
Primary Contact: Patrick Christiansen, Ph.D., Chief Executive Officer
CFO: Ronald Ewald, Chief Financial Officer
CMO: Joseph Hallal, M.D., Chief Medical Officer
CIO: Geoffrey Brown, Vice President Information Systems
CHR: Ken Hull, Director Human Resources
Web address: www.inova.org
Control: Other not–for–profit (including NFP Corporation) **Service**: General medical and surgical

Staffed Beds: 1002 **Admissions:** 49852 **Census:** 721 **Outpatient Visits:** 424359 **Births:** 10432 **Total Expense ($000):** 1387479 **Payroll Expense ($000):** 438758 **Personnel:** 5878

VA

Hospital, Medicare Provider Number, Address, Telephone, Approval, Facility, and Physician Codes, Health Care System
★ American Hospital Association (AHA) membership   ○ Healthcare Facilities Accreditation Program   ⇑ Center for Improvement in Healthcare Quality Accreditation ☐ The Joint Commission accreditation   ◇ DNV Healthcare Inc. accreditation   △ Commission on Accreditation of Rehabilitation Facilities (CARF) accreditation

☐ **NORTHERN VIRGINIA MENTAL HEALTH INSTITUTE (494010)**, 3302 Gallows Road, Zip 22042–3398; tel. 703/207–7100, (Nonreporting) **A**1 3 5 10 **S** Virginia Department of Mental Health, Richmond, VA
Primary Contact: Tammy Peacock, Ph.D., Facility Director
CFO: John Poffenbarger, Director Fiscal Services
CMO: R Maxilimien del Rio, M.D., Medical Director
CHR: Cynthia Lott, Director Human Resources
Web address: www.nvmhi.dbhds.virginia.gov
Control: State, Government, nonfederal **Service**: Psychiatric

Staffed Beds: 134

FARMVILLE—Prince Edward County

✠ **CENTRA SOUTHSIDE COMMUNITY HOSPITAL (490090)**, 800 Oak Street, Zip 23901–1199; tel. 434/392–8811, **A**1 5 10 20 **F**3 11 13 15 18 20 22 26 28 29 30 31 34 35 40 44 45 49 50 57 59 62 63 64 70 74 75 76 77 78 79 81 82 85 86 87 89 107 108 110 111 115 118 119 129 130 132 133 146 147 148 154 **S** Centra Health, Inc., Lynchburg, VA
Primary Contact: Thomas Angelo, Chief Executive Officer
Web address: www.sch.centrahealth.com/
Control: Other not-for-profit (including NFP Corporation) **Service**: General medical and surgical

Staffed Beds: 86 Admissions: 4057 Census: 35 Outpatient Visits: 107688 Births: 343 Total Expense ($000): 70890 Payroll Expense ($000): 25095 Personnel: 407

SOUTHSIDE COMMUNITY HOSPITAL See Centra Southside Community Hospital

FISHERSVILLE—Augusta County

✠ **AUGUSTA HEALTH (490018)**, 78 Medical Center Drive, Zip 22939–2332, Mailing Address: P.O. Box 1000, Zip 22939–1000; tel. 540/932–4000, **A**1 2 3 10 **F**3 5 7 11 13 15 18 20 22 26 28 29 30 31 34 35 38 40 41 45 46 47 48 49 50 51 53 54 57 58 59 62 63 64 65 66 68 70 74 75 76 77 78 79 81 82 84 85 86 87 89 90 91 93 94 96 97 98 100 102 103 104 107 108 110 111 112 114 115 118 119 120 121 123 124 126 128 129 130 131 132 135 144 146 147 148 153 154 **P**8
Primary Contact: Mary N. Mannix, FACHE, President and Chief Executive Officer
CMO: Richard Embrey, M.D., Chief Medical Officer
CIO: Michael Canfield, Chief Information Officer
CHR: Sue Krzastek, Vice President Human Resources
Web address: www.augustahealth.com
Control: Other not-for-profit (including NFP Corporation) **Service**: General medical and surgical

Staffed Beds: 215 Admissions: 10749 Census: 112 Outpatient Visits: 768166 Births: 1153 Total Expense ($000): 317600 Payroll Expense ($000): 130335 Personnel: 1865

FORT BELVOIR—Fairfax County

✠ **FORT BELVOIR COMMUNITY HOSPITAL**, 9300 Dewitt Loop, Zip 22060–5285; tel. 571/231–3224, (Nonreporting) **A**1 3 5 **S** Department of the Army, Office of the Surgeon General, Falls Church, VA
Primary Contact: Colonel Jason S. Wieman, Director
CMO: Lieutenant Colonel Mark D Harris, Deputy Commander Clinical Services
CIO: Terrance Branch, Chief Information Management
Web address: www.fbch.capmed.mil/SitePages/Home.aspx
Control: Army, Government, federal **Service**: General medical and surgical

Staffed Beds: 46

FRANKLIN—Franklin City County

✠ **SOUTHAMPTON MEMORIAL HOSPITAL (490092)**, 100 Fairview Drive, Zip 23851–1238, Mailing Address: P.O. Box 817, Zip 23851–0817; tel. 757/569–6100, (Nonreporting) **A**1 10 20 **S** Community Health Systems, Inc., Franklin, TN
Primary Contact: Kimberly W. Marks, Chief Executive Officer
CFO: Steve Ramey, Chief Financial Officer
CMO: Donald Bowling, M.D., Chief Medical Staff
CIO: Kristie Howell, System Information Technology Director
CHR: Loretha Ricks, Human Resources Supervisor
CNO: Laurie Ross, Chief Nursing Officer
Web address: www.smhfranklin.com
Control: Corporation, Investor-owned (for-profit) **Service**: General medical and surgical

Staffed Beds: 72

FREDERICKSBURG—Fredericksburg City County

✠ **ENCOMPASS HEALTH REHABILITATION HOSPITAL OF FREDERICKSBURG (493032)**, 300 Park Hill Drive, Zip 22401–3387; tel. 540/368–7300, (Nonreporting) **A**1 10 **S** Encompass Health Corporation, Birmingham, AL
Primary Contact: David Cashwell, Chief Executive Officer
Web address: www.fredericksburgrehabhospital.com
Control: Corporation, Investor-owned (for-profit) **Service**: Rehabilitation

Staffed Beds: 40

✠ **MARY WASHINGTON HOSPITAL (490022)**, 1001 Sam Perry Boulevard, Zip 22401–3354; tel. 540/741–1100, (Includes SNOWDEN AT FREDERICKSBURG, 1200 Sam Perry Boulevard, Fredericksburg, VA, Zip 22401–4456; tel. 540/741–3900; Charles Scercy, Corporate Director) **A**1 2 3 5 10 **F**3 5 13 15 18 20 22 24 26 28 29 30 31 34 35 36 40 43 44 45 46 47 48 49 50 54 55 57 58 59 62 64 70 72 74 75 76 77 78 79 81 83 84 85 86 87 89 92 93 96 98 99 100 101 102 104 105 107 108 111 114 115 118 119 120 121 124 126 129 130 131 132 135 146 147 148 149 152 153 154 **S** Mary Washington Healthcare, Fredericksburg, VA
Primary Contact: Michael P. McDermott, M.D., President and Chief Executive Officer
COO: Thomas Gettinger, Executive Vice President and Chief Operating Officer
CFO: Sean Barden, Executive Vice President and Chief Financial Officer
CMO: Rebecca Bigoney, Executive Vice President and Chief Medical Officer
CIO: Justin K. Box, Senior Vice President & Chief Information Officer
CHR: Kathryn S Wall, Executive Vice President, Human Resources and Organizational Development
CNO: Eileen L Dohmann, R.N., Senior Vice President and Chief Nursing Officer
Web address: www.marywashingtonhealthcare.com
Control: Other not-for-profit (including NFP Corporation) **Service**: General medical and surgical

Staffed Beds: 451 Admissions: 21464 Census: 287 Outpatient Visits: 347806 Births: 2609 Total Expense ($000): 404573 Payroll Expense ($000): 120666 Personnel: 1791

FREDERICKSBURG—Spotsylvania County

✠ **SPOTSYLVANIA REGIONAL MEDICAL CENTER (490141)**, 4600 Spotsylvania Parkway, Zip 22408–7762; tel. 540/498–4000, (Nonreporting) **A**1 10 **S** HCA Healthcare, Nashville, TN
Primary Contact: David McKnight, CPA, Chief Executive Officer
COO: Roberta Tinch, Chief Operations Officer
Web address: www.spotsrmc.com
Control: Corporation, Investor-owned (for-profit) **Service**: General medical and surgical

Staffed Beds: 100

FRONT ROYAL—Warren County

✠ **WARREN MEMORIAL HOSPITAL (490033)**, 1000 North Shenandoah Avenue, Zip 22630–3598; tel. 540/636–0300, (Total facility includes 120 beds in nursing home-type unit) **A**1 3 10 13 **F**3 11 13 15 28 29 30 34 35 36 40 50 53 54 56 57 59 64 65 67 70 75 76 77 79 81 82 85 86 87 93 96 107 108 111 114 118 119 128 130 132 135 144 146 147 148 154 **P**6 **S** Valley Health System, Winchester, VA
Primary Contact: Floyd Heater, President
CFO: Phillip Graybeal, CPA, Chief Financial Officer
CMO: Robert Meltvedt, M.D., Jr Vice President Medical Affairs
CNO: Terri Wright, Vice President and Chief Nursing Officer
Web address: www.valleyhealthlink.com/WMH
Control: Other not-for-profit (including NFP Corporation) **Service**: General medical and surgical

Staffed Beds: 164 Admissions: 2755 Census: 135 Outpatient Visits: 57561 Births: 373 Total Expense ($000): 59025 Payroll Expense ($000): 26950 Personnel: 433

GALAX—Galax City County

✠ **TWIN COUNTY REGIONAL HEALTHCARE (490115)**, 200 Hospital Drive, Zip 24333–2227; tel. 276/236–8181, **A**1 10 20 **F**3 13 14 15 28 29 30 31 32 34 35 38 40 45 50 51 53 57 64 65 68 70 75 76 77 78 79 81 82 85 87 89 93 98 100 101 102 104 107 108 110 111 116 117 119 132 146 147 **S** Duke LifePoint Healthcare, Brentwood, TN
Primary Contact: Dale Alward, Chief Executive Officer
CFO: Marita Caldwell, Chief Financial Officer
CHR: Kristal Herrington, Senior Director, Human Resources
CNO: Agnes A Smith, MSN, R.N., Chief Nursing Officer
Web address: www.tcrh.org
Control: Partnership, Investor-owned (for-profit) **Service**: General medical and surgical

Staffed Beds: 86 Admissions: 2725 Census: 25

VA

GLOUCESTER—Gloucester County

⇑ **RIVERSIDE WALTER REED HOSPITAL (490130)**, 7519 Hospital Drive,
Zip 23061–4178, Mailing Address: P.O. Box 1130, Zip 23061–1130;
tel. 804/693–8800, **A**2 10 21 **F**3 15 28 29 34 35 40 44 45 50 51 57 59 60 64
70 71 75 77 78 79 81 85 86 87 92 93 96 107 108 110 111 114 115 116 118
119 120 121 123 130 132 146 147 148 149 **P**6 **S** Riverside Health System,
Newport News, VA
Primary Contact: Esther Muscari. Desimini, Interim Administrator
CHR: Tabetha Holt, Director of Human Resources
Web address: www.riversideonline.com
Control: Other not–for–profit (including NFP Corporation) **Service**: General
medical and surgical

Staffed Beds: 30 **Admissions:** 2602 **Census:** 29 **Outpatient Visits:** 85131
Births: 0 **Total Expense ($000):** 58427 **Payroll Expense ($000):** 20627
Personnel: 357

GRUNDY—Buchanan County

⊞ **BUCHANAN GENERAL HOSPITAL (490127)**, 1535 Slate Creek Road,
Zip 24614–6974; tel. 276/935–1000, **A**1 10 20 **F**3 15 18 28 29 30 34 35 40
41 45 57 59 62 64 70 81 85 87 89 93 107 108 110 115 119 130 132 135
146 148
Primary Contact: Robert D. Ruchti, Chief Executive Officer
COO: Scott M Pittman, Chief Operating Officer
CFO: Kim Boyd, Chief Financial Officer
CIO: Rita Ramey, Director Information Systems
CHR: Wanda B. Stiltner, Director Human Resources
CNO: Patty Dorton, Director of Nursing
Web address: www.bgh.org
Control: Other not–for–profit (including NFP Corporation) **Service**: General
medical and surgical

Staffed Beds: 49 **Admissions:** 1120 **Census:** 15 **Outpatient Visits:** 45236
Births: 0 **Total Expense ($000):** 23360 **Payroll Expense ($000):** 8746
Personnel: 205

HAMPTON—Hampton City County

⊞ **HAMPTON VETERANS AFFAIRS MEDICAL CENTER**, 100 Emancipation Drive,
Zip 23667–0001; tel. 757/722–9961, (Total facility includes 122 beds in nursing
home–type unit) **A**1 3 5 **F**3 4 5 8 15 30 31 34 35 39 46 48 49 53 54 56 57
58 59 60 61 62 63 64 65 68 70 74 75 77 78 79 80 81 82 83 84 85 86 87
91 92 93 94 96 97 98 100 101 103 104 107 108 109 110 111 114 115 119
128 129 130 132 135 143 144 146 147 148 149 152 154 **S** Department of
Veterans Affairs, Perry Point, MD
Primary Contact: J. Ronald. Johnson, Medical Center Director
COO: Lorraine B Price, Associate Director
CFO: Terry Grew, Chief Business Office
CMO: Val Gibberman, M.D., Acting Chief of Staff
CIO: Cary Parks, Chief Information Resource Management
Web address: www.hampton.va.gov/
Control: Veterans Affairs, Government, federal **Service**: General medical and
surgical

Staffed Beds: 451 **Admissions:** 3070 **Census:** 160 **Births:** 0

★ ⇑ **SENTARA CAREPLEX HOSPITAL (490093)**, 3000 Coliseum Drive,
Zip 23666–5963; tel. 757/736–1000, **A**2 3 5 10 21 **F**3 8 11 12 13 15 18 20 22
26 28 29 30 31 33 34 35 36 37 38 39 40 41 44 45 46 47 48 49 51 54 56 57
58 59 60 61 63 64 68 70 71 74 75 76 77 78 79 80 81 82 83 84 85 86 87 91
92 93 95 96 100 101 107 110 111 113 117 118 119 120 126 129 130 131
134 135 141 146 147 148 149 154 **P**6 **S** Sentara Healthcare, Norfolk, VA
Primary Contact: Kirkpatrick Conley, President
COO: Rita A. Bunch, M.P.H., FACHE, Vice President of Operations
CFO: Cheryl Larner, Chief Financial Officer
CMO: Arthur Greene, M.D., Vice President Medical Affairs
CIO: Thomas Ewing, Director Information Technology
CHR: David Kidd, Manager Human Resources
Web address: www.sentara.com
Control: Other not–for–profit (including NFP Corporation) **Service**: General
medical and surgical

Staffed Beds: 169 **Admissions:** 8386 **Census:** 111 **Outpatient Visits:**
414389 **Births:** 0 **Total Expense ($000):** 216295 **Payroll Expense**
($000): 89315 **Personnel:** 1427

⊞ **U.S. AIR FORCE HOSPITAL**, 77 Nealy Avenue, Zip 23665–2040;
tel. 757/764–6969, **A**1 3 **F**3 7 13 15 18 29 30 33 34 39 40 59 64 65 68 70
72 74 75 76 77 79 81 85 87 91 92 93 97 104 107 110 111 119 130 135 146
147 149 154 **S** Department of the Air Force, Washington, DC
Primary Contact: Colonel Susan Pietrykowski, Commander
COO: Colonel Michael Dietz, Administrator
CFO: Major Steven Dadd, Flight Commander Resource Management
CMO: Colonel Paul Gourley, M.D., Chief Hospital Services
CIO: Major Merlinda Vergonio, Chief Information Management and Technology
CHR: Major Steven Dadd, Flight Commander Resource Management
CNO: Colonel Marlene Kerchenski, Chief Nurse
Web address: www.jble.af.mil
Control: Air Force, Government, federal **Service**: General medical and surgical

Staffed Beds: 60 **Admissions:** 6400 **Census:** 20 **Outpatient Visits:** 400000
Births: 65 **Total Expense ($000):** 70936 **Payroll Expense ($000):** 12573
Personnel: 1303

HARRISONBURG—Harrisonburg City County

★ ⇑ **SENTARA RMH MEDICAL CENTER (490004)**, 2010 Health Campus Drive,
Zip 22801–3293; tel. 540/689–1000, **A**2 5 10 21 **F**3 5 8 11 12 13 15 17 18 20
22 24 26 28 29 30 31 32 34 35 36 40 41 44 45 46 47 48 49 50 53 54 55 56
57 59 60 61 63 64 65 66 68 70 71 73 74 75 76 77 78 79 81 82 84 85 86 87
89 91 92 93 97 98 100 102 104 105 107 108 110 111 115 116 117 118 119
120 121 129 130 131 132 135 141 145 146 147 148 149 154 **P**6 8 **S** Sentara
Healthcare, Norfolk, VA
Primary Contact: Douglas J. Moyer, President
COO: Richard L Haushalter, Senior Vice President Operations and Chief Operating
Officer
CFO: Stewart R Nelson, Vice President and Chief Financial Officer
CMO: Susan McDonald, Vice President, Medical Affairs
CNO: Donna S Hahn, R.N., Vice President Acute Care and Chief Nurse Executive
Web address: www.rmhonline.com
Control: Other not–for–profit (including NFP Corporation) **Service**: General
medical and surgical

Staffed Beds: 244 **Admissions:** 13820 **Census:** 145 **Outpatient Visits:**
636979 **Births:** 1742 **Total Expense ($000):** 391653 **Payroll Expense**
($000): 149460 **Personnel:** 2323

HAYMARKET—Prince William County

⊞ **NOVANT HEALTH UVA HEALTH SYSTEM HAYMARKET MEDICAL CENTER**
(490144), 15225 Heathcote Boulevard, Zip 20155–4023, Mailing Address:
14535 John Marshall Hwy, Gainesville, Zip 20155–4023; tel. 571/284–1000,
(Nonreporting) **A**1 10 **S** Novant Health, Winston Salem, NC
Primary Contact: Greg Napps, President
CFO: Charles Coder, Vice President
CMO: Doug Reed, Vice President of Medical Affairs
CIO: David B Garrett, Senior Vice President and Chief Information Officer
CHR: Tracy Bowers, Vice President Human Resources and Administrative Services
CNO: Maggie C Conklin, M.P.H., Interim Chief Nursing Officer
Web address: www.novanthealth.org
Control: Other not–for–profit (including NFP Corporation) **Service**: General
medical and surgical

Staffed Beds: 18

HOPEWELL—Hopewell City County

⊞ **JOHN RANDOLPH MEDICAL CENTER (490020)**, 411 West Randolph Road,
Zip 23860–2938; tel. 804/541–1600, (Nonreporting) **A**1 2 10 **S** HCA Healthcare,
Nashville, TN
Primary Contact: Joseph Mazzo, Chief Executive Officer
CFO: Jennifer Honaker, Chief Financial Officer
CHR: MaDena DuChemin, Assistant Administrator Human Resources
Web address: www.johnrandolphmed.com
Control: Corporation, Investor–owned (for–profit) **Service**: General medical and
surgical

Staffed Beds: 112

VA

| ★ American Hospital Association (AHA) membership | ○ Healthcare Facilities Accreditation Program | ⇑ Center for Improvement in Healthcare Quality Accreditation |
| □ The Joint Commission accreditation | ◇ DNV Healthcare Inc. accreditation | △ Commission on Accreditation of Rehabilitation Facilities (CARF) accreditation |

Hospital, Medicare Provider Number, Address, Telephone, Approval, Facility, and Physician Codes, Health Care System

© 2018 AHA Guide   *Many Facility Codes have changed. Please refer to the AHA Guide Code Chart.*   Hospitals **A659**

HOT SPRINGS—Bath County

✠ **BATH COMMUNITY HOSPITAL (491300)**, 106 Park Drive, Zip 24445–2921,
Mailing Address: P.O. Box Z, Zip 24445–0750; tel. 540/839–7000, (Nonreporting)
A1 10 18
Primary Contact: Kathy Landreth, Chief Executive Officer
COO: Mitzi Grey, Chief Operating Officer
CMO: James Redington, M.D., Chief of Staff
CIO: Tracy Bartley, Manager Information Technology
CHR: Patricia Foutz, Director Human Resources
CNO: Kyna Moore, R.N., Director of Nursing
Web address: www.https://bathhospital.org
Control: Other not–for–profit (including NFP Corporation) **Service**: General
medical and surgical

Staffed Beds: 25

KILMARNOCK—Lancaster County

✠ **RAPPAHANNOCK GENERAL HOSPITAL (491308)**, 101 Harris Drive,
Zip 22482–3880, Mailing Address: P.O. Box 1449, Zip 22482–1449;
tel. 804/435–8000, **A**1 10 18 **F**3 11 15 18 26 28 29 30 31 34 35 38 40 44 45
46 50 57 59 64 68 74 75 77 78 79 81 85 93 98 100 102 103 104 107 108
110 111 115 118 119 129 130 131 132 133 146 148 149 153 154 **S** Bon
Secours Health System, Inc., Marriottsville, MD
Primary Contact: Chris Accashian, Chief Executive Officer
Web address: www.https://bonsecours.com/richmond/find–a–facility/
rappahannock–general–hospital
Control: Other not–for–profit (including NFP Corporation) **Service**: General
medical and surgical

**Staffed Beds: 35 Admissions: 1369 Census: 17 Outpatient Visits: 17197
Births: 4 Total Expense ($000): 35034 Payroll Expense ($000): 13329
Personnel: 256**

LEBANON—Russell County

☐ **RUSSELL COUNTY MEDICAL CENTER (490002)**, 58 Carroll Street, Zip 24266,
Mailing Address: P.O. Box 3600, Zip 24266–0200; tel. 276/883–8000, **A**1 10 **F**3
11 15 28 29 30 31 34 35 40 44 45 50 56 57 59 62 63 64 68 70 75 78 79 81
85 93 97 98 100 101 102 104 107 108 110 111 114 118 119 127 129 130
133 146 147 148 154 **S** Ballad Health, Johnson City, TN
Primary Contact: Stephen K. Givens, Assistant Vice President and Administrator
CMO: Brian Condit, M.D., Vice President Chief Medical Officer, Virginia Operations
Medical Staff Services
CHR: Beth Hill, Director Human Resources
CNO: Greta M. Morrison, Assistant Chief Nursing Officer
Web address: www.mountainstateshealth.com/rcmc
Control: Other not–for–profit (including NFP Corporation) **Service**: General
medical and surgical

**Staffed Beds: 78 Admissions: 1807 Census: 22 Outpatient Visits: 29114
Births: 0 Total Expense ($000): 24153 Payroll Expense ($000): 8342
Personnel: 144**

LEESBURG—Loudoun County

✠ **INOVA LOUDOUN HOSPITAL (490043)**, 44045 Riverside Parkway,
Zip 20176–5101, Mailing Address: P.O. Box 6000, Zip 20177–0600;
tel. 703/858–6000, (Total facility includes 100 beds in nursing–type unit) **A**1
2 5 10 **F**3 5 11 13 14 15 18 20 22 26 28 29 30 31 34 35 37 38 39 40 41 43
44 45 48 49 50 54 55 57 58 59 60 61 63 64 65 66 67 68 70 71 72 74 75 76
77 78 79 80 81 82 84 85 86 87 89 91 92 93 96 98 100 101 102 103 104 105
107 108 110 111 114 115 118 119 120 121 123 126 128 130 131 132 135
145 146 147 148 149 154 **P**6 **S** Inova Health System, Falls Church, VA
Primary Contact: Deborah Addo, Chief Executive Officer
CFO: William Bane, Chief Financial Officer
CMO: Christopher Chiantella, M.D., Chief Medical Officer
CHR: Sarah Pavik, Director Human Resources and Guest Services
CNO: Elizabeth Dugan, Ph.D., R.N., MSN, Chief Nursing Officer
Web address: www.inova.org
Control: Other not–for–profit (including NFP Corporation) **Service**: General
medical and surgical

**Staffed Beds: 279 Admissions: 13651 Census: 227 Outpatient Visits:
149611 Births: 2674 Total Expense ($000): 273129 Payroll Expense
($000): 95711 Personnel: 1585**

LEXINGTON—Lexington City County

✠ **CARILION STONEWALL JACKSON HOSPITAL (491304)**, 1 Health Circle,
Zip 24450–2492; tel. 540/458–3300, **A**1 10 18 **F**3 8 11 15 18 28 29 34 35
40 45 50 53 56 57 59 65 68 70 75 77 79 81 85 87 91 93 97 107 108 110
111 119 127 129 130 131 132 133 135 146 148 149 **P**6 **S** Carilion Clinic,
Roanoke, VA
Primary Contact: Greg T. Madsen, Chief Executive Officer
CMO: Lyle McClung, M.D., Chief of Staff
Web address: www.carilionclinic.org
Control: Other not–for–profit (including NFP Corporation) **Service**: General
medical and surgical

**Staffed Beds: 12 Admissions: 1239 Census: 14 Outpatient Visits: 28680
Births: 2 Total Expense ($000): 33346 Payroll Expense ($000): 12647
Personnel: 213**

LOW MOOR—Alleghany County

✠ **LEWISGALE HOSPITAL ALLEGHANY (490126)**, One ARH Lane, Zip 24457,
Mailing Address: P.O. Box 7, Zip 24457–0007; tel. 540/862–6011, (Nonreporting)
A1 10 20 **S** HCA Healthcare, Nashville, TN
Primary Contact: William Windham, Chief Executive Officer
CMO: Michele Ballou, M.D., Chief Medical Staff
CIO: Jeffrey Steelman, Director Information Systems
CHR: Bernard M Campbell, Administrator Human Resources
CNO: Robin Broughman, R.N., Ph.D., Chief Nursing Officer
Web address: www.alleghanyregional.com
Control: Corporation, Investor–owned (for–profit) **Service**: General medical and
surgical

Staffed Beds: 146

LURAY—Page County

✠ **PAGE MEMORIAL HOSPITAL (491307)**, 200 Memorial Drive, Zip 22835–1005;
tel. 540/743–4561, **A**1 10 18 **F**3 7 8 11 15 28 29 30 34 35 40 53 56 57 59
60 64 66 68 69 74 75 77 79 81 85 90 93 107 108 110 111 114 119 127 128
129 130 133 135 143 146 148 154 **P**2 **S** Valley Health System, Winchester, VA
Primary Contact: N Travis. Clark, President
CFO: Phillip Graybeal, CPA, Chief Financial Officer
Web address: www.valleyhealthlink.com/page
Control: Other not–for–profit (including NFP Corporation) **Service**: General
medical and surgical

**Staffed Beds: 25 Admissions: 501 Census: 9 Outpatient Visits: 79487
Births: 0 Total Expense ($000): 27950 Payroll Expense ($000): 14364
Personnel: 186**

LYNCHBURG—Lynchburg City County

CENTRA HEALTH See Centra Lynchburg General Hospital

✠ **CENTRA LYNCHBURG GENERAL HOSPITAL (490021)**, 1901 Tate Springs
Road, Zip 24501–1109; tel. 434/200–4700, (Includes CENTRA VIRGINIA
BAPTIST HOSPITAL, 3300 Rivermont Avenue, Lynchburg, VA, Zip 24503–2053;
tel. 434/200–4000; LYNCHBURG GENERAL HOSPITAL, 1901 Tate Springs Road,
Lynchburg, VA, Zip 24501–1167; tel. 434/200–3000) (Total facility includes 413
beds in nursing home–type unit) **A**1 2 3 5 10 **F**2 3 4 5 7 10 11 12 13 15 17 18
19 20 22 24 26 28 29 30 31 34 35 37 38 40 43 44 45 46 47 48 49 50 53 54
55 56 57 59 60 61 62 63 64 67 68 70 71 72 73 74 75 76 77 78 79 80 81
82 84 85 86 87 89 90 91 92 93 94 96 98 99 100 101 102 103 104 105 106
107 108 110 111 114 115 119 120 121 123 124 125 126 127 128 129 130
131 132 133 135 143 144 146 147 148 149 152 **P**7 **S** Centra Health, Inc.,
Lynchburg, VA
Primary Contact: E W. Tibbs, President and Chief Executive Officer
CFO: Lewis C Addison, Senior Vice President and Chief Financial Officer
CMO: Chalmers Nunn, M.D., Chief Medical Officer and Senior Vice President
CIO: Ben Clark, Vice President and Chief Information Officer
CHR: Jan Walker, Director Human Resources
Web address: www.centrahealth.com
Control: Other not–for–profit (including NFP Corporation) **Service**: General
medical and surgical

**Staffed Beds: 1029 Admissions: 29685 Census: 762 Outpatient Visits:
758089 Births: 2708 Total Expense ($000): 885165 Payroll Expense
($000): 389994 Personnel: 5807**

✠ **CENTRA SPECIALTY HOSPITAL (492010)**, 3300 Rivermont Avenue,
Zip 24503–2030; tel. 434/200–1799, **A**10 **F**1 3 29 44 50 68 75 77 149 **P**6
Primary Contact: Kay Bowling, Chief Executive Officer
Control: Other not–for–profit (including NFP Corporation) **Service**: Acute long–
term care hospital

**Staffed Beds: 26 Admissions: 214 Census: 20 Outpatient Visits: 0
Births: 0 Total Expense ($000): 9536 Payroll Expense ($000): 4174
Personnel: 73**

MADISON HEIGHTS—Amherst County

CENTRAL VIRGINIA TRAINING CENTER (490108), 210 East Colony Road,
Zip 24572–2005, Mailing Address: P.O. Box 1098, Lynchburg, Zip 24505–1098;
tel. 434/947–6326, (Nonreporting) **A**10 **S** Virginia Department of Mental Health,
Richmond, VA
Primary Contact: David Cole, Assistant Director of Administration, Chief Financial
Officer, Department of Behavioral Health and D
CFO: Charles Felmlee, Assistant Director Fiscal Services
CMO: Balraj Bawa, M.D., Assistant Director Medical Services
CHR: Burckhard Blob, Manager Human Resources
Web address: www.cvtc.dmhmrsas.virginia.gov/
Control: State, Government, nonfederal **Service**: Intellectual disabilities

Staffed Beds: 1112

Many Facility Codes have changed. Please refer to the AHA Guide Code Chart.   © 2018 AHA Guide

VA

MANASSAS—Manassas City County

✠ **NOVANT HEALTH UVA HEALTH SYSTEM PRINCE WILLIAM MEDICAL CENTER (490045)**, 8700 Sudley Road, Zip 20110–4418, Mailing Address: P.O. Box 2610, Zip 20108–0867; tel. 703/369–8000, (Nonreporting) **A**1 2 3 10 **S** Novant Health, Winston Salem, NC
Primary Contact: Greg Napps, President
CFO: Charles Coder, Vice President
CMO: Doug Wall, M.D., Vice President Medical Affairs
CIO: David B Garrett, Senior Vice President and Chief Information Officer
CHR: Tracy Bowers, Vice President Human Resources and Administrative Services
CNO: Maggie C Conklin, M.P.H., Interim Chief Nurse Officer
Web address: www.pwhs.org
Control: Other not–for–profit (including NFP Corporation) **Service**: General medical and surgical

Staffed Beds: 90

MARION—Smyth County

☐ **SMYTH COUNTY COMMUNITY HOSPITAL (490038)**, 245 Medical Park Drive, Zip 24354, Mailing Address: P.O. Box 880, Zip 24354–0880; tel. 276/378–1000, (Total facility includes 109 beds in nursing home–type unit) **A**1 10 **F**3 11 15 18 28 29 30 31 34 35 40 45 50 51 54 57 59 62 64 67 68 70 75 77 78 79 81 85 87 90 93 97 107 110 111 115 118 119 127 128 129 131 132 133 135 144 146 147 148 149 **S** Ballad Health, Johnson City, TN
Primary Contact: James E. Tyler, Chief Executive Officer
CHR: Sue Henderson, Human Resource Manager
CNO: Ethan Collins, R.N., Chief Nursing Officer
Web address: www.msha.com/scch
Control: Other not–for–profit (including NFP Corporation) **Service**: General medical and surgical

Staffed Beds: 153 Admissions: 1713 Census: 111 Outpatient Visits: 61062 Births: 0 Total Expense ($000): 40592 Payroll Expense ($000): 15415 Personnel: 210

☐ **SOUTHWESTERN VIRGINIA MENTAL HEALTH INSTITUTE (490105)**, 340 Bagley Circle, Zip 24354–3390; tel. 276/783–1200, (Nonreporting) **A**1 10 **S** Virginia Department of Mental Health, Richmond, VA
Primary Contact: Cynthia McClaskey, Ph.D., Director
CIO: Kim Ratliff, Director Health Information Management
Web address: www.swvmhi.dmhmrsas.virginia.gov/
Control: State, Government, nonfederal **Service**: Psychiatric

Staffed Beds: 166

MARTINSVILLE—Martinsville City County

✠ **SOVAH HEALTH–MARTINSVILLE (490079)**, 320 Hospital Drive, Zip 24112–1981, Mailing Address: P.O. Box 4788, Zip 24115–4788; tel. 276/666–7200, (Nonreporting) **A**1 2 10 19 **S** LifePoint Health, Brentwood, TN
Primary Contact: Michael Ehrat, Chief Executive Officer
CFO: Brandy Hanners, Chief Financial Officer
CIO: Jeff Butker, Chief Information Officer
CHR: Sherry Schofield, Director Human Resources
CNO: Michael Pittman, Chief Nursing Officer
Web address: www.martinsvillehospital.com
Control: Corporation, Investor–owned (for–profit) **Service**: General medical and surgical

Staffed Beds: 150

MECHANICSVILLE—Hanover County

✠ **BON SECOURS MEMORIAL REGIONAL MEDICAL CENTER (490069)**, 8260 Atlee Road, Zip 23116–1844; tel. 804/764–6000, (Nonreporting) **A**1 2 3 5 10 **S** Bon Secours Health System, Inc., Marriottsville, MD
Primary Contact: Mark M. Gordon, Chief Executive Officer
COO: Gary A. Welch, Assistant to the Chief Executive Officer and Administrative Director Support Systems
CFO: Stephan F Quiriconi, Vice President Finance
CMO: Sunil K. Sinha, M.D., FACHE, Chief Medical Officer
CIO: Gwen Harding, Site Manager Information Systems
CHR: Rebecca Kamguia, Administrative Director Human Resources
CNO: Jill M Kennedy, R.N., Vice President, Ambulatory Patient Care Services
Web address: www.bonsecours.com
Control: Church operated, Nongovernment, not–for–profit **Service**: General medical and surgical

Staffed Beds: 225

☐ **SHELTERING ARMS REHABILITATION HOSPITAL (493025)**, 8254 Atlee Road, Zip 23116–1844; tel. 804/764–1000, **A**1 3 10 **F**3 29 30 34 35 50 53 54 57 58 59 64 68 74 75 77 79 82 86 87 90 91 92 93 94 95 96 130 131 132 146 148 **P**6
Primary Contact: Mary A. Zweifel, MS, President and Chief Executive Officer
COO: Amy J Showalter, R.N., Chief Operating Officer
CFO: James Litsinger, CPA, Vice President and Chief Financial Officer
CMO: Hillary Hawkins, M.D., Medical Director
CIO: Chris Sorenson, Chief Information Officer
CHR: Ellen B Vance, Chief Human Resource Officer
CNO: Sandra Eyler, MS, Chief Nursing Officer
Web address: www.shelteringarms.com
Control: Other not–for–profit (including NFP Corporation) **Service**: Rehabilitation

Staffed Beds: 40 Admissions: 884 Census: 37 Outpatient Visits: 82926 Births: 0 Total Expense ($000): 29438 Payroll Expense ($000): 18318 Personnel: 131

MIDLOTHIAN—Chesterfield County

✠ **BON SECOURS ST. FRANCIS MEDICAL CENTER (490136)**, 13710 St Francis Boulevard, Zip 23114–3267; tel. 804/594–7300, (Nonreporting) **A**1 2 3 5 10 **S** Bon Secours Health System, Inc., Marriottsville, MD
Primary Contact: Chris Accashian, Chief Executive Officer
COO: Toni R Ardabell, Chief Executive Officer, Bon Secours Virginia
CFO: Stephan F Quiriconi, Vice President, Finance
CMO: Michael Menen, M.D., Chief Medical Officer
CIO: Terri Spence, Vice President and Regional Chief Information Officer
CHR: James C Godwin Jr Vice President, Human Resources
CNO: Barbara L. Gesme, MSN, Vice President Patient Care Services & Chief Nurse Executive
Web address: www.bonsecours.com/sfmc/default.asp
Control: Other not–for–profit (including NFP Corporation) **Service**: General medical and surgical

Staffed Beds: 124

☐ **SHELTERING ARMS HOSPITAL SOUTH (493030)**, 13700 St. Francis Boulevard, Suite 400, Zip 23114–3222; tel. 804/764–1000, **A**1 5 10 **F**3 29 30 34 35 50 54 57 58 59 64 68 74 75 77 79 82 86 87 90 91 92 93 94 95 96 100 104 130 131 132 146 148 154 **P**6
Primary Contact: Mary A. Zweifel, MS, President and Chief Executive Officer
COO: Amy J Showalter, R.N., Chief Operating Officer
CFO: James Litsinger, CPA, Chief Operating Officer
CMO: Timothy Silver, M.D., Medical Director, SAH–S
CIO: Chris Sorenson, Chief Health Information Officer
CHR: Ellen B Vance, Chief Human Resources Officer
CNO: Sandra Eyler, MS, Chief Nursing Officer
Web address: www.shelteringarms.com
Control: Other not–for–profit (including NFP Corporation) **Service**: Rehabilitation

Staffed Beds: 28 Admissions: 613 Census: 22 Outpatient Visits: 5748 Births: 0 Total Expense ($000): 10558 Payroll Expense ($000): 6034 Personnel: 78

NEW KENT—New Kent County

☐ **CUMBERLAND HOSPITAL FOR CHILDREN AND ADOLESCENTS (493300)**, 9407 Cumberland Road, Zip 23124–2029; tel. 804/966–2242, **A**1 10 **F**12 28 29 32 35 38 44 50 53 57 59 68 74 75 77 86 87 89 91 96 98 99 100 101 106 130 132 143 148 154 **P**6 **S** Universal Health Services, Inc., King of Prussia, PA
Primary Contact: Patrice Gay. Brooks, Chief Executive Officer
CFO: Joanne Rial, Chief Financial Officer
CMO: Daniel N Davidow, M.D., Medical Director
CIO: Leslie Bowery, Director of Standards and Compliance
CHR: Kim Ivey, Director of Human Resources
CNO: Paula Roberts, Chief Nursing Officer
Web address: www.cumberlandhospital.com
Control: Corporation, Investor–owned (for–profit) **Service**: Children's general medical and surgical

Staffed Beds: 118 Admissions: 274 Census: 100 Outpatient Visits: 0 Births: 0 Total Expense ($000): 20691 Payroll Expense ($000): 12006 Personnel: 238

VA

Hospital, Medicare Provider Number, Address, Telephone, Approval, Facility, and Physician Codes, Health Care System

★ American Hospital Association (AHA) membership
☐ The Joint Commission accreditation
○ Healthcare Facilities Accreditation Program
◇ DNV Healthcare Inc. accreditation
⇑ Center for Improvement in Healthcare Quality Accreditation
△ Commission on Accreditation of Rehabilitation Facilities (CARF) accreditation

© 2018 AHA Guide *Many Facility Codes have changed. Please refer to the AHA Guide Code Chart.* Hospitals **A661**

NEWPORT NEWS—Newport News City County

⊞ **BON SECOURS MARY IMMACULATE HOSPITAL (490041)**, 2 Bernardine Drive, Zip 23602–4499; tel. 757/886–6000, (Total facility includes 115 beds in nursing home–type unit) **A**1 10 **F**3 5 11 12 13 15 18 20 22 24 26 28 29 30 31 32 34 35 36 37 38 40 44 45 46 50 51 57 59 61 63 64 67 68 70 71 73 74 75 76 77 78 79 81 82 84 85 86 87 91 93 102 107 108 111 114 118 119 130 131 132 143 145 146 147 148 149 154 **P**6 **S** Bon Secours Health System, Inc., Marriottsville, MD
Primary Contact: Darlene Stephenson, Chief Executive Officer
COO: Darlene Stephenson, Vice President Operations
CIO: Terri Spence, Vice President Information Services
CHR: Vickie Witcher Humphries, Vice President Human Resources
Web address: www.bonsecourshamptonroads.com
Control: Other not–for–profit (including NFP Corporation) **Service**: General medical and surgical

Staffed Beds: 238 Admissions: 7899 Census: 157 Outpatient Visits: 106334 Births: 1617 Total Expense ($000): 163057 Payroll Expense ($000): 46597 Personnel: 837

⊞ **COASTAL VIRGINIA REHABILITATION (493027)**, 245 Chesapeake Avenue, Zip 23607–6038; tel. 757/928–8000, **A**1 3 5 10 **F**29 30 57 87 90 91 94 96 130 132 149 **S** Select Medical Corporation, Mechanicsburg, PA
Primary Contact: Daniel Ballin, Administrator
COO: William B Downey, President and Chief Executive Officer
CFO: Bill Austin, Senior Vice President of Finance
CMO: C Renee Moss, M.D., Chief Medical Officer
CIO: Dennis Loftis, Senior Vice President of Information Systems
CHR: Rob Cuthrell, Director of Human Resources
CNO: Debbie Outlaw, R.N., Director Patient Care Services
Web address: www.riversideonline.com/rri/index.cfm
Control: Partnership, Investor–owned (for–profit) **Service**: Rehabilitation

Staffed Beds: 35 Admissions: 431 Census: 16 Outpatient Visits: 0 Births: 0 Total Expense ($000): 8120 Payroll Expense ($000): 5773

☐ **NEWPORT NEWS BEHAVIORAL HEALTH CENTER**, 17579 Warwick Boulevard, Zip 23603–1343; tel. 757/888–0400, (Nonreporting) **A**1
Primary Contact: Paul Kirkham, Chief Executive Officer
COO: Paul Kirkham, Chief Executive Officer
CFO: Joe Brooks, Chief Financial Officer
CMO: Avtar Dhillon, M.D., Medical Director
CIO: Terry Rethamel, Director of Support Services
CHR: Shawn Marston, Director Human Resources
CNO: Karen Bruce, Director of Nursing
Web address: www.newportnewsbhc.com/
Control: Corporation, Investor–owned (for–profit) **Service**: Psychiatric

Staffed Beds: 132

⇑ **RIVERSIDE REGIONAL MEDICAL CENTER (490052)**, 500 J Clyde Morris Boulevard, Zip 23601–1929; tel. 757/594–2000, (Includes RIVERSIDE BEHAVIORAL HEALTH CENTER, 2244 Executive Drive, Hampton, VA, Zip 23666–2430; tel. 757/827–1001; Debra Campbell, R.N., Administrator) **A**2 3 5 10 13 21 **F**3 4 8 13 15 18 20 22 24 26 28 30 31 36 38 40 43 44 45 49 50 51 54 56 58 60 64 70 72 74 75 76 77 78 79 81 82 84 85 86 87 91 93 94 96 98 99 102 103 108 110 111 114 115 116 117 118 119 120 121 123 124 126 129 130 131 132 141 143 146 148 149 154 **P**6 **S** Riverside Health System, Newport News, VA
Primary Contact: Michael J. Doucette, Senior Vice President and Administrator
COO: William B Downey, Chief Operating Officer
CFO: Wade Broughman, Executive Vice President and Chief Financial Officer
CMO: Barry L Gross, M.D., Executive Vice President and Chief Medical Officer
CIO: Dennis Loftis, Senior Vice President and Chief Information Officer
CHR: Sally Hartman, Senior Vice President
CNO: Candice R. Carroll, Nurse Executive
Web address: www.riversideonline.com/rrmc/index.cfm
Control: Other not–for–profit (including NFP Corporation) **Service**: General medical and surgical

Staffed Beds: 307 Admissions: 19966 Census: 290 Outpatient Visits: 108632 Births: 2444 Total Expense ($000): 509533 Payroll Expense ($000): 128304 Personnel: 1789

★ ⇑ **SELECT SPECIALTY HOSPITAL HAMPTON ROADS (492008)**, 245 Chesapeake Avenue, Zip 23607–6038; tel. 757/534–5000, (Nonreporting) **A**10 21 **S** Select Medical Corporation, Mechanicsburg, PA
Primary Contact: Phillip L. Wright, FACHE, Chief Executive Officer
Web address: www.hamptonroadsspecialtyhospital.com
Control: Other not–for–profit (including NFP Corporation) **Service**: Acute long–term care hospital

Staffed Beds: 25

NORFOLK—Norfolk City County

⊞ ⇑ **BON SECOURS–DEPAUL MEDICAL CENTER (490011)**, 150 Kingsley Lane, Zip 23505–4650; tel. 757/889–5000, (Total facility includes 24 beds in nursing home–type unit) **A**1 2 3 5 10 21 **F**3 11 13 15 18 20 22 29 30 31 34 35 40 44 45 46 50 51 56 57 59 61 64 68 70 71 74 75 76 78 79 81 82 84 85 86 87 93 97 102 107 108 110 111 114 115 118 119 120 121 128 129 130 131 132 143 145 146 147 148 149 154 **P**6 **S** Bon Secours Health System, Inc., Marriottsville, MD
Primary Contact: Paul Gaden, Chief Executive Officer
CFO: Charmaine Rochester, Vice President Finance
CIO: Lynne Zultanky, Director Corporate Communications and Media Relations
CHR: Vickie Witcher Humphries, Vice President Human Resources
CNO: Michael J. Bratton, R.N., Chief Nurse Executive and Vice President Patient Care Services
Web address: www.bonsecourshamptonroads.com
Control: Other not–for–profit (including NFP Corporation) **Service**: General medical and surgical

Staffed Beds: 204 Admissions: 6695 Census: 89 Outpatient Visits: 347295 Births: 1322 Total Expense ($000): 208485 Payroll Expense ($000): 68603 Personnel: 1230

☐ **CHILDREN'S HOSPITAL OF THE KING'S DAUGHTERS (493301)**, 601 Children's Lane, Zip 23507–1910; tel. 757/668–7000, **A**1 3 5 10 **F**3 7 8 9 12 16 17 19 21 23 25 27 29 30 31 32 34 35 39 40 41 44 45 48 49 50 55 57 58 59 60 61 64 65 66 68 72 73 74 75 77 78 79 80 81 84 85 86 87 88 89 90 91 92 93 97 99 100 102 107 108 111 115 118 119 129 130 131 132 134 138 144 145 146 148 149 153 154 **P**8
Primary Contact: James D. Dahling, President and Chief Executive Officer
COO: John P Harding, Chief Operating Officer
CFO: Dennis Ryan, Senior Vice President and Chief Financial Officer
CMO: Chris Foley, Chief of Medicine
CIO: Deborah Barnes, Vice President and Chief Information Officer
CHR: Paul J Morlock, FACHE, Vice President Human Resources and Occupational Health
CNO: Karen Mitchell, Vice President Patient Care Services
Web address: www.chkd.org
Control: Other not–for–profit (including NFP Corporation) **Service**: Children's general medical and surgical

Staffed Beds: 206 Admissions: 5292 Census: 129 Outpatient Visits: 290447 Births: 0 Total Expense ($000): 352891 Payroll Expense ($000): 144462 Personnel: 2468

HOSPITAL FOR EXTENDED RECOVERY (492007), 600 Gresham Drive, Suite 700, Zip 23507–1904; tel. 757/388–1700, (Nonreporting) **A**10
Primary Contact: Aimee Vergara, Chief Executive Officer
Control: Other not–for–profit (including NFP Corporation) **Service**: Acute long–term care hospital

Staffed Beds: 25

☐ **KEMPSVILLE CENTER FOR BEHAVIORAL HEALTH**, 860 Kempsville Road, Zip 23502–3980; tel. 757/461–4565, (Nonreporting) **A**1
Primary Contact: Jaime Fernandez, Chief Executive Officer
Control: Corporation, Investor–owned (for–profit) **Service**: Psychiatric

Staffed Beds: 77

LAKE TAYLOR TRANSITIONAL CARE HOSPITAL (492001), 1309 Kempsville Road, Zip 23502–2286; tel. 757/461–5001, (Nonreporting) **A**3 5 10
Primary Contact: Thomas J. Orsini, President and Chief Executive Officer
CFO: Robert W Fogg, Director Finance
CMO: Kevin Murray, M.D., Director Medical Services
CIO: Mark Davis, Director Information Systems
CHR: LeeAnn Lowman, Director Human Resources
Web address: www.laketaylor.org
Control: Hospital district or authority, Government, nonfederal **Service**: Acute long–term care hospital

Staffed Beds: 284

★ ⇑ **SENTARA LEIGH HOSPITAL (490046)**, 830 Kempsville Road, Zip 23502–3920; tel. 757/261–6000, **A**2 3 5 10 21 **F**3 8 9 11 13 15 18 20 22 26 28 29 30 31 34 35 36 37 38 39 40 41 44 45 46 47 48 49 50 53 54 56 57 58 59 60 61 63 64 65 68 70 71 74 75 76 77 78 79 80 81 82 84 85 86 87 91 92 93 94 96 97 100 102 107 108 110 111 114 119 126 130 131 132 135 141 146 147 148 149 154 **P**6 **S** Sentara Healthcare, Norfolk, VA
Primary Contact: Joanne Inman, President
COO: Howard P Kern, President and Chief Operating Officer
CFO: Robert Broermann, Senior Vice President and Chief Financial Officer
CMO: Terry Gilliland, M.D., Chief Medical Officer
CIO: Bert Reese, Chief Information Officer
CHR: Michael V Taylor, Senior Vice President Human Resources
CNO: Genemarie McGee, R.N., MS, Chief Nursing Officer
Web address: www.sentara.com
Control: Other not–for–profit (including NFP Corporation) **Service**: General medical and surgical

Staffed Beds: 250 Admissions: 16926 Census: 196 Outpatient Visits: 454816 Births: 2176 Total Expense ($000): 291560 Payroll Expense ($000): 117433 Personnel: 1806

VA

★ ⇑ **SENTARA NORFOLK GENERAL HOSPITAL (490007)**, 600 Gresham Drive, Zip 23507–1904; tel. 757/388–3000, **A**2 3 5 8 10 21 **F**3 7 11 12 13 15 16 17 18 20 22 24 26 28 29 30 31 34 35 36 37 38 39 40 41 43 44 45 46 47 48 49 50 51 52 53 54 56 57 58 59 60 61 63 64 65 66 68 70 71 72 74 75 76 77 78 79 80 81 82 84 85 86 87 90 91 92 93 94 96 97 98 100 101 102 103 107 108 110 111 112 114 115 116 117 118 119 120 121 123 124 126 129 130 131 132 135 136 137 138 141 142 145 146 147 148 149 154 **P**6 **S** Sentara Healthcare, Norfolk, VA
Primary Contact: Kurt T. Hofelich, President
COO: Carolyn Carpenter, FACHE, Vice President and Chief Operating Officer
CFO: Robert Broermann, Senior Vice President and Chief Financial Officer
CIO: Bert Reese, Chief Information Officer
Web address: www.sentara.com
Control: Other not–for–profit (including NFP Corporation) **Service:** General medical and surgical

Staffed Beds: 495 **Admissions:** 25496 **Census:** 408 **Outpatient Visits:** 1121641 **Births:** 2888 **Total Expense ($000):** 797512 **Payroll Expense ($000):** 275173 **Personnel:** 3925

NORTON—Norton City County

★ **MOUNTAIN VIEW REGIONAL MEDICAL CENTER (490027)**, 310 Third Street NE, Zip 24273–1137; tel. 276/679–9100, (Total facility includes 44 beds in nursing home–type unit) **F**3 11 15 28 29 40 45 50 59 70 75 77 81 85 87 89 93 107 108 110 111 115 119 128 130 135 **S** Ballad Health, Johnson City, TN
Primary Contact: Dale Clark, President
CFO: Regina Day, Executive Director Finance
CMO: Michael Ketcham, Chief Medical Officer
CHR: Bobby Collins, Director Human Resources
Web address: www.wellmont.org
Control: Other not–for–profit (including NFP Corporation) **Service:** General medical and surgical

Staffed Beds: 70 **Admissions:** 1115 **Census:** 42 **Outpatient Visits:** 26587 **Total Expense ($000):** 24896 **Payroll Expense ($000):** 6979 **Personnel:** 151

○ **NORTON COMMUNITY HOSPITAL (490001)**, 100 15th Street NW, Zip 24273–1616; tel. 276/679–9600, **A**3 10 11 13 **F**3 11 13 15 18 28 29 30 31 32 34 35 40 44 45 46 51 53 55 56 57 58 59 62 63 64 65 66 68 70 75 76 77 78 79 81 82 87 90 93 107 108 110 111 115 116 117 118 119 129 130 131 133 135 146 147 148 154 **S** Ballad Health, Johnson City, TN
Primary Contact: Mark T. Leonard, Chief Executive Officer
CFO: Stephen Sawyer, Chief Financial Officer
CMO: Allen Mullens, M.D., Chief Medical Staff
CIO: Judy Lawson, Director Information Services
CHR: Valeri J Colyer, Director Human Resources
Web address: www.msha.com/nch
Control: Other not–for–profit (including NFP Corporation) **Service:** General medical and surgical

Staffed Beds: 70 **Admissions:** 3271 **Census:** 32 **Outpatient Visits:** 73597 **Births:** 210 **Total Expense ($000):** 50594 **Payroll Expense ($000):** 19684 **Personnel:** 367

ONANCOKE—Accomack County

★ ⇑ **RIVERSIDE SHORE MEMORIAL HOSPITAL (490037)**, 204800 Market Street, Zip 23417, Mailing Address: P.O. Box 17, Nassawadox, Zip 23413–0017; tel. 757/302–2100, **A**2 3 10 20 21 **F**3 11 13 15 18 28 29 30 31 34 40 45 49 50 59 64 70 74 75 76 77 78 79 81 85 93 107 110 111 114 118 119 121 129 130 132 146 **P**6 **S** Riverside Health System, Newport News, VA
Primary Contact: John Peterman, Vice President and Administrator
CFO: W William Austin Jr Senior Vice President Finance
CMO: David Jones, Service Chief
CHR: Nicole Miller, Director Human Resources
Web address: www.riversideonline.com
Control: Other not–for–profit (including NFP Corporation) **Service:** General medical and surgical

Staffed Beds: 24 **Admissions:** 2582 **Census:** 22 **Outpatient Visits:** 31841 **Births:** 147 **Total Expense ($000):** 64580 **Payroll Expense ($000):** 20203 **Personnel:** 321

⇑ **SHORE MEMORIAL HOSPITAL** See Riverside Shore Memorial Hospital

PEARISBURG—Giles County

⊞ **CARILION GILES COMMUNITY HOSPITAL (491302)**, 159 Hartley Way, Zip 24134–2471; tel. 540/921–6000, **A**1 10 18 **F**3 11 15 18 28 29 30 34 35 36 40 45 50 53 57 59 64 65 68 70 75 77 79 81 85 86 87 91 93 96 107 108 110 111 115 118 119 127 130 133 135 146 147 148 149 **P**6 **S** Carilion Clinic, Roanoke, VA
Primary Contact: William Flattery, Vice President and Administrator Western Division
CMO: John Tamminen, M.D., President Medical Staff
CHR: Carrie Boggess, Human Resource Generalist
CNO: Veronica Stump, Director of Nursing
Web address: www.carilionclinic.org
Control: Other not–for–profit (including NFP Corporation) **Service:** General medical and surgical

Staffed Beds: 10 **Admissions:** 1017 **Census:** 14 **Outpatient Visits:** 25669 **Births:** 1 **Total Expense ($000):** 30877 **Payroll Expense ($000):** 11725 **Personnel:** 199

PETERSBURG—Petersburg City County

□ **CENTRAL STATE HOSPITAL**, 26317 West Washington Street, Zip 23803–2727, Mailing Address: P.O. Box 4030, Zip 23803–0030; tel. 804/524–7000, **A**1 **F**29 30 35 38 77 87 98 101 106 130 132 143 149 **S** Virginia Department of Mental Health, Richmond, VA
Primary Contact: Rebecca Vauter, PsyD, Facility Director
COO: Ann Bailey, Assistant Director Administration
CFO: Robert Kaufman, Director Financial Services
CMO: Ronald O Forbes, M.D., Medical Director
CIO: Jonathan Baber, Director Information Technology
CHR: Tracy Salisbury, Regional Manager Human Resources
CNO: Eva Parham, R.N., Chief Nurse Executive
Web address: www.csh.dbhds.virginia.gov
Control: State, Government, nonfederal **Service:** Psychiatric

Staffed Beds: 277 **Admissions:** 827 **Census:** 240 **Outpatient Visits:** 0 **Births:** 0 **Total Expense ($000):** 65879 **Payroll Expense ($000):** 37786 **Personnel:** 869

⊞ **ENCOMPASS HEALTH REHABILITATION HOSPITAL OF PETERSBURG (493031)**, 95 Medical Park Boulevard, Zip 23805–9233; tel. 804/504–8100, (Nonreporting) **A**1 10 **S** Encompass Health Corporation, Birmingham, AL
Primary Contact: Louis Collier, Chief Executive Officer
Web address: www.encompasshealth.com
Control: Corporation, Investor–owned (for–profit) **Service:** Rehabilitation

Staffed Beds: 53

□ **HIRAM W. DAVIS MEDICAL CENTER (490104)**, 26317 West Washington Street, Zip 23803–2727, Mailing Address: P.O. Box 4030, Zip 23803–0030; tel. 804/524–7344, (Nonreporting) **A**1 10 **S** Virginia Department of Mental Health, Richmond, VA
Primary Contact: Brenda Buenvenida, Director
CFO: Robert Kaufman, Fiscal Officer
CHR: Tracy Salisbury, Director Human Resources
Control: State, Government, nonfederal **Service:** Other specialty treatment

Staffed Beds: 10

⊞ **POPLAR SPRINGS HOSPITAL (494022)**, 350 Poplar Drive, Zip 23805–9367; tel. 804/733–6874, (Nonreporting) **A**1 10 **S** Universal Health Services, Inc., King of Prussia, PA
Primary Contact: Nelson Smith, Chief Executive Officer
COO: Rachel Beal, Chief Operating Officer
CFO: Michael Felice, Chief Financial Officer
CMO: Thresa Simon, M.D., Medical Director
CHR: Morris Mitchell, Director Human Resources
Web address: www.poplarsprings.com
Control: Corporation, Investor–owned (for–profit) **Service:** Psychiatric

Staffed Beds: 180

VA

Hospital, Medicare Provider Number, Address, Telephone, Approval, Facility, and Physician Codes, Health Care System

★ American Hospital Association (AHA) membership
□ The Joint Commission accreditation
○ Healthcare Facilities Accreditation Program
◇ DNV Healthcare Inc. accreditation
⇑ Center for Improvement in Healthcare Quality Accreditation
△ Commission on Accreditation of Rehabilitation Facilities (CARF) accreditation

✠ **SOUTHSIDE REGIONAL MEDICAL CENTER (490067)**, 200 Medical Park Boulevard, Zip 23805–9274; tel. 804/765–5000, **A**1 2 3 10 **F**3 12 13 15 17 18 20 22 24 26 28 29 30 31 34 35 40 43 45 46 47 48 49 50 54 55 56 57 59 60 64 70 72 74 75 76 77 78 79 81 82 85 86 87 91 92 93 96 97 98 101 102 105 107 108 110 111 112 114 115 119 120 121 122 123 124 126 130 131 132 135 146 147 148 154 **P**6 **S** Community Health Systems, Inc., Franklin, TN
Primary Contact: Trent Nobles, Chief Executive Officer
COO: Jerad Hanlon, Chief Operating Officer
CMO: Boyd Wickizer, M.D., Jr Chief Medical Officer
CIO: Eric Synnestvedt, Director Information Technology
CHR: Irene Buskey, Director Human Resources
CNO: Beverly Bzdek Smith, Chief Nursing Officer
Web address: www.srmconline.com
Control: Corporation, Investor–owned (for–profit) **Service:** General medical and surgical

Staffed Beds: 294 **Admissions:** 13244 **Census:** 173 **Outpatient Visits:** 103359 **Births:** 1059 **Total Expense ($000):** 173176 **Payroll Expense ($000):** 68138 **Personnel:** 1173	

PORTSMOUTH—Portsmouth City County

✠ **BON SECOURS MARYVIEW MEDICAL CENTER (490017)**, 3636 High Street, Zip 23707–3270; tel. 757/398–2200, (Total facility includes 120 beds in nursing home–type unit) **A**1 2 3 5 10 **F**3 4 5 11 12 13 15 17 18 20 22 24 26 28 29 30 31 34 35 36 37 38 40 44 45 46 50 51 54 57 59 61 62 63 64 66 67 68 70 71 73 74 75 76 77 78 79 81 82 84 85 86 87 90 91 93 96 97 98 99 100 101 102 103 104 105 106 107 108 110 111 114 115 118 119 121 126 128 129 130 131 132 134 135 143 145 146 147 149 152 153 154 **P**6 **S** Bon Secours Health System, Inc., Marriottsville, MD
Primary Contact: Paul Gaden, Chief Executive Officer
CFO: Ernest C Padden, Chief Financial Officer
CMO: Warren Austin, M.D., Vice President Medical Affairs
CIO: Terri Spence, Chief Information Officer
CHR: Vickie Witcher Humphries, Director Human Resources
CNO: Leana Fox, MSN, Interim Chief Nurse Executive
Web address: www.bonsecourshamptonroads.com
Control: Other not–for–profit (including NFP Corporation) **Service:** General medical and surgical

Staffed Beds: 466 **Admissions:** 11495 **Census:** 256 **Outpatient Visits:** 589550 **Births:** 777 **Total Expense ($000):** 361552 **Payroll Expense ($000):** 127555 **Personnel:** 2177	

✠ **NAVAL MEDICAL CENTER**, 620 John Paul Jones Circle, Zip 23708–2197; tel. 757/953–1980, (Nonreporting) **A**1 2 3 5 **S** Bureau of Medicine and Surgery, Department of the Navy, Falls Church, VA
Primary Contact: Captain Matthew Case, MSC, USN, Executive Officer
CMO: Captain Cynthia J Gantt, Chief of Staff
CIO: Lieutenant Colonel Karen Albany, Chief Information Officer
Web address: www.nmcphc.med.navy.mil/
Control: Navy, Government, federal **Service:** General medical and surgical

Staffed Beds: 274	

PULASKI—Pulaski County

✠ **LEWISGALE HOSPITAL PULASKI (490116)**, 2400 Lee Highway, Zip 24301–2326, Mailing Address: P.O. Box 759, Zip 24301–0759; tel. 540/994–8100, (Nonreporting) **A**1 2 10 **S** HCA Healthcare, Nashville, TN
Primary Contact: Sean Pressman, Chief Executive Officer
CFO: Jeff Kurcab, Chief Financial Officer
CMO: Karanita Ojomo, M.D., Chief of Staff
CIO: Diron Lane, Director Information Systems
CHR: Jana Beckner, Director Human Resources
Web address: www.lewisgale.com/
Control: Corporation, Investor–owned (for–profit) **Service:** General medical and surgical

Staffed Beds: 54	

RESTON—Fairfax County

✠ **RESTON HOSPITAL CENTER (490107)**, 1850 Town Center Parkway, Zip 20190–3219; tel. 703/689–9000, (Nonreporting) **A**1 2 10 **S** HCA Healthcare, Nashville, TN
Primary Contact: John A. Deardorff, President and Chief Executive, Northern Virginia Market
COO: Jane Raymond, Vice President and Chief Operating Officer
CFO: Edward R Stojakovich, Chief Financial Officer
CMO: Walter R Zolkiwsky, M.D., Chief Medical Officer
CIO: Paresh Shah, Director Information Systems
CHR: Lesley Channell, Vice President Human Resources
CNO: Cynthia Glover, R.N., Vice President and Chief Nursing Officer
Web address: www.restonhospital.com
Control: Corporation, Investor–owned (for–profit) **Service:** General medical and surgical

Staffed Beds: 199	

RICHLANDS—Tazewell County

✠ **CLINCH VALLEY MEDICAL CENTER (490060)**, 6801 Governor G C Peery Highway, Zip 24641–2194; tel. 276/596–6000, (Total facility includes 14 beds in nursing home–type unit) **A**1 10 **F**3 12 13 14 15 17 18 20 22 28 29 30 31 34 35 39 40 41 45 49 50 55 56 57 59 64 70 75 76 77 78 79 81 85 86 87 89 90 93 94 97 107 108 110 111 114 115 118 119 120 121 128 129 130 132 134 135 143 144 146 147 148 149 150 154 **S** LifePoint Health, Brentwood, TN
Primary Contact: Peter Mulkey, Chief Executive Officer
COO: Jennifer Coello, Chief Operating Officer
CFO: Jason Schmiedt, Chief Financial Officer
CMO: George Farrell, M.D., Chief Medical Officer
CIO: Chris Perkins, Director Information Services
CHR: John Knowles, Director Human Resources
CNO: Clint Kendall, R.N., Chief Nursing Officer
Web address: www.clinchvalleymedicalcenter.com
Control: Corporation, Investor–owned (for–profit) **Service:** General medical and surgical

Staffed Beds: 111 **Admissions:** 3524 **Census:** 40 **Outpatient Visits:** 98010 **Births:** 290 **Personnel:** 470	

RICHMOND—Henrico County

✠ **BON SECOURS ST. MARY'S HOSPITAL (490059)**, 5801 Bremo Road, Zip 23226–1907; tel. 804/285–2011, (Includes BON SECOURS ST. MARY'S CHILDREN'S SERVICES, 5801 Bremo Road, Richmond, VA, Zip 23226–1907; tel. 804/285–2011) (Nonreporting) **A**1 2 3 5 10 **S** Bon Secours Health System, Inc., Marriottsville, MD
Primary Contact: Francine Barr, R.N., MS, Chief Executive Officer
COO: Francine Barr, R.N., MS, Vice President and Chief Operating Officer
CFO: Stephan F Quiriconi, Chief Financial Officer
CMO: Khiet Trinh, M.D., Chief Medical Officer
CIO: Terri Spence, Chief Information Officer
CHR: Kishah White, Director Human Resources
CNO: Jody A. Bishop, Vice President of Patient Care Services and Chief Nursing Executive
Web address: www.bonsecours.com
Control: Church operated, Nongovernment, not–for–profit **Service:** General medical and surgical

Staffed Beds: 391	

RICHMOND—Richmond City County

✠ **BON SECOURS–RICHMOND COMMUNITY HOSPITAL (490094)**, 1500 North 28th Street, Zip 23223–5396, Mailing Address: P.O. Box 27184, Zip 23261–7184; tel. 804/225–1700, (Nonreporting) **A**1 3 10 **S** Bon Secours Health System, Inc., Marriottsville, MD
Primary Contact: Mark M. Gordon, Chief Executive Officer
CIO: Jeff Burke, Chief Information Officer
CHR: Shelia White, Director Human Resources
Web address: www.bonsecours.com
Control: Church operated, Nongovernment, not–for–profit **Service:** General medical and surgical

Staffed Beds: 85	

★ **CHILDREN'S HOSPITAL OF RICHMOND AT VCU–BROOK ROAD CAMPUS (493302)**, 2924 Brook Road, Zip 23220–1298; tel. 804/321–7474, (Nonreporting) **A**3 5 10 **S** VCU Health System, Richmond, VA
Primary Contact: Elias Neujahr, Chief Executive Officer
CFO: James A Deyarmin, Controller
CMO: Eugene A Monasterio, M.D., Medical Director
CIO: Tim Gibbs, Director of Information Technology, Information Security Officer
CNO: Sharon Darby, R.N., FACHE, Vice President, Clinical Operations
Web address: www.chrichmond.org
Control: Other not–for–profit (including NFP Corporation) **Service:** Children's rehabilitation

Staffed Beds: 36	

✠ ⇑ **CHIPPENHAM HOSPITAL (490112)**, 7101 Jahnke Road, Zip 23225–4044; tel. 804/320–3911, (Includes CHIPPENHAM MEDICAL CENTER, 7101 Jahnke Road, Richmond, VA, Zip 23225; tel. 804/320–3911; JOHNSTON–WILLIS HOSPITAL, 1401 Johnston–Willis Drive, Richmond, VA, Zip 23235; tel. 804/330–2000; Zachary McCluskey, Chief Executive Officer) (Nonreporting) **A**1 2 3 5 10 21 **S** HCA Healthcare, Nashville, TN
Primary Contact: Greg Lowe, Chief Executive Officer
CFO: Lynn Strader, Chief Financial Officer
CMO: Georgean DeBlois, M.D., Chairman Medical Staff
CIO: Tracy Hechler, Healthcare Director Information Services
CHR: Kris Lukish, Human Resources Officer
Web address: www.cjwmedical.com
Control: Corporation, Investor–owned (for–profit) **Service:** General medical and surgical

Staffed Beds: 765	

Many Facility Codes have changed. Please refer to the AHA Guide Code Chart.

VA

RICHMOND—Henrico County

☒ **EMCOMPASS HEALTH REHABILITATION HOSPITAL OF VIRGINIA (493028)**, 5700 Fitzhugh Avenue, Zip 23226–1800; tel. 804/288–5700, **A**1 10 **F**28 29 30 34 35 50 57 59 68 74 75 86 87 90 91 92 93 95 96 97 130 132 148 **P**5 **S** Encompass Health Corporation, Birmingham, AL
Primary Contact: Dan Gaskell, Chief Executive Officer
CMO: Roger Giordano, M.D., Medical Director
CIO: Faye Encke, Director Information Management
CHR: Tonya Ferguson, Director Human Resources
CNO: Michelle Anthony, Chief Nursing Officer
Web address: www.encompasshealth.com
Control: Corporation, Investor–owned (for–profit) **Service**: Rehabilitation

Staffed Beds: 28 **Admissions**: 688 **Census**: 26 **Births**: 0

RICHMOND—Goochland County

HALLMARK YOUTHCARE – RICHMOND, 12800 West Creek Parkway, Zip 23238–1116; tel. 804/784–2200, (Nonreporting)
Primary Contact: Di Hayes, Chief Executive Officer
Web address: www.hallmarkyouthcare.org
Control: State, Government, nonfederal **Service**: Children's hospital psychiatric

Staffed Beds: 78

RICHMOND—Henrico County

☒ **HENRICO DOCTORS' HOSPITAL (490118)**, 1602 Skipwith Road, Zip 23229–5205; tel. 804/289–4500, (Includes HENRICO DOCTORS' HOSPITAL – FOREST, 1602 Skipwith Road, Richmond, VA, Zip 23229–5298; tel. 804/289–4500; HENRICO DOCTORS' HOSPITAL – PARHAM, 7700 East Parham Road, Richmond, VA, Zip 23294–4301; tel. 804/747–5600; David Donaldson, Chief Executive Officer; HENRICO DOCTORS' HOSPITAL – RETREAT CAMPUS, 2621 Grove Avenue, Richmond, VA, Zip 23220–4308; tel. 804/254–5100; William Wagnon, Chief Executive Officer) (Nonreporting) **A**1 2 10 **S** HCA Healthcare, Nashville, TN
Primary Contact: William Wagnon, Chief Executive Officer
COO: Zachary Reed, Chief Operating Officer
CFO: Christopher Denton, Chief Financial Officer
CIO: Daniel Patton, Director Information Systems
CHR: Steven Burgess, Administrator Human Resources
Web address: www.henricodoctorshospital.com
Control: Corporation, Investor–owned (for–profit) **Service**: General medical and surgical

Staffed Beds: 560

RICHMOND—Richmond City County

☒ △ **HUNTER HOLMES MCGUIRE VETERANS AFFAIRS MEDICAL CENTER-RICHMOND**, 1201 Broad Rock Boulevard, Zip 23249–0002; tel. 804/675–5000, (Nonreporting) **A**1 3 5 7 8 **S** Department of Veterans Affairs, Perry Point, MD
Primary Contact: John A. Brandecker, M.P.H., Director
COO: Alan Lombardo, Associate Director
CFO: Tanza Westry, Chief Financial Officer
CMO: Julie Beales, M.D., Chief of Staff
CIO: David Dahlstrand, Chief, OI&T
CHR: Adriana H Hamilton, Chief Human Resources Officer
CNO: Marjorie Lyne, Associate Director for Patient Care Services
Web address: www.richmond.va.gov/
Control: Veterans Affairs, Government, federal **Service**: General medical and surgical

Staffed Beds: 381

RICHMOND—Chesterfield County

JOHNSTON–WILLIS HOSPITAL See Chippenham Hospital, Richmond

RICHMOND—Henrico County

KINDRED HOSPITAL RICHMOND See Vibra Hospital of Richmond

RICHMOND—Richmond City County

☒ **VCU MEDICAL CENTER (490032)**, 1250 East Marshall Street, Zip 23298–5051; Mailing Address: P.O. Box 980510, Zip 23298–0510; tel. 804/828–9000, (Includes CHILDREN'S HOSPITAL OF RICHMOND AT VCU, 1000 East Broad Street, Richmond, VA, Zip 23219–1918, Mailing Address: PO Box 980646, Zip 23298–0646, tel. 804/828–2467; Elias Neujahr, Chief Executive Officer) **A**1 5 8 10 **F**2 3 5 6 8 9 11 12 13 15 16 17 18 19 20 21 22 23 24 25 26 27 28 29 30 31 32 34 35 36 37 38 39 40 41 43 44 45 46 47 48 49 50 51 52 54 55 56 57 58 59 60 61 62 64 65 66 68 70 72 73 74 75 76 78 79 80 81 82 83 84 85 86 87 88 89 90 91 92 93 95 96 97 98 99 100 101 102 103 104 107 108 109 110 111 114 115 116 117 118 119 120 121 123 124 126 129 130 131 132 134 135 136 137 138 139 141 142 143 145 146 147 148 149 150 153 154 **P**6 **S** VCU Health System, Richmond, VA
Primary Contact: Deborah W. Davis, Chief Executive Officer and Vice President Clinical Services
COO: Paul J Wesolowski, Chief Operating Officer
CFO: Melinda Hancock, Chief Financial Officer
CMO: Ron Clark, M.D., Vice President Clinical Activities and Chief Medical Officer
CIO: Susan Steagall, Vice President Information Services
CHR: Maria Curran, Vice President Human Resources
CNO: Deb Zimmermann, R.N., Chief Nursing Officer and Vice President Patient Care Services
Web address: www.vcuhealth.org
Control: Hospital district or authority, Government, nonfederal **Service**: General medical and surgical

Staffed Beds: 802 **Admissions**: 35450 **Census**: 648 **Outpatient Visits**: 820434 **Births**: 2505 **Total Expense ($000)**: 1409887 **Payroll Expense ($000)**: 478683 **Personnel**: 8202

RICHMOND—Henrico County

☒ **VIBRA HOSPITAL OF RICHMOND (492009)**, 2220 Edward Holland Drive, Zip 23230–2519; tel. 804/678–7000, (Nonreporting) **A**1 10 **S** Vibra Healthcare, Mechanicsburg, PA
Primary Contact: Linda Tiemens, Chief Executive Officer
CMO: Gerard Weeden, Chief Medical Officer
CHR: Jonnitra Peeples, Chief Human Resource Officer
CNO: Crystal Richardson, Chief Nursing Officer
Web address: www.vhrichmond.com
Control: Corporation, Investor–owned (for–profit) **Service**: Acute long–term care hospital

Staffed Beds: 60

ROANOKE—Roanoke City County

☒ **CARILION ROANOKE MEMORIAL HOSPITAL (490024)**, 1906 Belleview Avenue Southeast, Zip 24014–1838, Mailing Address: P.O. Box 13367, Zip 24033–3367; tel. 540/981–7000, (Includes CARILION CLINIC CHILDREN'S HOSPITAL, 1906 Belleview Avenue, SE, Roanoke, VA, Zip 24014–1838; tel. 540/981–7000; CARILION ROANOKE COMMUNITY HOSPITAL, 101 Elm Avenue SE, Roanoke, VA, Zip 24013–2230, Mailing Address: P.O. Box 12946, Zip 24029–2946, tel. 540/985–8000; ROANOKE MEMORIAL REHABILITATION CENTER, South Jefferson and McClanahan Streets, Roanoke, VA, Zip 24014, Mailing Address: P.O. Box 13367, Zip 24033, tel. 703/342–4541) **A**1 2 3 5 8 10 13 **F**3 5 7 8 9 11 12 13 15 17 18 19 20 22 24 26 28 29 30 31 32 33 34 35 36 37 38 39 40 41 43 44 45 46 47 48 49 50 51 52 53 54 55 56 57 58 59 60 61 62 63 64 65 66 68 70 71 72 73 74 75 76 77 78 79 81 82 83 84 85 86 87 88 89 90 91 92 93 96 97 98 99 100 101 102 103 104 106 107 108 110 111 113 114 115 116 117 118 119 120 121 123 124 126 129 130 131 132 134 135 143 144 146 147 148 149 **P**6 **S** Carilion Clinic, Roanoke, VA
Primary Contact: Steven C. Arner, President
COO: Steven C. Arner, President
CFO: Donald B Halliwill, Executive Vice President and Chief Financial Officer
CHR: Heather S Shepardson, Vice President Human Resources
CNO: Margaret M. Scheaffel, Chief Nursing Officer
Web address: www.carilionclinic.org
Control: Other not–for–profit (including NFP Corporation) **Service**: General medical and surgical

Staffed Beds: 620 **Admissions**: 38506 **Census**: 562 **Outpatient Visits**: 264064 **Births**: 3011 **Total Expense ($000)**: 1166788 **Payroll Expense ($000)**: 511903 **Personnel**: 6711

VA

ROCKY MOUNT—Franklin County

☒ **CARILION FRANKLIN MEMORIAL HOSPITAL (490089)**, 180 Floyd Avenue,
Zip 24151–1389; tel. 540/483–5277, **A**1 3 10 **F**3 11 15 18 28 29 30 34 35 40
45 50 53 57 59 62 63 65 68 70 75 81 84 85 91 93 96 107 110 115 119 130
132 135 146 149 **P**6 **S** Carilion Clinic, Roanoke, VA
Primary Contact: William D. Jacobsen, FACHE, Administrator and Hospital Vice
President
COO: Steven C. Arner, Executive Vice President of Administration
CFO: Donald B Halliwill, Chief Financial Officer
CMO: Patrice M Weiss, Executive Vice President, Administration
CIO: Robert Keith Perry, Senior Vice President, Chief Information Officer
CHR: Paul C. Hudgins, Senior Vice President
CNO: Margaret M. Scheaffel, Chief Nursing Officer
Web address: www.carilionclinic.org/CFMH
Control: Other not–for–profit (including NFP Corporation) **Service**: General
medical and surgical

Staffed Beds: 14 **Admissions:** 1313 **Census:** 12 **Outpatient Visits:** 39939 **Births:** 0 **Total Expense ($000):** 38279 **Payroll Expense ($000):** 15417 **Personnel:** 246	

SALEM—Salem City County

☒ **LEWIS–GALE MEDICAL CENTER (490048)**, 1900 Electric Road,
Zip 24153–7494; tel. 540/776–4000, (Includes LEWIS–GALE PAVILION, 1902
Braeburn Drive, Salem, VA, Zip 24153–7391; tel. 703/772–2800) (Nonreporting)
A1 2 10 **S** HCA Healthcare, Nashville, TN
Primary Contact: Thomas R. Pentz, Interim Chief Executive Officer
COO: Michael Abbott, Chief Operating Officer
CFO: Angela D Reynolds, Chief Financial Officer
CMO: Joseph Nelson, M.D., President Medical Staff
CIO: Beth Cole, Director Information Services
CHR: Dale Beaudoin, Vice President Human Resources
Web address: www.lewis–gale.com
Control: Corporation, Investor–owned (for–profit) **Service**: General medical and
surgical

Staffed Beds: 521	

☒ **SALEM VETERANS AFFAIRS MEDICAL CENTER**, 1970 Roanoke Boulevard,
Zip 24153–6478; tel. 540/982–2463, (Total facility includes 60 beds in nursing
home–type unit) **A**1 3 5 8 **F**3 4 11 18 20 22 29 30 31 35 36 38 39 40 44 45 46
53 55 56 57 58 59 60 61 63 64 67 70 74 75 77 78 79 80 81 82 83 84 85 86
87 90 92 93 94 96 97 98 100 101 102 104 107 108 111 115 118 119 128
129 130 132 135 146 147 148 149 154 **S** Department of Veterans Affairs, Perry
Point, MD
Primary Contact: Rebecca J. Stackhouse, Medical Center Director
CFO: Codie Walker, Chief Financial Officer
CMO: Anne Hutchins, M.D., Chief of Staff
CIO: Sharon Collins, Chief Information Officer
CHR: Brian Zeman, Chief Human Resources
CNO: Teresa England, R.N., Ph.D., Nurse Executive
Web address: www.salem.va.gov
Control: Veterans Affairs, Government, federal **Service**: General medical and
surgical

Staffed Beds: 212 **Admissions:** 4421 **Census:** 141 **Outpatient Visits:** 464067 **Births:** 0 **Total Expense ($000):** 354294 **Payroll Expense ($000):** 133577 **Personnel:** 1854	

SOUTH BOSTON—Halifax County

★ ⇧ **SENTARA HALIFAX REGIONAL HOSPITAL (490013)**, 2204 Wilborn Avenue,
Zip 24592–1638; tel. 434/517–3100, (Total facility includes 384 beds in nursing
home–type unit) **A**10 21 **F**3 5 11 13 14 15 18 20 22 28 29 30 31 34 35 38 39
40 41 45 46 47 48 50 56 57 59 61 62 63 64 65 68 70 74 75 76 77 78 79 81
82 84 85 86 87 91 92 93 94 96 97 100 101 102 104 107 108 110 111 114
115 118 119 127 128 129 130 131 132 135 141 145 146 147 148 149 153
P7 **S** Sentara Healthcare, Norfolk, VA
Primary Contact: Jason A. Studley, FACHE, President
CFO: Stewart R Nelson, Vice President and Chief Financial Officer
CMO: Said Iskandar, M.D., Chief Medical Officer
CIO: William Zirkle, Manager Information Systems
CHR: Catherine Howard, Director Human Resources
CNO: Patricia F Thomas, Chief Nursing Officer
Web address: www.hrhs.org
Control: Other not–for–profit (including NFP Corporation) **Service**: General
medical and surgical

Staffed Beds: 456 **Admissions:** 4363 **Census:** 403 **Outpatient Visits:** 125118 **Births:** 397 **Total Expense ($000):** 133780 **Payroll Expense ($000):** 53531 **Personnel:** 949	

SOUTH HILL—Mecklenburg County

☒ **VCU HEALTH COMMUNITY MEMORIAL HOSPITAL (490098)**, 125 Buena
Vista Circle, Zip 23970–1431, Mailing Address: P.O. Box 90, Zip 23970–0090;
tel. 434/447–3151, (Total facility includes 110 beds in nursing home–type unit) **A**1
2 10 20 **F**3 11 15 18 28 29 30 31 34 35 40 45 46 49 50 53 54 56 59 62 63
64 65 70 74 75 77 78 79 81 82 84 85 86 87 93 96 97 107 108 110 111 115
118 119 121 123 127 128 130 131 132 133 135 146 147 148 154 **S** VCU
Health System, Richmond, VA
Primary Contact: W Scott. Burnette, Chief Executive Officer
CFO: Kenneth Libby, Vice President Finance
CMO: Manhal Saleeby, M.D., Chief of Staff
CIO: Brian Rock, Director of Information Systems
CHR: Maria Stephens, Director Human Resources, Education and Occupational
Health and Wellness
CNO: Ursula N Butts, FACHE, Vice President of Patient Care Services
Web address: www.cmh–sh.org
Control: Other not–for–profit (including NFP Corporation) **Service**: General
medical and surgical

Staffed Beds: 178 **Admissions:** 3017 **Census:** 133 **Outpatient Visits:** 139961 **Births:** 0 **Total Expense ($000):** 95623 **Payroll Expense ($000):** 38426 **Personnel:** 669	

STAFFORD—Stafford County

☒ **STAFFORD HOSPITAL (490140)**, 101 Hospital Center Boulevard,
Zip 22554–6200; tel. 540/741–9000, **A**1 5 10 **F**3 13 15 18 20 22 26 29 30
31 34 35 36 39 40 44 45 46 47 48 49 50 54 57 58 59 64 70 73 74 75 76
77 78 79 81 84 85 86 87 92 93 96 102 107 108 110 111 115 118 119 120
122 129 130 131 132 135 146 147 148 149 **S** Mary Washington Healthcare,
Fredericksburg, VA
Primary Contact: Michael P. McDermott, M.D., President and Chief Executive
Officer
COO: Thomas Gettinger, Executive Vice President and Chief Operating Officer
CFO: Sean Barden, Executive Vice President and Chief Financial Officer
CMO: Rebecca Bigoney, Executive Vice President and Chief Medical Officer
CIO: Justin K. Box, Senior Vice President and Chief Information Officer
CHR: Kathryn S Wall, Executive Vice President Human Resources and
Organizational Development
CNO: Eileen L Dohmann, R.N., Senior Vice President and Chief Nursing Officer
Web address: www.mwhc.com
Control: Other not–for–profit (including NFP Corporation) **Service**: General
medical and surgical

Staffed Beds: 82 **Admissions:** 4595 **Census:** 43 **Outpatient Visits:** 65403 **Births:** 1177 **Total Expense ($000):** 86785 **Payroll Expense ($000):** 25708 **Personnel:** 357	

STAUNTON—Staunton City County

COMMONWEALTH CENTER FOR CHILDREN AND ADOLESCENTS, 1355
Richmond Road, Zip 24401–9146, Mailing Address: Box 4000, Zip 24402–4000;
tel. 540/332–2100, (Nonreporting) **A**3 5 **S** Virginia Department of Mental Health,
Richmond, VA
Primary Contact: Mary Clare. Smith, Acting Facility Director
Web address: www.ccca.dbhds.virginia.gov
Control: State, Government, nonfederal **Service**: Children's hospital psychiatric

Staffed Beds: 60	

☐ **WESTERN STATE HOSPITAL (494021)**, 103 Valley Center Drive,
Zip 24401–9146, Mailing Address: P.O. Box 2500, Zip 24402–2500;
tel. 540/332–8000, **A**1 3 5 10 **F**3 29 30 34 39 44 50 53 59 65 68 75 77 86
87 97 98 100 101 130 132 135 146 149 154 **S** Virginia Department of Mental
Health, Richmond, VA
Primary Contact: Mary Clare. Smith, Director
CFO: Jon Chapman, Fiscal Officer
CMO: Jonathan Anderson, Medical Director
CIO: Sharon Johnson, Director Health Information Management
CHR: Kimberly Harman, Regional Manager Human Resources
CNO: Diane Pavalonis, Chief Nurse Executive
Web address: www.dbhds.virginia.gov
Control: State, Government, nonfederal **Service**: Psychiatric

Staffed Beds: 246 **Admissions:** 1025 **Census:** 226 **Outpatient Visits:** 0 **Births:** 0 **Total Expense ($000):** 65073 **Payroll Expense ($000):** 33360	

VA

SUFFOLK—Suffolk City County

★ ⇑ **SENTARA OBICI HOSPITAL (490044)**, 2800 Godwin Boulevard, Zip 23434–8038; tel. 757/934–4000, **A**2 3 5 10 21 **F**3 8 11 13 15 18 20 22 28 29 30 31 34 35 36 37 38 39 40 41 44 45 46 47 48 49 50 54 56 57 58 59 60 61 63 64 65 68 70 71 74 75 76 77 78 79 81 82 84 85 86 87 91 92 93 96 97 98 100 107 108 110 111 114 115 118 119 120 121 126 129 130 131 132 135 141 142 145 146 147 148 149 154 **P**6 **S** Sentara Healthcare, Norfolk, VA
Primary Contact: Steve Julian, M.D., President
CFO: Mike Mounie, Director Finance
CMO: Steve Julian, M.D., Vice President Medical Affairs
CIO: Alice Oxton, Director Information Technology
CHR: Deborah Ferguson, Human Resources Consultant
Web address: www.sentara.com
Control: Other not–for–profit (including NFP Corporation) **Service:** General medical and surgical

Staffed Beds: 178 **Admissions:** 9977 **Census:** 115 **Outpatient Visits:** 355836 **Births:** 1373 **Total Expense ($000):** 191729 **Payroll Expense ($000):** 82799 **Personnel:** 1213

TAPPAHANNOCK—Essex County

⇑ **RIVERSIDE TAPPAHANNOCK HOSPITAL (490084)**, 618 Hospital Road, Zip 22560–5000; tel. 804/443–3311, **A**10 20 21 **F**3 11 15 18 26 29 30 31 34 35 36 37 38 40 44 45 46 47 48 52 55 56 57 59 60 62 63 64 70 74 75 77 78 79 81 82 84 85 86 87 91 92 93 97 100 102 103 107 108 110 111 115 116 117 118 119 129 130 131 132 133 135 144 146 147 148 **P**6 **S** Riverside Health System, Newport News, VA
Primary Contact: Esther Muscari. Desimini, Administrator
CFO: Jeri Sibley, Director Revenue Cycle
CMO: Richard Dunn, M.D., Chief Medical Officer
CHR: Lindsey Custer, Director Human Resources
CNO: Judith Matthews, Nurse Executive
Web address: www.riverside–online.com
Control: Other not–for–profit (including NFP Corporation) **Service:** General medical and surgical

Staffed Beds: 18 **Admissions:** 1854 **Census:** 17 **Outpatient Visits:** 28723 **Births:** 0 **Total Expense ($000):** 52059 **Payroll Expense ($000):** 16551 **Personnel:** 227

TAZEWELL—Tazewell County

✠ **CARILION TAZEWELL COMMUNITY HOSPITAL (490117)**, 141 Ben Bolt Avenue, Zip 24651–9700, Mailing Address: 388 Ben Bolt Avenue, Zip 24651; tel. 276/988–8700, **A**1 10 **F**3 11 15 29 30 34 40 44 45 50 57 59 62 64 65 68 75 77 85 87 91 93 107 111 114 119 133 135 146 149 **P**6 **S** Carilion Clinic, Roanoke, VA
Primary Contact: Kathren Dowdy, MSN, Regional Hospital Senior Director
CMO: Kevin Combs, Chief of Staff
CHR: Carrie Boggess, Human Resources Generalist
CNO: Kathren Dowdy, MSN, Senior Director, Chief Executive Officer and Chief Nursing Officer
Web address: www.carilionclinic.org
Control: Other not–for–profit (including NFP Corporation) **Service:** General medical and surgical

Staffed Beds: 5 **Admissions:** 567 **Census:** 6 **Outpatient Visits:** 14930 **Births:** 0 **Total Expense ($000):** 14753 **Payroll Expense ($000):** 5518 **Personnel:** 102

VIRGINIA BEACH—Virginia Beach City County

★ ⇑ **SENTARA PRINCESS ANNE HOSPITAL (490119)**, 2025 Glenn Mitchell Drive, Zip 23456–0178; tel. 757/507–1000, **A**2 3 5 10 21 **F**3 8 11 13 15 18 20 22 26 28 29 30 31 34 35 36 37 38 39 40 41 44 45 46 47 49 50 53 54 55 56 57 58 59 60 61 63 64 65 68 70 71 74 75 76 77 78 79 81 82 84 85 86 87 91 92 93 94 96 97 100 102 107 108 110 111 114 115 118 119 126 129 130 131 132 135 141 146 147 148 149 154 **P**6 **S** Sentara Healthcare, Norfolk, VA
Primary Contact: Thomas B. Thames, M.D., President
COO: Howard P Kern, Chief Operating Officer
CFO: Robert Broermann, Senior Vice President and Chief Financial Officer
CMO: Terry Gilliland, M.D., Senior Vice President and Chief Medical Officer
CIO: Bert Reese, Chief Information Officer
CHR: Michael V Taylor, Vice President Human Resources
CNO: Grace Myers, MSN, Vice President, Nurse Executive
Web address: www.sentara.com
Control: Other not–for–profit (including NFP Corporation) **Service:** General medical and surgical

Staffed Beds: 160 **Admissions:** 12156 **Census:** 140 **Outpatient Visits:** 381714 **Births:** 2473 **Total Expense ($000):** 215701 **Payroll Expense ($000):** 71725 **Personnel:** 1436

★ ⇑ **SENTARA VIRGINIA BEACH GENERAL HOSPITAL (490057)**, 1060 First Colonial Road, Zip 23454–3002; tel. 757/395–8000, **A**2 3 5 10 21 **F**3 11 15 17 18 20 22 24 26 28 29 30 31 33 34 35 36 37 38 39 40 41 43 44 45 46 47 48 49 50 51 53 54 55 56 57 58 59 60 61 63 64 65 68 70 71 74 75 77 78 79 81 82 84 85 86 87 90 91 92 93 94 96 97 98 100 101 102 107 108 110 111 114 115 118 119 120 121 123 126 131 132 135 141 142 145 146 147 148 149 154 **P**6 **S** Sentara Healthcare, Norfolk, VA
Primary Contact: Elwood Bernard. Boone III, FACHE, President
CFO: Marley Nacey, Director Finance
CHR: Michelle Meekins, Manager Human Resources
CNO: Peggy Braun, R.N., Vice President Patient Care Services and Chief Nurse Executive
Web address: www.sentara.com
Control: Other not–for–profit (including NFP Corporation) **Service:** General medical and surgical

Staffed Beds: 259 **Admissions:** 14320 **Census:** 203 **Outpatient Visits:** 444245 **Births:** 0 **Total Expense ($000):** 266189 **Payroll Expense ($000):** 116603 **Personnel:** 1749

☐ **VIRGINIA BEACH PSYCHIATRIC CENTER (494025)**, 1100 First Colonial Road, Zip 23454–2403; tel. 757/496–6000, (Nonreporting) **A**1 10 **S** Universal Health Services, Inc., King of Prussia, PA
Primary Contact: Jennifer Kelly, Chief Executive Officer
Web address: www.vbpcweb.com
Control: Corporation, Investor–owned (for–profit) **Service:** Psychiatric

Staffed Beds: 100

WARRENTON—Fauquier County

✠ △ **FAUQUIER HOSPITAL (490023)**, 500 Hospital Drive, Zip 20186–3099; tel. 540/316–5000, (Nonreporting) **A**1 2 5 7 10 **S** LifePoint Health, Brentwood, TN
Primary Contact: Chad Melton, Chief Executive Officer
CFO: Lionel J Phillips, Vice President Financial Services
CIO: Donna Staton, Chief Information Officer
CHR: Katy Reeves, Vice President Human Resources
CNO: Linda Sharkey, R.N., MSN, Vice President Patient Care Services and Chief Nurse Executive
Web address: www.fauquierhealth.org/
Control: Other not–for–profit (including NFP Corporation) **Service:** General medical and surgical

Staffed Beds: 86

WILLIAMSBURG—James City County

☐ **EASTERN STATE HOSPITAL (490109)**, 4601 Ironbound Road, Zip 23188–2652; tel. 757/253–5161, (Nonreporting) **A**1 3 5 10 **S** Virginia Department of Mental Health, Richmond, VA
Primary Contact: John M. Favret, Director
CFO: E Clifford Love, Director Fiscal Services
CMO: Guillermo Schrader, M.D., Acting Medical Director
CIO: Barbara Lambert, Director Healthcare Compliance
CHR: Edie Rogan, Manager Human Resources
Web address: www.esh.dmhmrsas.virginia.gov/
Control: State, Government, nonfederal **Service:** Psychiatric

Staffed Beds: 300

☐ ⇑ **RIVERSIDE DOCTORS' HOSPITAL WILLIAMSBURG (490143)**, 1500 Commonwealth Avenue, Zip 23185–5229; tel. 757/585–2200, **A**1 3 10 21 **F**3 11 28 29 34 35 40 44 45 50 57 59 64 70 74 75 77 79 81 82 85 86 87 91 92 107 108 115 118 119 120 121 123 130 132 146 148 149 **P**6 **S** Riverside Health System, Newport News, VA
Primary Contact: Steve C. McCary, Administrator
CNO: Arlene Messina, R.N., MSN, Director of Nursing
Web address: www.riversideonline.com/rdhw
Control: Other not–for–profit (including NFP Corporation) **Service:** General medical and surgical

Staffed Beds: 14 **Admissions:** 1678 **Census:** 14 **Outpatient Visits:** 24559 **Births:** 0 **Total Expense ($000):** 39260 **Payroll Expense ($000):** 12079 **Personnel:** 250

VA

Hospital, Medicare Provider Number, Address, Telephone, Approval, Facility, and Physician Codes, Health Care System

★ American Hospital Association (AHA) membership
☐ The Joint Commission accreditation
○ Healthcare Facilities Accreditation Program
◇ DNV Healthcare Inc. accreditation
⇑ Center for Improvement in Healthcare Quality Accreditation
△ Commission on Accreditation of Rehabilitation Facilities (CARF) accreditation

WILLIAMSBURG—York County

★ ⇑ **SENTARA WILLIAMSBURG REGIONAL MEDICAL CENTER (490066)**, 100 Sentara Circle, Zip 23188–5713; tel. 757/984–6000, **A**2 10 21 **F**3 8 11 13 15 18 20 22 28 29 30 31 34 35 36 37 38 39 40 41 43 44 45 46 47 48 49 50 51 54 55 56 57 58 59 60 61 63 64 65 68 70 74 75 76 77 78 79 81 82 84 85 86 87 89 90 91 92 93 94 96 97 100 102 107 108 110 111 114 115 118 119 126 129 130 131 132 135 141 142 146 147 148 149 154 **P**6 **S** Sentara Healthcare, Norfolk, VA
Primary Contact: David J. Masterson, President
CFO: Andreas Roehrle, Director Finance
CMO: Joe Robbins, M.D., Vice President Medical Affairs
CIO: Mike Freeman, Director Information Technology
CHR: Lois B Demerich, Director Human Resources
CNO: Donna Wilmoth, Vice President Patient Care Services and Chief Nursing Officer
Web address: www.sentara.com
Control: Other not–for–profit (including NFP Corporation) **Service**: General medical and surgical

Staffed Beds: 145 **Admissions:** 7515 **Census:** 85 **Outpatient Visits:** 291574 **Births:** 905 **Total Expense ($000):** 157860 **Payroll Expense ($000):** 66152 **Personnel:** 925

☐ **THE PAVILION AT WILLIAMSBURG PLACE (494032)**, 5483 Mooretown Road, Zip 23188–2108; tel. 757/565–0106, **A**1 10 **F**98 100 101 102 103 128
Primary Contact: Shirley Repta, Chief Executive Officer
CMO: Avtar Dhilion, Medical Director
CNO: Shedale Tindall, Chief Nursing Officer
Web address: www.pavilionwp.com
Control: Corporation, Investor–owned (for–profit) **Service**: Psychiatric

Staffed Beds: 66 **Admissions:** 1959 **Census:** 53 **Outpatient Visits:** 0 **Births:** 0

WINCHESTER—Winchester City County

⊠ **WINCHESTER MEDICAL CENTER (490005)**, 1840 Amherst Street, Zip 22601–2808, Mailing Address: P.O. Box 3340, Zip 22604–2540; tel. 540/536–8000, **A**1 2 3 5 10 20 **F**3 5 11 12 13 15 17 18 20 22 24 26 28 29 30 31 32 34 35 38 39 40 41 43 44 45 46 47 49 50 51 54 55 56 57 58 59 61 62 64 65 66 68 70 71 72 74 75 76 77 78 79 80 81 82 84 85 86 87 89 90 91 92 93 97 98 100 101 102 103 104 107 108 110 111 114 115 116 117 118 119 120 121 123 124 126 129 130 131 132 135 136 146 147 148 153 154 **P**5 **S** Valley Health System, Winchester, VA
Primary Contact: Grady W. Philips III, President
CFO: Robert Amos, Vice President and Chief Financial Officer
CMO: Nicolas Restrepo, M.D., Vice President Medical Affairs
CIO: Joan Roscoe, Chief Information Officer
CHR: Elizabeth Savage, Senior Vice President and Chief Human Resource Officer and Vice President Community Health and Wellness
CNO: Anne Whiteside, Vice President Nursing
Web address: www.valleyhealthlink.com/WMC
Control: Other not–for–profit (including NFP Corporation) **Service**: General medical and surgical

Staffed Beds: 485 **Admissions:** 22672 **Census:** 331 **Outpatient Visits:** 392637 **Births:** 2150 **Total Expense ($000):** 477167 **Payroll Expense ($000):** 182834 **Personnel:** 2638

WOODBRIDGE—Prince William County

★ ⇑ **SENTARA NORTHERN VIRGINIA MEDICAL CENTER (490113)**, 2300 Opitz Boulevard, Zip 22191–3399; tel. 703/523–1000, **A**2 10 21 **F**3 8 11 12 13 15 18 20 22 26 28 29 30 31 34 35 40 41 44 45 49 50 54 55 56 57 59 60 61 62 63 64 65 68 70 71 72 74 75 76 77 78 79 81 82 85 86 87 91 92 93 94 96 102 107 108 110 111 114 115 118 119 121 126 130 131 132 135 141 143 145 146 147 148 149 154 **P**6 **S** Sentara Healthcare, Norfolk, VA
Primary Contact: Katherine Johnson, Ph.D., President
CMO: David M Schwartz, D.O., Vice President, Medical Affairs
CIO: Thomas Ewing, Director Information Technology
CHR: Brett Willsie, Vice President Human Resources
CNO: Valerie E Keane, FACHE, Chief Nursing Executive
Web address: www.sentara.com/northernvirginia
Control: Other not–for–profit (including NFP Corporation) **Service**: General medical and surgical

Staffed Beds: 183 **Admissions:** 10168 **Census:** 120 **Outpatient Visits:** 323818 **Births:** 1537 **Total Expense ($000):** 231875 **Payroll Expense ($000):** 72274 **Personnel:** 1103

WOODSTOCK—Shenandoah County

⊠ **VALLEY HEALTH SHENANDOAH MEMORIAL HOSPITAL (491305)**, 759 South Main Street, Zip 22664–1127; tel. 540/459–1100, **A**1 10 18 **F**3 11 15 28 29 30 35 40 45 50 53 57 59 64 65 68 69 70 75 77 79 81 82 87 92 93 97 107 108 110 114 118 119 127 130 132 133 135 146 148 153 154 **S** Valley Health System, Winchester, VA
Primary Contact: N Travis. Clark, President
CFO: Phillip Graybeal, CPA, Vice President, Finance
CMO: Greg Byrd, Vice President Medical Affairs
CIO: James Burton, Vice President and Chief Information Officer, Valley Health
CHR: Abbey Rembold, Manager, Human Resource Business Partnerships
CNO: Lisa Heishman, R.N., Vice President
Web address: www.valleyhealthlink.com/shenandoah
Control: Other not–for–profit (including NFP Corporation) **Service**: General medical and surgical

Staffed Beds: 25 **Admissions:** 1542 **Census:** 15 **Outpatient Visits:** 99113 **Births:** 0 **Total Expense ($000):** 50545 **Payroll Expense ($000):** 24682 **Personnel:** 322

WYTHEVILLE—Wythe County

⊠ **WYTHE COUNTY COMMUNITY HOSPITAL (490111)**, 600 West Ridge Road, Zip 24382–1099; tel. 276/228–0200, **A**1 10 20 **F**3 13 15 18 26 28 29 32 34 35 37 40 45 50 51 55 57 59 62 63 64 65 68 70 75 76 77 79 81 82 84 85 86 87 91 92 93 107 110 111 114 119 128 129 131 132 133 135 146 147 148 **S** LifePoint Health, Brentwood, TN
Primary Contact: Joseph Wilkins, Chief Executive Officer
COO: Adam Martin, Chief Operating Officer
CFO: John D White, Chief Financial Officer
CMO: George Farrell, M.D., Chief of Staff
CIO: Andrea Harless, Director Information Services
CHR: Kristie E Walker, M.P.H., Director of Human Resources
CNO: Theresa Dix, R.N., Chief Nursing Officer
Web address: www.wcchcares.com
Control: Corporation, Investor–owned (for–profit) **Service**: General medical and surgical

Staffed Beds: 70 **Admissions:** 2308 **Census:** 23 **Outpatient Visits:** 62737 **Births:** 358 **Total Expense ($000):** 39553 **Payroll Expense ($000):** 14865 **Personnel:** 254

VA

Many Facility Codes have changed. Please refer to the AHA Guide Code Chart. © 2018 AHA Guide

WASHINGTON

ABERDEEN—Grays Harbor County

GRAYS HARBOR COMMUNITY HOSPITAL (500031), 915 Anderson Drive,
Zip 98520–1006; tel. 360/532–8330, (Nonreporting) **A**1 10 20
Primary Contact: Tom Jensen, Chief Executive Officer
CMO: Anne Marie Wong, M.D., Chief Medical Officer
CIO: Brad Wallace, Director Information Services
CHR: Julie Feller, Executive Director Human Resources
CNO: Melanie Brandt Esq Chief Nursing Officer
Web address: www.ghcares.org
Control: Other not–for–profit (including NFP Corporation) **Service**: General
medical and surgical

Staffed Beds: 105

ANACORTES—Skagit County

ISLAND HOSPITAL (500007), 1211 24th Street, Zip 98221–2562;
tel. 360/299–1300, **A**2 10 21 **F**3 8 11 13 15 28 29 30 31 34 35 40 43 45 50
53 57 59 64 70 75 76 77 78 79 81 82 85 86 89 93 96 97 99 100 104 107
108 110 111 114 115 116 119 127 129 130 132 134 135 144 146 147 148
149 **P**6
Primary Contact: Vincent Oliver, FACHE, Administrator
CFO: Elise Cutter, Chief Financial Officer
CIO: Tom Bluhm, Director Information Systems
CNO: Lois Pate, R.N., Chief Nursing Officer
Web address: www.islandhospital.org
Control: Hospital district or authority, Government, nonfederal **Service**: General
medical and surgical

Staffed Beds: 43 **Admissions:** 3011 **Census:** 25 **Outpatient Visits:** 171287
Births: 479 **Total Expense ($000):** 97198 **Payroll Expense ($000):** 42567
Personnel: 591

ARLINGTON—Snohomish County

CASCADE VALLEY HOSPITAL (500060), 330 South Stillaguamish Avenue,
Zip 98223–1642; tel. 360/435–2133, (Nonreporting) **A**10 21 **S** Skagit Regional
Health, Mount Vernon, WA
Primary Contact: Brian K. Ivie, President and Chief Executive Officer
COO: Jim Geist, Executive Vice President and Chief Operating Officer
CFO: Thomas Litaker, Regional Vice President and Chief Financial Officer
CMO: Rosana Go, M.D., Medical Staff President
CHR: Deborah Martin, Regional Vice President Human Resources
CNO: Michelle Sand, R.N., MSN, Vice President and Chief Nursing Officer
Web address: www.cascadevalley.org
Control: Hospital district or authority, Government, nonfederal **Service**: General
medical and surgical

Staffed Beds: 48

AUBURN—King County

MULTICARE AUBURN MEDICAL CENTER (500015), 202 North Division, Plaza
One, Zip 98001–4908; tel. 253/833–7711, **A**1 7 10 **F**3 13 18 20 22 28 29 30
34 35 40 41 43 45 49 51 57 64 65 68 70 73 74 75 76 77 79 81 84 85 87 93
96 98 102 103 107 108 111 114 115 119 126 129 130 132 135 146 147 148
149 **S** MultiCare Health System, Tacoma, WA
Primary Contact: Mark T. Smith, JD, CPA, President and Chief Operating Officer
CMO: Chad Krilich, M.D., Chief Med Officer–AMC/CMC
CHR: Kevin B Dull, Senior Vice President Human Potential
CNO: Roseanna Bell, Chief Nurse Executive
Web address: www.multicare.org/auburn–medical–center/
Control: Other not–for–profit (including NFP Corporation) **Service**: General
medical and surgical

Staffed Beds: 153 **Admissions:** 6962 **Census:** 107 **Outpatient Visits:**
67410 **Births:** 1217 **Total Expense ($000):** 184353 **Payroll Expense
($000):** 73942 **Personnel:** 804

BELLEVUE—King County

OVERLAKE MEDICAL CENTER (500051), 1035 116th Avenue NE,
Zip 98004–4604; tel. 425/688–5000, **A**1 2 3 10 **F**3 11 12 13 15 17 18 20 22
24 26 29 30 31 34 35 36 37 38 39 40 41 43 44 45 46 47 48 49 54 55 56 57
58 59 61 64 65 68 70 72 73 74 75 76 77 78 79 81 82 84 85 86 87 92 93 97
98 100 101 102 103 104 105 107 108 110 111 114 115 116 117 118 119
120 121 123 124 126 130 131 132 134 135 144 145 146 147 148 149 153
154 **P**6
Primary Contact: J. Michael. Marsh, President and Chief Executive Officer
COO: Thomas DeBord, Chief Operating Officer
CFO: Andrew Tokar, Chief Financial Officer
CMO: David Knoepfler, M.D., Chief Medical Officer
CHR: Lisa M Brock, Chief Human Resource Officer
CNO: Julie Clayton, Chief Nursing Officer and Vice President Patient Care Services
Web address: www.overlakehospital.org
Control: Other not–for–profit (including NFP Corporation) **Service**: General
medical and surgical

Staffed Beds: 282 **Admissions:** 18232 **Census:** 184 **Outpatient Visits:**
239226 **Births:** 3805 **Total Expense ($000):** 513218 **Payroll Expense
($000):** 219178 **Personnel:** 2166

BELLINGHAM—Whatcom County

PEACEHEALTH ST. JOSEPH MEDICAL CENTER (500030), 2901 Squalicum
Parkway, Zip 98225–1851; tel. 360/734–5400, **A**2 5 7 10 20 21 **F**3 11 13 18
20 22 24 26 28 29 30 31 34 35 36 39 40 43 45 47 48 49 50 51 57 58 59
63 64 68 70 73 75 76 77 81 83 85 87 89 90 93 96 98 100 102 107 108 111
115 119 120 121 123 124 126 130 132 146 148 149 154 **P**6 **S** PeaceHealth,
Vancouver, WA
Primary Contact: Dale Zender, President Hospital Services NW
COO: Stephen R Omta, Chief Operating Officer
CFO: Eric Brettner, NWN Chief Financial Officer
CMO: Chris Sprowl, M.D., Vice President
CIO: Kelly Lundy, Chief Information Officer
CHR: Cindy C Klein, Vice President Human Resources
Web address: www.peacehealth.org
Control: Other not–for–profit (including NFP Corporation) **Service**: General
medical and surgical

Staffed Beds: 225 **Admissions:** 14999 **Census:** 188 **Outpatient Visits:**
95148 **Total Expense ($000):** 504655 **Payroll Expense ($000):** 195860
Personnel: 2011

ST. JOSEPH HOSPITAL See Peacehealth St. Joseph Medical Center

BREMERTON—Kitsap County

HARRISON MEDICAL CENTER (500039), 2520 Cherry Avenue,
Zip 98310–4229; tel. 360/744–3911, **A**1 2 10 **F**3 11 12 13 15 18 20 22 24
26 28 29 30 31 34 35 38 40 43 44 45 46 49 50 54 57 59 64 70 73 74 75
76 77 78 79 80 81 82 84 85 86 87 93 94 96 107 108 110 111 114 115 117
119 121 124 126 129 130 132 135 144 146 147 148 149 154 **S** Catholic
Health Initiatives, Englewood, CO
Primary Contact: David W. Schultz, FACHE, President, Peninsula Region
COO: Matthew Wheelus, Vice President, Chief Operating Officer
CFO: Mike Fitzgerald, Chief Financial Officer
CMO: David Weiss, M.D., Vice President, Medical Operations, Peninsula Region
CIO: Rand Strobel, Regional Chief Information Officer, Information Technology
Services
CHR: Vickie Lackman, Human Resource Director, Peninsula Region
CNO: Jeanell Rasmussen, R.N., Vice President Patient Care Services and Chief
Nursing Officer
Web address: www.chifranciscan.org/harrison
Control: Church operated, Nongovernment, not–for–profit **Service**: General
medical and surgical

Staffed Beds: 260 **Admissions:** 12972 **Census:** 153 **Outpatient Visits:**
309051 **Births:** 2050 **Total Expense ($000):** 402454 **Payroll Expense
($000):** 119392 **Personnel:** 2098

WA

NAVAL HOSPITAL BREMERTON, One Boone Road, Zip 98312–1898; tel. 360/475–4000, (Nonreporting) **A**1 3 5 **S** Bureau of Medicine and Surgery, Department of the Navy, Falls Church, VA
Primary Contact: Captain Jeffrey Bitterman, Commanding Officer
CFO: Judith Hogan, Comptroller and Director Resources and Logistics
CIO: Patrick Flaherty, Director Management Information
Web address: www.med.navy.mil/sites/nhbrem/Pages/default.aspx
Control: Navy, Government, federal **Service:** General medical and surgical

Staffed Beds: 23

BREWSTER—Okanogan County

THREE RIVERS HOSPITAL (501324), 507 Hospital Way, Zip 98812–0577, Mailing Address: P.O. Box 577, Zip 98812–0577; tel. 509/689–2517, (Nonreporting) **A**10 18
Primary Contact: Scott Graham, Chief Executive Officer
CFO: Jennifer Munson, Chief Financial Officer
CMO: Gordon Tagge, M.D., President Medical Staff
CIO: Edgar Alejandro Arellano, Chief Information Technologist
CHR: Anita Fisk, Director Human Resources
CNO: Gretchen Aguilar, Director Patient Care and Chief Nursing Officer
Web address: www.threerivershospital.net
Control: Hospital district or authority, Government, nonfederal **Service:** General medical and surgical

Staffed Beds: 20

BURIEN—King County

HIGHLINE MEDICAL CENTER (500011), 16251 Sylvester Road SW, Zip 98166–3052; tel. 206/244–9970, **A**1 2 7 10 **F**3 8 11 13 15 18 29 30 34 35 38 40 43 44 45 49 50 51 57 59 70 72 74 75 76 79 80 81 85 86 87 92 93 107 108 110 111 114 115 117 119 130 132 135 146 147 149 **S** Catholic Health Initiatives, Englewood, CO
Primary Contact: Anthony McLean, President
COO: Russell Woolley, Chief Operating Officer
CMO: Dennis De Leon, M.D., Associate Chief Medical Officer and Vice President Medical Affairs
CHR: Sharon Royne, Senior Vice President: Human Resources
CNO: Kim Baisch, R.N., Associate Vice President Patient Care Services
Web address: www.chifranciscan.org/highline–medical–center.html
Control: Church operated, Nongovernment, not–for–profit **Service:** General medical and surgical

Staffed Beds: 128 Admissions: 7064 Census: 84 Outpatient Visits: 116575 Births: 952 Total Expense ($000): 188717 Payroll Expense ($000): 64431 Personnel: 781

REGIONAL HOSPITAL FOR RESPIRATORY AND COMPLEX CARE (502001), 16251 Sylvester Road SW, Zip 98166–3017; tel. 206/248–4548, **A**1 10 **F**1 29 30 44 50 75 85 87 130 135 148 149 154 **S** Catholic Health Initiatives, Englewood, CO
Primary Contact: Anne McBride, Chief Executive Officer
CMO: Embra Roper, Chief Medical Officer
CHR: Valerie Albano, Director, Human Resources
CNO: Christi Sifri, Chief Nursing Officer
Web address: www.regionalhospital.org
Control: Church operated, Nongovernment, not–for–profit **Service:** Acute long–term care hospital

Staffed Beds: 26 Admissions: 195 Census: 18 Outpatient Visits: 0 Births: 0 Total Expense ($000): 16531 Payroll Expense ($000): 7085 Personnel: 76

CENTRALIA—Lewis County

PROVIDENCE CENTRALIA HOSPITAL (500019), 914 S Scheuber RD, Zip 98531–9027, Mailing Address: 914 South Scheuber Road, Zip 98531–9027; tel. 360/736–2803, **A**1 3 10 20 **F**3 8 11 13 15 29 30 31 34 35 40 43 50 51 57 58 59 64 68 70 75 76 77 78 79 80 81 82 84 85 86 87 93 107 108 110 111 114 115 116 117 118 119 120 121 123 124 130 132 146 148 149 150 154 **S** Providence St. Joseph Health, Renton, WA
Primary Contact: Medrice Coluccio, R.N., Southwest Region Chief Executive
CFO: Denise Marroni, Chief Financial Officer
CMO: Kevin Caserta, M.D., Chief Medical Officer
CIO: Kerry Miles, Site Director
CHR: Susan Meenk, Vice President Service Area
CNO: Michelle James, Regional Chief Nursing Officer
Web address: www.providence.org
Control: Church operated, Nongovernment, not–for–profit **Service:** General medical and surgical

Staffed Beds: 91 Admissions: 4943 Census: 51 Outpatient Visits: 258464 Births: 676 Total Expense ($000): 104382 Payroll Expense ($000): 51779 Personnel: 634

CHELAN—Chelan County

LAKE CHELAN COMMUNITY HOSPITAL AND CLINICS (501334), 503 East Highland Avenue, Zip 98816–8631, Mailing Address: P.O. Box 908, Zip 98816–0908; tel. 509/682–3300, **A**3 10 18 **F**5 7 8 11 13 15 29 30 32 34 35 36 38 40 41 43 44 45 50 56 57 59 63 64 65 66 68 71 74 75 76 77 79 80 81 82 84 85 86 87 91 92 93 94 97 100 101 104 107 110 111 119 127 130 131 132 133 134 135 143 144 146 147 149 154 **P**6
Primary Contact: Steven D. Patonai, Interim Chief Executive Officer
COO: Brad Hankins, Chief Operating Quality Officer
CFO: Vickie Bodle, Chief Financial Officer
CMO: Ty Witt, M.D., Chief Medical Officer
CIO: Ross Hurd, Chief Information Officer
CHR: DeLynn K Barnett, Director Human Resources
Web address: www.lakechelancommunityhospital.com
Control: Hospital district or authority, Government, nonfederal **Service:** General medical and surgical

Staffed Beds: 25 Admissions: 767 Census: 17 Outpatient Visits: 26981 Births: 96 Total Expense ($000): 27618 Payroll Expense ($000): 16508 Personnel: 245

CHEWELAH—Stevens County

PROVIDENCE ST. JOSEPH'S HOSPITAL (501309), 500 East Webster Street, Zip 99109–9523; tel. 509/935–8211, (Total facility includes 40 beds in nursing home–type unit) **A**1 10 18 **F**3 8 10 11 15 29 30 34 35 40 43 44 45 57 59 65 75 79 81 82 84 87 91 93 107 114 119 128 133 146 148 **P**6 **S** Providence St. Joseph Health, Renton, WA
Primary Contact: Ronald G. Rehn, Chief Executive Officer
CFO: Helen Andrus, Chief Financial Officer
CMO: Jeff Collins, Chief Medical Officer
CNO: Deborah Watson, R.N., Chief Nursing Officer
Web address: www.washington.providence.org/hospitals/st–josephs–hospital/
Control: Church operated, Nongovernment, not–for–profit **Service:** General medical and surgical

Staffed Beds: 55 Admissions: 549 Census: 48 Outpatient Visits: 27141 Births: 0 Total Expense ($000): 22519 Payroll Expense ($000): 9759 Personnel: 115

CLARKSTON—Asotin County

TRI–STATE MEMORIAL HOSPITAL (501332), 1221 Highland Avenue, Zip 99403–2829, Mailing Address: P.O. Box 189, Zip 99403–0189; tel. 509/758–5511, (Nonreporting) **A**10 18 21
Primary Contact: Donald Wee, Chief Executive Officer
CFO: Alex Town, Vice President Finance
CMO: Don Greggain, M.D., Physician Network Director
CIO: Joleen Carper, Vice President Quality and Risk
CHR: Regana Davis, Vice President Human Resources
CNO: Rhonda Mason, Vice President of Patient Care Services
Web address: www.tsmh.org
Control: Other not–for–profit (including NFP Corporation) **Service:** General medical and surgical

Staffed Beds: 25

COLFAX—Whitman County

WHITMAN HOSPITAL AND MEDICAL CENTER (501327), 1200 West Fairview Street, Zip 99111–9579; tel. 509/397–3435, **A**10 18 **F**3 13 15 29 34 35 36 40 43 45 53 68 75 76 79 81 84 85 93 107 110 111 119 130 133 149 154 **P**5 6 **S** Providence St. Joseph Health, Renton, WA
Primary Contact: Hank Hanigan, FACHE, Chief Executive Officer
CFO: Hank Hanigan, FACHE, Interim Chief Financial Officer
CMO: Bryan N Johnson, M.D., Chief Medical Officer
CHR: Michelle Ellis, Director Human Resources
CNO: Pam Akin, R.N., MSN, Chief Nursing Officer
Web address: www.whitmanhospital.org
Control: Hospital district or authority, Government, nonfederal **Service:** General medical and surgical

Staffed Beds: 25 Admissions: 455 Census: 4 Outpatient Visits: 17948 Births: 33 Total Expense ($000): 28768 Payroll Expense ($000): 11009 Personnel: 148

COLVILLE—Stevens County

PROVIDENCE MOUNT CARMEL HOSPITAL (501326), 982 East Columbia Avenue, Zip 99114–3352; tel. 509/685–5100, **A**1 3 10 18 **F**3 11 13 15 29 30 34 40 43 44 45 57 59 64 70 75 76 77 79 81 82 84 85 86 87 93 107 108 115 118 119 123 129 131 132 133 135 146 148 **P**6 **S** Providence St. Joseph Health, Renton, WA
Primary Contact: Ronald G. Rehn, Chief Executive Officer
CFO: Helen Andrus, Chief Financial Officer
CNO: Deborah Watson, R.N., Chief Nursing Officer
Web address: www.mtcarmelhospital.org
Control: Church operated, Nongovernment, not–for–profit **Service:** General medical and surgical

Staffed Beds: 25 Admissions: 1206 Census: 15 Outpatient Visits: 74079 Births: 213 Total Expense ($000): 47801 Payroll Expense ($000): 16171 Personnel: 242

WA

Many Facility Codes have changed. Please refer to the AHA Guide Code Chart.
© 2018 AHA Guide

COUPEVILLE—Island County

WHIDBEYHEALTH (501339), 101 North Main Street, Zip 98239–3413;
tel. 360/678–5151, (Nonreporting) **A**2 10 18
Primary Contact: Geri Forbes, Chief Executive Officer
CMO: Gabe Barrio, M.D., Chief of Staff
CNO: Linda Stephens Gipson, MSN, Ph.D., Chief Nursing Officer
Web address: www.whidbeygen.org
Control: Hospital district or authority, Government, nonfederal **Service:** General medical and surgical

Staffed Beds: 25

DAVENPORT—Lincoln County

LINCOLN HOSPITAL (501305), 10 Nicholls Street, Zip 99122–9729;
tel. 509/725–7101, **A**10 18 **F**3 7 11 15 29 34 35 40 41 43 45 56 57 59 64 65
66 75 77 79 81 82 85 89 91 93 97 107 110 114 119 127 130 133 144 148
Primary Contact: Tyson Lacy, Chief Executive Officer and Superintendent
CFO: Tim O'Connell, Chief Financial Officer
CMO: Fred Reed, M.D., Chief of Staff
CIO: Elliott Donson, Chief Information Specialist
CHR: Becky Bailey, Director Human Resources
CNO: Jennifer Larmer, R.N., Chief Clinical Officer
Web address: www.lincolnhospital.org
Control: Hospital district or authority, Government, nonfederal **Service:** General medical and surgical

Staffed Beds: 50 **Admissions:** 364 **Census:** 3 **Outpatient Visits:** 20403
Births: 0

DAYTON—Columbia County

COLUMBIA COUNTY HEALTH SYSTEM (501302), 1012 South Third Street,
Zip 99328–1696; tel. 509/382–2531, (Nonreporting) **A**10 18
Primary Contact: Shane McGuire, Chief Executive Officer
CFO: Lee H Holter, Chief Financial Officer
CHR: Steven J Stahl, Director Human Resources
CNO: Stephanie Carpenter, Director of Nursing Services
Web address: www.cchd-wa.org
Control: County, Government, nonfederal **Service:** General medical and surgical

Staffed Beds: 44

EDMONDS—Snohomish County

STEVENS HEALTHCARE See Swedish/Edmonds

SWEDISH/EDMONDS (500026), 21601 76th Avenue West, Zip 98026–7506;
tel. 425/640–4000, **A**2 10 21 **F**2 3 11 13 15 18 20 22 26 28 29 30 31 34 35
38 40 41 43 45 49 56 59 60 61 64 65 68 70 73 74 75 76 77 78 79 81 82 84
85 87 91 92 93 96 98 100 101 102 104 107 108 111 114 115 116 119 124
126 129 130 131 132 135 141 146 147 148 149 154 **P**6 **S** Swedish Health
Services, Seattle, WA
Primary Contact: Sarah Zabel, Vice President, Operations
CMO: Sandeep Sachdeva, M.D., Vice President Medical Affairs
CNO: Jean Doerge, R.N., MSN, Nurse Executive
Web address: www.swedish.org
Control: Other not–for–profit (including NFP Corporation) **Service:** General medical and surgical

Staffed Beds: 186 **Admissions:** 10937 **Census:** 130 **Outpatient Visits:**
125524 **Births:** 1371 **Total Expense ($000):** 254503 **Payroll Expense
($000):** 90708 **Personnel:** 769

ELLENSBURG—Kittitas County

KITTITAS VALLEY HEALTHCARE (501333), 603 South Chestnut Street,
Zip 98926–3875; tel. 509/962–7302, **A**3 10 18 **F**3 11 13 15 29 30 34 35 37
40 41 43 44 45 46 50 56 57 59 62 63 64 65 68 70 73 75 76 77 79 81 82 84
85 87 89 93 96 102 104 107 110 111 115 119 127 130 131 132 144 146
147 149 154 **P**6
Primary Contact: Julie Petersen, CPA, Chief Executive Officer
CFO: Libby Allgood, Chief Financial Officer
CMO: Don Solberg, M.D., Chief Medical Officer
CIO: Jack Schwartz, Director Information Technology
CHR: Carrie Youngblood, Director of Human Resources
CNO: Vicky Machorro, R.N., Chief Nursing Officer
Web address: www.kvhealthcare.org
Control: Hospital district or authority, Government, nonfederal **Service:** General medical and surgical

Staffed Beds: 25 **Admissions:** 899 **Census:** 7 **Outpatient Visits:** 73963
Births: 322 **Total Expense ($000):** 70605 **Payroll Expense ($000):** 38215
Personnel: 459

ELMA—Grays Harbor County

SUMMIT PACIFIC MEDICAL CENTER (501304), 600 East Main Street,
Zip 98541–9560; tel. 360/346–2222, (Nonreporting) **A**10 18
Primary Contact: Josh Martin, Chief Executive Officer
COO: Josh Martin, Chief Operating Officer
CFO: James Hansen, Chief Financial Officer
CMO: William Hurley, M.D., Chief Medical Officer
CIO: Jeff Painter, Manager Information Technology
CHR: Mindy Portchy, Manager Human Resources
Web address: www.markreed.org
Control: Corporation, Investor–owned (for–profit) **Service:** General medical and surgical

Staffed Beds: 6

ENUMCLAW—King County

ST. ELIZABETH HOSPITAL (501335), 1455 Battersby Avenue,
Zip 98022–3634, Mailing Address: P.O. Box 218, Zip 98022–0218;
tel. 360/802–8800, **A**10 18 **F**3 13 15 18 29 30 34 35 38 40 44 45 50 57 64
70 74 75 76 79 81 85 87 107 108 110 111 115 119 130 135 146 149 154 **S**
Catholic Health Initiatives, Englewood, CO
Primary Contact: Syd Bersante, R.N., Market President
COO: Joseph Wilczek, Chief Executive Officer
CFO: Philip Hjembo, Chief Financial Officer
CHR: Jerilyn Ray, Manager Human Resources
Web address: www.fhshealth.org
Control: Church operated, Nongovernment, not–for–profit **Service:** General medical and surgical

Staffed Beds: 25 **Admissions:** 1639 **Census:** 14 **Outpatient Visits:** 36615
Births: 345 **Total Expense ($000):** 45524 **Payroll Expense ($000):** 16443
Personnel: 198

EPHRATA—Grant County

COLUMBIA BASIN HOSPITAL (501317), 200 Nat Washington Way,
Zip 98823–1982; tel. 509/754–4631, (Total facility includes 12 beds in nursing
home–type unit) **A**10 18 **F**3 10 11 15 29 30 34 35 40 50 56 59 65 75 77 84 91
93 97 107 108 111 114 119 125 127 130 132 133 146 147
Primary Contact: Rosalinda Kibby, Superintendent and Administrator
CFO: Rhonda Handley, Chief Financial Officer
CMO: Lowell C Allred, M.D., Chief of Staff
CHR: Suzanne Little, Human Resources Specialist
Web address: www.columbiabasinhospital.org
Control: Hospital district or authority, Government, nonfederal **Service:** General medical and surgical

Staffed Beds: 69 **Admissions:** 286 **Census:** 15 **Outpatient Visits:** 17813
Births: 0 **Total Expense ($000):** 17441 **Payroll Expense ($000):** 6718
Personnel: 128

EVERETT—Snohomish County

PROVIDENCE REGIONAL MEDICAL CENTER EVERETT (500014), 1321 Colby
Avenue, Zip 98201–1665, Mailing Address: P.O. Box 1147, Zip 98206–1147;
tel. 425/261–2000, (Includes PROVIDENCE EVERETT MEDICAL CENTER – COLBY
CAMPUS, 1321 Colby Avenue, Everett, WA, Zip 98206, Mailing Address: P.O. Box
1147, Zip 98206, tel. 425/261–2000; PROVIDENCE EVERETT MEDICAL CENTER
– PACIFIC CAMPUS, Pacific and Nassau Streets, Everett, WA, Zip 98201, Mailing
Address: P.O. Box 1067, Zip 98206–1067, tel. 206/258–7123) **A**1 2 3 5 7 10
F3 4 5 11 12 13 15 17 18 20 22 24 26 28 29 30 31 32 34 35 36 37 38 40 43
44 45 46 47 48 49 50 54 55 56 57 58 59 61 64 65 68 70 72 73 74 75 76 77
78 79 80 81 84 85 86 87 89 90 93 94 96 100 107 108 109 110 111 114 115
116 117 118 119 120 121 123 124 126 129 130 131 132 135 144 146 147
148 149 150 152 **P**6 **S** Providence St. Joseph Health, Renton, WA
Primary Contact: Kim Williams, R.N., MS, Chief Executive Officer
CFO: Sheri Feeney, Chief Financial Officer
CMO: Frank Andersen, Interim Chief Medical Officer
CIO: Matt Wonser, Director, Information Services
CHR: Lori A Vocca, Vice President Human Resources
CNO: Barbara M Hyland–Hill, R.N., Chief Nursing Officer
Web address: www.providence.org
Control: Church operated, Nongovernment, not–for–profit **Service:** General medical and surgical

Staffed Beds: 530 **Admissions:** 31150 **Census:** 408 **Outpatient Visits:**
470495 **Births:** 4540 **Total Expense ($000):** 564671 **Payroll Expense
($000):** 250178 **Personnel:** 2682

WA

FEDERAL WAY—King County

ST. FRANCIS HOSPITAL (500141), 34515 Ninth Avenue South, Zip 98003–6799; tel. 253/944–8100, **A**1 2 10 **F**3 8 11 12 13 15 18 20 22 29 30 34 35 38 40 43 44 45 49 50 51 57 59 64 70 73 74 75 76 78 79 80 81 85 86 87 92 93 107 108 110 111 114 117 119 126 129 130 132 135 146 147 154 **S** Catholic Health Initiatives, Englewood, CO
Primary Contact: Anthony McLean, Market President
COO: Dino Johnson, R.N., Chief Operationg Officer and Chief Nursing Officer
CFO: Mike Fitzgerald, Chief Financial Officer
CMO: Dennis deLeon, M.D., Chief Medical Officer, King Region
CIO: Rand Strobel, Regional Chief Information Officer
CHR: Les Soltis, Director – Human Resources
CNO: Dino Johnson, R.N., Chief Operating Officer and Chief Nursing Officer
Web address: www.fhshealth.org
Control: Church operated, Nongovernment, not-for-profit **Service:** General medical and surgical

Staffed Beds: 124 **Admissions:** 8684 **Census:** 91 **Outpatient Visits:** 169967 **Births:** 1314 **Total Expense ($000):** 194738 **Payroll Expense ($000):** 63613 **Personnel:** 807

FORKS—Clallam County

FORKS COMMUNITY HOSPITAL (501325), 530 Bogachiel Way, Zip 98331–9120; tel. 360/374–6271, (Nonreporting) **A**10 18 21
Primary Contact: Tim Cournyer, Administrator
CFO: Joe Bradick, Chief Financial Officer
CIO: Andrea Perkins–Peppers, Chief Information Officer
CHR: Cindy Paget, Chief Human Resources Officer
CNO: Laura Kripinski, Chief Nursing Officer
Web address: www.forkshospital.org
Control: Hospital district or authority, Government, nonfederal **Service:** General medical and surgical

Staffed Beds: 45

FRIDAY HARBOR—San Juan County

PEACEHEALTH PEACE ISLAND MEDICAL CENTER (501340), 1117 Spring Street, Zip 98250–9782; tel. 360/378–2141, **A**5 10 18 21 **F**3 30 31 34 40 45 59 64 65 68 77 79 81 100 104 107 115 130 146 149 154 **S** PeaceHealth, Vancouver, WA
Primary Contact: Merry Ann Keane, Chief Administrative Officer
CFO: Carolyn Foster, Chief Financial Officer
CMO: Michael Sullivan, M.D., Medical Director Emergency Services
CHR: Lorraine Allison, Human Resource Partner
CNO: Sheryl Murphy, Chief Nursing Officer and Director of Clinical Services
Web address: www.peacehealth.org
Control: Church operated, Nongovernment, not-for-profit **Service:** General medical and surgical

Staffed Beds: 10 **Admissions:** 89 **Census:** 1 **Outpatient Visits:** 13513 **Births:** 0 **Personnel:** 79

GIG HARBOR—Pierce County

ST. ANTHONY HOSPITAL (500151), 11567 Canterwood Boulevard NW, Zip 98332–5812; tel. 253/426–5000, **A**1 10 18 **F**3 11 12 15 18 20 29 30 31 34 38 40 44 45 49 50 51 57 59 60 64 70 74 75 77 78 79 81 85 87 92 93 107 108 110 111 114 115 119 126 129 130 132 135 146 147 154 **S** Catholic Health Initiatives, Englewood, CO
Primary Contact: David W. Schultz, FACHE, President, Peninsula Region
Web address: www.chifranciscan.org/
Control: Church operated, Nongovernment, not-for-profit **Service:** General medical and surgical

Staffed Beds: 80 **Admissions:** 5431 **Census:** 66 **Outpatient Visits:** 75899 **Births:** 0 **Total Expense ($000):** 126655 **Payroll Expense ($000):** 37932 **Personnel:** 481

GOLDENDALE—Klickitat County

KLICKITAT VALLEY HEALTH (501316), 310 South Roosevelt Avenue, Zip 98620–9201; tel. 509/773–4022, **A**3 10 18 **F**3 8 15 18 29 30 34 35 40 43 45 55 57 59 62 63 64 65 68 75 77 81 83 84 85 97 107 110 114 119 127 128 130 133 135 146 148 149
Primary Contact: Leslie Hiebert, Chief Executive Officer
CFO: Jamie Eldred, Controller
CMO: Rod Krehbiel, M.D., Chief of Staff
CIO: Jonathan Hatfield, Supervisor Information Technology
CHR: Herbert Hill, Director Human Resources
CNO: Gwen Cox, Director Nursing Services
Web address: www.kvhealth.net
Control: Hospital district or authority, Government, nonfederal **Service:** General medical and surgical

Staffed Beds: 17 **Admissions:** 244 **Census:** 4 **Outpatient Visits:** 5705 **Births:** 0 **Total Expense ($000):** 23707 **Payroll Expense ($000):** 11938 **Personnel:** 215

GRAND COULEE—Grant County

COULEE COMMUNITY HOSPITAL See Coulee Medical Center

COULEE MEDICAL CENTER (501308), 411 Fortuyn Road, Zip 99133–8718; tel. 509/633–1753, **A**10 18 **F**8 15 29 32 40 41 43 45 47 48 50 56 57 59 64 65 75 76 79 81 82 83 84 85 86 87 93 97 107 110 114 119 127 128 130 133 144 147 148 149 154
Primary Contact: Ramona Hicks, Interim Chief Executive Officer
CFO: Paul Babcock, Chief Financial Officer
CMO: Andrew Castrodale, M.D., Chief Medical Officer
CHR: Heather McCleary, Director Human Resources
Web address: www.cmccares.org
Control: Hospital district or authority, Government, nonfederal **Service:** General medical and surgical

Staffed Beds: 25 **Admissions:** 505 **Census:** 15 **Outpatient Visits:** 27365 **Births:** 69 **Total Expense ($000):** 31177 **Payroll Expense ($000):** 14398 **Personnel:** 187

ILWACO—Pacific County

OCEAN BEACH HOSPITAL (501314), 174 First Avenue North, Zip 98624–9137, Mailing Address: P.O. Box H, Zip 98624–0258; tel. 360/642–3181, **A**10 18 **F**3 11 15 18 28 29 30 31 34 35 40 45 56 57 59 68 75 77 78 79 81 85 86 87 93 97 102 107 111 114 119 127 128 130 132 133 135 149 154 **P**6
Primary Contact: Larry Cohen, Chief Executive Officer
CFO: Kathy Hubbard, Controller
CMO: Patty Malone, M.D., Chief Medical Officer
CIO: Julie P Oakes, R.N., Manager Risk and Quality
CHR: Beth Whitton, Director Human Resources
CNO: Linda Kaino, Chief Nursing Officer
Web address: www.oceanbeachhospital.com
Control: Hospital district or authority, Government, nonfederal **Service:** General medical and surgical

Staffed Beds: 15 **Admissions:** 412 **Census:** 5 **Outpatient Visits:** 29932 **Births:** 0 **Total Expense ($000):** 26318 **Payroll Expense ($000):** 10542 **Personnel:** 153

ISSAQUAH—King County

SWEDISH/ISSAQUAH (500152), 751 NE Blakely Drive, Zip 98029–6201; tel. 425/313–4000, **A**3 10 21 **F**2 12 13 15 18 20 22 29 30 31 34 35 37 38 40 41 45 48 49 50 56 57 58 59 60 61 64 65 68 70 73 74 75 76 77 78 79 81 82 85 86 87 89 92 93 96 97 102 107 108 110 111 114 115 119 126 129 130 131 132 134 135 141 143 146 147 148 149 154 **S** Swedish Health Services, Seattle, WA
Primary Contact: Guy Hudson, Chief Executive Officer
COO: Jeffery Robert, Chief Operaing Officer
Web address: www.swedish.org/issaquah
Control: Other not–for–profit (including NFP Corporation) **Service:** General medical and surgical

Staffed Beds: 134 **Admissions:** 7601 **Census:** 62 **Outpatient Visits:** 120471 **Births:** 1627 **Total Expense ($000):** 220114 **Payroll Expense ($000):** 58400 **Personnel:** 500

KENNEWICK—Benton County

TRIOS HEALTH (500053), 900 South Auburn Street, Zip 99336–5621, Mailing Address: P.O. Box 6128, Zip 99336–0128; tel. 509/586–6111, (Nonreporting) **A**1 2 3 10 13 **S** QHR, Brentwood, TN
Primary Contact: John H. Solheim, Chief Executive Officer
CFO: Jason Hotchkiss, CPA, Chief Financial Officer
CIO: Michael Cloutier, Director Information Services
CHR: Russ Keefer, Chief Human Resources Officer
Web address: www.trioshealth.org
Control: Hospital district or authority, Government, nonfederal **Service:** General medical and surgical

Staffed Beds: 111

KIRKLAND—King County

EVERGREEN HEALTHCARE See Evergreenhealth

EVERGREENHEALTH (500124), 12040 NE 128th Street, Zip 98034–3013; tel. 425/899–1000, **A**1 2 3 5 10 **F**3 8 11 12 13 15 18 20 22 28 29 30 34 35 37 38 40 43 44 45 46 49 50 51 54 55 56 58 59 61 62 63 64 65 68 70 71 72 73 74 75 76 78 79 80 81 82 84 85 86 87 89 90 91 92 93 94 95 96 97 100 107 108 110 111 114 115 119 120 121 123 124 126 129 130 131 132 134 135 144 146 147 148 149 154 **P**4 6
Primary Contact: Amy Beiter, M.D., Chief Executive Officer
CFO: Tina Mycroft, Senior Vice President, Chief Financial Officer
CMO: Jeff Tomlin, M.D., Chief Medical and Quality Officer
CIO: Tom Martin, Senior Vice President, Strategy and Information Technology Officer
CHR: Bob Sampson, Senior Vice President, Human Resources
CNO: Nancee Hofmeister, R.N., Senior Vice President, Chief Nursing Officer
Web address: www.evergreenhealth.com
Control: Hospital district or authority, Government, nonfederal **Service:** General medical and surgical

Staffed Beds: 318 **Admissions:** 15281 **Census:** 168 **Outpatient Visits:** 1134154 **Births:** 4525 **Total Expense ($000):** 665126 **Payroll Expense ($000):** 352532 **Personnel:** 3626

FAIRFAX BEHAVIORAL HEALTH (504002), 10200 NE 132nd Street, Zip 98034–2899; tel. 425/821–2000, (Includes FAIRFAX BEHAVIORAL HEALTH EVERETT, 916 Pacific Avenue, Everett, WA, Zip 98201–4147; tel. 425/821–2000) **A**1 10 **F**50 98 100 101 102 103 105 152 **P**6 **S** Universal Health Services, Inc., King of Prussia, PA
Primary Contact: Beckie Shauinger, Chief Executive Officer
COO: Todd Thama, Chief Operating Officer
CFO: Pam Rhoads, Chief Financial Officer
CMO: Samir Aziz, M.D., Medical Director
CHR: Anne Schreiber, Manager Human Resources
Web address: www.fairfaxhospital.com
Control: Corporation, Investor–owned (for–profit) **Service:** Psychiatric

Staffed Beds: 221 **Admissions:** 5281 **Census:** 173 **Outpatient Visits:** 0 **Births:** 0 **Total Expense ($000):** 71839 **Payroll Expense ($000):** 27381 **Personnel:** 420

LAKEWOOD—Pierce County

ST. CLARE HOSPITAL (500021), 11315 Bridgeport Way SW, Zip 98499–3004; tel. 253/985–1711, **A**1 2 3 7 10 **F**3 8 18 29 30 31 34 35 38 40 44 45 49 50 51 57 59 64 70 74 75 77 78 79 80 81 82 85 86 87 92 93 107 108 111 114 119 129 130 132 135 146 149 154 **S** Catholic Health Initiatives, Englewood, CO
Primary Contact: Syd Bersante, R.N., President
CFO: Mike Fitzgerald, Chief Financial Officer
CIO: Bruce Elkington, Regional Chief Information Officer
CHR: David C. Lawson, Senior Vice President Human Resources
Web address: www.fhshealth.org
Control: Church operated, Nongovernment, not–for–profit **Service:** General medical and surgical

Staffed Beds: 103 **Admissions:** 5997 **Census:** 83 **Outpatient Visits:** 102577 **Births:** 0 **Total Expense ($000):** 137220 **Payroll Expense ($000):** 46775 **Personnel:** 621

LEAVENWORTH—Chelan County

CASCADE MEDICAL CENTER (501313), 817 Commercial Street, Zip 98826–1316; tel. 509/548–5815, (Nonreporting) **A**5 10 18
Primary Contact: Diane Blake, Chief Executive Officer
COO: Amy Webb, Chief Operating Officer
CFO: Jim Hopkins, Chief Financial Officer
CMO: Karl Kranz, M.D., Chief of Staff
CIO: Charles Amstutz, Director of Information Technology
CHR: Reyne Boik, Director Human Resources
Web address: www.cascademedical.org
Control: Hospital district or authority, Government, nonfederal **Service:** General medical and surgical

Staffed Beds: 9

LONGVIEW—Cowlitz County

PEACEHEALTH ST. JOHN MEDICAL CENTER (500041), 1615 Delaware Street, Zip 98632–2367, Mailing Address: P.O. Box 3002, Zip 98632–0302; tel. 360/414–2000, (Nonreporting) **A**1 2 10 19 21 **S** PeaceHealth, Vancouver, WA
Primary Contact: Cherelle Montanye–Ireland, Chief Administrative Officer
CFO: Ronald K Benfield, Chief Financial Officer
CMO: Sheila Lynam, M.D., Chief Medical Officer
CHR: Kelley Frengle, Director, Human Resources
Web address: www.peacehealth.org
Control: Church operated, Nongovernment, not–for–profit **Service:** General medical and surgical

Staffed Beds: 180

MARYSVILLE—Snohomish County

SMOKEY POINT BEHAVIORAL HOSPITAL (504012), 3955 156th Street Northeast, Zip 98271; tel. 844/202–5555, (Nonreporting) **A**10
Primary Contact: Matt Crockett, Chief Executive Officer
Web address: www.smokeypointbehavioralhospital.com
Control: Other not–for–profit (including NFP Corporation) **Service:** Psychiatric

Staffed Beds: 115

MEDICAL LAKE—Spokane County

EASTERN STATE HOSPITAL (504004), Maple Street, Zip 99022–0045, Mailing Address: P.O. Box 800, Zip 99022–0800; tel. 509/565–4705, **A**1 3 10 **F**29 30 39 59 65 68 75 77 86 98 100 103 105 130 132 135 143
Primary Contact: Mark Kettner, Interim Chief Executive Officer
COO: Ronda Kenney, Chief Operating Officer
CMO: Kamal Floura, M.D., Medical Director
CNO: Chet Roshetko, Chief Nursing Officer
Web address: www.dshs.wa.gov/bha/division–state–hospitals/eastern–state–hospital–overview
Control: State, Government, nonfederal **Service:** Psychiatric

Staffed Beds: 317 **Admissions:** 532 **Census:** 274 **Births:** 0 **Total Expense ($000):** 80637 **Payroll Expense ($000):** 55840

MONROE—Snohomish County

EVERGREENHEALTH MONROE (500084), 14701 179th SE, Zip 98272–1108, Mailing Address: P.O. Box 646, Zip 98272–0646; tel. 360/794–7497, (Nonreporting) **A**10 21
Primary Contact: Renee K. Jensen, Senior Vice President and Chief Administrative Officer
CFO: Scott Olander, Chief Financial Officer
CMO: Jack Handley, M.D., Chief Medical Officer
CIO: John Gepford, Director Information Systems
CHR: Kathryn Rothberg, Director Human Resources
CNO: Brenda West, R.N., MSN, Chief Nursing Officer
Web address: www.evergreenhealthmonroe.com
Control: Hospital district or authority, Government, nonfederal **Service:** General medical and surgical

Staffed Beds: 68

MORTON—Lewis County

MORTON GENERAL HOSPITAL (501319), 521 Adams Avenue, Zip 98356–9323, Mailing Address: P.O. Box 1138, Zip 98356–0019; tel. 360/496–5112, (Nonreporting) **A**10 18
Primary Contact: Leianne Everett, Chief Executive Officer
CFO: Geoff Hamilton, Interim Chief Financial Officer
CIO: Randy Nielsen, Director Information Technology
CHR: Shannon Kelly, Director Human Resources
CNO: Heidi Anderson, Chief Nursing Officer
Web address: www.mortongeneral.org
Control: Hospital district or authority, Government, nonfederal **Service:** General medical and surgical

Staffed Beds: 25

MOSES LAKE—Grant County

SAMARITAN HEALTHCARE (500033), 801 East Wheeler Road, Zip 98837–1899; tel. 509/765–5606, **A**10 20 **F**3 8 13 15 28 29 30 34 35 40 43 45 50 57 59 64 65 68 75 76 79 80 81 85 86 87 97 107 108 110 111 115 118 119 127 130 132 135 144 146 147
Primary Contact: Theresa Sullivan, Chief Executive Officer
COO: Kris Neff, Chief Operating Officer
CFO: Alex Town, Chief Financial Officer
CMO: Andrea Carter, M.D., Chief Medical Officer
CNO: Becky DeMers, R.N., Chief Nursing Officer
Web address: www.samaritanhealthcare.com
Control: Hospital district or authority, Government, nonfederal **Service:** General medical and surgical

Staffed Beds: 50 **Admissions:** 3053 **Census:** 24 **Outpatient Visits:** 52630 **Births:** 1027 **Total Expense ($000):** 77223 **Payroll Expense ($000):** 35207 **Personnel:** 499

WA

Hospital, Medicare Provider Number, Address, Telephone, Approval, Facility, and Physician Codes, Health Care System

★ American Hospital Association (AHA) membership ○ Healthcare Facilities Accreditation Program ⇑ Center for Improvement in Healthcare Quality Accreditation
□ The Joint Commission accreditation ◇ DNV Healthcare Inc. accreditation △ Commission on Accreditation of Rehabilitation Facilities (CARF) accreditation

MOUNT VERNON—Skagit County

SKAGIT REGIONAL HEALTH (500003), 1415 East Kincaid, Zip 98274–4126, Mailing Address: P.O. Box 1376, Zip 98273–1376; tel. 360/424–4111, (Nonreporting) **A**2 3 5 10 13 19 21 **S** Skagit Regional Health, Mount Vernon, WA
Primary Contact: Brian K. Ivie, President and Chief Executive Officer
COO: Jim Geist, Executive Vice President and Chief Operating Officer
CFO: Paul Ishizuka, Chief Financial Officer
CMO: Jeffrey S. Gibbs, M.D., Regional Vice President Medical Affairs
CIO: John Dwight, Regional Vice President and Chief Information Officer
CHR: Deborah Martin, Regional Vice President Human Resources
CNO: Roxanne Olason, R.N., FACHE, Vice President and Chief Nursing Officer
Web address: www.skagitregionalhealth.org
Control: Hospital district or authority, Government, nonfederal **Service:** General medical and surgical

Staffed Beds: 137

NEWPORT—Pend Oreille County

NEWPORT HOSPITAL AND HEALTH SERVICES (501310), 714 West Pine Street, Zip 99156–9046; tel. 509/447–2441, (Nonreporting) **A**10 18
Primary Contact: Thomas W. Wilbur, Chief Executive Officer and Superintendent
COO: Shelley Froehlich, R.N., Director Nursing Services
CMO: Clay Kersting, M.D., Chief Medical Staff
CIO: Walter Price, Director Information Technology
CHR: Joseph Clouse, Chief Administrative Officer
Web address: www.newporthospitalandhealth.org
Control: Hospital district or authority, Government, nonfederal **Service:** General medical and surgical

Staffed Beds: 70

OAK HARBOR—Island County

NAVAL HOSPITAL OAK HARBOR, 3475 North Saratoga Street, Zip 98278–8800; tel. 360/257–9500, (Nonreporting) **A**1 **S** Bureau of Medicine and Surgery, Department of the Navy, Falls Church, VA
Primary Contact: Commander Frederick Joseph. McDonald, Commanding Officer
COO: Lieutenant Michael Bowers, Interim Director for Administration
CFO: Lieutenant Matthew Martin, Director Resource Management
CMO: Lieutenant Commander Catherine Borja, M.D., Chairman Executive Committee Medical Staff
CIO: Gregory Carruth, Head Information Management
CHR: Lieutenant Michael Bowers, Head Human Resources
CNO: Captain Karen Pruett–Baer, Senior Nurse Executive
Web address: www.med.navy.mil/sites/nhoh/Pages/default.aspx
Control: Navy, Government, federal **Service:** General medical and surgical

Staffed Beds: 29

ODESSA—Lincoln County

ODESSA MEMORIAL HEALTHCARE CENTER (501307), 502 East Amende Drive, Zip 99159–7003, Mailing Address: P.O. Box 368, Zip 99159–0368; tel. 509/982–2611, (Nonreporting) **A**10 18
Primary Contact: Mo P. Sheldon, FACHE, Chief Executive Officer and Administrator
CFO: Annette Edwards, Chief Financial Officer
CMO: Linda J Powel, M.D., Medical Director
CHR: Jodi J Bailey, Human Resources Director
CNO: Megan Shepard, Director Clinical Services
Web address: www.omhc.org
Control: Hospital district or authority, Government, nonfederal **Service:** General medical and surgical

Staffed Beds: 25

OLYMPIA—Thurston County

CAPITAL MEDICAL CENTER (500139), 3900 Capital Mall Drive SW, Zip 98502–5026; tel. 360/754–5858, (Nonreporting) **A**1 10 **S** RCCH HealthCare Partners, Brentwood, TN
Primary Contact: Mark S. Turner, Chief Executive Officer
CFO: Brian Anderson, Chief Financial Officer
CMO: Rojesh Sharangpani, M.D., Chief of Staff
CIO: Renee Crotty, Coordinator Marketing and Public Relations
CHR: Dana Vandewege, Director Human Resources
Web address: www.capitalmedical.com
Control: Partnership, Investor–owned (for–profit) **Service:** General medical and surgical

Staffed Beds: 85

PROVIDENCE ST. PETER HOSPITAL (500024)

PROVIDENCE ST. PETER HOSPITAL (500024), 413 Lilly Road NE, Zip 98506–5166; tel. 360/491–9480, **A**1 3 7 10 **F**3 5 8 11 13 15 17 18 20 22 24 26 28 29 30 31 34 35 38 40 43 44 46 49 51 53 56 57 58 59 64 68 70 73 74 75 76 77 78 79 80 81 82 84 85 86 87 89 90 91 92 93 95 96 98 99 100 101 102 104 107 108 111 114 115 118 119 126 129 130 132 135 145 146 148 149 150 152 154 **S** Providence St. Joseph Health, Renton, WA
Primary Contact: Medrice Coluccio, R.N., Chief Executive Officer
CFO: Denise Marroni, Chief Financial Officer
CMO: Kevin Caserta, M.D., Chief Medical Officer
CIO: Kerry Miles, Chief Information Officer
CHR: Susan Meenk, Vice President Human Resources
CNO: Michelle James, Chief Nursing Officer
Web address: www.providence.org/swsa/facilities/st_peter_hospital
Control: Church operated, Nongovernment, not–for–profit **Service:** General medical and surgical

Staffed Beds: 350 **Admissions:** 19388 **Census:** 265 **Outpatient Visits:** 357519 **Births:** 2041 **Total Expense ($000):** 323164 **Payroll Expense ($000):** 177057 **Personnel:** 2208

OMAK—Okanogan County

MID–VALLEY HOSPITAL (501328), 810 Jasmine, Zip 98841–9578, Mailing Address: P.O. Box 793, Zip 98841–0793; tel. 509/826–1760, **A**5 10 18 **F**3 8 13 15 18 19 29 34 35 38 39 40 41 43 45 50 56 57 59 65 68 75 76 77 79 81 85 87 93 102 107 108 109 110 111 114 119 127 130 131 133 147 148 149 152 154
Primary Contact: Alan Fisher, Chief Executive Officer
CFO: Scott Attridge, Chief Financial Officer
CMO: Jennifer Thill, Chief of Staff
CIO: Ethan Harris, Manager Information Systems
CHR: Randy Coffell, Manager Human Resources
CNO: Rebecca Christoph, Director Nursing and Patient Care Services
Web address: www.mvhealth.org
Control: Hospital district or authority, Government, nonfederal **Service:** General medical and surgical

Staffed Beds: 28 **Admissions:** 828 **Census:** 6 **Outpatient Visits:** 27684 **Births:** 229 **Total Expense ($000):** 18820 **Payroll Expense ($000):** 15145 **Personnel:** 199

OTHELLO—Adams County

OTHELLO COMMUNITY HOSPITAL (501318), 315 North 14th Avenue, Zip 99344–1297; tel. 509/488–2636, (Nonreporting) **A**10 18
Primary Contact: Connie Agenbroad, Chief Executive Officer
CFO: Mark Bunch, Director Finance
CHR: Mindy Gonzales, Chief Human Resources Officer
CNO: Tina Bernsen, Chief Nursing Officer
Web address: www.othellocommunityhospital.org
Control: Hospital district or authority, Government, nonfederal **Service:** General medical and surgical

Staffed Beds: 25

PASCO—Franklin County

LOURDES MEDICAL CENTER (501337), 520 North Fourth Avenue, Zip 99301–5257; tel. 509/547–7704, (Nonreporting) **A**1 7 10 18 **S** RCCH HealthCare Partners, Brentwood, TN
Primary Contact: John Serle, FACHE, President and Chief Executive Officer
CFO: Frank Becker, Chief Financial Officer
CMO: Venkataraman Sambasivan, M.D., Chief Medical Officer
CIO: Deb Carpenter, Director Information Technology
CHR: Barbara Blood, Executive Director Human Resources
CNO: Denise Clapp, Chief Nursing Officer
Web address: www.lourdeshealth.net
Control: Corporation, Investor–owned (for–profit) **Service:** General medical and surgical

Staffed Beds: 53

POMEROY—Garfield County

GARFIELD COUNTY PUBLIC HOSPITAL DISTRICT (501301), 66 North 6th Street, Zip 99347–9705; tel. 509/843–1591, (Nonreporting) **A**10 18
Primary Contact: Julie Leonard, Chief Executive Officer
CFO: Julie Leonard, Chief Financial Officer
CMO: Glenn Jefferson, Chief Medical Officer
CHR: Alicia Scharnhorst, Human Resources and Administrative Assistant
CNO: Barbara DeHerrera, Chief Nursing Officer
Web address: www.pomeroymd.com
Control: Hospital district or authority, Government, nonfederal **Service:** General medical and surgical

Staffed Beds: 45

WA

Many Facility Codes have changed. Please refer to the AHA Guide Code Chart. © 2018 AHA Guide

PORT ANGELES—Clallam County

OLYMPIC MEDICAL CENTER (500072), 939 Caroline Street, Zip 98362–3997;
tel. 360/417–7000, **A**2 3 5 10 21 **F**3 13 15 18 28 29 31 40 45 54 57 58 62 64
70 74 75 77 78 79 81 82 85 87 91 93 97 107 108 110 111 114 119 121 123
127 129 131 132 144 146 147 148
Primary Contact: Eric Lewis, Chief Executive Officer
COO: Lorraine Wall, Chief Nursing Officer and Chief Operating Officer
CFO: Darryl Wolfe, Chief Financial Officer
CMO: R. Scott Kennedy, M.D., Chief Medical Officer and Safety Officer
CHR: Richard Newman, Chief Human Resources Officer
CNO: Lorraine Wall, Chief Nursing Officer and Chief Operating Officer
Web address: www.olympicmedical.org
Control: Hospital district or authority, Government, nonfederal **Service**: General
medical and surgical

Staffed Beds: 67 **Admissions**: 4379 **Census**: 39 **Outpatient Visits**: 449981
Births: 487 **Total Expense ($000)**: 184055 **Payroll Expense ($000)**: 89103
Personnel: 1219

PORT TOWNSEND—Jefferson County

JEFFERSON HEALTHCARE (501323), 834 Sheridan Street, Zip 98368–2443;
tel. 360/385–2200, (Nonreporting) **A**10 18 21
Primary Contact: Mike Glenn, Chief Executive Officer
COO: Paula Dowdle, Chief Operating Officer
CFO: Hilary Whittington, Chief Financial Officer
CMO: Joe Mattern, M.D., Chief Medical Officer
CHR: Heather Bailey, Chief Human Resources Officer
CNO: Joyce Cardinal, Chief Nursing Executive
Web address: www.jeffersonhealthcare.org
Control: Hospital district or authority, Government, nonfederal **Service**: General
medical and surgical

Staffed Beds: 25

PROSSER—Benton County

PMH MEDICAL CENTER (501312), 723 Memorial Street, Zip 99350–1524;
tel. 509/786–2222, **A**3 10 18 **F**3 7 11 12 13 15 29 30 34 35 37 40 41 43 44
45 50 53 54 57 59 65 68 75 76 77 79 81 82 85 87 89 91 93 97 107 108 109
110 112 114 115 119 127 128 130 131 132 133 135 143 146 147 148 149
154 **P**8
Primary Contact: Craig J. Marks, FACHE, Chief Executive Officer
CFO: Tim Cooper, Chief Financial Officer
CIO: Jim Zoesch, Information Technology Director
CNO: Marla Davis, Interim Chief Nursing Officer
Web address: www.pmhmedicalcenter.com/
Control: Hospital district or authority, Government, nonfederal **Service**: General
medical and surgical

Staffed Beds: 25 **Admissions**: 1127 **Census**: 12 **Outpatient Visits**: 28822
Births: 389 **Total Expense ($000)**: 48053 **Payroll Expense ($000)**: 20444
Personnel: 234

PULLMAN—Whitman County

PULLMAN REGIONAL HOSPITAL (501331), 835 SE Bishop Boulevard,
Zip 99163–5512; tel. 509/332–2541, (Nonreporting) **A**10 18 21
Primary Contact: Scott K. Adams, FACHE, Chief Executive Officer
CFO: Steven Febus, Chief Financial Officer
CMO: Gerald L Early, M.D., Chief Medical Officer
CHR: Bernadette Berney, Director Human Resources
Web address: www.pullmanhospital.org
Control: Hospital district or authority, Government, nonfederal **Service**: General
medical and surgical

Staffed Beds: 25

PUYALLUP—Pierce County

GOOD SAMARITAN COMMUNITY HEALTHCARE See Multicare Good Samaritan
Hospital

MULTICARE GOOD SAMARITAN HOSPITAL (500079)

MULTICARE GOOD SAMARITAN HOSPITAL (500079), 401 15th Avenue
SE, Zip 98372–3770, Mailing Address: P.O. Box 1247, Zip 98371–0192;
tel. 253/697–4000, **A**1 2 3 7 10 13 **F**3 11 13 18 20 22 24 28 29 30 31 34 35
38 40 41 43 45 47 48 50 51 55 56 57 58 59 61 64 65 66 68 70 73 74 75 76
78 79 80 81 82 83 84 85 87 89 90 91 93 96 97 102 106 107 108 111 114
115 116 117 118 119 126 129 130 132 146 147 148 149 154 **S** MultiCare
Health System, Tacoma, WA
Primary Contact: Christopher Bredeson, President and Chief Operating Officer
COO: Christopher Bredeson, President and Chief Operating Officer
CMO: Walter Fink, Chief Medical Officer
CHR: Kevin B Dull, Senior Vice President Human Potential
CNO: Lucy Norris, Administrator Interim Chief Nursing Officer
Web address: www.multicare.org/good–samaritan–hospital/
Control: Other not–for–profit (including NFP Corporation) **Service**: General
medical and surgical

Staffed Beds: 287 **Admissions**: 18264 **Census**: 250 **Outpatient Visits**:
139989 **Births**: 2294 **Total Expense ($000)**: 425052 **Payroll Expense
($000)**: 164808 **Personnel**: 1771

QUINCY—Grant County

QUINCY VALLEY MEDICAL CENTER (501320), 908 10th Avenue SW,
Zip 98848–1376; tel. 509/787–3531, (Nonreporting) **A**10 18
Primary Contact: Glenda Bishop, Interim Chief Executive Officer
CFO: Dean Taplett, Controller
CMO: Mark Vance, M.D., Chief Medical Officer
CIO: Ruth Vance, Director Information Systems
CHR: Alene Walker, Director Human Resources
Web address: www.quincyhospital.org
Control: County, Government, nonfederal **Service**: General medical and surgical

Staffed Beds: 25

RENTON—King County

UW MEDICINE/VALLEY MEDICAL CENTER (500088), 400 South 43rd
Street, Zip 98055–5714, Mailing Address: P.O. Box 50010, Zip 98058–5010;
tel. 425/228–3450, **A**1 2 3 5 10 **F**3 8 11 13 15 18 19 20 22 26 28 29 30 31
32 34 35 36 37 38 40 43 44 45 48 49 50 51 53 54 55 57 58 59 60 64 65 66
68 70 72 74 75 76 77 78 79 81 82 83 84 85 86 87 89 91 92 93 94 96 97 100
101 102 104 107 110 111 114 115 118 119 120 121 123 124 126 129 130
131 132 135 144 146 147 148 149 153 **P**6 **S** UW Medicine, Seattle, WA
Primary Contact: Richard D. Roodman, Chief Executive Officer
CFO: Larry Smith, Senior Vice President and Chief Financial Officer
CMO: Kathryn Beattie, M.D., Senior Vice President and Chief Medical Officer
CHR: Barbara Mitchell, Senior Vice President Marketing and Human Resources
CNO: Scott Alleman, Senior Vice President Patient Care Services and Chief Nursing
Officer
Web address: www.valleymed.org
Control: Hospital district or authority, Government, nonfederal **Service**: General
medical and surgical

Staffed Beds: 295 **Admissions**: 18153 **Census**: 199 **Outpatient Visits**:
621545 **Births**: 3742 **Total Expense ($000)**: 633262 **Payroll Expense
($000)**: 294462 **Personnel**: 2944

REPUBLIC—Ferry County

FERRY COUNTY MEMORIAL HOSPITAL (501322), 36 Klondike Road,
Zip 99166–9701; tel. 509/775–3333, (Nonreporting) **A**10 18
Primary Contact: Aaron Edwards, Chief Executive Officer
CFO: Kelly Leslie, Chief Financial Officer
CMO: Farhad H Alrashedy, M.D., Chief Medical Officer
CIO: James Davidson, Director of Information Services
CHR: Michelle Loftis, Human Resources Officer
CNO: Thomas Durham, Chief Nursing Officer
Web address: www.fcphd.org
Control: Hospital district or authority, Government, nonfederal **Service**: General
medical and surgical

Staffed Beds: 25

WA

Hospital, Medicare Provider Number, Address, Telephone, Approval, Facility, and Physician Codes, Health Care System

★ American Hospital Association (AHA) membership
□ The Joint Commission accreditation
○ Healthcare Facilities Accreditation Program
◇ DNV Healthcare Inc. accreditation
⇑ Center for Improvement in Healthcare Quality Accreditation
△ Commission on Accreditation of Rehabilitation Facilities (CARF) accreditation

RICHLAND—Benton County

KADLEC REGIONAL MEDICAL CENTER (500058), 888 Swift Boulevard, Zip 99352–3514; tel. 509/946–4611, **A**1 2 3 7 10 **F**3 8 11 13 15 17 18 20 22 24 26 28 29 30 31 32 34 35 36 38 40 45 46 47 48 49 50 51 52 54 55 56 57 58 59 64 65 68 70 72 73 74 75 76 78 79 81 82 83 84 85 86 87 89 90 91 93 96 97 107 110 111 114 115 116 117 118 119 126 127 130 132 144 146 147 148 149 **S** Providence St. Joseph Health, Renton, WA
Primary Contact: Reza Kaleel, Chief Administrative Officer
CFO: Spencer Harris, Senior Director Finance
CMO: Dale Hoekema, M.D., Vice President Medical Affairs and Chief Medical Officer
CIO: David Roach, Vice President Information Systems
CHR: Jeffrey A Clark, Vice President Human Resources
CNO: Kirk Harper, R.N., Vice President, Nursing
Web address: www.kadlec.org
Control: Other not–for–profit (including NFP Corporation) **Service:** General medical and surgical

Staffed Beds: 260 **Admissions:** 15635 **Census:** 196 **Outpatient Visits:** 291440 **Births:** 2777 **Total Expense ($000):** 484156 **Payroll Expense ($000):** 249581 **Personnel:** 2739

LOURDES COUNSELING CENTER (504008), 1175 Carondelet Drive, Zip 99354–3300; tel. 509/943–9104, (Nonreporting) **A**3 10 **S** RCCH HealthCare Partners, Brentwood, TN
Primary Contact: Mark Gregson, Interim Chief Executive Officer
CFO: Frank Becker, Chief Financial Officer
CIO: Jared Fleming, Director, Information Services
CHR: Barbara Blood, Director Human Resources
CNO: Denise Clapp, Chief Nursing Officer
Web address: www.lourdeshealth.net
Control: Corporation, Investor–owned (for–profit) **Service:** Psychiatric

Staffed Beds: 20

RITZVILLE—Adams County

EAST ADAMS RURAL HEALTHCARE (501311), 903 South Adams Street, Zip 99169–2298; tel. 509/659–1200, (Nonreporting) **A**10 18
Primary Contact: Gary Bostrom, Chief Executive Officer and Chief Financial Officer
COO: Dina McBride, Chief Operating Officer and Director Human Resources
CFO: Gary Bostrom, Chief Executive Officer and Chief Financial Officer
CMO: Charles Sackmann, M.D., Chief of Staff
CIO: Kellie Ottmar, Manager Information Services
CHR: Dina McBride, Chief Operating Officer and Director Human Resources
CNO: Brenda Herr, Chief Nursing Officer
Web address: www.earh.com
Control: Hospital district or authority, Government, nonfederal **Service:** General medical and surgical

Staffed Beds: 20

SEATTLE—King County

KAISER PERMANENTE CAPITOL HILL CAMPUS (500052), 201 16th Avenue East, Zip 98112–5226; tel. 206/326–3000, (Nonreporting) **A**5 10 21
Primary Contact: Carol M. Taylor, R.N., Regional Director Clinical Operations
Web address: www.ghc.org/html/public/locations/capitol–hill
Control: Corporation, Investor–owned (for–profit) **Service:** General medical and surgical

Staffed Beds: 306

KINDRED HOSPITAL SEATTLE–NORTHGATE (502002), 10631 8th Avenue NE, Zip 98125–7213; tel. 206/364–2050, (Includes KINDRED HOSPITAL SEATTLE–FIRST HILL, 1334 Terry Avenue, Seattle, WA, Zip 98101–2747; tel. 206/682–2661; Doug McCoy, Chief Executive Officer) (Nonreporting) **A**1 10 **S** Kindred Healthcare, Louisville, KY
Primary Contact: Lerenda Johnson, Interim Chief Executive Officer
CFO: Bruce MacNeill, Chief Financial Officer
Web address: www.kindredhospitalseattle.com/
Control: Corporation, Investor–owned (for–profit) **Service:** Acute long–term care hospital

Staffed Beds: 80

NAVOS (504009), 2600 SW Holden Street, Zip 98126–3505; tel. 206/933–7299, **A**1 10 **F**98 100 101 102 103 104 106 130 153 **P**6
Primary Contact: David Johnson, Chief Executive Officer
COO: Cassie Undlin, Chief Operating Officer
CIO: Mary Sellers, Chief Information Officer
CHR: Karen White, Interim Vice President of Human Resources
CNO: Terry McInerney, Director of Nursing, Inpatient
Web address: www.navos.org
Control: Other not–for–profit (including NFP Corporation) **Service:** Psychiatric

Staffed Beds: 40 **Admissions:** 532 **Census:** 39 **Outpatient Visits:** 0 **Births:** 0 **Total Expense ($000):** 12870 **Payroll Expense ($000):** 7950 **Personnel:** 126

SCHICK SHADEL HOSPITAL, 12101 Ambaum Boulevard SW, Zip 98146–2651, Mailing Address: P.O. Box 48149, Zip 98148–0149; tel. 206/244–8100, **A**7 **F**4 130 132
Primary Contact: Philip Herink, Administrator
CFO: Troy Cherry, Chief Financial Officer
CMO: Kayyan Danbdala, M.D., Medical Director
CIO: Peter Vermulen, Director Information Technology
CHR: Elaine Oksendahl, Director Human Resources and Risk Management
Web address: www.schickshadel.com
Control: Corporation, Investor–owned (for–profit) **Service:** Alcoholism and other chemical dependency

Staffed Beds: 55 **Admissions:** 987 **Census:** 29 **Outpatient Visits:** 0 **Births:** 0 **Total Expense ($000):** 11005 **Payroll Expense ($000):** 5461 **Personnel:** 90

SEATTLE CANCER CARE ALLIANCE (500138), 825 Eastlake Avenue East, Zip 98109–4405, Mailing Address: P.O. Box 19023, Zip 98109–1023; tel. 206/288–1400, **A**1 2 3 10 **F**3 14 15 29 30 31 34 35 36 39 44 45 50 55 57 58 59 64 65 68 75 78 80 81 82 84 85 86 87 93 100 104 107 108 110 111 115 117 119 120 121 123 130 132 135 136 143 146 147 148 149 **P**1
Primary Contact: Norm Hubbard, Executive Vice President
CFO: Jonathan Tingstad, Vice President and Chief Financial Officer
CMO: Marc Stewart, M.D., Vice President and Medical Director
CIO: David Ackerson, Chief Information Officer
CHR: Han Nachtrieb, Vice President Human Resources
Web address: www.seattlecca.org
Control: Other not–for–profit (including NFP Corporation) **Service:** Cancer

Staffed Beds: 20 **Admissions:** 432 **Census:** 16 **Outpatient Visits:** 78695 **Births:** 0 **Total Expense ($000):** 526843 **Payroll Expense ($000):** 104480 **Personnel:** 1082

SEATTLE CHILDREN'S HOSPITAL (503300), 4800 Sand Point Way NE, Zip 98105–3901, Mailing Address: P.O. Box 5371, Zip 98145–5005; tel. 206/987–2000, (Nonreporting) **A**1 2 5 7 10 21
Primary Contact: Jeff Sperring, M.D., Chief Executive Officer
COO: Cindy Gazecki, Senior Vice President, Hospital Operations
CFO: Suzanne Beitel, Senior Vice President and Chief Financial Officer
CMO: David Fisher, M.D., Senior Vice President and Chief Medical Officer
CIO: Zafar Chaudry, M.D., Senior Vice President and Chief Information Officer
CHR: Steven Hurwitz, Senior Vice President Shared Services
CNO: Susan Heath, R.N., Senior Vice President and Chief Nursing Officer
Web address: www.seattlechildrens.org
Control: Other not–for–profit (including NFP Corporation) **Service:** Children's general medical and surgical

Staffed Beds: 316

SWEDISH MEDICAL CENTER–CHERRY HILL CAMPUS (500025), 500 17th Avenue, Zip 98122–5711; tel. 206/320–2000, **A**1 2 3 5 7 10 21 **F**3 8 11 17 18 20 21 22 23 24 26 27 28 29 30 31 34 35 37 38 40 45 46 53 57 58 59 61 64 65 68 74 75 77 78 79 80 81 82 83 84 85 87 90 91 92 93 97 100 101 102 107 108 109 111 118 119 124 126 129 130 131 132 135 141 143 146 148 149 154 **P**6 **S** Swedish Health Services, Seattle, WA
Primary Contact: June Altaras, R.N., Chief Executive Officer
CFO: Jeffrey Veilleux, Senior Vice President and Chief Financial Officer
CIO: Janice Newell, Chief Information Officer
Web address: www.swedish.org
Control: Other not–for–profit (including NFP Corporation) **Service:** General medical and surgical

Staffed Beds: 227 **Admissions:** 9850 **Census:** 150 **Outpatient Visits:** 160458 **Births:** 0 **Total Expense ($000):** 487619 **Payroll Expense ($000):** 125933 **Personnel:** 1061

SWEDISH MEDICAL CENTER–FIRST HILL (500027), 747 Broadway, Zip 98122–4307; tel. 206/386–6000, (Includes SWEDISH MEDICAL CENTER–BALLARD, 5300 Tallman Avenue NW, Seattle, WA, Zip 98107–3932; tel. 206/782–2700; Jennifer Graves, R.N., MS, Chief Executive) **A**1 2 3 5 10 21 **F**3 4 5 7 8 11 12 13 15 18 19 20 21 22 23 25 26 29 30 31 32 34 35 36 37 38 39 40 41 45 46 47 48 49 52 54 55 56 57 58 59 60 61 64 65 66 68 70 71 72 73 74 75 76 77 78 79 80 81 82 83 84 85 86 87 88 89 91 92 93 96 97 98 100 101 102 104 107 108 109 110 111 114 115 116 117 118 119 120 121 123 126 127 130 131 132 134 135 136 138 139 141 142 144 146 147 148 149 154 **P**6 **S** Swedish Health Services, Seattle, WA
Primary Contact: June Altaras, R.N., Chief Executive Officer
COO: Gary G Fybel, FACHE, Interim Chief Operating Officer
CFO: Jeffrey Veilleux, Executive Vice President and Chief Financial Officer
CIO: Janice Newell, Chief Information Officer
Web address: www.swedish.org
Control: Other not–for–profit (including NFP Corporation) **Service:** General medical and surgical

Staffed Beds: 659 **Admissions:** 38849 **Census:** 481 **Outpatient Visits:** 654218 **Births:** 8677 **Total Expense ($000):** 1382805 **Payroll Expense ($000):** 410623 **Personnel:** 3257

UNIVERSITY OF WASHINGTON MEDICAL CENTER (500008), 1959 NE Pacific Street, Zip 98195–6151; tel. 206/598–3300, **A**1 2 3 5 7 8 10 **F**3 9 11 12 13 15 17 18 20 22 24 26 29 30 31 32 34 35 36 40 44 45 46 47 48 49 50 52 54 55 56 57 58 59 60 61 64 65 68 70 72 74 75 76 77 78 79 81 82 84 85 86 87 90 91 92 93 94 95 97 98 100 101 102 104 107 108 110 111 114 115 116 117 118 119 120 121 123 124 126 130 131 132 135 136 137 138 139 140 141 142 144 145 146 147 148 149 154 **S** UW Medicine, Seattle, WA
Primary Contact: Geoff Austin, Executive Director
CFO: Jacque Cabe, Chief Financial Officer
CMO: Tom Staiger, Medical Director
CIO: Joy Grosser, Chief Information Officer
CHR: Jennifer J Petritz, Director Human Resources
CNO: Cindy Sayre, Ph.D., R.N., Chief Nursing Officer
Web address: www.uwmedicine.org/uw-medical–center
Control: State, Government, nonfederal **Service**: General medical and surgical

Staffed Beds: 452 **Admissions:** 18964 **Census:** 363 **Outpatient Visits:** 378264 **Births:** 1943 **Total Expense ($000):** 1216983 **Payroll Expense ($000):** 374826 **Personnel:** 4425

UW MEDICINE/HARBORVIEW MEDICAL CENTER (500064), 325 Ninth Avenue, Zip 98104–2499, Mailing Address: P.O. Box 359717, Zip 98195–9717; tel. 206/744–3000, **A**1 3 5 7 8 10 **F**3 5 6 16 17 20 22 26 29 30 31 32 34 35 36 37 38 40 41 43 45 46 47 48 49 50 56 58 59 60 61 64 65 66 68 70 72 73 74 75 77 78 79 80 81 82 84 85 86 87 88 89 90 91 92 93 94 96 97 98 100 101 102 104 107 108 111 114 115 118 119 124 129 130 131 132 135 146 147 148 149 150 154 **P**6 **S** UW Medicine, Seattle, WA
Primary Contact: Paul Hayes, R.N., Executive Director
CFO: Kera Dennis, Assistant Administrator, Finance
CMO: J. Richard Goss, M.D., Medical Director
CIO: James Fine, M.D., Chief Information Officer
CHR: Nicki McCraw, Assistant Vice President Human Resources
CNO: Darcy Jaffe, R.N., Chief Nursing Officer
Web address: www.uwmedicine.org/Patient–Care/Locations/HMC/Pages/default.aspx
Control: County, Government, nonfederal **Service**: General medical and surgical

Staffed Beds: 413 **Admissions:** 16981 **Census:** 396 **Outpatient Visits:** 378490 **Births:** 0 **Total Expense ($000):** 996523 **Payroll Expense ($000):** 367494 **Personnel:** 4867

UW MEDICINE/NORTHWEST HOSPITAL & MEDICAL CENTER (500001), 1550 North 115th Street, Zip 98133–8401; tel. 206/364–0500, **A**1 2 3 5 10 **F**3 9 13 15 18 20 22 24 26 28 29 30 31 34 35 40 41 43 44 45 46 47 49 50 51 53 54 56 57 58 59 61 64 68 70 73 74 75 76 77 78 79 80 81 84 85 86 87 92 93 96 97 98 100 102 103 104 105 107 108 110 111 114 115 119 126 130 131 132 146 148 **P**6 **S** UW Medicine, Seattle, WA
Primary Contact: Cynthia Hecker, R.N., Executive Director
CFO: Ketty Hsieh, Senior Director Finance
CMO: Greg Schroedl, M.D., Vice President, Medical and Chief Medical Officer
CIO: Eric Neil, Interim Chief Information Officer
CHR: Linda Olmstead, Director, Human Resources
CNO: Susan Manfredi, R.N., Vice President and Chief Nursing Officer
Web address: www.uwmedicine.org/Patient–Care/Locations/nwh/Pages/default.aspx
Control: Other not–for–profit (including NFP Corporation) **Service**: General medical and surgical

Staffed Beds: 197 **Admissions:** 10265 **Census:** 140 **Outpatient Visits:** 398618 **Births:** 1166 **Total Expense ($000):** 394285 **Payroll Expense ($000):** 166732 **Personnel:** 1912

VETERANS AFFAIRS PUGET SOUND HEALTH CARE SYSTEM, 1660 South Columbian Way, Zip 98108–1597; tel. 206/762–1010, (Includes VETERANS AFFAIRS PUGET SOUND HEALTH CARE SYSTEM–AMERICAN LAKE DIVISION, 9600 Veterans Drive, Tacoma, WA, Zip 98493–0003; tel. 253/582–8440) (Nonreporting) **A**1 2 3 5 7 8 **S** Department of Veterans Affairs, Perry Point, MD
Primary Contact: Michael C. Tadych, FACHE, Director
CFO: Kenneth J Hudson, Chief Financial Officer
CMO: Gordon Starkebaum, M.D., Chief of Staff
CIO: Glenn Zwinger, Manager Information Systems Services
Web address: www.pugetsound.va.gov/
Control: Veterans Affairs, Government, federal **Service**: General medical and surgical

Staffed Beds: 358

VIRGINIA MASON MEDICAL CENTER (500005), 1100 Ninth Avenue, Zip 98101–2756, Mailing Address: P.O. Box 900, Zip 98111–0900; tel. 206/223–6600, (Total facility includes 35 beds in nursing home–type unit) **A**1 2 3 5 7 10 **F**2 3 8 11 12 15 17 18 20 22 24 25 28 29 30 31 33 34 36 40 44 45 46 47 48 49 50 51 55 56 57 58 59 60 61 63 64 65 68 70 74 75 77 78 79 80 81 82 83 84 85 86 87 91 92 93 94 96 97 98 100 101 102 103 104 107 108 110 111 114 115 117 118 119 120 121 123 126 128 129 130 131 132 135 138 141 142 144 145 146 148 154 **P**6 **S** Virginia Mason Health System, Seattle, WA
Primary Contact: Gary Kaplan, M.D., FACHE, Chairman and Chief Executive Officer
CFO: Craig Goodrich, Chief Financial Officer
CMO: Michael Glenn, M.D., Chief Medical Officer
CIO: Bill Poppy, Chief Information Officer
CHR: Kathy J. Shingleton, Ed.D., Vice President, Human Resources
CNO: Charleen Tachibana, R.N., Senior Vice President and Chief Nursing Officer
Web address: www.VirginiaMason.org
Control: Other not–for–profit (including NFP Corporation) **Service**: General medical and surgical

Staffed Beds: 232 **Admissions:** 11348 **Census:** 198 **Outpatient Visits:** 893442 **Births:** 0 **Total Expense ($000):** 1017820 **Payroll Expense ($000):** 489201 **Personnel:** 4848

SEDRO—WOOLLEY–Skagit County

PEACEHEALTH UNITED GENERAL MEDICAL CENTER (501329), 2000 Hospital Drive, Zip 98284–4327; tel. 360/856–6021, **A**2 10 18 21 **F**3 11 15 29 30 31 34 35 40 43 45 50 57 59 64 68 70 75 77 78 79 81 85 89 92 93 107 108 110 115 118 119 120 121 123 129 130 132 133 143 146 148 149 **P**6 **S** PeaceHealth, Vancouver, WA
Primary Contact: Christopher Johnston, Chief Administrative Officer
CFO: Carolyn Haupt, Chief Financial Officer
CHR: Tracie Skrinde, Senior Human Resources Partner
Web address: www.peacehealth.org/united–general
Control: Church operated, Nongovernment, not–for–profit **Service**: General medical and surgical

Staffed Beds: 25 **Admissions:** 700 **Census:** 9 **Outpatient Visits:** 28671 **Births:** 0 **Total Expense ($000):** 43984 **Payroll Expense ($000):** 15931 **Personnel:** 218

SHELTON—Mason County

MASON GENERAL HOSPITAL AND FAMILY OF CLINICS (501336), 901 Mountain View Drive, Zip 98584–4401, Mailing Address: P.O. Box 1668, Zip 98584–5001; tel. 360/426–1611, **A**1 10 18 **F**3 11 13 15 29 30 34 35 40 45 50 57 59 68 70 75 76 79 81 83 85 93 97 104 107 110 111 119 127 130 132 146 147 148 149 154
Primary Contact: Eric Moll, Chief Executive Officer
COO: Eileen Branscome, Chief Operating Officer
CFO: Rick Smith, Chief Financial Officer
CMO: Dean Gushee, M.D., Medical Director
CIO: Tom Hornburg, Director Information Systems
CHR: Eileen Branscome, Director Human Resources
CNO: Melissa D Strong, Chief Nursing Officer
Web address: www.masongeneral.com
Control: Hospital district or authority, Government, nonfederal **Service**: General medical and surgical

Staffed Beds: 25 **Admissions:** 1638 **Census:** 14 **Outpatient Visits:** 90818 **Births:** 255 **Total Expense ($000):** 97841 **Payroll Expense ($000):** 46269 **Personnel:** 494

SNOQUALMIE—King County

SNOQUALMIE VALLEY HOSPITAL DISTRICT (501338), 9801 Frontier Avenue SE, Zip 98065–9577; tel. 425/831–2300, (Nonreporting) **A**10 18
Primary Contact: Thomas Parker, Chief Executive Officer
CHR: Kimberly D Washburn, Director Human Resources
Web address: www.snoqualmiehospital.org/
Control: Hospital district or authority, Government, nonfederal **Service**: General medical and surgical

Staffed Beds: 18

Hospital, Medicare Provider Number, Address, Telephone, Approval, Facility, and Physician Codes, Health Care System

★ American Hospital Association (AHA) membership
☐ The Joint Commission accreditation
○ Healthcare Facilities Accreditation Program
◇ DNV Healthcare Inc. accreditation
⇑ Center for Improvement in Healthcare Quality Accreditation
△ Commission on Accreditation of Rehabilitation Facilities (CARF) accreditation

SOUTH BEND—Pacific County

WILLAPA HARBOR HOSPITAL (501303), 800 Alder Street, Zip 98586–4900, Mailing Address: P.O. Box 438, Zip 98586–0438; tel. 360/875–5526, (Nonreporting) **A**10 18
Primary Contact: Carole Halsan, R.N., Chief Executive Officer
CFO: Terry Stone, Chief Financial Officer and Chief Information Officer
CIO: Terry Stone, Chief Financial Officer and Chief Information Officer
CHR: Krisy L Funkhouser, Manager Human Resources
Web address: www.willapaharborhospital.com
Control: Hospital district or authority, Government, nonfederal **Service**: General medical and surgical

Staffed Beds: 10

SPOKANE—Spokane County

MANN–GRANDSTAFF VETERANS AFFAIRS MEDICAL CENTER, 4815 North Assembly Street, Zip 99205–6197; tel. 509/434–7000, (Nonreporting) **A**1 3 5 **S** Department of Veterans Affairs, Perry Point, MD
Primary Contact: Tracye B. Davis, Interim Medical Center Director
COO: Perry Klein, Chief Engineering
CFO: Michael Stuhlmiller, Chief Financial Officer
CIO: Rob Fortenberry, Chief Information Officer
CHR: Jacqueline Ross, Chief Human Resources Officer
CNO: Nancy Benton, Assistant Director Patient Care Services
Web address: www.spokane.va.gov/
Control: Veterans Affairs, Government, federal **Service**: General medical and surgical

Staffed Beds: 70

MULTICARE DEACONESS HOSPITAL (500044), 800 West Fifth Avenue, Zip 99204–2803, Mailing Address: P.O. Box 248, Zip 99210–0248; tel. 509/458–5800, **A**1 3 10 **F**3 12 15 17 18 20 22 24 26 28 29 30 31 35 40 43 45 46 47 48 49 50 51 56 60 64 68 70 72 73 74 75 78 79 81 82 85 86 91 92 107 108 110 111 113 114 115 119 124 126 129 130 132 146 147 148 149 **S** MultiCare Health System, Tacoma, WA
Primary Contact: Laureen Driscoll, President
CFO: Rodney Higgins, Chief Financial Officer
CMO: David Chen, M.D., Chief Medical Officer
CIO: Richard DeRoche, Manager Information Technology
CHR: Melinda Moore, Director Human Resources
CNO: Jennifer Petrik, Interim Chief Nursing Officer
Web address: www.multicare.org/deaconess–hospital/
Control: Other not–for–profit (including NFP Corporation) **Service**: General medical and surgical

Staffed Beds: 352 Admissions: 10866 Census: 158 Outpatient Visits: 107516 Births: 1441 Total Expense ($000): 294880 Payroll Expense ($000): 97188 Personnel: 1078

PROVIDENCE HOLY FAMILY HOSPITAL (500077), 5633 North Lidgerwood Street, Zip 99208–1224; tel. 509/482–0111, **A**1 2 5 7 10 **F**3 8 11 12 13 15 18 29 30 31 34 35 37 38 39 40 41 43 45 46 47 48 49 50 53 56 57 58 59 60 61 64 68 70 73 74 75 76 77 78 79 80 81 82 84 85 86 87 92 100 107 108 129 130 131 132 135 143 145 146 147 148 149 154 **P**6 **S** Providence St. Joseph Health, Renton, WA
Primary Contact: Peggy M. Currie, R.N., Chief Operating Officer
COO: Cathy J Simchuk, Chief Operating Officer
CFO: Shelby Stokoe, Chief Financial Officer
CMO: Dean Martz, Chief Medical Officer
CIO: Mark Vogelsang, Director Information Services
CHR: Mark Smith, Director Human Resources
CNO: Sharon Hershman, R.N., Chief Nursing Officer
Web address: www.providence.org
Control: Church operated, Nongovernment, not–for–profit **Service**: General medical and surgical

Staffed Beds: 191 Admissions: 8732 Census: 96 Outpatient Visits: 189205 Births: 1227 Total Expense ($000): 201898 Payroll Expense ($000): 56839 Personnel: 874

PROVIDENCE SACRED HEART MEDICAL CENTER & CHILDREN'S HOSPITAL (500054), 101 West Eighth Avenue, Zip 99204–2364, Mailing Address: P.O. Box 2555, Zip 99220–2555; tel. 509/474–3131, (Includes SACRED HEART CHILDREN'S HOSPITAL, 101 West Eighth Avenue, Spokane, WA, Zip 99204–2307, Mailing Address: PO Box 2555, Zip 99220–2555, tel. 509/474–4841; Keith Georgeson, M.D., Chief Executive) **A**1 2 3 5 10 **F**3 8 13 17 18 19 20 21 22 23 24 25 26 27 29 30 31 35 36 37 40 41 43 45 46 47 48 49 56 60 68 70 72 73 74 75 76 78 79 81 82 83 84 85 86 87 88 89 92 98 99 100 101 102 103 104 105 106 107 108 109 110 111 112 114 115 118 119 120 121 123 124 126 130 131 132 136 137 138 142 145 146 147 148 149 154 **P**6 **S** Providence St. Joseph Health, Renton, WA
Primary Contact: Peggy M. Currie, R.N., Chief Operating Officer
CFO: Shelby Stokoe, Senior Director Finance
CMO: Dean Martz, Chief Medical Officer
CHR: Mark Smith, Director Human Resources
CNO: Susan Stacey, Chief Nursing Officer
Web address: www.shmc.org
Control: Church operated, Nongovernment, not–for–profit **Service**: General medical and surgical

Staffed Beds: 719 Admissions: 29185 Census: 468 Outpatient Visits: 481076 Births: 3103 Total Expense ($000): 940774 Payroll Expense ($000): 298406 Personnel: 3629

SHRINERS HOSPITALS FOR CHILDREN–SPOKANE (503302), 911 West Fifth Avenue, Zip 99204–2901, Mailing Address: P.O. Box 2472, Zip 99210–2472; tel. 509/455–7844, (Nonreporting) **A**1 3 10 **S** Shriners Hospitals for Children, Tampa, FL
Primary Contact: Peter G. Brewer, Administrator
CFO: Monica Hickman, Director Fiscal Services
CMO: Glen Baird, M.D., Chief of Staff
CIO: Mike Allen, Director Information Services
CHR: Karen Mattern, Director of Human Resources
CNO: Lynda Vilanova, Director Patient Care Services
Web address: www.shrinershospitalsforchildren.org/Hospitals/Locations/Spokane.aspx
Control: Other not–for–profit (including NFP Corporation) **Service**: Children's orthopedic

Staffed Beds: 30

ST. LUKE'S REHABILITATION INSTITUTE (503025), 711 South Cowley Street, Zip 99202–1388; tel. 509/473–6000, **A**1 7 10 **F**28 29 30 34 35 36 38 43 50 53 57 58 64 68 74 75 77 79 82 86 87 90 91 92 93 95 96 130 131 132 135 146 148 149 **P**6 **S** Providence St. Joseph Health, Renton, WA
Primary Contact: Nancy Webster, Administrator and Chief Operating Officer
CFO: Helen Andrus, Chief Financial Officer
CMO: Gregory Carter, M.D., Chief Medical Officer
CIO: Fred Galusha, Chief Information Officer
CHR: Staci Franz, Director Human Resources
CNO: Kimberly J Ward, Chief Nurse Officer
Web address: www.st–lukes.org
Control: Other not–for–profit (including NFP Corporation) **Service**: Rehabilitation

Staffed Beds: 78 Admissions: 1285 Census: 53 Outpatient Visits: 95004 Births: 0 Total Expense ($000): 48304 Payroll Expense ($000): 30086 Personnel: 639

VETERANS AFFAIRS MEDICAL CENTER See Mann–Grandstaff Veterans Affairs Medical Center

SPOKANE VALLEY—Spokane County

MULTICARE VALLEY HOSPITAL (500119), 12606 East Mission Avenue, Zip 99216–1090; tel. 509/924–6650, **A**1 3 10 **F**3 8 13 20 29 30 40 43 45 46 48 49 50 59 60 68 70 74 75 76 78 79 81 85 87 107 108 111 114 119 130 131 135 143 146 147 148 154 **S** MultiCare Health System, Tacoma, WA
Primary Contact: Gregory George. Repetti III, FACHE, Chief Executive Officer
COO: David Martin, Assistant Administrator
CFO: Justin Voelker, Chief Financial Officer
CMO: David Chen, M.D., Chief Medical Officer
CIO: Brain Jones, Director of Information Technology
CHR: Jamie Caine, Director of Human Resources
CNO: Shannon S Holland, R.N., MSN, Chief Nursing Officer
Web address: www.valleyhospital.org
Control: Other not–for–profit (including NFP Corporation) **Service**: General medical and surgical

Staffed Beds: 92 Admissions: 5757 Census: 57 Outpatient Visits: 57926 Births: 708 Total Expense ($000): 100460 Payroll Expense ($000): 43245 Personnel: 570

SUNNYSIDE—Yakima County

ASTRIA SUNNYSIDE HOSPITAL (501330), 1016 Tacoma Avenue, Zip 98944–2263, Mailing Address: P.O. Box 719, Zip 98944–0719; tel. 509/837–1500, **A**10 18 **F**8 11 13 15 18 20 22 26 29 30 31 32 34 35 40 41 45 46 50 51 59 60 62 64 65 68 70 74 76 77 78 79 81 82 87 89 93 100 104 107 108 110 111 115 116 117 119 127 129 130 131 132 133 144 148 153 154 **S** Astria Health, Sunnyside, WA
Primary Contact: Brian P. Gibbons Jr, Chief Executive Officer
CFO: Cary Rowan, Chief Financial Officer
CIO: John Andersen, Manager Information Systems
CHR: Elaina Wagner, Director Human Resources
CNO: Mary Beth Tubbs, Chief Nursing Officer
Web address: www.astria.health/
Control: Other not–for–profit (including NFP Corporation) **Service**: General medical and surgical

Staffed Beds: 25 Admissions: 1905 Census: 18 Outpatient Visits: 81111 Births: 530 Total Expense ($000): 93068 Payroll Expense ($000): 36881 Personnel: 488

TACOMA—Pierce County

ALLENMORE HOSPITAL See Multicare Tacoma General Hospital, Tacoma

Many Facility Codes have changed. Please refer to the AHA Guide Code Chart.   © 2018 AHA Guide

MADIGAN ARMY MEDICAL CENTER, Fitzsimmons Drive, Building 9040, Zip 98431–1100; tel. 253/968–1110, **A**1 2 3 **F**3 4 5 7 8 9 11 12 13 14 15 18 19 20 22 29 30 31 32 33 34 35 36 37 38 39 40 41 43 44 45 46 47 48 49 50 51 52 53 54 55 56 57 58 59 60 61 64 65 68 70 72 74 75 76 77 78 79 80 81 82 83 84 85 86 87 88 89 92 93 94 96 97 98 100 101 102 103 104 107 110 111 114 115 116 117 118 119 120 121 122 123 124 126 129 130 131 132 134 135 136 144 145 146 147 148 149 153 154 **S** Department of the Army, Office of the Surgeon General, Falls Church, VA
Primary Contact: Colonel Thomas S. Bundt, Commanding Officer
COO: Colonel R Neal David, Administrator and Chief of Staff
CFO: Lieutenant Colonel Bryan Longmuir, Chief Resource Management
CIO: Lieutenant Colonel Andrew Smith, Chief Information Management
CHR: David Aiken, Chief Human Resources Officer
Web address: www.mamc.health.mil/
Control: Army, Government, federal **Service**: General medical and surgical

Staffed Beds: 200 **Admissions**: 11748 **Census**: 110 **Outpatient Visits**: 1396065 **Births**: 1950 **Total Expense ($000)**: 591965 **Payroll Expense ($000)**: 270584

MULTICARE MARY BRIDGE CHILDREN'S HOSPITAL AND HEALTH CENTER (503301), 317 Martin Luther King Jr Way, Zip 98405–4234, Mailing Address: P.O. Box 5299, Zip 98415–0299; tel. 253/403–1400, **A**1 3 5 10 **F**3 8 18 19 21 23 25 27 29 30 31 32 34 35 38 39 40 41 43 45 46 48 49 53 54 55 57 58 59 60 61 62 64 65 66 68 71 74 75 78 79 81 82 84 85 86 87 88 89 91 92 93 94 96 97 100 104 107 108 111 114 115 116 117 119 120 121 123 124 126 129 130 131 132 143 144 146 148 149 150 153 154 **S** MultiCare Health System, Tacoma, WA
Primary Contact: Jeffrey S. Poltawsky, President and Market Leader
COO: Jennifer Hamilton, COO – Mary Bridge
CMO: Iain Asplin, Chief Medical Officer
CHR: Kevin B Dull, Senior Vice President Human Potential
CNO: Diana Brovold, Chief Nurse Executive
Web address: www.multicare.org/marybridge
Control: Other not–for–profit (including NFP Corporation) **Service**: Children's general medical and surgical

Staffed Beds: 75 **Admissions**: 3655 **Census**: 37 **Outpatient Visits**: 148920 **Births**: 0 **Total Expense ($000)**: 221923 **Payroll Expense ($000)**: 82331 **Personnel**: 691

MULTICARE TACOMA GENERAL HOSPITAL (500129), 315 Martin Luther King Jr Way, Zip 98405–4234, Mailing Address: P.O. Box 5299, Zip 98415–0299; tel. 253/403–1000, (Includes ALLENMORE HOSPITAL, 1901 South Union Avenue, Tacoma, WA, Zip 98405, Mailing Address: P.O. Box 11414, Zip 98411–0414, tel. 253/459–6633; Sharon Oxendale, President and Chief Operating Officer) **A**1 2 3 10 **F**3 8 12 13 15 17 18 20 22 24 26 28 29 30 31 34 35 36 40 43 45 46 47 48 49 50 51 53 54 55 57 58 59 64 70 72 73 74 75 76 78 79 80 81 82 84 85 87 98 99 100 102 107 108 109 111 114 115 116 117 119 120 121 123 124 126 129 130 131 132 135 146 147 148 149 154 **S** MultiCare Health System, Tacoma, WA
Primary Contact: Sharon Oxendale, President and Chief Operating Officer
COO: Julia Truman, Chief Operating Officer
CHR: Kevin B Dull, Senior Vice President Human Potential
CNO: Anita Wolfe, Chief Nurse Executive
Web address: www.multicare.org
Control: Other not–for–profit (including NFP Corporation) **Service**: General medical and surgical

Staffed Beds: 457 **Admissions**: 19974 **Census**: 298 **Outpatient Visits**: 203390 **Births**: 3005 **Total Expense ($000)**: 742082 **Payroll Expense ($000)**: 280815 **Personnel**: 2721

ST. JOSEPH MEDICAL CENTER (500108), 1717 South 'J' Street, Zip 98405–3004, Mailing Address: P.O. Box 2197, Zip 98401–2197; tel. 253/426–4101, **A**1 2 3 7 10 **F**3 8 11 12 13 17 18 20 22 24 26 28 29 30 31 34 35 38 40 43 44 45 46 47 48 49 50 51 53 54 55 56 59 60 63 64 65 70 72 73 74 75 76 77 78 79 81 82 84 85 86 87 90 92 93 98 102 107 108 111 114 115 119 124 126 130 131 132 135 145 146 148 149 154 **S** Catholic Health Initiatives, Englewood, CO
Primary Contact: Syd Bersante, R.N., President
COO: Tim O'Haver, Chief Operating Officer
CFO: Mike Fitzgerald, Chief Financial Officer
CIO: Rand Strobel, Vice President Information Technology and Compliance
CNO: Ruth Flint, Chief Nursing Officer
Web address: www.chifranciscan.org
Control: Church operated, Nongovernment, not–for–profit **Service**: General medical and surgical

Staffed Beds: 366 **Admissions**: 20410 **Census**: 305 **Outpatient Visits**: 261878 **Births**: 4327 **Total Expense ($000)**: 644815 **Payroll Expense ($000)**: 210612 **Personnel**: 2742

VETERANS AFFAIRS PUGET SOUND HEALTH CARE SYSTEM–AMERICAN LAKE DIVISION See Veterans Affairs Puget Sound Health Care System, Seattle

WESTERN STATE HOSPITAL (504003), 9601 Steilacoom Boulevard SW, Zip 98498–7213; tel. 253/582–8900, (Nonreporting) **A**1 5 10
Primary Contact: David Holt, Chief Executive Officer
CFO: Sue Breen, Chief Financial Officer
CMO: James A Polo, M.D., Chief Medical Officer
CHR: Lori Manning, Administrator Human Resources
CNO: Rae Simpson, R.N., Chief Nursing Officer
Web address: www.dshs.wa.gov/bhsia/division–state–hospitals/western–state–hospital
Control: State, Government, nonfederal **Service**: Psychiatric

Staffed Beds: 867

TONASKET—Okanogan County

NORTH VALLEY HOSPITAL (501321), 203 South Western Avenue, Zip 98855–8803; tel. 509/486–2151, (Nonreporting) **A**10 18
Primary Contact: Scott Graham, Chief Executive Officer
COO: John McReynolds, Chief Operating Officer
CMO: Paul Lacey, M.D., Chief Medical Staff
CIO: Kelly Cariker, Chief Information Officer
CHR: Jan Gonzales, Director Human Resources
Web address: www.nvhospital.org
Control: Hospital district or authority, Government, nonfederal **Service**: General medical and surgical

Staffed Beds: 67

TOPPENISH—Yakima County

ASTRIA TOPPENISH HOSPITAL (500037), 502 West Fourth Avenue, Zip 98948–1616, Mailing Address: P.O. Box 672, Zip 98948–0672; tel. 509/865–3105, (Nonreporting) **A**1 3 5 10 **S** Astria Health, Sunnyside, WA
Primary Contact: Eric P. Jensen, Chief Executive Officer
CFO: Curtis Herrin, Chief Financial Officer
CHR: Rosa Solorzano, Interim Director Human Resources
Web address: www.astria.health/
Control: Corporation, Investor–owned (for–profit) **Service**: General medical and surgical

Staffed Beds: 48

TUKWILA—King County

CASCADE BEHAVIORAL HOSPITAL (504011), 12844 Military Road South, Zip 98168–3045; tel. 206/244–0180, (Nonreporting) **A**1 10 **S** Acadia Healthcare Company, Inc., Franklin, TN
Primary Contact: Michael Uradnik, Chief Executive Officer
CFO: Gregg Terreson, Chief Financial Officer
CHR: Sherry Cochran, Manager Human Resources
Web address: www.cascadebh.com
Control: Corporation, Investor–owned (for–profit) **Service**: Psychiatric

Staffed Beds: 63

VANCOUVER—Clark County

LEGACY SALMON CREEK HOSPITAL See Legacy Salmon Creek Medical Center

LEGACY SALMON CREEK MEDICAL CENTER (500150), 2211 NE 139th Street, Zip 98686–2742; tel. 360/487–1000, **A**1 2 5 10 **F**3 11 13 15 18 20 26 28 29 30 31 32 34 35 37 38 39 40 41 44 45 46 47 49 50 51 55 57 59 60 65 68 70 72 74 75 76 77 78 79 80 81 82 84 85 87 93 94 96 97 107 108 110 111 114 115 116 117 118 119 120 121 126 129 130 132 146 147 148 149 150 **P**6 **S** Legacy Health, Portland, OR
Primary Contact: Bryce R. Helgerson, Chief Administrative Officer
COO: Michael Newcomb, D.O., Senior Vice President and Chief Operating Officer
CMO: Lewis Low, M.D., Senior Vice President and Chief Medical Officer
CHR: Sonja Steves, Senior Vice President Human Resources
CNO: Carol Bradley, MSN, R.N., Senior Vice President and Chief Nursing Officer
Web address: www.legacyhealth.org
Control: Other not–for–profit (including NFP Corporation) **Service**: General medical and surgical

Staffed Beds: 211 **Admissions**: 15308 **Census**: 161 **Outpatient Visits**: 298844 **Births**: 3313 **Total Expense ($000)**: 284499 **Payroll Expense ($000)**: 154414 **Personnel**: 1730

WA

PEACEHEALTH SOUTHWEST MEDICAL CENTER (500050), 400 NE Mother Joseph Place, Zip 98664–3200, Mailing Address: P.O. Box 1600, Zip 98668–1600; tel. 360/256–2000, (Includes VANCOUVER MEMORIAL CAMPUS, 3400 Main Street, Vancouver, WA, Zip 98663; tel. 360/514–2000; Sean Gregory, Chief Executive, Columbia Network) **A**2 3 5 7 10 21 **F**3 11 12 13 15 17 18 20 22 24 26 28 29 30 31 34 35 40 43 44 45 46 49 50 51 54 57 58 59 60 61 62 63 64 65 68 70 72 73 74 75 77 78 79 81 82 84 85 86 87 88 90 92 93 96 97 98 100 101 102 103 104 105 107 108 109 110 111 114 115 116 117 119 120 121 122 124 126 129 130 131 132 135 144 145 146 147 148 153 154 **S** PeaceHealth, Vancouver, WA
Primary Contact: Sean Gregory, Chief Executive
COO: Wade Hunt, Chief Operating Officer
CFO: Ronald K Benfield, Chief Financial Officer
CMO: Lawrence Neville, Chief Medical Officer
CIO: Donn McMillan, Senior Director, IST Client Liaison
CHR: Kelley Frengle, Senior Director, Human Resources
CNO: Helen Vos, R.N., Interim Chief Nursing Officer
Web address: www.peacehealth.org
Control: Church operated, Nongovernment, not–for–profit **Service**: General medical and surgical

Staffed Beds: 412 **Admissions**: 19154 **Census**: 247 **Outpatient Visits**: 260617 **Births**: 2102 **Total Expense ($000)**: 529026 **Payroll Expense ($000)**: 175211 **Personnel**: 2773

SOUTHWEST WASHINGTON MEDICAL CENTER See Peacehealth Southwest Medical Center

WALLA WALLA—Walla Walla County

PROVIDENCE ST. MARY MEDICAL CENTER (500002), 401 West Poplar Street, Zip 99362–2846, Mailing Address: P.O. Box 1477, Zip 99362–0312; tel. 509/897–3320, **A**1 2 7 10 19 **F**3 13 15 18 20 22 28 29 30 31 34 35 40 43 45 46 49 59 60 62 64 70 74 75 76 77 78 79 80 81 84 85 89 90 92 93 96 97 100 107 108 110 111 114 115 119 120 121 123 124 129 130 132 135 144 146 147 148 149 154 **P**6 **S** Providence St. Joseph Health, Renton, WA
Primary Contact: Susan Blackburn, Chief Administrative Officer
COO: Susan Blackburn, Chief Operating Officer
CMO: Tim Davidson, M.D., Chief Executive Physician Services
CIO: Martin Manny, Director, I.S.
CNO: Yvonne M Strader, Chief Nursing Officer
Web address: www.washington.providence.org/hospitals/st–mary/
Control: Church operated, Nongovernment, not–for–profit **Service**: General medical and surgical

Staffed Beds: 92 **Admissions**: 5605 **Census**: 55 **Outpatient Visits**: 200123 **Births**: 683 **Total Expense ($000)**: 222086 **Payroll Expense ($000)**: 97076 **Personnel**: 1169

STATE PENITENTIARY HOSPITAL, 1313 North 13th Street, Zip 99362–8817; tel. 509/525–3610, (Nonreporting)
Primary Contact: Karen Forest, Health Care Manager
Control: State, Government, nonfederal **Service**: Hospital unit of an institution (prison hospital, college infirmary, etc.)

Staffed Beds: 36

WENATCHEE—Chelan County

CONFLUENCE HEALTH/CENTRAL WASHINGTON HOSPITAL (500016), 1201 South Miller Street, Zip 98801–3201, Mailing Address: P.O. Box 1887, Zip 98807–1887; tel. 509/662–1511, (Nonreporting) **A**2 3 10 19 21
Primary Contact: Peter Rutherford, M.D., Chief Executive Officer
COO: Vikki Noyes, Executive Vice President and Chief Operating Officer
CFO: John Doyle, Chief Financial Officer
CMO: Stuart Freed, M.D., Chief Medical Officer
CIO: Robert Pageler, Chief Information Officer
CHR: Jim Wood, Chief Administrative Officer
CNO: Tracey A Kasnic, Senior Vice President Inpatient and Chief Nursing Officer
Web address: www.cwhs.com
Control: Other not–for–profit (including NFP Corporation) **Service**: General medical and surgical

Staffed Beds: 198

CONFLUENCE HEALTH/WENATCHEE VALLEY HOSPITAL (500148), 820 North Chelan Avenue, Zip 98801–2028; tel. 509/663–8711, (Total facility includes 22 beds in nursing home–type unit) **A**2 7 10 **F**3 13 17 18 20 22 24 26 28 29 30 31 34 35 40 43 45 46 47 49 50 62 63 64 68 69 70 73 74 75 76 78 79 81 84 85 86 89 91 93 94 95 107 111 114 115 119 127 128 130 146 148
Primary Contact: Peter Rutherford, M.D., Chief Executive Officer
COO: Kevin Gilbert, R.N., Vice President
CFO: John Doyle, Chief Financial Officer
CMO: Stuart Freed, M.D., Medical Director
CIO: Robert Pageler, Chief Information Officer
CHR: Jim Wood, Chief Human Resources Officer
CNO: Tracey A Kasnic, Chief Nursing Officer
Web address: www.confluencehealth.org
Control: Other not–for–profit (including NFP Corporation) **Service**: General medical and surgical

Staffed Beds: 198 **Admissions**: 11774 **Census**: 145 **Outpatient Visits**: 123453 **Births**: 1351 **Total Expense ($000)**: 320520 **Payroll Expense ($000)**: 96798 **Personnel**: 1421

WHITE SALMON—Klickitat County

SKYLINE HOSPITAL (501315), 211 Skyline Drive, Zip 98672–1918, Mailing Address: P.O. Box 99, Zip 98672–0099; tel. 509/493–1101, **A**10 18 **F**3 15 18 34 35 40 43 45 57 59 64 74 81 82 87 93 97 107 115 119 127 131 133 146 149 **P**6
Primary Contact: Robert P. Kimmes, Chief Executive Officer
CFO: Brenda Schneider, Chief Financial Officer
CMO: Christopher Samuels, Chief of Staff
CIO: Steve Opbroek, Manager Information Technology
CHR: Jessie Ramos, Manager Human Resources
CNO: Stefanie Boen, Chief Nursing Officer
Web address: www.skylinehospital.org
Control: Hospital district or authority, Government, nonfederal **Service**: General medical and surgical

Staffed Beds: 16 **Admissions**: 208 **Census**: 2 **Outpatient Visits**: 15303 **Births**: 0 **Total Expense ($000)**: 18783 **Payroll Expense ($000)**: 10092 **Personnel**: 142

YAKIMA—Yakima County

ASTRIA REGIONAL MEDICAL CENTER (500012), 110 South Ninth Avenue, Zip 98902–3315; tel. 509/575–5000, **A**1 7 10 **F**3 15 17 18 19 20 21 22 23 24 26 28 29 30 34 35 37 40 41 43 45 46 47 48 49 50 51 59 62 63 64 67 68 70 74 77 79 81 84 85 87 89 90 91 92 93 94 95 96 107 108 110 111 115 119 126 130 132 146 149 154 **S** Astria Health, Sunnyside, WA
Primary Contact: Richard H. Robinson, Chief Executive Officer
COO: Darrin Cook, Chief Operating Officer
CMO: John Zambito, M.D., Chief of Staff
CNO: Beth Gregory, Interim Chief Nursing Officer
Web address: www.astria.health/
Control: Other not–for–profit (including NFP Corporation) **Service**: General medical and surgical

Staffed Beds: 167 **Admissions**: 3143 **Census**: 48 **Outpatient Visits**: 33864 **Births**: 0 **Total Expense ($000)**: 42259 **Payroll Expense ($000)**: 32709 **Personnel**: 711

VIRGINIA MASON MEMORIAL (500036), 2811 Tieton Drive, Zip 98902–3761; tel. 509/575–8000, **A**1 2 3 5 10 **F**3 8 9 11 13 15 17 18 20 22 26 28 29 30 31 32 34 35 36 40 41 43 44 45 46 47 48 49 50 51 54 55 57 58 59 60 62 63 64 68 70 72 74 75 76 77 78 79 81 82 84 85 86 87 89 91 92 93 96 97 98 100 102 103 104 107 110 111 114 115 116 117 118 119 120 121 123 124 129 130 131 132 135 144 145 146 147 148 154 **P**6 **S** Virginia Mason Health System, Seattle, WA
Primary Contact: Russ Myers, Chief Executive Officer
COO: Diane Patterson, Senior Vice President, Chief Operating Officer and Chief Nursing Officer
CFO: Tim Reed, Vice President and Chief Financial Officer
CMO: Marty Brueggemann, Chief Medical Officer
CIO: Jeff Yamada, Vice President
CHR: Jolene R. Seda, Vice President People and Culture
CNO: Diane Patterson, Senior Vice President, Chief Operating Officer and Chief Nursing Officer
Web address: www.yakimamemorial.org
Control: Other not–for–profit (including NFP Corporation) **Service**: General medical and surgical

Staffed Beds: 220 **Admissions**: 12149 **Census**: 127 **Outpatient Visits**: 528273 **Births**: 2575 **Total Expense ($000)**: 470481 **Payroll Expense ($000)**: 195900 **Personnel**: 2526

WA

WEST VIRGINIA

BECKLEY—Raleigh County

☐ **BECKLEY ARH HOSPITAL (510062)**, 306 Stanaford Road, Zip 25801–3142; tel. 304/255–3000, **A**1 10 **F**3 6 11 15 17 18 20 28 29 30 31 34 35 40 43 44 45 46 47 48 49 50 51 54 56 57 59 60 61 62 64 65 70 74 75 77 78 79 81 82 84 85 86 87 89 92 93 97 98 99 100 101 102 103 107 108 109 110 111 114 115 116 118 119 129 130 132 146 148 **P**6 **S** Appalachian Regional Healthcare, Inc., Lexington, KY
Primary Contact: Rocco K. Massey, Community Chief Executive Officer
CMO: Ahmad Khiami, Chief of Staff
CHR: Sue Thomas, Manager Human Resources
CNO: Angela Rivera, Chief Nursing Officer
Web address: www.arh.org
Control: Other not–for–profit (including NFP Corporation) **Service**: General medical and surgical

Staffed Beds: 160 **Admissions**: 6542 **Census**: 100 **Outpatient Visits**: 88872 **Births**: 0 **Total Expense ($000)**: 91867 **Payroll Expense ($000)**: 25830 **Personnel**: 596

✠ **BECKLEY VETERANS AFFAIRS MEDICAL CENTER**, 200 Veterans Avenue, Zip 25801–6499; tel. 304/255–2121, (Nonreporting) **A**1 3 **S** Department of Veterans Affairs, Perry Point, MD
Primary Contact: Stacy J. Vasquez, Director
CFO: Terry Massey, Chief Fiscal Services
CMO: John David Berryman, M.D., Chief of Staff
CIO: Sherry Gregg, Chief Information Technology Officer
CNO: Debra Lynn Legg, Associate Director Patient Care Services and Nurse Executive
Web address: www.beckley.va.gov/
Control: Veterans Affairs, Government, federal **Service**: General medical and surgical

Staffed Beds: 173

✠ **RALEIGH GENERAL HOSPITAL (510070)**, 1710 Harper Road, Zip 25801–3397; tel. 304/256–4100, **A**1 10 19 **F**3 13 15 17 18 20 22 29 30 31 34 35 40 43 45 49 50 57 59 60 64 70 74 75 76 78 79 81 85 87 89 107 108 110 111 114 115 116 117 119 120 126 130 132 146 147 148 149 **S** LifePoint Health, Brentwood, TN
Primary Contact: Matthew S. Roberts, Chief Executive Officer
CFO: Randy Harrison, Chief Financial Officer
CMO: Syed Siddiqi, M.D., President Medical Staff
CIO: Kevin Sexton, Director Information Systems
CHR: Chris T Beebe, Director Human Resources
CNO: Alene Lewis, R.N., Chief Nursing Officer
Web address: www.raleighgeneral.com
Control: Corporation, Investor–owned (for–profit) **Service**: General medical and surgical

Staffed Beds: 229 **Admissions**: 10331 **Census**: 132 **Outpatient Visits**: 100294 **Births**: 1004 **Total Expense ($000)**: 140759 **Payroll Expense ($000)**: 43919 **Personnel**: 838

BERKELEY SPRINGS—Morgan County

★ **WAR MEMORIAL HOSPITAL (511309)**, One Healthy Way, Zip 25411–7463; tel. 304/258–1234, (Total facility includes 16 beds in nursing home–type unit) **A**10 18 **F**3 11 15 18 28 29 30 34 35 40 45 50 53 54 57 59 64 65 77 79 81 85 86 93 97 107 110 114 119 129 130 133 154 **P**6 **S** Valley Health System, Winchester, VA
Primary Contact: Thomas S. Kluge, President
CFO: Kathryn Morales, Director of Finance
CMO: Gerald Bechamps, M.D., Vice President Medical Affairs
CHR: Abbey Rembold, Human Resources Senior Generalist
CNO: Heather Sigel, Director of Clinical Services
Web address: www.valleyhealthlink.com/war
Control: Other not–for–profit (including NFP Corporation) **Service**: General medical and surgical

Staffed Beds: 41 **Admissions**: 412 **Census**: 24 **Outpatient Visits**: 28051 **Births**: 0 **Total Expense ($000)**: 21768 **Payroll Expense ($000)**: 9824 **Personnel**: 153

BLUEFIELD—Mercer County

✠ **BLUEFIELD REGIONAL MEDICAL CENTER (510071)**, 500 Cherry Street, Zip 24701–3390; tel. 304/327–1100, **A**1 10 12 13 19 **F**3 8 13 15 18 20 22 28 29 31 34 40 43 45 46 47 49 50 56 57 59 60 64 68 70 74 75 76 78 79 81 86 89 93 96 107 108 110 111 115 118 119 121 124 126 127 129 130 132 144 146 147 **P**8 **S** Community Health Systems, Inc., Franklin, TN
Primary Contact: Derek W. Cimala, Interim Chief Executive Officer
CMO: Joel Shor, M.D., Chief of Staff
CIO: Rose Lasker, Director Information Services
CHR: Sandee Cheynet, Vice President Administrative Services
Web address: www.bluefield.org
Control: Corporation, Investor–owned (for–profit) **Service**: General medical and surgical

Staffed Beds: 92 **Admissions**: 3572 **Census**: 36 **Outpatient Visits**: 69556 **Births**: 545 **Total Expense ($000)**: 85613 **Payroll Expense ($000)**: 21077 **Personnel**: 409

BRIDGEPORT—Harrison County

✠ **UNITED HOSPITAL CENTER (510006)**, 327 Medical Park Drive, Zip 26330–9006; tel. 681/342–1000, **A**1 2 3 5 10 12 13 **F**3 11 13 15 17 18 20 22 26 28 29 30 31 34 35 40 43 44 45 46 47 48 49 50 51 54 55 57 58 59 60 62 63 64 68 70 74 75 76 77 78 79 81 82 84 85 86 87 89 92 93 96 97 98 100 101 107 108 110 111 114 115 117 119 120 121 126 128 129 130 131 132 135 145 146 147 148 149 154 **P**1 6 **S** West Virginia University Health System, Morgantown, WV
Primary Contact: Michael C. Tillman, President and Chief Executive Officer
COO: John Fernandez, Chief Operating Officer
CFO: Jim Rutkowski, Chief Financial Officer
CMO: Eric Radcliffe, M.D., Medical Director
CIO: Brian Cottrill, Chief Information Officer
CHR: Timothy M Allen, Vice President Human Resources
CNO: Stephanie Smart, Chief Nursing Officer
Web address: www.thenewuhc.com
Control: Other not–for–profit (including NFP Corporation) **Service**: General medical and surgical

Staffed Beds: 264 **Admissions**: 12846 **Census**: 175 **Outpatient Visits**: 605693 **Births**: 1073 **Total Expense ($000)**: 323238 **Payroll Expense ($000)**: 123658 **Personnel**: 2149

BUCKEYE—Pocahontas County

★ **POCAHONTAS MEMORIAL HOSPITAL (511314)**, 150 Duncan Road, Zip 24924; tel. 304/799–7400, **A**10 18 **F**3 7 11 29 30 34 35 40 43 50 56 57 59 64 65 68 75 77 86 89 90 93 97 107 119 127 128 130 132 133 135 149
Primary Contact: Barbara Lay, Chief Executive Officer
COO: Terry Wagner, R.N., Chief Operating Officer
CFO: Jon Boyette, Chief Financial Officer
CMO: Jeffrey Pilney, Chief Medical Officer
CIO: Samuel Walker, Director of IT
CHR: Katie Brown, Coordinator Human Resources
CNO: Kyna Moore, R.N., Chief Nursing Officer
Web address: www.pmhwv.org/
Control: County, Government, nonfederal **Service**: General medical and surgical

Staffed Beds: 24 **Admissions**: 191 **Census**: 2 **Outpatient Visits**: 14355 **Births**: 1 **Total Expense ($000)**: 14325 **Payroll Expense ($000)**: 7663 **Personnel**: 202

WV

Hospital, Medicare Provider Number, Address, Telephone, Approval, Facility, and Physician Codes, Health Care System

★ American Hospital Association (AHA) membership
☐ The Joint Commission accreditation
○ Healthcare Facilities Accreditation Program
◇ DNV Healthcare Inc. accreditation
⇑ Center for Improvement in Healthcare Quality Accreditation
△ Commission on Accreditation of Rehabilitation Facilities (CARF) accreditation

BUCKHANNON—Upshur County

ST. JOSEPH'S HOSPITAL OF BUCKHANNON (511321), 1 Amalia Drive, Zip 26201-2276; tel. 304/473-2000, (Total facility includes 16 beds in nursing home-type unit) **A**1 10 18 **F**3 11 13 15 18 28 29 30 31 34 35 40 43 44 45 50 57 59 64 65 70 75 76 81 83 84 85 87 89 107 110 115 119 128 129 130 132 133 135 144 146 147 **P**6 **S** West Virginia University Health System, Morgantown, WV
Primary Contact: Skip Gjolberg, FACHE, Administrator
CFO: Russell J. Plywaczynski, CPA, Director of Finance
CMO: Bartley Brown, D.O., Chief of Staff
CIO: Brian Williams, Web Services and Information Technology Manager
CHR: Anissa J Hite Davis, Vice President Human Resources
CNO: Annamarie Chidester, R.N., Vice President, Patient Care Services
Web address: www.stj.net
Control: Other not-for-profit (including NFP Corporation) **Service:** General medical and surgical

Staffed Beds: 51 **Admissions:** 812 **Census:** 23 **Outpatient Visits:** 107653 **Births:** 278 **Total Expense ($000):** 44452 **Payroll Expense ($000):** 19335 **Personnel:** 383

CHARLESTON—Kanawha County

CAMC MEMORIAL HOSPITAL See Charleston Area Medical Center, Charleston

CAMC WOMEN AND CHILDREN'S HOSPITAL See Charleston Area Medical Center, Charleston

★ △ ⇑ **CHARLESTON AREA MEDICAL CENTER (510022)**, 501 Morris Street, Zip 25301-1300, Mailing Address: P.O. Box 1547, Zip 25326-1547; tel. 304/388-5432, (Includes CAMC MEMORIAL HOSPITAL, 3200 MacCorkle Avenue SE, Charleston, WV, Zip 25304; tel. 304/388-5973; Jeffrey L. Oskin, Vice President and Administrator; CAMC TEAYS VALLEY HOSPITAL, 1400 Hospital Drive, Hurricane, WV, Zip 25526-9202; tel. 304/757-1700; Randall H Hodges, FACHE, Vice President and Administrator; CAMC WOMEN AND CHILDREN'S HOSPITAL, 800 Pennsylvania Avenue, Charleston, WV, Zip 25302, Mailing Address: P.O. Box 6669, Zip 25362, tel. 304/388-5432; Andrew Weber, Vice President and Administrator; GENERAL HOSPITAL, 501 Morris Street, Charleston, WV, Zip 25301, Mailing Address: Box 1393, Zip 25325, tel. 304/388-5432; Michael D Williams, Vice President and Administrator) **A**2 3 5 7 8 10 12 13 21 **F**3 7 8 11 12 13 15 17 18 19 20 22 24 26 28 29 30 31 32 34 35 38 39 40 41 43 44 45 46 47 48 49 50 51 52 54 55 56 57 59 60 61 64 65 68 70 72 74 75 76 77 78 79 81 82 84 85 86 88 89 90 91 92 93 94 95 96 97 98 100 101 102 104 107 108 110 111 114 115 116 117 118 119 120 121 123 124 126 129 130 131 132 134 135 138 141 143 144 145 146 147 148 149 150 154 **P**6
Primary Contact: David L. Ramsey, President and Chief Executive Officer
COO: Glenn Crotty, M.D., Jr Executive Vice President and Chief Operating Officer
CFO: Larry C Hudson, Executive Vice President and Chief Financial Officer
CMO: T Pinckney McIlwain, M.D., Vice President and Chief Medical Officer
CIO: Eileen Clark, Vice President Information Services
CHR: Kristi Snyder, Vice President Human Resources
CNO: Ronald E Moore, R.N., MSN, Vice President Professional Practice and Chief Nursing Officer
Web address: www.camc.org
Control: Other not-for-profit (including NFP Corporation) **Service:** General medical and surgical

Staffed Beds: 846 **Admissions:** 37255 **Census:** 550 **Outpatient Visits:** 751233 **Births:** 2727 **Total Expense ($000):** 1110172 **Payroll Expense ($000):** 426015 **Personnel:** 6460

☐ **CHARLESTON SURGICAL HOSPITAL (510091)**, 1306 Kanawha Boulevard East, Zip 25301-3001, Mailing Address: P.O. Box 2271, Zip 25328-2271; tel. 304/343-4371, **A**1 10 **F**3 45 57 59 75 79 81 111 119 126 141
Primary Contact: Christina Arvon, Administrator and Chief Executive Officer
CMO: James W Candill, M.D., President Medical Staff
Web address: www.eyeandearclinicwv.org
Control: Corporation, Investor-owned (for-profit) **Service:** General medical and surgical

Staffed Beds: 6 **Admissions:** 236 **Census:** 1 **Births:** 0 **Personnel:** 124

GENERAL HOSPITAL See Charleston Area Medical Center, Charleston

HIGHLAND HOSPITAL (514001), 300 56th Street SE, Zip 25304-2361, Mailing Address: P.O. Box 4107, Zip 25364-4107; tel. 304/926-1600, **A**1 10 **F**3 34 35 38 57 59 98 99 101 106 130 132 135 143 154
Primary Contact: Cynthia A. Persily, Ph.D., R.N., President and Chief Executive Officer
COO: Rick Rucker, Chief Operating Officer
CFO: Chris K. Miller, Chief Financial Officer
CMO: Kiran S. Devaraj, Chief Medical Officer and Chief Clinical Officer
CIO: Damon Carradine, Director Information Technology
CNO: Leigh Dalton, Director of Nursing and Patient Care Services
Web address: www.highlandhosp.com
Control: Individual, Investor-owned (for-profit) **Service:** Psychiatric

Staffed Beds: 104 **Admissions:** 2227 **Census:** 67 **Outpatient Visits:** 0 **Births:** 0 **Total Expense ($000):** 23649 **Payroll Expense ($000):** 12178 **Personnel:** 344

SAINT FRANCIS HOSPITAL (510031), 333 Laidley Street, Zip 25301-1628, Mailing Address: P.O. Box 471, Zip 25322-0471; tel. 304/347-6500, (Total facility includes 25 beds in nursing home-type unit) **A**1 10 **F**3 11 15 18 20 22 26 29 30 33 34 35 45 48 49 51 57 58 59 60 64 68 69 70 74 75 77 81 82 84 86 87 97 107 108 110 111 115 119 128 130 144 146 147 148 **S** Thomas Health System, Inc., South Charleston, WV
Primary Contact: Daniel Lauffer, FACHE, President and Chief Executive Officer
COO: Brian Ulery, Senior Vice President and Chief Operating Officer
CFO: Renee Cross, Senior Vice President and Chief Financial Officer
CMO: Matthew Upton, Chief Medical Officer and Chief Medical Information Officer
CIO: Jeremy Taylor, Director Information Services
CHR: Patrick Rawlings, Chief Human Resource Officer
CNO: Rebecca Brannon, R.N., Senior Vice President and Chief Nursing Officer
Web address: www.stfrancishospital.com
Control: Other not-for-profit (including NFP Corporation) **Service:** General medical and surgical

Staffed Beds: 65 **Admissions:** 780 **Census:** 14 **Outpatient Visits:** 78253 **Births:** 0 **Total Expense ($000):** 71739 **Payroll Expense ($000):** 24231 **Personnel:** 432

SELECT SPECIALTY HOSPITAL-CHARLESTON (512002), 333 Laidley Street, 3rd Floor East, Zip 25301-1614; tel. 304/720-7234, **A**1 10 **F**1 29 74 75 85 130 148 149 **S** Select Medical Corporation, Mechanicsburg, PA
Primary Contact: Frank Weber, Chief Executive Officer
CHR: Sabrina White, Coordinator Human Resources
Web address: www.selectspecialtyhospitals.com/company/locations/charleston.aspx
Control: Corporation, Investor-owned (for-profit) **Service:** Acute long-term care hospital

Staffed Beds: 32 **Admissions:** 416 **Census:** 29 **Outpatient Visits:** 0 **Births:** 0 **Total Expense ($000):** 17472 **Payroll Expense ($000):** 7131 **Personnel:** 104

CLARKSBURG—Harrison County

☐ **HIGHLAND-CLARKSBURG HOSPITAL (514011)**, 3 Hospital Plaza, Zip 26301-9316; tel. 304/969-3100, **A**1 10 **F**98 99 103 **P**8
Primary Contact: Michael Casdorph, Chief Executive Officer
CFO: Shelly Giaguinto, Chief Financial Officer
CMO: Christi Cooper-Lehki, Chief Clinical Officer
CIO: Kimberly Samuelson, Director of Information Management
CHR: Robert L Boyles, Director of Human Resources
CNO: Melissa Hitt, Director of Nursing
Web address: www.highlandhosp.com
Control: Other not-for-profit (including NFP Corporation) **Service:** Psychiatric

Staffed Beds: 115 **Admissions:** 537 **Census:** 86 **Outpatient Visits:** 0 **Births:** 0 **Total Expense ($000):** 23211 **Payroll Expense ($000):** 12547 **Personnel:** 308

LOUIS A. JOHNSON VETERANS AFFAIRS MEDICAL CENTER, 1 Medical Center Drive, Zip 26301-4199; tel. 304/623-3461, (Nonreporting) **A**1 2 3 5 **S** Department of Veterans Affairs, Perry Point, MD
Primary Contact: Glenn R. Snider, M.D., Interim Director
CMO: Glenn R Snider, M.D., Chief of Staff
CIO: Michael Matthey, Facility Chief Information Officer
CHR: Ian Jacobs, Chief, Human Resource Management Service
Web address: www.clarksburg.va.gov
Control: Veterans Affairs, Government, federal **Service:** General medical and surgical

Staffed Beds: 71

ELKINS—Randolph County

DAVIS MEDICAL CENTER (510030), Gorman Avenue and Reed Street, Zip 26241, Mailing Address: P.O. Box 1484, Zip 26241-1484; tel. 304/636-3300, **A**1 2 10 20 **F**11 13 15 28 29 30 31 32 34 35 40 49 50 51 54 57 59 64 68 69 70 71 75 76 78 79 81 82 84 85 86 87 89 92 94 97 107 108 109 110 111 115 116 117 118 119 121 123 129 130 132 135 146 147 148 154 **P**3 8 **S** Davis Health System, Elkins, WV
Primary Contact: Vance Jackson, FACHE, Chief Executive Officer
COO: Greg Johnson, Vice President of Operations
CFO: Rebecca J Hammer, Chief Financial Officer
CMO: Anne Banfield, Chief, Medical Staff
CIO: Steve Crowl, Director of Information Services
CHR: Jon Steen, Director Human Resources
CNO: Pamela Smithson, R.N., Vice President Nursing
Web address: www.davishealthsystem.com
Control: Other not-for-profit (including NFP Corporation) **Service:** General medical and surgical

Staffed Beds: 80 **Admissions:** 2819 **Census:** 25 **Outpatient Visits:** 143257 **Births:** 319 **Total Expense ($000):** 96565 **Payroll Expense ($000):** 42979 **Personnel:** 688

FAIRMONT—Marion County

✠ **FAIRMONT REGIONAL MEDICAL CENTER (510047)**, 1325 Locust Avenue,
Zip 26554–1435; tel. 304/367–7100, (Nonreporting) **A**1 2 10 **S** Alecto
Healthcare, Irvine, CA
Primary Contact: Robert S. Adcock, Chief Executive Officer
CFO: Daniel Quance, Chief Financial Officer
CMO: Wes Steele, M.D., Chief of Staff
CIO: Mike Wooddell, Director Information Services
CHR: Jim Harris, Vice President Human Resources
CNO: Michelle L Luffey, MSN, R.N., Chief Nursing Officer
Web address: www.frmcwv.com
Control: Other not–for–profit (including NFP Corporation) **Service**: General
medical and surgical

Staffed Beds: 144

GASSAWAY—Braxton County

BRAXTON COUNTY MEMORIAL HOSPITAL (511308), 100 Hoylman DR,
Zip 26624–9318, Mailing Address: 100 Hoylman Drive, Zip 26624–9318;
tel. 304/364–5156, **A**10 18 **F**3 8 11 15 29 30 32 34 35 40 43 45 57 59 62 64
75 81 97 107 108 114 127 130 133 146 147 149 **P**6
Primary Contact: Ben Vincent, FACHE, Chief Executive Officer
CFO: Kimber Knight, Chief Financial Officer
CMO: Russell L Stewart, D.O., Medical Director
CNO: Julia Rose, R.N., Director of Nursing
Web address: www.braxtonmemorial.org
Control: Other not–for–profit (including NFP Corporation) **Service**: General
medical and surgical

Staffed Beds: 25 Admissions: 224 Census: 2 Outpatient Visits: 47269
Births: 0 Total Expense ($000): 17450 Payroll Expense ($000): 7460
Personnel: 142

GLEN DALE—Marshall County

✠ **REYNOLDS MEMORIAL HOSPITAL (510013)**, 800 Wheeling Avenue,
Zip 26038–1697; tel. 304/845–3211, (Nonreporting) **A**1 10 **S** West Virginia
University Health System, Morgantown, WV
Primary Contact: David F. Hess, M.D., Chief Executive Officer
COO: Kevin Britt, Chief Operating Officer
CFO: William Robert Hunt, Chief Financial Officer
CMO: David F Hess, M.D., President Medical Staff
CIO: Warren Kelley, Chief Information Officer
CHR: R. Craig Madden, Director Employee Relations
CNO: Carol R Miller, R.N., Chief Nursing Officer
Web address: www.reynoldsmemorial.com
Control: Other not–for–profit (including NFP Corporation) **Service**: General
medical and surgical

Staffed Beds: 90

GRAFTON—Taylor County

GRAFTON CITY HOSPITAL (511307), 1 Hospital Plaza, Zip 26354–1283;
tel. 304/265–0400, (Total facility includes 76 beds in nursing home–type unit) **A**10
18 **F**11 15 29 30 32 34 35 38 39 40 45 50 53 54 56 57 59 61 64 65 67 75 81
84 85 86 87 91 92 93 94 97 100 101 104 107 108 110 114 119 127 128 129
130 131 132 133 135 146 147 **P**6
Primary Contact: Patrick D. Shaw, Chief Executive Officer
CFO: Regina Pickens, Chief Financial Officer
CMO: David B Bender, M.D., Chief Medical Staff
CIO: Jim Harris, Director Information Technology
CHR: Missey Kimbrew, Director Human Resources
CNO: Violet Shaw, R.N., Director of Nursing
Web address: www.graftonhospital.org
Control: City, Government, nonfederal **Service**: General medical and surgical

Staffed Beds: 101 Admissions: 528 Census: 69 Outpatient Visits: 47652
Births: 0 Total Expense ($000): 19865 Payroll Expense ($000): 11061
Personnel: 241

GRANTSVILLE—Calhoun County

★ **MINNIE HAMILTON HEALTHCARE CENTER (511303)**, 186 Hospital Drive,
Zip 26147–7100; tel. 304/354–9244, (Nonreporting) **A**10 18
Primary Contact: Steve Whited, Chief Executive Officer
CMO: Suresh Balasubramony, M.D., Chief Medical Officer
CIO: Brent Barr, Chief Information Officer
CHR: Sheila Gherke, Director Human Resources
CNO: Kim Houchin, Chief Nursing Officer
Web address: www.mhhcc.com
Control: Other not–for–profit (including NFP Corporation) **Service**: General
medical and surgical

Staffed Beds: 42

HINTON—Summers County

☐ **SUMMERS COUNTY ARH HOSPITAL (511310)**, Terrace Street,
Zip 25951–2407, Mailing Address: Drawer 940, Zip 25951–0940;
tel. 304/466–1000, **A**1 10 18 **F**11 15 29 30 32 34 35 40 43 44 50 54 57 59
62 64 65 71 77 81 82 85 86 87 93 97 107 110 114 119 127 130 133 146
147 148 **P**6 **S** Appalachian Regional Healthcare, Inc., Lexington, KY
Primary Contact: Wesley Dangerfield, Community Chief Executive Officer
CMO: Waheed Khan, M.D., President Medical Staff
CIO: Brent Styer, Chief Information Officer
CHR: Beth Elswick, Administrative Assistant
CNO: Sharon Milburn, Chief Nursing Officer
Web address: www.arh.org
Control: Other not–for–profit (including NFP Corporation) **Service**: General
medical and surgical

Staffed Beds: 25 Admissions: 462 Census: 8 Outpatient Visits: 28645
Births: 0 Total Expense ($000): 13923 Payroll Expense ($000): 4827
Personnel: 119

HUNTINGTON—Cabell County

✠ **CABELL HUNTINGTON HOSPITAL (510055)**, 1340 Hal Greer Boulevard,
Zip 25701–0195; tel. 304/526–2000, (Includes HOOPS FAMILY CHILDREN'S
HOSPITAL, 1340 Hal Greer Boulevard, Huntington, WV, Zip 25701–3800;
tel. 304/526–2000) (Total facility includes 15 beds in nursing home–type unit) **A**1
2 3 5 8 10 **F**3 5 7 9 11 12 13 15 16 18 19 20 22 26 28 29 30 31 32 34 35 37
38 39 40 41 43 44 45 46 47 48 49 50 51 52 54 55 56 57 58 59 61 62 64 65
70 72 73 74 75 76 77 78 79 81 82 83 84 85 86 87 88 89 91 92 93 94 96 97
104 107 108 110 111 114 115 116 117 118 119 120 121 123 124 126 128
129 130 131 132 134 135 144 145 146 147 148 149 150 154
Primary Contact: Kevin N. Fowler, President and Chief Executive Officer
CFO: David M Ward, Chief Financial Officer and Chief Acquisition Officer
CMO: Hoyt J Burdick, M.D., Vice President Medical Affairs
CIO: Dennis Lee, Vice President and Chief Information Officer
CHR: Barry Tourigny, Vice President Human Resources and Organizational
Development
CNO: Joy S Pelfrey, R.N., MSN, Vice President and Chief Nursing Officer
Web address: www.cabellhuntington.org
Control: Other not–for–profit (including NFP Corporation) **Service**: General
medical and surgical

Staffed Beds: 303 Admissions: 27445 Census: 276 Outpatient Visits: 723624 Births: 2612 Total Expense ($000): 500185 Payroll Expense ($000): 165955 Personnel: 2629

☐ **CORNERSTONE HOSPITAL OF HUNTINGTON (512003)**, 2900 First Avenue,
Two East, Zip 25702–1241; tel. 304/399–2600, **A**1 10 **F**1 29 148 **S** Cornerstone
Healthcare Group, Dallas, TX
Primary Contact: Cynthia Isaacs, Chief Executive Officer
CFO: Frank Carter, Chief Financial Officer
CMO: William Beam, M.D., Chief of Staff
Web address: www.chghospitals.com
Control: Corporation, Investor–owned (for–profit) **Service**: Acute long–term care
hospital

Staffed Beds: 28 Admissions: 409 Census: 26 Outpatient Visits: 0
Births: 0 Total Expense ($000): 11537 Payroll Expense ($000): 4952
Personnel: 69

✠ **HEALTHSOUTH HUNTINGTON REHABILITATION HOSPITAL (513028)**, 6900
West Country Club Drive, Zip 25705–2000; tel. 304/733–1060, **A**1 10 **F**29 34
90 95 96 148 149 **S** Encompass Health Corporation, Birmingham, AL
Primary Contact: Michael E. Zuliani, Chief Executive Officer
CHR: Jenny Overcash, Director Human Resources
CNO: Ann Evans, Chief Nursing Officer
Web address: www.healthsouthhuntington.com
Control: Corporation, Investor–owned (for–profit) **Service**: Rehabilitation

Staffed Beds: 62 Admissions: 1392 Census: 48 Outpatient Visits: 0
Births: 0 Total Expense ($000): 15155 Payroll Expense ($000): 8041
Personnel: 164

WV

Hospital, Medicare Provider Number, Address, Telephone, Approval, Facility, and Physician Codes, Health Care System

★ American Hospital Association (AHA) membership ☐ The Joint Commission accreditation ○ Healthcare Facilities Accreditation Program ◇ DNV Healthcare Inc. accreditation ⇑ Center for Improvement in Healthcare Quality Accreditation △ Commission on Accreditation of Rehabilitation Facilities (CARF) accreditation

© 2018 AHA Guide   *Many Facility Codes have changed. Please refer to the AHA Guide Code Chart.*   Hospitals **A683**

HUNTINGTON—Wayne County

✠ **HUNTINGTON VETERANS AFFAIRS MEDICAL CENTER**, 1540 Spring Valley Drive, Zip 25704–9300; tel. 304/429–6741, (Nonreporting) **A**1 3 5 **S** Department of Veterans Affairs, Perry Point, MD
Primary Contact: Brian Nimmo, Director
CIO: Gary Henderson, Chief Information Resources Management Services
Web address: www.huntington.va.gov/
Control: Veterans Affairs, Government, federal **Service**: General medical and surgical

> **Staffed Beds**: 80

HUNTINGTON—Cabell County

☐ **MILDRED MITCHELL–BATEMAN HOSPITAL (514009)**, 1530 Norway Avenue, Zip 25705–1358, Mailing Address: P.O. Box 448, Zip 25709–0448; tel. 304/525–7801, **A**1 3 10 **F**3 4 11 30 68 86 87 97 98 103 130 132 135 143 146 148 149 150 154 **P**6
Primary Contact: Craig A. Richards, Chief Executive Officer
CFO: Lucille Gedies, Chief Financial Officer
CMO: Shahid Masood, M.D., Clinical Director
CIO: Elias Majdalani, Director Management Information Systems
CHR: Kieth Anne Worden, Director Human Resources
CNO: Patricia Hamilton, R.N., Director of Nursing
Web address: www.batemanhospital.org
Control: State, Government, nonfederal **Service**: Psychiatric

> **Staffed Beds**: 110 **Admissions**: 574 **Census**: 97 **Outpatient Visits**: 0
> **Births**: 0 **Total Expense ($000)**: 45286 **Payroll Expense ($000)**: 14681
> **Personnel**: 316

☐ **RIVER PARK HOSPITAL (514008)**, 1230 Sixth Avenue, Zip 25701–2312, Mailing Address: P.O. Box 1875, Zip 25719–1875; tel. 304/526–9111, (Nonreporting) **A**1 3 10 **S** Universal Health Services, Inc., King of Prussia, PA
Primary Contact: Terry A. Stephens, Chief Executive Officer
CFO: Steve Kuhn, Chief Financial Officer
CMO: Mark A. Hughes, M.D., Medical Director
CIO: James Martin, Chief Information Officer
CHR: Mary Stratton, Director Human Resources
CNO: Michelle Gilliland, Director of Nursing
Web address: www.riverparkhospital.net
Control: Corporation, Investor–owned (for–profit) **Service**: Psychiatric

> **Staffed Beds**: 175

✠ **ST. MARY'S MEDICAL CENTER (510007)**, 2900 First Avenue, Zip 25702–1272; tel. 304/526–1234, (Total facility includes 19 beds in nursing home–type unit) **A**1 2 3 10 **F**3 11 12 13 17 18 20 22 24 26 28 29 30 31 32 34 35 36 39 40 43 44 45 46 47 48 49 50 53 54 55 57 58 59 60 61 62 64 65 66 67 68 70 74 75 76 77 78 79 81 82 84 85 86 87 89 90 92 93 96 97 98 100 101 102 103 105 107 108 110 111 114 115 118 119 120 121 123 124 126 128 129 130 132 135 144 145 146 147 148 149 154 **P**8 **S** Pallottine Health Services, Huntington, WV
Primary Contact: Michael G. Sellards, President and Chief Executive Officer
COO: Todd Campbell, Senior Vice President and Chief Operating Officer
CFO: Angela Swearingen, Vice President Finance
CMO: Ernest Lee Taylor, M.D., Vice President Medical Affairs
CIO: David Wendell, Manager, Information Systems
CHR: Susan Beth Robinson, Vice President Human Resources
CNO: Elizabeth Bosley, R.N., FACHE, Vice President Patient Services and Chief Nursing Officer
Web address: www.st–marys.org
Control: Church operated, Nongovernment, not–for–profit **Service**: General medical and surgical

> **Staffed Beds**: 393 **Admissions**: 16249 **Census**: 253 **Outpatient Visits**: 259932 **Births**: 397 **Total Expense ($000)**: 385602 **Payroll Expense ($000)**: 129869 **Personnel**: 2478

KEYSER—Mineral County

✠ **POTOMAC VALLEY HOSPITAL (511315)**, 100 Pin Oak Lane, Zip 26726–5908; tel. 304/597–3500, (Nonreporting) **A**1 10 18 **S** West Virginia University Health System, Morgantown, WV
Primary Contact: Mark G. Boucot, FACHE, President and Chief Executive Officer
CFO: Marian Cardwell, Chief Financial Officer
CMO: Charles Bess, M.D., Medical Director
CIO: Micah Reel, Director of Bio–Med
CHR: Dianne Smith, Director Personnel and Human Resources
CNO: Mary Ann Billings, Director of Nursing
Web address: www.potomacvalleyhospital.com
Control: Other not–for–profit (including NFP Corporation) **Service**: General medical and surgical

> **Staffed Beds**: 25

KINGWOOD—Preston County

★ **PRESTON MEMORIAL HOSPITAL (511312)**, 150 Memorial Drive, Zip 26537–1495; tel. 304/329–1400, **A**10 18 **F**3 12 15 18 28 29 30 34 35 40 43 45 47 48 50 53 55 57 59 64 65 70 74 75 76 77 81 92 93 97 107 108 110 111 114 119 129 132 133 135 144 146 147 148 154 **P**6 **S** Mon Health System, Morgantown, WV
Primary Contact: Melissa Lockwood, Chief Executive Officer
CIO: Beth Horne, System Administrator Information Technology
CHR: Michele Batiste, Director Human Resources
Web address: www.prestonmemorial.org
Control: Other not–for–profit (including NFP Corporation) **Service**: General medical and surgical

> **Staffed Beds**: 25 **Admissions**: 663 **Census**: 7 **Outpatient Visits**: 69988
> **Births**: 2 **Total Expense ($000)**: 36530 **Payroll Expense ($000)**: 16250
> **Personnel**: 323

LOGAN—Logan County

✠ **LOGAN REGIONAL MEDICAL CENTER (510048)**, 20 Hospital Drive, Zip 25601–3452; tel. 304/831–1101, **A**1 10 20 **F**3 11 13 15 18 20 28 29 31 34 35 40 43 45 49 51 54 57 59 64 65 70 74 75 76 77 78 79 81 82 86 87 89 90 92 93 97 107 108 110 111 114 115 117 118 119 129 130 133 135 146 147 148 **P**6 **S** LifePoint Health, Brentwood, TN
Primary Contact: Kevin Zachary, Chief Executive Officer
COO: Simon Ratliff, Chief Operating Officer
CFO: Tim Matney, Chief Financial Officer
CMO: Kathy Harvey, D.O., Chief Medical Officer
CIO: Barry Hensley, Director Information Systems
CHR: Jessica Martin, Director Human Resources
CNO: Karen Barnes, Interim Chief Nursing Officer
Web address: www.loganregionalmedicalcenter.com
Control: Corporation, Investor–owned (for–profit) **Service**: General medical and surgical

> **Staffed Beds**: 129 **Admissions**: 4586 **Census**: 63 **Outpatient Visits**: 101165 **Births**: 171 **Total Expense ($000)**: 78417 **Payroll Expense ($000)**: 25624 **Personnel**: 634

MADISON—Boone County

✠ **BOONE MEMORIAL HOSPITAL (511313)**, 701 Madison Avenue, Zip 25130–1699; tel. 304/369–1230, (Nonreporting) **A**1 10 18
Primary Contact: Virgil Underwood, Chief Executive Officer
CFO: Randy Foxx, Chief Financial Officer
CMO: Ziad Chanaa, M.D., Chief of Staff
CIO: Susan Shreve, Executive Director Information Technology
CHR: Sheliah Cook, Director Human Resources
CNO: Teresa Meade, R.N., Chief Nursing Officer
Web address: www.bmh.org
Control: Other not–for–profit (including NFP Corporation) **Service**: General medical and surgical

> **Staffed Beds**: 25

MARTINSBURG—Berkeley County

✠ **BERKELEY MEDICAL CENTER (510008)**, 2500 Hospital Drive, Zip 25401–3402; tel. 304/264–1000, **A**1 2 3 5 10 **F**3 11 12 13 15 17 18 20 22 28 29 30 31 34 35 38 40 43 44 45 47 49 51 53 57 59 62 64 70 72 74 75 77 78 79 81 82 84 85 86 87 89 92 93 98 102 103 104 105 107 108 110 111 114 115 118 119 124 126 129 130 131 132 135 143 144 145 146 147 148 154 **S** West Virginia University Health System, Morgantown, WV
Primary Contact: Anthony Zelenka, President and Chief Operating Officer
CFO: Anna Buchanan, Vice President Finance and Chief Financial Officer
CIO: Mark Combs, Interim Director System Information Technology
CHR: Justin Ruble, Director, Human Resources
CNO: Donna Clews, Ph.D., R.N., Vice President Patient Care Services
Web address: www.cityhospital.org
Control: Other not–for–profit (including NFP Corporation) **Service**: General medical and surgical

> **Staffed Beds**: 195 **Admissions**: 8642 **Census**: 102 **Outpatient Visits**: 263510 **Births**: 1057 **Total Expense ($000)**: 194450 **Payroll Expense ($000)**: 61125 **Personnel**: 1220

WV

Many Facility Codes have changed. Please refer to the AHA Guide Code Chart.
© 2018 AHA Guide

MARTINSBURG VETERANS AFFAIRS MEDICAL CENTER, 510 Butler Avenue, Zip 25405–9990; tel. 304/263–0811, (Total facility includes 178 beds in nursing home–type unit) **A**1 3 5 **F**3 4 5 7 10 15 18 22 24 26 29 30 31 33 34 35 38 39 40 45 46 47 48 49 50 53 55 56 58 59 61 62 63 64 65 66 68 70 74 75 77 78 79 81 82 83 84 85 87 91 92 93 94 97 98 101 102 103 104 106 107 108 111 114 115 118 119 127 128 129 130 132 133 135 141 142 143 146 147 148 149 150 152 154 **S** Department of Veterans Affairs, Perry Point, MD
Primary Contact: Timothy J. Cooke, Medical Center Director and Chief Executive Officer
COO: Timothy J Cooke, Medical Center Director and Chief Executive Officer
CMO: Jonathan Fierer, M.D., Chief of Staff
CIO: Mary Ann Creel, Chief Information Resource Management
CHR: Brenda Byrd–Pelaez, Chief Human Resources Management Office
CNO: Susan George, R.N., M.P.H., Associate Director Patient Care Services
Web address: www.martinsburg.va.gov/
Control: Veterans Affairs, Government, federal **Service**: General medical and surgical

Staffed Beds: 487 **Admissions**: 3878 **Census**: 403 **Outpatient Visits**: 515032 **Births**: 0 **Total Expense ($000)**: 320040 **Payroll Expense ($000)**: 148429 **Personnel**: 2077

MONTGOMERY—Fayette County

MONTGOMERY GENERAL HOSPITAL (511318), 401 Sixth Avenue, Zip 25136–2116, Mailing Address: P.O. Box 270, Zip 25136–0270; tel. 304/442–5151, (Total facility includes 44 beds in nursing home–type unit) **A**1 10 18 **F**3 11 15 29 30 34 35 40 45 49 50 53 57 59 64 67 68 77 81 87 93 97 107 110 111 114 119 128 129 130 131 133 135 146 147 **P**6 8
Primary Contact: Vickie Gay, Chief Executive Officer
CFO: Sherri Murray, Chief Financial Officer
CMO: Traci Acklin, M.D., Chief of Staff
CIO: Denzil Blevins, Director Information Systems
CHR: Kelly D Frye, Director Human Resources
Web address: www.mghwv.com
Control: Other not–for–profit (including NFP Corporation) **Service**: General medical and surgical

Staffed Beds: 69 **Admissions**: 445 **Census**: 46 **Outpatient Visits**: 60078 **Births**: 0 **Total Expense ($000)**: 21393 **Payroll Expense ($000)**: 10729 **Personnel**: 214

MORGANTOWN—Monongalia County

CHESTNUT RIDGE HOSPITAL See West Virginia University Hospitals, Morgantown

HEALTHSOUTH MOUNTAINVIEW REGIONAL REHABILITATION HOSPITAL (513030), 1160 Van Voorhis Road, Zip 26505–3437; tel. 304/598–1100, **A**1 5 10 **F**3 29 34 57 59 64 74 75 79 86 87 90 91 93 94 96 107 130 132 148 **S** Encompass Health Corporation, Birmingham, AL
Primary Contact: Tracy Vinciguerra, Chief Executive Officer
CFO: Jason Gizzi, Controller
CMO: Govind Patel, M.D., Medical Director
CIO: Robin Wherry, Risk Manager and Director Quality Assurance and Health Information Management
CHR: Shannon Hyde, Director Human Resources
CNO: Stacy Jones, Chief Nursing Officer
Web address: www.healthsouthmountainview.com
Control: Corporation, Investor–owned (for–profit) **Service**: Rehabilitation

Staffed Beds: 96 **Admissions**: 2252 **Census**: 73 **Outpatient Visits**: 7449 **Births**: 0 **Total Expense ($000)**: 31805 **Payroll Expense ($000)**: 14731 **Personnel**: 258

MON HEALTH MEDICAL CENTER (510024), 1200 J D Anderson Drive, Zip 26505–3486; tel. 304/598–1200, **A**1 2 3 10 19 **F**3 13 15 17 18 20 22 24 26 28 29 30 31 32 34 35 40 43 45 46 49 50 51 54 55 57 59 60 64 65 68 70 74 75 76 77 78 79 81 82 84 85 86 87 89 97 107 108 110 111 114 115 116 118 119 120 121 123 126 127 129 130 132 135 145 146 147 148 149 154 **P**6 8 **S** Mon Health System, Morgantown, WV
Primary Contact: Thomas Senker, Interim Chief Executive Officer
CFO: Daris Rosencrance, Chief Financial Officer
CMO: Matthew P Darmelio, Chief of Staff
CIO: Steve Carter, Chief Information Officer
CHR: Melissa Shreves Shahnam, Director Human Resources
Web address: www.mongeneral.com
Control: Other not–for–profit (including NFP Corporation) **Service**: General medical and surgical

Staffed Beds: 185 **Admissions**: 8061 **Census**: 94 **Outpatient Visits**: 365339 **Births**: 1114 **Total Expense ($000)**: 272362 **Payroll Expense ($000)**: 99122 **Personnel**: 1538

WEST VIRGINIA UNIVERSITY HOSPITALS (510001), 1 Medical Center Drive, Zip 26506–4749; tel. 304/598–4000, (Includes CHESTNUT RIDGE HOSPITAL, 930 Chestnut Ridge Road, Morgantown, WV, Zip 26505–2854; tel. 304/293–4000; WEST VIRGINIA UNIVERSITY CHILDREN'S HOSPITAL, 1 Medical Center Drive, Morgantown, WV, Zip 26506–1200; tel. 800/982–6277) **A**1 3 5 8 10 19 **F**3 4 5 7 8 9 11 12 13 15 17 18 19 20 21 22 23 24 25 26 27 28 29 30 31 32 33 34 35 36 37 38 39 40 41 43 44 45 46 47 48 49 50 51 52 53 54 55 56 57 58 59 60 61 64 65 66 70 71 72 74 75 76 77 78 79 80 81 82 83 84 85 86 87 88 89 91 92 93 97 98 99 100 101 102 103 104 105 107 108 109 110 111 114 115 116 117 118 119 120 121 123 124 126 127 129 130 131 132 133 135 136 141 143 144 145 146 147 148 149 151 152 153 154 **P**1 **S** West Virginia University Health System, Morgantown, WV
Primary Contact: Albert L. Wright Jr, PharmD, President and Chief Executive Officer
COO: Ron Pellegrino, Chief Operating Officer
CFO: Melissa McCoy, Vice President and Chief Financial Officer
CMO: Judie Charlton, M.D., Chief Medical Officer
CIO: James Venturella, Vice President Information Technology
CHR: Leeann Cerimele, Vice President Human Resources
CNO: Douglas W Mitchell, Vice President and Chief Nursing Officer
Web address: www.health.wvu.edu
Control: Other not–for–profit (including NFP Corporation) **Service**: General medical and surgical

Staffed Beds: 631 **Admissions**: 31464 **Census**: 523 **Outpatient Visits**: 803292 **Births**: 1433 **Total Expense ($000)**: 1057742 **Payroll Expense ($000)**: 327724 **Personnel**: 6047

NEW MARTINSVILLE—Wetzel County

WETZEL COUNTY HOSPITAL (510072), 3 East Benjamin Drive, Zip 26155–2758; tel. 304/455–8000, **A**1 10 20 **F**3 8 15 28 30 31 34 40 43 45 57 59 64 65 70 75 77 81 85 90 93 94 107 108 114 118 119 127 130 132 133 135 146 148 **P**6
Primary Contact: Brian K. Felici, Chief Executive Officer
CFO: Edwin Szewczyk, Chief Financial Officer
CMO: Donald A. Blum, M.D., Chief of Staff
CIO: Amy Frazier, Supervisor Management Information Systems
CHR: Sarah Boley, Director Human Resources
Web address: www.wetzelcountyhospital.com
Control: County, Government, nonfederal **Service**: General medical and surgical

Staffed Beds: 44 **Admissions**: 461 **Census**: 6 **Outpatient Visits**: 83535 **Births**: 0 **Total Expense ($000)**: 19862 **Payroll Expense ($000)**: 8672 **Personnel**: 190

OAK HILL—Fayette County

PLATEAU MEDICAL CENTER (511317), 430 Main Street, Zip 25901–3455; tel. 304/469–8600, **A**1 10 18 **F**3 15 18 29 30 34 35 40 45 46 50 57 59 64 68 70 75 77 79 81 85 87 91 93 97 107 108 114 115 119 126 129 133 146 **S** Community Health Systems, Inc., Franklin, TN
Primary Contact: Derek W. Cimala, Interim Chief Executive Officer
CFO: Heather Hylton, Chief Financial Officer
CMO: Jacob McNeel, D.O., Chief of Staff
CIO: Nick Stover, Director Information Systems
CHR: Tammie Chinn, Director Marketing and Public Relations
CNO: Randell Thompson, Chief Nursing Officer
Web address: www.plateaumedicalcenter.com
Control: Corporation, Investor–owned (for–profit) **Service**: General medical and surgical

Staffed Beds: 25 **Admissions**: 1119 **Census**: 8 **Outpatient Visits**: 31204 **Births**: 0 **Total Expense ($000)**: 26384 **Payroll Expense ($000)**: 9358 **Personnel**: 209

PARKERSBURG—Wood County

CAMDEN CLARK MEDICAL CENTER (510058), 800 Garfield Avenue, Zip 26101–5378, Mailing Address: P.O. Box 718, Zip 26102–0718; tel. 304/424–2111, **A**1 3 5 10 **F**3 7 8 15 17 18 19 20 22 24 28 29 30 31 34 35 40 43 45 48 49 50 51 53 54 57 58 59 64 65 66 68 70 74 75 76 78 79 80 81 84 85 86 87 89 92 97 98 107 108 110 111 114 115 116 117 118 119 120 121 123 124 129 130 132 135 146 147 148 154 **P**6 8 **S** West Virginia University Health System, Morgantown, WV
Primary Contact: Steve Altmiller, President and Chief Executive Officer
CFO: Carolyn Allen, Vice President and Chief Financial Officer
CMO: David Gnegy, M.D., Vice President of Medical Affairs
CIO: Josh Woods, Director Information Systems
CHR: Tom Heller, Vice President Operations and Human Resources
CNO: Christine S. Daniels, R.N., Interim Chief Nursing Officer
Web address: www.camdenclark.org
Control: Other not–for–profit (including NFP Corporation) **Service**: General medical and surgical

Staffed Beds: 240 **Admissions**: 11684 **Census**: 150 **Outpatient Visits**: 265462 **Births**: 1315 **Total Expense ($000)**: 231906 **Payroll Expense ($000)**: 69937 **Personnel**: 1792

WV

Hospital, Medicare Provider Number, Address, Telephone, Approval, Facility, and Physician Codes, Health Care System

★ American Hospital Association (AHA) membership
☐ The Joint Commission accreditation
○ Healthcare Facilities Accreditation Program
◇ DNV Healthcare Inc. accreditation
⇧ Center for Improvement in Healthcare Quality Accreditation
△ Commission on Accreditation of Rehabilitation Facilities (CARF) accreditation

✠ **HEALTHSOUTH WESTERN HILLS REGIONAL REHABILITATION HOSPITAL (513027)**, 3 Western Hills Drive, Zip 26105–8122; tel. 304/420–1300, **A**1 10 **F**29 90 94 96 130 148 149 **S** Encompass Health Corporation, Birmingham, AL
Primary Contact: Alvin R. Lawson, FACHE, JD, Chief Executive Officer
CFO: Jessica Gum, Controller
CMO: Kalapala Rao, M.D., Medical Director
CHR: Julie Swanson, Coordinator Human Resources
CNO: Tonda Hockenberry, Chief Nursing Officer
Web address: www.healthsouthwesternhills.com
Control: Corporation, Investor–owned (for–profit) **Service:** Rehabilitation

Staffed Beds: 40 **Admissions:** 1105 **Census:** 36 **Outpatient Visits:** 4418
Births: 0 **Total Expense ($000):** 14565 **Payroll Expense ($000):** 6865
Personnel: 120

PETERSBURG—Grant County

★ **GRANT MEMORIAL HOSPITAL (511316)**, 117 Hospital Drive, Zip 26847–9566, Mailing Address: P.O. Box 1019, Zip 26847–1019; tel. 304/257–1026, (Total facility includes 20 beds in nursing home–type unit) **A**10 18 **F**3 11 13 15 18 28 29 30 34 35 40 45 50 57 59 64 65 67 68 70 75 76 77 79 81 84 85 86 87 93 102 107 108 110 114 118 119 128 130 131 132 133 135 146 147 148 149 **P**6
Primary Contact: Robert W. Milvet Jr, Chief Executive Officer
CMO: Bruce W Leslie, M.D., Chief of Staff
CIO: Derek Nesselrodt, Director Information Systems
CHR: Ronnie Arbaugh, Director Human Resources
CNO: Kimberly Linville, Chief Nursing Officer
Web address: www.grantmemorial.com
Control: County, Government, nonfederal **Service:** General medical and surgical

Staffed Beds: 45 **Admissions:** 1455 **Census:** 29 **Outpatient Visits:** 41643
Births: 258 **Total Expense ($000):** 36649 **Payroll Expense ($000):** 14130
Personnel: 304

PHILIPPI—Barbour County

★ **BROADDUS HOSPITAL (511300)**, 1 Healthcare Drive, Zip 26416–9405, Mailing Address: P.O. Box 930, Zip 26416–0930; tel. 304/457–1760, (Total facility includes 60 beds in nursing home–type unit) **A**10 18 **F**3 15 29 30 34 35 40 57 59 64 75 85 87 107 110 115 119 128 130 132 133 135 143 146 **P**3 8 **S** Davis Health System, Elkins, WV
Primary Contact: Dana L. Gould, Chief Executive Officer
CFO: Cathy Kalar, Chief Financial Officer
CHR: Penny D Brown, Director of Human Resources
Web address: www.davishealthsystem.org/
Control: Other not–for–profit (including NFP Corporation) **Service:** General medical and surgical

Staffed Beds: 72 **Admissions:** 206 **Census:** 56 **Outpatient Visits:** 20831
Births: 0 **Total Expense ($000):** 16724 **Payroll Expense ($000):** 7292
Personnel: 146

POINT PLEASANT—Mason County

✠ **PLEASANT VALLEY HOSPITAL (510012)**, 2520 Valley Drive, Zip 25550–2031; tel. 304/675–4340, (Total facility includes 100 beds in nursing home–type unit) **A**1 10 **F**3 11 13 15 17 18 24 26 28 29 30 31 34 35 40 43 45 46 47 48 50 53 56 57 59 64 65 70 74 75 76 77 78 79 81 85 86 87 89 93 107 108 110 111 114 115 119 128 129 130 131 132 135 143 144 146 147 148 **P**6
Primary Contact: Glen A. Washington, Chief Executive Officer
COO: William A Barker Jr Vice President Administration
CFO: Richard Hogan, Chief Financial Officer
CMO: Agnes Enrico–Simon, M.D., President Medical Staff
CIO: Paula Brooker, Director Information Services
CHR: David A Brown, Director Human Resources and Corporate Compliance
CNO: Amber Findley, Senior Director Nursing Services and NRC Administrator
Web address: www.pvalley.org
Control: Other not–for–profit (including NFP Corporation) **Service:** General medical and surgical

Staffed Beds: 201 **Admissions:** 2067 **Census:** 110 **Outpatient Visits:** 174425 **Births:** 122 **Total Expense ($000):** 62807 **Payroll Expense ($000):** 22821 **Personnel:** 532

PRINCETON—Mercer County

✠ **HEALTHSOUTH SOUTHERN HILLS REHABILITATION HOSPITAL (513026)**, 120 Twelfth Street, Zip 24740–2352; tel. 304/487–8000, (Nonreporting) **A**1 10 **S** Encompass Health Corporation, Birmingham, AL
Primary Contact: Robert Williams, Chief Executive Officer
CFO: Melinda Fanning, Chief Financial Officer and Controller
CMO: Robert Walker, M.D., Medical Director
CIO: Brian Bales, Director Plant Operations
CHR: Jan Thibodeau, Director Human Resources
CNO: Lisa Lester, Chief Nursing Officer
Web address: www.healthsouthsouthernhills.com
Control: Corporation, Investor–owned (for–profit) **Service:** Rehabilitation

Staffed Beds: 45

✠ **PRINCETON COMMUNITY HOSPITAL (510046)**, 122 12th Street, Zip 24740–2352, Mailing Address: P.O. Box 1369, Zip 24740–1369; tel. 304/487–7000, **A**1 2 10 19 **F**3 11 12 13 15 17 29 30 31 32 34 35 39 40 44 45 46 48 49 50 51 53 57 59 64 65 70 74 75 76 77 78 79 81 85 86 87 89 93 98 100 101 102 103 104 107 108 110 111 114 115 118 119 127 129 130 131 132 135 141 142 144 146 147 149 153 **P**1
Primary Contact: Jeffrey Lilley, CPA, Chief Executive Officer
CFO: Frank J Sinicrope Jr Vice President Financial Services
CMO: Wesley Asbury, M.D., President Medical Staff
CIO: Stephen A Curry, Director Information Services
CHR: Heather Poff, Director Human Resources
CNO: Rose Morgan, MS, R.N., Vice President Patient Care Services
Web address: www.pchonline.org
Control: City, Government, nonfederal **Service:** General medical and surgical

Staffed Beds: 210 **Admissions:** 7944 **Census:** 116 **Outpatient Visits:** 256156 **Births:** 702 **Total Expense ($000):** 138242 **Payroll Expense ($000):** 51088 **Personnel:** 1053

RANSON—Jefferson County

✠ **JEFFERSON MEDICAL CENTER (511319)**, 300 South Preston Street, Zip 25438–1631; tel. 304/728–1600, **A**1 3 5 10 18 **F**3 13 30 35 38 40 43 45 64 70 79 81 82 86 87 93 107 119 130 131 133 146 147 154 **S** West Virginia University Health System, Morgantown, WV
Primary Contact: Neil R. McLaughlin, R.N., Administrator and Vice President, Operations
CFO: Anna Buchanan, Vice President Finance and Chief Financial Officer
CMO: David A. Baltierra, M.D., President Medical Staff
CIO: Mark Combs, Chief Information Security Officer
CHR: Justin Ruble, Director Human Resources
CNO: Linda Blanc, R.N., Administrative Director of Nursing
Web address: www.wvuniversityhealthcare.com/locations/Jefferson–Medical–Center.aspx
Control: Other not–for–profit (including NFP Corporation) **Service:** General medical and surgical

Staffed Beds: 25 **Admissions:** 1341 **Census:** 10 **Outpatient Visits:** 68327
Births: 198 **Total Expense ($000):** 45189 **Payroll Expense ($000):** 15934
Personnel: 300

RIPLEY—Jackson County

☐ **JACKSON GENERAL HOSPITAL (511320)**, 122 Pinnell Street, Zip 25271–9101, Mailing Address: P.O. Box 720, Zip 25271–0720; tel. 304/372–2731, **A**1 10 18 **F**3 11 15 29 30 34 35 40 43 45 50 51 57 59 64 68 75 79 81 82 85 87 93 107 108 110 114 119 127 132 133 **P**6
Primary Contact: Stephanie McCoy, President and Chief Executive Officer
CFO: Angela Frame, Chief Financial Officer
CMO: James G Gaal, M.D., Chief of Medical Staff
CIO: John Manley, Director Information Systems
CHR: Jeffrey Tabor, Director Human Resources
Web address: www.jacksongeneral.com
Control: Other not–for–profit (including NFP Corporation) **Service:** General medical and surgical

Staffed Beds: 25 **Admissions:** 579 **Census:** 7 **Outpatient Visits:** 40789
Births: 0 **Total Expense ($000):** 22954 **Payroll Expense ($000):** 9847
Personnel: 241

ROMNEY—Hampshire County

✠ **HAMPSHIRE MEMORIAL HOSPITAL (511311)**, 363 Sunrise Boulevard, Zip 26757–4607; tel. 304/822–4561, (Total facility includes 30 beds in nursing home–type unit) **A**1 10 18 **F**3 15 18 29 30 40 45 50 54 59 64 65 71 77 79 81 85 86 93 97 107 110 114 119 127 128 129 130 133 148 154 **P**6 **S** Valley Health System, Winchester, VA
Primary Contact: Thomas S. Kluge, President
CFO: Kathryn Morales, Director of Finance
CMO: Gerald Bechamps, M.D., Vice President of Medical Affairs
CHR: Abbey Rembold, Human Resources Senior Generalist
CNO: Mary Sas, Director of Clinical Services
Web address: www.valleyhealthlink.com/hampshire
Control: Other not–for–profit (including NFP Corporation) **Service:** General medical and surgical

Staffed Beds: 44 **Admissions:** 388 **Census:** 35 **Outpatient Visits:** 53329
Births: 0 **Total Expense ($000):** 23149 **Payroll Expense ($000):** 10028
Personnel: 162

WV

Many Facility Codes have changed. Please refer to the AHA Guide Code Chart.
© 2018 AHA Guide

RONCEVERTE—Greenbrier County

★ ○ **GREENBRIER VALLEY MEDICAL CENTER (510002)**, 202 Maplewood Avenue, Zip 24970–1334, Mailing Address: P.O. Box 497, Zip 24970–0497; tel. 304/647–4411, **A**3 10 11 12 13 **F**13 15 18 20 29 34 40 45 49 51 57 59 60 68 70 75 76 79 81 86 87 107 108 110 111 114 116 119 120 129 133 146 **P**6 **S** Community Health Systems, Inc., Franklin, TN
Primary Contact: Jim Hobson, Chief Executive Officer
CFO: Paige Adkins, Chief Financial Officer
CMO: John Johnson, M.D., Chief of Staff
CIO: Matt Turley, Interim Director Information Systems
CHR: Melissa Wickline, Director Marketing
CNO: Charlene Warren, R.N., Chief Nursing Officer
Web address: www.gvmc.com
Control: Corporation, Investor–owned (for–profit) **Service:** General medical and surgical

Staffed Beds: 113 **Admissions:** 2834 **Census:** 30 **Outpatient Visits:** 56033 **Births:** 464 **Total Expense ($000):** 54587 **Payroll Expense ($000):** 18435 **Personnel:** 369

SISTERSVILLE—Tyler County

★ **SISTERSVILLE GENERAL HOSPITAL (511304)**, 314 South Wells Street, Zip 26175–1098; tel. 304/652–2611, (Nonreporting) **A**10 18
Primary Contact: Brandon Chadock, Interim Chief Executive Officer
COO: Brandon Chadock, Director of Operations
CMO: Amanda Nichols, M.D., Chief of Staff
CIO: Casey Tuttle, Director Information Technology
CNO: Stephen Todd Strickler, Director of Nursing
Web address: www.sistersvillehospital.com
Control: City, Government, nonfederal **Service:** General medical and surgical

Staffed Beds: 12

SOUTH CHARLESTON—Kanawha County

⊞ **THOMAS MEMORIAL HOSPITAL (510029)**, 4605 MacCorkle Avenue SW, Zip 25309–1398; tel. 304/766–3600, **A**1 5 10 **F**3 4 5 11 13 15 17 18 20 22 29 30 31 32 34 35 38 40 43 45 46 47 48 49 50 53 54 57 59 60 64 65 68 69 70 72 74 75 76 77 78 79 81 84 85 86 87 89 92 93 98 100 101 102 103 104 107 108 110 111 114 115 118 119 120 121 123 124 126 129 130 131 132 143 144 146 147 **S** Thomas Health System, Inc., South Charleston, WV
Primary Contact: Daniel Lauffer, FACHE, President and Chief Executive Officer
COO: Brian Ulery, Chief Operating Officer
CFO: Timothy Skeldon, Chief Financial Officer
CMO: Matthew Upton, Chief Medical Information Officer
CHR: Patrick Rawlings, Human Resources Director
CNO: Rebecca Brannon, R.N., Chief Nursing Officer
Web address: www.thomashealth.org
Control: Other not–for–profit (including NFP Corporation) **Service:** General medical and surgical

Staffed Beds: 211 **Admissions:** 8089 **Census:** 108 **Outpatient Visits:** 170920 **Births:** 1036 **Total Expense ($000):** 179521 **Payroll Expense ($000):** 51613 **Personnel:** 1008

SPENCER—Roane County

⊞ **ROANE GENERAL HOSPITAL (511306)**, 200 Hospital Drive, Zip 25276–1050; tel. 304/927–4444, (Total facility includes 35 beds in nursing home–type unit) **A**1 10 18 **F**1 3 11 15 18 28 29 34 35 40 43 45 53 57 59 64 65 67 68 81 82 85 89 90 93 97 107 108 110 114 119 127 128 130 132 133 135 148 **P**6
Primary Contact: Douglas E. Bentz, Chief Executive Officer
CFO: Kyle A. Pierson, Chief Financial Officer
CMO: Hong–Kin Ng, M.D., Chief Medical Officer
CIO: Tony Keaton, Director Information Systems
CHR: Jeffery B Hunt, Vice President, Business Development and Support Services
CNO: Julie R. Carr, Chief Nursing Officer
Web address: www.roanegeneralhospital.com
Control: Other not–for–profit (including NFP Corporation) **Service:** General medical and surgical

Staffed Beds: 60 **Admissions:** 198 **Census:** 35 **Outpatient Visits:** 44731 **Births:** 0 **Total Expense ($000):** 34734 **Payroll Expense ($000):** 15419 **Personnel:** 282

SUMMERSVILLE—Nicholas County

⊞ **SUMMERSVILLE REGIONAL MEDICAL CENTER (510082)**, 400 Fairview Heights Road, Zip 26651–9308; tel. 304/872–2891, (Nonreporting) **A**1 10 20 **S** QHR, Brentwood, TN
Primary Contact: Karen A. Fiducia, FACHE, President and Chief Executive Officer
CFO: Brian Kelbaugh, Chief Financial Officer
CMO: Bandy Mullins, M.D., Chief of Staff
CIO: Mike Ellison, Information Systems Lead
CHR: David M Henderson, Director Human Resources
CNO: Jennifer McCue, Director Patient Care
Web address: www.summersvilleregional.org/
Control: City, Government, nonfederal **Service:** General medical and surgical

Staffed Beds: 153

WEBSTER SPRINGS—Webster County

★ **WEBSTER COUNTY MEMORIAL HOSPITAL (511301)**, 324 Miller Mountain Drive, Zip 26288–1087, Mailing Address: P.O. Box 312, Zip 26288–0312; tel. 304/847–5682, **A**10 18 **F**7 28 30 34 35 40 57 59 64 75 82 87 93 97 107 114 119 127 130 133 135 146 147 148
Primary Contact: Jim Parker, FACHE, Chief Executive Officer
CIO: Jeannie Fisher, Coordinator Information Technology
CHR: Michelle Holcomb, Human Resources
Web address: www.wcmhw.org
Control: Other not–for–profit (including NFP Corporation) **Service:** General medical and surgical

Staffed Beds: 15 **Admissions:** 138 **Census:** 1 **Outpatient Visits:** 48470 **Total Expense ($000):** 15647 **Payroll Expense ($000):** 8874 **Personnel:** 143

WEIRTON—Brooke County

⊞ **WEIRTON MEDICAL CENTER (510023)**, 601 Colliers Way, Zip 26062–5091; tel. 304/797–6000, (Total facility includes 33 beds in nursing home–type unit) **A**1 10 **F**3 9 11 13 15 17 18 20 22 28 29 30 32 34 35 37 40 41 43 45 46 47 48 49 50 51 54 56 57 59 60 61 62 64 68 70 74 75 76 77 78 79 81 82 85 86 89 90 92 93 96 97 102 107 108 110 111 114 115 116 118 119 124 126 128 129 130 131 132 135 143 145 146 147 148 149 **P**6
Primary Contact: John C. Frankovitch, President and Chief Executive Officer
COO: David S Artman, Chief Operating Officer
CFO: Gene Trout, Chief Financial Officer
CMO: Atul Shetty, Chief of Staff
CIO: Cristen Nopwaskey, Chief Information Officer
CHR: Gabe D'Ortenzio, Director of Human Resources
CNO: Denise P Westwood, Chief Nursing Officer
Web address: www.weirtonmedical.com
Control: Other not–for–profit (including NFP Corporation) **Service:** General medical and surgical

Staffed Beds: 167 **Admissions:** 6309 **Census:** 88 **Outpatient Visits:** 473697 **Births:** 428 **Total Expense ($000):** 179654 **Payroll Expense ($000):** 78341 **Personnel:** 1187

WELCH—Mcdowell County

WELCH COMMUNITY HOSPITAL (510086), 454 McDowell Street, Zip 24801–2097; tel. 304/436–8461, (Total facility includes 59 beds in nursing home–type unit) **A**10 20 **F**3 13 15 29 35 40 45 50 57 59 64 65 66 67 68 70 75 76 81 86 87 97 107 110 114 119 127 130 135 146 147 148 **P**6
Primary Contact: Mark Simpson, Chief Executive Officer
COO: Heather Smith, Chief Operating Officer
CFO: Johnny Brant, Chief Financial Officer
CMO: Chandra Sharma, M.D., Chief of Staff
CHR: Diana Blankenship, Director Human Resources
Control: State, Government, nonfederal **Service:** General medical and surgical

Staffed Beds: 108 **Admissions:** 705 **Census:** 45 **Outpatient Visits:** 29294 **Births:** 40 **Total Expense ($000):** 29889 **Payroll Expense ($000):** 8926 **Personnel:** 287

WV

Hospital, Medicare Provider Number, Address, Telephone, Approval, Facility, and Physician Codes, Health Care System		
★ American Hospital Association (AHA) membership	○ Healthcare Facilities Accreditation Program	⇑ Center for Improvement in Healthcare Quality Accreditation
□ The Joint Commission accreditation	◇ DNV Healthcare Inc. accreditation	△ Commission on Accreditation of Rehabilitation Facilities (CARF) accreditation

WESTON—Lewis County

☒ **STONEWALL JACKSON MEMORIAL HOSPITAL (510038)**, 230 Hospital Plaza, Zip 26452–8558; tel. 304/269–8000, **A**1 10 **F**3 11 13 15 28 29 30 31 35 40 43 45 48 50 56 57 59 62 64 68 70 75 76 78 79 81 85 86 87 93 94 97 107 108 111 114 118 119 129 130 131 132 135 145 146 147 148 **P**6 **S** Mon Health System, Morgantown, WV
Primary Contact: Avah Stalnaker, Chief Executive Officer
COO: Kevin P Stalnaker, CPA, Assistant Chief Executive Officer
CFO: Joe Barnes, Chief Financial Officer
CMO: Joseph Snead, Chief of Medical Staff
CIO: Kay Butcher, Director Health Information Management
CHR: Rhonda K Mitchell, Director Human Resources
CNO: Carole Norton, Chief Nursing Officer
Web address: www.stonewallhospital.com
Control: Other not–for–profit (including NFP Corporation) **Service**: General medical and surgical

Staffed Beds: 70 **Admissions:** 1646 **Census:** 16 **Outpatient Visits:** 92408 **Births:** 191 **Total Expense ($000):** 50689 **Payroll Expense ($000):** 22788 **Personnel:** 407

☐ **WILLIAM R. SHARPE, JR. HOSPITAL (514010)**, 936 Sharpe Hospital Road, Zip 26452–8550; tel. 304/269–1210, **A**1 3 5 10 **F**3 11 30 50 53 56 68 75 86 87 98 100 101 103 130 132 143 146 **P**6
Primary Contact: Parker Haddix, Chief Executive Officer
COO: Terry L. Small, Assistant Chief Executive Officer
CFO: Robert J. Kimble, Chief Financial Officer
CIO: Pam Lewis, Chief Compliance Officer
CNO: Cheryl France, M.D., Chief Medical Officer
Web address: www.wvdhhr.org/sharpe
Control: State, Government, nonfederal **Service**: Psychiatric

Staffed Beds: 150 **Admissions:** 516 **Census:** 140 **Outpatient Visits:** 0 **Births:** 0 **Total Expense ($000):** 71570 **Payroll Expense ($000):** 13885 **Personnel:** 408

WHEELING—Ohio County

☐ ○ **OHIO VALLEY MEDICAL CENTER (510039)**, 2000 Eoff Street, Zip 26003–3870; tel. 304/234–0123, (Nonreporting) **A**1 2 3 10 11 12 13 **S** Alecto Healthcare, Irvine, CA
Primary Contact: Daniel C. Dunmyer, Chief Executive Officer
COO: Kelly Bettem, Vice President, Ambulatory Services
CFO: Lisa M. Simon, Senior Vice President and Chief Financial Officer
CIO: Michael Martz, Chief Information Officer
CHR: Robert Wright, Senior Human Resource Advisor
CNO: Patsy George, R.N., Vice President and Chief Nursing Officer
Web address: www.ovmc–eorh.com
Control: Corporation, Investor–owned (for–profit) **Service**: General medical and surgical

Staffed Beds: 189

★ **PETERSON HEALTHCARE AND REHABILITATION HOSPITAL (513025)**, Homestead Avenue, Zip 26003; tel. 304/234–0500, (Total facility includes 150 beds in nursing home–type unit) **A**10 **F**29 34 50 56 57 59 75 77 86 87 90 93 96 128 130 131 132 143 146 148 149
Primary Contact: Diane Miller, Administrator
CFO: Tammy Bortz, Director of Finance
CMO: William Mercer, M.D., Director
CIO: Hope Miller, Director of Medical Records
CHR: Spencer McIlvain, Director of Human Resources
CNO: Charlene Jones, Chief Nursing Officer
Web address: www.petersonrehabilitationhospital.com
Control: Corporation, Investor–owned (for–profit) **Service**: Rehabilitation

Staffed Beds: 172 **Admissions:** 778 **Census:** 153 **Outpatient Visits:** 3343 **Births:** 0 **Total Expense ($000):** 19654 **Payroll Expense ($000):** 5919 **Personnel:** 174

☐ **WHEELING HOSPITAL (510050)**, 1 Medical Park, Zip 26003–6379; tel. 304/243–3000, **A**1 2 3 10 13 **F**3 8 9 11 13 15 17 18 20 22 24 26 28 29 30 31 32 33 34 35 36 38 40 43 44 45 46 47 49 50 51 53 54 57 58 59 60 61 62 64 65 66 67 68 70 73 74 75 76 77 78 79 81 82 84 85 86 87 89 90 92 93 96 97 98 100 107 108 110 111 114 115 116 117 118 119 120 121 123 124 126 128 129 130 131 132 135 136 143 146 147 148 149 150 154 **P**5
Primary Contact: Ronald L. Violi, Chief Executive Officer
CMO: Angelo Georges, M.D., President Medical and Dental Staff
CIO: David Rapp, Chief Information Officer
CHR: Kareen Simon, Vice President of Operations
CNO: Kathy Stahl, Chief Nursing Officer
Web address: www.wheelinghospital.org
Control: Other not–for–profit (including NFP Corporation) **Service**: General medical and surgical

Staffed Beds: 223 **Admissions:** 10682 **Census:** 133 **Outpatient Visits:** 609283 **Births:** 1245 **Total Expense ($000):** 323591 **Payroll Expense ($000):** 138547 **Personnel:** 2215

WILLIAMSON—Mingo County

☒ **WILLIAMSON MEMORIAL HOSPITAL (510077)**, 859 Alderson Street, Zip 25661–3215, Mailing Address: P.O. Box 1980, Zip 25661–1980; tel. 304/235–2500, (Nonreporting) **A**1 10 **S** Community Health Systems, Inc., Franklin, TN
Primary Contact: Michael D. Makosky, Interim Chief Executive Officer
CFO: Robert Haralson, Chief Financial Officer
CMO: C. Donovan Beckett, Chief Medical Officer
CHR: Tammie Chinn, Chief Human Resource Officer
CNO: Stacey Markus, Chief Nursing Officer
Web address: www.williamsonmemorial.net
Control: Corporation, Investor–owned (for–profit) **Service**: General medical and surgical

Staffed Beds: 76

Many Facility Codes have changed. Please refer to the AHA Guide Code Chart. © 2018 AHA Guide

WISCONSIN

ALTOONA—Eau Claire County

☐ **OAKLEAF SURGICAL HOSPITAL (520196)**, 1000 OakLeaf Way,
Zip 54701–3016; tel. 715/831–8130, **A**1 10 **F**3 37 45 47 48 51 64 68 75
79 80 81 82 85 107 111 114 119 130 149 **S** National Surgical Healthcare,
Chicago, IL
Primary Contact: Anne Hargrave–Thomas, Chief Executive Officer
COO: Erma Radke, Director of Operations
CFO: Denise Freid–Scheppke, Chief Accounting Officer
CHR: Nikki Yankton, Director Human Resources
CNO: Jacquelyn Maki, Chief Nursing Officer
Web address: www.oakleafmedical.com
Control: Corporation, Investor–owned (for–profit) **Service:** General medical and
surgical

Staffed Beds: 13 **Admissions:** 674 **Census:** 4 **Outpatient Visits:** 11990
Births: 0 **Total Expense ($000):** 56036 **Payroll Expense ($000):** 14010
Personnel: 200

AMERY—Polk County

★ **AMERY HOSPITAL AND CLINIC (521308)**, 265 Griffin Street East,
Zip 54001–1439; tel. 715/268–8000, **A**3 10 18 **F**3 6 11 13 15 18 28 29 31
34 35 36 38 40 44 45 50 53 54 56 57 58 59 64 65 68 74 75 76 77 78 81
82 84 85 86 87 89 92 93 97 98 99 100 103 104 105 106 107 108 111 112
115 119 122 130 131 132 133 135 143 144 145 146 148 149 152 153 **P**6 **S**
HealthPartners, Bloomington, MN
Primary Contact: Debra Rudquist, FACHE, President and Chief Executive Officer
CMO: James Quenan, M.D., Chief Medical Officer
CIO: Patrice P Wolff, Director Management Information Systems
CHR: Joanne Jackson, Administrator Human Resources, Community Relations and
Quality Improvement
Web address: www.amerymedicalcenter.org
Control: Other not–for–profit (including NFP Corporation) **Service:** General
medical and surgical

Staffed Beds: 11 **Admissions:** 1024 **Census:** 11 **Outpatient Visits:** 120307
Births: 89 **Total Expense ($000):** 54084 **Payroll Expense ($000):** 30891
Personnel: 345

ANTIGO—Langlade County

⊞ **ASPIRUS LANGLADE HOSPITAL (521350)**, 112 East Fifth Avenue,
Zip 54409–2796; tel. 715/623–2331, **A**1 10 18 **F**2 3 6 10 11 12 13 15 28 29
30 31 34 35 36 40 43 50 53 54 56 57 59 60 63 64 65 68 69 70 75 76 77 78
79 81 82 84 85 86 87 89 92 93 96 97 99 100 101 103 104 107 108 110 111
115 118 119 121 127 129 130 131 132 133 144 146 147 148 154 **S** Aspirus,
Inc., Wausau, WI
Primary Contact: Andrew J. Barth, Executive Director
CFO: Pat Tincher, Director Finance
CHR: Janelle K. Markgraf, Director Human Resources and Off Campus Services
CNO: Sherry Bunten, Director Patient Care Services
Web address: www.aspirus.org
Control: Church operated, Nongovernment, not–for–profit **Service:** General
medical and surgical

Staffed Beds: 22 **Admissions:** 1318 **Census:** 11 **Outpatient Visits:** 120794
Births: 283 **Total Expense ($000):** 88142 **Payroll Expense ($000):** 33681
Personnel: 379

APPLETON—Outagamie County

⊞ **ASCENSION NORTHEAST WISCONSIN ST. ELIZABETH HOSPITAL (520009)**,
1506 South Oneida Street, Zip 54915–1305; tel. 920/738–2000, **A**1 2 3 5 10
F4 5 6 9 11 13 15 17 20 22 24 28 29 34 36 40 43 56 64 69 70 72 75 76 77
78 80 81 86 87 88 89 93 98 99 100 102 103 104 107 108 111 116 118 119
130 131 144 147 **S** Ascension Healthcare, Saint Louis, MO
Primary Contact: Monica Hilt, President and Regional Vice President
CFO: Jeff Badger, Chief Financial Officer
CMO: Lawrence Donatelle, M.D., Vice President Medical Affairs
CIO: Will Weider, Chief Information Officer
CHR: Vince Gallucci, Senior Vice President Human Resources
Web address: www.affinityhealth.org
Control: Church operated, Nongovernment, not–for–profit **Service:** General
medical and surgical

Staffed Beds: 190 **Admissions:** 7126 **Census:** 96 **Outpatient Visits:**
240148 **Births:** 1216 **Total Expense ($000):** 165522 **Payroll Expense
($000):** 51718 **Personnel:** 854

☐ **THEDACARE REGIONAL MEDICAL CENTER–APPLETON (520160)**, 1818
North Meade Street, Zip 54911–3496; tel. 920/731–4101, **A**1 2 3 5 10 **F**4 9 13
15 17 24 28 29 34 40 51 54 64 70 75 76 78 80 81 82 86 88 89 101 107 108
111 118 119 130 **S** ThedaCare, Inc., Appleton, WI
Primary Contact: Thomas J. Arquilla, Chief Strategy Officer
CFO: Tim Olson, Senior Vice President Finance
CMO: Gregory L Long, M.D., Chief Medical Officer
CIO: Keith Livingston, Senior Vice President and Chief Information Officer
Web address: www.thedacare.org
Control: Other not–for–profit (including NFP Corporation) **Service:** General
medical and surgical

Staffed Beds: 147 **Admissions:** 7707 **Census:** 79 **Outpatient Visits:**
162028 **Births:** 1048 **Total Expense ($000):** 223506 **Payroll Expense
($000):** 85244 **Personnel:** 1120

ASHLAND—Ashland County

⊞ **MEMORIAL MEDICAL CENTER OF ASHLAND (521359)**, 1615 Maple Lane,
Zip 54806–3689; tel. 715/685–5500, **A**1 10 18 **F**3 4 5 13 15 28 30 31 34 40
43 45 48 49 57 59 64 65 68 75 76 78 79 80 81 85 86 87 89 90 93 94 96 98
99 100 101 102 103 104 107 108 110 111 115 118 119 120 121 123 126
129 130 132 135 144 146 148 149 152 153
Primary Contact: Jason T. Douglas, Chief Executive Officer
COO: Karen Hansen, Vice President and Chief Operating Officer
CFO: Kent Dumonseau, Vice President Finance and Information Services
CIO: Todd Reynolds, Chief Information Officer
CHR: Diane Lulich, Director Human Resources
CNO: Kathryn Tuttle, R.N., Director of Nursing
Web address: www.ashlandmmc.com
Control: Other not–for–profit (including NFP Corporation) **Service:** General
medical and surgical

Staffed Beds: 35 **Admissions:** 2159 **Census:** 18 **Outpatient Visits:** 16214
Births: 212 **Total Expense ($000):** 67069 **Payroll Expense ($000):** 26128
Personnel: 420

BALDWIN—St. Croix County

★ **WESTERN WISCONSIN HEALTH (521347)**, 1100 Bergslien Street,
Zip 54002–2600; tel. 715/684–3311, **A**10 18 **F**1 3 8 11 13 15 17 28 29 31 32
34 35 36 40 41 43 53 55 57 59 64 65 68 70 71 75 76 77 78 79 80 81 82 85
86 87 89 90 91 93 96 97 99 100 102 103 104 107 108 110 111 114 115 117
119 127 130 131 133 144 146 147 148 149 150 154 **P**6
Primary Contact: Alison Page, Chief Executive Officer
CMO: Clint Semrau, Chief of Staff
CIO: Kendra Shaw, Chief Information Officer
CHR: Chris Riba, Director Human Resources
Web address: www.wwhealth.org
Control: Other not–for–profit (including NFP Corporation) **Service:** General
medical and surgical

Staffed Beds: 11 **Admissions:** 375 **Census:** 4 **Outpatient Visits:** 61495
Births: 168 **Total Expense ($000):** 39957 **Payroll Expense ($000):** 17970
Personnel: 254

BARABOO—Sauk County

⊞ **SSM HEALTH ST. CLARE HOSPITAL–BARABOO (520057)**, 707 14th Street,
Zip 53913–1597; tel. 608/356–1400, **A**1 3 5 10 **F**5 11 13 15 28 29 34 36 40
56 64 69 70 75 76 77 78 80 81 82 86 89 93 107 108 116 118 119 130 131
144 154 **S** SSM Health, Saint Louis, MO
Primary Contact: Laura Walczak, President
CFO: Troy Walker, Director Finance
CMO: Maureen Murphy, M.D., Director of Medical Affairs
CIO: Heather Stephens, Director of Information Health Technology
CHR: Jason Stelzer, Director Human Resources
CNO: Ginger Selle, Vice President Patient Care Services
Web address: www.stclare.com
Control: Church operated, Nongovernment, not–for–profit **Service:** General
medical and surgical

Staffed Beds: 43 **Admissions:** 2014 **Census:** 18 **Outpatient Visits:** 104418
Births: 210 **Total Expense ($000):** 53679 **Payroll Expense ($000):** 21119
Personnel: 281

WI

Hospital, Medicare Provider Number, Address, Telephone, Approval, Facility, and Physician Codes, Health Care System

★ American Hospital Association (AHA) membership   ○ Healthcare Facilities Accreditation Program   ⇑ Center for Improvement in Healthcare Quality Accreditation
☐ The Joint Commission accreditation   ◇ DNV Healthcare Inc. accreditation   △ Commission on Accreditation of Rehabilitation Facilities (CARF) accreditation

BARRON—Barron County

☐ **MAYO CLINIC HEALTH SYSTEM – NORTHLAND IN BARRON (521315)**, 1222 East Woodland Avenue, Zip 54812–1798; tel. 715/537–3186, **A**1 10 18 **F**3 6 8 13 15 18 28 29 30 31 32 34 35 36 40 43 44 45 53 54 56 57 59 60 64 65 69 75 76 77 78 79 80 81 82 84 85 86 87 89 90 93 96 97 100 104 107 110 115 118 130 131 132 133 135 144 145 146 147 148 149 154 **P**6 **S** Mayo Clinic, Rochester, MN
Primary Contact: Rita Sullivan, Vice President Operations
COO: Karolyn Bartlett, Assistant Administrator
CFO: Paul Bammel, Vice President
CMO: Richard Nagler, M.D., Chief of Staff
CIO: Todd Muden, Section Head Information Management
CHR: Blythe Rinaldi, Vice President
CNO: Patricia Keller, MSN, R.N., Nurse Administrator
Web address: www.luthermidelfortnorthland.org
Control: Other not–for–profit (including NFP Corporation) **Service:** General medical and surgical

Staffed Beds: 20 **Admissions:** 925 **Census:** 12 **Outpatient Visits:** 64382 **Births:** 108 **Total Expense ($000):** 59916 **Payroll Expense ($000):** 26263 **Personnel:** 307

BEAVER DAM—Dodge County

✠ **BEAVER DAM COMMUNITY HOSPITALS (520076)**, 707 South University Avenue, Zip 53916–3089; tel. 920/887–7181, (Total facility includes 115 beds in nursing home–type unit) **A**1 10 19 **F**3 6 8 10 11 13 15 17 28 29 30 31 33 34 36 37 40 41 43 44 45 47 53 56 57 59 62 63 64 65 69 70 74 75 76 77 78 79 80 81 82 85 86 87 89 93 96 97 107 110 111 114 115 119 126 128 129 130 131 132 135 143 144 146 147 148 149 150 154 **P**6
Primary Contact: Kimberly J. Miller, FACHE, President and Chief Executive Officer
COO: David Corso, Chief Operating Officer
CMO: Jason Smith, Chief Medical Officer
CHR: Melanie Bruins, Chief Talent Officer
CNO: Carolyn Catton, Interim Chief Patient Care Officer
Web address: www.bdch.com
Control: Other not–for–profit (including NFP Corporation) **Service:** General medical and surgical

Staffed Beds: 163 **Admissions:** 1807 **Census:** 109 **Outpatient Visits:** 95611 **Births:** 315 **Total Expense ($000):** 95610 **Payroll Expense ($000):** 32974 **Personnel:** 516

BELOIT—Rock County

☐ **BELOIT HEALTH SYSTEM (520100)**, 1969 West Hart Road, Zip 53511–2299; tel. 608/364–5011, **A**1 3 10 **F**5 6 9 10 11 12 13 15 17 20 22 24 28 29 34 36 40 43 51 53 54 56 60 62 75 76 77 78 80 81 82 86 87 89 93 99 100 101 102 103 104 108 111 116 118 119 130 131 144 147 154
Primary Contact: Timothy M. McKevett, President and Chief Executive Officer
CFO: William E Groeper, Vice President Finance
CMO: Kenneth Klein, M.D., Vice President Medical Affairs
CHR: Thomas J McCawley, Vice President
CNO: Doris Mulder, Vice President Nursing
Web address: www.beloithealthsystem.org
Control: Other not–for–profit (including NFP Corporation) **Service:** General medical and surgical

Staffed Beds: 103 **Admissions:** 4168 **Census:** 39 **Outpatient Visits:** 347980 **Births:** 459 **Total Expense ($000):** 226481 **Payroll Expense ($000):** 96618 **Personnel:** 1232

BERLIN—Green Lake County

☐ **THEDACARE MEDICAL CENTER–BERLIN (521355)**, 225 Memorial Drive, Zip 54923–1295; tel. 920/361–1313, **A**1 10 18 **F**11 13 15 17 24 28 29 34 40 43 51 53 56 70 75 76 78 80 81 82 86 87 88 89 90 93 107 108 111 116 119 130 131 144 147 154 **S** ThedaCare, Inc., Appleton, WI
Primary Contact: Tammy Bending, Vice President, Critical Access Hospital
CFO: Thomas P Krystowiak, Chief Financial Officer
Web address: www.chnwi.org
Control: Other not–for–profit (including NFP Corporation) **Service:** General medical and surgical

Staffed Beds: 25 **Admissions:** 1309 **Census:** 10 **Outpatient Visits:** 52355 **Births:** 110 **Total Expense ($000):** 38341 **Payroll Expense ($000):** 15042 **Personnel:** 291

BLACK RIVER FALLS—Jackson County

☐ **BLACK RIVER MEMORIAL HOSPITAL (521333)**, 711 West Adams Street, Zip 54615–9113; tel. 715/284–5361, **A**1 10 18 **F**3 11 13 29 34 35 40 44 45 53 56 57 59 62 63 65 69 75 76 77 81 84 85 86 89 93 107 111 115 116 118 119 129 130 131 132 133 135 144 146 148 154
Primary Contact: Mary Beth White–Jacobs, FACHE, R.N., Chief Executive Officer
COO: Holly Winn, FACHE, Chief Operating Officer
CFO: Robert Daley, CPA, Chief Financial Officer
CMO: Esteban Miller, Chief Medical Officer
CIO: Robert Daley, CPA, Vice President Fiscal and Information Technology Services
CNO: Melissa Bergerson, R.N., Chief Nursing Officer
Web address: www.brmh.net
Control: Other not–for–profit (including NFP Corporation) **Service:** General medical and surgical

Staffed Beds: 25 **Admissions:** 865 **Census:** 6 **Outpatient Visits:** 11759 **Births:** 146 **Total Expense ($000):** 43349 **Payroll Expense ($000):** 20230 **Personnel:** 308

BLOOMER—Chippewa County

☐ **MAYO CLINIC HEALTH SYSTEM – CHIPPEWA VALLEY IN BLOOMER (521314)**, 1501 Thompson Street, Zip 54724–1299; tel. 715/568–2000, **A**1 10 18 **F**3 8 15 18 28 29 30 32 34 35 40 43 44 45 53 54 56 57 59 64 65 75 77 78 80 81 84 85 86 87 90 93 96 97 107 115 119 130 132 133 135 144 146 147 148 149 154 **P**6 **S** Mayo Clinic, Rochester, MN
Primary Contact: Rita Sullivan, Vice President Operations
Web address: www.bloomermedicalcenter.org
Control: Other not–for–profit (including NFP Corporation) **Service:** General medical and surgical

Staffed Beds: 21 **Admissions:** 407 **Census:** 13 **Outpatient Visits:** 42938 **Births:** 0 **Total Expense ($000):** 33259 **Payroll Expense ($000):** 15896 **Personnel:** 199

BOSCOBEL—Grant County

GUNDERSEN BOSCOBEL AREA HOSPITAL AND CLINICS (521344), 205 Parker Street, Zip 53805–1698; tel. 608/375–4112, **A**10 18 **F**11 15 29 34 36 38 40 43 53 56 64 75 77 78 81 82 86 87 93 107 108 111 118 119 130 144 147 154 **P**2
Primary Contact: David Hartberg, Chief Executive Officer
CFO: Melissa Uselman, Chief Financial Officer
CMO: Marilu Bintz, M.D., Chief of Staff
CIO: Tonia Midtlien, Information Systems Support Specialist
CHR: Jennifer Dax, Director Human Resources
CNO: Theresa Lynn Braudt, Chief Nursing Officer
Web address: www.gundersenhealth.org/boscobel
Control: Other not–for–profit (including NFP Corporation) **Service:** General medical and surgical

Staffed Beds: 8 **Admissions:** 182 **Census:** 2 **Outpatient Visits:** 32550 **Births:** 0 **Total Expense ($000):** 16616 **Payroll Expense ($000):** 5208 **Personnel:** 111

BROOKFIELD—Waukesha County

★ **ASCENSION SOUTHEAST WISCONSIN HOSPITAL – ELMBROOK CAMPUS (520170)**, 19333 West North Avenue, Zip 53045–4198; tel. 262/785–2000, **F**3 4 11 12 13 15 17 18 20 22 24 26 28 29 30 31 34 35 36 40 41 43 44 45 46 47 48 49 50 51 54 56 58 59 64 65 68 70 72 74 75 76 77 78 79 80 81 82 83 84 85 86 87 89 90 92 93 97 100 107 108 109 110 111 112 114 115 116 117 118 119 120 121 122 123 124 126 130 131 132 135 145 146 148 149 154 **S** Ascension Healthcare, Saint Louis, MO
Primary Contact: Timothy Richman, President and Chief Executive Officer
CFO: Michael Petitt, Director of Finance
CMO: Rita Hanson, M.D., Vice President Medical Affairs
CIO: Andrew Donovan, Director Information Technology
CHR: Christopher Morris, Director Human Resources
Web address: www.wfhealthcare.org
Control: Church operated, Nongovernment, not–for–profit **Service:** General medical and surgical

Staffed Beds: 122 **Admissions:** 4652 **Census:** 53 **Outpatient Visits:** 71993 **Births:** 449 **Total Expense ($000):** 126368 **Payroll Expense ($000):** 35506 **Personnel:** 456

WI

Many Facility Codes have changed. Please refer to the AHA Guide Code Chart. © 2018 AHA Guide

BURLINGTON—Racine County

⊞ **AURORA MEMORIAL HOSPITAL OF BURLINGTON (520059)**, 252 McHenry Street, Zip 53105–1828; tel. 262/767–6000, **A**1 2 10 **F**3 8 11 15 16 17 18 20 26 28 29 30 34 35 36 40 43 44 45 47 48 49 50 51 53 56 57 59 60 68 70 74 75 79 80 81 82 85 86 87 88 89 93 94 96 100 107 108 109 110 111 115 116 118 119 130 131 132 134 135 146 148 149 154 **P**6 **S** Advocate Aurora Health, Downers Grove, IL
Primary Contact: Bob Miller, President
CFO: Stuart Arnett, Vice President Finance and Chief Financial Officer
CIO: Jean Chase, Regional Manager Information Services
CHR: Gene Krauklis, Regional Vice President Human Resources
Web address: www.aurorahealthcare.org
Control: Other not–for–profit (including NFP Corporation) **Service**: General medical and surgical

Staffed Beds: 55 **Admissions**: 2290 **Census**: 20 **Outpatient Visits**: 91426
Births: 0 **Total Expense ($000)**: 76970 **Payroll Expense ($000)**: 24374
Personnel: 503

CHILTON—Calumet County

⊞ **ASCENSION CALUMET HOSPITAL (521317)**, 614 Memorial Drive, Zip 53014–1597; tel. 920/849–2386, **A**1 10 18 **F**3 7 11 15 28 29 34 35 40 43 45 54 56 57 59 64 65 75 78 79 80 81 82 85 86 87 89 92 93 97 107 110 115 119 129 130 131 132 133 144 145 146 148 154 **S** Ascension Healthcare, Saint Louis, MO
Primary Contact: Jenny Derks, Chief Administrative Officer
CFO: Jeff Badger, Chief Financial Officer
CMO: Mark W Kehrberg, M.D., Chief Medical Officer
CIO: Will Weider, Chief Information Officer
CHR: Beth O'laire, Manager Human Resources
Web address: www.affinityhealth.org
Control: Other not–for–profit (including NFP Corporation) **Service**: General medical and surgical

Staffed Beds: 15 **Admissions**: 448 **Census**: 5 **Outpatient Visits**: 60216
Births: 0 **Total Expense ($000)**: 23797 **Payroll Expense ($000)**: 6636
Personnel: 97

CHIPPEWA FALLS—Chippewa County

⊞ **HSHS ST. JOSEPH'S HOSPITAL (520017)**, 2661 County Highway I, Zip 54729–5407; tel. 715/723–1811, **A**1 10 **F**3 4 5 11 13 15 17 19 28 29 30 34 38 40 43 54 56 59 62 63 64 68 69 70 75 76 79 80 81 82 83 84 86 87 88 89 93 100 101 102 104 107 110 111 115 119 129 130 132 135 145 146 147 148 149 154 **P**2 **S** HSHS Hospital Sisters Health System, Springfield, IL
Primary Contact: Charisse S. Oland, FACHE, President and Chief Executive Officer
CFO: David Nelson, FACHE, Divisional Chief Financial Officer
CIO: Kevin Groskreutz, Division Chief Information Officer, Ancillary Systems
CHR: Rick Tolson, Divisional Chief People Officer
CNO: Stella Clark, MSN, R.N., Chief Nursing Officer
Web address: www.stjoeschipfalls.com
Control: Church operated, Nongovernment, not–for–profit **Service**: General medical and surgical

Staffed Beds: 124 **Admissions**: 3046 **Census**: 38 **Outpatient Visits**: 67611
Births: 344 **Total Expense ($000)**: 60088 **Payroll Expense ($000)**: 25550
Personnel: 316

COLUMBUS—Columbia County

⊞ **COLUMBUS COMMUNITY HOSPITAL, INC. (521338)**, 1515 Park Avenue, Zip 53925–2402; tel. 920/623–2200, **A**1 10 18 **F**13 15 16 17 28 29 34 40 51 54 56 64 70 75 76 77 78 80 81 86 88 93 118 119 130 131 144 147 154 **P**6
Primary Contact: John D. Russell, President and Chief Executive Officer
CFO: Phillip G Roberts, Vice President Finance and Chief Financial Officer
CMO: Gary Galvin, M.D., Chief of the Medical Staff
CIO: Phillip G Roberts, Vice President Finance and Chief Financial Officer
CHR: Ann Roundy, Vice President Employee Services
CNO: Jamie Hendrix, Vice President Patient Care Services
Web address: www.cch–inc.com
Control: Other not–for–profit (including NFP Corporation) **Service**: General medical and surgical

Staffed Beds: 25 **Admissions**: 906 **Census**: 8 **Outpatient Visits**: 50531
Births: 87 **Total Expense ($000)**: 41522 **Payroll Expense ($000)**: 17033
Personnel: 242

CUBA CITY—Grant County

SOUTHWEST HEALTH CENTER NURSING HOME See Southwest Health, Platteville

CUDAHY—Milwaukee County

AURORA ST. LUKE'S SOUTH SHORE See Aurora St. Luke's Medical Center, Milwaukee

CUMBERLAND—Barron County

⊞ **CUMBERLAND HEALTHCARE (521353)**, 1110 Seventh Avenue, Zip 54829–9138; tel. 715/822–2741, **A**1 10 18 **F**11 13 15 28 29 34 40 43 53 55 56 64 75 76 77 78 81 82 86 87 89 93 99 100 103 104 107 130 131 144 154 **P**8
Primary Contact: Michael Gutsch, Chief Executive Officer and Administrator
COO: Bob Lindberg, Chief Operating Officer
CFO: Angela Martens, Chief Financial Officer
CMO: Tom Lingen, M.D., Chief of Staff
CIO: Jason Morse, Director Information Technology
CHR: Hilary Butzler, Director Human Resources
Web address: www.cumberlandhealthcare.com
Control: Other not–for–profit (including NFP Corporation) **Service**: General medical and surgical

Staffed Beds: 25 **Admissions**: 521 **Census**: 25 **Outpatient Visits**: 12846
Births: 45 **Total Expense ($000)**: 25236 **Payroll Expense ($000)**: 10885
Personnel: 161

DARLINGTON—Lafayette County

★ **MEMORIAL HOSPITAL OF LAFAYETTE COUNTY (521312)**, 800 Clay Street, Zip 53530–1228, Mailing Address: P.O. Box 70, Zip 53530–0070; tel. 608/776–4466, **A**10 18 **F**1 11 15 28 29 34 40 54 56 64 75 76 80 81 82 86 89 90 93 102 107 111 116 119 130 131 144 154 **S** UnityPoint Health, West Des Moines, IA
Primary Contact: Kathleen Kuepers, Chief Executive Officer
CFO: Marie Wamsley, Chief Financial Officer
Web address: www.memorialhospitaloflafayettecounty.org
Control: County, Government, nonfederal **Service**: General medical and surgical

Staffed Beds: 25 **Admissions**: 292 **Census**: 3 **Outpatient Visits**: 20699
Births: 0 **Total Expense ($000)**: 17907 **Payroll Expense ($000)**: 6321
Personnel: 125

DODGEVILLE—Iowa County

⊞ **UPLAND HILLS HEALTH (521352)**, 800 Compassion Way, Zip 53533–1956, Mailing Address: P.O. Box 800, Zip 53533–0800; tel. 608/930–8000, (Total facility includes 44 beds in nursing home–type unit) **A**1 10 18 **F**3 8 11 13 15 17 28 29 34 36 40 41 43 44 45 50 53 54 56 57 59 62 63 64 65 67 68 70 75 76 77 78 79 80 81 82 83 84 85 86 87 88 89 90 93 97 107 110 111 114 115 119 127 128 129 130 131 133 144 146 147 148 154 **P**6
Primary Contact: Lisa W. Schnedler, FACHE, President and Chief Executive Officer
CFO: Karl Pustina, Vice President Finance
CIO: Karen Thuli, Information Systems Coordinator
CHR: Troy Marx, Human Resources Director
CNO: Lynn Hebgen, MSN, R.N., Vice President of Nursing
Web address: www.uplandhillshealth.org
Control: Other not–for–profit (including NFP Corporation) **Service**: General medical and surgical

Staffed Beds: 69 **Admissions**: 1153 **Census**: 51 **Outpatient Visits**: 56322
Births: 238 **Total Expense ($000)**: 44845 **Payroll Expense ($000)**: 19548
Personnel: 271

DURAND—Pepin County

★ **CHIPPEWA VALLEY HOSPITAL (521307)**, 1220 Third Avenue West, Zip 54736–1600, Mailing Address: P.O. Box 224, Zip 54736–0224; tel. 715/672–4211, **A**10 18 **F**15 28 29 30 34 40 56 57 59 75 79 81 86 87 89 97 107 109 110 114 117 127 129 130 133 148 154 **S** Adventist Health System Sunbelt Health Care Corporation, Altamonte Springs, FL
Primary Contact: Douglas R. Peterson, President and Chief Executive Officer
Web address: www.chippewavalleyhospital.com/
Control: Church operated, Nongovernment, not–for–profit **Service**: General medical and surgical

Staffed Beds: 25 **Admissions**: 240 **Census**: 2 **Outpatient Visits**: 27380
Births: 0 **Total Expense ($000)**: 13311 **Payroll Expense ($000)**: 5200
Personnel: 88

WI

Hospital, Medicare Provider Number, Address, Telephone, Approval, Facility, and Physician Codes, Health Care System

★ American Hospital Association (AHA) membership
☐ The Joint Commission accreditation
○ Healthcare Facilities Accreditation Program
◇ DNV Healthcare Inc. accreditation
⇑ Center for Improvement in Healthcare Quality Accreditation
△ Commission on Accreditation of Rehabilitation Facilities (CARF) accreditation

EAGLE RIVER—Vilas County

★ **ASCENSION EAGLE RIVER HOSPITAL (521300)**, 201 Hospital Road, Zip 54521–8835; tel. 715/479–7411, **A**10 18 **F**11 15 28 29 34 40 64 75 81 82 86 87 89 93 107 111 119 130 154 **S** Ascension Healthcare, Saint Louis, MO
Primary Contact: Sandra L. Anderson, President
COO: Laurie Oungst, Vice President, Operations
CFO: Jamon Lamers, Director Finance
CMO: Roderick Brodhead, Chief Medical Officer
CIO: Howard Dobizl, Director Information Technology Services
CHR: Michelle Cornelius, Director Human Resources for Northern Region
CNO: Jacqualyn Monge, Director of Nursing
Web address: www.ministryhealth.org
Control: Church operated, Nongovernment, not–for–profit **Service**: General medical and surgical

Staffed Beds: 14 Admissions: 395 Census: 5 Outpatient Visits: 21468 **Births:** 0 **Total Expense ($000):** 13696 **Payroll Expense ($000):** 6262 **Personnel:** 70

EAU CLAIRE—Eau Claire County

✠ △ **HSHS SACRED HEART HOSPITAL (520013)**, 900 West Clairemont Avenue, Zip 54701–6122; tel. 715/717–4121, **A**1 2 3 5 7 10 19 **F**3 6 11 12 13 15 17 18 20 22 24 28 29 30 31 34 35 38 40 43 45 46 47 48 49 51 53 54 57 59 60 64 68 69 70 72 74 75 76 78 79 80 81 82 84 85 86 87 88 89 90 91 92 93 94 96 98 99 100 101 102 103 104 107 108 110 111 112 113 115 116 117 118 119 120 121 123 124 126 129 130 132 135 141 144 145 146 147 149 154 **P**2 6 **S** HSHS Hospital Sisters Health System, Springfield, IL
Primary Contact: Andrew Bagnall, President and Chief Executive Officer
CFO: David Nelson, FACHE, Chief Financial Officer
CMO: Humayun Khan, M.D., Chief Medical Officer
CIO: Kevin Groskreutz, Chief Information Officer
CHR: Craig Brenholt, Division Director People Services
CNO: Amy L. Dwyer, R.N., MSN, Chief Nursing Officer
Web address: www.sacredhearteauclaire.org
Control: Church operated, Nongovernment, not–for–profit **Service**: General medical and surgical

Staffed Beds: 216 Admissions: 9157 Census: 117 Outpatient Visits: 98432 **Births:** 881 **Total Expense ($000):** 182576 **Payroll Expense ($000):** 67393 **Personnel:** 922

MARSHFIELD MEDICAL CENTER – EAU CLAIRE HOSPITAL, 2310 Craig Road, Zip 54701–6128; tel. 715/858–8100, (Nonreporting) **S** Marshfield Clinic Health System, Marshfield, WI
Primary Contact: Scott Polenz, CPA, Chief Administrative Officer
Control: Other not–for–profit (including NFP Corporation) **Service**: General medical and surgical

Staffed Beds: 44

☐ **MAYO CLINIC HEALTH SYSTEM IN EAU CLAIRE (520070)**, 1221 Whipple Street, Zip 54703–5210, Mailing Address: P.O. Box 4105, Zip 54702; tel. 715/838–3311, **A**1 2 3 5 10 19 **F**3 4 5 6 8 12 13 15 17 18 20 22 24 26 28 29 30 31 32 34 35 36 37 40 43 44 45 46 48 49 53 55 56 57 58 59 60 64 65 70 71 72 74 75 76 78 79 80 81 82 83 84 85 86 87 89 90 92 93 94 96 97 98 99 100 101 102 103 104 105 107 108 110 111 115 117 118 119 120 121 124 126 129 130 132 135 144 145 146 147 148 149 154 **P**6 **S** Mayo Clinic, Rochester, MN
Primary Contact: Richard Helmers, M.D., Regional Vice President
COO: John M Dickey, Chief Administrative Officer
CFO: Denise Mattison, Director Finance and Accounting Services
CMO: Robert C Peck, M.D., Chief Medical Officer
CHR: Kenneth Lee, Division Chair, Human Resource Advisory
CNO: Pamela K. White, R.N., MSN, Chief Nursing Officer and Vice President
Web address: www.mhs.mayo.edu
Control: Other not–for–profit (including NFP Corporation) **Service**: General medical and surgical

Staffed Beds: 185 Admissions: 10148 Census: 117 Outpatient Visits: 380959 **Births:** 1062 **Total Expense ($000):** 506487 **Payroll Expense ($000):** 238900 **Personnel:** 2352

EDGERTON—Rock County

✠ **EDGERTON HOSPITAL AND HEALTH SERVICES (521319)**, 11101 North Sherman Road, Zip 53534–9002; tel. 608/884–3441, **A**1 10 18 **F**3 8 11 15 28 32 34 40 43 48 57 59 64 65 75 77 81 85 86 90 93 97 107 108 110 111 115 119 129 130 132 133 135 144 146 148 149 154
Primary Contact: Jim Schultz, Chief Executive Officer
CFO: Charles Roader, Vice President Finance
CMO: Brian Stubitsch, M.D., Chief Medical Officer
CIO: JT Johrendt, Information Technology Network Specialist
CHR: Mark Kindschi, Director Human Resources
CNO: Sue Alwin-Popp, Chief Clinical Officer
Web address: www.edgertonhospital.com
Control: Other not–for–profit (including NFP Corporation) **Service**: General medical and surgical

Staffed Beds: 18 Admissions: 425 Census: 9 Outpatient Visits: 16472 **Births:** 0 **Total Expense ($000):** 21291 **Payroll Expense ($000):** 10017 **Personnel:** 116

ELKHORN—Walworth County

✠ △ **AURORA LAKELAND MEDICAL CENTER (520102)**, W3985 County Road NN, Zip 53121–4389; tel. 262/741–2000, **A**1 2 3 7 10 **F**3 11 13 17 18 29 30 34 35 36 40 43 44 45 46 47 48 50 51 56 57 59 60 68 70 74 75 76 79 80 81 82 84 85 86 89 90 93 94 96 100 107 108 111 115 118 119 129 130 131 132 135 146 148 149 154 **P**6 **S** Advocate Aurora Health, Downers Grove, IL
Primary Contact: Bob Miller, President
CFO: Stuart Arnett, Regional Vice President Finance
CMO: Greg Gerber, M.D., Chief Medical Officer
CIO: Jean Chase, Regional Manager Information Services
CHR: Gene Krauklis, Regional Vice President Human Resources
Web address: www.aurorahealthcare.org
Control: Other not–for–profit (including NFP Corporation) **Service**: General medical and surgical

Staffed Beds: 67 Admissions: 2689 Census: 25 Outpatient Visits: 67714 **Births:** 626 **Total Expense ($000):** 55435 **Payroll Expense ($000):** 19298 **Personnel:** 396

FOND DU LAC—Fond Du Lac County

FOND DU LAC COUNTY MENTAL HEALTH CENTER (524025), 459 East First Street, Zip 54935–4599; tel. 920/929–3502, **A**10 **F**4 38 98 99 102 103 130 135 151 154 **P**6
Primary Contact: J.R. Musunuru, M.D., Executive Director
Web address: www.fdlco.wi.gov
Control: County, Government, nonfederal **Service**: Psychiatric

Staffed Beds: 25 Admissions: 915 Census: 13 Outpatient Visits: 537 **Births:** 0 **Total Expense ($000):** 4079 **Payroll Expense ($000):** 2615 **Personnel:** 47

✠ △ **ST. AGNES HOSPITAL (520088)**, 430 East Division Street, Zip 54935–4560, Mailing Address: P.O. Box 385, Zip 54936–0385; tel. 920/929–2300, **A**1 2 7 10 20 **F**2 3 5 6 8 11 13 15 18 20 22 24 26 28 29 30 31 33 34 35 36 38 40 43 44 45 46 47 48 49 50 51 53 54 55 56 57 59 60 62 63 64 66 67 68 69 74 75 76 77 78 79 80 81 82 84 85 86 87 90 92 93 96 97 98 99 100 101 102 103 104 105 107 108 109 110 111 115 118 119 120 121 123 124 126 129 130 132 134 135 143 144 146 147 148 149 150 152 153 154 **P**3 6 **S** SSM Health, Saint Louis, MO
Primary Contact: Katherine Vergos, President
CFO: Bonnie Schmitz, Vice President and Chief Financial Officer
CMO: Derek Colmenares, M.D., Chief Medical Officer
CIO: Nancy Birschbach, Vice President and Chief Information Officer
CHR: Sue Edminster, Vice President Human Resources
CNO: Tami Schattschneider, Chief Nursing Officer
Web address: www.agnesian.com
Control: Church operated, Nongovernment, not–for–profit **Service**: General medical and surgical

Staffed Beds: 140 Admissions: 6806 Census: 74 Outpatient Visits: 742348 **Births:** 816 **Total Expense ($000):** 363365 **Payroll Expense ($000):** 136067 **Personnel:** 1989

FORT ATKINSON—Jefferson County

✠ **FORT HEALTHCARE (520071)**, 611 East Sherman Avenue, Zip 53538–1998; tel. 920/568–5000, **A**1 10 **F**3 11 12 13 15 28 29 34 35 40 47 48 50 53 55 56 57 59 68 75 76 77 79 80 81 85 86 87 89 90 93 94 96 107 108 110 111 115 118 119 124 130 132 135 144 146 147 149 150 154 **P**1 5
Primary Contact: Michael S. Wallace, President and Chief Executive Officer
CFO: James J Nelson, Senior Vice President Finance and Strategic Planning
CMO: Thomas Nordland, Chief Medical Officer
CIO: Christopher Manakas, Chief Information Officer
CHR: Nancy Alstad, Director Human Resources
CNO: Marie Wiesmann, Vice President of Nursing and Chief Nursing Officer
Web address: www.forthealthcare.com
Control: Other not–for–profit (including NFP Corporation) **Service**: General medical and surgical

Staffed Beds: 72 Admissions: 1828 Census: 14 Outpatient Visits: 267737 **Births:** 405 **Total Expense ($000):** 116441 **Payroll Expense ($000):** 37384 **Personnel:** 432

FRANKLIN—Milwaukee County

✠ **MIDWEST ORTHOPEDIC SPECIALTY HOSPITAL (520205)**, 10101 South 27th Street, 2nd Floor, Zip 53132–7209; tel. 414/817–5800, **A**1 3 5 10 **F**3 29 30 34 50 57 68 79 80 81 82 85 86 91 92 94 96 114 130 131 149 154 **S** Ascension Healthcare, Saint Louis, MO
Primary Contact: Bernie Sherry, President, Ascension Wisconsin
CFO: Aaron Bridgeland, Director Finance
CMO: Daniel Guehlstorf, M.D., Chief of Staff
CIO: Gregory Smith, Senior Vice President and Chief Information Officer
Web address: www.mymosh.com/
Control: Partnership, Investor–owned (for–profit) **Service**: General medical and surgical

Staffed Beds: 16 Admissions: 1436 Census: 8 Outpatient Visits: 5979 **Births:** 0 **Total Expense ($000):** 38502 **Payroll Expense ($000):** 6127 **Personnel:** 107

Many Facility Codes have changed. Please refer to the AHA Guide Code Chart.

© 2018 AHA Guide

✠ **WHEATON FRANCISCAN HEALTHCARE – FRANKLIN (520204)**, 10101 South 27th Street, Zip 53132–7209; tel. 414/325–4700, **A**1 10 **F**3 15 18 20 22 26 29 30 34 35 40 43 44 45 48 49 50 57 59 64 65 68 70 74 75 77 79 81 82 85 86 87 91 92 93 96 97 107 108 110 111 115 119 126 130 131 135 146 154 **S** Ascension Healthcare, Saint Louis, MO
Primary Contact: Sheila Gansemer, R.N., Vice President Patient Care Services and Chief Nursing Officer
CFO: Aaron Bridgeland, Director Finance
CMO: Michelle Graham, M.D., Vice President Medical Affairs
CIO: Gregory Smith, Senior Vice President and Chief Information Officer
CNO: Sheila Gansemer, R.N., Vice President Patient Care Services and Chief Nursing Officer
Web address: www.mywheaton.org/
Control: Church operated, Nongovernment, not–for–profit **Service**: General medical and surgical

Staffed Beds: 44 **Admissions**: 2727 **Census**: 33 **Outpatient Visits**: 94178 **Births**: 0 **Total Expense ($000)**: 79067 **Payroll Expense ($000)**: 24848 **Personnel**: 327

FRIENDSHIP—Adams County

GUNDERSEN MOUNDVIEW MEMORIAL HOSPITAL & CLINICS (521309), 402 West Lake Street, Zip 53934–9699, Mailing Address: P.O. Box 40, Zip 53934–0040; tel. 608/339–3331, **A**10 18 **F**6 11 15 28 29 34 36 40 53 56 64 77 81 82 86 87 93 107 108 111 119 130 131 154 **P**6
Primary Contact: Francisco Perez–Guerra, Chief Executive Officer
Web address: www.moundview.org
Control: Other not–for–profit (including NFP Corporation) **Service**: General medical and surgical

Staffed Beds: 25 **Admissions**: 190 **Census**: 2 **Outpatient Visits**: 35850 **Births**: 0 **Total Expense ($000)**: 17823 **Payroll Expense ($000)**: 7878 **Personnel**: 136

GLENDALE—Milwaukee County

ORTHOPAEDIC HOSPITAL OF WISCONSIN – GLENDALE (520194), 475 West River Woods Parkway, Zip 53212–1081; tel. 414/961–6800, **A**10 **F**29 34 38 53 64 80 81 82 86 93 107 111 119 130 131
Primary Contact: Brian J. Cramer, Chief Executive Officer
CFO: Tom Swiderski, Chief Financial Officer
CMO: Rory Wright, M.D., President Medical Staff
CIO: Todd Heikkinen, Manager Sports Medicine and Rehabilitation Services
CNO: Nanette Johnson, Chief Nursing Officer
Web address: www.ohow.org
Control: Partnership, Investor–owned (for–profit) **Service**: General medical and surgical

Staffed Beds: 30 **Admissions**: 1394 **Census**: 9 **Outpatient Visits**: 36158 **Births**: 0 **Total Expense ($000)**: 38797 **Payroll Expense ($000)**: 13470 **Personnel**: 199

GRAFTON—Ozaukee County

✠ **AURORA MEDICAL CENTER GRAFTON (520207)**, 975 Port Washington Road, Zip 53024–9201; tel. 262/329–1000, **A**1 2 3 5 10 **F**3 8 13 15 17 18 20 22 24 26 28 29 30 31 34 35 36 37 40 43 44 45 46 47 48 49 50 51 53 54 59 60 64 65 68 70 72 74 75 76 79 80 81 82 84 85 86 87 89 90 91 93 94 96 107 108 110 111 114 115 116 117 118 119 120 121 124 126 130 131 135 146 147 148 149 154 **P**6 **S** Advocate Aurora Health, Downers Grove, IL
Primary Contact: David Graebner, Interim President
CMO: Doug McManus, Chief Medical Officer
CNO: Terry Kabitzke–Groth, R.N., Vice President Nursing
Web address: www.aurorahealthcare.org
Control: Other not–for–profit (including NFP Corporation) **Service**: General medical and surgical

Staffed Beds: 127 **Admissions**: 7683 **Census**: 77 **Outpatient Visits**: 128480 **Births**: 892 **Total Expense ($000)**: 194180 **Payroll Expense ($000)**: 54594 **Personnel**: 1151

GRANTSBURG—Burnett County

★ **BURNETT MEDICAL CENTER (521331)**, 257 West St George Avenue, Zip 54840–7827; tel. 715/463–5353, (Total facility includes 50 beds in nursing home–type unit) **A**10 18 **F**2 3 13 15 28 29 30 31 34 35 40 43 45 56 57 59 64 68 75 76 77 78 80 81 84 86 87 89 90 93 97 107 115 127 128 130 131 132 133 135 144 148 149 154 **P**6
Primary Contact: Gordon Lewis, Chief Executive Officer
CFO: Charles J Faught, Chief Financial Officer
CMO: Hans Rechsteiner, M.D., Chief of Staff
CIO: Andy Douglas, Manager Information Technology
CHR: Sandy Hinrichs, Director Human Resources
Web address: www.burnettmedicalcenter.com
Control: Other not–for–profit (including NFP Corporation) **Service**: General medical and surgical

Staffed Beds: 67 **Admissions**: 340 **Census**: 42 **Outpatient Visits**: 33292 **Births**: 18 **Total Expense ($000)**: 14956 **Payroll Expense ($000)**: 6978 **Personnel**: 126

GREEN BAY—Brown County

✠ △ **AURORA BAYCARE MEDICAL CENTER (520193)**, 2845 Greenbrier Road, Zip 54311–6519, Mailing Address: P.O. Box 8900, Zip 54308–8900; tel. 920/288–8000, **A**1 2 7 10 **F**3 12 13 15 17 20 22 24 28 29 36 40 43 53 54 64 70 72 75 76 78 80 81 82 86 87 89 90 93 107 108 111 116 118 119 130 131 144 147 149 154 **P**6 **S** Advocate Aurora Health, Downers Grove, IL
Primary Contact: Daniel T. Meyer, President
COO: Daniel T Meyer, President
CFO: Gwen Christensen, Vice President, Finance
CMO: Brian Johnson, M.D., Chief Medical Officer
CIO: Chuck Geurts, Manager Information Technology Client Services
CHR: Elizabeth A Kirby, Senior Director Human Resources
CNO: Heather Schroeder, R.N., Vice President Nursing
Web address: www.aurorabaycare.com
Control: Partnership, Investor–owned (for–profit) **Service**: General medical and surgical

Staffed Beds: 167 **Admissions**: 9560 **Census**: 109 **Outpatient Visits**: 355464 **Births**: 1413 **Total Expense ($000)**: 323639 **Payroll Expense ($000)**: 103241 **Personnel**: 1713

★ ⇑ **BELLIN MEMORIAL HOSPITAL (520049)**, 744 South Webster Avenue, Zip 54301–3581, Mailing Address: P.O. Box 23400, Zip 54305–3400; tel. 920/433–3500, **A**2 10 21 **F**3 12 13 15 17 18 20 22 24 26 28 29 30 31 32 35 36 37 40 43 44 45 46 47 48 49 51 53 54 59 62 64 71 74 75 76 77 78 79 80 81 82 83 84 85 86 87 89 90 91 92 96 97 107 108 110 111 115 116 117 118 119 121 123 124 126 127 129 130 131 132 133 144 145 146 148 149 154 **P**2 6
Primary Contact: George Kerwin, President and Chief Executive Officer
CFO: Jim Dietsche, Chief Financial Officer
CMO: Cynthia Lasecki, M.D., Chief Medical Officer
CIO: John Rocheleau, Vice President Business Support and Information Technology
CHR: Troy L Koebke, Director Human Resources Management
CNO: Laura Hieb, R.N., Chief Nursing Officer
Web address: www.bellin.org
Control: Church operated, Nongovernment, not–for–profit **Service**: General medical and surgical

Staffed Beds: 167 **Admissions**: 8626 **Census**: 81 **Outpatient Visits**: 1053054 **Births**: 1471 **Total Expense ($000)**: 443951 **Payroll Expense ($000)**: 213066 **Personnel**: 2670

⇑ **BELLIN PSYCHIATRIC CENTER (524038)**, 301 East St Joseph Street, Zip 54301, Mailing Address: P.O. Box 23725, Zip 54305–3725; tel. 920/433–3630, **A**3 10 21 **F**4 5 6 29 34 36 38 53 54 56 64 75 86 87 98 99 100 101 102 103 104 130 154 **P**2 6
Primary Contact: Sharla Baenen, MSN, R.N., President
COO: Chris Woleske, Chief Operating Officer
CFO: Kevin McGurk, Controller
CIO: Troy Schiesl, Director Information Services
CHR: Troy L Koebke, Director Human Resources
CNO: Crystal Malakar, Team Leader Inpatient Nursing
Web address: www.bellin.org
Control: Church operated, Nongovernment, not–for–profit **Service**: Psychiatric

Staffed Beds: 53 **Admissions**: 1632 **Census**: 20 **Outpatient Visits**: 79317 **Births**: 0 **Total Expense ($000)**: 21845 **Payroll Expense ($000)**: 14476 **Personnel**: 157

WI

Hospital, Medicare Provider Number, Address, Telephone, Approval, Facility, and Physician Codes, Health Care System

★ American Hospital Association (AHA) membership   ◯ Healthcare Facilities Accreditation Program   ⇑ Center for Improvement in Healthcare Quality Accreditation
☐ The Joint Commission accreditation   ◇ DNV Healthcare Inc. accreditation   △ Commission on Accreditation of Rehabilitation Facilities (CARF) accreditation

BROWN COUNTY COMMUNITY TREATMENT CENTER (524014), 3150 Gershwin Drive, Zip 54311–5899; tel. 920/391–4700, **A**10 **F**98 102 130 154
Primary Contact: Roberta Morschauser, Administrator
CFO: Margaret Hoff, Account Manager
CMO: Yogesh Pareek, M.D., Clinical Director
CIO: Dawn LaPlant, Manager Health Information Management
CHR: Brent R Miller, Manager Human Resources
Web address: www.co.brown.wi.us/
Control: County, Government, nonfederal **Service**: Psychiatric

Staffed Beds: 16 Admissions: 755 Census: 11 Outpatient Visits: 0
Births: 0 Total Expense ($000): 4063 Payroll Expense ($000): 2652
Personnel: 62

BROWN COUNTY HUMAN SERVICES MENTAL HEALTH CENTER See Brown County Community Treatment Center

☒ **HSHS ST. MARY'S HOSPITAL MEDICAL CENTER (520097)**, 1726 Shawano Avenue, Zip 54303–3282; tel. 920/498–4200, **A**1 2 10 **F**3 13 15 17 18 20 22 26 28 29 30 31 34 35 40 43 44 45 46 47 48 49 50 51 53 55 57 59 64 65 68 69 70 74 75 76 77 78 79 80 81 82 84 85 86 87 92 94 96 102 107 108 110 111 114 115 116 117 118 119 130 132 143 145 146 147 148 149 150 154 **P**2 **S** HSHS Hospital Sisters Health System, Springfield, IL
Primary Contact: Therese B. Pandl, President and Chief Executive Officer
COO: Lawrence J Connors, Chief Operating Officer
CFO: Greg Simia, Chief Financial Officer
CMO: Ken Johnson, Chief Physician Executive
CIO: Shane Miller, Chief Information Officer
CHR: Christine Jensema, Chief People Officer
CNO: Paula Hafeman, Chief Nursing Officer
Web address: www.stmgb.org
Control: Church operated, Nongovernment, not–for–profit **Service**: General medical and surgical

Staffed Beds: 83 Admissions: 4018 Census: 34 Outpatient Visits: 104395
Births: 456 Total Expense ($000): 116918 Payroll Expense ($000): 36346
Personnel: 411

☒ **HSHS ST. VINCENT HOSPITAL (520075)**, 835 South Van Buren Street, Zip 54301–3526, Mailing Address: P.O. Box 13508, Zip 54307–3508; tel. 920/433–0111, **A**1 2 10 **F**3 5 9 11 12 13 15 17 18 19 20 22 24 26 29 30 31 32 34 35 36 40 43 44 45 49 50 51 56 57 58 59 60 62 64 65 68 70 72 74 75 76 77 78 79 80 81 83 84 85 86 87 88 89 90 91 92 94 96 107 108 110 111 114 115 116 117 118 119 120 121 123 124 126 129 130 132 135 143 144 146 147 148 149 150 151 154 **P**2 **S** HSHS Hospital Sisters Health System, Springfield, IL
Primary Contact: Therese B. Pandl, President and Chief Executive Officer
COO: Brian Charlier, Chief Operating Officer, HSHS St. Vincent Hospital/Prevea Health
CFO: Greg Simia, Chief Financial Officer
CMO: Ken Johnson, Chief Physician Executive
CIO: Shane Miller, Chief Information Officer
CHR: Christine Jensema, Chief Human Resources Officer
CNO: Kenneth E Nelson, R.N., III Chief Nursing Officer
Web address: www.stvincenthospital.org
Control: Church operated, Nongovernment, not–for–profit **Service**: General medical and surgical

Staffed Beds: 255 Admissions: 10687 Census: 138 Outpatient Visits: 155218 Births: 1098 Total Expense ($000): 301040 Payroll Expense ($000): 88426 Personnel: 1453

WILLOW CREEK BEHAVIORAL HEALTH (524041), 1351 Ontario Road, Zip 54311–8302; tel. 920/328–1220, (Nonreporting) **S** Strategic Behavioral Health, LLC, Memphis, TN
Primary Contact: Teena Ahuja, Interim Chief Executive Officer and Regional Vice President of Operations
Web address: www.willowcreekbh.com
Control: Corporation, Investor–owned (for–profit) **Service**: Psychiatric

Staffed Beds: 72

GREENFIELD—Milwaukee County

KINDRED HOSPITAL–MILWAUKEE See Post Acute Medical Specialty Hospital of Milwaukee

☒ **POST ACUTE MEDICAL SPECIALTY HOSPITAL OF MILWAUKEE (522004)**, 5017 South 110th Street, Zip 53228–3131; tel. 414/427–8282, **A**1 10 **F**1 29 100 130 **S** Post Acute Medical, LLC, Enola, PA
Primary Contact: Paul E. Qualls, Chief Executive Officer
CMO: Alok Goyal, M.D., Medical Director
CNO: Nancy Cholka, R.N., Chief Nursing Officer
Web address: www.postacutemedical.com/
Control: Corporation, Investor–owned (for–profit) **Service**: Children's acute long–term Care

Staffed Beds: 56 Admissions: 496 Census: 33 Outpatient Visits: 0
Births: 0 Total Expense ($000): 19048 Payroll Expense ($000): 7028
Personnel: 121

HARTFORD—Washington County

☒ **AURORA MEDICAL CENTER IN WASHINGTON COUNTY (520038)**, 1032 East Sumner Street, Zip 53027–1698; tel. 262/673–2300, **A**1 2 10 **F**2 3 8 11 15 29 30 34 35 36 37 40 41 43 44 45 46 47 48 49 50 53 54 56 57 59 60 64 65 70 74 75 77 79 80 81 82 83 84 85 86 87 89 90 91 92 93 94 95 96 107 111 114 118 119 129 130 132 135 146 148 149 154 **P**6 **S** Advocate Aurora Health, Downers Grove, IL
Primary Contact: David Graebner, President
CIO: John Sipek, Supervisor Client Services
CNO: Terry Kabitzke–Groth, R.N., Chief Nursing Officer
Web address: www.aurorahealthcare.org
Control: Other not–for–profit (including NFP Corporation) **Service**: General medical and surgical

Staffed Beds: 34 Admissions: 1536 Census: 14 Outpatient Visits: 82461
Births: 0 Total Expense ($000): 50442 Payroll Expense ($000): 18516
Personnel: 328

HAYWARD—Sawyer County

★ **HAYWARD AREA MEMORIAL HOSPITAL AND WATER'S EDGE (521336)**, 11040 North State Road 77, Zip 54843–6391; tel. 715/934–4321, (Total facility includes 70 beds in nursing home–type unit) **A**10 18 **F**10 11 13 15 34 40 43 51 64 75 76 77 78 81 82 93 107 111 119 128 130 154
Primary Contact: Luke Beirl, PharmD, Chief Executive Officer
COO: Brad Zeller, Vice President Operations
CFO: Kent Dumonseau, Vice President Finance and Information Services
CHR: Rose Gates, Director Human Resources
Web address: www.https://haywardmemorialhospital.com
Control: Other not–for–profit (including NFP Corporation) **Service**: General medical and surgical

Staffed Beds: 75 Admissions: 880 Census: 75 Outpatient Visits: 13211
Births: 137 Total Expense ($000): 35334 Payroll Expense ($000): 14286
Personnel: 205

HILLSBORO—Vernon County

★ **GUNDERSEN ST. JOSEPH'S HOSPITAL AND CLINICS (521304)**, 400 Water Avenue, Zip 54634–9054, Mailing Address: P.O. Box 527, Zip 54634–0527; tel. 608/489–8000, **A**10 18 **F**3 15 29 30 34 35 40 41 43 44 45 46 50 53 56 57 59 64 65 66 68 69 75 77 79 80 81 82 84 85 86 87 89 90 93 97 99 100 101 103 104 107 108 114 127 128 130 131 133 135 144 145 146 147 148 154
Primary Contact: Danielle Gearhart, Chief Executive Officer
CFO: Robin Nelson, Chief Financial Officer
CMO: William Cooke, M.D., Chief of Staff
CIO: Danial Phetteplace, Director Information Technology
CHR: Kristie McCoic, Clinic Operations Officer and Director Human Resources
Web address: www.gundersenhealth.org/st-josephs
Control: Other not–for–profit (including NFP Corporation) **Service**: General medical and surgical

Staffed Beds: 13 Admissions: 201 Census: 2 Outpatient Visits: 37406
Births: 0 Total Expense ($000): 19951 Payroll Expense ($000): 8377
Personnel: 171

HUDSON—St. Croix County

☐ **HUDSON HOSPITAL AND CLINIC (521335)**, 405 Stageline Road, Zip 54016–7848; tel. 715/531–6000, **A**1 3 10 18 **F**5 13 15 28 29 34 38 40 43 53 55 56 64 75 76 78 80 81 86 87 89 93 107 111 119 130 154 **S** HealthPartners, Bloomington, MN
Primary Contact: Thomas Borowski, FACHE, President
CFO: Douglas E Johnson, Interim Vice President Operations and Chief Financial Officer
CMO: Paul Scott, M.D., Chief of Staff
CHR: Scott J Allen, Director Human Resources
Web address: www.hudsonhospital.org
Control: Other not–for–profit (including NFP Corporation) **Service**: General medical and surgical

Staffed Beds: 24 Admissions: 1413 Census: 10 Outpatient Visits: 35292
Births: 568 Total Expense ($000): 52699 Payroll Expense ($000): 19885
Personnel: 232

WI

Many Facility Codes have changed. Please refer to the AHA Guide Code Chart. © 2018 AHA Guide

JANESVILLE—Rock County

☒ **MERCYHEALTH HOSPITAL AND TRAUMA CENTER – JANESVILLE (520066)**, 1000 Mineral Point Avenue, Zip 53548–2982, Mailing Address: P.O. Box 5003, Zip 53547–5003; tel. 608/756–6000, (Total facility includes 28 beds in nursing home–type unit) **A**1 2 3 10 **F**3 4 5 6 9 11 12 13 15 17 18 20 22 24 26 28 29 30 31 32 34 37 38 40 43 44 45 49 50 51 54 55 56 57 58 59 60 61 65 66 68 69 70 74 75 76 77 78 79 80 81 82 84 85 87 88 89 90 92 93 94 96 97 98 100 101 102 103 104 105 107 108 110 111 114 115 116 118 119 120 121 126 128 129 130 131 132 135 144 146 147 148 149 153 154 **P**6 **S** Mercy Health System, Janesville, WI
Primary Contact: Javon R. Bea, President and Chief Executive Officer
CFO: John Cook, Vice President and Chief Financial Officer
CMO: Mark L. Goelzer, M.D., Director Medical Affairs
CHR: Kathy Harris, Vice President
CNO: Debra Potempa, Vice President
Web address: www.mercyhealthsystem.org
Control: Other not–for–profit (including NFP Corporation) **Service**: General medical and surgical

Staffed Beds: 135 **Admissions**: 8189 **Census**: 103 **Outpatient Visits**: 1064375 **Births**: 835 **Total Expense ($000)**: 423241 **Payroll Expense ($000)**: 139645 **Personnel**: 1686

☒ **SSM HEALTH ST. MARY'S HOSPITAL JANESVILLE (520208)**, 3400 East Racine Steeet, Zip 53546–2344; tel. 608/373–8000, **A**1 10 **F**11 13 28 29 34 38 40 70 75 76 77 80 81 82 86 87 89 90 93 107 108 111 118 119 130 154 **S** SSM Health, Saint Louis, MO
Primary Contact: Benjamin Layman, President
Web address: www.stmarysjanesville.com
Control: Church operated, Nongovernment, not–for–profit **Service**: General medical and surgical

Staffed Beds: 50 **Admissions**: 2570 **Census**: 22 **Outpatient Visits**: 33745 **Births**: 435 **Total Expense ($000)**: 62439 **Payroll Expense ($000)**: 20866 **Personnel**: 322

KENOSHA—Kenosha County

☒ **AURORA MEDICAL CENTER KENOSHA (520189)**, 10400 75th Street, Zip 53142–7884; tel. 262/948–5600, **A**1 2 10 **F**3 8 11 13 15 17 18 19 20 22 26 28 29 31 34 35 36 40 43 44 45 46 47 48 49 50 51 54 57 59 66 68 70 72 74 75 76 79 80 81 82 84 85 86 87 93 94 96 100 107 108 110 111 114 115 116 117 118 119 120 121 123 126 129 130 131 132 135 146 148 149 **P**6 **S** Advocate Aurora Health, Downers Grove, IL
Primary Contact: Douglas E. Koch, Market President
COO: Linda A. Gump, Chief Clinical Services Officer
CFO: Laurie B. Yake, Vice President Finance
CMO: James Santarelli, M.D., President Medical Staff
CIO: Debora R. Chapdelaine, Manager Information Technology
CHR: Kellie Nelson, Director Human Resources
CNO: Donna F. Jamieson, Ph.D., R.N., Chief Nursing Officer
Web address: www.aurorahealthcare.org
Control: Other not–for–profit (including NFP Corporation) **Service**: General medical and surgical

Staffed Beds: 79 **Admissions**: 5581 **Census**: 50 **Outpatient Visits**: 189736 **Births**: 740 **Total Expense ($000)**: 148871 **Payroll Expense ($000)**: 45299 **Personnel**: 1193

☐ **FROEDTERT SOUTH – KENOSHA MEDICAL CENTER (520021)**, 6308 Eighth Avenue, Zip 53143–5082; tel. 262/656–2011, (Includes FROEDTERT SOUTH – ST. CATHERINE'S MEDICAL CENTER, 9555 76th Street, Pleasant Prairie, WI, Zip 53158–1984, Mailing Address: 6308 Eighth Avenue, Kenosha, Zip 53143–5082, tel. 262/656–2011; Richard O Schmidt Jr, President and Chief Executive Officer) **A**1 2 10 **F**1 11 12 13 15 17 20 22 24 28 29 34 38 40 43 51 53 60 64 70 72 75 76 78 80 81 86 87 89 90 93 100 102 107 108 111 118 119 130 131 144 147 154
Primary Contact: Richard O. Schmidt Jr, President and Chief Executive Officer
CFO: Thomas J. Kelley, Executive Vice President and Chief Financial Officer
Web address: www.unitedhospitalsystem.org/
Control: Other not–for–profit (including NFP Corporation) **Service**: General medical and surgical

Staffed Beds: 232 **Admissions**: 7362 **Census**: 90 **Outpatient Visits**: 339531 **Births**: 1064 **Total Expense ($000)**: 285993 **Payroll Expense ($000)**: 129068 **Personnel**: 1844

LA CROSSE—La Crosse County

☒ △ **GUNDERSEN LUTHERAN MEDICAL CENTER (520087)**, 1900 South Avenue, Zip 54601–5467; tel. 608/782–7300, **A**1 2 3 5 7 8 10 **F**3 5 7 11 12 13 15 18 19 20 22 24 26 28 29 30 31 32 33 34 35 36 39 40 43 44 45 46 47 48 49 50 51 52 53 54 55 56 57 59 60 61 63 64 65 68 70 72 74 75 76 77 78 79 81 82 84 85 86 87 88 89 90 91 92 93 94 96 97 98 100 102 104 105 107 109 110 111 113 115 116 117 118 119 120 121 123 124 126 127 128 129 130 131 132 134 135 143 144 145 146 147 148 149 150 153 154
Primary Contact: Scott W. Rathgaber, M.D., Chief Executive Officer
COO: Kathy Klock, R.N., Senior Vice President Clinical Operations and Human Resources
CFO: Dara Bartels, Chief Financial Officer
CMO: Greg Thompson, Chief Medical Officer
CIO: Deb Rislow, Chief Information Officer
CHR: Kathy Klock, R.N., Senior Vice President Clinical Operations and Human Resources
Web address: www.gundluth.org
Control: Other not–for–profit (including NFP Corporation) **Service**: General medical and surgical

Staffed Beds: 544 **Admissions**: 14809 **Census**: 188 **Outpatient Visits**: 639692 **Births**: 1561 **Total Expense ($000)**: 853519 **Payroll Expense ($000)**: 385017 **Personnel**: 6047

☒ **MAYO CLINIC HEALTH SYSTEM – FRANCISCAN HEALTHCARE IN LA CROSSE (520004)**, 700 West Avenue South, Zip 54601–4783; tel. 608/785–0940, **A**1 2 3 5 10 **F**1 3 4 5 6 8 9 11 13 14 15 16 17 18 19 20 21 22 23 25 26 27 28 29 30 31 32 34 35 36 40 43 44 45 50 52 53 54 55 56 57 58 59 61 64 65 66 68 69 70 71 74 75 76 77 78 79 80 81 82 84 85 86 87 88 89 90 93 94 97 99 100 101 102 103 104 107 108 109 110 111 112 114 115 118 119 120 121 123 124 126 127 129 130 131 132 134 135 143 144 145 146 147 148 149 150 154 **S** Mayo Clinic, Rochester, MN
Primary Contact: Timothy Johnson, M.D., President and Chief Executive Officer
COO: Joseph J Kruse, Executive Vice President
CFO: Tom Tiggelaar, Vice President Finance
CMO: David Rushlow, Vice President Medical Affairs
CIO: Neal Sanger, Vice President Information Services
Web address: www.franciscanskemp.org
Control: Church operated, Nongovernment, not–for–profit **Service**: General medical and surgical

Staffed Beds: 91 **Admissions**: 5910 **Census**: 63 **Outpatient Visits**: 100064 **Births**: 846 **Total Expense ($000)**: 311615 **Payroll Expense ($000)**: 144734 **Personnel**: 1795

LADYSMITH—Rusk County

★ **MARSHFIELD MEDICAL CENTER – LADYSMITH (521328)**, 900 College Avenue West, Zip 54848–2116; tel. 715/532–5561, **A**10 18 **F**3 11 15 28 29 34 36 40 43 44 45 50 51 53 56 57 59 64 68 70 77 81 85 86 87 89 93 107 110 111 115 116 117 118 119 127 132 133 144 146 147 148 154 **P**6
Primary Contact: Jeff Euclide, R.N., Chief Executive Officer
CFO: David Kuehn, Chief Financial Officer
CMO: Ganesh Pawar, M.D., Chief of Staff
CHR: Rita Telitz, Chief Administrative Officer
Web address: www.ruskhospital.org
Control: County, Government, nonfederal **Service**: General medical and surgical

Staffed Beds: 25 **Admissions**: 487 **Census**: 5 **Outpatient Visits**: 32136 **Births**: 0 **Total Expense ($000)**: 25008 **Payroll Expense ($000)**: 10368 **Personnel**: 153

LAKE GENEVA—Walworth County

MERCYHEALTH HOSPITAL AND MEDICAL CENTER – WALWORTH (521357), N2950 State Road 67, Zip 53147–2655; tel. 262/245–0535, **A**10 18 **F**3 9 11 13 15 18 26 29 30 31 34 35 38 40 44 45 50 57 59 65 70 74 75 76 77 78 79 81 82 85 87 89 92 93 94 96 97 100 101 103 104 107 108 111 112 114 118 119 129 130 131 132 133 135 144 146 147 148 149 **P**6 **S** Mercy Health System, Janesville, WI
Primary Contact: Javon R. Bea, President and Chief Executive Officer
COO: Jennifer Hallatt, Vice President
CNO: Caryn Lynn Oleston, FACHE, MSN, R.N., Chief Nursing Officer
Web address: www.mercyhealthsystem.org
Control: Other not–for–profit (including NFP Corporation) **Service**: General medical and surgical

Staffed Beds: 17 **Admissions**: 1272 **Census**: 11 **Outpatient Visits**: 159402 **Births**: 166 **Total Expense ($000)**: 79719 **Payroll Expense ($000)**: 18510 **Personnel**: 335

WI

Hospital, Medicare Provider Number, Address, Telephone, Approval, Facility, and Physician Codes, Health Care System

★ American Hospital Association (AHA) membership
☐ The Joint Commission accreditation
○ Healthcare Facilities Accreditation Program
◇ DNV Healthcare Inc. accreditation
⇑ Center for Improvement in Healthcare Quality Accreditation
△ Commission on Accreditation of Rehabilitation Facilities (CARF) accreditation

LANCASTER—Grant County

☒ **GRANT REGIONAL HEALTH CENTER (521322)**, 507 South Monroe Street, Zip 53813–2054; tel. 608/723–2143, **A**1 10 18 **F**3 8 11 13 15 28 29 34 35 36 40 43 44 52 53 55 56 57 59 64 65 68 69 75 76 77 79 80 81 82 84 85 86 87 89 90 93 97 107 110 115 119 127 129 130 131 132 133 135 144 146 148 149 154 **P**6 **S** HealthTech Management Services, Brentwood, TN
Primary Contact: Nicole Clapp, R.N., MSN, FACHE, President and Chief Executive Officer
CFO: Dawn Bandy, Chief Financial Officer
CMO: Jessica Varnam, Chief of Staff
CIO: Ken Kaiser, Coordinator Information Systems
CHR: Stacy L Martin, Director Human Resources
CNO: Jennifer Rutkowski, R.N., MSN, Vice President Professional Services
Web address: www.grantregional.com
Control: Other not–for–profit (including NFP Corporation) **Service**: General medical and surgical

Staffed Beds: 4 **Admissions:** 618 **Census:** 21 **Outpatient Visits:** 27438 **Births:** 179 **Total Expense ($000):** 27796 **Payroll Expense ($000):** 13758 **Personnel:** 177

MADISON—Dane County

☐ **MENDOTA MENTAL HEALTH INSTITUTE (524008)**, 301 Troy Drive, Zip 53704–1599; tel. 608/301–1000, **A**1 3 5 10 **F**6 29 34 38 56 75 82 86 87 98 100 101 103 104 130 154
Primary Contact: Greg Van Rybroek, Chief Executive Officer
CFO: Stacie Schiereck, Director Management Services
CMO: Molli Martha Rolli, M.D., Medical Director
CNO: Jane Walters, Director of Nursing
Web address: www.dhfs.state.wi.us
Control: State, Government, nonfederal **Service**: Psychiatric

Staffed Beds: 293 **Admissions:** 572 **Census:** 281 **Outpatient Visits:** 0 **Births:** 0 **Total Expense ($000):** 81087 **Payroll Expense ($000):** 44305 **Personnel:** 767

☒ **SELECT SPECIALTY HOSPITAL–MADISON (522008)**, 801 Braxton Place, Zip 53715–1415; tel. 608/260–2700, **A**1 10 **F**1 29 34 60 75 86 119 130 **P**8 **S** Select Medical Corporation, Mechanicsburg, PA
Primary Contact: Mary Kay. Diderrich, R.N., Chief Executive Officer
CHR: Mallary Stramowski, Chief Human Resources Officer
CNO: Dana McKinney, Chief Nursing Officer
Web address: www.madison.selectspecialtyhospitals.com
Control: Corporation, Investor–owned (for–profit) **Service**: Acute long–term care hospital

Staffed Beds: 58 **Admissions:** 419 **Census:** 35 **Outpatient Visits:** 0 **Births:** 0 **Total Expense ($000):** 23471 **Payroll Expense ($000):** 9783 **Personnel:** 168

☒ **SSM HEALTH ST. MARY'S HOSPITAL (520083)**, 700 South Park Street, Zip 53715–1830; tel. 608/251–6100, **A**1 3 10 **F**2 9 11 13 15 17 20 22 24 28 29 34 40 43 53 56 64 70 72 76 77 78 80 81 82 86 88 89 90 98 100 101 102 103 107 108 118 119 130 141 154 **S** SSM Health, Saint Louis, MO
Primary Contact: Jon Rozenfeld, President
CFO: Steve Caldwell, Vice President Finance and Chief Financial Officer
CHR: Linda Taplin Statz, System Director, Employee Experience
CNO: Ginger Malone MSN, RN–B Chief Nursing Officer
Web address: www.stmarysmadison.com
Control: Church operated, Nongovernment, not–for–profit **Service**: General medical and surgical

Staffed Beds: 362 **Admissions:** 19504 **Census:** 241 **Outpatient Visits:** 99646 **Births:** 3007 **Total Expense ($000):** 372170 **Payroll Expense ($000):** 130916 **Personnel:** 1817

☒ **UNITYPOINT HEALTH MERITER (520089)**, 202 South Park Street, Zip 53715–1507; tel. 608/417–6000, **A**1 3 5 10 **F**3 4 5 9 11 12 13 15 17 18 20 22 24 26 28 29 30 31 32 34 35 36 37 40 41 43 45 46 48 49 50 53 56 57 58 59 64 65 66 68 70 71 72 74 75 76 78 79 80 81 84 85 86 87 90 92 93 96 97 98 99 100 101 102 103 104 107 108 110 111 115 118 119 126 130 132 135 145 146 147 148 149 154 **P**6 **S** UnityPoint Health, West Des Moines, IA
Primary Contact: Sue Erickson, President and Chief Executive Officer
CFO: Beth Erdman, Chief Financial Officer
CMO: Geoff Priest, M.D., Chief Medical Officer
CIO: Denise Gomez, Assistant Vice President Information Systems
CHR: James Arnett, Vice President Human Resources
CNO: Pat Grunwald, MSN, Chief Nursing Officer
Web address: www.meriter.com
Control: Other not–for–profit (including NFP Corporation) **Service**: General medical and surgical

Staffed Beds: 217 **Admissions:** 14860 **Census:** 172 **Outpatient Visits:** 206105 **Births:** 4138 **Total Expense ($000):** 413647 **Payroll Expense ($000):** 144287 **Personnel:** 2081

☒ **UNIVERSITY HOSPITAL (520098)**, 600 Highland Avenue, Zip 53792–0002; tel. 608/263–6400, (Includes AMERICAN FAMILY CHILDREN'S HOSPITAL, 1675 Highland Avenue, Madison, WI, Zip 53705; tel. 608/890–5437; Jeffrey S Poltawsky, Senior Vice President) **A**1 2 3 5 8 10 13 **F**3 5 8 9 12 15 16 17 18 19 20 21 22 23 24 25 26 27 28 29 30 31 32 33 34 35 36 37 40 41 43 45 46 47 48 49 50 51 52 53 54 55 56 57 58 59 60 61 62 64 68 70 72 74 77 78 79 80 81 82 83 84 85 86 87 88 89 92 93 94 95 97 98 100 102 103 107 108 110 111 112 114 115 116 117 118 119 120 121 123 124 126 129 130 131 132 134 135 136 137 138 139 140 141 142 145 146 147 148 153 154 **S** UW Health System, Madison, WI
Primary Contact: Alan Kaplan, M.D., Chief Executive Officer
COO: Ron Sliwinski, Chief of Hospital Division
CFO: Robert Flannery, Chief Financial Officer
CMO: Peter Newcomer, M.D., Chief Medical Officer
CIO: Jocelyn DeWitt, Ph.D., Vice President and Chief Information Officer
CHR: Elizabeth T Bolt, Chief Human Resources Officer
CNO: Beth Houlahan, R.N., Senior Vice President and Chief Nursing Officer
Web address: www.uwhealth.org
Control: Other not–for–profit (including NFP Corporation) **Service**: General medical and surgical

Staffed Beds: 621 **Admissions:** 33542 **Census:** 463 **Outpatient Visits:** 964117 **Births:** 0 **Total Expense ($000):** 1703031 **Payroll Expense ($000):** 577772 **Personnel:** 10287

UW HEALTH REHABILITATION HOSPITAL (523028), 5115 North Biltmore Lane, Zip 53718–2161; tel. 608/592–8100, **F**29 60 90 154 **P**3 **S** UW Health System, Madison, WI
Primary Contact: Gregory A. Banaszynski, Chief Executive Officer
CFO: Karen Bindl, CPA, Controller
Web address: www.uwhealth.org
Control: Corporation, Investor–owned (for–profit) **Service**: Rehabilitation

Staffed Beds: 25 **Admissions:** 902 **Census:** 25 **Outpatient Visits:** 0 **Births:** 0 **Total Expense ($000):** 17486 **Payroll Expense ($000):** 6990 **Personnel:** 143

☒ **WILLIAM S. MIDDLETON MEMORIAL VETERANS HOSPITAL**, 2500 Overlook Terrace, Zip 53705–2286; tel. 608/256–1901, (Nonreporting) **A**1 3 5 **S** Department of Veterans Affairs, Perry Point, MD
Primary Contact: John J. Rohrer, Director
CFO: Evarista Mikell, Assistant Finance Officer
CMO: Alan J Bridges, M.D., Chief of Staff
CIO: Randall Margenau, Chief Information Officer
CHR: Stuart Souders, Chief, Human Resources
CNO: Rebecca Kordahl, R.N., Associate Director, Patient Care Services
Web address: www.madison.va.gov
Control: Veterans Affairs, Government, federal **Service**: General medical and surgical

Staffed Beds: 87

MANITOWOC—Manitowoc County

☒ **HOLY FAMILY MEMORIAL (520107)**, 2300 Western Avenue, Zip 54220–3712, Mailing Address: P.O. Box 1450, Zip 54221–1450; tel. 920/320–2011, **A**1 2 10 **F**3 5 11 13 15 18 20 22 26 28 29 30 33 34 35 36 40 43 51 53 54 56 58 59 62 63 64 68 70 75 76 77 78 79 80 81 82 85 86 89 93 94 97 104 107 108 110 111 115 118 119 130 132 135 146 148 149 154 **P**6 **S** Franciscan Sisters of Christian Charity Sponsored Ministries, Inc., Manitowoc, WI
Primary Contact: Brett Norell, Interim Chief Executive Officer
COO: Jane Curran–Meuli, Chief Operating Officer
CFO: Patricia Huettl, Vice President Finance and Chief Financial Officer
CMO: Steve Driggers, M.D., Chief Medical Officer
CIO: Theron Pappas, Director Management Information Systems
CHR: Laura M Fielding, Administrative Director Organizational Development
CNO: Bonny Range, MSN, Chief Nursing Officer
Web address: www.hfmhealth.org
Control: Church operated, Nongovernment, not–for–profit **Service**: General medical and surgical

Staffed Beds: 67 **Admissions:** 2646 **Census:** 26 **Outpatient Visits:** 218386 **Births:** 173 **Total Expense ($000):** 126480 **Payroll Expense ($000):** 61677 **Personnel:** 685

MARINETTE—Marinette County

☒ **BAY AREA MEDICAL CENTER (520113)**, 3003 University Drive, Zip 54143–4110; tel. 715/735–6621, **A**1 10 20 **F**3 7 11 13 15 17 18 20 22 28 29 30 31 34 40 43 44 45 48 50 51 54 57 59 70 74 75 76 77 78 79 80 81 82 85 86 87 89 93 96 107 108 110 111 114 115 119 121 124 130 131 143 146 147 148 154 **P**8
Primary Contact: Edward A. Harding, FACHE, President and Chief Executive Officer
COO: Bernie VanCourt, Chief Operating Officer
CFO: Roger Sneath, Chief Financial Officer
CMO: Richard Stein, M.D., Chief Medical Officer
CIO: Pete Eisenzoph, Director Information Technology
CHR: Ken Joyner, Vice President of Employee Services
CNO: Bernie VanCourt, Interim Chief Nursing Officer
Web address: www.bamc.org
Control: Other not–for–profit (including NFP Corporation) **Service**: General medical and surgical

Staffed Beds: 49 **Admissions**: 2910 **Census**: 26 **Outpatient Visits**: 332368 **Births**: 213 **Total Expense ($000)**: 114299 **Payroll Expense ($000)**: 46564 **Personnel**: 516

MARSHFIELD—Wood County

☒ △ **MARSHFIELD MEDICAL CENTER (520037)**, 611 St Joseph Avenue, Zip 54449–1898; tel. 715/387–1713, (Includes MARSHFIELD CHILDEN'S HOSPITAL, 611 Saint Joseph Avenue, Marshfield, WI, Zip 54449–1832; tel. 715/387–1713) **A**1 2 5 7 10 **F**3 5 6 7 9 10 11 12 13 16 17 18 19 20 21 22 23 24 26 27 28 29 30 31 32 34 35 36 38 40 43 44 49 50 56 57 58 59 61 64 65 68 69 70 72 74 75 76 77 78 79 80 81 82 83 84 85 86 87 88 89 90 93 96 98 100 101 102 103 108 110 111 115 116 118 119 126 129 130 132 135 136 144 145 146 147 148 149 154 **S** Marshfield Clinic Health System, Marshfield, WI
Primary Contact: Ned H. Wolf, Chief Administrative Officer
CFO: William J Hinner, Vice President Financial Analysis and Planning Ministry Health Care
CMO: Peter Stamas, M.D., Vice President Medical Affairs
CIO: Will Weider, Chief Information Officer
CHR: Cheryl F Zima, Vice President Human Resources Ministry Health Care
CNO: Robin Kretschman, MSN, R.N., Vice President Patient Care Services
Web address: www.stjosephs–marshfield.org
Control: Church operated, Nongovernment, not–for–profit **Service**: General medical and surgical

Staffed Beds: 176 **Admissions**: 11894 **Census**: 176 **Outpatient Visits**: 42000 **Births**: 1011 **Total Expense ($000)**: 263883 **Payroll Expense ($000)**: 61543 **Personnel**: 747

NORWOOD HEALTH CENTER (524019), 1600 North Chestnut Avenue, Zip 54449–1499; tel. 715/384–2188, (Total facility includes 24 beds in nursing home–type unit) **A**10 **F**3 30 69 75 98 99 100 101 102 103 104 106 128 130 143 146 148 154 **P**6
Primary Contact: Jordan Bruce, Administrator
CFO: Jo Timmerman, Manager Accounting
CHR: Larry Shear, Administrative Assistant
Web address: www.co.wood.wi.us/norwood/index.htm
Control: County, Government, nonfederal **Service**: Psychiatric

Staffed Beds: 40 **Admissions**: 441 **Census**: 33 **Outpatient Visits**: 0 **Births**: 0 **Total Expense ($000)**: 3547 **Payroll Expense ($000)**: 1583 **Personnel**: 40

MAUSTON—Juneau County

☐ **MILE BLUFF MEDICAL CENTER (520109)**, 1050 Division Street, Zip 53948–1997; tel. 608/847–6161, (Total facility includes 116 beds in nursing home–type unit) **A**1 10 20 **F**10 11 13 15 28 29 34 36 40 43 56 60 62 69 75 76 77 78 80 81 82 86 87 89 93 107 108 111 118 119 125 128 130 131 144 154 **P**2
Primary Contact: James M. O'Keefe, President and Chief Executive Officer
CFO: Francis James Fish, Vice President and Chief Financial Officer
CMO: Tim Bjelland Esq Physician
CHR: Sue Wafle, Director, Human Resources
CNO: Jean Surguy, Vice President, Chief Nursing Officer
Web address: www.milebluff.com
Control: Other not–for–profit (including NFP Corporation) **Service**: General medical and surgical

Staffed Beds: 122 **Admissions**: 1263 **Census**: 110 **Outpatient Visits**: 179830 **Births**: 143 **Total Expense ($000)**: 80905 **Payroll Expense ($000)**: 40082 **Personnel**: 511

MEDFORD—Taylor County

☒ **ASPIRUS MEDFORD HOSPITAL & CLINICS, INC. (521324)**, 135 South Gibson Street, Zip 54451; tel. 715/748–8100, (Total facility includes 109 beds in nursing home–type unit) **A**1 10 18 **F**1 3 8 10 11 15 28 29 31 34 35 36 40 41 43 50 53 55 56 57 58 59 60 64 65 68 75 76 77 78 81 82 85 86 87 89 90 93 97 107 110 111 115 116 117 118 119 125 127 128 129 130 131 132 133 135 144 146 147 148 154 **S** Aspirus, Inc., Wausau, WI
Primary Contact: Dale Hustedt, Chief Executive Officer
CFO: Greg Shaw, Vice President, Finance
CMO: Erik Branstetter, M.D., Chief Medical Officer
CIO: Todd Richardson, Chief Information Officer
CHR: Angela C. Hupf, Vice President Human Resources and Community Relations
CNO: Barb Lato, Chief Nursing Officer
Web address: www.aspirus.org
Control: Other not–for–profit (including NFP Corporation) **Service**: General medical and surgical

Staffed Beds: 124 **Admissions**: 871 **Census**: 66 **Outpatient Visits**: 81281 **Births**: 271 **Total Expense ($000)**: 59531 **Payroll Expense ($000)**: 25380 **Personnel**: 346

MENOMONEE FALLS—Waukesha County

☒ △ **COMMUNITY MEMORIAL HOSPITAL (520103)**, W180 N8085 Town Hall Road, Zip 53051–3518, Mailing Address: P.O. Box 408, Zip 53052–0408; tel. 262/251–1000, **A**1 2 3 7 10 **F**3 5 9 11 13 15 20 22 24 26 28 29 30 31 34 35 36 38 40 44 45 46 47 49 50 51 56 57 59 60 62 64 65 66 68 72 74 75 76 77 78 79 80 81 82 83 84 85 86 87 90 93 97 98 100 101 102 103 104 107 108 110 111 114 115 116 117 118 119 120 121 123 126 129 130 131 132 135 145 146 147 148 149 150 154
Primary Contact: Teresa M. Lux, President and Chief Operating Officer
COO: Allen Ericson, Chief Operating Officer, Community Hospital Division and President, St. Joseph's Hospital
CFO: Scott Hawig, Senior Vice President of Finance, Chief Financial Officer and Treasurer
CMO: David Goldberg, M.D., Vice President Medical Affairs and Chief Medical Officer
CHR: Keith Allen, Senior Vice President and Chief Human Resources Officer
Web address: www.communitymemorial.com
Control: Other not–for–profit (including NFP Corporation) **Service**: General medical and surgical

Staffed Beds: 202 **Admissions**: 8409 **Census**: 96 **Outpatient Visits**: 101497 **Births**: 841 **Total Expense ($000)**: 227306 **Payroll Expense ($000)**: 76044 **Personnel**: 1131

MENOMONIE—Dunn County

☐ **MAYO CLINIC HEALTH SYSTEM – RED CEDAR IN MENOMONIE (521340)**, 2321 Stout Road, Zip 54751–2397; tel. 715/235–5531, **A**1 10 18 **F**3 8 11 13 15 17 18 28 29 30 31 32 34 35 36 40 43 44 45 53 54 55 56 57 59 60 64 65 70 75 76 77 78 79 80 81 82 84 85 86 87 89 90 93 94 96 97 99 100 101 102 103 104 107 108 110 111 115 119 127 129 130 131 132 133 135 144 146 147 148 149 154 **P**6 **S** Mayo Clinic, Rochester, MN
Primary Contact: Steven Lindberg, Chief Administrative Officer
CFO: Jeanie Lubinsky, Chief Financial Officer
CMO: Mark Deyo Svendsen, M.D., Medical Director
CIO: Frank Wrogg, Director Information Technology
CHR: Leann Wurtzel, Director Human Resources
Web address: www.rcmc–mhs.org
Control: Other not–for–profit (including NFP Corporation) **Service**: General medical and surgical

Staffed Beds: 25 **Admissions**: 1160 **Census**: 10 **Outpatient Visits**: 109712 **Births**: 285 **Total Expense ($000)**: 82317 **Payroll Expense ($000)**: 38649 **Personnel**: 405

RED CEDAR MEDICAL CENTER–MAYO HEALTH SYSTEM See Mayo Clinic Health System – Red Cedar In Menomonie

MEQUON—Ozaukee County

COLUMBIA CENTER BIRTH HOSPITAL (520195), 13125 North Port Washington Road, Zip 53097–2416; tel. 262/243–7408, **A**10 **F**13 34 64 76 81 86 87 104
Primary Contact: Candy J. Casey, R.N., MS, President and Chief Executive Officer
CMO: Daniel Hagerman, M.D., President Medical Staff
Web address: www.columbiacenter.org
Control: Other not–for–profit (including NFP Corporation) **Service**: General medical and surgical

Staffed Beds: 6 **Admissions**: 563 **Census**: 4 **Outpatient Visits**: 483 **Births**: 566 **Total Expense ($000)**: 6748 **Payroll Expense ($000)**: 3348 **Personnel**: 54

WI

COLUMBIA ST. MARY'S HOSPITAL OZAUKEE (520027), 13111 North Port Washington Road, Zip 53097–2416; tel. 262/243–7300, **A**1 2 10 **F**4 5 9 15 17 20 22 24 28 29 34 36 38 40 43 51 53 54 56 64 70 75 77 78 80 81 86 89 93 98 100 102 103 107 108 111 116 118 119 130 144 147 154 **P**6 **S** Ascension Healthcare, Saint Louis, MO
Primary Contact: Travis Andersen, President and Chief Executive Officer
CFO: Rhonda Anderson, Executive Vice President Finance and Chief Financial Officer
CMO: David Shapiro, M.D., Vice President Medical Affairs and Chief Medical Officer
CIO: Mary Paul, Chief Information Officer
CHR: Cheryl Hill, Vice President Human Resources
Web address: www.columbia–stmarys.org
Control: Church operated, Nongovernment, not–for–profit **Service**: General medical and surgical

Staffed Beds: 112 **Admissions:** 4465 **Census:** 58 **Outpatient Visits:** 320418 **Births:** 0 **Total Expense ($000):** 167409 **Payroll Expense ($000):** 53070 **Personnel:** 726	

MERRILL—Lincoln County

ASCENSION GOOD SAMARITAN HOSPITAL (521339), 601 South Center Avenue, Zip 54452–3404; tel. 715/536–5511, **A**1 10 18 **F**3 11 15 28 29 30 31 34 35 40 41 43 44 45 50 57 64 68 74 75 80 81 82 85 86 87 89 93 97 107 108 110 111 115 119 130 132 133 135 144 146 147 149 154 **S** Ascension Healthcare, Saint Louis, MO
Primary Contact: Jeremy Normington–Slay, FACHE, Chief Executive Officer
CFO: David Jirovec, Director Finance
CHR: Nancy Kwiesielewicz, Human Resources Manager
CNO: Kristine McGarigle, R.N., Vice President Patient Care
Web address: www.ministryhealth.org
Control: Church operated, Nongovernment, not–for–profit **Service**: General medical and surgical

Staffed Beds: 10 **Admissions:** 493 **Census:** 4 **Outpatient Visits:** 20326 **Births:** 0 **Total Expense ($000):** 19543 **Payroll Expense ($000):** 8140 **Personnel:** 68	

GOOD SAMARITAN HEALTH CENTER OF MERRILL See Ascension Good Samaritan Hospital

---

MILWAUKEE—Milwaukee County

★ △ **AURORA SINAI MEDICAL CENTER (520064)**, 945 North 12th Street, Zip 53233–1337, Mailing Address: P.O. Box 342, Zip 53201–0342; tel. 414/219–2000, **A**2 3 5 7 8 **F**3 6 11 12 13 15 18 20 22 26 29 30 31 32 34 35 36 37 38 40 44 45 46 49 50 51 54 56 57 59 60 64 70 75 76 77 78 79 80 81 82 84 85 86 87 89 90 91 92 93 94 96 102 103 107 108 110 111 114 119 120 121 123 126 129 130 131 132 135 144 146 147 148 149 150 154 **P**6 **S** Advocate Aurora Health, Downers Grove, IL
Primary Contact: Jessica Bauer, President
CHR: Heidi Grow, Director Human Resources
CNO: Ania Horner, R.N., MSN, Vice President and Chief Nurse Executive
Web address: www.aurorahealthcare.org
Control: Other not–for–profit (including NFP Corporation) **Service**: General medical and surgical

Staffed Beds: 202 **Admissions:** 8177 **Census:** 109 **Outpatient Visits:** 254706 **Births:** 2072 **Total Expense ($000):** 193007 **Payroll Expense ($000):** 69120 **Personnel:** 1725	

⊞ △ AURORA ST. LUKE'S MEDICAL CENTER (520138), 2900 West Oklahoma Avenue, Zip 53215–4330, Mailing Address: P.O. Box 2901, Zip 53201–2901; tel. 414/649–6000, (Includes AURORA ST. LUKE'S SOUTH SHORE, 5900 South Lake Drive, Cudahy, WI, Zip 53110–8903; tel. 414/769–9000) **A**1 2 3 5 7 8 10 **F**1 3 4 5 11 12 15 17 18 19 20 22 24 26 28 29 30 31 33 34 35 36 37 38 40 41 43 44 45 46 47 49 50 51 54 56 57 58 59 60 64 65 66 68 70 74 75 78 79 80 81 82 84 85 86 87 89 90 91 92 93 94 96 98 100 101 102 103 104 105 107 108 110 111 114 115 116 117 118 119 120 121 123 124 126 129 130 132 134 135 136 137 138 139 140 142 145 146 148 149 153 154 **P**6 **S** Advocate Aurora Health, Downers Grove, IL
Primary Contact: Marie Golanowski, R.N., MS, President
CFO: Nan Nelson, Senior Vice President Finance
CMO: Jeffrey A. Smith, M.D., Senior Vice President and Chief Medical Officer
CIO: Philip Loftus, Ph.D., Vice President and Chief Information Officer
CHR: Thomas C Ter Horst, Vice President Human Resources
CNO: Faye Zwieg, Vice President and Chief Nursing Officer
Web address: www.aurorahealthcare.org
Control: Other not–for–profit (including NFP Corporation) **Service**: General medical and surgical

Staffed Beds: 711 **Admissions:** 34785 **Census:** 558 **Outpatient Visits:** 601579 **Births:** 0 **Total Expense ($000):** 1129163 **Payroll Expense ($000):** 323633 **Personnel:** 6375	

CHILDREN'S HOSPITAL OF WISCONSIN (523300), 9000 West Wisconsin Avenue, Zip 53226–4810, Mailing Address: P.O. Box 1997, Zip 53201–1997; tel. 414/266–2000, **A**1 3 5 10 **F**12 20 22 24 28 29 34 36 38 40 43 51 54 60 61 64 72 75 77 78 81 82 86 87 88 89 93 99 100 104 107 108 111 118 119 130 131 136 137 138 140 141 154 **P**2 **S** Children's Hospital and Health System, Milwaukee, WI
Primary Contact: Peggy N. Troy, President and Chief Executive Officer
CFO: Marc Cadieux, Corporate Vice President and Chief Financial Officer
CMO: Michael Gutzeit, M.D., Chief Medical Officer
CIO: Michael B Nauman, Chief Information Officer
CHR: Thomas Shanahan, Vice President, Human Resources
CNO: Nancy K Korom, Chief Nursing Officer and Vice President
Web address: www.chw.org
Control: Other not–for–profit (including NFP Corporation) **Service**: Children's general medical and surgical

Staffed Beds: 193 **Admissions:** 9305 **Census:** 193 **Outpatient Visits:** 381128 **Births:** 0 **Total Expense ($000):** 587911 **Payroll Expense ($000):** 178247 **Personnel:** 2564	

⊞ △ CLEMENT J. ZABLOCKI VETERANS AFFAIRS MEDICAL CENTER, 5000 West National Avenue, Zip 53295–0001; tel. 414/384–2000, (Nonreporting) **A**1 2 3 5 7 **S** Department of Veterans Affairs, Perry Point, MD
Primary Contact: Daniel Zomchek, Ph.D., Chief Executive Officer and Medical Center Director
COO: James McClain, Deputy Director
CFO: John Lasota, Assistant Finance Officer
CMO: Michael Erdmann, M.D., Chief of Staff
CIO: Bryan Vail, Chief Information Officer
CHR: Kay Schwieger, Chief Human Resources Officer
CNO: Mary E. Brunn, R.N., Acting Associate Director Nursing
Web address: www.milwaukee.va.gov/
Control: Veterans Affairs, Government, federal **Service**: General medical and surgical

Staffed Beds: 637	

COLUMBIA ST. MARY'S HOSPITAL MILWAUKEE (520051), 2301 North Lake Drive, Zip 53211–4508; tel. 414/291–1000, (Includes COLUMBIA ST. MARY'S COLUMBIA HOSPITAL, 2025 East Newport Avenue, Milwaukee, WI, Zip 53211–2990; tel. 414/961–3300; COLUMBIA ST. MARY'S MILWAUKEE HOSPITAL, 2323 North Lake Drive, Milwaukee, WI, Zip 53211–9682, Mailing Address: P.O. Box 503, Zip 53201–0503, tel. 414/291–1000) (Nonreporting) **A**1 2 3 5 10 **S** Ascension Healthcare, Saint Louis, MO
Primary Contact: Travis Andersen, Chief Executive Officer
CFO: Rhonda Anderson, Executive Vice President Finance and Chief Financial Officer
CMO: David Shapiro, M.D., Vice President Medical Affairs and Chief Medical Officer
CIO: Mary Paul, Chief Information Officer
CHR: Cheryl Hill, Vice President Human Resources
Web address: www.columbia–stmarys.org
Control: Church operated, Nongovernment, not–for–profit **Service**: General medical and surgical

Staffed Beds: 277	

⊞ △ COLUMBIA ST. MARY'S MILWAUKEE HOSPITAL (523025), 2323 North Lake Drive, Zip 53211–4508, Mailing Address: 2301 North Lake Drive, Zip 53211–4508; tel. 414/585–1000, **A**1 7 10 **F**9 29 34 54 56 64 75 77 86 90 93 98 100 102 103 130 131 154 **P**6 **S** Ascension Healthcare, Saint Louis, MO
Primary Contact: Kelly Elkins, President and Chief Executive Officer
CFO: Rhonda Anderson, Executive Vice President Finance and Chief Financial Officer
CMO: David Shapiro, M.D., Vice President Medical Affairs and Chief Medical Officer
CIO: Mary Paul, Vice President and Chief Information Officer
CHR: Cheryl Hill, Vice President Human Resources
Web address: www.columbia–stmarys.org/SHRI
Control: Church operated, Nongovernment, not–for–profit **Service**: Rehabilitation

Staffed Beds: 31 **Admissions:** 304 **Census:** 15 **Outpatient Visits:** 10480 **Births:** 0 **Total Expense ($000):** 10971 **Payroll Expense ($000):** 5030 **Personnel:** 80	

⊞ △ FROEDTERT AND THE MEDICAL COLLEGE OF WISCONSIN FROEDTERT HOSPITAL (520177), 9200 West Wisconsin Avenue, Zip 53226–3596, Mailing Address: P.O. Box 26099, Zip 53226–0099; tel. 414/805–3000, **A**1 2 3 5 7 8 10 **F**3 6 8 9 12 13 15 17 18 20 22 24 26 29 30 31 34 35 37 38 40 43 44 45 46 47 48 49 50 51 52 54 55 56 57 58 59 60 61 64 66 68 70 74 75 76 77 78 79 80 81 84 85 86 87 90 91 92 93 94 95 96 97 100 107 108 110 111 112 113 114 115 116 117 118 119 120 121 123 124 126 129 130 131 132 135 136 137 138 139 140 141 142 145 146 147 148 149 150 154
Primary Contact: Catherine Buck, MSN, R.N., President
CFO: Scott Hawig, Senior Vice President Finance, Chief Financial Officer and Treasurer
CMO: Lee Biblo, M.D., Chief Medical Officer
CHR: Keith Allen, Senior Vice President and Chief Human Resources Officer
CNO: Kathleen Bechtel, MSN, R.N., Vice President Patient Care Services and Chief Nursing Officer
Web address: www.froedtert.com
Control: Other not–for–profit (including NFP Corporation) **Service**: General medical and surgical

Staffed Beds: 585 **Admissions:** 28270 **Census:** 448 **Outpatient Visits:** 809191 **Births:** 2736 **Total Expense ($000):** 1389568 **Payroll Expense ($000):** 345837 **Personnel:** 5438	

★ **MILWAUKEE COUNTY BEHAVIORAL HEALTH DIVISION (524001)**, 9455 Watertown Plank Road, Zip 53226–3559; tel. 414/257–6995, **A**3 5 10 **F**35 50 98 99 100 101 102 104 106 134 146 149 153 154 **P**6
Primary Contact: Michael Lappen, Chief Executive Officer
COO: Jennifer Bergersen, Interim Chief Operating Officer
CFO: Randy Oleszak, Director Fiscal Services
CMO: John Schneider, M.D., Medical Director
CIO: Chris Lindberg, Chief Information Officer
CHR: Ara Garcia, Manager Human Resources
CNO: Nancy Ann Marigomen, R.N., Director of Nursing
Web address: www.milwaukeecounty.org
Control: County, Government, nonfederal **Service**: Psychiatric

Staffed Beds: 54 **Admissions**: 1365 **Census**: 51 **Outpatient Visits**: 8496 **Births**: 0 **Total Expense ($000)**: 192887 **Payroll Expense ($000)**: 31488 **Personnel**: 453

⊞ **SELECT SPECIALTY HOSPITAL–MILWAUKEE (522006)**, 8901 West Lincoln Avenue, 2nd Floor, Zip 53227–2409, Mailing Address: West Allis, tel. 414/328–7700, **A**1 10 **F**1 29 60 78 100 130 **S** Select Medical Corporation, Mechanicsburg, PA
Primary Contact: Mary Kay. Diderrich, R.N., Chief Executive Officer
CMO: Matt Mathai, M.D., Medical Director
CHR: Chris Froh, Senior Coordinator Human Resources
CNO: Jane Cerra, Market Nurse Executive and Chief Nursing Officer
Web address: www.selectspecialtyhospitals.com/company/locations/milwaukee.aspx
Control: Corporation, Investor–owned (for–profit) **Service**: Acute long–term care hospital

Staffed Beds: 63 **Admissions**: 503 **Census**: 45 **Outpatient Visits**: 0 **Births**: 0 **Total Expense ($000)**: 28047 **Payroll Expense ($000)**: 10990 **Personnel**: 162

⊞ **WHEATON FRANCISCAN HEALTHCARE – ST. FRANCIS (520078)**, 3237 South 16th Street, Zip 53215; tel. 414/647–5000, **A**1 2 10 **F**3 5 11 13 15 18 20 22 24 26 28 30 31 38 40 44 45 46 47 49 50 54 56 64 65 66 68 72 74 75 76 77 78 79 80 81 82 84 85 86 87 92 93 98 100 101 102 103 104 105 107 108 110 111 114 115 118 119 121 122 129 130 131 135 144 145 146 147 149 152 154 **S** Ascension Healthcare, Saint Louis, MO
Primary Contact: Seth Teigen, President
CFO: Aaron Bridgeland, Director Finance
CMO: Michelle Graham, M.D., Vice President Medical Affairs
CIO: Gregory Smith, Senior Vice President and Chief Information Officer
Web address: www.mywheaton.org/stfrancis
Control: Church operated, Nongovernment, not–for–profit **Service**: General medical and surgical

Staffed Beds: 161 **Admissions**: 6944 **Census**: 98 **Outpatient Visits**: 168052 **Births**: 680 **Total Expense ($000)**: 171797 **Payroll Expense ($000)**: 58105 **Personnel**: 801

⊞ **WHEATON FRANCISCAN HEALTHCARE – ST. JOSEPH'S (520136)**, 5000 West Chambers Street, Zip 53210–1650; tel. 414/447–2000, **A**1 3 5 10 **F**6 11 13 15 17 20 22 28 29 40 43 53 54 56 64 70 72 76 77 78 80 81 87 89 90 93 107 108 111 118 119 130 131 144 147 **S** Ascension Healthcare, Saint Louis, MO
Primary Contact: Timothy Richman, President
CFO: Michael Petitt, Director of Finance
CMO: Rita Hanson, M.D., Vice President Medical Affairs
CIO: Andrew Donovan, Regional Director Information Services
CHR: Christopher Morris, Senior Director, Human Resources
Web address: www.mywheaton.org/stjoseph
Control: Church operated, Nongovernment, not–for–profit **Service**: General medical and surgical

Staffed Beds: 197 **Admissions**: 7433 **Census**: 104 **Outpatient Visits**: 285119 **Births**: 2281 **Total Expense ($000)**: 222702 **Payroll Expense ($000)**: 76296 **Personnel**: 858

☐ **MONROE CLINIC (520028)**, 515 22nd Avenue, Zip 53566–1598; tel. 608/324–2000, **A**1 3 10 13 **F**3 6 8 9 13 15 17 18 26 28 29 30 31 32 34 35 37 38 40 43 44 45 46 49 50 55 56 57 59 62 63 65 68 70 74 75 76 77 79 80 81 82 84 85 86 90 93 97 99 100 101 102 103 104 107 108 110 111 112 115 117 119 126 129 130 131 132 135 144 145 146 147 148 154 **P**6 **S** SSM Health, Saint Louis, MO
Primary Contact: Michael B. Sanders, President and Chief Executive Officer
CFO: Jim Nemeth, Chief Financial Officer
CMO: Mark Thompson, M.D., Chief Medical Officer
CIO: Carrie Blum, Chief Information Officer
CHR: Jane Monahan, Vice President Ministry, Spiritual Care and Human Resources
CNO: Paula Elmer, R.N., MSN, Vice President and Chief Nursing Officer
Web address: www.monroeclinic.org
Control: Other not–for–profit (including NFP Corporation) **Service**: General medical and surgical

Staffed Beds: 58 **Admissions**: 2544 **Census**: 23 **Outpatient Visits**: 270391 **Births**: 467 **Total Expense ($000)**: 163686 **Payroll Expense ($000)**: 82378 **Personnel**: 1039

☐ **CHILDREN'S HOSPITAL OF WISCONSIN–FOX VALLEY (523302)**, 130 Second Street, Zip 54956–2883; tel. 920/969–7900, **A**1 10 **F**34 64 72 75 86 89 93 130 154 **P**6 **S** Children's Hospital and Health System, Milwaukee, WI
Primary Contact: Peggy N. Troy, President and Chief Executive Officer
COO: Debra Franckowiak, Executive Director
CFO: Marc Cadieux, Corporate Vice President and Chief Financial Officer
CMO: Paul Myers, M.D., Neonatologist and Chief Medical Officer
CIO: Michael B Nauman, Chief Information Officer and Corporate Vice President
CHR: Thomas Shanahan, Vice President, Human Resources
CNO: Nancy K Korom, Chief Nursing Officer and Vice President
Web address: www.chw.org
Control: Other not–for–profit (including NFP Corporation) **Service**: Children's general medical and surgical

Staffed Beds: 14 **Admissions**: 551 **Census**: 14 **Outpatient Visits**: 14146 **Births**: 0 **Total Expense ($000)**: 27273 **Payroll Expense ($000)**: 10907 **Personnel**: 132

☐ **THEDACARE REGIONAL MEDICAL CENTER–NEENAH (520045)**, 130 Second Street, Zip 54956–2883, Mailing Address: P.O. Box 2021, Zip 54957–2021; tel. 920/729–3100, **A**1 2 3 10 **F**4 5 9 12 13 18 28 29 34 40 43 51 64 70 75 76 78 80 81 82 86 88 90 98 101 107 108 111 118 119 130 154 **S** ThedaCare, Inc., Appleton, WI
Primary Contact: Brian Burmeister, Senior Vice President, ThedaCare Medical Centers
CFO: Tim Olson, Senior Vice President Finance
CMO: Gregory L Long, M.D., Chief Medical Officer
CIO: Keith Livingston, Senior Vice President and Chief Information Officer
Web address: www.thedacare.org
Control: Other not–for–profit (including NFP Corporation) **Service**: General medical and surgical

Staffed Beds: 164 **Admissions**: 7602 **Census**: 84 **Outpatient Visits**: 108024 **Births**: 1425 **Total Expense ($000)**: 161542 **Payroll Expense ($000)**: 62659 **Personnel**: 851

★ **MEMORIAL MEDICAL CENTER – NEILLSVILLE (521323)**, 216 Sunset Place, Zip 54456–1799; tel. 715/743–3101, **A**10 18 **F**10 11 15 29 34 40 43 55 56 64 75 77 80 81 82 86 89 90 93 107 111 119 130 131 144 147 154 **P**6
Primary Contact: Ryan T. Neville, FACHE, President and Chief Executive Officer
CMO: Timothy Meyer, M.D., Chief of Staff
CIO: Derrick Longdo, Director Information Systems
CHR: Tamie Zarak, Director Human Resources
Web address: www.memorialmedcenter.org
Control: Other not–for–profit (including NFP Corporation) **Service**: General medical and surgical

Staffed Beds: 29 **Admissions**: 322 **Census**: 12 **Outpatient Visits**: 22652 **Births**: 0 **Total Expense ($000)**: 25876 **Payroll Expense ($000)**: 12405 **Personnel**: 200

WI

Hospital, Medicare Provider Number, Address, Telephone, Approval, Facility, and Physician Codes, Health Care System

★ American Hospital Association (AHA) membership   ○ Healthcare Facilities Accreditation Program   ⇑ Center for Improvement in Healthcare Quality Accreditation
☐ The Joint Commission accreditation   ◇ DNV Healthcare Inc. accreditation   △ Commission on Accreditation of Rehabilitation Facilities (CARF) accreditation

NEW LONDON—Outagamie County

☐ **THEDACARE MEDICAL CENTER–NEW LONDON (521326)**, 1405 Mill Street, Zip 54961–0307, Mailing Address: P.O. Box 307, Zip 54961–0307; tel. 920/531–2000, **A**1 10 18 **F**7 11 13 15 28 29 34 40 43 56 64 75 76 80 81 82 86 87 89 90 93 107 108 111 119 131 141 154 **S** ThedaCare, Inc., Appleton, WI
Primary Contact: William Schmidt, President and Chief Executive Officer
CFO: Betty Gehring, Finance Director, Operations
CMO: Paul Hoell, M.D., President Medical Staff
CNO: Peggy School, Director of Nursing
Web address: www.thedacare.org
Control: Other not–for–profit (including NFP Corporation) **Service:** General medical and surgical

Staffed Beds: 25 **Admissions:** 640 **Census:** 8 **Outpatient Visits:** 36594 **Births:** 97 **Total Expense ($000):** 23078 **Payroll Expense ($000):** 10484 **Personnel:** 134

NEW RICHMOND—St. Croix County

★ **WESTFIELDS HOSPITAL AND CLINIC (521345)**, 535 Hospital Road, Zip 54017–1449; tel. 715/243–2600, **A**3 10 18 **F**1 3 13 15 18 28 29 30 31 32 34 35 37 38 40 43 44 45 47 50 56 57 59 64 68 70 74 75 76 77 78 79 80 81 82 84 86 87 89 90 93 94 97 104 105 107 109 110 111 115 117 119 120 121 123 129 130 131 132 133 145 146 148 149 152 153 154 **P**8 **S** HealthPartners, Bloomington, MN
Primary Contact: Steven Massey, President and Chief Executive Officer
CFO: Jason J. Luhrs, Vice President Fiscal Services
CMO: David O DeGear, M.D., Vice President Medical Affairs
CIO: Patrice P Wolff, Director Information Services
CHR: Chad P Engstrom, Director Human Resources
Web address: www.westfieldshospital.com
Control: Other not–for–profit (including NFP Corporation) **Service:** General medical and surgical

Staffed Beds: 25 **Admissions:** 866 **Census:** 7 **Outpatient Visits:** 95251 **Births:** 127 **Total Expense ($000):** 56121 **Payroll Expense ($000):** 18885 **Personnel:** 313

OCONOMOWOC—Waukesha County

⊞ **OCONOMOWOC MEMORIAL HOSPITAL (520062)**, 791 Summit Avenue, Zip 53066–3896; tel. 262/569–9400, **A**1 2 10 **F**3 11 13 15 18 20 22 26 28 29 30 31 32 34 37 40 43 45 46 47 48 49 50 56 57 59 64 65 68 74 75 78 79 81 83 84 85 87 89 93 97 100 101 102 107 108 109 110 111 112 114 115 117 118 119 120 121 126 130 133 135 146 147 149 153 154 **S** ProHealth Care, Inc., Waukesha, WI
Primary Contact: Susan A. Edwards, President and Chief Executive Officer
COO: Mary Jo O'Malley, R.N., MS, Vice President Diagnostics and Support Services
CMO: Brian Lipman, M.D., Medical Director and Medical Staff Services
CIO: Christine Bessler, Vice President Information Services
CHR: Edward Malindzak, Chief Human Resources Officer
CNO: Catherine Rapp, R.N., MS, Vice President Nursing
Web address: www.prohealthcare.org/locations/locations–v2–detail/?id=1123
Control: Other not–for–profit (including NFP Corporation) **Service:** General medical and surgical

Staffed Beds: 58 **Admissions:** 2869 **Census:** 22 **Outpatient Visits:** 69244 **Births:** 309 **Total Expense ($000):** 91730 **Payroll Expense ($000):** 21513 **Personnel:** 320

⊞ **ROGERS MEMORIAL HOSPITAL, INC. (524018)**, 34700 Valley Road, Zip 53066–4599; tel. 262/646–4411, (Includes ROGERS MEMORIAL HOSPITAL–BROWN DEER, 4600 West Schroeder Drive, Brown Deer, WI, Zip 53223; tel. 414/865–2500; Jim Kubicek, Vice President, Operations; ROGERS MEMORIAL HOSPITAL–WEST ALLIS, 11101 West Lincoln Avenue, West Allis, WI, Zip 53227; tel. 414/327–3000; T Orvin Fillman, Dr.PH, Vice President, Operations) **A**1 3 10 **F**5 29 34 38 75 86 98 100 101 102 103 104 130 154
Primary Contact: Paul A. Mueller, Chief Executive Officer, Hospital Division
CFO: Gerald A Noll, Chief Financial Officer
CMO: Peter M Lake, M.D., Chief Medical Officer
CIO: Wayne Mattson, Management Information Systems Specialist
CHR: Renee A. Patterson, Vice President Employment and Training Services
CNO: Teresa L Schultz, R.N., Vice President of Patient Care
Web address: www.rogershospital.org
Control: Other not–for–profit (including NFP Corporation) **Service:** Psychiatric

Staffed Beds: 196 **Admissions:** 9464 **Census:** 157 **Outpatient Visits:** 90278 **Births:** 0 **Total Expense ($000):** 72365 **Payroll Expense ($000):** 42656 **Personnel:** 777

OCONTO—Oconto County

⇑ **BELLIN HEALTH OCONTO HOSPITAL (521356)**, 820 Arbutus Avenue, Zip 54153–2004, Mailing Address: P.O. Box 357, Zip 54153–0357; tel. 920/835–1100, **A**10 18 21 **F**15 29 40 43 51 62 64 78 80 81 82 90 99 100 101 104 107 111 119 130 147 154 **P**8
Primary Contact: Laura Hieb, R.N., Chief Executive Officer
CHR: Troy L Koebke, Human Resource Director
Web address: www.bellin.org/facilities_amenities/oconto_hospital_medical_center/
Control: Other not–for–profit (including NFP Corporation) **Service:** General medical and surgical

Staffed Beds: 10 **Admissions:** 173 **Census:** 1 **Outpatient Visits:** 18648 **Births:** 0 **Total Expense ($000):** 34886 **Payroll Expense ($000):** 15171 **Personnel:** 196

OCONTO FALLS—Oconto County

★ **HSHS ST. CLARE MEMORIAL HOSPITAL (521310)**, 855 South Main Street, Zip 54154–1296; tel. 920/846–3444, **A**10 18 **F**3 11 15 28 29 30 31 34 35 40 43 44 50 56 57 59 64 65 68 75 77 79 80 81 85 86 87 89 90 94 96 107 108 110 111 114 119 127 129 130 132 133 144 146 147 148 154 **P**2 5 **S** HSHS Hospital Sisters Health System, Springfield, IL
Primary Contact: Christopher Brabant, President and Chief Executive Officer
CFO: Greg Simia, Chief Financial Officer
CMO: Ken Johnson, Chief Physician Executive
CIO: Shane Miller, Chief Information Officer
CHR: Christine Jensema, Chief Human Resources Officer
CNO: Paula Hafeman, Chief Nursing Officer
Web address: www.stclarememorial.org
Control: Church operated, Nongovernment, not–for–profit **Service:** General medical and surgical

Staffed Beds: 20 **Admissions:** 503 **Census:** 5 **Outpatient Visits:** 19073 **Births:** 0 **Total Expense ($000):** 32365 **Payroll Expense ($000):** 9472 **Personnel:** 105

OSCEOLA—Polk County

★ **OSCEOLA MEDICAL CENTER (521318)**, 2600 65th Avenue, Zip 54020–4370, Mailing Address: P.O. Box 218, Zip 54020–0218; tel. 715/294–2111, **A**10 18 **F**3 8 11 13 15 28 29 31 32 34 35 40 41 43 45 50 53 56 57 59 65 66 70 75 76 77 78 81 85 86 87 89 93 96 97 107 110 111 115 119 127 129 133 135 144 145 146 148 149 150 154 **P**6
Primary Contact: Tom G. Geskermann, Chief Executive Officer
CMO: Rene Milner, Chief Medical Officer
CIO: Shawn Kammerud, Manager Information Services
CHR: Margie Evenson, Manager Human Resources
Web address: www.osceolamedicalcenter.com
Control: Other not–for–profit (including NFP Corporation) **Service:** General medical and surgical

Staffed Beds: 18 **Admissions:** 480 **Census:** 5 **Outpatient Visits:** 17805 **Births:** 94 **Total Expense ($000):** 32824 **Payroll Expense ($000):** 11681 **Personnel:** 216

OSHKOSH—Winnebago County

⊞ △ **ASCENSION NORTHEAST WISCONSIN MERCY HOSPITAL (520048)**, 500 South Oakwood Road, Zip 54904–7944; tel. 920/223–2000, **A**1 2 7 10 **F**4 5 11 13 15 16 17 20 22 28 29 34 38 40 43 51 53 56 64 70 75 76 78 80 81 82 86 87 88 90 93 98 103 104 107 108 111 119 130 131 144 147 154 **S** Ascension Healthcare, Saint Louis, MO
Primary Contact: Denise Parrish, Interim Chief Administrative Officer
CFO: Jeff Badger, Chief Financial Officer
CMO: Mark W Kehrberg, M.D., Senior Vice President and Chief Medical Officer
CIO: Will Weider, Chief Information Officer
CHR: Vince Gallucci, Senior Vice President Human Resources
Web address: www.affinityhealth.org
Control: Church operated, Nongovernment, not–for–profit **Service:** General medical and surgical

Staffed Beds: 120 **Admissions:** 4128 **Census:** 42 **Outpatient Visits:** 122986 **Births:** 551 **Total Expense ($000):** 88630 **Payroll Expense ($000):** 25608 **Personnel:** 347

⊞ **AURORA MEDICAL CENTER OF OSHKOSH (520198)**, 855 North Westhaven Drive, Zip 54904–7668; tel. 920/456–6000, **A**1 2 10 **F**3 8 11 12 13 15 17 18 20 22 26 29 30 34 37 40 41 43 47 49 53 54 56 60 64 68 70 71 74 75 76 78 79 80 81 82 84 85 86 87 89 92 93 94 107 108 109 110 111 113 114 115 117 118 119 120 121 122 123 129 130 131 145 146 147 148 149 154 **P**6 **S** Advocate Aurora Health, Downers Grove, IL
Primary Contact: Jeffrey Bard, President
CFO: Sandra Ewald, Vice President Finance
CMO: Bruce L Van Cleave, M.D., Senior Vice President and Chief Medical Officer
CIO: Philip Loftus, Ph.D., Vice President and Chief Information Officer
CHR: Linda Mingus, Director Human Resources
CNO: Mary Beth Kingston, R.N., MSN, Executive Vice President and Chief Nursing Officer
Web address: www.aurorahealthcare.com
Control: Other not–for–profit (including NFP Corporation) **Service:** General medical and surgical

Staffed Beds: 61 **Admissions:** 3580 **Census:** 31 **Outpatient Visits:** 154373 **Births:** 646 **Total Expense ($000):** 121635 **Payroll Expense ($000):** 34862 **Personnel:** 1005

WI

Many Facility Codes have changed. Please refer to the AHA Guide Code Chart.

© 2018 AHA Guide

OSSEO—Trempealeau County

☐ **MAYO CLINIC HEALTH SYSTEM – OAKRIDGE IN OSSEO (521302)**, 13025 Eighth Street, Zip 54758–7634, Mailing Address: P.O. Box 70, Zip 54758–0070; tel. 715/597–3121, **A**1 10 18 **F**3 15 18 28 29 30 32 34 35 40 43 44 45 53 54 56 57 59 64 65 75 77 80 84 85 86 87 90 93 96 97 107 110 115 130 132 133 135 143 144 146 148 149 154 **P**6 **S** Mayo Clinic, Rochester, MN
Primary Contact: Dean Eide, Vice President
Web address: www.mayoclinichealthsystem.org/locations/osseo
Control: Other not–for–profit (including NFP Corporation) **Service**: General medical and surgical

Staffed Beds: 16 **Admissions:** 377 **Census:** 11 **Outpatient Visits:** 27197 **Births:** 0 **Total Expense ($000):** 22062 **Payroll Expense ($000):** 11021 **Personnel:** 150

PARK FALLS—Price County

★ **FLAMBEAU HOSPITAL (521325)**, 98 Sherry Avenue, Zip 54552–1467, Mailing Address: P.O. Box 310, Zip 54552–0310; tel. 715/762–2484, **A**10 18 **F**3 8 11 15 19 28 29 31 34 35 40 41 45 46 47 48 49 50 53 56 59 62 63 64 65 69 75 77 80 81 82 86 87 89 90 93 94 96 107 108 110 112 113 114 115 117 119 130 131 132 133 148 149 150 154 **S** Marshfield Clinic Health System, Marshfield, WI
Primary Contact: James R. Braun, Chief Administrative Officer and Chief Financial Officer
CMO: Yusuf Kasirye, M.D., Chief of Staff
CHR: Elizabeth Harrop, Director, Human Resources
CNO: Elizabeth Schreiber, R.N., Director Patient Care Services
Web address: www.flambeauhospital.org
Control: Other not–for–profit (including NFP Corporation) **Service**: General medical and surgical

Staffed Beds: 25 **Admissions:** 570 **Census:** 4 **Outpatient Visits:** 27206 **Births:** 0 **Total Expense ($000):** 21639 **Payroll Expense ($000):** 8844 **Personnel:** 185

PEWAUKEE—Waukesha County

☒ **LIFECARE HOSPITALS OF WISCONSIN (522007)**, 2400 Golf Road, Zip 53072–5590; tel. 262/524–2600, **A**1 10 **F**1 29 34 77 86 93 107 130 **P**8 **S** LifeCare Management Services, Plano, TX
Primary Contact: David Chaudier, Chief Executive Officer
CMO: John Daniels, M.D., Medical Director
CHR: Stephanie Matter, Manager Human Resources
CNO: Angela Osowski, Chief Nursing Officer
Web address: www.lifecare–hospitals.com
Control: Corporation, Investor–owned (for–profit) **Service**: Acute long–term care hospital

Staffed Beds: 30 **Admissions:** 394 **Census:** 30 **Outpatient Visits:** 0 **Births:** 0 **Total Expense ($000):** 21540 **Payroll Expense ($000):** 10198 **Personnel:** 128

PLATTEVILLE—Grant County

☒ **SOUTHWEST HEALTH (521354)**, 1400 Eastside Road, Zip 53818–9800; tel. 608/348–2331, (Includes SOUTHWEST HEALTH CENTER NURSING HOME, 808 South Washington Street, Cuba City, WI, Zip 53807; tel. 608/744–2161) (Total facility includes 78 beds in nursing home–type unit) **A**1 10 18 **F**2 3 6 7 13 15 28 29 34 35 40 43 45 46 47 48 49 50 56 57 59 64 65 75 76 77 78 79 80 81 82 83 84 86 87 93 94 95 96 98 100 101 102 103 104 107 110 111 112 115 119 127 128 129 130 131 132 133 135 143 144 146 147 148 149 153 154
Primary Contact: Dan D. Rohrbach, President
CFO: Matthew Streeter, Chief Financial Officer
CMO: Andrew Klann, D.O., Chief of Staff
CIO: Todd Lull, Director Information Technology
CHR: Holly Beehn, Director Human Resources
CNO: Suzi Okey, Director of Nursing
Web address: www.southwesthealth.org
Control: Other not–for–profit (including NFP Corporation) **Service**: General medical and surgical

Staffed Beds: 113 **Admissions:** 989 **Census:** 86 **Outpatient Visits:** 58249 **Births:** 176 **Total Expense ($000):** 50600 **Payroll Expense ($000):** 24937 **Personnel:** 326

PORTAGE—Columbia County

☐ **DIVINE SAVIOR HEALTHCARE (520041)**, 2817 New Pinery Road, Zip 53901–9240, Mailing Address: P.O. Box 387, Zip 53901–0387; tel. 608/742–4131, (Total facility includes 123 beds in nursing home–type unit) **A**1 3 10 **F**3 4 7 8 11 12 13 15 28 30 31 34 35 36 40 43 45 54 55 57 58 59 60 62 64 65 69 70 75 76 77 78 79 80 81 82 85 86 87 90 92 93 96 97 107 108 110 111 114 115 118 119 128 129 130 131 132 133 144 147 148 154 **P**6
Primary Contact: Michael Decker, President and Chief Executive Officer
CFO: Marlin Pete Nelson, Vice President Fiscal Services
CMO: Elizabeth Strabel, M.D., Chief Medical Staff
CHR: Carol J Bank, Vice President Human Resources
Web address: www.dshealthcare.com
Control: Church operated, Nongovernment, not–for–profit **Service**: General medical and surgical

Staffed Beds: 133 **Admissions:** 2007 **Census:** 114 **Outpatient Visits:** 161210 **Births:** 193 **Total Expense ($000):** 82956 **Payroll Expense ($000):** 44436 **Personnel:** 667

PRAIRIE DU CHIEN—Crawford County

☒ **CROSSING RIVERS HEALTH MEDICAL CENTER (521330)**, 37868 US Highway 18, Zip 53821–8416; tel. 608/357–2000, **A**1 10 18 **F**10 11 13 15 28 29 30 31 34 35 36 40 41 50 53 56 57 59 62 63 64 65 68 74 75 76 77 79 81 82 83 84 86 87 93 97 104 107 110 111 115 117 119 126 129 130 131 132 133 135 144 146 147 148 154
Primary Contact: William P. Sexton, Chief Executive Officer
CFO: Dave Breitbach, Chief Financial Officer
CMO: Steven Bush, Chief Medical Officer
CIO: John Daane, Information Systems Officer
CHR: Samantha Donahue, Director Human Resources
Web address: www.crossingrivers.org
Control: Other not–for–profit (including NFP Corporation) **Service**: General medical and surgical

Staffed Beds: 25 **Admissions:** 984 **Census:** 10 **Outpatient Visits:** 9073 **Births:** 143 **Total Expense ($000):** 51526 **Payroll Expense ($000):** 21312 **Personnel:** 325

PRAIRIE DU SAC—Sauk County

○ **SAUK PRAIRIE HEALTHCARE (520095)**, 260 26th Street, Zip 53578–1599; tel. 608/643–3311, **A**3 10 11 **F**3 4 8 11 13 15 28 29 32 34 35 36 38 40 41 43 45 48 53 54 55 56 57 59 65 69 75 76 77 79 80 81 82 85 86 89 90 97 102 107 108 110 111 115 118 119 127 129 130 131 133 135 144 146 147 149 154 **P**7
Primary Contact: Shawn Lerch, Chief Executive Officer
CFO: James Dregney, Vice President Finance and Operations, Chief Financial Officer
CMO: John McAuliffe, M.D., Medical Director
CIO: Richard C Bonjour, Chief Information Officer
CHR: Robbi E Bos, Vice President Human Resources
CNO: Denise Marie Cole–Ouzounian, MSN, R.N., Vice President Patient Services
Web address: www.saukprairiehealthcare.org/
Control: Other not–for–profit (including NFP Corporation) **Service**: General medical and surgical

Staffed Beds: 36 **Admissions:** 1911 **Census:** 11 **Outpatient Visits:** 115683 **Births:** 350 **Total Expense ($000):** 87469 **Payroll Expense ($000):** 40374 **Personnel:** 481

RACINE—Racine County

☒ △ **ASCENSION ALL SAINTS (520096)**, 3801 Spring Street, Zip 53405–1690; tel. 262/687–4011, (Total facility includes 50 beds in nursing home–type unit) **A**1 2 7 10 **F**3 4 5 6 13 15 17 18 20 22 24 26 28 29 30 31 34 35 38 40 41 44 45 46 47 48 49 50 51 53 55 56 57 58 59 64 65 66 68 70 72 74 75 76 77 78 79 80 81 82 84 85 86 87 89 90 91 92 93 94 96 97 98 99 100 101 102 103 104 105 107 108 110 111 114 115 117 118 119 120 121 123 124 126 128 129 130 131 132 134 135 146 147 148 149 150 152 153 154 **P**6 **S** Ascension Healthcare, Saint Louis, MO
Primary Contact: Kristin McManmon, President
CFO: Jeanne Gramza, Director Finance
CMO: Jerry Hardacre, M.D., Chief of Staff
CIO: Joanne Bisterfeldt, Chief Information Officer
CHR: Mary Jo Wodicka, Vice President Human Resources
CNO: Mary Elizabeth Ouimet, MSN, R.N., Senior Vice President and Chief Nursing Officer
Web address: www.allsaintshealth.com
Control: Church operated, Nongovernment, not–for–profit **Service**: General medical and surgical

Staffed Beds: 338 **Admissions:** 13216 **Census:** 202 **Outpatient Visits:** 594198 **Births:** 1604 **Total Expense ($000):** 337148 **Payroll Expense ($000):** 105249 **Personnel:** 1859

WI

Hospital, Medicare Provider Number, Address, Telephone, Approval, Facility, and Physician Codes, Health Care System

★ American Hospital Association (AHA) membership
☐ The Joint Commission accreditation
○ Healthcare Facilities Accreditation Program
◇ DNV Healthcare Inc. accreditation
⇑ Center for Improvement in Healthcare Quality Accreditation
△ Commission on Accreditation of Rehabilitation Facilities (CARF) accreditation

© 2018 AHA Guide · *Many Facility Codes have changed. Please refer to the AHA Guide Code Chart.* · Hospitals **A701**

REEDSBURG—Sauk County

☒ **REEDSBURG AREA MEDICAL CENTER (521351)**, 2000 North Dewey Street, Zip 53959–1097; tel. 608/524–6487, **A**1 10 18 **F**3 8 11 13 15 17 18 26 28 29 30 31 34 40 41 43 45 50 51 53 54 57 59 64 65 66 70 75 76 77 78 79 80 81 82 85 86 87 88 89 93 96 97 107 110 111 115 127 129 130 131 132 133 135 144 146 147 148 154
Primary Contact: Robert Van Meeteren, President and Chief Executive Officer
COO: Dale Turner, Chief Operating Officer
CFO: Barry Borchert, Vice President Finance
Web address: www.ramchealth.com
Control: Other not–for–profit (including NFP Corporation) **Service**: General medical and surgical

Staffed Beds: 25 **Admissions**: 1073 **Census**: 8 **Outpatient Visits**: 69087
Births: 235 **Total Expense ($000)**: 66958 **Payroll Expense ($000)**: 30718
Personnel: 520

RHINELANDER—Oneida County

☒ **ASCENSION SAINT MARY'S HOSPITALS (520019)**, 2251 North Shore Drive, Zip 54501–6710; tel. 715/361–2000, (Includes ST. MARY'S HOSPITAL, 1044 Kabel Avenue, Rhinelander, WI, Zip 54501; tel. 715/369–6600) **A**1 3 10 20 **F**4 5 13 15 28 29 34 40 54 64 75 76 78 80 81 82 86 87 89 93 98 99 100 101 103 104 107 108 111 116 119 130 131 144 154 **S** Ascension Healthcare, Saint Louis, MO
Primary Contact: Sandra L. Anderson, President
COO: Laurie Oungst, Vice President and Chief Operating Officer
CFO: Jamon Lamers, Director Finance
CMO: Mark Banas, M.D., Chief Medical Officer
CIO: Howard Dobizl, Director Information Services for the Northern Region
CHR: Michelle Cornelius, Director Human Resources for the Northern Region
CNO: Christine Krebs, Director or Nursing
Web address: www.ministryhealth.org
Control: Church operated, Nongovernment, not–for–profit **Service**: General medical and surgical

Staffed Beds: 64 **Admissions**: 3034 **Census**: 31 **Outpatient Visits**: 98733
Births: 288 **Total Expense ($000)**: 122421 **Payroll Expense ($000)**: 49812
Personnel: 326

RICE LAKE—Barron County

☒ **MARSHFIELD MEDICAL CENTER – RICE LAKE (520011)**, 1700 West Stout Street, Zip 54868–5000; tel. 715/234–1515, **A**1 10 20 **F**3 7 8 11 13 15 18 22 26 28 29 31 32 34 35 40 43 45 51 53 56 57 59 60 62 63 64 65 70 75 76 77 78 79 80 81 82 84 85 86 89 93 107 111 114 115 119 124 129 130 132 135 146 147 154 **P**5 **S** Marshfield Clinic Health System, Marshfield, WI
Primary Contact: Bradley D. Groseth, Chief Administrative Officer
COO: Cindy Arts–Strenke, R.N., Chief Operating Officer and Chief Nursing Officer
CFO: Jacqueline Klein, Chief Financial Officer
CMO: John L. Olson, M.D., Medical Director
CIO: Brad Gerrits, Director Information Systems
CHR: Kathy Mitchell, Director Human Resources
Web address: www.lakeviewmedical.com
Control: Other not–for–profit (including NFP Corporation) **Service**: General medical and surgical

Staffed Beds: 40 **Admissions**: 2206 **Census**: 17 **Outpatient Visits**: 113688
Births: 478 **Total Expense ($000)**: 69317 **Payroll Expense ($000)**: 23318
Personnel: 433

RICHLAND CENTER—Richland County

☒ **RICHLAND HOSPITAL (521341)**, 333 East Second Street, Zip 53581–1914; tel. 608/647–6321, **A**1 10 18 **F**3 12 13 15 28 31 34 35 37 40 43 45 50 56 57 59 64 65 70 75 76 78 79 80 81 85 86 89 92 93 107 110 115 119 127 129 130 131 132 133 135 146 148 149 153 154
Primary Contact: Bruce E. Roesler, FACHE, Chief Executive Officer
CFO: Karen Traynor, Chief Financial Officer
CMO: David May, Chief of Staff
CIO: Jerry Cooper, Manager Data Processing
CHR: Rhonda Sutton, Director Human Resources
CNO: Cindy Hanold, Chief Nursing Officer
Web address: www.richlandhospital.com
Control: Other not–for–profit (including NFP Corporation) **Service**: General medical and surgical

Staffed Beds: 25 **Admissions**: 1162 **Census**: 11 **Outpatient Visits**: 41864
Births: 185 **Total Expense ($000)**: 40688 **Payroll Expense ($000)**: 17032
Personnel: 238

RIPON—Fond Du Lac County

☐ **RIPON MEDICAL CENTER (521321)**, 845 Parkside Street, Zip 54971–8505, Mailing Address: P.O. Box 390, Zip 54971–0390; tel. 920/748–3101, **A**1 10 18 **F**3 11 13 15 17 18 28 29 30 31 32 34 35 40 43 44 45 50 51 53 57 59 66 68 69 70 75 76 77 79 80 81 82 85 86 87 88 89 93 96 97 107 108 109 110 111 114 119 130 131 132 133 134 135 143 144 146 147 148 149 150 154 **P**2 6 **S** SSM Health, Saint Louis, MO
Primary Contact: DeAnn Thurmer, Interim Chief Operating Officer and Chief Nursing Officer
COO: DeAnn Thurmer, Interim Chief Operating Officer and Chief Nursing Officer
CFO: Bonnie Schmitz, Chief Financial Officer
CIO: Nancy Birschbach, Vice President and Chief Information Officer
CHR: Sue Edminster, Vice President Human Resources
CNO: DeAnn Thurmer, Interim Chief Operating Officer and Chief Nursing Officer
Web address: www.agnesian.com
Control: Church operated, Nongovernment, not–for–profit **Service**: General medical and surgical

Staffed Beds: 18 **Admissions**: 537 **Census**: 5 **Outpatient Visits**: 31160
Births: 33 **Total Expense ($000)**: 27319 **Payroll Expense ($000)**: 11054
Personnel: 129

RIVER FALLS—St. Croix County

☒ **RIVER FALLS AREA HOSPITAL (521349)**, 1629 East Division Street, Zip 54022–1571; tel. 715/425–6155, **A**1 2 10 18 **F**3 11 13 15 28 29 30 31 34 35 40 43 45 50 51 53 64 75 76 78 79 80 81 82 84 86 87 89 90 93 97 107 111 119 129 130 131 133 135 146 147 148 154 **S** Allina Health, Minneapolis, MN
Primary Contact: David R. Miller, President
COO: William Frommelt, Director Operations and Finance
CFO: William Frommelt, Director Operations and Finance
CHR: Kristen Novak, Manager Human Resources
Web address: www.allina.com
Control: Other not–for–profit (including NFP Corporation) **Service**: General medical and surgical

Staffed Beds: 18 **Admissions**: 831 **Census**: 6 **Outpatient Visits**: 19901
Births: 86 **Total Expense ($000)**: 38098 **Payroll Expense ($000)**: 13493
Personnel: 143

SHAWANO—Shawano County

☐ **THEDACARE MEDICAL CENTER–SHAWANO (521346)**, 100 County Road B, Zip 54166–2127; tel. 715/526–2111, **A**1 10 18 **F**11 13 15 28 29 34 40 53 64 75 76 77 78 80 81 82 86 87 90 102 107 108 111 119 130 131 154 **S** ThedaCare, Inc., Appleton, WI
Primary Contact: William Schmidt, Chief Executive Officer
CFO: Kerry Lee Blanke, Chief Financial Officer
CMO: Mindy Frimodig, D.O., President Medical Staff ThedaCare Physicians Shawano
CIO: Jennifer Quinn, Quality and Safety Coordinator
CNO: Patricia A Angelucci, MS, R.N., Director Patient Care Services
Web address: www.shawanomed.org
Control: Other not–for–profit (including NFP Corporation) **Service**: General medical and surgical

Staffed Beds: 22 **Admissions**: 1296 **Census**: 11 **Outpatient Visits**: 62953
Births: 251 **Total Expense ($000)**: 38459 **Payroll Expense ($000)**: 17337
Personnel: 210

SHEBOYGAN—Sheboygan County

☒ **AURORA SHEBOYGAN MEMORIAL MEDICAL CENTER (520035)**, 2629 North Seventh Street, Zip 53083–4998; tel. 920/451–5000, **A**1 2 10 **F**3 4 5 13 17 18 20 22 26 28 29 30 31 32 34 35 36 40 41 43 44 45 49 50 53 56 57 59 60 64 65 68 70 72 74 75 76 79 80 81 82 84 85 86 87 89 92 93 94 98 99 100 102 103 104 105 107 108 111 112 114 115 117 118 119 120 121 123 126 129 130 131 132 135 143 146 147 148 149 152 153 154 **P**6 **S** Advocate Aurora Health, Downers Grove, IL
Primary Contact: David Graebner, President
CFO: Pamela Ott, Vice President Finance
CMO: Andrea Gavin, M.D., Chief Medical officer
CIO: Steve Serketich, Manager Information Services
CHR: Stacie A Schneider, Director Human Resources
CNO: Lori Knitt, Chief Nursing Officer
Web address: www.aurorahealthcare.org
Control: Other not–for–profit (including NFP Corporation) **Service**: General medical and surgical

Staffed Beds: 136 **Admissions**: 5544 **Census**: 51 **Outpatient Visits**: 98351
Births: 800 **Total Expense ($000)**: 130348 **Payroll Expense ($000)**: 38427
Personnel: 721

Many Facility Codes have changed. Please refer to the AHA Guide Code Chart. © 2018 AHA Guide

⊠ **HSHS ST. NICHOLAS HOSPITAL (520044)**, 3100 Superior Avenue, Zip 53081–1948; tel. 920/459–8300, **A**1 2 10 F3 8 11 13 15 17 18 20 26 27 28 29 30 31 34 35 36 38 40 43 44 45 50 53 54 57 59 60 62 63 64 65 70 71 74 75 76 77 79 80 81 84 85 86 87 89 90 93 107 108 110 111 114 115 116 117 118 119 120 121 123 129 130 132 146 148 149 154 **P**2 **S** HSHS Hospital Sisters Health System, Springfield, IL
Primary Contact: Justin Selle, Chief Executive Officer
CFO: Greg Simia, Chief Financial Officer
CMO: Ken Johnson, Chief Physician Executive
CIO: Shane Miller, Chief Information Officer
CHR: Christine Jensema, Chief People Officer
CNO: Mary Martin, MSN, R.N., Chief Nursing Officer
Web address: www.stnicholashospital.org
Control: Church operated, Nongovernment, not–for–profit **Service**: General medical and surgical

Staffed Beds: 46 **Admissions**: 2361 **Census**: 22 **Outpatient Visits**: 77286 **Births**: 264 **Total Expense ($000)**: 73848 **Payroll Expense ($000)**: 22954 **Personnel**: 241	

SHELL LAKE—Washburn County

☐ **INDIANHEAD MEDICAL CENTER (521342)**, 113 Fourth Avenue, Zip 54871–4457, Mailing Address: P.O. Box 300, Zip 54871–0300; tel. 715/468–7833, **A**1 10 18 F15 28 34 40 43 56 62 64 80 81 86 89 93 107 119 130 144 **P**5
Primary Contact: Shannon Jack, Executive Vice President
CFO: Michael Elliott, Controller
CMO: Allan Haesemeyer, M.D., Chief of Staff
CHR: Gwen Nielsen, Manager Human Resources
Web address: www.indianheadmedicalcenter.com
Control: Corporation, Investor–owned (for–profit) **Service**: General medical and surgical

Staffed Beds: 16 **Admissions**: 322 **Census**: 4 **Outpatient Visits**: 15769 **Births**: 0 **Total Expense ($000)**: 8467 **Payroll Expense ($000)**: 3332 **Personnel**: 86	

SPARTA—Monroe County

MAYO CLINIC HEALTH SYSTEM – FRANCISCAN HEALTHCARE IN SPARTA (521305), 310 West Main Street, Zip 54656–2171; tel. 608/269–2132, **A**10 18 F1 5 6 11 14 15 28 29 30 34 35 40 43 53 56 57 59 64 65 66 68 75 77 80 81 85 86 87 89 90 93 97 107 108 119 127 130 132 133 143 144 146 149 150 154 **S** Mayo Clinic, Rochester, MN
Primary Contact: Kimberly Hawthorne, Administrator
COO: Joseph J Kruse, Chief Administrative Officer
CFO: Tom Tiggelaar, Vice President Finance ad Chief Financial Officer
CMO: Tracy Warsing, M.D., Site Leader Chief of Staff
CHR: Mike J Hesch, Regional Administrator Human Resources
Web address: www.mayoclinichealthsystem.org
Control: Church operated, Nongovernment, not–for–profit **Service**: General medical and surgical

Staffed Beds: 12 **Admissions**: 243 **Census**: 10 **Outpatient Visits**: 34336 **Births**: 0 **Total Expense ($000)**: 27791 **Payroll Expense ($000)**: 12320 **Personnel**: 145	

SPOONER—Washburn County

★ **SPOONER HEALTH (521332)**, 1280 Chandler Drive, Zip 54801–1299; tel. 715/635–2111, **A**10 18 F3 11 15 29 30 31 34 35 40 43 45 50 56 57 59 62 64 65 68 78 80 81 85 86 87 89 90 93 103 107 111 119 129 130 132 133 135 146 148 154 **S** HealthTech Management Services, Brentwood, TN
Primary Contact: Michael Schafer, Chief Executive Officer and Administrator
CFO: Rebecca Busch, Chief Financial Officer
CMO: Mark Van Etten, M.D., Chief of Staff
CHR: Cindy Rouzer, Director Human Resources
CNO: Clint Miller, Chief Nursing Officer
Web address: www.spoonerhealth.com
Control: Other not–for–profit (including NFP Corporation) **Service**: General medical and surgical

Staffed Beds: 20 **Admissions**: 445 **Census**: 6 **Outpatient Visits**: 21834 **Births**: 0 **Total Expense ($000)**: 20261 **Payroll Expense ($000)**: 7480 **Personnel**: 104	

ST CROIX FALLS—Polk County

★ **ST. CROIX REGIONAL MEDICAL CENTER (521337)**, 235 State Street, Zip 54024–4117; tel. 715/483–3261, **A**10 18 F6 9 11 13 15 28 29 34 36 40 43 51 55 56 64 70 75 76 77 78 81 82 86 87 93 99 100 101 104 107 108 111 116 118 119 130 131 144 147 154 **P**6
Primary Contact: David Dobosenski, Chief Executive Officer
CFO: Sally Bajak, Chief Financial Officer
CMO: Jeffrey Hall, DPM, Chief Medical Officer
CIO: Brent McCurdy, Director Management Information
CHR: Betsy Nordby, Director of Human Resources
CNO: Laura J. Jensen, Vice President Patient Care Services
Web address: www.scrmc.org
Control: Other not–for–profit (including NFP Corporation) **Service**: General medical and surgical

Staffed Beds: 25 **Admissions**: 1499 **Census**: 13 **Outpatient Visits**: 220868 **Births**: 280 **Total Expense ($000)**: 78261 **Payroll Expense ($000)**: 32785 **Personnel**: 451	

STANLEY—Chippewa County

★ **ASCENSION OUR LADY OF VICTORY HOSPITAL (521311)**, 1120 Pine Street, Zip 54768–1297; tel. 715/644–5571, **A**10 18 F15 28 29 34 40 43 64 75 80 81 86 87 89 93 107 130 131 144 147 154 **P**2 **S** Ascension Healthcare, Saint Louis, MO
Primary Contact: Jeremy Normington–Slay, FACHE, President
CFO: Terri Lewandowski, Director Financial Services
Web address: www.ministryhealth.org
Control: Church operated, Nongovernment, not–for–profit **Service**: General medical and surgical

Staffed Beds: 5 **Admissions**: 196 **Census**: 3 **Outpatient Visits**: 21731 **Births**: 0 **Total Expense ($000)**: 17506 **Payroll Expense ($000)**: 6048 **Personnel**: 58	

STEVENS POINT—Portage County

⊠ **ASCENSION ST. MICHAEL'S HOSPITAL (520002)**, 900 Illinois Avenue, Zip 54481–3196; tel. 715/346–5000, **A**1 3 10 19 F5 13 15 17 29 34 40 43 51 56 64 70 72 76 77 78 80 81 86 87 89 90 93 98 99 100 101 102 103 104 107 108 111 118 119 130 131 144 147 154 **S** Ascension Healthcare, Saint Louis, MO
Primary Contact: Jeremy Normington–Slay, FACHE, President, North Central Region
CFO: William J Hinner, Vice President Financial Analysis and Planning
CMO: Ryan Andrews, M.D., Chief Medical Officer
CIO: Will Weider, Chief Information Officer
CHR: Celia Shaunessy, Vice President Human Resources
CNO: Tom Veeser, Chief Nursing Officer
Web address: www.ministryhealth.org/SMH/home.nws
Control: Church operated, Nongovernment, not–for–profit **Service**: General medical and surgical

Staffed Beds: 50 **Admissions**: 4507 **Census**: 38 **Outpatient Visits**: 392484 **Births**: 494 **Total Expense ($000)**: 173179 **Payroll Expense ($000)**: 78104 **Personnel**: 427	

SAINT MICHAEL'S HOSPITAL See Ascension St. Michael's Hospital

STOUGHTON—Dane County

☐ **STOUGHTON HOSPITAL ASSOCIATION (521343)**, 900 Ridge Street, Zip 53589–1864; tel. 608/873–6611, **A**1 10 18 F3 4 6 8 15 28 29 34 35 36 40 41 43 50 53 54 56 57 59 62 64 65 68 70 71 74 75 77 79 80 81 85 86 87 89 90 91 93 98 100 103 107 115 129 130 131 132 133 135 144 146 147 148 149 152 154
Primary Contact: Daniel DeGroot, President and Chief Executive Officer
CFO: Karen Myers, Vice President Financial Services
CMO: Guirish Agni, M.D., Chief of Staff
CIO: Karen Myers, Vice President Financial Services
CHR: Christopher Schmitz, Associate Vice President, Director Human Resources
CNO: Teresa Lindfors, Chief Nursing Officer and Vice President, Patient Services
Web address: www.stoughtonhospital.com
Control: Other not–for–profit (including NFP Corporation) **Service**: General medical and surgical

Staffed Beds: 32 **Admissions**: 1022 **Census**: 16 **Outpatient Visits**: 56603 **Births**: 0 **Total Expense ($000)**: 42808 **Payroll Expense ($000)**: 17978 **Personnel**: 268	

WI

Hospital, Medicare Provider Number, Address, Telephone, Approval, Facility, and Physician Codes, Health Care System

★ American Hospital Association (AHA) membership
☐ The Joint Commission accreditation
○ Healthcare Facilities Accreditation Program
◇ DNV Healthcare Inc. accreditation
⇑ Center for Improvement in Healthcare Quality Accreditation
△ Commission on Accreditation of Rehabilitation Facilities (CARF) accreditation

STURGEON BAY—Door County

★ **DOOR COUNTY MEDICAL CENTER (521358)**, 323 South 18th Avenue, Zip 54235–1495; tel. 920/743–5566, (Total facility includes 30 beds in nursing home–type unit) **A**10 18 **F**3 11 13 15 17 28 29 30 31 32 34 35 36 40 43 56 57 59 61 64 65 66 68 70 75 76 77 78 79 80 81 82 84 85 86 87 89 90 93 107 108 110 111 115 118 119 127 128 129 130 132 133 135 144 145 147 148 149 154 **P**1
Primary Contact: Gerald M. Worrick, President and Chief Executive Officer
CFO: Adam Gingery, Chief Financial Officer
CMO: James Heise, Chief Medical Officer
CIO: Mary Lopas, Chief Information Officer
CHR: Kelli Bowling, Chief Culture Officer
CNO: Jody Boes, Vice President Patient Care Services
Web address: www.dcmedical.org
Control: Church operated, Nongovernment, not–for–profit **Service**: General medical and surgical

Staffed Beds: 55 Admissions: 1347 Census: 39 Outpatient Visits: 111008	
Births: 117 Total Expense ($000): 77685 Payroll Expense ($000): 40476	
Personnel: 524	

DOOR COUNTY MEMORIAL HOSPITAL See Door County Medical Center

SUMMIT—Waukesha County

✠ **AURORA MEDICAL CENTER SUMMIT (520206)**, 36500 Aurora Drive, Zip 53066–4899; tel. 262/434–1000, **A**1 2 10 **F**3 8 11 12 13 15 17 18 19 20 22 24 26 28 29 30 31 32 34 35 36 40 41 43 44 45 47 48 49 50 53 54 57 59 60 64 68 70 72 74 75 76 79 80 81 82 85 86 87 89 90 93 94 96 102 107 108 110 111 114 115 116 117 118 119 120 121 123 126 129 130 131 132 134 135 146 147 148 149 154 **P**6 **S** Advocate Aurora Health, Downers Grove, IL
Primary Contact: Michael Bergmann, President
Web address: www.aurorahealthcare.org
Control: Other not–for–profit (including NFP Corporation) **Service**: General medical and surgical

Staffed Beds: 91 Admissions: 3959 Census: 40 Outpatient Visits: 101724	
Births: 451 Total Expense ($000): 112909 Payroll Expense ($000): 34819	
Personnel: 919	

SUPERIOR—Douglas County

✠ **ESSENTIA HEALTH ST. MARY'S HOSPITAL OF SUPERIOR (521329)**, 3500 Tower Avenue, Zip 54880–5395; tel. 715/817–7000, **A**1 10 18 **F**3 8 11 15 26 28 29 30 32 40 45 46 48 49 56 57 59 65 75 77 78 79 80 81 82 86 87 90 93 96 97 107 110 114 119 127 130 132 133 135 146 149 154 **S** Essentia Health, Duluth, MN
Primary Contact: Terry Jacobson, Administrator and Chief Executive Officer
Web address: www.essentiahealth.org/ EssentiaHealthStMarysHospitalofSuperiorFoundation/overview.aspx
Control: Other not–for–profit (including NFP Corporation) **Service**: General medical and surgical

Staffed Beds: 25 Admissions: 542 Census: 8 Outpatient Visits: 52762	
Births: 0 Total Expense ($000): 45639 Payroll Expense ($000): 23765	
Personnel: 266	

TOMAH—Monroe County

✠ **TOMAH MEMORIAL HOSPITAL (521320)**, 321 Butts Avenue, Zip 54660–1412; tel. 608/372–2181, **A**1 10 18 **F**3 8 11 12 13 18 28 30 31 34 35 40 43 50 56 57 59 63 64 65 68 76 77 79 80 81 82 84 85 86 87 89 90 93 107 109 111 119 129 130 132 133 135 144 146 148 154 **P**5 6 **S** HealthTech Management Services, Brentwood, TN
Primary Contact: Philip J. Stuart, Administrator and Chief Executive Officer
CFO: Joseph Zeps, Vice President Finance
CIO: LaVonne Smith, Director Health Information Technology
CHR: Brenda Reinert, Director Human Resources
CNO: Tracy Myhre, R.N., MSN, Chief Nursing Officer
Web address: www.tomahhospital.org
Control: Other not–for–profit (including NFP Corporation) **Service**: General medical and surgical

Staffed Beds: 25 Admissions: 999 Census: 9 Outpatient Visits: 38864	
Births: 283 Total Expense ($000): 46537 Payroll Expense ($000): 19991	
Personnel: 306	

✠ **VA MEDICAL CENTER**, 500 East Veterans Street, Zip 54660–3105; tel. 608/372–3971, (Nonreporting) **A**1 3 **S** Department of Veterans Affairs, Perry Point, MD
Primary Contact: Victoria Brahm, R.N., MSN, Medical Center Director
CFO: Jane Mashak–Ekern, Fiscal Officer
CMO: David Houlihan, M.D., Chief of Staff
CIO: Edward Hensel, Chief Information Officer
CHR: David Dechant, Chief Human Resources Officer
Web address: www.tomah.va.gov
Control: Veterans Affairs, Government, federal **Service**: General medical and surgical

Staffed Beds: 71	

TOMAHAWK—Lincoln County

★ **ASCENSION SACRED HEART HOSPITAL (521313)**, 401 West Mohawk Drive, Zip 54487–2274; tel. 715/453–7700, **A**10 18 **F**5 15 28 29 34 40 75 77 80 81 86 87 89 93 99 100 101 104 107 119 130 131 154 **S** Ascension Healthcare, Saint Louis, MO
Primary Contact: Sandra L. Anderson, President and Chief Executive Officer
COO: Laurie Oungst, Vice President, Operations
CFO: Jamon Lamers, Director Finance
CMO: Russ Sudbury, M.D., President Medical Staff
CIO: Howard Dobizl, Director Information Technology Services
CHR: Michelle Cornelius, Director Human Resources
CNO: Christine Krebs, Director of Nursing
Web address: www.ministryhealth.org
Control: Church operated, Nongovernment, not–for–profit **Service**: General medical and surgical

Staffed Beds: 8 Admissions: 301 Census: 3 Outpatient Visits: 20521	
Births: 0 Total Expense ($000): 13794 Payroll Expense ($000): 7682	
Personnel: 61	

TWO RIVERS—Manitowoc County

✠ **AURORA MEDICAL CENTER – MANITOWOC COUNTY (520034)**, 5000 Memorial Drive, Zip 54241–3900; tel. 920/794–5000, **A**1 2 10 **F**11 13 28 29 36 40 43 56 64 75 76 78 80 81 82 86 87 89 93 107 108 111 119 130 131 147 149 154 **P**6 **S** Advocate Aurora Health, Downers Grove, IL
Primary Contact: Cathie A. Kocourek, President
COO: Carrie L Penovich, Chief Clinical Services Officer
CFO: Sandra Ewald, President (Green Bay/Manitowoc Market)
CMO: Paul Mihalakakos, M.D., Chief of Staff
CIO: Preston Simons, Chief Information Officer
CHR: Elizabeth A Kirby, Senior Director Human Resources
CNO: Betsy Benz, R.N., MS, Chief Nursing Officer
Web address: www.aurorahealthcare.org
Control: Other not–for–profit (including NFP Corporation) **Service**: General medical and surgical

Staffed Beds: 62 Admissions: 2280 Census: 17 Outpatient Visits: 89773	
Births: 387 Total Expense ($000): 60756 Payroll Expense ($000): 18770	
Personnel: 358	

VIROQUA—Vernon County

VERNON MEMORIAL HEALTHCARE (521348), 507 South Main Street, Zip 54665–2096; tel. 608/637–2101, **A**10 18 **F**3 5 13 15 18 26 28 29 31 34 35 36 37 40 43 45 53 56 57 59 62 63 64 65 68 75 76 77 79 80 81 82 85 86 87 89 93 97 99 100 103 104 107 110 115 119 126 127 129 130 131 132 133 135 144 146 148 154 **P**6
Primary Contact: Kyle Bakkum, Chief Executive Officer and Administrator
COO: Kristy Wiltrout, R.N., Chief Operating Officer
CFO: Mary Koenig, Chief Financial Officer
CIO: Scott Adkins, Manager Information Technology
CHR: Kay Starr, Manager Human Resources
Web address: www.vmh.org
Control: Other not–for–profit (including NFP Corporation) **Service**: General medical and surgical

Staffed Beds: 25 Admissions: 1183 Census: 8 Outpatient Visits: 133658	
Births: 155 Total Expense ($000): 73032 Payroll Expense ($000): 32299	
Personnel: 400	

WATERFORD—Racine County

☐ **LAKEVIEW SPECIALTY HOSPITAL AND REHAB (522005)**, 1701 Sharp Road, Zip 53185–5214; tel. 262/534–7297, **A**1 10 **F**1 29 34 38 53 60 64 75 86 87 90 93 130 **P**6
Primary Contact: Jerry Amato, President and Chief Operating Officer
Web address: www.lakeviewsystem.com
Control: Corporation, Investor–owned (for–profit) **Service**: Acute long–term care hospital

Staffed Beds: 39 Admissions: 241 Census: 26 Outpatient Visits: 3985	
Births: 0 Total Expense ($000): 17102 Payroll Expense ($000): 6670	
Personnel: 120	

WI

Many Facility Codes have changed. Please refer to the AHA Guide Code Chart.

WATERTOWN—Dodge County

☒ **WATERTOWN REGIONAL MEDICAL CENTER (520116)**, 125 Hospital Drive, Zip 53098–3303; tel. 920/261–4210, **A**1 10 **F**3 8 10 11 13 15 18 20 22 26 27 28 29 34 35 36 40 41 44 45 46 47 48 50 53 54 56 57 59 64 65 66 68 69 74 75 76 77 78 79 80 81 82 83 85 86 87 89 90 93 94 96 97 104 107 108 110 111 115 118 119 125 129 130 131 132 133 135 144 147 149 154 **P**8 **S** LifePoint Health, Brentwood, TN
Primary Contact: David Critchlow, Senior Vice President, Government Relations, LifePoint Health
COO: John P Kosanovich, President
CFO: John Graf, Senior Vice President
CIO: Jennifer Laughlin, Chief Information Officer
CHR: Duane Floyd, Vice President Human Resources and Professional Services
Web address: www.watertownregional.com/Main/Home.aspx
Control: Corporation, Investor–owned (for–profit) **Service:** General medical and surgical

Staffed Beds: 56 **Admissions:** 1863 **Census:** 16 **Outpatient Visits:** 80239 **Births:** 220 **Total Expense ($000):** 88978 **Payroll Expense ($000):** 38180 **Personnel:** 626	

WAUKESHA—Waukesha County

☐ **REHABILITATION HOSPITAL OF WISCONSIN (523027)**, 1625 Coldwater Creek Drive, Zip 53188–8028; tel. 262/521–8800, **A**1 10 **F**3 28 29 34 35 57 64 65 68 75 86 90 93 94 95 96 100 130 135 148 149 150 154 **S** Kindred Healthcare, Louisville, KY
Primary Contact: John R. Robertstad, FACHE, Chief Executive Officer
COO: Brad Anderson, Chief Operating Officer
CMO: Tim McAvoy, M.D., Medical Director
CHR: Jenny Franke, Director Human Resources
CNO: Sharon Behrens, R.N., MSN, Chief Clinical Officer
Web address: www.rehabhospitalwi.com
Control: Partnership, Investor–owned (for–profit) **Service:** Rehabilitation

Staffed Beds: 40 **Admissions:** 895 **Census:** 34 **Outpatient Visits:** 6233 **Births:** 0 **Total Expense ($000):** 14426 **Payroll Expense ($000):** 8052 **Personnel:** 151	

WAUKESHA COUNTY MENTAL HEALTH CENTER (524026), 2501 Airport Road, Zip 53188; tel. 262/548–7950, **A**10 **F**4 29 44 50 59 87 98 103 130 154
Primary Contact: Jeff Lewis, Administrator
CFO: Randy R Setzer, Financial Services Manager
Web address: www.waukeshacounty.gov/
Control: County, Government, nonfederal **Service:** Psychiatric

Staffed Beds: 28 **Admissions:** 685 **Census:** 17 **Outpatient Visits:** 0 **Births:** 0 **Total Expense ($000):** 7116 **Payroll Expense ($000):** 3831 **Personnel:** 53	

☒ **WAUKESHA MEMORIAL HOSPITAL (520008)**, 725 American Avenue, Zip 53188–5099; tel. 262/928–1000, **A**1 2 3 5 10 **F**3 4 5 6 11 12 13 18 20 22 24 26 28 29 30 31 32 33 34 37 40 43 45 46 47 48 49 50 53 56 57 58 59 64 65 66 68 72 74 75 76 78 79 80 81 82 83 84 85 87 89 93 97 98 100 101 102 104 105 107 108 109 110 111 112 114 115 116 117 118 119 120 121 126 129 130 132 133 135 146 147 148 149 151 152 153 154 **S** ProHealth Care, Inc., Waukesha, WI
Primary Contact: Susan A. Edwards, Chief Executive Officer
CMO: James D Gardner, M.D., Vice President and Chief Medical Officer
CIO: Rodney Dykehouse, Senior Vice President Information Services
CHR: Nadine T Guirl, Senior Vice President Human Resources
Web address: www.prohealthcare.org/locations/locations-v2-detail/?id=1119
Control: Other not–for–profit (including NFP Corporation) **Service:** General medical and surgical

Staffed Beds: 262 **Admissions:** 12666 **Census:** 131 **Outpatient Visits:** 336530 **Births:** 1742 **Total Expense ($000):** 423351 **Payroll Expense ($000):** 110484 **Personnel:** 1833	

WAUPACA—Waupaca County

☐ **THEDACARE MEDICAL CENTER–WAUPACA (521334)**, 800 Riverside Drive, Zip 54981–1999; tel. 715/258–1000, **A**1 10 18 **F**11 13 17 28 29 34 40 64 70 75 76 78 80 81 82 86 87 88 89 90 107 111 119 130 144 147 154 **S** ThedaCare, Appleton, WI
Primary Contact: Craig A. Kantos, Chief Executive Officer
CFO: Kerry Lee Blanke, Director Financial Services
CMO: James Williams, M.D., Chief of Staff
CHR: Kevin Gossens, Director Human Resources
Web address: www.riversidemedical.org
Control: Other not–for–profit (including NFP Corporation) **Service:** General medical and surgical

Staffed Beds: 25 **Admissions:** 908 **Census:** 8 **Outpatient Visits:** 47056 **Births:** 123 **Total Expense ($000):** 27210 **Payroll Expense ($000):** 14315 **Personnel:** 176	

WAUPUN—Dodge County

☐ ⇑ **WAUPUN MEMORIAL HOSPITAL (521327)**, 620 West Brown Street, Zip 53963–1799; tel. 920/324–5581, **A**1 10 18 21 **F**3 11 13 15 18 28 29 30 31 34 35 40 43 44 45 50 51 57 59 60 66 68 69 70 75 76 77 79 81 82 85 86 87 93 96 97 107 108 109 110 114 118 119 124 130 131 132 133 134 135 143 144 146 147 148 149 150 154 **P**6 **S** SSM Health, Saint Louis, MO
Primary Contact: DeAnn Thurmer, Chief Operating Officer
COO: DeAnn Thurmer, Chief Operating Officer
CFO: Bonnie Schmitz, Chief Financial Officer
CMO: Derek Colmenares, M.D., Chief Medical Officer
CIO: Nancy Birschbach, Vice President and Chief Information Officer
CHR: Sue Edminster, Vice President Human Resources
CNO: DeAnn Thurmer, Chief Nursing Officer
Web address: www.agnesian.com
Control: Church operated, Nongovernment, not–for–profit **Service:** General medical and surgical

Staffed Beds: 25 **Admissions:** 947 **Census:** 8 **Outpatient Visits:** 58609 **Births:** 141 **Total Expense ($000):** 35642 **Payroll Expense ($000):** 15376 **Personnel:** 191	

WAUSAU—Marathon County

☒ △ **ASPIRUS WAUSAU HOSPITAL, INC. (520030)**, 333 Pine Ridge Boulevard, Zip 54401–4187; tel. 715/847–2121, **A**1 2 3 5 7 10 **F**3 6 7 8 11 12 13 15 17 18 20 22 24 29 30 31 34 35 36 37 40 43 44 45 46 47 49 50 51 54 55 56 57 58 59 60 64 65 68 69 70 71 72 74 75 76 78 79 80 81 82 83 84 85 86 87 89 90 92 93 96 97 100 102 103 107 108 110 111 114 115 116 117 118 119 120 121 123 124 126 129 130 132 134 135 143 144 145 146 147 148 154 **P**8 **S** Aspirus, Inc., Wausau, WI
Primary Contact: Darrell Lentz, President
CFO: Sidney C Sczygelski, Senior Vice President Finance and Chief Financial Officer
CMO: William Wessels, M.D., Chief Medical Officer
CNO: Jeannine Burnat Nosko, Vice President Patient Care
Web address: www.aspirus.org
Control: Other not–for–profit (including NFP Corporation) **Service:** General medical and surgical

Staffed Beds: 263 **Admissions:** 13565 **Census:** 155 **Outpatient Visits:** 122533 **Births:** 1280 **Total Expense ($000):** 437966 **Payroll Expense ($000):** 144601 **Personnel:** 1712	

★ **NORTH CENTRAL HEALTH CARE (524017)**, 1100 Lake View Drive, Zip 54403–6785; tel. 715/848–4600, (Total facility includes 181 beds in nursing home–type unit) **A**3 10 **F**4 5 29 38 75 80 87 98 99 102 103 104 128 130 154
Primary Contact: Michael Loy, Interim Chief Executive Officer
CFO: Brenda Glodowski, Chief Financial Officer
CHR: Sue Matis, Director Human Resources
Web address: www.norcen.org
Control: County, Government, nonfederal **Service:** Psychiatric

Staffed Beds: 210 **Admissions:** 1174 **Census:** 198 **Outpatient Visits:** 146793 **Births:** 0 **Total Expense ($000):** 37949 **Payroll Expense ($000):** 15777 **Personnel:** 364	

NORTH CENTRAL HEALTH CARE FACILITIES See North Central Health Care

WAUWATOSA—Milwaukee County

☒ **AURORA PSYCHIATRIC HOSPITAL (524000)**, 1220 Dewey Avenue, Zip 53213–2598; tel. 414/454–6600, **A**1 3 5 10 **F**4 5 29 30 32 34 35 38 44 50 54 57 59 64 68 75 86 87 98 99 100 101 103 104 105 106 130 132 134 135 149 152 153 154 **P**6 **S** Advocate Aurora Health, Downers Grove, IL
Primary Contact: Peter Carlson, President, Behavioral Health Services
CFO: Susan Dwyer, Vice President Finance
CMO: Anthony Meyer, M.D., Medical Director
CIO: Philip Loftus, Ph.D., Vice President and Chief Information Officer
CHR: Pamela Gamb, Manager Human Resources
CNO: Jamie Lewiston, R.N., MSN, Chief Nursing Officer
Web address: www.aurorahealthcare.org
Control: Other not–for–profit (including NFP Corporation) **Service:** Psychiatric

Staffed Beds: 91 **Admissions:** 5450 **Census:** 67 **Outpatient Visits:** 79585 **Births:** 0 **Total Expense ($000):** 34934 **Payroll Expense ($000):** 18915 **Personnel:** 456	

WI

Hospital, Medicare Provider Number, Address, Telephone, Approval, Facility, and Physician Codes, Health Care System	

★ American Hospital Association (AHA) membership
☐ The Joint Commission accreditation
○ Healthcare Facilities Accreditation Program
◇ DNV Healthcare Inc. accreditation
⇑ Center for Improvement in Healthcare Quality Accreditation
△ Commission on Accreditation of Rehabilitation Facilities (CARF) accreditation

WEST ALLIS—Milwaukee County

⊞ **AURORA WEST ALLIS MEDICAL CENTER (520139)**, 8901 West Lincoln Avenue, Zip 53227–2409, Mailing Address: P.O. Box 27901, Zip 53227–0901; tel. 414/328–6000, **A**1 2 3 10 **F**3 11 12 13 15 29 30 31 32 34 35 37 38 40 43 44 45 46 49 50 52 54 55 56 57 59 64 65 68 70 72 74 75 76 78 79 80 81 82 84 85 86 87 91 93 94 95 96 97 107 108 110 111 114 115 116 117 118 119 120 121 123 126 130 132 134 135 146 147 148 149 154 **P**6 **S** Advocate Aurora Health, Downers Grove, IL
Primary Contact: Richard A. Kellar, President
COO: Gerard Colman, Chief Operating Officer
CFO: Chris Hemmer, Director Finance
CMO: Andrew McDonagh, M.D., Chief Medical Officer
CIO: Philip Loftus, Ph.D., Chief Information Officer
CHR: Shannon Christenson, Director Human Resources
CNO: Kathy Becker, Ph.D., R.N., Vice President and Chief Nursing Officer
Web address: www.aurorahealthcare.org
Control: Other not–for–profit (including NFP Corporation) **Service**: General medical and surgical

Staffed Beds: 218 **Admissions**: 11980 **Census**: 136 **Outpatient Visits**: 159027 **Births**: 3183 **Total Expense ($000)**: 208988 **Payroll Expense ($000)**: 68164 **Personnel**: 1910

WEST BEND—Washington County

⊞ **ST. JOSEPH'S HOSPITAL (520063)**, 3200 Pleasant Valley Road, Zip 53095–9274; tel. 262/836–5533, **A**1 2 3 5 10 **F**3 9 13 15 26 28 29 30 31 34 35 40 44 45 46 47 49 50 56 57 58 59 60 64 65 66 68 71 75 76 77 78 79 80 81 84 85 86 87 100 101 107 108 110 111 114 115 116 117 118 119 120 121 123 129 130 132 135 145 146 147 148 149 150 154 Primary Contact: Allen Ericson, President
COO: Allen Ericson, Chief Operating Officer, Community Hospital Division and President, St. Joseph's Hospital
CFO: Scott Hawig, Senior Vice President of Finance, Chief Financial Officer and Treasurer
CMO: Patrick Gardner, M.D., Associate Vice President, Medical Affairs, St. Joseph's Hospital
CHR: Eric Humphrey, Senior Vice President, Chief Human Resources Officer
CNO: Shelly Waala, Vice President Patient Care Services and Chief Nursing Officer
Web address: www.froedtert.com
Control: Other not–for–profit (including NFP Corporation) **Service**: General medical and surgical

Staffed Beds: 70 **Admissions**: 3585 **Census**: 36 **Outpatient Visits**: 87549 **Births**: 692 **Total Expense ($000)**: 126021 **Payroll Expense ($000)**: 34983 **Personnel**: 496

WESTON—Marathon County

⊞ **MINISTRY GOOD SAMARITAN HEALTH CENTER (520202)**, 3400 Ministry Parkway, Zip 54476–5220; tel. 715/393–3000, **A**1 10 19 **F**11 13 17 20 22 24 29 34 40 43 51 64 70 72 76 78 80 81 82 86 87 89 130 147 154 **S** Ascension Healthcare, Saint Louis, MO
Primary Contact: Jeremy Normington–Slay, FACHE, President, North Central Region
CFO: Charlotte Esselman, Director Finance
CMO: Ryan Andrews, M.D., Chief Medical Officer
CIO: Tammy Hawkey, Manager Information Technology Client Services
CHR: Nancy Kwiesielewicz, Human Resources Manager
CNO: Sally E. Zillman, Interim Vice President, Patient Care Services
Web address: www.ministryhealth.org
Control: Church operated, Nongovernment, not–for–profit **Service**: General medical and surgical

Staffed Beds: 99 **Admissions**: 5862 **Census**: 59 **Outpatient Visits**: 19373 **Births**: 568 **Total Expense ($000)**: 105582 **Payroll Expense ($000)**: 34158 **Personnel**: 343

WHITEHALL—Trempealeau County

★ **GUNDERSEN TRI–COUNTY HOSPITAL AND CLINICS (521316)**, 18601 Lincoln Street, Zip 54773–8605; tel. 715/538–4361, (Total facility includes 47 beds in nursing home–type unit) **A**10 18 **F**5 6 7 10 11 15 28 34 40 43 53 54 56 64 69 75 78 81 82 86 87 93 99 100 104 107 108 128 130 144 154 Primary Contact: Joni Olson, Chief Executive Officer
CFO: Roxane K Schliech, Chief Financial Officer
CMO: Kim B Breidenbach, Medical Director
CIO: John Waldera, Director Information Technology
CHR: Jill Wesener Dieck, Human Resources Operations Manager
CNO: Kelsey N Underwood, Director of Nursing
Web address: www.gundersenhealth.org/tri–county
Control: Other not–for–profit (including NFP Corporation) **Service**: General medical and surgical

Staffed Beds: 50 **Admissions**: 318 **Census**: 41 **Outpatient Visits**: 30464 **Births**: 0 **Total Expense ($000)**: 17515 **Payroll Expense ($000)**: 7370 **Personnel**: 136

WILD ROSE—Waushara County

THEDA CARE MEDICAL CENTER – WILD ROSE (521303), 601 Grove Avenue, Zip 54984–6903, Mailing Address: P.O. Box 243, Zip 54984–0243; tel. 920/622–3257, **A**10 18 **F**11 15 28 29 34 40 43 56 64 75 77 80 81 86 87 89 90 93 99 100 101 102 103 104 107 111 119 131 144 147 154 **S** ThedaCare, Inc., Appleton, WI
Primary Contact: Craig A. Kantos, Chief Executive Officer
CFO: Thomas P Krystowiak, Vice President Finance
CMO: Michael Staudinger, M.D., Chief of Staff
Web address: www.wildrosehospital.org
Control: Other not–for–profit (including NFP Corporation) **Service**: General medical and surgical

Staffed Beds: 25 **Admissions**: 261 **Census**: 5 **Outpatient Visits**: 14714 **Births**: 0 **Total Expense ($000)**: 9325 **Payroll Expense ($000)**: 5225 **Personnel**: 78

WINNEBAGO—Winnebago County

☐ **WINNEBAGO MENTAL HEALTH INSTITUTE (524002)**, 1300 South Drive, Zip 54985, Mailing Address: Box 9, Zip 54985–0009; tel. 920/235–4910, **A**1 3 5 10 **F**3 4 5 29 30 57 59 75 82 87 98 99 103 130 132 135 146 149 154 **P**7 Primary Contact: Thomas Speech, Ph.D., Director
COO: Chris Craggs, Deputy Director
CFO: Lisa Spanbauer, Financial Program Supervisor
CMO: Randy Kerswill, M.D., Medical Director
CIO: Terrance J. Sweet, Director Information Technology
CHR: Mary Howard, Director Human Resources
CNO: Lori Monroe, Director of Nursing
Web address: www.dhfs.state.wi.us/mh_winnebago
Control: State, Government, nonfederal **Service**: Psychiatric

Staffed Beds: 184 **Admissions**: 3675 **Census**: 184 **Outpatient Visits**: 0 **Births**: 0 **Total Expense ($000)**: 68159 **Payroll Expense ($000)**: 35743 **Personnel**: 680

WISCONSIN RAPIDS—Wood County

⊞ **ASPIRUS RIVERVIEW HOSPITAL AND CLINICS, INC. (520033)**, 410 Dewey Street, Zip 54494–4715, Mailing Address: P.O. Box 8080, Zip 54495–8080; tel. 715/423–6060, **A**1 2 10 **F**4 13 15 17 28 34 40 43 56 64 69 70 75 76 77 78 80 81 86 88 89 90 93 98 107 108 111 118 119 130 131 154 **S** Aspirus, Inc., Wausau, WI
Primary Contact: Todd Burch, Chief Executive Officer
CFO: Nancy Roth–Mallek, Vice President of Finance
CMO: Thomas Voelker, M.D., Chief Medical Officer
CIO: Marjorie Tell, Vice President Information Technology
CHR: Jessica Fox, Director of Human Resources
CNO: Peggy Ose, FACHE, MSN, R.N., Chief Nursing Officer
Web address: www.aspirus.org
Control: Other not–for–profit (including NFP Corporation) **Service**: General medical and surgical

Staffed Beds: 75 **Admissions**: 2944 **Census**: 23 **Outpatient Visits**: 52541 **Births**: 483 **Total Expense ($000)**: 103144 **Payroll Expense ($000)**: 38103 **Personnel**: 542

WOODRUFF—Oneida County

⊞ **HOWARD YOUNG MEDICAL CENTER (520091)**, 240 Maple Street, Zip 54568–9190, Mailing Address: P.O. Box 470, Zip 54568–0470; tel. 715/356–8000, **A**1 5 10 20 **F**11 13 15 28 29 34 40 43 64 75 76 77 80 81 82 86 87 88 89 93 107 111 119 130 154 **S** Ascension Healthcare, Saint Louis, MO
Primary Contact: Sandra L. Anderson, President and Chief Executive Officer
COO: Laurie Oungst, Vice President, Operations
CFO: Jamon Lamers, Director Finance
CMO: John Crump, M.D., Medical Staff President
CIO: Howard Dobizl, Director Information Technology Services
CHR: Michelle Cornelius, Director Human Resources
CNO: Jacqualyn Monge, Director of Nursing
Web address: www.ministryhealth.org
Control: Church operated, Nongovernment, not–for–profit **Service**: General medical and surgical

Staffed Beds: 50 **Admissions**: 2406 **Census**: 24 **Outpatient Visits**: 39980 **Births**: 253 **Total Expense ($000)**: 46269 **Payroll Expense ($000)**: 17557 **Personnel**: 206

WI

Many Facility Codes have changed. Please refer to the AHA Guide Code Chart.

WYOMING

AFTON—Lincoln County

★ **STAR VALLEY MEDICAL CENTER (531313)**, 901 Adams Street, Zip 83110–9621, Mailing Address: P.O. Box 579, Zip 83110–0579; tel. 307/885–5800, (Total facility includes 24 beds in nursing home–type unit) **A**10 18 **F**3 4 7 8 11 12 13 15 28 29 31 34 36 40 41 43 45 46 47 48 49 50 51 53 56 57 65 67 70 75 76 77 78 79 81 82 84 85 87 89 90 92 93 94 107 108 109 110 111 112 115 117 119 127 128 129 130 131 132 133 141 143 144 145 146 148 152 **P**6
Primary Contact: Bren Lowe, Chief Executive Officer
COO: Mike Hunsaker, Chief Operating Officer
CFO: Chad Turner, Chief Financial Officer
CMO: Donald Kirk, M.D., Chief of Staff
CIO: Amy R Johnson, R.N., Quality Improvement Safety Officer
CHR: Trevor Merritt, Director Human Resources
CNO: Derek Greenwald, Chief Nursing Officer
Web address: www.svmcwy.org
Control: Hospital district or authority, Government, nonfederal **Service:** General medical and surgical

| Staffed Beds: 46 | Admissions: 828 | Census: 26 | Outpatient Visits: 37960 |
| Births: 91 | Total Expense ($000): 45839 | Payroll Expense ($000): 19365 |
| Personnel: 303 |

BASIN—Big Horn County

SOUTH BIG HORN COUNTY HOSPITAL (531301), 388 South US Highway 20, Zip 82410–8902; tel. 307/568–3311, (Total facility includes 37 beds in nursing home–type unit) **A**10 18 **F**3 11 15 29 35 40 50 56 57 59 64 67 68 75 97 107 110 114 127 130 133 146
Primary Contact: Vincent DiFranco, Interim Chief Executive Officer
Web address: www.midwayclinic.com
Control: Hospital district or authority, Government, nonfederal **Service:** General medical and surgical

| Staffed Beds: 47 | Admissions: 156 | Census: 30 | Births: 0 | Total Expense ($000): 8443 |

BUFFALO—Johnson County

★ **JOHNSON COUNTY HEALTHCARE CENTER (531308)**, 497 West Lott Street, Zip 82834–1691; tel. 307/684–5521, (Total facility includes 44 beds in nursing home–type unit) **A**10 18 **F**3 11 13 15 28 34 40 45 53 57 59 62 63 67 70 76 79 81 93 97 107 119 130 131 132 133
Primary Contact: Nicole Hobbs, Administrator
CMO: Blaine Ruby, M.D., Chief of Staff
CIO: Laurie Hansen, Director Administrative Services
CHR: Karen Ferguson, Director Human Resources
CNO: Mary Whaley, Director of Acute Care
Web address: www.jchealthcare.com
Control: Hospital district or authority, Government, nonfederal **Service:** General medical and surgical

| Staffed Beds: 59 | Admissions: 421 | Census: 49 | Outpatient Visits: 17946 |
| Births: 48 | Total Expense ($000): 22589 | Payroll Expense ($000): 12076 |
| Personnel: 208 |

CASPER—Natrona County

☐ **ELKHORN VALLEY REHABILITATION HOSPITAL (533027)**, 5715 East 2nd Street, Zip 82609–4322; tel. 307/265–0005, (Nonreporting) **A**1 10 **S** Ernest Health, Inc., Albuquerque, NM
Primary Contact: Michael Phillips, Chief Executive Officer
Web address: www.evrh.ernesthealth.com/
Control: Corporation, Investor–owned (for–profit) **Service:** Rehabilitation

| Staffed Beds: 40 |

○ **MOUNTAIN VIEW REGIONAL HOSPITAL (530033)**, 6550 East Second Street, Zip 82609–4321, Mailing Address: P.O. Box 51888, Zip 82605–1888; tel. 307/995–8100, (Nonreporting) **A**10 11 **S** National Surgical Healthcare, Chicago, IL
Primary Contact: Thomas Kopitnik, Acting Chief Executive Officer
Web address: www.mountainviewregionalhospital.com
Control: Partnership, Investor–owned (for–profit) **Service:** Surgical

| Staffed Beds: 23 |

⇑ **SUMMIT MEDICAL CENTER (530034)**, 6350 East 2nd Street, Zip 82609–4264; tel. 307/232–6600, (Nonreporting) **A**21
Primary Contact: Dennis D. Jack, FACHE, Chief Executive Officer
CFO: Calvin Carey, Chief Financial Officer
CMO: Joseph Vigneri, M.D., Chief Medical Officer
CNO: Vanessa Sorensen, Chief Nursing Officer
Web address: www.summitmedicalcasper.com/
Control: Corporation, Investor–owned (for–profit) **Service:** General medical and surgical

| Staffed Beds: 16 |

☐ **WYOMING BEHAVIORAL INSTITUTE (534004)**, 2521 East 15th Street, Zip 82609–4126; tel. 307/237–7444, (Nonreporting) **A**1 10 **S** Universal Health Services, Inc., King of Prussia, PA
Primary Contact: Joseph Gallagher, Chief Executive Officer
CFO: Carmel Bickford, Chief Financial Officer
CMO: Steven Brown, M.D., Medical Director
CHR: Jon Barra, Director Human Resources
Web address: www.wbihelp.com
Control: Corporation, Investor–owned (for–profit) **Service:** Psychiatric

| Staffed Beds: 129 |

⊠ **WYOMING MEDICAL CENTER (530012)**, 1233 East Second Street, Zip 82601–2988; tel. 307/577–7201, **A**1 3 10 **F**3 7 11 12 13 18 20 22 24 28 29 30 31 34 35 40 41 43 45 46 48 49 50 51 53 57 59 60 61 68 70 74 76 79 81 82 85 86 87 89 97 102 107 108 115 118 119 120 121 123 124 126 129 130 132 135 144 146 147 148 **P**6
Primary Contact: Michele Chulick, President and Chief Executive Officer
COO: Chad Pew, Chief Operating Officer and Senior Vice President
CFO: Yvonne Wigington, Vice President, Chief Financial Officer
CMO: Carol M Solie, M.D., Chief Medical Officer
CIO: Rob Pettigrew, Director Information Technology
CNO: David Gardner, MSN, Chief Nursing Officer
Web address: www.https://wyomingmedicalcenter.org/
Control: Other not–for–profit (including NFP Corporation) **Service:** General medical and surgical

| Staffed Beds: 217 | Admissions: 8649 | Census: 88 | Outpatient Visits: 85172 | Births: 1023 | Total Expense ($000): 205176 | Payroll Expense ($000): 73906 | Personnel: 1121 |

CHEYENNE—Laramie County

⊠ △ **CHEYENNE REGIONAL MEDICAL CENTER (530014)**, 214 East 23rd Street, Zip 82001–3790; tel. 307/634–2273, **A**1 2 3 5 7 10 20 **F**3 5 8 13 15 18 20 22 24 26 28 29 30 31 32 34 35 37 38 40 43 44 45 46 47 48 49 50 51 56 57 59 60 61 62 63 64 65 68 70 73 74 76 77 78 79 81 82 83 84 85 86 87 89 90 91 92 93 96 97 98 100 101 102 104 107 108 111 115 116 117 118 119 120 121 122 123 124 126 128 130 131 135 143 146 147 148 149 153 154 **P**6
Primary Contact: Patrick Madigan, Interim Chief Executive Officer
COO: Robin Roling, FACHE, MS, R.N., Chief Operating Officer
CFO: Neil W Bertrand, Interim Chief Financial Officer
CMO: Jeffrey Chapman, M.D., Chief Medical Officer
CIO: Craig Luzinski, FACHE, MSN, R.N., Vice President Performance Optimization
CHR: Craig Luzinski, FACHE, MSN, R.N., Vice President Performance Optimization
CNO: Tracy Garcia, MS, Chief Nursing Officer
Web address: www.cheyenneregional.org/
Control: County, Government, nonfederal **Service:** General medical and surgical

| Staffed Beds: 238 | Admissions: 10044 | Census: 131 | Outpatient Visits: 182560 | Births: 1232 | Total Expense ($000): 288411 | Payroll Expense ($000): 117651 | Personnel: 1544 |

Hospital, Medicare Provider Number, Address, Telephone, Approval, Facility, and Physician Codes, Health Care System

★ American Hospital Association (AHA) membership
☐ The Joint Commission accreditation
○ Healthcare Facilities Accreditation Program
◇ DNV Healthcare Inc. accreditation
⇑ Center for Improvement in Healthcare Quality Accreditation
△ Commission on Accreditation of Rehabilitation Facilities (CARF) accreditation

WY

⊞ **CHEYENNE VETERANS AFFAIRS MEDICAL CENTER**, 2360 East Pershing Boulevard, Zip 82001–5392; tel. 307/778–7550, (Nonreporting) **A**1 3 **S** Department of Veterans Affairs, Perry Point, MD
Primary Contact: Paul L. Roberts, Director
CFO: Melvin Cranford, Chief Fiscal Services
CMO: Roger Johnson, M.D., Chief of Staff
CIO: Liz McCulloch, Chief Information Resource Management Systems
CHR: Ron Lester, Chief Human Resources
Web address: www.cheyenne.va.gov/
Control: Veterans Affairs, Government, federal **Service**: General medical and surgical

| Staffed Beds: 61 |

CODY—Park County

★ **WEST PARK HOSPITAL (531312)**, 707 Sheridan Avenue, Zip 82414–3409; tel. 307/527–7501, (Total facility includes 87 beds in nursing home–type unit) **A**10 18 **F**3 4 5 6 7 11 13 15 18 28 29 30 31 34 35 37 38 40 43 45 46 50 54 56 57 59 62 63 64 65 68 70 74 75 76 77 78 79 81 84 85 86 87 93 97 99 100 102 103 104 107 108 110 111 115 119 120 124 126 127 128 130 131 132 133 135 143 144 145 146 147 148 149 151 **P**6 **S** QHR, Brentwood, TN
Primary Contact: Douglas A. McMillan, Administrator and Chief Executive Officer
CFO: Patrick G McConnell, Chief Financial Officer
CMO: Gary Hart, M.D., Chief Medical Officer
CHR: Dick Smith, Director Human Resources
Web address: www.westparkhospital.org
Control: Hospital district or authority, Government, nonfederal **Service**: General medical and surgical

| Staffed Beds: 112 Admissions: 1702 Census: 90 Outpatient Visits: 94692 Births: 235 Total Expense ($000): 93844 Payroll Expense ($000): 36304 Personnel: 545 |

DOUGLAS—Converse County

★ **MEMORIAL HOSPITAL OF CONVERSE COUNTY (531302)**, 111 South Fifth Street, Zip 82633–2434, Mailing Address: P.O. Box 1450, Zip 82633–1450; tel. 307/358–2122, **A**10 18 **F**3 7 8 13 15 28 29 30 32 34 35 40 43 45 46 50 57 59 64 65 70 74 75 76 79 81 82 85 86 87 89 94 97 107 109 110 111 115 118 119 126 127 128 129 130 131 133 135 143 144 146 147 148 149 154 **P**6
Primary Contact: Ryan K. Smith, Chief Executive Officer
COO: Karl Edward Hertz, Assistant Administrator
CFO: Curtis R. Dugger, Chief Financial Officer
CMO: James Morgan, M.D., Chief Medical Officer
CIO: Dave Patterson, Chief Information Officer
CHR: Linda York, Director Human Resource
CNO: Cristy Dicklich-Cobb, Chief Nursing Officer
Web address: www.conversehospital.com
Control: County, Government, nonfederal **Service**: General medical and surgical

| Staffed Beds: 25 Admissions: 762 Census: 8 Outpatient Visits: 41887 Births: 151 Total Expense ($000): 52928 Payroll Expense ($000): 27613 Personnel: 306 |

EVANSTON—Uinta County

⊞ **EVANSTON REGIONAL HOSPITAL (530032)**, 190 Arrowhead Drive, Zip 82930–9266; tel. 307/789–3636, **A**1 10 20 **F**3 11 13 15 29 34 35 40 43 45 48 60 64 65 70 74 75 76 77 79 81 82 85 86 87 89 93 97 107 108 111 115 119 127 128 129 131 133 146 147 148 149 **P**6 **S** Quorum Health, Brentwood, TN
Primary Contact: Jeremy Davis, Chief Executive Officer
CHR: Joshua Jones, Director Human Resources
CNO: Cheri Willard, R.N., Chief Nursing Officer
Web address: www.evanstonregionalhospital.com
Control: Corporation, Investor–owned (for–profit) **Service**: General medical and surgical

| Staffed Beds: 42 Admissions: 683 Census: 4 Outpatient Visits: 21692 Births: 169 Total Expense ($000): 28640 Payroll Expense ($000): 12458 Personnel: 186 |

WYOMING STATE HOSPITAL (534001), 830 Highway 150 South, Zip 82931–5341, Mailing Address: P.O. Box 177, Zip 82931–0177; tel. 307/789–3464, **A**10 **F**29 30 39 53 57 61 74 98 154
Primary Contact: Rich Dunkley, Administrator
CFO: Paul Mullenax, Business Manager
CIO: Steve Baldwin, Manager Information Technology
Web address: www.health.wyo.gov/statehospital/index.html
Control: State, Government, nonfederal **Service**: Psychiatric

| Staffed Beds: 103 Admissions: 260 Census: 78 Births: 0 |

GILLETTE—Campbell County

★ ⇧ **CAMPBELL COUNTY HEALTH (530002)**, 501 South Burma Avenue, Zip 82716–3426, Mailing Address: P.O. Box 3011, Zip 82717–3011; tel. 307/682–8811, (Total facility includes 140 beds in nursing home–type unit) **A**10 20 21 **F**3 5 6 7 8 11 13 15 18 20 22 26 28 29 30 31 34 35 38 40 43 45 50 51 53 54 56 59 60 62 63 64 65 66 68 70 71 73 74 75 76 77 78 79 81 82 84 85 86 87 91 93 94 96 97 98 99 100 101 102 103 104 107 108 109 110 111 114 115 116 118 119 120 121 125 129 130 131 132 133 134 135 143 144 146 147 148 149 152 153 154 **P**6
Primary Contact: Andy Fitzgerald, Chief Executive Officer
CFO: Dalton Huber, Chief Financial Officer
CIO: Chris Harrison, Manager Information Systems
CHR: John A Fitch, Vice President Human Resources
CNO: Deb L Tonn, Vice President Patient Care
Web address: www.ccmh.net
Control: Hospital district or authority, Government, nonfederal **Service**: General medical and surgical

| Staffed Beds: 195 Admissions: 2353 Census: 152 Outpatient Visits: 182060 Births: 679 Total Expense ($000): 177766 Payroll Expense ($000): 81342 Personnel: 1098 |

JACKSON—Teton County

⊞ **ST. JOHN'S MEDICAL CENTER AND LIVING CENTER (530015)**, 625 East Broadway Street, Zip 83001–8642, Mailing Address: P.O. Box 428, Zip 83001–0428; tel. 307/733–3636, (Total facility includes 60 beds in nursing home–type unit) **A**1 5 10 20 **F**3 10 11 13 15 18 26 28 29 30 31 32 34 35 37 38 39 41 43 45 46 47 48 49 50 51 53 54 57 59 62 63 64 65 66 67 68 70 75 76 77 78 79 81 82 83 84 85 86 87 92 93 94 107 108 110 111 114 115 119 125 126 127 129 130 132 133 135 143 144 145 146 147 148 149 150 152 154
Primary Contact: Paul Beaupre', M.D., Chief Executive Officer
COO: Gary Tauner, Chief Operating Officer
CFO: John Kren, Chief Financial Officer
CIO: Lance Spranger, Chief Information Officer
CNO: Lynn Kirman, R.N., Chief Nursing Officer
Web address: www.tetonhospital.org
Control: Hospital district or authority, Government, nonfederal **Service**: General medical and surgical

| Staffed Beds: 108 Admissions: 1981 Census: 61 Outpatient Visits: 83275 Births: 453 Total Expense ($000): 107872 Payroll Expense ($000): 45628 Personnel: 637 |

KEMMERER—Lincoln County

★ **SOUTH LINCOLN MEDICAL CENTER (531315)**, 711 Onyx Street, Zip 83101–3214; tel. 307/877–4401, (Nonreporting) **A**10 18
Primary Contact: Kristin Housley, Co–Interim Chief Executive Officer
CFO: Curtis Nielson, Chief Financial Officer
CMO: G Christopher Krell, M.D., Chief of Staff
CIO: Kristin Housley, Chief Information Officer
CNO: Kathi Parks, Director of Nursing
Web address: www.southlincolnmedical.com
Control: Hospital district or authority, Government, nonfederal **Service**: General medical and surgical

| Staffed Beds: 38 |

LARAMIE—Albany County

⊞ **IVINSON MEMORIAL HOSPITAL (530025)**, 255 North 30th Street, Zip 82072–5140; tel. 307/742–2141, (Total facility includes 10 beds in nursing home–type unit) **A**1 10 20 **F**3 8 11 13 15 28 29 30 31 32 34 35 38 40 41 43 45 46 51 56 57 59 60 64 65 68 70 75 76 77 78 79 81 87 89 93 97 98 99 100 105 107 108 110 111 115 119 126 128 129 130 132 133 135 146 147 148 149 **P**6
Primary Contact: Doug Faus, FACHE, Chief Executive Officer
COO: Holly Zajic, Chief Operating Officer
CFO: James G Bands IV Chief Financial Officer
CMO: John Ullrich, M.D., Chief of Staff
CIO: Brandon Lewis, Director of Information Technology
CHR: Kayla Parry, Manager Human Resources
CNO: Nicole Roonery, Chief Nursing Officer
Web address: www.ivinsonhospital.org
Control: Other not–for–profit (including NFP Corporation) **Service**: General medical and surgical

| Staffed Beds: 99 Admissions: 2054 Census: 20 Outpatient Visits: 58038 Births: 399 Total Expense ($000): 77133 Payroll Expense ($000): 29465 Personnel: 465 |

WY

LOVELL—Big Horn County

★ **NORTH BIG HORN HOSPITAL DISTRICT (531309)**, 1115 Lane 12,
Zip 82431–9537; tel. 307/548–5200, (Nonreporting) **A**10 18
Primary Contact: Rick Schroeder, Chief Executive Officer
CFO: Lori Smith, Chief Financial Officer
CMO: Richard Jay, D.O., Chief of Staff
CIO: Lisa Strom, Director Information Systems
CHR: Barbara Shumway, Director Human Resources
CNO: Tina Toner, Director of Nursing
Web address: www.nbhh.com
Control: Hospital district or authority, Government, nonfederal **Service**: General medical and surgical

Staffed Beds: 100

LUSK—Niobrara County

★ **NIOBRARA HEALTH AND LIFE CENTER (531314)**, 921 Ballencee Avenue,
Zip 82225, Mailing Address: P.O. Box 780, Zip 82225–0780; tel. 307/334–4000,
(Nonreporting) **A**10 18
Primary Contact: Nathan Hough, Chief Executive Officer
Web address: www.niobrarahospital.com
Control: Hospital district or authority, Government, nonfederal **Service**: General medical and surgical

Staffed Beds: 24

NEWCASTLE—Weston County

★ **WESTON COUNTY HEALTH SERVICES (531303)**, 1124 Washington Boulevard,
Zip 82701–2972; tel. 307/746–4491, (Total facility includes 54 beds in nursing home–type unit) **A**10 18 **F**3 28 29 35 40 41 43 50 57 59 62 64 77 93 107 114 119 129 130 135 148 **S** Regional Health, Rapid City, SD
Primary Contact: Maureen K. Cadwell, Chief Executive Officer
CFO: Lynn Moller, Chief Financial Officer
CMO: Chuck Franklin, M.D., Chief Medical Staff
CIO: Terri Frye, Information Technology Officer
CHR: Julie A Sindlinger, Director of Human Resources
Web address: www.wchs–wy.org
Control: Hospital district or authority, Government, nonfederal **Service**: General medical and surgical

Staffed Beds: 66 Admissions: 92 Census: 57 Outpatient Visits: 13505
Births: 0 Total Expense ($000): 17941 Payroll Expense ($000): 7736
Personnel: 141

POWELL—Park County

★ **POWELL VALLEY HEALTHCARE (531310)**, 777 Avenue 'H', Zip 82435–2296;
tel. 307/754–2267, (Nonreporting) **A**10 18
Primary Contact: Terry Odom, Chief Executive Officer
CFO: Mike Long, Chief Financial Officer
CMO: Valerie Lengfelder, M.D., Chief of Staff
CIO: Joshua Baxter, Director, Information Systems
CHR: Cassie Tinsley, Director, Human Resources
CNO: Arleen Campeau, R.N., Vice President of Patient Care Services, Chief Nursing Officer
Web address: www.pvhc.org
Control: Other not–for–profit (including NFP Corporation) **Service**: General medical and surgical

Staffed Beds: 125

RAWLINS—Carbon County

★ **MEMORIAL HOSPITAL OF CARBON COUNTY (531316)**, 2221 West Elm Street, Zip 82301–5108, Mailing Address: P.O. Box 460, Zip 82301–0460;
tel. 307/324–2221, (Nonreporting) **A**10 18 **S** QHR, Brentwood, TN
Primary Contact: Dana Barnett, Chief Executive Officer
CFO: David Pike, Interim Chief Financial Officer
CMO: David Cesko, M.D., Chief of Staff
CIO: Toby Schaef, Director Information Technology
CNO: Amber Green, R.N., Chief Clinical Officer
Web address: www.imhcc.com
Control: County, Government, nonfederal **Service**: General medical and surgical

Staffed Beds: 25

RIVERTON—Fremont County

⊞ **SAGEWEST HEALTH CARE AT RIVERTON (530008)**, 2100 West Sunset Drive, Zip 82501–2274; tel. 307/856–4161, (Includes SAGEWEST HEALTH CARE AT LANDER, 1320 Bishop Randall Drive, Lander, WY, Zip 82520–3996; tel. 307/332–4420; Stephen M Erixon, Chief Executive Officer) **A**1 10 20 **F**3 11 12 13 15 28 29 34 35 39 40 43 45 50 57 59 68 70 74 75 76 77 79 81 82 85 87 93 97 98 103 106 107 108 110 111 114 115 119 129 130 131 132 146 147 148 149 **P**7 **S** LifePoint Health, Brentwood, TN
Primary Contact: Robert Alan. Daugherty, Chief Executive Officer
COO: Derrick Brumfield, Chief Operating Officer
CFO: Jennifer Hamilton, Chief Financial Officer
CMO: Cielette Karn, M.D., Chief of Staff
CIO: Linda Tice, Director Information Systems
CHR: Dawn Nelson, Director Human Resources
CNO: Vickie Bessey, MSN, R.N., Chief Nursing Officer
Web address: www.sagewesthealthcare.com
Control: Corporation, Investor–owned (for–profit) **Service**: General medical and surgical

Staffed Beds: 71 Admissions: 2663 Census: 26 Outpatient Visits: 51266
Births: 443 Total Expense ($000): 51644 Payroll Expense ($000): 21392
Personnel: 259

ROCK SPRINGS—Sweetwater County

ASPEN MOUNTAIN MEDICAL CENTER (530035), 4401 College Drive,
Zip 82901–3507; tel. 307/352–8900, (Nonreporting)
Primary Contact: Steve Perry, Chief Executive Officer
Web address: www.aspenmountainmc.com
Control: Partnership, Investor–owned (for–profit) **Service**: General medical and surgical

Staffed Beds: 16

⊞ **MEMORIAL HOSPITAL OF SWEETWATER COUNTY (530011)**, 1200 College Drive, Zip 82901–5868, Mailing Address: P.O. Box 1359, Zip 82902–1359;
tel. 307/362–3711, **A**1 10 20 **F**3 11 15 28 29 30 31 34 35 40 43 48 57 59 60 64 68 70 75 76 77 78 79 81 82 87 93 96 97 107 110 111 114 115 116 118 119 120 121 122 123 129 130 131 132 135 146 147 148 154 **P**6
Primary Contact: Irene Richardson, Chief Executive Officer
COO: Mandeep Gill, Chief Operating Officer
CFO: Tami Love, Chief Financial Officer
CMO: Sigsbee Duck, M.D., President, Medical Staff
CHR: Amber Fisk, Director Human Resources
CNO: Kallie Mikkelsen, Vice President Nursing
Web address: www.sweetwatermemorial.com/default.aspx
Control: County, Government, nonfederal **Service**: General medical and surgical

Staffed Beds: 58 Admissions: 1975 Census: 17 Outpatient Visits: 160181
Births: 512 Total Expense ($000): 95274 Payroll Expense ($000): 41500
Personnel: 475

SHERIDAN—Sheridan County

⊞ **SHERIDAN MEMORIAL HOSPITAL (530006)**, 1401 West Fifth Street,
Zip 82801–2799; tel. 307/672–1000, (Nonreporting) **A**1 10 20
Primary Contact: Michael McCafferty, Chief Executive Officer
CMO: John Addlesperger, D.O., Chief Medical Officer
CIO: Nyle Morgan, Chief Information Officer
CHR: Len Gross, Chief Human Resources Officer
Web address: www.sheridanhospital.org
Control: County, Government, nonfederal **Service**: General medical and surgical

Staffed Beds: 88

⊞ **SHERIDAN VETERANS AFFAIRS MEDICAL CENTER**, 1898 Fort Road,
Zip 82801–8320; tel. 307/672–3473, (Nonreporting) **A**1 **S** Department of Veterans Affairs, Perry Point, MD
Primary Contact: Pamela Crowell, Director
COO: Chandra Lake, Associate Director
CFO: Donna Fuerstenberg, Fiscal Chief
CMO: Wendell Robison, M.D., Chief of Staff
CIO: Anthony Giljum, Chief Information Officer
CHR: James Hardin, Human Resources Officer
Web address: www.sheridan.va.gov/
Control: Veterans Affairs, Government, federal **Service**: Psychiatric

Staffed Beds: 145

Hospital, Medicare Provider Number, Address, Telephone, Approval, Facility, and Physician Codes, Health Care System

★ American Hospital Association (AHA) membership
☐ The Joint Commission accreditation
○ Healthcare Facilities Accreditation Program
◇ DNV Healthcare Inc. accreditation
⇑ Center for Improvement in Healthcare Quality Accreditation
△ Commission on Accreditation of Rehabilitation Facilities (CARF) accreditation

SUNDANCE—Crook County

★ **CROOK COUNTY MEDICAL SERVICES DISTRICT (531311)**, 713 Oak Street, Zip 82729, Mailing Address: P.O. Box 517, Zip 82729–0517; tel. 307/283–3501, **A**10 18 **F**7 40 41 44 57 59 64 65 68 75 89 107 111 114 119 127 128 130 133 143 146 148 149 150 **S** Regional Health, Rapid City, SD
Primary Contact: Nathan Hough, Chief Executive Officer
CFO: Betty Meyers, Chief Financial Officer
CMO: Jeremi Villano, M.D., Chief of Staff
CHR: Patricia Feist, Manager Human Resources
Web address: www.ccmsd.org/
Control: Hospital district or authority, Government, nonfederal **Service**: Acute long–term care hospital

Staffed Beds: 16 **Admissions**: 4 **Census**: 1 **Outpatient Visits**: 3403
Births: 0 **Total Expense ($000)**: 6043 **Payroll Expense ($000)**: 4170
Personnel: 114

THERMOPOLIS—Hot Springs County

★ **HOT SPRINGS COUNTY MEMORIAL HOSPITAL (531304)**, 150 East Arapahoe Street, Zip 82443–2498; tel. 307/864–3121, **A**10 18 **F**3 11 13 15 28 29 31 34 35 40 43 45 50 57 59 64 68 75 76 81 82 85 89 97 107 108 110 111 115 119 127 130 133 135 145 146 148 **S** HealthTech Management Services, Brentwood, TN
Primary Contact: Margie Molitor, FACHE, R.N., Chief Executive Officer
CFO: Shelly Larson, Chief Financial Officer
CHR: Patti Jeunehomme, Director Human Resources
CNO: Sarah Aliff, Ph.D., Chief Nursing Officer
Web address: www.hscmh.org
Control: Hospital district or authority, Government, nonfederal **Service**: General medical and surgical

Staffed Beds: 25 **Admissions**: 266 **Census**: 4 **Outpatient Visits**: 12504
Births: 66 **Total Expense ($000)**: 16407 **Payroll Expense ($000)**: 5389
Personnel: 88

TORRINGTON—Goshen County

★ **COMMUNITY HOSPITAL (531307)**, 2000 Campbell Drive, Zip 82240–1597; tel. 307/532–4181, **A**10 18 **F**15 18 40 43 70 76 89 **S** Banner Health, Gilbert, AZ
Primary Contact: Shelby Olind, Interim Chief Executive Officer
CMO: Bonnie Randolph, M.D., Chief of Staff
CIO: Rod Miller, Chief Information Technology
Web address: www.bannerhealth.com/Locations/Wyoming/Community+Hospital/
Control: Other not–for–profit (including NFP Corporation) **Service**: General medical and surgical

Staffed Beds: 20 **Admissions**: 550 **Census**: 6 **Outpatient Visits**: 16974
Births: 80 **Total Expense ($000)**: 26086 **Payroll Expense ($000)**: 10511
Personnel: 185

WHEATLAND—Platte County

⊞ **PLATTE COUNTY MEMORIAL HOSPITAL (531305)**, 201 14th Street, Zip 82201–3201, Mailing Address: P.O. Box 848, Zip 82201–0848; tel. 307/322–3636, **A**1 10 18 **F**3 7 76 **S** Banner Health, Gilbert, AZ
Primary Contact: Shelby Olind, Chief Executive Officer
CFO: James Cussins, Chief Financial Officer
CMO: Willard Woods, M.D., Chief Medical Officer
CIO: Robin May, Director Information Systems
CHR: Sandy Dugger, Chief Human Resources Officer
Web address: www.bannerhealth.com/Locations/Wyoming/Platte+County+Memorial+Hospital
Control: Other not–for–profit (including NFP Corporation) **Service**: General medical and surgical

Staffed Beds: 25 **Admissions**: 403 **Census**: 4 **Outpatient Visits**: 13235
Births: 35 **Total Expense ($000)**: 22255 **Payroll Expense ($000)**: 9746
Personnel: 162

WORLAND—Washakie County

★ **WASHAKIE MEDICAL CENTER (531306)**, 400 South 15th Street, Zip 82401–3531, Mailing Address: P.O. Box 700, Zip 82401–0700; tel. 307/347–3221, **A**10 18 **F**3 8 11 13 15 29 31 37 39 40 43 46 53 56 57 59 64 65 68 70 75 76 78 81 85 93 107 109 110 111 115 119 133 146 148 149 154 **S** Banner Health, Gilbert, AZ
Primary Contact: Jay Stallings, Chief Executive Officer
CFO: Jennifer Montgomery, Chief Financial Officer
CMO: Ryan Clifford, M.D., Chief of Staff
CHR: Jerry Clipp, Manager Human Resources
Web address: www.washakiemedicalcenter.com
Control: Other not–for–profit (including NFP Corporation) **Service**: General medical and surgical

Staffed Beds: 18 **Admissions**: 417 **Census**: 4 **Births**: 34 **Total Expense ($000)**: 24490 **Payroll Expense ($000)**: 8353 **Personnel**: 101

AMERICAN SAMOA

PAGO PAGO—Washakie County

LYNDON B. JOHNSON TROPICAL MEDICAL CENTER (640001), Faga'alu Village, Zip 96799, Mailing Address: P.O. Box LBJ, Zip 96799; tel. 684/633–1222, **A**10 **F**7 15 29 30 39 40 44 45 46 50 59 60 66 68 70 72 75 76 77 79 81 82 87 89 93 98 100 101 102 104 105 106 107 110 114 115 119 130 133 144 146 148 153 154 **P**6
Primary Contact: Taufete's John. Faumuina, Chief Executive Officer
Web address: www.asmca.org
Control: State, Government, nonfederal **Service:** General medical and surgical

Staffed Beds: 144 **Admissions:** 5762 **Census:** 77 **Outpatient Visits:** 113208 **Births:** 978 **Total Expense ($000):** 54019 **Payroll Expense ($000):** 24318 **Personnel:** 755

GUAM

AGANA—Guam County

⊠ **U.S. NAVAL HOSPITAL GUAM**, Building #50 Farenholt Avenue, Zip 96910, Mailing Address: PSC 490, Box 208, FPO, Zip 96540; tel. 671/344–9340, (Nonreporting) **A**1 **S** Bureau of Medicine and Surgery, Department of the Navy, Falls Church, VA
Primary Contact: Captain Daniel Cornwell, Command Officer
Web address: www.med.navy.mil/sites/usnhguam/Pages/default.aspx
Control: Navy, Government, federal **Service:** General medical and surgical

Staffed Beds: 55

DEDEDO—Guam County

★ **GUAM REGIONAL MEDICAL CITY (650003)**, 133 Route 3, Zip 96932, Mailing Address: P.O. Box 3830, Hagatna, Zip 96932; tel. 671/645–5500, (Nonreporting) **A**10
Primary Contact: Gloria Long, Chief Operating Officer
Web address: www.grmc.gu/
Control: Corporation, Investor–owned (for–profit) **Service:** General medical and surgical

Staffed Beds: 130

TAMUNING—Guam County

☐ **GUAM MEMORIAL HOSPITAL AUTHORITY (650001)**, 850 Governor Carlos G Camacho Road, Zip 96913; tel. 671/647–2108, (Nonreporting) **A**1 10
Primary Contact: Joseph P. Verga, FACHE, Chief Executive Officer
CFO: Alan Ulrich, Chief Financial Officer
CMO: James J Stadler, M.D., Associate Administrator Medical Services
CIO: Vince Quichocho, Manager Information Systems
CHR: Elizabeth Claros, Administrator Personnel Services
Web address: www.gmha.org
Control: Hospital district or authority, Government, nonfederal **Service:** General medical and surgical

Staffed Beds: 104

MARSHALL ISLANDS

KWAJALEIN ISLAND—Guam County

KWAJALEIN HOSPITAL, US Army Kwajalein Atoll, Zip 96960, Mailing Address: Box 1702, APO, UNIT, Zip 96555–5000; tel. 805/355–2225, (Nonreporting) **S** Department of the Army, Office of the Surgeon General, Falls Church, VA
Primary Contact: Elaine McMahon, Administrator
Control: Army, Government, federal **Service:** General medical and surgical

Staffed Beds: 14

NORTHERN MARIANA ISLANDS

SAIPAN—Guam County

★ **COMMONWEALTH HEALTH CENTER (660001)**, Navy Hill Road, Zip 96950, Mailing Address: P.O. Box 500409, Zip 96950; tel. 670/234–8950, (Nonreporting) **A**10
Primary Contact: Esther L. Muna, FACHE, Chief Executive Officer
CFO: Priscilla Maratita Iakopo, Chief Financial Officer
CMO: John M Tudela, M.D., Director of Medical Affairs
CIO: Anthony Reyes, Information Technology Director
CHR: Clarinda Ngiraisui, Director, Human Resources
CNO: Leslie Camacho, R.N., Director of Nursing
Web address: www.chcc.gov.mp
Control: Corporation, Investor–owned (for–profit) **Service:** General medical and surgical

Staffed Beds: 86

PUERTO RICO

AGUADILLA—Aguadilla County

⊠ **HOSPITAL BUEN SAMARITANO (400079)**, Carr #2 Km 141–1 Ave Severiano Cuevas, Zip 603, Mailing Address: P.O. Box 4055, Zip 00605–4055; tel. 787/658–0000, **A**1 5 10 **F**3 13 14 15 29 30 34 40 41 45 50 57 59 65 70 74 75 76 77 78 79 81 82 87 89 107 111 114 119 130 146 148 149
Primary Contact: Marilyn Morales, Chief Executive Officer
CFO: Edwin Orama Acevedo, Financial Supervisor
CMO: Arturo Cedeno Llorens, M.D., Medical Director
CHR: Jose Garcia Rivera, Director Human Resources
CNO: Eneida Alicea Perez, Interim Nursing Director
Web address: www.hbspr.org
Control: Other not–for–profit (including NFP Corporation) **Service:** General medical and surgical

Staffed Beds: 138 **Admissions:** 4340 **Census:** 62 **Outpatient Visits:** 57566 **Births:** 18

AIBONITO—Aibonito County

⊠ **CENTRO DE SALUD CONDUCTUAL MENONITA–CIMA (404009)**, Carretera Estatal 14 Interior, Zip 705, Mailing Address: PO Box 871, Zip 705; tel. 787/714–2462, (Nonreporting) **A**1 5 10
Primary Contact: Pedro Melendez, Chief Executive Officer
Web address: www.menonitacima.org
Control: Other not–for–profit (including NFP Corporation) **Service:** Psychiatric

Staffed Beds: 20

Hospital, Medicare Provider Number, Address, Telephone, Approval, Facility, and Physician Codes, Health Care System

★ American Hospital Association (AHA) membership
☐ The Joint Commission accreditation
○ Healthcare Facilities Accreditation Program
◇ DNV Healthcare Inc. accreditation
⇑ Center for Improvement in Healthcare Quality Accreditation
△ Commission on Accreditation of Rehabilitation Facilities (CARF) accreditation

✠ **MENNONITE GENERAL HOSPITAL (400018)**, Calle Jose C Vasquez, Zip 705, Mailing Address: P.O. Box 372800, Cayey, Zip 00737-2800; tel. 787/535-1001, (Nonreporting) **A**1 10
Primary Contact: Pedro Melendez, Chief Executive Officer
COO: Marta R Mercado Suro, Chief Operating Officer
CFO: Jose E Solivan, Chief Financial Officer
CMO: Victor Hernandez Miranda, M.D., Chief of Staff
CIO: Daniza Morales, Manager Information System
CHR: Evelyn Padilla Ortiz, Director Human Resources
CNO: Gloria Mercado, Director of Nursing
Web address: www.hospitalmenonita.com
Control: Other not-for-profit (including NFP Corporation) **Service**: General medical and surgical

Staffed Beds: 143

ARECIBO—Arecibo County

★ **HOSPITAL METROPOLITANO DR. SUSONI (400117)**, Calle Palma #55, Zip 612, Mailing Address: P.O. Box 145200, Zip 614; tel. 787/650-1030, (Nonreporting) **A**10
Primary Contact: Yelitza Lucena, Executive Director
CFO: Francisco Silva, Financial Director
CMO: Ada S Miranda, M.D., Medical Director
CIO: Mayra Montano, Director Information Systems
CHR: Janira Hernandez, Coordinator Human Resources
CNO: Damaris Rios, Executive Nursing Director
Web address: www.metropavia.com/DrSusoni.cfm
Control: Corporation, Investor-owned (for-profit) **Service**: General medical and surgical

Staffed Beds: 134

✠ **HOSPITAL PAVIA ARECIBO (400087)**, 129 San Luis Avenue, Zip 612, Mailing Address: P.O. Box 659, Zip 613; tel. 787/650-7272, **A**1 10 **F**2 3 20 40 41 46 66 68 70 72 73 102 107 111 119 130
Primary Contact: Jose Luis Rodriguez Collazo, Executive Director
COO: Jamie Rivera, Chief Financial Officer
CFO: Agustin Gonzalez, Director Finance
CMO: Antoine Pavia, M.D., Medical Director
CIO: David Valle, Chief Information Officer
CHR: Yesenia Natal, Coordinator Human Resources
CNO: Iris Toledo, Chief Nursing Officer
Web address: www.cayetano@xsn.net
Control: City, Government, nonfederal **Service**: General medical and surgical

Staffed Beds: 184 **Admissions:** 7306 **Census:** 114 **Outpatient Visits:** 31247 **Births:** 452 **Total Expense ($000):** 53232 **Payroll Expense ($000):** 15049

BAYAMON—Bayamon County

★ **DOCTOR'S CENTER OF BAYAMON (400102)**, Extension Hermanas Davila, Zip 960, Mailing Address: P.O. Box 2957, Zip 960; tel. 787/622-5420, (Nonreporting) **A**10
Primary Contact: Maria Marte, Administrator
Web address: www.tuhospitalfamiliar.com
Control: Corporation, Investor-owned (for-profit) **Service**: General medical and surgical

Staffed Beds: 91

✠ **HOSPITAL HERMANOS MELENDEZ (400032)**, Route 2, KM 11-7, Zip 960, Mailing Address: P.O. Box 306, Zip 960; tel. 787/620-8181, (Includes PUERTO RICO CHILDREN'S HOSPITAL, P.O. Box 1999, Bayamon, PR, Zip 960; tel. 787/474-1378; Tania Conde, Administrator) (Nonreporting) **A**1 3 10
Primary Contact: Richard Machado, M.D., President and Chief Executive Officer
CFO: Luz D Medina, Controller
CMO: Norma Ortiz, M.D., Medical Director
CIO: Leticia Santana, Administrator Medical Records
Web address: www.hospitalhermanosmelendez.net
Control: Corporation, Investor-owned (for-profit) **Service**: General medical and surgical

Staffed Beds: 211

✠ **HOSPITAL SAN PABLO (400109)**, Calle Santa Cruz 70, Zip 00961-7020, Mailing Address: P.O. Box 236, Zip 00960-0236; tel. 787/740-4747, (Nonreporting) **A**1 3 5 10
Primary Contact: Claudia V. Guzman, Chief Executive Officer and Managing Director
Web address: www.sanpablo.com
Control: Corporation, Investor-owned (for-profit) **Service**: General medical and surgical

Staffed Beds: 431

✠ **HOSPITAL UNIVERSITARIO DR. RAMON RUIZ ARNAU (400105)**, Avenue Laurel #100, Santa Juanita, Zip 956; tel. 787/787-5151, (Nonreporting) **A**1 3 5 10 **S** Puerto Rico Department of Health, San Juan, PR
Primary Contact: Prudencio A. Laureano, Chief Executive Officer
CFO: Elsie Morales, Chief Financial Officer
CMO: Hector Cintron Principe, M.D., Director
CIO: Irma Duprey, Administrator Medical Records
CHR: Aurea De Leon, Chief Human Resources Officer
Web address: www.salud.gov.pr/Dept-de-Salud/Pages/Nuestros-Hospitales.aspx
Control: State, Government, nonfederal **Service**: General medical and surgical

Staffed Beds: 101

CABO ROJO—Cabo Rojo County

✠ **HOSPITAL PSIQUIATRICO METROPOLITANO (404007)**, 108 Munoz Rivera Street, Zip 00623-4060, Mailing Address: P.O. Box 910, Zip 00623-0910; tel. 787/851-2025, **A**1 10 **F**40 41 98 102 103 104 105
Primary Contact: Marco Reyes, Executive Director
Web address: www.metropavia.com/CaboRojo.cfm
Control: Corporation, Investor-owned (for-profit) **Service**: Psychiatric

Staffed Beds: 43 **Admissions:** 1233 **Census:** 19 **Births:** 0

CAGUAS—Caguas County

✠ **HIMA SAN PABLO CAGUAS (400120)**, Avenida Munoz Marin, Zip 726, Mailing Address: P.O. Box 4980, Zip 726; tel. 787/653-3434, (Nonreporting) **A**1 2 3 5 10
Primary Contact: Maria E. Jacobo Moreno, Administrator
CFO: Luis A Arroyo, Chief Financial Officer
CMO: Ivan E Del Toro, M.D., Medical Director
CIO: Giovanni Piereschi, Vice President Enterprise Information and Chief Information Officer
CHR: Elena Robinson, Chief Human Resources Officer
CNO: Elenia Berrios, Chief Nursing Officer
Web address: www.himasanpablo.com
Control: Partnership, Investor-owned (for-profit) **Service**: General medical and surgical

Staffed Beds: 415

✠ **HOSPITAL MENONITA DE CAGUAS (400104)**, P.O. Box 6660, Zip 00726-6660; tel. 787/653-0550, (Nonreporting) **A**1 5 10
Primary Contact: Pedro Melendez, Executive Director
Web address: www.sistemamenonita.com
Control: Other not-for-profit (including NFP Corporation) **Service**: General medical and surgical

Staffed Beds: 25

CAROLINA—Carolina County

✠ **HOSPITAL DE LA UNIVERSIDAD DE PUERTO RICO/DR. FEDERICO TRILLA (400112)**, 65th Infanteria, KM 8 3, Zip 984, Mailing Address: P.O. Box 6021, Zip 984; tel. 787/757-1800, (Nonreporting) **A**1 3 5 10
Primary Contact: Diraida Maldonado, Chief Executive Officer
COO: Diraida Maldonado, Chief Executive Officer
CFO: Yolanda Quinonez, Chief Financial Officer
CMO: Marina Roman, M.D., Medical Director
CIO: Francisco Perez, Manager Management Information Systems
CHR: Betzaida Jimenez, Director Human Resources
Web address: www.hospitalupr.org
Control: Corporation, Investor-owned (for-profit) **Service**: General medical and surgical

Staffed Beds: 250

CASTANER—Lares County

★ **CASTANER GENERAL HOSPITAL (400010)**, KM 64-2, Route 135, Zip 631, Mailing Address: P.O. Box 1003, Zip 631; tel. 787/829-5010, (Nonreporting) **A**5 10
Primary Contact: Domingo Monroig, Executive Director
COO: Agustin Ponce, Supervisor Maintenance
CFO: Guillermo Jimenez, Director Finance
CMO: Jose O Rodriguez, M.D., Medical Director
CIO: Domingo Monroig, Executive Director
CHR: Nydimar Salcedo, Chief Human Resources Officer
CNO: Margarita Rentas, R.N., Nursing Director
Web address: www.hospitalcastaner.com
Control: Other not-for-profit (including NFP Corporation) **Service**: General medical and surgical

Staffed Beds: 24

Many Facility Codes have changed. Please refer to the AHA Guide Code Chart.

CAYEY—Cayey County

☒ **HOSPITAL MENONITA DE CAYEY (400013)**, 4 H Mendoza Street, Zip 00736–3801, Mailing Address: P.O. Box 373130, Zip 00737–3130; tel. 787/263–1001, **A**1 5 10 **F**8 12 13 15 17 18 20 22 24 26 28 29 30 32 34 40 41 45 46 47 48 49 65 67 69 70 71 72 74 75 78 79 81 82 85 88 89 94 107 109 110 111 112 113 114 115 119 120 130 132 135 136 143 145 146
Primary Contact: Pedro Melendez, Chief Executive Director
COO: Leda Marta R Mercado, Chief Operating Officer
CFO: Jose E Solivan, Chief Financial Officer
CMO: Luis J Rodriquez Saenz, M.D., Medical Director
CIO: Daniza Morales, Chief Information Officer
CHR: Evelyn Padilla Ortiz, Director Human Resources
Web address: www.hospitalmenonita.com
Control: Other not–for–profit (including NFP Corporation) **Service**: General medical and surgical

Staffed Beds: 242 Admissions: 9794 **Census:** 161 **Outpatient Visits:** 107381 **Births:** 1011 **Total Expense ($000):** 94240 **Payroll Expense ($000):** 27087 **Personnel:** 964

CIDRA—Cidra County

☒ **FIRST HOSPITAL PANAMERICANO (404004)**, State Road 787 KM 1 5, Zip 739, Mailing Address: P.O. Box 1400, Zip 739; tel. 787/739–5555, (Nonreporting) **A**1 3 5 10 **S** Universal Health Services, Inc., King of Prussia, PA
Primary Contact: Astro Munoz, Executive Director
COO: Tim McCarthy, President Puerto Rico Division
CFO: Arthur Fernandez, Chief Financial Officer
CMO: Arlene Martinez–Nieto, M.D., Chief Medical Officer
CIO: Tomas Rodriguez, Chief Information Technology Officer
CHR: Shirley Ayala, Director Human Resources
Web address: www.hospitalpanamericano.com
Control: Corporation, Investor–owned (for–profit) **Service**: Psychiatric

Staffed Beds: 153

COTO LAUREL—Ponce County

★ **HOSPITAL SAN CRISTOBAL (400113)**, 506 Carr Road, Zip 780; tel. 787/848–2100, (Nonreporting) **A**3 5 10
Primary Contact: Pedro L. Benetti–Loyola, Administrator
COO: Pedro L Benetti–Loyola, Senior Executive and Vice President
CFO: Marian Collazo, Director Finance
CMO: Ramon Rodriguez Rivas, M.D., Medical Director
CIO: Ramon Acevedo, Supervisor Information Systems
CHR: Candie Rodriguez, Director Human Resources
Web address: www.hospitalsancristobal.com
Control: Corporation, Investor–owned (for–profit) **Service**: Other specialty treatment

Staffed Beds: 103

FAJARDO—Fajardo County

★ **CARIBBEAN MEDICAL CENTER (400131)**, 151 Avenue Osvaldo Molina, Zip 00738–4013, Mailing Address: Call Box 70006, Zip 00738–7006; tel. 787/801–0081, (Nonreporting) **A**10
Primary Contact: Ana Oliveras Laguna, Administrator
CMO: Miguel Rodriguez, Medical Director
Web address: www.caribbeanmedicalcenter.com
Control: Other not–for–profit (including NFP Corporation) **Service**: General medical and surgical

Staffed Beds: 39

☒ **HOSPITAL SAN PABLO DEL ESTE (400125)**, Avenida General Valero, 404, Zip 738, Mailing Address: P.O. Box 1028, Zip 00738–1028; tel. 787/863–0505, (Nonreporting) **A**1 10
Primary Contact: Venus V. Ramirez, Executive Director
CFO: Luis A Arroyo, Chief Financial Officer
CMO: Manuel Navas, M.D., Medical Director
CHR: Vilma Rodriguez, Director Human Resources
Web address: www.sanpablo.com
Control: Corporation, Investor–owned (for–profit) **Service**: General medical and surgical

Staffed Beds: 145

GUAYAMA—Guayama County

☒ **HOSPITAL EPISCOPAL SAN LUCAS GUAYAMA (400048)**, Avenue Pedro Albizu Campos, Zip 784, Mailing Address: PO Box 10011, Zip 00785–1006; tel. 787/864–4300, (Nonreporting) **A**1 3 5 10
Primary Contact: Elyonel Ponton, Executive Director
COO: Arnaldo Rodriguez Sanchez, M.D., Chief Operating Officer
CFO: Rosemary De La Cruz, Chief Financial Officer
CMO: Gerson Jimenez, M.D., Medical Director
CHR: Ivette Lacot, Director Human Resources
Web address: www.ssepr.com
Control: Church operated, Nongovernment, not–for–profit **Service**: General medical and surgical

Staffed Beds: 115

GUAYNABO—Guaynabo County

PROFESSIONAL HOSPITAL GUAYNABO (400122), Carretera 199 Km 1.2 Avenue, Zip 969, Mailing Address: PO Box 1609, Zip 970; tel. 787/708–6560, (Nonreporting) **A**5 10
Primary Contact: Leonardo Valentin, Chief Executive Officer
Web address: www.professionalhospital.com
Control: Other not–for–profit (including NFP Corporation) **Service**: Psychiatric

Staffed Beds: 54

HATO REY—San Juan County

☒ **I. GONZALEZ MARTINEZ ONCOLOGIC HOSPITAL (400012)**, Puerto Rico Medical Center, Zip 935, Mailing Address: P.O. Box 191811, Zip 00919–1811; tel. 787/765–2382, (Nonreporting) **A**1 2 3 5 10
Primary Contact: Jorge De Jesus, Executive Director
COO: Felix Ortiz Baez, Administrator
CFO: Yolanda Quinones, Director Finance
CMO: Carlos Chevere, M.D., Medical Director
CHR: Luz Maria Hernandez, Director Human Resources
Control: Other not–for–profit (including NFP Corporation) **Service**: Cancer

Staffed Beds: 57

HUMACAO—Humacao County

HOSPITAL DR. DOMINGUEZ See Hospital Oriente

☒ **HOSPITAL HIMA DE HUMACAO (400005)**, 3 Font Martelo Street, Zip 00791–3342, Mailing Address: P.O. Box 639, Zip 00792–0639; tel. 787/656–2424, (Nonreporting) **A**1 10
Primary Contact: Aixa Irizarry, Executive Director
COO: Carlos M Pineiro, President
CFO: Luis A Arroyo, Chief Financial Officer
CMO: Francisco R. Carballo, M.D., Medical Director
CIO: Giovanni Piereschi, Vice President Management Information Systems
CHR: Iris Abreu, Supervisor Human Resources
Web address: www.himasanpablo.com
Control: Corporation, Investor–owned (for–profit) **Service**: General medical and surgical

Staffed Beds: 64

★ **HOSPITAL ORIENTE (400011)**, 300 Font Martelo Street, Zip 00791–3230, Mailing Address: P.O. Box 699, Zip 00792–0699; tel. 787/852–0505, (Nonreporting) **A**10
Primary Contact: Efrain Pinero, Administrator
CFO: Ivonne Rivera, Director Finance
CMO: Carmelo Herrero, M.D., Medical Director
CHR: Ivonne Lopez, Director Human Resources
Control: Corporation, Investor–owned (for–profit) **Service**: General medical and surgical

Staffed Beds: 60

Hospital, Medicare Provider Number, Address, Telephone, Approval, Facility, and Physician Codes, Health Care System

★ American Hospital Association (AHA) membership ○ Healthcare Facilities Accreditation Program ⇑ Center for Improvement in Healthcare Quality Accreditation
☐ The Joint Commission accreditation ◇ DNV Healthcare Inc. accreditation △ Commission on Accreditation of Rehabilitation Facilities (CARF) accreditation

★ **RYDER MEMORIAL HOSPITAL (400007)**, 355 Font Martelo Street, Zip 00791–3249, Mailing Address: P.O. Box 859, Zip 00792–0859; tel. 787/852–0768, (Nonreporting) **A**5 10
Primary Contact: Jose R. Feliciano, Chief Executive Officer
CFO: Jose O Ortiz, Chief Financial Officer
CMO: Raul Ramos Pereira, M.D., Medical Director
CIO: Joseph V Cruz, Chief Information Officer
CHR: Maria Figueroa, Director Human Resources
CNO: Aurelis Burgus, Nursing Director
Web address: www.hryder@prtc.net
Control: Other not–for–profit (including NFP Corporation) **Service:** General medical and surgical

Staffed Beds: 165

MANATI—Manati County

⊞ **DOCTORS CENTER (400118)**, KM 47–7, Zip 674, Mailing Address: P.O. Box 30532, Zip 674; tel. 787/854–3322, (Nonreporting) **A**1 10
Primary Contact: Belinda L. Toro Palacios, Executive Director
Web address: www.tuhospitalfamiliar.com
Control: Corporation, Investor–owned (for–profit) **Service:** General medical and surgical

Staffed Beds: 250

★ **HEALTHSOUTH HOSPITAL OF MANATI (403026)**, Carretera 2, Kilometro 47 7, Zip 674; tel. 787/621–3800, (Nonreporting) **A**10 **S** Encompass Health Corporation, Birmingham, AL
Primary Contact: Enid Y. Gonzalez, Chief Executive Officer
CFO: Jesus M Corazon, Controller
CMO: Jamie L Marrero, M.D., Medical Director
CHR: Erika Landrau, Director Human Resources
CNO: Evelyn Diaz, R.N., Chief Nursing Officer
Web address: www.healthsouth.com
Control: Corporation, Investor–owned (for–profit) **Service:** Rehabilitation

Staffed Beds: 40

⊞ **HOSPITAL MANATI MEDICAL CENTER (400114)**, Calle Hernandez, Carrion 668, Zip 674, Mailing Address: P.O. Box 1142, Zip 00674–1142; tel. 787/621–3700, (Nonreporting) **A**1 3 5 10
Primary Contact: Jose S. Rosado, Executive Director
CFO: Noriselle Rivera–Pol, Vice President Finance
CMO: Luis R Rosa–Toledo, M.D., Medical Director
CIO: Alberto Medina, Information Technology Senior Consultant
CHR: Nilda Paravisini, Director Human Resources
Web address: www.manatimedical.com
Control: Corporation, Investor–owned (for–profit) **Service:** General medical and surgical

Staffed Beds: 235

MAYAGUEZ—Mayaguez County

⊞ **BELLA VISTA HOSPITAL (400014)**, State Road 349, Zip 680, Mailing Address: P.O. Box 1750, Zip 681; tel. 787/834–6000, (Nonreporting) **A**1 3 5 10
Primary Contact: Luis Rivera Maldonado, Executive Director
CFO: Enrique Rivera, Chief Financial Officer
CMO: Miguel Cruz, M.D., Medical Director
CHR: Benjamin Astacio, Director Human Resources
Web address: www.bvhpr.org
Control: Church operated, Nongovernment, not–for–profit **Service:** General medical and surgical

Staffed Beds: 157

⊞ **DR. RAMON E. BETANCES HOSPITAL–MAYAGUEZ MEDICAL CENTER BRANCH (400103)**, 410 Hostos Avenue, Zip 00680–1501, Mailing Address: P.O. Box 600, Zip 00681–0600; tel. 787/652–9200, (Nonreporting) **A**1 3 5 10
Primary Contact: Idelfonso Vargas, Executive Director
CMO: Milton D Carrero, M.D., Medical Director
CHR: Betsmari Medina, Director Human Resources
Web address: www.mayaguezmedical.com
Control: State, Government, nonfederal **Service:** General medical and surgical

Staffed Beds: 144

★ **HOSPITAL PEREA (400123)**, 15 Basora Street, Zip 681, Mailing Address: P.O. Box 170, Zip 681; tel. 787/834–0101, (Nonreporting) **A**3 10 **S** United Medical Corporation, Windermere, FL
Primary Contact: Jorge I. Martinez, Executive Director
CFO: Joannie Garcia, CPA, Director Finance
CMO: Humberto Olivencia, M.D., Medical Director
Web address: www.paviahealth.com/perea_hospital.htm
Control: Corporation, Investor–owned (for–profit) **Service:** General medical and surgical

Staffed Beds: 103

★ **HOSPITAL SAN ANTONIO (018487)**, Calle Dr Ramon Emeterio Betances N #18, Zip 680, Mailing Address: PO Box 546, Zip 00681–0546; tel. 787/834–0050, (Nonreporting) **A**3 5
Primary Contact: Francisco Martinez, Executive Director
Web address: www.hsaipr.com/
Control: Other not–for–profit (including NFP Corporation) **Service:** General medical and surgical

Staffed Beds: 25

MOCA—Moca County

★ **HOSPITAL SAN CARLOS BORROMEO (400111)**, 550 Concepcion Vera Ayala, Zip 676, Mailing Address: PO Box 68, Zip 676; tel. 787/877–8000, (Nonreporting) **A**10
Primary Contact: Rosaida M. Crespo, Executive Director
COO: Rosaida M Crespo, Executive Director
CFO: Irma Cabrera, Finance Director
CMO: Erick Nieves, M.D., Medical Director
CIO: Juan Carlos Soto, Director Information Systems
CHR: Migdalia Ortiz, Director Human Resources
CNO: Luz M Velez, Director–Administration of Nursing Services
Web address: www.hscbpr.org
Control: Other not–for–profit (including NFP Corporation) **Service:** General medical and surgical

Staffed Beds: 106

PONCE—Ponce County

⊞ **DR. PILA'S HOSPITAL (400003)**, Avenida Las Americas, Zip 731, Mailing Address: P.O. Box 1910, Zip 00733–1910; tel. 787/848–5600, (Nonreporting) **A**1 5 10
Primary Contact: Rafael Alvarado, Chief Executive Officer
Web address: www.drpila.com
Control: Other not–for–profit (including NFP Corporation) **Service:** General medical and surgical

Staffed Beds: 143

⊞ **HOSPITAL DE DAMAS (400022)**, 2213 Ponce Bypass, Zip 717; tel. 787/840–8686, (Nonreporting) **A**1 3 5 10
Primary Contact: Maria Mercedes Torres. Bernal, Administrator
CFO: Julio Colon, Financial Director
CMO: Pedro Benitez, M.D., Medical Director
CIO: Bienvenido Ortiz, Coordinator Information Systems
CHR: Gilberto Cuevas, Director Human Resources
CNO: Sandra Dominicci, Nursing Director
Web address: www.hospitaldamas.com/
Control: Other not–for–profit (including NFP Corporation) **Service:** General medical and surgical

Staffed Beds: 251

HOSPITAL DE PSIQUIATRIA FORENSE, Road 14, Zip 731; tel. 787/844–0210, (Nonreporting)
Primary Contact: Nemuel O. Artiles, FACHE, Administrator
Web address: www.bestmentalhealthfacilities.com/hospital–psiquiatria–forenseponce–in–ponce–pr–731/
Control: State, Government, nonfederal **Service:** Psychiatric

Staffed Beds: 25

★ **INSPIRA PONCE (404008)**, Calle Guadalupe, #184, Piso2, Zip 730; tel. 787/709–4130, (Nonreporting) **A**10
Primary Contact: Alberto M. Varela, M.D., President
Web address: www.inspirapr.com
Control: Corporation, Investor–owned (for–profit) **Service:** Psychiatric

Staffed Beds: 30

⊞ **ST. LUKE'S EPISCOPAL HOSPITAL (400044)**, 917 Tito Castro Avenue, Zip 00731–4717, Mailing Address: P.O. Box 336810, Zip 00733–6810; tel. 787/844–2080, **A**1 3 5 10 **F**3 8 12 13 15 17 18 19 20 22 24 26 28 29 30 34 40 41 43 45 46 49 50 57 59 70 72 73 74 75 76 78 79 81 85 86 87 88 89 91 92 93 107 110 111 113 114 115 118 119 130 144 146 148
Primary Contact: Jose M. Torres, Executive Director
CFO: Carlos Valentin, Chief Financial Officer
CMO: Jesus Cruz Correa, Chief Medical Officer
CIO: Jose Abrams, Chief Information Officer
CHR: Hector Troche Garcin, Human Resources Director
CNO: Zoraida Vega, MSN, R.N., Chief Nursing Officer
Web address: www.sanlucaspr.com
Control: Church operated, Nongovernment, not–for–profit **Service:** General medical and surgical

Staffed Beds: 291 Admissions: 16019 Census: 238 Outpatient Visits: 41847 Births: 1673

Many Facility Codes have changed. Please refer to the AHA Guide Code Chart.

RIO PIEDRAS—San Juan County

✠ **UNIVERSITY PEDIATRIC HOSPITAL (403301)**, Barrio Monacenno, Carretera 22, Zip 935, Mailing Address: P.O. Box 191079, San Juan, Zip 00910–1070; tel. 787/777–3535, (Nonreporting) **A**1 3 5 10 **S** Puerto Rico Department of Health, San Juan, PR
Primary Contact: Gloria Hernandez, Executive Director
CMO: Myrna Quinones Feliciano, M.D., Medical Director
Web address: www.md.rcm.upr.edu/pediatrics/university_pediatric_hospital.php
Control: State, Government, nonfederal **Service:** Children's general medical and surgical

Staffed Beds: 145

SAN GERMAN—San German County

✠ **HOSPITAL DE LA CONCEPCION (400021)**, Carr 2, Km 173, Bo Cain Alto, Zip 00683–3920, Mailing Address: P.O. Box 285, Zip 00683–0285; tel. 787/892–1860, **A**1 3 5 10 **F**3 13 15 18 20 29 30 31 34 35 39 40 41 45 47 57 64 65 68 70 72 73 74 75 76 77 79 81 85 87 89 90 92 93 96 102 107 108 109 110 111 112 115 119 130 145 146 147 148 149
Primary Contact: Felicita Bonilla, Administrator
COO: Gustavo Almodovar, Executive Director
CFO: Lizmari Calderon, Director Finance
CMO: Ivan Acosta, M.D., Medical Director
CIO: Daniel Ferreira, Director Management Information Systems
CHR: Ada Bermudez, Director Human Resources
CNO: Amanda Caraballo, Nursing Director
Web address: www.hospitalconcepcion.org
Control: Church operated, Nongovernment, not–for–profit **Service:** General medical and surgical

Staffed Beds: 187 Admissions: 7049 Census: 114 Births: 285 Total Expense ($000): 70170 Payroll Expense ($000): 25504

★ **HOSPITAL METROPOLITANO SAN GERMAN (400126)**, Calle Javilla Al Costado Parque de Bombas, Zip 683, Mailing Address: PO Box 63, Zip 683; tel. 787/892–5300, (Nonreporting) **A**10
Primary Contact: Luis A. Berdiel, Executive Director
Control: Corporation, Investor–owned (for–profit) **Service:** Other specialty treatment

Staffed Beds: 76

SAN JUAN—San Juan County

✠ **ASHFORD PRESBYTERIAN COMMUNITY HOSPITAL (400001)**, 1451 Avenue Ashford, Zip 00907–1511, Mailing Address: P.O. Box 9020032, Zip 00902–0032; tel. 787/721–2160, **A**1 3 5 10 **F**3 8 11 13 15 18 28 30 40 41 45 46 49 51 53 59 65 70 72 75 76 79 81 82 87 89 91 93 97 107 110 111 114 116 118 119 130 131 135 145 146 147 148 **P**5
Primary Contact: Pedro J. Gonzalez, FACHE, Chief Executive Officer
COO: Obdulia Medina, Associate Director for Administrative Support, Clinical Management and Ambulatory Care
CFO: Mayra Torres, CPA, Chief Financial Officer
CMO: Francisco de Torres, M.D., Medical Director
CIO: Sigfredo Irizarry, Information Technology Director
CHR: Irma Carrillo, Director Human Resources
CNO: Itza Soto, MSN, Nursing Executive
Web address: www.presbypr.com
Control: Other not–for–profit (including NFP Corporation) **Service:** General medical and surgical

Staffed Beds: 177 Admissions: 8701 Census: 115 Outpatient Visits: 44682 Births: 2381 Total Expense ($000): 64923 Payroll Expense ($000): 19965 Personnel: 696

✠ **AUXILIO MUTUO HOSPITAL (400016)**, Ponce De Leon Avenue, Zip 00918–1000, Mailing Address: P.O. Box 191227, Zip 00919–1227; tel. 787/758–2000, (Nonreporting) **A**1 3 5 10
Primary Contact: Jorge L Matta. Serrano, Administrator
COO: Carmen Martin, Associate Administrator
CFO: Maria L Marti, Director Fiscal Services
CMO: Jose Isado, M.D., Medical Director
CIO: Edgardo Rodriguez, Director Management Information Systems
CHR: Maria Vega, Director Human Resources
Web address: www.auxiliomutuo.com
Control: Other not–for–profit (including NFP Corporation) **Service:** General medical and surgical

Staffed Beds: 483

✠ **CARDIOVASCULAR CENTER OF PUERTO RICO AND THE CARIBBEAN (400124)**, Americo Miranda Centro Medico, Zip 936, Mailing Address: P.O. Box 366528, Zip 00936–6528; tel. 787/754–8500, (Nonreporting) **A**1 3 5 10 **S** Puerto Rico Department of Health, San Juan, PR
Primary Contact: Carlos Cabrera, Executive Director
COO: Wilfredo Rabelo Millan, Chief Operating Officer
CFO: Arthur J Fernandez del Valle, Chief Financial Officer
CMO: Jose E Novoa Loyola, M.D., Medical Director
CIO: Eugenio Torres Ayala, Director Information Systems
CHR: Myriam T Rodriguez Schmidt, Director Human Resources
CNO: Pedro Laureano Cantre, Chief Nursing Officer
Web address: www.cardiovascular.gobierno.pr
Control: State, Government, nonfederal **Service:** General medical and surgical

Staffed Beds: 154

★ **DOCTORS' CENTER HOSPITAL SAN JUAN (400006)**, 1395 San Rafael Street, Zip 00909–2518, Mailing Address: Box 11338, Santurce Station, Zip 00910–3428; tel. 787/999–7620, (Nonreporting) **A**10
Primary Contact: Norma Marrero, Executive Administrator
COO: Norma Marrero, Executive Administrator
CFO: Alejandro Santiago, Director Finance
CMO: Ubaldo Santiago, M.D., Chairman
CIO: Luis Alicea, Chief Information Officer
CHR: Carmen Perez, Director Human Resources
CNO: Lesbia Lopez, Chief Nursing Officer
Web address: www.tuhospitalfamiliar.com
Control: Corporation, Investor–owned (for–profit) **Service:** General medical and surgical

Staffed Beds: 152

★ **HEALTHSOUTH REHABILITATION HOSPITAL OF SAN JUAN (403025)**, University Hospital, 3rd Floor, Zip 923, Mailing Address: P.O. Box 70344, Zip 923; tel. 787/274–5100, (Nonreporting) **A**3 5 10 **S** Encompass Health Corporation, Birmingham, AL
Primary Contact: Daniel Del Castillo, Chief Executive Officer
CFO: Jesus M Corazon, Controller
CMO: Eduardo Ramos, M.D., Medical Director
CHR: Frances Fuentes, Coordinator Human Resources
CNO: Zamarys Rivera, R.N., Chief Nursing Officer
Web address: www.healthsouthsanjuan.com
Control: Corporation, Investor–owned (for–profit) **Service:** Rehabilitation

Staffed Beds: 32

HOSPITAL CUIDADO AGUDO ESPECIALIZADO EN PACIENTES POLITRAUMATIZADOS (400127), Carr. Num. 22 BO. Monacillos, Centro Medico, Zip 00922–2129, Mailing Address: PO Box 2129, Zip 00922–2129; tel. 787/777–3535, (Nonreporting)
Primary Contact: Victor L. Medina Cruz, M.D., Administrator
Web address: www.asempr.org
Control: Other not–for–profit (including NFP Corporation) **Service:** General medical and surgical

Staffed Beds: 25

★ **HOSPITAL DE PSIQUIATRIA (404006)**, Dr. Ramon Fernandez Marina, P O Box 2100, Zip 936; tel. 787/766–4646, (Nonreporting) **A**5
Primary Contact: Elizabeth De Santiago, Executive Director
CMO: Brunilda Vazquez, Medical Director
CHR: Idalia Garcia, Chief Human Resources Officer
Control: State, Government, nonfederal **Service:** Psychiatric

Staffed Beds: 153

✠ **HOSPITAL DEL MAESTRO (400004)**, 550 Sergio Cuevas, Zip 00918–3741, Mailing Address: P.O. Box 364708, Zip 00936–4708; tel. 787/758–8383, (Nonreporting) **A**1 10
Primary Contact: Jorge Torres. Otero, Executive Director
CFO: Marisol Vargas, Director Finance
CMO: Jose Montalvo, M.D., Medical Director
CIO: Laura Rodriguez, Director Medical Records
CHR: Orlando Santiago, Human Resources Officer
Web address: www.hospitaldelmaestro.org
Control: Corporation, Investor–owned (for–profit) **Service:** General medical and surgical

Staffed Beds: 250

Hospital, Medicare Provider Number, Address, Telephone, Approval, Facility, and Physician Codes, Health Care System

★ American Hospital Association (AHA) membership   ○ Healthcare Facilities Accreditation Program   ⇑ Center for Improvement in Healthcare Quality Accreditation
□ The Joint Commission accreditation   ◇ DNV Healthcare Inc. accreditation   △ Commission on Accreditation of Rehabilitation Facilities (CARF) accreditation

✠ **HOSPITAL METROPOLITAN (400106)**, 1785 Carr 21, Zip 00921–3399, Mailing Address: P.O. Box 11981, Zip 922; tel. 787/782–9999, (Nonreporting) **A**1 10
Primary Contact: Domingo Nevarez, Chief Executive Officer
CFO: Maritza Rodriguez, Chief Financial Officer
CMO: Maria de los Angeles Correa, M.D., Medical Director
CIO: Manuel Santiago, Chief Information Officer
Control: Corporation, Investor–owned (for–profit) **Service**: General medical and surgical

Staffed Beds: 127

✠ **HOSPITAL PAVIA–HATO REY (400128)**, 435 Ponce De Leon Avenue, Zip 00917–3428, Mailing Address: PO Box 190828, Zip 00917–3428; tel. 787/641–2323, (Nonreporting) **A**1 3 5 10 **S** United Medical Corporation, Windermere, FL
Primary Contact: Guillermo Pastrana, Executive Director
Web address: www.paviahealth.com
Control: Corporation, Investor–owned (for–profit) **Service**: General medical and surgical

Staffed Beds: 180

✠ **HOSPITAL PAVIA–SANTURCE (400019)**, 1462 Asia Street, Zip 00909–2143, Mailing Address: Box 11137, Santurce Station, Zip 00910–1137; tel. 787/727–6060, (Nonreporting) **A**1 10 **S** United Medical Corporation, Windermere, FL
Primary Contact: Jose Luis. Rodriguez, Chief Executive Officer
CFO: Francisco Espina, Director Finance
Web address: www.paviahealth.com
Control: Corporation, Investor–owned (for–profit) **Service**: General medical and surgical

Staffed Beds: 197

★ **HOSPITAL PSIQUIATRICO CORRECCIONAL**, PMB 302 P O Box 70344, Zip 936; tel. 939/225–2400, (Nonreporting)
Primary Contact: Felicia E. Alvarado, Administrator
Web address: www.www2.pr.gov/Directorios/Pages/InfoAgencia.aspx?PRIFA=220
Control: State, Government, nonfederal **Service**: General medical and surgical

Staffed Beds: 25

✠ **HOSPITAL SAN FRANCISCO (400098)**, 371 Avenida De Diego, Zip 00923–1711, Mailing Address: P.O. Box 29025, Zip 00929–0025; tel. 787/767–5100, (Nonreporting) **A**1 10 **S** United Medical Corporation, Windermere, FL
Primary Contact: Marcos Aguila, Chief Executive Officer
CFO: Lizzette Rodriguez, Director Finance
CMO: Hector L Cotto, M.D., Medical Director
CIO: Deborah Nieves, Director Management Information Systems
CHR: Sugehi Santiago, Director
Web address: www.metropavia.com/SanFrancisco.cfm
Control: Corporation, Investor–owned (for–profit) **Service**: General medical and surgical

Staffed Beds: 148

★ **HOSPITAL SAN GERARDO (400121)**, 138 Avenue Winston Churchill, Zip 00926–6013; tel. 787/761–8383, (Nonreporting) **A**10
Primary Contact: Henry Ruberte, Administrator
Web address: www.https://hospitales.cybo.com/PR–biz/hospital–san–gerardo_2P
Control: Other not–for–profit (including NFP Corporation) **Service**: Chronic disease

Staffed Beds: 60

★ **INDUSTRIAL HOSPITAL**, Puerto Rico Medical Center, Zip 936, Mailing Address: P.O. Box 365028, Zip 936; tel. 787/754–2525, (Nonreporting)
Primary Contact: Jane Vega, Executive Director
CFO: Robert Bernier Casanova, Chief Financial Officer
CMO: Carmen Carrasquillo, M.D., Medical Director
CHR: Sonia M Lebron, Human Resources Specialist
Control: State, Government, nonfederal **Service**: General medical and surgical

Staffed Beds: 108

✠ **SAN JUAN CAPESTRANO HOSPITAL (404005)**, Rural Route 2, Box 11, Zip 926; tel. 787/625–2900, (Nonreporting) **A**1 5 10 **S** Acadia Healthcare Company, Inc., Franklin, TN
Primary Contact: Marta Rivera. Plaza, Chief Executive Officer and Managing Director
CFO: Julia Cruz, Chief Financial Officer
CMO: Jose' Alonso, M.D., Medical Director
CIO: Ana Morandeira, Director Marketing
CHR: Luis Rivera, Director Human Resources
Web address: www.sjcapestrano.com
Control: Corporation, Investor–owned (for–profit) **Service**: Psychiatric

Staffed Beds: 108

✠ **SAN JUAN CITY HOSPITAL (400015)**, Puerto Rico Medical Center, Zip 928, Mailing Address: PMB 79, P O Box 70344, Zip 00936–8344; tel. 787/766–2222, (Nonreporting) **A**1 3 5 10
Primary Contact: James F. Nieves, Executive Director
COO: Norma Marcano, Chief Operating Officer
CFO: Jaime Rodriguez, Chief Financial Officer
CMO: Raul Reyes, M.D., Medical Director
CIO: Gustavo Mesa, Chief Information Officer
CHR: Jose Garcia, Chief Human Resources Officer
Web address: www.massalud.com
Control: City, Government, nonfederal **Service**: General medical and surgical

Staffed Beds: 267

★ **UNIVERSITY HOSPITAL (400061)**, Nineyas 869 Rio Piedras, Zip 922, Mailing Address: P.O. Box 2116, Zip 922; tel. 787/754–0101, (Nonreporting) **A**3 5 10 **S** Puerto Rico Department of Health, San Juan, PR
Primary Contact: Jorge Matta. Gonzalez, Executive Director
CFO: Janet Baez, Director
CMO: Ricardo Moscoso, M.D., Medical Director
CIO: Josue Martinez, Coordinator Information Systems
CHR: Ramomita Navarro, Director Human Resources
Control: State, Government, nonfederal **Service**: General medical and surgical

Staffed Beds: 220

✠ △ **VETERANS AFFAIRS CARIBBEAN HEALTHCARE SYSTEM**, 10 Casia Street, Zip 00921–3201; tel. 787/641–7582, (Nonreporting) **A**1 2 3 5 7 8 **S** Department of Veterans Affairs, Perry Point, MD
Primary Contact: Antonio Sanchez, M.D., Acting Director
CFO: Oscar Rodriguez, Chief Fiscal Officer
CMO: Antonio Sanchez, M.D., Chief of Staff
CIO: Manuel Negron, Chief Information Technology Service
CHR: Omar Ahmed, Acting Manager Human Resources
CNO: Kathleen Ruiz, M.D., Associate Director Patient Care Services
Web address: www.caribbean.va.gov/
Control: Veterans Affairs, Government, federal **Service**: General medical and surgical

Staffed Beds: 330

SANTURCE—San Juan County

✠ **SAN JORGE CHILDREN'S HOSPITAL**, 258 San Jorge Street, Santurce, Zip 00912–3310, Mailing Address: PO Box 6308, San Juan, Zip 00912–3310; tel. 787/727–1000, (Nonreporting) **A**1 3 5 **S** United Medical Corporation, Windermere, FL
Primary Contact: Domingo Cruz, Senior Vice President Operations
CFO: Jose Marrero, Director Finance
CMO: Luis Clavell, M.D., Medical Director
CIO: Rogelio Caballero, Chief Information Systems
CHR: Odette Burgos, Supervisor Human Resources
CNO: Leticia Fuentes, Nursing Director
Web address: www.sanjorgechildrenshospital.com
Control: Corporation, Investor–owned (for–profit) **Service**: Children's general medical and surgical

Staffed Beds: 125

UTUADO—San Juan County

★ **METROPOLITANO DE LA MONTANA (400130)**, Calle Issac Gonzalez Martinez, Zip 641, Mailing Address: P.O. Box 2600, Zip 641; tel. 787/933–1100, (Nonreporting) **A**10
Primary Contact: Yelitza Sanchez. Rodriguez, Executive Director
Web address: www.metropavia.com/DeLaMontana.cfm
Control: Corporation, Investor–owned (for–profit) **Service**: General medical and surgical

Staffed Beds: 25

VEGA BAJA—Vega Alta County

★ **WILMA N. VAZQUEZ MEDICAL CENTER (400115)**, KM 39 1/2 Road 2, Call Box 7001, Zip 694; tel. 787/858–1580, (Nonreporting) **A**10
Primary Contact: Ramon J. Vilar, Administrator
COO: Jose O Pabon, Director Operations
CFO: Youdie Reynolds–Gossette, Controller
CMO: Jorge Feria, M.D., President Medical Staff
CIO: Miguel Aponte, Supervisor Management Information Systems
CHR: Aymette Garcia, Manager Human Resources
Control: Corporation, Investor–owned (for–profit) **Service**: General medical and surgical

Staffed Beds: 150

YAUCO—Yauco County

⊠ **HOSPITAL PAVIA YAUCO (400110)**, Carretera 128 KM 1.0, Zip 698, Mailing Address: P.O. Box 5643, Zip 698; tel. 787/856–1000, (Nonreporting) **A**1 5 10
Primary Contact: Dinorah Hernandez Esq, Executive Director
CFO: Elizabeth Gonzalez, CPA, Financial Director
CMO: Juan Pillot, M.D., Esq Medical Director
CIO: Edson Ortiz, Chief Information Officer
Web address: www.metropavia.com/facilities/hospitals/pavia-yauco/?lang=en/
Control: Corporation, Investor–owned (for–profit) **Service**: General medical and surgical

Staffed Beds: 114

VIRGIN ISLANDS

CHRISTIANSTED—St. Croix County

☐ **GOVERNOR JUAN F. LUIS HOSPITAL (480002)**, 4007 Estate Diamond Ruby, Zip 00820–4421; tel. 340/778–6311, (Nonreporting) **A**1 10
Primary Contact: Darice S. Plaskett, R.N., FACHE, Interim Chief Executive Officer
CFO: Rosalie Javois, Chief Financial Officer
CMO: Robert Centeno, M.D., Chief Medical Officer
CIO: Reuben D Molloy, Chief Information Officer
CHR: Joan Jean–Baptiste, Vice President Human Resources
Web address: www.jflusvi.org
Control: State, Government, nonfederal **Service**: General medical and surgical

Staffed Beds: 165

SAINT THOMAS—St. Thomas County

☐ **SCHNEIDER REGIONAL MEDICAL CENTER (480001)**, 9048 Sugar Estate, Charlotte Amalie, Zip 802; tel. 340/776–8311, (Nonreporting) **A**1 10
Primary Contact: Bernard Wheatley, FACHE, Chief Executive Officer
CMO: Thelma Ruth Watson, M.D., Medical Director
CIO: J C Creque, Director Management Information Systems
CHR: Marlene J Adams, Director Human Resources
Web address: www.rlshospital.org
Control: State, Government, nonfederal **Service**: General medical and surgical

Staffed Beds: 86

Hospital, Medicare Provider Number, Address, Telephone, Approval, Facility, and Physician Codes, Health Care System

★ American Hospital Association (AHA) membership
☐ The Joint Commission accreditation
○ Healthcare Facilities Accreditation Program
◇ DNV Healthcare Inc. accreditation
⇑ Center for Improvement in Healthcare Quality Accreditation
△ Commission on Accreditation of Rehabilitation Facilities (CARF) accreditation

© 2018 AHA Guide   *Many Facility Codes have changed. Please refer to the AHA Guide Code Chart.*   Hospitals **A717**

U.S. Government Hospitals
Outside the United States, by Area

GERMANY

Heidelberg: ★ Heidelberg Army Community Hospital, APO, CMR 242, AE 09042

Landstuhl: ★ Landstuhl Army Regional Medical Center, APO, CMR 402, AE 09180

Wuerzburg: ★ Wuerzburg Army Community Hospital, APO, USAMEDDAC Wuerzburg, Ut 26610, AE 09244

ITALY

Naples: ★ U. S. Naval Hospital, FPO, none, AE 09619

JAPAN

Yokosuka: ★ U. S. Naval Hospital, Box 1487, UNIT 96350

SOUTH KOREA

Seoul: ★ Brian Allgood Army Community Hospital, 121st General Hospital, UNIT 96205

Yongsan: Medcom 18th Commander, Facilities Division Eamc L EM, UNIT 96205

SPAIN

Rota: ★ U. S. Naval Hospital, Rota, FPO, PSC 819, Box 18, AE 09645–2500

TAIWAN

Taipei: ★ U. S. Naval Hospital Taipei, No 300 Shin–Pai Road, Sec 2

Index of Hospitals

This section is an index of all hospitals in alphabetical order by hospital name, followed by the city, state, and page reference to the hospital's listing in Section A.

A

A. WEBB ROBERTS HOSPITAL, TX (see BAYLOR UNIVERSITY MEDICAL CENTER), p. A596
ABBEVILLE AREA MEDICAL CENTER, ABBEVILLE, SC, p. A549
ABBEVILLE GENERAL HOSPITAL, ABBEVILLE, LA, p. A262
ABBOTT NORTHWESTERN HOSPITAL, MINNEAPOLIS, MN, p. A335
ABBOTT NORTHWESTERN HOSPITAL, MINNEAPOLIS, MN (see SISTER KENNY REHABILITATION INSTITUTE), p. A335
ABILENE REGIONAL MEDICAL CENTER, ABILENE, TX, p. A582
ABINGTON HOSPITAL, ABINGTON, PA, p. A519
ABINGTON-LANSDALE HOSPITAL JEFFERSON HEALTH, LANSDALE, PA, p. A529
ABRAHAM LINCOLN MEMORIAL HOSPITAL, LINCOLN, IL, p. A188
ABRAZO ARIZONA HEART HOSPITAL, AZ (see ABRAZO ARROWHEAD CAMPUS), p. A30
ABRAZO ARROWHEAD CAMPUS, GLENDALE, AZ, p. A30
ABRAZO CENTRAL CAMPUS, PHOENIX, AZ, p. A32
ABRAZO SCOTTSDALE CAMPUS, PHOENIX, AZ, p. A32
ABRAZO WEST CAMPUS, GOODYEAR, AZ, p. A30
ABROM KAPLAN MEMORIAL HOSPITAL, KAPLAN, LA, p. A270
ACADIA GENERAL HOSPITAL, CROWLEY, LA, p. A266
ACADIA-ST. LANDRY HOSPITAL, CHURCH POINT, LA, p. A265
ACADIAN MEDICAL CENTER, LA (see MERCY REGIONAL MEDICAL CENTER), p. A280
ACCEL REHABILITATION HOSPITAL OF PLANO, PLANO, TX, p. A628
ACCESS HOSPITAL DAYTON, DAYTON, OH, p. A480
ACCORD REHABILITATION HOSPITAL, PLAQUEMINE, LA, p. A277
ACMH HOSPITAL, KITTANNING, PA, p. A528
ACOMA-CANONCITO-LAGUNA HOSPITAL, ACOMA, NM, p. A415
ACUITY HOSPITAL OF SOUTH TEXAS, SAN ANTONIO, TX, p. A632
ACUITY SPECIALTY HOSPITAL OF NEW JERSEY, ATLANTIC CITY, NJ, p. A402
ACUITY SPECIALTY HOSPITAL OF SOUTHERN NEW JERSEY, WILLINGBORO, NJ, p. A414
ACUITY SPECIALTY HOSPITALS OHIO VALLEY, STEUBENVILLE, OH, p. A490
ACUITY SPECIALTY HOSPITALS OHIO VALLEY AT BELMONT, OH (see ACUITY SPECIALTY HOSPITALS OHIO VALLEY), p. A490
AD HOSPITAL EAST, HOUSTON, TX, p. A609
ADAIR COUNTY HEALTH SYSTEM, GREENFIELD, IA, p. A223
ADAMS COUNTY REGIONAL MEDICAL CENTER, SEAMAN, OH, p. A490
ADAMS MEMORIAL HOSPITAL, DECATUR, IN, p. A202
ADCARE HOSPITAL OF WORCESTER, WORCESTER, MA, p. A306
ADDISON GILBERT HOSPITAL, GLOUCESTER, MA, p. A300
ADDISON GILBERT HOSPITAL, MA (see BEVERLY HOSPITAL), p. A295
ADENA GREENFIELD MEDICAL CENTER, GREENFIELD, OH, p. A483
ADENA MEDICAL CENTER, CHILLICOTHE, OH, p. A474
ADENA PIKE MEDICAL CENTER, WAVERLY, OH, p. A493
ADIRONDACK HEALTH, SARANAC LAKE, NY, p. A442
ADVANCED CARE HOSPITAL OF MONTANA, BILLINGS, MT, p. A373
ADVANCED CARE HOSPITAL OF SOUTHERN NEW MEXICO, LAS CRUCES, NM, p. A417
ADVANCED CARE HOSPITAL OF WHITE COUNTY, SEARCY-White County, AR, p. A48
ADVANCED DIAGNOSTICS HOSPITAL, HOUSTON, TX, p. A610
ADVANCED SPECIALTY HOSPITAL OF TOLEDO, TOLEDO, OH, p. A491
ADVANCED SURGICAL HOSPITAL, WASHINGTON, PA, p. A543
ADVENTIST BEHAVIORAL HEALTH AND WELLNESS SERVICES, ROCKVILLE, MD, p. A293

ADVENTIST BEHAVIORAL HEALTH AND WELLNESS SERVICES, MD (see POTOMAC RIDGE BEHAVIORAL HEALTH), p. A294
ADVENTIST HEALTH BAKERSFIELD, BAKERSFIELD, CA, p. A51
ADVENTIST HEALTH CASTLE, KAILUA, HI, p. A165
ADVENTIST HEALTH CLEAR LAKE, CLEARLAKE, CA, p. A54
ADVENTIST HEALTH FEATHER RIVER, PARADISE, CA, p. A77
ADVENTIST HEALTH GLENDALE, LOS ANGELES, CA, p. A66
ADVENTIST HEALTH HOWARD MEMORIAL, WILLITS, CA, p. A95
ADVENTIST HEALTH LODI MEMORIAL, LODI, CA, p. A64
ADVENTIST HEALTH MEDICAL CENTER - TEHACHAPI VALLEY, TEHACHAPI, CA, p. A91
ADVENTIST HEALTH SONORA, SONORA, CA, p. A90
ADVENTIST HEALTH ST. HELENA, SAINT HELENA, CA, p. A82
ADVENTIST HEALTH ST. HELENA, VALLEJO, CA, p. A93
ADVENTIST HEALTH WHITE MEMORIAL, LOS ANGELES, CA, p. A66
ADVENTIST HEALTHCARE PHYSICAL HEALTH AND REHABILITATION, ROCKVILLE, MD, p. A293
ADVENTIST HEALTHCARE SHADY GROVE MEDICAL CENTER, ROCKVILLE, MD, p. A294
ADVENTIST HEALTHCARE WASHINGTON ADVENTIST HOSPITAL, TAKOMA PARK, MD, p. A294
ADVENTIST MEDICAL CENTER - HANFORD, HANFORD, CA, p. A61
ADVENTIST MEDICAL CENTER-PORTLAND, PORTLAND, OR, p. A516
ADVENTIST MEDICAL CENTER-REEDLEY, REEDLEY, CA, p. A80
ADVENTIST MEDICAL CENTER-SELMA, CA (see ADVENTIST MEDICAL CENTER - HANFORD), p. A61
ADVOCATE BETHANY HOSPITAL, CHICAGO, IL, p. A176
ADVOCATE BROMENN MEDICAL CENTER, NORMAL, IL, p. A191
ADVOCATE BROMENN MEDICAL CENTER, IL (see ADVOCATE BROMENN REGIONAL MEDICAL CENTER), p. A191
ADVOCATE BROMENN REGIONAL MEDICAL CENTER, NORMAL, IL, p. A191
ADVOCATE BROMENN REGIONAL MEDICAL CENTER, IL (see ADVOCATE BROMENN MEDICAL CENTER), p. A191
ADVOCATE CHRIST MEDICAL CENTER, OAK LAWN, IL, p. A191
ADVOCATE CONDELL MEDICAL CENTER, LIBERTYVILLE, IL, p. A188
ADVOCATE EUREKA HOSPITAL, EUREKA, IL, p. A182
ADVOCATE EUREKA HOSPITAL, IL (see EUREKA COMMUNITY HOSPITAL), p. A182
ADVOCATE GOOD SAMARITAN HOSPITAL, DOWNERS GROVE, IL, p. A181
ADVOCATE GOOD SHEPHERD HOSPITAL, BARRINGTON, IL, p. A174
ADVOCATE HOPE CHILDREN'S HOSPITAL, IL (see ADVOCATE CHRIST MEDICAL CENTER), p. A191
ADVOCATE ILLINOIS MASONIC MEDICAL CENTER, CHICAGO, IL, p. A176
ADVOCATE LUTHERAN GENERAL HOSPITAL, PARK RIDGE, IL, p. A192
ADVOCATE SHERMAN HOSPITAL, ELGIN, IL, p. A182
ADVOCATE SHERMAN HOSPITAL, IL (see SHERMAN HOSPITAL), p. A182
ADVOCATE SOUTH SUBURBAN HOSPITAL, HAZEL CREST, IL, p. A185
ADVOCATE TRINITY HOSPITAL, CHICAGO, IL, p. A176
AHMC ANAHEIM REGIONAL MEDICAL CENTER, ANAHEIM, CA, p. A50
AIKEN REGIONAL MEDICAL CENTERS, AIKEN, SC, p. A549
AKRON CHILDREN'S HOSPITAL, AKRON, OH, p. A470
ALAMANCE REGIONAL MEDICAL CENTER, BURLINGTON, NC, p. A448
ALAMEDA HOSPITAL, ALAMEDA, CA, p. A50
ALASKA NATIVE MEDICAL CENTER, ANCHORAGE, AK, p. A25
ALASKA PSYCHIATRIC INSTITUTE, ANCHORAGE, AK, p. A25
ALASKA REGIONAL HOSPITAL, ANCHORAGE, AK, p. A25
ALBANY MEDICAL CENTER, ALBANY, NY, p. A421
ALBANY MEDICAL CENTER SOUTH-CLINICAL CAMPUS, NY (see ALBANY MEDICAL CENTER), p. A421
ALBANY MEMORIAL HOSPITAL, ALBANY, NY, p. A421
ALBANY STRATTON VETERANS AFFAIRS MEDICAL CENTER, ALBANY, NY, p. A421

ALBERT EINSTEIN MEDICAL CENTER, PHILADELPHIA, PA, p. A533
ALBERT J. SOLNIT PSYCHIATRIC CENTER - SOUTH CAMPUS, MIDDLETOWN, CT, p. A109
ALEDA E. LUTZ VETERANS AFFAIRS MEDICAL CENTER, SAGINAW, MI, p. A322
ALEXANDRIA VETERANS AFFAIRS HEALTH CARE SYSTEM, PINEVILLE, LA, p. A277
ALEXANDRIA VETERANS AFFAIRS HEALTH CARE SYSTEM, LA (see VETERANS AFFAIRS MEDICAL CENTER - ALEXANDRIA), p. A277
ALEXIAN BROTHERS BEHAVIORAL HEALTH HOSPITAL, HOFFMAN ESTATES, IL, p. A186
ALFRED I. DUPONT HOSPITAL FOR CHILDREN, WILMINGTON, DE, p. A114
ALHAMBRA HOSPITAL MEDICAL CENTER, ALHAMBRA, CA, p. A50
ALICE PECK DAY MEMORIAL HOSPITAL, LEBANON, NH, p. A399
ALLEGAN GENERAL HOSPITAL, ALLEGAN, MI, p. A307
ALLEGHANY MEMORIAL HOSPITAL, SPARTA, NC, p. A461
ALLEGHENY GENERAL HOSPITAL, PITTSBURGH, PA, p. A537
ALLEGHENY VALLEY HOSPITAL, NATRONA HEIGHTS, PA, p. A532
ALLEGIANCE BEHAVIORAL HEALTH CENTER OF PLAINVIEW, PLAINVIEW, TX, p. A628
ALLEGIANCE BEHAVIORAL HEALTH CENTERS OF MONROE, WEST MONROE, LA, p. A280
ALLEGIANCE HEALTH CENTER OF RUSTON, LA (see ALLEGIANCE BEHAVIORAL HEALTH CENTERS OF MONROE), p. A280
ALLEGIANCE SPECIALTY HOSPITAL OF GREENVILLE, GREENVILLE, MS, p. A346
ALLEGIANCE SPECIALTY HOSPITAL OF KILGORE, KILGORE, TX, p. A617
ALLEGIANCE SPECIALTY HOSPITAL OF LITTLE ROCK, LITTLE ROCK-Pulaski County, AR, p. A44
ALLEN COUNTY REGIONAL HOSPITAL, IOLA, KS, p. A237
ALLEN MEMORIAL HOSPITAL, WATERLOO, IA, p. A230
ALLEN PARISH HOSPITAL, KINDER, LA, p. A270
ALLENDALE COUNTY HOSPITAL, FAIRFAX, SC, p. A552
ALLENMORE HOSPITAL, TACOMA, WA, p. A678
ALLENMORE HOSPITAL, WA (see MULTICARE TACOMA GENERAL HOSPITAL), p. A679
ALLIANCE COMMUNITY HOSPITAL, ALLIANCE, OH, p. A470
ALLIANCE HEALTH CENTER, MERIDIAN, MS, p. A350
ALLIANCE HEALTHCARE SYSTEM, HOLLY SPRINGS, MS, p. A347
ALLIANCEHEALTH CLINTON, CLINTON, OK, p. A497
ALLIANCEHEALTH DURANT, DURANT, OK, p. A498
ALLIANCEHEALTH MADILL, MADILL, OK, p. A500
ALLIANCEHEALTH MIDWEST, MIDWEST CITY, OK, p. A501
ALLIANCEHEALTH PONCA CITY, PONCA CITY, OK, p. A505
ALLIANCEHEALTH SEMINOLE, SEMINOLE, OK, p. A506
ALLIANCEHEALTH WOODWARD, WOODWARD, OK, p. A510
ALLIED SERVICES REHABILITATION HOSPITAL, SCRANTON, PA, p. A540
ALOMERE HEALTH, ALEXANDRIA, MN, p. A327
ALTA BATES MEDICAL CENTER-HERRICK CAMPUS, CA (see ALTA BATES SUMMIT MEDICAL CENTER), p. A52
ALTA BATES SUMMIT MEDICAL CENTER - SUMMIT CAMPUS, OAKLAND, CA, p. A75
ALTA BATES SUMMIT MEDICAL CENTER, BERKELEY, CA, p. A52
ALTA VIEW HOSPITAL, SANDY, UT, p. A651
ALTA VISTA REGIONAL HOSPITAL, LAS VEGAS, NM, p. A418
ALTON MEMORIAL HOSPITAL, ALTON, IL, p. A173
ALTON MENTAL HEALTH CENTER, ALTON, IL, p. A173
ALTOONA REGIONAL HEALTH SYSTEM, ALTOONA, PA, p. A519
ALTRU HEALTH SYSTEM, GRAND FORKS, ND, p. A466
ALTRU HOSPITAL, ND (see ALTRU HEALTH SYSTEM), p. A466
ALTRU REHABILITATION CENTER, ND (see ALTRU HEALTH SYSTEM), p. A466
ALTUS BAYTOWN HOSPITAL, BAYTOWN, TX, p. A587
ALVARADO HOSPITAL MEDICAL CENTER, SAN DIEGO, CA, p. A83
ALVARADO PARKWAY INSTITUTE BEHAVIORAL HEALTH SYSTEM, LA MESA, CA, p. A63
ALVIN C. YORK CAMPUS, MURFREESBORO, TN, p. A576

BERTRAND CHAFFEE HOSPITAL, SPRINGVILLE, NY, p. A443
BERWICK HOSPITAL CENTER, BERWICK, PA, p. A520
BETH ISRAEL DEACONESS HOSPITAL PLYMOUTH, PLYMOUTH, MA, p. A303
BETH ISRAEL DEACONESS HOSPITAL-MILTON, MILTON, MA, p. A302
BETH ISRAEL DEACONESS HOSPITAL-NEEDHAM CAMPUS, NEEDHAM, MA, p. A302
BETH ISRAEL DEACONESS MEDICAL CENTER, BOSTON, MA, p. A296
BETH ISRAEL MEDICAL CENTER, NEW YORK (Includes all hospitals located within the five boroughs), NY, p. A431
BETH ISRAEL MEDICAL CENTER-KINGS HIGHWAY DIVISION, NEW YORK (Includes all hospitals located within the five boroughs), NY, p. A431
BETHANY BEHAVIORAL HEALTH, OK (see CEDAR RIDGE HOSPITAL), p. A503
BETHESDA BUTLER HOSPITAL, OH (see BETHESDA NORTH HOSPITAL), p. A474
BETHESDA HOSPITAL, SAINT PAUL, MN, p. A339
BETHESDA HOSPITAL, OH (see GENESIS HEALTHCARE SYSTEM), p. A494
BETHESDA HOSPITAL EAST, BOYNTON BEACH, FL, p. A118
BETHESDA HOSPITAL WEST, FL (see BETHESDA HOSPITAL EAST), p. A118
BETHESDA NORTH HOSPITAL, CINCINNATI, OH, p. A474
BETHESDA REHABILITATION HOSPITAL, BATON ROUGE, LA, p. A263
BEVERLY HOSPITAL, BEVERLY, MA, p. A295
BEVERLY HOSPITAL, MONTEBELLO, CA, p. A73
BEVERLY HOSPITAL, BEVERLY, MA (see ADDISON GILBERT HOSPITAL), p. A300
BHC ALHAMBRA HOSPITAL, ROSEMEAD, CA, p. A81
BIBB MEDICAL CENTER, CENTREVILLE, AL, p. A16
BIENVILLE MEDICAL CENTER, ARCADIA, LA, p. A263
BIG BEND REGIONAL MEDICAL CENTER, ALPINE, TX, p. A582
BIG HORN COUNTY MEMORIAL HOSPITAL, HARDIN, MT, p. A376
BIG SANDY MEDICAL CENTER, BIG SANDY, MT, p. A373
BIG SOUTH FORK MEDICAL CENTER, ONEIDA, TN, p. A578
BIG SPRING STATE HOSPITAL, BIG SPRING, TX, p. A589
BIGFORK VALLEY HOSPITAL, BIGFORK, MN, p. A328
BILLINGS CLINIC, BILLINGS, MT, p. A373
BINGHAM MEMORIAL HOSPITAL, BLACKFOOT, ID, p. A167
BINGHAMTON GENERAL HOSPITAL, BINGHAMTON, NY, p. A422
BINGHAMTON GENERAL HOSPITAL, NY (see UNITED HEALTH SERVICES HOSPITALS-BINGHAMTON), p. A423
BIRMINGHAM VETERANS AFFAIRS MEDICAL CENTER, BIRMINGHAM, AL, p. A14
BIRMINGHAM VETERANS AFFAIRS MEDICAL CENTER, PERRY POINT, AL (see VETERANS AFFAIRS MEDICAL CENTER), p. A15
BLACK HILLS SURGICAL HOSPITAL, RAPID CITY, SD, p. A563
BLACK RIVER MEDICAL CENTER, POPLAR BLUFF, MO, p. A366
BLACK RIVER MEMORIAL HOSPITAL, BLACK RIVER FALLS, WI, p. A690
BLACKFEET COMMUNITY HOSPITAL, SAINT MARY, MT, p. A379
BLACKFORD COMMUNITY HOSPITAL, HARTFORD CITY, IN, p. A205
BLACKWELL REGIONAL HOSPITAL, BLACKWELL, OK, p. A496
BLADEN COUNTY HOSPITAL, ELIZABETHTOWN, NC, p. A452
BLAIR E. BATSON HOSPITAL FOR CHILDREN, MS (see UNIVERSITY OF MISSISSIPPI MEDICAL CENTER), p. A348
BLAKE MEDICAL CENTER, BRADENTON, FL, p. A118
BLANCHARD VALLEY HOSPITAL, FINDLAY, OH, p. A482
BLANCHARD VALLEY HOSPITAL, OH (see BLANCHARD VALLEY HOSPITAL), p. A482
BLECKLEY MEMORIAL HOSPITAL, COCHRAN, GA, p. A150
BLESSING HOSPITAL, QUINCY, IL, p. A194
BLESSING HOSPITAL, IL (see BLESSING HOSPITAL), p. A194
BLOOMINGTON HOSPITAL, BLOOMINGTON, IN, p. A200
BLOOMINGTON HOSPITAL OF ORANGE COUNTY, PAOLI, IN, p. A213
BLOOMINGTON MEADOWS HOSPITAL, BLOOMINGTON, IN, p. A200
BLOUNT MEMORIAL HOSPITAL, MARYVILLE, TN, p. A574
BLUE HILL MEMORIAL HOSPITAL, BLUE HILL, ME, p. A283
BLUE MOUNTAIN HOSPITAL, BLANDING, UT, p. A646
BLUE MOUNTAIN HOSPITAL, JOHN DAY, OR, p. A514
BLUE RIDGE MEDICAL CENTER - YANCEY CAMPUS, NC (see BLUE RIDGE REGIONAL HOSPITAL), p. A461
BLUE RIDGE REGIONAL HOSPITAL, SPRUCE PINE, NC, p. A461
BLUE VALLEY HOSPITAL, OVERLAND PARK, KS, p. A243
BLUEFIELD REGIONAL MEDICAL CENTER, BLUEFIELD, WV, p. A681

BLUEGRASS COMMUNITY HOSPITAL, VERSAILLES, KY, p. A261
BLUFFTON HOSPITAL, BLUFFTON, OH, p. A472
BLUFFTON REGIONAL MEDICAL CENTER, BLUFFTON, IN, p. A200
BLYTHEDALE CHILDREN'S HOSPITAL, VALHALLA, NY, p. A445
BOB WILSON MEMORIAL GRANT COUNTY HOSPITAL, ULYSSES, KS, p. A247
BOCA RATON COMMUNITY HOSPITAL, BOCA RATON, FL, p. A118
BOCA RATON REGIONAL HOSPITAL, BOCA RATON, FL, p. A118
BOCA RATON REGIONAL HOSPITAL, FL (see BOCA RATON COMMUNITY HOSPITAL), p. A118
BOGALUSA COMMUNITY MEDICAL CENTER, LA (see OUR LADY OF THE ANGELS HOSPITAL), p. A264
BOISE BEHAVIORAL HEALTH HOSPITAL, BOISE, ID, p. A167
BOISE VETERANS AFFAIRS MEDICAL CENTER, BOISE, ID, p. A167
BOISE VETERANS AFFAIRS MEDICAL CENTER, ID (see VETERANS AFFAIRS MEDICAL CENTER), p. A168
BOLIVAR GENERAL HOSPITAL, BOLIVAR, TN, p. A566
BOLIVAR MEDICAL CENTER, CLEVELAND, MS, p. A345
BON SECOURS BALTIMORE HEALTH SYSTEM, BALTIMORE, MD, p. A287
BON SECOURS COMMUNITY HOSPITAL, PORT JERVIS, NY, p. A440
BON SECOURS-DEPAUL MEDICAL CENTER, NORFOLK, VA, p. A662
BON SECOURS MARY IMMACULATE HOSPITAL, NEWPORT NEWS, VA, p. A662
BON SECOURS MARYVIEW MEDICAL CENTER, PORTSMOUTH, VA, p. A664
BON SECOURS MEMORIAL REGIONAL MEDICAL CENTER, MECHANICSVILLE, VA, p. A661
BON SECOURS ST. FRANCIS HEALTH SYSTEM, GREENVILLE, SC, p. A553
BON SECOURS ST. FRANCIS HOSPITAL, CHARLESTON, SC, p. A549
BON SECOURS ST. FRANCIS MEDICAL CENTER, MIDLOTHIAN, VA, p. A661
BON SECOURS ST. MARY'S CHILDREN'S SERVICES, VA (see BON SECOURS ST. MARY'S HOSPITAL), p. A664
BON SECOURS ST. MARY'S HOSPITAL, RICHMOND, VA, p. A664
BON SECOURS-RICHMOND COMMUNITY HOSPITAL, RICHMOND, VA, p. A664
BONNER GENERAL HOSPITAL, SANDPOINT, ID, p. A172
BOONE COUNTY HEALTH CENTER, ALBION, NE, p. A381
BOONE COUNTY HOSPITAL, BOONE, IA, p. A218
BOONE HOSPITAL CENTER, COLUMBIA, MO, p. A358
BOONE MEMORIAL HOSPITAL, MADISON, WV, p. A684
BORGESS-LEE MEMORIAL HOSPITAL, DOWAGIAC, MI, p. A312
BORGESS MEDICAL CENTER, KALAMAZOO, MI, p. A316
BORGESS-PIPP HOSPITAL, MI (see BORGESS MEDICAL CENTER), p. A316
BOSTON CHILDREN'S HOSPITAL, BOSTON, MA, p. A296
BOSTON MEDICAL CENTER, BOSTON, MA, p. A296
BOTHWELL REGIONAL HEALTH CENTER, SEDALIA, MO, p. A370
BOULDER CITY HOSPITAL, BOULDER CITY, NV, p. A392
BOULDER COMMUNITY FOOTHILLS HOSPITAL, CO (see BOULDER COMMUNITY HEALTH), p. A96
BOULDER COMMUNITY HEALTH, BOULDER, CO, p. A96
BOUNDARY COMMUNITY HOSPITAL, BONNERS FERRY, ID, p. A168
BOURBON COMMUNITY HOSPITAL, PARIS, KY, p. A259
BOURNEWOOD HEALTH SYSTEMS, BROOKLINE, MA, p. A298
BOWDLE HOSPITAL, BOWDLE, SD, p. A559
BOX BUTTE GENERAL HOSPITAL, ALLIANCE, NE, p. A381
BOYS TOWN NATIONAL RESEARCH HOSPITAL, OMAHA, NE, p. A387
BOZEMAN HEALTH BIG SKY MEDICAL CENTER, BIG SKY, MT, p. A373
BOZEMAN HEALTH DEACONESS HOSPITAL, BOZEMAN, MT, p. A374
BRADFORD HEALTH SERVICES AT HUNTSVILLE, MADISON, AL, p. A20
BRADFORD HEALTH SERVICES AT WARRIOR LODGE, WARRIOR, AL, p. A24
BRADFORD REGIONAL MEDICAL CENTER, BRADFORD, PA, p. A521
BRADLEY CENTER OF ST. FRANCIS, COLUMBUS, GA, p. A150
BRADLEY CENTER OF ST. FRANCIS, GA (see ST. FRANCIS HOSPITAL), p. A151
BRADLEY COUNTY MEDICAL CENTER, WARREN-Bradley County, AR, p. A49
BRADLEY MEMORIAL, SOUTHINGTON, CT, p. A111

BRADLEY MEMORIAL, CT (see THE HOSPITAL OF CENTRAL CONNECTICUT), p. A109
BRANDON REGIONAL HOSPITAL, BRANDON, FL, p. A119
BRANDYWINE HOSPITAL, COATESVILLE, PA, p. A523
BRATTLEBORO MEMORIAL HOSPITAL, BRATTLEBORO, VT, p. A653
BRATTLEBORO RETREAT, BRATTLEBORO, VT, p. A653
BRAXTON COUNTY MEMORIAL HOSPITAL, GASSAWAY, WV, p. A683
BRECKINRIDGE MEMORIAL HOSPITAL, HARDINSBURG, KY, p. A253
BRENNER CHILDREN'S HOSPITAL & HEALTH SERVICES, WINSTON SALEM, NC, p. A462
BRENNER CHILDREN'S HOSPITAL & HEALTH SERVICES, NC (see WAKE FOREST BAPTIST MEDICAL CENTER), p. A463
BRENTWOOD BEHAVIORAL HEALTHCARE OF MISSISSIPPI, JACKSON, MS, p. A348
BRENTWOOD HOSPITAL, SHREVEPORT, LA, p. A278
BRENTWOOD SPRINGS, NEWBURGH, IN, p. A212
BRIDGEPOINT CONTINUING CARE HOSPITAL, MARRERO, LA, p. A273
BRIDGEPOINT HOSPITAL CAPITOL HILL, WASHINGTON, DC, p. A115
BRIDGEPOINT HOSPITAL NATIONAL HARBOR, WASHINGTON, DC, p. A115
BRIDGEPORT HOSPITAL, BRIDGEPORT, CT, p. A107
BRIDGES MEDICAL CENTER, ADA, MN, p. A327
BRIDGETON HEALTH CENTER, BRIDGETON, NJ, p. A403
BRIDGETON HEALTH CENTER, NJ (see INSPIRA MEDICAL CENTER-VINELAND), p. A413
BRIDGEWATER STATE HOSPITAL, BRIDGEWATER, MA, p. A297
BRIDGTON HOSPITAL, BRIDGTON, ME, p. A283
BRIGHAM AND WOMEN'S FAULKNER HOSPITAL, BOSTON, MA, p. A296
BRIGHAM AND WOMEN'S HOSPITAL, BOSTON, MA, p. A296
BRIGHAM CITY COMMUNITY HOSPITAL, BRIGHAM CITY, UT, p. A646
BRIGHTON CENTER FOR RECOVERY, BRIGHTON, MI, p. A308
BRISTOL BAY AREA HEALTH CORPORATION, DILLINGHAM, AK, p. A26
BRISTOL HOSPITAL, BRISTOL, CT, p. A107
BRISTOL-MYERS SQUIBB CHILDREN'S HOSPITAL, NJ (see ROBERT WOOD JOHNSON UNIVERSITY HOSPITAL), p. A408
BRISTOL REGIONAL MEDICAL CENTER, BRISTOL, TN, p. A566
BRISTOW MEDICAL CENTER, BRISTOW, OK, p. A496
BROADDUS HOSPITAL, PHILIPPI, WV, p. A686
BROADLAWNS MEDICAL CENTER, DES MOINES, IA, p. A221
BROADWATER HEALTH CENTER, TOWNSEND, MT, p. A379
BRODSTONE MEMORIAL HOSPITAL, SUPERIOR, NE, p. A390
BRONSON BATTLE CREEK HOSPITAL, BATTLE CREEK, MI, p. A308
BRONSON LAKEVIEW HOSPITAL, PAW PAW, MI, p. A320
BRONSON METHODIST HOSPITAL, KALAMAZOO, MI, p. A317
BRONSON METHODIST HOSPITAL, KALAMAZOO, MI (see BRONSON VICKSBURG HOSPITAL), p. A325
BRONSON SOUTH HAVEN HOSPITAL, SOUTH HAVEN, MI, p. A323
BRONSON SOUTH HAVEN HOSPITAL, MI (see SOUTH HAVEN COMMUNITY HOSPITAL), p. A323
BRONSON VICKSBURG HOSPITAL, VICKSBURG, MI, p. A325
BRONSON VICKSBURG HOSPITAL, MI (see BRONSON METHODIST HOSPITAL), p. A317
BRONX CHILDREN'S HOSPITAL PSYCHIATRIC CENTER, NY (see NEW YORK CITY CHILDREN'S CENTER), p. A434
BRONX-LEBANON SPECIAL CARE CENTER, NY (see BRONXCARE HEALTH SYSTEM), p. A431
BRONX PSYCHIATRIC CENTER, NEW YORK (Includes all hospitals located within the five boroughs), NY, p. A431
BRONXCARE HEALTH SYSTEM, NEW YORK (Includes all hospitals located within the five boroughs), NY, p. A431
BRONXCARE HEALTH SYSTEM, BRONX, NY (see CONCOURSE DIVISION), p. A432
BRONXCARE HEALTH SYSTEM, BRONX, NY (see FULTON DIVISION), p. A432
BROOK LANE HEALTH SERVICES, HAGERSTOWN, MD, p. A292
BROOKDALE HOSPITAL MEDICAL CENTER, NEW YORK (Includes all hospitals located within the five boroughs), NY, p. A431
BROOKE ARMY MEDICAL CENTER, FORT SAM HOUSTON, TX, p. A603
BROOKE ARMY MEDICAL CENTER, FORT SAM HOUSTON, TX, p. A604
BROOKE ARMY MEDICAL CENTER, TX (see BROOKE ARMY MEDICAL CENTER), p. A604

C

CHESTNUT RIDGE HOSPITAL, MORGANTOWN, WV, p. A685
CHESTNUT RIDGE HOSPITAL, WV (see WEST VIRGINIA UNIVERSITY HOSPITALS), p. A685
CHEYENNE COUNTY HOSPITAL, SAINT FRANCIS, KS, p. A245
CHEYENNE REGIONAL MEDICAL CENTER, CHEYENNE, WY, p. A707
CHEYENNE VETERANS AFFAIRS MEDICAL CENTER, CHEYENNE, WY, p. A708
CHG CORNERSTONE HOSPITAL CONROE, CONROE, TX, p. A593
CHG HOSPITAL TUCSON, LLC, TUCSON, AZ, p. A37
CHI HEALTH CREIGHTON UNIVERSITY MEDICAL CENTER - BERGAN MERCY, OMAHA, NE, p. A387
CHI HEALTH GOOD SAMARITAN, KEARNEY, NE, p. A385
CHI HEALTH GOOD SAMARITAN, NE (see GOOD SAMARITAN HEALTH SYSTEMS), p. A385
CHI HEALTH IMMANUEL, OMAHA, NE, p. A388
CHI HEALTH LAKESIDE, OMAHA, NE, p. A388
CHI HEALTH MERCY CORNING, CORNING, IA, p. A219
CHI HEALTH MERCY COUNCIL BLUFFS, COUNCIL BLUFFS, IA, p. A220
CHI HEALTH MIDLANDS, PAPILLION, NE, p. A389
CHI HEALTH MISSOURI VALLEY, MISSOURI VALLEY, IA, p. A226
CHI HEALTH NEBRASKA HEART, LINCOLN, NE, p. A386
CHI HEALTH PLAINVIEW, PLAINVIEW, NE, p. A390
CHI HEALTH SAINT FRANCIS, GRAND ISLAND, NE, p. A384
CHI HEALTH SCHUYLER, SCHUYLER, NE, p. A390
CHI HEALTH ST ELIZABETH, LINCOLN, NE, p. A386
CHI HEALTH ST. MARY'S, NEBRASKA CITY, NE, p. A387
CHI LAKEWOOD HEALTH, BAUDETTE, MN, p. A328
CHI LISBON HEALTH, LISBON, ND, p. A467
CHI MEMORIAL, CHATTANOOGA, TN, p. A567
CHI MEMORIAL HOSPITAL - GEORGIA, FORT OGLETHORPE, GA, p. A154
CHI MERCY HEALTH, VALLEY CITY, ND, p. A468
CHI OAKES HOSPITAL, OAKES, ND, p. A468
CHI ST ALEXIUS HEALTH CARRINGTON MEDICAL CENTER, CARRINGTON, ND, p. A464
CHI ST. ALEXIUS HEALTH - DICKINSON MEDICAL CENTER, DICKINSON, ND, p. A465
CHI ST. ALEXIUS HEALTH - WILLISTON MEDICAL CENTER, WILLISTON, ND, p. A469
CHI ST. ALEXIUS HEALTH, BISMARCK, ND, p. A464
CHI ST. ALEXIUS HEALTH DEVILS LAKE HOSPITAL, DEVILS LAKE, ND, p. A465
CHI ST. ALEXIUS HEALTH GARRISON, GARRISON, ND, p. A466
CHI ST. ANTHONY HOSPITAL, PENDLETON, OR, p. A515
CHI ST. FRANCIS HEALTH, BRECKENRIDGE, MN, p. A328
CHI ST. GABRIEL'S HEALTH, LITTLE FALLS, MN, p. A333
CHI ST. JOSEPH HEALTH BELLVILLE HOSPITAL, BELLVILLE, TX, p. A589
CHI ST. JOSEPH HEALTH BELLVILLE HOSPITAL, TX (see BELLVILLE GENERAL HOSPITAL), p. A589
CHI ST. JOSEPH HEALTH BURLESON HOSPITAL, CALDWELL, TX, p. A591
CHI ST. JOSEPH HEALTH GRIMES HOSPITAL, NAVASOTA, TX, p. A625
CHI ST. JOSEPH HEALTH MADISON HOSPITAL, MADISONVILLE, TX, p. A622
CHI ST. JOSEPH HEALTH REHABILITATION HOSPITAL, AN AFFILIATE OF ENCOMPASS HEALTH, BRYAN, TX, p. A591
CHI ST. JOSEPH REGIONAL HEALTH CENTER, BRYAN, TX, p. A591
CHI ST. JOSEPH'S HEALTH, PARK RAPIDS, MN, p. A337
CHI ST. LUKE'S HEALTH - PATIENTS MEDICAL CENTER, PASADENA, TX, p. A627
CHI ST. LUKE'S HEALTH - PATIENTS MEDICAL CENTER, TX (see PATIENTS MEDICAL CENTER), p. A627
CHI ST. LUKE'S HEALTH BRAZOSPORT, LAKE JACKSON, TX, p. A618
CHI ST. LUKE'S HEALTH MEMORIAL LIVINGSTON, LIVINGSTON, TX, p. A620
CHI ST. LUKE'S HEALTH MEMORIAL LUFKIN, LUFKIN, TX, p. A621
CHI ST. LUKE'S HEALTH MEMORIAL SAN AUGUSTINE, SAN AUGUSTINE, TX, p. A635
CHI ST. LUKE'S HEALTH MEMORIAL SPECIALTY HOSPITAL, LUFKIN, TX, p. A621
CHI ST. LUKE'S HEALTH-LAKESIDE HOSPITAL, THE WOODLANDS, TX, p. A639
CHI ST. LUKE'S HEALTH-THE WOODLANDS HOSPITAL, THE WOODLANDS, TX, p. A639
CHI ST. LUKE'S HOSPITAL - THE VINTAGE HOSPITAL, HOUSTON, TX, p. A610
CHI ST. VINCENT HOT SPRINGS, HOT SPRINGS-Garland County, AR, p. A43
CHI ST. VINCENT INFIRMARY MEDICAL CENTER, LITTLE ROCK-Pulaski County, AR, p. A45

CHI ST. VINCENT MEDICAL CENTER-NORTH, SHERWOOD-Pulaski County, AR, p. A48
CHI ST. VINCENT MORRILTON, MORRILTON-Conway County, AR, p. A46
CHI ST. VINCENT MORRILTON, AR (see ST. ANTHONY'S MEDICAL CENTER), p. A46
CHICAGO LAKESHORE HOSPITAL, CHICAGO, IL, p. A176
CHICAGO LYING-IN (CLI), CHICAGO, IL, p. A176
CHICAGO LYING-IN (CLI), IL (see UNIVERSITY OF CHICAGO MEDICAL CENTER), p. A180
CHICAGO-READ MENTAL HEALTH CENTER, CHICAGO, IL, p. A176
CHICKASAW NATION MEDICAL CENTER, ADA, OK, p. A495
CHICOT MEMORIAL MEDICAL CENTER, LAKE VILLAGE-Chicot County, AR, p. A44
CHILD AND ADOLESCENT BEHAVIORAL HEALTH SERVICES, WILLMAR, MN, p. A342
CHILDEN'S REGIONAL HOSPITAL AT COOPER, NJ (see COOPER UNIVERSITY HEALTH CARE), p. A403
CHILDREN AT PROVIDENCE ST. VINCENT, OR (see PROVIDENCE ST. VINCENT MEDICAL CENTER), p. A516
CHILDREN'S HEALTH CENTER, AZ (see ST. JOSEPH'S HOSPITAL AND MEDICAL CENTER), p. A34
CHILDREN'S HEALTHCARE OF ATLANTA, ATLANTA, GA, p. A146
CHILDREN'S HEALTHCARE OF ATLANTA AT EGLESTON, GA (see CHILDREN'S HEALTHCARE OF ATLANTA), p. A146
CHILDREN'S HEALTHCARE OF ATLANTA AT HUGHES SPALDING, GA (see CHILDREN'S HEALTHCARE OF ATLANTA), p. A146
CHILDREN'S HEALTHCARE OF ATLANTA AT SCOTTISH RITE, GA (see CHILDREN'S HEALTHCARE OF ATLANTA), p. A146
CHILDREN'S HEALTHCARE OF MISSISSIPPI, MS (see UNIVERSITY OF MISSISSIPPI MEDICAL CENTER), p. A348
CHILDREN'S HOSPITAL, NEW ORLEANS, LA, p. A275
CHILDREN'S HOSPITAL, OH (see CINCINNATI CHILDREN'S HOSPITAL MEDICAL CENTER), p. A474
CHILDREN'S HOSPITAL AND MEDICAL CENTER, OMAHA, NE, p. A388
CHILDREN'S HOSPITAL AT BRONSON, MI (see BRONSON METHODIST HOSPITAL), p. A317
CHILDREN'S HOSPITAL AT DARTMOUTH, NH (see DARTMOUTH-HITCHCOCK MEDICAL CENTER), p. A399
CHILDREN'S HOSPITAL AT MONMOUTH MEDICAL CENTER, NJ (see MONMOUTH MEDICAL CENTER, LONG BRANCH CAMPUS), p. A407
CHILDREN'S HOSPITAL AT PROVIDENCE, AK (see PROVIDENCE ALASKA MEDICAL CENTER), p. A25
CHILDREN'S HOSPITAL AT SAINT FRANCIS, OK (see SAINT FRANCIS HOSPITAL), p. A509
CHILDREN'S HOSPITAL COLORADO, AURORA, CO, p. A96
CHILDREN'S HOSPITAL LOS ANGELES, LOS ANGELES, CA, p. A66
CHILDREN'S HOSPITAL OF COLORADO AT MEMORIAL, CO (see CHILDREN'S HOSPITAL COLORADO), p. A96
CHILDREN'S HOSPITAL OF GEORGIA, GA (see AUGUSTA UNIVERSITY MEDICAL CENTER), p. A147
CHILDREN'S HOSPITAL OF ILLINOIS, IL (see OSF SAINT FRANCIS MEDICAL CENTER), p. A193
CHILDREN'S HOSPITAL OF MONTEFIORE, NY (see MONTEFIORE MEDICAL CENTER), p. A433
CHILDREN'S HOSPITAL OF NEVADA AT UMC, NV (see UNIVERSITY MEDICAL CENTER), p. A395
CHILDREN'S HOSPITAL OF NEW JERSEY, NJ (see NEWARK BETH ISRAEL MEDICAL CENTER), p. A408
CHILDREN'S HOSPITAL OF OKLAHOMA, OKLAHOMA CITY, OK, p. A503
CHILDREN'S HOSPITAL OF OKLAHOMA, OK (see OU MEDICAL CENTER), p. A504
CHILDREN'S HOSPITAL OF ORANGE COUNTY, ORANGE, CA, p. A76
CHILDREN'S HOSPITAL OF PHILADELPHIA, PHILADELPHIA, PA, p. A534
CHILDREN'S HOSPITAL OF PITTSBURGH OF UPMC, PITTSBURGH, PA, p. A537
CHILDREN'S HOSPITAL OF RICHMOND AT VCU, VA (see VCU MEDICAL CENTER), p. A665
CHILDREN'S HOSPITAL OF RICHMOND AT VCU-BROOK ROAD CAMPUS, RICHMOND, VA, p. A664
CHILDREN'S HOSPITAL OF SAN ANTONIO, TX (see CHRISTUS SANTA ROSA HEALTH SYSTEM), p. A632
CHILDREN'S HOSPITAL OF SHREVEPORT, LA (see UNIVERSITY HEALTH SHREVEPORT), p. A279
CHILDREN'S HOSPITAL OF SOUTH CAROLINA AT MUSC, SC (see MUSC HEALTH OF MEDICAL UNIVERSITY OF SOUTH CAROLINA), p. A550
CHILDREN'S HOSPITAL OF THE KING'S DAUGHTERS, NORFOLK, VA, p. A662
CHILDREN'S HOSPITAL OF WISCONSIN, MILWAUKEE, WI, p. A698

CHILDREN'S HOSPITAL OF WISCONSIN-FOX VALLEY, NEENAH, WI, p. A699
CHILDREN'S HOSPITAL, NAVICENT HEALTH, GA (see MEDICAL CENTER, NAVICENT HEALTH), p. A156
CHILDREN'S HOSPITALS AND CLINICS OF MINNESOTA, MINNEAPOLIS, MN, p. A335
CHILDREN'S HOSPITALS AND CLINICS OF MINNESOTA, MN (see CHILDREN'S HOSPITALS AND CLINICS OF MINNESOTA), p. A335
CHILDREN'S INN AT NIH, MD (see NATIONAL INSTITUTES OF HEALTH CLINICAL CENTER), p. A290
CHILDREN'S MEDICAL CENTER, NY (see NYU WINTHROP HOSPITAL), p. A430
CHILDREN'S MEDICAL CENTER DALLAS, DALLAS, TX, p. A596
CHILDREN'S MEDICAL CENTER PLANO, PLANO, TX, p. A628
CHILDREN'S MEMORIAL HERMANN HOSPITAL, TX (see MEMORIAL HERMANN - TEXAS MEDICAL CENTER), p. A612
CHILDREN'S MEMORIAL HOSPITAL, CHICAGO, IL, p. A176
CHILDREN'S MERCY HOSPITAL KANSAS, OVERLAND PARK, KS, p. A243
CHILDREN'S MERCY HOSPITAL KANSAS CITY, KANSAS CITY, MO, p. A361
CHILDREN'S NATIONAL HEALTH SYSTEM, WASHINGTON, DC, p. A115
CHILDREN'S OF ALABAMA, BIRMINGHAM, AL, p. A14
CHILDREN'S SPECIALIZED HOSPITAL, NEW BRUNSWICK, NJ, p. A408
CHILDREN'S SPECIALIZED HOSPITAL, NJ (see CHILDREN'S SPECIALIZED HOSPITAL), p. A408
CHILDRESS REGIONAL MEDICAL CENTER, CHILDRESS, TX, p. A592
CHILLICOTHE HOSPITAL DISTRICT, CHILLICOTHE, TX, p. A592
CHILLICOTHE VETERANS AFFAIRS MEDICAL CENTER, CHILLICOTHE, OH, p. A474
CHILLICOTHE VETERANS AFFAIRS MEDICAL CENTER, OH (see VETERANS AFFAIRS MEDICAL CENTER), p. A474
CHILTON MEDICAL CENTER, POMPTON PLAINS, NJ, p. A410
CHINESE HOSPITAL, SAN FRANCISCO, CA, p. A85
CHINLE COMPREHENSIVE HEALTH CARE FACILITY, CHINLE, AZ, p. A28
CHINO VALLEY MEDICAL CENTER, CHINO, CA, p. A54
CHIPPENHAM HOSPITAL, RICHMOND, VA, p. A664
CHIPPENHAM HOSPITAL, RICHMOND, VA (see JOHNSTON-WILLIS HOSPITAL), p. A665
CHIPPENHAM MEDICAL CENTER, VA (see CHIPPENHAM HOSPITAL), p. A664
CHIPPEWA COUNTY-MONTEVIDEO HOSPITAL, MONTEVIDEO, MN, p. A336
CHIPPEWA VALLEY HOSPITAL, DURAND, WI, p. A691
CHOATE MENTAL HEALTH CENTER, ANNA, IL, p. A173
CHOC CHILDREN'S AT MISSION HOSPITAL, MISSION VIEJO, CA, p. A72
CHOCTAW GENERAL HOSPITAL, BUTLER, AL, p. A15
CHOCTAW HEALTH CENTER, PHILADELPHIA, MS, p. A352
CHOCTAW MEMORIAL HOSPITAL, HUGO, OK, p. A500
CHOCTAW NATION HEALTH CARE CENTER, TALIHINA, OK, p. A507
CHOCTAW REGIONAL MEDICAL CENTER, ACKERMAN, MS, p. A343
CHRIS EVERT CHILDRENS HOSPITAL, FL (see BROWARD HEALTH MEDICAL CENTER), p. A122
CHRIST HOSPITAL, CINCINNATI, OH, p. A474
CHRISTIAN HEALTH CARE CENTER, WYCKOFF, NJ, p. A414
CHRISTIAN HOSPITAL, SAINT LOUIS, MO, p. A368
CHRISTIANA CARE HEALTH SYSTEM, NEWARK, DE, p. A113
CHRISTUS BOSSIER EMERGENCY HOSPITAL, LA (see CHRISTUS HEALTH SHREVEPORT-BOSSIER), p. A278
CHRISTUS COUSHATTA HEALTH CARE CENTER, COUSHATTA, LA, p. A266
CHRISTUS DUBUIS HOSPITAL OF ALEXANDRIA, ALEXANDRIA, LA, p. A262
CHRISTUS DUBUIS HOSPITAL OF BEAUMONT, BEAUMONT, TX, p. A588
CHRISTUS DUBUIS HOSPITAL OF FORT SMITH, FORT SMITH-Sebastian County, AR, p. A42
CHRISTUS DUBUIS HOSPITAL OF HOT SPRINGS, HOT SPRINGS NATIONAL PARK-Garland County, AR, p. A43
CHRISTUS DUBUIS HOSPITAL OF PARIS, PARIS, TX, p. A627
CHRISTUS DUBUIS HOSPITAL OF PORT ARTHUR, TX (see CHRISTUS DUBUIS HOSPITAL OF BEAUMONT), p. A588
CHRISTUS DUBUIS HOSPITAL OF PORT ARTHUR, TX (see DUBUIS HOSPITAL OF PORT ARTHUR), p. A629
CHRISTUS GOOD SHEPHERD MEDICAL CENTER, TX (see CHRISTUS GOOD SHEPHERD MEDICAL CENTER-MARSHALL), p. A622
CHRISTUS GOOD SHEPHERD MEDICAL CENTER-MARSHALL, MARSHALL, TX, p. A622

CHRISTUS HEALTH SHREVEPORT-BOSSIER, SHREVEPORT, LA, p. A278

CHRISTUS HIGHLAND MEDICAL CENTER, LA (see CHRISTUS HEALTH SHREVEPORT-BOSSIER), p. A278

CHRISTUS MOTHER FRANCES HOSPITAL - JACKSONVILLE, JACKSONVILLE, TX, p. A616

CHRISTUS MOTHER FRANCES HOSPITAL - SULPHUR SPRINGS, SULPHUR SPRINGS, TX, p. A637

CHRISTUS MOTHER FRANCES HOSPITAL - TYLER, TYLER, TX, p. A640

CHRISTUS MOTHER FRANCES HOSPITAL - WINNSBORO, WINNSBORO, TX, p. A644

CHRISTUS MOTHER FRANCES HOSPITAL - WINNSBORO, TX (see TEXAS HEALTH PRESBYTERIAN HOSPITAL WINNSBORO), p. A644

CHRISTUS OCHSNER LAKE AREA HOSPITAL, LAKE CHARLES, LA, p. A272

CHRISTUS OCHSNER ST. PATRICK HOSPITAL SOUTHWEST LOUISIANA, LAKE CHARLES, LA, p. A272

CHRISTUS SANTA ROSA HEALTH SYSTEM, SAN ANTONIO, TX, p. A632

CHRISTUS SANTA ROSA HOSPITAL - ALAMO HEIGHTS, TX (see CHRISTUS SANTA ROSA HEALTH SYSTEM), p. A632

CHRISTUS SANTA ROSA HOSPITAL - NEW BRAUNFELS, TX (see CHRISTUS SANTA ROSA HEALTH SYSTEM), p. A632

CHRISTUS SANTA ROSA-MEDICAL CENTER, TX (see CHRISTUS SANTA ROSA HEALTH SYSTEM), p. A632

CHRISTUS SOUTHEAST TEXAS HOSPITAL - ST. ELIZABETH, BEAUMONT, TX, p. A588

CHRISTUS SOUTHEAST TEXAS HOSPITAL-ST. MARY, TX (see CHRISTUS SOUTHEAST TEXAS HOSPITAL - ST. ELIZABETH), p. A588

CHRISTUS SOUTHEAST TEXAS JASPER MEMORIAL, JASPER, TX, p. A616

CHRISTUS SOUTHEAST TEXAS ORTHOPEDIC SPECIALTY CENTER, BEAUMONT, TX, p. A588

CHRISTUS SPOHN HOSPITAL ALICE, ALICE, TX, p. A582

CHRISTUS SPOHN HOSPITAL BEEVILLE, BEEVILLE, TX, p. A588

CHRISTUS SPOHN HOSPITAL CORPUS CHRISTI MEMORIAL, CORPUS CHRISTI, TX, p. A594

CHRISTUS SPOHN HOSPITAL CORPUS CHRISTI SHORELINE, TX (see CHRISTUS SPOHN HOSPITAL CORPUS CHRISTI MEMORIAL), p. A594

CHRISTUS SPOHN HOSPITAL CORPUS CHRISTI SOUTH, TX (see CHRISTUS SPOHN HOSPITAL CORPUS CHRISTI MEMORIAL), p. A594

CHRISTUS SPOHN HOSPITAL KLEBERG, KINGSVILLE, TX, p. A617

CHRISTUS ST. CATHERINE HOSPITAL, KATY, TX, p. A616

CHRISTUS ST. FRANCES CABRINI HOSPITAL, ALEXANDRIA, LA, p. A262

CHRISTUS ST. MICHAEL HEALTH SYSTEM, TEXARKANA, TX, p. A639

CHRISTUS ST. MICHAEL HOSPITAL-ATLANTA, TX (see CHRISTUS ST. MICHAEL HEALTH SYSTEM), p. A639

CHRISTUS ST. MICHAEL REHABILITATION HOSPITAL, TEXARKANA, TX, p. A639

CHRISTUS ST. VINCENT PHYSICIANS MEDICAL CENTER, NM (see CHRISTUS ST. VINCENT REGIONAL MEDICAL CENTER), p. A419

CHRISTUS ST. VINCENT REGIONAL MEDICAL CENTER, SANTA FE, NM, p. A419

CHRISTUS TRINITY MOTHER FRANCES REHABILITATION HOSPITAL, A PARTNER OF ENCOMPASS HEALTH, TYLER, TX, p. A641

CIBOLA GENERAL HOSPITAL, GRANTS, NM, p. A417

CIMARRON MEMORIAL HOSPITAL, BOISE CITY, OK, p. A496

CINCINNATI CHILDREN'S HOSPITAL MEDICAL CENTER, CINCINNATI, OH, p. A474

CINCINNATI VETERANS AFFAIRS MEDICAL CENTER, CINCINNATI, OH, p. A474

CINCINNATI VETERANS AFFAIRS MEDICAL CENTER, OH (see VETERANS AFFAIRS MEDICAL CENTER), p. A476

CIRCLES OF CARE, MELBOURNE, FL, p. A129

CITIZENS BAPTIST MEDICAL CENTER, TALLADEGA, AL, p. A23

CITIZENS MEDICAL CENTER, COLBY, KS, p. A233

CITIZENS MEDICAL CENTER, COLUMBIA, LA, p. A266

CITIZENS MEDICAL CENTER, VICTORIA, TX, p. A642

CITIZENS MEMORIAL HOSPITAL, BOLIVAR, MO, p. A355

CITRUS MEMORIAL HEALTH SYSTEM, INVERNESS, FL, p. A125

CITRUS VALLEY MEDICAL CENTER-INTER COMMUNITY CAMPUS, COVINA, CA, p. A56

CITRUS VALLEY MEDICAL CENTER-INTER-COMMUNITY CAMPUS, CA (see CITRUS VALLEY MEDICAL CENTER-INTER COMMUNITY CAMPUS), p. A56

CITRUS VALLEY MEDICAL CENTER-QUEEN OF THE VALLEY CAMPUS, CA (see CITRUS VALLEY MEDICAL CENTER-INTER COMMUNITY CAMPUS), p. A56

CITY HOSPITAL AT WHITE ROCK, DALLAS, TX, p. A596

CITY OF HOPE'S HELFORD CLINICAL RESEARCH HOSPITAL, DUARTE, CA, p. A57

CLAIBORNE COUNTY MEDICAL CENTER, PORT GIBSON, MS, p. A352

CLAIBORNE MEDICAL CENTER, TAZEWELL, TN, p. A580

CLAIBORNE MEMORIAL MEDICAL CENTER, HOMER, LA, p. A268

CLARA BARTON HOSPITAL, HOISINGTON, KS, p. A236

CLARA MAASS MEDICAL CENTER, BELLEVILLE, NJ, p. A402

CLAREMORE INDIAN HOSPITAL, CLAREMORE, OK, p. A497

CLARIAN ARNETT HOSPITAL, LAFAYETTE, IN, p. A209

CLARIAN HEALTH PARTNERS, INDIANAPOLIS, IN, p. A206

CLARIAN NORTH MEDICAL CENTER, CARMEL, IN, p. A201

CLARIAN WEST MEDICAL CENTER, AVON, IN, p. A199

CLARINDA REGIONAL HEALTH CENTER, CLARINDA, IA, p. A219

CLARION HOSPITAL, CLARION, PA, p. A522

CLARION PSYCHIATRIC CENTER, CLARION, PA, p. A522

CLARITY CHILD GUIDANCE CENTER, SAN ANTONIO, TX, p. A632

CLARK FORK VALLEY HOSPITAL, PLAINS, MT, p. A378

CLARK MEMORIAL HOSPITAL, JEFFERSONVILLE, IN, p. A208

CLARK REGIONAL MEDICAL CENTER, WINCHESTER, KY, p. A261

CLARKE COUNTY HOSPITAL, OSCEOLA, IA, p. A228

CLARKS SUMMIT STATE HOSPITAL, CLARKS SUMMIT, PA, p. A522

CLAXTON-HEPBURN MEDICAL CENTER, OGDENSBURG, NY, p. A439

CLAY COUNTY HOSPITAL, ASHLAND, AL, p. A13

CLAY COUNTY HOSPITAL, FLORA, IL, p. A183

CLAY COUNTY MEDICAL CENTER, CLAY CENTER, KS, p. A233

CLAY COUNTY MEMORIAL HOSPITAL, HENRIETTA, TX, p. A609

CLEAR LAKE REGIONAL MEDICAL CENTER, WEBSTER, TX, p. A643

CLEAR LAKE REGIONAL MEDICAL CENTER, WEBSTER, TX (see ALVIN DIAGNOSTIC AND URGENT CARE CENTER), p. A583

CLEAR LAKE REHABILITATION HOSPITAL, WEBSTER, TX, p. A643

CLEARVISTA HEALTH AND WELLNESS, LORAIN, OH, p. A485

CLEARWATER VALLEY HOSPITAL AND CLINICS, OROFINO, ID, p. A170

CLEMENT J. ZABLOCKI VETERANS AFFAIRS MEDICAL CENTER, MILWAUKEE, WI, p. A698

CLEVELAND AREA HOSPITAL, CLEVELAND, OK, p. A497

CLEVELAND CLINIC, CLEVELAND, OH, p. A476

CLEVELAND CLINIC AKRON GENERAL, AKRON, OH, p. A470

CLEVELAND CLINIC AKRON GENERAL LODI HOSPITAL, LODI, OH, p. A485

CLEVELAND CLINIC AVON HOSPITAL, AVON, OH, p. A471

CLEVELAND CLINIC CHILDREN'S HOSPITAL, OH (see CLEVELAND CLINIC), p. A476

CLEVELAND CLINIC CHILDREN'S HOSPITAL FOR REHABILITATION, CLEVELAND, OH, p. A476

CLEVELAND CLINIC FAIRVIEW HOSPITAL, CLEVELAND, OH, p. A476

CLEVELAND CLINIC FLORIDA, WESTON, FL, p. A144

CLEVELAND CLINIC REHABILITATION HOSPITAL, AVON, OH, p. A471

CLEVELAND CLINIC REHABILITATION HOSPITAL, OH (see CLEVELAND CLINIC REHABILITATION HOSPITAL), p. A471

CLEVELAND CLINIC UNION HOSPITAL, DOVER, OH, p. A481

CLEVELAND CLINIC, MEDINA HOSPITAL, MEDINA, OH, p. A486

CLEVELAND EMERGENCY HOSPITAL, CLEVELAND, TX, p. A592

CLIFTON SPRINGS HOSPITAL AND CLINIC, CLIFTON SPRINGS, NY, p. A424

CLIFTON T. PERKINS HOSPITAL CENTER, JESSUP, MD, p. A292

CLIFTON-FINE HOSPITAL, STAR LAKE, NY, p. A443

CLINCH MEMORIAL HOSPITAL, HOMERVILLE, GA, p. A155

CLINCH VALLEY MEDICAL CENTER, RICHLANDS, VA, p. A664

CLOUD COUNTY HEALTH CENTER, CONCORDIA, KS, p. A234

CLOVIS COMMUNITY MEDICAL CENTER, CLOVIS, CA, p. A55

CMH REGIONAL HEALTH SYSTEM, WILMINGTON, OH, p. A494

COAL COUNTY GENERAL HOSPITAL, COALGATE, OK, p. A497

COAST PLAZA DOCTORS HOSPITAL, NORWALK, CA, p. A75

COAST PLAZA HOSPITAL, NORWALK, CA, p. A75

COAST PLAZA HOSPITAL, CA (see COAST PLAZA DOCTORS HOSPITAL), p. A75

COASTAL CAROLINA HOSPITAL, HARDEEVILLE, SC, p. A554

COASTAL HARBOR TREATMENT CENTER, SAVANNAH, GA, p. A160

COASTAL VIRGINIA REHABILITATION, NEWPORT NEWS, VA, p. A662

COATESVILLE VETERANS AFFAIRS MEDICAL CENTER, COATESVILLE, PA, p. A523

COATESVILLE VETERANS AFFAIRS MEDICAL CENTER, PA (see VETERANS AFFAIRS MEDICAL CENTER), p. A523

COBALT REHABILITATION HOSPITAL, SURPRISE, AZ, p. A36

COBALT REHABILITATION HOSPITAL OF NEW ORLEANS, NEW ORLEANS, LA, p. A275

COBLESKILL REGIONAL HOSPITAL, COBLESKILL, NY, p. A424

COBRE VALLEY COMMUNITY HOSPITAL, GLOBE, AZ, p. A30

COBRE VALLEY REGIONAL MEDICAL CENTER, GLOBE, AZ, p. A30

COBRE VALLEY REGIONAL MEDICAL CENTER, AZ (see COBRE VALLEY COMMUNITY HOSPITAL), p. A30

COCHRAN MEMORIAL HOSPITAL, MORTON, TX, p. A624

COFFEE REGIONAL MEDICAL CENTER, DOUGLAS, GA, p. A152

COFFEY COUNTY HOSPITAL, BURLINGTON, KS, p. A233

COFFEYVILLE REGIONAL MEDICAL CENTER, COFFEYVILLE, KS, p. A233

COGDELL MEMORIAL HOSPITAL, SNYDER, TX, p. A636

COLEMAN COUNTY MEDICAL CENTER, COLEMAN, TX, p. A593

COLER REHABILITATION AND NURSING CARE CENTER, NY (see NYC HEALTH + HOSPITALS / HENRY J CARTER SPECIALTY HOSPITAL AND MEDICAL CENTER), p. A435

COLER-GOLDWATER SPECIALTY HOSPITAL AND NURSING FACILITY, NEW YORK (Includes all hospitals located within the five boroughs), NY, p. A432

COLISEUM CENTER FOR BEHAVIORAL HEALTH, GA (see COLISEUM MEDICAL CENTERS), p. A156

COLISEUM MEDICAL CENTERS, MACON, GA, p. A156

COLISEUM NORTHSIDE HOSPITAL, MACON, GA, p. A156

COLLEGE HOSPITAL CERRITOS, CERRITOS, CA, p. A54

COLLEGE HOSPITAL COSTA MESA, COSTA MESA, CA, p. A55

COLLEGE MEDICAL CENTER, LONG BEACH, CA, p. A65

COLLEGE STATION MEDICAL CENTER, COLLEGE STATION, TX, p. A593

COLLETON MEDICAL CENTER, WALTERBORO, SC, p. A557

COLLINGSWORTH GENERAL HOSPITAL, WELLINGTON, TX, p. A643

COLONEL FLORENCE A. BLANCHFIELD ARMY COMMUNITY HOSPITAL, FORT CAMPBELL, KY, p. A252

COLORADO ACUTE LONG TERM HOSPITAL, DENVER, CO, p. A98

COLORADO CANYONS HOSPITAL AND MEDICAL CENTER, FRUITA, CO, p. A101

COLORADO MENTAL HEALTH INSTITUTE AT FORT LOGAN, DENVER, CO, p. A98

COLORADO MENTAL HEALTH INSTITUTE AT PUEBLO, PUEBLO, CO, p. A104

COLORADO PLAINS MEDICAL CENTER, FORT MORGAN, CO, p. A100

COLORADO RIVER MEDICAL CENTER, NEEDLES, CA, p. A75

COLQUITT REGIONAL MEDICAL CENTER, MOULTRIE, GA, p. A158

COLUMBIA BASIN HOSPITAL, EPHRATA, WA, p. A671

COLUMBIA CENTER BIRTH HOSPITAL, MEQUON, WI, p. A697

COLUMBIA COUNTY HEALTH SYSTEM, DAYTON, WA, p. A671

COLUMBIA MEMORIAL HOSPITAL, ASTORIA, OR, p. A511

COLUMBIA MEMORIAL HOSPITAL, HUDSON, NY, p. A428

COLUMBIA ST. MARY'S COLUMBIA HOSPITAL, WI (see COLUMBIA ST. MARY'S HOSPITAL MILWAUKEE), p. A698

COLUMBIA ST. MARY'S HOSPITAL MILWAUKEE, MILWAUKEE, WI, p. A698

COLUMBIA ST. MARY'S HOSPITAL OZAUKEE, MEQUON, WI, p. A698

COLUMBIA ST. MARY'S MILWAUKEE HOSPITAL, MILWAUKEE, WI, p. A698

COLUMBIA ST. MARY'S MILWAUKEE HOSPITAL, WI (see COLUMBIA ST. MARY'S HOSPITAL MILWAUKEE), p. A698

COLUMBUS COMMUNITY HOSPITAL, COLUMBUS, NE, p. A383

COLUMBUS COMMUNITY HOSPITAL, COLUMBUS, TX, p. A593

COLUMBUS COMMUNITY HOSPITAL, INC., COLUMBUS, WI, p. A691

COLUMBUS DUBLIN SPRINGS, DUBLIN, OH, p. A481

COLUMBUS HOSPITAL LTACH, NEWARK, NJ, p. A408

COLUMBUS REGIONAL HEALTHCARE SYSTEM, WHITEVILLE, NC, p. A462

COLUMBUS REGIONAL HOSPITAL, COLUMBUS, IN, p. A201

COLUMBUS SPECIALTY HOSPITAL, COLUMBUS, GA, p. A150

COLUMBUS SPRINGS EAST HOSPITAL, OH (see COLUMBUS DUBLIN SPRINGS), p. A481

D

DEVEREUX HOSPITAL AND CHILDREN'S CENTER OF FLORIDA, MELBOURNE, FL, p. A129
DEVEREUX TEXAS TREATMENT NETWORK, LEAGUE CITY, TX, p. A619
DEWITT HOSPITAL, DEWITT-Arkansas County, AR, p. A41
DIAMOND CHILDREN'S HOSPITAL, AZ (see BANNER - UNIVERSITY MEDICAL CENTER TUCSON), p. A37
DICKENSON COMMUNITY HOSPITAL, CLINTWOOD, VA, p. A657
DICKINSON COUNTY HEALTHCARE SYSTEM, IRON MOUNTAIN, MI, p. A316
DIGNITY HEALTH ARIZONA GENERAL HOSPITAL, LAVEEN, AZ, p. A31
DILEY RIDGE MEDICAL CENTER, CANAL WINCHESTER, OH, p. A473
DIMMIT REGIONAL HOSPITAL, CARRIZO SPRINGS, TX, p. A591
DISTRICT ONE HOSPITAL, FARIBAULT, MN, p. A331
DIVINE PROVIDENCE HOSPITAL, WILLIAMSPORT, PA, p. A545
DIVINE SAVIOR HEALTHCARE, PORTAGE, WI, p. A701
DIXIE REGIONAL MEDICAL CENTER, SAINT GEORGE, UT, p. A650
DIXIE REGIONAL MEDICAL CENTER, UT (see DIXIE REGIONAL MEDICAL CENTER), p. A650
DMC - CHILDREN'S HOSPITAL OF MICHIGAN, DETROIT, MI, p. A310
DMC - DETROIT RECEIVING HOSPITAL, DETROIT, MI, p. A311
DMC HARPER UNIVERSITY HOSPITAL, DETROIT, MI, p. A311
DMC HARPER UNIVERSITY HOSPITAL, MI (see HARPER UNIVERSITY HOSPITAL), p. A311
DMC HURON VALLEY-SINAI HOSPITAL, COMMERCE TOWNSHIP, MI, p. A310
DMC HUTZEL WOMEN'S HOSPITAL, MI (see DMC HARPER UNIVERSITY HOSPITAL), p. A311
DMC - REHABILITATION INSTITUTE OF MICHIGAN, DETROIT, MI, p. A311
DMC - SINAI-GRACE HOSPITAL, DETROIT, MI, p. A311
DOCTOR'S CENTER OF BAYAMON, BAYAMON, PR, p. A712
DOCTOR'S HOSPITAL, LEAWOOD, KS, p. A239
DOCTOR'S HOSPITAL AT RENAISSANCE, EDINBURG, TX, p. A600
DOCTOR'S HOSPITAL OF DEER CREEK, LEESVILLE, LA, p. A272
DOCTOR'S MEMORIAL HOSPITAL, PERRY, FL, p. A136
DOCTORS CENTER, MANATI, PR, p. A714
DOCTORS' CENTER HOSPITAL SAN JUAN, SAN JUAN, PR, p. A715
DOCTORS COMMUNITY HOSPITAL, LANHAM, MD, p. A292
DOCTORS HOSPITAL, AUGUSTA, GA, p. A147
DOCTORS HOSPITAL OF JEFFERSON, LA (see EAST JEFFERSON GENERAL HOSPITAL), p. A274
DOCTORS HOSPITAL OF LAREDO, LAREDO, TX, p. A619
DOCTORS HOSPITAL OF MANTECA, MANTECA, CA, p. A71
DOCTORS' HOSPITAL OF MICHIGAN, PONTIAC, MI, p. A321
DOCTORS HOSPITAL OF SARASOTA, SARASOTA, FL, p. A138
DOCTORS HOSPITAL PARKWAY, TX (see UNITED MEMORIAL MEDICAL CARE), p. A614
DOCTORS MEDICAL CENTER OF MODESTO, MODESTO, CA, p. A72
DOCTORS MEMORIAL HOSPITAL, BONIFAY, FL, p. A118
DOCTORS NEUROPSYCHIATRIC HOSPITAL AND RESEARCH INSTITUTE, BREMEN, IN, p. A200
DODGE COUNTY HOSPITAL, EASTMAN, GA, p. A153
DOERNBECHER CHILDREN'S HOSPITAL, OR (see OHSU HOSPITAL), p. A516
DOMINICAN HOSPITAL, SANTA CRUZ, CA, p. A88
DOMINION HOSPITAL, FALLS CHURCH, VA, p. A657
DONALSONVILLE HOSPITAL, DONALSONVILLE, GA, p. A152
DOOR COUNTY MEDICAL CENTER, STURGEON BAY, WI, p. A704
DOOR COUNTY MEDICAL CENTER, WI (see DOOR COUNTY MEMORIAL HOSPITAL), p. A704
DOOR COUNTY MEMORIAL HOSPITAL, STURGEON BAY, WI, p. A704
DORMINY MEDICAL CENTER, FITZGERALD, GA, p. A153
DOROTHEA DIX PSYCHIATRIC CENTER, BANGOR, ME, p. A282
DOUGLAS COUNTY COMMUNITY MENTAL HEALTH CENTER, OMAHA, NE, p. A388
DOUGLAS COUNTY MEMORIAL HOSPITAL, ARMOUR, SD, p. A559
DOVER BEHAVIORAL HEALTH SYSTEM, DOVER, DE, p. A113
DOWN EAST COMMUNITY HOSPITAL, MACHIAS, ME, p. A285
DOYLESTOWN HOSPITAL, DOYLESTOWN, PA, p. A524
DR. DAN C. TRIGG MEMORIAL HOSPITAL, TUCUMCARI, NM, p. A420
DR. J. CORRIGAN MENTAL HEALTH CENTER, FALL RIVER, MA, p. A299
DR. PILA'S HOSPITAL, PONCE, PR, p. A714

DR. RAMON E. BETANCES HOSPITAL-MAYAGUEZ MEDICAL CENTER BRANCH, MAYAGUEZ, PR, p. A714
DR. SOLOMON CARTER FULLER MENTAL HEALTH CENTER, BOSTON, MA, p. A296
DREW MEMORIAL HEALTH SYSTEM, MONTICELLO-Drew County, AR, p. A46
DRISCOLL CHILDREN'S HOSPITAL, CORPUS CHRISTI, TX, p. A594
DRUMRIGHT REGIONAL HOSPITAL, DRUMRIGHT, OK, p. A497
DUANE L. WATERS HOSPITAL, JACKSON, MI, p. A316
DUBUIS HOSPITAL OF HOUSTON, HOUSTON, TX, p. A610
DUBUIS HOSPITAL OF PORT ARTHUR, PORT ARTHUR, TX, p. A629
DUKE CHILDREN'S HOSPITAL & HEALTH CENTER, NC (see DUKE UNIVERSITY HOSPITAL), p. A451
DUKE RALEIGH HOSPITAL, RALEIGH, NC, p. A459
DUKE REGIONAL HOSPITAL, DURHAM, NC, p. A451
DUKE REGIONAL HOSPITAL, NC (see DURHAM REGIONAL HOSPITAL), p. A451
DUKE UNIVERSITY HOSPITAL, DURHAM, NC, p. A451
DUKES MEMORIAL HOSPITAL, PERU, IN, p. A213
DUNCAN REGIONAL HOSPITAL, DUNCAN, OK, p. A498
DUNDY COUNTY HOSPITAL, BENKELMAN, NE, p. A382
DUNN MEMORIAL HOSPITAL, BEDFORD, IN, p. A199
DUPONT HOSPITAL, FORT WAYNE, IN, p. A203
DURHAM REGIONAL HOSPITAL, DURHAM, NC, p. A451
DURHAM VETERANS AFFAIRS MEDICAL CENTER, DURHAM, NC, p. A451
DWIGHT DAVID EISENHOWER ARMY MEDICAL CENTER, FORT GORDON, GA, p. A154

E

E. A. CONWAY MEDICAL CENTER, MONROE, LA, p. A274
EAGLEVILLE HOSPITAL, EAGLEVILLE, PA, p. A524
EARLE E. MORRIS ALCOHOL AND DRUG TREATMENT CENTER, COLUMBIA, SC, p. A551
EAST ADAMS RURAL HEALTHCARE, RITZVILLE, WA, p. A676
EAST ALABAMA MEDICAL CENTER, OPELIKA, AL, p. A22
EAST ALABAMA MEDICAL CENTER-LANIER, AL (see EAST ALABAMA MEDICAL CENTER), p. A22
EAST CAMPUS, NE (see FAITH REGIONAL HEALTH SERVICES), p. A387
EAST CARROLL PARISH HOSPITAL, LAKE PROVIDENCE, LA, p. A272
EAST CENTRAL REGIONAL HOSPITAL, AUGUSTA, GA, p. A147
EAST CENTRAL REGIONAL HOSPITAL, GRACEWOOD, GA, p. A154
EAST CENTRAL REGIONAL HOSPITAL, GA (see EAST CENTRAL REGIONAL HOSPITAL), p. A147
EAST CENTRAL REGIONAL HOSPITAL, AUGUSTA, GA (see EAST CENTRAL REGIONAL HOSPITAL), p. A154
EAST COOPER MEDICAL CENTER, MOUNT PLEASANT, SC, p. A555
EAST COOPER MEDICAL CENTER, SC (see EAST COOPER REGIONAL MEDICAL CENTER), p. A555
EAST COOPER REGIONAL MEDICAL CENTER, MOUNT PLEASANT, SC, p. A555
EAST EL PASO PHYSICIANS MEDICAL CENTER, EL PASO, TX, p. A601
EAST GEORGIA REGIONAL MEDICAL CENTER, STATESBORO, GA, p. A161
EAST JEFFERSON GENERAL HOSPITAL, METAIRIE, LA, p. A274
EAST LIVERPOOL CITY HOSPITAL, EAST LIVERPOOL, OH, p. A482
EAST LOS ANGELES DOCTORS HOSPITAL, LOS ANGELES, CA, p. A66
EAST MISSISSIPPI STATE HOSPITAL, MERIDIAN, MS, p. A350
EAST MORGAN COUNTY HOSPITAL, BRUSH, CO, p. A97
EAST MOUNTAIN HOSPITAL, BELLE MEAD, NJ, p. A402
EAST OHIO REGIONAL HOSPITAL, MARTINS FERRY, OH, p. A486
EAST ORANGE DIVISION, NJ (see VETERANS AFFAIRS NEW JERSEY HEALTH CARE SYSTEM), p. A404
EAST ORANGE GENERAL HOSPITAL, EAST ORANGE, NJ, p. A404
EAST RIDGE HOSPITAL, EAST RIDGE, TN, p. A569
EAST RIDGE HOSPITAL, TN (see PARKRIDGE MEDICAL CENTER), p. A567
EAST TENNESSEE CHILDREN'S HOSPITAL, KNOXVILLE, TN, p. A572
EASTAR HEALTH SYSTEM, EAST CAMPUS, MUSKOGEE, OK, p. A501

EASTAR HEALTH SYSTEM, EAST CAMPUS, OK (see SAINT FRANCIS HOSPITAL MUSKOGEE), p. A502
EASTERN IDAHO REGIONAL MEDICAL CENTER, IDAHO FALLS, ID, p. A169
EASTERN LONG ISLAND HOSPITAL, GREENPORT, NY, p. A427
EASTERN LOUISIANA MENTAL HEALTH SYSTEM, JACKSON, LA, p. A269
EASTERN MAINE MEDICAL CENTER, BANGOR, ME, p. A282
EASTERN NEW MEXICO MEDICAL CENTER, ROSWELL, NM, p. A419
EASTERN NIAGARA HOSPITAL, LOCKPORT, NY, p. A429
EASTERN NIAGARA HOSPITAL LOCKPORT, NY (see EASTERN NIAGARA HOSPITAL), p. A429
EASTERN NIAGARA HOSPITAL NEWFANE, NY (see EASTERN NIAGARA HOSPITAL), p. A429
EASTERN OKLAHOMA MEDICAL CENTER, POTEAU, OK, p. A505
EASTERN PLUMAS HEALTH CARE, PORTOLA, CA, p. A79
EASTERN SHORE HOSPITAL CENTER, CAMBRIDGE, MD, p. A290
EASTERN STATE HOSPITAL, LEXINGTON, KY, p. A254
EASTERN STATE HOSPITAL, MEDICAL LAKE, WA, p. A673
EASTERN STATE HOSPITAL, WILLIAMSBURG, VA, p. A667
EASTLAND MEMORIAL HOSPITAL, EASTLAND, TX, p. A600
EASTON HOSPITAL, EASTON, PA, p. A524
EASTPOINTE HOSPITAL, DAPHNE, AL, p. A16
EASTSIDE MEDICAL CENTER, SNELLVILLE, GA, p. A161
EASTSIDE PSYCHIATRIC HOSPITAL, TALLAHASSEE, FL, p. A140
EATON RAPIDS MEDICAL CENTER, EATON RAPIDS, MI, p. A312
ED FRASER MEMORIAL HOSPITAL AND BAKER COMMUNITY HEALTH CENTER, MACCLENNY, FL, p. A128
EDEN MEDICAL CENTER, CASTRO VALLEY, CA, p. A54
EDGEFIELD COUNTY HOSPITAL, EDGEFIELD, SC, p. A552
EDGERTON HOSPITAL AND HEALTH SERVICES, EDGERTON, WI, p. A692
EDGEWOOD SURGICAL HOSPITAL, TRANSFER, PA, p. A542
EDINBURG CHILDREN'S HOSPITAL, TX (see SOUTH TEXAS HEALTH SYSTEM), p. A601
EDINBURG REGIONAL MEDICAL CENTER, TX (see SOUTH TEXAS HEALTH SYSTEM), p. A601
EDWARD HINES, JR. VETERANS AFFAIRS HOSPITAL, HINES, IL, p. A185
EDWARD HINES, JR. VETERANS AFFAIRS HOSPITAL, IL (see VETERANS AFFAIRS EDWARD HINES, JR. HOSPITAL), p. A185
EDWARD HOSPITAL, NAPERVILLE, IL, p. A190
EDWARDS COUNTY MEDICAL CENTER, KINSLEY, KS, p. A238
EDWIN SHAW REHAB, CUYAHOGA FALLS, OH, p. A480
EFFINGHAM HOSPITAL, SPRINGFIELD, GA, p. A161
EINSTEIN MEDICAL CENTER ELKINS PARK, PA (see EINSTEIN MEDICAL CENTER PHILADELPHIA), p. A534
EINSTEIN MEDICAL CENTER MONTGOMERY, EAST NORRITON, PA, p. A524
EINSTEIN MEDICAL CENTER PHILADELPHIA, PHILADELPHIA, PA, p. A534
EINSTEIN MEDICAL CENTER PHILADELPHIA, PA (see ALBERT EINSTEIN MEDICAL CENTER), p. A533
EISENHOWER MEDICAL CENTER, RANCHO MIRAGE, CA, p. A79
EL CAMINO HOSPITAL, MOUNTAIN VIEW, CA, p. A74
EL CAMINO HOSPITAL LOS GATOS, CA (see EL CAMINO HOSPITAL), p. A74
EL CAMPO MEMORIAL HOSPITAL, EL CAMPO, TX, p. A601
EL CENTRO REGIONAL MEDICAL CENTER, EL CENTRO, CA, p. A57
EL PASO BEHAVIORAL HEALTH SYSTEM, EL PASO, TX, p. A601
EL PASO CHILDREN'S HOSPITAL, EL PASO, TX, p. A601
EL PASO LTAC HOSPITAL, EL PASO, TX, p. A601
EL PASO PSYCHIATRIC CENTER, EL PASO, TX, p. A601
EL PASO SPECIALTY HOSPITAL, EL PASO, TX, p. A601
ELBERT MEMORIAL HOSPITAL, ELBERTON, GA, p. A153
ELEAH MEDICAL CENTER, ELBOW LAKE, MN, p. A331
ELEANOR SLATER HOSPITAL, CRANSTON, RI, p. A547
ELECTRA MEMORIAL HOSPITAL, ELECTRA, TX, p. A603
ELGIN MENTAL HEALTH CENTER, ELGIN, IL, p. A182
ELIZA COFFEE MEMORIAL HOSPITAL, FLORENCE, AL, p. A18
ELIZABETH SETON PEDIATRIC CENTER, NY (see SISTERS OF CHARITY HOSPITAL OF BUFFALO), p. A424
ELKHART GENERAL HOSPITAL, ELKHART, IN, p. A202
ELKHORN VALLEY REHABILITATION HOSPITAL, CASPER, WY, p. A707
ELKVIEW GENERAL HOSPITAL, HOBART, OK, p. A499
ELLENVILLE REGIONAL HOSPITAL, ELLENVILLE, NY, p. A426
ELLETT MEMORIAL HOSPITAL, APPLETON CITY, MO, p. A355
ELLINWOOD DISTRICT HOSPITAL, ELLINWOOD, KS, p. A234
ELLIOT HOSPITAL, MANCHESTER, NH, p. A400

F

FAIRCHILD MEDICAL CENTER, YREKA, CA, p. A95

FAIRFAX BEHAVIORAL HEALTH, KIRKLAND, WA, p. A673

FAIRFAX BEHAVIORAL HEALTH EVERETT, WA (see FAIRFAX BEHAVIORAL HEALTH), p. A673

FAIRFAX COMMUNITY HOSPITAL, FAIRFAX, OK, p. A499

FAIRFAX COMMUNITY HOSPITAL, OK (see FAIRFAX MEMORIAL HOSPITAL), p. A499

FAIRFAX MEMORIAL HOSPITAL, FAIRFAX, OK, A499

FAIRFIELD MEDICAL CENTER, LANCASTER, OH, p. A484

FAIRFIELD MEMORIAL HOSPITAL, FAIRFIELD, IL, p. A183

FAIRFIELD MEMORIAL HOSPITAL, WINNSBORO, SC, p. A558

FAIRLAWN REHABILITATION HOSPITAL, WORCESTER, MA, p. A306

FAIRMONT HOSPITAL, SAN LEANDRO, CA, p. A87

FAIRMONT HOSPITAL, CA (see HIGHLAND HOSPITAL), p. A75

FAIRMONT REGIONAL MEDICAL CENTER, FAIRMONT, WV, p. A683

FAIRMOUNT BEHAVIORAL HEALTH SYSTEM, PHILADELPHIA, PA, p. A534

FAIRVIEW DEVELOPMENTAL CENTER, COSTA MESA, CA, p. A55

FAIRVIEW HOSPITAL, GREAT BARRINGTON, MA, p. A300

FAIRVIEW LAKES HEALTH SERVICES, WYOMING, MN, p. A342

FAIRVIEW NORTHLAND MEDICAL CENTER, PRINCETON, MN, p. A337

FAIRVIEW PARK HOSPITAL, DUBLIN, GA, p. A153

FAIRVIEW REGIONAL MEDICAL CENTER, FAIRVIEW, OK, p. A499

FAIRVIEW RIDGES HOSPITAL, BURNSVILLE, MN, p. A329

FAIRVIEW RIVERSIDE HOSPITAL, MINNEAPOLIS, MN, p. A335

FAIRVIEW RIVERSIDE HOSPITAL, MN (see UNIVERSITY OF MINNESOTA MEDICAL CENTER, FAIRVIEW), p. A335

FAIRVIEW SOUTHDALE HOSPITAL, EDINA, MN, p. A331

FAITH COMMUNITY HOSPITAL, JACKSBORO, TX, p. A616

FAITH REGIONAL HEALTH SERVICES, NORFOLK, NE, p. A387

FALL RIVER HOSPITAL, HOT SPRINGS, SD, p. A561

FALLON MEDICAL COMPLEX, BAKER, MT, p. A373

FALLS COMMUNITY HOSPITAL AND CLINIC, MARLIN, TX, p. A622

FALMOUTH HOSPITAL, FALMOUTH, MA, p. A299

FANNIN REGIONAL HOSPITAL, BLUE RIDGE, GA, p. A148

FANNY ALLEN CAMPUS, COLCHESTER, VT, p. A653

FANNY ALLEN CAMPUS, VT (see UNIVERSITY OF VERMONT MEDICAL CENTER), p. A653

FARGO VETERANS AFFAIRS HEALTH CARE SYSTEM, FARGO, ND, A465

FARGO VETERANS AFFAIRS HEALTH CARE SYSTEM, ND (see VETERANS AFFAIRS HEALTH CARE SYSTEM), p. A466

FAULKTON AREA MEDICAL CENTER, FAULKTON, SD, p. A560

FAUQUIER HOSPITAL, WARRENTON, VA, p. A667

FAWCETT MEMORIAL HOSPITAL, PORT CHARLOTTE, FL, p. A137

FAXTON CAMPUS, NY (see FAXTON ST. LUKE'S HEALTHCARE), p. A444

FAXTON ST. LUKE'S HEALTHCARE, UTICA, NY, p. A444

FAXTON ST. LUKE'S HEALTHCARE, UTICA, NY (see ST. LUKE'S CAMPUS), p. A444

FAYETTE COUNTY HOSPITAL, VANDALIA, IL, p. A197

FAYETTE COUNTY MEMORIAL HOSPITAL, WASHINGTON COURT HOUSE, OH, p. A493

FAYETTE MEDICAL CENTER, FAYETTE, AL, p. A18

FAYETTE REGIONAL HEALTH SYSTEM, CONNERSVILLE, IN, p. A201

FAYETTEVILLE VETERANS AFFAIRS MEDICAL CENTER, FAYETTEVILLE, NC, p. A452

FAYETTEVILLE VETERANS AFFAIRS MEDICAL CENTER, NC (see VETERANS AFFAIRS MEDICAL CENTER), p. A452

FEDERAL CORRECTIONAL INSTITUTE HOSPITAL, LITTLETON, CO, p. A103

FEDERAL MEDICAL CENTER, LEXINGTON, KY, p. A255

FERRELL HOSPITAL, ELDORADO, IL, p. A181

FERRY COUNTY MEMORIAL HOSPITAL, REPUBLIC, WA, p. A675

FHN MEMORIAL HOSPITAL, FREEPORT, IL, p. A183

FIELD MEMORIAL COMMUNITY HOSPITAL, CENTREVILLE, MS, p. A344

FIELDSTONE CENTER, MI (see BRONSON BATTLE CREEK HOSPITAL), p. A308

FILLMORE COMMUNITY HOSPITAL, FILLMORE, UT, p. A646

FILLMORE COUNTY HOSPITAL, GENEVA, NE, p. A384

FINGER LAKES HOSPITAL, GENEVA, NY, p. A426

FINLEY HOSPITAL, DUBUQUE, IA, p. A222

FIRELANDS REGIONAL HEALTH SYSTEM, SANDUSKY, OH, p. A490

FIRELANDS REGIONAL MEDICAL CENTER - MAIN CAMPUS, OH (see FIRELANDS REGIONAL HEALTH SYSTEM), p. A490

FIRELANDS REGIONAL MEDICAL CENTER SOUTH CAMPUS, OH (see FIRELANDS REGIONAL HEALTH SYSTEM), p. A490

FIRST BAPTIST MEDICAL CENTER, DALLAS, TX, p. A596

FIRST CARE HEALTH CENTER, PARK RIVER, ND, p. A468

FIRST CARE MEDICAL SERVICES, FOSSTON, MN, p. A331

FIRST HOSPITAL PANAMERICANO, CIDRA, PR, p. A713

FIRST HOSPITAL WYOMING VALLEY, KINGSTON, PA, p. A528

FIRST SURGICAL HOSPITAL, BELLAIRE, TX, p. A589

FIRST TEXAS HOSPITAL, HOUSTON, TX, p. A610

FIRSTHEALTH MONTGOMERY MEMORIAL HOSPITAL, TROY, NC, p. A461

FIRSTHEALTH MOORE REGIONAL HOSPITAL - HOKE, NC (see FIRSTHEALTH MOORE REGIONAL HOSPITAL), p. A458

FIRSTHEALTH MOORE REGIONAL HOSPITAL - RICHMOND, NC (see FIRSTHEALTH MOORE REGIONAL HOSPITAL), p. A458

FIRSTHEALTH MOORE REGIONAL HOSPITAL, PINEHURST, NC, p. A458

FIRSTLIGHT HEALTH SYSTEM, MORA, MN, p. A336

FISHER COUNTY HOSPITAL DISTRICT, ROTAN, TX, p. A631

FISHER-TITUS MEDICAL CENTER, NORWALK, OH, p. A488

FITZGIBBON HOSPITAL, MARSHALL, MO, p. A364

FIVE RIVERS MEDICAL CENTER, POCAHONTAS-Randolph County, AR, p. A48

FLAGET MEMORIAL HOSPITAL, BARDSTOWN, KY, p. A249

FLAGLER HOSPITAL, SAINT AUGUSTINE, FL, p. A137

FLAGSTAFF MEDICAL CENTER, FLAGSTAFF, AZ, p. A29

FLAMBEAU HOSPITAL, PARK FALLS, WI, p. A701

FLEMING COUNTY HOSPITAL, FLEMINGSBURG, KY, p. A251

FLINT RIVER COMMUNITY HOSPITAL, MONTEZUMA, GA, p. A157

FLORIDA HOSPITAL, ORLANDO, FL, p. A134

FLORIDA HOSPITAL AT CONNERTON LONG TERM ACUTE CARE, LAND O'LAKES, FL, p. A127

FLORIDA HOSPITAL CARROLLWOOD, TAMPA, FL, p. A140

FLORIDA HOSPITAL CELEBRATION HEALTH, CELEBRATION, FL, p. A119

FLORIDA HOSPITAL CELEBRATION HEALTH, FL (see FLORIDA HOSPITAL), p. A134

FLORIDA HOSPITAL DADE CITY, DADE CITY, FL, p. A121

FLORIDA HOSPITAL DELAND, DELAND, FL, p. A121

FLORIDA HOSPITAL EAST ORLANDO, FL (see FLORIDA HOSPITAL), p. A134

FLORIDA HOSPITAL FISH MEMORIAL, ORANGE CITY, FL, p. A133

FLORIDA HOSPITAL FLAGLER, PALM COAST, FL, p. A135

FLORIDA HOSPITAL FOR CHILDREN-WALT DISNEY PAVILION, FL (see FLORIDA HOSPITAL), p. A134

FLORIDA HOSPITAL HEARTLAND MEDICAL CENTER, SEBRING, FL, p. A139

FLORIDA HOSPITAL KISSIMMEE, KISSIMMEE, FL, p. A126

FLORIDA HOSPITAL KISSIMMEE, FL (see FLORIDA HOSPITAL), p. A134

FLORIDA HOSPITAL LAKE PLACID, FL (see FLORIDA HOSPITAL HEARTLAND MEDICAL CENTER), p. A139

FLORIDA HOSPITAL MEMORIAL MEDICAL CENTER, DAYTONA BEACH, FL, p. A121

FLORIDA HOSPITAL NEW SMYRNA, NEW SMYRNA BEACH, FL, p. A132

FLORIDA HOSPITAL NORTH PINELLAS, TARPON SPRINGS, FL, p. A142

FLORIDA HOSPITAL OCALA, OCALA, FL, p. A133

FLORIDA HOSPITAL-OCEANSIDE, FL (see FLORIDA HOSPITAL MEMORIAL MEDICAL CENTER), p. A121

FLORIDA HOSPITAL, ORLANDO, FL (see FLORIDA HOSPITAL CELEBRATION HEALTH), p. A119

FLORIDA HOSPITAL, ORLANDO, FL (see FLORIDA HOSPITAL KISSIMMEE), p. A126

FLORIDA HOSPITAL, ORLANDO, FL (see FLORIDA HOSPITAL-ALTAMONTE), p. A116

FLORIDA HOSPITAL, ORLANDO, FL (see FLORIDA HOSPITAL-APOPKA), p. A117

FLORIDA HOSPITAL, ORLANDO, FL (see WINTER PARK MEMORIAL HOSPITAL), p. A144

FLORIDA HOSPITAL TAMPA, TAMPA, FL, p. A140

FLORIDA HOSPITAL WATERMAN, TAVARES, FL, p. A142

FLORIDA HOSPITAL WAUCHULA, WAUCHULA, FL, p. A143

FLORIDA HOSPITAL WESLEY CHAPEL, WESLEY CHAPEL, FL, p. A143

FLORIDA HOSPITAL ZEPHYRHILLS, ZEPHYRHILLS, FL, p. A144

FLORIDA HOSPITAL-ALTAMONTE, ALTAMONTE SPRINGS, FL, p. A116

FLORIDA HOSPITAL-APOPKA, APOPKA, FL, p. A117

FLORIDA MEDICAL CENTER - A CAMPUS OF NORTH SHORE, FL (see FLORIDA MEDICAL CENTER), p. A122

FLORIDA MEDICAL CENTER - A CAMPUS OF NORTH SHORE, FL (see NORTH SHORE MEDICAL CENTER), p. A130

FLORIDA MEDICAL CENTER, FORT LAUDERDALE, FL, p. A122

FLORIDA STATE HOSPITAL, CHATTAHOOCHEE, FL, p. A119

FLOWERS HOSPITAL, DOTHAN, AL, p. A17

FLOYD CHEROKEE MEDICAL CENTER, CENTRE, AL, p. A16

FLOYD COUNTY MEDICAL CENTER, CHARLES CITY, IA, p. A219

FLOYD MEDICAL CENTER, ROME, GA, p. A159

FLOYD VALLEY HEALTHCARE, LE MARS, IA, p. A225

FLUSHING HOSPITAL MEDICAL CENTER, NEW YORK (Includes all hospitals located within the five boroughs), NY, p. A432

FOND DU LAC COUNTY MENTAL HEALTH CENTER, FOND DU LAC, WI, p. A692

FOOTHILL PRESBYTERIAN HOSPITAL, GLENDORA, CA, p. A60

FOOTHILL REGIONAL MEDICAL CENTER, TUSTIN, CA, p. A92

FORBES HOSPITAL, MONROEVILLE, PA, p. A532

FORBES HOSPITAL, PA (see WESTERN PENNSYLVANIA HOSPITAL - FORBES REGIONAL CAMPUS), p. A532

FOREST HEALTH MEDICAL CENTER, YPSILANTI, MI, p. A326

FOREST VIEW PSYCHIATRIC HOSPITAL, GRAND RAPIDS, MI, p. A314

FORKS COMMUNITY HOSPITAL, FORKS, WA, p. A672

FORREST CITY MEDICAL CENTER, FORREST CITY-St. Francis County, AR, p. A42

FORREST GENERAL HOSPITAL, HATTIESBURG, MS, p. A347

FORT BELKNAP SERVICE UNIT, HARLEM, MT, p. A376

FORT BELVOIR COMMUNITY HOSPITAL, FORT BELVOIR, VA, p. A658

FORT DUNCAN REGIONAL MEDICAL CENTER, EAGLE PASS, TX, p. A600

FORT HAMILTON HOSPITAL, HAMILTON, OH, p. A483

FORT HEALTHCARE, FORT ATKINSON, WI, p. A692

FORT LAUDERDALE HOSPITAL, FORT LAUDERDALE, FL, p. A122

FORT LOUDOUN MEDICAL CENTER, LENOIR CITY, TN, p. A573

FORT MADISON COMMUNITY HOSPITAL, FORT MADISON, IA, p. A223

FORT SANDERS REGIONAL MEDICAL CENTER, KNOXVILLE, TN, p. A572

FORT WALTON BEACH MEDICAL CENTER, FORT WALTON BEACH, FL, p. A123

FORT WASHINGTON MEDICAL CENTER, OXEN HILL, MD, p. A293

FOUNDATION SURGICAL HOSPITAL OF EL PASO, EL PASO, TX, p. A602

FOUNDATION SURGICAL HOSPITAL OF EL PASO, TX (see EAST EL PASO PHYSICIANS MEDICAL CENTER), p. A601

FOUNDATION SURGICAL HOSPITAL OF SAN ANTONIO, SAN ANTONIO, TX, p. A633

FOUNDATIONS BEHAVIORAL HEALTH, DOYLESTOWN, PA, p. A524

FOUNTAIN VALLEY REGIONAL HOSPITAL AND MEDICAL CENTER, FOUNTAIN VALLEY, CA, p. A58

FOUR COUNTY COUNSELING CENTER, LOGANSPORT, IN, p. A210

FOUR WINDS HOSPITAL, KATONAH, NY, p. A428

FOUR WINDS HOSPITAL, SARATOGA SPRINGS, NY, p. A442

FOX CHASE CANCER CENTER-AMERICAN ONCOLOGIC HOSPITAL, PHILADELPHIA, PA, p. A534

FRAMINGHAM UNION HOSPITAL, MA (see METROWEST MEDICAL CENTER), p. A300

FRANCES MAHON DEACONESS HOSPITAL, GLASGOW, MT, p. A374

FRANCISCAN CHILDREN'S, BRIGHTON, MA, p. A297

FRANCISCAN HEALTH CARMEL, CARMEL, IN, p. A201

FRANCISCAN HEALTH CRAWFORDSVILLE, CRAWFORDSVILLE, IN, p. A202

FRANCISCAN HEALTH CRAWFORDSVILLE, IN (see ST. CLARE MEDICAL CENTER), p. A202

FRANCISCAN HEALTH CROWN POINT, CROWN POINT, IN, p. A202

FRANCISCAN HEALTH CROWN POINT, IN (see ST. ANTHONY MEDICAL CENTER), p. A202

FRANCISCAN HEALTH DYER, DYER, IN, p. A202

FRANCISCAN HEALTH DYER, IN (see SAINT MARGARET MERCY HEALTHCARE CENTERS-SOUTH CAMPUS), p. A202

FRANCISCAN HEALTH HAMMOND, HAMMOND, IN, p. A205

FRANCISCAN HEALTH HAMMOND, IN (see SAINT MARGARET MERCY HEALTHCARE CENTERS), p. A205

FRANCISCAN HEALTH INDIANAPOLIS, INDIANAPOLIS, IN, p. A206

FRANCISCAN HEALTH INDIANAPOLIS, IN (see ST. FRANCIS HOSPITAL AND HEALTH CENTERS - SOUTH CAMPUS), p. A207

FRANCISCAN HEALTH LAFAYETTE CENTRAL, IN (see FRANCISCAN HEALTH LAFAYETTE EAST), p. A209

FRANCISCAN HEALTH LAFAYETTE CENTRAL, IN (see ST. ELIZABETH CENTRAL), p. A209

FRANCISCAN HEALTH LAFAYETTE EAST, LAFAYETTE, IN, p. A209

FRANCISCAN HEALTH MICHIGAN CITY, MICHIGAN CITY, IN, p. A211

FRANCISCAN HEALTH MICHIGAN CITY, IN (see SAINT ANTHONY MEMORIAL), p. A211

FRANCISCAN HEALTH MOORESVILLE, MOORESVILLE, IN, p. A211

FRANCISCAN HEALTH MOORESVILLE, IN (see ST. FRANCIS HOSPITAL-MOORESVILLE), p. A211
FRANCISCAN HEALTH OLYMPIA FIELDS, OLYMPIA FIELDS, IL, p. A192
FRANCISCAN HEALTH OLYMPIA FIELDS, IL (see FRANCISCAN HEALTH OLYMPIA FIELDS), p. A192
FRANCISCAN HEALTH OLYMPIA FIELDS, IL (see ST. JAMES HOSPITAL AND HEALTH CENTERS), p. A192
FRANCISCAN HEALTH OLYMPIA FIELDS, OLYMPIA FIELDS, IL (see ST. JAMES HOSPITAL AND HEALTH CENTERS - CHICAGO HEIGHTS CAMPUS), p. A180
FRANCISCAN HEALTH RENSSELEAR, RENSSELAER, IN, p. A214
FRANCISCAN HEALTHCARE MUNSTER, MUNSTER, IN, p. A212
FRANKFORD CAMPUS, PA (see JEFFERSON HEALTH NORTHEAST), p. A535
FRANKFORT REGIONAL MEDICAL CENTER, FRANKFORT, KY, p. A252
FRANKLIN COUNTY MEDICAL CENTER, PRESTON, ID, p. A171
FRANKLIN COUNTY MEMORIAL HOSPITAL, FRANKLIN, NE, p. A383
FRANKLIN COUNTY MEMORIAL HOSPITAL, MEADVILLE, MS, p. A350
FRANKLIN FOUNDATION HOSPITAL, FRANKLIN, LA, p. A267
FRANKLIN GENERAL HOSPITAL, HAMPTON, IA, p. A223
FRANKLIN HOSPITAL DISTRICT, BENTON, IL, p. A174
FRANKLIN MEDICAL CENTER, WINNSBORO, LA, p. A281
FRANKLIN MEMORIAL HOSPITAL, FARMINGTON, ME, p. A284
FRANKLIN REGIONAL HOSPITAL, FRANKLIN, NH, p. A399
FRANKLIN SQUARE HOSPITAL CENTER, BALTIMORE, MD, p. A287
FRANKLIN WOODS COMMUNITY HOSPITAL, JOHNSON CITY, TN, p. A571
FRANKLIN WOODS COMMUNITY HOSPITAL, TN (see NORTH SIDE HOSPITAL), p. A572
FRAZIER REHAB INSTITUTE, KY (see JEWISH HOSPITAL), p. A256
FREDERICK REGIONAL HEALTH SYSTEM, FREDERICK, MD, p. A291
FREDONIA REGIONAL HOSPITAL, FREDONIA, KS, p. A235
FREEMAN HEALTH SYSTEM, JOPLIN, MO, p. A361
FREEMAN HOSPITAL EAST, MO (see FREEMAN HEALTH SYSTEM), p. A361
FREEMAN NEOSHO HOSPITAL, NEOSHO, MO, p. A365
FREEMAN REGIONAL HEALTH SERVICES, FREEMAN, SD, p. A561
FREESTONE MEDICAL CENTER, FAIRFIELD, TX, p. A603
FREMONT HEALTH, FREMONT, NE, p. A384
FREMONT HOSPITAL, FREMONT, CA, p. A59
FREMONT MEDICAL CENTER, YUBA CITY, CA, p. A95
FREMONT MEDICAL CENTER, CA (see RIDEOUT MEMORIAL HOSPITAL), p. A72
FRENCH HOSPITAL MEDICAL CENTER, SAN LUIS OBISPO, CA, p. A87
FRESNO HEART AND SURGICAL HOSPITAL, FRESNO, CA, p. A59
FRESNO MEDICAL CENTER, FRESNO, CA, p. A59
FRESNO SURGICAL HOSPITAL, FRESNO, CA, p. A59
FRIEND COMMUNITY HEALTHCARE SYSTEM, FRIEND, NE, p. A384
FRIENDS HOSPITAL, PHILADELPHIA, PA, p. A534
FRIO REGIONAL HOSPITAL, PEARSALL, TX, p. A627
FRISBIE MEMORIAL HOSPITAL, ROCHESTER, NH, p. A401
FROEDTERT AND THE MEDICAL COLLEGE OF WISCONSIN FROEDTERT HOSPITAL, MILWAUKEE, WI, p. A698
FROEDTERT SOUTH - KENOSHA MEDICAL CENTER, KENOSHA, WI, p. A695
FROEDTERT SOUTH - ST. CATHERINE'S MEDICAL CENTER, WI (see FROEDTERT SOUTH - KENOSHA MEDICAL CENTER), p. A695
FRYE REGIONAL MEDICAL CENTER, HICKORY, NC, p. A454
FRYE REGIONAL MEDICAL CENTER-SOUTH CAMPUS, NC (see FRYE REGIONAL MEDICAL CENTER), p. A454
FULTON COUNTY HEALTH CENTER, WAUSEON, OH, p. A493
FULTON COUNTY HOSPITAL, SALEM-Fulton County, AR, p. A48
FULTON COUNTY MEDICAL CENTER, MC CONNELLSBURG, PA, p. A530
FULTON DIVISION, NEW YORK (Includes all hospitals located within the five boroughs), NY, p. A432
FULTON DIVISION, NY (see BRONXCARE HEALTH SYSTEM), p. A431
FULTON MEDICAL CENTER, FULTON, MO, p. A359
FULTON STATE HOSPITAL, FULTON, MO, p. A359

G

G. WERBER BRYAN PSYCHIATRIC HOSPITAL, COLUMBIA, SC, p. A551
G.V. (SONNY) MONTGOMERY VETERANS AFFAIRS MEDICAL CENTER, JACKSON, MS, p. A348
GADSDEN REGIONAL MEDICAL CENTER, GADSDEN, AL, p. A18
GAINESVILLE VETERANS AFFAIRS MEDICAL CENTER, FL (see NORTH FLORIDA/SOUTH GEORGIA VETERAN'S HEALTH SYSTEM), p. A123
GALESBURG COTTAGE HOSPITAL, GALESBURG, IL, p. A183
GALION HOSPITAL, GALION, OH, p. A483
GALLUP INDIAN MEDICAL CENTER, GALLUP, NM, p. A417
GARDEN CITY HOSPITAL, GARDEN CITY, MI, p. A313
GARDEN GROVE HOSPITAL AND MEDICAL CENTER, GARDEN GROVE, CA, p. A60
GARDEN PARK MEDICAL CENTER, GULFPORT, MS, p. A346
GARFIELD COUNTY HEALTH CENTER, JORDAN, MT, p. A376
GARFIELD COUNTY PUBLIC HOSPITAL DISTRICT, POMEROY, WA, p. A674
GARFIELD MEDICAL CENTER, MONTEREY PARK, CA, p. A73
GARFIELD MEMORIAL HOSPITAL, PANGUITCH, UT, p. A649
GARFIELD PARK HOSPITAL, CHICAGO, IL, p. A176
GARLAND BEHAVIORAL HOSPITAL, GARLAND, TX, p. A606
GARRETT REGIONAL MEDICAL CENTER, OAKLAND, MD, p. A293
GASTON MEMORIAL HOSPITAL, GASTONIA, NC, p. A453
GATEWAY REGIONAL MEDICAL CENTER, GRANITE CITY, IL, p. A184
GATEWAY REHABILITATION HOSPITAL, FLORENCE, KY, p. A251
GATEWAYS HOSPITAL AND MENTAL HEALTH CENTER, LOS ANGELES, CA, p. A67
GAYLORD HOSPITAL, WALLINGFORD, CT, p. A111
GEARY COMMUNITY HOSPITAL, JUNCTION CITY, KS, p. A238
GEISINGER HEALTHSOUTH REHABILITATION HOSPITAL, DANVILLE, PA, p. A523
GEISINGER HOLY SPIRIT, CAMP HILL, PA, p. A521
GEISINGER JERSEY SHORE HOSPITAL, JERSEY SHORE, PA, p. A528
GEISINGER MEDICAL CENTER, DANVILLE, PA, p. A523
GEISINGER WYOMING VALLEY MEDICAL CENTER, WILKES BARRE, PA, p. A544
GEISINGER-BLOOMSBURG HOSPITAL, BLOOMSBURG, PA, p. A521
GEISINGER-COMMUNITY MEDICAL CENTER, SCRANTON, PA, p. A540
GEISINGER-COMMUNITY MEDICAL CENTER, PA (see COMMUNITY MEDICAL CENTER HEALTHCARE SYSTEM), p. A540
GEISINGER-LEWISTOWN HOSPITAL, LEWISTOWN, PA, p. A530
GEISINGER-SHAMOKIN AREA COMMUNITY HOSPITAL, PA (see GEISINGER MEDICAL CENTER), p. A523
GENERAL HOSPITAL, CHARLESTON, WV, p. A682
GENERAL HOSPITAL, CA (see LAC+USC MEDICAL CENTER), p. A68
GENERAL HOSPITAL, CA (see ST. JOSEPH HOSPITAL), p. A57
GENERAL HOSPITAL, WV (see CHARLESTON AREA MEDICAL CENTER), p. A682
GENERAL LEONARD WOOD ARMY COMMUNITY HOSPITAL, FORT LEONARD WOOD, MO, p. A359
GENESIS BEHAVIORAL HOSPITAL, BREAUX BRIDGE, LA, p. A265
GENESIS HEALTHCARE SYSTEM, ZANESVILLE, OH, p. A494
GENESIS MEDICAL CENTER, DAVENPORT, DAVENPORT, IA, p. A220
GENESIS MEDICAL CENTER, DEWITT, DE WITT, IA, p. A220
GENESIS MEDICAL CENTER, SILVIS, SILVIS, IL, p. A196
GENESIS MEDICAL CENTER-ALEDO, ALEDO, IL, p. A173
GENESIS MEDICAL CENTER-EAST CAMPUS, IA (see GENESIS MEDICAL CENTER, DAVENPORT), p. A220
GENESIS MEDICAL CENTER-WEST CAMPUS, IA (see GENESIS MEDICAL CENTER, DAVENPORT), p. A220
GENESYS REGIONAL MEDICAL CENTER, GRAND BLANC, MI, p. A313
GENOA MEDICAL FACILITIES, GENOA, NE, p. A384
GEORGE AND MARIE BACKUS CHILDREN'S HOSPITAL, SAVANNAH, GA, p. A160
GEORGE C GRAPE COMMUNITY HOSPITAL, HAMBURG, IA, p. A223
GEORGE E. WEEMS MEMORIAL HOSPITAL, APALACHICOLA, FL, p. A117
GEORGE REGIONAL HOSPITAL, LUCEDALE, MS, p. A349

GEORGE W. TRUETT MEMORIAL HOSPITAL, TX (see BAYLOR UNIVERSITY MEDICAL CENTER), p. A596
GEORGE WASHINGTON UNIVERSITY HOSPITAL, WASHINGTON, DC, p. A115
GEORGETOWN BEHAVIORAL HEALTH INSTITUTE, GEORGETOWN, TX, p. A607
GEORGETOWN COMMUNITY HOSPITAL, GEORGETOWN, KY, p. A252
GEORGETOWN UNIVERSITY HOSPITAL, WASHINGTON, DC, p. A115
GEORGIA REGIONAL HOSPITAL AT ATLANTA, DECATUR, GA, p. A152
GEORGIA REGIONAL HOSPITAL AT SAVANNAH, SAVANNAH, GA, p. A160
GEORGIANA HOSPITAL, GEORGIANA, AL, p. A18
GERALD CHAMPION REGIONAL MEDICAL CENTER, ALAMOGORDO, NM, p. A415
GHS CHILDREN'S HOSPITAL, SC (see GHS GREENVILLE MEMORIAL HOSPITAL), p. A553
GHS GREENVILLE MEMORIAL HOSPITAL, GREENVILLE, SC, p. A553
GHS GREER MEMORIAL HOSPITAL, GREER, SC, p. A554
GHS HILLCREST MEMORIAL HOSPITAL, SIMPSONVILLE, SC, p. A556
GHS - LAURENS COUNTY MEMORIAL HOSPITAL, SC (see GREENVILLE HEALTH SYSTEM - LAURENS COUNTY MEMORIAL HOSPITAL), p. A550
GIBSON AREA HOSPITAL AND HEALTH SERVICES, GIBSON CITY, IL, p. A184
GIBSON GENERAL HOSPITAL, PRINCETON, IN, p. A213
GIFFORD MEDICAL CENTER, RANDOLPH, VT, p. A654
GILA REGIONAL MEDICAL CENTER, SILVER CITY, NM, p. A420
GILLETTE CHILDREN'S SPECIALTY HEALTHCARE, SAINT PAUL, MN, p. A339
GILMORE MEMORIAL HOSPITAL, AMORY, MS, p. A343
GIRARD MEDICAL CENTER, GIRARD, KS, p. A235
GIRARD MEDICAL CENTER, PA (see NORTH PHILADELPHIA HEALTH SYSTEM), p. A536
GLACIAL RIDGE HEALTH SYSTEM, GLENWOOD, MN, p. A332
GLADES GENERAL HOSPITAL, BELLE GLADE, FL, p. A117
GLADYS SPELLMAN SPECIALTY HOSPITAL AND NURSING CENTER, CHEVERLY, MD, p. A290
GLEN COVE HOSPITAL, GLEN COVE, NY, p. A426
GLEN OAKS HOSPITAL, GREENVILLE, TX, p. A608
GLEN ROSE MEDICAL CENTER, GLEN ROSE, TX, p. A607
GLENBEIGH HOSPITAL AND OUTPATIENT CENTERS, ROCK CREEK, OH, p. A489
GLENCOE REGIONAL HEALTH SERVICES, GLENCOE, MN, p. A332
GLENDALE MEMORIAL HOSPITAL AND HEALTH CENTER, GLENDALE, CA, p. A60
GLENDIVE MEDICAL CENTER, GLENDIVE, MT, p. A375
GLENDORA COMMUNITY HOSPITAL, GLENDORA, CA, p. A61
GLENN MEDICAL CENTER, WILLOWS, CA, p. A95
GLENS FALLS HOSPITAL, GLENS FALLS, NY, p. A427
GLENWOOD REGIONAL MEDICAL CENTER, WEST MONROE, LA, p. A280
GLENWOOD SURGERY CENTER, LA (see GLENWOOD REGIONAL MEDICAL CENTER), p. A280
GOLDEN PLAINS COMMUNITY HOSPITAL, BORGER, TX, p. A589
GOLDEN VALLEY MEMORIAL HEALTHCARE, CLINTON, MO, p. A357
GOLETA VALLEY COTTAGE HOSPITAL, SANTA BARBARA, CA, p. A88
GOLISANO CHILDREN'S HOSPITAL, NY (see STRONG MEMORIAL HOSPITAL OF THE UNIVERSITY OF ROCHESTER), p. A441
GOLISANO CHILDREN'S HOSPITAL, NY (see UPSTATE UNIVERSITY HOSPITAL), p. A444
GOLISANO CHILDREN'S HOSPITAL OF SOUTHWEST FLORIDA, FORT MYERS, FL, p. A123
GOLISANO CHILDREN'S HOSPITAL OF SOUTHWEST FLORIDA, FL (see LEE MEMORIAL HOSPITAL), p. A123
GONZALES HEALTHCARE SYSTEMS, GONZALES, TX, p. A607
GOOD SAMARITAN COMMUNITY HEALTHCARE, PUYALLUP, WA, p. A675
GOOD SAMARITAN HEALTH CENTER OF MERRILL, MERRILL, WI, p. A698
GOOD SAMARITAN HEALTH SYSTEMS, KEARNEY, NE, p. A385
GOOD SAMARITAN HOSPITAL, BAKERSFIELD, CA, p. A52
GOOD SAMARITAN HOSPITAL, CINCINNATI, OH, p. A475
GOOD SAMARITAN HOSPITAL, LOS ANGELES, CA, p. A67
GOOD SAMARITAN HOSPITAL, SAN JOSE, CA, p. A86
GOOD SAMARITAN HOSPITAL, VINCENNES, IN, p. A216
GOOD SAMARITAN HOSPITAL AND MEDICAL CENTER, PORTLAND, OR, p. A516

H

HOSPITAL SAN PABLO DEL ESTE, FAJARDO, PR, p. A713
HOSPITAL UNIVERSITARIO DR. RAMON RUIZ ARNAU, BAYAMON, PR, p. A712
HOT SPRINGS COUNTY MEMORIAL HOSPITAL, THERMOPOLIS, WY, p. A710
HOULTON REGIONAL HOSPITAL, HOULTON, ME, p. A284
HOUSTON BEHAVIORAL HEALTHCARE HOSPITAL, HOUSTON, TX, p. A611
HOUSTON COUNTY COMMUNITY HOSPITAL, ERIN, TN, p. A569
HOUSTON MEDICAL CENTER, WARNER ROBINS, GA, p. A163
HOUSTON METHODIST BAYTOWN HOSPITAL, BAYTOWN, TX, p. A587
HOUSTON METHODIST CLEAR LAKE HOSPITAL, NASSAU BAY, TX, p. A625
HOUSTON METHODIST CONTINUING CARE HOSPITAL, KATY, TX, p. A616
HOUSTON METHODIST CONTINUING CARE HOSPITAL, TX (see CHRISTUS ST. CATHERINE HOSPITAL), p. A616
HOUSTON METHODIST HOSPITAL, HOUSTON, TX, p. A611
HOUSTON METHODIST HOSPITAL, TX (see THE METHODIST HOSPITAL), p. A613
HOUSTON METHODIST SAN JACINTO HOSPITAL - ALEXANDER, TX (see HOUSTON METHODIST BAYTOWN HOSPITAL), p. A587
HOUSTON METHODIST SUGAR LAND HOSPITAL, SUGAR LAND, TX, p. A637
HOUSTON METHODIST SUGAR LAND HOSPITAL, TX (see METHODIST SUGAR LAND HOSPITAL), p. A637
HOUSTON METHODIST THE WOODLANDS HOSPITAL, THE WOODLANDS, TX, p. A640
HOUSTON METHODIST WEST HOSPITAL, HOUSTON, TX, p. A611
HOUSTON METHODIST WEST HOSPITAL, TX (see METHODIST WEST HOUSTON HOSPITAL), p. A612
HOUSTON METHODIST WILLOWBROOK HOSPITAL, HOUSTON, TX, p. A611
HOUSTON METHODIST WILLOWBROOK HOSPITAL, TX (see METHODIST WILLOWBROOK HOSPITAL), p. A612
HOUSTON NORTHWEST MEDICAL CENTER, HOUSTON, TX, p. A611
HOUSTON PHYSICIANS HOSPITAL, WEBSTER, TX, p. A643
HOWARD A. RUSK REHABILITATION CENTER, COLUMBIA, MO, p. A358
HOWARD COUNTY COMMUNITY HOSPITAL, SAINT PAUL, NE, p. A390
HOWARD COUNTY GENERAL HOSPITAL, COLUMBIA, MD, p. A291
HOWARD COUNTY MEDICAL CENTER, SAINT PAUL, NE, p. A390
HOWARD COUNTY MEDICAL CENTER, NE (see HOWARD COUNTY COMMUNITY HOSPITAL), p. A390
HOWARD MEMORIAL HOSPITAL, NASHVILLE-Howard County, AR, p. A46
HOWARD REGIONAL HEALTH SYSTEM, KOKOMO, IN, p. A209
HOWARD REGIONAL HEALTH SYSTEM WEST CAMPUS SPECIALTY HOSPITAL, KOKOMO, IN, p. A209
HOWARD UNIVERSITY HOSPITAL, WASHINGTON, DC, p. A115
HOWARD YOUNG MEDICAL CENTER, WOODRUFF, WI, p. A706
HSHS GOOD SHEPHERD HOSPITAL, SHELBYVILLE, IL, p. A195
HSHS HOLY FAMILY HOSPITAL IN GREENVILLE, GREENVILLE, IL, p. A184
HSHS SACRED HEART HOSPITAL, EAU CLAIRE, WI, p. A692
HSHS ST. ANTHONY'S MEMORIAL HOSPITAL, EFFINGHAM, IL, p. A181
HSHS ST. CLARE MEMORIAL HOSPITAL, OCONTO FALLS, WI, p. A700
HSHS ST. ELIZABETH'S HOSPITAL, O'FALLON, IL, p. A192
HSHS ST. FRANCIS HOSPITAL, LITCHFIELD, IL, p. A188
HSHS ST. JOHN'S HOSPITAL, SPRINGFIELD, IL, p. A196
HSHS ST. JOSEPH'S HOSPITAL, BREESE, IL, p. A174
HSHS ST. JOSEPH'S HOSPITAL, CHIPPEWA FALLS, WI, p. A691
HSHS ST. JOSEPH'S HOSPITAL, HIGHLAND, IL, p. A185
HSHS ST. MARY'S HOSPITAL, DECATUR, IL, p. A181
HSHS ST. MARY'S HOSPITAL MEDICAL CENTER, GREEN BAY, WI, p. A694
HSHS ST. NICHOLAS HOSPITAL, SHEBOYGAN, WI, p. A703
HSHS ST. VINCENT HOSPITAL, GREEN BAY, WI, p. A694
HUDSON COUNTY MEADOWVIEW PSYCHIATRIC HOSPITAL, SECAUCUS, NJ, p. A411
HUDSON HOSPITAL AND CLINIC, HUDSON, WI, p. A694
HUDSON REGIONAL HOSPITAL, SECAUCUS, NJ, p. A411
HUDSON REGIONAL HOSPITAL, NJ (see LIBERTYHEALTH-MEADOWLANDS HOSPITAL MEDICAL CENTER), p. A411
HUGGINS HOSPITAL, WOLFEBORO, NH, p. A401
HUGH CHATHAM MEMORIAL HOSPITAL, ELKIN, NC, p. A452
HUGHSTON HOSPITAL, COLUMBUS, GA, p. A150

HUHUKAM MEMORIAL HOSPITAL, SACATON, AZ, p. A35
HUMBOLDT COUNTY MEMORIAL HOSPITAL, HUMBOLDT, IA, p. A224
HUMBOLDT COUNTY MENTAL HEALTH, EUREKA, CA, p. A57
HUMBOLDT GENERAL HOSPITAL, WINNEMUCCA, NV, p. A397
HUNT REGIONAL MEDICAL CENTER, GREENVILLE, TX, p. A608
HUNTER HOLMES MCGUIRE VETERANS AFFAIRS MEDICAL CENTER-RICHMOND, RICHMOND, VA, p. A665
HUNTERDON MEDICAL CENTER, FLEMINGTON, NJ, p. A405
HUNTINGTON BEACH HOSPITAL, HUNTINGTON BEACH, CA, p. A62
HUNTINGTON CREEK RECOVERY CENTER, SHICKSHINNY, PA, p. A541
HUNTINGTON HOSPITAL, HUNTINGTON, NY, p. A428
HUNTINGTON MEMORIAL HOSPITAL, PASADENA, CA, p. A78
HUNTINGTON VETERANS AFFAIRS MEDICAL CENTER, HUNTINGTON, WV, p. A684
HUNTSVILLE HOSPITAL, HUNTSVILLE, AL, p. A19
HUNTSVILLE HOSPITAL FOR WOMEN AND CHILDREN, AL (see HUNTSVILLE HOSPITAL), p. A19
HUNTSVILLE MEMORIAL HOSPITAL, HUNTSVILLE, TX, p. A615
HURLEY CHILDREN'S HOSPITAL, MI (see HURLEY MEDICAL CENTER), p. A312
HURLEY MEDICAL CENTER, FLINT, MI, p. A312
HURON REGIONAL MEDICAL CENTER, HURON, SD, p. A561
HUTCHINSON HEALTH, HUTCHINSON, MN, p. A333
HUTCHINSON REGIONAL MEDICAL CENTER, HUTCHINSON, KS, p. A237

I

I-70 COMMUNITY HOSPITAL, SWEET SPRINGS, MO, p. A371
I. GONZALEZ MARTINEZ ONCOLOGIC HOSPITAL, HATO REY, PR, p. A713
IBERIA EXTENDED CARE HOSPITAL, LA (see LOUISIANA EXTENDED CARE HOSPITAL OF LAFAYETTE), p. A271
IBERIA MEDICAL CENTER, NEW IBERIA, LA, p. A275
IBERIA REHABILITATION HOSPITAL, NEW IBERIA, LA, p. A275
ICARE REHABILITATION HOSPITAL, FLOWER MOUND, TX, p. A603
ICON HOSPITAL, HUMBLE, TX, p. A615
IDAHO ELKS REHABILITATION HOSPITAL, BOISE, ID, p. A167
ILLINI COMMUNITY HOSPITAL, PITTSFIELD, IL, p. A193
ILLINOIS VALLEY COMMUNITY HOSPITAL, PERU, IL, p. A193
IMPERIAL POINT MEDICAL CENTER, FORT LAUDERDALE, FL, p. A122
INCLINE VILLAGE COMMUNITY HOSPITAL, INCLINE VILLAGE, NV, p. A393
INDIAN HEALTH SERVICE - QUENTIN N. BURDICK MEMORIAL HEALTH CARE FACILITY, BELCOURT, ND, p. A464
INDIAN HEALTH SERVICE HOSPITAL, RAPID CITY, SD, p. A563
INDIAN PATH MEDICAL CENTER, KINGSPORT, TN, p. A572
INDIAN RIVER MEDICAL CENTER, VERO BEACH, FL, p. A143
INDIANA REGIONAL MEDICAL CENTER, INDIANA, PA, p. A528
INDIANA UNIVERSITY HEALTH ARNETT HOSPITAL, LAFAYETTE, IN, p. A209
INDIANA UNIVERSITY HEALTH ARNETT HOSPITAL, IN (see CLARIAN ARNETT HOSPITAL), p. A209
INDIANA UNIVERSITY HEALTH BALL MEMORIAL HOSPITAL, MUNCIE, IN, p. A212
INDIANA UNIVERSITY HEALTH BALL MEMORIAL HOSPITAL, IN (see BALL MEMORIAL HOSPITAL), p. A211
INDIANA UNIVERSITY HEALTH BEDFORD HOSPITAL, BEDFORD, IN, p. A199
INDIANA UNIVERSITY HEALTH BEDFORD HOSPITAL, IN (see BEDFORD REGIONAL MEDICAL CENTER), p. A199
INDIANA UNIVERSITY HEALTH BLACKFORD HOSPITAL, HARTFORD CITY, IN, p. A206
INDIANA UNIVERSITY HEALTH BLACKFORD HOSPITAL, IN (see BLACKFORD COMMUNITY HOSPITAL), p. A205
INDIANA UNIVERSITY HEALTH BLOOMINGTON HOSPITAL, BLOOMINGTON, IN, p. A200
INDIANA UNIVERSITY HEALTH BLOOMINGTON HOSPITAL, IN (see BLOOMINGTON HOSPITAL), p. A200
INDIANA UNIVERSITY HEALTH FRANKFORT, FRANKFORT, IN, p. A204
INDIANA UNIVERSITY HEALTH JAY HOSPITAL, PORTLAND, IN, p. A213
INDIANA UNIVERSITY HEALTH METHODIST HOSPITAL, INDIANAPOLIS, IN, p. A206
INDIANA UNIVERSITY HEALTH METHODIST HOSPITAL, IN (see INDIANA UNIVERSITY HEALTH UNIVERSITY HOSPITAL), p. A207

INDIANA UNIVERSITY HEALTH METHODIST HOSPITAL, IN (see METHODIST HOSPITAL), p. A207
INDIANA UNIVERSITY HEALTH NORTH HOSPITAL, CARMEL, IN, p. A201
INDIANA UNIVERSITY HEALTH NORTH HOSPITAL, IN (see CLARIAN NORTH MEDICAL CENTER), p. A201
INDIANA UNIVERSITY HEALTH PAOLI HOSPITAL, PAOLI, IN, p. A213
INDIANA UNIVERSITY HEALTH PAOLI HOSPITAL, IN (see BLOOMINGTON HOSPITAL OF ORANGE COUNTY), p. A213
INDIANA UNIVERSITY HEALTH SAXONY HOSPITAL, IN (see INDIANA UNIVERSITY HEALTH UNIVERSITY HOSPITAL), p. A207
INDIANA UNIVERSITY HEALTH TIPTON HOSPITAL, TIPTON, IN, p. A215
INDIANA UNIVERSITY HEALTH TIPTON HOSPITAL, IN (see TIPTON HOSPITAL), p. A215
INDIANA UNIVERSITY HEALTH UNIVERSITY HOSPITAL, INDIANAPOLIS, IN, p. A207
INDIANA UNIVERSITY HEALTH UNIVERSITY HOSPITAL, IN (see CLARIAN HEALTH PARTNERS), p. A206
INDIANA UNIVERSITY HEALTH UNIVERSITY HOSPITAL, INDIANAPOLIS, IN (see INDIANA UNIVERSITY HEALTH METHODIST HOSPITAL), p. A206
INDIANA UNIVERSITY HEALTH UNIVERSITY HOSPITAL, INDIANAPOLIS, IN (see INDIANA UNIVERSITY HOSPITAL), p. A207
INDIANA UNIVERSITY HEALTH UNIVERSITY HOSPITAL, INDIANAPOLIS, IN (see RILEY HOSPITAL FOR CHILDREN AT INDIANA UNIVERSITY HEALTH), p. A207
INDIANA UNIVERSITY HEALTH WEST HOSPITAL, AVON, IN, p. A199
INDIANA UNIVERSITY HEALTH WEST HOSPITAL, IN (see CLARIAN WEST MEDICAL CENTER), p. A199
INDIANA UNIVERSITY HEALTH WHITE MEMORIAL HOSPITAL, MONTICELLO, IN, p. A211
INDIANA UNIVERSITY HOSPITAL, INDIANAPOLIS, IN, p. A207
INDIANA UNIVERSITY HOSPITAL, IN (see INDIANA UNIVERSITY HEALTH UNIVERSITY HOSPITAL), p. A207
INDIANHEAD MEDICAL CENTER, SHELL LAKE, WI, p. A703
INDUSTRIAL HOSPITAL, SAN JUAN, PR, p. A716
INFIRMARY LONG TERM ACUTE CARE HOSPITAL, MOBILE, AL, p. A20
INGALLS MEMORIAL HOSPITAL, HARVEY, IL, p. A185
INLAND HOSPITAL, WATERVILLE, ME, p. A286
INLAND VALLEY MEDICAL CENTER, CA (see SOUTHWEST HEALTHCARE SYSTEM), p. A74
INNOVIS HEALTH, FARGO, ND, p. A465
INOVA ALEXANDRIA HOSPITAL, ALEXANDRIA, VA, p. A655
INOVA FAIR OAKS HOSPITAL, FAIRFAX, VA, p. A657
INOVA FAIRFAX HOSPITAL, FALLS CHURCH, VA, p. A657
INOVA FAIRFAX HOSPITAL FOR CHILDREN, VA (see INOVA FAIRFAX HOSPITAL), p. A657
INOVA LOUDOUN HOSPITAL, LEESBURG, VA, p. A660
INOVA MOUNT VERNON HOSPITAL, ALEXANDRIA, VA, p. A655
INSPIRA MEDICAL CENTER-ELMER, ELMER, NJ, p. A404
INSPIRA MEDICAL CENTER-VINELAND, VINELAND, NJ, p. A413
INSPIRA MEDICAL CENTER-VINELAND, VINELAND, NJ (see BRIDGETON HEALTH CARE), p. A403
INSPIRA MEDICAL CENTER-WOODBURY, WOODBURY, NJ, p. A414
INSPIRA PONCE, PONCE, PR, p. A714
INSTITUTE FOR ORTHOPAEDIC SURGERY, LIMA, OH, p. A484
INSTITUTE OF LIVING, CT (see HARTFORD HOSPITAL), p. A108
INTEGRIS BAPTIST MEDICAL CENTER, OKLAHOMA CITY, OK, p. A503
INTEGRIS BAPTIST MEDICAL CENTER, OKLAHOMA CITY, OK (see INTEGRIS MENTAL HEALTH SYSTEM-SPENCER), p. A507
INTEGRIS BASS BAPTIST HEALTH CENTER, ENID, OK, p. A498
INTEGRIS BASS BEHAVIORAL HEALTH SYSTEM, ENID, OK, p. A498
INTEGRIS BASS MEADOWLAKE, OK (see INTEGRIS BASS BAPTIST HEALTH CENTER), p. A498
INTEGRIS BASS MEADOWLAKE, OK (see INTEGRIS BASS BEHAVIORAL HEALTH SYSTEM), p. A498
INTEGRIS BASS PAVILION, ENID, OK, p. A498
INTEGRIS CANADIAN VALLEY HOSPITAL, YUKON, OK, p. A510
INTEGRIS DEACONESS, OKLAHOMA CITY, OK, p. A502
INTEGRIS GROVE HOSPITAL, GROVE, OK, p. A499
INTEGRIS HEALTH EDMOND, EDMOND, OK, p. A498
INTEGRIS MENTAL HEALTH SYSTEM-SPENCER, SPENCER, OK, p. A507
INTEGRIS MENTAL HEALTH SYSTEM-SPENCER, OK (see INTEGRIS BAPTIST MEDICAL CENTER), p. A503

INTEGRIS MIAMI HOSPITAL, MIAMI, OK, p. A501
INTEGRIS SOUTHWEST MEDICAL CENTER, OKLAHOMA CITY, OK, p. A503
INTEGRITY TRANSITIONAL HOSPITAL, DENTON, TX, p. A599
INTERFAITH MEDICAL CENTER, NEW YORK (Includes all hospitals located within the five boroughs), NY, p. A432
INTERMOUNTAIN HOSPITAL, BOISE, ID, p. A167
INTERMOUNTAIN MEDICAL CENTER, MURRAY, UT, p. A648
INTRACARE NORTH HOSPITAL, HOUSTON, TX, p. A611
IOWA CITY VETERANS AFFAIRS HEALTH CARE SYSTEM, IOWA CITY, IA, p. A224
IOWA LUTHERAN HOSPITAL, DES MOINES, IA, p. A221
IOWA MEDICAL AND CLASSIFICATION CENTER, CORALVILLE, IA, p. A219
IOWA SPECIALTY HOSPITAL-BELMOND, BELMOND, IA, p. A217
IOWA SPECIALTY HOSPITAL-CLARION, CLARION, IA, p. A219
IRA DAVENPORT MEMORIAL HOSPITAL, BATH, NY, p. A422
IRAAN GENERAL HOSPITAL, IRAAN, TX, p. A615
IREDELL HEALTH SYSTEM, STATESVILLE, NC, p. A461
IRON COUNTY MEDICAL CENTER, PILOT KNOB, MO, p. A366
IROQUOIS MEMORIAL HOSPITAL AND RESIDENT HOME, WATSEKA, IL, p. A197
IRWIN ARMY COMMUNITY HOSPITAL, JUNCTION CITY, KS, p. A238
IRWIN COUNTY HOSPITAL, OCILLA, GA, p. A158
ISLAND HOSPITAL, ANACORTES, WA, p. A669
IVINSON MEMORIAL HOSPITAL, LARAMIE, WY, p. A708
IZARD COUNTY MEDICAL CENTER, CALICO ROCK-Logan County, AR, p. A40

J

J. ARTHUR DOSHER MEMORIAL HOSPITAL, SOUTHPORT, NC, p. A460
J. C. BLAIR MEMORIAL HOSPITAL, HUNTINGDON, PA, p. A527
J. D. MCCARTY CENTER FOR CHILDREN WITH DEVELOPMENTAL DISABILITIES, NORMAN, OK, p. A502
JACK C. MONTGOMERY VETERANS AFFAIRS MEDICAL CENTER, MUSKOGEE, OK, p. A501
JACK D WEILER HOSPITAL OF ALBERT EINSTEIN COLLEGE OF MEDICINE, NEW YORK (Includes all hospitals located within the five boroughs), NY, p. A432
JACK D WEILER HOSPITAL OF ALBERT EINSTEIN COLLEGE OF MEDICINE, NY (see MONTEFIORE MEDICAL CENTER), p. A433
JACK HUGHSTON MEMORIAL HOSPITAL, PHENIX CITY, AL, p. A22
JACKSON BEHAVIORAL HEALTH HOSPITAL, MIAMI, FL, p. A130
JACKSON BEHAVIORAL HEALTH HOSPITAL, FL (see JACKSON HEALTH SYSTEM), p. A130
JACKSON COUNTY HOSPITAL DISTRICT, EDNA, TX, p. A601
JACKSON COUNTY MEMORIAL HOSPITAL, ALTUS, OK, p. A495
JACKSON COUNTY REGIONAL HEALTH CENTER, MAQUOKETA, IA, p. A226
JACKSON GENERAL HOSPITAL, RIPLEY, WV, p. A686
JACKSON HEALTH SYSTEM, MIAMI, FL, p. A130
JACKSON HEALTH SYSTEM, MIAMI, FL (see JACKSON BEHAVIORAL HEALTH HOSPITAL), p. A130
JACKSON HEALTH SYSTEM, MIAMI, FL (see JACKSON NORTH MEDICAL CENTER), p. A132
JACKSON HEALTH SYSTEM, MIAMI, FL (see JACKSON SOUTH COMMUNITY HOSPITAL), p. A130
JACKSON HOSPITAL, MARIANNA, FL, p. A129
JACKSON HOSPITAL AND CLINIC, MONTGOMERY, AL, p. A21
JACKSON MEDICAL CENTER, JACKSON, AL, p. A19
JACKSON MEMORIAL HOSPITAL, FL (see JACKSON HEALTH SYSTEM), p. A130
JACKSON NORTH MEDICAL CENTER, NORTH MIAMI BEACH, FL, p. A132
JACKSON NORTH MEDICAL CENTER, FL (see JACKSON HEALTH SYSTEM), p. A130
JACKSON PARISH HOSPITAL, JONESBORO, LA, p. A269
JACKSON PARK HOSPITAL AND MEDICAL CENTER, CHICAGO, IL, p. A177
JACKSON PURCHASE MEDICAL CENTER, MAYFIELD, KY, p. A257
JACKSON SOUTH COMMUNITY HOSPITAL, MIAMI, FL, p. A130
JACKSON SOUTH COMMUNITY HOSPITAL, FL (see JACKSON HEALTH SYSTEM), p. A130
JACKSON-MADISON COUNTY GENERAL HOSPITAL, JACKSON, TN, p. A571

JACOBSON MEMORIAL HOSPITAL CARE CENTER, ELGIN, ND, p. A465
JAMAICA HOSPITAL MEDICAL CENTER, NEW YORK (Includes all hospitals located within the five boroughs), NY, p. A432
JAMES A. HALEY VETERANS' HOSPITAL-TAMPA, TAMPA, FL, p. A141
JAMES AND CONNIE MAYNARD CHILDREN'S HOSPITAL, NC (see VIDANT MEDICAL CENTER), p. A454
JAMES CANCER HOSPITAL AND SOLOVE RESEARCH INSTITUTE, COLUMBUS, OH, p. A478
JAMES E. VAN ZANDT VETERANS AFFAIRS MEDICAL CENTER, ALTOONA, PA, p. A519
JAMES H. QUILLEN VETERANS AFFAIRS MEDICAL CENTER, MOUNTAIN HOME, TN, p. A576
JAMES J. PETERS VETERANS AFFAIRS MEDICAL CENTER, NEW YORK (Includes all hospitals located within the five boroughs), NY, p. A432
JAMES J. PETERS VETERANS AFFAIRS MEDICAL CENTER, NY (see VETERANS AFFAIRS MEDICAL CENTER), p. A437
JAMESTOWN REGIONAL MEDICAL CENTER, JAMESTOWN, ND, p. A467
JAMESTOWN REGIONAL MEDICAL CENTER, JAMESTOWN, TN, p. A467
JANE PHILLIPS MEDICAL CENTER, BARTLESVILLE, OK, p. A496
JANE PHILLIPS NOWATA HEALTH CENTER, NOWATA, OK, p. A502
JANE TODD CRAWFORD HOSPITAL, GREENSBURG, KY, p. A252
JASPER GENERAL HOSPITAL, BAY SPRINGS, MS, p. A343
JASPER MEMORIAL HOSPITAL, MONTICELLO, GA, p. A158
JAY HOSPITAL, JAY, FL, p. A126
JEANES HOSPITAL, PHILADELPHIA, PA, p. A535
JEFF DAVIS HOSPITAL, HAZLEHURST, GA, p. A154
JEFFERSON COMMUNITY HEALTH AND LIFE, FAIRBURY, NE, p. A383
JEFFERSON COUNTY HEALTH CENTER, FAIRFIELD, IA, p. A222
JEFFERSON COUNTY HOSPITAL, FAYETTE, MS, p. A345
JEFFERSON COUNTY HOSPITAL, WAURIKA, OK, p. A510
JEFFERSON COUNTY MEMORIAL HOSPITAL, WINCHESTER, KS, p. A248
JEFFERSON DAVIS COMMUNITY HOSPITAL, PRENTISS, MS, p. A352
JEFFERSON HEALTH NORTHEAST, PHILADELPHIA, PA, p. A535
JEFFERSON HEALTH NORTHEAST, PHILADELPHIA, PA (see BUCKS COUNTY CAMPUS), p. A529
JEFFERSON HEALTHCARE, PORT TOWNSEND, WA, p. A675
JEFFERSON HOSPITAL, JEFFERSON HILLS, PA, p. A528
JEFFERSON HOSPITAL, LOUISVILLE, GA, p. A156
JEFFERSON MEDICAL CENTER, RANSON, WV, p. A686
JEFFERSON METHODIST HOSPITAL, PHILADELPHIA, PA, p. A535
JEFFERSON METHODIST HOSPITAL, PA (see THOMAS JEFFERSON UNIVERSITY HOSPITALS), p. A536
JEFFERSON REGIONAL MEDICAL CENTER, PINE BLUFF-Jefferson County, AR, p. A47
JEFFERSON STRATFORD HOSPITAL, STRATFORD, NJ, p. A412
JEFFERSON STRATFORD HOSPITAL, NJ (see JEFFERSON STRATFORD HOSPITAL), p. A412
JEFFERSON STRATFORD HOSPITAL, NJ (see KENNEDY MEMORIAL HOSPITALS-UNIVERSITY MEDICAL CENTER), p. A412
JEFFERSON STRATFORD HOSPITAL, STRATFORD, NJ (see JEFFERSON WASHINGTON TOWNSHIP HOSPITAL), p. A413
JEFFERSON WASHINGTON TOWNSHIP HOSPITAL, TURNERSVILLE, NJ, p. A413
JEFFERSON WASHINGTON TOWNSHIP HOSPITAL, NJ (see JEFFERSON STRATFORD HOSPITAL), p. A412
JELLICO COMMUNITY HOSPITAL, JELLICO, TN, p. A571
JENNERSVILLE HOSPITAL, WEST GROVE, PA, p. A544
JENNIE EDMUNDSON HOSPITAL, COUNCIL BLUFFS, IA, p. A220
JENNIE M. MELHAM MEMORIAL MEDICAL CENTER, BROKEN BOW, NE, p. A382
JENNIE STUART MEDICAL CENTER, HOPKINSVILLE, KY, p. A253
JENNINGS AMERICAN LEGION HOSPITAL, JENNINGS, LA, p. A269
JENNINGS SENIOR CARE HOSPITAL, JENNINGS, LA, p. A269
JEROLD PHELPS COMMUNITY HOSPITAL, GARBERVILLE, CA, p. A60
JEROME GOLDEN CENTER FOR BEHAVIORAL HEALTH, INC., WEST PALM BEACH, FL, p. A143
JERSEY CITY MEDICAL CENTER, JERSEY CITY, NJ, p. A406
JERSEY COMMUNITY HOSPITAL, JERSEYVILLE, IL, p. A186
JESSE BROWN VETERANS AFFAIRS MEDICAL CENTER, CHICAGO, IL, p. A177

JEWELL COUNTY HOSPITAL, MANKATO, KS, p. A240
JEWISH HOME OF SAN FRANCISCO, SAN FRANCISCO, CA, p. A85
JEWISH HOSPITAL, LOUISVILLE, KY, p. A256
JEWISH HOSPITAL-SHELBYVILLE, SHELBYVILLE, KY, p. A260
JFK MEDICAL CENTER, ATLANTIS, FL, p. A117
JFK MEDICAL CENTER NORTH CAMPUS, WEST PALM BEACH, FL, p. A143
JIM TALIAFERRO COMMUNITY MENTAL HEALTH, LAWTON, OK, p. A500
JOE DIMAGGIO CHILDREN'S HOSPITAL, FL (see MEMORIAL REGIONAL HOSPITAL), p. A124
JOHN C. FREMONT HEALTHCARE DISTRICT, MARIPOSA, CA, p. A71
JOHN C. STENNIS MEMORIAL HOSPITAL, DE KALB, MS, p. A345
JOHN D. ARCHBOLD MEMORIAL HOSPITAL, THOMASVILLE, GA, p. A161
JOHN D. DINGELL VETERANS AFFAIRS MEDICAL CENTER, DETROIT, MI, p. A311
JOHN F. KENNEDY MEMORIAL HOSPITAL, INDIO, CA, p. A62
JOHN GEORGE PSYCHIATRIC HOSPITAL, CA (see HIGHLAND HOSPITAL), p. A75
JOHN H. STROGER JR. HOSPITAL OF COOK COUNTY, CHICAGO, IL, p. A177
JOHN HEINZ INSTITUTE OF REHABILITATION MEDICINE, WILKES, PA, p. A544
JOHN J. MADDEN MENTAL HEALTH CENTER, HINES, IL, p. A185
JOHN J. PERSHING VETERANS AFFAIRS MEDICAL CENTER, POPLAR BLUFF, MO, p. A366
JOHN MUIR BEHAVIORAL HEALTH CENTER, CONCORD, CA, p. A55
JOHN MUIR MEDICAL CENTER, CONCORD, CONCORD, CA, p. A55
JOHN MUIR MEDICAL CENTER, WALNUT CREEK, WALNUT CREEK, CA, p. A94
JOHN PETER SMITH HOSPITAL, FORT WORTH, TX, p. A604
JOHN PETER SMITH HOSPITAL, TX (see JPS HEALTH NETWORK), p. A604
JOHN RANDOLPH MEDICAL CENTER, HOPEWELL, VA, p. A659
JOHN T. MATHER MEMORIAL HOSPITAL, PORT JEFFERSON, NY, p. A440
JOHNS COMMUNITY HOSPITAL, TAYLOR, TX, p. A638
JOHNS HOPKINS ALL CHILDREN'S HOSPITAL, SAINT PETERSBURG, FL, p. A138
JOHNS HOPKINS BAYVIEW MEDICAL CENTER, BALTIMORE, MD, p. A287
JOHNS HOPKINS CHILDREN'S CENTER, MD (see JOHNS HOPKINS HOSPITAL), p. A287
JOHNS HOPKINS HOSPITAL, BALTIMORE, MD, p. A287
JOHNSON CITY MEDICAL CENTER, JOHNSON CITY, TN, p. A571
JOHNSON COUNTY COMMUNITY HOSPITAL, MOUNTAIN CITY, TN, p. A576
JOHNSON COUNTY HEALTHCARE CENTER, BUFFALO, WY, p. A707
JOHNSON COUNTY HOSPITAL, TECUMSEH, NE, p. A391
JOHNSON MEMORIAL HEALTH SERVICES, DAWSON, MN, p. A330
JOHNSON MEMORIAL HOSPITAL, FRANKLIN, IN, p. A204
JOHNSON MEMORIAL MEDICAL CENTER, STAFFORD SPRINGS, CT, p. A111
JOHNSON REGIONAL MEDICAL CENTER, CLARKSVILLE-Johnson County, AR, p. A40
JOHNSTON HEALTH, SMITHFIELD, NC, p. A460
JOHNSTON MEMORIAL HOSPITAL, ABINGDON, VA, p. A655
JOHNSTON MEMORIAL HOSPITAL, TISHOMINGO, OK, p. A507
JOHNSTON R. BOWMAN HEALTH CENTER, CHICAGO, IL, p. A177
JOHNSTON R. BOWMAN HEALTH CENTER, IL (see RUSH UNIVERSITY MEDICAL CENTER), p. A179
JOHNSTON-WILLIS HOSPITAL, RICHMOND, VA, p. A665
JOHNSTON-WILLIS HOSPITAL, VA (see CHIPPENHAM HOSPITAL), p. A664
JOINT TOWNSHIP DISTRICT MEMORIAL HOSPITAL, SAINT MARYS, OH, p. A490
JONES MEMORIAL HOSPITAL, WELLSVILLE, NY, p. A445
JORDAN VALLEY MEDICAL CENTER, WEST JORDAN, UT, p. A652
JORDAN VALLEY MEDICAL CENTER WEST VALLEY CAMPUS, WEST VALLEY CITY, UT, p. A652
JOYCE EISENBERG-KEEFER MEDICAL CENTER, RESEDA, CA, p. A80
JPS HEALTH NETWORK, FORT WORTH, TX, p. A604
JPS HEALTH NETWORK, FORT WORTH, TX (see JOHN PETER SMITH HOSPITAL), p. A604

JULIAN F. KEITH ALCOHOL AND DRUG ABUSE TREATMENT CENTER, BLACK MOUNTAIN, NC, p. A448
JUPITER MEDICAL CENTER, JUPITER, FL, p. A126

K

K. HOVNANIAN CHILDREN'S HOSPITAL, NJ (see HACKENSACK MERIDIAN HEALTH JERSEY SHORE UNIVERSITY MEDICAL CENTER), p. A408
KA'U HOSPITAL, PAHALA, HI, p. A166
KADLEC REGIONAL MEDICAL CENTER, RICHLAND, WA, p. A676
KAHUKU MEDICAL CENTER, KAHUKU, HI, p. A165
KAISER FOUNDATION HOSPITAL, MARTINEZ, CA, p. A71
KAISER FOUNDATION HOSPITAL, CA (see KAISER PERMANENTE WALNUT CREEK MEDICAL CENTER), p. A94
KAISER FOUNDATION HOSPITAL WESTSIDE MEDICAL CENTER, HILLSBORO, OR, p. A513
KAISER FOUNDATION MENTAL HEALTH CENTER, LOS ANGELES, CA, p. A67
KAISER FOUNDATION MENTAL HEALTH CENTER, CA (see KAISER PERMANENTE LOS ANGELES MEDICAL CENTER), p. A67
KAISER PERMANENTE ANTIOCH MEDICAL CENTER, ANTIOCH, CA, p. A50
KAISER PERMANENTE BALDWIN PARK MEDICAL CENTER, BALDWIN PARK, CA, p. A52
KAISER PERMANENTE BALDWIN PARK MEDICAL CENTER, CA (see BALDWIN PARK MEDICAL CENTER), p. A52
KAISER PERMANENTE CAPITOL HILL CAMPUS, SEATTLE, WA, p. A676
KAISER PERMANENTE DOWNEY MEDICAL CENTER, DOWNEY, CA, p. A56
KAISER PERMANENTE FONTANA MEDICAL CENTER, FONTANA, CA, p. A58
KAISER PERMANENTE FREMONT MEDICAL CENTER, FREMONT, CA, p. A59
KAISER PERMANENTE FRESNO MEDICAL CENTER, FRESNO, CA, p. A59
KAISER PERMANENTE FRESNO MEDICAL CENTER, CA (see FRESNO MEDICAL CENTER), p. A59
KAISER PERMANENTE LOS ANGELES MEDICAL CENTER, LOS ANGELES, CA, p. A67
KAISER PERMANENTE LOS ANGELES MEDICAL CENTER, CA (see LOS ANGELES MEDICAL CENTER), p. A68
KAISER PERMANENTE LOS ANGELES MEDICAL CENTER, LOS ANGELES, CA (see KAISER FOUNDATION MENTAL HEALTH CENTER), p. A67
KAISER PERMANENTE MANTECA MEDICAL CENTER, MANTECA, CA, p. A71
KAISER PERMANENTE MANTECA MEDICAL CENTER, MANTECA, CA (see MODESTO MEDICAL CENTER), p. A73
KAISER PERMANENTE MEDICAL CENTER, HONOLULU, HI, p. A164
KAISER PERMANENTE MORENO VALLEY MEDICAL CENTER, MORENO VALLEY, CA, p. A73
KAISER PERMANENTE OAKLAND MEDICAL CENTER, OAKLAND, CA, p. A76
KAISER PERMANENTE OAKLAND MEDICAL CENTER, CA (see OAKLAND MEDICAL CENTER), p. A76
KAISER PERMANENTE OAKLAND MEDICAL CENTER, OAKLAND, CA (see KAISER PERMANENTE RICHMOND MEDICAL CENTER), p. A80
KAISER PERMANENTE ONTARIO MEDICAL CENTER, CA (see KAISER PERMANENTE FONTANA MEDICAL CENTER), p. A58
KAISER PERMANENTE ORANGE COUNTY ANAHEIM MEDICAL CENTER, ANAHEIM, CA, p. A50
KAISER PERMANENTE ORANGE COUNTY ANAHEIM MEDICAL CENTER, CA (see ANAHEIM MEDICAL CENTER), p. A50
KAISER PERMANENTE ORANGE COUNTY ANAHEIM MEDICAL CENTER, ANAHEIM, CA (see ORANGE COUNTY IRVINE MEDICAL CENTER), p. A62
KAISER PERMANENTE PANORAMA CITY MEDICAL CENTER, LOS ANGELES, CA, p. A67
KAISER PERMANENTE PANORAMA CITY MEDICAL CENTER, CA (see PANORAMA CITY MEDICAL CENTER), p. A69
KAISER PERMANENTE REDWOOD CITY MEDICAL CENTER, REDWOOD CITY, CA, p. A80
KAISER PERMANENTE RICHMOND MEDICAL CENTER, RICHMOND, CA, p. A80
KAISER PERMANENTE RICHMOND MEDICAL CENTER, CA (see KAISER PERMANENTE OAKLAND MEDICAL CENTER), p. A76
KAISER PERMANENTE RIVERSIDE MEDICAL CENTER, RIVERSIDE, CA, p. A81
KAISER PERMANENTE RIVERSIDE MEDICAL CENTER, CA (see RIVERSIDE MEDICAL CENTER), p. A81

KAISER PERMANENTE ROSEVILLE MEDICAL CENTER, ROSEVILLE, CA, p. A81
KAISER PERMANENTE SACRAMENTO MEDICAL CENTER, SACRAMENTO, CA, p. A81
KAISER PERMANENTE SAN DIEGO MEDICAL CENTER, SAN DIEGO, CA, p. A83
KAISER PERMANENTE SAN DIEGO MEDICAL CENTER, CA (see KAISER PERMANENTE SAN DIEGO MEDICAL CENTER), p. A83
KAISER PERMANENTE SAN DIEGO MEDICAL CENTER, CA (see SAN DIEGO MEDICAL CENTER), p. A84
KAISER PERMANENTE SAN FRANCISCO MEDICAL CENTER, SAN FRANCISCO, CA, p. A85
KAISER PERMANENTE SAN FRANCISCO MEDICAL CENTER, CA (see SAN FRANCISCO MEDICAL CENTER), p. A85
KAISER PERMANENTE SAN JOSE MEDICAL CENTER, SAN JOSE, CA, p. A86
KAISER PERMANENTE SAN JOSE MEDICAL CENTER, CA (see SAN JOSE MEDICAL CENTER), p. A87
KAISER PERMANENTE SAN LEANDRO MEDICAL CENTER, SAN LEANDRO, CA, p. A87
KAISER PERMANENTE SAN RAFAEL MEDICAL CENTER, SAN RAFAEL, CA, p. A87
KAISER PERMANENTE SANTA CLARA MEDICAL CENTER, SANTA CLARA, CA, p. A88
KAISER PERMANENTE SANTA ROSA MEDICAL CENTER, SANTA ROSA, CA, p. A89
KAISER PERMANENTE SOUTH BAY MEDICAL CENTER, LOS ANGELES, CA, p. A67
KAISER PERMANENTE SOUTH SACRAMENTO MEDICAL CENTER, SACRAMENTO, CA, p. A82
KAISER PERMANENTE SOUTH SACRAMENTO MEDICAL CENTER, CA (see SOUTH SACRAMENTO MEDICAL CENTER), p. A82
KAISER PERMANENTE SOUTH SAN FRANCISCO, SOUTH SAN FRANCISCO, CA, p. A90
KAISER PERMANENTE VACAVILLE MEDICAL CENTER, VACAVILLE, CA, p. A93
KAISER PERMANENTE VALLEJO MEDICAL CENTER, VALLEJO, CA, p. A93
KAISER PERMANENTE WALNUT CREEK MEDICAL CENTER, WALNUT CREEK, CA, p. A94
KAISER PERMANENTE WALNUT CREEK MEDICAL CENTER, WALNUT CREEK, CA (see KAISER FOUNDATION HOSPITAL), p. A71
KAISER PERMANENTE WEST LOS ANGELES MEDICAL CENTER, LOS ANGELES, CA, p. A67
KAISER PERMANENTE WEST LOS ANGELES MEDICAL CENTER, CA (see WEST LOS ANGELES MEDICAL CENTER), p. A70
KAISER PERMANENTE WOODLAND HILLS MEDICAL CENTER, LOS ANGELES, CA, p. A67
KAISER PERMANENTE WOODLAND HILLS MEDICAL CENTER, CA (see WOODLAND HILLS MEDICAL CENTER), p. A70
KAISER SUNNYSIDE MEDICAL CENTER, CLACKAMAS, OR, p. A512
KALAMAZOO PSYCHIATRIC HOSPITAL, KALAMAZOO, MI, p. A317
KALEIDA HEALTH, BUFFALO, NY, p. A423
KALISPELL REGIONAL HEALTHCARE, KALISPELL, MT, p. A377
KALKASKA MEMORIAL HEALTH CENTER, KALKASKA, MI, p. A317
KANE COUNTY HOSPITAL, KANAB, UT, p. A647
KANSAS CITY ORTHOPAEDIC INSTITUTE, LEAWOOD, KS, p. A240
KANSAS CITY VETERANS AFFAIRS MEDICAL CENTER, KANSAS CITY, MO, p. A361
KANSAS HEART HOSPITAL, WICHITA, KS, p. A247
KANSAS MEDICAL CENTER, ANDOVER, KS, p. A232
KANSAS NEUROLOGICAL INSTITUTE, TOPEKA, KS, p. A246
KANSAS REHABILITATION HOSPITAL, TOPEKA, KS, p. A246
KANSAS SPINE AND SPECIALTY HOSPITAL, WICHITA, KS, p. A247
KANSAS SURGERY AND RECOVERY CENTER, WICHITA, KS, p. A248
KAPIOLANI MEDICAL CENTER FOR WOMEN & CHILDREN, HONOLULU, HI, p. A164
KARL AND ESTHER HOBLITZELLE MEMORIAL HOSPITAL, TX (see BAYLOR UNIVERSITY MEDICAL CENTER), p. A596
KARMANOS CANCER CENTER, DETROIT, MI, p. A311
KATE DISHMAN REHABILITATION HOSPITAL, BEAUMONT, TX, p. A588
KATHERINE SHAW BETHEA HOSPITAL, DIXON, IL, p. A181
KAUAI VETERANS MEMORIAL HOSPITAL, WAIMEA, HI, p. A166
KAWEAH DELTA MEDICAL CENTER, VISALIA, CA, p. A94
KEARNEY COUNTY HEALTH SERVICES, MINDEN, NE, p. A386
KEARNEY REGIONAL MEDICAL CENTER, KEARNEY, NE, p. A385

KEARNY COUNTY HOSPITAL, LAKIN, KS, p. A239
KECK HOSPITAL OF USC, LOS ANGELES, CA, p. A68
KECK HOSPITAL OF USC, CA (see USC UNIVERSITY HOSPITAL), p. A70
KEDREN COMMUNITY MENTAL HEALTH CENTER, LOS ANGELES, CA, p. A68
KEEFE MEMORIAL HOSPITAL, CHEYENNE WELLS, CO, p. A97
KELL WEST REGIONAL HOSPITAL, WICHITA FALLS, TX, p. A644
KELLER ARMY COMMUNITY HOSPITAL, WEST POINT, NY, p. A446
KEMPSVILLE CENTER FOR BEHAVIORAL HEALTH, NORFOLK, VA, p. A662
KENDALL REGIONAL MEDICAL CENTER, MIAMI, FL, p. A130
KENMARE COMMUNITY HOSPITAL, KENMARE, ND, p. A467
KENMORE MERCY HOSPITAL, KENMORE, NY, p. A428
KENNEDY KRIEGER INSTITUTE, BALTIMORE, MD, p. A287
KENNEDY MEMORIAL HOSPITALS-UNIVERSITY MEDICAL CENTER, STRATFORD, NJ, p. A412
KENSINGTON HOSPITAL, PHILADELPHIA, PA, p. A535
KENT COUNTY MEMORIAL HOSPITAL, WARWICK, RI, p. A548
KENTFIELD REHABILITATION AND SPECIALTY HOSPITAL, KENTFIELD, CA, p. A62
KENTUCKIANA MEDICAL CENTER, CLARKSVILLE, IN, p. A201
KENTUCKY CHILDREN'S HOSPITAL, KY (see UNIVERSITY OF KENTUCKY ALBERT B. CHANDLER HOSPITAL), p. A255
KENTUCKY RIVER MEDICAL CENTER, JACKSON, KY, p. A254
KEOKUK COUNTY HEALTH CENTER, SIGOURNEY, IA, p. A229
KERN MEDICAL CENTER, BAKERSFIELD, CA, p. A52
KERN VALLEY HEALTHCARE DISTRICT, LAKE ISABELLA, CA, p. A63
KERNERSVILLE MEDICAL CENTER, NC (see NOVANT HEALTH FORSYTH MEDICAL CENTER), p. A462
KERRVILLE DIVISION, KERRVILLE, TX, p. A617
KERRVILLE DIVISION, TX (see SOUTH TEXAS VETERANS HEALTH CARE SYSTEM), p. A634
KERRVILLE STATE HOSPITAL, KERRVILLE, TX, p. A617
KERSHAWHEALTH, CAMDEN, SC, p. A549
KESSLER INSTITUTE FOR REHABILITATION, CHESTER, NJ, p. A403
KESSLER INSTITUTE FOR REHABILITATION, SADDLE BROOK, NJ, p. A411
KESSLER INSTITUTE FOR REHABILITATION, WEST ORANGE, NJ, p. A413
KESSLER INSTITUTE FOR REHABILITATION, NJ (see KESSLER INSTITUTE FOR REHABILITATION), p. A413
KESSLER INSTITUTE FOR REHABILITATION, WEST ORANGE, NJ (see KESSLER INSTITUTE FOR REHABILITATION), p. A403
KESSLER INSTITUTE FOR REHABILITATION, WEST ORANGE, NJ (see KESSLER INSTITUTE FOR REHABILITATION), p. A411
KESSLER INSTITUTE FOR REHABILITATION, WEST ORANGE, NJ (see KESSLER INSTITUTE FOR REHABILITATION), p. A413
KESSLER MARLTON REHABILITATION, MARLTON, NJ, p. A407
KETTERING BEHAVIORAL MEDICAL CENTER, OH (see SYCAMORE MEDICAL CENTER), p. A487
KETTERING MEDICAL CENTER, KETTERING, OH, p. A484
KIDSPEACE CHILDREN'S HOSPITAL, OREFIELD, PA, p. A533
KIMBALL HEALTH SERVICES, KIMBALL, NE, p. A385
KIMBALL-RIDGE CENTER, IA (see COVENANT MEDICAL CENTER), p. A230
KIMBLE HOSPITAL, JUNCTION, TX, p. A616
KINDRED CHICAGO LAKESHORE, CHICAGO, IL, p. A177
KINDRED CHICAGO LAKESHORE, IL (see KINDRED CHICAGO-CENTRAL HOSPITAL), p. A177
KINDRED CHICAGO-CENTRAL HOSPITAL, CHICAGO, IL, p. A177
KINDRED CHICAGO-CENTRAL HOSPITAL, CHICAGO, IL (see KINDRED CHICAGO LAKESHORE), p. A177
KINDRED CHICAGO-CENTRAL HOSPITAL, CHICAGO, IL (see KINDRED HOSPITAL CHICAGO NORTH), p. A177
KINDRED HOSPITAL BAY AREA-TAMPA, TAMPA, FL, p. A141
KINDRED HOSPITAL CENTRAL TAMPA, TAMPA, FL, p. A141
KINDRED HOSPITAL CHICAGO NORTH, CHICAGO, IL, p. A177
KINDRED HOSPITAL CHICAGO NORTH, IL (see KINDRED CHICAGO-CENTRAL HOSPITAL), p. A177
KINDRED HOSPITAL CHICAGO-NORTHLAKE, NORTHLAKE, IL, p. A191
KINDRED HOSPITAL CLEAR LAKE, WEBSTER, TX, p. A643
KINDRED HOSPITAL DALLAS CENTRAL, DALLAS, TX, p. A596
KINDRED HOSPITAL DENVER SOUTH, DENVER, CO, p. A99
KINDRED HOSPITAL EL PASO, EL PASO, TX, p. A602
KINDRED HOSPITAL EL PASO, TX (see TRIUMPH HOSPITAL EL PASO), p. A602
KINDRED HOSPITAL FARGO, FARGO, ND, p. A465
KINDRED HOSPITAL HOUSTON MEDICAL CENTER, HOUSTON, TX, p. A611

L

M

MAINE VETERANS AFFAIRS MEDICAL CENTER, ME (see VETERANS AFFAIRS MEDICAL CENTER), p. A282

MAINEGENERAL MEDICAL CENTER, AUGUSTA, ME, p. A282

MAINEGENERAL MEDICAL CENTER, AUGUSTA, ME (see MAINEGENERAL MEDICAL CENTER-AUGUSTA CAMPUS), p. A282

MAINEGENERAL MEDICAL CENTER-AUGUSTA CAMPUS, AUGUSTA, ME, p. A282

MAINEGENERAL MEDICAL CENTER-AUGUSTA CAMPUS, ME (see MAINEGENERAL MEDICAL CENTER), p. A282

MAINLAND MEDICAL CENTER, TX (see CLEAR LAKE REGIONAL MEDICAL CENTER), p. A643

MAJOR HOSPITAL, SHELBYVILLE, IN, p. A214

MALVERN INSTITUTE, MALVERN, PA, p. A530

MAMMOTH HOSPITAL, MAMMOTH LAKES, CA, p. A71

MANATEE MEMORIAL HOSPITAL, BRADENTON, FL, p. A118

MANCHESTER MEMORIAL HOSPITAL, MANCHESTER, CT, p. A108

MANCHESTER MEMORIAL HOSPITAL, MANCHESTER, KY, p. A257

MANCHESTER VETERANS AFFAIRS MEDICAL CENTER, MANCHESTER, NH, p. A400

MANCHESTER VETERANS AFFAIRS MEDICAL CENTER, NH (see VETERANS AFFAIRS MEDICAL CENTER), p. A400

MANGUM REGIONAL MEDICAL CENTER, MANGUM, OK, p. A501

MANHASSET AMBULATORY CARE PAVILION, NY (see LONG ISLAND JEWISH MEDICAL CENTER), p. A433

MANHATTAN EYE, EAR AND THROAT HOSPITAL, NY (see LENOX HILL HOSPITAL), p. A433

MANHATTAN PSYCHIATRIC CENTER-WARD'S ISLAND, NEW YORK (Includes all hospitals located within the five boroughs), NY, p. A433

MANHATTAN SURGICAL, MANHATTAN, KS, p. A240

MANIILAQ HEALTH CENTER, KOTZEBUE, AK, p. A26

MANN-GRANDSTAFF VETERANS AFFAIRS MEDICAL CENTER, SPOKANE, WA, p. A678

MANN-GRANDSTAFF VETERANS AFFAIRS MEDICAL CENTER, WA (see VETERANS AFFAIRS MEDICAL CENTER), p. A678

MANNING REGIONAL HEALTHCARE CENTER, MANNING, IA, p. A226

MANSFIELD HOSPITAL, OH (see OHIOHEALTH MEDCENTRAL MANSFIELD HOSPITAL), p. A485

MAPLE GROVE HOSPITAL, MAPLE GROVE, MN, p. A334

MARCUS DALY MEMORIAL HOSPITAL, HAMILTON, MT, p. A376

MARGARET MARY HEALTH, BATESVILLE, IN, p. A199

MARGARET R. PARDEE MEMORIAL HOSPITAL, HENDERSONVILLE, NC, p. A454

MARGARETVILLE HOSPITAL, MARGARETVILLE, NY, p. A429

MARIA FARERI CHILDREN'S HOSPITAL, NY (see WESTCHESTER MEDICAL CENTER), p. A445

MARIA PARHAM MEDICAL CENTER, HENDERSON, NC, p. A454

MARIAN CENTER, SALT LAKE CITY, UT, p. A650

MARIAN REGIONAL MEDICAL CENTER, SANTA MARIA, CA, p. A89

MARIAS MEDICAL CENTER, SHELBY, MT, p. A379

MARICOPA INTEGRATED HEALTH SYSTEM, PHOENIX, AZ, p. A33

MARIETTA MEMORIAL HOSPITAL, MARIETTA, OH, p. A485

MARIN GENERAL HOSPITAL, GREENBRAE, CA, p. A61

MARINA DEL REY HOSPITAL, MARINA DEL REY, CA, p. A71

MARION COUNTY MEDICAL CENTER, MULLINS, SC, p. A556

MARION GENERAL HOSPITAL, COLUMBIA, MS, p. A345

MARION GENERAL HOSPITAL, MARION, IN, p. A211

MARION VETERANS AFFAIRS MEDICAL CENTER, MARION, IL, p. A188

MARK TWAIN MEDICAL CENTER, SAN ANDREAS, CA, p. A83

MARLETTE REGIONAL HOSPITAL, MARLETTE, MI, p. A318

MARSHALL BROWNING HOSPITAL, DU QUOIN, IL, p. A181

MARSHALL COUNTY HEALTHCARE CENTER AVERA, BRITTON, SD, p. A559

MARSHALL COUNTY HOSPITAL, BENTON, KY, p. A249

MARSHALL I. PICKENS HOSPITAL, SC (see GHS GREENVILLE MEMORIAL HOSPITAL), p. A553

MARSHALL MEDICAL CENTER, LEWISBURG, TN, p. A573

MARSHALL MEDICAL CENTER, PLACERVILLE, CA, p. A78

MARSHALL MEDICAL CENTER NORTH, GUNTERSVILLE, AL, p. A19

MARSHALL MEDICAL CENTER SOUTH, BOAZ, AL, p. A15

MARSHFIELD CHILDEN'S HOSPITAL, WI (see MARSHFIELD MEDICAL CENTER), p. A697

MARSHFIELD MEDICAL CENTER - EAU CLAIRE HOSPITAL, EAU CLAIRE, WI, p. A692

MARSHFIELD MEDICAL CENTER - LADYSMITH, LADYSMITH, WI, p. A695

MARSHFIELD MEDICAL CENTER - RICE LAKE, RICE LAKE, WI, p. A702

MARSHFIELD MEDICAL CENTER, MARSHFIELD, WI, p. A697

MARTHA'S VINEYARD HOSPITAL, OAK BLUFFS, MA, p. A303

MARTIN ARMY COMMUNITY HOSPITAL, FORT BENNING, GA, p. A154

MARTIN COUNTY HOSPITAL DISTRICT, STANTON, TX, p. A637

MARTIN GENERAL HOSPITAL, WILLIAMSTON, NC, p. A462

MARTIN HEALTH SYSTEM, STUART, FL, p. A139

MARTIN LUTHER KING, JR. COMMUNITY HOSPITAL, LOS ANGELES, CA, p. A68

MARTIN MEMORIAL HOSPITAL SOUTH, FL (see MARTIN HEALTH SYSTEM), p. A139

MARTINSBURG VETERANS AFFAIRS MEDICAL CENTER, MARTINSBURG, WV, p. A685

MARY BLACK HEALTH SYSTEM - GAFFNEY, GAFFNEY, SC, p. A553

MARY BLACK HEALTH SYSTEM-SPARTANBURG, SPARTANBURG, SC, p. A557

MARY BRECKINRIDGE ARH HOSPITAL, HYDEN, KY, p. A254

MARY FREE BED REHABILITATION HOSPITAL, GRAND RAPIDS, MI, p. A314

MARY GREELEY MEDICAL CENTER, AMES, IA, p. A217

MARY LANNING HEALTHCARE, HASTINGS, NE, p. A384

MARY RUTAN HOSPITAL, BELLEFONTAINE, OH, p. A472

MARY S HARPER GERIATRIC PSYCHIATRY CENTER, TUSCALOOSA, AL, p. A24

MARY SHIELS HOSPITAL, DALLAS, TX, p. A596

MARY WASHINGTON HOSPITAL, FREDERICKSBURG, VA, p. A658

MARYMOUNT HOSPITAL, GARFIELD HEIGHTS, OH, p. A483

MASON DISTRICT HOSPITAL, HAVANA, IL, p. A185

MASON GENERAL HOSPITAL AND FAMILY OF CLINICS, SHELTON, WA, p. A677

MASONICARE HEALTH CENTER, WALLINGFORD, CT, p. A111

MASSAC MEMORIAL HOSPITAL, METROPOLIS, IL, p. A189

MASSACHUSETTS EYE AND EAR, BOSTON, MA, p. A296

MASSACHUSETTS GENERAL HOSPITAL, BOSTON, MA, p. A297

MASSENA MEMORIAL HOSPITAL, MASSENA, NY, p. A430

MASSGENERAL FOR CHILDREN AT NEWTON-WELLESLEY HOSPITAL, MA (see NEWTON-WELLESLEY HOSPITAL), p. A302

MASSGENERAL FOR CHILDREN AT NORTH SHORE MEDICAL CENTER, MA (see NORTH SHORE CHILDREN'S HOSPITAL), p. A303

MASSGENERAL FOR CHILDREN AT NORTH SHORE MEDICAL CENTER, MA (see NORTH SHORE MEDICAL CENTER), p. A304

MASSGENERAL HOSPITAL FOR CHILDREN, MA (see MASSACHUSETTS GENERAL HOSPITAL), p. A297

MAT-SU REGIONAL MEDICAL CENTER, PALMER, AK, p. A27

MATAGORDA REGIONAL MEDICAL CENTER, BAY CITY, TX, p. A587

MATHENY MEDICAL AND EDUCATIONAL CENTER, PEAPACK, NJ, p. A409

MATTEL CHILDREN'S HOSPITAL, CA (see RONALD REAGAN UCLA MEDICAL CENTER), p. A69

MAUI MEMORIAL MEDICAL CENTER, WAILUKU, HI, p. A166

MAURY REGIONAL HOSPITAL, COLUMBIA, TN, p. A568

MAYERS MEMORIAL HOSPITAL DISTRICT, FALL RIVER MILLS, CA, p. A58

MAYHILL HOSPITAL, DENTON, TX, p. A599

MAYO CLINIC HEALTH SYSTEM - ALBERT LEA AND AUSTIN, ALBERT LEA, MN, p. A327

MAYO CLINIC HEALTH SYSTEM - ALBERT LEA AND AUSTIN, MN (see MAYO CLINIC HEALTH SYSTEM - ALBERT LEA AND AUSTIN), p. A327

MAYO CLINIC HEALTH SYSTEM - CHIPPEWA VALLEY IN BLOOMER, BLOOMER, WI, p. A690

MAYO CLINIC HEALTH SYSTEM - FRANCISCAN HEALTHCARE IN LA CROSSE, LA CROSSE, WI, p. A695

MAYO CLINIC HEALTH SYSTEM - FRANCISCAN HEALTHCARE IN SPARTA, SPARTA, WI, p. A703

MAYO CLINIC HEALTH SYSTEM - NORTHLAND IN BARRON, BARRON, WI, p. A690

MAYO CLINIC HEALTH SYSTEM - OAKRIDGE IN OSSEO, OSSEO, WI, p. A701

MAYO CLINIC HEALTH SYSTEM - RED CEDAR IN MENOMONIE, MENOMONIE, WI, p. A697

MAYO CLINIC HEALTH SYSTEM - RED CEDAR IN MENOMONIE, WI (see RED CEDAR MEDICAL CENTER-MAYO HEALTH SYSTEM), p. A697

MAYO CLINIC HEALTH SYSTEM IN CANNON FALLS, CANNON FALLS, MN, p. A329

MAYO CLINIC HEALTH SYSTEM IN EAU CLAIRE, EAU CLAIRE, WI, p. A692

MAYO CLINIC HEALTH SYSTEM IN FAIRMONT, FAIRMONT, MN, p. A331

MAYO CLINIC HEALTH SYSTEM IN LAKE CITY, LAKE CITY, MN, p. A333

MAYO CLINIC HEALTH SYSTEM IN MANKATO, MANKATO, MN, p. A334

MAYO CLINIC HEALTH SYSTEM IN NEW PRAGUE, NEW PRAGUE, MN, p. A336

MAYO CLINIC HEALTH SYSTEM IN RED WING, RED WING, MN, p. A338

MAYO CLINIC HEALTH SYSTEM IN SAINT JAMES, SAINT JAMES, MN, p. A339

MAYO CLINIC HEALTH SYSTEM IN SPRINGFIELD, SPRINGFIELD, MN, p. A340

MAYO CLINIC HEALTH SYSTEM IN WASECA, WASECA, MN, p. A342

MAYO CLINIC HOSPITAL - METHODIST CAMPUS, MN (see MAYO CLINIC HOSPITAL - ROCHESTER), p. A338

MAYO CLINIC HOSPITAL - ROCHESTER, ROCHESTER, MN, p. A338

MAYO CLINIC HOSPITAL - SAINT MARYS CAMPUS, MN (see MAYO CLINIC HOSPITAL - ROCHESTER), p. A338

MAYO CLINIC HOSPITAL, PHOENIX, AZ, p. A33

MAYO CLINIC HOSPITAL IN FLORIDA, JACKSONVILLE, FL, p. A125

MAYO EUGENIO LITTA CHILDREN'S HOSPITAL, MN (see MAYO CLINIC HOSPITAL - ROCHESTER), p. A338

MAYO REGIONAL HOSPITAL, DOVER, ME, p. A284

MCALESTER REGIONAL HEALTH CENTER, MCALESTER, OK, p. A501

MCALLEN HEART HOSPITAL, TX (see SOUTH TEXAS HEALTH SYSTEM), p. A601

MCALLEN MEDICAL CENTER, TX (see SOUTH TEXAS HEALTH SYSTEM), p. A601

MCBRIDE ORTHOPEDIC HOSPITAL, OKLAHOMA CITY, OK, p. A503

MCCAMEY COUNTY HOSPITAL DISTRICT, MCCAMEY, TX, p. A623

MCCONE COUNTY HEALTH CENTER, CIRCLE, MT, p. A374

MCCREADY HEALTH, CRISFIELD, MD, p. A291

MCCULLOUGH-HYDE MEMORIAL HOSPITAL/TRIHEALTH, OXFORD, OH, p. A489

MCCURTAIN MEMORIAL HOSPITAL, IDABEL, OK, p. A500

MCDONOUGH DISTRICT HOSPITAL, MACOMB, IL, p. A188

MCDOWELL ARH HOSPITAL, MCDOWELL, KY, p. A258

MCDOWELL HOSPITAL, MARION, NC, p. A456

MCGEHEE HOSPITAL, MCGEHEE-Desha County, AR, p. A46

MCKAY-DEE HOSPITAL, OGDEN, UT, p. A648

MCKEE MEDICAL CENTER, LOVELAND, CO, p. A104

MCKENZIE COUNTY HEALTHCARE SYSTEM, WATFORD CITY, ND, p. A469

MCKENZIE HEALTH SYSTEM, SANDUSKY, MI, p. A323

MCKENZIE REGIONAL HOSPITAL, MCKENZIE, TN, p. A574

MCKENZIE-WILLAMETTE MEDICAL CENTER, SPRINGFIELD, OR, p. A518

MCLANE CHILDREN'S HOSPITAL SCOTT & WHITE, TEMPLE, TX, p. A638

MCLANE CHILDREN'S HOSPITAL SCOTT & WHITE, TX (see SCOTT & WHITE MEDICAL CENTER - TEMPLE), p. A638

MCLAREN BAY REGION, BAY CITY, MI, p. A308

MCLAREN BAY REGION-WEST CAMPUS, MI (see MCLAREN BAY REGION), p. A308

MCLAREN BAY SPECIAL CARE, BAY CITY, MI, p. A308

MCLAREN CARO REGION, CARO, MI, p. A309

MCLAREN CENTRAL MICHIGAN, MOUNT PLEASANT, MI, p. A319

MCLAREN FLINT, FLINT, MI, p. A312

MCLAREN GREATER LANSING, LANSING, MI, p. A317

MCLAREN GREATER LANSING, MI (see MCLAREN GREATER LANSING), p. A317

MCLAREN LAPEER REGION, LAPEER, MI, p. A317

MCLAREN MACOMB, MOUNT CLEMENS, MI, p. A319

MCLAREN NORTHERN MICHIGAN, PETOSKEY, MI, p. A320

MCLAREN OAKLAND, PONTIAC, MI, p. A321

MCLAREN ORTHOPEDIC HOSPITAL, MI (see MCLAREN GREATER LANSING), p. A317

MCLAREN PORT HURON, PORT HURON, MI, p. A321

MCLAREN THUMB REGION, BAD AXE, MI, p. A308

MCLEAN HOSPITAL, BELMONT, MA, p. A295

MCLEOD HEALTH CHERAW, CHERAW, SC, p. A550

MCLEOD HEALTH CLARENDON, MANNING, SC, p. A555

MCLEOD LORIS SEACOAST HOSPITAL, LORIS, SC, p. A555

MCLEOD MEDICAL CENTER DARLINGTON, DARLINGTON, SC, p. A552

MCLEOD MEDICAL CENTER DILLON, DILLON, SC, p. A552

MCLEOD REGIONAL MEDICAL CENTER, FLORENCE, SC, p. A553

MCLEOD SEACOAST, SC (see MCLEOD LORIS SEACOAST HOSPITAL), p. A555

MCPHERSON HOSPITAL, MCPHERSON, KS, p. A241

MCPHERSON HOSPITAL, KS (see MEMORIAL HOSPITAL), p. A241

MEADE DISTRICT HOSPITAL, MEADE, KS, p. A241

MEADOW WOOD BEHAVIORAL HEALTH SYSTEM, NEW CASTLE, DE, p. A113
MEADOWBROOK REHABILITATION HOSPITAL, GARDNER, KS, p. A235
MEADOWBROOK SPECIALTY HOSPITAL OF TULSA, TULSA, OK, p. A508
MEADOWS PSYCHIATRIC CENTER, CENTRE HALL, PA, p. A522
MEADOWS REGIONAL MEDICAL CENTER, VIDALIA, GA, p. A162
MEADOWVIEW REGIONAL MEDICAL CENTER, MAYSVILLE, KY, p. A257
MEADVILLE MEDICAL CENTER, MEADVILLE, PA, p. A531
MEASE COUNTRYSIDE HOSPITAL, SAFETY HARBOR, FL, p. A137
MEASE DUNEDIN HOSPITAL, DUNEDIN, FL, p. A122
MEDCENTRAL - MANSFIELD HOSPITAL, MANSFIELD, OH, p. A485
MEDICAL ARTS HOSPITAL, LAMESA, TX, p. A618
MEDICAL BEHAVIORAL HOSPITAL OF MISHAWAKA, KNOX, IN, p. A208
MEDICAL CENTER AT BOWLING GREEN, BOWLING GREEN, KY, p. A250
MEDICAL CENTER AT FRANKLIN, FRANKLIN, KY, p. A252
MEDICAL CENTER AT SCOTTSVILLE, SCOTTSVILLE, KY, p. A260
MEDICAL CENTER BARBOUR, EUFAULA, AL, p. A17
MEDICAL CENTER ENTERPRISE, ENTERPRISE, AL, p. A17
MEDICAL CENTER HEALTH SYSTEM, ODESSA, TX, p. A626
MEDICAL CENTER HEALTH SYSTEM, TX (see MEDICAL CENTER HOSPITAL), p. A626
MEDICAL CENTER HOSPITAL, ODESSA, TX, p. A626
MEDICAL CENTER HOSPITAL CAMPUS, VT (see UNIVERSITY OF VERMONT MEDICAL CENTER), p. A653
MEDICAL CENTER OF AURORA, AURORA, CO, p. A96
MEDICAL CENTER OF AURORA, CO (see MEDICAL CENTER OF AURORA), p. A96
MEDICAL CENTER OF AURORA NORTH, CO (see MEDICAL CENTER OF AURORA), p. A96
MEDICAL CENTER OF LOUISIANA AT NEW ORLEANS, NEW ORLEANS, LA, p. A275
MEDICAL CENTER OF PEACH COUNTY, NAVICENT HEALTH, BRYON, GA, p. A149
MEDICAL CENTER OF SOUTH ARKANSAS, EL DORADO-Union County, AR, p. A41
MEDICAL CENTER OF SOUTHEAST TEXAS, BEAUMONT, TX, p. A588
MEDICAL CENTER OF TRINITY, TRINITY, FL, p. A142
MEDICAL CENTER OF TRINITY, TRINITY, FL (see COMMUNITY HOSPITAL), p. A142
MEDICAL CENTER, NAVICENT HEALTH, MACON, GA, p. A156
MEDICAL CITY ALLIANCE, FORT WORTH, TX, p. A605
MEDICAL CITY ARLINGTON, ARLINGTON, TX, p. A584
MEDICAL CITY CHILDREN'S HOSPITAL, TX (see MEDICAL CITY DALLAS), p. A597
MEDICAL CITY DALLAS, DALLAS, TX, p. A597
MEDICAL CITY DENTON, DENTON, TX, p. A599
MEDICAL CITY FORT WORTH, FORT WORTH, TX, p. A605
MEDICAL CITY FRISCO, TX (see MEDICAL CITY PLANO), p. A628
MEDICAL CITY GREEN OAKS HOSPITAL, DALLAS, TX, p. A597
MEDICAL CITY LAS COLINAS, IRVING, TX, p. A615
MEDICAL CITY LEWISVILLE, LEWISVILLE, TX, p. A619
MEDICAL CITY MCKINNEY, MCKINNEY, TX, p. A623
MEDICAL CITY NORTH HILLS, NORTH RICHLAND HILLS, TX, p. A626
MEDICAL CITY PLANO, PLANO, TX, p. A628
MEDICAL CITY WEATHERFORD, WEATHERFORD, TX, p. A643
MEDICAL COLLEGE OF GEORGIA HEALTH, AUGUSTA, GA, p. A147
MEDICAL PARK HOSPITAL, WINSTON, NC, p. A462
MEDICAL WEST, BESSEMER, AL, p. A14
MEDICINE LODGE MEMORIAL HOSPITAL, MEDICINE LODGE, KS, p. A241
MEDINA COMMUNITY HOSPITAL, HONDO, TX, p. A609
MEDINA MEMORIAL HOSPITAL, MEDINA, NY, p. A430
MEDINA REGIONAL HOSPITAL, HONDO, TX, p. A609
MEDINA REGIONAL HOSPITAL, TX (see MEDINA COMMUNITY HOSPITAL), p. A609
MEDSTAR FRANKLIN SQUARE MEDICAL CENTER, BALTIMORE, MD, p. A288
MEDSTAR FRANKLIN SQUARE MEDICAL CENTER, MD (see FRANKLIN SQUARE HOSPITAL CENTER), p. A287
MEDSTAR GEORGETOWN UNIVERSITY HOSPITAL, WASHINGTON, DC, p. A115
MEDSTAR GEORGETOWN UNIVERSITY HOSPITAL, DC (see GEORGETOWN UNIVERSITY HOSPITAL), p. A115
MEDSTAR GOOD SAMARITAN HOSPITAL, BALTIMORE, MD, p. A288

MEDSTAR GOOD SAMARITAN HOSPITAL, MD (see GOOD SAMARITAN HOSPITAL OF MARYLAND), p. A287
MEDSTAR HARBOR HOSPITAL, BALTIMORE, MD, p. A288
MEDSTAR HARBOR HOSPITAL, MD (see HARBOR HOSPITAL), p. A287
MEDSTAR MONTGOMERY MEDICAL CENTER, OLNEY, MD, p. A293
MEDSTAR NATIONAL REHABILITATION HOSPITAL, WASHINGTON, DC, p. A115
MEDSTAR NATIONAL REHABILITATION HOSPITAL, DC (see NATIONAL REHABILITATION HOSPITAL), p. A116
MEDSTAR SOUTHERN MARYLAND HOSPITAL CENTER, CLINTON, MD, p. A290
MEDSTAR SOUTHERN MARYLAND HOSPITAL CENTER, MD (see SOUTHERN MARYLAND HOSPITAL CENTER), p. A291
MEDSTAR ST. MARY'S HOSPITAL, LEONARDTOWN, MD, p. A292
MEDSTAR UNION MEMORIAL HOSPITAL, BALTIMORE, MD, p. A288
MEDSTAR UNION MEMORIAL HOSPITAL, MD (see UNION MEMORIAL HOSPITAL), p. A289
MEDSTAR WASHINGTON HOSPITAL CENTER, WASHINGTON, DC, p. A116
MEDSTAR WASHINGTON HOSPITAL CENTER, DC (see WASHINGTON HOSPITAL CENTER), p. A116
MEE MEMORIAL HOSPITAL, KING CITY, CA, p. A62
MEEKER MEMORIAL HOSPITAL, LITCHFIELD, MN, p. A333
MELBOURNE REGIONAL MEDICAL CENTER, MELBOURNE, FL, p. A129
MELISSA MEMORIAL HOSPITAL, HOLYOKE, CO, p. A102
MELROSE-WAKEFIELD HOSPITAL, MA (see MELROSEWAKEFIELD HEALTHCARE), p. A301
MELROSEWAKEFIELD HEALTHCARE, MELROSE, MA, p. A301
MELROSEWAKEFIELD HEALTHCARE, MELROSE, MA (see LAWRENCE MEMORIAL HOSPITAL OF MEDFORD), p. A301
MEMORIAL BEHAVIORAL HEALTH, MS (see MEMORIAL HOSPITAL AT GULFPORT), p. A346
MEMORIAL CAMPUS, MA (see UMASS MEMORIAL MEDICAL CENTER), p. A306
MEMORIAL CHILDREN'S HOSPITAL, GA (see GEORGE AND MARIE BACKUS CHILDREN'S HOSPITAL), p. A160
MEMORIAL CHILDREN'S HOSPITAL, GA (see MEMORIAL HEALTH), p. A160
MEMORIAL COMMUNITY HEALTH, AURORA, NE, p. A381
MEMORIAL COMMUNITY HEALTH, NE (see MEMORIAL HOSPITAL), p. A381
MEMORIAL COMMUNITY HOSPITAL AND HEALTH SYSTEM, BLAIR, NE, p. A382
MEMORIAL HEALTH, MARYSVILLE, OH, p. A486
MEMORIAL HEALTH, SAVANNAH, GA, p. A160
MEMORIAL HEALTH CARE SYSTEMS, SEWARD, NE, p. A390
MEMORIAL HEALTH SYSTEM, ABILENE, KS, p. A232
MEMORIAL HEALTHCARE, OWOSSO, MI, p. A320
MEMORIAL HERMAN CYPRESS, TX (see MEMORIAL HERMANN - TEXAS MEDICAL CENTER), p. A612
MEMORIAL HERMANN - TEXAS MEDICAL CENTER, HOUSTON, TX, p. A612
MEMORIAL HERMANN BAPTIST FANNIN BEHAVIORAL HEALTH CENTER, BEAUMONT, TX, p. A588
MEMORIAL HERMANN FIRST COLONY HOSPITAL, SUGAR LAND, TX, p. A637
MEMORIAL HERMANN GREATER HEIGHTS HOSPITAL, HOUSTON, TX, p. A612
MEMORIAL HERMANN GREATER HEIGHTS HOSPITAL, HOUSTON, TX (see MEMORIAL HERMANN SOUTHEAST HOSPITAL), p. A612
MEMORIAL HERMANN GREATER HEIGHTS HOSPITAL, HOUSTON, TX (see MEMORIAL HERMANN SOUTHWEST HOSPITAL), p. A612
MEMORIAL HERMANN GREATER HEIGHTS HOSPITAL, HOUSTON, TX (see MEMORIAL HERMANN THE WOODLANDS HOSPITAL), p. A640
MEMORIAL HERMANN KATY HOSPITAL, KATY, TX, p. A616
MEMORIAL HERMANN MEMORIAL CITY MEDICAL CENTER, HOUSTON, TX, p. A612
MEMORIAL HERMANN NORTHEAST, HUMBLE, TX, p. A615
MEMORIAL HERMANN ORTHOPEDIC AND SPINE HOSPITAL, TX (see MEMORIAL HERMANN - TEXAS MEDICAL CENTER), p. A612
MEMORIAL HERMANN PEARLAND MEDICAL CENTER, TX (see MEMORIAL HERMANN GREATER HEIGHTS HOSPITAL), p. A612
MEMORIAL HERMANN REHABILITATION HOSPITAL - KATY, KATY, TX, p. A616
MEMORIAL HERMANN SOUTHEAST HOSPITAL, HOUSTON, TX, p. A612
MEMORIAL HERMANN SOUTHEAST HOSPITAL, TX (see MEMORIAL HERMANN GREATER HEIGHTS HOSPITAL), p. A612

MEMORIAL HERMANN SOUTHWEST HOSPITAL, HOUSTON, TX, p. A612
MEMORIAL HERMANN SOUTHWEST HOSPITAL, TX (see MEMORIAL HERMANN GREATER HEIGHTS HOSPITAL), p. A612
MEMORIAL HERMANN SUGAR LAND HOSPITAL, SUGAR LAND, TX, p. A637
MEMORIAL HERMANN SURGICAL HOSPITAL KINGWOOD, KINGWOOD, TX, p. A618
MEMORIAL HERMANN SURGICAL HOSPITAL KINGWOOD, TX (see KINGWOOD SPECIALTY HOSPITAL), p. A618
MEMORIAL HERMANN THE WOODLANDS HOSPITAL, THE WOODLANDS, TX, p. A640
MEMORIAL HERMANN THE WOODLANDS HOSPITAL, TX (see MEMORIAL HERMANN GREATER HEIGHTS HOSPITAL), p. A612
MEMORIAL HERMANN TOMBALL HOSPITAL, TOMBALL, TX, p. A640
MEMORIAL HOSPITAL, AURORA, NE, p. A381
MEMORIAL HOSPITAL, BELLEVILLE, IL, p. A174
MEMORIAL HOSPITAL, CARTHAGE, IL, p. A175
MEMORIAL HOSPITAL, CHESTER, IL, p. A176
MEMORIAL HOSPITAL, MCPHERSON, KS, p. A241
MEMORIAL HOSPITAL, NORTH CONWAY, NH, p. A400
MEMORIAL HOSPITAL, SEMINOLE, TX, p. A635
MEMORIAL HOSPITAL AND HEALTH CARE CENTER, JASPER, IN, p. A208
MEMORIAL HOSPITAL AND MANOR, BAINBRIDGE, GA, p. A148
MEMORIAL HOSPITAL AT GULFPORT, GULFPORT, MS, p. A346
MEMORIAL HOSPITAL EAST, SHILOH, IL, p. A196
MEMORIAL HOSPITAL HIXSON, TN (see CHI MEMORIAL), p. A567
MEMORIAL HOSPITAL JACKSONVILLE, JACKSONVILLE, FL, p. A125
MEMORIAL HOSPITAL LOS BANOS, LOS BANOS, CA, p. A70
MEMORIAL HOSPITAL MIRAMAR, MIRAMAR, FL, p. A132
MEMORIAL HOSPITAL OF CARBON COUNTY, RAWLINS, WY, p. A709
MEMORIAL HOSPITAL OF CARBONDALE, CARBONDALE, IL, p. A175
MEMORIAL HOSPITAL OF CONVERSE COUNTY, DOUGLAS, WY, p. A708
MEMORIAL HOSPITAL OF GARDENA, GARDENA, CA, p. A60
MEMORIAL HOSPITAL OF LAFAYETTE COUNTY, DARLINGTON, WI, p. A691
MEMORIAL HOSPITAL OF SALEM COUNTY, SALEM, NJ, p. A411
MEMORIAL HOSPITAL OF SOUTH BEND, SOUTH BEND, IN, p. A215
MEMORIAL HOSPITAL OF STILWELL, STILWELL, OK, p. A507
MEMORIAL HOSPITAL OF SWEETWATER COUNTY, ROCK SPRINGS, WY, p. A709
MEMORIAL HOSPITAL OF TAMPA, TAMPA, FL, p. A141
MEMORIAL HOSPITAL OF TEXAS COUNTY, GUYMON, OK, p. A499
MEMORIAL HOSPITAL PEMBROKE, PEMBROKE PINES, FL, p. A135
MEMORIAL HOSPITAL WEST, PEMBROKE PINES, FL, p. A135
MEMORIAL MEDICAL CENTER, LAS CRUCES, NM, p. A418
MEMORIAL MEDICAL CENTER, MODESTO, CA, p. A73
MEMORIAL MEDICAL CENTER, PORT LAVACA, TX, p. A629
MEMORIAL MEDICAL CENTER, SPRINGFIELD, IL, p. A196
MEMORIAL MEDICAL CENTER, CA (see MEMORIAL MEDICAL CENTER), p. A73
MEMORIAL MEDICAL CENTER - LEE CAMPUS, JOHNSTOWN, PA, p. A528
MEMORIAL MEDICAL CENTER - LEE CAMPUS, PA (see CONEMAUGH MEMORIAL MEDICAL CENTER), p. A528
MEMORIAL MEDICAL CENTER - NEILLSVILLE, NEILLSVILLE, WI, p. A699
MEMORIAL MEDICAL CENTER OF ASHLAND, ASHLAND, WI, p. A689
MEMORIAL REGIONAL HEALTH, CRAIG, CO, p. A98
MEMORIAL REGIONAL HOSPITAL, HOLLYWOOD, FL, p. A124
MEMORIAL REGIONAL HOSPITAL SOUTH, FL (see MEMORIAL REGIONAL HOSPITAL), p. A124
MEMORIAL SATILLA HEALTH, WAYCROSS, GA, p. A163
MEMORIAL SLOAN-KETTERING CANCER CENTER, NEW YORK (Includes all hospitals located within the five boroughs), NY, p. A433
MEMORIAL SPECIALTY HOSPITAL, LAKE CHARLES, LA, p. A272
MEMORIALCARE, LONG BEACH MEMORIAL MEDICAL CENTER, LONG BEACH, CA, p. A65
MEMORIALCARE, MILLER CHILDREN'S & WOMEN'S HOSPITAL LONG BEACH, LONG BEACH, CA, p. A65
MEMORIALCARE, ORANGE COAST MEMORIAL MEDICAL CENTER, FOUNTAIN VALLEY, CA, p. A58

MEMORIALCARE, SADDLEBACK MEMORIAL MEDICAL CENTER, LAGUNA HILLS, CA, p. A63

MEMPHIS MENTAL HEALTH INSTITUTE, MEMPHIS, TN, p. A575

MEMPHIS VETERANS AFFAIRS MEDICAL CENTER, MEMPHIS, TN, p. A575

MEMPHIS VETERANS AFFAIRS MEDICAL CENTER, TN (see VETERANS AFFAIRS MEDICAL CENTER), p. A576

MENA REGIONAL HEALTH SYSTEM, MENA-Polk County, AR, p. A46

MENDOCINO COAST DISTRICT HOSPITAL, FORT BRAGG, CA, p. A58

MENDOTA MENTAL HEALTH INSTITUTE, MADISON, WI, p. A696

MENIFEE VALLEY MEDICAL CENTER, SUN CITY, CA, p. A91

MENLO PARK SURGICAL HOSPITAL, MENLO PARK, CA, p. A72

MENNINGER CLINIC, HOUSTON, TX, p. A612

MENNONITE GENERAL HOSPITAL, AIBONITO, PR, p. A712

MENORAH MEDICAL CENTER, OVERLAND PARK, KS, p. A243

MENTAL HEALTH CENTER, NM (see UNIVERSITY OF NEW MEXICO HOSPITALS), p. A416

MENTAL HEALTH INSTITUTE, CHEROKEE, IA, p. A219

MENTAL HEALTH INSTITUTE, INDEPENDENCE, IA, p. A224

MENTAL HEALTH SERVICES FOR CLARK AND MADISON COUNTIES, SPRINGFIELD, OH, p. A490

MERCER HEALTH, COLDWATER, OH, p. A478

MERCY ALLEN HOSPITAL, OBERLIN, OH, p. A488

MERCY CHILDREN'S HOSPITAL, OH (see MERCY ST. VINCENT MEDICAL CENTER), p. A491

MERCY CHILDREN'S HOSPITAL SPRINGFIELD, MO (see MERCY HOSPITAL SPRINGFIELD), p. A370

MERCY CHILDREN'S HOSPITAL ST. LOUIS, MO (see MERCY HOSPITAL ST. LOUIS), p. A368

MERCY CHILDREN'S HOSPITAL ST. LOUIS, MO (see ST. JOHN'S MERCY CHILDREN'S HOSPITAL), p. A369

MERCY FITZGERALD HOSPITAL, DARBY, PA, p. A524

MERCY FITZGERALD HOSPITAL, PA (see MERCY FITZGERALD HOSPITAL), p. A524

MERCY FITZGERALD HOSPITAL, DARBY, PA (see MERCY PHILADELPHIA HOSPITAL), p. A535

MERCY GENERAL HOSPITAL, SACRAMENTO, CA, p. A82

MERCY GILBERT MEDICAL CENTER, GILBERT, AZ, p. A29

MERCY HEALTH - ANDERSON HOSPITAL, CINCINNATI, OH, p. A475

MERCY HEALTH - CLERMONT HOSPITAL, BATAVIA, OH, p. A471

MERCY HEALTH - FAIRFIELD HOSPITAL, FAIRFIELD, OH, p. A482

MERCY HEALTH - MARCUM AND WALLACE, IRVINE, KY, p. A254

MERCY HEALTH - ST. CHARLES HOSPITAL, OREGON, OH, p. A488

MERCY HEALTH - ST. CHARLES HOSPITAL, OH (see ST. CHARLES MERCY HOSPITAL), p. A488

MERCY HEALTH - ST. ELIZABETH BOARDMAN HOSPITAL, BOARDMAN, OH, p. A472

MERCY HEALTH - ST. ELIZABETH YOUNGSTOWN HOSPITAL, YOUNGSTOWN, OH, p. A494

MERCY HEALTH - ST. JOSEPH WARREN HOSPITAL, WARREN, OH, p. A492

MERCY HEALTH - WEST HOSPITAL, CINCINNATI, OH, p. A475

MERCY HEALTH - WILLARD HOSPITAL, WILLARD, OH, p. A493

MERCY HEALTH HACKLEY CAMPUS, MUSKEGON, MI, p. A319

MERCY HEALTH LOVE COUNTY, MARIETTA, OK, p. A501

MERCY HEALTH ROCKFORD, MI (see MERCY HEALTH SAINT MARY'S), p. A314

MERCY HEALTH SAINT MARY'S, GRAND RAPIDS, MI, p. A314

MERCY HEALTH, GENERAL CAMPUS, MI (see MERCY HEALTH HACKLEY CAMPUS), p. A319

MERCY HEALTH, LAKESHORE CAMPUS, SHELBY, MI, p. A323

MERCY HEALTH, MERCY CAMPUS, MI (see MERCY HEALTH HACKLEY CAMPUS), p. A319

MERCY HOSPITAL - A CAMPUS OF PLANTATION GENERAL HOSPITAL, FL (see PLANTATION GENERAL HOSPITAL), p. A136

MERCY HOSPITAL, BUFFALO, NY, p. A423

MERCY HOSPITAL, COON RAPIDS, MN, p. A330

MERCY HOSPITAL, MOOSE LAKE, MN, p. A336

MERCY HOSPITAL, MOUNDRIDGE, KS, p. A241

MERCY HOSPITAL ADA, ADA, OK, p. A495

MERCY HOSPITAL AND MEDICAL CENTER, CHICAGO, IL, p. A178

MERCY HOSPITAL ARDMORE, ARDMORE, OK, p. A495

MERCY HOSPITAL AURORA, AURORA, MO, p. A355

MERCY HOSPITAL BERRYVILLE, BERRYVILLE-Carroll County, AR, p. A39

MERCY HOSPITAL BOONEVILLE, BOONEVILLE-Logan County, AR, p. A40

MERCY HOSPITAL CARTHAGE, CARTHAGE, MO, p. A357

MERCY HOSPITAL CASSVILLE, CASSVILLE, MO, p. A357

MERCY HOSPITAL COLUMBUS, COLUMBUS, KS, p. A233

MERCY HOSPITAL EL RENO, EL RENO, OK, p. A498

MERCY HOSPITAL EL RENO, OK (see PARKVIEW HOSPITAL), p. A498

MERCY HOSPITAL FORT SCOTT, FORT SCOTT, KS, p. A235

MERCY HOSPITAL FORT SMITH, FORT SMITH-Sebastian County, AR, p. A42

MERCY HOSPITAL HEALDTON, HEALDTON, OK, p. A499

MERCY HOSPITAL JEFFERSON, CRYSTAL CITY, MO, p. A358

MERCY HOSPITAL JOPLIN, JOPLIN, MO, p. A361

MERCY HOSPITAL KINGFISHER, KINGFISHER, OK, p. A500

MERCY HOSPITAL LEBANON, LEBANON, MO, p. A363

MERCY HOSPITAL LINCOLN, TROY, MO, p. A371

MERCY HOSPITAL LOGAN COUNTY, GUTHRIE, OK, p. A499

MERCY HOSPITAL OF DEFIANCE, DEFIANCE, OH, p. A481

MERCY HOSPITAL OF FOLSOM, FOLSOM, CA, p. A58

MERCY HOSPITAL OF FRANCISCAN SISTERS, OELWEIN, IA, p. A227

MERCY HOSPITAL OF PORTLAND, PORTLAND, ME, p. A285

MERCY HOSPITAL OF SCRANTON, SCRANTON, PA, p. A540

MERCY HOSPITAL OKLAHOMA CITY, OKLAHOMA CITY, OK, p. A503

MERCY HOSPITAL OZARK, OZARK-Franklin County, AR, p. A47

MERCY HOSPITAL PARIS, PARIS-Logan County, AR, p. A47

MERCY HOSPITAL ROGERS, ROGERS-Benton County, AR, p. A48

MERCY HOSPITAL SPRINGFIELD, SPRINGFIELD, MO, p. A370

MERCY HOSPITAL ST. LOUIS, SAINT LOUIS, MO, p. A368

MERCY HOSPITAL ST. LOUIS, MO (see ST. JOHN'S MERCY MEDICAL CENTER), p. A369

MERCY HOSPITAL TISHOMINGO, TISHOMINGO, OK, p. A508

MERCY HOSPITAL TISHOMINGO, OK (see JOHNSTON MEMORIAL HOSPITAL), p. A507

MERCY HOSPITAL WALDRON, WALDRON-Scott County, AR, p. A49

MERCY HOSPITAL WASHINGTON, WASHINGTON, MO, p. A372

MERCY HOSPITAL WATONGA, WATONGA, OK, p. A510

MERCY HOSPITALS OF BAKERSFIELD, BAKERSFIELD, CA, p. A52

MERCY IOWA CITY, IOWA CITY, IA, p. A224

MERCY MEDICAL CENTER, BALTIMORE, MD, p. A288

MERCY MEDICAL CENTER, CANTON, OH, p. A473

MERCY MEDICAL CENTER, CEDAR RAPIDS, IA, p. A218

MERCY MEDICAL CENTER, NAMPA, ID, p. A170

MERCY MEDICAL CENTER, ROCKVILLE CENTRE, NY, p. A442

MERCY MEDICAL CENTER, ROSEBURG, OR, p. A517

MERCY MEDICAL CENTER, SPRINGFIELD, MA, p. A304

MERCY MEDICAL CENTER MERCED, MERCED, CA, p. A72

MERCY MEDICAL CENTER MERCED-DOMINICAN CAMPUS, CA (see MERCY MEDICAL CENTER MERCED), p. A72

MERCY MEDICAL CENTER MOUNT SHASTA, MOUNT SHASTA, CA, p. A74

MERCY MEDICAL CENTER NORTH, POWELL, TN, p. A579

MERCY MEDICAL CENTER REDDING, REDDING, CA, p. A79

MERCY MEDICAL CENTER WEST, KNOXVILLE, TN, p. A572

MERCY MEDICAL CENTER - WEST LAKES, IA (see MERCY MEDICAL CENTER-DES MOINES), p. A221

MERCY MEDICAL CENTER-CENTERVILLE, CENTERVILLE, IA, p. A218

MERCY MEDICAL CENTER-CLINTON, CLINTON, IA, p. A219

MERCY MEDICAL CENTER-DES MOINES, DES MOINES, IA, p. A221

MERCY MEDICAL CENTER-DUBUQUE, DUBUQUE, IA, p. A222

MERCY MEDICAL CENTER-DYERSVILLE, DYERSVILLE, IA, p. A222

MERCY MEDICAL CENTER-NEW HAMPTON, NEW HAMPTON, IA, p. A227

MERCY MEDICAL CENTER-NORTH IOWA, MASON CITY, IA, p. A226

MERCY MEDICAL CENTER-SIOUX CITY, SIOUX CITY, IA, p. A229

MERCY MEMORIAL HOSPITAL, URBANA, OH, p. A492

MERCY ORTHOPEDIC HOSPITAL FORT SMITH, AR (see MERCY HOSPITAL FORT SMITH), p. A42

MERCY ORTHOPEDIC HOSPITAL SPRINGFIELD, MO (see MERCY HOSPITAL SPRINGFIELD), p. A370

MERCY PHILADELPHIA HOSPITAL, PHILADELPHIA, PA, p. A535

MERCY PHILADELPHIA HOSPITAL, PA (see MERCY FITZGERALD HOSPITAL), p. A524

MERCY REGIONAL MEDICAL CENTER, DURANGO, CO, p. A99

MERCY REGIONAL MEDICAL CENTER, LORAIN, OH, p. A485

MERCY REGIONAL MEDICAL CENTER, VILLE PLATTE, LA, p. A280

MERCY REHABILITATION HOSPITAL OKLAHOMA CITY, OKLAHOMA CITY, OK, p. A503

MERCY REHABILITATION HOSPITAL ST. LOUIS, CHESTERFIELD, MO, p. A357

MERCY REHABILITATION HOSPITAL SPRINGFIELD, SPRINGFIELD, MO, p. A370

MERCY SAN JUAN MEDICAL CENTER, CARMICHAEL, CA, p. A54

MERCY SERVICES FOR AGING, IA (see MERCY MEDICAL CENTER-CLINTON), p. A219

MERCY SOUTHWEST HOSPITAL, CA (see MERCY HOSPITALS OF BAKERSFIELD), p. A52

MERCY ST. ANNE HOSPITAL, TOLEDO, OH, p. A491

MERCY ST. FRANCIS HOSPITAL, MOUNTAIN VIEW, MO, p. A365

MERCY ST. VINCENT MEDICAL CENTER, TOLEDO, OH, p. A491

MERCY TIFFIN HOSPITAL, TIFFIN, OH, p. A491

MERCYHEALTH HOSPITAL - ROCKTON AVENUE, ROCKFORD, IL, p. A194

MERCYHEALTH HOSPITAL AND MEDICAL CENTER - HARVARD, HARVARD, IL, p. A184

MERCYHEALTH HOSPITAL AND MEDICAL CENTER - WALWORTH, LAKE GENEVA, WI, p. A695

MERCYHEALTH HOSPITAL AND TRAUMA CENTER - JANESVILLE, JANESVILLE, WI, p. A695

MERIDIAN HEALTH SERVICES, MUNCIE, IN, p. A212

MERIT HEALTH BILOXI, BILOXI, MS, p. A343

MERIT HEALTH CENTRAL, JACKSON, MS, p. A348

MERIT HEALTH MADISON, CANTON, MS, p. A344

MERIT HEALTH NATCHEZ, NATCHEZ, MS, p. A351

MERIT HEALTH RANKIN, BRANDON, MS, p. A344

MERIT HEALTH RIVER OAKS, FLOWOOD, MS, p. A345

MERIT HEALTH RIVER REGION, VICKSBURG, MS, p. A354

MERIT HEALTH WESLEY, HATTIESBURG, MS, p. A347

MERIT HEALTH WOMAN'S HOSPITAL, FLOWOOD, MS, p. A346

MERITCARE MAYVILLE UNION HOSPITAL, MAYVILLE, ND, p. A467

MERITCARE MEDICAL CENTER, FARGO, ND, p. A465

MERITCARE THIEF RIVER FALLS NORTHWEST MEDICAL CENTER, THIEF RIVER FALLS, MN, p. A340

MERITUS MEDICAL CENTER, HAGERSTOWN, MD, p. A292

MERITUS MEDICAL CENTER, MD (see WASHINGTON COUNTY HEALTH SYSTEM), p. A292

MERRICK MEDICAL CENTER, CENTRAL CITY, NE, p. A382

MESA HILLS SPECIALTY HOSPITAL, EL PASO, TX, p. A602

MESA SPRINGS, FORT WORTH, TX, p. A605

MESA VIEW REGIONAL HOSPITAL, MESQUITE, NV, p. A395

MESCALERO PUBLIC HEALTH SERVICE INDIAN HOSPITAL, MESCALERO, NM, p. A418

MESILLA VALLEY HOSPITAL, LAS CRUCES, NM, p. A418

MESQUITE REHABILITATION INSTITUTE, MESQUITE, TX, p. A623

MESQUITE SPECIALTY HOSPITAL, MESQUITE, TX, p. A623

METHODIST AMBULATORY SURGERY HOSPITAL - NORTHWEST, SAN ANTONIO, TX, p. A633

METHODIST BEHAVIORAL HOSPITAL OF ARKANSAS, MAUMELLE-Pulaski County, AR, p. A46

METHODIST CHARLTON MEDICAL CENTER, DALLAS, TX, p. A597

METHODIST CHILDREN'S HOSPITAL, TX (see METHODIST HOSPITAL), p. A633

METHODIST DALLAS MEDICAL CENTER, DALLAS, TX, p. A597

METHODIST HEALTHCARE MEMPHIS HOSPITALS, MEMPHIS, TN, p. A575

METHODIST HEALTHCARE MEMPHIS HOSPITALS, MEMPHIS, TN (see LE BONHEUR CHILDREN'S HOSPITAL), p. A575

METHODIST HEALTHCARE MEMPHIS HOSPITALS, MEMPHIS, TN (see METHODIST LE BONHEUR GERMANTOWN HOSPITAL), p. A570

METHODIST HEALTHCARE OLIVE BRANCH HOSPITAL, OLIVE BRANCH, MS, p. A351

METHODIST HEALTHCARE-NORTH HOSPITAL, TN (see METHODIST HEALTHCARE MEMPHIS HOSPITALS), p. A575

METHODIST HEALTHCARE-SOUTH HOSPITAL, TN (see METHODIST HEALTHCARE MEMPHIS HOSPITALS), p. A575

METHODIST HOSPITAL, HENDERSON, KY, p. A253

METHODIST HOSPITAL, INDIANAPOLIS, IN, p. A207

METHODIST HOSPITAL, SAN ANTONIO, TX, p. A633

METHODIST HOSPITAL FOR SURGERY, ADDISON, TX, p. A582

METHODIST HOSPITAL OF CHICAGO, CHICAGO, IL, p. A178

METHODIST HOSPITAL OF SACRAMENTO, SACRAMENTO, CA, p. A82

METHODIST HOSPITAL OF SOUTHERN CALIFORNIA, ARCADIA, CA, p. A51

METHODIST HOSPITAL SOUTH, JOURDANTON, TX, p. A616

METHODIST HOSPITAL UNION COUNTY, MORGANFIELD, KY, p. A258

METHODIST HOSPITALS, GARY, IN, p. A204

METHODIST HOSPITALS, GARY, IN (see SOUTHLAKE CAMPUS), p. A211

METHODIST JENNIE EDMUNDSON HOSPITAL, COUNCIL BLUFFS, IA, p. A220

MONTGOMERY DIVISION, AL (see CENTRAL ALABAMA VETERANS HEALTH CARE SYSTEM), p. A21
MONTGOMERY GENERAL HOSPITAL, MONTGOMERY, WV, p. A685
MONTPELIER HOSPITAL, MONTPELIER, OH, p. A487
MONTPELIER HOSPITAL, OH (see COMMUNITY HOSPITALS AND WELLNESS CENTERS), p. A473
MONTROSE MEMORIAL HOSPITAL, MONTROSE, CO, p. A104
MOORE COUNTY HOSPITAL DISTRICT, DUMAS, TX, p. A600
MOREHOUSE GENERAL HOSPITAL, BASTROP, LA, p. A263
MORGAN COUNTY ARH HOSPITAL, WEST LIBERTY, KY, p. A261
MORGAN MEMORIAL HOSPITAL, MADISON, GA, p. A157
MORGAN STANLEY CHILDREN'S HOSPITAL OF NEW YORK-PRESBYTERIAN, NEW YORK (Includes all hospitals located within the five boroughs), NY, p. A433
MORGAN STANLEY CHILDREN'S HOSPITAL OF NEW YORK-PRESBYTERIAN, NY (see NEW YORK-PRESBYTERIAN HOSPITAL), p. A434
MORRILL COUNTY COMMUNITY HOSPITAL, BRIDGEPORT, NE, p. A382
MORRIS COUNTY HOSPITAL, COUNCIL GROVE, KS, p. A234
MORRIS HOSPITAL & HEALTHCARE CENTERS, MORRIS, IL, p. A190
MORRISON COMMUNITY HOSPITAL, MORRISON, IL, p. A190
MORRISTOWN MEDICAL CENTER, MORRISTOWN, NJ, p. A408
MORRISTOWN-HAMBLEN HEALTHCARE SYSTEM, MORRISTOWN, TN, p. A576
MORROW COUNTY HOSPITAL, MOUNT GILEAD, OH, p. A487
MORTON COUNTY HEALTH SYSTEM, ELKHART, KS, p. A234
MORTON GENERAL HOSPITAL, MORTON, WA, p. A673
MORTON HOSPITAL AND MEDICAL CENTER, TAUNTON, MA, p. A305
MORTON PLANT HOSPITAL, CLEARWATER, FL, p. A119
MORTON PLANT NORTH BAY HOSPITAL, NEW PORT RICHEY, FL, p. A132
MOSAIC LIFE CARE, SAINT JOSEPH, MO, p. A367
MOSES H. CONE MEMORIAL HOSPITAL, GREENSBORO, NC, p. A453
MOSES H. CONE MEMORIAL HOSPITAL, GREENSBORO, NC (see ANNIE PENN HOSPITAL), p. A459
MOSES LUDINGTON HOSPITAL, NY (see THE UNIVERSITY OF VERMONT HEALTH NETWORK ELIZABETHTOWN COMMUNITY HOSPITAL), p. A426
MOSES TAYLOR HOSPITAL, SCRANTON, PA, p. A540
MOTION PICTURE AND TELEVISION FUND HOSPITAL AND RESIDENTIAL SERVICES, LOS ANGELES, CA, p. A68
MOUNT AUBURN HOSPITAL, CAMBRIDGE, MA, p. A298
MOUNT CARMEL, COLUMBUS, OH, p. A478
MOUNT CARMEL EAST HOSPITAL, OH (see MOUNT CARMEL), p. A478
MOUNT CARMEL NEW ALBANY SURGICAL HOSPITAL, NEW ALBANY, OH, p. A487
MOUNT CARMEL ST. ANN'S, WESTERVILLE, OH, p. A493
MOUNT CARMEL WEST HOSPITAL, OH (see MOUNT CARMEL), p. A478
MOUNT DESERT ISLAND HOSPITAL, BAR HARBOR, ME, p. A282
MOUNT GRANT GENERAL HOSPITAL, HAWTHORNE, NV, p. A393
MOUNT NITTANY MEDICAL CENTER, STATE COLLEGE, PA, p. A541
MOUNT SINAI BETH ISRAEL, NEW YORK (Includes all hospitals located within the five boroughs), NY, p. A434
MOUNT SINAI BETH ISRAEL, NY (see BETH ISRAEL MEDICAL CENTER), p. A431
MOUNT SINAI BETH ISRAEL BROOKLYN, NY (see BETH ISRAEL MEDICAL CENTER-KINGS HIGHWAY DIVISION), p. A431
MOUNT SINAI BETH ISRAEL BROOKLYN, NY (see MOUNT SINAI BETH ISRAEL), p. A434
MOUNT SINAI HOSPITAL, CHICAGO, IL, p. A178
MOUNT SINAI HOSPITAL, NEW YORK (Includes all hospitals located within the five boroughs), NY, p. A434
MOUNT SINAI MEDICAL CENTER, MIAMI BEACH, FL, p. A131
MOUNT SINAI MEDICAL CENTER, MIAMI BEACH, FL (see MIAMI HEART CAMPUS AT MOUNT SINAI MEDICAL CENTER), p. A131
MOUNT SINAI QUEENS, NY (see MOUNT SINAI HOSPITAL), p. A434
MOUNT SINAI REHABILITATION HOSPITAL, HARTFORD, CT, p. A108
MOUNT SINAI WEST, NEW YORK (Includes all hospitals located within the five boroughs), NY, p. A434
MOUNT SINAI WEST HOSPITAL, NEW YORK (Includes all hospitals located within the five boroughs), NY, p. A434
MOUNT SINAI WEST HOSPITAL, NY (see MOUNT SINAI WEST), p. A434

MOUNT SINAI WEST HOSPITAL, NY (see ROOSEVELT HOSPITAL), p. A437
MOUNT SINAI WEST, NEW YORK, NY (see MOUNT SINAI WEST HOSPITAL), p. A434
MOUNT ST. MARY'S HOSPITAL AND HEALTH CENTER, LEWISTON, NY, p. A429
MOUNTAIN CREST HOSPITAL, CO (see UCHEALTH POUDRE VALLEY HOSPITAL), p. A100
MOUNTAIN LAKES MEDICAL CENTER, CLAYTON, GA, p. A150
MOUNTAIN POINT MEDICAL CENTER, UT (see JORDAN VALLEY MEDICAL CENTER), p. A652
MOUNTAIN RIVER BIRTHING AND SURGERY CENTER, BLACKFOOT, ID, p. A167
MOUNTAIN VALLEY REGIONAL REHABILITATION HOSPITAL, PRESCOTT VALLEY, AZ, p. A34
MOUNTAIN VIEW HOSPITAL, GADSDEN, AL, p. A18
MOUNTAIN VIEW HOSPITAL, IDAHO FALLS, ID, p. A169
MOUNTAIN VIEW HOSPITAL, PAYSON, UT, p. A649
MOUNTAIN VIEW REGIONAL HOSPITAL, CASPER, WY, p. A707
MOUNTAIN VIEW REGIONAL MEDICAL CENTER, NORTON, VA, p. A663
MOUNTAIN VISTA MEDICAL CENTER, MESA, AZ, p. A31
MOUNTAIN WEST MEDICAL CENTER, TOOELE, UT, p. A651
MOUNTAIN'S EDGE HOSPITAL, LAS VEGAS, NV, p. A394
MOUNTAINVIEW HOSPITAL, LAS VEGAS, NV, p. A394
MOUNTAINVIEW MEDICAL CENTER, WHITE SULPHUR SPRINGS, MT, p. A380
MOUNTAINVIEW REGIONAL MEDICAL CENTER, LAS CRUCES, NM, p. A418
MOUNTRAIL COUNTY MEDICAL CENTER, STANLEY, ND, p. A468
MT. ASCUTNEY HOSPITAL AND HEALTH CENTER, WINDSOR, VT, p. A654
MT. GRAHAM REGIONAL MEDICAL CENTER, SAFFORD, AZ, p. A35
MT. SAN RAFAEL HOSPITAL, TRINIDAD, CO, p. A106
MT. WASHINGTON PEDIATRIC HOSPITAL, BALTIMORE, MD, p. A288
MUENSTER MEMORIAL HOSPITAL, MUENSTER, TX, p. A625
MULESHOE AREA MEDICAL CENTER, MULESHOE, TX, p. A625
MULTICARE AUBURN MEDICAL CENTER, AUBURN, WA, p. A669
MULTICARE DEACONESS HOSPITAL, SPOKANE, WA, p. A678
MULTICARE GOOD SAMARITAN HOSPITAL, PUYALLUP, WA, p. A675
MULTICARE GOOD SAMARITAN HOSPITAL, WA (see GOOD SAMARITAN COMMUNITY HEALTHCARE), p. A675
MULTICARE MARY BRIDGE CHILDREN'S HOSPITAL AND HEALTH CENTER, TACOMA, WA, p. A679
MULTICARE TACOMA GENERAL HOSPITAL, TACOMA, WA, p. A679
MULTICARE TACOMA GENERAL HOSPITAL, TACOMA, WA (see ALLENMORE HOSPITAL), p. A678
MULTICARE VALLEY HOSPITAL, SPOKANE VALLEY, WA, p. A678
MUNISING MEMORIAL HOSPITAL, MUNISING, MI, p. A319
MUNSON HEALTHCARE CADILLAC HOSPITAL, CADILLAC, MI, p. A309
MUNSON HEALTHCARE CHARLEVOIX HOSPITAL, CHARLEVOIX, MI, p. A309
MUNSON HEALTHCARE GRAYLING HOSPITAL, GRAYLING, MI, p. A314
MUNSON HEALTHCARE MANISTEE HOSPITAL, MANISTEE, MI, p. A318
MUNSON HEALTHCARE OTSEGO MEMORIAL HOSPITAL, GAYLORD, MI, p. A313
MUNSON MEDICAL CENTER, TRAVERSE CITY, MI, p. A324
MURRAY COUNTY MEDICAL CENTER, SLAYTON, MN, p. A340
MURRAY MEDICAL CENTER, CHATSWORTH, GA, p. A150
MURRAY-CALLOWAY COUNTY HOSPITAL, MURRAY, KY, p. A258
MUSC HEALTH OF MEDICAL UNIVERSITY OF SOUTH CAROLINA, CHARLESTON, SC, p. A550
MUSCOGEE CREEK NATION MEDICAL CENTER, OKMULGEE, OK, p. A505
MUSCOGEE CREEK NATION PHYSICAL REHABILITATION CENTER, OKMULGEE, OK, p. A505
MUSKOGEE REGIONAL MEDICAL CENTER, MUSKOGEE, OK, p. A502
MYRTUE MEDICAL CENTER, HARLAN, IA, p. A224

N

N.C. WOMEN'S HOSPITAL, NC (see UNIVERSITY OF NORTH CAROLINA HOSPITALS), p. A449
NACOGDOCHES MEDICAL CENTER, NACOGDOCHES, TX, p. A625
NACOGDOCHES MEMORIAL HOSPITAL, NACOGDOCHES, TX, p. A625
NANTICOKE MEMORIAL HOSPITAL, SEAFORD, DE, p. A114
NANTUCKET COTTAGE HOSPITAL, NANTUCKET, MA, p. A302
NAPA STATE HOSPITAL, NAPA, CA, p. A74
NASH HEALTH CARE SYSTEMS, ROCKY MOUNT, NC, p. A459
NASHOBA VALLEY MEDICAL CENTER, AYER, MA, p. A295
NASHVILLE CAMPUS, TN (see TENNESSEE VALLEY HEALTHCARE SYSTEM), p. A577
NASHVILLE GENERAL HOSPITAL, NASHVILLE, TN, p. A577
NASSAU UNIVERSITY MEDICAL CENTER, EAST MEADOW, NY, p. A426
NATCHAUG HOSPITAL, MANSFIELD CENTER, CT, p. A108
NATCHITOCHES REGIONAL MEDICAL CENTER, NATCHITOCHES, LA, p. A275
NATHAN LITTAUER HOSPITAL AND NURSING HOME, GLOVERSVILLE, NY, p. A427
NATIONAL INSTITUTES OF HEALTH CLINICAL CENTER, BETHESDA, MD, p. A290
NATIONAL JEWISH HEALTH, DENVER, CO, p. A99
NATIONAL NAVAL MEDICAL CENTER, BETHESDA, MD, p. A290
NATIONAL PARK MEDICAL CENTER, HOT SPRINGS-Garland County, AR, p. A43
NATIONAL REHABILITATION HOSPITAL, WASHINGTON, DC, p. A116
NATIONWIDE CHILDREN'S HOSPITAL, COLUMBUS, OH, p. A478
NATIVIDAD MEDICAL CENTER, SALINAS, CA, p. A83
NATURE COAST REGIONAL HOSPITAL, WILLISTON, FL, p. A144
NAVAL HOSPITAL BEAUFORT, BEAUFORT, SC, p. A549
NAVAL HOSPITAL BREMERTON, BREMERTON, WA, p. A670
NAVAL HOSPITAL CAMP LEJEUNE, CAMP LEJEUNE, NC, p. A449
NAVAL HOSPITAL CAMP PENDLETON, CAMP PENDLETON, CA, p. A54
NAVAL HOSPITAL JACKSONVILLE, JACKSONVILLE, FL, p. A125
NAVAL HOSPITAL LEMOORE, LEMOORE, CA, p. A64
NAVAL HOSPITAL OAK HARBOR, OAK HARBOR, WA, p. A674
NAVAL HOSPITAL PENSACOLA, PENSACOLA, FL, p. A136
NAVAL MEDICAL CENTER, PORTSMOUTH, VA, p. A664
NAVAL MEDICAL CENTER SAN DIEGO, SAN DIEGO, CA, p. A84
NAVARRO REGIONAL HOSPITAL, CORSICANA, TX, p. A595
NAVICENT HEALTH BALDWIN, MILLEDGEVILLE, GA, p. A157
NAVOS, SEATTLE, WA, p. A676
NAZARETH HOSPITAL, PHILADELPHIA, PA, p. A535
NCH BAKER HOSPITAL, NAPLES, FL, p. A132
NCH NORTH NAPLES HOSPITAL, FL (see NCH BAKER HOSPITAL), p. A132
NEA BAPTIST MEMORIAL HOSPITAL, JONESBORO-Craighead County, AR, p. A44
NEBRASKA MEDICINE - BELLEVUE, BELLEVUE, NE, p. A382
NEBRASKA MEDICINE - NEBRASKA MEDICAL CENTER, OMAHA, NE, p. A388
NEBRASKA METHODIST HOSPITAL, OMAHA, NE, p. A388
NEBRASKA METHODIST HOSPITAL, OMAHA, NE (see METHODIST WOMEN'S HOSPITAL), p. A383
NEBRASKA PENAL AND CORRECTIONAL HOSPITAL, LINCOLN, NE, p. A386
NEBRASKA SPINE HOSPITAL, OMAHA, NE, p. A388
NELL J. REDFIELD MEMORIAL HOSPITAL, MALAD CITY, ID, p. A170
NELSON COUNTY HEALTH SYSTEM, MCVILLE, ND, p. A468
NEMAHA COUNTY HOSPITAL, AUBURN, NE, p. A381
NEMAHA VALLEY COMMUNITY HOSPITAL, SENECA, KS, p. A245
NEMOURS CHILDREN'S HOSPITAL, ORLANDO, FL, p. A134
NEOSHO MEMORIAL REGIONAL MEDICAL CENTER, CHANUTE, KS, p. A233
NESHOBA COUNTY GENERAL HOSPITAL, PHILADELPHIA, MS, p. A352
NESS COUNTY HOSPITAL DISTRICT NO 2, NESS CITY, KS, p. A242
NEUROPSYCHIATRIC HOSPITAL OF INDIANAPOLIS, INDIANAPOLIS, IN, p. A207
NEVADA REGIONAL MEDICAL CENTER, NEVADA, MO, p. A365

NEW BRAUNFELS REGIONAL REHABILITATION HOSPITAL, NEW BRAUNFELS, TX, p. A625
NEW BRIDGE MEDICAL CENTER, PARAMUS, NJ, p. A409
NEW BRITAIN GENERAL, CT (see THE HOSPITAL OF CENTRAL CONNECTICUT), p. A109
NEW ENGLAND BAPTIST HOSPITAL, BOSTON, MA, p. A297
NEW ENGLAND REHABILITATION HOSPITAL OF PORTLAND, PORTLAND, ME, p. A285
NEW ENGLAND SINAI HOSPITAL AND REHABILITATION CENTER, STOUGHTON, MA, p. A305
NEW HAMPSHIRE HOSPITAL, CONCORD, NH, p. A398
NEW HANOVER REGIONAL MEDICAL CENTER, WILMINGTON, NC, p. A462
NEW LONDON HOSPITAL, NEW LONDON, NH, p. A400
NEW MEXICO BEHAVIORAL HEALTH INSTITUTE AT LAS VEGAS, LAS VEGAS, NM, p. A418
NEW MEXICO REHABILITATION CENTER, ROSWELL, NM, p. A419
NEW MEXICO VETERANS AFFAIRS HEALTH CARE SYSTEM - RAYMOND G. MURPHY MEDICAL CENTER, ALBUQUERQUE, NM, p. A416
NEW MILFORD HOSPITAL, CT (see DANBURY HOSPITAL), p. A107
NEW ORLEANS EAST HOSPITAL, NEW ORLEANS, LA, p. A275
NEW ULM MEDICAL CENTER, NEW ULM, MN, p. A336
NEW YORK CITY CHILDREN'S CENTER, NEW YORK (Includes all hospitals located within the five boroughs), NY, p. A434
NEW YORK CITY CHILDREN'S CENTER, NY (see QUEENS Children's hospital psychiatric CENTER), p. A436
NEW YORK COMMUNITY HOSPITAL, NEW YORK (Includes all hospitals located within the five boroughs), NY, p. A434
NEW YORK EYE AND EAR INFIRMARY OF MOUNT SINAI, NEW YORK (Includes all hospitals located within the five boroughs), NY, p. A434
NEW YORK-PRESBYTERIAN HOSPITAL, NEW YORK (Includes all hospitals located within the five boroughs), NY, p. A434
NEW YORK-PRESBYTERIAN HOSPITAL, NEW YORK, NY (see MORGAN STANLEY CHILDREN'S HOSPITAL OF NEW YORK-PRESBYTERIAN), p. A433
NEW YORK-PRESBYTERIAN HOSPITAL, NEW YORK, NY (see NEW YORK-PRESBYTERIAN HOSPITAL, WESTCHESTER DIVISION), p. A446
NEW YORK-PRESBYTERIAN HOSPITAL, NEW YORK, NY (see PAYNE WHITNEY PSYCHIATRIC CLINIC), p. A436
NEW YORK-PRESBYTERIAN HOSPITAL, NEW YORK, NY (see THE ALLEN PAVILION), p. A437
NEW YORK-PRESBYTERIAN HOSPITAL, WESTCHESTER DIVISION, WHITE PLAINS, NY, p. A446
NEW YORK-PRESBYTERIAN HOSPITAL, WESTCHESTER DIVISION, NY (see NEW YORK-PRESBYTERIAN HOSPITAL), p. A434
NEW YORK-PRESBYTERIAN HOSPITAL/WEILL CORNELL MEDICAL CENTER, NY (see NEW YORK-PRESBYTERIAN HOSPITAL), p. A434
NEW YORK PRESBYTERIAN LOWER MANHATTAN HOSPITAL, NY (see NEW YORK-PRESBYTERIAN HOSPITAL), p. A434
NEW YORK-PRESBYTERIAN QUEENS, NEW YORK (Includes all hospitals located within the five boroughs), NY, p. A435
NEW YORK-PRESBYTERIAN/COLUMBIA UNIVERSITY MEDICAL CENTER, NY (see NEW YORK-PRESBYTERIAN HOSPITAL), p. A434
NEW YORK-PRESBYTERIAN/HUDSON VALLEY HOSPITAL, CORTLANDT MANOR, NY, p. A425
NEW YORK-PRESBYTERIAN/LAWRENCE HOSPITAL, NY (see NEW YORK-PRESBYTERIAN HOSPITAL), p. A434
NEW YORK STATE PSYCHIATRIC INSTITUTE, NEW YORK (Includes all hospitals located within the five boroughs), NY, p. A434
NEWARK BETH ISRAEL MEDICAL CENTER, NEWARK, NJ, p. A408
NEWARK-WAYNE COMMUNITY HOSPITAL, NEWARK, NY, p. A438
NEWBERRY COUNTY MEMORIAL HOSPITAL, NEWBERRY, SC, p. A556
NEWMAN MEMORIAL HOSPITAL, SHATTUCK, OK, p. A506
NEWMAN REGIONAL HEALTH, EMPORIA, KS, p. A234
NEWPORT BAY HOSPITAL, NEWPORT BEACH, CA, p. A75
NEWPORT HOSPITAL, NEWPORT, RI, p. A547
NEWPORT HOSPITAL AND HEALTH SERVICES, NEWPORT, WA, p. A674
NEWPORT NEWS BEHAVIORAL HEALTH CENTER, NEWPORT NEWS, VA, p. A662
NEWTON MEDICAL CENTER, NEWTON, KS, p. A242
NEWTON MEDICAL CENTER, NEWTON, NJ, p. A409
NEWTON-WELLESLEY HOSPITAL, NEWTON LOWER FALLS, MA, p. A302
NEWYORK-PRESBYTERIAN BROOKLYN METHODIST HOSPITAL, NEW YORK (Includes all hospitals located within the five boroughs), NY, p. A435
NEXUS SPECIALTY HOSPITAL, SHENANDOAH, TX, p. A635

NEXUS SPECIALTY HOSPITAL THE WOODLANDS, THE WOODLANDS, TX, p. A640
NIAGARA FALLS MEMORIAL MEDICAL CENTER, NIAGARA FALLS, NY, p. A438
NICHOLAS H. NOYES MEMORIAL HOSPITAL, DANSVILLE, NY, p. A425
NICKLAUS CHILDREN'S HOSPITAL, MIAMI, FL, p. A130
NIOBRARA HEALTH AND LIFE CENTER, LUSK, WY, p. A709
NIOBRARA VALLEY HOSPITAL, LYNCH, NE, p. A386
NISWONGER CHILDREN'S HOSPITAL, TN (see JOHNSON CITY MEDICAL CENTER), p. A571
NIX HEALTH CARE SYSTEM, SAN ANTONIO, TX, p. A633
NOCONA GENERAL HOSPITAL, NOCONA, TX, p. A626
NOLAND HOSPITAL ANNISTON, ANNISTON, AL, p. A13
NOLAND HOSPITAL BIRMINGHAM, BIRMINGHAM, AL, p. A14
NOLAND HOSPITAL DOTHAN, DOTHAN, AL, p. A17
NOLAND HOSPITAL MONTGOMERY, MONTGOMERY, AL, p. A21
NOLAND HOSPITAL MONTGOMERY, AL (see LONG TERM CARE HOSPITAL), p. A21
NOLAND HOSPITAL SHELBY, ALABASTER, AL, p. A13
NOLAND HOSPITAL TUSCALOOSA, TUSCALOOSA, AL, p. A24
NOR-LEA HOSPITAL DISTRICT, LOVINGTON, NM, p. A418
NORMAN REGIONAL HEALTH SYSTEM, NORMAN, OK, p. A502
NORMAN REGIONAL HEALTH SYSTEM, NORMAN, OK (see NORMAN REGIONAL MOORE), p. A501
NORMAN REGIONAL HOSPITAL, OK (see NORMAN REGIONAL HEALTH SYSTEM), p. A502
NORMAN REGIONAL MOORE, MOORE, OK, p. A501
NORMAN REGIONAL MOORE, OK (see NORMAN REGIONAL HEALTH SYSTEM), p. A502
NORRISTOWN STATE HOSPITAL, NORRISTOWN, PA, p. A533
NORTH ALABAMA SPECIALTY HOSPITAL, ATHENS, AL, p. A13
NORTH ARKANSAS REGIONAL MEDICAL CENTER, HARRISON-Boone County, AR, p. A43
NORTH BALDWIN INFIRMARY, BAY MINETTE, AL, p. A14
NORTH BIG HORN HOSPITAL DISTRICT, LOVELL, WY, p. A709
NORTH CADDO MEDICAL CENTER, VIVIAN, LA, p. A280
NORTH CANYON MEDICAL CENTER, GOODING, ID, p. A169
NORTH CAROLINA CHILDREN'S HOSPITAL, NC (see UNIVERSITY OF NORTH CAROLINA HOSPITALS), p. A449
NORTH CAROLINA SPECIALTY HOSPITAL, DURHAM, NC, p. A451
NORTH CENTRAL BAPTIST HOSPITAL, TX (see BAPTIST MEDICAL CENTER), p. A632
NORTH CENTRAL HEALTH CARE, WAUSAU, WI, p. A705
NORTH CENTRAL HEALTH CARE, WI (see NORTH CENTRAL HEALTH CARE FACILITIES), p. A705
NORTH CENTRAL HEALTH CARE FACILITIES, WAUSAU, WI, p. A705
NORTH CENTRAL SURGICAL CENTER, DALLAS, TX, p. A597
NORTH COLORADO MEDICAL CENTER, GREELEY, CO, p. A101
NORTH COUNTRY HOSPITAL AND HEALTH CENTER, NEWPORT, VT, p. A654
NORTH COUNTRY REGIONAL HOSPITAL, BEMIDJI, MN, p. A328
NORTH CYPRESS MEDICAL CENTER, CYPRESS, TX, p. A595
NORTH DAKOTA STATE HOSPITAL, JAMESTOWN, ND, p. A467
NORTH FLORIDA REGIONAL MEDICAL CENTER, GAINESVILLE, FL, p. A123
NORTH FLORIDA/SOUTH GEORGIA VETERAN'S HEALTH SYSTEM, GAINESVILLE, FL, p. A123
NORTH GREENVILLE HOSPITAL, TRAVELERS REST, SC, p. A557
NORTH HAWAII COMMUNITY HOSPITAL, KAMUELA, HI, p. A165
NORTH KANSAS CITY HOSPITAL, NORTH KANSAS CITY, MO, p. A365
NORTH LITTLE ROCK DIVISION, NORTH LITTLE ROCK-Pulaski County, AR, p. A47
NORTH LITTLE ROCK DIVISION, AR (see CENTRAL ARKANSAS VETERANS HEALTHCARE SYSTEM), p. A45
NORTH MEMORIAL HEALTH HOSPITAL, ROBBINSDALE, MN, p. A338
NORTH METRO MEDICAL CENTER, JACKSONVILLE-Pulaski County, AR, p. A44
NORTH MISSISSIPPI MEDICAL CENTER - TUPELO, TUPELO, MS, p. A353
NORTH MISSISSIPPI MEDICAL CENTER-EUPORA, EUPORA, MS, p. A345
NORTH MISSISSIPPI MEDICAL CENTER-HAMILTON, HAMILTON, AL, p. A19
NORTH MISSISSIPPI MEDICAL CENTER-IUKA, IUKA, MS, p. A347
NORTH MISSISSIPPI MEDICAL CENTER-PONTOTOC, PONTOTOC, MS, p. A352

NORTH MISSISSIPPI MEDICAL CENTER-WEST POINT, WEST POINT, MS, p. A354
NORTH MISSISSIPPI STATE HOSPITAL, TUPELO, MS, p. A353
NORTH OAK REGIONAL MEDICAL CENTER, SENATOBIA, MS, p. A353
NORTH OAKS MEDICAL CENTER, HAMMOND, LA, p. A268
NORTH OAKS REHABILITATION HOSPITAL, HAMMOND, LA, p. A268
NORTH OKALOOSA MEDICAL CENTER, CRESTVIEW, FL, p. A120
NORTH OTTAWA COMMUNITY HOSPITAL, GRAND HAVEN, MI, p. A313
NORTH PHILADELPHIA HEALTH SYSTEM, PHILADELPHIA, PA, p. A536
NORTH RUNNELS HOSPITAL, WINTERS, TX, p. A644
NORTH SHORE CHILDREN'S HOSPITAL, SALEM, MA, p. A303
NORTH SHORE HEALTH, GRAND MARAIS, MN, p. A332
NORTH SHORE MEDICAL CENTER, MIAMI, FL, p. A130
NORTH SHORE MEDICAL CENTER, SALEM, MA, p. A304
NORTH SHORE MEDICAL CENTER, SALEM, MA (see UNION CAMPUS), p. A301
NORTH SHORE UNIVERSITY HOSPITAL, MANHASSET, NY, p. A429
NORTH SIDE HOSPITAL, JOHNSON CITY, TN, p. A572
NORTH STAR BEHAVIORAL HEALTH, AK (see NORTH STAR BEHAVIORAL HEALTH SYSTEM), p. A25
NORTH STAR BEHAVIORAL HEALTH SYSTEM, ANCHORAGE, AK, p. A25
NORTH SUBURBAN MEDICAL CENTER, THORNTON, CO, p. A105
NORTH SUNFLOWER MEDICAL CENTER, RULEVILLE, MS, p. A353
NORTH TAMPA BEHAVIORAL HEALTH, WESLEY CHAPEL, FL, p. A143
NORTH TEXAS MEDICAL CENTER, GAINESVILLE, TX, p. A606
NORTH TEXAS STATE HOSPITAL, VERNON, TX, p. A642
NORTH TEXAS STATE HOSPITAL, WICHITA FALLS CAMPUS, WICHITA FALLS, TX, p. A644
NORTH VALLEY HEALTH CENTER, WARREN, MN, p. A341
NORTH VALLEY HOSPITAL, TONASKET, WA, p. A679
NORTH VALLEY HOSPITAL, WHITEFISH, MT, p. A380
NORTH VISTA HOSPITAL, NORTH LAS VEGAS, NV, p. A396
NORTHBAY MEDICAL CENTER, FAIRFIELD, CA, p. A57
NORTHBAY MEDICAL CENTER, FAIRFIELD, CA (see NORTHBAY VACAVALLEY HOSPITAL), p. A93
NORTHBAY VACAVALLEY HOSPITAL, VACAVILLE, CA, p. A93
NORTHBAY VACAVALLEY HOSPITAL, CA (see NORTHBAY MEDICAL CENTER), p. A57
NORTHBROOK BEHAVIORAL HEALTH HOSPITAL, BLACKWOOD, NJ, p. A402
NORTHCOAST BEHAVIORAL HEALTHCARE, NORTHFIELD, OH, p. A488
NORTHCREST MEDICAL CENTER, SPRINGFIELD, TN, p. A580
NORTHEAST BAPTIST HOSPITAL, TX (see BAPTIST MEDICAL CENTER), p. A632
NORTHEAST GEORGIA MEDICAL CENTER, GAINESVILLE, GA, p. A154
NORTHEAST GEORGIA MEDICAL CENTER BARROW, WINDER, GA, p. A163
NORTHEAST GEORGIA MEDICAL CENTER BRASELTON, BRASELTON, GA, p. A148
NORTHEAST METHODIST HOSPITAL, TX (see METHODIST HOSPITAL), p. A633
NORTHEAST REGIONAL MEDICAL CENTER, KIRKSVILLE, MO, p. A362
NORTHEAST REHABILITATION HOSPITAL, SALEM, NH, p. A401
NORTHEASTERN CENTER, AUBURN, IN, p. A199
NORTHEASTERN HEALTH SYSTEM, TAHLEQUAH, OK, p. A507
NORTHEASTERN HEALTH SYSTEM SEQUOYAH, SALLISAW, OK, p. A506
NORTHEASTERN NEVADA REGIONAL HOSPITAL, ELKO, NV, p. A392
NORTHEASTERN VERMONT REGIONAL HOSPITAL, SAINT JOHNSBURY, VT, p. A654
NORTHERN ARIZONA VETERANS AFFAIRS HEALTH CARE SYSTEM, PRESCOTT, AZ, p. A34
NORTHERN CALIFORNIA REHABILITATION HOSPITAL, REDDING, CA, p. A80
NORTHERN COCHISE COMMUNITY HOSPITAL, WILLCOX, AZ, p. A38
NORTHERN COLORADO LONG TERM ACUTE HOSPITAL, JOHNSTOWN, CO, p. A102
NORTHERN COLORADO REHABILITATION HOSPITAL, JOHNSTOWN, CO, p. A102
NORTHERN DUTCHESS HOSPITAL, RHINEBECK, NY, p. A441
NORTHERN HOSPITAL OF SURRY COUNTY, MOUNT AIRY, NC, p. A457
NORTHERN IDAHO ADVANCED CARE HOSPITAL, POST FALLS, ID, p. A171

O

P

PAGE HOSPITAL, PAGE, AZ, p. A32
PAGE MEMORIAL HOSPITAL, LURAY, VA, p. A660
PAGOSA SPRINGS MEDICAL CENTER, PAGOSA SPRINGS, CO, p. A104
PALACIOS COMMUNITY MEDICAL CENTER, PALACIOS, TX, p. A626
PALESTINE REGIONAL MEDICAL CENTER, PALESTINE, TX, p. A626
PALESTINE REGIONAL MEDICAL CENTER-EAST, PALESTINE, TX, p. A626
PALI MOMI MEDICAL CENTER, AIEA, HI, p. A164
PALM BEACH CHILDREN'S HOSPITAL, FL (see ST. MARY'S MEDICAL CENTER), p. A143
PALM BEACH GARDENS MEDICAL CENTER, PALM BEACH GARDENS, FL, p. A135
PALM SPRINGS GENERAL HOSPITAL, HIALEAH, FL, p. A124
PALMDALE REGIONAL MEDICAL CENTER, PALMDALE, CA, p. A77
PALMETTO GENERAL HOSPITAL, HIALEAH, FL, p. A124
PALMETTO HEALTH BAPTIST, COLUMBIA, SC, p. A551
PALMETTO HEALTH BAPTIST PARKRIDGE, COLUMBIA, SC, p. A551
PALMETTO HEALTH CHILDREN'S HOSPITAL, SC (see PALMETTO HEALTH RICHLAND), p. A551
PALMETTO HEALTH RICHLAND, COLUMBIA, SC, p. A551
PALMETTO HEALTH TUOMEY, SUMTER, SC, p. A557
PALMETTO LOWCOUNTRY BEHAVIORAL HEALTH, CHARLESTON, SC, p. A550
PALMS OF PASADENA HOSPITAL, SAINT PETERSBURG, FL, p. A138
PALMS WEST HOSPITAL, LOXAHATCHEE, FL, p. A128
PALO ALTO COUNTY HEALTH SYSTEM, EMMETSBURG, IA, p. A222
PALO ALTO DIVISION, CA (see VA PALO ALTO HEALTH CARE SYSTEM), p. A77
PALO PINTO GENERAL HOSPITAL, MINERAL WELLS, TX, p. A624
PALO VERDE BEHAVIORAL HEALTH, TUCSON, AZ, p. A37
PALO VERDE HOSPITAL, BLYTHE, CA, p. A53
PALOMAR MEDICAL CENTER, ESCONDIDO, CA, p. A57
PALOS HEALTH, PALOS HEIGHTS, IL, p. A192
PAM REHABILITATION HOSPITAL OF BEAUMONT, BEAUMONT, TX, p. A588
PAM REHABILITATION HOSPITAL OF TULSA, TULSA, OK, p. A508
PAM REHABILITATION HOSPITAL OF VICTORIA, VICTORIA, TX, p. A642
PAM SPECIALTY HOSPITAL OF CORPUS CHRISTI SOUTH, CORPUS CHRISTI, TX, p. A594
PAM SPECIALTY HOSPITAL OF CORPUS CHRISTI SOUTH, TX (see KINDRED HOSPITAL-CORPUS CHRISTI), p. A594
PAM SPECIALTY HOSPITAL OF COVINGTON, COVINGTON, LA, p. A266
PAM SPECIALTY HOSPITAL OF COVINGTON, LA (see NORTHSHORE SPECIALTY HOSPITAL), p. A266
PAM SPECIALTY HOSPITAL OF HAMMOND, HAMMOND, LA, p. A268
PAM SPECIALTY HOSPITAL OF VICTORIA NORTH, VICTORIA, TX, p. A642
PAM SPECIALTY HOSPITAL OF VICTORIA SOUTH, VICTORIA, TX, p. A642
PAM SPECIALTY HOSPITAL OF WILKES-BARRE, WILKES BARRE, PA, p. A544
PAMPA REGIONAL MEDICAL CENTER, PAMPA, TX, p. A627
PANA COMMUNITY HOSPITAL, PANA, IL, p. A192
PANOLA MEDICAL CENTER, BATESVILLE, MS, p. A343
PANORAMA CITY MEDICAL CENTER, LOS ANGELES, CA, p. A69
PAOLI HOSPITAL, PAOLI, PA, p. A533
PAPPAS REHABILITATION HOSPITAL FOR CHILDREN, CANTON, MA, p. A299
PARADISE VALLEY HOSPITAL, NATIONAL CITY, CA, p. A74
PARIS COMMUNITY HOSPITAL, PARIS, IL, p. A192
PARIS REGIONAL MEDICAL CENTER, PARIS, TX, p. A627
PARIS REGIONAL MEDICAL CENTER, TX (see PARIS REGIONAL MEDICAL CENTER), p. A627
PARK CITY HOSPITAL, PARK CITY, UT, p. A649
PARK NICOLLET METHODIST HOSPITAL, SAINT LOUIS PARK, MN, p. A339
PARK PLACE SURGICAL HOSPITAL, LAFAYETTE, LA, p. A271
PARK PLAZA HOSPITAL, HOUSTON, TX, p. A612
PARK RIDGE HEALTH, HENDERSONVILLE, NC, p. A454
PARK ROYAL HOSPITAL, FORT MYERS, FL, p. A123
PARKER ADVENTIST HOSPITAL, PARKER, CO, p. A104
PARKLAND HEALTH & HOSPITAL SYSTEM, DALLAS, TX, p. A597
PARKLAND HEALTH CENTER - FARMINGTON COMMUNITY, FARMINGTON, MO, p. A359
PARKLAND HEALTH CENTER-BONNE TERRE, BONNE TERRE, MO, p. A355

PARKLAND MEDICAL CENTER, DERRY, NH, p. A398
PARKRIDGE EAST HOSPITAL, TN (see PARKRIDGE MEDICAL CENTER), p. A567
PARKRIDGE MEDICAL CENTER, CHATTANOOGA, TN, p. A567
PARKRIDGE MEDICAL CENTER, CHATTANOOGA, TN (see EAST RIDGE HOSPITAL), p. A569
PARKRIDGE VALLEY CHILD AND ADOLESCENT CAMPUS, TN (see PARKRIDGE MEDICAL CENTER), p. A567
PARKRIDGE WEST HOSPITAL, TN (see PARKRIDGE MEDICAL CENTER), p. A567
PARKSIDE PSYCHIATRIC HOSPITAL AND CLINIC, TULSA, OK, p. A508
PARKVIEW COMMUNITY HOSPITAL MEDICAL CENTER, RIVERSIDE, CA, p. A81
PARKVIEW HOSPITAL, EL RENO, OK, p. A498
PARKVIEW HOSPITAL, WHEELER, TX, p. A644
PARKVIEW HOSPITAL RANDALLIA, IN (see PARKVIEW REGIONAL MEDICAL CENTER), p. A204
PARKVIEW HUNTINGTON HOSPITAL, HUNTINGTON, IN, p. A206
PARKVIEW LAGRANGE HOSPITAL, LAGRANGE, IN, p. A210
PARKVIEW MEDICAL CENTER, PUEBLO, CO, p. A104
PARKVIEW NOBLE HOSPITAL, KENDALLVILLE, IN, p. A208
PARKVIEW NORTH HOSPITAL, IN (see PARKVIEW REGIONAL MEDICAL CENTER), p. A204
PARKVIEW ORTHO HOSPITAL, FORT WAYNE, IN, p. A204
PARKVIEW REGIONAL HOSPITAL, MEXIA, TX, p. A624
PARKVIEW REGIONAL MEDICAL CENTER, FORT WAYNE, IN, p. A204
PARKVIEW WABASH COUNTY HOSPITAL, WABASH, IN, p. A216
PARKVIEW WHITLEY HOSPITAL, COLUMBIA CITY, IN, p. A201
PARKWAY MEDICAL CENTER, DECATUR, AL, p. A16
PARKWEST MEDICAL CENTER, KNOXVILLE, TN, p. A572
PARKWOOD BEHAVIORAL HEALTH SYSTEM, OLIVE BRANCH, MS, p. A351
PARMER COUNTY COMMUNITY HOSPITAL, FRIONA, TX, p. A606
PARMER MEDICAL CENTER, FRIONA, TX, p. A606
PARMER MEDICAL CENTER, TX (see PARMER COUNTY COMMUNITY HOSPITAL), p. A606
PARRISH MEDICAL CENTER, TITUSVILLE, FL, p. A142
PARSONS STATE HOSPITAL AND TRAINING CENTER, PARSONS, KS, p. A244
PASSAVANT AREA HOSPITAL, JACKSONVILLE, IL, p. A186
PATEWOOD MEMORIAL HOSPITAL, GREENVILLE, SC, p. A553
PATHWAY REHABILITATION HOSPITAL, BOSSIER CITY, LA, p. A265
PATHWAYS OF TENNESSEE, JACKSON, TN, p. A571
PATHWAYS TREATMENT CENTER, MT (see KALISPELL REGIONAL HEALTHCARE), p. A377
PATIENTS CHOICE MEDICAL CENTER OF SMITH COUNTY, RALEIGH, MS, p. A352
PATIENTS MEDICAL CENTER, PASADENA, TX, p. A627
PATIENTS' HOSPITAL OF REDDING, REDDING, CA, p. A80
PATRICK B. HARRIS PSYCHIATRIC HOSPITAL, ANDERSON, SC, p. A549
PATTON STATE HOSPITAL, PATTON, CA, p. A78
PAUL B. HALL REGIONAL MEDICAL CENTER, PAINTSVILLE, KY, p. A259
PAUL OLIVER MEMORIAL HOSPITAL, FRANKFORT, MI, p. A313
PAULDING COUNTY HOSPITAL, PAULDING, OH, p. A489
PAULS VALLEY GENERAL HOSPITAL, PAULS VALLEY, OK, p. A505
PAWHUSKA HOSPITAL, PAWHUSKA, OK, p. A505
PAWNEE COUNTY MEMORIAL HOSPITAL AND RURAL HEALTH CLINIC, PAWNEE CITY, NE, p. A389
PAWNEE VALLEY COMMUNITY HOSPITAL, LARNED, KS, p. A239
PAYNE WHITNEY PSYCHIATRIC CLINIC, NEW YORK (Includes all hospitals located within the five boroughs), NY, p. A436
PAYNE WHITNEY PSYCHIATRIC CLINIC, NY (see NEW YORK-PRESBYTERIAN HOSPITAL), p. A434
PEACEHEALTH COTTAGE GROVE COMMUNITY MEDICAL CENTER, COTTAGE GROVE, OR, p. A512
PEACEHEALTH KETCHIKAN MEDICAL CENTER, KETCHIKAN, AK, p. A26
PEACEHEALTH PEACE HARBOR MEDICAL CENTER, FLORENCE, OR, p. A512
PEACEHEALTH PEACE ISLAND MEDICAL CENTER, FRIDAY HARBOR, WA, p. A672
PEACEHEALTH SACRED HEART MEDICAL CENTER AT RIVERBEND, SPRINGFIELD, OR, p. A518
PEACEHEALTH SACRED HEART MEDICAL CENTER UNIVERSITY DISTRICT, EUGENE, OR, p. A512
PEACEHEALTH SOUTHWEST MEDICAL CENTER, VANCOUVER, WA, p. A680
PEACEHEALTH SOUTHWEST MEDICAL CENTER, WA (see SOUTHWEST WASHINGTON MEDICAL CENTER), p. A680

PEACEHEALTH ST. JOHN MEDICAL CENTER, LONGVIEW, WA, p. A673
PEACEHEALTH ST. JOSEPH MEDICAL CENTER, BELLINGHAM, WA, p. A669
PEACEHEALTH ST. JOSEPH MEDICAL CENTER, WA (see ST. JOSEPH HOSPITAL), p. A669
PEACEHEALTH UNITED GENERAL MEDICAL CENTER, SEDRO, WA, p. A677
PEACHFORD BEHAVIORAL HEALTH SYSTEM, ATLANTA, GA, p. A146
PEAK BEHAVIORAL HEALTH SERVICES, SANTA TERESA, NM, p. A419
PEAK VIEW BEHAVIORAL HEALTH, COLORADO SPRINGS, CO, p. A97
PEARL RIVER COUNTY HOSPITAL, POPLARVILLE, MS, p. A352
PEARLAND MEDICAL CENTER, PEARLAND, TX, p. A627
PECONIC BAY MEDICAL CENTER, RIVERHEAD, NY, p. A441
PECOS COUNTY MEMORIAL HOSPITAL, FORT STOCKTON, TX, p. A604
PECOS VALLEY LODGE, NM (see NEW MEXICO REHABILITATION CENTER), p. A419
PELHAM MEDICAL CENTER, GREER, SC, p. A554
PELLA REGIONAL HEALTH CENTER, PELLA, IA, p. A228
PEMBINA COUNTY MEMORIAL HOSPITAL AND WEDGEWOOD MANOR, CAVALIER, ND, p. A465
PEMBROKE HOSPITAL, PEMBROKE, MA, p. A303
PEMISCOT MEMORIAL HEALTH SYSTEM, HAYTI, MO, p. A360
PEN BAY MEDICAL CENTER, ROCKPORT, ME, p. A286
PEN BAY MEDICAL CENTER, ME (see PENOBSCOT BAY MEDICAL CENTER), p. A286
PENDER COMMUNITY HOSPITAL, PENDER, NE, p. A389
PENDER MEMORIAL HOSPITAL, BURGAW, NC, p. A448
PENINSULA HOSPITAL, TN (see PARKWEST MEDICAL CENTER), p. A572
PENINSULA REGIONAL MEDICAL CENTER, SALISBURY, MD, p. A294
PENN HIGHLANDS BROOKVILLE, BROOKVILLE, PA, p. A521
PENN HIGHLANDS CLEARFIELD, CLEARFIELD, PA, p. A522
PENN HIGHLANDS DUBOIS, DUBOIS, PA, p. A524
PENN HIGHLANDS ELK, SAINT MARYS, PA, p. A540
PENN MEDICINE LANCASTER GENERAL HOSPITAL, LANCASTER, PA, p. A529
PENN MEDICINE PRINCETON MEDICAL CENTER, PLAINSBORO, NJ, p. A410
PENN MEDICINE PRINCETON MEDICAL CENTER, PLAINSBORO, NJ (see UNIVERSITY MEDICAL CENTER AT PRINCETON), p. A410
PENN PRESBYTERIAN MEDICAL CENTER, PHILADELPHIA, PA, p. A536
PENN STATE CHILDREN'S HOSPITAL, PA (see PENN STATE MILTON S. HERSHEY MEDICAL CENTER), p. A527
PENN STATE HEALTH ST. JOSEPH - DOWNTOWN CAMPUS, PA (see PENN STATE HEALTH ST. JOSEPH), p. A539
PENN STATE HEALTH ST. JOSEPH, READING, PA, p. A539
PENN STATE HERSHEY REHABILITATION HOSPITAL, HUMMELSTOWN, PA, p. A527
PENN STATE MILTON S. HERSHEY MEDICAL CENTER, HERSHEY, PA, p. A527
PENNSYLVANIA HOSPITAL, PHILADELPHIA, PA, p. A536
PENNSYLVANIA PSYCHIATRIC INSTITUTE, HARRISBURG, PA, p. A526
PENOBSCOT BAY MEDICAL CENTER, ROCKPORT, ME, p. A286
PENOBSCOT VALLEY HOSPITAL, LINCOLN, ME, p. A284
PENROSE HOSPITAL, CO (see PENROSE-ST. FRANCIS HEALTH SERVICES), p. A98
PENROSE-ST. FRANCIS HEALTH SERVICES, COLORADO SPRINGS, CO, p. A98
PERHAM HEALTH, PERHAM, MN, p. A337
PERKINS COUNTY HEALTH SERVICES, GRANT, NE, p. A384
PERMIAN REGIONAL MEDICAL CENTER, ANDREWS, TX, p. A583
PERRY COMMUNITY HOSPITAL, LINDEN, TN, p. A573
PERRY COUNTY GENERAL HOSPITAL, RICHTON, MS, p. A352
PERRY COUNTY MEMORIAL HOSPITAL, PERRYVILLE, MO, p. A366
PERRY COUNTY MEMORIAL HOSPITAL, TELL CITY, IN, p. A215
PERRY HOSPITAL, PERRY, GA, p. A158
PERRY MEMORIAL HOSPITAL, PERRY, OK, p. A505
PERRY MEMORIAL HOSPITAL, PRINCETON, IL, p. A194
PERSHING GENERAL HOSPITAL, LOVELOCK, NV, p. A395
PERSHING MEMORIAL HOSPITAL, BROOKFIELD, MO, p. A356
PERSON MEMORIAL HOSPITAL, ROXBORO, NC, p. A460
PERTH AMBOY DIVISION, NJ (see HACKENSACK MERIDIAN HEALTH RARITAN BAY MEDICAL CENTER), p. A410
PETALUMA VALLEY HOSPITAL, PETALUMA, CA, p. A78
PETERSBURG MEDICAL CENTER, PETERSBURG, AK, p. A27

PRESENCE SAINT JOSEPH MEDICAL CENTER, JOLIET, IL, p. A187
PRESENCE SAINT JOSEPH MEDICAL CENTER, IL (see PROVENA SAINT JOSEPH MEDICAL CENTER), p. A187
PRESENCE SAINTS MARY & ELIZABETH MEDICAL CENTER, CHICAGO, IL, p. A178
PRESENCE SAINTS MARY & ELIZABETH MEDICAL CENTER, IL (see SAINTS MARY & ELIZABETH MEDICAL CENTER), p. A179
PRESENCE SAINTS MARY & ELIZABETH MEDICAL CENTER, CLAREMONT AVENUE, IL (see PRESENCE SAINTS MARY & ELIZABETH MEDICAL CENTER), p. A178
PRESENCE ST. MARY'S HOSPITAL, KANKAKEE, IL, p. A187
PRESENCE ST. MARY'S HOSPITAL, IL (see PROVENA ST. MARY'S HOSPITAL), p. A187
PRESENTATION MEDICAL CENTER, ROLLA, ND, p. A468
PRESTON MEMORIAL HOSPITAL, KINGWOOD, WV, p. A684
PREVOST MEMORIAL HOSPITAL, DONALDSONVILLE, LA, p. A267
PRIMARY CHILDREN'S HOSPITAL, SALT LAKE CITY, UT, p. A650
PRINCETON BAPTIST MEDICAL CENTER, BIRMINGHAM, AL, p. A15
PRINCETON COMMUNITY HOSPITAL, PRINCETON, WV, p. A686
PROFESSIONAL HOSPITAL GUAYNABO, GUAYNABO, PR, p. A713
PROGRESS WEST HOSPITAL, O'FALLON, MO, p. A365
PROMEDICA BAY PARK HOSPITAL, OREGON, OH, p. A488
PROMEDICA BIXBY HOSPITAL, ADRIAN, MI, p. A307
PROMEDICA COLDWATER REGIONAL HOSPITAL, COLDWATER, MI, p. A310
PROMEDICA DEFIANCE REGIONAL HOSPITAL, DEFIANCE, OH, p. A481
PROMEDICA FLOWER HOSPITAL, SYLVANIA, OH, p. A491
PROMEDICA FOSTORIA COMMUNITY HOSPITAL, FOSTORIA, OH, p. A482
PROMEDICA HERRICK HOSPITAL, TECUMSEH, MI, p. A324
PROMEDICA MEMORIAL HOSPITAL, FREMONT, OH, p. A482
PROMEDICA MONROE REGIONAL HOSPITAL, MONROE, MI, p. A319
PROMEDICA TOLEDO HOSPITAL, TOLEDO, OH, p. A491
PROMEDICA WILDWOOD ORTHOPAEDIC AND SPINE HOSPITAL, OH (see PROMEDICA TOLEDO HOSPITAL), p. A491
PROMISE HOSPITAL BATON ROUGE - MAIN CAMPUS, BATON ROUGE, LA, p. A264
PROMISE HOSPITAL OF BATON ROUGE - MID-CITY CAMPUS, LA (see PROMISE HOSPITAL OF BATON ROUGE - OCHSNER CAMPUS), p. A264
PROMISE HOSPITAL OF BATON ROUGE - OCHSNER CAMPUS, BATON ROUGE, LA, p. A264
PROMISE HOSPITAL OF DALLAS, DALLAS, TX, p. A597
PROMISE HOSPITAL OF EAST LOS ANGELES, LOS ANGELES, CA, p. A69
PROMISE HOSPITAL OF EAST LOS ANGELES, SUBURBAN MEDICAL CENTER CAMPUS, CA (see PROMISE HOSPITAL OF EAST LOS ANGELES), p. A69
PROMISE HOSPITAL OF FLORIDA AT THE VILLAGES, OXFORD, FL, p. A134
PROMISE HOSPITAL OF FORT MYERS, FORT MYERS, FL, p. A123
PROMISE HOSPITAL OF LOUISIANA - BOSSIER CITY CAMPUS, LA (see PROMISE HOSPITAL OF LOUISIANA - SHREVEPORT CAMPUS), p. A278
PROMISE HOSPITAL OF LOUISIANA - SHREVEPORT CAMPUS, SHREVEPORT, LA, p. A278
PROMISE HOSPITAL OF LOUISIANA - SHREVEPORT CAMPUS, LA (see PROMISE SPECIALTY HOSPITAL OF SHREVEPORT), p. A279
PROMISE HOSPITAL OF MIAMI, MIAMI, FL, p. A131
PROMISE HOSPITAL OF MISS LOU, VIDALIA, LA, p. A280
PROMISE HOSPITAL OF OVERLAND PARK, OVERLAND PARK, KS, p. A243
PROMISE HOSPITAL OF PHOENIX, MESA, AZ, p. A31
PROMISE HOSPITAL OF SALT LAKE, SALT LAKE CITY, UT, p. A650
PROMISE HOSPITAL OF SAN DIEGO, SAN DIEGO, CA, p. A84
PROMISE HOSPITAL OF VICKSBURG, VICKSBURG, MS, p. A354
PROMISE HOSPITAL OF WICHITA FALLS, WICHITA FALLS, TX, p. A644
PROMISE SPECIALTY HOSPITAL OF SHREVEPORT, SHREVEPORT, LA, p. A279
PROVENA MERCY MEDICAL CENTER, AURORA, IL, p. A174
PROVENA SAINT JOSEPH HOSPITAL, ELGIN, IL, p. A182
PROVENA SAINT JOSEPH MEDICAL CENTER, JOLIET, IL, p. A187
PROVENA ST. MARY'S HOSPITAL, KANKAKEE, IL, p. A187

PROVIDENCE ALASKA MEDICAL CENTER, ANCHORAGE, AK, p. A25
PROVIDENCE CENTRALIA HOSPITAL, CENTRALIA, WA, p. A670
PROVIDENCE CHILDREN'S HOSPITAL, TX (see THE HOSPITALS OF PROVIDENCE MEMORIAL CAMPUS), p. A602
PROVIDENCE EVERETT MEDICAL CENTER - COLBY CAMPUS, WA (see PROVIDENCE REGIONAL MEDICAL CENTER EVERETT), p. A671
PROVIDENCE EVERETT MEDICAL CENTER - PACIFIC CAMPUS, WA (see PROVIDENCE REGIONAL MEDICAL CENTER EVERETT), p. A671
PROVIDENCE HEALTHCARE NETWORK, WACO, TX, p. A642
PROVIDENCE HOLY CROSS MEDICAL CENTER, MISSION HILLS, CA, p. A72
PROVIDENCE HOLY FAMILY HOSPITAL, SPOKANE, WA, p. A678
PROVIDENCE HOOD RIVER MEMORIAL HOSPITAL, HOOD RIVER, OR, p. A513
PROVIDENCE HOSPITAL, COLUMBIA, SC, p. A551
PROVIDENCE HOSPITAL, MOBILE, AL, p. A20
PROVIDENCE HOSPITAL, WASHINGTON, DC, p. A116
PROVIDENCE HOSPITAL NORTHEAST, COLUMBIA, SC, p. A551
PROVIDENCE HOSPITAL NORTHEAST, SC (see PROVIDENCE HOSPITAL), p. A551
PROVIDENCE HOSPITAL OF NORTH HOUSTON, HOUSTON, TX, p. A613
PROVIDENCE HOSPITAL, COLUMBIA, SC (see PROVIDENCE HOSPITAL NORTHEAST), p. A551
PROVIDENCE KODIAK ISLAND MEDICAL CENTER, KODIAK, AK, p. A26
PROVIDENCE LITTLE COMPANY OF MARY MEDICAL CENTER - TORRANCE, TORRANCE, CA, p. A92
PROVIDENCE LITTLE COMPANY OF MARY MEDICAL CENTER SAN PEDRO, LOS ANGELES, CA, p. A69
PROVIDENCE MEDFORD MEDICAL CENTER, MEDFORD, OR, p. A515
PROVIDENCE MEDICAL CENTER, KANSAS CITY, KS, p. A238
PROVIDENCE MEDICAL CENTER, WAYNE, NE, p. A391
PROVIDENCE MILWAUKIE HOSPITAL, MILWAUKIE, OR, p. A515
PROVIDENCE MOUNT CARMEL HOSPITAL, COLVILLE, WA, p. A670
PROVIDENCE NEWBERG MEDICAL CENTER, NEWBERG, OR, p. A515
PROVIDENCE PORTLAND MEDICAL CENTER, PORTLAND, OR, p. A516
PROVIDENCE - PROVIDENCE PARK HOSPITAL, NOVI CAMPUS, NOVI, MI, p. A320
PROVIDENCE - PROVIDENCE PARK HOSPITAL, NOVI CAMPUS, MI (see PROVIDENCE-PROVIDENCE PARK HOSPITALS), p. A323
PROVIDENCE REGIONAL MEDICAL CENTER EVERETT, EVERETT, WA, p. A671
PROVIDENCE SACRED HEART MEDICAL CENTER & CHILDREN'S HOSPITAL, SPOKANE, WA, p. A678
PROVIDENCE SAINT JOHN'S HEALTH CENTER, SANTA MONICA, CA, p. A89
PROVIDENCE SAINT JOSEPH MEDICAL CENTER, BURBANK, CA, p. A53
PROVIDENCE SEASIDE HOSPITAL, SEASIDE, OR, p. A518
PROVIDENCE SEWARD MEDICAL CENTER, SEWARD, AK, p. A27
PROVIDENCE ST. JOSEPH MEDICAL CENTER, POLSON, MT, p. A378
PROVIDENCE ST. JOSEPH'S HOSPITAL, CHEWELAH, WA, p. A670
PROVIDENCE ST. MARY MEDICAL CENTER, WALLA WALLA, WA, p. A680
PROVIDENCE ST. PETER HOSPITAL, OLYMPIA, WA, p. A674
PROVIDENCE ST. VINCENT MEDICAL CENTER, PORTLAND, OR, p. A516
PROVIDENCE TARZANA MEDICAL CENTER, LOS ANGELES, CA, p. A69
PROVIDENCE VALDEZ MEDICAL CENTER, VALDEZ, AK, p. A27
PROVIDENCE VETERANS AFFAIRS MEDICAL CENTER, PROVIDENCE, RI, p. A547
PROVIDENCE VETERANS AFFAIRS MEDICAL CENTER, RI (see VETERANS AFFAIRS MEDICAL CENTER), p. A548
PROVIDENCE WILLAMETTE FALLS MEDICAL CENTER, OREGON CITY, OR, p. A515
PROVIDENCE-PROVIDENCE PARK HOSPITALS, SOUTHFIELD, MI, p. A323
PROVIDENCE-PROVIDENCE PARK HOSPITALS, SOUTHFIELD, MI (see PROVIDENCE - PROVIDENCE PARK HOSPITAL, NOVI CAMPUS), p. A320

PROVIDENT HOSPITAL OF COOK COUNTY, CHICAGO, IL, p. A179
PROVO CANYON BEHAVIORAL HOSPITAL, OREM, UT, p. A649
PROWERS MEDICAL CENTER, LAMAR, CO, p. A103
PSYCHIATRIC INSTITUTE OF WASHINGTON, WASHINGTON, DC, p. A116
PSYCHIATRIC MEDICINE CENTER, OR (see SALEM HOSPITAL), p. A517
PSYCHIATRIC PAVILION NEW ORLEANS, NEW ORLEANS, LA, p. A276
PUERTO RICO CHILDREN'S HOSPITAL, PR (see HOSPITAL HERMANOS MELENDEZ), p. A712
PULASKI MEMORIAL HOSPITAL, WINAMAC, IN, p. A216
PULLMAN REGIONAL HOSPITAL, PULLMAN, WA, p. A675
PUNXSUTAWNEY AREA HOSPITAL, PUNXSUTAWNEY, PA, p. A539
PURCELL MUNICIPAL HOSPITAL, PURCELL, OK, p. A506
PUSHMATAHA HOSPITAL, ANTLERS, OK, p. A495
PUTNAM COMMUNITY MEDICAL CENTER, PALATKA, FL, p. A134
PUTNAM COUNTY HOSPITAL, GREENCASTLE, IN, p. A205
PUTNAM COUNTY MEMORIAL HOSPITAL, UNIONVILLE, MO, p. A371
PUTNAM GENERAL HOSPITAL, EATONTON, GA, p. A153
PUTNAM HOSPITAL CENTER, CARMEL, NY, p. A424

Q

QUAIL RUN BEHAVIORAL HEALTH, PHOENIX, AZ, p. A34
QUEEN OF THE VALLEY MEDICAL CENTER, NAPA, CA, p. A74
QUEEN'S MEDICAL CENTER - WEST OAHU, HI (see THE QUEEN'S MEDICAL CENTER), p. A165
QUEENS CHILDREN'S HOSPITAL PSYCHIATRIC CENTER, NEW YORK (Includes all hospitals located within the five boroughs), NY, p. A436
QUENTIN MEASE HOSPITAL, TX (see HARRIS HEALTH SYSTEM), p. A611
QUILLEN REHABILITATION HOSPITAL, JOHNSON CITY, TN, p. A572
QUINCY VALLEY MEDICAL CENTER, QUINCY, WA, p. A675

R

RADY CHILDREN'S HOSPITAL - SAN DIEGO, SAN DIEGO, CA, p. A84
RADY CHILDREN'S HOSPITAL - SAN DIEGO, CA (see RADY CHILDREN'S HOSPITAL AND HEALTH CENTER), p. A84
RADY CHILDREN'S HOSPITAL AND HEALTH CENTER, SAN DIEGO, CA, p. A84
RAINBOW BABIES AND CHILDREN'S HOSPITAL, OH (see UNIVERSITY HOSPITALS CLEVELAND MEDICAL CENTER), p. A477
RAINY LAKE MEDICAL CENTER, INTERNATIONAL FALLS, MN, p. A333
RALEIGH GENERAL HOSPITAL, BECKLEY, WV, p. A681
RALPH H. JOHNSON VETERANS AFFAIRS MEDICAL CENTER, CHARLESTON, SC, p. A550
RANCHO LOS AMIGOS NATIONAL REHABILITATION CENTER, DOWNEY, CA, p. A56
RANCHO SPRINGS MEDICAL CENTER, CA (see SOUTHWEST HEALTHCARE SYSTEM), p. A74
RANDALL CHILDREN'S HOSPITAL, OR (see LEGACY EMANUEL MEDICAL CENTER), p. A516
RANDOLPH HOSPITAL, ASHEBORO, NC, p. A447
RANGE REGIONAL HEALTH SERVICES, HIBBING, MN, p. A333
RANGELY DISTRICT HOSPITAL, RANGELY, CO, p. A105
RANKEN JORDAN PEDIATRIC BRIDGE HOSPITAL, MARYLAND HEIGHTS, MO, p. A364
RANKIN COUNTY HOSPITAL DISTRICT, RANKIN, TX, p. A630
RANSOM MEMORIAL HOSPITAL, OTTAWA, KS, p. A243
RAPID CITY REGIONAL HOSPITAL, RAPID CITY, SD, p. A563
RAPIDES REGIONAL MEDICAL CENTER, ALEXANDRIA, LA, p. A262
RAPPAHANNOCK GENERAL HOSPITAL, KILMARNOCK, VA, p. A660
RAULERSON HOSPITAL, OKEECHOBEE, FL, p. A133
RAWLINS COUNTY HEALTH CENTER, ATWOOD, KS, p. A232
RAY COUNTY MEMORIAL HOSPITAL, RICHMOND, MO, p. A366
RC HOSPITAL AND CLINICS, OLIVIA, MN, p. A336

S

SAINT MARY'S REGIONAL MEDICAL CENTER, RUSSELLVILLE-Pope County, AR, p. A48
SAINT MICHAEL'S HOSPITAL, STEVENS POINT, WI, p. A703
SAINT MICHAEL'S MEDICAL CENTER, NEWARK, NJ, p. A409
SAINT PETER'S UNIVERSITY HOSPITAL, NEW BRUNSWICK, NJ, p. A408
SAINT SIMONS BY-THE-SEA HOSPITAL, SAINT SIMONS ISLAND, GA, p. A159
SAINT THOMAS DEKALB HOSPITAL, SMITHVILLE, TN, p. A580
SAINT THOMAS HICKMAN HOSPITAL, CENTERVILLE, TN, p. A567
SAINT THOMAS HIGHLANDS HOSPITAL, SPARTA, TN, p. A580
SAINT THOMAS HOSPITAL FOR SPINAL SURGERY, NASHVILLE, TN, p. A577
SAINT THOMAS MIDTOWN HOSPITAL, NASHVILLE, TN, p. A577
SAINT THOMAS RIVER PARK HOSPITAL, MC MINNVILLE, TN, p. A574
SAINT THOMAS RUTHERFORD HOSPITAL, MURFREESBORO, TN, p. A576
SAINT THOMAS STONES RIVER HOSPITAL, WOODBURY, TN, p. A581
SAINT THOMAS WEST HOSPITAL, NASHVILLE, TN, p. A577
SAINT VINCENT HOSPITAL, ERIE, PA, p. A525
SAINT VINCENT HOSPITAL, WORCESTER, MA, p. A306
SAINTS MARY & ELIZABETH MEDICAL CENTER, CHICAGO, IL, p. A179
SAINTS MEDICAL CENTER, LOWELL, MA, p. A301
SAKAKAWEA MEDICAL CENTER, HAZEN, ND, p. A466
SALEM CAMPUS, MA (see NORTH SHORE MEDICAL CENTER), p. A304
SALEM CAMPUS, MA (see SALEM HOSPITAL), p. A304
SALEM HEALTH REHABILITATION CENTER, OR (see SALEM HOSPITAL), p. A517
SALEM HEALTH WEST VALLEY, DALLAS, OR, p. A512
SALEM HOSPITAL, SALEM, MA, p. A304
SALEM HOSPITAL, SALEM, OR, p. A517
SALEM MEMORIAL DISTRICT HOSPITAL, SALEM, MO, p. A370
SALEM REGIONAL MEDICAL CENTER, SALEM, OH, p. A490
SALEM TOWNSHIP HOSPITAL, SALEM, IL, p. A195
SALEM VETERANS AFFAIRS MEDICAL CENTER, SALEM, VA, p. A666
SALINA REGIONAL HEALTH CENTER, SALINA, KS, p. A245
SALINA REGIONAL HEALTH CENTER- PENN CAMPUS, KS (see SALINA REGIONAL HEALTH CENTER), p. A245
SALINA REGIONAL HEALTH CENTER-SANTA FE CAMPUS, KS (see SALINA REGIONAL HEALTH CENTER), p. A245
SALINA SURGICAL HOSPITAL, SALINA, KS, p. A245
SALINAS VALLEY MEMORIAL HEALTHCARE SYSTEM, SALINAS, CA, p. A83
SALINE MEMORIAL HOSPITAL, BENTON-Saline County, AR, p. A39
SALT LAKE BEHAVIORAL HEALTH, SALT LAKE CITY, UT, p. A650
SALT LAKE REGIONAL MEDICAL CENTER, SALT LAKE CITY, UT, p. A650
SAM RAYBURN MEMORIAL VETERANS CENTER, BONHAM, TX, p. A589
SAM RAYBURN MEMORIAL VETERANS CENTER, TX (see VETERANS AFFAIRS NORTH TEXAS HEALTH CARE SYSTEM), p. A598
SAMARITAN ALBANY GENERAL HOSPITAL, ALBANY, OR, p. A511
SAMARITAN BEHAVIORAL HEALTH CENTER-DESERT SAMARITAN MEDICAL CENTER, MESA, AZ, p. A31
SAMARITAN BEHAVIORAL HEALTH CENTER-DESERT SAMARITAN MEDICAL CENTER, AZ (see BANNER DESERT MEDICAL CENTER), p. A31
SAMARITAN HEALTHCARE, MOSES LAKE, WA, p. A673
SAMARITAN HOSPITAL, MACON, MO, p. A364
SAMARITAN HOSPITAL, TROY, NY, p. A444
SAMARITAN LEBANON COMMUNITY HOSPITAL, LEBANON, OR, p. A514
SAMARITAN MEDICAL CENTER, WATERTOWN, NY, p. A445
SAMARITAN NORTH LINCOLN HOSPITAL, LINCOLN CITY, OR, p. A514
SAMARITAN PACIFIC COMMUNITIES HOSPITAL, NEWPORT, OR, p. A515
SAME DAY SURGERY CENTER, RAPID CITY, SD, p. A563
SAMPSON REGIONAL MEDICAL CENTER, CLINTON, NC, p. A450
SAMUEL MAHELONA MEMORIAL HOSPITAL, KAPAA, HI, p. A166
SAMUEL SIMMONDS MEMORIAL HOSPITAL, BARROW, AK, p. A25
SAN ANGELO COMMUNITY MEDICAL CENTER, SAN ANGELO, TX, p. A632
SAN ANTONIO BEHAVIORAL HEALTHCARE HOSPITAL, SAN ANTONIO, TX, p. A634

SAN ANTONIO DIVISION, TX (see SOUTH TEXAS VETERANS HEALTH CARE SYSTEM), p. A634
SAN ANTONIO REGIONAL HOSPITAL, UPLAND, CA, p. A93
SAN ANTONIO STATE HOSPITAL, SAN ANTONIO, TX, p. A634
SAN BERNARDINO MOUNTAINS COMMUNITY HOSPITAL DISTRICT, LAKE ARROWHEAD, CA, p. A63
SAN CARLOS APACHE HEALTHCARE CORPORATION, PERIDOT, AZ, p. A32
SAN DIEGO COUNTY PSYCHIATRIC HOSPITAL, SAN DIEGO, CA, p. A84
SAN DIEGO MEDICAL CENTER, SAN DIEGO, CA, p. A84
SAN DIMAS COMMUNITY HOSPITAL, SAN DIMAS, CA, p. A85
SAN FRANCISCO MEDICAL CENTER, SAN FRANCISCO, CA, p. A85
SAN FRANCISCO VA MEDICAL CENTER, SAN FRANCISCO, CA, p. A86
SAN FRANCISCO VA MEDICAL CENTER, CA (see VETERANS AFFAIRS MEDICAL CENTER), p. A86
SAN GABRIEL VALLEY MEDICAL CENTER, SAN GABRIEL, CA, p. A86
SAN GORGONIO MEMORIAL HOSPITAL, BANNING, CA, p. A52
SAN JOAQUIN GENERAL HOSPITAL, FRENCH CAMP, CA, p. A59
SAN JOAQUIN VALLEY REHABILITATION HOSPITAL, FRESNO, CA, p. A59
SAN JORGE CHILDREN'S HOSPITAL, SANTURCE, PR, p. A716
SAN JOSE BEHAVORIAL HEALTH, SAN JOSE, CA, p. A87
SAN JOSE MEDICAL CENTER, SAN JOSE, CA, p. A87
SAN JUAN CAPESTRANO HOSPITAL, SAN JUAN, PR, p. A716
SAN JUAN CITY HOSPITAL, SAN JUAN, PR, p. A716
SAN JUAN HEALTH SERVICE DISTRICT, MONTICELLO, UT, p. A648
SAN JUAN REGIONAL MEDICAL CENTER, FARMINGTON, NM, p. A417
SAN JUAN REGIONAL MEDICAL CENTER REHABILITATION HOSPITAL, NM (see SAN JUAN REGIONAL MEDICAL CENTER), p. A417
SAN LEANDRO HOSPITAL, SAN LEANDRO, CA, p. A87
SAN LUIS VALLEY HEALTH, ALAMOSA, CO, p. A96
SAN LUIS VALLEY HEALTH CONEJOS COUNTY HOSPITAL, LA JARA, CO, p. A102
SAN MATEO MEDICAL CENTER, SAN MATEO, CA, p. A87
SAN RAMON REGIONAL MEDICAL CENTER, SAN RAMON, CA, p. A88
SANFORD ABERDEEN MEDICAL CENTER, ABERDEEN, SD, p. A559
SANFORD BAGLEY MEDICAL CENTER, BAGLEY, MN, p. A328
SANFORD BEMIDJI MEDICAL CENTER, BEMIDJI, MN, p. A328
SANFORD BEMIDJI MEDICAL CENTER, MN (see NORTH COUNTRY REGIONAL HOSPITAL), p. A328
SANFORD BISMARCK, BISMARCK, ND, p. A464
SANFORD BISMARCK, ND (see SANFORD HEALTH), p. A464
SANFORD CANBY MEDICAL CENTER, CANBY, MN, p. A329
SANFORD CANTON-INWOOD MEDICAL CENTER, CANTON, SD, p. A559
SANFORD CHAMBERLAIN MEDICAL CENTER, CHAMBERLAIN, SD, p. A560
SANFORD CHAMBERLAIN MEDICAL CENTER, SD (see SANFORD MID DAKOTA MEDICAL CENTER), p. A560
SANFORD CHILDREN'S HOSPITAL, SD (see SANFORD USD MEDICAL CENTER), p. A564
SANFORD CLEAR LAKE MEDICAL CENTER, CLEAR LAKE, SD, p. A560
SANFORD HEALTH, BISMARCK, ND, p. A464
SANFORD HILLSBORO MEDICAL CENTER, HILLSBORO, ND, p. A467
SANFORD JACKSON MEDICAL CENTER, JACKSON, MN, p. A333
SANFORD LUVERNE MEDICAL CENTER, LUVERNE, MN, p. A334
SANFORD MAYVILLE MEDICAL CENTER, MAYVILLE, ND, p. A467
SANFORD MAYVILLE MEDICAL CENTER, ND (see MERITCARE MAYVILLE UNION HOSPITAL), p. A467
SANFORD MEDICAL CENTER FARGO, FARGO, ND, p. A466
SANFORD MEDICAL CENTER FARGO, ND (see MERITCARE MEDICAL CENTER), p. A465
SANFORD MEDICAL CENTER THIEF RIVER FALLS, THIEF RIVER FALLS, MN, p. A340
SANFORD MEDICAL CENTER THIEF RIVER FALLS, MN (see MERITCARE THIEF RIVER FALLS NORTHWEST MEDICAL CENTER), p. A340
SANFORD MERRILL MEDICAL CENTER, ROCK RAPIDS, IA, p. A228
SANFORD MID DAKOTA MEDICAL CENTER, CHAMBERLAIN, SD, p. A560
SANFORD REGIONAL HOSPITAL WORTHINGTON, WORTHINGTON, MN, p. A342
SANFORD ROCK RAPIDS MEDICAL CENTER, ROCK RAPIDS, IA, p. A228

SANFORD ROCK RAPIDS MEDICAL CENTER, IA (see SANFORD MERRILL MEDICAL CENTER), p. A228
SANFORD SHELDON MEDICAL CENTER, SHELDON, IA, p. A229
SANFORD SOUTH UNIVERSITY, ND (see SANFORD MEDICAL CENTER FARGO), p. A466
SANFORD THIEF RIVER FALLS BEHAVIORAL HEALTH CENTER, THIEF RIVER FALLS, MN, p. A341
SANFORD TRACY MEDICAL CENTER, TRACY, MN, p. A341
SANFORD USD MEDICAL CENTER, SIOUX FALLS, SD, p. A564
SANFORD VERMILLION MEDICAL CENTER, VERMILLION, SD, p. A564
SANFORD WEBSTER MEDICAL CENTER, WEBSTER, SD, p. A565
SANFORD WEBSTER MEDICAL CENTER, SD (see SANFORD WEBSTER MEDICAL CENTER), p. A565
SANFORD WESTBROOK MEDICAL CENTER, WESTBROOK, MN, p. A342
SANFORD WHEATON MEDICAL CENTER, WHEATON, MN, p. A342
SANFORD WORTHINGTON MEDICAL CENTER, WORTHINGTON, MN, p. A342
SANFORD WORTHINGTON MEDICAL CENTER, MN (see SANFORD REGIONAL HOSPITAL WORTHINGTON), p. A342
SANPETE VALLEY HOSPITAL, MOUNT PLEASANT, UT, p. A648
SANTA BARBARA COTTAGE HOSPITAL, SANTA BARBARA, CA, p. A88
SANTA BARBARA COTTAGE HOSPITAL, SANTA BARBARA, CA (see COTTAGE REHABILITATION HOSPITAL), p. A88
SANTA BARBARA COUNTY PSYCHIATRIC HEALTH FACILITY, SANTA BARBARA, CA, p. A88
SANTA CLARA VALLEY MEDICAL CENTER, SAN JOSE, CA, p. A87
SANTA CRUZ VALLEY REGIONAL HOSPITAL, GREEN VALLEY, AZ, p. A30
SANTA ROSA MEDICAL CENTER, MILTON, FL, p. A131
SANTA ROSA MEMORIAL HOSPITAL, SANTA ROSA, CA, p. A89
SANTA YNEZ VALLEY COTTAGE HOSPITAL, SOLVANG, CA, p. A90
SANTIAM HOSPITAL, STAYTON, OR, p. A518
SARAH BUSH LINCOLN HEALTH CENTER, MATTOON, IL, p. A188
SARAH D. CULBERTSON MEMORIAL HOSPITAL, RUSHVILLE, IL, p. A195
SARASOTA MEMORIAL HEALTH CARE SYSTEM, SARASOTA, FL, p. A139
SARATOGA HOSPITAL, SARATOGA SPRINGS, NY, p. A442
SARTORI MEMORIAL HOSPITAL, CEDAR FALLS, IA, p. A218
SATANTA DISTRICT HOSPITAL AND LONG TERM CARE, SATANTA, KS, p. A245
SAUK PRAIRIE HEALTHCARE, PRAIRIE DU SAC, WI, p. A701
SAUNDERS MEDICAL CENTER, WAHOO, NE, p. A391
SAVOY MEDICAL CENTER, MAMOU, LA, p. A273
SAYRE MEMORIAL HOSPITAL, SAYRE, OK, p. A506
SCA HOUSTON HOSPITAL FOR SPECIALIZED SURGERY, HOUSTON, TX, p. A613
SCENIC MOUNTAIN MEDICAL CENTER, BIG SPRING, TX, p. A589
SCHEIE EYE INSTITUTE OF THE HOSPITAL OF THE UNIVERSITY OF PENNSYLVANIA, PA (see HOSPITAL OF THE UNIVERSITY OF PENNSYLVANIA), p. A535
SCHEURER HOSPITAL, PIGEON, MI, p. A320
SCHICK SHADEL HOSPITAL, SEATTLE, WA, p. A676
SCHLEICHER COUNTY MEDICAL CENTER, ELDORADO, TX, p. A603
SCHNECK MEDICAL CENTER, SEYMOUR, IN, p. A214
SCHNEIDER REGIONAL MEDICAL CENTER, SAINT THOMAS, VI, p. A717
SCHOOLCRAFT MEMORIAL HOSPITAL, MANISTIQUE, MI, p. A318
SCHUYLER HOSPITAL, MONTOUR FALLS, NY, p. A430
SCHWAB REHABILITATION HOSPITAL, CHICAGO, IL, p. A179
SCOTLAND COUNTY HOSPITAL, MEMPHIS, MO, p. A364
SCOTLAND COUNTY HOSPITAL, MO (see SCOTLAND COUNTY MEMORIAL HOSPITAL), p. A364
SCOTLAND COUNTY MEMORIAL HOSPITAL, MEMPHIS, MO, p. A364
SCOTLAND HEALTH CARE SYSTEM, LAURINBURG, NC, p. A456
SCOTT & WHITE HOSPITAL - BRENHAM, BRENHAM, TX, p. A590
SCOTT & WHITE HOSPITAL - COLLEGE STATION, COLLEGE STATION, TX, p. A593
SCOTT & WHITE MEDICAL CENTER - TEMPLE, TEMPLE, TX, p. A638
SCOTT & WHITE MEDICAL CENTER - TEMPLE, TEMPLE, TX (see MCLANE CHILDREN'S HOSPITAL SCOTT & WHITE), p. A638
SCOTT COUNTY HOSPITAL, SCOTT CITY, KS, p. A245

SEVEN RIVERS REGIONAL MEDICAL CENTER, CRYSTAL RIVER, FL, p. A120
SEVIER VALLEY HOSPITAL, RICHFIELD, UT, p. A649
SEWICKLEY VALLEY HOSPITAL, (A DIVISION OF VALLEY MEDICAL FACILITIES), SEWICKLEY, PA, p. A541
SEYMOUR HOSPITAL, SEYMOUR, TX, p. A635
SHADOW MOUNTAIN BEHAVIORAL HEALTH SYSTEM, TULSA, OK, p. A509
SHAMROCK GENERAL HOSPITAL, SHAMROCK, TX, p. A635
SHANDS LAKE SHORE REGIONAL MEDICAL CENTER, LAKE CITY, FL, p. A127
SHANDS LIVE OAK REGIONAL MEDICAL CENTER, LIVE OAK, FL, p. A128
SHANDS STARKE, STARKE, FL, p. A139
SHANDS STARKE REGIONAL MEDICAL CENTER, STARKE, FL, p. A139
SHANDS STARKE REGIONAL MEDICAL CENTER, FL (see SHANDS STARKE), p. A139
SHANNON MEDICAL CENTER, SAN ANGELO, TX, p. A632
SHANNON MEDICAL CENTER- ST. JOHN'S CAMPUS, TX (see SHANNON MEDICAL CENTER), p. A632
SHARE MEDICAL CENTER, ALVA, OK, p. A495
SHARKEY-ISSAQUENA COMMUNITY HOSPITAL, ROLLING FORK, MS, p. A353
SHARON HOSPITAL, SHARON, CT, p. A110
SHARON REGIONAL MEDICAL CENTER, SHARON, PA, p. A541
SHARP CHULA VISTA MEDICAL CENTER, CHULA VISTA, CA, p. A54
SHARP CORONADO HOSPITAL AND HEALTHCARE CENTER, CORONADO, CA, p. A55
SHARP GROSSMONT HOSPITAL, LA MESA, CA, p. A63
SHARP MCDONALD CENTER, CA (see SHARP MESA VISTA HOSPITAL), p. A84
SHARP MEMORIAL HOSPITAL, SAN DIEGO, CA, p. A84
SHARP MESA VISTA HOSPITAL, SAN DIEGO, CA, p. A84
SHASTA REGIONAL MEDICAL CENTER, REDDING, CA, p. A80
SHAWNEE MISSION MEDICAL CENTER, SHAWNEE MISSION, KS, p. A246
SHELBY BAPTIST MEDICAL CENTER, ALABASTER, AL, p. A13
SHELTERING ARMS HOSPITAL SOUTH, MIDLOTHIAN, VA, p. A661
SHELTERING ARMS REHABILITATION HOSPITAL, MECHANICSVILLE, VA, p. A661
SHENANDOAH MEDICAL CENTER, SHENANDOAH, IA, p. A229
SHENANGO VALLEY CAMPUS, FARRELL, PA, p. A526
SHENANGO VALLEY CAMPUS, PA (see UPMC HORIZON), p. A526
SHEPHERD CENTER, ATLANTA, GA, p. A147
SHEPPARD PRATT HEALTH SYSTEM, BALTIMORE, MD, p. A289
SHERIDAN COMMUNITY HOSPITAL, SHERIDAN, MI, p. A323
SHERIDAN COUNTY HEALTH COMPLEX, HOXIE, KS, p. A237
SHERIDAN MEMORIAL HOSPITAL, PLENTYWOOD, MT, p. A378
SHERIDAN MEMORIAL HOSPITAL, SHERIDAN, WY, p. A709
SHERIDAN VETERANS AFFAIRS MEDICAL CENTER, SHERIDAN, WY, p. A709
SHERMAN HOSPITAL, ELGIN, IL, p. A182
SHERMAN OAKS HOSPITAL, LOS ANGELES, CA, p. A69
SHIRLEY RYAN ABILITYLAB, CHICAGO, IL, p. A179
SHOALS HOSPITAL, MUSCLE SHOALS, AL, p. A22
SHODAIR CHILDREN'S HOSPITAL, HELENA, MT, p. A376
SHORE MEDICAL CENTER, SOMERS POINT, NJ, p. A411
SHORE MEMORIAL HOSPITAL, ONANCOKE, VA, p. A663
SHOSHONE MEDICAL CENTER, KELLOGG, ID, p. A169
SHRINERS HOSPITALS FOR CHILDREN-BOSTON, BOSTON, MA, p. A297
SHRINERS HOSPITALS FOR CHILDREN-CHICAGO, CHICAGO, IL, p. A179
SHRINERS HOSPITALS FOR CHILDREN - CINCINNATI, CINCINNATI, OH, p. A475
SHRINERS HOSPITALS FOR CHILDREN-GALVESTON, GALVESTON, TX, p. A606
SHRINERS HOSPITALS FOR CHILDREN-GREENVILLE, GREENVILLE, SC, p. A554
SHRINERS HOSPITALS FOR CHILDREN-HONOLULU, HONOLULU, HI, p. A165
SHRINERS HOSPITALS FOR CHILDREN-HOUSTON, HOUSTON, TX, p. A613
SHRINERS HOSPITALS FOR CHILDREN-NORTHERN CALIFORNIA, SACRAMENTO, CA, p. A82
SHRINERS HOSPITALS FOR CHILDREN-PHILADELPHIA, PHILADELPHIA, PA, p. A536
SHRINERS HOSPITALS FOR CHILDREN-PORTLAND, PORTLAND, OR, p. A516
SHRINERS HOSPITALS FOR CHILDREN-SALT LAKE CITY, SALT LAKE CITY, UT, p. A650
SHRINERS HOSPITALS FOR CHILDREN-SHREVEPORT, SHREVEPORT, LA, p. A279

SHRINERS HOSPITALS FOR CHILDREN-SPOKANE, SPOKANE, WA, p. A678
SHRINERS HOSPITALS FOR CHILDREN-SPRINGFIELD, SPRINGFIELD, MA, p. A304
SHRINERS HOSPITALS FOR CHILDREN-ST. LOUIS, SAINT LOUIS, MO, p. A368
SHRINERS HOSPITALS FOR CHILDREN-TAMPA, TAMPA, FL, p. A141
SHRINERS HOSPITALS FOR CHILDREN-TWIN CITIES, MINNEAPOLIS, MN, p. A335
SIBLEY MEMORIAL HOSPITAL, WASHINGTON, DC, p. A116
SIDNEY HEALTH CENTER, SIDNEY, MT, p. A379
SIDNEY REGIONAL MEDICAL CENTER, SIDNEY, NE, p. A390
SIERRA NEVADA MEMORIAL HOSPITAL, GRASS VALLEY, CA, p. A61
SIERRA SURGERY HOSPITAL, NV (see CARSON TAHOE HEALTH), p. A392
SIERRA TUCSON, TUCSON, AZ, p. A37
SIERRA VIEW MEDICAL CENTER, PORTERVILLE, CA, p. A79
SIERRA VISTA HOSPITAL, SACRAMENTO, CA, p. A82
SIERRA VISTA HOSPITAL, TRUTH OR CONSEQUENCES, NM, p. A420
SIERRA VISTA REGIONAL MEDICAL CENTER, SAN LUIS OBISPO, CA, p. A87
SIGNATURE HEALTHCARE BROCKTON HOSPITAL, BROCKTON, MA, p. A298
SIGNATURE PSYCHIATRIC HOSPITAL, KANSAS CITY, MO, p. A362
SILOAM SPRINGS REGIONAL HOSPITAL, SILOAM SPRINGS-Benton County, AR, p. A48
SILVER CROSS HOSPITAL, NEW LENOX, IL, p. A191
SILVER HILL HOSPITAL, NEW CANAAN, CT, p. A109
SILVER LAKE MEDICAL CENTER, LOS ANGELES, CA, p. A69
SILVER LAKE MEDICAL CENTER-INGLESIDE HOSPITAL, CA (see SILVER LAKE MEDICAL CENTER), p. A69
SIMI VALLEY HOSPITAL, SIMI VALLEY, CA, p. A90
SIMPSON GENERAL HOSPITAL, MENDENHALL, MS, p. A350
SINAI CHILDREN'S HOSPITAL, IL (see MOUNT SINAI HOSPITAL), p. A178
SINAI HOSPITAL OF BALTIMORE, BALTIMORE, MD, p. A289
SINGING RIVER HEALTH SYSTEM, PASCAGOULA, MS, p. A351
SINGING RIVER HEALTH SYSTEM, PASCAGOULA, MS (see OCEAN SPRINGS HOSPITAL), p. A351
SINGING RIVER HOSPITAL, MS (see SINGING RIVER HEALTH SYSTEM), p. A351
SIOUX CENTER HEALTH, SIOUX CENTER, IA, p. A229
SIOUX FALLS SPECIALTY HOSPITAL, SIOUX FALLS, SD, p. A564
SIOUX FALLS VETERANS AFFAIRS HEALTH CARE SYSTEM, SIOUX FALLS, SD, p. A564
SIOUXLAND SURGERY CENTER, DAKOTA DUNES, SD, p. A560
SISKIN HOSPITAL FOR PHYSICAL REHABILITATION, CHATTANOOGA, TN, p. A567
SISTER EMMANUEL HOSPITAL, MIAMI, FL, p. A131
SISTER KENNY REHABILITATION INSTITUTE, MINNEAPOLIS, MN, p. A335
SISTER KENNY REHABILITATION INSTITUTE, MN (see ABBOTT NORTHWESTERN HOSPITAL), p. A335
SISTERS OF CHARITY HOSPITAL OF BUFFALO, BUFFALO, NY, p. A424
SISTERSVILLE GENERAL HOSPITAL, SISTERSVILLE, WV, p. A687
SITKA COMMUNITY HOSPITAL, SITKA, AK, p. A27
SKAGIT REGIONAL HEALTH, MOUNT VERNON, WA, p. A674
SKIFF MEDICAL CENTER, NEWTON, IA, p. A227
SKY LAKES MEDICAL CENTER, KLAMATH FALLS, OR, p. A514
SKY RIDGE MEDICAL CENTER, LONE TREE, CO, p. A103
SKYLINE HOSPITAL, WHITE SALMON, WA, p. A680
SKYRIDGE MEDICAL CENTER - WESTSIDE CAMPUS, TN (see TENNOVA HEALTHCARE - CLEVELAND), p. A568
SLEEPY EYE MEDICAL CENTER, SLEEPY EYE, MN, p. A340
SLIDELL MEMORIAL HOSPITAL, SLIDELL, LA, p. A279
SMDC MEDICAL CENTER, DULUTH, MN, p. A330
SMITH COUNTY MEMORIAL HOSPITAL, SMITH CENTER, KS, p. A246
SMITH NORTHVIEW HOSPITAL, GA (see SOUTH GEORGIA MEDICAL CENTER), p. A162
SMOKEY POINT BEHAVIORAL HOSPITAL, MARYSVILLE, WA, p. A673
SMYTH COUNTY COMMUNITY HOSPITAL, MARION, VA, p. A661
SNOQUALMIE VALLEY HOSPITAL DISTRICT, SNOQUALMIE, WA, p. A677
SNOWDEN AT FREDERICKSBURG, VA (see MARY WASHINGTON HOSPITAL), p. A658
SOCORRO GENERAL HOSPITAL, SOCORRO, NM, p. A420
SOIN MEDICAL CENTER, BEAVERCREEK, OH, p. A472
SOLARA HOSPITAL - BROWNSVILLE CAMPUS, TX (see SOLARA HOSPITAL HARLINGEN), p. A609

SOLARA HOSPITAL HARLINGEN, HARLINGEN, TX, p. A609
SOLARA HOSPITAL MCALLEN, MCALLEN, TX, p. A623
SOLDIERS AND SAILORS MEMORIAL HOSPITAL OF YATES COUNTY, PENN YAN, NY, p. A440
SOMERSET HOSPITAL, SOMERSET, PA, p. A541
SOMERVILLE HOSPITAL, SOMERVILLE, MA, p. A304
SOMERVILLE HOSPITAL, MA (see CAMBRIDGE HEALTH ALLIANCE), p. A298
SONOMA DEVELOPMENTAL CENTER, ELDRIDGE, CA, p. A57
SONOMA VALLEY HOSPITAL, SONOMA, CA, p. A90
SONOMA WEST MEDICAL CENTER, SEBASTOPOL, CA, p. A89
SONORA BEHAVIORAL HEALTH HOSPITAL, TUCSON, AZ, p. A38
SOUTH BALDWIN REGIONAL MEDICAL CENTER, FOLEY, AL, p. A18
SOUTH BATON ROUGE REHABILITATION HOSPITAL, GONZALES, LA, p. A267
SOUTH BAY HOSPITAL, SUN CITY CENTER, FL, p. A140
SOUTH BEACH PSYCHIATRIC CENTER, NEW YORK (Includes all hospitals located within the five boroughs), NY, p. A437
SOUTH BIG HORN COUNTY HOSPITAL, BASIN, WY, p. A707
SOUTH CAMERON MEMORIAL HOSPITAL, CAMERON, LA, p. A265
SOUTH CAMPUS, CA (see KAWEAH DELTA MEDICAL CENTER), p. A94
SOUTH CAMPUS, CO (see MEDICAL CENTER OF AURORA), p. A96
SOUTH CAROLINA DEPARTMENT OF CORRECTIONS HOSPITAL, COLUMBIA, SC, p. A551
SOUTH CENTRAL KANSAS MEDICAL CENTER, ARKANSAS CITY, KS, p. A232
SOUTH CENTRAL REGIONAL MEDICAL CENTER, LAUREL, MS, p. A349
SOUTH COAST GLOBAL MEDICAL CENTER, SANTA ANA, CA, p. A88
SOUTH COUNTY HOSPITAL, WAKEFIELD, RI, p. A548
SOUTH DAVIS COMMUNITY HOSPITAL, BOUNTIFUL, UT, p. A646
SOUTH FLORIDA BAPTIST HOSPITAL, PLANT CITY, FL, p. A136
SOUTH FLORIDA STATE HOSPITAL, HOLLYWOOD, FL, p. A124
SOUTH GEORGIA MEDICAL CENTER, VALDOSTA, GA, p. A162
SOUTH GEORGIA MEDICAL CENTER BERRIEN CAMPUS, NASHVILLE, GA, p. A158
SOUTH GEORGIA MEDICAL CENTER LANIER CAMPUS, LAKELAND, GA, p. A156
SOUTH HAVEN COMMUNITY HOSPITAL, SOUTH HAVEN, MI, p. A323
SOUTH LAKE HOSPITAL, CLERMONT, FL, p. A120
SOUTH LINCOLN MEDICAL CENTER, KEMMERER, WY, p. A708
SOUTH LYON MEDICAL CENTER, YERINGTON, NV, p. A397
SOUTH MISSISSIPPI COUNTY REGIONAL MEDICAL CENTER, OSCEOLA-Mississippi County, AR, p. A47
SOUTH MISSISSIPPI STATE HOSPITAL, PURVIS, MS, p. A352
SOUTH NASSAU COMMUNITIES HOSPITAL, OCEANSIDE, NY, p. A438
SOUTH OAKS HOSPITAL, AMITYVILLE, NY, p. A421
SOUTH PENINSULA HOSPITAL, HOMER, AK, p. A26
SOUTH POINTE HOSPITAL, WARRENSVILLE HEIGHTS, OH, p. A492
SOUTH SACRAMENTO MEDICAL CENTER, SACRAMENTO, CA, p. A82
SOUTH SHORE HOSPITAL, CHICAGO, IL, p. A179
SOUTH SHORE HOSPITAL, SOUTH WEYMOUTH, MA, p. A304
SOUTH SUNFLOWER COUNTY HOSPITAL, INDIANOLA, MS, p. A347
SOUTH TEXAS BEHAVIORAL HEALTH CENTER, TX (see SOUTH TEXAS HEALTH SYSTEM), p. A601
SOUTH TEXAS HEALTH CARE SYSTEM, TX (see RIO GRANDE STATE CENTER/SOUTH TEXAS HEALTH CARE SYSTEM), p. A608
SOUTH TEXAS HEALTH SYSTEM, EDINBURG, TX, p. A601
SOUTH TEXAS REHABILITATION HOSPITAL, BROWNSVILLE, TX, p. A590
SOUTH TEXAS SPINE AND SURGICAL HOSPITAL, SAN ANTONIO, TX, p. A634
SOUTH TEXAS SURGICAL HOSPITAL, CORPUS CHRISTI, TX, p. A594
SOUTH TEXAS VETERANS HEALTH CARE SYSTEM, SAN ANTONIO, TX, p. A634
SOUTH TEXAS VETERANS HEALTH CARE SYSTEM, SAN ANTONIO, TX (see KERRVILLE DIVISION), p. A617
SOUTHAMPTON MEMORIAL HOSPITAL, FRANKLIN, VA, p. A658
SOUTHCOAST BEHAVIORAL HEALTH, DARTMOUTH, MA, p. A299
SOUTHCOAST HOSPITALS GROUP, FALL RIVER, MA, p. A299

SSM HEALTH SAINT LOUIS UNIVERSITY HOSPITAL-SOUTH, MO (see SSM HEALTH SAINT LOUIS UNIVERSITY HOSPITAL), p. A369
SSM HEALTH ST. ANTHONY HOSPITAL - OKLAHOMA CITY, OKLAHOMA CITY, OK, p. A504
SSM HEALTH ST. ANTHONY HOSPITAL - SHAWNEE, SHAWNEE, OK, p. A506
SSM HEALTH ST. ANTHONY HOSPITAL - SHAWNEE, OK (see UNITY HEALTH CENTER), p. A506
SSM HEALTH ST. ANTHONY SOUTH, OK (see SSM HEALTH ST. ANTHONY HOSPITAL - OKLAHOMA CITY), p. A504
SSM HEALTH ST. CLARE HOSPITAL - FENTON, FENTON, MO, p. A359
SSM HEALTH ST. CLARE HOSPITAL-BARABOO, BARABOO, WI, p. A689
SSM HEALTH ST. FRANCIS HOSPITAL - MARYVILLE, MARYVILLE, MO, p. A364
SSM HEALTH ST. JOSEPH - ST. CHARLES, SAINT CHARLES, MO, p. A367
SSM HEALTH ST. JOSEPH - ST. CHARLES, SAINT CHARLES, MO (see SSM HEALTH ST. JOSEPH - WENTZVILLE), p. A372
SSM HEALTH ST. JOSEPH - WENTZVILLE, WENTZVILLE, MO, p. A372
SSM HEALTH ST. JOSEPH - WENTZVILLE, MO (see SSM HEALTH ST. JOSEPH - ST. CHARLES), p. A367
SSM HEALTH ST. JOSEPH HOSPITAL - LAKE SAINT LOUIS, LAKE SAINT LOUIS, MO, p. A363
SSM HEALTH ST. MARY'S HOSPITAL - AUDRAIN, MEXICO, MO, p. A364
SSM HEALTH ST. MARY'S HOSPITAL - JEFFERSON CITY, JEFFERSON CITY, MO, p. A360
SSM HEALTH ST. MARY'S HOSPITAL - ST. LOUIS, SAINT LOUIS, MO, p. A369
SSM HEALTH ST. MARY'S HOSPITAL, MADISON, WI, p. A696
SSM HEALTH ST. MARY'S HOSPITAL CENTRALIA, CENTRALIA, IL, p. A175
SSM HEALTH ST. MARY'S HOSPITAL JANESVILLE, JANESVILLE, WI, p. A695
SSM SELECT REHABILITATION HOSPITAL, RICHMOND HEIGHTS, MO, p. A366
SSM SELECT REHABILITATION HOSPITAL, MO (see SSM SELECT REHABILITATION HOSPITAL), p. A366
ST LUKE'S HOSPITAL - ALLENTOWN CAMPUS, ALLENTOWN, PA, p. A519
ST LUKE'S HOSPITAL - ALLENTOWN CAMPUS, PA (see ST. LUKE'S UNIVERSITY HOSPITAL - BETHLEHEM CAMPUS), p. A521
ST. AGNES HOSPITAL, FOND DU LAC, WI, p. A692
ST. ALEXIUS HOSPITAL - BROADWAY CAMPUS, SAINT LOUIS, MO, p. A369
ST. ALEXIUS HOSPITAL - FOREST PARK CAMPUS, MO (see ST. ALEXIUS HOSPITAL - BROADWAY CAMPUS), p. A369
ST. ALOISIUS MEDICAL CENTER, HARVEY, ND, p. A466
ST. ANDREW'S HEALTH CENTER, BOTTINEAU, ND, p. A464
ST. ANTHONY COMMUNITY HOSPITAL, WARWICK, NY, p. A445
ST. ANTHONY HOSPITAL, GIG HARBOR, WA, p. A672
ST. ANTHONY HOSPITAL, LAKEWOOD, CO, p. A103
ST. ANTHONY MEDICAL CENTER, CROWN POINT, IN, p. A202
ST. ANTHONY NORTH HEALTH CAMPUS, WESTMINSTER, CO, p. A106
ST. ANTHONY REGIONAL HOSPITAL, CARROLL, IA, p. A218
ST. ANTHONY SUMMIT MEDICAL CENTER, FRISCO, CO, p. A100
ST. ANTHONY'S HOSPITAL, SAINT PETERSBURG, FL, p. A138
ST. ANTHONY'S MEDICAL CENTER, MORRILTON-Conway County, AR, p. A46
ST. ANTHONY'S MERCY, SAINT LOUIS, MO, p. A369
ST. ANTHONY'S REHABILITATION HOSPITAL, LAUDERDALE LAKES, FL, p. A128
ST. BARNABAS HOSPITAL, NEW YORK (Includes all hospitals located within the five boroughs), NY, p. A437
ST. BERNARD HOSPITAL AND HEALTH CARE CENTER, CHICAGO, IL, p. A179
ST. BERNARD PARISH HOSPITAL, CHALMETTE, LA, p. A265
ST. BERNARDINE MEDICAL CENTER, SAN BERNARDINO, CA, p. A83
ST. BERNARDS MEDICAL CENTER, JONESBORO-Craighead County, AR, p. A44
ST. CATHERINE HOSPITAL, EAST CHICAGO, IN, p. A202
ST. CATHERINE HOSPITAL, GARDEN CITY, KS, p. A235
ST. CATHERINE MEMORIAL HOSPITAL, NEW ORLEANS, LA, p. A276
ST. CATHERINE OF SIENA MEDICAL CENTER, SMITHTOWN, NY, p. A443
ST. CATHERINE'S REHABILITATION HOSPITAL, NORTH MIAMI, FL, p. A132
ST. CHARLES BEND, BEND, OR, p. A511
ST. CHARLES HOSPITAL, PORT JEFFERSON, NY, p. A440
ST. CHARLES MADRAS, MADRAS, OR, p. A514

ST. CHARLES MERCY HOSPITAL, OREGON, OH, p. A488
ST. CHARLES PARISH HOSPITAL, LULING, LA, p. A273
ST. CHARLES PRINEVILLE, PRINEVILLE, OR, p. A517
ST. CHARLES REDMOND, REDMOND, OR, p. A517
ST. CHARLES SURGICAL HOSPITAL, NEW ORLEANS, LA, p. A276
ST. CHRISTOPHER'S HOSPITAL FOR CHILDREN, PHILADELPHIA, PA, p. A536
ST. CLAIR HOSPITAL, PITTSBURGH, PA, p. A537
ST. CLAIRE HEALTHCARE, MOREHEAD, KY, p. A258
ST. CLARE HOSPITAL, LAKEWOOD, WA, p. A673
ST. CLARE MEDICAL CENTER, CRAWFORDSVILLE, IN, p. A202
ST. CLOUD HOSPITAL, SAINT CLOUD, MN, p. A338
ST. CLOUD REGIONAL MEDICAL CENTER, SAINT CLOUD, FL, p. A138
ST. CLOUD VETERANS AFFAIRS HEALTH CARE SYSTEM, SAINT CLOUD, MN, p. A339
ST. CLOUD VETERANS AFFAIRS HEALTH CARE SYSTEM, MN (see VETERANS AFFAIRS MEDICAL CENTER), p. A339
ST. CROIX REGIONAL MEDICAL CENTER, ST CROIX FALLS, WI, p. A703
ST. DAVID'S GEORGETOWN HOSPITAL, TX (see ST. DAVID'S MEDICAL CENTER), p. A586
ST. DAVID'S MEDICAL CENTER, AUSTIN, TX, p. A586
ST. DAVID'S NORTH AUSTIN MEDICAL CENTER, AUSTIN, TX, p. A586
ST. DAVID'S REHABILITATION CENTER, TX (see ST. DAVID'S MEDICAL CENTER), p. A586
ST. DAVID'S ROUND ROCK MEDICAL CENTER, ROUND ROCK, TX, p. A631
ST. DAVID'S SOUTH AUSTIN MEDICAL CENTER, AUSTIN, TX, p. A587
ST. DOMINIC-JACKSON MEMORIAL HOSPITAL, JACKSON, MS, p. A348
ST. ELIAS SPECIALTY HOSPITAL, ANCHORAGE, AK, p. A25
ST. ELIZABETH CENTRAL, LAFAYETTE, IN, p. A209
ST. ELIZABETH COMMUNITY HOSPITAL, RED BLUFF, CA, p. A79
ST. ELIZABETH COVINGTON, KY (see ST. ELIZABETH EDGEWOOD), p. A251
ST. ELIZABETH COVINGTON, KY (see ST. ELIZABETH MEDICAL CENTER-NORTH), p. A251
ST. ELIZABETH EDGEWOOD, EDGEWOOD, KY, p. A251
ST. ELIZABETH EDGEWOOD, KY (see ST. ELIZABETH HEALTHCARE-EDGEWOOD), p. A251
ST. ELIZABETH FALMOUTH, KY (see ST. ELIZABETH FORT THOMAS), p. A252
ST. ELIZABETH FLORENCE, FLORENCE, KY, p. A252
ST. ELIZABETH FLORENCE, KY (see ST. ELIZABETH HEALTHCARE FLORENCE), p. A252
ST. ELIZABETH FORT THOMAS, FORT THOMAS, KY, p. A252
ST. ELIZABETH FORT THOMAS, KY (see ST. ELIZABETH HEALTHCARE FORT THOMAS), p. A252
ST. ELIZABETH GRANT, WILLIAMSTOWN, KY, p. A261
ST. ELIZABETH GRANT, KY (see ST. ELIZABETH MEDICAL CENTER-GRANT COUNTY), p. A261
ST. ELIZABETH HEALTH SERVICES, BAKER CITY, OR, p. A511
ST. ELIZABETH HEALTHCARE FLORENCE, FLORENCE, KY, p. A252
ST. ELIZABETH HEALTHCARE FORT THOMAS, FORT THOMAS, KY, p. A252
ST. ELIZABETH HEALTHCARE-EDGEWOOD, EDGEWOOD, KY, p. A251
ST. ELIZABETH HOSPITAL, ENUMCLAW, WA, p. A671
ST. ELIZABETH HOSPITAL, GONZALES, LA, p. A268
ST. ELIZABETH MEDICAL CENTER, UTICA, NY, p. A444
ST. ELIZABETH MEDICAL CENTER-GRANT COUNTY, WILLIAMSTOWN, KY, p. A261
ST. ELIZABETH MEDICAL CENTER-NORTH, COVINGTON, KY, p. A251
ST. ELIZABETH'S MEDICAL CENTER, BRIGHTON, MA, p. A297
ST. ELIZABETH'S MEDICAL CENTER, MA (see CARITAS ST. ELIZABETH'S MEDICAL CENTER), p. A297
ST. FRANCIS CAMPUS, KS (see VIA CHRISTI HOSPITAL ON ST. FRANCIS), p. A248
ST. FRANCIS EASTSIDE, SC (see BON SECOURS ST. FRANCIS HEALTH SYSTEM), p. A553
ST. FRANCIS HOSPITAL, COLUMBUS, GA, p. A151
ST. FRANCIS HOSPITAL, FEDERAL WAY, WA, p. A672
ST. FRANCIS HOSPITAL, WILMINGTON, DE, p. A114
ST. FRANCIS HOSPITAL AND HEALTH CENTERS - SOUTH CAMPUS, INDIANAPOLIS, IN, p. A207
ST. FRANCIS HOSPITAL, COLUMBUS, GA (see BRADLEY CENTER OF ST. FRANCIS), p. A150
ST. FRANCIS HOSPITAL, THE HEART CENTER, ROSLYN, NY, p. A442
ST. FRANCIS HOSPITAL-MOORESVILLE, MOORESVILLE, IN, p. A211
ST. FRANCIS MEDICAL CENTER, LYNWOOD, CA, p. A70

ST. FRANCIS MEDICAL CENTER, MONROE, LA, p. A274
ST. FRANCIS MEDICAL CENTER, TRENTON, NJ, p. A413
ST. FRANCIS MEDICAL CENTER, CO (see PENROSE-ST. FRANCIS HEALTH SERVICES), p. A98
ST. FRANCIS MEDICAL PLAZA, NE (see CHI HEALTH SAINT FRANCIS), p. A384
ST. FRANCIS MEMORIAL HOSPITAL, WEST POINT, NE, p. A391
ST. FRANCIS REGIONAL MEDICAL CENTER, SHAKOPEE, MN, p. A340
ST. FRANCIS SPECIALTY HOSPITAL, MONROE, LA, p. A274
ST. HELENA PARISH HOSPITAL, GREENSBURG, LA, p. A268
ST. JAMES BEHAVIORAL HEALTH HOSPITAL, GONZALES, LA, p. A268
ST. JAMES HEALTHCARE, BUTTE, MT, p. A374
ST. JAMES HOSPITAL AND HEALTH CENTERS - CHICAGO HEIGHTS CAMPUS, CHICAGO HEIGHTS, IL, p. A180
ST. JAMES HOSPITAL AND HEALTH CENTERS - CHICAGO HEIGHTS CAMPUS, IL (see FRANCISCAN HEALTH OLYMPIA FIELDS), p. A192
ST. JAMES HOSPITAL AND HEALTH CENTERS, OLYMPIA FIELDS, IL, p. A192
ST. JAMES MERCY HOSPITAL, HORNELL, NY, p. A427
ST. JAMES PARISH HOSPITAL, LUTCHER, LA, p. A273
ST. JOHN BROKEN ARROW, BROKEN ARROW, OK, p. A496
ST. JOHN MACOMB-OAKLAND HOSPITAL, WARREN, MI, p. A325
ST. JOHN MACOMB-OAKLAND HOSPITAL, MADISON HEIGHTS CAMPUS, MI (see ST. JOHN MACOMB-OAKLAND HOSPITAL), p. A325
ST. JOHN MACOMB-OAKLAND HOSPITAL, WARREN CAMPUS, MI (see ST. JOHN MACOMB-OAKLAND HOSPITAL), p. A325
ST. JOHN MEDICAL CENTER, TULSA, OK, p. A509
ST. JOHN MEDICAL CENTER, WESTLAKE, OH, p. A493
ST. JOHN MEDICAL CENTER, OH (see ST. JOHN WEST SHORE HOSPITAL), p. A493
ST. JOHN OWASSO, OWASSO, OK, p. A505
ST. JOHN REHABILITATION HOSPITAL, BROKEN ARROW, OK, p. A496
ST. JOHN RIVER DISTRICT HOSPITAL, EAST CHINA, MI, p. A312
ST. JOHN SAPULPA, SAPULPA, OK, p. A506
ST. JOHN VIANNEY HOSPITAL, DOWNINGTOWN, PA, p. A524
ST. JOHN WEST SHORE HOSPITAL, WESTLAKE, OH, p. A493
ST. JOHN'S CHILDREN'S HOSPITAL, IL (see HSHS ST. JOHN'S HOSPITAL), p. A196
ST. JOHN'S EPISCOPAL HOSPITAL-SOUTH SHORE, NEW YORK (Includes all hospitals located within the five boroughs), NY, p. A437
ST. JOHN'S HOSPITAL, MAPLEWOOD, MN, p. A334
ST. JOHN'S MEDICAL CENTER AND LIVING CENTER, JACKSON, WY, p. A708
ST. JOHN'S MERCY CHILDREN'S HOSPITAL, SAINT LOUIS, MO, p. A369
ST. JOHN'S MERCY MEDICAL CENTER, SAINT LOUIS, MO, p. A369
ST. JOHN'S PLEASANT VALLEY HOSPITAL, CAMARILLO, CA, p. A53
ST. JOHN'S REGIONAL MEDICAL CENTER, OXNARD, CA, p. A77
ST. JOHN'S REHABILITATION CENTER, MO (see MERCY HOSPITAL JOPLIN), p. A361
ST. JOHN'S RIVERSIDE HOSPITAL - DOBBS FERRY PAVILION, NY (see ST. JOHN'S RIVERSIDE HOSPITAL), p. A446
ST. JOHN'S RIVERSIDE HOSPITAL - PARK CARE PAVILION, NY (see ST. JOHN'S RIVERSIDE HOSPITAL), p. A446
ST. JOHN'S RIVERSIDE HOSPITAL, YONKERS, NY, p. A446
ST. JOHN'S RIVERSIDE HOSPITAL, YONKERS, NY (see ANDRUS PAVILION), p. A446
ST. JOSEPH CAMPUS, KS (see VIA CHRISTI HOSPITAL ON ST. FRANCIS), p. A248
ST. JOSEPH HEALTH SERVICES OF RHODE ISLAND, NORTH PROVIDENCE, RI, p. A547
ST. JOSEPH HEALTH SERVICES OF RHODE ISLAND, NORTH PROVIDENCE, RI (see ST. JOSEPH HOSPITAL FOR SPECIALTY CARE), p. A548
ST. JOSEPH HEALTH SYSTEM, TAWAS CITY, MI, p. A324
ST. JOSEPH HOSPITAL, BANGOR, ME, p. A282
ST. JOSEPH HOSPITAL, BELLINGHAM, WA, p. A669
ST. JOSEPH HOSPITAL, BETHPAGE, NY, p. A422
ST. JOSEPH HOSPITAL, EUREKA, CA, p. A57
ST. JOSEPH HOSPITAL, FORT WAYNE, IN, p. A204
ST. JOSEPH HOSPITAL, NASHUA, NH, p. A400
ST. JOSEPH HOSPITAL, ORANGE, CA, p. A76
ST. JOSEPH HOSPITAL, NY (see SISTERS OF CHARITY HOSPITAL OF BUFFALO), p. A424
ST. JOSEPH HOSPITAL FOR SPECIALTY CARE, PROVIDENCE, RI, p. A548
ST. JOSEPH HOSPITAL FOR SPECIALTY CARE, RI (see ST. JOSEPH HEALTH SERVICES OF RHODE ISLAND), p. A547

T

THEDACARE MEDICAL CENTER-WAUPACA, WAUPACA, WI, p. A705

THEDACARE REGIONAL MEDICAL CENTER-APPLETON, APPLETON, WI, p. A689

THEDACARE REGIONAL MEDICAL CENTER-NEENAH, NEENAH, WI, p. A699

THIBODAUX REGIONAL MEDICAL CENTER, THIBODAUX, LA, p. A280

THOMAS B. FINAN CENTER, CUMBERLAND, MD, p. A291

THOMAS H. BOYD MEMORIAL HOSPITAL, CARROLLTON, IL, p. A175

THOMAS HOSPITAL, FAIRHOPE, AL, p. A17

THOMAS JEFFERSON UNIVERSITY HOSPITALS, PHILADELPHIA, PA, p. A536

THOMAS JEFFERSON UNIVERSITY HOSPITALS, PHILADELPHIA, PA (see JEFFERSON METHODIST HOSPITAL), p. A535

THOMAS MEMORIAL HOSPITAL, SOUTH CHARLESTON, WV, p. A687

THOMPSON HEALTH, CANANDAIGUA, NY, p. A424

THOREK MEMORIAL HOSPITAL, CHICAGO, IL, p. A180

THORNTON HOSPITAL, CA (see UC SAN DIEGO HEALTH), p. A84

THOUSAND OAKS SURGICAL HOSPITAL, CA (see LOS ROBLES HOSPITAL AND MEDICAL CENTER), p. A91

THREE GABLES SURGERY CENTER, PROCTORVILLE, OH, p. A489

THREE RIVERS BEHAVIORAL HEALTH, WEST COLUMBIA, SC, p. A558

THREE RIVERS HEALTH, THREE RIVERS, MI, p. A324

THREE RIVERS HOSPITAL, BREWSTER, WA, p. A670

THREE RIVERS HOSPITAL, WAVERLY, TN, p. A580

THREE RIVERS MEDICAL CENTER, LOUISA, KY, p. A255

THROCKMORTON COUNTY MEMORIAL HOSPITAL, THROCKMORTON, TX, p. A640

TIDELANDS GEORGETOWN MEMORIAL HOSPITAL, GEORGETOWN, SC, p. A553

TIDELANDS WACCAMAW COMMUNITY HOSPITAL, MURRELLS INLET, SC, p. A556

TIFT REGIONAL MEDICAL CENTER, TIFTON, GA, p. A162

TILLAMOOK REGIONAL MEDICAL CENTER, TILLAMOOK, OR, p. A518

TIMBERLAWN MENTAL HEALTH SYSTEM, DALLAS, TX, p. A598

TIMPANOGOS REGIONAL HOSPITAL, OREM, UT, p. A649

TIOGA MEDICAL CENTER, TIOGA, ND, p. A468

TIPPAH COUNTY HOSPITAL, RIPLEY, MS, p. A353

TIPTON HOSPITAL, TIPTON, IN, p. A215

TIRR MEMORIAL HERMANN, HOUSTON, TX, p. A614

TITUS REGIONAL MEDICAL CENTER, MOUNT PLEASANT, TX, p. A624

TITUSVILLE AREA HOSPITAL, TITUSVILLE, PA, p. A542

TLC HEALTH NETWORK - LAKE SHORE HOSPITAL, NY (see BROOKS MEMORIAL HOSPITAL), p. A425

TMC BEHAVIORAL HEALTH CENTER, TX (see TEXOMA MEDICAL CENTER), p. A599

TMC BONHAM HOSPITAL, BONHAM, TX, p. A589

TMC FOR CHILDREN, TUCSON, AZ, p. A38

TMC FOR CHILDREN, AZ (see TMC HEALTHCARE), p. A38

TMC HEALTHCARE, TUCSON, AZ, p. A38

TMC HEALTHCARE, TUCSON, AZ (see TMC FOR CHILDREN), p. A38

TOBEY HOSPITAL, WAREHAM, MA, p. A305

TOBEY HOSPITAL, MA (see SOUTHCOAST HOSPITALS GROUP), p. A299

TOLEDO CHILDREN'S HOSPITAL, OH (see PROMEDICA TOLEDO HOSPITAL), p. A491

TOMAH MEMORIAL HOSPITAL, TOMAH, WI, p. A704

TOMBALL REGIONAL MEDICAL CENTER, TOMBALL, TX, p. A640

TOPS SURGICAL SPECIALTY HOSPITAL, HOUSTON, TX, p. A614

TORRANCE MEMORIAL MEDICAL CENTER, TORRANCE, CA, p. A92

TORRANCE STATE HOSPITAL, TORRANCE, PA, p. A542

TOUCHETTE REGIONAL HOSPITAL, CENTREVILLE, IL, p. A175

TOURO INFIRMARY, NEW ORLEANS, LA, p. A276

TOURO REHABILITATION CENTER, LA (see TOURO INFIRMARY), p. A276

TOWNER COUNTY MEDICAL CENTER, CANDO, ND, p. A464

TRACE REGIONAL HOSPITAL, HOUSTON, MS, p. A347

TRADITION MEDICAL CENTER, FL (see MARTIN HEALTH SYSTEM), p. A139

TRANSYLVANIA REGIONAL HOSPITAL, BREVARD, NC, p. A448

TREASURE VALLEY HOSPITAL, BOISE, ID, p. A168

TREGO COUNTY-LEMKE MEMORIAL HOSPITAL, WAKEENEY, KS, p. A247

TRENTON PSYCHIATRIC HOSPITAL, TRENTON, NJ, p. A413

TRI PARISH REHABILITATION HOSPITAL, LEESVILLE, LA, p. A272

TRI VALLEY HEALTH SYSTEM, CAMBRIDGE, NE, p. A382

TRI-CITY MEDICAL CENTER, OCEANSIDE, CA, p. A76

TRI-COUNTY HOSPITAL, WADENA, MN, p. A341

TRI-STATE MEMORIAL HOSPITAL, CLARKSTON, WA, p. A670

TRI-WARD GENERAL HOSPITAL, BERNICE, LA, p. A264

TRIANGLE EAST NURSING CARE CENTER, WILSON, NC, p. A462

TRIANGLE SPRINGS HOSPITAL, RALEIGH, NC, p. A459

TRIDENT MEDICAL CENTER, CHARLESTON, SC, p. A550

TRIGG COUNTY HOSPITAL, CADIZ, KY, p. A250

TRIHEALTH EVENDALE HOSPITAL, CINCINNATI, OH, p. A476

TRIHEALTH REHABILITATION HOSPITAL, CINCINNATI, OH, p. A476

TRINITAS HOSPITAL, NJ (see TRINITAS REGIONAL MEDICAL CENTER), p. A404

TRINITAS REGIONAL MEDICAL CENTER - NEW POINT CAMPUS, NJ (see TRINITAS REGIONAL MEDICAL CENTER), p. A404

TRINITAS REGIONAL MEDICAL CENTER, ELIZABETH, NJ, p. A404

TRINITY HEALTH, MINOT, ND, p. A468

TRINITY HEALTH SYSTEM, STEUBENVILLE, OH, p. A491

TRINITY HOSPITAL, WEAVERVILLE, CA, p. A95

TRINITY HOSPITAL, WOLF POINT, MT, p. A380

TRINITY HOSPITAL TWIN CITY, DENNISON, OH, p. A481

TRINITY HOSPITAL-ST. JOSEPH'S, ND (see TRINITY HEALTH), p. A468

TRINITY MEDICAL CENTER EAST, OH (see TRINITY HEALTH SYSTEM), p. A491

TRINITY MEDICAL CENTER WEST, OH (see TRINITY HEALTH SYSTEM), p. A491

TRINITY SPRINGS PAVILION, TX (see JPS HEALTH NETWORK), p. A604

TRIOS HEALTH, KENNEWICK, WA, p. A672

TRIPLER ARMY MEDICAL CENTER, HONOLULU, HI, p. A165

TRIPOINT MEDICAL CENTER, OH (see LAKE HEALTH), p. A479

TRISTAR ASHLAND CITY MEDICAL CENTER, ASHLAND CITY, TN, p. A566

TRISTAR CENTENNIAL MEDICAL CENTER, NASHVILLE, TN, p. A577

TRISTAR CENTENNIAL MEDICAL CENTER, TN (see CENTENNIAL MEDICAL CENTER), p. A577

TRISTAR CENTENNIAL WOMEN'S & CHILDREN'S, TN (see TRISTAR CENTENNIAL MEDICAL CENTER), p. A577

TRISTAR GREENVIEW REGIONAL HOSPITAL, BOWLING GREEN, KY, p. A250

TRISTAR HENDERSONVILLE MEDICAL CENTER, HENDERSONVILLE, TN, p. A570

TRISTAR HORIZON MEDICAL CENTER, DICKSON, TN, p. A569

TRISTAR SKYLINE MADISON CAMPUS, TN (see TRISTAR SKYLINE MEDICAL CENTER), p. A577

TRISTAR SKYLINE MEDICAL CENTER, NASHVILLE, TN, p. A577

TRISTAR SOUTHERN HILLS MEDICAL CENTER, NASHVILLE, TN, p. A578

TRISTAR STONECREST MEDICAL CENTER, SMYRNA, TN, p. A580

TRISTAR SUMMIT MEDICAL CENTER, HERMITAGE, TN, p. A570

TRIUMPH HOSPITAL - CENTRAL DAKOTAS, MANDAN, ND, p. A467

TRIUMPH HOSPITAL EL PASO, EL PASO, TX, p. A602

TRIUMPH HOSPITAL LIMA, LIMA, OH, p. A485

TRIUMPH HOSPITAL NORTHWEST, HOUSTON, TX, p. A614

TRIUMPH HOSPITAL NORTHWEST INDIANA, HAMMOND, IN, p. A205

TRIUMPH HOSPITAL PHILADELPHIA, PHILADELPHIA, PA, p. A536

TRIUMPH HOSPITAL SOUTHWEST, SUGAR LAND, TX, p. A637

TROUSDALE MEDICAL CENTER, HARTSVILLE, TN, p. A570

TROY COMMUNITY HOSPITAL, TROY, PA, p. A542

TROY REGIONAL MEDICAL CENTER, TROY, AL, p. A23

TRUMAN MEDICAL CENTER-HOSPITAL HILL, KANSAS CITY, MO, p. A362

TRUMAN MEDICAL CENTER-LAKEWOOD, KANSAS CITY, MO, p. A362

TRUMBULL MEMORIAL HOSPITAL, WARREN, OH, p. A492

TRUSTPOINT HOSPITAL, MURFREESBORO, TN, p. A576

TRUSTPOINT REHABILITATION HOSPITAL OF LUBBOCK, LUBBOCK, TX, p. A621

TSEHOOTSOOI MEDICAL CENTER, FORT DEFIANCE, AZ, p. A29

TUALITY COMMUNITY HOSPITAL, OR (see TUALITY HEALTHCARE), p. A513

TUALITY FOREST GROVE HOSPITAL, FOREST GROVE, OR, p. A513

TUALITY FOREST GROVE HOSPITAL, OR (see TUALITY HEALTHCARE), p. A513

TUALITY HEALTHCARE, HILLSBORO, OR, p. A513

TUALITY HEALTHCARE, HILLSBORO, OR (see TUALITY FOREST GROVE HOSPITAL), p. A513

TUBA CITY REGIONAL HEALTH CARE CORPORATION, TUBA CITY, AZ, p. A36

TUFTS MEDICAL CENTER, BOSTON, MA, p. A297

TUG VALLEY ARH REGIONAL MEDICAL CENTER, SOUTH WILLIAMSON, KY, p. A260

TULANE HEALTH SYSTEM, NEW ORLEANS, LA, p. A276

TULANE-LAKESIDE HOSPITAL, LA (see TULANE HEALTH SYSTEM), p. A276

TULSA SPINE AND SPECIALTY HOSPITAL, TULSA, OK, p. A509

TURNING POINT HOSPITAL, MOULTRIE, GA, p. A158

TURQUOISE LODGE HOSPITAL, ALBUQUERQUE, NM, p. A416

TUSCALOOSA VETERANS AFFAIRS MEDICAL CENTER, TUSCALOOSA, AL, p. A24

TUSKEGEE DIVISION, TUSKEGEE, AL, p. A24

TUSKEGEE DIVISION, AL (see CENTRAL ALABAMA VETERANS HEALTH CARE SYSTEM), p. A21

TWIN CITIES COMMUNITY HOSPITAL, TEMPLETON, CA, p. A91

TWIN CITIES HOSPITAL, NICEVILLE, FL, p. A132

TWIN COUNTY REGIONAL HEALTHCARE, GALAX, VA, p. A658

TWIN LAKES REGIONAL MEDICAL CENTER, LEITCHFIELD, KY, p. A254

TWIN VALLEY BEHAVIORAL HEALTHCARE, COLUMBUS, OH, p. A479

TWO RIVERS BEHAVIORAL HEALTH SYSTEM, KANSAS CITY, MO, p. A362

TYLER CONTINUECARE HOSPITAL, TYLER, TX, p. A641

TYLER COUNTY HOSPITAL, WOODVILLE, TX, p. A645

TYLER HOLMES MEMORIAL HOSPITAL, WINONA, MS, p. A354

TYLER MEMORIAL HOSPITAL, TUNKHANNOCK, PA, p. A542

TYRONE HOSPITAL, TYRONE, PA, p. A542

U

U.S. AIR FORCE HOSPITAL, HAMPTON, VA, p. A659

U.S. AIR FORCE MEDICAL CENTER KEESLER, KEESLER AFB, MS, p. A348

U.S. AIR FORCE REGIONAL HOSPITAL, EGLIN AFB, FL, p. A122

U.S. AIR FORCE REGIONAL HOSPITAL, ELMENDORF AFB, AK, p. A26

U.S. NAVAL HOSPITAL GUAM, AGANA, GU, p. A711

U.S. PENITENTIARY INFIRMARY, LEWISBURG, PA, p. A530

U.S. PUBLIC HEALTH SERVICE INDIAN HOSPITAL, CASS LAKE, MN, p. A329

U.S. PUBLIC HEALTH SERVICE INDIAN HOSPITAL, CROWNPOINT, NM, p. A416

U.S. PUBLIC HEALTH SERVICE INDIAN HOSPITAL, EAGLE BUTTE, SD, p. A560

U.S. PUBLIC HEALTH SERVICE INDIAN HOSPITAL, PARKER, AZ, p. A32

U.S. PUBLIC HEALTH SERVICE INDIAN HOSPITAL, PINE RIDGE, SD, p. A562

U.S. PUBLIC HEALTH SERVICE INDIAN HOSPITAL, ROSEBUD, SD, p. A563

U.S. PUBLIC HEALTH SERVICE INDIAN HOSPITAL, WINNEBAGO, NE, p. A391

U.S. PUBLIC HEALTH SERVICE INDIAN HOSPITAL, ZUNI, NM, p. A420

U.S. PUBLIC HEALTH SERVICE INDIAN HOSPITAL-SELLS, SELLS, AZ, p. A36

U.S. PUBLIC HEALTH SERVICE INDIAN HOSPITAL-WHITERIVER, WHITERIVER, AZ, p. A38

U.S. PUBLIC HEALTH SERVICE PHOENIX INDIAN MEDICAL CENTER, PHOENIX, AZ, p. A34

UAB HIGHLANDS, BIRMINGHAM, AL, p. A15

UAB HIGHLANDS, AL (see UNIVERSITY OF ALABAMA HOSPITAL), p. A15

UAMS MEDICAL CENTER, LITTLE ROCK-Pulaski County, AR, p. A45

UC IRVINE MEDICAL CENTER, ORANGE, CA, p. A76

UC SAN DIEGO HEALTH, SAN DIEGO, CA, p. A84

UC SAN DIEGO HEALTH, CA (see UNIVERSITY OF CALIFORNIA SAN DIEGO MEDICAL CENTER), p. A84

UC SAN DIEGO SHILEY EYE INSTITUTE, CA (see UC SAN DIEGO HEALTH), p. A84

UCHEALTH BROOMFIELD HOSPITAL, BROOMFIELD, CO, p. A97

UCHEALTH GRANDVIEW HOSPITAL, COLORADO SPRINGS, CO, p. A98

UCHEALTH MEDICAL CENTER OF THE ROCKIES, LOVELAND, CO, p. A104

V

WASHINGTON COUNTY HOSPITAL, WASHINGTON, KS, p. A247
WASHINGTON COUNTY HOSPITAL AND CLINICS, WASHINGTON, IA, p. A230
WASHINGTON COUNTY MEMORIAL HOSPITAL, POTOSI, MO, p. A366
WASHINGTON COUNTY REGIONAL MEDICAL CENTER, SANDERSVILLE, GA, p. A160
WASHINGTON DC VETERANS AFFAIRS MEDICAL CENTER, WASHINGTON, DC, p. A116
WASHINGTON DC VETERANS AFFAIRS MEDICAL CENTER, DC (see VETERANS AFFAIRS MEDICAL CENTER), p. A116
WASHINGTON HEALTH SYSTEM GREENE, WAYNESBURG, PA, p. A543
WASHINGTON HOSPITAL, WASHINGTON, PA, p. A543
WASHINGTON HOSPITAL CENTER, WASHINGTON, DC, p. A116
WASHINGTON HOSPITAL HEALTHCARE SYSTEM, FREMONT, CA, p. A59
WASHINGTON REGIONAL MEDICAL CENTER, FAYETTEVILLE-Washington County, AR, p. A42
WATAUGA MEDICAL CENTER, BOONE, NC, p. A448
WATERBURY HOSPITAL, WATERBURY, CT, p. A112
WATERTOWN REGIONAL MEDICAL CENTER, WATERTOWN, WI, p. A705
WATSONVILLE COMMUNITY HOSPITAL, WATSONVILLE, CA, p. A94
WAUKESHA COUNTY MENTAL HEALTH CENTER, WAUKESHA, WI, p. A705
WAUKESHA MEMORIAL HOSPITAL, WAUKESHA, WI, p. A705
WAUPUN MEMORIAL HOSPITAL, WAUPUN, WI, p. A705
WAVERLY HEALTH CENTER, WAVERLY, IA, p. A231
WAYNE COUNTY HOSPITAL, CORYDON, IA, p. A220
WAYNE COUNTY HOSPITAL, MONTICELLO, KY, p. A258
WAYNE GENERAL HOSPITAL, WAYNESBORO, MS, p. A354
WAYNE HEALTHCARE, GREENVILLE, OH, p. A483
WAYNE MEDICAL CENTER, WAYNESBORO, TN, p. A581
WAYNE MEMORIAL HOSPITAL, HONESDALE, PA, p. A527
WAYNE MEMORIAL HOSPITAL, JESUP, GA, p. A155
WAYNE UNC HEALTH CARE, GOLDSBORO, NC, p. A453
WAYNESBORO HOSPITAL, WAYNESBORO, PA, p. A543
WEATHERFORD REGIONAL HOSPITAL, WEATHERFORD, OK, p. A510
WEATHERFORD REHABILITATION HOSPITAL, WEATHERFORD, TX, p. A643
WEBSTER COUNTY COMMUNITY HOSPITAL, RED CLOUD, NE, p. A390
WEBSTER COUNTY MEMORIAL HOSPITAL, WEBSTER SPRINGS, WV, p. A687
WEED ARMY COMMUNITY HOSPITAL, FORT IRWIN, CA, p. A58
WEEKS MEDICAL CENTER, LANCASTER, NH, p. A399
WEIRTON MEDICAL CENTER, WEIRTON, WV, p. A687
WEISBROD MEMORIAL COUNTY HOSPITAL, EADS, CO, p. A100
WEISER MEMORIAL HOSPITAL, WEISER, ID, p. A172
WEISMAN CHILDREN'S REHABILITATION HOSPITAL, MARLTON, NJ, p. A407
WEKIVA SPRINGS, JACKSONVILLE, FL, p. A126
WELCH COMMUNITY HOSPITAL, WELCH, WV, p. A687
WELLBRIDGE HEALTHCARE GREATER DALLAS, PLANO, TX, p. A629
WELLBRIDGE HEALTHCARE OF FORT WORTH, FORT WORTH, TX, p. A605
WELLBRIDGE HEATLHCARE OF SAN MARCOS, SAN MARCOS, TX, p. A635
WELLINGTON REGIONAL MEDICAL CENTER, WELLINGTON, FL, p. A143
WELLSPAN EPHRATA COMMUNITY HOSPITAL, EPHRATA, PA, p. A525
WELLSPAN GETTYSBURG HOSPITAL, GETTYSBURG, PA, p. A526
WELLSPAN GOOD SAMARITAN HOSPITAL, LEBANON, PA, p. A529
WELLSPAN PHILHAVEN, MOUNT GRETNA, PA, p. A532
WELLSPAN SURGERY AND REHABILLITATION HOSPITAL, YORK, PA, p. A546
WELLSPAN YORK HOSPITAL, YORK, PA, p. A546
WELLSTAR ATLANTA MEDICAL CENTER - SOUTH CAMPUS, GA (see WELLSTAR ATLANTA MEDICAL CENTER), p. A147
WELLSTAR ATLANTA MEDICAL CENTER, ATLANTA, GA, p. A147
WELLSTAR COBB HOSPITAL, AUSTELL, GA, p. A148
WELLSTAR DOUGLAS HOSPITAL, DOUGLASVILLE, GA, p. A152
WELLSTAR KENNESTONE HOSPITAL, MARIETTA, GA, p. A157
WELLSTAR NORTH FULTON HOSPITAL, ROSWELL, GA, p. A159
WELLSTAR PAULDING HOSPITAL, HIRAM, GA, p. A155

WELLSTAR SPALDING REGIONAL HOSPITAL, GRIFFIN, GA, p. A154
WELLSTAR SYLVAN GROVE HOSPITAL, JACKSON, GA, p. A155
WELLSTAR WEST GEORGIA MEDICAL CENTER, LAGRANGE, GA, p. A155
WELLSTAR WINDY HILL HOSPITAL, MARIETTA, GA, p. A157
WELLSTONE REGIONAL HOSPITAL, JEFFERSONVILLE, IN, p. A208
WENTWORTH-DOUGLASS HOSPITAL, DOVER, NH, p. A398
WERNERSVILLE STATE HOSPITAL, WERNERSVILLE, PA, p. A543
WESLACO REGIONAL REHABILITATION HOSPITAL, WESLACO, TX, p. A643
WESLEY CHILDREN'S HOSPITAL, KS (see WESLEY HEALTHCARE CENTER), p. A248
WESLEY HEALTHCARE CENTER, WICHITA, KS, p. A248
WESLEY LONG COMMUNITY HOSPITAL, NC (see MOSES H. CONE MEMORIAL HOSPITAL), p. A453
WESLEY REHABILITATION HOSPITAL, WICHITA, KS, p. A248
WESLEY WOODLAWN HOSPITAL & ER, KS (see WESLEY HEALTHCARE CENTER), p. A248
WESLEY WOODS GERIATRIC HOSPITAL OF EMORY UNIVERSITY, ATLANTA, GA, p. A147
WEST ANAHEIM MEDICAL CENTER, ANAHEIM, CA, p. A50
WEST BOCA MEDICAL CENTER, BOCA RATON, FL, p. A118
WEST CALCASIEU CAMERON HOSPITAL, SULPHUR, LA, p. A280
WEST CAMPUS, NE (see FAITH REGIONAL HEALTH SERVICES), p. A387
WEST CARROLL MEMORIAL HOSPITAL, OAK GROVE, LA, p. A277
WEST CENTRAL GEORGIA REGIONAL HOSPITAL, COLUMBUS, GA, p. A151
WEST CHESTER HOSPITAL, WEST CHESTER, OH, p. A493
WEST CHESTER HOSPITAL SURGICAL CENTER, OH (see WEST CHESTER HOSPITAL), p. A493
WEST COVINA MEDICAL CENTER, WEST COVINA, CA, p. A95
WEST FELICIANA PARISH HOSPITAL, SAINT FRANCISVILLE, LA, p. A278
WEST FLORIDA COMMUNITY CARE CENTER, MILTON, FL, p. A131
WEST FLORIDA HOSPITAL, PENSACOLA, FL, p. A136
WEST FLORIDA HOSPITAL, PENSACOLA, FL (see WEST FLORIDA REHABILITATION INSTITUTE), p. A136
WEST FLORIDA REHABILITATION INSTITUTE, PENSACOLA, FL, p. A136
WEST FLORIDA REHABILITATION INSTITUTE, FL (see WEST FLORIDA HOSPITAL), p. A136
WEST GABLES REHABILITATION HOSPITAL, MIAMI, FL, p. A131
WEST HAVEN DIVISION, CT (see VETERANS AFFAIRS CONNECTICUT HEALTHCARE SYSTEM), p. A112
WEST HILLS HOSPITAL, RENO, NV, p. A396
WEST HILLS HOSPITAL AND MEDICAL CENTER, LOS ANGELES, CA, p. A70
WEST HOLT MEDICAL SERVICES, ATKINSON, NE, p. A381
WEST HOUSTON MEDICAL CENTER, HOUSTON, TX, p. A614
WEST JEFFERSON MEDICAL CENTER, MARRERO, LA, p. A273
WEST LOS ANGELES MEDICAL CENTER, LOS ANGELES, CA, p. A70
WEST MARION COMMUNITY HOSPITAL, FL (see OCALA REGIONAL MEDICAL CENTER), p. A133
WEST OAKS HOSPITAL, HOUSTON, TX, p. A614
WEST PALM BEACH VETERANS AFFAIRS MEDICAL CENTER, WEST PALM BEACH, FL, p. A143
WEST PALM BEACH VETERANS AFFAIRS MEDICAL CENTER, FL (see VETERANS AFFAIRS MEDICAL CENTER), p. A143
WEST PARK HOSPITAL, CODY, WY, p. A708
WEST PENN HOSPITAL, PITTSBURGH, PA, p. A538
WEST RIVER REGIONAL MEDICAL CENTER, HETTINGER, ND, p. A467
WEST SPRINGS HOSPITAL, GRAND JUNCTION, CO, p. A101
WEST SUBURBAN MEDICAL CENTER, OAK PARK, IL, p. A192
WEST TENNESSEE HEALTHCARE DYERSBURG HOSPITAL, DYERSBURG, TN, p. A569
WEST TENNESSEE HEALTHCARE NORTH HOSPITAL, TN (see JACKSON-MADISON COUNTY GENERAL HOSPITAL), p. A571
WEST TENNESSEE HEALTHCARE VOLUNTEER HOSPITAL, MARTIN, TN, p. A574
WEST TEXAS VETERANS AFFAIRS HEALTH CARE SYSTEM, BIG SPRING, TX, p. A589
WEST VALLEY MEDICAL CENTER, CALDWELL, ID, p. A168
WEST VIRGINIA UNIVERSITY CHILDREN'S HOSPITAL, WV (see WEST VIRGINIA UNIVERSITY HOSPITALS), p. A685
WEST VIRGINIA UNIVERSITY HOSPITALS, MORGANTOWN, WV, p. A685

WEST VIRGINIA UNIVERSITY HOSPITALS, MORGANTOWN, WV (see CHESTNUT RIDGE HOSPITAL), p. A685
WESTCHESTER GENERAL HOSPITAL, MIAMI, FL, p. A131
WESTCHESTER GENERAL HOSPITAL, MIAMI, FL (see SOUTHERN WINDS HOSPITAL), p. A124
WESTCHESTER MEDICAL CENTER, VALHALLA, NY, p. A445
WESTERLY HOSPITAL, WESTERLY, RI, p. A548
WESTERN ARIZONA REGIONAL MEDICAL CENTER, BULLHEAD CITY, AZ, p. A28
WESTERN MARYLAND HOSPITAL CENTER, HAGERSTOWN, MD, p. A292
WESTERN MARYLAND REGIONAL MEDICAL CENTER, CUMBERLAND, MD, p. A291
WESTERN MASSACHUSETTS HOSPITAL, WESTFIELD, MA, p. A306
WESTERN MENTAL HEALTH INSTITUTE, BOLIVAR, TN, p. A566
WESTERN MISSOURI MEDICAL CENTER, WARRENSBURG, MO, p. A371
WESTERN NEW YORK CHILDREN'S HOSPITAL PSYCHIATRIC CENTER, WEST SENECA, NY, p. A446
WESTERN PENNSYLVANIA HOSPITAL - FORBES REGIONAL CAMPUS, MONROEVILLE, PA, p. A532
WESTERN PLAINS MEDICAL COMPLEX, DODGE CITY, KS, p. A234
WESTERN PSYCHIATRIC INSTITUTE AND CLINIC, PITTSBURGH, PA, p. A538
WESTERN PSYCHIATRIC INSTITUTE AND CLINIC, PA (see UPMC PRESBYTERIAN), p. A538
WESTERN REGIONAL MEDICAL CENTER, GOODYEAR, AZ, p. A30
WESTERN RESERVE HOSPITAL, CUYAHOGA FALLS, OH, p. A480
WESTERN RESERVE HOSPITAL, OH (see CUYAHOGA FALLS GENERAL HOSPITAL), p. A480
WESTERN STATE HOSPITAL, HOPKINSVILLE, KY, p. A253
WESTERN STATE HOSPITAL, STAUNTON, VA, p. A666
WESTERN STATE HOSPITAL, TACOMA, WA, p. A679
WESTERN WISCONSIN HEALTH, BALDWIN, WI, p. A689
WESTFIELD MEMORIAL HOSPITAL, WESTFIELD, NY, p. A446
WESTFIELDS HOSPITAL AND CLINIC, NEW RICHMOND, WI, p. A700
WESTLAKE HOSPITAL, MELROSE PARK, IL, p. A189
WESTON COUNTY HEALTH SERVICES, NEWCASTLE, WY, p. A709
WESTPARK SPRINGS, RICHMOND, TX, p. A630
WESTSIDE REGIONAL MEDICAL CENTER, PLANTATION, FL, p. A136
WESTSIDE SURGICAL HOSPITAL, HOUSTON, TX, p. A614
WETZEL COUNTY HOSPITAL, NEW MARTINSVILLE, WV, p. A685
WHEATLAND MEMORIAL HEALTHCARE, HARLOWTON, MT, p. A376
WHEATON FRANCISCAN HEALTHCARE - FRANKLIN, FRANKLIN, WI, p. A693
WHEATON FRANCISCAN HEALTHCARE - ST. FRANCIS, MILWAUKEE, WI, p. A699
WHEATON FRANCISCAN HEALTHCARE - ST. JOSEPH'S, MILWAUKEE, WI, p. A699
WHEELING HOSPITAL, WHEELING, WV, p. A688
WHIDBEYHEALTH, COUPEVILLE, WA, p. A671
WHIDDEN MEMORIAL HOSPITAL, EVERETT, MA, p. A299
WHIDDEN MEMORIAL HOSPITAL, MA (see CAMBRIDGE HEALTH ALLIANCE), p. A298
WHITE COMMUNITY HOSPITAL, AURORA, MN, p. A327
WHITE MOUNTAIN REGIONAL MEDICAL CENTER, SPRINGERVILLE, AZ, p. A36
WHITE PLAINS HOSPITAL CENTER, WHITE PLAINS, NY, p. A446
WHITE RIVER JUNCTION VETERANS AFFAIRS MEDICAL CENTER, WHITE RIVER JUNCTION, VT, p. A654
WHITE RIVER MEDICAL CENTER, BATESVILLE, AR, p. A39
WHITESBURG ARH HOSPITAL, WHITESBURG, KY, p. A261
WHITFIELD MEDICAL SURGICAL HOSPITAL, MS (see MISSISSIPPI STATE HOSPITAL), p. A354
WHITING FORENSIC HOSPITAL, MIDDLETOWN, CT, p. A109
WHITING FORENSIC HOSPITAL, CT (see CONNECTICUT VALLEY HOSPITAL), p. A109
WHITINSVILLE MEDICAL CENTER, WHITINSVILLE, MA, p. A306
WHITINSVILLE MEDICAL CENTER, MA (see MILFORD REGIONAL MEDICAL CENTER), p. A302
WHITMAN HOSPITAL AND MEDICAL CENTER, COLFAX, WA, p. A670
WHITTEN CENTER, CLINTON, SC, p. A551
WHITTIER HOSPITAL MEDICAL CENTER, WHITTIER, CA, p. A95
WHITTIER PAVILION, HAVERHILL, MA, p. A300
WHITTIER REHABILITATION HOSPITAL, BRADFORD, MA, p. A297

Y

Z

This section is an index of the key health care professionals for the hospitals and/or health care systems listed in this publication. The index is in alphabetical order, by individual, followed by the title, institutional affiliation, city, state and page reference to the hospital and/or health care system listing in section A and/or B.

A

AAGARD, Kim, Chief Financial Officer, Tri-County Hospital, Wadena, MN, p. A341

AALBORG, Chase, Vice President and Chief Financial Officer, Amita Health Adventist Medical Center Glenoaks, Glendale Heights, IL, p. A184

AASVED, Craig E., Chief Executive Officer, Shodair Children's Hospital, Helena, MT, p. A376

ABAIR, Cynthia, Associate Director, Va San Diego Healthcare System, San Diego, CA, p. A84

ABANG, Toni, M.D., Medical Director, Healthsouth Lakeview Rehabilitation Hospital, Elizabethtown, KY, p. A251

ABBATE, Anthony, Director of Information Services, San Ramon Regional Medical Center, San Ramon, CA, p. A88

ABBATIELLO, Michael, Chief Financial Officer, Spring Harbor Hospital, Westbrook, ME, p. A286

ABBEY, Kurt, Chief Nursing Officer, Ozarks Medical Center, West Plains, MO, p. A372

ABBOTT, Dana, Market Human Resources Director, Shands Live Oak Regional Medical Center, Live Oak, FL, p. A128

ABBOTT, Jody, Senior Vice President and Chief Operating Officer, North Kansas City Hospital, North Kansas City, MO, p. A365

ABBOTT, Justin, M.D., Medical Director, Sevier Valley Hospital, Richfield, UT, p. A649

ABBOTT, Michael, Chief Operating Officer, Lewis-Gale Pavilion, VA, p. A666

ABBOTT, Peggy L., President and Chief Executive Officer, Ouachita County Medical Center, Camden-Ouachita County, AR, p. A40

ABDA, William, Chief Human Resources Officer, Clarks Summit State Hospital, Clarks Summit, PA, p. A522

ABDELKARIM, Riad Z., M.D., Vice President and Chief Medical Officer, St. Mary Medical Center, Apple Valley, CA, p. A51

ABDELNASER, Mohammad, Chief Nursing Officer, Centinela Hospital Medical Center, Inglewood, CA, p. A62

ABE, Ann
    Administrator and Chief Operating Officer, Orange County Global Medical Center, Inc., Santa Ana, CA, p. A88
    Interim Chief Executive Officer, Orange County Global Medical Center, Inc., Santa Ana, CA, p. A88

ABEL, Danielle, Vice President of Patient Care Services, Chi Lakewood Health, Baudette, MN, p. A328

ABEL, Doug, Chief Information Officer, North Kansas City Hospital, North Kansas City, MO, p. A365

ABEL, Jeffrey, M.D., Chief Medical Officer, Ogden Regional Medical Center, Ogden, UT, p. A648

ABEL, Kevin, Chief Executive Officer, North Valley Hospital, Whitefish, MT, p. A380

ABEL, Stacy L, Director Human Resources, Craig Hospital, Englewood, CO, p. A100

ABELLERA, Roland, Vice President and Chief Operating Officer, St. Bernard Hospital And Health Care Center, Chicago, IL, p. A179

ABELY, Susan Cerrone
    Chief Information Officer, St. Joseph Hospital For Specialty Care, RI, p. A547
    Vice President and Chief Information Officer, Roger Williams Medical Center, Providence, RI, p. A548

ABERCROMBIE, David
    Controller, Baptist Health South Florida, Homestead Hospital, Homestead, FL, p. A125
    Controller, Baptist Health South Florida, Mariners Hospital, Tavernier, FL, p. A142

ABERCROMBIE, David E., Chief Executive Officer, Montgomery County Memorial Hospital, Red Oak, IA, p. A228

ABERCROMBIE, Zach, Chief Financial Officer, Citizens Baptist Medical Center, Talladega, AL, p. A23

ABERNATHY, Clint, President and Chief Operating Officer, Texas Health Harris Methodist Hospital Alliance, Fort Worth, TX, p. A605

ABERNETHY, Robert, Interim Chief Financial Officer, Medical Center Health System, Odessa, TX, p. A626

ABLA, Mike, Director of Nursing, Griffin Memorial Hospital, Norman, OK, p. A502

ABNEY, Stuart, Controller, Jasper Memorial Hospital, Monticello, GA, p. A158

ABOUD, Al, CPA, Chief Financial Officer, Hackensack Meridian Health Mountainside Medical Center, Montclair, NJ, p. A407

ABRAHAM, Akram, M.D., Chief of Staff, Harmon Memorial Hospital, Hollis, OK, p. A500

ABRAHAM, Brian, Chief Executive Officer, Mesquite Rehabilitation Institute, Mesquite, TX, p. A623

ABRAHAM, JiJi
    Area Chief Financial Officer, Kaiser Permanente Moreno Valley Medical Center, Moreno Valley, CA, p. A73
    Chief Financial Officer, Kaiser Permanente Riverside Medical Center, Riverside, CA, p. A81

ABRAHAM, Paul B., FACHE, Chief Executive Officer, Cumberland Surgical Hospital, San Antonio, TX, p. A633

ABRAHAMSON-BATY, Sherri, Director Patient Care Services, Cambridge Medical Center, Cambridge, MN, p. A329

ABRAHAMY, Ran, M.D., Chief of Staff, University Pavilion, FL, p. A140

ABRAMS, Jose, Chief Information Officer, St. Luke's Episcopal Hospital, Ponce, PR, p. A714

ABREU, Iris, Supervisor Human Resources, Hospital Hima De Humacao, Humacao, PR, p. A713

ABREU, John, Vice President and Chief Financial Officer, Portneuf Medical Center, Pocatello, ID, p. A171

ABRINA, Sofia, R.N.
    Administrator, Montclair Hospital Medical Center, Montclair, CA, p. A73
    Chief Executive Officer, Glendora Community Hospital, Glendora, CA, p. A61

ABROMOVICH, Sari, Chief Executive Officer, Harbor Oaks Hospital, New Baltimore, MI, p. A320

ABRUTZ, Joseph F., Jr, Administrator, Cameron Regional Medical Center, Cameron, MO, p. A356

ABSALON, Jeffrey, M.D.
    Chief Physician Officer, St. Charles Bend, Bend, OR, p. A511
    Chief Physician Officer, St. Charles Redmond, Redmond, OR, p. A517

ABSHIER, Trey
    Chief Executive Officer, Florida Medical Center - A Campus Of North Shore, FL, p. A130
    Chief Executive Officer, Palm Beach Gardens Medical Center, Palm Beach Gardens, FL, p. A135

ABUNDO, Manuel, M.D., Chief of Staff, Wahiawa General Hospital, Wahiawa, HI, p. A166

ABY, Sherry, Director Information Management, Upmc Pinnacle Carlisle, Carlisle, PA, p. A522

ACCASHIAN, Chris
    Chief Executive Officer, Bon Secours St. Francis Medical Center, Midlothian, VA, p. A661
    Chief Executive Officer, Rappahannock General Hospital, Kilmarnock, VA, p. A660

ACETO, Anthony, Vice President Human Resources, Norwalk Hospital, Norwalk, CT, p. A110

ACEVEDO, Edwin Orama, Financial Supervisor, Hospital Buen Samaritano, Aguadilla, PR, p. A711

ACEVEDO, Elizabeth, Director Human Resources, Houston Methodist Willowbrook Hospital, Houston, TX, p. A611

ACEVEDO, Ramon, Supervisor Information Systems, Hospital San Cristobal, Coto Laurel, PR, p. A713

ACEVEDO, Vanessa, Interim Chief Executive Officer, Chg Hospital Tucson, Llc, Tucson, AZ, p. A37

ACHARYA, Ganesh, Chief Executive Officer, Good Samaritan Hospital, Bakersfield, CA, p. A52

ACHEBE, James Bob, M.D., President Medical Staff, South Shore Hospital, Chicago, IL, p. A179

ACHTER, Dick, Chief Financial Officer, Barrett Hospital & Healthcare, Dillon, MT, p. A375

ACHURY, Dario, Director of Information Management, St. Anthony's Rehabilitation Hospital, Lauderdale Lakes, FL, p. A128

ACKER, David B., FACHE, President and Chief Executive Officer, Canton-Potsdam Hospital, Potsdam, NY, p. A440

ACKER, Peter W., President and Chief Executive Officer, Carolinas Healthcare System Lincoln, Lincolnton, NC, p. A456

ACKERMAN, F. Kenneth, FACHE
    Chair, Hospital Operation, Mayo Clinic Hospital - Saint Marys Campus, MN, p. A338
    Hospital Administrator, Mayo Eugenio Litta Children's Hospital, MN, p. A338

ACKERSON, David, Chief Information Officer, Seattle Cancer Care Alliance, Seattle, WA, p. A676

ACKERT, Sara, Associate Director, Sioux Falls Veterans Affairs Health Care System, Sioux Falls, SD, p. A564

ACKLAND, Jeanne, Director of Finance, Fillmore County Hospital, Geneva, NE, p. A384

ACKLEY, Michael
    Chief Financial Officer, Kentucky River Medical Center, Jackson, KY, p. A254
    Chief Financial Officer, Three Rivers Medical Center, Louisa, KY, p. A255

ACKLIN, Traci, M.D., Chief of Staff, Montgomery General Hospital, Montgomery, WV, p. A685

ACKMAN, Jeffrey D., M.D., Chief of Staff, Shriners Hospitals For Children-Chicago, Chicago, IL, p. A179

ACKMAN, Laura, Chief Operating Officer and Administrator, Essentia Health Northern Pines Medical Center, Aurora, MN, p. A327

ACOSTA, Ivan, M.D., Medical Director, Hospital De La Concepcion, San German, PR, p. A715

ACOSTA, Louis, M.D., Chief of Staff, Silver Lake Medical Center-Ingleside Hospital, CA, p. A69

ACOSTA-CARLSON, Francisca, M.D., Chief of Staff, Lexington Regional Health Center, Lexington, NE, p. A385

ACOSTA-CRUZ, Maridel, Chief Executive Officer, First Texas Hospital, Houston, TX, p. A610

ACREE, Charis L, Vice President and Chief Operating Officer, Wellstar West Georgia Medical Center, Lagrange, GA, p. A155

ADAIR, Dale K, M.D., Chief Medical Officer, Wernersville State Hospital, Wernersville, PA, p. A543

ADAIR, Julie, Interim Corporate Chief Human Resources Officer, Fresno Heart And Surgical Hospital, Fresno, CA, p. A59

ADAIR-TRIPLETT, Alonna, Chief Nurse Executive, Claremore Indian Hospital, Claremore, OK, p. A497

ADAM, Sheryl, Chief Financial Officer, Hanover Hospital, Hanover, KS, p. A236

ADAM, Suzanne, D.O., Medical Director, Healthsouth Reading Rehabilitation Hospital, Reading, PA, p. A539

ADAMO, James D., M.D., Medical Director, Harbor Oaks Hospital, New Baltimore, MI, p. A320

ADAMO, Peter J., President and Chief Executive Officer, Waterbury Hospital, Waterbury, CT, p. A112

ADAMOLEKUN, Michelle
    Chief Human Resource Officer, St. Vincent's Medical Center Riverside, Jacksonville, FL, p. A126
    Vice President Human Resource Market Lead Florida/ Alabama Ministry Market, Sacred Heart Hospital Pensacola, Pensacola, FL, p. A136

ADAMS, Alan L., Administrator, Memorial Hospital Of Stilwell, Stilwell, OK, p. A507

ADAMS, Bob, Director Information Services, Bay Area Hospital, Coos Bay, OR, p. A512

ADAMS, Brian
    President and Chief Executive Officer, Florida Hospital At Connerton Long Term Acute Care, Land O'Lakes, FL, p. A127
    President and Chief Executive Officer, Florida Hospital Tampa, Tampa, FL, p. A140

ADAMS, Carla, Chief Nursing Officer, Northern Nevada Medical Center, Sparks, NV, p. A397

ADAMS, Cathleen, Chief Nursing Officer, Carepartners Health Services, Asheville, NC, p. A447

ADAMS, Charlotte, Director of Human Resources, Carolina Pines Regional Medical Center, Hartsville, SC, p. A554

ADAMS, Chris, Vice President Patient Care Services, Good Samaritan Regional Health Center, Mount Vernon, IL, p. A190

ADAMS, Cynthia, Vice President Human Resources, Tristar Stonecrest Medical Center, Smyrna, TN, p. A580

ADAMS, Denise, Human Resources Generalist, Hancock County Hospital, Sneedville, TN, p. A580

ADAMS, Emmy
    Chief Financial Officer, Mayhill Hospital, Denton, TX, p. A599
    Chief Financial Officer, Provo Canyon Behavioral Hospital, Orem, UT, p. A649

ADAMS, Essie, Director of Nursing, Kedren Community Mental Health Center, Los Angeles, CA, p. A68

ADAMS, Felicia M, MS, Chief Nursing Officer, Mid-Columbia Medical Center, The Dalles, OR, p. A518

ADAMS, Gini, Director Employee and Public Relations, Yuma District Hospital, Yuma, CO, p. A106

ADAMS, Heather, Chief Nursing Officer, John F. Kennedy Memorial Hospital, Indio, CA, p. A62

ADAMS, J'Dee, Chief Operating Officer, North Canyon Medical Center, Gooding, ID, p. A169

ADAMS, Jason, M.D.
Medical Staff President, Forest Health Medical Center, Ypsilanti, MI, p. A326
Chief Operating Officer, Christus St. Vincent Physicians Medical Center, NM, p. A419

ADAMS, Jennifer B, Chief Operating Officer and Chief Financial Officer, Lake City Medical Center, Lake City, FL, p. A127

ADAMS, Jo, Director Human Resources, Donalsonville Hospital, Donalsonville, GA, p. A152

ADAMS, Karen, Vice President Human Resources, Baxter Regional Medical Center, Mountain Home-Baxter County, AR, p. A46

ADAMS, Kelly, Chief Executive Officer, Santa Cruz Valley Regional Hospital, Green Valley, AZ, p. A30

ADAMS, Kimberly, Manager Human Resources, Carroll County Memorial Hospital, Carrollton, KY, p. A250

ADAMS, Lana, Chief Financial Officer, Lafayette General Orthopedic Hospital, LA, p. A271

ADAMS, Leslie, Chief Nursing Executive, Saint Joseph Berea, Berea, KY, p. A249

ADAMS, Mark A., President and Chief Executive Officer, Methodist Rehabilitation Center, Jackson, MS, p. A348

ADAMS, Mark B., Chief Executive Officer, Ogden Regional Medical Center, Ogden, UT, p. A648

ADAMS, Mark C., M.D., Chief Medical Officer, El Camino Hospital Los Gatos, CA, p. A74

ADAMS, Marlene J, Director Human Resources, Schneider Regional Medical Center, Saint Thomas, VI, p. A717

ADAMS, Marsha, Interim Director Human Resources, Texas Health Harris Methodist Hospital Cleburne, Cleburne, TX, p. A592

ADAMS, Martin D., CPA, Vice President Finance and Chief Financial Officer, Paris Community Hospital, Paris, IL, p. A192

ADAMS, Mary Jane, R.N., MSN, Senior Vice President and Chief Nursing Officer, University Of Louisville Hospital, Louisville, KY, p. A257

ADAMS, Matthew, Administrator, Oklahoma State University Medical Center, Tulsa, OK, p. A508

ADAMS, Michael, Chief Operating Officer, Scottsdale Liberty Hospital, Scottsdale, AZ, p. A35

ADAMS, Mike, M.D., Chief Medical Officer, Gateway Regional Medical Center, Granite City, IL, p. A184

ADAMS, Nancy D., R.N., Senior Vice President and Chief Operating Officer, Western Maryland Regional Medical Center, Cumberland, MD, p. A291

ADAMS, Norma, Director Human Resources, Southern Regional Medical Center, Riverdale, GA, p. A159

ADAMS, Patsy, Vice President Human Resources, Redmond Regional Medical Center, Rome, GA, p. A159

ADAMS, Renee, Director Information Technology, Chan Soon-Shiong Medical Center, Windber, PA, p. A545

ADAMS, Robert H, Vice President Operations, K. Hovnanian Children's Hospital, NJ, p. A408

ADAMS, Robin, Director Human Resources, Reeves Memorial Medical Center, Bernice, LA, p. A264

ADAMS, Russell, M.D., Chief Medical Officer, Unitypoint Health - Marshalltown, Marshalltown, IA, p. A226

ADAMS, Scott K., FACHE, Chief Executive Officer, Pullman Regional Hospital, Pullman, WA, p. A675

ADAMS, Shannon, Chief Financial Officer, Avera Holy Family Hospital, Estherville, IA, p. A222

ADAMS, Sharon
Chief Nursing Officer, New Milford Hospital, CT, p. A107
Chief Operating Officer, New Milford Hospital, CT, p. A107

ADAMS, Shaun, Chief Financial Officer, Tennova Healthcare-Harton, Tullahoma, TN, p. A580

ADAMS, Shawn, Chief Financial Officer, Christus Southeast Texas Hospital-St. Mary, TX, p. A588

ADAMS, Shelah, Chief Executive Officer, Timberlawn Mental Health System, Dallas, TX, p. A598

ADAMS, Susan, Chief Nursing Officer and Chief Operating Officer, Specialty Hospital Of Lorain, Amherst, OH, p. A470

ADAMS, T Gard, M.D., Chief of Staff, Mclaren Caro Region, Caro, MI, p. A309

ADAMS, Tony, President, Barix Clinics Of Pennsylvania, Langhorne, PA, p. A529

ADAMSKI, Joseph, Chief Nursing Officer, Healthsouth Rehabilitation Hospital, Concord, NH, p. A398

ADAMSON, James, Chief Executive Officer, Mountain View Hospital, Idaho Falls, ID, p. A169

ADAMSON, Nancy, Chief Nursing Officer, Banner Del E. Webb Medical Center, Sun City West, AZ, p. A36

ADCOCK, Robert S., Chief Executive Officer, Fairmont Regional Medical Center, Fairmont, WV, p. A683

ADCOCK, Tanya M., President, St. Mary's Good Samaritan Hospital, Greensboro, GA, p. A154

ADCOCK, William, Chief Financial Officer, Union General Hospital, Farmerville, LA, p. A267

ADCOCK MOHR, Barbara, Chief Executive Officer, Uva-Healthsouth Rehabilitation Hospital, Charlottesville, VA, p. A656

ADDINGTON, Tom, Chief Information Officer, Saint Michael's Medical Center, Newark, NJ, p. A409

ADDISON, Holland M, M.D., Medical Director, Select Specialty Hospital - Belhaven, Jackson, MS, p. A348

ADDISON, John Bruce, D.O., Chief Medical Officer, Mccamey County Hospital District, Mccamey, TX, p. A623

ADDISON, Lenora, Vice President Patient Care and Nursing, Medstar Harbor Hospital, Baltimore, MD, p. A288

ADDISON, Lewis C, Senior Vice President and Chief Financial Officer, Lynchburg General Hospital, VA, p. A660

ADDLESPERGER, John, D.O., Chief Medical Officer, Sheridan Memorial Hospital, Sheridan, WY, p. A709

ADDO, Deborah, Chief Executive Officer, Inova Loudoun Hospital, Leesburg, VA, p. A660

ADEEL, Mohammed, Medical Director, Healthsouth Deaconess Rehabilitation Hospital, Evansville, IN, p. A203

ADEMA, Carolyn, Vice President, Human Resources, St. Tammany Parish Hospital, Covington, LA, p. A266

ADEN, Susie, Director of IP Services, Pocahontas Community Hospital, Pocahontas, IA, p. A228

ADER, Michael H, M.D., Vice President Medical Affairs, Upmc Pinnacle Hanover, Hanover, PA, p. A526

ADERS, Deb, MS, R.N., Interim Chief Nursing Officer, Yuma Regional Medical Center, Yuma, AZ, p. A38

ADESSO, Patrick
Director Information Technology and Systems, Memorial Hospital Jacksonville, Jacksonville, FL, p. A125
Director Information Technology and Systems, Specialty Hospital Jacksonville, Jacksonville, FL, p. A126

ADKINS, Garry, Chief Information Officer, University Of South Alabama Children's And Women's Hospital, Mobile, AL, p. A20

ADKINS, Gary W, Chief Executive Officer, Parkview Noble Hospital, Kendallville, IN, p. A208

ADKINS, Gary W., President, Parkview Noble Hospital, Kendallville, IN, p. A208

ADKINS, Kedrick D., Chief Financial Officer, Mayo Eugenio Litta Children's Hospital, MN, p. A338

ADKINS, Kevin, Director Human Resources, Medical City Green Oaks Hospital, Dallas, TX, p. A597

ADKINS, Melisa, Chief Executive Officer, Heartland Regional Medical Center, Marion, IL, p. A188

ADKINS, Michael, Chief Operating Officer, Houston Northwest Medical Center, Houston, TX, p. A611

ADKINS, Paige, Chief Financial Officer, Greenbrier Valley Medical Center, Ronceverte, WV, p. A687

ADKINS, Raymond, Chief Information Officer, Peninsula Regional Medical Center, Salisbury, MD, p. A294

ADKINS, Scott, Manager Information Technology, Vernon Memorial Healthcare, Viroqua, WI, p. A704

ADKINS, Tyler, Chief Financial Officer, Vaughan Regional Medical Center, Selma, AL, p. A23

ADLER, Josh, M.D., Chief Medical Officer, Ucsf Medical Center Mission Bay, CA, p. A86

ADLER, Kenneth, M.D., Medical Director, Arrowhead Behavioral Health Hospital, Maumee, OH, p. A486

ADLER, Maurita, Director Information Services, Gottlieb Memorial Hospital, Melrose Park, IL, p. A189

ADMA, Vishal, M.D., Medical Director, Kvc Prairie Ridge Psychiatric Hospital, Kansas City, KS, p. A238

ADORNATO, Sara F., Executive Director, Barnes-Kasson County Hospital, Susquehanna, PA, p. A542

ADORNETTO-GARCIA, Debra, MSN, R.N., Chief Nursing Officer, Banner Gateway Medical Center, Gilbert, AZ, p. A29

ADREAN, Christina
Chief Executive Officer, Pam Specialty Hospital Of Victoria North, Victoria, TX, p. A642
Chief Executive Officer, Pam Specialty Hospital Of Victoria South, Victoria, TX, p. A642

ADRIAANSE, Steven W, Vice President and Chief Human Resources Officer, Tallahassee Memorial Healthcare, Tallahassee, FL, p. A140

ADVEY, Linda, Manager Information Systems, Glenbeigh Hospital And Outpatient Centers, Rock Creek, OH, p. A489

AEMMER, Anthony, Director of Nursing, Wellstone Regional Hospital, Jeffersonville, IN, p. A208

AFENYA, Kenneth, M.D., Chief of Staff, Baptist Memorial Hospital-Tipton, Covington, TN, p. A568

AFIFI, Alaa Y, M.D., Chief of Staff, Corona Regional Medical Center-Rehabilitation, CA, p. A55

AFLAK, Ziba, Chief Financial Officer, Kindred Hospital-San Francisco Bay Area, San Leandro, CA, p. A87

AFZAL, Muhammed, M.D., Chief of Staff, Sutter General Hospital, CA, p. A82

AGANA, Ben, M.D., Medical Director, Encompass Health Rehabilitation Hospital The Woodlands, Conroe, TX, p. A594

AGEE, Joan, Vice President Patient Care Services, St. Joseph Regional Medical Center, Lewiston, ID, p. A170

AGENBROAD, Connie, Chief Executive Officer, Othello Community Hospital, Othello, WA, p. A674

AGLOINGA, Roy, Chief Administrative Officer, Norton Sound Regional Hospital, Nome, AK, p. A27

AGNEW, Mary Christine, R.N., Senior Vice President and Chief Nursing Officer, Reading Hospital, West Reading, PA, p. A544

AGNI, Guirish, M.D., Chief of Staff, Stoughton Hospital Association, Stoughton, WI, p. A703

AGOSTINI, Irene, M.D., Chief Medical Officer, Unm Children's Hospital, NM, p. A416

AGOSTO, Paula M, R.N., MSN, Senior Vice President and Chief Nursing Officer, Children's Hospital Of Philadelphia, Philadelphia, PA, p. A534

AGRELA, Ramona, Associate Chancellor & Chief Human Resources Executive, Uc Irvine Medical Center, Orange, CA, p. A76

AGRESTI, Katie, R.N., Director Patient Care Services, Lecom Health Millcreek Community Hospital, Erie, PA, p. A525

AGUAS, Hugo, Vice President Human Resources, Inova Alexandria Hospital, Alexandria, VA, p. A655

AGUERO, Samuel, Chief Operating Officer, Florida Hospital Deland, Deland, FL, p. A121

AGUILA, Marcos, Chief Executive Officer, Hospital San Francisco, San Juan, PR, p. A716

AGUILAR, Gretchen, Director Patient Care and Chief Nursing Officer, Three Rivers Hospital, Brewster, WA, p. A670

AGUILAR, Marisa
Chief Operating Officer, Valley Baptist Medical Center-Brownsville, Brownsville, TX, p. A590
Interim Chief Nursing Officer, Valley Baptist Medical Center-Brownsville, Brownsville, TX, p. A590

AGUILERA, Louie, Director Information Technology, Foundation Surgical Hospital Of El Paso, El Paso, TX, p. A602

AGUINAGA, Miguel, M.D., FACS, Medical Director, Advanced Care Hospital Of White County, Searcy-White County, AR, p. A48

AGUIRRE, Jose, M.D., Medical Director, Carson Tahoe Continuing Care Hospital, Carson City, NV, p. A392

AGUIRRE, Kim, Director Finance, Northern Cochise Community Hospital, Willcox, AZ, p. A38

AGWUNOBI, Andrew, M.D., Chief Executive Officer, Uconn, John Dempsey Hospital, Farmington, CT, p. A108

AHAINE, Israel, Chief Nursing Officer, West Oaks Hospital, Houston, TX, p. A614

AHEARN, Patrick
Chief Operating Officer and Senior Vice President, Saint Barnabas Medical Center, Livingston, NJ, p. A406
Chief Operating Officer, Community Medical Center, Toms River, NJ, p. A412

AHL, Dennis, Director Information Technology, Jefferson Community Health And Life, Fairbury, NE, p. A383

AHLERS, Tim
Chief Financial Officer, Unitypoint Health - Finley Hospital, Dubuque, IA, p. A222
Chief Operating Officer, Unitypoint Health - Finley Hospital, Dubuque, IA, p. A222

AHMAD, Shariq, M.D., Chief of Staff, Baptist Hospitals Of Southeast Texas Fannin Behavioral Health Center, TX, p. A588

AHMED, Ashraf, M.D., Senior Vice President Physician and Hospital Services, Alliance Community Hospital, Alliance, OH, p. A470

AHMED, Bilal, M.D., Medical Director, Wyoming County Community Hospital, Warsaw, NY, p. A445

AHMED, Imtiaz, Chief of Staff, Mercy Hospital Ada, Ada, OK, p. A495

AHMED, Mohammed Shafeeq, M.D., Vice President of Medical Affairs and Chief Medical Officer, Howard County General Hospital, Columbia, MD, p. A291

AHMED, Omar, Acting Manager Human Resources, Veterans Affairs Caribbean Healthcare System, San Juan, PR, p. A716

AHMED, Sajid, Chief Information and Innovation Officer, Martin Luther King, Jr. Community Hospital, Los Angeles, CA, p. A68

AHMED, Shabeer A, M.D., Clinical Director, Community Behavioral Health Hospital - Annandale, Annandale, MN, p. A327

AHNER, Dawn, Chief Financial Officer, Renown Rehabilitation Hospital, Reno, NV, p. A396

AHRENS, C Todd., President and Chief Executive Officer, Hannibal Regional Hospital, Hannibal, MO, p. A360

AHUJA, Teena, Interim Chief Executive Officer and Regional Vice President of Operations, Willow Creek Behavioral Health, Green Bay, WI, p. A694

AIELLO, Louis
  Chief Financial Officer, St. Elizabeth Medical Center, Utica, NY, p. A444
  Senior Vice President and Chief Financial Officer, St. Luke's Campus, NY, p. A444

AIKEN, David, Chief Human Resources Officer, Madigan Army Medical Center, Tacoma, WA, p. A679

AIKEN, Patsy, Coordinator Human Resource, Spearfish Regional Surgery Center, SD, p. A564

AIKEN, Richard, M.D., Medical Director, Lakeland Behavioral Health System, Springfield, MO, p. A370

AILOR, Lorie, Chief Executive Officer, Orthopaedic Hospital Of Lutheran Health Network, Fort Wayne, IN, p. A204

AINTABLIAN, Susan, Chief Information Officer, Lac-Olive View-Ucla Medical Center, Los Angeles, CA, p. A68

AIONA, Michael, M.D., Chief of Staff, Shriners Hospitals For Children-Portland, Portland, OR, p. A516

AIRHART, Steven
  Chief Executive Officer, Garfield Park Hospital, Chicago, IL, p. A176
  Chief Executive Officer, Hartgrove Hospital, Chicago, IL, p. A177

AIROSUS, Diane, Chief Financial Officer, Pembroke Hospital, Pembroke, MA, p. A303

AISEN, Mindy, M.D., Chief Medical Officer, Rancho Los Amigos National Rehabilitation Center, Downey, CA, p. A56

AISENBREY, Lisa, Administrator Human Resources and Support Services, Sidney Health Center, Sidney, MT, p. A379

AIYELAWO, Pius, Chief Operating Officer, Children's Inn At Nih, MD, p. A290

AJANAH, Muhammed, M.D., Clinical Director, Clifton T. Perkins Hospital Center, Jessup, MD, p. A292

AJMAL, Farooq, Vice President and Chief Information Officer, Nassau University Medical Center, East Meadow, NY, p. A426

AKENS, Rick, Director Human Resources and Labor Relations, Methodist Medical Center Of Oak Ridge, Oak Ridge, TN, p. A578

AKERS, Earl, Supervisor Information Technology, Salina Surgical Hospital, Salina, KS, p. A245

AKERSON, Jeffrey D., M.D., Chief Medical Officer, Nebraska Medicine - Bellevue, Bellevue, NE, p. A382

AKHRAS, Omar, M.D., Chief of Staff, Putnam General Hospital, Eatonton, GA, p. A153

AKHTAR, M. Osman, Chief Operating Officer, St. John's Hospital, Maplewood, MN, p. A334

AKIF, Joe, Chief Clinical Officer and Chief Nursing Officer, Warren General Hospital, Warren, PA, p. A543

AKIN, Pam, R.N., MSN, Chief Nursing Officer, Whitman Hospital And Medical Center, Colfax, WA, p. A670

AKINS, Tina, Director Human Resources, Lost Rivers Medical Center, Arco, ID, p. A167

AKIYOSHI, Derek, Chief Executive Officer, Leahi Hospital, Honolulu, HI, p. A164

AKOPYAN, George, Director Human Resources, Centinela Hospital Medical Center, Inglewood, CA, p. A62

ALAGAR, Ravi, M.D., Medical Director, Curahealth Pittsburgh, Oakdale, PA, p. A533

ALAM, Md
  Chief Information Officer, Nyc Health + Hospitals / Jacobi, New York (Includes All Hospitals Located Within The Five Boroughs), NY, p. A435
  Chief Information Officer, Nyc Health + Hospitals / Metropolitan, New York (Includes All Hospitals Located Within The Five Boroughs), NY, p. A436

ALAM, Muhammad M, M.D., Medical Director, Turning Point Hospital, Moultrie, GA, p. A158

ALAMEDDINE, Hala, Chief Nursing Executive, Kindred Hospital Sugar Land, Sugar Land, TX, p. A637

ALASZEWSKI, Lydia, Chief Nursing Officer, Select Specialty Hospital-Macomb County, Mount Clemens, MI, p. A319

ALBANO, Valerie, Director, Human Resources, Regional Hospital For Respiratory And Complex Care, Burien, WA, p. A670

ALBANY, Karen, Chief Information Officer, Naval Medical Center, Portsmouth, VA, p. A664

ALBAUM, Michael, M.D., Senior Vice President and Chief Medical Officer, Southern Maine Health Care - Biddeford Medical Center, ME, p. A283

ALBERS, Craig, President and Chief Operating Officer, Mercy Health - St. Charles Hospital, Oregon, OH, p. A488

ALBERT, Debra, MSN, R.N., Senior Vice President Patient Care and Chief Nursing Officer, Comer Children's Hospital, IL, p. A180

ALBERT, Todd, M.D., Surgeon-in-Chief and Medical Director, Hospital For Special Surgery, New York (Includes All Hospitals Located Within The Five Boroughs), NY, p. A432

ALBERTINI, Bernie, Chief Administrative Officer, East Ohio Regional Hospital, Martins Ferry, OH, p. A486

ALBERTS, Patrick J, Senior Vice President and Chief Operating Officer, Monongahela Valley Hospital, Monongahela, PA, p. A532

ALBERTSON, Chris
  Chief Executive Officer, Presentation Medical Center, Rolla, ND, p. A468
  Director Human Resources, Presentation Medical Center, Rolla, ND, p. A468

ALBERTSON, Robert, M.D., Chief Medical Officer, Henry Ford Allegiance Specialty Hospital, Jackson, MI, p. A316

ALBIN, James
  Chief Information Officer, Baylor St. Luke's Medical Center, Houston, TX, p. A610
  Chief Information Officer, Regional Medical Center, Orangeburg, SC, p. A556

ALBIN, Lonnie, M.D., Interim Chief Executive Officer, Highlands Medical Center, Scottsboro, AL, p. A23

ALBOSTA, Kevin, Vice President, Chief Financial Officer, Covenant Medical Center-Harrison, MI, p. A322

ALBRECHT, David L.
  President, District One Hospital, Faribault, MN, p. A331
  President, Owatonna Hospital, Owatonna, MN, p. A337

ALBRECHT, John, Chief of Staff, Union Hospital Clinton, Clinton, IN, p. A201

ALBRECHT, Sandra, Interim Chief Financial Officer, Singing River Hospital, MS, p. A351

ALBRIGHT, Bill, Director Human Resources, Stewart Memorial Community Hospital, Lake City, IA, p. A225

ALBRIGHT, Leslie, Vice President Information Systems, Bethesda Hospital West, FL, p. A118

ALBRIGHT, Sara Z, Vice President Human Resources, Bassett Medical Center, Cooperstown, NY, p. A425

ALBRIGHT, Tammy, President, Takoma Regional Hospital, Greeneville, TN, p. A570

ALBRIGHT, Tina, Director Human Resources, National Park Medical Center, Hot Springs-Garland County, AR, p. A43

ALCOCER, Deborah, Chief Information Officer, South Texas Rehabilitation Hospital, Brownsville, TX, p. A590

ALDANA, Eladio, Manager Information Systems, College Hospital Costa Mesa, Costa Mesa, CA, p. A55

ALDER, Cal, Director Information Technology, Rock County Hospital, Bassett, NE, p. A381

ALDERFER, Jennifer, President, Good Samaritan Medical Center, Lafayette, CO, p. A102

ALDERMAN, Una, Chief Executive Officer, Northern Idaho Advanced Care Hospital, Post Falls, ID, p. A171

ALDIS, Karen, Director of Nursing, Hospital District 6 - Anthony Campus, KS, p. A236

ALDRED, Linda W, Senior Vice President, Texas Children's Hospital West Campus, TX, p. A613

ALDREDGE, Sarah, M.D., Chief Medical Officer, Essentia Health Sandstone, Sandstone, MN, p. A340

ALDRICH, Alan, Chief Financial Officer, Central Montana Medical Center, Lewistown, MT, p. A377

ALDRICH, Jim, Chief Executive Officer, Select Specialty Hospital - Spectrum Health, Grand Rapids, MI, p. A314

ALDRIDGE, Cassandra Haynes, Chief Human Resources Officer, Phoebe Sumter Medical Center, Americus, GA, p. A145

ALDRIDGE, Kenneth, M.D., Vice President Medical Affairs, Northport Medical Center, AL, p. A24

ALEEM, Asaf, M.D., Medical Director, Peachford Behavioral Health System, Atlanta, GA, p. A146

ALEMAN, Ralph A., President and Chief Executive Officer, Citrus Memorial Health System, Inverness, FL, p. A125

ALEXAITIS, Irene, R.N., Vice President of Nursing and Patient Services and Chief Nursing Officer, Uf Health Shands Rehab Hospital, FL, p. A124

ALEXANDA, Lisa, M.D., Vice President Medical Affairs, Parrish Medical Center, Titusville, FL, p. A142

ALEXANDER, Alan B., FACHE, Vice President and Administrator, The Medical Center At Caverna, Horse Cave, KY, p. A253

ALEXANDER, Angie, Chief Executive Officer, Allegiance Behavioral Health Center Of Plainview, Plainview, TX, p. A628

ALEXANDER, April, Director Human Resources, Nyc Health + Hospitals / Metropolitan, New York (Includes All Hospitals Located Within The Five Boroughs), NY, p. A436

ALEXANDER, Bobby, R.N., Chief Nursing Officer, Pinnacle Pointe Hospital, Little Rock-Pulaski County, AR, p. A45

ALEXANDER, Brenda, System Vice President, Human Resources, Ssm Health St. Mary's Hospital Centralia, Centralia, IL, p. A175

ALEXANDER, Brian, Chief Executive Officer, Sutter Roseville Medical Center, Roseville, CA, p. A81

ALEXANDER, Craig, Chief Operating Officer, Thomas B. Finan Center, Cumberland, MD, p. A291

ALEXANDER, David, Senior Vice President and Chief Financial Officer, St. Joseph's Wayne Hospital, NJ, p. A409

ALEXANDER, Dean, President and Chief Executive Officer, Christus Santa Rosa-Medical Center, TX, p. A632

ALEXANDER, Debra, Chief Information Officer, Safe Haven Hospital Of Treasure Valley, Boise, ID, p. A167

ALEXANDER, Drew, Chief Nursing Officer, Cedar County Memorial Hospital, El Dorado Springs, MO, p. A358

ALEXANDER, Fred, M.D., Medical Director, Kaiser Permanente West Los Angeles Medical Center, Los Angeles, CA, p. A67

ALEXANDER, Jack, M.D., Chief Medical Officer, Mayo Clinic Health System In Red Wing, Red Wing, MN, p. A338

ALEXANDER, Jane, Director Facility Administrative Services, Sagamore Children's Hospital Psychiatric Center, Dix Hills, NY, p. A425

ALEXANDER, Jeffrey, Chief Executive Officer, Healthsouth Rehabilitation Hospital Of Spring Hill, Brooksville, FL, p. A119

ALEXANDER, Jeremy, Chief Executive Officer, Fort Madison Community Hospital, Fort Madison, IA, p. A223

ALEXANDER, Josette, Director, Human Resources, Ohiohealth Rehabilitation Hospital, Columbus, OH, p. A478

ALEXANDER, Lisa, Vice President Patient Services and Chief Nursing Officer, University Of Kansas Health System St. Francis Campus, Topeka, KS, p. A246

ALEXANDER, Pat, Chief Executive Officer, Select Specialty Hospital-York, PA, p. A522

ALEXANDER, Thomas, Chief Executive Officer, Vibra Specialty Hospital At Desoto, Desoto, TX, p. A600

ALEXANDER-HINES, Joyce, R.N., MSN, Associate Director, Patient Care Services, Fayetteville Veterans Affairs Medical Center, Fayetteville, NC, p. A452

ALFANO, Alan, M.D., Medical Director, Uva-Healthsouth Rehabilitation Hospital, Charlottesville, VA, p. A656

ALFANO, Anthony, Vice President Executive Director, Montefiore New Rochelle, New Rochelle, NY, p. A431

ALFORD, Charles, Vice President Financial Services, Vidant Edgecombe Hospital, Tarboro, NC, p. A461

ALFORD, Jon, Chief Financial Officer, Medical City Frisco, TX, p. A628

ALFORD, Karla, Chief Information Officer, Greater Regional Medical Center, Creston, IA, p. A220

ALFORD, Michelle, R.N., MSN, Director of Nursing, Washington County Hospital, Chatom, AL, p. A16

ALFRED, Lorrie, Director Human Resources, Southern Surgical Hospital, Slidell, LA, p. A279

ALGER, Steve, Senior Vice President and Chief Financial Officer, Lakes Regional Healthcare, Spirit Lake, IA, p. A230

ALHADEFF, Joseph, M.D., President, Oss Orthopaedic Hospital, York, PA, p. A545

AL-HASHMI, Samer, M.D., Chief Medical Staff, Stevens County Hospital, Hugoton, KS, p. A237

ALI, Irfan, Director Information Services, Saint Agnes Medical Center, Fresno, CA, p. A59

ALI, Mirza Z, M.D., Chief of Staff, Wilkes-Barre Veterans Affairs Medical Center, Wilkes, PA, p. A544

ALI, Muhammad, M.D., Chief Medical Officer, Sanford Tracy Medical Center, Tracy, MN, p. A341

ALI, Syed Asif, M.D., Chief of Staff, Syracuse Veterans Affairs Medical Center, Syracuse, NY, p. A444

ALI-KHAN, Mir, M.D., Medical Director, Canyon Ridge Hospital, Chino, CA, p. A54

ALI-KHAN, Mujtaba, D.O., Chief Medical Officer, Conroe Regional Medical Center, Conroe, TX, p. A594

ALICE, Patricia K., Chief Executive Officer, Arizona Orthopedic Surgical Hospital, Chandler, AZ, p. A28

ALICEA, Luis, Chief Information Officer, Doctors' Center Hospital San Juan, San Juan, PR, p. A715

ALICEA PEREZ, Eneida, Interim Nursing Director, Hospital Buen Samaritano, Aguadilla, PR, p. A711

ALIFF, Sarah, Ph.D., Chief Nursing Officer, Hot Springs County Memorial Hospital, Thermopolis, WY, p. A710

ALKHOULI, Hassan, M.D.
  Chief Medical Officer, Garden Grove Hospital And Medical Center, Garden Grove, CA, p. A60
  Chief Medical Officer, West Anaheim Medical Center, Anaheim, CA, p. A50
  Medical Director, Huntington Beach Hospital, Huntington Beach, CA, p. A62

ALLA, Vamseedhar, M.D., Director Medical Staff, Connecticut Veterans Home And Hospital, Rocky Hill, CT, p. A110

ALLARD, Joan, Director Human Resources, Heart Of Florida Regional Medical Center, Davenport, FL, p. A121

ALLARD, Marie, Finance Manager, Brighton Center For Recovery, Brighton, MI, p. A308

ALLATT, Richard, M.D., Medical Director, Healthsouth Nittany Valley Rehabilitation Hospital, Pleasant Gap, PA, p. A538

ALLDREDGE, Kim, Director Human Resources, Lawrence County Memorial Hospital, Lawrenceville, IL, p. A187

ALLEMAN, Scott, Senior Vice President Patient Care Services and Chief Nursing Officer, Uw Medicine/Valley Medical Center, Renton, WA, p. A675

ALLEN, Audrey, Coordinator Benefits, Dallas County Medical Center, Fordyce-Dallas County, AR, p. A42

ALLEN, Brian, M.D., President Medical Staff, Georgetown Community Hospital, Georgetown, KY, p. A252

ALLEN, Candice, Director of Nursing, Rio Grande Hospital, Del Norte, CO, p. A98

ALLEN, Carolyn, Vice President and Chief Financial Officer, Camden Clark Medical Center, Parkersburg, WV, p. A685

ALLEN, Dawn, R.N., Chief Clinical Officer, Redwood Area Hospital, Redwood Falls, MN, p. A338

ALLEN, Devon, M.D., Chief of Medical Staff, Samuel Simmonds Memorial Hospital, Barrow, AK, p. A25

ALLEN, Donald, Chief Operating Officer, Unity Medical & Surgical Hospital, Mishawaka, IN, p. A211

ALLEN, Jason
Chief Operating Officer, Brook Lane Health Services, Hagerstown, MD, p. A292
Director Patient Care Services, Brook Lane Health Services, Hagerstown, MD, p. A292

ALLEN, Jean, Human Resources Director, Bleckley Memorial Hospital, Cochran, GA, p. A150

ALLEN, Jennifer, Vice President Human Resources, Mercy Hospital - A Campus Of Plantation General Hospital, FL, p. A136

ALLEN, John, Chief Information Officer, Holzer Medical Center, Gallipolis, OH, p. A483

ALLEN, John P., President, St. Mary's Medical Center, San Francisco, CA, p. A86

ALLEN, Judy, Human Resource Specialist, Carl Albert Community Mental Health Center, Mcalester, OK, p. A501

ALLEN, Kandice K., R.N., Chief Executive Officer, Share Medical Center, Alva, OK, p. A495

ALLEN, Karen A, R.N., Chief Nursing Officer, Butler Health System, Butler, PA, p. A521

ALLEN, Keith
Senior Vice President and Chief Human Resources Officer, Community Memorial Hospital, Menomonee Falls, WI, p. A697
Senior Vice President and Chief Human Resources Officer, Froedtert And The Medical College Of Wisconsin Froedtert Hospital, Milwaukee, WI, p. A698

ALLEN, Kent, Director Human Resources, Midmichigan Medical Center - West Branch, West Branch, MI, p. A326

ALLEN, Linda M, Vice President Human Resources, The Children's Institute Of Pittsburgh, Pittsburgh, PA, p. A538

ALLEN, Lucretia, Director Human Resources, Sweetwater Hospital, Sweetwater, TN, p. A580

ALLEN, Mark, Chief Operating Officer, Marian Regional Medical Center, Santa Maria, CA, p. A89

ALLEN, Mary Beth, Vice President Human Resources, Emory Wesley Woods Geriatric Hospital, GA, p. A146

ALLEN, Mike
Director Information Services, Shawnee Mission Medical Center, Shawnee Mission, KS, p. A246
Director Information Services, Shriners Hospitals For Children-Spokane, Spokane, WA, p. A678
Director Information Technology, Shriners Hospitals For Children-Salt Lake City, Salt Lake City, UT, p. A650

ALLEN, Myrna, R.N., MS, Chief Operating and Nursing Officer, Martin Luther King, Jr. Community Hospital, Los Angeles, CA, p. A68

ALLEN, Nancy, R.N., MS, Director, Patient Services and Chief Nursing Executive, Advocate Eureka Hospital, Eureka, IL, p. A182

ALLEN, Nikki, Patient Care Executive, Sutter Amador Hospital, Jackson, CA, p. A62

ALLEN, Patty, St. John's Vice President Finance, St. John's Children's Hospital, IL, p. A196

ALLEN, R Keith, Senior Vice President Human Resources, University Of Maryland Hospital For Children, MD, p. A289

ALLEN, Richard
Chief Executive Officer, Palmdale Regional Medical Center, Palmdale, CA, p. A77
Chief Executive Officer, Warren General Hospital, Warren, PA, p. A543

ALLEN, Rob, Chief Executive Officer, Sitka Community Hospital, Sitka, AK, p. A27

ALLEN, Robert, M.D.
Chief Medical Officer, Mercy Hospital Of Folsom, Folsom, CA, p. A58
President and Chief Executive Officer, Hollywood Presbyterian Medical Center, Los Angeles, CA, p. A67

ALLEN, Scott J, Director Human Resources, Hudson Hospital And Clinic, Hudson, WI, p. A694

ALLEN, Steve, M.D., Chief Executive Officer, Nationwide Children's Hospital, Columbus, OH, p. A478

ALLEN, Timothy J., FACHE
Chief Executive Officer, Leonard J. Chabert Medical Center, Houma, LA, p. A269
Chief Executive Officer, Ochsner St. Anne General Hospital, Raceland, LA, p. A277

ALLEN, Timothy M, Vice President Human Resources, United Hospital Center, Bridgeport, WV, p. A681

ALLEN, Vicki, R.N., MS
Vice President Patient Care Services and Chief Nursing Officer, Central Hartnett Hospital, NC, p. A451
Chief Financial Officer, Chicot Memorial Medical Center, Lake Village-Chicot County, AR, p. A44

ALLEN, Wain, M.D., Medical Director, Park City Hospital, Park City, UT, p. A649

ALLEN, Zac, CPA, Chief Financial Officer, Floyd Cherokee Medical Center, Centre, AL, p. A16

ALLENSWORTH, Ed, M.D., Medical Director, Saint Francis Hospital Vinita, Vinita, OK, p. A509

ALLEY, David, Chief Financial Officer, Starr Regional Medical Center, Athens, TN, p. A566

ALLEY, John L., Chief Executive Officer, Woodlawn Hospital, Rochester, IN, p. A214

ALLEY, Jon, D.O., President Medical Staff, Cameron Memorial Community Hospital, Angola, IN, p. A199

ALLEY, Steve B, M.D., Chief of Staff, Crosbyton Clinic Hospital, Crosbyton, TX, p. A595

ALLGEIER, Patricia, R.N., Chief Nursing Officer, Boys Town National Research Hospital, Omaha, NE, p. A387

ALLGOOD, Libby, Chief Financial Officer, Kittitas Valley Healthcare, Ellensburg, WA, p. A671

ALLICON, Keary T, Vice President Finance and Chief Financial Officer, Baystate Wing Hospital, Palmer, MA, p. A303

ALLIES, Karla, Director Human Resources, Rosebud Health Care Center, Forsyth, MT, p. A375

ALLINSON, Randy, R.N., Chief Nursing Officer, Central Valley Medical Center, Nephi, UT, p. A648

ALLISON, Lorraine, Human Resource Partner, Peacehealth Peace Island Medical Center, Friday Harbor, WA, p. A672

ALLISON, Steve, Director Human Resources, Logan County Hospital, Oakley, KS, p. A242

ALLISON, William E., Senior Vice President and Chief Operating Officer, Administration, South Nassau Communities Hospital, Oceanside, NY, p. A438

ALLMAN, Rex, M.D., President Medical Staff, Pulaski Memorial Hospital, Winamac, IN, p. A216

ALLORE, Gary, President, Mercy Health, Mercy Campus, MI, p. A319

ALLPHIN, Allan, M.D., Chief of Staff, Mercy Orthopedic Hospital Springfield, MO, p. A370

ALLPORT, Jeff, Vice President, Chief Information Officer, Valley Presbyterian Hospital, Los Angeles, CA, p. A70

ALLRED, Al W, Chief Financial Officer, Florida Hospital New Smyrna, New Smyrna Beach, FL, p. A132

ALLRED, B Dee, M.D., President Medical Staff, Mountain Point Medical Center, UT, p. A652

ALLRED, Lowell C, M.D., Chief of Staff, Columbia Basin Hospital, Ephrata, WA, p. A671

ALLRED, William, M.D., Vice President Medical Affairs, St. John Medical Center, Tulsa, OK, p. A509

ALLSOP, Brian, Director Human Resources, Central Valley Medical Center, Nephi, UT, p. A648

ALLSTOTT, Patti, Administrative Coordinator Human Resources and Grant Writer, Pioneer Memorial Hospital, Heppner, OR, p. A513

ALLUSON, Valerie, M.D., Chief Medical Officer, Hackensack Meridian Health Mountainside Medical Center, Montclair, NJ, p. A407

ALMAUHY, Deborah, R.N., Chief Nursing Officer, Emory Rehabilitation Hospital, Atlanta, GA, p. A146

ALMEIDA, Sergio, Director Information Systems, West Houston Medical Center, Houston, TX, p. A614

ALMEIDA-SUAREZ, Mario, M.D., Chief of Staff, Larkin Community Hospital, South Miami, FL, p. A139

ALMENDINGER, J Todd., President and Chief Executive Officer, Magruder Memorial Hospital, Port Clinton, OH, p. A489

ALMETER, Connie, Director of Nursing (Acute), Wyoming County Community Hospital, Warsaw, NY, p. A445

ALMETER, Marilyn, Chief Nursing Officer, United Memorial Medical Center-North Street, NY, p. A422

ALMODOVAR, Gustavo, Executive Director, Hospital De La Concepcion, San German, PR, p. A715

ALMOHAMMED, Salah, Chief of Staff, Ut Health Carthage, Carthage, TX, p. A592

ALO, Kathleen, Chief Nursing Officer, Mammoth Hospital, Mammoth Lakes, CA, p. A71

ALONSO, Gwen, Chief Nursing Officer, Florida Hospital Zephyrhills, Zephyrhills, FL, p. A144

ALONSO, Jose', M.D., Medical Director, San Juan Capestrano Hospital, San Juan, PR, p. A716

ALONZO, Patti, Manager Human Resources, Pacifica Hospital Of The Valley, Los Angeles, CA, p. A69

ALPERT, Jeffrey, M.D., Medical Director, Wichita County Health Center, Leoti, KS, p. A240

ALPERT, Len, Director Human Resources, Larkin Community Hospital Behavioral Health Services, Hollywood, FL, p. A124

ALRASHEDY, Farhad H, M.D., Chief Medical Officer, Ferry County Memorial Hospital, Republic, WA, p. A675

ALSADON, Danielle, Clinic/Hospital Manager, Kenmare Community Hospital, Kenmare, ND, p. A467

ALSIP, Bryan, M.D., Executive Vice President, Chief Medical Officer, University Hospital, TX, p. A634

ALSTAD, Nancy, Director Human Resources, Fort Healthcare, Fort Atkinson, WI, p. A692

ALT, Melinda, Chief Financial Officer, Audubon County Memorial Hospital, Audubon, IA, p. A217

ALTARAS, June, R.N.
Chief Executive Officer, Swedish Medical Center-Ballard, WA, p. A676
Chief Executive Officer, Swedish Medical Center-Cherry Hill Campus, Seattle, WA, p. A676

ALTENBURGER, Andy, Chief Information Officer, Marietta Memorial Hospital, Marietta, OH, p. A485

ALTENDORF, Amanda, Chief Human Resources and Quality Management, Red River Behavioral Health System, Grand Forks, ND, p. A466

ALTHOEN, David, Director Financial Planning and Analysis, Forest Health Medical Center, Ypsilanti, MI, p. A326

ALTHOUSE, Douglas, Chief Medical Staff, Kearney County Health Services, Minden, NE, p. A386

ALTMAN, Alexander B, III, Chief Financial Officer, Union County General Hospital, Clayton, NM, p. A416

ALTMAN, Angie, Director Human Resources, Shands Lake Shore Regional Medical Center, Lake City, FL, p. A127

ALTMAN, Brett, Chief Executive Officer, Cass County Memorial Hospital, Atlantic, IA, p. A217

ALTMAN, Deana, Interim Chief Nursing Officer, Harney District Hospital, Burns, OR, p. A511

ALTMAN, Harold, M.D., Chief Medical Officer, Acmh Hospital, Kittanning, PA, p. A528

ALTMILLER, Steve, President and Chief Executive Officer, Camden Clark Medical Center, Parkersburg, WV, p. A685

ALTOM, Andy, President and Chief Executive Officer, Methodist Behavioral Hospital Of Arkansas, Maumelle-Pulaski County, AR, p. A46

ALTOSE, Murray, M.D., Chief of Staff, Louis Stokes Cleveland Veterans Affairs Medical Center, Cleveland, OH, p. A477

ALTSHULER, Keith, President and Chief Administrative Officer, Fort Sanders Regional Medical Center, Knoxville, TN, p. A572

ALUISE, Tony, Chief Executive Officer, Three Gables Surgery Center, Proctorville, OH, p. A489

ALURI, Bapu, M.D., Chief Medical Officer, Yuma Rehabilitation Hospital, A Partnership Of Encompass Health And Yrmc, Yuma, AZ, p. A38

ALVARADO, Felicita E., Administrator, Hospital Psiquiatrico Correccional, San Juan, PR, p. A716

ALVARADO, Rafael, Chief Executive Officer, Dr. Pila's Hospital, Ponce, PR, p. A714

ALVARADO, Ramona, Interim Manager Human Resources, Adventist Medical Center-Reedley, Reedley, CA, p. A80

ALVAREZ, Dena C, R.N., COO & Chief Compliance Officer, Brodstone Memorial Hospital, Superior, NE, p. A390

ALVAREZ, Janie, Accounting Director, Cornerstone Regional Hospital, Edinburg, TX, p. A600

ALVAREZ, Jose, M.D., Chief Medical Staff, Circles Of Care, Melbourne, FL, p. A129

ALVAREZ, Maria Charlotte, M.D., Chief of Staff, Sheridan Community Hospital, Sheridan, MI, p. A323

ALVAREZ, Valerie, Executive Assistant, Adventist Medical Center-Reedley, Reedley, CA, p. A80

ALVEY, Raymond, Chief Financial Officer, Ssm Health Saint Louis University Hospital-South, MO, p. A369

ALWARD, Dale, Chief Executive Officer, Twin County Regional Healthcare, Galax, VA, p. A658

ALWIN-POPP, Sue, Chief Clinical Officer, Edgerton Hospital And Health Services, Edgerton, WI, p. A692

ALWINE, Steven, Chief Executive Officer, Healthsouth Rehabilitation Hospital Of York, York, PA, p. A545

ALZEIN, Bashar, M.D., President Medical Staff, Illini Community Hospital, Pittsfield, IL, p. A193

AMADO, Mitchell, Senior Vice President Finance and Chief Financial Officer, Glens Falls Hospital, Glens Falls, NY, p. A427

AMANTEA, Paul, Director Finance, University Hospitals Geauga Medical Center, Chardon, OH, p. A474

AMAR, Eugene, Jr, Administrator, Kohala Hospital, Kohala, HI, p. A166

AMARANTOS, Stacie, Chief Operating Officer, Catalina Island Medical Center, Avalon, CA, p. A51

AMATO, Jerry, President and Chief Operating Officer, Lakeview Specialty Hospital And Rehab, Waterford, WI, p. A704

AMBERSON, Rosemarie, Vice President Human Resources, Aventura Hospital And Medical Center, Aventura, FL, p. A117

AMBROSE, Sherie, Chief Nurse Executive, Sequoia Hospital, Redwood City, CA, p. A80

AMBROSIANI, Michael, Chief Financial Officer, Knox Community Hospital, Mount Vernon, OH, p. A487

AMBROSINI, Joseph, Director Human Resources, Olympia Medical Center, Los Angeles, CA, p. A69

AMENT, Arlinda K, R.N., Interim Chief Nursing Officer, Beatrice Community Hospital And Health Center, Beatrice, NE, p. A382

AMENT, Rick, Chief Executive Officer, Robert J. Dole Veterans Affairs Medical Center, Wichita, KS, p. A248

AMERSON, Jeff, Director Information System, West Florida Rehabilitation Institute, FL, p. A136

AMES, Becky, Chief Executive Officer, Medical Center Of Southeast Texas, Beaumont, TX, p. A588

AMES, Lance
Interim Chief Executive Officer, Edinburg Regional Medical Center, TX, p. A601
Interim Chief Executive Officer, South Texas Behavioral Health Center, TX, p. A601

AMIN, Saad, Medical Director Hospital, Kindred Hospital-Greensboro, Greensboro, NC, p. A453

AMMAZZALORSO, Michael, M.D., Chief Medical Officer, Children's Medical Center, NY, p. A430

AMMONS, Angela, Administrator, Clinch Memorial Hospital, Homerville, GA, p. A155

AMMONS, Eric, President, Mercy Hospital Jefferson, Crystal City, MO, p. A358

AMODO, Mitch, Vice President and Chief Financial Officer, Orange Regional Medical Center, Middletown, NY, p. A430

AMOROSE, Carl, Vice President Finance, Norton Women's And Children's Hospital, KY, p. A256

AMOROSO, Mitze, Chief Information Officer, Terence Cardinal Cooke Health Care Center, New York (Includes All Hospitals Located Within The Five Boroughs), NY, p. A437

AMOS, John R.
Chief Executive Officer, Yavapai Regional Medical Center - East, AZ, p. A34
President and Chief Executive Officer, Yavapai Regional Medical Center - East, AZ, p. A34

AMOS, Robert, Vice President and Chief Financial Officer, Winchester Medical Center, Winchester, VA, p. A668

AMOX, Mark J., Chief Operating Officer, Sunrise Hospital And Medical Center, Las Vegas, NV, p. A395

AMSBERRY, Shelly, Director of Nursing, Jennie M. Melham Memorial Medical Center, Broken Bow, NE, p. A382

AMSTUTZ, Charles, Director of Information Technology, Cascade Medical Center, Leavenworth, WA, p. A673

AMSTUTZ, Terry L., FACHE, Chief Executive Officer, Anson General Hospital, Anson, TX, p. A584

AMYX, Maleigha, Chief Information Officer, Rockcastle Regional Hospital And Respiratory Care Center, Mount Vernon, KY, p. A258

ANASTASI, Frank, Chief Financial Officer, Pennsylvania Hospital, Philadelphia, PA, p. A536

ANAYA, Sandra J., R.N., Chief Executive Officer, Palo Verde Hospital, Blythe, CA, p. A53

ANCHONDO, Laura, Administrator Human Resources, Kindred Hospital El Paso, El Paso, TX, p. A602

ANCZAK, Deb, Director Performance Improvement, Livingston Healthcare, Livingston, MT, p. A377

ANDERER, Tammy, Acting President, Geisinger Jersey Shore Hospital, Jersey Shore, PA, p. A528

ANDERS, Anna, Vice President and Chief Nursing Officer, Sierra Surgery Hospital, NV, p. A392

ANDERS, James M, Jr, Administrator and Chief Operating Officer, Kennedy Krieger Institute, Baltimore, MD, p. A287

ANDERS, Mark, Administrator, Villa Feliciana Medical Complex, Jackson, LA, p. A269

ANDERS, Robert, Chief Financial Officer, Ouachita County Medical Center, Camden-Ouachita County, AR, p. A40

ANDERSEN, Connie, R.N., MS, Chief Nursing Officer, Sarasota Memorial Health Care System, Sarasota, FL, p. A139

ANDERSEN, Donia L, Director of Nursing, Centennial Peaks Hospital, Louisville, CO, p. A104

ANDERSEN, Frank, Interim Chief Medical Officer, Providence Everett Medical Center - Pacific Campus, WA, p. A671

ANDERSEN, Janet
Chief Financial Officer, Ut Health Pittsburg, Pittsburg, TX, p. A628
Chief Financial Officer, Ut Health Quitman, Quitman, TX, p. A629

ANDERSEN, John, Manager Information Systems, Astria Sunnyside Hospital, Sunnyside, WA, p. A678

ANDERSEN, Sue
Chief Financial Officer, French Hospital Medical Center, San Luis Obispo, CA, p. A87
Vice President and Service Area and Chief Financial Officer, Marian Regional Medical Center, Santa Maria, CA, p. A89

ANDERSEN, Tracy, Chief Information Officer, St. Mary's Regional Medical Center, Enid, OK, p. A498

ANDERSEN, Travis
Chief Executive Officer, Columbia St. Mary's Milwaukee Hospital, WI, p. A698
President and Chief Executive Officer, Columbia St. Mary's Hospital Ozaukee, Mequon, WI, p. A698

ANDERSEN, Wendy, Director Human Resources, Eastern Idaho Regional Medical Center, Idaho Falls, ID, p. A169

ANDERSON, Alison, Chief Nursing Officer, Select Specialty Hospital-Sioux Falls, Sioux Falls, SD, p. A564

ANDERSON, Allen, Administrator, Avera Tyler Hospital, Tyler, MN, p. A341

ANDERSON, Allyson, President, Legacy Meridian Park Medical Center, Tualatin, OR, p. A518

ANDERSON, Angie, Director Information Technology, Crawford County Memorial Hospital, Denison, IA, p. A221

ANDERSON, Benjamin, Chief Executive Officer and Administrator, Kearny County Hospital, Lakin, KS, p. A239

ANDERSON, Bill, Chief Executive Officer, Lakeview Behavioral Health, Norcross, GA, p. A158

ANDERSON, Brad
Chief Financial Officer, Community Memorial Hospital, Cloquet, MN, p. A329
Chief Operating Officer, Rehabilitation Hospital Of Wisconsin, Waukesha, WI, p. A705

ANDERSON, Brian
Chief Financial Officer, Capital Medical Center, Olympia, WA, p. A674
Chief Financial Officer, Simi Valley Hospital, Simi Valley, CA, p. A90

ANDERSON, Brian A., D.O., Chief of Staff, Myrtue Medical Center, Harlan, IA, p. A224

ANDERSON, Calandra, Vice President Patient Care and Chief Nursing Officer, Mclaren Oakland, Pontiac, MI, p. A321

ANDERSON, Charles, M.D., Chief Medical Officer, Desert Regional Medical Center, Palm Springs, CA, p. A77

ANDERSON, Cherri, Chief Nursing Officer, Banner Behavioral Health Hospital - Scottsdale, Scottsdale, AZ, p. A35

ANDERSON, Christine, Chief Nursing Officer and Vice President of Patient Care Services, Lincolnhealth St. Andrews Campus, ME, p. A283

ANDERSON, Conde Nevin, M.D., Chief of Staff, Detar Hospital North, TX, p. A642

ANDERSON, Craig, Director Management Information Systems, River Bend Hospital, West Lafayette, IN, p. A216

ANDERSON, Dale, RN, Chief Executive Officer, North Metro Medical Center, Jacksonville-Pulaski County, AR, p. A44

ANDERSON, Dana, Administrator, Long-Term Acute Care Hospital, Mosaic Life Care At St. Joseph, Saint Joseph, MO, p. A367

ANDERSON, Darla, Chief Financial Officer, Ridgeview Sibley Medical Center, Arlington, MN, p. A327

ANDERSON, Dave, FACHE
Vice President Administration, Carolinas Healthcare System Union, Monroe, NC, p. A457
Vice President and Administrator, Carolinas Healthcare System Anson, Wadesboro, NC, p. A461

ANDERSON, David, Chief Executive Officer, Jackson Purchase Medical Center, Mayfield, KY, p. A257

ANDERSON, Dianne J., MS, R.N., President and Chief Executive Officer, Lawrence General Hospital, Lawrence, MA, p. A300

ANDERSON, Donna K, R.N., Chief Nursing Officer, Anmed Health Cannon, Pickens, SC, p. A556

ANDERSON, Duke, President and Chief Executive Officer, Hillsdale Hospital, Hillsdale, MI, p. A315

ANDERSON, Edwin, M.D., Chief of Staff and Chief Medical Officer, Bigfork Valley Hospital, Bigfork, MN, p. A328

ANDERSON, Gaynell, M.D., Medical Director, Ssm Health St. Anthony Hospital - Shawnee, Shawnee, OK, p. A506

ANDERSON, Gina, Human Resources Officer, Riverview Regional Medical Center, Carthage, TN, p. A566

ANDERSON, Heidi, Chief Nursing Officer, Morton General Hospital, Morton, WA, p. A673

ANDERSON, Holly, Supervisor Human Resources, Sanford Rock Rapids Medical Center, Rock Rapids, IA, p. A228

ANDERSON, Jason, Chief Financial Officer, Mackinac Straits Health System, Inc., Saint Ignace, MI, p. A322

ANDERSON, Jay
President, Northwestern Medicine Kishwaukee Hospital, Dekalb, IL, p. A181
President, Northwestern Medicine Valley West Hospital, Sandwich, IL, p. A195

ANDERSON, Joann, President and Chief Executive Officer, Southeastern Health, Lumberton, NC, p. A456

ANDERSON, Jodie, Director Human Resources, Mitchell County Regional Health Center, Osage, IA, p. A227

ANDERSON, John D., FACHE, Administrator, Marshall Medical Center South, Boaz, AL, p. A15

ANDERSON, John G., FACHE
President and Chief Executive Officer, Anderson Regional Health System South, Meridian, MS, p. A350
President and Chief Executive Officer, Anderson Regional Health System, Meridian, MS, p. A350

ANDERSON, Jonathan, Medical Director, Western State Hospital, Staunton, VA, p. A666

ANDERSON, Kathleen, Director, Acute Clinical Systems, Ghs - Laurens County Memorial Hospital, SC, p. A550

ANDERSON, Kenneth, M.D., Senior Vice President and Chief Medical Officer, Baptist Health Louisville, Louisville, KY, p. A256

ANDERSON, Kimball S., FACHE, Chief Executive Officer, Timpanogos Regional Hospital, Orem, UT, p. A649

ANDERSON, Kristin, Director, Human Resources, California Hospital Medical Center, Los Angeles, CA, p. A66

ANDERSON, Libby, Chief Financial Officer, Satanta District Hospital And Long Term Care, Satanta, KS, p. A245

ANDERSON, Louis, Chief Financial Officer, Mcleod Health Cheraw, Cheraw, SC, p. A550

ANDERSON, Lucia E, Senior Vice President Operations and Chief Nurse Executive, Lake Region Healthcare, Fergus Falls, MN, p. A331

ANDERSON, Lynne, Chief Executive Officer, Stephens County Hospital, Toccoa, GA, p. A162

ANDERSON, Mark
Chief Financial Officer, North Oaks Medical Center, Hammond, LA, p. A268
Chief Financial Officer, North Oaks Rehabilitation Hospital, Hammond, LA, p. A268

ANDERSON, Mark T, Chief Financial Officer, Sovah Health-Danville, Danville, VA, p. A657

ANDERSON, Michael, M.D., President, Ucsf Benioff Children's Hospital, CA, p. A86

ANDERSON, Michael Bruce, Ph.D., Chief Operating Officer, Metropolitan St. Louis Psychiatric Center, Saint Louis, MO, p. A368

ANDERSON, Mickey, M.D., Vice President Medical Affairs, Flaget Memorial Hospital, Bardstown, KY, p. A249

ANDERSON, Patricia, Chief Nursing Officer, Riverview Regional Medical Center, Carthage, TN, p. A566

ANDERSON, Patrick
Chief Information Officer and Senior Vice President, Hoag Hospital Irvine, CA, p. A75
Chief Information Officer, Memorial Medical Center, CA, p. A73

ANDERSON, Paula, Administrative Director Human Resources, Endless Mountain Health Systems, Montrose, PA, p. A532

ANDERSON, Rhena
Chief Nursing Officer, Nexus Specialty Hospital The Woodlands, The Woodlands, TX, p. A640
Chief Nursing Officer, Nexus Specialty Hospital, Shenandoah, TX, p. A635

ANDERSON, Rhonda
Executive Vice President Finance and Chief Financial Officer, Columbia St. Mary's Hospital Ozaukee, Mequon, WI, p. A698
Executive Vice President Finance and Chief Financial Officer, Columbia St. Mary's Milwaukee Hospital, Milwaukee, WI, p. A698
Executive Vice President Finance and Chief Financial Officer, Columbia St. Mary's Milwaukee Hospital, WI, p. A698

ANDERSON, Rick, M.D., Senior Vice President and Chief Medical Officer, Tmc For Children, AZ, p. A38

ANDERSON, Robert C, Interim Chief Financial Officer, Alameda Hospital, Alameda, CA, p. A50

ANDERSON, Robert G., Jr, President, Children's Hospital Of Illinois, IL, p. A193

ANDERSON, Rohan, Chief Information Officer, Doctors Memorial Hospital, Bonifay, FL, p. A118

ANDERSON, Rosemary, Administrator, Ccc At Pineview Hospital, Lakeside, AZ, p. A31

ANDERSON, Sandra L.
President and Chief Executive Officer, Ascension Sacred Heart Hospital, Tomahawk, WI, p. A704
President and Chief Executive Officer, Howard Young Medical Center, Woodruff, WI, p. A706
President, Ascension Eagle River Hospital, Eagle River, WI, p. A692
President, St. Mary's Hospital, WI, p. A702

ANDERSON, Scott, Chief Medical Officer, Banner Del E. Webb Medical Center, Sun City West, AZ, p. A36

ANDERSON, Sharla, Chief Executive Officer, Christus Trinity Mother Frances Rehabilitation Hospital, A Partner Of Encompass Health, Tyler, TX, p. A641

ANDERSON, Shawn, Chief Operating Officer, Cary Medical Center, Caribou, ME, p. A283

ANDERSON, Sims, Manager Facility Automation, Terrell State Hospital, Terrell, TX, p. A639

ANDERSON, Stephanie, Executive Vice President and Chief Operating Officer, Woman's Hospital, Baton Rouge, LA, p. A264

ANDERSON, Stephen, M.D.
Chief Medical Officer, Plymouth Medical Center, Plymouth, IN, p. A213
Chief Medical Officer, Saint Joseph Health System, Mishawaka, IN, p. A211

ANDERSON, Steven, Chief Executive Officer, University Of Kansas Health System St. Francis Campus, Topeka, KS, p. A246

ANDERSON, Susan, Director Information Systems, Texas Health Presbyterian Hospital Plano, Plano, TX, p. A629

ANDERSON, Suzanne P., Nurse Administrator, Intermountain Medical Center, Murray, UT, p. A648

ANDERSON, Terry, R.N., Director of Nursing Services, Chippewa County-Montevideo Hospital, Montevideo, MN, p. A336

ANDERSON, Thomas, M.D.
Vice President Medical Affairs, Chambersburg Hospital, Chambersburg, PA, p. A522
Vice President Medical Affairs, Waynesboro Hospital, Waynesboro, PA, p. A543
Vice President Medical Affairs, Lakeview Hospital, Stillwater, MN, p. A340

ANDERSON, Tim, Controller, Van Matre Healthsouth Rehabilitation Hospital, Rockford, IL, p. A195

ANDERSON, Timothy Craig, Jr, Chief Nursing Officer, Bristol Regional Medical Center, Bristol, TN, p. A566

ANDERSON, Traci, Chief Financial Officer, Memorial Hospital, Seminole, TX, p. A635

ANDERSON, Valerie, Chief Nursing Officer, Select Specialty Hospital-Tri Cities, Bristol, TN, p. A566

ANDERSON, William, M.D., Medical Director, Rosebud Health Care Center, Forsyth, MT, p. A375

ANDERT, Nancy, Director Human Resources, Murray County Medical Center, Slayton, MN, p. A340

ANDERT, Vicki
Chief Executive Officer, Eureka Springs Hospital, Eureka Springs-Carroll County, AR, p. A41
Chief Executive Officer, River Valley Medical Center, Dardanelle-Yell County, AR, p. A41

ANDERTON, Scott, Chief Financial Officer, Coliseum Center For Behavioral Health, GA, p. A156

ANDRADA, Sally, Chief Information Officer, Los Alamitos Medical Center, Los Alamitos, CA, p. A65

ANDRADE, Marise, Controller, Southern Inyo Healthcare District, Lone Pine, CA, p. A65

ANDRAE, Andrea, Chief Financial Officer, St. Luke's - Palmerton Campus, PA, p. A530

ANDRE, Katelyn, Human Resource Coordinator, Select Specialty Hospital-Macomb County, Mount Clemens, MI, p. A319

ANDREAS, Ginger, Coordinator Personnel and Credentialing, El Campo Memorial Hospital, El Campo, TX, p. A601

ANDREAS, Lori, Chief Executive Officer and Administrator, Appleton Area Health Services, Appleton, MN, p. A327

ANDREASEN, Raymond, M.D., Chief Medical Officer-Inpatient, California Medical Facility, Vacaville, CA, p. A93

ANDRES, Chad, Chief Information Officer, Desert View Hospital, Pahrump, NV, p. A396

ANDRES, Elizabeth, Director Human Resources, Atascadero State Hospital, Atascadero, CA, p. A51

ANDRES, Leonidas, M.D., Chief of Staff, Riceland Medical Center, Winnie, TX, p. A644

ANDRESEN, Daniel, Chief information Officer, Mercy Medical Center Merced-Dominican Campus, CA, p. A72

ANDREW, Sigrid, Director, James E. Van Zandt Veterans Affairs Medical Center, Altoona, PA, p. A519

ANDREWS, Callie, President, Wellstar Cobb Hospital, Austell, GA, p. A148

ANDREWS, Carolle, Vice President, Interim Human Resources Officer, Uconn, John Dempsey Hospital, Farmington, CT, p. A108

ANDREWS, Charles, Director Information Technology, West Springs Hospital, Grand Junction, CO, p. A101

ANDREWS, David, Manager Information Systems, Chicot Memorial Medical Center, Lake Village-Chicot County, AR, p. A44

ANDREWS, Jim, Chief Financial Officer, North Okaloosa Medical Center, Crestview, FL, p. A120

ANDREWS, John, M.D., Chief of Staff, Ut Health Behavioral Health Center, TX, p. A641

ANDREWS, Kathy, Chief Financial Officer, Kindred Hospital Philadelphia - Havertown, PA, p. A535

ANDREWS, Lisa, Director Human Resources, Lancaster Rehabilitation Hospital, Lancaster, PA, p. A528

ANDREWS, Michael, Coordinator Information Systems, Harlan County Health System, Alma, NE, p. A381

ANDREWS, Michele, Chief Clinical Officer, Integrity Transitional Hospital, Denton, TX, p. A599

ANDREWS, Mike, Associate Administrator and Chief Operating Officer, Och Regional Medical Center, Starkville, MS, p. A353

ANDREWS, Paul
Chief Executive Officer, The Brook At Dupont, Louisville, KY, p. A256
Chief Executive Officer, The Brook Hospital - Kmi, Louisville, KY, p. A257

ANDREWS, Rebecca, Chief Financial Officer, Vibra Hospital Of Northern California, Redding, CA, p. A80

ANDREWS, Ryan, M.D.
Chief Medical Officer, Ascension St. Michael's Hospital, Stevens Point, WI, p. A703
Chief Medical Officer, Ministry Good Samaritan Health Center, Weston, WI, p. A706

ANDREWS, Steve, Chief Financial Officer, Three Rivers Health, Three Rivers, MI, p. A324

ANDREWS, Sue E., Chief Financial Officer, O'Connor Hospital, Delhi, NY, p. A425

ANDREWS, Susan E., Chief Executive Officer, Touro Rehabilitation Center, LA, p. A276

ANDREWS, Terri, Director Information Technology, Alamance Regional Medical Center, Burlington, NC, p. A448

ANDRO, Ronald J., R.N., MS, President and Chief Executive Officer, West Penn Hospital, Pittsburgh, PA, p. A538

ANDRUS, Helen
Chief Financial Officer, Providence Mount Carmel Hospital, Colville, WA, p. A670
Chief Financial Officer, Providence St. Joseph's Hospital, Chewelah, WA, p. A670
Chief Financial Officer, St. Luke's Rehabilitation Institute, Spokane, WA, p. A678

ANDRUS, Jonathon, Chief Executive Officer, Fairchild Medical Center, Yreka, CA, p. A95

ANDURSKY, John, Chief Financial Officer, Highlands Hospital, Connellsville, PA, p. A523

ANFINSON, Julie, Director Human Resources, Mercy Medical Center-Sioux City, Sioux City, IA, p. A229

ANGELI, Maribeth, Chief Nursing Officer, Berwick Hospital Center, Berwick, PA, p. A520

ANGELL, Deborah, Chief Financial Officer, Syracuse Veterans Affairs Medical Center, Syracuse, NY, p. A444

ANGELL, Nancy, Associate Administrator Personnel, Sagamore Children's Hospital Psychiatric Center, Dix Hills, NY, p. A425

ANGELO, Gregory, Chief Fiscal Program, James J. Peters Veterans Affairs Medical Center, New York (Includes All Hospitals Located Within The Five Boroughs), NY, p. A432

ANGELO, Thomas, Chief Executive Officer, Centra Southside Community Hospital, Farmville, VA, p. A658

ANGELUCCI, Patricia A, MS, R.N., Director Patient Care Services, Thedacare Medical Center-Shawano, Shawano, WI, p. A702

ANGERAMI, Deborah
Chief Operating Officer, Health First Community Hospitals, Health First Cape Canaveral Hospital, Cocoa Beach, FL, p. A120
Chief Operating Officer, Health First Community Hospitals, Health First Palm Bay Hospital, Palm Bay, FL, p. A135
Chief Operating Officer, Health First Viera Hospital, Melbourne, FL, p. A129

ANGERMEIER, Elizabeth, Director of Nursing, Evansville Psychiatric Children Center, Evansville, IN, p. A203

ANGLE, Mary Ann, R.N., FACHE, Chief Nursing Officer, Tristar Summit Medical Center, Hermitage, TN, p. A570

ANGLIM, John, Human Resources Client Manager, Providence Seaside Hospital, Seaside, OR, p. A518

ANGLIN, Jason, Chief Executive Officer, Memorial Medical Center, Port Lavaca, TX, p. A629

ANGLIN, Kristine, Human Resources Manager, Willow Springs Center, Reno, NV, p. A396

ANGUS, Jolyn M, R.N., Chief Nursing Officer, Miami Valley Hospital South, OH, p. A480

ANISKO RYAN, Karen, Director Business Development and Communications, Uc San Diego Shiley Eye Institute, CA, p. A84

ANMUTH, Craig, M.D., Medical Director, Bacharach Institute For Rehabilitation, Pomona, NJ, p. A410

ANNARINO, Phillip, Vice President Human Resources, Fisher-Titus Medical Center, Norwalk, OH, p. A488

ANNARUMO, Beverly, R.N., MSN, President, Ellwood City Medical Center, Ellwood City, PA, p. A525

ANNECHARICO, Mary Alice
System Vice President and Chief Information Officer, Henry Ford Hospital, Detroit, MI, p. A311
System Vice President and Chief Information Officer, Henry Ford West Bloomfield Hospital, West Bloomfield, MI, p. A325
System Vice President and Chief Information Officer, Henry Ford Wyandotte Hospital, Wyandotte, MI, p. A326

ANNESSER, Sue, Director Information Systems, Freeman Neosho Hospital, Neosho, MO, p. A365

ANOATUBBY, Chris, Deputy Secretary of Health, Chickasaw Nation Medical Center, Ada, OK, p. A495

ANOLIK, Adam, Chief Financial Officer, Highland Hospital, Rochester, NY, p. A441

ANSALDO, Luanne, Chief Operating Officer, Aventura Hospital And Medical Center, Aventura, FL, p. A117

ANSELL, David A, M.D., Senior Vice President Clinical Affairs and Chief Medical Officer, Rush Children's Hospital, IL, p. A179

ANSHUTZ, Margie, Chief Development Officer, Hamilton Center, Terre Haute, IN, p. A215

ANSI, Azena, Manager Health Information Management, Horizon Specialty Hospital, Las Vegas, NV, p. A394

ANSLEY, Pamela, Director Finance, Sutter Center For Psychiatry, Sacramento, CA, p. A82

ANSON, Ashley, Chief Executive Officer, Texas Health Hospital, Carrollton, TX, p. A592

ANTCZAK, Brett, Chief Executive Officer, Palo Alto County Health System, Emmetsburg, IA, p. A222

ANTCZAK, Kenneth, Vice President Human Resources, St. Mary Mercy Hospital, Livonia, MI, p. A318

ANTES, John, President, Missouri Baptist Medical Center, Saint Louis, MO, p. A368

ANTHONY, Ashley, R.N., Chief Executive Officer, Delta Memorial Hospital, Dumas-Desha County, AR, p. A41

ANTHONY, Harry C., M.D., Chief Medical Officer, Nanticoke Memorial Hospital, Seaford, DE, p. A114

ANTHONY, Jean, R.N., President and Chief Executive Officer, Hills & Dales General Hospital, Cass City, MI, p. A309

ANTHONY, Kim, Director Human Resources, Burke Medical Center, Waynesboro, GA, p. A163

ANTHONY, Mark, Executive Vice President and Chief Operating Officer, Borgess-Pipp Hospital, MI, p. A316

ANTHONY, Michelle, Chief Nursing Officer, Emcompass Health Rehabilitation Hospital Of Virginia, Richmond, VA, p. A665

ANTHONY, Paula
Vice President Information Services, Ut Health Behavioral Health Center, TX, p. A641
Vice President Information Services, Ut Health Pittsburg, Pittsburg, TX, p. A628
Vice President Information Services, Ut Health Rehabilitation Hospital, Tyler, TX, p. A641
Vice President Information Services, Ut Health Specialty Hospital, Tyler, TX, p. A641

ANTHONY, Robert, Chief Financial Officer, Kirkbride Center, Philadelphia, PA, p. A535

ANTINELLI, Mark, Manager Human Resources, Syracuse Veterans Affairs Medical Center, Syracuse, NY, p. A444

ANTINORI, James, M.D., Chief of Staff, Mountain West Medical Center, Tooele, UT, p. A651

ANTLE, Sue, Director of Nursing, Casey County Hospital, Liberty, KY, p. A255

ANTOINE, Greg, M.D., Chief of Staff, Fayetteville Veterans Affairs Medical Center, Fayetteville, NC, p. A452

ANTON, Lourdes, Director Human Resources, Palm Springs General Hospital, Hialeah, FL, p. A124

ANTONACCI, Amy, MSN, R.N., Vice President Nursing Services, Alliance Community Hospital, Alliance, OH, p. A470

ANTONECCHIA, Paul, M.D., Vice President Medical Affairs and Chief Medical Officer, St. John's Riverside Hospital - Dobbs Ferry Pavilion, NY, p. A446

ANTONSON, Pete, Chief Executive Officer, Northwood Deaconess Health Center, Northwood, ND, p. A468

ANTONUCCI, Lawrence, M.D.
President and Chief Executive Officer, Cape Coral Hospital, Cape Coral, FL, p. A119

President and Chief Executive Officer, Gulf Coast Medical Center, Fort Myers, FL, p. A123

President and Chief Executive Officer, The Rehabilitation Hospital, FL, p. A123

ANTRUM, Sheila, R.N., President, Ucsf Medical Center Mission Bay, CA, p. A86

ANTRUM, Vi-Anne, Chief Nursing Officer, Olean General Hospital, Olean, NY, p. A439

ANUSZKIEWICZ, Dawn, Chief Executive Officer, Ochsner Baptist Medical Center, LA, p. A276

ANWAR, Muhammad, M.D., Chief Medical Officer, Encino Hospital Medical Center, Los Angeles, CA, p. A66

ANYASO, Vanessa, Chief Human Resources, Kindred Hospital The Heights, TX, p. A640

ANYEBE, Abiola

Interim Chief Executive Officer, Kindred Hospital San Antonio Central, San Antonio, TX, p. A633

Interim Chief Executive Officer, Kindred Hospital-San Antonio, San Antonio, TX, p. A633

ANZURES, Rosey, Acting Chief Financial Officer, Central Texas Veterans Health Care System, Doris Miller Veterans Medical Center, TX, p. A638

APIKI, Zessica L, Accountant, Molokai General Hospital, Kaunakakai, HI, p. A166

APKON, Michael, MD, PhD, Chief Executive Officer, Tufts Medical Center, Boston, MA, p. A297

APLAND, Wendy, Interim Chief Financial Officer, Peacehealth Sacred Heart Medical Center University District, Eugene, OR, p. A512

APOLINAR, Adam, Chief Nursing Officer, Uvalde Memorial Hospital, Uvalde, TX, p. A641

APOLIONA, Nicole, M.D., Medical Director, Kula Hospital, Kula, HI, p. A166

APONTE, Miguel, Supervisor Management Information Systems, Wilma N. Vazquez Medical Center, Vega Baja, PR, p. A716

APPLEBAUM, Jon D., President and Chief Operating Officer, Novant Health Thomasville Medical Center, Thomasville, NC, p. A461

APPLEGEET, Carol, MSN, R.N., Vice President and Chief Nursing Officer, Fort Hamilton Hospital, Hamilton, OH, p. A483

APPLETON, Joe, M.D., Chief of Surgery, Milan General Hospital, Milan, TN, p. A576

APRILE, Patricia, Chief Operating Officer, Southern Maine Health Care - Biddeford Medical Center, ME, p. A283

AQUILINA, Anthony, D.O., Chief Medical Officer, Geisinger-Community Medical Center, Scranton, PA, p. A540

AQUILINA, Joanne, Vice President Finance and Chief Financial Officer, Bethesda Hospital West, FL, p. A118

AQUILINA, Salvatore, Chief Executive Officer, Pam Specialty Hospital Of Wilkes-Barre, Wilkes Barre, PA, p. A544

AQUINO, Jonathon F., Chief Executive Officer, San Gabriel Valley Medical Center, San Gabriel, CA, p. A86

ARA, Farideh, Interim Chief Nursing Officer, Hollywood Presbyterian Medical Center, Los Angeles, CA, p. A67

ARABIT, Aleen D., Chief Executive Officer, San Antonio Behavioral Healthcare Hospital, San Antonio, TX, p. A634

ARAD, Lana

Chief Financial Officer, Good Samaritan Hospital, San Jose, CA, p. A86

Chief Financial Officer, Mountainview Hospital, Las Vegas, NV, p. A394

ARAGON, Juliette, Finance Director, Turquoise Lodge Hospital, Albuquerque, NM, p. A416

ARAKELIAN, Armen

Chief Information Officer, Fulton County Medical Center, Mc Connellsburg, PA, p. A530

Chief Information Officer, J. C. Blair Memorial Hospital, Huntingdon, PA, p. A527

ARANDA, Heather R, R.N., MSN, Chief Nursing Officer, F. W. Huston Medical Center, Winchester, KS, p. A248

ARANIO, Lani, Regional Director Human Resources, Samuel Mahelona Memorial Hospital, Kapaa, HI, p. A166

ARATOW, Michael, M.D., Chief Information Officer, San Mateo Medical Center, San Mateo, CA, p. A87

ARAU, Molly, Chief Nursing Officer, Memorial Hospital Of Tampa, Tampa, FL, p. A141

ARAUJO, Marianne D, R.N., Ph.D., FACHE, Vice President Nursing and Chief Nurse Executive, Advocate Good Shepherd Hospital, Barrington, IL, p. A174

ARAUJO, Markeeta, Chief Nursing Officer, Desert View Hospital, Pahrump, NV, p. A396

ARBAUGH, Ronnie, Director Human Resources, Grant Memorial Hospital, Petersburg, WV, p. A686

ARBON, Terron, R.N., Chief Nursing Officer, Salt Lake Regional Medical Center, Salt Lake City, UT, p. A650

ARBUTHNOT, Rena, Director Human Resources, Shriners Hospitals For Children-Shreveport, Shreveport, LA, p. A279

ARCANGELI, Barbara J., Vice President Human Resources, Newport Hospital, Newport, RI, p. A547

ARCE, Daisy, President Medical Staff, Weslaco Regional Rehabilitation Hospital, Weslaco, TX, p. A643

ARCENEAUX, Larrie, Chief Clinical Officer, Promise Hospital Baton Rouge - Main Campus, Baton Rouge, LA, p. A264

ARCENEAUX, Trina, Assistant Chief Financial Officer, Promise Hospital Baton Rouge - Main Campus, Baton Rouge, LA, p. A264

ARCH, Chrissy, Chief Financial Officer, Cherokee Indian Hospital, Cherokee, NC, p. A450

ARCH, John K., FACHE, Director, Boys Town National Research Hospital, Omaha, NE, p. A387

ARCHAMBEAULT, Shirley, Chief Information Officer, Medical City Lewisville, Lewisville, TX, p. A619

ARCHER, David, Director Information Systems, Tristar Ashland City Medical Center, Ashland City, TN, p. A566

ARCHER, Doug, Administrator, Memorial Hospital Los Banos, Los Banos, CA, p. A70

ARCHER, Joe, Chief Information Officer, Victor Valley Global Medical Center, Victorville, CA, p. A94

ARCHER, Matt

Chief Executive Officer, Complex Care Hospital At Tenaya, Las Vegas, NV, p. A394

Chief Executive Officer, Tahoe Pacific Hospitals, NV, p. A397

ARCHER, Stuart

Chief Executive Officer, Oceans Behavioral Hospital Katy, Katy, TX, p. A616

Chief Executive Officer, Oceans Behavioral Hospital Of De Ridder, Deridder, LA, p. A267

ARCHER-DUSTE, Helen, Chief Operating Officer, Kaiser Permanente San Francisco Medical Center, San Francisco, CA, p. A85

ARCHEY, Eugene, Chief Information Technology, Va Greater Los Angeles Healthcare System, Los Angeles, CA, p. A70

ARCHIBOLD, Robert, Director, Human Resources, St. Anthony North Health Campus, Westminster, CO, p. A106

ARCHIBONG, Henry, Vice President, Information Services and Technology, University Of Maryland Capital Region Health Prince George's Hospital Center, Cheverly, MD, p. A290

ARCHULETA, Michael, Chief Information Technology Officer, Mt. San Rafael Hospital, Trinidad, CO, p. A106

ARCIDI, Alfred J., M.D.

Senior Vice President, Whittier Rehabilitation Hospital, Bradford, MA, p. A297

Senior Vice President, Whittier Rehabilitation Hospital, Westborough, MA, p. A305

ARCIDI, Alfred L., M.D., Chief Executive Officer, Whittier Pavilion, Haverhill, MA, p. A300

ARCILLA, Jelden, R.N., Vice President and Chief Nursing Officer, Honorhealth John C. Lincoln Medical Center, Phoenix, AZ, p. A33

ARD, Sheila, Chief Nursing Officer, Huntsville Memorial Hospital, Huntsville, TX, p. A615

ARDABELL, Toni R, Chief Executive Officer, Bon Secours Virginia, Bon Secours St. Francis Medical Center, Midlothian, VA, p. A661

ARDEMAGNI, Jeff, Chief Financial Officer, Medical City Arlington, Arlington, TX, p. A584

ARDESHNA, Harish, Pulmonologist & Chief Medical Officer, Bluffton Regional Medical Center, Bluffton, IN, p. A200

ARDION, Doug, M.D., Chief Medical Officer, Nch North Naples Hospital, FL, p. A132

ARDOIN, Cody, Director Human Resources, Acadian Medical Center, LA, p. A280

AREAUX, Rene, Vice President and Chief Operating Officer, Springhill Memorial Hospital, Mobile, AL, p. A20

ARELLANO, Edgar Alejandro, Chief Information Technologist, Three Rivers Hospital, Brewster, WA, p. A670

ARENDS, Candace, R.N., Chief Nursing Officer, United Hospital District, Blue Earth, MN, p. A328

ARETINO, Sandi, M.D., Chief Executive Officer, Tsehootsooi Medical Center, Fort Defiance, AZ, p. A29

ARGUELLO-VASQUEZ, Mabel, R.N., Executive Nurse Administrator, New Mexico Behavioral Health Institute At Las Vegas, Las Vegas, NM, p. A418

ARGYROS, Gregory J., M.D., Senior Vice President and President, Medstar Washington Hospital Center, Washington, DC, p. A116

ARIAS, Taffy J., Chief Executive Officer, Gila Regional Medical Center, Silver City, NM, p. A420

ARISPE, Joe, Director Information Systems, Wise Regional Health System, West Campus Medical Center, TX, p. A598

ARIZMENDEZ, Maria Elena, M.D., Medical Director, Vibra Rehabilitation Hospital Lake Travis, Lakeway, TX, p. A618

ARIZPE, Robert C., Superintendent, San Antonio State Hospital, San Antonio, TX, p. A634

ARKEMA, Ashley, Manager Human Resources, Pella Regional Health Center, Pella, IA, p. A228

ARKIN, Melissa, Chief Executive Officer, Parkridge Valley Child And Adolescent Campus, TN, p. A567

ARLEDGE, Denton, Vice President and Chief Information Officer, Wakemed Cary Hospital, Cary, NC, p. A449

ARLEDGE, William, Administrator and Chief Financial Officer, Genesis Behavioral Hospital, Breaux Bridge, LA, p. A265

ARLIEN, Dana, M.D., Chief Medical Officer, Willow Springs Center, Reno, NV, p. A396

ARMAND, Sandra, Director, Lafayette Behavioral Health, LA, p. A271

ARMBRUSTER, Kent A W, M.D., Vice President Medical Affairs, Little Company Of Mary Hospital And Health Care Centers, Evergreen Park, IL, p. A183

ARMBRUSTER, Rebecca, M.D., Chief Medical Officer, Jeanes Hospital, Philadelphia, PA, p. A535

ARMFIELD, Ben

Associate Administrator, Fresno Heart And Surgical Hospital, Fresno, CA, p. A59

Chief Financial Officer, Fresno Heart And Surgical Hospital, Fresno, CA, p. A59

ARMOUR, Dale, Chief Financial Officer, Melbourne Regional Medical Center, Melbourne, FL, p. A129

ARMOUR, John, Chief Financial Officer, Bayshore Medical Center, Pasadena, TX, p. A627

ARMOUR, Meri, President, Le Bonheur Children's Hospital, TN, p. A575

ARMSTRONG, Alan, M.D., Chief Medical Officer, Pine Rest Christian Mental Health Services, Grand Rapids, MI, p. A314

ARMSTRONG, Deborah, Chief Executive Officer, Piedmont Henry Hospital, Stockbridge, GA, p. A161

ARMSTRONG, Eleze, Chief Operating Officer, Sierra Vista Regional Medical Center, San Luis Obispo, CA, p. A87

ARMSTRONG, Gary, Executive Vice President, Methodist Rehabilitation Center, Jackson, MS, p. A348

ARMSTRONG, Jeffery, CPA, Chief Financial Officer, Granville Health System, Oxford, NC, p. A458

ARMSTRONG, Jeremy, FACHE, Chief Executive Officer, Mitchell County Hospital Health Systems, Beloit, KS, p. A232

ARMSTRONG, Kim, Chief Financial Officer, Windom Area Hospital, Windom, MN, p. A342

ARMSTRONG, Kyle, President, Baylor Medical Center At Mckinney, Mckinney, TX, p. A623

ARMSTRONG, Lori, R.N., MSN, Chief Nursing Officer, Kaiser Permanente Santa Clara Medical Center, Santa Clara, CA, p. A88

ARMSTRONG, Mark, M.D., Medical Director, Baylor Medical Center At Uptown, Dallas, TX, p. A595

ARMSTRONG, Neil G, FACHE, Vice President and Chief Operating Officer, Divine Providence Hospital, Williamsport, PA, p. A545

ARMSTRONG, Paula, Chief Financial Officer, Kaiser Permanente Fresno Medical Center, Fresno, CA, p. A59

ARMSTRONG, Robert E., Senior Vice President and Chief Operating Officer, Lima Memorial Health System, Lima, OH, p. A484

ARMSTRONG, Roger

Interim Chief Financial Officer, Pioneers Memorial Healthcare District, Brawley, CA, p. A53

Vice President Finance and Chief Financial Officer, Unitypoint Health - Proctor, Peoria, IL, p. A193

ARMSTRONG, William C

Senior Vice President and Chief Financial Officer, Mercy Medical Center, Rockville Centre, NY, p. A442

Vice President and Chief Financial Officer, St. Francis Hospital, The Heart Center, Roslyn, NY, p. A442

ARMSTRONG-HUFF, Glenda, Assistant Superintendent, Texas Center For Infectious Disease, San Antonio, TX, p. A634

ARNDELL, Scott, Chief Financial Officer, Twin Lakes Regional Medical Center, Leitchfield, KY, p. A254

ARNER, Steven C.

Executive Vice President of Administration, Carilion Franklin Memorial Hospital, Rocky Mount, VA, p. A666

President, Roanoke Memorial Rehabilitation Center, VA, p. A665

ARNESON, Brenda, Administrative Assistant, St. Andrew's Health Center, Bottineau, ND, p. A464

ARNESON, Garrett, FACHE, R.N., Chief Operating Officer, Acuity Specialty Hospital Of Southern New Jersey, Willingboro, NJ, p. A414

ARNETT, Jacob, Chief Information Technology Officer, Lakeside Behavioral Health System, Memphis, TN, p. A575

ARNETT, James, Vice President Human Resources, Unitypoint Health Meriter, Madison, WI, p. A696

ARNETT, Randal M., President and Chief Executive Officer, Southern Ohio Medical Center, Portsmouth, OH, p. A489

ARNETT, Sallie, Vice President Information Systems, Licking Memorial Hospital, Newark, OH, p. A488

ARNETT, Stuart
  Regional Vice President Finance, Aurora Lakeland Medical Center, Elkhorn, WI, p. A692
  Vice President Finance and Chief Financial Officer, Aurora Memorial Hospital Of Burlington, Burlington, WI, p. A691
ARNHART, Carol, Vice President Finance and Chief Financial Officer, Siskin Hospital For Physical Rehabilitation, Chattanooga, TN, p. A567
ARNOLD, Ann, M.D., Medical Director, Medical City Frisco, TX, p. A628
ARNOLD, Bill, President and Chief Executive Officer, Children's Hospital At Monmouth Medical Center, NJ, p. A407
ARNOLD, Dustin, D.O., Chief Medical Officer, Unitypoint Health - St. Luke's Hospital, Cedar Rapids, IA, p. A218
ARNOLD, Jeffrey, M.D., Chief Medical Officer, Santa Clara Valley Medical Center, San Jose, CA, p. A87
ARNOLD, Kimberly N, R.N., Chief Nursing Officer and Interim Chief Quality Officer, Alliancehealth Woodward, Woodward, OK, p. A510
ARNOLD, Leslie, Chief Executive Officer and Administrator, Chi St. Vincent Morrilton, Morrilton-Conway County, AR, p. A46
ARNOLD, Scott, Senior Vice President Information Systems, Tampa General Hospital Children's Medical Center, FL, p. A141
ARNTZ, Mary, Manager Business Office and Executive Assistant, Physicians' Medical Center, New Albany, IN, p. A212
AROCHA, Joe, Chief of Staff, Alleghany Memorial Hospital, Sparta, NC, p. A461
AROCHO, Jacqueline, Administrator, Baycare Alliant Hospital, Dunedin, FL, p. A122
ARORA, Pamela
  Senior Vice President and Chief Information Officer, Children's Medical Center Plano, Plano, TX, p. A628
  Senior Vice President Information Systems, Children's Medical Center Dallas, Dallas, TX, p. A596
ARORA, Sat, M.D., President Medical and Dental Staff, Taylor Hospital, PA, p. A543
ARQUILLA, Thomas J., Chief Strategy Officer, Thedacare Regional Medical Center-Appleton, Appleton, WI, p. A689
ARRANTS, Diane, Chief Information Officer, Kershawhealth, Camden, SC, p. A549
ARROGANTE, Revelyn, M.D., Medical Director, Northern Colorado Rehabilitation Hospital, Johnstown, CO, p. A102
ARROWOOD, Al, Interim President, Washington County Hospital, Plymouth, NC, p. A458
ARROWOOD, Melina, Interim President and Chief Nursing Officer, Transylvania Regional Hospital, Brevard, NC, p. A448
ARROYO, Luis A
  Chief Financial Officer, Hima San Pablo Caguas, Caguas, PR, p. A712
  Chief Financial Officer, Hospital Hima De Humacao, Humacao, PR, p. A713
  Chief Financial Officer, Hospital San Pablo Del Este, Fajardo, PR, p. A713
ARSENAULT, Lisa, Vice President Human Resources and Compliance, Millinocket Regional Hospital, Millinocket, ME, p. A285
ARSLANPAY, Robin F., Director Human Resources, Lifecare Hospitals Of Pittsburgh - Suburban, PA, p. A537
ARSURA, Edward, M.D., Chief Medical Officer, Richmond University Medical Center, New York (Includes All Hospitals Located Within The Five Boroughs), NY, p. A437
ARTENSTEIN, Andrew, M.D., Chief Physician Executive, Chief Academic Officer and President, Baystate Medical Practices, Baystate Children's Hospital, MA, p. A304
ARTERBURN, Catherine T, R.N., Vice President Human Resources, Sidney Regional Medical Center, Sidney, NE, p. A390
ARTHUR, John
  Chief Financial Officer, St. Vincent Mercy Hospital, Elwood, IN, p. A203
  Chief Financial Officer, St. Vincent Randolph Hospital, Winchester, IN, p. A216
ARTHUR, Rita K, Director Human Resources, Littleton Adventist Hospital, Littleton, CO, p. A103
ARTILES, Nemuel O., FACHE, Administrator, Hospital De Psiquiatria Forense, Ponce, PR, p. A714
ARTMAN, David S, Chief Operating Officer, Weirton Medical Center, Weirton, WV, p. A687
ARTS-STRENKE, Cindy, R.N., Chief Operating Officer and Chief Nursing Officer, Marshfield Medical Center - Rice Lake, Rice Lake, WI, p. A702
ARUNAMATA, Peti, Interim Area Director Information Technology, Kaiser Permanente San Francisco Medical Center, San Francisco, CA, p. A85
ARVIDSON, Betty, Chief Financial Officer, Riverview Health, Crookston, MN, p. A330

ARVIN, Douglas, Vice President Finance and Chief Financial Officer, Wellstar Kennestone Hospital, Marietta, GA, p. A157
ARVIN, Jon A, M.D., Chief Medical Officer, Rockcastle Regional Hospital And Respiratory Care Center, Mount Vernon, KY, p. A258
ARVON, Christina, Administrator and Chief Executive Officer, Charleston Surgical Hospital, Charleston, WV, p. A682
ARZOUMANIAN, Aimee, Chief Operating Officer, Sparks Regional Medical Center, Fort Smith-Sebastian County, AR, p. A42
ASADA, Bonnie, Chief Nursing Officer, Alvarado Parkway Institute Behavioral Health System, La Mesa, CA, p. A63
ASAFTEI, Laura, Administrative Director, Florida Hospital Zephyrhills, Zephyrhills, FL, p. A144
ASAOKA, Danny
  Executive Director Information Systems, Memorialcare, Long Beach Memorial Medical Center, Long Beach, CA, p. A65
  Executive Director Information Systems, Memorialcare, Miller Children's & Women's Hospital Long Beach, Long Beach, CA, p. A65
ASBURY, Wesley, M.D., President Medical Staff, Princeton Community Hospital, Princeton, WV, p. A686
ASCHOFF, Jodi, Chief Financial Officer, Osmond General Hospital, Osmond, NE, p. A389
ASH, Michael A, Chief Transformation Officer, Nebraska Medicine - Nebraska Medical Center, Omaha, NE, p. A388
ASH, Richard M., Chief Executive Officer, United Hospital District, Blue Earth, MN, p. A328
ASHBY, F Michael, M.D., Vice President and Medical Director, Sentara Martha Jefferson Hospital, Charlottesville, VA, p. A656
ASHBY, Fred, Director Information Technology, Fort Washington Medical Center, Oxen Hill, MD, p. A293
ASHBY, Kim, Vice President of Finance, Baptist Health Madisonville, Madisonville, KY, p. A257
ASHBY, Pamela, Vice President Human Resources, Medstar National Rehabilitation Hospital, Washington, DC, p. A115
ASHBY, Rae A., Director Human Resources, Sullivan County Memorial Hospital, Milan, MO, p. A364
ASHCOM, Thomas L., M.D., Ph.D., Chief Executive Officer, Kansas Heart Hospital, Wichita, KS, p. A247
ASHENFELTER, Kathy, Chief Financial Officer, Swedish Medical Center, Englewood, CO, p. A100
ASHKENASE, Donald L, Executive Vice President and Chief Operating Officer, Nassau University Medical Center, East Meadow, NY, p. A426
ASHLEY, Ada, HIM Director, Lifebrite Community Hospital Of Stokes, Danbury, NC, p. A450
ASHLEY, Dennis H
  Vice President Human Resources, Montefiore Mount Vernon, Mount Vernon, NY, p. A430
  Vice President Human Resources, Montefiore New Rochelle, New Rochelle, NY, p. A431
ASHLEY, Kent, Chief Financial Officer, Mesa Springs, Fort Worth, TX, p. A605
ASHLEY, Sharon, MSN, Chief Nursing Officer, Adams County Regional Medical Center, Seaman, OH, p. A490
ASHLEY, Stanley, M.D., Senior Vice President Medical Affairs and Chief Medical Officer, Brigham And Women's Hospital, Boston, MA, p. A296
ASHMENT, Kerry, Chief Executive Officer, Kindred Hospital-San Diego, San Diego, CA, p. A83
ASHRAF, Mirza, M.D., Medical Director, Carthage Area Hospital, Carthage, NY, p. A424
ASHTON, Michael, Administrator, Bayhealth Medical Center, Milford Memorial Hospital, DE, p. A113
ASHWORTH, Fred, Chief Financial Officer, Regional Medical Center Of San Jose, San Jose, CA, p. A86
ASHWORTH, James, M.D., Medical Director, University Of Utah Neuropsychiatric Institute, Salt Lake City, UT, p. A651
ASHWORTH, Jerry
  Chief Operating Officer, Tirr Memorial Hermann, Houston, TX, p. A614
  Interim Chief Executive Officer, Memorial Hermann Rehabilitation Hospital - Katy, Katy, TX, p. A616
  Interim Chief Executive Officer, Tirr Memorial Hermann, Houston, TX, p. A614
ASIC, Jason, Chief Operating Officer, Mercy Health - West Hospital, Cincinnati, OH, p. A475
ASKEW, Pam, R.N., Vice President Patient Care Services, Unitypoint Health - Trinity Muscatine, Muscatine, IA, p. A227
ASKINS, Stephen, M.D., Chief of Staff, Lake City Community Hospital, Lake City, SC, p. A555
ASLIN, Judy, MSN, R.N., Vice President and Chief Nursing Officer, Southeast Hospital, Cape Girardeau, MO, p. A357
ASPEL, Tracy, Chief Nursing Officer, Northern Inyo Hospital, Bishop, CA, p. A53

ASPLIN, Iain, Chief Medical Officer, Multicare Mary Bridge Children's Hospital And Health Center, Tacoma, WA, p. A679
ASPLUND, David, Chief Operating Officer, Motion Picture And Television Fund Hospital And Residential Services, Los Angeles, CA, p. A68
ASSAAD, Haney, Vice President Medical Affairs, North Ottawa Community Hospital, Grand Haven, MI, p. A313
ASSAVAPISITKUL, Colleen, Chief Nursing Officer, Adventist Health Clear Lake, Clearlake, CA, p. A54
ASTACIO, Benjamin, Director Human Resources, Bella Vista Hospital, Mayaguez, PR, p. A714
ASTLEFORD, Daniel, Vice President Operations, Lafayette Regional Health Center, Lexington, MO, p. A363
ATADERO, Robyn, R.N., Chief Nursing Officer, Pioneers Memorial Healthcare District, Brawley, CA, p. A53
ATCHISON, Garfield, Chief Executive Officer, Frye Regional Medical Center-South Campus, NC, p. A454
ATCHISON, Marcie
  Vice President Human Resources, Memorialcare, Long Beach Memorial Medical Center, Long Beach, CA, p. A65
  Vice President Human Resources, Memorialcare, Miller Children's & Women's Hospital Long Beach, Long Beach, CA, p. A65
ATCHLEY, Mark, Vice President and Chief Financial Officer, Medical City Children's Hospital, TX, p. A597
ATHERTON, Dorie, Manager Human Resources, University Behavioral Health Of Denton, Denton, TX, p. A599
ATHEY, Alycia, Director of Nursing, Prairie Ridge Hospital And Health Services, Elbow Lake, MN, p. A331
ATKIN, Suzanne, M.D., Chief Medical Officer, University Hospital, Newark, NJ, p. A409
ATKINS, Christa, Administrator, Commonwealth Regional Specialty Hospital, Bowling Green, KY, p. A249
ATKINS, James, PharmD, Chief Operating Officer, Piedmont Henry Hospital, Stockbridge, GA, p. A161
ATKINS, Jim, Director Employee Services, St. Luke's Rehabilitation Hospital, Boise, ID, p. A168
ATKINS, Melissa, CPA, Chief Executive Officer, Graham County Hospital, Hill City, KS, p. A236
ATKINS, Tracy, Chief Operating and Nursing Officer, Orchard Hospital, Gridley, CA, p. A61
ATKINSON, Andrew, Chief Operating Officer, Fulton State Hospital, Fulton, MO, p. A359
ATKINSON, James, M.D., Medical Director, Ucla Medical Center-Santa Monica, Santa Monica, CA, p. A89
ATKINSON, Jodi, President and Chief Executive Officer, St. Andrew's Health Center, Bottineau, ND, p. A464
ATKINSON, Johnie M, Chief Human Resources Officer, Saint Vincent Hospital, Erie, PA, p. A525
ATTAR, Nichol, Chief Executive Officer, Mayhill Hospital, Denton, TX, p. A599
ATTEBURY, Mary, Chief Operating Officer, Northwest Missouri Psychiatric Rehabilitation Center, Saint Joseph, MO, p. A367
ATTENBURY, Kristen, Commanding Officer, Naval Hospital Lemoore, Lemoore, CA, p. A64
ATTERBERG, Linda, Chief Information Officer, Unitypoint Health-Keokuk, Keokuk, IA, p. A225
ATTLESEY-PRIES, Jacqueline M, MS, R.N., Chief Nursing Officer, Vice President, Boulder Community Foothills Hospital, CO, p. A96
ATTRIDGE, Scott
  Chief Financial Officer, Chi St. Anthony Hospital, Pendleton, OR, p. A515
  Chief Financial Officer, Mid-Valley Hospital, Omak, WA, p. A674
ATTY, James, Chief Executive Officer, Waverly Health Center, Waverly, IA, p. A231
ATWAL, Money, Chief Information Officer, Hilo Medical Center, Hilo, HI, p. A164
ATWOOD, Julie, Director Human Resources, San Bernardino Mountains Community Hospital District, Lake Arrowhead, CA, p. A63
ATWOOD, Linda, Chief Nursing Officer, Merit Health Woman's Hospital, Flowood, MS, p. A346
AUBEL, Eugenia, President, St. Elizabeth Boardman Hospital, Mercy Health - St. Elizabeth Boardman Hospital, Boardman, OH, p. A472
AUBIN, Michael D, President, Wolfson Children's Hospital, FL, p. A125
AUBRY, Michael, Director Information Systems, Adventist Medical Center-Selma, CA, p. A61
AUBUCHON, Christy, Director Personnel, Washington County Memorial Hospital, Potosi, MO, p. A366
AUCKER, Kendra A.
  President and Chief Executive Officer, Evangelical Community Hospital, Lewisburg, PA, p. A530
  Vice President Operations, Evangelical Community Hospital, Lewisburg, PA, p. A530

AUCKERMAN, Graydon Todd, Chief Nursing Officer, Ohiohealth Rehabilitation Hospital, Columbus, OH, p. A478

AUD, Pam, Chief Clinical Officer, Andalusia Health, Andalusia, AL, p. A13

AUDETT, John R, M.D., Medical Director Clinical Affairs, Overlook Medical Center, Summit, NJ, p. A412

AUERBACH, Lorraine P., FACHE, President and Chief Executive Officer, Dameron Hospital, Stockton, CA, p. A90

AUGSBURGER, Marc, R.N., President and Chief Executive Officer, Mclaren Caro Region, Caro, MI, p. A309

AUGSBURGER, Tod, FACHE
President and Chief Executive Officer, Lexington Medical Center, West Columbia, SC, p. A558
Senior Vice President and Chief Operating Officer, Lexington Medical Center, West Columbia, SC, p. A558

AUGUST, Brad, Director Information Systems, Fairfield Memorial Hospital, Fairfield, IL, p. A183

AUGUST, Prudence, Chief Information Officer, Palomar Medical Center, Escondido, CA, p. A57

AUGUSTIN, Robert, Director Human Resources, Southern Tennessee Regional Health System-Lawrenceburg, Lawrenceburg, TN, p. A573

AUGUSTIN, W Walter, CPA, III, Vice President Financial Services and Chief Financial Officer, University Of Maryland Rehabilitation & Orthopaedic Institute, Baltimore, MD, p. A289

AUGUSTINE, David, Chief Executive Officer, Trego County-Lemke Memorial Hospital, Wakeeney, KS, p. A247

AUGUSTUS, Richard, M.D., Chief Medical Officer, West Valley Medical Center, Caldwell, ID, p. A168

AUGUSTYNIAK, Becky, Director Human Resources, Piedmont Columbus Regional Northside, Columbus, GA, p. A150

AUKES, Amy
Human Resources Analyst, Avera Flandreau Hospital, Flandreau, SD, p. A561
Regional Manager of Human Resources, Avera Dells Area Hospital, Dell Rapids, SD, p. A560

AURAND, Brendan, Director, Human Resources, Fairmount Behavioral Health System, Philadelphia, PA, p. A534

AURILIO, Lisa, R.N., MSN, Chief Operating Officer, Akron Children's Hospital, Akron, OH, p. A470

AUSMAN, Dan F., President and Chief Executive Officer, Methodist Hospital Of Southern California, Arcadia, CA, p. A51

AUSTIN, Aaron
Market Vice President Human Resources, Chi St. Vincent Hot Springs, Hot Springs-Garland County, AR, p. A43
Market Vice President Human Resources, Chi St. Vincent Infirmary Medical Center, Little Rock-Pulaski County, AR, p. A45
Market Vice President Human Resources, Chi St. Vincent Morrilton, Morrilton-Conway County, AR, p. A46

AUSTIN, Bill, Senior Vice President of Finance, Coastal Virginia Rehabilitation, Newport News, VA, p. A662

AUSTIN, Dan
Director Information Technology, Arkansas Methodist Medical Center, Paragould-Greene County, AR, p. A47
Manager Data Processing, Ashley County Medical Center, Crossett-Ashley County, AR, p. A40

AUSTIN, Debbie W, MSN, R.N., Vice President Patient Care Services, P & S Surgical Hospital, Monroe, LA, p. A274

AUSTIN, Donnica, Vice President, Operations, Holy Cross Hospital, Chicago, IL, p. A177

AUSTIN, Geoff, Executive Director, University Of Washington Medical Center, Seattle, WA, p. A677

AUSTIN, Joe, Executive Vice President and Chief Operating Officer, Phoebe North, GA, p. A145

AUSTIN, Laura, Vice President Finance and Chief Financial Officer, Community Hospital Of Anaconda, Anaconda, MT, p. A373

AUSTIN, Sherri, MSN, R.N., Chief Nursing Officer, Wrangell Medical Center, Wrangell, AK, p. A27

AUSTIN, W William, Jr, Senior Vice President Finance, Riverside Shore Memorial Hospital, Onancoke, VA, p. A663

AUSTIN, Warren, M.D., Vice President Medical Affairs, Bon Secours Maryview Medical Center, Portsmouth, VA, p. A664

AUSTIN-MOORE, Gale, Director Area Technology, Kaiser Permanente Vallejo Medical Center, Vallejo, CA, p. A93

AUSTRIA, Ramon, R.N., Chief Nursing Officer, Vibra Rehabilitation Hospital Lake Travis, Lakeway, TX, p. A618

AUTELLI, Oscar, Chief Information Officer, Women's And Children's Hospital, CA, p. A68

AUTREY, Pamela Spencer, R.N., Ph.D., MSN, Chief Nursing Officer, Medical West, Bessemer, AL, p. A14

AUTRY, Paula R., FACHE, Chief Executive Officer, Lutheran Hospital Of Indiana, Fort Wayne, IN, p. A203

AVANT, Andre, Facility Automation Manager, Texas Center For Infectious Disease, San Antonio, TX, p. A634

AVATO, Rich, Director, Palm Beach Children's Hospital, FL, p. A143

AVELINO, Joseph, Chief Executive Officer, College Medical Center, Long Beach, CA, p. A65

AVERETT, Elaine, Chief Financial Officer, Grove Hill Memorial Hospital, Grove Hill, AL, p. A19

AVERILL, Clark, Director Information Technology, St. Luke's Hospital, Duluth, MN, p. A331

AVERNA, Russell
Vice President Human Resources, Spaulding Rehabilitation Hospital, Charlestown, MA, p. A299
Vice President of Human Resources, Spaulding Rehabilitation Hospital Cape Cod, East Sandwich, MA, p. A299

AVERY, Danny, Chief Financial Officer and Chief Operating Officer, Mangum Regional Medical Center, Mangum, OK, p. A501

AVERY, Donald R., FACHE, President and Chief Executive Officer, Fairview Park Hospital, Dublin, GA, p. A153

AVERY, John B., III, Administrator, Perry Community Hospital, Linden, TN, p. A573

AVERY, Jonathan, Chief Administrative Officer, Rehabilitation Institute Of Oregon, OR, p. A516

AVERY, Scott B., Chief Operating Officer, Paris Regional Medical Center, TX, p. A627

AVIADO, Gail, Chief Nursing Officer, Montclair Hospital Medical Center, Montclair, CA, p. A73

AVIGDOR, Lauren, Director Human Resources, Advanced Specialty Hospital Of Toledo, Toledo, OH, p. A491

AVIGNONE, Frank, Chief Executive Officer, Mangum Regional Medical Center, Mangum, OK, p. A501

AVILA, Brandi, Chief Nursing Officer, Martin County Hospital District, Stanton, TX, p. A637

AVILA, Patrick, Chief Operating Officer, Belton Regional Medical Center, Belton, MO, p. A355

AVVISATO, Michael, Senior Vice President and Chief Financial Officer, Allied Services Rehabilitation Hospital, Scranton, PA, p. A540

AVVISATO, Mike, Vice President and Chief Financial Officer, John Heinz Institute Of Rehabilitation Medicine, Wilkes, PA, p. A544

AWALD, Tamara, Chief Nursing Officer and Chief Operating Officer, Plymouth Medical Center, Plymouth, IN, p. A213

AWALT, Scott, Chief Financial Officer, Sanford Hillsboro Medical Center, Hillsboro, ND, p. A467

AWAN, Naveed, FACHE, Chief Executive Officer, St. Helena Parish Hospital, Greensburg, LA, p. A268

AWOLOWO, Yinusa, Business Officer, Kingsboro Psychiatric Center, New York (Includes All Hospitals Located Within The Five Boroughs), NY, p. A432

AWWAD, Emad, Director Care Delivery Sites Information Systems and Technology, Lakeview Hospital, Stillwater, MN, p. A340

AXTELL, Vicki, Director Human Resources, Livingston Healthcare, Livingston, MT, p. A377

AYALA, Jose L, M.D., Chief Medical Officer, Valley Baptist Medical Center-Brownsville, Brownsville, TX, p. A590

AYALA, Lisa, R.N., Director Human Resources, Specialty Hospital Jacksonville, Jacksonville, FL, p. A126

AYALA, Shirley, Director Human Resources, First Hospital Panamericano, Cidra, PR, p. A713

AYCOCK, Mark, Chief Operating Officer, Spartanburg Medical Center, Spartanburg, SC, p. A557

AYERS, James G, Chief Financial Officer, Piedmont Geriatric Hospital, Burkeville, VA, p. A656

AYERS, Jessi, Chief Financial Officer, Person Memorial Hospital, Roxboro, NC, p. A460

AYERS, Matthew, Chief Administrative Officer, Norton Women's And Children's Hospital, KY, p. A256

AYERS, Pam, Chief Nursing Officer, North Oak Regional Medical Center, Senatobia, MS, p. A353

AYOUB, John J., FACHE, Chief Executive Officer, Mobridge Regional Hospital, Mobridge, SD, p. A562

AYRES, Robert, Director Information Systems, Firelands Regional Medical Center South Campus, OH, p. A490

AYRES, Shane, Chief Financial Officer, Sanford Wheaton Medical Center, Wheaton, MN, p. A342

AZCONA, Alain
Chief Executive Officer, Aurora Behavioral Healthcare San Diego, San Diego, CA, p. A83
Director Business Development, Aurora Behavioral Healthcare San Diego, San Diego, CA, p. A83

AZCUY, Karla, Acting Chief Human Resources Officer, Va Portland Healthcare System, Portland, OR, p. A517

AZEVEDO, Michael, M.D., Medical Director, San Joaquin Valley Rehabilitation Hospital, Fresno, CA, p. A59

AZIZ, Samir, M.D., Medical Director, Fairfax Behavioral Health Everett, WA, p. A673

AZIZKHAN, Richard G., M.D., President and Chief Executive Officer, Children's Hospital And Medical Center, Omaha, NE, p. A388

AZURE, Vernon, Clinical Director, Indian Health Service - Quentin N. Burdick Memorial Health Care Facility, Belcourt, ND, p. A464

B

BAAS, Dina, Director Financial Services, Orange City Area Health System, Orange City, IA, p. A227

BABAKANIAN, Ed, Chief Information Officer, Uc San Diego Shiley Eye Institute, CA, p. A84

BABB, A. Mitch, Vice President, Operations, Duke Regional Hospital, Durham, NC, p. A451

BABB, Cindy, Executive Director Human Resources and Organizational Effectiveness, St. Vincent Kokomo, Kokomo, IN, p. A209

BABB, Dan, Chief Financial Officer, Dmc - Rehabilitation Institute Of Michigan, Detroit, MI, p. A311

BABB, Donald J., Chief Executive Officer, Citizens Memorial Hospital, Bolivar, MO, p. A355

BABB, Kathy, Manager Human Resources, Clifton Springs Hospital And Clinic, Clifton Springs, NY, p. A424

BABCOCK, Daniel, Chief Executive Officer, Marlette Regional Hospital, Marlette, MI, p. A318

BABCOCK, Jordon, Interim Chief Executive Officer, Springwoods Behavioral Health Hospital, Fayetteville-Washington County, AR, p. A41

BABCOCK, Kimberly, Administrative Director of Operations, Kalkaska Memorial Health Center, Kalkaska, MI, p. A317

BABCOCK, Paul, Chief Financial Officer, Coulee Medical Center, Grand Coulee, WA, p. A672

BABCOCK, Robert, M.D., Interim Chief of Staff, Bath Veterans Affairs Medical Center, Bath, NY, p. A422

BABE, Heather, M.D., Chief of Staff, Shenandoah Medical Center, Shenandoah, IA, p. A229

BABER, Jonathan, Director Information Technology, Central State Hospital, Petersburg, VA, p. A663

BABICH, Eli, Chief Nursing Officer, Select Specialty Hospital-Pittsburgh/Upmc, Pittsburgh, PA, p. A537

BABUSCIO, Cathy, Director Human Resources, Mat-Su Regional Medical Center, Palmer, AK, p. A27

BACA, Modesto, Chief Information Officer, Amarillo Veterans Affairs Health Care System, Amarillo, TX, p. A583

BACH, Dawn M, MS, Chief Clinical Officer, Buena Vista Regional Medical Center, Storm Lake, IA, p. A230

BACHA, Fadi, M.D., Chief Medical Officer, Select Specialty Hospital-Lexington, Lexington, KY, p. A255

BACHELDOR, H Lee, D.O., Chief Medical Officer, St. John River District Hospital, East China, MI, p. A312

BACHELIER, Erin, Human Resource Administrator, Ranken Jordan Pediatric Bridge Hospital, Maryland Heights, MO, p. A364

BACHER, Beth, Chief Executive Officer, Encompass Health Valley Of The Sun Rehabilitation Hospital, Glendale, AZ, p. A30

BACHMAN, John Page, Corporate Vice President, St. John Medical Center, Tulsa, OK, p. A509

BACHMAN, Judith Lynn
Chief Operating Officer, Fox Chase Cancer Center-American Oncologic Hospital, Philadelphia, PA, p. A534
Chief Operating Officer, Jeanes Hospital, Philadelphia, PA, p. A535

BACHMAN, Roberta, Director Human Resources, Riverview Behavioral Health, Texarkana-Miller County, AR, p. A49

BACHMEIER, Susan T., MSN, R.N., Chief Nursing Officer, Wake Forest Baptist Health-Davie Medical Center, Bermuda Run, NC, p. A448

BACK, Barbara, Manager Human Resources, Encino Hospital Medical Center, Los Angeles, CA, p. A66

BACON, Jeff, D.O., Chief Medical Officer, Sterling Regional Medcenter, Sterling, CO, p. A105

BADEN, Robert M, Chief Financial Officer, Lompoc Valley Medical Center, Lompoc, CA, p. A65

BADEN, Thomas, Jr, Chief Information Officer, Community Behavioral Health Hospital - Rochester, Rochester, MN, p. A338

BADGER, Jeff
Chief Financial Officer, Ascension Calumet Hospital, Chilton, WI, p. A691
Chief Financial Officer, Ascension Northeast Wisconsin Mercy Hospital, Oshkosh, WI, p. A700
Chief Financial Officer, Ascension Northeast Wisconsin St. Elizabeth Hospital, Appleton, WI, p. A689

BALCAVAGE, Thomas, Vice President Chief Patient Safety and Quality Officer, Jefferson Washington Township Hospital, NJ, p. A412

BALCEZAK, Thomas, M.D., Senior Vice President Medical Affairs and Chief Medical Officer, Yale-New Haven Psychiatric Hospital, CT, p. A110

BALDAUF, Robb, Coordinator Information Systems, Cleveland Clinic Akron General Lodi Hospital, Lodi, OH, p. A485

BALDERRAMA, Jose, Vice President Human Resources, Valley Hospital, Ridgewood, NJ, p. A411

BALDOSARO, Thomas
  Chief Financial Officer, Bridgeton Health Center, NJ, p. A413
  Chief Financial Officer, Inspira Medical Center-Elmer, Elmer, NJ, p. A404

BALDRIDGE, Dava, R.N., Chief Nursing Officer, Hillcrest Hospital - South, Tulsa, OK, p. A508

BALDWIN, Barbara, Chief Information Officer, Anne Arundel Medical Center, Annapolis, MD, p. A287

BALDWIN, Bruce A., Chief Executive Officer, Newberry County Memorial Hospital, Newberry, SC, p. A556

BALDWIN, Chad, Interim Chief Executive Officer, Westside Surgical Hospital, Houston, TX, p. A614

BALDWIN, Ellen, R.N., Chief Nursing Officer, Texas Health Center For Diagnostic & Surgery, Plano, TX, p. A629

BALDWIN, Erin, M.P.H., Chief Operating Officer, Mahaska Health Partnership, Oskaloosa, IA, p. A228

BALDWIN, Linda, Chief Nursing Officer, Ogallala Community Hospital, Ogallala, NE, p. A387

BALDWIN, Nathan, M.D., President Medical Staff, Baptist Memorial Hospital-Booneville, Booneville, MS, p. A344

BALDWIN, Steve
  Manager Information Technology, Wyoming State Hospital, Evanston, WY, p. A708
  Vice President Finance, The Willough At Naples, Naples, FL, p. A132

BALDWIN, William, Chief Information Officer, Ashe Memorial Hospital, Jefferson, NC, p. A455

BALES, Brian, Director Plant Operations, Healthsouth Southern Hills Rehabilitation Hospital, Princeton, WV, p. A686

BALES, Correen, Executive Director Human Resources, Unm Sandoval Regional Medical Center, Inc., Rio Rancho, NM, p. A419

BALES, Glenn, Chief Financial Officer, Providence Saint Joseph Medical Center, Burbank, CA, p. A53

BALES-CHUBB, Denyse, President and Chief Executive Officer, Florida Hospital Wesley Chapel, Wesley Chapel, FL, p. A143

BALKO, Tom, Manager Information Systems, Redwood Area Hospital, Redwood Falls, MN, p. A338

BALL, Cassie, Chief Financial Officer, Colleton Medical Center, Walterboro, SC, p. A557

BALL, Charlie, Chief Operating Officer, Specialty Rehabilitation Hospital Of Coushatta, Coushatta, LA, p. A266

BALL, Connie, Chief Financial Officer, Specialty Rehabilitation Hospital Of Coushatta, Coushatta, LA, p. A266

BALL, Craig, Chief Executive Officer, Specialty Rehabilitation Hospital Of Coushatta, Coushatta, LA, p. A266

BALL, James, Chief Operating Officer, Executive, St. Anthony's Rehabilitation Hospital, Lauderdale Lakes, FL, p. A128

BALL, Jim, Chief Operating Officer, St. Catherine's Rehabilitation Hospital, North Miami, FL, p. A132

BALL, Johnny Percy, III, Assistant Administrator Human Resources, Smith Northview Hospital, GA, p. A162

BALL, Rodney, Vice President Finance, Carolinas Healthcare System Northeast, Concord, NC, p. A450

BALLANCE, William, Chief of Medical Staff, Vidant Bertie Hospital, Windsor, NC, p. A462

BALLARD, Christine, Vice President Human Resources, Upmc Susquehanna Soldiers + Sailors, Wellsboro, PA, p. A543

BALLARD, Jerry, Director Information Systems, Central Florida Regional Hospital, Sanford, FL, p. A138

BALLARD, John, Ph.D., Chief Executive Officer, Kentucky River Medical Center, Jackson, KY, p. A254

BALLARD, Lorraine L, Director Human Resources, St. Helena Parish Hospital, Greensburg, LA, p. A268

BALLARD, Marsha, Human Resources, Christus Mother Frances Hospital - Jacksonville, Jacksonville, TX, p. A616

BALLARD, Terri, Chief Nursing Officer, Healthsouth Northern Kentucky Rehabilitation Hospital, Edgewood, KY, p. A251

BALLESTERO, Susan, Vice President and Chief Human Resources Officer, The Children's Hospital At Saint Peter's University, NJ, p. A408

BALLEW, Cheryl, Human Resources Director, Healthsouth Rehabilitation Hospital-Las Vegas, Las Vegas, NV, p. A394

BALLIETT, Matt, Chief Information Officer, Coal County General Hospital, Coalgate, OK, p. A497

BALLIN, Daniel, Administrator, Coastal Virginia Rehabilitation, Newport News, VA, p. A662

BALLINGHOFF, James R, MSN, R.N., Chief Nursing Officer and Associate Executive Director, Penn Presbyterian Medical Center, Philadelphia, PA, p. A536

BALLMAN, Patricia, Director, Westfield Memorial Hospital, Westfield, NY, p. A446

BALLOU, Michele, M.D., Chief Medical Staff, Lewisgale Hospital Alleghany, Low Moor, VA, p. A660

BALOGA-ALTIERI, Bonnie, Ph.D., R.N., Vice President Patient Care Services and Chief Nursing Officer, Children's Specialized Hospital, NJ, p. A408

BALSANO, Tony, Vice President Finance, Saint Francis Medical Center, Cape Girardeau, MO, p. A356

BALSAR, Jeffrey R., President and Chief Executive Officer Vanderbilt Medical Center and Dean, Vanderbilt University Scho, Vanderbilt Psychiatric Hospital, TN, p. A578

BALT, David, D.O., Chief Medical Officer, Avera Queen Of Peace Hospital, Mitchell, SD, p. A562

BALTIERRA, David A., M.D., President Medical Staff, Jefferson Medical Center, Ranson, WV, p. A660

BALTZ, Phyllis, Chief Executive Officer, Methodist Hospital Of Sacramento, Sacramento, CA, p. A82

BALUKOFF, Sam, Interim Administrator, Geisinger-Shamokin Area Community Hospital, PA, p. A523

BALULGA, Josefina, M.D., Clinical Director, Florida State Hospital, Chattahoochee, FL, p. A119

BALUNTANSKI, Brian, Chief Financial Officer, Mclaren Macomb, Mount Clemens, MI, p. A319

BALZ, Pat, Vice President Operations Human Resources, Mclane Children's Hospital Scott & White, TX, p. A638

BALZANO, Janice, President and Chief Executive Officer, St. Petersburg General Hospital, Saint Petersburg, FL, p. A138

BAMAN, Raj, D.O., President Medical Staff, Samaritan North Lincoln Hospital, Lincoln City, OR, p. A514

BAME, Jeremiah, R.N., Chief Nursing Officer, Piedmont Newton Hospital, Covington, GA, p. A151

BAMMEL, Paul, Vice President, Mayo Clinic Health System - Northland In Barron, Barron, WI, p. A690

BANAS, Mark, M.D., Chief Medical Officer, St. Mary's Hospital, WI, p. A702

BANASZYNSKI, Gregory A., Chief Executive Officer, Uw Health Rehabilitation Hospital, Madison, WI, p. A696

BANBURY, Brian, Director Site Information Systems, Advocate Hope Children's Hospital, IL, p. A191

BANCHY, Pamela, Chief Information Officer, Western Reserve Hospital, Cuyahoga Falls, OH, p. A480

BANCO, Leonard, M.D., Senior Vice President and Chief Medical Officer, Bristol Hospital, Bristol, CT, p. A107

BANDA, Venkat, M.D., President Medical Staff, Promise Hospital Of Baton Rouge - Mid-City Campus, LA, p. A264

BANDFIELD-KEOUGH, Kathryn, Vice President Patient Care Services, Munson Healthcare Cadillac Hospital, Cadillac, MI, p. A309

BANDLA, H., M.D., Chief Clinical Affairs, Walter P. Reuther Psychiatric Hospital, Westland, MI, p. A326

BANDS, James G, IV, Chief Financial Officer, Ivinson Memorial Hospital, Laramie, WY, p. A708

BANDY, Dawn, Chief Financial Officer, Grant Regional Health Center, Lancaster, WI, p. A696

BANDY, Don, Director Information Technology, Integris Deaconess, Oklahoma City, OK, p. A502

BANDY, Jennifer, Human Resource Business Partner, Wake Forest Baptist Health-Davie Medical Center, Bermuda Run, NC, p. A448

BANDY, P Ross, M.D., Chief Medical Officer and Chief of Staff, Levi Hospital, Hot Springs National Park-Garland County, AR, p. A43

BANE, Brian R, Vice President Human Resources, Rush Memorial Hospital, Rushville, IN, p. A214

BANE, Harrison, President, Good Samaritan Medical Center - Cushing Campus, MA, p. A298

BANE, William, Chief Financial Officer, Inova Loudoun Hospital, Leesburg, VA, p. A660

BANFIELD, Anne, Chief, Medical Staff, Davis Medical Center, Elkins, WV, p. A682

BANG, W J, M.D., Chief of Staff, Reeves County Hospital, Pecos, TX, p. A628

BANGA, Alok, M.D., Medical Director, Sierra Vista Hospital, Sacramento, CA, p. A82

BANIEWICZ, John, M.D., Chief Medical Officer, Tripoint Medical Center, OH, p. A479

BANK, Carol J, Vice President Human Resources, Divine Savior Healthcare, Portage, WI, p. A701

BANKER, Julie G, R.N., MSN, Chief Nursing Officer, Lehigh Regional Medical Center, Lehigh Acres, FL, p. A128

BANKERS, Diane, Senior Vice President, Nursing Services, Firstlight Health System, Mora, MN, p. A336

BANKS, Chester, Director Human Resources, East Orange General Hospital, East Orange, NJ, p. A404

BANKS, Elizabeth, Chief Executive Officer, Summit Behavioral Healthcare, Cincinnati, OH, p. A475

BANKS, Matthew, Chief Executive Officer, Davis Regional Medical Center, Statesville, NC, p. A461

BANKS, Maureen, FACHE, MS, R.N.
  Chief Operating Officer, Spaulding Rehabilitation Hospital, Charlestown, MA, p. A299
  President, Spaulding Hospital For Continuing Medical Care Cambridge, Cambridge, MA, p. A298
  President, Spaulding Rehabilitation Hospital Cape Cod, East Sandwich, MA, p. A299

BANKS, Robbi, Vice President, Human Resources, Medical Center Health System, Odessa, TX, p. A626

BANKS, Walter, Director Human Resources, Baptist Memorial Hospital-Desoto, Southaven, MS, p. A353

BANKSTON, Doug, Director Technical Services, North Oaks Medical Center, Hammond, LA, p. A268

BANKTSON, Julie, Manager Human Resources, Paul Oliver Memorial Hospital, Frankfort, MI, p. A313

BANNER, Fred, Chief Information Officer, Shore Medical Center, Somers Point, NJ, p. A411

BANTZ, Steve, Manager Information Technology, Grundy County Memorial Hospital, Grundy Center, IA, p. A223

BANUEDOS, Jorge, Director Human Resources, Metropolitan State Hospital, Norwalk, CA, p. A75

BAPTISTE, Ernest J., Chief Executive Officer, Stony Brook Southampton Hospital, NY, p. A443

BAQUET, Shawn, Chief of Staff, Iberia Medical Center, New Iberia, LA, p. A275

BARACSKAY, Donald J., II, M.D., Chief Executive Officer, The Centers, Ocala, FL, p. A133

BARANSKI, David J, Vice President Human Resources, Phoebe North, GA, p. A145

BARANSKI, Kenneth, Chief Financial Officer, Hills & Dales General Hospital, Cass City, MI, p. A309

BARANSKI, Monica, MS, R.N.
  President, Mclaren Bay Region-West Campus, MI, p. A308
  President, Mclaren Bay Special Care, Bay City, MI, p. A308

BARBA, James J., President and Chief Executive Officer, Albany Medical Center South-Clinical Campus, NY, p. A421

BARBAREE, Jerry, Director Human Resources, Baptist Memorial Hospital - Memphis, Memphis, TN, p. A574

BARBARIN, LaSharndra, Chief Executive Officer, Medical City Lewisville, Lewisville, TX, p. A619

BARBAROTTA, Ann Marie., Executive Director, Creedmoor Psychiatric Center, New York (Includes All Hospitals Located Within The Five Boroughs), NY, p. A432

BARBEE, Daniel, Chief Executive Officer, The University Of Toledo Medical Center, Toledo, OH, p. A492

BARBEE, Ovell, Senior Vice President, Human Resources, Spectrum Health, MI, p. A314

BARBER, Chris B., FACHE, President and Chief Executive Officer, St. Bernards Medical Center, Jonesboro-Craighead County, AR, p. A44

BARBER, Eric A., President and Chief Executive Officer, Mary Lanning Healthcare, Hastings, NE, p. A384

BARBER, Karen, R.N., Chief Executive Officer, Yoakum Community Hospital, Yoakum, TX, p. A645

BARBER, Keith, CPA, Chief Executive Officer, Houston Methodist Willowbrook Hospital, Houston, TX, p. A611

BARBER, Michael, Chief Operating Officer, Chester County Hospital, West Chester, PA, p. A544

BARBER, Richard, M.D., Chief Medical Officer, Wake Forest Baptist Health - Wilkes Medical Center, North Wilkesboro, NC, p. A458

BARBER, Roxann E, Regional Ambulatory Care and Ancillary Services Officer, Presence Mercy Medical Center, Aurora, IL, p. A173

BARBER, Scott
  Chief Executive Officer, Decatur County General Hospital, Parsons, TN, p. A578
  Vice President, Camden General Hospital, Camden, TN, p. A566

BARBER, Wendi, Vice President Finance and Chief Financial Officer, Park Ridge Health, Hendersonville, NC, p. A454

BARBINI, Gerald J., President and Chief Executive Officer, Allegan General Hospital, Allegan, MI, p. A307

BARBO, Steve, RN, Chief Executive Officer, Citizens Medical Center, Columbia, LA, p. A266

BARBOUR, Alexis, Director Finance, Columbus Springs East Hospital, OH, p. A481

BARBOUR, Michael B, Chief Nursing Officer, Emerald Coast Behavioral Hospital, Panama City, FL, p. A135

BARBUAT, James P, Chief Financial Officer, Gunnison Valley Hospital, Gunnison, CO, p. A101

BARCELLONA, Nicholas J., Chief Financial Officer, Children's Hospital Of Pittsburgh Of Upmc, Pittsburgh, PA, p. A537

BARCHI, Daniel, Senior Vice President, Technical Services and Chief Information Officer, Bridgeport Hospital, Bridgeport, CT, p. A107

BARCLAY, Bonnie, Chief Nursing Officer, Lifecare Hospitals Of Chester County, West Chester, PA, p. A544

BARCLAY, Duane, D.O., Chief Medical Officer, Dekalb Medical At Hillandale, Lithonia, GA, p. A156

BARCLAY, Emily, Vice President Human Resources, Dana-Farber Cancer Institute, Boston, MA, p. A296

BARCLAY, Jeremy, Chief Executive Officer, St. David's Round Rock Medical Center, Round Rock, TX, p. A631

BARCLAY, Rick, Vice President Support Services, Mercy Hospital Rogers, Rogers-Benton County, AR, p. A48

BARCUS, Krista, Human Resources Leader, Ssm Health St. Francis Hospital - Maryville, Maryville, MO, p. A364

BARD, Jeffrey, President, Aurora Medical Center Of Oshkosh, Oshkosh, WI, p. A700

BARDEN, Sean
Executive Vice President and Chief Financial Officer, Snowden At Fredericksburg, VA, p. A658
Executive Vice President and Chief Financial Officer, Stafford Hospital, Stafford, VA, p. A666

BARDIER, Catherine, Vice President, Human Resources, Elliot Hospital, Manchester, NH, p. A400

BARDWELL, Carol A, R.N., MSN, Chief Nurse Executive, Martha's Vineyard Hospital, Oak Bluffs, MA, p. A303

BARDWELL, Sheila, Director Information Systems, Baptist Memorial Hospital-Golden Triangle, Columbus, MS, p. A345

BARE, Christina, Director of Business Operations, Carle Richland Memorial Hospital, Olney, IL, p. A192

BAREFOOT, Denise, Director of Information Technology, Carolina Pines Regional Medical Center, Hartsville, SC, p. A554

BAREIS, Charles, M.D., Medical Director, Macneal Hospital, Berwyn, IL, p. A174

BARELA, Barbara, Director Human Resources, Gila Regional Medical Center, Silver City, NM, p. A420

BARFIELD, Donna, Chief Nursing Officer, West Tennessee Healthcare Volunteer Hospital, Martin, TN, p. A574

BARHAM, Ed, M.D., Chief of Staff, Merit Health Woman's Hospital, Flowood, MS, p. A346

BARIOLA, Christopher L., Chief Executive Officer, Baptist Memorial Rehabilitation Hospital, Germantown, TN, p. A570

BARKER, Alanna, Director Human Resources, Metrosouth Medical Center, Blue Island, IL, p. A174

BARKER, James, Chief Executive Officer, Munson Healthcare Manistee Hospital, Manistee, MI, p. A318

BARKER, Karen, Vice President and Chief Information Officer, Sinai Hospital Of Baltimore, Baltimore, MD, p. A289

BARKER, Kathryn L, Chief Human Resources Management, Veterans Health Care System Of The Ozarks, Fayetteville-Washington County, AR, p. A42

BARKER, Kendra, Administrator, Pawnee Valley Community Hospital, Larned, KS, p. A239

BARKER, Louise, R.N., Chief Executive Officer, Central Louisiana Surgical Hospital, Alexandria, LA, p. A262

BARKER, Richard, Administrator and Chief Executive Officer, Mercy Health Love County, Marietta, OK, p. A501

BARKER, Russell
Community Chief Executive Officer, Mcdowell Arh Hospital, Mcdowell, KY, p. A258
Information Officer, U.S. Public Health Service Indian Hospital-Whiteriver, Whiteriver, AZ, p. A38

BARKER, William A, Jr, Vice President Administration, Pleasant Valley Hospital, Point Pleasant, WV, p. A686

BARKHYMER, Mary C, R.N., MSN, Vice President Patient Care Services and Chief Nursing Officer, Upmc St. Margaret, Pittsburgh, PA, p. A538

BARKMAN, Joseph, Vice President Financial Services, Oaklawn Psychiatric Center, Goshen, IN, p. A205

BARKSDALE, Mary, Director Human Resources, Person Memorial Hospital, Roxboro, NC, p. A460

BARLAGE, Seth, Associate Medical Center Director, John J. Pershing Veterans Affairs Medical Center, Poplar Bluff, MO, p. A366

BARLEY, Leonard, M.D., Chief Medical Officer, Windsor-Laurelwood Center For Behavioral Medicine, Willoughby, OH, p. A493

BARLEY, Tammy, Director, Human Resources, Healthsouth Rehabilitation Hospital Of Jonesboro, Jonesboro-Craighead County, AR, p. A44

BARLIS, Ellen, Chief Financial Officer, Nyc Health + Hospitals / Jacobi, New York (Includes All Hospitals Located Within The Five Boroughs), NY, p. A435

BARLOW, Mark, M.D., Chief Medical Officer and President Medical Staff, Cornerstone Hospital Of Houston - Bellaire, TX, p. A643

BARLOW, Roddex, Chief Operating Officer, Providence Children's Hospital, TX, p. A602

BARMECHA, Jitendra, M.D., M.P.H., Senior Vice President and Chief Information Officer, St. Barnabas Hospital, New York (Includes All Hospitals Located Within The Five Boroughs), NY, p. A437

BARNARD, Jeanna, FACHE, Chief Executive Officer, Bayshore Medical Center, Pasadena, TX, p. A627

BARNARD, Kerri, Director Human Resources, Larned State Hospital, Larned, KS, p. A239

BARNARD, Lawrence, President and Chief Executive Officer, St. Rose Dominican Hospitals - San Martin Campus, Las Vegas, NV, p. A395

BARNCORD, Sharon, Human Resource Business Partner, Kaiser Permanente South San Francisco, South San Francisco, CA, p. A90

BARNELL, Phil, Chief Medical Officer, Hshs St. Mary's Hospital, Decatur, IL, p. A181

BARNES, Alan, Chief Financial Officer, North Star Behavioral Health, AK, p. A25

BARNES, Becky, Chief Operating Officer, St. David's North Austin Medical Center, Austin, TX, p. A586

BARNES, Bridget, Vice President and Chief Information Officer, Doernbecher Children's Hospital, OR, p. A516

BARNES, Deborah, Vice President and Chief Information Officer, Children's Hospital Of The King's Daughters, Norfolk, VA, p. A662

BARNES, Donald K, Chief Human Resources Officer, Duke Raleigh Hospital, Raleigh, NC, p. A459

BARNES, Douglas A, M.D., Chief of Staff, Shriners Hospitals For Children-Houston, Houston, TX, p. A613

BARNES, Elbert, M.D., Chief Medical Officer, Medical Center Of Trinity, Trinity, FL, p. A142

BARNES, Gary, Senior Vice President, Chief Information Officer, Medical Center Health System, Odessa, TX, p. A626

BARNES, Gloria V., MSN, Assistant Vice President Patient Care Services, Southeastern Regional Medical Center, Newnan, GA, p. A158

BARNES, Jacqueline, Manager Health Information, Select Specialty Hospital-Jackson, Jackson, MS, p. A348

BARNES, Jeff, Director Information Technology, Girard Medical Center, Girard, KS, p. A235

BARNES, Joe, Chief Financial Officer, Stonewall Jackson Memorial Hospital, Weston, WV, p. A688

BARNES, John, Administrative Director Human Resources, Beverly Hospital, Montebello, CA, p. A73

BARNES, Karen, Interim Chief Nursing Officer, Logan Regional Medical Center, Logan, WV, p. A684

BARNES, Larry, Director Information Technology, Salina Regional Health Center-Santa Fe Campus, KS, p. A245

BARNES, Leslie, Chief Financial Officer, Parkview Medical Center, Pueblo, CO, p. A104

BARNES, Marla, Director of Nursing, Pushmataha Hospital, Antlers, OK, p. A495

BARNES, Michael, Chief Information Officer, North Valley Hospital, Whitefish, MT, p. A380

BARNES, P. Marie, Director, Human Resources, North Mississippi Medical Center-Pontotoc, Pontotoc, MS, p. A352

BARNES, Sherry, Director Health Information and Quality Management, Rolling Hills Hospital, Ada, OK, p. A495

BARNES, William, FACHE, Administrator, Kimble Hospital, Junction, TX, p. A616

BARNETT, Dana, Chief Executive Officer, Memorial Hospital Of Carbon County, Rawlins, WY, p. A709

BARNETT, DeLynn K, Director Human Resources, Lake Chelan Community Hospital And Clinics, Chelan, WA, p. A670

BARNETT, Frederick, M.D., Chief of Staff, Metroplex Behavioral Health Center, TX, p. A617

BARNETT, Julia, Chief Nursing Officer, Union General Hospital, Blairsville, GA, p. A148

BARNETT, Kelly, Human Resource Officer, Brownfield Regional Medical Center, Brownfield, TX, p. A590

BARNETT, Laura, Executive Director, Human Resources, Brigham And Women's Faulkner Hospital, Boston, MA, p. A296

BARNETT, Lori, R.N., MSN, Chief Nursing Officer, Troy Community Hospital, Troy, PA, p. A542

BARNETT, Pam, R.N., Director of Nursing, Highland District Hospital, Hillsboro, OH, p. A484

BARNETT, Shawn
Senior Vice President and Chief Financial Officer, Chi St. Vincent Hot Springs, Hot Springs-Garland County, AR, p. A43
Senior Vice President and Chief Financial Officer, Chi St. Vincent Infirmary Medical Center, Little Rock-Pulaski County, AR, p. A45
Senior Vice President and Chief Financial Officer, Chi St. Vincent Medical Center-North, Sherwood-Pulaski County, AR, p. A48
Senior Vice President and Chief Financial Officer, Chi St. Vincent Morrilton, Morrilton-Conway County, AR, p. A46

BARNETT, Steve, President and Chief Executive Officer, Mckenzie Health System, Sandusky, MI, p. A323

BARNETT, Tom, Chief Information Officer, Highland Hospital, Rochester, NY, p. A441

BARNETTE, Brian, Chief Information Officer, Shepherd Center, Atlanta, GA, p. A147

BARNHARDT, Bonnie, Executive Director Human Resources, Ridgeview Le Sueur Medical Center, Le Sueur, MN, p. A333

BARNHART, Ann, Chief Executive Officer, Heart Of Florida Regional Medical Center, Davenport, FL, p. A121

BARNHART, David, Director Information Systems, Rockledge Regional Medical Center, Rockledge, FL, p. A137

BARNHART, J. T., Chief Executive Officer, Dallas Medical Center, Dallas, TX, p. A596

BARNHART, Jeff, Chief Executive Officer, Hereford Regional Medical Center, Hereford, TX, p. A609

BARNO, Jill, M.D., Chief Medical Officer, Berger Health System, Circleville, OH, p. A476

BARONE, Richard, M.D., Medical Director, Montefiore New Rochelle, New Rochelle, NY, p. A431

BARR, Ann
Chief Information Officer - Bay Area, California Pacific Medical Center-St. Luke's Campus, San Francisco, CA, p. A85
Chief Information Officer - Bay Area, California Pacific Medical Center, San Francisco, CA, p. A85
Chief Information Officer, Sutter Health Bay Area, Sutter Maternity And Surgery Center Of Santa Cruz, Santa Cruz, CA, p. A89
Interim Chief Financial Officer, Florida Hospital Dade City, Dade City, FL, p. A121

BARR, Brent, Chief Information Officer, Minnie Hamilton Healthcare Center, Grantsville, WV, p. A683

BARR, Bret A., President and Chief Executive Officer, Conway Medical Center, Conway, SC, p. A552

BARR, Francine, R.N., MS
Chief Executive Officer, Bon Secours St. Mary's Children's Services, VA, p. A664
Vice President and Chief Operating Officer, Bon Secours St. Mary's Children's Services, VA, p. A664

BARR, Kristine, Vice President Communication Services, O'Bleness Memorial Hospital, Athens, OH, p. A471

BARR, Kyle, Senior Vice President, Chief Team Resources Officer, Mease Countryside Hospital, Safety Harbor, FL, p. A137

BARR, Kyle J
Senior Vice President, Chief Team Resources Officer, Mease Dunedin Hospital, Dunedin, FL, p. A122
Senior Vice President, Chief Team Resources Officer, Morton Plant North Bay Hospital, New Port Richey, FL, p. A132

BARR, Laurie C
Vice President Human Resources, Salem Health Rehabilitation Center, OR, p. A517
Vice President Human Resources, Salem Health West Valley, Dallas, OR, p. A512

BARRA, Jon, Director Human Resources, Wyoming Behavioral Institute, Casper, WY, p. A707

BARRACLOUGH, Grant, R.N., Chief Nursing Officer, Castleview Hospital, Price, UT, p. A649

BARRALL, Audrey
Director Human Resources, Adventist Health Clear Lake, Clearlake, CA, p. A54
Director Human Resources, Adventist Health St. Helena, Saint Helena, CA, p. A82

BARRERA, Edward, Director Communications, Encino Hospital Medical Center, Los Angeles, CA, p. A66

BARRERA, Liflor, Manager Human Resources, Wahiawa General Hospital, Wahiawa, HI, p. A166

BARRERA-RICHARDS, Ursula, Human Resource Director, Northwest Ohio Psychiatric Hospital, Toledo, OH, p. A491

BARRERE, Davie Ann, Coordinator Information Technology, Dahl Memorial Healthcare Association, Ekalaka, MT, p. A375

BARRETT, Anne J, Associate Executive Director Human Resources, Southside Hospital, Bay Shore, NY, p. A422

BARRETT, Bill, Manager Human Resources, Wilson N. Jones Regional Medical Center, Sherman, TX, p. A636

BARRETT, Cindy, Administrative Assistant, Patton State Hospital, Patton, CA, p. A78

BARRETT, Hannah, Director of Nursing, North Sunflower Medical Center, Ruleville, MS, p. A353

BARRETT, James W., Jr, Chief Executive Officer, Richardson Medical Center, Rayville, LA, p. A278

BARRETT, Jason P., Chief Executive Officer, Flagler Hospital, Saint Augustine, FL, p. A137

BARRETT, John, Regional Director Human Resources, Franciscan Health Michigan City, Michigan City, IN, p. A211

BARRETT, Kerry Flynn, Vice President Human Resources, Northern Westchester Hospital, Mount Kisco, NY, p. A430

BARRETT, Kristen, Chief Executive Officer, Promise Hospital Of Overland Park, Overland Park, KS, p. A243

BROSKEY, Steven, Associate Director, Veterans Affairs Roseburg Healthcare System, Roseburg, OR, p. A517

BROSNAHAN, Jan, Chief Financial Officer, Winona Health, Winona, MN, p. A342

BROSNAN, Kimberly, Director Human Resources, Norwood Hospital, Norwood, MA, p. A303

BROSS, James B., President, St. Luke's Hospital, Columbus, NC, p. A450

BROST, Wade, Executive Director, Anoka-Metropolitan Regional Treatment Center, Anoka, MN, p. A327

BROTEN, Kurt
Chief Financial Officer, Palmdale Regional Medical Center, Palmdale, CA, p. A77
Chief Financial Officer, Vista Del Mar Hospital, Ventura, CA, p. A94

BROTHMAN, Joe, Assistant Vice President, Information Systems, Medstar Washington Hospital Center, Washington, DC, p. A116

BROUGHMAN, Robin, R.N., Ph.D., Chief Nursing Officer, Lewisgale Hospital Alleghany, Low Moor, VA, p. A660

BROUGHMAN, Wade
Chief Financial Officer, Tobey Hospital, MA, p. A299
Executive Vice President and Chief Financial Officer, Riverside Behavioral Health Center, VA, p. A662

BROUSSARD, Heidi, Chief Nursing Officer, Abbeville General Hospital, Abbeville, LA, p. A262

BROUSSARD, Kari, Chief Nursing Officer, Oakdale Community Hospital, Oakdale, LA, p. A277

BROUWER, Heath, Administrator, Douglas County Memorial Hospital, Armour, SD, p. A559

BROVOLD, Diana, Chief Nurse Executive, Multicare Mary Bridge Children's Hospital And Health Center, Tacoma, WA, p. A679

BROWDER, Renate, R.N., Director of Nursing, Lake City Community Hospital, Lake City, SC, p. A555

BROWER, Laura E, R.N., MSN, Chief Nursing Officer, Children's Hospital Of Georgia, GA, p. A147

BROWN, Alisa, Administrative Assistant, Dewitt Hospital, Dewitt-Arkansas County, AR, p. A41

BROWN, Angel, Director Human Resources, Morton Plant Hospital, Clearwater, FL, p. A119

BROWN, Ann R., M.D., Director, Va Greater Los Angeles Healthcare System, Los Angeles, CA, p. A70

BROWN, Austin, Chief Operating Officer, Bayfront Health St. Petersburg, Saint Petersburg, FL, p. A138

BROWN, B Blaine, Vice President and General Counsel, Prattville Baptist Hospital, Prattville, AL, p. A22

BROWN, Barbra, MS, R.N., Interim Chief Nursing Officer and Vice President of Nursing, Alice Peck Day Memorial Hospital, Lebanon, NH, p. A399

BROWN, Bartley, D.O., Chief of Staff, St. Joseph's Hospital Of Buckhannon, Buckhannon, WV, p. A682

BROWN, Benjamin, Chief Operating Officer, Stonesprings Hospital Center, Dulles, VA, p. A657

BROWN, Bryan, Executive Director, Mercy Orthopedic Hospital Fort Smith, AR, p. A42

BROWN, Chad J., M.P.H., President, Wake Forest Baptist Health-Davie Medical Center, Bermuda Run, NC, p. A448

BROWN, Cheryl, Chief Executive Officer, Henderson Health Care Services, Henderson, NE, p. A385

BROWN, Chistiane, Assistant Vice President, Medstar Montgomery Medical Center, Olney, MD, p. A293

BROWN, Christi, Director Human Resources, Bogalusa Community Medical Center, LA, p. A264

BROWN, Chuck, Administrator, Bethesda Butler Hospital, OH, p. A474

BROWN, Crystal, M.D., Medical Director, Medical Center Of Peach County, Navicent Health, Bryon, GA, p. A149

BROWN, Cynthia, Director of Nursing, Hill Hospital Of Sumter County, York, AL, p. A24

BROWN, Darin, Vice President Finance, Henry Community Health, New Castle, IN, p. A212

BROWN, David A, Director Human Resources and Corporate Compliance, Pleasant Valley Hospital, Point Pleasant, WV, p. A686

BROWN, Deana, Director Administrative Services, Franciscan Health Rensselear, Rensselaer, IN, p. A214

BROWN, Deborah, Chief Nursing Officer, Logan Memorial Hospital, Russellville, KY, p. A260

BROWN, Debra L, Area Financial Officer, Modesto Medical Center, CA, p. A71

BROWN, Debra M., Vice President, Chief Nursing Officer and Chief Operating Officer, Dell Children's Medical Center Of Central Texas, Austin, TX, p. A585

BROWN, Denise, Vice President Human Resources, Presence Saint Joseph Hospital, Chicago, IL, p. A178

BROWN, Derek, Chief Information Officer, Jellico Community Hospital, Jellico, TN, p. A571

BROWN, Ed
Chief Financial Officer, Cibola General Hospital, Grants, NM, p. A417
Chief Information Officer, Children's Hospital, Navicent Health, GA, p. A156

BROWN, Eric, M.D., Physician Executive, Palmetto Health Children's Hospital, SC, p. A551

BROWN, Geoffrey
Chief Information Officer, Piedmont Fayette Hospital, Fayetteville, GA, p. A153
Chief Information Officer, Piedmont Mountainside Hospital, Jasper, GA, p. A155
Vice President Information Systems, Inova Fairfax Hospital For Children, VA, p. A657

BROWN, Greg, Administrator, St. Vincent's Blount, Oneonta, AL, p. A22

BROWN, Howard, Chief Financial Officer, Florida Medical Center - A Campus Of North Shore, FL, p. A130

BROWN, Hugh, Chief Executive Officer, St. David's Georgetown Hospital, TX, p. A586

BROWN, James H, Chief Financial Officer, Centerpoint Medical Center, Independence, MO, p. A360

BROWN, Janice, Chief Financial Officer, Coosa Valley Medical Center, Sylacauga, AL, p. A23

BROWN, Jason, M.D.
Chief Medical Officer, Banner Goldfield Medical Center, Apache Junction, AZ, p. A28
Director Information Systems, Sanford Sheldon Medical Center, Sheldon, IA, p. A229
Director, Kettering Behavioral Medical Center, OH, p. A487

BROWN, Jay
Senior Vice President, Chief Information Officer, West Chester Hospital Surgical Center, OH, p. A493
Vice President and Chief Information Officer, University Of Cincinnati Medical Center, Cincinnati, OH, p. A476

BROWN, Jayma, R.N., Director of Nursing, Oakland Mercy Hospital, Oakland, NE, p. A387

BROWN, Jeffrey P, M.D., Chief Medical Officer, Indiana University Health Arnett Hospital, Lafayette, IN, p. A209

BROWN, Jenny, Director of Human Resources, Vidant Beaufort Hospital, Washington, NC, p. A462

BROWN, Jill, Chief Financial Officer, Miller County Hospital, Colquitt, GA, p. A150

BROWN, Jim
Chief Executive Officer, North Cypress Medical Center, Cypress, TX, p. A595
Director Information Technology, Lynn County Hospital District, Tahoka, TX, p. A638

BROWN, Jon, Chief Information Officer, Mission Hospital, NC, p. A447

BROWN, Joni, Director Human Resources, Rehabilitation Hospital Of Indiana, Indianapolis, IN, p. A207

BROWN, Joseph C.
Vice President Operations, Baylor Regional Medical Center At Plano, Plano, TX, p. A628
Vice President Operations, Baylor Scott & White Medical Center - Lakeway, TX, p. A631

BROWN, Judy, Executive Vice President and Chief Operating Officer, Doctors Hospital Of Jefferson, LA, p. A274

BROWN, Karen
Manager Information Technology, Guthrie Towanda Memorial Hospital, Towanda, PA, p. A542
Senior Director of Human Resources, Bridgepoint Hospital Capitol Hill, Washington, DC, p. A115

BROWN, Karen C, Vice President Chief Operating Officer, Osf Saint Anthony Medical Center, Rockford, IL, p. A195

BROWN, Katie, Coordinator Human Resources, Pocahontas Memorial Hospital, Buckeye, WV, p. A681

BROWN, Kendra, MSN, R.N.
Director of Nursing, Kearney County Health Services, Minden, NE, p. A386
Job Requisition Coordinator, Rusk State Hospital, Rusk, TX, p. A631

BROWN, Kenneth A, Vice President and Chief Human Resource Officer, Pratt Regional Medical Center, Pratt, KS, p. A244

BROWN, Kevin, Chief Executive Officer, La Paz Regional Hospital, Parker, AZ, p. A32

BROWN, Kris, Associate Director, Bay Pines Veterans Affairs Healthcare System, Bay Pines, FL, p. A117

BROWN, LaRay, President and Chief Executive Officer, Interfaith Medical Center, New York (Includes All Hospitals Located Within The Five Boroughs), NY, p. A432

BROWN, Lewis, Director Information Technology, Bsa Hospital, Llc, Amarillo, TX, p. A583

BROWN, Lisa, Director of Nursing, Pearl River County Hospital, Poplarville, MS, p. A352

BROWN, Liz, Manager Human Resources, Gunnison Valley Hospital, Gunnison, UT, p. A647

BROWN, Lorenzo, Chief Executive Officer, Florida Hospital Deland, Deland, FL, p. A121

BROWN, Lori, Chief Nursing Officer, Baptist Memorial Hospital-Union City, Union City, TN, p. A580

BROWN, Lori J, R.N., FACHE, Vice President and Chief Nursing Executive, Borgess-Pipp Hospital, MI, p. A316

BROWN, Margaret, Director Medical Records, Vantage Point Of Northwest Arkansas, Fayetteville-Washington County, AR, p. A42

BROWN, Mark R, Chief Nursing Officer, Seton Medical Center, Daly City, CA, p. A56

BROWN, Markham, M.D., Chief Medical Staff, Mike O'Callaghan Federal Hospital, Nellis Afb, NV, p. A395

BROWN, Marlon, Human Resources, Essex County Hospital Center, Cedar Grove, NJ, p. A403

BROWN, Martin, Vice President Information Services and Chief Information Officer, Nathan Littauer Hospital And Nursing Home, Gloversville, NY, p. A427

BROWN, Mary Beth, Director Human Resources, Bertrand Chaffee Hospital, Springville, NY, p. A443

BROWN, Mary W, Senior Vice President Operations, St. Joseph's Hospital Health Center, Syracuse, NY, p. A444

BROWN, Michael, D.O., Chief of Staff, Tmc Bonham Hospital, Bonham, TX, p. A589

BROWN, Michael L.
Regional President and Chief Executive Officer, Presence Mercy Medical Center, Aurora, IL, p. A173
Regional President and Chief Executive Officer, Presence Saint Joseph Hospital, Elgin, IL, p. A182

BROWN, Mike, Chief Financial Officer, Carlinville Area Hospital, Carlinville, IL, p. A175

BROWN, Molly B., Chief Operating Officer, University Of Mississippi Medical Center Grenada, Grenada, MS, p. A346

BROWN, Natalie, Chief Human Resources Management Services, Memphis Veterans Affairs Medical Center, Memphis, TN, p. A575

BROWN, Pam, Human Resources Manager, Unity Psychiatric Care-Columbia, Columbia, TN, p. A568

BROWN, Pat, R.N., Chief Nursing Officer, San Gorgonio Memorial Hospital, Banning, CA, p. A52

BROWN, Patsy, Site Coordinator Human Resources, Erlanger Bledsoe Hospital, Pikeville, TN, p. A579

BROWN, Penny D, Director of Human Resources, Broaddus Hospital, Philippi, WV, p. A686

BROWN, Philip, D.O., Vice President Medical Affairs, The University Of Vermont Health Network Central Vermont Medical Center, Berlin, VT, p. A653

BROWN, Phyllis, Chief Executive Officer, Marshall Medical Center, Lewisburg, TN, p. A573

BROWN, Randal, M.D., Chief of Medical Staff, Guadalupe County Hospital, Santa Rosa, NM, p. A419

BROWN, Regenia, Vice President Human Resources, Magnolia Regional Health Center, Corinth, MS, p. A345

BROWN, Rex H., President and Chief Executive Officer, Hillsboro Area Hospital, Hillsboro, IL, p. A185

BROWN, Rickie F, Chief Financial Officer, Monroe County Medical Center, Tompkinsville, KY, p. A261

BROWN, Rita, Director Human Resources, Richardson Medical Center, Rayville, LA, p. A278

BROWN, Robert, Chief Operating Officer, Parkview Community Hospital Medical Center, Riverside, CA, p. A81

BROWN, Roberta, Chief Nursing Officer, Community Hospital Of Staunton, Staunton, IL, p. A197

BROWN, Robin, Chief Information Officer and Compliance Officer, St. Joseph Medical Center In The Heights, TX, p. A613

BROWN, Scott, Chief Financial Officer, Valir Rehabilitation Hospital, Oklahoma City, OK, p. A505

BROWN, Sharon, R.N., MSN
Vice President Patient Care and Chief Nursing Officer, St. Mary Medical Center, Langhorne, PA, p. A529
Deputy Commander Nursing, Winn Army Community Hospital, Hinesville, GA, p. A155
Vice President Human Resources, Sierra View Medical Center, Porterville, CA, p. A79

BROWN, Sherry, Director Human Resources, Cleveland Area Hospital, Cleveland, OK, p. A497

BROWN, Stephen A, Chief Financial Officer, Grace Cottage Hospital, Townshend, VT, p. A654

BROWN, Steve, M.D.
Chief Quality Officer, Saint Alphonsus Regional Medical Center, Boise, ID, p. A168
Chief Information Officer, Wellstar Sylvan Grove Hospital, Jackson, GA, p. A155
Director Information Systems, Wellstar Spalding Regional Hospital, Griffin, GA, p. A154
Health Services Director, U.S. Penitentiary Infirmary, Lewisburg, PA, p. A530

Vice President Finance and Chief Financial Officer, Jefferson Medical Center, Ranson, WV, p. A686

BUCHANAN, Donald E., Chief Executive Officer, Haskell County Community Hospital, Stigler, OK, p. A507

BUCHANAN, Donna, Director Nursing, Stroud Regional Medical Center, Stroud, OK, p. A507

BUCHANAN, Jean, Director Human Resources, Broughton Hospital, Morganton, NC, p. A457

BUCHANAN, Robert, Chief Information Officer, Anna Jaques Hospital, Newburyport, MA, p. A302

BUCHANAN, Toni, Chief Financial Officer, Unicoi County Memorial Hospital, Erwin, TN, p. A569

BUCHANAN, Tracy, Chief Executive Officer and President, Carepartners Health Services, Asheville, NC, p. A447

BUCHART, Phyllis, Chief Operating Officer, Marina Del Rey Hospital, Marina Del Rey, CA, p. A71

BUCHE, Karen, Chief Human Resource Officer, Douglas County Community Mental Health Center, Omaha, NE, p. A388

BUCHELE, Paula, Chief Human Resources, Bay Pines Veterans Affairs Healthcare System, Bay Pines, FL, p. A117

BUCHER, Ben, Chief Executive Officer, Towner County Medical Center, Cando, ND, p. A464

BUCHHEIT, Anne, Coordinator Mental Health Local Information Systems, Buffalo Psychiatric Center, Buffalo, NY, p. A423

BUCHHEIT, Joe, Chief Financial Officer, Our Lady Of Bellefonte Hospital, Ashland, KY, p. A249

BUCHHOLZ, Kari, Director Health Information Management, Wishek Community Hospital And Clinics, Wishek, ND, p. A469

BUCHNESS, Michael P., M.D., Director Medical, Deer's Head Hospital Center, Salisbury, MD, p. A294

BUCIENSKI, Jennifer C, Vice President Human Resources, Hayes Green Beach Memorial Hospital, Charlotte, MI, p. A309

BUCK, Catherine, MSN, R.N., President, Froedtert And The Medical College Of Wisconsin Froedtert Hospital, Milwaukee, WI, p. A698

BUCK, Linda K, Vice President Human Resources, Unitypoint Health - Proctor, Peoria, IL, p. A193

BUCK, Nathan, R.N., Nursing Manager, Mountain River Birthing And Surgery Center, Blackfoot, ID, p. A167

BUCK, Phylis, Controller, Encompass Health Rehabilitation Hospital Of Texarkana, Texarkana, TX, p. A639

BUCK, Shelly, Chief Nursing Executive and Chief Operating Officer, Bon Secours Baltimore Health System, Baltimore, MD, p. A287

BUCK, Tavia, Chief Nursing Officer, Roper St. Francis Mount Pleasant Hospital, Mount Pleasant, SC, p. A555

BUCK, William, Chief of Staff, Horton Community Hospital, Horton, KS, p. A237

BUCKHOY, Sandra, Chief Clinical Officer, Kindred Hospital Chicago-Northlake, Northlake, IL, p. A191

BUCKLEY, David, Acting Chief Information Management Services, Oklahoma City Veterans Affairs Medical Center, Oklahoma City, OK, p. A504

BUCKLEY, John, M.D., President Medical Staff, Vibra Hospital Of Denver, Thornton, CO, p. A106

BUCKLEY, Kalvin, Director Information Systems, Woodland Heights Medical Center, Lufkin, TX, p. A622

BUCKLEY, Karen L, R.N., Chief Nursing Officer, Community Behavioral Health Center, Fresno, CA, p. A59

BUCKLEY, Martha, Chief Medical Informatics Officer, Fairfield Medical Center, Lancaster, OH, p. A484

BUCKMINSTER, Joe, Manager Information Technology, Community Medical Center, Inc., Falls City, NE, p. A383

BUCKNER, Marlys, Chief Nursing Officer, Cox Barton County Memorial Hospital, Lamar, MO, p. A363

BUCKNER, Twila, R.N., Chief Nursing Officer, Cass Regional Medical Center, Harrisonville, MO, p. A360

BUCKWORTH, Albert Bennett, Human Resources Administrative Director, Primary Children's Hospital, Salt Lake City, UT, p. A650

BUDA, Jeff, Chief Information Officer, Floyd Medical Center, Rome, GA, p. A159

BUDD, Edward, President and Chief Executive Officer, Thorek Memorial Hospital, Chicago, IL, p. A180

BUDZINSKY, Chris
    Vice President Nursing and Chief Nursing Officer Alexian Brothers Acute Care Ministries, Amita Health Women & Children's Hospital, IL, p. A186
    Vice President, Nursing and Chief Nursing Officer, Amita Health Rehabilitation Hospital, IL, p. A182

BUE, Cheryl, Health Information Transcriptionist, Faulkton Area Medical Center, Faulkton, SD, p. A560

BUEHLER, Bonnie, Chief Information Officer, St. Mary Medical Center, Langhorne, PA, p. A529

BUEHRLE, Jeff, Chief Financial Officer, Banner - University Medical Center South, Tucson, AZ, p. A36

BUELL, Jack, Director Information Services, Sutter Lakeside Hospital, Lakeport, CA, p. A64

BUENVENIDA, Brenda, Director, Hiram W. Davis Medical Center, Petersburg, VA, p. A663

BUER, Shane, Vice President, Human Resources, Mercy Services For Aging, IA, p. A219

BUFFENBARGER, Andrew, Chief Compliance Officer, Kirby Medical Center, Monticello, IL, p. A190

BUFFINGTON, John, Chief Operating Officer, San Juan Regional Medical Center Rehabilitation Hospital, NM, p. A417

BUFFINGTON, Mike, Manager Information Technology, Kansas Medical Center, Andover, KS, p. A232

BUFKIN, Ben, Human Resource Director, Bolivar Medical Center, Cleveland, MS, p. A345

BUGALLO-MUROS, Mariana, Vice President Chief Human Resources Officer, H. Lee Moffitt Cancer Center And Research Institute, Tampa, FL, p. A140

BUGAYONG, Carol, Human Resources Director, Healthsouth Rehabilitation Hospital Of Tallahassee, Tallahassee, FL, p. A140

BUGNA, Eric, M.D., Chief of Staff, Eastern Plumas Health Care, Portola, CA, p. A79

BUHLKE, Brian, M.D., Medical Director, Genoa Medical Facilities, Genoa, NE, p. A384

BUI, Steven, M.D., Chief of Staff, Orange County Global Medical Center, Inc., Santa Ana, CA, p. A88

BUIT, Timothy, Executive Vice President and Chief Financial Officer, Bellevue Hospital, Bellevue, OH, p. A472

BULAU, Chris, Manager Information Technology, Ridgeview Sibley Medical Center, Arlington, MN, p. A327

BULEN, Susan R., M.D., Medical Director, Encompass Health Rehabilitation Hospital Of Northwest Tucson, Tucson, AZ, p. A37

BULFIN, Joey, R.N., Interim Chief Executive Officer, Palm Beach Children's Hospital, FL, p. A143

BULLARD, Brandon
    Chief Financial Officer, Bailey Medical Center, Owasso, OK, p. A505
    Chief Financial Officer, Hillcrest Hospital Claremore, Claremore, OK, p. A497
    Chief Financial Officer, Sparks Regional Medical Center, Fort Smith-Sebastian County, AR, p. A42
    Interim Chief Executive Officer, Sparks Medical Center - Van Buren, Van Buren-Crawford County, AR, p. A49
    Interim Chief Executive Officer, Sparks Regional Medical Center, Fort Smith-Sebastian County, AR, p. A42

BULLARD, Elizabeth, Chief Executive Officer, Northern Colorado Rehabilitation Hospital, Johnstown, CO, p. A102

BULLARD, John, Director Information Technology, St. Mary's Hospital And Medical Center, Grand Junction, CO, p. A101

BULLARD, Patrick, Chief Financial Officer, Fayetteville Veterans Affairs Medical Center, Fayetteville, NC, p. A452

BULLINGTON, Benjamin P., M.D., Chief of Staff, Pioneer Medical Center, Big Timber, MT, p. A373

BULLINGTON, Gina, Chief Nursing Officer, Tristar Horizon Medical Center, Dickson, TN, p. A569

BULLOCK, David, Director Information Services, Northwest Medical Center, Tucson, AZ, p. A37

BULLOCK, Lance, M.D., Medical Director, St. James Behavioral Health Hospital, Gonzales, LA, p. A268

BULLOCK, Scott, Director Information Systems, Barstow Community Hospital, Barstow, CA, p. A52

BULMAN, Laurie, Director Human Resources, Winneshiek Medical Center, Decorah, IA, p. A221

BULMASH, Jack, M.D., Chief of Staff, Edward Hines, Jr. Veterans Affairs Hospital, Hines, IL, p. A185

BUMAN, Karen, MSN, Chief Nursing Executive, Myrtue Medical Center, Harlan, IA, p. A224

BUMANN, Tim, D.O., Chief of Staff, Abilene Regional Medical Center, Abilene, TX, p. A582

BUMBAUGH, Christopher, Executive Director Human Resource and Organizational Development, Western Maryland Regional Medical Center, Cumberland, MD, p. A291

BUMGARDNER, Charles
    Chief Information Officer, Southeast Georgia Health System Brunswick Campus, Brunswick, GA, p. A149
    Director, Southeast Georgia Health System Camden Campus, Saint Marys, GA, p. A159

BUMGARNER, William J., President, Spencer Hospital, Spencer, IA, p. A230

BUMP, Cathy, R.N., Chief Nursing Officer, Methodist Ambulatory Surgery Hospital - Northwest, San Antonio, TX, p. A633

BUNCH, David V., President and Chief Administrative Officer, Cumberland Medical Center, Crossville, TN, p. A569

BUNCH, Elicia
    Chief Executive Officer, Centennial Peaks Hospital, Louisville, CO, p. A104
    Chief Executive Officer, Highlands Behavioral Health System, Littleton, CO, p. A103

BUNCH, Jimm, President and Chief Executive Officer, Park Ridge Health, Hendersonville, NC, p. A454

BUNCH, Kim, Director Information Technology, Marshall Medical Center North, Guntersville, AL, p. A19

BUNCH, Mark, Director Finance, Othello Community Hospital, Othello, WA, p. A674

BUNCH, Mike, Executive Vice President, Chief Operating Officer and Chief Financial Officer, Kershawhealth, Camden, SC, p. A549

BUNCH, Rita A., M.P.H., FACHE, Vice President of Operations, Sentara Careplex Hospital, Hampton, VA, p. A659

BUNCH, Terri, MSN, R.N., MSN, Chief Nursing Officer, White River Medical Center, Batesville, AR, p. A39

BUND, Linda, Chief Information Officer and Director Education, James J. Peters Veterans Affairs Medical Center, New York (Includes All Hospitals Located Within The Five Boroughs), NY, p. A432

BUNDT, Thomas S., Commanding Officer, Madigan Army Medical Center, Tacoma, WA, p. A679

BUNDY, Michael N, Chief Operating Officer, Cape Cod Hospital, Hyannis, MA, p. A300

BUNKER, Marla, Vice President Nursing and Chief Operating Officer, War Memorial Hospital, Sault Sainte Marie, MI, p. A323

BUNN, Barry, M.D., Chief of Staff, Vidant Edgecombe Hospital, Tarboro, NC, p. A461

BUNNELL, Emily Ann, Chief Nurse Executive, Senior Director of Acute Care, Upmc Cole, Coudersport, PA, p. A523

BUNNER, Blake, Chief Executive Officer, Healthsouth Deaconess Rehabilitation Hospital, Evansville, IN, p. A203

BUNSELMEYER, Becky, Director Information Services, Memorial Hospital, Chester, IL, p. A176

BUNTEN, Sherry, Director Patient Care Services, Aspirus Langlade Hospital, Antigo, WI, p. A689

BUNTING, Katherine, Esq, Chief Executive Officer, Fairfield Memorial Hospital, Fairfield, IL, p. A183

BUNTYN, Diane, MSN, R.N., Vice President Patient Care Services, Southeast Alabama Medical Center, Dothan, AL, p. A17

BUNYARD, Steve
    President, Ohiohealth Dublin Methodist Hospital, Dublin, OH, p. A481
    President, Ohiohealth Grady Memorial Hospital, Delaware, OH, p. A481

BUONGIORNO, Michael J
    Executive Vice President Finance and Chief Financial Officer, Bryn Mawr Hospital, Bryn Mawr, PA, p. A521
    Vice President Finance, Lankenau Medical Center, Wynnewood, PA, p. A545

BUPP, Steven, M.D., Medical Director, Sonora Behavioral Health Hospital, Tucson, AZ, p. A38

BURBANK, Jimmy, Chief Information Officer, U.S. Public Health Service Indian Hospital, Crownpoint, NM, p. A416

BURCH, Debra, Chief Nursing Officer, Burke Medical Center, Waynesboro, GA, p. A163

BURCH, Lee, Director Management Information Systems, Bayfront Health Spring Hill, FL, p. A119

BURCH, Todd, Chief Executive Officer, Aspirus Riverview Hospital And Clinics, Inc., Wisconsin Rapids, WI, p. A706

BURCHELL, Pam, Director Human Resources, Lawnwood Pavilion, FL, p. A123

BURCHETT, Claudia L, R.N., Vice President of Patient Services, Southern Ohio Medical Center, Portsmouth, OH, p. A489

BURCHETT, Travis, Troop Commander Human Resources, Colonel Florence A. Blanchfield Army Community Hospital, Fort Campbell, KY, p. A252

BURCZEUSKI, Jason
    Controller, Arms Acres, Carmel, NY, p. A424
    Controller, Conifer Park, Glenville, NY, p. A427

BURD, David, Chief Executive Officer, Thayer County Health Services, Hebron, NE, p. A384

BURDEN, Jennifer, Human Resources Director, Tristar Centennial Women's & Children'S, TN, p. A577

BURDETTE, Marie, Chief Nursing Officer, East Georgia Regional Medical Center, Statesboro, GA, p. A161

BURDICK, Ginny
    Senior Vice President and Chief Human Resources Officer, Clovis Community Medical Center, Clovis, CA, p. A55
    Vice President Human Resources, Community Behavioral Health Center, Fresno, CA, p. A59
    Vice President Human Resources, Community Regional Medical Center, Fresno, CA, p. A59

BURDICK, Hoyt J, M.D., Vice President Medical Affairs, Hoops Family Children's Hospital, WV, p. A683

BURGE, Eugene H., Chief Executive Officer, Savoy Medical Center, Mamou, LA, p. A273

BURGER, Janice, Chief Executive, Children At Providence St. Vincent, OR, p. A516

BURGESS, Angela, Chief Information Officer, Randolph Hospital, Asheboro, NC, p. A447

BURGESS, Daniel, Chief Information Officer, Mainegeneral Medical Center-Augusta Campus, ME, p. A282

BURGESS, Deborah, R.N., Chief Nursing Officer, Chi St. Luke's Health Memorial Specialty Hospital, Lufkin, TX, p. A621

BURGESS, John, Director Information Services, Hocking Valley Community Hospital, Logan, OH, p. A485

BURGESS, Robert L., President and Chief Executive Officer, St. Elizabeth Hospital, Gonzales, LA, p. A268

BURGESS, Steven, Administrator Human Resources, Henrico Doctors' Hospital - Retreat Campus, VA, p. A665

BURGESS, Ty, Chief Executive Officer, Select Specialty Hospital-Dallas, Carrollton, TX, p. A592

BURGHART, Steven, President, Ssm Cardinal Glennon Children's Hospital, Saint Louis, MO, p. A368

BURGOS, Odette, Supervisor Human Resources, San Jorge Children's Hospital, Santurce, PR, p. A716

BURGUILLOS, Richard, Chief Financial Officer, Careone At Raritan Bay Medical Center, Perth Amboy, NJ, p. A410

BURGUS, Aurelis, Nursing Director, Ryder Memorial Hospital, Humacao, PR, p. A714

BURICK, Adam, M.D.
Chief Medical Officer, Pam Specialty Hospital Of Covington, Covington, LA, p. A266
Chief Medical Officer, Pam Specialty Hospital Of Victoria North, Victoria, TX, p. A642
Chief Medical Officer, Pam Specialty Hospital Of Victoria South, Victoria, TX, p. A642

BURICK, Marsha, Chief Financial Officer, Central Florida Behavioral Hospital, Orlando, FL, p. A134

BURINGRUD, Duane, M.D., Chief Medical and Quality Officer, Palomar Medical Center, Escondido, CA, p. A57

BURISH, Brent, Chief Executive Officer, St. Cloud Regional Medical Center, Saint Cloud, FL, p. A138

BURK, Kaye, Administrator, Noland Hospital Dothan, Dothan, AL, p. A17

BURK, Thomas J, Chief Operating Officer, Danville State Hospital, Danville, PA, p. A523

BURKE, Brian, M.D., President Medical Staff, Fairview Hospital, Great Barrington, MA, p. A300

BURKE, Brigid, Chief Financial Officer, Pondera Medical Center, Conrad, MT, p. A374

BURKE, Christopher D., Ph.D., Chief Executive Officer, Cedar Springs Hospital, Colorado Springs, CO, p. A97

BURKE, David J, Director Finance and Chief Financial Officer, Nantucket Cottage Hospital, Nantucket, MA, p. A302

BURKE, Dennis E., President and Chief Executive Officer, Good Shepherd Health Care System, Hermiston, OR, p. A513

BURKE, Dorothy, Chief Financial Officer, Southeast Colorado Hospital District, Springfield, CO, p. A105

BURKE, Greg, M.D., Medical Director, Geisinger Healthsouth Rehabilitation Hospital, Danville, PA, p. A523

BURKE, Jack J, MS, R.N., Chief Operating Officer and Chief Nursing Officer, Antelope Valley Hospital, Lancaster, CA, p. A64

BURKE, James, M.D.
Senior Vice President and Chief Medical Officer, Honorhealth Scottsdale Osborn Medical Center, Scottsdale, AZ, p. A35
Senior Vice President and Chief Medical Officer, Honorhealth Scottsdale Shea Medical Center, Scottsdale, AZ, p. A35

BURKE, James M., Vice President Finance, Chief Nursing Executive Medical Surgical Hospitals, Kent County Memorial Hospital, Warwick, RI, p. A548

BURKE, Jeff, Chief Information Officer, Bon Secours-Richmond Community Hospital, Richmond, VA, p. A664

BURKE, John, Chief Financial Officer, Nyack Hospital, Nyack, NY, p. A438

BURKE, Julie, Director Human Resources, New England Sinai Hospital And Rehabilitation Center, Stoughton, MA, p. A305

BURKE, Marsha, Senior Vice President and Chief Financial Officer, Wellstar Windy Hill Hospital, Marietta, GA, p. A157

BURKE, Michael, Senior Vice President and Corporate Chief Financial Officer, Rusk Institute At Nyu-Hjd, NY, p. A436

BURKE, Paul, Administrator, Schleicher County Medical Center, Eldorado, TX, p. A603

BURKE, Rebecca, R.N., MS, Senior Vice President and Chief Nursing Officer, Kent County Memorial Hospital, Warwick, RI, p. A548

BURKE, Richard Aron, M.D., Chief Medical Officer, Community Hospital-Fairfax, Fairfax, MO, p. A359

BURKE, Rose, Associate Director Patient Care Services, Marion Veterans Affairs Medical Center, Marion, IL, p. A188

BURKE, Ryan, Esq, Vice President, Human Resources, Citrus Valley Medical Center-Queen Of The Valley Campus, CA, p. A56

BURKE, Timothy, M.D., Medical Director, The Brook Hospital - Kmi, Louisville, KY, p. A257

BURKEL, Greg, Chief Financial Officer, Regional Health Services Of Howard County, Cresco, IA, p. A220

BURKEL, Gregory, Chief Financial Officer, Mitchell County Regional Health Center, Osage, IA, p. A227

BURKET, Mark, Chief Executive Officer, Platte Health Center Avera, Platte, SD, p. A562

BURKETT, Doug, Manager Information Technology, L. V. Stabler Memorial Hospital, Greenville, AL, p. A19

BURKETT, Eric, M.D., Vice President Medical Affairs, Children's Hospital At Monmouth Medical Center, NJ, p. A407

BURKETT, Evan, Chief Human Resource Officer, Sanford Children's Hospital, SD, p. A564

BURKEY, Kathleen, R.N., MSN, Vice President, Patient Care Service and Chief Nursing Officer, Grand View Health, Sellersville, PA, p. A541

BURKHARDT, Raye, Chief Nurse Executive, Fontana Medical Center, Kaiser Permanente Ontario Medical Center, CA, p. A58

BURKHART, Brad, Assistant Administrator, Harlan Arh Hospital, Harlan, KY, p. A253

BURKHART, Steven, M.D., Chief Medical Officer, Crittenden County Hospital, Marion, KY, p. A257

BURKHART, Tracy, Vice President Information Services, St. Luke's Sacred Heart Campus, Allentown, PA, p. A519

BURKHOLDER, Adrienne, Director Human Resources, Amg Specialty Hospital-Wichita, Wichita, KS, p. A247

BURKHOLDER-MCNUTT, Kim, Chief Executive Officer, Advanced Specialty Hospital Of Toledo, Toledo, OH, p. A491

BURKS, Felicia, Chief Financial Officer, U.S. Air Force Regional Hospital, Elmendorf Afb, AK, p. A26

BURKS, Matt, Director Information Technology, Unity Medical Center, Manchester, TN, p. A574

BURKS, Melvin, Chief Executive Officer, Hamilton Center, Terre Haute, IN, p. A215

BURKS, Tami
Chief Fiscal Services, Iraan General Hospital, Iraan, TX, p. A615
Comptroller, Rankin County Hospital District, Rankin, TX, p. A630

BURLESON, Linda, Administrative Secretary, Clay County Memorial Hospital, Henrietta, TX, p. A609

BURLESON, Stan, M.D., Chief Medical Staff, Dewitt Hospital, Dewitt-Arkansas County, AR, p. A41

BURLING, Chris, M.D., Chief of Staff, Titus Regional Medical Center, Mount Pleasant, TX, p. A624

BURLINGAME DEAL, Penney, FACHE, R.N., Chief Executive Officer, Onslow Memorial Hospital, Jacksonville, NC, p. A455

BURMAN, Don
Director, Lincoln Division, NE, p. A386
Director, Veterans Affairs Nebraska-Western Iowa Health Care System, Omaha, NE, p. A389

BURMEISTER, Brian, Senior Vice President, ThedaCare Medical Centers, Thedacare Regional Medical Center-Neenah, Neenah, WI, p. A699

BURMESTER, Mark A, Vice President Strategy and Communications, Kaiser Sunnyside Medical Center, Clackamas, OR, p. A512

BURNAM, Gregg, Chief Information Officer and Manager Business Office, Mangum Regional Medical Center, Mangum, OK, p. A501

BURNELL, Lori, R.N., Ph.D., Senior Vice President and Chief Nursing Officer, Valley Presbyterian Hospital, Los Angeles, CA, p. A70

BURNES BOLTON, Linda, Dr.PH, R.N., Vice President and Chief Nurse Executive, Cedars-Sinai Medical Center, Los Angeles, CA, p. A66

BURNETT, Anthony, M.D., Medical Director, Julian F. Keith Alcohol And Drug Abuse Treatment Center, Black Mountain, NC, p. A448

BURNETT, Brad, Chief Financial Officer, Heart Of Texas Memorial Hospital, Brady, TX, p. A590

BURNETT, Brenda, R.N., Vice President Patient Care Services and Chief Nursing Officer, Titusville Area Hospital, Titusville, PA, p. A542

BURNETT, Cindi, Chief Human Resources Officer, Madison County Memorial Hospital, Madison, FL, p. A128

BURNETT, Mark, President and Chief Executive Officer, Scott County Hospital, Scott City, KS, p. A245

BURNETT, Michael, Chief Executive Officer, Piedmont Fayette Hospital, Fayetteville, GA, p. A153

BURNETT, Rob, Director Human Resources, Jordan Valley Medical Center West Valley Campus, West Valley City, UT, p. A652

BURNETT, Tasha, Director of Nursing, Falls Community Hospital And Clinic, Marlin, TX, p. A622

BURNETTE, Linda, R.N., Chief Nursing Officer, Southern Virginia Regional Medical Center, Emporia, VA, p. A657

BURNETTE, Peg, Chief Financial Officer, Denver Health, Denver, CO, p. A98

BURNETTE, Sheri, R.N., Chief Executive Officer and Administrator, Cornerstone Hospital Of Bossier City, Bossier City, LA, p. A265

BURNETTE, W Scott., Chief Executive Officer, Vcu Health Community Memorial Hospital, South Hill, VA, p. A666

BURNEY, Sibte, M.D., Senior Vice President Medical Affairs and Chief Medical Officer, Kingsbrook Jewish Medical Center, New York (Includes All Hospitals Located Within The Five Boroughs), NY, p. A433

BURNHAM, Sharon, Director of Nursing, Simpson General Hospital, Mendenhall, MS, p. A350

BURNS, Barry, Vice President, Methodist Ambulatory Surgery Hospital - Northwest, San Antonio, TX, p. A633

BURNS, Becky L, Manager Health Information Management, Ellinwood District Hospital, Ellinwood, KS, p. A234

BURNS, Bruce R., Chief Financial Officer, Concord Hospital, Concord, NH, p. A398

BURNS, Helen K, Ph.D., R.N.
Senior Vice President and Chief Nursing Officer, Excela Frick Hospital, Mount Pleasant, PA, p. A532
Senior Vice President and Chief Nursing Officer, Excela Health Westmoreland Hospital, Greensburg, PA, p. A526
Senior Vice President and Chief Nursing Officer, Excela Latrobe Area Hospital, Latrobe, PA, p. A529

BURNS, Helene M, MSN, R.N., Chief Nursing Executive, Jefferson Washington Township Hospital, NJ, p. A412

BURNS, Jeff, Manager of Information Technology, Mary Free Bed Rehabilitation Hospital, Grand Rapids, MI, p. A314

BURNS, Jon P
Chief Information Officer, University Of Maryland Hospital For Children, MD, p. A289
Senior Vice President and Chief Information Officer, University Of Maryland Baltimore Washington Medical Center, Glen Burnie, MD, p. A292
Senior Vice President and Chief Information Officer, University Of Maryland Medical Center Midtown Campus, Baltimore, MD, p. A289

BURNS, Katherine, Vice President Human Resources, High Point Regional Health System, High Point, NC, p. A454

BURNS, Kathryn I., R.N., Director of Nursing, Medicine Lodge Memorial Hospital, Medicine Lodge, KS, p. A241

BURNS, Larry P, Jr, Chief Operating Officer, Yavapai Regional Medical Center - East, AZ, p. A34

BURNS, Patricia, Chief Executive Officer, Jfk Medical Center North Campus, West Palm Beach, FL, p. A143

BURNS, Patrick, Vice President Finance, Acmh Hospital, Kittanning, PA, p. A528

BURNS, Rhonda, Director Human Resources, Caldwell Medical Center, Princeton, KY, p. A260

BURNS, Sonda, Chief Executive Officer, Select Specialty Hospital-Akron, Akron, OH, p. A470

BURNS, Steve, Chief Operating Officer, Cumberland County Hospital, Burkesville, KY, p. A250

BURNS, Steven, Director Fiscal Services, Summit Behavioral Healthcare, Cincinnati, OH, p. A475

BURNS, Terry M., President, Kettering Medical Center, Kettering, OH, p. A484

BURNS, Tom, M.D., Chief of Staff, The Hospital At Westlake Medical Center, Austin, TX, p. A587

BURNS-CHISTENSON, Katherine, Human Resource Director, Grand Itasca Clinic And Hospital, Grand Rapids, MN, p. A332

BURNS-TISDALE, Susan, Senior Vice President Clinical Operations, Interim CNO, Exeter Hospital, Exeter, NH, p. A399

BURRELL, Carol H.
Chief Executive Officer, Northeast Georgia Medical Center Braselton, Braselton, GA, p. A148
Chief Executive Officer, Northeast Georgia Medical Center, Gainesville, GA, p. A154

BURRESS, Lori, Vice President Patient Services and Chief Nursing Officer, Mt. Graham Regional Medical Center, Safford, AZ, p. A35

BURRIS, Bradley D., Chief Executive Officer, Pipestone County Medical Center Avera, Pipestone, MN, p. A337

BURRIS, Don, Chief Executive Officer, Foundation Surgical Hospital Of El Paso, El Paso, TX, p. A602

BURRIS, Lisa, Director Human Resources, Southern Indiana Rehabilitation Hospital, New Albany, IN, p. A212

BURRIS, Olga, Human Resource/Executive Assistant, North Oak Regional Medical Center, Senatobia, MS, p. A353

BURRISS, Jessica, Chief Financial Officer, Encompass Health Rehabilitation Hospital Of Columbia, Columbia, SC, p. A551

BURRISS, Stephen W., President, Unc Rex Health Care, Raleigh, NC, p. A459

BURROUGHS, Shawn, Director of Information Services, Northeastern Vermont Regional Hospital, Saint Johnsbury, VT, p. A654

BURROUGHS, Steven, Chief Financial Officer, Palms West Hospital, Loxahatchee, FL, p. A128

BURROUGHS, Susan R, FACHE, Chief Operating Officer, Kershawhealth, Camden, SC, p. A549

BURROUGHS, Valentine, M.D., Chief Medical Officer, East Orange General Hospital, East Orange, NJ, p. A404

BURROW, Debbie, R.N., Chief Nursing Officer, Saline Memorial Hospital, Benton-Saline County, AR, p. A39

BURROWS, Susan M, Vice President Human Resources, Martin Luther King, Jr. Community Hospital, Los Angeles, CA, p. A68

BURRUS, Gary, Director Information Technology, Winner Regional Healthcare Center, Winner, SD, p. A565

BURT, Alan, Director Information Services, Sunrise Hospital And Medical Center, Las Vegas, NV, p. A395

BURT, Linda K, Corporate Vice President Finance, Methodist Women's Hospital, NE, p. A388

BURT, Noel F, Ph.D., Chief Human Resources Officer, Women's Hospital Of Greensboro, NC, p. A453

BURT, Suzanne M., Director Human Resources, Kimball-Ridge Center, IA, p. A230

BURTCH, Gloria, Director Human Resources, Cornerstone Of Medical Arts Center Hospital, Fresh Meadows, NY, p. A426

BURTCHELL, Scott, Director Information Systems, Maine Coast Memorial Hospital, Ellsworth, ME, p. A284

BURTHAY, Darcy, MSN, R.N., President and Chief Executive Officer, Providence Hospital, Washington, DC, p. A116

BURTON, Angela, Privacy Officer, Wayne County Hospital, Monticello, KY, p. A258

BURTON, Becky, R.N., Chief Executive Officer and Market Chief Executive Officer, Vibra Hospital Of Amarillo, Amarillo, TX, p. A583

BURTON, Charles, Chief Human Resources, Carl R. Darnall Army Medical Center, Fort Hood, TX, p. A603

BURTON, Cynthia, R.N., Chief Nursing Officer, Rockcastle Regional Hospital And Respiratory Care Center, Mount Vernon, KY, p. A258

BURTON, James, Vice President and Chief Information Officer, Valley Health, Valley Health Shenandoah Memorial Hospital, Woodstock, VA, p. A668

BURTON, Luanne, Director Human Resources, Encompass Health Rehabilitation Hospital Of Columbia, Columbia, SC, p. A551

BURTON, Robert, Manager Finance, Utah State Hospital, Provo, UT, p. A649

BURTON, Stacey R., Director Human Resources, Muscogee Creek Nation Medical Center, Okmulgee, OK, p. A505

BURY, Peter, Vice President Finance, Ohiohealth Riverside Methodist Hospital, Columbus, OH, p. A479

BUSBY, Jay, M.D., President Medical Staff, Franklin Medical Center, Winnsboro, LA, p. A281

BUSBY, Kathy, Medical Record Technician, Chillicothe Hospital District, Chillicothe, TX, p. A592

BUSCH, Michael D
Executive Vice President and Chief Operating Officer, Excela Frick Hospital, Mount Pleasant, PA, p. A532
Executive Vice President and Chief Operating Officer, Excela Health Westmoreland Hospital, Greensburg, PA, p. A526
Executive Vice President and Chief Operating Officer, Excela Latrobe Area Hospital, Latrobe, PA, p. A529

BUSCH, Michael D.
Executive Vice President and Chief Operating Officer, Excela Frick Hospital, Mount Pleasant, PA, p. A532
Executive Vice President and Chief Operating Officer, Excela Latrobe Area Hospital, Latrobe, PA, p. A529

BUSCH, Rebecca, Chief Financial Officer, Spooner Health, Spooner, WI, p. A703

BUSCH, Steve, Chief Operating Officer, Midwest Medical Center, Galena, IL, p. A183

BUSH, Amy, Vice President Operations, Upmc Mckeesport, Mckeesport, PA, p. A531

BUSH, Bruce A, M.D., Senior Vice President Medical Affairs, Indiana Regional Medical Center, Indiana, PA, p. A528

BUSH, Doug, President, Promedica Defiance Regional Hospital, Defiance, OH, p. A481

BUSH, Michael, M.D., Chief Medical Officer, Holy Rosary Healthcare, Miles City, MT, p. A377

BUSH, Stephen, Chief Financial Officer, Tmc For Children, AZ, p. A38

BUSH, Steven, Chief Medical Officer, Crossing Rivers Health Medical Center, Prairie Du Chien, WI, p. A701

BUSH, Wayne, M.D., Chief of Staff, Tristar Greenview Regional Hospital, Bowling Green, KY, p. A250

BUSHART, Phyllis, R.N., Chief Operating Officer, Providence Tarzana Medical Center, Los Angeles, CA, p. A69

BUSHART, Stephanie, Chief Financial Officer, Ochsner Medical Center - Baton Rouge, Baton Rouge, LA, p. A263

BUSHELL, Michael, President, Saint Anne's Hospital, Fall River, MA, p. A299

BUSHEY, Dale, Chief Financial Officer, Oss Orthopaedic Hospital, York, PA, p. A545

BUSHMAN, Jerry, Chief Nursing Officer, Brigham City Community Hospital, Brigham City, UT, p. A646

BUSHNELL, Andrew, M.D., Interim Chief Medical Officer, Rome Memorial Hospital, Rome, NY, p. A442

BUSHNELL, Kim, MSN, R.N., Vice President, Patient Care Services, Mercy Medical Center, Baltimore, MD, p. A288

BUSINELLE, Denise, Chief Financial Officer, Avala, Covington, LA, p. A266

BUSKEY, Irene, Director Human Resources, Southside Regional Medical Center, Petersburg, VA, p. A664

BUSS, Theresa L, Regional Vice President Human Resources, Windham Hospital, Willimantic, CT, p. A112

BUSSELL, Walter
Chief Financial Officer, Memorial Hospital West, Pembroke Pines, FL, p. A135
Chief Financial Officer, Memorial Regional Hospital South, FL, p. A124

BUSSIERE, Mark, Administrator Human Resources, New Hampshire Hospital, Concord, NH, p. A398

BUSSLER, David, Chief Information Officer, Sheridan Community Hospital, Sheridan, MI, p. A323

BUSTLE, John P., M.D., Chief Executive Officer, Bates County Memorial Hospital, Butler, MO, p. A356

BUTCHER, Gina, Chief Financial Officer, Garden City Hospital, Garden City, MI, p. A313

BUTCHER, Kay, Director Health Information Management, Stonewall Jackson Memorial Hospital, Weston, WV, p. A688

BUTE, Phil, Manager Information Technology, Clay County Hospital, Flora, IL, p. A183

BUTERBAUGH, Roger W, Chief Human Resources Officer, Charlie Norwood Veterans Affairs Medical Center, Augusta, GA, p. A147

BUTKER, Jeff, Chief Information Officer, Sovah Health-Martinsville, Martinsville, VA, p. A661

BUTLER, Anita M., Chief Executive Officer, Spartanburg Hospital For Restorative Care, Spartanburg, SC, p. A557

BUTLER, Brad, Network Administrator, Cox Barton County Memorial Hospital, Lamar, MO, p. A363

BUTLER, Carol A, R.N., MSN, VP Patient Care Services & Operations, St. Anthony North Health Campus, Westminster, CO, p. A106

BUTLER, Catherine, M.D., Chief Medical Staff, Hancock County Health System, Britt, IA, p. A218

BUTLER, Chris, Chief Information Officer, Children's Hospital At Monmouth Medical Center, NJ, p. A407

BUTLER, Dana, M.D., Medical Director, Sunrise Canyon Hospital, Lubbock, TX, p. A621

BUTLER, David, President and Chief Executive Officer, Tillamook Regional Medical Center, Tillamook, OR, p. A518

BUTLER, Debby
Director Human Resources, Wadley Regional Medical Center At Hope, Hope-Hempstead County, AR, p. A43
Director Human Resources, Wadley Regional Medical Center, Texarkana, TX, p. A639

BUTLER, Keith L., Chief Executive Officer, Iraan General Hospital, Iraan, TX, p. A615

BUTLER, LaDonna, Esq, Chief Nursing Officer, Healthsouth Tustin Rehabilitation Hospital, Tustin, CA, p. A92

BUTLER, Linda H., M.D., Chief Medical Officer, Unc Rex Health Care, Raleigh, NC, p. A459

BUTLER, Margaret, Vice President Human Resources, Sister Kenny Rehabilitation Institute, MN, p. A335

BUTLER, Margaret E, Vice President Chief Operating Officer, Seton Northwest Hospital, Seton Northwest Hospital, Austin, TX, p. A586

BUTLER, Monique, MD
Chief Medical Officer, Swedish Medical Center, Englewood, CO, p. A100
Chief Operating Officer, Dmc - Children's Hospital Of Michigan, Detroit, MI, p. A310

BUTLER, Randy, Chief Financial Officer, West Florida Rehabilitation Institute, FL, p. A136

BUTLER, Rosemary M, R.N., MSN, Chief Nurse Executive, Kaiser Permanente Riverside Medical Center, Riverside, CA, p. A81

BUTLER, Scott A., Chief Executive Officer, Select Specialty Hospital-Evansville, Evansville, IN, p. A203

BUTLER, Stuart, Director Information Technology, Sweeny Community Hospital, Sweeny, TX, p. A638

BUTT, Zaahra, Chief Executive Officer, Select Specialty Hospital-Grosse Pointe, Grosse Pointe, MI, p. A315

BUTTELL, Phil, Chief Operating Officer, Centerpoint Medical Center, Independence, MO, p. A360

BUTTER, Hazel, Manager Human Resources, Hammond-Henry Hospital, Geneseo, IL, p. A184

BUTTERFIELD, Cindy, Director, Fiscal and Administrative Services, Whiting Forensic Hospital, CT, p. A109

BUTTERFIELD, Jon
Administrator and Chief Operating Officer, Jordan Valley Medical Center West Valley Campus, West Valley City, UT, p. A652
Chief Operating Officer, Mountain Point Medical Center, UT, p. A652

BUTTERFIELD, Jon R., Administrator and Chief Executive Officer, Jordan Valley Medical Center West Valley Campus, West Valley City, UT, p. A652

BUTTERMORE, Bruce
Director Human Resources, Parkview Lagrange Hospital, Lagrange, IN, p. A210
Manager Human Resources, Parkview Noble Hospital, Kendallville, IN, p. A208

BUTTON, Charlie A., Chief Executive Officer, Regional Medical Center, Manchester, IA, p. A226

BUTTS, Paula Yvonne, Chief Nursing Officer, Piedmont Henry Hospital, Stockbridge, GA, p. A161

BUTTS, Ursula N, FACHE, Vice President of Patient Care Services, Vcu Health Community Memorial Hospital, South Hill, VA, p. A666

BUTZINE, Bart, Director Information Technology, Community Hospital, Grand Junction, CO, p. A101

BUTZLER, Hilary, Director Human Resources, Cumberland Healthcare, Cumberland, WI, p. A691

BUUCK, Brian, Chief Executive Officer, Ridgeview Psychiatric Hospital And Center, Oak Ridge, TN, p. A578

BUZACHERO, Victor, Corporate Senior Vice President for Innovation, Human Resources and Performance Management, Scripps Green Hospital, La Jolla, CA, p. A62

BYARS, Stephanie, Chief Nursing Officer, Unity Medical Center, Manchester, TN, p. A574

BYDA, Jeff, Vice President Information Technology, Mercy Philadelphia Hospital, PA, p. A524

BYERS, John, M.D., Medical Director, Select Specialty Hospital-Tri Cities, Bristol, TN, p. A566

BYERS, Suzann, Director of Nursing, Southern Indiana Rehabilitation Hospital, New Albany, IN, p. A212

BYERS, Tracy, Chief Executive Officer, Drumright Regional Hospital, Drumright, OK, p. A497

BYERS, William J., Chief Information Officer, Western Maryland Regional Medical Center, Cumberland, MD, p. A291

BYLER, Karen, Information Technology Generalist, Warren State Hospital, Warren, PA, p. A543

BYNUM, Justin, Chief Financial Officer, Saint Anthony Hospital, Chicago, IL, p. A179

BYORICK, Joseph, Senior Vice President and Chief Financial Officer, Penn Medicine Lancaster General Hospital, Lancaster, PA, p. A529

BYRD, Catherine, Vice President Patient Services, Parkview Noble Hospital, Kendallville, IN, p. A208

BYRD, David, Chief Financial Officer, The Hospitals Of Providence Transmountain Campus, El Paso, TX, p. A602

BYRD, Greg, Vice President Medical Affairs, Valley Health Shenandoah Memorial Hospital, Woodstock, VA, p. A668

BYRD, Lu, R.N., MSN, Vice President Hospital Operations and Chief Nursing Officer, Billings Clinic, Billings, MT, p. A373

BYRD, O Wayne, M.D., Chief of Staff, H. C. Watkins Memorial Hospital, Quitman, MS, p. A352

BYRD, Rebecca, President Medical Staff, Grandview Medical Center, Birmingham, AL, p. A14

BYRD-PELAEZ, Brenda, Chief Human Resources Management Office, Martinsburg Veterans Affairs Medical Center, Martinsburg, WV, p. A685

BYRNE, Frank J, Vice President Finance, Newport Hospital, Newport, RI, p. A547

BYRNES, Matthew C, M.D., Chief Medical Officer, St. Catherine Hospital, Garden City, KS, p. A235

BYROM, David, Chief Executive Officer, Coryell Memorial Hospital, Gatesville, TX, p. A607

C

CAAMANO, Tero, Director Information Technology, Saint Clare's Hospital/Dover, NJ, p. A403

CABALLERO, Rogelio, Chief Information Systems, San Jorge Children's Hospital, Santurce, PR, p. A716

CABE, Jacque, Chief Financial Officer, University Of Washington Medical Center, Seattle, WA, p. A677

CABIGAO, Edwin, Chief Nursing Officer, Jewish Home Of San Francisco, San Francisco, CA, p. A85

CABIRO, Michael, Chief Executive Officer, Encompass Health Rehabilitation Hospital Of Pearland, Pearland, TX, p. A627

CABRERA, Carlos, Executive Director, Cardiovascular Center Of Puerto Rico And The Caribbean, San Juan, PR, p. A715

CABRERA, Irma, Finance Director, Hospital San Carlos Borromeo, Moca, PR, p. A714

CABRERA, Sheelah, Chief Information Officer, La Rabida Children's Hospital, Chicago, IL, p. A177

CABUNOC, Brenda, Chief Human Resources, Va Greater Los Angeles Healthcare System, Los Angeles, CA, p. A70

CACCAMISE, Chad, Director Information Services, United Memorial Medical Center-North Street, NY, p. A422

CACCAMO, Michael, M.D.
Chief Medical Officer, Greene Memorial Hospital, Xenia, OH, p. A494
Chief Medical Officer, Soin Medical Center, Beavercreek, OH, p. A472

CACCIAMANI, John D., M.D., Chief Executive Officer, Chestnut Hill Hospital, Philadelphia, PA, p. A534

CADE, Paul, Administrator and Chief Executive Officer, Baptist Memorial Hospital-Golden Triangle, Columbus, MS, p. A345

CADIEUX, Marc
Corporate Vice President and Chief Financial Officer, Children's Hospital Of Wisconsin-Fox Valley, Neenah, WI, p. A699
Corporate Vice President and Chief Financial Officer, Children's Hospital Of Wisconsin, Milwaukee, WI, p. A698

CADIGAN, Elizabeth, R.N., MSN, Senior Vice President Patient Care Services and Chief Nursing Officer, Whidden Memorial Hospital, MA, p. A298

CADOGAN, David, Chief Medical Officer, Alaska Regional Hospital, Anchorage, AK, p. A25

CADORETTE, Brenda E, Chief Nursing Officer, Hillcrest Hospital, MA, p. A303

CADWELL, Carrie, M.D., Chief Clinical Officer, Four County Counseling Center, Logansport, IN, p. A210

CADWELL, Jason, Chief Financial Officer, Four County Counseling Center, Logansport, IN, p. A210

CADWELL, Maureen K., Chief Executive Officer, Weston County Health Services, Newcastle, WY, p. A709

CADY, Kathy, Coordinator Human Resources, Accounts Payable and Payroll, Safe Haven Hospital Of Treasure Valley, Boise, ID, p. A167

CADY, Thomas, Vice President Human Resources, Heywood Hospital, Gardner, MA, p. A300

CADY, Tina, Controller, The Women's Hospital, Newburgh, IN, p. A213

CAFASSO, Michael
Chief Executive Officer, St. Mary-Corwin Medical Center, Pueblo, CO, p. A105
Chief Operating Officer, St. Mary-Corwin Medical Center, Pueblo, CO, p. A105

CAGLE, Jennifer, Director of Nursing, North Mississippi Medical Center-Hamilton, Hamilton, AL, p. A19

CAGLE, Karen, Chief Nursing Officer, Select Specialty Hospital-Nashville, Nashville, TN, p. A577

CAGLE, LaDonna, HIM Appeals Coordinator III, Monroe Hospital, Bloomington, IN, p. A200

CAGNA, Ralph A
Director Information Technology Operations, Cleveland Clinic Health System South Market, Marymount Hospital, Garfield Heights, OH, p. A483
Director Information Technology, South Pointe Hospital, Warrensville Heights, OH, p. A492

CAHALAN, Jay P., Chief Executive Officer, Columbia Memorial Hospital, Hudson, NY, p. A428

CAHILL, Joseph, Executive Vice President and Chief Operating Officer, South Shore Hospital, South Weymouth, MA, p. A304

CAHILL, Marty, Chief Executive Officer, Samaritan Lebanon Community Hospital, Lebanon, OR, p. A514

CAHILL, Patricia, R.N., Vice President, Patient Care Services and Chief Nursing Officer, Highbridge Woodycrest Center, NY, p. A431

CAHO-MOONEY, Linda, Chief Financial Officer, Claiborne County Medical Center, Port Gibson, MS, p. A352

CAHOE, Mary, Chief Nursing Officer, Iroquois Memorial Hospital And Resident Home, Watseka, IL, p. A197

CAHOJ, Lindsey, Chief Nursing Officer, Select Specialty Hospital-Wichita, Wichita, KS, p. A248

CAICEDO, Christian H., President, Upmc Pinnacle Carlisle, Carlisle, PA, p. A522

CAIN, Amy, District Director Human Resources, Kindred Hospital South Philadelphia, Philadelphia, PA, p. A535

CAIN, Donna, Director Information Systems Department, Cypress Fairbanks Medical Center, Houston, TX, p. A610

CAIN, Mark, Chief Executive Officer, Tennova Healthcare-Lafollette Medical Center, La Follette, TN, p. A573

CAIN, Roxie, Chief Financial Officer, Big Horn County Memorial Hospital, Hardin, MT, p. A376

CAIN, William, Controller, Penn Highlands Clearfield, Clearfield, PA, p. A522

CAINE, Jamie, Director of Human Resources, Multicare Valley Hospital, Spokane Valley, WA, p. A678

CAIRNS, Craig, M.D., Vice President Medical Affairs, Licking Memorial Hospital, Newark, OH, p. A488

CALAIS, C Matthew, Senior Vice President and Chief Information Officer, Rehabilitation Institute Of Oregon, OR, p. A516

CALAIS, Daniel, Jr, Superintendent, Bridgewater State Hospital, Bridgewater, MA, p. A297

CALAMARI, Frank A., President and Chief Executive Officer, Calvary Hospital, New York (Includes All Hospitals Located Within The Five Boroughs), NY, p. A431

CALAMARI, Jacquelyn, MSN, MS, Chief Nursing Officer and Vice President, Patient Care Services, Middlesex Hospital, Middletown, CT, p. A109

CALANDRELLA, Paul, Chief Operating Officer, Mt. Ascutney Hospital And Health Center, Windsor, VT, p. A654

CALANDRIELLO, John, Vice President and Chief Financial Officer, Hackensack Meridian Health Palisades Medical Center, North Bergen, NJ, p. A409

CALARCO, Marge, Chief Nursing Executive, C. S. Mott Children's Hospital, MI, p. A307

CALAWAY, Shearmaine, Director Human Resources, East Mississippi State Hospital, Meridian, MS, p. A350

CALBONE, Angelo G., President and Chief Executive Officer, Saratoga Hospital, Saratoga Springs, NY, p. A442

CALBY, Elizabeth, Vice President Human Resources, Advocate Good Samaritan Hospital, Downers Grove, IL, p. A181

CALDARI, Patricia, Vice President, Richmond University Medical Center, New York (Includes All Hospitals Located Within The Five Boroughs), NY, p. A437

CALDAS, Robert, D.O., Chief Medical Officer, Tobey Hospital, MA, p. A299

CALDEIRA, Amy, Director Information Technology and Systems, Fort Walton Beach Medical Center, Fort Walton Beach, FL, p. A123

CALDERA, Ken, Director Human Resources, Kessler Institute For Rehabilitation, NJ, p. A413

CALDERON, Lizmari, Director Finance, Hospital De La Concepcion, San German, PR, p. A715

CALDWELL, Carolyn P., FACHE, President and Chief Executive Officer, St. Mary Medical Center, Long Beach, CA, p. A65

CALDWELL, Charles, M.D., Chief of Staff, Byrd Regional Hospital, Leesville, LA, p. A272

CALDWELL, Dan, Chief Executive Officer, Mcallen Heart Hospital, TX, p. A601

CALDWELL, Dari, R.N., Ph.D., FACHE, President and Chief Operating Officer, Novant Health Rowan Medical Center, Salisbury, NC, p. A460

CALDWELL, Darren, Vice President and Administrator, Unity Health Harris Medical Center, AR, p. A48

CALDWELL, Eric, Director Finance, Northside Hospital-Forsyth, Cumming, GA, p. A151

CALDWELL, Marita, Chief Financial Officer, Twin County Regional Healthcare, Galax, VA, p. A658

CALDWELL, Matthew T.
President and Chief Executive Officer, Mercy Memorial Hospital, Urbana, OH, p. A492
President and Chief Executive Officer, Springfield Regional Medical Center, Springfield, OH, p. A490

CALDWELL, Nesa, Chief Nursing Officer, Solara Hospital - Brownsville Campus, TX, p. A609

CALDWELL, Noah, Vice President and Chief Information Officer, South Nassau Communities Hospital, Oceanside, NY, p. A438

CALDWELL, Paul, Facility Coordinator Information Technology Customer Relations, Page Hospital, Page, AZ, p. A32

CALDWELL, Steve, Vice President Finance and Chief Financial Officer, Ssm Health St. Mary's Hospital, Madison, WI, p. A696

CALDWELL, William E., Jr, FACHE, Chief Executive Officer, Wilson Medical Center, Wilson, NC, p. A462

CALEY, Carl
Chief Financial Officer, Spring Valley Hospital Medical Center, Las Vegas, NV, p. A395
Chief Financial Officer, St. Cloud Regional Medical Center, Saint Cloud, FL, p. A138

CALHOUN, Cathy, Director Human Resources, River Point Behavioral Health, Jacksonville, FL, p. A125

CALHOUN, Joshua, M.D., Medical Director, Hawthorn Children Psychiatric Hospital, Saint Louis, MO, p. A368

CALHOUN, Kirk A., M.D., President, Ut Health North Campus Tyler, Tyler, TX, p. A641

CALHOUN, Robert, Chief Executive Officer, Merit Health Biloxi, Biloxi, MS, p. A343

CALHOUN, Timothy
Vice President Finance and Chief Financial Officer, Lakeland Hospital, Niles, MI, p. A323
Vice President Finance, Chief Financial Officer, Lakeland Hospital, Watervliet, Watervliet, MI, p. A325

CALHOUN, William, Chief Executive Officer, Kearney Regional Medical Center, Kearney, NE, p. A385

CALIA, Christopher, Vice President Human Resources, Chi St. Luke's Health Brazosport, Lake Jackson, TX, p. A618

CALIFORNIA, Randy, Chief Operating Officer, Warren General Hospital, Warren, PA, p. A543

CALIME, Erica, Director Human Resources, Baylor Scott & White Medical Center - Carrollton, Carrollton, TX, p. A592

CALIVA, Todd, FACHE, Chief Executive Officer, Mainland Medical Center, TX, p. A643

CALKIN, Steven, D.O., Vice President Medical Affairs, Mclaren Oakland, Pontiac, MI, p. A321

CALKINS, Paul, M.D., Chief Medical Officer, Indiana University Health North Hospital, Carmel, IN, p. A201

CALL, Carie, Computer Support, Cassia Regional Hospital, Burley, ID, p. A168

CALL, Stacie, R.N.
Vice President Patient Care and Chief Nursing Officer, East Liverpool City Hospital, East Liverpool, OH, p. A482
Chief Nursing Officer, Mercy Health - St. Elizabeth Boardman Hospital, Boardman, OH, p. A472

CALLAGHAN, James, III, M.D., President and Chief Executive Officer, Franciscan Health Indianapolis, Indianapolis, IN, p. A206

CALLAGHAN, Peter, President and Chief Executive Officer, Columbus Hospital Ltach, Newark, NJ, p. A408

CALLAHAN, Ame, Acting Manager Resource Management Service, Northern Arizona Veterans Affairs Health Care System, Prescott, AZ, p. A34

CALLAHAN, Charles D, Ph.D., Executive Vice President and Chief Operating Officer, Memorial Medical Center, Springfield, IL, p. A196

CALLAHAN, Christopher M, Vice President Human Resources, Exeter Hospital, Exeter, NH, p. A399

CALLAHAN, Kelly, Public Information Officer, Elgin Mental Health Center, Elgin, IL, p. A182

CALLAHAN, Kevin J., President and Chief Executive Officer, Exeter Hospital, Exeter, NH, p. A399

CALLAHAN, Larry A., Senior Vice President Human Resources, Grady Memorial Hospital, Atlanta, GA, p. A146

CALLAHAN, Mark, Chief Operating Officer, Mary Lanning Healthcare, Hastings, NE, p. A384

CALLAHAN, Mary Beth, Chief Financial Officer, Mclaren Lapeer Region, Lapeer, MI, p. A317

CALLAHAN, Neil, Chief Executive Officer, Brooke Glen Behavioral Hospital, Fort Washington, PA, p. A526

CALLAHAN, Robert W., Jr, Interim Director, Wilmington Veterans Affairs Medical Center, Wilmington, DE, p. A114

CALLAHAN, Shannon, Director Human Resources, Sitka Community Hospital, Sitka, AK, p. A27

CALLAHAN, William, Chief Information Management Division, Bayne-Jones Army Community Hospital, Fort Polk, LA, p. A267

CALLAN, Michael, Executive Vice President and Chief Financial Officer, Kidspeace Children's Hospital, Orefield, PA, p. A533

CALLANAN, Patrick, Vice President Patient Care Services, Mercy Hospital Fort Scott, Fort Scott, KS, p. A235

CALLAS, Robin B, R.N., Vice President Human Resources, Rutherford Regional Health System, Rutherfordton, NC, p. A460

CALLAWAY, Blair, Chief Financial Officer, Texas Orthopedic Hospital, Houston, TX, p. A613

CALLENS, Don, M.D., Chief Medical Officer, Liberty Dayton Regional Medical Center, Liberty, TX, p. A619

CALLENS, Paul A., Ph.D., Director, North Mississippi State Hospital, Tupelo, MS, p. A353

CALLISTE, Gregory, Ph.D., FACHE, Chief Executive Officer, Nyc Health + Hospitals / Woodhull, New York (Includes All Hospitals Located Within The Five Boroughs), NY, p. A436

CALLISTER, T Brian, M.D., Chief Medical Officer, Tahoe Pacific Hospitals, NV, p. A397

CALLMAN, Mark, M.D., Chief Medical Officer, Fawcett Memorial Hospital, Port Charlotte, FL, p. A137

CALLOWAY, Maria, R.N., MSN, Chief Nursing Officer, Central Florida Regional Hospital, Sanford, FL, p. A138

CALUBAQUIB, Evelyn, Chief Nursing Officer, Greater El Monte Community Hospital, South El Monte, CA, p. A90

CALVARUSO, Gaspare, President, Capital Region Medical Center, Jefferson City, MO, p. A360

CALVERT, Mandy, Director Information Systems, Southern Coos Hospital And Health Center, Bandon, OR, p. A511

CALVERT, Sarah, Chief Nursing Officer, Mcgehee Hospital, Mcgehee-Desha County, AR, p. A46

CALVIN, Harley, D.O., Chief Medical Officer, Rush County Memorial Hospital, La Crosse, KS, p. A239

CALVIN, Irene, Vice President Human Resources, South Oaks Hospital, Amityville, NY, p. A421

CALVIN, Jeff, Chief Financial Officer, Michiana Behavioral Health Center, Plymouth, IN, p. A213

CAMACHO, Leslie, R.N., Director of Nursing, Commonwealth Health Center, Saipan, MP, p. A711

CAMARDELLO, Heidi, Vice President Patient Care Services and Chief Nursing Officer, Little Falls Hospital, Little Falls, NY, p. A429

CAMERON, Carl, Director Information Systems, Holyoke Medical Center, Holyoke, MA, p. A300

CAMERON, Don, Chief Operating Officer, Allegiance Behavioral Health Center Of Plainview, Plainview, TX, p. A628

CAMERON, Kim, Manager Health Information Services, Patients' Hospital Of Redding, Redding, CA, p. A80

CAMMACK, Geri, R.N., Director of Nursing, Lost Rivers Medical Center, Arco, ID, p. A167

CAMMENGA, Randall, M.D., Vice President Medical Affairs, Goshen Health, Goshen, IN, p. A205

CAMP, Claude E Chip''., III, FACHE, Chief Executive Officer, Brownwood Regional Medical Center, Brownwood, TX, p. A590

CAMP, David, Director Human Resources, St. Mary's Regional Medical Center, Enid, OK, p. A498

CAMP, Kendra, R.N., Chief Executive Officer, Amg Specialty Hospital-Albuquerque, Albuquerque, NM, p. A415

CAMPA, Melissa, Controller, Kindred Hospital El Paso, El Paso, TX, p. A602

CAMPANA, Thomas, M.D., Chief of Staff, Spectrum Health Reed City Hospital, Reed City, MI, p. A321

CAMPANELLA, Alfred, Chief Information Officer, Voorhees Pediatric Facility, NJ, p. A413

CAMPAS, Janice, Chief Financial Officer, Wichita County Health Center, Leoti, KS, p. A240

CAMPBELL, Al, Senior Vice President and Chief Operating Officer, Fort Washington Medical Center, Oxen Hill, MD, p. A293

CAMPBELL, Amy, Chief Financial Officer, Community Hospital North, Indianapolis, IN, p. A206

CAMPBELL, Andrew, Associate Executive Director, Nyc Health + Hospitals / Coney Island, New York (Includes All Hospitals Located Within The Five Boroughs), NY, p. A435

CAMPBELL, April, Director Human Resources, Broadwater Health Center, Townsend, MT, p. A379

CAMPBELL, Bernard M, Administrator Human Resources, Lewisgale Hospital Alleghany, Low Moor, VA, p. A660

CAMPBELL, Brian, Director Professional Services, U.S. Public Health Service Indian Hospital-Whiteriver, Whiteriver, AZ, p. A38

CAMPBELL, C Scott, Market Chief Executive Officer, Physicians Regional, FL, p. A132

CAMPBELL, Carla, R.N., Chief Nurse Officer, Mercy Hospital And Medical Center, Chicago, IL, p. A178

CAMPBELL, Christine, Controller, Vanderbilt Stallworth Rehabilitation Hospital, Nashville, TN, p. A578

CAMPBELL, Cinthia, Chief Nursing Officer, Healthsouth Chattanooga Rehabilitation Hospital, Chattanooga, TN, p. A567

CAMPBELL, David, Administrator, Perry Hospital, Perry, GA, p. A158

CAMPBELL, Dean, Vice President Information Services and Chief Information Officer, Good Samaritan Hospital, Los Angeles, CA, p. A67

CAMPBELL, Deborah, Administrator, Thomas H. Boyd Memorial Hospital, Carrollton, IL, p. A175

CAMPBELL, Debra, R.N., Administrator, Riverside Behavioral Health Center, VA, p. A662

CAMPBELL, Emily, Vice President Human Resources, The University Of Vermont Health Network - Alice Hyde Medical Center, Malone, NY, p. A429

CAMPBELL, Eric, Chief Financial Officer, Oswego Hospital, Oswego, NY, p. A439

CAMPBELL, Gary, Chief Executive Officer, St. Vincent General Hospital District, Leadville, CO, p. A103

CAMPBELL, Ivy, Director of Nursing, Community Medical Center, Inc., Falls City, NE, p. A383

CAMPBELL, Jennie, Chief Financial Officer, Baylor Scott & White Medical Center - Llano, Llano, TX, p. A620

CAMPBELL, John
Chief Information Officer, Spaulding Hospital For Continuing Medical Care Cambridge, Cambridge, MA, p. A298
Chief Information Officer, Spaulding Rehabilitation Hospital Cape Cod, East Sandwich, MA, p. A299
Chief Information Officer, Spaulding Rehabilitation Hospital, Charlestown, MA, p. A299

CAMPBELL, Kathy, Interim Chief Nursing Officer, Holston Valley Medical Center, Kingsport, TN, p. A572

CAMPBELL, Kevin, Chief Executive Officer, Saint Thomas Hickman Hospital, Centerville, TN, p. A567

CAMPBELL, Matthew J., Esq, Chief Executive Officer, Select Specialty Hospital-Saginaw, Saginaw, MI, p. A322

CAMPBELL, Melissa, Chief Financial Officer and Controller, Mercy Rehabilition Hospital Springfield, Springfield, MO, p. A370

CAMPBELL, Melvin, M.D., Medical Staff Chairman, Brown County Hospital, Ainsworth, NE, p. A381

CAMPBELL, Pamela, M.D., Medical Director, Lincoln Prairie Behavioral Health Center, Springfield, IL, p. A196

CAMPBELL, Philip, Vice President Information Services, Calverthealth Medical Center, Prince Frederick, MD, p. A293

CAMPBELL, Sandra M., R.N., Chief Nursing Officer, Dodge County Hospital, Eastman, GA, p. A153

CAMPBELL, Scott, Chief Executive Officer, Bay Medical Sacred Heart, Panama City, FL, p. A135

CAMPBELL, Shari, Chief Operating Officer, Kearny County Hospital, Lakin, KS, p. A239

CAMPBELL, Sharon J, Director, Human Resources, Park Ridge Health, Hendersonville, NC, p. A454

CAMPBELL, Sherry May, Director of Human Resources, Medical Records, Seaside Behavioral Center, New Orleans, LA, p. A276

CAMPBELL, Stephen J, Chief Operating Officer, Pioneers Memorial Healthcare District, Brawley, CA, p. A53

CAMPBELL, Susie, Chief Executive Officer, Community Hospital Of Staunton, Staunton, IL, p. A197

CAMPBELL, Suzannah, Administrator, St. Vincent's Chilton Hospital, Clanton, AL, p. A16

CAMPBELL, Suzanne, Director Patient Services, Spearfish Regional Surgery Center, SD, p. A564

CAMPBELL, Teresa, R.N., Chief Nursing Executive, Sutter Lakeside Hospital, Lakeport, CA, p. A64

CAMPBELL, Todd, Senior Vice President and Chief Operating Officer, St. Mary's Medical Center, Huntington, WV, p. A684

CAMPBELL, Vicky, Vice President Mental Health and Support Services, Depaul Center, TX, p. A642

CAMPEAU, Arleen, R.N., Vice President of Patient Care Services, Chief Nursing Officer, Powell Valley Healthcare, Powell, WY, p. A709

CAMPO, Mary Beth, MS, R.N., Director of Nursing, Eastern Niagara Hospital Newfane, NY, p. A429

CAMPOS, Christina, Administrator, Guadalupe County Hospital, Santa Rosa, NM, p. A419

CAMPOS, Emilio, Deparment Head Information Technology, Guadalupe County Hospital, Santa Rosa, NM, p. A419

CAMPOVERDE, Jacqueline, Business Manager, Essex County Hospital Center, Cedar Grove, NJ, p. A403

CAMPS, Lourdes, Chief Operating Officer, Hialeah Hospital, Hialeah, FL, p. A124

CANADY, Carolyn, Chief Financial Officer, Sierra Nevada Memorial Hospital, Grass Valley, CA, p. A61

CANADY, Michael, M.D.
Chief Executive Officer, Holzer Medical Center - Jackson, Jackson, OH, p. A484
Interim Chief Executive Officer, Holzer Medical Center, Gallipolis, OH, p. A483

CANALE, Joseph, Business Manager, Trenton Psychiatric Hospital, Trenton, NJ, p. A413

CANALES, Joe
Director Human Resources, Seton Edgar B. Davis Hospital, Luling, TX, p. A622
Director Human Resources, Seton Shoal Creek Hospital, Austin, TX, p. A586
Vice President Human Resources, Ministry Market Texas, Dell Seton Medical Center At The University Of Texas, Austin, TX, p. A586
Vice President Human Resources, Seton Medical Center Austin, Austin, TX, p. A586
Vice President, Ascension and Human Resources Officer, Texas Market, Seton Northwest Hospital, Austin, TX, p. A586

CANCEL, Diana, Director Human Resources, Glendora Community Hospital, Glendora, CA, p. A61

CANDELA, Chris, President and Chief Executive Officer, Mclaren Lapeer Region, Lapeer, MI, p. A317

CANDILL, James W, M.D., President Medical Staff, Charleston Surgical Hospital, Charleston, WV, p. A682

CANDIO, Christine M., R.N., FACHE, President and Chief Executive Officer, St. Luke's Hospital, Chesterfield, MO, p. A357

CANDULLO, Carl, Chief Information Officer, Florida Hospital Ocala, Ocala, FL, p. A133

CANEDO, Jim, Chief Financial Officer, College Medical Center, Long Beach, CA, p. A65

CANFIELD, Brian, Chief Operating Officer, Firsthealth Moore Regional Hospital - Richmond, NC, p. A458

CANFIELD, Michael, Chief Information Officer, Augusta Health, Fishersville, VA, p. A658

CANIZARO, Tom, Vice President and Chief Financial Officer, South Central Regional Medical Center, Laurel, MS, p. A349

CANLAS, Emma, Chief Financial Officer, Valley View Medical Center, Fort Mohave, AZ, p. A29

CANNARA, Christopher, Chief Executive Officer, Kindred Hospital New Jersey - Rahway, NJ, p. A404

CANNIFF, Christopher, Executive Director, Human Resources, Harrington Hospital, Southbridge, MA, p. A304

CANNING, John, Chief Financial Officer, Blythedale Children's Hospital, Valhalla, NY, p. A445

CANNINGTON, H D., Interim Chief Executive Officer, George E. Weems Memorial Hospital, Apalachicola, FL, p. A117

CANNON, Brenda, R.N., Director of Nursing, Laughlin Memorial Hospital, Greeneville, TN, p. A570

CANNON, Gayle, Director Human Resources, Childress Regional Medical Center, Childress, TX, p. A592

CANNON, Heather, M.D., Medical Director, Neshoba County General Hospital, Philadelphia, MS, p. A352

CANNON, Linda, Chief Medical Records Services, San Diego County Psychiatric Hospital, San Diego, CA, p. A84

CANNON, Robert W., President, Barnes-Jewish Hospital Psychiatric Support Center, MO, p. A367

CANO, Daniel, M.D., Chief Medical Officer, Citizens Medical Center, Victoria, TX, p. A642

CANSLER, Vicki A, Chief Human Resource Officer, Piedmont Hospital, Atlanta, GA, p. A146

CANTLEY, J Scott., President and Chief Executive Officer, Marietta Memorial Hospital, Marietta, OH, p. A485

CANTRE, Pedro Laureano, Chief Nursing Officer, Cardiovascular Center Of Puerto Rico And The Caribbean, San Juan, PR, p. A715

CANTRELL, David, CPA, Vice President and Chief Financial Officer, West Hills Hospital And Medical Center, Los Angeles, CA, p. A70

CANTRELL, Dedra
Chief Information Officer, Emory Saint Joseph's Hospital Of Atlanta, Atlanta, GA, p. A146
Chief Information Officer, Emory University Hospital Midtown, Atlanta, GA, p. A146

CANTRELL, Eric
Chief Executive Officer, Nexus Specialty Hospital The Woodlands, The Woodlands, TX, p. A640
Chief Executive Officer, Nexus Specialty Hospital, Shenandoah, TX, p. A635

CANTU, Andrew, Chief Financial Officer, Kern Medical Center, Bakersfield, CA, p. A52

CANTU, Janie, Director Human Resources, Crosbyton Clinic Hospital, Crosbyton, TX, p. A595

CAPECE, Vincent G., Jr, President and Chief Executive Officer, Middlesex Hospital, Middletown, CT, p. A109

CAPERS, Travis, FACHE, President, Ssm Health St. Mary's Hospital - St. Louis, Saint Louis, MO, p. A369

CAPILI, Anthony, M.D., Chief of Staff, Bayside Community Hospital, Anahuac, TX, p. A583

CAPIOLA, Richard, M.D., Chief Medical Officer, Baton Rouge Behavioral Hospital, Baton Rouge, LA, p. A263

CAPITELLI, Robert, M.D., Senior Vice President and Chief Medical Officer, St. Tammany Parish Hospital, Covington, LA, p. A266

CAPITULO, Kathleen, Ph.D., R.N., Chief Nurse Executive, James J. Peters Veterans Affairs Medical Center, New York (Includes All Hospitals Located Within The Five Boroughs), NY, p. A432

CAPIZZI, Thomas, Vice President Human Resources, Choc Children's At Mission Hospital, Mission Viejo, CA, p. A72

CAPLAN, Margaret B., Director, Veterans Affairs Hudson Valley Health Care System-Montrose Campus, NY, p. A430

CAPLE, Jocelyn, M.D.
Chief Medical Officer, Frisbie Memorial Hospital, Rochester, NH, p. A401
Interim President and Chief Executive Officer, Frisbie Memorial Hospital, Rochester, NH, p. A401

CAPLES, Greg, Chief Executive Officer, Coliseum Northside Hospital, Macon, GA, p. A156

CAPO, Ann Marie, R.N., Chief Nursing Officer, Uconn, John Dempsey Hospital, Farmington, CT, p. A108

CAPOROSO, Robyn, Chief Executive Officer, Trenton Psychiatric Hospital, Trenton, NJ, p. A413

CAPOTE, Henry, Interim Chief Financial Officer, Coral Gables Hospital, Coral Gables, FL, p. A120

CAPPEL, Blaine, Director Information Systems, Memorial Health System, Abilene, KS, p. A232

CAPPLEMAN, Troy, M.D., Chief of Staff, Tippah County Hospital, Ripley, MS, p. A353

CAPPS, Anita, R.N., Chief Nursing Executive, Community Hospital South, Indianapolis, IN, p. A206

CAPPS, Kim, Chief Financial Officer, Hayes Green Beach Memorial Hospital, Charlotte, MI, p. A309

CAPPS, Melissa, Site Leader Information Technology, St. Luke's Magic Valley Medical Center, Twin Falls, ID, p. A172

CAPPS, Rick, Chief Financial Officer, Cumberland County Hospital, Burkesville, KY, p. A250

CAPRICO, Rick, Chief Financial Officer, Catskill Regional Medical Center, Harris, NY, p. A427

CAPSHAW, Marcia, Chief Operating Officer, West Central Georgia Regional Hospital, Columbus, GA, p. A151

CAPSHEW, Ryan, Chief Executive Officer, De Queen Medical Center, De Queen-Sevier County, AR, p. A41

CAPUANO, Terry Ann, R.N., MSN, FACHE
Executive Vice President and Chief Operating Officer, Lehigh Valley Health Network Pediatrics, PA, p. A519
Executive Vice President and Chief Operating Officer, Lehigh Valley Hospital-Muhlenberg, Bethlehem, PA, p. A520

CAPUANO, Tony, Chief Operating Officer, Eastar Health System, East Campus, OK, p. A502

CAPUTO, Louis, Chief Executive Officer, Tristar Stonecrest Medical Center, Smyrna, TN, p. A580

CAPUTO, Michael, Chief Information Officer, Children's Hospital Of South Carolina At Musc, SC, p. A550

CARABALLO, Amanda, Nursing Director, Hospital De La Concepcion, San German, PR, p. A715

CARACCIOLO, Kevin, Chief Human Resources Officer, Palm Beach Gardens Medical Center, Palm Beach Gardens, FL, p. A135

CARACCIOLO, Mary Jo, Human Resource Director, Wellington Regional Medical Center, Wellington, FL, p. A143

CARALIS, George P, Interim Chief Executive Officer, University Hospital Of Brooklyn At Long Island College Hospital, NY, p. A437

CARBALLO, Francisco R., M.D., Medical Director, Hospital Hima De Humacao, Humacao, PR, p. A713

CARBONE, Davide M., FACHE, Chief Executive Officer, Osceola Regional Medical Center, Kissimmee, FL, p. A126

CARBONE, Dominick, M.D., Chief of Staff, Hugh Chatham Memorial Hospital, Elkin, NC, p. A452

CARD, Dean
Chief Financial Officer, Kindred Hospital South Florida-Hollywood, FL, p. A123
Chief Financial Officer, Kindred Hospital The Palm Beaches, Riviera Beach, FL, p. A137

CARD, Edwin, President Medical Staff, Mcdonough District Hospital, Macomb, IL, p. A188

CARD, Mike, Chief Information Officer, Audubon County Memorial Hospital, Audubon, IA, p. A217

CARDA, Greg, Vice President Finance, Missouri Delta Medical Center, Sikeston, MO, p. A370

CARDALI, Paul, M.D., Chief of Staff, Lakeway Regional Hospital, Morristown, TN, p. A576

CARDELL, Melinda H.
Interim Chief Information Officer, Roper St. Francis Mount Pleasant Hospital, Mount Pleasant, SC, p. A555
Interim Vice President and Chief Information Officer, Roper St. Francis, Charleston, SC, p. A550

CARDENAS, Lydia, Director Human Resources, River Crest Hospital, San Angelo, TX, p. A632

CARDENAS, Mark, Director Plant Operations, Vibra Hospital Of Northern California, Redding, CA, p. A80

CARDENAS, Mitzi
Chief Information Officer, Truman Medical Center-Hospital Hill, Kansas City, MO, p. A362
Chief Information Officer, Truman Medical Center-Lakewood, Kansas City, MO, p. A362

CARDIFF, Michael, Systems Supervisor, Abrom Kaplan Memorial Hospital, Kaplan, LA, p. A270

CARDINAL, Joyce, Chief Nursing Executive, Jefferson Healthcare, Port Townsend, WA, p. A675

CARDLE, Lori, Senior Vice President, Chief Operating Officer, Valley Presbyterian Hospital, Los Angeles, CA, p. A70

CARDOZA, Phuong, Interim Chief Executive Officer, Cypress Creek Hospital, Houston, TX, p. A610

CARDWELL, Marian, Chief Financial Officer, Potomac Valley Hospital, Keyser, WV, p. A684

CAREY, Ann
Chief Information Officer, St. Vincent's Medical Center Southside, Jacksonville, FL, p. A126
Vice President and Chief Information Officer, St. Vincent's Medical Center Riverside, Jacksonville, FL, p. A126

CAREY, Calvin, Chief Financial Officer, Summit Medical Center, Casper, WY, p. A707

CAREY, Eric R, Vice President Information Systems and Chief Information Officer, Valley Hospital, Ridgewood, NJ, p. A411

CAREY, Jeannie, R.N., Director Patient Care, Perry Memorial Hospital, Perry, OK, p. A505

CAREY, Robin, Director of Nursing, Jasper Memorial Hospital, Monticello, GA, p. A158

CARIGSON, John, Chief Financial Officer, Covenant Specialty Hospital, Lubbock, TX, p. A621

CARIKER, Kelly, Chief Information Officer, North Valley Hospital, Tonasket, WA, p. A679

CARLE, Chris, Senior Vice President and Chief Operating Officer, St. Elizabeth Florence, Florence, KY, p. A252

CARLETON, David
Chief Information Officer, Heritage Valley Health System, Beaver, PA, p. A520

Chief Information Officer, Sewickley Valley Hospital, (A Division Of Valley Medical Facilities), Sewickley, PA, p. A541

CARLINO, Tracy, R.N., Chief Nursing Officer, Virtua Marlton, Marlton, NJ, p. A407

CARLISLE, Charles, Director, East Mississippi State Hospital, Meridian, MS, p. A350

CARLISLE, Sandy, Manager Human Resources, Holzer Medical Center - Jackson, Jackson, OH, p. A484

CARLOCK, Carey, Chief Executive Officer, Riveredge Hospital, Forest Park, IL, p. A183

CARLOS, Ilona, M.D., President Medical Staff, Thorek Memorial Hospital, Chicago, IL, p. A180

CARLSON, Bev, Chief Financial Officer, Delta County Memorial Hospital, Delta, CO, p. A98

CARLSON, Brian J., FACHE
Chief Executive Officer, Sanford Thief River Falls Behavioral Health Center, Thief River Falls, MN, p. A341
Executive Director, Sanford Medical Center Thief River Falls, Thief River Falls, MN, p. A340

CARLSON, Daniel, M.D., Chief Medical Officer, Holston Valley Medical Center, Kingsport, TN, p. A572

CARLSON, Dennis, Chief Executive Officer, Bear Lake Memorial Hospital, Montpelier, ID, p. A170

CARLSON, Kellie, Director Human Resources, Coastal Harbor Treatment Center, Savannah, GA, p. A160

CARLSON, Kim
Director Human Resources, Essentia Health Northern Pines Medical Center, Aurora, MN, p. A327
Senior Vice President Human Resources, Firstlight Health System, Mora, MN, p. A336

CARLSON, Kurt, Chief Executive Officer, Otis R. Bowen Center For Human Services, Warsaw, IN, p. A216

CARLSON, Lisa, Chief Financial Officer, Adena Pike Medical Center, Waverly, OH, p. A493

CARLSON, Peter, President, Behavioral Health Services, Aurora Psychiatric Hospital, Wauwatosa, WI, p. A705

CARLSON, Richard, Chief Financial Officer, Crawford Memorial Hospital, Robinson, IL, p. A194

CARLSON, Sandee, Director of Nursing, Essentia Health Duluth, Duluth, MN, p. A330

CARLSON, Sarah, Director Human Resources, Essentia Health St. Joseph's Medical Center, Brainerd, MN, p. A328

CARLSON, Scott, Director, Mary Greeley Medical Center, Ames, IA, p. A217

CARLSON, Wendie, Chief Human Resources Officer, West Tennessee Healthcare North Hospital, TN, p. A571

CARLSON, Wendy, Director Human Resources, Pathways Of Tennessee, Jackson, TN, p. A571

CARLTON, Andrew, Administrator, Atrium Medical Center Of Corinth, Corinth, TX, p. A594

CARLTON, Roy, Chief Financial Officer, Walter B. Jones Alcohol And Drug Abuse Treatment Center, Greenville, NC, p. A454

CARLTON, Terrie, R.N., Vice President & Chief Nursing Officer, Palmetto Health Tuomey, Sumter, SC, p. A557

CARLYLE, Dave, Director Human Resources, Wayne County Hospital, Corydon, IA, p. A220

CARMAN, Susan, Chief Information Officer, Wilson Memorial Regional Medical Center, NY, p. A423

CARMAN, Thomas H., President and Chief Executive Officer, Samaritan Medical Center, Watertown, NY, p. A445

CARMELLINI, Tracy, M.D., Chief of Staff, Jennersville Hospital, West Grove, PA, p. A544

CARMEN, Lee, Associate Vice President Health Care Information Systems, University Of Iowa Stead Family Children's Hospital, IA, p. A224

CARMICHAEL, Cindy
Administrator, Mercy Hospital El Reno, El Reno, OK, p. A498
Administrator, Mercy Hospital Watonga, Watonga, OK, p. A510

CARMICHAEL, Craig, Vice President, Operations, University Of Maryland St. Joseph Medical Center, Towson, MD, p. A294

CARMICHAEL, Gavin H, FACHE, Chief Operating Officer, Alaska Psychiatric Institute, Anchorage, AK, p. A25

CARMIK, Richard, Facility Director and Hospital Administrator, Chicago-Read Mental Health Center, Chicago, IL, p. A176

CARMODY, James, Vice President Human Resources, Wilkes-Barre General Hospital, PA, p. A544

CARNAHAN, David, Chief Executive Officer, Quail Run Behavioral Health, Phoenix, AZ, p. A34

CARNAHAN, Robert H., II, R.N., Chief Executive Officer, Banner Churchill Community Hospital, Fallon, NV, p. A392

CARNES, Ruth, Manager Human Resources, Jennings American Legion Hospital, Jennings, LA, p. A269

CARNEVALE, Raymond
Interim Chief Executive Officer, Select Specialty Hospital - Cincinnati North, Cincinnati, OH, p. A475

Interim Chief Executive Officer, Select Specialty Hospital-Tulsa Midtown, Tulsa, OK, p. A509

CARNEY, Adrienne, R.N., Director Nursing and Surgical Services, Kearney Regional Medical Center, Kearney, NE, p. A385

CARNEY, Glenn, Chief Operating Officer, Central Florida Regional Hospital, Sanford, FL, p. A138

CARNEY, Judi, M.D., President Medical Staff, Baptist Memorial Hospital For Women, Memphis, TN, p. A574

CARNEY, Kevin, Senior Information Systems Analyst, Pine Creek Medical Center, Dallas, TX, p. A597

CARNEY, Michael J., Chief Executive Officer, Brentwood Behavioral Healthcare Of Mississippi, Jackson, MS, p. A348

CARNEY, Mike, Interim President and Chief Executive Officer, Gibson General Hospital, Princeton, IN, p. A213

CARO, Vique, Chief Information Officer, Cincinnati Veterans Affairs Medical Center, Cincinnati, OH, p. A474

CAROLINA, Dorinda, Chief Human Resources Officer, Frankford Campus, PA, p. A535

CARON, Jacqueline, Chief Human Resources, Birmingham Veterans Affairs Medical Center, Birmingham, AL, p. A14

CARON, William J., Director, Southern Arizona Veterans Affairs Health Care System, Tucson, AZ, p. A38

CAROSELLI, Cynthia A., R.N., Ph.D., Chief Nursing Officer, Veterans Affairs New York Harbor Healthcare System - Manhattan Campus, NY, p. A437

CAROZZA, Sally, Director Human Resources, West Penn Hospital, Pittsburgh, PA, p. A538

CARPEL, Emmett, M.D., Medical Director and Chief of Staff, Phillips Eye Institute, Minneapolis, MN, p. A335

CARPENTER, Carolyn, FACHE, Vice President and Chief Operating Officer, Sentara Norfolk General Hospital, Norfolk, VA, p. A663

CARPENTER, Curt, Manager Information Technology, Coquille Valley Hospital, Coquille, OR, p. A512

CARPENTER, Deb, Director Information Technology, Lourdes Medical Center, Pasco, WA, p. A674

CARPENTER, Jackie, Office Manager, Rock County Hospital, Bassett, NE, p. A381

CARPENTER, Leah A., Administrator and Chief Executive Officer, Memorial Hospital West, Pembroke Pines, FL, p. A135

CARPENTER, Posie, R.N., MSN, Chief Administrative Officer, Ucla Medical Center-Santa Monica, Santa Monica, CA, p. A89

CARPENTER, Stephanie, Director of Nursing Services, Columbia County Health System, Dayton, WA, p. A671

CARPER, Joleen, Vice President Quality and Risk, Tri-State Memorial Hospital, Clarkston, WA, p. A670

CARR, Ann, R.N., Chief Nursing Officer, Saint Francis Hospital Vinita, Vinita, OK, p. A509

CARR, David, M.D., Physician Medical Director, The Rehabilitation Institute Of St. Louis, Saint Louis, MO, p. A369

CARR, Deborah, Vice President Human Resources, Orange Regional Medical Center, Middletown, NY, p. A430

CARR, Diane, Chief Information Officer, Nyc Health + Hospitals / North Central Bronx, New York (Includes All Hospitals Located Within The Five Boroughs), NY, p. A436

CARR, George, Chief Information Officer, Bryan Medical Center-West, NE, p. A385

CARR, James
Chief Information Officer, Nyc Health + Hospitals / Bellevue, New York (Includes All Hospitals Located Within The Five Boroughs), NY, p. A435
Chief Information Officer, Nyc Health + Hospitals / Lincoln, New York (Includes All Hospitals Located Within The Five Boroughs), NY, p. A436

CARR, Julie R., Chief Nursing Officer, Roane General Hospital, Spencer, WV, p. A687

CARR, Kay
Chief Information Officer, Bryn Mawr Hospital, Bryn Mawr, PA, p. A521
Chief Information Officer, Bryn Mawr Rehabilitation Hospital, Malvern, PA, p. A530
Chief Information Officer, Lankenau Medical Center, Wynnewood, PA, p. A545
Senior Vice President and Chief Information Officer, Paoli Hospital, Paoli, PA, p. A533

CARR, Randall
Director Human Resources, Peninsula Hospital, TN, p. A572
Director Human Resources, Roane Medical Center, Harriman, TN, p. A570

CARR, Sheila, Chief Executive Officer, Wekiva Springs, Jacksonville, FL, p. A126

CARR, Tim, Chief Financial Officer, Methodist Ambulatory Surgery Hospital - Northwest, San Antonio, TX, p. A633

CARRADINE, Damon, Director Information Technology, Highland Hospital, Charleston, WV, p. A682

CARRANZA, Diana
  Associate Director, Veterans Affairs Illiana Health Care System, Danville, IL, p. A180
  Interim Director, Veterans Affairs Illiana Health Care System, Danville, IL, p. A180
CARRASCO, Carlos, Chief Operating Officer, Winnie Palmer Hospital For Women And Babies, FL, p. A134
CARRASCO, Michelle, Director Human Resources, Palo Verde Behavioral Health, Tucson, AZ, p. A37
CARRASCO, Victor, Chief Executive Officer, Kindred Hospital Rancho, Rancho Cucamonga, CA, p. A79
CARRASQUILLO, Carmen, M.D., Medical Director, Industrial Hospital, San Juan, PR, p. A716
CARREJO, Angela, Director Human Resources, Nor-Lea Hospital District, Lovington, NM, p. A418
CARRELLI, Bobbie, Director Human Resources, Summit Behavioral Healthcare, Cincinnati, OH, p. A475
CARREON, Aleana, Executive Director, Sonoma Developmental Center, Eldridge, CA, p. A57
CARRERA, Lavern H, Senior Vice President Human Resources, Northside Medical Center, OH, p. A494
CARRERO, Milton D, M.D., Medical Director, Dr. Ramon E. Betances Hospital-Mayaguez Medical Center Branch, Mayaguez, PR, p. A714
CARRICO, Tom, Vice President of Operations, Hardin Memorial Health, Elizabethtown, KY, p. A251
CARRIER, Jeffrey, R.N., Chief Clinical Officer, Freeman Hospital East, MO, p. A361
CARRIERE, Archie, Information Technology Technician, Northlake Behavioral Health System, Mandeville, LA, p. A273
CARRIGG, John M.
  Executive Vice President and Chief Operating Officer, Wilson Memorial Regional Medical Center, NY, p. A423
  President and Chief Executive Officer, Binghamton General Hospital, NY, p. A423
  President and Chief Executive Officer, Wilson Memorial Regional Medical Center, NY, p. A423
CARRILLO, Irma, Director Human Resources, Ashford Presbyterian Community Hospital, San Juan, PR, p. A715
CARRILLO, Todd, Chief Information Officer, Yoakum County Hospital, Denver City, TX, p. A599
CARRILLO, Zulema, Superintendent, El Paso Psychiatric Center, El Paso, TX, p. A601
CARRINGER, Rick, Vice President and Chief Financial Officer, Methodist Medical Center Of Oak Ridge, Oak Ridge, TN, p. A578
CARRINGTON, Ebone', Chief Executive Officer and Chief Operating Officer, Nyc Health + Hospitals / Harlem, New York (Includes All Hospitals Located Within The Five Boroughs), NY, p. A435
CARROCINO, Joanne, FACHE, President and Chief Executive Officer, Cape Regional Health System, Cape May Court House, NJ, p. A403
CARROLL, Jonathan, Chief Information Officer, Uconn, John Dempsey Hospital, Farmington, CT, p. A108
CARROLL, Candice R., Nurse Executive, Riverside Behavioral Health Center, VA, p. A662
CARROLL, Eric, Chief Executive Officer, Unicoi County Memorial Hospital, Erwin, TN, p. A569
CARROLL, Jack, Director Human Resources, Spaulding Hospital For Continuing Medical Care Cambridge, Cambridge, MA, p. A298
CARROLL, Jack A., Ph.D., President and Chief Executive Officer, Magee Rehabilitation Hospital, Philadelphia, PA, p. A535
CARROLL, Jacqueline, Director Human Resources, Los Alamos Medical Center, Los Alamos, NM, p. A418
CARROLL, Jaime, R.N.
  Vice President Nursing, Sentara Albemarle Medical Center, Elizabeth City, NC, p. A452
  Department Head, Walter Reed National Military Medical Center, Bethesda, MD, p. A290
CARROLL, James H, Chief Information Officer, St. John Medical Center, Westlake, OH, p. A493
CARROLL, Jan, MSN, M.P.H., R.N., Chief Nursing Officer, Canton-Potsdam Hospital, Potsdam, NY, p. A440
CARROLL, John, M.D., Chief Medical Officer, St. James Mercy Hospital, Hornell, NY, p. A427
CARROLL, Karen Manuel, R.N., Vice President Patient Care Services, Beaufort Memorial Hospital, Beaufort, SC, p. A549
CARROLL, Kristen, M.D., Chief of Staff, Shriners Hospitals For Children-Salt Lake City, Salt Lake City, UT, p. A650
CARROLL, Leonard, M.D., Chief of Staff, Hendry Regional Medical Center, Clewiston, FL, p. A120
CARROLL, Michael W., Administrator, Richland Parish Hospital, Delhi, LA, p. A267
CARROLL, Peggy, Chief Information Officer, Palos Health, Palos Heights, IL, p. A192

CARROLL, Richard, M.D.
  Chief Medical officer, Amita Health Adventist Medical Center Bolingbrook, Bolingbrook, IL, p. A174
  Vice President and Chief Medical Officer, Amita Health Adventist Medical Center Glenoaks, Glendale Heights, IL, p. A184
CARROLL, Susan, Chief Executive Officer, Inova Alexandria Hospital, Alexandria, VA, p. A655
CARROLL, Terri L, Vice President Financial Services, Hillsboro Area Hospital, Hillsboro, IL, p. A185
CARROLL, William, M.D., Chief Medical Executive, Warrack Campus, CA, p. A89
CARRON, Patrick E., FACHE, President and Chief Executive Officer, Perry County Memorial Hospital, Perryville, MO, p. A366
CARRUTH, Gregory, Head Information Management, Naval Hospital Oak Harbor, Oak Harbor, WA, p. A674
CARRUTH, Keith, Chief Executive Officer, Amg Specialty Hospital At Mercy, Oklahoma City, OK, p. A502
CARSON, Carole, Director of Nursing Operations, Rehabilitation Hospital Of Southern New Mexico, Las Cruces, NM, p. A418
CARSON, Debbie, Director Human Resources, Promise Hospital Of Vicksburg, Vicksburg, MS, p. A354
CARSON, Kara Jo, Chief Financial Officer, Pinckneyville Community Hospital, Pinckneyville, IL, p. A193
CARSTENS, Cynthia L., R.N., President and Chief Executive Officer, Stewart Memorial Community Hospital, Lake City, IA, p. A225
CARSTENSEN, Karla, Director Patient Care, Avera Dells Area Hospital, Dell Rapids, SD, p. A560
CARTAGENA, Maria, M.D., Chief Medical Officer, Brylin Hospitals, Buffalo, NY, p. A423
CARTER, Andrea, M.D., Chief Medical Officer, Samaritan Healthcare, Moses Lake, WA, p. A673
CARTER, Barbara, Chief Nursing Officer, Cimarron Memorial Hospital, Boise City, OK, p. A496
CARTER, Billie, Chief Operating Officer and Assistant Administrator, Stonewall Memorial Hospital, Aspermont, TX, p. A584
CARTER, Bob, Interim Chief Executive Officer, Eastern Oklahoma Medical Center, Poteau, OK, p. A505
CARTER, Carolyn Lizann, Chief Nursing Officer, Broward Health Coral Springs, Coral Springs, FL, p. A120
CARTER, Charla, Human Resource Officer, Uvalde Memorial Hospital, Uvalde, TX, p. A641
CARTER, Christen, Director Public Relations, Roosevelt Warm Springs Rehabilitation Hospital - Rehab, Warm Springs, GA, p. A162
CARTER, D. Montez., Chief Executive Officer, St. Mary's Health Care System, Athens, GA, p. A145
CARTER, Dennis, M.D., Chief of Staff, Eastern Oklahoma Medical Center, Poteau, OK, p. A505
CARTER, Donna, MSN, R.N.
  Chief Nursing Officer, Minden Medical Center, Minden, LA, p. A274
  Chief Information Officer and Security Officer, Russell Medical, Alexander City, AL, p. A13
CARTER, Douglas S, M.D., Vice President and Chief Medical Officer, Major Hospital, Shelbyville, IN, p. A214
CARTER, Frank, Chief Financial Officer, Cornerstone Hospital Of Huntington, Huntington, WV, p. A683
CARTER, Gary L, M.D., Vice President and Chief Medical Officer, North Kansas City Hospital, North Kansas City, MO, p. A365
CARTER, Gregory, M.D., Chief Medical Officer, St. Luke's Rehabilitation Institute, Spokane, WA, p. A678
CARTER, Jessica Y, Chief Financial Officer, Crisp Regional Hospital, Cordele, GA, p. A151
CARTER, Jim, Chief Operating Officer, Grady General Hospital, Cairo, GA, p. A149
CARTER, Josh, Chief Executive Officer, Memphis Mental Health Institute, Memphis, TN, p. A575
CARTER, Leonard, Campus Administrator, Smith Northview Hospital, GA, p. A162
CARTER, Leonard M, Chief Human Resources Officer, Fhn Memorial Hospital, Freeport, IL, p. A183
CARTER, Leslia, Administrator, North Mississippi Medical Center-Pontotoc, Pontotoc, MS, p. A352
CARTER, Lisa, Chief Executive Officer, Niswonger Children's Hospital, TN, p. A571
CARTER, Malinda Yvonne, Vice President Human Resources, Saint Anthony Hospital, Chicago, IL, p. A179
CARTER, Marcia, Director Human Resources, Bluegrass Community Hospital, Versailles, KY, p. A261
CARTER, Michael, M.D.
  Chief Medical Officer, Houston County Community Hospital, Erin, TN, p. A569
  Administrator Information Technology, Northwest Ohio Psychiatric Hospital, Toledo, OH, p. A491

CARTER, Misty, Vice President Human Resources and Ancillary Services, Great Plains Regional Medical Center, Elk City, OK, p. A498
CARTER, Priscilla, Chief Financial Officer, Mesa Hills Specialty Hospital, El Paso, TX, p. A602
CARTER, Rebecca W, MSN, R.N., FACHE, Chief Executive Officer and Chief Nursing Officer, Blue Ridge Medical Center - Yancey Campus, NC, p. A461
CARTER, Rebecca W., MSN, R.N., FACHE, Chief Executive Officer and Chief Nursing Officer, Blue Ridge Medical Center - Yancey Campus, NC, p. A461
CARTER, Richard, M.D.
  Chief Medical Director, Hamilton County Hospital, Syracuse, KS, p. A246
  Chief of Staff, Tennova Healthcare-Jefferson Memorial Hospital, Jefferson City, TN, p. A571
  District Chief Executive Officer, Hunt Regional Medical Center, Greenville, TX, p. A608
CARTER, Shanti, Chief Executive Officer, Kingwood Pines Hospital, Kingwood, TX, p. A618
CARTER, Steve, Chief Information Officer, Mon Health Medical Center, Morgantown, WV, p. A685
CARTER, Teresa, Vice President Patient Care Services, Onecore Health, Oklahoma City, OK, p. A504
CARTER, Tomika, Deputy Chief Executive Officer, Greystone Park Psychiatric Hospital, Morris Plains, NJ, p. A407
CARTER, Vickie, Information Systems Director, Sumner Regional Medical Center, Gallatin, TN, p. A570
CARTWRIGHT, Bryan, Chief Information Technology Officer, Missouri River Medical Center, Fort Benton, MT, p. A375
CARTWRIGHT, David, Director Management Information Systems, Sovah Health-Danville, Danville, VA, p. A657
CARTWRIGHT, David A, Vice President Finance and Support Services, Advocate Condell Medical Center, Libertyville, IL, p. A188
CARTWRIGHT, Debra, Chief Financial Officer, St. Joseph Medical Center, Kansas City, MO, p. A362
CARTWRIGHT, Michelle, Chief Financial Officer, Palm Beach Children's Hospital, FL, p. A143
CARUCCI, Dean, Chief Executive Officer, Portsmouth Regional Hospital, Portsmouth, NH, p. A401
CARUGATI, Diane, Chief Operating Officer, Friends Hospital, Philadelphia, PA, p. A534
CARUSO, Diane M, MSN, Chief Nursing Officer, Encompass Health Rehabilitation Hospital Of Scottsdale, Scottsdale, AZ, p. A35
CARUSO, Don, M.D.
  Chief Executive Officer and President, Cheshire Medical Center, Keene, NH, p. A399
  Chief Medical Officer, Cheshire Medical Center, Keene, NH, p. A399
CARUSO, Maria, Chief Financial Officer, Venice Regional Bayfront Health, Venice, FL, p. A142
CARVER, Carol, MSN, R.N., Vice President Patient Services, Clarity Child Guidance Center, San Antonio, TX, p. A632
CARVER, Deborah, Chief Nursing Officer, Providence Tarzana Medical Center, Los Angeles, CA, p. A69
CARVER, Gary J., M.D., Chief Medical Officer, Coshocton Regional Medical Center, Coshocton, OH, p. A479
CARVETH, Barbara, Chief Financial Officer, University Of Colorado Hospital, Aurora, CO, p. A96
CARYER, Steve, Chief Financial Officer, Community Memorial Hospital, Hicksville, OH, p. A484
CARYNSKI, Paula A., MS, R.N., President, Osf Saint Anthony Medical Center, Rockford, IL, p. A195
CASABONA, Nicholas, Chief Information Officer, Children's Medical Center, NY, p. A430
CASANO, Jayleen, Ph.D., FACHE, Chief Operations and Nursing Officer, Abrazo Central Campus, Phoenix, AZ, p. A32
CASANOVA, Robert Bernier, Chief Financial Officer, Industrial Hospital, San Juan, PR, p. A716
CASAREZ, Margaret, Chief Financial Officer, San Joaquin Valley Rehabilitation Hospital, Fresno, CA, p. A59
CASAREZ, Teresa, Director Human Resources, Pecos Valley Lodge, NM, p. A419
CASDORPH, Michael, Chief Executive Officer, Highland-Clarksburg Hospital, Clarksburg, WV, p. A682
CASE, Cliff, Chief Financial Officer, Mineral Community Hospital, Superior, MT, p. A379
CASE, Ed, Executive Vice President and Chief Financial Officer, Shirley Ryan Abilitylab, Chicago, IL, p. A179
CASE, Harvey, President, Vidant Beaufort Hospital, Washington, NC, p. A462
CASE, Helen M, Chief Nursing Officer, Nemours Children's Hospital, Orlando, FL, p. A134
CASE, Jeannia, Chief Nursing Officer, Central Hospital Of Bowie, Bowie, TX, p. A590
CASE, Matthew, MSC, USN, Executive Officer, Naval Medical Center, Portsmouth, VA, p. A664

CASE, Nancy, Chief Nursing Officer, Daviess Community Hospital, Washington, IN, p. A216

CASERTA, Kevin, M.D.
Chief Medical Officer, Providence Centralia Hospital, Centralia, WA, p. A670
Chief Medical Officer, Providence St. Peter Hospital, Olympia, WA, p. A674

CASEY, Candy J., R.N., MS, President and Chief Executive Officer, Columbia Center Birth Hospital, Mequon, WI, p. A697

CASEY, Dina, Human Resources Officer, Lane County Hospital, Dighton, KS, p. A234

CASEY, Joseph, Interim President and Chief Executive Officer, Sturdy Memorial Hospital, Attleboro, MA, p. A295

CASEY, Kevin, M.D., Chief Clinical Officer, St. Rita's Medical Center, Lima, OH, p. A485

CASH, Jeff, Senior Vice President and Chief Information Officer, Mercy Medical Center, Cedar Rapids, IA, p. A218

CASH, Jordan, President, Integris Southwest Medical Center, Oklahoma City, OK, p. A503

CASHEN CHACON, Chanda, Executive Vice President and Chief Operating Officer, Arkansas Children's Hospital, Little Rock-Pulaski County, AR, p. A44

CASHMAN, Tim, Chief Financial Officer, Estes Park Medical Center, Estes Park, CO, p. A100

CASHWELL, David, Chief Executive Officer, Encompass Health Rehabilitation Hospital Of Fredericksburg, Fredericksburg, VA, p. A658

CASIANO, Manuel, M.D., Senior Vice President Medical Affairs, Frederick Regional Health System, Frederick, MD, p. A291

CASILLAS, Rosalind C, Chief Nursing Officer, Lawrence Memorial Hospital, Walnut Ridge-Lawrence County, AR, p. A49

CASNER, Trina, President and Chief Executive Officer, Pana Community Hospital, Pana, IL, p. A192

CASOLA, Frances, Senior Vice President Operations, Saint Joseph's Medical Center, Yonkers, NY, p. A446

CASON, Amy, MSN, Chief Nursing Officer, Tristar Stonecrest Medical Center, Smyrna, TN, p. A580

CASON, Cathy, Chief Financial Officer, Jeff Davis Hospital, Hazlehurst, GA, p. A154

CASON, Diane, Chief Information Officer, Controller and Director Human Resources, Lake Butler Hospital Hand Surgery Center, Lake Butler, FL, p. A127

CASON, Randall R., FACHE, Senior Administrator, Via Christi Hospital Pittsburg, Pittsburg, KS, p. A244

CASON, Will, Vice President Human Resources, St. Rita's Medical Center, Lima, OH, p. A485

CASPERSON, William, M.D.
Vice President Medical Affairs, Memorial Hospital, Belleville, IL, p. A174
Vice President Medical Affairs, Memorial Hospital East, Shiloh, IL, p. A196

CASS, Julene J, R.N., Director of Nursing, Community Memorial Hospital, Redfield, SD, p. A563

CASS, Paul, D.O., Chief Medical & Clinical Integration Officer, Wentworth-Douglass Hospital, Dover, NH, p. A398

CASSADY, Perry, M.D., Medical Director, Physicians' Medical Center, New Albany, IN, p. A212

CASSAGNE, Nancy R., FACHE, Chief Executive Officer, West Jefferson Medical Center, Marrero, LA, p. A273

CASSEDY, Ryan, Chief Administrative Officer, Rehabilitation Hospital Of Fort Wayne, Fort Wayne, IN, p. A204

CASSEL, Asenath, Chief Nursing Officer, Wellington Regional Medical Center, Wellington, FL, p. A143

CASSEL, Kari
Senior Vice President and Chief Information Officer, Uf Health Jacksonville, Jacksonville, FL, p. A126
Senior Vice President and Chief Information Officer, Uf Health Shands Rehab Hospital, FL, p. A124

CASSELL, Sally D, Manager Human Resources, Ozark Health Medical Center, Clinton-Van Buren County, AR, p. A40

CASSIDAY, Cheryl, R.N., Director of Nursing, Chadron Community Hospital And Health Services, Chadron, NE, p. A383

CASSIDY, Donna
Administrator, Borgess-Pipp Hospital, MI, p. A316
Chief Nursing Executive, Bronson South Haven Hospital, South Haven, MI, p. A323

CASSIDY, Joseph J, Vice President, Holy Redeemer Hospital, Meadowbrook, PA, p. A531

CASSINGHAM, Brandi, Chief Nursing Officer, Memorialcare, Saddleback Memorial Medical Center, Laguna Hills, CA, p. A63

CASSLE, Susie, R.N., MSN, Vice President Nursing Services, Hendrick Health System, Abilene, TX, p. A582

CASTALDO, Jennifer, R.N., Vice President, Patient Care and Chief Nursing Officer, Henry Mayo Newhall Hospital, Valencia, CA, p. A93

CASTANEDA, Edmundo, President, Mercy General Hospital, Sacramento, CA, p. A82

CASTANEDA, Marissa, Chief Operating Officer and Director Marketing, Doctor's Hospital At Renaissance, Edinburg, TX, p. A600

CASTANEDA, Trevor, Chief Executive Officer, Baylor Medical Center At Frisco, Frisco, TX, p. A606

CASTEEL, Brian, Information Technology Technician, Hardin County General Hospital, Rosiclare, IL, p. A195

CASTEEL, Karen, Director Human Resources, Palms Of Pasadena Hospital, Saint Petersburg, FL, p. A138

CASTEEL, Lisa, Chief Executive Officer, Henry County Medical Center, Paris, TN, p. A578

CASTEEL, Rick
Vice President Management Information Systems and Chief Information Officer, University Of Maryland Harford Memorial Hospital, Havre De Grace, MD, p. A292
Vice President Management Information Systems and Chief Information Officer, University Of Maryland Upper Chesapeake Medical Center, Bel Air, MD, p. A289

CASTILLO, Carol, Medical Director, Sonoma Developmental Center, Eldridge, CA, p. A57

CASTILLO, Dan A., FACHE, Chief Executive Officer, Women's And Children's Hospital, CA, p. A68

CASTILLO, Edgar, Chief Financial Officer, Larkin Community Hospital, South Miami, FL, p. A139

CASTILLO, Paul, Chief Financial Officer, C. S. Mott Children's Hospital, MI, p. A307

CASTILLO, Ralph A., CPA, Chief Executive Officer, Morgan Memorial Hospital, Madison, GA, p. A157

CASTILLO, Renee, Chief Nursing Officer, Plains Memorial Hospital, Dimmitt, TX, p. A600

CASTILLO, Rita S, R.N., Vice President, Quality, Risk and Safety, Methodist Hospital South, Jourdanton, TX, p. A616

CASTLE, Dorothy, Director Human Resources, North Mississippi Medical Center-Eupora, Eupora, MS, p. A345

CASTLE, Eric, Director Information Services, Lawnwood Pavilion, FL, p. A123

CASTLE, Samantha, Chief Executive Officer, Carrollton Springs, Carrollton, TX, p. A592

CASTLEBERRY, Ginger, Corporate Risk Manager, Quality and Patient Safety, Valir Rehabilitation Hospital, Oklahoma City, OK, p. A505

CASTLEDINE, Ed, Chief Executive Officer, St. Luke's Nampa, Nampa, ID, p. A170

CASTLEMAN, Pam, MSN, Chief Nursing Officer, Regional One Health, Memphis, TN, p. A575

CASTOR, Susan, Chief Nursing Officer, Healthsouth Rehabilitation Hospital Of Toms River, Toms River, NJ, p. A412

CASTRO, Ana, Director Information Technology, Gerald Champion Regional Medical Center, Alamogordo, NM, p. A415

CASTRO, Craig
Chief Executive Officer, Clovis Community Medical Center, Clovis, CA, p. A55
Chief Information Officer, Community Regional Medical Center, Fresno, CA, p. A59

CASTRO, Darcy, Director Human Resources, Garfield Medical Center, Monterey Park, CA, p. A73

CASTRO, Jill, M.D., Medical Director, Healthsouth Rehabilitation Hospital Of Littleton, Littleton, CO, p. A103

CASTRO, Pete, D.O., Chief of Staff, Heart Of Texas Memorial Hospital, Brady, TX, p. A590

CASTRO, Richard
Chief Executive Officer, Ahmc Anaheim Regional Medical Center, Anaheim, CA, p. A50
Chief Executive Officer, Whittier Hospital Medical Center, Whittier, CA, p. A95

CASTRODALE, Andrew, M.D., Chief Medical Officer, Coulee Medical Center, Grand Coulee, WA, p. A672

CASTRONUEVO, Joseph, Director Information Management, St. Lawrence Rehabilitation Center, Lawrenceville, NJ, p. A406

CASWELL, Lori, Director Information Technology, Good Samaritan Medical Center - Cushing Campus, MA, p. A298

CASWELL, Penny, Director of Nursing, Bloomington Meadows Hospital, Bloomington, IN, p. A200

CATALA, Lucy, Vice President Finance, Baylor All Saints Medical Center At Fort Worth, Fort Worth, TX, p. A604

CATALDO, Linda, Human Resources Secretary, Prevost Memorial Hospital, Donaldsonville, LA, p. A267

CATALDO, Vincent A., Administrator, Prevost Memorial Hospital, Donaldsonville, LA, p. A267

CATALIOTTI, Palmira, Senior Vice President, Chief Financial Officer and Treasurer, Children's Medical Center, NY, p. A430

CATANIA, Joseph M., Chief Executive Officer, St. Anthony's Rehabilitation Hospital, Lauderdale Lakes, FL, p. A128

CATAUDELLA, Mary, Corporate Director Human Resources, Jersey City Medical Center, Jersey City, NJ, p. A406

CATENA, Cornelio R., President and Chief Executive Officer, Wilkes-Barre General Hospital, PA, p. A544

CATES, Brett, Director Information Services, Medical City Weatherford, Weatherford, TX, p. A643

CATES, Jessica, Fiscal Manager, Western State Hospital, Hopkinsville, KY, p. A253

CATHEY, Michele, Interim Chief Financial officer, Martin County Hospital District, Stanton, TX, p. A637

CATHEY, Walt, Chief Executive Officer, Covenant Medical Center-Lakeside, TX, p. A621

CATINO, Anne, MS, R.N., Vice President and Chief Nursing Officer, Holy Redeemer Hospital, Meadowbrook, PA, p. A531

CATTALANI, Mark, M.D., Clinical Director, Richard H. Hutchings Psychiatric Center, Syracuse, NY, p. A443

CATTELL, JoAnne, Chief Nursing Officer, St. Petersburg General Hospital, Saint Petersburg, FL, p. A138

CATTELL, Nancy E, Vice President Human Resources, Liberty Hospital, Liberty, MO, p. A363

CATTON, Carolyn, Interim Chief Patient Care Officer, Beaver Dam Community Hospitals, Beaver Dam, WI, p. A690

CATTON, Jane, R.N., Chief Operating Officer and Chief Nursing Officer, Northwestern Medical Center, Saint Albans, VT, p. A654

CAUBLE, David, Executive Vice President and Chief Financial Officer, Children's Mercy Hospital Kansas City, Kansas City, MO, p. A361

CAUDILL, Allan, M.D., Chief of Staff, Bronson South Haven Hospital, South Haven, MI, p. A323

CAUDILL, David, Administrator, Grisell Memorial Hospital District One, Ransom, KS, p. A244

CAUGHELL, David, M.D., Chief of Staff, Jane Phillips Nowata Health Center, Nowata, OK, p. A502

CAUGHEY, Michelle, M.D., Physician In Chief, Kaiser Permanente South San Francisco, South San Francisco, CA, p. A90

CAUGHMAN, Katie
Chief Financial Officer, St. John Broken Arrow, Broken Arrow, OK, p. A496
Chief Financial Officer, St. John Owasso, Owasso, OK, p. A505

CAUSEY, Cynthia, Associate Administrator Human and Mission Services, Mcleod Medical Center Dillon, Dillon, SC, p. A552

CAUSEY, Jack M., Chief Executive Officer, Leesville Rehabilitation Hospital, Leesville, LA, p. A272

CAUSEY, Jennifer, Chief Executive Officer, Select Specialty Hospital-Nashville, Nashville, TN, p. A577

CAUWENBERG, Jude, M.D., Chief of Staff, Ashtabula County Medical Center, Ashtabula, OH, p. A471

CAVA, Anthony V., MS, RPH, FACHE, President, Robert Wood Johnson University Hospital Somerset, Somerville, NJ, p. A411

CAVAGNARO, Charles E, M.D., III, Interim Chief Medical officer, University Campus, MA, p. A306

CAVANAUGH, Cheryl, Senior Director Human Resources, Valley Regional Hospital, Claremont, NH, p. A398

CAVANAUGH, Paul, Director Human Resources, Friends Hospital, Philadelphia, PA, p. A534

CAVAZOS, David-Paul, Chief Executive Officer, Republic County Hospital, Belleville, KS, p. A232

CAVE, Chuck, CPA, Chief Financial Officer, Wilson N. Jones Regional Medical Center, Sherman, TX, p. A636

CAVELL, Richard, M.D., Medical Director, University Health Conway, Monroe, LA, p. A274

CAVEN, Tom, M.D., Vice President, Medical Director, Dell Seton Medical Center At The University Of Texas, Austin, TX, p. A586

CAVENEY, Timothy, President, South Shore Hospital, Chicago, IL, p. A179

CAVERNO, John
Chief Human Resources Officer, Excela Frick Hospital, Mount Pleasant, PA, p. A532
Chief Human Resources Officer, Excela Health Westmoreland Hospital, Greensburg, PA, p. A526

CAWLEY, Karen, Chief Executive Officer, Curahealth Phoenix, AZ, p. A33

CAWLEY, Kevin J, Interim Chief Financial Officer, Mclaren Thumb Region, Bad Axe, MI, p. A308

CAWLEY, Patrick J, Chief Executive Officer, MUSC Health and Vice President for Health Affairs, University, Children's Hospital Of South Carolina At Musc, SC, p. A550

CAWLEY, Patrick J., Chief Executive Officer, MUSC Health and Vice President for Health Affairs, University, Children's Hospital Of South Carolina At Musc, SC, p. A550

CAWOOD, Marina, Administrative Assistant, Middlesboro Arh Hospital, Middlesboro, KY, p. A258

CAYER, Gerald, Chief Executive Officer, Lewis County General Hospital, Lowville, NY, p. A429

CAYTON, Mical, Area Information Officer, Kaiser Permanente Antioch Medical Center, Antioch, CA, p. A50

CAZARES, Erik, Chief Nursing Officer, The Hospitals Of Providence Sierra Campus, El Paso, TX, p. A602

CAZAYOUX, John, Chief Financial Officer, Pointe Coupee General Hospital, New Roads, LA, p. A276

CAZES, Anna Leah
Interim Chief Nursng Officer, Senior Vice President, Chief Operating Officer, Lake Charles Memorial Hospital For Women, LA, p. A272
Senior Vice President, Chief Operating Officer, Lake Charles Memorial Hospital For Women, LA, p. A272

CECAVA, Eric
Chief Operating Officer, Adena Medical Center, Chillicothe, OH, p. A474
Chief Operating Officer, Adena Pike Medical Center, Waverly, OH, p. A493

CECCHINI, Marina T., Administrator, Uf Health Shands Rehab Hospital, FL, p. A124

CECH, Bob, Regional Finance Officer, Presence Saints Mary & Elizabeth Medical Center, Claremont Avenue, IL, p. A178

CECIL, Bruce, Chief Financial Officer, Fresno Surgical Hospital, Fresno, CA, p. A59

CECIL, Janell, R.N., MSN, Senior Vice President and Chief Nursing Officer, University Of Tennessee Medical Center, Knoxville, TN, p. A572

CECIL, Jason, Vice President, Information, Capital Region Medical Center, Jefferson City, MO, p. A360

CECIL, Jon C
Chief Human Resource Officer, Cape Coral Hospital, Cape Coral, FL, p. A119
Chief Human Resource Officer, Gulf Coast Medical Center, Fort Myers, FL, p. A123
Chief Human Resource Officer, The Rehabilitation Hospital, FL, p. A123

CEDENO LLORENS, Arturo, M.D., Medical Director, Hospital Buen Samaritano, Aguadilla, PR, p. A711

CEDILLO, Alaina, Interim Administrator, Marion General Hospital, Columbia, MS, p. A345

CEDOTAL, Kiley P, FACHE, Chief Executive Officer, Promise Hospital Of Baton Rouge - Mid-City Campus, LA, p. A264

CEDOTAL, Kiley P., FACHE
Chief Executive Officer, Promise Hospital Baton Rouge - Main Campus, Baton Rouge, LA, p. A264
Chief Executive Officer, Promise Hospital Of Baton Rouge - Mid-City Campus, LA, p. A264

CEHELYK, Bohdan, M.D., Chief Medical Officer, East Mountain Hospital, Belle Mead, NJ, p. A402

CELLA, Ann S, R.N., Senior Vice President, Patient Care Services, St. Francis Hospital, The Heart Center, Roslyn, NY, p. A442

CELLA, Robert, M.D.
Chief Medical Officer, Albany Memorial Hospital, Albany, NY, p. A421
Chief Medical Officer, St. Peter's Hospital, Albany, NY, p. A421

CELSOR, Reba, Chief Executive Officer, West Tennessee Healthcare Dyersburg Hospital, Dyersburg, TN, p. A569

CELUCH, Paul
Chief Human Resource Officer, East Los Angeles Doctors Hospital, Los Angeles, CA, p. A66
Corporate Human Resources Director, Community Hospital Of Huntington Park, Huntington Park, CA, p. A62

CEMATE, David D, FACHE, Senior Vice President and Chief Operating Officer, Mercy Medical Center, Canton, OH, p. A473

CEMENO, Michael J, Chief Information Officer, Waterbury Hospital, Waterbury, CT, p. A112

CENTENO, Robert, M.D., Chief Medical Officer, Governor Juan F. Luis Hospital, Christiansted, VI, p. A717

CEPEDA, Aaron, Director Nursing Operations, South Texas Rehabilitation Hospital, Brownsville, TX, p. A590

CERALDI, Christopher, M.D., Chief of Staff, Abbeville Area Medical Center, Abbeville, SC, p. A549

CERCEO, Richard, Executive Vice President and Chief Operating Officer, Mercy Hospital And Medical Center, Chicago, IL, p. A178

CERIMELE, Joseph, D.O., Medical Director, Hillside Rehabilitation Hospital, Warren, OH, p. A492

CERIMELE, Leeann, Vice President Human Resources, West Virginia University Children's Hospital, WV, p. A685

CERISE, Fred, M.D., Chief Executive Officer, Parkland Health & Hospital System, Dallas, TX, p. A597

CERNAVA, Joanne, Director Human Resources, Kessler Marlton Rehabilitation, Marlton, NJ, p. A407

CERNOCH, Desiree, Director of Nurses, El Campo Memorial Hospital, El Campo, TX, p. A601

CERRA, Jane, Market Nurse Executive and Chief Nursing Officer, Select Specialty Hospital-Milwaukee, Milwaukee, WI, p. A699

CERULLO, Timothy J., Chief Executive Officer, Bayfront Health Port Charlotte, Port Charlotte, FL, p. A137

CERVANTES, Jason
Chief Information Officer, East Los Angeles Doctors Hospital, Los Angeles, CA, p. A66
Corporate Chief Information Officer, Community Hospital Of Huntington Park, Huntington Park, CA, p. A62

CERVINO, Noel A., President and Chief Executive Officer, University Of Maryland Charles Regional Medical Center, La Plata, MD, p. A292

CESAREZ, Margaret, Chief Financial Officer, Gateway Rehabilitation Hospital, Florence, KY, p. A251

CESCA, Ken, Vice President Human Resources, Midstate Medical Center, Meriden, CT, p. A108

CESKO, David, M.D., Chief of Staff, Memorial Hospital Of Carbon County, Rawlins, WY, p. A709

CHA, Wontae, Chief Operating Officer, Hollywood Presbyterian Medical Center, Los Angeles, CA, p. A67

CHA BRIDIER, Vicky, Chief Operating Officer, College Station Medical Center, College Station, TX, p. A593

CHABALOWSKI, Edward, Chief Financial Officer, Phoenixville Hospital, Phoenixville, PA, p. A537

CHABOT, Judy, Chief Nursing Officer, Los Alamitos Medical Center, Los Alamitos, CA, p. A65

CHACKO, Benson
Chief Operating Officer, The Hospitals Of Providence Sierra Campus, El Paso, TX, p. A602
Vice President, Operations, Baylor Scott & White Medical Center - Lake Pointe, Rowlett, TX, p. A631

CHACON, Barbara, Chief Financial Officer, The Core Institute Specialty Hospital, Phoenix, AZ, p. A34

CHADEK, Richard, M.D., Clinical Director, Lawton Indian Hospital, Lawton, OK, p. A500

CHADHA, Beenu, Chief Financial Officer, San Ramon Regional Medical Center, San Ramon, CA, p. A88

CHADOCK, Brandon
Director of Operations, Sistersville General Hospital, Sistersville, WV, p. A687
Interim Chief Executive Officer, Sistersville General Hospital, Sistersville, WV, p. A687

CHADWICK, Maureen C, R.N., Chief Nursing Officer, Saint Vincent Hospital, Erie, PA, p. A525

CHADWICK, Robyn, President, Via Christi Hospital On St. Teresa, Wichita, KS, p. A248

CHADWICK, Sharon M, Director Human Resources, Abrazo Arizona Heart Hospital, AZ, p. A30

CHAFFIN, Linda, Director Medical Review, Baptist Memorial Hospital-Booneville, Booneville, MS, p. A344

CHAHANOVICH, Jen, President and Chief Executive Officer, Wilcox Medical Center, Lihue, HI, p. A166

CHALFANT, Cathie, Director Human Resources, Harrison County Community Hospital, Bethany, MO, p. A355

CHALIAN, Christopher, M.D., Medical Director, Casa Colina Hospital And Health Systems, Pomona, CA, p. A78

CHALK, Jackie, Director Human Resources, Healthsouth Rehabilitation Hospital Of Largo, Largo, FL, p. A128

CHALKE, Dennis, Senior Vice President, Chief Financial Officer and Treasurer, Baystate Children's Hospital, MA, p. A304

CHALONER, Robert S, Chief Administrative Officer, Stony Brook Southampton Hospital, NY, p. A443

CHALPHANT, Steve, Director Information Management Service Line, Wm. Jennings Bryan Dorn Veterans Affairs Medical Center, Columbia, SC, p. A552

CHALTRY, Richard, M.D., Director Medical Staff, Aspirus Ontonagon Hospital, Inc., Ontonagon, MI, p. A320

CHALTRY, William, Chief Nursing Officer, Pecos Valley Lodge, NM, p. A419

CHALUPA, Rebecca, MSN, R.N., Chief Nursing Officer, Houston Methodist San Jacinto Hospital - Alexander, TX, p. A587

CHAMBERLIN, Kim, Vice President Patient Services and Chief Nursing Officer, Mercy Medical Center-North Iowa, Mason City, IA, p. A226

CHAMBERS, Bradley
President and Senior Vice President, MedStar Health, Medstar Good Samaritan Hospital, Baltimore, MD, p. A288
President, Medstar Union Memorial Hospital, Baltimore, MD, p. A288

CHAMBERS, Gwen, Executive Director Human Resources, Methodist Hospital Of Southern California, Arcadia, CA, p. A51

CHAMBERS, Matthew
Chief Information Officer, Baylor Scott & White Medical Center - Lakeway, TX, p. A631
Chief Information Officer, Mclane Children's Hospital Scott & White, TX, p. A638

CHAMBERS, Regina, Vice President Human Resource, Rome Memorial Hospital, Rome, NY, p. A442

CHAMBLEE, Jane, Manager Human Resources, North Mississippi Medical Center-Iuka, Iuka, MS, p. A347

CHAMBLESS, Lesley
Assistant Vice President Human Resources, Carolinas Healthcare System Lincoln, Lincolnton, NC, p. A456
Assistant Vice President Workforce Relations, Carolinas Healthcare System Northeast, Concord, NC, p. A450

CHAMBLISS, James W, Chief of Staff, Magnolia Regional Medical Center, Magnolia-Columbia County, AR, p. A45

CHAMPAGNE, Charles D., Chief Financial Officer, Northeast Rehabilitation Hospital, Salem, NH, p. A401

CHAMPAGNE, Laurie, Controller, Curahealth New Orleans, New Orleans, LA, p. A275

CHAMPAVANNARATH, Vilakon, Director Information Systems, Bartow Regional Medical Center, Bartow, FL, p. A117

CHAMPION, Joshua I, Director, Florida Hospital Flagler, Palm Coast, FL, p. A135

CHAN, Eric, M.D., Chief Executive Officer, Surgery Specialty Hospitals Of America, Pasadena, TX, p. A627

CHAN, Fred, Chief Financial Officer, Intracare North Hospital, Houston, TX, p. A611

CHAN, Joyce, Chief Human Resources Officer, Centracare Health-Melrose, Melrose, MN, p. A334

CHAN, Thomas T., Chief Financial Officer, Meritus Medical Center, Hagerstown, MD, p. A292

CHANAA, Ziad, M.D., Chief of Staff, Boone Memorial Hospital, Madison, WV, p. A684

CHANAGA, Luis, Chief Financial Officer, Southview Medical Center, OH, p. A480

CHANCE, Andre, Chief Financial Officer, Veterans Affairs New York Harbor Healthcare System - Manhattan Campus, NY, p. A437

CHANDLER, Carla, Vice President and Chief Financial Officer, Emory Wesley Woods Geriatric Hospital, GA, p. A146

CHANDLER, Christopher, Chief Executive Officer, Monroe Regional Hospital, Aberdeen, MS, p. A343

CHANDLER, Laurie
Chairman, Prairie Community Hospital, Terry, MT, p. A379
Financial Director, Prairie Community Hospital, Terry, MT, p. A379

CHANDLER, Loren, President, Sinai Children's Hospital, IL, p. A178

CHANDLER, Mike, Administrator, Wk Bossier Health Center, LA, p. A279

CHANDLER, Ryan
Chief Executive Officer, Midtown Medical Center West, GA, p. A150
Chief Executive Officer, Northwest Texas Surgery Center, TX, p. A583

CHANDLER, Vincent, Director Information Services, Porterville Developmental Center, Porterville, CA, p. A79

CHANDLER, Wendy
Assistant Administrator Human Resources, Christus Ochsner St. Patrick Hospital Southwest Louisiana, Lake Charles, LA, p. A272
Regional Vice President Human Resources, Christus St. Frances Cabrini Hospital, Alexandria, LA, p. A262
Vice President Human Resources, Christus Highland Medical Center, LA, p. A278

CHANDRAN, Kutty, M.D., Regional Medical Officer, Broward Health Coral Springs, Coral Springs, FL, p. A120

CHANDRASENA, Anita, M.D., Vice President Medical Affairs, Sequoia Hospital, Redwood City, CA, p. A80

CHANDY, Joseph, Administrator, Methodist Hospital Of Chicago, Chicago, IL, p. A178

CHANG, Alex, Chief Operating Officer, Englewood Community Hospital, Englewood, FL, p. A122

CHANG, Jason
Chief Medical Officer and Vice President of Medical Affairs, Rehabilitation Hospital Of The Pacific, Honolulu, HI, p. A165
Executive Vice President and Chief Operating Officer, Queen's Medical Center - West Oahu, HI, p. A165

CHANG, Myrna, Chief Nursing Executive, Sutter Davis Hospital, Davis, CA, p. A56

CHANG, Sang-ick, M.D., M.P.H., Chief Medical Officer, John George Psychiatric Hospital, CA, p. A75

CHANNELL, Lesley
Vice President Human Resources, Reston Hospital Center, Reston, VA, p. A664
Vice President Human Resources, Dominion Hospital, Falls Church, VA, p. A657

CHAPDELAINE, Debora R., Manager Information Technology, Aurora Medical Center Kenosha, Kenosha, WI, p. A695

CHAPITAL, Alyssa B, M.D., Medical Director, Mayo Clinic Hospital, Mayo Clinic Hospital, Phoenix, AZ, p. A33

CHAPLIN, Steven, M.D., Medical Director, Sutter Health Kahi Mohala, Ewa Beach, HI, p. A164

CHAPMAN, Bradley, President, Penn Highlands Elk, Saint Marys, PA, p. A540

CHAPMAN, Cully, Chief Financial Officer, Lutheran Hospital Of Indiana, Fort Wayne, IN, p. A203

CHAPMAN, Emily, Chief Medical Officer, Children's Hospitals And Clinics Of Minnesota, MN, p. A335

CHAPMAN, Jeffrey, M.D., Chief Medical Officer, Cheyenne Regional Medical Center, Cheyenne, WY, p. A707

CHAPMAN, John, Chief Administrative Officer, Alameda Hospital, Alameda, CA, p. A50

CHAPMAN, Jon, Fiscal Officer, Western State Hospital, Staunton, VA, p. A666

CHAPMAN, Judy, Interim Director Information Systems, Upmc Susquehanna Lock Haven, Lock Haven, PA, p. A530

CHAPMAN, Karen
Director Human Resources, Chester Regional Medical Center, Chester, SC, p. A550
Human Resources Director, Springs Memorial Hospital, Lancaster, SC, p. A555

CHAPMAN, Kathleen, Esq, Deputy Director, Patient Care Services, Va Portland Healthcare System, Portland, OR, p. A517

CHAPMAN, Kathy, R.N., Chief Clinical Officer and Vice President of Patient Services, Allegan General Hospital, Allegan, MI, p. A307

CHAPMAN, Patrick, Ed.D.
Chief Executive Officer, Tippah County Hospital, Ripley, MS, p. A353
Assistant Vice President Operations, Jfk Medical Center North Campus, West Palm Beach, FL, p. A143

CHAPMAN, Rachel, Nurse Manager, Noland Hospital Birmingham, Birmingham, AL, p. A14

CHAPMAN, Rick, Chief Information Officer, Kindred Hospital North Florida, Green Cove Springs, FL, p. A124

CHAPMAN, Roland, Chief Information Officer, Northern Navajo Medical Center, Shiprock, NM, p. A420

CHAPMAN, Teresa, Vice President Human Resources, Northwestern Medicine Marianjoy Rehabilitation Hospital, Wheaton, IL, p. A198

CHAPMAN, Terina, Director of Nursing, Northern Utah Rehabilitation Hospital, South Ogden, UT, p. A651

CHAPPELL, Brandee, Director of Nursing, Lifecare Hospitals Of North Carolina, Rocky Mount, NC, p. A459

CHAPPELL, Pamela, R.N.
Assistant Administrator, Louisiana Extended Care Hospital West Monroe, West Monroe, LA, p. A281
Assistant Administrator, Specialty Hospital, Monroe, LA, p. A274

CHAPPELL, Robert, M.D., Chief Medical Officer and Chief Quality Officer, Madison Hospital, AL, p. A19

CHAPPELL, Teresa, Chief Information Officer, Johnston Health, Smithfield, NC, p. A460

CHAPPLE, Albert J., R.N., Chief Clinical Officer, Kindred Rehabilitation Hospital Northeast Houston, Humble, TX, p. A615

CHAPPLE, Scott, Chief Operating Officer, Oroville Hospital, Oroville, CA, p. A77

CHARARA, Kassem, Chief Medical Officer, Beaumont Hospital - Taylor, Taylor, MI, p. A324

CHARBENEAU, Ryan, M.D., Chief Medical Officer, St. David's North Austin Medical Center, Austin, TX, p. A586

CHARDAVOYNE, Alan, Chief Financial Officer, Moses Ludington Hospital, NY, p. A426

CHARETTE, Deborah, Director of Nursing, East Mountain Hospital, Belle Mead, NJ, p. A402

CHARLAT, Richard A, Chief of Staff, Iowa City Veterans Affairs Health Care System, Iowa City, IA, p. A224

CHARLES, Charlotte, Director Acute Patient Services, Madison Regional Health System, Madison, SD, p. A561

CHARLES, John, M.D., Chief Medical Officer, Mcleod Seacoast, SC, p. A555

CHARLES, Sally, Coordinator Human Resources, Grace Medical Center, Lubbock, TX, p. A621

CHARLES, Timothy L., President and Chief Executive Officer, Mercy Medical Center, Cedar Rapids, IA, p. A218

CHARLIER, Brian, Chief Operating Officer, HSHS St. Vincent Hospital/Prevea Health, Hshs St. Vincent Hospital, Green Bay, WI, p. A694

CHARLTON, Beth, Vice President Patient Services and Chief Nursing Officer, Covenant Medical Center-Harrison, MI, p. A322

CHARLTON, Francis, M.D., Jr, Chief Medical Staff, St. Mary's Medical Center, San Francisco, CA, p. A86

CHARLTON, Judie, M.D., Chief Medical Officer, West Virginia University Children's Hospital, WV, p. A685

CHARMEL, Patrick, President and Chief Executive Officer, Griffin Hospital, Derby, CT, p. A107

CHARTIER, Bridgett, Director of Nursing, Beartooth Billings Clinic, Red Lodge, MT, p. A378

CHARTIER, Terry
Director, Information Systems, Mercy Medical Center-New Hampton, New Hampton, IA, p. A227
Director, Information Systems, Mercy Medical Center-North Iowa, Mason City, IA, p. A226

CHARVAT, Peter, Chief Medical Officer, Johnston Health, Smithfield, NC, p. A460

CHASE, Jean
Regional Manager Information Services, Aurora Lakeland Medical Center, Elkhorn, WI, p. A692
Regional Manager Information Services, Aurora Memorial Hospital Of Burlington, Burlington, WI, p. A691

CHASE, Kyle, Chief Financial Officer, Glacial Ridge Health System, Glenwood, MN, p. A332

CHASE, Layla, Interim Chief Financial Officer, Bunkie General Hospital, Bunkie, LA, p. A265

CHASE, Pansy, Director Human Resources, Vidant Duplin Hospital, Kenansville, NC, p. A455

CHASE, Robert, M.D.
Chief Medical Officer, Westlake Hospital, Melrose Park, IL, p. A189
Physician Advisor, West Suburban Medical Center, Oak Park, IL, p. A192

CHASE, Susan, Vice President, Carolinas Rehabilitation, Charlotte, NC, p. A449

CHASIN, Marc, M.D., Chief Information Officer, St. Luke's Meridian Medical Center, ID, p. A168

CHASSE, Floyd, Vice President Human Resources, Willie D. Miller Eye Center, TN, p. A567

CHASTAIN, James G., FACHE, Director, Whitfield Medical Surgical Hospital, MS, p. A354

CHASTAIN, Katherine L, R.N., Chief Nursing Officer, Sacred Heart Hospital On The Gulf, Port St Joe, FL, p. A137

CHASTAIN, Stephen L, M.D., Chief Medical Officer, Healthsouth Rehabilitation Hospital At Martin Health, Stuart, FL, p. A139

CHASTANG, Mark J., M.P.H., Chief Executive Officer, Saint Elizabeths Hospital, Washington, DC, p. A116

CHASTANT, Lee, Chief Executive Officer, West Feliciana Parish Hospital, Saint Francisville, LA, p. A278

CHATANI, Kumar
Chief Information Officer, Mount Sinai Health System, Mount Sinai West Hospital, NY, p. A434
Chief Information Officer, Mount Sinai Health System, New York Eye And Ear Infirmary Of Mount Sinai, New York (Includes All Hospitals Located Within The Five Boroughs), NY, p. A434
Senior Vice President and Chief Information Officer Mount Sinai Health System, Mount Sinai Beth Israel Brooklyn, NY, p. A434
Senior Vice President and Chief Information Officer Mount Sinai Health System, Mount Sinai Queens, NY, p. A434

CHATELAIN, Alicia, Director Human Resource, Hood Memorial Hospital, Amite, LA, p. A262

CHATELAIN, Vincent, Director Business Development, River Oaks Child And Adolescent Hospital, LA, p. A276

CHATLEY, Alice M, R.N., MSN, Vice President Acute Care Services, Ssm Health St. Mary's Hospital - Jefferson City, Jefferson City, MO, p. A360

CHATMAN, Hubert, Chief Civilian Personnel, Wright Patterson Medical Center, Wright, OH, p. A494

CHATMAN, Jim, Chief Financial Officer, Maria Parham Medical Center, Henderson, NC, p. A454

CHATMAN, Mary, Ph.D.
Chief Executive Officer, Wellstar Kennestone Hospital, Marietta, GA, p. A157
Senior Vice President, Chief Operating Officer and Chief Nursing Officer, Memorial Children's Hospital, GA, p. A160

CHATTERJEE, Kanan, M.D., Chief of Staff, Lebanon Veterans Affairs Medical Center, Lebanon, PA, p. A529

CHATTERTON, Bryan, Chief Executive Officer, Kindred Hospital-Indianapolis, Indianapolis, IN, p. A207

CHAUDHARY, Shahid, M.D., Chief Medical Officer, Avera St. Luke's Hospital, Aberdeen, SD, p. A559

CHAUDHRY, Riaz, M.D., Chief Medical Officer, Mercy Health - St. Charles Hospital, Oregon, OH, p. A488

CHAUDIER, David, Chief Executive Officer, Lifecare Hospitals Of Wisconsin, Pewaukee, WI, p. A701

CHAUDRY, Zafar, M.D., Senior Vice President and Chief Information Officer, Seattle Children's Hospital, Seattle, WA, p. A676

CHAUHAN, Varun, Chief Executive Officer, Select Specialty Hospital - Boardman, Boardman, OH, p. A472

CHAUSSARD, David, Chief Executive Officer, Hillcrest Hospital Claremore, Claremore, OK, p. A497

CHAVEZ, Irene, Senior Vice President and Area Manager, Kaiser Permanente San Jose Medical Center, San Jose, CA, p. A86

CHAVEZ, Shari, Chief Nursing Officer, Swedish Medical Center, Englewood, CO, p. A100

CHAVEZ, Steven, Vice President Finance and Operations, Kettering Medical Center, Kettering, OH, p. A484

CHAVEZ, Virgil, Director Information Technology, Tsehootsooi Medical Center, Fort Defiance, AZ, p. A29

CHAVIS, Anthony D, M.D., Vice President Enterprise Medical Officer, Community Hospital Foundation, Community Hospital Of The Monterey Peninsula, Monterey, CA, p. A73

CHAWLA, Nikki, M.D., Medical Director, Alliancehealth Seminole, Seminole, OK, p. A506

CHAYER, Olivia, Director, Human Resources, York Hospital, York, ME, p. A286

CHAYKIN, Lee B., Chief Executive Officer, Aventura Hospital And Medical Center, Aventura, FL, p. A117

CHECK, Arthur, M.D., Chief Medical Officer, Story County Medical Center, Nevada, IA, p. A227

CHECKETTS, Lannie
Chief Financial Officer, Saint Alphonsus Medical Center - Nampa, Nampa, ID, p. A170
Chief Financial Officer, Saint Alphonsus Medical Center - Ontario, Ontario, OR, p. A515

CHEEK, Collin, Administrator, Baptist Memorial Hospital - Calhoun, Calhoun City, MS, p. A344

CHEEK, Holly, Vice President and Chief Nursing Officer, Columbus Regional Hospital, Columbus, IN, p. A201

CHEEK, Michael, Chief Financial Officer, Christus Good Shepherd Medical Center, TX, p. A622

CHEEK, Ramona, MS, R.N., Chief Nursing Officer, Mercy Health - Fairfield Hospital, Fairfield, OH, p. A482

CHEEMA, Linde, Vice President Human Resources, Sequoia Hospital, Redwood City, CA, p. A80

CHEESEMAN, Karen, Chief Executive Officer, Mackinac Straits Health System, Inc., Saint Ignace, MI, p. A322

CHEEVER, Liz, Administrator, Miracle Mile Medical Center, Los Angeles, CA, p. A68

CHEKURU, Naidu, M.D., Chief Medical Officer, Covenant Specialty Hospital, Lubbock, TX, p. A621

CHELLAPPA, Sheila, M.D., Chief of Staff, Coatesville Veterans Affairs Medical Center, Coatesville, PA, p. A523

CHEN, Bonny, M.D., Vice President and Chief Medical Officer, Amita Health Adventist Medical Center - Hinsdale, Hinsdale, IL, p. A186

CHEN, David, M.D.
Chief Medical Officer, Multicare Deaconess Hospital, Spokane, WA, p. A678
Chief Medical Officer, Multicare Valley Hospital, Spokane Valley, WA, p. A678

CHEN, Helen, M.D., Chief Medical Officer, Hebrew Rehabilitation Center, Roslindale, MA, p. A303

CHEN, Stephen, M.D., Chief Medicare, Alhambra Hospital Medical Center, Alhambra, CA, p. A50

CHEN, Van, M.D., Medical Director, Ballard Rehabilitation Hospital, San Bernardino, CA, p. A83

CHENEY, David, Chief Executive Officer, Sutter General Hospital, CA, p. A82

CHENG, Alice, President and Chief Executive Officer, Beverly Hospital, Montebello, CA, p. A73

CHENG, Rebecca
Chief Financial Officer, California Hospital Medical Center, Los Angeles, CA, p. A66
Chief Financial Officer, Glendale Memorial Hospital And Health Center, Glendale, CA, p. A60

CHENG, Ringo, Director Information Technology, Surgery Specialty Hospitals Of America, Pasadena, TX, p. A627

CHENNAULT, Paula, Administrator, Unity Psychiatric Care-Columbia, Columbia, TN, p. A568

CHENOWETH, Judy, Chief Nursing Officer, Russell County Hospital, Russell Springs, KY, p. A260

CHERAMIE, Bennett, Vice President Information Technology, Baton Rouge General Medical Center-Bluebonnet, LA, p. A263

CHERAY, James, M.D., Chief Medical Officer, Menorah Medical Center, Overland Park, KS, p. A243

CHERMSIDE, Paula L, Chief Executive Officer, Aspirus Ironwood Hospitals & Clinics, Inc., Ironwood, MI, p. A316

CHERMSIDE, Paula L., Chief Executive Officer, Aspirus Ironwood Hospitals & Clinics, Inc., Ironwood, MI, p. A316

CHERONE, Nancy, Executive Director and Administrator, Nazareth Hospital, Philadelphia, PA, p. A535

CHERRY, Deano, Chief Information Officer, Upmc Kane, Kane, PA, p. A528

CHERRY, Jean, Executive Vice President, Commonwealth Regional Specialty Hospital, Bowling Green, KY, p. A249

CHERRY, Jonathan M., President and Chief Executive Officer, Lifestream Behavioral Center, Leesburg, FL, p. A128

CHERRY, Kris, Ph.D., R.N., Chief Nursing Officer, Saint Francis Hospital-Bartlett, Bartlett, TN, p. A566

CHERRY, Michael, Chief Financial Officer, Tennova Healthcare-Lafollette Medical Center, La Follette, TN, p. A573

CHERRY, Robert, M.D., Chief Medical and Quality Officer, Mattel Children's Hospital, CA, p. A69

CHERRY, Troy, Chief Financial Officer, Schick Shadel Hospital, Seattle, WA, p. A676

CHESLEK, Ingrid, R.N., Chief Nursing Officer, Mary Free Bed Rehabilitation Hospital, Grand Rapids, MI, p. A314

CHESLEY, Jeanine, Chief Executive Officer, New England Rehabilitation Hospital Of Portland, Portland, ME, p. A285

CHESLEY, Judy S, M.D., Chief of Staff, Sanford Luverne Medical Center, Luverne, MN, p. A334

CHESLEY, Randy, Director Information Technology, Copley Hospital, Morrisville, VT, p. A654

CHESLEY, Walter, Senior Vice President Human Resources, Hcmc Department Of Pediatrics, MN, p. A335

CHESNOS, Richard C, Senior Vice President Finance and Chief Financial Officer, St. Clair Hospital, Pittsburgh, PA, p. A537

CHESSARE, John B., M.D., M.P.H., FACHE, President and Chief Executive Officer, Greater Baltimore Medical Center, Baltimore, MD, p. A287

CHESSON, Andrew, Chief Medical Officer, Catawba Valley Medical Center, Hickory, NC, p. A454

CHESSUM, George
Senior Vice President and Chief Information Officer, Community First Medical Center, Chicago, IL, p. A176
Senior Vice President Information Systems and Chief Information Officer, Presence Saint Joseph Hospital, Chicago, IL, p. A178
Vice President Information Systems, Presence Saint Francis Hospital, Evanston, IL, p. A182

CHESTER, Julie, Vice President Human Resources, University Macdonald Women's Hospital, OH, p. A477

CHESTER, Linnes L, USAF, MSC, Administrator, Mike O'Callaghan Federal Hospital, Nellis Afb, NV, p. A395

CHESTER, William, Manager Human Resources, Grand Junction Veterans Health Care System, Grand Junction, CO, p. A101

CHESTNUT-RAULS, Monica, Vice President Human Resources, Peconic Bay Medical Center, Riverhead, NY, p. A441

CHEUNG, Alan, M.D., Vice President Medical Affairs, Adventist Health Castle, Kailua, HI, p. A165

CHEUNG, Marilou, Assistant Administrator Finance, Kaiser Permanente Woodland Hills Medical Center, Los Angeles, CA, p. A67

CHEUNG, Raymond, M.D., Chief of Staff, San Ramon Regional Medical Center, San Ramon, CA, p. A88

CHEVERE, Carlos, M.D., Medical Director, I. Gonzalez Martinez Oncologic Hospital, Hato Rey, PR, p. A713

CHEYNET, Sandee, Vice President Administrative Services, Bluefield Regional Medical Center, Bluefield, WV, p. A681

CHHABRA, Ankit, Director Finance, Cleveland Clinic Fairview Hospital, Cleveland, OH, p. A476

CHIACCHIARO, Peter, Vice President Human Resources, St. Joseph Hospital, Bethpage, NY, p. A422

CHIANESE, Charles, Vice President, Chief Operating Officer, Children's Specialized Hospital, NJ, p. A408

CHIANTELLA, Christopher, M.D., Chief Medical Officer, Inova Loudoun Hospital, Leesburg, VA, p. A660

CHIAVETTA, Robert, Vice President Finance, United Memorial Medical Center-North Street, NY, p. A422

CHIBAYA, Daniel, Chief Information Officer, Fremont Medical Center, CA, p. A72

CHICK, Melanie, Chief Executive Officer, Baylor Medical Center At Trophy Club, Trophy Club, TX, p. A640

CHICKEN, Kurt, Director Support Services, Gundersen Palmer Lutheran Hospital And Clinics, West Union, IA, p. A231

CHIDESTER, Annamarie, R.N., Vice President, Patient Care Services, St. Joseph's Hospital Of Buckhannon, Buckhannon, WV, p. A682

CHIEFFO, Ron, Chief Information Officer, Colorado River Medical Center, Needles, CA, p. A75

CHILCOTT, Stephen, Associate Director Human Resources, University Of California Davis Children's Hospital, CA, p. A82

CHILD, Clint L, R.N., Chief Nursing Officer, Saint Alphonsus Medical Center - Nampa, Nampa, ID, p. A170

CHILDERS, Bethany, Director Human Resources, Fremont Health, Fremont, NE, p. A384

CHILDERS, Christy, Director Information Technology, P & S Surgical Hospital, Monroe, LA, p. A274

CHILDERS, James R, Vice President & Chief Financial Officer, Gibson General Hospital, Princeton, IN, p. A213

CHILDERS, Linda, Director Human Resources, Wallowa Memorial Hospital, Enterprise, OR, p. A512

CHILDERS, Scott W., Administrator, Mercy Hospital Lebanon, Lebanon, MO, p. A363

CHILDERS, Susan M., CPA, Chief Executive Officer, Mee Memorial Hospital, King City, CA, p. A62

CHILDS, Joe, M.D., Vice President Medical Services, East Tennessee Children's Hospital, Knoxville, TN, p. A572

CHILDS, Michelle, Chief Human Resources Officer, Salinas Valley Memorial Healthcare System, Salinas, CA, p. A83

CHILES, Kevin, Vice President Human Resources, Hutchinson Regional Medical Center, Hutchinson, KS, p. A237

CHILES, Morton, M.D., Chief Medical Officer, Novant Health Uva Health System Culpeper Medical Center, Culpeper, VA, p. A657

CHILESE, Melody, Chief Nurse Executive, Hawthorn Children Psychiatric Hospital, Saint Louis, MO, p. A368

CHILESKI, Andy, Chief Information Officer and Vice President Facilities, Berger Health System, Circleville, OH, p. A476

CHILL, Martha O'Regan
Chief Information Officer, Bristol Regional Medical Center, Bristol, TN, p. A566
Interim Chief Information Officer, Hancock County Hospital, Sneedville, TN, p. A580

CHILSON, Terrance, Chief of Staff, Tyler Memorial Hospital, Tunkhannock, PA, p. A542

CHILTON, Bryan, Director Information Systems, Navarro Regional Hospital, Corsicana, TX, p. A595

CHILTON, Hal, Senior Vice President and Chief Operating Officer, Adventist Health St. Helena, Saint Helena, CA, p. A82

CHIN, Ellyn, Vice President Finance, Gottlieb Memorial Hospital, Melrose Park, IL, p. A189

CHINBURG, Paul, M.D., Medical Director, Lane County Hospital, Dighton, KS, p. A234

CHING, Angelica
Director Information Systems, Garfield Medical Center, Monterey Park, CA, p. A73
Director Information Systems, Monterey Park Hospital, Monterey Park, CA, p. A73

CHINN, Tammie
Chief Human Resource Officer, Williamson Memorial Hospital, Williamson, WV, p. A688
Director Marketing and Public Relations, Plateau Medical Center, Oak Hill, WV, p. A685

CHINN, Terri, Vice President Finance, St. Mary's Hospital And Medical Center, Grand Junction, CO, p. A101

CHINNOCK, Rachel, Chief Human Resources Officer, Latimer County General Hospital, Wilburton, OK, p. A510

CHINNOCK, Richard, Chief Medical Officer, LLUCH, Loma Linda University Children's Hospital, Loma Linda, CA, p. A64

CHIOLO, Denise, Chief Human Resources Officer, Phoenixville Hospital, Phoenixville, PA, p. A537

CHIPMAN, Glen, Chief Financial Officer, Healthsource Saginaw, Inc., Saginaw, MI, p. A322

CHIRICHELLA, Joseph, President and Chief Executive Officer, Deborah Heart And Lung Center, Browns Mills, NJ, p. A403

CHISHOLM, Sharon, Entity Human Resource Officer, Texas Health Presbyterian Hospital Allen, Allen, TX, p. A582

CHISSELL, Herbert G, M.D., Chief Medical Officer, Torrance State Hospital, Torrance, PA, p. A542

CHITCHYAN, Ara, M.D., Medical Director, Roosevelt Warm Springs Rehabilitation Hospital - Rehab, Warm Springs, GA, p. A162

CHIUSANO, Jennifer, R.N., Chief Nursing Officer, Saint Francis Hospital, Memphis, TN, p. A576

CHIVERS, John
Chief Financial Officer, Ridgecrest Regional Hospital, Ridgecrest, CA, p. A80
Senior Vice President Finance, Sierra View Medical Center, Porterville, CA, p. A79

CHMURA, David, Chief Information Officer, Copper Queen Community Hospital, Bisbee, AZ, p. A28

CHOATE, Charlotte, Director Information Systems, University Hospital Summerville, Augusta, GA, p. A148

CHOATE, Matthew, Chief Nursing Officer, The University Of Vermont Health Network Central Vermont Medical Center, Berlin, VT, p. A653

CHOCKLETT, Wyatt, Chief Operating Officer, Doctors Hospital Of Sarasota, Sarasota, FL, p. A138

CHOINIERE, Leon, Vice President, Chief Financial Officer, St. Mary Medical Center, Long Beach, CA, p. A65

CHOINKA, Keith A, Vice President Information Systems and Chief Information Officer, St. Joseph Hospital, Nashua, NH, p. A400

CHOKSHI, Sushil, M.D., Chief Medical Officer, Faith Community Hospital, Jacksboro, TX, p. A616

CHOLGER, Dave, Chief Financial Officer, Woodlawn Hospital, Rochester, IN, p. A214

CHOLKA, Nancy, R.N., Chief Nursing Officer, Post Acute Medical Specialty Hospital Of Milwaukee, Greenfield, WI, p. A694

CHONG, Johnnette, Chief Financial Officer, Los Angeles Community Hospital Of Norwalk, CA, p. A68

CHOPIN, Candice, Vice President Human Resources, Women's And Children's Hospital, Lafayette, LA, p. A272

CHORD, Ginger, Coordinator Human Resources, Sturgis Regional Hospital, Sturgis, SD, p. A564

CHOREY, Raymond M., President and Chief Executive Officer, Southeastern Ohio Regional Medical Center, Cambridge, OH, p. A473

CHOU, David, Vice President, Chief Information and Digital Officer, Children's Mercy Hospital Kansas City, Kansas City, MO, p. A361

CHOU, Rebecca
Director Information Systems, Palestine Regional Medical Center-East, Palestine, TX, p. A626
Directory Information Systems, Palestine Regional Medical Center, Palestine, TX, p. A626

CHOUDHURY, Golam, Chief of Staff, Desert Springs Hospital Medical Center, Las Vegas, NV, p. A394

CHOUDHURY, Seleem, R.N., MSN, Chief Nursing Officer, Northeastern Vermont Regional Hospital, Saint Johnsbury, VT, p. A654

CHOY, Ann N., Manager Human Resources and Payroll, Kuakini Medical Center, Honolulu, HI, p. A164

CHOZINSKI, Joseph P, M.D., Deputy Commander Clinical Services, Brooke Army Medical Center, Fort Sam Houston, TX, p. A603

CHRICEOL, Earlene, Chief Nursing Officer, Richardson Medical Center, Rayville, LA, p. A278

CHRISTENSEN, Carl
Senior Vice President and Chief Information Officer, Northwestern Memorial HealthCare, Stone Institute Of Psychiatry, IL, p. A178
Senior Vice President, Chief Information Officer, Northwestern Medicine Kishwaukee Hospital, Dekalb, IL, p. A181

CHRISTENSEN, Claudia, Director, Human Resources, Mills-Peninsula Medical Center, CA, p. A53

CHRISTENSEN, Connie, Chief Financial Officer, Morrill County Community Hospital, Bridgeport, NE, p. A382

CHRISTENSEN, David, M.D., Senior Vice President and Chief Medical Officer, Valley Children's Healthcare, Madera, CA, p. A71

CHRISTENSEN, Elizabeth B, Director Human Resources, Mercy Hospital Of Portland, Portland, ME, p. A285

CHRISTENSEN, G N, M.D., Chief Medical Officer, William Bee Ririe Hospital, Ely, NV, p. A392

CHRISTENSEN, Gwen, Vice President, Finance, Aurora Baycare Medical Center, Green Bay, WI, p. A693

CHRISTENSEN, Jeffrey, Chief Executive Officer, Encompass Health Rehabilitation Institute Of Tucson, Tucson, AZ, p. A37

CHRISTENSEN, Kim, Interim Chief Nursing Executive, Sheridan Community Hospital, Sheridan, MI, p. A323

CHRISTENSEN, Mark
Chief Financial Officer, Weiser Memorial Hospital, Weiser, ID, p. A172
Director, Finance, Cassia Regional Hospital, Burley, ID, p. A168

CHRISTENSEN, Marti, Director of Psychiatric Nursing, Douglas County Community Mental Health Center, Omaha, NE, p. A388

CHRISTENSEN, Scott, FACHE, Chief Executive Officer, The King's Daughters Hospital, MS, p. A346

CHRISTENSEN, Todd, Vice President, Finance, Grand Itasca Clinic And Hospital, Grand Rapids, MN, p. A332

CHRISTENSEN, Troy, Chief Financial Officer, Madison Memorial Hospital, Rexburg, ID, p. A171

CHRISTENSEN, W R, M.D., Chief of Staff, Ut Health Pittsburg, Pittsburg, TX, p. A628

CHRISTENSEN-MORES, Donna, JD, Director Human Resources, Myrtue Medical Center, Harlan, IA, p. A224

CHRISTENSON, Ron, Chief Financial Officer, Morris County Hospital, Council Grove, KS, p. A234

CHRISTENSON, Shannon, Director Human Resources, Aurora West Allis Medical Center, West Allis, WI, p. A706

CHRISTIAN, Bruce C.
Chief Executive Officer, Amita Health Adventist Medical Center Bolingbrook, Bolingbrook, IL, p. A174
President and Chief Executive Officer, Amita Health Adventist Medical Center Glenoaks, Glendale Heights, IL, p. A184

CHRISTIAN, Glenn, Administrator, Mayo Clinic Health System In Cannon Falls, Cannon Falls, MN, p. A329

CHRISTIAN, Greg
Senior Vice President, Area Manager - San Bernardino County Area, Kaiser Permanente Ontario Medical Center, CA, p. A58
Sr Vice President, Area Manager - San Bernardino County Area, Kaiser Permanente Ontario Medical Center, CA, p. A58

CHRISTIAN, Karolyne, Director Human Resources, Byrd Regional Hospital, Leesville, LA, p. A272

CHRISTIAN, Lynn, R.N., MSN, Division Director, Acute Care Nursing, Centracare Health-Monticello, Monticello, MN, p. A336

CHRISTIAN, Michael, Chief Operating Officer, St. John Sapulpa, Sapulpa, OK, p. A506

CHRISTIANO, Barbara, Vice President, Patient Care Services and Chief Nursing Officer, Penn Medicine Princeton Medical Center, Plainsboro, NJ, p. A410

CHRISTIANSEN, Anne, Chief Financial Officer, Pioneer Memorial Hospital And Health Services, Viborg, SD, p. A565

CHRISTIANSEN, Hilary, Chief Financial Officer, George C Grape Community Hospital, Hamburg, IA, p. A223

CHRISTIANSEN, Keith, Chief Nursing Officer, Select Specialty Hospital-Erie, Erie, PA, p. A525

CHRISTIANSEN, Lia
Chief Operating Officer, Acute Care Hospitals, Fairview Lakes Health Services, Wyoming, MN, p. A342
Chief Operating Officer, Acute Care Hospitals, Fairview Northland Medical Center, Princeton, MN, p. A337
Chief Operating Officer, Acute Care Hospitals, St. John's Hospital, Maplewood, MN, p. A334
Chief Operating Officer, Acute Care Hospitals, St. Joseph's Hospital, Saint Paul, MN, p. A339
Chief Operating Officer, Acute Care Hospitals, Woodwinds Health Campus, Woodbury, MN, p. A342

CHRISTIANSEN, Patrick, Ph.D., Chief Executive Officer, Inova Fairfax Hospital For Children, VA, p. A657

CHRISTIANSEN, Sara, Interim Director Human Resources, Ridgeview Sibley Medical Center, Arlington, MN, p. A327

CHRISTIANSON, Chad, Chief Executive Officer, West Marion Community Hospital, FL, p. A133

CHRISTIANSON, Delano, Administrator, Centracare Health-Sauk Centre, Sauk Centre, MN, p. A340

CHRISTIE, Janet L., Senior Vice President Human Resources, Uf Health Shands Rehab Hospital, FL, p. A124

CHRISTINE, Gerald, Chief Financial Officer, Lakewood Ranch Medical Center, Bradenton, FL, p. A118

CHRISTION, Lydia, Director Human Resources, Encompass Health Rehabilitation Hospital Of Dothan, Dothan, AL, p. A17

CHRISTISON, George, M.D., Medical Director, Patton State Hospital, Patton, CA, p. A78

CHRISTMAN, Lawrence, Chief Financial Officer and Chief Operating Officer, Riverview Health, Noblesville, IN, p. A213

CHRISTMAN, Thomas C, Director Plant Operations, Kindred Hospital St. Louis-St. Anthony'S, MO, p. A368

CHRISTNER, Jane, Chief Nursing Officer, Mclaren Thumb Region, Bad Axe, MI, p. A308

CHRISTOPH, Rebecca, Director Nursing and Patient Care Services, Mid-Valley Hospital, Omak, WA, p. A674

CHRISTOPHEL, Randal, President and Chief Executive Officer, Goshen Health, Goshen, IN, p. A205

CHRISTOPHER, Candi, CPA, Chief Financial Officer, Stonesprings Hospital Center, Dulles, VA, p. A657

CHRISTOPHER, Sue, Vice President, Human Resources, Baptist Health Floyd, New Albany, IN, p. A212

CHRISTOPHERSEN, Kristin, Chief Nursing Officer, Fountain Valley Regional Hospital And Medical Center, Fountain Valley, CA, p. A58

CHRISTY, Rose, Executive Director of Medical Services, Hamilton Center, Terre Haute, IN, p. A215

CHU, Betty, M.D., Chief Medical Officer and Vice President of Medical Affairs, Henry Ford West Bloomfield Hospital, West Bloomfield, MI, p. A325

CHU, Edward, Chief Financial Officer, Leahi Hospital, Honolulu, HI, p. A164

CHUA, Jesus, M.D., Chief of Staff, Franklin Foundation Hospital, Franklin, LA, p. A267

CHUE, Bevins, M.D., Medical Director, Healthsouth Desert Canyon Rehabilitation Hospital, Las Vegas, NV, p. A394

CHUGDEN, Robert, M.D., Chief Medical Officer, West Jefferson Medical Center, Marrero, LA, p. A273

CHUKWUMA, Lilian, Chief Financial Officer, United Medical Center, Washington, DC, p. A116

CHULICK, Michele, President and Chief Executive Officer, Wyoming Medical Center, Casper, WY, p. A707

CHUN, Ryan, Information Resources Management, San Francisco Va Medical Center, San Francisco, CA, p. A86

CHUNG, Esther, Chief Operating Officer, St. David's Rehabilitation Center, TX, p. A586

CHUNG, Maria, CPA, Director Fiscal Services, Shriners Hospitals For Children-Boston, Boston, MA, p. A297

CHUNG, Michael, Chief Financial Officer, Greater El Monte Community Hospital, South El Monte, CA, p. A90

CHUNG, William, M.D., Chief of Staff, Chinese Hospital, San Francisco, CA, p. A85

CHUNN, Ashley, Director of Nursing, Atmore Community Hospital, Atmore, AL, p. A14

CHURCH, Brian, Senior Vice President and Chief Financial Officer, Phoebe North, GA, p. A145

CHURCH, Kim
Manager Human Resources, G. Werber Bryan Psychiatric Hospital, Columbia, SC, p. A551

Manager Human Resources, William S. Hall Psychiatric Institute, Columbia, SC, p. A551

CHURCH, Rhonda, Director Human Resources, Bastrop Rehabilitation Hospital, Monroe, LA, p. A274

CHURCHILL, Brigitte, Director of Human Resources, Memorial Satilla Health, Waycross, GA, p. A163

CHURCHILL, Larry, Director Information Services, Alliancehealth Woodward, Woodward, OK, p. A510

CHURCHILL, Sandi, Vice President Business Development and Operations, Professional Services, Advocate Good Samaritan Hospital, Downers Grove, IL, p. A181

CHURCHILL, Timothy A.
Interim Chief Executive Officer, Franklin Memorial Hospital, Farmington, ME, p. A284
President, Stephens Memorial Hospital, Norway, ME, p. A285

CHURCHWELL, Kevin B, M.D., Chief Operating Officer and Executive Vice President Health Affairs, Boston Children's Hospital, Boston, MA, p. A296

CIAMPA, Amy, Chief Financial Officer, Park Royal Hospital, Fort Myers, FL, p. A123

CIAMPA, Steve, Vice President Finance, Porter Medical Center, Middlebury, VT, p. A653

CIANCIOTTO CROYLE, Allison, Vice President of Human Resources, Mercy Medical Center, Rockville Centre, NY, p. A442

CIANFLONE, Laura, Director Human Resources, Kenmore Mercy Hospital, Kenmore, NY, p. A428

CIAREFELLA, Donna, Director Human Resources, Vibra Hospital Of Western Massachusetts-Central Campus, MA, p. A304

CICCARELLI, John, Director Information Technology, Parkview Community Hospital Medical Center, Riverside, CA, p. A81

CICCARELLI, Thomas, Chief Information Officer, East Orange General Hospital, East Orange, NJ, p. A404

CICCONE, Josie, Director, Human Resources, Garden City Hospital, Garden City, MI, p. A313

CICERI, David P, M.D., Chief Medical Officer, Baylor Scott And White Continuing Care Hospital, Temple, TX, p. A638

CICIRETTI, Mary Louise, Director Human Resources, Riddle Hospital, Media, PA, p. A531

CIENCEWICKI, Michael, M.D., Vice President Medical Affairs, Perth Amboy Division, NJ, p. A410

CIHA, Clayton, President and Chief Executive Officer, Alexian Brothers Behavioral Health Hospital, Hoffman Estates, IL, p. A186

CIHAK, Scott A., President and Chief Executive Officer, Tristar Centennial Women's & Children'S, TN, p. A577

CIMA, Robert R., M.D., Medical Director, Hospital Operations, Mayo Eugenio Litta Children's Hospital, MN, p. A338

CIMALA, Derek W.
Interim Chief Executive Officer, Bluefield Regional Medical Center, Bluefield, WV, p. A681
Interim Chief Executive Officer, Plateau Medical Center, Oak Hill, WV, p. A685

CIMINO, Michael A., Jr, Chief Financial Officer, Banner Behavioral Health Hospital - Scottsdale, Scottsdale, AZ, p. A35

CIMMINO, Denise, MSN, R.N., Assistant Vice President, Nursing and Patient Care Services, Carepoint Health Christ Hospital, Jersey City, NJ, p. A406

CINTRON, Jacob, FACHE, President and Chief Executive Officer, University Medical Center Of El Paso, El Paso, TX, p. A603

CIOFFI, Cheryl, R.N., Senior Vice President Patient Care Services and Chief Nursing Officer, Frederick Regional Health System, Frederick, MD, p. A291

CIOTA, Mark, M.D., Chief Executive Officer, Mayo Clinic Health System - Albert Lea And Austin, MN, p. A327

CIRALDO, Lou, Information Services Representative, University Hospitals Geauga Medical Center, Chardon, OH, p. A474

CIRBA, Michael, Chief Information Officer, Good Shepherd Specialty Hospital, Bethlehem, PA, p. A520

CIRO, Maria, Director Human Resources, Acuity Specialty Hospital Of New Jersey, Atlantic City, NJ, p. A402

CIROCCO, Anthony, Chief Financial Officer, Dignity Health Arizona General Hospital, Laveen, AZ, p. A31

CIRONE, Laura, Manager Human Resources, Rochelle Community Hospital, Rochelle, IL, p. A194

CIRPILI, Avni, Senior Vice President, Chief Nursing Officer, Menninger Clinic, Houston, TX, p. A612

CITA, Bob, Chief Information Officer, Searhc Mt. Edgecumbe Hospital, Sitka, AK, p. A27

CITAK, Michael, M.D., Chief Medical Officer, Lake Cumberland Regional Hospital, Somerset, KY, p. A260

CITRO, Tina, R.N., Chief Nursing Officer, Vice President, Patient Services, Wellspan Ephrata Community Hospital, Ephrata, PA, p. A525

CIUFO, Donna, R.N., Vice President and Chief Nurse Executive, Hackensack Meridian Health Southern Ocean Medical Center, Manahawkin, NJ, p. A407

CIVIC, Dave, M.D., Associate Director Clinical Services, U.S. Public Health Service Phoenix Indian Medical Center, Phoenix, AZ, p. A34

CIVITELLO, Dean
Vice President Human Resources, Saint Joseph's Medical Center, Yonkers, NY, p. A446
Vice President, Human Resources, Public Relations and Development, The University Of Vermont Health Network-Champlain Valley Physicians Hospital, Plattsburgh, NY, p. A440

CLAASSENS, Nicolise, Nurse Executive, West Central Georgia Regional Hospital, Columbus, GA, p. A151

CLABAUGH, John, Director Human Resources, Saint Luke's East Hospital, Lee's Summit, MO, p. A363

CLABUESCH, Paul, President and Chief Executive Officer, Harbor Beach Community Hospital, Harbor Beach, MI, p. A315

CLACK, Deborah, Chief Nursing Officer, Hunt Regional Medical Center, Greenville, TX, p. A608

CLAEYS, David, FACHE, Chief Executive Officer, Beaumont Hospital - Dearborn, Dearborn, MI, p. A310

CLAIR OLIVER, Delores, Chief Clinical Officer and Chief Operating Officer, Bridgepoint Hospital Capitol Hill, Washington, DC, p. A115

CLANCY, Mikki, Chief Operating Officer, Miami Valley Hospital South, OH, p. A480

CLANCY, Patricia, M.D., Director Medical Services, Maniilaq Health Center, Kotzebue, AK, p. A26

CLAPP, Ann R, Director Human Resources, Encompass Health Rehabilitation Hospital Of Texarkana, Texarkana, TX, p. A639

CLAPP, Denise
Chief Nursing Officer, Lourdes Counseling Center, Richland, WA, p. A676
Chief Nursing Officer, Lourdes Medical Center, Pasco, WA, p. A674

CLAPP, Nicole, R.N., MSN, FACHE, President and Chief Executive Officer, Grant Regional Health Center, Lancaster, WI, p. A676

CLAPP, William, M.D., Chief of Medical Staff, Methodist Hospital Union County, Morganfield, KY, p. A258

CLARK, Allan W, M.D., Medical Director, Southwood Psychiatric Hospital, Pittsburgh, PA, p. A537

CLARK, Ashley, Coordinator Human Resources, Noland Hospital Birmingham, Birmingham, AL, p. A14

CLARK, Ben, Vice President and Chief Information Officer, Lynchburg General Hospital, VA, p. A660

CLARK, Christopher, D.O., President and Chief Executive Officer, Saint Vincent Hospital, Erie, PA, p. A525

CLARK, Dale
Chief Operating Officer, Holston Valley Medical Center, Kingsport, TN, p. A572
President, Mountain View Regional Medical Center, Norton, VA, p. A663

CLARK, Dave, FACHE, Interim Chief Executive Officer, Hardeman County Memorial Hospital, Quanah, TX, p. A629

CLARK, Debra, Chief Nursing Officer, Bayfront Health Port Charlotte, Port Charlotte, FL, p. A137

CLARK, Denise, Chief Nursing Officer, Holy Cross Hospital, Taos, NM, p. A420

CLARK, Ed, M.D., Chief Medical Officer, Primary Children's Hospital, Salt Lake City, UT, p. A650

CLARK, Eileen, Vice President Information Services, General Hospital, WV, p. A682

CLARK, Janice, Manager Human Resources, Garfield Park Hospital, Chicago, IL, p. A176

CLARK, Jason, Director Quality Improvement, Risk Management and Information System, Greenwood County Hospital, Eureka, KS, p. A235

CLARK, Jeff, Director Information Systems, Graham Regional Medical Center, Graham, TX, p. A607

CLARK, Jeffrey, Chief Executive Officer, Cornerstone Hospital Of Southwest Louisiana, Sulphur, LA, p. A280

CLARK, Jeffrey A, Vice President Human Resources, Kadlec Regional Medical Center, Richland, WA, p. A676

CLARK, Jeremy L., Market Chief Executive Officer, Hilton Head Hospital, Hilton Head Island, SC, p. A554

CLARK, Judith, Chief Financial Officer, Takoma Regional Hospital, Greeneville, TN, p. A570

CLARK, Karen, MS, R.N.
Vice President Operations, Advocate South Suburban Hospital, Hazel Crest, IL, p. A185
Director Administrative Services, Sonoma Developmental Center, Eldridge, CA, p. A57
Vice President Patient Care Services, St. Mary's Regional Medical Center, Lewiston, ME, p. A284

CLARK, Kent, M.D., Chief Medical Affairs and Quality, Waldo County General Hospital Maine Health, Belfast, ME, p. A283

CLARK, Lisa, Director Human Resources, Willamette Valley Medical Center, Mcminnville, OR, p. A514

COATES, Jennifer, Coordinator Information Technology, Purcell Municipal Hospital, Purcell, OK, p. A506

COATES, Robert, M.D., Vice President, Medical Affairs, Hunterdon Medical Center, Flemington, NJ, p. A405

COATS, Daniel J, Vice President Operations, Mercy Hospital Ada, Ada, OK, p. A495

COATS, Daniel J., Interim Chief Executive Officer, Holdenville General Hospital, Holdenville, OK, p. A500

COATS, John, M.D., Chief Medical Staff, Morehouse General Hospital, Bastrop, LA, p. A263

COATS, Kevin
Chief Financial Officer, Baylor Medical Center At Frisco, Frisco, TX, p. A606
Chief Operating Officer and Chief Financial Officer, Baylor Medical Center At Frisco, Frisco, TX, p. A606

COBARRUBIAS, Samuel, M.D., Chief of Staff, Clinch Memorial Hospital, Homerville, GA, p. A155

COBB, April, Chief Nursing Officer, Encompass Health Lakeshore Rehabilitation Hospital, Birmingham, AL, p. A14

COBB, Heidi, R.N., Chief Nursing Officer, Medical Arts Hospital, Lamesa, TX, p. A618

COBB, Janice M, R.N., Chief Nursing Officer, Nashville Campus, TN, p. A577

COBB, Jason E., FACHE, Chief Executive Officer, Rapides Regional Medical Center, Alexandria, LA, p. A262

COBB, Jeff, Information Technologist, Guthrie County Hospital, Guthrie Center, IA, p. A223

COBB, Lindsay, Director Human Resources, Cypress Grove Behavioral Health, Bastrop, LA, p. A263

COBB, Stephen, M.D., Chief Medical Officer, Rocky Mountain Hospital For Children, CO, p. A99

COBB, Tammy, Chief Financial Officer, Tennova Healthcare-Shelbyville, Shelbyville, TN, p. A579

COBBLE, Emlyn, Vice President and Chief Support Officer, Peninsula Hospital, TN, p. A572

COBBS, Wendy, Director of Human Resources, Promise Hospital Of Baton Rouge - Mid-City Campus, LA, p. A264

COBURN, Meridith
Vice President Information Services, Saint Francis Heart Hospital, OK, p. A509
Vice President, Information Systems, Saint Francis Hospital South, Tulsa, OK, p. A509

COBURN, Paul, Chief Financial Officer, Cypress Grove Behavioral Health, Bastrop, LA, p. A263

COBURN, Thomas C., M.D., Chief Medical Officer, Middle Park Medical Center - Granby, CO, p. A102

COCCA, Lisa, Chief Executive Officer, Belmont Pines Hospital, Youngstown, OH, p. A494

COCCHI, Dean, Chief Financial Officer, Kindred Hospital Ocala, Ocala, FL, p. A133

COCH, William, M.D., Medical Director, Jones Memorial Hospital, Wellsville, NY, p. A445

COCHRAN, Avril, R.N., Vice President Patient Care Services, North Country Hospital And Health Center, Newport, VT, p. A654

COCHRAN, Bill, Interim Chief Executive Officer, Oswego Community Hospital, Oswego, KS, p. A243

COCHRAN, Dan, Chief Operating Officer, Mountain River Birthing And Surgery Center, Blackfoot, ID, p. A167

COCHRAN, Daniel, Vice President and Chief Financial Officer, Adventist Healthcare Shady Grove Medical Center, Rockville, MD, p. A294

COCHRAN, Janice, R.N., Director Patient Care, Christus Dubuis Hospital Of Paris, Paris, TX, p. A627

COCHRAN, Kenneth, R.N., FACHE, President and Chief Executive Officer, Opelousas General Health System-South Campus, LA, p. A277

COCHRAN, Lena, Director of Finance, Highlands-Cashiers Hospital, Highlands, NC, p. A455

COCHRAN, Lynn, R.N., System Vice President Operations,Chief Nursing Officer, Edward Hospital, Naperville, IL, p. A190

COCHRAN, Sherry, Manager Human Resources, Cascade Behavioral Hospital, Tukwila, WA, p. A679

COCHRAN, Willie, M.D., Jr, Chief of Staff, Southern Regional Medical Center, Riverdale, GA, p. A159

COCHRANE, Andrew S., Chief Executive Officer, Maple Grove Hospital, Maple Grove, MN, p. A334

COCHRANE, Donna R., Chief Nursing Officer, Liberty Regional Medical Center, Hinesville, GA, p. A154

COCHRANE, Robert K., Vice President Finance and Chief Financial Officer, Frisbie Memorial Hospital, Rochester, NH, p. A401

COCKAYNE, Heather, Chief Financial Officer, Clifton-Fine Hospital, Star Lake, NY, p. A443

COCKFIELD, Costa, Chief Nursing Officer, Carolinas Hospital System, Florence, SC, p. A552

COCKING, Kathy, R.N., Director of Clinical Services, Carson Valley Medical Center, Gardnerville, NV, p. A393

COCKRELL, Christopher, Executive Director Human Resources, Providence Hospital, Mobile, AL, p. A20

COCKRELL, Dennis, Director Human Resources, Gritman Medical Center, Moscow, ID, p. A170

COCKRELL, Tim, Chief Executive Officer, Patients Choice Medical Center Of Smith County, Raleigh, MS, p. A352

COCO, Jeffrey, M.D., Chief Medical Officer, Touro Rehabilitation Center, LA, p. A276

CODER, Charles
Vice President, Novant Health Uva Health System Haymarket Medical Center, Haymarket, VA, p. A659
Vice President, Novant Health Uva Health System Prince William Medical Center, Manassas, VA, p. A661

CODER, Denise, Chief Human Resource Officer, Cass County Memorial Hospital, Atlantic, IA, p. A217

CODY, Robert J., MD, MBA, Interim President and Chief Executive Officer, Hunterdon Medical Center, Flemington, NJ, p. A405

COE, Jason, M.D., Medical Director, Covington Behavior Health, Covington, LA, p. A266

COE, Susan
Regional Vice President Human Resources, University Of Maryland Shore Medical Center At Dorchester, Cambridge, MD, p. A290
Regional Vice President Human Resources, University Of Maryland Shore Medical Center At Easton, Easton, MD, p. A291
Vice President Human Resources, University Of Maryland Shore Medical Center At Chestertown, Chestertown, MD, p. A290

COELLO, Jennifer, Chief Operating Officer, Clinch Valley Medical Center, Richlands, VA, p. A664

COEN, Vickie, Chief Clinical Officer and Nurse Executive, Pana Community Hospital, Pana, IL, p. A192

COFFEE, Paula, Director Human Resources, St. Mary's Of Michigan, Saginaw, MI, p. A322

COFFEE, Robert, Chief Information Officer, Creek Nation Community Hospital, Okemah, OK, p. A502

COFFELL, Randy, Manager Human Resources, Mid-Valley Hospital, Omak, WA, p. A674

COFFEY, Douglas W, R.N., MSN, Chief Nursing Officer, St. Mary's Regional Medical Center, Enid, OK, p. A498

COFFEY, Joseph, Director Facility Administration, Rochester Psychiatric Center, Rochester, NY, p. A441

COFFEY, Judy, R.N.
Senior Vice President and Area Manager, Kaiser Permanente San Rafael Medical Center, San Rafael, CA, p. A87
Senior Vice President and Area Manager, Kaiser Permanente Santa Rosa Medical Center, Santa Rosa, CA, p. A89

COFFEY, Kevin, Chief Executive Officer, Winner Regional Healthcare Center, Winner, SD, p. A565

COFFEY, M. Justin, Vice President and Chief Information Officer, Medical Director Center for Brain Stimulation, Menninger Clinic, Houston, TX, p. A612

COFFING, Sylvia K, R.N., MSN, Chief Nursing and Compliance Officer, Unity Medical & Surgical Hospital, Mishawaka, IN, p. A211

COFFMAN, Brian, Director Information System, National Park Medical Center, Hot Springs-Garland County, AR, p. A43

COFFMAN, Courtney, Vice President, Finance and Chief Financial Officer, Penn State Health St. Joseph - Downtown Campus, PA, p. A539

COFFMAN, Joan, FACHE, President and Chief Executive Officer, St. Tammany Parish Hospital, Covington, LA, p. A266

COFFMAN BARNES, Julie, M.D., Chief Medical Officer, Redmond Regional Medical Center, Rome, GA, p. A159

COGGINS, David, MS, Chief Executive Officer, Healthsouth New England Rehabilitation Hospital, Woburn, MA, p. A306

COGGINS, Lisa, Chief Nursing Officer, Morton Hospital And Medical Center, Taunton, MA, p. A305

COGGINS, Parkes, Chief Executive Officer, Mary Black Health System-Spartanburg, Spartanburg, SC, p. A557

COHEN, Jason, M.D., Chief Medical Officer, North Valley Hospital, Whitefish, MT, p. A380

COHEN, Jeffrey, M.D., President, Allegheny General Hospital, Pittsburgh, PA, p. A537

COHEN, Kathleena, MSN, R.N., Director of Nursing, Hampton Behavioral Health Center, Westampton, NJ, p. A414

COHEN, Larry, Chief Executive Officer, Ocean Beach Hospital, Ilwaco, WA, p. A672

COHEN, Lisa, Chief Financial Officer, New London Hospital, New London, NH, p. A400

COHEN, Mark, M.D., Chief Medical Officer, Piedmont Hospital, Atlanta, GA, p. A146

COHEN, Philip A., Chief Executive Officer, Monterey Park Hospital, Monterey Park, CA, p. A73

COHICK, Jim, Chief Executive Officer, Kindred Hospital-Sycamore, Sycamore, IL, p. A197

COKER, Cindy, Vice President, Patient Care Services, Vidant Chowan Hospital, Edenton, NC, p. A452

COKER, Tina, MSN, Chief Nursing Officer, Henderson Hospital, Henderson, NV, p. A393

COLADONATO, Angela R., R.N., MSN, Chief Nursing Officer, Chester County Hospital, West Chester, PA, p. A544

COLAMARIA, James, Director of Nursing, Four Winds Hospital, Saratoga Springs, NY, p. A442

COLAS, Chuck, M.D., Medical Director, Surprise Valley Health Care District, Cedarville, CA, p. A54

COLBURN, Douglas, Chief Information Officer, Piedmont Columbus Regional Northside, Columbus, GA, p. A150

COLBURN, Tim A., President and Chief Executive Officer, Berger Health System, Circleville, OH, p. A476

COLBY, Dennis, M.D., Chief of Staff, Iowa Specialty Hospital-Clarion, Clarion, IA, p. A219

COLBY, Karen M, MS, Chief Nursing Officer, Shirley Ryan Abilitylab, Chicago, IL, p. A179

COLBY, Ruth A., President and Chief Executive Officer, Silver Cross Hospital, New Lenox, IL, p. A191

COLBY, Scott, President, Upper Connecticut Valley Hospital, Colebrook, NH, p. A398

COLCHER, Marian W., President and Chief Executive Officer, Valley Forge Medical Center And Hospital, Norristown, PA, p. A533

COLCHER, Robert E, M.D., Medical Director, Valley Forge Medical Center And Hospital, Norristown, PA, p. A533

COLE, Annette E., R.N., MSN, Vice President and Chief Nursing Officer, Sky Lakes Medical Center, Klamath Falls, OR, p. A514

COLE, Bernadette Green, R.N., Chief Nursing Officer, Munson Healthcare Charlevoix Hospital, Charlevoix, MI, p. A309

COLE, Beth, Director Information Services, Lewis-Gale Pavilion, VA, p. A666

COLE, Cal, Director Information Systems, Winter Haven Hospital, Winter Haven, FL, p. A144

COLE, Carlene, Manager Human Resources, Kittson Memorial Healthcare Center, Hallock, MN, p. A332

COLE, Dale, Director, Human Resources, Corona Regional Medical Center-Rehabilitation, CA, p. A55

COLE, David, Assistant Director of Administration, Chief Financial Officer, Department of Behavioral Health and D, Central Virginia Training Center, Madison Heights, VA, p. A660

COLE, Donas, FACHE, President, Baylor Scott & White Medical Center - Lake Pointe, Rowlett, TX, p. A631

COLE, Dylan, Chief Medical Officer, Moab Regional Hospital, Moab, UT, p. A647

COLE, F Sessions, M.D., Chief Medical Officer, St. Louis Children's Hospital, Saint Louis, MO, p. A369

COLE, Georgeanne, Chief Executive Officer, Rehabilitation Hospital Of Southwest Virginia, Bristol, VA, p. A656

COLE, Harry, Jr, Administrator, Georgiana Hospital, Georgiana, AL, p. A18

COLE, James B., President and Chief Executive Officer, Virginia Hospital Center, Arlington, VA, p. A655

COLE, Jason
Regional Chief Financial Officer, Baylor Scott & White Medical Center - Lakeway, TX, p. A631
Senior Director, Management Information Systems, Suburban Hospital, Bethesda, MD, p. A290

COLE, Lori, Director Information Technology, Wayne Unc Health Care, Goldsboro, NC, p. A453

COLE, Missy, Director Human Resources, Healthsouth Rehabilitation Hospital, Fayetteville-Washington County, AR, p. A41

COLE, Nancye, R.N.
Chief Nursing Officer and Chief Operating Officer, Lovelace Westside Hospital, Albuquerque, NM, p. A415
Chief Operating Officer, Lovelace Westside Hospital, Albuquerque, NM, p. A415

COLE, Robert, Chief Operating Officer, Connecticut Mental Health Center, New Haven, CT, p. A109

COLE, Sherman W., Interim Chief Executive Officer, Osawatomie State Hospital At Adair Acute Care, Osawatomie, KS, p. A242

COLE, William Clifford, M.D., Chief of Staff, Leconte Medical Center, Sevierville, TN, p. A579

COLE-OUZOUNIAN, Denise Marie, MSN, R.N., Vice President Patient Services, Sauk Prairie Healthcare, Prairie Du Sac, WI, p. A701

COLEMAN, Alisa, Chief Executive Officer, Ferrell Hospital, Eldorado, IL, p. A181

COLEMAN, Anne, Administrator, St. Vincent Women's Hospital, IN, p. A208

COLEMAN, Curt, FACHE
Administrator, Jackson County Regional Health Center, Maquoketa, IA, p. A226

Chief Executive Officer, Genesis Medical Center, Dewitt, De Witt, IA, p. A220

COLEMAN, D. Scott, M.D., Medical Director, Livingston Healthcare, Livingston, MT, p. A377

COLEMAN, Donna, Coordinator Human Resources, Jackson County Hospital District, Edna, TX, p. A601

COLEMAN, Jim L, Jr, Chief Operating Officer, Parkridge West Hospital, TN, p. A567

COLEMAN, Karen, Director of Nursing, Grove Hill Memorial Hospital, Grove Hill, AL, p. A19

COLEMAN, Kevin, M.D., Chief Medical Officer, Grand River Hospital District, Rifle, CO, p. A105

COLEMAN, Melissa, Director Human Resources, Healthsouth Rehabilitation Hospital Of Sewickley, Sewickley, PA, p. A541

COLEMAN, Robert
Chief Executive Officer, Baptist Medical Center Attala, Kosciusko, MS, p. A349
Chief Executive Officer, Baptist Medical Center Yazoo, Yazoo City, MS, p. A354

COLEMAN, Shane, Chief Information Officer, Palo Pinto General Hospital, Mineral Wells, TX, p. A624

COLEMAN, Stanley, Director Human Resources, Texas Rehabilitation Hospital Of Arlington, Arlington, TX, p. A584

COLERICK, Steven, Chief Executive Officer, Buena Vista Regional Medical Center, Storm Lake, IA, p. A230

COLETTA, Antonio
Vice President Human Resources, Advocate Bromenn Regional Medical Center, IL, p. A191
Vice President Human Resources, Advocate Eureka Hospital, Eureka, IL, p. A182

COLETTA, Diane, Vice President Human Resources, Royal Oaks Hospital, Windsor, MO, p. A372

COLETTI, Edmund, Chief Executive Officer, Helen Hayes Hospital, West Haverstraw, NY, p. A445

COLEY, Aaron, Chief Financial Officer, Orange County, Memorialcare, Saddleback Memorial Medical Center, Laguna Hills, CA, p. A63

COLEY, Brenda
Executive Director, Metroplex Behavioral Health Center, TX, p. A617
Executive Director, Rollins Brook Community Hospital, Lampasas, TX, p. A619

COLGAN, Teresa, Vice President Nursing, Great River Medical Center, West Burlington, IA, p. A231

COLGLAZIER, Garrett, Director Health Information Management, Sabetha Community Hospital, Sabetha, KS, p. A245

COLINERI, Lori, R.N., Senior Vice President Nursing and Chief Nursing Officer, Bristol-Myers Squibb Children's Hospital, NJ, p. A408

COLL, Shawni, D.O., Chief Medical Officer, Tahoe Forest Hospital District, Truckee, CA, p. A92

COLLADO, Raquel, Vice President Human Resources, New York Community Hospital, New York (Includes All Hospitals Located Within The Five Boroughs), NY, p. A434

COLLAZO, Marian, Director Finance, Hospital San Cristobal, Coto Laurel, PR, p. A713

COLLETT, John, Vice President and Chief Financial Officer, Cayuga Medical Center At Ithaca, Ithaca, NY, p. A428

COLLETT, Josh, Director Human Resources, Southeastern Kentucky Medical Center, Pineville, KY, p. A259

COLLETTI, Teresa, Director Patient Services, South Florida Baptist Hospital, Plant City, FL, p. A136

COLLEY, Sarah, Senior Vice President Human Resources, Regional One Health, Memphis, TN, p. A575

COLLIER, Betty, Chief Human Resources Officer, Johnson Regional Medical Center, Clarksville-Johnson County, AR, p. A40

COLLIER, Brad, Director, Piedmont Newton Hospital, Covington, GA, p. A151

COLLIER, Jack, M.D., Chief of Staff, Mountainview Hospital, Las Vegas, NV, p. A394

COLLIER, Louis, Chief Executive Officer, Encompass Health Rehabilitation Hospital Of Petersburg, Petersburg, VA, p. A663

COLLIER, Shari, Chief Financial Officer, Rocky Mountain Hospital For Children, CO, p. A99

COLLINI, M. Patrick, M.D., President Medical Staff, Usmd Hospital At Arlington, Arlington, TX, p. A584

COLLINS, Alesha Danielle, MSN, R.N., Chief Nursing Officer, Howard Memorial Hospital, Nashville-Howard County, AR, p. A46

COLLINS, Annasue, Chief Nursing Officer, Ten Broeck Tennessee Treatment Facility, Cookeville, TN, p. A568

COLLINS, Ava Jo, FACHE, Chief Operating Officer, Saint Vincent Hospital, Worcester, MA, p. A306

COLLINS, Ava Jo., FACHE, Interim Chief Executive Officer, Saint Vincent Hospital, Worcester, MA, p. A306

COLLINS, Bobby
Director Human Resources, Lonesome Pine Hospital, Big Stone Gap, VA, p. A655

Director Human Resources, Mountain View Regional Medical Center, Norton, VA, p. A663

COLLINS, Chauncey, Chief Operating Officer and Chief Financial Officer, Austen Riggs Center, Stockbridge, MA, p. A305

COLLINS, Daniel, M.D., Clinical Director, New Mexico Behavioral Health Institute At Las Vegas, Las Vegas, NM, p. A418

COLLINS, Dennis, Chief Financial Officer, The Brook Hospital - Kmi, Louisville, KY, p. A257

COLLINS, Edmund, Chief Information Officer, Tradition Medical Center, FL, p. A139

COLLINS, Ethan, R.N., Chief Nursing Officer, Smyth County Community Hospital, Marion, VA, p. A661

COLLINS, Frances, Director of Nursing, Andrew Mcfarland Mental Health Center, Springfield, IL, p. A196

COLLINS, Harold E, JD, Chief Financial Officer, Franciscan Healthcare Munster, Munster, IN, p. A212

COLLINS, James M., President and Chief Executive Officer, St. Clair Hospital, Pittsburgh, PA, p. A537

COLLINS, Jeff, Chief Medical Officer, Providence St. Joseph's Hospital, Chewelah, WA, p. A670

COLLINS, Jeffrey A, M.D., Chief Executive Officer, Kaiser Permanente Richmond Medical Center, CA, p. A76

COLLINS, Jeffrey A., M.D., Senior Vice President and Area Manager, Kaiser Permanente Richmond Medical Center, CA, p. A76

COLLINS, John
Corporate Chief Financial Officer, Chapman Global Medical Center, Orange, CA, p. A76
Chief Financial Officer, Anaheim Global Medical Center, Anaheim, CA, p. A50
Chief Financial Officer, Orange County Global Medical Center, Inc., Santa Ana, CA, p. A88
Chief Financial Officer, South Coast Global Medical Center, Santa Ana, CA, p. A88

COLLINS, John F., President and Chief Executive Officer, Children's Medical Center, NY, p. A430

COLLINS, John P., FACHE, Medical Center Director, Veterans Affairs Central Western Massachusetts Healthcare System, Leeds, MA, p. A301

COLLINS, John R, Chief Financial Officer, Hemet Valley Medical Center, Hemet, CA, p. A61

COLLINS, Karen S., R.N., Chief Executive Officer, Lady Of The Sea General Hospital, Cut Off, LA, p. A266

COLLINS, Kevin J., M.D., Medical Director, St. Vincent Rehabilitation Hospital, Sherwood-Pulaski County, AR, p. A48

COLLINS, Kimberly, M.D., Chief of Staff, Saint Thomas Dekalb Hospital, Smithville, TN, p. A580

COLLINS, Lainie, Human Resources Partner, St. Vincent Clay Hospital, Brazil, IN, p. A200

COLLINS, Leonora, Chief Nursing Officer, Nashville General Hospital, Nashville, TN, p. A577

COLLINS, Michael F.
Chief Executive Officer, Manchester Memorial Hospital, Manchester, CT, p. A108
Chief Executive Officer, Rockville General Hospital, Vernon, CT, p. A111

COLLINS, Pam, Director Human Resources, Avala, Covington, LA, p. A266

COLLINS, Pamela, Vice President Chief Patient Services Officer, Mccullough-Hyde Memorial Hospital/Trihealth, Oxford, OH, p. A489

COLLINS, Richard F, M.D., Executive Vice President and Chief Medical Officer, Jefferson Hospital, Jefferson Hills, PA, p. A528

COLLINS, Ricky M, M.D., Chief of Staff, Whitesburg Arh Hospital, Whitesburg, KY, p. A261

COLLINS, Ronald, Chief Financial Officer, Pampa Regional Medical Center, Pampa, TX, p. A627

COLLINS, Sharon
Chief Information Officer, Salem Veterans Affairs Medical Center, Salem, VA, p. A666
Director Human Resources and Chief Operating Officer, Russell Regional Hospital, Russell, KS, p. A245
Interim Chief Executive Officer, Russell Regional Hospital, Russell, KS, p. A245

COLLINS, Teresa, R.N., Chief Executive Officer and Chief Nursing Officer, Saint Luke's Community Hospital At Leawood, Leawood, KS, p. A240

COLLINS, Thomas M., President, Chairman and Chief Executive Officer, Medical City Green Oaks Hospital, Dallas, TX, p. A597

COLLIPP, Dan, M.D., Chief of Staff, Wayne Memorial Hospital, Jesup, GA, p. A155

COLLISON, June, President, Community Hospital Of San Bernardino, San Bernardino, CA, p. A83

COLLOM, Bobbie, Nursing Director, North Runnels Hospital, Winters, TX, p. A644

COLMAN, Gerard, Chief Operating Officer, Aurora West Allis Medical Center, West Allis, WI, p. A706

COLMENARES, Derek, M.D.
Chief Medical Officer, St. Agnes Hospital, Fond Du Lac, WI, p. A692
Chief Medical Officer, Waupun Memorial Hospital, Waupun, WI, p. A705

COLOMBO, Armando, Chief Operating Officer, Sheppard Pratt Health System, Baltimore, MD, p. A289

COLOMBO, Lisa, R.N., Senior Vice President Patient Care Services and Chief Nursing Officer, University Campus, MA, p. A306

COLON, Julio, Financial Director, Hospital De Damas, Ponce, PR, p. A714

COLON, Omar, M.D., Medical Director, Encompass Health Rehabilitation Hospital Of Plano, Plano, TX, p. A628

COLONES, Robert L., President and Chief Executive Officer, Mcleod Regional Medical Center, Florence, SC, p. A553

COLONNELLI, Kim, Chief Nursing Officer, Corona Regional Medical Center-Rehabilitation, CA, p. A55

COLORADO, Judy, R.N., Chief Nursing Officer, Monmouth Medical Center, Southern Campus, Lakewood, NJ, p. A406

COLPITTS, Robert, Chief Human Resource Service, Bedford Veterans Affairs Medical Center, Edith Nourse Rogers Memorial Veterans Hospital, Bedford, MA, p. A295

COLSDEN, Kristen, Director of Nursing, Osmond General Hospital, Osmond, NE, p. A389

COLSON, Wayne, Chief Financial Officer, Southwestern Medical Center, Lawton, OK, p. A500

COLTHARP, Missy, Director, Baptist Memorial Hospital-Union County, New Albany, MS, p. A351

COLTON, Jan, M.D., Acting Clinical Director, U.S. Public Health Service Indian Hospital, Pine Ridge, SD, p. A562

COLUCCI, Eugene, Vice President Finance, Greenwich Hospital, Greenwich, CT, p. A108

COLUCCIO, Medrice, R.N.
Chief Executive Officer, Providence St. Peter Hospital, Olympia, WA, p. A674
Southwest Region Chief Executive, Providence Centralia Hospital, Centralia, WA, p. A670

COLVARD, Dusty, Manager Information Technology, Adventist Health Medical Center - Tehachapi Valley, Tehachapi, CA, p. A91

COLVERT, Richard, Chief Information Officer, Royal Oaks Hospital, Windsor, MO, p. A372

COLVIN, Garren
Chief Executive Officer, St. Elizabeth Covington, KY, p. A251
Chief Executive Officer, St. Elizabeth Falmouth, KY, p. A252
Chief Executive Officer, St. Elizabeth Florence, Florence, KY, p. A252
Chief Executive Officer, St. Elizabeth Grant, Williamstown, KY, p. A261

COLVIN, William, Human Resources Officer, Claiborne Memorial Medical Center, Homer, LA, p. A268

COLWELL, Dean, D.O., Vice President Medical Affairs, Ohiohealth Doctors Hospital, Columbus, OH, p. A478

COLWELL, Melodie, Chief Financial Officer, Drew Memorial Health System, Monticello-Drew County, AR, p. A46

COLYER, Valeri J
Director Human Resources, Dickenson Community Hospital, Clintwood, VA, p. A657
Director Human Resources, Norton Community Hospital, Norton, VA, p. A663

COMAIANNI, Sheri, Vice President Human Resources, Bakersfield Memorial Hospital, Bakersfield, CA, p. A52

COMBEST, Felton, M.D., Vice President Medical Affairs, Magnolia Regional Health Center, Corinth, MS, p. A345

COMBETTA, Jeffery, M.D., Medical Director, Bastrop Rehabilitation Hospital, Monroe, LA, p. A274

COMBS, Kevin, Chief of Staff, Carilion Tazewell Community Hospital, Tazewell, VA, p. A667

COMBS, Mark
Chief Information Security Officer, Jefferson Medical Center, Ranson, WV, p. A686
Interim Director System Information Technology, Berkeley Medical Center, Martinsburg, WV, p. A684

COMBS, Meri, R.N., Vice President and Chief Nursing Officer, Madera Community Hospital, Madera, CA, p. A71

COMBS, Mike, Manager Information Technology, Holdenville General Hospital, Holdenville, OK, p. A500

COMBS, Will, Director Information Technology, Harrison Community Hospital, Cadiz, OH, p. A473

COMER, Fannessa, Chief Executive Officer, Northern Navajo Medical Center, Shiprock, NM, p. A420

COMER, Jennifer, M.D., Medical Director, Valle Vista Hospital, Greenwood, IN, p. A205

COMER, Randy
Chief Financial Officer, Athens-Limestone Hospital, Athens, AL, p. A13
Chief Operating Officer, Athens-Limestone Hospital, Athens, AL, p. A13

COMER, Scott M, Vice President Human Resources, Marshall Medical Center, Placerville, CA, p. A78

COMERFORD, Jennifer, Manager Information Services, Midstate Medical Center, Meriden, CT, p. A108

COMITTO, Judy, Vice President Information Services and Chief Information Officer, Trinitas Regional Medical Center - New Point Campus, NJ, p. A404

COMP, Susan, Senior Vice President and Chief Nursing Officer, Pinnaclehealth West Shore Hospital, PA, p. A527

COMPTON, Brenda, Manager Information Technology, Plumas District Hospital, Quincy, CA, p. A79

COMPTON, Carri, Administrative Officer, Heartland Behavioral Health Services, Nevada, MO, p. A365

COMPTON, Mark, Chief Financial Officer, Laughlin Memorial Hospital, Greeneville, TN, p. A570

COMPTON, Randy, Information Technology and System Director, Logan Memorial Hospital, Russellville, KY, p. A260

COMPTON, Ty, Chief Nursing Officer, Horton Community Hospital, Horton, KS, p. A237

CONANT, Cathy, Chief Human Resources and Personnel, Eastern Plumas Health Care, Portola, CA, p. A79

CONANT, Merrill, M.D., Chief of Staff, Western Plains Medical Complex, Dodge City, KS, p. A234

CONANT, Sonya, Senior Director Human Resources, Alaska Native Medical Center, Anchorage, AK, p. A25

CONAWAY, E Edwin, M.D., Vice President Medical Affairs and Chief Medical Officer, Southeastern Ohio Regional Medical Center, Cambridge, OH, p. A473

CONCANNON, Laura, M.D., Regional Chief Medical Officer, Presence Saints Mary & Elizabeth Medical Center, Claremont Avenue, IL, p. A178

CONCEPCION, Walter, Chief Executive Officer, West Gables Rehabilitation Hospital, Miami, FL, p. A131

CONDE, Tania, Administrator, Puerto Rico Children's Hospital, PR, p. A712

CONDIT, Brian, M.D.
Chief Medical Officer, Johnston Memorial Hospital, Abingdon, VA, p. A655
Vice President Chief Medical Officer, Virginia Operations Medical Staff Services, Russell County Medical Center, Lebanon, VA, p. A660

CONDIT, Edward, President and Chief Executive Officer, St. Mary's General Hospital, Passaic, NJ, p. A409

CONDOLUCI, David, M.D., Senior Vice President and Chief Medical Officer, Jefferson Washington Township Hospital, NJ, p. A412

CONDON, Joseph
Director Human Resources, Texas Health Specialty Hospital, Fort Worth, TX, p. A605
Entity Human Resources Officer, Texas Health Harris Methodist Hospital Fort Worth, Fort Worth, TX, p. A605

CONDRY, Donna, Director Human Resources, Unitypoint Health - Jones Regional Medical Center, Anamosa, IA, p. A217

CONE, Maryann, Chief Operating Officer, Sharp Grossmont Hospital, La Mesa, CA, p. A63

CONEJO, David, Chief Executive Officer, Rehoboth Mckinley Christian Health Care Services, Gallup, NM, p. A417

CONFALONE, Daniel, Chief Financial Officer and Vice President Finance, St. Mary Medical Center, Langhorne, PA, p. A529

CONFER, James, Manager Information Systems, Clarion Hospital, Clarion, PA, p. A522

CONGDON, James B, M.D., Medical Director, Horsham Clinic, Ambler, PA, p. A520

CONGER, Sue, Chief Operating Officer, Eastside Psychiatric Hospital, Tallahassee, FL, p. A140

CONKLIN, Maggie C, M.P.H.
Interim Chief Nurse Officer, Novant Health Uva Health System Prince William Medical Center, Manassas, VA, p. A661
Interim Chief Nursing Officer, Novant Health Uva Health System Haymarket Medical Center, Haymarket, VA, p. A659

CONKLIN, Michael E, Jr, Chief Financial Officer, St. Joseph Hospital For Specialty Care, RI, p. A547

CONKLIN, Robin, R.N., Chief Nursing Officer, Carondelet St. Joseph's Hospital, Tucson, AZ, p. A37

CONKLING, Victoria, Vice President, Patient Services and Chief Nursing Officer, Uhs Delaware Valley Hospital, Walton, NY, p. A445

CONLEY, Christopher, M.D., President of the Medical Staff, Tristar Skyline Madison Campus, TN, p. A577

CONLEY, Joanna J., FACHE, Chief Executive Officer, Tristar Southern Hills Medical Center, Nashville, TN, p. A578

CONLEY, Kenneth, Chief Financial Officer, Baptist Memorial Hospital - Calhoun, Calhoun City, MS, p. A344

CONLEY, Kirkpatrick, President, Sentara Careplex Hospital, Hampton, VA, p. A659

CONLEY, Melissa, Director Human Resources, Midwest Medical Center, Galena, IL, p. A183

CONLEY, Michelle E, R.N., Chief Nursing Officer, Frankford Campus, PA, p. A535

CONLEY, Teressa
President and Chief Executive Officer, St. Rose Dominican Hospitals - Rose De Lima Campus, Henderson, NV, p. A393
Vice President and Chief Operating Officer, St. Rose Dominican Hospitals - Rose De Lima Campus, Henderson, NV, p. A393

CONLEY, Theresa, Manager Human Resources, Cherokee Regional Medical Center, Cherokee, IA, p. A219

CONLEY, Thomas C, Vice President, Human Resources and Organizational Development, Northwestern Medical Center, Saint Albans, VT, p. A654

CONLON, John, M.D., Chief Medical Officer, Saint Anne's Hospital, Fall River, MA, p. A299

CONN, Stephanie, Administrator and Chief Nursing Officer, Coshocton Regional Medical Center, Coshocton, OH, p. A479

CONNAWAY, Jessica, Director Human Resources, Crossroads Community Hospital, Mount Vernon, IL, p. A190

CONNEL, Lorene, Chief Human Resources Management Service, Veterans Affairs Eastern Colorado Health Care System, Denver, CO, p. A99

CONNELL, Faith, Director of Nursing, Turning Point Hospital, Moultrie, GA, p. A158

CONNELL, Pam, Manager Human Resources, Windsor-Laurelwood Center For Behavioral Medicine, Willoughby, OH, p. A493

CONNELLEY, Bertha Mary, Director Human Resources, Austen Riggs Center, Stockbridge, MA, p. A305

CONNELLY, Jac, Chief Financial Officer, Rose Medical Center, Denver, CO, p. A99

CONNELLY, Kathryn, Manager Information Technology, Whiting Forensic Hospital, CT, p. A109

CONNELLY, Michael P., CPA, FACHE, Executive Vice President and Chief Financial Officer, Melrose-Wakefield Hospital, MA, p. A301

CONNELLY, Steven, M.D., President and Chief Medical Officer, Park Nicollet Methodist Hospital, Saint Louis Park, MN, p. A339

CONNER, Chad, Administrator, Green Clinic Surgical Hospital, LA, p. A278

CONNER, Jeff, M.D., Chief Medical Staff, Loma Linda University Medical Center-Murrieta, Murrieta, CA, p. A74

CONNER, June, R.N., Chief Operating Officer, Emory University Orthopaedic And Spine Hospital, GA, p. A146

CONNER, Laurie A., FACHE, Chief Executive Officer, Skiff Medical Center, Newton, IA, p. A227

CONNER, Stacey, Director Personnel, Ed Fraser Memorial Hospital And Baker Community Health Center, Macclenny, FL, p. A128

CONNERS, Stephanie, Senior Executive Vice President Chief Operating Officer and Chief Nursing Officer, Childen's Regional Hospital At Cooper, NJ, p. A403

CONNERTON, Kathryn, President and Chief Executive Officer, Our Lady Of Lourdes Memorial Hospital, Inc., Binghamton, NY, p. A422

CONNOLLY, Christine, M.D., Chief of Staff, Keefe Memorial Hospital, Cheyenne Wells, CO, p. A97

CONNOLLY, Seam, Commissioner, Connecticut Veterans Home And Hospital, Rocky Hill, CT, p. A110

CONNOLLY, Teresa, R.N., Chief Nursing Officer, Mayo Clinic Hospital, Phoenix, AZ, p. A33

CONNOR, Brian, FACHE
President, Christus Spohn Hospital Corpus Christi Shoreline, TX, p. A594
President, Christus Spohn Hospital Corpus Christus South, TX, p. A594

CONNOR, Paul J., lll, President and Chief Executive Officer, Eastern Long Island Hospital, Greenport, NY, p. A427

CONNOR, Starr, Chief Nursing Officer, Fairfield Memorial Hospital, Winnsboro, SC, p. A558

CONNOR, William, Assistant Administrator and Director Human Resources, River Hospital, Alexandria Bay, NY, p. A421

CONNORS, Alfred, M.D., Executive Vice President and Chief Quality Officer and Interim Chief Medical Officer, Metrohealth Medical Center, Cleveland, OH, p. A477

CONNORS, Lawrence J, Chief Operating Officer, Hshs St. Mary's Hospital Medical Center, Green Bay, WI, p. A694

CONNORS, Michael
Senior Vice President and Chief Financial Officer, Cape Cod Hospital, Hyannis, MA, p. A300
Senior Vice President and Chief Financial Officer, Falmouth Hospital, Falmouth, MA, p. A299

CONNORS, Robert, M.D., President, Helen DeVos Children's Hospital, Helen Devos Children's Hospital, MI, p. A314

CONNOVICH, Ron D
Chief Financial Officer and Chief Operating Officer, Soin Medical Center, Beavercreek, OH, p. A472
Chief Financial Officer, Greene Memorial Hospital, Xenia, OH, p. A494

CONNY, Sophia, Deputy Administrative Officer, U.S. Public Health Service Indian Hospital, Pine Ridge, SD, p. A562

CONRAD, Daniel S., M.D., President, Phillips Eye Institute, Minneapolis, MN, p. A335

CONRAD, Elizabeth P., Senior Vice President and Chief Human Resource Officer, Lahey Medical Center, Peabody, MA, p. A298

CONRAD, Heidi, Vice President and Chief Financial Officer, Regions Hospital, Saint Paul, MN, p. A339

CONRATH, Mark, Chief Financial Officer, Drumright Regional Hospital, Drumright, OK, p. A497

CONROW-VERVERIS, Stacy, Director Human Resources, Mineral Community Hospital, Superior, MT, p. A379

CONROY, Joanne M., M.D., President and Chief Executive Officer, Children's Hospital At Dartmouth, NH, p. A399

CONROY, Michael, Chief Financial Officer, Pine Creek Medical Center, Dallas, TX, p. A597

CONROY, Mike, Chief Financial Officer, Methodist Mckinney Hospital, Mckinney, TX, p. A623

CONROY, Tracy, Chief Executive Officer, Daviess Community Hospital, Washington, IN, p. A216

CONSBRUCK, Todd
Chief Executive Officer, Avera Creighton Hospital, Creighton, NE, p. A383
President and Chief Executive Officer, Avera St. Anthony's Hospital, O'Neill, NE, p. A389

CONSIDINE, William H., President, Akron Children's Hospital, Akron, OH, p. A470

CONSIGLIO, Gayle, Chief Information Officer, Mclaren Lapeer Region, Lapeer, MI, p. A317

CONSIGNEY, Ginger, Vice President Human Resources, Lake Charles Memorial Hospital For Women, LA, p. A272

CONSOLVER, Roberta, Chief Information Officer, Healthbridge Children's Hospital, Orange, CA, p. A76

CONSTANT, Jean-Charles, Administrator, Dover Behavioral Health System, Dover, DE, p. A113

CONSTANTINE-CASTILLO, Candida, MSN, R.N., Chief Nursing Officer, South Texas Behavioral Health Center, TX, p. A601

CONTE, John, Director Facility Services and Real Estate, Wayne Memorial Hospital, Honesdale, PA, p. A527

CONTI, John, Director Finance, Shriners Hospitals For Children-Greenville, Greenville, SC, p. A554

CONTRERAS, Amy, Esq, Chief Nursing Officer, Milford Valley Memorial Hospital, Milford, UT, p. A647

CONTRERAS, Marta, Chief Nursing Officer and Chief Operating Officer, Foundation Surgical Hospital Of El Paso, El Paso, TX, p. A602

CONVERY, Luanne, Vice President Patient Care Services, Putnam Hospital Center, Carmel, NY, p. A424

CONWAY, Jimmy, M.D., President Medical Staff, Northwest Surgical Hospital, Oklahoma City, OK, p. A503

CONWAY, Kevin, Chief Information Officer, Upmc Mercy, Pittsburgh, PA, p. A538

CONWILL, Michael, Director Human Resources, Corpus Christi Medical Center Bay Area, TX, p. A594

CONYERS, Robin, Administrator, Lasting Hope Recovery Center, NE, p. A387

COOGAN, Ben, Chief Operating Officer, Medical City Arlington, Arlington, TX, p. A584

COOK, Aaron, Director Information Services, Christus Ochsner Lake Area Hospital, Lake Charles, LA, p. A272

COOK, Alan, Chief Medical Officer, Central Regional Hospital, Butner, NC, p. A448

COOK, Anthony, M.D., Chief of Staff, Avera Holy Family Hospital, Estherville, IA, p. A222

COOK, Brooke, Director of Nursing, Strategic Behavioral Health - Wilmington, Leland, NC, p. A456

COOK, Carla, Director of Nursing, Scotland County Hospital, Memphis, MO, p. A364

COOK, Darrin
Chief Executive Officer and Administrator, Horizon Specialty Hospital, Las Vegas, NV, p. A394
Chief Operating Officer, Astria Regional Medical Center, Yakima, WA, p. A680

COOK, David, Manager Information Systems, Christus Dubuis Hospital Of Hot Springs, Hot Springs National Park-Garland County, AR, p. A43

COOK, David A, Vice President and Chief Financial Officer, University Hospitals Elyria Medical Center, Elyria, OH, p. A482

COOK, Elizabeth, Chief Information Officer, Mizell Memorial Hospital, Opp, AL, p. A22

COOK, G. Anthony, M.D., Medical Director, Hemphill County Hospital, Canadian, TX, p. A591

COOK, Greg, Chief Financial Officer, Castleview Hospital, Price, UT, p. A649

COOK, Heidi, Chief Nursing Officer, Warner Hospital And Health Services, Clinton, IL, p. A180

COOK, Jana, Vice President and Chief Financial Officer, Phelps County Regional Medical Center, Rolla, MO, p. A366

COOK, Janie, Director Information Systems, Passavant Area Hospital, Jacksonville, IL, p. A186

COOK, John
   Interim Chief Information Officer, University Of California Davis Children's Hospital, CA, p. A82
   Senior Vice President & Chief Financial Officer, Mercyhealth Hospital - Rockton Avenue, Rockford, IL, p. A194
   Vice President and Chief Financial Officer, Mercyhealth Hospital And Trauma Center - Janesville, Janesville, WI, p. A695

COOK, Katheryn, R.N., Nurse Executive, Cincinnati Veterans Affairs Medical Center, Cincinnati, OH, p. A474

COOK, Kathy, FACHE, MSN, President, Mercy Health - St. Joseph Warren Hospital, Warren, OH, p. A492

COOK, Kevin S., Chief Executive Officer, Children's Healthcare Of Mississippi, MS, p. A348

COOK, Kim, Interim Clinical Applications Services Manager, Tri-City Medical Center, Oceanside, CA, p. A76

COOK, LaMont, Administrator, F. W. Huston Medical Center, Winchester, KS, p. A248

COOK, Linda, Vice President Human Resources, General Hospital, CA, p. A57

COOK, Lottie, Superintendent, Evansville Psychiatric Children Center, Evansville, IN, p. A203

COOK, Marcia, Director Information Technology, Bates County Memorial Hospital, Butler, MO, p. A356

COOK, Mary Ann, R.N., Director of Nursing, Red Lake Indian Health Service Hospital, Red Lake, MN, p. A337

COOK, Natalie
   Administrative Director of Human Resources, Manchester Memorial Hospital, Manchester, CT, p. A108
   Administrative Director, Human Resources, Rockville General Hospital, Vernon, CT, p. A111

COOK, Pamela W, Chief Financial Officer, Trace Regional Hospital, Houston, MS, p. A347

COOK, Patrick, Vice President Support Services, Morgan Memorial Hospital, Madison, GA, p. A157

COOK, Paul, M.D., Chief Medical Officer, Baylor Scott & White Medical Center - Llano, Llano, TX, p. A620

COOK, Scott
   Chief Financial Officer, Garland Behavioral Hospital, Garland, TX, p. A606
   Chief Information Officer, Johnson Regional Medical Center, Clarksville-Johnson County, AR, p. A40

COOK, Sheliah, Director Human Resources, Boone Memorial Hospital, Madison, WV, p. A684

COOK, Sherry P, R.N., MSN, Chief Nursing Executive, Merit Health River Oaks, Flowood, MS, p. A345

COOK, Stacey M, MS, Vice President, Human Resources, University Of Maryland Charles Regional Medical Center, La Plata, MD, p. A292

COOK, Thomas M, Chief Financial Officer, Good Samaritan Hospital, Vincennes, IN, p. A216

COOK, Wayne, Chief Executive Officer, Plano Specialty Hospital, Plano, TX, p. A628

COOK, Wendy J., Chief Financial Officer, Piedmont Athens Regional Medical Center, Athens, GA, p. A145

COOK, William
   Associate Warden Business Service, California Mens Colony Correctional Treatment Center, San Luis Obispo, CA, p. A87
   Director, Southern Virginia Mental Health Institute, Danville, VA, p. A657
   President and Chief Executive Officer, University Of Colorado Hospital, Aurora, CO, p. A96

COOKE, Barbara, Director Health Information Systems, Montefiore Mount Vernon, Mount Vernon, NY, p. A430

COOKE, David, R.N.
   Chief Nursing Officer, Sutter Surgical Hospital - North Valley, Yuba City, CA, p. A95
   Chief Operating Officer, Hi-Desert Medical Center, Joshua Tree, CA, p. A62

COOKE, Jordan, Director Human Resources, Shadow Mountain Behavioral Health System, Tulsa, OK, p. A509

COOKE, Nancy, Chief Financial Officer, Medical City Weatherford, Weatherford, TX, p. A643

COOKE, Rebecca L, Director Human Resources, Kearney County Health Services, Minden, NE, p. A386

COOKE, Timothy J, Medical Center Director and Chief Executive Officer, Martinsburg Veterans Affairs Medical Center, Martinsburg, WV, p. A685

COOKE, Timothy J., Medical Center Director and Chief Executive Officer, Martinsburg Veterans Affairs Medical Center, Martinsburg, WV, p. A685

COOKE, William, M.D., Chief of Staff, Gundersen St. Joseph's Hospital And Clinics, Hillsboro, WI, p. A694

COOLEY, Andrew, M.D., Chief Medical Officer, Eastern State Hospital, Lexington, KY, p. A254

COOLEY-JOHNSON, Sonja, Chief Nursing Officer, Fairlawn Rehabilitation Hospital, Worcester, MA, p. A306

COOMBS, James, Chief Executive Officer, Grand River Hospital District, Rifle, CO, p. A105

COOMBS, Teri, R.N., Director Nursing Services, Cascade Medical Center, Cascade, ID, p. A168

COOMES, Larry, Chief Executive Officer, Queen Of The Valley Medical Center, Napa, CA, p. A74

COOMLER, Mimi, R.N., Vice President and Chief Nursing Officer, Tmc For Children, AZ, p. A38

COONER, Suzanne, R.N., MSN, Chief Executive Officer, Audubon County Memorial Hospital, Audubon, IA, p. A217

COONEY, Darlene, Director Nursing, Sumner Regional Medical Center, Wellington, KS, p. A247

COONEY, Lauri Ann, Director Nursing, Wheatland Memorial Healthcare, Harlowton, MT, p. A376

COONEY, Marina, Medical Director, Montgomery County Emergency Service, Norristown, PA, p. A533

COONS, Jennifer, Chief Executive Officer, Seiling Regional Medical Center, Seiling, OK, p. A506

COOPER, Alisa, Manager Financial Resources, Michael E. Debakey Veterans Affairs Medical Center, Houston, TX, p. A612

COOPER, Alison, Chief Financial Officer, Ward Memorial Hospital, Monahans, TX, p. A624

COOPER, Allison, Administrator, Physicians Behavioral Hospital, Shreveport, LA, p. A278

COOPER, Ben, Administrator, Oceans Behavioral Hospital Of Alexandria, Alexandria, LA, p. A262

COOPER, Brenda, Director Quality and Human Resources, Corry Memorial Hospital, Corry, PA, p. A523

COOPER, Casey, Chief Executive Officer, Cherokee Indian Hospital, Cherokee, NC, p. A450

COOPER, Curtis, Manager Information Systems, Pioneers Medical Center, Meeker, CO, p. A104

COOPER, Donald, Director Information Systems, Tennova Healthcare-Harton, Tullahoma, TN, p. A580

COOPER, Douglas, M.D., Chief Medical Officer, Grundy County Memorial Hospital, Grundy Center, IA, p. A223

COOPER, Jerry, Manager Data Processing, Richland Hospital, Richland Center, WI, p. A702

COOPER, Jon, Chief Administrative Officer, Norton Audubon Hospital, KY, p. A256

COOPER, Pamela, Director Finance, Providence Seaside Hospital, Seaside, OR, p. A518

COOPER, Shawnee, Director Human Resources, Magnolia Regional Medical Center, Magnolia-Columbia County, AR, p. A45

COOPER, Tim, Chief Financial Officer, Pmh Medical Center, Prosser, WA, p. A675

COOPER-LEHKI, Christi, Chief Clinical Officer, Highland-Clarksburg Hospital, Clarksburg, WV, p. A682

COOPER-LOHR, Willie, Chief Financial Officer, Barnesville Hospital, Barnesville, OH, p. A471

COOPERMAN, Todd, M.D., Medical Director, Healthsouth Rehabilitation Hospital Of Tinton Falls, Tinton Falls, NJ, p. A412

COOPWOOD, Reginald W., M.D., President and Chief Executive Officer, Regional One Health, Memphis, TN, p. A575

COOTS, Aaron, Information Technology Director, Mason District Hospital, Havana, IL, p. A185

COOTS, Lawrence, M.D., Chief Medical Officer, Orange Park Medical Center, Orange Park, FL, p. A133

COPE, Brent A., Chief Executive Officer, Silver Lake Medical Center-Ingleside Hospital, CA, p. A69

COPE, Dave, Director Information Systems, Marshall County Hospital, Benton, KY, p. A249

COPE, Mary, R.N., Chief Clinical Officer, Spanish Peaks Regional Health Center, Walsenburg, CO, p. A106

COPE, Yvette Renee, Chief Nurse Executive, Lompoc Valley Medical Center, Lompoc, CA, p. A65

COPELAND, Carolyn, Business Administrator, Madison State Hospital, Madison, IN, p. A210

COPELAND, Darlinda, Chief Operating Officer, Florida Hospital-Oceanside, FL, p. A121

COPELAND, Gail, Director Management Information Systems, Crossridge Community Hospital, Wynne-Cross County, AR, p. A49

COPELAND, Gearline, R.N., Chief Nursing Officer, Saint Thomas Highlands Hospital, Sparta, TN, p. A580

COPELAND, Kristie M., Interim Chief Nursing Officer, Claiborne Memorial Medical Center, Homer, LA, p. A268

COPELAND, Robert, Interim Chief Executive Officer, Covenant Hospital Plainview, Plainview, TX, p. A628

COPELAND, Stephen, Chief Financial Officer, Cypress Creek Hospital, Houston, TX, p. A610

COPELAND, Willie Mae, Chief Financial Officer, Harmon Memorial Hospital, Hollis, OK, p. A500

COPELAND, Yolanda, R.N., Senior Vice President Patient Care Services and Chief Nursing Officer, Saint Agnes Healthcare, Baltimore, MD, p. A288

COPEN, Greg, Chief Information Officer, Haywood Regional Medical Center, Clyde, NC, p. A450

COPENHAVER, Kathy, Director Human Resources, Haven Behavioral Hospital Of Eastern Pennsylvania, Reading, PA, p. A539

COPES, Tammy, Director Information Systems, St. Mary's Of Michigan Standish Hospital, Standish, MI, p. A324

COPPEDGE, Mitch, M.D., Chief Medical Officer, Grady Memorial Hospital, Chickasha, OK, p. A497

COPPLE, Brad
   Vice President Operations, Northwestern Medicine Valley West Hospital, Sandwich, IL, p. A195
   Vice President, Operations, Northwestern Medicine Kishwaukee Hospital, Dekalb, IL, p. A181

COPPLE, Robert C., FACHE, Senior Administrator, Via Christi Hospital Manhattan, Inc., Manhattan, KS, p. A240

CORA, Michelle, Director Human Resources, Beaumont Hospital - Trenton, Trenton, MI, p. A324

CORAZON, Jesus M
   Controller, Healthsouth Hospital Of Manati, Manati, PR, p. A714
   Controller, Healthsouth Rehabilitation Hospital Of San Juan, San Juan, PR, p. A715

CORBEIL, John, Chief Operating Officer, Medical City Fort Worth, Fort Worth, TX, p. A605

CORBET, Mark, Interim Chief Financial Officer, Women's And Children's Hospital, CA, p. A68

CORBETT, David, M.D., Chief of Staff, Northwest Medical Center, Winfield, AL, p. A24

CORBI, Kelly, Chief Operating Officer, Northwest Hospital, Randallstown, MD, p. A293

CORBIN, Michelle, M.D., Chief of Staff, Deer Lodge Medical Center, Deer Lodge, MT, p. A375

CORCIMIGLIA, Michael, Chief Operating Officer, Wyoming County Community Hospital, Warsaw, NY, p. A445

CORCORAN, John Russell, Vice President Medical Affairs, South County Hospital, Wakefield, RI, p. A548

CORCORAN, Joseph C., D.O.
   Chief Medical Officer, Brandon Regional Hospital, Brandon, FL, p. A119
   Chief Medical Officer, South Bay Hospital, Sun City Center, FL, p. A140

CORCORAN, Kevin, Chief Financial Officer, Westside Regional Medical Center, Plantation, FL, p. A136

CORCORAN, Nancy R, Senior Vice President Human Resources and Quality Service, The Joseph M. Sanzari Children's Hospital, NJ, p. A405

CORCORAN, Rose, R.N., Chief Nursing Executive, Sutter Coast Hospital, Crescent City, CA, p. A56

CORD, Jennifer, R.N., Chief Nursing Officer, Mission Hospital Laguna Beach, CA, p. A72

CORDDRY, David, Chief Financial Officer, Ten Broeck Tennessee Treatment Facility, Cookeville, TN, p. A568

CORDEAU, Peter, Chief Executive Officer, Sharon Hospital, Sharon, CT, p. A110

CORDER, Earline, Chief Fiscal, Charlie Norwood Veterans Affairs Medical Center, Augusta, GA, p. A147

CORDER, Scott, Controller, Healthsouth Rehabilitation Hospital Of Cincinnati At Norwood, OH, p. A475

CORDERO, Edwin, Chief Financial Officer, Valley Baptist Medical Center-Brownsville, Brownsville, TX, p. A590

CORDES, Debra, Chief Nursing Officer, Rehabilitation Hospital Of Indiana, Indianapolis, IN, p. A207

CORDIA, Jennifer, Vice President and Chief Nursing Executive, Christian Hospital, Saint Louis, MO, p. A368

CORDOVA, Mandelyn, R.N., Director of Nurses, Guadalupe County Hospital, Santa Rosa, NM, p. A419

CORDOVA, Martin, Director Information Services, Centinela Hospital Medical Center, Inglewood, CA, p. A62

CORDOVA, Sheila
   Chief Operating Officer and Chief Nursing Officer, Aurora Charter Oak Hospital, Covina, CA, p. A55
   Director Clinical Services and Chief Operating Officer, Aurora Charter Oak Hospital, Covina, CA, p. A55

CORDOVES, America, Controller, Jerome Golden Center For Behavioral Health, Inc., West Palm Beach, FL, p. A143

CORDUM, Shelly L., R.N., MSN, Vice President Nursing and Chief Nursing Officer, Ssm Health Depaul Hospital - St. Louis, Bridgeton, MO, p. A356

CORDY, Roy, M.D., President Medical Staff, Presentation Medical Center, Rolla, ND, p. A468

COREA, Rohan, Director Healthcare Information Technology, College Medical Center, Long Beach, CA, p. A65

COREY, Mark, Chief Financial Officer, Behavioral Center Of Michigan, Warren, MI, p. A325

CORFITS, Joe, Chief Financial Officer, Unitypoint Health-Iowa Lutheran Hospital, Des Moines, IA, p. A221

CORKERY, Thomas B, D.O., Chief Medical Officer, Canonsburg Hospital, Canonsburg, PA, p. A522

CORLEW, Scott, M.D., Chief Medical Officer, Saint Thomas Rutherford Hospital, Murfreesboro, TN, p. A576

CORLEY, Becky, Director Human Resources, Tyler Holmes Memorial Hospital, Winona, MS, p. A354

CORLEY, Janet, Accountant, Malvern Institute, Malvern, PA, p. A530

CORLEY, Juli, Chief Information Officer, Edgefield County Hospital, Edgefield, SC, p. A552

CORMACK, Julie, Administrator, Christus Dubuis Hospital Of Fort Smith, Fort Smith-Sebastian County, AR, p. A42

CORMIER, Philip M., Chief Executive Officer, Addison Gilbert Hospital, MA, p. A295

CORN, Rick, Chief Information Officer, Madison Hospital, AL, p. A19

CORNEJO, C Susan
  Chief Financial Officer, Sacred Heart Hospital Pensacola, Pensacola, FL, p. A136
  Chief Operating Officer, Providence Hospital, Mobile, AL, p. A20

CORNEJO, Juan, M.D., Chief of Staff, Perry County Memorial Hospital, Tell City, IN, p. A215

CORNELIUS, David, Director Information Systems, Parkridge West Hospital, TN, p. A567

CORNELIUS, Margaret E, Vice President Human Resources, Wyckoff Heights Medical Center, New York (Includes All Hospitals Located Within The Five Boroughs), NY, p. A438

CORNELIUS, Michelle
  Director Human Resources for Northern Region, Ascension Eagle River Hospital, Eagle River, WI, p. A692
  Director Human Resources for the Northern Region, St. Mary's Hospital, WI, p. A702
  Director Human Resources, Ascension Sacred Heart Hospital, Tomahawk, WI, p. A704
  Director Human Resources, Howard Young Medical Center, Woodruff, WI, p. A706

CORNELIUS, Senta, Director Human Resources, West Valley Medical Center, Caldwell, ID, p. A168

CORNELIUS, Teresa, R.N., Interim Chief Nursing Officer, Hshs St. Joseph's Hospital, Highland, IL, p. A185

CORNELL, John, Vice President Finance, Meadows Regional Medical Center, Vidalia, GA, p. A162

CORNET, Trina, JD, Vice President Human Resources, Jamaica Hospital Medical Center, New York (Includes All Hospitals Located Within The Five Boroughs), NY, p. A432

CORNETT, Sheila, Manager Human Resources, Hazard Arh Regional Medical Center, Hazard, KY, p. A253

CORNETT, Suzanne, Director Human Resources, Southern Kentucky Rehabilitation Hospital, Bowling Green, KY, p. A250

CORNICELLI, Kari
  Chief Financial Officer, Sharp Grossmont Hospital, La Mesa, CA, p. A63
  Chief Financial Officer, Sharp Mcdonald Center, CA, p. A84
  Chief Financial Officer, Sharp Memorial Hospital, San Diego, CA, p. A84

CORNWALL, Thomas, M.D., Medical Director, Holly Hill Hospital, Raleigh, NC, p. A459

CORNWELL, Cheryl, Chief Financial Officer, Great Falls Clinic Hospital, Great Falls, MT, p. A376

CORNWELL, Cheryl J, Chief Financial Officer, Lake District Hospital, Lakeview, OR, p. A514

CORNWELL, Daniel, Command Officer, U.S. Naval Hospital Guam, Agana, GU, p. A711

CORNWELL, Richard, Chief Executive Officer, Surprise Valley Health Care District, Cedarville, CA, p. A54

CORONA, Robert, D.O., Interim Chief Executive Officer, Upstate University Hospital At Community General, NY, p. A444

CORONEL, Jorge, Chief Information Officer, Regional Hospital Of Scranton, Scranton, PA, p. A540

CORPORA, Don, Executive Vice President and Chief Human Resources Officer, Cleveland Clinic Akron General, Akron, OH, p. A470

CORRADO, Bob, Chief Information Officer, Canandaigua Veterans Affairs Medical Center, Canandaigua, NY, p. A424

CORRADO, Theresa, Director Finance, St. Luke's Hospital - Quakertown Campus, Quakertown, PA, p. A539

CORREA, Elizabeth, Director Information Management, Big Spring State Hospital, Big Spring, TX, p. A589

CORREA, Leo, Chief Executive Officer and Administrator, St. Catherine Hospital, East Chicago, IN, p. A202

CORREA, Maria de los Angeles, M.D., Medical Director, Hospital Metropolitano, San Juan, PR, p. A716

CORREA, Omar, Chief Financial Officer, Texas Neurorehab Center, Austin, TX, p. A587

CORREA, Sharon, Vice President and Chief Information Officer, Adventist Health Glendale, Los Angeles, CA, p. A66

CORRELL, Anne, Chief Clinical Officer, Kindred Hospital-Greensboro, Greensboro, NC, p. A453

CORRIGAN, Heidi, Manager Human Resources, Trinity Hospital, Weaverville, CA, p. A95

CORRIGAN, Jeffrey T.
  Vice President Human Resources, Brattleboro Retreat, Brattleboro, VT, p. A653
  Vice President Human Resources, Day Kimball Hospital, Putnam, CT, p. A110

CORRIGAN, Paula, Vice President and Chief Financial Officer, Osf Saint James - John W. Albrecht Medical Center, Pontiac, IL, p. A194

CORS, William K., M.D., Senior Medical Director, Lehigh Valley Hospital - Pocono, East Stroudsburg, PA, p. A524

CORSO, David, Chief Operating Officer, Beaver Dam Community Hospitals, Beaver Dam, WI, p. A690

CORTI, Ronald J., President and Chief Executive Officer, St. John's Riverside Hospital - Dobbs Ferry Pavilion, NY, p. A446

CORUM, Sharon, Chief Financial Officer, Kingwood Pines Hospital, Kingwood, TX, p. A618

CORWIN, Nancy
  Chief Nursing Officer, Summit Surgical, Hutchinson, KS, p. A237
  Chief Operating Officer, Summit Surgical, Hutchinson, KS, p. A237

CORWIN, Steven J., M.D., President and Chief Executive Officer, The Allen Pavilion, NY, p. A434

CORZINE, Judy, Administrative Director and Chief Information Officer, Stormont Vail Health, Topeka, KS, p. A246

COSBY, Christopher, Chief Executive Officer, Poinciana Medical Center, Kissimmee, FL, p. A127

COSBY, Dwan, Manager Human Resources, Mclaren Oakland, Pontiac, MI, p. A321

COSBY, Ernestine Y., Vice President Clinical Services and Chief Nursing Officer, Sheppard Pratt Health System, Baltimore, MD, p. A289

COSLETT, John, R.N., Chief Nursing Officer, Kansas Spine And Specialty Hospital, Wichita, KS, p. A247

COSTA, Christopher P., M.D., Chief of Staff, Gordon Memorial Health Services, Gordon, NE, p. A384

COSTA, Joe
  Acting Chief Fiscal Officer, Veterans Affairs Medical Center West Roxbury Division, MA, p. A298
  Chief Financial Officer, Veterans Affairs Boston Healthcare System, West Roxbury, MA, p. A305

COSTA, Mark E, Executive Director, Orange County Irvine Medical Center, CA, p. A50

COSTA, Mark E., Executive Director, Orange County Irvine Medical Center, CA, p. A50

COSTA, Michael G, Vice President Human Resources, Chi St. Joseph Regional Health Center, Bryan, TX, p. A591

COSTAKIS, Angie, Chief Information Officer, Claiborne Memorial Medical Center, Homer, LA, p. A268

COSTALAS, Peter, Chief Financial Officer, Huntington Hospital, Huntington, NY, p. A428

COSTANTINO, Vincent, Vice President Operations and Human Resources, Perth Amboy Division, NJ, p. A410

COSTANZO, Kristin L., Direct-In-Market Lead Human Relations Partner, St. Vincent's Blount, Oneonta, AL, p. A22

COSTELLA, Jeane L, Vice President, New York-Presbyterian/Hudson Valley Hospital, Cortlandt Manor, NY, p. A425

COSTELLO, Jeff
  Chief Financial Officer, Beacon Health System, Beacon Children's Hospital, IN, p. A215
  Chief Financial Officer, Elkhart General Hospital, Elkhart, IN, p. A202

COSTELLO, Jodi, Chief Executive Officer, Select Specialty Hospital-Youngstown, Boardman Campus, OH, p. A494

COSTELLO, Kenneth, Administrator, Christus Dubuis Hospital Of Hot Springs, Hot Springs National Park-Garland County, AR, p. A43

COSTIC, Andrew
  Regional Chief Financial Officer, Abraham Lincoln Memorial Hospital, Lincoln, IL, p. A188
  Regional Chief Financial Officer, Taylorville Memorial Hospital, Taylorville, IL, p. A197

COSTNER, Marc, Chief Financial Officer, Chestnut Hill Hospital, Philadelphia, PA, p. A534

COTA, Scott, M.D., Director Medical Services, Naval Hospital Lemoore, Lemoore, CA, p. A64

COTE, Gerri, Chief Operating Officer, Brattleboro Retreat, Brattleboro, VT, p. A653

COTE, Mary, Director Human Resources, New England Rehabilitation Hospital Of Portland, Portland, ME, p. A285

COTT, Gary, M.D., Executive Vice President Medical and Clinical Services, National Jewish Health, Denver, CO, p. A99

COTTEN, Brandon, Chief Financial Officer, Dewitt Hospital, Dewitt-Arkansas County, AR, p. A41

COTTER, Bonny, Chief Nursing Officer, Baraga County Memorial Hospital, L'Anse, MI, p. A317

COTTER, Carole
  Senior Vice President and Chief Information Officer, Emma Pendleton Bradley Hospital, East Providence, RI, p. A547
  Senior Vice President and Chief Information Officer, Hasbro Children's Hospital, RI, p. A548
  Vice President and Chief Information Officer, Miriam Hospital, Providence, RI, p. A547

COTTERILL, Allison, Chief Nursing Officer, Mercy General Hospital, Sacramento, CA, p. A82

COTTERMAN, Rob, Chief Executive Officer, Middle Tennessee Mental Health Institute, Nashville, TN, p. A577

COTTINGHAM, Jerod, Director Information Systems, Carlinville Area Hospital, Carlinville, IL, p. A175

COTTLE, Jeremy, Ph.D., Chief Executive Officer, Provo Canyon Behavioral Hospital, Orem, UT, p. A649

COTTLE, Mike, Chief Information Officer, Newton Medical Center, Newton, KS, p. A242

COTTO, Hector L, M.D., Medical Director, Hospital San Francisco, San Juan, PR, p. A716

COTTON, C Gerald, Interim Chief Operating Officer, Baptist Medical Center Leake, Carthage, MS, p. A344

COTTON, Michael, Chief Financial Officer, Gadsden Regional Medical Center, Gadsden, AL, p. A18

COTTRILL, Brian, Chief Information Officer, United Hospital Center, Bridgeport, WV, p. A681

COUCH, Beulah, Director Human Resources, Mary Breckinridge Arh Hospital, Hyden, KY, p. A254

COUCH, Bill, Chief Financial Officer, Ashley County Medical Center, Crossett-Ashley County, AR, p. A40

COUCH, Chad, Chief Medical Officer, Bristol Regional Medical Center, Bristol, TN, p. A566

COUCHMAN, Diane, Vice President Patient Care Services and Chief Nursing Executive, Calverthealth Medical Center, Prince Frederick, MD, p. A293

COUGHENOUR, James, Administrator, Community Behavioral Health Hospital - Baxter, Baxter, MN, p. A328

COUGHLIN, Ann, Director Human Resources, Boundary Community Hospital, Bonners Ferry, ID, p. A168

COUGHLIN, Cynthia, MS, R.N., Chief Nursing Officer, Cheshire Medical Center, Keene, NH, p. A399

COUGHLIN, Kevin B., President and Chief Executive Officer, Beth Israel Deaconess Hospital Plymouth, Plymouth, MA, p. A303

COULTER, Barbara
  Director Information Systems, Franciscan Health Indianapolis, Indianapolis, IN, p. A206
  Director Information Systems, Franciscan Health Mooresville, Mooresville, IN, p. A211

COUNTS, Virginia, Manager Human Resources, Scott & White Hospital - Brenham, Brenham, TX, p. A590

COUNTY-TEEMER, Vickie, Coordinator Human Resources, Mitchell County Hospital, Camilla, GA, p. A149

COURIS, John D., Chief Executive Officer, Tampa General Hospital Children's Medical Center, FL, p. A141

COURNYER, Tim, Administrator, Forks Community Hospital, Forks, WA, p. A672

COURREGE, Gary, Chief Information Officer, Jennings American Legion Hospital, Jennings, LA, p. A269

COURTOIS, Harold, Chief Executive Officer, Memorial Health System, Abilene, KS, p. A232

COURTOIS, Robert, Vice President Finance, Munson Healthcare Otsego Memorial Hospital, Gaylord, MI, p. A313

COURY, Justin, Chief Operating Officer, Tristar Centennial Women's & Children'S, TN, p. A577

COURY, Tiffany, Chief Operating Officer, Northern Nevada Medical Center, Sparks, NV, p. A397

COUSAR, Myra, Director Human Resources, Baptist Memorial Hospital-Tipton, Covington, TN, p. A568

COUSINEAU, Cathy, Director Human Resources, Kaiser Permanente Woodland Hills Medical Center, Los Angeles, CA, p. A67

COUTURE, Maureen, Chief Nursing Officer and Vice President Nursing, Cardinal Hill Rehabilitation Hospital, Lexington, KY, p. A254

COUVILLON, Larry, M.D., Chief Medical Officer, Memorial Behavioral Health, MS, p. A346

COVAULT, Julie, Vice President Finance, Wilson Memorial Hospital, Sidney, OH, p. A490

COVAULT, Myra, Associate Vice President of Human Resources, Hardin Memorial Health, Elizabethtown, KY, p. A251

COVELL, Nancy, Director Human Resources, Cameron Memorial Community Hospital, Angola, IN, p. A199

COVELLI, Margaret, R.N., Chief Nursing Officer, Spring Valley Hospital Medical Center, Las Vegas, NV, p. A395

COVERT, David G., Chief Executive Officer, South Texas Surgical Hospital, Corpus Christi, TX, p. A594

COVERT, Kathy, MSN, Vice President Workforce Development and Organizational Development, Schneck Medical Center, Seymour, IN, p. A214

COVERT, Terri, Vice President Human Resources, Mission Hospital Laguna Beach, CA, p. A72

COVEY, Staci, R.N., MS
President, Guthrie Towanda Memorial Hospital, Towanda, PA, p. A542
President, Troy Community Hospital, Troy, PA, p. A542

COVINGTON, Casey, M.D., President Elect, Medical Staff, Jennie Stuart Medical Center, Hopkinsville, KY, p. A253

COVINGTON, Celia, MSN, R.N., Director of Nursing, St. Mary's Good Samaritan Hospital, Greensboro, GA, p. A154

COVINGTON, Jerome, M.D., Chief Medical Officer, De Poo Hospital, FL, p. A126

COVONE, Ann Marie, Senior Vice President and Chief Financial Officer, Terence Cardinal Cooke Health Care Center, New York (Includes All Hospitals Located Within The Five Boroughs), NY, p. A437

COWAN, Christopher, Senior Vice President and Chief Human Resources Officer, Christiana Care Health System, Newark, DE, p. A113

COWAN, J W., Administrator, Choctaw General Hospital, Butler, AL, p. A15

COWAN, Leslie, R.N., Chief Nursing Officer, Henry Community Health, New Castle, IN, p. A212

COWAN, Ronald M, Vice President Information Systems, Geisinger-Lewistown Hospital, Lewistown, PA, p. A530

COWART, Mark, Facility Chief Information Officer, Carl Vinson Veterans Affairs Medical Center, Dublin, GA, p. A153

COWART, Timothy, Administrator, Springbrook Hospital, Brooksville, FL, p. A119

COWLES, John, Chief Financial Officer, Silver Lake Medical Center-Ingleside Hospital, CA, p. A69

COWLING, Phyllis A., CPA, President and Chief Executive Officer, United Regional Health Care System-Eleventh Street Campus, TX, p. A644

COX, Amber, Director Human Resources, Ut Health Carthage, Carthage, TX, p. A592

COX, Brian, Director Information Systems, Baptist Health Floyd, New Albany, IN, p. A212

COX, Carla C., Chief Nursing Officer, Indiana University Health Ball Memorial Hospital, Muncie, IN, p. A212

COX, Chandler, Director Human Resources, Mena Regional Health System, Mena-Polk County, AR, p. A46

COX, Christopher, Chief Nursing Officer, Baptist Health Extended Care Hospital, Little Rock-Pulaski County, AR, p. A44

COX, David W, Chief Financial Officer, Marin General Hospital, Greenbrae, CA, p. A61

COX, Debbie D, Administrative Director Human Resources, Central Texas Medical Center, San Marcos, TX, p. A635

COX, Denida A., Chief Nursing Officer, Smith Northview Hospital, GA, p. A162

COX, Dianne E, Vice President of Human Resources, South Campus, CA, p. A94

COX, Dina, Director Human Resources, Kansas Rehabilitation Hospital, Topeka, KS, p. A246

COX, Dorothy, Manager Information Systems, Hackettstown Medical Center, Hackettstown, NJ, p. A405

COX, Gwen, Director Nursing Services, Klickitat Valley Health, Goldendale, WA, p. A672

COX, Jeffrey
Chief Information Officer, Glendora Community Hospital, Glendora, CA, p. A61
Director Information Technology, San Dimas Community Hospital, San Dimas, CA, p. A85

COX, Keith, Chief Executive Officer and Administrator, Lifecare Hospitals Of South Shreveport-Willis Knighton North, LA, p. A278

COX, Kenneth, Interim Chief Financial Officer, Mckenzie County Healthcare System, Watford City, ND, p. A469

COX, Leigh, Chief Information Officer, Wellstar Windy Hill Hospital, Marietta, GA, p. A157

COX, Lisa D., R.N., MSN, Chief Nursing Officer, Cypress Fairbanks Medical Center, Houston, TX, p. A610

COX, Lynna B, Director Health Information Services, Anson General Hospital, Anson, TX, p. A584

COX, Randy, Chief Information Officer, St. Vincent Women's Hospital, IN, p. A208

COX, Raymond L., M.D., Chief Medical Officer, Providence Hospital, Washington, DC, p. A116

COX, Sandra, Controller, Permian Regional Medical Center, Andrews, TX, p. A583

COX, Sharon K., FACHE, Chief Executive Officer, Rawlins County Health Center, Atwood, KS, p. A232

COX, Sheila, Director Human Resources, Cibola General Hospital, Grants, NM, p. A417

COX, Steven, M.D., Chief Medical Officer, Ut Health North Campus Tyler, Tyler, TX, p. A641

COY, Nelson, Director Human Resources, Tahoe Pacific Hospitals, NV, p. A397

COYE, Ed
Director Information Technology Mission Health System Hospitals, Angel Medical Center, Franklin, NC, p. A452
Director Information Technology, Transylvania Regional Hospital, Brevard, NC, p. A448

COYLE, Michael F., Chief Executive Officer, Ely-Bloomenson Community Hospital, Ely, MN, p. A331

COYNE, Rose, Interim CFO, Haywood Regional Medical Center, Clyde, NC, p. A450

COZART, Adrienne, Senior Vice President Human Resources, University Medical Center, Lubbock, TX, p. A621

CRABB, David W, M.D., Chief Medical Officer, Eskenazi Health, Indianapolis, IN, p. A206

CRABB, Ian, M.D., Chief Medical Officer, Orthonebraska Hospital, Omaha, NE, p. A388

CRABBE, Amy J.
Senior Vice President Human Resources, Watauga Medical Center, Boone, NC, p. A448
Vice President People Services, Charles A. Cannon Memorial Hospital, Newland, NC, p. A458

CRABDREE, Nathan, Chief Financial Officer, Rapides Regional Medical Center, Alexandria, LA, p. A262

CRABTREE, Gordon
Chief Financial Officer, University Of Utah Health, Salt Lake City, UT, p. A651
Interim Chief Executive Officer, University Of Utah Health, Salt Lake City, UT, p. A651

CRABTREE, John D, M.D., Chief of Staff, Tennova Healthcare-Harton, Tullahoma, TN, p. A580

CRABTREE, Robert, M.D., Chief of Staff and Medical Director, Physicians Surgical Hospital - Panhandle Campus, TX, p. A583

CRABTREE, Susan, Director Human Resources, Simi Valley Hospital, Simi Valley, CA, p. A90

CRACOLICI, Frank J., President and Chief Executive Officer, St. Vincent Medical Center, Los Angeles, CA, p. A70

CRACROFT, Davis, M.D., Senior Director Medical Affairs, Scripps Mercy Hospital Chula Vista, CA, p. A84

CRAFT, Brian, Group Finance Officer, Texas Health Presbyterian Hospital Dallas, Dallas, TX, p. A598

CRAFT, Christina, Director Information Systems, Washington County Hospital, Plymouth, NC, p. A458

CRAFT, Kirby, Chief Information Officer, Magee General Hospital, Magee, MS, p. A349

CRAFTS, Nicholas, Chief Executive Officer, Houston Physicians Hospital, Webster, TX, p. A643

CRAGGS, Chris, Deputy Director, Winnebago Mental Health Institute, Winnebago, WI, p. A706

CRAIG, Alan, M.D., Chief Medical Officer, Princeton Baptist Medical Center, Birmingham, AL, p. A15

CRAIG, Celine H, Director Human Resources, King's Daughters Medical Center, Brookhaven, MS, p. A344

CRAIG, Cheniere, Director Human Resources, P & S Surgical Hospital, Monroe, LA, p. A274

CRAIG, Donnette, Director Human Resources, Christus Coushatta Health Care Center, Coushatta, LA, p. A266

CRAIG, Elizabeth J, MSN, Chief Nursing Officer and Vice President Patient Services, Temple University Hospital - Episcopal Division, PA, p. A536

CRAIG, Emmett
Chief Human Resources Officer, Knapp Medical Center, Weslaco, TX, p. A643
Director Human Resources, Harlingen Medical Center, Harlingen, TX, p. A608

CRAIG, Jeff, Chief Human Resource Management, Veterans Affairs Maryland Health Care System-Perry Point Division, MD, p. A289

CRAIG, Mike
Chief Financial Officer, Indiana University Health Bloomington Hospital, Bloomington, IN, p. A200
Vice President, Chief Financial Officer, Indiana University Health Bedford Hospital, Bedford, IN, p. A199

CRAIG, Pamela, R.N., Chief Nursing Officer, Seton Medical Center Harker Heights, Harker Heights, TX, p. A608

CRAIG, Patrice, Manager Human Resources, Southern Arizona Veterans Affairs Health Care System, Tucson, AZ, p. A38

CRAIG, Rebecca W, Vice President and Chief Financial Officer, Wayne Unc Health Care, Goldsboro, NC, p. A453

CRAIG, Scott, M.D., Medical Director, Healthsouth Rehabilitation Hospital Of Franklin, Franklin, TN, p. A569

CRAIG, Sherry, Director Human Resources, Trace Regional Hospital, Houston, MS, p. A347

CRAIG, Steven, Ph.D., Chief Operating Officer and Acting Chief Executive Officer, Oakland Regional Hospital, Southfield, MI, p. A323

CRAIG, William J, CPA, Chief Financial Officer, Howard Memorial Hospital, Nashville-Howard County, AR, p. A46

CRAIGER, Lisa, Chief Nursing Officer, Indiana University Health Jay Hospital, Portland, IN, p. A213

CRAIGIN, Jane, Chief Executive Officer, St. Vincent Williamsport Hospital, Williamsport, IN, p. A216

CRAIN, Greg, FACHE, Senior Vice President and Administrator, Baptist Health Medical Center-Little Rock, Little Rock-Pulaski County, AR, p. A45

CRAIN, Michelle B., R.N., MSN, Administrator and Chief Operating Officer, Heart Hospital Of Lafayette, Lafayette, LA, p. A271

CRAMBES, Terry, Manager Finance, Warren State Hospital, Warren, PA, p. A543

CRAMER, Brian J., Chief Executive Officer, Orthopaedic Hospital Of Wisconsin - Glendale, Glendale, WI, p. A693

CRAMER, James R
Vice President and Chief Information Officer, Honorhealth Scottsdale Osborn Medical Center, Scottsdale, AZ, p. A35
Vice President and Chief Information Officer, Honorhealth Scottsdale Shea Medical Center, Scottsdale, AZ, p. A35

CRAMER, Lonnie, Chief Operating Officer, St. Francis Medical Center, CO, p. A98

CRANDELL, Kristy, M.D., Medical Staff President, Red Bay Hospital, Red Bay, AL, p. A23

CRANFORD, Melvin, Chief Fiscal Services, Cheyenne Veterans Affairs Medical Center, Cheyenne, WY, p. A708

CRANK, Christina, Chief Nursing Officer, St. Vincent Jennings Hospital, North Vernon, IN, p. A213

CRATON, Deborah W, M.D., Chief Medical Officer, St. Vincent Dunn Hospital, Bedford, IN, p. A200

CRATTY, Michael, M.D.
Chief Medical Officer, Heritage Valley Health System, Beaver, PA, p. A520
Chief Medical Officer, Sewickley Valley Hospital, (A Division Of Valley Medical Facilities), Sewickley, PA, p. A541

CRAVEN, Brian, Senior Vice President Finance, Magnolia Regional Health Center, Corinth, MS, p. A345

CRAVEN, Darcy
President, De Graff Memorial Hospital, NY, p. A423
President, Millard Fillmore Suburban Hospital, NY, p. A423

CRAVENS, Marc
Chief Financial Officer, Pinnacle Specialty Hospital, Tulsa, OK, p. A508
Interim Chief Executive Officer, Pinnacle Specialty Hospital, Tulsa, OK, p. A508

CRAVEY, Lavonda, Chief Financial Officer, Coffee Regional Medical Center, Douglas, GA, p. A152

CRAW, David, Coordinator Information Technology, Dundy County Hospital, Benkelman, NE, p. A382

CRAWFORD, Allen, Chief Nursing Officer, Jeff Davis Hospital, Hazlehurst, GA, p. A154

CRAWFORD, Arnita, Director Human Resources, Woman's Hospital Of Texas, Houston, TX, p. A614

CRAWFORD, Jim, Chief Financial Officer, Lawrence Medical Center, Moulton, AL, p. A21

CRAWFORD, John W
Chief Financial Officer, Muscogee Creek Nation Medical Center, Okmulgee, OK, p. A505
Chief Financial Officer, St. John Sapulpa, Sapulpa, OK, p. A506

CRAWFORD, Linda, R.N., MSN, Chief Nursing Officer, Cookeville Regional Medical Center, Cookeville, TN, p. A568

CRAWFORD, Lucinda
Vice President Financial Services, Vidant Duplin Hospital, Kenansville, NC, p. A455
Vice President of Patient Care Services, Vidant Beaufort Hospital, Washington, NC, p. A462

CRAWFORD, Pam, R.N., Ph.D., Vice President of Nursing and Chief Nursing Officer, Mansfield Hospital, OH, p. A485

CRAWFORD, Ryan, Director Talent, Southwestern Regional Medical Center, Tulsa, OK, p. A509

CRAWFORD, Susan, Manager Human Resources, Fayette County Hospital, Vandalia, IL, p. A197

CRAWFORD, Thomas, Chicago Market Chief Information Officer, Louis A. Weiss Memorial Hospital, Chicago, IL, p. A177

CRAWFORD, Tom
Vice President Human Resources, Dekalb Medical At Downtown Decatur, Decatur, GA, p. A152
Vice President Human Resources, Dekalb Medical At Hillandale, Lithonia, GA, p. A156

CRAWFORD, Traci, R.N., Commander, Moncrief Army Community Hospital, Fort Jackson, SC, p. A553

CRAWFORD, Wendy, Chief Human Resource Officer, Honorhealth Scottsdale Thompson Peak Medical Center, Scottsdale, AZ, p. A35

CRAWFORD, Wes, Chief Executive Officer, Covington Behavior Health, Covington, LA, p. A266

CRAYTON, Cory
Director Information Systems, Northeast Georgia Medical Center Barrow, Winder, GA, p. A163
Director of Information Systems, Piedmont Walton Hospital, Monroe, GA, p. A157

CREAL, Sharon, Vice President Financial Operations, Scripps Memorial Hospital-Encinitas, Encinitas, CA, p. A57

CREAMER, Julie L., President, Northwestern Memorial Hospital and Senior Vice President Northwestern Memorial HealthCare, Stone Institute Of Psychiatry, IL, p. A178

CREAMER, Ken, Chief Human Resource, Amarillo Veterans Affairs Health Care System, Amarillo, TX, p. A583

CREASMAN, Ginny L, Associate Director, Richard L. Roudebush Veterans Affairs Medical Center, Indianapolis, IN, p. A207

CREEL, Keith, Vice President Operations, Christus Good Shepherd Medical Center, TX, p. A622

CREEL, Mary Ann, Chief Information Resource Management, Martinsburg Veterans Affairs Medical Center, Martinsburg, WV, p. A685

CREIGHTON, Peggy F, R.N., Director of Nursing, Methodist Hospital Union County, Morganfield, KY, p. A258

CRENSHAW, Neville, D.O., Chief of Staff, Unitypoint Health-Keokuk, Keokuk, IA, p. A225

CRENSHAW, Rachel H., Chief Operating Officer, Jack Hughston Memorial Hospital, Phenix City, AL, p. A22

CRENSHAW, William, M.D., Chief of Staff, Lady Of The Sea General Hospital, Cut Off, LA, p. A266

CREPEAU, Diana, Director Human Resources, Healthsouth Rehabilitation Hospital Of Colorado Springs, Colorado Springs, CO, p. A97

CREPS, Barbara, Director Human Resources and Accounting, Okeene Municipal Hospital, Okeene, OK, p. A502

CREQUE, J C, Director Management Information Systems, Schneider Regional Medical Center, Saint Thomas, VI, p. A717

CRESPO, Rosaida M, Executive Director, Hospital San Carlos Borromeo, Moca, PR, p. A714

CRESPO, Rosaida M., Executive Director, Hospital San Carlos Borromeo, Moca, PR, p. A714

CRESWELL, Linda, Director Human Resource, Cypress Fairbanks Medical Center, Houston, TX, p. A610

CREVLING, Charles, Chief Financial Officer, Valley View Hospital, Glenwood Springs, CO, p. A101

CREWS, Carol
Chief Financial Officer, Higgins General Hospital, Bremen, GA, p. A148
Chief Financial Officer, Tanner Medical Center-Carrollton, Carrollton, GA, p. A149
Senior Vice President and Chief Financial Officer, Willowbrooke At Tanner, GA, p. A162

CREWS, Kimberly, Vice President and Chief Financial Officer, Catawba Valley Medical Center, Hickory, NC, p. A454

CREWS, Paul, Director, Durham Veterans Affairs Medical Center, Durham, NC, p. A451

CRIBBS, Sammie, Vice President Clinical Services and Chief Nursing Officer, North Arkansas Regional Medical Center, Harrison-Boone County, AR, p. A43

CRIBBS, Susan, D.O., Chief of Staff, Adventist Health Medical Center - Tehachapi Valley, Tehachapi, CA, p. A91

CRIDER, Terry, Information Technology Site Manager, Nea Baptist Memorial Hospital, Jonesboro-Craighead County, AR, p. A44

CRIGER, Sara J., President, Unity Hospital, MN, p. A330

CRILLY, Tom
Executive Vice President and Chief Financial Officer, Unity Hospital, Rochester, NY, p. A441
Executive Vice President, Chief Financial Officer, Rochester Regional Health, Newark-Wayne Community Hospital, Newark, NY, p. A438

CRIM, Marcia, R.N., MSN
Chief Executive Officer, Usmd Hospital At Arlington, Arlington, TX, p. A584
Chief Nursing Officer and Chief Executive Officer, Usmd Hospital At Arlington, Arlington, TX, p. A584

CRINER, Mark, Director Information Technology, Memorial Health Care Systems, Seward, NE, p. A390

CRINER, Tonya, Human Resource Lead, Blackwell Regional Hospital, Blackwell, OK, p. A496

CRIPE, Kimberly C.
President and Chief Executive Officer, Children's Hospital Of Orange County, Orange, CA, p. A76
President and Chief Executive Officer, Choc Children's At Mission Hospital, Mission Viejo, CA, p. A72

CRIPPS, Eric, Chief Financial Officer, De Soto Regional Health System, Mansfield, LA, p. A273

CRISTY, Kirk, Chief Financial Officer, Sanford Bismarck, Bismarck, ND, p. A464

CRISWELL, Jodie, Vice President of Fiscal Services, Hammond-Henry Hospital, Geneseo, IL, p. A184

CRITCHLEY, Dan, Chief Information Officer, Diamond Children's Hospital, AZ, p. A37

CRITCHLOW, David, Senior Vice President, Government Relations, LifePoint Health, Watertown Regional Medical Center, Watertown, WI, p. A705

CRITTENDEN, Shana, Chief Operating Officer, Florida Medical Center - A Campus Of North Shore, FL, p. A130

CROCE, Martin, MD, Senior Vice President and Chief Medical Officer, Regional One Health, Memphis, TN, p. A575

CROCKER, Daniel, M.D., Chief Medical Officer, Lifecare Hospitals Of North Carolina, Rocky Mount, NC, p. A459

CROCKETT, James Scott, M.D., Chief of Staff, Falls Community Hospital And Clinic, Marlin, TX, p. A622

CROCKETT, John, Chief Information Officer, Guidance Center, Flagstaff, AZ, p. A29

CROCKETT, Mandy Lee
Director Human Resources, San Luis Valley Health Conejos County Hospital, La Jara, CO, p. A102
Director Human Resources, San Luis Valley Health, Alamosa, CO, p. A96

CROCKETT, Matt, Chief Executive Officer, Smokey Point Behavioral Hospital, Marysville, WA, p. A673

CROCKETT, Richard, Director, Overton Brooks Veterans Affairs Medical Center, Shreveport, LA, p. A278

CROCKETT, Timothy D, Chief Financial Officer, Breckinridge Memorial Hospital, Hardinsburg, KY, p. A253

CROFFUT, Tom, Chief Financial Officer, Centerpointe Hospital, Saint Charles, MO, p. A367

CROFT, Kim, R.N., Executive Director Human Resources, Pomerene Hospital, Millersburg, OH, p. A487

CROFTON, Michael
Chief Financial Officer, Good Samaritan Hospital, Cincinnati, OH, p. A475
Chief Financial Officer, Trihealth Evendale Hospital, Cincinnati, OH, p. A476
Senior Vice President and Chief Financial Officer, Bethesda Butler Hospital, OH, p. A474

CROKER, James, Director Information Systems, St. Bernardine Medical Center, San Bernardino, CA, p. A83

CROLEY, John S, Vice President Business Operations, Texas Institute For Surgery At Texas Health Presbyterian Dallas, Dallas, TX, p. A598

CRONER, Robert, Senior Vice President and Chief Human Resources Officer, Children's Hospital Of Philadelphia, Philadelphia, PA, p. A534

CRONIN, Annamarie, Director Human Resources, Healthsouth New England Rehabilitation Hospital, Woburn, MA, p. A306

CRONIN, David J, Regional Vice President Human Resources, Good Samaritan Medical Center - Cushing Campus, MA, p. A298

CRONIN-WAELDE, Deborah L, MSN, R.N., Senior Vice President Clinical Operations and Chief Nursing Officer, Melrose-Wakefield Hospital, MA, p. A301

CROOKS, John, Chair Information Services, Mayo Clinic Hospital In Florida, Jacksonville, FL, p. A125

CROOM, Jon-Paul, President, Wellstar North Fulton Hospital, Roswell, GA, p. A159

CROPPER, Ronnie, Chief Operating Officer, Warren State Hospital, Warren, PA, p. A543

CROSBY, Evalie M, CPA, Vice President Finance and Chief Financial Officer, Alice Peck Day Memorial Hospital, Lebanon, NH, p. A399

CROSBY, Robert
Chief Financial Officer, Athol Hospital, Athol, MA, p. A295
Senior Vice President and Chief Financial Officer, Heywood Hospital, Gardner, MA, p. A300

CROSHAW, Diane S, Vice President Human Resources, Bacharach Institute For Rehabilitation, Pomona, NJ, p. A410

CROSLAND, Telita, Commander, Colonel Florence A. Blanchfield Army Community Hospital, Fort Campbell, KY, p. A252

CROSS, Carol, CPA, Chief Financial Officer, Northeast Regional Medical Center, Kirksville, MO, p. A362

CROSS, John D., Chief Executive Officer, Kindred Hospital Sugar Land, Sugar Land, TX, p. A637

CROSS, Lynda, R.N., Director of Nurses, Nemaha Valley Community Hospital, Seneca, KS, p. A245

CROSS, Patricia, Chief Executive Officer, Life Line Hospital, Steubenville, OH, p. A490

CROSS, Renee, Senior Vice President and Chief Financial Officer, Saint Francis Hospital, Charleston, WV, p. A682

CROSSAN, Eric, Chief Executive Officer, Walton Rehabilitation Hospital, Augusta, GA, p. A147

CROSSLAND, Jeanne, Director of Nursing, Shamrock General Hospital, Shamrock, TX, p. A635

CROSSLEY, Kent, M.D., Chief of Staff, Minneapolis Veterans Affairs Health Care System, Minneapolis, MN, p. A335

CROSSMAN, Margaret, M.D., Chief Medical Officer, Halifax Health Medical Center Of Port Orange, FL, p. A121

CROTEAU, Gary, Assistant Vice President and Chief Information Officer, South County Hospital, Wakefield, RI, p. A548

CROTTY, Glenn, M.D., Jr, Executive Vice President and Chief Operating Officer, General Hospital, WV, p. A682

CROTTY, Renee, Coordinator Marketing and Public Relations, Capital Medical Center, Olympia, WA, p. A674

CROUCH, Amy, Chief Financial Officer, Promedica Coldwater Regional Hospital, Coldwater, MI, p. A310

CROUCH, James, Vice President Technical Services, Northwest Medical Center, Albany, MO, p. A355

CROUCH, Matthew, Chief Executive Officer and Managing Director, Peachford Behavioral Health System, Atlanta, GA, p. A146

CROUT, Tom, MS, Director Human Resources, Central Louisiana State Hospital, Pineville, LA, p. A277

CROW, Angie, Director Finance, Saint Thomas Hospital For Spinal Surgery, Nashville, TN, p. A577

CROW, Regina W, R.N., Chief Nursing Officer, Bothwell Regional Health Center, Sedalia, MO, p. A370

CROW, Ronda, Chief Nursing Officer, Moore County Hospital District, Dumas, TX, p. A600

CROWDER, Andy, Chief Information Officer and Corporate Senior Vice President, Scripps Green Hospital, La Jolla, CA, p. A62

CROWDER, Lonna, Director of Nursing, Phillips County Hospital, Malta, MT, p. A377

CROWE, Arthur, Director Information Systems, Peconic Bay Medical Center, Riverhead, NY, p. A441

CROWE, Darren, Chief Executive Officer, Crow/Northern Cheyenne Hospital, Crow Agency, MT, p. A374

CROWELL, Lynn, Chief Executive Officer, Arkansas Valley Regional Medical Center, La Junta, CO, p. A102

CROWELL, Pamela, Director, Sheridan Veterans Affairs Medical Center, Sheridan, WY, p. A709

CROWELL, Robin, Chief Nursing Officer and Chief Operating Officer, Saint Thomas Hickman Hospital, Centerville, TN, p. A567

CROWL, Steve, Director of Information Services, Davis Medical Center, Elkins, WV, p. A682

CROWLEY, Karen, Chief Executive Officer, Select Specialty Hospital-Phoenix, Phoenix, AZ, p. A34

CROWLEY, Thomas, President and Chief Executive Officer, Saint Elizabeth's Medical Center, Wabasha, MN, p. A341

CRUCETTI, Carol, R.N., Chief Nursing Officer, Seton Health System-St. Mary's Hospital, NY, p. A444

CRUDDAS, Brian, Chief Operating Officer, Bayfront Health Port Charlotte, Port Charlotte, FL, p. A137

CRUICKSHANK, Roland, President, Chi St. Luke's Hospital - The Vintage Hospital, Houston, TX, p. A610

CRUIKSHANK, Jennifer, R.N., Chief Executive Officer, Riverside University Health System-Medical Center, Moreno Valley, CA, p. A74

CRUM, Aaron, M.D., Senior Vice President, Assistant Chief Executive Officer and Chief Medical Officer, Pikeville Medical Center, Pikeville, KY, p. A259

CRUM, Dennis L, Senior Vice President and Chief Financial Officer, Tift Regional Medical Center, Tifton, GA, p. A162

CRUM, Jarett, Hospital Director, Baypointe Behavioral Health, Mobile, AL, p. A20

CRUMB, Robert, MS, Chief Executive Officer, Schoolcraft Memorial Hospital, Manistique, MI, p. A318

CRUMLEY, Vickie L, Chief Human Resources Officer, Mary Rutan Hospital, Bellefontaine, OH, p. A472

CRUMP, John, M.D., Medical Staff President, Howard Young Medical Center, Woodruff, WI, p. A706

CRUMP, Rick, Chief Financial Officer, Lakeland Behavioral Health System, Springfield, MO, p. A370

CRUMPTON, Patsy Sue, R.N., Chief Nursing Officer, National Park Medical Center, Hot Springs-Garland County, AR, p. A43

CRUNK, Frances H, Vice President and Chief Financial Officer, Florida Hospital Waterman, Tavares, FL, p. A142

CRUSE, Ray, Chief Executive Officer, Lakeland Hospital, Watervliet, Watervliet, MI, p. A325

CRUSON, Jim, Chief Information Officer, Riverview Behavioral Health, Texarkana-Miller County, AR, p. A49

CRUTCHFIELD, David, Vice President, Information Services & Chief Information Officer, Conway Medical Center, Conway, SC, p. A552

CRUTHIRDS, Richard, Director Information Systems, Peterson Regional Medical Center, Kerrville, TX, p. A617

CRUZ, Arlene, Director, Rush Oak Park Hospital, Oak Park, IL, p. A191

CRUZ, Domingo, Senior Vice President Operations, San Jorge Children's Hospital, Santurce, PR, p. A716

CRUZ, Joseph V, Chief Information Officer, Ryder Memorial Hospital, Humacao, PR, p. A714

CRUZ, Julia, Chief Financial Officer, San Juan Capestrano Hospital, San Juan, PR, p. A716

CRUZ, Michael, Senior Vice President Operations, Bsa Hospital, Llc, Amarillo, TX, p. A583

CRUZ, Miguel, M.D.
Medical Director, Bella Vista Hospital, Mayaguez, PR, p. A714
Medical Staff Credentialing Coordinator, Healthsouth Rehabilitation Hospital Of Miami, Cutler Bay, FL, p. A120

CRUZ, Obed, Vice President and Chief Nursing Officer, Amita Health Adventist Medical Center Bolingbrook, Bolingbrook, IL, p. A174

CRUZ CORREA, Jesus, Chief Medical Officer, St. Luke's Episcopal Hospital, Ponce, PR, p. A714

CRYER, Betty, R.N., Administrator/Chief Nursing Officer, Anderson Regional Health System South, Meridian, MS, p. A350

CRYER, Selena, Director Human Resources, Ennis Regional Medical Center, Ennis, TX, p. A603

CRYNES, Kristin, Executive Director of Nursing, Greene County General Hospital, Linton, IN, p. A210

CSEPKE, Cheryl, Controller, Kindred Rehabilitation Hospital Northeast Houston, Humble, TX, p. A615

CUELLAR, Eddie, Vice President Information Systems, Northeast Methodist Hospital, TX, p. A633

CUELLAR, Jacob, M.D., Chief Executive Officer, Laurel Ridge Treatment Center, San Antonio, TX, p. A633

CUENCA, Derrick, Chief Executive Officer, Mountainview Regional Medical Center, Las Cruces, NM, p. A418

CUEVAS, Gilberto, Director Human Resources, Hospital De Damas, Ponce, PR, p. A714

CUEVAS, Jacki, Director Health Information Services, Regional Rehabilitation Hospital, Phenix City, AL, p. A22

CUFF, Randy, Chief Operating Officer, Central Valley Medical Center, Nephi, UT, p. A648

CULBERSON, David K., Chief Executive Officer, San Joaquin General Hospital, French Camp, CA, p. A59

CULBERT, Devon, Controller, The Hospital At Westlake Medical Center, Austin, TX, p. A587

CULLEN, Barry, Chief Executive Officer, Southeast Michigan Surgical Hospital, Warren, MI, p. A325

CULLEN, John, M.D.
Chief of Staff and Medical Director Long Term Care, Providence Valdez Medical Center, Valdez, AK, p. A27
Chief Executive Officer, Thomas B. Finan Center, Cumberland, MD, p. A291

CULLEN, Kelly, R.N., Executive Vice President and Chief Operating Officer, Tampa General Hospital Children's Medical Center, FL, p. A141

CULLEN, Michael, Senior Vice President and Chief Financial Officer, South Shore Hospital, South Weymouth, MA, p. A304

CULLEN, Neil, Director Human Resources, Encompass Health Rehabilitation Hospital Of Northwest Tucson, Tucson, AZ, p. A37

CULLEN, Paul T, M.D., Vice President Medical Affairs, Washington Hospital, Washington, PA, p. A543

CULLITON, Gerald F., Medical Center Director, West Haven Division, CT, p. A112

CULP, Judy, Chief Financial Officer, Hill Regional Hospital, Hillsboro, TX, p. A609

CULPEPPER, Michelle, Director Human Resources, Chicago Lakeshore Hospital, Chicago, IL, p. A176

CULVER, Douglas, Chief Financial Officer, Mercy Hospital Carthage, Carthage, MO, p. A357

CULVER, Shawna, Director Information Systems, Western Plains Medical Complex, Dodge City, KS, p. A234

CUMBEE, Lib, Director Information Systems, Providence Hospital Northeast, SC, p. A551

CUMBIE, Dan L, Chief Nursing Officer, Flowers Hospital, Dothan, AL, p. A17

CUMBO, Adam, Chief Financial Officer, Dukes Memorial Hospital, Peru, IN, p. A213

CUMING, Richard, R.N., MSN, Ed.D., Chief Nurse Executive, Christiana Care Health System, Newark, DE, p. A113

CUMMINGS, Allana, Chief Information Officer, Children's Healthcare Of Atlanta At Scottish Rite, GA, p. A146

CUMMINGS, Brooke, Chief Financial Officer, Bogalusa Community Medical Center, LA, p. A264

CUMMINGS, Gabrielle, President, Northshore Highland Park Hospital, IL, p. A182

CUMMINGS, Greg, Chief Financial Officer, Baylor Scott & White Texas Spine & Joint Hospital, Tyler, TX, p. A641

CUMMINGS, Jerry, Chief Operating Officer, Putnam County Memorial Hospital, Unionville, MO, p. A371

CUMMINGS, Kelly, Chief Nursing Officer, Abington-Lansdale Hospital Jefferson Health, Lansdale, PA, p. A529

CUMMINGS, Steve, M.D., Chief of Medical Staff, Stillwater Medical Center, Stillwater, OK, p. A507

CUMMINGS, Steven, Chief Operating Officer and Chief Information Officer, Baystate Noble Hospital, Westfield, MA, p. A305

CUMMINS, Frank L, Vice President Human Resources, Honorhealth Deer Valley Medical Center, Phoenix, AZ, p. A33

CUMMINS, Thomas H., M.D., Chief Medical Officer, St. Francis Eastside, SC, p. A553

CUNNIGHAM, James, D.O., Chief of Staff, Audubon County Memorial Hospital, Audubon, IA, p. A217

CUNNINGHAM, Becky, Controller, Salem Memorial District Hospital, Salem, MO, p. A370

CUNNINGHAM, Brian, Chief Executive Officer, Wahiawa General Hospital, Wahiawa, HI, p. A166

CUNNINGHAM, Carol, Administrative Assistant, Highland Ridge Hospital, Midvale, UT, p. A647

CUNNINGHAM, Connie, Chief Information Officer, Ellwood City Medical Center, Ellwood City, PA, p. A525

CUNNINGHAM, Debbie, R.N.
President, Women's Hospital Of Greensboro, NC, p. A453
Senior Vice President, Cone Health and President, Maternal, Child and Behavioral Health Services, Behavioral Health Center, NC, p. A453

CUNNINGHAM, Dennis J., M.D., Chief Medical Officer, Mclaren Macomb, Mount Clemens, MI, p. A319

CUNNINGHAM, Gail, Interim Chief Medical Officer, University Of Maryland St. Joseph Medical Center, Towson, MD, p. A294

CUNNINGHAM, Gary, Chief Nursing Officer, Dixie Regional Medical Center, UT, p. A650

CUNNINGHAM, James C, M.D., Chief Medical Officer, Cook Children's Medical Center, Fort Worth, TX, p. A604

CUNNINGHAM, Julie, Associate Administrator and Chief Human Resources Officer, Pioneers Memorial Healthcare District, Brawley, CA, p. A53

CUNNINGHAM, Keith W, M.D., Medical Director, Encompass Health Rehabilitation Hospital Of Scottsdale, Scottsdale, AZ, p. A35

CUNNINGHAM, M Edward., Chief Executive Officer, Gateway Regional Medical Center, Granite City, IL, p. A184

CUNNINGHAM, Michelle P., Chief Executive Officer, Highlands Hospital, Connellsville, PA, p. A523

CUNNINGHAM, Peggy, Chief Executive Officer, Peak Behavioral Health Services, Santa Teresa, NM, p. A419

CUNNINGHAM, Regina, Ph.D., R.N., Chief Executive Officer, Scheie Eye Institute Of The Hospital Of The University Of Pennsylvania, PA, p. A535

CUPPS, Cheryl, Director Finance, Griffin Memorial Hospital, Norman, OK, p. A502

CURD, R Blake., M.D., Chief Executive Officer, Sioux Falls Specialty Hospital, Sioux Falls, SD, p. A564

CURLING, Susan, M.D., Chief Medical Officer, Memorial Hermann Northeast, Humble, TX, p. A615

CURNEL, Robin, MSN, Chief Operating Officer and Chief Nursing Officer, Crittenden County Hospital, Marion, KY, p. A257

CURPHY, Rona, President and Chief Executive Officer, Banner Casa Grande Medical Center, Casa Grande, AZ, p. A28

CURRAN, Dezerae, Director Human Resources, Osawatomie State Hospital At Adair Acute Care, Osawatomie, KS, p. A242

CURRAN, Maria, Vice President Human Resources, Children's Hospital Of Richmond At Vcu, VA, p. A665

CURRAN, Michael, President, Taylor Hospital, PA, p. A543

CURRAN, Todd A., M.D., President Medical Staff, Oss Orthopaedic Hospital, York, PA, p. A545

CURRAN-MEULI, Jane, Chief Operating Officer, Holy Family Memorial, Manitowoc, WI, p. A696

CURRANS, Sheila, Chief Executive Officer, Harrison Memorial Hospital, Cynthiana, KY, p. A251

CURREN, Robert
Director Information Technology, Center For Behavioral Medicine, Kansas City, MO, p. A361
Western Region Chief Information Technology Officer, Northwest Missouri Psychiatric Rehabilitation Center, Saint Joseph, MO, p. A367

CURRIE, Michelle, Chief Financial Officer, Red River Behavioral Health System, Grand Forks, ND, p. A466

CURRIE, Peggy M., R.N.
Chief Operating Officer, Providence Holy Family Hospital, Spokane, WA, p. A678
Chief Operating Officer, Sacred Heart Children's Hospital, WA, p. A678

CURRIE, Scott D, Vice President and Chief Financial Officer, Midmichigan Medical Center-Midland, Midland, MI, p. A319

CURRIN, Randy, Chief Executive Officer, Blake Medical Center, Bradenton, FL, p. A118

CURRY, Cheryl, Chief Financial Officer, Littleton Adventist Hospital, Littleton, CO, p. A103

CURRY, Christopher, Chief Executive Officer, Kindred Hospital Peoria, Peoria, IL, p. A193

CURRY, Jeffrey T
Executive Vice President and Chief Financial Officer, Excela Frick Hospital, Mount Pleasant, PA, p. A532
Executive Vice President and Chief Financial Officer, Excela Health Westmoreland Hospital, Greensburg, PA, p. A526

CURRY, Robert H
President and Chief Executive Officer, Citrus Valley Medical Center-Inter-Community Campus, CA, p. A56
President and Chief Executive Officer, Citrus Valley Medical Center-Queen Of The Valley Campus, CA, p. A56

CURRY, Robert H.
President and Chief Executive Officer, Citrus Valley Medical Center-Queen Of The Valley Campus, CA, p. A56
President and Chief Executive Officer, Foothill Presbyterian Hospital, Glendora, CA, p. A60

CURRY, Stephen A, Director Information Services, Princeton Community Hospital, Princeton, WV, p. A686

CURRY, Steve, Regional Director Human Resources, Four County Counseling Center, Logansport, IN, p. A210

CURRY, Tim, Chief Operating Officer, Avoyelles Hospital, Marksville, LA, p. A273

CURRY-PELYAK, Mary Jane, R.N., Vice President and Chief Clinical Officer, The Villages Regional Hospital, The Villages, FL, p. A142

CURTI, Tate, Senior Vice President and Chief Operating Officer, Southern New Hampshire Medical Center, Nashua, NH, p. A400

CURTIN, Sean, Chief Financial Officer, The University Of Vermont Health Network - Alice Hyde Medical Center, Malone, NY, p. A429

CURTIS, Bryan, Chief Information Officer, Memorial Regional Health, Craig, CO, p. A98

CURTIS, Edgar J., FACHE, President and Chief Executive Officer, Memorial Medical Center, Springfield, IL, p. A196

CURTIS, George, Chief Information Officer, Houston Medical Center, Warner Robins, GA, p. A163

CURTIS, Janis, Interim Director Information Technology, Duke Raleigh Hospital, Raleigh, NC, p. A459

CURTIS, Joy U, Senior Vice President Human Resources, Whidden Memorial Hospital, MA, p. A298

CURTIS, Lorna, Chief Financial Officer, John F. Kennedy Memorial Hospital, Indio, CA, p. A62

CURTIS, Michael, Chief Administrative Officer, Mckenzie County Healthcare System, Watford City, ND, p. A469

CURTIS, Scott A., Administrator and Chief Executive Officer, Kossuth Regional Health Center, Algona, IA, p. A217

CURTIS, Tracie, Business Partner Human Resources, Cleveland Clinic, Medina Hospital, Medina, OH, p. A486

CURTRIGHT, Jonathan W., Chief Executive Officer and Chief Operating Officer, Women's And Children's Hospital, MO, p. A358

CURVIN, Thomas J, M.D., Chief of Staff, Rankin County Hospital District, Rankin, TX, p. A630

CUSA, Philip L., Hospital Director, Eastpointe Hospital, Daphne, AL, p. A16

CUSACK, Michele, Senior Vice President and Chief Financial Officer, Southside Hospital, Bay Shore, NY, p. A422

CUSACK, Susan, Executive Director, Mercy Philadelphia Hospital, PA, p. A524

CUSACK-MCGUIRK, Joan, President and Chief Executive Officer, St. Luke's Cornwall Hospital - Newburgh Campus, NY, p. A438

CUSANO, Susan, Director Human Resources, Four Winds Hospital, Katonah, NY, p. A428

CUSENZ, Bruce J, M.D., Medical Director, Eastern Niagara Hospital Newfane, Newfane, NY, p. A429

CUSHING, Ginger, Chief Executive Officer, Lifebrite Community Hospital Of Early, Blakely, GA, p. A148

CUSHING, Heidi, Chief Financial Officer, Harlan County Health System, Alma, NE, p. A381

CUSHING, Herbert, M.D., Chief Medical Officer, Temple University Hospital - Episcopal Division, PA, p. A536

CUSHMAN, Bonnie, Chief Financial Officer, Northern Colorado Rehabilitation Hospital, Johnstown, CO, p. A102

CUSSINS, James, Chief Financial Officer, Platte County Memorial Hospital, Wheatland, WY, p. A710

CUSTER, Joshua, Director Finance, St. Luke's Magic Valley Medical Center, Twin Falls, ID, p. A172

CUSTER, Lindsey, Director Human Resources, Riverside Tappahannock Hospital, Tappahannock, VA, p. A667

CUSTER-MITCHELL, Marilyn J., President, Parkview Wabash County Hospital, Wabash, IN, p. A216

CUSTIN, Melinda, Chief Information Officer, Trinity Springs Pavilion, TX, p. A604

CUSTODIO, David, M.D., President Summa Health System Akron, Summa Saint Thomas Hospital, OH, p. A470

CUSUMANO, Margaret M, R.N., MSN, Vice President Patient Care Services and Chief Nursing Officer, Saint Joseph's Medical Center, Yonkers, NY, p. A446

CUTHRELL, Rob, Director of Human Resources, Coastal Virginia Rehabilitation, Newport News, VA, p. A662

CUTLIFF, Bryan, Chief Executive Officer, Select Specialty Hospital-Ann Arbor, Ypsilanti, MI, p. A326

CUTOLO, Edward, M.D., Jr, Chief of Staff, James A. Haley Veterans' Hospital-Tampa, Tampa, FL, p. A141

CUTRELL, Carrie, Chief Nursing Officer, Arkansas Valley Regional Medical Center, La Junta, CO, p. A102

CUTRIGHT, Bruce E, MS, Vice President Human Resources, Mary Lanning Healthcare, Hastings, NE, p. A384

CUTSFORTH, Shawn, Information Systems Officer, Pioneer Memorial Hospital, Heppner, OR, p. A513

CUTTER, Elise, Chief Financial Officer, Island Hospital, Anacortes, WA, p. A669

CUZZOLA, Anthony, Vice President and Administrator, Hackensack Meridian Health Jfk Johnson Rehabilitation Institute, Edison, NJ, p. A404

CYBORON, Abigail, Chief Financial Officer, Chase County Community Hospital, Imperial, NE, p. A385

CYE, Mark, Chief Executive Officer, Medina Memorial Hospital, Medina, NY, p. A430

CYR, Kristin, R.N., MSN, Senior Nursing Executive and Vice President of Patient Care Services, Maine Coast Memorial Hospital, Ellsworth, ME, p. A284

CYTLAK, David
  Chief Financial Officer, Blanchard Valley Hospital, OH, p. A482
  Vice President Finance, Bluffton Hospital, Bluffton, OH, p. A472

CZAHOR, John, IT Site Executive, University Of Maryland Charles Regional Medical Center, La Plata, MD, p. A292

CZAJKOWSKI, Cheryl, Associate Director Patient and Nursing Services, Syracuse Veterans Affairs Medical Center, Syracuse, NY, p. A444

CZEREW, Jane, Vice President Clinical Services and Quality, Spectrum Health Zeeland Community Hospital, Zeeland, MI, p. A326

CZYMBOR, Mary, Chief Medical Officer, Whitinsville Medical Center, MA, p. A302

CZYZ, AnneMarie, R.N., MS, Ed.D., Senior Vice President Operations, Chief Operating Officer and Chief Nursing Officer, St. Joseph's Hospital Health Center, Syracuse, NY, p. A444

D

DAANE, John, Information Systems Officer, Crossing Rivers Health Medical Center, Prairie Du Chien, WI, p. A701

DABNEY, Ann, Manager Human Resources, Spring View Hospital, Lebanon, KY, p. A254

DACE, Linda, Vice President Finance, Mcdonough District Hospital, Macomb, IL, p. A188

D'ACCURZIO, Albert, M.D., Medical Director, St. Elizabeth Medical Center, Utica, NY, p. A444

DADD, Steven, Flight Commander Resource Management, U.S. Air Force Hospital, Hampton, VA, p. A659

DADO, Joe
  Chief Information Officer, Conemaugh Miners Medical Center, Hastings, PA, p. A527
  Chief Information Officer, Memorial Medical Center - Lee Campus, PA, p. A528

DAEGER, Brian, Chief Financial Officer and Vice President Financial Services, Margaret Mary Health, Batesville, IN, p. A199

DAFFRON, Eric Allen, Division Director, Information Systems, Southeast Alabama Medical Center, Dothan, AL, p. A17

DAGENBACH, Pete, Chief Financial Officer, Adams County Regional Medical Center, Seaman, OH, p. A490

DAGGETT, Jake, Chief Executive Officer, Texas Rehabilitation Hospital Of Fort Worth, Fort Worth, TX, p. A605

DAGLIO, Michael, President, Norwalk Hospital, Norwalk, CT, p. A110

DAHDUL, Adnan, M.D., Medical Director, Healthsouth Rehabilitation Hospital Of Western Massachusetts, Ludlow, MA, p. A301

DAHL, Robert, President and Chief Executive Officer, Presence Resurrection Medical Center, Chicago, IL, p. A178

DAHLBERG, Connie, Director Business and Employee, Sleepy Eye Medical Center, Sleepy Eye, MN, p. A340

DAHLHAUSEN, Daniel J, M.D., President of Medical Staff/ Chief Medical Officer, Anmed Health Cannon, Pickens, SC, p. A556

DAHLING, James D., President and Chief Executive Officer, Children's Hospital Of The King's Daughters, Norfolk, VA, p. A662

DAHLQUIST, Clay, M.D., Chief Medical Officer, Waverly Health Center, Waverly, IA, p. A231

DAHLSTRAND, David, Chief, OI&T, Hunter Holmes Mcguire Veterans Affairs Medical Center-Richmond, Richmond, VA, p. A665

DAHLSTROM, Sheri, R.N., Chief Nursing Officer, Banner Estrella Medical Center, Phoenix, AZ, p. A33

DAIGLE, Cindy, Chief Financial Officer, Northern Maine Medical Center, Fort Kent, ME, p. A284

DAIGLE, Jennifer, R.N., Director of Nursing and Utilization Review, Carolina Center For Behavioral Health, Greer, SC, p. A554

DAIGLE, Richard
  Chief Information Officer, Manchester Memorial Hospital, Manchester, CT, p. A108
  Chief Information Officer, Rockville General Hospital, Vernon, CT, p. A111

DAIKER, David, Chief Information Resource Management, Lincoln Division, NE, p. A386

DAILEY, Gina, Chief Financial Officer, Pinnacle Pointe Hospital, Little Rock-Pulaski County, AR, p. A45

DAILEY, Jacqueline, Chief Information Officer, West Penn Hospital, Pittsburgh, PA, p. A538

DAILEY, Richard R, D.O., President Medical Staff, Ellett Memorial Hospital, Appleton City, MO, p. A355

DAISLEY, Samuel, D.O., Vice President Medical Affairs, Shenango Valley Campus, PA, p. A526

DAJCZAK, Stanislaw, M.D., Chief of Staff, Promedica Defiance Regional Hospital, Defiance, OH, p. A481

DALBY, William, Director Fiscal Services, Shriners Hospitals For Children-Northern California, Sacramento, CA, p. A82

DALE, Jackson
  Director Management Information Services, Johnston Memorial Hospital, Abingdon, VA, p. A655
  Site Manager Information Systems, Indian Path Medical Center, Kingsport, TN, p. A572

DALE, Jae, Chief Executive Officer, Oro Valley Hospital, Oro Valley, AZ, p. A32

DALEBOUT, Kenneth, Site Administrator, Arroyo Grande Community Hospital, Arroyo Grande, CA, p. A51

DALEY, Robert, CPA
  Chief Financial Officer, Black River Memorial Hospital, Black River Falls, WI, p. A690
  Vice President Fiscal and Information Technology Services, Black River Memorial Hospital, Black River Falls, WI, p. A690

DALGAI, Netrisha, Director of Operations, Sage Memorial Hospital, Ganado, AZ, p. A29

DALL, Jamie, Chief Financial Officer, New Hampshire Hospital, Concord, NH, p. A398

DALLER, Sue, R.N., Assistant Administrator Nursing, Hermann Area District Hospital, Hermann, MO, p. A360

DALLEY, Mark F., Administrator, Gunnison Valley Hospital, Gunnison, UT, p. A647

DALLIS, Donna, R.N., Vice President Patient Care, Northeastern Health System, Tahlequah, OK, p. A507

DALPOAS, Dolan, President and Chief Executive Officer, Abraham Lincoln Memorial Hospital, Lincoln, IL, p. A188

DALTON, Deana, Human Resources, San Juan Health Service District, Monticello, UT, p. A648

DALTON, Eric
  Administrator, Willowbrooke At Tanner, GA, p. A162
  Chief Financial Officer, Memorial Medical Center, CA, p. A73
  Chief Financial Officer, Sutter Tracy Community Hospital, Tracy, CA, p. A92

DALTON, John, President and Chief Executive Officer, Inland Hospital, Waterville, ME, p. A286

DALTON, Leigh, Director of Nursing and Patient Care Services, Highland Hospital, Charleston, WV, p. A682

DALTON, Nissi, Manager Human Resources, Baylor Institute For Rehabilitation At Fort Worth, Fort Worth, TX, p. A604

DALTON, Valerie, R.N., Administrator, Oceans Behavioral Hospital Of Baton Rouge, Baton Rouge, LA, p. A263

DALTON, Wayne, Chief Financial Officer, Lakeview Hospital, Bountiful, UT, p. A646

DALY, Cindy, R.N., Director of Nursing, Syringa Hospital And Clinics, Grangeville, ID, p. A169

DALY, Derek, Chief Executive Officer, Blue Mountain Hospital, John Day, OR, p. A514

DALY, Linda, Vice President Human Resources, Auburn Community Hospital, Auburn, NY, p. A422

DALY, Thomas M, CPA, Chief Financial Officer, University Hospital, Newark, NJ, p. A409

DALY, William, Chief Executive Officer, Pennsylvania Psychiatric Institute, Harrisburg, PA, p. A526

DAMA, Sunil, M.D., Medical Director, Select Specialty Hospital - Cincinnati North, Cincinnati, OH, p. A475

DAMBOISE, Robin, Director Human Resources, Northern Maine Medical Center, Fort Kent, ME, p. A284

D'AMBROSIO, Matthew, MSN, R.N., Chief Nursing Officer, Encompass Health Rehabilitation Hospital Of San Antonio, San Antonio, TX, p. A633

D'AMBROSIO, Paul, Chief Operating Officer, Complex Care Hospital At Tenaya, Las Vegas, NV, p. A394

DAMIANO, Louis, M.D., President, Holy Cross Hospital, Silver Spring, MD, p. A294

D'AMICO, David, Chief Financial Officer, St. Anthony's Rehabilitation Hospital, Lauderdale Lakes, FL, p. A128

D'AMICO, Paul, M.D., Chief of Staff, Carolinas Healthcare System Stanly, Albemarle, NC, p. A447

DAMM, Julie, Chief Financial Officer, Hancock County Health System, Britt, IA, p. A218

DAMMEYER, Matt, Ph.D., Chief Operating Officer, Central Peninsula Hospital, Soldotna, AK, p. A27

DAMODARAN, A N, M.D., President Medical Staff, Starke Hospital, Knox, IN, p. A208

DAMON, Chad, Contractor, St. Vincent Dunn Hospital, Bedford, IN, p. A200

DAMON, Kerry, Director Human Resources, Baystate Franklin Medical Center, Greenfield, MA, p. A300

D'AMORE, Seanna, Director Human Resources, Penn Highlands Elk, Saint Marys, PA, p. A540

DAMRON, Greg, Vice President Finance and Chief Financial Officer, Children's Hospital Of Georgia, GA, p. A147

DAMRON, Paul, Chief Financial Officer, Highlands Regional Medical Center, Sebring, FL, p. A139

DAMRON, Tony, Senior Vice President and Chief Information Officer, Pikeville Medical Center, Pikeville, KY, p. A259

DAMSCHRODER, Robin, Chief Operating Officer, St. Joseph Mercy Livingston Hospital, Howell, MI, p. A315

DANBDALA, Kayyan, M.D., Medical Director, Schick Shadel Hospital, Seattle, WA, p. A676

DANCER, Stephanie, Manager Human Resources, Pauls Valley General Hospital, Pauls Valley, OK, p. A505

DANCY, Peter C., Jr, Director, Alexandria Veterans Affairs Health Care System, Pineville, LA, p. A277

DANDORPH, Michael J, President and Chief Operating Officer, Rush Children's Hospital, IL, p. A179

DANE, Brenda, Director, Human Resources, Highlands Regional Medical Center, Sebring, FL, p. A139

DANE, Jeff, Executive Vice President and Chief Financial Officer, University Medical Center, Lubbock, TX, p. A621

DANEFF, Jeffrey, Chief Financial Officer, Porter Regional Hospital, Valparaiso, IN, p. A215

DANELLO, Sherry, MSN, R.N.
  Vice President and Chief Nursing Officer, Candler Hospital, Savannah, GA, p. A160
  Vice President and Chief Nursing Officer, St. Joseph's Hospital, Savannah, GA, p. A160

DANESHMAND, Alex, D.O., Chief Patient Safety Officer, The Rehabilitation Hospital, FL, p. A123

DANG, Cynthia, Vice President Human Resources, Medical City North Hills, North Richland Hills, TX, p. A626

D'ANGELO, Jennifer, Vice President Information Services, Christian Health Care Center, Wyckoff, NJ, p. A414

DANGERFIELD, Wesley, Community Chief Executive Officer, Summers County Arh Hospital, Hinton, WV, p. A683

D'ANGINA, Joseph, Area Finance Officer, Kaiser Permanente Vallejo Medical Center, Vallejo, CA, p. A93

DANIEL, Christopher W., Administrator, Sterling Surgical Hospital, Slidell, LA, p. A279

DANIEL, Dena, Director Information Systems, Jackson County Memorial Hospital, Altus, OK, p. A495

DANIEL, Joyce, Chief Nursing Officer, Blackwell Regional Hospital, Blackwell, OK, p. A496

DANIEL, Karen
  Chief Executive Officer, Warm Springs Medical Center, Warm Springs, GA, p. A163
  Director Human Resources, Bibb Medical Center, Centreville, AL, p. A16

DANIEL, Ron, Manager Information Systems, Matheny Medical And Educational Center, Peapack, NJ, p. A409

DANIEL, S., M.D., Chief Medical Officer, Spring Valley Hospital Medical Center, Las Vegas, NV, p. A395

DANIELS, Alex, Chief Nurse Executive, U.S. Public Health Service Indian Hospital, Crownpoint, NM, p. A416

DANIELS, Andrew J., Chief Executive Officer, Memorial Regional Health, Craig, CO, p. A98

DANIELS, Andy, Chief Operating Officer, Bucyrus Hospital, Bucyrus, OH, p. A473

DANIELS, Anita, Director, Bronx Psychiatric Center, New York (Includes All Hospitals Located Within The Five Boroughs), NY, p. A431

DANIELS, Betty, M.D., Chief of Staff, St. Bernardine Medical Center, San Bernardino, CA, p. A83

DANIELS, Buddy, Chief Executive Officer, San Angelo Community Medical Center, San Angelo, TX, p. A632

DANIELS, Christine S., R.N., Interim Chief Nursing Officer, Camden Clark Medical Center, Parkersburg, WV, p. A685

DANIELS, Craig M, Chief Financial Officer, Moab Regional Hospital, Moab, UT, p. A647

DANIELS, D. Jeffery., Chief Executive Officer, Mountain River Birthing And Surgery Center, Blackfoot, ID, p. A167

DANIELS, Don, M.D.
Chief Medical Officer, Rollins Brook Community Hospital, Lampasas, TX, p. A619
Executive Vice President and Chief Operating Officer, Swedishamerican - A Division Of Uw Health, Rockford, IL, p. A195

DANIELS, John, M.D., Medical Director, Lifecare Hospitals Of Wisconsin, Pewaukee, WI, p. A701

DANIELS, Judy, Vice President Human Resources, Our Lady Of Bellefonte Hospital, Ashland, KY, p. A249

DANIELS, Karen, MSN, R.N., Chief Nursing Officer, Halifax Regional Medical Center, Roanoke Rapids, NC, p. A459

DANIELS, Kristin, Manager Human Resources, Sutter Center For Psychiatry, Sacramento, CA, p. A82

DANIELS, Mark, M.D., Vice President Physician Enterprise, Northwestern Medicine Delnor Hospital, Geneva, IL, p. A184

DANIELS, S Janette, Director Human Resources, Healthsouth Rehabilitation Hospital Of Fort Smith, Fort Smith-Sebastian County, AR, p. A42

DANIELS, Sarah, Vice President, Information Technology, Mayo Clinic Health System In Mankato, Mankato, MN, p. A334

DANIELS, Susan, Chief Financial Officer, Pawnee County Memorial Hospital And Rural Health Clinic, Pawnee City, NE, p. A389

DANIELS, Todd, M.D., Medical Director, Encompass Health Rehabilitation Hospital Of Arlington, Arlington, TX, p. A584

DANIELS, Troy P, Chief Human Resources Officer, Pine Grove Behavioral Health And Addiction Services, MS, p. A347

DANIELS, W. Peter, FACHE, Executive Vice President and Chief Operating Officer, Carepoint Health Bayonne Medical Center, Bayonne, NJ, p. A402

DANIELSON, Carol, R.N., Senior Vice President and Chief Nursing Officer, Gwinnett Medical Center, GA, p. A156

DANIELYAN, Arman, M.D., Chief of Staff, John Muir Behavioral Health Center, Concord, CA, p. A55

DANN, Doreen, R.N., Chief Operating Officer, Victor Valley Global Medical Center, Victorville, CA, p. A94

DANNA, Denise, Esq, Chief Nursing Officer, University Medical Center, New Orleans, LA, p. A276

DANNENBERG, Walt, Director, Va Long Beach Healthcare System, Long Beach, CA, p. A65

DANNER, Cynthia, Chief Nursing Officer, Northeast Georgia Medical Center Braselton, Braselton, GA, p. A148

DANOWSKI, Dale G, R.N., Senior Vice President, Chief Nursing Officer, St. Vincent's Behavioral Health, CT, p. A107

DANSBY, Tommy, Chief Medical Officer, Cypress Grove Behavioral Health, Bastrop, LA, p. A263

DANUSER, James, Chief Information Officer, Knoxville Division, IA, p. A221

DAOUD, Joudat, M.D., Chief of Staff, Promedica Coldwater Regional Hospital, Coldwater, MI, p. A310

D'APOLLO, Julie, R.N., Director of Nursing, Hampstead Hospital, Hampstead, NH, p. A399

D'AQUILA, Richard, President, Yale-New Haven Hospital-Saint Raphael Campus, CT, p. A110

DARBONNE, Tina, Chief Financial Officer, Central Louisiana State Hospital, Pineville, LA, p. A277

DARBY, Kristin, Chief Information Officer, Cancer Treatment Centers Of America-Eastern Regional Medical Center, Philadelphia, PA, p. A534

DARBY, Sharon, R.N., FACHE, Vice President, Clinical Operations, Children's Hospital Of Richmond At Vcu-Brook Road Campus, Richmond, VA, p. A664

DARCY, Deborah, Human Resources, Chg Hospital Tucson, Llc, Tucson, AZ, p. A37

DARDANO, Anthony, M.D., Chief Medical Officer, Pinecrest Rehabilitation Hospital, FL, p. A121

DARDEAU, Sean T., FACHE, Chief Executive Officer, Porter Regional Hospital, Valparaiso, IN, p. A215

DARDENELLO, Stephanie, Administrator, Lakeside Medical Center, Belle Glade, FL, p. A117

DAREY, Roland, M.D., Medical Director, Wamego Health Center, Wamego, KS, p. A247

DARLING, Cory, Chief Operating Officer, Memorial Hospital Jacksonville, Jacksonville, FL, p. A125

DARMELIO, Matthew P, Chief of Staff, Mon Health Medical Center, Morgantown, WV, p. A685

DARNAUER, Kristina, M.D., Chief of Staff, Hospital District No 1 Of Rice County, Lyons, KS, p. A240

DARNELL, Linda, Director Management Information Systems, King's Daughters' Health, Madison, IN, p. A210

DARRINGTON, Gilbert, Director Human Resources, Jackson Hospital And Clinic, Montgomery, AL, p. A21

DARVIN, Ken, M.D., Chief of Staff, Stroud Regional Medical Center, Stroud, OK, p. A507

DASARO, Lynda, Director Human Resources, Sutter Roseville Medical Center, Roseville, CA, p. A81

DASCENZO, Douglas R, MSN, R.N., Chief Nursing Officer, St. Joseph Mercy Oakland, Pontiac, MI, p. A321

DASHIELD, Luanne G, Personnel Administrator, Deer's Head Hospital Center, Salisbury, MD, p. A294

DASKALAKIS, Tom G, Chief Administrative Officer, West Chester Hospital Surgical Center, OH, p. A493

DASKALAKIS, Tom G., Chief Administrative Officer, West Chester Hospital Surgical Center, OH, p. A493

DASKEVICH, Cris, Chief Executive Officer, Children's Hospital Of San Antonio, TX, p. A632

DASS, Karla, Director Human Resources, Regional General Hospital, Williston, FL, p. A144

DASSENKO, Dennis, Chief Information Officer, Essentia Health Duluth, Duluth, MN, p. A330

DAUBERT, Stephanie
Chief Financial Officer, Nebraska Medicine - Bellevue, Bellevue, NE, p. A382
Chief Financial Officer, Nebraska Medicine - Nebraska Medical Center, Omaha, NE, p. A388

DAUBY, Randall W., CPA, Chief Executive Officer, Pinckneyville Community Hospital, Pinckneyville, IL, p. A193

DAUGHDRILL, Diane, Director Human Resources, Jefferson Davis Community Hospital, Prentiss, MS, p. A352

DAUGHDRILL, Richard, R.N., Chief Executive Officer, Curahealth New Orleans, New Orleans, LA, p. A275

DAUGHERTY, Beth Ann, R.N., M.P.H., Vice President Care Services and Chief Nursing Executive, Sparrow Clinton Hospital, Saint Johns, MI, p. A322

DAUGHERTY, Don, Director Information Systems, Fleming County Hospital, Flemingsburg, KY, p. A251

DAUGHERTY, Marney, Worklife Services Consultant, Brighton Center For Recovery, Brighton, MI, p. A308

DAUGHERTY, Robert Alan., Chief Executive Officer, Sagewest Health Care At Lander, Lander, WY, p. A709

DAUGHERTY, Stephen J.
Chief Executive Officer, Coliseum Center For Behavioral Health, GA, p. A156
Interim Chief Executive Officer, Coliseum Center For Behavioral Health, GA, p. A156

DAUGHTRY, Chris, Chief Executive Officer, Encompass Health Rehabilitation Hospital Of Columbia, Columbia, SC, p. A551

DAUM, Karen, R.N., MS, Vice President and Chief Nursing Officer, Passavant Area Hospital, Jacksonville, IL, p. A186

D'AURIA, Joseph, Director Finance, Goryeb Children's Hospital, NJ, p. A408

DAUTERIVE, F Ralph, M.D., Vice President Medical Affairs, Ochsner Medical Center - Baton Rouge, Baton Rouge, LA, p. A263

DAVACHI, Khosrow, Chief Medical Officer, Bridgepoint Hospital National Harbor, Washington, DC, p. A115

DAVE, Bhasker J, M.D., Superintendent, Mental Health Institute, Independence, IA, p. A224

DAVE, Bhasker J., M.D., Superintendent, Mental Health Institute, Independence, IA, p. A224

DAVE', Rajesh J, M.D., Executive Vice President and Chief Medical Officer, Wilson Memorial Regional Medical Center, NY, p. A423

DAVENPORT, David, Director Human Resources, Washington County Hospital, Nashville, IL, p. A191

DAVENPORT, Douglas, Interim Chief Financial Officer, Mercy Iowa City, Iowa City, IA, p. A224

DAVENPORT, Ginger, Director Human Resources, Promise Hospital Of Dallas, Dallas, TX, p. A597

DAVENPORT, Paula, Chief Nursing Officer, Princeton Baptist Medical Center, Birmingham, AL, p. A15

DAVENPORT, Polly J., BSN, DSC, FACHE
President, Chi St. Vincent Medical Center-North, Sherwood-Pulaski County, AR, p. A48
President, Chi St. Vincent Infirmary Medical Center, Little Rock-Pulaski County, AR, p. A45

DAVES, Ronnie, Chief Executive Officer, North Okaloosa Medical Center, Crestview, FL, p. A119

DAVID, Biff, R.N., Administrator, St. Landry Extended Care Hospital, Opelousas, LA, p. A277

DAVID, Daphne G., President and Chief Executive Officer, North Suburban Medical Center, Thornton, CO, p. A105

DAVID, Michelle, Chief Executive Officer, Valley Hospital Phoenix, Phoenix, AZ, p. A34

DAVID, R Neal, Administrator and Chief of Staff, Madigan Army Medical Center, Tacoma, WA, p. A679

DAVID, Robert G., President, St. John Medical Center, Westlake, OH, p. A493

DAVIDOFF, Ravin, M.D., Chief Medical Officer, Boston Medical Center, Boston, MA, p. A296

DAVIDOW, Daniel N, M.D., Medical Director, Cumberland Hospital For Children And Adolescents, New Kent, VA, p. A661

DAVIDSON, Brian, M.D., President and Chief Medical Officer, St. Mary's Hospital And Medical Center, Grand Junction, CO, p. A101

DAVIDSON, Camille, Director Human Resources, Stanton County Hospital, Johnson, KS, p. A237

DAVIDSON, Diane, Senior Vice President Human Resources, Essentia Health Duluth, Duluth, MN, p. A330

DAVIDSON, Dianne, Chief Operating Officer, Union General Hospital, Farmerville, LA, p. A267

DAVIDSON, Elizabeth, R.N., MSN, Vice President, Patient Care Services, Osf Saint James - John W. Albrecht Medical Center, Pontiac, IL, p. A194

DAVIDSON, Gary, M.D.
Medical Director, Select Specialty Hospital-Johnstown, Johnstown, PA, p. A528
Senior Vice President and Chief Information Officer, Penn Medicine Lancaster General Hospital, Lancaster, PA, p. A529

DAVIDSON, James
Chief Executive Officer, Saint Mary's Regional Medical Center, Russellville-Pope County, AR, p. A48
Director of Information Services, Ferry County Memorial Hospital, Republic, WA, p. A675

DAVIDSON, James N., Troop Commander, Tripler Army Medical Center, Honolulu, HI, p. A165

DAVIDSON, Judy, R.N., I, Chief Nursing Officer, Porter Regional Hospital, Valparaiso, IN, p. A215

DAVIDSON, Nancy, Senior Vice President and Chief Financial Officer, Jackson County Memorial Hospital, Altus, OK, p. A495

DAVIDSON, Rocky, Chief Financial Officer, Larkin Community Hospital Behavioral Health Services, Hollywood, FL, p. A124

DAVIDSON, Stephen, Director Human Resources, Lafayette Regional Health Center, Lexington, MO, p. A363

DAVIDSON, Stuart, President Medical Staff, Mount Desert Island Hospital, Bar Harbor, ME, p. A282

DAVIDSON, Tim, M.D., Chief Executive Physician Services, Providence St. Mary Medical Center, Walla Walla, WA, p. A680

DAVIDSON, Tori, R.N., Chief Nursing Officer, Tsehootsooi Medical Center, Fort Defiance, AZ, p. A29

DAVILA, Susan, Chief Executive Officer, Desert View Hospital, Pahrump, NV, p. A396

DAVIN, Joni, Director Information and Business Management Service Line, Veterans Affairs Eastern Kansas Health Care System-Dwight D. Eisenhower Veterans Affairs Medical Center, KS, p. A246

DAVINI, John, Vice President, St. Rose Hospital, Hayward, CA, p. A61

DAVIS, Adam
Chief Information Officer, Cornerstone Hospital-West Monroe, West Monroe, LA, p. A280
Director Information Technology, Chg Hospital Tucson, Llc, Tucson, AZ, p. A37

DAVIS, Amelia, Director of Nursing, Crossridge Community Hospital, Wynne-Cross County, AR, p. A49

DAVIS, Andrea, Chief Executive Officer, Healthsouth Desert Canyon Rehabilitation Hospital, Las Vegas, NV, p. A394

DAVIS, Andrew L, Jr, Chief Operating Officer, Erie County Medical Center, Buffalo, NY, p. A423

DAVIS, Andy, Chief Operating Officer, St. Vincent's Birmingham, Birmingham, AL, p. A15

DAVIS, Anne, Director Human Resources, Mason District Hospital, Havana, IL, p. A185

DAVIS, Astrid, R.N., Chief Nursing Officer, Wellspan York Hospital, York, PA, p. A546

DAVIS, Autherine, Director Human Resources, D. W. Mcmillan Memorial Hospital, Brewton, AL, p. A15

DAVIS, Barry L., FACHE, President and Chief Executive Officer, Arkansas Methodist Medical Center, Paragould-Greene County, AR, p. A47

DAVIS, Ben, Chief Executive Officer, Osceola Community Hospital, Sibley, IA, p. A229

DAVIS, Betty, Director Administrative Services, Porterville Developmental Center, Porterville, CA, p. A79

DAVIS, Brenda, Vice President Patient Services, Indiana University Health Bedford Hospital, Bedford, IN, p. A199

DAVIS, Brent, Chief Financial Officer, Central Valley Medical Center, Nephi, UT, p. A648

DAVIS, C.J., Chief Executive Officer and Executive Director, Four County Counseling Center, Logansport, IN, p. A210

DAVIS, Charissa, Chief Nursing Officer and Director of Nursing, Oasis Behavioral Health - Chandler, Chandler, AZ, p. A28

DAVIS, Charles, President, Saint Alphonsus Medical Center - Baker City, Baker City, OR, p. A511

DAVIS, Charlotte C, Director Human Resources, Lincoln Trail Behavioral Health System, Radcliff, KY, p. A260

DAVIS, Cheryl, M.D., Chief Medical Officer, Scotland Health Care System, Laurinburg, NC, p. A456

DAVIS, Dan, Managing Director and Chief Financial Officer, Integris Southwest Medical Center, Oklahoma City, OK, p. A503

DAVIS, Daniel E, Chief Financial Officer, Kingwood Medical Center, Kingwood, TX, p. A618

DAVIS, Darcy, Chief Financial Officer, Lakeside Medical Center, Belle Glade, FL, p. A117

DAVIS, David, Chief Operating Officer, Western Maryland Hospital Center, Hagerstown, MD, p. A292

DAVIS, Deborah W., Chief Executive Officer and Vice President Clinical Services, Children's Hospital Of Richmond At Vcu, VA, p. A665

DAVIS, Debra K., Director of Operations, Winner Regional Healthcare Center, Winner, SD, p. A565

DAVIS, Deland, Chief Financial Officer, Indian Health Service - Quentin N. Burdick Memorial Health Care Facility, Belcourt, ND, p. A464

DAVIS, Dell, Director Information Systems, Doctors Hospital Parkway, TX, p. A614

DAVIS, Dustin, Chief Executive Officer, Woodland Springs Hospital, Conroe, TX, p. A594

DAVIS, Elaine, Chief Nursing Officer and Vice President Patient Services, Rmc Anniston, Anniston, AL, p. A13

DAVIS, Evan, Director Technology and Environmental Services, Barbourville Arh Hospital, Barbourville, KY, p. A249

DAVIS, Gannon, Director Human Resources, Medical West, Bessemer, AL, p. A14

DAVIS, Gary, Vice President Information Systems, St. Luke's Baptist Hospital, TX, p. A632

DAVIS, Heather, M.D.
Chief of Staff, Pender Memorial Hospital, Burgaw, NC, p. A448
Administrator, Scott Regional Hospital, Morton, MS, p. A351

DAVIS, Howard Z, M.D., Chief Medical Officer, Providence Tarzana Medical Center, Los Angeles, CA, p. A69

DAVIS, Jack, Vice President Human Resources, St. Luke's Campus, NY, p. A444

DAVIS, James R.
Chief Executive Officer, University Hospital Summerville, Augusta, GA, p. A148
Chief Executive Officer, University Hospital, Augusta, GA, p. A147

DAVIS, Janet, R.N., MS, Senior Vice President and Chief Nursing Officer, Tampa General Hospital Children's Medical Center, FL, p. A141

DAVIS, Janice, Interim Director Human Resources, Gifford Medical Center, Randolph, VT, p. A654

DAVIS, Jeff
Chief Financial Officer, Harrison County Hospital, Corydon, IN, p. A201
Senior Vice President Human Resources, Massgeneral Hospital For Children, MA, p. A297

DAVIS, Jeffrey, D.O., Chief Medical Officer, Palm Beach Children's Hospital, FL, p. A143

DAVIS, Jeremy, Chief Executive Officer, Evanston Regional Hospital, Evanston, WY, p. A708

DAVIS, John, Chief Human Resources Officer, Bristol Bay Area Health Corporation, Dillingham, AK, p. A26

DAVIS, John William Bill".
Chief Executive Officer, Ochsner Medical Center - North Shore, Slidell, LA, p. A279
Chief Executive Officer, Slidell Memorial Hospital, Slidell, LA, p. A279

DAVIS, Johnnie, Director Human Resources, Medicine Lodge Memorial Hospital, Medicine Lodge, KS, p. A241

DAVIS, Jon, Chief Financial Officer, Community Hospital-Fairfax, Fairfax, MO, p. A359

DAVIS, Jonathan S., FACHE, President, Sentara Martha Jefferson Hospital, Charlottesville, VA, p. A656

DAVIS, Karen
Chief Nursing Officer and Vice President, Nursing, Howard County General Hospital, Columbia, MD, p. A291
Interim Chief Executive Officer, Behavioral Health Center, FL, p. A143

DAVIS, Kassi, Director Patient Care Services, Willow Crest Hospital, Miami, OK, p. A501

DAVIS, Kelly, Chief Nursing Officer, Anmed Health Rehabilitation Hospital, Anderson, SC, p. A549

DAVIS, Kenneth, M.D.
Chief Medical Officer, Christus Santa Rosa-Medical Center, TX, p. A632
Assistant Vice President Information Systems, Kennedy Krieger Institute, Baltimore, MD, p. A287

DAVIS, LaKeitha, Director Human Resources, Medical Center Of South Arkansas, El Dorado-Union County, AR, p. A41

DAVIS, Lance, PharmD, Associate Director, Miami Veterans Affairs Healthcare System, Miami, FL, p. A130

DAVIS, Leslie C., President, Magee-Womens Hospital Of Upmc, Pittsburgh, PA, p. A537

DAVIS, Lora, FACHE, Chief Executive Officer, Regional Rehabilitation Hospital, Phenix City, AL, p. A22

DAVIS, Lorraine, Vice President Human Resources, Horn Memorial Hospital, Ida Grove, IA, p. A224

DAVIS, Lyle E., Administrator, Cozad Community Health System, Cozad, NE, p. A383

DAVIS, Malene S., R.N., President and Chief Executive Officer, Capital Hospice, Arlington, VA, p. A655

DAVIS, Margaret, Chief Operating Officer, Pecos County Memorial Hospital, Fort Stockton, TX, p. A604

DAVIS, Mark, M.D.
Chief of Staff, Newberry County Memorial Hospital, Newberry, SC, p. A556
Director Information Systems, Lake Taylor Transitional Care Hospital, Norfolk, VA, p. A662

DAVIS, Marla, Interim Chief Nursing Officer, Pmh Medical Center, Prosser, WA, p. A675

DAVIS, Matt, FACHE, Chief Executive Officer, Conroe Regional Medical Center, Conroe, TX, p. A594

DAVIS, Myra, Senior Vice President and Chief Information Officer, Texas Children's Hospital West Campus, TX, p. A613

DAVIS, Myrna, Manager Human Resources, Palo Verde Hospital, Blythe, CA, p. A53

DAVIS, Natalie, R.N., Interim Chief Nursing Officer, Mcleod Health Clarendon, Manning, SC, p. A555

DAVIS, Pam, Chief Nursing Officer, Galesburg Cottage Hospital, Galesburg, IL, p. A183

DAVIS, Patricia, Chief Nursing Officer, South Central Kansas Medical Center, Arkansas City, KS, p. A232

DAVIS, Paula M, Chief Human Resources Officer, Sonoma Valley Hospital, Sonoma, CA, p. A90

DAVIS, Rachel, Director, Sharp Coronado Hospital And Healthcare Center, Coronado, CA, p. A55

DAVIS, Randy
Chief Executive Officer, Houston County Community Hospital, Erin, TN, p. A569
Chief Executive Officer, Northcrest Medical Center, Springfield, TN, p. A580
Vice President and Chief Information Officer, Cgh Medical Center, Sterling, IL, p. A197

DAVIS, Ray
Administrative Director Information Systems, The Hospitals Of Providence Sierra Campus, El Paso, TX, p. A602
Administrative Director, Providence Children's Hospital, TX, p. A602
Chief Information Officer, The Hospitals Of Providence Transmountain Campus, El Paso, TX, p. A602

DAVIS, Regana, Vice President Human Resources, Tri-State Memorial Hospital, Clarkston, WA, p. A670

DAVIS, Richard
Chief Executive Officer, Central Peninsula Hospital, Soldotna, AK, p. A27
Chief Financial Officer, George Washington University Hospital, Washington, DC, p. A115
Chief Financial Officer, Saint Barnabas Medical Center, Livingston, NJ, p. A406

DAVIS, Richard O., Ph.D., President, Sibley Memorial Hospital, Washington, DC, p. A116

DAVIS, Rick, Chief Operating Officer and Support Services, Coshocton Regional Medical Center, Coshocton, OH, p. A479

DAVIS, Robert, Chief Nursing Officer, Florida Hospital Flagler, Palm Coast, FL, p. A135

DAVIS, Roger K, Director Human Resources, Bourbon Community Hospital, Paris, KY, p. A259

DAVIS, Ronald Anthony, Chief Financial Officer - UCLA Hospital System, Stewart & Lynda Resnick Neuropsychiatric Hospital At Ucla, Los Angeles, CA, p. A70

DAVIS, Roy, M.D., Chief Medical Officer, Children's Hospital At Providence, AK, p. A25

DAVIS, Scott
Chief Executive Officer, Methodist Ambulatory Surgery Hospital - Northwest, San Antonio, TX, p. A633
Chief Executive Officer, Methodist Texsan Hospital, TX, p. A633
Manager Information Technology, Arkansas Surgical Hospital, North Little Rock-Pulaski County, AR, p. A46

DAVIS, Shawn, Chief Information Officer, Tuba City Regional Health Care Corporation, Tuba City, AZ, p. A36

DAVIS, Sondra, Vice President Human Resources & System Development, Central Hartnett Hospital, NC, p. A451

DAVIS, Stephanie, Controller, Healthsouth Rehabilitation Hospital Of Colorado Springs, Colorado Springs, CO, p. A97

DAVIS, Steve, Chief Financial Officer, Shands Lake Shore Regional Medical Center, Lake City, FL, p. A127

DAVIS, Takeisha C., M.D., M.P.H., President and Chief Executive Officer, New Orleans East Hospital, New Orleans, LA, p. A275

DAVIS, Tammy, Director Human Resources, Union County Hospital, Anna, IL, p. A173

DAVIS, Terry, Manager Information Systems, Atchison Hospital, Atchison, KS, p. A232

DAVIS, Teshia, Chief Clinical Officer, Carolinas Continuecare Hospital At Pineville, Charlotte, NC, p. A449

DAVIS, Toby, Chief Nursing Officer, Good Samaritan Hospital, Bakersfield, CA, p. A52

DAVIS, Todd, M.D., Vice President Medical Affairs, Patient Safety Officer, Caromont Regional Medical Center, Gastonia, NC, p. A453

DAVIS, Tommy, M.D., Chief of Staff, Oakdale Community Hospital, Oakdale, LA, p. A277

DAVIS, Tracy, Chief Executive Officer, Neuropsychiatric Hospital Of Indianapolis, Indianapolis, IN, p. A207

DAVIS, Tracye B., Interim Medical Center Director, Mann-Grandstaff Veterans Affairs Medical Center, Spokane, WA, p. A678

DAVIS, Trish, Chief Nursing Officer, Santa Rosa Medical Center, Milton, FL, p. A131

DAVIS, Verlene, Director Human Resources, Blue Mountain Hospital, John Day, OR, p. A514

DAVIS, Wayne, Manager Human Resources, Jesse Brown Veterans Affairs Medical Center, Chicago, IL, p. A177

DAVIS, Wendy, Associate Vice President and Chief Human Resource Officer, The University Of Toledo Medical Center, Toledo, OH, p. A492

DAVIS, MSN, Dan, R.N., Nurse Administrator, Park City Hospital, Park City, UT, p. A649

DAVIS-HAGENS, Patricia, R.N., Central Market Leader and President, The Jewish Hospital - Mercy Health, Cincinnati, OH, p. A476

DAVISON, Katie, Executive Director, Human Resources, Nash Health Care Systems, Rocky Mount, NC, p. A459

DAVISON, Trish, R.N., Chief Nursing Officer, Regional West Garden County, Oshkosh, NE, p. A389

DAVISSON, Deborah, MSN, Chief Nursing Officer and Vice President, Patient Care Services, Holy Cross Hospital, Chicago, IL, p. A177

DAVY, Larry, Chief Executive Officer, Wallowa Memorial Hospital, Enterprise, OR, p. A512

DAWE, Jacqueline, R.N., Chief Nursing Officer, Lakes Region General Hospital, Laconia, NH, p. A399

DAWES, John M., FACHE, Chief Executive Officer, Howard A. Rusk Rehabilitation Center, Columbia, MO, p. A358

DAWKINS, David, Director Human Resources, Doctor's Memorial Hospital, Perry, FL, p. A136

DAWSON, Cindy, MSN, R.N., Chief Nursing Executive, University Of Iowa Stead Family Children's Hospital, IA, p. A224

DAWSON, Kane A., Chief Executive Officer, Mission Regional Medical Center, Mission, TX, p. A624

DAWSON, Theresa, MSN, R.N., Chief Nursing Officer, Oaklawn Hospital, Marshall, MI, p. A319

DAWSON, Trang, Chief Information Officer, Baylor Emergency Medical Centers - Keller, TX, p. A585

DAWSON, Troy, M.D., President Medical Staff, Antelope Memorial Hospital, Neligh, NE, p. A387

DAWSON, Zackary L., Chief Executive Officer, Select Specialty Hospital-Oklahoma City, Oklahoma City, OK, p. A504

DAX, Jennifer, Director Human Resources, Gundersen Boscobel Area Hospital And Clinics, Boscobel, WI, p. A690

DAY, Gordy, M.D., Medical Director, Schleicher County Medical Center, Eldorado, TX, p. A603

DAY, John M., Chief Executive Officer, Unity Medical & Surgical Hospital, Mishawaka, IN, p. A211

DAY, Mark, Chief Financial Officer, Twin Cities Hospital, Niceville, FL, p. A132

DAY, Regina
Chief Executive Officer, Hawkins County Memorial Hospital, Rogersville, TN, p. A579
Director of Finance, Hancock County Hospital, Sneedville, TN, p. A580
Executive Director Finance, Mountain View Regional Medical Center, Norton, VA, p. A663
Executive Vice President of Finance, Lonesome Pine Hospital, Big Stone Gap, VA, p. A655

DAY, Scott, Vice President Human Resources, Exempla West Pines, CO, p. A106

DAY, Sherry Clouse, CPA
Chief Financial Officer, Mercy Hospital Cassville, Cassville, MO, p. A357
Chief Financial Officer, Mercy St. Francis Hospital, Mountain View, MO, p. A365
Vice President Finance and Regional Chief Financial Officer, Mercy Hospital Aurora, Aurora, MO, p. A355

DAY, Therese, Chief Financial Officer, University Campus, MA, p. A306

DAY, Victoria, Chief Financial Officer and Vice President of Ancillary Services, Sharp Coronado Hospital And Healthcare Center, Coronado, CA, p. A55

DAYAO, Jerome, MSN, Chief Nursing Officer, Arrowhead Regional Medical Center, Colton, CA, p. A55

DE BOND, Virginia, Chief Financial Officer, Woodlands Specialty Hospital, The Woodlands, TX, p. A640

DE FARIA, Ludmila, M.D., Chief Medical Officer, Eastside Psychiatric Hospital, Tallahassee, FL, p. A140

DE JESUS, Alexander, M.D., Medical Director, Healthsouth Rehabilitation Hospital Of Sarasota, Sarasota, FL, p. A139

DE JESUS, Jorge, Executive Director, I. Gonzalez Martinez Oncologic Hospital, Hato Rey, PR, p. A713

DE LA CRUZ, Rosemary, Chief Financial Officer, Hospital Episcopal San Lucas Guayama, Guayama, PR, p. A713

DE LA GARZA, Josiah, Chief Operating Officer, Baylor Scott & White Medical Center - Sunnyvale, Sunnyvale, TX, p. A638

DE LA PAZ, Christine, Director Human Resources, Aurora Charter Oak Hospital, Covina, CA, p. A55

DE LEON, Aurea, Chief Human Resources Officer, Hospital Universitario Dr. Ramon Ruiz Arnau, Bayamon, PR, p. A712

DE LEON, Darcy, Executive Director, Human Resources, Adventist Health Howard Memorial, Willits, CA, p. A95

DE LEON, Dennis, M.D., Associate Chief Medical Officer and Vice President Medical Affairs, Highline Medical Center, Burien, WA, p. A670

DE LOS REYES, Jay, Chief Executive Officer, Lake Huron Medical Center, Port Huron, MI, p. A321

DE LOS SANTOS, Conrad, President Medical Staff, Medical West, Bessemer, AL, p. A14

DE LOS SANTOS, Ruben, M.D., Chief Medical Officer, Fort Duncan Regional Medical Center, Eagle Pass, TX, p. A600

DE NESHEREA, Alexander, M.D., Chief Medical Officer, Children's Hospital At Dartmouth, NH, p. A399

DE ONIS, Luis, Interim Chief Human Resources Officer, Stony Brook Southampton Hospital, NY, p. A443

DE PIANO, Linda, Ph.D., Chief Executive Officer, Jerome Golden Center For Behavioral Health, Inc., West Palm Beach, FL, p. A143

DE SANTIAGO, Elizabeth, Executive Director, Hospital De Psiquiatria, San Juan, PR, p. A715

DE SHAZO, Sherri, R.N., Senior Vice President and Hospital Administrator, Wakemed North Family Health And Women's Hospital, NC, p. A459

DE TORRES, Francisco, M.D., Medical Director, Ashford Presbyterian Community Hospital, San Juan, PR, p. A715

DEAK, Terry, Chief Financial Officer, Lodi Memorial Hospital West, CA, p. A64

DEAKYNE, John R, Chief Financial Officer, Saint Mary's Regional Medical Center, Reno, NV, p. A396

DEAL, Larry, R.N., Chief Executive Officer, Vibra Hospital Of Northwestern Indiana, Crown Point, IN, p. A202

DEAL, Lisa, Budget Analyst, U.S. Public Health Service Indian Hospital, Eagle Butte, SD, p. A560

DEAL, Roy, Chief Medical Officer, Emerald Coast Behavioral Hospital, Panama City, FL, p. A135

DEAN, Douglas B, Chief Human Resources Officer, Children's Of Alabama, Birmingham, AL, p. A14

DEAN, Douglas F., Jr, Chief Executive Officer, Elliot Hospital, Manchester, NH, p. A400

DEAN, Joel, Director Information Services, Piedmont Medical Center, Rock Hill, SC, p. A556

DEAN, Laura L, Director Human Resources, Wilson Medical Center, Neodesha, KS, p. A241

DEAN, Les, President and Chief Executive Officer, Sumner Regional Medical Center, Wellington, KS, p. A247

DEAN, Marty, Chief Executive Officer, Northlake Behavioral Health System, Mandeville, LA, p. A273

DEAN, Morre, Chief Executive Officer, Porter Adventist Hospital, Denver, CO, p. A99

DEAN, Ronald, Chief Executive Officer, Troy Regional Medical Center, Troy, AL, p. A23

DEAN, Sam, Administrator, Usa Health University Hospital, Mobile, AL, p. A21

DEAN, Thomas, M.D., Chief of Staff, Avera Weskota Memorial Hospital, Wessington Springs, SD, p. A565

DEANGELIS, Lisa, MD, Acting Physician-in-Chief, Memorial Sloan-Kettering Cancer Center, New York (Includes All Hospitals Located Within The Five Boroughs), NY, p. A433

DEARDORFF, John A., President and Chief Executive, Northern Virginia Market, Reston Hospital Center, Reston, VA, p. A664

DEARY, Shirley, Director Human Resources, Glenbeigh Hospital And Outpatient Centers, Rock Creek, OH, p. A489

DEASON, Lori, Director, Lakeside Behavioral Health System, Memphis, TN, p. A575

DEATER, Gary A, Vice President Administration, Human Resources and Risk Management, Witham Health Services, Lebanon, IN, p. A210

DEATON, David, Chief Executive Officer, Ozark Health Medical Center, Clinton-Van Buren County, AR, p. A40

DEATON, Eric, Executive Vice President, Chief Operating Officer and Corporate Operating, Hancock County Hospital, Sneedville, TN, p. A580

DEATON, Mike, Chief Financial Officer, Ozark Health Medical Center, Clinton-Van Buren County, AR, p. A40

DEATON, Susan Renodin, Human Resources Director, Logan Memorial Hospital, Russellville, KY, p. A260

DEATON, Timothy C., Chief Executive Officer, Curahealth Nashville, Nashville, TN, p. A577

DEBBAS, Elias, M.D., President Medical Staff, Fort Washington Medical Center, Oxen Hill, MD, p. A293

DEBEVEC, Teresa, Chief Executive Officer and Administrator, Cook Hospital & Care Center, Cook, MN, p. A329

DEBLANC, Hunt, M.D., Chief of Staff, Opelousas General Health System-South Campus, LA, p. A277

DEBLASIS, John
Vice President, Belmont Community Hospital, Bellaire, OH, p. A472
Vice President, Harrison Community Hospital, Cadiz, OH, p. A473

DEBLIEUX, Dawna, Vice President Patient Care Services and Chief Nurse Executive, Natchitoches Regional Medical Center, Natchitoches, LA, p. A275

DEBLOIS, Georgean, M.D., Chairman Medical Staff, Johnston-Willis Hospital, VA, p. A664

DEBLOUW, Christina, Chief Executive Officer, Select Specialty Hospital-Flint, Flint, MI, p. A313

DEBOER, Cynthia D, Chief Financial Officer, Cedar Springs Hospital, Colorado Springs, CO, p. A97

DEBOER, K. C., President and Chief Executive Officer, Prairie Lakes Healthcare System, Watertown, SD, p. A565

DEBOLT, Larry W, Chief Financial Officer, Bluffton Regional Medical Center, Bluffton, IN, p. A200

DEBONA, Paul, Chief Executive Officer, Baylor Surgical Hospital At Fort Worth, Fort Worth, TX, p. A604

DEBONO, Julie, Director, Human Resources, Umass Memorial Healthalliance-Clinton Hospital, MA, p. A301

DEBOOY, Ann, R.N., Chief Nursing Officer, Memorial Medical Center, Las Cruces, NM, p. A418

DEBORD, Thomas, Chief Operating Officer, Overlake Medical Center, Bellevue, WA, p. A669

DEBRUYCKER, Allison, Administrator, Magnolia Behavioral Hospital Of East Texas, Longview, TX, p. A620

DECASPERIS, Ilyssa, Director of Human Resources, Parkview Community Hospital Medical Center, Riverside, CA, p. A81

DECELIS, Lori, Director Human Resources, Hampton Behavioral Health Center, Westampton, NJ, p. A414

DECELL, Daniela, Chief Executive Officer, Medical City Las Colinas, Irving, TX, p. A615

DECHABERT, Rebecca, Acting Director Personnel, New York State Psychiatric Institute, New York (Includes All Hospitals Located Within The Five Boroughs), NY, p. A434

DECHANT, David, Chief Human Resources Officer, Va Medical Center, Tomah, WI, p. A704

DECKARD, Rick, Chief Fiscal Service, Chillicothe Veterans Affairs Medical Center, Chillicothe, OH, p. A474

DECKARD, Steven D, Vice President Human Resources, Indiana University Health Bloomington Hospital, Bloomington, IN, p. A200

DECKER, Diann, Chief Human Resource Officer, Provo Canyon Behavioral Hospital, Orem, UT, p. A649

DECKER, Janet, Assistant Vice President, Information Systems, Medstar Union Memorial Hospital, Baltimore, MD, p. A288

DECKER, Jeanine, Manager Human Resources, Arizona State Hospital, Phoenix, AZ, p. A32

DECKER, Kevin, Chief Executive Officer, Forrest City Medical Center, Forrest City-St. Francis County, AR, p. A42

DECKER, Michael, President and Chief Executive Officer, Divine Savior Healthcare, Portage, WI, p. A701

DECKER, Wyatt, Chief Executive Officer, Mayo Clinic in Arizona, Mayo Clinic Hospital, Phoenix, AZ, p. A33

DECORTE, Raymond P, M.D., Chief Medical Officer, Doctors Hospital Of Jefferson, LA, p. A274

DECREMER, Dean, Information Systems Manager, Dickinson County Healthcare System, Iron Mountain, MI, p. A316

DEE, Thomas A., President and Chief Executive Officer, Southwestern Vermont Medical Center, Bennington, VT, p. A653

DEEN, Cecelia, Esq, Chief Nursing Officer, Southeast Colorado Hospital District, Springfield, CO, p. A105

DEERING, Linda, MSN, R.N., President, Advocate Sherman Hospital, Elgin, IL, p. A182

DEERING, Lisa
Administrator, Heatherhill Care Communities, Chardon, OH, p. A474
Chief Executive Officer, Regency Hospital Of Cleveland - West, OH, p. A492

DEETER, Joe, MS, Director Information Systems, Clifton-Fine Hospital, Star Lake, NY, p. A443

DEFIGUIEREDO, Kathy, Director, Information Technology, Chi St. Luke's Health Memorial Livingston, Livingston, TX, p. A620

DEFOE, Mike, Chief Financial Officer, Perry Memorial Hospital, Princeton, IL, p. A194

DEFORD, Drexel, Chief Information Officer, Scripps Mercy Hospital Chula Vista, CA, p. A84

DEFRANCESCO, Anthony, Associate Director, Va Long Beach Healthcare System, Long Beach, CA, p. A65

DEFREECE, Daniel, M.D., Interim President, Chi Health St. Mary'S, Nebraska City, NE, p. A387

DEFURIO, Anthony C, Executive Vice President Chief Financial Officer, Levine Children's Hospital, NC, p. A449

DEFURIO, Ken, President and Chief Executive Officer, Butler Health System, Butler, PA, p. A521

DEGEAR, David O, M.D., Vice President Medical Affairs, Westfields Hospital And Clinic, New Richmond, WI, p. A700

DEGENNARO, Vincent, M.D., Chief of Staff, Miami Veterans Affairs Healthcare System, Miami, FL, p. A130

DEGINA, Anthony M, President and Chief Executive Officer, Largo Medical Center - Indian Rocks, FL, p. A128

DEGNAN, William, Vice President Finance, Frankford Campus, PA, p. A535

DEGRAVELLE, Eric, Director Human Resources, Thibodaux Regional Medical Center, Thibodaux, LA, p. A280

DEGROOD, Robert, M.D., Chief Medical Staff, Carolinas Hospital System Marion, Mullins, SC, p. A555

DEGROOT, Daniel, President and Chief Executive Officer, Stoughton Hospital Association, Stoughton, WI, p. A703

DEGROOT, Randy, President and Chief Executive Officer, Promedica Coldwater Regional Hospital, Coldwater, MI, p. A310

DEHAAI, Sarah, R.N., Director of Nursing, Avera Hand County Memorial Hospital, Miller, SD, p. A562

DEHART, Kristen, Chief Executive Officer, Excelsior Springs Hospital, Excelsior Springs, MO, p. A359

DEHAVEN, Bryce, Chief Financial Officer, South Campus, CO, p. A96

DEHERRERA, Barbara, Chief Nursing Officer, Garfield County Public Hospital District, Pomeroy, WA, p. A674

DEHNING, Cielo, M.D., Medical Director, Mid-America Rehabilitation Hospital, Shawnee Mission, KS, p. A246

DEIBEL, Justin, Senior Vice President and Chief Financial Officer, Mercy Medical Center, Baltimore, MD, p. A288

DEININGER, Robert, Chief Executive Officer, Florida Hospital Fish Memorial, Orange City, FL, p. A133

DEIS, Terrence G., CPA, FACHE
President, Saint Joseph Berea, Berea, KY, p. A249
President, Saint Joseph London, London, KY, p. A255
President, Saint Joseph Mount Sterling, Mount Sterling, KY, p. A258

DEITRICK, Diana, Director Information Services, Devereux Hospital And Children's Center Of Florida, Melbourne, FL, p. A129

DEJACO, Lynn S, Chief Financial Officer, Firsthealth Moore Regional Hospital - Richmond, NC, p. A458

DEJESUS, David, Senior Vice President Human Resources, Tobey Hospital, MA, p. A299

DEJONG, Tyler, Director of Operational Finance, Chi Health Midlands, Papillion, NE, p. A389

DEKEYZER, Ron, Regional Director Information Systems, Christus St. Vincent Physicians Medical Center, NM, p. A419

DEKOK, Joni, Chief Nursing Officer, Sanford Sheldon Medical Center, Sheldon, IA, p. A229

DEKONING, Bernard L., M.D., Chief of Staff, Wm. Jennings Bryan Dorn Veterans Affairs Medical Center, Columbia, SC, p. A552

DEKREY, Dale, MS, Associate Director Operations and Resources, Fargo Veterans Affairs Health Care System, Fargo, ND, p. A465

DEKREY, Daniel, M.D., Chief of Staff, Sanford Bemidji Medical Center, Bemidji, MN, p. A328

DEKRUSE, Jet L., Administrator, Humboldt County Mental Health, Eureka, CA, p. A57

DEL CASTILLO, Daniel, Chief Executive Officer, Healthsouth Rehabilitation Hospital Of San Juan, San Juan, PR, p. A715

DEL GAUDIO, Frank J., Director and Chief Executive Officer, Essex County Hospital Center, Cedar Grove, NJ, p. A403

DEL GUIDICE, Mary Margaret, MSN, R.N., Chief Nursing Officer, Pennsylvania Hospital, Philadelphia, PA, p. A536

DEL RIO, R Maxilimien, M.D., Medical Director, Northern Virginia Mental Health Institute, Falls Church, VA, p. A658

DEL TORO, Gustavo, M.D., Chief Medical Officer, Wyckoff Heights Medical Center, New York (Includes All Hospitals Located Within The Five Boroughs), NY, p. A438

DEL TORO, Ivan E, M.D., Medical Director, Hima San Pablo Caguas, Caguas, PR, p. A712

DELA TORRE, Victor, Command Legal Officer, Naval Hospital Lemoore, Lemoore, CA, p. A64

DELAGARDELLE, Pamela K., President and Chief Executive Officer, Unitypoint Health - Allen Hospital, Waterloo, IA, p. A231

DELAHANTY, Paula
Regional Chief Nursing Officer, Pen Bay Medical Center, Rockport, ME, p. A286
Regional Chief Nursing Officer, Waldo County General Hospital Maine Health, Belfast, ME, p. A283

DELANCEY, Darlene, Interim Director, Albany Stratton Veterans Affairs Medical Center, Albany, NY, p. A421

DELANEY, Bryan, Director Information Technology, Crossroads Community Hospital, Mount Vernon, IL, p. A190

DELANEY, Kristi, Director, Human Resources, Siskin Hospital For Physical Rehabilitation, Chattanooga, TN, p. A567

DELANEY, Patrick, Administrative Director, Operations, Robert Wood Johnson University Hospital Somerset, Somerville, NJ, p. A411

DELATTE, Sandra, Director Human Resources, Villa Feliciana Medical Complex, Jackson, LA, p. A269

DELAVAN, Karen, Interim Director Human Resources, Comanche County Medical Center, Comanche, TX, p. A593

DELEON, Arsenio V, M.D., Chief Medical Officer, Select Specialty Hospital-Macomb County, Mount Clemens, MI, p. A319

DELEON, Dennis, M.D., Chief Medical Officer, King Region, St. Francis Hospital, Federal Way, WA, p. A672

DELEON, Joseph, President, Texas Health Harris Methodist Hospital Fort Worth, Fort Worth, TX, p. A605

DELEON, Marcos
Vice President Community Engagement, Truman Medical Center-Hospital Hill, Kansas City, MO, p. A362
Vice President Community Engagement, Truman Medical Center-Lakewood, Kansas City, MO, p. A362

DELEON, Sherilene, Chief Financial Officer, Spring Mountain Treatment Center, Las Vegas, NV, p. A395

DELFS, Michael, Chief Executive Officer, Mercy Hospital, Moose Lake, MN, p. A336

DELGADO, Eric
Chief Financial Officer, Lakewood Regional Medical Center, Lakewood, CA, p. A64
Chief Financial Officer, Placentia-Linda Hospital, Placentia, CA, p. A78

DELGADO, Lupe, Coordinator Human Resources, Kindred Hospital Sugar Land, Sugar Land, TX, p. A637

DELGADO, Pete, President and Chief Executive Officer, Salinas Valley Memorial Healthcare System, Salinas, CA, p. A83

DELGRECO, Trish, Director of Nursing, Ohiohealth Medcentral Shelby Hospital, Shelby, OH, p. A490

D'ELIA, Peter, Chief Financial Officer, Saint Vincent Hospital, Worcester, MA, p. A306

DELIEN, Rudie, Director of Human Resources, Devereux Advanced Behavioral Health Georgia, Kennesaw, GA, p. A155

DELLA FLORA, Thomas, Vice President and Chief Information Officer, Catholic Medical Center, Manchester, NH, p. A400

DELLEA, Eugene A., President, Fairview Hospital, Great Barrington, MA, p. A300

DELLER, Jerry, Administrator, United Medical Rehabilitation Hospital, Gretna, LA, p. A268

DELLICKER, Sandra, Director of Human Resources, Saint Anne's Hospital, Fall River, MA, p. A299

DELLOCONO, John, Senior Vice President and Chief Financial Officer, Centrastate Healthcare System, Freehold, NJ, p. A405

DELLSPERGER, Kevin, M.D., Chief Medical Officer, Children's Hospital Of Georgia, GA, p. A147

DELONG, Patricia, Chief Nursing Officer, Essentia Health St. Joseph's Medical Center, Brainerd, MN, p. A328

DELORENZO, David, Senior Director Human Resources, St. Joseph Hospital, NY, p. A424

DELORME, Robert, Vice President Medical Affairs, Community Memorial Hospital, Hamilton, NY, p. A427

DELVEAUX, Joe, Manager Information Services, St. Francis Regional Medical Center, Shakopee, MN, p. A340

DEMAIO, Joan, Vice President Nursing, Milford Hospital, Milford, CT, p. A109

DEMARCO, Victor, Chief Financial Officer, Highbridge Woodycrest Center, NY, p. A431

DEMAREST, Pamela, MSN, R.N., Chief Nursing Officer, Unm Sandoval Regional Medical Center, Inc., Rio Rancho, NM, p. A419

DEMASIE, Dennis, Vice President Information Systems and Chief Information Officer, Rush-Copley Medical Center, Aurora, IL, p. A174

DEMATTEO, Kathleen, Chief Information Officer, New Milford Hospital, CT, p. A107

DEMBLA, Preeti, Chief Medical Officer and Medical Director, Rehabilitation Hospital Of Fort Wayne, Fort Wayne, IN, p. A204

DEMERICH, Lois B, Director Human Resources, Sentara Williamsburg Regional Medical Center, Williamsburg, VA, p. A668

DEMERS, Becky, R.N., Chief Nursing Officer, Samaritan Healthcare, Moses Lake, WA, p. A673

DEMETRIADES, James, Vice President, Operations, Penn Medicine Princeton Medical Center, Plainsboro, NJ, p. A410

DEMING, Mark, Administrator, Finance and Support, Beaumont Hospital - Taylor, Taylor, MI, p. A324

DEMING, Peggy, Executive Vice President and Chief Financial Officer, University Hospital, TX, p. A634

DEMING, Terra, Director Human Resources, Munson Healthcare Otsego Memorial Hospital, Gaylord, MI, p. A313

DEMLAKIAN, Vahan, Director of Human Resources, Gateways Hospital And Mental Health Center, Los Angeles, CA, p. A67

DEMMEL, Ruth, M.D., Chief Medical Officer, Perkins County Health Services, Grant, NE, p. A384

DEMOE, Sara, Chief Financial Officer, North Canyon Medical Center, Gooding, ID, p. A169

DEMORLIS, John, M.D., Chief Medical Staff, Salem Memorial District Hospital, Salem, MO, p. A370

DEMORROW, Dawn P, Chief Human Resources Service, Wilkes-Barre Veterans Affairs Medical Center, Wilkes, PA, p. A544

DEMOSS, Jill, Finance Manager, Guttenberg Municipal Hospital, Guttenberg, IA, p. A223

DEMPSEY, Jeffrey, President, Mercy Children's Hospital, OH, p. A491

DEMPSEY, John J., Chief Executive Officer, Little Colorado Medical Center, Winslow, AZ, p. A38

DEMURO, Rob, M.D., Chief Medical Officer, Moses Ludington Hospital, NY, p. A426

DENCKLAU, Larry, D.O., Chief of Staff, Baylor Scott & White Medical Center - Lake Pointe, Rowlett, TX, p. A631

DENEFF, Randall, Vice President Finance, Mary Free Bed Rehabilitation Hospital, Grand Rapids, MI, p. A314

DENEGRI, David, Chief Financial Officer, Parkwood Behavioral Health System, Olive Branch, MS, p. A351

DENG, Mei, Chief Financial Officer, T. J. Samson Community Hospital, Glasgow, KY, p. A252

DENHAM, Stephanie, Chief Financial Officer and Human Resources Officer, Phillips County Hospital, Malta, MT, p. A377

DENICOLA, Joseph, Chief Executive Officer and Managing Director, Arrowhead Behavioral Health Hospital, Maumee, OH, p. A486

DENIGRIS, Deborah, Chief Nursing Officer, Kingsboro Psychiatric Center, New York (Includes All Hospitals Located Within The Five Boroughs), NY, p. A432

DENIKE, Michael, D.O., Vice President, Medical Affairs, Blanchard Valley Hospital, OH, p. A482

DENIO, Arthur E, Vice President and Chief Financial Officer, Northbay Vacavalley Hospital, CA, p. A57

DENIRO, Lori, Regional Chief Nursing Officer, Mercy Health - St. Elizabeth Youngstown Hospital, Youngstown, OH, p. A494

DENISIENKO, Mary, Vice President Human Resources, Palos Health, Palos Heights, IL, p. A192

DENISON, Rita, Director of Information Systems, Sturgis Hospital, Sturgis, MI, p. A324

DENKER, Jill, Executive Director Human Resources, Lexington Regional Health Center, Lexington, NE, p. A385

DENKINGER, Marshall, M.D., Interim Chief Executive Officer, St. Anthony Summit Medical Center, Frisco, CO, p. A100

DENMARK, Donald, M.D.
Chief Medical Officer, Carondelet St. Joseph's Hospital, Tucson, AZ, p. A37
Chief Medical Officer, Carondelet St. Mary's Hospital, Tucson, AZ, p. A37

DENNETT, Bryan, M.D., Chief of Staff, William Newton Hospital, Winfield, KS, p. A248

DENNIS, Kera, Assistant Administrator, Finance, Uw Medicine/Harborview Medical Center, Seattle, WA, p. A677

DENNIS, Michael, Director, William J. Mccord Adolescent Treatment Facility, Orangeburg, SC, p. A556

DENNISON, Cynthia, Chief Financial Officer, Mercy Allen Hospital, Oberlin, OH, p. A488

DENNY, Donald, M.D., Senior Vice President, Medical Affairs, Penn Medicine Princeton Medical Center, Plainsboro, NJ, p. A410

DENO, Mark S, Chief Operating Officer, South Campus, CO, p. A96

DENSLEY, Tina, R.N., Chief Executive Officer, Weatherford Rehabilitation Hospital, Weatherford, TX, p. A643

DENSON, Anna, Human Resources Specialist, Choctaw Health Center, Philadelphia, MS, p. A352

DENSON, Paula Lajean, M.D., President, Tyler County Hospital, Woodville, TX, p. A645

DENT, Bob, R.N., Senior Vice President, Chief Operating Officer and Chief Nursing Officer, Midland Memorial Hospital, TX, p. A624

DENT, Bruce, Human Resources Director, Heber Valley Medical Center, Heber City, UT, p. A647

DENTEN, Jane, MSN, R.N., Chief Nurse Executive, Advocate Lutheran General Hospital, Park Ridge, IL, p. A192

DENTON, Brian, Administrator, Mercy Hospital Kingfisher, Kingfisher, OK, p. A500

DENTON, Christopher, Chief Financial Officer, Henrico Doctors' Hospital - Retreat Campus, VA, p. A665

DENTON, Genise, Manager Human Resources, John J. Pershing Veterans Affairs Medical Center, Poplar Bluff, MO, p. A366

DENTON, Joe, Executive Vice President and Chief Financial Officer, Rotary Rehabilitation Hospital, AL, p. A20

DENTON, Renee, Chief Operating Officer, Freeman Neosho Hospital, Neosho, MO, p. A365

DENTON, Roy, M.D., Chief Medical Officer, Conway Regional Rehabilitation Hospital, Conway-Faulkner County, AR, p. A40

DENTON, Tony, JD, Senior Vice President and Chief Operating Officer, University of Michigan Health System, C. S. Mott Children's Hospital, MI, p. A307

DENTONI, Terry, Chief Nursing Officer, Zuckerberg San Francisco General Hospital And Trauma Center, San Francisco, CA, p. A86

DENUCCI, Alex, Chief Financial Officer, Franciscan Children'S, Brighton, MA, p. A297

DEPASQUALE, Joseph, M.D., Interim Chief Medical Officer, Saint Michael's Medical Center, Newark, NJ, p. A409

DEPAULIS, Hugh, Interim Vice President and Chief Financial Officer, Mercy Medical Center-Sioux City, Sioux City, IA, p. A229

DEPKO, Mike, Director Information Technology, Brown County Hospital, Ainsworth, NE, p. A381

DEPLONTY, Sandy, Senior Director Clinical Services, War Memorial Hospital, Sault Sainte Marie, MI, p. A323

DEPOMPEI, Patricia
President, Rainbow Babies And Children's Hospital, OH, p. A477
President, University Macdonald Women's Hospital, OH, p. A477

DEPOOTER, Stephen, Chief Information Officer, Norwegian American Hospital, Chicago, IL, p. A178

DEPPERMAN, Kristi, Chief Financial Officer, Memphis Veterans Affairs Medical Center, Memphis, TN, p. A575

DEPPERT, Eric, M.D., Chief Medical Officer, Manatee Memorial Hospital, Bradenton, FL, p. A118

DEPRATO, Jeremy, Director Information Technology, Spine Hospital Of Louisiana (Formally The Neuromedical Center Surgical Hospital), Baton Rouge, LA, p. A264

D'ERAMO, John, Chief Operating Officer, Whiting Forensic Hospital, CT, p. A109

DERAMUS, Brenda, Manager Human Resources, Sutter Lakeside Hospital, Lakeport, CA, p. A64

DERBY, Richard P, Vice President Finance, Barton Memorial Hospital, South Lake Tahoe, CA, p. A90

DERFLINGER, Terri, Site Administrator, Mercy Hospital Of Franciscan Sisters, Oelwein, IA, p. A227

DERK, Tammy, Chief Executive Officer, Lancaster Rehabilitation Hospital, Lancaster, PA, p. A528

DERKS, Jenny, Chief Administrative Officer, Ascension Calumet Hospital, Chilton, WI, p. A691

DERMAN, Nancy, Director Human Resources, Southwest Connecticut Mental Health System, Bridgeport, CT, p. A107

DEROCHE, Richard, Manager Information Technology, Multicare Deaconess Hospital, Spokane, WA, p. A678

DERONCEREY, Josiane, Director Human Resources, Carepoint Health Christ Hospital, Jersey City, NJ, p. A406

DERONDE, Kevin, Chief Executive Officer, Mahaska Health Partnership, Oskaloosa, IA, p. A228

DEROSSITT, James, M.D., Chief of Staff, Forrest City Medical Center, Forrest City-St. Francis County, AR, p. A42

DEROUEN, Jason, Director Management Information Systems, Grace Medical Center, Lubbock, TX, p. A621

DERRICO, Patricia, FACHE, R.N., Chief Nursing Officer, Coliseum Northside Hospital, Macon, GA, p. A156

DERSCH, Stephen, M.D., President Medical Staff, Regency Hospital Of Florence, Florence, SC, p. A553

DERUS, Charles, M.D., Vice President Medical Management, Advocate Good Samaritan Hospital, Downers Grove, IL, p. A181

DERUYTER, David N., M.D., President Medical Staff, Select Specialty Hospital Midtown Atlanta, Atlanta, GA, p. A147

DERYNCK, Dodie, Chief Nursing Officer, Avera Marshall Regional Medical Center, Marshall, MN, p. A334

DESAI, Colleen, Chief Nursing Officer, Holyoke Medical Center, Holyoke, MA, p. A300

DESAI, Nimesh, M.D., Medical Director, Massena Memorial Hospital, Massena, NY, p. A430

DESAI, Shailesh, M.D., Chief of Staff, Baum Harmon Mercy Hospital, Primghar, IA, p. A228

DESALVO, Susan, Manager Human Resources, Bath Veterans Affairs Medical Center, Bath, NY, p. A422

DESANTIS, Vincent, Vice President Finance, Phelps Memorial Hospital Center, Sleepy Hollow, NY, p. A442

DESART, Amy, Vice President, Chief Financial Officer, Missouri Baptist Medical Center, Saint Louis, MO, p. A368

DESCENT, Karen T., Chief Nursing Officer, Parkview Community Hospital Medical Center, Riverside, CA, p. A81

DESCHAMBEAU, Wayne G., President and Chief Executive Officer, Wayne Healthcare, Greenville, OH, p. A483

DESCHENE, Normand E., FACHE, Chief Executive Officer, Lowell General Hospital, Saints Campus, MA, p. A301

DESCHRYVER, Joseph, Chief Executive Officer, Good Samaritan Hospital, San Jose, CA, p. A86

DESEI, Nitin, M.D., Medical Director, Regional Rehabilitation Hospital, Phenix City, AL, p. A22

DESIMINI, Esther Muscari.
    Administrator, Riverside Tappahannock Hospital, Tappahannock, VA, p. A667
    Interim Administrator, Riverside Walter Reed Hospital, Gloucester, VA, p. A659

DESIMONE, Maureen, Chief Operating Officer, Blythedale Children's Hospital, Valhalla, NY, p. A445

DESIMONE, Shane, M.D., Chief of Staff, Jane Todd Crawford Hospital, Greensburg, KY, p. A252

DESJARDINS, Isabelle, M.D., Chief Medical Officer, Vermont Children's Hospital, VT, p. A653

DESJEUNES, Carol, Vice President and Chief Operating Officer, Psychiatric Institute Of Washington, Washington, DC, p. A116

DESMARTEAU, Lisa Jo, Chief Financial Officer, Miami Jewish Home And Hospital For Aged, Miami, FL, p. A130

DESMOND, Debbie, Director Human Resources, Sentara Martha Jefferson Hospital, Charlottesville, VA, p. A656

DESMOND, Heather, Chief Financial Officer, Bibb Medical Center, Centreville, AL, p. A16

DESMOND, Jeffrey, M.D., Chief Medical Officer, C. S. Mott Children's Hospital, MI, p. A307

DESMOND, P Craig., Chief Executive Officer, Southwest General Hospital, San Antonio, TX, p. A634

DESOTELLE, Robert C., President and Chief Executive Officer, Continuing Care Hospital, Lexington, KY, p. A254

DESOTO, James, M.D.
    Vice President Medical Affairs, Mercy Medical Center Redding, Redding, CA, p. A79
    Vice President Medical Affairs, St. Elizabeth Community Hospital, Red Bluff, CA, p. A79

DESOUZA, Jacqueline, Chief Executive Officer, Research Psychiatric Center, MO, p. A361

DESPRES, Paul J., Chief Executive Officer, Eleanor Slater Hospital, Cranston, RI, p. A547

DESROCHES, Jeff, Director Information Systems, Ahmc Anaheim Regional Medical Center, Anaheim, CA, p. A50

DESTEFANO, Geraldine, R.N., MS, Chief Nursing Officer, Jfk Medical Center North Campus, West Palm Beach, FL, p. A143

DESTEFANO, Stephen, Chief Financial Officer, Magee Rehabilitation Hospital, Philadelphia, PA, p. A535

DETILLIO, Joshua, Chief Executive Officer, Palms West Hospital, Loxahatchee, FL, p. A128

DETTERMAN, B Lynn.
    President and Chief Executive Officer, Mercy Health - Willard Hospital, Willard, OH, p. A493
    President and Chief Executive Officer, Mercy Hospital Of Defiance, Defiance, OH, p. A481
    President and Chief Executive Officer, Mercy Tiffin Hospital, Tiffin, OH, p. A491

DETTMER, Brantley, Administrator and Chief Operating Officer, Kaiser Foundation Hospital Westside Medical Center, Hillsboro, OR, p. A513

DETWILER, Eric, Director Information Technology, Barnes-Kasson County Hospital, Susquehanna, PA, p. A542

DEURMIER, Carol, Chief Executive Officer, St. Michael's Hospital Avera, Tyndall, SD, p. A564

DEUTSCH, Stephen, Vice President Operations and Support, Spencer Hospital, Spencer, IA, p. A230

DEVANATHAN, Raja, M.D., Chief Medical Officer, Vibra Hospital Of Northwestern Indiana, Crown Point, IN, p. A202

DEVARAJ, Kiran S., Chief Medical Officer and Chief Clinical Officer, Highland Hospital, Charleston, WV, p. A682

DEVARAJAN, Vadakkipalayam N., Chief Medical Staff, St. Charles Parish Hospital, Luling, LA, p. A273

DEVAULT, Jennifer, Vice President Associate Services, F. F. Thompson Hospital, Canandaigua, NY, p. A424

DEVAULT, Rosanne, Chief Financial Officer, Mckenzie-Willamette Medical Center, Springfield, OR, p. A518

DEVAULT, Roseann M, Chief Financial Officer, Tennova Healthcare-Jefferson Memorial Hospital, Jefferson City, TN, p. A571

DEVAUX, Sheri, Information Technology Manager, Connecticut Veterans Home And Hospital, Rocky Hill, CT, p. A110

DEVERA, Rozelle, Director of Information Systems, Gateways Hospital And Mental Health Center, Los Angeles, CA, p. A67

DEVEREUX, Chris, Human Resources Director, Business Partner, Edward Hospital, Naperville, IL, p. A190

DEVILLE, Linda F., Chief Executive Officer, Bunkie General Hospital, Bunkie, LA, p. A265

DEVIN, Brian V., Chief Executive Officer, Pappas Rehabilitation Hospital For Children, Canton, MA, p. A299

DEVIN, Joseph, Chief Financial Officer, Boone County Hospital, Boone, IA, p. A218

DEVINE, Joseph W, FACHE, President, New Jersey Division Jefferson Health, Jefferson Washington Township Hospital, NJ, p. A412

DEVINE, Kathryn, Vice President Human Resources, Western Psychiatric Institute And Clinic, PA, p. A538

DEVITA, James, M.D., Chief Medical Officer, Tewksbury Hospital, Tewksbury, MA, p. A305

DEVITO, Joseph M, Vice President Finance and Chief Operating Officer, Geisinger-Bloomsburg Hospital, Bloomsburg, PA, p. A521

DEVLIN, James, Director Information Systems, St. Cloud Regional Medical Center, Saint Cloud, FL, p. A138

DEVOCELLE, Frank H., President and Chief Executive Officer, Olathe Medical Center, Olathe, KS, p. A242

DEVORE, Druery, Chief of Medical Staff, Northern Hospital Of Surry County, Mount Airy, NC, p. A457

DEVORE, Paul A, M.D., Medical Director, Gladys Spellman Specialty Hospital And Nursing Center, Cheverly, MD, p. A290

DEVORSETZ, Marc, Chief Executive Officer, Baylor Scott & White Surgical Hospital At Sherman, Sherman, TX, p. A635

DEW, Douglas, M.D., President Medical Staff, Flagler Hospital, Saint Augustine, FL, p. A137

DEWAN, Vijay, M.D., Clinical Director, Lincoln Regional Center, Lincoln, NE, p. A386

DEWANE, Patti, Vice President Finance and Treasurer, Swedishamerican - A Division Of Uw Health, Rockford, IL, p. A195

DEWAR, William, M.D., Chief of Staff, Wayne Memorial Hospital, Honesdale, PA, p. A527

DEWBERRY, Robbie, Chief Executive Officer, Mitchell County Hospital, Colorado City, TX, p. A593

DEWERFF, Michael, Chief Financial Officer, Younker Memorial Rehabilitation Center, IA, p. A221

DEWISPELARE, Cheryl M, Chief Human Resources Officer, Veterans Affairs Nebraska-Western Iowa Health Care System, Omaha, NE, p. A389

DEWITT, Alan Neil, Chief Medical Officer, Summit Healthcare Regional Medical Center, Show Low, AZ, p. A36

DEWITT, Jocelyn, Ph.D., Vice President and Chief Information Officer, American Family Children's Hospital, WI, p. A696

DEWORTH, Gerald M, Associate Director, Carl Vinson Veterans Affairs Medical Center, Dublin, GA, p. A153

DEXTER, Heather, Chief Executive Officer, Emory Saint Joseph's Hospital Of Atlanta, Atlanta, GA, p. A146

DEXTER, Sue, Administrative Department Leader Human Resources, Mcdonough District Hospital, Macomb, IL, p. A188

DEYARMIN, James A, Controller, Children's Hospital Of Richmond At Vcu-Brook Road Campus, Richmond, VA, p. A664

DEYNOODT, Mary, Interim Chief Executive Officer and Chief Operating Officer, Ochsner Medical Center - West Bank, LA, p. A276

DEYO-ALLERS, Margaret, Vice President, Chief Nursing Officer, St. Luke's Cornwall Hospital - Newburgh Campus, NY, p. A438

DEYOUNG, Keith, M.D., Chief Medical Staff, Wallowa Memorial Hospital, Enterprise, OR, p. A512

DHAWAN, Ajay, M.D., Chief of Staff, Veterans Affairs Northern Indiana Health Care System-Marion Campus, IN, p. A204

DHAWAN, Rahul, M.D., Chief Medical Officer, St. Francis Medical Center, Lynwood, CA, p. A70

DHILION, Avtar, Medical Director, The Pavilion At Williamsburg Place, Williamsburg, VA, p. A668

DHILLON, Avtar, M.D., Medical Director, Newport News Behavioral Health Center, Newport News, VA, p. A662

DHULIPALA, Vasudeva, M.D., Medical Director, Healthsouth Rehabilitation Hospital Of Alexandria, Alexandria, LA, p. A262

DHUPER, Aman, President and Chief Executive Officer, St. Rose Hospital, Hayward, CA, p. A61

DI BERNARDO, Deborah, Chief Information Officer, Saint Joseph's Medical Center, Yonkers, NY, p. A446

DIAL, Jody S, Chief Financial Officer, Timpanogos Regional Hospital, Orem, UT, p. A649

DIAL, Ray D., Director of Nursing, Nebraska Medicine - Bellevue, Bellevue, NE, p. A382

DIALTO, Margaret, Regional Chief Human Resource Officer, Staten Island University Hospital, New York (Includes All Hospitals Located Within The Five Boroughs), NY, p. A437

DIAMOND, Anne, President and Chief Executive Officer, Day Kimball Hospital, Putnam, CT, p. A110

DIAMOND, Kevin M., M.D., Chief Medical Officer, Lawrence Memorial Hospital, Walnut Ridge-Lawrence County, AR, p. A49

DIAMOND, Lester K., President, St. Dominic-Jackson Memorial Hospital, Jackson, MS, p. A348

DIAMOND, Timothy, Chief Information Officer, Southlake Campus, IN, p. A204

DIANDA-MARTIN, Barb, Chief Nursing Officer, Mercy St. Anne Hospital, Toledo, OH, p. A491

DIANGELO, John A.
    President and Chief Executive Officer, Bridgeton Health Center, NJ, p. A413
    President and Chief Executive Officer, Inspira Medical Center-Elmer, Elmer, NJ, p. A404
    President and Chief Executive Officer, Inspira Medical Center-Woodbury, Woodbury, NJ, p. A414

DIASIO, Anthony J, Chief Financial Officer, Fox Chase Cancer Center-American Oncologic Hospital, Philadelphia, PA, p. A534

DIATI, Raquel, Chief Executive Officer, Sacred Oak Medical Center, Houston, TX, p. A613

DIAZ, Al, M.D., Chief Executive Officer, Kindred Hospital Rome, Rome, GA, p. A159

DIAZ, Evelyn, R.N., Chief Nursing Officer, Healthsouth Hospital Of Manati, Manati, PR, p. A714

DIAZ, Georgina
    Chief Executive Officer, Jackson South Community Hospital, FL, p. A130
    Chief Operating Officer, Palmetto General Hospital, Hialeah, FL, p. A124

DIAZ, Janine, Human Resources Manager, Emory Rehabilitation Hospital, Atlanta, GA, p. A146

DIAZ, Jesse, Chief Information Officer, Phoebe North, GA, p. A145

DIAZ, Jimmy, Director Information Technology, Odessa Regional Medical Center, Odessa, TX, p. A626

DIAZ, Jose, Director Information Systems, St. Vincent Evansville, Evansville, IN, p. A203

DIAZ, Ron, Manager Operations, Albany Stratton Veterans Affairs Medical Center, Albany, NY, p. A421

DIAZ, Sandra, Administrator, Baptist Emergency Hospital - Schertz, TX, p. A632

DIAZ, Steve, M.D., Chief Medical Officer, Mainegeneral Medical Center-Augusta Campus, ME, p. A282

DIBBLE, Lynn, Vice President Patient Care Services, Guthrie Towanda Memorial Hospital, Towanda, PA, p. A542

DIBNER, David A, FACHE
    Senior Vice President Hospital Operations and Musculoskeletal Strategic Areas, Nyu Langone Orthopedic Hospital, NY, p. A436
    Senior Vice President Hospital Operations and Musculoskeletal Strategic Areas, Rusk Institute At Nyu-Hjd, NY, p. A436

DICESARE, Jan, Vice President Financial Operations, St. Vincent's East, Birmingham, AL, p. A15

DICICCO, Marilyn, Director Human Resources, Chestnut Hill Hospital, Philadelphia, PA, p. A534

DICK, Andy, Director Information Services, Saline Memorial Hospital, Benton-Saline County, AR, p. A39

DICK, David, Chief Executive Officer, Huron Regional Medical Center, Huron, SD, p. A561

DICK, Lynette, Director of Support Services, Ellsworth County Medical Center, Ellsworth, KS, p. A234

DICK, Mollie, Coordinator Human Resources, Wayne County Hospital, Monticello, KY, p. A258

DICK, Myra, Manager Business Office, Amg Specialty Hospital-Wichita, Wichita, KS, p. A247

DICKENS, Betty, Director Human Resources, Sierra Tucson, Tucson, AZ, p. A37

DICKENS, Shelby, Director, Patient Care Services, Fort Madison Community Hospital, Fort Madison, IA, p. A223

DICKERSON, Gene, M.D., Vice President Medical Affairs, Palmetto Health Tuomey, Sumter, SC, p. A557

DICKERSON, Kathy, Chief Financial Officer, Encompass Health Rehabilitation Hospital Of Arlington, Arlington, TX, p. A584

DICKERSON, Michelle, Chief Nursing Officer, Frye Regional Medical Center-South Campus, NC, p. A454

DICKERSON, Sandra, Chief Executive Officer, Greenwood County Hospital, Eureka, KS, p. A235

DICKERSON, Taylor, Chief Information Officer, Lake City Medical Center, Lake City, FL, p. A127

DICKERSON, Toby, Chief Information Resources Management Services, Durham Veterans Affairs Medical Center, Durham, NC, p. A451

DICKEY, Ashley, Director Human Resources, Benson Hospital, Benson, AZ, p. A28

DICKEY, John M, Chief Administrative Officer, Mayo Clinic Health System In Eau Claire, Eau Claire, WI, p. A692

DICKEY, Mark, Director Business Development, Valir Rehabilitation Hospital, Oklahoma City, OK, p. A505

DICKEY, Sarah J., Human Resource Directory of People and Culture, Mahaska Health Partnership, Oskaloosa, IA, p. A228

DICKINSON, Ashley, Chief Executive Officer, La Porte Hospital, La Porte, IN, p. A209

DICKINSON, Cathy C, Vice President Human Resources, Baptist Health Medical Center - North Little Rock, North Little Rock-Pulaski County, AR, p. A47

DICKINSON, Galen, Chief Financial Officer, Cary Medical Center, Caribou, ME, p. A283

DICKINSON, Lani, Chief Executive Officer, Emanuel Medical Center, Turlock, CA, p. A92

DICKLICH-COBB, Cristy, Chief Nursing Officer, Memorial Hospital Of Converse County, Douglas, WY, p. A708

DICKMAN, Kathy, Director of Information Systems, Highpoint Health, Lawrenceburg, IN, p. A210

DICKREITER, Adrian, Vice President Technology, Nix Health Care System, San Antonio, TX, p. A633

DICKS, Mandy, Director of Nursing, Lake Butler Hospital Hand Surgery Center, Lake Butler, FL, p. A127

DICKSON, Anita, Director Human Resources, Five Rivers Medical Center, Pocahontas-Randolph County, AR, p. A48

DICKSON, Scott, Director Information Technology, Reeves Memorial Medical Center, Bernice, LA, p. A264

DICKSON, William, Executive Director, Capital District Psychiatric Center, Albany, NY, p. A421

DIDDLE, Derrick, Chief Information Officer, Colorado Canyons Hospital And Medical Center, Fruita, CO, p. A101

DIDENKO, Dima, Chief Financial Officer, Florida Hospital Tampa, Tampa, FL, p. A140

DIDERRICH, Mary Kay., R.N.
Chief Executive Officer, Select Specialty Hospital-Madison, Madison, WI, p. A696
Chief Executive Officer, Select Specialty Hospital-Milwaukee, Milwaukee, WI, p. A699

DIDRIKSON, Lynne, M.D., Chief Medical Officer, Cavalier County Memorial Hospital And Clinics, Langdon, ND, p. A467

DIEBLING, Tara, Chief Executive Officer, Cardinal Hill Rehabilitation Hospital, Lexington, KY, p. A254

DIEDERICH, John A, Senior Vice President Operations and Chief Operating Officer, Rush-Copley Medical Center, Aurora, IL, p. A174

DIEDRICH, Michele, R.N., Chief Nursing Officer, Vice President Patient Care, Baptist Health Medical Center-Little Rock, Little Rock-Pulaski County, AR, p. A45

DIEGEL, James A., FACHE, Chief Executive Officer, Howard University Hospital, Washington, DC, p. A115

DIEHL, Robert, President, Mark Twain Medical Center, San Andreas, CA, p. A83

DIENER, D Michael., Chief Executive Officer, Fayette County Memorial Hospital, Washington Court House, OH, p. A493

DIERKENS, Janelle, Chief Administration Officer, New York State Psychiatric Institute, New York (Includes All Hospitals Located Within The Five Boroughs), NY, p. A434

DIERKER, Anne, Vice President Hospital Services, Unitypoint Health-Pekin Hospital, Pekin, IL, p. A193

DIERS, Suzanne, R.N., Director Patient Care Services, Shriners Hospitals For Children-Portland, Portland, OR, p. A516

DIESTEL, Peter, Senior Vice President and Chief Operating Officer, Valley Hospital, Ridgewood, NJ, p. A411

DIETER, Brian, President and Chief Executive Officer, Mary Greeley Medical Center, Ames, IA, p. A217

DIETERICH, Kevin, Director Information Services, Inland Hospital, Waterville, ME, p. A286

DIETLIN, Steve, Chief Executive Officer, Tri-City Medical Center, Oceanside, CA, p. A76

DIETRICH, Brenda, Chief Human Resources Officer, Banner Boswell Medical Center, Sun City, AZ, p. A36

DIETRICK, Brian, Director Information Systems, Wilson Medical Center, Wilson, NC, p. A462

DIETSCH, Barry, Chief Financial Officer, Virginia Gay Hospital, Vinton, IA, p. A230

DIETSCHE, Jim, Chief Financial Officer, Bellin Memorial Hospital, Green Bay, WI, p. A693

DIETZ, Brian, Interim Chief Executive Officer, Mcdonough District Hospital, Macomb, IL, p. A188

DIETZ, Michael, Administrator, U.S. Air Force Hospital, Hampton, VA, p. A659

DIETZE, Zachary K., Chief Executive Officer, Seton Medical Center Harker Heights, Harker Heights, TX, p. A608

DIFRANCO, Vincent, Interim Chief Executive Officer, South Big Horn County Hospital, Basin, WY, p. A707

DIGUILIO, Jason, Controller, Uh Avon Rehabilitation Hospital, Avon, OH, p. A471

DIIESO, Nicholas T, R.N., Chief Operating Officer, Mount Auburn Hospital, Cambridge, MA, p. A298

DIIORIO, Emil, M.D., Chief Executive Officer, Surgical Specialty Center At Coordinated Health, Allentown, PA, p. A519

DIKE, Charles, M.D., Chief of Staff, Sanford Worthington Medical Center, Worthington, MN, p. A342

DIKOS, Julie A., MSN, R.N., President and Chief Executive Officer, Asheville Specialty Hospital, Asheville, NC, p. A447

DILALLO, Kevin, Chief Executive Officer, Manatee Memorial Hospital, Bradenton, FL, p. A118

DILISI, Jeffrey P, Vice President and Chief Medical Officer, Virginia Hospital Center, Arlington, VA, p. A655

DILLARD, Evan S., M.P.H., FACHE, Chief Executive Officer, Pine Grove Behavioral Health And Addiction Services, MS, p. A347

DILLARD, Sharon, Chief Nursing Officer, Poinciana Medical Center, Kissimmee, FL, p. A127

DILLEHUNT, David B
Chief Information Officer, Firsthealth Montgomery Memorial Hospital, Troy, NC, p. A461
Chief Information Officer, Firsthealth Moore Regional Hospital - Richmond, NC, p. A458

DILLIE, Codie, Chief Executive Officer, Select Specialty Hospital-Quad Cities, Davenport, IA, p. A220

DILLION, Tim, Vice President of Human Resources, Devereux Hospital And Children's Center Of Florida, Melbourne, FL, p. A129

DILLON, Jim, Chief Financial Officer, Rangely District Hospital, Rangely, CO, p. A105

DILLON, Lorie, Chief Executive Officer, Geisinger Healthsouth Rehabilitation Hospital, Danville, PA, p. A523

DILLON, Mary E, MS, R.N., Vice President Patient Care Services, St. Joseph Hospital, NY, p. A424

DILORENZO, Randolph, M.D., Medical Director, Syosset Hospital, Syosset, NY, p. A443

DILORETO, David, M.D., Executive Vice President and Chief Medical Officer, Presence Saint Francis Hospital, Evanston, IL, p. A182

DIMAMBRO, Christina, Chief Financial Officer, Havasu Regional Medical Center, Lake Havasu City, AZ, p. A30

DIMARCO, Lisa, R.N., FACHE, Vice President Patient Care Service and Chief Nursing Officer, Little Company Of Mary Hospital And Health Care Centers, Evergreen Park, IL, p. A183

DIMARE, John, M.D., Medical Director, Foothill Presbyterian Hospital, Glendora, CA, p. A60

DIMEK, Carolyn, Acting Superintendent, Dorothea Dix Psychiatric Center, Bangor, ME, p. A282

DIMICHELE, Maria, Administrative Assistant, Kensington Hospital, Philadelphia, PA, p. A535

DIMITROVA, Gergana, M.D., Medical Director, Carolina Center For Behavioral Health, Greer, SC, p. A554

DIMM, Adam, Chief Executive Officer, J. C. Blair Memorial Hospital, Huntingdon, PA, p. A527

DIMMICK, Scott, Senior Vice President and Chief Human Resources Officer, Lakeland Regional Health Medical Center, Lakeland, FL, p. A127

DIMOND, Margaret, Ph.D., President and Chief Executive Officer, Mclaren Oakland, Pontiac, MI, p. A321

DIMURIA, Asja, Chief Financial Officer, Abrazo West Campus, Goodyear, AZ, p. A30

DINARDO, Mark, Chief Nursing Officer, Healthsouth Rehabilitation Hospital Of Modesto, Modesto, CA, p. A72

DINGER, Bradley
Chief Financial Offical, Upmc Hamot, Erie, PA, p. A525
Financial Representative, Upmc Northwest, Seneca, PA, p. A541

DINGILIAN, John, M.D., Chief Medical Officer, Simi Valley Hospital, Simi Valley, CA, p. A90

DINGLE, Steve, M.D., Chief Medical Officer, Arizona State Hospital, Phoenix, AZ, p. A32

DINGLEDINE, Jon, Senior Director Human Resources and Support Services, Mercer Health, Coldwater, OH, p. A478

DINGLER, Chance, M.D., Chief Medical Officer, Nocona General Hospital, Nocona, TX, p. A626

DINHAM, Vilma L, R.N., Chief Nursing Officer, Encino Hospital Medical Center, Los Angeles, CA, p. A66

DINKHA, Duncan, M.D., Chief of Staff, Morrison Community Hospital, Morrison, IL, p. A190

DINKINS, Vicki, Director Human Resources, South Georgia Medical Center Lanier Campus, Lakeland, GA, p. A156

DINON, Nancy, Vice President Human Resources, Health Central Hospital, Ocoee, FL, p. A133

DINSLAGE, Dennis, Vice President Finance and Chief Financial Officer, St. Francis Memorial Hospital, West Point, NE, p. A391

DINSMORE, Brad, Chief Executive Officer, Encompass Health Rehabilitation Hospital Of Austin, Austin, TX, p. A586

DION, Jeffrey P.
Vice President Finance and Chief Financial Officer, Massgeneral For Children At Newton-Wellesley Hospital, MA, p. A302
Vice President Finance, St. Elizabeth's Medical Center, Brighton, MA, p. A297

DIPALMA, Maureen, Chief Financial Officer, Tewksbury Hospital, Tewksbury, MA, p. A305

DIPAOLO, Joseph, FACHE, MBA
President, Hackettstown Medical Center, Hackettstown, NJ, p. A405
President, Newton Medical Center, Newton, NJ, p. A409

DIPIETRO, Sandra P, Chief Financial Officer, St. Tammany Parish Hospital, Covington, LA, p. A266

DISANTE, Ginger, Chief Nursing Executive, Christus Highland Medical Center, LA, p. A278

DISESA, Verdi, M.D., President and Chief Executive Officer, Temple University Hospital - Episcopal Division, PA, p. A536

DISLER, Jordi K., President, Parkview Lagrange Hospital, Lagrange, IN, p. A210

DISPOTO, Martha, R.N., I, Chief Nurse Executive, Anaheim Medical Center, Orange County Irvine Medical Center, CA, p. A50

DISWOOD, Lavenia, R.N., Chief Nurse Executive, Northern Navajo Medical Center, Shiprock, NM, p. A420

DITMANSON, Paul, M.D., Clinical Director, Red Lake Indian Health Service Hospital, Red Lake, MN, p. A337

DITORO, Michael, Chief Operating Officer, Westlake Hospital, Melrose Park, IL, p. A189

DITTBENNER, Beth, Regional Director, Human Resources, Mayo Clinic Health System In Mankato, Mankato, MN, p. A334

DITTMANN, Gerald P, Vice President Human Resources, Mount Nittany Medical Center, State College, PA, p. A541

DITTO, Debbie, CPA, Controller, Lincoln Trail Behavioral Health System, Radcliff, KY, p. A260

DITURO, Beth, Divisional Chief Information Officer, Manhattan Eye, Ear And Throat Hospital, NY, p. A433

DITZLER, Andru, Chief Information Officer, Lebanon Veterans Affairs Medical Center, Lebanon, PA, p. A529

DIVELLO, Douglas F., President and Chief Executive Officer, Grace Cottage Hospital, Townshend, VT, p. A654

DIX, Roger J, Vice President Finance, Hannibal Regional Hospital, Hannibal, MO, p. A360

DIX, Theresa, R.N., Chief Nursing Officer, Wythe County Community Hospital, Wytheville, VA, p. A668

DIXON, Christy, Chief Human Resources Officer, Encompass Health Rehabilitation Hospital Of Humble, Humble, TX, p. A614

DIXON, Debbie, Director Human Resources, Pampa Regional Medical Center, Pampa, TX, p. A627

DIXON, Del, Chief Information Officer, South Shore Hospital, South Weymouth, MA, p. A304

DIXON, Florine, Chief Operating Officer, Memorial Hospital, Carthage, IL, p. A175

DIXON, Gregg
Chief Financial Officer, Asheville Specialty Hospital, Asheville, NC, p. A447
Chief Financial Officer, Carepartners Health Services, Asheville, NC, p. A447

DIXON, John, Chief Medical Officer, Rotary Rehabilitation Hospital, AL, p. A20

DIXON, Lisa, Business Partner and Human Resource Director, Linden Oaks Hospital, Naperville, IL, p. A190

DIXON, Mary E., MSN, R.N., Interim Chief Nursing Officer, University Of Virginia Children's Hospital, VA, p. A656

DIXON, Michael, Director Human Resources, Self Regional Healthcare, Greenwood, SC, p. A554

DIXON, Michael L, Vice President, Human Resources, Beaumont Children's Hospital, MI, p. A322

DIXON, Shannon, Manager Business Office, Weisbrod Memorial County Hospital, Eads, CO, p. A100

DIXON, Todd, R.N., Chief Executive Officer, Navicent Health Baldwin, Milledgeville, GA, p. A157

DOAK, Scott
System Vice President, Human Resources, Unc Lineberger Comprehensive Cancer Center, NC, p. A449
Vice President, Human Resources, Unc Rex Health Care, Raleigh, NC, p. A459

DOAN, Angela, Chief Financial Officer, Scott Memorial Hospital, Scottsburg, IN, p. A214

DOANE, Peter, M.D.
Chief Medical Officer, Franklin Regional Hospital, Franklin, NH, p. A399
Chief Medical Officer, Lakes Region General Hospital, Laconia, NH, p. A399

DOBBINS, Jim, Vice President Human Resources, Unc Lenoir Healthcare, Kinston, NC, p. A456

DOBBS, Jacee, Chief Information Officer, Citizens Medical Center, Colby, KS, p. A233

DOBBS, Stephanie, Chief Nursing Officer, Sanford Clear Lake Medical Center, Clear Lake, SD, p. A560

DOBIE, Linda, R.N., JD, Vice President, Legal Affairs, Torrance Memorial Medical Center, Torrance, CA, p. A92

DOBIN, Jennifer, Executive Vice President Human Resources, Carepoint Health Bayonne Medical Center, Bayonne, NJ, p. A402

DOBIZL, Howard
Director Information Services for the Northern Region, St. Mary's Hospital, WI, p. A702
Director Information Technology Services, Ascension Eagle River Hospital, Eagle River, WI, p. A692
Director Information Technology Services, Ascension Sacred Heart Hospital, Tomahawk, WI, p. A704
Director Information Technology Services, Howard Young Medical Center, Woodruff, WI, p. A706

DOBKIN, Eric D, M.D., Vice President Medical Affairs, Suburban Hospital, Bethesda, MD, p. A290

DOBOSENSKI, David, Chief Executive Officer, St. Croix Regional Medical Center, St Croix Falls, WI, p. A703

DOBOSH, Joseph J, Jr, Vice President and Chief Financial Officer, Children's Specialized Hospital, NJ, p. A408

DOBRAWA, Stanley
Area Information Officer, Kaiser Permanente San Rafael Medical Center, San Rafael, CA, p. A87
Area Information Officer, Kaiser Permanente Santa Rosa Medical Center, Santa Rosa, CA, p. A89

DOBRINSKI, Sandra, Director of Nursing, Comanche County Hospital, Coldwater, KS, p. A233

DOBROVICH, Michael, M.D., Chief Medical Officer, St. John Medical Center, Westlake, OH, p. A493

DOBSON, Glenda, Chief Executive Officer, Cypress Pointe Surgical Hospital, Hammond, LA, p. A268

DOBSON, Glenn E, Vice President, Finance and Chief Financial Officer, Aspirus Iron River Hospitals & Clinics, Inc., Iron River, MI, p. A316

DOBSON, Trey, M.D., Chief Medical Officer, Southwestern Vermont Medical Center, Bennington, VT, p. A653

DODD, John, Vice President Human Resources, Central Peninsula Hospital, Soldotna, AK, p. A27

DODD, Kathy M, Director of Nursing, Southern Virginia Mental Health Institute, Danville, VA, p. A657

DODD, Pam, Chief Operating Officer, Harper County Community Hospital, Buffalo, OK, p. A496

DODDS, George, M.D., Medical Director, Gouverneur Hospital, Gouverneur, NY, p. A427

DODDS, Rick A.
President, Greene Memorial Hospital, Xenia, OH, p. A494
President, Soin Medical Center, Beavercreek, OH, p. A472

DODDS, Sheryl, Chief Clinical Officer, Winter Park Memorial Hospital, FL, p. A134

DODERER, Marcella, FACHE
President and Chief Executive Officer, Arkansas Children's Hospital, Little Rock-Pulaski County, AR, p. A44
President and Chief Executive Officer, Arkansas Children's Northwest, Springdale-Washington County, AR, p. A48

DODGE, Cynthia J., Director Human Resources, Vibra Hospital Of Springfield, Springfield, IL, p. A196

DODGE, Terry, M.D., Chief of Staff, Chester Regional Medical Center, Chester, SC, p. A550

DODSON, Louise, R.N.
Chief Nursing Officer, Wagoner Community Hospital, Wagoner, OK, p. A510

Chief Operating Officer and Chief Nursing Officer, Wagoner Community Hospital, Wagoner, OK, p. A510

DODSON, Paige, M.D., M.P.H., Chief Medical Officer, Susan B. Allen Memorial Hospital, El Dorado, KS, p. A234

DOEHRING, Christopher, M.D.
Vice President Medical Affairs, Franciscan Health Indianapolis, Indianapolis, IN, p. A206
Vice President of Medical Affairs, Franciscan Health Carmel, Carmel, IN, p. A201

DOELING, Mariann, R.N., President, Chi St Alexius Health Carrington Medical Center, Carrington, ND, p. A464

DOELLING, James, Chief Nurse Executive, Va Greater Los Angeles Healthcare System, Los Angeles, CA, p. A70

DOERFLER, Mary P., Chief Human Resources Officer, Central Texas Veterans Health Care System, Doris Miller Veterans Medical Center, TX, p. A638

DOERGE, Jean, R.N., MSN, Nurse Executive, Swedish/Edmonds, Edmonds, WA, p. A671

DOERGE, Jean B, MS, R.N., Chief Nursing Executive, Unitypoint Health - Trinity Bettendorf, Bettendorf, IA, p. A217

DOERING, Dean, Chief Executive Officer, Central Prison Hospital, Raleigh, NC, p. A458

DOERR, Brian, Chief Information Officer, Continuecare Hospital At Baptist Health Corbin, Corbin, KY, p. A250

DOGGETT, Geri, Director Business, East Mississippi State Hospital, Meridian, MS, p. A350

DOGGETT, Sherri L, Vice President Patient Services, Mercy Medical Center-Centerville, Centerville, IA, p. A218

DOHERTY, Allison, Chief Financial Officer, Spine Hospital Of Louisiana (Formerly The Neuromedical Center Surgical Hospital), Baton Rouge, LA, p. A264

DOHERTY, Bryan, Management Information Technology Services I, Sagamore Children's Hospital Psychiatric Center, Dix Hills, NY, p. A425

DOHERTY, Dan, Vice President, Operations, Advocate Trinity Hospital, Chicago, IL, p. A176

DOHERTY, Donna, R.N., Vice President of Nursing and Chief Nursing Officer, Beth Israel Deaconess Hospital Plymouth, Plymouth, MA, p. A303

DOHERTY, Donnie, Director Information Systems, Fairfield Memorial Hospital, Winnsboro, SC, p. A558

DOHERTY, John
Co-President, M Health, University Of Minnesota Masonic Children's Hospital, MN, p. A335
Vice President Finance, University Of Minnesota Masonic Children's Hospital, MN, p. A335

DOHERTY, Randy, CPA, Chief Executive Officer, Healthsouth Braintree Rehabilitation Hospital, Braintree, MA, p. A297

DOHERTY, Ray, Director Information Technology, Cmh Regional Health System, Wilmington, OH, p. A494

DOHMANN, Eileen L, R.N.
Senior Vice President and Chief Nursing Officer, Snowden At Fredericksburg, VA, p. A658
Senior Vice President and Chief Nursing Officer, Stafford Hospital, Stafford, VA, p. A666

DOIDGE, John C, Vice President Finance, Glencoe Regional Health Services, Glencoe, MN, p. A332

DOKKEN, Susan, Chief Human Resources, St. Joseph Regional Medical Center, Lewiston, ID, p. A170

DOKSUM, Kathryn, Director Finance, Samaritan North Lincoln Hospital, Lincoln City, OR, p. A514

DOLAN, Lisa, Interim Chief Executive Officer, St. Joseph Hospital, Fort Wayne, IN, p. A204

DOLAN, Mary, Regional Director Information Services and HIPAA Security Official, Shriners Hospitals For Children-Boston, Boston, MA, p. A297

DOLAN, Steve, Chief Information Officer, Eastpointe Hospital, Daphne, AL, p. A16

DOLBEE, Hilary, Chief Financial Officer, Monroe Hospital, Bloomington, IN, p. A200

DOLBIN, Kathy, Director of Human Resources, Mercy Allen Hospital, Oberlin, OH, p. A488

DOLEN, Cassie, Vice President Finance and Chief Financial Officer, Hutchinson Regional Medical Center, Hutchinson, KS, p. A237

DOLLINS, Gary, Director Management Information Systems, Poplar Bluff Regional Medical Center-South Campus, MO, p. A366

DOLOHANTY-JOHNSON, Bridget, MSN, R.N., Vice President Patient Care Services, Parkview Whitley Hospital, Columbia City, IN, p. A201

DOLORESCO, Laureen, R.N., Associate Director for Patient Care and Nursing Services, James A. Haley Veterans' Hospital-Tampa, Tampa, FL, p. A141

DOMALESKI, Vareen O'Keefe, MS, R.N., Vice Patient Care Services and Chief Nursing Officer, Emma Pendleton Bradley Hospital, East Providence, RI, p. A547

DOMANICO, Lee, Chief Executive Officer, Marin General Hospital, Greenbrae, CA, p. A61

DOMANN, Debbie, Director of Operations, Fillmore County Hospital, Geneva, NE, p. A384

DOMANSKY, John, Vice President Operations, Rutherford Regional Health System, Rutherfordton, NC, p. A460

DOMAYER, Cory, Chief Financial Officer, Florida Hospital Flagler, Palm Coast, FL, p. A135

DOMBROUSKI, Joyce, R.N., Chief Executive Officer, St. Patrick Hospital, Missoula, MT, p. A378

DOMEIER, Sandy, Director Patient Care Services, Ridgeview Sibley Medical Center, Arlington, MN, p. A327

DOMINGO, Connie, M.D., Medical Director, Weisman Children's Rehabilitation Hospital, Marlton, NJ, p. A407

DOMINGUE, Buffy, Chief Executive Officer, Lafayette Surgical Specialty Hospital, Lafayette, LA, p. A271

DOMINGUEZ, Brenda, Director Human Resources, Cypress Creek Hospital, Houston, TX, p. A610

DOMINGUEZ, Ed, President Medical Staff, Vibra Specialty Hospital At Desoto, Desoto, TX, p. A600

DOMINGUEZ, Marie, Commander, Martin Army Community Hospital, Fort Benning, GA, p. A154

DOMINICCI, Sandra, Nursing Director, Hospital De Damas, Ponce, PR, p. A714

DOMINIQUE, Ravon, Chief Nursing Officer, Brentwood Hospital, Shreveport, LA, p. A278

DOMINSKI, Paul, Vice President Human Resources, Park Nicollet Methodist Hospital, Saint Louis Park, MN, p. A339

DOMMER, Matthew, M.D., Chief Medical Officer, Bronson Lakeview Hospital, Paw Paw, MI, p. A320

DOMON, Steven, M.D., Medical Director, Arkansas State Hospital, Little Rock-Pulaski County, AR, p. A44

DONAHEY, Kenneth C., Chief Executive Officer, Oviedo Medical Center, Oviedo, FL, p. A134

DONAHUE, Edward, M.D., Chief Medical Officer, St. Joseph's Westgate Medical Center, AZ, p. A34

DONAHUE, Kristine Marie, Administrator, Clinical Operations, Beaumont Hospital - Taylor, Taylor, MI, p. A324

DONAHUE, Michael, M.D., Medical Director, Select Specialty Hospital-Pittsburgh/Upmc, Pittsburgh, PA, p. A537

DONAHUE, Ruth, R.N., Chief Nursing Officer, Harrison County Hospital, Corydon, IN, p. A201

DONAHUE, Samantha, Director Human Resources, Crossing Rivers Health Medical Center, Prairie Du Chien, WI, p. A701

DONALD, Steve, M.D., Chief of Staff, Washington County Hospital, Chatom, AL, p. A16

DONALDSON, Brooke G, Assistant Administrator Human Resources, Jackson Hospital, Marianna, FL, p. A129

DONALDSON, David, Chief Executive Officer, Henrico Doctors' Hospital - Parham, VA, p. A665

DONALDSON, Jill, Vice President Operations, Medstar Harbor Hospital, Baltimore, MD, p. A288

DONALDSON, Les, M.D., Chief of Staff, Roosevelt General Hospital, Portales, NM, p. A418

DONALDSON, Lori, Chief Financial Officer, Uc San Diego Shiley Eye Institute, CA, p. A84

DONALDSON, Nesha, Chief Financial Officer, Cullman Regional Medical Center, Cullman, AL, p. A16

DONALDSON, Shirley, Chief Financial Officer, Pecos Valley Lodge, NM, p. A419

DONATELLE, Lawrence, M.D., Vice President Medical Affairs, Ascension Northeast Wisconsin St. Elizabeth Hospital, Appleton, WI, p. A689

DONATO, Cyndy, Vice President, Human Resources, Missouri Baptist Medical Center, Saint Louis, MO, p. A368

DONAWAY, Duane, Director Information Technology, Hendrick Health System, Abilene, TX, p. A582

DONELAN, Matthias B, M.D., Chief of Staff, Shriners Hospitals For Children-Boston, Boston, MA, p. A297

DONENWIRTH, Karl, Vice President Information Services, Northcoast Behavioral Healthcare, Northfield, OH, p. A488

DONGILLI, Paul, Jr, Ph.D., FACHE
President and Chief Executive Officer, Madonna Rehabilitation Hospital, Lincoln, NE, p. A386
President and Chief Executive Officer, Madonna Rehabilitation Specialty Hospital, Bellevue, NE, p. A382

DONHAM, Guyle, M.D., Chief of Staff, Comanche County Medical Center, Comanche, TX, p. A593

DONICA, Joanna, Director Human Resource, Pam Rehabilitation Hospital Of Beaumont, Beaumont, TX, p. A588

DONLEY, Linda, Vice President Operations, Ira Davenport Memorial Hospital, Bath, NY, p. A422

DONLIN, Bruce, Director Information Services, Mount Desert Island Hospital, Bar Harbor, ME, p. A282

DONLIN, John
Director Human Resources, Shriners Hospitals For Children-Springfield, Springfield, MA, p. A304
Regional Director Human Resources - Boston, Erie, and Springfield, Shriners Hospitals For Children-Boston, Boston, MA, p. A297

DONLIN, Michael T., FACHE, Administrator, Floyd Valley Healthcare, Le Mars, IA, p. A225

DONNELLY, James E, Chief Nursing Officer and Vice President Patient Care Services, Upmc Hamot, Erie, PA, p. A525

DONNELLY, Margaret, Interim President, Crittenton Children's Center, MO, p. A362

DONNELLY, Sheryl, Human Resources Specialist, State Hospital South, Blackfoot, ID, p. A167

DONNELY, Lisa, Controller II, Central Texas Rehabilitation Hospital, Austin, TX, p. A585

DONOFRIO, Kathryn, Chief Nursing Officer, Swedish Covenant Hospital, Chicago, IL, p. A180

DONOGHUE, Alicia, Director Human Resources, Eastpointe Hospital, Daphne, AL, p. A16

DONOHUE, Mary Ann T, Ph.D., R.N., Chief Patient Care Services Officer, Stony Brook Southampton Hospital, NY, p. A443

DONOHUE-RYAN, MaryAnn, Ph.D., Vice President Patient Care Services, Englewood Hospital And Medical Center, Englewood, NJ, p. A405

DONOVAN, Andrew
  Director Information Technology, Ascension Southeast Wisconsin Hospital - Elmbrook Campus, Brookfield, WI, p. A690
  Regional Director Information Services, Wheaton Franciscan Healthcare - St. Joseph'S, Milwaukee, WI, p. A699

DONOVAN, James W, President and Chief Executive Officer, Lincolnhealth Miles Campus, ME, p. A283

DONOVAN, James W., President and Chief Executive Officer, Lincolnhealth St. Andrews Campus, ME, p. A283

DONOVAN, Jenny, Director Human Resources, Wright Memorial Hospital, Trenton, MO, p. A371

DONOVAN, Kevin, FACHE
  President and Chief Executive Officer, Franklin Regional Hospital, Franklin, NH, p. A399
  President and Chief Executive Officer, Lakes Region General Hospital, Laconia, NH, p. A399

DONOVAN, Mary, Controller, Encompass Health Rehabilitation Institute Of Tucson, Tucson, AZ, p. A37

DONOVAN, Mike, Chief Financial Officer, Lemuel Shattuck Hospital, Jamaica Plain, MA, p. A300

DONOVAN, Patrick, M.D., Director Medical Staff, Encompass Health Rehabilitation Hospital Of Fort Worth, Fort Worth, TX, p. A604

DONSON, Elliott, Chief Information Specialist, Lincoln Hospital, Davenport, WA, p. A671

DONZE, Richard D, D.O., Senior Vice President Medical Affairs, Chester County Hospital, West Chester, PA, p. A544

DOODY, Kris A., R.N., Chief Executive Officer, Cary Medical Center, Caribou, ME, p. A283

DOOKEERAM, David, Chief Operating Officer, Porter Adventist Hospital, Denver, CO, p. A99

DOOLEY, Jerry, Interim Chief Executive Officer, Castleview Hospital, Price, UT, p. A649

DOOLEY, Kimberly H., Administrator, Lafayette General Surgical Hospital, Lafayette, LA, p. A271

DOOLEY, Lisa, Health Information Officer, Middlesboro Arh Hospital, Middlesboro, KY, p. A258

DOOLEY, Mark J., Chief Executive Officer, Putnam Community Medical Center, Palatka, FL, p. A134

DOOLING, Edward, Vice President, Human Resources, Masonicare Health Center, Wallingford, CT, p. A111

DOOLITTLE, Jon D., Regional President, Northwest Medical Center, Albany, MO, p. A355

DOORENBOS, Pamela, M.D., Vice President, Medical Affairs, Maple Grove Hospital, Maple Grove, MN, p. A334

DOORN, Douglas, Chief Executive Officer, Lewis And Clark Specialty Hospital, Yankton, SD, p. A565

DOPERAK, Martin, Commander, Weed Army Community Hospital, Fort Irwin, CA, p. A58

DORAN, Judy, R.N., Vice President of Hospital Services and Chief Nurse Executive, Carolinas Healthcare System Stanly, Albemarle, NC, p. A447

DORAN, Ken, Interim Chief Executive Officer, Sierra Surgery Hospital, NV, p. A392

DORAN, T, M.D., Chief of Staff, Perry Memorial Hospital, Princeton, IL, p. A194

DORIA, Thomas
  Vice President and Patient Services - West, Morton Plant North Bay Hospital, New Port Richey, FL, p. A132
  Vice President and Patient Services West, St. Anthony's Hospital, Saint Petersburg, FL, p. A138
  Vice President Patient Services - West, Morton Plant Hospital, Clearwater, FL, p. A119
  Vice President, Patient Services and Chief Nursing Officer, Mease Countryside Hospital, Safety Harbor, FL, p. A137
  Vice President, Patient Services and Chief Nursing Officer, Mease Dunedin Hospital, Dunedin, FL, p. A122

DORION, Heath, Physician Administrator, Mercy Health - St. Elizabeth Boardman Hospital, Boardman, OH, p. A472

DORITY, Paula, Director Human Resources, Martin County Hospital District, Stanton, TX, p. A637

DORMAN, Christopher, President and Chief Executive Officer, Tift Regional Medical Center, Tifton, GA, p. A162

DORMAN, Doug, Vice President Human Resources, Roger C. Peace Rehabilitation Hospital, SC, p. A553

DORMAN, Julie, Human Resources Director, Parkwood Behavioral Health System, Olive Branch, MS, p. A351

DORMAN, Stephen, M.D., Chief Medical Officer, Pecos Valley Lodge, NM, p. A419

DORNOFF, Edward G., Associate Director, Battle Creek Veterans Affairs Medical Center, Battle Creek, MI, p. A308

DOROGY, Sharon, Chief Information Officer, The Children's Institute Of Pittsburgh, Pittsburgh, PA, p. A538

DOROTHY, Jonnie, Senior Director Human Resources, Massena Memorial Hospital, Massena, NY, p. A430

DORR, Amy
  Vice President Human Resources, Mclaren Lapeer Region, Lapeer, MI, p. A317
  Vice President Human Resources, Mclaren Orthopedic Hospital, MI, p. A317

DORRIS, Steve, Chief Financial Officer, Poplar Bluff Regional Medical Center-South Campus, MO, p. A366

DORSCH, Anthony, Chief Financial Officer, Children's Hospital At Providence, AK, p. A25

DORSEY, Bob, Human Resources Coordinator, Select Specialty Hospital - Lincoln, Lincoln, NE, p. A386

DORSEY, John T, M.D., Vice President Physician Services and Chief Medical Officer, Mercyhealth Hospital - Rockton Avenue, Rockford, IL, p. A194

DORSEY, Michael A., FACHE, Chief Executive Officer, Johnson Regional Medical Center, Clarksville-Johnson County, AR, p. A40

DORSEY, William, M.D., Board Chairman and Chief Executive Officer, Jackson Park Hospital And Medical Center, Chicago, IL, p. A177

DORST, Jake, Chief Information Officer, Tahoe Forest Hospital District, Truckee, CA, p. A92

D'ORTENZIO, Gabe, Director of Human Resources, Weirton Medical Center, Weirton, WV, p. A687

DORTON, Patty, Director of Nursing, Buchanan General Hospital, Grundy, VA, p. A659

D'ORTONA, Cary, President, Arnold Palmer Hospital For Children, FL, p. A134

DOSCHER, Suzanne C., Chief Executive Officer, Fairfield Memorial Hospital, Winnsboro, SC, p. A558

DOSHI, Nikunj, D.O., Chief Medical Officer, Banner Gateway Medical Center, Gilbert, AZ, p. A29

DOSI, Abhishek, Chief Executive Officer, Sutter Solano Medical Center, Vallejo, CA, p. A93

DOSS, Delilah, Director, Human Resources, Mountainview Regional Medical Center, Las Cruces, NM, p. A418

DOSS, Mounir F
  Executive Vice President and Chief Financial Officer, Flushing Hospital Medical Center, New York (Includes All Hospitals Located Within The Five Boroughs), NY, p. A432
  Executive Vice President and Chief Financial Officer, Jamaica Hospital Medical Center, New York (Includes All Hospitals Located Within The Five Boroughs), NY, p. A432

DOSSETT, Jeffrey, Chief Operating Officer, Abrazo West Campus, Goodyear, AZ, p. A30

DOSSETT, Phyllis, Director of Clinical Services, Hancock County Hospital, Sneedville, TN, p. A580

DOSTAL, Drew H., R.N., FACHE, Chief Executive Officer, Ogallala Community Hospital, Ogallala, NE, p. A387

DOTEN, Charles, Chief Executive Officer, Promise Hospital Of Miami, Miami, FL, p. A131

DOTTS-MCCOOL, Michelle, Chief Nursing Officer, St. Vincent Dunn Hospital, Bedford, IN, p. A200

DOTY, Lisa, Manager Human Resources, Desert View Hospital, Pahrump, NV, p. A396

DOUBLE, Ron
  Chief Information Officer, Parkview Huntington Hospital, Huntington, IN, p. A206
  Chief Information Officer, Parkview Noble Hospital, Kendallville, IN, p. A208
  Chief Information Technology Officer, Parkview Lagrange Hospital, Lagrange, IN, p. A210

DOUCETTE, Diane, R.N., President, Mount Carmel New Albany Surgical Hospital, New Albany, OH, p. A487

DOUCETTE, Elmer H, Chief Financial Officer, Redington-Fairview General Hospital, Skowhegan, ME, p. A286

DOUCETTE, Michael J., Senior Vice President and Administrator, Riverside Behavioral Health Center, VA, p. A662

DOUD, Tony
  Controller, St. Joseph Health System, Tawas City, MI, p. A324
  Controller, St. Mary's Of Michigan Standish Hospital, Standish, MI, p. A324

DOUGHERTY, Chuck, Chief Information Officer, Shenandoah Medical Center, Shenandoah, IA, p. A229

DOUGHERTY, David, Chief Information Management Officer, Irwin Army Community Hospital, Junction City, KS, p. A238

DOUGHERTY, James, Commander, U.S. Air Force Medical Center Keesler, Keesler Afb, MS, p. A348

DOUGHERTY, Terry, Director Human Resources, Bryn Mawr Hospital, Bryn Mawr, PA, p. A521

DOUGHTY, Cathy, Vice President Human Resources, Sheppard Pratt Health System, Baltimore, MD, p. A289

DOUGHTY, Linda, Chief Nursing Officer, Alaska Regional Hospital, Anchorage, AK, p. A25

DOUGHTY, Stephanie
  Chief Financial Officer, Mountain Crest Hospital, CO, p. A100
  Chief Financial Officer, Uchealth Medical Center Of The Rockies, Loveland, CO, p. A104

DOUGLAS, Andy, Manager Information Technology, Burnett Medical Center, Grantsburg, WI, p. A693

DOUGLAS, Bill, Senior Vice President and Chief Financial Officer, Riverside Medical Center, Kankakee, IL, p. A187

DOUGLAS, Debbie, Director Human Resources, Putnam County Memorial Hospital, Unionville, MO, p. A371

DOUGLAS, Doug, Interim Vice President Human Resources, Beaufort Memorial Hospital, Beaufort, SC, p. A549

DOUGLAS, Errol A., MS, Vice President, Human Resources, Roswell Park Cancer Institute, Buffalo, NY, p. A423

DOUGLAS, Jason T., Chief Executive Officer, Memorial Medical Center Of Ashland, Ashland, WI, p. A689

DOUGLAS, Johnna, Human Resources Manager, Massac Memorial Hospital, Metropolis, IL, p. A189

DOUGLAS, Kay, Human Resources Director, Carolinas Hospital System, Florence, SC, p. A552

DOUGLAS, Pam, Chief Nursing Officer, Putnam General Hospital, Eatonton, GA, p. A153

DOUGLAS, Paul, Vice President Human Resources, Baton Rouge General Medical Center-Bluebonnet, LA, p. A263

DOUGLAS, Phillip B, Chairman and Chief Executive Officer, Lifecare Hospitals Of North Texas-Fort Worth, TX, p. A596

DOUGLAS-WALSH, Marlene, Chief Executive Officer, Kirkbride Center, Philadelphia, PA, p. A535

DOUVILLE, Arthur, M.D.
  Chief Medical Officer, O'Connor Hospital, San Jose, CA, p. A86
  Chief Medical Officer, Saint Louise Regional Hospital, Gilroy, CA, p. A60

DOVEL, Melissa, Manager Human Resources, Atrium Medical Center Of Corinth, Corinth, TX, p. A594

DOVER, Jaems F., FACHE, Interim Chief Executive Officer, Hshs Holy Family Hospital In Greenville, Greenville, IL, p. A184

DOVER, Jerry, Chief Executive Officer, Sullivan County Memorial Hospital, Milan, MO, p. A364

DOVNARSKY, James, M.D., Director Pulmonary Medical, Kindred Hospital South Philadelphia, Philadelphia, PA, p. A535

DOW, Janet, R.N., Chief Nursing Officer, Santiam Hospital, Stayton, OR, p. A518

DOW, Korry, Interim President, Nashoba Valley Medical Center, Ayer, MA, p. A295

DOW, Laura, Chief Financial Officer, Memorial Children's Hospital, GA, p. A160

DOWDLE, Paula, Chief Operating Officer, Jefferson Healthcare, Port Townsend, WA, p. A675

DOWDY, Kathren, MSN
  Regional Hospital Senior Director, Carilion Tazewell Community Hospital, Tazewell, VA, p. A667
  Senior Director, Chief Executive Officer and Chief Nursing Officer, Carilion Tazewell Community Hospital, Tazewell, VA, p. A667

DOWDY, Michael, Chief Executive Officer, Central Montana Medical Center, Lewistown, MT, p. A377

DOWELL, James, Administrator and Chief Executive Officer, Little River Memorial Hospital, Ashdown, AR, p. A39

DOWERS, Cindy, Chief Nursing Officer, Harsha Behavioral Center, Terre Haute, IN, p. A215

DOWGUN, Richard, Chief Information Officer, St. Francis Medical Center, Trenton, NJ, p. A413

DOWIS, Jeff, M.D., Interim Chief Executive Officer, Mountain Lakes Medical Center, Clayton, GA, p. A150

DOWLING, Deanna, R.N., Chief Nursing Officer, Promise Hospital Of Wichita Falls, Wichita Falls, TX, p. A644

DOWLING, Lisa, Manager Finance, Mercy Hospital Tishomingo, Tishomingo, OK, p. A508

DUGGAL, Harpreet, M.D., Medical Director, Department of Health and Human Services, Humboldt County Mental Health, Eureka, CA, p. A57

DUGGAN, James E, Director Human Resources, Western Massachusetts Hospital, Westfield, MA, p. A306

DUGGAN, Margaret M., M.D., Chief Medical Officer, Brigham And Women's Faulkner Hospital, Boston, MA, p. A296

DUGGAN, Tonya, Director Human Resources, Green Clinic Surgical Hospital, LA, p. A278

DUGGAR, Susan, R.N., MSN, Vice President Nursing, Spartanburg Medical Center, Spartanburg, SC, p. A557

DUGGER, Curtis R., Chief Financial Officer, Memorial Hospital Of Converse County, Douglas, WY, p. A708

DUGGER, Sandy, Chief Human Resources Officer, Platte County Memorial Hospital, Wheatland, WY, p. A710

DUHAIME, Robert A, R.N., Senior Vice President Clinical Operations and Chief Nursing Officer, Catholic Medical Center, Manchester, NH, p. A400

DUHANEY-WEST, Aphreikah, Chief Executive Officer, Teche Regional Medical Center, Morgan City, LA, p. A274

DUHE, Louis, Senior Director Information Technology, George Washington University Hospital, Washington, DC, p. A115

DUHE, Louis H., Executor Director, Information Services, Piedmont Athens Regional Medical Center, Athens, GA, p. A145

DUHON, Thomas, Director Human Resources, Heart Hospital Of Lafayette, Lafayette, LA, p. A271

DUKE, Ezekiel, M.D., Chief of Staff, Knox County Hospital, Knox City, TX, p. A618

DUKE, Lee M, M.D., II, Senior Vice President and Chief Physician Executive, Penn Medicine Lancaster General Hospital, Lancaster, PA, p. A529

DUKES, Brenda, Director Human Resources, Sonoma Developmental Center, Eldridge, CA, p. A57

DUKOFF, Ruth, M.D., Medical Director, North Star Behavioral Health, AK, p. A25

DULANEY, Paul, M.D., Chief of Staff, Troy Regional Medical Center, Troy, AL, p. A23

DULIN, Misty, CAH, Director, Baum Harmon Mercy Hospital, Primghar, IA, p. A228

DULING, Ruth, Chief Executive Officer, Girard Medical Center, Girard, KS, p. A235

DULL, David, M.D., Chief Medical Officer, St. Francis Medical Center, CO, p. A98

DULL, Kevin B
Senior Vice President Human Potential, Allenmore Hospital, WA, p. A679
Senior Vice President Human Potential, Multicare Auburn Medical Center, Auburn, WA, p. A669
Senior Vice President Human Potential, Multicare Good Samaritan Hospital, Puyallup, WA, p. A675
Senior Vice President Human Potential, Multicare Mary Bridge Children's Hospital And Health Center, Tacoma, WA, p. A679

DULNY, David
Chief Financial Officer, Providence Medical Center, Kansas City, KS, p. A238
Chief Financial Officer, Saint John Hospital, Leavenworth, KS, p. A239

DUMAIS, Mark, M.D., Chief Medical Officer, Mercy Medical Center, Springfield, MA, p. A304

DUMAL, Jennifer, R.N., Chief Operating Officer of Clinical and Chief Nursing Officer, Memorial Behavioral Health, MS, p. A346

DUMKE, Steve, FACHE, Executive Vice President and Chief Operating Officer, Christian Health Care Center, Wyckoff, NJ, p. A414

DUMONSEAU, Kent
Vice President Finance and Information Services, Hayward Area Memorial Hospital And Water's Edge, Hayward, WI, p. A694
Vice President Finance and Information Services, Memorial Medical Center Of Ashland, Ashland, WI, p. A689

DUMONT, Amy, R.N., MSN, Chief Nursing Officer, Concord Hospital, Concord, NH, p. A398

DUMONT, Frank, Assistant Vice President Human Resources and Corporate Compliance, Eastern Long Island Hospital, Greenport, NY, p. A427

DUNAVAN, Chad, R.N., Vice President, Chief Nursing Officer, Medical Center Health System, Odessa, TX, p. A626

DUNCAN, Allison, Chief Financial Officer, Arrowhead Behavioral Health Hospital, Maumee, OH, p. A486

DUNCAN, Barbara
Chief Financial Officer, Habersham Medical Center, Demorest, GA, p. A152
Interim Chief Executive Officer, Habersham Medical Center, Demorest, GA, p. A152

DUNCAN, Charles, M.D., Medical Director, Kindred Hospital-San Antonio, San Antonio, TX, p. A633

DUNCAN, Cindy
Director Human Resources, Roosevelt General Hospital, Portales, NM, p. A418

Manager Human Resources, Plains Regional Medical Center, Clovis, NM, p. A416

DUNCAN, Cynthia, Chief Executive Officer, Roger Mills Memorial Hospital, Cheyenne, OK, p. A497

DUNCAN, Erika, Vice President Human Resources, St. Joseph's Hospital Health Center, Syracuse, NY, p. A444

DUNCAN, Jeremy, Director Information Systems, Lawrence Medical Center, Moulton, AL, p. A21

DUNCAN, Jimmy, Vice President Human Resources, Wellstar Kennestone Hospital, Marietta, GA, p. A157

DUNCAN, Joani, Chief Human Resource Officer, Ann & Robert H. Lurie Children's Hospital Of Chicago, Chicago, IL, p. A176

DUNCAN, Leeann, Director Patient Care Services, Harbor Oaks Hospital, New Baltimore, MI, p. A320

DUNCAN, Linda, Director Human Resources, Lee's Summit Medical Center, Lee's Summit, MO, p. A363

DUNCAN, Lyman, Chief Financial Officer, San Juan Health Service District, Monticello, UT, p. A648

DUNCAN, Michael J., President and Chief Executive Officer, Chester County Hospital, West Chester, PA, p. A544

DUNCAN, Nathan, Chief Executive Officer, Lakeland Behavioral Health System, Springfield, MO, p. A370

DUNCAN, Thomas M, Executive Vice President and Chief Financial Officer, Miami Valley Hospital South, OH, p. A480

DUNCAN, Traci A, Vice President, Chief Nursing Officer, Northbay Vacavalley Hospital, CA, p. A57

DUNFORD, Bill, Manager, Northside Hospital-Cherokee, Canton, GA, p. A149

DUNHAM, Cathy, Vice President Human Resources, Mcpherson Hospital, Mcpherson, KS, p. A241

DUNHAM, Shelly, Chief Executive Officer, Okeene Municipal Hospital, Okeene, OK, p. A502

DUNIO, Gina, Chief Human Resources, James E. Van Zandt Veterans Affairs Medical Center, Altoona, PA, p. A519

DUNKEL, Jason, President and Chief Executive Officer, Florida Hospital North Pinellas, Tarpon Springs, FL, p. A142

DUNKER, Karla, Director Finance, Sedgwick County Health Center, Julesburg, CO, p. A102

DUNKIEL, Barbara, Director Human Resources, Healthsouth Sunrise Rehabilitation Hospital, Sunrise, FL, p. A140

DUNKIN, Jackie J., Director Human Resources, Platte Valley Medical Center, Brighton, CO, p. A97

DUNKIN, John, Executive Director, Amita Health Rehabilitation Hospital, IL, p. A182

DUNKLE, David, Vice President Medical Affairs, Johnson Memorial Hospital, Franklin, IN, p. A204

DUNKLEY, Rich, Administrator, Wyoming State Hospital, Evanston, WY, p. A708

DUNLAP, Cyndy, R.N., FACHE, Chief Nursing Officer, Depaul Center, TX, p. A642

DUNLAY, Sherry, R.N., MSN
Vice President Chief Nursing Officer, Integris Bass Pavilion, Enid, OK, p. A498
Vice President Patient Care Services and Chief Nursing Officer, Ssm Health St. Mary's Hospital Centralia, Centralia, IL, p. A175

DUNLEAVY, Christopher, Senior Vice President Finance and Chief Financial Officer, Brigham And Women's Hospital, Boston, MA, p. A296

DUNLEY, Pamela L., MS, R.N., Chief Executive Officer, Elmhurst Hospital, Elmhurst, IL, p. A182

DUNLOP, James H, CPA, Jr
Chief Financial Officer, St. Joseph Hospital, NY, p. A424
Executive Vice President and Chief Financial Officer, Kenmore Mercy Hospital, Kenmore, NY, p. A428
Senior Vice President Finance and Chief Financial Officer, Mercy Hospital, Buffalo, NY, p. A423

DUNMYER, Daniel C., Chief Executive Officer, Ohio Valley Medical Center, Wheeling, WV, p. A688

DUNN, Daniel N, Vice President Operations, Wentworth-Douglass Hospital, Dover, NH, p. A398

DUNN, Denise, R.N., Chief Nursing Officer, Baptist Health Madisonville, Madisonville, KY, p. A257

DUNN, E D, Vice President Human Resources, Virtua Memorial, Mount Holly, NJ, p. A408

DUNN, Hope, Chief Nursing Officer, Emcompass Health Rehabilitation Hospital Of East, Mesa, AZ, p. A31

DUNN, Jack, M.D., Chief of Staff, La Paz Regional Hospital, Parker, AZ, p. A32

DUNN, Janice
Chief Financial Officer, Plymouth Medical Center, Plymouth, IN, p. A213
Chief Financial Officer, Southeast Georgia Health System Camden Campus, Saint Marys, GA, p. A159
Vice President and Chief Financial Officer, Southeast Georgia Health System Brunswick Campus, Brunswick, GA, p. A149

DUNN, Jim, Ph.D., Chief Human Resource Officer, Levine Children's Hospital, NC, p. A449

DUNN, Leonard, M.D., Chief Medical Officer, Baycare Alliant Hospital, Dunedin, FL, p. A122

DUNN, Marcy
Vice President Information Services and Chief Information Officer, Good Samaritan Hospital Medical Center, West Islip, NY, p. A445
Vice President Information Services and Chief Information Officer, Mercy Medical Center, Rockville Centre, NY, p. A442
Vice President Information Services and Chief Information Officer, St. Francis Hospital, The Heart Center, Roslyn, NY, p. A442

DUNN, Margie, Director Human Resources, Middle Tennessee Mental Health Institute, Nashville, TN, p. A577

DUNN, Nicholas, Director Information Systems, Mena Regional Health System, Mena-Polk County, AR, p. A46

DUNN, Patrick A, R.N., Chief Nursing Officer, Lea Regional Medical Center, Hobbs, NM, p. A417

DUNN, Richard, M.D., Chief Medical Officer, Riverside Tappahannock Hospital, Tappahannock, VA, p. A667

DUNN, Rosemary, R.N., Chief Nursing Officer, Cape Regional Health System, Cape May Court House, NJ, p. A403

DUNN, Sheila, Assistant Administrator Human Resources, Dale Medical Center, Ozark, AL, p. A22

DUNN, Tandra, Director of Nursing, San Luis Valley Health Conejos County Hospital, La Jara, CO, p. A102

DUNN, Terry, Director Information Technology, Battle Mountain General Hospital, Battle Mountain, NV, p. A392

DUNNAM, Lorie, Chief Executive Officer, Oceans Behavioral Health Center Permian Basin, Midland, TX, p. A624

DUNNING, David K., Medical Center Director and Chief Executive Officer, Memphis Veterans Affairs Medical Center, Memphis, TN, p. A575

DUNPHY-ALEXANDER, Shannon, Director, Mercyhealth Hospital And Medical Center - Harvard, Harvard, IL, p. A184

DUNWOODY, Robert, Chief Financial Officer, Lawnwood Pavilion, FL, p. A123

DUPPER, Harold, Chief Financial Officer, Platte Valley Medical Center, Brighton, CO, p. A97

DUPRE, Charlotte W., Chief Executive Officer, Southern Regional Medical Center, Riverdale, GA, p. A159

DUPREE, Lucy G, Director Human Resources, Columbia Memorial Hospital, Astoria, OR, p. A511

DUPREY, Irma, Administrator Medical Records, Hospital Universitario Dr. Ramon Ruiz Arnau, Bayamon, PR, p. A712

DUPUIS, Pamela M, R.N., Senior Vice President Patient Care Services, Montefiore New Rochelle, New Rochelle, NY, p. A431

DUQUETTE, Connie, Director Human Resources, Sharp Memorial Hospital, San Diego, CA, p. A84

DUQUETTE, William M., Chief Executive Officer, Baptist Health South Florida, Homestead Hospital, Homestead, FL, p. A125

DURAN, Jody, Manager Information Systems, Livingston Healthcare, Livingston, MT, p. A377

DURAND, Crista F., President, Newport Hospital, Newport, RI, p. A547

DURAND, Mark, Assistant Administrator Operations, Christus Southeast Texas Jasper Memorial, Jasper, TX, p. A616

DURANT, Charles E., Jr, FACHE, Chief Executive Officer, Calhoun-Liberty Hospital, Blountstown, FL, p. A118

DURBAK, Ivan, Chief Information Officer, Highbridge Woodycrest Center, NY, p. A431

DURBIN, Melissa, R.N., MSN, Chief Nursing Officer, Boca Raton Regional Hospital, Boca Raton, FL, p. A118

DURDEN, Rhonda, Chief Financial Officer, Emanuel Medical Center, Swainsboro, GA, p. A161

DURFLINGER, Kathy
Vice President and Chief Nursing Officer, Avita Ontario Hospital, Ontario, OH, p. A488
Vice President and Chief Nursing Officer, Galion Hospital, Galion, OH, p. A483

DURGIN, Manal, Network Medical Director, Devereux Hospital And Children's Center Of Florida, Melbourne, FL, p. A129

DURHAM, Karla, Director of Information Systems, Baptist Health Madisonville, Madisonville, KY, p. A257

DURHAM, Laurie Lea, Chief Executive Officer, Prairie Community Hospital, Terry, MT, p. A379

DURHAM, Linda, Director Human Resources, Henderson County Community Hospital, Lexington, TN, p. A573

DURHAM, Thomas, Chief Nursing Officer, Ferry County Memorial Hospital, Republic, WA, p. A675

DURIS, Deb, Director of Nursing, Northwest Ohio Psychiatric Hospital, Toledo, OH, p. A491

DURNEY, Gerry, Chief Operating Officer, Good Samaritan Regional Medical Center, Suffern, NY, p. A443

DURNIAT-SUSHRSTEDT, Karen, Nurse Executive, Appalachian Behavioral Healthcare, Athens, OH, p. A471

DURNIOK, Brian
President, Upmc Northwest, Seneca, PA, p. A541
Vice President Operations, Upmc Northwest, Seneca, PA, p. A541

E

EDELMAN, Marc D, Vice President Operations, Bristol Hospital, Bristol, CT, p. A107

EDEN, Tina M, Director of Nursing, Virginia Gay Hospital, Vinton, IA, p. A230

EDENFIELD, Janet, Director Financial Services, Georgia Regional Hospital At Savannah, Savannah, GA, p. A160

EDGAR, Joseph H, Senior Vice President Operations, Wellspan Gettysburg Hospital, Gettysburg, PA, p. A526

EDGAR, Nancy, Vice President Human Resources, Northeast Methodist Hospital, TX, p. A633

EDGAR, Steven, FACHE, President and Chief Executive Officer, Medical City Denton, Denton, TX, p. A599

EDIN, Scott D, Vice President, Finance and Chief Financial Officer, Northfield Hospital And Clinics, Northfield, MN, p. A336

EDINGTON, Brent, Director Information Services, Pomerene Hospital, Millersburg, OH, p. A487

EDLER, Susie, R.N., Chief Nursing Officer, Dallas Behavioral Healthcare Hospital, Desoto, TX, p. A599

EDMINSTER, Sue
  Vice President Human Resources, Ripon Medical Center, Ripon, WI, p. A702
  Vice President Human Resources, St. Agnes Hospital, Fond Du Lac, WI, p. A692
  Vice President Human Resources, Waupun Memorial Hospital, Waupun, WI, p. A705

EDMONDS, Kelly, Chief Financial Officer, Western Maryland Hospital Center, Hagerstown, MD, p. A292

EDMONDSON, Bobby, Controller, Regional Rehabilitation Hospital, Phenix City, AL, p. A22

EDMONDSON, James H., Chief Executive Officer, Southern Tennessee Regional Health System-Pulaski, Pulaski, TN, p. A579

EDMONSON, Cole, R.N., MS, FACHE, Vice President and Chief Nursing Officer, Texas Health Presbyterian Hospital Dallas, Dallas, TX, p. A598

EDMUNDS, Liza, Director Human Resources, Tennova Healthcare-Clarksville, Clarksville, TN, p. A568

EDNEY, Daniel, M.D., Chief of Staff, Promise Hospital Of Vicksburg, Vicksburg, MS, p. A354

EDWARD, Adolphe, Chief Executive Officer, El Centro Regional Medical Center, El Centro, CA, p. A57

EDWARDS, Aaron, Chief Executive Officer, Ferry County Memorial Hospital, Republic, WA, p. A675

EDWARDS, Angela Imelda, R.N., Chief Nurse Executive, Nyc Health + Hospitals / Woodhull, New York (Includes All Hospitals Located Within The Five Boroughs), NY, p. A436

EDWARDS, Annette, Chief Financial Officer, Odessa Memorial Healthcare Center, Odessa, WA, p. A674

EDWARDS, Becky, Manager Human Resources, Irwin County Hospital, Ocilla, GA, p. A158

EDWARDS, Bob S., Jr, FACHE, Chief Executive Officer, Mendocino Coast District Hospital, Fort Bragg, CA, p. A58

EDWARDS, Bruce
  Vice President Human Resources, Heritage Valley Health System, Beaver, PA, p. A520
  Vice President Human Resources, Sewickley Valley Hospital, (A Division Of Valley Medical Facilities), Sewickley, PA, p. A541

EDWARDS, Chris, M.D., Chief Medical Officer, Maury Regional Hospital, Columbia, TN, p. A568

EDWARDS, Dana, Chief Financial Officer, Sea Pines Rehabilitation Hospital, Melbourne, FL, p. A129

EDWARDS, Dennis, M.D., Vice President Medical Affairs, Richard H. Young Behavioral Health Center, NE, p. A385

EDWARDS, Gregg
  Chief People Officer, Asante Rogue Regional Medical Center, Medford, OR, p. A515
  Chief People Officer, Asante Three Rivers Medical Center, Grants Pass, OR, p. A513
  Vice President Human Resources, Asante Ashland Community Hospital, Ashland, OR, p. A511

EDWARDS, Jeff, Manager Information Services, Mendocino Coast District Hospital, Fort Bragg, CA, p. A58

EDWARDS, Jonita, Director Human Resources, Dmc - Children's Hospital Of Michigan, Detroit, MI, p. A310

EDWARDS, Kathleen, Manager Information Systems Operation, Healthsouth Rehabilitation Hospital Of Altoona, Altoona, PA, p. A519

EDWARDS, Marti, MSN, R.N., Chief Nursing Officer, Rml Specialty Hospital, IL, p. A186

EDWARDS, Matt, Vice President Nursing Services and Chief Nursing Officer, Anderson Regional Health System, Meridian, MS, p. A350

EDWARDS, Michelle, Executive Vice President Information Technology, Palmetto Health Baptist, Columbia, SC, p. A551

EDWARDS, Nicki E, Ph.D., R.N., Interim Chief Nursing Officer, Sierra Vista Regional Medical Center, San Luis Obispo, CA, p. A87

EDWARDS, Rebecca
  Chief Human Resources Officer, Penn Highlands Brookville, Brookville, PA, p. A521
  Director Human Resources, Martin General Hospital, Williamston, NC, p. A462

EDWARDS, Rick, Vice President and Chief Financial Officer, Hancock Regional Hospital, Greenfield, IN, p. A205

EDWARDS, Samuel, M.D., Chief of Staff, Florida Hospital Deland, Deland, FL, p. A121

EDWARDS, Steven D., President and Chief Executive Officer, Cox Medical Center South, MO, p. A370

EDWARDS, Susan, Vice President Human Resources, Novant Health Uva Health System Culpeper Medical Center, Culpeper, VA, p. A657

EDWARDS, Susan A.
  Chief Executive Officer, Waukesha Memorial Hospital, Waukesha, WI, p. A705
  President and Chief Executive Officer, Oconomowoc Memorial Hospital, Oconomowoc, WI, p. A700

EDWARDS, Terry, Controller, Carolinas Healthcare System Kings Mountain, Kings Mountain, NC, p. A455

EDWARDS, Todd, Director Information Management Systems, Chi St. Luke's Health Brazosport, Lake Jackson, TX, p. A618

EDWARDS, William, Information Technology Generalist, Wernersville State Hospital, Wernersville, PA, p. A543

EESLEY, Michael S, Chief Executive Officer, Centegra Hospital-Huntley, IL, p. A189

EESLEY, Michael S.
  Chief Executive Officer, Centegra Hospital - Woodstock, Woodstock, IL, p. A198
  Chief Executive Officer, Centegra Hospital-Huntley, IL, p. A189

EGAN, Carol, R.N., MSN, Chief Nursing Officer, Rutland Regional Medical Center, Rutland, VT, p. A654

EGAN, Kim, Executive Director Human Resources, Regions Hospital, Saint Paul, MN, p. A339

EGAN, Timothy, President and Chief Executive Officer, Roseland Community Hospital, Chicago, IL, p. A179

EGBERT, James, Chief of Staff, Vidant Beaufort Hospital, Washington, NC, p. A462

EGERTON, W Eugene, M.D., Chief Medical Officer, University Of Maryland Medical Center Midtown Campus, Baltimore, MD, p. A289

EGGEN, Caity, Chief Human Resource Officer, Cuyuna Regional Medical Center, Crosby, MN, p. A330

EGGERS, Judy, Manager Human Resources, Alliance Healthcare System, Holly Springs, MS, p. A347

EGGLESTON, Brett, Chief Financial Officer, Callaway District Hospital, Callaway, NE, p. A382

EGGLESTON, Kirk W., Commanding Officer, Winn Army Community Hospital, Hinesville, GA, p. A155

EGGLESTON, Lara
  Finance Manager, University Hospitals Conneaut Medical Center, Conneaut, OH, p. A479
  Finance Manager, University Hospitals Geneva Medical Center, Geneva, OH, p. A483

EGGLESTON, Ryan, Chief Financial Officer, Desert View Hospital, Pahrump, NV, p. A396

EGYUD, Amber, R.N., Chief Nursing Officer and Chief Operating Officer, Chesapeake Regional Medical Center, Chesapeake, VA, p. A656

EHASZ, James, Chief Financial Officer, Copper Queen Community Hospital, Bisbee, AZ, p. A28

EHLER, Phyllis, Director Human Resources, Avera St. Benedict Health Center, Parkston, SD, p. A562

EHLERS, Jeffrey, Chief Financial Officer, Memorial Health, Marysville, OH, p. A486

EHLINGER, Forrest, System Chief Financial Officer, Benefis Health Care-West Campus, MT, p. A376

EHLKE, Ranae, Administrative Secretary and Coordinator Risk Management and Human Resources, Kenmare Community Hospital, Kenmare, ND, p. A467

EHLY, Ronda S, R.N., Chief Nursing Officer, Mary Lanning Healthcare, Hastings, NE, p. A384

EHN, Jerry, Chief Operating Officer, Northfield Hospital And Clinics, Northfield, MN, p. A336

EHN, Nicole, M.D., Chief of Staff, Van Diest Medical Center, Webster City, IA, p. A231

EHRAT, Michael, Chief Executive Officer, Sovah Health-Martinsville, Martinsville, VA, p. A661

EHRENBERGER, David, M.D., Chief Medical Officer, Avista Adventist Hospital, Louisville, CO, p. A103

EHRICH, Laurie, Chief Communications Officer, Wayne County Hospital, Corydon, IA, p. A220

EHRLICH, Frank, M.D.
  Chief Medical Officer, Health Alliance Hospital - Broadway Campus, Kingston, NY, p. A428
  Chief Medical Officer, Health Alliance Hospital - Mary's Avenue Campus, Kingston, NY, p. A428

EHRLICH, Susan P., M.D., Chief Executive Officer, Zuckerberg San Francisco General Hospital And Trauma Center, San Francisco, CA, p. A86

EHTISHAM, Saad, R.N., FACHE
  Senior Vice President and Chief Operating Officer, Leesburg Regional Medical Center, Leesburg, FL, p. A128
  Vice President and Chief Operating Officer, The Villages Regional Hospital, The Villages, FL, p. A142

EICHENAUER, Donald T., Chief Executive Officer, Wyoming County Community Hospital, Warsaw, NY, p. A445

EICHENBERGER, Daniel J., M.D., President and Chief Executive Officer, Baptist Health Floyd, New Albany, IN, p. A212

EICHER, Natasha, President and Chief Executive Officer, Dekalb Health, Auburn, IN, p. A199

EIDAM, JoEllen, FACHE, Chief Executive Officer, Adams Memorial Hospital, Decatur, IN, p. A202

EIDE, Dean, Vice President, Mayo Clinic Health System - Oakridge In Osseo, Osseo, WI, p. A701

EIDE, Tom, Chief Financial Officer, Prairie St. John'S, Fargo, ND, p. A466

EIG, Blair, M.D., Senior Vice President Medical Affairs, Holy Cross Hospital, Silver Spring, MD, p. A294

EIKE, Gail, Chief Financial Officer, Sanford Jackson Medical Center, Jackson, MN, p. A333

EILBRACHT, Hans, Chief Information Officer, Hamilton Center, Terre Haute, IN, p. A215

EILER, John M., Administrative Director, Barnes-Jewish Hospital Psychiatric Support Center, MO, p. A367

EIMERS, Katy, Human Resources Officer, Syringa Hospital And Clinics, Grangeville, ID, p. A169

EIPE, Joseph, M.D., Chief Medical Officer, Pacifica Hospital Of The Valley, Los Angeles, CA, p. A69

EISCHENS, Shelby, Chief Medical Officer, Brookings Health System, Brookings, SD, p. A559

EISEL, Tom, Chief Financial Officer, Poinciana Medical Center, Kissimmee, FL, p. A127

EISELE, Karla, M.D., Clinical Director, State Hospital North, Orofino, ID, p. A171

EISEMANN, Bradley, Administrator, Beacon Children's Hospital, Luverne, AL, p. A20

EISEN, Robert A, Vice President Human Resources, Northern California Region, Queen Of The Valley Medical Center, Napa, CA, p. A74

EISENMAN, Edward, Chief Executive Officer, Sunnyview Rehabilitation Hospital, Schenectady, NY, p. A442

EISENTRAGER, Steve, President, Ohio Valley Surgical Hospital, Springfield, OH, p. A490

EISENZOPH, Pete, Director Information Technology, Bay Area Medical Center, Marinette, WI, p. A697

EISMAN, Michael, M.D., Medical Director, Schuyler Hospital, Montour Falls, NY, p. A430

EISNER, Nina W., Chief Executive Officer and Managing Director, Ridge Behavioral Health System, Lexington, KY, p. A255

EITZEN, Tamara, Chief Nursing Officer, Fairview Regional Medical Center, Fairview, OK, p. A499

EIXENBERGER, Timothy D., Chief Nursing Officer, Tobey Hospital, MA, p. A299

EKENGREN, Francie H, M.D., Chief Medical Officer, Wesley Woodlawn Hospital & Er, KS, p. A248

EKEREN, Douglas R., Regional President and Chief Executive Officer, Avera Sacred Heart Hospital, Yankton, SD, p. A565

EKPO, Felix, Manager, Information Systems, Arrowhead Regional Medical Center, Colton, CA, p. A55

EL KHALILI, Nizar, M.D., Medical Director, Sycamore Springs Hospital, Lafayette, IN, p. A209

EL-DALATI, Sam, M.D., Chief Medical Officer, Mercy Regional Medical Center, Lorain, OH, p. A485

EL-MELIGI, Christi J., R.N., Chief Executive Officer, Sage Memorial Hospital, Ganado, AZ, p. A24

EL-SOLH, Ali, M.D., Interim Chief of Staff, Veterans Affairs Western New York Healthcare System-Buffalo Division, Buffalo, NY, p. A424

ELAM, Lora, R.N., Chief Nursing Officer, Wayne County Hospital, Monticello, KY, p. A258

ELAM, Moses D, M.D., Physician-in-Chief, Modesto Medical Center, CA, p. A71

ELARBEE, Vernon, Director of Human Resources, Florida Hospital North Pinellas, Tarpon Springs, FL, p. A142

ELBERT, Darlene M, R.N., MS, Assistant Administrator and Chief Nursing Officer, Kossuth Regional Health Center, Algona, IA, p. A217

ELDER, Deborah, Director Human Resources, Scenic Mountain Medical Center, Big Spring, TX, p. A589

ELDIDY, Rene, M.D., Chief of Staff, Centracare Health-Long Prairie, Long Prairie, MN, p. A333

ELDRED, Jamie, Controller, Klickitat Valley Health, Goldendale, WA, p. A672

ELDRIDGE, Janet, Director Human Resources and Personnel, Brooks County Hospital, Quitman, GA, p. A158

ELDRIDGE, Jim, Area Financial Officer, Kaiser Permanente Sacramento Medical Center, Sacramento, CA, p. A81

ELDRIDGE, Laurie, Chief Financial Officer, Marshall Medical Center, Placerville, CA, p. A78

ELDRIDGE, Lisa, Human Resources Officer, Thomas H. Boyd Memorial Hospital, Carrollton, IL, p. A175

ELEGANT, Bruce M., FACHE, President and Chief Executive Officer, Rush Oak Park Hospital, Oak Park, IL, p. A191

ELFERT, Mike, Director Information Services, Lourdes Medical Center Of Burlington County, Willingboro, NJ, p. A414

ELGARICO, David, Chief Executive Officer, Mckenzie-Willamette Medical Center, Springfield, OR, p. A518

ELI, Bev, Chief Nursing Officer, Cox Monett Hospital, Monett, MO, p. A365

ELIAS, Jose, Director Information Technology, Fort Duncan Regional Medical Center, Eagle Pass, TX, p. A600

ELICH, Elizabeth, Chief Human Resources Officer, Piedmont Medical Center, Rock Hill, SC, p. A556

ELIOT, Jason L, Vice President Human Resources, Integris Mental Health System-Spencer, OK, p. A503

ELKINGTON, Bruce, Regional Chief Information Officer, St. Clare Hospital, Lakewood, WA, p. A673

ELKINGTON, Mark, M.D., Chief Medical Officer, Willow Crest Hospital, Miami, OK, p. A501

ELKINS, Carl, Director Information Technology, Rollins Brook Community Hospital, Lampasas, TX, p. A619

ELKINS, James N., FACHE, Director, Texas Center For Infectious Disease, San Antonio, TX, p. A634

ELKINS, Kelly, President and Chief Executive Officer, Columbia St. Mary's Milwaukee Hospital, Milwaukee, WI, p. A698

ELKINS, Wendy, Director Operations, Dundy County Hospital, Benkelman, NE, p. A382

ELLEDGE, David, Controller, Select Specialty Hospital-Knoxville, TN, p. A579

ELLEN, Jonathan D, M.D., Medical Director, Healthsouth Rehabilitation Hospital Of Memphis, Memphis, TN, p. A575

ELLEN, Jonathan M., M.D., President, Johns Hopkins All Children's Hospital, Saint Petersburg, FL, p. A138

ELLENBURG, Cynthia, Director Health Information Services, Baptist Easley Hospital, Easley, SC, p. A552

ELLER, Bill, Director Information Technology, El Campo Memorial Hospital, El Campo, TX, p. A601

ELLER, Steven M
    Chief Human Resources Officer, Beacon Children's Hospital, IN, p. A215
    Vice President Human Resources, Elkhart General Hospital, Elkhart, IN, p. A202

ELLER, Troy, Chief Financial Officer, Guthrie County Hospital, Guthrie Center, IA, p. A223

ELLERSON, Thomas, Chief Information Officer, Our Lady Of Lourdes Memorial Hospital, Inc., Binghamton, NY, p. A422

ELLEY, Michael, Chief Information Officer, Healthpark, KY, p. A258

ELLINGTON, Christopher, Executive Vice President and Chief Financial Officer, Unc Lineberger Comprehensive Cancer Center, NC, p. A449

ELLIOTT, Amy, M.D., Director Medical Affairs, District One Hospital, Faribault, MN, p. A331

ELLIOTT, Barb
    Chief Financial Officer, Fairbanks, Indianapolis, IN, p. A206
    Interim President and Chief Executive Officer, Fairbanks, Indianapolis, IN, p. A206

ELLIOTT, Charles W., Jr, Chief Executive Officer, Johnston Health, Smithfield, NC, p. A460

ELLIOTT, Jim
    Director Human Resources, Bryce Hospital, Tuscaloosa, AL, p. A23
    Director Human Resources, Mary S Harper Geriatric Psychiatry Center, Tuscaloosa, AL, p. A24

ELLIOTT, Laura, Director Human Resources, Northeastern Nevada Regional Hospital, Elko, NV, p. A392

ELLIOTT, Lee Ann, R.N., Director of Nursing, Select Rehabilitation Hospital Of Denton, Denton, TX, p. A599

ELLIOTT, Marye, Chief Nursing Officer, Brookwood Baptist Medical Center, Birmingham, AL, p. A14

ELLIOTT, Michael, M.D.
    Chief Medical Officer and Senior Vice President of Medical Affairs, Avera Children's Hospital, SD, p. A563
    Controller, Indianhead Medical Center, Shell Lake, WI, p. A703

ELLIOTT, Peyton, Chief Executive Officer, Park Plaza Hospital, Houston, TX, p. A612

ELLIOTT, R James, Vice President Human Resources, Charlotte Hungerford Hospital, Torrington, CT, p. A111

ELLIOTT, Randi, MSN, Chief Nursing Officer, Baylor Medical Center At Frisco, Frisco, TX, p. A606

ELLIOTT, Rhonda M., Director Information Technology and Meaningful Use, Person Memorial Hospital, Roxboro, NC, p. A460

ELLIOTT, Robin, Personnel Officer, Community Memorial Hospital, Sumner, IA, p. A230

ELLIOTT, Shane, Associate Director Administration, Veterans Affairs Loma Linda Healthcare System, Loma Linda, CA, p. A64

ELLIS, Amanda, Chief Financial Officer, Barbourville Arh Hospital, Barbourville, KY, p. A249

ELLIS, Angela, R.N., Chief Nursing Officer, Terre Haute Regional Hospital, Terre Haute, IN, p. A215

ELLIS, Ashley, Chief Executive Officer, Haven Senior Horizons, Phoenix, AZ, p. A33

ELLIS, Bob, Director of Nursing, D. W. Mcmillan Memorial Hospital, Brewton, AL, p. A15

ELLIS, Cynthia, Chief Nursing Officer, Merit Health Rankin, Brandon, MS, p. A344

ELLIS, Deb, Director Human Resources, Perry Memorial Hospital, Perry, OK, p. A505

ELLIS, Kristin, Controller, Munson Healthcare Cadillac Hospital, Cadillac, MI, p. A309

ELLIS, Lisa, Chief Operating Officer, Alliancehealth Midwest, Midwest City, OK, p. A501

ELLIS, Mark, Director Information Technology, Lakeview Hospital, Bountiful, UT, p. A646

ELLIS, Michael, M.D., Chief Medical Officer, The University Of Toledo Medical Center, Toledo, OH, p. A492

ELLIS, Michael J., FACHE, Chief Executive Officer, Hill Regional Hospital, Hillsboro, TX, p. A609

ELLIS, Michelle, Director Human Resources, Whitman Hospital And Medical Center, Colfax, WA, p. A670

ELLIS, Mike, Chief Financial Officer, Mendocino Coast District Hospital, Fort Bragg, CA, p. A58

ELLIS, Nichole, Chief Medical Officer, Hillsdale Hospital, Hillsdale, MI, p. A315

ELLIS, Paula, Administrator, Saint John Hospital, Leavenworth, KS, p. A239

ELLIS, Richard, Chief Executive Officer, Tennova Healthcare-Harton, Tullahoma, TN, p. A580

ELLIS, Scott, D.O., Chief Medical Officer, Memorial Regional Health, Craig, CO, p. A98

ELLIS, Susan Renee', R.N., MSN, Vice President of Human Resources, Highlands Regional Medical Center, Prestonsburg, KY, p. A259

ELLIS, Tammy, FACHE, R.N., Vice President Patient Services, Texas Health Huguley Hospital Fort Worth South, Burleson, TX, p. A591

ELLIS, Thomas J, Vice President Human Resources, Mt. Washington Pediatric Hospital, Baltimore, MD, p. A288

ELLIS, Wendel, D.O., Chief Medical Staff, Greeley County Health Services, Tribune, KS, p. A247

ELLISON, Darcy, R.N., MSN, Senior Vice President, Chief Nursing Officer and Inpatient Flow, St. Vincent Evansville, Evansville, IN, p. A203

ELLISON, Keith, Chief Nursing Officer, Big Bend Regional Medical Center, Alpine, TX, p. A582

ELLISON, Laura, Chief Financial Officer, Bon Secours Baltimore Health System, Baltimore, MD, p. A287

ELLISON, Mike, Information Systems Lead, Summersville Regional Medical Center, Summersville, WV, p. A687

ELLISON, Patricia, Chief Financial Officer, Galesburg Cottage Hospital, Galesburg, IL, p. A183

ELLSWORTH, Anthon, Director Information Technology, Mt. Graham Regional Medical Center, Safford, AZ, p. A35

ELLZEY, Bob S., FACHE, President, Texas Health Harris Methodist Hospital Azle, Azle, TX, p. A587

ELMER, Paula, R.N., MSN, Vice President and Chief Nursing Officer, Monroe Clinic, Monroe, WI, p. A699

ELMORE, Kevin, Chief Information Officer, Covenant Hospital-Levelland, Levelland, TX, p. A619

ELMORE, Nadine, Chief Executive Officer, Dahl Memorial Healthcare Association, Ekalaka, MT, p. A375

ELROD, Emily, R.N.
    Chief Nursing Officer, Saint Thomas Dekalb Hospital, Smithville, TN, p. A580
    Director of Nursing, Saint Thomas Stones River Hospital, Woodbury, TN, p. A581

ELROD, James K., FACHE, Chief Executive Officer, Wk Bossier Health Center, LA, p. A279

ELROD, Keri, Administrator, Willis-Knighton South - The Center For Women's Health, LA, p. A279

ELROD, Sonya, Chief Nursing Officer, Elbert Memorial Hospital, Elberton, GA, p. A153

ELS, Veronica, Chief Nursing Officer, Lafayette General Surgical Hospital, Lafayette, LA, p. A271

ELSBERRY, Kevin, Senior Vice President Human Resources, Mercy Medical Center - West Lakes, IA, p. A221

ELSBREE, Heidi, Vice President People and Culture, Mercyhealth Hospital - Rockton Avenue, Rockford, IL, p. A194

ELSE, Ryan, M.D., Vice President Medical Affairs, Unity Hospital, MN, p. A330

ELSESSER, William, Chief Executive Officer, Kindred Hospital The Heights, TX, p. A640

ELSWICK, Beth, Administrative Assistant, Summers County Arh Hospital, Hinton, WV, p. A683

ELWELL, Richard, Senior Vice President and Chief Financial Officer, Elliot Hospital, Manchester, NH, p. A400

ELWELL, Russell, M.D., Medical Director, Westfield Memorial Hospital, Westfield, NY, p. A446

ELY, Thomas L, D.O., Chief Medical Officer, Tennova Healthcare-Clarksville, Clarksville, TN, p. A568

EMAMGHORAISHI, Anna, Human Resources, Midwest City Specialty Hospital, Midwest City, OK, p. A501

EMANUEL, Kate, Director Human Resources, Clarke County Hospital, Osceola, IA, p. A228

EMBREE, Steve, Chief Financial Officer, Up Health System-Marquette, Marquette, MI, p. A318

EMBREY, Jeffrey, M.D., Chief Medical Officer, Baylor Scott & White Medical Center-Irving, Irving, TX, p. A615

EMBREY, Richard, M.D., Chief Medical Officer, Augusta Health, Fishersville, VA, p. A658

EMBURY, Stuart, M.D., Chief Medical Officer, Phelps Memorial Health Center, Holdrege, NE, p. A385

EMDUR, Larry, D.O.
    Chief Medical Officer, Alvarado Hospital Medical Center, San Diego, CA, p. A83
    Chief of Staff, Promise Hospital Of San Diego, San Diego, CA, p. A84

EMEOTT, Sandra, R.N., Chief Nursing Officer, Northwest Medical Center, Margate, FL, p. A129

EMERSON, Leah, Director of Nursing, St. Luke Community Healthcare, Ronan, MT, p. A378

EMERSON, Sherri Leigh, Chief Operating Officer, Texas Health Heart & Vascular Hospital Arlington, Arlington, TX, p. A584

EMERY, Andrew, Chief Executive Officer, Bayfront Health Punta Gorda, Punta Gorda, FL, p. A137

EMERY, John, Chief Executive Officer, Shands Starke Regional Medical Center, Starke, FL, p. A139

EMGE, Joann, Chief Executive Officer, Sparta Community Hospital, Sparta, IL, p. A196

EMIG, Laura, Director Marketing Operations, Healthsouth Rehabilitation Hospital Of York, York, PA, p. A545

EMMINGER, Dianne, Vice President Information Services, Acmh Hospital, Kittanning, PA, p. A528

EMMONS, Jennifer, Chief Operating Officer & Director of Physician Services, Carle Richland Memorial Hospital, Olney, IL, p. A192

EMON, Dee, R.N., Chief Information Officer, Wake Forest Baptist Health-Lexington Medical Center, Lexington, NC, p. A456

EMPEDRAD, Globert, Chief Clinical Officer, Curahealth Tucson, Tucson, AZ, p. A37

EMPEY, Dennis
    Chief Financial Officer, Kenmare Community Hospital, Kenmare, ND, p. A467
    Chief Financial Officer, Trinity Hospital-St. Joseph'S, ND, p. A468

ENCAPERA, Kimberly, M.D., Medical Director, Rehabilitation Hospital Of Southern New Mexico, Las Cruces, NM, p. A418

ENCE, Michael, Computer Specialist, Sanpete Valley Hospital, Mount Pleasant, UT, p. A648

ENCKE, Faye, Director Information Management, Emcompass Health Rehabilitation Hospital Of Virginia, Richmond, VA, p. A665

ENDEN, Jay, M.D., Medical Director, Southside Hospital, Bay Shore, NY, p. A422

ENDERS, Robert A., Jr, President, Chatham Hospital, Siler City, NC, p. A460

ENDOM, Beth W, R.N., MSN, Vice President and Chief Nursing Officer, South Central Regional Medical Center, Laurel, MS, p. A349

ENDRES, Jack A., FACHE, JD, Administrator, Ut Health Athens, Athens, TX, p. A585

ENG, Bland, Chief Executive Officer, Brandon Regional Hospital, Brandon, FL, p. A119

ENG, Jeffrey, M.D., Medical Director, Encompass Health Rehabilitation Hospital Of Montgomery, Montgomery, AL, p. A21

ENGBERS, Jon, M.D., President, Hegg Health Center Avera, Rock Valley, IA, p. A229

ENGBRECHT, Chad, Chief Financial Officer, Alvarado Parkway Institute Behavioral Health System, La Mesa, CA, p. A63

ENGEL, David, Chief Executive Officer and Administrator, Southeast Colorado Hospital District, Springfield, CO, p. A105

ENGEL, Dawn M, Chief Nursing Officer, Geary Community Hospital, Junction City, KS, p. A238

ENGELKE, Brian, Chief Financial Officer, Community Hospital Of Staunton, Staunton, IL, p. A197

ENGESSER, Edward, Chief Financial Officer and Chief Information Officer, Barlow Respiratory Hospital, Los Angeles, CA, p. A66

ENGFEHR, Tricia A, Chief Human Resources, Selby General Hospital, Marietta, OH, p. A486

ENGLAND, Dave, Director Human Resources, Lakeland Behavioral Health System, Springfield, MO, p. A370

ENGLAND, Leslie, Chief of Staff, Merit Health Natchez, Natchez, MS, p. A351

ENGLAND, Mary Ann, Chief Nurse Executive, Wilcox Medical Center, Lihue, HI, p. A166

ENGLAND, Richard N, Chief Financial Officer, Palo Verde Behavioral Health, Tucson, AZ, p. A37

ENGLAND, Stacy, Community Chief Nursing Officer, Middlesboro Arh Hospital, Middlesboro, KY, p. A258

ENGLAND, Teresa, R.N., Ph.D., Nurse Executive, Salem Veterans Affairs Medical Center, Salem, VA, p. A666

ENGLE, Dana E., Chief Executive Officer, Madison Health, London, OH, p. A485

ENGLE, Lisa, Director Information Technology, Tmc Behavioral Health Center, TX, p. A599

ENGLE, Sharon, Director Clinical Services, Noland Hospital Birmingham, Birmingham, AL, p. A14

ENGLE-RAMIREZ, Jeanette, Chief Executive Officer, Menlo Park Surgical Hospital, Menlo Park, CA, p. A72

ENGLEHART, Jay, M.D., Medical Director, Southeast Missouri Mental Health Center, Farmington, MO, p. A359

ENGLERT, William, Chief Executive Officer, Allegheny Valley Hospital, Natrona Heights, PA, p. A532

ENGLERTH, LaDonna, Administrator, East Carroll Parish Hospital, Lake Providence, LA, p. A272

ENGLISH, Anne L, Director Human Resources, Uhs Chenango Memorial Hospital, Norwich, NY, p. A438

ENGLISH, Brett, Chief Financial Officer, Mary Black Health System-Spartanburg, Spartanburg, SC, p. A557

ENGLISH, Dennis, M.D., Vice President Medical Affairs, Magee-Womens Hospital Of Upmc, Pittsburgh, PA, p. A537

ENGLISH, Jeff

  President, St. Mary's Sacred Heart Hospital, Lavonia, GA, p. A156

  Vice President Human Resources, St. Mary's Health Care System, Athens, GA, p. A145

ENGLISH, Julene, Director Human Resources, Kentfield Rehabilitation And Specialty Hospital, Kentfield, CA, p. A62

ENGLISH, Kathy L, R.N., MSN, Executive Vice President and Chief Operating Officer, Children's Hospital And Medical Center, Omaha, NE, p. A388

ENGLISH, Laurie, Senior Vice President and Chief Human Resource Officer, Excela Latrobe Area Hospital, Latrobe, PA, p. A529

ENGSTROM, Chad P, Director Human Resources, Westfields Hospital And Clinic, New Richmond, WI, p. A700

ENGSTROM, Frederick, M.D., Chief Medical Officer, Brattleboro Retreat, Brattleboro, VT, p. A653

ENICKS, Charles, Chief Information Officer, Children's Hospital Of Georgia, GA, p. A147

ENJADY, Rainey, Administrative Officer, Mescalero Public Health Service Indian Hospital, Mescalero, NM, p. A418

ENNEN, Mark S, Director of Finance, Hshs Holy Family Hospital In Greenville, Greenville, IL, p. A184

ENNEN, Philip L.

  President and Chief Executive Officer, Community Hospitals And Wellness Centers-Montpelier, Montpelier, OH, p. A487

  Vice President and Chief Executive Officer, Montpelier Hospital, OH, p. A473

ENNIS, Debra, R.N., Vice President and Chief Nursing Officer, Texas Health Harris Methodist Hospital Southlake, Southlake, TX, p. A636

ENNIS, Virgil, Chief Information Officer, Helen Hayes Hospital, West Haverstraw, NY, p. A445

ENOCHS, Darren, Director Human Resources, Promise Hospital Of Overland Park, Overland Park, KS, p. A243

ENOKA, Christina, Director Human Resources and Risk Management, Sutter Health Kahi Mohala, Ewa Beach, HI, p. A164

ENRICO-SIMON, Agnes, M.D., President Medical Staff, Pleasant Valley Hospital, Point Pleasant, WV, p. A686

ENRIQUEZ, Kelly, Chief Executive Officer, Sebastian River Medical Center, Sebastian, FL, p. A139

ENSEY, Jeremy, Chief Executive Officer, St. Luke Hospital And Living Center, Marion, KS, p. A241

ENSLEY, Terrasina, Director Human Resources, Fannin Regional Hospital, Blue Ridge, GA, p. A148

ENSMINGER, Jennifer, Chief Operating Officer, College Medical Center, Long Beach, CA, p. A65

ENSRUDE, Layne, Chief Financial Officer, First Care Health Center, Park River, ND, p. A468

ENTIN, Ari, Chief Information Officer, Natividad Medical Center, Salinas, CA, p. A83

ENTLER, Paul, D.O., Medical Director, Sparrow Specialty Hospital, Lansing, MI, p. A317

ENTWISTLE, David, President and Chief Executive Officer, Stanford Health Care, Palo Alto, CA, p. A77

ENTZMINGER, Julie, Manager Human Resources, Chi Oakes Hospital, Oakes, ND, p. A468

EOLOFF, Eric J., President, Mercy Hospital Washington, Washington, MO, p. A372

EPPERSON, Edward L., Chief Executive Officer, Sierra Surgery Hospital, NV, p. A392

EPPERSON, Elysia, Director Human Resources, Ut Health Jacksonville, Jacksonville, TX, p. A616

EPPERSON, James, Interim Chief Nursing Officer, Grandview Medical Center, Birmingham, AL, p. A14

EPPERSON, Jeff, Chief Financial Officer, Millwood Hospital, Arlington, TX, p. A584

EPPLER, Todd, FACHE, Chief Executive Officer, De Soto Regional Health System, Mansfield, LA, p. A273

EPPS, Donna

  Vice President and Chief Human Resources Officer, Lawrence + Memorial Hospital, New London, CT, p. A110

  Vice President, Chief Human Resource Officer, Westerly Hospital, Westerly, RI, p. A548

EPPS, Jerry, M.D., Senior Vice President and Chief Medical Officer, University Of Tennessee Medical Center, Knoxville, TN, p. A572

EPPS, Michelle L., MSN, R.N., Chief Nursing Officer, Stonesprings Hospital Center, Dulles, VA, p. A657

EPSTEIN, Michael, M.D., Senior Vice President Medical Affairs, Johns Hopkins All Children's Hospital, Saint Petersburg, FL, p. A138

ERDMAN, Beth, Chief Financial Officer, Unitypoint Health Meriter, Madison, WI, p. A696

ERDMAN, Donja, Chief Financial Officer, Marcus Daly Memorial Hospital, Hamilton, MT, p. A376

ERDMAN, John, M.D., Chief of Staff, Chi Memorial Hospital - Georgia, Fort Oglethorpe, GA, p. A154

ERDMANN, Michael, M.D., Chief of Staff, Clement J. Zablocki Veterans Affairs Medical Center, Milwaukee, WI, p. A698

ERDOS, Joseph, M.D., Chief Information Officer, West Haven Division, CT, p. A112

ERDRICH, Louis P., Acting Chief Executive Officer, U.S. Public Health Service Indian Hospital, Cass Lake, MN, p. A329

EREMAN, Melissa, R.N., Chief Nursing Officer, Coleman County Medical Center, Coleman, TX, p. A593

ERGLE, Jeanine, Chief Financial Officer, Bay Pines Veterans Affairs Healthcare System, Bay Pines, FL, p. A117

ERICKSON, Ashley M., Chief Executive Officer, Sanford Aberdeen Medical Center, Aberdeen, SD, p. A559

ERICKSON, Brent J, Administrator, Wright Patterson Medical Center, Wright, OH, p. A494

ERICKSON, Brent J., Administrator, Wright Patterson Medical Center, Wright, OH, p. A494

ERICKSON, Doug, Chief Financial Officer, Prague Community Hospital, Prague, OK, p. A506

ERICKSON, Jake, Chief Executive Officer, Bingham Memorial Hospital, Blackfoot, ID, p. A167

ERICKSON, Karyn, Director Human Resources, Delta Medical Center, Memphis, TN, p. A575

ERICKSON, Kerrie, Vice President Finance, Stevens Community Medical Center, Morris, MN, p. A336

ERICKSON, Laura, R.N., Chief Nursing Officer, Pondera Medical Center, Conrad, MT, p. A374

ERICKSON, Nancy

  Administrator Information Systems, Kossuth Regional Health Center, Algona, IA, p. A217

  Human Resource Director, Southern Inyo Healthcare District, Lone Pine, CA, p. A65

ERICKSON, Robert J., President, Presence Saint Joseph Medical Center, Joliet, IL, p. A187

ERICKSON, Sue, President and Chief Executive Officer, Unitypoint Health Meriter, Madison, WI, p. A696

ERICKSON, Vonnie, Human Resource Manager, Chippewa County-Montevideo Hospital, Montevideo, MN, p. A336

ERICSON, Allen

  Chief Operating Officer, Community Hospital Division and President, St. Joseph's Hospital, Community Memorial Hospital, Menomonee Falls, WI, p. A697

  Chief Operating Officer, Community Hospital Division and President, St. Joseph's Hospital, St. Joseph's Hospital, West Bend, WI, p. A706

President, St. Joseph's Hospital, West Bend, WI, p. A706

ERICSON, Bob, Chief Financial Officer, Hemphill County Hospital, Canadian, TX, p. A591

ERICSON, Kim

  Vice President Finance, Fairview Lakes Health Services, Wyoming, MN, p. A342

  Vice President Finance, Fairview Northland Medical Center, Princeton, MN, p. A337

ERIXON, Stephen M, Chief Executive Officer, Sagewest Health Care At Lander, WY, p. A709

ERKEN, Carole L, Human Resources Leader, Kaiser Permanente Panorama City Medical Center, Los Angeles, CA, p. A67

ERLING, Brian

  Group Chief Medical Officer, St. Anthony Hospital, Lakewood, CO, p. A103

  Interim Chief Executive Officer, Penrose Hospital, CO, p. A98

  Interim Chief Executive Officer, St. Francis Medical Center, CO, p. A98

ERMANN, William, President and Chief Executive Officer, Southwest Medical Center, Liberal, KS, p. A240

ERTEL, Matthew, Chief Financial Officer, Gibson Area Hospital And Health Services, Gibson City, IL, p. A184

ERUKHIMOU, Jeffrey, M.D., Medical Director, Curahealth Heritage Valley, Beaver, PA, p. A520

ERVIN, Fulton

  Chief Financial Officer, Mcleod Regional Medical Center, Florence, SC, p. A553

  Senior Vice President and Chief Financial Officer, Mcleod Medical Center Dillon, Dillon, SC, p. A552

ERVIN, Joan, Administrator, Mcleod Medical Center Dillon, Dillon, SC, p. A552

ERVIN, Paul D, Chief Financial Officer, Valley Behavioral Health System, Barling, AR, p. A39

ERVIN, Richard, Chief Financial Officer, Kindred Hospital The Heights, TX, p. A640

ERVING-MENGEL, Tammi, R.N., MSN, Vice President, Chief Nursing Officer, High Point Regional Health System, High Point, NC, p. A454

ERWAY, Robert, Director for Administration, Bronx Psychiatric Center, New York (Includes All Hospitals Located Within The Five Boroughs), NY, p. A431

ERWIN, Connie, Manager, Samaritan Lebanon Community Hospital, Lebanon, OR, p. A514

ESCHENBRENNER, Wade, Chief Financial Officer, Lexington Regional Health Center, Lexington, NE, p. A385

ESHLEMAN, James, D.O., President Medical Staff, Stephens Memorial Hospital, Norway, ME, p. A285

ESKER, Jerry, President and Chief Executive Officer, Sarah Bush Lincoln Health Center, Mattoon, IL, p. A188

ESLAVA, Lee, Chief Medical Officer, South Baldwin Regional Medical Center, Foley, AL, p. A18

ESPARZA, Becky, Human Resources, Crane Memorial Hospital, Crane, TX, p. A595

ESPARZA, Caroline

  Senior Vice President, Chief Operating Officer and Chief Nurse Officer, Simi Valley Hospital, Simi Valley, CA, p. A90

  Sr. VP, COO & CNO, Simi Valley Hospital, Simi Valley, CA, p. A90

ESPELAND, Darryl, D.O.

  Chief Medical Staff, Fallon Medical Complex, Baker, MT, p. A373

  Medical Director, Dahl Memorial Healthcare Association, Ekalaka, MT, p. A375

ESPELAND, David, Chief Executive Officer, Fallon Medical Complex, Baker, MT, p. A373

ESPINA, Francisco, Director Finance, Hospital Pavia-Santurce, San Juan, PR, p. A716

ESPINOZA, John, Chief Human Resources Officer, Children's Hospital Of Nevada At Umc, NV, p. A395

ESPINOZA, Judy, Chief Human Resources Officer, St. Joseph Campus, KS, p. A248

ESPINOZA, Richard, Chief Administrative Officer, Fairmont Hospital, CA, p. A75

ESPOSITO, Mary H, Assistant Executive Director, Devereux Advanced Behavioral Health Georgia, Kennesaw, GA, p. A155

ESPOSITO, Pamela, Director Administration, Buffalo Psychiatric Center, Buffalo, NY, p. A423

ESPY, Christine, Division Director, Mid-Columbia Medical Center, The Dalles, OR, p. A518

ESROCK, Brett A., FACHE, Chief Executive Officer, Health First Holmes Regional Medical Center, Melbourne, FL, p. A129

ESSELMAN, Charlotte, Director Finance, Ministry Good Samaritan Health Center, Weston, WI, p. A706

ESSENPREIS, Helen, MSN, R.N., Chief Nursing Officer, Hshs St. Joseph's Hospital, Breese, IL, p. A174

F

FABRICK, Peter, Vice President Clinical Operations, Mountain View Hospital, Idaho Falls, ID, p. A169

FABRY, Joseph, D.O., Chief of Staff, Sutter Maternity And Surgery Center Of Santa Cruz, Santa Cruz, CA, p. A89

FACKRELL, Sherlyn, Finance Controller, Grover C. Dils Medical Center, Caliente, NV, p. A392

FACTEAU, Patrick M., Chief Financial Officer, Massena Memorial Hospital, Massena, NY, p. A430

FADALE, Sean, President and Chief Executive Officer, Community Memorial Hospital, Hamilton, NY, p. A427

FADLER, Jeannie, R.N., Vice President Patient Care Services, Saint Francis Medical Center, Cape Girardeau, MO, p. A356

FAGAN, Erin, Manager Human Resources, George Washington University Hospital, Washington, DC, p. A115

FAGAN, Mary, MSN, R.N., Chief Nursing Officer, Rady Children's Hospital - San Diego, San Diego, CA, p. A84

FAGAN, Michael, Senior Vice President Finance, Newyork-Presbyterian Brooklyn Methodist Hospital, New York (Includes All Hospitals Located Within The Five Boroughs), NY, p. A435

FAGBONGBE, Eniola, M.D., Chief Medical Staff, Grove Hill Memorial Hospital, Grove Hill, AL, p. A19

FAGERBERG, Lesley, Vice President Fiscal Services, Heart Of The Rockies Regional Medical Center, Salida, CO, p. A105

FAGERHAUG, Larry, Director Human Resources, Carson Tahoe Continuing Care Hospital, Carson City, NV, p. A392

FAGERSTROM, Joel, Executive Vice President and Chief Operating Officer, St. Luke's Hospital - Miners Campus, Coaldale, PA, p. A523

FAGG, Cindy, Fiscal Officer, Battle Mountain General Hospital, Battle Mountain, NV, p. A392

FAHERTY, Jay, Chief Executive Officer, Select Specialty Hospital-Tallahassee, Tallahassee, FL, p. A140

FAHEY, Dana, Manager Management Information Systems, Santa Barbara County Psychiatric Health Facility, Santa Barbara, CA, p. A88

FAHEY, Linda L, R.N., Chief Information Officer and Senior Vice President Quality Systems, Decatur Memorial Hospital, Decatur, IL, p. A180

FAHEY, Patrick, M.D., Chief Medical Officer, Rml Specialty Hospital, IL, p. A186

FAHEY, Stephen P, Executive Director, Sierra Tucson, Tucson, AZ, p. A37

FAHEY, Stephen P., Executive Director, Sierra Tucson, Tucson, AZ, p. A37

FAHEY, Walter, Chief Information Officer, Maimonides Infants And Children's Hospital Of Brooklyn, NY, p. A433

FAILE, J Gene., Chief Executive Officer and President, Wake Forest Baptist Health - Wilkes Medical Center, North Wilkesboro, NC, p. A458

FAILLA, Richard
Chief Executive Officer, Montevista Hospital, Las Vegas, NV, p. A394
Chief Executive Officer, Red Rock Behavioral Hospital, Las Vegas, NV, p. A394

FAIN, Marilyn, R.N., MSN, Chief Operating Officer, Banner Fort Collins Medical Center, Fort Collins, CO, p. A100

FAIN, Nona, Ph.D., R.N., Director of Nursing, Belmont Behavioral Hospital, Philadelphia, PA, p. A533

FAIRBANKS, Bruce, Vice President and Chief Financial Officer, Southeast Hospital, Cape Girardeau, MO, p. A357

FAIRBANKS, Trish, R.N., Associate Vice President and Chief Nursing Officer, Linden Oaks Hospital, Naperville, IL, p. A190

FAIRCHILD, David, M.D., Chief Medical Officer, Tufts Medical Center, Boston, MA, p. A297

FAIRCLOTH, Karen, Chief Financial Officer, Memorial Hospital And Manor, Bainbridge, GA, p. A148

FAIRFAX, Tom, Director Information Systems, Bothwell Regional Health Center, Sedalia, MO, p. A370

FAIRFAX, Walter, M.D., Chief Medical Officer, Kootenai Behavioral Health, ID, p. A169

FAIRLEY, Dawn Ann, M.D., Chief of Staff, Putnam County Memorial Hospital, Unionville, MO, p. A371

FAIRLEY, Susan, Chief Nursing Officer, Barton Memorial Hospital, South Lake Tahoe, CA, p. A90

FAISAL, Mohammad, President Medical Staff, Shands Lake Shore Regional Medical Center, Lake City, FL, p. A127

FALCON, Hugo, M.D., Director Medical Services, Piedmont Geriatric Hospital, Burkeville, VA, p. A656

FALCONE, Lynn, Chief Executive Officer, Cuero Community Hospital, Cuero, TX, p. A595

FALGOUT, Charlene, Chief Nursing Officer, Bradley Center Of St. Francis, GA, p. A151

FALIVENA, Richard, D.O., M.P.H., Vice President and Chief Medical Officer, Saratoga Hospital, Saratoga Springs, NY, p. A442

FALK, Chelsie, Chief Nursing Officer, Sanford Wheaton Medical Center, Wheaton, MN, p. A342

FALKENBERRY, Jody, Director Information Systems, Monroe County Hospital, Monroeville, AL, p. A21

FALL, J Mark., Chief Executive Officer, Henry Ford Allegiance Specialty Hospital, Jackson, MI, p. A316

FALLIS, Susan, Chief Nursing Officer, Buffalo Psychiatric Center, Buffalo, NY, p. A423

FALLON, Angela, Acting Chief Executive Officer, U.S. Public Health Service Indian Hospital-Sells, Sells, AZ, p. A36

FALLON, Jeanne M.
Chief Information Officer, Falmouth Hospital, Falmouth, MA, p. A299
Senior Vice President and Chief Information Officer, Cape Cod Hospital, Hyannis, MA, p. A300

FALLON, L J, JD, Executive Vice President, Chief Legal and Human Resources Officer, Carle Foundation Hospital, Urbana, IL, p. A197

FALO, Carol, RN, BSN, MBA, Chief Executive Officer, Curahealth Pittsburgh, Oakdale, PA, p. A533

FALTERMAN, James B, M.D., Jr, Medical Director, University Hospital And Clinics, Lafayette, LA, p. A271

FAMMARTINO, Gary
Regional President, St. Vincent Carmel Hospital, Carmel, IN, p. A201
Regional President, St. Vincent Fishers Hospital, Fishers, IN, p. A203

FANALE, Linda, Chief Financial Officer, Conemaugh Miners Medical Center, Hastings, PA, p. A527

FANNIN, Allyson, Human Resources Officer, Lasalle General Hospital, Jena, LA, p. A269

FANNIN, Pam, Coordinator Human Resources, Lifecare Hospital Of Dayton, Miamisburg, OH, p. A486

FANNING, Melinda, Chief Financial Officer and Controller, Healthsouth Southern Hills Rehabilitation Hospital, Princeton, WV, p. A686

FANNON, Susan, Chief Nursing Officer, Indian Path Medical Center, Kingsport, TN, p. A572

FANSLER, Janet, R.N., Executive Vice President and Chief Nurse Executive, Lakeland Regional Health Medical Center, Lakeland, FL, p. A127

FANTANO, Gene, Chief Financial Officer, Aurora Behavioral Healthcare San Diego, San Diego, CA, p. A83

FARAH, Tony, M.D., President Medical Staff, Allegheny General Hospital, Pittsburgh, PA, p. A537

FARBER, Bobbi, M.D., Chief Medical Officer, Bradley Center Of St. Francis, GA, p. A151

FARBER, Nancy J, Chief Executive Officer, Washington Hospital Healthcare System, Fremont, CA, p. A59

FARBER, Niceta, Chief Executive Officer, Sheridan County Health Complex, Hoxie, KS, p. A237

FARBER, Stephen D., Chief Financial Officer, Kindred Hospital New Jersey - Wayne, NJ, p. A404

FARELL, Clay, Chief Operation Officer, Los Alamitos Medical Center, Los Alamitos, CA, p. A65

FARGASON, Crayton A, M.D., Medical Director, Children's Of Alabama, Birmingham, AL, p. A14

FARGUSON, Jack, Director Information Technology, Tmc Bonham Hospital, Bonham, TX, p. A589

FARINA, Albert M, Chief Financial Officer, Montefiore Mount Vernon, Mount Vernon, NY, p. A430

FARINA, Jonathan, Chief Information Officer, Brattleboro Memorial Hospital, Brattleboro, VT, p. A653

FARISH, Audra, Vice President Human Resources, Emory Saint Joseph's Hospital Of Atlanta, Atlanta, GA, p. A146

FARKAS, Laura, Director Human Resources, Fairview Hospital, Great Barrington, MA, p. A300

FARLEY, Chris, Chief Financial Officer, Willow Springs Center, Reno, NV, p. A396

FARMER, Kathleen, Assistant Administrator Finance and Chief Financial Officer, El Centro Regional Medical Center, El Centro, CA, p. A57

FARMER, Pat, Coordinator Human Resources and Safety Officer, Institute For Orthopaedic Surgery, Lima, OH, p. A484

FARMER, William, M.D., Chief of Staff, Evergreen Medical Center, Evergreen, AL, p. A17

FARNHAM, Diane, Acting Director Human Resources, Lallie Kemp Medical Center, Independence, LA, p. A269

FARNHAM, Krista, Chief Executive, Providence Portland Medical Center, Portland, OR, p. A516

FARO, Joan, M.D., Chief Medical Officer, John T. Mather Memorial Hospital, Port Jefferson, NY, p. A440

FARR, Lorraine, Manager Human Resources, Georgia Regional Hospital At Atlanta, Decatur, GA, p. A152

FARR, Ronald, Chief Financial Officer, Frazier Rehab Institute, KY, p. A256

FARR, William L, M.D., Chief Medical Officer, University Hospital, Augusta, GA, p. A147

FARRAGE, Jim, M.D., Medical Director, Southern Kentucky Rehabilitation Hospital, Bowling Green, KY, p. A250

FARRAND, Cynthia B, President, Annie Penn Hospital, NC, p. A453

FARRAR, William, M.D., Interim Chief Executive Officer, James Cancer Hospital And Solove Research Institute, Columbus, OH, p. A478

FARRAUTO, Joseph, Director Human Resources, Eastern Niagara Hospital Newfane, NY, p. A429

FARRELL, America S., FACHE, Chief Executive Officer, College Station Medical Center, College Station, TX, p. A593

FARRELL, Brenda, Vice President Finance, Long Island Community Hospital, Patchogue, NY, p. A440

FARRELL, Coleen M, Vice President Human Resources, Mid Coast Hospital, Brunswick, ME, p. A283

FARRELL, George, M.D.
Chief Medical Officer, Clinch Valley Medical Center, Richlands, VA, p. A664
Chief of Staff, Wythe County Community Hospital, Wytheville, VA, p. A668

FARRELL, Kathleen, Chief Administrative Officer, Abington-Lansdale Hospital Jefferson Health, Lansdale, PA, p. A529

FARRELL, Roy, M.D., Chief Medical Officer, Carondelet Holy Cross Hospital, Nogales, AZ, p. A32

FARRELL, Scott, M.D., Vice President Medical Affairs, Promedica Memorial Hospital, Fremont, OH, p. A482

FARRELL, Steven E, M.D., Chief Medical Officer, Pine Grove Behavioral Health And Addiction Services, MS, p. A347

FARRELL, Teresa, Chief Human Resources Officer, Nacogdoches Medical Center, Nacogdoches, TX, p. A625

FARRELL, Timothy, Executive Director, St. Lawrence Psychiatric Center, Ogdensburg, NY, p. A439

FARRELLY, Irene, Vice President and Chief Information Officer, Brooklyn Hospital Center, New York (Includes All Hospitals Located Within The Five Boroughs), NY, p. A431

FARRINGTON, Robyn, Chief Nursing Officer, Chris Evert Childrens Hospital, FL, p. A122

FARRIS, James R., FACHE, Chief Executive Officer, Union County Hospital, Anna, IL, p. A173

FARRIS, Jason, Chief Nursing Officer, Midwest City Specialty Hospital, Midwest City, OK, p. A501

FARRISH, John, Health Information Director, University Of Mississippi Medical Center Grenada, Grenada, MS, p. A346

FARROW, Diane, Manager Information Technology and Systems, Willamette Valley Medical Center, Mcminnville, OR, p. A514

FARRUGIA, Gianrico, M.D., Vice President and Chief Executive Officer, Mayo Clinic Hospital In Florida, Jacksonville, FL, p. A125

FARSHAO, Nosratian, M.D., Chief Medical Staff, Memorial Hospital Of Gardena, Gardena, CA, p. A60

FARUGIA, Celeste, R.N., MSN, Chief Nurse Executive, Kaiser Permanente Panorama City Medical Center, Los Angeles, CA, p. A67

FARWELL, Brenda
Director Human Resources, Providence Medical Center, Kansas City, KS, p. A238
Director Human Resources, Saint John Hospital, Leavenworth, KS, p. A239

FASANO, Philip, Chief Information Officer, Kaiser Permanente Sacramento Medical Center, Sacramento, CA, p. A81

FASHINA, Olawale, M.D., Chief of Staff, Central Texas Veterans Health Care System, Doris Miller Veterans Medical Center, TX, p. A638

FAST, Gary, M.D., Medical Director, Prairie View, Newton, KS, p. A242

FASTHORSE, Lena, Supervisor Human Resource, U.S. Public Health Service Indian Hospital-Whiteriver, Whiteriver, AZ, p. A38

FATCH, Casey, Chief Executive Officer, Shasta Regional Medical Center, Redding, CA, p. A80

FATTIG, Marty, Chief Executive Officer, Nemaha County Hospital, Auburn, NE, p. A381

FATULA, Suzette
Chief Financial Officer, Oakdale Community Hospital, Oakdale, LA, p. A277
Chief Financial Officer, Winn Parish Medical Center, Winnfield, LA, p. A281

FAUBION, Matthew, M.D., Clinical Director, Kerrville State Hospital, Kerrville, TX, p. A617

FAUCETT, Michael, Chief Operating Officer, Lake City Community Hospital, Lake City, SC, p. A555

FAUCHER, Kimberly, M.D., Chief Medical Officer, Adventist Health Howard Memorial, Willits, CA, p. A95

FAUCHEUX, Lisa, Director Human Resources, St. James Parish Hospital, Lutcher, LA, p. A273

FAUGHT, Charles J, Chief Financial Officer, Burnett Medical Center, Grantsburg, WI, p. A693

FAUL, Jennifer, Chief Operating Officer, Prairie St. John'S, Fargo, ND, p. A466

FAULIS, Karen, Chief Executive Officer, Hi-Desert Medical Center, Joshua Tree, CA, p. A62

FAULKNER, Cheryl, Director of Nursing, Mckenzie County Healthcare System, Watford City, ND, p. A469

FAULKNER, Cynthia, R.N., Chief Nursing Executive, Pender Memorial Hospital, Burgaw, NC, p. A448

FAULKNER, David, Interim Chief Executive Officer, Sierra Vista Hospital, Truth Or Consequences, NM, p. A420

FAULKNER, Kristi, Vice President Organizational Growth, United Regional Health Care System-Eleventh Street Campus, TX, p. A644

FAULKNER, Laura, Chief Human Resource Management Service, Lexington Veterans Affairs Medical Center, Lexington, KY, p. A255

FAULKNER, Sharon
Administrator, Sage Specialty Hospital (Ltac), Denham Springs, LA, p. A267
Chief Nursing Officer, Sage Specialty Hospital (Ltac), Denham Springs, LA, p. A267

FAUMUINA, Taufete's John., Chief Executive Officer, Lyndon B. Johnson Tropical Medical Center, Pago Pago, AS, p. A711

FAUS, Doug, FACHE, Chief Executive Officer, Ivinson Memorial Hospital, Laramie, WY, p. A708

FAUST, Cheryl, Chief Nursing Officer, Edgefield County Hospital, Edgefield, SC, p. A552

FAUTHEREE, Greg, M.D., Medical Director, Spine Hospital Of Louisiana (Formally The Neuromedical Center Surgical Hospital), Baton Rouge, LA, p. A264

FAVATA, Valerie, R.N., MS, Chief Nursing Officer, Oswego Hospital, Oswego, NY, p. A439

FAVRET, John M., Director, Eastern State Hospital, Williamsburg, VA, p. A667

FAY, Brian, Director Information Systems, Sidney Health Center, Sidney, MT, p. A379

FAYEN, Edward J, Associate Administrator Operations and Support, Washington Hospital Healthcare System, Fremont, CA, p. A59

FAYRE, Gail, M.D., Medical Director, Anna Jaques Hospital, Newburyport, MA, p. A302

FAZIO, Charles, Chief Health Officer and Medical Director Health Plan, Regions Hospital, Saint Paul, MN, p. A339

FEAGIN, Bridgett
Chief Financial Officer, Dmc - Detroit Receiving Hospital, Detroit, MI, p. A311
Chief Financial Officer, Dmc Hutzel Women's Hospital, MI, p. A311

FEASEL, Jeff, Chief Executive Officer, Halifax Health Medical Center Of Port Orange, FL, p. A121

FEATHER, Leroy P, Vice President Finance, Montpelier Hospital, OH, p. A473

FEAZELL, Kayla, Chief Executive Officer, Encompass Health Rehabilitation Hospital Of Gadsden, Gadsden, AL, p. A18

FEBRY, Ricardo, M.D., Medical Director, St. Theresa Specialty Hospital, Kenner, LA, p. A270

FEBUS, Steven, Chief Financial Officer, Pullman Regional Hospital, Pullman, WA, p. A675

FEDELE, Jerry J., President and Chief Executive Officer, Boca Raton Regional Hospital, Boca Raton, FL, p. A118

FEDER, Diane, R.N., FACHE, Senior Vice President and Chief Operating Officer, Witham Health Services, Lebanon, IN, p. A210

FEDERICO, Skip, Director Information Systems, Avala, Covington, LA, p. A266

FEDERINKO, David, Chief Information Officer, Allegan General Hospital, Allegan, MI, p. A307

FEDIE, Corey J, Chief Operating Officer, Kit Carson County Health Service District, Burlington, CO, p. A97

FEDIE, Corey J., Chief Operating Officer, Kit Carson County Health Service District, Burlington, CO, p. A97

FEDORA, Deborah, Director Human Resources, Paoli Hospital, Paoli, PA, p. A533

FEELEY, Daniel, Interim Chief Financial Officer, Medstar Southern Maryland Hospital Center, Clinton, MD, p. A290

FEEMAN, Kimberly, Senior Vice President and Chief Operating Officer, Wellspan Good Samaritan Hospital, Lebanon, PA, p. A529

FEEN, Jim, Senior Vice President and Chief Information Officer, Tobey Hospital, MA, p. A299

FEENEY, Daniel, M.D., Medical Director, Brentwood Hospital, Shreveport, LA, p. A278

FEENEY, Sheri, Chief Financial Officer, Providence Everett Medical Center - Pacific Campus, WA, p. A671

FEESS, David, President and Chief Executive Officer, Liberty Hospital, Liberty, MO, p. A363

FEGAN, Claudia, M.D., Chief Medical Officer, John H. Stroger Jr. Hospital Of Cook County, Chicago, IL, p. A177

FEGAN, Theresa, R.N., Chief Clinical Officer, Tahoe Pacific Hospitals, NV, p. A397

FEGHALI, Georges, M.D.
Senior Vice President Quality and Chief Medical Officer, Bethesda Butler Hospital, OH, p. A474

Senior Vice President Quality and Chief Medical Officer, Good Samaritan Hospital, Cincinnati, OH, p. A475

FEH, Godwin, Interim Administrator, Pawhuska Hospital, Pawhuska, OK, p. A505

FEHRING, Marcia, Chief Financial Officer, Horn Memorial Hospital, Ida Grove, IA, p. A224

FEICKERT, Brent, Chief Financial Officer, Unitypoint Health - Trinity Regional Medical Center, Fort Dodge, IA, p. A222

FEIDT, Leslie, Chief Information Officer, Erie County Medical Center, Buffalo, NY, p. A423

FEIGENBAUM, Avi, LNHA, Chief Executive Officer, Northbrook Behavioral Health Hospital, Blackwood, NJ, p. A402

FEIKE, Jeffrey, President and Chief Administrative Officer, Fort Loudoun Medical Center, Lenoir City, TN, p. A573

FEILMEIER, Patricia A., R.N., Chief Nursing Officer, Piedmont Medical Center, Rock Hill, SC, p. A556

FEILNER, Margaret, Director Information Services, Ssm Health St. Joseph - Wentzville, MO, p. A367

FEINBERG, Daniel, M.D., Chief Medical Officer, Pennsylvania Hospital, Philadelphia, PA, p. A536

FEINBERG, Jason, M.D.
Vice President Medical Affairs and Chief Medical Officer, Finger Lakes Hospital, Geneva, NY, p. A426
Vice President Medical Affairs and Chief Medical Officer, Soldiers And Sailors Memorial Hospital Of Yates County, Penn Yan, NY, p. A440

FEISAL, J Philip., President and Chief Executive Officer, Spartanburg Medical Center, Spartanburg, SC, p. A557

FEIST, Patricia, Manager Human Resources, Crook County Medical Services District, Sundance, WY, p. A710

FEISTRITZER, Nancye R., Chief Nursing Officer, Emory Wesley Woods Geriatric Hospital, GA, p. A146

FELDMAN, David L, Executive Vice President and Treasurer, Circles Of Care, Melbourne, FL, p. A129

FELDMAN, David L., President and Chief Executive Officer, Circles Of Care, Melbourne, FL, p. A129

FELDMAN, Deborah A., President and Chief Executive Officer, Dayton Children's Hospital, Dayton, OH, p. A480

FELDMAN, Joel
Regional President, St. Vincent Seton Specialty Hospital, Indianapolis, IN, p. A208
Regional President, St. Vincent Women's Hospital, IN, p. A208

FELDMAN, Mitchell S., Chief Executive Officer, West Boca Medical Center, Boca Raton, FL, p. A118

FELDMANN, Scott, Director Information Technology, Ssm Health Depaul Hospital - St. Louis, Bridgeton, MO, p. A356

FELDSTEIN, Charles S., M.D., Vice President Medical Affairs, St. Rose Hospital, Hayward, CA, p. A61

FELEGE, Lester, Controller, Healthsouth New England Rehabilitation Hospital, Woburn, MA, p. A306

FELICE, Michael, Chief Financial Officer, Poplar Springs Hospital, Petersburg, VA, p. A663

FELICETTI, Jacqueline, Chief Human Resource Officer, Chester County Hospital, West Chester, PA, p. A544

FELICI, Brian K., Chief Executive Officer, Wetzel County Hospital, New Martinsville, WV, p. A685

FELICIANO, Jose R., Chief Executive Officer, Ryder Memorial Hospital, Humacao, PR, p. A714

FELICIANO, Myrna Quinones, M.D., Medical Director, University Pediatric Hospital, Rio Piedras, PR, p. A715

FELICIANO, Pablo, Manager Human Resources, Veterans Affairs Central Western Massachusetts Healthcare System, Leeds, MA, p. A301

FELIZ, Miriam, M.D., Medical Director, St. Catherine's Rehabilitation Hospital, North Miami, FL, p. A132

FELKNER, Joseph G
Chief Financial Officer, Health First Viera Hospital, Melbourne, FL, p. A129
Executive Vice President and Chief Financial Officer, Health First Palm Bay Hospital, Palm Bay, FL, p. A135
Executive Vice President/Chief Financial Officer, Health First Holmes Regional Medical Center, Melbourne, FL, p. A129
Senior Vice President Finance and Chief Financial Officer, Health First Cape Canaveral Hospital, Cocoa Beach, FL, p. A120

FELL, David, M.D., Chief Medical Officer, Tulsa Spine And Specialty Hospital, Tulsa, OK, p. A509

FELLER, Alicia, Chief Executive Officer, Southwest Connecticut Mental Health System, Bridgeport, CT, p. A107

FELLER, Julie, Executive Director Human Resources, Grays Harbor Community Hospital, Aberdeen, WA, p. A669

FELLOWS, Rhonda, R.N., Chief Nursing Officer, Van Buren County Hospital, Keosauqua, IA, p. A225

FELLOWS, Steven A
Executive Vice President and Chief Operating Officer, Cottage Rehabilitation Hospital, CA, p. A88

Executive Vice President and Chief Operating Officer, Goleta Valley Cottage Hospital, Santa Barbara, CA, p. A88

Executive Vice President and Chief Operating Officer, Santa Ynez Valley Cottage Hospital, Solvang, CA, p. A90

FELMLEE, Charles, Assistant Director Fiscal Services, Central Virginia Training Center, Madison Heights, VA, p. A660

FELTMAN, Steven, CPA, Chief Financial Officer, Essentia Health-Virginia, Virginia, MN, p. A341

FELTON, David
Manager Information Systems, Waldo County General Hospital Maine Health, Belfast, ME, p. A283
Regional Chief Information Officer, Lincolnhealth St. Andrews Campus, ME, p. A283

FELTS, Dave, Chief Information Systems, Logan Regional Hospital, Logan, UT, p. A647

FELTZ, Stacy, Manager Human Resource, Hillsdale Hospital, Hillsdale, MI, p. A315

FENDER, Tamra, Chief Nursing Officer, Marias Medical Center, Shelby, MT, p. A379

FENDT, Phil, Chief Financial Officer, Memorial Community Health, Aurora, NE, p. A381

FENELLO, Michael A., Administrator and West Region Chief Executive Officer, St. Luke's Magic Valley Medical Center, Twin Falls, ID, p. A172

FENER, Michael
Executive Director, Plainview Hospital, Plainview, NY, p. A440
Executive Director, Syosset Hospital, Syosset, NY, p. A443

FENN, Mark, Director Human Resources, Pulaski Memorial Hospital, Winamac, IN, p. A216

FENNELL, Charles, Vice President Information Management, St. Joseph's Hospital Health Center, Syracuse, NY, p. A444

FENNELL, Colin, M.D., Chief Medical Officer, Riverview Health, Crookston, MN, p. A330

FENNELL, David, M.D., Acting Medical Director, Atascadero State Hospital, Atascadero, CA, p. A51

FENSKE, Bill, Chief Financial Officer, Rice Memorial Hospital, Willmar, MN, p. A342

FENSKE, Candace, Chief Executive Officer, Madelia Community Hospital, Madelia, MN, p. A334

FENSTERLE, Chris, Chief Operating Officer, Frye Regional Medical Center-South Campus, NC, p. A454

FENWICK, Sandra L., M.P.H., President and Chief Executive Officer, Boston Children's Hospital, Boston, MA, p. A296

FEOLA, Ferd, Chief Information Officer, Lehigh Valley Hospital - Pocono, East Stroudsburg, PA, p. A524

FERCH, Wayne
President and Chief Executive Officer, Adventist Medical Center-Reedley, Reedley, CA, p. A80
President and Chief Executive Officer, Adventist Medical Center-Selma, CA, p. A61
President and Chief Executive Officer, Central Valley General Hospital, Hanford, CA, p. A61

FERDOUS, Riza, Health Services Director, Ossining Correctional Facilities Hospital, Ossining, NY, p. A439

FERGUS, Janie
Director and Chief Information Officer, Saint Joseph Hospital, Lexington, KY, p. A255
Director and Chief Information Officer, Women's Hospital Saint Joseph East, KY, p. A255

FERGUS, Linda, Manager Information Technology, Allegheny Valley Hospital, Natrona Heights, PA, p. A532

FERGUSON, Allison, Director Human Resources, Avoyelles Hospital, Marksville, LA, p. A273

FERGUSON, Cathy, R.N., MSN, Vice President and Chief Nursing Officer, Hamilton Medical Center, Dalton, GA, p. A152

FERGUSON, Cheryl L, Associate Administrator, Sanford Canby Medical Center, Canby, MN, p. A329

FERGUSON, Clifford, Director Information Technology and Systems, Bayshore Medical Center, Pasadena, TX, p. A627

FERGUSON, Daniel, Chief of Staff, Grove City Medical Center, Grove City, PA, p. A526

FERGUSON, Deborah
Director, Human Resources, Sentara Albemarle Medical Center, Elizabeth City, NC, p. A452
Human Resources Consultant, Sentara Obici Hospital, Suffolk, VA, p. A667

FERGUSON, Denise, Chief Nursing Officer, Baptist Memorial Hospital-Collierville, Collierville, TN, p. A568

FERGUSON, G Thomas, Senior Vice President and Chief Human Resources Officer, The Allen Pavilion, NY, p. A434

FERGUSON, Gordon B., President and Chief Executive Officer, Saint Thomas Rutherford Hospital, Murfreesboro, TN, p. A576

FERGUSON, Karen, Director Human Resources, Johnson County Healthcare Center, Buffalo, WY, p. A707

FERGUSON, Marla J., Commanding Officer, Bayne-Jones Army Community Hospital, Fort Polk, LA, p. A267

FERGUSON, Michael, Chief Financial Officer, Harbor Oaks Hospital, New Baltimore, MI, p. A320

FERGUSON, Nina L, Director Human Resources, Little Colorado Medical Center, Winslow, AZ, p. A38

FERGUSON, Randy, Information Systems Manager, Fairchild Medical Center, Yreka, CA, p. A95

FERGUSON, Rick, Chief Executive Officer, Oklahoma Surgical Hospital, Tulsa, OK, p. A508

FERGUSON, Tonya, Director Human Resources, Emcompass Health Rehabilitation Hospital Of Virginia, Richmond, VA, p. A665

FERGUSON, Zeta, Chief Human Resources, Atlanta Veterans Affairs Medical Center, Decatur, GA, p. A152

FERIA, Jorge, M.D., President Medical Staff, Wilma N. Vazquez Medical Center, Vega Baja, PR, p. A716

FERNANDES, Roxanne, R.N., Chief Nursing Officer, Children's Hospitals And Clinics Of Minnesota, MN, p. A335

FERNANDEZ, Alexander, Chief Financial Officer, Chris Evert Childrens Hospital, FL, p. A122

FERNANDEZ, Arthur, Chief Financial Officer, First Hospital Panamericano, Cidra, PR, p. A713

FERNANDEZ, Benigno J, M.D., Executive Medical Director, Laurel Ridge Treatment Center, San Antonio, TX, p. A633

FERNANDEZ, Darlene, Chief Financial Officer, Unm Sandoval Regional Medical Center, Inc., Rio Rancho, NM, p. A419

FERNANDEZ, Jaime, Chief Executive Officer, Kempsville Center For Behavioral Health, Norfolk, VA, p. A662

FERNANDEZ, Jean, Chief Information Officer, Beth Israel Deaconess Hospital-Milton, Milton, MA, p. A302

FERNANDEZ, John, Chief Operating Officer, United Hospital Center, Bridgeport, WV, p. A681

FERNANDEZ, John R., President and Chief Executive Officer, Massachusetts Eye And Ear, Boston, MA, p. A296

FERNANDEZ, Marco, R.N., MSN, Chief Nursing Officer, Saint Thomas Midtown Hospital, Nashville, TN, p. A577

FERNANDEZ, Mark, M.D., Chief of Staff and President Medical Staff, Illinois Valley Community Hospital, Peru, IL, p. A193

FERNANDEZ, Richard W., President and Chief Executive Officer, Beth Israel Deaconess Hospital-Milton, Milton, MA, p. A302

FERNANDEZ, Ruben D, R.N., Vice President and Chief Nursing Officer, Hackensack Meridian Health Palisades Medical Center, North Bergen, NJ, p. A409

FERNANDEZ, Tracey, Chief Financial Officer, St. Mary Medical Center, Apple Valley, CA, p. A51

FERNANDEZ DEL VALLE, Arthur J, Chief Financial Officer, Cardiovascular Center Of Puerto Rico And The Caribbean, San Juan, PR, p. A715

FERNANDEZ-BRAVO, Grisel, R.N., Administrator and Chief Executive Officer, Memorial Hospital Miramar, Miramar, FL, p. A132

FERNYAK, Susan, M.D., Interim Chief Medical Officer & Chief Quality Officer, San Mateo Medical Center, San Mateo, CA, p. A87

FERRACANE, Tony, Vice President Human Resources, St. Mary Medical Center, Hobart, IN, p. A206

FERRANTI, Jeffrey, M.D., Chief Information Officer, Duke Children's Hospital & Health Center, NC, p. A451

FERRARO, Lisa, Senior Vice President and Chief Operating Officer, Virtua Marlton, Marlton, NJ, p. A407

FERRAROTTI, Gianna, Director Human Resources North Region, Ohiohealth Marion General Hospital, Marion, OH, p. A486

FERREIRA, Daniel, Director Management Information Systems, Hospital De La Concepcion, San German, PR, p. A715

FERRELL, Angie
Director Human Resources, Mercy Health - Anderson Hospital, Cincinnati, OH, p. A475
Director Human Resources, Mercy Health - Clermont Hospital, Batavia, OH, p. A471

FERRELL, Eileen Brennan, MS, R.N., Vice President and Chief Nursing Officer, Medstar Georgetown University Hospital, Washington, DC, p. A115

FERRELL, Jennifer, Chief Nursing Officer, Healthsouth Rehabilitation Hospital Of Memphis, Memphis, TN, p. A575

FERRELL, Leslie, Chief Nursing Officer, Harrisburg Medical Center, Harrisburg, IL, p. A184

FERRELL, Ronald, Chief Information Officer, New Mexico Veterans Affairs Health Care System - Raymond G. Murphy Medical Center, Albuquerque, NM, p. A416

FERREN, Alison, Vice President Information Technology and Chief Information Officer, Abington-Lansdale Hospital Jefferson Health, Lansdale, PA, p. A536

FERRIS, David, Chief Nursing Officer and Vice President Patient Care Services, Claxton-Hepburn Medical Center, Ogdensburg, NY, p. A439

FERRIS, Joseph, Chief Financial Officer, Veterans Affairs Medical Center Hot Springs Campus, SD, p. A561

FERRIS, Michael, M.D., Chief Medical Officer, Chi Health St Elizabeth, Lincoln, NE, p. A386

FERRIS, Norma, R.N., MS, Chief Nursing Officer, Spring Mountain Treatment Center, Las Vegas, NV, p. A395

FERRONI, Karen, M.D., Medical Director, Holyoke Medical Center, Holyoke, MA, p. A300

FERRY, Jane, M.D., Vice President Medical Affairs, Grand View Health, Sellersville, PA, p. A541

FERTIG, Ashley
Chief Nursing Officer, University Hospitals Conneaut Medical Center, Conneaut, OH, p. A479
Chief Nursing Officer, University Hospitals Geneva Medical Center, Geneva, OH, p. A483

FESSER, James, Chief Nursing Officer, Palo Pinto General Hospital, Mineral Wells, TX, p. A624

FETTEROLF, Kim, R.N., Chief Clinical Officer, Acuity Specialty Hospital Of Southern New Jersey, Willingboro, NJ, p. A414

FETTO, Julie, R.N., Chief Nursing Officer, Cleveland Clinic, Medina Hospital, Medina, OH, p. A486

FEUCHT, Jason, Chief Financial Officer, Kossuth Regional Health Center, Algona, IA, p. A217

FEUER, Tammy, Chief Executive Officer, Healthsouth Rehabilitation Hospital Of Vineland, Vineland, NJ, p. A413

FEUNNING, Charles, M.D., Chief Medical Officer, Western Reserve Hospital, Cuyahoga Falls, OH, p. A480

FIBIYI, Abayomi, Chief Human Resources Officer, North Vista Hospital, North Las Vegas, NV, p. A396

FICCHI, Adrienne, Vice President Information Management, Philadelphia Veterans Affairs Medical Center, Philadelphia, PA, p. A536

FICICCHY, Teri, R.N., MSN, Chief Nursing Officer, St. Francis Eastside, SC, p. A553

FICK, Beverly
Chief Nursing Officer, Desert Regional Medical Center, Palm Springs, CA, p. A77
Chief Nursing Officer, Doctors Hospital Of Manteca, Manteca, CA, p. A71

FIDLER, Soniya, MS, Chief Human Resources and Compliance Officer, Uchealth Yampa Valley Medical Center, Steamboat Springs, CO, p. A105

FIDUCIA, Karen A., FACHE, President and Chief Executive Officer, Summersville Regional Medical Center, Summersville, WV, p. A687

FIELD, Clifford, M.D., Medical Director, Ka'U Hospital, Pahala, HI, p. A166

FIELD, Edward, Administrator, Loma Linda University Behavioral Medicine Center, Redlands, CA, p. A80

FIELD, Kori, Director of Nursing, Brodstone Memorial Hospital, Superior, NE, p. A390

FIELD, Laurie, Director Human Resources, Eaton Rapids Medical Center, Eaton Rapids, MI, p. A312

FIELDER, Barb, Vice President Finance, St. Joseph Mercy Chelsea, Chelsea, MI, p. A309

FIELDING, Colene, Manager Business Office, Baylor Medical Center At Uptown, Dallas, TX, p. A595

FIELDING, Laura M, Administrative Director Organizational Development, Holy Family Memorial, Manitowoc, WI, p. A696

FIELDS, Donald R., Community Chief Executive Officer, Harlan Arh Hospital, Harlan, KY, p. A253

FIELDS, Greg, Director Information Technology, Elbert Memorial Hospital, Elberton, GA, p. A153

FIERER, Jonathan, M.D., Chief of Staff, Martinsburg Veterans Affairs Medical Center, Martinsburg, WV, p. A685

FIERRO, Barbara, Director, Human Resources, St. Francis Hospital, The Heart Center, Roslyn, NY, p. A442

FIETEK, Denise, Information Technology, Rio Grande Hospital, Del Norte, CO, p. A98

FIFE, Stephen, Chief Financial Officer, Cape Fear Valley - Bladen County Hospital, Elizabethtown, NC, p. A452

FIFIELD, Michael, Vice President Human Resources, Oneida Healthcare, Oneida, NY, p. A439

FIGGINS, Tara, Director Human Resources, Davis Hospital And Medical Center, Layton, UT, p. A647

FIGUEROA, Maria, Director Human Resources, Ryder Memorial Hospital, Humacao, PR, p. A714

FIGUEROA, Roseann, Director Human Resources, Doctors Hospital Of Laredo, Laredo, TX, p. A619

FIKE, Ruthita J, Chief Executive Officer, Loma Linda University Behavioral Medicine Center, Redlands, CA, p. A80

FILADORA, Victor A, M.D., MS, II, Chief Clinical Services, Roswell Park Cancer Institute, Buffalo, NY, p. A423

FILER, Christine, Director Human Resources, Healthsouth Rehabilitation Hospital Of Altoona, Altoona, PA, p. A519

FILES, Ashley S, Director Human Resources and Public Relations and Marketing, Winn Parish Medical Center, Winnfield, LA, p. A281

FILES, Carol, Chief Financial Officer, Advanced Diagnostics Hospital, Houston, TX, p. A610

FILIPINI, Alfred, Manager Human Resources, Ancora Psychiatric Hospital, Hammonton, NJ, p. A405

FILIPOWICZ, Thomas, M.D., Medical Director, St. Luke's Hospital - Quakertown Campus, Quakertown, PA, p. A539

FILLER, Richard, Chief Financial Officer, Berger Health System, Circleville, OH, p. A476

FILLER, Scott, Chief Executive Officer, Healthsouth Rehabilitation Hospital Of Altoona, Altoona, PA, p. A519

FILLINGIM, Jed, Acting Chief Operating Officer and Associate Director, G.V. (Sonny) Montgomery Veterans Affairs Medical Center, Jackson, MS, p. A348

FILLIPO, Brian, M.D., Chief Medical Officer, Guthrie Robert Packer Hospital, Sayre, PA, p. A540

FILLMAN, Donald, M.D., Chief Medical Officer, Guthrie County Hospital, Guthrie Center, IA, p. A223

FILLMAN, T Orvin, Dr.PH, Vice President, Operations, Rogers Memorial Hospital-West Allis, WI, p. A700

FILOSA, Frank, Fiscal Manager, Washington Dc Veterans Affairs Medical Center, Washington, DC, p. A116

FILOSA, Shannon M., Executive Director Women's and Children, Children's Hospital At Saint Francis, OK, p. A509

FILSON, Debbie, Chief Financial Officer, Ashland Health Center, Ashland, KS, p. A232

FINAN, Timothy J., FACHE
President and Chief Executive Officer, Bradford Regional Medical Center, Bradford, PA, p. A521
President and Chief Executive Officer, Olean General Hospital, Olean, NY, p. A439

FINCH, John
Chief Information and Community Officer, Health Alliance Hospital - Mary's Avenue Campus, Kingston, NY, p. A428
Vice President Information Services, Health Alliance Hospital - Broadway Campus, Kingston, NY, p. A428

FINCH, Kenneth A., President and Chief Executive Officer, Texas Health Huguley Hospital Fort Worth South, Burleson, TX, p. A591

FINCH, Kim
Chief Nursing Officer, Kosciusko Community Hospital, Warsaw, IN, p. A216
Interim Chief Executive Officer Chief Nursing Officer, Kosciusko Community Hospital, Warsaw, IN, p. A216

FINCH, Robert D., Director, Human Resources, Piedmont Athens Regional Medical Center, Athens, GA, p. A145

FINCH, Roy
Chief Executive Officer, Palestine Regional Medical Center-East, Palestine, TX, p. A626
Chief Executive Officer, Palestine Regional Medical Center, Palestine, TX, p. A626
Chief Operating Officer, Longview Regional Medical Center, Longview, TX, p. A620

FINCH, Steve, Chief Financial Officer, Guidance Center, Flagstaff, AZ, p. A29

FINCH, Teresa, Chief Financial Officer, Summerville Medical Center, SC, p. A550

FINCHER, Jodi
Administrator, St. Joseph Medical Center, Kansas City, MO, p. A362
Vice President Patient Care Services, Saint John Hospital, Leavenworth, KS, p. A239

FINDLAY, Andrew L., Deputy Commander Clinical Services, Tripler Army Medical Center, Honolulu, HI, p. A165

FINDLAY, Kelly, Director of Nurses, Pawnee County Memorial Hospital And Rural Health Clinic, Pawnee City, NE, p. A389

FINDLEY, Amber, Senior Director Nursing Services and NRC Administrator, Pleasant Valley Hospital, Point Pleasant, WV, p. A686

FINDLEY, John T, M.D., Chief Medical Officer, Beatrice Community Hospital And Health Center, Beatrice, NE, p. A382

FINE, James, M.D., Chief Information Officer, Uw Medicine/Harborview Medical Center, Seattle, WA, p. A677

FINE, Mathew N., M.D., Chief Medical Officer, Oroville Hospital, Oroville, CA, p. A77

FINELLI, Frederick, M.D., Vice President Medical Affairs, Medstar Montgomery Medical Center, Olney, MD, p. A293

FINELLI, Peter, Chief Financial Officer, Banner Payson Medical Center, Payson, AZ, p. A32

FINESTEIN, Brian, Chief Executive Officer, Saint Clare's Hospital/Dover, NJ, p. A403

FINETTI, Yoany, R.N., Chief Nursing Officer, Barnes-Jewish West County Hospital, Saint Louis, MO, p. A367

FINK, Renee, CPA, Chief Financial Officer, Dundy County Hospital, Benkelman, NE, p. A382

FINK, Tom, Vice President Regional Finance Officer, Range Regional Health Services, Hibbing, MN, p. A333

FINK, Walter, Chief Medical Officer, Multicare Good Samaritan Hospital, Puyallup, WA, p. A675

FINKEL, Naomi, Nurse Executive, Montgomery County Emergency Service, Norristown, PA, p. A533

FIX, Judith A, R.N., MSN, Senior Vice President and Chief Nursing Officer, Memorialcare, Long Beach Memorial Medical Center, Long Beach, CA, p. A65

FLACH, Shannan, Chief Executive Officer, Kingman Community Hospital, Kingman, KS, p. A238

FLACK, Charles, Interim Chief Information Officer, Orange County Global Medical Center, Inc., Santa Ana, CA, p. A88

FLAHERTY, John
Chief Financial Officer, Healthsouth Rehabilitation Hospital Of Western Massachusetts, Ludlow, MA, p. A301
Controller, Fairlawn Rehabilitation Hospital, Worcester, MA, p. A306

FLAHERTY, Linda, R.N., Senior Vice President, Patient Care Services, Mclean Hospital, Belmont, MA, p. A295

FLAHERTY, Patrick, Director Management Information, Naval Hospital Bremerton, Bremerton, WA, p. A670

FLAHERTY, Steve, Chief Executive Officer, Warm Springs Rehabilitation Hospital Of Westover Hills, TX, p. A634

FLAHERTY, Tom, Assistant Administrator, Los Angeles County Central Jail Hospital, Los Angeles, CA, p. A68

FLAKE, Robert
Chief Executive Officer, Middle Park Medical Center - Granby, CO, p. A102
Chief Financial Officer, Middle Park Medical Center - Granby, CO, p. A102

FLAMING, Patrick, R.N., Director Inpatient Operations, Prairie View, Newton, KS, p. A242

FLAMM, Cindy, Manager Quality, Choate Mental Health Center, Anna, IL, p. A173

FLANAGAN, Carl J., Chief Financial Officer, La Paz Regional Hospital, Parker, AZ, p. A32

FLANAGAN, Craig, Chief Financial Officer, Unitypoint Health - Allen Hospital, Waterloo, IA, p. A231

FLANAGAN, Michael J, Senior Vice President and Chief Operating Officer, St. Clair Hospital, Pittsburgh, PA, p. A537

FLANAGAN, Thomas, M.D., Medical Director, Aurora Behavioral Healthcare San Diego, San Diego, CA, p. A83

FLANAGAN, Tom, Chief Executive Officer, Osage Beach Center For Cognitive Disorders, Osage Beach, MO, p. A366

FLANARY, Tresha, R.N., Chief Clinical Services Officer, Wamego Health Center, Wamego, KS, p. A247

FLANDERS, David, Chief Operating Officer, Candler County Hospital, Metter, GA, p. A157

FLANIGAN, Erin, Vice President Human Resources, Wentworth-Douglass Hospital, Dover, NH, p. A398

FLANIGAN, Kevin, M.D., Chief Executive Officer, Northern Inyo Hospital, Bishop, CA, p. A53

FLANNERY, Lindsay, R.N., Vice President Patient Care Services, Avera Sacred Heart Hospital, Yankton, SD, p. A565

FLANNERY, Maureen, Vice President Clinic Operations, Straub Medical Center, Honolulu, HI, p. A165

FLANNERY, Patrick, Administrator, Christus St. Michael Rehabilitation Hospital, Texarkana, TX, p. A639

FLANNERY, Robert, Chief Financial Officer, American Family Children's Hospital, WI, p. A696

FLANZ, Bruce J.
President and Chief Executive Officer, Flushing Hospital Medical Center, New York (Includes All Hospitals Located Within The Five Boroughs), NY, p. A432
President and Chief Executive Officer, Jamaica Hospital Medical Center, New York (Includes All Hospitals Located Within The Five Boroughs), NY, p. A432

FLASCHENRIEM, Julie, Chief Information Officer, Park Nicollet Methodist Hospital, Saint Louis Park, MN, p. A339

FLASHER, Sara, Chief Nurse Executive, Warren State Hospital, Warren, PA, p. A543

FLATOW, Evan, M.D., President, Mount Sinai West Hospital, NY, p. A434

FLATT, G Wayne, D.O., Chief Medical Director, Pushmataha Hospital, Antlers, OK, p. A495

FLATTERY, William
Vice President and Administrator Western Division, Carilion Clinic Saint Albans Hospital, VA, p. A656
Vice President and Administrator Western Division, Carilion Giles Community Hospital, Pearisburg, VA, p. A663

FLAVIO, Chuck, Chief Executive Officer, Saint Simons By-The-Sea Hospital, Saint Simons Island, GA, p. A159

FLECHSIG, Randolph K, Administrator, Sheridan Community Hospital, Sheridan, MI, p. A323

FLECHSIG, Randolph K., Administrator, Sheridan Community Hospital, Sheridan, MI, p. A323

FLECK, Julie, Chief Operating Officer, Parkview Ortho Hospital, Fort Wayne, IN, p. A204

FLECKENSTEIN, Casey, Nurse Manager, Monroe County Hospital, Forsyth, GA, p. A153

FLEEGEL, Monica, Director Human Resources, Mayo Clinic Health System - Albert Lea And Austin, MN, p. A327

FLEENOR, Dennis, R.N., Administrator, Muleshoe Area Medical Center, Muleshoe, TX, p. A625

FLEET, Aaron, R.N., Chief Nursing Officer, Baylor Scott & White Texas Spine & Joint Hospital, Tyler, TX, p. A641

FLEISCHMANN, Craig, Vice President Finance, University Of Maryland Medical Center Midtown Campus, Baltimore, MD, p. A289

FLEISCHMANN, Tim, Chief Financial Officer, Tuality Forest Grove Hospital, OR, p. A513

FLEISHMAN, Samuel A, M.D., Chief Medical Officer, Cape Fear Valley Rehabilitation Center, NC, p. A452

FLEITES, Fernando, Senior Vice President Human Resources, St. Francis Eastside, SC, p. A553

FLEMER, Andrew, Chief Operating Officer, Smith Northview Hospital, GA, p. A162

FLEMING, Jared, Director, Information Services, Lourdes Counseling Center, Richland, WA, p. A676

FLEMING, Joshua, Vice President Chief Clinical Officer, Leesburg Regional Medical Center, Leesburg, FL, p. A128

FLEMING, Michael, Chief People Officer, Banner - University Medical Center Phoenix, Phoenix, AZ, p. A33

FLEMING, Shane
Chief Financial Officer, Capital Health Medical Center-Hopewell, Pennington, NJ, p. A410
Chief Financial Officer, Capital Health Regional Medical Center, Trenton, NJ, p. A413

FLEMING, William P, Chief Operating Officer, Norwood Hospital, Norwood, MA, p. A303

FLEMMING, Libby, Controller and Chief Information Officer, South Georgia Medical Center Lanier Campus, Lakeland, GA, p. A156

FLEMMING, Michael, Administrator, Cornerstone Behavioral Health Hospital Of Union County, Berkeley Heights, NJ, p. A402

FLESNER, Lynn, Director of Nursing, Glacial Ridge Health System, Glenwood, MN, p. A332

FLETCHALL, Terry L., President and Chief Executive Officer, Santiam Memorial Hospital, Stayton, OR, p. A518

FLETCHER, Adam, Chief Nursing Officer, Blake Medical Center, Bradenton, FL, p. A118

FLETCHER, Audrey, Chief Operating Officer, Madison Memorial Hospital, Rexburg, ID, p. A171

FLETCHER, Bill, Director Information Technology, Cooper County Community Hospital, Boonville, MO, p. A356

FLETCHER, Jennifer, Chief of Staff, Decatur County Memorial Hospital, Greensburg, IN, p. A205

FLETCHER, John, Chief Executive Officer, Patrick B. Harris Psychiatric Hospital, Anderson, SC, p. A549

FLETCHER, John R., President, Lehigh Valley Hospital - Hazleton, Hazleton, PA, p. A527

FLETCHER, Josie, Interim Chief Nursing Officer, Iberia Medical Center, New Iberia, LA, p. A275

FLETCHER, Kathy, R.N., MSN, Interim Chief Nursing Officer, Val Verde Regional Medical Center, Del Rio, TX, p. A598

FLETCHER, Kevin, Director Information Systems, Wysong Campus, TX, p. A623

FLETCHER, Melissa, Chief Executive Officer, Ellett Memorial Hospital, Appleton City, MO, p. A355

FLETCHER, Michael, M.D., Vice President and Chief Medical Officer, Hancock Regional Hospital, Greenfield, IN, p. A205

FLETCHER, Stephanie L, CPA, Chief Financial Officer, Union General Hospital, Blairsville, GA, p. A148

FLETCHER-JANZEN, David, Chief Executive Officer, Chicago Lakeshore Hospital, Chicago, IL, p. A176

FLETT, Will, Vice President Finance and Chief Financial Officer, Avera Queen Of Peace Hospital, Mitchell, SD, p. A562

FLICEK, David, President and Chief Executive Officer, Avera Children's Hospital, SD, p. A563

FLICKEMA, James, Vice President Market Development, Munson Healthcare Otsego Memorial Hospital, Gaylord, MI, p. A313

FLICKINGER, Kenneth E, Chief Financial Officer, Chester County Hospital, West Chester, PA, p. A544

FLINCHBAUGH, Robert, D.O., Chief Medical Officer, Winneshiek Medical Center, Decorah, IA, p. A221

FLINN, Charles, Vice President, Chief Operating Officer, Saint Mary's Hospital, Waterbury, CT, p. A111

FLINN, James, JD, FACHE, Chief Executive Officer, Tempe St. Luke's Hospital, AZ, p. A34

FLINT, Jennifer, Chief Financial Officer, Laird Hospital, Union, MS, p. A353

FLINT, Ruth, Chief Nursing Officer, St. Joseph Medical Center, Tacoma, WA, p. A679

FLIPPO, Mary Elizabeth, R.N., MSN, Vice President and Chief Nursing Officer, Tradition Medical Center, FL, p. A139

FLIS, James D, Chief Financial Officer, Livengrin Foundation, Bensalem, PA, p. A520

FLOOD, James, Director Information Systems, Claxton-Hepburn Medical Center, Ogdensburg, NY, p. A439

FLOREN, Joshua, President, Texas Health Presbyterian Hospital Plano, Plano, TX, p. A629

FLORENTINE, Erich
Chief People Officer, Bridgeton Health Center, NJ, p. A413
Chief People Officer, Inspira Medical Center-Elmer, Elmer, NJ, p. A404

FLORES, Andrea, Director, Information Systems, Providence Little Company Of Mary Medical Center - Torrance, Torrance, CA, p. A92

FLORES, Debbie
Chief Executive Officer, Banner Del E. Webb Medical Center, Sun City West, AZ, p. A36
Interim Chief Executive Officer, Banner Boswell Medical Center, Sun City, AZ, p. A36

FLORES, Debra A, R.N., MS, President and Chief Operating Officer, Valley Children's Healthcare, Madera, CA, p. A71

FLORES, Jacob, Chief Information Officer, Frio Regional Hospital, Pearsall, TX, p. A627

FLORES, Jerome
Chief Financial Officer and Chief Operating Officer, Kahuku Medical Center, Kahuku, HI, p. A165
Chief Financial Officer, Sunrise Canyon Hospital, Lubbock, TX, p. A621

FLORES, Linda, R.N., MSN, Vice President Nursing Services, Parkview Medical Center, Pueblo, CO, p. A104

FLORES, Rick, Interim Chief Executive Officer, Big Bend Regional Medical Center, Alpine, TX, p. A582

FLORKOWSKI, Douglas, Chief Executive Officer, Crawford Memorial Hospital, Robinson, IL, p. A194

FLOURA, Kamal, M.D., Medical Director, Eastern State Hospital, Medical Lake, WA, p. A673

FLOWE, Kenneth, M.D., Chief Medical Officer, Rice Memorial Hospital, Willmar, MN, p. A342

FLOWERS, Deborah, Director Human Resources, Monroe County Hospital, Forsyth, GA, p. A153

FLOWERS, Frank M., M.D.
Area Medical Director, Kaiser Permanente Moreno Valley Medical Center, Moreno Valley, CA, p. A73
Area Medical Director, Kaiser Permanente Riverside Medical Center, Riverside, CA, p. A81

FLOWERS, Michael, Director Information Management, Calhoun-Liberty Hospital, Blountstown, FL, p. A118

FLOWERS, Scott, Vice President Professional Services, Thibodaux Regional Medical Center, Thibodaux, LA, p. A280

FLOWERS, Susan S, MSN, R.N., Chief Nursing Officer, Cumberland County Hospital, Burkesville, KY, p. A250

FLOWERS, Taylor, Senior Vice President Human Resources, Onslow Memorial Hospital, Jacksonville, NC, p. A455

FLOYD, Dorothy, Ph.D., Superintendent, Terrell State Hospital, Terrell, TX, p. A639

FLOYD, Duane, Vice President Human Resources and Professional Services, Watertown Regional Medical Center, Watertown, WI, p. A705

FLOYD, Kiley, Chief Executive Officer, Nemaha Valley Community Hospital, Seneca, KS, p. A245

FLOYD, Miranda, R.N., Chief Nursing Officer, Northwest Medical Center, Albany, MO, p. A355

FLOYD, Robert, D.O., Chief Medical Staff, Davis County Hospital, Bloomfield, IA, p. A218

FLOYD, Terri, Chief Financial Officer, Bates County Memorial Hospital, Butler, MO, p. A356

FLOYD, William Brian., President, University Health Systems Children's Hospital, NC, p. A454

FLUGUM, Aaron, Chief Executive Officer, Mercy Medical Center-New Hampton, New Hampton, IA, p. A227

FLUKE, Cinda, R.N., Chief Nursing Officer, Saint Joseph Mount Sterling, Mount Sterling, KY, p. A258

FLUTY, Lisa, Director Information Services, Baptist Health Lexington, Lexington, KY, p. A254

FLYGARE, Matthew, Director Human Resources, Mountain West Medical Center, Tooele, UT, p. A651

FLYNN, Brian, Chief Human Resources Officer, Veterans Affairs Northern Indiana Health Care System-Marion Campus, IN, p. A204

FLYNN, Chanda, R.N., MSN, Chief Nursing Officer, Mary Black Health System-Spartanburg, Spartanburg, SC, p. A557

FLYNN, Cheryl, Senior Vice President Chief Human Resources Officer, Methodist Charlton Medical Center, Dallas, TX, p. A597

FLYNN, James, Chief Executive Officer, Galesburg Cottage Hospital, Galesburg, IL, p. A183

FLYNN, Julianne, M.D., Chief of Staff, San Antonio Division, TX, p. A634

FLYNN, Kristin, Chief Human Resources Officer, Sierra Vista Regional Medical Center, San Luis Obispo, CA, p. A87

FLYNN, Matthew J, Chief Financial Officer West Region, Northwestern Medicine Valley West Hospital, Sandwich, IL, p. A195

FLYNN, Patrick, Chief Financial Officer, Warm Springs Medical Center, Warm Springs, GA, p. A163

FOARD, Mesa, Director Information technology, William S. Hall Psychiatric Institute, Columbia, SC, p. A551

FOGARTY, John M., President and Chief Executive Officer, Beth Israel Deaconess Hospital-Needham Campus, Needham, MA, p. A302

FOGARTY, Kathleen R., MS, Director, Kansas City Veterans Affairs Medical Center, Kansas City, MO, p. A361

FOGELSON, Julia, R.N., Chief Operating Officer and Chief Nursing Executive, French Hospital Medical Center, San Luis Obispo, CA, p. A87

FOGG, Jay Trevor, R.N., Chief Nursing Officer, Western Plains Medical Complex, Dodge City, KS, p. A234

FOGG, Robert W, Director Finance, Lake Taylor Transitional Care Hospital, Norfolk, VA, p. A662

FOJTASEK, Georgia R., President and Chief Executive Officer, Henry Ford Allegiance Health, Jackson, MI, p. A316

FOLDS, Jesse, Director of Information Technologies, Merit Health Wesley, Hattiesburg, MS, p. A347

FOLEY, Chris, Chief of Medicine, Children's Hospital Of The King's Daughters, Norfolk, VA, p. A662

FOLEY, Crystal, Director Human Resources, Rockdale Hospital, Rockdale, TX, p. A630

FOLEY, James T, CPA, Vice President and Chief Financial Officer, Shore Medical Center, Somers Point, NJ, p. A411

FOLEY, Jay, President and Chief Executive Officer, Southwestern Regional Medical Center, Tulsa, OK, p. A509

FOLEY, John, Chief Information Officer, Allegheny General Hospital, Pittsburgh, PA, p. A537

FOLEY, Michael, M.D., Chief Medical Officer, North Okaloosa Medical Center, Crestview, FL, p. A120

FOLEY, Regina, R.N., FACHE
   Chief Operating Officer, Hackensack Meridian Health Southern Ocean Medical Center, Manahawkin, NJ, p. A407
   Vice President Nursing and Operations, Hackensack Meridian Health Ocean Medical Center, Brick Township, NJ, p. A403

FOLK, Jeffrey R, M.D., Vice President Medical Affairs and Chief Medical Officer, Piedmont Newnan Hospital, Newnan, GA, p. A158

FOLKENBERG, Todd, Chief Executive Officer, Castle Rock Adventist Hospital, Castle Rock, CO, p. A97

FOLL, Gary R, Chief Financial Officer, Atchison Hospital, Atchison, KS, p. A232

FOLLETT, Traci, Director Clinical Infomatics, Sierra View Medical Center, Porterville, CA, p. A79

FOLSKE, Lance, Chief Executive Officer, Sun Behavioral Columbus, Columbus, OH, p. A479

FOLSOM, Lori S, Assistant Vice President Human Resources, Tift Regional Medical Center, Tifton, GA, p. A162

FOLTZ, JoAnn M., R.N., Chief Executive Officer, Sanford Wheaton Medical Center, Wheaton, MN, p. A342

FONDESSY, Terrence, M.D., Vice President Medical Affairs, Promedica Fostoria Community Hospital, Fostoria, OH, p. A482

FONDREN, Shay, Administrator, Hale County Hospital, Greensboro, AL, p. A18

FONG, Joseph, Administrator, Providence Seward Medical Center, Seward, AK, p. A27

FONKEN, Paul, M.D., Chief of Staff, Estes Park Medical Center, Estes Park, CO, p. A100

FONTAINE-WESTHART, Mark, Associate Director, Bedford Veterans Affairs Medical Center, Edith Nourse Rogers Memorial Veterans Hospital, Bedford, MA, p. A295

FONTENAULT, Richard, Director Information Systems, Medical City Green Oaks Hospital, Dallas, TX, p. A597

FONTENELLE, Mary, Executive Nurse Director, Eastern Louisiana Mental Health System, Jackson, LA, p. A269

FONTENOT, Jude, Administrator, Lafayette General Orthopedic Hospital, LA, p. A271

FONTENOT, Teri G., FACHE, President and Chief Executive Officer, Woman's Hospital, Baton Rouge, LA, p. A264

FONTENOT, Terrie, Chief Nursing Officer, Sacred Heart Hospital Pensacola, Pensacola, FL, p. A136

FONZIE, Juril, Director Human Resources, Helena Regional Medical Center, Helena-Phillips County, AR, p. A43

FOOTE, Donald E, Fiscal Officer, Wilkes-Barre Veterans Affairs Medical Center, Wilkes, PA, p. A544

FOOTE, John, Chief Information Officer, Manchester Veterans Affairs Medical Center, Manchester, NH, p. A400

FOOTE, Mark, Chief Financial Officer, Madera Community Hospital, Madera, CA, p. A71

FORAND, Angela, Director, William S. Hall Psychiatric Institute, Columbia, SC, p. A551

FORBES, Bill
   Interim Chief Executive Officer, Big Horn County Memorial Hospital, Hardin, MT, p. A376

   Interim Chief Executive Officer, Smith Northview Hospital, GA, p. A162

FORBES, Brenda, Controller, Healthsouth Rehabilitation Hospital Of Fort Smith, Fort Smith-Sebastian County, AR, p. A42

FORBES, Dan, Vice President Human Resources, Doernbecher Children's Hospital, OR, p. A516

FORBES, Geri, Chief Executive Officer, Whidbeyhealth, Coupeville, WA, p. A671

FORBES, Jonathan, Director Human Resources, Ashtabula County Medical Center, Ashtabula, OH, p. A471

FORBES, Ronald O, M.D., Medical Director, Central State Hospital, Petersburg, VA, p. A663

FORBORT, Gordy, Chief Financial Officer, Firstlight Health System, Mora, MN, p. A336

FORD, Alisa, Vice President Human Resources, The University Of Kansas Hospital - Indian Creek Campus, KS, p. A238

FORD, Angelique, Administrator Human Resources, Spring Valley Hospital Medical Center, Las Vegas, NV, p. A395

FORD, Cora, Vice President Human Resources, Our Lady Of The Lake Children's Hospital, LA, p. A264

FORD, James, Director Human Resources, Sparks Medical Center - Van Buren, Van Buren-Crawford County, AR, p. A49

FORD, Karen, Chief Nursing Officer, Sabine Medical Center, Many, LA, p. A273

FORD, LeeAnn, Director Human Resources and Imaging, The Physicians Centre Hospital, Bryan, TX, p. A591

FORD, Marcia F, Chief Operating Officer, Hawthorn Children Psychiatric Hospital, Saint Louis, MO, p. A368

FORD, Mary Carroll, Chief Information Officer, Einstein Medical Center Montgomery, East Norriton, PA, p. A524

FORD, Michael, Vice President Patient Services, Wood County Hospital, Bowling Green, OH, p. A472

FORD, Timothy R., President and Chief Executive Officer, Springfield Hospital, Springfield, VT, p. A654

FORD, Veronica, Vice President Human Resources, University Of Maryland Capital Region Health Prince George's Hospital Center, Cheverly, MD, p. A290

FORDE, Steve, Chief Executive Officer, Nelson County Health System, Mcville, ND, p. A468

FORDHAM, Karen, Chief Executive Officer, Venice Regional Bayfront Health, Venice, FL, p. A142

FORDYCE, Brian, Director Information Technology, Roosevelt Medical Center, Culbertson, MT, p. A374

FORDYCE, Michael L., President and Chief Executive Officer, Craig Hospital, Englewood, CO, p. A100

FOREMAN, Christopher, Director Human Resources, Santa Rosa Medical Center, Milton, FL, p. A131

FOREMAN, Kim, M.D., Chief of Staff, Baylor Scott & White Texas Spine & Joint Hospital, Tyler, TX, p. A641

FOREMAN, Lee Ann
   Vice President Human Resources, Mississippi Baptist Medical Center, Jackson, MS, p. A348
   Vice President Human Resources, Select Specialty Hospital - Belhaven, Jackson, MS, p. A348

FOREMAN, Nena, Chief Nursing Officer, Palo Verde Hospital, Blythe, CA, p. A53

FORESE, Laura, M.D., M.P.H., Executive Vice President and Chief Medical Officer, The Allen Pavilion, NY, p. A434

FOREST, Karen, Health Care Manager, State Penitentiary Hospital, Walla Walla, WA, p. A680

FORET, Chris, M.D., Chief of Staff, Riverside Medical Center, Franklinton, LA, p. A267

FORET, Robert, Chief Financial Officer, Yoakum Community Hospital, Yoakum, TX, p. A645

FORGE, Brenda J, Vice President, Human Resources, Regional West Medical Center, Scottsbluff, NE, p. A390

FORGEY, Warren, CPA, FACHE, President and Chief Executive Officer, Schneck Medical Center, Seymour, IN, p. A214

FORKEL, Todd
   Interim Chief Executive Officer, Avera St. Mary's Hospital, Pierre, SD, p. A562
   President and Chief Executive Officer, Avera St. Luke's Hospital, Aberdeen, SD, p. A559

FORKNER, Christine, Executive Vice President and Chief Financial Officer, National Jewish Health, Denver, CO, p. A99

FORNIER-JOHNSON, Michelle, Group Vice President Human Resources, St. Anthony Hospital, Lakewood, CO, p. A103

FORREST, Brian, Vice President Human Resources, Cayuga Medical Center At Ithaca, Ithaca, NY, p. A428

FORREST, Mary Helen, R.N., Chief Nursing Officer, Uams Medical Center, Little Rock-Pulaski County, AR, p. A45

FORREST, Molly, President and Chief Executive Officer, Joyce Eisenberg-Keefer Medical Center, Reseda, CA, p. A80

FORRESTER, John M, Director Information Services, Hamilton Medical Center, Dalton, GA, p. A152

FORSCH, Randall T, M.D., M.P.H., Chief Medical Officer, St. Joseph Mercy Chelsea, Chelsea, MI, p. A309

FORSTER, Tracy B, R.N., Senior Director of Nursing, Novant Health Matthews Medical Center, Matthews, NC, p. A457

FORSTNER, Jim, Chief Operating Officer, Dekalb Medical At North Decatur, Decatur, GA, p. A152

FORSYTH, Beth, Chief Operating Officer, Good Samaritan Medical Center, Lafayette, CO, p. A102

FORSYTH, Larry, Director Information Services, Presbyterian Tower, OK, p. A504

FORT, Claudio D., President and Chief Executive Officer, Rutland Regional Medical Center, Rutland, VT, p. A654

FORT, Glenn, Chief Medical Officer, Landmark Medical Center-Woonsocket Unit, RI, p. A548

FORTENBERRY, Denise, Chief Nursing Officer and Chief Compliance Officer, Cypress Pointe Surgical Hospital, Hammond, LA, p. A268

FORTENBERRY, Doris, Coordinator Human Resources, Delta Memorial Hospital, Dumas-Desha County, AR, p. A41

FORTENBERRY, Rob, Chief Information Officer, Mann-Grandstaff Veterans Affairs Medical Center, Spokane, WA, p. A678

FORTIER, Jeanne M, R.N., Chief Nursing Officer and Interim Chief Operating Officer, Grace Cottage Hospital, Townshend, VT, p. A654

FORTIN, Amanda, Manager Finance, Decatur Health Systems, Oberlin, KS, p. A242

FORTIN, Laura, R.N., Chief Operating Officer, St. Joseph Medical Center In The Heights, TX, p. A613

FORTNEY, John
   Chief Medical Officer, Adena Pike Medical Center, Waverly, OH, p. A493
   Senior System Medical Advisor, Adena Medical Center, Chillicothe, OH, p. A474

FORTNEY, Robert, MS, R.N., Chief Nursing Officer and Vice President of Patient Care, Illinois Valley Community Hospital, Peru, IL, p. A193

FOSBERG, Renee, Chief Information Officer, Emerson Hospital, Concord, MA, p. A299

FOSINA, Michael, M.P.H., FACHE, President, New York-Presbyterian/Lawrence Hospital, NY, p. A434

FOSNESS, Nick, Chief Executive Officer, Marshall County Healthcare Center Avera, Britton, SD, p. A559

FOSNOCHT, Kevin, M.D., Chief Medical Officer and Associate Executive Director, Penn Presbyterian Medical Center, Philadelphia, PA, p. A536

FOSS, David, Chief Information Officer, New London Hospital, New London, NH, p. A400

FOSS, R Coleman, Chief Executive Officer, Skyridge Medical Center - Westside Campus, TN, p. A568

FOSS, R Coleman., Chief Executive Officer, Skyridge Medical Center - Westside Campus, TN, p. A568

FOSTER, Barbara A, Regional Human Resources Director, Select Specialty Hospital-Wilmington, Wilmington, DE, p. A114

FOSTER, Becky
   Employee Relations Specialist, Sanford Tracy Medical Center, Tracy, MN, p. A341
   Employee Relations Specialist, Sanford Westbrook Medical Center, Westbrook, MN, p. A342

FOSTER, Beverly, Chief Executive Officer, Kindred Hospital Chicago-Northlake, Northlake, IL, p. A191

FOSTER, Bob, Chief Information Officer, Smith Northview Hospital, GA, p. A162

FOSTER, Brian, Chief Information Officer, Vail Health, Vail, CO, p. A106

FOSTER, Carolyn, Chief Financial Officer, Peacehealth Peace Island Medical Center, Friday Harbor, WA, p. A672

FOSTER, Charles, Regional Director Human Resources, Christus Southeast Texas Hospital-St. Mary, TX, p. A588

FOSTER, Chris, Director Health Information Management, Deer Lodge Medical Center, Deer Lodge, MT, p. A375

FOSTER, Daniel J, Chief Financial Officer, Northern Utah Rehabilitation Hospital, South Ogden, UT, p. A651

FOSTER, Don, Chief Executive Officer, St. Luke's Rehabilitation Hospital, Chesterfield, MO, p. A357

FOSTER, Gary, R.N.
   Associate Administrator, Banner Estrella Medical Center, Phoenix, AZ, p. A33
   Vice President and Chief Financial Officer, Saratoga Hospital, Saratoga Springs, NY, p. A442

FOSTER, Kennetha, Chief Nursing Officer, Mission Regional Medical Center, Mission, TX, p. A624

FOSTER, Larry, R.N., MSN, Chief Executive Officer, Kindred Hospital Chicago North, IL, p. A177

FOSTER, Michael, Director Information Systems, East Cooper Medical Center, Mount Pleasant, SC, p. A555

FOSTER, Mickey, President, Women's Hospital Of Greensboro, NC, p. A453

FOSTER, Mike, Manager Information Systems, Moab Regional Hospital, Moab, UT, p. A647

FOSTER, Mitzi, Director Information Services, Southern Tennessee Regional Health System-Pulaski, Pulaski, TN, p. A579

FOSTER, Rebecca, MSN, R.N., Chief Nursing Officer, Cumberland Medical Center, Crossville, TN, p. A569

FOSTER, Robert, Director Human Resources, L. V. Stabler Memorial Hospital, Greenville, AL, p. A19

FOSTER, Shane, R.N., Chief Nursing Officer, Vibra Hospital Of Springfield, Springfield, IL, p. A196

FOSTER, Stephanie, MSN, R.N., Chief Nursing Officer, Longview Regional Medical Center, Longview, TX, p. A620

FOSTER, Steven, Chief Executive Officer, Chi St. Luke's Health - Patients Medical Center, Pasadena, TX, p. A627

FOSTER, Terri, Hospital Finance Officer, Baylor Regional Medical Center At Grapevine, Grapevine, TX, p. A607

FOSTER, Timothy, Acting Chief Medical Officer, Massgeneral For Children At Newton-Wellesley Hospital, MA, p. A302

FOSTER, Wanda, R.N., MS, FACHE, MSN, Vice President Nursing, Mcdonough District Hospital, Macomb, IL, p. A188

FOTIADIS, George, M.D., Chief of Staff, Clarke County Hospital, Osceola, IA, p. A228

FOTTER, Robert, Chief Financial Officer, Pennsylvania Psychiatric Institute, Harrisburg, PA, p. A526

FOTTER, Robert L, Chief Financial Officer, Littleton Regional Healthcare, Littleton, NH, p. A400

FOUGHT, Scott, Vice President Finance, Promedica Bay Park Hospital, Oregon, OH, p. A488

FOULKE, Elvia, Executive Vice President and Chief Operating Officer, Foothill Presbyterian Hospital, Glendora, CA, p. A60

FOUNTAIN, Aaron, Chief Information Officer, Brandon Regional Hospital, Brandon, FL, p. A119

FOUNTAIN, Wesley D, Chief Financial Officer, St. David's South Austin Medical Center, Austin, TX, p. A587

FOUREZ, Yvonne, Chief Financial Officer, Washington County Memorial Hospital, Potosi, MO, p. A366

FOURNIER, Warren, Chief Executive Officer and Medical Director, Richmond State Hospital, Richmond, IN, p. A214

FOURRE, Mark
  Chief Executive Officer, Waldo County General Hospital Maine Health, Belfast, ME, p. A283
  President and Chief Executive Officer, Pen Bay Medical Center, Rockport, ME, p. A286

FOUSE, Carla
  Administrator and Chief Nursing Officer, St. Vincent Randolph Hospital, Winchester, IN, p. A216
  Chief Nursing Officer, St. Vincent Randolph Hospital, Winchester, IN, p. A216

FOUSE, Sarah, Associate Director of Patient Services, Captain James A. Lovell Federal Health Care Center, North Chicago, IL, p. A191

FOUST, Lisa
  Senior Vice President Human Resources, John Muir Behavioral Health Center, Concord, CA, p. A55
  Senior Vice President Human Resources, John Muir Medical Center, Concord, Concord, CA, p. A55
  Senior Vice President, Human Resources, John Muir Medical Center, Walnut Creek, Walnut Creek, CA, p. A94

FOUST-COFIELD, Misti, R.N., Vice President and Chief Nursing Officer, Reid Health, Richmond, IN, p. A214

FOUTS, Phillip, Chief Financial Officer, Fannin Regional Hospital, Blue Ridge, GA, p. A148

FOUTZ, Patricia, Director Human Resources, Bath Community Hospital, Hot Springs, VA, p. A660

FOWLER, Andrew, Vice President Information Services, Atlantic General Hospital, Berlin, MD, p. A290

FOWLER, Barry, Director Human and System Resources, Clark Fork Valley Hospital, Plains, MT, p. A378

FOWLER, Brian, Information Technology Director, Jeff Davis Hospital, Hazlehurst, GA, p. A154

FOWLER, Jennifer, Chief Nurse Officer, Central State Hospital, Louisville, KY, p. A256

FOWLER, Kate, Chief Financial Officer, West Valley Medical Center, Caldwell, ID, p. A168

FOWLER, Kevin, Director Finance, Putnam County Hospital, Greencastle, IN, p. A205

FOWLER, Kevin N., President and Chief Executive Officer, Hoops Family Children's Hospital, WV, p. A683

FOWLER, Marcia, Chief Executive Officer, Bournewood Health Systems, Brookline, MA, p. A298

FOWLER, Maureen, Director Human Resources, Conifer Park, Glenville, NY, p. A427

FOWLER, Ruth, Senior Vice President and Chief Financial Officer, Children's Healthcare Of Atlanta At Scottish Rite, GA, p. A146

FOWLER, Ryan, Chief Administrative Officer, Lower Umpqua Hospital District, Reedsport, OR, p. A517

FOWLER, Sean, Chief Executive Officer, Southern California Hospital At Culver City, Culver City, CA, p. A56

FOWLER, Steven, M.D., President Medical Staff, Genesis Medical Center, Dewitt, De Witt, IA, p. A220

FOX, Alan, Chief Financial Officer, Saint Francis Memorial Hospital, San Francisco, CA, p. A85

FOX, Carol J., M.D., Senior Vice President and Chief Medical Officer, Excela Latrobe Area Hospital, Latrobe, PA, p. A529

FOX, David R., Vice President and Chief Operating Officer, Baxter Regional Medical Center, Mountain Home-Baxter County, AR, p. A46

FOX, Debra, Chief Nursing Officer, Children's Hospital Of Nevada At Umc, NV, p. A395

FOX, Devin, M.D., Vice President Medical Operations, Lasting Hope Recovery Center, NE, p. A387

FOX, E. Kay, Director of Nursing, Black River Medical Center, Poplar Bluff, MO, p. A366

FOX, Jay
  Director Operations, Baylor Scott & White Medical Center - Taylor, Taylor, TX, p. A638
  President, Baylor Scott & White Medical Center - Lakeway, TX, p. A631

FOX, Jerry, Jr, Chief Information Officer, Alton Memorial Hospital, Alton, IL, p. A173

FOX, Jessica, Director of Human Resources, Aspirus Riverview Hospital And Clinics, Inc., Wisconsin Rapids, WI, p. A706

FOX, John, M.D., Medical Director, Vibra Hospital Of San Diego, San Diego, CA, p. A85

FOX, John A., M.D., Chief of Staff, Shriners Hospitals For Children-Shreveport, Shreveport, LA, p. A279

FOX, Leana, MSN, Interim Chief Nurse Executive, Bon Secours Maryview Medical Center, Portsmouth, VA, p. A664

FOX, Randy, Director Performance Improvement and Risk Management, Lakeland Behavioral Health System, Springfield, MO, p. A370

FOX, Starla, Director of Nursing, Bristol Bay Area Health Corporation, Dillingham, AK, p. A26

FOX, Susan, President and Chief Executive Officer, White Plains Hospital Center, White Plains, NY, p. A446

FOX, William, Chief Executive Officer, Amg Specialty Hospital - Las Vegas, Las Vegas, NV, p. A393

FOXX, Randy, Chief Financial Officer, Boone Memorial Hospital, Madison, WV, p. A684

FOY, Gregory S., Human Resources System Leader, Scheurer Hospital, Pigeon, MI, p. A320

FRABLE, Arthur H., Chief Executive Officer, Humboldt General Hospital, Winnemucca, NV, p. A397

FRACHISEUR, Kenny, Chief Information Officer, Ouachita County Medical Center, Camden-Ouachita County, AR, p. A40

FRACICA, Phil, M.D., Vice President and Chief Medical Officer, Mercy Gilbert Medical Center, Gilbert, AZ, p. A29

FRACK, Darla, R.N., RN, Vice President, Patient Services, St. Luke's Hospital - Anderson Campus, Easton, PA, p. A525

FRACK, Gina, Chief Executive Officer, Norton County Hospital, Norton, KS, p. A242

FRAGEN, Andrew, M.D., Chief Medical Officer, Community Hospital Of San Bernardino, San Bernardino, CA, p. A83

FRAHER, Francis D, Vice President, Finance, Northwestern Memorial Hospital, Stone Institute Of Psychiatry, IL, p. A178

FRAIOLA, Anthony, Associate Administrator Administrative and Support Services, Hawaii State Hospital, Kaneohe, HI, p. A166

FRAKER, Steve, Chief Financial Officer, Banner Churchill Community Hospital, Fallon, NV, p. A392

FRALICKER, Tammy, MS, R.N., Chief Nursing Officer, Crawford Memorial Hospital, Robinson, IL, p. A194

FRAME, Angela, Chief Financial Officer, Jackson General Hospital, Ripley, WV, p. A686

FRAME, Ken, Chief Nursing Officer, Ashtabula County Medical Center, Ashtabula, OH, p. A471

FRANCE, Cheryl, M.D., Chief Medical Officer, William R. Sharpe, Jr. Hospital, Weston, WV, p. A688

FRANCE, James, M.D., Chief of Staff, Conway Regional Medical Center, Conway-Faulkner County, AR, p. A40

FRANCETICH, Kane, Chief Information Officer, Gritman Medical Center, Moscow, ID, p. A170

FRANCIOLI, Carl H, Vice President Finance, Johns Hopkins Bayview Medical Center, Baltimore, MD, p. A287

FRANCIS, Carolyn, R.N., MSN, Director of Nursing, Lasalle General Hospital, Jena, LA, p. A269

FRANCIS, Christy, Chief Executive Officer, Hemphill County Hospital, Canadian, TX, p. A591

FRANCIS, Duane, Interim Chief Executive Officer, Wilson Memorial Hospital, Sidney, OH, p. A490

FRANCIS, Jeffrey, Vice President Finance and Chief Financial Officer, Methodist Jennie Edmundson Hospital, Council Bluffs, IA, p. A220

FRANCIS, Lana B., Chief Executive Officer, Lasalle General Hospital, Jena, LA, p. A269

FRANCIS, Mark J, President and Chief Executive Officer, Colorado Canyons Hospital And Medical Center, Fruita, CO, p. A101

FRANCIS, Mark J., President and Chief Executive Officer, Colorado Canyons Hospital And Medical Center, Fruita, CO, p. A101

FRANCIS, Perry, Supervisory Information Technology Specialist, Chinle Comprehensive Health Care Facility, Chinle, AZ, p. A28

FRANCIS, Rebekah, JD
  Chief Financial Officer, Aurora Behavioral Health System East, Tempe, AZ, p. A36
  Chief Financial Officer, Aurora Behavioral Health System West, Glendale, AZ, p. A30

FRANCISCO, Gerard E, M.D., Chief Medical Officer, Tirr Memorial Hermann, Houston, TX, p. A614

FRANCKOWIAK, Debra, Executive Director, Children's Hospital Of Wisconsin-Fox Valley, Neenah, WI, p. A699

FRANCO, Glenda, Director, Human Resources, Vibra Hospital Of Sacramento, Folsom, CA, p. A58

FRANCO, Luis, M.D., Medical Director, United Medical Rehabilitation Hospital - Gonzales, LA, p. A268

FRANCO, Richard, Chief Financial Officer, Community First Medical Center, Chicago, IL, p. A176

FRANCO, Richard A., Vice President and Chief Financial Officer, Northwestern Medicine Lake Forest Hospital, Lake Forest, IL, p. A187

FRANCO, Roger, Director Human Resources, St. John's Episcopal Hospital-South Shore, New York (Includes All Hospitals Located Within The Five Boroughs), NY, p. A437

FRANCO, Rosemary, Chief Nursing Officer, Cochran Memorial Hospital, Morton, TX, p. A624

FRANCOIS, Fritz, M.D., Chief Medical Officer, Rusk Institute At Nyu-Hjd, NY, p. A436

FRANDSEN, Jeff, Chief Executive Officer, Healthsouth Rehabilitation Hospital Of Utah, Sandy, UT, p. A651

FRANK, Barbara, Human Resource Specialist, Caro Center, Caro, MI, p. A309

FRANK, Cathrine, M.D., Chairperson, Henry Ford Kingswood Hospital, Ferndale, MI, p. A312

FRANK, Daniel, Chief Financial Officer, Longmont United Hospital, Longmont, CO, p. A103

FRANK, Debra, Chief Financial Officer, Ness County Hospital District No 2, Ness City, KS, p. A242

FRANK, James, CPA, Chief Executive Officer, Providence Medical Center, Wayne, NE, p. A391

FRANK, Kevin
  Administrator, Eunice Extended Care Hospital, LA, p. A271
  Administrator, Iberia Extended Care Hospital, LA, p. A271

FRANK, Kim, Chief Human Resources Officer, Virginia Gay Hospital, Vinton, IA, p. A230

FRANK, Patricia, Chief Nursing Officer, Henry County Hospital, Napoleon, OH, p. A487

FRANK, Robert A
  Senior Vice President of Operations, University Of Maryland Shore Medical Center At Chestertown, Chestertown, MD, p. A290
  Senior Vice President of Operations, University Of Maryland Shore Medical Center At Easton, Easton, MD, p. A291
  Senior Vice President Operations, University Of Maryland Shore Medical Center At Dorchester, Cambridge, MD, p. A290

FRANK, Stanley, Chief Executive Officer, Ohio Hospital For Psychiatry, Columbus, OH, p. A478

FRANK, Thomas
  Chief Operating Officer, North Country Hospital And Health Center, Newport, VT, p. A654
  Interim Chief Executive Officer, North Country Hospital And Health Center, Newport, VT, p. A654

FRANK-LIGHTFOOT, Loraine, Vice President, Patient Care Services and Chief Nursing Officer, Munson Medical Center, Traverse City, MI, p. A324

FRANKE, Craig, M.D., Medical Director, Texas Star Recovery, Austin, TX, p. A587

FRANKE, Jenny, Director Human Resources, Rehabilitation Hospital Of Wisconsin, Waukesha, WI, p. A705

FRANKE, John, Chief Financial Officer, Baptist Health Lexington, Lexington, KY, p. A254

FRANKE, Paul, M.D., Chief Medical Officer, Alaska Native Medical Center, Anchorage, AK, p. A25

FRANKEL, Harris, M.D., Interim Chief Medical Officer, Nebraska Medicine - Nebraska Medical Center, Omaha, NE, p. A388

FRANKEL, Michele, Associate Executive Director Finance, Glen Cove Hospital, Glen Cove, NY, p. A426

FRANKEN, Stephanie, Vice President Operational Finance, Chi St. Alexius Health - Dickinson Medical Center, Dickinson, ND, p. A465

FRANKENSTEIN, Richard, M.D., Vice President and Chief Medical Officer, Henry Mayo Newhall Hospital, Valencia, CA, p. A93

FRANKL, Angie, Director Human Resources, Adair County Health System, Greenfield, IA, p. A223

FRANKLIN, Chuck, M.D., Chief Medical Staff, Weston County Health Services, Newcastle, WY, p. A709

FRANKLIN, Clay, Chief Executive Officer, Alliancehealth Midwest, Midwest City, OK, p. A501

FRANKLIN, Ed, Chief Human Resources Officer, Page Hospital, Page, AZ, p. A32

FRANKLIN, Jennifer, R.N., Chief Clinical Officer, Yoakum Community Hospital, Yoakum, TX, p. A645

FRANKLIN, Matthew, Director Human Resources, Warren General Hospital, Warren, PA, p. A543

FRANKLIN, Michael A., FACHE, President and Chief Executive Officer, Atlantic General Hospital, Berlin, MD, p. A290

FRANKLIN, Michelle, Chief Executive Officer, Sullivan County Community Hospital, Sullivan, IN, p. A215

FRANKLIN, Tammy, Manager Personnel and Marketing, Covenant Hospital-Levelland, Levelland, TX, p. A619

FRANKO, Stephen
  Senior Vice President and Chief Financial Officer, St. Vincent's Behavioral Health, CT, p. A107
  Vice President Finance and Chief Financial Officer, Mount St. Mary's Hospital And Health Center, Lewiston, NY, p. A429
  Vice President Finance and Chief Financial Officer, Regional Hospital Of Scranton, Scranton, PA, p. A540

FRANKOVITCH, John C., President and Chief Executive Officer, Weirton Medical Center, Weirton, WV, p. A687

FRANKS, Cathy, RN, Chief Operating Officer, Izard County Medical Center, Calico Rock-Logan County, AR, p. A40

FRANKS, Charles, Chief Human Resources, Louis Stokes Cleveland Veterans Affairs Medical Center, Cleveland, OH, p. A477

FRANKS, Dennis, FACHE
  Chief Executive Officer, Neosho Memorial Regional Medical Center, Chanute, KS, p. A233
  Interim Chief Financial Officer, Doctors' Hospital Of Michigan, Pontiac, MI, p. A321
  Vice President Operations, Doctors' Hospital Of Michigan, Pontiac, MI, p. A321

FRANSEN, Mitchell, Chief Financial Officer, Mesa View Regional Hospital, Mesquite, NV, p. A395

FRANSON, John K., M.D., Chief Medical Staff, Caribou Memorial Hospital And Living Center, Soda Springs, ID, p. A172

FRANTZ, Steven, Chief Financial Officer, Saint Francis Hospital, Memphis, TN, p. A576

FRANTZ, Vincent, M.D., Chief of Staff, Plumas District Hospital, Quincy, CA, p. A79

FRANTZ, Zoe, Chief Executive Officer, Sycamore Springs Hospital, Lafayette, IN, p. A209

FRANZ, Eric, Vice President, Finance and Chief Financial Officer, Graham Hospital Association, Canton, IL, p. A175

FRANZ, Staci, Director Human Resources, St. Luke's Rehabilitation Institute, Spokane, WA, p. A678

FRANZELLA, Susan, Human Resource Business Partner, Kaiser Permanente San Jose Medical Center, San Jose, CA, p. A86

FRARDO, Virgil, M.D., Medical Director, Encompass Health Rehabilitation Hospital Of Wichita Falls, Wichita Falls, TX, p. A644

FRASCA, Edith, Controller and Chief Financial Officer, The Pavilion, Champaign, IL, p. A175

FRASCH, Sara, Chief Human Resource Officer, Unm Children's Hospital, NM, p. A416

FRASER, Cathryn H., Chief Human Resources Officer, Mayo Eugenio Litta Children's Hospital, MN, p. A338

FRASER, James, Administrator Finance, Via Christi Hospital Manhattan, Inc., Manhattan, KS, p. A240

FRASIER, Nora, R.N., FACHE, Chief Nursing Officer, Methodist Mansfield Medical Center, Mansfield, TX, p. A622

FRASURE, Jane, Human Resources, Baylor Scott & White Medical Center - Llano, Llano, TX, p. A620

FRATZKE, Mark, R.N., President and Chief Executive Officer, Seton Medical Center, Daly City, CA, p. A56

FRAUENHOFER, Chris, Chief Financial Officer, Maine Coast Memorial Hospital, Ellsworth, ME, p. A284

FRAZIER, Amy, Supervisor Management Information Systems, Wetzel County Hospital, New Martinsville, WV, p. A685

FRAZIER, Brandon, Chief Financial Officer, River Oaks Child And Adolescent Hospital, LA, p. A276

FRAZIER, Derrick A., FACHE, Chief Executive Officer, Morehouse General Hospital, Bastrop, LA, p. A263

FRAZIER, Joel L., M.D., Medical Director, Onecore Health, Oklahoma City, OK, p. A504

FRAZIER, Kimberly, R.N., Chief Nursing Officer, East Los Angeles Doctors Hospital, Los Angeles, CA, p. A66

FRAZIER, Shane, Chief Executive Officer, Pinnacle Pointe Hospital, Little Rock-Pulaski County, AR, p. A45

FREAS, Mary Ann, Senior Vice President and Chief Financial Officer, Southwest General Health Center, Middleburg Heights, OH, p. A487

FRED, Mark, R.N., Chief Operating Officer, Kirby Medical Center, Monticello, IL, p. A190

FREDEBOELLING, Elizabeth E., MSN, R.N., Chief Nursing Officer, Dell Children's Medical Center Of Central Texas, Austin, TX, p. A585

FREDERICK, Brenda, Director Human Resources, Laurel Ridge Treatment Center, San Antonio, TX, p. A633

FREDERICK, Dessa, Manager Human Resources, St. James Behavioral Health Hospital, Gonzales, LA, p. A268

FREDERICK, Gretchen A, R.N., Director Patient Care Services, Buffalo Hospital, Buffalo, MN, p. A329

FREDERICK, John, Chief Financial Officer, West Central Georgia Regional Hospital, Columbus, GA, p. A151

FREDERICK, Ryannon, Chief Nursing Officer, Mayo Clinic Hospital In Florida, Jacksonville, FL, p. A125

FREDERICKS, Raymond F, President and Chief Executive Officer, Hackensack Meridian Health Jfk Medical Center, Edison, NJ, p. A404

FREDERICKSON, Kathy, Information Systems Site Lead, Sutter Delta Medical Center, Antioch, CA, p. A50

FREDETTE, Beth, Chief Information Officer, Dayton Children's Hospital, Dayton, OH, p. A480

FREDRICH, Nancy, R.N., Chief Clinical Officer, Cooper County Community Hospital, Boonville, MO, p. A356

FREDRICK, Joyce, Associate Director, Veterans Affairs Central Western Massachusetts Healthcare System, Leeds, MA, p. A301

FREDRICK, Rick, Director Information Technology, Cottage Hospital, Woodsville, NH, p. A401

FREDRICKSON, Kelley, Director Information Services, Medical City Fort Worth, Fort Worth, TX, p. A605

FREDRICKSON, Mark A, M.D., Medical Director, Encompass Health Rehabilitation Hospital Midland Odessa, Midland, TX, p. A624

FREEBERN, Joseph, Executive Director, Mid-Hudson Forensic Psychiatric Center, New Hampton, NY, p. A431

FREEBORN, Fawn, Human Resources Generalist, Schoolcraft Memorial Hospital, Manistique, MI, p. A318

FREEBURG, Rick, Chief Executive Officer, Baptist Health South Florida, Mariners Hospital, Tavernier, FL, p. A142

FREEBURN, Mark, Chief Executive Officer, Helen M. Simpson Rehabilitation Hospital, Harrisburg, PA, p. A526

FREED, Nancy, Chief Financial Officer, Seiling Regional Medical Center, Seiling, OK, p. A506

FREED, Stuart, M.D.
  Chief Medical Officer, Confluence Health/Central Washington Hospital, Wenatchee, WA, p. A680
  Medical Director, Confluence Health/Wenatchee Valley Hospital, Wenatchee, WA, p. A680

FREED-SIGURDSSON, Anna, M.D., Medical Director, Encompass Health Rehabilitation Hospital Of Dallas, Dallas, TX, p. A596

FREEDMAN, Barry R, President and Chief Executive Officer, Einstein Medical Center Elkins Park, PA, p. A534

FREEDMAN, Barry R., President and Chief Executive Officer, Einstein Medical Center Elkins Park, PA, p. A534

FREEDMAN, Kenneth, M.D., Chief Medical Officer, Lemuel Shattuck Hospital, Jamaica Plain, MA, p. A300

FREEDMAN, Rick, Commanding Officer, Naval Hospital Camp Lejeune, Camp Lejeune, NC, p. A449

FREEHILL, Sarah, Chief Nursing Officer, Arbuckle Memorial Hospital, Sulphur, OK, p. A507

FREEHOF, Leonard, Chief Executive Officer and Managing Director, Spring Valley Hospital Medical Center, Las Vegas, NV, p. A395

FREELAND, R Alan, M.D., Chief Clinical Officer, Twin Valley Behavioral Healthcare, Columbus, OH, p. A479

FREEMAN, Brian, President, Carolinas Healthcare System Stanly, Albemarle, NC, p. A447

FREEMAN, Diane, R.N., Assistant Vice President and Chief Nursing Officer, Chi St. Luke's Health-Lakeside Hospital, The Woodlands, TX, p. A639

FREEMAN, Gail, Chief Nursing Officer, San Gabriel Valley Medical Center, San Gabriel, CA, p. A86

FREEMAN, Jerry, Chief, Human Resources Management Services, Durham Veterans Affairs Medical Center, Durham, NC, p. A451

FREEMAN, Kimberlee, MS, R.N., Vice President Patient Care Services and Chief Nursing Officer, Wayne Healthcare, Greenville, OH, p. A483

FREEMAN, Marianne, Vice President Human Resources, Piedmont Rockdale Hospital, Conyers, GA, p. A151

FREEMAN, Michael
  Director Human Resources, Alta Vista Regional Hospital, Las Vegas, NM, p. A418
  Director Human Resources, Huhukam Memorial Hospital, Sacaton, AZ, p. A35

FREEMAN, Mike, Director Information Technology, Sentara Williamsburg Regional Medical Center, Williamsburg, VA, p. A668

FREEMAN, Peggy, Chief Physicians Services Officer, Dickinson County Healthcare System, Iron Mountain, MI, p. A316

FREEMAN, Richard
  Chief Medical Officer, St. Vincent Women's Hospital, IN, p. A208
  President and Chief Executive Officer, Robert Wood Johnson University Hospital At Hamilton, Hamilton, NJ, p. A405

FREEMAN, Robert, Director Human Resources, Sparks Regional Medical Center, Fort Smith-Sebastian County, AR, p. A42

FREESE DECKER, Christina, FACHE, Executive Vice President and Chief Operating Officer, Spectrum Health, MI, p. A314

FREGOLI, Fabian, M.D., Chief Medical Officer, St. Joseph Mercy Oakland, Pontiac, MI, p. A321

FREID-SCHEPPKE, Denise, Chief Accounting Officer, Oakleaf Surgical Hospital, Altoona, WI, p. A689

FREIER, Toby, President, New Ulm Medical Center, New Ulm, MN, p. A336

FREIJ, Walid, M.D., Chief of Staff, Vaughan Regional Medical Center, Selma, AL, p. A23

FREILICH, Josh, Vice President and Chief Nurse Executive, Mercy Hospital Of Folsom, Folsom, CA, p. A58

FREIMARK, Jeffrey P., Chief Executive Officer, Miami Jewish Home And Hospital For Aged, Miami, FL, p. A130

FREISCHLAG, Julie Ann., M.D., Chief Executive Officer, Brenner Children's Hospital & Health Services, NC, p. A463

FREITAG, Donald, M.D., Chief Medical Officer, Lynn County Hospital District, Tahoka, TX, p. A638

FRELING, Eric, M.D., Director Medical Staff Affairs, Memorial Hospital West, Pembroke Pines, FL, p. A135

FRENCH, Dean, M.D., Chief Executive Officer, Community Medical Center, Missoula, MT, p. A377

FRENCH, Dean O, M.D., Chief of Staff, West Campus, NE, p. A387

FRENCH, Holly, Chief Financial Officer, Newman Regional Health, Emporia, KS, p. A234

FRENCH, Lori, Manager Human Resources, Fulton State Hospital, Fulton, MO, p. A359

FRENCH, Toni, Manager Human Resources, Callaway District Hospital, Callaway, NE, p. A382

FRENCH, Tracy
  Chief Financial Officer, Banner Goldfield Medical Center, Apache Junction, AZ, p. A28
  Chief Financial Officer, Banner Ironwood Medical Center, San Tan Valley, AZ, p. A35

FRENGLE, Kelley
  Director, Human Resources, Peacehealth St. John Medical Center, Longview, WA, p. A673
  Senior Director, Human Resources, Vancouver Memorial Campus, WA, p. A680

FRENIER, Karen, President, Orlando Health South Seminole Hospital, FL, p. A134

FRERER, Mary
  Chief Human Resources Officer, Freeman Hospital East, MO, p. A361
  Chief Human Resources Officer, Freeman Neosho Hospital, Neosho, MO, p. A365

FRERICHS, Craig, Chief Information Technology Service, Grand Junction Veterans Health Care System, Grand Junction, CO, p. A101

FREUDENBERG, Liz, Chief Financial Officer, Healthsouth Rehabilitation Hospital Of Littleton, Littleton, CO, p. A103

FREUDENBERGER, Joe
  Chief Executive Officer, Hospital For Surgical Excellence, TX, p. A630
  Chief Executive Officer, Oakbend Medical Center Williams Way Campus, TX, p. A630

FREY, Jack, Acting Business Manager, Greystone Park Psychiatric Hospital, Morris Plains, NJ, p. A407

FREY, James, Jr, Acting Manager Human Resources, Greystone Park Psychiatric Hospital, Morris Plains, NJ, p. A407

FREY, Jeff, Business Administrator, Andrew Mcfarland Mental Health Center, Springfield, IL, p. A196

FREY, Paul, Director Information Technology Applications, Orthoindy Hospital, Indianapolis, IN, p. A207

FREY, Rachel, Director Human Resources, Athens-Limestone Hospital, Athens, AL, p. A13

FREYER, Mary, Chief Operating Officer, Little Company Of Mary Hospital And Health Care Centers, Evergreen Park, IL, p. A183

FREYER, Sharon, R.N., Chief Nursing Officer, Baptist Health Paducah, Paducah, KY, p. A259

FREYMULLER, Robert S., Chief Executive Officer, Summerlin Hospital Medical Center, Las Vegas, NV, p. A395

FREYSINGER, Edward E., Chief Administrative Officer, Peacehealth Ketchikan Medical Center, Ketchikan, AK, p. A26

FREYTAG, Peter, Senior Vice President Finance and Chief Financial Officer, Bristol Hospital, Bristol, CT, p. A107

FRIARTE, Pedro, Director of Physician Services, Coral Gables Hospital, Coral Gables, FL, p. A120

FRIAS, Patricio A., M.D., President and Chief Executive Officer, Rady Children's Hospital - San Diego, San Diego, CA, p. A84

FRICK, Mark P, Senior Vice President Human Resources, Somerset Hospital, Somerset, PA, p. A541

FRICK, Mary Jo, Director Finance, St. Catherine's Rehabilitation Hospital, North Miami, FL, p. A132

FRICKE, Rhett D., Chief Executive Officer, Ballinger Memorial Hospital, Ballinger, TX, p. A587

FRIDAY, Jason, M.D., Medical Director, Aurora Behavioral Health System East, Tempe, AZ, p. A36

FRIDAY, Lisa, Director Human Resources, Christus Ochsner Lake Area Hospital, Lake Charles, LA, p. A272

FRIDKIN, Marjorie, M.D., Chief Medical Officer, Garrett Regional Medical Center, Oakland, MD, p. A293

FRIED, Guy, M.D., Chief Medical Officer, Magee Rehabilitation Hospital, Philadelphia, PA, p. A535

FRIED, Jeffrey M., FACHE, President and Chief Executive Officer, Beebe Healthcare, Lewes, DE, p. A113

FRIED, Tera, Manager Human Resources, West River Regional Medical Center, Hettinger, ND, p. A467

FRIEDEN, Robert
Vice President Information Systems, Genesis Medical Center, Silvis, Silvis, IL, p. A196
Vice President Information Systems, Genesis Medical Center-West Campus, IA, p. A220
Vice President, Information Services and Chief Information Officer, Genesis Medical Center-Aledo, Aledo, IL, p. A173

FRIEDENBACH, Daryl, Director Fiscal Services, Floyd Valley Healthcare, Le Mars, IA, p. A225

FRIEDLY, Jennifer
Chief Operating Officer and Vice President, Unitypoint Health - Allen Hospital, Waterloo, IA, p. A231
President, Unitypoint Health - Marshalltown, Marshalltown, IA, p. A226

FRIEDMAN, Jonathan, Public Affairs Officer, Captain James A. Lovell Federal Health Care Center, North Chicago, IL, p. A191

FRIEDMAN, Lloyd, M.D.
Interim President and Chief Operating Officer, Milford Hospital, Milford, CT, p. A109
Vice President Medical Affairs and Chief Operating Officer, Milford Hospital, Milford, CT, p. A109

FRIEDMAN, Ross, Chief Executive Officer, Summit Oaks Hospital, Summit, NJ, p. A412

FRIEL, Donald F., Executive Vice President, Holy Redeemer Hospital, Meadowbrook, PA, p. A531

FRIEL, John P., Chief Executive Officer, Bear Valley Community Hospital, Big Bear Lake, CA, p. A53

FRIELING, Jeff
Chief Information Officer, Pathways Of Tennessee, Jackson, TN, p. A571
Vice President and Chief Information Officer, West Tennessee Healthcare North Hospital, TN, p. A571
Vice President Information Systems, Camden General Hospital, Camden, TN, p. A566

FRIEND, Chad, Director, T. J. Samson Community Hospital, Glasgow, KY, p. A252

FRIEND, Lori, Human Resources Director, Alliancehealth Seminole, Seminole, OK, p. A506

FRIERSON, Cathy, Chief Human Resource Officer, New Milford Hospital, CT, p. A107

FRIES, Richard W, Vice President Finance, Allegheny General Hospital, Pittsburgh, PA, p. A537

FRIESEN, Dale L, Chief Financial Officer, Henry Ford Allegiance Specialty Hospital, Jackson, MI, p. A316

FRIESEN, Lynette, Manager Human Resources, Henderson Health Care Services, Henderson, NE, p. A385

FRIGEN, Karen, Director Human Resources, Shriners Hospitals For Children-Twin Cities, Minneapolis, MN, p. A335

FRIGO, Dave
Vice President Financial Planning and Treasury, Cleveland Clinic Akron General, Akron, OH, p. A470
Chief Financial Officer, Edwin Shaw Rehab, Cuyahoga Falls, OH, p. A480
Director Finance and Controller, Cleveland Clinic Akron General Lodi Hospital, Lodi, OH, p. A485

FRIGON, Shelby, Chief Financial Officer, Saint Luke's South Hospital, Overland Park, KS, p. A243

FRIGY, Alan, M.D., President Medical Staff, Pana Community Hospital, Pana, IL, p. A192

FRIMODIG, Mindy, D.O., President Medical Staff ThedaCare Physicians Shawano, Thedacare Medical Center-Shawano, Shawano, WI, p. A702

FRISBEE, Kent, Director Human Resources, Saint Thomas Highlands Hospital, Sparta, TN, p. A580

FRISINA, Marcy, Chief Nursing Officer, South Bay Hospital, Sun City Center, FL, p. A140

FRITSCH, William, M.D., Medical Director, Landmark Hospital Of Cape Girardeau, Cape Girardeau, MO, p. A356

FRITTON, Amy, Controller, Sierra Tucson, Tucson, AZ, p. A37

FRITTS, Doris, R.N., Executive Director, Same Day Surgery Center, Rapid City, SD, p. A563

FRITTS, Robert G, Chief Financial Officer and Senior Vice President, Valdese General Hospital, NC, p. A457

FRITZ, Robert, Chief Information Officer, Brook Lane Health Services, Hagerstown, MD, p. A292

FROCHTZWAJG, Stanley, M.D., Chief Medical Officer, Community Memorial Hospital, CA, p. A94

FROEHLICH, Shelley, R.N., Director Nursing Services, Newport Hospital And Health Services, Newport, WA, p. A674

FROEMKE, Janet, Human Resources Officer, Chi Lisbon Health, Lisbon, ND, p. A467

FROESE, Kristi, R.N.
Chief Nursing Officer, Chi St. Luke's Health Memorial Livingston, Livingston, TX, p. A620
Vice President Clinical Operations, Chi St. Luke's Health Memorial Livingston, Livingston, TX, p. A620

FROH, Chris, Senior Coordinator Human Resources, Select Specialty Hospital-Milwaukee, Milwaukee, WI, p. A699

FROHNHOFER, Erin J
Director Human Resources, Southwood Psychiatric Hospital, Pittsburgh, PA, p. A537
Vice President Human Resources, Ohio Valley Hospital, Mckees Rocks, PA, p. A531

FROISLAND, Jeffrey R, Chief Financial Officer, Mayo Clinic Hospital, Phoenix, AZ, p. A33

FROMHOLD, John A., FACHE, President and Chief Executive Officer, Hackensack Meridian Health Mountainside Medical Center, Montclair, NJ, p. A407

FROMM, Daniel
Chief Financial Officer, Bethesda Hospital, Saint Paul, MN, p. A339
Chief Financial Officer, St. John's Hospital, Maplewood, MN, p. A334
Chief Financial Officer, St. Joseph's Hospital, Saint Paul, MN, p. A339
Chief Financial Officer, Woodwinds Health Campus, Woodbury, MN, p. A342

FROMME, Richard, Chief Financial Officer, Cavalier County Memorial Hospital And Clinics, Langdon, ND, p. A467

FROMMELT, William, Director Operations and Finance, River Falls Area Hospital, River Falls, WI, p. A702

FRONZA, Sarah, President, Legacy Silverton Medical Center, Silverton, OR, p. A518

FROSCH, Kevin, Chief Financial Officer, Medina Regional Hospital, Hondo, TX, p. A609

FROST, Eric, Associate Vice President Human Resources, Upstate University Hospital At Community General, NY, p. A444

FROST, Joan, R.N., Chief Operating Officer, Mercy Hospital Washington, Washington, MO, p. A372

FROST, Mark I, M.D.
Senior Vice President Medical Affairs, Saint Francis Health System, Saint Francis Heart Hospital, OK, p. A509
Senior Vice President Medical Affairs, Laureate Psychiatric Clinic And Hospital, Tulsa, OK, p. A508
Senior Vice President Medical Affairs, Saint Francis Hospital South, Tulsa, OK, p. A509

FROST, Sarah
Administrator and Chief Operating Officer, Banner - University Medical Center South, Tucson, AZ, p. A36
Chief Executive Officer, Banner - University Medical Center South, Tucson, AZ, p. A36
Chief Executive Officer, Diamond Children's Hospital, AZ, p. A37
Chief Operating Officer and Administrator, University of Arizona Medical Center - South Campus, Diamond Children's Hospital, AZ, p. A37

FROWNFELTER, Penny, Chief Nursing Officer, Healthsouth Nittany Valley Rehabilitation Hospital, Pleasant Gap, PA, p. A538

FRUGE, Janie, R.N., MSN, FACHE, Chief Executive Officer, West Calcasieu Cameron Hospital, Sulphur, LA, p. A280

FRUM, Judy, R.N., Chief Nursing Officer, Memorial Hospital Pembroke, Pembroke Pines, FL, p. A135

FRUM, R David.
President, Bridgton Hospital, Bridgton, ME, p. A283
President, Rumford Hospital, Rumford, ME, p. A286

FRY, Kenneth, Chief Financial Officer, Saint Alphonsus Regional Medical Center, Boise, ID, p. A168

FRY, Robin, CPA, Market Controller, Kindred Hospital Dallas Central, Dallas, TX, p. A596

FRY, Terry, R.N., Chief Nursing Officer, Upper Valley Medical Center, Troy, OH, p. A492

FRYE, Kelly D, Director Human Resources, Montgomery General Hospital, Montgomery, WV, p. A685

FRYE, Terri, Information Technology Officer, Weston County Health Services, Newcastle, WY, p. A709

FRYFOGLE, Anthoney, Chief Information Officer, George Regional Hospital, Lucedale, MS, p. A349

FUCCI, Thomas, FACHE, Chief Executive Officer, Select Specialty Hospital-Erie, Erie, PA, p. A525

FUCHS, Mary Ann, R.N., Vice President Patient Care and System Chief Nurse Executive, Duke Children's Hospital & Health Center, NC, p. A451

FUEHRER, Susan, Director, Louis Stokes Cleveland Veterans Affairs Medical Center, Cleveland, OH, p. A477

FUENTES, Frances, Coordinator Human Resources, Healthsouth Rehabilitation Hospital Of San Juan, San Juan, PR, p. A715

FUENTES, Leticia, Nursing Director, San Jorge Children's Hospital, Santurce, PR, p. A716

FUENTES, Michelle, President, Adventist Health Sonora, Sonora, CA, p. A90

FUENTES, Miguel A, Jr
President and Chief Executive Officer, Concourse Division, NY, p. A431
President and Chief Executive Officer, Fulton Division, NY, p. A431

FUENTES, Miguel A., Jr, President and Chief Executive Officer, Highbridge Woodycrest Center, NY, p. A431

FUERSTENBERG, Donna, Fiscal Chief, Sheridan Veterans Affairs Medical Center, Sheridan, WY, p. A709

FUGATTE, Cheryl, MSN, Vice President and Chief Nursing Officer, Frazier Rehab Institute, KY, p. A256

FUGITT, Jacki L., Director Employee Relations, Children's Hospital Of Illinois, IL, p. A193

FUGLER, Shawna, R.N., Chief Nursing Officer, Memorial Hermann Surgical Hospital Kingwood, Kingwood, TX, p. A618

FUHRMAN, Bradley, M.D., Physician in Chief, El Paso Children's Hospital, El Paso, TX, p. A601

FUHRMAN, Dennis, Vice President Finance, Essentia Health Fargo, Fargo, ND, p. A465

FUHRO, Mary, Chief Nursing Officer, Children's Hospital Of New Jersey, NJ, p. A408

FUHS, Veronica, Chief Executive Officer, Monroe County Hospital And Clinics, Albia, IA, p. A217

FUJINAKA, Jason, Manager Information System, Wahiawa General Hospital, Wahiawa, HI, p. A166

FULCHER, Cathe, Superintendent, Evansville State Hospital, Evansville, IN, p. A203

FULCHER, Kimberly, Chief Human Resources Officer, Halifax Health Medical Center Of Port Orange, FL, p. A121

FULCHER, Martha, Chief Nursing Officer, Och Regional Medical Center, Starkville, MS, p. A353

FULCO, Mark M., President, Mercy Medical Center, Springfield, MA, p. A304

FULKERSON, Judy, Director Human Resources, Tristar Greenview Regional Hospital, Bowling Green, KY, p. A250

FULKERSON, Kimberly, Chief Nursing Officer, Dupont Hospital, Fort Wayne, IN, p. A203

FULKERSON, Richard, Director Fiscal Services, Shriners Hospitals For Children-Springfield, Springfield, MA, p. A304

FULKERSON, William T., Chief Operating Officer, University Of Virginia Children's Hospital, VA, p. A656

FULKS, Chris, Vice President Finance, Lake Huron Medical Center, Port Huron, MI, p. A321

FULKS, Gerald N., President, Wellstar West Georgia Medical Center, Lagrange, GA, p. A155

FULLBRIGHT, Gary D., Comptroller, Citizens Memorial Hospital, Bolivar, MO, p. A355

FULLER, Cara
Vice President Human Resources, Unitypoint Health - Trinity Bettendorf, Bettendorf, IA, p. A217
Vice President Human Resources, Unitypoint Health - Trinity Moline, IL, p. A194

FULLER, Cheryl, Director Information Resources, Kansas Neurological Institute, Topeka, KS, p. A246

FULLER, Dale, Vice President and Chief Information Officer, Upmc Altoona, Altoona, PA, p. A520

FULLER, David, Vice President of Human Resources, Porter Medical Center, Middlebury, VT, p. A653

FULLER, Debbie, Director Health Information Systems and Chief Information Officer, Doctors Medical Center Of Modesto, Modesto, CA, p. A72

FULLER, Harrington, Information Technology Director, Hendry Regional Medical Center, Clewiston, FL, p. A120

FULLER, Jane, Vice President Human Resources, North Florida Regional Medical Center, Gainesville, FL, p. A123

FULLER, Jeremy, Director Information Systems, Conroe Regional Medical Center, Conroe, TX, p. A594

FULLER, Marion, Chief of Staff, Munson Healthcare Manistee Hospital, Manistee, MI, p. A318

FULLER, Scott O.
President and Chief Executive Officer, Seton Edgar B. Davis Hospital, Luling, TX, p. A622
President and Chief Executive Officer, Seton Highland Lakes, Burnet, TX, p. A591
President and Chief Executive Officer, Seton Smithville Regional Hospital, Smithville, TX, p. A636

FULLER-WILLIAMS, Vonetta, Director Human Resources Strategic and Business Services, Baylor Scott & White Medical Center-Irving, Irving, TX, p. A615

FULLMER, John, Chief Financial Officer, Bingham Memorial Hospital, Blackfoot, ID, p. A167

FULLUM, Jane, Vice President Patient Care Services, East Alabama Medical Center-Lanier, AL, p. A22

FULTON, Lorna, Director Human Resources, Vibra Hospital Of Denver, Thornton, CO, p. A106

FULTON, Lynn, President, Osf St. Joseph Medical Center, Bloomington, IL, p. A174

FUNDERBURG, Michelle, Director Human Resources, Stephens Memorial Hospital, Breckenridge, TX, p. A590

FUNDERBURK, Mark, President and Chief Executive Officer, University Medical Center, Lubbock, TX, p. A621

FUNG, Adrian, Director Information Systems, Tennova Healthcare-Lebanon Mcfarland Campus, TN, p. A573

FUNK, Luann A, Administrative Assistant and Manager Human Resources, Pana Community Hospital, Pana, IL, p. A192

FUNKHOUSER, Krisy L, Manager Human Resources, Willapa Harbor Hospital, South Bend, WA, p. A678

FUQUA, David, Director Human Resources Management, Children's Hospital Of Shreveport, LA, p. A279

FUQUA, David G., Chief Executive Officer, Marshall County Hospital, Benton, KY, p. A249

FUQUA, Leon, Chief Operating Officer, Wise Regional Health System, West Campus Decatur, TX, p. A598

FURER, Darnell F, MS, R.N.
Vice President of Patient Care Services, Lehigh Valley Hospital - Schuylkill East Norwegian Street, Pottsville, PA, p. A539
Vice President Patient Care Services and Chief Nursing Officer, Lehigh Valley Hospital - Schuylkill, Pottsville, PA, p. A539

FURGURSON, Carol, Chief Operating Officer, Saint Louise Regional Hospital, Gilroy, CA, p. A60

FURLOW, Pete, Director Information Technology Services, Rmc Anniston, Anniston, AL, p. A13

FURNAS, David, Chief Information Officer, Gila Regional Medical Center, Silver City, NM, p. A420

FURNEY, June, R.N., Director of Nursing, Brooks County Hospital, Quitman, GA, p. A158

FURNISS, Scott, Vice President and Chief Financial Officer, Saint Agnes Healthcare, Baltimore, MD, p. A288

FURR, Robert, Director Information Services, Anmed Health Cannon, Pickens, SC, p. A556

FUSCHILLO, Ronald
Chief Information Officer, Renown Rehabilitation Hospital, Reno, NV, p. A396
Chief Information Officer, Renown South Meadows Medical Center, Reno, NV, p. A396

FUSCO, Gina, Chief Executive Officer, Foundations Behavioral Health, Doylestown, PA, p. A524

FUSELIER, Gerald, Chief Operating Officer, Savoy Medical Center, Mamou, LA, p. A273

FUSELIER, Michael, FACHE, CPA, R.N., Chief Financial Officer, Central Louisiana Surgical Hospital, Alexandria, LA, p. A262

FUSILERO, Jane, Vice President Chief Nursing Officer, H. Lee Moffitt Cancer Center And Research Institute, Tampa, FL, p. A140

FUSTON, Kathie, Director Human Resources, Moore County Hospital District, Dumas, TX, p. A600

FUTCH, Margaret A., Chief Executive Officer, Encompass Health Rehabilitation Hospital Of Dothan, Dothan, AL, p. A17

FUTRAL, Cindy, Director Human Resources, Elmore Community Hospital, Wetumpka, AL, p. A24

FUTRELL, Cynthia, MSN, R.N., Chief Nursing Officer, Marion General Hospital, Marion, IN, p. A211

FYBEL, Gary G, FACHE, Interim Chief Operating Officer, Swedish Medical Center-Ballard, WA, p. A676

G

GAAL, James G, M.D., Chief of Medical Staff, Jackson General Hospital, Ripley, WV, p. A686

GAASCH, Andrew
Chief Financial Officer, Parker Adventist Hospital, Parker, CO, p. A104
Chief Financial Officer, Porter Adventist Hospital, Denver, CO, p. A99

GABALDON, Karen, Chief Management Information Systems, West Palm Beach Veterans Affairs Medical Center, West Palm Beach, FL, p. A143

GABEL, Christopher, Chief Operating Officer, Larkin Community Hospital Behavioral Health Services, Hollywood, FL, p. A124

GABEL, Kelly, Chief of Staff, Citizens Medical Center, Colby, KS, p. A233

GABEL, Marcia, Chief Financial Officer, Lane County Hospital, Dighton, KS, p. A234

GABLE, Beth, Administrative Assistant, Jasper General Hospital, Bay Springs, MS, p. A343

GABLENZ, Gordon, Vice President Finance, Ridgeview Medical Center, Waconia, MN, p. A341

GABORIAULT, Randall, Chief Information Officer, Christiana Care Health System, Newark, DE, p. A113

GABRIEL, Scott F, President, Parkview Whitley Hospital, Columbia City, IN, p. A201

GABRIEL, Scott F., President, Parkview Whitley Hospital, Columbia City, IN, p. A201

GABRIEL, Shirley, Vice President and Chief Information Officer, University Hospital, Augusta, GA, p. A147

GABRIEL, Stacey, R.N., President and Chief Executive Officer, Hocking Valley Community Hospital, Logan, OH, p. A485

GABRIELE, Joan, Deputy Executive Director, Nyc Health + Hospitals / Queens, New York (Includes All Hospitals Located Within The Five Boroughs), NY, p. A436

GABRYEL, Timothy, M.D., Vice President Medical Affairs and Medical Director, Mercy Hospital, Buffalo, NY, p. A423

GABUAT, Jesse, Chief Nursing Officer, Mercy Hospital - A Campus Of Plantation General Hospital, FL, p. A136

GAC, Deborah, Vice President Human Resources, Valley Presbyterian Hospital, Los Angeles, CA, p. A70

GADALLAH, Yousri, M.D., Chief Medical Officer, Pershing General Hospital, Lovelock, NV, p. A395

GADDAM, Sumalatha, Senior Vice President and Chief Information Officer, Kent County Memorial Hospital, Warwick, RI, p. A548

GADDAM, Summa, Chief Information Officer, Butler Hospital, Providence, RI, p. A547

GADDIS, Cathryn H, Director Human Resources, Rivervalley Behavioral Health Hospital, Owensboro, KY, p. A259

GADDY, Pam, Director, Patient Care Services and Chief Nursing Officer, Firsthealth Montgomery Memorial Hospital, Troy, NC, p. A461

GADDY, Roger A, Jr, Chief Medical Officer, Fairfield Memorial Hospital, Winnsboro, SC, p. A558

GADE, Swami P, M.D., Medical Director, Tioga Medical Center, Tioga, ND, p. A468

GADEN, Paul
Chief Executive Officer, Bon Secours Maryview Medical Center, Portsmouth, VA, p. A664
Chief Executive Officer, Bon Secours-Depaul Medical Center, Norfolk, VA, p. A662

GAEDE, John, Director Information Systems, El Centro Regional Medical Center, El Centro, CA, p. A57

GAFFOLI, Jill, Director Human Resources, Physicians Regional, FL, p. A132

GAFFORD, Deborah, Chief Financial Officer, Menorah Medical Center, Overland Park, KS, p. A243

GAFFORD, Grady Paul, Chief Financial Officer, Brownfield Regional Medical Center, Brownfield, TX, p. A590

GAGE, Bobby, Director Information Technology, Wabash General Hospital, Mount Carmel, IL, p. A190

GAGE, Eileen, R.N.
Vice President Nursing, Finger Lakes Hospital, Geneva, NY, p. A426
Vice President Nursing, Soldiers And Sailors Memorial Hospital Of Yates County, Penn Yan, NY, p. A440

GAGE, Kevin, Chief Financial Officer, Stamford Hospital, Stamford, CT, p. A111

GAGE, Mark, D.O., Medical Director, Brookhaven Hospital, Tulsa, OK, p. A508

GAGE, Susan, Financial Manager, Veterans Affairs Western New York Healthcare System-Buffalo Division, Buffalo, NY, p. A424

GAGE, Weldon, Chief Financial Officer, University Of Texas M.D. Anderson Cancer Center, Houston, TX, p. A614

GAGLIARDI, Teresa, R.N.
Chief Nursing Officer, Trinity Hospital Twin City, Dennison, OH, p. A481
Vice President of Hospital Operations and Site Administrator, Trinity Hospital Twin City, Dennison, OH, p. A481

GAGLIO, Anthony, CPA
Interim President and Chief Executive Officer, Menninger Clinic, Houston, TX, p. A612
Senior Vice President and Chief Financial Officer, Menninger Clinic, Houston, TX, p. A612

GAGNE, Cheryl, I, Vice President Patient Care Services and Chief Nursing Officer, Southern New Hampshire Medical Center, Nashua, NH, p. A400

GAGNON, Andy, Manager Information Technology, Via Christi Hospital Manhattan, Inc., Manhattan, KS, p. A240

GAINER, Rolf B., Ph.D., Chief Executive Officer, Brookhaven Hospital, Tulsa, OK, p. A508

GAINEY, Rachel, Administrator, Mcleod Health Clarendon, Manning, SC, p. A555

GAINEY, Shari W
Chief Human Resource Officer, Willowbrooke At Tanner, GA, p. A162
Human Resource Director, Higgins General Hospital, Bremen, GA, p. A148

GAJ, Steve, Facility Chief Information Officer, Louis Stokes Cleveland Veterans Affairs Medical Center, Cleveland, OH, p. A477

GAJEWSKI, Christie, Director Human Resources, Pinckneyville Community Hospital, Pinckneyville, IL, p. A193

GALANG, Michael, M.D.
Chief Information Officer, Mercy Hospital, Buffalo, NY, p. A423
Chief Information Officer, St. Joseph Hospital, NY, p. A424

GALARNEAU, Ciprian, Director Information Systems, Tri Valley Health System, Cambridge, NE, p. A382

GALARNEAU, Gerard, M.D., Regional Chief Medical Officer, Catskill Regional Medical Center, Harris, NY, p. A427

GALATI, John P, Chief Executive Officer, Tlc Health Network - Lake Shore Hospital, NY, p. A425

GALAVIZ, Veronica, Chief Financial Officer, Lovelace Regional Hospital - Roswell, Roswell, NM, p. A419

GALBRAITH, Kathleen B., FACHE, President, Duke Regional Hospital, Durham, NC, p. A451

GALDIERI, Lou, R.N.
President, Mease Countryside Hospital, Safety Harbor, FL, p. A137
President, Mease Dunedin Hospital, Dunedin, FL, p. A122

GALE, Gabrielle, Chief Financial Officer, Lighthouse Behavioral Health Hospital, Conway, SC, p. A552

GALE, Melissa, Chief Executive Officer, Landmann-Jungman Memorial Hospital Avera, Scotland, SD, p. A563

GALE, Michael, Chief Financial Officer, Bournewood Health Systems, Brookline, MA, p. A298

GALEY, John P, M.D., Chief Medical Officer, Schoolcraft Memorial Hospital, Manistique, MI, p. A318

GALFANO, Victor J., FACHE, Chief Executive Officer, Amg Specialty Hospital - Muncie, Muncie, IN, p. A211

GALIPEAU, Michelle, Director Human Resources, St. Vincent's Birmingham, Birmingham, AL, p. A15

GALKOWSKI, James, Associate Director for Operations, Fayetteville Veterans Affairs Medical Center, Fayetteville, NC, p. A452

GALLAGHER, Chris, M.D., Chief Medical Officer, Christus Mother Frances Hospital - Sulphur Springs, Sulphur Springs, TX, p. A637

GALLAGHER, Deborah, Manager Human Resources, Ojai Valley Community Hospital, Ojai, CA, p. A76

GALLAGHER, Doug, Director Human Resources, Carolinas Continuecare Hospital At Pineville, Charlotte, NC, p. A449

GALLAGHER, J. P., President and Chief Executive Officer, Northshore Skokie Hospital, IL, p. A182

GALLAGHER, James
Chief Executive Officer, First Hospital Wyoming Valley, Kingston, PA, p. A528
Chief Executive Officer, Oasis Behavioral Health - Chandler, Chandler, AZ, p. A28

GALLAGHER, Jeannie
Chief Human Resource Officer, North Colorado Medical Center, Greeley, CO, p. A101
jeanie.gallagher@bannerhealth.com, Mckee Medical Center, Loveland, CO, p. A104

GALLAGHER, Joseph, Chief Executive Officer, Wyoming Behavioral Institute, Casper, WY, p. A707

GALLAGHER, Karen, Vice President Human Resources and Learning, Brooks Rehabilitation Hospital, Jacksonville, FL, p. A125

GALLAGHER, Karen M, MSN, Chief Nursing Office, Vice President Operations, Presence St. Mary's Hospital, Kankakee, IL, p. A187

GALLAGHER, Pamela, Chief Financial Officer, Providence Hospital Northeast, SC, p. A551

GALLAGHER, Regen, D.O., Chief Medical Officer, Cary Medical Center, Caribou, ME, p. A283

GALLAGHER, Sherry, Director Nursing, Department of Health and Human Services, Humboldt County Mental Health, Eureka, CA, p. A57

GALLAHOM, Gerty, Director Human Resources, Maniilaq Health Center, Kotzebue, AK, p. A26

GALLARDO, Kathleen, Chief Nursing Officer, Select Specialty Hospital-Flint, Flint, MI, p. A313

GALLARDO, Ysidro, Associate Administrator Human Resources, William And Inez Mabie Skilled Nursing Facility, CA, p. A61

GALLATI, Todd, FACHE, President and Chief Executive Officer, Summerville Medical Center, SC, p. A550

GALLAY, Emily, Vice President and Chief Information Officer, Lakeland Hospital, Niles, MI, p. A323

GALLEGOS, Colleen, Director Human Resources, Guadalupe County Hospital, Santa Rosa, NM, p. A419

GALLEGOS, Enrique, Chief Executive Officer, Laredo Medical Center, Laredo, TX, p. A619

GALLEGOS, Kelly, Administrator, San Luis Valley Health Conejos County Hospital, La Jara, CO, p. A102

GALLEGOS, Ken, Director Support Services and Information Technology, Medina Regional Hospital, Hondo, TX, p. A609

GALLI, Jodi B., R.N., Chief Nursing Officer, Kaiser Permanente Redwood City Medical Center, Redwood City, CA, p. A80

GALLIART, Mark, Chief Executive Officer, Mcbride Orthopedic Hospital, Oklahoma City, OK, p. A503

GALLIK, Becky, Information Systems Manager, Firstlight Health System, Mora, MN, p. A336

GALLO, Carrie, Chief Nursing Officer, Western Reserve Hospital, Cuyahoga Falls, OH, p. A480

GALLO, Ronald, Director Human Resources, Blythedale Children's Hospital, Valhalla, NY, p. A445

GALLOGLY-SIMON, Catherine A, R.N., MS, Chief Nursing Officer, Wyckoff Heights Medical Center, New York (Includes All Hospitals Located Within The Five Boroughs), NY, p. A438

GALLUCCI, Vince
Senior Vice President Human Resources, Ascension Northeast Wisconsin Mercy Hospital, Oshkosh, WI, p. A700
Senior Vice President Human Resources, Ascension Northeast Wisconsin St. Elizabeth Hospital, Appleton, WI, p. A689

GALT, Nick
Chief Financial Officer, Medical City Las Colinas, Irving, TX, p. A615
Chief Financial Officer, Medical City North Hills, North Richland Hills, TX, p. A626

GALUSHA, Fred, Chief Information Officer, St. Luke's Rehabilitation Institute, Spokane, WA, p. A678

GALVIN, Gary, M.D., Chief of the Medical Staff, Columbus Community Hospital, Inc., Columbus, WI, p. A691

GALYON, Darlene, Director Human Resources, Choctaw Memorial Hospital, Hugo, OK, p. A500

GAMACHE, Cynde, R.N., Vice President and Chief Nursing Officer, Baptist Hospital, Pensacola, FL, p. A136

GAMB, Pamela, Manager Human Resources, Aurora Psychiatric Hospital, Wauwatosa, WI, p. A705

GAMBA, William, Chief Nursing Officer, Twin Cities Community Hospital, Templeton, CA, p. A91

GAMBLA, Kurt, D.O., Chief Medical Officer, Beaufort Memorial Hospital, Beaufort, SC, p. A549

GAMBLE, Allen J., Interim Chief Executive Officer, Gordon Memorial Health Services, Gordon, NE, p. A384

GAMBLE, Brian, Chief Financial Officer, Karmanos Cancer Center, Detroit, MI, p. A311

GAMBLE, Kathleen, Fiscal Officer, Patton State Hospital, Patton, CA, p. A78

GAMBLE, Laura, Director of Critical Access Hospitals, Oakland Mercy Hospital, Oakland, NE, p. A387

GAMBLE, Robert, M.D., Chief of Staff, Terrebonne General Medical Center, Houma, LA, p. A269

GAMBOA, Eileen, Director Human Resources, Oakbend Medical Center Williams Way Campus, TX, p. A630

GAMBRELL, Titus E., Vice President and Chief Nursing Officer, St. Mary's Health Care System, Athens, GA, p. A145

GAMET, Nicki, R.N.
Administrator, Mercy Hospital Aurora, Aurora, MO, p. A355
Administrator, Mercy Hospital Cassville, Cassville, MO, p. A357

GAMEZ, Kriss, Director Human Resources, Baylor Regional Medical Center At Plano, Plano, TX, p. A628

GAMINO, Randall, Director Perot Site, St. Joseph's Medical Center, Stockton, CA, p. A91

GAMMIERE, Thomas A, Chief Executive Officer, Scripps Mercy Hospital Chula Vista, CA, p. A84

GAMMIERE, Thomas A., Chief Executive, Senior Vice President, Scripps Mercy Hospital Chula Vista, CA, p. A84

GAMMON, Jonathon
Interim Chief Executive Officer, Glen Oaks Hospital, Greenville, TX, p. A608
Interim Chief Executive Officer, The Bridgeway, North Little Rock-Pulaski County, AR, p. A47

GANDHI, Tejas, Ph.D., Chief Operating Officer, Baystate Children's Hospital, MA, p. A304

GANDY, Galina, Vice President Information Technology, Columbia Memorial Hospital, Astoria, OR, p. A511

GANDY, Patrick W., Jr, CPA, Executive Vice President and Chief Executive Officer, Lafayette General Orthopedic Hospital, LA, p. A271

GANGULY, Devabrata, M.D., Medical Director, Christus Dubuis Hospital Of Paris, Paris, TX, p. A627

GANGULY, Indranil, Vice President and Chief Information Officer, Hackensack Meridian Health Jfk Medical Center, Edison, NJ, p. A404

GANGULY, Neal, Chief Information Officer, Hackensack Meridian Health Jfk Johnson Rehabilitation Institute, Edison, NJ, p. A404

GANLEY, Evan, Manager Human Resources, Lifecare Hospitals Of Chester County, West Chester, PA, p. A544

GANN, Lisa, R.N., Chief Nursing Officer, Tristar Hendersonville Medical Center, Hendersonville, TN, p. A570

GANN, Michele, Vice President Patient Services, Mercy Hospital Berryville, Berryville-Carroll County, AR, p. A39

GANNON, Ronnie, Director Information Services, Tristar Southern Hills Medical Center, Nashville, TN, p. A578

GANNOTTA, Richard
Chief Executive Officer, Uc Irvine Medical Center, Orange, CA, p. A76
Chief Operaing Officer, Uc Irvine Medical Center, Orange, CA, p. A76

GANS, Bruce M, M.D., Executive Vice President and Chief Medical Officer, Kessler Institute For Rehabilitation, NJ, p. A413

GANSEMER, Sheila, R.N., Vice President Patient Care Services and Chief Nursing Officer, Wheaton Franciscan Healthcare - Franklin, Franklin, WI, p. A693

GANSKE, Jary, Chief Financial Officer, Methodist Mansfield Medical Center, Mansfield, TX, p. A622

GANTNER, John J., President and Chief Executive Officer, Bristol-Myers Squibb Children's Hospital, NJ, p. A408

GANTT, Cynthia J, Chief of Staff, Naval Medical Center, Portsmouth, VA, p. A664

GANTZER, Ann M, Ph.D., R.N., Vice President Patient Services and Chief Nursing Officer, Swedishamerican - A Division Of Uw Health, Rockford, IL, p. A195

GAPSTUR, Roxanna L., Ph.D., R.N., President, Park Nicollet Methodist Hospital, Saint Louis Park, MN, p. A339

GARAY, Kenneth, M.D., Chief Medical Officer, Jersey City Medical Center, Jersey City, NJ, p. A406

GARBANZOS, Del, Director Human Resources, Delano Regional Medical Center, Delano, CA, p. A56

GARBARINO, James, Chief Financial Officer, Clay County Medical Center, Clay Center, KS, p. A233

GARBER, Mary, Vice President Finance, Mercy Hospital Ada, Ada, OK, p. A495

GARCIA, Andrew T., Acting Associate Director, Central Texas Veterans Health Care System, Doris Miller Veterans Medical Center, TX, p. A638

GARCIA, Antonio M., Chief Nursing Officer, Emanuel Medical Center, Turlock, CA, p. A92

GARCIA, Ara, Manager Human Resources, Milwaukee County Behavioral Health Division, Milwaukee, WI, p. A699

GARCIA, Aymette, Manager Human Resources, Wilma N. Vazquez Medical Center, Vega Baja, PR, p. A716

GARCIA, Danette, Director Human Resources, Encompass Health Valley Of The Sun Rehabilitation Hospital, Glendale, AZ, p. A30

GARCIA, Estevan, M.D., Chief Medical Officer, Cooley Dickinson Hospital, Northampton, MA, p. A303

GARCIA, Evangeline, M.D., Clinical Director, Eastern Shore Hospital Center, Cambridge, MD, p. A290

GARCIA, Georgina R., R.N., Executive Director, Kaiser Permanente West Los Angeles Medical Center, Los Angeles, CA, p. A67

GARCIA, Gerard, Chief Human Resource Officer, University Hospital, Newark, NJ, p. A409

GARCIA, Idalia, Chief Human Resources Officer, Hospital De Psiquiatria, San Juan, PR, p. A715

GARCIA, Iris, Director, Information Services, Jerome Golden Center For Behavioral Health, Inc., West Palm Beach, FL, p. A143

GARCIA, Irma, Job Coordinator, South Texas Health Care System, TX, p. A608

GARCIA, Jacob, Chief Information Officer, Little Colorado Medical Center, Winslow, AZ, p. A38

GARCIA, Jannina, Director of Human Resources, Florida Hospital Fish Memorial, Orange City, FL, p. A133

GARCIA, Joanne, Chief Operating Officer, Kindred Hospital Chicago North, IL, p. A177

GARCIA, Joannie, CPA, Director Finance, Hospital Perea, Mayaguez, PR, p. A714

GARCIA, Jose, M.D.
Chief Medical Staff, Dundy County Hospital, Benkelman, NE, p. A382
Chief Human Resources Officer, San Juan City Hospital, San Juan, PR, p. A716

GARCIA, Kathleen, Controller, St. John's Episcopal Hospital-South Shore, New York (Includes All Hospitals Located Within The Five Boroughs), NY, p. A437

GARCIA, Luis Mario, Jr, Director Human Resources, Houston Methodist Sugar Land Hospital, Sugar Land, TX, p. A637

GARCIA, Margaret, Manager Human Resources, Baylor Medical Center At Frisco, Frisco, TX, p. A606

GARCIA, Michael A, Vice President and Chief Information Officer, Jackson South Community Hospital, FL, p. A130

GARCIA, Orlando, M.D., Chief Medical Officer, Hialeah Hospital, Hialeah, FL, p. A124

GARCIA, Robert W, M.D., Chief Medical Officer, Iraan General Hospital, Iraan, TX, p. A615

GARCIA, Roland
Senior Vice President and Chief Information Officer, Baptist Medical Center Beaches, Jacksonville Beach, FL, p. A126
Senior Vice President and Chief Information Officer, Wolfson Children's Hospital, FL, p. A125

GARCIA, Rudy, Chief Executive Officer, Southern Winds Hospital, FL, p. A131

GARCIA, Sharon, Human Resources Representative, Medina Regional Hospital, Hondo, TX, p. A609

GARCIA, Shawn, Manager Human Resources, Memorial Hospital Los Banos, Los Banos, CA, p. A70

GARCIA, Sylvia, Chief Accounting Officer, South Texas Spine And Surgical Hospital, San Antonio, TX, p. A634

GARCIA, Tracy, MS, Chief Nursing Officer, Cheyenne Regional Medical Center, Cheyenne, WY, p. A707

GARCIN, Hector Troche, Human Resources Director, St. Luke's Episcopal Hospital, Ponce, PR, p. A714

GARD, Emily, Chief Clinical Officer, Kindred Hospital-San Francisco Bay Area, San Leandro, CA, p. A87

GARDEPE, Cynthia, Director, Human Resources, Uhs Delaware Valley Hospital, Walton, NY, p. A445

GARDINER, Greg, Chief Clinical Officer, Ashley Regional Medical Center, Vernal, UT, p. A651

GARDINER, Karen, Human Resources Director, Bayfront Health Port Charlotte, Port Charlotte, FL, p. A137

GARDNER, Carla, Director of Nursing, Munson Healthcare Grayling Hospital, Grayling, MI, p. A314

GARDNER, David, MSN, Chief Nursing Officer, Wyoming Medical Center, Casper, WY, p. A707

GARDNER, Debra C., R.N., MSN, Administrator, Ten Lakes Center, Dennison, OH, p. A481

GARDNER, Greg, Senior Vice President and Chief Financial Officer, Behavioral Health Center, FL, p. A143

GARDNER, Jacque, Administrative Assistant, Clinic Manager, Co-Chief Financial Officer and Chief Human Resources, Mccone County Health Center, Circle, MT, p. A374

GARDNER, James D, M.D., Vice President and Chief Medical Officer, Waukesha Memorial Hospital, Waukesha, WI, p. A705

GARDNER, Joel, D.O., Chief Medical Officer, Brigham City Community Hospital, Brigham City, UT, p. A646

GARDNER, Kristin Day, Chief Nursing Officer, Berger Health System, Circleville, OH, p. A476

GARDNER, Michelle, M.D., Clinical Director, Dorothea Dix Psychiatric Center, Bangor, ME, p. A282

GARDNER, Nancy, Chief Nursing Officer, I-70 Community Hospital, Sweet Springs, MO, p. A371

GARDNER, Patrick, M.D., Associate Vice President, Medical Affairs, St. Joseph's Hospital, St. Joseph's Hospital, West Bend, WI, p. A706

GARDNER, Robb, Chief Executive Officer, Henry County Health Center, Mount Pleasant, IA, p. A226

GARDNER, Sharon, Manager Information Systems, Ssm Health St. Joseph Hospital - Lake Saint Louis, Lake Saint Louis, MO, p. A363

GARDNER, William, Chief Clinical Officer, Bartlett Regional Hospital, Juneau, AK, p. A26

GARDNER, Zoe, Manager Human Resources, Sharp Chula Vista Medical Center, Chula Vista, CA, p. A54

GARES, Donna, R.N., FACHE, MSN, Chief Executive Officer, Select Specialty Hospital-Wilmington, Wilmington, DE, p. A114

GARISON, Jerri, R.N.
Interim Chief Executive Officer and Chief Operating Officer, Baylor Scott & White Medical Center - Carrollton, Carrollton, TX, p. A592
Interim Chief Executve Officer and Chief Operating Officer, Baylor Scott & White Medical Center - Carrollton, Carrollton, TX, p. A592
President, Baylor Regional Medical Center At Plano, Plano, TX, p. A628

GARKO, Michael, Chief Financial Officer, St. Vincent Medical Center, Los Angeles, CA, p. A70

GARLETS, Mary, Director Human Resources, Mayo Clinic Health System In Cannon Falls, Cannon Falls, MN, p. A329

GARMAN, Denise M, Director Human Resources, Wellspan Good Samaritan Hospital, Lebanon, PA, p. A529

GARMAN, Michael, Chief Financial Officer, Avera St. Anthony's Hospital, O'Neill, NE, p. A389

GARMAN, Patrick M., Commander, Evans U.S. Army Community Hospital, Fort Carson, CO, p. A100

GARNAS, David, Administrator, Cloud County Health Center, Concordia, KS, p. A234

GARNER, Douglas, Vice President, Thomas Hospital, Fairhope, AL, p. A17

GARNER, Ethnee, R.N., Vice President Patient Care Services, Memorial Hospital, North Conway, NH, p. A400

GARNETT, Mark, M.D., Chief of Staff, Hansford Hospital, Spearman, TX, p. A636

GARONE, Marlene, M.D., Vice President Medical Affairs and Medical Director, Upmc Chautauqua Wca, Jamestown, NY, p. A428

GARRARD, Michael Eric., FACHE, Chief Executive Officer, Emory Rehabilitation Hospital, Atlanta, GA, p. A146

GARRED, John, M.D., Sr, Chief Medical Officer, Burgess Health Center, Onawa, IA, p. A227

GARREN-OSTER, Cynthia, Human Resource Manager, South Coast Global Medical Center, Santa Ana, CA, p. A88

GARRETT, Alan H., President and Chief Executive Officer, St. Mary Medical Center, Apple Valley, CA, p. A51

GARRETT, Courtney, CPA, Senior Vice President, Chief Financial Officer, Children's Hospital, New Orleans, LA, p. A275

GARRETT, Dana M., R.N., Nursing Services Administrator, Taylor Regional Hospital, Campbellsville, KY, p. A250

GARRETT, David B
Senior Vice President and Chief Information Officer, Novant Health Brunswick Medical Center, Bolivia, NC, p. A448
Senior Vice President and Chief Information Officer, Novant Health Charlotte Orthopaedic Hospital, Charlotte, NC, p. A450
Senior Vice President and Chief Information Officer, Novant Health Clemmons Medical Center, NC, p. A462
Senior Vice President and Chief Information Officer, Novant Health Huntersville Medical Center, Huntersville, NC, p. A455
Senior Vice President and Chief Information Officer, Novant Health Matthews Medical Center, Matthews, NC, p. A457
Senior Vice President and Chief Information Officer, Novant Health Medical Park Hospital, Winston, NC, p. A463
Senior Vice President and Chief Information Officer, Novant Health Rowan Medical Center, Salisbury, NC, p. A460
Senior Vice President and Chief Information Officer, Novant Health Thomasville Medical Center, Thomasville, NC, p. A461
Senior Vice President and Chief Information Officer, Novant Health Uva Health System Haymarket Medical Center, Haymarket, VA, p. A659
Senior Vice President and Chief Information Officer, Novant Health Uva Health System Prince William Medical Center, Manassas, VA, p. A661
Senior Vice President Information Technology, Presbyterian Hemby Children's Hospital, NC, p. A450

GARRETT, Josh, Chief of Staff, Habersham Medical Center, Demorest, GA, p. A152

GARRETT, Kevin C., M.D.
Medical Executive East Region, St. Joseph's Hospital, Saint Paul, MN, p. A339
Medical Executive, East Region, Woodwinds Health Campus, Woodbury, MN, p. A342

GARRETT, Matthew, Director Information Systems, Flowers Hospital, Dothan, AL, p. A17

GARRETT, Nancy, Chief Analytics and Information Technology Officer, Hcmc Department Of Pediatrics, MN, p. A335

GARRETT, Scott, Director of IS, Ottumwa Regional Health Center, Ottumwa, IA, p. A228

GARRICK, Renee, M.D., Executive Medical Director, Midhudson Regional Hospital Of Westchester Medical Center, NY, p. A445

GARRIOTT, Edie, Director Human Resources, Community Hospital South, Indianapolis, IN, p. A206

GARRISON, Christopher, M.D., Medical Director, Central Texas Rehabilitation Hospital, Austin, TX, p. A585

GARRISON, Eric L, Chief Information Officer, Laughlin Memorial Hospital, Greeneville, TN, p. A570

GARRISON, Tina, President, Ssm Health St. Clare Hospital - Fenton, Fenton, MO, p. A359

GARRISON, Wes, Chief Nurse Officer, St. Luke's Sugar Land Hospital, Sugar Land, TX, p. A637

GARRITY, Elizabeth, Director Human Resources, Hudson Regional Hospital, Secaucus, NJ, p. A411

GARRITY, Nerissa, Chief Financial Officer, Kula Hospital, Kula, HI, p. A166

GARROW, Dina, Chief Nursing Officer and Chief Operating Officer, Kindred Hospital-Baldwin Park, Baldwin Park, CA, p. A52

GARTLAND, Bryce D., M.D., Chief Executive Officer, Emory Wesley Woods Geriatric Hospital, GA, p. A146

GARTMAN, Kathy Degenstein, Chief Nursing Officer, Medical Center Of South Arkansas, El Dorado-Union County, AR, p. A41

GARTNER, Katie, Director Health Information Management, Richard H. Young Behavioral Health Center, NE, p. A385

GARTON, Debra, R.N., Chief Nursing Officer, Oss Orthopaedic Hospital, York, PA, p. A545

GARVEY, James
Hospital Operations, Essentia Health Duluth, Duluth, MN, p. A330
Senior Vice President Hospital Practice, Essentia Health East, St. Mary's Children's Hospital, MN, p. A330

GARVEY, Rita, Chief Nursing Officer, Lawrence County Memorial Hospital, Lawrenceville, IL, p. A187

GARVEY, Thomas J, Senior Vice President Operations and Chief Financial Officer, Swedish Covenant Hospital, Chicago, IL, p. A180

GARVIN, Jan, Vice President Human Resources, Bryan Medical Center-West, NE, p. A385

GARY, Al, COO, Simpson General Hospital, Mendenhall, MS, p. A350

GARZA, Art, FACHE, Chief Executive Officer, Valley Regional Medical Center, Brownsville, TX, p. A590

GARZA, Ismelda, Director Information Systems, Comanche County Medical Center, Comanche, TX, p. A593

GARZA, Laura, Director Human Resources, Pine Valley Specialty Hospital, Houston, TX, p. A613

GARZA, Leo, Chief Executive Officer, South Texas Rehabilitation Hospital, Brownsville, TX, p. A590

GARZA, Oscar, M.D., Chief Medical Staff, Frio Regional Hospital, Pearsall, TX, p. A627

GARZA, Teri, Director Health Information Services, Knapp Medical Center, Weslaco, TX, p. A643

GARZA, Tom, Director Fiscal and Support, South Texas Health Care System, TX, p. A608

GASBARRE, Christopher, D.O., Community Medical Director, Spearfish Regional Surgery Center, SD, p. A564

GASH, Deborah
Chief Information Officer, Crittenton Children's Center, MO, p. A362
Chief Information Officer, Saint Luke's South Hospital, Overland Park, KS, p. A243

GASKELL, Dan, Chief Executive Officer, Emcompass Health Rehabilitation Hospital Of Virginia, Richmond, VA, p. A665

GASKILL, Harold, III, M.D., Chief Executive Officer, First Baptist Medical Center, Dallas, TX, p. A596

GASKILL, Paulette Sue, Executive Director of Nursing, St. Vincent Clay Hospital, Brazil, IN, p. A200

GASKILL-HAMES, Michelle, R.N., Senior Vice President & Area Manager, Kaiser Permanente Redwood City Medical Center, Redwood City, CA, p. A80

GASKINS, Michael, Director Information Technology, Lincoln Community Hospital And Nursing Home, Hugo, CO, p. A102

GASKINS, Michael W., President, Upmc Pinnacle Hanover, Hanover, PA, p. A526

GASPAR, Gabrielle, M.D., Chief Medical Officer, Doctors Medical Center Of Modesto, Modesto, CA, p. A72

GASQUE, James, M.D., Chief Hospital Services, U.S. Air Force Medical Center Keesler, Keesler Afb, MS, p. A348

GASSEN, Bill, Chief Human Resource Officer, Sanford South University, ND, p. A466

GASTINEAU, Trent, Chief Executive Officer, Tulsa Spine And Specialty Hospital, Tulsa, OK, p. A509

GASTON, Jan, Administrator, Jasper Memorial Hospital, Monticello, GA, p. A158

GASTON, Kathy, Chief Nursing Officer, Baptist Medical Center East, Montgomery, AL, p. A21

GASTON, Tammy, Chief Information Officer, Smith County Memorial Hospital, Smith Center, KS, p. A246

GATES, Misty, Chief Financial Officer, Forrest City Medical Center, Forrest City-St. Francis County, AR, p. A42

GATES, Rose, Director Human Resources, Hayward Area Memorial Hospital And Water's Edge, Hayward, WI, p. A694

GATES, Tracy, Vice President Operations and Chief Operating Officer, Cortland Regional Medical Center, Cortland, NY, p. A425

GATHERS, Mary
Director Information Systems, Mckay-Dee Hospital, Ogden, UT, p. A648
Director Information Systems, Utah Valley Hospital, Provo, UT, p. A649
Manager Information Systems, American Fork Hospital, American Fork, UT, p. A646

GATLIFF, Peggy, Chief Financial Officer, Northside Hospital, Saint Petersburg, FL, p. A138

GATLIFF, Rob, Chief of Medical Staff, Washington County Regional Medical Center, Sandersville, GA, p. A160

GATO, Carlos A, Director of Human Resources, Fort Lauderdale Hospital, Fort Lauderdale, FL, p. A122

GATTMAN, Gregory B., Chief Operating Officer, Palmetto Health Baptist, Columbia, SC, p. A551

GATTO, Tony, Director Management Information Systems, Flushing Hospital Medical Center, New York (Includes All Hospitals Located Within The Five Boroughs), NY, p. A432

GAUBERT, Steve C, Chief Financial Officer, Thibodaux Regional Medical Center, Thibodaux, LA, p. A280

GAUER, Natalie, Administrator, Milbank Area Hospital Avera, Milbank, SD, p. A562

GAUG, Mathew P., Executive Director of Information Techology, Lima Memorial Health System, Lima, OH, p. A484

GAUGHAN, Thomas, M.D., Chief Medical Officer, Kingman Regional Medical Center, Kingman, AZ, p. A30

GAUL, Mike, Director Information Technology, Golden Valley Memorial Healthcare, Clinton, MO, p. A357

GAULKE, Becky, Chief Nursing Officer, Ely-Bloomenson Community Hospital, Ely, MN, p. A331

GAULT, Cindy L., Chief Financial Officer, Union Medical Center, Union, SC, p. A557

GAURON, Patricia, Director Human Resources, Holy Family Hospital At Merrimack Valley, MA, p. A302

GAUSE, Levi Nathan, M.D., Chief Information Officer and Vice President Health System Informatics, Great River Medical Center, West Burlington, IA, p. A231

GAUTHIER, Paul, Chief Information Resources Management, Veterans Affairs Montana Health Care System, Fort Harrison, MT, p. A375

GAUTNEY, Steven, Chief Executive Officer, Crisp Regional Hospital, Cordele, GA, p. A151

GAVALCHIK, Stephen M., FACHE, Community Chief Executive Officer, Morgan County Arh Hospital, West Liberty, KY, p. A261

GAVIN, Andrea, M.D., Chief Medical officer, Aurora Sheboygan Memorial Medical Center, Sheboygan, WI, p. A702

GAVIN, Donald, Chief Financial Officer, Southern Tennessee Regional Health System-Pulaski, Pulaski, TN, p. A579

GAVIN, Todd, Chief Medical Officer, Madelia Community Hospital, Madelia, MN, p. A334

GAVORA, George, Director Program Evaluation, Kingsboro Psychiatric Center, New York (Includes All Hospitals Located Within The Five Boroughs), NY, p. A432

GAVULIC, Melany
President & Chief Executive Officer, Hurley Children's Hospital, MI, p. A312
Senior Vice President Operations & COO, Hurley Children's Hospital, MI, p. A312

GAW, Kris, Executive Vice President and Chief Operating Officer, Arizona Children's Center, AZ, p. A33

GAWALUCK, David
Vice President and Chief Information Officer, Excela Frick Hospital, Mount Pleasant, PA, p. A532
Vice President and Chief Information Officer, Excela Health Westmoreland Hospital, Greensburg, PA, p. A526
Vice President and Chief Information Officer, Excela Latrobe Area Hospital, Latrobe, PA, p. A529

GAWITH, Marlene, Director of Nursing, Ottawa County Health Center, Minneapolis, KS, p. A241

GAWLER, William, Chief Information Officer, Chillicothe Veterans Affairs Medical Center, Chillicothe, OH, p. A474

GAWNE, Bernard B, M.D., Vice President and Chief Medical Officer, Christ Hospital, Cincinnati, OH, p. A474

GAY, Christophe, M.D., Chief of Staff, Chi St. Joseph Health Bellville Hospital, Bellville, TX, p. A589

GAY, Don, Director Human Resources, West Hills Hospital, Reno, NV, p. A396

GAY, Kent E., M.D., Chief of Medical Staff, Arkansas Valley Regional Medical Center, La Junta, CO, p. A102

GAY, Kristi
Chief Financial Officer, Chi St. Luke's Health Memorial Lufkin, Lufkin, TX, p. A621
Chief Financial Officer, Chi St. Luke's Health Memorial San Augustine, San Augustine, TX, p. A635
GAY, Michael, Chief Operating Officer, Habersham Medical Center, Demorest, GA, p. A152
GAY, Perry, President and Chief Executive Officer, Logansport Memorial Hospital, Logansport, IN, p. A210
GAY, Vickie, Chief Executive Officer, Montgomery General Hospital, Montgomery, WV, p. A685
GAYNE, William, Chief Financial Officer, Medstar Washington Hospital Center, Washington, DC, p. A116
GAYNOR, Sheila, Director Human Resources, Perry County Memorial Hospital, Tell City, IN, p. A215
GAYTKO, Caren, Chief Nursing Officer, Regency Hospital Of Minneapolis, Golden Valley, MN, p. A332
GAZAWAY, William, Information Technology Security Officer, Alliancehealth Ponca City, Ponca City, OK, p. A505
GAZECKI, Cindy, Senior Vice President, Hospital Operations, Seattle Children's Hospital, Seattle, WA, p. A676
GEARHART, Danielle, Chief Executive Officer, Gundersen St. Joseph's Hospital And Clinics, Hillsboro, WI, p. A694
GEARHART, Heidi, Director Information Systems, Arkansas Valley Regional Medical Center, La Junta, CO, p. A102
GEARY, David S, Chief Financial Officer, Cache Valley Hospital, North Logan, UT, p. A648
GEARY, Herb J
Chief Nursing Officer, Santa Ynez Valley Cottage Hospital, Solvang, CA, p. A90
Vice President Patient Care Services and Chief Nursing Officer, Cottage Rehabilitation Hospital, CA, p. A88
GEBAUER, Laurie, Director Patient Care, Orange City Area Health System, Orange City, IA, p. A227
GEBHARD, Scott
Chief Operating Officer, Hackensack Meridian Health Jfk Johnson Rehabilitation Institute, Edison, NJ, p. A404
Executive VP and Chief Operating Officer, Hackensack Meridian Health Jfk Medical Center, Edison, NJ, p. A404
GEBHART, Cheryl
Chief Human Resources Officer, Tuality Forest Grove Hospital, OR, p. A513
Director Human Resources Providence Health Plan and Providence Medical Group, Providence Newberg Medical Center, Newberg, OR, p. A515
GEBHART, Jim, Jr, FACHE, President, Mercy Hospital Oklahoma City, Oklahoma City, OK, p. A503
GEBHART, Ronald J, M.D., Chief of Staff, Veterans Affairs Salt Lake City Health Care System, Salt Lake City, UT, p. A651
GECKLE, Rachel, Chief Human Resource Officer, Fulton County Health Center, Wauseon, OH, p. A493
GEDDINGS, Toni, Director Human Resources, Cullman Regional Medical Center, Cullman, AL, p. A16
GEDIES, Lucille, Chief Financial Officer, Mildred Mitchell-Bateman Hospital, Huntington, WV, p. A684
GEE, Kyle
Chief Financial Officer, Beartooth Billings Clinic, Red Lodge, MT, p. A378
Chief Financial Officer, Pioneer Medical Center, Big Timber, MT, p. A373
Regional Vice President Financial Operations, Roundup Memorial Healthcare, Roundup, MT, p. A378
GEER, Nicholas, Chief Financial Officer, Dallas Medical Center, Dallas, TX, p. A596
GEERTS, Jodi, Chief Nursing Officer, Henry County Health Center, Mount Pleasant, IA, p. A226
GEESEY, Wanda, Director Human Resources, Pennsylvania Psychiatric Institute, Harrisburg, PA, p. A526
GEHA, Andrew, D.O., President Medical Staff, Floyd Valley Healthcare, Le Mars, IA, p. A225
GEHLAUF, Dee Ann, Senior Vice President Business and Organization Development, Marietta Memorial Hospital, Marietta, OH, p. A485
GEHLHAUSEN, Sherri, Assistant Chief Financial Officer, Logansport Memorial Hospital, Logansport, IN, p. A210
GEHRIG, Ryan, President, Mercy Orthopedic Hospital Fort Smith, AR, p. A42
GEHRING, Betty, Finance Director, Operations, Thedacare Medical Center-New London, New London, WI, p. A700
GEHRING, Jay, Director Information Systems, Kingman Community Hospital, Kingman, KS, p. A238
GEHRING, Mikaela, Chief Operating Officer, Compass Memorial Healthcare, Marengo, IA, p. A226
GEHRING, Samuel, M.D., Chief of Staff, Fleming County Hospital, Flemingsburg, KY, p. A251
GEHRING, Terri
President and Chief Executive Officer, Mcpherson Hospital, Mcpherson, KS, p. A241
Vice President Operations, Mcpherson Hospital, Mcpherson, KS, p. A241

GEHRKE, Ryan, Chief Executive Officer, Eminent Medical Center, Richardson, TX, p. A630
GEIER, Joyce, Director Nursing, Girard Medical Center, Girard, KS, p. A235
GEIER, Kathy, Director of Nursing, Chase County Community Hospital, Imperial, NE, p. A385
GEIGER, Deb, Executive Director of Acute Care, Harbor Beach Community Hospital, Harbor Beach, MI, p. A315
GEIGER, Judy, R.N., Chief Nursing Officer, Primary Children's Hospital, Salt Lake City, UT, p. A650
GEIGER, Ralph, M.D., Chief of Staff, Sebastian River Medical Center, Sebastian, FL, p. A139
GEIGLE, Joseph, Director Human Resources, Fort Hamilton Hospital, Hamilton, OH, p. A483
GEIL, Kristie A, Vice President, Chief Nursing Officer, Cgh Medical Center, Sterling, IL, p. A197
GEISLER, Linda W, R.N., FACHE, Vice President Patient Services, Centrastate Healthcare System, Freehold, NJ, p. A405
GEISSLER, Bonnie, R.N., Chief Nursing Officer, Vice President Patient Care Services, Clara Maass Medical Center, Belleville, NJ, p. A402
GEIST, Jim
Executive Vice President and Chief Operating Officer, Cascade Valley Hospital, Arlington, WA, p. A669
Executive Vice President and Chief Operating Officer, Skagit Regional Health, Mount Vernon, WA, p. A674
GEITZ, Cheri, Director Human Resources, Hansen Family Hospital, Iowa Falls, IA, p. A225
GEITZ, James, M.D., Chief of Staff, Newman Regional Health, Emporia, KS, p. A234
GEIVER, Betsy, Chief Human Resources Officer, Sioux Falls Veterans Affairs Health Care System, Sioux Falls, SD, p. A564
GELBS, Hannah, Chief Operating Officer, Cypress Fairbanks Medical Center, Houston, TX, p. A610
GELDHOF, Jay
Director Information Systems, Greater El Monte Community Hospital, South El Monte, CA, p. A90
Director Information Systems, Whittier Hospital Medical Center, Whittier, CA, p. A95
GELFAND, Andrew, M.D., Medical Director, Our Children's House, Dallas, TX, p. A597
GELL, Michael, Director Human Resources, Boys Town National Research Hospital, Omaha, NE, p. A387
GELLASCH, Tara L, Chief Medical Officer, United Memorial Medical Center-North Street, NY, p. A422
GELLER, Harold S., Chief Executive Officer, Chi St. Anthony Hospital, Pendleton, OR, p. A515
GELLER, Mark, M.D., President and Chief Executive Officer, Nyack Hospital, Nyack, NY, p. A438
GELLER, Warren, President and Chief Executive Officer, Englewood Hospital And Medical Center, Englewood, NJ, p. A405
GEMBOL, Leslie, MSN, R.N., Chief Nursing Officer, Baylor Scott & White Medical Center - Lakeway, TX, p. A631
GENESIO, Sabina, Finance Officer for Institutes, Colorado Mental Health Institute At Fort Logan, Denver, CO, p. A98
GENEVRO, Thomas A, Vice President Human Resources, Butler Health System, Butler, PA, p. A521
GENGLE, Tim F, Director Human Resources, North Ottawa Community Hospital, Grand Haven, MI, p. A313
GENGLER, Laraine, Chief Financial Officer, Lindsborg Community Hospital, Lindsborg, KS, p. A240
GENNA, Nick, Administrator, Treasure Valley Hospital, Boise, ID, p. A168
GENNARO, John, FACHE, Director, Erie Veterans Affairs Medical Center, Erie, PA, p. A525
GENOVESE, Vincent P, M.D., President Medical Staff, Owensboro Health Muhlenberg Community Hospital, Greenville, KY, p. A252
GENSERT, Kurt G, FACHE, R.N., Vice President Operations, Platte Valley Medical Center, Brighton, CO, p. A97
GENTILE, John, M.D.
Vice President Medical Affairs, Alta Bates Medical Center-Herrick Campus, CA, p. A52
Vice President Medical Affairs, Alta Bates Summit Medical Center - Summit Campus, Oakland, CA, p. A75
GENTILE, Serge, Director Human Resources, Belmont Community Hospital, Bellaire, OH, p. A472
GENTNER, Kim, Chief Financial Officer, Deckerville Community Hospital, Deckerville, MI, p. A310
GENTNER, Rocky, Chief Financial Officer, Newport Bay Hospital, Newport Beach, CA, p. A75
GENTRY, Jeanine, Chief Executive Officer, Steele Memorial Medical Center, Salmon, ID, p. A172
GENTRY, Jennifer, R.N., Chief Nursing Officer, Christus Spohn Hospital Corpus Christus South, TX, p. A594
GENTRY, Kristen, Chief Operating Officer, Venice Regional Bayfront Health, Venice, FL, p. A142

GENTRY, Lee, FACHE, Vice President and Administrator, Baptist Health Extended Care Hospital, Little Rock-Pulaski County, AR, p. A44
GENTRY, Margie, Controller, T. J. Samson Community Hospital, Glasgow, KY, p. A252
GEOGHEGAN, Jeffrey, Chief Financial Officer, Uconn, John Dempsey Hospital, Farmington, CT, p. A108
GEORGE, Alan E, Chief Operating Officer, Bradley Center Of St. Francis, GA, p. A151
GEORGE, Brad, Director Information Systems, Parkland Medical Center, Derry, NH, p. A398
GEORGE, Dana, Chief Human Resources Officer, Abrazo Central Campus, Phoenix, AZ, p. A32
GEORGE, Daniel M, Executive Vice President, Operations, Covenant Medical Center-Harrison, MI, p. A322
GEORGE, Denise, R.N., President, Northern Dutchess Hospital, Rhinebeck, NY, p. A441
GEORGE, Gary, Senior Vice President Human Resources, Mercy Children's Hospital, OH, p. A491
GEORGE, P A, M.D., Chief of Staff, Madison Medical Center, Fredericktown, MO, p. A359
GEORGE, Patsy, R.N., Vice President and Chief Nursing Officer, Ohio Valley Medical Center, Wheeling, WV, p. A688
GEORGE, Saju, Chief Executive Officer, Garden City Hospital, Garden City, MI, p. A313
GEORGE, Shayne, Chief Executive Officer, Memorial Children's Hospital, GA, p. A160
GEORGE, Susan, R.N., M.P.H., Associate Director Patient Care Services, Martinsburg Veterans Affairs Medical Center, Martinsburg, WV, p. A685
GEORGE, Tracy L, Chief Financial Officer, St. James Parish Hospital, Lutcher, LA, p. A273
GEORGE, William, M.D., Chief of Staff, Beartooth Billings Clinic, Red Lodge, MT, p. A378
GEORGES, Angelo, M.D., President Medical and Dental Staff, Wheeling Hospital, Wheeling, WV, p. A688
GEORGESON, Keith, M.D., Chief Executive, Sacred Heart Children's Hospital, WA, p. A678
GEORGOFF, Julie, Vice President of Finance and Chief Financial Officer, Magruder Memorial Hospital, Port Clinton, OH, p. A489
GEPFORD, John, Director Information Systems, Evergreenhealth Monroe, Monroe, WA, p. A673
GERARD, Greg Donavan., President, Baptist Health Richmond, Richmond, KY, p. A260
GERBER, Allen, M.D., Chief of Staff, Baptist Health Medical Center-Hot Spring County, Malvern-Hot Spring County, AR, p. A45
GERBER, Andrew, M.D., Ph.D., Medical Director and Chief Executive Officer, Austen Riggs Center, Stockbridge, MA, p. A305
GERBER, Greg, M.D., Chief Medical Officer, Aurora Lakeland Medical Center, Elkhorn, WI, p. A692
GERDES, Isaac, Chief Executive Officer, Sanford Webster Medical Center, Webster, SD, p. A565
GERDTS, Elizabeth, Chief Nursing Officer, Nyc Health + Hospitals / North Central Bronx, New York (Includes All Hospitals Located Within The Five Boroughs), NY, p. A436
GERE, Zsaber, Chief Human Resource Officer, Banner Behavioral Health Hospital - Scottsdale, Scottsdale, AZ, p. A35
GERETY, Meghan, M.D., Chief of Staff, New Mexico Veterans Affairs Health Care System - Raymond G. Murphy Medical Center, Albuquerque, NM, p. A416
GERHART, Paul, Chief Financial Officer, Sanford Canton-Inwood Medical Center, Canton, SD, p. A559
GERIG, Stacey L.
Chief Executive Officer, Odessa Regional Medical Center South Campus, Odessa, TX, p. A626
Chief Executive Officer, Odessa Regional Medical Center, Odessa, TX, p. A626
GERING, Paul, M.D., Vice President Medical Affairs, Saint Alphonsus Medical Center - Ontario, Ontario, OR, p. A515
GERKE, Daniel, Chief Nursing Officer, Wright Patterson Medical Center, Wright, OH, p. A494
GERKE, Sarah, Manager Human Resources, Warner Hospital And Health Services, Clinton, IL, p. A180
GERLACH, Carl, Chief Financial Officer, Curry General Hospital, Gold Beach, OR, p. A513
GERLACH, Judith LeAnn, Chief Nursing Officer, Helena Regional Medical Center, Helena-Phillips County, AR, p. A43
GERLACH, Matthew S
Chief Operating Officer, Children's Hospital Of Orange County, Orange, CA, p. A76
Chief Operating Officer, Choc Children's At Mission Hospital, Mission Viejo, CA, p. A72
GERMANY, Alan, Chief Executive Officer and Chief Restructuring Officer, Southern Inyo Healthcare District, Lone Pine, CA, p. A65

GERNDT, Angie, Human Resources Manager, Central Community Hospital, Elkader, IA, p. A222

GERNHART, Diana, Senior Vice President and Hospital Chief Financial Officer, Doernbecher Children's Hospital, OR, p. A516

GERRIOR, Marilyn, R.N., MSN, Chief Nursing Executive, Saint Louise Regional Hospital, Gilroy, CA, p. A60

GERRITS, Brad, Director Information Systems, Marshfield Medical Center - Rice Lake, Rice Lake, WI, p. A702

GERSON, Elaine, Chief Clinical Officer and General Counsel, Aspen Valley Hospital, Aspen, CO, p. A96

GERSTENBERGER, Linda
Vice President Human Resources, St. Rose Dominican Hospitals - San Martin Campus, Las Vegas, NV, p. A395
Vice President Human Resources, St. Rose Dominican Hospitals - Siena Campus, Henderson, NV, p. A393

GERSTNER, Nancy, Manager Human Resources, Robert J. Dole Veterans Affairs Medical Center, Wichita, KS, p. A248

GERTH, P. Kevin, Chief of Staff, Spectrum Health Gerber Memorial, Fremont, MI, p. A313

GERVELER, Patrick M, Vice President Finance and Chief Financial Officer, Blessing Hospital, p. A194

GESKERMANN, Tom G., Chief Executive Officer, Osceola Medical Center, Osceola, WI, p. A700

GESME, Barbara L., MSN, Vice President Patient Care Services & Chief Nurse Executive, Bon Secours St. Francis Medical Center, Midlothian, VA, p. A661

GESSLING, Heather, M.D., Chief Medical Officer, Moberly Regional Medical Center, Moberly, MO, p. A364

GESSNER, Christopher A., President, Children's Hospital Of Pittsburgh Of Upmc, Pittsburgh, PA, p. A537

GETCHIUS, Joseph, Director Information Technology, Benewah Community Hospital, Saint Maries, ID, p. A171

GETMAN, Sylvia, President and Chief Executive Officer, Adirondack Health, Saranac Lake, NY, p. A442

GETSAY, Timothy, Chief Information Officer, Vice President of Performance & Information Mgmt, Gillette Children's Specialty Healthcare, Saint Paul, MN, p. A339

GETTINGER, Thomas
Executive Vice President and Chief Operating Officer, Snowden At Fredericksburg, VA, p. A658
Executive Vice President and Chief Operating Officer, Stafford Hospital, Stafford, VA, p. A666

GETTINGS, Scott, M.D., Senior Vice President and Chief Medical Officer, Health First Viera Hospital, Melbourne, FL, p. A129

GETTYS, Sky, Chief Financial Officer, Fairfield Medical Center, Lancaster, OH, p. A484

GETZ, Liz, Chief Information Officer, Aultman Hospital Pediatric Services, OH, p. A473

GEUDER, Denise, Vice President Patient Care Service and Chief Nursing Officer, Southwestern Regional Medical Center, Tulsa, OK, p. A509

GEURTS, Chuck, Manager Information Technology Client Services, Aurora Baycare Medical Center, Green Bay, WI, p. A693

GEWECKE, Tyler, Information Technology Technician, Fillmore County Hospital, Geneva, NE, p. A384

GFELLER, Michael, Director Information Systems, Medical City Frisco, TX, p. A628

GHAEMMAGHAMI, Chris A., M.D., Chief Medical Officer, University Of Virginia Children's Hospital, VA, p. A656

GHAFFARI, Bahram, President, Delano Regional Medical Center, Delano, CA, p. A56

GHALI, Sara, Chief Financial Officer, Santa Cruz Valley Regional Hospital, Green Valley, AZ, p. A30

GHERINGHELLI, Thomas, Senior Vice President, Chief Financial Officer, New England Baptist Hospital, Boston, MA, p. A297

GHERKE, Sheila, Director Human Resources, Minnie Hamilton Healthcare Center, Grantsville, WV, p. A683

GHIDOTTI, Craig J, Vice President Human Resources, Tripoint Medical Center, OH, p. A479

GHINASSI, Frank A., Ph.D., President and Chief Executive Officer, University Behavioral Healthcare, Piscataway, NJ, p. A410

GHION, christopher, Vice President and Chief Information Officer, Adventist Healthcare Shady Grove Medical Center, Rockville, MD, p. A294

GHULUM, Evelyn, Chief Financial Officer, Jellico Community Hospital, Jellico, TN, p. A571

GIAGUINTO, Shelly, Chief Financial Officer, Highland-Clarksburg Hospital, Clarksburg, WV, p. A682

GIAMPA, Patricia L, Chief Nursing Officer, Searhc Mt. Edgecumbe Hospital, Sitka, AK, p. A27

GIANCOLA, Louis R., President and Chief Executive Officer, South County Hospital, Wakefield, RI, p. A548

GIANELLI, Arthur A., M.P.H., President, Mount Sinai West Hospital, NY, p. A434

GIANG, Vernon, M.D.
Chief Medical Executive, California Pacific Medical Center-St. Luke's Campus, San Francisco, CA, p. A85
Chief Medical Executive, California Pacific Medical Center, San Francisco, CA, p. A85

GIANGARDELLA, Mike, Vice President Finance and Administration, Salem Regional Medical Center, Salem, OH, p. A490

GIANNONE, John, M.D., Delaware Valley Hospital Medical Director, Uhs Delaware Valley Hospital, Walton, NY, p. A445

GIANNOSA, Amy, Director Human Resources, Havenwyck Hospital, Auburn Hills, MI, p. A307

GIANNUZZI, Donna, R.N., Chief Nursing Officer, The Rehabilitation Hospital, FL, p. A123

GIANSANTE, Joseph, Vice President Human Resources, Ellis Hospital Health Center, NY, p. A442

GIARDINA, Deborah, Director Human Resources and Medical Staff Services, Rehabilitation Hospital Of Fort Wayne, Fort Wayne, IN, p. A204

GIBB, Matthew, M.D., Executive Vice President and System Chief Medical Officer, Carle Foundation Hospital, Urbana, IL, p. A197

GIBB, Randall K., M.D., Chief Executive Officer, Billings Clinic, Billings, MT, p. A373

GIBBENS, Lori, Controller, Healthsouth Rehabilitation Hospital Of Erie, Erie, PA, p. A525

GIBBERMAN, Val, M.D., Acting Chief of Staff, Hampton Veterans Affairs Medical Center, Hampton, VA, p. A659

GIBBES, Gregg, Chief Executive Officer, Covington County Hospital, Collins, MS, p. A345

GIBBONS, Barbara, Vice President Patient Care Services, St. Joseph Hospital, Bethpage, NY, p. A422

GIBBONS, Brian P., Jr, Chief Executive Officer, Astria Sunnyside Hospital, Sunnyside, WA, p. A678

GIBBONS, David, President, Upmc Hamot, Erie, PA, p. A525

GIBBONS, Jason, Chief Financial Officer, Minidoka Memorial Hospital, Rupert, ID, p. A171

GIBBS, Christopher Michael, Director Information Management Systems, Taylor Regional Hospital, Campbellsville, KY, p. A250

GIBBS, Jeffrey S., M.D., Regional Vice President Medical Affairs, Skagit Regional Health, Mount Vernon, WA, p. A674

GIBBS, Kenneth, President and Chief Executive Officer, Maimonides Infants And Children's Hospital Of Brooklyn, NY, p. A433

GIBBS, Michael, President, Avera Heart Hospital Of South Dakota, Sioux Falls, SD, p. A563

GIBBS, Parker, M.D., Chief Medical Officer, Uf Health Shands Rehab Hospital, FL, p. A124

GIBBS, Tim, Director of Information Technology, Information Security Officer, Children's Hospital Of Richmond At Vcu-Brook Road Campus, Richmond, VA, p. A664

GIBBS, Vickie, Director Nursing, Phillips County Hospital, Phillipsburg, KS, p. A244

GIBBS-MCELVY, Shelana, M.D., Medical Director, Healthsouth Rehabilitation Hospital Of Sewickley, Sewickley, PA, p. A541

GIBNEY, Thomas, Senior Vice President and Chief Financial Officer, St. Luke's Cornwall Hospital - Newburgh Campus, NY, p. A438

GIBSON, Armetria, Human Resources Generalist, Select Specialty Hospital Midtown Atlanta, Atlanta, GA, p. A147

GIBSON, Belinda D, R.N., Senior Vice President Patient Services, Bsa Hospital, Llc, Amarillo, TX, p. A583

GIBSON, Connie, R.N., Director Human Resources, Mary Black Health System - Gaffney, Gaffney, SC, p. A553

GIBSON, David R., Chief Executive Officer, Carl R. Darnall Army Medical Center, Fort Hood, TX, p. A603

GIBSON, Elizabeth, Director Human Resources, Mid-America Rehabilitation Hospital, Shawnee Mission, KS, p. A246

GIBSON, J. Francis., Administrator and Chief Executive Officer, Orem Community Hospital, Orem, UT, p. A648

GIBSON, Jack, Administrator, Noland Hospital Tuscaloosa, Tuscaloosa, AL, p. A24

GIBSON, Joel, Vice President Human Resources, St. Joseph's Mercy-North, MI, p. A310

GIBSON, Mary Helen, Director Human Resources, Floyd Valley Healthcare, Le Mars, IA, p. A225

GIBSON, Megan, Nurse Manager, River Bend Hospital, West Lafayette, IN, p. A216

GIBSON, Todd, Chief Financial Officer, Medical City Denton, Denton, TX, p. A599

GICCA, Ron, Chief Executive Officer, Melbourne Regional Medical Center, Melbourne, FL, p. A129

GICZI, Mary Beth, Director Human Resources, Encompass Health Rehabilitation Hospital Of Scottsdale, Scottsdale, AZ, p. A35

GIDDINGS, Carleen, Information Technology System Leader, Scheurer Hospital, Pigeon, MI, p. A320

GIDEON, Daniel L., FACHE, Chief Executive Officer, Pine Creek Medical Center, Dallas, TX, p. A597

GIEGER, Julie
Chief Financial Officer, Lackey Memorial Hospital, Forest, MS, p. A346
Chief Financial Officer, Monroe Regional Hospital, Aberdeen, MS, p. A343

GIER, Jennifer, Director Human Resources, Brynn Marr Hospital, Jacksonville, NC, p. A455

GIERTUGA, Garry, Site Manager Human Resources, Amita Health Adventist La Grange Medical Center, La Grange, IL, p. A187

GIESE, Kristine A, Chief Operating Officer, Providence Medical Center, Wayne, NE, p. A391

GIFFORD, Ellen, Director Human Resources, Integris Deaconess, Oklahoma City, OK, p. A502

GIGLIO, Aimee M., Chief Human Resources Officer, Children's Hospital At Dartmouth, NH, p. A399

GIGLIOTTI, Vicki, Chief Clinical Officer, Moab Regional Hospital, Moab, UT, p. A647

GIJANTO, Charles
Interim Chief Executive Officer, Claxton-Hepburn Medical Center, Ogdensburg, NY, p. A439
Interim Chief Executive Officer, Massena Memorial Hospital, Massena, NY, p. A430

GIL, Julio, Manager Information Services, William And Inez Mabie Skilled Nursing Facility, CA, p. A61

GILBERT, Andrea F., FACHE, President, Bryn Mawr Hospital, Bryn Mawr, PA, p. A521

GILBERT, Carla, Director Finance, Cedar County Memorial Hospital, El Dorado Springs, MO, p. A358

GILBERT, Christy
Interim Chief Executive Officer, Doctors Neuropsychiatric Hospital And Research Institute, Bremen, IN, p. A200
President and Chief Operating Officer, Medical Behavioral Hospital Of Mishawaka, Knox, IN, p. A208

GILBERT, Jack, Vice President Finance and Facilities, Advocate Illinois Masonic Medical Center, Chicago, IL, p. A176

GILBERT, Kevin, R.N., Vice President, Confluence Health/Wenatchee Valley Hospital, Wenatchee, WA, p. A680

GILBERT, Kim, R.N., Chief Nursing Officer, Electra Memorial Hospital, Electra, TX, p. A603

GILBERT, Thomas, Director Information Technology Services, Lake Cumberland Regional Hospital, Somerset, KY, p. A260

GILBERT, Thomas D., FACHE
Chief Executive Officer, Wadley Regional Medical Center At Hope, Hope-Hempstead County, AR, p. A43
Chief Executive Officer, Wadley Regional Medical Center, Texarkana, TX, p. A639

GILBERT, Valarie, R.N., Chief Nursing Officer, Texas Health Harris Methodist Hospital Azle, Azle, TX, p. A587

GILBERT, William L., Hospital Director, Arrowhead Regional Medical Center, Colton, CA, p. A55

GILBERTSON, Gerry, FACHE, Administrator, Centracare Health-Melrose, Melrose, MN, p. A334

GILCHRIST, Doug, Chief Operating Officer, Summit Healthcare Regional Medical Center, Show Low, AZ, p. A36

GILDAY, Matt, Vice President of Human Resources, Tristar Hendersonville Medical Center, Hendersonville, TN, p. A570

GILDON, Lisa
Group Financial Officer, Texas Health Presbyterian Hospital Allen, Allen, TX, p. A582
Vice President and Chief Financial Officer, Texas Health Presbyterian Hospital Plano, Plano, TX, p. A629

GILES, Charles, M.D., President Medical Staff, T.J. Health Columbia, Columbia, KY, p. A250

GILES, Jared, Chief Operating Officer, Rancho Springs Medical Center, CA, p. A74

GILES, Steve, Chief Information Officer, Hollywood Presbyterian Medical Center, Los Angeles, CA, p. A67

GILES, William, Chief Executive Officer, Regional West Garden County, Oshkosh, NE, p. A389

GILG, Ronald, Assistant Vice President Talent, Cancer Treatment Centers Of America-Eastern Regional Medical Center, Philadelphia, PA, p. A534

GILGEN, Steve, Chief Financial Officer, Erlanger Murphy Medical Center, Murphy, NC, p. A457

GILJUM, Anthony, Chief Information Officer, Sheridan Veterans Affairs Medical Center, Sheridan, WY, p. A709

GILKEY, Edward, M.D., Vice President Medical Affairs, St. Luke's Hospital - Warren Campus, Phillipsburg, NJ, p. A410

GILL, Brian, Chief Administrative Officer, Saint Thomas Stones River Hospital, Woodbury, TN, p. A581

GILL, Mandeep, Chief Operating Officer, Memorial Hospital Of Sweetwater County, Rock Springs, WY, p. A709

GILL, Margaret, Chief Executive Officer, Pinecrest Rehabilitation Hospital, FL, p. A121

GILL, Mark, Vice President Finance and Chief Financial Officer, Cape Regional Health System, Cape May Court House, NJ, p. A403

GILLAM, Sally A, R.N., Chief Nursing Officer, St. David's South Austin Medical Center, Austin, TX, p. A587

GILLARD, Austin M., Chief Executive Officer, Clay County Medical Center, Clay Center, KS, p. A233

GILLEN, Mark T
Director Finance and Operations, Owatonna Hospital, Owatonna, MN, p. A337
Director of Operations, Owatonna Hospital, Owatonna, MN, p. A337

GILLES, Ken
Associate Chief Information Officer, Essentia Health St. Mary's - Detroit Lakes, Detroit Lakes, MN, p. A330
Chief Information Officer, Essentia Health Fargo, Fargo, ND, p. A465

GILLESPIE, Anne, R.N., Associate Director Patient Care and Nursing Services, Veterans Affairs Loma Linda Healthcare System, Loma Linda, CA, p. A64

GILLESPIE, Bob
Chief Information Technology Officer, Connally Memorial Medical Center, Floresville, TX, p. A603
Chief Operating Officer, Connally Memorial Medical Center, Floresville, TX, p. A603

GILLESPIE, Curt, Chief Executive Officer, Mental Health Services For Clark And Madison Counties, Springfield, OH, p. A490

GILLESPIE, Karen, Director Human Resources, Anderson County Hospital, Garnett, KS, p. A235

GILLESPIE, Lisa, M.D., Chief Medical Officer, Piedmont Rockdale Hospital, Conyers, GA, p. A151

GILLESPIE, Richard, Chief Executive Officer, Jefferson County Hospital, Waurika, OK, p. A510

GILLESPIE, Tim, Manager Information Systems, Carle Richland Memorial Hospital, Olney, IL, p. A192

GILLESPIE, Tina, Chief Executive Officer, Harrison County Community Hospital, Bethany, MO, p. A355

GILLETTE, Karen, Associate Director Patient Care Services, Memphis Veterans Affairs Medical Center, Memphis, TN, p. A575

GILLETTE, Nicole, R.N., Chief Nursing Officer, Midmichigan Medical Center - West Branch, West Branch, MI, p. A326

GILLETTE, Robert, Chief Information Officer, St. Elizabeth Medical Center, Utica, NY, p. A444

GILLETTE, Tom, Senior Vice President and Chief Information Officer, Miami Heart Campus At Mount Sinai Medical Center, FL, p. A131

GILLIAM, David, M.D., Medical Director, Bloomington Meadows Hospital, Bloomington, IN, p. A200

GILLIAM, Eric, President, Women's Hospital Saint Joseph East, KY, p. A255

GILLIAM, Leslie, Director Health Information Management, Dominion Hospital, Falls Church, VA, p. A657

GILLIAN, Tom, Chief Operating Officer, River Bend Hospital, West Lafayette, IN, p. A216

GILLIAND, Michael, M.D., Chief of Staff, Chi St. Luke's Health Brazosport, Lake Jackson, TX, p. A618

GILLILAND, Michelle, Director of Nursing, River Park Hospital, Huntington, WV, p. A684

GILLILAND, Sharon, Chief of Staff, Baraga County Memorial Hospital, L'Anse, MI, p. A317

GILLILAND, Terry, M.D.
Chief Medical Officer, Sentara Leigh Hospital, Norfolk, VA, p. A662
Senior Vice President and Chief Medical Officer, Sentara Princess Anne Hospital, Virginia Beach, VA, p. A667

GILLIS, Anne, Chief Financial Officer, Holy Cross Hospital, Silver Spring, MD, p. A294

GILLMAN, Kreg, Chief Executive Officer, Salt Lake Behavioral Health, Salt Lake City, UT, p. A650

GILLY, Mike, Chief Information Officer, Bogalusa Community Medical Center, LA, p. A264

GILMAN, Howard, M.D., Medical Executive, Christian Health Care Center, Wyckoff, NJ, p. A414

GILMAN, James K., M.D., Chief Executive Officer, Children's Inn At Nih, MD, p. A290

GILMAN, Kim
Chief Executive Officer and Chief Nursing Officer, Southwest Georgia Regional Medical Center, Cuthbert, GA, p. A151
Chief Executive Officer, Phoebe Worth Medical Center, Sylvester, GA, p. A161
Chief Nursing Officer, Phoebe Worth Medical Center, Sylvester, GA, p. A161

GILMORE, Hugh V, M.D., Vice President Medical Affairs, Seton Medical Center Williamson, Round Rock, TX, p. A631

GILMORE, Joshua, Chief Executive Officer, Iron County Medical Center, Pilot Knob, MO, p. A366

GILMORE, Phillip K., FACHE, Chief Executive Officer, Ashley County Medical Center, Crossett-Ashley County, AR, p. A40

GILMORE, Stephen, Chief Financial Officer, Piedmont Medical Center, Rock Hill, SC, p. A556

GILPIN, Michael W., Vice President Human Resources, Sampson Regional Medical Center, Clinton, NC, p. A450

GILSON, Sheila, R.N., Chief Operating Officer, Kaiser Permanente Redwood City Medical Center, Redwood City, CA, p. A80

GILTNER, Michelle, Interim Chief Nursing Officer, University Hospitals Richmond Medical Center, OH, p. A477

GIN, Nancy, M.D., Area Associate Medical Director, Orange County Irvine Medical Center, CA, p. A50

GINDER, Phil, Chief Executive Officer, Hodgeman County Health Center, Jetmore, KS, p. A237

GINGERY, Adam, Chief Financial Officer, Door County Medical Center, Sturgeon Bay, WI, p. A704

GINGRAS, Sean, CPA, Chief Financial Officer, Centerstone Hospital, Bradenton, FL, p. A118

GINGRICH, Joye, Director Patient Care Services and Chief Nursing Officer, J. C. Blair Memorial Hospital, Huntingdon, PA, p. A527

GINGRICH, Mary, Director Health Care Services, Kansas Neurological Institute, Topeka, KS, p. A246

GINN, Bobby, Chief Operating Officer, Crestwood Medical Center, Huntsville, AL, p. A19

GINN, Doug, Executive Vice President Operations, Peak Behavioral Health Services, Santa Teresa, NM, p. A419

GINNATY, Rayn, Vice President Nursing, Benefis Health Care-West Campus, MT, p. A376

GINSBERG, Jo-Ann M., R.N., MSN, Director, Marion Veterans Affairs Medical Center, Marion, IL, p. A188

GINSBERG, Ronald L, M.D., Vice President Medical Affairs, Northwest Hospital, Randallstown, MD, p. A293

GINSBURG, J Lawrence, M.D., Vice President Medical Affairs, Evangelical Community Hospital, Lewisburg, PA, p. A530

GINTER, Gary, System Vice President and Chief Information Officer, Miami Valley Hospital South, OH, p. A480

GINTOLI, Eric, Administrator, Seaside Health System, Baton Rouge, LA, p. A264

GINTZIG, Donald R.
President and Chief Executive Officer, Wakemed Cary Hospital, Cary, NC, p. A449
President and Chief Executive Officer, Wakemed North Family Health And Women's Hospital, NC, p. A459

GIOIA, Anthony, Chief Financial Officer, Orthoindy Hospital, Indianapolis, IN, p. A207

GIORDANO, Paul D., Senior Vice President, Human Resources, South Nassau Communities Hospital, Oceanside, NY, p. A438

GIORDANO, Peter, Senior Director Human Resources, Harrison Community Hospital, Cadiz, OH, p. A473

GIORDANO, Roger, M.D., Medical Director, Emcompass Health Rehabilitation Hospital Of Virginia, Richmond, VA, p. A665

GIORDANO, Susan, R.N., Chief Nursing Officer, Hackensack Meridian Health Pascack Valley Medical Center, Westwood, NJ, p. A414

GIPP, Jana, Chief Executive Officer, Standing Rock Service Unit, Fort Yates Hospital, Indian Health Service, Dhhs, Fort Yates, ND, p. A466

GIPSON, Linda Stephens, MSN, Ph.D., Chief Nursing Officer, Whidbeyhealth, Coupeville, WA, p. A671

GIRALT, Juana
Chief Financial Officer, River Crest Hospital, San Angelo, TX, p. A632
Interim Chief Executive Officer, River Crest Hospital, San Angelo, TX, p. A632

GIRARD, Thomas R
Vice President Human Resources, Lincolnhealth St. Andrews Campus, ME, p. A283
Vice President Human Resources, Pen Bay Medical Center, Rockport, ME, p. A286

GIRARDEAU, Brian, Director Information System, East Georgia Regional Medical Center, Statesboro, GA, p. A161

GIRARDIER, Cheryl, Director Information Technology, Lecom Health Millcreek Community Hospital, Erie, PA, p. A525

GIRARDY, James, M.D., Vice President, Chief Surgical Officer, Osf Saint Anthony Medical Center, Rockford, IL, p. A195

GIRTY, Tara, Director Human Resources, Kiowa District Healthcare, Kiowa, KS, p. A238

GISH, Kevin, Administrator and Vice President, Essentia Health Fosston, Fosston, MN, p. A331

GISLER, Greg, Chief Financial Officer, Mcbride Orthopedic Hospital, Oklahoma City, OK, p. A503

GISLESON, Joni, Director Finance, Gundersen Palmer Lutheran Hospital And Clinics, West Union, IA, p. A231

GITMAN, Michael, M.D., Medical Director, North Shore University Hospital, Manhasset, NY, p. A429

GITTELMAN, Michael B
Administrator, Bascom Palmer Eye Institute-Anne Bates Leach Eye Hospital, FL, p. A131
Chief Executive Officer, University Of Miami Hospital, FL, p. A131

GITTELMAN, Michael B., Chief Executive Officer, University Of Miami Hospital, FL, p. A131

GITTLER, Michelle, M.D., Medical Director, Schwab Rehabilitation Hospital, Chicago, IL, p. A179

GITZINGER, Matthew, Director of Operations, Vidant Duplin Hospital, Kenansville, NC, p. A455

GIUDICE, William A, Vice President and Chief Financial Officer, Tallahassee Memorial Healthcare, Tallahassee, FL, p. A140

GIULIANELLI, Victor, FACHE, President and Chief Executive Officer, St. Mary's Healthcare, NY, p. A421

GIVENS, Michael K, FACHE, Administrator, St. Bernards Medical Center, Jonesboro-Craighead County, AR, p. A44

GIVENS, Patricia, R.N., Chief Nursing Officer, Children's Hospital Of Colorado At Memorial, CO, p. A96

GIVENS, Seth, Chief Human Resource Officer, Drew Memorial Health System, Monticello-Drew County, AR, p. A46

GIVENS, Stephen K., Assistant Vice President and Administrator, Russell County Medical Center, Lebanon, VA, p. A660

GIZZI, Jason, Controller, Healthsouth Mountainview Regional Rehabilitation Hospital, Morgantown, WV, p. A685

GJOLBERG, Skip, FACHE, Administrator, St. Joseph's Hospital Of Buckhannon, Buckhannon, WV, p. A682

GLADEN, Tracy, Chief Financial Officer, Twin Valley Behavioral Healthcare, Columbus, OH, p. A479

GLADSTONE, Art, R.N.
Chief Executive Officer, Pali Momi Medical Center, Aiea, HI, p. A164
Chief Executive Officer, Straub Medical Center, Honolulu, HI, p. A165

GLANVILLE, Tristan, Chief Financial Officer, Adirondack Health, Saranac Lake, NY, p. A442

GLANZER, Elgin, Chief Financial Officer, Memorial Health System, Abilene, KS, p. A232

GLASBERG, Michael, Senior Vice President, Chief Operating Officer, Dameron Hospital, Stockton, CA, p. A90

GLASER, Elaine, Chief Executive Officer, Valley Hospital Medical Center, Las Vegas, NV, p. A395

GLASER, Ruth, President, Pender Memorial Hospital, Burgaw, NC, p. A448

GLASNAPP, Sherry L., Director, Douglas County Community Mental Health Center, Omaha, NE, p. A388

GLASS, Ian, M.D., Chief Medical Officer, Kindred Hospital The Heights, TX, p. A640

GLASS, Ina Louise, Administrator, Ephraim Mcdowell Fort Logan Hospital, Stanford, KY, p. A261

GLASS, Ina Louise., Administrator, Ephraim Mcdowell Fort Logan Hospital, Stanford, KY, p. A261

GLASS, Kyle, Chief Financial Officer, Florida Hospital Deland, Deland, FL, p. A121

GLASS, Steven, Chief Financial Officer, Cleveland Clinic Children's Hospital, OH, p. A476

GLASS, Wendy, Director Human Resources, Colleton Medical Center, Walterboro, SC, p. A557

GLASSBURN, David, Vice President Finance and Chief Financial Officer, Harlingen Medical Center, Harlingen, TX, p. A608

GLASSCOCK, Sheryl, Chief Nursing Officer, Lake Cumberland Regional Hospital, Somerset, KY, p. A260

GLASSMAN, Kimberly S, Ph.D., R.N., Chief Nursing Officer, Rusk Institute At Nyu-Hjd, NY, p. A436

GLAUBKE, Nancy, Chief Executive Officer, Valley County Health System, Ord, NE, p. A389

GLAVIN, Jolene, R.N., MSN, Director Nursing, Salina Surgical Hospital, Salina, KS, p. A245

GLAZIER, Stephen, Chief Operating Officer, University Of Texas Harris County Psychiatric Center, Houston, TX, p. A614

GLEASON, Jeffrey J, M.D., Chief Medical Officer, Cookeville Regional Medical Center, Cookeville, TN, p. A568

GLEASON, Vallerie L., President and Chief Executive Officer, Newton Medical Center, Newton, KS, p. A242

GLEN, Diane M, Assistant Administrator, Barnes-Jewish West County Hospital, Saint Louis, MO, p. A367

GLENN, Daphne, Chief Executive Officer, Trihealth Rehabilitation Hospital, Cincinnati, OH, p. A476

GLENN, Gary
Director Information Technology, Carrus Rehabilitation Hospital, Sherman, TX, p. A636
Director Information Technology, Carrus Specialty Hospital, Sherman, TX, p. A636

GLENN, Jeannette, Vice President Human Resources, Education and Training, Mcleod Regional Medical Center, Florence, SC, p. A553

GLENN, Michael, M.D., Chief Medical Officer, Virginia Mason Medical Center, Seattle, WA, p. A677

GLENN, Mike, Chief Executive Officer, Jefferson Healthcare, Port Townsend, WA, p. A675

GLENN, Wil A, Director Communications, Larry B. Zieverink, Sr. Alcoholism Treatment Center, Raleigh, NC, p. A459

GLENNING, Robert, Executive Vice President Finance and Chief Financial Officer, The Joseph M. Sanzari Children's Hospital, NJ, p. A405

GLESSNER, Theresa, Chief Nursing Officer, Eastern Region, Newark-Wayne Community Hospital, Newark, NY, p. A438

GLICK, Jennifer, Manager Clinical Informatics, Oaklawn Psychiatric Center, Goshen, IN, p. A205

GLIDDEN, Nancy
Chief Financial Officer and Vice President Finance, Mayo Regional Hospital, Dover, ME, p. A284
Chief Financial Officer, Calais Regional Hospital, Calais, ME, p. A283

GLIDEWELL, Calvin E, Jr, Chief Executive Officer, Chris Evert Childrens Hospital, FL, p. A122

GLIHA, Frank, Vice President of Patient Care, Mary Rutan Hospital, Bellefontaine, OH, p. A472

GLIHA, Jennie, Chief Human Resource Officer, Aurelia Osborn Fox Memorial Hospital, Oneonta, NY, p. A439

GLIMCHER, Laurie H., M.D., President and Chief Executive Officer, Dana-Farber Cancer Institute, Boston, MA, p. A296

GLIMP, Richard, M.D.
Chief Medical Officer, Providence Little Company Of Mary Medical Center - Torrance, Torrance, CA, p. A92
Chief Medical Officer, Providence Little Company Of Mary Medical Center San Pedro, Los Angeles, CA, p. A69

GLINES, Grant L, Vice President Operation Finance, Mercy Medical Center, Roseburg, OR, p. A517

GLODOWSKI, Brenda, Chief Financial Officer, North Central Health Care, Wausau, WI, p. A705

GLOFF, Vicki, Chief Financial Officer, Goodall-Witcher Hospital Authority, Clifton, TX, p. A593

GLOGGNER, Peter, Chief Human Resources Officer, Jupiter Medical Center, Jupiter, FL, p. A126

GLONER, James, Senior Vice President, Girard Medical Center, PA, p. A536

GLORIA-BARRAZA, Patricia, Coordinator Human Resources, Mayhill Hospital, Denton, TX, p. A599

GLOTZBACK, Lee, Director Human Resources, Citrus Memorial Health System, Inverness, FL, p. A125

GLOVER, Cynthia, R.N., Vice President and Chief Nursing Officer, Reston Hospital Center, Reston, VA, p. A664

GLOVER, Doug, Controller, William S. Hall Psychiatric Institute, Columbia, SC, p. A551

GLOVER, Leslie, Director Operations, Mary Black Health System - Gaffney, Gaffney, SC, p. A553

GLOWA, Meghan, Director Human Resources, Sunnyview Rehabilitation Hospital, Schenectady, NY, p. A442

GLOWCZEWSKI, Jason
Chief Operating Officer, University Hospitals Conneaut Medical Center, Conneaut, OH, p. A479
Chief Operating Officer, University Hospitals Geneva Medical Center, Geneva, OH, p. A483

GLUCHOWSKI, Jeanne, Executive Director, Conifer Park, Glenville, NY, p. A427

GLUCK, Michael, M.D., Medical Director, Lifecare Hospitals Of Mechanicsburg, Mechanicsburg, PA, p. A531

GLUECK, Dane, M.D., Chief of Staff, Progress West Hospital, O'Fallon, MO, p. A365

GLYER, David
Vice President Finance, Community Memorial Hospital, CA, p. A94
Vice President Finance, Ojai Valley Community Hospital, Ojai, CA, p. A76

GLYNN, Cindy, Director Human Resources, Regional Rehabilitation Hospital, Phenix City, AL, p. A22

GLYNN, John
Chief Information Officer, Rochester General Hospital, Rochester, NY, p. A441
Executive Vice President, Chief Information Officer, Rochester Regional Health, Newark-Wayne Community Hospital, Newark, NY, p. A438
Senior Vice President and Chief Information Officer, Unity Hospital, Rochester, NY, p. A441

GLYNN, Margaret, M.D., Chief Medical Officer, North Mississippi Medical Center-Iuka, Iuka, MS, p. A347

GLYNN, Shari, Vice President Finance and Chief Financial Officer, Eaton Rapids Medical Center, Eaton Rapids, MI, p. A312

GNAGEY, Keith, Chief Executive Officer, Teton Valley Health Care, Driggs, ID, p. A169

GNAM, Gwen, R.N., MSN, Chief Nursing Officer, Henry Ford Hospital, Detroit, MI, p. A311

GNANN, Andrew, Vice President Operations, St. Vincent's East, Birmingham, AL, p. A15

GNEGY, David, M.D., Vice President of Medical Affairs, Camden Clark Medical Center, Parkersburg, WV, p. A685

GO, Rosana, M.D., Medical Staff President, Cascade Valley Hospital, Arlington, WA, p. A669

GOACHER, Brad, Vice President Administration, Alton Memorial Hospital, Alton, IL, p. A173

GOAD, Pat, Director Human Resources, Hillcrest Hospital Claremore, Claremore, OK, p. A497

GOBEL, Bret, Chief Financial Officer, Sierra Vista Hospital, Truth Or Consequences, NM, p. A420

GOBELL, James, Chief Financial Officer, Unitypoint Health - St. Lukes's Sioux City, Sioux City, IA, p. A230

GOBER, Kirby, Chief Executive Officer, Throckmorton County Memorial Hospital, Throckmorton, TX, p. A640

GOBLE, Jonathan R., FACHE, Interim President, Ingalls Memorial Hospital, Harvey, IL, p. A185

GOBLE, Mandy C., President and Chief Executive Officer, Mary Rutan Hospital, Bellefontaine, OH, p. A472

GOCHENOUR, Julia, Manager Information Systems, West River Regional Medical Center, Hettinger, ND, p. A467

GOCHNOUR, Eric, Director Human Resources, Minidoka Memorial Hospital, Rupert, ID, p. A171

GODAMUNNE, Karim, M.D., Chief Medical Officer, Wellstar North Fulton Hospital, Roswell, GA, p. A159

GODBEE, Mitchell, Chief of Staff, Capital Region Medical Center, Jefferson City, MO, p. A360

GODBOLD, Steven, Vice President Operations and Chief Operating Officer, East Tennessee Children's Hospital, Knoxville, TN, p. A572

GODDARD, Mark, M.D., Medical Director, Healthsouth Rehabilitation Hospital Of Cincinnati At Norwood, OH, p. A475

GODDARD, Nichole, Chief Operating Officer, South Region, Community Hospital South, Indianapolis, IN, p. A206

GODFREY, John, M.D., Vice President and Chief Executive Officer, Hardin Memorial Health, Elizabethtown, KY, p. A251

GODFREY, Katrina, Director Human Resources, Mercy Hospital Ada, Ada, OK, p. A495

GODFREY, Kristine, Director Human Resources, Skyridge Medical Center - Westside Campus, TN, p. A568

GODINA, Gabriel, M.D., Chief of Staff, Ogallala Community Hospital, Ogallala, NE, p. A387

GODINEZ, Roxanna M., Chief Executive Officer, Cornerstone Regional Hospital, Edinburg, TX, p. A600

GODLEY, James R, Vice President of Human Resources, Mayo Regional Hospital, Dover, ME, p. A284

GODLEY, Patrick, Chief Financial Officer, Contra Costa Regional Medical Center, Martinez, CA, p. A71

GODWIN, Herman A, M.D., Jr, Senior Vice President and Medical Director, Watauga Medical Center, Boone, NC, p. A448

GODWIN, James C, Jr, Vice President, Human Resources, Bon Secours St. Francis Medical Center, Midlothian, VA, p. A661

GODWIN, Kristi, Interim Human Resource Director, Fairfield Memorial Hospital, Winnsboro, SC, p. A558

GOEB-BURKETT, Michele, R.N., MSN, Chief Nursing Officer, Florida Hospital-Oceanside, FL, p. A121

GOEBEL, Bret, Chief Financial Officer, Guadalupe County Hospital, Santa Rosa, NM, p. A419

GOEBEL, Cecilia B, R.N., Chief Nursing Officer, Susan B. Allen Memorial Hospital, El Dorado, KS, p. A234

GOEBEL, Dennis, Chief Executive Officer, Murray County Medical Center, Slayton, MN, p. A340

GOEBEL, Donna, M.D., Chief Nursing Officer, Mitchell County Hospital, Colorado City, TX, p. A593

GOEBEL, Michael, Chief Executive Officer, Parker Adventist Hospital, Parker, CO, p. A104

GOEHRING, Jennifer, R.N., Assistant Chief Nursing Officer, Via Christi Hospital Manhattan, Inc., Manhattan, KS, p. A240

GOEL, Amitabh, M.D., Chief Medical Officer, University Hospitals Geneva Medical Center, Geneva, OH, p. A483

GOEL, Ash, Senior Vice President Information Technology & Chief Information Officer, Bronson Lakeview Hospital, Paw Paw, MI, p. A320

GOEL, Vineet, Chief Medical Officer, Carolinas Healthcare System Lincoln, Lincolnton, NC, p. A456

GOELZ, Gary, R.N., Chief Nursing Officer, Shands Lake Shore Regional Medical Center, Lake City, FL, p. A127

GOELZER, Mark L., M.D., Director Medical Affairs, Mercyhealth Hospital And Trauma Center - Janesville, Janesville, WI, p. A695

GOERINGER, Dawn Marie, Chief Clinical Care Officer, O'Connor Hospital, San Jose, CA, p. A86

GOESER, Stephen L., FACHE, President and Chief Executive Officer, Methodist Women's Hospital, NE, p. A388

GOETTSCH, Barry, FACHE, Chief Executive Officer, Compass Memorial Healthcare, Marengo, IA, p. A226

GOFF, Gary E., M.D., Medical Director, Promise Hospital Of Dallas, Dallas, TX, p. A597

GOFF, Kerry, Chief Executive Officer, Reeves Memorial Medical Center, Bernice, LA, p. A264

GOFF, Vivian, R.N., Chief Executive Officer, Landmark Hospital Of Athens, Athens, GA, p. A145

GOGGIN, Daniel
Senior Vice President and Chief Financial Officer, Chi St. Joseph Health Burleson Hospital, Caldwell, TX, p. A591
Senior Vice President and Chief Financial Officer, Chi St. Joseph Health Grimes Hospital, Navasota, TX, p. A625

GOGGIN, Kathy, Director of Finance, Devereux Advanced Behavioral Health Georgia, Kennesaw, GA, p. A155

GOINS, Rick, Chief Executive Officer, Massac Memorial Hospital, Metropolis, IL, p. A189

GOLAN, Marc
Chief Financial Officer, Franciscan Health Crown Point, Crown Point, IN, p. A202
Chief Financial Officer, Saint Margaret Mercy Healthcare Centers-North Campus, IN, p. A205
Regional Chief Financial Officer, Franciscan Health Michigan City, Michigan City, IN, p. A211

GOLANOWSKI, Marie, R.N., MS, President, Aurora St. Luke's South Shore, WI, p. A698

GOLBIN, Jason, M.D., Chief Medical Officer, St. Catherine Of Siena Medical Center, Smithtown, NY, p. A443

GOLD, Barbara, M.D., Chief Medical Officer, University Of Minnesota Masonic Children's Hospital, MN, p. A335

GOLD, Joseph, M.D., Chief Medical Officer, Mclean Hospital, Belmont, MA, p. A295

GOLD, Larry, Vice President, Information Services, Southern Virginia Regional Medical Center, Emporia, VA, p. A657

GOLDAMMER, Kyle, Chief Financial Officer, Sioux Falls Specialty Hospital, Sioux Falls, SD, p. A564

GOLDBERG, Andrew S, Associate Executive Director, Syosset Hospital, Syosset, NY, p. A443

GOLDBERG, David, M.D., Vice President Medical Affairs and Chief Medical Officer, Community Memorial Hospital, Menomonee Falls, WI, p. A697

GOLDBERG, Frederick, M.D., Vice President Medical Affairs and Chief Medical Officer, Nathan Littauer Hospital And Nursing Home, Gloversville, NY, p. A427

GOLDBERG, Gary, M.D., Chief Medical Officer, North Hawaii Community Hospital, Kamuela, HI, p. A165

GOLDBERG, Jonathan, Senior Vice President and Chief Information Officer, Arkansas Children's Hospital, Little Rock-Pulaski County, AR, p. A44

GOLDBERG, Michael, Executive Director, Zucker Hillside Hospital, NY, p. A433

GOLDBERG, Paul R, Chief Financial Officer, Jersey City Medical Center, Jersey City, NJ, p. A406

GOLDBERG, Stephanie J, MSN, R.N., Senior Vice President and Chief Nursing Officer, Hospital For Special Surgery, New York (Includes All Hospitals Located Within The Five Boroughs), NY, p. A432

GOLDEN, Joy, Chief Executive Officer, Lakeside Behavioral Health System, Memphis, TN, p. A575

GOLDEN, William, M.D., Chief Medical Officer, East Alabama Medical Center-Lanier, AL, p. A22

GOLDENSTEIN, Rachel, R.N., Chief Nursing Officer, Buchanan County Health Center, Independence, IA, p. A224

GOLDFARB, I William, Chief Medical Officer, West Penn Hospital, Pittsburgh, PA, p. A538

GOLDFARB, Timothy, Interim Chief Executive Officer, Doernbecher Children's Hospital, OR, p. A516

GOLDFRACH, Andrew, Chief Executive Officer, Uh Avon Rehabilitation Hospital, Avon, OH, p. A471

GOLDHAGEN, Michele, M.D., Chief Medical Officer, Russell Medical, Alexander City, AL, p. A13

GOLDIS, Glenn, Chief Medical Officer, Kern Medical Center, Bakersfield, CA, p. A52

GOLDMAN, Eric, Chief Executive Officer, Lawnwood Pavilion, FL, p. A123

GOLDMAN, Kris, Director Human Resources, Shriners Hospitals For Children-Salt Lake City, Salt Lake City, UT, p. A650

GOLDSMITH, Cheri L.
Director Financial Services, Parkland Health Center - Farmington Community, Farmington, MO, p. A359
Director Financial Services, Parkland Health Center-Bonne Terre, Bonne Terre, MO, p. A355

GOLDSMITH, Dana L, M.D., Vice President Medical Affairs, Pen Bay Medical Center, Rockport, ME, p. A286

GOLDSTEIN, Allan, M.D., Medical Director and Chief of Staff, Select Specialty Hospital-Birmingham, Birmingham, AL, p. A15

GOLDSTEIN, David, M.D., Chief Medical Officer, Contra Costa Regional Medical Center, Martinez, CA, p. A71

GOLDSTEIN, Gerald, M.D., Senior Vice President and Chief Medical Officer, Western Maryland Regional Medical Center, Cumberland, MD, p. A291

GOLDSTEIN, Lawrence, M.D., Chief Medical Officer, Vibra Hospital Of Mahoning Valley-Trumbull Campus, OH, p. A472

GOLDSTEIN, Lisa, Executive Vice President and Chief Operating Officer, Hospital For Special Surgery, New York (Includes All Hospitals Located Within The Five Boroughs), NY, p. A432

GOLDSTEIN, Mark L., President and Chief Executive Officer, Anna Jaques Hospital, Newburyport, MA, p. A302

GOLDSTEIN, Steven I.
President and Chief Executive Officer, Golisano Children's Hospital, NY, p. A441
President and Chief Executive Officer, Highland Hospital, Rochester, NY, p. A441

GOLDSZER, Robert, M.D., Senior Vice President and Chief Medical Officer, Miami Heart Campus At Mount Sinai Medical Center, FL, p. A131

GOLICH, Jacob, Chief Executive Officer, Mountain Vista Medical Center, Mesa, AZ, p. A31

GOLIGHTLY, Beverly, Director Information Technology, St. Vincent's East, Birmingham, AL, p. A15

GOLKE, Rynae, Director Human Resources, Jacobson Memorial Hospital Care Center, Elgin, ND, p. A465

GOLL, Cheri, MSN, R.N., Chief Nursing Executive, Advocate Sherman Hospital, Elgin, IL, p. A182

GOLLAHER, Jeffrey, Chief Executive Officer, Hendricks Community Hospital Association, Hendricks, MN, p. A332

GOLLINGER, Mary A, MS, R.N., Director of Nursing, Schwab Rehabilitation Hospital, Chicago, IL, p. A179

GOLOLOBOV, Alexey, Chief Financial Officer, Columbus Hospital Ltach, Newark, NJ, p. A408

GOLOVAN, Ronald, M.D., Vice President Medical Operations, Lutheran Hospital, Cleveland, OH, p. A477

GOMBAR, Greg A, Chief Financial Officer, Carolinas Healthcare System University, Charlotte, NC, p. A449

GOMBERG, Sandra, Chief Operating Officer, Frankford Campus, PA, p. A535

GOMBERT, Laurie H., Administrator, Coordinated Health-Bethlehem, Bethlehem, PA, p. A520

GOMES, Bob, FACHE, President and Chief Executive Officer, Canyon Vista Medical Center, Sierra Vista, AZ, p. A36

GOMES, Carol, FACHE, Chief Operating Officer, Stony Brook Southampton Hospital, NY, p. A443

GOMEZ, Carmen, Director Human Resources, Florida Medical Center - A Campus Of North Shore, FL, p. A130

GOMEZ, Denise, Assistant Vice President Information Systems, Unitypoint Health Meriter, Madison, WI, p. A696

GOMEZ, Dianna, Controller, Uva-Healthsouth Rehabilitation Hospital, Charlottesville, VA, p. A656

GOMEZ, Dolores S., R.N., Chief Operating Officer, Mills-Peninsula Medical Center, CA, p. A53

GOMEZ, Gloria, M.D., Medical Director, East Mississippi State Hospital, Meridian, MS, p. A350

GOMEZ, Jay Michael, Chief Financial Officer, Memorial Hermann Surgical Hospital Kingwood, Kingwood, TX, p. A618

GOMEZ, Jesse, Vice President Human Resources, Ut Health North Campus Tyler, Tyler, TX, p. A641

GOMEZ, Mike, Site Manager Medical Information Systems, Our Lady Of Bellefonte Hospital, Ashland, KY, p. A249

GOMEZ, Omar, M.D., Chief of Staff, Cornerstone Regional Hospital, Edinburg, TX, p. A600

GOMEZ, Richard, Assistant Vice President Information Technology Division, Hillcrest Medical Center, Tulsa, OK, p. A508

GOMEZ, Robin, R.N., MSN, Administrator, Alvarado Hospital Medical Center, San Diego, CA, p. A83

GOMEZ-LUNA, Sandra, Medical Director, Southwest Connecticut Mental Health System, Bridgeport, CT, p. A107

GOMILA, Michael, Administrator, Baton Rouge Behavioral Hospital, Baton Rouge, LA, p. A263

GOMPF, Shelly, Director Human Resources, Alomere Health, Alexandria, MN, p. A327

GONCZ, Gray, Vice President of Medical Affairs, Trinity Medical Center West, OH, p. A491

GONDER, Christie, R.N., Chief Nursing Officer, Salinas Valley Memorial Healthcare System, Salinas, CA, p. A83

GONGAWARE, Robert, Senior Vice President Finance, Indiana Regional Medical Center, Indiana, PA, p. A528

GONZALES, Amy, Director of Human Resources, Mckenzie County Healthcare System, Watford City, ND, p. A469

GONZALES, Angela, Manager Human Resources, San Mateo Medical Center, San Mateo, CA, p. A87

GONZALES, Ed
Vice President Human Resources, Marian Regional Medical Center, Santa Maria, CA, p. A89
Vice President Human Resources, St. John's Pleasant Valley Hospital, Camarillo, CA, p. A53
Vice President Human Resources, St. John's Regional Medical Center, Oxnard, CA, p. A77

GONZALES, Jan, Director Human Resources, North Valley Hospital, Tonasket, WA, p. A679

GONZALES, Mike, Chief Financial Officer, Vibra Hospital Of San Diego, San Diego, CA, p. A85

GONZALES, Mindy, Chief Human Resources Officer, Othello Community Hospital, Othello, WA, p. A674

GONZALES, Rachel Ann, Chief Executive Officer, Madison Memorial Hospital, Rexburg, ID, p. A171

GONZALEZ, Agustin, Director Finance, Hospital Pavia Arecibo, Arecibo, PR, p. A712

GONZALEZ, Alan, Chief Operating Officer, Fort Duncan Regional Medical Center, Eagle Pass, TX, p. A600

GONZALEZ, Aurelio, Chief Financial Officer, University Pavilion, FL, p. A140

GONZALEZ, David, M.D.
Medical Director, Brook Lane Health Services, Hagerstown, MD, p. A292
Chief Clinical Officer, Advanced Diagnostics Hospital, Houston, TX, p. A610

GONZALEZ, Dinah L., Chief Financial Officer, Knapp Medical Center, Weslaco, TX, p. A643

GONZALEZ, Elizabeth, CPA, Financial Director, Hospital Pavia Yauco, Yauco, PR, p. A717

GONZALEZ, Enid Y., Chief Executive Officer, Healthsouth Hospital Of Manati, Manati, PR, p. A714

GONZALEZ, Hugo, M.D., Chief Medical Officer, Sister Emmanuel Hospital, Miami, FL, p. A131

GONZALEZ, Jacqueline, Senior Vice President and Chief Nursing Officer, Nicklaus Children's Hospital, Miami, FL, p. A130

GONZALEZ, Jaime, Administrator, St. Catherine's Rehabilitation Hospital, North Miami, FL, p. A132

GONZALEZ, Jerry, Interim Chief Nursing Officer, Las Palmas Rehabilitation Hospital, TX, p. A602

GONZALEZ, Jorge F, M.D.
Chief Medical Officer, Florida Hospital Lake Placid, FL, p. A139
Vice President and Chief Nursing Officer, Florida Hospital Wauchula, Wauchula, FL, p. A143

GONZALEZ, Jorge Matta., Executive Director, University Hospital, San Juan, PR, p. A716

GONZALEZ, Laura, Interim Chief Nurse Executive, South Shore Hospital, Chicago, IL, p. A179

GONZALEZ, Pedro J., FACHE, Chief Executive Officer, Ashford Presbyterian Community Hospital, San Juan, PR, p. A715

GONZALEZ, Roberto, Executive Director Human Resources, Carepoint Health Hoboken University Medical Center, Hoboken, NJ, p. A406

GONZALEZ, Susan, Director of Clinical Services, Stanislaus Surgical Hospital, Modesto, CA, p. A73

GONZALEZ, Victoria, Chief Financial Officer, The Hospitals Of Providence Sierra Campus, El Paso, TX, p. A602

GONZALEZ-FAJARDO, Ana, Human Resources Director, Palmetto General Hospital, Hialeah, FL, p. A124

GOOCH, Mathew, Chief Executive Officer, Healthsouth Rehabilitation Hospital Of Middletown, Middletown, DE, p. A113

GOOD, Jo, Director of Nursing, Palmetto Lowcountry Behavioral Health, Charleston, SC, p. A550

GOOD, Vance A, M.D., Chief Medical Staff, Troy Community Hospital, Troy, PA, p. A542

GOODALL, David, M.D., Chief Medical Staff, Essentia Health-Deer River, Deer River, MN, p. A330

GOODBALIAN, Terry
Regional Chief Financial Officer, Henry Ford West Bloomfield Hospital, West Bloomfield, MI, p. A325
Vice President Finance and Chief Financial Officer, St. Joseph's Mercy-North, MI, p. A310
Vice President, Finance and Chief Financial Officer, Henry Ford Wyandotte Hospital, Wyandotte, MI, p. A326

GOODE, Jennifer, Director Human Resources, Russell County Hospital, Russell Springs, KY, p. A260

GOODE, Lori, Director Human Resources, Baptist Memorial Hospital-Union County, New Albany, MS, p. A351

GOODE, Richard P., Executive Vice President and Chief Financial Officer, Children's Medical Center Dallas, Dallas, TX, p. A596

GOODE, Vicky, Director Human Resources, Lifecare Hospitals Of North Carolina, Rocky Mount, NC, p. A459

GOODIN, Antonia M., Chief Executive Officer and Chief Financial Officer, Claiborne Memorial Medical Center, Homer, LA, p. A268

GOODIN, Scott, Chief Financial Officer, Chinese Hospital, San Francisco, CA, p. A85

GOODING, Lari, Chief Executive Officer, Allendale County Hospital, Fairfax, SC, p. A552

GOODLETT, Lisa
Administrator Finance and Support Services, Children's Hospital Of South Carolina At Musc, SC, p. A550

Senior Vice President and Chief Financial Officer, University Of Maryland Capital Region Health At Laurel Regional Hospital, Laurel, MD, p. A292

GOODMAN, Brenda, Chief Nursing Officer, Medical Center Of Peach County, Navicent Health, Bryon, GA, p. A149

GOODMAN, Charlene, Director Human Resources, Rush County Memorial Hospital, La Crosse, KS, p. A239

GOODMAN, Darrell, Chief Information Officer, Hi-Desert Medical Center, Joshua Tree, CA, p. A62

GOODMAN, David M, Ph.D., Chief Information Officer, Veterans Affairs Boston Healthcare System, West Roxbury, MA, p. A305

GOODMAN, Doug, Vice President Human Resources, Brandon Regional Hospital, Brandon, FL, p. A119

GOODMAN, Josie, Hospital Director, Central State Hospital, Louisville, KY, p. A256

GOODMAN, Larry J., M.D., Chief Executive Officer, Rush Children's Hospital, IL, p. A179

GOODMAN, Louis, Senior Vice President Human Resources, Monongahela Valley Hospital, Monongahela, PA, p. A532

GOODMAN, Mary Jo, Chief Operating Officer, Park Plaza Hospital, Houston, TX, p. A612

GOODMAN, Shane, Chief Nursing Officer, De Soto Regional Health System, Mansfield, LA, p. A273

GOODMAN, Steven, Chief Operating Officer, Willow Crest Hospital, Miami, OK, p. A501

GOODMAN, William H., Vice President Medical Affairs, Chief Medical Officer, Catholic Medical Center, Manchester, NH, p. A400

GOODNER, Beth, Chief Executive Officer, Trustpoint Hospital, Murfreesboro, TN, p. A576

GOODNOW, John H., Chief Executive Officer, Benefis Health Care-West Campus, MT, p. A376

GOODPASTER, Amber, Chief Financial Officer, Clark Regional Medical Center, Winchester, KY, p. A261

GOODRICH, C Harlan, Vice President and Chief Information Officer, Midmichigan Medical Center-Midland, Midland, MI, p. A319

GOODRICH, Craig, Chief Financial Officer, Virginia Mason Medical Center, Seattle, WA, p. A677

GOODROW, Darrin
Chief Information Officer, Moses Ludington Hospital, NY, p. A426
Chief Information Officer, The University Of Vermont Health Network - Alice Hyde Medical Center, Malone, NY, p. A429

GOODSPEED, Darwin, Director, Sioux Falls Veterans Affairs Health Care System, Sioux Falls, SD, p. A564

GOODSTEIN, Ruth, Controller, Healthsouth Sunrise Rehabilitation Hospital, Sunrise, FL, p. A140

GOODWIN, Jeremy, M.D., President, Medical Staff, Monroe County Hospital, Forsyth, GA, p. A153

GOODWIN, Jeronica, Senior Director Human Resources, Howard University Hospital, Washington, DC, p. A115

GOODWIN, Keith D., President and Chief Executive Officer, East Tennessee Children's Hospital, Knoxville, TN, p. A572

GOODWIN, Linda, Chief Operating Officer and Chief Nursing Executive, Mercy Medical Center - West Lakes, IA, p. A221

GOODWIN, W Jarrad, M.D., Director, University Of Miami Hospital, FL, p. A131

GOOLSBY, Elizabeth, Director, Fayetteville Veterans Affairs Medical Center, Fayetteville, NC, p. A452

GOPALAKRISHNAN, Paari, M.D., Chief Medical Officer, Kent County Memorial Hospital, Warwick, RI, p. A548

GOPALAM, Gopinath, Chief Executive Officer, Apollo Behavioral Health Hospital, Baton Rouge, LA, p. A263

GOPINATH, Anil, FACHE, M.D., Regional Chief Medical Officer, Presence Mercy Medical Center, Aurora, IL, p. A173

GORAB, Robert, M.D., Chief Medical Officer, Hoag Orthopedic Institute, Irvine, CA, p. A62

GORANSON, Ken, Chief Financial Officer, Benson Hospital, Benson, AZ, p. A28

GORBY, Cherie, Chief Operations Officer, Uchealth Memorial Hospital North, CO, p. A98

GORBY, Karen S., R.N., MSN, FACHE, President and Chief Nursing Officer, Angel Medical Center, Franklin, NC, p. A452

GORCZYCA, Julie A, R.N., Chief Nursing Officer, Genesys Regional Medical Center, Grand Blanc, MI, p. A313

GORDNER, Barbie, Director Human Resources, Acuity Hospital Of South Texas, San Antonio, TX, p. A632

GORDON, Cyndy, Chief Operating Officer, Fremont Medical Center, CA, p. A72

GORDON, Dan, Chief Financial Officer, Adventist Health Feather River, Paradise, CA, p. A77

GORDON, Kevin, M.D., Chief of Staff, Alliancehealth Durant, Durant, OK, p. A498

GORDON, Mandy, Human Resource Coordinator, Phoebe Worth Medical Center, Sylvester, GA, p. A161

GORDON, Mark, Chief Nursing Officer, Kern Valley Healthcare District, Lake Isabella, CA, p. A63

GORDON, Mark M.
Chief Executive Officer, Bon Secours Memorial Regional Medical Center, Mechanicsville, VA, p. A661
Chief Executive Officer, Bon Secours-Richmond Community Hospital, Richmond, VA, p. A664

GORDON, Nancy Gail, R.N., MSN, Chief Nursing Officer and Vice President of Nursing, Baptist Health South Florida, Homestead Hospital, Homestead, FL, p. A125

GORDON, Robert, Manager Information Systems, Halifax Regional Medical Center, Roanoke Rapids, NC, p. A459

GORDON, Steve
Chief Operating Officer, Osceola Regional Medical Center, Kissimmee, FL, p. A126
Director Human Resources, Lake City Medical Center, Lake City, FL, p. A127

GORDON, Steven R., President and Chief Executive Officer, Brattleboro Memorial Hospital, Brattleboro, VT, p. A653

GORDON, Susan, R.N., Chief Nursing Officer, Upmc Pinnacle Memorial, York, PA, p. A546

GORDON, Thomas, Chief Information Officer, Virtua Marlton, Marlton, NJ, p. A407

GORDON, Wayne
Chief Financial Officer, Memorial Hermann Rehabilitation Hospital - Katy, Katy, TX, p. A616
Chief Financial Officer, Tirr Memorial Hermann, Houston, TX, p. A614

GORE, Carol, MSN, R.N., Chief Nursing Officer, Saint Mary's Regional Medical Center, Russellville-Pope County, AR, p. A48

GORE, Tim, Chief Financial Officer, Rivendell Behavioral Health, Bowling Green, KY, p. A250

GOREAU, Judy, R.N., Director of Nursing, Eastside Psychiatric Hospital, Tallahassee, FL, p. A140

GORELICK, Marc, M.D., President and Chief Executive Officer, Children's Hospitals And Clinics Of Minnesota, MN, p. A335

GOREY, Peter, Administrative Coordinator, Rockland Children's Hospital Psychiatric Center, Orangeburg, NY, p. A439

GORLEWSKI, Todd, Senior Vice President and Chief Financial Officer, St. Barnabas Hospital, New York (Includes All Hospitals Located Within The Five Boroughs), NY, p. A437

GORMAN, Brandon, Chief Financial Officer, Bradley County Medical Center, Warren-Bradley County, AR, p. A49

GORMAN, Jodie, Director Human Resources, Salem Memorial District Hospital, Salem, MO, p. A370

GORMAN, Kathleen, MSN, R.N., Executive Vice President Patient Care Services and Chief Operating Officer, Children's National Health System, Washington, DC, p. A115

GORMLEY, Ann H, Senior Vice President Human Resources, Pinnaclehealth West Shore Hospital, PA, p. A527

GORMSEN, David, D.O., Vice President and Chief Medical Officer, Mercy Medical Center, Canton, OH, p. A473

GORN, Angela, Vice President, Norton Sound Regional Hospital, Nome, AK, p. A27

GORSUCH, Penelope Franklin, Associate Director Patient Care Services, Dayton Veterans Affairs Medical Center, Dayton, OH, p. A480

GOSA, Dallas, Interim Chief Financial Officer, Conway Regional Medical Center, Conway-Faulkner County, AR, p. A40

GOSCH, Shawn, Chief Financial Officer, Burgess Health Center, Onawa, IA, p. A227

GOSEY, J, M.D., Medical Director, Southern Surgical Hospital, Slidell, LA, p. A279

GOSHE, Nick, Chief Executive Officer, Rangely District Hospital, Rangely, CO, p. A105

GOSHIA, Rob, Chief Financial Officer, Paulding County Hospital, Paulding, OH, p. A489

GOSLEE, Belle, Chief Nursing Officer, Healthsouth Chesapeake Rehabilitation Hospital, Salisbury, MD, p. A294

GOSNEY, Brett, Chief Executive Officer, Animas Surgical Hospital, Durango, CO, p. A99

GOSS, Ella M., MSN, R.N., Chief Executive Officer, Children's Hospital At Providence, AK, p. A25

GOSS, J. Richard, M.D., Medical Director, Uw Medicine/ Harborview Medical Center, Seattle, WA, p. A677

GOSS, Norma, R.N., Chief Nursing Officer, Flaget Memorial Hospital, Bardstown, KY, p. A249

GOSS, Roger, Chief Information Officer, North Sunflower Medical Center, Ruleville, MS, p. A353

GOSSELIN, Gail
Director Human Resources, Landmark Medical Center-Woonsocket Unit, RI, p. A548
Director Human Resources, Rehabilitation Hospital Of Rhode Island, North Smithfield, RI, p. A547

GOSSENS, Kevin, Director Human Resources, Thedacare Medical Center-Waupaca, Waupaca, WI, p. A705

GOSSETT, Lisa, MSN, R.N., Chief Nursing Officer, Ohiohealth Riverside Methodist Hospital, Columbus, OH, p. A479

GOTSOULIAS, Kostas, Interim Chief Executive Officer, Aspire Hospital, Conroe, TX, p. A593

GOTTI, Sreekant, Director Information Systems, Desert Valley Hospital, Victorville, CA, p. A94

GOTTLE, L. Gill, Senior Vice President and Chief Financial Officer, Robert Wood Johnson University Hospital At Hamilton, Hamilton, NJ, p. A405

GOTTLIEB, Harold, M.D., Chief Medical Officer, Memorial Hermann Memorial City Medical Center, Houston, TX, p. A612

GOTTLIEB, Jonathan, M.D., Senior Vice President and Chief Medical Officer, University Of Maryland Hospital For Children, MD, p. A289

GOTTSCHALK, Amy, M.D., Chief Medical Officer, Verde Valley Medical Center; Vice President Quality, Northern Arizona Healthcare, Verde Valley Medical Center, Cottonwood, AZ, p. A29

GOTTSCHALL, Dan, Senior Vice President and Chief Clinical Officer, St. Vincent's Behavioral Health, CT, p. A107

GOUGEON, Michele L, Executive Vice President and Chief Operating Officer, Mclean Hospital, Belmont, MA, p. A295

GOUGH, Galal S, M.D., Chief of Staff, Coast Plaza Hospital, Norwalk, CA, p. A75

GOUGH, Michelle, MSN, RN-B, Chief Nursing Officer, Southwest Mississippi Regional Medical Center, Mccomb, MS, p. A350

GOULD, Christine, Director Human Resources, Martha's Vineyard Hospital, Oak Bluffs, MA, p. A303

GOULD, Dana L., Chief Executive Officer, Broaddus Hospital, Philippi, WV, p. A686

GOULD, Jacquelyn M, MS, R.N., Vice President Patient Care Services and Chief Nursing Officer, Wellspan Good Samaritan Hospital, Lebanon, PA, p. A529

GOULD, Robert, President and Chief Executive Officer, Western Regional Medical Center, Goodyear, AZ, p. A30

GOULD, Tamara, R.N., Vice President Clinical Services and Chief Nursing Officer, Wabash General Hospital, Mount Carmel, IL, p. A190

GOULD, William R, Vice President Human Resources, Saint Joseph Hospital, Denver, CO, p. A99

GOULET, James P, Vice President Operations, Columbus Community Hospital, Columbus, NE, p. A383

GOULSON, Dan, M.D., Chief Medical Officer, Our Lady Of Bellefonte Hospital, Ashland, KY, p. A249

GOURLEY, Paul, M.D., Chief Hospital Services, U.S. Air Force Hospital, Hampton, VA, p. A659

GOUX, L Rene', Chief Executive Officer, Avoyelles Hospital, Marksville, LA, p. A273

GOVE, Cynthia A, Chief Operating Officer, Hampstead Hospital, Hampstead, NH, p. A399

GOVERO, Chris, Director of Operations, Hshs St. Joseph's Hospital, Highland, IL, p. A185

GOVINDAIAH, Rajesh G, M.D., Chief Medical Officer, Memorial Medical Center, Springfield, IL, p. A196

GOVORCHIN, Pete, Senior Vice President Operations, Midwestern Regional Medical Center, Zion, IL, p. A198

GOWEN, Tina, System Controller, Westfield Memorial Hospital, Westfield, NY, p. A446

GOWER, Gary, Chief Information Officer, Appling Healthcare System, Baxley, GA, p. A148

GOYAL, Alok, M.D., Medical Director, Post Acute Medical Specialty Hospital Of Milwaukee, Greenfield, WI, p. A694

GOYAL, Deepak, M.D., Chief of Staff, Jacobson Memorial Hospital Care Center, Elgin, ND, p. A465

GOYKOVICH, Stephen, D.O., Chief Medical Officer, Geisinger Jersey Shore Hospital, Jersey Shore, PA, p. A528

GOYTIA-LEOS, Dina, M.D., Chief of Staff, Nix Health Care System, San Antonio, TX, p. A633

GOZA, Brian, Chief Information Officer, Hemphill County Hospital, Canadian, TX, p. A591

GRABER, Donald, M.D., Medical Director, Richmond State Hospital, Richmond, IN, p. A214

GRABOSO, Rebecca, Vice President and Chief Nurse Executive, Hackensack Meridian Health Riverview Medical Center, Red Bank, NJ, p. A411

GRACE, Jeffery, M.D., Clinical Director, Buffalo Psychiatric Center, Buffalo, NY, p. A423

GRACE, Michael A., President, Upmc Mercy, Pittsburgh, PA, p. A538

GRACE, Richard, Chief Administrative Officer, Mayo Clinic Health System In Saint James, Saint James, MN, p. A339

GRACE, Robert, Chief Financial Officer, Kendall Regional Medical Center, Miami, FL, p. A130

GRACE, Walter, Chief Executive Officer and Administrator, Baptist Memorial Hospital-Union County, New Albany, MS, p. A351

GRACIE, Michael, Chief Information Officer, Veterans Health Care System Of The Ozarks, Fayetteville-Washington County, AR, p. A42

GRADDY, Steve W
Chief Financial Officer, Freeman Hospital East, MO, p. A361

Chief Financial Officer, Freeman Neosho Hospital, Neosho, MO, p. A365

GRADNEY, Angel, Chief Executive Officer, Kindred Hospital Clear Lake, Webster, TX, p. A643

GRADY, John M, Associate Director, Veterans Affairs Hudson Valley Health Care System-Montrose Campus, NY, p. A430

GRADY, Kevin, M.D., Chief Medical Officer, Ascension St. John Hospital, Detroit, MI, p. A310

GRADY, Phillip L., Administrator, Shriners Hospitals For Children-St. Louis, Saint Louis, MO, p. A368

GRADY, Raymond, FACHE, President and Chief Executive Officer, Southlake Campus, IN, p. A204

GRAEBER, Tod
Administrator, Chi St. Alexius Health Garrison, Garrison, ND, p. A466
Administrator, Community Memorial Hospital, Turtle Lake, ND, p. A468

GRAEBNER, David
Interim President, Aurora Medical Center Grafton, Grafton, WI, p. A693
President, Aurora Medical Center In Washington County, Hartford, WI, p. A694
President, Aurora Sheboygan Memorial Medical Center, Sheboygan, WI, p. A702

GRAEBNER, Nancy Kay., President and Chief Executive Officer, St. Joseph Mercy Chelsea, Chelsea, MI, p. A309

GRAF, John, Senior Vice President, Watertown Regional Medical Center, Watertown, WI, p. A705

GRAFTON, Jennifer, Chief Financial Officer, Shands Live Oak Regional Medical Center, Live Oak, FL, p. A128

GRAGG, Connie, Director Human Resources, Saint Mary's Regional Medical Center, Russellville-Pope County, AR, p. A48

GRAH, John A., FACHE, Chief Executive Officer, Lakewood Regional Medical Center, Lakewood, CA, p. A64

GRAHAM, Bill, President, Sequoia Hospital, Redwood City, CA, p. A80

GRAHAM, Bonnie S., Director, San Francisco Va Medical Center, San Francisco, CA, p. A86

GRAHAM, Brenda, Chief Nursing Officer, Barbourville Arh Hospital, Barbourville, KY, p. A249

GRAHAM, Brooke, Human Resources Manager, Franklin Woods Community Hospital, Johnson City, TN, p. A571

GRAHAM, Christopher W, Chief Financial Officer, Community Memorial Hospital, Hamilton, NY, p. A427

GRAHAM, Connie, Public Information Officer, Mercy Health Love County, Marietta, OK, p. A501

GRAHAM, David B, M.D., Senior Vice President and Chief Information Officer, Memorial Medical Center, Springfield, IL, p. A196

GRAHAM, Gail L., Director, Knoxville Division, IA, p. A221

GRAHAM, Jeff, President and Chief Executive Officer, Adena Medical Center, Chillicothe, OH, p. A474

GRAHAM, John, M.D.
Vice President Medical Affairs, Day Kimball Hospital, Putnam, CT, p. A110
Chief Financial Officer, Jefferson Hospital, Louisville, GA, p. A156

GRAHAM, Jon, Chief Finance Officer, Vidant Roanoke-Chowan Hospital, Ahoskie, NC, p. A447

GRAHAM, Kathryn, Director Communications and Community Relations, Novato Community Hospital, Novato, CA, p. A75

GRAHAM, Larry M., FACHE, President and Chief Executive Officer, Lake Charles Memorial Hospital For Women, LA, p. A272

GRAHAM, Michelle, M.D.
Vice President Medical Affairs, Wheaton Franciscan Healthcare - Franklin, Franklin, WI, p. A693
Vice President Medical Affairs, Wheaton Franciscan Healthcare - St. Francis, Milwaukee, WI, p. A699

GRAHAM, Scott
Chief Executive Officer, North Valley Hospital, Tonasket, WA, p. A679
Chief Executive Officer, Three Rivers Hospital, Brewster, WA, p. A670

GRAHAM, Shauna, Director of Professional Services Human Resources, Marketing Foundation, Merrick Medical Center, Central City, NE, p. A382

GRAHAM, Sheri
Director Human Resources and Administrative Services, Parkland Health Center - Farmington Community, Farmington, MO, p. A359
Director Human Resources and Administrative Services, Parkland Health Center-Bonne Terre, Bonne Terre, MO, p. A359

GRAHAM, Susan, R.N., Nurse Executive, Healthsource Saginaw, Inc., Saginaw, MI, p. A322

GRAHAM, Yolanda, M.D., Medical Director, Devereux Advanced Behavioral Health Georgia, Kennesaw, GA, p. A155

GRAMER, Johanna, Director Human Resources, Mimbres Memorial Hospital, Deming, NM, p. A417

GRAMS, Shannon, Chief Executive Officer, Select Specialty Hospital-Fort Smith, Fort Smith-Sebastian County, AR, p. A42

GRAMZA, Jeanne, Director Finance, Ascension All Saints, Racine, WI, p. A701

GRANADO-VILLAR, Deise, M.D., Chief Medical Officer and Senior Vice President Medical Affairs, Nicklaus Children's Hospital, Miami, FL, p. A130

GRANATH, Brad, M.D., Chief of Staff, Humboldt General Hospital, Winnemucca, NV, p. A397

GRANATO, Jerome, M.D.
  Senior Vice President and Chief Medical Officer, Excela Frick Hospital, Mount Pleasant, PA, p. A532
  Senior Vice President and Chief Medical Officer, Excela Health Westmoreland Hospital, Greensburg, PA, p. A526

GRAND, Lawrence N, MS, R.N., Chief Operating Officer, Hunterdon Medical Center, Flemington, NJ, p. A405

GRANDIOSI, Joe, Director Information Technology, Southern Hills Hospital And Medical Center, Las Vegas, NV, p. A394

GRANER, Terry J., R.N., Chief Nursing Officer, Hutchinson Health, Hutchinson, MN, p. A333

GRANNELL, James, Chief Medical Officer, Sturgis Hospital, Sturgis, MI, p. A324

GRANT, Chad M., President and Chief Executive Officer, Mclaren Flint, Flint, MI, p. A312

GRANT, Cheryl, Director Information Systems, Coastal Carolina Hospital, Hardeeville, SC, p. A554

GRANT, Gail, Director Human Resources, Chi St. Francis Health, Breckenridge, MN, p. A328

GRANT, Mikki, Chief Information Officer, Fort Belknap Service Unit, Harlem, MT, p. A376

GRANT, Samuel, Chief Financial Officer, Stephens Memorial Hospital, Breckenridge, TX, p. A590

GRANT, Timothy M., M.D., Chief Medical Officer, Parkridge West Hospital, TN, p. A567

GRANT, Tonya, Director Human Resources, T.J. Health Columbia, Columbia, KY, p. A250

GRANT, Will, Chief Financial Officer, Anmed Health Cannon, Pickens, SC, p. A556

GRANTHAM, Charlie, Manager Information Systems, Carolinas Hospital System Marion, Mullins, SC, p. A555

GRANTHAM, James, Administrator and Chief Executive Officer, Baptist Memorial Hospital-Booneville, Booneville, MS, p. A344

GRANVILLE, Sabrina M, Senior Vice President and Chief Human Resources Officer, Lowell General Hospital, Saints Campus, MA, p. A301

GRANZOW, Steven L., Chief Executive Officer, Lincoln County Hospital, Lincoln, KS, p. A240

GRASER, David, Vice President and Chief Information Officer, Hillcrest Hospital - South, Tulsa, OK, p. A508

GRASS, Linda J., Chief Executive Officer, Northside Medical Center, OH, p. A494

GRASSER, Tierney Lynn, Senior Vice President and Chief Financial Officer, Olathe Medical Center, Olathe, KS, p. A242

GRATCH, Amie, Director Financial Services, Lifecare Hospitals Of North Texas-Plano, TX, p. A596

GRATE, Anthony, Controller, Kindred Hospital-Greensboro, Greensboro, NC, p. A453

GRATRIX, Katie E., Administrative Assistant III, Alaska Psychiatric Institute, Anchorage, AK, p. A25

GRATZ, Silvia, D.O., Chief Medical Officer, Fairmount Behavioral Health System, Philadelphia, PA, p. A534

GRAU, Leah, Director Human Resources, Tulane-Lakeside Hospital, LA, p. A276

GRAUMANN, Julie, Director, Alliancehealth Clinton, Clinton, OK, p. A497

GRAVES, Amanda, Chief Information Systems, Washington Dc Veterans Affairs Medical Center, Washington, DC, p. A116

GRAVES, Bruce, M.D., Chief of Staff, Hale Ho'Ola Hamakua, Honokaa, HI, p. A164

GRAVES, Buddy, Chief Information Officer, Southern Surgical Hospital, Slidell, LA, p. A279

GRAVES, Elsie, Chief Nursing Officer, Central Texas Medical Center, San Marcos, TX, p. A635

GRAVES, Jared, Chief Financial Officer, Byrd Regional Hospital, Leesville, LA, p. A272

GRAVES, Jennifer, R.N., MS, Chief Executive, Swedish Medical Center-Ballard, WA, p. A676

GRAVES, Jimmy, Interim Chief Executive Officer, Jefferson Davis Community Hospital, Prentiss, MS, p. A352

GRAVES, John A., Chief Executive Officer, Dimmit Regional Hospital, Carrizo Springs, TX, p. A591

GRAY, Albert, Chief Executive Officer, The Children's Center Rehabilitation Hospital, Bethany, OK, p. A496

GRAY, Amy, Chief Executive Officer, Chi St. Joseph Health Rehabilitation Hospital, An Affiliate Of Encompass Health, Bryan, TX, p. A591

GRAY, Anthony, Chief Financial Officer, Lac-Olive View-Ucla Medical Center, Los Angeles, CA, p. A68

GRAY, Bob, Chief Financial Officer, Aspire Hospital, Conroe, TX, p. A593

GRAY, Brett, Director Human Resource, Sanpete Valley Hospital, Mount Pleasant, UT, p. A648

GRAY, Carrie, Director of Nursing, Riverview Behavioral Health, Texarkana-Miller County, AR, p. A49

GRAY, Clarence, Chief Financial Officer, Tristar Horizon Medical Center, Dickson, TN, p. A569

GRAY, Cynthia, Interim Chief Financial Officer, Alliancehealth Midwest, Midwest City, OK, p. A501

GRAY, Eric, Chief Financial Officer, Healthsouth Rehabilitation Hospital Of Memphis, Memphis, TN, p. A575

GRAY, Gary, D.O., Chief Executive Officer, Natividad Medical Center, Salinas, CA, p. A83

GRAY, Janis
  Chief Information Officer, Dupont Hospital, Fort Wayne, IN, p. A203
  Chief Information Officer, Rehabilitation Hospital Of Fort Wayne, Fort Wayne, IN, p. A204

GRAY, Jason, M.D., Chief Medical Officer, Mercy Medical Center, Roseburg, OR, p. A517

GRAY, Jeremy, Chief Operating Officer, Saint Thomas Midtown Hospital, Nashville, TN, p. A577

GRAY, Judy
  Vice President Human Resources, Albany Memorial Hospital, Albany, NY, p. A421
  Vice President Human Resources, St. Peter's Hospital, Albany, NY, p. A421

GRAY, Karen D, Director Human Resources, Vibra Hospital Of Southeastern Michigan, Llc, Lincoln Park, MI, p. A318

GRAY, Kris David, Chief Medical Officer, Florida Hospital-Oceanside, FL, p. A121

GRAY, Larry W., President, Baptist Health Louisville, Louisville, KY, p. A256

GRAY, Marty, R.N., Director of Nursing, Wyandot Memorial Hospital, Upper Sandusky, OH, p. A492

GRAY, Mary, Director Human Resources, Lehigh Regional Medical Center, Lehigh Acres, FL, p. A128

GRAY, Michelle, Nurse Executive, Atrium Medical Center Of Corinth, Corinth, TX, p. A594

GRAY, Mike, Corporate Vice President Human Resources, Ut Health Behavioral Health Center, TX, p. A641

GRAY, Patricia, Director Health Information Management, Cumberland Hall Hospital, Hopkinsville, KY, p. A253

GRAY, Roshanda, Assistant Administrator, Memorial Medical Center, Port Lavaca, TX, p. A629

GRAY, Sarah, Vice President Information Services, East Alabama Medical Center-Lanier, AL, p. A22

GRAY, Stephen, Chief Executive Officer, Eden Medical Center, Castro Valley, CA, p. A54

GRAY, Tami, Chief Financial Officer, Irwin County Hospital, Ocilla, GA, p. A158

GRAY, Teresa
  Chief Nursing Officer and Assistant Vice President, Integris Canadian Valley Hospital, Yukon, OK, p. A510
  President, Integris Canadian Valley Hospital, Yukon, OK, p. A510

GRAY, Terry, Vice President Human Resources, Emanuel Medical Center, Turlock, CA, p. A92

GRAY, Thomas, M.D., Medical Director, Montana State Hospital, Warm Springs, MT, p. A379

GRAY, Tracy
  Chief Information Officer, Grady General Hospital, Cairo, GA, p. A149
  Chief Information Officer, Mitchell County Hospital, Camilla, GA, p. A149
  Senior Vice President Information Services, John D. Archbold Memorial Hospital, Thomasville, GA, p. A161

GRAYBEAL, Phillip, CPA
  Chief Financial Officer, Page Memorial Hospital, Luray, VA, p. A660
  Chief Financial Officer, Warren Memorial Hospital, Front Royal, VA, p. A658
  Vice President, Finance, Valley Health Shenandoah Memorial Hospital, Woodstock, VA, p. A668

GRAYBILL, Matthew P, Vice President, Human Resources and Chief Administrative Officer, Dayton Children's Hospital, Dayton, OH, p. A480

GRAYSON, Barbara, Vice President Human Resources, Mercy Hospital Washington, Washington, MO, p. A372

GREAKER, Mark, Chief Information Officer, New York-Presbyterian Queens, New York (Includes All Hospitals Located Within The Five Boroughs), NY, p. A435

GREAR, Esther, Director Hospital Social Work and Assistant Hospital Administrator, Windhaven Psychiatric Hospital, Prescott Valley, AZ, p. A35

GREASON, Linda, Vice President Human Resources, Whitinsville Medical Center, MA, p. A302

GREBOSKY, Jamie, M.D., Vice President of Medical Affairs, Asante Rogue Regional Medical Center, Medford, OR, p. A515

GRECCO, Jamie
  Chief Human Resource Executive, Nyc Health + Hospitals / Jacobi, New York (Includes All Hospitals Located Within The Five Boroughs), NY, p. A435
  Director Human Resources Post Acute, Henry J. Carter Specialty Hospital & Nursing Facility, NY, p. A435

GRECO, Andrew, Chief Financial Officer, Calvary Hospital, New York (Includes All Hospitals Located Within The Five Boroughs), NY, p. A431

GRECO, Margaret, Chief Human Resources, Keller Army Community Hospital, West Point, NY, p. A446

GREELEY, Donna, Director Human Resources, Spalding Rehabilitation Hospital, Aurora, CO, p. A96

GREELEY, Gerald, Chief Information Officer, Signature Healthcare Brockton Hospital, Brockton, MA, p. A298

GREEN, Amber, R.N., Chief Clinical Officer, Memorial Hospital Of Carbon County, Rawlins, WY, p. A709

GREEN, Angela, Chief Executive Officer, Kindred Hospital St. Louis-St. Anthony'S, MO, p. A368

GREEN, Barbara, Director Human Resources, O'Connor Hospital, Delhi, NY, p. A425

GREEN, Brenda, Director of Nursing, Ruby Valley Hospital, Sheridan, MT, p. A379

GREEN, Calvin, Chief Executive Officer, Acadian Medical Center, LA, p. A280

GREEN, Christi, R.N., MS, Vice President, Human Resources, Frisbie Memorial Hospital, Rochester, NH, p. A401

GREEN, Dante, Assistant Vice President Operations, New Orleans East Hospital, New Orleans, LA, p. A275

GREEN, Darryl, Director Administration, Naval Hospital Jacksonville, Jacksonville, FL, p. A125

GREEN, David, Chief Human Resources, West Palm Beach Veterans Affairs Medical Center, West Palm Beach, FL, p. A143

GREEN, David F., M.D., Chief Medical Officer, Concord Hospital, Concord, NH, p. A398

GREEN, Debra Jane, R.N., Director of Nursing, Turquoise Lodge Hospital, Albuquerque, NM, p. A416

GREEN, Elizabeth, Chief Human Resources Officer, Childen's Regional Hospital At Cooper, NJ, p. A403

GREEN, Garry Kim., FACHE, Administrator, Shriners Hospitals For Children-Shreveport, Shreveport, LA, p. A279

GREEN, Gayle, Director of Nursing, Hale Ho'Ola Hamakua, Honokaa, HI, p. A164

GREEN, Gene E., M.D., President and Chief Executive Officer, South Shore Hospital, South Weymouth, MA, p. A304

GREEN, Jack W., Administrator, Antelope Memorial Hospital, Neligh, NE, p. A387

GREEN, John
  Chief Operating Officer, Iredell Health System, Statesville, NC, p. A461
  Vice President Finance, St. Peter's Hospital, Helena, MT, p. A376

GREEN, Jon, R.N., Chief Executive Officer, Bleckley Memorial Hospital, Cochran, GA, p. A150

GREEN, Julie, Vice President Human Resources, Cheshire Medical Center, Keene, NH, p. A399

GREEN, Karen, Chief Information Officer, Brooks Rehabilitation Hospital, Jacksonville, FL, p. A125

GREEN, Kaye, FACHE, Chief Executive Officer, Roosevelt General Hospital, Portales, NM, p. A418

GREEN, Ladonna, Director Human Resources, Glen Rose Medical Center, Glen Rose, TX, p. A607

GREEN, Larry D., Jr, Chief Executive Officer, Windhaven Psychiatric Hospital, Prescott Valley, AZ, p. A35

GREEN, Marsha, Administrator and Chief Operating Officer, Essentia Health-Deer River, Deer River, MN, p. A330

GREEN, Meredith, Senior Vice President and Chief Nursing Officer, Washington Regional Medical Center, Fayetteville-Washington County, AR, p. A42

GREEN, Patrick, FACHE
  President and Chief Executive Officer, Lawrence + Memorial Hospital, New London, CT, p. A110
  President and Chief Executive Officer, Westerly Hospital, Westerly, RI, p. A548

GREEN, Paul, Chief Clinical Officer, Kindred Hospital-Aurora, Aurora, CO, p. A96

GREEN, Rhonda G., Administrator, Lallie Kemp Medical Center, Independence, LA, p. A269

GREEN, Rose Marie, Director Human Resources, Humboldt General Hospital, Winnemucca, NV, p. A397

GREEN, Steve, Comptroller, Jasper General Hospital, Bay Springs, MS, p. A343

GREEN, Susan, Senior Vice President Finance, Chief Financial Officer, Lowell General Hospital, Saints Campus, MA, p. A301

GREEN, Tracy V., Chief Financial Officer, Nyc Health + Hospitals / Metropolitan, New York (Includes All Hospitals Located Within The Five Boroughs), NY, p. A436

GREEN, Trent, President, Randall Children's Hospital, OR, p. A516

GREEN, Vince, Chief Operating Officer, St. Joseph Hospital, Fort Wayne, IN, p. A204

GREEN, Vincent, Medical Director, Ghs - Laurens County Memorial Hospital, SC, p. A550

GREENBERG, Mark, M.D.
Chief Medical Officer, Cape Coral Hospital, Cape Coral, FL, p. A119
Medical Director, Gulf Coast Medical Center, Fort Myers, FL, p. A123

GREENBLATT, James, M.D., Chief Medical Officer, Vice President Medical Clinical Services, Walden Behavioral Care, Waltham, MA, p. A305

GREENE, Arthur, M.D., Vice President Medical Affairs, Sentara Careplex Hospital, Hampton, VA, p. A659

GREENE, Beth, Chief Operating Officer, Cherokee Indian Hospital, Cherokee, NC, p. A450

GREENE, Bradley, Chief Financial Officer, Wellstar Douglas Hospital, Douglasville, GA, p. A152

GREENE, Chelsea, Manager Human Resources, Guttenberg Municipal Hospital, Guttenberg, IA, p. A223

GREENE, Cora, Senior Director, Chief Nursing Officer, Novant Health Rowan Medical Center, Salisbury, NC, p. A460

GREENE, Dustin, Chief Executive Officer, Tristar Horizon Medical Center, Dickson, TN, p. A569

GREENE, Erin, Coordinator Human Resources, Kindred Hospital-San Francisco Bay Area, San Leandro, CA, p. A87

GREENE, Kathleen, Director Human Resources, Promise Hospital Of San Diego, San Diego, CA, p. A84

GREENE, Melodi, R.N., MS, Chief Nursing Officer, Community Howard Regional Health, Kokomo, IN, p. A209

GREENE, Palmer, R.N., Chief Nursing Officer, Sierra Vista Hospital, Truth Or Consequences, NM, p. A420

GREENE, Robert, Director Information Technology, Promise Hospital Of Miss Lou, Vidalia, LA, p. A280

GREENE, Scott, Chief Information Officer, Tennova Healthcare-Clarksville, Clarksville, TN, p. A568

GREENE, Todd
Chief Executive Officer, Arizona Spine And Joint Hospital, Mesa, AZ, p. A31
Chief Executive Officer, Physicians Surgical Hospital - Panhandle Campus, TX, p. A583

GREENE, Tracie, Director Human Resources, Brigham City Community Hospital, Brigham City, UT, p. A646

GREENFIELD, Tadd, Executive Vice President and Chief Operating Officer, Regional West Medical Center, Scottsbluff, NE, p. A390

GREENLEE, Kathryn M, R.N.
Vice President, Clinical Services/CNO, Promedica Bixby Hospital, Adrian, MI, p. A307
Vice President, Clinical Services/CNO, Promedica Herrick Hospital, Tecumseh, MI, p. A324

GREENMAN, Jennifer, Vice President Chief Information Officer, H. Lee Moffitt Cancer Center And Research Institute, Tampa, FL, p. A140

GREENMAN, Sharon, Director Human Resources, Melissa Memorial Hospital, Holyoke, CO, p. A102

GREENWALD, Derek, Chief Nursing Officer, Star Valley Medical Center, Afton, WY, p. A707

GREENWOOD, Annette June, Chief Nursing Officer, Riverside Community Hospital, Riverside, CA, p. A81

GREENWOOD, Les, M.D., President, Medical Staff, Davis Hospital And Medical Center, Layton, UT, p. A647

GREENWOOD, Susan, R.N., Vice President and Chief Nursing Officer, St. Bernards Medical Center, Jonesboro-Craighead County, AR, p. A44

GREER, Troy, Chief Executive Officer, Heart Hospital Of New Mexico, NM, p. A415

GREGERSON, Scott, President and Chief Executive Officer, Valley Memorial, CA, p. A78

GREGG, Richard, M.D., Medical Director, Lifecare Hospital Of Dayton, Miamisburg, OH, p. A486

GREGG, Shawna, Director Human Resources, Porterville Developmental Center, Porterville, CA, p. A79

GREGG, Sherry, Chief Information Technology Officer, Beckley Veterans Affairs Medical Center, Beckley, WV, p. A681

GREGG, Tom, Vice President Human Resources, Chi St. Alexius Health, Bismarck, ND, p. A464

GREGG, Travis, Director Support Services, Kearney Regional Medical Center, Kearney, NE, p. A385

GREGGAIN, Don, M.D., Physician Network Director, Tri-State Memorial Hospital, Clarkston, WA, p. A670

GREGONIS, Michael, Comptroller, Naval Hospital Jacksonville, Jacksonville, FL, p. A125

GREGOR, Brian, Manager Information Technology Operations, Glendale Memorial Hospital And Health Center, Glendale, CA, p. A60

GREGORIAN, Myra, Vice President and Chief Human Resources Officer, Children's Hospital Los Angeles, Los Angeles, CA, p. A66

GREGORICH, Miki, Director Human Resources, Pioneer Medical Center, Big Timber, MT, p. A373

GREGORY, Adina
Chief Nursing Officer, University Of Kansas Health System Great Bend Campus, Great Bend, KS, p. A236
Chief Operating Officer, University Of Kansas Health System Great Bend Campus, Great Bend, KS, p. A236

GREGORY, Audrey, R.N., MSN, Chief Executive Officer, Saint Francis Hospital, Memphis, TN, p. A576

GREGORY, Ben, Chief Executive Officer, Walter B. Jones Alcohol And Drug Abuse Treatment Center, Greenville, NC, p. A454

GREGORY, Beth, Interim Chief Nursing Officer, Astria Regional Medical Center, Yakima, WA, p. A680

GREGORY, Jan, Chief of Human Resources, Crittenden County Hospital, Marion, KY, p. A257

GREGORY, Jay, M.D., Chief Medical Officer, Eastar Health System, East Campus, OK, p. A502

GREGORY, Jim, Controller, Methodist Hospital Of Chicago, Chicago, IL, p. A178

GREGORY, Jody S, R.N., Chief Nursing Officer, Encompass Health Rehabilitation Hospital Of Wichita Falls, Wichita Falls, TX, p. A644

GREGORY, Luke, Chief Executive Officer, Monroe Carell Jr. Children's Hospital At Vanderbilt, TN, p. A578

GREGORY, Phyllis, Registered Health Information Administrator, Southern Inyo Healthcare District, Lone Pine, CA, p. A65

GREGORY, Sean
Chief Executive, Columbia Network, Vancouver Memorial Campus, WA, p. A680
Chief Executive, Vancouver Memorial Campus, WA, p. A680

GREGORY, Shawn, Chief Financial Officer, St. Petersburg General Hospital, Saint Petersburg, FL, p. A138

GREGORY, Trip, Senior Vice President Human Resources, Palmetto Health Baptist, Columbia, SC, p. A551

GREGOS, Ruth, Director Finance, Shriners Hospitals For Children-Tampa, Tampa, FL, p. A141

GREGSON, Mark, Interim Chief Executive Officer, Lourdes Counseling Center, Richland, WA, p. A676

GREIMAN, Alan W., Chief Executive Officer and President, Royal Oaks Hospital, Windsor, MO, p. A372

GREINER, Walter, Chief Financial Officer, Atlanticare Regional Medical Center-Mainland Division, NJ, p. A402

GREINER, William, M.D., Chief of Staff, F. W. Huston Medical Center, Winchester, KS, p. A248

GRENALDO, Paul, Executive Vice President and Chief Operating Officer, Doctors Community Hospital, Lanham, MD, p. A292

GRENDON, M Todd, M.D., President Medical Staff, Presence Saint Joseph Hospital, Chicago, IL, p. A178

GRENIER, Raymond, Chief Financial Officer, Memorial Medical Center, Las Cruces, NM, p. A418

GRENNAN, M. Joseph, M.D., Jr, Senior Vice President and Chief Medical Officer, Reading Hospital, West Reading, PA, p. A544

GRESHAM, Paula, Vice President, Hospital Administrator, Willowbrooke At Tanner, GA, p. A162

GRESSLE, Charles, Chief Executive Officer, Medical City Frisco, TX, p. A628

GREW, Kate, MSN, R.N., Vice President/Chief Nurse Executive, Carolinas Healthcare System Northeast, Concord, NC, p. A450

GREW, Terry, Chief Business Office, Hampton Veterans Affairs Medical Center, Hampton, VA, p. A659

GREY, Michael, M.D., Interim Chief Medical Officer, Saint Francis Hospital And Medical Center, Hartford, CT, p. A108

GREY, Mitzi, Chief Operating Officer, Bath Community Hospital, Hot Springs, VA, p. A660

GRIBBIN, John, FACHE, President and Chief Executive Officer, Centrastate Healthcare System, Freehold, NJ, p. A405

GRICE, William N., Executive Director, Kaiser Foundation Mental Health Center, Hayward, CA, p. A67

GRICUS, Peggy, R.N., Vice President, Patient Care Services and Chief Nursing Officer, Silver Cross Hospital, New Lenox, IL, p. A191

GRIDLEY, Mark, FACHE, President and Chief Executive Officer, Fhn Memorial Hospital, Freeport, IL, p. A183

GRIEP, John, M.D., Chief Medical Director, St. Catherine Hospital, East Chicago, IN, p. A202

GRIESHEIM, Glen, Chief Executive Officer, Select Specialty Hospital-Des Moines, Des Moines, IA, p. A221

GRIEST, Mary, Vice President Finance and Chief Financial Officer, University Hospitals Samaritan Medical Center, Ashland, OH, p. A470

GRIFFES, Carol, Administrator, Duane L. Waters Hospital, Jackson, MI, p. A316

GRIFFIN, Amy, Vice President Patient Care Services, John D. Archbold Memorial Hospital, Thomasville, GA, p. A161

GRIFFIN, Barbara J, MSN, R.N., Chief Nursing Officer, Rapides Regional Medical Center, Alexandria, LA, p. A262

GRIFFIN, Betty, Interim Chief Nursing Officer, Chester Regional Medical Center, Chester, SC, p. A550

GRIFFIN, Brad, Chief Executive Officer, Gulf Coast Regional Medical Center, Panama City, FL, p. A135

GRIFFIN, Brian, Director Information Services, Springhill Medical Center, Springhill, LA, p. A279

GRIFFIN, Charles, Director of Nursing, Clay County Hospital, Ashland, AL, p. A13

GRIFFIN, Christopher B., Chief Executive Officer, D. W. Mcmillan Memorial Hospital, Brewton, AL, p. A15

GRIFFIN, Cindy
Chief Nursing Officer, Liberty Dayton Regional Medical Center, Liberty, TX, p. A619
Director Human Resources, Medical Center Barbour, Eufaula, AL, p. A17

GRIFFIN, Dean A., Chief Executive Officer, Lawrence Medical Center, Moulton, AL, p. A21

GRIFFIN, Douglas, M.D., Vice President Medical Officer, Sanford South University, ND, p. A466

GRIFFIN, Holly, R.N., Chief Nursing Officer, Lady Of The Sea General Hospital, Cut Off, LA, p. A266

GRIFFIN, James, Manager Information Systems, Martin General Hospital, Williamston, NC, p. A462

GRIFFIN, Jeannine, M.D., Chief of Staff, Memorial Medical Center, Port Lavaca, TX, p. A629

GRIFFIN, Jeff, Assistant Vice President Finance, Carolinas Healthcare System Anson, Wadesboro, NC, p. A461

GRIFFIN, Joe, Controller, Encompass Health Rehabilitation Hospital Of Round Rock, Round Rock, TX, p. A631

GRIFFIN, Kathryn, Chief Nurse Executive, Terrell State Hospital, Terrell, TX, p. A639

GRIFFIN, Margaret Elizabeth., Chief Executive Officer, Honorhealth John C. Lincoln Medical Center, Phoenix, AZ, p. A33

GRIFFIN, Matthew, M.D., Chief Medical Officer, St. Mary Mercy Hospital, Livonia, MI, p. A318

GRIFFIN, Paulette, Director Human Resources, Dmc - Sinai-Grace Hospital, Detroit, MI, p. A311

GRIFFIN, Philip, Director of Operations, Rochester Psychiatric Center, Rochester, NY, p. A441

GRIFFIN-JONES, Christie, R.N., Chief Nursing Officer, Encompass Health Rehabilitation Hospital Of Humble, Humble, TX, p. A614

GRIFFIN-MAHON, Selena, Assistant Vice President Human Resources, Highbridge Woodycrest Center, NY, p. A431

GRIFFIS, Daniel, M.D., Chief Medical Officer, Syringa Hospital And Clinics, Grangeville, ID, p. A169

GRIFFITH, Barbara, M.D.
Chief Medical Officer, Duke Regional Hospital, Durham, NC, p. A451
Vice President Human Resources, St. Anthony's Rehabilitation Hospital, Lauderdale Lakes, FL, p. A128

GRIFFITH, David, M.D., Medical Director, Texas Center For Infectious Disease, San Antonio, TX, p. A634

GRIFFITH, H. Wes, Chief Financial Officer, Skyridge Medical Center - Westside Campus, TN, p. A568

GRIFFITH, James D
Chief Operating Officer, Higgins General Hospital, Bremen, GA, p. A148
Chief Operating Officer, Tanner Medical Center-Carrollton, Carrollton, GA, p. A149

GRIFFITH, Jeanne, Chief Nursing Officer, Coryell Memorial Hospital, Gatesville, TX, p. A607

GRIFFITH, John H., Ph.D., President and Chief Executive Officer, Kedren Community Mental Health Center, Los Angeles, CA, p. A68

GRIFFITH, Joshua, Manager Human Resources, Presbyterian Espanola Hospital, Espanola, NM, p. A417

GRIFFITH, Leah, Chief Executive Officer, Big Sandy Medical Center, Big Sandy, MT, p. A373

GRIFFITH, Maria, Director Human Resources, Signature Psychiatric Hospital, Kansas City, MO, p. A362

GRIFFITH, Patti, R.N., MS, Chief Nursing Officer, Methodist Hospital For Surgery, Addison, TX, p. A582

GRIFFITHS, Mark, Director Management Information Systems, Incline Village Community Hospital, Incline Village, NV, p. A393

GRIGG, Dan, Chief Executive Officer, Harney District Hospital, Burns, OR, p. A511

GRIGG, William E., Senior Vice President and Chief Financial Officer, Methodist Hospital Of Southern California, Arcadia, CA, p. A51

GRIGGS, Shannon, Interim Chief Executive Officer, Research Psychiatric Center, MO, p. A361

GRIGGS, Stacie, MIS Analyst, North Mississippi Medical Center-West Point, West Point, MS, p. A354

GRIGSBY, Jan, Vice President and Chief Financial Officer, Springhill Memorial Hospital, Mobile, AL, p. A20

GRIGSON, John A, Vice President and Chief Financial Officer, Covenant Medical Center-Lakeside, TX, p. A621

GRILL, Laura D, R.N., Executive Vice President and Administrator, East Alabama Medical Center-Lanier, AL, p. A22

GRILL, Laura D., Chief Executive Officer, East Alabama Medical Center-Lanier, AL, p. A22

GRILLO, Jorge C, Chief Information Officer, Canton-Potsdam Hospital, Potsdam, NY, p. A440

GRILLS, Kathy, Director Human Resources, Healthsouth Harmarville Rehabilitation Hospital, Pittsburgh, PA, p. A537

GRIM, Andrew, Chief Financial Officer, San Gabriel Valley Medical Center, San Gabriel, CA, p. A86

GRIMES, Paula, R.N., MSN, Chief Nursing Officer, Nea Baptist Memorial Hospital, Jonesboro-Craighead County, AR, p. A44

GRIMES, Teresa G., Chief Executive Officer, Washington County Hospital, Chatom, AL, p. A16

GRIMES, Walter, Director Information Technology, Christus Good Shepherd Medical Center, TX, p. A622

GRIMLEY, Karen A, Chief Nursing Executive, Mattel Children's Hospital, CA, p. A69

GRIMM, Debra, DPN, MS, RN, Vice President and Chief Nursing Officer, Long Island Community Hospital, Patchogue, NY, p. A440

GRIMM, Tamara, R.N., Chief Clinical Officer and Chief Nursing Officer, Cornerstone Hospital Of Bossier City, Bossier City, LA, p. A265

GRIMM, William, Chief Information Officer, Henry County Hospital, Napoleon, OH, p. A487

GRIMMER, Michael, Chief Operating Officer, Athol Hospital, Athol, MA, p. A295

GRIMSHAW, Bruce P., FACHE, Chief Executive Officer, Southern California Hospital At Van Nuys, CA, p. A70

GRIMSHAW, Matthew, Market Chief Executive Officer, Trinity Medical Center West, OH, p. A491

GRIMSLEY, Denise, R.N., Vice President and Administrator, Florida Hospital Wauchula, Wauchula, FL, p. A143

GRINER, Alisa R, Director, Human Resources, Memorial Children's Hospital, GA, p. A160

GRINER, Ginny, Director Human Resources, George E. Weems Memorial Hospital, Apalachicola, FL, p. A117

GRIPPI, Michael, M.D., Chief Medical Officer, Good Shepherd Penn Partners Specialty Hospital At Rittenhouse, Philadelphia, PA, p. A534

GRISH, John, Chief Financial Officer, Johnson Memorial Medical Center, Stafford Springs, CT, p. A111

GRISHOW, Cathy, Director Human Resources, Ellett Memorial Hospital, Appleton City, MO, p. A355

GRISIER, Douglas, D.O., Medical Director, Healthsouth Rehabilitation Hospital Of Erie, Erie, PA, p. A525

GRISNAK, Karen, R.N., Chief Operating Officer and Assistant Administrator Quality Services, Kaiser Permanente Vallejo Medical Center, Vallejo, CA, p. A93

GRISPINO, Frank, Vice President Operations, Ssm Health St. Francis Hospital - Maryville, Maryville, MO, p. A364

GRISSLER, Brian G., President and Chief Executive Officer, Stamford Hospital, Stamford, CT, p. A111

GRISSOM, Robyn, Director of Human Resources, Osf Healthcare Saint Clare's Hospital, IL, p. A173

GRISSOM, Tina, Chief Information Technology Officer, Arkansas State Hospital, Little Rock-Pulaski County, AR, p. A44

GROCE, Vicky, Chief Nursing Officer, Lincoln County Health System, Fayetteville, TN, p. A569

GROCHALA, Eugene
Vice President Information Systems, Capital Health Medical Center-Hopewell, Pennington, NJ, p. A410
Vice President Information Systems, Capital Health Regional Medical Center, Trenton, NJ, p. A413

GROCHOLSKI, James F., FACHE, Chief Executive Officer, Wesley Rehabilitation Hospital, Wichita, KS, p. A248

GROENIG, Matt, Vice President Finance, St. Luke's Mccall, Mccall, ID, p. A170

GROEPER, William E, Vice President Finance, Beloit Health System, Beloit, WI, p. A690

GROEPPER, Ronald
Senior Vice President and Area Manager, Kaiser Permanente San Francisco Medical Center, San Francisco, CA, p. A85

Senior Vice President and Area Manager, Kaiser Permanente South San Francisco, South San Francisco, CA, p. A90

GRONDIN, Tom, Chief Operating Officer, Memorial Hospital Of Tampa, Tampa, FL, p. A141

GRONERT, Thomas, Chief Information Officer, University Of Maryland St. Joseph Medical Center, Towson, MD, p. A294

GRONEWOLD, Russell, Chief Financial Officer, Bryan Medical Center-West, NE, p. A385

GRONOW, Thomas, Chief Operating Officer, University Of Colorado Hospital, Aurora, CO, p. A96

GROOM, Scott C, Senior Vice President and Chief Information Officer, Huntington Hospital, Huntington, NY, p. A428

GROOMS, Kim, Administrator, King's Daughters Medical Center Ohio, Portsmouth, OH, p. A489

GROOMS, Richard Walter, Jr, Chief Human Resources Officer, Anmed Health Women's And Children's Hospital, SC, p. A549

GROS, Albert, M.D., Chief Medical Officer, St. David's South Austin Medical Center, Austin, TX, p. A587

GROS, Mark, Director Human Resources, United Medical Rehabilitation Hospital - Gonzales, LA, p. A268

GROSECLOSE, Cathy, Vice President Patient Care Services, Grady Memorial Hospital, Chickasha, OK, p. A497

GROSETH, Bradley D., Chief Administrative Officer, Marshfield Medical Center - Rice Lake, Rice Lake, WI, p. A702

GROSHANS, Adam, Chief Operating Officer, Springfield Regional Medical Center, Springfield, OH, p. A490

GROSKREUTZ, Kevin
Chief Information Officer, Hshs Sacred Heart Hospital, Eau Claire, WI, p. A692
Division Chief Information Officer, Ancillary Systems, Hshs St. Joseph's Hospital, Chippewa Falls, WI, p. A691

GROSS, Barry L, M.D., Executive Vice President and Chief Medical Officer, Riverside Behavioral Health Center, VA, p. A662

GROSS, Cathy, Director Health Information Management Systems, Wrangell Medical Center, Wrangell, AK, p. A27

GROSS, Cindy, Director of Finance, Barnes-Jewish St. Peters Hospital, Saint Peters, MO, p. A370

GROSS, Denton, Director Information Services, Larue D. Carter Memorial Hospital, Indianapolis, IN, p. A207

GROSS, Kevin J., FACHE, Chief Executive Officer, Hillcrest Medical Center, Tulsa, OK, p. A508

GROSS, Kristin, Director Information Technology Center, Avera Children's Hospital, SD, p. A563

GROSS, Len, Chief Human Resources Officer, Sheridan Memorial Hospital, Sheridan, WY, p. A709

GROSS, Mark
Executive Vice President and Chief Financial Officer, Bronson South Haven Hospital, South Haven, MI, p. A323
Senior Business Director Finance, Mercy Health, Lakeshore Campus, Shelby, MI, p. A323
Vice President Finance and Chief Financial Officer, North Ottawa Community Hospital, Grand Haven, MI, p. A313

GROSS, Matthew, Chief Executive Officer, Fisher-Titus Medical Center, Norwalk, OH, p. A488

GROSS, Paul, Human Services and Finance Officer, Larry B. Zieverink, Sr. Alcoholism Treatment Center, Raleigh, NC, p. A459

GROSS, Peter A, M.D., Senior Vice President and Chief Medical Officer, The Joseph M. Sanzari Children's Hospital, NJ, p. A405

GROSS, Randy, Chief Operating Officer, Kendall Regional Medical Center, Miami, FL, p. A130

GROSS, Tina, MSN, R.N., Chief Nursing Officer, Sparrow Specialty Hospital, Lansing, MI, p. A317

GROSSER, Joy, Chief Information Officer, University Of Washington Medical Center, Seattle, WA, p. A677

GROSSMAN, Hannah, M.D., Chief Medical Officer, Thousand Oaks Surgical Hospital, CA, p. A91

GROSSMAN, Martin, Chief of Staff, Aventura Hospital And Medical Center, Aventura, FL, p. A117

GROSSMAN, Robert I., M.D., Chief Executive Officer, Rusk Institute At Nyu-Hjd, NY, p. A436

GROSSO, Michael, M.D., Senior Vice President Medical Affairs, Huntington Hospital, Huntington, NY, p. A428

GROTELUSCHEN, Ronald J., Chief Financial Officer, Coastal Carolina Hospital, Hardeeville, SC, p. A554

GROTH, McGarrett, Chief of Staff, Atchison Hospital, Atchison, KS, p. A232

GROVE, Gene, M.D., Chief of Staff, Elkhart General Hospital, Elkhart, IN, p. A202

GROVE, Julia, Chief Nursing Officer, Jackson Purchase Medical Center, Mayfield, KY, p. A257

GROVER, James, Manager Data Processing, Atascadero State Hospital, Atascadero, CA, p. A51

GROVES, Ned, Executive Vice President and Administrator, Memorial Sloan-Kettering Cancer Center, New York (Includes All Hospitals Located Within The Five Boroughs), NY, p. A433

GROVES, Tandy, Coordinator Human Resources, Bailey Medical Center, Owasso, OK, p. A505

GROW, Heidi, Director Human Resources, Aurora Sinai Medical Center, Milwaukee, WI, p. A698

GROW, Julie E, Chief Financial Officer, Hocking Valley Community Hospital, Logan, OH, p. A485

GROWSE, Michael, M.D., Clinical Director, Federal Medical Center, Lexington, KY, p. A255

GRUBB, Michael
Chief Financial Officer, Bridgepoint Hospital Capitol Hill, Washington, DC, p. A115
Chief Financial Officer, Bridgepoint Hospital National Harbor, Washington, DC, p. A115

GRUBB, Nora, Chief Financial Officer, Big Sandy Medical Center, Big Sandy, MT, p. A373

GRUBER, Scott, M.D., Chief of Staff, John D. Dingell Veterans Affairs Medical Center, Detroit, MI, p. A311

GRUEBER, Cynthia M, Senior Vice President and Chief Operating Officer, Doernbecher Children's Hospital, OR, p. A516

GRUEN, Jeremy, Director Information Systems, Pike County Memorial Hospital, Louisiana, MO, p. A363

GRUHONJIC, Osman, Chief Financial Officer, Lehigh Regional Medical Center, Lehigh Acres, FL, p. A128

GRUN, Joseph, Chief Information Officer, New York State Psychiatric Institute, New York (Includes All Hospitals Located Within The Five Boroughs), NY, p. A434

GRUNDIG, Kevin, Chief Human Resource Officer, Veterans Affairs New York Harbor Healthcare System - Manhattan Campus, NY, p. A437

GRUNHOVD, April, Chief Nursing Officer, Riverview Health, Crookston, MN, p. A330

GRUNWALD, Pat, MSN, Chief Nursing Officer, Unitypoint Health Meriter, Madison, WI, p. A696

GRUVER, Laquita, Fiscal Officer, Grand Junction Veterans Health Care System, Grand Junction, CO, p. A101

GRUZENSKY, Denton, Director Human Resources, Adventist Health Feather River, Paradise, CA, p. A77

GRZYBOWSKI, John, M.D., Medical Director, Mayo Clinic Health System - Albert Lea And Austin, MN, p. A327

GUACCIO, Anthony, President and Chief Executive Officer, Swedish Covenant Hospital, Chicago, IL, p. A180

GUADAGNOLI, Donald, M.D., Chief Medical Officer, Cape Cod Hospital, Hyannis, MA, p. A300

GUAJARDO, Carlos, Chief Financial Officer, South Texas Behavioral Health Center, TX, p. A601

GUAJARDO, Michael, Director Finance, Christus Spohn Hospital Alice, Alice, TX, p. A582

GUARINO, Celia, R.N., MSN, Vice President and Chief Nursing Officer, Holy Cross Hospital, Silver Spring, MD, p. A294

GUARINO, Rick, M.D., Vice President Medical Affairs, Wilson Medical Center, Wilson, NC, p. A462

GUARNESCHELLI, Philip
Interim Chief Executive Officer, Pinnaclehealth West Shore Hospital, PA, p. A527
Senior Vice President and Chief Operating Officer, Pinnaclehealth West Shore Hospital, PA, p. A527

GUARNI, Andrew, Chief Financial Officer, Hoag Hospital Irvine, CA, p. A75

GUARNIERI, Candace
Chief Financial Officer, Phoebe Worth Medical Center, Sylvester, GA, p. A161
Chief Financial Officer, Southwest Georgia Regional Medical Center, Cuthbert, GA, p. A151

GUARRACINO, Joseph, Senior Vice President and Chief Financial Officer, White Plains Hospital Center, White Plains, NY, p. A446

GUARRERA, Frank, Executive Vice President and Chief Financial Officer, Motion Picture And Television Fund Hospital And Residential Services, Los Angeles, CA, p. A68

GUBERMAN, Wayne, Director Finance, Matheny Medical And Educational Center, Peapack, NJ, p. A409

GUDAHL, Shanna, Manager Human Resources, United Hospital District, Blue Earth, MN, p. A328

GUEHLSTORF, Daniel, M.D., Chief of Staff, Midwest Orthopedic Specialty Hospital, Franklin, WI, p. A692

GUELKER, Rhonda, Senior Director Finance, Rolling Plains Memorial Hospital, Sweetwater, TX, p. A638

GUERIN, Stephanie, Chief Nursing Officer, Encompass Health Rehabilitation Hospital Of Round Rock, Round Rock, TX, p. A631

GUERMONPREZ, D. Scott., FACHE, Director, Northport Veterans Affairs Medical Center, Northport, NY, p. A438

GUERRERO, Bonnie, Director Human Resources, Valley View Medical Center, Fort Mohave, AZ, p. A29

GUERRERO, Kerrie, R.N., MSN, Vice President and Chief Nursing Officer, Houston Methodist The Woodlands Hospital, The Woodlands, TX, p. A640

GUERRERO, Marisa, Director Human Resources, Laredo Specialty Hospital, Laredo, TX, p. A619

GUERRIERO, John A., Chief of Staff, Berwick Hospital Center, Berwick, PA, p. A520

GUERRIERO, Marianne, Nurse Executive, Christian Health Care Center, Wyckoff, NJ, p. A414

GUESMAN, Kim, R.N., Chief Nursing Officer, Beaumont Hospital - Farmington Hills, Farmington Hills, MI, p. A312

GUEST, William, M.D., Senior Vice President and Chief Medical Officer, Tift Regional Medical Center, Tifton, GA, p. A162

GUEVARA, Al, Jr, FACHE, President, Chi St. Luke's Health Brazosport, Lake Jackson, TX, p. A618

GUFFEY, Jay, Chief Executive Officer, Mercy Rehabilition Hospital Springfield, Springfield, MO, p. A370

GUGEL, Paul, Manager Information Technology, Marlette Regional Hospital, Marlette, MI, p. A318

GUGLIELMI, Diane, Vice President, Human Resources, Berger Health System, Circleville, OH, p. A476

GUGLIELMO, Elaine, Vice President Human Resources and Organizational Development, Stamford Hospital, Stamford, CT, p. A111

GUIDERA, Kenneth, M.D., Chief of Staff, Shriners Hospitals For Children-Twin Cities, Minneapolis, MN, p. A335

GUIDO-ALLEN, Debra, Vice President and Chief Nursing Officer, Beaumont Hospital - Troy, Troy, MI, p. A325

GUIDRY, Charles W, Chief Operating Officer, Abbeville General Hospital, Abbeville, LA, p. A262

GUIDRY, Linda, Human Resources Generalist, Abrom Kaplan Memorial Hospital, Kaplan, LA, p. A270

GUIDRY, Lloyd, Chief Operating Officer, Lady Of The Sea General Hospital, Cut Off, LA, p. A266

GUIDRY, Ruth, Chief Nursing Officer, Lafayette Surgical Specialty Hospital, Lafayette, LA, p. A271

GUIDRY, Stephanie, Chief Executive Officer, Franklin Foundation Hospital, Franklin, LA, p. A267

GUIDRY, Trisha, Administrator, Baton Rouge Rehabilitation Hospital, Baton Rouge, LA, p. A263

GUIGNIER, Liz, Vice President Human Resources, Eisenhower Medical Center, Rancho Mirage, CA, p. A79

GUILD, Anthony, Chief Executive Officer, Rolling Hills Hospital, Ada, OK, p. A495

GUILFOIL, Thomas, Director Human Resources, Baystate Wing Hospital, Palmer, MA, p. A303

GUILLORY, Larry, Chief Human Resources Officer, Baylor Emergency Medical Centers - Keller, TX, p. A585

GUILLORY, Pamela
Chief Nursing Officer, Methodist Hospital South, Jourdanton, TX, p. A616
Interim Chief Executive Officer, Methodist Hospital South, Jourdanton, TX, p. A616

GUIMARAES, Antonio, M.D., Clinical Director, U.S. Public Health Service Indian Hospital, Cass Lake, MN, p. A329

GUIMENTO, Robert, President, Newyork-Presbyterian Brooklyn Methodist Hospital, New York (Includes All Hospitals Located Within The Five Boroughs), NY, p. A435

GUINA, Michelle, Manager Human Resources, Sutter Surgical Hospital - North Valley, Yuba City, CA, p. A95

GUINANE, Gerard, Vice President Human Resources, Swedishamerican - A Division Of Uw Health, Rockford, IL, p. A195

GUIRL, Nadine T, Senior Vice President Human Resources, Waukesha Memorial Hospital, Waukesha, WI, p. A705

GUISE, Linda, Senior Human Resource Consultant, Indiana University Health Jay Hospital, Portland, IN, p. A213

GULARTE, Steven, Chief Executive Officer, Bayside Community Hospital, Anahuac, TX, p. A583

GULL, Joann Bernadette, Chief Nursing Officer, Nyc Health + Hospitals / Elmhurst, New York (Includes All Hospitals Located Within The Five Boroughs), NY, p. A435

GULRICH, Erica, Chief Executive Officer, Northwest Medical Center, Margate, FL, p. A129

GUM, Jessica, Controller, Healthsouth Western Hills Regional Rehabilitation Hospital, Parkersburg, WV, p. A686

GUMATO, Sixta, M.D., Chief Medical Officer, Crane Memorial Hospital, Crane, TX, p. A595

GUMBEL, Wendy, Director of Human Resources, Healthsouth Deaconess Rehabilitation Hospital, Evansville, IN, p. A203

GUMBS, Milton A, M.D., Vice President and Medical Director, Highbridge Woodycrest Center, NY, p. A431

GUMMADI, Subhaker, M.D., Chief Medical Staff, Promise Hospital Baton Rouge - Main Campus, Baton Rouge, LA, p. A264

GUMP, Linda A., Chief Clinical Services Officer, Aurora Medical Center Kenosha, Kenosha, WI, p. A695

GUNABALAN, Ryan, Chief Executive Officer, Behavioral Center Of Michigan, Warren, MI, p. A325

GUNDLAPALLI, Madhu, M.D., Clinical Director, Utah State Hospital, Provo, UT, p. A649

GUNDT, Kristin, Chief Nursing Officer, Community Hospital, Grand Junction, CO, p. A101

GUNKEL, Jeff, Chief Information Officer, Jamestown Regional Medical Center, Jamestown, ND, p. A467

GUNN, Deborah, Chief Information Officer, W. G. (Bill) Heffner Veterans Affairs Medical Center, Salisbury, NC, p. A460

GUNN, Terry, FACHE, Chief Executive Officer, Kershawhealth, Camden, SC, p. A549

GUNNELL, Nancy
Chief Human Resource Officer, West Suburban Medical Center, Oak Park, IL, p. A192
Chief Human Resource Officer, Westlake Hospital, Melrose Park, IL, p. A189

GUNNERSEN, Nils, Administrator, Bertrand Chaffee Hospital, Springville, NY, p. A443

GUNTLOW, Ann Marie, Chief Nursing Officer, Ellenville Regional Hospital, Ellenville, NY, p. A426

GUNUKULA, Srinivas, M.D., Chief of Staff, Dallas Regional Medical Center, Mesquite, TX, p. A623

GUOYAVATIN, Kora
Chief Financial Officer, Garden Grove Hospital And Medical Center, Garden Grove, CA, p. A60
Chief Financial Officer, West Anaheim Medical Center, Anaheim, CA, p. A50

GUPTA, Anil, M.D., Chief of Staff, Kindred Hospital-Baldwin Park, Baldwin Park, CA, p. A52

GUPTA, Arun, M.D., Vice President Medical Affairs, South Pointe Hospital, Warrensville Heights, OH, p. A492

GUPTA, Ashok K, M.D., Chief of Staff, Eaton Rapids Medical Center, Eaton Rapids, MI, p. A312

GUPTA, John, Executive Vice President and Chief Operating Officer, Brooklyn Hospital Center, New York (Includes All Hospitals Located Within The Five Boroughs), NY, p. A431

GUPTA, Saurabh, Chief Medical Officer, Rockford Center, Newark, DE, p. A113

GUPTA, Vijay D, M.D., President and Chief Executive Officer, Franciscan Healthcare Munster, Munster, IN, p. A212

GURR, Lory, Chief Human Resources Division, Evans U.S. Army Community Hospital, Fort Carson, CO, p. A100

GURRAD, Trece, Vice President Patient Care Services, Columbia Memorial Hospital, Astoria, OR, p. A511

GURROLA, Jose, Administrator, Pecos Valley Lodge, NM, p. A419

GURULE, Eric, Chief Information Officer, Turquoise Lodge Hospital, Albuquerque, NM, p. A416

GURUNG, Anju, M.D., Chief Medical Officer, Mahnomen Health Center, Mahnomen, MN, p. A334

GUSHEE, Dean, M.D., Medical Director, Mason General Hospital And Family Of Clinics, Shelton, WA, p. A677

GUSHO, Michael, Chief Financial Officer, St. Joseph Mercy Oakland, Pontiac, MI, p. A321

GUSMANO, Jane
Interim Vice President Finance, Memorial Hospital East, Shiloh, IL, p. A196
Interim Vice President Finance, Memorial Hospital, Belleville, IL, p. A174

GUSTAFSON, Brian, Chief Financial Officer, Veterans Affairs Montana Health Care System, Fort Harrison, MT, p. A375

GUSTAFSON, Connie, Director of Nursing, Jacobson Memorial Hospital Care Center, Elgin, ND, p. A465

GUSTAFSON, Michael, M.D., President, University Campus, MA, p. A306

GUSTAFSON, Philip P., Interim President, Ssm Health St. Mary's Hospital - Jefferson City, Jefferson City, MO, p. A360

GUSTER, Cherie M, R.N., MSN, Senior Vice President and Chief Nursing Officer, Cleveland Clinic Akron General, Akron, OH, p. A470

GUSTILO, Maria, M.D., Medical Director, Osawatomie State Hospital At Adair Acute Care, Osawatomie, KS, p. A242

GUSTIN, Michael, Information Technology, John J. Pershing Veterans Affairs Medical Center, Poplar Bluff, MO, p. A366

GUTHMILLER, Martin W., Chief Executive Officer, Orange City Area Health System, Orange City, IA, p. A227

GUTHRIE, Pamela A, Chief Human Resources Officer, Hillcrest Hospital Pryor, Pryor, OK, p. A506

GUTHRIE, Todd, Chief of Staff, Mercy Medical Center Mount Shasta, Mount Shasta, CA, p. A74

GUTIERREZ, Lori, Chief Financial Officer, Rochelle Community Hospital, Rochelle, IL, p. A194

GUTIERREZ, Michelle
Executive Director Human Resources, Orange County, Memorialcare, Saddleback Memorial Medical Center, Laguna Hills, CA, p. A63
Executive Director Human Resources, Memorialcare, Orange Coast Memorial Medical Center, Fountain Valley, CA, p. A58

GUTIERREZ, Noe, Chief Financial Officer, Lake Granbury Medical Center, Granbury, TX, p. A607

GUTIERREZ, Santiago, M.D., Chief Medical Officer, Doctors Hospital Of Laredo, Laredo, TX, p. A619

GUTIERREZ, Vickie, Director of Patient Care, Dr. Dan C. Trigg Memorial Hospital, Tucumcari, NM, p. A420

GUTIERREZ, Victor A, M.D., Medical Director, Allegiance Behavioral Health Center Of Plainview, Plainview, TX, p. A628

GUTJAHR, Susan, Reimbursement Specialist, Sparta Community Hospital, Sparta, IL, p. A196

GUTMAN, Luisa, Senior Vice President and Chief Operating Officer, Holy Cross Hospital, Fort Lauderdale, FL, p. A122

GUTNICK, Michael, Executive Vice President and Chief Financial Officer, Memorial Sloan-Kettering Cancer Center, New York (Includes All Hospitals Located Within The Five Boroughs), NY, p. A433

GUTOW, Andrew, M.D., Medical Director, Menlo Park Surgical Hospital, Menlo Park, CA, p. A72

GUTOWSKI, Jennifer S., FACHE, Director, Veterans Affairs Pacific Islands Health Care System, Honolulu, HI, p. A165

GUTSCH, Michael, Chief Executive Officer and Administrator, Cumberland Healthcare, Cumberland, WI, p. A691

GUTSCHENRITTER, John, Chief Financial Officer, Wilson Medical Center, Neodesha, KS, p. A241

GUTTENBERG, Ellen, Chief Operating Officer, Frances Mahon Deaconess Hospital, Glasgow, MT, p. A375

GUTTIN, Enrique, M.D., FACS, Chief of Staff, Wilmington Veterans Affairs Medical Center, Wilmington, DE, p. A114

GUTTMACHER, Laurence, M.D., Clinical Director, Rochester Psychiatric Center, Rochester, NY, p. A441

GUTZEIT, Michael, M.D., Chief Medical Officer, Children's Hospital Of Wisconsin, Milwaukee, WI, p. A698

GUY, Glenda, Director, Health Information Management, Ten Broeck Tennessee Treatment Facility, Cookeville, TN, p. A568

GUY, Kimberly, President, St. Joseph's Women's Hospital, FL, p. A141

GUYETTE, William, M.D., President Medical Staff, Livingston Hospital And Healthcare Services, Salem, KY, p. A260

GUZ, Andrew, Chief Executive Officer, Lakewood Ranch Medical Center, Bradenton, FL, p. A118

GUZAK, Jason, Chief Financial Officer, Rock Springs, Georgetown, TX, p. A607

GUZMAN, Claudia V., Chief Executive Officer and Managing Director, Hospital San Pablo, Bayamon, PR, p. A712

GUZMAN, David, Chief Financial Officer, Nyc Health + Hospitals / Elmhurst, New York (Includes All Hospitals Located Within The Five Boroughs), NY, p. A435

GUZMAN, Lisa, Human Resource Vice President, Redlands Community Hospital, Redlands, CA, p. A80

GWATKIN, Elizabeth, Vice President Human Resources, Northeastern Vermont Regional Hospital, Saint Johnsbury, VT, p. A654

GWYN, Andrea, Chief Operating Officer, Terre Haute Regional Hospital, Terre Haute, IN, p. A215

GWYN, Brian
President and Chief Executive Officer, Carolinas Healthcare System Cleveland, Shelby, NC, p. A460
President and Chief Executive Officer, Carolinas Healthcare System Kings Mountain, Kings Mountain, NC, p. A455
President Chief Operating Officer, Carolinas Healthcare System Cleveland, Shelby, NC, p. A460

GYIMAH, Ed, Chief Financial Officer, Howard University Hospital, Washington, DC, p. A115

GYNTHER, Tracy, R.N., Vice President and Chief Nursing Officer, Wellstar West Georgia Medical Center, Lagrange, GA, p. A155

H

HAACK, Sally, Vice President and Director of Human Resources, St. Francis Regional Medical Center, Shakopee, MN, p. A340

HAACK, Wanda, MSN, R.N., Chief Nursing Officer, Genesis Medical Center, Dewitt, De Witt, IA, p. A220

HAAG, Adam, Manager Information Technology, Coffey County Hospital, Burlington, KS, p. A233

HAAGENSON, Deb, R.N., Vice President of Patient Care, Chi St. Joseph's Health, Park Rapids, MN, p. A337

HAAK, Karen S., R.N., MSN, Chief Nursing Officer, Good Samaritan Hospital, Vincennes, IN, p. A216

HAAS, Christine, Chief Information Officer, Geisinger Jersey Shore Hospital, Jersey Shore, PA, p. A528

HAAS, Robert, M.D., Chief Medical Officer, Liberty Hospital, Liberty, MO, p. A363

HAAS, Steven J
Chief Financial Officer, Health Alliance Hospital - Broadway Campus, Kingston, NY, p. A428
Chief Financial Officer, Health Alliance Hospital - Mary's Avenue Campus, Kingston, NY, p. A428
HAAS, Susan, Director Human Resources, Aurora Behavioral Healthcare San Diego, San Diego, CA, p. A83
HAASE, Patricia, Director Information Technology and Communications, Marian Regional Medical Center, Santa Maria, CA, p. A89
HAASE, Ronald
Chief Human Resources Officer, Northern Arizona Healthcare, Flagstaff Medical Center, Flagstaff, AZ, p. A29
Chief Human Resources Officer, Northern Arizona Healthcare, Verde Valley Medical Center, Cottonwood, AZ, p. A29
HAASKEN, Timothy W, Chief Financial Officer, Lewisgale Hospital Montgomery, Blacksburg, VA, p. A655
HABIB, Noel, M.D., Chief Medical Officer, Huhukam Memorial Hospital, Sacaton, AZ, p. A35
HABIS, Saba, M.D., Chief Medical Officer, Freeman Hospital East, MO, p. A361
HABOWSKI, Michael J., President and Chief Executive Officer, Ashtabula County Medical Center, Ashtabula, OH, p. A471
HACHEY, Michael
Senior Vice President and Chief Financial Officer, Emerson Hospital, Concord, MA, p. A299
Senior Vice President and Chief Financial Officer, Mercy Hospital Of Portland, Portland, ME, p. A285
HACKBARTH, John, CPA, Senior Vice President Finance and Chief Financial Officer, Healthpark, KY, p. A258
HACKER, Daniel, Human Resource Business Partner, Eastern State Hospital, Lexington, KY, p. A254
HACKER, Leanne, Chief Financial Officer, Eastern New Mexico Medical Center, Roswell, NM, p. A419
HACKER, Mary Dee, R.N., Vice President, Patient Care Services and Chief Nursing Officer, Children's Hospital Los Angeles, Los Angeles, CA, p. A66
HACKER, Phil, Chief Financial Officer, Lane Regional Medical Center, Zachary, LA, p. A281
HACKER, Phillip
Chief Financial Officer, Stone County Medical Center, Mountain View-Stone County, AR, p. A46
Chief Financial Officer, White River Medical Center, Batesville, AR, p. A39
HACKETT, Leslie, Chief Nursing Officer, Covenant Hospital Plainview, Plainview, TX, p. A628
HACKSTEDDE, Anita, M.D.
President and Chief Executive Officer, Salem Regional Medical Center, Salem, OH, p. A490
Vice President Medical Affairs, Salem Regional Medical Center, Salem, OH, p. A490
HADAWAY, Krystal, Director Human Resources, Healthsource Saginaw, Inc., Saginaw, MI, p. A322
HADDAD, Housam, M.D., Chief of Staff, Casey County Hospital, Liberty, KY, p. A255
HADDADIN, Maen, M.D., President Medical Staff, Chi Health Mercy Corning, Corning, IA, p. A219
HADDIX, Parker, Chief Executive Officer, William R. Sharpe, Jr. Hospital, Weston, WV, p. A688
HADDOX, Melissa, Controller, Encompass Health Rehabilitation Hospital Of Cypress, Houston, TX, p. A610
HADLEY, Gerard, Vice President Finance for Brigham & Women's Faulkner Hospital and Vice President Finance and Controller, Brigham And Women's Faulkner Hospital, Boston, MA, p. A296
HADLEY, H Roger, M.D., Vice President, Medical Affairs, Loma Linda University Heart & Surgical Hospital, CA, p. A64
HADLEY, Steven N, Chief Financial Officer, Kansas Medical Center, Andover, KS, p. A232
HADLEY, Susan, MS, Chief Nursing Officer, Dickinson County Healthcare System, Iron Mountain, MI, p. A316
HADZEGA, Angela, Chief Financial Officer, Upmc Kane, Kane, PA, p. A528
HAEFELE, John, M.D., Chief Medical Officer, Community Memorial Healthcare, Marysville, KS, p. A241
HAEHN, Debra, Chief Financial Officer, Clay County Memorial Hospital, Henrietta, TX, p. A609
HAENELT, Michael, Chief Information Management, Weed Army Community Hospital, Fort Irwin, CA, p. A58
HAESEMEYER, Allan, M.D., Chief of Staff, Indianhead Medical Center, Shell Lake, WI, p. A703
HAESEMEYER, Christa, Chief Nursing Officer, Lincoln County Hospital, Lincoln, KS, p. A240
HAFEMAN, Paula
Chief Nursing Officer, Hshs St. Clare Memorial Hospital, Oconto Falls, WI, p. A700
Chief Nursing Officer, Hshs St. Mary's Hospital Medical Center, Green Bay, WI, p. A694

HAFFEY, Robert, R.N.
President and Chief Operating Officer, Kent County Memorial Hospital, Warwick, RI, p. A548
President, Delaware County Memorial Hospital, Drexel Hill, PA, p. A524
HAFIZ, Irfan
Vice President Medical Affairs, Centegra Hospital - Woodstock, Woodstock, IL, p. A198
Vice President Medical Affairs, Centegra Hospital-Huntley, IL, p. A189
HAGAN, Donald E, Chief Financial Officer, Detar Hospital North, TX, p. A642
HAGAN, Eric, R.N., Executive Vice President and Administrator, Medical Center At Scottsville, Scottsville, KY, p. A260
HAGAN, Frank, Senior Vice President Finance, Saint Joseph's Medical Center, Yonkers, NY, p. A446
HAGEDORN, Tammy, Chief Human Resource Officer, Genesis Medical Center-Aledo, Aledo, IL, p. A173
HAGEL, Bonnie, Chief Financial Officer, Logan County Hospital, Oakley, KS, p. A242
HAGELBERG, Robbi, Vice President Nursing Services and Chief Nursing Officer, Lakeview Hospital, Stillwater, MN, p. A340
HAGELTHORN, Diane, Human Resources Generalist, Modoc Medical Center, Alturas, CA, p. A50
HAGEN, Bruce P., President, Ohiohealth Marion General Hospital, Marion, OH, p. A486
HAGEN, Lynne D, Human Resources Officer, Avera Children's Hospital, SD, p. A563
HAGEN, Mary, R.N., MSN, VP and Chief Nursing Officer, Unitypoint Health - Allen Hospital, Waterloo, IA, p. A231
HAGEN, Paulette, Human Resources and Administrative Services Director, Centracare Health-Paynesville, Paynesville, MN, p. A337
HAGENS, Paul, Vice President Human Resources, Doctors Community Hospital, Lanham, MD, p. A292
HAGERMAN, Daniel, M.D., President Medical Staff, Columbia Center Birth Hospital, Mequon, WI, p. A697
HAGERSTROM, Paige A, System Director of Talent Management, St. Joseph Hospital, Bangor, ME, p. A282
HAGERTY, Cindy, Assistant Chief Nurse Officer and Administrator of Operations, Via Christi Rehabilitation Hospital, Wichita, KS, p. A248
HAGGARD, Tommy, Chief Executive Officer, Bluegrass Community Hospital, Versailles, KY, p. A261
HAGGERTY, Cheryl Kay, Chief Nursing Officer, Assistant Chief Executive Officer, Mercy Medical Center-New Hampton, New Hampton, IA, p. A227
HAGLER, Dan, M.D., Vice President and Chief Medical Officer, Carolinas Healthcare System Northeast, Concord, NC, p. A450
HAGLUND, Nicole, Vice President of Nursing Services, Providence Medical Center, Wayne, NE, p. A391
HAGOOD, Teena, Chief Nursing Officer, Kimble Hospital, Junction, TX, p. A616
HAGY, Kelly, Director Human Resources, Cumberland Hall Hospital, Hopkinsville, KY, p. A253
HAGY, Michelle, Senior Vice President and Chief Financial Officer, Pikeville Medical Center, Pikeville, KY, p. A259
HAHEY, Joanne A
Senior Vice President and Chief Financial Officer, University Of Maryland Shore Medical Center At Dorchester, Cambridge, MD, p. A290
Senior Vice President and Chief Financial Officer, University Of Maryland Shore Medical Center At Easton, Easton, MD, p. A291
Vice President Finance and Chief Financial Officer, University Of Maryland Shore Medical Center At Chestertown, Chestertown, MD, p. A290
HAHN, Donna S, R.N., Vice President Acute Care and Chief Nurse Executive, Sentara Rmh Medical Center, Harrisonburg, VA, p. A659
HAHN, Jen, Finance Manager, Uh Portage Medical Center, Ravenna, OH, p. A489
HAHN, Joseph, M.D., Chief of Staff, Cleveland Clinic Children's Hospital, OH, p. A476
HAHN, Kurt, M.D., Acting Clinical Director, Elmira Psychiatric Center, Elmira, NY, p. A426
HAHN, Lisa, R.N., Chief Nursing Officer, Ahmc Anaheim Regional Medical Center, Anaheim, CA, p. A50
HAHN, Lori, Vice President Nursing Services, Chi St. Alexius Health - Williston Medical Center, Williston, ND, p. A469
HAHN, Peter, Chief Medical Officer, Metro Health - University Of Michigan Health, Wyoming, MI, p. A326
HAHN, Stephen, Deputy to the President and Chief Operating Officer, University Of Texas M.D. Anderson Cancer Center, Houston, TX, p. A614
HAHS, Seth, Chief of Staff, Salem Township Hospital, Salem, IL, p. A195

HAIGH, Sara, Associate Director, Durham Veterans Affairs Medical Center, Durham, NC, p. A451
HAIGLER, Tonda V., Chief Operating Officer, Merit Health Biloxi, Biloxi, MS, p. A343
HAIL, Brian, Chief Executive Officer, Cherokee Nation W.W. Hastings Indian Hospital, Tahlequah, OK, p. A507
HAIN, Jim, Chief Operating Officer, Lexington Regional Health Center, Lexington, NE, p. A385
HAINES, Christopher, D.O., Vice President and Chief Medical Officer, Children's Specialized Hospital, NJ, p. A408
HAIR, Denise J., Vice President of Nursing Services and Chief Nursing Officer, Dameron Hospital, Stockton, CA, p. A90
HAIR, Kelly, Director Information Systems and Data Analytics, Abbeville General Hospital, Abbeville, LA, p. A262
HAIR, Troy, Chief Financial Officer, Abbeville General Hospital, Abbeville, LA, p. A262
HAISLIP, Heidi, M.D., Chief of Staff, Alliancehealth Madill, Madill, OK, p. A500
HAIZLIP, Thomas M, M.D., Jr, Chief of Staff, Charles A. Cannon Memorial Hospital, Newland, NC, p. A458
HAJEK, Julie, Director Human Resources, St. David's Rehabilitation Center, TX, p. A586
HAKENSON, Diana, Director of Patient Care Services, Newport Bay Hospital, Newport Beach, CA, p. A75
HALAMA, George, Vice President Finance, Mcpherson Hospital, Mcpherson, KS, p. A241
HALAMKA, John, M.D., Chief Information Officer, Beth Israel Deaconess Medical Center, Boston, MA, p. A296
HALDEMAN, Larry, M.D., Executive Vice President and Chief Medical Officer, Wellstar Windy Hill Hospital, Marietta, GA, p. A157
HALDER, Ranjay, M.D., Chief Medical Director, Centerstone Hospital, Bradenton, FL, p. A118
HALE, Becky, Director Human Resources, Hill Regional Hospital, Hillsboro, TX, p. A609
HALE, Byron, Chief Financial Officer, Ut Health Behavioral Health Center, TX, p. A641
HALE, Danny, Director Human Resources, Southwestern Medical Center, Lawton, OK, p. A500
HALE, Donna, Director of Nursing, Baptist Memorial Rehabilitation Hospital, Germantown, TN, p. A570
HALE, Ken, Executive Director of Operations, Mercy Allen Hospital, Oberlin, OH, p. A488
HALE, Kirsten
Coordinator Health Information Services, University Hospitals Conneaut Medical Center, Conneaut, OH, p. A479
Coordinator Health Informations Systems and Coding, University Hospitals Geneva Medical Center, Geneva, OH, p. A483
HALE, Margie, R.N., MSN, Chief Executive Officer, Baraga County Memorial Hospital, L'Anse, MI, p. A317
HALE, Marshall, M.D., Chief Medical Officer, Passavant Area Hospital, Jacksonville, IL, p. A186
HALE, Renae, Chief Nursing Officer, Lincoln Prairie Behavioral Health Center, Springfield, IL, p. A196
HALE, Ron, Superintendent, Colorado Mental Health Institute At Pueblo, Pueblo, CO, p. A104
HALE, Ron B., Chief Executive Officer, Alaska Psychiatric Institute, Anchorage, AK, p. A25
HALE, Steven D., FACHE, Chief Executive Officer, Weiser Memorial Hospital, Weiser, ID, p. A172
HALE, Tonia, Chief Nursing Officer, Tennova Newport Medical Center, Newport, TN, p. A578
HALEN, Catherine, Vice President Human Resources, Beebe Healthcare, Lewes, DE, p. A113
HALES, Brent, Chief Financial Officer, Uintah Basin Medical Center, Roosevelt, UT, p. A650
HALES, Joe, Chief Information Officer, Primary Children's Hospital, Salt Lake City, UT, p. A650
HALEY, DeLeigh, Chief Executive Officer, Ut Health Jacksonville, Jacksonville, TX, p. A616
HALEY, James, M.D., Senior Vice President and Chief Medical Officer, Unity Hospital, Rochester, NY, p. A441
HALEY, Leon L., Jr, M.D., Chief Executive Officer, Uf Health Jacksonville, Jacksonville, FL, p. A126
HALEY, Thomas
Division Assistant Vice President Business Relationship Management, Lasting Hope Recovery Center, NE, p. A387
Information Technology Services Site Director, Chi Health Mercy Council Bluffs, Council Bluffs, IA, p. A220
Information Technology Systems Site Director, Chi Health Lakeside, Omaha, NE, p. A388
Information Technology Systems Site Director, Chi Health Midlands, Papillion, NE, p. A389
HALFEN, John, M.D., Medical Director, Lakewood Health System, Staples, MN, p. A340
HALFORD, Dianne, Chief Financial Officer, Saint Clare's Hospital/Dover, NJ, p. A403

HALIMI, Hamid, M.D., Medical Director, Select Specialty Hospital-Ann Arbor, Ypsilanti, MI, p. A326

HALL, Becky, R.N., Director Nursing, Rumford Hospital, Rumford, ME, p. A286

HALL, Catherine, Manager Human Resources, Jefferson Hospital, Louisville, GA, p. A156

HALL, Dan, R.N., Chief Operating Officer, St. John Owasso, Owasso, OK, p. A505

HALL, David
Chief Information Officer, Southeastern Kentucky Medical Center, Pineville, KY, p. A259
Senior Vice President and Chief Operating Officer, University Of Tennessee Medical Center, Knoxville, TN, p. A572

HALL, Gary, Vice President of Information Technology, Estes Park Medical Center, Estes Park, CO, p. A100

HALL, Geoffrey, Chief Executive Officer, Edwin Shaw Rehab, Cuyahoga Falls, OH, p. A480

HALL, George, M.D.
Vice President Medical Affairs, St. Elizabeth Falmouth, KY, p. A252
Vice President Medical Affairs, St. Elizabeth Florence, Florence, KY, p. A252

HALL, James, M.D., Chief Medical Officer, Pampa Regional Medical Center, Pampa, TX, p. A627

HALL, Jeanne, Director Information Systems, Shriners Hospitals For Children-St. Louis, Saint Louis, MO, p. A368

HALL, Jeffrey, DPM, Chief Medical Officer, St. Croix Regional Medical Center, St Croix Falls, WI, p. A703

HALL, Jeremy, Assistant Administrator and Chief Financial Officer, Middlesboro Arh Hospital, Middlesboro, KY, p. A258

HALL, Jim, Acting Chief Information Officer, North Little Rock Division, AR, p. A45

HALL, Kathy J., Administrator, St. Vincent Warrick Hospital, Boonville, IN, p. A200

HALL, Kenneth C, R.N., Chief Nursing Officer, Saint Joseph Health System, Mishawaka, IN, p. A211

HALL, Kent, M.D., Vice President and Chief Medical Officer, The University Of Vermont Health Network-Champlain Valley Physicians Hospital, Plattsburgh, NY, p. A440

HALL, Linda, Administrator and Chief Executive Officer, Chillicothe Hospital District, Chillicothe, TX, p. A592

HALL, Margaret, M.D., Chief Medical Officer, Lakeside Women's Hospital, Oklahoma City, OK, p. A503

HALL, Mary A, Chief Medical Staff, Mcdowell Arh Hospital, Mcdowell, KY, p. A258

HALL, Melissa
Chief Executive Officer, Munising Memorial Hospital, Munising, MI, p. A319
Chief Nursing Officer, Coffey County Hospital, Burlington, KS, p. A233

HALL, Morrison, Chief Financial Officer, Pender Memorial Hospital, Burgaw, NC, p. A448

HALL, Patricia, MSN, Ph.D., R.N., Director, John J. Pershing Veterans Affairs Medical Center, Poplar Bluff, MO, p. A366

HALL, Richard, Chief Executive Officer, Samuel Simmonds Memorial Hospital, Barrow, AK, p. A25

HALL, Roger L.
President, Sacred Heart Hospital On The Emerald Coast, Miramar Beach, FL, p. A132
President, Sacred Heart Hospital On The Gulf, Port St Joe, FL, p. A137

HALL, Ryan, Vice President, Providence Hospital Northeast, SC, p. A551

HALL, Sally, Manager Human Resources, South Texas Spine And Surgical Hospital, San Antonio, TX, p. A634

HALL, Stephanie, M.D.
Chief Medical Officer, Keck Hospital Of Usc, Los Angeles, CA, p. A68
Chief Medical Officer, Usc Verdugo Hills Hospital, Glendale, CA, p. A60
Medical Director, Usc Norris Comprehensive Cancer Center, Los Angeles, CA, p. A70

HALL, Steve, Chief Financial Officer, Unitypoint Health-Pekin Hospital, Pekin, IL, p. A193

HALL, Terry E., Chief of Staff, Harrison County Community Hospital, Bethany, MO, p. A355

HALL, Trudy, M.D.
Vice President Medical Affairs and Interim Chief Executive Officer, University Of Maryland Capital Region Health At Laurel Regional Hospital, Laurel, MD, p. A292
Vice President Medical Affairs, University Of Maryland Capital Region Health At Laurel Regional Hospital, Laurel, MD, p. A292

HALL, Veronica, R.N., Interim President and Chief Executive Officer, Henry Ford Hospital, Detroit, MI, p. A311

HALL, Wyatt, M.D., Chief Medical Officer, Longmont United Hospital, Longmont, CO, p. A103

HALL-OLSEN, Kathy, MA, Administrator, Weisman Children's Rehabilitation Hospital, Marlton, NJ, p. A407

HALLAL, Joseph, M.D., Chief Medical Officer, Inova Fairfax Hospital For Children, VA, p. A657

HALLATT, Jennifer
Chief Operating Officer, Mercyhealth Hospital And Medical Center - Harvard, Harvard, IL, p. A184
Vice President, Mercyhealth Hospital And Medical Center - Walworth, Lake Geneva, WI, p. A695

HALLEY, Andrea, Vice President of Non-Clinical Operations/ Director Human Resources, Hopedale Medical Complex, Hopedale, IL, p. A186

HALLEY, Lisa B, Vice President Human Resources, Holzer Medical Center, Gallipolis, OH, p. A483

HALLIDAY, Lisa, Director Accounting Services, Taylor Regional Hospital, Hawkinsville, GA, p. A154

HALLIWILL, Donald B
Chief Financial Officer, Carilion Franklin Memorial Hospital, Rocky Mount, VA, p. A666
Executive Vice President and Chief Financial Officer, Roanoke Memorial Rehabilitation Center, VA, p. A665

HALLMARK, Todd
Chief Executive Officer, Choctaw Nation Health Care Center, Talihina, OK, p. A507
Chief Operating Officer, Choctaw Nation Health Care Center, Talihina, OK, p. A507

HALLOCK, Mirya, Administrator, Webster County Community Hospital, Red Cloud, NE, p. A390

HALLORAN, Abigail, Chief Executive Officer, Haven Behavioral Hospital Of Philadelphia, Philadelphia, PA, p. A535

HALLORAN, Teresa, Ph.D., R.N.
Vice President Nursing Services, Memorial Hospital East, Shiloh, IL, p. A196
Vice President Nursing Services, Memorial Hospital, Belleville, IL, p. A174

HALPIN, Jean
President, Mansfield Hospital, OH, p. A485
President, Ohiohealth Medcentral Shelby Hospital, Shelby, OH, p. A490

HALPIN, Kim, Director Human Resources, Arms Acres, Carmel, NY, p. A424

HALSAN, Carole, R.N., Chief Executive Officer, Willapa Harbor Hospital, South Bend, WA, p. A678

HALSELL, David, Senior Vice President and Chief Financial Officer, Lake Regional Health System, Osage Beach, MO, p. A365

HALSTEAD, Lisa, Chief Nursing Officer, Integris Miami Hospital, Miami, OK, p. A501

HALSTEAD, Rhonda, President, Penn Highlands Clearfield, Clearfield, PA, p. A522

HALTER, Bev, Director Human Resources and Payroll, Liberty Medical Center, Chester, MT, p. A374

HALTER, Kevin, Chief Executive Officer, Our Lady Of Bellefonte Hospital, Ashland, KY, p. A249

HALTOM, Shannon, Vice President, Patient Care Services, Chi St. Luke's Health Brazosport, Lake Jackson, TX, p. A618

HALVORSEN, Lisa, Chief Nurse Executive, Providence Milwaukie Hospital, Milwaukie, OR, p. A515

HALVORSON, Marla, Director Human Resources, St. Luke's Hospital, Duluth, MN, p. A331

HAM, Michael, Chief Executive Officer, Park Royal Hospital, Fort Myers, FL, p. A123

HAMAM, Hisham, M.D., Chief of Staff, Northern Cochise Community Hospital, Willcox, AZ, p. A38

HAMAN, Timothy, M.D., Vice President Medical Affairs, Christus Ochsner St. Patrick Hospital Southwest Louisiana, Lake Charles, LA, p. A272

HAMATY, Edward G., D.O., Chief Medical Officer, Acuity Specialty Hospital Of Southern New Jersey, Willingboro, NJ, p. A414

HAMB, Aaron, M.D., Chief Medical Officer, Provident Hospital Of Cook County, Chicago, IL, p. A179

HAMBLIN, Garth, Chief Financial Officer, Bear Valley Community Hospital, Big Bear Lake, CA, p. A53

HAMBLIN, James, Chief Financial Officer, White Mountain Regional Medical Center, Springerville, AZ, p. A36

HAMBLIN, Scott, M.D., President Medical Staff, White Mountain Regional Medical Center, Springerville, AZ, p. A36

HAMBRIDGE, Mark, Director Information Systems, Livingston Regional Hospital, Livingston, TN, p. A573

HAMBY, Kelley, Vice President Patient Care, Baptist Health Medical Center - North Little Rock, North Little Rock-Pulaski County, AR, p. A47

HAMEL, Cathleen, Chief Nurse Executive, St. Rose Dominican Hospitals - Siena Campus, Henderson, NV, p. A393

HAMEL, Loren, M.D., President and Chief Executive Officer, Lakeland Hospital, Niles, MI, p. A323

HAMEL, Susan, Chief Nursing Officer, St. Luke's Hospital, Duluth, MN, p. A331

HAMILL, Dave H., President and Chief Executive Officer, Hampton Regional Medical Center, Varnville, SC, p. A557

HAMILTON, Adriana H, Chief Human Resources Officer, Hunter Holmes Mcguire Veterans Affairs Medical Center-Richmond, Richmond, VA, p. A665

HAMILTON, Aggie, Chief Human Resources, Veterans Affairs Montana Health Care System, Fort Harrison, MT, p. A375

HAMILTON, Brandy, Chief Executive Officer, Suncoast Behavioral Health Center, Bradenton, FL, p. A119

HAMILTON, Catherine, Chief Nursing Officer, Hedrick Medical Center, Chillicothe, MO, p. A357

HAMILTON, Chanda, Chief Information Officer, Clifton T. Perkins Hospital Center, Jessup, MD, p. A292

HAMILTON, Dan, Chief Operating Officer, Nor-Lea Hospital District, Lovington, NM, p. A418

HAMILTON, David, Chief Information Officer, Southwest Mississippi Regional Medical Center, Mccomb, MS, p. A350

HAMILTON, Gary, Chief Executive Officer, Pioneer Medical Center, Big Timber, MT, p. A373

HAMILTON, Geoff, Interim Chief Financial Officer, Morton General Hospital, Morton, WA, p. A673

HAMILTON, Jennifer
Chief Financial Officer, Sagewest Health Care At Lander, WY, p. A709
COO - Mary Bridge, Multicare Mary Bridge Children's Hospital And Health Center, Tacoma, WA, p. A679

HAMILTON, Kevin M., M.D., Chief Medical Officer, Tristar Summit Medical Center, Hermitage, TN, p. A570

HAMILTON, Marci, Chief Nursing Officer, Orthopaedic Hospital Of Lutheran Health Network, Fort Wayne, IN, p. A204

HAMILTON, Marilyn, Director Human Resources, Promise Hospital Baton Rouge - Main Campus, Baton Rouge, LA, p. A264

HAMILTON, Matthew, Chief Executive Officer, United Medical Center, Washington, DC, p. A116

HAMILTON, Michelle, Human Resource Manager, Turning Point Hospital, Moultrie, GA, p. A158

HAMILTON, Nancy, Chief Human and Learning Resources, Lyons Division, NJ, p. A404

HAMILTON, Patricia, R.N.
Director of Nursing, Mildred Mitchell-Bateman Hospital, Huntington, WV, p. A684
Chief Executive Officer, Rebound Behavioral Health, Lancaster, SC, p. A555

HAMILTON, Peggy, Chief Financial Officer, Bayside Community Hospital, Anahuac, TX, p. A583

HAMILTON, Phil, R.N., Chief Executive Officer, Pershing Memorial Hospital, Brookfield, MO, p. A356

HAMILTON, Randal S., Chief Executive Officer, Select Specialty Hospital-Panama City, Panama City, FL, p. A135

HAMILTON, Scott, Vice President and Chief Financial Officer, Peninsula Hospital, TN, p. A572

HAMILTON, Sharon, Chief Nursing Officer, Healthsouth Emerald Coast Rehabilitation Hospital, Panama City, FL, p. A135

HAMILTON, Terry
President, St. John Macomb-Oakland Hospital, Madison Heights Campus, MI, p. A325
President, St. John Macomb-Oakland Hospital, Warren Campus, MI, p. A325

HAMILTON, Tom, M.D., Chief of Staff, Decatur County General Hospital, Parsons, TN, p. A578

HAMILTON-BEYER, Maggie, Chief Financial Officer, Knoxville Hospital & Clinics, Knoxville, IA, p. A225

HAMLIN, Faye, Manager Human Resources, Julian F. Keith Alcohol And Drug Abuse Treatment Center, Black Mountain, NC, p. A448

HAMM, Jay, R.N., FACHE, Chief Operating Officer, Palmetto Health Children's Hospital, SC, p. A551

HAMM, Sonja, Vice President Human and Foundation Resources, Lakes Regional Healthcare, Spirit Lake, IA, p. A230

HAMMAKER, Barry, M.D., Chief Medical Officer and Chief Clinical Officer, Vail Health, Vail, CO, p. A106

HAMMAN, Baron L, M.D., Chief Medical Officer, Texas Health Heart & Vascular Hospital Arlington, Arlington, TX, p. A584

HAMMEL, Leah, Acting Administrator, Chester Mental Health Center, Chester, IL, p. A176

HAMMER, Kristine, Director of Finance, Centracare Health-Monticello, Monticello, MN, p. A336

HAMMER, Rebecca J, Chief Financial Officer, Davis Medical Center, Elkins, WV, p. A682

HAMMERAN, Kevin R., Chief Executive Officer and Administrator, Baptist Memorial Hospital For Women, Memphis, TN, p. A574

HAMMES, Paul, Chief Executive Officer, Hugh Chatham Memorial Hospital, Elkin, NC, p. A452

HAMMETT, Doran, Chief Financial Officer, Petersburg Medical Center, Petersburg, AK, p. A27

HAMMETT, Richard A., President and Chief Executive Officer, Swedish Medical Center, Englewood, CO, p. A100

HAMMETT, Troy, Senior Vice President and Chief Financial Officer South Eastern Division, Memorial Hospital Hixson, TN, p. A567

HAMMOCK, Preston W., President, Alamance Regional Medical Center, Burlington, NC, p. A448

HAMMON, Selene Q., Chief Executive Officer, Dallas Behavioral Healthcare Hospital, Desoto, TX, p. A599

HAMMOND, Flora, M.D., Chief Medical Affairs, Rehabilitation Hospital Of Indiana, Indianapolis, IN, p. A207

HAMMOND, Michael
Chief Financial Officer, Lourdes Medical Center Of Burlington County, Willingboro, NJ, p. A414
Chief Financial Officer, Our Lady Of Lourdes Medical Center, Camden, NJ, p. A403

HAMMOND, Nancy, M.D., Vice President, Chief Medical Officer, Saint Agnes Healthcare, Baltimore, MD, p. A288

HAMMOND, Patti, Chief Operating Officer, Adirondack Health, Saranac Lake, NY, p. A442

HAMMOND, Reed, Chief Operating Officer, Conroe Regional Medical Center, Conroe, TX, p. A594

HAMMONDS, Janie, Human Resources Officer, Columbus Community Hospital, Columbus, TX, p. A593

HAMNER, Candy, Vice President and Chief Nursing Officer, Levindale Hebrew Geriatric Center And Hospital, Baltimore, MD, p. A288

HAMON, Beta, Chief Medical Officer, Sanford Rock Rapids Medical Center, Rock Rapids, IA, p. A228

HAMON, Eric
Executive Vice President and Chief Financial Officer, Driscoll Children's Hospital, Corpus Christi, TX, p. A594
Interim President and Chief Executive Officer, Driscoll Children's Hospital, Corpus Christi, TX, p. A594

HAMPF, Carl, M.D., Chief Medical Officer, Saint Thomas Hospital For Spinal Surgery, Nashville, TN, p. A577

HAMPTON, Angie, Director Human Resources, Porter Regional Hospital, Valparaiso, IN, p. A215

HAMPTON, Connie, R.N., Associate Director for Patient Care Services, Carl Vinson Veterans Affairs Medical Center, Dublin, GA, p. A153

HAMPTON, Jeff, Director Information Systems, Lehigh Regional Medical Center, Lehigh Acres, FL, p. A128

HAMPTON, Mary Ann, MSN, R.N., Chief Nursing Officer, St. Luke's Des Peres Hospital, Saint Louis, MO, p. A369

HAMRICK, Jan, Chief Financial Officer, Dodge County Hospital, Eastman, GA, p. A153

HAMSTRA, Nancy, Chief Operating Officer, University Hospital, Newark, NJ, p. A409

HAMULA, Michelle, Director of Nursing and Quality, Chan Soon-Shiong Medical Center, Windber, PA, p. A545

HANCOCK, Brian, M.D., Director, Richard L. Roudebush Veterans Affairs Medical Center, Indianapolis, IN, p. A207

HANCOCK, J Brian, M.D., Chief of Staff, Fargo Veterans Affairs Health Care System, Fargo, ND, p. A465

HANCOCK, Katherine, R.N., Executive Chief Nursing Officer, Cleveland Clinic Children's Hospital, OH, p. A476

HANCOCK, Kerry, Director Human Resources, Bacon County Hospital And Health System, Alma, GA, p. A145

HANCOCK, Lori, Chief Business Officer, West Palm Beach Veterans Affairs Medical Center, West Palm Beach, FL, p. A143

HANCOCK, Melinda, Chief Financial Officer, Children's Hospital Of Richmond At Vcu, VA, p. A665

HANCOCK, Myrna, Director Financial Services, Choctaw Health Center, Philadelphia, MS, p. A352

HANCOCK, Sharon, Chief Human Resources Officer, Mccullough-Hyde Memorial Hospital/Trihealth, Oxford, OH, p. A489

HANCOCK, Todd, President and Chief Executive Officer, Christus Good Shepherd Medical Center, TX, p. A622

HANDEL, Daniel, M.D., Chief Medical Officer, Children's Hospital Of South Carolina At Musc, SC, p. A550

HANDLER, Michael, M.D., Vice President Medical Affairs and Chief Medical Officer, Ssm Health St. Joseph Hospital - Lake Saint Louis, Lake Saint Louis, MO, p. A363

HANDLEY, Charles
Chief Financial Officer, Plaza Specialty Hospital, Houston, TX, p. A613
Chief Financial Officer, Providence Children's Hospital, TX, p. A602

HANDLEY, Donna
President, The William W. Backus Hospital, Norwich, CT, p. A110
President, Windham Hospital, Willimantic, CT, p. A112

HANDLEY, Jack, M.D., Chief Medical Officer, Evergreenhealth Monroe, Monroe, WA, p. A673

HANDLEY, Rhonda, Chief Financial Officer, Columbia Basin Hospital, Ephrata, WA, p. A671

HANDOL, Nelson, M.D., Medical Director, Laurel Oaks Behavioral Health Center, Dothan, AL, p. A17

HANDWERK, Ashley, Director, Human Resources, Medstar Union Memorial Hospital, Baltimore, MD, p. A288

HANDY, Steven P., CPA, Chief Executive Officer, Uniontown Hospital, Uniontown, PA, p. A542

HANEFELD, Darlene, Chief Human Resources Officer, Banner Churchill Community Hospital, Fallon, NV, p. A392

HANENBURG, Thomas S., Senior Vice President and Area Manager, Kaiser Permanente San Leandro Medical Center, San Leandro, CA, p. A87

HANEY, Kathryn, Controller, Encompass Health Valley Of The Sun Rehabilitation Hospital, Glendale, AZ, p. A30

HANEY, Lisa, Chief Executive Officer, St. Mary Rehabilitation Hospital, Langhorne, PA, p. A529

HANGER, Kelvin, Chief Executive Officer, Trihealth Evendale Hospital, Cincinnati, OH, p. A476

HANIGAN, Hank, FACHE
Chief Executive Officer, Whitman Hospital And Medical Center, Colfax, WA, p. A670
Interim Chief Financial Officer, Whitman Hospital And Medical Center, Colfax, WA, p. A670

HANISCH, Denise, M.D., Chief of Staff, Avera St. Mary's Hospital, Pierre, SD, p. A562

HANKINS, Brad, Chief Operating Quality Officer, Lake Chelan Community Hospital And Clinics, Chelan, WA, p. A670

HANKS, John, Director Information Systems, East Tennessee Children's Hospital, Knoxville, TN, p. A572

HANKS, Susan, Chief Information Officer, Riverton Hospital, Riverton, UT, p. A650

HANLEY, Bob, Chief Human Resources Officer, Comer Children's Hospital, IL, p. A180

HANLEY, Darlene S., R.N., President and Chief Executive Officer, St. Lawrence Rehabilitation Center, Lawrenceville, NJ, p. A406

HANLEY, Mathew, Chief Financial Officer, Osf Healthcare Saint Clare's Hospital, IL, p. A173

HANLEY, Patrick, D.O., Interim Vice President Medical Affairs, St. Luke's - Palmerton Campus, PA, p. A530

HANLON, Jerad, Chief Operating Officer, Southside Regional Medical Center, Petersburg, VA, p. A664

HANLON, John, MD, President and Chief Executive Officer, Little Company Of Mary Hospital And Health Care Centers, Evergreen Park, IL, p. A183

HANNA, Casey, M.D., Chief of Staff, Wagoner Community Hospital, Wagoner, OK, p. A510

HANNA, Mitchell J.
Chief Executive Officer, Sutter Auburn Faith Hospital, Auburn, CA, p. A51
Chief Executive Officer, Sutter Coast Hospital, Crescent City, CA, p. A56

HANNA, Philip S., Chief Executive Officer, North Oak Regional Medical Center, Senatobia, MS, p. A353

HANNA, Robb, Executive Director Information Technology, Lexington Regional Health Center, Lexington, NE, p. A385

HANNAH, Jill, Director Human Resources, James Cancer Hospital And Solove Research Institute, Columbus, OH, p. A478

HANNAPEL, Andrew, Chief Medical Officer, Chatham Hospital, Siler City, NC, p. A460

HANNERS, Brandy, Chief Financial Officer, Sovah Health-Martinsville, Martinsville, VA, p. A661

HANNERS, Rodney B.
Chief Executive Officer, Keck Hospital Of Usc, Los Angeles, CA, p. A68
Chief Executive Officer, Usc Norris Comprehensive Cancer Center, Los Angeles, CA, p. A70

HANNON, Barbara A, R.N., Interim Chief Nursing Officer and Chief Clinical Officer, Curry General Hospital, Gold Beach, OR, p. A513

HANNON, Edward J., FACHE, President, St. Francis Medical Plaza, NE, p. A384

HANNON, Patricia, Chief Nursing Officer, Vaughan Regional Medical Center, Selma, AL, p. A23

HANOLD, Cindy, Chief Nursing Officer, Richland Hospital, Richland Center, WI, p. A702

HANS, Christopher, Chief Financial Officer, Riverside University Health System-Medical Center, Moreno Valley, CA, p. A74

HANSCOM, Kristine, Chief Financial Officer, Tufts Medical Center, Boston, MA, p. A297

HANSCOME, Joyce, Chief Information Officer, Doctors Community Hospital, Lanham, MD, p. A292

HANSEL, Jimmie W., Ph.D., Chief Executive Officer, Edwards County Medical Center, Kinsley, KS, p. A238

HANSEN, Carolyn, Chief Nursing Officer, Bingham Memorial Hospital, Blackfoot, ID, p. A167

HANSEN, Chris, Senior Vice President Ambulatory Services and Chief Information Officer, The University Of Kansas Hospital - Indian Creek Campus, KS, p. A238

HANSEN, Gayle B, R.N.
Chief Integration Officer, Mayo Clinic Health System In Saint James, Saint James, MN, p. A339
Chief Operating Officer, Mayo Clinic Health System In Fairmont, Fairmont, MN, p. A331

HANSEN, James, Chief Financial Officer, Summit Pacific Medical Center, Elma, WA, p. A671

HANSEN, Jay, Director Information Services, Oconee Memorial Hospital, Seneca, SC, p. A556

HANSEN, Karen, Vice President and Chief Operating Officer, Memorial Medical Center Of Ashland, Ashland, WI, p. A689

HANSEN, Kristy, CPA, Chief Financial Officer, Myrtue Medical Center, Harlan, IA, p. A224

HANSEN, Kyle, Corporate Director Information Systems, Riverside Medical Center, Kankakee, IL, p. A187

HANSEN, Kyle A., Chief Executive Officer, Logan Regional Hospital, Logan, UT, p. A647

HANSEN, Laurie
Director Administrative Services, Johnson County Healthcare Center, Buffalo, WY, p. A707
Vice President of Operations, Emory Johns Creek Hospital, Johns Creek, GA, p. A155

HANSEN, Linda, Director Human Resources, Bakersfield Heart Hospital, Bakersfield, CA, p. A51

HANSEN, Michael T., FACHE, President and Chief Executive Officer, Columbus Community Hospital, Columbus, NE, p. A383

HANSEN, Michelle, Director, Richard H. Young Behavioral Health Center, NE, p. A385

HANSEN, Misty, Chief Financial Officer, Diamond Children's Hospital, AZ, p. A37

HANSEN, Paul, Administrator, Maniilaq Health Center, Kotzebue, AK, p. A26

HANSEN, Steven, Director Information Technology, Healdsburg District Hospital, Healdsburg, CA, p. A61

HANSEN, Tim, Interim Chief Human Resource Officer, Denver Health, Denver, CO, p. A98

HANSERT, Benjamin K., Administrator, North Baldwin Infirmary, Bay Minette, AL, p. A14

HANSON, Debbie, Interim Chief Financial Officer, Dickinson County Healthcare System, Iron Mountain, MI, p. A316

HANSON, Denise, Information Technology Specialist, St. Cloud Veterans Affairs Health Care System, Saint Cloud, MN, p. A339

HANSON, Emily, M.D., President, Medical Staff, St. Joseph Memorial Hospital, Murphysboro, IL, p. A190

HANSON, Gregory S., M.D., Chief Executive Officer, Clark Fork Valley Hospital, Plains, MT, p. A378

HANSON, Jane E, R.N.
Chief Operating Officer, Chandler Regional Medical Center, Chandler, AZ, p. A28
Chief Operating Officer, Mercy Gilbert Medical Center, Gilbert, AZ, p. A29

HANSON, Jane E., R.N.
Interim Chief Executive Officer, Chandler Regional Medical Center, Chandler, AZ, p. A28
Interim President and Chief Executive Officer, Mercy Gilbert Medical Center, Gilbert, AZ, p. A29

HANSON, Jesica, Vice President and Chief Financial Officer, Bakersfield Memorial Hospital, Bakersfield, CA, p. A52

HANSON, Jim, Director Information Systems, Avera Queen Of Peace Hospital, Mitchell, SD, p. A562

HANSON, Lesley, Director Human Resources, Lake District Hospital, Lakeview, OR, p. A514

HANSON, Mary Ann, Director Personnel, Mental Health Institute, Cherokee, IA, p. A219

HANSON, Paul A., FACHE, President, Sanford Children's Hospital, SD, p. A564

HANSON, Rhonda, Director Human Resources, Huron Regional Medical Center, Huron, SD, p. A561

HANSON, Rita, M.D.
Vice President Medical Affairs, Ascension Southeast Wisconsin Hospital - Elmbrook Campus, Brookfield, WI, p. A690
Vice President Medical Affairs, Wheaton Franciscan Healthcare - St. Joseph'S, Milwaukee, WI, p. A699

HANSON, Samantha, Chief Human Resources Officer, Children's Hospitals And Clinics Of Minnesota, MN, p. A335

HANSON, Tamra, Human Resource Manager, Dorothea Dix Psychiatric Center, Bangor, ME, p. A282

HANYAK, Diana, Chief Executive Officer, Healthsouth Tustin Rehabilitation Hospital, Tustin, CA, p. A92

HANZLIK, Debra Dawn, R.N., Director of Nursing, Niobrara Valley Hospital, Lynch, NE, p. A386

HAPNEY, Sherry, Chief Financial Officer, Encompass Health Rehabilitation Hospital Of Fort Worth, Fort Worth, TX, p. A604

HAPPEL, Terry J, M.D., Vice President and Chief Medical Officer, Chandler Regional Medical Center, Chandler, AZ, p. A28

HAQQANI, Rahim, M.D., Medical Director, Dallas Behavioral Healthcare Hospital, Desoto, TX, p. A599

HAQUE, Haroon, M.D., Medical Director, Chg Hospital Tucson, Llc, Tucson, AZ, p. A37

HAQUE, Syed, Vice President and Chief Information Officer, Loretto Hospital, Chicago, IL, p. A177

HARA, Karen, Personnel Management Specialist, Hawaii State Hospital, Kaneohe, HI, p. A166

HARALDSON, Richard, CPA, FACHE
Chief Executive Officer, Beatrice Community Hospital And Health Center, Beatrice, NE, p. A382
Chief Executive Officer, Sidney Health Center, Sidney, MT, p. A379

HARALSON, Gregory, FACHE, Senior Vice President and Chief Executive Officer, Memorial Hermann Orthopedic And Spine Hospital, TX, p. A612

HARALSON, Robert, Chief Financial Officer, Williamson Memorial Hospital, Williamson, WV, p. A688

HARARI, Jack L, M.D., Chief Medical Officer, West Boca Medical Center, Boca Raton, FL, p. A118

HARBAUGH, Charles, Director Human Resources, Mountain Lakes Medical Center, Clayton, GA, p. A150

HARBAUGH, Ken, Vice President and Chief Financial Officer, Children's Hospital Of Illinois, IL, p. A193

HARBERTS, Jerry, Information Technologist, Madison Healthcare Services, Madison, MN, p. A334

HARBIN, Cathy
Chief Nursing Officer, Roosevelt Warm Springs Rehabilitation And Specialty Hospitals - Ltac, Warm Springs, GA, p. A162
Chief Nursing Officer, Roosevelt Warm Springs Rehabilitation Hospital - Rehab, Warm Springs, GA, p. A162

HARBIN, Jason, Director of Nursing, Ward Memorial Hospital, Monahans, TX, p. A624

HARBISON, Damon R., President, Ssm Health St. Mary's Hospital Centralia, Centralia, IL, p. A175

HARCHENKO, Vern, M.D., Chief of Staff, Chi St. Alexius Health Garrison, Garrison, ND, p. A466

HARCLERODE, Timothy
Chief Executive Officer, Conemaugh Miners Medical Center, Hastings, PA, p. A527
Chief Executive Officer, Conemaugh Nason Medical Center, Roaring Spring, PA, p. A540

HARCOMBE, Douglas
Administrator, Winter Park Memorial Hospital, FL, p. A134
Chief Executive Officer, Florida Hospital Celebration Health, FL, p. A134

HARCOURT, Jenifer, Chief Operating Officer, Riverwoods Behavioral Health System, Riverdale, GA, p. A159

HARCOURT, Roxane, Interim Administrator, Uf Health Shands Psychiatric Hospital, FL, p. A124

HARCUP, Craig, M.D., Hospital Medical Director, Complex Care Hospital At Ridgelake, Sarasota, FL, p. A138

HARDACRE, Jerry, M.D., Chief of Staff, Ascension All Saints, Racine, WI, p. A701

HARDAGE, Tony, Assistant Vice President and Administrator, Baptist Health Medical Center-Arkadelphia, Arkadelphia, AR, p. A39

HARDAN, Terry, Director Human Resources, Longview Regional Medical Center, Longview, TX, p. A620

HARDCASTLE, Brad, Chief Financial Officer, South Baldwin Regional Medical Center, Foley, AL, p. A18

HARDCASTLE, Kathy, Director Human Resources, Texas Health Presbyterian Hospital Denton, Denton, TX, p. A599

HARDEE, Gary R, M.D., Medical Director, Plains Memorial Hospital, Dimmitt, TX, p. A600

HARDEMAN, Diane, Director Personnel, Stephens County Hospital, Toccoa, GA, p. A162

HARDEN, Diane P
Chief Financial Officer, Leesburg Regional Medical Center, Leesburg, FL, p. A128
Senior Vice President and Chief Financial Officer, The Villages Regional Hospital, The Villages, FL, p. A142

HARDESTY, Keith, Chief Financial Officer, Springfield Hospital Center, Sykesville, MD, p. A294

HARDICK, Cindy, Human Resources Coordinator, Select Specialty Hospital-Ann Arbor, Ypsilanti, MI, p. A326

HARDIE, Rebecca Kay, Chief Nursing Officer, Baylor Scott & White Medical Center - Hillcrest, Waco, TX, p. A642

HARDIN, Cecil, CPA, Chief Financial Officer, Catawba Hospital, Catawba, VA, p. A656

HARDIN, James, Human Resources Officer, Sheridan Veterans Affairs Medical Center, Sheridan, WY, p. A709

HARDIN, Leslie, Chief Executive Officer and Chief Financial Officer, Seymour Hospital, Seymour, TX, p. A635

HARDIN, Marci, Manager Information Technology, Nevada Regional Medical Center, Nevada, MO, p. A365

HARDIN, Mark, M.D., Medical Director, Ed Fraser Memorial Hospital And Baker Community Health Center, Macclenny, FL, p. A128

HARDIN, Nicholas, FACHE, Chief Executive Officer, Encompass Health Rehabilitation Hospital Of Sugar Land, Sugar Land, TX, p. A637

HARDING, Andrew D., R.N.
Chief Nursing Officer, Leonard Morse Hospital, MA, p. A300
Interim Chief Executive Officer, Leonard Morse Hospital, MA, p. A300

HARDING, Barry, Interim Chief Executive Officer and Chief Financial Officer, Sumner Regional Medical Center, Wellington, KS, p. A247

HARDING, Christina, Vice President Finance, Mount Desert Island Hospital, Bar Harbor, ME, p. A282

HARDING, Denise, Director Human Resources, Plumas District Hospital, Quincy, CA, p. A79

HARDING, Edward A., FACHE, President and Chief Executive Officer, Bay Area Medical Center, Marinette, WI, p. A697

HARDING, Geoff, Chief Clinical Officer, Promise Hospital Of Salt Lake, Salt Lake City, UT, p. A650

HARDING, Gwen, Site Manager Information Systems, Bon Secours Memorial Regional Medical Center, Mechanicsville, VA, p. A661

HARDING, Helen, Chief Nursing Officer, Fairfield Medical Center, Lancaster, OH, p. A484

HARDING, John P, Chief Operating Officer, Children's Hospital Of The King's Daughters, Norfolk, VA, p. A662

HARDING, Rick, Chief Executive Officer, Sun Behavioral Houston, Houston, TX, p. A613

HARDISON, Randall, M.D., Chief Medical Officer, Arizona Orthopedic Surgical Hospital, Chandler, AZ, p. A28

HARDMAN, Joe, M.D., Chief Medical Officer, Tuality Forest Grove Hospital, OR, p. A513

HARDWICK, Garry, R.N., Chief Operating Officer, Newport Bay Hospital, Newport Beach, CA, p. A75

HARDY, Bob, Chief Operating Officer, Opelousas General Health System-South Campus, LA, p. A277

HARDY, James, D.O.
Chief Executive Officer, Dayton Veterans Affairs Medical Center, Dayton, OH, p. A480
Chief of Staff, Dayton Veterans Affairs Medical Center, Dayton, OH, p. A480

HARDY, Janice, Chief Human Resource Management Service, Tuskegee Division, AL, p. A21

HARDY, Kevin, Chief Financial Officer, Healthsouth Treasure Coast Rehabilitation Hospital, Vero Beach, FL, p. A142

HARDY, LaBon, Chief Information Officer, Ralph H. Johnson Veterans Affairs Medical Center, Charleston, SC, p. A550

HARDY, Melanie, D.O., Chief of Staff, Marias Medical Center, Shelby, MT, p. A379

HARDY, Raymond, Controller, Healthsouth Rehabilitation Hospital-Las Vegas, Las Vegas, NV, p. A394

HARDY, Valonia, Chief Healthy Living Officer, Tsehootsooi Medical Center, Fort Defiance, AZ, p. A29

HARGENS, Scott James
Administrator and Chief Executive Officer, Avera Dells Area Hospital, Dell Rapids, SD, p. A560
Administrator and Chief Executive Officer, Avera Flandreau Hospital, Flandreau, SD, p. A561

HARGER, Anita
Chief Human Resource Officer, Kingman Regional Medical Center, Kingman, AZ, p. A30
Director Human Resources, Mercy Gilbert Medical Center, Gilbert, AZ, p. A29

HARGETT, Fred M
Executive Vice President and Chief Financial Officer, Novant Health Brunswick Medical Center, Bolivia, NC, p. A448
Executive Vice President and Chief Financial Officer, Novant Health Charlotte Orthopaedic Hospital, Charlotte, NC, p. A450
Executive Vice President and Chief Financial Officer, Novant Health Clemmons Medical Center, NC, p. A462
Executive Vice President and Chief Financial Officer, Novant Health Huntersville Medical Center, Huntersville, NC, p. A455
Executive Vice President and Chief Financial Officer, Novant Health Matthews Medical Center, Matthews, NC, p. A457
Executive Vice President and Chief Financial Officer, Novant Health Medical Park Hospital, Winston, NC, p. A463
Executive Vice President and Chief Financial Officer, Novant Health Rowan Medical Center, Salisbury, NC, p. A460
Executive Vice President and Chief Financial Officer, Novant Health Thomasville Medical Center, Thomasville, NC, p. A461
Executive Vice President and Chief Financial Officer, Presbyterian Hemby Children's Hospital, NC, p. A450

HARGETT, Stephen A, Senior Vice President and Chief Financial Officer, Marina Del Rey Hospital, Marina Del Rey, CA, p. A71

HARGIS, Chris, Manager Finance, Alta View Hospital, Sandy, UT, p. A651

HARGRAVE, Dallas, Human Resources Director, Bartlett Regional Hospital, Juneau, AK, p. A26

HARGRAVE, David, Chief Information Officer, Ward Memorial Hospital, Monahans, TX, p. A624

HARGRAVE-THOMAS, Anne, Chief Executive Officer, Oakleaf Surgical Hospital, Altoona, WI, p. A689

HARGRODER, Ty, M.D., Chief of Staff, Acadia-St. Landry Hospital, Church Point, LA, p. A265

HARGROVE, Ben, Human Resources Director, Lifestream Behavioral Center, Leesburg, FL, p. A128

HARGROVE, Jeno, R.N., Director of Nursing, Columbus Community Hospital, Columbus, TX, p. A593

HARGROVE, Tressa B, Director Human Resources, Jackson Purchase Medical Center, Mayfield, KY, p. A257

HARIHARAN, Parma, M.D., Chief of Staff, Mercy Health - Clermont Hospital, Batavia, OH, p. A471

HARKER, Jodie, Director Human Resources, Van Diest Medical Center, Webster City, IA, p. A231

HARKEY, FACHE, Shirley S, R.N., Vice President, Patient Services, Wayne Unc Health Care, Goldsboro, NC, p. A453

HARKINS, Shelly, M.D.
Chief Medical Officer, Hshs St. Elizabeth's Hospital, O'Fallon, IL, p. A192
Chief Medical Officer, St. Peter's Hospital, Helena, MT, p. A376

HARKLEROAD, Rod, R.N., Chief Executive Officer, Haywood Regional Medical Center, Clyde, NC, p. A450

HARKNESS, Charles, D.O., Vice President Medical Affairs, Southeast Alabama Medical Center, Dothan, AL, p. A17

HARLAN, Kevin W., President, Joint Township District Memorial Hospital, Saint Marys, OH, p. A490

HARLAN, Thomas P., Chief Executive Officer, Continuecare Hospital At Palmetto Health Baptist, Columbia, SC, p. A551

HARLE, Connie, Chief Nursing Officer, Range Regional Health Services, Hibbing, MN, p. A333

HARLESS, Andrea, Director Information Services, Wythe County Community Hospital, Wytheville, VA, p. A668

HARLESS, Cheryl, Chief Nursing Officer, Doctors Medical Center Of Modesto, Modesto, CA, p. A72

HARLIN, Tim, M.D., Chief Operations Officer, Denver Health, Denver, CO, p. A98

HARLING, Roxanne, Chief Nursing Officer, Abraham Lincoln Memorial Hospital, Lincoln, IL, p. A188

HARLOVIC, Michael, R.N., President and Chief Executive Officer, Oswego Hospital, Oswego, NY, p. A439

HARLOW, Donald, Director of Information Services, Mountainview Regional Medical Center, Las Cruces, NM, p. A418

HARLOW, Tammy
Chief Nurse Executive, Riverview Regional Medical Center, Gadsden, AL, p. A18
Director of Nursing, Grady General Hospital, Cairo, GA, p. A149

HARLOW, Thomas R., FACHE, President, Wellspan Good Samaritan Hospital, Lebanon, PA, p. A529

HARLOWE, Michael, President and Chief Executive Officer, Indiana University Health Tipton Hospital, Tipton, IN, p. A215

HARMAN, Kenneth, Chief Executive Officer, Pioneers Medical Center, Meeker, CO, p. A104

HARMAN, Kimberly, Regional Manager Human Resources, Western State Hospital, Staunton, VA, p. A666

HARMATZ, Alan, M.D., Chief Medical Officer, Blake Medical Center, Bradenton, FL, p. A118

HARMON, Amy, Chief Financial Officer, Elkview General Hospital, Hobart, OK, p. A499

HARMON, Connie, Director of Nursing, Lakeland Hospital, Watervliet, Watervliet, MI, p. A325

HARMON, David, D.O., Vice President Medical Services, Rivervalley Behavioral Health Hospital, Owensboro, KY, p. A259

HARMON, James
Information Technology, Cypress Creek Hospital, Houston, TX, p. A610
Network Administrator, West Oaks Hospital, Houston, TX, p. A614

HARMON, Jennifer, Director of Human Resources, St. Cloud Regional Medical Center, Saint Cloud, FL, p. A138

HARMON, Thomas, M.D., Vice President Medical Affairs, Ohiohealth Riverside Methodist Hospital, Columbus, OH, p. A479

HARMOND, Joshua, Assistant Chief Financial Officer, Physicians' Specialty Hospital, Fayetteville-Washington County, AR, p. A41

HARMS, Arlene, Chief Executive Officer, Rio Grande Hospital, Del Norte, CO, p. A98

HARMS, George
Chief Financial Officer, Hays Medical Center, Hays, KS, p. A236
Chief Financial Officer, Pawnee Valley Community Hospital, Larned, KS, p. A239

HARNED, Barbara, R.N., MSN, Chief Nursing Officer, Monroe County Hospital, Monroeville, AL, p. A21

HARNESS, Phil, Chief Executive Officer, Doctor's Hospital, Leawood, KS, p. A239

HARNEY, Geraldine, Chief Financial Officer, U.S. Public Health Service Phoenix Indian Medical Center, Phoenix, AZ, p. A34

HARPE, Michael, Vice President Human Resources, Community Hospital Of Anderson & Madison County, Anderson, IN, p. A199

HARPER, Cindy, Manager Patient Data, Westfield Memorial Hospital, Westfield, NY, p. A446

HARPER, Corwin N
Administrator, Modesto Medical Center, CA, p. A71
Senior Vice President and Area Manager, Modesto Medical Center, CA, p. A71

HARPER, Corwin N.
Senior Vice President and Area Manager, Kaiser Permanente Vallejo Medical Center, Vallejo, CA, p. A93
Senior Vice President and Area Manager, Modesto Medical Center, CA, p. A71

HARPER, David
Chief Information Officer, Wills Memorial Hospital, Washington, GA, p. A163
Director, Site Information Systems, Advocate Eureka Hospital, Eureka, IL, p. A182

HARPER, Eric, Chief Information Officer, Southeastern Health, Lumberton, NC, p. A456

HARPER, Heather L., FACHE, Chief Executive Officer, Lovelace Regional Hospital - Roswell, Roswell, NM, p. A419

HARPER, James F, Senior Vice President and Chief Human Resources Officer, Tidelands Georgetown Memorial Hospital, Georgetown, SC, p. A553

HARPER, Kirk, R.N., Vice President, Nursing, Kadlec Regional Medical Center, Richland, WA, p. A676

HARPER, R Andrew, M.D., Medical Director, University Of Texas Harris County Psychiatric Center, Houston, TX, p. A614

HARPER, Wally G, Vice President Human Resources, Gaylord Hospital, Wallingford, CT, p. A111

HARPER, William F, M.D., Chief of Staff, Birmingham Veterans Affairs Medical Center, Birmingham, AL, p. A14

HARPER-O'CONNOR, Paul
Interim Administrator, Lanai Community Hospital, Lanai City, HI, p. A166
Interim Chief Executive Officer, Kula Hospital, Kula, HI, p. A166

HARR, Donald, Controller, Ray County Memorial Hospital, Richmond, MO, p. A366

HARREL, Mark, Chief Executive Officer, Phelps Memorial Health Center, Holdrege, NE, p. A385

HARRELL, Aaron, Director, Grove Hill Memorial Hospital, Grove Hill, AL, p. A19

HARRELL, Joy, R.N., Chief Nursing Officer, Mimbres Memorial Hospital, Deming, NM, p. A417

HARRELL, Michael, R.N.
Chief Executive Officer, Promise Hospital Of Miss Lou, Vidalia, LA, p. A280
Chief Executive Officer, Promise Hospital Of Vicksburg, Vicksburg, MS, p. A354

HARRELL, Paula, Chief Nursing Officer, Regional One Health Extended Care Hospital, Memphis, TN, p. A575

HARRELL, Steven W, FACHE, Chief Operating Officer, Florida Hospital New Smyrna, New Smyrna Beach, FL, p. A132

HARRELL, Thomas, M.D., Commander, U.S. Air Force Medical Center Keesler, Keesler Afb, MS, p. A348

HARRELSON, Rick, M.D., President Medical Staff, Medical Center Enterprise, Enterprise, AL, p. A17

HARRIER, Margie, MSN, R.N., Medical Center Chief Operations Officer, Orange County Irvine Medical Center, CA, p. A50

HARRIGER, Richard, Director of Emergency Services, Kimball Health Services, Kimball, NE, p. A385

HARRILSON, Annette, Chief Executive Officer, Select Specialty Hospital Midtown Atlanta, Atlanta, GA, p. A147

HARRINGTON, Dawn, Chief Information Officer, Unm Children's Hospital, NM, p. A416

HARRINGTON, Hal, Vice President Human Resources, River Region West Campus, MS, p. A354

HARRINGTON, Jason, FACHE, President and Chief Executive Officer, Lakes Regional Healthcare, Spirit Lake, IA, p. A230

HARRINGTON, Jeff, Chief Financial Officer, Children's Hospital Of Colorado At Memorial, CO, p. A96

HARRINGTON, Joseph P., Interim Chief Executive Officer, Healdsburg District Hospital, Healdsburg, CA, p. A61

HARRINGTON, Kathleen, Vice President Human Resources, Beth Israel Deaconess Hospital-Milton, Milton, MA, p. A302

HARRIS, Alicia, Director Fiscal Services, Whitfield Medical Surgical Hospital, MS, p. A354

HARRIS, Allen, M.D., Clinical Director, South Mississippi State Hospital, Purvis, MS, p. A352

HARRIS, Betty J, Director Human Resources, Southern California Hospital At Culver City, Culver City, CA, p. A56

HARRIS, Burt
Acting Chief Executive Officer, Canyon Ridge Hospital, Chino, CA, p. A54
Chief Financial Officer, Canyon Ridge Hospital, Chino, CA, p. A54

HARRIS, C Martin, M.D.
Chief Information Officer, Cleveland Clinic Children's Hospital For Rehabilitation, Cleveland, OH, p. A476
Chief Information Officer, Cleveland Clinic Fairview Hospital, Cleveland, OH, p. A476
Chief Information Officer, Lutheran Hospital, Cleveland, OH, p. A477

HARRIS, David, Director Information Systems, De Queen Medical Center, De Queen-Sevier County, AR, p. A41

HARRIS, Denise H., R.N., MSN, Chief Nursing Officer, Baptist Health South Florida, West Kendall Baptist Hospital, Miami, FL, p. A130

HARRIS, Diana, Chief Nursing Officer, Cape Fear Valley - Bladen County Hospital, Elizabethtown, NC, p. A452

HARRIS, Donna, Chief Executive Officer, Healthsouth Rehabilitation Hospital Of Jonesboro, Jonesboro-Craighead County, AR, p. A44

HARRIS, Dory, Director Human Resource, Teton Valley Health Care, Driggs, ID, p. A169

HARRIS, Ethan, Manager Information Systems, Mid-Valley Hospital, Omak, WA, p. A674

HARRIS, Howard, Vice President Human Resources, Regional Medical Center, Orangeburg, SC, p. A556

HARRIS, Jan, R.N., Director of Nursing, Stonewall Memorial Hospital, Aspermont, TX, p. A584

HARRIS, Janice M, Director Human Resources, University Medical Center Of El Paso, El Paso, TX, p. A603

HARRIS, Jen, Director Health Information Management, Chase County Community Hospital, Imperial, NE, p. A385

HARRIS, Jerald, Chief Information Officer, Cornerstone Hospital Of Houston - Bellaire, TX, p. A643

HARRIS, Jim
Director Information Technology, Grafton City Hospital, Grafton, WV, p. A683
Vice President Human Resources, Fairmont Regional Medical Center, Fairmont, WV, p. A683

HARRIS, Jo ell, R.N., Chief Nursing Officer, Forest View Psychiatric Hospital, Grand Rapids, MI, p. A314

HARRIS, Joanne, Director Human Resources, Mount Desert Island Hospital, Bar Harbor, ME, p. A282

HARRIS, John, Chief Executive Officer, Memorial Medical Center, Las Cruces, NM, p. A418

HARRIS, John B., Vice President Finance and Chief Financial Officer, Community Hospital Of Anderson & Madison County, Anderson, IN, p. A199

HARRIS, Julie
Chief Financial Officer, Riceland Medical Center, Winnie, TX, p. A644
Controller, Anmed Health Rehabilitation Hospital, Anderson, SC, p. A549

HARRIS, Karen, R.N., Chief Nursing and Operations Officer, Henry Ford West Bloomfield Hospital, West Bloomfield, MI, p. A325

HARRIS, Kathy, Vice President, Mercyhealth Hospital And Trauma Center - Janesville, Janesville, WI, p. A695

HARRIS, Kevin, Director Information Systems, Titus Regional Medical Center, Mount Pleasant, TX, p. A624

HARRIS, Kristin, Chief Executive Officer, Garland Behavioral Hospital, Garland, TX, p. A606

HARRIS, Laurie, Chief Accountant, Kerrville State Hospital, Kerrville, TX, p. A617

HARRIS, Lee, Assistant Administrator Support Services, Memorial Hospital And Manor, Bainbridge, GA, p. A148

HARRIS, Leslie, Chief Nursing Officer, Forrest City Medical Center, Forrest City-St. Francis County, AR, p. A42

HARRIS, Lisa E., M.D., Chief Executive Officer, Eskenazi Health, Indianapolis, IN, p. A206

HARRIS, Madeline, R.N., Vice President and Chief Nursing Officer, Queen's Medical Center - West Oahu, HI, p. A165

HARRIS, Marianna, Administrator, Osborne County Memorial Hospital, Osborne, KS, p. A243

HARRIS, Mark D, Deputy Commander Clinical Services, Fort Belvoir Community Hospital, Fort Belvoir, VA, p. A658

HARRIS, Merilyn, Administrator, Ka'U Hospital, Pahala, HI, p. A166

HARRIS, Michael, M.D., Chief Medical Officer, Englewood Hospital And Medical Center, Englewood, NJ, p. A405

HARRIS, Miriam, Director Finance, Oklahoma Forensic Center, Vinita, OK, p. A509

HARRIS, R Brian, M.D., Chief of Staff, Reeves Memorial Medical Center, Bernice, LA, p. A264

HARRIS, Robert M, M.D., President Medical and Dental Staff, New Bridge Medical Center, Paramus, NJ, p. A409

HARRIS, Shelly, Chief Executive Officer, Indian Health Service - Quentin N. Burdick Memorial Health Care Facility, Belcourt, ND, p. A464

HARRIS, Shirley, M.D., President Medical Staff, Ssm Health St. Francis Hospital - Maryville, Maryville, MO, p. A364

HARRIS, Spencer, Senior Director Finance, Kadlec Regional Medical Center, Richland, WA, p. A676

HARRIS, Stuart, M.D., Chief of Staff, Trigg County Hospital, Cadiz, KY, p. A250

HARRIS, Sue, Vice President and Chief Nursing Officer, Methodist Medical Center Of Oak Ridge, Oak Ridge, TN, p. A578

HARRIS, Susan, R.N.
Chief Operating Officer, Children's Hospital, Navicent Health, GA, p. A156
Director Fiscal Services, Shriners Hospitals For Children - Cincinnati, Cincinnati, OH, p. A475

HARRIS, Sylvia, Fiscal Director, Moccasin Bend Mental Health Institute, Chattanooga, TN, p. A567

HARRIS, Timothy, M.D., Chief Quality Officer, Texas Health Presbyterian Hospital Denton, Denton, TX, p. A599

HARRIS, Vena, Director Human Resources, Minneola District Hospital, Minneola, KS, p. A241

HARRIS, William R, Chief Information Officer, Lawton Indian Hospital, Lawton, OK, p. A500

HARRISON, Allen, Chief Executive Officer, Northeast Methodist Hospital, TX, p. A633

HARRISON, Charles, Chief Executive Officer, San Bernardino Mountains Community Hospital District, Lake Arrowhead, CA, p. A63

HARRISON, Chris, Manager Information Systems, Campbell County Health, Gillette, WY, p. A708

HARRISON, Denise, Associate Director, Veterans Affairs Nebraska-Western Iowa Health Care System, Omaha, NE, p. A389

HARRISON, Dyan, Manager Health Information, Ochiltree General Hospital, Perryton, TX, p. A628

HARRISON, George E., M.D., Chief Medical Officer, Fairview Park Hospital, Dublin, GA, p. A153

HARRISON, Jo L, Vice President of Patient Care Services, Southwest Medical Center, Liberal, KS, p. A240

HARRISON, Kathleen, Chief Executive Officer, Mccready Health, Crisfield, MD, p. A291

HARRISON, Marva, R.N., Vice President and Chief Nursing Officer, Integris Southwest Medical Center, Oklahoma City, OK, p. A503

HARRISON, Randy, Chief Financial Officer, Raleigh General Hospital, Beckley, WV, p. A681

HARROD, Tracy, Director of Nursing, Greenwood County Hospital, Eureka, KS, p. A235

HARRON, Rick, Chief Financial Officer, Dominican Hospital, Santa Cruz, CA, p. A88

HARROP, Elizabeth, Director, Human Resources, Flambeau Hospital, Park Falls, WI, p. A701

HARSHAWAT, Paras, M.D., Medical Director, Harsha Behavioral Center, Terre Haute, IN, p. A215

HARSHAWAT, Roopam, Chief Executive Officer, Harsha Behavioral Center, Terre Haute, IN, p. A215

HARSHBARGER, Catherine S., R.N., Chief Executive Officer, Banner Lassen Medical Center, Susanville, CA, p. A91

HARSY, Brice, Chief Financial Officer, Marshall Browning Hospital, Du Quoin, IL, p. A181

HART, Amy, Chief Operating Officer, Cuyuna Regional Medical Center, Crosby, MN, p. A330

HART, Denise, Director Human Resources, Sullivan County Community Hospital, Sullivan, IN, p. A215

HART, Donna, Chief Information Officer, Provident Hospital Of Cook County, Chicago, IL, p. A179

HART, Elizabeth, R.N., MSN, Chief Nursing Officer, Providence Saint Joseph Medical Center, Burbank, CA, p. A53

HART, Gary, M.D., Chief Medical Officer, West Park Hospital, Cody, WY, p. A708

HART, James, M.D., Medical Director, Rolling Hills Hospital, Franklin, TN, p. A570

HART, Joline, Vice President Human Resources, Franklin Memorial Hospital, Farmington, ME, p. A284

HART, Joseph, Director Finance and Support Services, Putnam Hospital Center, Carmel, NY, p. A424

HART, Kenneth, President, Saint Alphonsus Medical Center - Ontario, Ontario, OR, p. A515

HART, Lisa, Chief Executive Officer, Elkview General Hospital, Hobart, OK, p. A499

HART, Monique, Chief Financial Officer, Baptist Memorial Hospital-Tipton, Covington, TN, p. A568

HART, Pat, Director Human Resources, Three Rivers Medical Center, Louisa, KY, p. A255

HART, Richard, Chief Financial Officer, Stanislaus Surgical Hospital, Modesto, CA, p. A73

HART, Scott, Controller, Healthsouth Lakeview Rehabilitation Hospital, Elizabethtown, KY, p. A251

HART-FLYNN, Wilma, MSN, Ph.D., R.N., Chief Nursing Officer, Morristown-Hamblen Healthcare System, Morristown, TN, p. A576

HARTBERG, David, Chief Executive Officer, Gundersen Boscobel Area Hospital And Clinics, Boscobel, WI, p. A690

HARTGRAVES, Steve L., President and Chief Executive Officer, Jackson County Memorial Hospital, Altus, OK, p. A495

HARTKE, Michael, Executive Vice President, Chief Operating Officer, Northwest Community Hospital, Arlington Heights, IL, p. A173

HARTLEY, Barbara, Chief Medical Officer, Benson Hospital, Benson, AZ, p. A28

HARTLEY, Diane L, Director of Patient Care Services, Beaumont Hospital, Wayne, Wayne, MI, p. A325

HARTLEY, Melinda D., R.N., Vice President Patient Care Services, Perry Hospital, Perry, GA, p. A158

HARTLEY, Michael, MS, Chief Nursing Officer, Holly Hill Hospital, Raleigh, NC, p. A459

HARTLEY, Randall W, Chief Operating Officer, Nemours Children's Hospital, Orlando, FL, p. A134

HARTLEY, Shauna, Administrator, Turquoise Lodge Hospital, Albuquerque, NM, p. A416

HARTLEY, Shawn
 Chief Financial Officer, Caldwell Unc Health Care, Lenoir, NC, p. A456
 Chief Financial Officer, Nash Health Care Systems, Rocky Mount, NC, p. A459

HARTLEY, Wannah, Controller, Winkler County Memorial Hospital, Kermit, TX, p. A617

HARTMAN, Daphane, Director Information Systems, College Station Medical Center, College Station, TX, p. A593

HARTMAN, Don, Director Human Resources, Sutter Davis Hospital, Davis, CA, p. A56

HARTMAN, Kathleen, Chief Nursing Officer, Metrosouth Medical Center, Blue Island, IL, p. A174

HARTMAN, Mark, Interim Chief Financial Officer, St. Joseph Medical Center In The Heights, TX, p. A613

HARTMAN, Sally, Senior Vice President, Riverside Behavioral Health Center, VA, p. A662

HARTMAN, Susan, Chief Executive Officer, Healthsouth Nittany Valley Rehabilitation Hospital, Pleasant Gap, PA, p. A538

HARTMANN, Doreen, Chief Financial Officer, St. Joseph's Behavioral Health Center, Stockton, CA, p. A91

HARTMANN, Margot, M.D., Ph.D., President and Chief Executive Officer, Nantucket Cottage Hospital, Nantucket, MA, p. A302

HARTMANN, Peter M, M.D., Vice President Medical Affairs, Wellspan York Hospital, York, PA, p. A546

HARTMANN, Rob, Assistant Director Human Resources Management, University Health Conway, Monroe, LA, p. A274

HARTNETT, Tammy, Employee Relations Manager, Unitypoint Health - St. Lukes's Sioux City, Sioux City, IA, p. A230

HARTSELL, Henry, Ph.D., Executive Director, Griffin Memorial Hospital, Norman, OK, p. A502

HARTSELL, Scott, Chief Operating Officer, Bayfront Health Spring Hill, FL, p. A119

HARTTER, Lynn E, Jr, Director Human Resources, Nemaha Valley Community Hospital, Seneca, KS, p. A245

HARTUNG, Andy, Director Information Systems, Self Regional Healthcare, Greenwood, SC, p. A554

HARTWELL, Tim, Chief Human Resources, Marion Veterans Affairs Medical Center, Marion, IL, p. A188

HARTWICK, Bryan
 Vice President Human Resources, Alton Memorial Hospital, Alton, IL, p. A173
 Vice President Human Resources, Christian Hospital, Saint Louis, MO, p. A368

HARTWIG, Michael, M.D., Chief of Staff, Perry Memorial Hospital, Perry, OK, p. A505

HARTZOG, Rick, Chief Information Officer, Merit Health Madison, Canton, MS, p. A344

HARVEY, Alice, Director of Nursing, Heatherhill Care Communities, Chardon, OH, p. A474

HARVEY, Anne, MSN, Chief Nursing Officer, El Paso Specialty Hospital, El Paso, TX, p. A601

HARVEY, Jennifer, Director Human Resources, Golden Plains Community Hospital, Borger, TX, p. A589

HARVEY, John, M.D.
 Chief Executive Officer, Oklahoma Heart Hospital South Campus, Oklahoma City, OK, p. A504
 Chief Executive Officer, Oklahoma Heart Hospital, Oklahoma City, OK, p. A504

HARVEY, Kathy, D.O., Chief Medical Officer, Logan Regional Medical Center, Logan, WV, p. A684

HARVEY, Kevin, Chief Financial Officer, Mckenzie Regional Hospital, Mckenzie, TN, p. A574

HARVEY, Linda, Chief Financial Officer, West Feliciana Parish Hospital, Saint Francisville, LA, p. A278

HARVEY, Michael, FACHE, President and Chief Executive Officer, Community Memorial Hospital, Syracuse, NE, p. A390

HARVEY, Paul
 Chief Executive Officer, Christus Mother Frances Hospital - Winnsboro, Winnsboro, TX, p. A644
 President and Chief Executive Officer, Christus Mother Frances Hospital - Sulphur Springs, Sulphur Springs, TX, p. A637

HARVILL, Brian
 Vice President Financial Services, Vidant Bertie Hospital, Windsor, NC, p. A462
 Vice President Financial Services, Vidant Chowan Hospital, Edenton, NC, p. A452

HARVIN, Schley, Information Technology Technician, Hood Memorial Hospital, Amite, LA, p. A262

HASBROUCK, Matthew Steven, Chief Operating Officer, Memorial Children's Hospital, GA, p. A160

HASELTON, David, Chief Medical Officer, Riverton Hospital, Riverton, UT, p. A650

HASHMI, Faraz
 Chief Executive Officer, Central Hospital Of Bowie, Bowie, TX, p. A590
 Chief Executive Officer, Texas General Hospital - Van Zandt Regional Medical Center, Grand Saline, TX, p. A607

HASHMI, Mubashir, Chief Information Officer, Pacifica Hospital Of The Valley, Los Angeles, CA, p. A69

HASHMI, Suleman, President and Chief Executive Officer, Texas General Hospital, Grand Prairie, TX, p. A607

HASKELL, Jeffrey, M.D., Chief Medical Staff, Lost Rivers Medical Center, Arco, ID, p. A167

HASKINS, Don, Administrative Director Human Resources, Southwest Mississippi Regional Medical Center, Mccomb, MS, p. A350

HASLETT, Tom, Interim Chief Information Officer, Macneal Hospital, Berwyn, IL, p. A174

HASNI, Kamran, M.D., Chief of Medical Staff, Barbourville Arh Hospital, Barbourville, KY, p. A249

HASS, Roxanne, Director of Nursing, Chi St. Joseph Health Madison Hospital, Madisonville, TX, p. A622

HASSAN, Tariq, M.D., Associate Director of Patient Care, Captain James A. Lovell Federal Health Care Center, North Chicago, IL, p. A191

HASSANI, Dahlia, Vice President of Medical Affairs, Baylor All Saints Medical Center At Fort Worth, Fort Worth, TX, p. A604

HASSELBRACK, Jeni, Director Human Resources, Gordon Hospital, Calhoun, GA, p. A149

HAST, Anne S, R.N., Director of Nursing, Advanced Surgical Hospital, Washington, PA, p. A543

HAST, Anne S., R.N., Chief Executive Officer, Advanced Surgical Hospital, Washington, PA, p. A543

HASTIN, Kathy, Administrative Assistant Human Resources, River Valley Medical Center, Dardanelle-Yell County, AR, p. A41

HASTINGS, Clare, R.N., Ph.D., Chief Nurse Officer, Children's Inn At Nih, MD, p. A290

HASTINGS, Sarah M, Executive Director, Ridgeview Medical Center, Waconia, MN, p. A341

HATCH, Brooke, Director Human Resource, Bradley County Medical Center, Warren-Bradley County, AR, p. A49

HATCH, Tammy, Manager, Sebasticook Valley Health, Pittsfield, ME, p. A285

HATCHER, Amy, Senior Vice President and Chief Financial Officer, Children's Hospital And Medical Center, Omaha, NE, p. A388

HATCHER, Julie, Vice President Human Resources, O'Connor Hospital, San Jose, CA, p. A86

HATCHES, Ann
 Director, Human Resources, Holy Cross Hospital, Chicago, IL, p. A177
 Interim Director Human Resources, Sinai Children's Hospital, IL, p. A178

HATFIELD, Chad, Chief Executive Officer, Northeast Georgia Medical Center Barrow, Winder, GA, p. A163

HATFIELD, Jonathan, Supervisor Information Technology, Klickitat Valley Health, Goldendale, WA, p. A672

HATFIELD, Timothy A., Community Chief Executive Officer, Tug Valley Arh Regional Medical Center, South Williamson, KY, p. A260

HATHAWAY, William, M.D., Chief Medical Officer, Mission Hospital, NC, p. A447

HATHCOCK, Claudette
 Administrative Director Human Resources, University Of Mississippi Medical Center Grenada, Grenada, MS, p. A346
 Human Resources Director, University Of Mississippi Medical Center Holmes County, Lexington, MS, p. A349

HATIRAS, Spiros, FACHE, President and Chief Executive Officer, Holyoke Medical Center, Holyoke, MA, p. A300

HATLESTAD, Jill, Vice President Human Resources and Marketing, Glencoe Regional Health Services, Glencoe, MN, p. A332

HATMAKER, Michael, Vice President Support Services and Admin Nursing Home, Leconte Medical Center, Sevierville, TN, p. A579

HATTEM-SCHIFFMAN, Marita, President, Midmichigan Medical Center-Gratiot, Alma, MI, p. A307

HATTER, Jason, Chief Human Resource Officer, Princeton Baptist Medical Center, Birmingham, AL, p. A15

HATTERER-HOAG, Dawn, Director Human Resources, Psychiatric Institute Of Washington, Washington, DC, p. A116

HATTON, Tad
 Chief Operating Officer, St. David's Round Rock Medical Center, Round Rock, TX, p. A631
 Vice President Chief Operating Officer, Seton Medical Center Austin, Austin, TX, p. A586

HAUBL, Eileen, Senior Vice President and Chief Financial Officer, Mission Hospital Laguna Beach, CA, p. A72

HAUG, Darin L., D.O.
 President & Chief Executive Officer, Fitzgibbon Hospital, Marshall, MO, p. A364
 President and Chief Executive Officer, Fitzgibbon Hospital, Marshall, MO, p. A364

HAUGE, Meri, R.N., MSN, Associate Director of Patient Care Services and Nurse Executive, St. Cloud Veterans Affairs Health Care System, Saint Cloud, MN, p. A339

HAUGER, Clint, Chief Executive Officer, Palmetto Lowcountry Behavioral Health, Charleston, SC, p. A550

HAUGH, William, Administrator, Georgetown Community Hospital, Georgetown, KY, p. A252

HAUGHEY, Tracie, Chief Executive Officer and Chief Financial Officer, Wills Memorial Hospital, Washington, GA, p. A163

HAULER, Jennifer, D.O., Chief Medical Officer, Upper Valley Medical Center, Troy, OH, p. A492

HAUPERT, John M., FACHE, President and Chief Executive Officer, Grady Memorial Hospital, Atlanta, GA, p. A146

HAUPT, Carolyn, Chief Financial Officer, Peacehealth United General Medical Center, Sedro, WA, p. A677

HAUPT, William, Administrator, Florida Hospital Kissimmee, FL, p. A134

HAUSAUER, Patricia K, Director Finance, Baptist Medical Center Nassau, Fernandina Beach, FL, p. A122

HAUSE, Eileen, Chief Executive Officer, Kensington Hospital, Philadelphia, PA, p. A535

HAUSER, Mark J, M.D., Chief Medical Officer, Baptist Children's Hospital, FL, p. A129

HAUSER, Megan, Director Human Resources, Shriners Hospitals For Children-Philadelphia, Philadelphia, PA, p. A536

HAUSHALTER, Brandon, Chief Executive Officer, Kendall Regional Medical Center, Miami, FL, p. A130

HAUSHALTER, Richard L, Senior Vice President Operations and Chief Operating Officer, Sentara Rmh Medical Center, Harrisonburg, VA, p. A659

HAUSMANN, Jena, President and Chief Executive Officer, Children's Hospital Of Colorado At Memorial, CO, p. A96

HAVARD, Greg, Chief Executive Officer, George Regional Hospital, Lucedale, MS, p. A349

HAVEN, Adrian C, Site Manager, Gallup Indian Medical Center, Gallup, NM, p. A417

HAVENS, Jennifer, Chief Executive Officer, Unitypoint Health - Grinnell Regional Medical Center, Grinnell, IA, p. A223

HAVERSTOCK, Loren, Manager Human Resources, Harrison County Hospital, Corydon, IN, p. A201

HAVICAN, Gary C.
 President, Midstate Medical Center, Meriden, CT, p. A108
 President, New Britain General, CT, p. A109

HAVRILLA, David A, Chief Financial Officer, Medstar Montgomery Medical Center, Olney, MD, p. A293

HAWIG, Scott
 Senior Vice President Finance, Chief Financial Officer and Treasurer, Froedtert And The Medical College Of Wisconsin Froedtert Hospital, Milwaukee, WI, p. A698
 Senior Vice President of Finance, Chief Financial Officer and Treasurer, Community Memorial Hospital, Menomonee Falls, WI, p. A697
 Senior Vice President of Finance, Chief Financial Officer and Treasurer, St. Joseph's Hospital, West Bend, WI, p. A706

HAWK, Kevin, Chief Executive Officer, Hillcrest Hospital Cushing, Cushing, OK, p. A497

HAWKEY, Tammy, Manager Information Technology Client Services, Ministry Good Samaritan Health Center, Weston, WI, p. A706

HAWKINS, Bryan, Controller, Firsthealth Montgomery Memorial Hospital, Troy, NC, p. A461

HAWKINS, Ellis, President, Ssm Health Depaul Hospital - St. Louis, Bridgeton, MO, p. A356

HAWKINS, Hillary, M.D., Medical Director, Sheltering Arms Rehabilitation Hospital, Mechanicsville, VA, p. A661

HAWKINS, Jason F., Chief Administrative Officer, Peacehealth Peace Harbor Medical Center, Florence, OR, p. A512

HAWKINS, Kidada, Chief Executive Officer, Shoals Hospital, Muscle Shoals, AL, p. A22

HAWKINS, Roy L., Jr, Senior Vice President and Chief Executive Officer, Jackson North Medical Center, FL, p. A130

HAWKINS, Sheri, Chief Nursing Officer, Shawnee Mission Medical Center, Shawnee Mission, KS, p. A246

HAWKINS, Tami, R.N., MSN, Vice President Patient Care and Chief Nursing Officer, Texas Health Presbyterian Hospital Of Rockwall, Rockwall, TX, p. A631

HAWKINSON, Curtis R., Chief Executive Officer, Community Memorial Healthcare, Marysville, KS, p. A241

HAWLEY, Jason, Director of Information Services and Security, Yuma District Hospital, Yuma, CO, p. A106

HAWLEY, William, President and Chief Executive Officer, Fawcett Memorial Hospital, Port Charlotte, FL, p. A137

HAWLIK, Teresa, MSN, Chief Nurse Executive, Nebraska Spine Hospital, Omaha, NE, p. A388

HAWS, Bradley, Chief Financial Officer, University Of Iowa Stead Family Children's Hospital, IA, p. A224

HAWTHORNE, Caryn, Vice President Finance and Chief Finance Officer, East Tennessee Children's Hospital, Knoxville, TN, p. A572

HAWTHORNE, Kimberly, Administrator, Mayo Clinic Health System - Franciscan Healthcare In Sparta, Sparta, WI, p. A703

HAWTOF, Jeffrey, M.D., Vice President Medical Operations and Informatics, Beebe Healthcare, Lewes, DE, p. A113

HAY, Fraser, President, Texas Health Springwood, TX, p. A588

HAYDEN, Crystal, MSN, R.N., Senior Vice President and Chief Nursing Officer, Nash Health Care Systems, Rocky Mount, NC, p. A459

HAYDEN, James, M.D., Chief Medical Officer, J. C. Blair Memorial Hospital, Huntingdon, PA, p. A527

HAYDEN, Jamie, Chief Financial Officer, Eastland Memorial Hospital, Eastland, TX, p. A600

HAYDEN, John
Senior Vice President and Chief Human Resources Officer, Bronson Lakeview Hospital, Paw Paw, MI, p. A320
Senior Vice President and Human Resources Officer, Main Campus, MI, p. A308
Vice President and Chief Human Resources Officer, Children's Hospital At Bronson, MI, p. A317

HAYDEN, Karen, Director Health Information Services, Performance Improvement and Risk Management, Valle Vista Hospital, Greenwood, IN, p. A205

HAYDEN-PUGH, Beverly P., R.N., Senior Vice President and Chief Nursing Officer, Valley Children's Healthcare, Madera, CA, p. A71

HAYEK, Anthony, D.O., Medical Director, Edwin Shaw Rehab, Cuyahoga Falls, OH, p. A480

HAYES, Barbara, Chief Executive Officer, Palacios Community Medical Center, Palacios, TX, p. A626

HAYES, David R, Chief Financial Officer, T.J. Health Columbia, Columbia, KY, p. A250

HAYES, Deborah Marie, R.N., MS, MSN, Chief Operating Officer, Christ Hospital, Cincinnati, OH, p. A474

HAYES, Di, Chief Executive Officer, Hallmark Youthcare - Richmond, Richmond, VA, p. A665

HAYES, Donna, Controller, Decatur County General Hospital, Parsons, TN, p. A578

HAYES, Elaine, Controller, Sts. Mary & Elizabeth Hospital, Louisville, KY, p. A256

HAYES, Farrell, Chief Financial Officer, Chi Memorial Hospital - Georgia, Fort Oglethorpe, GA, p. A154

HAYES, James L, Director Human Resources, Western State Hospital, Hopkinsville, KY, p. A253

HAYES, Jo, Chief Nursing Officer, Horn Memorial Hospital, Ida Grove, IA, p. A224

HAYES, June, Chief Financial Officer, Harrisburg Medical Center, Harrisburg, IL, p. A184

HAYES, Kathe, Executive Director, Western New York Children's Hospital Psychiatric Center, West Seneca, NY, p. A446

HAYES, Kelly, Chief Financial Officer, Methodist Hospital For Surgery, Addison, TX, p. A582

HAYES, Kevin, M.D., Chief of Staff, Monroe Regional Hospital, Aberdeen, MS, p. A343

HAYES, Lisa G., Chief Clinical Officer, Amg Specialty Hospital - Muncie, Muncie, IN, p. A211

HAYES, Lynnette, Chief Nursing Officer, Golden Valley Memorial Healthcare, Clinton, MO, p. A357

HAYES, Paul, R.N., Executive Director, Uw Medicine/ Harborview Medical Center, Seattle, WA, p. A677

HAYES, Stacy, R.N., Chief Nursing Officer, Arizona Spine And Joint Hospital, Mesa, AZ, p. A31

HAYES, Susan, Director Human Resources, Southeastern Health, Lumberton, NC, p. A456

HAYES, Tammy A., R.N., MS, Chief Nurse Executive and Long Term Care Administrator, Northfield Hospital And Clinics, Northfield, MN, p. A336

HAYES, Thomas P., Chief Executive Officer, Eastern Plumas Health Care, Portola, CA, p. A79

HAYES, Warren, Chief of Staff, Montgomery County Memorial Hospital, Red Oak, IA, p. A228

HAYES, William M., Chief Executive Officer, Northside Hospital-Cherokee, Canton, GA, p. A149

HAYGOOD, Rachel Joy, Director Information Technology, Tyler County Hospital, Woodville, TX, p. A645

HAYHURST, Leslie, Director Information Systems, Washington Health System Greene, Waynesburg, PA, p. A543

HAYMAN, Judy A., Ph.D., Director, Syracuse Veterans Affairs Medical Center, Syracuse, NY, p. A444

HAYN, Jed, Chief Information Officer, Walter B. Jones Alcohol And Drug Abuse Treatment Center, Greenville, NC, p. A454

HAYNES, Deatosha D., Interim Associates Director for Patient, Veterans Affairs Gulf Coast Veterans Health Care System, Biloxi, MS, p. A343

HAYNES, Elaine S, R.N., MSN, Vice President Patient Services and Chief Nursing Executive, Carolinas Healthcare System Lincoln, Lincolnton, NC, p. A456

HAYNES, Jamil, Regional Director Human Resources, Integris Miami Hospital, Miami, OK, p. A501

HAYNES, Jill, Financial Coach, Bath Veterans Affairs Medical Center, Bath, NY, p. A422

HAYNES, John H, M.D., Jr, Chief of Medical Staff, North Caddo Medical Center, Vivian, LA, p. A280

HAYNES, Laurie, Chief Financial Officer, Gulf Coast Regional Medical Center, Panama City, FL, p. A135

HAYNES, Mark, M.D., Chief of Staff, Claiborne Memorial Medical Center, Homer, LA, p. A268

HAYNES, Robert Gerard., FACHE, Chief Executive Officer, Guadalupe Regional Medical Center, Seguin, TX, p. A635

HAYNES, William, Director Information Technology, Central Louisiana State Hospital, Pineville, LA, p. A277

HAYREH, Davinder, M.D., Medical Director, Metropolitan St. Louis Psychiatric Center, Saint Louis, MO, p. A368

HAYS, Cheryl M, FACHE, Administrator and Chief Operating Officer, Marshall Medical Center North, Guntersville, AL, p. A19

HAYS, Cheryl M., FACHE, Administrator and Chief Operating Officer, Marshall Medical Center North, Guntersville, AL, p. A19

HAYS, Chuck, President and Chief Executive Officer, Mainegeneral Medical Center-Augusta Campus, ME, p. A282

HAYS, Harry, Chief Executive Officer, Carroll County Memorial Hospital, Carrollton, KY, p. A250

HAYS, Kathie, MSN, R.N., Chief Nursing Officer, West Chester Hospital Surgical Center, OH, p. A493

HAYS, Larry, Director Information Technology, Southern Virginia Mental Health Institute, Danville, VA, p. A657

HAYS, Richard, M.D., Chief Medical Officer, Wellington Regional Medical Center, Wellington, FL, p. A143

HAYS, Richard O, Chief Fiscal Service, Veterans Affairs Southern Nevada Healthcare System, North Las Vegas, NV, p. A396

HAYS, Timothy A, Vice President Human Resources, Johnston Health, Smithfield, NC, p. A460

HAYTAIAN, Mike, Head Director Information Resources Management, Naval Hospital Jacksonville, Jacksonville, FL, p. A125

HAYWOOD, Nancy
Chief Financial Officer, Genesys Regional Medical Center, Grand Blanc, MI, p. A313
Chief Financial Officer, St. Mary's Of Michigan, Saginaw, MI, p. A322

HAYWOOD, Stephanie, Director Human Resources, Southern Virginia Mental Health Institute, Danville, VA, p. A657

HAZELBAKER, Matthew, M.D., President Medical Staff, Memorial Health, Marysville, OH, p. A486

HEAD, David, M.D., Chief Medical Staff, Norton Sound Regional Hospital, Nome, AK, p. A27

HEAD, Susan, Director Nursing Services, Blackfeet Community Hospital, Saint Mary, MT, p. A379

HEALY, John, Manager Information Technology, Friends Hospital, Philadelphia, PA, p. A534

HEALY-COLLIER, Kathy, Chief Operating Officer, Brookwood Baptist Medical Center, Birmingham, AL, p. A14

HEARD, Alex, M.D., Chief Medical Officer, Falmouth Hospital, Falmouth, MA, p. A299

HEARD, Charles, M.D., Chief of Staff, Winnie Palmer Hospital For Women And Babies, FL, p. A134

HEARD, Heather, Director Human Resources, Holdenville General Hospital, Holdenville, OK, p. A500

HEARD, John E., Chief Executive Officer, Mcgehee Hospital, Mcgehee-Desha County, AR, p. A46

HEARD, M Denise, Director Business Services, North Mississippi Medical Center-Pontotoc, Pontotoc, MS, p. A352

HEARING, Ava, Chief Nursing Officer, Atrium Medical Center, Stafford, TX, p. A636

HEARING, Tim, Associate Information Technology Director, Raulerson Hospital, Okeechobee, FL, p. A133

HEARNE, Diane, Director Human Resources, Arizona Spine And Joint Hospital, Mesa, AZ, p. A31

HEARNSBERGER, John, M.D., Chief of Staff, Howard Memorial Hospital, Nashville-Howard County, AR, p. A46

HEATER, Floyd, President, Warren Memorial Hospital, Front Royal, VA, p. A658

HEATH, Ed, FACHE, Chief Executive Officer, Owensboro Health Muhlenberg Community Hospital, Greenville, KY, p. A252

HEATH, Lisa, M.D., President Medical Staff, Saint Luke's South Hospital, Overland Park, KS, p. A243

HEATH, Megan, Chief Nursing Officer, Gordon Memorial Health Services, Gordon, NE, p. A384

HEATH, Merry, Chief Nursing Officer, Piedmont Fayette Hospital, Fayetteville, GA, p. A153

HEATH, Susan, R.N., Senior Vice President and Chief Nursing Officer, Seattle Children's Hospital, Seattle, WA, p. A676

HEATHERLY, Neil, President and Chief Administrative Officer, Peninsula Hospital, TN, p. A572

HEATHERLY, Steve
Chief Executive Officer, Harris Regional Hospital, Sylva, NC, p. A461
Chief Executive Officer, Swain Community Hospital, Bryson City, NC, p. A448

HEATHERLY-LLOYD, Sara, Chief Operating Officer, Tennova Healthcare-Lafollette Medical Center, La Follette, TN, p. A573

HEATLEY, Mark A, Associate Administrator, Turning Point Hospital, Moultrie, GA, p. A158

HEATON, Crystal, Director of Finance, St. Vincent Warrick Hospital, Boonville, IN, p. A200

HEBBERD, Hilda, R.N., MSN, Senior Director Clinical Services, Marlette Regional Hospital, Marlette, MI, p. A318

HEBEL, Barbara, Vice President Human Resources, Doylestown Hospital, Doylestown, PA, p. A524

HEBERT, Bryan, Director Information Systems, The Medical Center Of Southeast Texas, Port Arthur, TX, p. A629

HEBERT, Carol, Director Human Resources, The Medical Center Of Southeast Texas, Port Arthur, TX, p. A629

HEBERT, Gerard, Chief Financial Officer, Tmc Behavioral Health Center, TX, p. A599

HEBERT, Jeff, Interim Vice President Finance, Gifford Medical Center, Randolph, VT, p. A654

HEBERT, Katherine D., Chief Executive Officer, University Hospital And Clinics, Lafayette, LA, p. A271

HEBERT, Rachel, Chief Financial Officer, Heart Hospital Of Lafayette, Lafayette, LA, p. A271

HEBERT, Timothy, Director Human Resources, Teche Regional Medical Center, Morgan City, LA, p. A274

HEBGEN, Lynn, MSN, R.N., Vice President of Nursing, Upland Hills Health, Dodgeville, WI, p. A691

HEBL, James, M.D., Regional Vice President, Mayo Clinic Health System In Mankato, Mankato, MN, p. A334

HEBRA, Andre, M.D., Chief Medical Officer, Nemours Children's Hospital, Orlando, FL, p. A134

HECHLER, Tracy, Healthcare Director Information Services, Johnston-Willis Hospital, VA, p. A664

HECHT, David, M.D., Chief of Staff, James H. Quillen Veterans Affairs Medical Center, Mountain Home, TN, p. A576

HECKATHORNE, Daniel R, Chief Financial Officer, Memorial Hospital Of Gardena, Gardena, CA, p. A60

HECKER, Cynthia, R.N., Executive Director, Uw Medicine/ Northwest Hospital & Medical Center, Seattle, WA, p. A677

HECKER, Julie, Vice President, Operations, Upmc Mercy, Pittsburgh, PA, p. A538

HECKER, Lisa, Director Human Resources, Hedrick Medical Center, Chillicothe, MO, p. A357

HECKERMAN, Ray, Chief Executive Officer and Managing Director, Coastal Harbor Treatment Center, Savannah, GA, p. A160

HECKERT, Robert J., Jr, Chief Executive Officer, Gerald Champion Regional Medical Center, Alamogordo, NM, p. A415

HEDBERG, Beth, R.N., Director Nursing, Lindsborg Community Hospital, Lindsborg, KS, p. A240

HEDDE, Charles C, M.D., Chief Medical Officer, Good Samaritan Hospital, Vincennes, IN, p. A216

HEDDEN, Tyler, Chief Operating Officer, Santa Rosa Memorial Hospital, Santa Rosa, CA, p. A89

HEDDERMAN, Michael, Senior Vice President Finance and Chief Financial Officer, Northwestern Medicine Marianjoy Rehabilitation Hospital, Wheaton, IL, p. A198

HEDGES, David, Chief Financial Officer, Southwestern Regional Medical Center, Tulsa, OK, p. A509

HEDLUND, Chris, Director Information Systems, Community Hospital-Fairfax, Fairfax, MO, p. A359

HEDRIX, Michael D., Administrator and President, Essentia Health Sandstone, Sandstone, MN, p. A340

HEEGAARD, William, M.D., Chief Medical Officer, Hcmc Department Of Pediatrics, MN, p. A335

HEEMANN, John, Vice President and Chief Information Officer, Aspire Hospital, Conroe, TX, p. A593

HEFFERNAN, Paul F, Vice President Human Resources, Women & Infants Hospital Of Rhode Island, Providence, RI, p. A548

HEFFERNAN, Rebecca, Director Human Resources, Leonard Morse Hospital, MA, p. A300

HEFFERS, Margaret, Assistant Vice President Human Resources, Geisinger Wyoming Valley Medical Center, Wilkes Barre, PA, p. A544

HEFFLINGER, Larry, Chief Information Officer, Fulton County Health Center, Wauseon, OH, p. A493

HEFLIN, Clyde, M.D., Chief Medical Officer, Curahealth Nashville, Nashville, TN, p. A577

HEFNER, Donna J., R.N., President and Chief Executive Officer, Sierra View Medical Center, Porterville, CA, p. A79

HEFNER, Katherine, MSN, Chief Nursing Officer, St. Luke's Hospital, Columbus, NC, p. A450

HEFNER, Kathy, Chief Nursing Officer, Mcdowell Hospital, Marion, NC, p. A456

HEGGEM, Mark, M.D., Chief Medical Officer, Riverwood Healthcare Center, Aitkin, MN, p. A327

HEGGEN, Steve, Administrative Director Human Resources, St. Joseph Hospital, Fort Wayne, IN, p. A204

HEGGER, John, Director Information Systems, Union County Hospital, Anna, IL, p. A173

HEGLAND, Larry T, M.D., Chief Medical Officer, Decatur Memorial Hospital, Decatur, IL, p. A180

HEGLAND, Sandra, Chief Executive Officer, Kindred Rehabilitation Hospital Clear Lake, Webster, TX, p. A643

HEGSTROM, Michael T, M.D., Chief Medical Officer, Geisinger-Lewistown Hospital, Lewistown, PA, p. A530

HEICHERT, Susan
Chief Information Officer, Unity Hospital, MN, p. A330
Senior Vice President and Chief Information Officer, Sister Kenny Rehabilitation Institute, MN, p. A335
Senior Vice President, United Hospital, Saint Paul, MN, p. A339

HEIDT, Robert, Director Information Systems, Pembina County Memorial Hospital And Wedgewood Manor, Cavalier, ND, p. A465

HEIFNER, Bruce, Chief Financial Officer, Pella Regional Health Center, Pella, IA, p. A228

HEIFNER, Robert A., FACHE, Chief Executive Officer, St. Luke's Sugar Land Hospital, Sugar Land, TX, p. A637

HEIKKINEN, Todd, Manager Sports Medicine and Rehabilitation Services, Orthopaedic Hospital Of Wisconsin - Glendale, Glendale, WI, p. A693

HEILMAN, Brooke, Chief Financial Officer, Bowdle Hospital, Bowdle, SD, p. A559

HEIM, Chad, Management Information System Director, Lifestream Behavioral Center, Leesburg, FL, p. A128

HEIM, Nicole, Chief Information Officer, Whitinsville Medical Center, MA, p. A302

HEIM, Tonya, R.N., MSN, Vice President Patient Services and Chief Nursing Officer, Memorial Hospital And Health Care Center, Jasper, IN, p. A208

HEIMALL, Michael S., Director, Walter Reed National Military Medical Center, Bethesda, MD, p. A290

HEIMAN, Thomas, Vice President Information Services and Chief Information Officer, John T. Mather Memorial Hospital, Port Jefferson, NY, p. A440

HEIN, Jodi, R.N., Chief Nursing Officer, Providence Holy Cross Medical Center, Mission Hills, CA, p. A72

HEINE, Ann, Chief Executive Officer, Surgical Specialty Center Of Baton Rouge, Baton Rouge, LA, p. A264

HEINEMANN, Don, Administrator and Chief Executive Officer, Blount Memorial Hospital, Maryville, TN, p. A574

HEINEMEIER, Robert, Interim Chief Financial Officer, Sonoma West Medical Center, Sebastopol, CA, p. A89

HEINISCH, Sheri, Compliance Officer, Chi Lisbon Health, Lisbon, ND, p. A467

HEINRICH, Bill, Chief Financial Officer, Florida Hospital Zephyrhills, Zephyrhills, FL, p. A144

HEINRICH, Caleb, Chief Financial Officer, Florida Hospital North Pinellas, Tarpon Springs, FL, p. A142

HEINRICH, Kerry, JD
Chief Executive Officer, Loma Linda University Children's Hospital, Loma Linda, CA, p. A64
Chief Executive Officer, Loma Linda University Heart & Surgical Hospital, CA, p. A64

HEINRICH, Michael G., Senior Vice President and Chief Financial Officer, Unitypoint Health - St. Luke's Hospital, Cedar Rapids, IA, p. A218

HEINRICHS, Alice, CPA, Chief Financial Officer, Van Diest Medical Center, Webster City, IA, p. A231

HEINRICHS, Leann, M.D., Chief of Staff, Thayer County Health Services, Hebron, NE, p. A384

HEINS, Patrick, President, Vidant Roanoke-Chowan Hospital, Ahoskie, NC, p. A447

HEINSOHN, Carmel, M.D., Medical Director, Bournewood Health Systems, Brookline, MA, p. A298

HEINTZ, Shirley, R.N., MS, Vice President Patient Care, Liberty Hospital, Liberty, MO, p. A363

HEINZE, Kyle, Coordinator Information Technology, Riveredge Hospital, Forest Park, IL, p. A183

HEINZMAN, Jerry, Senior Vice President and Chief Financial Officer, Sampson Regional Medical Center, Clinton, NC, p. A450

HEINZMANN, Bill, Director Human Resources, Tmc Behavioral Health Center, TX, p. A599

HEISE, James, Chief Medical Officer, Door County Medical Center, Sturgeon Bay, WI, p. A704

HEISE, Teresa, Coordinator Management Information Systems, Pender Community Hospital, Pender, NE, p. A389

HEISEL, Diane, Acting Director, Center For Forensic Psychiatry, Saline, MI, p. A323

HEISER, Eric, Chief Information Resource Management, Sioux Falls Veterans Affairs Health Care System, Sioux Falls, SD, p. A564

HEISHMAN, Lisa, R.N., Vice President, Valley Health Shenandoah Memorial Hospital, Woodstock, VA, p. A668

HEISMEYER, Joyce, Chief Operating Officer, Kansas Heart Hospital, Wichita, KS, p. A247

HEISSER, Randy, M.D., Medical Director, Kindred Hospital-Chattanooga, Chattanooga, TN, p. A567

HEIT, Ryan, Chief Financial Officer, Northern Nevada Medical Center, Sparks, NV, p. A397

HEITHAUS, Carolyn, Chief Financial Officer, Calverthealth Medical Center, Prince Frederick, MD, p. A293

HEITMEYER, Paulette, Administrator and Chief Operating Officer, Marina Del Rey Hospital, Marina Del Rey, CA, p. A71

HEITZENRATER, James F., FACHE, Chief Executive Officer, W. J. Mangold Memorial Hospital, Lockney, TX, p. A620

HEITZMAN, Cynthia, R.N., Chief Nursing Officer, Seven Rivers Regional Medical Center, Crystal River, FL, p. A120

HELDRETH, Karen, Director Data Processing, Mercy Hospital El Reno, El Reno, OK, p. A498

HELDT, Katie, Chief Nursing Officer, Greene County Medical Center, Jefferson, IA, p. A225

HELFER, Cassandra, Chief Financial Officer, Ralph H. Johnson Veterans Affairs Medical Center, Charleston, SC, p. A550

HELFER, David, FACHE, President, Texas Institute For Surgery At Texas Health Presbyterian Dallas, Dallas, TX, p. A598

HELGERSON, Bryce R., Chief Administrative Officer, Legacy Salmon Creek Medical Center, Vancouver, WA, p. A679

HELGESEN, Roald, Chief Executive Officer, Alaska Native Medical Center, Anchorage, AK, p. A25

HELGESON, Heidi E, M.D., Chief Medical Officer, Rio Grande Hospital, Del Norte, CO, p. A98

HELGET, Peggy, R.N., MSN, Vice President Patient Services and Chief Nursing Officer, Methodist Jennie Edmundson Hospital, Council Bluffs, IA, p. A220

HELLA, Timothy, Chief Information Officer, Munson Healthcare Otsego Memorial Hospital, Gaylord, MI, p. A313

HELLAND, Don, M.D., Chief Medical Officer, Roosevelt Medical Center, Culbertson, MT, p. A374

HELLE, Dan, Human Resources Officer, Iowa City Veterans Affairs Health Care System, Iowa City, IA, p. A224

HELLE, Tara, Human Resources Lead, Palo Alto County Health System, Emmetsburg, IA, p. A222

HELLELAND, Brian, Chief Executive Officer, St. Jude Medical Center, Fullerton, CA, p. A60

HELLER, Michael, Chief Financial Officer, Corry Memorial Hospital, Corry, PA, p. A523

HELLER, Tom, Vice President Operations and Human Resources, Camden Clark Medical Center, Parkersburg, WV, p. A685

HELM, Carrie, Chief Executive Officer, Arkansas Surgical Hospital, North Little Rock-Pulaski County, AR, p. A46

HELM, Pamela E., Executive Director, Devereux Texas Treatment Network, League City, TX, p. A619

HELMERS, Richard, M.D., Regional Vice President, Mayo Clinic Health System In Eau Claire, Eau Claire, WI, p. A692

HELMES, Claudia, R.N., Chief Nursing Officer, Banner Lassen Medical Center, Susanville, CA, p. A91

HELMICKI, Soni, Chief Executive Officer, Wellbridge Healthcare Of Fort Worth, Fort Worth, TX, p. A605

HELMS, Candace, Director Information Services, Good Samaritan Medical Center, West Palm Beach, FL, p. A143

HELMS, Ella Raye., Chief Executive Officer, Cogdell Memorial Hospital, Snyder, TX, p. A636

HELMS, James, Vice President Finance, Jones Memorial Hospital, Wellsville, NY, p. A445

HELMS, Joseph, Director Information Systems, Dekalb Regional Medical Center, Fort Payne, AL, p. A18

HELPER, Mark A, Corporate Vice President and Chief Financial Officer, Munson Medical Center, Traverse City, MI, p. A324

HELSEL, David S., M.D., Chief Executive Officer, Spring Grove Hospital Center, Baltimore, MD, p. A289

HELSEL, Elizabeth, Chief Executive Officer, U.S. Public Health Service Indian Hospital, Parker, AZ, p. A32

HELSPER, Richard S, Chief Operating Officer, Good Samaritan Medical And Rehabilitation Center, OH, p. A494

HELSTROM, James, Chief Medical Officer, Fox Chase Cancer Center-American Oncologic Hospital, Philadelphia, PA, p. A534

HELTON, Deirdre, Director Human Resources, Lakeway Regional Hospital, Morristown, TN, p. A576

HELTON, Fay, Director Medical Records, Red River Hospital, Llc, Wichita Falls, TX, p. A644

HELTON, R.J., D.O., Chief of Staff, Coal County General Hospital, Coalgate, OK, p. A497

HELTON, Stephanie, Chief Financial Officer, Weatherford Regional Hospital, Weatherford, OK, p. A510

HELVEY, John, Chief Information Officer, Orchard Hospital, Gridley, CA, p. A61

HEMATILLAKE, M. Ganga, M.D., Chief of Staff, White River Junction Veterans Affairs Medical Center, White River Junction, VT, p. A654

HEMBREE, Greg, Senior Vice President and Chief Financial Officer, Bradley Center Of St. Francis, GA, p. A151

HEMKER, Debbie, Senior Vice President and Area Manager, Kaiser Permanente Fresno Medical Center, Fresno, CA, p. A59

HEMMER, Chris, Director Finance, Aurora West Allis Medical Center, West Allis, WI, p. A706

HEMMING, Stuart, Chief Operating Officer, Portsmouth Regional Hospital, Portsmouth, NH, p. A401

HEMPEL, Stephen, M.D., President Medical Staff, Lakeland Hospital, Niles, MI, p. A323

HEMPHILL, Dana, Manager Human Resources, Shoshone Medical Center, Kellogg, ID, p. A169

HEMPHILL, Robyn, Chief Executive Officer and Chief Nursing Officer, Monroe Surgical Hospital, Monroe, LA, p. A274

HEMPLER, Shannan, Director Human Resources, Norton County Hospital, Norton, KS, p. A242

HEMSATH, Randolph, M.D., Medical Director, Suncoast Behavioral Health Center, Bradenton, FL, p. A119

HENDEE, Daniel, Director, Philadelphia Veterans Affairs Medical Center, Philadelphia, PA, p. A536

HENDEL, Dawna, R.N., Chief Nursing Officer and Vice President Patient Care Services, Providence Saint John's Health Center, Santa Monica, CA, p. A89

HENDERSHOT, Richard
Chief Financial Officer, Casey County Hospital, Liberty, KY, p. A255
Chief Financial Officer, Jane Todd Crawford Hospital, Greensburg, KY, p. A252

HENDERSON, Claudia, Chief Human Resources, St. Elizabeth's Medical Center, Brighton, MA, p. A297

HENDERSON, David K, M.D., Deputy Director Clinical Care, Children's Inn At Nih, MD, p. A290

HENDERSON, David M, Director Human Resources, Summersville Regional Medical Center, Summersville, WV, p. A687

HENDERSON, Deborah, Acting Chief Financial Officer, Harry S. Truman Memorial Veterans Hospital, Columbia, MO, p. A358

HENDERSON, Donald G., FACHE
President and Chief Executive Officer, Leesburg Regional Medical Center, Leesburg, FL, p. A128
President and Chief Executive Officer, The Villages Regional Hospital, The Villages, FL, p. A142

HENDERSON, Gary, Chief Information Resources Management Services, Huntington Veterans Affairs Medical Center, Huntington, WV, p. A684

HENDERSON, Jace, Chief Financial Officer, Parkview Hospital, Wheeler, TX, p. A644

HENDERSON, Jessica, Manager Human Resources, Fitzgibbon Hospital, Marshall, MO, p. A364

HENDERSON, John, M.D.
Chief Medical Officer, Unity Health Specialty Care, AR, p. A48
Chief Human Resources Management, James H. Quillen Veterans Affairs Medical Center, Mountain Home, TN, p. A576
Chief Information Officer, Choc Children's At Mission Hospital, Mission Viejo, CA, p. A72
Vice President and Chief Information Officer, Children's Hospital Of Orange County, Orange, CA, p. A76

HENDERSON, Katherine
President and Chief Executive Officer, Seton Medical Center Hays, Kyle, TX, p. A618
President and Chief Executive Officer, Seton Medical Center Williamson, Round Rock, TX, p. A631
President and Chief Executive Officer, Seton Northwest Hospital, Austin, TX, p. A586
President and Chief Executive Officer, Seton Southwest Hospital, Austin, TX, p. A586

HENDERSON, Kathy, Director Human Resources, Willow Crest Hospital, Miami, OK, p. A501

HENDERSON, Larry, M.D., Medical Director, Greene County Hospital, Leakesville, MS, p. A349

HENDERSON, Lisa
Chief Operating Officer, Palacios Community Medical Center, Palacios, TX, p. A626
Chief Operations Officer, Palacios Community Medical Center, Palacios, TX, p. A626

HENDERSON, Lori, Chief Nursing Officer, Vice President Clinical, Colorado Canyons Hospital And Medical Center, Fruita, CO, p. A101

HENDERSON, Lorrie, Ph.D., Chief Executive Officer, Huhukam Memorial Hospital, Sacaton, AZ, p. A35

HENDERSON, Melody, Ph.D., R.N., Chief Operating Officer and Chief Nursing Officer, Golden Plains Community Hospital, Borger, TX, p. A589

HENDERSON, Mike, Human Resources Director, Forest View Psychiatric Hospital, Grand Rapids, MI, p. A314

HENDERSON, Pamela S, Vice President Human Resources, Memorial Hospital Of Carbondale, Carbondale, IL, p. A175

HENDERSON, Patricia, R.N., Vice President Nursing and Clinical Services, Glencoe Regional Health Services, Glencoe, MN, p. A332

HENDERSON, Paula
Chief Human Resources Officer, Children's Healthcare Of Mississippi, MS, p. A348
Vice President Human Resources, University Of Maryland Medical Center Midtown Campus, Baltimore, MD, p. A289
Vice President Human Resources, University Of Maryland Rehabilitation & Orthopaedic Institute, Baltimore, MD, p. A289

HENDERSON, Peggy, Director Health Information, Rmc-Stringfellow Memorial Hospital, Anniston, AL, p. A13

HENDERSON, Rex, M.D., Chief of Staff, Mcdowell Hospital, Marion, NC, p. A456

HENDERSON, Sue, Human Resource Manager, Smyth County Community Hospital, Marion, VA, p. A661

HENDERSON, Travis, M.D., Chief of Staff, Mobridge Regional Hospital, Mobridge, SD, p. A562

HENDERSON, Vickie, M.D., Chief Medical Officer, Saint Mary's Regional Medical Center, Russellville-Pope County, AR, p. A48

HENDERSON, Volante, Director Human Resources, Walton Rehabilitation Hospital, Augusta, GA, p. A147

HENDRICK, Kirk, Director Information Systems, Northside Hospital, Saint Petersburg, FL, p. A138

HENDRICKS, Barbara, Interim Human Resources Director, Galesburg Cottage Hospital, Galesburg, IL, p. A183

HENDRICKS, Marcia, FACHE, R.N.
Chief Executive Officer, Adair County Health System, Greenfield, IA, p. A223
Chief Executive Officer, Madison County Health Care System, Winterset, IA, p. A231

HENDRICKSEN, Sherry, R.N., MSN, Chief Nursing Officer, Continuecare Hospital At Hendrick Medical Center, Abilene, TX, p. A582

HENDRICKS, Leslie, Director Human Resources, Coteau Des Prairies Hospital, Sisseton, SD, p. A564

HENDRICKSON, Roman, M.D., Medical Director, Ruby Valley Hospital, Sheridan, MT, p. A379

HENDRIX, Angie, Director of Nursing, Evergreen Medical Center, Evergreen, AL, p. A17

HENDRIX, Billie, R.N., Director of Nursing, W. J. Mangold Memorial Hospital, Lockney, TX, p. A620

HENDRIX, Jamie, Vice President Patient Care Services, Columbus Community Hospital, Inc., Columbus, WI, p. A691

HENDRIX, Michael, Chief Financial Officer, St. Mary's Regional Medical Center, Lewiston, ME, p. A284

HENDRIX, Michael A., Jr, Chief Financial Officer, St. Joseph Hospital, Bangor, ME, p. A282

HENDRIXSON, Mark, M.D., Chief Medical Officer, Jamestown Regional Medical Center, Jamestown, TN, p. A571

HENDRY, Christopher, M.D., Chief Medical Officer, Children's Hospital, Navicent Health, GA, p. A156

HENDRYX, Joel, M.D., Chief Medical Officer, University Medical Center Of El Paso, El Paso, TX, p. A603

HENES, Jean M., MSN, R.N., Director of Nursing, Avera Creighton Hospital, Creighton, NE, p. A383

HENESSEE, Nolan, Vice President and Chief Information Officer, St. Joseph's Hospital, Savannah, GA, p. A160

HENINGER, Bev, Director of Nursing, Kenmare Community Hospital, Kenmare, ND, p. A467

HENKE, Georgia, Operational Account Manager, Osf Healthcare Saint Clare's Hospital, IL, p. A173

HENKE, Mark, Chief Financial Officer, Mena Regional Health System, Mena-Polk County, AR, p. A46

HENKENIUS, Jim, Chief Financial Officer, Stewart Memorial Community Hospital, Lake City, IA, p. A225

HENLEY, Donald, Vice President Human Resources, Grove City Medical Center, Grove City, PA, p. A526

HENNEBOLD, Julie, R.N., Interim Chief Nursing Officer, Winner Regional Healthcare Center, Winner, SD, p. A565

HENNELLY, John, Chief Executive Officer, Saint Louise Regional Hospital, Gilroy, CA, p. A60

HENNENBERG, Shayla, Director Human Resources, Essentia Health Ada, Ada, MN, p. A327

HENNESSEY, Ruth, Executive Vice President and Chief Administrative Officer, St. Francis Hospital, The Heart Center, Roslyn, NY, p. A442

HENNESSY, John, Chief Financial Officer, Bonner General Hospital, Sandpoint, ID, p. A172

HENNESSY, Mark, Chief Financial Officer, Riveredge Hospital, Forest Park, IL, p. A183

HENNIGAN, Michael, M.D., Medical Director, Healthsouth Emerald Coast Rehabilitation Hospital, Panama City, FL, p. A135

HENNIKA, Billi Jo, Vice President Operations, Mckenzie Health System, Sandusky, MI, p. A323

HENNING, Cindy, R.N., Chief Nursing Officer, Houston Northwest Medical Center, Houston, TX, p. A611

HENNING, William C., Administrator and Chief Executive Officer, Baptist Memorial Hospital-North Mississippi, Oxford, MS, p. A351

HENNIS, Michelle, Administrative Director Financial Services, Grace Hospital, Cleveland, OH, p. A476

HENRICI, Michael, Associate Administrator, Roxborough Memorial Hospital, Philadelphia, PA, p. A536

HENRICKS, William, Ph.D., Vice President and Chief Operating Officer, Seton Shoal Creek Hospital, Austin, TX, p. A586

HENRY, Aden, R.N., Vice President, Patient Care, La Rabida Children's Hospital, Chicago, IL, p. A177

HENRY, Andrea, Director of Nursing, Sweetwater Hospital, Sweetwater, TN, p. A580

HENRY, Anna, Chief Information Officer, Kimble Hospital, Junction, TX, p. A616

HENRY, Chris, Associate Administrator and Chief Financial Officer, Washington Hospital Healthcare System, Fremont, CA, p. A59

HENRY, Dane W., Chief Executive Officer, Lake Regional Health System, Osage Beach, MO, p. A365

HENRY, David, President and Chief Executive Officer, Northern Montana Health Care, Havre, MT, p. A376

HENRY, Debbie, Vice President and Chief Financial Officer, Baxter Regional Medical Center, Mountain Home-Baxter County, AR, p. A46

HENRY, Donna, Vice President of Nursing Services, Four County Counseling Center, Logansport, IN, p. A210

HENRY, Edwina J, Assistant Chief Nursing Officer, Parkview Regional Hospital, Mexia, TX, p. A624

HENRY, Hannah, Interim Vice President of Human Resources, Emory Johns Creek Hospital, Johns Creek, GA, p. A155

HENRY, Heather, Information Technology Manager, Hammond-Henry Hospital, Geneseo, IL, p. A184

HENRY, James L, Director Human Resources, Sea Pines Rehabilitation Hospital, Melbourne, FL, p. A129

HENRY, Joy, R.N., Chief of Nursing, Faith Community Hospital, Jacksboro, TX, p. A616

HENRY, Joyce, Controller, Healthsouth Rehabilitation Hospital Of York, York, PA, p. A545

HENRY, Kelsea, Chief Financial Offical, Memorial Regional Health, Craig, CO, p. A98

HENRY, Peter, M.D., Chief Medical Officer, Essentia Health St. Joseph's Medical Center, Brainerd, MN, p. A328

HENRY, Roshonda, Chief Nursing Officer, Encompass Health Rehabilitation Hospital Of Cypress, Houston, TX, p. A610

HENRY, Ryan, Chief Operating Officer, Kindred Hospital The Heights, TX, p. A640

HENRY, Tim, Accountant, Chatuge Regional Hospital And Nursing Home, Hiawassee, GA, p. A154

HENRY, William
Director Human Resources, Ut Health Henderson, Henderson, TX, p. A609
Director Human Resources, Ut Health Quitman, Quitman, TX, p. A629

HENSEL, David, Director Financial Operations, Ohiohealth Grady Memorial Hospital, Delaware, OH, p. A481

HENSEL, Edward, Chief Information Officer, Va Medical Center, Tomah, WI, p. A704

HENSLEIGH, David, Director Medical Staff, Clay County Hospital, Ashland, AL, p. A13

HENSLEY, Angela, Director of Nursing, Pathways Of Tennessee, Jackson, TN, p. A571

HENSLEY, Anna
Chief Operating Officer, Ohiohealth Dublin Methodist Hospital, Dublin, OH, p. A481
Chief Operating Officer, Ohiohealth Grady Memorial Hospital, Delaware, OH, p. A481

HENSLEY, Barry, Director Information Systems, Logan Regional Medical Center, Logan, WV, p. A684

HENSLEY, Kristy, Director Human Resources, Orthoindy Hospital, Indianapolis, IN, p. A207

HENSON, Judith
Vice President Patient Care Services, Southeast Georgia Health System Brunswick Campus, Brunswick, GA, p. A149
Vice President, Patient Care Services, Southeast Georgia Health System Camden Campus, Saint Marys, GA, p. A159

HENSON, Lily, M.D., Chief Medical Officer, Piedmont Henry Hospital, Stockbridge, GA, p. A161

HENSON, Maureen, Vice President Human Resources, Rapid City Regional Hospital, Rapid City, SD, p. A563

HENSON, Pam, Executive Director, Pathways Of Tennessee, Jackson, TN, p. A571

HENSON, Steve, Chief Executive Officer, Bradley County Medical Center, Warren-Bradley County, AR, p. A49

HENTHORN, Cheryl, Chief Executive Officer, Summa Rehab Hospital, Akron, OH, p. A470

HENTON, Thomas, Chief Executive Officer, Carnegie Tri-County Municipal Hospital, Carnegie, OK, p. A496

HENTZEN PAGE, Ann, M.D.
Chief Executive Officer, Summit Surgical, Hutchinson, KS, p. A237
Medical Director, Summit Surgical, Hutchinson, KS, p. A237

HENZE, Rick, Chief Financial Officer, St. Mary's Healthcare, NY, p. A421

HEPNER, Tim, M.D., Chief Medical Officer, St. John Owasso, Owasso, OK, p. A505

HERALD, Kathleen R, Vice President and Chief Information Officer, Lexington Medical Center, West Columbia, SC, p. A558

HERB, Beth, Administrator, State Correctional Institution At Camp Hill, Camp Hill, PA, p. A522

HERBECK, Marilyn, Coordinator Human Resources, Community Hospital Of Staunton, Staunton, IL, p. A197

HERBEL, Aaron, Administrator, Mercy Hospital, Moundridge, KS, p. A241

HERBER, Steven, M.D., FACS
President and Chief Executive Officer, Adventist Health St. Helena, Saint Helena, CA, p. A82
President and Chief Executive Officer, Adventist Health St. Helena, Vallejo, CA, p. A93

HERBERGER, Eva, Administrator Human Resources, Usc Verdugo Hills Hospital, Glendale, CA, p. A60

HERBERT, Daniel, M.D., Medical Administrative Officer, Millinocket Regional Hospital, Millinocket, ME, p. A285

HERBERT, Laurie, Vice President Operations, Three Rivers Health, Three Rivers, MI, p. A324

HERBOLD, Charlotte, Manager Business Officer, Garfield County Health Center, Jordan, MT, p. A376

HERBST, Gary, Chief Executive Officer, South Campus, CA, p. A94

HERD, Jacqueline, R.N., MSN, Chief Nursing Officer, Grady Memorial Hospital, Atlanta, GA, p. A146

HERDER, Debbie, Controller, Promise Hospital Of Wichita Falls, Wichita Falls, TX, p. A644

HERDON, Lori, President and Chief Executive Officer, Atlanticare Regional Medical Center-Mainland Division, NJ, p. A402

HERFORT, Oliver, M.D., Chief Medical Officer, Valley Regional Hospital, Claremont, NH, p. A398

HERGET, Jordan
Chief Operating Officer, Good Samaritan Hospital, San Jose, CA, p. A86
President and Chief Executive Officer, O'Connor Hospital, San Jose, CA, p. A86
Senior Vice President and Manager, Kaiser Permanente Roseville Medical Center, Roseville, CA, p. A81
HERING, John, M.D., Chief Medical Officer, Centracare Health-Monticello, Monticello, MN, p. A336
HERING, Kristine, R.N., Chief Nursing Officer, Speare Memorial Hospital, Plymouth, NH, p. A401
HERINK, Philip, Administrator, Schick Shadel Hospital, Seattle, WA, p. A676
HERKIMER, Eileen, Director Human Resources, United Memorial Medical Center-North Street, NY, p. A422
HERLONG, John, Medical Staff President, Unc Lenoir Healthcare, Kinston, NC, p. A456
HERMAN, Jeff, Chief Executive Officer, Prairie St. John'S, Fargo, ND, p. A466
HERMAN, Michael
Chief Executive Officer, Riverview Regional Medical Center, Carthage, TN, p. A566
Chief Executive Officer, Trousdale Medical Center, Hartsville, TN, p. A570
HERMANN, Terri, R.N., Chief Nursing Officer, Franklin Hospital District, Benton, IL, p. A174
HERMES, Dina, Chief Financial Officer, Golden Plains Community Hospital, Borger, TX, p. A589
HERMOSA, Mercy, Director of Information System, Coral Gables Hospital, Coral Gables, FL, p. A120
HERNANDEZ, Ashley, Chief Information Technology Officer, Pender Memorial Hospital, Burgaw, NC, p. A448
HERNANDEZ, Debra T.
Vice President, Chief Operating Officer and Chief Nursing Officer, Dell Seton Medical Center At The University Of Texas, Austin, TX, p. A586
Vice President, Chief Operation Officer and Chief Nursing Officer, Dell Seton Medical Center At The University Of Texas, Austin, TX, p. A586
HERNANDEZ, Dennis, Chief Medical Officer, Florida Hospital New Smyrna, New Smyrna Beach, FL, p. A132
HERNANDEZ, Diane
Area Finance Officer, Kaiser Permanente San Rafael Medical Center, San Rafael, CA, p. A87
Area Finance Officer, Kaiser Permanente Santa Rosa Medical Center, Santa Rosa, CA, p. A89
HERNANDEZ, Dinorah, Esq, Executive Director, Hospital Pavia Yauco, Yauco, PR, p. A717
HERNANDEZ, George B., Jr, President and Chief Executive Officer, University Hospital, TX, p. A634
HERNANDEZ, Gloria, Executive Director, University Pediatric Hospital, Rio Piedras, PR, p. A715
HERNANDEZ, Janira, Coordinator Human Resources, Hospital Metropolitano Dr. Susoni, Arecibo, PR, p. A712
HERNANDEZ, Kim, Chief Human Resources Officer, Sage Specialty Hospital (Ltac), Denham Springs, LA, p. A267
HERNANDEZ, Kristen, Director Human Resources, Healthsouth Rehabilitation Hospital Of New Mexico, Albuquerque, NM, p. A415
HERNANDEZ, Leonard, Chief Executive Officer, Coffey County Hospital, Burlington, KS, p. A233
HERNANDEZ, Lilly, Human Resources Director, Catalina Island Medical Center, Avalon, CA, p. A51
HERNANDEZ, Lisa J., R.N., Vice President, Patient Care Continuum and Chief Nursing Officer, Sarah Bush Lincoln Health Center, Mattoon, IL, p. A188
HERNANDEZ, Luz Maria, Director Human Resources, I. Gonzalez Martinez Oncologic Hospital, Hato Rey, PR, p. A713
HERNANDEZ, Matt, Director of Information Technology and System, Kendall Regional Medical Center, Miami, FL, p. A130
HERNANDEZ, Reyna, Chief Financial Officer, Healthsouth Rehabilitation Hospital Of Miami, Cutler Bay, FL, p. A120
HERNANDEZ, Sandi, Controller, Lafayette General Surgical Hospital, Lafayette, LA, p. A271
HERNANDEZ, Susan, R.N.
Chief Nurse Executive, University Of Texas Southwestern Medical Center - Zale Lipshy, TX, p. A598
Chief Nursing Officer, Rice Medical Center, Eagle Lake, TX, p. A600
HERNANDEZ-KEEBLE, Sonia, Superintendent, South Texas Health Care System, TX, p. A608
HERNANDEZ-LICHTL, Javier, Chief Executive Officer, Baptist Health South Florida, West Kendall Baptist Hospital, Miami, FL, p. A130
HERNDON, Amy, Chief Finance Officer, Morristown-Hamblen Healthcare System, Morristown, TN, p. A576
HERNDON, David N, M.D., Chief of Staff, Shriners Hospitals For Children-Galveston, Galveston, TX, p. A606

HERNDON, Lori S., R.N., President and Chief Executive Officer, Atlanticare Regional Medical Center-Mainland Division, NJ, p. A402
HERNDON, Robert Scott
Chief Financial Officer, Seton Shoal Creek Hospital, Austin, TX, p. A586
Vice President Chief Financial Officer, Seton Medical Center Austin, Austin, TX, p. A586
HERNDON, Sandra, CPA, Chief Financial Officer, Bleckley Memorial Hospital, Cochran, GA, p. A150
HERNDON, Scott, FACHE
Chief Financial Officer, Ministry Market Texas, Dell Seton Medical Center At The University Of Texas, Austin, TX, p. A586
Chief Financial Officer, Texas Market, Seton Northwest Hospital, Austin, TX, p. A586
HERNE, Mose, Chief Executive Officer, Hopi Health Care Center, Keams Canyon, AZ, p. A30
HEROLD, Mary, Director Human Resources, Share Medical Center, Alva, OK, p. A495
HERPFER, Caroline, Chief Nursing Officer, Arizona Orthopedic Surgical Hospital, Chandler, AZ, p. A28
HERR, Brenda, Chief Nursing Officer, East Adams Rural Healthcare, Ritzville, WA, p. A676
HERR, Michael, Chief Operating Officer, Starr Regional Medical Center, Athens, TN, p. A566
HERRARA, Espie, Chief Financial Officer, Peak Behavioral Health Services, Santa Teresa, NM, p. A419
HERRERA, Jocelyn A.
Director Human Resources, Orange County Irvine Medical Center, CA, p. A50
Human Resources Director, Kaiser Permanente San Diego Medical Center, CA, p. A83
HERRERA, Veronica, Director Human Resources, Las Encinas Hospital, Pasadena, CA, p. A78
HERRERA, Yamila, Director Human Resources, Hialeah Hospital, Hialeah, FL, p. A124
HERRERO, Carmelo, M.D., Medical Director, Hospital Oriente, Humacao, PR, p. A713
HERRIN, Curtis
Chief Financial Officer, Astria Toppenish Hospital, Toppenish, WA, p. A679
Chief Financial Officer, Upmc Pinnacle Memorial, York, PA, p. A546
HERRING, Davey, M.D., Chief Medical Officer, Dorminy Medical Center, Fitzgerald, GA, p. A153
HERRING, Donnette, Chief Information Officer, University Health Systems Children's Hospital, NC, p. A454
HERRING, Randy, M.D., Chief of Staff, Coon Memorial Hospital, Dalhart, TX, p. A595
HERRING, Sherry, Chief Nursing Officer, Uva-Healthsouth Rehabilitation Hospital, Charlottesville, VA, p. A656
HERRINGTON, Bruce, M.D., Chief Medical Officer, South Georgia Medical Center Lanier Campus, Lakeland, GA, p. A156
HERRINGTON, Kristal, Senior Director, Human Resources, Twin County Regional Healthcare, Galax, VA, p. A658
HERRMAN, Edward, R.N., FACHE, President and Chief Executive Officer, Hays Medical Center, Hays, KS, p. A236
HERRMANN, Deborah, M.D., Chief of Staff, I-70 Community Hospital, Sweet Springs, MO, p. A371
HERRMANN, Lee, Chief Healthcare Technology Officer, Santa Clara Valley Medical Center, San Jose, CA, p. A87
HERRMANN, Tim, R.N., Administrator, Peacehealth Cottage Grove Community Medical Center, Cottage Grove, OR, p. A512
HERRON, Katherine, Director Human Resources, Richard H. Hutchings Psychiatric Center, Syracuse, NY, p. A443
HERRON, Mary Beth, Director of Human Resources, Illinois Valley Community Hospital, Peru, IL, p. A193
HERSEY, Robert, Chief Financial Officer, Northeastern Vermont Regional Hospital, Saint Johnsbury, VT, p. A654
HERSHBERGER, Brandy, Chief Nursing Officer, Fawcett Memorial Hospital, Port Charlotte, FL, p. A137
HERSHBERGER, Scott, Acting Chief Information Management Services, Battle Creek Veterans Affairs Medical Center, Battle Creek, MI, p. A308
HERSHMAN, Sharon, R.N., Chief Nursing Officer, Providence Holy Family Hospital, Spokane, WA, p. A678
HERSHMANN, Michael, Medical Center Director, Veterans Affairs Northern Indiana Health Care System-Marion Campus, IN, p. A204
HERTEL, Holly, Director Nursing, Larned State Hospital, Larned, KS, p. A239
HERTZ, Karl Edward, Assistant Administrator, Memorial Hospital Of Converse County, Douglas, WY, p. A708
HERWIG, Brian J., Chief Executive Officer, Perry County Memorial Hospital, Tell City, IN, p. A215
HERZBERG, Deborah L., R.N., MS, FACHE, Chief Executive Officer, Tri Valley Health System, Cambridge, NE, p. A382

HERZL-BETZ, Kenneth, M.D.
Chief Medical Officer and Senior Vice President Medical Affairs, St. Joseph's Hospital, Elmira, NY, p. A426
Chief Medical Officer, Arnot Ogden Medical Center, Elmira, NY, p. A426
HERZOG, Dean, Chief Financial Officer, Kona Community Hospital, Kealakekua, HI, p. A166
HERZOG, Vearnail, Chief Executive Officer, Allegiance Specialty Hospital Of Greenville, Greenville, MS, p. A346
HESCH, Dennis, Executive Vice President Finance, System Chief Financial Officer, Carle Foundation Hospital, Urbana, IL, p. A197
HESCH, Mike J, Regional Administrator Human Resources, Mayo Clinic Health System - Franciscan Healthcare In Sparta, Sparta, WI, p. A703
HESS, David F, M.D., President Medical Staff, Reynolds Memorial Hospital, Glen Dale, WV, p. A683
HESS, David F., M.D., Chief Executive Officer, Reynolds Memorial Hospital, Glen Dale, WV, p. A683
HESS, Heidi, Chief Nursing Officer, Genesis Medical Center-Aledo, Aledo, IL, p. A173
HESS, Jim, Chief Operations Officer, Salt Lake Behavioral Health, Salt Lake City, UT, p. A650
HESS, Michael, M.D., Chief Medical Officer, Lakeview Hospital, Bountiful, UT, p. A646
HESS, Pamela
Chief Financial Officer, Saint Thomas Midtown Hospital, Nashville, TN, p. A577
Chief Financial Officer, Saint Thomas West Hospital, Nashville, TN, p. A577
HESS, Phil, Chief Executive Officer, Wellspan Philhaven, Mount Gretna, PA, p. A532
HESS, Steve
Vice President & Chief Information Officer, Uchealth Medical Center Of The Rockies, Loveland, CO, p. A104
Vice President Information Services and Chief Information Officer, University Of Colorado Hospital, Aurora, CO, p. A96
HESS, Susan, Director Human Resources, J. C. Blair Memorial Hospital, Huntingdon, PA, p. A527
HESSE, Fred, M.D., Medical Director, Arms Acres, Carmel, NY, p. A424
HESSE, Nancy, MSN, R.N., President and Chief Executive Officer, Cancer Treatment Centers Of America-Eastern Regional Medical Center, Philadelphia, PA, p. A534
HESSELRODE, Renee, Director Health Information Management, Landmark Hospital Of Cape Girardeau, Cape Girardeau, MO, p. A356
HESSHEIMER, Susan, Director Human Resources, Johnson County Hospital, Tecumseh, NE, p. A391
HESSING, Jeffrey, M.D., Medical Director, Treasure Valley Hospital, Boise, ID, p. A168
HESSMAN, Mary Pat, Chief Fiscal, Northport Veterans Affairs Medical Center, Northport, NY, p. A438
HESTER, Amber, Chief Executive Officer, Healthsouth Rehabilitation Hospital Of Gulfport, Gulfport, MS, p. A346
HESTER, Charles H., CPA, Jr, Chief Financial Officer, Northwest Mississippi Medical Center, Clarksdale, MS, p. A344
HESTER, Josh, Chief Operating Officer, Gadsden Regional Medical Center, Gadsden, AL, p. A18
HESTER, Joyce, CPA, Senior Vice President and Chief Financial Officer, Louis & Peaches Owen Heart Hospital, TX, p. A640
HESTER, Kathy, Chief Nursing Officer, Orange Park Medical Center, Orange Park, FL, p. A133
HESTER, Michael, Chief Executive Officer, Liberty Regional Medical Center, Hinesville, GA, p. A154
HESTON, Cathy, Chief Nursing Officer, Three Rivers Medical Center, Louisa, KY, p. A255
HETHERINGTON, Ray, Network Administrator, Wheatland Memorial Healthcare, Harlowton, MT, p. A376
HETLETVED, Beth, Director of Nurses, Chi St. Alexius Health Garrison, Garrison, ND, p. A466
HETMANSKI, Jeff, President and Chief Operating Officer, Novant Health Uva Health System Culpeper Medical Center, Culpeper, VA, p. A657
HETT, Samantha, Manager Human Resources, Satanta District Hospital And Long Term Care, Satanta, KS, p. A245
HETTICH, E Paul, Chief Financial Officer, Brylin Hospitals, Buffalo, NY, p. A423
HETTINGER, JoAnn, R.N., Director of Patient Care Services, Avera Weskota Memorial Hospital, Wessington Springs, SD, p. A565
HETTINGER, MaryLou, Director Quality Management, Devereux Children's Behavioral Health Center, Malvern, PA, p. A530
HETTINGER, Tiffany Erin, Associate Chief Nursing Officer, North Colorado Medical Center, Greeley, CO, p. A101

HETU, Maureen, Chief Information Officer, Our Lady Of Lourdes Medical Center, Camden, NJ, p. A403

HETZ, Mark
Chief Information Officer, Asante Ashland Community Hospital, Ashland, OR, p. A511
Chief Information Officer, Asante Rogue Regional Medical Center, Medford, OR, p. A515
Chief Information Officer, Asante Three Rivers Medical Center, Grants Pass, OR, p. A513

HEURING, Ron, Director Information Systems, Perry County Memorial Hospital, Perryville, MO, p. A366

HEURTIN, John, Chief Financial Officer, Lee's Summit Medical Center, Lee's Summit, MO, p. A363

HEUSER, Keith E., Market President, Chi Mercy Health, Valley City, ND, p. A468

HEUSTON, Melanie M, Chief Nursing Office, Meritus Medical Center, Hagerstown, MD, p. A292

HEWSTON, MaryAnn, R.N., Chief Nurse Executive, Meadville Medical Center, Meadville, PA, p. A531

HEYDON, Larry, President and Chief Executive Officer, Johnson Memorial Hospital, Franklin, IN, p. A204

HEYN, Matthew M., Chief Executive Officer, Ransom Memorial Hospital, Ottawa, KS, p. A243

HIATT, Tim, Chief Information Officer, Brodstone Memorial Hospital, Superior, NE, p. A390

HIBBARD, Carrie, Human Resource Business Partner, Adventist Healthcare Physical Health And Rehabilitation, Rockville, MD, p. A293

HIBBS, Cathy, Chief Executive Officer, Carlsbad Medical Center, Carlsbad, NM, p. A416

HIBEN, Daniel, Chief Executive Officer, Crittenden County Hospital, Marion, KY, p. A257

HIBSCHMAN, Kimberly, Chief Financial Officer, Riverview Behavioral Health, Texarkana-Miller County, AR, p. A49

HICK, Claire, Chief Executive Officer, Longleaf Hospital, Alexandria, LA, p. A262

HICKEY, Beth, Vice President, Finance, Advocate Lutheran General Hospital, Park Ridge, IL, p. A192

HICKEY, Christopher, Chief Financial Officer, Northwestern Medical Center, Saint Albans, VT, p. A654

HICKEY, Conner, Chief Operating Officer, Woodland Heights Medical Center, Lufkin, TX, p. A622

HICKEY, Marcia H, Senior Vice President Operations, Hebrew Senior Care, West Hartford, CT, p. A112

HICKEY-BOYNTON, Meg, Director Human Resources and Marketing, Community Hospital Of Anaconda, Anaconda, MT, p. A373

HICKLING, Andrea, Vice President of Finance and Chief Financial Officer, Northern Hospital Of Surry County, Mount Airy, NC, p. A457

HICKLING, Karen, Director Human Resources, Palmdale Regional Medical Center, Palmdale, CA, p. A77

HICKMAN, George, Executive Vice President and Chief Information Officer, Albany Medical Center South-Clinical Campus, NY, p. A421

HICKMAN, Louise, R.N., Vice President of Patient Care Services, Jefferson Regional Medical Center, Pine Bluff-Jefferson County, AR, p. A47

HICKMAN, Monica, Director Fiscal Services, Shriners Hospitals For Children-Spokane, Spokane, WA, p. A678

HICKMAN, Troy, Director Human Resources, Hospital District 6 - Anthony Campus, KS, p. A236

HICKS, Christia, Vice President Human Resources, Eskenazi Health, Indianapolis, IN, p. A206

HICKS, Crystal, R.N., Chief Nursing Officer, Harrison County Community Hospital, Bethany, MO, p. A355

HICKS, Dana, Director of Nursing, Izard County Medical Center, Calico Rock-Logan County, AR, p. A40

HICKS, Janelle, R.N., Vice President Patient Services, Hocking Valley Community Hospital, Logan, OH, p. A485

HICKS, Joan, Chief Information Officer, Uab Highlands, AL, p. A15

HICKS, John R., President and Chief Executive Officer, Platte Valley Medical Center, Brighton, CO, p. A97

HICKS, Michael L, Senior Vice President and Chief Operating Officer, Ingalls Memorial Hospital, Harvey, IL, p. A185

HICKS, Ramona, Interim Chief Executive Officer, Coulee Medical Center, Grand Coulee, WA, p. A672

HICKS, Scott, Vice President, Clark Memorial Hospital, Jeffersonville, IN, p. A208

HICKS, Susan, Chief Executive Officer, Sky Ridge Medical Center, Lone Tree, CO, p. A103

HICKS, Terri, Chief Operating Officer and Chief Financial Officer, P & S Surgical Hospital, Monroe, LA, p. A274

HICKS, Tim
Administrator, Muscogee Creek Nation Medical Center, Okmulgee, OK, p. A505
Administrator, Muscogee Creek Nation Physical Rehabilitation Center, Okmulgee, OK, p. A505

HICKS, William, Chief Executive Officer, Nyc Health + Hospitals / Bellevue, New York (Includes All Hospitals Located Within The Five Boroughs), NY, p. A435

HICKSON, Stan, FACHE, Chief Executive Officer, Woodridge Hospital, TN, p. A571

HIDAY, Holly, Director Human Resources, Kalamazoo Psychiatric Hospital, Kalamazoo, MI, p. A317

HIEB, Dorothy, Director Human Resources, Sanford Chamberlain Medical Center, Chamberlain, SD, p. A560

HIEB, Laura, R.N.
Chief Executive Officer, Bellin Health Oconto Hospital, Oconto, WI, p. A700
Chief Nursing Officer, Bellin Memorial Hospital, Green Bay, WI, p. A693

HIEBERT, Leslie, Chief Executive Officer, Klickitat Valley Health, Goldendale, WA, p. A672

HIGA, Russel, JD, Regional Director Human Resources, Leahi Hospital, Honolulu, HI, p. A164

HIGDON, Kevin J, Chief Financial Officer, Saint Joseph Health System, Mishawaka, IN, p. A211

HIGGINBOTHAM, G Douglas, President and Chief Executive Officer, South Central Regional Medical Center, Laurel, MS, p. A349

HIGGINBOTHAM, Lee, Chief Executive Officer, Dominion Hospital, Falls Church, VA, p. A657

HIGGINBOTHAM, Michael, Chief Executive Officer, Cornerstone Hospital-Medical Center Of Houston, Houston, TX, p. A610

HIGGINS, Alana
Regional Information Management Executive, Christus St. Michael Hospital-Atlanta, TX, p. A639
Regional Information Management Executive, Christus St. Michael Rehabilitation Hospital, Texarkana, TX, p. A639

HIGGINS, John, Vice President and Chief Financial Officer, Good Samaritan Medical Center, Lafayette, CO, p. A102

HIGGINS, Kevin A, Chief Financial Officer, Olmsted Medical Center, Rochester, MN, p. A338

HIGGINS, Larisa, Administrator and Chief Operating Officer, Laredo Rehabilitation Hospital, Laredo, TX, p. A619

HIGGINS, Larry, Vice President Human Resources, King's Daughters Medical Center, Ashland, KY, p. A249

HIGGINS, Michael, Commander, David Grant Usaf Medical Center, Travis Afb, CA, p. A92

HIGGINS, Rodney, Chief Financial Officer, Multicare Deaconess Hospital, Spokane, WA, p. A678

HIGGINS, Thomas, M.D., Chief Medical Officer, Baystate Franklin Medical Center, Greenfield, MA, p. A300

HIGGINS, William, M.D., Vice President Medical Affairs, New York-Presbyterian/Hudson Valley Hospital, Cortlandt Manor, NY, p. A425

HIGGINS BOWERS, Shirley, Senior Vice President Human Resources, Hackensack Meridian Health Jfk Medical Center, Edison, NJ, p. A404

HIGGINSON, David, Executive Vice President and Chief Administrative Officer, Phoenix Children's Hospital, Phoenix, AZ, p. A33

HIGH, Kim, Chief Financial Officer, Baptist Memorial Hospital-Union County, New Albany, MS, p. A351

HIGHTOWER, Bernita, Chief Human Resources, Martin Army Community Hospital, Fort Benning, GA, p. A154

HIGHTOWER, Skip
Chief Financial Officer, Brooks County Hospital, Quitman, GA, p. A158
Chief Financial Officer, Grady General Hospital, Cairo, GA, p. A149
Senior Vice President and Chief Financial Officer, John D. Archbold Memorial Hospital, Thomasville, GA, p. A161
Senior Vice President and Chief Financial Officer, Mitchell County Hospital, Camilla, GA, p. A149

HIJECK, Thomas W., R.N., MS, Vice President Nursing Services and Chief Nursing Officer, Harrington Hospital, Southbridge, MA, p. A304

HILAMAN, Brad L, M.D., Chief Medical Officer, J. Arthur Dosher Memorial Hospital, Southport, NC, p. A460

HILDEBRAND, Randall, M.D., Chief Medical Officer, University Of Kansas Health System Great Bend Campus, Great Bend, KS, p. A236

HILDEBRANDT, James, D.O., Vice President Medical Affairs, Sarah Bush Lincoln Health Center, Mattoon, IL, p. A188

HILDRETH, Beth, Vice President Human Resources, Mansfield Hospital, OH, p. A485

HILDRETH, Joe, Director Information Technology, Three Rivers Hospital, Waverly, TN, p. A580

HILDWEIN, Robin, Chief Information Officer, Boca Raton Regional Hospital, Boca Raton, FL, p. A118

HILFIGER, Janie, Chief Administrative Officer, Upmc Susquehanna Soldiers + Sailors, Wellsboro, PA, p. A543

HILL, Beth, Director Human Resources, Russell County Medical Center, Lebanon, VA, p. A660

HILL, Cheryl
Vice President Human Resources, Columbia St. Mary's Hospital Ozaukee, Mequon, WI, p. A698
Vice President Human Resources, Columbia St. Mary's Milwaukee Hospital, Milwaukee, WI, p. A698
Vice President Human Resources, Columbia St. Mary's Milwaukee Hospital, WI, p. A698

HILL, Chris, Information Technology, Anchor Hospital, Atlanta, GA, p. A145

HILL, Herbert, Director Human Resources, Klickitat Valley Health, Goldendale, WA, p. A672

HILL, Jack
Chief Operating Officer and Administrator, The Jewish Hospital - Mercy Health, Cincinnati, OH, p. A476
Vice President and Chief Operating Officer, Union Hospital Clinton, Clinton, IN, p. A201

HILL, James P, Senior Vice President Administrative Services, Medstar Washington Hospital Center, Washington, DC, p. A116

HILL, Janice, R.N., Administrator, Baptist Memorial Restorative Care Hospital, Memphis, TN, p. A574

HILL, Jason, M.D., Chief Medical Officer, Choctaw Nation Health Care Center, Talihina, OK, p. A507

HILL, Jill, Director Information Technology, Utah State Hospital, Provo, UT, p. A649

HILL, Joe B, Jr, Vice President Human Resources, Summerville Medical Center, SC, p. A550

HILL, John, President and Chief Executive Officer, Bozeman Health Deaconess Hospital, Bozeman, MT, p. A374

HILL, Kalisha, M.D., Chief Medical Officer, Presence St. Mary's Hospital, Kankakee, IL, p. A187

HILL, Karen
Departmental Personnel Officer, Zuckerberg San Francisco General Hospital And Trauma Center, San Francisco, CA, p. A86
Director Human Resources, Baylor Institute For Rehabilitation, Dallas, TX, p. A595

HILL, Karen S, R.N., FACHE, Chief Operating Officer and Chief Nursing Officer, Baptist Health Lexington, Lexington, KY, p. A254

HILL, Kerry
Chief Financial Officer, Vista Medical Center East, Waukegan, IL, p. A198
Chief Financial Officer, Vista Medical Center West, Waukegan, IL, p. A198

HILL, Leo, Chief Information Officer, Massachusetts Eye And Ear, Boston, MA, p. A296

HILL, M. Scott
President and Chief Executive Officer, Midtown Medical Center West, GA, p. A150
President and Chief Executive Officer, Piedmont Columbus Regional Northside, Columbus, GA, p. A150

HILL, Nancy, R.N., Chief Nursing Officer, Johnson Regional Medical Center, Clarksville-Johnson County, AR, p. A40

HILL, Nancy L, R.N., MSN, Chief Operating Officer, Medical City North Hills, North Richland Hills, TX, p. A626

HILL, Ned, Chief Executive Officer, Mesa View Regional Hospital, Mesquite, NV, p. A395

HILL, Robert, M.D.
Chief Medical Officer, Borgess-Lee Memorial Hospital, Dowagiac, MI, p. A312
Vice President Medical Staff Affairs, Borgess-Pipp Hospital, MI, p. A316

HILL, Stephen, Vice President and Chief Nursing Officer, Valley Baptist Medical Center-Harlingen, Harlingen, TX, p. A609

HILL, Stuart, Vice President and Treasurer, Unity Health Specialty Care, AR, p. A48

HILL, Timothy, Chief Operating Officer, Uams Medical Center, Little Rock-Pulaski County, AR, p. A45

HILL-DAVIS, Nancy L, Vice President Human Resources, Mercy Hospital And Medical Center, Chicago, IL, p. A178

HILLARD, Mary, R.N., MSN, Vice President Patient Care Services and Clinical Operations, Chief Nursing Executive, Advocate Condell Medical Center, Libertyville, IL, p. A188

HILLARY, Maureen, Chief Nursing Officer, Hayes Green Beach Memorial Hospital, Charlotte, MI, p. A309

HILLEGASS, Bonnie Essex., Chief Executive Officer, Harmon Medical And Rehabilitation Hospital, Las Vegas, NV, p. A394

HILLEMEIER, A. Craig., M.D., Chief Executive Officer, Penn State Children's Hospital, PA, p. A527

HILLESTAD, Catherine, Interim Chief Executive Officer, Davis County Hospital, Bloomfield, IA, p. A218

HILLESTAD, Tammy, Chief Nursing Officer, Brookings Health System, Brookings, SD, p. A559

HILLIARD, David J, D.O., Chief of Staff, Barnesville Hospital, Barnesville, OH, p. A471

HILLIARD, Jamie, Director of Information Technology, University Of Kansas Health System St. Francis Campus, Topeka, KS, p. A246

HILLIS, David W., Chairman and Chief Executive Officer, Adcare Hospital Of Worcester, Worcester, MA, p. A306

HILLIS, Jeffrey W, Chief Operating Officer, Adcare Hospital Of Worcester, Worcester, MA, p. A306

HILLMAN, Annette, Director Human Resources, Doctor's Hospital Of Deer Creek, Leesville, LA, p. A272

HILLMAN, Brandon, Interim Administrator, Director of Hospital Services, Christus Coushatta Health Care Center, Coushatta, LA, p. A266

HILLS, Cindi, Director Human Resources, Riverwood Healthcare Center, Aitkin, MN, p. A327

HILLYER, Lisa L, Human Resources Manager, Box Butte General Hospital, Alliance, NE, p. A381

HILT, Monica, President and Regional Vice President, Ascension Northeast Wisconsin St. Elizabeth Hospital, Appleton, WI, p. A689

HILTON, Craig, Chief Executive Officer and Managing Director, Hampton Behavioral Health Center, Westampton, NJ, p. A414

HILTON, Daniel, M.D., Chief of Staff, Fountain Valley Regional Hospital And Medical Center, Fountain Valley, CA, p. A58

HILTON, Lois, Director Human Resources, Desoto Memorial Hospital, Arcadia, FL, p. A117

HILTON, Neil A., FACHE, President and Chief Executive Officer, Perkins County Health Services, Grant, NE, p. A384

HILTON-SIEBERT, Stephanie, MSN, President and Chief Executive Officer, Marion General Hospital, Marion, IN, p. A211

HILTUNEN, Theresa, Entity Information Officer, Penn Presbyterian Medical Center, Philadelphia, PA, p. A536

HILTZ, Paul C., FACHE, Interim Chief Executive Officer, Mercy Medical Center, Canton, OH, p. A473

HIMES, Judy N., MSN, R.N., Chief Nursing Officer, Penn State Children's Hospital, PA, p. A527

HINCHEY, Paul P.
President and Chief Executive Officer, Candler Hospital, Savannah, GA, p. A160
President and Chief Executive Officer, St. Joseph's Hospital, Savannah, GA, p. A160

HINCKLEY, Fran X., Chief Information Officer, Union Campus, MA, p. A304

HINDMAN, Robbie, Vice President Patient Care Services and Chief Nursing Officer, Walker Baptist Medical Center, Jasper, AL, p. A20

HINDS, Bob, Executive Director, Bradford Health Services At Huntsville, Madison, AL, p. A20

HINE, Kristy, Associate Vice President Finance, Geisinger-Lewistown Hospital, Lewistown, PA, p. A530

HINE, Rhonda, R.N., Interim Chief Nursing Executive, Mason District Hospital, Havana, IL, p. A185

HINEMAN, Elizabeth, M.D., Chief Medical Staff, Scott County Hospital, Scott City, KS, p. A245

HINER, Jill, Vice President and Chief Financial Officer, Western Reserve Hospital, Cuyahoga Falls, OH, p. A480

HINER, Peggy, Director Human Resources, Wheatland Memorial Healthcare, Harlowton, MT, p. A376

HINES, Andrew, Administrator, St. James Behavioral Health Hospital, Gonzales, LA, p. A268

HINES, Darlene, Chief Operating Officer, Fairfield Memorial Hospital, Winnsboro, SC, p. A558

HINES, Frederick W., President and Chief Executive Officer, Clarity Child Guidance Center, San Antonio, TX, p. A632

HINES, JeDonne, Chief Financial Officer, Intermountain Hospital, Boise, ID, p. A167

HINES, Linda, Vice President Information Technology and Information Systems, University Of Maryland Rehabilitation & Orthopaedic Institute, Baltimore, MD, p. A289

HINES, Lisa, Director Nursing, Eastern Shore Hospital Center, Cambridge, MD, p. A290

HINES, Mary Beth, D.O., Chief Medical Officer, Up Health System-Portage, Hancock, MI, p. A315

HINESLEY, Jay, FACHE, Chief Executive Officer, Tennova Healthcare-Lebanon Mcfarland Campus, TN, p. A573

HINKLE, Stacey, Director Information Technology, Samaritan Behavioral Health Center-Desert Samaritan Medical Center, AZ, p. A31

HINNER, William J
Vice President Financial Analysis and Planning Ministry Health Care, Marshfield Childen's Hospital, WI, p. A697
Vice President Financial Analysis and Planning, Ascension St. Michael's Hospital, Stevens Point, WI, p. A703

HINOJOSA, Anna, MSN, R.N., Interim Chief Nursing Officer, Knapp Medical Center, Weslaco, TX, p. A643

HINRICHS, Becky Kay, Vice President Human Resources, Riverside Medical Center, Kankakee, IL, p. A187

HINRICHS, Sandy, Director Human Resources, Burnett Medical Center, Grantsburg, WI, p. A693

HINSHAW, Bruce, Director Human Resources, Artesia General Hospital, Artesia, NM, p. A416

HINSON, Lee, Chief Nursing Officer, Merit Health Natchez, Natchez, MS, p. A351

HINTZ, Lori, Coordinator Information Systems, Rochester Psychiatric Center, Rochester, NY, p. A441

HINTZE, Hart, Chief Nursing Officer, Banner Payson Medical Center, Payson, AZ, p. A32

HINTZE, Hartland, Chief Nursing Officer, Green Clinic Surgical Hospital, LA, p. A278

HINTZE, Paul, M.D., Vice President Medical Affairs, Mercy Children's Hospital St. Louis, MO, p. A368

HIOTT, Jimmy O., III, Chief Executive Officer, Colleton Medical Center, Walterboro, SC, p. A557

HIPKISS, Tom, Vice President Finance, Forbes Hospital, Monroeville, PA, p. A532

HIRKALER, Kim, Director Human Resources, Bon Secours Community Hospital, Port Jervis, NY, p. A440

HIROMOTO, Brenda, Director of Nursing, Rehabilitation Hospital Of The Pacific, Honolulu, HI, p. A165

HIROSE, Mivic, Executive Administrator, Laguna Honda Hospital And Rehabilitation Center, San Francisco, CA, p. A85

HIRSCH, Edward, M.D., Vice President Chief Medical and Quality Officer, South Campus, CA, p. A94

HIRSCH, Leslie D., FACHE, Interim Chief Executive Officer and President, The Children's Hospital At Saint Peter's University, NJ, p. A408

HIRSCH, Ted W, Senior Executive Director, Pathways Treatment Center, MT, p. A377

HIRSCHBERG, Paula, R.N., Director of Nursing, Timberlawn Mental Health System, Dallas, TX, p. A598

HIRST, Barb, R.N., Vice President Human Resources and Chief Nursing Officer, Salem Regional Medical Center, Salem, OH, p. A490

HISE, Landon E., Chief Executive Officer, Alliancehealth Clinton, Clinton, OK, p. A497

HISEY, Commie, D.O., Chief of Staff, Gonzales Healthcare Systems, Gonzales, TX, p. A607

HITE DAVIS, Anissa J, Vice President Human Resources, St. Joseph's Hospital Of Buckhannon, Buckhannon, WV, p. A682

HITT, John, M.D., Executive Vice President and Chief Medical Officer, Arizona Children's Center, AZ, p. A33

HITT, Melissa, Director of Nursing, Highland-Clarksburg Hospital, Clarksburg, WV, p. A682

HITT, Patricia A, Associate Director, Grand Junction Veterans Health Care System, Grand Junction, CO, p. A101

HIXENBAUGH, Cynthia, Director Human Resources, Pershing General Hospital, Lovelock, NV, p. A395

HIXSON, Kim, Vice President of Financial Officer and Chief Financial Officer, Providence Medical Center, Wayne, NE, p. A391

HJEMBO, Philip, Chief Financial Officer, St. Elizabeth Hospital, Enumclaw, WA, p. A671

HLAHOL, Jan, Manager Human Resources, Cleveland Clinic Children's Hospital For Rehabilitation, Cleveland, OH, p. A476

HLUCHY, Nicholas, Business Analyst, Support Services Manager, Baton Rouge Rehabilitation Hospital, Baton Rouge, LA, p. A263

HO-SHING, Viodelda, Deputy Director Administration, Creedmoor Psychiatric Center, New York (Includes All Hospitals Located Within The Five Boroughs), NY, p. A432

HOAG, Abby, Director, Human Resources, Uh Avon Rehabilitation Hospital, Avon, OH, p. A471

HOAGBIN, Joseph, M.D.
Chief Medical Officer, Chi Health Immanuel, Omaha, NE, p. A388
Chief Quality Officer, Chi Health Mercy Council Bluffs, Council Bluffs, IA, p. A220

HOAR, Brad, Director Information and Technology, Cedar Park Regional Medical Center, Cedar Park, TX, p. A592

HOARD, Kaylee S., Chief Financial Officer, Cook Hospital & Care Center, Cook, MN, p. A329

HOBACK, Kim, Supervisor Information Systems, Athens-Limestone Hospital, Athens, AL, p. A13

HOBAN, Donna, M.D., Senior Vice President and Chief Medical Officer, Beaumont Hospital - Grosse Pointe, Grosse Pointe, MI, p. A315

HOBAN, Douglas M, Vice President and Chief Financial Officer, Mercy Hospital Lebanon, Lebanon, MO, p. A363

HOBAN, Robert E.
President, Ascension St. John Hospital, Detroit, MI, p. A310
President, St. John River District Hospital, East China, MI, p. A312

HOBART, Robert, Director Management Information Systems, Heartland Behavioral Healthcare, Massillon, OH, p. A486

HOBBS, Donna, Nurse Executive, U.S. Public Health Service Indian Hospital-Sells, Sells, AZ, p. A36

HOBBS, Ed, Director Information Services, Dekalb Health, Auburn, IN, p. A199

HOBBS, Emilie, Director Human Resources, Woodland Heights Medical Center, Lufkin, TX, p. A622

HOBBS, Keith, Chief Executive Officer, Usc Verdugo Hills Hospital, Glendale, CA, p. A60

HOBBS, Mike, Chief Financial Officer, Clay County Hospital, Flora, IL, p. A183

HOBBS, Nicole, Administrator, Johnson County Healthcare Center, Buffalo, WY, p. A707

HOBBS, Steve E.
Chief Financial Officer, Eliza Coffee Memorial Hospital, Florence, AL, p. A18
Chief Financial Officer, Shoals Hospital, Muscle Shoals, AL, p. A22

HOBBS, Tommy, Chief Executive Officer, Illinois Valley Community Hospital, Peru, IL, p. A193

HOBGOOD, Lisa, Chief Information Officer, The Heart Hospital At Deaconess Gateway, Newburgh, IN, p. A212

HOBGOOD, Marcus, Director Information Services, Children's Hospital Of Shreveport, LA, p. A279

HOBSON, Christopher Brian, Chief Operating Officer, Bristol Regional Medical Center, Bristol, TN, p. A566

HOBSON, Jim, Chief Executive Officer, Greenbrier Valley Medical Center, Ronceverte, WV, p. A687

HOCATE, Crispin P, Professional and Support Services Officer, Texas Health Presbyterian Hospital Allen, Allen, TX, p. A582

HOCE, N. Kristopher., President, Morton Plant Hospital, Clearwater, FL, p. A119

HOCHENBERG, Paul S, Executive Director, Midhudson Regional Hospital Of Westchester Medical Center, NY, p. A445

HOCHSTETLER, Amy, Chief Financial Officer, Orthopaedic Hospital Of Lutheran Health Network, Fort Wayne, IN, p. A204

HOCK, Douglas G, Executive Vice President and Chief Operating Officer, Children's Hospital Of Philadelphia, Philadelphia, PA, p. A534

HOCKADAY, Christina, FACHE, Chief Executive Officer, Assumption Community Hospital, Napoleonville, LA, p. A274

HOCKENBERRY, Michael A., Senior Vice President and Chief Operating Officer, Upmc Pinnacle Hanover, Hanover, PA, p. A526

HOCKENBERRY, Tonda, Chief Nursing Officer, Healthsouth Western Hills Regional Rehabilitation Hospital, Parkersburg, WV, p. A686

HOCKENBURY, Debbie, Assistant Administrator and Chief Financial Officer, William Newton Hospital, Winfield, KS, p. A248

HOCKERSMITH, Lisa K., Vice President Human Resources, Kern Medical Center, Bakersfield, CA, p. A52

HOCKERT, Steve, Chief Executive Officer, Onecore Health, Oklahoma City, OK, p. A504

HOCKING, Barbara, Chief Nursing Officer, St. Luke's Meridian Medical Center, ID, p. A168

HOCKING, Dale E, Chief Financial Officer, Jupiter Medical Center, Jupiter, FL, p. A126

HOCKING, Patrick
Chief Financial Officer, Asante Ashland Community Hospital, Ashland, OR, p. A511
Chief Financial Officer, Asante Rogue Regional Medical Center, Medford, OR, p. A515
Chief Financial Officer, Asante Three Rivers Medical Center, Grants Pass, OR, p. A513

HOCUM, Timothy, Chief Financial Officer, Providence Kodiak Island Medical Center, Kodiak, AK, p. A26

HODGE, Ian, Chief Executive Officer, Yuma Rehabilitation Hospital, A Partnership Of Encompass Health And Yrmc, Yuma, AZ, p. A38

HODGE, Lisa, Director, Human Resources, Rolling Hills Hospital, Franklin, TN, p. A570

HODGE, Montie, Vice President Information Technology and Chief Information Officer, Regional West Medical Center, Scottsbluff, NE, p. A390

HODGE, Pamela, R.N., Chief Nursing Officer and Coordinator Performance Improvement, Jellico Community Hospital, Jellico, TN, p. A571

HODGES, Alan, Chief Executive Officer, Hancock Medical Center, Bay Saint Louis, MS, p. A343

HODGES, Calvin, Director Human Resources, Alliancehealth Ponca City, Ponca City, OK, p. A505

HODGES, Craig, Director Information Services, Hancock Medical Center, Bay Saint Louis, MS, p. A343

HODGES, Dawn, Director Human Resources, Grand River Hospital District, Rifle, CO, p. A105

HODGES, Jay, Chief Financial Officer, Tmc Bonham Hospital, Bonham, TX, p. A589

HODGES, Leisha, Human Resources Officer, Eastland Memorial Hospital, Eastland, TX, p. A600

HODGES, Randall H, FACHE, Vice President and Administrator, Camc Teays Valley Hospital, WV, p. A682

HODGIN, Robin, R.N., Vice President of Patient Services and Chief Nursing Officer, Northern Hospital Of Surry County, Mount Airy, NC, p. A457

HODGSON, Judith Ann, Chief Nursing Officer, Cheyenne County Hospital, Saint Francis, KS, p. A245

HODNETT, Laura, Interim Chief Nursing Officer, Glen Rose Medical Center, Glen Rose, TX, p. A607

HODSON, Don, M.D., Chief Medical Officer, St. Luke Hospital And Living Center, Marion, KS, p. A241

HOEFER, Bill, Chief Operating Officer, St. Anthony's Mercy, Saint Louis, MO, p. A369

HOEFLING, Tracy, Chief Financial Officer, The Heart Hospital At Deaconess Gateway, Newburgh, IN, p. A212

HOEFS, Dennis, Manager Information Technology, Pecos Valley Lodge, NM, p. A419

HOEHN, Charles, President, Medical Staff, Van Wert County Hospital, Van Wert, OH, p. A492

HOEHNS, Brent, M.D., Chief of Medical Staff, Knoxville Hospital & Clinics, Knoxville, IA, p. A225

HOEKEMA, Dale, M.D., Vice President Medical Affairs and Chief Medical Officer, Kadlec Regional Medical Center, Richland, WA, p. A676

HOELL, Paul, M.D., President Medical Staff, Thedacare Medical Center-New London, New London, WI, p. A700

HOELSCHER, Steven C, Chief Operating Officer, Valley Regional Medical Center, Brownsville, TX, p. A590

HOERTZ, Joanne, Vice President of Nursing, Brooks Rehabilitation Hospital, Jacksonville, FL, p. A125

HOESCH, Marty, Director Information Systems, North Suburban Medical Center, Thornton, CO, p. A105

HOEY, Amy J, R.N., MS, Executive Vice President and Chief Operating Officer, Lowell General Hospital, Saints Campus, MA, p. A301

HOFELICH, Kurt T., President, Sentara Norfolk General Hospital, Norfolk, VA, p. A663

HOFER, Maggie, Human Resources Representative, Hawarden Regional Healthcare, Hawarden, IA, p. A224

HOFF, David L., Chief Executive Officer, Wayne Memorial Hospital, Honesdale, PA, p. A527

HOFF, Deanna, R.N., Director of Nursing, Bacon County Hospital And Health System, Alma, GA, p. A145

HOFF, Linda, Senior Vice President and Chief Financial Officer, Legacy Mount Hood Medical Center, Gresham, OR, p. A513

HOFF, Margaret, Account Manager, Brown County Community Treatment Center, Green Bay, WI, p. A694

HOFFER, Nolan, Senior Director, St. Luke's Rehabilitation Hospital, Boise, ID, p. A168

HOFFMAN, Brad, Administrative Director Human Resources, Shawnee Mission Medical Center, Shawnee Mission, KS, p. A246

HOFFMAN, Brian, M.D.
Chief Medical Services, Veterans Affairs Boston Healthcare System, West Roxbury, MA, p. A305
Director Human Resources, Upmc Pinnacle Lancaster, Lancaster, PA, p. A529

HOFFMAN, Carole, Vice President, Parkridge West Hospital, TN, p. A567

HOFFMAN, Chris, Chief Operating Officer, Highlands Regional Medical Center, Prestonsburg, KY, p. A259

HOFFMAN, Daniel, M.D., Administrative Medical Director, Good Samaritan Regional Health Center, Mount Vernon, IL, p. A190

HOFFMAN, Debbie, Vice President Patient Services, Ssm Health St. Francis Hospital - Maryville, Maryville, MO, p. A364

HOFFMAN, Debra, Human Resources Manager, Kern Valley Healthcare District, Lake Isabella, CA, p. A63

HOFFMAN, Howard, M.D., Medical Director, Psychiatric Institute Of Washington, Washington, DC, p. A116

HOFFMAN, Jerry, Chief Financial Officer, Platte Health Center Avera, Platte, SD, p. A562

HOFFMAN, Joseph E, III, Senior Vice President and Chief Financial Officer, University Of Maryland Hospital For Children, MD, p. A289

HOFFMAN, Marcus, Area Chief Financial Officer, Orange County Irvine Medical Center, CA, p. A50

HOFFMAN, Robert P, Chief Nursing Officer, Wilkes-Barre General Hospital, PA, p. A544

HOFFMAN, Tom, Manager Information Systems, Wayne Memorial Hospital, Honesdale, PA, p. A527

HOFFMAN, Trudy, Executive Director, Northwest Center For Behavioral Health, Fort Supply, OK, p. A499

HOFFMAN, Val, Chief Financial Officer, Granite Falls Health, Granite Falls, MN, p. A332

HOFFMANN, Wanda, Director Human Resources, River Oaks Child And Adolescent Hospital, LA, p. A276

HOFIUS, Chuck, Chief Executive Officer, Perham Health, Perham, MN, p. A337

HOFLER, Linda D, Ph.D., R.N., FACHE, Senior Vice President, Nurse Executive, University Health Systems Children's Hospital, NC, p. A454

HOFMAN, William, Manager Information Technology, Wake Forest Baptist Health - Wilkes Medical Center, North Wilkesboro, NC, p. A458

HOFMEIER, Sara, Executive Director, Veritas Collaborative, Durham, NC, p. A451

HOFMEISTER, Nancee, R.N., Senior Vice President, Chief Nursing Officer, Evergreenhealth, Kirkland, WA, p. A673

HOFSTETTER, Peter A.
Chief Executive Officer, Petersburg Medical Center, Petersburg, AK, p. A27
Chief Executive Officer, Willamette Valley Medical Center, Mcminnville, OR, p. A514

HOGAN, Dan, Chief Financial Officer, Desoto Memorial Hospital, Arcadia, FL, p. A117

HOGAN, Judith, Comptroller and Director Resources and Logistics, Naval Hospital Bremerton, Bremerton, WA, p. A670

HOGAN, Michael, Chief Resource Management, General Leonard Wood Army Community Hospital, Fort Leonard Wood, MO, p. A359

HOGAN, Richard, Chief Financial Officer, Pleasant Valley Hospital, Point Pleasant, WV, p. A686

HOGAN, Richard H, CPA, Chief Financial Officer, Landmark Hospital Of Cape Girardeau, Cape Girardeau, MO, p. A356

HOGAN, Sean, FACHE, President, St. Anthony's Mercy, Saint Louis, MO, p. A369

HOGAN, Timothy J., FACHE
President, RMC and BMC, Hackensack Meridian Health Bayshore Community Hospital, Holmdel, NJ, p. A406
President, RMC and BMC, Hackensack Meridian Health Riverview Medical Center, Red Bank, NJ, p. A411

HOGDSON, Judy, R.N., Chief Nursing Officer, Hospital District No 1 Of Rice County, Lyons, KS, p. A240

HOGGARD GREEN, Jill, Ph.D., R.N., President, Mission Hospital, NC, p. A447

HOGUE, Vicky, R.N., Vice President Patient Services and Chief Nursing Officer, Wellstar Paulding Hospital, Hiram, GA, p. A155

HOHENBERGER, Joseph, Chief Financial Officer, Ferrell Hospital, Eldorado, IL, p. A181

HOHENSHELL, Valerie, Director of Clinical Services, Gonzales Healthcare Systems, Gonzales, TX, p. A607

HOLBERT, Brandon, Director, Information Services, West Marion Community Hospital, FL, p. A133

HOLBROOK, Chip, M.D., Chief of Staff, Simpson General Hospital, Mendenhall, MS, p. A350

HOLBROOK, Curtis, M.D., Chief Medical Officer, Baylor Scott & White Surgical Hospital At Sherman, Sherman, TX, p. A635

HOLCOMB, Holly, R.N.
Chie Operating Officer, Childress Regional Medical Center, Childress, TX, p. A592
Chief Operating Officer, Childress Regional Medical Center, Childress, TX, p. A592

HOLCOMB, Michelle, Human Resources, Webster County Memorial Hospital, Webster Springs, WV, p. A687

HOLDEMAN, Royce, Chief Financial Officer, Mercy Hospital, Moundridge, KS, p. A241

HOLDEN, Teal A., Chief Executive Officer, Memorial Hermann Surgical Hospital Kingwood, Kingwood, TX, p. A618

HOLDER, Hal
Director Finance, Ssm Health Depaul Hospital - St. Louis, Bridgeton, MO, p. A356
Regional Chief Financial Officer-Hospital Operations, Ssm Health St. Clare Hospital - Fenton, Fenton, MO, p. A359
Regional Chief Financial Officer, Ssm Health St. Joseph Hospital - Lake Saint Louis, Lake Saint Louis, MO, p. A363

HOLDER, Jennifer, Chief Nursing Officer, Trousdale Medical Center, Hartsville, TN, p. A570

HOLDER, Kasey, M.D., Vice President Medical Affairs, St. Bernards Medical Center, Jonesboro-Craighead County, AR, p. A44

HOLDER, Michelle, Nurse Executive, Straith Hospital For Special Surgery, Southfield, MI, p. A324

HOLDER, Spencer, Chief Financial Officer, Riverland Medical Center, Ferriday, LA, p. A267

HOLDER-HOOPER, Donna, Chief Human Resource Officer, Healthsouth Rehabilitation Hospital At Martin Health, Stuart, FL, p. A139

HOLEKAMP, Nicholas, M.D., Chief Medical Officer, Ranken Jordan Pediatric Bridge Hospital, Maryland Heights, MO, p. A364

HOLGUIN, Brenda, Manager Human Resources, El Paso Behavioral Health System, El Paso, TX, p. A601

HOLGUIN, Mindee, Manager Human Resources, Sierra Vista Hospital, Truth Or Consequences, NM, p. A420

HOLIFIELD, Tracy, Director Information Systems, Merit Health Central, Jackson, MS, p. A348

HOLINER, Joel, M.D., Executive Medical Director, Medical City Green Oaks Hospital, Dallas, TX, p. A597

HOLIVER, John J., Chief Executive Officer, St. Joseph Hospital For Specialty Care, RI, p. A547

HOLLAND, Baxter C, M.D., Chief Medical Officer, Rutland Regional Medical Center, Rutland, VT, p. A654

HOLLAND, Brad D., Chief Executive Officer, Cedar Park Regional Medical Center, Cedar Park, TX, p. A592

HOLLAND, Charles, President and Chief Executive Officer, St. Bernard Hospital And Health Care Center, Chicago, IL, p. A179

HOLLAND, Cheyenne, Chief Financial Officer, The University Of Vermont Health Network Central Vermont Medical Center, Berlin, VT, p. A653

HOLLAND, David
Chief Information Officer, Herrin Hospital, Herrin, IL, p. A185
Vice President Chief Innovation Officer, Memorial Hospital Of Carbondale, Carbondale, IL, p. A175
Vice President Information Services, St. Joseph Memorial Hospital, Murphysboro, IL, p. A190

HOLLAND, Gabrielle, Chief Financial Officer, Baylor Surgical Hospital At Las Colinas, Irving, TX, p. A615

HOLLAND, Kevin, MHSA, MBA
Chief Executive Officer, CHRISTUS Southwestern Louisiana, Christus Ochsner Lake Area Hospital, Lake Charles, LA, p. A272
Chief Executive Officer, CHRISTUS Southwestern Louisiana, Christus Ochsner St. Patrick Hospital Southwest Louisiana, Lake Charles, LA, p. A272

HOLLAND, Kwi, Vice President Information Services, Knox Community Hospital, Mount Vernon, OH, p. A487

HOLLAND, Megan, Chief Medical Officer and Family Practitioner, Southern Coos Hospital And Health Center, Bandon, OR, p. A511

HOLLAND, Michael, M.D., Chief Executive Officer, Rehabilitation Hospital Of Jennings, Jennings, LA, p. A269

HOLLAND, Penny, Associate Director for Patient Care Services, Aleda E. Lutz Veterans Affairs Medical Center, Saginaw, MI, p. A322

HOLLAND, Shannon S, R.N., MSN, Chief Nursing Officer, Multicare Valley Hospital, Spokane Valley, WA, p. A678

HOLLAND, Sharron, Chief Financial Officer, Baptist Memorial Hospital-Huntingdon, Huntingdon, TN, p. A571

HOLLAND, Stephen, M.D., Vice President Chief Medical Officer and Medical Director, Gaylord Hospital, Wallingford, CT, p. A111

HOLLEMAN, James, M.D., Chief of Staff, St. Luke's Hospital, Columbus, NC, p. A450

HOLLEMAN, Stephen B, Chief Financial Officer, Shepherd Center, Atlanta, GA, p. A147

HOLLIDAY, Jonathan, Manager Information Technology, Central Community Hospital, Elkader, IA, p. A222

HOLLIMAN, Emily L., Chief Executive Officer, Hackensack Meridian Health Pascack Valley Medical Center, Westwood, NJ, p. A414

HOLLIN, Sheara, Chief Operating Officer, Scheie Eye Institute Of The Hospital Of The University Of Pennsylvania, PA, p. A535

HOLLINGSWORTH, Carl, Chief Financial Officer, Artesia General Hospital, Artesia, NM, p. A416

HOLLINGSWORTH, Christine, Chief Financial Officer, Phoenix Veterans Affairs Health Care System, Phoenix, AZ, p. A34

HOLLINGSWORTH, Nancy, R.N., MSN, President and Chief Executive Officer, Saint Agnes Medical Center, Fresno, CA, p. A59

HOLLINGSWORTH, Sherri, Chief Human Resources Officer, Pih Health Hospital - Downey, Downey, CA, p. A56

HOLLIS, Carla, Chief Executive Officer, Triangle Springs Hospital, Raleigh, NC, p. A459

HOLLIS, Gary W, Comptroller, Arkansas State Hospital, Little Rock-Pulaski County, AR, p. A44

HOLLIS, Roy, Chief Executive Officer, Houston Behavioral Healthcare Hospital, Houston, TX, p. A611

HOLLISTER, Jerry, Chief Executive Officer, Northeastern Center, Auburn, IN, p. A199

HOLLISTER, Richard, President of Medical Staff, Exeter Hospital, Exeter, NH, p. A399

HOLLON, Kim Norton., FACHE, President and Chief Executive Officer, Signature Healthcare Brockton Hospital, Brockton, MA, p. A298

HOLLOWAY, Kristina, Chief Human Resources Officer, Healdsburg District Hospital, Healdsburg, CA, p. A61

HOLLOWAY, Myra, Director Human Resources Management, Central State Hospital, Milledgeville, GA, p. A157

HOLLOWAY, Walter R, Chief Medical Officer, Ozarks Medical Center, West Plains, MO, p. A372

HOLLOWAY, Whitney, Chief Financial Officer, Berwick Hospital Center, Berwick, PA, p. A520

HOLM, Mary Ann, Office Clerk, Tioga Medical Center, Tioga, ND, p. A468

HOLM, Stan, Chief Executive Officer, Abrazo West Campus, Goodyear, AZ, p. A30

HOLMAN, Steve M., Chief Executive Officer, Union Hospital, Terre Haute, IN, p. A215

HOLMBERG, Daniel, M.D., Director of Medical Affairs, New Ulm Medical Center, New Ulm, MN, p. A336

HOLMES, Dawne
Chief Financial Officer, Greenwood Leflore Hospital, Greenwood, MS, p. A346
Interim Chief Executive Officer, Greenwood Leflore Hospital, Greenwood, MS, p. A346

HOLMES, Diana, Chief Nursing Officer, Central Regional Hospital, Butner, NC, p. A448

HOLMES, Ginnie, Chief Financial Officer, Electra Memorial Hospital, Electra, TX, p. A603

HOLMES, Heather, Director Health Information Systems, Merit Health Rankin, Brandon, MS, p. A344

HOLMES, Heidi, Chief Information Officer, Oklahoma State University Medical Center, Tulsa, OK, p. A508

HOLMES, James R., President and Chief Executive Officer, Redlands Community Hospital, Redlands, CA, p. A80

HOLMES, John, Business Manager, Ancora Psychiatric Hospital, Hammonton, NJ, p. A405

HOLMES, Phillip Walter, M.D., Chief of Staff, Prairie Ridge Hospital And Health Services, Elbow Lake, MN, p. A331

HOLMES, Terry R, M.D., Clinical Director, Moccasin Bend Mental Health Institute, Chattanooga, TN, p. A567

HOLMES, Troy, Director Finance, Advanced Specialty Hospital Of Toledo, Toledo, OH, p. A491

HOLMSTROM, Tallulah, M.D.
Chief Medical Officer, Carolina Pines Regional Medical Center, Hartsville, SC, p. A554
Chief Medical Officer, Kershawhealth, Camden, SC, p. A549

HOLOM, Randall G., Chief Executive Officer, Frances Mahon Deaconess Hospital, Glasgow, MT, p. A375

HOLSAPPLE, Kim, Human Resource Specialist, Chester Mental Health Center, Chester, IL, p. A176

HOLSCHBACH, Dennis, Chief Financial Officer, Ruby Valley Hospital, Sheridan, MT, p. A379

HOLSON, Debbie C, R.N., MSN, Chief Operating Officer, The Hsc Pediatric Center, Washington, DC, p. A116

HOLSON, Debbie C., R.N., MSN, Chief Operating Officer, The Hsc Pediatric Center, Washington, DC, p. A116

HOLSTEN, Robyn, Human Resources Director, Salt Lake Behavioral Health, Salt Lake City, UT, p. A650

HOLT, Clayton, Chief Executive Officer, San Juan Health Service District, Monticello, UT, p. A648

HOLT, David, Chief Executive Officer, Western State Hospital, Tacoma, WA, p. A679

HOLT, Kory
Assistant Vice President for Financial Integration, Avera Flandreau Hospital, Flandreau, SD, p. A561
Division Controller Network Operations, Avera Dells Area Hospital, Dell Rapids, SD, p. A560

HOLT, Peter, M.D., Director Medical Affairs, Crittenton Children's Center, MO, p. A362

HOLT, Richard, R.N., Associate Director Patient Care Services, Veterans Affairs St. Louis Health Care System, Saint Louis, MO, p. A370

HOLT, Sherry, Director Human Resources, Unity Medical Center, Manchester, TN, p. A574

HOLT, Stephen R., M.D., Director, Sam Rayburn Memorial Veterans Center, TX, p. A598

HOLT, Tabetha, Director of Human Resources, Riverside Walter Reed Hospital, Gloucester, VA, p. A659

HOLT, Thomas, M.D., Medical Staff President, Good Shepherd Health Care System, Hermiston, OR, p. A513

HOLT, Thomas A, Chief Financial Officer, Conroe Regional Medical Center, Conroe, TX, p. A594

HOLT, Will, Director Information Technology, Harrison County Community Hospital, Bethany, MO, p. A355

HOLTER, Lee H, Chief Financial Officer, Columbia County Health System, Dayton, WA, p. A671

HOLTHAUS, Julie K, Director Human Resources, Sabetha Community Hospital, Sabetha, KS, p. A245

HOLTHAUS, Monica, Chief Financial Officer, Community Healthcare System, Onaga, KS, p. A242

HOLTMAN, Jean, Vice President, Human Resources, St. Mary Medical Center, Apple Valley, CA, p. A51

HOLTZ, George, Director Human Resources, Sharp Grossmont Hospital, La Mesa, CA, p. A63

HOLTZ, Jennifer, Director Finance, Centracare Health-Paynesville, Paynesville, MN, p. A337

HOLTZ, Noel, M.D., Chief Medical Officer, Wellstar Douglas Hospital, Douglasville, GA, p. A152

HOLTZMAN, Michael, M.D., Medical Director, Kindred Hospital St. Louis-St. Anthony'S, MO, p. A368

HOLUBEK, William, M.D., Chief Medical Officer, Carepoint Health Christ Hospital, Jersey City, NJ, p. A406

HOLYFIELD, Asia, Manager Business Office, Lifecare Hospitals Of Pittsburgh - Suburban, PA, p. A537

HOLYFIELD, Linda S., R.N., MSN, President and Chief Executive Officer, P & S Surgical Hospital, Monroe, LA, p. A274

HOLZER, Traci, Chief Human Resources Officer, Doctors Hospital Of Manteca, Manteca, CA, p. A71

HOMA, Jim, Chief Executive Officer, Heatherhill Care Communities, Chardon, OH, p. A474

HOMER, Kenneth, M.D., Chief Medical Officer, Holy Cross Hospital, Fort Lauderdale, FL, p. A122

HOMYK, Linda
Chief Nursing Officer, Heritage Valley Health System, Beaver, PA, p. A520
Chief Nursing Officer, Sewickley Valley Hospital, (A Division Of Valley Medical Facilities), Sewickley, PA, p. A541

HONAKER, Jennifer, Chief Financial Officer, John Randolph Medical Center, Hopewell, VA, p. A659

HONEA, Bert, M.D.
Associate Chief Medical Officer Northern Colorado, Banner Fort Collins Medical Center, Fort Collins, CO, p. A100
Medical Director, Mckee Medical Center, Loveland, CO, p. A104

HONEA, Bruce, Director Information Services, Christus Coushatta Health Care Center, Coushatta, LA, p. A266

HONEA, Michael, Chief Financial Officer, Glen Rose Medical Center, Glen Rose, TX, p. A607

HONEYCUTT, Cynthia, Director Human Resources, Moccasin Bend Mental Health Institute, Chattanooga, TN, p. A567

HONEYCUTT, Robert C.
Chief Executive Officer, Ennis Regional Medical Center, Ennis, TX, p. A603
Chief Executive Officer, Parkview Regional Hospital, Mexia, TX, p. A624

HONSINGER, Melissa, Chief Operating Officer, St. Luke's Rehabilitation Hospital, Boise, ID, p. A168

HONTS, Gary, Chief Executive Officer, John F. Kennedy Memorial Hospital, Indio, CA, p. A62

HOOD, Brenda, Chief Executive Officer, Curahealth Oklahoma, OK, p. A503

HOOD, Cliff, Chief Operating Officer, Central Regional Hospital, Butner, NC, p. A448

HOOD, Gary, Chief Information Officer, Fayette County Hospital, Vandalia, IL, p. A197

HOOD, Kathy, Administrative Assistant Human Resources, Union General Hospital, Blairsville, GA, p. A148

HOOD, Ron, M.D., Chief of Staff, Sutter Amador Hospital, Jackson, CA, p. A62

HOOD, Sam, Director Human Resources, Heartland Regional Medical Center, Marion, IL, p. A188

HOOD, Thomas, Chief Operating Officer, King's Daughters Medical Center, Brookhaven, MS, p. A344

HOOK, Diane, Chief Financial Officer, Wayne County Hospital, Corydon, IA, p. A220

HOOKER, Melvin, Chief Human Resources, New Mexico Veterans Affairs Health Care System - Raymond G. Murphy Medical Center, Albuquerque, NM, p. A416

HOOKER, Rita, Administrative Director Information Services, St. Francis Eastside, SC, p. A553

HOOLAHAN, Susan E, R.N., MSN, Vice President Patient Care Services and Chief Nursing Officer, Upmc Passavant Cranberry, PA, p. A538

HOOP, Heather, Human Resources Generalist, Adams County Regional Medical Center, Seaman, OH, p. A490

HOOPER, Grady A., Chief Executive Officer, Hamilton General Hospital, Hamilton, TX, p. A608

HOOPER, Jason R., President and Chief Executive Officer, Kvc Prairie Ridge Psychiatric Hospital, Kansas City, KS, p. A238

HOOPER, Joseph, President and Chief Executive Officer, Community Howard Regional Health, Kokomo, IN, p. A209

HOOPER, Robert A, Director Human Resources, Tristar Skyline Madison Campus, TN, p. A577

HOOPINGARNER, Darrick, Chief Operating Officer, Dupont Hospital, Fort Wayne, IN, p. A203

HOOPINGARNER, Traci, R.N., Chief Nursing Officer, Lawrence Memorial Hospital, Lawrence, KS, p. A239

HOOVER, Alvin, FACHE, Chief Executive Officer, King's Daughters Medical Center, Brookhaven, MS, p. A344

HOOVER, Garrett W., FACHE, President, Guthrie Corning Hospital, Corning, NY, p. A425

HOOVER, Jeremy Steven, Chief Information Officer, Kiowa County Memorial Hospital, Greensburg, KS, p. A236

HOPE, Lisa R, Director Human Resources, Owensboro Health Muhlenberg Community Hospital, Greenville, KY, p. A252

HOPE, Steve, Vice President Corporate Services, Methodist Rehabilitation Center, Jackson, MS, p. A348

HOPE, William, IV, Chief of Medical Staff, Vidant Chowan Hospital, Edenton, NC, p. A452

HOPKINS, Chris, Chief Executive Officer, Garfield County Health Center, Jordan, MT, p. A376

HOPKINS, Frances F, Chief Financial Officer, Sabine Medical Center, Many, LA, p. A273

HOPKINS, Jason, Director, Human Resources, Hamilton Medical Center, Dalton, GA, p. A152

HOPKINS, Jim, Chief Financial Officer, Cascade Medical Center, Leavenworth, WA, p. A673

HOPKINS, John, M.D., Chief of Staff, Avera Hand County Memorial Hospital, Miller, SD, p. A562

HOPKINS, Joy, Vice President Patient Care Services, Osf St. Francis Hospital And Medical Group, Escanaba, MI, p. A312

HOPKINS, Kelli, Director Human Resources, Baptist Health Medical Center-Hot Spring County, Malvern-Hot Spring County, AR, p. A45

HOPKINS, Ken, Vice President Finance and Chief Financial Officer, Norman Regional Moore, OK, p. A502

HOPKINS, Kevin, Vice President of Operations, Chi Memorial Hospital - Georgia, Fort Oglethorpe, GA, p. A154

HOPKINS, Larry, Chief Medical Officer, Indiana University Health Tipton Hospital, Tipton, IN, p. A215

HOPKINS, Ronald, D.O., Chief of Staff, Nor-Lea Hospital District, Lovington, NM, p. A418

HOPKINS, William, Director Finance, Carolinas Rehabilitation, Charlotte, NC, p. A449

HOPP, Eva, Chief Nurse Executive, Pinckneyville Community Hospital, Pinckneyville, IL, p. A193

HOPPER, Tasha
Chief Executive Officer, The Hospitals Of Providence Transmountain Campus, El Paso, TX, p. A602
Chief Operating Officer, The Hospitals Of Providence Transmountain Campus, El Paso, TX, p. A602

HOPPS, Deborah, R.N., FACHE, Chief Executive Officer, Vibra Rehabilitation Hospital Lake Travis, Lakeway, TX, p. A618

HOPSON, W Briggs, M.D., Clinical Medical Director, River Region West Campus, MS, p. A354

HOPSTAD, Kyle, Chief Executive Officer, Broadwater Health Center, Townsend, MT, p. A379

HOPWOOD, James, Chief Financial Officer, Promise Hospital Of Miss Lou, Vidalia, LA, p. A280

HOPWOOD, Jennifer, Vice President, Chief Nursing Officer, Children's Hospital Of Illinois, IL, p. A193

HORAN, Gary S, FACHE
President and Chief Executive Officer, Trinitas Hospital, NJ, p. A404
President and Chief Executive Officer, Trinitas Regional Medical Center - New Point Campus, NJ, p. A404

HORAN, Gary S., FACHE, President and Chief Executive Officer, Trinitas Regional Medical Center - New Point Campus, NJ, p. A404

HORATH, Kevin, Vice President Human Resources, Decatur Memorial Hospital, Decatur, IL, p. A180

HORCH, David, Chief Executive, California Medical Facility, Vacaville, CA, p. A93

HORECKA, Richard, Chief Medical Officer, Swift County - Benson Health Services, Benson, MN, p. A328

HORINEK, ReChelle, Chief Financial Officer, Trego County-Lemke Memorial Hospital, Wakeeney, KS, p. A247

HORN, Debbie, Controller, Texas Rehabilitation Hospital Of Arlington, Arlington, TX, p. A584

HORN, Jeff, Director of Support Services, Indiana University Health Jay Hospital, Portland, IN, p. A213

HORN, Jon, M.D., Chief of Staff, Northeast Georgia Medical Center Barrow, Winder, GA, p. A163

HORN, LeeAnn, Chief Nurse Executive, Providence Kodiak Island Medical Center, Kodiak, AK, p. A26

HORN, Sarah
Chief Nursing Officer, Salem Health Rehabilitation Center, OR, p. A517
Chief Nursing Officer, Salem Health West Valley, Dallas, OR, p. A517

HORN, Syndi, Director Information Systems, Memorial Hospital, Carthage, IL, p. A175

HORNBURG, Tom, Director Information Systems, Mason General Hospital And Family Of Clinics, Shelton, WA, p. A677

HORNE, Beth, System Administrator Information Technology, Preston Memorial Hospital, Kingwood, WV, p. A684

HORNE, Eilene, Manager Human Resources, Mountain View Hospital, Idaho Falls, ID, p. A169

HORNE, Harry, D.O., Chief of Staff, Cumberland River Hospital, Celina, TN, p. A566

HORNE, J Mark, Senior Vice President, Ambulatory Services and Chief Operating Officer, Grand View Health, Sellersville, PA, p. A541

HORNE, Perry, Chief Nursing Officer, St. Cloud Regional Medical Center, Saint Cloud, FL, p. A138

HORNER, Ania, R.N., MSN, Vice President and Chief Nurse Executive, Aurora Sinai Medical Center, Milwaukee, WI, p. A698

HORNER, Bryan, President and Chief Executive Officer, Shannon Medical Center- St. John's Campus, TX, p. A632

HORNER, Cheryl, Supervisor Data Processing, Community Hospital Of Staunton, Staunton, IL, p. A197

HORNER, Eva, Assistant Executive Director Operations, Devereux Hospital And Children's Center Of Florida, Melbourne, FL, p. A129

HORNER, John M., President and Chief Executive Officer, Major Hospital, Shelbyville, IN, p. A214

HORNICK, Gregory, MSN, Chief Nursing Officer, Martin General Hospital, Williamston, NC, p. A462

HORNSBY, Donny, Director Fiscal Services, Memphis Mental Health Institute, Memphis, TN, p. A575

HORNUNG, Dona, Director Information and Technology Services, Doctors Hospital, Augusta, GA, p. A147

HORNUNG, Kurt, Director, Medical Center Of Trinity, Trinity, FL, p. A142

HORRIGAN, Timothy, M.D., Chief Quality Officer, Unitypoint Health - Allen Hospital, Waterloo, IA, p. A231

HORSLEY, Steve, Vice President and Chief Information Officer, Women's Hospital Of Greensboro, NC, p. A453

HORSMAN, Sandra, Director, Veterans Affairs Medical Center Hot Springs Campus, SD, p. A561

HORST, Brad, Director Human Resources, Mainland Medical Center, TX, p. A643

HORST, Joanna, MSN, R.N., Chief Nursing Officer, St. Christopher's Hospital For Children, Philadelphia, PA, p. A536

HORSTMAN, Jennifer M, R.N., Chief Nursing Officer and Chief Information Officer, Fairbanks, Indianapolis, IN, p. A206

HORSTMANN, Steve, Vice President Operations, North Memorial Health Hospital, Robbinsdale, MN, p. A338

HORTILLOSA, Maria, M.D., Chief of Staff, Middlesboro Arh Hospital, Middlesboro, KY, p. A258

HORTON, Alan, Administrator, Putnam General Hospital, Eatonton, GA, p. A153

HORTON, Greg, Director Support Services, State Hospital South, Blackfoot, ID, p. A167

HORTON, Jerrilyn, R.N., Chief Nursing Officer, Dewitt Hospital, Dewitt-Arkansas County, AR, p. A41

HORTON, Jim, Chief Executive Officer, Rankin County Hospital District, Rankin, TX, p. A630

HORTON, Kenny, Director Information Systems, Walker Baptist Medical Center, Jasper, AL, p. A20

HORTON, Kimberly, R.N., MSN, Chief Executive Officer, Vibra Hospital Of Sacramento, Folsom, CA, p. A58

HORTON, Landon, Director of Nursing, Valley Behavioral Health System, Barling, AR, p. A39

HORTON, Marie, Director Associate Relations, Bartow Regional Medical Center, Bartow, FL, p. A117

HORTON, Sammy, Chief of Staff, Brownwood Regional Medical Center, Brownwood, TX, p. A590

HORTON, Warren, Information Technologist, Baptist Health Medical Center-Stuttgart, Stuttgart-Arkansas County, AR, p. A49

HORVAT, Kami, Chief Financial Officer, West Covina Medical Center, West Covina, CA, p. A95

HORVATH, Alex
Vice President and Chief Human Resources Officer, Tmc For Children, AZ, p. A38
Vice President Human Resources, Southlake Campus, IN, p. A204

HORVATH, Holly, Director of Nursing, Jerome Golden Center For Behavioral Health, Inc., West Palm Beach, FL, p. A143

HOSKINS, Pearly Graham, M.D., President Medical Staff, Cape Fear Valley - Bladen County Hospital, Elizabethtown, NC, p. A452

HOSS, Laurna, Human Resource Coordinator, Select Specialty Hospital-Omaha, Omaha, NE, p. A388

HOSTEENEZ, Vivie, Chief Financial Officer, San Carlos Apache Healthcare Corporation, Peridot, AZ, p. A32

HOSTETTER, Lynne, Vice President Human Resources, The Hsc Pediatric Center, Washington, DC, p. A116

HOTA, Bala, Interim Chief Information Officer, John H. Stroger Jr. Hospital Of Cook County, Chicago, IL, p. A177

HOTALING, Andrew, Chief Executive Officer, Forest View Psychiatric Hospital, Grand Rapids, MI, p. A314

HOTCHKISS, Jason, CPA
Chief Financial Officer, Ottumwa Regional Health Center, Ottumwa, IA, p. A228
Chief Financial Officer, Trios Health, Kennewick, WA, p. A672

HOTCHKISS, Kaleigh, Controller, Encompass Health Rehabilitation Hospital Of Northwest Tucson, Tucson, AZ, p. A37

HOTES, Lawrence S, M.D., Chief Medical Officer, New England Sinai Hospital And Rehabilitation Center, Stoughton, MA, p. A305

HOTOVY, Patrick, M.D., Chief of Staff, York General, York, NE, p. A391

HOUCHIN, Kim, Chief Nursing Officer, Minnie Hamilton Healthcare Center, Grantsville, WV, p. A683

HOUCK, Nanette, R.N., Chief Nursing Executive, Excelsior Springs Hospital, Excelsior Springs, MO, p. A359

HOUGH, Nathan
Chief Executive Officer, Crook County Medical Services District, Sundance, WY, p. A710
Chief Executive Officer, Niobrara Health And Life Center, Lusk, WY, p. A709

HOUGHTON, Roxan, Director Human Resources, Promise Hospital Of Miss Lou, Vidalia, LA, p. A280

HOULAHAN, Beth, R.N., Senior Vice President and Chief Nursing Officer, American Family Children's Hospital, WI, p. A696

HOULE, David, Executive Vice President and Chief Financial Officer, Hebrew Senior Care, West Hartford, CT, p. A112

HOULIHAN, David, M.D., Chief of Staff, Va Medical Center, Tomah, WI, p. A704

HOULTON, Andrew, M.D., Chief Medical Officer, North Memorial Health Hospital, Robbinsdale, MN, p. A338

HOUMANN, Lars D, President, Florida Hospital For Children-Walt Disney Pavilion, FL, p. A134

HOUNSHELL, Jacqueline, Chief Financial Officer, Leconte Medical Center, Sevierville, TN, p. A579

HOURANY, Joseph, Chief Medical Officer, Montclair Hospital Medical Center, Montclair, CA, p. A73

HOUSAND, Jill, Director Human Resources, Mesa Springs, Fort Worth, TX, p. A605

HOUSE, David
Vice President and Chief Information Officer, Baptist Health Medical Center - North Little Rock, North Little Rock-Pulaski County, AR, p. A47
Vice President and Chief Information Officer, Baptist Health Medical Center-Arkadelphia, Arkadelphia, AR, p. A39
Vice President and Chief Information Officer, Baptist Health Medical Center-Little Rock, Little Rock-Pulaski County, AR, p. A45
Vice President and Chief Information Officer, Baptist Health Rehabilitation Institute, Little Rock-Pulaski County, AR, p. A45
Vice President, Baptist Health Extended Care Hospital, Little Rock-Pulaski County, AR, p. A44

HOUSE, John, M.D., Chief of Staff, Eureka Springs Hospital, Eureka Springs-Carroll County, AR, p. A41

HOUSER, David, M.D., Vice President Medical Affairs, Rapid City Regional Hospital, Rapid City, SD, p. A563

HOUSER, Robert, FACHE, Chief Executive Officer, Pioneer Memorial Hospital, Heppner, OR, p. A513

HOUSER, Sara, Chief Nursing Officer, Ashe Memorial Hospital, Jefferson, NC, p. A455

HOUSER-HANFELDER, Sallie, FACHE, Director, Veterans Affairs Eastern Colorado Health Care System, Denver, CO, p. A99

HOUSH, Joe, District Director Human Resources, Kindred Hospital-Indianapolis, Indianapolis, IN, p. A207

HOUSLEY, Kristin
Chief Information Officer, South Lincoln Medical Center, Kemmerer, WY, p. A708
Co-Interim Chief Executive Officer, South Lincoln Medical Center, Kemmerer, WY, p. A708

HOUSMAN, Bradley W., M.D., Chief Medical Officer, Baptist Health Paducah, Paducah, KY, p. A259

HOUSTON, Anthony, FACHE, President, Chi St Vincent Hot Springs, Hot Springs-Garland County, AR, p. A43

HOUSTON, Jerry, Director Information Systems, Jennie Stuart Medical Center, Hopkinsville, KY, p. A253

HOUSTON, Sally, M.D., Executive Vice President and Chief Medical Officer, Tampa General Hospital Children's Medical Center, FL, p. A141

HOVAN, Keith A, R.N.
President and Chief Executive Officer, Charlton Memorial Hospital, MA, p. A299

President and Chief Executive Officer, St. Luke's Hospital, MA, p. A299

President and Chief Executive Officer, Tobey Hospital, MA, p. A299

HOVAN, Keith A., R.N., President and Chief Executive Officer, Tobey Hospital, MA, p. A299

HOVDENES, Jodi Lynn, Vice President Patient Care, Chi St Alexius Health Carrington Medical Center, Carrington, ND, p. A464

HOVENS, Michael R., M.D., Chief Medical Officer, Panola Medical Center, Batesville, MS, p. A343

HOWARD, Andrew, Chief Executive Officer, Select Specialty Hospital-Knoxville, TN, p. A579

HOWARD, Catherine, Director Human Resources, Sentara Halifax Regional Hospital, South Boston, VA, p. A666

HOWARD, Cindy, Director Financial Services, Nell J. Redfield Memorial Hospital, Malad City, ID, p. A170

HOWARD, Dan, Director, Information Services, San Gorgonio Memorial Hospital, Banning, CA, p. A52

HOWARD, Daniel, Chief Financial Officer, Maine Veterans Affairs Medical Center, Augusta, ME, p. A282

HOWARD, Darcy, Chief Financial Officer, Citizens Medical Center, Colby, KS, p. A233

HOWARD, Eddie L, Chief Operating Officer, Ut Health Rehabilitation Hospital, Tyler, TX, p. A641

HOWARD, Gary L, Senior Vice President and Chief Financial Officer, Hamilton Medical Center, Dalton, GA, p. A152

HOWARD, Greg M
Director Human Resource, Health Alliance Hospital - Broadway Campus, Kingston, NY, p. A428
Vice President Human Resources, Health Alliance Hospital - Mary's Avenue Campus, Kingston, NY, p. A428

HOWARD, Gwenyth, Vice President Finance, St. Thomas More Hospital, Canon City, CO, p. A97

HOWARD, Kari, Interim Director of Nursing, Pauls Valley General Hospital, Pauls Valley, OK, p. A505

HOWARD, Lisa M, Associate Director, Veterans Affairs Sierra Nevada Health Care System, Reno, NV, p. A396

HOWARD, Lisa M., Director, Veterans Affairs Sierra Nevada Health Care System, Reno, NV, p. A396

HOWARD, Loy M., Chief Operating Officer, Tanner Medical Center-Carrollton, Carrollton, GA, p. A149

HOWARD, Mary, Director Human Resources, Winnebago Mental Health Institute, Winnebago, WI, p. A706

HOWARD, Melissa, Chief Nurse Executive, ICH & FPH, Citrus Valley Medical Center-Queen Of The Valley Campus, CA, p. A56

HOWARD, Michele, Vice President Nursing Services, Perry County Memorial Hospital, Tell City, IN, p. A215

HOWARD, Mike, Chief Operating Officer, Eliza Coffee Memorial Hospital, Florence, AL, p. A18

HOWARD, Opal R, Executive Director Human Resources, Florida Hospital-Oceanside, FL, p. A121

HOWARD, Pamela B., R.N., Chief Executive Officer, Administrator and Risk Manager, Lake Butler Hospital Hand Surgery Center, Lake Butler, FL, p. A127

HOWARD, Ron, Chief Financial Officer, Holly Hill Hospital, Raleigh, NC, p. A459

HOWARD, Sabra, Manager Human Resources, Harlan Arh Hospital, Harlan, KY, p. A253

HOWARD, Shawn, Interim Chief Executive Officer, Atoka County Medical Center, Atoka, OK, p. A496

HOWARD, Teresa, Manager Human Resources, Yoakum County Hospital, Denver City, TX, p. A599

HOWARD, Tom, Chief Financial Officer, Texas Health Presbyterian Hospital Flower Mound, Flower Mound, TX, p. A603

HOWARD, Win, Chief Executive Officer, Asante Three Rivers Medical Center, Grants Pass, OR, p. A513

HOWARD-CROW, Dallis, Chief Human Resources Officer, Emory University Hospital Midtown, Atlanta, GA, p. A146

HOWAT, Greg, Vice President Human Resources, Eastern Maine Medical Center, Bangor, ME, p. A282

HOWDEN, William, Vice President Nursing, Good Samaritan Regional Medical Center, Corvallis, OR, p. A512

HOWE, Debbie, Chief Executive Officer, Weatherford Regional Hospital, Weatherford, OK, p. A510

HOWE, James L, Director Human Resources, Pinnacle Pointe Hospital, Little Rock-Pulaski County, AR, p. A45

HOWE, Judson, Chief Financial Officer, Adventist Health Howard Memorial, Willits, CA, p. A95

HOWE, Vicki, Health Information Management, Ness County Hospital District No 2, Ness City, KS, p. A242

HOWELL, Amy M, Director Human Resources, St. Luke's Behavioral Health Center, Phoenix, AZ, p. A34

HOWELL, Bradley, Chief Executive Officer, Roundup Memorial Healthcare, Roundup, MT, p. A378

HOWELL, Carrie, Chief Financial Officer, Barstow Community Hospital, Barstow, CA, p. A52

HOWELL, Diana, Director Human Resources, Conroe Regional Medical Center, Conroe, TX, p. A594

HOWELL, Jerry, Administrator, Sabine County Hospital, Hemphill, TX, p. A609

HOWELL, Jill, Chief Nursing Officer, St. Luke's Jerome, Jerome, ID, p. A169

HOWELL, Kathy A, Vice President Human Resources, Lexington Medical Center, West Columbia, SC, p. A558

HOWELL, Kristie, System Information Technology Director, Southampton Memorial Hospital, Franklin, VA, p. A658

HOWELL, Nathan, Chief Executive Officer, Southern Maine Health Care - Biddeford Medical Center, ME, p. A283

HOWELL, Pat, Chief Nursing Officer, Community Memorial Hospital, Syracuse, NE, p. A390

HOWELL, Ronene, Director Health Information Management, Bryce Hospital, Tuscaloosa, AL, p. A23

HOWELL, Sheri, Deputy Commander Nursing, Brooke Army Medical Center, Fort Sam Houston, TX, p. A603

HOWELL, Timothy W., R.N., Senior Vice President and Chief Nursing Officer, University Medical Center, Lubbock, TX, p. A621

HOWELLS, Stephen, Chief Financial Officer, Kane County Hospital, Kanab, UT, p. A647

HOWERTER, Mark, M.D., President Medical Staff, Columbus Community Hospital, Columbus, NE, p. A383

HOWERTON, Russell M, M.D., Chief Medical Officer, Brenner Children's Hospital & Health Services, NC, p. A463

HOWERTON, Shawn, M.D., Chief Executive Officer and President, Medical Staff, Sampson Regional Medical Center, Clinton, NC, p. A450

HOY, Jonathan B, Chief Financial Officer, Duke Regional Hospital, Durham, NC, p. A451

HOYER, Sara, Director Administrative Services, Kansas Neurological Institute, Topeka, KS, p. A246

HOYES, Garry W, Chief Executive Officer, Columbus Springs East Hospital, OH, p. A481

HOYES, Garry W., Chief Executive Officer, Columbus Springs East Hospital, OH, p. A481

HOYOS, Kent, Chief Information Officer, Pomona Valley Hospital Medical Center, Pomona, CA, p. A79

HOYT, Nancy Gerilyn, R.N., Vice President Operations/Clinical and Chief Nursing Officer, Mercy Regional Medical Center, Durango, CO, p. A99

HRDLICKA, Stephanie, Chief Executive Officer, Vermilion Behavioral Health Systems South, LA, p. A271

HRIT, Barbara, Controller, Beaumont Hospital - Farmington Hills, Farmington Hills, MI, p. A312

HRITZ, Diane, Chief Financial Officer, Advanced Surgical Hospital, Washington, PA, p. A543

HRUBIAK, Dan, Associate Computer Program Analyst, Western New York Children's Hospital Psychiatric Center, West Seneca, NY, p. A446

HRUBY, Deidre, Director of Patient Care, Madelia Community Hospital, Madelia, MN, p. A334

HSIEH, Ketty, Senior Director Finance, Uw Medicine/Northwest Hospital & Medical Center, Seattle, WA, p. A677

HSU, Wah Chung, Senior Vice President Finance, San Antonio Regional Hospital, Upland, CA, p. A93

HUANG, Hanna, Chief Executive Officer, Laredo Specialty Hospital, Laredo, TX, p. A619

HUANG, Joseph, M.D., Chief Medical and Quality Officer, Legacy Silverton Medical Center, Silverton, OR, p. A518

HUBBARD, Bill, Vice President, Operations, Carolinas Healthcare System Northeast, Concord, NC, p. A450

HUBBARD, Blake W., FACHE, Chief Executive Officer, Foundation Surgical Hospital Of San Antonio, San Antonio, TX, p. A633

HUBBARD, Brent
  Chief Operating Officer, Mercy Hospital Ozark, Ozark-Franklin County, AR, p. A47
  Chief Operating Officer, Mercy Hospital Paris, Paris-Logan County, AR, p. A47
  Chief Operating Officer, Mercy Hospital Waldron, Waldron-Scott County, AR, p. A49
  Chief Operating Officer, Mercy Orthopedic Hospital Springfield, MO, p. A370

HUBBARD, Daniel, Chief Financial Officer, Sioux Falls Veterans Affairs Health Care System, Sioux Falls, SD, p. A564

HUBBARD, Gwen, Chief Nursing Officer, Sierra Vista Hospital, Sacramento, CA, p. A82

HUBBARD, Kathy
  Controller, Ocean Beach Hospital, Ilwaco, WA, p. A672
  Manager Human Resources, Nell J. Redfield Memorial Hospital, Malad City, ID, p. A170

HUBBARD, Lisa, Vice President and Chief Nursing Executive, Mercy Medical Center Mount Shasta, Mount Shasta, CA, p. A74

HUBBARD, Mark, Vice President Risk Management, Loma Linda University Behavioral Medicine Center, Redlands, CA, p. A80

HUBBARD, Norm, Executive Vice President, Seattle Cancer Care Alliance, Seattle, WA, p. A676

HUBBARD, Tyson, Director Human Resources, Stanislaus Surgical Hospital, Modesto, CA, p. A73

HUBBS, Olas A., III, FACHE, President and Chief Executive Officer, Memorial Health, Marysville, OH, p. A486

HUBEL, Edward T., FACHE, President, Baptist Medical Center Nassau, Fernandina Beach, FL, p. A122

HUBER, Dalton, Chief Financial Officer, Campbell County Health, Gillette, WY, p. A708

HUBER, Joseph M, Chief Financial Officer, Scheie Eye Institute Of The Hospital Of The University Of Pennsylvania, PA, p. A535

HUBER, Timothy
  Vice President and Chief Financial Officer, Kimball-Ridge Center, IA, p. A230
  Vice President and Chief Financial Officer, Mercy Hospital Of Franciscan Sisters, Oelwein, IA, p. A227
  Vice President and Chief Financial Officer, Sartori Memorial Hospital, Cedar Falls, IA, p. A218

HUBER, Vicki Lynn, R.N., MSN, Chief Nursing Officer, Abrazo Scottsdale Campus, Phoenix, AZ, p. A32

HUBLEY, Grover, M.D., President Medical Staff, Chi St. Joseph Health Madison Hospital, Madisonville, TX, p. A622

HUBSCHMAN, Gary
  Administrative Director Finance, Sutter Auburn Faith Hospital, Auburn, CA, p. A51
  Administrative Director Finance, Sutter Roseville Medical Center, Roseville, CA, p. A81

HUCK, Karma, Chief Operating Officer, Scott County Hospital, Scott City, KS, p. A245

HUCKABEE, Mike, Network Administrator, Coryell Memorial Hospital, Gatesville, TX, p. A607

HUCKABY, Don, Chief Information Management Service, Veterans Affairs Eastern Colorado Health Care System, Denver, CO, p. A99

HUDA, Edith, Director Human Resources, Daniels Memorial Healthcare Center, Scobey, MT, p. A379

HUDAK, Corey, Director Human Resources, Upmc Pinnacle Memorial, York, PA, p. A546

HUDDLESTON, Tina, R.N., Chief Nursing Officer, Baylor Medical Center At Trophy Club, Trophy Club, TX, p. A640

HUDGENS, Roselyn, Director Human Resources, Ballinger Memorial Hospital, Ballinger, TX, p. A587

HUDGINS, Laura E, Assistant Administrator, Jasper Memorial Hospital, Monticello, GA, p. A158

HUDGINS, Paul C., Senior Vice President, Carilion Franklin Memorial Hospital, Rocky Mount, VA, p. A666

HUDSON, Beth, Chief Nursing Officer, Baylor Institute For Rehabilitation, Dallas, TX, p. A595

HUDSON, Delilah, Controller, Covington County Hospital, Collins, MS, p. A345

HUDSON, Gary Mikeal, Administrator, Ut Health Carthage, Carthage, TX, p. A592

HUDSON, Gary Mikeal., Administrator, Ut Health Carthage, Carthage, TX, p. A592

HUDSON, Guy, Chief Executive Officer, Swedish/Issaquah, Issaquah, WA, p. A672

HUDSON, Janell, Director, Nursing and Clinical Services, Sanford Medical Center Thief River Falls, Thief River Falls, MN, p. A340

HUDSON, Jason Dan, RN, BSN, Chief Executive Officer, Healthsouth Rehabilitation Hospital Of Tinton Falls, Tinton Falls, NJ, p. A412

HUDSON, Kenneth J, Chief Financial Officer, Veterans Affairs Puget Sound Health Care System-American Lake Division, WA, p. A677

HUDSON, Kent, Chief Financial Officer, Kingman Community Hospital, Kingman, KS, p. A238

HUDSON, Larry C, Executive Vice President and Chief Financial Officer, General Hospital, WV, p. A682

HUDSON, Maggie, Chief Financial and Operations Officer, Santiam Hospital, Stayton, OR, p. A518

HUDSON, Mike, Administrator, Federal Correctional Institute Hospital, Littleton, CO, p. A103

HUDSON, Pamela, M.D., Chief Executive Officer, Crestwood Medical Center, Huntsville, AL, p. A19

HUDSON, Robbi, Chief Executive Officer, Encompass Health Rehabilitation Hospital Of Wichita Falls, Wichita Falls, TX, p. A644

HUDSON-JINKS, Therese M., R.N., MSN, Chief Nursing Officer, Tufts Medical Center, Boston, MA, p. A297

HUELSKAMP, Donald, Interim Chief Financial Officer, Harrison Community Hospital, Cadiz, OH, p. A473

HUENERGARDT, Sam D., Chief Executive Officer, Shawnee Mission Medical Center, Shawnee Mission, KS, p. A246

HUERTA, Brad, Chief Executive Officer and Administrator, Lost Rivers Medical Center, Arco, ID, p. A167

HUERTA, Guillermo, M.D., Chief Medical Officer, Select Specialty Hospital-Omaha, Omaha, NE, p. A388

HUERTA, Jose, Chief Executive Officer, Mesa Hills Specialty Hospital, El Paso, TX, p. A602

HUERTER, Holly
  Vice President Human Resources, Methodist Jennie Edmundson Hospital, Council Bluffs, IA, p. A220
  Vice President Human Resources, Methodist Women's Hospital, NE, p. A388

HUESMAN, Carol, Chief Information Officer, Major Hospital, Shelbyville, IN, p. A214

HUETTL, Patricia, Vice President Finance and Chief Financial Officer, Holy Family Memorial, Manitowoc, WI, p. A696

HUFF, Jeff, Assistant Administrator Finance, Fayette Medical Center, Fayette, AL, p. A18

HUFF, Michael H., Chief Executive Officer, Hamilton Hospital, Olney, TX, p. A626

HUFF, Shelly E, Manager Human Resources, Indiana University Health Tipton Hospital, Tipton, IN, p. A215

HUFFINE, Daniel, Chief Financial Officer, St. David's Rehabilitation Center, TX, p. A586

HUFFMAN, David, Vice President and Controller, Select Specialty Hospital-Wilmington, Wilmington, DE, p. A114

HUFFMAN, James, Chief Executive Officer and Administrator, Baptist Memorial Hospital-Desoto, Southaven, MS, p. A353

HUFFMAN, Joshua, M.D., Chief Medical Staff, Saint Joseph Berea, Berea, KY, p. A249

HUFFMAN, Sherry, Administrator Human Resources, Beaumont Hospital - Dearborn, Dearborn, MI, p. A310

HUFFMAN, Teresa, Chief Executive Officer, Texas Rehabilitation Hospital Of Arlington, Arlington, TX, p. A584

HUFFMAN, Tim, Western Region Director, Information Systems Business Relationships, Baylor Scott & White Medical Center-Irving, Irving, TX, p. A615

HUFFNER, William, M.D.
  Chief Medical Officer, University Of Maryland Shore Medical Center At Chestertown, Chestertown, MD, p. A290
  Chief Medical Officer, University Of Maryland Shore Medical Center At Easton, Easton, MD, p. A291
  Vice President Medical Affairs, University Of Maryland Shore Medical Center At Dorchester, Cambridge, MD, p. A290

HUFFSTUTLER, Brandon, Chief Information Officer, Electra Memorial Hospital, Electra, TX, p. A603

HUFNAGEL, Keith, Director Human Resources, Stillwater Medical Center, Stillwater, OK, p. A507

HUGAR, Joseph G., President, Sharon Regional Medical Center, Sharon, PA, p. A541

HUGGINS, Lois, Chief Human Resources Officer and Senior Vice President Human Resources, Shirley Ryan Abilitylab, Chicago, IL, p. A179

HUGGINS, Michael C, Administrator Network System, Eastern Oklahoma Medical Center, Poteau, OK, p. A505

HUGHES, April, Chief Financial Officer, Peachford Behavioral Health System, Atlanta, GA, p. A146

HUGHES, Beth, President, Mercy Medical Center-Sioux City, Sioux City, IA, p. A229

HUGHES, Bill, Chief Nursing Officer, Granville Health System, Oxford, NC, p. A458

HUGHES, Brandon, Director Human Resources, Hermann Area District Hospital, Hermann, MO, p. A360

HUGHES, Chad
  Chief Information Officer, North Texas State Hospital, Wichita Falls Campus, Wichita Falls, TX, p. A644
  Information Officer, North Texas State Hospital, Vernon, TX, p. A642

HUGHES, David L., Adminstrator, Crenshaw Community Hospital, Luverne, AL, p. A20

HUGHES, David S, Chief Financial Officer, University Health Systems Children's Hospital, NC, p. A454

HUGHES, Dustan, M.D., Vice President Medical Affairs, Saint Alphonsus Medical Center - Nampa, Nampa, ID, p. A170

HUGHES, Elisabeth, Director Human Resources and Community Relations, Fairview Regional Medical Center, Fairview, OK, p. A499

HUGHES, James, Director Human Resources, Lake Cumberland Regional Hospital, Somerset, KY, p. A260

HUGHES, Jessica, Director Finance, Hawarden Regional Healthcare, Hawarden, IA, p. A224

HUGHES, Lee, R.N., Chief Nursing Officer, Flint River Community Hospital, Montezuma, GA, p. A157

HUGHES, Leigh Ann, Chief Financial Officer, Hardin Medical Center, Savannah, TN, p. A579

HUGHES, Lori, R.N., MSN
  Chief Nursing Officer, Vice President Operations & Patient Care Services, Cottage Hospital, Woodsville, NH, p. A401
  Chief Nursing Officer, Vice President Operations and Patient Care Services, Cottage Hospital, Woodsville, NH, p. A401

HUGHES, Mark A., M.D., Medical Director, River Park Hospital, Huntington, WV, p. A684

HUGHES, Michael, M.D., President, Summa Health System Barberton, Summa Health System Barberton Hospital, OH, p. A470

HUGHES, Robert K.
Chief Executive Officer, Coler Rehabilitation And Nursing Care Center, NY, p. A435
Chief Executive Officer, Henry J. Carter Specialty Hospital & Nursing Facility, NY, p. A435

HUGHES, Sandra, Chief Financial Officer, Clinch Memorial Hospital, Homerville, GA, p. A155

HUGHES, Susan, Interim Director Human Resources, Winner Regional Healthcare Center, Winner, SD, p. A565

HUGHES, Terry, Director Information Systems, Nantucket Cottage Hospital, Nantucket, MA, p. A302

HUGHES, Thomas, President, Our Lady Of Fatima Hospital, RI, p. A547

HUGHES, Veronica, Chief Nursing Officer, Mesilla Valley Hospital, Las Cruces, NM, p. A418

HUGHES-MICKEL, Leann, Chief Information Officer, Touro Rehabilitation Center, LA, p. A276

HUGHS, Mary, Chief Human Resources Officer, Our Lady Of Lourdes Memorial Hospital, Inc., Binghamton, NY, p. A422

HUGHSON, John R., Chief Executive Officer, Gonzales Healthcare Systems, Gonzales, TX, p. A607

HUGO, Chris, M.D., Chief of Staff, Guttenberg Municipal Hospital, Guttenberg, IA, p. A223

HULBERT, Kim, R.N., Chief Clinical Officer, Madison County Health Care System, Winterset, IA, p. A231

HULETT, Rachelle, Vice President Human Resources, Mclaren Flint, Flint, MI, p. A312

HULETT, Wendi, Chief Nursing Officer, Artesia General Hospital, Artesia, NM, p. A416

HULL, Brad, Chief Financial Officer, Dale Medical Center, Ozark, AL, p. A22

HULL, Debbie, Chief Financial Officer, Fisher County Hospital District, Rotan, TX, p. A631

HULL, Kathy, President and Chief Executive Officer, Illini Community Hospital, Pittsfield, IL, p. A193

HULL, Ken, Director Human Resources, Inova Fairfax Hospital For Children, VA, p. A657

HULL, Lauren, Chief Operating Officer, Porter Regional Hospital, Valparaiso, IN, p. A215

HULLANDER, Angie, Administrator and Special Operations, Chi Memorial Hospital - Georgia, Fort Oglethorpe, GA, p. A154

HULSE, Mark, MSN, Chief Digital Officer, City Of Hope's Helford Clinical Research Hospital, Duarte, CA, p. A57

HULSEY, Cathy, Manager of Human Resources, Chi Memorial Hospital - Georgia, Fort Oglethorpe, GA, p. A154

HULSEY, Grant, Director Information Technology, Baylor Scott & White Surgical Hospital At Sherman, Sherman, TX, p. A635

HULSEY, Kelly, MSN, R.N., Chief Nursing Officer, Piedmont Hospital, Atlanta, GA, p. A146

HUMBERT, Gilbert Glenn, Jr, Interim Chief Nursing Officer, Eliza Coffee Memorial Hospital, Florence, AL, p. A18

HUMBLE, Kathryn G., Chief Human Resources Officer, Beatrice Community Hospital And Health Center, Beatrice, NE, p. A382

HUMBLE, Linnea, Director of Finance, Sutter Lakeside Hospital, Lakeport, CA, p. A64

HUME, Diana, Manager Human Resources, Methodist Mckinney Hospital, Mckinney, TX, p. A623

HUMES, Karen, Chief Information Officer, Titusville Area Hospital, Titusville, PA, p. A542

HUMES, Ronny, Chief Executive Officer, Magnolia Regional Health Center, Corinth, MS, p. A345

HUMME, Sarah, MSN, R.N.
Chief Nursing Officer, Southwest General Hospital, San Antonio, TX, p. A634
Chief Operating Officer, Southwest General Hospital, San Antonio, TX, p. A634

HUMMEL, Angela, Vice President Human Resources, Evangelical Community Hospital, Lewisburg, PA, p. A530

HUMMELKE, Arlita, Manager Human Resources, Mercy Hospital Tishomingo, Tishomingo, OK, p. A508

HUMMER, Christopher R., President, Carolinas Healthcare System Pineville, Charlotte, NC, p. A449

HUMMER, Denise, R.N., Vice President Administrative Services, Community Memorial Hospital, Hamilton, NY, p. A427

HUMPHREY, Dale, Chief Executive Officer, Saint Thomas River Park Hospital, Mc Minnville, TN, p. A574

HUMPHREY, Eric, Senior Vice President, Chief Human Resources Officer, St. Joseph's Hospital, West Bend, WI, p. A706

HUMPHREY, James, Vice President Talent Resources and Human Resources for South Side Operating Group, St. Francis Medical Center, CO, p. A98

HUMPHREY, Randy, Chief Financial Officer, Merit Health Wesley, Hattiesburg, MS, p. A347

HUMPHREY, Richard, Executive Vice President and Chief Financial Officer, Parkland Health & Hospital System, Dallas, TX, p. A597

HUMPHREYS, Corina
Chief Executive Officer, Weslaco Regional Rehabilitation Hospital, Weslaco, TX, p. A643
Chief Operating Officer, Weslaco Regional Rehabilitation Hospital, Weslaco, TX, p. A643

HUMPHREYS, Lynn, Director Human Resources, Henry County Health Center, Mount Pleasant, IA, p. A226

HUMPHRIES, Vickie Witcher
Director Human Resources, Bon Secours Maryview Medical Center, Portsmouth, VA, p. A664
Vice President Human Resources, Bon Secours Mary Immaculate Hospital, Newport News, VA, p. A662
Vice President Human Resources, Bon Secours-Depaul Medical Center, Norfolk, VA, p. A662

HUNDAL, Ranjit, M.D., Chief Medical Executive, Mills-Peninsula Medical Center, CA, p. A53

HUNGER, Bryan, Chief Executive Officer, Jefferson County Health Center, Fairfield, IA, p. A222

HUNGER, Dennis, Chief Operating Officer, Ottumwa Regional Health Center, Ottumwa, IA, p. A228

HUNSAKER, Mike, Chief Operating Officer, Star Valley Medical Center, Afton, WY, p. A707

HUNSBERGER, Tom, Director Human Resources, Olmsted Medical Center, Rochester, MN, p. A338

HUNSICKER, Elizabeth, Chief Executive Officer, West Valley Medical Center, Caldwell, ID, p. A168

HUNT, Amy, Director Human Resources, Menorah Medical Center, Overland Park, KS, p. A243

HUNT, Cecile, Interim Chief Executive Officer, Ut Health Behavioral Health Center, TX, p. A641

HUNT, Cheri, R.N., Vice President Patient Care Services and Chief Nursing Officer, Children's Mercy Hospital Kansas City, Kansas City, MO, p. A361

HUNT, Cheryl, Esq, Chief Nursing Officer, St. Peter's Hospital, Helena, MT, p. A376

HUNT, Chris, President, Clay County Hospital, Flora, IL, p. A183

HUNT, Christopher, Director, Information Technologies, FISO, Helena Regional Medical Center, Helena-Phillips County, AR, p. A43

HUNT, D Deann, Director of Human Resources, Gibson General Hospital, Princeton, IN, p. A213

HUNT, Deloris, Chief Human Resources Officer, C. S. Mott Children's Hospital, MI, p. A307

HUNT, Don, M.D., Vice President Patient Centered Care and Chief Nursing Officer, Ut Health North Campus Tyler, Tyler, TX, p. A641

HUNT, Jeffery B, Vice President, Business Development and Support Services, Roane General Hospital, Spencer, WV, p. A687

HUNT, John R., Chief Executive Officer, Healthsouth Rehabilitation Hospital Of Western Massachusetts, Ludlow, MA, p. A301

HUNT, Julie, R.N., MS, Chief Nursing Officer, Oro Valley Hospital, Oro Valley, AZ, p. A32

HUNT, Karen, Executive Director, Harsha Behavioral Center, Terre Haute, IN, p. A215

HUNT, Kathy, Chief Executive Officer, Elmwood Healthcare Center At The Springs, Green Springs, OH, p. A483

HUNT, Lynelle, Director of Nursing, Indian Health Service - Quentin N. Burdick Memorial Health Care Facility, Belcourt, ND, p. A464

HUNT, Mary Miles., Chief Executive Officer, Ballard Rehabilitation Hospital, San Bernardino, CA, p. A83

HUNT, MaryJane, Chief Clinical Officer, Knoxville Hospital & Clinics, Knoxville, IA, p. A225

HUNT, Nick, Interim Director of Nursing, Mercy Hospital Waldron, Waldron-Scott County, AR, p. A49

HUNT, Richard, M.D., Chief Operating Officer, Kaiser Sunnyside Medical Center, Clackamas, OR, p. A512

HUNT, Sharon, Interim Chief Financial Officer, Pecos County Memorial Hospital, Fort Stockton, TX, p. A604

HUNT, W. Jeffrey., Chief Executive Officer, Brandywine Hospital, Coatesville, PA, p. A523

HUNT, Wade, Chief Operating Officer, Vancouver Memorial Campus, WA, p. A680

HUNT, William Robert, Chief Financial Officer, Reynolds Memorial Hospital, Glen Dale, WV, p. A683

HUNTER, Bridgette, Chief Executive Officer, Select Specialty Hospital-Kansas City, Kansas City, KS, p. A238

HUNTER, Byron, Vice President Human Resources, Cape Regional Health System, Cape May Court House, NJ, p. A403

HUNTER, Diana, Director of Nursing, Fort Belknap Service Unit, Harlem, MT, p. A376

HUNTER, Fred, R.N., Chief Executive Officer, Desert Valley Hospital, Victorville, CA, p. A94

HUNTER, George, Interim Chief Human Resources Officer, Tuba City Regional Health Care Corporation, Tuba City, AZ, p. A36

HUNTER, John G., M.D., FACS, Chief Executive Officer, Doernbecher Children's Hospital, OR, p. A516

HUNTER, Ken, R.N., Chief Executive Officer, Kimball Health Services, Kimball, NE, p. A385

HUNTER, Linda, Chief Nursing Officer, Spring View Hospital, Lebanon, KY, p. A254

HUNTER, Mary Ann, Director Nursing Services, Baptist Easley Hospital, Easley, SC, p. A552

HUNTER, Melissa, Senior Vice President Clinical Services, Lake Regional Health System, Osage Beach, MO, p. A365

HUNTER, Shelly
Chief Financial Officer, Mercy Hospital Fort Scott, Fort Scott, KS, p. A235
Chief Financial Officer, St. John's Rehabilitation Center, MO, p. A361

HUNTER, Stephanie, Chief Human Resources Officer, Veterans Affairs Ann Arbor Healthcare System, Ann Arbor, MI, p. A307

HUNTER, Terri Lynn, R.N., Nurse Administrator, American Fork Hospital, American Fork, UT, p. A646

HUNTER, Tracy, Chief Human Resources Officer, East Cooper Medical Center, Mount Pleasant, SC, p. A555

HUNTLEY, Adrienne
Chief Human Resources Officer, Saint Francis Hospital-Bartlett, Bartlett, TN, p. A566
Director Human Resources, Healthsouth Rehabilitation Hospital Memphis-North, Memphis, TN, p. A575

HUNTLEY, Devin, Vice President Operations, Community Medical Center, Missoula, MT, p. A377

HUNTON, David, M.D., Chief Medical Officer, Mercy Orthopedic Hospital Fort Smith, AR, p. A42

HUNTSINGER, Kelli, Chief Operating Officer, Northern Inyo Hospital, Bishop, CA, p. A53

HUPF, Angela C., Vice President Human Resources and Community Relations, Aspirus Medford Hospital & Clinics, Inc., Medford, WI, p. A697

HUPP, Diane, R.N., Vice President Support Services and Patient Care Services, Children's Hospital Of Pittsburgh Of Upmc, Pittsburgh, PA, p. A537

HURD, Debra J., MS, R.N.
Vice President and Chief Nursing Officer, St. Joseph's Hospital, Saint Paul, MN, p. A339
Vice President and Chief Nursing Officer, Woodwinds Health Campus, Woodbury, MN, p. A342

HURD, Ross, Chief Information Officer, Lake Chelan Community Hospital And Clinics, Chelan, WA, p. A670

HURFORD, Bill, Chief Medical Officer, University Of Cincinnati Medical Center, Cincinnati, OH, p. A476

HURLBUT, Marty, M.D., Medical Director, Healthsouth Rehabilitation Hospital, Fayetteville-Washington County, AR, p. A41

HURLEY, Al, Clinic Chief Operating Officer, Sanford Bismarck, Bismarck, ND, p. A464

HURLEY, Jeff, Vice President Human Resources, Flagler Hospital, Saint Augustine, FL, p. A137

HURLEY, Sandra, MS, R.N., Chief Nursing Officer, Valley View Hospital, Glenwood Springs, CO, p. A101

HURLEY, William, M.D., Chief Medical Officer, Summit Pacific Medical Center, Elma, WA, p. A671

HUROWITZ, Marc P., D.O., President and Chief Executive Officer, Jeanes Hospital, Philadelphia, PA, p. A535

HURSH, John, Vice President Human Resources, Cox Medical Center South, MO, p. A370

HURSHE, Joseph R, President, Providence - Providence Park Hospital, Novi Campus, MI, p. A323

HURSHE, Joseph R. President, Providence - Providence Park Hospital, Novi Campus, MI, p. A323

HURST, Kyle, Chief Operations Officer, Northwest Ohio Psychiatric Hospital, Toledo, OH, p. A491

HURST, Paul, M.D., Chief Medical Officer, Banner Heart Hospital, Mesa, AZ, p. A31

HURST, Steve, Information Technology Specialist, Haskell County Community Hospital, Stigler, OK, p. A507

HURT, Carol Anne, Chief Nursing Officer, Tippah County Hospital, Ripley, MS, p. A353

HURT, Christie, M.D., Chief of Staff and Medical Director, Mercy Hospital Aurora, Aurora, MO, p. A355

HURT, Kelly, Chief Human Resources Officer Northern Colorado and Western Region, Banner Fort Collins Medical Center, Fort Collins, CO, p. A100

HURT, Todd, Administrator, State Hospital North, Orofino, ID, p. A171

HURTADO, Xochy, FACHE, Chief Executive Officer, Val Verde Regional Medical Center, Del Rio, TX, p. A598

HURWITZ, Steven, Senior Vice President Shared Services, Seattle Children's Hospital, Seattle, WA, p. A676

HUSAIN, Syed Arshad, M.D., Executive Vice President and Chief Medical Officer, Royal Oaks Hospital, Windsor, MO, p. A372

HUSEBY, Custer, Chief Executive Officer, Vibra Hospital Of Fargo, Fargo, ND, p. A466

HUSHER, Phil, Chief Financial Officer, Winner Regional Healthcare Center, Winner, SD, p. A565

HUSHING-KLINE, Bob, Hospital Administrator, Atascadero State Hospital, Atascadero, CA, p. A51

HUSKEY, Jeff, Chief Executive Officer and Administrator, Clay County Memorial Hospital, Henrietta, TX, p. A609

HUSS, Cathy, Chief Financial Officer, Lifecare Medical Center, Roseau, MN, p. A338

HUSSAIN, Hamid, M.D., Medical Director, Bogalusa Community Medical Center, LA, p. A264

HUSSAIN, Iftikhar, Chief Financial Officer, El Camino Hospital Los Gatos, CA, p. A74

HUSSEY, Jamie, Chief Information Officer, Jackson Hospital, Marianna, FL, p. A129

HUSSEY, Stephen, M.D., Chief of Staff, Lake District Hospital, Lakeview, OR, p. A514

HUSSON, Charles, Regional Chief Medical Officer, Genesys Regional Medical Center, Grand Blanc, MI, p. A313

HUSTEDT, Dale, Chief Executive Officer, Aspirus Medford Hospital & Clinics, Inc., Medford, WI, p. A697

HUSTON, Jennifer, Chief Nursing Officer, Lake Wales Medical Center, Lake Wales, FL, p. A127

HUSTON, William R, Senior Vice President and Chief Financial Officer, Texas Scottish Rite Hospital For Children, Dallas, TX, p. A598

HUTCHENRIDER, E. Kenneth., Jr, FACHE, President, Methodist Richardson Medical Center, Richardson, TX, p. A630

HUTCHENS, Zachary, M.D., Chief Medical Officer, Saint Thomas Hickman Hospital, Centerville, TN, p. A567

HUTCHES, Trampas, Chief Executive Officer, Melissa Memorial Hospital, Holyoke, CO, p. A102

HUTCHESON, Lorie, Vice President of Human Resources, Shepherd Center, Atlanta, GA, p. A147

HUTCHESON, Lou Ellen, M.D., Chief of Staff, Bacon County Hospital And Health System, Alma, GA, p. A145

HUTCHINGS, Lisa, Chief Financial Officer, Dmc - Children's Hospital Of Michigan, Detroit, MI, p. A310

HUTCHINS, Anne, M.D., Chief of Staff, Salem Veterans Affairs Medical Center, Salem, VA, p. A666

HUTCHINS, Michael T., Administrator, Jay Hospital, Jay, FL, p. A126

HUTCHINS-OTERO, Kathy, Chief Clinical Officer, Kindred Rehabilitation Hospital Clear Lake, Webster, TX, p. A643

HUTCHISON, Barbra, Director Medical Records, Richland Parish Hospital, Delhi, LA, p. A267

HUTCHISON, Florence N., M.D., Chief of Staff, Ralph H. Johnson Veterans Affairs Medical Center, Charleston, SC, p. A550

HUTCHISON, Harry, Vice President Fiscal Services, St. Bernards Medical Center, Jonesboro-Craighead County, AR, p. A44

HUTCHISON, Lewis, Vice President Operations and Quality, Ashtabula County Medical Center, Ashtabula, OH, p. A471

HUTCHSIN, Joel, M.D., Chief Medical Staff, Holton Community Hospital, Holton, KS, p. A237

HUTH, Michael, Chief Financial Officer, Sycamore Springs Hospital, Lafayette, IN, p. A209

HUTH, Richard
Administrator, South Georgia Medical Center Berrien Campus, Nashville, GA, p. A158
Administrator, South Georgia Medical Center Lanier Campus, Lakeland, GA, p. A156

HUTH, Thomas, M.D., Vice President Medical Affairs, Reid Health, Richmond, IN, p. A214

HUTSELL, Dick, Vice President Information Technology Services, Saint Louise Regional Hospital, Gilroy, CA, p. A60

HUTSELL, Richard, Vice President and Chief Information Officer, Daughters of Charity Health System, O'Connor Hospital, San Jose, CA, p. A86

HUTSON, Donald, President and Chief Executive Officer, Harrisburg Medical Center, Harrisburg, IL, p. A184

HUTSON, Joy M, Director Human Resources, Merit Health Rankin, Brandon, MS, p. A344

HUTSON, Marty, Chief Financial Officer, St. Mary's Health Care System, Athens, GA, p. A145

HUTSON, Vivian T., Director, Cincinnati Veterans Affairs Medical Center, Cincinnati, OH, p. A474

HUTSON, Wayne
Chief Financial Officer, Union Hospital Clinton, Clinton, IN, p. A201
Executive Vice President and Chief Financial Officer, Union Hospital, Terre Haute, IN, p. A215

HUTT, Si William., Administrator, Park City Hospital, Park City, UT, p. A649

HUTTER, Elizabeth, Chief Executive Officer, Cedar Hills Hospital, Portland, OR, p. A516

HUVAL, Shadelle, Director Finance, St. Martin Hospital, Breaux Bridge, LA, p. A265

HUYNH, Thai, M.D., Chief of Medical Staff, El Campo Memorial Hospital, El Campo, TX, p. A601

HYATT, Charlotte, MSN, R.N., Chief Operating Officer and Chief Nursing Officer, Henry Ford Allegiance Specialty Hospital, Jackson, MI, p. A316

HYATT, David W.
President, Indiana University Health Blackford Hospital, Hartford City, IN, p. A206
President, Indiana University Health Jay Hospital, Portland, IN, p. A213

HYATT, Ronnie, Senior Vice President Finance and Chief Financial Officer, St. Francis Eastside, SC, p. A553

HYBERGER, Trey, Director Information Technology, Hardin Memorial Health, Elizabethtown, KY, p. A251

HYDE, Devon, Vice President, Chief Administrative Officer, Presbyterian Rust Medical Center, NM, p. A416

HYDE, Jane E., President, Wellspan Gettysburg Hospital, Gettysburg, PA, p. A526

HYDE, Keith, Chief Executive, Providence Milwaukie Hospital, Milwaukie, OR, p. A515

HYDE, Robert, Human Resources Business Partner, Kaiser Permanente Santa Clara Medical Center, Santa Clara, CA, p. A88

HYDE, Shannon, Director Human Resources, Healthsouth Mountainview Regional Rehabilitation Hospital, Morgantown, WV, p. A685

HYDE, Stephanie, R.N., MSN, Chief Executive Officer, Tyler Continuecare Hospital, Tyler, TX, p. A641

HYDE, Steve, Chief Executive Officer, Paris Regional Medical Center, TX, p. A627

HYDER, LouAnn, Director Information Integrity Management, Cardinal Hill Rehabilitation Hospital, Lexington, KY, p. A254

HYDER, Shiraz, M.D., Director Medical Affairs, Chi St. Alexius Health, Bismarck, ND, p. A464

HYLAND, Donna W., President and Chief Executive Officer, Children's Healthcare Of Atlanta At Scottish Rite, GA, p. A146

HYLAND, Jaquelyn, M.D., Chief Medical Officer, University Of Kansas Health System St. Francis Campus, Topeka, KS, p. A246

HYLAND-HILL, Barbara M, R.N., Chief Nursing Officer, Providence Everett Medical Center - Pacific Campus, WA, p. A671

HYLTON, Heather, Chief Financial Officer, Plateau Medical Center, Oak Hill, WV, p. A685

HYMAN, Bruce, M.D., Vice President Clinical Performance, Advocate Sherman Hospital, Elgin, IL, p. A182

HYMBAUGH, Mitzi, Chief Personnel, Ringgold County Hospital, Mount Ayr, IA, p. A226

HYMEL, Paul, Chief Financial Officer, Abrazo Central Campus, Phoenix, AZ, p. A32

HYNES, Kristi, Director Human Resources, Georgetown Behavioral Health Institute, Georgetown, TX, p. A607

HYNES, Mary, Manager Information Services, United Hospital District, Blue Earth, MN, p. A328

HYNOSKI, Michael, Chief Information Resource Management, James E. Van Zandt Veterans Affairs Medical Center, Altoona, PA, p. A519

I

IACOBACCI, Margaret, Vice President Patient Care, Lankenau Medical Center, Wynnewood, PA, p. A545

IACUONE, Karen
Chief Nursing Officer and Chief Operating Officer, Pioneers Medical Center, Meeker, CO, p. A104
Chief Nursing Officer, Pioneers Medical Center, Meeker, CO, p. A104

IAKOPO, Priscilla Maratita, Chief Financial Officer, Commonwealth Health Center, Saipan, MP, p. A711

IANNACCONE, Robert C., JD, Chief Executive Officer, Saint Michael's Medical Center, Newark, NJ, p. A409

IBARRA, Daniel, Chief Financial Officer, Crane Memorial Hospital, Crane, TX, p. A595

IBARRA, Kyle, Director Information Systems, Geary Community Hospital, Junction City, KS, p. A238

IBRAHIM, Tajudeen, Interim Business Administrator, Elgin Mental Health Center, Elgin, IL, p. A182

ICKOWSKI, Michael F, Vice President and Chief Financial Officer, Regional West Medical Center, Scottsbluff, NE, p. A390

IDBEIS, Badr, M.D., Chief Executive Officer, Kansas Medical Center, Andover, KS, p. A232

IDOINE-FRIES, Julie, Chief Executive Officer, Select Specialty Hospital - Cleveland Fairhill, OH, p. A477

IDSTEIN, Mary, Chief Financial Officer, Porter-Starke Services, Valparaiso, IN, p. A216

IERARDI, Joseph P., Chief Executive Officer, Wayne Memorial Hospital, Jesup, GA, p. A155

IERO, Tony, Director Management Information Systems, Girard Medical Center, PA, p. A536

IFTINIUK, Alan, Chief Executive Officer, French Hospital Medical Center, San Luis Obispo, CA, p. A87

IGO, Angela, MSN, R.N., Chief Nursing Officer, Fitzgibbon Hospital, Marshall, MO, p. A364

IMBIMBO, Richard, Chief Financial Officer, Hahnemann University Hospital, Philadelphia, PA, p. A534

IMHOFF, Sarah, Business Administrator, Chester Mental Health Center, Chester, IL, p. A176

IMLAY, Ralph, M.D., Chief of Staff, Hospital District 6 - Anthony Campus, KS, p. A236

IMLER, Jim
Director Human Resources, Gothenburg Health, Gothenburg, NE, p. A384
Director Human Resources, Kimball Health Services, Kimball, NE, p. A385

IMMITI, Vincent F., FACHE, Director, Lyons Division, NJ, p. A404

IMMORDINO, Jonathan R, Chief Financial Officer, Rockledge Regional Medical Center, Rockledge, FL, p. A137

IMSEIS, Mikhail, M.D., Chief of Staff, Ness County Hospital District No 2, Ness City, KS, p. A242

IN, Henry, Director Human Resources, Dallas Behavioral Healthcare Hospital, Desoto, TX, p. A599

INGE, Laura, Chief Executive Officer, Kindred Hospital Northland, Kansas City, MO, p. A361

INGE, Ray, Vice President Human Resources, Pomona Valley Hospital Medical Center, Pomona, CA, p. A79

INGHAM, Raymond V., Ph.D., President and Chief Executive Officer, Witham Health Services, Lebanon, IN, p. A210

INGLIS, Suzanne, MSN, FACHE, Senior Vice President Nursing Services, Fisher-Titus Medical Center, Norwalk, OH, p. A488

INGRAM, Karen, Director Human Resources, Baptist Memorial Hospital For Women, Memphis, TN, p. A574

INGRAM, Nathan Daniel., Chief Executive Officer and Owner, Lone Star Behavioral Health, Cypress, TX, p. A595

INGWERSON, Connie, Chief Financial Officer, Nemaha Valley Community Hospital, Seneca, KS, p. A245

INHOFE, Kyle, Chief Human Resources Officer, Oklahoma City Veterans Affairs Medical Center, Oklahoma City, OK, p. A504

INMAN, Debbie, Chief Nursing Officer, Physicians Surgical Hospital - Panhandle Campus, TX, p. A583

INMAN, Joanne, President, Sentara Leigh Hospital, Norfolk, VA, p. A662

INMAN, Julie, Regional Executive Officer, Southeast Missouri Mental Health Center, Farmington, MO, p. A359

INNOCENTI, John, Sr
President and Chief Executive Officer, Upmc Montefiore, PA, p. A538
President and Chief Executive Officer, Western Psychiatric Institute And Clinic, PA, p. A538

INO, Alan, Chief Financial Officer, Good Samaritan Hospital, Los Angeles, CA, p. A67

INOUYE, Valerie, Chief Financial Officer, Zuckerberg San Francisco General Hospital And Trauma Center, San Francisco, CA, p. A86

INSCHO, Kimberly, Vice President Human Resources and Marketing, Margaret Mary Health, Batesville, IN, p. A199

INSERRA, Toni A., Interim Administrator, South Lyon Medical Center, Yerington, NV, p. A397

INSKEEP, Johnathan, Chief Information Officer, Caribou Memorial Hospital And Living Center, Soda Springs, ID, p. A172

INZANA, Lou, Senior Vice President and Chief Financial Officer, Maine Medical Center, Brighton Campus, ME, p. A285

IPSAN, Charlotte, Chief Administrative Officer, Norton Women's And Children's Hospital, KY, p. A256

IQBAL, Nayyar, M.D., Director Medical Staff, Western State Hospital, Hopkinsville, KY, p. A253

IRELAND, Amy, Chief Financial Officer, Carroll County Memorial Hospital, Carrollton, MO, p. A357

IRELAND, Daniel P., FACHE, President, United Memorial Medical Center-North Street, NY, p. A422

IRISH, Kevin
Chief Information Officer, Franklin Regional Hospital, Franklin, NH, p. A399
Chief Information Officer, Lakes Region General Hospital, Laconia, NH, p. A399
IRISH-CLARDY, Katherine, M.D., Chief Medical Officer, Sparks Regional Medical Center, Fort Smith-Sebastian County, AR, p. A42
IRIZARRI, David, Director Information Technology, Northwest Medical Center, Margate, FL, p. A129
IRIZARRY, Aixa, Executive Director, Hospital Hima De Humacao, Humacao, PR, p. A713
IRIZARRY, Lourdes, M.D., Chief of Staff, Albany Stratton Veterans Affairs Medical Center, Albany, NY, p. A421
IRIZARRY, Sigfredo, Information Technology Director, Ashford Presbyterian Community Hospital, San Juan, PR, p. A715
IRVIN, Debbie, Director Health Information Management, Bhc Alhambra Hospital, Rosemead, CA, p. A81
IRVIN, Donna, Director Human Resources, Baylor Medical Center At Trophy Club, Trophy Club, TX, p. A640
IRVIN, Mary, R.N., MSN, Senior Vice President and Chief Nursing Officer, Bethesda Butler Hospital, OH, p. A474
IRVIN, Michael, Chief Executive Officer, Bayfront Health Spring Hill, FL, p. A119
IRVIN, Miriam, CNO, Healthsouth Rehabilitation Hospital, Fayetteville-Washington County, AR, p. A41
IRVING, Edith E, R.N., MS, FACHE, Chief Nursing Officer, West Valley Medical Center, Caldwell, ID, p. A168
IRVING, Kelly Ann, MSN, RN-B, Associate Director for Patient Care Services, Michael E. Debakey Veterans Affairs Medical Center, Houston, TX, p. A612
IRVING, Mark, Manager Management Information Systems, Osf St. Francis Hospital And Medical Group, Escanaba, MI, p. A312
IRWIN, Robert G, Vice President Information Systems, Bristol-Myers Squibb Children's Hospital, NJ, p. A408
IRWIN, Ruth, Associate Director Clinical Operations, Stewart & Lynda Resnick Neuropsychiatric Hospital At Ucla, Los Angeles, CA, p. A70
IRWIN, Vivian, Chief Financial Officer and Controller, Encompass Health Rehabilitation Hospital Midland Odessa, Midland, TX, p. A624
ISAAC, Lisa, Chief Nursing Officer, Choctaw Nation Health Care Center, Talihina, OK, p. A507
ISAAC, Regina, Director of Nursing, Choctaw Health Center, Philadelphia, MS, p. A352
ISAACKS, David, Director, Harry S. Truman Memorial Veterans Hospital, Columbia, MO, p. A358
ISAACKS, Scott R., FACHE, Director and Chief Executive Officer, Ralph H. Johnson Veterans Affairs Medical Center, Charleston, SC, p. A550
ISAACS, Cynthia, Chief Executive Officer, Cornerstone Hospital Of Huntington, Huntington, WV, p. A683
ISAACS, Diane, Director of Nursing, Ouachita County Medical Center, Camden-Ouachita County, AR, p. A40
ISAACS, Michael R
Vice President Human Resources, Vista Medical Center East, Waukegan, IL, p. A198
Vice President Human Resources, Vista Medical Center West, Waukegan, IL, p. A198
ISAACSON, Alan, Superintendent, Austin State Hospital, Austin, TX, p. A585
ISAACSON, Sara, Chief Nursing Officer, Mad River Community Hospital, Arcata, CA, p. A51
ISADO, Jose, M.D., Medical Director, Auxilio Mutuo Hospital, San Juan, PR, p. A715
ISBELL, Samantha, R.N., Chief Nursing Officer, Hamilton Hospital, Olney, TX, p. A626
ISBELL, Sherri, Chief Information Officer, Virginia Gay Hospital, Vinton, IA, p. A230
ISEMANN, William R., President and Chief Executive Officer, Kidspeace Children's Hospital, Orefield, PA, p. A533
ISENMANN, Debra, Human Resources Generalist, Cox Monett Hospital, Monett, MO, p. A365
ISHIZUKA, Paul, Chief Financial Officer, Skagit Regional Health, Mount Vernon, WA, p. A674
ISHKANIAN, Gary, M.D., Vice President Medical Affairs, Montefiore Mount Vernon, Mount Vernon, NY, p. A430
ISKANDAR, Said, M.D., Chief Medical Officer, Sentara Halifax Regional Hospital, South Boston, VA, p. A666
ISLAM, Asad, M.D., Chief Medical Officer, Mayhill Hospital, Denton, TX, p. A599
ISLEY, L Lee., FACHE, Ph.D., President and Chief Executive Officer, Nash Health Care Systems, Rocky Mount, NC, p. A459
ISMAIL, Asad, M.D., Medical Director, Wellstone Regional Hospital, Jeffersonville, IN, p. A208
ISMAIL, Hummayun, M.D., Medical Director, Select Specialty Hospital-Wilmington, Wilmington, DE, p. A114

ISOM, Julie, Director Human Resources, Lakeview Hospital, Bountiful, UT, p. A646
ISON, Tamara
Chief Financial Officer, Wellstar Sylvan Grove Hospital, Jackson, GA, p. A155
Chief Operating Officer, Wellstar Spalding Regional Hospital, Griffin, GA, p. A154
Senior Vice President and President, Wellstar Spalding Regional Hospital, Griffin, GA, p. A154
Senior Vice President and President, Wellstar Sylvan Grove Hospital, Jackson, GA, p. A155
ISON, William G, Human Resources Manager, Select Specialty Hospital-Tri Cities, Bristol, TN, p. A566
ISQUIERDO, Maria E.
Executive Director, Human Resources, Saint Francis Heart Hospital, OK, p. A509
Executive Director, Human Resources, Saint Francis Hospital South, Tulsa, OK, p. A509
ISRAEL, Corry, Director Human Resources, Western Plains Medical Complex, Dodge City, KS, p. A234
ISRAEL, Michael D., President and Chief Executive Officer, Midhudson Regional Hospital Of Westchester Medical Center, NY, p. A445
ISSAI, Alice H., President, Adventist Health Glendale, Los Angeles, CA, p. A66
ITAGAKI, Brian, M.D., Chief of Staff, St. Vincent Medical Center, Los Angeles, CA, p. A70
ITO, Derek, Director Human Resources, Shriners Hospitals For Children-Honolulu, Honolulu, HI, p. A165
IVES, Matthew
Administrator and Chief Financial Officer, Keokuk County Health Center, Sigourney, IA, p. A229
Interim Chief Executive Officer and Chief Financial Officer, Keokuk County Health Center, Sigourney, IA, p. A229
IVES ERICKSON, Jeanette R, MS, R.N., Senior Vice President Patient Care and Chief Nurse, Massgeneral Hospital For Children, MA, p. A297
IVEY, Kim, Director of Human Resources, Cumberland Hospital For Children And Adolescents, New Kent, VA, p. A661
IVEY, Misty, Human Resources Manager, Washington County Regional Medical Center, Sandersville, GA, p. A160
IVIE, Brian K.
President and Chief Executive Officer, Cascade Valley Hospital, Arlington, WA, p. A669
President and Chief Executive Officer, Skagit Regional Health, Mount Vernon, WA, p. A674
IVORY, Brenda, Chief Executive Officer, Harlingen Medical Center, Harlingen, TX, p. A608
IVY, Michael, M.D.
Senior Vice President for Medical Affairs and Chief Medical Officer, Bridgeport Hospital, Bridgeport, CT, p. A107
Interim Chief Executive Officer, Bridgeport Hospital, Bridgeport, CT, p. A107
IZAKOVIC, Martin, M.D., Vice President Medical Staff Affairs and Chief Medical Officer, Mercy Iowa City, Iowa City, IA, p. A224
IZZI, Denine, Senior Director Information Technology, Robert Wood Johnson University Hospital Rahway, Rahway, NJ, p. A411

J

JABBARPOUR, Yad, M.D., Chief of Staff, Catawba Hospital, Catawba, VA, p. A656
JABERG, Janie, FACHE, President and Chief Executive Officer, Wayne Unc Health Care, Goldsboro, NC, p. A453
JABLONSKI, Kevin, Chief Nursing Officer, Christus Mother Frances Hospital - Winnsboro, Winnsboro, TX, p. A644
JABLONSKI, Kevin M, Chief Nursing Officer, Ut Health Athens, Athens, TX, p. A585
JABLONSKI, Mark, Vice President Mission Integration, St. Jude Medical Center, Fullerton, CA, p. A60
JABOUR, Leon John
Regional Chief Information Officer, Wellspan Ephrata Community Hospital, Ephrata, PA, p. A525
Regional Chief Information Officer, Wellspan Good Samaritan Hospital, Lebanon, PA, p. A529
JACK, Claudia L, Director Associate Relations, Bayfront Health Spring Hill, FL, p. A119
JACK, Dennis D., FACHE, Chief Executive Officer, Summit Medical Center, Casper, WY, p. A707
JACK, Shannon, Executive Vice President, Indianhead Medical Center, Shell Lake, WI, p. A703

JACKES, Frederick D, Assistant Administrator and Director Human Resources, Valley Forge Medical Center And Hospital, Norristown, PA, p. A533
JACKLIN, Bonnie, R.N., MSN, Chief Nursing Officer, Mckay-Dee Hospital, Ogden, UT, p. A648
JACKSON, Alan, M.D., Medical Director, Roseland Community Hospital, Chicago, IL, p. A179
JACKSON, Angelica, Director of Nursing, Anchor Hospital, Atlanta, GA, p. A145
JACKSON, Anthony
Chief Executive Officer, Bon Secours St. Francis Hospital, Charleston, SC, p. A549
Chief Executive Officer, Roper St. Francis Mount Pleasant Hospital, Mount Pleasant, SC, p. A555
JACKSON, Barbara, Ed.D., Acting Facility Director, Taylor Hardin Secure Medical Facility, Tuscaloosa, AL, p. A24
JACKSON, Bryan G, Vice President and Chief Financial Officer, Jefferson Regional Medical Center, Pine Bluff-Jefferson County, AR, p. A47
JACKSON, Carolyn, Chief Operating Officer, Scheie Eye Institute Of The Hospital Of The University Of Pennsylvania, PA, p. A535
JACKSON, Cindy, Director Human Resources, Phelps Memorial Health Center, Holdrege, NE, p. A385
JACKSON, Collette, R.N., Director of Clinical Services, St. Theresa Specialty Hospital, Kenner, LA, p. A270
JACKSON, Corey D., Executive Vice President and Chief Talent Officer, Parkland Health & Hospital System, Dallas, TX, p. A597
JACKSON, Cynthia, Vice President Human Resources, Raulerson Hospital, Okeechobee, FL, p. A133
JACKSON, Daniel, Vice President, Administrator, Wellstar Atlanta Medical Center - South Campus, GA, p. A147
JACKSON, Darryl, D.O., Chief of Staff, Prague Community Hospital, Prague, OK, p. A506
JACKSON, David, Chief Financial Officer, Baptist Medical Center Leake, Carthage, MS, p. A344
JACKSON, Erin, Human Resources Specialist, Baptist Medical Center Nassau, Fernandina Beach, FL, p. A122
JACKSON, Evan, Vice President Information Technology, Middlesex Hospital, Middletown, CT, p. A109
JACKSON, Frank D., III, Facility Chief Information Officer, Veterans Affairs Illiana Health Care System, Danville, IL, p. A180
JACKSON, Gary, D.O., Medical Director, Lincoln County Medical Center, Ruidoso, NM, p. A419
JACKSON, Holly, Chief Operating Officer, Gulf Coast Regional Medical Center, Panama City, FL, p. A135
JACKSON, James, M.D., Chief of Staff, Cornerstone Hospital Of Bossier City, Bossier City, LA, p. A265
JACKSON, James E T., M.P.H., Chief Administrative Officer, San Leandro Hospital, San Leandro, CA, p. A87
JACKSON, James H., Jr, Chief Executive Officer, Och Regional Medical Center, Starkville, MS, p. A353
JACKSON, James V., Budget Director, Saint Elizabeths Hospital, Washington, DC, p. A116
JACKSON, Jeffrey, M.D., Medical Director, Houston Methodist Sugar Land Hospital, Sugar Land, TX, p. A637
JACKSON, Jennifer, Director Human Resources, Madison County Health Care System, Winterset, IA, p. A231
JACKSON, Joanne, Administrator Human Resources, Community Relations and Quality Improvement, Amery Hospital And Clinic, Amery, WI, p. A689
JACKSON, Jodie A., Associate Director, Veterans Affairs New York Harbor Healthcare System - Manhattan Campus, NY, p. A437
JACKSON, John J, President, Firsthealth Moore Regional Hospital - Richmond, NC, p. A458
JACKSON, Judy, Director Health Information Management and Privacy Officer, Shodair Children's Hospital, Helena, MT, p. A376
JACKSON, Kevin
Interim Chief Executive Officer, Central Hartnett Hospital, NC, p. A451
On Site Administrator, Highsmith-Rainey Specialty Hospital, Fayetteville, NC, p. A452
JACKSON, Kiland, Chief Information Officer, Bunkie General Hospital, Bunkie, LA, p. A265
JACKSON, Lynn, Administrator, Northside Hospital-Forsyth, Cumming, GA, p. A151
JACKSON, Margaret G., R.N., Vice President Patient Care Services and Chief Nursing Officer, University Hospital Of Brooklyn At Long Island College Hospital, NY, p. A437
JACKSON, Meg, Director Information Technology, Beauregard Health System, De Ridder, LA, p. A266
JACKSON, Melinda R, Director Human Resources, Bates County Memorial Hospital, Butler, MO, p. A356
JACKSON, Melonie, Human Resource Business Partner, Spectrum Health Big Rapids Hospital, Big Rapids, MI, p. A308

JACKSON, Michelle, Chief Financial Officer, Bhc Alhambra Hospital, Rosemead, CA, p. A81

JACKSON, Patsy, Director of Nursing, Jay Hospital, Jay, FL, p. A126

JACKSON, Phillip E.
Vice President & CEO, Erlanger East Hospital, TN, p. A567
Vice President and CEO, Erlanger North Hospital, TN, p. A567

JACKSON, Reese, President and Chief Executive Officer, Chesapeake Regional Medical Center, Chesapeake, VA, p. A656

JACKSON, Robert, Jr
Chief Executive Officer, Grove City Medical Center, Grove City, PA, p. A526
Chief Financial Officer, Alliance Health Center, Meridian, MS, p. A350
Chief Financial Officer, Signature Psychiatric Hospital, Kansas City, MO, p. A362

JACKSON, Robin E., Ph.D., Interim Acting Director, Charlie Norwood Veterans Affairs Medical Center, Augusta, GA, p. A147

JACKSON, Stephanie, M.D., Vice President and Chief Medical Officer, Honorhealth Scottsdale Thompson Peak Medical Center, Scottsdale, AZ, p. A35

JACKSON, Tamara, Chief Nursing Officer, Piedmont Athens Regional Medical Center, Athens, GA, p. A145

JACKSON, Thomas W., Chief Executive Officer, St. David's North Austin Medical Center, Austin, TX, p. A586

JACKSON, Tom, Chief Financial Officer, Parkridge West Hospital, TN, p. A567

JACKSON, Valarie, President, Westfield Memorial Hospital, Westfield, NY, p. A446

JACKSON, Vance, FACHE, Chief Executive Officer, Davis Medical Center, Elkins, WV, p. A682

JACKSON, Victor, Chief Executive Officer, Vibra Specialty Hospital Of Portland, Portland, OR, p. A517

JACKSON, William, Director Medical Records, Millwood Hospital, Arlington, TX, p. A584

JACKSON, William L, Chief Medical Officer, Inova Alexandria Hospital, Alexandria, VA, p. A655

JACKSON, William L., M.D., Jr, Executive Vice President, Chief Medical Officer, Willie D. Miller Eye Center, TN, p. A567

JACO, Angela, Chief Executive Officer, Hamlin Memorial Hospital, Hamlin, TX, p. A608

JACO, Mary, Administrator, Shriners Hospitals For Children-Galveston, Galveston, TX, p. A606

JACOB, Jan, R.N., Interim Administrator, St. Joseph Health System, Tawas City, MI, p. A324

JACOBI, Diane, Chief of Staff, Ssm Health St. Mary's Hospital - Audrain, Mexico, MO, p. A364

JACOBI, Elizabeth
Associate Director Human Resources, Rancho Los Amigos National Rehabilitation Center, Downey, CA, p. A56
Human Resources Director, Women's And Children's Hospital, CA, p. A68

JACOBO MORENO, Maria E., Administrator, Hima San Pablo Caguas, Caguas, PR, p. A712

JACOBS, Anastasia, Chief Human Resources Officer, Robert Wood Johnson University Hospital Somerset, Somerville, NJ, p. A411

JACOBS, Andrea, Chief Operating Officer, South Pointe Hospital, Warrensville Heights, OH, p. A492

JACOBS, Barbara S, MSN, Vice President, Nursing and Chief Nursing Officer, Anne Arundel Medical Center, Annapolis, MD, p. A287

JACOBS, Brian, M.D., Vice President Chief Information Officer and Chief Medical Information Officer, Children's National Health System, Washington, DC, p. A115

JACOBS, Donna K., FACHE, President, Ssm Health St. Mary's Hospital - Audrain, Mexico, MO, p. A364

JACOBS, Greg, Manager, Mclaren Bay Special Care, Bay City, MI, p. A308

JACOBS, Ian, Chief, Human Resource Management Service, Louis A. Johnson Veterans Affairs Medical Center, Clarksburg, WV, p. A682

JACOBS, Jenny
Director Human Resources, Osf Holy Family Medical Center, Monmouth, IL, p. A189
Director Human Resources, Osf St. Mary Medical Center, Galesburg, IL, p. A183

JACOBS, Julie
Chief Financial Officer, Warren General Hospital, Warren, PA, p. A543
Director Human Resources, Oklahoma Forensic Center, Vinita, OK, p. A509

JACOBS, Lori, Chief Financial Officer, Edgefield County Hospital, Edgefield, SC, p. A552

JACOBS, Michael, Vice President Human Resources, Gladys Spellman Specialty Hospital And Nursing Center, Cheverly, MD, p. A290

JACOBS, Richard, Vice President Finance and Chief Financial Officer, Canton-Potsdam Hospital, Potsdam, NY, p. A440

JACOBS, Robert
Regional Director Information Management, Christus Southeast Texas Hospital-St. Mary, TX, p. A588
Regional Information Management Executive, Christus Southeast Texas Jasper Memorial, Jasper, TX, p. A616

JACOBS, Ronnie, M.D., Chief Medical Officer, Asheville Specialty Hospital, Asheville, NC, p. A447

JACOBS, Trace, Director Information Technology, Santiam Hospital, Stayton, OR, p. A518

JACOBS, Yolanda, Coordinator Human Resources, Cornerstone Hospital Of Houston - Bellaire, TX, p. A643

JACOBSEN, Barry, CPA, Chief Executive Officer, Myrtue Medical Center, Harlan, IA, p. A224

JACOBSEN, William D., FACHE, Administrator and Hospital Vice President, Carilion Franklin Memorial Hospital, Rocky Mount, VA, p. A666

JACOBSON, Becky, Vice President Finance, St. Vincent Heart Center, Indianapolis, IN, p. A208

JACOBSON, Carlton, Vice President of Finance, Adventist Health Clear Lake, Clearlake, CA, p. A54

JACOBSON, Carolyn
Chief Human Resource Officer, St. Joseph's Hospital, Saint Paul, MN, p. A339
Chief Human Resource Officer, Woodwinds Health Campus, Woodbury, MN, p. A342
Chief Human Resources Officer, Bethesda Hospital, Saint Paul, MN, p. A339
Chief Human Resources Officer, St. John's Hospital, Maplewood, MN, p. A334

JACOBSON, Gary, M.D., Chief Medical Officer, Pembroke Hospital, Pembroke, MA, p. A303

JACOBSON, Janet, Director Human Resources, Lakewood Health System, Staples, MN, p. A340

JACOBSON, Jenny, Manager Human Resources, Sanford Hillsboro Medical Center, Hillsboro, ND, p. A467

JACOBSON, John
Chief Financial Officer, Martin General Hospital, Williamston, NC, p. A462
Interim Chief Executive Officer, Martin General Hospital, Williamston, NC, p. A462

JACOBSON, John L., Chief Executive Officer, Atchison Hospital, Atchison, KS, p. A232

JACOBSON, Lisa, Director of Nursing, Community Hospital Of Huntington Park, Huntington Park, CA, p. A62

JACOBSON, Mark, D.O., Vice President Medical Affairs, Wellspan Ephrata Community Hospital, Ephrata, PA, p. A525

JACOBSON, Mary Jo, Chief Executive Officer, San Joaquin Valley Rehabilitation Hospital, Fresno, CA, p. A59

JACOBSON, Peter, President, Essentia Health St. Mary's - Detroit Lakes, Detroit Lakes, MN, p. A330

JACOBSON, Randolph
Chief Financial Officer, Carrier Clinic, Belle Mead, NJ, p. A402
Chief Financial Officer, East Mountain Hospital, Belle Mead, NJ, p. A402

JACOBSON, Renae A., Human Resources Officer, Ralph H. Johnson Veterans Affairs Medical Center, Charleston, SC, p. A550

JACOBSON, Sam, Director Management Information Systems, Community Memorial Hospital, Cloquet, MN, p. A329

JACOBSON, Shirley
Chief Financial Officer, Community Behavioral Health Hospital - Alexandria, Alexandria, MN, p. A327
Chief Financial Officer, Community Behavioral Health Hospital - Rochester, Rochester, MN, p. A338

JACOBSON, Terry, Administrator and Chief Executive Officer, Essentia Health St. Mary's Hospital Of Superior, Superior, WI, p. A704

JACOBY, Jamie, Chief Financial Officer, Cimarron Memorial Hospital, Boise City, OK, p. A496

JACQUAY, Dena M, Chief Human Resource Officer, Parkview Huntington Hospital, Huntington, IN, p. A206

JACQUES, Alistar
Chief Information Officer, Bethesda Hospital, Saint Paul, MN, p. A339
Chief Information Officer, St. John's Hospital, Maplewood, MN, p. A334

JACQUES, Shane
Regional Chief Financial Officer - U.P., Aspirus Keweenaw Hospital, Inc., Laurium, MI, p. A318
Regional Chief Financial Officer, Aspirus Ironwood Hospitals & Clinics, Inc., Ironwood, MI, p. A316

JACQUES, Teresa, Interim Chief Financial Officer, Adventist Medical Center-Reedley, Reedley, CA, p. A80

JADCZAK, Audrey, R.N., FACHE
Vice President Chief Nursing Officer, Our Lady Of Lourdes Medical Center, Camden, NJ, p. A403
Vice President/Chief Nursing Officer, Lourdes Medical Center Of Burlington County, Willingboro, NJ, p. A414

JADEJA, Neerav, Administrator, Bayview Behavioral Health Campus, CA, p. A74

JADWIN, Anne, R.N., MSN, Chief Nursing Officer, Fox Chase Cancer Center-American Oncologic Hospital, Philadelphia, PA, p. A534

JAEGER, Shiuvaun, M.D., Chief of Staff, Tri Valley Health System, Cambridge, NE, p. A382

JAFF, Michael R., D.O., President, Massgeneral For Children At Newton-Wellesley Hospital, MA, p. A302

JAFFE, Darcy, R.N., Chief Nursing Officer, Uw Medicine/Harborview Medical Center, Seattle, WA, p. A677

JAFFE, Richard, M.D., Medical Director, Belmont Behavioral Hospital, Philadelphia, PA, p. A533

JAFFER, Amir, M.D., Senior Vice President Medical Affairs, New York-Presbyterian Queens, New York (Includes All Hospitals Located Within The Five Boroughs), NY, p. A435

JAGER, Jonathon R, Chief Information Officer, Bradley Center Of St. Francis, GA, p. A151

JAGER, Linda, Director Finance, Avera Weskota Memorial Hospital, Wessington Springs, SD, p. A565

JAGGI, Michael, D.O., Vice President and Chief Medical Officer, Hurley Children's Hospital, MI, p. A312

JAGOE, Patricia, Assistant Vice President Patient Care, Johnson Memorial Medical Center, Stafford Springs, CT, p. A111

JAHAN, Mohammad S, M.D., Clinical Director, Middle Tennessee Mental Health Institute, Nashville, TN, p. A577

JAHN, Barbara A., Chief Operating Officer, Saint Joseph Hospital, Denver, CO, p. A99

JAHN, David B., President and Chief Executive Officer, War Memorial Hospital, Sault Sainte Marie, MI, p. A323

JAHN, Gregory L., R.N., Chief Executive Officer, St. Luke's Behavioral Health Center, Phoenix, AZ, p. A34

JAHN, Kim C, Chief Plant Operations and Chief Information Officer, Manning Regional Healthcare Center, Manning, IA, p. A226

JAHNIG, Jay A, Chief Executive Officer, Faulkton Area Medical Center, Faulkton, SD, p. A560

JAHRE, Jeffrey, M.D., Vice President Medical and Academic Affairs, St Luke's Hospital - Allentown Campus, PA, p. A521

JAIN, Anil, Chief Financial Officer, St. Francis Medical Center, Lynwood, CA, p. A70

JAIN, Ashok, M.D., Senior Vice President and Chief Medical Officer, Beaumont Hospital, Wayne, Wayne, MI, p. A325

JAKOUBECK, Denise, Director Human Resources, Hancock County Health System, Britt, IA, p. A218

JAKUBOWSKI, Michael, M.D., Chief Medical Officer, Mary Free Bed Rehabilitation Hospital, Grand Rapids, MI, p. A314

JALBERT, Susan L, R.N., MS, Vice President Patient Care Services and Chief Nursing Officer, Northwest Hospital, Randallstown, MD, p. A293

JALOMO, Angie, Chief Nursing Officer, Lynn County Hospital District, Tahoka, TX, p. A638

JAMES, Annette, R.N., MSN, Chief Nursing Officer, Creek Nation Community Hospital, Okemah, OK, p. A502

JAMES, Bruce, President and Chief Executive Officer, Cleveland Clinic Union Hospital, Dover, OH, p. A481

JAMES, Craig, President, Alleghany Memorial Hospital, Sparta, NC, p. A461

JAMES, Donald, D.O., Senior Vice President and Chief Medical Officer, Phelps County Regional Medical Center, Rolla, MO, p. A366

JAMES, Douglas, Chief Nursing Officer, Caldwell Medical Center, Princeton, KY, p. A260

JAMES, Gregory L, D.O., Chief Medical Officer, St. Vincent's Birmingham, Birmingham, AL, p. A15

JAMES, Jaime, Entity Finance Officer, Texas Health Springwood, TX, p. A588

JAMES, Janet, Director Human Resources, Trigg County Hospital, Cadiz, KY, p. A250

JAMES, Jobie, Chief Financial Officer, West Calcasieu Cameron Hospital, Sulphur, LA, p. A280

JAMES, Karen, Regional Director, Human Resources, The William W. Backus Hospital, Norwich, CT, p. A110

JAMES, Ken, President and Chief Executive Officer of East Market, Mercy Health - Anderson Hospital, Cincinnati, OH, p. A475

JAMES, Laura, Director Human Resources, St. Francis Medical Center, Trenton, NJ, p. A413

JAMES, Michael
Chief Operations Officer, Jackson Hospital And Clinic, Montgomery, AL, p. A21
Information Technology Technical Support Specialist 1, Villa Feliciana Medical Complex, Jackson, LA, p. A269

JAMES, Michelle
Chief Nursing Officer, Providence St. Peter Hospital, Olympia, WA, p. A674
Regional Chief Nursing Officer, Providence Centralia Hospital, Centralia, WA, p. A670

JAMES, Robert L, Director Human Resources, Beaumont Hospital, Wayne, Wayne, MI, p. A325

JAMES, Shelia, Director of Nursing, Riverland Medical Center, Ferriday, LA, p. A267

JAMES, Sherelle, Interim Chief Nursing Officer and Clinical Manager, Our Lady Of Lourdes Regional Medical Center, Lafayette, LA, p. A271

JAMES, Sherrie, R.N., Chief Executive Officer, Riverview Behavioral Health, Texarkana-Miller County, AR, p. A49

JAMES, Taya, Director, Mercy Hospital Berryville, Berryville-Carroll County, AR, p. A39

JAMES, Teri, Chief Financial Officer, Lafayette Regional Health Center, Lexington, MO, p. A363

JAMES, Thomas L, M.D., Chief Medical Officer, Trumbull Memorial Hospital, Warren, OH, p. A492

JAMES, Wesley, Chief Financial Officer, Piedmont Henry Hospital, Stockbridge, GA, p. A161

JAMES, William B., FACHE, President, Wake Forest Baptist Health-Lexington Medical Center, Lexington, NC, p. A456

JAMES-NIELSEN, Lori, President, Tuality Forest Grove Hospital, OR, p. A513

JAMESON, David, M.D., Chief of Staff, Annie Jeffrey Memorial County Health Center, Osceola, NE, p. A389

JAMESON, Eileen, Chief Operating Officer, Abington Hospital, Abington, PA, p. A519

JAMIESON, Donna F., Ph.D., R.N., Chief Nursing Officer, Aurora Medical Center Kenosha, Kenosha, WI, p. A695

JAMIESON, Pamela, Vice President Patient Care Services and Chief Nursing Officer, University Of Maryland St. Joseph Medical Center, Towson, MD, p. A294

JAMIN, David, Chief Financial Officer, St. Mary's Regional Medical Center, Enid, OK, p. A498

JANDIAL, Rajnish, M.D., Chief Medical Officer, San Dimas Community Hospital, San Dimas, CA, p. A85

JANEK, James D., Chief Executive Officer, Rice Medical Center, Eagle Lake, TX, p. A600

JANERELLA, Wendy, Controller, Bucktail Medical Center, Renovo, PA, p. A540

JANGDHARI, Kalautie, Director, West Texas Veterans Affairs Health Care System, Big Spring, TX, p. A589

JANICAK, Dan, Chief Financial Officer, Children's Healthcare Of Mississippi, MS, p. A348

JANIS, Terry, Assistant Vice President, Park Plaza Hospital, Houston, TX, p. A612

JANKE, Paul, FACHE, President and Chief Executive Officer, Bay Area Hospital, Coos Bay, OR, p. A512

JANKOWSKI, Stan, Vice President and Chief Information Officer, Hospital For Special Care, New Britain, CT, p. A109

JANLOO, Arman, M.D., Chief Medical Staff, Fairfax Community Hospital, Fairfax, OK, p. A499

JANOSO, John R., Chief Executive Officer, Fairfield Medical Center, Lancaster, OH, p. A484

JANSEN, David, Vice President Human Resources, Karmanos Cancer Center, Detroit, MI, p. A311

JANSEN, John, Management Information Specialist, Hawaii State Hospital, Kaneohe, HI, p. A166

JANSEN, Robert, M.D., Chief Medical Officer, Grady Memorial Hospital, Atlanta, GA, p. A146

JANSSEN, Kathy, Director Medical Records, Mountrail County Medical Center, Stanley, ND, p. A468

JANSSEN, Paul, President and Chief Executive Officer, Henry Community Health, New Castle, IN, p. A212

JANTZEN, Daniel, Chief Financial Officer, Children's Hospital At Dartmouth, NH, p. A399

JANTZEN, Tammi, Chief Operating Officer, Okeene Municipal Hospital, Okeene, OK, p. A502

JANUS, Tammy, Senior Vice President Human Resources, Mercy Medical Center, Baltimore, MD, p. A288

JANZEN, Wes, Chief Information Officer, Wamego Health Center, Wamego, KS, p. A247

JAQUEZ, Jason
Director Human Resources, Greater El Monte Community Hospital, South El Monte, CA, p. A90
Human Resource Director, Ahmc Anaheim Regional Medical Center, Anaheim, CA, p. A50

JARAMILLO, Charles, Chief Operating Officer, New Mexico Behavioral Health Institute At Las Vegas, Las Vegas, NM, p. A418

JARBOE, Joe, Director Human Resources, Kosciusko Community Hospital, Warsaw, IN, p. A216

JARBOE, Lori, Chief Executive Officer, Healthsouth Lakeview Rehabilitation Hospital, Elizabethtown, KY, p. A251

JARMER, Ryan, Chief Information Officer, Naval Medical Center San Diego, San Diego, CA, p. A84

JAROPILLO, Erwin, Director Information Systems, Lake Wales Medical Center, Lake Wales, FL, p. A127

JARREAU, Jeff
Chief Human Resources Officer, North Oaks Medical Center, Hammond, LA, p. A268
Senior Vice President, Human Resources, North Oaks Health System, North Oaks Rehabilitation Hospital, Hammond, LA, p. A268

JARREAU, Valerie Sparks, R.N., Chief Nursing Officer, Pointe Coupee General Hospital, New Roads, LA, p. A276

JARRELL, Lindsey, Vice President Information Services, St. Joseph's Women's Hospital, FL, p. A141

JARRETT, Adam D, M.D., Executive Vice President and Chief Medical Officer, Holy Name Medical Center, Teaneck, NJ, p. A412

JARRY, Jacques, Administrator, Bullock County Hospital, Union Springs, AL, p. A24

JARRY, Patricia, Manager Human Resources, Crenshaw Community Hospital, Luverne, AL, p. A20

JARVIS, Dinah, Director of Nursing, Southeastern Kentucky Medical Center, Pineville, KY, p. A259

JARVIS, Keith, Director Information Systems, Longview Regional Medical Center, Longview, TX, p. A620

JARVIS, Susan, Vice President Operations, Sanford South University, ND, p. A466

JARVIS, Tammy, Vice President Clinical Services and Chief Nursing Officer, Texas Institute For Surgery At Texas Health Presbyterian Dallas, Dallas, TX, p. A598

JASPER, Harry, Chief Financial Officer, Jerold Phelps Community Hospital, Garberville, CA, p. A60

JASPER, Jerry, Chief Executive Officer, Brownfield Regional Medical Center, Brownfield, TX, p. A590

JATCZAK, Tracy E, CPA, Chief Financial Officer, Box Butte General Hospital, Alliance, NE, p. A381

JAUERSACK, Dawn, Vice President and Chief Financial Officer, Boca Raton Regional Hospital, Boca Raton, FL, p. A118

JAURON, Jason, Director Human Resources, Orange City Area Health System, Orange City, IA, p. A227

JAVOIS, Laurent D.
Chief Executive Officer, St. Louis Psychiatric Rehabilitation Center, Saint Louis, MO, p. A369
Regional Executive Officer, Hawthorn Children Psychiatric Hospital, Saint Louis, MO, p. A368
Regional Executive Officer, Metropolitan St. Louis Psychiatric Center, Saint Louis, MO, p. A368

JAVOIS, Rosalie, Chief Financial Officer, Governor Juan F. Luis Hospital, Christiansted, VI, p. A717

JAY, Richard, D.O., Chief of Staff, North Big Horn Hospital District, Lovell, WY, p. A709

JEAKLE, James, Chief Medical Officer, Munson Healthcare Charlevoix Hospital, Charlevoix, MI, p. A309

JEAN-BAPTISTE, Joan, Vice President Human Resources, Governor Juan F. Luis Hospital, Christiansted, VI, p. A717

JEAN-LOUIS, Marie S, R.N., Chief Nursing Officer, Creedmoor Psychiatric Center, New York (Includes All Hospitals Located Within The Five Boroughs), NY, p. A432

JEANS, Joe, CPA, Chief Financial Officer, Johnson Regional Medical Center, Clarksville-Johnson County, AR, p. A40

JEANSONNE, Corey, Chief Nursing Officer, Bunkie General Hospital, Bunkie, LA, p. A265

JEDLICKA, Colleen, R.N., JD, Chief Nursing Officer, Comanche County Medical Center, Comanche, TX, p. A593

JEFFERIES, Kanika, Executive Director, Brooklyn Children's Hospital Psychiatric Center, NY, p. A434

JEFFERSON, Glenn, Chief Medical Officer, Garfield County Public Hospital District, Pomeroy, WA, p. A674

JEFFERSON, Kelly, Vice President, Operations, Osf St. Francis Hospital And Medical Group, Escanaba, MI, p. A312

JEFFRESS, Chuck, Vice President Fiscal Services, Chi St. Luke's Health Brazosport, Lake Jackson, TX, p. A618

JEFFREY, Paul A, President, Wesley Long Community Hospital, NC, p. A453

JEFFRIES, John, Director Finance, Hshs St. Joseph's Hospital, Breese, IL, p. A174

JEHAN, Sayed, M.D., Interim Medical Director, Larned State Hospital, Larned, KS, p. A239

JELALIAN, Christine, M.D., Medical Director, St. Luke's Cornwall Hospital - Newburgh Campus, NY, p. A438

JELDEN, Dennis, M.D., Chief of Staff, Melissa Memorial Hospital, Holyoke, CO, p. A102

JELKS, Kim, Fiscal Officer, Villa Feliciana Medical Complex, Jackson, LA, p. A269

JEMJEMIAN, Norair, Senior Vice President and Area Manager, Kaiser Permanente Vacaville Medical Center, Vacaville, CA, p. A93

JENE, Suzanne L., Chief Operating Officer, Nashville Campus, TN, p. A577

JENKINS, Bonnie
Chief Financial Officer, Mercy General Hospital, Sacramento, CA, p. A82

Chief Financial Officer, Methodist Hospital Of Sacramento, Sacramento, CA, p. A82

JENKINS, Brian, Director Human Resources, Arbour-Fuller Hospital, Attleboro, MA, p. A295

JENKINS, Debbie, Chief Human Resources Management Service, Veterans Affairs Sierra Nevada Health Care System, Reno, NV, p. A396

JENKINS, Denise, Chief Clinical Officer, Kindred Hospital-Brea, Brea, CA, p. A53

JENKINS, Jimmy, M.D., Chief Medical Officer, Geary Community Hospital, Junction City, KS, p. A238

JENKINS, Keith, Director, Human Resources, Southview Medical Center, OH, p. A480

JENKINS, Kevin, President and Chief Executive Officer, St. Anthony North Health Campus, Westminster, CO, p. A106

JENKINS, Linda, R.N., Vice President Patient Care Services, St. Jude Medical Center, Fullerton, CA, p. A60

JENKINS, Maynard, Regional Vice President Human Resources, Sutter Maternity And Surgery Center Of Santa Cruz, Santa Cruz, CA, p. A89

JENKINS, Michelle, M.D., President Medical Staff, Herrin Hospital, Herrin, IL, p. A185

JENKINS, Rebecca, Director Human Resources Management, Harrison Memorial Hospital, Cynthiana, KY, p. A251

JENKINS, Roger T., Chief Executive Officer, Ethicus Hospital - Grapevine, Grapevine, TX, p. A608

JENKINS, Ruth, Chief Financial Officer, Ridgeview Institute, Smyrna, GA, p. A160

JENKINS, Timothy, M.D., Area Medical Director and Chief of Staff, Kaiser Permanente Ontario Medical Center, CA, p. A58

JENNER, Jody J., President and Chief Executive Officer, Broadlawns Medical Center, Des Moines, IA, p. A221

JENNETTE, Brian, Chief Financial Officer, Northside Hospital-Cherokee, Canton, GA, p. A149

JENNINGS, Jason, FACHE
President, Scott & White Hospital - Brenham, Brenham, TX, p. A590
President, Scott & White Hospital - College Station, College Station, TX, p. A593

JENNINGS, Keith, Chief Information Officer, Massgeneral Hospital For Children, MA, p. A297

JENNINGS, Lawrence, Chief of Staff, Wabash General Hospital, Mount Carmel, IL, p. A190

JENNINGS, Lee Ann, R.N., Vice President, Nursing Services, Wise Regional Health System, West Campus Decatur, TX, p. A598

JENNINGS, Marilyn, Director Human Resources, Arise Austin Medical Center, Austin, TX, p. A585

JENNINGS, Mark, Chief Information Officer, Saint Anthony Hospital, Chicago, IL, p. A179

JENNINGS, Peter, M.D., Chief Medical Officer, Sacred Heart Hospital Pensacola, Pensacola, FL, p. A136

JENNINGS, Shayla, Human Resources Director, Montgomery County Memorial Hospital, Red Oak, IA, p. A228

JENSEMA, Christine
Chief Human Resources Officer, Hshs St. Clare Memorial Hospital, Oconto Falls, WI, p. A700
Chief Human Resources Officer, Hshs St. Vincent Hospital, Green Bay, WI, p. A694
Chief People Officer, Hshs St. Mary's Hospital Medical Center, Green Bay, WI, p. A694
Chief People Officer, Hshs St. Nicholas Hospital, Sheboygan, WI, p. A703

JENSEN, Amy, Director Human Resources, Promedica Coldwater Regional Hospital, Coldwater, MI, p. A310

JENSEN, Annelise, Vice President and Chief Nursing Officer, Methodist Healthcare Olive Branch Hospital, Olive Branch, MS, p. A351

JENSEN, Beth, Director Clinic Operations, Mobridge Regional Hospital, Mobridge, SD, p. A562

JENSEN, Camille, R.N., Chief Nursing Officer, Mclaren Orthopedic Hospital, MI, p. A317

JENSEN, Christopher, Chief Financial Officer, Three Rivers Behavioral Health, West Columbia, SC, p. A558

JENSEN, Dave, Director Human Resources, Performance Improvement and Risk Management, Mountain View Hospital, Gadsden, AL, p. A18

JENSEN, Eric P., Chief Executive Officer, Astria Toppenish Hospital, Toppenish, WA, p. A679

JENSEN, Janette, Manager Human Resources, Avera Holy Family Hospital, Estherville, IA, p. A222

JENSEN, Jeff, D.O.
Vice President, Medical Affairs, Morton Plant Hospital, Clearwater, FL, p. A119
Vice President, Medical Affairs, Morton Plant North Bay Hospital, New Port Richey, FL, p. A132

JENSEN, Laura J., Vice President Patient Care Services, St. Croix Regional Medical Center, St Croix Falls, WI, p. A703

JENSEN, Mary, Controller, Mountain View Hospital, Gadsden, AL, p. A18

JENSEN, Michael, Chief Executive Officer, Davis Hospital And Medical Center, Layton, UT, p. A647

JENSEN, Neal, Chief Executive Officer, Cobre Valley Regional Medical Center, Globe, AZ, p. A30

JENSEN, Pamela M., FACHE
President, Promedica Fostoria Community Hospital, Fostoria, OH, p. A482
President, Promedica Memorial Hospital, Fremont, OH, p. A482

JENSEN, Paul, M.D., Chief of Staff, Regional Health Services Of Howard County, Cresco, IA, p. A220

JENSEN, Renee K., Senior Vice President and Chief Administrative Officer, Evergreenhealth Monroe, Monroe, WA, p. A673

JENSEN, Ron, D.O., Chief Medical Officer and Vice President, Baylor Regional Medical Center At Grapevine, Grapevine, TX, p. A607

JENSEN, Ryan, Chief Executive Officer, Desert Springs Hospital Medical Center, Las Vegas, NV, p. A394

JENSEN, Sherry, Chief Financial Officer, Halifax Regional Medical Center, Roanoke Rapids, NC, p. A459

JENSEN, Tom, Chief Executive Officer, Grays Harbor Community Hospital, Aberdeen, WA, p. A669

JENSEN, Troy, Director Human Resources, Healthsouth Rehabilitation Hospital Of Utah, Sandy, UT, p. A651

JENSEN, Twyla, Director Human Resources, Pioneers Medical Center, Meeker, CO, p. A104

JENTZ, Amy, M.D., Chief of Staff, Sparrow Ionia Hospital, Ionia, MI, p. A316

JEPPESEN, Kelly, Chief Medical Officer, San Juan Health Service District, Monticello, UT, p. A648

JEPSEN, Christina, R.N., Chief Nursing Officer, Mahaska Health Partnership, Oskaloosa, IA, p. A228

JEPSON, Brian, President, Ohiohealth Riverside Methodist Hospital, Columbus, OH, p. A479

JEPSON, Mark, Vice President, Silver Cross Hospital, New Lenox, IL, p. A191

JERGER, Greg, Chief Financial Officer, Memorial Health Care Systems, Seward, NE, p. A390

JERINA, Anthony T., Chief Nursing Officer, Hereford Regional Medical Center, Hereford, TX, p. A609

JERNIGAN, Pam, Chief Financial Officer, Unity Medical Center, Manchester, TN, p. A574

JESCH, Doug, Director Human Resources, Starke Hospital, Knox, IN, p. A208

JESIOLOWSKI, Craig A, FACHE, President, Holy Family Hospital At Merrimack Valley, MA, p. A302

JESIOLOWSKI, Craig A., FACHE, President, Holy Family Hospital At Merrimack Valley, MA, p. A302

JESSOP, Reuben, Chief Operating Officer, Northern Utah Rehabilitation Hospital, South Ogden, UT, p. A651

JESSUP, Daniel
Chief Financial Officer, Legacy Silverton Medical Center, Silverton, OR, p. A518
Chief Financial Officer, Wallowa Memorial Hospital, Enterprise, OR, p. A512

JESTER, Denise, Chief Financial Officer, Nanticoke Memorial Hospital, Seaford, DE, p. A114

JESTILA-PELTOLA, Gail, Chief Financial Officer, Baraga County Memorial Hospital, L'Anse, MI, p. A317

JESURASA, Jebashini, Vice President, Chief Information Technology Officer, Wyckoff Heights Medical Center, New York (Includes All Hospitals Located Within The Five Boroughs), NY, p. A438

JETER, John, Chief Executive Officer, Johnston Memorial Hospital, Abingdon, VA, p. A655

JETT, Chris, Administrator, University Of South Alabama Children's And Women's Hospital, Mobile, AL, p. A20

JETTERGREN, Tess, Director Clinical Informatics, St. Mary's Children's Hospital, MN, p. A330

JEUNEHOMME, Patti, Director Human Resources, Hot Springs County Memorial Hospital, Thermopolis, WY, p. A710

JEWETT, Lori, R.N., Chief Executive Officer, Falmouth Hospital, Falmouth, MA, p. A299

JEWETT, Sherri R., Chief Executive Officer, Valle Vista Hospital, Greenwood, IN, p. A205

JEX, Kerri, R.N., Chief Nursing Officer, Bear Valley Community Hospital, Big Bear Lake, CA, p. A53

JEYAKUMAR, Panch, M.D., Chief of Staff, Olympia Medical Center, Los Angeles, CA, p. A69

JEZIORSKE, John J, Director Human Resources, Abilene Regional Medical Center, Abilene, TX, p. A582

JEZSU, Peggy, Chief Nursing Officer, Alvarado Hospital Medical Center, San Diego, CA, p. A83

JIMENEZ, Betzaida, Director Human Resources, Hospital De La Universidad De Puerto Rico/Dr. Federico Trilla, Carolina, PR, p. A712

JIMENEZ, Cristina, Chief Executive Officer, Coral Gables Hospital, Coral Gables, FL, p. A120

JIMENEZ, Edward
Chief Executive Officer, Uf Health Shands Cancer Hospital, FL, p. A124
Chief Executive Officer, Uf Health Shands Children's Hospital, FL, p. A124
Chief Executive Officer, Uf Health Shands Rehab Hospital, FL, p. A124

JIMENEZ, Gerson, M.D., Medical Director, Hospital Episcopal San Lucas Guayama, Guayama, PR, p. A713

JIMENEZ, Guillermo, Director Finance, Castaner General Hospital, Castaner, PR, p. A712

JIMENEZ, Ronald, M.D., Chief Executive Officer, Florida Hospital Flagler, Palm Coast, FL, p. A135

JIMESON, Jean-Marie, Manager Human Resources, Kansas Spine And Specialty Hospital, Wichita, KS, p. A247

JIMMERSON, Kevin, Business Manager, Mental Health Institute, Independence, IA, p. A224

JIN, Marvin, M.D., Medical Director, Parkside Psychiatric Hospital And Clinic, Tulsa, OK, p. A508

JIRON, Feliciano, Chief Executive Officer, Valley View Medical Center, Fort Mohave, AZ, p. A29

JIROVEC, David, Director Finance, Ascension Good Samaritan Hospital, Merrill, WI, p. A698

JOBBITT, Patty, Chief Operating Officer, Dmc - Rehabilitation Institute Of Michigan, Detroit, MI, p. A311

JOBE, Kenneth Lynn, Director Human Resources, Tyler County Hospital, Woodville, TX, p. A645

JOCHIM, Steven, Administrator, Cape Cod & Island Community Mental Health Center, Pocasset, MA, p. A303

JODWAY, Timothy, Chief Financial Administrator, Beaumont Hospital - Dearborn, Dearborn, MI, p. A310

JOHANNSEN, Lee, M.D., Chief Medical Officer, Central Texas Medical Center, San Marcos, TX, p. A635

JOHANSON, Amanda, Chief Executive Officer, Holly Hill Hospital, Raleigh, NC, p. A459

JOHE, David, M.D., President Medical Staff, Penn Highlands Elk, Saint Marys, PA, p. A540

JOHN, Aleyamma, R.N., Director of Nursing, Kensington Hospital, Philadelphia, PA, p. A535

JOHN, Janene, Chief Human Resource Officer, Broward Health Coral Springs, Coral Springs, FL, p. A120

JOHNS, Dale, FACHE, Chief Executive Officer, Salt Lake Regional Medical Center, Salt Lake City, UT, p. A650

JOHNS, Dawn, Director Human Resources, Colquitt Regional Medical Center, Moultrie, GA, p. A158

JOHNS, Jeffery, M.D., Medical Director, Vanderbilt Stallworth Rehabilitation Hospital, Nashville, TN, p. A578

JOHNS, Paul, Chief Operating Officer, South Lake Hospital, Clermont, FL, p. A120

JOHNS, Thomas Bradford, M.D., Medical Director, Ridgeview Institute, Smyrna, GA, p. A160

JOHNSEN, Timothy J., MS, President, Integris Mental Health System-Spencer, OK, p. A503

JOHNSON, Aaron, Vice President Patient Care Services and Chief Nursing Officer, Chi St. Alexius Health Devils Lake Hospital, Devils Lake, ND, p. A465

JOHNSON, Alan, Interim Chief Information Officer, United Medical Center, Washington, DC, p. A116

JOHNSON, Allen
Chief Financial Officer, Truman Medical Center-Hospital Hill, Kansas City, MO, p. A362
Chief Financial Officer, Truman Medical Center-Lakewood, Kansas City, MO, p. A362

JOHNSON, Amy R, R.N., Quality Improvement Safety Officer, Star Valley Medical Center, Afton, WY, p. A707

JOHNSON, Angela, Executive Director, Unitypoint Health - Trinity Muscatine, Muscatine, IA, p. A227

JOHNSON, Arlan D., Chief Executive Officer, Howard County Medical Center, Saint Paul, NE, p. A390

JOHNSON, Ashley, Director Human Resource, Mccamey County Hospital District, Mccamey, TX, p. A623

JOHNSON, Ashley L., Chief Operations Officer, Canyon Vista Medical Center, Sierra Vista, AZ, p. A36

JOHNSON, Becky, Director Human Resources, Oakdale Community Hospital, Oakdale, LA, p. A277

JOHNSON, Belinda, R.N., Chief Nursing Officer/Chief Clinical Officer, Russellville Hospital, Russellville, AL, p. A23

JOHNSON, Betty, Associate Administrator, Children's Hospital Of Shreveport, LA, p. A279

JOHNSON, Billy, Chief Executive Officer, Coal County General Hospital, Coalgate, OK, p. A497

JOHNSON, Blake, M.D., Chief of Staff, Salt Lake Regional Medical Center, Salt Lake City, UT, p. A650

JOHNSON, Bonnie, R.N., Vice President of Patient Services, Perham Health, Perham, MN, p. A337

JOHNSON, Brandi, Site Manager Technology Information Systems, Spectrum Health Reed City Hospital, Reed City, MI, p. A321

JOHNSON, Brenda
Director Human Resources, Baptist Memorial Hospital-Collierville, Collierville, TN, p. A568
Director Human Resources, North Mississippi Medical Center-West Point, West Point, MS, p. A354

JOHNSON, Bret
Chief Financial Officer, Bon Secours St. Francis Hospital, Charleston, SC, p. A549
Chief Financial Officer, Roper St. Francis Mount Pleasant Hospital, Mount Pleasant, SC, p. A555
Chief Financial Officer, Roper St. Francis, Charleston, SC, p. A550

JOHNSON, Brett M., Chief Executive Officer, Northwest Ohio Psychiatric Hospital, Toledo, OH, p. A491

JOHNSON, Brian, M.D., Chief Medical Officer, Aurora Baycare Medical Center, Green Bay, WI, p. A693

JOHNSON, Bryan N, M.D., Chief Medical Officer, Whitman Hospital And Medical Center, Colfax, WA, p. A670

JOHNSON, C Thomas, III, Vice President Finance and Chief Financial Officer, Southeastern Health, Lumberton, NC, p. A456

JOHNSON, Candace, Ph.D., President and Chief Executive Officer, Roswell Park Cancer Institute, Buffalo, NY, p. A423

JOHNSON, Casey R, Chief Financial Officer, Riverwood Healthcare Center, Aitkin, MN, p. A327

JOHNSON, Charles, M.D., Chief of Staff, Renown Children's Hospital, NV, p. A396

JOHNSON, Cheryl, Regional Chief Information Officer, St. Joseph Medical Center, Kansas City, MO, p. A362

JOHNSON, Chris
Chief of Staff, Mercy Hospital Rogers, Rogers-Benton County, AR, p. A48
Chief Nursing Officer, Davis Hospital And Medical Center, Layton, UT, p. A647

JOHNSON, Christina, M.D.
Chief Executive Officer, Longmont United Hospital, Longmont, CO, p. A103
Vice President and Chief Clinical and Quality Officer, Exempla West Pines, CO, p. A106

JOHNSON, Collette, Chief Financial Officer, Palo Alto County Health System, Emmetsburg, IA, p. A222

JOHNSON, Craig A., Chief Executive Officer, Boundary Community Hospital, Bonners Ferry, ID, p. A168

JOHNSON, Cynthia J, R.N., Chief Nursing Officer, Thousand Oaks Surgical Hospital, CA, p. A91

JOHNSON, Danielle, Chief Operating Officer, Florida Hospital Fish Memorial, Orange City, FL, p. A133

JOHNSON, Darren, M.D., Chief of Staff, West Tennessee Healthcare Dyersburg Hospital, Dyersburg, TN, p. A569

JOHNSON, David
Chief Executive Officer, Kindred Hospital Louisville At Jewish Hospital, KY, p. A256
Chief Executive Officer, Navos, Seattle, WA, p. A676
Manager Information Services, Providence Kodiak Island Medical Center, Kodiak, AK, p. A26

JOHNSON, Debra, R.N., Chief Administrator, Lakeland Hospital, Niles, MI, p. A323

JOHNSON, Deeann, Director Human Resources, Saint Thomas River Park Hospital, Mc Minnville, TN, p. A574

JOHNSON, Denise, M.D., Medical Director, Meadville Medical Center, Meadville, PA, p. A531

JOHNSON, Dennis B., President and Chief Executive Officer, Hardin Memorial Health, Elizabethtown, KY, p. A251

JOHNSON, Derek, Sr
Chief Operating Officer, Franklin Hospital District, Benton, IL, p. A174
Chief Executive Officer, Laurel Oaks Behavioral Health Center, Dothan, AL, p. A17

JOHNSON, Diana G, Acting Chief Human Resources Officer, Novato Community Hospital, Novato, CA, p. A75

JOHNSON, Dino, R.N.
Chief Operating Officer and Chief Nursing Officer, St. Francis Hospital, Federal Way, WA, p. A672
Chief Operationg Officer and Chief Nursing Officer, St. Francis Hospital, Federal Way, WA, p. A672

JOHNSON, Douglas E
Chief Financial Officer, Lakeview Hospital, Stillwater, MN, p. A340
Interim Vice President Operations and Chief Financial Officer, Hudson Hospital And Clinic, Hudson, WI, p. A694

JOHNSON, Douglas V., Chief Executive Officer, Stanislaus Surgical Hospital, Modesto, CA, p. A73

JOHNSON, Drew, Chief Financial Officer, Holdenville General Hospital, Holdenville, OK, p. A500

JOHNSON, Earle
Area Information Officer, Kaiser Permanente Panorama City Medical Center, Los Angeles, CA, p. A67
Area Information Officer, Kaiser Permanente Woodland Hills Medical Center, Los Angeles, CA, p. A67

JOHNSON, Eddie, Chief Information Technology Officer, Kansas City Veterans Affairs Medical Center, Kansas City, MO, p. A361

JOHNSON, Eric M., Director, United Medical Center, Washington, DC, p. A116

JOHNSON, Eunice, M.D., Chief Medical Staff, Kentucky River Medical Center, Jackson, KY, p. A254

JOHNSON, Fred, M.D., Chief Medical Officer, Dignity Health Arizona General Hospital, Laveen, AZ, p. A31

JOHNSON, Gigi, Chief Nursing Officer, Kindred Hospital-Chattanooga, Chattanooga, TN, p. A567

JOHNSON, Greg
IT Coordinator, North Shore Health, Grand Marais, MN, p. A332
Vice President of Operations, Davis Medical Center, Elkins, WV, p. A682

JOHNSON, Greg K, Chief Operating Officer, Colquitt Regional Medical Center, Moultrie, GA, p. A158

JOHNSON, Heather, Director of Finance, Operations and Business Development, Buffalo Hospital, Buffalo, MN, p. A329

JOHNSON, Helen, R.N., MSN, Vice President Patient Services, Spectrum Health Ludington Hospital, Ludington, MI, p. A318

JOHNSON, J David, M.D., Chief of Staff, Ut Health Specialty Hospital, Tyler, TX, p. A641

JOHNSON, J. Ronald., Medical Center Director, Hampton Veterans Affairs Medical Center, Hampton, VA, p. A659

JOHNSON, Jack, R.N., Director of Nursing, Sanford Rock Rapids Medical Center, Rock Rapids, IA, p. A228

JOHNSON, James, Chief Executive Officer, Franklin Hospital District, Benton, IL, p. A174

JOHNSON, Jamie, R.N.
Vice President Nursing, Community Hospital Of Anaconda, Anaconda, MT, p. A373
Director Human Resources, Miners' Colfax Medical Center, NM, p. A418

JOHNSON, Jani L., R.N., MSN, Chief Executive Officer, Crittenton Children's Center, MO, p. A362

JOHNSON, Jason, Controller, F. W. Huston Medical Center, Winchester, KS, p. A248

JOHNSON, Jay, Chief Financial Officer, Alliancehealth Clinton, Clinton, OK, p. A497

JOHNSON, Jay R., FACHE, President and Chief Executive Officer, Duncan Regional Hospital, Duncan, OK, p. A498

JOHNSON, Jayne, Director Human Resources, Great Plains Health, North Platte, NE, p. A387

JOHNSON, Jeff, Director Information Systems, Saint Thomas River Park Hospital, Mc Minnville, TN, p. A574

JOHNSON, Jeffrey
Commander, Brooke Army Medical Center, Fort Sam Houston, TX, p. A603
Vice President, Uchealth Memorial Hospital North, CO, p. A98

JOHNSON, Jimmy, Chief Financial Officer, Blue Mountain Hospital, Blanding, UT, p. A646

JOHNSON, Joel, M.D., Chief Medical Staff, First Care Health Center, Park River, ND, p. A468

JOHNSON, John, M.D.
Chief of Staff, Greenbrier Valley Medical Center, Ronceverte, WV, p. A687
Clinical Director, U.S. Public Health Service Indian Hospital, Crownpoint, NM, p. A416

JOHNSON, Juantina, Chief of Staff, Choctaw Health Center, Philadelphia, MS, p. A352

JOHNSON, Judith, Controller, Healthsouth Rehabilitation Hospital Of Largo, Largo, FL, p. A128

JOHNSON, Juli, MSN, R.N., President, Parkview Huntington Hospital, Huntington, IN, p. A206

JOHNSON, Katherine, Ph.D., President, Sentara Northern Virginia Medical Center, Woodbridge, VA, p. A668

JOHNSON, Kathi, Chief Financial Officer, Eskenazi Health, Indianapolis, IN, p. A206

JOHNSON, Kathryn
Chief Nursing Officer, Casa Colina Hospital And Health Systems, Pomona, CA, p. A78
Manager Human Resources, Marketing and Public Relations, St. Vincent Jennings Hospital, North Vernon, IN, p. A213

JOHNSON, Kawanda, Director of Nursing, Specialty Hospital Of Meridian, Meridian, MS, p. A350

JOHNSON, Kayla, R.N., Vice President Patient Care Services and Chief Nursing Officer, St. Francis Medical Center, Monroe, LA, p. A274

JOHNSON, Kelly, R.N.
Chief Nursing Officer, St. John Sapulpa, Sapulpa, OK, p. A506
Director Human Resources, Madison Healthcare Services, Madison, MN, p. A334

JOHNSON, Kelly M, Chief Nursing Officer, Lucile Salter Packard Children's Hospital Stanford, Palo Alto, CA, p. A77

JOHNSON, Ken
Chief Physician Executive, Hshs St. Clare Memorial Hospital, Oconto Falls, WI, p. A700
Chief Physician Executive, Hshs St. Mary's Hospital Medical Center, Green Bay, WI, p. A694
Chief Physician Executive, Hshs St. Nicholas Hospital, Sheboygan, WI, p. A703
Chief Physician Executive, Hshs St. Vincent Hospital, Green Bay, WI, p. A694
President and Chief Executive Officer, Hutchinson Regional Medical Center, Hutchinson, KS, p. A237

JOHNSON, Kendall, Chief Financial Officer, Baton Rouge General Medical Center-Bluebonnet, LA, p. A263

JOHNSON, Kenneth, Vice President, Sts. Mary & Elizabeth Hospital, Louisville, KY, p. A256

JOHNSON, Kerri, Human Resources Operations Consultant, Integris Bass Pavilion, Enid, OK, p. A498

JOHNSON, Kevin, Chief Executive Officer, Mountain View Hospital, Payson, UT, p. A649

JOHNSON, Kristen, Chief Nursing Officer, Rancho Springs Medical Center, CA, p. A74

JOHNSON, Kyle
Chief Information Officer, Community General Health Center, ME, p. A286
Vice President Finance, East Liverpool City Hospital, East Liverpool, OH, p. A482

JOHNSON, Laurie, Director - Human Resources, Via Christi Hospital Pittsburg, Pittsburg, KS, p. A244

JOHNSON, Lerenda, Interim Chief Executive Officer, Kindred Hospital Seattle-First Hill, WA, p. A676

JOHNSON, Linda, R.N., Vice President, Patient Services Risk Management and Chief Nursing Officer, Heart Of The Rockies Regional Medical Center, Salida, CO, p. A105

JOHNSON, Lois, Chief Financial Officer, Twin Cities Community Hospital, Templeton, CA, p. A91

JOHNSON, Margaret M., President, St. Vincent Northwest Region, St. Vincent Kokomo, Kokomo, IN, p. A209

JOHNSON, Marianne, Chief Nursing Officer, Trace Regional Hospital, Houston, MS, p. A347

JOHNSON, Marie
Chief Nursing Officer, Carrus Rehabilitation Hospital, Sherman, TX, p. A636
Chief Nursing Officer, Carrus Specialty Hospital, Sherman, TX, p. A636

JOHNSON, Marisa, M.D., Vice President Medical Affairs, Christus Highland Medical Center, LA, p. A278

JOHNSON, Mark
Chief Financial Officer, Norwood Hospital, Norwood, MA, p. A303
Chief Information Officer, West Holt Medical Services, Atkinson, NE, p. A381

JOHNSON, Mary, Chief Nursing Officer, Falmouth Hospital, Falmouth, MA, p. A299

JOHNSON, Marylynn, Director of Nursing, Springbrook Behavioral Health System, Travelers Rest, SC, p. A557

JOHNSON, Matthew, Chief Executive Officer and President, Cherokee Regional Medical Center, Cherokee, IA, p. A219

JOHNSON, Melissa, Chief Financial Officer, Baptist Medical Center South, Montgomery, AL, p. A21

JOHNSON, Michael, M.D.
Medical Director, Salina Surgical Hospital, Salina, KS, p. A245
Chief Executive Officer, Piedmont Walton Hospital, Monroe, GA, p. A157

JOHNSON, Michael A, M.D., Chief of Staff, Bucyrus Hospital, Bucyrus, OH, p. A473

JOHNSON, Michael G., CPA, Chief Financial Officer, Abrom Kaplan Memorial Hospital, Kaplan, LA, p. A270

JOHNSON, Michael T., FACHE, President and Chief Executive Officer, Regional Medical Center Of San Jose, San Jose, CA, p. A86

JOHNSON, Mike
Chief Financial Officer, Upmc Pinnacle Lancaster, Lancaster, PA, p. A529
Vice President, Chief Information Officer, Caromont Regional Medical Center, Gastonia, NC, p. A453

JOHNSON, Monte, Vice President, Medical Affairs, St. Francis Regional Medical Center, Shakopee, MN, p. A340

JOHNSON, Nancy, Chief Nursing Officer, Select Specialty Hospital-Knoxville, TN, p. A579

JOHNSON, Nanette, Chief Nursing Officer, Orthopaedic Hospital Of Wisconsin - Glendale, Glendale, WI, p. A693

JOHNSON, Nate, Chief Information Officer, Highlands Regional Medical Center, Sebring, FL, p. A139

JOHNSON, Neil, Chief Operating Officer, Eskenazi Health, Indianapolis, IN, p. A206

JOHNSON, Nikki, Interim Chief Executive Officer, Cooperstown Medical Center, Cooperstown, ND, p. A465

JOHNSON, Pamela, R.N.
Chief Nursing Officer, Mccurtain Memorial Hospital, Idabel, OK, p. A500
Treasurer and Chief Financial Officer, Finger Lakes Hospital, Geneva, NY, p. A426
Treasurer and Chief Financial Officer, Soldiers And Sailors Memorial Hospital Of Yates County, Penn Yan, NY, p. A440

JOHNSON, Pamela O., MS, R.N., Chief Nursing Officer, Mayo Eugenio Litta Children's Hospital, MN, p. A338

JOHNSON, Patricia, R.N., Senior Vice President, Woman's Hospital, Baton Rouge, LA, p. A264

JOHNSON, Patrick, Director Human Resources, Pondera Medical Center, Conrad, MT, p. A374

JOHNSON, Penny, Chief Financial Officer, Metroplex Behavioral Health Center, TX, p. A617

JOHNSON, Peri, Human Resources Director, West Central Georgia Regional Hospital, Columbus, GA, p. A151

JOHNSON, Peter A, Interim Chief Information Officer, Monadnock Community Hospital, Peterborough, NH, p. A401

JOHNSON, Phillip, Vice President, Chief Human Resources Officer, St. Luke's Meridian Medical Center, ID, p. A168

JOHNSON, Ralph
Chief Information Officer, Franklin Memorial Hospital, Farmington, ME, p. A284
Chief Information Officer, Southern Maine Health Care - Biddeford Medical Center, ME, p. A283

JOHNSON, Randall, Administrator, Beacon Behavioral Hospital, Bunkie, LA, p. A265

JOHNSON, Rashard
President, Advocate South Suburban Hospital, Hazel Crest, IL, p. A185
President, Advocate Trinity Hospital, Chicago, IL, p. A176

JOHNSON, Ric, Associate Administrator, Mountain View Hospital, Payson, UT, p. A649

JOHNSON, Richard, M.D., Chief of Medical Staff, Chi St. Alexius Health Devils Lake Hospital, Devils Lake, ND, p. A465

JOHNSON, Rick, Chief Executive Officer, Spire Cane Creek Rehabilitation Hospital, Martin, TN, p. A574

JOHNSON, Robb, Director Operations, Hamilton Center, Terre Haute, IN, p. A215

JOHNSON, Roger, M.D., Chief of Staff, Cheyenne Veterans Affairs Medical Center, Cheyenne, WY, p. A708

JOHNSON, Ronald W., FACHE, President and Chief Executive Officer, Shore Medical Center, Somers Point, NJ, p. A411

JOHNSON, Russell W., President and Chief Executive Officer, Lawrence Memorial Hospital, Lawrence, KS, p. A239

JOHNSON, Ryan K, Controller, Spectrum Health Kelsey Hospital, MI, p. A314

JOHNSON, Sam, M.D., Chief Medical Officer, Northeast Georgia Medical Center, Gainesville, GA, p. A154

JOHNSON, Scott H., Vice President Finance and Chief Financial Officer, St. Luke's Hospital, Chesterfield, MO, p. A357

JOHNSON, Sharon, Director Health Information Management, Western State Hospital, Staunton, VA, p. A666

JOHNSON, Shelia B., Director of Nursing, St. Landry Extended Care Hospital, Opelousas, LA, p. A277

JOHNSON, Shelly, Chief Operating Officer, Spectrum Health Gerber Memorial, Fremont, MI, p. A313

JOHNSON, Sheryl, Chief Information Officer, Swedishamerican - A Division Of Uw Health, Rockford, IL, p. A195

JOHNSON, Shirley, MS, R.N., Senior Vice President Nursing and Patient Care Services, Chief Nursing Officer, Roswell Park Cancer Institute, Buffalo, NY, p. A423

JOHNSON, Shrea, Director Human Resources, Alliance Health Center, Meridian, MS, p. A350

JOHNSON, Stacy, Chief Financial Officer, Loring Hospital, Sac City, IA, p. A228

JOHNSON, Steven P., FACHE, President, Upmc Susquehanna Williamsport Regional Medical Center, Williamsport, PA, p. A545

JOHNSON, Sy
Executive Vice President, Chief Operating Officer, Renown Children's Hospital, NV, p. A396
Executive Vice President, Chief Operating Officer, Renown South Meadows Medical Center, Reno, NV, p. A396

JOHNSON, Talicia, Director Human Resources, Brentwood Hospital, Shreveport, LA, p. A278

JOHNSON, Tamatha, Director Human Resources, Rmc-Stringfellow Memorial Hospital, Anniston, AL, p. A13

JOHNSON, Thomas, Director Information Systems, Penn Highlands Brookville, Brookville, PA, p. A521

JOHNSON, Timothy, M.D.
President and Chief Executive Officer, Mayo Clinic Health System - Franciscan Healthcare In La Crosse, La Crosse, WI, p. A695

President and Chief Executive Officer, Eaton Rapids Medical Center, Eaton Rapids, MI, p. A312

JOHNSON, Todd, Chief Financial Officer, Longview Regional Medical Center, Longview, TX, p. A620

JOHNSON, Tom, Chief Human Resource Officer, Minneapolis Veterans Affairs Health Care System, Minneapolis, MN, p. A335

JOHNSON, Trudy, R.N., RN, Chief Nursing Officer, Santa Clara Valley Medical Center, San Jose, CA, p. A87

JOHNSON, Vern, Director Information Technology, Sullivan County Memorial Hospital, Milan, MO, p. A364

JOHNSON, Vernon, Administrator, Dale Medical Center, Ozark, AL, p. A22

JOHNSON, Victoria, R.N., Nursing Director of Surgical and Medical Services, The Healthcenter, Kalispell, MT, p. A377

JOHNSON, Wade C., MS, FACHE, Chief Executive Officer, St. Peter's Hospital, Helena, MT, p. A376

JOHNSON, William, Director Information Systems, Shoals Hospital, Muscle Shoals, AL, p. A22

JOHNSON, William F, Chief Medical Officer, Skyridge Medical Center - Westside Campus, TN, p. A568

JOHNSON, William Micah, Administrator and Chief Nursing Officer, Christus St. Michael Hospital-Atlanta, TX, p. A639

JOHNSON, William P., Interim Chief Executive Officer, Fairlawn Rehabilitation Hospital, Worcester, MA, p. A306

JOHNSON-HATCHER, Dawn, Chief Financial Officer, Christus Ochsner Lake Area Hospital, Lake Charles, LA, p. A272

JOHNSON-MEKOTA, Judith, Director, Iowa City Veterans Affairs Health Care System, Iowa City, IA, p. A224

JOHNSON-MILLER, Kimberly, Chief Financial Officer, Carl Vinson Veterans Affairs Medical Center, Dublin, GA, p. A153

JOHNSON-THREAT, Yvette, Vice President Medical Affairs, Medstar Southern Maryland Hospital Center, Clinton, MD, p. A290

JOHNSRUD, Carolyn, Manager Human Resources, Missouri River Medical Center, Fort Benton, MT, p. A375

JOHNSRUD, Jill, Director of Nursing, Essentia Health-Graceville, Graceville, MN, p. A332

JOHNSTON, Charles, Chief Executive Officer, Cascade Medical Center, Cascade, ID, p. A168

JOHNSTON, Christopher, Chief Administrative Officer, Peacehealth United General Medical Center, Sedro, WA, p. A677

JOHNSTON, Diann, R.N., MSN, Vice President of Patient Care Services, Children's Hospital At Monmouth Medical Center, NJ, p. A407

JOHNSTON, Don, Chief Information Officer, San Joaquin General Hospital, French Camp, CA, p. A59

JOHNSTON, John, Chief Medical Officer, Specialty Hospital Of Meridian, Meridian, MS, p. A350

JOHNSTON, Lori, Chief Information Officer, Promedica Flower Hospital, Sylvania, OH, p. A491

JOHNSTON, Michael Eric., President and Chief Executive Officer, Mclaren Thumb Region, Bad Axe, MI, p. A308

JOHNSTON, Michael V, M.D., Chief Medical Officer and Senior Vice President Medical Programs, Kennedy Krieger Institute, Baltimore, MD, p. A287

JOHNSTON, Mike, Director Facilities Operations, Union General Hospital, Blairsville, GA, p. A148

JOHNSTON, Monte, Manager Human Resources, Coquille Valley Hospital, Coquille, OR, p. A512

JOHNSTON, Patricia, Vice President Information Services, Texas Health Harris Methodist Hospital Azle, Azle, TX, p. A587

JOHNSTON, Phyllis M., Vice President, Catawba Valley Medical Center, Hickory, NC, p. A454

JOHNSTON, Scott, Chief of Staff, Onslow Memorial Hospital, Jacksonville, NC, p. A455

JOHNSTON, Susan, Vice President Human Resources, East Alabama Medical Center-Lanier, AL, p. A22

JOHNSTON, Susanne, Manager Human Resources, Lincoln County Medical Center, Ruidoso, NM, p. A419

JOHNSTON, Word, Medical Director, Covington County Hospital, Collins, MS, p. A345

JOHNSTONE, Jennifer, Chief Clinical Officer, Kindred Hospital Rome, Rome, GA, p. A159

JOHRENDT, JT, Information Technology Network Specialist, Edgerton Hospital And Health Services, Edgerton, WI, p. A692

JOICE, Jason, M.D., Chief Medical Staff, Hillcrest Hospital Pryor, Pryor, OK, p. A506

JOLLEY, Colby, D.O., Acting Chief of Staff, Haxtun Hospital District, Haxtun, CO, p. A102

JOLLEY, Sherry, Director of Operations and Nursing, Red Bay Hospital, Red Bay, AL, p. A23

JOLLY, Gaye, FACHE, President and Chief Administrative Officer, Leconte Medical Center, Sevierville, TN, p. A579

JONASON, Anna, Ph.D., R.N., Chief Nursing Officer, Colleton Medical Center, Walterboro, SC, p. A557

JONES, Adrienne, Director Human Resources, Creedmoor Psychiatric Center, New York (Includes All Hospitals Located Within The Five Boroughs), NY, p. A432

JONES, Alesia, Chief Human Resources Officer, Uab Highlands, AL, p. A15

JONES, Allan, Controller, Healthsouth Rehabilitation Hospital Of Jonesboro, Jonesboro-Craighead County, AR, p. A44

JONES, America, R.N., Chief Executive Officer, Kindred Hospital El Paso, El Paso, TX, p. A602

JONES, Anetra, R.N., M.P.H.
Chief Nursing Officer, La Porte Hospital, La Porte, IN, p. A209
Chief Nursing Officer, Starke Hospital, Knox, IN, p. A208

JONES, Austin, CPA, Chief Financial Officer, Physicians Surgical Hospital - Panhandle Campus, TX, p. A583

JONES, Beth
Chief Operating Officer, Reeves Memorial Medical Center, Bernice, LA, p. A264
Director of Nursing, Reeves Memorial Medical Center, Bernice, LA, p. A264

JONES, Bill
Chief Executive Officer, Jackson County Hospital District, Edna, TX, p. A601
Chief Financial Officer, Florida State Hospital, Chattahoochee, FL, p. A119

JONES, Brain, Director of Information Technology, Multicare Valley Hospital, Spokane Valley, WA, p. A678

JONES, Carol, Controller and Manager Business Office, Coryell Memorial Hospital, Gatesville, TX, p. A607

JONES, Carol S., MSN, R.N., Interim Chief Nursing Officer, Goryeb Children's Hospital, NJ, p. A408

JONES, Carolyn, R.N., MSN, Chief Nursing Officer, Box Butte General Hospital, Alliance, NE, p. A381

JONES, Charlene, Chief Nursing Officer, Peterson Healthcare And Rehabilitation Hospital, Wheeling, WV, p. A688

JONES, Cheryl L, Vice President Human Resources and Organizational Development, Bsa Hospital, Llc, Amarillo, TX, p. A583

JONES, Chris, Chief Executive Officer, Vibra Hospital Of Northern California, Redding, CA, p. A80

JONES, Christian, Chief Operating Officer, Poplar Bluff Regional Medical Center-South Campus, MO, p. A366

JONES, Connie, Director Human Resources, Community Behavioral Health Hospital - Rochester, Rochester, MN, p. A338

JONES, Dale, Administrator, Noland Hospital Montgomery, Montgomery, AL, p. A21

JONES, Dana R., R.N., MSN, Chief Nursing Officer and Chief Operating Officer, Springhill Medical Center, Springhill, LA, p. A279

JONES, Danny L., Jr, FACHE, Chief Executive Officer, Bradley Center Of St. Francis, GA, p. A151

JONES, David, M.D.
Chief Medical Officer, Beauregard Health System, De Ridder, LA, p. A266
Chief Financial Officer, Alexian Brothers Behavioral Health Hospital, Hoffman Estates, IL, p. A186
Chief Nursing Officer, Encompass Health Rehabilitation Hospital Of Arlington, Arlington, TX, p. A584
Service Chief, Riverside Shore Memorial Hospital, Onancoke, VA, p. A663

JONES, David C., Administrator, North Caddo Medical Center, Vivian, LA, p. A280

JONES, Debbie, Director of Nursing, Brookhaven Hospital, Tulsa, OK, p. A508

JONES, Deborah, Controller, Sca Houston Hospital For Specialized Surgery, Houston, TX, p. A613

JONES, Derrick, Chief Executive Officer, Lovelace Rehabilitation Hospital, Albuquerque, NM, p. A415

JONES, Don, M.D., Chief Medical Officer, Marshall Medical Center North, Guntersville, AL, p. A19

JONES, Donald J., FACHE, Administrator, Fayette Medical Center, Fayette, AL, p. A18

JONES, Douglas A, Chief Operating Officer, Pine Grove Behavioral Health And Addiction Services, MS, p. A347

JONES, Elaine, M.D., President Medical Staff, Roger Williams Medical Center, Providence, RI, p. A548

JONES, Elizabeth
Chief Operating Officer, Lake Cumberland Regional Hospital, Somerset, KY, p. A260
Interim Chief Executive Officer, Lake Cumberland Regional Hospital, Somerset, KY, p. A260

JONES, Evan, Executive Vice President and Chief Financial Officer, Lakeland Regional Health Medical Center, Lakeland, FL, p. A127

JONES, Evelyn, R.N., Vice President Nursing Services, St. Bernard Hospital And Health Care Center, Chicago, IL, p. A179

JONES, Florence, President, Methodist Healthcare-North Hospital, TN, p. A575

JONES, Greg, Chief Financial Officer, Wayne Memorial Hospital, Jesup, GA, p. A155

JONES, Holly A, Administrative Director Nursing Services, Illini Community Hospital, Pittsfield, IL, p. A193

JONES, Janice G, Interim Chief Financial Officer, Controller and Compliance Officer, Acadian Medical Center, LA, p. A280

JONES, Jason L., R.N., Chief Nursing Officer, Fannin Regional Hospital, Blue Ridge, GA, p. A148

JONES, Jeff, Director Human Resources, Greene Memorial Hospital, Xenia, OH, p. A494

JONES, Jeffrey, Chief Financial Officer, Women's Hospital Of Greensboro, NC, p. A453

JONES, Jeremy A., Chief Executive Officer, Arbuckle Memorial Hospital, Sulphur, OK, p. A507

JONES, Joshua, Director Human Resources, Evanston Regional Hospital, Evanston, WY, p. A708

JONES, Joyce, Director Human Resources, Healthsouth Rehabilitation Hospital, Kingsport, TN, p. A572

JONES, Judy, Chief Clinical Officer, Arkansas Surgical Hospital, North Little Rock-Pulaski County, AR, p. A46

JONES, Julie L, Chief Nursing Officer, Community Hospital-Fairfax, Fairfax, MO, p. A359

JONES, Karen, Administrative Director Human Resources, Marion General Hospital, Marion, IN, p. A211

JONES, Karin, Interim Chief Nursing Officer, Healthsouth Rehabilitation Hospital Of New Mexico, Albuquerque, NM, p. A415

JONES, Karol, Chief Nursing Officer, Madison Hospital, AL, p. A19

JONES, Kathy, Director Human Resources, Jackson Medical Center, Jackson, AL, p. A19

JONES, Keith, Chief Information Officer, Fulton State Hospital, Fulton, MO, p. A359

JONES, Ken M, Chief Operating Officer, Ucsf Medical Center Mission Bay, CA, p. A86

JONES, Kenneth, President, Presence Saint Francis Hospital, Evanston, IL, p. A182

JONES, Kimberly, Director Human Resources, Spine Hospital Of Louisiana (Formally The Neuromedical Center Surgical Hospital), Baton Rouge, LA, p. A264

JONES, Kyle, Chief Financial Officer, Marshall Medical Center, Lewisburg, TN, p. A573

JONES, Lance, Chief Executive Officer, Stonesprings Hospital Center, Dulles, VA, p. A657

JONES, Liston, M.D., Medical Director, Springhill Memorial Hospital, Mobile, AL, p. A20

JONES, Louis, Director Management Information Systems, Heart Of Florida Regional Medical Center, Davenport, FL, p. A121

JONES, M Steven, President, University Hospitals Geauga Medical Center, Chardon, OH, p. A474

JONES, M Steven.
President, Uh Portage Medical Center, Ravenna, OH, p. A489
President, University Hospitals Conneaut Medical Center, Conneaut, OH, p. A479
President, University Hospitals Geauga Medical Center, Chardon, OH, p. A474
President, University Hospitals Geneva Medical Center, Geneva, OH, p. A483

JONES, Mark, Chief Financial Officer, Hill Country Memorial Hospital, Fredericksburg, TX, p. A606

JONES, Mark A., President, Winnie Palmer Hospital For Women And Babies, FL, p. A134

JONES, Marsha, R.N.
Director Nursing, Baptist Medical Center Yazoo, Yazoo City, MS, p. A354
Director of Nursing, Baptist Medical Center Yazoo, Yazoo City, MS, p. A354

JONES, Marshall, Senior Vice President Human Resources, Arizona Children's Center, AZ, p. A33

JONES, Mary Jane, R.N., MSN, Vice President Nursing Operations, Northridge Hospital Medical Center, Los Angeles, CA, p. A69

JONES, Matthew, Vice President Support Services and Facilities, The University Of Vermont Health Network - Alice Hyde Medical Center, Malone, NY, p. A429

JONES, Maud, Manager Medical Records, Tops Surgical Specialty Hospital, Houston, TX, p. A614

JONES, MaxAnne, Director Human Resources, Rock Prairie Behavioral Health, College Station, TX, p. A593

JONES, Melinda, R.N., Chief Nursing Officer, Morehouse General Hospital, Bastrop, LA, p. A263

JONES, Mike, Executive Director, Marshall Medical Center, Placerville, CA, p. A78

JONES, Mitchell, Director Information Technology, Little River Memorial Hospital, Ashdown, AR, p. A39

JUNO, Russell, M.D., Chief of Staff, St. Mark's Medical Center, La Grange, TX, p. A618

JURCZYK, John A., FACHE, Senior Vice President and President, St. Joseph Hospital, Nashua, NH, p. A400

JUREK, Chuck
Business Office Manager, Specialty Hospital Of Winnfield, Winnfield, LA, p. A281
Interim Administrator and Chief Operating Officer, Specialty Hospital Of Winnfield, Winnfield, LA, p. A281

JURGENS, Chad, Chief Executive Officer, Jefferson Community Health And Life, Fairbury, NE, p. A383

JURIS, Susan V., President, University Hospitals Ahuja Medical Center, Beachwood, OH, p. A471

JURKUS, Patti
Director Human Resources, Carilion Clinic Saint Albans Hospital, VA, p. A656
Vice President and Chief Executive Officer, Centra Bedford Memorial Hospital, Bedford, VA, p. A655

JURY, Tina M., MSN, Chief Nursing Officer, Anmed Health Women's And Children's Hospital, SC, p. A549

JUST, Paula
Chief Human Resources Officer, Health First Holmes Regional Medical Center, Melbourne, FL, p. A129
Chief Human Resources Officer, Health First Palm Bay Hospital, Palm Bay, FL, p. A135
Chief Human Resources Officer, Health First Viera Hospital, Melbourne, FL, p. A129
Vice President Human Resources, Health First Cape Canaveral Hospital, Cocoa Beach, FL, p. A120

JUSTICE, Jay D.
Chief Human Resource Officer, Adena Medical Center, Chillicothe, OH, p. A474
Chief Human Resources Officer, Adena Pike Medical Center, Waverly, OH, p. A493

JUSTICE, Kansas, Senior Vice President and Chief Operating Officer, Pikeville Medical Center, Pikeville, KY, p. A259

JUSTICE, Kim, Vice President Planning and Operations, Atlantic General Hospital, Berlin, MD, p. A290

JUSTIN, Patrick, Chief Financial Officer, United Hospital District, Blue Earth, MN, p. A328

JUSTIN-TANNER, Karen, R.N., Chief Nursing Officer, Fairbanks Memorial Hospital, Fairbanks, AK, p. A26

JUSTUS, Jason, Vice President Finance and Chief Financial Officer, Pomerene Hospital, Millersburg, OH, p. A487

JUTILA, Kathy, M.D., Chief of Staff, Wheatland Memorial Healthcare, Harlowton, MT, p. A376

JYRKAS, Wade A, Director Computer Information Systems, Lake Region Healthcare, Fergus Falls, MN, p. A331

K

KA'AKIMAKA, Holly, Director Human Resources, Hilo Medical Center, Hilo, HI, p. A164

KABERLINE, Gene, Chief Financial Officer, Susan B. Allen Memorial Hospital, El Dorado, KS, p. A234

KABITZKE-GROTH, Terry, R.N.
Chief Nursing Officer, Aurora Medical Center In Washington County, Hartford, WI, p. A694
Vice President Nursing, Aurora Medical Center Grafton, Grafton, WI, p. A693

KACHIGION, Claudia, M.D., Medical Director, Alton Mental Health Center, Alton, IL, p. A173

KADDOURI, Sami, M.D., Medical Director, Cornerstone Of Medical Arts Center Hospital, Fresh Meadows, NY, p. A426

KADIVAR, Aryan, M.D., Chief Medical Officer, Southwestern Medical Center, Lawton, OK, p. A500

KAFKA, Rich, M.D., Chief Medical Officer, Avera Gregory Hospital, Gregory, SD, p. A561

KAHL, Larry, Chief Operating Officer, Mid-Columbia Medical Center, The Dalles, OR, p. A518

KAHL, Vicky, Director Human Resources, Valley Regional Medical Center, Brownsville, TX, p. A590

KAHLE, Russ, Chief Information Officer, Logan County Hospital, Oakley, KS, p. A242

KAHLE, Ty
Assistant Vice President Human Resources, Methodist Hospital Union County, Morganfield, KY, p. A258
Vice President Human Resources, Methodist Hospital, Henderson, KY, p. A253

KAHLER, John G., M.D., Radiologist, Bryan W. Whitfield Memorial Hospital, Demopolis, AL, p. A16

KAHLY-MCMAHON, Heidi
Interim Vice President Human Resources, Genesis Medical Center-West Campus, IA, p. A220

Vice President Human Resources, Genesis Medical Center, Silvis, Silvis, IL, p. A196

KAHN, Jalil, M.D., Chief of Staff, Atrium Medical Center Of Corinth, Corinth, TX, p. A594

KAHN, Maureen A., R.N., President and Chief Executive Officer, Blessing Hospital, IL, p. A194

KAHO, Clint
President, Baptist Health La Grange, La Grange, KY, p. A254
Vice President, Baptist Health Louisville, Louisville, KY, p. A256

KAHRS, Amy, Director of Finance, Franklin County Memorial Hospital, Franklin, NE, p. A383

KAINO, Linda, Chief Nursing Officer, Ocean Beach Hospital, Ilwaco, WA, p. A672

KAISER, Brenda, Director Human Resources, University Of Kansas Health System Great Bend Campus, Great Bend, KS, p. A236

KAISER, James, Site Director Information Technology, Upper Valley Medical Center, Troy, OH, p. A492

KAISER, Janet, R.N., Chief Nursing Officer, Kansas Medical Center, Andover, KS, p. A232

KAISER, Ken, Coordinator Information Systems, Grant Regional Health Center, Lancaster, WI, p. A696

KAISER, Russell, Interim Chief Executive Officer and Chief Nursing Officer, The Colony Er Hospital, The Colony, TX, p. A639

KAJIWARA, Gary K, President and Chief Executive Officer, Kuakini Medical Center, Honolulu, HI, p. A164

KAJIWARA, Gary K., President and Chief Executive Officer, Kuakini Medical Center, Honolulu, HI, p. A164

KAKAVAS, Connie, Chief Human Resources Officer, Summit Healthcare Regional Medical Center, Show Low, AZ, p. A36

KAKUDA, James, M.D., Chief of Staff, Pali Momi Medical Center, Aiea, HI, p. A164

KALAFUS, Lisa, MSN, R.N., Chief Nursing Officer, Gaylord Hospital, Wallingford, CT, p. A111

KALAJAINEN, Kimberly
Vice President Operations and Chief Information Officer, Lawrence + Memorial Hospital, New London, CT, p. A110
Vice President, Operations and Information Technology, Chief Information Officer, Westerly Hospital, Westerly, RI, p. A548

KALANIHUIA, Janice, President, Molokai General Hospital, Kaunakakai, HI, p. A166

KALAR, Cathy, Chief Financial Officer, Broaddus Hospital, Philippi, WV, p. A686

KALAVAR, Jagadeesh S, M.D., Chief of Staff, Michael E. Debakey Veterans Affairs Medical Center, Houston, TX, p. A612

KALCHIK, Kevin, Chief Financial Officer, War Memorial Hospital, Sault Sainte Marie, MI, p. A323

KALE, Debra
Director Human Resources, Carolinas Healthcare System Kings Mountain, Kings Mountain, NC, p. A455
Vice President Human Resources, Carolinas Healthcare System Cleveland, Shelby, NC, p. A460

KALEEL, Reza
Chief Administrative Officer, Kadlec Regional Medical Center, Richland, WA, p. A676
Executive Vice President and Chief Operating Officer, St. Mary's Hospital And Medical Center, Grand Junction, CO, p. A101

KALINA, Andrea, Vice President External Affairs and Chief Human Resources Officer, St. Clair Hospital, Pittsburgh, PA, p. A537

KALINSKI, Cami, Director Financial Services, Frances Mahon Deaconess Hospital, Glasgow, MT, p. A375

KALKA, Gina, R.N., Chief Nursing Officer, Pecos County Memorial Hospital, Fort Stockton, TX, p. A604

KALKOWSKI, Kelly, Chief Executive Officer, Niobrara Valley Hospital, Lynch, NE, p. A386

KALKUT, Gary, M.D., Senior Vice President and Chief Medical Officer, Montefiore Medical Center - North Division, NY, p. A433

KALL, Greg, Chief Information Officer, Summa Saint Thomas Hospital, OH, p. A470

KALLEVIG, Daryl, Chief Information Officer, Riverwood Healthcare Center, Aitkin, MN, p. A327

KALMAN, Jill, Executive Director, Manhattan Eye, Ear And Throat Hospital, NY, p. A433

KALSMAN, Stephen L, Area Finance Officer, Kaiser Permanente San Jose Medical Center, San Jose, CA, p. A86

KALTENBACH, Gretchen, R.N., Chief Operating Officer, Genesis Behavioral Hospital, Breaux Bridge, LA, p. A265

KALUA, Patricia, Chief Nurse Executive, Kona Community Hospital, Kealakekua, HI, p. A166

KAMBER, Sean, Chief Executive Officer, Medical City Weatherford, Weatherford, TX, p. A643

KAMBEROS, Peter N, Chief Operating Officer, Thorek Memorial Hospital, Chicago, IL, p. A180

KAMBEROV, Denis, M.D., Chief of Staff, De Soto Regional Health System, Mansfield, LA, p. A273

KAMBIC, Phillip M., President and Chief Executive Officer, Riverside Medical Center, Kankakee, IL, p. A187

KAMENS, Eric, Regional Director Information Systems, Shriners Hospitals For Children-Springfield, Springfield, MA, p. A304

KAMERMAYER, Angela K, MS, Chief Nursing Officer, Integris Health Edmond, Edmond, OK, p. A498

KAMGUIA, Rebecca, Administrative Director Human Resources, Bon Secours Memorial Regional Medical Center, Mechanicsville, VA, p. A661

KAMIKAWA, Cynthia, R.N., MSN, President, North Hawaii Community Hospital, Kamuela, HI, p. A165

KAMINSKI, Gene, Vice President Human Resources and Hospitality Services, Mclaren Northern Michigan, Petoskey, MI, p. A320

KAMINSKI, Tammy
Director Human Resources, Alaska Regional Hospital, Anchorage, AK, p. A25
Vice President Human Relations, Riverside Community Hospital, Riverside, CA, p. A81

KAMINSKI, Toni, Director Human Resources, Medical Center Enterprise, Enterprise, AL, p. A17

KAMMERER, James M., Vice President Support Services, Great River Medical Center, West Burlington, IA, p. A231

KAMMERUD, Shawn, Manager Information Services, Osceola Medical Center, Osceola, WI, p. A700

KAMOWSKI, David, Vice President and Chief Information Officer, Temple University Hospital - Episcopal Division, PA, p. A536

KAMPHUIS, Jan, Ph.D., R.N., Executive Vice President and Chief Nurse Executive, Sanford Bismarck, Bismarck, ND, p. A464

KAMPSCHNIEDER, Carol, Vice President Clinical and Regulatory Services, St. Francis Memorial Hospital, West Point, NE, p. A391

KAMPWERTH, Dennis, Director Management Information Systems, Gateway Regional Medical Center, Granite City, IL, p. A184

KAMRAN, Khurram, M.D.
Vice President Medical Affairs, Toledo Children's Hospital, OH, p. A491
Vice President, Physician Services, Winter Haven Hospital, Winter Haven, FL, p. A144

KANAPARTI, V.R., M.D., Director Medical Services, Kalamazoo Psychiatric Hospital, Kalamazoo, MI, p. A317

KANDOW, Casey
Chief Operating Officer, Mclaren Orthopedic Hospital, MI, p. A317
Interim President and Chief Executive Officer, Mclaren Orthopedic Hospital, MI, p. A317

KANE, Addy, Chief Financial Officer, Roger Williams Medical Center, Providence, RI, p. A548

KANE, Audrey, Interim Chief Financial Officer, Prowers Medical Center, Lamar, CO, p. A103

KANE, Kelli R, Director of Finance, Barnes-Kasson County Hospital, Susquehanna, PA, p. A542

KANE, Nancy, Assistant Vice President Finance LifeBridge Health, Northwest Hospital, Randallstown, MD, p. A293

KANE, Robert E., Chief Administrative Officer, Divine Providence Hospital, Williamsport, PA, p. A545

KANE, Steve, Director Information Technology, Lower Bucks Hospital, Bristol, PA, p. A521

KANE, Thomas, R.N., Vice President Patient Services and Chief Nursing Officer, Munson Healthcare Manistee Hospital, Manistee, MI, p. A318

KANE, Trisha, Director Human Resources, Continuecare Hospital At Hendrick Medical Center, Abilene, TX, p. A582

KANIA, Kathy, Associate Executive Director and Chief Information Officer, Staten Island University Hospital, New York (Includes All Hospitals Located Within The Five Boroughs), NY, p. A437

KANNADAY, Colleen, FACHE
President, Advocate Bromenn Regional Medical Center, IL, p. A191
President, Advocate Eureka Hospital, Eureka, IL, p. A182

KANTELAS, Sandra Jean, Chief Nursing Officer, University Hospitals Elyria Medical Center, Elyria, OH, p. A482

KANTOS, Craig A.
Chief Executive Officer, Theda Care Medical Center - Wild Rose, Wild Rose, WI, p. A706
Chief Executive Officer, Thedacare Medical Center-Waupaca, Waupaca, WI, p. A705

KANUCH, James A
  Vice President Finance, Allegheny Valley Hospital, Natrona Heights, PA, p. A532
  Vice President Finance, West Penn Hospital, Pittsburgh, PA, p. A538
KAPER, Jonathan, Chief Medical Officer, Beaumont Hospital - Trenton, Trenton, MI, p. A324
KAPLAN, Alan, M.D., Chief Executive Officer, American Family Children's Hospital, WI, p. A696
KAPLAN, Gary, M.D., FACHE, Chairman and Chief Executive Officer, Virginia Mason Medical Center, Seattle, WA, p. A677
KAPLAN, Ronald, Chief Financial Officer, Girard Medical Center, PA, p. A536
KAPLAN, Tamra, PharmD, Chief Operating Officer, Memorialcare, Miller Children's & Women's Hospital Long Beach, Long Beach, CA, p. A65
KAPLANIS, Gene, Director Information Technology, Alaska Regional Hospital, Anchorage, AK, p. A25
KAPRE, Sheela, M.D., Chief Medical Officer, San Joaquin General Hospital, French Camp, CA, p. A59
KARA, Amynah, M.D., Chief Medical Officer, Baylor Emergency Medical Centers - Keller, TX, p. A585
KARAM, Annah, Director Human Resources, San Gorgonio Memorial Hospital, Banning, CA, p. A52
KARAM, Chris, FACHE, President and Chief Executive Officer, Senior Vice President Group Operations, Christus St. Frances Cabrini Hospital, Alexandria, LA, p. A262
KARAM, Christopher J, Chief Operating Officer, Saint Joseph Health System, Mishawaka, IN, p. A211
KARAM, Christopher J., President, Plymouth Medical Center, Plymouth, IN, p. A213
KARANJA, Diana, R.N., Director of Nursing, St. John Vianney Hospital, Downingtown, PA, p. A524
KARANJAI, Rajohn, M.D., Chief Medical Officer, Sidney Health Center, Sidney, MT, p. A379
KARCZ, Chrisi, Chief Nursing Officer, Van Matre Healthsouth Rehabilitation Hospital, Rockford, IL, p. A195
KARDOW, Vivian
  Chief Human Resources Officer, Memorial Hermann Orthopedic And Spine Hospital, TX, p. A612
  Chief Human Resources Officer, Tirr Memorial Hermann, Houston, TX, p. A614
KAREL, Thomas L, Vice President Organization and Talent Effectiveness, Mercy Health Rockford, MI, p. A314
KARG, Gary, Interim Vice President Finance, Christus St. Frances Cabrini Hospital, Alexandria, LA, p. A262
KARIM, Parvez, M.D., Chief Medical Officer, Allegiance Specialty Hospital Of Greenville, Greenville, MS, p. A346
KARL, Don
  Chief Operating Officer, Las Palmas Rehabilitation Hospital, TX, p. A602
  Interim Chief Executive Officer, Las Palmas Rehabilitation Hospital, TX, p. A602
KARL, Thomas P., President, Parkland Health Center - Farmington Community, Farmington, MO, p. A359
KARMACH, Izabela, R.N., Administrator, San Diego County Psychiatric Hospital, San Diego, CA, p. A84
KARN, Cielette, M.D., Chief of Staff, Sagewest Health Care At Lander, WY, p. A709
KARNER, Diana M., R.N., MSN
  Chief Nursing Executive, California Pacific Medical Center-St. Luke's Campus, San Francisco, CA, p. A85
  Chief Nursing Officer, California Pacific Medical Center, San Francisco, CA, p. A85
KARNS, Kristopher, Chief Executive Officer, Post Acute Medical Specialty Hospital Of Tulsa, Tulsa, OK, p. A508
KARP, Bob, M.D., Chief Medical Officer, United Hospital District, Blue Earth, MN, p. A328
KARRE, Kris, Director Finance and Accounting, Unitypoint Health-Keokuk, Keokuk, IA, p. A225
KARSOS, Felicia, R.N.
  Chief Nursing Officer, Hudson Regional Hospital, Secaucus, NJ, p. A411
  President and Chief Executive Officer, Hudson Regional Hospital, Secaucus, NJ, p. A411
KARSTEN, Margo, Ph.D., MSN
  Chief Executive Officer, Banner Fort Collins Medical Center, Fort Collins, CO, p. A100
  Chief Executive Officer, Mckee Medical Center, Loveland, CO, p. A104
  Chief Executive Officer, North Colorado Medical Center, Greeley, CO, p. A101
KARSTEN, Paul H, Vice President Finance and Chief Financial Officer, Pine Rest Christian Mental Health Services, Grand Rapids, MI, p. A314
KARSTETTER, James M., R.N., II, Vice President & Chief Nursing Officer, Western Maryland Regional Medical Center, Cumberland, MD, p. A291

KASIRYE, Yusuf, M.D., Chief of Staff, Flambeau Hospital, Park Falls, WI, p. A701
KASITZ, Todd, Vice President Finance, Newton Medical Center, Newton, KS, p. A242
KASNIC, Tracey A
  Chief Nursing Officer, Confluence Health/Wenatchee Valley Hospital, Wenatchee, WA, p. A680
  Senior Vice President Inpatient and Chief Nursing Officer, Confluence Health/Central Washington Hospital, Wenatchee, WA, p. A680
KASPER, Katie, Chief Clinical Officer, Uh Avon Rehabilitation Hospital, Avon, OH, p. A471
KASPER, Yobi, Chief Information Officer, Advanced Diagnostics Hospital, Houston, TX, p. A610
KASS, Andrew J A, M.D., Assistant Superintendent, Albert J. Solnit Psychiatric Center - South Campus, Middletown, CT, p. A109
KASSAB, Jerry, President and Chief Executive Officer, Aspire Health Partners, Orlando, FL, p. A134
KASSAHN, Kristine, Chief Executive Officer, Fresno Surgical Hospital, Fresno, CA, p. A59
KASSER, Michael
  Chief Financial Officer, Herrin Hospital, Herrin, IL, p. A185
  Vice President Chief Financial Officer and Treasurer, Memorial Hospital Of Carbondale, Carbondale, IL, p. A175
KASSIS, Charles, President, Mercy Medical Center Merced-Dominican Campus, CA, p. A72
KASSIS, Maher, M.D., Chief Medical Staff, Mercy Health - Marcum And Wallace, Irvine, KY, p. A254
KASTANIS, John N., FACHE, President and Chief Executive Officer, University Hospital, Newark, NJ, p. A409
KASTER, Steven, M.D., Chief Medical Officer, Wysong Campus, TX, p. A623
KATEN-BAHENSKY, Donna, Director, West Palm Beach Veterans Affairs Medical Center, West Palm Beach, FL, p. A143
KATES, Josh, Information Technology Analyst, Andrew Mcfarland Mental Health Center, Springfield, IL, p. A196
KATES, Kenneth P., Chief Executive Officer, University Of Iowa Stead Family Children's Hospital, IA, p. A224
KATHRINS, Richard J., Ph.D., President and Chief Executive Officer, Bacharach Institute For Rehabilitation, Pomona, NJ, p. A410
KATNENI, Jitendra P., M.D., Medical Director, Select Specialty Hospital-Flint, Flint, MI, p. A313
KATO, Laura
  Vice President Human Resources, St. Francis Medical Center, Lynwood, CA, p. A70
  Vice President of Human Resources, San Antonio Regional Hospital, Upland, CA, p. A93
KATSCHKE, R William, M.D., Jr, Medical Director, Grover C. Dils Medical Center, Caliente, NV, p. A392
KATZ, Benjamin, M.D., Vice President Medical Affairs, Glens Falls Hospital, Glens Falls, NY, p. A427
KATZ, Jeffrey, M.D., Chief Medical Officer, Memorial Hermann Orthopedic And Spine Hospital, TX, p. A612
KATZ, Michelle, Director Human Resources, Healthsouth Nittany Valley Rehabilitation Hospital, Pleasant Gap, PA, p. A538
KATZ, Richard, M.D., Vice President Medical Affairs, Mt. Washington Pediatric Hospital, Baltimore, MD, p. A288
KATZ, Robert, M.D., Chief of Staff, Columbus Community Hospital, Columbus, TX, p. A593
KATZ, Yair
  Chief Financial Officer, Memorialcare, Long Beach Memorial Medical Center, Long Beach, CA, p. A65
  Chief Financial Officer, Memorialcare, Miller Children's & Women's Hospital Long Beach, Long Beach, CA, p. A65
KAUFFMAN, Angie, Chief Executive Officer, South Texas Spine And Surgical Hospital, San Antonio, TX, p. A634
KAUFMAN, Cheryl
  Director Health Information Management, Florida Hospital Dade City, Dade City, FL, p. A121
  Information Technology Technician, Coteau Des Prairies Hospital, Sisseton, SD, p. A564
KAUFMAN, Dan, Director Information Services, Paulding County Hospital, Paulding, OH, p. A489
KAUFMAN, Irvin A, M.D., Chief Medical Officer, Rady Children's Hospital - San Diego, San Diego, CA, p. A84
KAUFMAN, Robert
  Director Financial Services, Central State Hospital, Petersburg, VA, p. A663
  Fiscal Officer, Hiram W. Davis Medical Center, Petersburg, VA, p. A663
KAUFMAN, Samuel, Chief Executive Officer, Henderson Hospital, Henderson, NV, p. A393
KAUFMAN, Seth, M.D., Chief Medical Officer, Northbay Vacavalley Hospital, CA, p. A57

KAUPA, Michael, Executive Vice President and Chief Operating Officer, Park Nicollet Methodist Hospital, Saint Louis Park, MN, p. A339
KAUPAS, Bill, Chief Executive Officer, Post Acute/Warm Springs Rehabilitation Hospital Of Allen, Allen, TX, p. A582
KAUTZ, Peter, Chief Executive Officer, Meadowbrook Rehabilitation Hospital, Gardner, KS, p. A235
KAUTZ, Terri, Manager Human Resources, Weiser Memorial Hospital, Weiser, ID, p. A172
KAUZLARICH, Sidney A., M.D., Medical Director, Douglas County Community Mental Health Center, Omaha, NE, p. A388
KAVALIER, MaryJo, Administrator, Sartori Memorial Hospital, Cedar Falls, IA, p. A218
KAVANAGH, Darina, R.N., MSN, Chief Nursing Officer, Good Samaritan Hospital, San Jose, CA, p. A86
KAVANAGH, Sean, Director Information Technology, Pondera Medical Center, Conrad, MT, p. A374
KAVANAUGH, Paul B., President and Chief Executive Officer, Community Care Hospital, New Orleans, LA, p. A275
KAVANAUGH, Samantha, Chief Financial Officer, Riverview Psychiatric Center, Augusta, ME, p. A282
KAVTARADZE, David, M.D., Chief of Staff, Crisp Regional Hospital, Cordele, GA, p. A151
KAY, Kirk, Chief Financial Officer, Veterans Affairs Nebraska-Western Iowa Health Care System, Omaha, NE, p. A389
KAY, Robert W, Senior Vice President and Chief Financial Officer, Memorial Medical Center, Springfield, IL, p. A196
KAY-GARCIA, Lisa, Chief Information Officer, Kearny County Hospital, Lakin, KS, p. A239
KAYE, Jessie, Chief Executive Officer, Prairie View, Newton, KS, p. A242
KAYGA, Alicia R., R.N., Chief Nursing Officer, Brownwood Regional Medical Center, Brownwood, TX, p. A590
KAYROUZ, Thomas, M.D., Chief Medical Officer, Anmed Health Women's And Children's Hospital, SC, p. A549
KAYSER, Sonya J, Human Resources Officer, Avera Marshall Regional Medical Center, Marshall, MN, p. A334
KAZMIERCZAK, Sara Marie, R.N., Director of Nursing, North Valley Health Center, Warren, MN, p. A341
KAZMIERCZAK, Stanley, Controller, Presence Saint Joseph Hospital, Chicago, IL, p. A178
KEANE, Dennis M., Vice President Finance and Chief Financial Officer, St. John's Riverside Hospital - Dobbs Ferry Pavilion, NY, p. A446
KEANE, Fran, Vice President Human Resources, Centrastate Healthcare System, Freehold, NJ, p. A405
KEANE, Merry Ann, Chief Administrative Officer, Peacehealth Peace Island Medical Center, Friday Harbor, WA, p. A672
KEANE, Valerie E, FACHE, Chief Nursing Executive, Sentara Northern Virginia Medical Center, Woodbridge, VA, p. A668
KEARNEY, Elizabeth, R.N., Chief Nursing Officer, Mountain Vista Medical Center, Mesa, AZ, p. A31
KEARNEY, Karen
  Vice President Inpatient Rehabilitation Services, Allied Services Rehabilitation Hospital, Scranton, PA, p. A540
  Vice President Inpatient Rehabilitation Services, John Heinz Institute Of Rehabilitation Medicine, Wilkes, PA, p. A544
KEARNEY, Lynn, Vice President Nursing, Robert Wood Johnson University Hospital Somerset, Somerville, NJ, p. A411
KEARNEY, M Clark, Vice President Human Resources, Saint Mary's Hospital, Waterbury, CT, p. A111
KEARNS, Debbie
  Chief Executive Officer, Community Hospital, Oklahoma City, OK, p. A503
  Chief Executive Officer, Northwest Surgical Hospital, Oklahoma City, OK, p. A503
KEARNS, Peggy W., MS, FACHE, Executive Director, Veterans Affairs Southern Nevada Healthcare System, North Las Vegas, NV, p. A396
KEASTER, Lorna, Interim Chief Nursing Officer, Hshs Holy Family Hospital In Greenville, Greenville, IL, p. A184
KEATING, Michael, President and Chief Executive Officer, Christ Hospital, Cincinnati, OH, p. A474
KEATING, Todd, Chief Financial Officer, Vermont Children's Hospital, VT, p. A653
KEATON, Tony, Director Information Systems, Roane General Hospital, Spencer, WV, p. A687
KECK, Paul, M.D., President and Chief Executive Officer, Lindner Center Of Hope, Mason, OH, p. A486
KEE, Agnes, Financial Manager, Gallup Indian Medical Center, Gallup, NM, p. A417
KEE, Robert, Chief Information Officer, Nyc Health + Hospitals / Coney Island, New York (Includes All Hospitals Located Within The Five Boroughs), NY, p. A435
KEEF, Shaun, Chief Financial Officer, Eastern Oklahoma Medical Center, Poteau, OK, p. A505
KEEFE, Eileen, Chief Nursing Officer, Parkland Medical Center, Derry, NH, p. A398

KEEFE, John, Chief Financial Officer, Hollywood Presbyterian Medical Center, Los Angeles, CA, p. A67

KEEFER, Russ, Chief Human Resources Officer, Trios Health, Kennewick, WA, p. A672

KEEGAN, Julie, Vice President Finance, Craig Hospital, Englewood, CO, p. A100

KEEGAN, Justin, Director Support Services, Avera Gregory Hospital, Gregory, SD, p. A561

KEEL, Barry L., Administration, North Mississippi Medical Center-West Point, West Point, MS, p. A354

KEEL, Patricia, Senior Vice President and Chief Financial Officer, St. Jude Children's Research Hospital, Memphis, TN, p. A576

KEELE, Paula
   Manager Information Systems, Osf Heart Of Mary Medical Center, Urbana, IL, p. A197
   Manager Information Systems, Osf Sacred Heart Medical Center, Danville, IL, p. A180

KEELE, Ryan, Chief Executive Officer, Northern Utah Rehabilitation Hospital, South Ogden, UT, p. A651

KEELER, Dave, Chief Financial Officer, Pipestone County Medical Center Avera, Pipestone, MN, p. A337

KEELER, Jason, Executive Vice President and Chief Operating Officer, Comer Children's Hospital, IL, p. A180

KEELER, Jean M., President and Chief Executive Officer, Grand View Health, Sellersville, PA, p. A541

KEELER, Karl, President, Mercy Medical Center - West Lakes, IA, p. A221

KEELEY, Katherine, M.D., Chief of Staff, Sunrise Hospital And Medical Center, Las Vegas, NV, p. A395

KEELINE, Leah, Clinical Infirmatics Specialist, Catalina Island Medical Center, Avalon, CA, p. A51

KEELING, Kathy, Director of Nursing, Rehabilitation Hospital Of Rhode Island, North Smithfield, RI, p. A547

KEELING, Kevin, Chief Financial Officer, St. Lucie Medical Center, Port St Lucie, FL, p. A137

KEELING, Michele A., Senior Vice President and Administrator, Laureate Psychiatric Clinic And Hospital, Tulsa, OK, p. A508

KEELING, Terri, Vice President Information Systems, Upmc Mckeesport, Mckeesport, PA, p. A531

KEEN, Kris, Chief Information Officer, Cameron Memorial Community Hospital, Angola, IN, p. A199

KEEN, Michael, Senior Vice President and Chief Financial Officer, Grand View Health, Sellersville, PA, p. A541

KEEN, Scott R., Chief Executive Officer, Honorhealth Rehabilitation Hospital, Scottsdale, AZ, p. A35

KEENAN, Bob, Chief Medical Officer, H. Lee Moffitt Cancer Center And Research Institute, Tampa, FL, p. A140

KEENAN, Kevin, M.D., Physician Advisor, East Cooper Medical Center, Mount Pleasant, SC, p. A555

KEENAN, Nancy C, R.N., Senior Vice President and Chief Nursing Officer, Houston Methodist Willowbrook Hospital, Houston, TX, p. A611

KEENAN, Richard, Senior Vice President Finance and Chief Financial Officer, Valley Hospital, Ridgewood, NJ, p. A411

KEENE, Emilie, Interim Chief Operating Officer, Palmetto Health Baptist Parkridge, Columbia, SC, p. A551

KEENE, Kimberly, Chief Executive Officer, St. Bernard Parish Hospital, Chalmette, LA, p. A265

KEENER, Vicki, Administrative Assistant and Director Human Resources, Little River Memorial Hospital, Ashdown, AR, p. A39

KEEPSEAGLE, Joelle, Director of Nursing, Standing Rock Service Unit, Fort Yates Hospital, Indian Health Service, Dhhs, Fort Yates, ND, p. A466

KEESBURY, Drew
   Chief Financial Officer, La Porte Hospital, La Porte, IN, p. A209
   Chief Financial Officer, Starke Hospital, Knox, IN, p. A208

KEEVER, Jerry, Administrator, Sharkey-Issaquena Community Hospital, Rolling Fork, MS, p. A353

KEFALAS, George, Chief Medical Officer, Aultman Specialty Hospital, Canton, OH, p. A473

KEGLEY, Carl J, System Director Information Technology, Fairbanks Memorial Hospital, Fairbanks, AK, p. A26

KEGLEY, Glen, Chief Operating Officer, Hutchinson Health, Hutchinson, MN, p. A333

KEGLEY, Shawn, Director Information Services, Research Psychiatric Center, MO, p. A361

KEHIAYAN, Nancy, Director of Nursing, Colorado Mental Health Institute At Fort Logan, Denver, CO, p. A98

KEHRBERG, Mark W, M.D.
   Chief Medical Officer, Ascension Calumet Hospital, Chilton, WI, p. A691
   Senior Vice President and Chief Medical Officer, Ascension Northeast Wisconsin Mercy Hospital, Oshkosh, WI, p. A700

KEHUS, Frank, Associate Director for Operations, Marion Veterans Affairs Medical Center, Marion, IL, p. A188

KEIL, James, M.D., Chief Medical Officer, Niobrara Valley Hospital, Lynch, NE, p. A386

KEIM, Thomas, Chief Executive Officer, Ste. Genevieve County Memorial Hospital, Ste Genevieve, MO, p. A371

KEIRNS, Melody, Manager Human Resources, F. W. Huston Medical Center, Winchester, KS, p. A248

KEISER, Trish, Comptroller, Avera Gregory Hospital, Gregory, SD, p. A561

KEISTER, Catharine L, Chief Nursing Officer, Upmc Susquehanna Sunbury, Sunbury, PA, p. A542

KEITEL, Kal, Executive Director Human Resources, Baptist Health Paducah, Paducah, KY, p. A259

KEITH, Bridgette, Director Human Resources, Healthsouth Northern Kentucky Rehabilitation Hospital, Edgewood, KY, p. A251

KEITH, Christopher, Chief Executive Officer, Select Specialty Hospital-Wichita, Wichita, KS, p. A248

KEITH, Darlene, Chief Information Systems, Alleghany Memorial Hospital, Sparta, NC, p. A461

KEITH, David N., FACHE, President and Chief Executive Officer, Mcalester Regional Health Center, Mcalester, OK, p. A501

KEITH, Jeannie, Director Patient Care Services and Nurse Executive, Shriners Hospitals For Children-Houston, Houston, TX, p. A613

KEITH, Lorraine
   Chief Nursing Officer, St. Vincent's Medical Center Riverside, Jacksonville, FL, p. A126
   Chief Nursing Officer, St. Vincent's Medical Center Southside, Jacksonville, FL, p. A126

KELBAUGH, Brian, Chief Financial Officer, Summersville Regional Medical Center, Summersville, WV, p. A687

KELBLY, Kevin, Senior Vice President Finance and Corporate Fiscal Affairs, Carroll Hospital Center, Westminster, MD, p. A294

KELL, Douglas B, Chief Financial Officer, Scottsdale Liberty Hospital, Scottsdale, AZ, p. A35

KELLAR, Brian, Chief Executive Officer, Page Hospital, Page, AZ, p. A32

KELLAR, Mark, R.N., Interim Chief Nursing Officer, Bogalusa Community Medical Center, LA, p. A264

KELLAR, Richard A., President, Aurora West Allis Medical Center, West Allis, WI, p. A706

KELLEHER, Cynthia, M.P.H., President and Chief Executive Officer, University Of Maryland Rehabilitation & Orthopaedic Institute, Baltimore, MD, p. A289

KELLEHER, Mary, Vice President Human Resources, Holyoke Medical Center, Holyoke, MA, p. A300

KELLEHER, Mary Lou, R.N., MSN, Vice President, Nursing, Franciscan Children'S, Brighton, MA, p. A297

KELLEHER, Michael, Chief Medical Officer, Ann & Robert H. Lurie Children's Hospital Of Chicago, Chicago, IL, p. A176

KELLEHER, William H, Director, Veterans Affairs Medical Center West Roxbury Division, MA, p. A298

KELLENBARGER, Lance, Site Director Information Systems, St. Catherine Hospital, Garden City, KS, p. A235

KELLER, Allen, Director Human Resources, Sumner Regional Medical Center, Wellington, KS, p. A247

KELLER, Anita M., R.N., MSN, Chief Nursing Officer, Johnson Memorial Hospital, Franklin, IN, p. A204

KELLER, Ann, Supervisor Health Information Management, Walton Rehabilitation Hospital, Augusta, GA, p. A147

KELLER, Christine, Chief Administrative Officer, Bluffton Hospital, Bluffton, OH, p. A472

KELLER, Diane R., Chief Executive Officer, Memorial Community Health, Aurora, NE, p. A381

KELLER, Gretchen, Director Health Information, Neosho Memorial Regional Medical Center, Chanute, KS, p. A233

KELLER, James, M.D.
   Vice President, Medical Management, Advocate Trinity Hospital, Chicago, IL, p. A176
   Chief Information Officer, Borgess-Lee Memorial Hospital, Dowagiac, MI, p. A312
   Director Human Resources, Nea Baptist Memorial Hospital, Jonesboro-Craighead County, AR, p. A44

KELLER, Jill, R.N., MSN, Vice President for Nursing Services, Quality and Risk Management, Waynesboro Hospital, Waynesboro, PA, p. A543

KELLER, Jim, Site Director Information Services, Mercy Health Rockford, MI, p. A314

KELLER, Justin, Chief Information Officer, Murray County Medical Center, Slayton, MN, p. A340

KELLER, Marsha, Director Human Resources, Upmc Kane, Kane, PA, p. A528

KELLER, Maryalice, Vice President Brand and Talent Management, Unity Hospital, Rochester, NY, p. A441

KELLER, Patricia, MSN, R.N., Nurse Administrator, Mayo Clinic Health System - Northland In Barron, Barron, WI, p. A690

KELLER, Ruey, Acting Chief Information Officer, Va San Diego Healthcare System, San Diego, CA, p. A84

KELLER, Stewart, M.D., Medical Director, Mesa Springs, Fort Worth, TX, p. A605

KELLER, Thomas, President and Chief Executive Officer, Ozarks Medical Center, West Plains, MO, p. A372

KELLER, Wendy, Director Health Information Management, Atrium Medical Center Of Corinth, Corinth, TX, p. A594

KELLERMAN, Laurie, MSN, Chief Clinical Officer, Marshall Browning Hospital, Du Quoin, IL, p. A181

KELLERMAN, Scott, Chief Financial Officer, Ely-Bloomenson Community Hospital, Ely, MN, p. A331

KELLEY, Brent, Director Information Technology, Nor-Lea Hospital District, Lovington, NM, p. A418

KELLEY, Danny, Administrative Director, Health Information Technology, Norman Regional Moore, OK, p. A502

KELLEY, Jalinda, Secretary of Interior Services, Chickasaw Nation Medical Center, Ada, OK, p. A495

KELLEY, James, Chief Human Resources Officer, Desert Regional Medical Center, Palm Springs, CA, p. A77

KELLEY, Janice, Chief Financial Officer, Marshall County Hospital, Benton, KY, p. A249

KELLEY, Julie, M.D., Chief of Staff, Red Bud Regional Hospital, Red Bud, IL, p. A194

KELLEY, Lewis
   Chief Operating Officer, Union General Hospital, Blairsville, GA, p. A148
   Interim Chief Executive Officer, Union General Hospital, Blairsville, GA, p. A148

KELLEY, Mary, Director Human Resources, The Outer Banks Hospital, Nags Head, NC, p. A458

KELLEY, Neal, Vice President and Chief Operating Officer, Seton Medical Center Hays, Kyle, TX, p. A618

KELLEY, Patti, Vice President, Nurisng and Chief Nursing Officer, Ssm Health Saint Louis University Hospital-South, MO, p. A369

KELLEY, Randall, FACHE
   President, Spectrum Health Gerber Memorial, Fremont, MI, p. A313
   President, Spectrum Health Ludington Hospital, Ludington, MI, p. A318

KELLEY, Sarah Jo, Executive Director of Human Resources and Support Services, Ste. Genevieve County Memorial Hospital, Ste Genevieve, MO, p. A371

KELLEY, Sharon, Chief Financial Officer, Clifton Springs Hospital And Clinic, Clifton Springs, NY, p. A424

KELLEY, Steven L., President and Chief Executive Officer, Ellenville Regional Hospital, Ellenville, NY, p. A426

KELLEY, Sue, Chief Financial Officer, Cordell Memorial Hospital, Cordell, OK, p. A497

KELLEY, Thomas J., Executive Vice President and Chief Financial Officer, Froedtert South - St. Catherine's Medical Center, WI, p. A695

KELLEY, Vicky, Chief Financial Officer, Dequincy Memorial Hospital, Dequincy, LA, p. A267

KELLEY, Warren, Chief Information Officer, Reynolds Memorial Hospital, Glen Dale, WV, p. A683

KELLIHER, Brandon, Chief Information Officer, Great Plains Health, North Platte, NE, p. A387

KELLOGG, Benjamin, M.D., Chief of Staff, Rhea Medical Center, Dayton, TN, p. A569

KELLOGG, Brewster, D.O., Chief Medical Officer, Rawlins County Health Center, Atwood, KS, p. A232

KELLOGG, Jason, M.D., Chief of Staff, Newport Bay Hospital, Newport Beach, CA, p. A75

KELLOGG, Susan, Administrator Patient Care Services, Carthage Area Hospital, Carthage, NY, p. A424

KELLS, Anne, Interim Chief Financial Officer, Appleton Area Health Services, Appleton, MN, p. A327

KELLUM, Craig, Director Management Information Systems, Cape Fear Valley - Bladen County Hospital, Elizabethtown, NC, p. A452

KELLY, Brian, M.D.
   Vice President Medical Affairs and Medical Director, Sturdy Memorial Hospital, Attleboro, MA, p. A295
   Acting Chief Fiscal Service, San Francisco Va Medical Center, San Francisco, CA, p. A86
   Vice President Finance, Advocate South Suburban Hospital, Hazel Crest, IL, p. A185

KELLY, Brian E., M.D., President Medical Staff, Saint Elizabeth's Medical Center, Wabasha, MN, p. A341

KELLY, Charlene, Chief Nursing Officer, Kane County Hospital, Kanab, UT, p. A647

KELLY, Charles, D.O., Vice President Medical Affairs and Chief Medical Officer, St. Joseph's Mercy-North, MI, p. A310

KELLY, Colan, Chief Financial Officer, Southeastern Kentucky Medical Center, Pineville, KY, p. A259

KELLY, Dan, R.N., Chief Nursing Officer, Memorial Hermann Memorial City Medical Center, Houston, TX, p. A612

KELLY, Daniel R., Chief Executive Officer, Mckenzie County Healthcare System, Watford City, ND, p. A469

KELLY, Diane, Chief Operating Officer, Greenwich Hospital, Greenwich, CT, p. A108

KELLY, Edward, Chief Executive Officer and President, Whitinsville Medical Center, MA, p. A302

KELLY, James J., Jr, Senior Vice President and Chief Financial Officer, Uf Health Shands Rehab Hospital, FL, p. A124

KELLY, James P., FACHE, Administrator, Community Behavioral Health Hospital - Annandale, Annandale, MN, p. A327

KELLY, Jennifer, Chief Executive Officer, Virginia Beach Psychiatric Center, Virginia Beach, VA, p. A667

KELLY, Jim, Chief Operating Officer, Nantucket Cottage Hospital, Nantucket, MA, p. A302

KELLY, John, R.N., Chief Nursing Officer and Chief Operating Officer, Umass Memorial-Marlborough Hospital, Marlborough, MA, p. A301

KELLY, Kecia, R.N., Chief Nurse Executive, Kaiser Permanente Medical Center, Honolulu, HI, p. A164

KELLY, Laurence E., President and Chief Executive Officer, Nathan Littauer Hospital And Nursing Home, Gloversville, NY, p. A427

KELLY, Leo, Vice President Medical Management, Advocate Lutheran General Hospital, Park Ridge, IL, p. A192

KELLY, Mark
  Administrator, Regional One Health Extended Care Hospital, Memphis, TN, p. A575
  Vice President Finance, St. Francis Medical Center, Trenton, NJ, p. A413

KELLY, Maura, Vice President Fiscal Services, Pen Bay Medical Center, Rockport, ME, p. A286

KELLY, Melissa, Chief Executive Officer and Chief Financial Officer, Pender Community Hospital, Pender, NE, p. A389

KELLY, Michael
  Vice President Operations, Missouri Baptist Medical Center, Saint Louis, MO, p. A368
  Vice President, Christian Hospital, Saint Louis, MO, p. A368

KELLY, Patrick J., FACHE, Director, Minneapolis Veterans Affairs Health Care System, Minneapolis, MN, p. A335

KELLY, Peter, President, Putnam Hospital Center, Carmel, NY, p. A424

KELLY, Ray, R.N., MSN, Vice President Chief Nursing Officer, Texas Health Springwood, TX, p. A588

KELLY, Robert E., M.D., President, New York Presbyterian Lower Manhattan Hospital, NY, p. A434

KELLY, Shannon, Director Human Resources, Morton General Hospital, Morton, WA, p. A673

KELLY, Stephen, M.D., Chief Medical Officer, Ssm Health St. Mary's Hospital - St. Louis, Saint Louis, MO, p. A368

KELLY, Steve, Interim Chief Executive Officer, Austin Oaks Hospital, Austin, TX, p. A585

KELLY, Teresa M, MSN, R.N., Chief Nursing Officer, Chestnut Hill Hospital, Philadelphia, PA, p. A534

KELLY, Vicky, Chief Financial Officer, De Queen Medical Center, De Queen-Sevier County, AR, p. A41

KELLY, Virginia, Chief Financial Officer, Eastside Psychiatric Hospital, Tallahassee, FL, p. A140

KELMAN, Gregory, M.D., Area Medical Director, Kaiser Permanente Woodland Hills Medical Center, Los Angeles, CA, p. A67

KEM, Mark, Vice President Finance and Chief Financial Officer, Chandler Regional Medical Center, Chandler, AZ, p. A28

KEMKER, S E, M.D., President Medical Staff, St. Vincent Salem Hospital, Salem, IN, p. A214

KEMMERER, Jan, Director of Nursing, Mitchell County Hospital Health Systems, Beloit, KS, p. A232

KEMP, Marlo, Vice President and Chief Financial Officer, Roseland Community Hospital, Chicago, IL, p. A179

KEMP, Susie, Chief Financial Officer, Fulton State Hospital, Fulton, MO, p. A359

KEMPF, Gary L., R.N., Administrator, Houston Methodist Continuing Care Hospital, Katy, TX, p. A616

KEMPIAK, Matthew, Director Human Resources and Administrative Services, Memorial Hospital Of Gardena, Gardena, CA, p. A60

KEMPINSKI, Paul D, Chief Operating Officer, Alfred I. Dupont Hospital For Children, Wilmington, DE, p. A114

KEMPTON, Matthew, Chief Executive Officer and Administrator, Stephens Memorial Hospital, Breckenridge, TX, p. A590

KENAGY, John Jay, Ph.D.
  Senior Vice President and Chief Information Officer, Legacy Meridian Park Medical Center, Tualatin, OR, p. A518
  Senior Vice President and Chief Information Officer, Legacy Mount Hood Medical Center, Gresham, OR, p. A513

KENAGY, Rob, M.D., Senior Vice President and Chief Medical Officer, Stormont Vail Health, Topeka, KS, p. A246

KENDALL, Abigail, Chief Nursing Officer, Lake Granbury Medical Center, Granbury, TX, p. A607

KENDALL, Anthony
  Vice President Human Resources, Baptist Health Extended Care Hospital, Little Rock-Pulaski County, AR, p. A44
  Vice President Human Resources, Baptist Health Medical Center-Arkadelphia, Arkadelphia, AR, p. A39
  Vice President Human Resources, Baptist Health Medical Center-Little Rock, Little Rock-Pulaski County, AR, p. A45
  Vice President Human Resources, Baptist Health Rehabilitation Institute, Little Rock-Pulaski County, AR, p. A45

KENDALL, Clint, R.N., Chief Nursing Officer, Clinch Valley Medical Center, Richlands, VA, p. A664

KENDALL, Dorothy, Medical Director, William J. Mccord Adolescent Treatment Facility, Orangeburg, SC, p. A556

KENDLE, Melinda
  Director Fiscal Management, Evansville State Hospital, Evansville, IN, p. A203
  Manager Business Office, Evansville Psychiatric Children Center, Evansville, IN, p. A203

KENDLER, Lisa
  Chief Financial Officer, Memorial Hermann Memorial City Medical Center, Houston, TX, p. A612
  Chief Financial Officer, Memorial Hermann Sugar Land Hospital, Sugar Land, TX, p. A637

KENDRICK, Donovan, M.D., Chief Medical Officer, Baptist Medical Center South, Montgomery, AL, p. A21

KENDRICK, Gary G., FACHE, Interim Chief Executive Officer, Nacogdoches Memorial Hospital, Nacogdoches, TX, p. A625

KENDRICK, Ray, Chief Human Resources Officer, Memorial Hospital Miramar, Miramar, FL, p. A132

KENINGER, Luke, Information Technology Client Leader, Winona Health, Winona, MN, p. A342

KENNEDY, Anita J, Vice President Operations, Methodist Hospital Of Sacramento, Sacramento, CA, p. A82

KENNEDY, Carol, Chief Clinical Officer, Barrett Hospital & Healthcare, Dillon, MT, p. A375

KENNEDY, Connie, Director Human Resources, Marlette Regional Hospital, Marlette, MI, p. A318

KENNEDY, Darla, Chief Information Officer, Foothill Regional Medical Center, Tustin, CA, p. A92

KENNEDY, Diana, Director Human Resources, Meadowview Regional Medical Center, Maysville, KY, p. A257

KENNEDY, Eric, Chief Executive Officer, Arbour Hospital, Boston, MA, p. A295

KENNEDY, Jack L, R.N., MS, Vice President and Chief Nursing Officer, Pratt Regional Medical Center, Pratt, KS, p. A244

KENNEDY, Jessica, D.O., Chief Medical Officer, Adair County Health System, Greenfield, IA, p. A223

KENNEDY, Jill M, R.N., Vice President, Ambulatory Patient Care Services, Bon Secours Memorial Regional Medical Center, Mechanicsville, VA, p. A661

KENNEDY, John, M.D., Vice President of Medical Affairs, Mercy Health - Fairfield Hospital, Fairfield, OH, p. A482

KENNEDY, Kay, Chief Nurse Executive, Wellstar Cobb Hospital, Austell, GA, p. A148

KENNEDY, Kimberly, Manager Human Resources, Osf Saint Paul Medical Center, Mendota, IL, p. A189

KENNEDY, Larkin, Chief Executive Officer, Rush Foundation Hospital, Meridian, MS, p. A350

KENNEDY, Nancy A., M.D., Chief Medical Officer, Highpoint Health, Lawrenceburg, IN, p. A210

KENNEDY, Peter, Chief Operating Officer, Northside Hospital, Saint Petersburg, FL, p. A138

KENNEDY, R. Scott, M.D., Chief Medical Officer and Safety Officer, Olympic Medical Center, Port Angeles, WA, p. A675

KENNEDY, Ryan
  Chief Financial Officer, Holy Name Medical Center, Teaneck, NJ, p. A412
  Chief Operating Officer, Kingman Regional Medical Center, Kingman, AZ, p. A30

KENNEDY, Tiffany, Chief Nursing Officer, Breckinridge Memorial Hospital, Hardinsburg, KY, p. A253

KENNEDY, Timea, Director Human Resources, St. Mary-Corwin Medical Center, Pueblo, CO, p. A105

KENNEDY, Todd S., President and Chief Executive Officer, Providence Hospital, Mobile, AL, p. A20

KENNEMER, Darline, Controller, Methodist Rehabilitation Hospital, Dallas, TX, p. A597

KENNETT, Jerry, M.D., Chief Medical Officer, Boone Hospital Center, Columbia, MO, p. A358

KENNEY, Mary Ellen, Chief Human Services, Manchester Veterans Affairs Medical Center, Manchester, NH, p. A400

KENNEY, Ronda, Chief Operating Officer, Eastern State Hospital, Medical Lake, WA, p. A673

KENNINGTON, Lynn, Chief Financial Officer, Alaska Regional Hospital, Anchorage, AK, p. A25

KENNISON, Barbara, Director Clinical Services, Aurora Behavioral Healthcare San Diego, San Diego, CA, p. A83

KENNY, Carolyn, Executive Vice President Clinical Care, Children's Healthcare Of Atlanta At Scottish Rite, GA, p. A146

KENNY, Virginia, Chief Nursing Officer, Hancock Medical Center, Bay Saint Louis, MS, p. A343

KENSINGER, Brooke, Chief Executive Officer, Central Community Hospital, Elkader, IA, p. A222

KENT, Alan, Chief Executive Officer, Meadows Regional Medical Center, Vidalia, GA, p. A162

KENT, David, M.D.
  Chief Medical Officer, Safe Haven Hospital Of Treasure Valley, Boise, ID, p. A167
  Chief Operating Officer, Southeastern Regional Medical Center, Newnan, GA, p. A158

KENT, Robert, D.O., President and Chief Executive Officer, Western Reserve Hospital, Cuyahoga Falls, OH, p. A480

KENTERA, Amy, Chief Information Officer, Conifer Park, Glenville, NY, p. A427

KENTFIELD, Melinda Johanna, R.N., Director of Nursing and Interim Chief Nursing Officer, Fremont Health, Fremont, NE, p. A384

KENTON, Bart, Chief Financial Officer, Holton Community Hospital, Holton, KS, p. A237

KENWOOD, Linda S, R.N., MSN, Chief Nursing Officer and Chief Operating Officer, Shore Medical Center, Somers Point, NJ, p. A411

KEOWN, Janet, Vice President Human Resources, Behavioral Health Network, Natchaug Hospital, Mansfield Center, CT, p. A108

KEPLINGER, Ron, Chief Information Officer, Western Maryland Hospital Center, Hagerstown, MD, p. A292

KEPNER, Donald L, Chief Financial Officer, Ashtabula County Medical Center, Ashtabula, OH, p. A471

KEPPLE, Jeffrey, M.D., Chief Executive Officer, Plumas District Hospital, Quincy, CA, p. A79

KEPPLER, Edward L., M.D., Chief Medical Officer, Marion General Hospital, Marion, IN, p. A211

KEPSHIRE, Bob, R.N., MS, Administrator and Chief Nursing Officer, University Hospital Mcduffie, Thomson, GA, p. A162

KERBS, Curtis, Regional Chief Information Officer, Memorial Hospital, North Conway, NH, p. A400

KERCHENSKI, Marlene, Chief Nurse, U.S. Air Force Hospital, Hampton, VA, p. A659

KERI, Alison, Director Human Resources, Hiawatha Community Hospital, Hiawatha, KS, p. A236

KERIAN-MASTERS, RN, Carol, Chief Nursing Officer, Regional Health Services Of Howard County, Cresco, IA, p. A220

KERLIN, Kerry, Chief Information Officer, Roswell Park Cancer Institute, Buffalo, NY, p. A423

KERMEN, John, D.O., Chief Medical Staff, Mendocino Coast District Hospital, Fort Bragg, CA, p. A58

KERN, Daniel, Chief Executive Officer, Strategic Behavioral Health - Wilmington, Leland, NC, p. A456

KERN, Douglas W., Chief Executive Officer, Northcoast Behavioral Healthcare, Northfield, OH, p. A488

KERN, Gordon, M.D., Medical Director, Oswego Community Hospital, Oswego, KS, p. A243

KERN, Howard P
  Chief Operating Officer, Sentara Princess Anne Hospital, Virginia Beach, VA, p. A667
  President and Chief Operating Officer, Sentara Leigh Hospital, Norfolk, VA, p. A662

KERNAN, Jacqueline D., President, Osf Saint Luke Medical Center, Kewanee, IL, p. A187

KERNDL, John, Executive Vice President and Chief Financial Officer, Beaumont Children's Hospital, MI, p. A322

KERNELL, Shane, Chief Executive Officer, Graham Regional Medical Center, Graham, TX, p. A607

KERNIVAN, Lina, Chief Operating Officer, Palms West Hospital, Loxahatchee, FL, p. A128

KERNS, Elizabeth, Senior Vice President and Chief Information Officer, Lakeland Regional Health Medical Center, Lakeland, FL, p. A127

KEROACK, Mark A., M.D., M.P.H., President and Chief Executive Officer, Baystate Health, Baystate Children's Hospital, MA, p. A304

KERR, Jeff, M.D., Chief Medical Officer, Baylor Medical Center At Mckinney, Mckinney, TX, p. A623

KERR, Karen, R.N., President, South Florida Baptist Hospital, Plant City, FL, p. A136

KERR, Michael D, Chief Executive Officer, Promise Hospital Of East Los Angeles, Suburban Medical Center Campus, CA, p. A69

KERR, Michael D.
  Chief Executive Officer, Kindred Hospital South Bay, Gardena, CA, p. A60
  Chief Executive Officer, Promise Hospital Of East Los Angeles, Suburban Medical Center Campus, CA, p. A69

KERRINS, David, Vice President Information Services and Chief Information Officer, Dameron Hospital, Stockton, CA, p. A90

KERRWOOD, Patrick, Chief Executive Officer, Siloam Springs Regional Hospital, Siloam Springs-Benton County, AR, p. A48

KERSCHEN, Susan, MS, R.N., Vice President and Chief Nursing Officer, Good Samaritan Medical Center, Lafayette, CO, p. A102

KERSTETTER, Kathleen, R.N., MSN, Chief Clinical Officer, Acuity Specialty Hospital Of New Jersey, Atlantic City, NJ, p. A402

KERSTING, Clay, M.D., Chief Medical Staff, Newport Hospital And Health Services, Newport, WA, p. A674

KERSWILL, Randy, M.D., Medical Director, Winnebago Mental Health Institute, Winnebago, WI, p. A706

KERWIN, George, President and Chief Executive Officer, Bellin Memorial Hospital, Green Bay, WI, p. A693

KERWOOD, Christine, Chief Nursing Officer, East Ohio Regional Hospital, Martins Ferry, OH, p. A486

KERWOOD, Lori A, Director Human Resources, Cooley Dickinson Hospital, Northampton, MA, p. A303

KESSEL, Jennifer, Chief Executive Officer, Aultman Orrville Hospital, Orrville, OH, p. A488

KESSLER, Alexander, M.D., Chief of Staff, Northside Hospital-Cherokee, Canton, GA, p. A149

KESSLER, David, M.D., Clinical Director, U.S. Public Health Service Indian Hospital, Zuni, NM, p. A420

KESSLER, Jeffrey R, Vice President Information Services, Dana-Farber Cancer Institute, Boston, MA, p. A296

KESSLER, Joseph, Executive Vice President and Chief Financial Officer, Women And Children's Hospital, NY, p. A423

KESSNER, Jennifer, Financial Director, Roosevelt Medical Center, Culbertson, MT, p. A374

KESTER, Bonnie J, R.N., MSN, Vice President Patient Care Services and Chief Nursing Officer, Nantucket Cottage Hospital, Nantucket, MA, p. A302

KESTERSON, Matt
Director Information Services, Wadley Regional Medical Center At Hope, Hope-Hempstead County, AR, p. A43
Director Information Services, Wadley Regional Medical Center, Texarkana, TX, p. A639

KETCH, Lynn
Human Resources Recruiter Generalist, Integris Canadian Valley Hospital, Yukon, OK, p. A510
Regional Director Integris Southwest Medical Center, Integris Southwest Medical Center, Oklahoma City, OK, p. A503

KETCHAM, Krista, Chief Financial Officer, Buena Vista Regional Medical Center, Storm Lake, IA, p. A230

KETCHAM, Michael
Chief Medical Officer, Mountain View Regional Medical Center, Norton, VA, p. A663
President, Medical Staff, Lonesome Pine Hospital, Big Stone Gap, VA, p. A655

KETCHEM, Tami, Human Resource Director, Up Health System-Bell, Ishpeming, MI, p. A316

KETTERHAGEN, James P, M.D., Senior Vice President and Chief Medical Officer, Frazier Rehab Institute, KY, p. A256

KETTERING, Lisa, Chief Medical Officer, Uchealth Yampa Valley Medical Center, Steamboat Springs, CO, p. A105

KETTERLING, Kimberly A., R.N., Vice President of Nursing, Chi Oakes Hospital, Oakes, ND, p. A468

KETTERMAN, Patricia P., R.N., President and Chief Administrative Officer, Claiborne Medical Center, Tazewell, TN, p. A580

KETTLER, Paul, M.D., Vice President Medical Affairs, Fairview Ridges Hospital, Burnsville, MN, p. A329

KETTNER, Mark, Interim Chief Executive Officer, Eastern State Hospital, Medical Lake, WA, p. A673

KEY, Jennifer, Chief Nursing Officer, Piedmont Newnan Hospital, Newnan, GA, p. A158

KEY, Lora, Chief Executive Officer, Sabetha Community Hospital, Sabetha, KS, p. A245

KEYONNIE, Christine, CPA, Chief Financial Officer, Tuba City Regional Health Care Corporation, Tuba City, AZ, p. A36

KEYS, Janice C., FACHE, Senior Vice President, Chief Nurse Executive, Willie D. Miller Eye Center, TN, p. A567

KHADE, Kashmira, Coordinator Non-Clinical Services, Behavioral Center Of Michigan, Warren, MI, p. A325

KHALEGHI, Trisha
Chief Executive Officer, Sharp Mcdonald Center, CA, p. A84
Senior Vice President and Chief Executive Officer, Sharp Mcdonald Center, CA, p. A84

KHALIQUE, Tania, Director Human Resources, Vibra Hospital Of San Diego, San Diego, CA, p. A85

KHAN, Atique, M.D., Medical Director, University Behavioral Health Of Denton, Denton, TX, p. A599

KHAN, Dan, M.D., Chief Medical Officer, Yoakum County Hospital, Denver City, TX, p. A599

KHAN, Faraz, Chief Financial Officer, Doctors Hospital Of Laredo, Laredo, TX, p. A619

KHAN, Humayun, M.D., Chief Medical Officer, Hshs Sacred Heart Hospital, Eau Claire, WI, p. A692

KHAN, Sarfraz, Medical Director, Meridian Health Services, Muncie, IN, p. A212

KHAN, Shahbaz, M.D., Medical Director, Two Rivers Behavioral Health System, Kansas City, MO, p. A362

KHAN, Waheed, M.D., President Medical Staff, Summers County Arh Hospital, Hinton, WV, p. A683

KHANCHANDANI, Ashok, Chief Financial Officer, Oroville Hospital, Oroville, CA, p. A77

KHANDELWAL, Ashish, M.D., Medical Director, Healthsouth Rehabilitation Hospital Of Middletown, Middletown, DE, p. A113

KHANNA, Rajive
Chief Executive Officer, Grace Hospital, Cleveland, OH, p. A476
Chief Executive Officer, Specialty Hospital Of Lorain, Amherst, OH, p. A470

KHARONOV, Arthur, Vice President Nursing, Columbus Hospital Ltach, Newark, NJ, p. A408

KHATAMI, Manoochehr, M.D., Medical Director, Hickory Trail Hospital, Desoto, TX, p. A600

KHATUA, Sanjeeb, M.D., Chief Medical Officer and Vice President, Edward Hospital, Naperville, IL, p. A190

KHAVKIN, Lisa, Vice President Human Resources, Huntington Hospital, Huntington, NY, p. A428

KHDOUR, Adel, M.D., Chief Medical Officer, Indiana University Health White Memorial Hospital, Monticello, IN, p. A211

KHEMKA, Hemant
Chief Financial Officer, Surgery Specialty Hospitals Of America, Pasadena, TX, p. A627
Chief Operating Officer, Surgery Specialty Hospitals Of America, Pasadena, TX, p. A627

KHIAMI, Ahmad, Chief of Staff, Beckley Arh Hospital, Beckley, WV, p. A681

KHIM FUGATE, Guay, Chief Operations Officer, Kindred Hospital Riverside, Perris, CA, p. A78

KHOERL, Thomas, Vice President Finance, Spectrum Health Big Rapids Hospital, Big Rapids, MI, p. A308

KHOO, Alex, Interim Area Finance Officer, Kaiser Permanente San Francisco Medical Center, San Francisco, CA, p. A85

KIBAR, Nizar, M.D., Chief Medical Staff, Kiowa County Memorial Hospital, Greensburg, KS, p. A236

KIBBY, Rosalinda, Superintendent and Administrator, Columbia Basin Hospital, Ephrata, WA, p. A671

KIDA, Sue, PT, MHA
President, Kessler Institute For Rehabilitation, NJ, p. A413
Chief Executive Officer, Kessler Institute For Rehabilitation, NJ, p. A413

KIDD, David, Manager Human Resources, Sentara Careplex Hospital, Hampton, VA, p. A659

KIDD, Monica, R.N., MSN, Administrator, Parkview Hospital, Wheeler, TX, p. A644

KIDD, Sabrina, M.D., Chief Medical Officer, Sonoma Valley Hospital, Sonoma, CA, p. A90

KIDD, Sue, Chief Financial Officer, Horton Community Hospital, Horton, KS, p. A237

KIDD, Thomas J., CPA, Chief Executive Officer, Macon Community Hospital, Lafayette, TN, p. A573

KIDDER, David M., D.O., Chief Medical Officer, Garfield County Health Center, Jordan, MT, p. A376

KIDDER, Suzanne F, Human Resources Officer, Opelousas General Health System-South Campus, LA, p. A277

KIEBZAK, Stanley F, R.N., Chief Nursing Officer, Encompass Health Rehabilitation Hospital The Vintage, Houston, TX, p. A610

KIEDROWSKI, Brian, M.D., Chief Medical Director, Miami Jewish Home And Hospital For Aged, Miami, FL, p. A130

KIEFER, William
Chief Nursing Officer, Tmc Bonham Hospital, Bonham, TX, p. A589
Chief Operating Officer, Rehoboth Mckinley Christian Health Care Services, Gallup, NM, p. A417

KIEFFER, Kelley
Chief Nursing Officer, Banner Baywood Medical Center, Mesa, AZ, p. A31
Chief Nursing Officer, Banner Heart Hospital, Mesa, AZ, p. A31

KIEHL, Tiffany, Chief Executive Officer, Mid-America Rehabilitation Hospital, Shawnee Mission, KS, p. A246

KIEHLE, Jessica, R.N., Chief Nursing Officer, Abilene Regional Medical Center, Abilene, TX, p. A582

KIELY, Sharon, M.D., Senior Vice President Medical Affairs and Chief Medical Officer, Stamford Hospital, Stamford, CT, p. A111

KIERNAN, Richard
Regional Chief Human Resources Officer, Monmouth Medical Center, Southern Campus, Lakewood, NJ, p. A406
Vice President Human Resources, Children's Hospital At Monmouth Medical Center, NJ, p. A407

KIGER, Tom, Director Information Systems, Trinity Medical Center West, OH, p. A491

KIGHT, Sheila, Director Human Resources, Tristar Horizon Medical Center, Dickson, TN, p. A569

KILARSKI, David J., FACHE, Chief Executive Officer, Firsthealth Moore Regional Hospital - Richmond, NC, p. A458

KILBORN, Mark, Director Information Systems, Springhill Memorial Hospital, Mobile, AL, p. A20

KILDAY, Kevin
Chief Financial Officer, Anna Jaques Hospital, Newburyport, MA, p. A302
Vice President Finance, Holy Family Hospital At Merrimack Valley, MA, p. A302

KILE, Steven E, Vice President Human Resources, Indiana University Health North Hospital, Carmel, IN, p. A201

KILEY, David, M.D., Vice President, Community Hospital South, Indianapolis, IN, p. A206

KILEY, Dennis, Interim President and Chief Executive Officer, Metroplex Behavioral Health Center, TX, p. A617

KILGORE, Julie, Vice President, Human Resources, Broadlawns Medical Center, Des Moines, IA, p. A221

KILLINGSWORTH, Meri, Chief Operating Officer, Hereford Regional Medical Center, Hereford, TX, p. A609

KILMER, Michael T., Director, Grand Junction Veterans Health Care System, Grand Junction, CO, p. A101

KILPATRICK, Von
Chief Nursing Officer, South Peninsula Hospital, Homer, AK, p. A26
Chief Nursing Officer, St. Vincent General Hospital District, Leadville, CO, p. A103

KIM, Donald, M.D., Chief Medical Officer, Memorial Regional Hospital South, FL, p. A124

KIM, Eric, Chief Information Officer, Las Encinas Hospital, Pasadena, CA, p. A78

KIM, Eugene P., M.D., Chief Medical Officer, St. Jude Medical Center, Fullerton, CA, p. A60

KIM, Hyon Su, M.D., Medical Director, Northlake Behavioral Health System, Mandeville, LA, p. A273

KIM, John, Chief Financial Officer, Anchor Hospital, Atlanta, GA, p. A145

KIMBALL, Kevin, Director Information Technology, Tlc Health Network - Lake Shore Hospital, NY, p. A425

KIMBALL, Mark E., Chief Executive Officer, Erlanger Murphy Medical Center, Murphy, NC, p. A457

KIMBALL, Tim, Chief Nursing Officer, Physicians' Specialty Hospital, Fayetteville-Washington County, AR, p. A41

KIMBLE, Becky, R.N., Chief Nursing Officer, Healthsouth Rehabilitation Hospital Of Jonesboro, Jonesboro-Craighead County, AR, p. A44

KIMBLE, D. Gay, Chief Human Resource Officer, Susan B. Allen Memorial Hospital, El Dorado, KS, p. A234

KIMBLE, Robert J., Chief Financial Officer, William R. Sharpe, Jr. Hospital, Weston, WV, p. A688

KIMBREW, Missey, Director Human Resources, Grafton City Hospital, Grafton, WV, p. A683

KIMBRO, George, Vice President Finance, Angel Medical Center, Franklin, NC, p. A452

KIMBROUGH, Pam, M.D., Vice President Medical Affairs, Mercy Hospital Ardmore, Ardmore, OK, p. A495

KIMMEL, Kyle, Chief Financial Officer, Bacon County Hospital And Health System, Alma, GA, p. A145

KIMMEL, Stephen, Chief Financial Officer, Cook Children's Medical Center, Fort Worth, TX, p. A604

KIMMES, Robert P., Chief Executive Officer, Skyline Hospital, White Salmon, WA, p. A680

KIMMET, Jackie, Chief Human Resource Officer, River's Edge Hospital And Clinic, Saint Peter, MN, p. A340

KIMPLE, Robin, Director Information Services, Wellspan Gettysburg Hospital, Gettysburg, PA, p. A526

KIMZEY, Mike, Chief Executive Officer and Administrator, Oklahoma Center For Orthopedic And Multi-Specialty Surgery, Oklahoma City, OK, p. A504

KINARD, Tifani, Administrator and Chief Nursing Officer, Polk Medical Center, Cedartown, GA, p. A150

KINCAID, Kevin, Chief Executive Officer, Knoxville Hospital & Clinics, Knoxville, IA, p. A225

KINCAID, Steve, Information Technology Manager, Eastern State Hospital, Lexington, KY, p. A254

KINDER, Barbara, R.N., Chief Clinical Officer, Clark Regional Medical Center, Winchester, KY, p. A261

KINDRED, Deanne, Vice President Finance, Baylor Regional Medical Center At Plano, Plano, TX, p. A628

KINDSCHI, Mark, Director Human Resources, Edgerton Hospital And Health Services, Edgerton, WI, p. A692

KING, Abner
Chief Executive Officer, Syringa Hospital And Clinics, Grangeville, ID, p. A169
Chief Operating Officer, Steele Memorial Medical Center, Salmon, ID, p. A172

KING, Beth, Chief Financial Officer, Jersey Community Hospital, Jerseyville, IL, p. A186

KING, Brent R, Chief Medical Officer and Chief Physician, Alfred I. Dupont Hospital For Children, Wilmington, DE, p. A114

KING, Bruce, President and Chief Executive Officer, New London Hospital, New London, NH, p. A400

KING, Chris, Director Information Services, Ohiohealth Marion General Hospital, Marion, OH, p. A486

KING, Christopher, Director Operations and Administrative Services, Matheny Medical And Educational Center, Peapack, NJ, p. A409

KING, Donna, R.N., FACHE, Vice President Clinical Operations and Chief Nursing Executive, Advocate Illinois Masonic Medical Center, Chicago, IL, p. A176

KING, Doug, M.D., Director Clinical Services, Western Mental Health Institute, Bolivar, TN, p. A566

KING, Glenn, R.N., MSN
Vice President and Chief Nursing Officer, Midmichigan Medical Center-Gladwin, Gladwin, MI, p. A313
Vice President, Chief Nursing Officer, Midmichigan Medical Center-Clare, Clare, MI, p. A310

KING, Heath, Chief Financial Officer, Orange Park Medical Center, Orange Park, FL, p. A133

KING, Janine, M.D., Chief of Staff, East Los Angeles Doctors Hospital, Los Angeles, CA, p. A66

KING, Jay, Vice President Human Resources, Mercy Southwest Hospital, CA, p. A52

KING, Jo Nell, Director of Nursing, Northlake Behavioral Health System, Mandeville, LA, p. A273

KING, Joanie, Chief Financial Officer, Carteret Health Care, Morehead City, NC, p. A457

KING, JoAnne, Chief Operating Officer, Florida Hospital Flagler, Palm Coast, FL, p. A135

KING, Katie, R.N., Chief Nursing Officer, Mountain View Hospital, Payson, UT, p. A649

KING, Katrina, R.N., Senior Director, Nursing, Novant Health Huntersville Medical Center, Huntersville, NC, p. A455

KING, Kim, Director Human Resources and Public Relations, Baptist Memorial Hospital-Huntingdon, Huntingdon, TN, p. A571

KING, Levi J., Director Human Resources, Conway Behavioral Health Hospital, Conway-Faulkner County, AR, p. A40

KING, Louie
Chief Executive Officer, Benefis Teton Medical Center, Choteau, MT, p. A374
President, Harry Bold Nursing Home Administrator, Missouri River Medical Center, Fort Benton, MT, p. A375

KING, Micheal, Controller, Spectrum Health Pennock, Hastings, MI, p. A315

KING, Paul, M.D., Medical Director, Parkwood Behavioral Health System, Olive Branch, MS, p. A351

KING, Paul A, Executive Director, C. S. Mott Children's Hospital, MI, p. A307

KING, Ray, M.D., Senior Vice President, Medical Affairs and Chief Medical Officer, Henry Ford Allegiance Health, Jackson, MI, p. A316

KING, Sam, Chief Financial Officer, Renown Children's Hospital, NV, p. A396

KING, Sammy, Controller, Healthsouth Rehabilitation Hospital Of Ocala, Ocala, FL, p. A133

KING, Sandra, Chief Nursing Officer, Sagamore Children's Hospital Psychiatric Center, Dix Hills, NY, p. A425

KING, Tamara, R.N., MSN, Chief Nurse Executive, Shepherd Center, Atlanta, GA, p. A147

KING, Val, Chief Information Officer, Val Verde Regional Medical Center, Del Rio, TX, p. A598

KINGHAM, Darrell L, CPA, Vice President Finance, Beauregard Health System, De Ridder, LA, p. A266

KINGRY, Jennifer, Chief Financial Officer, St. Vincent's Blount, Oneonta, AL, p. A22

KINGSLEY, Christi, Vice President Human Resources, West Calcasieu Cameron Hospital, Sulphur, LA, p. A280

KINGSTON, Eileen M, R.N., Nurse Executive, Associate Director Patient Care, Veterans Affairs Nebraska-Western Iowa Health Care System, Omaha, NE, p. A389

KINGSTON, Mary Beth, R.N., MSN, Executive Vice President and Chief Nursing Officer, Aurora Medical Center Of Oshkosh, Oshkosh, WI, p. A700

KINGSTON, Mary E., FACHE, R.N., Chief Executive, Peacehealth Sacred Heart Medical Center At Riverbend, Springfield, OR, p. A518

KINGSTON, Peggy, Chief Executive Officer, Select Specialty Hospital-Pontiac, Pontiac, MI, p. A321

KINI, M Narendra., M.D., President and Chief Executive Officer, Nicklaus Children's Hospital, Miami, FL, p. A130

KINKAID, Steve, Director Information Systems, St. Luke's - Palmerton Campus, PA, p. A530

KINLEN, Thomas, Superintendent, Larned State Hospital, Larned, KS, p. A239

KINMAN, Amanda, Director of Finance, Saint Joseph Mount Sterling, Mount Sterling, KY, p. A258

KINNAIRD, Adriene, Chief Executive Officer, Select Specialty Hospital Midtown Atlanta, Atlanta, GA, p. A147

KINNEER, James W, Vice President Organizational Development, Indiana Regional Medical Center, Indiana, PA, p. A528

KINNEMAN, Mary, R.N., MSN, Chief Nursing Officer, Vice President Patient Care Services, Norwood Hospital, Norwood, MA, p. A303

KINNEY, Janet, Chief Operating Officer, Northwest Florida Community Hospital, Chipley, FL, p. A119

KINSALA, Edeli, Chief Executive Officer, Sonora Behavioral Health Hospital, Tucson, AZ, p. A38

KINSEL, Mike, Controller, Federal Medical Center, Lexington, KY, p. A255

KINSELLA, Daniel F
Executive Vice President Information Technology, Northwestern Medicine Delnor Hospital, Geneva, IL, p. A184
Vice President and Chief Information Officer, Behavioral Health Center, IL, p. A198

KINSEY, Daniel, M.D., Medical Director, Oaklawn Psychiatric Center, Goshen, IN, p. A205

KINSEY, Wayne
Chief Executive Officer, Promise Hospital Of Phoenix, Mesa, AZ, p. A31
Chief Executive Officer, Promise Hospital Of Salt Lake, Salt Lake City, UT, p. A650

KINSLOW, Kathleen, Ed.D., Chief Executive Officer, Frankford Campus, PA, p. A535

KINTZ, Ronald J
Chief Financial Officer, Ira Davenport Memorial Hospital, Bath, NY, p. A422
Senior Vice President Finance and Chief Financial Officer, St. Joseph's Hospital, Elmira, NY, p. A426
Vice President and Treasurer, Arnot Ogden Medical Center, Elmira, NY, p. A426

KINYON, Craig C., President, Reid Health, Richmond, IN, p. A214

KINYON, David, Vice President of Operations and Outpatient Services, Asante Three Rivers Medical Center, Grants Pass, OR, p. A513

KINZIC, Elizabeth, M.D., Chief of Staff, Share Medical Center, Alva, OK, p. A495

KINZIE, Wesley, M.D., Chief of Staff, Stanislaus Surgical Hospital, Modesto, CA, p. A73

KIO, Kenneth, Manager Human Resources, Albany Stratton Veterans Affairs Medical Center, Albany, NY, p. A421

KIPP, Kris M, Executive Director, Patient Services and Chief Nursing Officer, James Cancer Hospital And Solove Research Institute, Columbus, OH, p. A478

KIRACOFE, Darin, Director Information Resource Management, Broughton Hospital, Morganton, NC, p. A457

KIRALY, Denise G, Director, Human Resources and Organization Development, Lima Memorial Health System, Lima, OH, p. A484

KIRBOW, Keith, R.N., Vice President and Chief Nursing Officer, Christus Good Shepherd Medical Center, TX, p. A622

KIRBY, Adrienne, Ph.D., FACHE, President and Executive Chairman/Chief Executive Chair, Childen's Regional Hospital At Cooper, NJ, p. A403

KIRBY, Brendan, M.D., Medical Director, Riverview Psychiatric Center, Augusta, ME, p. A282

KIRBY, Elizabeth A
Senior Director Human Resources, Aurora Baycare Medical Center, Green Bay, WI, p. A693
Senior Director Human Resources, Aurora Medical Center - Manitowoc County, Two Rivers, WI, p. A704

KIRBY, James M., II, President and Chief Executive Officer, Margaret R. Pardee Memorial Hospital, Hendersonville, NC, p. A454

KIRBY, John
Senior Vice President and Chief Financial Officer, Virtua Memorial, Mount Holly, NJ, p. A408
Senior Vice President and Chief Operating Officer, Virtua Memorial, Mount Holly, NJ, p. A408

KIRBY, Juliana Kay, R.N., MSN, Chief Nursing Officer, Adventist Health Medical Center - Tehachapi Valley, Tehachapi, CA, p. A91

KIRBY, Penny V, MSN, Chief Nursing Officer, Livingston Regional Hospital, Livingston, TN, p. A573

KIRBY, Ruby, Administrator, Bolivar General Hospital, Bolivar, TN, p. A566

KIRBY, Tracy
Assistant Vice President Business Relationship Management, Chi St. Vincent Hot Springs, Hot Springs-Garland County, AR, p. A43
Assistant Vice President Business Relationship Management, Chi St. Vincent Infirmary Medical Center, Little Rock-Pulaski County, AR, p. A45
Assistant Vice President Business Relationship Management, Chi St. Vincent Morrilton, Morrilton-Conway County, AR, p. A46

KIRCH, Cyndi
Vice President Human Resources, Mercy General Hospital, Sacramento, CA, p. A82
Vice President Human Resources, Methodist Hospital Of Sacramento, Sacramento, CA, p. A82

KIRCHER, Janelle, R.N., MSN, Chief Executive Officer, Kindred Hospital-Denver, Denver, CO, p. A99

KIRCHNER, Doris, President and Chief Executive Officer, Vail Health, Vail, CO, p. A106

KIRCHNER, Kent, M.D., Chief of Staff, G.V. (Sonny) Montgomery Veterans Affairs Medical Center, Jackson, MS, p. A348

KIRCHNER, Susan M, Director Human Resources, Four Winds Hospital, Saratoga Springs, NY, p. A442

KIRISITS, Christopher, Chief Nursing Officer, Rochester Psychiatric Center, Rochester, NY, p. A441

KIRITANI, Tracy, Vice President and Chief Financial Officer, Clovis Community Medical Center, Clovis, CA, p. A55

KIRK, Darlene, Manager Finance, U.S. Public Health Service Indian Hospital, Crownpoint, NM, p. A416

KIRK, Donald, M.D., Chief of Staff, Star Valley Medical Center, Afton, WY, p. A707

KIRK, H Lee., Jr, FACHE, Administrator, Shriners Hospitals For Children-Springfield, Springfield, MA, p. A304

KIRK, J. Douglas, M.D., Chief Medical Officer, University Of California Davis Children's Hospital, CA, p. A82

KIRK, Jean, Chief Financial Officer, Bennett County Hospital And Nursing Home, Martin, SD, p. A562

KIRK, Paul, Vice President, Woman's Hospital, Baton Rouge, LA, p. A264

KIRK, Peggy, Senior Vice President Clinical Operations, Shirley Ryan Abilitylab, Chicago, IL, p. A179

KIRK, Roger L, President and Chief Executive Officer, Bethesda Hospital West, FL, p. A118

KIRK, Roger L., President and Chief Executive Officer, Bethesda Hospital West, FL, p. A118

KIRK, Vanessa, Director of Nursing, Kiowa County Memorial Hospital, Greensburg, KS, p. A236

KIRK, Warren J., Chief Executive Officer, Doctors Medical Center Of Modesto, Modesto, CA, p. A72

KIRKBRIDE, James B., President and Chief Executive Officer, Susan B. Allen Memorial Hospital, El Dorado, KS, p. A234

KIRKER, Donna, R.N., MS, Vice President Patient Services and Chief Nursing Officer, Glens Falls Hospital, Glens Falls, NY, p. A427

KIRKER, Lynda I, Chief Financial Officer, Flagler Hospital, Saint Augustine, FL, p. A137

KIRKHAM, Brett, Chief Operating Officer, Integris Deaconess, Oklahoma City, OK, p. A502

KIRKHAM, Paul, Chief Executive Officer, Newport News Behavioral Health Center, Newport News, VA, p. A662

KIRKLAND-ROSE, Tina, Coordinator Human Resources, Select Specialty Hospital-Lexington, Lexington, KY, p. A255

KIRKLEY, Scott, M.D., BJC CHief Medical Officer Group Liaison, Parkland Health Center - Farmington Community, Farmington, MO, p. A359

KIRKPATRICK, Brett, Executive Director, Mccullough-Hyde Memorial Hospital/Trihealth, Oxford, OH, p. A489

KIRKPATRICK, Kyle
Chief Executive Officer, Baylor Emergency Medical Center Murphy, TX, p. A585
Chief Executive Officer, Baylor Emergency Medical Centers - Colleyville, TX, p. A585
Chief Executive Officer, Baylor Emergency Medical Centers - Keller, TX, p. A585
Chief Executive Officer, Baylor Emergency Medical Centers - Mansfield, TX, p. A591
Chief Executive Officer, Baylor Emergency Medical Centers - Rockwall, Rockwall, TX, p. A630
Chief Executive Officer, Baylor Scott & White Emergency Medical Center- Cedar Park, Cedar Park, TX, p. A592

KIRKS, Linda, Vice President and Chief Financial Officer, Christus Santa Rosa-Medical Center, TX, p. A632

KIRMAN, Lynn, R.N., Chief Nursing Officer, St. John's Medical Center And Living Center, Jackson, WY, p. A708

KIRSHNER, Arthur N, Chief Information Management, Winn Army Community Hospital, Hinesville, GA, p. A155

KIRSHNER, David L., Chief Financial Officer, Golisano Children's Hospital, NY, p. A441

KIRSTEIN, Susan N., R.N., MSN, Chief Nursing Officer, Broadlawns Medical Center, Des Moines, IA, p. A221

KIRTON, Carl, Ph.D., Chief Nursing Officer, University Hospital, Newark, NJ, p. A409

KISACKY, Christina A, Vice President, Operations, Uhs Chenango Memorial Hospital, Norwich, NY, p. A438

KISER, Greg, Chief Executive Officer, Three Rivers Medical Center, Louisa, KY, p. A255

KISER, Harrison, Chief Operating Officer, Saint Thomas West Hospital, Nashville, TN, p. A577

KISER, James R., II, Chief Executive Officer, Montrose Memorial Hospital, Montrose, CO, p. A104

KISER, Pamela, R.N., MS, Chief Nursing Executive and Vice President of Nursing, St. John Medical Center, Tulsa, OK, p. A509

KISHNER, Janice, R.N., FACHE, Chief Clinical Officer, St. Bernard Parish Hospital, Chalmette, LA, p. A265

KISKADDON, Robert, M.D., Chief Medical Officer, Margaret R. Pardee Memorial Hospital, Hendersonville, NC, p. A454

KISNER, Angela, Director Human Resources and Coordinator Medical Staff, Landmark Hospital Of Cape Girardeau, Cape Girardeau, MO, p. A356

KISS, Meredith, Administrator, Elgin Mental Health Center, Elgin, IL, p. A182

KISSNER, Michael, Chief Executive Officer, Healthsouth Treasure Coast Rehabilitation Hospital, Vero Beach, FL, p. A142

KISTLER, Beckie, Director of Finance, Our Lady Of Peace, Louisville, KY, p. A256

KISTNER, Kasondra, R.N., Chief Executive Officer, Warm Springs Rehabilitation Hospital Of Thousand Oaks, TX, p. A634

KITCH, Barrett, MD, Senior Vice President, Clinical Affairs and Chief Medical Officer, Emerson Hospital, Concord, MA, p. A299

KITCHEN, Steven, M.D., Chief Medical Officer, Phoebe North, GA, p. A145

KITTNER, Bonnie, R.N., Chief Nursing Officer, Mendocino Coast District Hospital, Fort Bragg, CA, p. A58

KJERGAARD, Holly, Chief Nursing Officer, Audubon County Memorial Hospital, Audubon, IA, p. A217

KJOSA, Ann Marie, R.N., MSN, Chief Nursing Officer, Eastern Idaho Regional Medical Center, Idaho Falls, ID, p. A169

KLAMFOTH, William E., Administrator, Christus Dubuis Hospital Of Port Arthur, TX, p. A588

KLANN, Andrew, D.O., Chief of Staff, Southwest Health Center Nursing Home, WI, p. A701

KLARNER, Lea Ann H., Chief Executive Officer, Continuecare Hospital At Madisonville, Madisonville, KY, p. A257

KLASEK, Chance, CPA, Chief Financial Officer, Jefferson Community Health And Life, Fairbury, NE, p. A383

KLASKO, Stephen K, M.D., President, Jefferson Methodist Hospital, PA, p. A536

KLASS, Cheryl, President, Women And Children's Hospital, NY, p. A423

KLASSEN, Brad, Information Technology Coordinator, Sanford Worthington Medical Center, Worthington, MN, p. A342

KLASSEN, Karen, Controller, Healthsouth Chattanooga Rehabilitation Hospital, Chattanooga, TN, p. A567

KLAUSTERMEIER, Lisa, R.N., MSN, Chief Nursing Officer, Anderson Hospital, Maryville, IL, p. A188

KLAWITTER, Kyle, Vice President Human Resources, Summa Saint Thomas Hospital, OH, p. A470

KLAY, Chris, President and Chief Executive Officer, Hshs St. Joseph's Hospital, Breese, IL, p. A174

KLEAM, Douglas V., President, St. Bernardine Medical Center, San Bernardino, CA, p. A83

KLEAS, Tara, Area Director Human Resources, Encompass Health Rehabilitation Hospital Of Fort Worth, Fort Worth, TX, p. A604

KLEEN, Kathy, Chief Nursing Officer, Tri-County Hospital, Wadena, MN, p. A341

KLEFFMAN, Angela, Director of Ancillary Services, Bigfork Valley Hospital, Bigfork, MN, p. A328

KLEHN, Paul, Chief Information Technology Officer, Liberty Hospital, Liberty, MO, p. A363

KLEIN, Aron
  Vice President Finance, Advocate Bromenn Regional Medical Center, IL, p. A191
  Vice President of Finance, Advocate Eureka Hospital, Eureka, IL, p. A182

KLEIN, Barbara, R.N., Director of Nursing, Arms Acres, Carmel, NY, p. A424

KLEIN, Bernard, M.D., Chief Executive, Providence Holy Cross Medical Center, Mission Hills, CA, p. A72

KLEIN, Cindy, Chief Executive Officer, Lamb Healthcare Center, Littlefield, TX, p. A620

KLEIN, Cindy C, Vice President Human Resources, Peacehealth St. Joseph Medical Center, Bellingham, WA, p. A669

KLEIN, David, Ph.D., Vice President Operations, Behavioral Health Network, Natchaug Hospital, Mansfield Center, CT, p. A108

KLEIN, David G., M.D., President, Saint Francis Memorial Hospital, San Francisco, CA, p. A85

KLEIN, Diany, Vice President Human Resources, Community Memorial Hospital, CA, p. A94

KLEIN, Edward A, Chief Financial Officer, Johnston Health, Smithfield, NC, p. A460

KLEIN, Jacqueline, Chief Financial Officer, Marshfield Medical Center - Rice Lake, Rice Lake, WI, p. A702

KLEIN, Jillyn, Chief Operating Officer, Howard County Medical Center, Saint Paul, NE, p. A390

KLEIN, Julie, Chief Operating Officer, Mckee Medical Center, Loveland, CO, p. A104

KLEIN, Kenneth, M.D., Vice President Medical Affairs, Beloit Health System, Beloit, WI, p. A690

KLEIN, Kyle, Assistant Chief Financial Officer, Mercy Health - West Hospital, Cincinnati, OH, p. A475

KLEIN, Perry, Chief Engineering, Mann-Grandstaff Veterans Affairs Medical Center, Spokane, WA, p. A678

KLEIN, Terrence, Ph.D., Vice President and Chief Operating Officer, Franciscan Health Crawfordsville, Crawfordsville, IN, p. A202

KLEINBECK, Seth M., M.D., Chief of Staff, Baptist Health Medical Center-Stuttgart, Stuttgart-Arkansas County, AR, p. A49

KLEINE, Doug, IT Director, St. Mary Medical Center, Apple Valley, CA, p. A51

KLEINHANZL, Thomas A., President and Chief Executive Officer, Frederick Regional Health System, Frederick, MD, p. A291

KLEINSASSER, Dustin, Information Technology and BioMed, Fall River Hospital, Hot Springs, SD, p. A561

KLEINSMITH, Carmen, MSN, R.N., Vice President, Chief Nurse Executive, Unitypoint Health - St. Luke's Hospital, Cedar Rapids, IA, p. A218

KLEINSTEUBER, Kathy, Chief Executive Officer, Rehabilitation Hospital Of Savannah, Savannah, GA, p. A160

KLENKE, Lisa R., R.N., Chief Executive Officer, Mercer Health, Coldwater, OH, p. A478

KLENNER, Susan, Chief Nursing Officer and Vice President of Hospital Operations, Olmsted Medical Center, Rochester, MN, p. A338

KLEPIN, Michael R, Administrator, Hunt Regional Medical Center, Greenville, TX, p. A608

KLESS, Adam
  Chief Nursing Officer, Highlands Regional Medical Center, Sebring, FL, p. A139
  Chief Nursing Officer, Raulerson Hospital, Okeechobee, FL, p. A133

KLESSENS, Thomas
  Chief Financial Officer, Landmark Medical Center-Woonsocket Unit, RI, p. A548
  Chief Financial Officer, Rehabilitation Hospital Of Rhode Island, North Smithfield, RI, p. A547

KLEVEN, Brian, Chief Financial Officer, St. Rose Dominican Hospitals - Siena Campus, Henderson, NV, p. A393

KLICKSTEIN, Judith S, Chief Information Officer, Whidden Memorial Hospital, MA, p. A298

KLIEWER, Chad, Information Technology Specialist, Mercy Hospital Kingfisher, Kingfisher, OK, p. A500

KLIMEK, David
  Chief Human Resources Officer, Miami County Medical Center, Paola, KS, p. A244
  Vice President Human Resources, Olathe Medical Center, Olathe, KS, p. A242

KLIMP, Mary J., FACHE, Interim Administrator, Mayo Clinic Health System In New Prague, New Prague, MN, p. A336

KLINE, Brian S, Vice President and Chief Financial Officer, Penn Highlands Dubois, Dubois, PA, p. A524

KLINE, Burke, Chief Executive Officer, Greeley County Health Services, Tribune, KS, p. A247

KLINE, Daniel B, Vice President, Site Administrator, St. Joseph's Wayne Hospital, NJ, p. A409

KLINE, Donald E., President and Chief Executive Officer, Mercy Health - St. Elizabeth Youngstown Hospital, Youngstown, OH, p. A494

KLINE, Jack, M.D., Chief of Staff, Mercy Medical Center-New Hampton, New Hampton, IA, p. A227

KLINE, Julie, Senior Vice President Patient Services, Adventist Health Sonora, Sonora, CA, p. A90

KLINE, Mark W, M.D., Physician in Chief, Texas Children's Hospital West Campus, TX, p. A613

KLINE, Melissa, Chief Nursing Officer, Metrohealth Medical Center, Cleveland, OH, p. A477

KLINGA, Maria, Director Management Information Systems, Silver Hill Hospital, New Canaan, CT, p. A109

KLINGEMAN, Jennifer, Director of Nursing, Chester Mental Health Center, Chester, IL, p. A176

KLINGENBERG, Pat, Director Human Resources, Towner County Medical Center, Cando, ND, p. A464

KLINGLER, Stacie, R.N., Vice President of Patient Services, Franciscan Health Rensselaer, Rensselaer, IN, p. A214

KLINGSEIS, Robert, Director Information Systems, Desert Regional Medical Center, Palm Springs, CA, p. A77

KLINK, Sheryl, Chief Financial Officer, Piedmont Hospital, Atlanta, GA, p. A146

KLINKER, Suzanne M., Director, Bay Pines Veterans Affairs Healthcare System, Bay Pines, FL, p. A117

KLINKNER, Donna M, Chief Financial Officer, Madelia Community Hospital, Madelia, MN, p. A334

KLOCK, Kathy, R.N., Senior Vice President Clinical Operations and Human Resources, Gundersen Lutheran Medical Center, La Crosse, WI, p. A695

KLOCKMAN, Dena, Chief Financial Officer, Ogallala Community Hospital, Ogallala, NE, p. A387

KLOCKO, Daniel, Vice President Human Resources, Kootenai Behavioral Health, ID, p. A169

KLOECKNER, Vicki, Director Human Resources, Hshs Holy Family Hospital In Greenville, Greenville, IL, p. A184

KLOEWER, Ron, Chief Information Officer, Montgomery County Memorial Hospital, Red Oak, IA, p. A228

KLOPFER, Anthony Rudy., FACHE, Director, Veterans Affairs Eastern Kansas Health Care System-Dwight D. Eisenhower Veterans Affairs Medical Center, KS, p. A246

KLOPP, Amanda, Director, Innovation and Clinical Integration, Penn State Health St. Joseph - Downtown Campus, PA, p. A539

KLOPPE, William, Chief Financial Officer, Geary Community Hospital, Junction City, KS, p. A238

KLOSTERMEIER, Janice, Senior Vice President and Chief Financial Officer, Valley Presbyterian Hospital, Los Angeles, CA, p. A70

KLUGE, Thomas S.
  President, Hampshire Memorial Hospital, Romney, WV, p. A686
  President, War Memorial Hospital, Berkeley Springs, WV, p. A681

KLUGHERZ, Greg, Vice President Corporate Services and Chief Financial Officer, St. Cloud Hospital, Saint Cloud, MN, p. A338

KNACKSTEDT, Cameron, D.O., Chief Medical Staff, Harlan County Health System, Alma, NE, p. A381

KNACKSTEDT, Nathan, D.O., Chief of Staff, Clara Barton Hospital, Hoisington, KS, p. A236

KNAK, Roger, Administrator and Chief Executive Officer, Fairview Regional Medical Center, Fairview, OK, p. A499

KNAPHEIDE, Debbie, MSN, Site Administrator, Chief Nursing Officer and Chief Operating Officer, Carondelet Holy Cross Hospital, Nogales, AZ, p. A32

KNAPIK, Steven, M.D., Chief of Staff, Bear Valley Community Hospital, Big Bear Lake, CA, p. A53

KNAPP, Brian A, Vice President Operations, Fairview Ridges Hospital, Burnsville, MN, p. A329

KNE, Tanya, M.D., Chief Medical Officer, Samaritan Behavioral Health Center-Desert Samaritan Medical Center, AZ, p. A31

KNECHT, Brian J, Chief Operating Officer, Regional Medical Center Of San Jose, San Jose, CA, p. A86

KNECHT, John, Chief Medical Staff, Linton Hospital, Linton, ND, p. A467

KNEDLER, Marie E., R.N., FACHE, President, Chi Health Mercy Council Bluffs, Council Bluffs, IA, p. A220

KNEELAND, Misty, Chief Medical Staff, Medical Center Of South Arkansas, El Dorado-Union County, AR, p. A41

KNEISEL, Kristin, Interim Director, Information Services, Alice Peck Day Memorial Hospital, Lebanon, NH, p. A399

KNEPP, Gary, D.O., Regional Chief Medical Officer and Chief Quality Officer, Unitypoint Health - Peoria, Peoria, IL, p. A193

KNEPP, Keith, M.D., President, UnityPoint Health - Methodist, UnityPoint Health - Proctor, UnityPoint Clinic, ProHealth Medical Group, Unitypoint Health - Peoria, Peoria, IL, p. A193

KNIEVEL, Lon, Chief Executive Officer, Osmond General Hospital, Osmond, NE, p. A389

KNIFFIN, Fred, M.D.
  Chief Executive Officer, Porter Medical Center, Middlebury, VT, p. A653
  Chief Medical Officer, Porter Medical Center, Middlebury, VT, p. A653

KNIGHT, Beth, Chief Nursing Officer, Nacogdoches Memorial Hospital, Nacogdoches, TX, p. A625

KNIGHT, Bethany, M.D., Chief of Staff, Izard County Medical Center, Calico Rock-Logan County, AR, p. A40

KNIGHT, Christopher D., Vice President Finance and Chief Financial Officer, Reid Health, Richmond, IN, p. A214

KNIGHT, Deana, Chief Executive Officer, Select Specialty Hospital-Greensboro, Greensboro, NC, p. A453

KNIGHT, Don, Assistant Administrator and Risk Manager, Teche Regional Medical Center, Morgan City, LA, p. A274

KNIGHT, Jennifer, Manager Human Resources, Waynesboro Hospital, Waynesboro, PA, p. A543

KNIGHT, Kimber, Chief Financial Officer, Braxton County Memorial Hospital, Gassaway, WV, p. A683

KNIGHT, Laura, Chief Nursing Officer, Merit Health Central, Jackson, MS, p. A348

KNIGHT, Mark T, Executive Vice President and Chief Financial Officer, Jackson South Community Hospital, FL, p. A130

KNIGHT, Michael, M.D., Medical Director, Hampstead Hospital, Hampstead, NH, p. A399

KNIGHT, Reginald Q., Chief Medical Officer, Aurelia Osborn Fox Memorial Hospital, Oneonta, NY, p. A439

KNIGHT, Ricardo, Interim Medical Director, Van Matre Healthsouth Rehabilitation Hospital, Rockford, IL, p. A195

KNIGHT, Ronny, President and Chief Executive Officer, The Connecticut Hospice, Branford, CT, p. A107

KNIGHT, Sue, CPA, Chief Operating Officer, St. Elizabeth Hospital, Gonzales, LA, p. A268

KNIGHT, Terry, Public Information Officer and Administrative Assistant, California Mens Colony Correctional Treatment Center, San Luis Obispo, CA, p. A87

KNIGHT, Warren, Chief Financial Officer, Baton Rouge Behavioral Hospital, Baton Rouge, LA, p. A263

KNIGHT, Wayne
Chief Financial Officer, Indiana University Health Frankfort, Frankfort, IN, p. A204
Director Finance, St. Vincent Clay Hospital, Brazil, IN, p. A200

KNIGHT, Wesley, Chief Financial Officer, Ut Health Henderson, Henderson, TX, p. A609

KNIPP, Cindi, Director Human Resources, Rooks County Health Center, Plainville, KS, p. A244

KNISLEY, Shane, Chief Operating Officer, Mercy Health - Fairfield Hospital, Fairfield, OH, p. A482

KNITT, Lori, Chief Nursing Officer, Aurora Sheboygan Memorial Medical Center, Sheboygan, WI, p. A702

KNITTEL, Monty E., Chief Executive Officer, Adventist Health Feather River, Paradise, CA, p. A77

KNOBLOCH, Stanley
Director Fiscal Services, Sanford Luverne Medical Center, Luverne, MN, p. A334
Director Fiscal Services, Sanford Rock Rapids Medical Center, Rock Rapids, IA, p. A228

KNOCKE, Michael, Chief Information Officer, Kansas Spine And Specialty Hospital, Wichita, KS, p. A247

KNODE, Scott, Chief Financial Officer, Veterans Memorial Hospital, Waukon, IA, p. A231

KNOEPFFLER, Susan, R.N., Vice President Nursing, Huntington Hospital, Huntington, NY, p. A428

KNOEPFLEIN, Susan, Chief Nurse Executive, Fulton State Hospital, Fulton, MO, p. A359

KNOEPFLER, David, M.D., Chief Medical Officer, Overlake Medical Center, Bellevue, WA, p. A669

KNOERL, Thomas, Vice President Finance, Spectrum Health Reed City Hospital, Reed City, MI, p. A321

KNORR, Kelly, Chief Financial Officer, First Hospital Wyoming Valley, Kingston, PA, p. A528

KNOWLES, B K, D.O., Chief of Staff, Pershing Memorial Hospital, Brookfield, MO, p. A356

KNOWLES, Christy, Chief Human Resources Officer, Coosa Valley Medical Center, Sylacauga, AL, p. A23

KNOWLES, John, Director Human Resources, Clinch Valley Medical Center, Richlands, VA, p. A664

KNOWLES, Robert, M.D., Chief of Staff, Saint Thomas Highlands Hospital, Sparta, TN, p. A580

KNOWLES-SMITH, Peter, M.D., Medical Director, Bennett County Hospital And Nursing Home, Martin, SD, p. A562

KNOX, Dennis M., Chief Executive Officer, Mid-Columbia Medical Center, The Dalles, OR, p. A518

KNOX, Jody, Chief Operating Officer, Kindred Hospital Rancho, Rancho Cucamonga, CA, p. A79

KNOX, John, Senior Vice President and Chief Information Officer, Carolinas Healthcare System University, Charlotte, NC, p. A449

KNOX, John E, FACHE, Chief Executive Officer, St. Luke's Baptist Hospital, TX, p. A632

KNOX, Jud, Chief Executive Officer, York Hospital, York, ME, p. A286

KNOX, Roland, Chief Executive Officer, Northern Cochise Community Hospital, Willcox, AZ, p. A38

KNOX, Stacey A., Administrator, Rock County Hospital, Bassett, NE, p. A381

KNUDSEN, Jessica, Chief Operating Officer and Director Performance Improvement and Risk Management, Holly Hill Hospital, Raleigh, NC, p. A459

KNUDSEN, Mark, Director Fiscal Services, Shriners Hospitals For Children-Portland, Portland, OR, p. A516

KNUDSEN, Matthew, Director, Information Systems, Sheppard Pratt Health System, Baltimore, MD, p. A289

KNUDSON, Jenny, Controller, Hiawatha Community Hospital, Hiawatha, KS, p. A236

KNUDTEN, Kristine, M.D., Vice President Medical Affairs, Glencoe Regional Health Services, Glencoe, MN, p. A332

KNUTH, Kerry, Chief Operating Officer, Mercy Hospital Of Defiance, Defiance, OH, p. A481

KNUTSON, Holly, Manager Information Technology, Kittson Memorial Healthcare Center, Hallock, MN, p. A332

KNUTSON, John P, M.D., Chief Medical Staff, Delta County Memorial Hospital, Delta, CO, p. A98

KNUTSON, Larry, Director Finance, Centracare Health-Long Prairie, Long Prairie, MN, p. A333

KO, Dicken S.C., M.D., Vice President of Medical Affairs and Chief Medical Officer, St. Elizabeth's Medical Center, Brighton, MA, p. A297

KO, Tommy, M.D., Chief Medical Officer, St. Joseph Medical Center, Kansas City, MO, p. A362

KOCH, Douglas E., Market President, Aurora Medical Center Kenosha, Kenosha, WI, p. A695

KOCH, Eric, Chief Nursing Officer, Northern Montana Health Care, Havre, MT, p. A376

KOCH, Holly, Chief Financial Officer, Girard Medical Center, Girard, KS, p. A235

KOCH, Jamie, R.N., Chief Nursing Officer, Thayer County Health Services, Hebron, NE, p. A384

KOCH, Joseph G., Chief Executive Officer, Meadowview Regional Medical Center, Maysville, KY, p. A257

KOCHIE, Daniel A, CPA
Chief Financial Officer, Samaritan Hospital, Troy, NY, p. A444
Chief Financial Officer, Seton Health System-St. Mary's Hospital, NY, p. A444

KOCHIS, Mary Ellen, MSN, R.N., Administrator Nursing Operations, Beaumont Hospital - Dearborn, Dearborn, MI, p. A310

KOCIOLA, Matthew, Senior Vice President and Chief Financial Officer, Somerset Hospital, Somerset, PA, p. A541

KOCOUREK, Cathie A., President, Aurora Medical Center - Manitowoc County, Two Rivers, WI, p. A704

KOCSIS, Dana
Vice President Nursing and Operations, Cleveland Clinic Akron General Lodi Hospital, Lodi, OH, p. A485
Vice President, Nursing and Operations, Cleveland Clinic Akron General Lodi Hospital, Lodi, OH, p. A485

KOCSIS, Violet, Chief Human Resources Officer, Hunterdon Medical Center, Flemington, NJ, p. A405

KOCZENT, Kurt, Executive Vice President and Chief Operating Officer, F. F. Thompson Hospital, Canandaigua, NY, p. A424

KODROFF, Kurt, M.D., Chief Executive Officer, Kingsbrook Jewish Medical Center, New York (Includes All Hospitals Located Within The Five Boroughs), NY, p. A433

KOEBKE, Troy L
Director Human Resources Management, Bellin Memorial Hospital, Green Bay, WI, p. A693
Director Human Resources, Bellin Psychiatric Center, Green Bay, WI, p. A693
Human Resource Director, Bellin Health Oconto Hospital, Oconto, WI, p. A700

KOEHLER, Amy, Director Human Resources, Hshs Good Shepherd Hospital, Shelbyville, IL, p. A195

KOELE, Craig, Chief Executive Officer, Cornerstone Hospital Of Oklahoma-Broken Arrow, OK, p. A501

KOENIG, Donald E., Jr
Chief Operating Officer, Mercy Health - St. Joseph Warren Hospital, Warren, OH, p. A492
Executive Vice President and Regional Chief Operating Officer, President, St. Elizabeth Youngstown Hospital, Mercy Health - St. Elizabeth Youngstown Hospital, Youngstown, OH, p. A494

KOENIG, Harris F., President and Chief Executive Officer, San Antonio Regional Hospital, Upland, CA, p. A93

KOENIG, Lori, Assistant Finance Director, Cleveland Clinic Avon Hospital, Avon, OH, p. A471

KOENIG, Mary, Chief Financial Officer, Vernon Memorial Healthcare, Viroqua, WI, p. A704

KOEPKE, Eldon, Chief Financial Officer, Mitchell County Hospital Health Systems, Beloit, KS, p. A232

KOEPKE, Jennifer, R.N., Vice President of Patient Care Services and Chief Nursing Officer, Western Missouri Medical Center, Warrensburg, MO, p. A371

KOEPPEL-OLSEN, Carol, Vice President, Patient Care Services, Winter Haven Hospital, Winter Haven, FL, p. A144

KOERNER, Jill, Manager Employee Relations, Weisman Children's Rehabilitation Hospital, Marlton, NJ, p. A407

KOESSL, Brenda, R.N., Director of Nursing Services, Frances Mahon Deaconess Hospital, Glasgow, MT, p. A375

KOESTER, Jean, Manager Human Resources, Limestone Medical Center, Groesbeck, TX, p. A608

KOESTERER, Susan, Vice President, Finance, Alton Memorial Hospital, Alton, IL, p. A173

KOETHE, Lori, MS, Vice President of Nursing and Chief Nursing Officer, Magruder Memorial Hospital, Port Clinton, OH, p. A489

KOETTING, Edward, Chief Financial Officer, Bedford Veterans Affairs Medical Center, Edith Nourse Rogers Memorial Veterans Hospital, Bedford, MA, p. A295

KOHANKE, Crystal H, Group Vice President, Human Resources, Christus Santa Rosa-Medical Center, TX, p. A632

KOHL, Randy T., M.D., Deputy Director, Health Services, Nebraska Penal And Correctional Hospital, Lincoln, NE, p. A386

KOHLENBERG, Chris, Chief Financial Officer, Lafayette Surgical Specialty Hospital, Lafayette, LA, p. A271

KOHLER, Douglas, M.D., Vice President Medical Operations, Marymount Hospital, Garfield Heights, OH, p. A483

KOHLER, Tracy
Chief Executive Officer, Kindred Hospital Spring, TX, p. A640
Chief Executive Officer, Kindred Hospital-Bay Area, TX, p. A612

KOHR, Kathy, Chief Financial Officer, Midmichigan Medical Center - West Branch, West Branch, MI, p. A326

KOHRER, Tammy, Director of Nursing-Acute, Wahiawa General Hospital, Wahiawa, HI, p. A166

KOINZAN, Leigh Jean, Director Finance, Boys Town National Research Hospital, Omaha, NE, p. A387

KOKJOHN, Bradley J, Chief Financial Officer, Fort Madison Community Hospital, Fort Madison, IA, p. A223

KOKJOHN, Vicki, Director Employee Relations, Fort Madison Community Hospital, Fort Madison, IA, p. A223

KOLACZ, Nicole, Chief Nursing Officer, Aultman Hospital Pediatric Services, OH, p. A473

KOLB, Andy, Chief Executive Officer, Stonewall Memorial Hospital, Aspermont, TX, p. A584

KOLB, Edward, M.D., Medical Director, Boys Town National Research Hospital, Omaha, NE, p. A387

KOLB, Pat, Manager Information Technology, Mcleod Health Clarendon, Manning, SC, p. A555

KOLHEDE, Deborah, Vice President and Chief Operating Officer, St. Mary's Medical Center, San Francisco, CA, p. A86

KOLLMEYER, Sherry, Vice President Human Resources, Youth Villages Inner Harbour Campus, Douglasville, GA, p. A152

KOLMAN, Bret, CPA, FACHE, Chief Executive Officer, Centerpoint Medical Center, Independence, MO, p. A360

KOLODZIEJCYK, Wanda S, Director Human Resources, Cuero Community Hospital, Cuero, TX, p. A595

KOLODZIEJCZYK, Clayton, Chief Financial Officer, Meadowview Regional Medical Center, Maysville, KY, p. A257

KOLOSKY, John A, Executive Vice President and Chief Operating Officer, H. Lee Moffitt Cancer Center And Research Institute, Tampa, FL, p. A140

KOLSETH, Shelley V, Chief Financial Officer, Memorial Hospital Of Tampa, Tampa, FL, p. A141

KOMAN, Stuart, Ph.D., President and Chief Executive Officer, Walden Behavioral Care, Waltham, MA, p. A305

KOMANDURI, Ramanujam, M.D., Chief of Staff, Veterans Affairs Southern Nevada Healthcare System, North Las Vegas, NV, p. A396

KOMAR, Ellen M, R.N., Vice President Patient Care Services and Chief Nursing Officer, Stamford Hospital, Stamford, CT, p. A111

KOME, Hunter, Campus President, Oconee Memorial Hospital, Seneca, SC, p. A556

KOMENDA, John, Chief Financial Officer, Hendricks Regional Health, Danville, IN, p. A202

KOMINS, Jeff, M.D., Chief Medical Officer, Mercy Philadelphia Hospital, PA, p. A524

KOMORNIK, Jeffrey, Director Human Resources, Milford Hospital, Milford, CT, p. A109

KONARSKI, Debbie, Interim Chief Financial Officer, Pottstown Hospital, Pottstown, PA, p. A539

KONECNE, Robin, Manager Human Resources, Kit Carson County Health Service District, Burlington, CO, p. A97

KONG, Mei, Chief Operating Officer, Nyc Health + Hospitals / Coney Island, New York (Includes All Hospitals Located Within The Five Boroughs), NY, p. A435

KONGARA, Rama, Chief Financial Officer, St. James Behavioral Health Hospital, Gonzales, LA, p. A268

KONIECZEK, Raymond, Chief Human Resources Officer, John F. Kennedy Memorial Hospital, Indio, CA, p. A62

KONKEL, Robert, Manager Finance, James A. Haley Veterans' Hospital-Tampa, Tampa, FL, p. A141

KONSAVAGE, Christian, M.D., Chief of Staff, Cumberland County Hospital, Burkesville, KY, p. A250

KONSKE, Paul, Chief Executive Officer, Bridgepoint Continuing Care Hospital, Marrero, LA, p. A273

KOOIMAN, Thomas, Chief Executive Officer, Granite Falls Health, Granite Falls, MN, p. A332

KOOKEN, Kyron J., MS
Chief Executive Officer, Kindred Hospital Dallas Central, Dallas, TX, p. A596
Chief Executive Officer, Kindred Hospital-Dallas, TX, p. A596

KOON, Rion, Chief Information Management Division, William Beaumont Army Medical Center, El Paso, TX, p. A603

KOOP, Steven, M.D., Chief Medical Officer, Medical Director, Gillette Children's Specialty Healthcare, Saint Paul, MN, p. A339

KOOVAKADA, Philip, Chief Executive Officer, Nacogdoches Medical Center, Nacogdoches, TX, p. A625

KOOYMAN, James, Human Resources Manager, Seneca Healthcare District, Chester, CA, p. A54

KOPEL, Samuel, M.D., Medical Director, Maimonides Infants And Children's Hospital Of Brooklyn, NY, p. A433

KOPFLE, Sue, Chief Human Resources Officer, Women's And Children's Hospital, MO, p. A358

KOPIN, Jeffrey D., Senior Vice President and Chief Medical Officer, Northwestern Medicine Lake Forest Hospital, Lake Forest, IL, p. A187

KOPITNIK, Thomas, Acting Chief Executive Officer, Mountain View Regional Hospital, Casper, WY, p. A707

KOPPELMAN, Benjamin
Interim President, Chi Lakewood Health, Baudette, MN, p. A328
President, Chi St. Joseph's Health, Park Rapids, MN, p. A337

KOPPENHAVER, Colleen, Interim Chief Financial Officer, Presence Resurrection Medical Center, Chicago, IL, p. A178

KOPPERUD, Gordon, Director Operations, Sanford Westbrook Medical Center, Westbrook, MN, p. A342

KORBEL, Tamara, Director Management Information Systems, Ridgeview Medical Center, Waconia, MN, p. A341

KORDAHL, Rebecca, R.N., Associate Director, Patient Care Services, William S. Middleton Memorial Veterans Hospital, Madison, WI, p. A696

KORDUCKI, Stanley R., President, Wood County Hospital, Bowling Green, OH, p. A472

KORDUPEL, Maureen
Director Information Technology Relationship Manager, Mercy Health - St. Elizabeth Boardman Hospital, Boardman, OH, p. A472
Director Relationship Manager, Mercy Health - St. Elizabeth Youngstown Hospital, Youngstown, OH, p. A494

KORF, Rick, Chief Financial Officer, Yuma District Hospital, Yuma, CO, p. A106

KORICH, Frank, FACHE
Senior Vice President, Operations, Finger Lakes Hospital, Geneva, NY, p. A426
Senior Vice President, Operations, Soldiers And Sailors Memorial Hospital Of Yates County, Penn Yan, NY, p. A440

KORKMAS, Ross, Chief Executive Officer, Alliancehealth Woodward, Woodward, OK, p. A510

KORN, Roy, M.D., Medical Director, Cobleskill Regional Hospital, Cobleskill, NY, p. A424

KORNBLATT, Lynne R, Chief Human Resources Officer, Einstein Medical Center Elkins Park, PA, p. A534

KORNFIELD, Lee, M.D., Medical Director, St. Luke's Rehabilitation Hospital, Boise, ID, p. A168

KOROLY, Marla, M.D., Chief Medical Officer and Senior Vice President Medical Affairs, Northern Westchester Hospital, Mount Kisco, NY, p. A430

KOROM, Nancy K
Chief Nursing Officer and Vice President, Children's Hospital Of Wisconsin-Fox Valley, Neenah, WI, p. A699
Chief Nursing Officer and Vice President, Children's Hospital Of Wisconsin, Milwaukee, WI, p. A698

KORPELA, Donita, R.N., Director of Patient Care Services, Mercy Hospital, Moose Lake, MN, p. A336

KORPIEL, Michael, FACHE, Chief Executive Officer, Mercy San Juan Medical Center, Carmichael, CA, p. A54

KORRELL, Charlene, Interim Chief Executive Officer, Weisbrod Memorial County Hospital, Eads, CO, p. A100

KORTE, Fred, Chief Financial Officer, Mclaren Flint, Flint, MI, p. A312

KORTEMEYER, Jay, Chief Executive Officer, Brynn Marr Hospital, Jacksonville, NC, p. A455

KORTH, Paul
Chief Executive Officer, Cookeville Regional Medical Center, Cookeville, TN, p. A568
Chief Financial Officer, Cookeville Regional Medical Center, Cookeville, TN, p. A568

KORTH, Susan, M.P.H., Ph.D., Vice President and Chief Operating Officer, Methodist Women's Hospital, NE, p. A388

KORTH-WHITE, Kirsten
Interim President, Munson Healthcare Grayling Hospital, Grayling, MI, p. A314
Vice President Physician Network and Ambulatory Service, Munson Healthcare Grayling Hospital, Grayling, MI, p. A314
Vice President Physician Network and Ambulatory Services, Munson Healthcare Grayling Hospital, Grayling, MI, p. A314

KOSANOVICH, John, M.D., Executive Vice President Physician Enterprise and Chief Executive Officer, Covenant Medical Group, Covenant Medical Center-Harrison, MI, p. A322

KOSANOVICH, John P, President, Watertown Regional Medical Center, Watertown, WI, p. A705

KOSE, William H, M.D., Vice President Quality and Medical Affairs, Bluffton Hospital, Bluffton, OH, p. A472

KOSEK, Kevin, Associate Director Operations, Iowa City Veterans Affairs Health Care System, Iowa City, IA, p. A224

KOSIER, Douglas D., Chief Executive Officer, Mason District Hospital, Havana, IL, p. A185

KOSLOW, Howard B, President and Chief Executive Officer, Promise Hospital Of Miss Lou, Vidalia, LA, p. A280

KOSMAN, Beth, Director Health Information Management, Ringgold County Hospital, Mount Ayr, IA, p. A226

KOSNIK, Linda, R.N., MSN, Chief Nursing Officer and Vice President, Patient Care Services, Sinai Hospital Of Baltimore, Baltimore, MD, p. A289

KOSNOSKY, David, M.D., Chief Medical Officer, University Hospitals Geauga Medical Center, Chardon, OH, p. A474

KOSTER, Tracy, Director Human Resources, Carlinville Area Hospital, Carlinville, IL, p. A175

KOSTERS, Gregory J, D.O., Chief Medical Officer, Osceola Community Hospital, Sibley, IA, p. A229

KOSTOK, Barbara, Manager Human Resources, Punxsutawney Area Hospital, Punxsutawney, PA, p. A539

KOSTURKO, MaryEllen, R.N., Senior Vice President Patient Care Operations and Chief Nursing Officer, Bridgeport Hospital, Bridgeport, CT, p. A107

KOSYLA, Gail, Chief Financial Officer and Senior Vice President Strategy, Hunterdon Medical Center, Flemington, NJ, p. A405

KOTIL, Drew, Director Information Technology, Crete Area Medical Center, Crete, NE, p. A383

KOTIN, Kathy, Chief Financial Officer, Banner - University Medical Center Phoenix, Phoenix, AZ, p. A33

KOTRBA, Mitchell, Chief Financial Officer, North Valley Health Center, Warren, MN, p. A341

KOTTENBROOK, Susan, Chief Executive Officer, Red River Behavioral Center, Bossier City, LA, p. A265

KOTTMANN, Bill, President and Chief Executive Officer, Edward Hospital, Naperville, IL, p. A190

KOUNS, Jaccel, R.N., MS, Vice President and Executive Director, Montefiore Mount Vernon, Mount Vernon, NY, p. A430

KOUNTZ, David, M.D., Senior Vice President Medical Affairs, K. Hovnanian Children's Hospital, NJ, p. A408

KOUSKOLEKAS, Anthony, FACHE, President, Pelham Medical Center, Greer, SC, p. A554

KOUTOUZOS, Connie L., R.N., MSN, Chief Executive Officer, Aspirus Iron River Hospitals & Clinics, Inc., Iron River, MI, p. A316

KOVAC, John, Facility Chief Information Officer, Veterans Affairs Medical Center, PA, p. A538

KOVACH, Andrew L, Vice President Human Resources and Chief Administrative Officer, Newton Medical Center, Newton, NJ, p. A409

KOVACS, Tina, Chief Financial Officer, Saint Francis Hospital-Bartlett, Bartlett, TN, p. A566

KOVAL, Matthew, M.D., Vice President Medical Affairs, Kidspeace Children's Hospital, Orefield, PA, p. A533

KOVALSKI, Jerry, Director Information Systems, Madera Community Hospital, Madera, CA, p. A71

KOWALSKI, Brad, Director Information Technology, Marcus Daly Memorial Hospital, Hamilton, MT, p. A376

KOWALSKI, David, Chief Executive Officer, Kindred Hospital Santa Ana, CA, p. A63

KOWALSKI, Patrick A, Chief Financial Officer, Mercy Health - Anderson Hospital, Cincinnati, OH, p. A475

KOWNACKI, Dawn, Director Human Resources, Brooke Glen Behavioral Hospital, Fort Washington, PA, p. A526

KOWNACKI, Hamila
Chief Operating Officer, California Pacific Medical Center-St. Luke's Campus, San Francisco, CA, p. A85
Chief Operating Officer, California Pacific Medical Center, San Francisco, CA, p. A85

KOZAI, Gerald T., PharmD, President and Chief Executive Officer, St. Francis Medical Center, Lynwood, CA, p. A70

KOZAR, Michael A., Chief Executive Officer, Northwest Florida Community Hospital, Chipley, FL, p. A119

KOZEL, Kenneth D., FACHE
President and Chief Executive Officer, University Of Maryland Shore Medical Center At Chestertown, Chestertown, MD, p. A290
President and Chief Executive Officer, University Of Maryland Shore Medical Center At Dorchester, Cambridge, MD, p. A290
President and Chief Executive Officer, University Of Maryland Shore Medical Center At Easton, Easton, MD, p. A291

KOZEL, Mary Ann, Chief Fiscal, Wilmington Veterans Affairs Medical Center, Wilmington, DE, p. A114

KOZIK, Kelly, Director Human Resources, Healthsouth Reading Rehabilitation Hospital, Reading, PA, p. A539

KOZIKUSKI, Courtney, Chief Financial Officer, Perry Memorial Hospital, Perry, OK, p. A505

KOZIN, Scott, M.D., Chief of Staff, Shriners Hospitals For Children-Philadelphia, Philadelphia, PA, p. A536

KOZIOL, Michael J, Chief Financial Officer, Holyoke Medical Center, Holyoke, MA, p. A300

KOZOROSKY, Laurie, Chief Executive Officer, Select Specialty Hospital - Cleveland Fairhill, OH, p. A477

KRABILL, Emma, Chief Executive Officer, Scenic Mountain Medical Center, Big Spring, TX, p. A589

KRABLIN, Brett, M.D., Chief of Staff, Mercy Hospital Kingfisher, Kingfisher, OK, p. A500

KRAFT, Chris, Director Information Systems, York General, York, NE, p. A391

KRAFVE, Jake Matthew, Chief Financial Officer, Royal Oaks Hospital, Windsor, MO, p. A372

KRAHNERT, John F, M.D., Chief Medical Officer, Firsthealth Moore Regional Hospital - Richmond, NC, p. A458

KRAJEWSKI, David, Senior Vice President and Chief Financial Officer, Sinai Hospital Of Baltimore, Baltimore, MD, p. A289

KRAMER, Blake, Chief Executive Officer, Franklin Medical Center, Winnsboro, LA, p. A281

KRAMER, Danette, Chief Financial Officer, Regional Medical Center, Manchester, IA, p. A226

KRAMER, Janie, Chief Operating Officer, Sharp Memorial Hospital, San Diego, CA, p. A84

KRAMER, Karen, R.N., Vice President and System Chief Nursing Officer, Cox Medical Center South, MO, p. A370

KRAMER, Kathryn, M.D., President Medical Staff, Unitypoint Health-Pekin Hospital, Pekin, IL, p. A193

KRAMER, Kevin, Chief Executive Officer, Modoc Medical Center, Alturas, CA, p. A50

KRAMER, Lynette, M.D., Chief Medical Officer, Boone County Health Center, Albion, NE, p. A381

KRAMER, Michael, Chief Executive Officer, Mercy Health - West Hospital, Cincinnati, OH, p. A475

KRAMER, Susan, Director of Human Resources, Levi Hospital, Hot Springs National Park-Garland County, AR, p. A43

KRAMPITS, Carrie, Director Human Resources, Mckenzie Health System, Sandusky, MI, p. A323

KRANZ, Karl, M.D., Chief of Staff, Cascade Medical Center, Leavenworth, WA, p. A673

KRASON, Jane E., R.N., Chief Executive Officer, Appalachian Behavioral Healthcare, Athens, OH, p. A471

KRASS, Todd, Chief Executive Officer, Belton Regional Medical Center, Belton, MO, p. A355

KRAUKLIS, Gene
Regional Vice President Human Resources, Aurora Lakeland Medical Center, Elkhorn, WI, p. A692
Regional Vice President Human Resources, Aurora Memorial Hospital Of Burlington, Burlington, WI, p. A691

KRAUS, Jason, Director Human Resources, Magruder Memorial Hospital, Port Clinton, OH, p. A489

KRAUS, John, M.D., Chief Medical Officer, Bryn Mawr Rehabilitation Hospital, Malvern, PA, p. A530

KRAUSE, Donna, Chief Information Officer, Harry S. Truman Memorial Veterans Hospital, Columbia, MO, p. A358

KRAUSE, Jill A., Director, Kalamazoo Psychiatric Hospital, Kalamazoo, MI, p. A317

KRAUSE, Kim, Director Human Resources, Baylor Jack And Jane Hamilton Heart And Vascular Hospital, Dallas, TX, p. A595

KRAUSE, Steven, Manager Information Technology, Franciscan Healthcare Munster, Munster, IN, p. A212

KRAUSE, Wade, M.D., Chief Medical Officer, Connally Memorial Medical Center, Floresville, TX, p. A603

KRAUTSCHEID, Steven P, Ancillary Services Administrator, Tuality Forest Grove Hospital, OR, p. A513

KRAVETZ, Michael, M.D., Medical Director, Encompass Health Valley Of The Sun Rehabilitation Hospital, Glendale, AZ, p. A30

KRAVETZ, Todd, Chief of Staff, Wickenburg Community Hospital, Wickenburg, AZ, p. A38

KREATSOULAS, Nicholas, Vice President Medical Affairs, Mercy Health - St. Joseph Warren Hospital, Warren, OH, p. A492

KREBS, Anne, Chief Financial Officer, Butler Health System, Butler, PA, p. A521

KREBS, Christine
Director of Nursing, Ascension Sacred Heart Hospital, Tomahawk, WI, p. A704
Director or Nursing, St. Mary's Hospital, WI, p. A702

KREBS, Cindy, District Director Human Resources, Matagorda Regional Medical Center, Bay City, TX, p. A587

KREBS, George, M.D., Chief Medical Officer, Broughton Hospital, Morganton, NC, p. A457

KREBS, Mary Jane, FACHE, President, Spring Harbor Hospital, Westbrook, ME, p. A286

KREBSBACH, Mayla, Chief Executive Officer, Vista Del Mar Hospital, Ventura, CA, p. A94

KREELEY, Chris, Director Nursing, Kessler Marlton Rehabilitation, Marlton, NJ, p. A407

KREHBIEL, Rod, M.D., Chief of Staff, Klickitat Valley Health, Goldendale, WA, p. A672

KREIDER, David, Controller, Wellspan Ephrata Community Hospital, Ephrata, PA, p. A525

KREIDLER, Marlene, Executive Director Human Resources, Adventist Health Bakersfield, Bakersfield, CA, p. A51

KREITINGER, Tate J., Chief Executive Officer, The Healthcenter, Kalispell, MT, p. A377

KREITZER, Teri, Director Human Resources, Saint Francis Medical Center, Cape Girardeau, MO, p. A356

KREJCI, Kathy Blair, Chief Nursing Officer, Marshall Medical Center, Placerville, CA, p. A78

KRELL, G Christopher, M.D., Chief of Staff, South Lincoln Medical Center, Kemmerer, WY, p. A708

KRELSTEIN, Michael, M.D., Medical Director, San Diego County Psychiatric Hospital, San Diego, CA, p. A84

KREN, John, Chief Financial Officer, St. John's Medical Center And Living Center, Jackson, WY, p. A708

KRESHON, James, M.D., Medical Director, Healthsouth Harmarville Rehabilitation Hospital, Pittsburgh, PA, p. A537

KRETSCHMAN, Robin, MSN, R.N., Vice President Patient Care Services, Marshfield Childen's Hospital, WI, p. A697

KRETSCHMER, Suzanne, Chief Executive Officer, Chg Cornerstone Hospital Conroe, Conroe, TX, p. A593

KRETZ, Blake, FACHE, President, Texas Health Arlington Memorial Hospital, Arlington, TX, p. A584

KRETZINGER, Curt, Chief Operating Officer, Mosaic Life Care, Saint Joseph, MO, p. A367

KRETZSCHMER, Kendra, Patient Care System Leader, Scheurer Hospital, Pigeon, MI, p. A320

KREUTNER, Ron, Chief Financial Officer, San Joaquin General Hospital, French Camp, CA, p. A59

KREUTZER, Kevin, Chief Financial Officer, Russell Regional Hospital, Russell, KS, p. A245

KREUZ, Betsy, Chief Financial Officer, Upmc Altoona, Altoona, PA, p. A520

KREUZER, Jay E., FACHE, Chief Executive Officer, Kona Community Hospital, Kealakekua, HI, p. A166

KRHOVSKY, David, M.D., Vice President, Medical Affairs, Spectrum Health, MI, p. A314

KRIEGER, Cathy, Human Resources Director, Greene County Medical Center, Jefferson, IA, p. A225

KRIEGER, Mark, Vice President and Chief Financial Officer, Barnes-Jewish Hospital Psychiatric Support Center, MO, p. A367

KRIEGER, Tim, Director Information Systems, Central Hartnett Hospital, NC, p. A451

KRIER, Jennifer, Vice President Human Resources, Wesley Woodlawn Hospital & Er, KS, p. A248

KRILICH, Chad, M.D.
Chief Med Officer-AMC/CMC, Multicare Auburn Medical Center, Auburn, WA, p. A669
Chief Medical Officer, Santa Rosa Memorial Hospital, Santa Rosa, CA, p. A89

KRINKE, Susan, Chief Executive Officer, Kindred Hospital Lima, Lima, OH, p. A484

KRIPAKARAN, Kasturi, M.D., Medical Director, Andrew Mcfarland Mental Health Center, Springfield, IL, p. A196

KRIPINSKI, Laura, Chief Nursing Officer, Forks Community Hospital, Forks, WA, p. A672

KRISHNAN, Radha, M.D., Chief Medical Officer, Antelope Valley Hospital, Lancaster, CA, p. A64

KRISHNASWAMY, Jaikumar, President, Baylor Scott & White Medical Center - Centennial, Frisco, TX, p. A606

KRISTEL, John, President and Chief Executive Officer, Good Shepherd Rehabilitation Hospital, Allentown, PA, p. A519

KRMPOTIC, Debra J., R.N., Chief Executive Officer, Banner Behavioral Health Center-Thunderbird Campus, AZ, p. A30

KRODEL, Scott, Vice President Information Systems, Johnson Memorial Hospital, Franklin, IN, p. A204

KROESE, Brandi, Director Operations, West Springs Hospital, Grand Junction, CO, p. A101

KROESE, Robert D, FACHE, Chief Executive Officer, Pella Regional Health Center, Pella, IA, p. A228

KROESE, Robert D., FACHE, Chief Executive Officer, Pella Regional Health Center, Pella, IA, p. A228

KROLICKI, Karen, Director, Human Resources, Beaumont Hospital - Taylor, Taylor, MI, p. A324

KROMER, Harold, Director Site Information Systems, Advocate Condell Medical Center, Libertyville, IL, p. A188

KRONENBERG, Seth, M.D., Chief Medical Officer, Crouse Health, Syracuse, NY, p. A443

KROSOFF, Mary June, Chief Human Resources Officer, Highlands Hospital, Connellsville, PA, p. A523

KROUSE, Donald, M.D., Chief of Staff, Trinity Hospital, Weaverville, CA, p. A95

KROUSE, Michael
Chief Information Officer Information Services, Ohiohealth Grady Memorial Hospital, Delaware, OH, p. A481
Chief Information Officer, Ohiohealth Doctors Hospital, Columbus, OH, p. A478
Chief Information Officer, Ohiohealth Grant Medical Center, Columbus, OH, p. A478
Chief Information Officer, Ohiohealth Riverside Methodist Hospital, Columbus, OH, p. A479
Senior Vice President Chief Information Officer, Ohiohealth Dublin Methodist Hospital, Dublin, OH, p. A481

KRUEGER, Christine, M.D., Chief of Staff, Munising Memorial Hospital, Munising, MI, p. A319

KRUEGER, Ellen, Director Human Resources, Chadron Community Hospital And Health Services, Chadron, NE, p. A383

KRUEGER, Eric, Chief Financial Officer, Mercy Hospital And Medical Center, Chicago, IL, p. A178

KRUEGER, James G., M.D., Ph.D., Chief Executive Officer, Rockefeller University Hospital, New York (Includes All Hospitals Located Within The Five Boroughs), NY, p. A437

KRUEGER, Justin, FACHE, President, Mercy Health - Clermont Hospital, Batavia, OH, p. A471

KRUEGER, Mary, Commanding Officer, Tripler Army Medical Center, Honolulu, HI, p. A165

KRUG, Robert J., M.D., Chief Executive Officer, Mount Sinai Rehabilitation Hospital, Hartford, CT, p. A108

KRUGEL, Gary M, Chief Financial Officer, Norwegian American Hospital, Chicago, IL, p. A178

KRUGER, Dale K., Chief Executive Officer, Mahnomen Health Center, Mahnomen, MN, p. A334

KRUGER, George, CPA, Chief Financial Officer, Comanche County Memorial Hospital, Lawton, OK, p. A500

KRUMMEL, Dere, Director Information Systems, Ochsner Medical Center - Kenner, Kenner, LA, p. A270

KRUMREY, Arthur J, Chief Information Officer, Ronald Mcdonald Children's Hospital, IL, p. A189

KRUMWIED, Robert D., President and Chief Executive Officer, Regional Mental Health Center, Merrillville, IN, p. A211

KRUPALA, Judith, R.N., Chief Nursing Officer, Cuero Community Hospital, Cuero, TX, p. A595

KRUSE, Joseph J
Chief Administrative Officer, Mayo Clinic Health System - Franciscan Healthcare In Sparta, Sparta, WI, p. A703
Executive Vice President, Mayo Clinic Health System - Franciscan Healthcare In La Crosse, La Crosse, WI, p. A695

KRUSE, Marcia, R.N., Director Nursing, Logan County Hospital, Oakley, KS, p. A242

KRUSE, Victoria, Manager Human Resources, Franklin General Hospital, Hampton, IA, p. A223

KRUSIE, Kathleen R, FACHE, President, Community Heart And Vascular Hospital, IN, p. A206

KRUSIE, Kathleen R., FACHE, President, Community Hospital North, Indianapolis, IN, p. A206

KRUYER-COLLINS, Emyle, Chief Human Resources Officer, Unity Medical & Surgical Hospital, Mishawaka, IN, p. A211

KRUZEL, Janet, Business Office Manager, Centracare Health-Melrose, Melrose, MN, p. A334

KRUZICK, Michael, Acting Chief Financial Officer, Norwalk Hospital, Norwalk, CT, p. A110

KRUZNER, Melinda, Chief Financial Officer, Lexington Medical Center, West Columbia, SC, p. A558

KRYSTOWIAK, Thomas P
Chief Financial Officer, Thedacare Medical Center-Berlin, Berlin, WI, p. A690
Vice President Finance, Theda Care Medical Center - Wild Rose, Wild Rose, WI, p. A706

KRYZANIAK, Larry, Chief Financial Officer, Hcmc Department Of Pediatrics, MN, p. A335

KRZASTEK, Sue, Vice President Human Resources, Augusta Health, Fishersville, VA, p. A658

KRZYMOWSKI, David, M.D., Chief of Staff, Sanpete Valley Hospital, Mount Pleasant, UT, p. A648

KUBALA, Joseph
Chief Financial Officer, St. Vincent Jennings Hospital, North Vernon, IN, p. A213
Director Financial and Support Services, St. Vincent Salem Hospital, Salem, IN, p. A214

KUBALL, Lana, Director Administrative Services, Lucas County Health Center, Chariton, IA, p. A219

KUBE, Don, M.D., Chief Medical Officer, Dickinson County Healthcare System, Iron Mountain, MI, p. A316

KUBIAK, Phillip J., President, Hampstead Hospital, Hampstead, NH, p. A399

KUBICEK, Jim, Vice President, Operations, Rogers Memorial Hospital-Brown Deer, WI, p. A700

KUBOTA, Andrea, R.N., MSN, Director Patient Care Services and Nurse Executive, Shriners Hospitals For Children-Honolulu, Honolulu, HI, p. A165

KUBOUSHEK, David, Chief, Fiscal Service, Durham Veterans Affairs Medical Center, Durham, NC, p. A451

KUCERA, Doug, Chief Financial Officer, Crete Area Medical Center, Crete, NE, p. A383

KUCERA, Kim, Chief Operating Officer, Mille Lacs Health System, Onamia, MN, p. A336

KUCICH, Vincent, FACHE, FACS, M.D.
Chief Medical Officer, Osf Heart Of Mary Medical Center, Urbana, IL, p. A197
Chief Medical Officer, Osf Sacred Heart Medical Center, Danville, IL, p. A180

KUCKEWICH, Mike, Director Information Systems, Terre Haute Regional Hospital, Terre Haute, IN, p. A215

KUCZORA, Paul, Chief Executive Officer, Grant-Blackford Mental Health Center, Marion, IN, p. A210

KUDER, Merlin, Chief Information Officer, Hamilton County Hospital, Syracuse, KS, p. A246

KUDLA, Angela, MSN, R.N., Chief Nursing Officer, Select Specialty Hospital-Downriver, Wyandotte, MI, p. A326

KUEHLER, Sheila, R.N., Director of Nursing, Knox County Hospital, Knox City, TX, p. A618

KUEHLER, Stephen A., Administrator, Knox County Hospital, Knox City, TX, p. A618

KUEHN, David, Chief Financial Officer, Marshfield Medical Center - Ladysmith, Ladysmith, WI, p. A695

KUEHNEMUND, Bonnie, Comptroller, Heart Of America Medical Center, Rugby, ND, p. A468

KUENY, Patrick
Chief Operating Officer, Lee's Summit Medical Center, Lee's Summit, MO, p. A363
Interim Chief Executive Officer, Lee's Summit Medical Center, Lee's Summit, MO, p. A363

KUEPERS, Kathleen, Chief Executive Officer, Memorial Hospital Of Lafayette County, Darlington, WI, p. A691

KUESTERSTEFFEN, Vicki, Director and Chief Executive Officer, J. D. Mccarty Center For Children With Developmental Disabilities, Norman, OK, p. A502

KUEVEN, John, Senior Vice President and President, Wellstar Paulding Hospital, Hiram, GA, p. A155

KUGHN, Yvonne, Chief Executive Officer, Select Specialty Hospital-Pittsburgh/Upmc, Pittsburgh, PA, p. A537

KUHAR, Peggy A, R.N., MSN, Chief Nursing Officer, University Hospitals Geauga Medical Center, Chardon, OH, p. A474

KUHARICH, Ryan J., Chief Executive Officer, Aultman Specialty Hospital, Canton, OH, p. A473

KUHLMAN, Ian, Manager Information Technology, Hshs Good Shepherd Hospital, Shelbyville, IL, p. A195

KUHN, Anita, Controller, Texas County Memorial Hospital, Houston, MO, p. A360

KUHN, Brenda, Ph.D., R.N., FACHE
Chief Nursing Officer, Greene Memorial Hospital, Xenia, OH, p. A494
Chief Nursing Officer, Kettering Medical Center, Kettering, OH, p. A484

KUHN, Keith, Chief Executive Officer, Haven Behavioral Senior Care Of Dayton, Dayton, OH, p. A480

KUHN, Margueritte, M.D., Vice President Medical Affairs, Midmichigan Medical Center-Midland, Midland, MI, p. A319

KUHN, Mark, Chief Executive Officer, Hammond-Henry Hospital, Geneseo, IL, p. A184

KUHN, Steve, Chief Financial Officer, River Park Hospital, Huntington, WV, p. A684

KUHNS, Jay, Vice President Human Resources, Johns Hopkins All Children's Hospital, Saint Petersburg, FL, p. A138

KUHRT, Sharon, Chief Nursing Officer, New England Rehabilitation Hospital Of Portland, Portland, ME, p. A285

KUIPER, Evert J., Interim President and Chief Executive Officer, Hshs St. Mary's Hospital, Decatur, IL, p. A181

KUKELHAN, Alison, Manager Human Resources, Adams Memorial Hospital, Decatur, IN, p. A202

KULHANEK, Linda, Chief Financial Officer, Memorial Hermann Katy Hospital, Katy, TX, p. A616

KULICK, Daniel, M.D., Chief of Staff, Marlette Regional Hospital, Marlette, MI, p. A318

KULIK, Alec G, Administrator, Cleveland Clinic Children's Hospital For Rehabilitation, Cleveland, OH, p. A476

KULISZ, Michael, D.O.
Chief Medical Officer, Northwestern Medicine Kishwaukee Hospital, Dekalb, IL, p. A181
Vice President, Chief Medical Officer, Northwestern Medicine Valley West Hospital, Sandwich, IL, p. A195

KULLMAN, Betsy, R.N., MSN, Executive Vice President and Chief Nursing Officer, Medical Center At Bowling Green, Bowling Green, KY, p. A250

KULMA, Mariarose, R.N., Vice President Patient Services, Ut Health Behavioral Health Center, TX, p. A641

KUMAR, Deborah W, MSN, Chief Nursing Officer, Florida Hospital Carrollwood, Tampa, FL, p. A140

KUMAR, Nanda, M.D., Chief of Staff, Vibra Hospital Of Northern California, Redding, CA, p. A80

KUMMER, Margaret, Chief Human Resource Officer, Citizens Medical Center, Colby, KS, p. A233

KUNERT, Alicia, MS, Executive Director, Conway Regional Rehabilitation Hospital, Conway-Faulkner County, AR, p. A40

KUNES, Courtney, Director Human Resources, Upmc Susquehanna Lock Haven, Lock Haven, PA, p. A530

KUNKEL, Elisabeth J., M.D., Professor, Pennsylvania State College of Medicine, Pennsylvania Psychiatric Institute, Harrisburg, PA, p. A526

KUNKEL, Stephanie, Vice President of Human Resources, Tampa Community Hospital, Tampa, FL, p. A141

KUNNAPPILLY, Chester, M.D., Interim Chief Executive Officer, San Mateo Medical Center, San Mateo, CA, p. A87

KUNSTLING, Ted, M.D., Chief Medical Officer, Duke Raleigh Hospital, Raleigh, NC, p. A459

KUNTZ, Alicia, Nurse Manager, Lifecare Hospitals Of Mechanicsburg, Mechanicsburg, PA, p. A531

KUNZ, Donna
System Director Human Resources, Saint Luke's Cushing Hospital, Leavenworth, KS, p. A239
System Director Human Resources, Saint Luke's North Hospital-Smithville Campus, MO, p. A362
System Director Human Resources, Saint Luke's South Hospital, Overland Park, KS, p. A243

KUNZA, Mary Kay, Manager Human Resources, Mercy Hospital Lincoln, Troy, MO, p. A371

KUOPUS, Lisa, Chief Nursing Officer, Cumberland Surgical Hospital, San Antonio, TX, p. A633

KUPER, Kandi, Chief Nursing Officer, Kit Carson County Health Service District, Burlington, CO, p. A97

KUPFERSTEIN, Ron, Chief Executive Officer, Monrovia Memorial Hospital, Monrovia, CA, p. A73

KUPLEN, Carol, R.N., MSN, President and Chief Executive Officer, St Luke's Hospital - Allentown Campus, PA, p. A521

KUPPLER, Sylvia, Chief Financial Officer, Belmont Pines Hospital, Youngstown, OH, p. A494

KURAITIS, Kestutis V, M.D., Chief of Staff, Pioneers Memorial Healthcare District, Brawley, CA, p. A53

KURCAB, Jeff, Chief Financial Officer, Lewisgale Hospital Pulaski, Pulaski, VA, p. A664

KUROKI, Helen, Senior Vice President and Chief Medical Officer, Memorial Hospital Hixson, TN, p. A567

KURRA, Shankar, M.D., Senior Vice President Medical Affairs, Fisher-Titus Medical Center, Norwalk, OH, p. A488

KURTZ, Kris, Chief Financial Officer, Metro Health - University Of Michigan Health, Wyoming, MI, p. A326

KURTZ, Maria
Director Human Resources, Lutheran Hospital Of Indiana, Fort Wayne, IN, p. A203
Director Human Resources, Orthopaedic Hospital Of Lutheran Health Network, Fort Wayne, IN, p. A204

KURTZ, Thomas F, Jr, Chief Operating Officer, Georgia Regional Hospital At Savannah, Savannah, GA, p. A160

KURTZ, Thomas M., President and Chief Executive Officer, Chan Soon-Shiong Medical Center, Windber, PA, p. A545

KURTZ, Tom, Vice President Information Services and Chief Information Officer, Memorial Healthcare, Owosso, MI, p. A320

KURZ, Kenneth R, M.D., Chief of Staff, Midstate Medical Center, Meriden, CT, p. A108

KURZ, Sharon H., Ph.D., Chief Executive Officer, St. Elias Specialty Hospital, Anchorage, AK, p. A25

KUSHNER, Michael S., Senior Vice President and Chief Talent Officer, Nicklaus Children's Hospital, Miami, FL, p. A130

KUSLER, Julie, Manager Information Services, Avera St. Luke's Hospital, Aberdeen, SD, p. A559

KUSNIERZ, William J., Vice President and Chief Financial Officer, Springfield Regional Medical Center, Springfield, OH, p. A490

KUTCH, John M., President, Trinity Hospital-St. Joseph'S, ND, p. A468

KUTILEK, Richard J, Chief Operating Officer, Calvary Hospital, New York (Includes All Hospitals Located Within The Five Boroughs), NY, p. A431

KUTNER, Jean, M.D., Chief Medical Officer, University Of Colorado Hospital, Aurora, CO, p. A96

KUVSHINOFF, Boris, M.D., II, Chief Medical Officer, Roswell Park Cancer Institute, Buffalo, NY, p. A423

KUYKENDALL, Jana, Chief Executive Officer, Post Acute/ Warm Springs Specialty Hospital Of Luling, Luling, TX, p. A622

KUZAS, Betsy, Executive Vice President and Chief Operating Officer, Phoenix Children's Hospital, Phoenix, AZ, p. A33

KUZEE, Ann, Executive Director Human Resources, Riverview Health, Noblesville, IN, p. A213

KWIATEK, Susan, R.N., Executive Director, Glen Cove Hospital, Glen Cove, NY, p. A426

KWIESIELEWICZ, Nancy
Human Resources Manager, Ascension Good Samaritan Hospital, Merrill, WI, p. A698
Human Resources Manager, Ministry Good Samaritan Health Center, Weston, WI, p. A706

KYHNELL, Koreen H, Vice President Human Resources, Indiana University Health Arnett Hospital, Lafayette, IN, p. A209

KYLER, Yvonne
Director Human Resources, Texas Health Arlington Memorial Hospital, Arlington, TX, p. A584
Director Human Resources, Texas Health Heart & Vascular Hospital Arlington, Arlington, TX, p. A584

KYRIACOU, George M., President and Chief Executive Officer, Gaylord Hospital, Wallingford, CT, p. A111

KYWI, Alberto
Chief Information Officer, Cottage Rehabilitation Hospital, CA, p. A88
Chief Information Officer, Goleta Valley Cottage Hospital, Santa Barbara, CA, p. A88

L

LA CAVA, Joseph, Chief Nursing Officer and Director Of Anesthesia, Desoto Memorial Hospital, Arcadia, FL, p. A117

LA CROIX, Kent, Chief Information Officer, Schoolcraft Memorial Hospital, Manistique, MI, p. A318

LABADIE, Wendy, Chief Human Resource Officer, Banner Estrella Medical Center, Phoenix, AZ, p. A33

LABAGNARA, James, M.D., Vice President Medical Affairs, St. Joseph's Wayne Hospital, NJ, p. A409

LABARGE, Robert J., President and Chief Executive Officer, Sturgis Hospital, Sturgis, MI, p. A324

LABELLE, Douglas, M.D., Chief Medical Officer, Up Health System-Bell, Ishpeming, MI, p. A316

LABELLE, James, M.D.
Chief Medical Officer, Scripps Green Hospital, La Jolla, CA, p. A62
Chief Medical Officer, Scripps Memorial Hospital-La Jolla, La Jolla, CA, p. A63

LABER, Susan, R.N., Chief Nursing Officer, Tampa Community Hospital, Tampa, FL, p. A141

LABONTE, Karen Y, Chief Nursing Officer, Willow Creek Women's Hospital, AR, p. A49

LABONTE, Robin, Leader Financial Care, York Hospital, York, ME, p. A286

LABORANTI, Sarah M, Interim Director Human Resources, Tennova Turkey Creek Medical Center, TN, p. A572

LABOUCHARDIERE, Mark, Interim Facility Administrator, Lincoln Regional Center, Lincoln, NE, p. A386

LABRIOLA, Suzanne M., D.O., Chief Medical Officer, Allegheny Valley Hospital, Natrona Heights, PA, p. A532

LABRIOLA, Terri, Human Resources Officer, Sierra Nevada Memorial Hospital, Grass Valley, CA, p. A61

LABRUM, Chad, Chief Financial Officer, Ashley Regional Medical Center, Vernal, UT, p. A651

LACAZE, Todd, Chief Financial Officer, Riverside Community Hospital, Riverside, CA, p. A81

LACEFIELD, Gayla, Director Human Resources, Howard Memorial Hospital, Nashville-Howard County, AR, p. A46

LACEY, Carmen, MSN, R.N.
President and Director of Patient Care Services, Charles A. Cannon Memorial Hospital, Newland, NC, p. A458
President, Charles A. Cannon Memorial Hospital, Newland, NC, p. A458

LACEY, Paul, M.D., Chief Medical Staff, North Valley Hospital, Tonasket, WA, p. A679

LACHANCE, Eric, Chief Financial Officer, Florida Hospital Ocala, Ocala, FL, p. A133

LACHAPELLE, Diana, CPA, Chief Executive Officer, Healthsouth Rehabilitation Hospital, Concord, NH, p. A398

LACHER, Paula A, MSN, R.N., Chief Nursing Officer, West Penn Hospital, Pittsburgh, PA, p. A538

LACHINA, Ignazio, M.D., Medical Director, Encompass Health Rehabilitation Hospital Of Cypress, Houston, TX, p. A610

LACHNEY, Cheryl, Director of Nursing, Compass Behavioral Center Of Alexandria, Alexandria, LA, p. A262

LACHOWSKY, John, M.D., Chief Medical Officer, Mercy Hospital Ozark, Ozark-Franklin County, AR, p. A47

LACINA, Amy, R.N., Director of Nursing, North Shore Health, Grand Marais, MN, p. A332

LACKEY, Lori, Chief Financial Officer, Sabetha Community Hospital, Sabetha, KS, p. A245

LACKMAN, Vickie, Human Resource Director, Peninsula Region, Harrison Medical Center, Bremerton, WA, p. A669

LACKNEY, Christopher J, Director Human Resources, Grace Cottage Hospital, Townshend, VT, p. A654

LACOT, Ivette, Director Human Resources, Hospital Episcopal San Lucas Guayama, Guayama, PR, p. A713

LACY, Albert, Associate Director of Information Technology, Tampa Community Hospital, Tampa, FL, p. A141

LACY, Angela, Director of Nursing, Bolivar General Hospital, Bolivar, TN, p. A566

LACY, Dwight A., Chief Executive Officer, Millwood Hospital, Arlington, TX, p. A584

LACY, Edward L., FACHE, Vice President and Administrator, Baptist Health Medical Center-Heber Springs, Heber Springs-Cleburne County, AR, p. A43

LACY, Tyson, Chief Executive Officer and Superintendent, Lincoln Hospital, Davenport, WA, p. A671

LADAROLA, Sandra, Chief Nursing Officer, Waterbury Hospital, Waterbury, CT, p. A112

LADD, Bill, Director Information Services, Western Missouri Medical Center, Warrensburg, MO, p. A371

LADWIG, Michael, M.D., Chief of Staff, Marion Veterans Affairs Medical Center, Marion, IL, p. A188

LADY, Brian, Administrator and Chief Executive Officer, Concho County Hospital, Eden, TX, p. A600

LAFERNEY, Jimmy, M.D., Vice President Medical Staff Affairs, Baylor Medical Center At Frisco, Frisco, TX, p. A606

LAFFEY, Leah, R.N., Chief Executive Officer, Healthsouth Rehabilitation Hospital Of Sewickley, Sewickley, PA, p. A541

LAFLAMME, Christine, R.N., MSN, Chief Nursing Officer, Seton Smithville Regional Hospital, Smithville, TX, p. A636

LAFRANCOIS, Gregory, President, Community General Health Center, ME, p. A286

LAFRANCOIS, Mary, Vice President Human Resources, Christus Spohn Hospital Corpus Christus South, TX, p. A594

LAGASSE, David A, Senior Vice President Fiscal Affairs, Mclean Hospital, Belmont, MA, p. A295

LAGNESE, John, M.D., Vice President Medical Affairs, Upmc St. Margaret, Pittsburgh, PA, p. A538

LAGROU, Robert, D.O., Medical Director, Henry Ford Kingswood Hospital, Ferndale, MI, p. A312

LAHASKY, Douglas, Chief Financial Officer, Avoyelles Hospital, Marksville, LA, p. A273

LAHAYE, Daniel, Manager, Savoy Medical Center, Mamou, LA, p. A273

LAHOOD, Amy, R.N., Director of Nursing, Vermilion Behavioral Health Systems South, LA, p. A271

LAHOUT, Brenda, Chief Nurse Executive, Danville State Hospital, Danville, PA, p. A523

LAHTI, Molly, Director Human Resources, Parkland Medical Center, Derry, NH, p. A398

LAI, Iris, Chief Executive Officer, Alhambra Hospital Medical Center, Alhambra, CA, p. A50

LAIBINIS, Walter, M.D., Chief Medical Officer, Upmc Susquehanna Soldiers + Sailors, Wellsboro, PA, p. A543

LAIGN, Michael B., President and Chief Executive Officer, Holy Redeemer Hospital, Meadowbrook, PA, p. A531

LAIL, Steve, Vice President Operations and Chief Operating Officer, Down East Community Hospital, Machias, ME, p. A285

LAIOSA, Sarah, M.D., Chief Medical Staff, Harney District Hospital, Burns, OR, p. A511

LAIRD, Alan, M.D., Chief Medical Officer, Orange City Area Health System, Orange City, IA, p. A227

LAIRD, Charles, Chief Executive Officer, Menorah Medical Center, Overland Park, KS, p. A243

LAIRD, David, Chief Executive Officer, Heart Hospital Of Austin, TX, p. A586

LAIRD, Jeff, Controller, Stephens County Hospital, Toccoa, GA, p. A162

LAIRD, Laci, Chief Executive Officer, Oceans Behavioral Hospital Lufkin, Lufkin, TX, p. A621

LAIRD, Shaw, Chief Information Officer, Chester Regional Medical Center, Chester, SC, p. A550

LAISTER, Judy K, Director, Human Resources, Methodist Mansfield Medical Center, Mansfield, TX, p. A622

LAKE, Chandra, Associate Director, Sheridan Veterans Affairs Medical Center, Sheridan, WY, p. A709

LAKE, Monica, Chief Nursing Officer, Iberia Extended Care Hospital, LA, p. A271

LAKE, Nathan, Vice President Human Resources, Prairie Lakes Healthcare System, Watertown, SD, p. A565

LAKE, Peter M, M.D., Chief Medical Officer, Rogers Memorial Hospital-West Allis, WI, p. A700

LAKE, Rob, Interim Chief Executive Officer, Mccurtain Memorial Hospital, Idabel, OK, p. A500

LAKE, Ryan, Director Information Technology, Glencoe Regional Health Services, Glencoe, MN, p. A332

LAKEY, Travis, Chief Financial Officer, Mayers Memorial Hospital District, Fall River Mills, CA, p. A58

LAKINS, Tom, Director Information Systems, Tennova Turkey Creek Medical Center, TN, p. A572

LALAS, Angela, Senior Vice President, Finance, Loma Linda University Children's Hospital, Loma Linda, CA, p. A64

LALIBERTE, John, Chief Information Officer, St. Vincent's Blount, Oneonta, AL, p. A22

LALIOTIS, Anna, Chief Executive Officer, Mesilla Valley Hospital, Las Cruces, NM, p. A418

LALLY, James M., D.O., President and Chief Medical Officer, Chino Valley Medical Center, Chino, CA, p. A54

LALLY, Robert P, Jr, Vice President Finance, Medstar Franklin Square Medical Center, Baltimore, MD, p. A288

LAM, Shiva, M.D., Executive Medical Director, Austin Lakes Hospital, Austin, TX, p. A585

LAM, Thomas, Chief Medical Officer, Garfield Medical Center, Monterey Park, CA, p. A73

LAMADELEINE, Joseph, Chief Financial Officer, West Haven Division, CT, p. A112

LAMANTEER, Mike, M.D., Senior Vice President Medical Affairs, Bsa Hospital, Llc, Amarillo, TX, p. A583

LAMARCHE, Heather, Manager Human Resources, Amg Specialty Hospital-Lafayette, Lafayette, LA, p. A270

LAMARCHE, Maximo, M.D., Chief Medical Officer, Amg Specialty Hospital-Lafayette, Lafayette, LA, p. A270

LAMB, Andrew, M.D., Chief of Staff, Alamance Regional Medical Center, Burlington, NC, p. A448

LAMB, Cindy, Director Human Resources, Marias Medical Center, Shelby, MT, p. A379

LAMB, Deanna, Director Human Resources, Central Carolina Hospital, Sanford, NC, p. A460

LAMB, Hope, Manager Human Resources, Kimble Hospital, Junction, TX, p. A616

LAMB, Joshua, Vice President Operations, Christus Highland Medical Center, LA, p. A278

LAMB, Mollee, Manager Human Resources, Lds Hospital, Salt Lake City, UT, p. A650

LAMB-PAGONE, Jerilynn, Nurse Executive, Whiting Forensic Hospital, CT, p. A109

LAMBERT, Amand, Director Human Resources, Allen Parish Hospital, Kinder, LA, p. A270

LAMBERT, Barbara, Director Healthcare Compliance, Eastern State Hospital, Williamsburg, VA, p. A667

LAMBERT, Cheryl, Chief Financial Officer, Acuity Specialty Hospital Of New Jersey, Atlantic City, NJ, p. A402

LAMBERT, James M., FACHE, Chief Executive Officer, Memorial Hospital And Manor, Bainbridge, GA, p. A148

LAMBERT, Karen A.
President, Advocate Condell Medical Center, Libertyville, IL, p. A188
President, Advocate Good Shepherd Hospital, Barrington, IL, p. A174

LAMBERT, Lynn, Chief Financial Officer, Central Hartnett Hospital, NC, p. A451

LAMBERT, Paul, M.D., Chief of Staff, Boise Veterans Affairs Medical Center, Boise, ID, p. A167

LAMBERT, Suzanne, R.N., Regional Chief Nursing Officer and Support Services, Presence Saints Mary & Elizabeth Medical Center, Claremont Avenue, IL, p. A178

LAMBETH, Laura, Chief Executive Officer, Ashe Memorial Hospital, Jefferson, NC, p. A455

LAMBRECHT, Craig, M.D., President, Sanford Bismarck, Bismarck, ND, p. A464

LAMEBULL, Charlotte, Administrative Officer, Fort Belknap Service Unit, Harlem, MT, p. A376

LAMEN, Drake M., M.D., President, Chief Executive Officer and Chief Medical Officer, Uhs Chenango Memorial Hospital, Norwich, NY, p. A438

LAMERS, Jamon
Director Finance, Ascension Eagle River Hospital, Eagle River, WI, p. A692
Director Finance, Ascension Sacred Heart Hospital, Tomahawk, WI, p. A704
Director Finance, Howard Young Medical Center, Woodruff, WI, p. A706
Director Finance, St. Mary's Hospital, WI, p. A702

LAMEY, Mark, Commander, U.S. Air Force Regional Hospital, Elmendorf Afb, AK, p. A26

LAMEY, Rebecca, Vice President Human Resources, Mainegeneral Medical Center-Augusta Campus, ME, p. A282

LAMLE, Sandra, Chief Financial Officer, Okeene Municipal Hospital, Okeene, OK, p. A502

LAMMERS, Sandra, Coordinator Human Resources and Finance, Chi Health Mercy Corning, Corning, IA, p. A219

LAMONT, Jennifer
Chief Financial Officer, West Suburban Medical Center, Oak Park, IL, p. A192
Chief Financial Officer, Westlake Hospital, Melrose Park, IL, p. A189

LAMORELLA, Vincent M, Chief Financial Officer, Clarion Hospital, Clarion, PA, p. A522

LAMOUREUX, John P., Commander, Dwight David Eisenhower Army Medical Center, Fort Gordon, GA, p. A154

LAMOUREUX, Laurie, Director of Finance, Cooley Dickinson Hospital, Northampton, MA, p. A303

LAMPE, Michael, M.D., Chief of Staff, Kossuth Regional Health Center, Algona, IA, p. A217

LAMPE, Tammy K, Director Human Resources, Edwards County Medical Center, Kinsley, KS, p. A238

LAMPIE, Abbie, Director of Nursing, Kirkbride Center, Philadelphia, PA, p. A535

LAMPLEY, Danny, Chief Operating Officer, Harrisburg Medical Center, Harrisburg, IL, p. A184

LAMPLEY, Joseph, D.O., Chief of Staff, Fisher County Hospital District, Rotan, TX, p. A631

LAMPTON, Lucius, M.D., Medical Director, Beacham Memorial Hospital, Magnolia, MS, p. A349

LANCASTER, Brian, Executive Director Information Management, Nebraska Medicine - Bellevue, Bellevue, NE, p. A382

LANCASTER, Penny, Controller, Cascade Medical Center, Cascade, ID, p. A168

LANCASTER, Tim, FACHE, President and Chief Executive Officer, Hendrick Health System, Abilene, TX, p. A582

LANCTIN, Henri, M.D., Chief of Staff, Prairie Lakes Healthcare System, Watertown, SD, p. A565

LAND, Laura M, Chief Human Resource Officer, North Mississippi Medical Center - Tupelo, Tupelo, MS, p. A353

LAND, Steve, Senior Administrator, Wamego Health Center, Wamego, KS, p. A247

LAND, Susann, M.D., Chief Medical Officer, Texas Health Springwood, TX, p. A588

LANDERS, Alice, Administrative Director Operations, Texas Health Springwood, TX, p. A588

LANDERS, Kimberly A., MS, R.N., Vice President Patient Care Services, Morris Hospital & Healthcare Centers, Morris, IL, p. A190

LANDERS, Lalah, R.N., Director of Nursing, Saunders Medical Center, Wahoo, NE, p. A391

LANDINI, Kristin
Vice President Human Resources, Advocate South Suburban Hospital, Hazel Crest, IL, p. A185
Vice President, Human Resources, Advocate Trinity Hospital, Chicago, IL, p. A176

LANDIS, Janie, Chief Financial Officer, Russell County Hospital, Russell Springs, KY, p. A260

LANDMAN, Adam, M.D., Chief Information Officer, Brigham And Women's Hospital, Boston, MA, p. A296

LANDMAN, Paul, Director Human Resources, Ellwood City Medical Center, Ellwood City, PA, p. A525

LANDOLL, Therese, Interim Chief Financial Officer, Community Memorial Healthcare, Marysville, KS, p. A241

LANDON, Anna, Chief Nursing Officer, Mercy Hospital Washington, Washington, MO, p. A372

LANDRAU, Erika, Director Human Resources, Healthsouth Hospital Of Manati, Manati, PR, p. A714

LANDRENEAU, John Derrick
Director of Nursing and Marketing Manager, Baton Rouge Rehabilitation Hospital, Baton Rouge, LA, p. A263
Director of Nursing, Baton Rouge Rehabilitation Hospital, Baton Rouge, LA, p. A263

LANDRETH, Jonathan, Administrator, United Medical Rehabilitation Hospital - Gonzales, LA, p. A268

LANDRETH, Kathy, Chief Executive Officer, Bath Community Hospital, Hot Springs, VA, p. A660

LANDRETH, Sandy, Director Human Resources, Seiling Regional Medical Center, Seiling, OK, p. A506

LANDRETH, Shannan, Information Systems, Livingston Hospital And Healthcare Services, Salem, KY, p. A260

LANDRUM, David, Chief Police Services, Atascadero State Hospital, Atascadero, CA, p. A51

LANDRUM, Scott M., Interim Chief Executive Officer, Wilbarger General Hospital, Vernon, TX, p. A642

LANDRY, Adam, Director of Information Systems, Northern Maine Medical Center, Fort Kent, ME, p. A284

LANDRY, Candy, Chief Human Resource Officer, Eastside Psychiatric Hospital, Tallahassee, FL, p. A140

LANDRY, Donna F., Chief Operating Officer, Our Lady Of Lourdes Regional Medical Center, Lafayette, LA, p. A271

LANDRY, Lisa G., Human Resources Director, Redington-Fairview General Hospital, Skowhegan, ME, p. A286

LANDRY, Nobie, Chief Financial Officer, Prevost Memorial Hospital, Donaldsonville, LA, p. A267

LANDRY, Ray A., Chief Executive Officer, Abbeville General Hospital, Abbeville, LA, p. A262

LANDRY NUNEZ, Lexis, Chief Executive Officer, St. Catherine Memorial Hospital, New Orleans, LA, p. A276

LANDSMAN, Joseph, President and Chief Executive Officer, University Of Tennessee Medical Center, Knoxville, TN, p. A572

LANDSTROM, John, Director Human Resources, Rml Specialty Hospital, IL, p. A186

LANE, Andrea, Chief Financial Officer, Conway Behavioral Health Hospital, Conway-Faulkner County, AR, p. A40

LANE, Charles A., Chief Medical Officer, Anderson Hospital, Maryville, IL, p. A188

LANE, Diron
Director Information Systems, Lewisgale Hospital Montgomery, Blacksburg, VA, p. A655
Director Information Systems, Lewisgale Hospital Pulaski, Pulaski, VA, p. A664

LANE, Kevin, D.O.
Chief of Staff, Hardeman County Memorial Hospital, Quanah, TX, p. A629
Vice President Information Systems, Silver Cross Hospital, New Lenox, IL, p. A191

LANE, Kim, Chief Fiscal Service, Overton Brooks Veterans Affairs Medical Center, Shreveport, LA, p. A278

LANE, Mike, Chief Operating Officer, Twin Cities Community Hospital, Templeton, CA, p. A91

LANE, Richard, Chief Financial Officer, Mid-America Rehabilitation Hospital, Shawnee Mission, KS, p. A246

LANE, Sonia, Interim Chief Nursing Officer, Uc Irvine Medical Center, Orange, CA, p. A76

LANEAUX, Eleanor, Director Information Systems, Placentia-Linda Hospital, Placentia, CA, p. A78

LANER, Richard, Jr, Manager Information Systems, Miners' Colfax Medical Center, NM, p. A418

LANEY, Samuel Mark., M.D., Chief Executive Officer, Mosaic Life Care, Saint Joseph, MO, p. A367

LANG, Cyndi, Director Information Services, French Hospital Medical Center, San Luis Obispo, CA, p. A87

LANG, Gary, M.D., Clinical Director, Claremore Indian Hospital, Claremore, OK, p. A497

LANG, Gordon, M.D., Chief of Staff, Trego County-Lemke Memorial Hospital, Wakeeney, KS, p. A247

LANG, Jeff, Chief Executive Officer, Coquille Valley Hospital, Coquille, OR, p. A512

LANG, John Christopher., Chief Executive Officer, Cass Regional Medical Center, Harrisonville, MO, p. A360

LANG, Joseph, M.D., Chief of Staff, Carolinas Continuecare Hospital At Pineville, Charlotte, NC, p. A449

LANG, Linda, Chief Human Resources Officer, Marin General Hospital, Greenbrae, CA, p. A61

LANG, Nicholas P, M.D., Chief Medical Officer, Uams Medical Center, Little Rock-Pulaski County, AR, p. A45

LANG, Richard, Ed.D., Vice President and Chief Information Officer, Doylestown Hospital, Doylestown, PA, p. A524

LANG, Richard T, Chief Financial Officer, Gouverneur Hospital, Gouverneur, NY, p. A427

LANGAN, Lynn, Chief Nursing Officer, Quillen Rehabilitation Hospital, Johnson City, TN, p. A572

LANGBEHN, Cody, Administrator, St. Luke's Wood River Medical Center, Ketchum, ID, p. A170

LANGBEHN, Jennifer, Medical Director, Mayo Clinic Health System In Saint James, Saint James, MN, p. A339

LANGBERG, Michael L, M.D., Senior Vice President Medical Affairs and Chief Medical Officer, Cedars-Sinai Medical Center, Los Angeles, CA, p. A66

LANGDON, Ashlee, Controller, Yalobusha General Hospital, Water Valley, MS, p. A354

LANGDORF, Brad, Vice President Clinical Services and Chief Nursing Officer, Community Hospital, Mccook, NE, p. A386

LANGE, Connie, R.N., Vice President Quality, Inpatient and Community Services, Lakes Regional Healthcare, Spirit Lake, IA, p. A230

LANGENBERG, Shannon, Director Human Resources, Jackson County Regional Health Center, Maquoketa, IA, p. A226

LANGENFELD, John, Medical Records Coordinator, Arizona Orthopedic Surgical Hospital, Chandler, AZ, p. A28

LANGFORD, Scott
  Administrator, Beaver Valley Hospital, Beaver, UT, p. A646
  Administrator, Milford Valley Memorial Hospital, Milford, UT, p. A647

LANGFORD, Terrie, Director Human Resources, Baylor Scott & White Surgical Hospital At Sherman, Sherman, TX, p. A635

LANGHOFF, Erik, M.D., Ph.D., Director, James J. Peters Veterans Affairs Medical Center, New York (Includes All Hospitals Located Within The Five Boroughs), NY, p. A432

LANGLAND, Robert, Senior Vice President and Chief Financial Officer, Stormont Vail Health, Topeka, KS, p. A246

LANGLEY, Kim
  Business Partner, Promedica Bixby Hospital, Adrian, MI, p. A307
  Business Partner, Promedica Herrick Hospital, Tecumseh, MI, p. A324

LANGLITZ, Sara, Controller, Kindred Hospital Houston Medical Center, Houston, TX, p. A611

LANGLOIS, John, Chief Executive Officer, Riverview Regional Medical Center, Gadsden, AL, p. A18

LANGMEAD, Paula A., Chief Executive Officer, Springfield Hospital Center, Sykesville, MD, p. A294

LANGSTON, David L
  Corporate Vice President Human Resources, Ut Health Rehabilitation Hospital, Tyler, TX, p. A641
  Corporate Vice President Human Resources, Ut Health Specialty Hospital, Tyler, TX, p. A641

LANIER, Donna, R.N., Chief Nursing Officer, Delta Medical Center, Memphis, TN, p. A575

LANIER, Mary, Vice President, Post Acute Services and Site Administrator, California Pacific Medical Center-Davies Campus, San Francisco, CA, p. A85

LANIER, Regina, MSN, R.N., Senior Vice President and Chief Nursing Officer, Onslow Memorial Hospital, Jacksonville, NC, p. A455

LANKFORD, Deanna, Business Office Manager, Plano Specialty Hospital, Plano, TX, p. A628

LANKOWICZ, Andrew, FACHE, President, Chi St. Alexius Health Devils Lake Hospital, Devils Lake, ND, p. A465

LANNING, John, Chief Operating Officer, Kearney Regional Medical Center, Kearney, NE, p. A385

LANNOYE, Craig, Vice President Operations, Wilson Memorial Hospital, Sidney, OH, p. A490

LANOUE, Cheryl, Chief Financial Officer, Ottawa County Health Center, Minneapolis, KS, p. A241

LANSDOWNE, Lynn M., Administrator Human Resources, Lehigh Valley Hospital - Pocono, East Stroudsburg, PA, p. A524

LANTOS, Phyllis R, Executive Vice President, Corporate Chief Financial Officer and Treasurer, The Allen Pavilion, NY, p. A434

LANTZY, William, Chief Financial Officer, Dmc Huron Valley-Sinai Hospital, Commerce Township, MI, p. A310

LANZ, April, Interim Administrator, Mayo Clinic Health System In Waseca, Waseca, MN, p. A342

LANZA, Nicholas, Controller, St. Mary's General Hospital, Passaic, NJ, p. A409

LAPERLE, Linda M, Vice President Administrative Services, Androscoggin Valley Hospital, Berlin, NH, p. A398

LAPHAM, Lisa, President and Chief Executive Officer, Healthsource Saginaw, Inc., Saginaw, MI, p. A322

LAPLANT, Dawn, Manager Health Information Management, Brown County Community Treatment Center, Green Bay, WI, p. A694

LAPOSTA, Mary Jo, Ph.D., R.N., Senior Vice President Patient Care and Organizational Excellence, Saratoga Hospital, Saratoga Springs, NY, p. A442

LAPPEN, Michael, Chief Executive Officer, Milwaukee County Behavioral Health Division, Milwaukee, WI, p. A699

LARA, Anne, Chief Information Officer, Union Hospital, Elkton, MD, p. A291

LARA, Sergio, M.D., Chief Medical Officer, Covenant Hospital Plainview, Plainview, TX, p. A628

LARAMIE, Robert, Chief Information Officer, Addison Gilbert Hospital, MA, p. A295

LARAMIE, Wayne, Vice President Nursing, Ssm Health St. Clare Hospital - Fenton, Fenton, MO, p. A359

LARCAS, John, M.D., Acting Medical Director, Choate Mental Health Center, Anna, IL, p. A173

LAREAU, Daniel, Executive Director, Operations and Information, St. Vincent Carmel Hospital, Carmel, IN, p. A201

LAREAU, Kim, Vice President and Chief Information Officer, Regions Hospital, Saint Paul, MN, p. A339

LARET, Mark R., Chief Executive Officer, Ucsf Medical Center Mission Bay, CA, p. A86

LARIMER, Cynthia, M.D., Chief of Staff, Lake Butler Hospital Hand Surgery Center, Lake Butler, FL, p. A127

LARIMORE, Rhonda
  Vice President Human Resources, Magee-Womens Hospital Of Upmc, Pittsburgh, PA, p. A537
  Vice President, Human Resources, Children's Hospital Of Pittsburgh Of Upmc, Pittsburgh, PA, p. A537

LARISCY, Christopher, M.D., Chief of Staff, Davis Regional Medical Center, Statesville, NC, p. A461

LARISCY, Robin Barton, M.D., Medical Director, Mary S Harper Geriatric Psychiatry Center, Tuscaloosa, AL, p. A24

LARIVEE, Theresa M., Chief Executive Officer, Pennsylvania Hospital, Philadelphia, PA, p. A536

LARIVIERE, Beckye, Controller, Encompass Health Rehabilitation Hospital Of Charleston, Charleston, SC, p. A550

LARKIN, Kevin
  Regional Chief Financial Officer, Presence Mercy Medical Center, Aurora, IL, p. A173
  Regional Chief Financial Officer, Presence Saint Joseph Hospital, Elgin, IL, p. A182

LARKIN, Kim, Chief Information Officer, Washington County Hospital, Nashville, IL, p. A191

LARKIN-SKINNER, Melissa, Chief Executive Officer, Centerstone Hospital, Bradenton, FL, p. A118

LARMER, Jennifer, R.N., Chief Clinical Officer, Lincoln Hospital, Davenport, WA, p. A671

LARNER, Cheryl, Chief Financial Officer, Sentara Careplex Hospital, Hampton, VA, p. A659

LAROSA, Vincent
  Director of Information Systems, Landmark Medical Center-Woonsocket Unit, RI, p. A548
  Director of Information Technology Services, Rehabilitation Hospital Of Rhode Island, North Smithfield, RI, p. A547

LAROWE, Mary E., FACHE, President and Chief Executive Officer, Tlc Health Network - Lake Shore Hospital, NY, p. A425

LARRISON, Robert G., Jr, President, Carolinas Rehabilitation, Charlotte, NC, p. A449

LARSEN, Bill, Vice President Human Resources, Driscoll Children's Hospital, Corpus Christi, TX, p. A594

LARSEN, Catherine M, Director Marketing, Sutter Tracy Community Hospital, Tracy, CA, p. A92

LARSEN, Donald, M.D., Chief Medical Officer, Providence Saint John's Health Center, Santa Monica, CA, p. A89

LARSEN, Kevin, Associate Vice President, Business and Ancillary Services, Uconn, John Dempsey Hospital, Farmington, CT, p. A108

LARSEN, Ryan C., FACHE, Administrator, Community Medical Center, Inc., Falls City, NE, p. A383

LARSON, Alan, Chief Executive Officer, Sovah Health-Danville, Danville, VA, p. A657

LARSON, Bill, Vice President Finance and Chief Financial Officer, Torrance Memorial Medical Center, Torrance, CA, p. A92

LARSON, Derek, Information Technology Network, Lakes Regional Healthcare, Spirit Lake, IA, p. A230

LARSON, Erick, Vice President and Chief Information Officer, Mid-Columbia Medical Center, The Dalles, OR, p. A518

LARSON, Jennifer, M.D., Chief of Staff, Blue Ridge Medical Center - Yancey Campus, NC, p. A461

LARSON, Jon, M.D., Medical Director, Encompass Health Rehabilitation Institute Of Tucson, Tucson, AZ, p. A37

LARSON, Karla, Director Human Resources, Stevens Community Medical Center, Morris, MN, p. A336

LARSON, Kay, R.N., Chief Nursing Officer, Essentia Health St. Mary's - Detroit Lakes, Detroit Lakes, MN, p. A330

LARSON, Michael, Vice President Chief Information Officer, Midmichigan Medical Center-Clare, Clare, MI, p. A310

LARSON, Mike, Chief Operating Officer, Essentia Health St. Joseph's Medical Center, Brainerd, MN, p. A328

LARSON, Pamela, Division Director Financial Services, Hutchinson Health, Hutchinson, MN, p. A333

LARSON, Rodney, M.D., Medical Director, Fall River Hospital, Hot Springs, SD, p. A561

LARSON, Ronald, Chief Financial Officer, Va San Diego Healthcare System, San Diego, CA, p. A84

LARSON, Scott, M.D., Vice President Medical Affairs and Chief Medical Officer, Children's Hospital At Bronson, MI, p. A317

LARSON, Scott C., Chief Executive Officer, Sanford Canton-Inwood Medical Center, Canton, SD, p. A559

LARSON, Shelly, Chief Financial Officer, Hot Springs County Memorial Hospital, Thermopolis, WY, p. A710

LARSON, Steve, M.D., Director Information Systems, Mercy Medical Center-Sioux City, Sioux City, IA, p. A229

LARSON, Tammy, Chief Financial Officer, Towner County Medical Center, Cando, ND, p. A464

LARSON, Tracy, MS, Vice President Patient Care Services and Chief Nursing Officer, Mercy Medical Center-Sioux City, Sioux City, IA, p. A229

LARSON, Walt, Vice President Finance, Tillamook Regional Medical Center, Tillamook, OR, p. A518

LARSON, Wendy, Chief Clinical Officer, Promise Hospital Of Phoenix, Mesa, AZ, p. A31

LASATER, Laci, R.N., Chief Nursing Officer, Christus Spohn Hospital Kleberg, Kingsville, TX, p. A617

LASCANO, Terrance, Administrative Officer, U.S. Public Health Service Indian Hospital, Cass Lake, MN, p. A329

LASECKI, Cynthia, M.D., Chief Medical Officer, Bellin Memorial Hospital, Green Bay, WI, p. A693

LASECKI, Matt, Interim Vice President Human Resources, Providence Hospital, Washington, DC, p. A116

LASHBROOK, Amy, Chief Financial Officer, Community Hospital Of Bremen, Bremen, IN, p. A200

LASHER, Karen, Chief Nursing Officer, Vanderbilt Stallworth Rehabilitation Hospital, Nashville, TN, p. A578

LASHKARI, Haady, Chief Administrative Officer, Ojai Valley Community Hospital, Ojai, CA, p. A76

LASKER, Rose, Director Information Services, Bluefield Regional Medical Center, Bluefield, WV, p. A681

LASKOWSKI, Rose, R.N., Director, Caro Center, Caro, MI, p. A309

LASKY, John, Jr, Vice President, Chief Human Resources Officer, Temple University Hospital - Episcopal Division, PA, p. A536

LASOTA, John, Assistant Finance Officer, Clement J. Zablocki Veterans Affairs Medical Center, Milwaukee, WI, p. A698

LATER, Elizabeth B., R.N., Chief Nursing Officer, Ogden Regional Medical Center, Ogden, UT, p. A648

LATIBEAUDIERE, Jorge, Chief Financial Officer, Lea Regional Medical Center, Hobbs, NM, p. A417

LATIMER, Kevin, Chief Executive Officer, Childress Regional Medical Center, Childress, TX, p. A592

LATIMER, Timothy, Chief Financial Officer, University Of Kansas Health System Great Bend Campus, Great Bend, KS, p. A236

LATIOLAIS, Ryan J, Director Information Systems, Our Lady Of Lourdes Regional Medical Center, Lafayette, LA, p. A271

LATNEY, Cynthia, Chief Nursing Officer, St. Francis Medical Center, CO, p. A98

LATO, Barb, Chief Nursing Officer, Aspirus Medford Hospital & Clinics, Inc., Medford, WI, p. A697

LATREILLE, William, M.D., Chief Medical Officer, The University Of Vermont Health Network - Alice Hyde Medical Center, Malone, NY, p. A429

LATTERNER, Renee, Director Human Resources, Lake Wales Medical Center, Lake Wales, FL, p. A127

LATTO, Janet B., Chief Nursing Officer and Disaster Officer, Pacifica Hospital Of The Valley, Los Angeles, CA, p. A69

LATUCHIE, Richard
  Chief Information Officer, Spearfish Regional Surgery Center, SD, p. A564
  Vice President Business Development, Rapid City Regional Hospital, Rapid City, SD, p. A563

LATULIPPE, Steve, President Medical Staff, East Liverpool City Hospital, East Liverpool, OH, p. A482

LAU, James, M.D., Area Medical Director, Kaiser Permanente Panorama City Medical Center, Los Angeles, CA, p. A67

LAUBENTHAL, Sherrie L, R.N., Chief Nursing Officer, Clarinda Regional Health Center, Clarinda, IA, p. A219

LAUDON, Larry A., Administrator, Community Behavioral Health Hospital - Bemidji, Bemidji, MN, p. A328

LAUE, Edward, M.D., Chief Medical Officer, Texas Health Huguley Hospital Fort Worth South, Burleson, TX, p. A591

LAUE, Jerry
  Administrator, St. Vincent Clay Hospital, Brazil, IN, p. A200
  Administrator, St. Vincent Dunn Hospital, Bedford, IN, p. A200

LAUER, Bill, Chief Information Officer, Morris County Hospital, Council Grove, KS, p. A234

LAUF, Michael K., President and Chief Executive Officer, Cape Cod Hospital, Hyannis, MA, p. A300

LAUFFER, Daniel, FACHE
  President and Chief Executive Officer, Saint Francis Hospital, Charleston, WV, p. A682
  President and Chief Executive Officer, Thomas Memorial Hospital, South Charleston, WV, p. A687

LAUFLE, Chuck, Director of Information Services, San Luis Valley Health, Alamosa, CO, p. A96

LAUGHLIN, Jennifer, Chief Information Officer, Watertown Regional Medical Center, Watertown, WI, p. A705

LAUGHLIN, Warren, Vice President Human Resources, Longmont United Hospital, Longmont, CO, p. A103

LAUGHLIN WAGNER, Nancy, R.N., Chief Executive Officer, Select Specialty Hospital-Omaha, Omaha, NE, p. A388

LAUKAITIS, Fran, R.N., FACHE, President, Methodist Charlton Medical Center, Dallas, TX, p. A597

LAUNIUS, Billie, Director Business Finance, Dallas County Medical Center, Fordyce-Dallas County, AR, p. A42

LAUREANO, Prudencio A., Chief Executive Officer, Hospital Universitario Dr. Ramon Ruiz Arnau, Bayamon, PR, p. A712

LAURENTS, W Robert, CPA, Chief Financial Officer, Madison Parish Hospital, Tallulah, LA, p. A280

LAURETANO, Arthur, M.D., Chief Medical Officer, Lowell General Hospital, Saints Campus, MA, p. A301

LAURETO, Rose Ann
Chief Information Officer, Promedica Fostoria Community Hospital, Fostoria, OH, p. A482
Chief Information Officer, Toledo Children's Hospital, OH, p. A491
Corporate Vice President Information Resources, Promedica Bay Park Hospital, Oregon, OH, p. A488

LAURIDSEN, Amy, Director Human Resources, Northern Colorado Rehabilitation Hospital, Johnstown, CO, p. A102

LAURIN, George M, Interim Director Human Resources, Crisp Regional Hospital, Cordele, GA, p. A151

LAUTER, Keith A.
Chief Financial Officer, Franciscan Health Carmel, Carmel, IN, p. A201
Regional Chief Financial Officer, Franciscan Health Indianapolis, Indianapolis, IN, p. A206
Vice President Finance, Franciscan Health Crawfordsville, Crawfordsville, IN, p. A202

LAUTEREN, Mark, Chief Information Officer, Usa Health University Hospital, Mobile, AL, p. A21

LAUTNER, Marty, Vice President Finance and Chief Financial Officer, Cardinal Hill Rehabilitation Hospital, Lexington, KY, p. A254

LAUVE, Lisa R., R.N., Regional Chief Nursing Executive and Chief Operating Officer, Christus St. Frances Cabrini Hospital, Alexandria, LA, p. A262

LAUVER, David, M.D., Chief Division Hospital Based Care, Central Maine Medical Center, Lewiston, ME, p. A284

LAUZAU, Paul, Controller, Beaumont Hospital - Trenton, Trenton, MI, p. A324

LAVELLE, John P., M.D., Chief Medical Officer, Parkview Hospital, Wheeler, TX, p. A644

LAVELY, Patricia A, FACHE, Senior Vice President and Chief Information Officer, Gwinnett Medical Center, GA, p. A156

LAVENDER, John Kenneth, Chief Information Officer, Lincoln County Health System, Fayetteville, TN, p. A569

LAVER, Joseph H., M.D., Chief Medical Officer, Stony Brook Southampton Hospital, NY, p. A443

LAVERY FRASCA, Denise Anne, MSN, R.N., Vice President Patient Care Services and Chief Nursing Officer, Jeanes Hospital, Philadelphia, PA, p. A535

LAVIGNETTE, Brooke, Director of Nursing, Sycamore Springs Hospital, Lafayette, IN, p. A209

LAVIOLETTE, Judy, M.D.
Chief Medical Officer, Texas Health Harris Methodist Hospital Azle, Azle, TX, p. A587
Chief Medical Officer, Texas Health Harris Methodist Hospital Cleburne, Cleburne, TX, p. A592

LAVOIE, Brad, Chief Financial Officer, Coastal Harbor Treatment Center, Savannah, GA, p. A160

LAW, Charles, Ph.D., Chief Operating Officer, Catawba Hospital, Catawba, VA, p. A656

LAW, Johnny, Area Information Officer, Kaiser Permanente Richmond Medical Center, CA, p. A76

LAWHORN, David, M.D., Chief Medical Officer, Shoshone Medical Center, Kellogg, ID, p. A169

LAWHORN, Renee, Director Medical Records, Ut Health Carthage, Carthage, TX, p. A592

LAWHORNE, Thomas
Chief Financial Officer, Regional Medical Center Bayonet Point, Hudson, FL, p. A125
Interim Chief Executive Officer, Regional Medical Center Bayonet Point, Hudson, FL, p. A125

LAWLER, Anne, Director Human Resources, North Mississippi Medical Center-Hamilton, Hamilton, AL, p. A19

LAWLER, Kay, Business Office Manager, North Mississippi Medical Center-West Point, West Point, MS, p. A354

LAWLER, Patrick, Chief Executive Officer, Youth Villages Inner Harbour Campus, Douglasville, GA, p. A152

LAWLESS, JoBeth, Chief Nursing Officer, Nursing Services and Director Emergency Management Services, Lucas County Health Center, Chariton, IA, p. A219

LAWLESS, Rosalie, Director Human Resources, Fairlawn Rehabilitation Hospital, Worcester, MA, p. A306

LAWONN, Kenneth
Senior Vice President and Chief Information Officer, Chi Health Mercy Corning, Corning, IA, p. A219

Senior Vice President and Chief Information Officer, Chi Health Schuyler, Schuyler, NE, p. A390

Senior Vice President and Chief Information Officer, Sharp Grossmont Hospital, La Mesa, CA, p. A63

Senior Vice President and Chief Information Officer, Sharp Memorial Hospital, San Diego, CA, p. A84

Senior Vice President Information Systems, Sharp Mcdonald Center, CA, p. A84

LAWRASON, Jock, M.D., Chief Medical Officer, Nantucket Cottage Hospital, Nantucket, MA, p. A302

LAWRENCE, Glenda, R.N., Chief Nursing Officer, Red River Hospital, Llc, Wichita Falls, TX, p. A644

LAWRENCE, Jonathan I.
President and Chief Executive Officer, St. Joseph's Hospital, Elmira, NY, p. A426
System Chief Operating Officer, Arnot Ogden Medical Center, Elmira, NY, p. A426

LAWRENCE, Kelsey, Manager Information Technology, Union County General Hospital, Clayton, NM, p. A416

LAWRENCE, Mark, Chief Information Systems, Saint Francis Hospital-Bartlett, Bartlett, TN, p. A566

LAWRENCE, Michael, Chief Financial Officer, Ingalls Memorial Hospital, Harvey, IL, p. A185

LAWRENCE, Paige, Assistant Administrator, University Of Mississippi Medical Center Holmes County, Lexington, MS, p. A349

LAWRENCE, Sandra A J, Executive Vice President and Chief Financial Officer, Children's Mercy Hospital Kansas, Overland Park, KS, p. A243

LAWRENCE, Stephanie
Chief Financial Officer, Kentfield Rehabilitation And Specialty Hospital, Kentfield, CA, p. A62
Chief Financial Officer, Vibra Specialty Hospital Of Portland, Portland, OR, p. A517

LAWRENCE, Tiffany, Vice President of Finance, Sanford South University, ND, p. A466

LAWRENSON, Victoria
Chief Operating Officer, Bullock County Hospital, Union Springs, AL, p. A24
Chief Operating Officer, Crenshaw Community Hospital, Luverne, AL, p. A20

LAWS, Stephanie, Vice President, Administrator, Union Hospital Clinton, Clinton, IN, p. A201

LAWSON, Alvin R., FACHE, JD, Chief Executive Officer, Healthsouth Western Hills Regional Rehabilitation Hospital, Parkersburg, WV, p. A686

LAWSON, Beth, Chief Nursing Officer, Union Medical Center, Union, SC, p. A557

LAWSON, Chad, Chief Information Officer, St. Anthony Regional Hospital, Carroll, IA, p. A218

LAWSON, David C., Senior Vice President Human Resources, St. Clare Hospital, Lakewood, WA, p. A673

LAWSON, Eric, Chief Executive Officer, North Florida Regional Medical Center, Gainesville, FL, p. A123

LAWSON, Jessica, Director of Nursing, Greenwood Regional Rehabilitation Hospital, Greenwood, SC, p. A554

LAWSON, Judy, Director Information Services, Norton Community Hospital, Norton, VA, p. A663

LAWSON, Linda B., Chief Nursing Officer, The Hospitals Of Providence Transmountain Campus, El Paso, TX, p. A602

LAWSON, Michael, President and Chief Operating Officer, Ohiohealth Grant Medical Center, Columbus, OH, p. A478

LAWSON, Penny, Human Resource Director, Quillen Rehabilitation Hospital, Johnson City, TN, p. A572

LAWSON, Ralph E, Executive Vice President and Chief Financial Officer, Baptist Children's Hospital, FL, p. A129

LAWSON, Sandra K., Interim Director Fiscal Services, Shriners Hospitals For Children-St. Louis, Saint Louis, MO, p. A368

LAWTON, Geoff, Vice President Operations, Littleton Adventist Hospital, Littleton, CO, p. A103

LAY, A K, M.D., Jr, Chief Medical Officer, Jasper General Hospital, Bay Springs, MS, p. A343

LAY, Barbara, Chief Executive Officer, Pocahontas Memorial Hospital, Buckeye, WV, p. A681

LAYFIELD, Michael G., Interim Chief Executive Officer, Lauderdale Community Hospital, Ripley, TN, p. A579

LAYMAN, Benjamin, President, Ssm Health St. Mary's Hospital Janesville, Janesville, WI, p. A695

LAYNE, Kristine, R.N., Chief Nursing Officer, Riverwood Healthcare Center, Aitkin, MN, p. A327

LAYTON, Ann, M.D., Chief of Staff, North Metro Medical Center, Jacksonville-Pulaski County, AR, p. A44

LAYUGAN, Melvin, Director Human Resources, Horizon Specialty Hospital, Las Vegas, NV, p. A394

LAZARUS, David, M.D., Medical Director Clinical Affairs, Newton Medical Center, Newton, NJ, p. A409

LAZENBY, John, M.D., Chief Medical Officer, Memorial Hospital Jacksonville, Jacksonville, FL, p. A125

LAZO, Nelson, Chief Executive Officer, Baptist Health South Florida, Doctors Hospital, Coral Gables, FL, p. A120

LAZO, Wendy, President, St. Luke's Hospital - Miners Campus, Coaldale, PA, p. A523

LAZROFF, Gary, Vice President Human Resources, St. John Medical Center, Westlake, OH, p. A493

LAZZARO, Frank A., III, Chief Human Resources Officer, Phelps County Regional Medical Center, Rolla, MO, p. A366

LE, Emily, Director Information Technology and Services, Woman's Hospital Of Texas, Houston, TX, p. A614

LE, Jennifer, Chief Financial Officer, Southern Hills Hospital And Medical Center, Las Vegas, NV, p. A394

LE, Tuan
Chief Executive Officer, Christus Dubuis Hospital Of Port Arthur, TX, p. A588
Chief Executive Officer, Continuecare Hospital At Baptist Health Corbin, Corbin, KY, p. A250

LEA, Hampton P S., Acting Chief Executive Officer, Eastern Louisiana Mental Health System, Jackson, LA, p. A269

LEA, Randy, M.D., M.P.H., Vice President and Chief Medical Officer, Alice Peck Day Memorial Hospital, Lebanon, NH, p. A399

LEA, Rich, Vice President Operations, Euclid Hospital, Euclid, OH, p. A482

LEACH, Craig, President and Chief Executive Officer, Torrance Memorial Medical Center, Torrance, CA, p. A92

LEACH, Dana, Director Human Resources, Alliancehealth Midwest, Midwest City, OK, p. A501

LEACH, Deonca, Director, Human Resources, Carolinas Rehabilitation, Charlotte, NC, p. A449

LEACH, Ryan, Chief Information Officer, St. John's Children's Hospital, IL, p. A196

LEACH, Todd, Vice President and Chief Information Officer, Angleton Danbury Campus, TX, p. A606

LEACH, Travis, President, Saint Alphonsus Medical Center - Nampa, Nampa, ID, p. A170

LEADBETTER, Dan, Information Technology Systems Site Lead, Chi Lakewood Health, Baudette, MN, p. A328

LEADBETTER, Raymond J., Jr
Revenue Cycle Consultant, Appling Healthcare System, Baxley, GA, p. A148
Interim Chief Executive Officer, Appling Healthcare System, Baxley, GA, p. A148

LEAHY, Mary, M.D.
Chief Executive Officer, Bon Secours Community Hospital, Port Jervis, NY, p. A440
Chief Executive Officer, Good Samaritan Regional Medical Center, Suffern, NY, p. A443
Chief Executive Officer, St. Anthony Community Hospital, Warwick, NY, p. A445

LEAHY, Mary P, Regional Vice Presiden, Chief Human Resources Officer, St. Joseph Hospital, Orange, CA, p. A76

LEAHY, Rosanne, Vice President Nursing Services, Carolinaeast Health System, New Bern, NC, p. A458

LEAKE, Neta F, Administrative Assistant Human Resources, West Feliciana Parish Hospital, Saint Francisville, LA, p. A278

LEAKE, Sandy, MSN, R.N., Associate Director, Nursing and Patient Care Services, Atlanta Veterans Affairs Medical Center, Decatur, GA, p. A152

LEAKEY, Kim, R.N., Chief Nursing Officer, Lafayette Regional Health Center, Lexington, MO, p. A363

LEAL, Carlos, Director Information Technology, Valley Regional Medical Center, Brownsville, TX, p. A590

LEAL, Enrique A, M.D., III, Chief of Staff, Sweeny Community Hospital, Sweeny, TX, p. A638

LEAL, Joseph M, M.D., Jr, Chief of Staff, Glendive Medical Center, Glendive, MT, p. A375

LEAMING, Larry E., Ph.D., FACHE, Chief Executive Officer, Estes Park Medical Center, Estes Park, CO, p. A100

LEAMON, Jim, Chief Financial Officer, Jfk Medical Center, Atlantis, FL, p. A117

LEAR, Richard
Director Information Systems, St. David's Rehabilitation Center, TX, p. A586
Director Information Systems, St. David's South Austin Medical Center, Austin, TX, p. A587

LEARSON, Jerome, Manager Information Technology and Chief Security Officer, Palo Verde Hospital, Blythe, CA, p. A53

LEARY, Edward B.
Chief Executive Officer, Vibra Hospital Of Southeastern Massachusetts, New Bedford, MA, p. A302
Interim Chief Executive Officer, Vibra Hospital Of Western Massachusetts-Central Campus, MA, p. A304

LEASE, Faye, Director of Nursing, Reeves County Hospital, Pecos, TX, p. A628

LEASE-HOMEYER, Cheryl, Lead Information Technology Business Partner, Mercy Hospital Carthage, Carthage, MO, p. A357

LEIF, Sue, R.N., Director Human Resources, Annie Jeffrey Memorial County Health Center, Osceola, NE, p. A389

LEIGHTON, Heather, Director, Revenue Cycle and Privacy Officer, Upper Connecticut Valley Hospital, Colebrook, NH, p. A398

LEIGHTON, Martha, Senior Vice President and Chief Nursing Officer, Elliot Hospital, Manchester, NH, p. A400

LEIGHTON, Richard, Financial Application Analyst, Unity Medical & Surgical Hospital, Mishawaka, IN, p. A211

LEINEN, Rick J, Chief Financial Officer, Montgomery County Memorial Hospital, Red Oak, IA, p. A228

LEININGER, Bethany, Manager Human Resource, Hillcrest Hospital Cushing, Cushing, OK, p. A497

LEISHER, George, Jr
Chief Human Resources Officer, Antelope Valley Hospital, Lancaster, CA, p. A64
Vice President Human Resources, Hollywood Presbyterian Medical Center, Los Angeles, CA, p. A67

LEISHER, Karla, Business Office Manager, Beaver County Memorial Hospital, Beaver, OK, p. A496

LEISING, Elizabeth, Chief Nursing Officer and Vice President Patient Services, Margaret Mary Health, Batesville, IN, p. A199

LEIST, Frank, Human Resources Manager, Piedmont Mountainside Hospital, Jasper, GA, p. A155

LEIST, Vincent, President and Chief Executive Officer, North Arkansas Regional Medical Center, Harrison-Boone County, AR, p. A43

LEITERMAN, Gretchen, Chief Operating Officer, Ssm Health Saint Louis University Hospital-South, MO, p. A369

LEITNER, Mark, FACHE, Administrator, Ut Health Henderson, Henderson, TX, p. A609

LEJEUNE, Lucille, Assistant Administrator and Chief Financial Officer, Acadia-St. Landry Hospital, Church Point, LA, p. A265

LEJSEK, Shari, Administrator, Patients' Hospital Of Redding, Redding, CA, p. A80

LELAND, Joni, Director Human Resources, Gonzales Healthcare Systems, Gonzales, TX, p. A607

LEM, Alan
Vice President Finance, Fairview Ridges Hospital, Burnsville, MN, p. A329
Vice President Finance, Fairview Southdale Hospital, Edina, MN, p. A331

LEMAIRE, Joseph M
Executive Vice President Finance and Partner Company Operations, Hackensack Meridian Health Bayshore Community Hospital, Holmdel, NJ, p. A406
Executive Vice President Finance, Hackensack Meridian Health Riverview Medical Center, Red Bank, NJ, p. A411
Executive Vice President, Hackensack Meridian Health Southern Ocean Medical Center, Manahawkin, NJ, p. A407

LEMAISTRE, Court, FACHE, Chief Operating Officer, Lafayette General Orthopedic Hospital, LA, p. A271

LEMANSKI, Dennis R, D.O., Senior Vice President Medical Affairs and Medical Education/CMO, Henry Ford Wyandotte Hospital, Wyandotte, MI, p. A326

LEMASTERS, Debra J, Director Human Resources, Woodlawn Hospital, Rochester, IN, p. A214

LEMAY, Catherine, Vice President Finance, Millinocket Regional Hospital, Millinocket, ME, p. A285

LEMAY, Robert Raymond, R.N., Chief Nursing Officer, The Physicians Centre Hospital, Bryan, TX, p. A591

LEMBCKE, Brad, M.D., Vice President Medical Staff Affairs, Karl And Esther Hoblitzelle Memorial Hospital, TX, p. A596

LEMEL, Mark, Chief of Staff, Transylvania Regional Hospital, Brevard, NC, p. A448

LEMIEUX, Harry, Chief Information Officer, Harrington Hospital, Southbridge, MA, p. A304

LEMIEUX, Kandie, Administrative Assistant and Director Human Resources, Northern Rockies Medical Center, Cut Bank, MT, p. A374

LEMKE, Michelle, Administrator Human Resources and Support Services, Ridgecrest Regional Hospital, Ridgecrest, CA, p. A80

LEMLE, Trent, Chief Financial Officer, Fayette County Memorial Hospital, Washington Court House, OH, p. A493

LEMMER, Donn J, Chief Financial Officer and Chief Operating Officer, Munson Healthcare Manistee Hospital, Manistee, MI, p. A318

LEMMERMAN, Deborah, Chief People Officer, Hebrew Rehabilitation Center, Roslindale, MA, p. A303

LEMMONS, Joe, D.O., Chief of Staff, Lehigh Regional Medical Center, Lehigh Acres, FL, p. A128

LEMOINE, Kirk, Chief Executive Officer, Bienville Medical Center, Arcadia, LA, p. A263

LEMON, Brian J.
President, Behavioral Health Center, IL, p. A198

President, Northwestern Medicine Marianjoy Rehabilitation Hospital, Wheaton, IL, p. A198

LEMON, Marc, Chief Executive Officer, Kindred Hospital Denver South, Denver, CO, p. A99

LEMON, Rita, Director Human Resources, Avera Queen Of Peace Hospital, Mitchell, SD, p. A562

LEMON, Thomas R., Chief Executive Officer, Munson Healthcare Otsego Memorial Hospital, Gaylord, MI, p. A313

LEMONTE, David, Vice President and Chief Operating Officer, Christus Spohn Hospital Kleberg, Kingsville, TX, p. A617

LENA, Ela C
Administrator and Vice President Operations, Bethesda Hospital West, FL, p. A118
Interim System Chief Nursing Officer, Bethesda Hospital West, FL, p. A118

LENAHAN, Kevin
Director Corporate Accounting, Budgets, Grants and Reimbursements, Newton Medical Center, Newton, NJ, p. A409
Vice President Finance and Chief Financial Officer, Overlook Medical Center, Summit, NJ, p. A412

LENAMOND, Kevin, Information Management Service Line Executive, Michael E. Debakey Veterans Affairs Medical Center, Houston, TX, p. A612

LENARD, Gary, Director Human Resources, Hendricks Regional Health, Danville, IN, p. A202

LENARZ, Sandy, Chief Nursing Officer, Grand Itasca Clinic And Hospital, Grand Rapids, MN, p. A332

LENDARIS, Nia, Regional Vice President Patient Care, Adventist Health St. Helena, Saint Helena, CA, p. A82

LENFANT, Rodney, Chief Financial Officer, Oakbend Medical Center Williams Way Campus, TX, p. A630

LENGFELDER, Valerie, M.D., Chief of Staff, Powell Valley Healthcare, Powell, WY, p. A709

LENIOR, Frank, Vice President Human Resources, St. Dominic-Jackson Memorial Hospital, Jackson, MS, p. A348

LENKO, Paul, Section Head Information Technology, Mayo Clinic Hospital, Phoenix, AZ, p. A33

LENKOWSKI, Thomas, Chief Financial Officer, Speare Memorial Hospital, Plymouth, NH, p. A401

LENNARTZ, Randal P., CPA, President and Chief Executive Officer, Highland District Hospital, Hillsboro, OH, p. A484

LENNON, Colin, Chief Financial Officer, Richard L. Roudebush Veterans Affairs Medical Center, Indianapolis, IN, p. A207

LENNON, Roslyn J, R.N., MS, Chief Nursing Officer, West Suburban Medical Center, Oak Park, IL, p. A192

LENTENBRINK, Laura, Vice President, Human Resources, Borgess-Pipp Hospital, MI, p. A316

LENTZ, Darrell, President, Aspirus Wausau Hospital, Inc., Wausau, WI, p. A705

LENTZ, Matt, R.N., Director of Patient Services, Brown County Hospital, Ainsworth, NE, p. A381

LENZ, Jan, Chief Nursing Officer, Athens-Limestone Hospital, Athens, AL, p. A13

LENZA, Robert, Chief Executive Officer, Methodist Children's Hospital, TX, p. A633

LENZO, Julie, Director Business Office, Amg Specialty Hospital-Albuquerque, Albuquerque, NM, p. A415

LEO, Elizabeth, Chief Human Resources Officer, Moses Taylor Hospital, Scranton, PA, p. A540

LEON, Daniel, Chief Financial Officer, Sherman Oaks Hospital, Los Angeles, CA, p. A69

LEON, Edwin, Chief Executive Officer, Pampa Regional Medical Center, Pampa, TX, p. A627

LEON, Luis, Chief Operating Officer, Desert Valley Hospital, Victorville, CA, p. A94

LEONARD, Anne, R.N., Chief Nursing Officer, Tristar Greenview Regional Hospital, Bowling Green, KY, p. A250

LEONARD, Barry, I, Vice President of Finance, Healthsouth Braintree Rehabilitation Hospital, Braintree, MA, p. A297

LEONARD, Beckie, R.N., Chief Nursing Officer, Foundation Surgical Hospital Of San Antonio, San Antonio, TX, p. A633

LEONARD, Bruce, M.D., Medical Director and Chief of Psychiatry, Colorado Mental Health Institute At Fort Logan, Denver, CO, p. A98

LEONARD, Donavan, Chief Financial Officer, Baptist Memorial Hospital-Booneville, Booneville, MS, p. A344

LEONARD, Edward F, Executive Vice President and Chief Operating Officer, White Plains Hospital Center, White Plains, NY, p. A446

LEONARD, James C., M.D., President and Chief Executive Officer, Carle Foundation Hospital, Urbana, IL, p. A197

LEONARD, Jayne, M.D., Family Medicine, Ashe Memorial Hospital, Jefferson, NC, p. A455

LEONARD, Julie
Chief Executive Officer, Garfield County Public Hospital District, Pomeroy, WA, p. A674
Chief Financial Officer, Garfield County Public Hospital District, Pomeroy, WA, p. A674

LEONARD, Kevin, Vice President, Finance, Henry Ford Allegiance Health, Jackson, MI, p. A316

LEONARD, Mark, Vice President Finance, Beaumont Hospital - Troy, Troy, MI, p. A325

LEONARD, Mark T.
Chief Executive Officer, Dickenson Community Hospital, Clintwood, VA, p. A657
Chief Executive Officer, Norton Community Hospital, Norton, VA, p. A663
Interim Chief Executive Officer, Lonesome Pine Hospital, Big Stone Gap, VA, p. A655

LEONARD, Robert, Director Information Services, Sierra Vista Regional Medical Center, San Luis Obispo, CA, p. A87

LEONARD, Steven E., President and Chief Executive Officer, Peninsula Regional Medical Center, Salisbury, MD, p. A294

LEONARD, Wes, Chief Executive Officer, Whitten Center, Clinton, SC, p. A551

LEONARD, William H., President, Carolinas Healthcare System University, Charlotte, NC, p. A449

LEONDAR, Kimberly, Director Human Resources, Texas Health Harris Methodist Hospital Stephenville, Stephenville, TX, p. A637

LEONELIS, Lisa, Chief Information Officer, Veterans Affairs Salt Lake City Health Care System, Salt Lake City, UT, p. A651

LEOPARD, Erik, Manager Human Resource, Methodist Hospital For Surgery, Addison, TX, p. A582

LEOPARD, Jimmy, FACHE, Chief Executive Officer, Wagoner Community Hospital, Wagoner, OK, p. A510

LEOPOLD, Michael, Chief Operating Officer, Broward Health Coral Springs, Coral Springs, FL, p. A120

LEPAK, Jason, M.D.
Medical Director, St. John Broken Arrow, Broken Arrow, OK, p. A496
Medical Director, St. John Sapulpa, Sapulpa, OK, p. A506

LEPPER, Dale, Chief Information Officer, Antelope Valley Hospital, Lancaster, CA, p. A64

LEPPKE, Ben, Chief Information Officer, Satanta District Hospital And Long Term Care, Satanta, KS, p. A245

LEQUEUX, Veronica, Vice President Human Resources, Blake Medical Center, Bradenton, FL, p. A118

LERASH, Terrance, President and Chief Executive Officer, Scheurer Hospital, Pigeon, MI, p. A320

LERCH, Gail, R.N.
Executive Vice President Human Resources, Straub Medical Center, Honolulu, HI, p. A165
Vice President Human Resources, Pali Momi Medical Center, Aiea, HI, p. A164
Vice President, Kapiolani Medical Center For Women & Children, Honolulu, HI, p. A164

LERCH, Shawn, Chief Executive Officer, Sauk Prairie Healthcare, Prairie Du Sac, WI, p. A701

LERMA, Robert J., MS, Chief Executive Officer, Austin Lakes Hospital, Austin, TX, p. A585

LERNER, Jerome, M.D., Medical Director, Sierra Tucson, Tucson, AZ, p. A37

LEROY, Michael
Senior Vice President and Chief Information Officer, Dmc - Detroit Receiving Hospital, Detroit, MI, p. A311
Senior Vice President and Chief Information Officer, Dmc Hutzel Women's Hospital, MI, p. A311

LESCH, Jason, Chief Financial Officer, Auburn Community Hospital, Auburn, NY, p. A422

LESCHER, Mary, Chief Clinical Officer, Doctor's Memorial Hospital, Perry, FL, p. A136

LESHER, Jennifer, Chief Financial Officer, Upmc Susquehanna Lock Haven, Lock Haven, PA, p. A530

LESIAK, Cindy, Vice President Patient Care Services and Director of Nursing, Boone County Health Center, Albion, NE, p. A381

LESINS, Ross, Chief Information Officer, Casa Colina Hospital And Health Systems, Pomona, CA, p. A78

LESKO, Joan, Director Technical Support and Services, Kidspeace Children's Hospital, Orefield, PA, p. A533

LESLIE, Andrea M., MSN, R.N., President, Spectrum Health Kelsey Hospital, MI, p. A314

LESLIE, Bruce W, M.D., Chief of Staff, Grant Memorial Hospital, Petersburg, WV, p. A686

LESLIE, Desdemona, Finance Officer, U.S. Public Health Service Indian Hospital-Whiteriver, Whiteriver, AZ, p. A38

LESLIE, Donald P, M.D., Medical Director, Shepherd Center, Atlanta, GA, p. A147

LESLIE, Kelly, Chief Financial Officer, Ferry County Memorial Hospital, Republic, WA, p. A675

LESLIE, Steve, Chief Financial Officer, Fairbanks Memorial Hospital, Fairbanks, AK, p. A26

LESMEISTER, Danielle, Chief Executive Officer, Prairie Ridge Hospital And Health Services, Elbow Lake, MN, p. A331

LESNIAK, Jacklynn, R.N., MS, Vice President Patient Care Services and Chief Nursing Officer, Midwestern Regional Medical Center, Zion, IL, p. A198

LESNICK, Kelly, Resource Manager Flight Commander, Wright Patterson Medical Center, Wright, OH, p. A494

LESNIEWSKI, Amy, Associate Director Patient Care Services, Alexandria Veterans Affairs Health Care System, Pineville, LA, p. A277

LESSMANN, Eric, Chief of Staff, South Sunflower County Hospital, Indianola, MS, p. A347

LESTER, Lisa, Chief Nursing Officer, Healthsouth Southern Hills Rehabilitation Hospital, Princeton, WV, p. A686

LESTER, Ron, Chief Human Resources, Cheyenne Veterans Affairs Medical Center, Cheyenne, WY, p. A708

LESTER, Wade K, Administrator, Riverside Hospital Of Louisiana, Alexandria, LA, p. A262

LESTER, Wade K., Administrator, Mid-Jefferson Extended Care Hospital, Nederland, TX, p. A625

LESTER, William, M.D., Vice President Medical Affairs, Cardinal Hill Rehabilitation Hospital, Lexington, KY, p. A254

LETCHWORTH, Mike, Manager Information Systems, Cherry Hospital, Goldsboro, NC, p. A453

LETEXIER, Lisa, Interim Chief Executive Officer, Pembina County Memorial Hospital And Wedgewood Manor, Cavalier, ND, p. A465

LETHI, Scott, R.N., FACHE, Chief Nursing Officer, Fort Duncan Regional Medical Center, Eagle Pass, TX, p. A600

LETT, Bryan W., Chief Executive Officer, Haven Behavioral Hospital Of Eastern Pennsylvania, Reading, PA, p. A539

LEU, Christopher, President, Texas Health Harris Methodist Hospital Stephenville, Stephenville, TX, p. A637

LEUBNER, Kristel, D.O., Chief of Staff, Chi St. Joseph Health Burleson Hospital, Caldwell, TX, p. A591

LEUDECKE, Amelia, Director Human Resources, Encompass Health Rehabilitation Hospital Of Round Rock, Round Rock, TX, p. A631

LEUNG, Lawrence, M.D., Chief of Staff, Veterans Affairs Palo Alto Health Care System, Livermore Division, CA, p. A77

LEURCK, Mary P, Human Resources Director, Amita Health Adventist Medical Center - Hinsdale, Hinsdale, IL, p. A186

LEVANGER, Nathan, M.D., Chief of Staff, Teton Valley Health Care, Driggs, ID, p. A169

LEVECK, Dianna, Chief Human Resources Officer, Good Samaritan Medical And Rehabilitation Center, OH, p. A494

LEVEILLEE, Mary, Senior Vice President Patient Care Services and Chief Nursing Officer, Butler Hospital, Providence, RI, p. A547

LEVELING, Jim, Director Information Technology, Kansas City Orthopaedic Institute, Leawood, KS, p. A240

LEVENDOFSKY, Randy, Director Information Technology, Thayer County Health Services, Hebron, NE, p. A384

LEVER, Roger, M.D., President Medical Staff, The Outer Banks Hospital, Nags Head, NC, p. A458

LEVERING, Theresa, Director Human Resources, Doctors Hospital Of Sarasota, Sarasota, FL, p. A138

LEVESQUE, David, Director, Information Systems, New Hampshire Hospital, Concord, NH, p. A398

LEVI, Dina, Director, Business Development, Psychiatric Institute Of Washington, Washington, DC, p. A116

LEVI, John, Director Human Resources, St. Lawrence Rehabilitation Center, Lawrenceville, NJ, p. A406

LEVIN, Alan M., MSN, R.N., Chief Nursing Officer, New York-Presbyterian Queens, New York (Includes All Hospitals Located Within The Five Boroughs), NY, p. A435

LEVINE, Larry L., President and Chief Executive Officer, Blythedale Children's Hospital, Valhalla, NY, p. A445

LEVINE, Peter H, M.D., Executive Medical Director Behavioral Health Services, Adventist Behavioral Health And Wellness Services, Rockville, MD, p. A293

LEVINE, Robert V, Executive Vice President and Chief Operating Officer, Flushing Hospital Medical Center, New York (Includes All Hospitals Located Within The Five Boroughs), NY, p. A432

LEVINE, Stuart M., M.D., President and Chief Medical Officer, Medstar Harbor Hospital, Baltimore, MD, p. A288

LEVINSON, Adam, Associate Director, Information Services, University Behavioral Healthcare, Piscataway, NJ, p. A410

LEVIS, Randolph, Chief Financial Officer, Saint Vincent Hospital, Erie, PA, p. A525

LEVISON, Julie, Director Human Resources, Providence Medford Medical Center, Medford, OR, p. A515

LEVITAN, Kenneth, Chief Administrative Officer, Einstein Medical Center Montgomery, East Norriton, PA, p. A524

LEVITOW, John, Vice President Patient Care Services and Chief Nursing Officer, Frisbie Memorial Hospital, Rochester, NH, p. A401

LEVITZ, Michele, Director Finance, St. Luke's Hospital - Miners Campus, Coaldale, PA, p. A523

LEVY, Becky
Chief Financial Officer, Bayview Behavioral Health Campus, CA, p. A74
Chief Financial Officer, Shasta Regional Medical Center, Redding, CA, p. A80
Chief Operating Officer, Shasta Regional Medical Center, Redding, CA, p. A80

LEVY, Dana, Chief Nursing Officer, University Of Maryland Charles Regional Medical Center, La Plata, MD, p. A292

LEVY, Jennifer C., Director Human Resources, Texas Institute For Surgery At Texas Health Presbyterian Dallas, Dallas, TX, p. A598

LEVY, Scott S, M.D., Vice President and Chief Medical Officer, Doylestown Hospital, Doylestown, PA, p. A524

LEVY, Susan M, M.D., Vice President Medical Affairs, Levindale Hebrew Geriatric Center And Hospital, Baltimore, MD, p. A288

LEWANDOWSKI, James, Vice President Human Resources, Perry Memorial Hospital, Princeton, IL, p. A194

LEWANDOWSKI, Jim, Interim Director of Human Resources, Sierra Surgery Hospital, NV, p. A392

LEWANDOWSKI, Terri, Director Financial Services, Ascension Our Lady Of Victory Hospital, Stanley, WI, p. A703

LEWELLEN, Patsy, Interim Chief Nursing Officer, Moberly Regional Medical Center, Moberly, MO, p. A364

LEWELLEN, Thomas, D.O., Chief of Staff, Delta Memorial Hospital, Dumas-Desha County, AR, p. A41

LEWERKE, Jane, Manager Human Resources, Northern Arizona Veterans Affairs Health Care System, Prescott, AZ, p. A34

LEWIS, Alene, R.N., Chief Nursing Officer, Raleigh General Hospital, Beckley, WV, p. A681

LEWIS, Angel
Senior Vice President Administration, Cookeville Regional Medical Center, Cookeville, TN, p. A568
Senior Vice President, Cumberland River Hospital, Celina, TN, p. A566

LEWIS, Barbara, Chief Nursing Officer, Alliancehealth Seminole, Seminole, OK, p. A506

LEWIS, Brandon, Director of Information Technology, Ivinson Memorial Hospital, Laramie, WY, p. A708

LEWIS, Brinsley, FACHE, President, Mount Carmel East Hospital, OH, p. A478

LEWIS, Caren, R.N., Chief Nursing Officer, Lawrence + Memorial Hospital, New London, CT, p. A110

LEWIS, Carlisle, III, Senior Vice President Legal and Human Resources, Sharp Mcdonald Center, CA, p. A84

LEWIS, Christine, Assistant Administrator, Finance, Hermann Area District Hospital, Hermann, MO, p. A360

LEWIS, Colleen, Director Human Resources, Texas Neurorehab Center, Austin, TX, p. A587

LEWIS, Courtney, Director Human Resources, Houston Methodist San Jacinto Hospital - Alexander, TX, p. A587

LEWIS, Craig, Chief Financial Officer, Sentara Albemarle Medical Center, Elizabeth City, NC, p. A452

LEWIS, Dana, Director Clinical Services, Southern Kentucky Rehabilitation Hospital, Bowling Green, KY, p. A250

LEWIS, Daniel
Chief Medical Officer, Takoma Regional Hospital, Greeneville, TN, p. A570
Executive Vice President and Chief Operating Officer, Metrohealth Medical Center, Cleveland, OH, p. A477

LEWIS, Darlene, Vice President Human Resources, Canton-Potsdam Hospital, Potsdam, NY, p. A440

LEWIS, Dave, Director Information Services, Ssm Health St. Francis Hospital - Maryville, Maryville, MO, p. A364

LEWIS, Dennis, M.D., Chief of Staff, Ashley Regional Medical Center, Vernal, UT, p. A651

LEWIS, Doug
Chief Financial Officer, St. Luke's Rehabilitation Hospital, Boise, ID, p. A168
Chief Financial Officer, Wheatland Memorial Healthcare, Harlowton, MT, p. A376

LEWIS, Douglas, Chief Financial Officer, Boulder City Hospital, Boulder City, NV, p. A392

LEWIS, Eric, Chief Executive Officer, Olympic Medical Center, Port Angeles, WA, p. A675

LEWIS, Gerry
Chief Information Officer, Seton Highland Lakes, Burnet, TX, p. A591
Chief Information Officer, Seton Medical Center Williamson, Round Rock, TX, p. A631

LEWIS, Gordon, Chief Executive Officer, Burnett Medical Center, Grantsburg, WI, p. A693

LEWIS, Irvan Wick", Vice President Human Resources, Mt. Graham Regional Medical Center, Safford, AZ, p. A35

LEWIS, J Steve, Director Finance, Youth Villages Inner Harbour Campus, Douglasville, GA, p. A152

LEWIS, Jacob, Chief Financial Officer, Mark Twain Medical Center, San Andreas, CA, p. A83

LEWIS, Jeff, Administrator, Waukesha County Mental Health Center, Waukesha, WI, p. A705

LEWIS, John I., President and Chief Executive Officer, Acmh Hospital, Kittanning, PA, p. A528

LEWIS, Kent, Director Information Services, Southwestern Medical Center, Lawton, OK, p. A500

LEWIS, Lawrence E., Chief Executive Officer, Pioneers Memorial Healthcare District, Brawley, CA, p. A53

LEWIS, Luther J., FACHE, Chief Executive Officer, Five Rivers Medical Center, Pocahontas-Randolph County, AR, p. A48

LEWIS, Marcus, Chief Executive Officer and Administrator, First Care Health Center, Park River, ND, p. A468

LEWIS, Marie, Human Resources Liaison, Veterans Affairs St. Louis Health Care System, Saint Louis, MO, p. A370

LEWIS, Nannette M., Chief Executive Officer, Three Rivers Behavioral Health, West Columbia, SC, p. A558

LEWIS, Nicholas P., Chief Executive Officer, Hardin Medical Center, Savannah, TN, p. A579

LEWIS, Pam, Chief Compliance Officer, William R. Sharpe, Jr. Hospital, Weston, WV, p. A688

LEWIS, Paul, M.D.
Chief Medical Officer, Vice President, Boulder Community Foothills Hospital, CO, p. A96
Chief Executive Officer, Holy Rosary Healthcare, Miles City, MT, p. A377

LEWIS, Paula, Interim Chief Nursing Officer, Five Rivers Medical Center, Pocahontas-Randolph County, AR, p. A48

LEWIS, Rebecca, President, Southview Medical Center, OH, p. A480

LEWIS, Robin, Chief Financial Officer, Kiowa District Healthcare, Kiowa, KS, p. A238

LEWIS, Ron, President, Spectrum Health Zeeland Community Hospital, Zeeland, MI, p. A326

LEWIS, Rosalind, R.N., MSN, Director of Ancillary Services, Community Healthcare System, Onaga, KS, p. A242

LEWIS, Sharon, Director Information Systems, Forbes Hospital, Monroeville, PA, p. A532

LEWIS, Sheila, Administrator, Harmon Memorial Hospital, Hollis, OK, p. A500

LEWIS, Sherlyn, Manager Finance, The Orthopedic Specialty Hospital, Murray, UT, p. A648

LEWIS, Stephen, Chief Executive Officer, Chase County Community Hospital, Imperial, NE, p. A385

LEWIS, Thomas D, Chief Operating Officer, Clifton T. Perkins Hospital Center, Jessup, MD, p. A292

LEWIS, Vicki, R.N., MS, FACHE, President and Chief Executive Officer, Coffee Regional Medical Center, Douglas, GA, p. A152

LEWIS, Vickie, Chief Executive Officer, Central Florida Behavioral Hospital, Orlando, FL, p. A134

LEWIS-TAYLOR, Tracey, Chief Operating Officer, Valley Memorial, CA, p. A78

LEWISTON, Jamie, R.N., MSN, Chief Nursing Officer, Aurora Psychiatric Hospital, Wauwatosa, WI, p. A705

LEYDEN, Andrea, RN, Chief Nursing Officer, Washington County Hospital And Clinics, Washington, IA, p. A230

LI, Eric, M.D., Chief Medical Officer, United Medical Center, Washington, DC, p. A116

LI, Ronald, Vice President Management Information Systems, New Bridge Medical Center, Paramus, NJ, p. A409

LI, Stephen, Vice President Management Information Systems, Jersey City Medical Center, Jersey City, NJ, p. A406

LI, Xiao H., M.D., Chief of Staff, Surgery Specialty Hospitals Of America, Pasadena, TX, p. A627

LIANG, Bonnie, Divisional Finance Officer, Sutter Maternity And Surgery Center Of Santa Cruz, Santa Cruz, CA, p. A89

LIBBY, Kenneth, Vice President Finance, Vcu Health Community Memorial Hospital, South Hill, VA, p. A666

LIBCKE, Julia, R.N., MSN
Chief Nursing Officer, Mclaren Macomb, Mount Clemens, MI, p. A319
VP Patient Care Services, Dmc - Rehabilitation Institute Of Michigan, Detroit, MI, p. A311

LIBERATORE, Kristi, Vice President and Chief Financial Officer, St. Joseph Hospital, Orange, CA, p. A76

LICHIUS, Sylvia Marie, R.N., Chief Nursing Officer, Morrill County Community Hospital, Bridgeport, NE, p. A382

LICHTENFELS, Suellen, Vice President and Chief Nursing Officer, Somerset Hospital, Somerset, PA, p. A541

LICHTENWALNER, Tom, Vice President Finance, St Luke's Hospital - Allentown Campus, PA, p. A521

LICHTY, Scott, M.D., Physician, Sanford Sheldon Medical Center, Sheldon, IA, p. A229

LICINA, Leonard, Chief Executive Officer, Sutter Health Kahi Mohala, Ewa Beach, HI, p. A164

LIDDELL, Sean, Manager Regional Service Information Technology, Unitypoint Health - Trinity Muscatine, Muscatine, IA, p. A227

LIDHOLM, Helen, Chief Executive Officer, Saint Mary's Regional Medical Center, Reno, NV, p. A396

LIEBER, Alan R., President, Overlook Medical Center, Summit, NJ, p. A412

LIEBERMAN, Jeffrey A., M.D., Executive Director, New York State Psychiatric Institute, New York (Includes All Hospitals Located Within The Five Boroughs), NY, p. A434

LIEBERMAN, Steven L, M.D., Chief of Staff, Lyons Division, NJ, p. A404

LIEBERS, David, M.D., Chief Medical Officer and Vice President Medical Affairs, Ellis Hospital Health Center, NY, p. A442

LIEFER, Alan, M.D., President Medical Staff, Memorial Hospital, Chester, IL, p. A176

LIESEN, Daniel, M.D.
Chief Medical Officer, Vista Medical Center East, Waukegan, IL, p. A198
Chief Medical Officer, Vista Medical Center West, Waukegan, IL, p. A198

LIESMANN, George, M.D., Chief Medical Officer, Blessing Hospital, IL, p. A194

LIETTE, Cindy, Vice President Patient Care Services, Mercer Health, Coldwater, OH, p. A478

LIEZERT, Timothy, Medical Center Director, Orlando Va Medical Center, Orlando, FL, p. A134

LIFFERTH, Geoffrey, M.D., Chief Medical Officer, Sumner Regional Medical Center, Gallatin, TN, p. A570

LIGHT, Asher, M.D., Medical Director, Baylor Institute For Rehabilitation At Fort Worth, Fort Worth, TX, p. A604

LIGHT, Gary, Vice President and Chief Information Officer, Memorial Hospital And Health Care Center, Jasper, IN, p. A208

LIGHT, Laura, Director Human Resources, St. David's North Austin Medical Center, Austin, TX, p. A586

LIGHTBOURNE, Olieth, Chief Nursing Officer, Streamwood Behavioral Health Center, Streamwood, IL, p. A197

LIGHTCAP, Debora, Director Human Resources, Mercy Medical Center, Roseburg, OR, p. A517

LIGHTFOOT, William M, M.D., Vice President Medical Services, Providence Hospital, Mobile, AL, p. A20

LIGON, Kim, Director Information Services, Northport Medical Center, AL, p. A24

LIGON, Lynda, Chief Nursing Officer, Warm Springs Medical Center, Warm Springs, GA, p. A163

LIKES, Randle L, M.D., Chief Medical Officer, Timpanogos Regional Hospital, Orem, UT, p. A649

LILES, Bart, M.D., Chief of Staff, P & S Surgical Hospital, Monroe, LA, p. A274

LILES, Jerry, Chief Medical Officer, Christus Spohn Hospital Alice, Alice, TX, p. A582

LILES, Richard A, M.D., Medical Director, Healthsouth Rehabilitation Hospital Of Largo, Largo, FL, p. A128

LILJEBERT, Sam, Chief Executive Officer, St. Theresa Specialty Hospital, Kenner, LA, p. A270

LILLEBOE, Linda, R.N., MSN, Director Operations, Carson Valley Medical Center, Gardnerville, NV, p. A393

LILLEY, Jeffrey, CPA, Chief Executive Officer, Princeton Community Hospital, Princeton, WV, p. A686

LILLY, Ryan S., Director, Maine Veterans Affairs Medical Center, Augusta, ME, p. A282

LIM, Rosemarie, M.D., Chief Medical Officer, Bayview Behavioral Health Campus, CA, p. A74

LIMA, Robert, Director Information Systems, Pappas Rehabilitation Hospital For Children, Canton, MA, p. A299

LIMAJ, Idriz, Chief Operating Officer and Executive Director, Levindale Hebrew Geriatric Center And Hospital, Baltimore, MD, p. A288

LIMBAGA, Aries, R.N., Chief Nursing Officer, Rancho Los Amigos National Rehabilitation Center, Downey, CA, p. A56

LIMBAUGH, Jason K, Vice President and Chief Financial Officer, Wellstar Atlanta Medical Center - South Campus, GA, p. A147

LIMBOCKER, Jeff, Chief Financial Officer, Our Lady Of The Lake Children's Hospital, LA, p. A264

LIMM, Whitney, M.D., Executive Vice President and Chief Physician Executive, Queen's Medical Center - West Oahu, HI, p. A165

LIN, Dean Q., FACHE, Regional President, Hackensack Meridian Health Ocean Medical Center, Brick Township, NJ, p. A403

LIN, George, M.D., Physician Advisor, Hackensack Meridian Health Pascack Valley Medical Center, Westwood, NJ, p. A414

LIN, James Y, D.O., Chief of Staff, Lecom Health Millcreek Community Hospital, Erie, PA, p. A525

LINAFELTER, Robb, Chief Executive Officer, Lincoln Surgical Hospital, Lincoln, NE, p. A386

LINCK, Cindy, Chief Nursing Officer, Cornerstone Hospital Of Oklahoma-Shawnee, Shawnee, OK, p. A506

LINCKS, Brad, R.N., Chief Nursing Officer and Vice President, Our Lady Of Peace, Louisville, KY, p. A256

LIND, Jonathan, Chief Operating Officer, Swedish Covenant Hospital, Chicago, IL, p. A180

LIND, Mark, Chief Information Officer, Mammoth Hospital, Mammoth Lakes, CA, p. A71

LIND, Sharon, MSN, FACHE
Chief Executive Officer, Banner Goldfield Medical Center, Apache Junction, AZ, p. A28
Chief Executive Officer, Banner Ironwood Medical Center, San Tan Valley, AZ, p. A35

LIND, Trent, Chief Executive Officer, Eastside Medical Center, Snellville, GA, p. A161

LINDBERG, Bob, Chief Operating Officer, Cumberland Healthcare, Cumberland, WI, p. A691

LINDBERG, Chris, Chief Information Officer, Milwaukee County Behavioral Health Division, Milwaukee, WI, p. A699

LINDBERG, Michael, M.D., Chief Medical Officer, Monadnock Community Hospital, Peterborough, NH, p. A401

LINDBERG, Steven, Chief Administrative Officer, Mayo Clinic Health System - Red Cedar In Menomonie, Menomonie, WI, p. A697

LINDELL, Jonathan, Director Information Technology, Miracle Mile Medical Center, Los Angeles, CA, p. A68

LINDEMAN, Barry K, Director Human Resources, Cardinal Hill Rehabilitation Hospital, Lexington, KY, p. A254

LINDEMAN, Gretchen, Director of Human Resources, Monterey Park Hospital, Monterey Park, CA, p. A73

LINDEMANN, Fran, Director Finance, Kell West Regional Hospital, Wichita Falls, TX, p. A644

LINDEMANN, Steve, Chief Financial Officer, Brookings Health System, Brookings, SD, p. A559

LINDEN, Kelly, Chief Executive Officer, Providence Saint Joseph Medical Center, Burbank, CA, p. A53

LINDER, James, M.D., Chief Executive Officer, Nebraska Medicine - Nebraska Medical Center, Omaha, NE, p. A388

LINDFORS, Teresa, Chief Nursing Officer and Vice President, Patient Services, Stoughton Hospital Association, Stoughton, WI, p. A703

LINDQUIST, James
Chief Nursing Officer, Hackensack Meridian Health Jfk Johnson Rehabilitation Institute, Edison, NJ, p. A404
Chief Nursing Officer, Hackensack Meridian Health Jfk Medical Center, Edison, NJ, p. A404

LINDQUIST, Peter, Vice President and Chief Nursing Officer, Providence Hospital, Mobile, AL, p. A20

LINDQUIST, Steve, Assistant Vice President, Behavioral Health, Avera Behavioral Health Center, SD, p. A563

LINDSAY, Kelly, Chief Operating Officer, Coliseum Center For Behavioral Health, GA, p. A156

LINDSAY-BELL, Davida, Area Human Resources Leader, Kaiser Permanente Antioch Medical Center, Antioch, CA, p. A50

LINDSAY-WOOD, Elizabeth, Interim Chief Information Officer, Overlook Medical Center, Summit, NJ, p. A412

LINDSEY, Don, Vice President and Chief Information Officer, Tallahassee Memorial Healthcare, Tallahassee, FL, p. A140

LINDSEY, Hugh, M.D., Chief Medical Officer, Hayes Green Beach Memorial Hospital, Charlotte, MI, p. A309

LINDSEY, Jay, Chief Executive Officer, Plano Surgical Hospital, Plano, TX, p. A629

LINDSEY, Kim, Chief Human Resources Officer, Lourdes Hospital, Paducah, KY, p. A259

LINDSEY, Robbie, Chief Information Officer, Twin Lakes Regional Medical Center, Leitchfield, KY, p. A254

LINDSEY, Tony, M.D., Chief of Staff, Unc Lineberger Comprehensive Cancer Center, NC, p. A449

LINDSTROM, David, M.D., Vice President Medical Affairs, Promedica Bay Park Hospital, Oregon, OH, p. A488

LINES, Brian, Chief Operating Officer, Ogden Regional Medical Center, Ogden, UT, p. A648

LING, Lori, Information Technician, Windom Area Hospital, Windom, MN, p. A342

LINGEN, Tom, M.D., Chief of Staff, Cumberland Healthcare, Cumberland, WI, p. A691

LINGLE, Dan, Chief Nursing Officer, Banner Casa Grande Medical Center, Casa Grande, AZ, p. A28

LINGLE, David, Directors Council Chairman and Chief of Staff, Vidant Roanoke-Chowan Hospital, Ahoskie, NC, p. A447

LINGO, Jessica, Human Resource Generalist, Story County Medical Center, Nevada, IA, p. A227

LINHARES, James, Chief Executive Officer, Bridgepoint Hospital Capitol Hill, Washington, DC, p. A115

LINK, Nathan, M.D., Medical Director, Nyc Health + Hospitals / Bellevue, New York (Includes All Hospitals Located Within The Five Boroughs), NY, p. A435

LINKENHOKER, Ellen Y, Chief Nursing Officer, Lewisgale Hospital Montgomery, Blacksburg, VA, p. A655

LINN, Steven C, M.D.
Chief Medical Officer, Bridgeton Health Center, NJ, p. A413

Chief Medical Officer, Inspira Medical Center-Elmer, Elmer, NJ, p. A404

LINNA, Gina, Manager Human Resources, Aspirus Ontonagon Hospital, Inc., Ontonagon, MI, p. A320

LINNELL, Jon E., Interim Chief Executive Officer, North Valley Health Center, Warren, MN, p. A341

LINNINGTON, Darryl, Chief Financial Officer, Mcalester Regional Health Center, Mcalester, OK, p. A501

LINSCHEID, Carol, Vice President Human Resources, Enloe Medical Center-Cohasset, CA, p. A54

LINSCOTT, Jason, CPA, Chief Financial Officer, Texas Health Presbyterian Hospital Of Rockwall, Rockwall, TX, p. A631

LINSE, Margaret, Administrative Secretary and Director Human Resources, West Holt Medical Services, Atkinson, NE, p. A381

LINSKEY, Chris, M.D., Acting Chief Medical Officer, Guidance Center, Flagstaff, AZ, p. A29

LINSTROM, Joseph, Vice President Operations, Suburban Hospital, Bethesda, MD, p. A290

LINTON, Dwight, Director Human Resources, Detar Hospital North, TX, p. A642

LINTZ, Gordon, President and Chief Administrative Officer, Morristown-Hamblen Healthcare System, Morristown, TN, p. A576

LINVILLE, Kimberly, Chief Nursing Officer, Grant Memorial Hospital, Petersburg, WV, p. A686

LINZMAN, Rob, D.O., Chief of Staff, Jefferson County Hospital, Waurika, OK, p. A510

LIPE, Curt, Vice President, Chief Financial Officer, Osf St. Mary Medical Center, Galesburg, IL, p. A183

LIPINSKI, Gary, M.D., Chief Medical Officer, Presence Saint Joseph Medical Center, Joliet, IL, p. A187

LIPMAN, Brian, M.D., Medical Director and Medical Staff Services, Oconomowoc Memorial Hospital, Oconomowoc, WI, p. A700

LIPMAN, Henry D
Senior Vice President, Financial Strategy and External Relations, Franklin Regional Hospital, Franklin, NH, p. A399
Senior Vice President, Financial Strategy and External Relations, Lakes Region General Hospital, Laconia, NH, p. A399

LIPNER, Zach, Vice President Human Resources, Children's Hospital Of New Jersey, NJ, p. A408

LIPPERT, Brandt, Vice President Human Resources, Adena Greenfield Medical Center, Greenfield, OH, p. A483

LIPPINCOTT, Ken, M.D., Chief of Staff, North Mississippi State Hospital, Tupelo, MS, p. A353

LIPSCOMB, Teresa, Director Human Resources, Springbrook Behavioral Health System, Travelers Rest, SC, p. A557

LIPSCOMB, Tiffiny J, Manager Human Resources, Intermountain Medical Center, Murray, UT, p. A648

LIPSCOMB, Tracy, CPA, Vice President Financial Services and Chief Financial Officer, Garrett Regional Medical Center, Oakland, MD, p. A293

LIPSON, Wayne, M.D., Chief Physician Executive, Baptist Health Madisonville, Madisonville, KY, p. A257

LIPTAK, Valenda M., Chief Executive Officer, Western Massachusetts Hospital, Westfield, MA, p. A306

LIPTON, Pat
Director Team Resources, South Florida Baptist Hospital, Plant City, FL, p. A136
Director Team Resources, St. Joseph's Women's Hospital, FL, p. A141

LIRAKIS, Kathy, R.N., Chief Nursing Officer, Blue Hill Memorial Hospital, Blue Hill, ME, p. A283

LIRIO, Ruel R., M.D., Clinical Physician Advisor, Spectrum Health Zeeland Community Hospital, Zeeland, MI, p. A326

LISA, Mark P., FACHE
Chief Executive Officer, Sierra Vista Regional Medical Center, San Luis Obispo, CA, p. A87
Chief Executive Officer, Twin Cities Community Hospital, Templeton, CA, p. A91

LISELL, Susan C, Vice President of Clinical Services, Lifecare Medical Center, Roseau, MN, p. A338

LISKA, Lee Ann, Chief Executive Officer, Children's Hospital Of Georgia, GA, p. A147

LISKO, Stuart, Vice President, Chief Financial Officer and Compliance Officer, Levi Hospital, Hot Springs National Park-Garland County, AR, p. A43

LISKOV, David, M.D., Medical Director, First Hospital Wyoming Valley, Kingston, PA, p. A528

LISONBEE, Rod, Chief Financial Officer, Utah Valley Hospital, Provo, UT, p. A649

LISS, Rita, Vice President Fiscal Services and Chief Financial Officer, Boone County Health Center, Albion, NE, p. A381

LIST, Alan F., M.D., President and Chief Executive Officer, H. Lee Moffitt Cancer Center And Research Institute, Tampa, FL, p. A140

LISTER, Jack, Director Human Resources, Takoma Regional Hospital, Greeneville, TN, p. A570

LISTI, Daniel, Chief Executive Officer, Shelby Baptist Medical Center, Alabaster, AL, p. A13

LISTON, Allison, Director, Human Resources, Cedar Crest Hospital And Residential Treatment Center, Belton, TX, p. A589

LISTON, John, Chief Operating Officer, Mclaren Port Huron, Port Huron, MI, p. A321

LITAKER, Thomas, Regional Vice President and Chief Financial Officer, Cascade Valley Hospital, Arlington, WA, p. A669

L'ITALIEN, Mark, Director Information Services, Salem Regional Medical Center, Salem, OH, p. A490

LITER, Jennifer Lynn, Vice President of Inpatient Services, King's Daughters' Health, Madison, IN, p. A210

LITKA, Calvin, R.N., Director of Nursing, Horsham Clinic, Ambler, PA, p. A520

LITOVITZ, Gary, M.D., Medical Director, Dominion Hospital, Falls Church, VA, p. A657

LITSINGER, James, CPA
Chief Operating Officer, Sheltering Arms Hospital South, Midlothian, VA, p. A661
Vice President and Chief Financial Officer, Sheltering Arms Rehabilitation Hospital, Mechanicsville, VA, p. A661

LITTERER, Karen, R.N., MSN, Administrator and Chief Operating Officer, Seton Highland Lakes, Burnet, TX, p. A591

LITTLE, Christopher M, Vice President and Chief Financial Officer, Ellwood City Medical Center, Ellwood City, PA, p. A525

LITTLE, Denise, Director Human Resources, St. Elizabeth Community Hospital, Red Bluff, CA, p. A79

LITTLE, Gary, M.D., Medical Director, George Washington University Hospital, Washington, DC, p. A115

LITTLE, James P, M.D., Medical Director, Healthsouth Rehabilitation Hospital, Kingsport, TN, p. A572

LITTLE, Lisa, Chief Nursing Officer, Washington County Hospital, Nashville, IL, p. A191

LITTLE, Lou, President and Chief Executive Officer, Sparrow Specialty Hospital, Lansing, MI, p. A317

LITTLE, Monica, Coordinator Human Resources, Kindred Rehabilitation Hospital Clear Lake, Webster, TX, p. A643

LITTLE, Suzanne, Human Resources Specialist, Columbia Basin Hospital, Ephrata, WA, p. A671

LITTLE, William, Chief Executive Officer, Carolina Pines Regional Medical Center, Hartsville, SC, p. A554

LITTLEDEER, Lenora, R.N., Director of Nursing, Lawton Indian Hospital, Lawton, OK, p. A500

LITTLEFIELD, Karen, Director Human Resources, Waldo County General Hospital Maine Health, Belfast, ME, p. A283

LITTLEJOHN, Edward, Chief Operating Officer, Fountain Valley Regional Hospital And Medical Center, Fountain Valley, CA, p. A58

LITTLEJOHN, Traxler, Human Resources Director, Encompass Health Rehabilitation Hospital Of Charleston, Charleston, SC, p. A550

LITTLEPAGE, Dana, Interim Chief Nursing Officer, St. John's Pleasant Valley Hospital, Camarillo, CA, p. A53

LITTRELL, Angela P., CPA, Chief Financial Officer and Chief Operating Officer, Fitzgibbon Hospital, Marshall, MO, p. A364

LITTRELL, Mark
Chief Executive Officer, Lincoln Prairie Behavioral Health Center, Springfield, IL, p. A196
Group Director, The Pavilion, Champaign, IL, p. A175

LIU, Marsha, Executive Vice President and Chief Financial Officer, Northwest Community Hospital, Arlington Heights, IL, p. A173

LIUZZA, Jed M, Chief Human Resources Officer, Presbyterian Tower, OK, p. A504

LIUZZO, Gary, Director Information Systems, Scotland Health Care System, Laurinburg, NC, p. A456

LIVELY, Corey, Chief Executive Officer, Great Plains Regional Medical Center, Elk City, OK, p. A498

LIVELY, David, Chief Nursing Officer, Atoka County Medical Center, Atoka, OK, p. A496

LIVERMAN, Brett, Chief Financial Officer, Alleghany Memorial Hospital, Sparta, NC, p. A461

LIVERSAGE, Lavonne, Director, Fargo Veterans Affairs Health Care System, Fargo, ND, p. A465

LIVESAY, William, D.O., Jr, Medical Director, Encompass Health Rehabilitation Hospital Of Charleston, Charleston, SC, p. A550

LIVIN, Lee, Chief Financial Officer, Yavapai Regional Medical Center - East, AZ, p. A34

LIVINGSTON, Carolyn, Director Human Resources, Salt Lake Regional Medical Center, Salt Lake City, UT, p. A650

LIVINGSTON, Charles
Administrator, Dakota Plains Surgical Center, Aberdeen, SD, p. A559
Chief Executive Officer, Midwest Surgical Hospital, Omaha, NE, p. A388

LIVINGSTON, Denise, Director Human Resources, St. Mary Medical Center, Long Beach, CA, p. A65

LIVINGSTON, Keith
Senior Vice President and Chief Information Officer, Thedacare Regional Medical Center-Appleton, Appleton, WI, p. A689
Senior Vice President and Chief Information Officer, Thedacare Regional Medical Center-Neenah, Neenah, WI, p. A699

LIVINGSTON, Richard, M.D., Medical Director, Valley Behavioral Health System, Barling, AR, p. A39

LIVINGSTON, Sam, Information Resource Consultant, G. Werber Bryan Psychiatric Hospital, Columbia, SC, p. A551

LIVSEY, Don, Vice President and Chief Information Officer, Ucsf Benioff Children's Hospital Oakland, Oakland, CA, p. A76

LIZZA, Beth, Chief Nursing Officer, Ohio Valley Surgical Hospital, Springfield, OH, p. A490

LLANO, Manuel R., Chief Executive Officer, Fort Lauderdale Hospital, Fort Lauderdale, FL, p. A122

LLEWELLYN, Michael R, Chief Operating Officer, Laguna Honda Hospital And Rehabilitation Center, San Francisco, CA, p. A85

LLOYD, Richard, D.O., Chief of Staff, Harbor Beach Community Hospital, Harbor Beach, MI, p. A315

LLOYD, Russell E., Director, Wilkes-Barre Veterans Affairs Medical Center, Wilkes, PA, p. A544

LOBBAN, Victoria, Vice President Finance, New England Sinai Hospital And Rehabilitation Center, Stoughton, MA, p. A305

LOBECK, Charles C., Administrator, Shriners Hospitals For Children-Twin Cities, Minneapolis, MN, p. A335

LOCEY, Vicky, R.N., MSN, Chief Operating Officer and Chief Nursing Executive, Kaiser Permanente Santa Rosa Medical Center, Santa Rosa, CA, p. A89

LOCHALA, Richard, Chief of Staff, Mena Regional Health System, Mena-Polk County, AR, p. A46

LOCK, Lesa, Chief Nursing Officer, Valley View Medical Center, Fort Mohave, AZ, p. A29

LOCKARD, Dennis, FACHE, Chief Financial Officer, Coshocton Regional Medical Center, Coshocton, OH, p. A479

LOCKCUFF, Todd, Chief Financial Officer, Inova Alexandria Hospital, Alexandria, VA, p. A655

LOCKE, Cheryl, Vice President and Chief Human Resource Officer, Brenner Children's Hospital & Health Services, NC, p. A463

LOCKE, Christopher, Chief Executive Officer, Saint Francis Hospital-Bartlett, Bartlett, TN, p. A566

LOCKE, Marianne, R.N., MSN, Associate Director Patient Care Services, Edward Hines, Jr. Veterans Affairs Hospital, Hines, IL, p. A185

LOCKE, Stuart, Chief Executive Officer, Southern Kentucky Rehabilitation Hospital, Bowling Green, KY, p. A250

LOCKERD, Marie Paul, M.D., Chief Medical Officer, Sanford Jackson Medical Center, Jackson, MN, p. A333

LOCKETT, Kevin, Interim Chief Financial Officer, Mayo Clinic Hospital In Florida, Jacksonville, FL, p. A125

LOCKEY, Chris, Chief Executive Officer, Sun Behavioral Kentucky, Erlanger, KY, p. A251

LOCKHART, Jimmy Wayne, M.D., Medical Director, Healthsouth Treasure Coast Rehabilitation Hospital, Vero Beach, FL, p. A142

LOCKLEAR, Ann, Vice President, Human Resources, Scotland Health Care System, Laurinburg, NC, p. A456

LOCKRIDGE, Michael, Chief Financial Officer, Green Clinic Surgical Hospital, LA, p. A278

LOCKWOOD, Melissa, Chief Executive Officer, Preston Memorial Hospital, Kingwood, WV, p. A684

LOE, Cindy, R.N., Director of Nursing, Essentia Health Northern Pines Medical Center, Aurora, MN, p. A327

LOEB, Amy E, Ed.D., R.N., Chief Nursing Officer, Peconic Bay Medical Center, Riverhead, NY, p. A441

LOEFFELHOLZ, Tim, Account Executive Information Technology, Unitypoint Health - Finley Hospital, Dubuque, IA, p. A222

LOELIGER, Eric, Vice President of Medical Affairs, Asante Three Rivers Medical Center, Grants Pass, OR, p. A513

LOEPP, Robert A., Jr, FACHE, Chief Executive Officer, Amg Specialty Hospital-Wichita, Wichita, KS, p. A247

LOERA, Arnold, M.D., Clinical Director, Bristol Bay Area Health Corporation, Dillingham, AK, p. A26

LOERINC, Albert, M.D., Medical Director, Vibra Hospital Of Southeastern Massachusetts, New Bedford, MA, p. A302

LOESCHER, Cori, R.N., Chief Nursing Officer and Vice President of Patient Care Services, Brigham And Women's Faulkner Hospital, Boston, MA, p. A296

LOEWENSTEIN, Howard, Chief Information Resource Management Services, Jesse Brown Veterans Affairs Medical Center, Chicago, IL, p. A177

LOFFING, David, Chief Operating Officer, University Of Illinois Hospital & Health Sciences System, Chicago, IL, p. A180

LOFTIS, Dennis
Senior Vice President and Chief Information Officer, Riverside Behavioral Health Center, VA, p. A662
Senior Vice President of Information Systems, Coastal Virginia Rehabilitation, Newport News, VA, p. A662

LOFTIS, Michelle, Human Resources Officer, Ferry County Memorial Hospital, Republic, WA, p. A675

LOFTON, Jason, M.D., Medical Director, De Queen Medical Center, De Queen-Sevier County, AR, p. A41

LOFTON, Veronica, Acting Chief Executive Officer, Twin Valley Behavioral Healthcare, Columbus, OH, p. A479

LOFTUS, John, M.D., Chief of Staff, Kaiser Permanente Richmond Medical Center, CA, p. A76

LOFTUS, Mary Virginia, Chief Nursing Officer, Specialists Hospital - Shreveport, Shreveport, LA, p. A279

LOFTUS, Philip, Ph.D.
Chief Information Officer, Aurora West Allis Medical Center, West Allis, WI, p. A706
Vice President and Chief Information Officer, Aurora Medical Center Of Oshkosh, Oshkosh, WI, p. A700
Vice President and Chief Information Officer, Aurora Psychiatric Hospital, Wauwatosa, WI, p. A705
Vice President and Chief Information Officer, Aurora St. Luke's South Shore, WI, p. A698

LOFTUS, Terry, M.D., Chief Medical Officer, Medical City Fort Worth, Fort Worth, TX, p. A605

LOFURNO, Justin A, Director Human Resources, Providence Hospital Northeast, SC, p. A551

LOGAN, Angela, Chief Nursing Officer, Lutheran Hospital Of Indiana, Fort Wayne, IN, p. A203

LOGAN, Ann P., R.N., Ph.D., Chief Operating Officer, Carepoint Health Hoboken University Medical Center, Hoboken, NJ, p. A406

LOGAN, Denise, Director Human Resources, Specialty Rehabilitation Hospital Of Coushatta, Coushatta, LA, p. A266

LOGAN, John, M.D., Chief Medical Officer, Methodist Hospital, Henderson, KY, p. A253

LOGAN, Renee, Chief Financial Officer, Murray County Medical Center, Slayton, MN, p. A340

LOGAN-OWENS, Michelle, Ph.D., R.N., Chief Operating Officer, Palmetto Health Tuomey, Sumter, SC, p. A557

LOGAR, Michael, Assistant Superintendent, Larue D. Carter Memorial Hospital, Indianapolis, IN, p. A207

LOGDSON, David, Chief Nursing Officer, Twin Lakes Regional Medical Center, Leitchfield, KY, p. A254

LOGOZZO, Vince, Director Information Technology, Aultman Orrville Hospital, Orrville, OH, p. A488

LOGSDON, Terri
Chief Financial Officer, Covington Behavior Health, Covington, LA, p. A266
Chief Financial Officer, Hickory Trail Hospital, Desoto, TX, p. A600

LOGUE, Amy Antani, Ph.D., Vice President Human Resources, Advocate Condell Medical Center, Libertyville, IL, p. A188

LOH, Marcel C., FACHE, Chief Executive Officer, Providence Saint John's Health Center, Santa Monica, CA, p. A89

LOHMAN, Eric, M.D., Chief of Staff, Meadowview Regional Medical Center, Maysville, KY, p. A257

LOHMEIER, Justin, M.D., Chief of Staff, Baptist Memorial Hospital-Union County, New Albany, MS, p. A351

LOHN, Eric
Chief Financial Officer, Lake View Hospital, Two Harbors, MN, p. A341
Vice President and Chief Financial Officer, St. Luke's Hospital, Duluth, MN, p. A331

LOHR, Daniel E, Regional Vice President Finance, Windham Hospital, Willimantic, CT, p. A112

LOHRMAN, Joseph W, Chief Executive Officer, Annie Jeffrey Memorial County Health Center, Osceola, NE, p. A389

LOHRMAN, Joseph W., Chief Executive Officer, Annie Jeffrey Memorial County Health Center, Osceola, NE, p. A389

LOHSTRETER, Thomas, M.D., Chief of Staff, Kittson Memorial Healthcare Center, Hallock, MN, p. A332

LOKKEN, Christine, Chief Financial Officer, Bigfork Valley Hospital, Bigfork, MN, p. A328

LOLLEY, Tim, MSN, Chief Nursing Officer, Merit Health Madison, Canton, MS, p. A344

LOLLIS, Sylvia, Director Human Resources, Osceola Regional Medical Center, Kissimmee, FL, p. A126

LOLLO, Trisha, President, Barnes-Jewish West County Hospital, Saint Louis, MO, p. A367

LOMAN, Sarah, Director Human Resources, Penobscot Valley Hospital, Lincoln, ME, p. A284

LOMBA, Maria R, Medical Director, New Braunfels Regional Rehabilitation Hospital, New Braunfels, TX, p. A625

LOMBARD, Lisa, Chief Medical Officer, Ohiohealth Rehabilitation Hospital, Columbus, OH, p. A478

LOMBARDO, Alan, Associate Director, Hunter Holmes Mcguire Veterans Affairs Medical Center-Richmond, Richmond, VA, p. A665

LOMEO, Jody, Chief Executive Officer, Women And Children's Hospital, NY, p. A423

LONEY, Chris, Director Personnel, Thomas B. Finan Center, Cumberland, MD, p. A291

LONG, Amy, Administrator, Mayo Clinic Health System In Fairmont, Fairmont, MN, p. A331

LONG, Angela S, Vice President Clinical Services and Chief Nursing Officer, Southeastern Ohio Regional Medical Center, Cambridge, OH, p. A473

LONG, Brian, FACHE, President and Chief Executive Officer, Memorial Healthcare, Owosso, MI, p. A320

LONG, Dennis, Director Human Resources, Western Missouri Medical Center, Warrensburg, MO, p. A371

LONG, Douglas, President and Chief Executive Officer, West Hills Hospital And Medical Center, Los Angeles, CA, p. A70

LONG, Erik, Controller, Baptist Health South Florida, South Miami Hospital, Miami, FL, p. A130

LONG, Floyd R, Chief Executive Officer, Henry J. Carter Specialty Hospital & Nursing Facility, NY, p. A435

LONG, Gloria, Chief Operating Officer, Guam Regional Medical City, Dededo, GU, p. A711

LONG, Gregory L, M.D.
Chief Medical Officer, Thedacare Regional Medical Center-Appleton, Appleton, WI, p. A689
Chief Medical Officer, Thedacare Regional Medical Center-Neenah, Neenah, WI, p. A699

LONG, Gretchen, Manager Human Resources, Shriners Hospitals For Children - Cincinnati, Cincinnati, OH, p. A475

LONG, Jeremy
Chief Information Officer, St. Vincent Heart Center, Indianapolis, IN, p. A208
Manager Information Systems, St. Vincent Salem Hospital, Salem, IN, p. A214

LONG, Jonathan Ray, M.D., Chief of Staff, Weatherford Regional Hospital, Weatherford, OK, p. A510

LONG, Judy M, R.N., MS, Chief Nursing Officer and Chief Operating Officer, Appling Healthcare System, Baxley, GA, p. A148

LONG, Karen, R.N., FACHE, Vice President Nursing, Bayfront Health St. Petersburg, Saint Petersburg, FL, p. A138

LONG, Michelle
Human Resources Business Partner, Abraham Lincoln Memorial Hospital, Lincoln, IL, p. A188
Regional Human Resource Manager, Taylorville Memorial Hospital, Taylorville, IL, p. A197

LONG, Mike, Chief Financial Officer, Powell Valley Healthcare, Powell, WY, p. A709

LONG, Richard, M.D., Chief Medical Officer, Upmc Hamot, Erie, PA, p. A525

LONG, Stephanie, President and Chief Executive Officer, River Bend Hospital, West Lafayette, IN, p. A216

LONG, Steven V., FACHE, President and Chief Executive Officer, Hancock Regional Hospital, Greenfield, IN, p. A205

LONG, Theresa, Chief Executive Officer, Danville State Hospital, Danville, PA, p. A523

LONGABAUGH, James, M.D., Chief Medical Staff, Sabetha Community Hospital, Sabetha, KS, p. A245

LONGACRE, Mark E, FACHE, Chief Operating Officer, Orthonebraska Hospital, Omaha, NE, p. A388

LONGDO, Derrick, Director Information Systems, Memorial Medical Center - Neillsville, Neillsville, WI, p. A699

LONGEST, Bruce, M.D., President Medical Staff, Baptist Memorial Hospital - Calhoun, Calhoun City, MS, p. A344

LONGEST, Sonya, M.D., Chief Medical Officer, Walter B. Jones Alcohol And Drug Abuse Treatment Center, Greenville, NC, p. A454

LONGLEY, Frank, Business Partner Information Technology, Cleveland Clinic, Medina Hospital, Medina, OH, p. A486

LONGMORE, David, Chief Information Officer, Wilkes-Barre Veterans Affairs Medical Center, Wilkes, PA, p. A544

LONGMUIR, Bryan, Chief Resource Management, Madigan Army Medical Center, Tacoma, WA, p. A679

LONGMUIR, Marla, M.D., Chief Medical Officer, Mountrail County Medical Center, Stanley, ND, p. A468

LONGNECKER, Stacy, Chief of Staff, Ortonville Area Health Services, Ortonville, MN, p. A337

LONGO, Marybeth, Manager Human Resources, Trenton Psychiatric Hospital, Trenton, NJ, p. A413

LONGTIN, Brett
Chief Financial Officer, Lake Region Healthcare, Fergus Falls, MN, p. A331
Chief Financial Officer, Prairie Ridge Hospital And Health Services, Elbow Lake, MN, p. A331

LONGWORTH, David L., MD, Chief Executive Officer, Lahey Medical Center, Peabody, MA, p. A298

LONIS, Robert M, CPA, Chief Financial Officer, Lincoln County Health System, Fayetteville, TN, p. A569

LOOMIS, Greg, Interim President and Chief Operating Officer, Mercy Health, General Campus, MI, p. A319

LOOMIS, Randy, Chief Financial Officer, Dallas County Hospital, Perry, IA, p. A228

LOONEY, Zane, Chief Information Officer, St. Bernard Parish Hospital, Chalmette, LA, p. A265

LOOSBROCK, Tammy
Chief Executive Officer, Sanford Rock Rapids Medical Center, Rock Rapids, IA, p. A228
Senior Director, Sanford Luverne Medical Center, Luverne, MN, p. A334

LOOSEMORE, Tim
Director, Franciscan Health Crown Point, Crown Point, IN, p. A202
Regional Director Information Systems, Franciscan Health Michigan City, Michigan City, IN, p. A211

LOOSLI, Angela, Assistant Administrator, Operations, State Hospital South, Blackfoot, ID, p. A167

LOPACHIN, Vicki, M.D., Chief Medical Officer, Mount Sinai Queens, NY, p. A434

LOPAS, Mary, Chief Information Officer, Door County Medical Center, Sturgeon Bay, WI, p. A704

LOPES, Michelle Anne, MSN, R.N., Senior Vice President, Patient Care Services & Chief Nursing Officer, John Muir Medical Center, Walnut Creek, Walnut Creek, CA, p. A94

LOPEZ, Augustine, Chief Financial Officer, Salinas Valley Memorial Healthcare System, Salinas, CA, p. A83

LOPEZ, Cesar, R.N., Director of Nurses, Chi St. Joseph Health Grimes Hospital, Navasota, TX, p. A625

LOPEZ, David S, FACHE, Executive Vice President and Chief Operating Officer, Parkland Health & Hospital System, Dallas, TX, p. A597

LOPEZ, Enrique, M.D., Medical Director, Larry B. Zieverink, Sr. Alcoholism Treatment Center, Raleigh, NC, p. A459

LOPEZ, Ericca, Director Human Resources, Canyon Ridge Hospital, Chino, CA, p. A54

LOPEZ, Ivonne, Director Human Resources, Hospital Oriente, Humacao, PR, p. A713

LOPEZ, Jose, M.D., Medical Staff President, Indiana University Health Paoli Hospital, Paoli, IN, p. A213

LOPEZ, Leonard H, Chief Operating Officer, Hopi Health Care Center, Keams Canyon, AZ, p. A30

LOPEZ, Leonardo, President Medical Staff, Osf Saint Paul Medical Center, Mendota, IL, p. A189

LOPEZ, Lesbia, Chief Nursing Officer, Doctors' Center Hospital San Juan, San Juan, PR, p. A715

LOPEZ, Lisa M, Director Human Resources, San Joaquin General Hospital, French Camp, CA, p. A59

LOPEZ, Maria Rose, R.N., Chief of Nursing, Nix Health Care System, San Antonio, TX, p. A633

LOPEZ, Maritza, M.D., Chief of Staff, Sanford Canby Medical Center, Canby, MN, p. A329

LOPEZ, Rene, Chief Executive Officer, Knapp Medical Center, Weslaco, TX, p. A643

LOPEZ, Robert, Chief Medical Officer, Highland Community Hospital, Picayune, MS, p. A352

LOPEZ, Rosalio J, M.D., Senior Vice President and Chief Medical Officer, Pih Health Hospital - Whittier, Whittier, CA, p. A95

LOPEZ, Steve Kelley, Chief Financial Officer, Colorado River Medical Center, Needles, CA, p. A75

LOPEZ, Steve Kelley, Chief Executive Officer, Colorado River Medical Center, Needles, CA, p. A75

LOPEZ, Steven, M.D., Chief Medical Officer, Palmetto Lowcountry Behavioral Health, Charleston, SC, p. A550

LOPEZ, Susan Nordstrom, President, Advocate Illinois Masonic Medical Center, Chicago, IL, p. A176

LOPEZ, Trish, Area Chief Financial Officer, Kaiser Permanente Ontario Medical Center, CA, p. A58

LOPEZ, Valerie, CPA, Chief Financial Officer, Uvalde Memorial Hospital, Uvalde, TX, p. A641

LOPREATO, Elayne
Chief Clinical Officer, Kindred Hospital The Palm Beaches, Riviera Beach, FL, p. A137
Chief Executive Officer, Kindred Hospital The Palm Beaches, Riviera Beach, FL, p. A137

LORAH, Kelly M., FACHE, Chief Executive Officer, Lower Bucks Hospital, Bristol, PA, p. A521

LORD, David, President, Osf St. Francis Hospital And Medical Group, Escanaba, MI, p. A312

LORD, Gregory D, M.D.
Chief Medical Officer, Leesville Rehabilitation Hospital, Leesville, LA, p. A272
Medical Director, Doctor's Hospital Of Deer Creek, Leesville, LA, p. A272

LORD, Jeff, Director of Nursing, Connecticut Veterans Home And Hospital, Rocky Hill, CT, p. A110

LORD, Robert L., JD, President and Chief Executive Officer, Tradition Medical Center, FL, p. A139

LORENTZ, Derick, Chief Financial Officer, Perkins County Health Services, Grant, NE, p. A384

LORENZ, Paul E., Chief Executive Officer, Santa Clara Valley Medical Center, San Jose, CA, p. A87

LORENZ, Todd, Chief Executive Officer, Pam Rehabilitation Hospital Of Beaumont, Beaumont, TX, p. A588

LORENZEN, Shelli, Chief Human Resources Officer, Manning Regional Healthcare Center, Manning, IA, p. A226

LORENZO, Heather, M.D., Vice President and Chief Medical Officer, Meritus Medical Center, Hagerstown, MD, p. A292

LORIMER, Lee, IV, Regional Director Human Resources, Mckay-Dee Hospital, Ogden, UT, p. A648

LORMAN, William J, Ph.D., Clinical Director, Livengrin Foundation, Bensalem, PA, p. A520

LORMAND, Jared, Vice President Information Technology, Opelousas General Health System-South Campus, LA, p. A277

LORTON, Donald E, Executive Vice President, Centra Bedford Memorial Hospital, Bedford, VA, p. A655

LOSITO, Glenna, R.N., MSN, Chief Nursing Officer, Cibola General Hospital, Grants, NM, p. A417

LOTHE, Eric L, FACHE
Executive Vice President and Chief Operating Officer, Younker Memorial Rehabilitation Center, IA, p. A221
Senior Vice President and Chief Operating Officer, Unitypoint Health-Iowa Lutheran Hospital, Des Moines, IA, p. A221

LOTT, Benjamin, Chief Executive Officer, Copiah County Medical Center, Hazlehurst, MS, p. A347

LOTT, Cynthia, Director Human Resources, Northern Virginia Mental Health Institute, Falls Church, VA, p. A658

LOTT, Laura, Administrative Director, Eastern Louisiana Mental Health System, Jackson, LA, p. A269

LOTT, Rodney, Director Management Information Systems and Facility Operations, Baylor Scott & White Medical Center - Llano, Llano, TX, p. A620

LOTZE, Eberhard, M.D., Chief Medical Officer, Woman's Hospital Of Texas, Houston, TX, p. A614

LOUBERT, Cheryl, M.D., Chief Medical Staff, Midmichigan Medical Center-Gladwin, Gladwin, MI, p. A313

LOUDEN CORBETT, Jeanette L, Chief Human Resources Officer, John George Psychiatric Hospital, CA, p. A75

LOUGHERY, Vicki, R.N., MS, Chief Nursing Officer, Monadnock Community Hospital, Peterborough, NH, p. A401

LOUGHRAN, Lisa, Chief Nursing Officer, Gunnison Valley Hospital, Gunnison, CO, p. A101

LOUGHRAN, Michael, Vice President Human Resources, Kennedy Krieger Institute, Baltimore, MD, p. A287

LOUIS, Alfred, M.D., Chief Medical Staff, Pine Valley Specialty Hospital, Houston, TX, p. A613

LOUK, Rodney, Vice President Information Systems, Washington Hospital, Washington, PA, p. A543

LOUKATOS, George, M.D., President Medical Staff Affairs, Merit Health Biloxi, Biloxi, MS, p. A343

LOVATO, Anthony, Director Information Technology, Coon Memorial Hospital, Dalhart, TX, p. A595

LOVDAHL, Brian A., Chief Executive Officer, Chippewa County-Montevideo Hospital, Montevideo, MN, p. A336

LOVE, Alex, Acting Manager Human Resources, Alexandria Veterans Affairs Health Care System, Pineville, LA, p. A277

LOVE, Bianca, Assistant Administrator Human Resources, Trinity Hospital Twin City, Dennison, OH, p. A481

LOVE, E Clifford, Director Fiscal Services, Eastern State Hospital, Williamsburg, VA, p. A667

LOVE, Glenn Neil, M.D., Medical Director, Hilton Head Hospital, Hilton Head Island, SC, p. A554

LOVE, Tami, Chief Financial Officer, Memorial Hospital Of Sweetwater County, Rock Springs, WY, p. A709

LOVE, Tim, Director Information Services, Reid Health, Richmond, IN, p. A214

LOVE, Valerie, Manager Business Office, Heatherhill Care Communities, Chardon, OH, p. A474

LOVEJOY, David, Chief Operations Officer, Riverview Psychiatric Center, Augusta, ME, p. A282

LOVEJOY, Leslie, R.N., Ph.D., Chief Nursing and Quality Officer, Sonoma Valley Hospital, Sonoma, CA, p. A90

LOVEJOY, Rob
Chief Operating Officer, Sanford Thief River Falls Behavioral Health Center, Thief River Falls, MN, p. A341
Director, Operations, Sanford Medical Center Thief River Falls, Thief River Falls, MN, p. A340

LOVELACE, Alan, Vice President and Chief Financial Officer, Stillwater Medical Center, Stillwater, OK, p. A507

LOVELACE, Christina, Director Human Resources, Gunnison Valley Hospital, Gunnison, CO, p. A101

LOVELESS, Craig, Chief Executive Officer, Prowers Medical Center, Lamar, CO, p. A103

LOVELESS, Jane Doll, Vice President, Chief Information Officer, Grand View Health, Sellersville, PA, p. A541

LOVELESS, Kurt, Chief Executive Officer, The Core Institute Specialty Hospital, Phoenix, AZ, p. A34

LOVELESS, Steve, President and Chief Executive Officer, St. Vincent Healthcare, Billings, MT, p. A373

LOVELL, Charles D., Jr, FACHE, Chief Executive Officer, Barbourville Arh Hospital, Barbourville, KY, p. A249

LOVELL, Mark, Vice President and Chief Financial Officer, Palmetto Health Tuomey, Sumter, SC, p. A557

LOVELL, Stephanie, Vice President and General Counsel, Boston Medical Center, Boston, MA, p. A296

LOVELL, Terrence, Vice President Human Resources, Union Hospital, Elkton, MD, p. A291

LOVELLETTE, Teresa A, Manager Human Resources, Herrin Hospital, Herrin, IL, p. A185

LOVERA, Carlos, Director Information Systems, Montrose Memorial Hospital, Montrose, CO, p. A104

LOVERING, Keith, Information Technician, Miller County Hospital, Colquitt, GA, p. A150

LOVERING, Richard, Corporate Vice President Human Resources and Organizational Development, Atlanticare Regional Medical Center-Mainland Division, NJ, p. A402

LOVERN, Ed, Chief Operating Officer, Piedmont Hospital, Atlanta, GA, p. A146

LOVERSO, Felice L., Ph.D., President and Chief Executive Officer, Casa Colina Hospital And Health Systems, Pomona, CA, p. A78

LOVETT, Chad, Chief Executive Officer, Kindred Hospital-Greensboro, Greensboro, NC, p. A453

LOVING, David E., FACHE, Chief Executive Officer, St. Luke's Des Peres Hospital, Saint Louis, MO, p. A369

LOVING, Tonya, Director of Human Resources, Uva-Healthsouth Rehabilitation Hospital, Charlottesville, VA, p. A656

LOVINGER, Warren, M.D., Chief Medical Officer, Nevada Regional Medical Center, Nevada, MO, p. A365

LOVINGOOD, Toni, Chief Operating Officer, Erlanger Murphy Medical Center, Murphy, NC, p. A457

LOVRICH, John
Chief Financial Officer, Catalina Island Medical Center, Avalon, CA, p. A51
Chief Financial Officer, Glenn Medical Center, Willows, CA, p. A95

LOW, Kern, M.D.
Chief Medical Officer, St. Mary-Corwin Medical Center, Pueblo, CO, p. A105
Chief Medical Officer, St. Thomas More Hospital, Canon City, CO, p. A97

LOW, Lewis, M.D.
Chief Medical Officer, Legacy Mount Hood Medical Center, Gresham, OR, p. A513
Senior Vice President and Chief Medical Officer, Legacy Meridian Park Medical Center, Tualatin, OR, p. A518
Senior Vice President and Chief Medical Officer, Legacy Salmon Creek Medical Center, Vancouver, WA, p. A679

LOW, Melissa, Chief Executive Officer, Amg Specialty Hospital, San Antonio, TX, p. A632

LOWE, Bren, Chief Executive Officer, Star Valley Medical Center, Afton, WY, p. A707

LOWE, E Rick, FACHE, Operations Support Risk Management and Compliance, Bradley Center Of St. Francis, GA, p. A151

LOWE, E Rick., FACHE, Chief Executive Officer, Select Specialty Hospital-Augusta, Augusta, GA, p. A147

LOWE, Greg, Chief Executive Officer, Johnston-Willis Hospital, VA, p. A664

LOWE, Joe, Director Management Information Systems, Cumberland Medical Center, Crossville, TN, p. A569

LOWE, Kristen, Chief Executive Officer, Post Acute/Warm Springs Specialty Hospital Of San Antonio, San Antonio, TX, p. A634

LOWE, Lavah Boyers, Chief Nursing Officer, Avista Adventist Hospital, Louisville, CO, p. A103

LOWE, Rob, Director, Healthcare Information Management, Onslow Memorial Hospital, Jacksonville, NC, p. A455

LOWE, Scott
Director Human Resource, Mcalester Regional Health Center, Mcalester, OK, p. A501
Interim Market Chief Executive Officer, Physicians Regional, FL, p. A132

LOWELL, David, M.D., Chief Medical Officer, Spaulding Rehabilitation Hospital Cape Cod, East Sandwich, MA, p. A299

LOWENTHAL, David, M.D., Clinical Director, New York State Psychiatric Institute, New York (Includes All Hospitals Located Within The Five Boroughs), NY, p. A434

LOWENTHAL, Steve B, M.D., M.P.H., FACS, Senior Vice President Medical Affairs and Chief Medical Officer, Rush-Copley Medical Center, Aurora, IL, p. A174

LOWERY, Elizabeth, Interim Director, Amarillo Veterans Affairs Health Care System, Amarillo, TX, p. A583

LOWERY, John, M.D., Deputy Commander Clinical Services, General Leonard Wood Army Community Hospital, Fort Leonard Wood, MO, p. A359

LOWERY, Josh, Director of Human Resources, Baptist Memorial Hospital-North Mississippi, Oxford, MS, p. A351

LOWMAN, LeeAnn, Director Human Resources, Lake Taylor Transitional Care Hospital, Norfolk, VA, p. A662

LOWREY, Linda, Human Resources Officer, Atmore Community Hospital, Atmore, AL, p. A14

LOWRY, Claudia Jean, R.N., Director of Nursing, Community Howard Specialty Hospital, Kokomo, IN, p. A209

LOWRY, David, M.D., Chief Medical Officer, Caldwell Unc Health Care, Lenoir, NC, p. A456

LOY, Michael, Interim Chief Executive Officer, North Central Health Care, Wausau, WI, p. A705

LOYA, John R, Vice President Human Resources and Organizational Development, Columbus Regional Hospital, Columbus, IN, p. A201

LOYA, Theresa, R.N., Chief Nursing Officer, John C. Fremont Healthcare District, Mariposa, CA, p. A71

LOYA, Velma, Administrative Human Resource Coordinator, Rice Medical Center, Eagle Lake, TX, p. A600

LOYD, Chris, Director Human Resources, Methodist Richardson Medical Center, Richardson, TX, p. A630

LOYD, Stephana, Vice President, Chief Nursing Officer, Baptist Health Medical Center - Conway, Conway-Faulkner County, AR, p. A40

LOYKE, Christopher, Chief Medical Officer, University Hospitals Parma Medical Center, Parma, OH, p. A489

LOYO-RODRIGUEZ, Raul J, Administrative Analyst III, San Diego County Psychiatric Hospital, San Diego, CA, p. A84

LOZADA, Leonardo J, M.D., Chief Physician Executive, Saint Luke's North Hospital-Smithville Campus, MO, p. A362

LOZANO, Elias B., Executive Officer, Tripler Army Medical Center, Honolulu, HI, p. A165

LOZANO, Melanie, Chief Financial Officer, Concho County Hospital, Eden, TX, p. A600

LOZANO, Michelle, Chief Executive Officer, Lifecare Hospitals Of San Antonio, San Antonio, TX, p. A633

LOZAR, Beverly, Chief Nursing Executive, St. Vincent Charity Medical Center, Cleveland, OH, p. A477

LOZIER, Tim, Director Human Resources, Vibra Specialty Hospital At Desoto, Desoto, TX, p. A600

LUBARSKY, Neil, Senior Vice President, Finance and Chief Financial Officer, Jefferson Methodist Hospital, PA, p. A536

LUBIN, Bertram, M.D., President and Chief Executive Officer, Ucsf Benioff Children's Hospital Oakland, Oakland, CA, p. A76

LUBINSKY, Jeanie, Chief Financial Officer, Mayo Clinic Health System - Red Cedar In Menomonie, Menomonie, WI, p. A697

LUBITZ, Robert, M.D., Vice President of Medical Affairs, Wellstar Kennestone Hospital, Marietta, GA, p. A157

LUCAS, Benny Lee, Jr, Chief Nursing Executive, St. Joseph's Behavioral Health Center, Stockton, CA, p. A91

LUCAS, Bob, Vice President Operations, King's Daughters Medical Center, Ashland, KY, p. A249

LUCAS, Christine, Chief of Staff, Union County Hospital, Anna, IL, p. A173

LUCAS, Denise, R.N., MSN, Vice President Clinical Services and Chief Nursing Officer, Margaret R. Pardee Memorial Hospital, Hendersonville, NC, p. A454

LUCAS, Kasey, Chief Executive Officer, Hospital Administrator, Salem Memorial District Hospital, Salem, MO, p. A370

LUCAS, Kelly, Chief Information Officer, Sampson Regional Medical Center, Clinton, NC, p. A450

LUCAS, Marshall, M.D., Medical Director, Cypress Creek Hospital, Houston, TX, p. A610

LUCCHESI, Michael, M.D., Chief Medical Officer; Chair, Emergency Medicine, University Hospital Of Brooklyn At Long Island College Hospital, NY, p. A437

LUCE, Glenda, Chief Nursing Officer, Memorial Hospital Of Gardena, Gardena, CA, p. A60

LUCE, Paul W., R.N., MSN, Vice President Operations, Miami County Medical Center, Paola, KS, p. A244

LUCE, Randall, R.N., Director of Nursing, Rock Springs, Georgetown, TX, p. A607

LUCENA, Ann, Chief Executive Officer, San Ramon Regional Medical Center, San Ramon, CA, p. A88

LUCENA, Yelitza, Executive Director, Hospital Metropolitano Dr. Susoni, Arecibo, PR, p. A712

LUCERO, Brenda, Chief Clinical Officer, Cornerstone Hospital Of Houston - Bellaire, TX, p. A643

LUCERO, Lupe, Manager Business Office, Presbyterian Espanola Hospital, Espanola, NM, p. A417

LUCEY, Jeffery, M.D., Clinical Director, Kingsboro Psychiatric Center, New York (Includes All Hospitals Located Within The Five Boroughs), NY, p. A432

LUCHSINGER, Catherine, MSN, Chief Nursing Officer, Halifax Health Medical Center Of Port Orange, FL, p. A121

LUCIA, Sandra J, Director Health Information and Corporate Compliance Officer, Hampstead Hospital, Hampstead, NH, p. A399

LUCIANO, Lisa, D.O., Medical Director, Hackensack Meridian Health Shore Rehabilitation Institute, Brick, NJ, p. A402

LUCIER, Robbyn, Director Human Resources, Up Health System-Portage, Hancock, MI, p. A315

LUCKE, Kim, Vice President Finance, Northern Montana Health Care, Havre, MT, p. A376

LUCORE, Charles, M.D., President and Chief Executive Officer, St. John's Children's Hospital, IL, p. A196

LUDFORD, Brad, Chief Financial Officer, Bozeman Health Deaconess Hospital, Bozeman, MT, p. A374

LUDWIG, John A., President and Chief Operating Officer, Hshs St. Joseph's Hospital, Highland, IL, p. A185

LUDWIG, Walter, President and Chief Executive Officer, Kenmore Mercy Hospital, Kenmore, NY, p. A428

LUDWIGSEN, Kevin, Chief Information Officer, Southeastern Ohio Regional Medical Center, Cambridge, OH, p. A473

LUEBBERING, Tom, Vice President Finance, Capital Region Medical Center, Jefferson City, MO, p. A360

LUEBCKE, Diane, R.N., Director Nursing, Community Memorial Healthcare, Marysville, KS, p. A241

LUECHT, Jackie
Chief Human Resources Officer, Mercy Medical Center-North Iowa, Mason City, IA, p. A226
Director, Human Resources, Mercy Medical Center-New Hampton, New Hampton, IA, p. A227

LUEDDERS, Keith, Chief Operations Officer, Tri Valley Health System, Cambridge, NE, p. A382

LUEDERS, Kathy, R.N., Director of Nursing-Acute Care, Saint Elizabeth's Medical Center, Wabasha, MN, p. A341

LUEHRS, Bill, Chief Human Resources Officer, Northshore Skokie Hospital, IL, p. A182

LUEHRS, Paul R, Chief Operating Officer, Mercy San Juan Medical Center, Carmichael, CA, p. A54

LUELLEN, John, M.D.
Chief Operating Officer, Heritage Valley Health System, Beaver, PA, p. A520
Chief Operating Officer, Sewickley Valley Hospital, (A Division Of Valley Medical Facilities), Sewickley, PA, p. A541

LUFF, Brian, Chief Executive Officer, Quillen Rehabilitation Hospital, Johnson City, TN, p. A572

LUFFEY, Michelle L, MSN, R.N., Chief Nursing Officer, Fairmont Regional Medical Center, Fairmont, WV, p. A683

LUFKIN, Kirk, M.D., VPMA, Mclaren Northern Michigan, Petoskey, MI, p. A320

LUGER, Gerald, M.D., President Medical Staff, Gottlieb Memorial Hospital, Melrose Park, IL, p. A189

LUGO, Cesar, Director Human Resources, Victor Valley Global Medical Center, Victorville, CA, p. A94

LUHRS, Jason J., Vice President Fiscal Services, Westfields Hospital And Clinic, New Richmond, WI, p. A700

LUKE, Leslie Paul., President and Chief Executive Officer, St. Joseph's Hospital Health Center, Syracuse, NY, p. A444

LUKENS, Tammy, Director Information, Kosciusko Community Hospital, Warsaw, IN, p. A216

LUKER, Patricia A., President, Osf Holy Family Medical Center, Monmouth, IL, p. A189

LUKISH, Kris, Human Resources Officer, Johnston-Willis Hospital, VA, p. A664

LULICH, Diane, Director Human Resources, Memorial Medical Center Of Ashland, Ashland, WI, p. A689

LULL, Todd, Director Information Technology, Southwest Health Center Nursing Home, WI, p. A701

LULOFF, Lynn, Chief Financial Officer, Winneshiek Medical Center, Decorah, IA, p. A221

LUMPKINS, Deborah, MSN, Chief Nursing Officer, Maury Regional Hospital, Columbia, TN, p. A568

LUMPP, Karen, Senior Vice President and Chief Financial Officer, Trinitas Regional Medical Center - New Point Campus, NJ, p. A404

LUMSDEN, Chris A., President and Chief Executive Officer, Northern Hospital Of Surry County, Mount Airy, NC, p. A457

LUNA, Raul D., Chief Nurse Executive, El Paso Psychiatric Center, El Paso, TX, p. A601

LUNA, Tony, M.D., Chief of Staff, Minneola District Hospital, Minneola, KS, p. A241

LUND, Dennis, M.D.
Chief Medical Officer, Lucile Salter Packard Children's Hospital Stanford, Palo Alto, CA, p. A77

Interim Chief Executive Officer, Lucile Salter Packard Children's Hospital Stanford, Palo Alto, CA, p. A77

LUND, Elizabeth, M.D., Chief of Staff, West Tennessee Healthcare Volunteer Hospital, Martin, TN, p. A574

LUNDAL, David, Senior Vice President Information Systems and Chief Information Officer, Presence Holy Family Medical Center, Des Plaines, IL, p. A181

LUNDBERG, Lanetta, Vice President Culture and People, Peacehealth Ketchikan Medical Center, Ketchikan, AK, p. A26

LUNDBLAD, Jackie, Chief Financial Officer, Wickenburg Community Hospital, Wickenburg, AZ, p. A38

LUNDE, Susan, R.N., Director of Nursing, Fallon Medical Complex, Baker, MT, p. A373

LUNDQUIST, David W., President and Chief Executive Officer, Rome Memorial Hospital, Rome, NY, p. A442

LUNDY, Kelly, Chief Information Officer, Peacehealth St. Joseph Medical Center, Bellingham, WA, p. A669

LUNDY, Marcel, Chief Information Officer, Putnam General Hospital, Eatonton, GA, p. A153

LUNDY, Noah, Director of Human Resources, Maine Coast Memorial Hospital, Ellsworth, ME, p. A284

LUNDY-PAINE, Robert, Director Information Systems, Alameda Hospital, Alameda, CA, p. A50

LUNN, William, MD, President and Chief Executive Officer, Tulane-Lakeside Hospital, LA, p. A276

LUNNEBORG, Brandi, Chief Executive Officer, Phoebe Sumter Medical Center, Americus, GA, p. A145

LUNNEY, Kathleen, MS, R.N., Vice President Patient Care Services and Chief Nursing Officer, Nyack Hospital, Nyack, NY, p. A438

LUNSFORD, Cindy, Executive Vice President and Chief Operating Officer, Peninsula Regional Medical Center, Salisbury, MD, p. A294

LUNSFORD, Kaye W, System Director Human Resources, St. Vincent's Medical Center Southside, Jacksonville, FL, p. A126

LUNT, Kimberly, Controller, Healthsouth Rehabilitation Hospital Of Spring Hill, Brooksville, FL, p. A119

LUNTZ, Adam, Chief Financial Officer, Aultman Orrville Hospital, Orrville, OH, p. A488

LUOMA, Michael, M.D., Chief of Staff, Aspirus Keweenaw Hospital, Inc., Laurium, MI, p. A318

LUPINACCI, Michael, M.D., Medical Director, Healthsouth Rehabilitation Hospital Of Mechanicsburg, Mechanicsburg, PA, p. A531

LUSKIN-HAWK, Roberta, M.D.
Chief Executive, General Hospital, CA, p. A57
Chief Executive, Redwood Memorial Hospital, Fortuna, CA, p. A58

LUSSIER, Shirley G, Vice President Human Resources, Northeast Rehabilitation Hospital, Salem, NH, p. A401

LUSTERIO, Efren, Director of Nursing, Behavioral Center Of Michigan, Warren, MI, p. A325

LUTES, Adrianne, Chief Executive Officer, Select Specialty Hospital Daytona Beach, Daytona Beach, FL, p. A121

LUTES, Michael, President, Carolinas Healthcare System Union, Monroe, NC, p. A457

LUTHER, Lori, CPA, Chief Operating Officer, Indiana University Health Ball Memorial Hospital, Muncie, IN, p. A212

LUTHER, Tracie, Director Employee and Labor Relations, Tlc Health Network - Lake Shore Hospital, NY, p. A425

LUTHER, Vera, M.D., Chief of Staff, Sabine County Hospital, Hemphill, TX, p. A609

LUTKENHAUS, Tiffany, Chief Nursing Officer, Muenster Memorial Hospital, Muenster, TX, p. A625

LUTZ, Barbara, Vice President Human Resources, Heart Of The Rockies Regional Medical Center, Salida, CO, p. A105

LUTZ, Denise, Chief Human Resources Officer, Chi St. Alexius Health - Dickinson Medical Center, Dickinson, ND, p. A465

LUTZ, Don, Director Information Technology, Easton Hospital, Easton, PA, p. A524

LUTZ, Kevin, DPM, Chief Operating Officer, Grant, Ohiohealth Grant Medical Center, Columbus, OH, p. A478

LUTZ, Terry, Chief Financial Officer, Scheurer Hospital, Pigeon, MI, p. A320

LUX, Teresa M., President and Chief Operating Officer, Community Memorial Hospital, Menomonee Falls, WI, p. A697

LUZINSKI, Craig, FACHE, MSN, R.N., Vice President Performance Optimization, Cheyenne Regional Medical Center, Cheyenne, WY, p. A707

LYDICK, Bryan, Chief Executive Officer, Redwood Area Hospital, Redwood Falls, MN, p. A338

LYDON, Jean, MS, R.N., System Vice President Operations, Chief Nursing Officer, Elmhurst Hospital, Elmhurst, IL, p. A182

LYLE, Janet, Chief Human Resources and Allied Health Services, Springfield Hospital, Springfield, VT, p. A654

LYLE, Jeffrey, Chief Executive Officer, Falls Community Hospital And Clinic, Marlin, TX, p. A622

LYMAN, Jeremy, Chief Executive Officer, Blue Mountain Hospital, Blanding, UT, p. A646

LYNAM, Sheila, M.D., Chief Medical Officer, Peacehealth St. John Medical Center, Longview, WA, p. A673

LYNCE, Danialle
Business Partner Human Resources, University Hospitals Conneaut Medical Center, Conneaut, OH, p. A479
Business Partner Human Resources, University Hospitals Geneva Medical Center, Geneva, OH, p. A483
Manager Human Resources, University Hospitals Geauga Medical Center, Chardon, OH, p. A474

LYNCH, Becky, Manager Business Entity Management and Information Systems, Osf St. Mary Medical Center, Galesburg, IL, p. A183

LYNCH, Cecelia, R.N., MS, Vice President Patient Care Services and Chief Nursing Officer, Lowell General Hospital, Saints Campus, MA, p. A301

LYNCH, Danile, Chief Operating Officer, Saint Luke Institute, Silver Spring, MD, p. A294

LYNCH, Elizabeth A, Vice President Human Resources, New Britain General, CT, p. A109

LYNCH, Ernest C., III, FACHE, President and Chief Executive Officer, Wysong Campus, TX, p. A623

LYNCH, G Michael, M.D., Chief Medical Officer, Inova Fair Oaks Hospital, Fairfax, VA, p. A657

LYNCH, James, Senior Vice President and Chief Medical Officer, Beaumont Hospital - Troy, Troy, MI, p. A325

LYNCH, Jim, Chief Executive Officer, Fairbanks Memorial Hospital, Fairbanks, AK, p. A26

LYNCH, John, M.D.
Vice President and Chief Medical Officer, Barnes-Jewish Hospital Psychiatric Support Center, MO, p. A367
Vice President and Chief Information Officer, St. Luke's Campus, NY, p. A444

LYNCH, Lisa, Chief Financial Officer, Illinois Valley Community Hospital, Peru, IL, p. A193

LYNCH, Marc, D.O., Chief of Staff, Kindred Hospital-Ontario, Ontario, CA, p. A76

LYNCH, Megan, Manager Human Resources, Johnson Memorial Health Services, Dawson, MN, p. A330

LYNCH, Torie A, Manager Human Resources, Central Montana Medical Center, Lewistown, MT, p. A377

LYNCH, William, Executive Vice President and Chief Operating Officer, Jamaica Hospital Medical Center, New York (Includes All Hospitals Located Within The Five Boroughs), NY, p. A432

LYNCH-KILIC, Cathy, Vice President Human Resources, St. Mary's General Hospital, Passaic, NJ, p. A409

LYND, Samuel, Administrator and Chief Executive Officer, Baptist Memorial Hospital-Tipton, Covington, TN, p. A568

LYNE, Marjorie, Associate Director for Patient Care Services, Hunter Holmes Mcguire Veterans Affairs Medical Center-Richmond, Richmond, VA, p. A665

LYNN, Christina, M.D., Medical Director, Three Rivers Behavioral Health, West Columbia, SC, p. A558

LYNN, Jason, Director Finance, St. Vincent's St. Clair, Pell City, AL, p. A22

LYNN, Lynne Warner, DNP, RN, Administrator, Ephraim Mcdowell James B. Haggin Memorial Hospital, Harrodsburg, KY, p. A253

LYNN, Samuel, Director Human Resources, Northwest Texas Surgery Center, TX, p. A583

LYNSKEY, Jeanne, Vice President and Chief Financial Officer, Whitinsville Medical Center, MA, p. A302

LYON, Tami, Director Human Resources, Community Memorial Hospital, Burke, SD, p. A559

LYONS, Althea C, Vice President Human Resources and Development, Addison Gilbert Hospital, MA, p. A295

LYONS, Denise, Chief Nursing Officer, Cumberland Hall Hospital, Hopkinsville, KY, p. A253

LYONS, Jim, Chief Clinic Officer, Hutchinson Health, Hutchinson, MN, p. A333

LYONS, Lenny
Administrator, Delta Community Medical Center, Delta, UT, p. A646
Administrator, Fillmore Community Hospital, Fillmore, UT, p. A646

LYONS, Michael
Regional Director Information Services, Shriners Hospitals For Children-Galveston, Galveston, TX, p. A606
Regional Information Systems Director, Shriners Hospitals For Children-Shreveport, Shreveport, LA, p. A279

LYONS, Timothy, M.D., Chief Medical Officer, Adventist Health St. Helena, Saint Helena, CA, p. A82

LYREN, Joseph, Chief Financial Officer, Mansfield Hospital, OH, p. A485

LYSAGHT, Marcia C, R.N., MSN, Associate Director Patient Care Services, Miami Veterans Affairs Healthcare System, Miami, FL, p. A130

LYSAGHT, William, Chief Financial Officer, Kindred Hospital-Flamingo, NV, p. A393

LYTHGOE, Derek
Chief Financial Officer, Banner Baywood Medical Center, Mesa, AZ, p. A31
Chief Financial Officer, Banner Heart Hospital, Mesa, AZ, p. A31

M

MAAS, Vernon, M.D., Vice President, Medical Affairs, St. Vincent Evansville, Evansville, IN, p. A203

MABRY, Jerry D., FACHE, Chief Executive Officer, National Park Medical Center, Hot Springs-Garland County, AR, p. A43

MACAFEE, Francis M, Vice President Finance and Chief Financial Officer, Guthrie Corning Hospital, Corning, NY, p. A425

MACAFFEE, Laurie, Director of Nursing, Willow Springs Center, Reno, NV, p. A396

MACARONAS, Thomas, Chief Financial Officer, Labette Health, Parsons, KS, p. A244

MACATOL, Matthew, M.D., President Medical Staff, Marietta Memorial Hospital, Marietta, OH, p. A485

MACDONALD, Joan, R.N., MSN, Chief Nursing Officer, Aurelia Osborn Fox Memorial Hospital, Oneonta, NY, p. A439

MACDONALD, Laurie, Vice President Finance, Penn Highlands Elk, Saint Marys, PA, p. A540

MACDONALD, Neil, Vice President, Operations, Medstar Union Memorial Hospital, Baltimore, MD, p. A288

MACDOUGALL, David, Chief Financial Officer, Wilson Memorial Regional Medical Center, NY, p. A423

MACE, T. Paul, Chief Medical Officer, Garden Park Medical Center, Gulfport, MS, p. A346

MACEVOY, Bonnie, Chief of Staff, Mad River Community Hospital, Arcata, CA, p. A51

MACFADYEN, James, M.D., Medical Director, St. John Vianney Hospital, Downingtown, PA, p. A524

MACH, Robert, Chief Executive Officer, Select Specialty Hospital-Battle Creek, Battle Creek, MI, p. A308

MACHADO, James, President, St. Vincent'S Medical Center Clay County, Middleburg, FL, p. A131

MACHADO, Richard, M.D., President and Chief Executive Officer, Puerto Rico Children'S Hospital, PR, p. A712

MACHORRO, Vicky, R.N., Chief Nursing Officer, Kittitas Valley Healthcare, Ellensburg, WA, p. A671

MACIAS, R.N., R.N., Chief Nursing Officer, Angleton Danbury Campus, TX, p. A606

MACIEL, Maureen, M.D., Chief of Staff, Shriners Hospitals For Children-Tampa, Tampa, FL, p. A141

MACK, Charles, Vice President Finance and Chief Financial Officer, Merit Health Natchez, Natchez, MS, p. A351

MACK, Kristina, Manager, Human Resources, San Dimas Community Hospital, San Dimas, CA, p. A85

MACKAY, Cristal, Chief Operating Officer, Samaritan Behavioral Health Center-Desert Samaritan Medical Center, AZ, p. A31

MACKENROTH, Robin D., Chief Operating Officer, Kaiser Permanente Riverside Medical Center, Riverside, CA, p. A81

MACKENZIE, Susan, Ph.D., Medical Center Director, Providence Veterans Affairs Medical Center, Providence, RI, p. A547

MACKETT, Charles, M.D., Senior Vice President and Chief Medical Officer, Behavioral Health Center, FL, p. A143

MACKEY, Denise, Administrator, Hale Ho'Ola Hamakua, Honokaa, HI, p. A164

MACKIN, Stephen, President, Mercy Children'S Hospital St. Louis, MO, p. A368

MACKINNON, Paul, R.N., Chief Operating Officer, Umass Memorial Healthalliance-Clinton Hospital, MA, p. A301

MACKSOOD, Dan, Regional Senior Vice President and Chief Financial Officer, Good Samaritan Hospital Medical Center, West Islip, NY, p. A445

MACLAUGHLIN, Jeremy, Director Human Resources, Citizens Memorial Hospital, Bolivar, MO, p. A355

MACLEAN, Scott, Administrator, Vibra Hospital Of Western Massachusetts-Central Campus, MA, p. A304

MACLENNAN, Alex, Chief Human Resources Officer, Tahoe Forest Hospital District, Truckee, CA, p. A92

MACLEOD, Deborah, MS, R.N., Vice President Nursing and Patient Care Services, Mid Coast Hospital, Brunswick, ME, p. A283

MACNEILL, Bruce, Chief Financial Officer, Kindred Hospital Seattle-First Hill, WA, p. A676

MACNICOL, Daniel, Chief Executive Officer, Encompass Health Rehabilitation Hospital Of Dallas, Dallas, TX, p. A596

MACOGAY, Melissa, Vice Presiident and Chief Nursing Officer, Johns Hopkins All Children'S Hospital, Saint Petersburg, FL, p. A138

MACPHEE, Alan, Chief Executive Officer, Kahuku Medical Center, Kahuku, HI, p. A165

MACRI, Fredrick, Executive Vice President, Hasbro Children'S Hospital, RI, p. A548

MADAN, Sunil, M.D., Chief Medical Officer and Chief Population Health Officer, Doctors Community Hospital, Lanham, MD, p. A292

MADDEN, Ann Marie, MS, R.N., Vice President of Patient Care Services and Chief Nursing Officer, Women'S Hospital Of Greensboro, NC, p. A453

MADDEN, R. Craig, Director Employee Relations, Reynolds Memorial Hospital, Glen Dale, WV, p. A683

MADDOX, Dale, Chief Financial Officer, Medical Center Of South Arkansas, El Dorado-Union County, AR, p. A41

MADDOX, Jamie, Chief Nursing Officer, Christus Mother Frances Hospital - Jacksonville, Jacksonville, TX, p. A616

MADER, Elaine, M.D., Chief of Staff, Integris Miami Hospital, Miami, OK, p. A501

MADER, Frank, Director Information Services, East Liverpool City Hospital, East Liverpool, OH, p. A482

MADER, Vikki, Director Health Information Services, Pratt Regional Medical Center, Pratt, KS, p. A244

MADIGAN, Catherine, Chief Nursing Officer, Unc Lineberger Comprehensive Cancer Center, NC, p. A449

MADIGAN, Patrick, Interim Chief Executive Officer, Cheyenne Regional Medical Center, Cheyenne, WY, p. A707

MADISON, Jeffrey, FACHE, Chief Executive Officer, Rockdale Hospital, Rockdale, TX, p. A630

MADKINS, Catrina, Controller and Chief Financial Officer, Encompass Health Rehabilitation Hospital Of Plano, Plano, TX, p. A628

MADRID, Melissa, R.N., Chief Nursing Officer, Harper County Community Hospital, Buffalo, OK, p. A496

MADSEN, Greg T., Chief Executive Officer, Carilion Stonewall Jackson Hospital, Lexington, VA, p. A660

MAEKAWA, Steve, Chief Financial Officer, Garfield Medical Center, Monterey Park, CA, p. A73

MAENIUS, Linda, Chief Financial Officer, Laurel Ridge Treatment Center, San Antonio, TX, p. A633

MAERTENS, Mary B., FACHE, President and Chief Executive Officer, Avera Marshall Regional Medical Center, Marshall, MN, p. A334

MAES, Jillian, Director Marketing and Public Relations, St. Thomas More Hospital, Canon City, CO, p. A97

MAES, Stephen, Director Information Systems, St. James Hospital And Health Centers - Chicago Heights Campus, IL, p. A192

MAESTAS, Sadie, Interim Chief Nursing Officer, Copper Queen Community Hospital, Bisbee, AZ, p. A28

MAGDANGAL, Connie, Executive Vice President and Chief Financial Officer, New Bridge Medical Center, Paramus, NJ, p. A409

MAGEE, Becky, Chief Information Officer, Washington Regional Medical Center, Fayetteville-Washington County, AR, p. A42

MAGEE, James L., Executive Director, Piggott Community Hospital, Piggott-Clay County, AR, p. A47

MAGEE, Michael J, Chief Financial Officer, Riverside Medical Center, Franklinton, LA, p. A267

MAGEE, Robert A
  Director Human Resources, Shriners Hospitals For Children-Galveston, Galveston, TX, p. A606
  Director Human Resources, Shriners Hospitals For Children-Houston, Houston, TX, p. A613

MAGEE, William F, Chief Financial Officer, Alliance Healthcare System, Holly Springs, MS, p. A347

MAGES, Michael, Chief Executive Officer, Ashland Health Center, Ashland, KS, p. A232

MAGESTRO, Ben, Chief Operating Officer, North Central Surgical Center, Dallas, TX, p. A597

MAGGARD, Amanda
  Chief Executive Officer, Florida Hospital Dade City, Dade City, FL, p. A121
  Chief Executive Officer, Florida Hospital Zephyrhills, Zephyrhills, FL, p. A144

MAGHAZEHE, Al, Ph.D., FACHE
  President and Chief Executive Officer, Capital Health Medical Center-Hopewell, Pennington, NJ, p. A410
  President and Chief Executive Officer, Capital Health Regional Medical Center, Trenton, NJ, p. A413

MAGID, Philip, Director Fiscal Services, Shriners Hospitals For Children-Chicago, Chicago, IL, p. A179

MAGILL, Marc, MS, Medical Center Director, Jesse Brown Veterans Affairs Medical Center, Chicago, IL, p. A177

MAGNER, Johanna, Interim Chief Nursing Officer, Saint Michael's Medical Center, Newark, NJ, p. A409

MAGNER, Kile, Administrator, Ellinwood District Hospital, Ellinwood, KS, p. A234

MAGNUSON, Johna, Director Nursing, Hillsboro Community Hospital, Hillsboro, KS, p. A236

MAGOON, Patrick M., President and Chief Executive Officer, Ann & Robert H. Lurie Children's Hospital Of Chicago, Chicago, IL, p. A176

MAGRUDER, Joan, President, St. Louis Children's Hospital, Saint Louis, MO, p. A369

MAGU, Bharat, M.D., Chief Medical Officer, Yuma Regional Medical Center, Yuma, AZ, p. A38

MAGUIRE, David L, M.D., Vice President Medical Affairs, Baystate Wing Hospital, Palmer, MA, p. A303

MAGUIRE, Kimberly, R.N., Chief Nursing Officer, Mercy Health, Mercy Campus, MI, p. A319

MAGUREAN, Vickie
  Chief Financial Officer, Englewood Community Hospital, Englewood, FL, p. A122
  Chief Financial Officer, Fawcett Memorial Hospital, Port Charlotte, FL, p. A137
  Chief Financial Officer, Seven Rivers Regional Medical Center, Crystal River, FL, p. A120

MAGUTA, Sam, Coordinator Information Systems, Devereux Advanced Behavioral Health Georgia, Kennesaw, GA, p. A155

MAHAJAN, Naman, Chief Executive Officer, Cypress Fairbanks Medical Center, Houston, TX, p. A610

MAHAN, Michelle K, Senior Vice President and Chief Financial Officer, Frederick Regional Health System, Frederick, MD, p. A291

MAHAN, Vic
  Chief Information Officer, Chino Valley Medical Center, Chino, CA, p. A54
  Director Information Systems, Garden Grove Hospital And Medical Center, Garden Grove, CA, p. A60
  Director Information Technology, La Palma Intercommunity Hospital, La Palma, CA, p. A63
  Director Information Technology, West Anaheim Medical Center, Anaheim, CA, p. A50

MAHAR, Priscilla, Chief Operating Officer, Spectrum Health Kelsey Hospital, MI, p. A314

MAHER, Donna, R.N., Chief Operating Officer, Morton Hospital And Medical Center, Taunton, MA, p. A305

MAHER, John P, Executive Vice President and Chief Financial Officer, Nassau University Medical Center, East Meadow, NY, p. A426

MAHER, Sean, Director Human Resources, Devereux Children's Behavioral Health Center, Malvern, PA, p. A530

MAHER, Thomas, Chief Executive Officer and Administrator, Boulder City Hospital, Boulder City, NV, p. A392

MAHERA, Tina, M.D., Chief Medical Officer, Garfield Park Hospital, Chicago, IL, p. A176

MAHESHWARI, Narendra, M.D., Chief of Staff, Broward Health North, Deerfield Beach, FL, p. A121

MAHEUX, Diane, Vice President Finance, Memorial Hospital, North Conway, NH, p. A400

MAHIDA, Chaitanya, M.D., Chief of Staff, Oak Valley Hospital District, Oakdale, CA, p. A75

MAHL, Morgan G, Director Human Resources, St. Luke's Hospital - Warren Campus, Phillipsburg, NJ, p. A410

MAHLE, Thomas J., Chief Executive Officer, Las Encinas Hospital, Pasadena, CA, p. A78

MAHMOOD, Ahsan, M.D., Chief Medical Officer, Hamilton Center, Terre Haute, IN, p. A215

MAHMOOD, Khalid, M.D., President and Chairman, Crescent Medical Center Lancaster, Lancaster, TX, p. A619

MAHNEKE, Suzette, Associate Vice President of Nursing, Amita Health Adventist Medical Center Glenoaks, Glendale Heights, IL, p. A184

MAHONE, William, President and Chief Executive Officer, Halifax Regional Medical Center, Roanoke Rapids, NC, p. A459

MAHONEY, Bryan, Chief Financial Officer, Columbia Memorial Hospital, Hudson, NY, p. A428

MAHONEY, James, Chief Information Officer, Upmc Pinnacle Memorial, York, PA, p. A546

MAHONEY, Nicole, Chief Financial Officer, Pioneer Memorial Hospital, Heppner, OR, p. A513

MAHONEY, William K., FACHE, President and Chief Executive Officer, Cox Medical Center Branson, Branson, MO, p. A356

MAHR-CHAN, Lydia, Director of Human Resources, Chinese Hospital, San Francisco, CA, p. A85

MAIBERGER, Michael J., President, Miami Valley Hospital South, OH, p. A480

MAIDEN, Phillip G, M.D., Medical Director, Belmont Pines Hospital, Youngstown, OH, p. A494

MAIER, Cindy, R.N., Director of Nursing, Ness County Hospital District No 2, Ness City, KS, p. A242

MAIER, Curtis, Administrator, St. Luke's Jerome, Jerome, ID, p. A169

MAIER, Walter M., Chief of Staff, San Bernardino Mountains Community Hospital District, Lake Arrowhead, CA, p. A63

MAIETTA, Carol, Vice President Human Resources and Chief Learning Officer, St. Vincent's East, Birmingham, AL, p. A15

MAIJALA, Jussi, Vice President, Human Resources, Phelps Memorial Hospital Center, Sleepy Hollow, NY, p. A442

MAIN, Cleo, Finance Officer, Blackfeet Community Hospital, Saint Mary, MT, p. A379

MAINARDI, Carlo, M.D., Vice President Medical Affairs and Chief Medical Officer, Park Ridge Health, Hendersonville, NC, p. A454

MAINES, Stephanie, Chief Nursing Officer, Crossroads Community Hospital, Mount Vernon, IL, p. A190

MAINIERI, Kathy, Human Resource Specialist, Sister Emmanuel Hospital, Miami, FL, p. A131

MAIZE, Makyla, Director Information Services, Washington County Hospital And Clinics, Washington, IA, p. A230

MAJAUSKAS, Joel, Chief Information Officer, Clifton Springs Hospital And Clinic, Clifton Springs, NY, p. A424

MAJCHRZAK, John, Chief Financial Officer, Touchette Regional Hospital, Centreville, IL, p. A175

MAJDALANI, Elias, Director Management Information Systems, Mildred Mitchell-Bateman Hospital, Huntington, WV, p. A684

MAJERUS, Michelle, Chief Information Officer, Olmsted Medical Center, Rochester, MN, p. A338

MAJESKI, Denise J., Vice President Operations and Chief Nurse Executive, Northwestern Medicine Lake Forest Hospital, Lake Forest, IL, p. A187

MAJETICH, Stephen D, CPA, Chief Financial Officer, Southwestern Vermont Medical Center, Bennington, VT, p. A653

MAJHAIL, Ruby, Chief Financial Officer, St. Luke's Behavioral Health Center, Phoenix, AZ, p. A34

MAJOR, Aprille, Director Human Resources, Foothill Regional Medical Center, Tustin, CA, p. A92

MAJOR, Kerry, R.N., MSN, Chief Nursing Officer, Cleveland Clinic Florida, Weston, FL, p. A144

MAJOR, Pattie, Chief Financial Officer, Paul B. Hall Regional Medical Center, Paintsville, KY, p. A259

MAJORS, Ed, Chief Executive Officer, Newman Memorial Hospital, Shattuck, OK, p. A506

MAJORS, Valerie, Director Information Services, Western State Hospital, Hopkinsville, KY, p. A253

MAJZUN, Rick, FACHE, President and Chief Operating Officer, Women & Infants Hospital Of Rhode Island, Providence, RI, p. A548

MAK, David, Chief Financial Officer, El Campo Memorial Hospital, El Campo, TX, p. A601

MAKAROFF, Jason, Chief Operating Officer and Associate Vice President, Adventist Healthcare Physical Health And Rehabilitation, Rockville, MD, p. A293

MAKELA, Taylor, Director Information Technology, Baraga County Memorial Hospital, L'Anse, MI, p. A317

MAKEPEACE, Anne, Director Human Resources, New Ulm Medical Center, New Ulm, MN, p. A336

MAKI, Jacquelyn, Chief Nursing Officer, Oakleaf Surgical Hospital, Altoona, WI, p. A689

MAKI, Richard, R.N., Vice President Nursing and Chief Nursing Officer, Anna Jaques Hospital, Newburyport, MA, p. A302

MAKIEVSKY, Inna, Interim Chief Nursing Officer, Fremont Medical Center, CA, p. A72

MAKORO, Leslie, Director Information management Systems, Merit Health Natchez, Natchez, MS, p. A351

MAKOSKY, Michael D.
  Chief Executive Officer, Fulton County Medical Center, Mc Connellsburg, PA, p. A530
  Interim Chief Executive Officer, Williamson Memorial Hospital, Williamson, WV, p. A688

MAKSOUD, Jane, R.N.
  Senior Vice President Human Resources and Labor Relations, Mount Sinai Health System, Mount Sinai Beth Israel Brooklyn, NY, p. A434
  Senior Vice President Human Resources and Labor Relations, Mount Sinai Health System, Mount Sinai West Hospital, NY, p. A434
  Senior Vice President Human Resources and Labor Relations, Mount Sinai Health System, New York Eye And Ear Infirmary Of Mount Sinai, New York (Includes All Hospitals Located Within The Five Boroughs), NY, p. A434
  Senior Vice President Human Resources and Labor Relations, Mount Sinai Queens, NY, p. A434

MAKSYMOW, Michael, Vice President Information Systems, Beebe Healthcare, Lewes, DE, p. A113

MAKUNDA, Beejadi, M.D., Chief Medical Officer, Heatherhill Care Communities, Chardon, OH, p. A474

MALAER, Gary, Chief Executive Officer, Detar Hospital North, TX, p. A642

MALAKAR, Crystal, Team Leader Inpatient Nursing, Bellin Psychiatric Center, Green Bay, WI, p. A693

MALAKOFF, Stacey, Executive Vice President and Chief Financial Officer, Hospital For Special Surgery, New York (Includes All Hospitals Located Within The Five Boroughs), NY, p. A432

MALAMED, Michael, M.D., Chief of Staff, Sherman Oaks Hospital, Los Angeles, CA, p. A69

MALAN, Glen, Vice President Information Technology and Chief Information Officer, Northwest Community Hospital, Arlington Heights, IL, p. A173

MALANEY, Scott C., FACHE, President and Chief Executive Officer, Blanchard Valley Hospital, OH, p. A482

MALCOLM, Dru, Vice President and Chief Nursing Officer, Woodridge Hospital, TN, p. A571

MALCOLMSON, James F, M.D., Chief of Staff, Sierra Vista Hospital, Truth Or Consequences, NM, p. A420

MALDONADO, Diraida, Chief Executive Officer, Hospital De La Universidad De Puerto Rico/Dr. Federico Trilla, Carolina, PR, p. A712

MALENSEK, Frank, M.D., Chief Medical Officer, St. Vincent's East, Birmingham, AL, p. A15

MALEY, Shelley, Director Human Resources, St. Luke's Hospital - Quakertown Campus, Quakertown, PA, p. A539

MALIK, Aamir, M.D., Chief Medical Officer, Acuity Hospital Of South Texas, San Antonio, TX, p. A632

MALIK, Azfar, M.D.
Chief Medical Officer, Centerpointe Hospital, Saint Charles, MO, p. A367
Chief Medical Officer, Signature Psychiatric Hospital, Kansas City, MO, p. A362

MALIK, Chuck
Director Information Systems, Advocate Good Shepherd Hospital, Barrington, IL, p. A174
Director Information Systems, Advocate Illinois Masonic Medical Center, Chicago, IL, p. A176

MALIN, Seth, M.D., President Medical and Dental Staff, Delaware County Memorial Hospital, Drexel Hill, PA, p. A524

MALINA, Joanne J, M.D., Chief of Staff, Veterans Affairs Hudson Valley Health Care System-Montrose Campus, NY, p. A430

MALINDZAK, Edward, Chief Human Resources Officer, Oconomowoc Memorial Hospital, Oconomowoc, WI, p. A700

MALJOVEC, John, M.D., Medical Director, Warren General Hospital, Warren, PA, p. A543

MALKO, Jennifer, Market Chief Executive Officer, Lifecare Hospitals Of Pittsburgh - Suburban, PA, p. A537

MALLETT, Belinda, R.N., MS, Vice President, Patient Care and Clinical Services, Soin Medical Center, Beavercreek, OH, p. A472

MALLETT, Conrad L., Jr, Chief Executive Officer, Dmc - Sinai-Grace Hospital, Detroit, MI, p. A311

MALLETT, Teresa, Chief Financial Officer, Madison Regional Health System, Madison, SD, p. A561

MALLICOAT, Robert E., Chief Executive Officer, Complex Care Hospital At Ridgelake, Sarasota, FL, p. A138

MALLIK, Subodh, M.D., Chief of Staff, Pecos County Memorial Hospital, Fort Stockton, TX, p. A604

MALLING, Timothy, M.D., Chief of Staff, Centracare Health-Paynesville, Paynesville, MN, p. A337

MALLONEE, Teresa, Director Human Resources, Angel Medical Center, Franklin, NC, p. A452

MALLORY, Brenda, M.D., Medical Director, Penn State Hershey Rehabilitation Hospital, Hummelstown, PA, p. A527

MALLOY, Patrick C., M.D., Chief of Staff, Veterans Affairs New York Harbor Healthcare System - Manhattan Campus, NY, p. A437

MALLOY, Peter, Chief Information Officer, Cheshire Medical Center, Keene, NH, p. A399

MALM, Brad, Director Human Resources and Education, Lindsborg Community Hospital, Lindsborg, KS, p. A240

MALMSTROM, Ron, Information Research Specialist, Parsons State Hospital And Training Center, Parsons, KS, p. A244

MALONE, Donald A., Jr, President, Lutheran Hospital, Cleveland, OH, p. A477

MALONE, Ginger, MSN, RN-B, Chief Nursing Officer, Ssm Health St. Mary's Hospital, Madison, WI, p. A696

MALONE, Meredith, Chief Financial Officer, West Tennessee Healthcare Dyersburg Hospital, Dyersburg, TN, p. A569

MALONE, Michael, Vice President and Chief Human Resources Officer, Virginia Hospital Center, Arlington, VA, p. A655

MALONE, Patty, M.D., Chief Medical Officer, Ocean Beach Hospital, Ilwaco, WA, p. A672

MALONEY, Christopher, M.D., Senior Vice President, Medical Affairs and Chief Medical Officer, Children's Hospital And Medical Center, Omaha, NE, p. A388

MALONEY, Jay, M.D., Chief of Staff, Cabinet Peaks Medical Center, Libby, MT, p. A377

MALONEY, Patrick J.
Chief Executive Officer, Franciscan Health Dyer, Dyer, IN, p. A202
Chief Executive Officer, Franciscan Healthcare Munster, Munster, IN, p. A212
Chief Executive Officer, Saint Margaret Mercy Healthcare Centers-North Campus, IN, p. A205

MALONEY, Paul V, Vice President Finance, Behavioral Health Network, Natchaug Hospital, Mansfield Center, CT, p. A108

MALONEY, Robert, Jr, Chief Operating Officer, Mercy Health - Anderson Hospital, Cincinnati, OH, p. A475

MALOTT, Deanna, Director Human Resources, Henry Community Health, New Castle, IN, p. A212

MALOTT, Gregg, Chief Financial Officer, Pulaski Memorial Hospital, Winamac, IN, p. A216

MALOTTE, Rebecca, Executive Director and Chief Nursing Officer, The Heart Hospital At Deaconess Gateway, Newburgh, IN, p. A212

MALSED, Brad, Area Chief Financial Officer, Kaiser Foundation Mental Health Center, CA, p. A67

MALSEED, Timothy James, Chief Information Officer, Keck Hospital Of Usc, Los Angeles, CA, p. A68

MALSEED, TJ, Vice President and Chief Information Officer, Children's Hospital Los Angeles, Los Angeles, CA, p. A66

MALYSZEK, Richard, M.D., Chief of Staff, Pikes Peak Regional Hospital, Woodland Park, CO, p. A106

MAMBOURG, Rolland, M.D., Vice President Medical Affairs, Mercy Health Rockford, MI, p. A314

MANAKAS, Christopher, Chief Information Officer, Fort Healthcare, Fort Atkinson, WI, p. A692

MANCHUR, Richard, President, Southview Medical Center, OH, p. A480

MANDAL, Alan, Vice President Financial Operations, Scripps Memorial Hospital-La Jolla, La Jolla, CA, p. A63

MANDAL, Konoy, M.D., Medical Director, Centennial Peaks Hospital, Louisville, CO, p. A104

MANDANAS, Renato, M.D., Chief Medical Officer, Oswego Hospital, Oswego, NY, p. A439

MANDERINO, Michelle, Chief Human Resources, Lake City Veterans Affairs Medical Center, FL, p. A123

MANDHAN, Narain, M.D., Chief Medical Officer, Kirby Medical Center, Monticello, IL, p. A190

MANDI, Deepak, M.D., Chief of Staff, West Palm Beach Veterans Affairs Medical Center, West Palm Beach, FL, p. A143

MANDRACCHIA, Vincent, DPM, Chief Medical Officer, Broadlawns Medical Center, Des Moines, IA, p. A221

MANESTRINA, Robert, Vice President Human Resources, Inspira Medical Center-Woodbury, Woodbury, NJ, p. A414

MANFREDI, Susan, R.N., Vice President and Chief Nursing Officer, Uw Medicine/Northwest Hospital & Medical Center, Seattle, WA, p. A677

MANFREDO, John, Chief Operating Officer, Norman Regional Moore, OK, p. A502

MANGIN, Paul, Vice President Finance, Mercy Services For Aging, IA, p. A219

MANGIONE, Ellen, M.D., Chief of Staff, Veterans Affairs Eastern Colorado Health Care System, Denver, CO, p. A99

MANGONA, John, Vice President, Chief Information Officer and Compliance Officer, Saratoga Hospital, Saratoga Springs, NY, p. A442

MANGUM, Cody, Director Operations, St. Luke's Elmore, Mountain Home, ID, p. A170

MANGUM, Lisa, Chief Nursing Officer, North Canyon Medical Center, Gooding, ID, p. A169

MANGUM, Rozanne, Administrative Assistant and Director Human Resources, Grover C. Dils Medical Center, Caliente, NV, p. A392

MANIATIS, Theodore, M.D., Medical Director, Staten Island University Hospital, New York (Includes All Hospitals Located Within The Five Boroughs), NY, p. A437

MANIGAULT, Merald, Chief Financial Officer, Acuity Hospital Of South Texas, San Antonio, TX, p. A632

MANKER, Marcia
Chief Executive Officer, Memorialcare, Orange Coast Memorial Medical Center, Fountain Valley, CA, p. A58
Chief Executive Officer, Memorialcare, Saddleback Memorial Medical Center, Laguna Hills, CA, p. A63

MANKINS, Mark L, M.D., Chief of Staff, Hamilton Hospital, Olney, TX, p. A626

MANKOSKI, Susan, Vice President Human Resources, Ssm Health St. Mary's Hospital - Jefferson City, Jefferson City, MO, p. A360

MANLAGNIT, Maybelle, Senior Accounting Officer, Metropolitan State Hospital, Norwalk, CA, p. A75

MANLEY, Dennis, R.N., Chief Nursing Officer, St. John's Rehabilitation Center, MO, p. A361

MANLEY, John, Director Information Systems, Jackson General Hospital, Ripley, WV, p. A686

MANN, Brian, Chief Executive Officer, Select Specialty Hospital-Danville, Danville, PA, p. A524

MANN, Corey, Director Human Resources, Memorial Health Care Systems, Seward, NE, p. A390

MANN, Erin, R.N., Chief Nursing Officer, Mccamey County Hospital District, Mccamey, TX, p. A623

MANN, Julie D, Vice President and Chief Administrative Officer, Katherine Shaw Bethea Hospital, Dixon, IL, p. A181

MANN, Karen, R.N., Chief Nursing Officer, Shoshone Medical Center, Kellogg, ID, p. A169

MANN, Lori, R.N., MSN, Chief Nursing Officer, Howard A. Rusk Rehabilitation Center, Columbia, MO, p. A358

MANN, Rex, M.D., Chief Medical Officer, Ochiltree General Hospital, Perryton, TX, p. A628

MANN, Rhonda, Chief Nursing Officer, Franklin Woods Community Hospital, Johnson City, TN, p. A571

MANN, Todd, Chief Executive Officer, Mcallen Medical Center, TX, p. A601

MANNI, Joseph, Executive Vice President and Chief Operating Officer, Deborah Heart And Lung Center, Browns Mills, NJ, p. A403

MANNICH, Andy, Regional Administrator, Georgia Regional Hospital At Savannah, Savannah, GA, p. A160

MANNING, Angela, Director Health Information Services, Healthsouth Sunrise Rehabilitation Hospital, Sunrise, FL, p. A140

MANNING, Austin Lane
Chief Operating Officer, Thousand Oaks Surgical Hospital, CA, p. A91
Chief Operating Officer, Timpanogos Regional Hospital, Orem, UT, p. A649

MANNING, Claude, Chief Financial Officer, Palacios Community Medical Center, Palacios, TX, p. A626

MANNING, Donald, M.D., Clinical Director, Georgia Regional Hospital At Savannah, Savannah, GA, p. A160

MANNING, James, Administrator, Pathway Rehabilitation Hospital, Bossier City, LA, p. A265

MANNING, JoAnn, Chief Financial Officer, Emory Johns Creek Hospital, Johns Creek, GA, p. A155

MANNING, Kevin, Chief Nursing Officer, Kingwood Medical Center, Kingwood, TX, p. A618

MANNING, Kimberly, Chief Nursing Officer, Washington County Hospital, Plymouth, NC, p. A458

MANNING, Laura, Administrative Director, Guthrie Corning Hospital, Corning, NY, p. A425

MANNING, Lori, Administrator Human Resources, Western State Hospital, Tacoma, WA, p. A679

MANNION, Stephen, Assistant Vice President Information Systems Customer Service, Medstar Franklin Square Medical Center, Baltimore, MD, p. A288

MANNIX, Mary N., FACHE, President and Chief Executive Officer, Augusta Health, Fishersville, VA, p. A658

MANNS, Bill, President, Mercy Health Rockford, MI, p. A314

MANNY, Martin, Director, I.S., Providence St. Mary Medical Center, Walla Walla, WA, p. A680

MANOHARA, Anand, Chief Operating Officer, Good Samaritan Hospital, Bakersfield, CA, p. A52

MANSEAU, Jani, Vice President Operations and Chief Nursing Officer, Scottsdale Liberty Hospital, Scottsdale, AZ, p. A35

MANSFIELD, David, M.D., Chief of Staff, El Paso Specialty Hospital, El Paso, TX, p. A601

MANSFIELD, Deena, Director Human Resources, Ashley Regional Medical Center, Vernal, UT, p. A651

MANSFIELD, Jerry A, Ph.D., R.N., Executive Chief Nursing Officer & Chief Patient Experience Officer, Children's Hospital Of South Carolina At Musc, SC, p. A550

MANSKE, Kristin, Chief Executive Officer, Greenwood Regional Rehabilitation Hospital, Greenwood, SC, p. A554

MANSKE, Lou Ann, Director Human Resources, Madonna Rehabilitation Hospital, Lincoln, NE, p. A386

MANSON, David, Manager Human Resources, Santa Clara Valley Medical Center, San Jose, CA, p. A87

MANSON, Kelly, Chief Financial Officer, Veterans Affairs Sierra Nevada Health Care System, Reno, NV, p. A396

MANSON, Lisa, Director Ambulatory Services, Guttenberg Municipal Hospital, Guttenberg, IA, p. A223

MANSON, Stephanie, Chief Operating Officer, Our Lady Of The Lake Children's Hospital, LA, p. A264

MANSON, William T, III, FACHE, Chief Executive Officer, Anmed Health Women's And Children's Hospital, SC, p. A549

MANSON, William T., III, FACHE, Chief Executive Officer, Anmed Health Women's And Children's Hospital, SC, p. A549

MANSOOR, Ureej, M.D., Chief of Staff, Southeast Health Center Of Ripley County, Doniphan, MO, p. A358

MANSTEDT, Chase, Chief Financial Officer, Saunders Medical Center, Wahoo, NE, p. A391

MANSUKHANI, Martin, Chief Financial Officer, Desert Valley Hospital, Victorville, CA, p. A94

MANSURE, John F., FACHE, President, Ghs Greer Memorial Hospital, Greer, SC, p. A554

MANTERNACH, Paul, M.D., Senior Vice President Physician Integration, Mercy Medical Center-North Iowa, Mason City, IA, p. A226

MANTOOTH, Charles, President and Chief Executive Officer, Watauga Medical Center, Boone, NC, p. A448

MANTZ, David, Chief Executive Officer, Chicot Memorial Medical Center, Lake Village-Chicot County, AR, p. A44

MANUBENS, Claudio, M.D., Chief of Staff, Heart Of Florida Regional Medical Center, Davenport, FL, p. A121

MANUEL, Shasta, Executive Director Finance, Ssm Health St. Anthony South, OK, p. A504

MANUEL, Wendy, Vice President and Chief Financial Officer, Rehabilitation Hospital Of The Pacific, Honolulu, HI, p. A165

MANZO, Arnold D, Vice President Human Resources, Saint Barnabas Medical Center, Livingston, NJ, p. A406

MANZO-LUNA, Hilda, Chief Nursing Officer, La Palma Intercommunity Hospital, La Palma, CA, p. A63

MANZOOR, Amir, M.D., Medical Director, Select Specialty Hospital-Panama City, Panama City, FL, p. A135

MAPARA, Anupam, M.D., Chief of Staff, Sutter Delta Medical Center, Antioch, CA, p. A50

MAPLES, Michael, M.D., Vice President and Chief Medical Officer, Mississippi Baptist Medical Center, Jackson, MS, p. A348

MAPLES, Rickie, Interim Chief Financial Officer, Southeast Health Center Of Ripley County, Doniphan, MO, p. A358

MAPPIN, F Gregory, M.D., Vice President Medical Affairs and Chief Medical Officer, Self Regional Healthcare, Greenwood, SC, p. A554

MARAAN, Sheila, Director of Nursing, Brynn Marr Hospital, Jacksonville, NC, p. A455

MARANDI, Hossain, M.D., FACHE
President and Chief Executive Officer, Peyton Manning Children's Hospital At St. Vincent, IN, p. A208
President and Chief Executive Officer, Peyton Manning Children's Hospital, IN, p. A208

MARANO, Deena, Human Resources Director, Community Hospital Of San Bernardino, San Bernardino, CA, p. A83

MARAS, Greg, Vice President Human Resources, Meadville Medical Center, Meadville, PA, p. A531

MARASA, Richard, M.D., President Medical Staff, Springfield Hospital, Springfield, VT, p. A654

MARBLE, Kevin, Director Information Technology, Oklahoma Forensic Center, Vinita, OK, p. A509

MARCANO, Norma, Chief Operating Officer, San Juan City Hospital, San Juan, PR, p. A716

MARCANTEL, Bill, Chief Information Systems, Allen Parish Hospital, Kinder, LA, p. A270

MARCEAUX, Caroline, MSN, R.N., Chief Nursing Officer, Acadia General Hospital, Crowley, LA, p. A266

MARCELIN, Fitzgerald, M.D., Chief of Staff, Southern Virginia Regional Medical Center, Emporia, VA, p. A657

MARCH, Riley, Manager Information Technology, Southeast Health Center Of Ripley County, Doniphan, MO, p. A358

MARCHANT, Joseph, Administrator, Bibb Medical Center, Centreville, AL, p. A16

MARCHETTI, Mark E., President and Chief Executive Officer, Mt. Graham Regional Medical Center, Safford, AZ, p. A35

MARCHIK, Katie A
Chief Financial Officer, Unitypoint Health - Trinity Moline, IL, p. A194
Vice President, Consolidated Services, UnityPoint Health and Chief Financial Officer, Trinity Regional Health System, Unitypoint Health - Trinity Muscatine, Muscatine, IA, p. A227

MARCIANO, Paolo G, M.D., Chief Medical Officer, Beaumont Hospital - Dearborn, Dearborn, MI, p. A310

MARCO, James E, Jr, Interim Vice President, Human Resources, Oswego Hospital, Oswego, NY, p. A439

MARCOTTE, Eric, M.D., Chief Medical Officer, Riverview Health, Noblesville, IN, p. A213

MARCOTTE, Lynn, Chief Financial Officer, Mclaren Oakland, Pontiac, MI, p. A321

MARCOTTE, Melissa, Chief Financial Officer, Rainy Lake Medical Center, International Falls, MN, p. A333

MARCOVICI, Mia, M.D., Chief Medical Officer, Norristown State Hospital, Norristown, PA, p. A533

MARCOWITZ, David, M.D., Chief of Staff, Lucas County Health Center, Chariton, IA, p. A219

MARCRUM, Jennifer, Chief Financial Officer, Sumner County Hospital District One, Caldwell, KS, p. A233

MARCUCCI, John, M.D., Vice President Medical Affairs, Baylor Regional Medical Center At Plano, Plano, TX, p. A628

MARCUM, Amie, Human Resources Coordinator, Continuecare Hospital At Baptist Health Corbin, Corbin, KY, p. A250

MARCZEWSKI, Les, M.D., Chief Medical Officer, Loring Hospital, Sac City, IA, p. A229

MARDY, Paul, Chief Information Technology Officer, Nashville Campus, TN, p. A577

MAREK, Kyle, Chief Information Officer, Carteret Health Care, Morehead City, NC, p. A457

MAREK, Rick, Vice President Medical Information Systems, Warm Springs Rehabilitation Hospital Of Westover Hills, TX, p. A634

MARGENAU, Randall, Chief Information Officer, William S. Middleton Memorial Veterans Hospital, Madison, WI, p. A696

MARGER, Brian, Chief Executive Officer, Tristar Summit Medical Center, Hermitage, TN, p. A570

MARGOLIS, Marilyn, MSN, Chief Executive Officer, Emory Johns Creek Hospital, Johns Creek, GA, p. A155

MARGULIS, Richard T., President and Chief Executive Officer, Long Island Community Hospital, Patchogue, NY, p. A440

MARIANI, Marilyn, R.N., Chief Nursing Officer, Lakeview Hospital, Bountiful, UT, p. A646

MARIANI, Meleah, Chief Nursing Officer, Spectrum Health Gerber Memorial, Fremont, MI, p. A313

MARICN, Tanya, Interim Vice President Human Resources, Mercy Orthopedic Hospital Springfield, MO, p. A370

MARIETTA, John, M.D., Chief Medical Officer, St. David's Rehabilitation Center, TX, p. A586

MARIETTA, Megan, Chief Executive Officer, West Houston Medical Center, Houston, TX, p. A614

MARIETTA, Richard, M.D., Medical Director, Mainland Medical Center, TX, p. A643

MARIGOMEN, Nancy Ann, R.N., Director of Nursing, Milwaukee County Behavioral Health Division, Milwaukee, WI, p. A699

MARIN, Loyman, Chief Human Resources, Miami Veterans Affairs Healthcare System, Miami, FL, p. A130

MARIN, Octavio, Vice President Long Term Care and Ambulatory Care Services, Bronx-Lebanon Special Care Center, NY, p. A431

MARINARO, Jon, M.D., Chief Medical Officer, Kindred Hospital-Albuquerque, Albuquerque, NM, p. A415

MARINELLO, Anthony, Chief Operating Officer, Children's Hospital Of Nevada At Umc, NV, p. A395

MARINI, Frank, Senior Vice President and Chief Information Officer, Tmc For Children, AZ, p. A38

MARINICH, Patsy
Chief Administrative Officer and Chief Nursing Officer, Cumberland River Hospital, Celina, TN, p. A566
Chief Adminstrative Officer and Chief Nursing Officer, Cumberland River Hospital, Celina, TN, p. A566

MARINO, A Michael, M.D., Senior Vice President Medical Administration, Greenwich Hospital, Greenwich, CT, p. A108

MARINO, Christopher, M.D., Chief of Staff, Memphis Veterans Affairs Medical Center, Memphis, TN, p. A575

MARINO, Joseph, Chief Financial Officer, Suburban Community Hospital, Norristown, PA, p. A533

MARINO, Marchita H, Vice President Human Resources, Rockledge Regional Medical Center, Rockledge, FL, p. A137

MARINOFF, Peter, President, Paul Oliver Memorial Hospital, Frankfort, MI, p. A313

MARION, Amy, Chief Human Resource Officer, Walter B. Jones Alcohol And Drug Abuse Treatment Center, Greenville, NC, p. A454

MARION, Kristie, Chief Nurse Executive, Memorial Hospital Los Banos, Los Banos, CA, p. A70

MARIOTTI, Denise J., Chief Human Resource Officer, Scheie Eye Institute Of The Hospital Of The University Of Pennsylvania, PA, p. A535

MARIS, Peter, Director Human Resources, Nyc Health + Hospitals / Elmhurst, New York (Includes All Hospitals Located Within The Five Boroughs), NY, p. A435

MARKENSON, David, M.D., Chief Medical Officer, Sky Ridge Medical Center, Lone Tree, CO, p. A103

MARKER, John, MSN, R.N., Chief Nursing Officer, Medical City North Hills, North Richland Hills, TX, p. A626

MARKESINO, Patricia A, FACHE, Chief Nurse Executive and Chief Operating Officer, Providence Willamette Falls Medical Center, Oregon City, OR, p. A515

MARKGRAF, Janelle K., Director Human Resources and Off Campus Services, Aspirus Langlade Hospital, Antigo, WI, p. A689

MARKHAM, Barbara, Chief Financial Officer, Glendive Medical Center, Glendive, MT, p. A375

MARKHAM, Kevin, Chief Financial Officer, Eastpointe Hospital, Daphne, AL, p. A16

MARKOS, Dennis R., Chief Executive Officer, Ed Fraser Memorial Hospital And Baker Community Health Center, Macclenny, FL, p. A128

MARKOS, Valerie, Chief Nursing Officer, Ed Fraser Memorial Hospital And Baker Community Health Center, Macclenny, FL, p. A128

MARKOWITZ, Christine, Chief Financial Officer, East Georgia Regional Medical Center, Statesboro, GA, p. A161

MARKOWITZ, Stuart, M.D., Chief Medical Officer, Institute Of Living, CT, p. A108

MARKOWSKI, Stan, Chief Financial Officer, Palmetto Lowcountry Behavioral Health, Charleston, SC, p. A550

MARKS, Craig J., FACHE, Chief Executive Officer, Pmh Medical Center, Prosser, WA, p. A675

MARKS, Jerry, Vice President Finance, Decatur County Memorial Hospital, Greensburg, IN, p. A205

MARKS, Kimberly W., Chief Executive Officer, Southampton Memorial Hospital, Franklin, VA, p. A658

MARKS, Kindra, Chief Executive Officer, Select Specialty Hospital - Columbus East, OH, p. A479

MARKS, Marie, Chief Nursing Officer, Lake Norman Regional Medical Center, Mooresville, NC, p. A457

MARKS, Michael, M.D., Chief of Staff, Norwalk Hospital, Norwalk, CT, p. A110

MARKS, Michelle, D.O., Medical Director, Cleveland Clinic Children's Hospital For Rehabilitation, Cleveland, OH, p. A476

MARKS, Peter, Vice President & Chief Information Officer, Wakemed North Family Health And Women's Hospital, NC, p. A459

MARKS, Stanley, M.D., FACS
Chief Medical Officer, Memorial Hospital Miramar, Miramar, FL, p. A132
Chief Medical Officer, Memorial Hospital Pembroke, Pembroke Pines, FL, p. A135

MARKSTROM, Susan, M.D., Chief of Staff, St. Cloud Veterans Affairs Health Care System, Saint Cloud, MN, p. A339

MARKUS, Stacey, Chief Nursing Officer, Williamson Memorial Hospital, Williamson, WV, p. A688

MARLATT, Pam, Business Systems Director, Essentia Health St. Joseph's Medical Center, Brainerd, MN, p. A328

MARLER, Ruth, Chief Nursing Officer and Chief Operating Officer, Johnston Health, Smithfield, NC, p. A460

MARLER, Steven R, Assistant Administrator, Parkland Health Center - Farmington Community, Farmington, MO, p. A359

MARLEY, Charles, D.O., Vice President Medical Affairs, Wellspan Gettysburg Hospital, Gettysburg, PA, p. A526

MARLEY, Lee, VP/Information Services Chief Application Officer, Presbyterian Rust Medical Center, NM, p. A416

MARLEY, Michael, Chief Information Officer, Veterans Affairs Central Western Massachusetts Healthcare System, Leeds, MA, p. A301

MARLIN, Chris, Director Human Resources, Orange Park Medical Center, Orange Park, FL, p. A133

MARLOW, Gary P, Chief Financial Officer, Addison Gilbert Hospital, MA, p. A295

MARLOWE, Justin, Information Technology Director, Shands Live Oak Regional Medical Center, Live Oak, FL, p. A128

MARMANDE, Susanne, Administrator, Infirmary Long Term Acute Care Hospital, Mobile, AL, p. A20

MARNEY, Terri A, R.N., Director of Nursing, Plains Regional Medical Center, Clovis, NM, p. A416

MARON, Michael, President and Chief Executive Officer, Holy Name Medical Center, Teaneck, NJ, p. A412

MARONEY, Gerry, Chief Information Officer and Security Officer, Gaylord Hospital, Wallingford, CT, p. A111

MAROSTICA, Tony, Chief Compliance and Human Resource Officer, Spanish Peaks Regional Health Center, Walsenburg, CO, p. A106

MAROTTA, Diane, Vice President Human Resources, John T. Mather Memorial Hospital, Port Jefferson, NY, p. A440

MAROUN, Christiane, M.D., Chief of Staff, Lifescape, Sioux Falls, SD, p. A563

MARQUES, John, Vice President Human Resources, Diamond Children's Hospital, AZ, p. A37

MARQUES, Tony, Director Information Systems, Grace Cottage Hospital, Townshend, VT, p. A654

MARQUSEE, Joanne, President and Chief Executive Officer, Cooley Dickinson Hospital, Northampton, MA, p. A303

MARR, Debbie, Administrative Assistant and Director Human Resources, Fredonia Regional Hospital, Fredonia, KS, p. A235

MARRAN, Mary, MS, President and Chief Operating Officer, Butler Hospital, Providence, RI, p. A547

MARRERO, Jamie L, M.D., Medical Director, Healthsouth Hospital Of Manati, Manati, PR, p. A714

MARRERO, Jose, Director Finance, San Jorge Children's Hospital, Santurce, PR, p. A716

MARRERO, Norma, Executive Administrator, Doctors' Center Hospital San Juan, San Juan, PR, p. A715

MARRONI, Denise
Chief Financial Officer, Providence Centralia Hospital, Centralia, WA, p. A670
Chief Financial Officer, Providence St. Peter Hospital, Olympia, WA, p. A674

MARRUFO, Gabriel, Chief Financial Officer, Methodist Stone Oak Hospital, San Antonio, TX, p. A633

MARSEE, DeWayne, Director Information Systems, Mercer Health, Coldwater, OH, p. A478

MARSH, Amy, Chief Financial Officer, Fairfield Memorial Hospital, Fairfield, IL, p. A183

MARSH, J. Michael., President and Chief Executive Officer, Overlake Medical Center, Bellevue, WA, p. A669

MARSH, Leslie, Chief Executive Officer, Lexington Regional Health Center, Lexington, NE, p. A385

MARSH, Linda, Vice President Financial Services and Chief Financial Officer, Alhambra Hospital Medical Center, Alhambra, CA, p. A50

MARSH, Mark A., President, Health Central Hospital, Ocoee, FL, p. A133

MARSH, Mitch, Interim Executive Director, Terence Cardinal Cooke Health Care Center, New York (Includes All Hospitals Located Within The Five Boroughs), NY, p. A437

MARSH, Rob, Chief Executive Officer, San Jose Behavorial Health, San Jose, CA, p. A87

MARSH, Toby, MSN, R.N., Interim Chief Patient Care Services Officer, University Of California Davis Children's Hospital, CA, p. A82

MARSH, Wallace, Director of Information Technology, Willow Springs Center, Reno, NV, p. A396

MARSHAK, Glenn, M.D., Chief of Staff, Mission Community Hospital, Los Angeles, CA, p. A68

MARSHALL, Deborah K, Vice President Public Relations, Good Samaritan Regional Medical Center, Suffern, NY, p. A443

MARSHALL, Erika, Interim Chief Nursing Officer, Calais Regional Hospital, Calais, ME, p. A283

MARSHALL, James I., President and Chief Executive Officer, Uintah Basin Medical Center, Roosevelt, UT, p. A650

MARSHALL, Jerry, Director Information Services, Information Technology Security Officer, United Regional Health Care System-Eleventh Street Campus, TX, p. A644

MARSHALL, Jim, Chief Executive Officer and Administrator, Pemiscot Memorial Health System, Hayti, MO, p. A360

MARSHALL, Joe, Chief Operating Officer, Lillian M. Hudspeth Memorial Hospital, Sonora, TX, p. A636

MARSHALL, Judy, Director Human Resources, Holy Cross Hospital, Taos, NM, p. A420

MARSHALL, Julie, Chief Nursing Officer, The University Of Vermont Health Network - Alice Hyde Medical Center, Malone, NY, p. A429

MARSHALL, Ken, M.D., Chief Medical Officer, Indiana University Health Bloomington Hospital, Bloomington, IN, p. A200

MARSHALL, Kenneth P., President and Chief Executive Officer, University Of Louisville Hospital, Louisville, KY, p. A257

MARSHALL, Michael, Vice President Finance and Chief Financial Officer, Anderson Hospital, Maryville, IL, p. A188

MARSHALL, Patricia, Assistant Administrator Human Resources, Washington Health System Greene, Waynesburg, PA, p. A543

MARSHALL, Penny, Chief Nursing Officer, Bear River Valley Hospital, Tremonton, UT, p. A651

MARSHALL, Robert L., Jr, FACHE, Chief Executive Officer, Bolivar Medical Center, Cleveland, MS, p. A345

MARSHBURN, Deborah, R.N., Chief Nursing Executive, Cape Fear Valley Rehabilitation Center, NC, p. A452

MARSICO, Nick, Vice President and Chief Operating Officer, Magruder Memorial Hospital, Port Clinton, OH, p. A489

MARSO, Paul, Vice President Human Resources, Avera St. Mary's Hospital, Pierre, SD, p. A562

MARSTON, Shawn, Director Human Resources, Newport News Behavioral Health Center, Newport News, VA, p. A662

MARTANIUK, Jean, Director Human Resources, Mt. Ascutney Hospital And Health Center, Windsor, VT, p. A654

MARTE, Maria, Administrator, Doctor's Center Of Bayamon, Bayamon, PR, p. A712

MARTELL, Gustavo, M.D., Chief Medical Officer, The Hospitals Of Providence Transmountain Campus, El Paso, TX, p. A602

MARTENS, Angela, Chief Financial Officer, Cumberland Healthcare, Cumberland, WI, p. A691

MARTENS, Troy, Chief Operating Officer, Unitypoint Health - Trinity Regional Medical Center, Fort Dodge, IA, p. A222

MARTHONE, Frances, Ph.D., R.N., Chief Nursing Officer, Mercy Medical Center, Springfield, MA, p. A304

MARTI, Maria L, Director Fiscal Services, Auxilio Mutuo Hospital, San Juan, PR, p. A715

MARTIN, Adam, Chief Operating Officer, Wythe County Community Hospital, Wytheville, VA, p. A668

MARTIN, Amanda, Manager Human Resources, Ohio Valley Surgical Hospital, Springfield, OH, p. A490

MARTIN, Andrew Shane., Administrator, Good Shepherd Specialty Hospital, Bethlehem, PA, p. A520

MARTIN, Angelia, M.D., Chief of Staff, Northwest Medical Center, Albany, MO, p. A355

MARTIN, Barbara, Chief Nursing Officer, Mercy Children's Hospital, OH, p. A491

MARTIN, Brent, Administrator, Lifecare Hospitals Of South Shreveport-Willis Knighton North, LA, p. A278

MARTIN, Brian
Chief Executive Officer, Loring Hospital, Sac City, IA, p. A229
Vice President Medical Affairs, Children's Hospital Of Pittsburgh Of Upmc, Pittsburgh, PA, p. A537

MARTIN, Bruce A, Vice President Human Resources, Carolinaeast Health System, New Bern, NC, p. A458

MARTIN, Carmen, Associate Administrator, Auxilio Mutuo Hospital, San Juan, PR, p. A715

MARTIN, Cary, Chief Executive Officer, Houston Medical Center, Warner Robins, GA, p. A163

MARTIN, Charity, Controller and Regional Business Officer Manager, Greenwood Regional Rehabilitation Hospital, Greenwood, SC, p. A554

MARTIN, Cheryl
Chief Information Officer, Kingman Regional Medical Center, Kingman, AZ, p. A30
Chief Information Officer, Palmetto Health Tuomey, Sumter, SC, p. A557

MARTIN, Christine M, Vice President and Chief Financial Officer, Carolinas Healthcare System Cleveland, Shelby, NC, p. A460

MARTIN, Clifford G, M.D.
Regional Vice President and Chief Medical Officer, Osf Holy Family Medical Center, Monmouth, IL, p. A189
Regional Vice President and Chief Medical Officer, Osf Saint Luke Medical Center, Kewanee, IL, p. A187
Regional Vice President and Chief Medical Officer, Osf St. Mary Medical Center, Galesburg, IL, p. A183

MARTIN, Connie
Chief Executive Officer and Administrator, Physicians Medical Center, Houma, LA, p. A269
Vice President and Chief Support Officer, Methodist Medical Center Of Oak Ridge, Oak Ridge, TN, p. A578

MARTIN, Corey, M.D., Director Medical Affairs, Buffalo Hospital, Buffalo, MN, p. A329

MARTIN, Cyndie, Director, Coal County General Hospital, Coalgate, OK, p. A497

MARTIN, David, Assistant Administrator, Multicare Valley Hospital, Spokane Valley, WA, p. A678

MARTIN, David T., President, Upmc Passavant Cranberry, PA, p. A538

MARTIN, David W, M.D., Vice President Chief Medical Officer, Seton Medical Center Austin, Austin, TX, p. A586

MARTIN, Deanna, Chief Executive Officer, Encompass Health Rehabilitation Hospital Of Rock Hill, Rock Hill, SC, p. A556

MARTIN, Deborah
Regional Vice President Human Resources, Cascade Valley Hospital, Arlington, WA, p. A669
Regional Vice President Human Resources, Skagit Regional Health, Mount Vernon, WA, p. A674

MARTIN, Debra, Chief Nursing Officer, Hamilton General Hospital, Hamilton, TX, p. A608

MARTIN, Garland, M.D., Chief of Staff, Appling Healthcare System, Baxley, GA, p. A148

MARTIN, Gregg
Chief Information Officer, Arnot Ogden Medical Center, Elmira, NY, p. A426
Chief Information Officer, Ira Davenport Memorial Hospital, Bath, NY, p. A422
Chief Information Officer, St. Joseph's Hospital, Elmira, NY, p. A426

MARTIN, Harvey C, M.D., Medical Director, Red River Hospital, Llc, Wichita Falls, TX, p. A644

MARTIN, Holly
Director Human Resource, Iowa Specialty Hospital-Belmond, Belmond, IA, p. A217
Human Resources Leader, Iowa Specialty Hospital-Clarion, Clarion, IA, p. A219

MARTIN, Jackie, Chief Financial Officer, Saint Luke's Cushing Hospital, Leavenworth, KS, p. A239

MARTIN, James, Chief Information Officer, River Park Hospital, Huntington, WV, p. A684

MARTIN, James D
Chief Financial Officer, Hawthorn Children Psychiatric Hospital, Saint Louis, MO, p. A368
Chief Financial Officer, Metropolitan St. Louis Psychiatric Center, Saint Louis, MO, p. A368

Chief Financial Officer, St. Louis Psychiatric Rehabilitation Center, Saint Louis, MO, p. A369

MARTIN, Janice S, R.N., Chief Nursing Officer, Davis Regional Medical Center, Statesville, NC, p. A461

MARTIN, Jason, M.D., Medical Director, Seton Northwest Hospital, Austin, TX, p. A586

MARTIN, Jeanene R, M.P.H.
Senior Vice President Human Resources and Chief People Officer, Wakemed Cary Hospital, Cary, NC, p. A449
Senior Vice President Human Resources, Wakemed North Family Health And Women's Hospital, NC, p. A459

MARTIN, Jeffrey H, M.D., Chief of Staff, Erlanger Murphy Medical Center, Murphy, NC, p. A457

MARTIN, Jeremy, Chief Support Services Officer, St. James Parish Hospital, Lutcher, LA, p. A273

MARTIN, Jessica, Director Human Resources, Logan Regional Medical Center, Logan, WV, p. A684

MARTIN, Jessie, R.N., Chief Nursing Executive, Community Memorial Hospital, Turtle Lake, ND, p. A468

MARTIN, Josh
Chief Executive Officer, Summit Pacific Medical Center, Elma, WA, p. A671
Chief Operating Officer, Summit Pacific Medical Center, Elma, WA, p. A671

MARTIN, Karen, R.N., MSN
Chief Nursing Officer, Marshall Medical Center, Lewisburg, TN, p. A573
Chief Nursing Officer, Springs Memorial Hospital, Lancaster, SC, p. A555

MARTIN, Keith, M.D.
Vice President, Chief Medical Officer, Cgh Medical Center, Sterling, IL, p. A197
Chief Medical Officer, Fhn Memorial Hospital, Freeport, IL, p. A183

MARTIN, Kelly, Chief Financial Officer, Fairchild Medical Center, Yreka, CA, p. A95

MARTIN, Kelly K, Human Resource Officer, Texas Health Presbyterian Hospital Plano, Plano, TX, p. A629

MARTIN, Kenneth A, M.D., Chief of Staff, Arkansas Surgical Hospital, North Little Rock-Pulaski County, AR, p. A46

MARTIN, Kevin, M.P.H., R.N., FACHE, Administrator, Shriners Hospitals For Children-Salt Lake City, Salt Lake City, UT, p. A650

MARTIN, Kevin P., M.D., Chief Medical Officer, Four Winds Hospital, Saratoga Springs, NY, p. A442

MARTIN, Konnie, Chief Executive Officer, San Luis Valley Health, Alamosa, CO, p. A96

MARTIN, Kory Lann, M.D., Chief of Staff, Seymour Hospital, Seymour, TX, p. A635

MARTIN, Kristina, Chief Information Officer, Curry General Hospital, Gold Beach, OR, p. A513

MARTIN, Leslee, Manager Information Technology, Hshs St. Elizabeth's Hospital, O'Fallon, IL, p. A192

MARTIN, Marlana, Director Human Resources, Benewah Community Hospital, Saint Maries, ID, p. A171

MARTIN, Mary, MSN, R.N., Chief Nursing Officer, Hshs St. Nicholas Hospital, Sheboygan, WI, p. A703

MARTIN, Matthew, Director Resource Management, Naval Hospital Oak Harbor, Oak Harbor, WA, p. A674

MARTIN, Nick, Chief Information Officer, Minidoka Memorial Hospital, Rupert, ID, p. A171

MARTIN, Nikki, Chief Financial Officer, Christus Southeast Texas Jasper Memorial, Jasper, TX, p. A616

MARTIN, Patrick, M.D.
Medical Director, Wilmington Treatment Center, Wilmington, NC, p. A462
Director Information Systems, Calvary Hospital, New York (Includes All Hospitals Located Within The Five Boroughs), NY, p. A431

MARTIN, Patsy, Manager Human Resources, Select Rehabilitation Hospital Of Denton, Denton, TX, p. A599

MARTIN, Paul, Chief Medical Officer, Southview Medical Center, OH, p. A480

MARTIN, Paul J, Director Human Resources, Kaiser Foundation Mental Health Center, CA, p. A67

MARTIN, Ric, Information Specialist, Madison State Hospital, Madison, IN, p. A210

MARTIN, Richard A, MSN, R.N., Senior Vice President and Chief Nursing Officer, Hoag Hospital Irvine, CA, p. A75

MARTIN, Sabrina, Chief Executive Officer, Rehabilitation Hospital Of Southern New Mexico, Las Cruces, NM, p. A418

MARTIN, Sharon E, M.D., Ph.D., President Medical Staff, Fulton County Medical Center, Mc Connellsburg, PA, p. A530

MARTIN, Sheila, Chief Nursing Officer, Cmh Regional Health System, Wilmington, OH, p. A494

MARTIN, Sherri, M.D., President Medical Staff, Shawnee Mission Medical Center, Shawnee Mission, KS, p. A246

MARTIN, Stacy L, Director Human Resources, Grant Regional Health Center, Lancaster, WI, p. A696

MARTIN, Susan, Vice President Finance, Middlesex Hospital, Middletown, CT, p. A109

MARTIN, Tom, Senior Vice President, Strategy and Information Technology Officer, Evergreenhealth, Kirkland, WA, p. A673

MARTIN, Tracie, M.D., Chief Medical Officer, Oakland Mercy Hospital, Oakland, NE, p. A387

MARTIN, Val, Director Financial Management Services Center, Veterans Affairs Salt Lake City Health Care System, Salt Lake City, UT, p. A651

MARTIN, W. Carl, Chief Operating Officer, Providence Hospital Northeast, SC, p. A551

MARTIN, Wendy, Chief Financial Officer, Shands Starke Regional Medical Center, Starke, FL, p. A139

MARTIN-LINNARD, Tamara, R.N., Chief Clinical Officer, Great Plains Health, North Platte, NE, p. A387

MARTIN-PRATT, Diane, Director Information Systems, Niagara Falls Memorial Medical Center, Niagara Falls, NY, p. A438

MARTINEZ, Albino, Director Budget and Finance, Miners' Colfax Medical Center, NM, p. A418

MARTINEZ, Angel, R.N., RN, BSN,, Director Patient Care Services, Shriners Hospitals For Children-Galveston, Galveston, TX, p. A606

MARTINEZ, Darlene, Director Finance, New Mexico Behavioral Health Institute At Las Vegas, Las Vegas, NM, p. A418

MARTINEZ, Eddie, Chief Financial Officer, El Paso Ltac Hospital, El Paso, TX, p. A601

MARTINEZ, Edward, Chief Information Officer, Nicklaus Children's Hospital, Miami, FL, p. A130

MARTINEZ, Eleanor, Chief Nursing Officer, Alhambra Hospital Medical Center, Alhambra, CA, p. A50

MARTINEZ, Fernando, Senior Vice President and Chief Information Officer, Parkland Health & Hospital System, Dallas, TX, p. A597

MARTINEZ, Francisco, Executive Director, Hospital San Antonio, Mayaguez, PR, p. A714

MARTINEZ, Frank, Senior Vice President Human Resources, Doctors Hospital Of Jefferson, LA, p. A274

MARTINEZ, Jason, Director Information Technology, West Valley Medical Center, Caldwell, ID, p. A168

MARTINEZ, Jeanine, Director Human Resources, Putnam General Hospital, Eatonton, GA, p. A153

MARTINEZ, Jorge I., Executive Director, Hospital Perea, Mayaguez, PR, p. A714

MARTINEZ, Jose, M.D., Chief Medical Officer, Northwest Medical Center, Margate, FL, p. A129

MARTINEZ, Josue, Coordinator Information Systems, University Hospital, San Juan, PR, p. A716

MARTINEZ, Katherine, Chief Nursing Officer, North Central Surgical Center, Dallas, TX, p. A597

MARTINEZ, Kathryn J, Chief Nursing Officer, Fhn Memorial Hospital, Freeport, IL, p. A183

MARTINEZ, Leanne, Chief Executive Officer and Administrator, Fisher County Hospital District, Rotan, TX, p. A631

MARTINEZ, Lee, Chief Information Officer, Cooley Dickinson Hospital, Northampton, MA, p. A303

MARTINEZ, Louisa, Director of Nursing, Frio Regional Hospital, Pearsall, TX, p. A627

MARTINEZ, Maria, Chief Nursing Officer, La Paz Regional Hospital, Parker, AZ, p. A32

MARTINEZ, Michelle
Chief Executive Officer, U.S. Public Health Service Indian Hospital-Whiteriver, Whiteriver, AZ, p. A38
Controller, Healthsouth Rehabilitation Hospital Of New Mexico, Albuquerque, NM, p. A415

MARTINEZ, Ozalina, R.N., Director of Nursing, Northeastern Health System Sequoyah, Sallisaw, OK, p. A506

MARTINEZ, Regina M, Director Human Resources, La Paz Regional Hospital, Parker, AZ, p. A32

MARTINEZ, Rosette, Acting Chief Executive Officer, Lemuel Shattuck Hospital, Jamaica Plain, MA, p. A300

MARTINEZ, Suzanne, Director Human Resources, Centennial Peaks Hospital, Louisville, CO, p. A104

MARTINEZ, Terri, Chief Financial Officer, Plains Memorial Hospital, Dimmitt, TX, p. A600

MARTINEZ, Tina, Director Human Resources, J. D. Mccarty Center For Children With Developmental Disabilities, Norman, OK, p. A502

MARTINEZ, Virginia, Director Human Resources, Copper Queen Community Hospital, Bisbee, AZ, p. A28

MARTINEZ, Yolanda, Chief Fiscal Services, Edward Hines, Jr. Veterans Affairs Hospital, Hines, IL, p. A185

MARTINEZ, Yvette, Director Human Resources, Sutter Auburn Faith Hospital, Auburn, CA, p. A51

MARTINEZ-NIETO, Arlene, M.D., Chief Medical Officer, First Hospital Panamericano, Cidra, PR, p. A713

MARTING, Bill, Senior Vice President and Chief Financial Officer, The University Of Kansas Hospital - Indian Creek Campus, KS, p. A238

MARTINSON, Erling, M.D., Medical Director, Nelson County Health System, Mcville, ND, p. A468

MARTINSON, Tiffany, Director Human Resources, Norton Sound Regional Hospital, Nome, AK, p. A27

MARTOCCIO, Debora, R.N., Chief Operating Officer, Florida Hospital At Connerton Long Term Acute Care, Land O'Lakes, FL, p. A127

MARTORANO, Ann, Chief Operating Officer, Halifax Health Medical Center Of Port Orange, FL, p. A121

MARTUCCI, Kathleen, Chief Operating Officer, Helen Hayes Hospital, West Haverstraw, NY, p. A445

MARTZ, Dean
Chief Medical Officer, Providence Holy Family Hospital, Spokane, WA, p. A678
Chief Medical Officer, Sacred Heart Children's Hospital, WA, p. A678

MARTZ, Michael, Chief Information Officer, Ohio Valley Medical Center, Wheeling, WV, p. A688

MARVIN, Ryan, Support Services Director, Rawlins County Health Center, Atwood, KS, p. A232

MARX, Edward, Chief Information Officer, Cleveland Clinic Children's Hospital, OH, p. A476

MARX, Kenneth, Chief Financial Officer, Ranken Jordan Pediatric Bridge Hospital, Maryland Heights, MO, p. A364

MARX, Tomasine, Chief Financial Officer and Chief Operating Officer, Ascension Crittenton Hospital Medical Center, Rochester, MI, p. A321

MARX, Troy, Human Resources Director, Upland Hills Health, Dodgeville, WI, p. A691

MARZELLA, Robert, Chief Operations Officer, Upstate University Hospital At Community General, NY, p. A444

MARZOLF, Steve, R.N., Chief Nursing Officer, Spectrum Health Pennock, Hastings, MI, p. A315

MASE, Kerin A., President and Chief Executive Officer, Marian Regional Medical Center, Santa Maria, CA, p. A89

MASHAK-EKERN, Jane, Fiscal Officer, Va Medical Center, Tomah, WI, p. A704

MASI, George V., Chief Executive Officer, Quentin Mease Hospital, TX, p. A611

MASIELLO, Matthew, M.D., Chief Medical Officer, The Children's Institute Of Pittsburgh, Pittsburgh, PA, p. A538

MASKELL, Denise, Chief Information Officer, Springfield Hospital Center, Sykesville, MD, p. A294

MASON, Bill A., Chief Executive Officer, Meadow Wood Behavioral Health System, New Castle, DE, p. A113

MASON, Drew, Chief Executive Officer, Grandview Medical Center, Birmingham, AL, p. A14

MASON, Jeffrey, President and Chief Executive Officer, Glencoe Regional Health Services, Glencoe, MN, p. A332

MASON, Jill K, MS, R.N., Chief Nursing Officer, Blessing Hospital, IL, p. A194

MASON, John, Chief Information Officer, Hill Country Memorial Hospital, Fredericksburg, TX, p. A606

MASON, Kathy, R.N., MSN
Chief Nursing Officer, Lifecare Hospitals Of North Texas-Plano, TX, p. A596
Chief Operating Officer, Atrium Medical Center Of Corinth, Corinth, TX, p. A594

MASON, Kay, Chief Financial Officer, Texas Health Heart & Vascular Hospital Arlington, Arlington, TX, p. A584

MASON, Keith, Chief Executive Officer, Bailey Medical Center, Owasso, OK, p. A505

MASON, Phyllis, M.D., Chief Medical Officer, Natchitoches Regional Medical Center, Natchitoches, LA, p. A275

MASON, Rhonda, Vice President of Patient Care Services, Tri-State Memorial Hospital, Clarkston, WA, p. A670

MASON, Sandra, MSN, R.N., Director Nursing Services and Senior Nurse Executive, Robert E. Bush Naval Hospital, Twentynine Palms, CA, p. A92

MASON, Stacie, Vice President and Chief Financial Officer, Integris Grove Hospital, Grove, OK, p. A499

MASON, William R, Chief Operating Officer, Brooke Glen Behavioral Hospital, Fort Washington, PA, p. A526

MASON-JONES, Taryn, Chief Nurse Executive, Norristown State Hospital, Norristown, PA, p. A533

MASOOD, Shahid, M.D., Clinical Director, Mildred Mitchell-Bateman Hospital, Huntington, WV, p. A684

MASSA, Rhonda, Director of Nursing, Clarion Psychiatric Center, Clarion, PA, p. A522

MASSAAD, Aziz, M.D., Medical Staff President, Down East Community Hospital, Machias, ME, p. A285

MASSELLA, Joan, Administrative Vice President and Chief Nursing Officer, St. Clair Hospital, Pittsburgh, PA, p. A537

MASSENGALE, David
Chief Financial Officer, Methodist Hospital Union County, Morganfield, KY, p. A258

Vice President and Chief Financial Officer, Methodist Hospital, Henderson, KY, p. A253

MASSENGILL, Leigh, Chief Executive Officer, Medical Center Of Trinity, Trinity, FL, p. A142

MASSEY, Gina, Vice President Human Resources, Clarity Child Guidance Center, San Antonio, TX, p. A632

MASSEY, Rocco K., Community Chief Executive Officer, Beckley Arh Hospital, Beckley, WV, p. A681

MASSEY, Steven, President and Chief Executive Officer, Westfields Hospital And Clinic, New Richmond, WI, p. A700

MASSEY, Tami, M.D., Chief of Medical Staff, Edgefield County Hospital, Edgefield, SC, p. A552

MASSEY, Terry, Chief Fiscal Services, Beckley Veterans Affairs Medical Center, Beckley, WV, p. A681

MASSIELLO, Martin, Executive Vice President and Chief Operating Officer, Eisenhower Medical Center, Rancho Mirage, CA, p. A79

MASSIMILLA, John P, FACHE, Vice President and Chief Operating Officer, Chambersburg Hospital, Chambersburg, PA, p. A522

MASSINI, Stephen M.
Chief Financial Officer, Penn State Children's Hospital, PA, p. A527
Chief Operating Officer, Penn State Children's Hospital, PA, p. A527

MASSMAN, Patty, Director of Nursing, Granite Falls Health, Granite Falls, MN, p. A332

MASSOUH, Rafik, M.D., Chief of Staff, Mercy Allen Hospital, Oberlin, OH, p. A488

MAST, Delvin, R.N., Director of Nursing, Weatherford Regional Hospital, Weatherford, OK, p. A510

MAST, Duane, M.D., Medical Director, Hocking Valley Community Hospital, Logan, OH, p. A485

MAST, Joelle, Ph.D., M.D., Chief Medical Officer, Blythedale Children's Hospital, Valhalla, NY, p. A445

MAST, Nathan, Chief Executive Officer, Vibra Hospital Of Mahoning Valley-Trumbull Campus, OH, p. A472

MASTER, Moiz, M.D., Medical Director of Quality, Piedmont Mountainside Hospital, Jasper, GA, p. A155

MASTERS, Emily, Chief Human Relations Officer, Windom Area Hospital, Windom, MN, p. A342

MASTERS, Ken, Director Information Technology, Chambers Memorial Hospital, Danville-Yell County, AR, p. A41

MASTERS, Kim, M.D., Medical Director, Saint Simons By-The-Sea Hospital, Saint Simons Island, GA, p. A159

MASTERS, Regina, R.N., MSN, Director of Nursing, Continuing Care Hospital, Lexington, KY, p. A254

MASTERSON, David J., President, Sentara Williamsburg Regional Medical Center, Williamsburg, VA, p. A668

MASTERSON, Paul, Chief Financial Officer, Good Samaritan Medical And Rehabilitation Center, OH, p. A494

MASTERSON, Sammie, Director Human Resources, Harney District Hospital, Burns, OR, p. A511

MASTERTON, William J., President and Chief Executive Officer, University Medical Center, New Orleans, LA, p. A276

MASTROIANNI, Anthony, Regional Vice President Finance, The William W. Backus Hospital, Norwich, CT, p. A110

MASTROIANNI, Thomas, Administrative Director of Human Resources, Halifax Regional Medical Center, Roanoke Rapids, NC, p. A459

MASTROMANNO, Christopher
Chief Operating Officer, Nyc Health + Hospitals / Jacobi, New York (Includes All Hospitals Located Within The Five Boroughs), NY, p. A435
Interim Chief Executive Officer, Nyc Health + Hospitals / Jacobi, New York (Includes All Hospitals Located Within The Five Boroughs), NY, p. A435

MASTROPIETRO, N. A., M.D., Medical Director, Upmc Pinnacle Lancaster, Lancaster, PA, p. A529

MATA, Maribel, Director Information Services, Doctors Hospital Of Laredo, Laredo, TX, p. A619

MATA-GUERRERO, Rita, Director of Nursing, Weslaco Regional Rehabilitation Hospital, Weslaco, TX, p. A643

MATAMOROS, Mary L., R.N., Chief Executive Officer, Seaside Behavioral Center, New Orleans, LA, p. A276

MATEJICKA, Anthony, D.O., M.P.H., Vice President, Chief Medical Officer, Nyack Hospital, Nyack, NY, p. A438

MATEJKA, Cheryl
Chief Financial Officer, Mercy Children's Hospital St. Louis, MO, p. A368
Chief Financial Officer, Mercy Hospital Washington, Washington, MO, p. A372

MATENAER, Thomas M, Chief Financial Officer, Banner Gateway Medical Center, Gilbert, AZ, p. A29

MATHAI, George, M.D., Chief of Staff, Three Rivers Hospital, Waverly, TN, p. A580

MATHAI, Matt, M.D., Medical Director, Select Specialty Hospital-Milwaukee, Milwaukee, WI, p. A699

MATHEIS, Tracey
  Chief Financial Officer, Moberly Regional Medical Center, Moberly, MO, p. A364
  Chief Operating Officer, Moberly Regional Medical Center, Moberly, MO, p. A364
MATHER, Kelly, Chief Executive Officer, Sonoma Valley Hospital, Sonoma, CA, p. A90
MATHER, Martha S, Chief Operating Officer and Vice President, Our Lady Of Peace, Louisville, KY, p. A256
MATHERS, Larry, M.D., Chief of Staff, Tennova Newport Medical Center, Newport, TN, p. A578
MATHES, Lisa L, Human Resources Director, Southwest Medical Center, Liberal, KS, p. A240
MATHESON, John A., Interim Chief Executive Officer, Dequincy Memorial Hospital, Dequincy, LA, p. A267
MATHEW, Finny
  President, Integris Bass Meadowlake, OK, p. A498
  President, Integris Bass Pavilion, Enid, OK, p. A498
MATHEWS, Arun, M.D., Chief Medical Officer (Acute), Medical Center Health System, Odessa, TX, p. A626
MATHEWS, Christine, R.N., MSN, Vice President Nursing Services, Geisinger-Lewistown Hospital, Lewistown, PA, p. A530
MATHEWS, Gary, M.D., Medical Doctor, Beaver County Memorial Hospital, Beaver, OK, p. A496
MATHEWS, Nimmy, Acting Director Quality Management, San Carlos Apache Healthcare Corporation, Peridot, AZ, p. A32
MATHEWS, Paul G., CPA, Administrator, Hardtner Medical Center, Olla, LA, p. A277
MATHIAS, Matt, Chief Operating Officer, Lewisgale Hospital Montgomery, Blacksburg, VA, p. A655
MATHIEU, Angie, System Director Information Technology and Regional Chief Information Officer, The William W. Backus Hospital, Norwich, CT, p. A110
MATHIEU, Lori, MSN, Chief Nursing Officer, Glenwood Surgery Center, LA, p. A280
MATHIS, Alison, Chief Nursing Officer, Copiah County Medical Center, Hazlehurst, MS, p. A347
MATHIS, Ashley, Privacy Officer, Columbus Community Hospital, Columbus, TX, p. A593
MATHIS, Jane, Chief Financial Officer, Baylor Surgical Hospital At Fort Worth, Fort Worth, TX, p. A604
MATHIS, Patricia, Associate Director Patient Care Service, Richard L. Roudebush Veterans Affairs Medical Center, Indianapolis, IN, p. A207
MATHIS, Rebecca
  Chief Financial Officer, Amita Health Adventist La Grange Medical Center, La Grange, IL, p. A187
  Chief Financial Officer, Amita Health Adventist Medical Center Bolingbrook, Bolingbrook, IL, p. A174
  Vice President and Chief Financial Officer, Amita Health Adventist Medical Center - Hinsdale, Hinsdale, IL, p. A186
MATHIS, Richard C., Chief Executive Officer, North Runnels Hospital, Winters, TX, p. A644
MATHIS, Robin, Director Human Resources, Methodist Healthcare Olive Branch Hospital, Olive Branch, MS, p. A351
MATHISEN, Arthur, FACHE, President and Chief Executive Officer, Copley Hospital, Morrisville, VT, p. A654
MATHUR, Ashish, M.D., Chief of Staff, Siloam Springs Regional Hospital, Siloam Springs-Benton County, AR, p. A48
MATHURIN, Emile, M.D., Jr, Medical Director, Encompass Health Rehabilitation Hospital Of Humble, Humble, TX, p. A614
MATHURIN, Venra, Vice President Human Resources, Interfaith Medical Center, New York (Includes All Hospitals Located Within The Five Boroughs), NY, p. A432
MATIS, Sue, Director Human Resources, North Central Health Care, Wausau, WI, p. A705
MATLACK, Victoria L.
  Director and Human Resources Business Partner, Ohiohealth Dublin Methodist Hospital, Dublin, OH, p. A481
  Director and Human Resources Business Partner, Ohiohealth Grady Memorial Hospital, Delaware, OH, p. A481
MATNEY, James L., President and Chief Executive Officer, Colquitt Regional Medical Center, Moultrie, GA, p. A158
MATNEY, Patty, Human Resources Consultant, Saint Thomas Hickman Hospital, Centerville, TN, p. A567
MATNEY, Tim, Chief Financial Officer, Logan Regional Medical Center, Logan, WV, p. A684
MATOS, Patricia, Chief Nursing Officer, Stewart & Lynda Resnick Neuropsychiatric Hospital At Ucla, Los Angeles, CA, p. A70
MATSINGER, John, D.O., Chief Medical Officer, Virtua Marlton, Marlton, NJ, p. A407
MATT, Christine K., Interim Associate Chief, Uva Transitional Care Hospital, Charlottesville, VA, p. A656

MATT, Robert Lawrence, Vice President and Chief Operating Officer, Hancock Regional Hospital, Greenfield, IN, p. A205
MATTER, Stephanie, Manager Human Resources, Lifecare Hospitals Of Wisconsin, Pewaukee, WI, p. A701
MATTERN, Bonnie, Director Human Resources, Chi St. Alexius Health Devils Lake Hospital, Devils Lake, ND, p. A465
MATTERN, Joe, M.D., Chief Medical Officer, Jefferson Healthcare, Port Townsend, WA, p. A675
MATTERN, Karen, Director of Human Resources, Shriners Hospitals For Children-Spokane, Spokane, WA, p. A678
MATTES, Bryan, Associate Administrator, Crossridge Community Hospital, Wynne-Cross County, AR, p. A49
MATTES, James A., President and Chief Executive Officer, Grande Ronde Hospital, La Grande, OR, p. A514
MATTEUCCI, Dolly, Executive Director, Napa State Hospital, Napa, CA, p. A74
MATTHEI, Ruth, R.N., MS, Chief Nursing Officer, Westlake Hospital, Melrose Park, IL, p. A189
MATTHEW, Mathew, M.D., Chief Medical Officer, Nazareth Hospital, Philadelphia, PA, p. A535
MATTHEWS, Adora, M.D., Medical Director, Encompass Health Rehabilitation Hospital Of Florence, Florence, SC, p. A552
MATTHEWS, Carol, Director Human Resources, Saline Memorial Hospital, Benton-Saline County, AR, p. A39
MATTHEWS, Clinton
  President and Chief Executive Officer, Reading Hospital Rehabilitation At Wyomissing, Wyomissing, PA, p. A545
  President and Chief Executive Officer, Reading Hospital, West Reading, PA, p. A544
MATTHEWS, Deborah
  Chief Nursing Officer, Tanner Medical Center-Carrollton, Carrollton, GA, p. A149
  Senior Vice President, Willowbrooke At Tanner, GA, p. A162
MATTHEWS, Edward, Chief Financial Officer, San Dimas Community Hospital, San Dimas, CA, p. A85
MATTHEWS, Gwen, R.N., MSN, Chief Executive Officer, Ukiah Valley Medical Center, Ukiah, CA, p. A93
MATTHEWS, Judith, Nurse Executive, Riverside Tappahannock Hospital, Tappahannock, VA, p. A667
MATTHEWS, Kristopher, Chief Operating Officer, Decatur Health Systems, Oberlin, KS, p. A242
MATTHEWS, Lori
  Vice President Information Technology System, Banner Baywood Medical Center, Mesa, AZ, p. A31
  Vice President, Information Technology System, Banner Heart Hospital, Mesa, AZ, p. A31
MATTHEWS, Melissa, Director Human Resources, Dahl Memorial Healthcare Association, Ekalaka, MT, p. A375
MATTHEWS, Michael, Vice President Human Resources, Holland Hospital, Holland, MI, p. A315
MATTHEWS, Oliver, M.D., Chief Medical Officer, Eliza Coffee Memorial Hospital, Florence, AL, p. A18
MATTHEWS, Ted, Chief Executive Officer, Eastland Memorial Hospital, Eastland, TX, p. A600
MATTHEY, Michael, Facility Chief Information Officer, Louis A. Johnson Veterans Affairs Medical Center, Clarksburg, WV, p. A682
MATTHIAS, Mark, M.D., Vice President of Medical Affairs, St. Cloud Hospital, Saint Cloud, MN, p. A338
MATTHIESSEN, Matthew
  Chief Financial Officer, John C. Fremont Healthcare District, Mariposa, CA, p. A71
  Interim Chief Executive Officer, John C. Fremont Healthcare District, Mariposa, CA, p. A71
MATTICE, Gloria, R.N., Director Patient Care, George C Grape Community Hospital, Hamburg, IA, p. A223
MATTINGLY, Marty, Chief Human Resources Officer, St. Vincent Evansville, Evansville, IN, p. A203
MATTISON, Denise, Director Finance and Accounting Services, Mayo Clinic Health System In Eau Claire, Eau Claire, WI, p. A692
MATTISON, Kenneth R., Chief Executive Officer, Florida Hospital New Smyrna, New Smyrna Beach, FL, p. A132
MATTLY, Sheila, Chief Nursing Officer, Wayne County Hospital, Corydon, IA, p. A220
MATTNER, Matthew, Chief Operating Officer, Lutheran Hospital, Cleveland, OH, p. A477
MATTSON, Jodi, Director of Nursing, Cedar Springs Hospital, Colorado Springs, CO, p. A97
MATTSON, Wayne, Management Information Systems Specialist, Rogers Memorial Hospital-West Allis, WI, p. A700
MATUS, Jose, M.D., Director Medical, Carrus Rehabilitation Hospital, Sherman, TX, p. A636
MATUSZKIEWICZ, Marcin, M.D., Chief of Staff and Medical Director, Jerold Phelps Community Hospital, Garberville, CA, p. A60
MATZENBACHER, Elaine, Chief Financial Officer, Washington County Hospital, Nashville, IL, p. A191

MATZIGKEIT, Linda, Senior Vice President Human Resources, Children's Healthcare Of Atlanta At Scottish Rite, GA, p. A146
MAURER, Gregory L., Chief Executive Officer, Sheridan Memorial Hospital, Plentywood, MT, p. A378
MAURER, Jackie, Fiscal Officer, Julian F. Keith Alcohol And Drug Abuse Treatment Center, Black Mountain, NC, p. A448
MAURER, Linda, Vice President Patient Care Services, Wilson Memorial Hospital, Sidney, OH, p. A490
MAURER, Marsha L., R.N., MS, Chief Nursing Officer Patient Care Services, Beth Israel Deaconess Medical Center, Boston, MA, p. A296
MAURICE, Timothy, Chief Financial Officer, University Of California Davis Children's Hospital, CA, p. A82
MAURIN, Michael J, Chief Financial Officer, Southern Surgical Hospital, Slidell, LA, p. A279
MAVROMATIS, Lou, Vice President Information Technology, Medstar Southern Maryland Hospital Center, Clinton, MD, p. A290
MAVROS, George, Chief Operating Officer, Citrus Memorial Health System, Inverness, FL, p. A125
MAXIE, Bryan K., Administrator, Walthall County General Hospital, Tylertown, MS, p. A353
MAXSON, Diana, Director Human Resources, University Hospital Summerville, Augusta, GA, p. A148
MAXWELL, Dale, Executive Vice President and Chief Financial Officer, Presbyterian Rust Medical Center, NM, p. A416
MAXWELL, Jody, Manager Business Office, Smith County Memorial Hospital, Smith Center, KS, p. A246
MAXWELL, Ronnie, Director Information Systems, Glenwood Surgery Center, LA, p. A280
MAY, Brandon
  Chief Executive Officer, Doctors Hospital Of Manteca, Manteca, CA, p. A71
  Chief Operating Officer, The Hospitals Of Providence East Campus, El Paso, TX, p. A602
MAY, David, Chief of Staff, Richland Hospital, Richland Center, WI, p. A702
MAY, Frank, Chief Executive Officer, Uchealth Yampa Valley Medical Center, Steamboat Springs, CO, p. A105
MAY, Kevin B
  Chief Financial Officer, Watauga Medical Center, Boone, NC, p. A448
  System Director Finance, Charles A. Cannon Memorial Hospital, Newland, NC, p. A458
MAY, Robin, Director Information Systems, Platte County Memorial Hospital, Wheatland, WY, p. A710
MAY, Ronald B, M.D., Vice President Medical Affairs, Carolinaeast Health System, New Bern, NC, p. A458
MAY, Scott, Area Director Technology, Kaiser Permanente Santa Clara Medical Center, Santa Clara, CA, p. A88
MAY, Sonja, Director Human Resources, Morton County Health System, Elkhart, KS, p. A234
MAY, Todd, M.D., Chief Medical Officer, Zuckerberg San Francisco General Hospital And Trauma Center, San Francisco, CA, p. A86
MAY, Troy, Chief Information Officer, University Of Louisville Hospital, Louisville, KY, p. A257
MAY, William J., Administrator, Hawaii State Hospital, Kaneohe, HI, p. A166
MAYBEN, Casey, Chief Nursing Officer, Ut Health Pittsburg, Pittsburg, TX, p. A628
MAYEAUX, Rachel, Chief Executive Officer, Amg Specialty Hospital-Lafayette, Lafayette, LA, p. A270
MAYER, David, Chief of Staff, Wayne County Hospital, Monticello, KY, p. A258
MAYER, Karen M, Ph.D., R.N., FACHE, Senior Vice President Patient Care Services, Rush Oak Park Hospital, Oak Park, IL, p. A191
MAYER, Peter, Director Information Systems, Bakersfield Heart Hospital, Bakersfield, CA, p. A51
MAYER, William, M.D., Vice President Medical Staff Services, St. Mary's Healthcare, NY, p. A421
MAYES, Libby, Human Resource Director, Ephraim Mcdowell Regional Medical Center, Danville, KY, p. A251
MAYEWSKI, Raymond, M.D.
  Chief Medical Officer, Golisano Children's Hospital, NY, p. A441
  Chief Medical Officer, Highland Hospital, Rochester, NY, p. A441
MAYFIELD, Michael Bradley, M.D., Chief of Staff, Chicot Memorial Medical Center, Lake Village-Chicot County, AR, p. A44
MAYFIELD, William, M.D., Chief of Staff, Tristar Stonecrest Medical Center, Smyrna, TN, p. A580
MAYHLE, Douglas, M.D., Medical Director, Nicholas H. Noyes Memorial Hospital, Dansville, NY, p. A425
MAYLE, Connie, Vice President Administrative Services, Shenango Valley Campus, PA, p. A526

MAYNARD, Bob, Chief Information Officer, Fairview Regional Medical Center, Fairview, OK, p. A499

MAYNARD, Rhonda, Chief Financial Officer, Tennova Turkey Creek Medical Center, TN, p. A572

MAYO, Andrew, Ph.D., Chief Executive Officer and Managing Director, North Star Behavioral Health, AK, p. A25

MAYO, Cindy, R.N., FACHE, Chief Executive, Providence Medford Medical Center, Medford, OR, p. A515

MAYO, Hal, Chief Financial Officer, Liberty Dayton Regional Medical Center, Liberty, TX, p. A619

MAYO, Jim, M.D., Clinical Director, Cherry Hospital, Goldsboro, NC, p. A453

MAYO, Michael A., FACHE, President, Wolfson Children's Hospital, FL, p. A125

MAYO, Randy, Director Information Technology, William Newton Hospital, Winfield, KS, p. A248

MAYO, Robert, M.D.
  Chief Medical Officer, Rochester General Hospital, Rochester, NY, p. A441
  Executive Vice President, Chief Medical Officer, Rochester Regional Health, Newark-Wayne Community Hospital, Newark, NY, p. A438

MAYO, Sarah, Vice President Financial Services, Unc Lenoir Healthcare, Kinston, NC, p. A456

MAYORGA, Oliver, M.D.
  Chief Medical Officer, Lawrence + Memorial Hospital, New London, CT, p. A110
  Chief Medical Officer, Westerly Hospital, Westerly, RI, p. A548

MAYS, Christine, R.N., MSN
  Chief Operating Officer and Chief Nurse Executive, Saint Joseph Hospital, Lexington, KY, p. A255
  Chief Operating Officer and Chief Nurse Executive, Women's Hospital Saint Joseph East, KY, p. A255

MAYS, Dawn, Chief Nursing Officer, Scott Memorial Hospital, Scottsburg, IN, p. A214

MAYS, Raymond, M.D., Medical Director, River Crest Hospital, San Angelo, TX, p. A632

MAYS, Sherrie, MSN, R.N., Vice President and Chief Nursing Officer, Baptist Health Corbin, Corbin, KY, p. A250

MAYSENT, Patty, Chief Executive Officer, Uc San Diego Shiley Eye Institute, CA, p. A84

MAYSILLES, Nancy, R.N., Chief Nursing Officer, Medical Center Of Trinity, Trinity, FL, p. A142

MAYSON, Mark J, M.D., Medical Director, Palmetto Health Baptist, Columbia, SC, p. A551

MAZANEC, Lori
  Chief Operating Officer, Box Butte General Hospital, Alliance, NE, p. A381
  Interim Chief Executive Officer, Box Butte General Hospital, Alliance, NE, p. A381

MAZEK, Mariusz, Vice President Information Technology and Chief Information Officer, Roseland Community Hospital, Chicago, IL, p. A179

MAZOUR, Linda, M.D., President, Franklin County Memorial Hospital, Franklin, NE, p. A383

MAZUREK, Michele A, Interim Vice President Patient Care Services and Chief Nursing Officer, Sinai Children's Hospital, IL, p. A178

MAZZA, Mary, Director Human Resources, Healthsouth Rehabilitation Hospital Of Western Massachusetts, Ludlow, MA, p. A301

MAZZARELLA, Frank, M.D., Chief Medical Officer, Clara Maass Medical Center, Belleville, NJ, p. A402

MAZZARELLI, Anthony J, JD, M.D., Co-President, Childen's Regional Hospital At Cooper, NJ, p. A403

MAZZO, Joseph, Chief Executive Officer, John Randolph Medical Center, Hopewell, VA, p. A659

MAZZOLA, Joe, D.O., Senior Vice President Medical Affairs and Chief Medical Officer, Valdese General Hospital, NC, p. A457

MAZZONI, Dean, President and Chief Executive Officer, Franciscan Health Michigan City, Michigan City, IN, p. A211

MAZZUCA, Darryl, Director Management Information Systems, Little Company Of Mary Hospital And Health Care Centers, Evergreen Park, IL, p. A183

MBENGA, Saul, Manager Information Technology, Alliance Healthcare System, Holly Springs, MS, p. A347

MC KELLAR, Grey, Chief Operating Officer and Director of Performance Improvement and Risk, Kingwood Pines Hospital, Kingwood, TX, p. A618

MCADAMS, David, Chief Financial Officer, Lindner Center Of Hope, Mason, OH, p. A486

MCADOO, Jackie, Chief Financial Officer, Grady Memorial Hospital, Chickasha, OK, p. A497

MCAFEE, Thomas J., President, North Region, Northwestern Medicine Lake Forest Hospital, Lake Forest, IL, p. A187

MCALISTER, Julene, Administrator, Accord Rehabilitation Hospital, Plaquemine, LA, p. A277

MCALISTER, Michael, Chief Executive Officer, Select Specialty Hospital - Dallas Downtown, Dallas, TX, p. A598

MCALISTER, Stephanie, Controller, Tippah County Hospital, Ripley, MS, p. A353

MCALLISTER, Guy, Vice President and Chief Information Officer, Tift Regional Medical Center, Tifton, GA, p. A162

MCALLISTER, Ric, Chief Executive Officer, Windsor-Laurelwood Center For Behavioral Medicine, Willoughby, OH, p. A493

MCALLISTER, Yvonne, Senior Director Human Resources, Southern Maine Health Care - Biddeford Medical Center, ME, p. A283

MCALOON, Richard, Vice President Human Resources, Institute Of Living, CT, p. A108

MCANDREWS, Kevin
  Vice President Human Resources, Nexus Specialty Hospital, Shenandoah, TX, p. A635
  Vice President, Human Resources, Nexus Specialty Hospital The Woodlands, The Woodlands, TX, p. A640

MCARTHUR, Ronald L., Chief Executive Officer, Summit Healthcare Regional Medical Center, Show Low, AZ, p. A36

MCARTHUR, Shelley, R.N., Chief Nursing Officer, Mckenzie Regional Hospital, Mckenzie, TN, p. A574

MCARTOR, Dana, R.N., Director of Nursing, Perkins County Health Services, Grant, NE, p. A384

MCASKILL, L. Craig, M.D., Chief Medical Officer, Englewood Community Hospital, Englewood, FL, p. A122

MCAULIFFE, Gregory, M.D.
  Chief Medical Officer, San Luis Valley Health Conejos County Hospital, La Jara, CO, p. A102
  Chief Medical Officer, San Luis Valley Health, Alamosa, CO, p. A96

MCAULIFFE, John, M.D., Medical Director, Sauk Prairie Healthcare, Prairie Du Sac, WI, p. A701

MCAVOY, Tim, M.D., Medical Director, Rehabilitation Hospital Of Wisconsin, Waukesha, WI, p. A705

MCBEE, Jeff, Administrator, Presbyterian Rust Medical Center, NM, p. A416

MCBEE, John, Chief of Staff, Chi St. Anthony Hospital, Pendleton, OR, p. A515

MCBREARTY, Michael, M.D., Vice President Medical Affairs, Thomas Hospital, Fairhope, AL, p. A17

MCBRIDE, Anne, Chief Executive Officer, Regional Hospital For Respiratory And Complex Care, Burien, WA, p. A670

MCBRIDE, Brandon, Operations Officer, Logan Regional Hospital, Logan, UT, p. A647

MCBRIDE, Dina, Chief Operating Officer and Director Human Resources, East Adams Rural Healthcare, Ritzville, WA, p. A676

MCBRIDE, Grace, Regional Chief Nursing Officer, Presence Mercy Medical Center, Aurora, IL, p. A173

MCBRIDE, Lamar, Chief Executive Officer, Northern Colorado Long Term Acute Hospital, Johnstown, CO, p. A102

MCBRIDE, Thomas Y, III, Executive Vice President and Chief Financial Officer, Gwinnett Medical Center, GA, p. A156

MCBROOM, Robert, M.D., Medical Director, Promise Hospital Of Wichita Falls, Wichita Falls, TX, p. A644

MCBRYDE, Robin, Chief Information Officer, Alexandria Veterans Affairs Health Care System, Pineville, LA, p. A277

MCCAA, Karen, R.N., Vice President Patient Care Services and Chief Nursing Officer, Baptist Medical Center South, Montgomery, AL, p. A21

MCCABE, Mary, Chief Financial Officer, North Colorado Medical Center, Greeley, CO, p. A101

MCCABE, Patrick, Senior Vice President Finance and Chief Financial Officer, Bridgeport Hospital, Bridgeport, CT, p. A107

MCCABE, Patrick G., Jr, FACHE, President and Chief Executive Officer, Levi Hospital, Hot Springs National Park-Garland County, AR, p. A43

MCCABE, Steve, Chief Executive Officer, Hill Crest Behavioral Health Services, Birmingham, AL, p. A14

MCCAFFERTY, Michael, Chief Executive Officer, Sheridan Memorial Hospital, Sheridan, WY, p. A709

MCCAFFREY, Anne E., President and Chief Executive Officer, Eastern Niagara Hospital Newfane, NY, p. A429

MCCAFFREY, Roberta A, R.N., Vice President and Chief Nursing Officer, Methodist Hospital Of Southern California, Arcadia, CA, p. A51

MCCAHILL, Connie, R.N., President and Chief Executive Officer, Cameron Memorial Community Hospital, Angola, IN, p. A199

MCCAHILL, Mary, Chief Nursing Officer, Thorek Memorial Hospital, Chicago, IL, p. A180

MCCAIN, Rebecca J., Chief Executive Officer, Electra Memorial Hospital, Electra, TX, p. A603

MCCALL, Harlo, Chief Executive Officer, Encompass Health Rehabilitation Hospital Of Texarkana, Texarkana, TX, p. A639

MCCALL, Lee, Chief Executive Officer, Neshoba County General Hospital, Philadelphia, MS, p. A352

MCCALL, Pam, Director Human Resources, Heatherhill Care Communities, Chardon, OH, p. A474

MCCALLISTER, Bob, Director Human Resources, Baptist Memorial Hospital-Golden Triangle, Columbus, MS, p. A345

MCCALLISTER, Darla, Chief Financial Officer, Lakeside Women's Hospital, Oklahoma City, OK, p. A503

MCCALLISTER, Dianne, M.D., Chief Medical Officer, South Campus, CO, p. A96

MCCALLISTER, Sean, Administrator, St. Luke's Mccall, Mccall, ID, p. A170

MCCAMMON, Colleen, Chief Executive Officer, Westpark Springs, Richmond, TX, p. A630

MCCAMPBELL, Kellie, Coordinator Human Resources, Kindred Hospital-Chattanooga, Chattanooga, TN, p. A567

MCCAMPBELL, Marcia, M.D., Chief Medical Officer, Shasta Regional Medical Center, Redding, CA, p. A80

MCCANDLESS, Barbara, Vice President Human Resources, Seton Health System-St. Mary's Hospital, NY, p. A444

MCCANDLESS, David, Vice President Medical Affairs, Upmc Northwest, Seneca, PA, p. A541

MCCANN, Barbara, Director Human Resources, Sunrise Canyon Hospital, Lubbock, TX, p. A621

MCCANN, Kyle, Chief Operating Officer, St. Joseph's Hospital, Savannah, GA, p. A160

MCCANN, Lew, Director Management Information Systems, Osf Holy Family Medical Center, Monmouth, IL, p. A189

MCCARTAN, Mary E, Manager Human Resources, Va Long Beach Healthcare System, Long Beach, CA, p. A65

MCCARTER, Alyssa, Chief Financial Officer, W. J. Mangold Memorial Hospital, Lockney, TX, p. A620

MCCARTER, Scott, Chief Information Officer, Karmanos Cancer Center, Detroit, MI, p. A311

MCCARTHY, Barbara, Chief Executive Officer, Specialty Hospital Jacksonville, Jacksonville, FL, p. A126

MCCARTHY, Brian, Director Information Systems, Memorial Hospital of Salem County, Salem, NJ, p. A411

MCCARTHY, Cynthia L, MS, R.N., Chief Nursing Officer, Texas Health Harris Methodist Hospital Stephenville, Stephenville, TX, p. A637

MCCARTHY, Maureen, M.D., Chief of Staff, Phoenix Veterans Affairs Health Care System, Phoenix, AZ, p. A34

MCCARTHY, Rick
  Chief Information Officer, St. Vincent's Behavioral Health, CT, p. A107
  Chief Information Officer, White Plains Hospital Center, White Plains, NY, p. A446

MCCARTHY, Sandra Mac
  Chief Nursing Officer, Arnot Ogden Medical Center, Elmira, NY, p. A426
  Chief Nursing Officer, St. Joseph's Hospital, Elmira, NY, p. A426

MCCARTHY, Tim, President Puerto Rico Division, First Hospital Panamericano, Cidra, PR, p. A713

MCCARTY, Daniel P, Chief Operating Officer, Orange City Area Health System, Orange City, IA, p. A227

MCCARTY, Jacob M., Chief Executive Officer, Kindred Hospital-San Francisco Bay Area, San Leandro, CA, p. A87

MCCARTY, Melany, R.N., Chief Clinical Officer, Vibra Hospital Of Amarillo, Amarillo, TX, p. A583

MCCARTY, Tim, Chief Information Officer, Oakbend Medical Center Williams Way Campus, TX, p. A630

MCCARTY, Wendy, Director Human Resources, Hillsboro Community Hospital, Hillsboro, KS, p. A236

MCCARY, Steve C., Administrator, Riverside Doctors' Hospital Williamsburg, Williamsburg, VA, p. A667

MCCASLIN, Anna, Chief Financial Officer, Orthonebraska Hospital, Omaha, NE, p. A388

MCCASLIN, Jami, Director Human Resources, Providence Hood River Memorial Hospital, Hood River, OR, p. A513

MCCAULEY, Bryan, Chief Financial Officer, West Jefferson Medical Center, Marrero, LA, p. A273

MCCAULEY, Cynthia, Chief Financial Officer, Good Samaritan Medical Center, West Palm Beach, FL, p. A143

MCCAULEY, Dudley, Controller, Lincoln County Medical Center, Ruidoso, NM, p. A419

MCCAULEY, Jason, Administrator, Jane Phillips Nowata Health Center, Nowata, OK, p. A502

MCCAULEY, Sue E, Director Finance, Baum Harmon Mercy Hospital, Primghar, IA, p. A228

MCCAWLEY, Thomas J, Vice President, Beloit Health System, Beloit, WI, p. A690

MCCHESNEY, Lisa D, R.N., Senior Director Information Systems, Upmc Hamot, Erie, PA, p. A525

MCCLAIN, Barbara, Human Resources, Horton Community Hospital, Horton, KS, p. A237

MCCLAIN, James, Deputy Director, Clement J. Zablocki Veterans Affairs Medical Center, Milwaukee, WI, p. A698

MCCLAIN, Richard, M.D., Chief Medical Officer, Chickasaw Nation Medical Center, Ada, OK, p. A495

MCCLAIN, Tami, Human Resources Operations Specialist, Leconte Medical Center, Sevierville, TN, p. A579

MCDONALD, Amanda, MSN, Chief Nurse Executive, Kerrville State Hospital, Kerrville, TX, p. A617

MCDONALD, Carl
Chief Human Resources Officer, Broward Health North, Deerfield Beach, FL, p. A121
Regional Director Human Resources, Broward Health Imperial Point, Fort Lauderdale, FL, p. A122

MCDONALD, Connie, Chief Financial Officer, Marion Veterans Affairs Medical Center, Marion, IL, p. A188

MCDONALD, Edward A, Chief Financial Officer, Adventist Health St. Helena, Vallejo, CA, p. A93

MCDONALD, Elizabeth, Director Human Resources, Wayne Memorial Hospital, Honesdale, PA, p. A527

MCDONALD, Frederick Joseph., Commanding Officer, Naval Hospital Oak Harbor, Oak Harbor, WA, p. A674

MCDONALD, Gary
Associate Administrator Human Resources, Stone County Medical Center, Mountain View-Stone County, AR, p. A46
Chief Facilities and Personnel Officer, White River Medical Center, Batesville, AR, p. A39

MCDONALD, Gregory, Vice President Finance and Chief Financial Officer, Roswell Park Cancer Institute, Buffalo, NY, p. A423

MCDONALD, Holly, Controller, Boundary Community Hospital, Bonners Ferry, ID, p. A168

MCDONALD, Jeff, Information Technology Manager, Florida Hospital Wauchula, Wauchula, FL, p. A143

MCDONALD, John, M.D.
Chief Medical Officer, Medical City North Hills, North Richland Hills, TX, p. A626
Chief Operating Officer, Northwest Texas Surgery Center, TX, p. A583

MCDONALD, Larry, Director Human Resources, Miami Jewish Home And Hospital For Aged, Miami, FL, p. A130

MCDONALD, Mark, M.D., President and Chief Executive Officer, Institute For Orthopaedic Surgery, Lima, OH, p. A484

MCDONALD, Michael S., Jr, Chief Executive Officer, Friends Hospital, Philadelphia, PA, p. A534

MCDONALD, Shari, Vice President Patient Care Services, Mercy Hospital, Buffalo, NY, p. A423

MCDONALD, Shelly, Chief Human Resources Officer, Ness County Hospital District No 2, Ness City, KS, p. A242

MCDONALD, Stanton B, M.D., Medical Director, Heber Valley Medical Center, Heber City, UT, p. A647

MCDONALD, Stuart, M.D., President Medical Staff, Kindred Hospital Tarrant County-Fort Worth Southwest, TX, p. A604

MCDONALD, Susan, Vice President, Medical Affairs, Sentara Rmh Medical Center, Harrisonburg, VA, p. A659

MCDONALD, Tedd, M.D., Chief Medical Officer, Banner Churchill Community Hospital, Fallon, NV, p. A392

MCDONALD-PINKETT, Shelly, Chief Medical Officer, Howard University Hospital, Washington, DC, p. A115

MCDONNELL, M. Therese, M.D., Interim Vice President Patient Safety, Quality and Medical Affairs, Sibley Memorial Hospital, Washington, DC, p. A116

MCDONNELL, Michael, M.D., Chief Medical Officer, Mercy Hospital And Medical Center, Chicago, IL, p. A178

MCDONNELL, Nancy, Manager Information Systems, Illinois Valley Community Hospital, Peru, IL, p. A193

MCDONNELL, Stephen C, Chief Financial Officer, Chesapeake Regional Medical Center, Chesapeake, VA, p. A656

MCDOUGLE, Mark, Executive Vice President and Chief Operating Officer, Maimonides Infants And Children's Hospital Of Brooklyn, NY, p. A433

MCDOWELL, Arthur V, M.D., III, Vice President Clinical Affairs, Middlesex Hospital, Middletown, CT, p. A109

MCDOWELL, Jean, Chief Financial Officer, Kindred Hospital-Dallas, Dallas, TX, p. A596

MCDOWELL, Paul L
Deputy Chief Financial Officer, Mission Hospital, NC, p. A447
Vice President Finance and Chief Financial Officer, King's Daughters Medical Center, Ashland, KY, p. A249

MCDOWELL, Richard, M.D.
Medical Director, Kona Community Hospital, Kealakekua, HI, p. A166
Chief Financial Officer, Ridge Behavioral Health System, Lexington, KY, p. A255

MCDOWELL, Wendy, R.N., Director of Nursing, Weisbrod Memorial County Hospital, Eads, CO, p. A100

MCDOWN, Missy, Director Information Systems, Via Christi Hospital Pittsburg, Pittsburg, KS, p. A244

MCDRURY, Martha M, R.N., Chief Operating Officer and Chief Nursing Officer, Holy Family Hospital At Merrimack Valley, MA, p. A302

MCEACHERN, John, Controller, Sebastian River Medical Center, Sebastian, FL, p. A139

MCEACHIN, Brenda, Human Resources Director, Jeff Davis Hospital, Hazlehurst, GA, p. A154

MCELDOWNEY, Erin, Manager Human Resources, Haven Senior Horizons, Phoenix, AZ, p. A33

MCELMURRAY, Dodie, Chief Operating Officer, Greenwood Leflore Hospital, Greenwood, MS, p. A346

MCELRATH, Matthew
Chief Human Resources Officer, Keck Hospital Of Usc, Los Angeles, CA, p. A68
Chief Human Resources Officer, Usc Norris Comprehensive Cancer Center, Los Angeles, CA, p. A70

MCELROY, Kevin, Chief Human Resources Officer, Mackinac Straits Health System, Inc., Saint Ignace, MI, p. A322

MCENTEE, Chris, Network Specialist, Van Buren County Hospital, Keosauqua, IA, p. A225

MCENTEE, Kara, Chief Financial Officer, Van Buren County Hospital, Keosauqua, IA, p. A225

MCENTIRE, Ann, MSN, R.N., Chief Nursing Officer, Citizens Baptist Medical Center, Talladega, AL, p. A23

MCEUEN, Jacqueline, Coordinator Human Resources, Chi St. Joseph Health Bellville Hospital, Bellville, TX, p. A589

MCEWAN, Kevin K, MSN, R.N., Vice President of Patient Care Service and Chief Nursing Officer, Down East Community Hospital, Machias, ME, p. A285

MCEWEN, Michelle, President and Chief Executive Officer, Speare Memorial Hospital, Plymouth, NH, p. A401

MCFADDEN, Krista, Interim Chief Executive Officer, Hillside Rehabilitation Hospital, Warren, OH, p. A492

MCFADYEN, David M., Administrator, St. Luke's Meridian Medical Center, ID, p. A168

MCFALL, Cathy, Human Resources Manager, Kiowa County Memorial Hospital, Greensburg, KS, p. A236

MCFALL, Michael, Chief Financial Officer, Kindred Rehabilitation Hospital Clear Lake, Webster, TX, p. A643

MCFALL, Vicky, Chief Executive Officer, Monroe County Medical Center, Tompkinsville, KY, p. A261

MCFALL-ROBERTS, Ebuni, Director Human Resources, Holly Hill Hospital, Raleigh, NC, p. A459

MCFARLAND, Kenneth D., Chief Executive Officer, Fountain Valley Regional Hospital And Medical Center, Fountain Valley, CA, p. A58

MCFARLAND, Nita, Director of Nursing, Kingman Community Hospital, Kingman, KS, p. A238

MCFARLAND, Rhonda
Director Human Resources, Carolinas Healthcare System Anson, Wadesboro, NC, p. A461
Director Human Resources, Carolinas Healthcare System Union, Monroe, NC, p. A457

MCFARLAND, Rodney, M.D., Medical Director, Freeman Neosho Hospital, Neosho, MO, p. A365

MCFARLAND, Tracee, Chief Financial Officer, Claiborne Medical Center, Tazewell, TN, p. A580

MCFARLANE, Michael
Chief Human Resource Officer, St. Louis Psychiatric Rehabilitation Center, Saint Louis, MO, p. A369
Director Human Resource, Hawthorn Children Psychiatric Hospital, Saint Louis, MO, p. A368
Director Human Resources, Metropolitan St. Louis Psychiatric Center, Saint Louis, MO, p. A368

MCFERRAN, Virginia, Chief Information Officer, Ucla Medical Center-Santa Monica, Santa Monica, CA, p. A89

MCGAHAN, Thomas P., M.D., Chief Medical Officer, Emory Saint Joseph's Hospital Of Atlanta, Atlanta, GA, p. A146

MCGAHEY, Nikki, Information Officer, Jefferson County Hospital, Waurika, OK, p. A510

MCGARIGLE, Kristine, R.N., Vice President Patient Care, Ascension Good Samaritan Hospital, Merrill, WI, p. A698

MCGARVEY, Missy, Chief Information Officer, Twin Valley Behavioral Healthcare, Columbus, OH, p. A479

MCGEACHEY, Edward J, President and Chief Executive Officer, Southern Maine Health Care - Biddeford Medical Center, ME, p. A283

MCGEE, Angela, Vice President Nursing Services, Aultman Orrville Hospital, Orrville, OH, p. A488

MCGEE, Genemarie, R.N., MS, Chief Nursing Officer, Sentara Leigh Hospital, Norfolk, VA, p. A662

MCGEE, Jessica
Chief Financial Officer, Amg Specialty Hospital-Lafayette, Lafayette, LA, p. A270
Chief Financial Officer, Sage Specialty Hospital (Ltac), Denham Springs, LA, p. A267

MCGEE, Kevin, Chief Executive Officer, River Point Behavioral Health, Jacksonville, FL, p. A125

MCGEE, Mark F, M.D., Chief Clinical Officer, Appalachian Behavioral Healthcare, Athens, OH, p. A471

MCGEE, Terry, Chief Operations Officer, Central State Hospital, Milledgeville, GA, p. A157

MCGEEHAN, Paul, M.D., Chief Medical Staff, Corry Memorial Hospital, Corry, PA, p. A523

MCGETTIGAN, Ryan, Chief Information Officer, Coatesville Veterans Affairs Medical Center, Coatesville, PA, p. A523

MCGHEE, Kenneth, Vice President and Chief Financial Officer, Loretto Hospital, Chicago, IL, p. A177

MCGHEE, Michael, M.D., Medical Director, Unity Psychiatric Care-Clarksville, Clarksville, TN, p. A568

MCGIBBON, Monica, Chief Nursing Officer, Terence Cardinal Cooke Health Care Center, New York (Includes All Hospitals Located Within The Five Boroughs), NY, p. A437

MCGILL, Brittini, MSN, R.N., Chief Nursing Officer, Norman Regional Moore, OK, p. A502

MCGILL, Martha, Executive Vice President and Chief Operating Officer, Nicklaus Children's Hospital, Miami, FL, p. A130

MCGILL, Rusty, System Director Information Technology, Indiana University Health Arnett Hospital, Lafayette, IN, p. A209

MCGILL, Steve, Vice President Finance and Chief Financial Officer, Wabash General Hospital, Mount Carmel, IL, p. A190

MCGILL, Thomas, M.D., Chief Information Officer, Butler Health System, Butler, PA, p. A521

MCGILL, Timothy W., Chief Executive Officer, Livingston Regional Hospital, Livingston, TN, p. A573

MCGILVRAY, Greg, Chief Financial Officer, Medical Center Enterprise, Enterprise, AL, p. A17

MCGIMSEY, Erika, Controller, Jewish Hospital-Shelbyville, Shelbyville, KY, p. A260

MCGINLEY, Mary Ann, Ph.D., Senior Vice President, Patient Services and Chief Nursing Officer, Jefferson Methodist Hospital, PA, p. A536

MCGINNIS, Christina, Director Information Technology, Menorah Medical Center, Overland Park, KS, p. A243

MCGINNIS, Jeff, M.D., President Medical Staff, Saint Joseph Mount Sterling, Mount Sterling, KY, p. A258

MCGINNIS, Paula, Chief Executive Officer, St. Joseph's Hospital - North, FL, p. A141

MCGIRL, John, Chief Human Resources Officer, Nch North Naples Hospital, FL, p. A132

MCGLADE, James, Director Human Resources, United Hospital, Saint Paul, MN, p. A339

MCGLEW, Timothy, Chief Executive Officer, Kern Valley Healthcare District, Lake Isabella, CA, p. A63

MCGLON, Tracy, Director Human Resources, Gulf Coast Regional Medical Center, Panama City, FL, p. A135

MCGLYNN, Mia, Director Management Information Systems, Mercy Hospital - A Campus Of Plantation General Hospital, FL, p. A136

MCGOLDRICK, Margaret M., President, Abington Hospital, Abington, PA, p. A519

MCGOVERN, Charles, Chief of Staff, Margaret Mary Health, Batesville, IN, p. A199

MCGOVERN, Joanne, MSN, R.N., Chief Nursing Officer, Cancer Treatment Centers Of America-Eastern Regional Medical Center, Philadelphia, PA, p. A534

MCGOVERN, Julia, Vice President Human Resources, Chilton Medical Center, Pompton Plains, NJ, p. A410

MCGOVERN, Julie, Vice President Human Resources, Anne Arundel Medical Center, Annapolis, MD, p. A287

MCGOVERN, Kimberly, Manager Human Resources, Hackettstown Medical Center, Hackettstown, NJ, p. A405

MCGOVERN, Pam, Director Technology, Huggins Hospital, Wolfeboro, NH, p. A401

MCGOVERN, Sandra, Chief Nursing Officer, Up Health System-Bell, Ishpeming, MI, p. A316

MCGOWEN, Bernard A, M.D., Medical Director, Kindred Hospital Tarrant County-Arlington, Arlington, TX, p. A584

MCGOWIN, Norman F, M.D., III, Chief of Staff, L. V. Stabler Memorial Hospital, Greenville, AL, p. A19

MCGRAIL, David, Vice President Finance, Carney Hospital, Boston, MA, p. A296

MCGRAIL, Robert, Chief Executive Officer, Midmichigan Medical Center - West Branch, West Branch, MI, p. A326

MCGRATH, Denise B., Chief Executive Officer, Sea Pines Rehabilitation Hospital, Melbourne, FL, p. A129

MCGRATH, John, Chief Information Officer, Mclaren Port Huron, Port Huron, MI, p. A321

MCGRATH, Kelly, Chief Medical Officer, Clearwater Valley Hospital And Clinics, Orofino, ID, p. A170

MCGRATH, Lynn, M.D., Vice President Medical Affairs, Deborah Heart And Lung Center, Browns Mills, NJ, p. A403

MCGRAW, Belinda
Director Human Resources, Boulder City Hospital, Boulder City, NV, p. A392
Director Human Resources, Complex Care Hospital At Tenaya, Las Vegas, NV, p. A394

MCGRAW, Karin L., MSN, FACHE, Director, Veterans Affairs Medical Center, PA, p. A538

MCGRAW, Kathleen, M.D., Chief Medical Officer, Brattleboro Memorial Hospital, Brattleboro, VT, p. A653

MCGRAW, Scott, M.D., Medical Director, Baylor Surgical Hospital At Las Colinas, Irving, TX, p. A615

MCGREEVY, John, FACHE
Chief Executive Officer, Louis & Peaches Owen Heart Hospital, TX, p. A640
President, Methodist Southlake Hospital, Southlake, TX, p. A636

MCGREGOR, Catherine, Deputy Director Facility and Administrative Services, Capital District Psychiatric Center, Albany, NY, p. A421

MCGREGOR, Julie
Director Human Resources, Sts. Mary & Elizabeth Hospital, Louisville, KY, p. A256
Vice President and Chief People Officer, Frazier Rehab Institute, KY, p. A256

MCGREGOR, Robert, M.D., Chief Medical Officer, Akron Children's Hospital, Akron, OH, p. A470

MCGREW, David S, Chief Financial Officer, San Mateo Medical Center, San Mateo, CA, p. A87

MCGREW, Deborah A, Vice President and Chief Operating Officer, Angleton Danbury Campus, TX, p. A606

MCGREW, Diane, Chief Nurse Executive, Montgomery County Memorial Hospital, Red Oak, IA, p. A228

MCGRIFF, Marchelle M, Chief Nursing Executive, Sutter General Hospital, CA, p. A82

MCGUCKEN, Holly, R.N., Chief Nursing Officer, Fort Walton Beach Medical Center, Fort Walton Beach, FL, p. A123

MCGUE, Lisa, Controller, Healthsouth Northern Kentucky Rehabilitation Hospital, Edgewood, KY, p. A251

MCGUE, Thomas E., M.D., Vice President Medical Affairs and Chief Medical Officer, Newport Hospital, Newport, RI, p. A547

MCGUFFIN, Patty, R.N., Chief Nursing Officer, Allen County Regional Hospital, Iola, KS, p. A237

MCGUIGAN, Kevin, M.D., Medical Director, St. Lawrence Rehabilitation Center, Lawrenceville, NJ, p. A406

MCGUILL, Gail, R.N., MSN, Chief Nursing Officer and Administrative Director of Patient Care Services, Shriners Hospitals For Children-Salt Lake City, Salt Lake City, UT, p. A650

MCGUINNESS, Patrick, Chief Information Management, Keller Army Community Hospital, West Point, NY, p. A446

MCGUIRE, Ann M., Regional Vice President Human Resources, Indiana University Health Ball Memorial Hospital, Muncie, IN, p. A212

MCGUIRE, Cynthia, FACHE, President and Chief Executive Officer, Monadnock Community Hospital, Peterborough, NH, p. A401

MCGUIRE, Patrick, Chief Financial Officer, Michigan Market, St. John Macomb-Oakland Hospital, Warren Campus, MI, p. A325

MCGUIRE, Shane, Chief Executive Officer, Columbia County Health System, Dayton, WA, p. A671

MCGUIRK, Christina Marie, R.N., Chief Nursing Officer, Health Central Hospital, Ocoee, FL, p. A133

MCGUIRL, Mary, Director Information Systems, Oneida Healthcare, Oneida, NY, p. A439

MCGUIRT, Jacob, Chief Executive Officer, Lifecare Hospitals Of Mechanicsburg, Mechanicsburg, PA, p. A531

MCGURK, Kevin, Controller, Bellin Psychiatric Center, Green Bay, WI, p. A693

MCHARDY, Bryson, M.D., President Medical Staff, Hannibal Regional Hospital, Hannibal, MO, p. A360

MCHUGH, Matthew, Director Information Services, Vaughan Regional Medical Center, Selma, AL, p. A23

MCHUGH, Ryan, M.D., Chief of Staff, The Medical Center Of Southeast Texas, Port Arthur, TX, p. A629

MCHUGH, William, M.D., Medical Director and Chief Medical Officer, Trinitas Regional Medical Center - New Point Campus, NJ, p. A404

MCILROY, Gail, Director Medical Records, Promise Hospital Of Wichita Falls, Wichita Falls, TX, p. A644

MCILVAIN, Spencer, Director of Human Resources, Peterson Healthcare And Rehabilitation Hospital, Wheeling, WV, p. A688

MCILWAIN, T Pinckney, M.D., Vice President and Chief Medical Officer, General Hospital, WV, p. A682

MCINERNEY, Terry, Director of Nursing, Inpatient, Navos, Seattle, WA, p. A676

MCINTOSH, Craig, Chief Information Officer, Northwest Specialty Hospital, Post Falls, ID, p. A171

MCINTOSH, Eric D., Vice President Human Resources, Upmc Jameson, New Castle, PA, p. A533

MCINTOSH, Ernasha, Interim Director of Nursing, Sage Memorial Hospital, Ganado, AZ, p. A29

MCINTOSH, Joe, Director Management Information Systems, Logansport State Hospital, Logansport, IN, p. A210

MCINTOSH, Tyler, Chief Financial Officer, Creek Nation Community Hospital, Okemah, OK, p. A502

MCINTYRE, Cindy, R.N., Administrative Director Clinical Services, Magee General Hospital, Magee, MS, p. A349

MCINTYRE, Daniel J., President, Charlotte Hungerford Hospital, Torrington, CT, p. A111

MCIWAIN, John, Director Human Resources, Wayne Memorial Hospital, Jesup, GA, p. A155

MCKAIN, Rick, Chief Executive Officer, Anderson County Hospital, Garnett, KS, p. A235

MCKALE, Brigitte, MSN, FACHE, Vice President and Chief Nurse Executive, Pali Momi Medical Center, Aiea, HI, p. A164

MCKAY, Amy, Chief Nursing Officer, Mid-America Rehabilitation Hospital, Shawnee Mission, KS, p. A246

MCKAY, Daniel E., Chief Executive Officer, Ephraim Mcdowell Regional Medical Center, Danville, KY, p. A251

MCKAY, Danny H., Administrator, Noxubee General Hospital, Macon, MS, p. A349

MCKAY, Michael, Chief Information Officer, Wickenburg Community Hospital, Wickenburg, AZ, p. A38

MCKAY, Rebecca, Director Human Resources, Sweeny Community Hospital, Sweeny, TX, p. A638

MCKAY, Ronda, R.N., Vice President Patient Care Services, Chief Nursing Officer, Community Hospital, Munster, IN, p. A212

MCKEE, Debra, R.N., Chief Clinical Officer and Chief Nursing Officer, Joint Township District Memorial Hospital, Saint Marys, OH, p. A490

MCKEE, Michele, Vice President and Chief Financial Officer, St. Louis Children's Hospital, Saint Louis, MO, p. A369

MCKEE, Robert J, Vice President Human Resources, Penn Highlands Dubois, Dubois, PA, p. A524

MCKEE, Willis P, M.D., Jr, Chief Medical Officer, Frankfort Regional Medical Center, Frankfort, KY, p. A252

MCKEEBY, Ben, Senior Vice President and Chief Information Officer, Grady Memorial Hospital, Atlanta, GA, p. A146

MCKEEBY, Jon W, Chief Information Officer, Children's Inn At Nih, MD, p. A290

MCKEEN, Marcia, Director Human Resources, Twin Valley Behavioral Healthcare, Columbus, OH, p. A479

MCKELDIN, Pat, Human Resource Business Partner, Modesto Medical Center, CA, p. A71

MCKENDREE, Rodney, Senior Vice President and Chief Financial Officer, Nemours Children's Hospital, Orlando, FL, p. A134

MCKENNA, Dennis, M.D., Interim Vice President Medical Affairs, Albany Medical Center South-Clinical Campus, NY, p. A421

MCKENNA, Donald, President and Chief Executive Officer, Jupiter Medical Center, Jupiter, FL, p. A126

MCKENNA, John F., Chief Executive Officer and Managing Director, Rockford Center, Newark, DE, p. A113

MCKENNA, Quinn, Chief Operating Officer, Stanford Health Care, Palo Alto, CA, p. A77

MCKENNERY, Kay, Interim Chief Executive Officer, Hickory Trail Hospital, Desoto, TX, p. A600

MCKENNEY, Jennifer, M.D., Chief Medical Officer, Fredonia Regional Hospital, Fredonia, KS, p. A235

MCKENZIE, Christine, Director Human Resources, Davis Regional Medical Center, Statesville, NC, p. A461

MCKENZIE, Jackie, Director Administrative Services, Beacham Memorial Hospital, Magnolia, MS, p. A349

MCKENZIE, Kimberly, R.N., MSN
Chief Nursing Officer and Chief Operations Officer, Harbor-Ucla Medical Center, Torrance, CA, p. A91
Interim Chief Executive Officer, Harbor-Ucla Medical Center, Torrance, CA, p. A91

MCKENZIE, Margaret, M.D., President, South Pointe Hospital, Warrensville Heights, OH, p. A492

MCKENZIE, Sandra D., Executive Vice President and Chief Operating Officer, Hamilton Medical Center, Dalton, GA, p. A152

MCKENZIE, Troy, Chief information Officer, Faith Community Hospital, Jacksboro, TX, p. A616

MCKEON, John, Vice President Human Resources, Kingsbrook Jewish Medical Center, New York (Includes All Hospitals Located Within The Five Boroughs), NY, p. A433

MCKEON, Sean, Director, Information Technology, Franciscan Children'S, Brighton, MA, p. A297

MCKEOWN, Colleen
Senior Vice President and Area Manager, Kaiser Foundation Hospital, CA, p. A94
Senior Vice President and Area Manager, Kaiser Permanente Antioch Medical Center, Antioch, CA, p. A50

MCKERNAN, James E., Chief Operating Officer, Main Campus, MI, p. A308

MCKERNAN, Kathleen S., Director Information Systems, Pioneers Memorial Healthcare District, Brawley, CA, p. A53

MCKEVETT, Timothy M., President and Chief Executive Officer, Beloit Health System, Beloit, WI, p. A690

MCKEWAN, Jason, Interim Chief Executive Officer, Dewitt Hospital, Dewitt-Arkansas County, AR, p. A41

MCKIBBEN, Leeanna, R.N., MSN
Vice President Patient Services and Chief Nursing Officer, Upmc Mckeesport, Mckeesport, PA, p. A531
Vice President Patient Services and Chief Nursing Officer, Upmc Mercy, Pittsburgh, PA, p. A538

MCKIBBEN, Sean, President and Chief Operating Officer, Mount Carmel West Hospital, OH, p. A478

MCKIDDY, Paul, Director Information Technology, Monroe County Medical Center, Tompkinsville, KY, p. A261

MCKIE, Kathy, Director Human Resources, Montrose Memorial Hospital, Montrose, CO, p. A104

MCKILLIP, Ed, Vice President Finance, Riddle Hospital, Media, PA, p. A531

MCKIMMY, Doyle L., FACHE, Chief Executive Officer, Jewell County Hospital, Mankato, KS, p. A240

MCKINLEY, Alton, Chief Financial Officer, Sam Rayburn Memorial Veterans Center, TX, p. A598

MCKINLEY, Bryan, Chief Financial Officer, St. Mark's Hospital, Salt Lake City, UT, p. A651

MCKINLEY, Ivy
Director Human Resources, Presence Holy Family Medical Center, Des Plaines, IL, p. A181
Regional Human Resources Officer, Community First Medical Center, Chicago, IL, p. A176
Regional Lead Human Resources, Presence Resurrection Medical Center, Chicago, IL, p. A178

MCKINLEY, John, Director, Information Technology, Community Mental Health Center, Lawrenceburg, IN, p. A210

MCKINLEY, Mike, Information Security Officer, West Texas Veterans Affairs Health Care System, Big Spring, TX, p. A589

MCKINLEY, Ronald, Ph.D., Vice President Human Resources and Employee Services, Angleton Danbury Campus, TX, p. A606

MCKINNEY, Brenda, Chief Executive Officer, Reeves County Hospital, Pecos, TX, p. A628

MCKINNEY, Bruce, Business Officer, Administrative Services, Central Prison Hospital, Raleigh, NC, p. A458

MCKINNEY, Dan, Administrator, Hermann Area District Hospital, Hermann, MO, p. A360

MCKINNEY, Dana, Chief Nursing Officer, Select Specialty Hospital-Madison, Madison, WI, p. A696

MCKINNEY, Daniel, Chief Executive Officer, South Baldwin Regional Medical Center, Foley, AL, p. A18

MCKINNEY, James, Warden, Iowa Medical And Classification Center, Coralville, IA, p. A219

MCKINNEY, Jillyan, Chief Executive Officer, Avista Adventist Hospital, Louisville, CO, p. A103

MCKINNEY, Rachael, FACHE, Chief Executive Officer, Sutter Davis Hospital, Davis, CA, p. A56

MCKINNEY, Rex, President and Chief Executive Officer, Decatur County Memorial Hospital, Greensburg, IN, p. A205

MCKINNEY, Thomas
President, Christus Spohn Hospital Alice, Alice, TX, p. A582
President, Christus Spohn Hospital Kleberg, Kingsville, TX, p. A617

MCKINNON, Mark, M.D., Chief of Staff, North Runnels Hospital, Winters, TX, p. A644

MCKINNON, Ron, Chief Information Officer, Ellis Hospital Health Center, NY, p. A442

MCKINNON, Scott, President and Chief Executive Officer, Memorial Hospital, North Conway, NH, p. A400

MCKINSTRY, Merissa, Chief Operating Officer, Columbus Springs East Hospital, OH, p. A481

MCKNIGHT, David, CPA, Chief Executive Officer, Spotsylvania Regional Medical Center, Fredericksburg, VA, p. A658

MCKNIGHT, Stephanie, Hospital Nursing Manager, Sanford Bagley Medical Center, Bagley, MN, p. A328

MCKNIGHT, Tim, M.D., Chief of Staff, Trinity Hospital Twin City, Dennison, OH, p. A481

MCKOY, Lori, Business Partner, Pender Memorial Hospital, Burgaw, NC, p. A448

MCKULA, Tim, Vice President Information Systems and Chief Information Officer, Shirley Ryan Abilitylab, Chicago, IL, p. A179

MCKUNE, Jeff, Chief Health Informatics Officer, Phelps County Regional Medical Center, Rolla, MO, p. A366

MCLAIN, Allen, M.D., Chief of Staff, Grisell Memorial Hospital District One, Ransom, KS, p. A244

MCLAIN, John R., President and Chief Executive Officer, Bayfront Health St. Petersburg, Saint Petersburg, FL, p. A138

MCLANE, Kerry, Chief Executive Officer, Select Specialty Hospital-Muskegon, Muskegon, MI, p. A320

MCLARIN, Benita, Chief Operating Officer, Santa Clara Valley Medical Center, San Jose, CA, p. A87

MCLARTY, Walter L
  Chief Human Resources Officer, Bethesda Butler Hospital, OH, p. A474
  Chief Human Resources Officer, Good Samaritan Hospital, Cincinnati, OH, p. A475
MCLAUGHLIN, Amy, CPA, Chief Financial Officer, Manning Regional Healthcare Center, Manning, IA, p. A226
MCLAUGHLIN, Cathy, R.N., MSN, Chief Nursing Officer, Medical City Arlington, Arlington, TX, p. A584
MCLAUGHLIN, Dan C.
  Chief Executive Officer, Menifee Valley Medical Center, Sun City, CA, p. A91
  Chief Hospital Executive Officer, Hemet Valley Medical Center, Hemet, CA, p. A61
MCLAUGHLIN, Kathryn, Chief Nursing Officer, Hemet Valley Medical Center, Hemet, CA, p. A61
MCLAUGHLIN, Leslie, Director of Business Development, Michiana Behavioral Health Center, Plymouth, IN, p. A213
MCLAUGHLIN, Maribeth, R.N., Vice President Patient Care Services, Magee-Womens Hospital Of Upmc, Pittsburgh, PA, p. A537
MCLAUGHLIN, Matthew, President and Chief Executive Officer, Upmc Susquehanna Muncy, Muncy, PA, p. A532
MCLAUGHLIN, Mederic D., Executive Director, Veritas Collaborative, Atlanta, GA, p. A147
MCLAUGHLIN, Neil R., R.N., Administrator and Vice President, Operations, Jefferson Medical Center, Ranson, WV, p. A686
MCLAUGHLIN, Pamela, Chief Financial Officer, Encompass Health Rehabilitation Hospital Of Austin, Austin, TX, p. A586
MCLAUGHLIN, Rebecca, Chief Human Resource Officer, Banner Goldfield Medical Center, Apache Junction, AZ, p. A28
MCLAUGHLIN, Sherry, Director Human Resources, Forrest City Medical Center, Forrest City-St. Francis County, AR, p. A42
MCLAURIN, Monty E.
  Chief Executive Officer, Northwest Market, Indian Path Medical Center, Kingsport, TN, p. A572
  Interim Chief Executive Officer, Holston Valley Medical Center, Kingsport, TN, p. A572
MCLAWS, Douglas, D.O., Chief Medical Officer, Manning Regional Healthcare Center, Manning, IA, p. A226
MCLEAN, Anthony
  Market President, St. Francis Hospital, Federal Way, WA, p. A672
  President, Highline Medical Center, Burien, WA, p. A670
MCLEAN, Chris, Chief Administrative Officer, Methodist Le Bonheur Germantown Hospital, TN, p. A575
MCLEAN, Cindy J, R.N., MSN, Director of Nursing, Central Prison Hospital, Raleigh, NC, p. A458
MCLEAN, Georgia, Director Human Resources, Miami Heart Campus At Mount Sinai Medical Center, FL, p. A131
MCLEAN, Robb, M.D., Chief Medical Officer, Unm Sandoval Regional Medical Center, Inc., Rio Rancho, NM, p. A419
MCLENDON, Carla
  Director Human Resources, Appling Healthcare System, Baxley, GA, p. A148
  Director Information Resource Management Services, Charles George Veterans Affairs Medical Center, Asheville, NC, p. A447
MCLENDON, John
  Senior Vice President and Chief Information Officer, Amita Health Adventist Medical Center Bolingbrook, Bolingbrook, IL, p. A174
  Vice President and Chief Information Officer, Johns Hopkins All Children's Hospital, Saint Petersburg, FL, p. A138
MCLENDON, Tom, Administrator, Evergreen Medical Center, Evergreen, AL, p. A17
MCLEOD, Les, Director of Nursing Services, Blue Mountain Hospital, John Day, OR, p. A514
MCLEOD, Margie, Director Information Technology, North Canyon Medical Center, Gooding, ID, p. A169
MCLEOD, Michael, M.D., Chief Medical Officer, Cuero Community Hospital, Cuero, TX, p. A595
MCLEOD, Sheldon
  Chief Executive Officer, Nyc Health + Hospitals / Kings County, New York (Includes All Hospitals Located Within The Five Boroughs), NY, p. A436
  Chief Operating Officer, Nyc Health + Hospitals / North Central Bronx, New York (Includes All Hospitals Located Within The Five Boroughs), NY, p. A436
MCLIN, Robert D., President and Chief Executive Officer, Good Samaritan Hospital, Vincennes, IN, p. A216
MCLOONE, Mark, Chief Executive Officer, Suburban Community Hospital, Norristown, PA, p. A533
MCLOONE, Paul, M.D.
  Chief Medical Officer, Unitypoint Health - Trinity Bettendorf, Bettendorf, IA, p. A217

  Chief Medical Officer, Unitypoint Health - Trinity Moline, IL, p. A194
MCMACKIN, Ann, President, Vassar Brothers Medical Center, Poughkeepsie, NY, p. A441
MCMAHAN, Mike, President, St. Francis Regional Medical Center, Shakopee, MN, p. A340
MCMAHAN, Steve, M.D., Chief Medical Officer, Glenwood Surgery Center, LA, p. A280
MCMAHON, Alisha, Director Human Resources, Mountrail County Medical Center, Stanley, ND, p. A468
MCMAHON, Andrew, Chief Fiscal Officer, Veterans Affairs Central Western Massachusetts Healthcare System, Leeds, MA, p. A301
MCMAHON, Chris, Chief Operating Officer, The Medical Center Of Southeast Texas, Port Arthur, TX, p. A629
MCMAHON, Elaine, Administrator, Kwajalein Hospital, Kwajalein Island, MH, p. A711
MCMAHON, Eugene
  Senior Vice President and Chief Medical Officer, Capital Health Medical Center-Hopewell, Pennington, NJ, p. A410
  Senior Vice President and Chief Medical Officer, Capital Health Regional Medical Center, Trenton, NJ, p. A413
MCMAHON, Leigh, MS, R.N., Senior Vice President Patient Care Services and Chief Nursing Officer, White Plains Hospital Center, White Plains, NY, p. A446
MCMAHON, Nancy, Vice President Human Resources, Miriam Hospital, Providence, RI, p. A547
MCMANAMAN, Craig, M.D., Chief of Staff, Mclaren Thumb Region, Bad Axe, MI, p. A308
MCMANMON, Kristin, President, Ascension All Saints, Racine, WI, p. A701
MCMANUS, Doug, Chief Medical Officer, Aurora Medical Center Grafton, Grafton, WI, p. A693
MCMANUS, Michael T
  Chief Operating Officer, Memorial Hospital East, Shiloh, IL, p. A196
  Chief Operating Officer, Memorial Hospital, Belleville, IL, p. A174
MCMANUS, Ronald, Senior Vice President Clinical Services and Business Entities, Peconic Bay Medical Center, Riverhead, NY, p. A441
MCMASTER, Sandra
  Regional Chief Information Officer, Kauai Veterans Memorial Hospital, Waimea, HI, p. A166
  Regional Chief Information Officer, Samuel Mahelona Memorial Hospital, Kapaa, HI, p. A166
MCMATH, Mark W
  Chief Information Officer, Indiana University Health Bloomington Hospital, Bloomington, IN, p. A200
  Chief Information Officer, Methodist Le Bonheur Germantown Hospital, TN, p. A575
MCMENAMIN, Anneliese, Senior Vice President Information Technology and Program Services, Jefferson Washington Township Hospital, NJ, p. A412
MCMICHEN, Diane, Director Human Resources, Dekalb Regional Medical Center, Fort Payne, AL, p. A18
MCMILLAN, Deborah, Director Human Resources, Glenn Medical Center, Willows, CA, p. A95
MCMILLAN, Donn
  Chief Information Officer, Peacehealth Sacred Heart Medical Center University District, Eugene, OR, p. A512
  Senior Director, IST Client Liaison, Vancouver Memorial Campus, WA, p. A680
MCMILLAN, Douglas A., Administrator and Chief Executive Officer, West Park Hospital, Cody, WY, p. A708
MCMILLAN, Jon R, Chief Financial Officer, Banner Lassen Medical Center, Susanville, CA, p. A91
MCMILLAN, Sheila, Chief Financial Officer, Park Nicollet Methodist Hospital, Saint Louis Park, MN, p. A339
MCMILLEN, Eric, Chief Executive Officer, Ochsner Medical Center - Baton Rouge, Baton Rouge, LA, p. A263
MCMILLIN, Lori, Administrator, Mercy Hospital Tishomingo, Tishomingo, OK, p. A508
MCMILLION, Kelley, Chief Nursing Officer, Clay County Memorial Hospital, Henrietta, TX, p. A609
MCMINN, Ken, Director Information Technology, Scotland County Hospital, Memphis, MO, p. A364
MCMINN, Melvin, Director Human Resources, Wernersville State Hospital, Wernersville, PA, p. A543
MCMINOWAY, Kelly, R.N., Vice President, Nursing, Baptist Health Floyd, New Albany, IN, p. A212
MCMULLAN, Cheryl, Chief Financial Officer, Baylor Scott & White Medical Center At Waxahachie, Waxahachie, TX, p. A642
MCMULLAN, Heidi, R.N., Chief Nursing Officer, Wellspan Philhaven, Mount Gretna, PA, p. A532
MCMULLAN, Rosemary, Chief Human Resources, Mayo Clinic Hospital In Florida, Jacksonville, FL, p. A125

MCMULLIN, John, Chief Financial Officer, Rehoboth Mckinley Christian Health Care Services, Gallup, NM, p. A417
MCMURRAY, Rob, Chief Financial Officer, Christiana Care Health System, Newark, DE, p. A113
MCMURRAY, Sharon, Director, Human Resources, Rock Springs, Georgetown, TX, p. A607
MCMURREN, Mary Anne, R.N., Chief Administrative Officer, Peacehealth Sacred Heart Medical Center University District, Eugene, OR, p. A512
MCMURREY, Jean Ann, R.N., MSN, Chief Nursing Officer, Southern Tennessee Regional Health System-Sewanee, TN, p. A581
MCNABB, Dana, Human Resources Manager, Field Memorial Community Hospital, Centreville, MS, p. A344
MCNABB, Teresita, R.N., FACHE, Vice President Nursing Services, Terrebonne General Medical Center, Houma, LA, p. A269
MCNAIR, Lisa, CPA, Senior Vice President and Chief Financial Officer, Chi St. Joseph Regional Health Center, Bryan, TX, p. A591
MCNAIR, Rebekah, Director Human Resources, Healthsouth Chattanooga Rehabilitation Hospital, Chattanooga, TN, p. A567
MCNAIR, Scott, Chief Financial Officer, Neshoba County General Hospital, Philadelphia, MS, p. A352
MCNALLY, Joseph, M.D., Medical Director, Streamwood Behavioral Health Center, Streamwood, IL, p. A197
MCNALLY, Kathy, Chief Nursing Officer, Healthsouth Rehabilitation Hospital Of Cincinnati At Norwood, OH, p. A475
MCNALLY, Lou-Ann, Executive Director Human Resources and Staff Development, Claxton-Hepburn Medical Center, Ogdensburg, NY, p. A439
MCNALLY, Michael, Vice President Human Resources, Wilson Memorial Regional Medical Center, NY, p. A423
MCNAMARA, John, M.D., Senior Vice President, Chief Medical Officer, Torrance Memorial Medical Center, Torrance, CA, p. A92
MCNAMARA, Marilyn, M.D., Chief Medical Officer, Southwest General Health Center, Middleburg Heights, OH, p. A487
MCNAMARA, Mike, Chief Information Officer, Mee Memorial Hospital, King City, CA, p. A62
MCNAMARA, Steve, Chief Financial Officer, Memorialcare, Orange Coast Memorial Medical Center, Fountain Valley, CA, p. A58
MCNAMARA, Thomas, D.O., Vice President Medical Affairs, Wellstar Cobb Hospital, Austell, GA, p. A148
MCNAMARA, Timothy M
  Senior Vice President Human Resources, Bradford Regional Medical Center, Bradford, PA, p. A521
  Senior Vice President Human Resources, Olean General Hospital, Olean, NY, p. A439
MCNAMEE, Hugar, D.O., Chief Medical Officer, Florida Hospital Zephyrhills, Zephyrhills, FL, p. A144
MCNATT, James, Chief Financial Officer, Baylor Scott & White Medical Center - Carrollton, Carrollton, TX, p. A592
MCNAUGHTON, Kathy, Chief Information Officer, Nemaha County Hospital, Auburn, NE, p. A381
MCNAUGHTON, Richard, Chief Information Management Service, Maine Veterans Affairs Medical Center, Augusta, ME, p. A282
MCNEA, Melvin, Chief Executive Officer, Great Plains Health, North Platte, NE, p. A387
MCNEAR, Michael, M.D., Chief Medical Officer, Jersey Community Hospital, Jerseyville, IL, p. A186
MCNEECE, Steve
  Interim Chief Executive Officer, Mineral Community Hospital, Superior, MT, p. A379
  President and Chief Executive Officer, Community Hospital Of Anaconda, Anaconda, MT, p. A373
MCNEEL, Jacob, D.O., Chief of Staff, Plateau Medical Center, Oak Hill, WV, p. A685
MCNEEL, Wakelin, M.D., Medical Director, Bhc Alhambra Hospital, Rosemead, CA, p. A81
MCNEIL, Ane, Vice President Human Resources, St. Joseph Mercy Oakland, Pontiac, MI, p. A321
MCNEIL, Karen, President, University Hospitals Samaritan Medical Center, Ashland, OH, p. A470
MCNEILL, Michael, Chief Financial Management, New Mexico Veterans Affairs Health Care System - Raymond G. Murphy Medical Center, Albuquerque, NM, p. A416
MCNEY, Jim, Senior Vice President Finance and Chief Financial Officer, North Kansas City Hospital, North Kansas City, MO, p. A365
MCNICHOLS, Janiece, Chief Financial Officer, St. Mary-Corwin Medical Center, Pueblo, CO, p. A105
MCNULTY, Bruce, Chief Medical Officer, Swedish Covenant Hospital, Chicago, IL, p. A180

MCNULTY, Stephanie
Chief Operating Officer, Largo Medical Center - Indian Rocks, FL, p. A128
Chief Operating Officer, St. Petersburg General Hospital, Saint Petersburg, FL, p. A138

MCNULTY, Timothy, Director Human Resources, Spring Harbor Hospital, Westbrook, ME, p. A286

MCNUTT, Elena, Chief Nursing Officer, Desert Springs Hospital Medical Center, Las Vegas, NV, p. A394

MCNUTT, Mike, Assistant Administrator, Covenant Hospital Plainview, Plainview, TX, p. A628

MCNUTT, Pamela
Senior Vice President and Chief Information Officer, Methodist Dallas Medical Center, Dallas, TX, p. A597
Senior Vice President and Chief Information Officer, Methodist Mansfield Medical Center, Mansfield, TX, p. A622
Senior Vice President and Chief Information Officer, Methodist Richardson Medical Center, Richardson, TX, p. A630
Vice President Information Systems, Methodist Charlton Medical Center, Dallas, TX, p. A597

MCPEAK, Sara, Chief Nursing Officer, Carlinville Area Hospital, Carlinville, IL, p. A175

MCPHERSON, Jason, Chief Executive Officer, Rock Springs, Georgetown, TX, p. A607

MCPHERSON, Lon, M.D., Senior Vice President Medical Affairs and Chief Quality Officer, Florida Hospital Ocala, Ocala, FL, p. A133

MCPHERSON, Rhonda, Vice President Human Resources, Fayette Regional Health System, Connersville, IN, p. A201

MCPHERSON, Valarie, MSN, Chief Nursing Executive, California Hospital Medical Center, Los Angeles, CA, p. A66

MCQUAID, David P, FACHE, Chief Operating Officer, Ohio State University Hospitals East, OH, p. A478

MCQUAID, David P., FACHE, Chief Operating Officer, Ohio State University Hospitals East, OH, p. A478

MCQUAIDE, Ben, M.D., Chief of Staff, Clark Regional Medical Center, Winchester, KY, p. A261

MCQUILLEN, Paul, M.D., Chief Medical Officer, Jane Phillips Medical Center, Bartlesville, OK, p. A496

MCQUISTAN, Bob, Vice President Finance, York General, York, NE, p. A391

MCQUISTON, Mike, Administrative Director Human Resources, Wise Regional Health System, West Campus Decatur, TX, p. A598

MCRAE, Ashley, Chief Clinical Officer, Kindred Hospital North Florida, Green Cove Springs, FL, p. A124

MCRAE, Colin, Chief Executive Officer, Tennova Healthcare-Jefferson Memorial Hospital, Jefferson City, TN, p. A571

MCREYNOLDS, John, Chief Operating Officer, North Valley Hospital, Tonasket, WA, p. A679

MCRIMMON, Dana, Chief Financial Officer, Mesilla Valley Hospital, Las Cruces, NM, p. A418

MCROBERTS, Kevin G, FACHE, Senior Vice President of Operations, Lake Regional Health System, Osage Beach, MO, p. A365

MCSWAIN, Marilyn, MSN, R.N., Administrator, Lake Charles Memorial Hospital For Women, LA, p. A272

MCTAGGART, Jac
Chief Executive Officer, Sanford Hillsboro Medical Center, Hillsboro, ND, p. A467
Chief Executive Officer, Sanford Mayville Medical Center, Mayville, ND, p. A467

MCTIGRIT, Chris, Manager Information Technology, Delta Memorial Hospital, Dumas-Desha County, AR, p. A41

MCTIGUE, Mary, Vice President Patient Care Services and Chief Nursing Officer, Trinitas Regional Medical Center - New Point Campus, NJ, p. A404

MCTIGUE, Michael
Chief Information Officer, Clara Maass Medical Center, Belleville, NJ, p. A402
Chief Information Officer, Saint Barnabas Medical Center, Livingston, NJ, p. A406

MCVAY, Tara, Chief Nursing Officer, Logansport Memorial Hospital, Logansport, IN, p. A210

MCVEIGH, Kevin, Chief Human Resources Officer, Samaritan Behavioral Health Center-Desert Samaritan Medical Center, AZ, p. A31

MCVEY, Eric A, M.D., Executive Vice President Medical Affairs and Quality, St. Dominic-Jackson Memorial Hospital, Jackson, MS, p. A348

MCVEY, Lynn, Chief Operating Officer, Hudson Regional Hospital, Secaucus, NJ, p. A411

MCVEY, Marian Lorraine, Chief Nursing Officer, North Greenville Hospital, Travelers Rest, SC, p. A557

MCVEY, Patrick, Chief Executive Officer, Kindred Hospital North Florida, Green Cove Springs, FL, p. A124

MCWAY, Jacob, Senior Vice President and Chief Financial Officer, Cox Medical Center South, MO, p. A370

MCWEY, Russ, M.D., Vice President and Chief Information Officer, Virginia Hospital Center, Arlington, VA, p. A655

MCWHERTER, Joe, Chief Financial Officer, Baptist Memorial Hospital-Desoto, Southaven, MS, p. A353

MCWILLIAMS, Jill, Chief Nursing Officer, Sierra Nevada Memorial Hospital, Grass Valley, CA, p. A61

MEACHAM, Byanka, Director Human Resources, Montgomery County Emergency Service, Norristown, PA, p. A533

MEACHEM, Michelle, Director Human Resources, Moses Ludington Hospital, NY, p. A426

MEAD, Linda, Director Human Resources, Margaretville Hospital, Margaretville, NY, p. A429

MEAD, Richard, Senior Director Human Resources, Saint Francis Memorial Hospital, San Francisco, CA, p. A85

MEAD, Rick, Human Resources Leader, Kaiser Permanente Richmond Medical Center, CA, p. A76

MEADE, Andrew, Chief Executive Officer, Select Specialty Hospital-Longview, Longview, TX, p. A620

MEADE, Robert C., Chief Executive Officer, Doctors Hospital Of Sarasota, Sarasota, FL, p. A138

MEADE, Stephanie, R.N., MSN, Chief Nursing Officer, Mercy Health - West Hospital, Cincinnati, OH, p. A475

MEADE, Teresa, R.N., Chief Nursing Officer, Boone Memorial Hospital, Madison, WV, p. A684

MEADOWS, Barbara, Chief Financial Manager, Captain James A. Lovell Federal Health Care Center, North Chicago, IL, p. A191

MEADOWS, Danny, M.D., Medical Director, Logansport State Hospital, Logansport, IN, p. A210

MEADOWS, Hal, M.D., Chief Medical Officer, Banner Lassen Medical Center, Susanville, CA, p. A91

MEADOWS, Mark, Chief Executive Officer, Lone Peak Hospital, Draper, UT, p. A646

MEADOWS, Nancy, Chief Financial Officer, Northeast Methodist Hospital, TX, p. A633

MEADOWS, Sheila M, Chief Human Resources Officer, Mission Hospital, NC, p. A447

MEADOWS, Theresa, Chief Information Officer, Cook Children's Medical Center, Fort Worth, TX, p. A604

MEANS, Dennis, M.D., Vice President Medical Affairs, Carilion Clinic Saint Albans Hospital, VA, p. A656

MEANS, Paul, M.D., President Medical Staff, Highlands Hospital, Connellsville, PA, p. A523

MEANS, William H., Jr, Administrator, Bastrop Rehabilitation Hospital, Monroe, LA, p. A274

MEARNS, Stephanie, R.N.
Vice President and Chief Nursing Officer, West Hills Hospital And Medical Center, Los Angeles, CA, p. A70
Vice President Patient Care Services and Chief Nurse Executive, Seton Medical Center, Daly City, CA, p. A56

MEARS, Edith, Chief Executive Officer, Regional General Hospital, Williston, FL, p. A144

MEARS, Terry, Director Information Systems, Duke Regional Hospital, Durham, NC, p. A451

MECHAM, Cindy, Health Information Director, Mountain View Hospital, Payson, UT, p. A649

MEDAGLIA, Guy A., President and Chief Executive Officer, Saint Anthony Hospital, Chicago, IL, p. A179

MEDCIROS, Ron, Director Applied Information Technology, Worcester Recovery Center And Hospital, Worcester, MA, p. A306

MEDEIROS, Katherine A., President and Chief Executive Officer, Sierra Nevada Memorial Hospital, Grass Valley, CA, p. A61

MEDEROS, Ana J., Chief Executive Officer, Palmetto General Hospital, Hialeah, FL, p. A124

MEDINA, Alberto, Information Technology Senior Consultant, Hospital Manati Medical Center, Manati, PR, p. A714

MEDINA, Betsmari, Director Human Resources, Dr. Ramon E. Betances Hospital-Mayaguez Medical Center Branch, Mayaguez, PR, p. A714

MEDINA, Ed, M.D., Medical Director, Phillips County Hospital, Malta, MT, p. A377

MEDINA, Eleanor, M.D., Chief Medical Officer, Behavioral Center Of Michigan, Warren, MI, p. A325

MEDINA, Luz D, Controller, Puerto Rico Children's Hospital, PR, p. A712

MEDINA, Marco, Chief Information Officer, Stanton County Hospital, Johnson, KS, p. A237

MEDINA, Obdulia, Associate Director for Administrative Support, Clinical Management and Ambulatory Care, Ashford Presbyterian Community Hospital, San Juan, PR, p. A715

MEDINA, Shelby, Chief Executive Officer, Windom Area Hospital, Windom, MN, p. A342

MEDINA CRUZ, Victor L., M.D., Administrator, Hospital Cuidado Agudo Especializado En Pacientes Politraumatizados, San Juan, PR, p. A715

MEDLAND, Jacqueline, MS, Ph.D., President and Chief Nursing Officer, Highlands-Cashiers Hospital, Highlands, NC, p. A455

MEDLEY, Adron, M.D., Chief Medical Staff, Northern Rockies Medical Center, Cut Bank, MT, p. A374

MEDLEY, Barry, Director Information Systems, Cook Medical Center-A Campus Of Tift Regional Medical Center, Adel, GA, p. A145

MEDLEY, Dennis
Chief Executive Officer and Administrator, Physicians' Medical Center, New Albany, IN, p. A212
Chief Executive Officer, Physicians' Medical Center, New Albany, IN, p. A212

MEDLEY, Wathen, M.D., Chief Medical Officer, Healthpark, KY, p. A258

MEDLIN, John, Chief Nursing Officer, North Carolina Specialty Hospital, Durham, NC, p. A451

MEDLIN, Marcia, Chief Executive Officer, Select Specialty Hospital-York, PA, p. A522

MEDLIN, Marsha, Senior Vice President of Clinical and Operations, Pam Specialty Hospital Of Covington, Covington, LA, p. A266

MEDLOCK, Darci, Manager Human Resources, St. Vincent Dunn Hospital, Bedford, IN, p. A200

MEDOVICH, Lisa, Chief Financial Officer, Peterson Regional Medical Center, Kerrville, TX, p. A617

MEEKER, Brian, D.O., President Medical Staff, Virginia Gay Hospital, Vinton, IA, p. A230

MEEKER, Chris, M.D., Chief Medical Officer, Sanford Bismarck, Bismarck, ND, p. A464

MEEKER, Christina, Director Human Resources, Strategic Behavioral Health - Raleigh, Garner, NC, p. A453

MEEKINS, Lance, Chief Executive Officer, Nocona General Hospital, Nocona, TX, p. A626

MEEKINS, Michelle, Manager Human Resources, Sentara Virginia Beach General Hospital, Virginia Beach, VA, p. A667

MEEKS, Deborah, Chief Nursing Officer, Harlingen Medical Center, Harlingen, TX, p. A608

MEENK, Susan
Vice President Human Resources, Providence St. Peter Hospital, Olympia, WA, p. A674
Vice President Service Area, Providence Centralia Hospital, Centralia, WA, p. A670

MEESE, John, Acting Director, Gallup Indian Medical Center, Gallup, NM, p. A417

MEESE, Larry, Chief Executive Officer, Lane Regional Medical Center, Zachary, LA, p. A281

MEESIG, Deborah, M.D., Chief of Staff, Chillicothe Veterans Affairs Medical Center, Chillicothe, OH, p. A474

MEGEHEE, Mark, Vice President and Chief Information Officer, Decatur Morgan Hospital-West, AL, p. A16

MEGGS, Christi, Director, Carolinas Hospital System Marion, Mullins, SC, p. A555

MEGLEMRE, Amy J, R.N., MSN, Senior Vice President and Chief Nursing Officer, Olathe Medical Center, Olathe, KS, p. A242

MEGLI, Cami, Controller, Morrison Community Hospital, Morrison, IL, p. A190

MEGLIOLA, Donna M, Assistant Vice President, Johnson Memorial Medical Center, Stafford Springs, CT, p. A111

MEGOW, Kimberly, M.D., Chief Medical Officer, Smith Northview Hospital, GA, p. A162

MEGUIAR, Ramon V, M.D., Chief Medical Officer, Memorial Children's Hospital, GA, p. A160

MEHAFFEY, M. Beth, Senior Vice President Human Resources, Wolfson Children's Hospital, FL, p. A125

MEHINDRU, Vinay, M.D.
Medical Director, Rockledge Regional Medical Center, Rockledge, FL, p. A137
Vice President/Chief Medical Officer, Florida Hospital Waterman, Tavares, FL, p. A142

MEHLHAUS, Brian, M.D., Chief of Staff, Boone County Hospital, Boone, IA, p. A218

MEHR, Nicholle, Vice President Operations, Mclaren Oakland, Pontiac, MI, p. A321

MEHTA, Kalpana, Chief Fiscal Services, Jesse Brown Veterans Affairs Medical Center, Chicago, IL, p. A177

MEHTA, Sonia, M.D., Chief Medical Officer, Loretto Hospital, Chicago, IL, p. A177

MEHTA, Umesh, M.D., Interim Chief Medical Officer, Carrier Clinic, Belle Mead, NJ, p. A402

MEIDINGER, Sue, Manager Business Office, Linton Hospital, Linton, ND, p. A467

MEIER, Suzanne S, System Director, Compensation and Human Resources Technology, Memorial Hermann Memorial City Medical Center, Houston, TX, p. A612

MEIERGERD, Jean, Chief Information Officer, St. Francis Memorial Hospital, West Point, NE, p. A391

MEIERS, Dawn, Coordinator Medical Staff and Personnel Services, Southeast Michigan Surgical Hospital, Warren, MI, p. A325

MEIGS, Jeffrey L, Chief Financial Officer, Louis A. Weiss Memorial Hospital, Chicago, IL, p. A177

MEIGS, John, M.D., Jr, Chief of Staff, Bibb Medical Center, Centreville, AL, p. A16

MEINDEL, Nympha, R.N., Chief Information Officer, North Shore University Hospital, Manhasset, NY, p. A429

MEINKE, Kenneth, Senior Vice President Administrative Services, Finance and Chief Financial Officer, Spartanburg Medical Center, Spartanburg, SC, p. A557

MEINKE, Victor E, Chief Financial Officer, Jewish Home Of San Francisco, San Francisco, CA, p. A85

MEINKOTH, Jennifer
Executive Director I.S., Memorial Hospital East, Shiloh, IL, p. A196

Executive Director, IS, Memorial Hospital, Belleville, IL, p. A174

MEISINGER, Alan, Chief Financial Officer, Herington Municipal Hospital, Herington, KS, p. A236

MEISNER, Anne, MSN, President and Chief Executive Officer, Southeastern Regional Medical Center, Newnan, GA, p. A158

MEKHAEL, Hani, M.D., Chief Staff, Havenwyck Hospital, Auburn Hills, MI, p. A307

MELAHN, William L, M.D., Vice President Medical Affairs and Chief Medical Officer, St. Claire Healthcare, Morehead, KY, p. A258

MELAN, Kristen, Director Human Resources Administration, Good Shepherd Specialty Hospital, Bethlehem, PA, p. A520

MELANCON, Eric, Chief of Staff, Teche Regional Medical Center, Morgan City, LA, p. A274

MELAND, Jeff, M.D., Vice President, Chief Medical Officer, Northfield Hospital And Clinics, Northfield, MN, p. A336

MELARAGNO, Robert, Vice President Finance, O'Bleness Memorial Hospital, Athens, OH, p. A471

MELBOURNE, John, M.D., Medical Director, Conifer Park, Glenville, NY, p. A427

MELBY, Gina, Chief Executive Officer, Jfk Medical Center, Atlantis, FL, p. A117

MELBY, Larry, Chief Executive Officer, Select Specialty Hospital-Palm Beach, Lake Worth, FL, p. A127

MELBY, Rachel, Vice President, Chief Financial Officer, Crawford County Memorial Hospital, Denison, IA, p. A221

MELCHER, Nancy, Chief Nursing Officer, Wellstar North Fulton Hospital, Roswell, GA, p. A159

MELCHIOR, Eric L, Executive Vice President and Chief Financial Officer, Greater Baltimore Medical Center, Baltimore, MD, p. A287

MELEAR, Brian, Chief Executive Officer, Raulerson Hospital, Okeechobee, FL, p. A133

MELENDEZ, Alma, Controller, Dimmit Regional Hospital, Carrizo Springs, TX, p. A591

MELENDEZ, Jose, M.D., Chief Medical Officer, Uchealth Memorial Hospital North, CO, p. A98

MELENDEZ, Pedro
Chief Executive Director, Hospital Menonita De Cayey, Cayey, PR, p. A713

Chief Executive Officer, Centro De Salud Conductual Menonita-Cima, Aibonito, PR, p. A711

Chief Executive Officer, Mennonite General Hospital, Aibonito, PR, p. A712

Executive Director, Hospital Menonita De Caguas, Caguas, PR, p. A712

MELINE, Brenda, Manager Human Resources, Patients' Hospital Of Redding, Redding, CA, p. A80

MELL, Kevin, Vice President Operations, Medstar Montgomery Medical Center, Olney, MD, p. A293

MELLETT, David, Chief Financial Officer, Harrison Memorial Hospital, Cynthiana, KY, p. A251

MELLGREN, Gustave, M.D., Chief of Staff, Glacial Ridge Health System, Glenwood, MN, p. A332

MELLO, Brett, Chief Information Officer, Cayuga Medical Center At Ithaca, Ithaca, NY, p. A428

MELLO, Paul, Manager Data Processing, Metropolitan State Hospital, Norwalk, CA, p. A75

MELLOWS, George, Facility Director, Hawthorn Center, Northville, MI, p. A320

MELNIKOFF, Jean, Vice President Human Resources, Kaiser Permanente Medical Center, Honolulu, HI, p. A164

MELO, Kathleen, Administrator, The Willough At Naples, Naples, FL, p. A132

MELTON, Anne, Chief Nursing Officer, Sumner Regional Medical Center, Gallatin, TN, p. A570

MELTON, Chad, Chief Executive Officer, Fauquier Hospital, Warrenton, VA, p. A667

MELTON, Josh, Chief Information Officer, St. Bernards Medical Center, Jonesboro-Craighead County, AR, p. A44

MELTVEDT, Robert, M.D., Jr, Vice President Medical Affairs, Warren Memorial Hospital, Front Royal, VA, p. A658

MELTZER, David B, Chief Financial Officer, Texas Health Presbyterian Hospital Denton, Denton, TX, p. A599

MELVILLE, Carol, Director Human Resources, West Houston Medical Center, Houston, TX, p. A614

MELVIN, Susan, D.O., Chief Medical Officer, Memorialcare, Long Beach Memorial Medical Center, Long Beach, CA, p. A65

MENA, Theodore, Chief Executive Officer, Select Specialty Hospital-Orlando South, FL, p. A134

MENDELOWITZ, Susan, R.N., FACHE, Executive Vice President and Chief Operating Officer, New Bridge Medical Center, Paramus, NJ, p. A409

MENDEZ, Alex A, Executive Vice President of Operations and Chief Financial Officer, Miami Heart Campus At Mount Sinai Medical Center, FL, p. A131

MENDEZ, Kim K, Ed.D., R.N., Chief Nurse Officer, Nyc Health + Hospitals / Bellevue, New York (Includes All Hospitals Located Within The Five Boroughs), NY, p. A435

MENDEZ, Lincoln S., Chief Executive Officer, Baptist Health South Florida, South Miami Hospital, Miami, FL, p. A130

MENDEZ, Nicholas Paul., Chief Executive Officer, Pam Specialty Hospital Of Hammond, Hammond, LA, p. A268

MENDEZ, Samantha, Human Resources, Scottsdale Liberty Hospital, Scottsdale, AZ, p. A35

MENDIOLA-BALDERAS, Rosie L, Director Information Systems, South Texas Behavioral Health Center, TX, p. A601

MENDIZABAL, Oscar, Chief Nursing Officer, Highlands Rehabilitation Hospital, El Paso, TX, p. A602

MENDOZA, Carlos, Controller, Baptist Memorial Rehabilitation Hospital, Germantown, TN, p. A570

MENDOZA, Christopher, Chief Executive Officer, Alliancehealth Ponca City, Ponca City, OK, p. A505

MENDOZA, Dana, Chief Information Officer, Maui Memorial Medical Center, Wailuku, HI, p. A166

MENDOZA, Joseph, M.D.
Medical Director, Porterville Developmental Center, Porterville, CA, p. A79

Chief Financial Officer, Hillcrest Hospital Cushing, Cushing, OK, p. A497

Chief Financial Officer, Hillcrest Hospital Henryetta, Henryetta, OK, p. A499

MENDOZA, Yolanda, Director Human Resources, Rehabilitation Hospital Of Southern New Mexico, Las Cruces, NM, p. A418

MENDYKA, Nick, Chief Financial Officer, University Of Virginia Children's Hospital, VA, p. A656

MENEFEE, Jason J, Chief Financial Officer, Mccamey County Hospital District, Mccamey, TX, p. A623

MENEN, Michael, M.D., Chief Medical Officer, Bon Secours St. Francis Medical Center, Midlothian, VA, p. A661

MENGLE, Scott, Vice President Human Resources, Penn State Health St. Joseph - Downtown Campus, PA, p. A539

MENKES, Jeffrey, President and Chief Executive Officer, Burke Rehabilitation Hospital, White Plains, NY, p. A446

MENNONNA, Guy, Senior Vice President Human Resources, New Bridge Medical Center, Paramus, NJ, p. A409

MENON, Rema, M.D., Clinical Director, Parsons State Hospital And Training Center, Parsons, KS, p. A244

MENSCH, Alan, M.D., Senior Vice President Medical Affairs, Plainview Hospital, Plainview, NY, p. A440

MENSEN, Amy, Chief Administrative Officer, Regional Medical Center, Manchester, IA, p. A226

MENTGEN, John, FACHE, President and Chief Executive Officer, Regional West Medical Center, Scottsbluff, NE, p. A390

MENTHCOAST, Lynn, Chief Fiscal Service, Nashville Campus, TN, p. A577

MENTINK, Terri, Chief Financial Officer, Oakland Mercy Hospital, Oakland, NE, p. A387

MENTZEL, Bridget, Director Human Resources, Mercy Health - West Hospital, Cincinnati, OH, p. A475

MENTZER, Larry, Chief Human Resources Officer, Veterans Affairs Roseburg Healthcare System, Roseburg, OR, p. A517

MENZEL, Colette, Ph.D., Chief Operating Officer and Chief Financial Officer, Antelope Valley Hospital, Lancaster, CA, p. A64

MENZIE, Sue, R.N., Director Patient Care, Sierra Tucson, Tucson, AZ, p. A37

MERCADO, Felix V., Chief Financial Officer, Lawrence General Hospital, Lawrence, MA, p. A300

MERCADO, Gloria, Director of Nursing, Mennonite General Hospital, Aibonito, PR, p. A712

MERCADO, Leda Marta R, Chief Operating Officer, Hospital Menonita De Cayey, Cayey, PR, p. A713

MERCER, David, Coordinator Information Systems, Baptist Memorial Hospital-Union City, Union City, TN, p. A580

MERCER, Shawna, Director Human Resources, Kansas Neurological Institute, Topeka, KS, p. A246

MERCER, William, M.D., Director, Peterson Healthcare And Rehabilitation Hospital, Wheeling, WV, p. A688

MERCHANT, Deven, M.D., Chief Medical Executive, Sutter Davis Hospital, Davis, CA, p. A56

MERCURI, Ralph, Vice President and Chief Financial Officer, Major Hospital, Shelbyville, IN, p. A214

MEREDITH, Katie, Chief Nursing Officer, Select Specialty Hospital-Lexington, Lexington, KY, p. A255

MEREDITH, Keith, Chief Operating Officer, Salem Regional Medical Center, Salem, OH, p. A490

MEREK, Gloria, Director of Nursing, Springfield Hospital Center, Sykesville, MD, p. A294

MERIDA, Andy, Director Management Information Systems, Fayette Regional Health System, Connersville, IN, p. A201

MERILLO, Myra, Supervisor Health Information Management, Healthsouth Rehabilitation Hospital Of Spring Hill, Brooksville, FL, p. A119

MERINGOLO, Francis, Vice President Human Resources, Umass Memorial-Marlborough Hospital, Marlborough, MA, p. A301

MERIWETHER, Wayne, Chief Executive Officer, Twin Lakes Regional Medical Center, Leitchfield, KY, p. A254

MERK, Richard
Director Human Resources, Allegiance Behavioral Health Center Of Plainview, Plainview, TX, p. A628

Executive Vice President, Allegiance Behavioral Health Center Of Plainview, Plainview, TX, p. A628

MERKEL, Rebecca, Privacy Officer, Franciscan Health Carmel, Carmel, IN, p. A201

MERKLE, John F., Medical Center Director, Tuscaloosa Veterans Affairs Medical Center, Tuscaloosa, AL, p. A24

MERKLEY, Jason R., Chief Executive Officer, Brookings Health System, Brookings, SD, p. A559

MERKLIN, Paul, Vice President Finance and Chief Financial Officer, Manchester Memorial Hospital, Manchester, KY, p. A257

MERRIFIELD, Matt
Chief Operating Officer, Aurora Pavilion, SC, p. A549

Interim Chief Executive Officer, Aurora Pavilion, SC, p. A549

MERRIGAN, Mary C, Manager Public Relations, Sanford Vermillion Medical Center, Vermillion, SD, p. A564

MERRILL, Cheryl Bhima, MSN, R.N., Senior Vice President Patient Care Services and Chief Nursing Officer, Union Campus, MA, p. A304

MERRILL, Chuck, M.D., Vice President Medical Affairs, Marian Regional Medical Center, Santa Maria, CA, p. A89

MERRILL, Doug, Executive Vice President Chief Medical and Acad Officer, Renown Rehabilitation Hospital, Reno, NV, p. A396

MERRILL, Rick W., System President and Chief Executive Officer, Cook Children's Medical Center, Fort Worth, TX, p. A604

MERRILL, Stacie, Chief Nursing Officer, Baylor Surgical Hospital At Fort Worth, Fort Worth, TX, p. A604

MERRITT, Becky A, Director Human Resources, Houston Methodist Clear Lake Hospital, Nassau Bay, TX, p. A625

MERRITT, Belinda, M.D., Medical Director, Spire Cane Creek Rehabilitation Hospital, Martin, TN, p. A574

MERRITT, Bradley, M.D., Medical Director, Christus Trinity Mother Frances Rehabilitation Hospital, A Partner Of Encompass Health, Tyler, TX, p. A641

MERRITT, Janet, Chief Financial Officer, St. Vincent Williamsport Hospital, Williamsport, IN, p. A216

MERRITT, Tim E., Chief Executive Officer, Summitridge Hospital, Lawrenceville, GA, p. A156

MERRITT, Trevor, Director Human Resources, Star Valley Medical Center, Afton, WY, p. A707

MERRY, Duane, Chief Information Officer, Little Falls Hospital, Little Falls, NY, p. A429

MERRYMAN, Angela, Chief Executive Officer, Select Specialty Hospital-Mckeesport, Mckeesport, PA, p. A531

MERRYMAN, Mary, Regional Director Information Management, Christus Highland Medical Center, LA, p. A278

MERRYMAN, Scott
Chief Financial Officer, Christus Coushatta Health Care Center, Coushatta, LA, p. A266

Chief Financial Officer, Christus Highland Medical Center, LA, p. A278

Chief Financial Officer, Christus Ochsner St. Patrick Hospital Southwest Louisiana, Lake Charles, LA, p. A272

MERRYWELL, Paul, Chief Information Officer, Sycamore Shoals Hospital, Elizabethton, TN, p. A569

MERSON, John, M.D., Chief of Staff, John Muir Medical Center, Concord, Concord, CA, p. A55

MERSON, Wendy, Chief Executive Officer, Windmoor Healthcare Of Clearwater, Clearwater, FL, p. A120

MESA, Gustavo, Chief Information Officer, San Juan City Hospital, San Juan, PR, p. A716

MESAROS, Dennis, Administrator, St. Luke's Meridian Medical Center, ID, p. A168

MESIC, John, M.D., Chief Medical Officer, Sutter Auburn Faith Hospital, Auburn, CA, p. A51

MESICK, Marc, Vice President and Chief Financial Officer, Ellis Hospital Health Center, NY, p. A442

MESKAN, Paula, R.N., Chief Nursing Officer, River's Edge Hospital And Clinic, Saint Peter, MN, p. A340

MESORAS, Amber, Chief Human Resources Officer, Veterans Affairs Medical Center, PA, p. A538

MESSA-GILL, Nicole, Manager Human Resources, Northlake Behavioral Health System, Mandeville, LA, p. A273

MESSELT, Mary Jo
Manager Human Resources, Mercy Hospital Watonga, Watonga, OK, p. A510
Senior Human Resources Manager, Mercy Hospital Logan County, Guthrie, OK, p. A499

MESSER, Kelly, Director of Finance, Devereux Hospital And Children's Center Of Florida, Melbourne, FL, p. A129

MESSER, Mark, D.O., Clinical Director, Terrell State Hospital, Terrell, TX, p. A639

MESSERSMITH, Scott E, Director Human Resources, Columbus Community Hospital, Columbus, NE, p. A383

MESSINA, Arlene, R.N., MSN, Director of Nursing, Riverside Doctors' Hospital Williamsburg, Williamsburg, VA, p. A667

MESSINA, Daniel J., Ph.D., FACHE, President and Chief Executive Officer, Richmond University Medical Center, New York (Includes All Hospitals Located Within The Five Boroughs), NY, p. A437

MESSMAN, Catherine, Chief Financial Officer, Mills-Peninsula Medical Center, CA, p. A53

MESTAS, Lisa, Associate Administrator and System Chief Nursing Officer, Usa Health University Hospital, Mobile, AL, p. A21

MESTER, Sulynn, R.N., Chief Nursing Officer, Childress Regional Medical Center, Childress, TX, p. A592

MESZLER, Lori A., Chief Financial Officer, Helen Hayes Hospital, West Haverstraw, NY, p. A445

METCALF, Angie L, Vice President and Chief Human Resource Officer, Tradition Medical Center, FL, p. A139

METCALF, Chris, Director of Nursing, Utah State Hospital, Provo, UT, p. A649

METCALF, Emma, MSN, R.N., Director, Lexington Veterans Affairs Medical Center, Lexington, KY, p. A255

METCALF, Kathleen, Chief Information Officer, University Hospitals Samaritan Medical Center, Ashland, OH, p. A470

METCALF, Peter, M.D., President Medical Staff, Genesis Medical Center, Silvis, Silvis, IL, p. A196

METER, Rex Van, President, Integris Deaconess, Oklahoma City, OK, p. A502

METHE, Joan, Chief Information Officer, Mercy Medical Center, Springfield, MA, p. A304

METHVEN, Jeffrey M, Vice President Ambulatory Services and Chief Human Resources Officer, Saratoga Hospital, Saratoga Springs, NY, p. A442

METHVIN, Jeff, Manager Information Technology, St. Luke Hospital And Living Center, Marion, KS, p. A241

METIKO, Olushola, M.D., Medical Director, Central Prison Hospital, Raleigh, NC, p. A458

METINKO, Andrew, M.D., Chief Medical Officer, The Hsc Pediatric Center, Washington, DC, p. A116

METIVIER, Roberta, Vice President Human Resources and Administrator, Western Main Nursing Home, Stephens Memorial Hospital, Norway, ME, p. A285

METRO, Michelle, Vice President Nursing, Cloud County Health Center, Concordia, KS, p. A234

METTEAUER, Kenneth, Chief Financial Officer, Redmond Regional Medical Center, Rome, GA, p. A159

METZ, Amy, Chief Executive Officer, Regency Hospital Of Florence, Florence, SC, p. A553

METZ, Bruce, Ph.D., Senior Vice President and Chief Information Officer, Lahey Medical Center, Peabody, MA, p. A298

METZ, Carl, Vice President, Ephraim Mcdowell Fort Logan Hospital, Stanford, KY, p. A261

METZGER, Alysha, Director Human Resources, Hill Country Memorial Hospital, Fredericksburg, TX, p. A606

METZGER, Cynthia, Chief Nursing and Operations Officer, Little River Memorial Hospital, Ashdown, AR, p. A39

METZGER, Terry
Chief Financial Officer, St. Vincent Seton Specialty Hospital, Indianapolis, IN, p. A208
Vice President, Finance, St. Vincent Women's Hospital, IN, p. A208

MEUER, Lynn, Interim Chief Nursing Officer, Sibley Memorial Hospital, Washington, DC, p. A116

MEURER, Bryan, Director Information Systems, Mat-Su Regional Medical Center, Palmer, AK, p. A27

MEURER, Lynn, MSN, R.N., Interim Chief Nursing Officer, Wellstar Kennestone Hospital, Marietta, GA, p. A157

MEWHIRTER, Michael, President, Fort Hamilton Hospital, Hamilton, OH, p. A483

MEYER, Anthony, M.D., Medical Director, Aurora Psychiatric Hospital, Wauwatosa, WI, p. A705

MEYER, Barb, Executive Director of Nursing, Gibson Area Hospital And Health Services, Gibson City, IL, p. A184

MEYER, Cameron, CPA, Chief Financial Officer, Excelsior Springs Hospital, Excelsior Springs, MO, p. A359

MEYER, Cheryl, MSN
Director of Nursing, Haven Behavioral Senior Care Of Dayton, Dayton, OH, p. A480
Director Human Resources, Gundersen Palmer Lutheran Hospital And Clinics, West Union, IA, p. A231

MEYER, Daniel T, President, Aurora Baycare Medical Center, Green Bay, WI, p. A693

MEYER, Daniel T., President, Aurora Baycare Medical Center, Green Bay, WI, p. A693

MEYER, Francis, Vice President Information Systems Technology, Women And Children's Hospital, NY, p. A423

MEYER, Gordon, Director Human Resources, Oakland Regional Hospital, Southfield, MI, p. A323

MEYER, Joe S, Chief Financial Officer, Scott County Hospital, Scott City, KS, p. A245

MEYER, June, MSN, R.N., Vice President Chief Nursing Officer, University Of Maryland Capital Region Health At Laurel Regional Hospital, Laurel, MD, p. A292

MEYER, Karen, Vice President Finance and Chief Financial Officer, Rush Memorial Hospital, Rushville, IN, p. A214

MEYER, Kurt A
Chief Human Resource Officer, Saint Joseph Health System, Mishawaka, IN, p. A211
Chief Human Resources Officer, Plymouth Medical Center, Plymouth, IN, p. A213

MEYER, Mark, Chief Financial Officer, Grady Memorial Hospital, Atlanta, GA, p. A146

MEYER, Michele C, Vice President of Operations, Mercy Hospital Jefferson, Crystal City, MO, p. A358

MEYER, Michele C., Chief Executive Officer, Washington County Memorial Hospital, Potosi, MO, p. A366

MEYER, Morgan, Chief Financial Officer, Howard County Medical Center, Saint Paul, NE, p. A390

MEYER, Nate, Director Finance, Alomere Health, Alexandria, MN, p. A327

MEYER, Robert L., President and Chief Executive Officer, Phoenix Children's Hospital, Phoenix, AZ, p. A33

MEYER, Roger, M.D., Chief of Staff, Friend Community Healthcare System, Friend, NE, p. A384

MEYER, Timothy, M.D., Chief of Staff, Memorial Medical Center - Neillsville, Neillsville, WI, p. A699

MEYER, Traci, Director Human Resources, Canyon Vista Medical Center, Sierra Vista, AZ, p. A36

MEYER, Wessel H., M.D., Chief of Staff, Veterans Affairs Central California Health Care System, Fresno, CA, p. A60

MEYERHOEFER, Todd, M.D., Vice President Medical Affairs, Cleveland Clinic Union Hospital, Dover, OH, p. A481

MEYERS, Audrey, FACHE, President and Chief Executive Officer, Valley Hospital, Ridgewood, NJ, p. A411

MEYERS, Betty, Chief Financial Officer, Crook County Medical Services District, Sundance, WY, p. A710

MEYERS, J Cullen, Chief Executive Officer, Pam Specialty Hospital Of Covington, Covington, LA, p. A266

MEYERS, Larry, Chief Information Officer, Wilson Memorial Hospital, Sidney, OH, p. A490

MEYERS, Mark S., M.D., Chief of Staff, Battle Mountain General Hospital, Battle Mountain, NV, p. A392

MEYERS, Russell, FACHE, President and Chief Executive Officer, Midland Memorial Hospital, TX, p. A624

MEYERS, William, Chief Information Officer, St. Luke's Hospital, Chesterfield, MO, p. A357

MEZA, Eduardo, M.D., Medical Director, Prairie St. John'S, Fargo, ND, p. A466

MEZA, Lourdes, Coordinator Human Resources, West Covina Medical Center, West Covina, CA, p. A95

MEZOFF, Adam, M.D., Vice President and Chief Medical Officer, Dayton Children's Hospital, Dayton, OH, p. A480

MHERABI, Nader, Senior Vice President and Vice Dean, Chief Information Officer, Rusk Institute At Nyu-Hjd, NY, p. A436

MIANO, Christena, Human Resources Director, Medical Center Of Trinity, Trinity, FL, p. A142

MICAN, Deborah, R.N., Chief Nursing Officer, Capital Health Medical Center-Hopewell, Pennington, NJ, p. A410

MICCOLI, Vincent
Executive Director, Kirby Forensic Psychiatric Center, New York (Includes All Hospitals Located Within The Five Boroughs), NY, p. A433
Executive Director, Manhattan Psychiatric Center-Ward's Island, New York (Includes All Hospitals Located Within The Five Boroughs), NY, p. A433

MICHAEL, Amy J, Chief Operating Officer, Sullivan County Memorial Hospital, Milan, MO, p. A364

MICHAEL, Elizabeth, R.N., MS, Vice President Patient Care Services and Chief Nursing Officer, Stillwater Medical Center, Stillwater, OK, p. A507

MICHAELS, Stephen T., M.D., Chief Operating Officer and Chief Medical Officer, Medstar St. Mary's Hospital, Leonardtown, MD, p. A292

MICHALEK, Debra, Chief Financial Officer, Fayette Regional Health System, Connersville, IN, p. A201

MICHALSKI, Carrie, President and Chief Executive Officer, Riverview Health, Crookston, MN, p. A330

MICHEL, Diane, Senior Vice President, Chief Nursing Officer, Children's Hospital, New Orleans, LA, p. A275

MICHEL, George J, Chief Operating Officer, Larkin Community Hospital, South Miami, FL, p. A139

MICHEL, Randall, M.D., Chief of Staff, Lompoc Valley Medical Center, Lompoc, CA, p. A65

MICHEL-OGBORN, Deborah, Chief Information Resource Management, Lake City Veterans Affairs Medical Center, FL, p. A123

MICHELE, Margorie, Chief Human Resources Officer, Penn Presbyterian Medical Center, Philadelphia, PA, p. A536

MICHELEN, Jeannith
Chief Implementation Officer, Nyc Health + Hospitals / Elmhurst, New York (Includes All Hospitals Located Within The Five Boroughs), NY, p. A435
Senior Associate Executive Director, Nyc Health + Hospitals / Lincoln, New York (Includes All Hospitals Located Within The Five Boroughs), NY, p. A436
Senior Associate Executive Director, Nyc Health + Hospitals / Queens, New York (Includes All Hospitals Located Within The Five Boroughs), NY, p. A436

MICHELL, Pamela W, R.N., Vice President, Chief Nursing Officer, Florida Hospital Ocala, Ocala, FL, p. A133

MICHELSON, Soad, M.D., Senior Medical Director, Clarity Child Guidance Center, San Antonio, TX, p. A632

MICHENER, Scott, M.D., Chief Medical Officer, Comanche County Memorial Hospital, Lawton, OK, p. A500

MICHL, Michelle, Director Human Resources, Mercy Medical Center Mount Shasta, Mount Shasta, CA, p. A74

MICKAL, Donald, M.D., Chief Medical Officer, Women's And Children's Hospital, Lafayette, LA, p. A272

MICKIEWICZ, Nanette, M.D., President, Dominican Hospital, Santa Cruz, CA, p. A88

MIDDENDORF, Bruce, M.D., Chief Medical Officer, St. Mary's Health Care System, Athens, GA, p. A145

MIDDLEBROOKS, Mark, M.D., Medical Director, Noland Hospital Birmingham, Birmingham, AL, p. A14

MIDDLETON, Jackie, Vice President Human Resources, Methodist Dallas Medical Center, Dallas, TX, p. A597

MIDDLETON, James, MSN, R.N., Chief Nursing Officer, Knox Community Hospital, Mount Vernon, OH, p. A487

MIDDLETON, Robert Eldon, MSN, R.N., III, Chief Nursing Officer, Gerald Champion Regional Medical Center, Alamogordo, NM, p. A415

MIDGETT, Steve, R.N., Chief Nursing Officer, Encompass Health Rehabilitation Hospital Of Sugar Land, Sugar Land, TX, p. A637

MIDKIFF, Stephen L., Chief Executive Officer, Lake Norman Regional Medical Center, Mooresville, NC, p. A457

MIDTLIEN, Tonia, Information Systems Support Specialist, Gundersen Boscobel Area Hospital And Clinics, Boscobel, WI, p. A690

MIEDLER, Michael, M.D., Chief Medical Officer, Continuing Care Hospital, Lexington, KY, p. A254

MIESNER, Gail, Chief Financial Officer, Memorial Hospital, Chester, IL, p. A176

MIGLIETTA, Steve, Chief Financial Officer, Winnie Palmer Hospital For Women And Babies, FL, p. A134

MIGOYA, Carlos A., President and Chief Executive Officer, Jackson South Community Hospital, FL, p. A130

MIHALAKAKOS, Paul, M.D., Chief of Staff, Aurora Medical Center - Manitowoc County, Two Rivers, WI, p. A704

MIHALJEVIC, Tomislav, M.D., President and Chief Executive Officer, Cleveland Clinic Children's Hospital, OH, p. A476

MIKELL, Evarista, Assistant Finance Officer, William S. Middleton Memorial Veterans Hospital, Madison, WI, p. A696

MIKHAIL, Ashraf, M.D., Medical Director, Brynn Marr Hospital, Jacksonville, NC, p. A455

MIKI, Nobuyuki, M.D., Vice President Medical Services and Chief Medical Officer, Kuakini Medical Center, Honolulu, HI, p. A164

MIKITARIAN, George, Jr, FACHE, President and Chief Executive Officer, Parrish Medical Center, Titusville, FL, p. A142

MIKITKA, Joseph, Vice President Human Resources, St. Luke's Sacred Heart Campus, Allentown, PA, p. A519

MIKKELSEN, Kallie, Vice President Nursing, Memorial Hospital Of Sweetwater County, Rock Springs, WY, p. A709

MIKKELSON, Tom, M.D.
Interim Chief Operating Officer, Touchette Regional Hospital, Centreville, IL, p. A175
Vice President Medical Affairs, Touchette Regional Hospital, Centreville, IL, p. A175

MIKLAVIC, Kirk
Director Human Resources, Bridgton Hospital, Bridgton, ME, p. A283
Director, Human Resources, Central Maine Medical Center, Lewiston, ME, p. A284

MIKLOS, Maggie, Director Human Resources, Northside Hospital, Saint Petersburg, FL, p. A138

MIKOS, Kathleen A, R.N., Vice President and Chief Nursing Officer, Ingalls Memorial Hospital, Harvey, IL, p. A185

MIKOS, Ken, Director Information Technology, Wilbarger General Hospital, Vernon, TX, p. A642

MIKULIC, Jeannie, Director Human Resources, Providence Portland Medical Center, Portland, OR, p. A516

MILAM, Wendy, Chief Nursing Officer, Healthsouth Rehabilitation Hospital Of Ocala, Ocala, FL, p. A133

MILAN, Isabel, R.N., Chief Nursing Officer, Women's And Children's Hospital, CA, p. A68

MILAND, Shelly
Chief Financial Officer, Texas Health Specialty Hospital, Fort Worth, TX, p. A605
Group Finance Officer, Texas Health Harris Methodist Hospital Cleburne, Cleburne, TX, p. A592
Group Financial Officer, Texas Health Harris Methodist Hospital Fort Worth, Fort Worth, TX, p. A605

MILANES, Carlos, Chief Executive Officer, Edgefield County Hospital, Edgefield, SC, p. A552

MILANO, Arthur D, Vice President Human Resources, Hillcrest Hospital, MA, p. A303

MILATOVICH, Natasha, Association Vice President Human Resources, Adventist Health White Memorial, Los Angeles, CA, p. A66

MILAZZO, John, Chief Financial Officer, River Region West Campus, MS, p. A354

MILBRANDT, David, M.D., Vice President Medical Affairs, Fairview Lakes Health Services, Wyoming, MN, p. A342

MILBURN, Sandra, Director Human Resources, Healthsouth Rehabilitation Hospital Of Memphis, Memphis, TN, p. A575

MILBURN, Sharon, Chief Nursing Officer, Summers County Arh Hospital, Hinton, WV, p. A683

MILES, Ben, President, Parkview North Hospital, IN, p. A204

MILES, Dana, Chief Nursing Officer and Chief Clinical Officer, Delta Memorial Hospital, Dumas-Desha County, AR, p. A41

MILES, John, Chief Financial Officer, Piedmont Newnan Hospital, Newnan, GA, p. A158

MILES, Karen, M.D., Medical Director, Strategic Behavioral Health - Raleigh, Garner, NC, p. A453

MILES, Kerry
Chief Information Officer, Providence St. Peter Hospital, Olympia, WA, p. A674
Site Director, Providence Centralia Hospital, Centralia, WA, p. A670

MILES, Lee Ann, Chief Financial Officer, Harrison County Community Hospital, Bethany, MO, p. A355

MILES, Paul V
Chief Operating Officer, Morgan County Arh Hospital, West Liberty, KY, p. A261
Vice President Administration, Whitesburg Arh Hospital, Whitesburg, KY, p. A261

MILETO, Dottie, Chief Nursing Officer, Heart Of Florida Regional Medical Center, Davenport, FL, p. A121

MILHALTSES, Dean, Chief Operating Officer, Nyc Health + Hospitals / Queens, New York (Includes All Hospitals Located Within The Five Boroughs), NY, p. A436

MILIAN, Tony, Chief Financial Officer, Palm Springs General Hospital, Hialeah, FL, p. A124

MILICEVIC, Heather, Director Human Resources, Western Reserve Hospital, Cuyahoga Falls, OH, p. A480

MILIUS, Hank A., Chief Executive Officer, Meridian Health Services, Muncie, IN, p. A212

MILLAN, Wilfredo Rabelo, Chief Operating Officer, Cardiovascular Center Of Puerto Rico And The Caribbean, San Juan, PR, p. A715

MILLARD, Kathleen, Acting Director Nursing, Kalamazoo Psychiatric Hospital, Kalamazoo, MI, p. A317

MILLEN, Peter S, Chief Medical Officer MHSATS, Community Behavioral Health Hospital - Rochester, Rochester, MN, p. A338

MILLER, Alicia, Director Human Resources, Aspen Valley Hospital, Aspen, CO, p. A96

MILLER, Andy, Chief Financial Officer, Memorial Hospital Jacksonville, Jacksonville, FL, p. A125

MILLER, Barbara, Manager Business Office, Regional General Hospital, Williston, FL, p. A144

MILLER, Bob
President, Aurora Lakeland Medical Center, Elkhorn, WI, p. A692
President, Aurora Memorial Hospital Of Burlington, Burlington, WI, p. A691

MILLER, Brent R, Manager Human Resources, Brown County Community Treatment Center, Green Bay, WI, p. A694

MILLER, Carol R, R.N., Chief Nursing Officer, Reynolds Memorial Hospital, Glen Dale, WV, p. A683

MILLER, Carrie, Director Human Resources, Promedica Defiance Regional Hospital, Defiance, OH, p. A481

MILLER, Chad J., President and Chief Executive Officer, Morrow County Hospital, Mount Gilead, OH, p. A487

MILLER, Chandra, Director of Nursing, John J. Pershing Veterans Affairs Medical Center, Poplar Bluff, MO, p. A366

MILLER, Che', M.D., Chief of Staff, Duncan Regional Hospital, Duncan, OK, p. A498

MILLER, Chris K., Chief Financial Officer, Highland Hospital, Charleston, WV, p. A682

MILLER, Christine
Chief Human Resources Management Services, Maine Veterans Affairs Medical Center, Augusta, ME, p. A282
General Counsel and Vice President Human Resources, Upmc Pinnacle Hanover, Hanover, PA, p. A526

MILLER, Clint, Chief Nursing Officer, Spooner Health, Spooner, WI, p. A703

MILLER, Connie, Vice President Human Resources, Overland Park Regional Medical Center, Overland Park, KS, p. A243

MILLER, Daniel, FACHE
President and Chief Executive Officer, Medical Center Of Aurora, CO, p. A96
President and Chief Executive Officer, South Campus, CO, p. A96
President and Chief Executive Officer, Spalding Rehabilitation Hospital, Aurora, CO, p. A96
Human Resources Business Partner, University Hospitals Parma Medical Center, Parma, OH, p. A489
Vice President Human Resources, University Hospitals Elyria Medical Center, Elyria, OH, p. A482

MILLER, David R., President, River Falls Area Hospital, River Falls, WI, p. A702

MILLER, Debra, Administrator, Crosbyton Clinic Hospital, Crosbyton, TX, p. A595

MILLER, Derek, Senior Vice President and Chief Financial Officer, Southeast Alabama Medical Center, Dothan, AL, p. A17

MILLER, Diane, Administrator, Peterson Healthcare And Rehabilitation Hospital, Wheeling, WV, p. A688

MILLER, Dillon D, M.D., Chief Medical Officer, Fannin Regional Hospital, Blue Ridge, GA, p. A148

MILLER, Dionne, Chief Operating Officer, Sutter Roseville Medical Center, Roseville, CA, p. A81

MILLER, Donald L, FACHE, Vice President, Operations, St. Luke's Hospital, Chesterfield, MO, p. A357

MILLER, Duane
Chief Financial Officer, Chi St. Luke's Health Memorial Livingston, Livingston, TX, p. A620
Chief Financial Officer, Chi St. Luke's Health Memorial Specialty Hospital, Lufkin, TX, p. A621
Chief Financial Officer, Integris Bass Meadowlake, OK, p. A498

MILLER, Dyrek, M.D., Chief Medical Staff, Vidant Duplin Hospital, Kenansville, NC, p. A455

MILLER, Elaine G, Director of Nursing, Oaklawn Psychiatric Center, Goshen, IN, p. A205

MILLER, Elizabeth, Director of Nursing, Harlan County Health System, Alma, NE, p. A381

MILLER, Esteban, Chief Medical Officer, Black River Memorial Hospital, Black River Falls, WI, p. A690

MILLER, Gary L
Regional Director Information Systems, Plymouth Medical Center, Plymouth, IN, p. A213
Senior Director Information Systems, Saint Joseph Health System, Mishawaka, IN, p. A211

MILLER, Gene, Interim Chief Executive Officer, Jellico Community Hospital, Jellico, TN, p. A571

MILLER, George, President and Chief Executive Officer, Loretto Hospital, Chicago, IL, p. A177

MILLER, Greg, Senior Vice President Operations, Uf Health Jacksonville, Jacksonville, FL, p. A126

MILLER, Hope, Director of Medical Records, Peterson Healthcare And Rehabilitation Hospital, Wheeling, WV, p. A688

MILLER, J D, M.D.
Chief Medical Officer, Hazard Arh Regional Medical Center, Hazard, KY, p. A253
Vice President Medical Affairs, Morgan County Arh Hospital, West Liberty, KY, p. A261
Vice President Medical Affairs, Tug Valley Arh Regional Medical Center, South Williamson, KY, p. A260

MILLER, James, Chief Financial Officer, Women's And Children's Hospital, Lafayette, LA, p. A272

MILLER, James L, Chief Financial Officer, Baptist Medical Center Yazoo, Yazoo City, MS, p. A354

MILLER, Jane E.
Director Human Resources, Avera Creighton Hospital, Creighton, NE, p. A383
Human Resources Officer, Avera Sacred Heart Hospital, Yankton, SD, p. A565

MILLER, Jason R., Chief Financial Officer, The Medical Center Of Southeast Texas, Port Arthur, TX, p. A629

MILLER, Jeff, M.D.
Chief of Staff, Parkview Wabash County Hospital, Wabash, IN, p. A216
Chief Operating Officer, Citizens Memorial Hospital, Bolivar, MO, p. A355

MILLER, Jon, Director Accounting and Information Services, Hancock Regional Hospital, Greenfield, IN, p. A205

MILLER, Joshua, Director Information Systems, Joint Township District Memorial Hospital, Saint Marys, OH, p. A490

MILLER, Joy, Chief Nursing Officer, Cornerstone Hospital Of Little Rock, Little Rock-Pulaski County, AR, p. A45

MILLER, Julie, Chief Operating Officer, Williamson Medical Center, Franklin, TN, p. A570

MILLER, Karen, Chief Financial Officer, San Juan Regional Medical Center Rehabilitation Hospital, NM, p. A417

MILLER, Kay J, R.N., MSN, Chief Nursing Officer, Uchealth Memorial Hospital North, CO, p. A98

MILLER, Keith, Chief Operating Officer, Daviess Community Hospital, Washington, IN, p. A216

MILLER, Ken, Chief Financial Officer, Beaufort Memorial Hospital, Beaufort, SC, p. A549

MILLER, Kevin
President, Chi Health Lakeside, Omaha, NE, p. A388
President, Chi Health Midlands, Papillion, NE, p. A389

MILLER, Kimberly J., FACHE, President and Chief Executive Officer, Beaver Dam Community Hospitals, Beaver Dam, WI, p. A690

MILLER, Kris, Senior Human Resources Business Partner, Spectrum Health Reed City Hospital, Reed City, MI, p. A321

MILLER, Krista, R.N., Chief Nursing Officer, Shriners Hospitals For Children-Philadelphia, Philadelphia, PA, p. A536

MILLER, Laurie, Administrative Assistant, Sakakawea Medical Center, Hazen, ND, p. A466

MILLER, Leanne R, Director Human Resources, Community Hospital, Mccook, NE, p. A386

MILLER, Lisa, Director Human Resources, Hendry Regional Medical Center, Clewiston, FL, p. A120

MILLER, Maria, Controller, Beaumont Hospital - Grosse Pointe, Grosse Pointe, MI, p. A315

MILLER, Mark, FACHE
Chief Operating Officer, Grand Strand Regional Medical Center, Myrtle Beach, SC, p. A556
Chief Financial Officer, Freeman Regional Health Services, Freeman, SD, p. A561
Director Information Systems, Perry County Memorial Hospital, Tell City, IN, p. A215

MILLER, Mark A., FACHE, Interim Chief Executive Officer, Harlan County Health System, Alma, NE, p. A381

MILLER, Mary, Vice President Finance and Business Development, Mt. Washington Pediatric Hospital, Baltimore, MD, p. A288

MILLER, Mary Beth, M.D., Chief of Staff, Cheyenne County Hospital, Saint Francis, KS, p. A245

MILLER, Mathew, M.D., Vice President and Chief Medical Officer, General Hospital, CA, p. A57

MILLER, Melissa, Director Human Resources, St. Elizabeth Hospital, Gonzales, LA, p. A268

MILLER, Michael J
Director Human Resources, Barnes-Jewish St. Peters Hospital, Saint Peters, MO, p. A370
Director Human Resources, Progress West Hospital, O'Fallon, MO, p. A365

MILLER, Michele A, R.N., MSN, Vice President, Acute and Nursing Services, University Behavioral Healthcare, Piscataway, NJ, p. A410

MILLER, Michelle, Chief Human Resources, Placentia-Linda Hospital, Placentia, CA, p. A78

MILLER, Nicole, Director Human Resources, Riverside Shore Memorial Hospital, Onancoke, VA, p. A663

MILLER, Patrick, Technology Coordinator, San Bernardino Mountains Community Hospital District, Lake Arrowhead, CA, p. A63

MILLER, Paul, Director of Operations, Sanford Chamberlain Medical Center, Chamberlain, SD, p. A560

MILLER, Peter S, Chief Financial Officer, North Vista Hospital, North Las Vegas, NV, p. A396

MILLER, Phil, Chief Information Officer, Unity Health Specialty Care, AR, p. A48

MILLER, Redonda G., M.D., President, Johns Hopkins Children's Center, MD, p. A287

MILLER, Richard, Administrator Finance, Banner Behavioral Health Center-Thunderbird Campus, AZ, p. A30

MILLER, Richard B., Ph.D., Vice President Hospital Affairs and Chief Financial Officer, University Hospital Of Brooklyn At Long Island College Hospital, NY, p. A437

MILLER, Rick
    Chief Financial Officer, District One Hospital, Faribault, MN, p. A331
    Director, Operations and Finance, District One Hospital, Faribault, MN, p. A331
    President and Chief Operating Officer, Nationwide Children's Hospital, Columbus, OH, p. A478

MILLER, Rod, Chief Information Technology, Community Hospital, Torrington, WY, p. A710

MILLER, Ryan, FACHE
    Administrator and Executive Director, Christus Southeast Texas Orthopedic Specialty Center, Beaumont, TX, p. A588
    Administrator, Christus Southeast Texas Hospital-St. Mary, TX, p. A588

MILLER, Sam, Chief Executive Officer, North Sunflower Medical Center, Ruleville, MS, p. A353

MILLER, Shane
    Chief Information Officer, Hshs St. Clare Memorial Hospital, Oconto Falls, WI, p. A700
    Chief Information Officer, Hshs St. Mary's Hospital Medical Center, Green Bay, WI, p. A694
    Chief Information Officer, Hshs St. Nicholas Hospital, Sheboygan, WI, p. A703
    Chief Information Officer, Hshs St. Vincent Hospital, Green Bay, WI, p. A694

MILLER, Stacy, Entity Human Resources Officer, Texas Health Presbyterian Hospital Dallas, Dallas, TX, p. A598

MILLER, Steve, Director Information Systems, Baptist Medical Center South, Montgomery, AL, p. A21

MILLER, Susan, Financial Administrator, Faulkton Area Medical Center, Faulkton, SD, p. A560

MILLER, Suzanne, R.N., MSN, Senior Director Patient Care Services and Nursing, St. Luke's Wood River Medical Center, Ketchum, ID, p. A170

MILLER, Tamara, FACHE, Chief Executive Officer and Administrator, Madison Regional Health System, Madison, SD, p. A561

MILLER, Ted, Vice President and Chief Financial Officer, Memorial Hospital And Health Care Center, Jasper, IN, p. A208

MILLER, Thomas, M.D., Medical Director, University Of Utah Health, Salt Lake City, UT, p. A651

MILLER, Valerie L, MSN, R.N., Director of Nursing, Major Hospital, Shelbyville, IN, p. A214

MILLER, Weston, M.D., Chief Medical Officer, Abbeville General Hospital, Abbeville, LA, p. A262

MILLER, William, Coordinator Management Information Systems, Livengrin Foundation, Bensalem, PA, p. A520

MILLER-BALFOUR, Pam, Director Human Resources, Socorro General Hospital, Socorro, NM, p. A420

MILLER-COLLETTE, Melody M, Director Human Resources, North Okaloosa Medical Center, Crestview, FL, p. A120

MILLICAN, Sharon, Associate Director, Patient Care Services, San Antonio Division, TX, p. A634

MILLIS, David, M.D., Clinical Director, Thomas B. Finan Center, Cumberland, MD, p. A291

MILLS, Amanda, Chief Nursing Officer, Mcleod Seacoast, SC, p. A555

MILLS, Aundrea, Chief Nursing Officer, Sovah Health-Danville, Danville, VA, p. A657

MILLS, Craig
    Chief Financial Officer, Heber Valley Medical Center, Heber City, UT, p. A647
    Vice President Human Resources, Peacehealth Sacred Heart Medical Center University District, Eugene, OR, p. A512

MILLS, Dennis, Chief Human Resources Officer, San Ramon Regional Medical Center, San Ramon, CA, p. A88

MILLS, Gene, Director Information Technology, Scenic Mountain Medical Center, Big Spring, TX, p. A589

MILLS, Jerry, Chief Human Resources Management Services, San Francisco Va Medical Center, San Francisco, CA, p. A86

MILLS, Jim, Regional Director Information Technology, Sutter General Hospital, CA, p. A82

MILLS, John, Chief Operating Officer, Cleveland Clinic Avon Hospital, Avon, OH, p. A471

MILLS, John C, Senior Vice President Operations, Cleveland Clinic Fairview Hospital, Cleveland, OH, p. A476

MILLS, Kalen M, Director Human Resources, Southern Coos Hospital And Health Center, Bandon, OR, p. A511

MILLS, Marianne, R.N., Chairperson, Stanton County Hospital, Johnson, KS, p. A237

MILLS, Scott, M.D., Vice President Medical Staff Administration and Chief Medical Officer, Mid Coast Hospital, Brunswick, ME, p. A283

MILLS, Sean
    Chief Financial Officer, Our Lady Of Lourdes Memorial Hospital, Inc., Binghamton, NY, p. A422
    Chief Financial Officer, Samaritan Medical Center, Watertown, NY, p. A445

MILLS, Tylie, Chief Executive Officer, Pike County Memorial Hospital, Louisiana, MO, p. A363

MILLS, Vicki L, Chief Financial Officer, Anderson County Hospital, Garnett, KS, p. A235

MILLS, William, M.D.
    Senior Vice President Quality and Professional Affairs, Bradford Regional Medical Center, Bradford, PA, p. A521
    Senior Vice President Quality and Professional Affairs, Olean General Hospital, Olean, NY, p. A439

MILLS-MATHEWS, Marcy, Director Human Resources, Palms West Hospital, Loxahatchee, FL, p. A128

MILLSAP, Debra, Director of Nursing, River Crest Hospital, San Angelo, TX, p. A632

MILLSAPS, Janet
    Chief Human Resources Officer, Harris Regional Hospital, Sylva, NC, p. A461
    Vice President Human Resources, Haywood Regional Medical Center, Clyde, NC, p. A450

MILLSAPS, Jarrett B., Jr, FACHE
    Chief Executive Officer, East Ridge Hospital, TN, p. A567
    Chief Executive Officer, Parkridge East Hospital, TN, p. A567

MILNE, C Dean, D.O., Medical Director, Complex Care Hospital At Tenaya, Las Vegas, NV, p. A394

MILNER, Mark W, Chief Nursing Officer, Ephraim Mcdowell Regional Medical Center, Danville, KY, p. A251

MILNER, Rene, Chief Medical Officer, Osceola Medical Center, Osceola, WI, p. A700

MILONE, Sheri, Chief Executive Officer and Administrator, Lovelace Women's Hospital, Albuquerque, NM, p. A415

MILOVICH, David, Vice President Human Resources, Saint Mary's Regional Medical Center, Reno, NV, p. A396

MILSTEIN, Marc E., Vice President Information Resources, University Of Texas Southwestern Medical Center - Zale Lipshy, TX, p. A598

MILSTIEN, Kim S., Chief Executive Officer, Ventura County Medical Center, Ventura, CA, p. A94

MILTON, Kerry K., R.N., Chief Nursing Officer, St. Tammany Parish Hospital, Covington, LA, p. A266

MILTON, Paul A, Executive Vice President and Chief Operating Officer, Ellis Hospital Health Center, NY, p. A442

MILTON, Paul A., President and Chief Executive Officer, Ellis Hospital Health Center, NY, p. A442

MILTON, S. Byron, M.D., Medical Director, Emory Rehabilitation Hospital, Atlanta, GA, p. A146

MILUS, Lori, R.N., MSN, Director of Nursing, Aurora Behavioral Health System West, Glendale, AZ, p. A30

MILVET, Robert W., Jr, Chief Executive Officer, Grant Memorial Hospital, Petersburg, WV, p. A686

MIMOSO, Michael, FACHE, President and Chief Executive Officer, Community Medical Center, Toms River, NJ, p. A412

MIMS, Staci, Chief Nursing Officer, Dorminy Medical Center, Fitzgerald, GA, p. A153

MIMS, Tammy, Chief Executive Officer, Jeff Davis Hospital, Hazlehurst, GA, p. A154

MINARD, Keith, Chief Information Officer, Chinese Hospital, San Francisco, CA, p. A85

MINCEY, Wallace D, Chief Executive Officer, Clinch Memorial Hospital, Homerville, GA, p. A155

MINDEN, Philip, Chief Executive Officer, Bartow Regional Medical Center, Bartow, FL, p. A117

MINEAR, Michael N.
    Senior Vice President and Chief Information Officer, Lehigh Valley Health Network Pediatrics, PA, p. A519
    Senior Vice President and Chief Information Officer, Lehigh Valley Hospital-Muhlenberg, Bethlehem, PA, p. A520

MINEAU, Francine, Chief Nursing Officer, Baton Rouge Behavioral Hospital, Baton Rouge, LA, p. A263

MINER, Bill, M.D., Chief of Staff, Huron Regional Medical Center, Huron, SD, p. A561

MINER, Edwina A, R.N., Chief Nursing Officer, Ennis Regional Medical Center, Ennis, TX, p. A603

MINER, Greg, Administrator, Siouxland Surgery Center, Dakota Dunes, SD, p. A560

MINER, John, Chief Financial Officer, Kindred Hospital Central Tampa, Tampa, FL, p. A141

MINGLE, Regina, Senior Vice President and Chief Leadership Officer, Penn Medicine Lancaster General Hospital, Lancaster, PA, p. A529

MINGS, William, M.D., Medical Director, Carl Albert Community Mental Health Center, Mcalester, OK, p. A501

MINGUS, Linda, Director Human Resources, Aurora Medical Center Of Oshkosh, Oshkosh, WI, p. A700

MINIER, Lori
    Chief Executive Officer, Benewah Community Hospital, Saint Maries, ID, p. A171
    Chief Financial Officer, Benewah Community Hospital, Saint Maries, ID, p. A171

MINIER, Mary, President, Indiana University Health White Memorial Hospital, Monticello, IN, p. A211

MINIOR, Devin, M.D., Chief Medical Officer, Banner Casa Grande Medical Center, Casa Grande, AZ, p. A28

MINISSALE, Joseph, President, Methodist Mckinney Hospital, Mckinney, TX, p. A623

MINKS, Michael H.
    Chief Information Officer VI, Dell Seton Medical Center At The University Of Texas, Austin, TX, p. A586
    Chief Information Officer VI, Seton Medical Center Austin, Austin, TX, p. A586
    Chief Information Officer, Seton Edgar B. Davis Hospital, Luling, TX, p. A622
    Chief Information Officer, Seton Northwest Hospital, Austin, TX, p. A586
    Chief Information Officer, Seton Shoal Creek Hospital, Austin, TX, p. A586

MINNICK, Paul E, R.N., MSN, Senior Vice President and Chief Operating Officer, Voorhees Pediatric Facility, NJ, p. A413

MINNICK, Peggy, R.N., Chief Executive Officer, Bhc Alhambra Hospital, Rosemead, CA, p. A81

MINNIS, Rosanne, Business Officer, Rochester Psychiatric Center, Rochester, NY, p. A441

MINON, Maria, M.D.
    Vice President Medical Affairs and Chief Medical Officer, Children's Hospital Of Orange County, Orange, CA, p. A76
    Vice President Medical Affairs and Chief Medical Officer, Choc Children's At Mission Hospital, Mission Viejo, CA, p. A72

MINOR, Amy, Chief Nursing Officer, Troy Regional Medical Center, Troy, AL, p. A23

MINOR, Athena, Chief Nursing Officer, Ohio County Hospital, Hartford, KY, p. A253

MINOR, Beverly, Chief Human Resources, Schleicher County Medical Center, Eldorado, TX, p. A603

MINOR, Blaine, M.D., Chief of Staff, Murray Medical Center, Chatsworth, GA, p. A150

MINSHEW, Tony L., Vice President, Patient Care Services, Conway Medical Center, Conway, SC, p. A552

MINSINGER, Linda, Vice President Hospital Division, Gifford Medical Center, Randolph, VT, p. A654

MINSKY, Bart R, Interim Vice President Human Resources, Fremont Medical Center, CA, p. A72

MINTEER, Laura, Chief Human Resource Officer, Meritus Medical Center, Hagerstown, MD, p. A292

MINTON, Tamra, R.N., MSN, Vice President Patient Care Services and Chief Nursing Officer, Upmc East, Monroeville, PA, p. A532

MINTONYE, Traci, Chief Financial Officer, River Hospital, Alexandria Bay, NY, p. A421

MINTZ, Michael, M.D., Chief Medical Officer, South Texas Surgical Hospital, Corpus Christi, TX, p. A594

MIRABELLA, Ilene, Director Human Resources, Vibra Hospital Of Southeastern Massachusetts, New Bedford, MA, p. A302

MIRANDA, Ada S, M.D., Medical Director, Hospital Metropolitano Dr. Susoni, Arecibo, PR, p. A712

MIRANDA, Casey D., Executive Vice President and Chief Operating Officer, Jackson County Memorial Hospital, Altus, OK, p. A495

MIRANDA, Ivette, Chief Executive Officer, Healthsouth Rehabilitation Hospital At Martin Health, Stuart, FL, p. A139

MIRANDA, Kim, Chief Financial Officer, St. Elizabeth Community Hospital, Red Bluff, CA, p. A79

MIRANDA, Kimberly
    Chief Financial Officer, Mercy Medical Center Mount Shasta, Mount Shasta, CA, p. A74
    Regional Vice President Finance and Chief Financial Officer, Mercy Medical Center Redding, Redding, CA, p. A79

MIRANDA, Lisa, Vice President Operations, University Medical Center, New Orleans, LA, p. A276

MIRANDA, Michael, Chief of Staff, Mercy Hospital Booneville, Booneville-Logan County, AR, p. A40

MIRANDA, Samuel, Jr, Chief Nursing Officer, Good Shepherd Specialty Hospital, Bethlehem, PA, p. A520

MIRANDA, Vicki, Vice President Human Resources, Dominican Hospital, Santa Cruz, CA, p. A88

MIRANDA, Victor Hernandez, M.D., Chief of Staff, Mennonite General Hospital, Aibonito, PR, p. A712

MIRZA, Irfan, Chief Financial Officer, Mercy Hospital - A Campus Of Plantation General Hospital, FL, p. A136

MIRZABEGIAN, Edward
Chief Executive Officer, La Palma Intercommunity Hospital, La Palma, CA, p. A63
Chief Executive Officer, West Anaheim Medical Center, Anaheim, CA, p. A50

MISHKIND, Steven, M.D., Chief of Staff, Desoto Memorial Hospital, Arcadia, FL, p. A117

MISHLER, Sheila, Chief Executive Officer, St. Vincent Stress Center, IN, p. A208

MISITI, Joseph, M.D., President Medical Staff, Medina Memorial Hospital, Medina, NY, p. A430

MISKIMEN, Theresa, M.D., Vice President Medical Services, University Behavioral Healthcare, Piscataway, NJ, p. A410

MISLAN, Tim, MS, Vice President and Chief Nurse Executive, Missouri Baptist Medical Center, Saint Louis, MO, p. A368

MISRA, Sahana, Acting Chief of Staff, Va Portland Healthcare System, Portland, OR, p. A517

MISSERITTI, Colomba, Director Human Resources, Rochester Psychiatric Center, Rochester, NY, p. A441

MITCHAM, Debbie, Chief Financial Officer, Northside Hospital, Atlanta, GA, p. A146

MITCHELL, Adonna, Director Fiscal Services, North Mississippi Medical Center-Eupora, Eupora, MS, p. A345

MITCHELL, Andrew J., President and Chief Executive Officer, Peconic Bay Medical Center, Riverhead, NY, p. A441

MITCHELL, Barbara
Director Human Resources, Oasis Behavioral Health - Chandler, Chandler, AZ, p. A28
Senior Vice President Marketing and Human Resources, Uw Medicine/Valley Medical Center, Renton, WA, p. A675

MITCHELL, Bridgett, Chief Clinical Officer, Advanced Specialty Hospital Of Toledo, Toledo, OH, p. A491

MITCHELL, Camelia, M.D., Medical Director, Texas Rehabilitation Hospital Of Arlington, Arlington, TX, p. A584

MITCHELL, Dave, Manager Information Services, Spectrum Health Gerber Memorial, Fremont, MI, p. A313

MITCHELL, David
Chief Executive Officer, Baptist Emergency Hospital - Hausman, TX, p. A632
Chief Executive Officer, Baptist Emergency Hospital - Overlook, TX, p. A632
Chief Executive Officer, Baptist Emergency Hospital - Westover Hills, TX, p. A632
Interim Chief Executive Officer, Baptist Emergency Hospital - Westover Hills, TX, p. A632

MITCHELL, Douglas W, Vice President and Chief Nursing Officer, West Virginia University Children's Hospital, WV, p. A685

MITCHELL, Elizabeth C, Chief Operating Officer, Specialty Hospital Of Meridian, Meridian, MS, p. A350

MITCHELL, Elizabeth C., Chief Executive Officer and Chief Operating Officer, Specialty Hospital Of Meridian, Meridian, MS, p. A350

MITCHELL, Errol, Chief Financial Officer, Integris Canadian Valley Hospital, Yukon, OK, p. A510

MITCHELL, Heath, Chief Operating Officer, Memorial Hospital, Seminole, TX, p. A635

MITCHELL, Ivan, Chief Operating Officer, Great Plains Health, North Platte, NE, p. A387

MITCHELL, Jack C., FACHE, Chief Executive Officer, Healthsouth Rehabilitation Hospital, Fayetteville-Washington County, AR, p. A41

MITCHELL, Jenifer, R.N., Director of Nursing Services, Mineral Community Hospital, Superior, MT, p. A379

MITCHELL, Jodie, Facility Financial Director, Sturgis Regional Hospital, Sturgis, SD, p. A564

MITCHELL, Joe J., Chief Executive Officer, Acadia General Hospital, Crowley, LA, p. A266

MITCHELL, Karen, Vice President Patient Care Services, Children's Hospital Of The King's Daughters, Norfolk, VA, p. A662

MITCHELL, Kathy, R.N.
Chief Nursing Officer, Doctors Hospital Of Sarasota, Sarasota, FL, p. A138
Chief Nursing Officer, Owensboro Health Muhlenberg Community Hospital, Greenville, KY, p. A252
Director Human Resources, Marshfield Medical Center - Rice Lake, Rice Lake, WI, p. A702

MITCHELL, Kent, Chief Financial Officer, Hamilton Memorial Hospital District, Mcleansboro, IL, p. A189

MITCHELL, Leah, R.N., Interim Chief Information Officer, Salem Health Rehabilitation Center, OR, p. A517

MITCHELL, Marsha, Director Human Resources, Fleming County Hospital, Flemingsburg, KY, p. A251

MITCHELL, Mary S, Chief Resource Management Services, Birmingham Veterans Affairs Medical Center, Birmingham, AL, p. A14

MITCHELL, Morris, Director Human Resources, Poplar Springs Hospital, Petersburg, VA, p. A663

MITCHELL, Naomi, Director Human Resources, Kentucky River Medical Center, Jackson, KY, p. A254

MITCHELL, Perry, M.D., Chief of Staff, Little Colorado Medical Center, Winslow, AZ, p. A38

MITCHELL, Rebekah, Chief Financial Officer, Madison County Health Care System, Winterset, IA, p. A231

MITCHELL, Rhonda K, Director Human Resources, Stonewall Jackson Memorial Hospital, Weston, WV, p. A688

MITCHELL, Richard R, Director Information Technology, Eagleville Hospital, Eagleville, PA, p. A524

MITCHELL, Sarah, Director Finance, Mary S Harper Geriatric Psychiatry Center, Tuscaloosa, AL, p. A24

MITCHELL, Scot, FACHE, Chief Executive Officer and Administrator, Cordova Community Medical Center, Cordova, AK, p. A26

MITCHELL, Steve, Chief Operating Officer, Memorial Medical Center, CA, p. A73

MITCHELL, Timothy, R.N.
Chief Nursing Officer, Complex Care Hospital At Ridgelake, Sarasota, FL, p. A138
Chief Financial Officer, Fairfield Memorial Hospital, Winnsboro, SC, p. A558

MITCHELL, Walton F., III, Director, Catawba Hospital, Catawba, VA, p. A656

MITCHELL, William, Chief Executive Officer and Administrator, Kindred Hospital Riverside, Perris, CA, p. A78

MITCHELL SANCHEZ, Lexi, D.O., Chief of Staff, Clay County Memorial Hospital, Henrietta, TX, p. A609

MITCHUM, Linda, Director of Nursing, William J. Mccord Adolescent Treatment Facility, Orangeburg, SC, p. A556

MITHUN, Robert, M.D., Physician in Chief, Kaiser Permanente San Francisco Medical Center, San Francisco, CA, p. A85

MITRICK, Joseph M., FACHE, President, Baptist Medical Center Beaches, Jacksonville Beach, FL, p. A126

MITRY, Norman F.
President and Chief Executive Officer, Heritage Valley Health System, Beaver, PA, p. A520
President and Chief Executive Officer, Sewickley Valley Hospital, (A Division Of Valley Medical Facilities), Sewickley, PA, p. A541

MITTAL, Vikrant, M.D., Chief Medical Officer, Danville State Hospital, Danville, PA, p. A523

MIX, Sherry, Chief Executive Officer and Administrator, The Neuromedical Center Rehabilitation Hospital, Baton Rouge, LA, p. A264

MIXON, Robin, Interim Chief Executive Officer, North Mississippi Medical Center-Eupora, Eupora, MS, p. A345

MIYAMOTO, Faye, Assistant Vice President Human Resources, Rehabilitation Hospital Of The Pacific, Honolulu, HI, p. A165

MIYASAWA, Patricia, CPA, Director Fiscal Service, Shriners Hospitals For Children-Honolulu, Honolulu, HI, p. A165

MIYAUCHI, Kimberly, R.N., Chief Nursing Officer, Kingman Regional Medical Center, Kingman, AZ, p. A30

MIZE, William D, Chief Operating Officer, Trousdale Medical Center, Hartsville, TN, p. A570

MIZELL, Philip L, M.D., Medical Director, The Bridgeway, North Little Rock-Pulaski County, AR, p. A47

MIZER, Alison, Chief Financial Officer, St. Anthony North Health Campus, Westminster, CO, p. A106

MIZIA, Robert, Director Information Systems and Chief Information Officer, Inspira Medical Center-Woodbury, Woodbury, NJ, p. A414

MIZONO, Gary, M.D., Physician-in-Chief, Kaiser Permanente San Rafael Medical Center, San Rafael, CA, p. A87

MLAWSKY, Karen, Senior Vice President and Chief Operations Officer, Tmc For Children, AZ, p. A38

MMEJE, Ikenna, Chief Operating Officer, Memorialcare, Long Beach Memorial Medical Center, Long Beach, CA, p. A65

MO, Lin H, M.P.H., President, Mount Sinai Beth Israel Brooklyn, NY, p. A434

MOAD, Sharon, Human Resources Director Health Information Management, Elkview General Hospital, Hobart, OK, p. A499

MOAK, Jennifer, Business Office Manager, Lawrence County Hospital, Monticello, MS, p. A351

MOAKLER, Thomas J., Chief Executive Officer, Houlton Regional Hospital, Houlton, ME, p. A284

MOATS, Susan K., R.N.
Vice President Patient Care Services and Chief Nursing Officer, The Heart Hospital Baylor Denton, Denton, TX, p. A599
Vice President Patient Care Services and Chief Nursing Officer, The Heart Hospital Baylor Plano, Plano, TX, p. A629

MOAWAD, Gerald, Chief Medical Officer, Bridgepoint Hospital Capitol Hill, Washington, DC, p. A115

MOCK, Presley, M.D., Chief of Staff, Texas Institute For Surgery At Texas Health Presbyterian Dallas, Dallas, TX, p. A598

MOE, Jonathan, Chief Operating Officer, Shenandoah Medical Center, Shenandoah, IA, p. A229

MOEEN, Farida, M.D., Chief Executive Officer, Doctors Hospital Parkway, TX, p. A614

MOELLER, Deborah A, R.N., MS, Interim Chief Nursing Officer, Baylor Scott & White Medical Center - Sunnyvale, Sunnyvale, TX, p. A638

MOEN, Belinda, R.N., MSN, Interim Director of Nursing, Mountrail County Medical Center, Stanley, ND, p. A468

MOEN, Daniel P., President, St. Francis Medical Center, Trenton, NJ, p. A413

MOEN, Larry, Chief Financial Officer, Coteau Des Prairies Hospital, Sisseton, SD, p. A564

MOFFA, Salvatore, M.D., Vice President, Medical Affairs and Chief Medical Officer, Robert Wood Johnson University Hospital Somerset, Somerville, NJ, p. A411

MOFFAT, Jeanne, Manager Information Technology, Keefe Memorial Hospital, Cheyenne Wells, CO, p. A97

MOFFAT, Jennifer, Staff Accountant, Regional West Garden County, Oshkosh, NE, p. A389

MOFFATT, Dan, Chief Information Officer, Sanford Bemidji Medical Center, Bemidji, MN, p. A328

MOFFET, Chris, Director Information Services, Bob Wilson Memorial Grant County Hospital, Ulysses, KS, p. A247

MOFFITT, Brenda L., Chief Nursing Officer, Memorial Health System, Abilene, KS, p. A232

MOFFITT SOD, Rhonda, Chief Nursing Officer, First Hospital Wyoming Valley, Kingston, PA, p. A528

MOGERMAN, Shauna, Chief Executive Officer, Roxbury Treatment Center, Shippensburg, PA, p. A541

MOGG, Cassie, Chief Financial Officer, Covenant Hospital Plainview, Plainview, TX, p. A628

MOHAMED, Antonia, Acting Chief Information Officer, Birmingham Veterans Affairs Medical Center, Birmingham, AL, p. A14

MOHAMMED, Ehtaisham, M.D., Chief Medical Officer, Ridgeview Sibley Medical Center, Arlington, MN, p. A327

MOHAN, Amit, President and Chief Executive Officer, Barlow Respiratory Hospital, Los Angeles, CA, p. A66

MOHAN, Rajesh, M.D., Chief Medical Officer, Monmouth Medical Center, Southern Campus, Lakewood, NJ, p. A406

MOHANDAS, Arjun, M.D., Chief of Staff, Seton Edgar B. Davis Hospital, Luling, TX, p. A622

MOHLER, Brittany, Director Human Resources, Essentia Health-Deer River, Deer River, MN, p. A330

MOHNK, Richard, Vice President Corporate Services, Bayhealth Medical Center, Milford Memorial Hospital, DE, p. A113

MOHNKERN, Pearl, Vice President and Director Human Resources, Christus St. Vincent Physicians Medical Center, NM, p. A419

MOHR, Amanda, Chief Nursing Officer, Greater Regional Medical Center, Creston, IA, p. A220

MOHR, Amy, Coordinator Human Resources, Forest Health Medical Center, Ypsilanti, MI, p. A326

MOHR, Angela, R.N., MS, Vice President Nursing and Chief Operating Officer, Ssm Health St. Anthony Hospital - Shawnee, Shawnee, OK, p. A506

MOHR, Catherine, R.N., MSN, Chief Nursing Officer, Guthrie Robert Packer Hospital, Sayre, PA, p. A540

MOHR, Liz, Assistant Chief Financial Officer, Mercy Health - Fairfield Hospital, Fairfield, OH, p. A482

MOHR, Steve
Senior Vice President Finance and Chief Financial Officer, Loma Linda University Behavioral Medicine Center, Redlands, CA, p. A80
Senior Vice President Finance and Chief Financial Officer, Loma Linda University Heart & Surgical Hospital, CA, p. A64

MOISAN, Terrence, M.D., Chief Executive Officer, Palos Health, Palos Heights, IL, p. A192

MOK, Michelle, Chief Financial Officer, Redlands Community Hospital, Redlands, CA, p. A80

MOKDESSI, Margot, Interim Chief Financial Officer, Vermilion Behavioral Health Systems South, LA, p. A271

MOKRY, Deborah, Chief Nurse Executive, St. Louis Psychiatric Rehabilitation Center, Saint Louis, MO, p. A369

MOL, Stacy E, CPA, Director Finance, Spencer Hospital, Spencer, IA, p. A230

MOLACEK, Shane, Chief Information Officer, Valley County Health System, Ord, NE, p. A389

MOLELUS, Elena, Manager Human Resources, Santa Barbara County Psychiatric Health Facility, Santa Barbara, CA, p. A88

MOLINA, Isabel, M.D., Chief Medical Officer, Lamb Healthcare Center, Littlefield, TX, p. A620

MOLINA, Luis F., Chief Executive Officer and Administrator, Community Hospital, Munster, IN, p. A212

MOLINA, Ricky, Director Marketing and Business Development, Rehabilitation Hospital Of Southern New Mexico, Las Cruces, NM, p. A418

MOLINARO, Frank L.
Chief Executive Officer, Abrazo Central Campus, Phoenix, AZ, p. A32
Chief Executive Officer, Abrazo Scottsdale Campus, Phoenix, AZ, p. A32

MOLITOR, Margie, FACHE, R.N., Chief Executive Officer, Hot Springs County Memorial Hospital, Thermopolis, WY, p. A710

MOLL, Ben, Assistant Chief Financial Officer, Nashoba Valley Medical Center, Ayer, MA, p. A295

MOLL, Eric, Chief Executive Officer, Mason General Hospital And Family Of Clinics, Shelton, WA, p. A677

MOLL, Gudrun, R.N., MSN, Chief Nursing Officer, San Antonio Regional Hospital, Upland, CA, p. A93

MOLL, Jeffrey, M.D., Medical Director, Clarion Psychiatric Center, Clarion, PA, p. A522

MOLL, Michael A., M.D., Chief Medical Officer and Chief of Staff, Spanish Peaks Regional Health Center, Walsenburg, CO, p. A106

MOLLER, Dan, M.D., Chief Medical Officer, Wk Bossier Health Center, LA, p. A279

MOLLER, Lynn, Chief Financial Officer, Weston County Health Services, Newcastle, WY, p. A709

MOLLOHAN, Joan, Vice President Human Resources, Ochsner Medical Center For Children, LA, p. A276

MOLLOY, Kevin
Senior Vice President and Chief Operating Officer, Mount Sinai Beth Israel Brooklyn, NY, p. A434
Senior Vice President and Chief Operating Officer, Mount Sinai West Hospital, NY, p. A434

MOLLOY, Laurel, Vice President Nursing and Rehab Services, Unc Lenoir Healthcare, Kinston, NC, p. A456

MOLLOY, Reuben D, Chief Information Officer, Governor Juan F. Luis Hospital, Christiansted, VI, p. A717

MOLMEN, David R, M.P.H.
Chief Executive Officer, Altru Hospital, ND, p. A466
Chief Executive Officer, Altru Rehabilitation Center, ND, p. A466

MOLMEN, David R., M.P.H., Chief Executive Officer, Altru Rehabilitation Center, ND, p. A466

MOLNAR, Becky, Director of Finance, Cleveland Clinic, Medina Hospital, Medina, OH, p. A486

MOLT, Brianna, Human Resources Director, Genoa Medical Facilities, Genoa, NE, p. A384

MOLYNEUX, Phyllis, Associate Administrator Human Resources and Education, Williamson Medical Center, Franklin, TN, p. A570

MOMEYER, Polly, Manager Human Resources, Lecom Health Millcreek Community Hospital, Erie, PA, p. A525

MONAHAN, Jane, Vice President Ministry, Spiritual Care and Human Resources, Monroe Clinic, Monroe, WI, p. A699

MONASTERIO, Eugene A, M.D., Medical Director, Children's Hospital Of Richmond At Vcu-Brook Road Campus, Richmond, VA, p. A664

MONCHER, Daniel J, Vice President and Chief Financial Officer, Firelands Regional Medical Center South Campus, OH, p. A490

MONCHER, Daniel J., Interim President and Chief Executive Officer, Firelands Regional Medical Center South Campus, OH, p. A490

MONCRIEF, William, ORH IT Client Executive, Oakland Regional Hospital, Southfield, MI, p. A323

MONCZEWSKI, Ted, Vice President Human Resources, St. Vincent Charity Medical Center, Cleveland, OH, p. A477

MONDA, Cam, D.O., Medical Director, Greenwood Regional Rehabilitation Hospital, Greenwood, SC, p. A554

MONETTE, Steven, Chief Financial Officer, Brattleboro Retreat, Brattleboro, VT, p. A653

MONEY, Lourene, R.N., Resource Chief Executive Officer, Kindred Hospital St. Louis-St. Anthony'S, MO, p. A368

MONGE, Candice, R.N., Chief Nurse Executive Officer, Marian Regional Medical Center, Santa Maria, CA, p. A89

MONGE, Jacqualyn
Director of Nursing, Ascension Eagle River Hospital, Eagle River, WI, p. A692
Director of Nursing, Howard Young Medical Center, Woodruff, WI, p. A706

MONGELL, Mitchell P., FACHE, Chief Executive Officer, Fort Walton Beach Medical Center, Fort Walton Beach, FL, p. A123

MONGER, Shelton, Director Information Technology, Wayne Healthcare, Greenville, OH, p. A483

MONIACI, Cathy, R.N., MS, Administrator, Shriners Hospitals For Children-Houston, Houston, TX, p. A613

MONJE, Mary Anne
Chief Financial Officer and Chief Operating Officer, Whittier Hospital Medical Center, Whittier, CA, p. A95
Chief Financial Officer, Ahmc Anaheim Regional Medical Center, Anaheim, CA, p. A50
Chief Operations Officer, Ahmc Anaheim Regional Medical Center, Anaheim, CA, p. A50

MONJESKY, Kimberly, Chief Executive Officer, Pikes Peak Regional Hospital, Woodland Park, CO, p. A106

MONKRES, Paula, Administrative Assistant and Director Human Resources, Nocona General Hospital, Nocona, TX, p. A626

MONROE, Ame, Director Human Resources, Rolling Plains Memorial Hospital, Sweetwater, TX, p. A638

MONROE, Lori, Director of Nursing, Winnebago Mental Health Institute, Winnebago, WI, p. A706

MONROE, Temple, Director Nursing Operations, Wilson Medical Center, Neodesha, KS, p. A241

MONROIG, Domingo, Executive Director, Castaner General Hospital, Castaner, PR, p. A712

MONROY-MILLER, Cherry, M.D., Acting Medical Director, Greystone Park Psychiatric Hospital, Morris Plains, NJ, p. A407

MONSANTO, Monte, Chief Information Systems, Russell County Hospital, Russell Springs, KY, p. A260

MONSRUD, Michele, Director Human Resources, Piedmont Walton Hospital, Monroe, GA, p. A157

MONTAGNESE, Robert A., President and Chief Executive Officer, Licking Memorial Hospital, Newark, OH, p. A488

MONTALBO, Tripp, Chief Executive Officer, Mainland Medical Center, TX, p. A643

MONTALVO, Cary L., Chief Executive Officer, Solara Hospital - Brownsville Campus, TX, p. A609

MONTALVO, Eladio, Chief Executive Officer, Fort Duncan Regional Medical Center, Eagle Pass, TX, p. A600

MONTALVO, Jose, M.D., Medical Director, Hospital Del Maestro, San Juan, PR, p. A715

MONTANA, Jennifer, Manager Human Resources, Community Memorial Hospital, Hamilton, NY, p. A427

MONTANA-RHODES, Lou, Vice President of Patient Care Services, Vidant Beaufort Hospital, Washington, NC, p. A462

MONTANIO, John, Chief Financial Officer, Longleaf Hospital, Alexandria, LA, p. A262

MONTANO, Maxine, R.N., Chief Nursing Officer, Rolling Plains Memorial Hospital, Sweetwater, TX, p. A638

MONTANO, Mayra, Director Information Systems, Hospital Metropolitano Dr. Susoni, Arecibo, PR, p. A712

MONTANTE, Carl, Director Information Systems and Information Technology, Shriners Hospitals For Children-Portland, Portland, OR, p. A516

MONTANYE, Richard, Director Information Systems, Hunt Regional Medical Center, Greenville, TX, p. A608

MONTANYE-IRELAND, Cherelle, Chief Administrative Officer, Peacehealth St. John Medical Center, Longview, WA, p. A673

MONTELONGO, Rick J., Chief Executive Officer, St. Mark's Medical Center, La Grange, TX, p. A618

MONTENEGRO, Diana, Director Human Resources, Baptist Health South Florida, South Miami Hospital, Miami, FL, p. A130

MONTER, Brian, MSN, R.N., President, University Hospitals Richmond Medical Center, OH, p. A477

MONTESI, Michael W, M.D., Chief of Staff, North Sunflower Medical Center, Ruleville, MS, p. A353

MONTESINO-KING, Becky, MS, R.N., MSN, Vice President and Chief Nursing Officer, Baptist Children's Hospital, FL, p. A129

MONTGOMERY, Brigett, Director Human Resource, Lawrence Memorial Hospital, Walnut Ridge-Lawrence County, AR, p. A49

MONTGOMERY, Daniel, Chief Financial Officer, Specialists Hospital - Shreveport, Shreveport, LA, p. A279

MONTGOMERY, James, Interim Chief Executive Officer, Bear River Valley Hospital, Tremonton, UT, p. A651

MONTGOMERY, Jennifer, FACHE, R.N.
President and Chief Executive Officer, Mclaren Port Huron, Port Huron, MI, p. A321
Chief Financial Officer, Washakie Medical Center, Worland, WY, p. A710

MONTGOMERY, Mark, M.D., Chief Medical Officer, Texas Health Hospital Clearfork, TX, p. A605

MONTGOMERY, Mary Jim, R.N., MSN, FACHE, Chief Operating Officer, Crisp Regional Hospital, Cordele, GA, p. A151

MONTGOMERY, Peggy, Director Medical Records, Arrowhead Behavioral Health Hospital, Maumee, OH, p. A486

MONTGOMERY, Roxie, Director of Nursing, Jane Todd Crawford Hospital, Greensburg, KY, p. A252

MONTGOMERY, Susan, Chief Nursing Officer, Asante Ashland Community Hospital, Ashland, OR, p. A511

MONTGOMERY, Tina, Chief Financial Officer, Sidney Health Center, Sidney, MT, p. A379

MONTMENY, Richard, Vice President Professional Services, On-Site Administrator, St. John's Pleasant Valley Hospital, Camarillo, CA, p. A53

MONTOIS, John D., Interim Chief Executive Officer, Highlands Regional Medical Center, Sebring, FL, p. A139

MONTOUR, Vina, Director Information Technology, U.S. Public Health Service Phoenix Indian Medical Center, Phoenix, AZ, p. A34

MONTOYA, Alfred, Director, Manchester Veterans Affairs Medical Center, Manchester, NH, p. A400

MONTOYA, Brooke, Director Human Resources, Lake Granbury Medical Center, Granbury, TX, p. A607

MONTOYA, Lillian, President and Chief Executive Officer, Christus St. Vincent Physicians Medical Center, NM, p. A419

MONTOYA, Lionel J., Chief Financial Officer, Spanish Peaks Regional Health Center, Walsenburg, CO, p. A106

MONZINGO, Ashley, Human Resources, Accounts Payable and Payroll, Tops Surgical Specialty Hospital, Houston, TX, p. A614

MONZON, Rogelio, Chief Financial Officer, Good Samaritan Hospital, Bakersfield, CA, p. A52

MOODY, Christy, R.N., Chief Nursing Officer, Carolina Pines Regional Medical Center, Hartsville, SC, p. A554

MOODY, Crystal R, Director Human Resources, Izard County Medical Center, Calico Rock-Logan County, AR, p. A40

MOODY, David, Vice President Human Resources, Salina Regional Health Center-Santa Fe Campus, KS, p. A245

MOODY, James, Chief Financial Officer, Donalsonville Hospital, Donalsonville, GA, p. A152

MOODY, Vicky, Director Human Resources, Houlton Regional Hospital, Houlton, ME, p. A284

MOON, Bob, Chief Financial Officer, Christus St. Vincent Physicians Medical Center, NM, p. A419

MOON, David, Jr, Director Information Systems, Lake City Community Hospital, Lake City, SC, p. A555

MOON, Diane, Chief Financial Officer, Fremont Medical Center, CA, p. A72

MOON, James, Chief Financial Officer, Pana Community Hospital, Pana, IL, p. A192

MOON, John, Associate Director, Veterans Affairs Eastern Kansas Health Care System-Dwight D. Eisenhower Veterans Affairs Medical Center, KS, p. A246

MOONEY, Claire Bradley, Vice President and Chief Nursing Officer, Jennersville Hospital, West Grove, PA, p. A544

MOONEY, Melissa, Director Human Resources, Mercy Rehabilitation Hospital Springfield, Springfield, MO, p. A370

MOONEY, Robert W, M.D., Medical Director, Willingway Hospital, Statesboro, GA, p. A161

MOONEY, Susan E., M.D., MS, President and Chief Executive Officer, Alice Peck Day Memorial Hospital, Lebanon, NH, p. A399

MOORE, Amy, Human Resources, Hamilton Hospital, Olney, TX, p. A626

MOORE, Ben, III, President and Chief Executive Officer, River Hospital, Alexandria Bay, NY, p. A421

MOORE, Betty, Business Manager, North Mississippi Medical Center-Iuka, Iuka, MS, p. A347

MOORE, Bill, Chief Human Resources, El Centro Regional Medical Center, El Centro, CA, p. A57

MOORE, Brandon, FACHE, Administrator and Chief Executive Officer, Park Place Surgical Hospital, Lafayette, LA, p. A271

MOORE, Brett, CPA, Assistant Administrator Finance, Sutter Amador Hospital, Jackson, CA, p. A62

MOORE, C Christy, FACHE, Chief Financial Officer, The King's Daughters Hospital, MS, p. A346

MOORE, Carrie, Director Human Resources, Meadowbrook Rehabilitation Hospital, Gardner, KS, p. A235

MOORE, Cecelia B, CPA, Associate Vice Chancellor Finance, Vanderbilt Psychiatric Hospital, TN, p. A578

MOORE, Christie, Director Human Resources, Encompass Health Rehabilitation Hospital Of The Mid-Cities, Bedford, TX, p. A588

MOORE, Christy
Chief Nursing Officer, Medical Center Barbour, Eufaula, AL, p. A17
Interim Chief Executive Officer, Medical Center Barbour, Eufaula, AL, p. A17

MOORE, Dana, Chief Information Officer, Children's Hospital Of Colorado At Memorial, CO, p. A96

MOORE, Deborah, Director Human Resources, Walter P. Reuther Psychiatric Hospital, Westland, MI, p. A326

MOORE, Diane C., Chief Financial Officer, Memorial Medical Center, Port Lavaca, TX, p. A629

MOORE, Edward H., President and Chief Executive Officer, Harrington Hospital, Southbridge, MA, p. A304

MOORE, Elizabeth, Chief Operating Officer, Silver Hill Hospital, New Canaan, CT, p. A109

MOORE, Emily, Director Human Resources and Information Technology, Haskell Memorial Hospital, Haskell, TX, p. A609

MOORE, Ethel L, M.D., Director of Medical Affairs, Fort Belknap Service Unit, Harlem, MT, p. A376

MOORE, Harold, Chief Information Technology Officer, Spartanburg Medical Center, Spartanburg, SC, p. A557

MOORE, Jason H, Vice President and Chief Operating Officer, Tallahassee Memorial Healthcare, Tallahassee, FL, p. A140

MOORE, Jeffrey Steve, Chief Financial Officer, Fort Walton Beach Medical Center, Fort Walton Beach, FL, p. A123

MOORE, Jody Dewen, District Director Human Resources, Kindred Hospital-San Diego, San Diego, CA, p. A83

MOORE, John, M.D.
Medical Director, Granite County Medical Center, Philipsburg, MT, p. A378
Vice President Medical Affairs, Ssm Health Depaul Hospital - St. Louis, Bridgeton, MO, p. A356
President, South Lake Hospital, Clermont, FL, p. A120

MOORE, John G, Vice President and Chief Financial Officer, Carolinas Healthcare System Union, Monroe, NC, p. A457

MOORE, Kandi, Administrator, Specialists Hospital - Shreveport, Shreveport, LA, p. A279

MOORE, Karen, Vice President Information Technology and Chief Information Officer, Southern Regional Medical Center, Riverdale, GA, p. A159

MOORE, Karen O., FACHE, Senior Vice President Operations and Chief Nursing Officer, Lawrence General Hospital, Lawrence, MA, p. A300

MOORE, Keri, Vice President Human Resources and Support Services, Rocky Mountain Hospital For Children, CO, p. A99

MOORE, Kermit, R.N., Chief Operating Officer and Chief Nursing Officer, Nemaha County Hospital, Auburn, NE, p. A381

MOORE, Kyna, R.N.
Chief Nursing Officer, Pocahontas Memorial Hospital, Buckeye, WV, p. A681
Director of Nursing, Bath Community Hospital, Hot Springs, VA, p. A660

MOORE, Leigh, Administrative Assistant Human Resources, H. C. Watkins Memorial Hospital, Quitman, MS, p. A352

MOORE, Linda, Manager Human Resources, Seymour Hospital, Seymour, TX, p. A635

MOORE, Margaret, Director Business Office, Sabine County Hospital, Hemphill, TX, p. A609

MOORE, Matthew, Director of Financial Reporting, Effingham Hospital, Springfield, GA, p. A161

MOORE, Melinda, Director Human Resources, Multicare Deaconess Hospital, Spokane, WA, p. A678

MOORE, Michael, Director Information Systems, Troy Regional Medical Center, Troy, AL, p. A23

MOORE, Mike, President and Chief Operating Officer, Jane Phillips Medical Center, Bartlesville, OK, p. A496

MOORE, Nelda, Director Data Processing, Memorial Hospital And Manor, Bainbridge, GA, p. A148

MOORE, Patricia J, Director Human Resource, Valley Behavioral Health System, Barling, AR, p. A39

MOORE, Paul, R.N.
Chief Clinical Officer, Mercy Rehabilitation Hospital Springfield, Springfield, MO, p. A370
Chief Information Officer, Connecticut Mental Health Center, New Haven, CT, p. A109

MOORE, Paula, R.N., Chief Clinical Officer, Hugh Chatham Memorial Hospital, Elkin, NC, p. A452

MOORE, Randy, Chief Information Officer, Banner Lassen Medical Center, Susanville, CA, p. A91

MOORE, Rick
Chief Information Officer, Bethesda Butler Hospital, OH, p. A474
Chief Information Officer, Good Samaritan Hospital, Cincinnati, OH, p. A475

MOORE, Robin A., Chief Human Resources Officer, Concord Hospital, Concord, NH, p. A398

MOORE, Ronald E, R.N., MSN, Vice President Professional Practice and Chief Nursing Officer, General Hospital, WV, p. A682

MOORE, Samuel, Chief Financial Officer, University Of Kansas Health System St. Francis Campus, Topeka, KS, p. A246

MOORE, Sandee, Chief Operating Officer, Eastern Idaho Regional Medical Center, Idaho Falls, ID, p. A169

MOORE, Saunya, Chief Financial Officer, Parkside Psychiatric Hospital And Clinic, Tulsa, OK, p. A508

MOORE, Shari, Chief Executive Officer, Methodist Rehabilitation Hospital, Dallas, TX, p. A597

MOORE, Steve, Chief Financial Officer, Southern Tennessee Regional Health System-Sewanee, TN, p. A581

MOORE, Susan, MS, R.N., Chief Nursing Officer, Gothenburg Health, Gothenburg, NE, p. A384

MOORE, Sylvia, Vice President and Chief Operating Officer, Southeast Hospital, Cape Girardeau, MO, p. A357

MOORE, Tim
Chief Accounting Officer and Vice President Ancillary Services and Finance, Blessing Hospital, IL, p. A194
Vice President Finance, Illini Community Hospital, Pittsfield, IL, p. A193

MOORE, Vernon, Senior Vice President Chief Business and Finance, Ut Health North Campus Tyler, Tyler, TX, p. A641

MOORE, VonDa, Administrator, Mercy Hospital Berryville, Berryville-Carroll County, AR, p. A39

MOORE, Warren E., FACHE, President and Chief Executive Officer, Children's Specialized Hospital, NJ, p. A408

MOORE, Wayne, Interim Administrator, Christus Southeast Texas Jasper Memorial, Jasper, TX, p. A616

MOORE, William, Chief Information Officer, Parrish Medical Center, Titusville, FL, p. A142

MOORE-CONNELLY, Marci, M.D., Vice President Chief Medical Officer, Memorial Hospital Of Carbondale, Carbondale, IL, p. A175

MOORE-HARDY, Cynthia, FACHE, President and Chief Executive Officer, Tripoint Medical Center, OH, p. A479

MOORE-JONES, Debra, Chief Executive Officer, Parkside Psychiatric Hospital And Clinic, Tulsa, OK, p. A508

MOOREHOUSE, Brett, FACHE
Interim Chief Executive Officer and Chief Operating Officer, Ranken Jordan Pediatric Bridge Hospital, Maryland Heights, MO, p. A364
Vice President and Chief Operating Officer, Ranken Jordan Pediatric Bridge Hospital, Maryland Heights, MO, p. A364

MOORER, Thad, Chief Information Officer, Eastside Psychiatric Hospital, Tallahassee, FL, p. A140

MOORHEAD, David, M.D., Chief Medical Officer, Winter Park Memorial Hospital, FL, p. A134

MOORMAN, Gary L., D.O., Chief Medical Officer and Senior Vice President Medical Affairs, Promedica Monroe Regional Hospital, Monroe, MI, p. A319

MORA, Debbie, Director, Southwest General Hospital, San Antonio, TX, p. A634

MORACA, Lynn, Director Human Resources, Cleveland Clinic Akron General Lodi Hospital, Lodi, OH, p. A485

MORAHAN, John, Vice President Finance, St. Joseph Hospital, Bethpage, NY, p. A422

MORAHAN, John R, President and Chief Executive Officer, Penn State Health St. Joseph - Downtown Campus, PA, p. A539

MORAHAN, John R., President and Chief Executive Officer, Penn State Health St. Joseph - Downtown Campus, PA, p. A539

MORALES, Autumn, Chief Medical Staff Officer, Clarinda Regional Health Center, Clarinda, IA, p. A219

MORALES, Daniza
Chief Information Officer, Hospital Menonita De Cayey, Cayey, PR, p. A713
Manager Information System, Mennonite General Hospital, Aibonito, PR, p. A712

MORALES, Elsie, Chief Financial Officer, Hospital Universitario Dr. Ramon Ruiz Arnau, Bayamon, PR, p. A712

MORALES, Joel, Chief Financial Officer, Fort Duncan Regional Medical Center, Eagle Pass, TX, p. A600

MORALES, John R, Chief Financial Officer, John H. Stroger Jr. Hospital Of Cook County, Chicago, IL, p. A177

MORALES, Kathryn
Director of Finance, Hampshire Memorial Hospital, Romney, WV, p. A686
Director of Finance, War Memorial Hospital, Berkeley Springs, WV, p. A681

MORALES, Kristin, Chief Operating Officer, Harrington Hospital, Southbridge, MA, p. A304

MORALES, Marilyn, Chief Executive Officer, Hospital Buen Samaritano, Aguadilla, PR, p. A711

MORALES, Trish, Director Human Resources, Lakewood Ranch Medical Center, Bradenton, FL, p. A118

MORAN, Alina, Chief Executive Officer, Nyc Health + Hospitals / Metropolitan, New York (Includes All Hospitals Located Within The Five Boroughs), NY, p. A436

MORAN, Debbie, Executive Director, Carl Albert Community Mental Health Center, Mcalester, OK, p. A501

MORAN, Mary, M.D., Pediatrician In Chief, St. Christopher's Hospital For Children, Philadelphia, PA, p. A536

MORAN, Michael Francis., President and Chief Administrative Officer, Baystate Wing Hospital, Palmer, MA, p. A303

MORAN, Timothy M., Chief Executive Officer, Glenn Medical Center, Willows, CA, p. A95

MORANDEIRA, Ana, Director Marketing, San Juan Capestrano Hospital, San Juan, PR, p. A716

MORASKO, Jerome
Chief Executive Officer, Bucyrus Hospital, Bucyrus, OH, p. A473
President and Chief Executive Officer, Avita Ontario Hospital, Ontario, OH, p. A488
President and Chief Executive Officer, Galion Hospital, Galion, OH, p. A483

MORASKO, Robert A., Chief Executive Officer, Heart Of The Rockies Regional Medical Center, Salida, CO, p. A105

MORAVICK, Donna, R.N., MSN, Executive Director, Southside Hospital, Bay Shore, NY, p. A422

MORDACH, John P, Senior Vice President and Chief Financial Officer, Rush Children's Hospital, IL, p. A179

MORDECAI, Steve, Director Human Resources, Griffin Hospital, Derby, CT, p. A107

MOREFIELD, Terri, Deputy Chief Human Resources Division, Bassett Army Community Hospital, Fort Wainwright, AK, p. A26

MOREH, Swenda
Interim Chief Executive Officer, Bridgepoint Hospital National Harbor, Washington, DC, p. A115
Vice President and Chief Operating Officer, Bridgepoint Hospital National Harbor, Washington, DC, p. A115

MOREIN, Sandy, Chief Nursing Officer, Acadian Medical Center, LA, p. A280

MORELAND, John, M.D., Chief Medical Officer, Marcus Daly Memorial Hospital, Hamilton, MT, p. A376

MORELAND, Tresha, MS, Regional Vice President Human Resources, Dameron Hospital, Stockton, CA, p. A90

MORELL, Ixel, Chief Operating Officer, Sierra Vista Hospital, Sacramento, CA, p. A82

MORELLI, Gerald, Director Human Resources, Philadelphia Veterans Affairs Medical Center, Philadelphia, PA, p. A536

MORENO, Debbie, R.N., Chief Nursing Officer, Lodi Memorial Hospital West, CA, p. A64

MORENO, Jorge, Director Information Technology Operations, Canyon Vista Medical Center, Sierra Vista, AZ, p. A36

MORENO, Robin
Chief Financial Officer, North Texas State Hospital, Wichita Falls Campus, Wichita Falls, TX, p. A644
Financial Officer, North Texas State Hospital, Vernon, TX, p. A642

MORENO, Sandra, Chief Nursing Officer, Orange County Global Medical Center, Inc., Santa Ana, CA, p. A88

MORETTE, Joseph M, Executive Vice President, Methodist Rehabilitation Center, Jackson, MS, p. A348

MOREY, Scott David, Chief Nursing Officer, Abrazo West Campus, Goodyear, AZ, p. A30

MORGAN, Bradley, Vice President of Operations, The Heart Hospital Baylor Denton, Denton, TX, p. A599

MORGAN, Charlene, Chief Nursing Officer, Henderson County Community Hospital, Lexington, TN, p. A573

MORGAN, David, Vice President and Chief Financial Officer, Bristol Bay Area Health Corporation, Dillingham, AK, p. A26

MORGAN, Dennis P, Chief of Staff, Baptist Memorial Hospital-North Mississippi, Oxford, MS, p. A351

MORGAN, Derek
Vice President Human Resources, Kettering Behavioral Medical Center, OH, p. A487
Vice President Human Resources, Kettering Medical Center, Kettering, OH, p. A484

MORGAN, Eric, Chief Executive Officer, Prattville Baptist Hospital, Prattville, AL, p. A22

MORGAN, James, M.D., Chief Medical Officer, Memorial Hospital Of Converse County, Douglas, WY, p. A708

MORGAN, Janelle, Interim Director of Nursing, Howard County Medical Center, Saint Paul, NE, p. A390

MORGAN, Jeff, Director Information Systems, Northeastern Nevada Regional Hospital, Elko, NV, p. A392

MORGAN, Jeffrey H., Vice President Finance and Chief Financial Officer, Tlc Health Network - Lake Shore Hospital, NY, p. A425

MORGAN, John, R.N., Chief Executive Officer, Jackson Parish Hospital, Jonesboro, LA, p. A269

MORGAN, Kelly C., President and Chief Executive Officer, Mercy Medical Center, Roseburg, OR, p. A517

MORGAN, Lois, R.N., MSN, Vice President and Chief Nursing Officer, Gibson General Hospital, Princeton, IN, p. A213

MORGAN, Loretta Y, Director Human Resources, Connally Memorial Medical Center, Floresville, TX, p. A603

MORGAN, Lori J., M.D., President and Chief Executive Officer, Huntington Memorial Hospital, Pasadena, CA, p. A78

MORGAN, Mace, Director Information Systems, Minden Medical Center, Minden, LA, p. A274

MORGAN, MacGregor, R.N., Chief Executive Officer, Curahealth Hospital Stoughton, Stoughton, MA, p. A305

MORGAN, Marguerite J., Administrator, Florida State Hospital, Chattahoochee, FL, p. A119

MORGAN, Mark E., Medical Center Director, Jack C. Montgomery Veterans Affairs Medical Center, Muskogee, OK, p. A501

MORGAN, Matthew, Associate Administrator, Hillcrest Hospital - South, Tulsa, OK, p. A508

MORGAN, Michael, Interim Chief Executive Officer, Huntsville Memorial Hospital, Huntsville, TX, p. A615

MORGAN, Nyle, Chief Information Officer, Sheridan Memorial Hospital, Sheridan, WY, p. A709

MORGAN, Rose, MS, R.N., Vice President Patient Care Services, Princeton Community Hospital, Princeton, WV, p. A686

MORGAN, Shawn, Finance Officer, Northern Navajo Medical Center, Shiprock, NM, p. A420

MORGAN, Susan, Director of Nursing Services, Prairie Community Hospital, Terry, MT, p. A379

MORGAN, Teresa
Assistant Vice President Human Resources, Shannon Medical Center- St. John's Campus, TX, p. A632
Chief Financial Officer, Mcgehee Hospital, Mcgehee-Desha County, AR, p. A46

MORGAN-FINE, Richard, IT Director, Clarinda Regional Health Center, Clarinda, IA, p. A219

MORGESE, Vincent, M.D., Executive Vice President, Chief Operating Officer and Chief Medical Officer, Queen Of The Valley Medical Center, Napa, CA, p. A74

MORIN, Robert J., Vice President Finance and Chief Financial Officer, Sturgis Hospital, Sturgis, MI, p. A324

MORIN-SCRIBNER, Nicole, Director Human Resources, St. Mary's Regional Medical Center, Lewiston, ME, p. A284

MORISCO, Antonietta, M.D., Medical Director, Chairman Anesthesiology, Jamaica Hospital Medical Center, New York (Includes All Hospitals Located Within The Five Boroughs), NY, p. A432

MORITZ, Mary, Administrator Human Resources, Humboldt County Memorial Hospital, Humboldt, IA, p. A224

MORK, David L., Jr
Chief Executive Officer, Roosevelt Warm Springs Rehabilitation And Specialty Hospitals - Ltac, Warm Springs, GA, p. A162
Chief Executive Officer, Roosevelt Warm Springs Rehabilitation Hospital - Rehab, Warm Springs, GA, p. A162

MORKRID, Shirley, Chief Nursing Officer, Liberty Medical Center, Chester, MT, p. A374

MORLOCK, Paul J, FACHE, Vice President Human Resources and Occupational Health, Children's Hospital Of The King's Daughters, Norfolk, VA, p. A662

MORON, David, M.D., Clinical Director, South Texas Health Care System, TX, p. A608

MORONY, David, Chief Financial Officer, Casa Colina Hospital And Health Systems, Pomona, CA, p. A78

MORQUECHO, Adam, Director Information Technology, Huntington Beach Hospital, Huntington Beach, CA, p. A62

MORREALE, Daniel
Chief Information Officer, Hunterdon Medical Center, Flemington, NJ, p. A405
Vice President and Chief Information Officer, Kingsbrook Jewish Medical Center, New York (Includes All Hospitals Located Within The Five Boroughs), NY, p. A433

MORREALE, Gene, President and Chief Executive Officer, Oneida Healthcare, Oneida, NY, p. A439

MORRELL, Dan, Manager Information Systems, Sierra Vista Hospital, Truth Or Consequences, NM, p. A420

MORRELL, Jeffrey F., Chief Executive Officer, Intermountain Hospital, Boise, ID, p. A167

MORRICAL, Michael, Chief Executive Officer, Mckenzie Regional Hospital, Mckenzie, TN, p. A574

MORRIONE, Thomas, Medical Director, New England Rehabilitation Hospital Of Portland, Portland, ME, p. A285

MORRIS, Alexander, Corporate Director Human Resources, Fort Washington Medical Center, Oxen Hill, MD, p. A293

MORRIS, Barbara, R.N., Chief Nursing Officer, Pam Rehabilitation Hospital Of Beaumont, Beaumont, TX, p. A588

MORRIS, Christi, Director of Nursing, Bayside Community Hospital, Anahuac, TX, p. A583

MORRIS, Christopher
Director Human Resources, Ascension Southeast Wisconsin Hospital - Elmbrook Campus, Brookfield, WI, p. A690
Senior Director, Human Resources, Wheaton Franciscan Healthcare - St. Joseph'S, Milwaukee, WI, p. A699

MORRIS, Clayton, Medical Director, Griffin Memorial Hospital, Norman, OK, p. A502

MORRIS, David, Chief Executive Officer, Denver Springs, Englewood, CO, p. A100

MORRIS, Debbie M, Director Human Resources, Marcus Daly Memorial Hospital, Hamilton, MT, p. A376

MORRIS, Debra D., R.N., MSN, Chief Nursing Officer, Great Plains Regional Medical Center, Elk City, OK, p. A498

MORRIS, Dennis, Area Finance Officer, Kaiser Permanente Richmond Medical Center, CA, p. A76

MORRIS, Donald, Vice President Human Resources, Hillcrest Medical Center, Tulsa, OK, p. A508

MORRIS, Douglas
Chief Financial Officer, Elmwood Healthcare Center At The Springs, Green Springs, OH, p. A483
Chief Financial Officer, Vibra Hospital Of Northwestern Indiana, Crown Point, IN, p. A202
Chief Financial Officer, Vibra Hospital Of Southeastern Michigan, Llc, Lincoln Park, MI, p. A318

MORRIS, Janet, Director Human Resources, Healthsouth Lakeview Rehabilitation Hospital, Elizabethtown, KY, p. A251

MORRIS, Janice, Accountant, Crossridge Community Hospital, Wynne-Cross County, AR, p. A49

MORRIS, Jarrett L
Controller and Chief Information Officer, Carolinas Healthcare System Lincoln, Lincolnton, NC, p. A456
Controller, Carolinas Healthcare System Lincoln, Lincolnton, NC, p. A456

MORRIS, Jerry
Administrator, Higgins General Hospital, Bremen, GA, p. A148
Administrator, Tanner Medical Center/East Alabama, Wedowee, AL, p. A24

MORRIS, Jim
Vice President Finance, Baptist Health La Grange, La Grange, KY, p. A254
Vice President Finance, Baptist Health Louisville, Louisville, KY, p. A256

MORRIS, Jonathan B, M.D.
Senior Vice President and Chief Information Officer, Wellstar Cobb Hospital, Austell, GA, p. A148
Senior Vice President and Chief Information Officer, Wellstar Kennestone Hospital, Marietta, GA, p. A157

MORRIS, Lisa, Vice President Human Resources, Swedish Medical Center, Englewood, CO, p. A100

MORRIS, Luke P
Assistant Vice President Talent, American Fork Hospital, American Fork, UT, p. A646
Assistant Vice President Talent, Utah Valley Hospital, Provo, UT, p. A649

MORRIS, Marsha, Manager Information Services, Fairview Park Hospital, Dublin, GA, p. A153

MORRIS, Mary, Chief Financial Officer, Purcell Municipal Hospital, Purcell, OK, p. A506

MORRIS, Nerissa E., Senior Vice President and Chief Human Resource Officer, Children's Hospital, OH, p. A474

MORRIS, Philip, Chief Operating Officer, West Houston Medical Center, Houston, TX, p. A614

MORRIS, R Randall., Administrator, West Carroll Memorial Hospital, Oak Grove, LA, p. A277

MORRIS, Rosanna, R.N., President Royal Oak Hospital, Beaumont Children's Hospital, MI, p. A322

MORRIS, Scott, Vice President Information Systems, Eskenazi Health, Indianapolis, IN, p. A206

MORRIS, Tony, Business Manager, Mental Health Institute, Cherokee, IA, p. A219

MORRIS, Will, Director Information Technology, Panola Medical Center, Batesville, MS, p. A343

MORRISON, Christopher, Chief Executive Officer, Ancora Psychiatric Hospital, Hammonton, NJ, p. A405

MORRISON, Deane, Chief Information Officer, Concord Hospital, Concord, NH, p. A398

MORRISON, Dereck, Assistant Administrator, Bryan W. Whitfield Memorial Hospital, Demopolis, AL, p. A16

MORRISON, Devin
Director Administration, Naval Hospital Pensacola, Pensacola, FL, p. A136
Director for Administration, Naval Hospital Pensacola, Pensacola, FL, p. A136

MORRISON, Dianne, Director Human Resources, Mizell Memorial Hospital, Opp, AL, p. A22

MORRISON, Greta M., Assistant Chief Nursing Officer, Russell County Medical Center, Lebanon, VA, p. A660

MORRISON, J. E., M.D., M.P.H., Chief Medical Officer, Baylor Scott & White Medical Center - Hillcrest, Waco, TX, p. A642

MORRISON, Kathy E, Executive Director Human Resources, St. Catherine Hospital, Garden City, KS, p. A235

MORRISON, Kevin, Chief Financial Officer, Dickenson Community Hospital, Clintwood, VA, p. A657

MORRISON, Maureen, Vice President, Finance, Advocate Trinity Hospital, Chicago, IL, p. A176

MORRISON, Michael, Chief Financial Officer, Tristar Skyline Madison Campus, TN, p. A577

MORRISON, Sarah, President and Chief Executive Officer, Shepherd Center, Atlanta, GA, p. A147

MORRISSETT, Barbara, Vice President Human Resources, St. Mary's Medical Center, San Francisco, CA, p. A86

MORRISSETTE, Daniel, Chief Financial Officer, Stanford Health Care, Palo Alto, CA, p. A77

MORRISSEY, Moira, Chief Operating Officer and General Counsel, Four Winds Hospital, Katonah, NY, p. A428

MORRISSEY, Una E, R.N., MSN, Senior Vice President Operations, Chief Operating Officer and Chief Nursing Officer, New York Community Hospital, New York (Includes All Hospitals Located Within The Five Boroughs), NY, p. A434

MORROW, Charles, M.D., Chief Medical Officer, Spartanburg Medical Center, Spartanburg, SC, p. A557

MORROW, Ginger, Executive Vice President Human Resources, Christus Good Shepherd Medical Center, TX, p. A622

MORROW, Jennifer, Director Human Resources, San Joaquin Valley Rehabilitation Hospital, Fresno, CA, p. A59

MORROW, Laurie, Executive Director Human Resources, Washington Regional Medical Center, Fayetteville-Washington County, AR, p. A42

MORROW, Pat, Director Human Resources, Walker Baptist Medical Center, Jasper, AL, p. A20

MORROW, Randy, Vice President and Chief Operating Officer, Boone Hospital Center, Columbia, MO, p. A358

MORROW, Sarah, Vice President Human Resources, Capital Region Medical Center, Jefferson City, MO, p. A360

MORROW, Shawn, Administrator, Heber Valley Medical Center, Heber City, UT, p. A647

MORROW, W. Robert, M.D., Executive Vice President and Chief Medical Officer, Children's Medical Center Dallas, Dallas, TX, p. A596

MORSCHAUSER, Roberta, Administrator, Brown County Community Treatment Center, Green Bay, WI, p. A694

MORSE, Craig, Chief Financial Officer, Carlsbad Medical Center, Carlsbad, NM, p. A416

MORSE, Douglas E., Chief Executive Officer, Hansen Family Hospital, Iowa Falls, IA, p. A225

MORSE, Jason, Director Information Technology, Cumberland Healthcare, Cumberland, WI, p. A691

MORSTAD, Joan, Director Information Systems, Coliseum Center For Behavioral Health, GA, p. A156

MORTENSEN, Lorrie, MSN, R.N., Director, Patient Care, Floyd Valley Healthcare, Le Mars, IA, p. A225

MORTENSEN, Shane
Chief Financial Officer, San Luis Valley Health Conejos County Hospital, La Jara, CO, p. A102
Chief Financial Officer, San Luis Valley Health, Alamosa, CO, p. A96

MORTENSON, June, R.N., Director of Nursing, Power County Hospital District, American Falls, ID, p. A167

MORTINSEN, Roy, M.D., Chief of Staff, Sanford Vermillion Medical Center, Vermillion, SD, p. A564

MORTON, David, M.D., Clinical Director, West Central Georgia Regional Hospital, Columbus, GA, p. A151

MORTON, Leslie, Manager Human Resources, Riverview Regional Medical Center, Gadsden, AL, p. A18

MORTON, Lucas
Regional Chief Financial Officer, Osf Heart Of Mary Medical Center, Urbana, IL, p. A197
Regional Chief Financial Officer, Osf Sacred Heart Medical Center, Danville, IL, p. A180

MORTON, Robert, M.D., Medical Director, Rolling Hills Hospital, Ada, OK, p. A495

MORTON, Stephanie, Chief Information Officer, Children's Hospital At Providence, AK, p. A25

MORTON, Steve, M.D., Chief Medical Officer, Continuecare Hospital At Baptist Health Corbin, Corbin, KY, p. A250

MORTON ROWE, Laura, Director of Human Resources, Providence Saint John's Health Center, Santa Monica, CA, p. A89

MORTOZA, Angela, Chief Executive Officer, Dallas County Hospital, Perry, IA, p. A228

MOSBY, Charmaine T, Area Director Health Information Management, Promise Hospital Baton Rouge - Main Campus, Baton Rouge, LA, p. A264

MOSCA, Philip, M.D., President, Medical Staff, Integris Southwest Medical Center, Oklahoma City, OK, p. A503

MOSCATO, Mary K., FACHE, President, Hebrew Rehabilitation Center, Roslindale, MA, p. A303

MOSCHKAU, Don, Senior Director Human Resources, University Of Minnesota Masonic Children's Hospital, MN, p. A335

MOSCOSO, Ricardo, M.D., Medical Director, University Hospital, San Juan, PR, p. A716

MOSEL, Lindy, Director of Nursing, Memorial Community Health, Aurora, NE, p. A381

MOSELY, Chisty, Director Information Management, Saint Simons By-The-Sea Hospital, Saint Simons Island, GA, p. A159

MOSER, Cindy, Director Human Resources, Allegheny Valley Hospital, Natrona Heights, PA, p. A532

MOSER, Joseph, M.D., Chief Medical Officer, University Of Maryland Charles Regional Medical Center, La Plata, MD, p. A292

MOSER, Kevin, Vice President of Operations, Baptist Health Madisonville, Madisonville, KY, p. A257

MOSER, Neal, M.D., Medical Director, Healthsouth Northern Kentucky Rehabilitation Hospital, Edgewood, KY, p. A251

MOSESIAN, Robert, Controller, Healthsouth Bakersfield Rehabilitation Hospital, Bakersfield, CA, p. A52

MOSHER, Guy W, III
Manager Information Systems, Finger Lakes Hospital, Geneva, NY, p. A426
Manager Information Systems, Soldiers And Sailors Memorial Hospital Of Yates County, Penn Yan, NY, p. A440

MOSHIER, John, Director Human Resources, Clara Barton Hospital, Hoisington, KS, p. A236

MOSHIRPUR, Jasmin, M.D.
Chief Medical Officer, Nyc Health + Hospitals / Queens, New York (Includes All Hospitals Located Within The Five Boroughs), NY, p. A436
Dean and Medical Director, Nyc Health + Hospitals / Elmhurst, New York (Includes All Hospitals Located Within The Five Boroughs), NY, p. A435

MOSHOFSKY, Bill, M.D., Chief of Staff, Peacehealth Sacred Heart Medical Center University District, Eugene, OR, p. A512

MOSIER, Dawn, Director Human Resources, Encompass Health Rehabilitation Institute Of Tucson, Tucson, AZ, p. A37

MOSIER, John, D.O., Chief of Staff, Herington Municipal Hospital, Herington, KS, p. A236

MOSKOWITZ, Samuel E., President, Medstar Franklin Square Medical Center, Baltimore, MD, p. A288

MOSLEY, J. Christopher., Chief Executive Officer, Cartersville Medical Center, Cartersville, GA, p. A149

MOSLEY, Tonja
Chief Financial Officer, Heart Of Florida Regional Medical Center, Davenport, FL, p. A121
Chief Financial Officer, Wellington Regional Medical Center, Wellington, FL, p. A143

MOSMEYER, Kathleen C, Director Human Resources, Citizens Medical Center, Victoria, TX, p. A642

MOSS, Austin, Vice President Human Resources, Jennie Stuart Medical Center, Hopkinsville, KY, p. A253

MOSS, Barry, Chief Executive Officer, Merit Health Central, Jackson, MS, p. A348

MOSS, Bradley, Administrator, Unity Psychiatric Care-Huntsville, Huntsville, AL, p. A19

MOSS, C Renee, M.D., Chief Medical Officer, Coastal Virginia Rehabilitation, Newport News, VA, p. A662

MOSS, Jennifer, MS, R.N., Chief Clinical Officer, Kirby Medical Center, Monticello, IL, p. A190

MOSS, Keith A, Vice President & Chief Medical Informatics Officers, Riverside Medical Center, Kankakee, IL, p. A187

MOSS, Misty, Director Business Administration, Logansport State Hospital, Logansport, IN, p. A210

MOSS, Ray, Vice President and Chief Information Officer, Henry Mayo Newhall Hospital, Valencia, CA, p. A93

MOSS, Shelby, Human Resource Officer, Sheridan County Health Complex, Hoxie, KS, p. A237

MOSS, Stuart, Chief Financial Officer, Kessler Marlton Rehabilitation, Marlton, NJ, p. A407

MOSS, Tyler, Chief Financial Officer, Milford Valley Memorial Hospital, Milford, UT, p. A647

MOST, Kevin, D.O., Vice President Medical Affairs, Behavioral Health Center, IL, p. A198

MOSTOFI, Ann R, MSN, R.N., Vice President Patient Care and Chief Nursing Officer, Eisenhower Medical Center, Rancho Mirage, CA, p. A79

MOTAKEF, Shahin, FACHE
President, Baylor Scott And White Continuing Care Hospital, Temple, TX, p. A638
President, Mclane Children's Hospital Scott & White, TX, p. A638

MOTEJZIK, Thomas, Director Information Systems, Carlsbad Medical Center, Carlsbad, NM, p. A416

MOTONAGA, Gregg, M.D., Chief of Staff, Central Peninsula Hospital, Soldotna, AK, p. A27

MOTT, Daman, MSN, Chief Nursing Officer, Doctors Hospital Of Laredo, Laredo, TX, p. A619

MOTT, Joseph, Chief Executive Officer, Intermountain Medical Center, Murray, UT, p. A648

MOTT, William, Chief Operating Officer, St. John Macomb-Oakland Hospital, Warren Campus, MI, p. A325

MOTTE, Michael J., Chief Executive Officer, St. Alexius Hospital - Forest Park Campus, MO, p. A369

MOUGHAN, Jennifer L, Chief Human Resources Officer, Our Lady Of Lourdes Medical Center, Camden, NJ, p. A403

MOUISSET, Rena B, Director Human Resources and Contract Compliance, St. Martin Hospital, Breaux Bridge, LA, p. A265

MOULTON, Susan, Director Health Information Management, Spring Harbor Hospital, Westbrook, ME, p. A286

MOUNIE, Mike, Director Finance, Sentara Obici Hospital, Suffolk, VA, p. A667

MOUNTAIN, J Michael, Chief Financial Officer, Rivervalley Behavioral Health Hospital, Owensboro, KY, p. A259

MOUSA, Ayman, R.N., Ph.D., Chief Executive Officer, Pacifica Hospital Of The Valley, Los Angeles, CA, p. A69

MOUSA, Cindy, Director Human Resources, Touro Rehabilitation Center, LA, p. A276

MOUSTAKAKIS, John, Senior Vice President Information Systems and Chief Information Officer, Midhudson Regional Hospital Of Westchester Medical Center, NY, p. A445

MOVSESIAN, Gregory, M.D., Acting Chief of Staff, Aleda E. Lutz Veterans Affairs Medical Center, Saginaw, MI, p. A322

MOWAN, Chris, Chief Executive Officer, Medical City Children's Hospital, TX, p. A597

MOYA, Linda, Director Human Resources, Mesilla Valley Hospital, Las Cruces, NM, p. A418

MOYER, Dale, Vice President Information Systems, Evangelical Community Hospital, Lewisburg, PA, p. A530

MOYER, Debra, R.N.
Chief Nurse Executive, Unitypoint Health-Iowa Lutheran Hospital, Des Moines, IA, p. A221
Chief Nursing Executive and Vice President Nursing Services, Younker Memorial Rehabilitation Center, IA, p. A221

MOYER, Douglas J., President, Sentara Rmh Medical Center, Harrisonburg, VA, p. A659

MOYER, Karen W, R.N., Senior Vice President and Chief Nursing Officer, Miami Heart Campus At Mount Sinai Medical Center, FL, p. A131

MOYER, William, President, St Luke's Hospital - Allentown Campus, PA, p. A521

MRAMOR, Joann, Director Human Resources, Seven Rivers Regional Medical Center, Crystal River, FL, p. A120

MUCARIA, Jaclyn, President, New York-Presbyterian Queens, New York (Includes All Hospitals Located Within The Five Boroughs), NY, p. A435

MUCK, Erin, Vice President, Clinical Nursing, Crawford County Memorial Hospital, Denison, IA, p. A221

MUDEN, Todd, Section Head Information Management, Mayo Clinic Health System - Northland In Barron, Barron, WI, p. A690

MUDRY, Janel, Chief Operating Officer, Washington Health System Greene, Waynesburg, PA, p. A543

MUELLER, Arthur, Director Management Information Systems, Cuero Community Hospital, Cuero, TX, p. A595

MUELLER, Charles, M.D., Chief of Staff, Texas County Memorial Hospital, Houston, MO, p. A360

MUELLER, Donald, Vice President and CEO, T. C. Thompson Children's Hospital, TN, p. A567

MUELLER, Karen, R.N., Chief Nursing Officer, Mount Desert Island Hospital, Bar Harbor, ME, p. A282

MUELLER, Michael E, Chief Financial Officer, Health Central Hospital, Ocoee, FL, p. A133

MUELLER, Paul, Chief Financial Officer, Sparta Community Hospital, Sparta, IL, p. A196

MUELLER, Paul A., Chief Executive Officer, Hospital Division, Rogers Memorial Hospital-West Allis, WI, p. A700

MUGGLI, David D., FACHE, Chief Executive Officer, Select Specialty Hospital-Cincinnati, Cincinnati, OH, p. A475

MUHAMMAD, Mark, Manager Human Resources, Michael E. Debakey Veterans Affairs Medical Center, Houston, TX, p. A612

MUHS, David, Chief Financial Officer, Henry County Health Center, Mount Pleasant, IA, p. A226

MUILENBURG, Jeff, Chief of Staff, Memorial Community Health, Aurora, NE, p. A381

MUIR, Brian, Chief of Staff, Minidoka Memorial Hospital, Rupert, ID, p. A171

MULDER, Doris, Vice President Nursing, Beloit Health System, Beloit, WI, p. A690

MULDER, Steven, M.D., President and Chief Executive Officer, Hutchinson Health, Hutchinson, MN, p. A333

MULDERIG, Marsha L., R.N., MSN, Chief Nursing Officer, Crisp Regional Hospital, Cordele, GA, p. A151

MULDOON, Sean R, M.D.
Chief Medical Officer, Kindred Hospital New Jersey - Wayne, NJ, p. A404
Senior Vice President and Chief Medical Officer-Kindred Healthcare, Hospital Division, Kindred Hospital Northland, Kansas City, MO, p. A361

MULIS, Becky, Director of Health Information Management Systems, Four County Counseling Center, Logansport, IN, p. A210

MULKEY, Peter, Chief Executive Officer, Clinch Valley Medical Center, Richlands, VA, p. A664

MULLEN, Thomas R., President and Chief Executive Officer, Mercy Medical Center, Baltimore, MD, p. A288

MULLENAX, Paul, Business Manager, Wyoming State Hospital, Evanston, WY, p. A708

MULLENDER, Monica, Director of Nursing, Osborne County Memorial Hospital, Osborne, KS, p. A243

MULLENS, Allen, M.D., Chief Medical Staff, Norton Community Hospital, Norton, VA, p. A663

MULLER, Donna L., Interim Chief Financial Officer, Upmc Pinnacle Hanover, Hanover, PA, p. A526

MULLER, Lynn, Chief Financial Officer, North Metro Medical Center, Jacksonville-Pulaski County, AR, p. A44

MULLER, Oz, Director Human Resources, Porter Adventist Hospital, Denver, CO, p. A99

MULLERY, Barbara M, Vice President Administration, Robert Wood Johnson University Hospital Rahway, Rahway, NJ, p. A411

MULLIGAN, Marie, R.N., MSN, Vice President Nursing, John T. Mather Memorial Hospital, Port Jefferson, NY, p. A440

MULLINAX, Bradley, Chief Administrative Officer, Saint Thomas Dekalb Hospital, Smithville, TN, p. A580

MULLINGS, Donna, Director of Nursing, Assumption Community Hospital, Napoleonville, LA, p. A274

MULLINS, Bandy, M.D., Chief of Staff, Summersville Regional Medical Center, Summersville, WV, p. A687

MULLINS, Brad, Director Information Technology, Gove County Medical Center, Quinter, KS, p. A244

MULLINS, Bryan, Chief Operating Officer, Johnston Memorial Hospital, Abingdon, VA, p. A655

MULLINS, Cindy, Director Information Technology, Saint Mary's Regional Medical Center, Reno, NV, p. A396

MULLINS, Dustin
Chief Human Resources, Bayne-Jones Army Community Hospital, Fort Polk, LA, p. A267
Chief Resource Management, Bayne-Jones Army Community Hospital, Fort Polk, LA, p. A267

MULLINS, Erin, D.O., Chief Medical Staff, Dickenson Community Hospital, Clintwood, VA, p. A657

MULLINS, Michelle, Chief Information Officer, Oklahoma Heart Hospital, Oklahoma City, OK, p. A504

MULLIS, Jeffrey
Interim Chief Financial Officer, Bayfront Health Port Charlotte, Port Charlotte, FL, p. A137
Interim Chief Financial Officer, Piedmont Walton Hospital, Monroe, GA, p. A157

MULROONEY, JoAnn M, R.N., Chief Operating Officer, Trinity Medical Center West, OH, p. A491

MULTACH, Mark, M.D., Chief Medical Officer, Sinai Children's Hospital, IL, p. A178

MULTACK, Richard, D.O., Vice President Medical Management, Advocate South Suburban Hospital, Hazel Crest, IL, p. A185

MULVEHILL, Mitchell, Group Financial Officer, Texas Health Harris Methodist Hospital Southlake, Southlake, TX, p. A636

MULVEY, Lee, Human Resource Officer, Texas Health Springwood, TX, p. A588

MUMFORD, Stephen, Chief Operating Officer, Baton Rouge General Medical Center-Bluebonnet, LA, p. A263

MUMOLIE, Gina
Senior Vice President and Chief Nurse Executive, Inspira Medical Center-Woodbury, Woodbury, NJ, p. A414
Senior Vice President Hospital Administration, Capital Health Regional Medical Center, Trenton, NJ, p. A413

MUMPOWER, Rebecca, Director Marketing, Mesilla Valley Hospital, Las Cruces, NM, p. A418

MUNA, Esther L., FACHE, Chief Executive Officer, Commonwealth Health Center, Saipan, MP, p. A711

MUNCHEL, Bryan, Senior Vice President and Chief Information Officer, Pam Specialty Hospital Of Covington, Covington, LA, p. A266

MUNFORD, Thedosia, Senior Vice President and Chief Nursing Officer, Providence Hospital, Washington, DC, p. A116

MUNGER, Richard, Administrator, Mount Grant General Hospital, Hawthorne, NV, p. A393

MUNGOVAN, Sandy, Chief Information Officer, Harbor-Ucla Medical Center, Torrance, CA, p. A91

MUNHOLLAND, Cleta
Administrator, Louisiana Extended Care Hospital West Monroe, West Monroe, LA, p. A281
Administrator, Specialty Hospital, Monroe, LA, p. A274

MUNIR, Amjad, M.D., Medical Director, Healthsouth Chattanooga Rehabilitation Hospital, Chattanooga, TN, p. A567

MUNLEY, Bill, Administrator, Shriners Hospitals For Children-Greenville, Greenville, SC, p. A554

MUNOZ, Alejandro, M.D., Chief Medical Officer, Cedar Crest Hospital And Residential Treatment Center, Belton, TX, p. A589

MUNOZ, Astro, Executive Director, First Hospital Panamericano, Cidra, PR, p. A713

MUNOZ, Thalia H., R.N., MS, Chief Executive Officer, Starr County Memorial Hospital, Rio Grande City, TX, p. A630

MUNSHI, Imtiaz A, M.D., Chief of Staff, Richard L. Roudebush Veterans Affairs Medical Center, Indianapolis, IN, p. A207

MUNSON, Bill, Vice President and Chief Financial Officer, Boulder Community Foothills Hospital, CO, p. A96

MUNSON, Jennifer, Chief Financial Officer, Three Rivers Hospital, Brewster, WA, p. A670

MUNSON, John, Vice President and Chief Financial Officer, St. Anthony Regional Hospital, Carroll, IA, p. A218

MUNSON, Kris, Director Human Resources, Arbour H. R. I. Hospital, Brookline, MA, p. A298

MUNTEFERING, Denise, Vice President Patient Care Services, Avera St. Benedict Health Center, Parkston, SD, p. A562

MUNTZ, Dana M., Chief Executive Officer, St. Vincent Salem Hospital, Salem, IN, p. A214

MUNTZ, Tim, President and Chief Executive Officer, St. Margaret's Hospital, Spring Valley, IL, p. A196

MUNYAN, Lori, Director, Human Resources, Healthsouth Rehabilitation Hospital Of Toms River, Toms River, NJ, p. A412

MURANSKY, Ed, Owner, Surgical Hospital At Southwoods, Youngstown, OH, p. A494

MURCHISON, Sandra, Director Medical Records, Coosa Valley Medical Center, Sylacauga, AL, p. A23

MURDAUGH, Laura, Finance Director, William J. Mccord Adolescent Treatment Facility, Orangeburg, SC, p. A556

MURDOCH, William, M.D., Medical Director, Loma Linda University Behavioral Medicine Center, Redlands, CA, p. A80

MURDOCK, Guy, Vice President Human Resources, Healthbridge Children's Hospital Of Houston, Houston, TX, p. A611

MURDOCK, Holly, Human Resources Coordinator, Kindred Hospital Rome, Rome, GA, p. A159

MURDOCK, Mark, FACHE, Director, Chillicothe Veterans Affairs Medical Center, Chillicothe, OH, p. A474

MURDOCK-LANGAN, Patricia, M.D.
Chief Medical Officer, Chi Health Lakeside, Omaha, NE, p. A388
Chief Medical Officer, Chi Health Midlands, Papillion, NE, p. A389

MURDY, James B, Chief Financial Officer, Belmont Community Hospital, Bellaire, OH, p. A472

MURILLO, Jeremias, M.D., Chief Medical Officer, Children's Hospital Of New Jersey, NJ, p. A408

MURIN, William J, Chief Human Resources Officer, Uc San Diego Shiley Eye Institute, CA, p. A84

MURO, Deborah, Chief Information Officer, El Camino Hospital Los Gatos, CA, p. A74

MURPHREE, Shari, Chief Executive Officer, Willow Crest Hospital, Miami, OK, p. A501

MURPHY, Brian, Senior Director Admissions and Referral Services, Hebrew Rehabilitation Center, Roslindale, MA, p. A303

MURPHY, Bruce, M.D., President and Chief Executive Officer, Arkansas Heart Hospital, Little Rock-Pulaski County, AR, p. A44

MURPHY, Charles J, Associate Vice President Human Resources, Golisano Children's Hospital, NY, p. A441

MURPHY, Christine, MS, Chief Operating Officer, Cypress Grove Behavioral Health, Bastrop, LA, p. A263

MURPHY, Colleen, M.D., Chief of Staff, Clay County Hospital, Flora, IL, p. A183

MURPHY, Dee, Vice President Human Resources, Southwest General Health Center, Middleburg Heights, OH, p. A487

MURPHY, Elizabeth A, R.N., FACHE, Vice President for Patient Care Services, Mercy Health Rockford, MI, p. A314

MURPHY, Evelyn, R.N., Chief Nursing Officer, St. Mary's Sacred Heart Hospital, Lavonia, GA, p. A156

MURPHY, J Patrick, Chief Financial Officer, North Baldwin Infirmary, Bay Minette, AL, p. A14

MURPHY, James M., M.D., Chief Medical Officer Regional Development and Outpatient Services, New London Hospital, New London, NH, p. A400

MURPHY, John B, M.D., Vice President Medical Affairs and Chief Medical Officer, Hasbro Children's Hospital, RI, p. A548

MURPHY, John M, M.D., President and Chief Executive Officer, Western Connecticut Health Network, New Milford Hospital, CT, p. A107

MURPHY, John M., M.D., President, New Milford Hospital, CT, p. A107

MURPHY, Julie, Chief Financial Officer, Saint Luke's North Hospital-Smithville Campus, MO, p. A362

MURPHY, Kathy, Site Manager, Mescalero Public Health Service Indian Hospital, Mescalero, NM, p. A418

MURPHY, Kelly, Vice President Human Resources, Colorado Canyons Hospital And Medical Center, Fruita, CO, p. A101

MURPHY, Kevin, Director, Information Technology Services, Bayfront Health St. Petersburg, Saint Petersburg, FL, p. A138

MURPHY, Kyle, Director Information Technology, Mayhill Hospital, Denton, TX, p. A599

MURPHY, Linda, Chief Financial Officer, Osborne County Memorial Hospital, Osborne, KS, p. A243

MURPHY, Lionel
Chief Executive Officer and Administrator, Bethesda Rehabilitation Hospital, Baton Rouge, LA, p. A263
Chief Executive Officer, Southeast Regional Medical Center, Kentwood, LA, p. A270

MURPHY, Margaret M, Chief Executive Officer, Kindred Hospital Philadelphia - Havertown, PA, p. A535

MURPHY, Marie, Director Human Resources, Effingham Hospital, Springfield, GA, p. A161

MURPHY, Mary S, MSN
Regional Chief Nursing Officer, Amita Health Adventist La Grange Medical Center, La Grange, IL, p. A187
Vice President and Chief Nursing Officer, Amita Health Adventist Medical Center - Hinsdale, Hinsdale, IL, p. A186

MURPHY, Matthew, Chief Financial Officer, Compass Memorial Healthcare, Marengo, IA, p. A226

MURPHY, Maureen, M.D., Director of Medical Affairs, Ssm Health St. Clare Hospital-Baraboo, Baraboo, WI, p. A689

MURPHY, Michael, M.D., JD, Chief Medical Officer, Sharp Grossmont Hospital, La Mesa, CA, p. A63

MURPHY, Michael D., FACHE, Chief Executive Officer, Abilene Regional Medical Center, Abilene, TX, p. A582

MURPHY, Nancy, Vice President, Human Resources, Franciscan Children'S, Brighton, MA, p. A297

MURPHY, Paul, Chief Information Officer, Lane Regional Medical Center, Zachary, LA, p. A281

MURPHY, Peter J., Senior Vice President and Chief Operating Officer, Franciscan Health Mooresville, Mooresville, IN, p. A211

MURPHY, Richard J., President and Chief Executive Officer, South Nassau Communities Hospital, Oceanside, NY, p. A438

MURPHY, Rita, Director Human Resources, Cobre Valley Regional Medical Center, Globe, AZ, p. A30

MURPHY, Sheryl, Chief Nursing Officer and Director of Clinical Services, Peacehealth Peace Island Medical Center, Friday Harbor, WA, p. A672

MURPHY, Steve
Director Information Systems, Ssm Health St. Mary's Hospital Centralia, Centralia, IL, p. A175
FM-East Region IS, Good Samaritan Regional Health Center, Mount Vernon, IL, p. A190

MURPHY, Steven, Executive Director, Devereux Hospital And Children's Center Of Florida, Melbourne, FL, p. A129

MURPHY, Terry
Director Information Services, Phoenixville Hospital, Phoenixville, PA, p. A537
President and Chief Executive Officer, Bayhealth Medical Center, Milford Memorial Hospital, DE, p. A113

MURPHY, Theresa, Chief Nursing Officer, Usc Verdugo Hills Hospital, Glendale, CA, p. A60

MURPHY, Timothy, R.N.
Chief Nursing Officer, Healthsouth Desert Canyon Rehabilitation Hospital, Las Vegas, NV, p. A394
Vice President Human Resources, Mercy Hospital Fort Scott, Fort Scott, KS, p. A235
Vice President Human Resources, St. John's Rehabilitation Center, MO, p. A361

MURPHY, Tom, Chief Executive Officer, Minidoka Memorial Hospital, Rupert, ID, p. A171

MURPHY-FROBISH, Erin, Vice President Human Resources, Morris Hospital & Healthcare Centers, Morris, IL, p. A190

MURPHY-MIJARES, Monique, Chief Information Officer, Valley View Medical Center, Fort Mohave, AZ, p. A29

MURRAY, Alexander, Interim Associate Director, Veterans Affairs Gulf Coast Veterans Health Care System, Biloxi, MS, p. A343

MURRAY, Beverly, Director of Human Resources, Providence Tarzana Medical Center, Los Angeles, CA, p. A69

MURRAY, Brian, M.D.
Medical Director, Erie County Medical Center, Buffalo, NY, p. A423
Chief Financial Officer, Gunnison Valley Hospital, Gunnison, UT, p. A647

MURRAY, Cindy, R.N., Chief Nursing Officer and Chief Operating Officer, Baylor Scott & White Medical Center At Waxahachie, Waxahachie, TX, p. A642

MURRAY, Denise R., Chief Executive Officer, Anmed Health Rehabilitation Hospital, Anderson, SC, p. A549

MURRAY, Diana, Director Information Systems, Grand River Hospital District, Rifle, CO, p. A105

MURRAY, Gerald
President, Upmc Altoona, Altoona, PA, p. A520
President, Upmc Bedford Memorial, Everett, PA, p. A526

MURRAY, J. Patrick., FACHE, President and Chief Executive Officer, Peterson Regional Medical Center, Kerrville, TX, p. A617

MURRAY, Julie, Chief Executive Officer, Merrick Medical Center, Central City, NE, p. A382

MURRAY, Kent, M.D., Chief of Staff, Robert J. Dole Veterans Affairs Medical Center, Wichita, KS, p. A248

MURRAY, Kevin, M.D., Medical Director, Lake Taylor Transitional Care Hospital, Norfolk, VA, p. A662

MURRAY, Kevin J, Senior Vice President, John T. Mather Memorial Hospital, Port Jefferson, NY, p. A440

MURRAY, Lorraine, Chief Executive Officer, Post Acute Medical Specialty Hospital Of Texarkana - North, Texarkana, TX, p. A639

MURRAY, Marisa, CPA, Director Finance, Hshs St. Francis Hospital, Litchfield, IL, p. A188

MURRAY, Michael, Chief Financial Officer, Christus Dubuis Hospital Of Paris, Paris, TX, p. A627

MURRAY, Sherri, Chief Financial Officer, Montgomery General Hospital, Montgomery, WV, p. A685

MURRAY, Susan, FACHE
Chief Operating Officer, Queen's Medical Center - West Oahu, HI, p. A165
Director Information Services, Summerville Medical Center, SC, p. A550

MURRAY, Wesley E., Chief Executive Officer, Texas County Memorial Hospital, Houston, MO, p. A360

MURRELL, Joseph, Chief Executive Officer, Wayne County Hospital, Monticello, KY, p. A258

MURRILL, Michael, President and Chief Executive Officer, Amita Health Adventist La Grange Medical Center, La Grange, IL, p. A187

MURROW, Carol, Vice President Business Development, Cox Medical Center Branson, Branson, MO, p. A356

MURRY, Jim, Chief Information Officer, Stony Brook Southampton Hospital, NY, p. A443

MURT, Mary Lou, R.N., Senior Vice President Nursing, Monongahela Valley Hospital, Monongahela, PA, p. A532

MURTHY, Anandhi, Chief Medical Officer, Harrison Community Hospital, Cadiz, OH, p. A473

MURTHY, Bangalore, M.D., Director Medical Staff, Jackson Park Hospital And Medical Center, Chicago, IL, p. A177

MURTHY, Krishna, M.D., Chief of Medical Staff, Gibson General Hospital, Princeton, IN, p. A213

MURZYN, Derek
Chief Executive Officer, Carolinas Continuecare Hospital At Kings Mountain, Kings Mountain, NC, p. A455
Chief Executive Officer, Carolinas Continuecare Hospital At University, Charlotte, NC, p. A449
Market Chief Executive Officer, Carolinas Continuecare Hospital At Pineville, Charlotte, NC, p. A449

MUSACK, Scott, Chief Information Officer, Silver Lake Medical Center-Ingleside Hospital, CA, p. A69

MUSANTE, David, M.D., Medical Director, North Carolina Specialty Hospital, Durham, NC, p. A451

MUSGRAVE, Chelsea, Director of Human Resources, Clay County Hospital, Flora, IL, p. A183

MUSICH, Trisha E, R.N.
Chief Nursing Officer, Vista Medical Center East, Waukegan, IL, p. A198
Chief Nursing Officer, Vista Medical Center West, Waukegan, IL, p. A198

MUSOIU, Robert, Director Human Resources, Fairfield Memorial Hospital, Fairfield, IL, p. A183

MUSSI, Natalie, President and Chief Executive Officer, Thousand Oaks Surgical Hospital, CA, p. A91

MUSSMAN, Rebekah, Chief Executive Officer, Crete Area Medical Center, Crete, NE, p. A383

MUSSO, Lewis C, Vice President Human Resources, Trinity Medical Center West, OH, p. A491

MUSTACCHIA, Michele, Chief Human Resources Officer, Banner Gateway Medical Center, Gilbert, AZ, p. A29

MUSTARD, Ruth W., R.N., MSN, Associate Director Nursing and Patient Services, Wm. Jennings Bryan Dorn Veterans Affairs Medical Center, Columbia, SC, p. A552

MUSTIAN, J Perry., President and Chief Executive Officer, John D. Archbold Memorial Hospital, Thomasville, GA, p. A161

MUSUNURU, J.R., M.D., Executive Director, Fond Du Lac County Mental Health Center, Fond Du Lac, WI, p. A692

MUTHU, Karthik, Chief Executive Officer, Healthsouth Rehabilitation Hospital Of Ocala, Ocala, FL, p. A133

MUTTERER, Michael, Senior Vice President and Chief Nursing Officer, Riverside Medical Center, Kankakee, IL, p. A187

MUTZIGER, John, M.D., Chief Medical Officer, Laird Hospital, Union, MS, p. A353

MWANIKI, Mary, Chief Financial Officer, Encompass Health Rehabilitation Hospital Of The Mid-Cities, Bedford, TX, p. A588

MWEBE, David, M.D., Chief of Staff, Osmond General Hospital, Osmond, NE, p. A389

MYATT, Kevin A, Senior Vice President Human Resources, Yale-New Haven Psychiatric Hospital, CT, p. A110

MYCROFT, Tina, Senior Vice President, Chief Financial Officer, Evergreenhealth, Kirkland, WA, p. A673

MYDLER, Todd, M.D., Vice President and Chief Medical Officer, Good Samaritan Medical Center, Lafayette, CO, p. A102

MYER, Amber, Director Medical Technology, Throckmorton County Memorial Hospital, Throckmorton, TX, p. A640

MYERS, Becky, Human Resources Specialist, Illini Community Hospital, Pittsfield, IL, p. A193

MYERS, Chrissy, R.N., Director of Nursing, Unity Psychiatric Care-Clarksville, Clarksville, TN, p. A568

MYERS, Douglas, Executive Vice President and Chief Financial Officer, Phoenix Children's Hospital, Phoenix, AZ, p. A33

MYERS, Ed, Administrator, Shriners Hospitals For Children-Philadelphia, Philadelphia, PA, p. A536

MYERS, Gabby, Human Resources Director, Advanced Diagnostics Hospital, Houston, TX, p. A610

MYERS, Gary, Chief Executive Officer, Mammoth Hospital, Mammoth Lakes, CA, p. A71

MYERS, Grace, MSN, Vice President, Nurse Executive, Sentara Princess Anne Hospital, Virginia Beach, VA, p. A667

MYERS, Jeffrey D., President and Chief Executive Officer, Hamilton Medical Center, Dalton, GA, p. A152

MYERS, Jerry, M.D., Chief Executive Officer and Medical Director, Kell West Regional Hospital, Wichita Falls, TX, p. A644

MYERS, Joseph, Interim Administrator, J. C. Blair Memorial Hospital, Huntingdon, PA, p. A527

MYERS, Josette M., Chief Executive Officer, Healthsouth Rehabilitation Hospital Of Mechanicsburg, Mechanicsburg, PA, p. A531

MYERS, Julie
Chief Executive Officer, Kindred Hospital San Gabriel Valley, CA, p. A63
Chief Executive Officer, Kindred Hospital-Westminster, Westminster, CA, p. A95

MYERS, Karen, Vice President Financial Services, Stoughton Hospital Association, Stoughton, WI, p. A703

MYERS, Kathy R, MS, R.N., Chief Nursing Officer, Tennova Healthcare-Lafollette Medical Center, La Follette, TN, p. A573

MYERS, Kevin
Director Information Systems, Lake Granbury Medical Center, Granbury, TX, p. A607
Director Information Technology, Wilson Medical Center, Neodesha, KS, p. A241

MYERS, Kimberly, Director Human Resources, Guthrie County Hospital, Guthrie Center, IA, p. A223

MYERS, Lisa, Director Human Resources, Heritage Oaks Hospital, Sacramento, CA, p. A81

MYERS, Mary, R.N., MSN, Chief Nursing Officer, St. Vincent Women's Hospital, IN, p. A208

MYERS, Michael D., R.N., Chief Executive Officer, Veterans Memorial Hospital, Waukon, IA, p. A231

MYERS, Michelle F., Director Human Resources, Florida Hospital Wauchula, Wauchula, FL, p. A143

MYERS, Paul, M.D., Neonatologist and Chief Medical Officer, Children's Hospital Of Wisconsin-Fox Valley, Neenah, WI, p. A699

MYERS, Philip, M.D., Vice President Medical Affairs, University Hospitals Samaritan Medical Center, Ashland, OH, p. A470

MYERS, Randy, Chief Information Officer, Rehoboth Mckinley Christian Health Care Services, Gallup, NM, p. A417

MYERS, Robert T, Chief Operating Officer, Goshen Health, Goshen, IN, p. A205

MYERS, Rosemary, Manager, Team Resources, Winter Haven Hospital, Winter Haven, FL, p. A144

MYERS, Russ, Chief Executive Officer, Virginia Mason Memorial, Yakima, WA, p. A680

MYERS, Shane P, Chief Operating Officer, Iberia Medical Center, New Iberia, LA, p. A275

MYERS, Sheri, Vice President Patient Care Services, Mclaren Central Michigan, Mount Pleasant, MI, p. A319

MYERS, Stephen
Chief Executive Officer, Providence Hospital Of North Houston, Houston, TX, p. A613
Interim Chief Executive Officer, Icon Hospital, Humble, TX, p. A615

MYERS, Theresa, Personnel Director, Fallon Medical Complex, Baker, MT, p. A373

MYERS, William, Chief Executive Officer, Montgomery County Emergency Service, Norristown, PA, p. A533

MYHRE, Tracy, R.N., MSN, Chief Nursing Officer, Tomah Memorial Hospital, Tomah, WI, p. A704

MYLAVARAPU, Sarada, M.D., Chief Medical Officer, Woodland Healthcare, Woodland, CA, p. A95

MYSTER, Jennifer, President, Buffalo Hospital, Buffalo, MN, p. A329

N

NABEL, Elizabeth, M.D., President, Brigham And Women's Hospital, Boston, MA, p. A296

NACEY, Marley, Director Finance, Sentara Virginia Beach General Hospital, Virginia Beach, VA, p. A667

NACHIMUTHU, Anbu, Chief Financial Officer, Atrium Medical Center Of Corinth, Corinth, TX, p. A594

NACHTIGAL, Amy, Chief Financial Officer, Crittenton Children's Center, MO, p. A362

NACHTRIEB, Han, Vice President Human Resources, Seattle Cancer Care Alliance, Seattle, WA, p. A676

NACION, Glenn, Vice President Human Resources, Trinitas Regional Medical Center - New Point Campus, NJ, p. A404

NADEAU, Barbara, Chief Human Resources Management Service, White River Junction Veterans Affairs Medical Center, White River Junction, VT, p. A654

NADEAU, Stephen, Senior Vice President Human Resources, Gwinnett Medical Center, GA, p. A156

NADER, Daniel, D.O., Chief of Staff, Southwestern Regional Medical Center, Tulsa, OK, p. A509

NADER, Keoni, Director Human Resources, Louis A. Weiss Memorial Hospital, Chicago, IL, p. A177

NADER, Rick Lee, Chief Financial Officer, Haxtun Hospital District, Haxtun, CO, p. A102

NADKARNI, Manasi, M.D., Vice President Medical Affairs, Unitypoint Health - Trinity Muscatine, Muscatine, IA, p. A227

NADLE, Patricia A, R.N., Chief Nursing Officer, St. Joseph Hospital For Specialty Care, RI, p. A547

NADLER, Tammy R, Chief Financial Officer, Golden Valley Memorial Healthcare, Clinton, MO, p. A357

NADOLNY, Stephanie, Vice President of Hospital Operations, Spaulding Rehabilitation Hospital Cape Cod, East Sandwich, MA, p. A299

NAEGLER, Rick, Chief Executive Officer, Lake City Medical Center, Lake City, FL, p. A127

NAFZIGER, Laurie N., President and Chief Executive Officer, Oaklawn Psychiatric Center, Goshen, IN, p. A205

NAFZIGER, Steve, M.D., Vice President Medical Affairs, Parkview Medical Center, Pueblo, CO, p. A104

NAG, Pratip, Vice President, Chief Medical Officer, Katherine Shaw Bethea Hospital, Dixon, IL, p. A181

NAGARAJ, Alaka, M.D., Medical Director, Regency Hospital Of Minneapolis, Golden Valley, MN, p. A332

NAGARAJ, Raghava, Chief Medical Officer, Wake Forest Baptist Health-Lexington Medical Center, Lexington, NC, p. A456

NAGATOSHI, Holly, R.N., Chief Nursing Officer, San Dimas Community Hospital, San Dimas, CA, p. A85

NAGLER, Richard, M.D., Chief of Staff, Mayo Clinic Health System - Northland In Barron, Barron, WI, p. A690

NAGOWSKI, Michael, Chief Executive Officer, Cape Fear Valley Rehabilitation Center, NC, p. A452

NAGY, Jeff, Chief Financial Officer, River Bend Hospital, West Lafayette, IN, p. A216

NAGY, Kimberly, R.N., MS, Chief Nursing Officer, Northwest Community Hospital, Arlington Heights, IL, p. A173

NAGY, Linda J., MSN, R.N., Chief Nursing Officer, Brattleboro Retreat, Brattleboro, VT, p. A653

NAGY, Ryan, M.D.
Interim President and Chief Medical Officer, Indiana University Health Methodist Hospital, IN, p. A207
Interim President and Chief Medical Officer, Riley Hospital For Children At Indiana University Health, IN, p. A207

NAHAPETIAN, Arby, M.D., Vice President Medical Affairs and Quality, Adventist Health Glendale, Los Angeles, CA, p. A66

NAHM, Christopher, M.D., Chief Medical Officer, Livingston Regional Hospital, Livingston, TN, p. A573

NAHMENSEN, Robert, Chief Financial Officer and Chief Operations Officer, Stanton County Hospital, Johnson, KS, p. A237

NAIBERK, Donald T., Administrator, Butler County Health Care Center, David City, NE, p. A383

NAIL, Cheryl, R.N., Chief Nursing Officer, City Hospital At White Rock, Dallas, TX, p. A596

NAIR, Chand, M.D., Medical Director, Brooke Glen Behavioral Hospital, Fort Washington, PA, p. A526

NAIR, Vijayachandran, M.D., Chief of Staff, John J. Pershing Veterans Affairs Medical Center, Poplar Bluff, MO, p. A366

NAJIEB, LaDonna, Service Area Director Human Resources, Providence Saint Joseph Medical Center, Burbank, CA, p. A53

NAJJAR, Maher, M.D., Medical Director, Kindred Hospital Chicago-Northlake, Northlake, IL, p. A191

NAJJAR, Milad, Information Technology, Scottsdale Liberty Hospital, Scottsdale, AZ, p. A35

NAKAMOTO, Kenneth, M.D., Vice President Medical Affairs, Pomona Valley Hospital Medical Center, Pomona, CA, p. A79

NAKAMURA, Bridget, Director Information Systems, Simi Valley Hospital, Simi Valley, CA, p. A90

NAKASUJI, Jody, Chief Financial Officer, Harbor-Ucla Medical Center, Torrance, CA, p. A91

NALDI, Robert, Chief Financial Officer, Maimonides Infants And Children's Hospital Of Brooklyn, NY, p. A433

NALL, Wes
Chief Financial Officer, Monroe County Hospital, Monroeville, AL, p. A21
Interim Chief Executive Officer, Monroe County Hospital, Monroeville, AL, p. A21

NALLEY, Leanna W, Director Human Resources, Texas Health Hospital Clearfork, TX, p. A605

NANCE, Christi, R.N., MSN, Chief Nursing Officer, Northwest Specialty Hospital, Post Falls, ID, p. A171

NAPIER, Frank, Interim Chief Financial Officer, Cobre Valley Regional Medical Center, Globe, AZ, p. A30

NAPIERKOWSKI, Daniel, M.D.
President, Euclid Hospital, Euclid, OH, p. A482
President, Marymount Hospital, Garfield Heights, OH, p. A483

NAPOLITANO, Mary Pat, Director Human Resources, Specialty Hospital Of Central Jersey, Lakewood, NJ, p. A406

NAPPER, Rick D., Chief Executive Officer, Medical Center Health System, Odessa, TX, p. A626

NAPPS, Greg
President, Novant Health Uva Health System Haymarket Medical Center, Haymarket, VA, p. A659
President, Novant Health Uva Health System Prince William Medical Center, Manassas, VA, p. A661

NARAMORE, G Harold, M.D., Chief Medical Officer and In house Legal Counsel, Blount Memorial Hospital, Maryville, TN, p. A574

NARANG, Steve, M.D., Chief Executive Officer, Banner - University Medical Center Phoenix, Phoenix, AZ, p. A33

NARANJO, Maria, Director Human Resources, Memorial Hospital West, Pembroke Pines, FL, p. A135

NARIELWALA, Dhruv, Interim Chief Executive Officer, Behavioral Hospital Of Bellaire, Houston, TX, p. A610

NARROW, Ann, Director of Nursing, River Hospital, Alexandria Bay, NY, p. A421

NASER, Bashar, Chief Financial Officer, Gerald Champion Regional Medical Center, Alamogordo, NM, p. A415

NASET-PAYNE, Janet, MS, R.N., Chief Nursing Officer, Van Diest Medical Center, Webster City, IA, p. A231

NASH, Daniel J, Chief Information Officer, Citrus Valley Medical Center-Queen Of The Valley Campus, CA, p. A56

NASH, Ernest
Chief Financial Officer, South Texas Rehabilitation Hospital, Brownsville, TX, p. A590
Chief Financial Officer, Weslaco Regional Rehabilitation Hospital, Weslaco, TX, p. A643

NASH, Gayle, R.N., M.P.H., Chief Nursing Officer, Mountainview Regional Medical Center, Las Cruces, NM, p. A418

NASH, Jacqueline, Controller, Beaumont Hospital, Wayne, Wayne, MI, p. A325

NASH, John D., FACHE, President and Chief Executive Officer, Franciscan Children'S, Brighton, MA, p. A297

NASH, Mary G, Ph.D., R.N., Chief Nursing Officer, Ohio State University Hospitals East, OH, p. A478

NASH, Robert, M.D., Chief of Staff, Carle Richland Memorial Hospital, Olney, IL, p. A192

NASH, Sandra, Chief Fiscal Service, James H. Quillen Veterans Affairs Medical Center, Mountain Home, TN, p. A576

NASH, Tim, M.D., Chief of Staff, Board Vice Chairman, Marshall Medical Center, Lewisburg, TN, p. A573

NASHID, Nadia, M.D., Chief of Staff, Windham Hospital, Willimantic, CT, p. A112

NASLUND, Kevin, Manager Information Technology, Cherokee Regional Medical Center, Cherokee, IA, p. A219

NASR, Anthony, M.D., Chief Medical Staff, Adventist Health Feather River, Paradise, CA, p. A77

NASRALLAH, Fadi, M.D., Vice President Medical Affairs, Louis & Peaches Owen Heart Hospital, TX, p. A640

NASSIEF, Raymond, Senior Vice President, Hospital Operations and Support Services, John Muir Medical Center, Walnut Creek, Walnut Creek, CA, p. A94

NASSTROM, Jeff, D.O., Chief of Staff, Mitchell County Regional Health Center, Osage, IA, p. A227

NAST, Ed, M.D., Chief Medical Officer, Oak Hill Hospital, Brooksville, FL, p. A119

NATAL, Yesenia, Coordinator Human Resources, Hospital Pavia Arecibo, Arecibo, PR, p. A712

NATCHER, Charles, Chief Financial Officer, Kindred Hospital-Los Angeles, Los Angeles, CA, p. A68

NATELSON, Richard, M.D., Chief of Staff, Steele Memorial Medical Center, Salmon, ID, p. A172

NATEMAN, Barry, Manager Human Resources, French Hospital Medical Center, San Luis Obispo, CA, p. A87

NATH, Dilip, Sc.D., Associate Chief Information Officer, University Hospital Of Brooklyn At Long Island College Hospital, NY, p. A437

NATH, Pravene, Chief Information Officer, Stanford Health Care, Palo Alto, CA, p. A77

NATHANSON, Andrea, Director Finance, Baystate Franklin Medical Center, Greenfield, MA, p. A300

NATHEM, Joanne, MSN, R.N., Chief Clinical and Nursing Officer, Waverly Health Center, Waverly, IA, p. A231

NATRAJAN, Sunil, M.D., Medical Director, Curahealth Tucson, Tucson, AZ, p. A37

NAU, James, Manager Computer and Applications Support, Delaware Psychiatric Center, New Castle, DE, p. A113

NAUMAN, Michael B
Chief Information Officer and Corporate Vice President, Children's Hospital Of Wisconsin-Fox Valley, Neenah, WI, p. A699
Chief Information Officer, Children's Hospital Of Wisconsin, Milwaukee, WI, p. A698

NAUMOWICH, Sarah, Interim President, Morton Plant North Bay Hospital, New Port Richey, FL, p. A132

NAVA, Madeline, Chief Executive Officer, Mercy Hospital - A Campus Of Plantation General Hospital, FL, p. A136

NAVARRO, Beth Ann, Chief Clinical Officer, Kindred Hospital-Sycamore, Sycamore, IL, p. A197

NAVARRO, Israel, Chief Executive Officer, Integrity Transitional Hospital, Denton, TX, p. A599

NAVARRO, Ramomita, Director Human Resources, University Hospital, San Juan, PR, p. A716

NAVARRO, Tess, Chief Financial Officer, Laguna Honda Hospital And Rehabilitation Center, San Francisco, CA, p. A85

NAVAS, Manuel, M.D., Medical Director, Hospital San Pablo Del Este, Fajardo, PR, p. A713

NAWROCKI, Bernie
Administrative Director Finance, Promedica Bixby Hospital, Adrian, MI, p. A307
Administrative Director Finance, Promedica Herrick Hospital, Tecumseh, MI, p. A324

NAWROCKI, Edward, President, St. Luke's Hospital - Anderson Campus, Easton, PA, p. A525

NAYAK, Yeshavanth, M.D., Interim Chief Medical Officer, Community Medical Center, Toms River, NJ, p. A412

NAZ, Haroon, Chief Executive Officer, Pinnacle Hospital, Crown Point, IN, p. A202

NAZARIAN, Alexander, CPA
Chief Financial Officer, Kirby Medical Center, Monticello, IL, p. A190
Director Information Technology, Kirby Medical Center, Monticello, IL, p. A190

NAZARIO, Uriel, M.D., Chief of Medical Staff, Kindred Hospital North Florida, Green Cove Springs, FL, p. A124

NAZE, Jesse, Chief Financial Officer, Fall River Hospital, Hot Springs, SD, p. A561

NAZEER, Imran, M.D., Chief of Staff, Woodland Heights Medical Center, Lufkin, TX, p. A622

NAZIR, Tariq, Interim Director Information Technology, Signature Psychiatric Hospital, Kansas City, MO, p. A362

NDOMEA, Feisal, Director Case Management, Kindred Hospital Sugar Land, Sugar Land, TX, p. A637

NDOW, Emmanuel, Chief Information Officer, Marion General Hospital, Marion, IN, p. A211

NEAL, Bob, Information Technology, Sparrow Ionia Hospital, Ionia, MI, p. A316

NEAL, Greg, FACHE, President, Bristol Regional Medical Center, Bristol, TN, p. A566

NEAL, Kaley, Chief Financial Officer, Shenandoah Medical Center, Shenandoah, IA, p. A229

NEAL, Robert, Manager Information Technology Services, Newman Memorial Hospital, Shattuck, OK, p. A506

NEAL, Roger, Vice President Operations, Duncan Regional Hospital, Duncan, OK, p. A498

NEAL, Terrell, R.N., Chief Operating Officer and Chief Nursing Officer, St. Charles Parish Hospital, Luling, LA, p. A273

NEAL, Thomas, Chief Executive Officer, Berwick Hospital Center, Berwick, PA, p. A520

NEALE, Debra, R.N., Chief Nursing Officer, O'Connor Hospital, Delhi, NY, p. A425

NEALON, Matthew, Vice President, Chief Financial Officer, University Of Cincinnati Medical Center, Cincinnati, OH, p. A476

NEAPOLITAN, David, Chief Financial Officer, Emanuel Medical Center, Turlock, CA, p. A92

NEAR, Holly, Chief Administrative Officer, Harsha Behavioral Center, Terre Haute, IN, p. A215

NEAT, Gary
Chief Information Officer, Ephraim Mcdowell Regional Medical Center, Danville, KY, p. A251
Director Information Systems, Ephraim Mcdowell Fort Logan Hospital, Stanford, KY, p. A261

NECAS, Kevin, Chief Financial Officer, Women's And Children's Hospital, MO, p. A358

NEEB, Verette, R.N., MSN, Chief Nursing Officer, Baylor Medical Center At Uptown, Dallas, TX, p. A595

NEECE, Patrick, Chief Information Officer, Jefferson Regional Medical Center, Pine Bluff-Jefferson County, AR, p. A47

NEEDHAM, Kim
Assistant Chief Executive Officer, Vista Medical Center East, Waukegan, IL, p. A198
Assistant Chief Executive Officer, Vista Medical Center West, Waukegan, IL, p. A198

NEEDHAM, Tammy, Chief Nursing Officer, Chatham Hospital, Siler City, NC, p. A460

NEEDLES, Kim, Manager Business Office, Patients' Hospital Of Redding, Redding, CA, p. A80

NEELAGARU, Narasimhulu, M.D., Chief of Staff, Northridge Medical Center, Commerce, GA, p. A151

NEELY, Denise, R.N., Vice President and Chief Nursing Officer, Children's Hospital At Bronson, MI, p. A317

NEELY, Jill, Chief Financial Officer, Titusville Area Hospital, Titusville, PA, p. A542

NEELY, K. Dale., FACHE, Chief Executive Officer, Healthsouth Rehabilitation Hospital Of Tallahassee, Tallahassee, FL, p. A140

NEELY, Kathy E., R.N.
Interim Vice President Patient Care Services, Chi St. Vincent Infirmary Medical Center, Little Rock-Pulaski County, AR, p. A45
Interim Vice President Patient Care Services, Chi St. Vincent Morrilton, Morrilton-Conway County, AR, p. A46

NEELY, Randall
CEO, Simpson General Hospital, Mendenhall, MS, p. A350
Chief Executive Officer, Simpson General Hospital, Mendenhall, MS, p. A350

NEENAN, Sharon, R.N., Interim Chief Nursing Officer, Grant, Ohiohealth Grant Medical Center, Columbus, OH, p. A478

NEERGHEEN, Chabilal, M.D., Medical Director, Western Massachusetts Hospital, Westfield, MA, p. A306

NEESEN, Cindy, Director of Information Technology, Butler County Health Care Center, David City, NE, p. A383

NEET, Bradley D, FACHE, Chief Executive Officer, Inland Valley Medical Center, CA, p. A74

NEET, Bradley D., FACHE, Chief Executive Officer, Rancho Springs Medical Center, CA, p. A74

NEFCY, Christine
Chief Medical Officer, Munson Healthcare, Munson Medical Center, Traverse City, MI, p. A324
Chief Medical Officer, Mckay-Dee Hospital, Ogden, UT, p. A648

NEFF, Kris, Chief Operating Officer, Samaritan Healthcare, Moses Lake, WA, p. A673

NEFF, Mark J., FACHE, President and Chief Executive Officer, St. Claire Healthcare, Morehead, KY, p. A258

NEFF, Richard, M.D., Interim Chief Medical Officer, Flagstaff Medical Center, Flagstaff, AZ, p. A29

NEFF, William, M.D., Chief Medical Officer, Uchealth Medical Center Of The Rockies, Loveland, CO, p. A104

NEGRON, Manuel, Chief Information Technology Service, Veterans Affairs Caribbean Healthcare System, San Juan, PR, p. A716

NEIDENBACH, John, Vice President and Chief Operating Officer, West Hills Hospital And Medical Center, Los Angeles, CA, p. A70

NEIKIRK, Richard, Chief Executive Officer, Cumberland County Hospital, Burkesville, KY, p. A250

NEIL, Eric, Interim Chief Information Officer, Uw Medicine/Northwest Hospital & Medical Center, Seattle, WA, p. A677

NEIL, William, Vice President and Chief Information Officer, Behavioral Health Center, FL, p. A143

NEILSEN SWANSON, Verbelee, Administrator, Florida Hospital-Apopka, FL, p. A134

NEILSON, Carol, CPA, Controller, Encompass Health Rehabilitation Hospital Of Sugar Land, Sugar Land, TX, p. A637

NEILSON, Erinn, Chief Nursing Officer, Minidoka Memorial Hospital, Rupert, ID, p. A171

NEILSON, Karen, Administrator, Safe Haven Hospital Of Pocatello, Pocatello, ID, p. A171

NEILSON, Richard, Director of Information Services, Timpanogos Regional Hospital, Orem, UT, p. A649

NEIMAN, Carla A, Chief Financial Officer, Clark Fork Valley Hospital, Plains, MT, p. A378

NEISWONGER, Randy, Chief Executive Officer, Up Health System-Portage, Hancock, MI, p. A315

NEITZEL, Monte, Chief Executive Officer, Greater Regional Medical Center, Creston, IA, p. A220

NELKIN MCCORMICK, Elizabeth, MSN, R.N., Senior Vice President and Chief Nursing Officer, Memorial Sloan-Kettering Cancer Center, New York (Includes All Hospitals Located Within The Five Boroughs), NY, p. A433

NELL, Sergio, Director Information Systems, Watsonville Community Hospital, Watsonville, CA, p. A94

NELLSCH, Verner, M.D., Chief of Staff, Chi St. Luke's Health Memorial Livingston, Livingston, TX, p. A620

NELSON, Allison
Chief Financial Officer, Sanford Canby Medical Center, Canby, MN, p. A329
Chief Financial Officer, Sanford Clear Lake Medical Center, Clear Lake, SD, p. A560

NELSON, Barbara J, Ph.D., R.N., Chief Nursing Executive, Sutter Roseville Medical Center, Roseville, CA, p. A81

NELSON, Bill, Chief Executive Officer, Mille Lacs Health System, Onamia, MN, p. A336

NELSON, Carol, Director Human Resources, Montevista Hospital, Las Vegas, NV, p. A394

NELSON, Cory D., Administrator, Sioux Center Health, Sioux Center, IA, p. A229

NELSON, David, FACHE
Chief Financial Officer, Hshs Sacred Heart Hospital, Eau Claire, WI, p. A692
Divisional Chief Financial Officer, Hshs St. Joseph's Hospital, Chippewa Falls, WI, p. A691
Medical Director, Barlow Respiratory Hospital, Los Angeles, CA, p. A66

NELSON, David A., President and Chief Executive Officer, Chi St. Francis Health, Breckenridge, MN, p. A328

NELSON, Dawn, Director Human Resources, Sagewest Health Care At Lander, WY, p. A709

NELSON, Diane, R.N., Chief Nursing Officer, Kindred Hospital-Albuquerque, Albuquerque, NM, p. A415

NELSON, Elaine, R.N., MSN, Chief Nursing Officer, Texas Health Harris Methodist Hospital Fort Worth, Fort Worth, TX, p. A605

NELSON, Frederick, MA, Administrator, Oceans Behavioral Hospital Of Kentwood, Kentwood, LA, p. A270

NELSON, Gina, Chief Financial Officer, Renown South Meadows Medical Center, Reno, NV, p. A396

NELSON, Jack, Vice President Finance and Chief Financial Officer, Ohio Valley Hospital, Mckees Rocks, PA, p. A531

NELSON, Jackie, Director Human Resources, Hansford Hospital, Spearman, TX, p. A636

NELSON, James J, Senior Vice President Finance and Strategic Planning, Fort Healthcare, Fort Atkinson, WI, p. A692

NELSON, Jamie, Vice President and Chief Information Officer, Hospital For Special Surgery, New York (Includes All Hospitals Located Within The Five Boroughs), NY, p. A432

NELSON, Jennifer, Senior Human Resource Business Partner, Spectrum Health Kelsey Hospital, MI, p. A314

NELSON, Jodi, Interim Chief Executive Officer, St. Luke's Medical Center, Crosby, ND, p. A465

NELSON, Joseph, M.D., President Medical Staff, Lewis-Gale Pavilion, VA, p. A666

NELSON, Julia, Vice President of Human Resources, Northern Hospital Of Surry County, Mount Airy, NC, p. A457

NELSON, Katey, Director Human Resources, Sevier Valley Hospital, Richfield, UT, p. A649

NELSON, Kathy
Chief Financial Officer, Marshall Medical Center North, Guntersville, AL, p. A19
Chief Financial Officer, Marshall Medical Center South, Boaz, AL, p. A15

NELSON, Kellie, Director Human Resources, Aurora Medical Center Kenosha, Kenosha, WI, p. A695

NELSON, Kenneth E, R.N., III, Chief Nursing Officer, Hshs St. Vincent Hospital, Green Bay, WI, p. A694

NELSON, Kerri, Chief Financial Officer, Spectrum Health Ludington Hospital, Ludington, MI, p. A318

NELSON, Lucy, Director Finance, Vice President, Maniilaq Health Center, Kotzebue, AK, p. A26

NELSON, Lynn M., R.N., R.N., Chief Nursing Officer and Chief Operating Officer, St. John's Riverside Hospital - Dobbs Ferry Pavilion, NY, p. A446

NELSON, Marlin Pete, Vice President Fiscal Services, Divine Savior Healthcare, Portage, WI, p. A701

NELSON, Martha
Chief Financial Officer, Antelope Memorial Hospital, Neligh, NE, p. A387
Chief Financial Officer, Niobrara Valley Hospital, Lynch, NE, p. A386

NELSON, Melissa, Assistant Administrator, Baptist Memorial Hospital For Women, Memphis, TN, p. A574

NELSON, Meredith, Chief Financial Officer, Willamette Valley Medical Center, Mcminnville, OR, p. A514

NELSON, Michael
Chief Financial Officer, Select Specialty Hospital Midtown Atlanta, Atlanta, GA, p. A147
Executive Vice President and Chief Financial Officer, Pomona Valley Hospital Medical Center, Pomona, CA, p. A79

NELSON, Nan, Senior Vice President Finance, Aurora St. Luke's South Shore, WI, p. A698

NELSON, Nancy, Director Human Resources, Intermountain Hospital, Boise, ID, p. A167

NELSON, Nick, Director Support Services, Adams Memorial Hospital, Decatur, IN, p. A202

NELSON, Raymond, Acting Chief Information Resource Management, Fargo Veterans Affairs Health Care System, Fargo, ND, p. A465

NELSON, Richard, Chief of Human Resources Management Services, North Little Rock Division, AR, p. A45

NELSON, RimaAnn O., R.N., Director, Phoenix Veterans Affairs Health Care System, Phoenix, AZ, p. A34

NELSON, Robin, Chief Financial Officer, Gundersen St. Joseph's Hospital And Clinics, Hillsboro, WI, p. A694

NELSON, Selena, Chief Financial Officer, Fallon Medical Complex, Baker, MT, p. A373

NELSON, Siri, Chief Executive Officer, Renown South Meadows Medical Center, Reno, NV, p. A396

NELSON, Stewart R
Vice President and Chief Financial Officer, Sentara Halifax Regional Hospital, South Boston, VA, p. A666
Vice President and Chief Financial Officer, Sentara Martha Jefferson Hospital, Charlottesville, VA, p. A656
Vice President and Chief Financial Officer, Sentara Rmh Medical Center, Harrisonburg, VA, p. A659

NELSON, Suzanne, R.N., Director of Nursing, Salt Lake Behavioral Health, Salt Lake City, UT, p. A650

NELSON, Tricia, Chief Financial Officer, Riverwoods Behavioral Health System, Riverdale, GA, p. A159

NELSON, Trudy, Chief Human Resource Officer, Niobrara Valley Hospital, Lynch, NE, p. A386

NELSON-JONES, Susan, Director Human Resources, Adventist Health Medical Center - Tehachapi Valley, Tehachapi, CA, p. A91

NEMECHEK, Victor, M.D., Chief of Staff and Chief Medical Officer, Sheridan County Health Complex, Hoxie, KS, p. A237

NEMETH, Jim
Chief Financial Officer, Monroe Clinic, Monroe, WI, p. A699
Senior Vice President of Patient Care Services and Chief Nursing Officer, Memorial Healthcare, Owosso, MI, p. A320

NEMI, Neil, Administrator Facility Information Center, Richard H. Hutchings Psychiatric Center, Syracuse, NY, p. A443

NEONAKIS, Stephanie W, Manager Human Resources, University Hospitals Richmond Medical Center, OH, p. A477

NERMOE, Bryan, Executive Vice President, Sanford Bemidji Medical Center, Bemidji, MN, p. A328

NERO, Theresa R, R.N., MS, Chief Nursing Officer, Kaiser Permanente San Jose Medical Center, San Jose, CA, p. A86

NESBITT, William, M.D., President, Texas Health Heart & Vascular Hospital Arlington, Arlington, TX, p. A584

NESMITH, Nikki
Chief Executive Officer and Chief Nursing Officer, Evans Memorial Hospital, Claxton, GA, p. A150
Chief Nursing Officer, Evans Memorial Hospital, Claxton, GA, p. A150

NESPOLI, John L., Chief Executive Officer, St. Luke's Sacred Heart Campus, Allentown, PA, p. A519

NESS, David L, Vice President Operations, Unitypoint Health - Grinnell Regional Medical Center, Grinnell, IA, p. A223

NESS, Jon, Chief Executive Officer, Kootenai Behavioral Health, ID, p. A169

NESSEL, Mark
Chief Operating Officer, Our Lady Of Lourdes Medical Center, Camden, NJ, p. A403
Executive Vice President and Chief Operating Officer, Lourdes Medical Center Of Burlington County, Willingboro, NJ, p. A414

NESSELRODT, Derek, Director Information Systems, Grant Memorial Hospital, Petersburg, WV, p. A686

NESTER, Brian A., D.O.
President and Chief Executive Officer, Lehigh Valley Health Network Peditatrics, PA, p. A519
President and Chief Executive Officer, Lehigh Valley Hospital-Muhlenberg, Bethlehem, PA, p. A520

NESTER, Darlene E.
Chief Human Resources Officer, Hilton Head Hospital, Hilton Head Island, SC, p. A554
Market Chief Human Resources Officer, Coastal Carolina Hospital, Hardeeville, SC, p. A554

NESTER, Michael, Administrator, H. C. Watkins Memorial Hospital, Quitman, MS, p. A352

NESTER WOLFE, Cheryl R., President and Chief Executive Officer, Salem Health Rehabilitation Center, OR, p. A517

NESTLER, Nicole, Division Director Human Resources, Chi Mercy Health, Valley City, ND, p. A468

NETH, Marvin, Chief Executive Officer, Callaway District Hospital, Callaway, NE, p. A382

NETTERVILLE, Chad, Administrator, Field Memorial Community Hospital, Centreville, MS, p. A344

NETTLES, Angela F, Vice President, Human Resources and Support Services, Kershawhealth, Camden, SC, p. A549

NETTLES, Robert, Director Human Resources, Mountainview Hospital, Las Vegas, NV, p. A394

NETZER, Craig, M.D., President Medical Staff, Wilcox Medical Center, Lihue, HI, p. A166

NEUBERT, Todd, Chief Executive Officer, Riverton Hospital, Riverton, UT, p. A650

NEUENDORF, Deborah, Vice President Administration, New York-Presbyterian/Hudson Valley Hospital, Cortlandt Manor, NY, p. A425

NEUENDORF, James, M.D., Medical Director, Saint Joseph's Medical Center, Yonkers, NY, p. A446

NEUENDORF, Michael, Chief Executive Officer, Princeton Baptist Medical Center, Birmingham, AL, p. A15

NEUFELD, Ellis, M.D., Chief Medical Officer, St. Jude Children's Research Hospital, Memphis, TN, p. A576

NEUFELDER, Daniel, President, Indiana University Health Arnett Hospital, Lafayette, IN, p. A209

NEUGENT, Kevin, Chief Information Officer, Hayes Green Beach Memorial Hospital, Charlotte, MI, p. A309

NEUHAUS, Joan E
Chief Operating Officer, Chi Health Mercy Council Bluffs, Council Bluffs, IA, p. A220
Division Senior Vice President Chief Operating Officer, Chi Health Lakeside, Omaha, NE, p. A388
Division Senior Vice President, Chief Operating Officer, Chi Health Midlands, Papillion, NE, p. A389

NEUJAHR, Elias
Chief Executive Officer, Children's Hospital Of Richmond At Vcu-Brook Road Campus, Richmond, VA, p. A664
Chief Executive Officer, Children's Hospital Of Richmond At Vcu, VA, p. A665

NEUMAN, Keith A.
Chief Information Officer, Lutheran Hospital Of Indiana, Fort Wayne, IN, p. A203
Chief Information Officer, Orthopaedic Hospital Of Lutheran Health Network, Fort Wayne, IN, p. A204

NEUMAN, Michael J, Vice President Finance, Kennedy Krieger Institute, Baltimore, MD, p. A287

NEUMANN, Charles W., President and Chief Medical Officer, Frazier Rehab Institute, KY, p. A256

NEUMANN, Jamie, Director Human Resources, Iroquois Memorial Hospital And Resident Home, Watseka, IL, p. A197

NEUMEISTER, Daniel P, Senior Vice President and Chief Operating Officer, Searhc Mt. Edgecumbe Hospital, Sitka, AK, p. A27

NEUNER, Kathy, R.N., Chief Nursing Officer, Clark Memorial Hospital, Jeffersonville, IN, p. A208

NEUVIRTH, Stephanie, Chief Human Resource and Diversity Officer, City Of Hope's Helford Clinical Research Hospital, Duarte, CA, p. A57

NEVAREZ, Domingo, Chief Executive Officer, Hospital Metropolitan, San Juan, PR, p. A716

NEVILL, David S., Chief Executive Officer, Healthsouth Rehabilitation Hospital Of New Mexico, Albuquerque, NM, p. A415

NEVILLE, Bette, R.N., MSN, Vice President and Chief Nursing Officer, Mercy Hospital Of Portland, Portland, ME, p. A285

NEVILLE, Lawrence, Chief Medical Officer, Vancouver Memorial Campus, WA, p. A680

NEVILLE, Ryan T., FACHE, President and Chief Executive Officer, Memorial Medical Center - Neillsville, Neillsville, WI, p. A699

NEVIN, James, M.D., Vice President Medical Management, Advocate Bromenn Regional Medical Center, IL, p. A191

NEVIN, Janice E., M.D., M.P.H., Chief Executive Officer, Christiana Care Health System, Newark, DE, p. A113

NEVINS, Norm, Manager Human Resources, Kansas Medical Center, Andover, KS, p. A232

NEWBURN, Lorance, M.D., Medical Chief of Staff, Saunders Medical Center, Wahoo, NE, p. A391

NEWBY, Doug, Chief Information Officer, Highlands Medical Center, Scottsboro, AL, p. A23

NEWBY, Glenda, Chief Executive Officer, Dallas Regional Medical Center, Mesquite, TX, p. A623

NEWBY, Nancy M., FACHE, Ph.D., R.N., President and Chief Executive Officer, Washington County Hospital, Nashville, IL, p. A191

NEWCOMB, James, M.D.
Vice President Medical Affairs, Slidell Memorial Hospital, Slidell, LA, p. A279
Vice President Medical Affairs, Ochsner Medical Center - North Shore, Slidell, LA, p. A279

NEWCOMB, Michael, D.O.
Senior Vice President and Chief Operating Officer, Legacy Meridian Park Medical Center, Tualatin, OR, p. A518
Senior Vice President and Chief Operating Officer, Legacy Mount Hood Medical Center, Gresham, OR, p. A513
Senior Vice President and Chief Operating Officer, Legacy Salmon Creek Medical Center, Vancouver, WA, p. A679

NEWCOMER, Jeremy, Director Information Services, Elmira Psychiatric Center, Elmira, NY, p. A426

NEWCOMER, Peter, M.D., Chief Medical Officer, American Family Children's Hospital, WI, p. A696

NEWELL, Dan, Chief Financial Officer, Highlands Medical Center, Scottsboro, AL, p. A23

NEWELL, Janice
Chief Information Officer, Swedish Medical Center-Ballard, WA, p. A676
Chief Information Officer, Swedish Medical Center-Cherry Hill Campus, Seattle, WA, p. A676

NEWELL, Richard, Chief Executive Officer, Pottstown Hospital, Pottstown, PA, p. A539

NEWEY, Mark, D.O., Chief of Staff, Mercy Hospital Healdton, Healdton, OK, p. A499

NEWHOUSE, Chuck, M.D., Chief of Staff, Boundary Community Hospital, Bonners Ferry, ID, p. A168

NEWHOUSE, Paul R., President, Union Medical Center, Union, SC, p. A557

NEWLAND, Judy, R.N.
Chief Nursing Officer, Incline Village Community Hospital, Incline Village, NV, p. A393
Chief Operating Officer, Tahoe Forest Hospital District, Truckee, CA, p. A92

NEWMAN, Billy, Department Head, Naval Hospital Lemoore, Lemoore, CA, p. A64

NEWMAN, Carlotta Hannah, Human Resources Manager, Northeast Georgia Medical Center Barrow, Winder, GA, p. A163

NEWMAN, Christopher, M.D., Vice President Medical Affairs and Chief Medical Officer, Penn State Health St. Joseph - Downtown Campus, PA, p. A539

NEWMAN, Cynthia, Manager Human Resources, Petersburg Medical Center, Petersburg, AK, p. A27

NEWMAN, Dan, Chief Executive Officer, Houston Methodist Clear Lake Hospital, Nassau Bay, TX, p. A625

NEWMAN, Diane, FACHE, Administrator, Johnson County Hospital, Tecumseh, NE, p. A391

NEWMAN, Edith, Interim Administrator, John J. Madden Mental Health Center, Hines, IL, p. A185

NEWMAN, Karen, Ed.D., MSN, R.N., Vice President and Chief Nursing Officer, Baptist Health Louisville, Louisville, KY, p. A256

NEWMAN, Kurt, M.D., President and Chief Executive Officer, Children's National Health System, Washington, DC, p. A115

NEWMAN, Mark, M.D., Executive Vice President of Health Affairs, Uk Healthcare Good Samaritan Hospital, KY, p. A255

NEWMAN, Richard, Chief Human Resources Officer, Olympic Medical Center, Port Angeles, WA, p. A675

NEWMAN, Sonya, R.N., Chief Nursing Officer, Blount Memorial Hospital, Maryville, TN, p. A574

NEWMAN, Thomas M
Chief Financial Officer, Upmc Passavant Cranberry, PA, p. A538
Vice President Finance, Upmc St. Margaret, Pittsburgh, PA, p. A538

NEWMILLER, Vicki, Chief Executive Officer, Great Falls Clinic Hospital, Great Falls, MT, p. A376

NEWPOWER, Nicole, Coordinator Human Resources, Kindred Hospital Tarrant County-Fort Worth Southwest, TX, p. A604

NEWQUIST, Dennis, Director Information Systems, Abilene Regional Medical Center, Abilene, TX, p. A582

NEWSOM, Cynthia, Chief Executive Officer, Vibra Hospital Of Boise, Boise, ID, p. A168

NEWSOM, Paul, Chief Operating Officer, Kentuckiana Medical Center, Clarksville, IN, p. A201

NEWSOM, Terri T., Vice President of Finance and Chief Financial Officer, Roger C. Peace Rehabilitation Hospital, SC, p. A553

NEWSOME, Samuel C, M.D., Chief of Staff, Lifebrite Community Hospital Of Stokes, Danbury, NC, p. A450

NEWSWANGER, Jeff, M.D., Chief Medical Officer, Manchester Memorial Hospital, Manchester, KY, p. A257

NEWTON, Gail, R.N., MSN, Vice President Patient Care Services, St. Luke's Hospital - Warren Campus, Phillipsburg, NJ, p. A410

NEWTON, Jennifer, R.N., Chief Nursing Officer, Neosho Memorial Regional Medical Center, Chanute, KS, p. A233

NEWTON, Keith, Interim Chief Executive Officer, Green Clinic Surgical Hospital, LA, p. A278

NEWTON, Steven R., FACHE, President, Karl And Esther Hoblitzelle Memorial Hospital, TX, p. A596

NEWTON, Susan, Chief Operating Officer, Broward Health North, Deerfield Beach, FL, p. A121

NEWTON, Terri, Chief Nursing Officer, Lakewood Regional Medical Center, Lakewood, CA, p. A64

NEWTON, Wilma, Executive Vice President and Chief Financial Officer, St. Vincent's Birmingham, Birmingham, AL, p. A15

NEZBETH, Jacqueline, Human Resources Officer, Select Specialty Hospital Of Southeast Ohio, Newark, OH, p. A488

NG, Anthony, M.D., Vice President and Chief Medical Officer, The Acadia Hospital, Bangor, ME, p. A282

NG, Hong-Kin, M.D., Chief Medical Officer, Roane General Hospital, Spencer, WV, p. A687

NG, Thomas T., Chief Information Officer, Collingsworth General Hospital, Wellington, TX, p. A643

NG, Vincent
Director, Veterans Affairs Boston Healthcare System, West Roxbury, MA, p. A305
Director, Veterans Affairs Medical Center West Roxbury Division, MA, p. A298

NGIRAISUI, Clarinda, Director, Human Resources, Commonwealth Health Center, Saipan, MP, p. A711

NGUYEN, Abby, R.N., Chief Nursing Officer, Good Samaritan Medical And Rehabilitation Center, OH, p. A494

NGUYEN, Bach, Director Information Systems, Northwest Texas Surgery Center, TX, p. A583

NGUYEN, Harry, M.D., Medical Director, The Woods At Parkside, Gahanna, OH, p. A482

NGUYEN, Nga, Manager Human Resources and Organizational Development, Glendale Memorial Hospital And Health Center, Glendale, CA, p. A60

NIBLOCK, Jenny, Chief Clinical Officer, Citizens Medical Center, Colby, KS, p. A233

NICASTRO, Pamela, Director Human Resources, Brylin Hospitals, Buffalo, NY, p. A423

NICAUD, Kent, President and Chief Executive Officer, Memorial Behavioral Health, MS, p. A346

NICE, Andrew, Chief Operating Officer, Wysong Campus, TX, p. A623

NICHELSON, Kathleen, Director Human Resources, Horsham Clinic, Ambler, PA, p. A520

NICHOLAS, Angela, Vice President, Medical Affairs, Einstein Medical Center Montgomery, East Norriton, PA, p. A524

NICHOLAS, Chris, Administrator of Rehabilitation Hospital, Renown Rehabilitation Hospital, Reno, NV, p. A396

NICHOLAS, David, Chief Executive Officer, St. John Rehabilitation Hospital, Broken Arrow, OK, p. A496

NICHOLS, Amanda, M.D., Chief of Staff, Sistersville General Hospital, Sistersville, WV, p. A687

NICHOLS, Barbara, R.N., President and Chief Executive Officer, Corry Memorial Hospital, Corry, PA, p. A523

NICHOLS, Bryan
Chief Financial Officer, The Heart Hospital Baylor Denton, Denton, TX, p. A599
Chief Financial Officer, The Heart Hospital Baylor Plano, Plano, TX, p. A629

NICHOLS, Christopher, Chief Executive Officer, Fillmore County Hospital, Geneva, NE, p. A384

NICHOLS, Cynthia, R.N., MSN, Chief Executive Officer, Lakeland Community Hospital, Haleyville, AL, p. A19

NICHOLS, Dia, Chief Executive Officer, Northside Hospital, Saint Petersburg, FL, p. A138

NICHOLS, Donna, R.N., Chief Nursing Officer, Goodall-Witcher Hospital Authority, Clifton, TX, p. A593

NICHOLS, Greg, Chief Executive Officer, East Alabama Medical Center-Lanier, AL, p. A22

NICHOLS, Gretchen, R.N., President, Legacy Mount Hood Medical Center, Gresham, OR, p. A513

NICHOLS, Laura L, Director Human Resources, Hancock Regional Hospital, Greenfield, IN, p. A205

NICHOLS, Lisa, R.N., Administrator, St. Vincent's St. Clair, Pell City, AL, p. A22

NICHOLS, Mark, FACHE, Chief Executive Officer, Starr Regional Medical Center, Athens, TN, p. A566

NICHOLS, Michael, Chief Information Officer, Masonicare Health Center, Wallingford, CT, p. A111

NICHOLS, Randy
Chief Financial Officer, Great River Medical Center, Blytheville-Mississippi County, AR, p. A39
Chief Financial Officer, South Mississippi County Regional Medical Center, Osceola-Mississippi County, AR, p. A47

NICHOLS, Robert R, M.D., Vice President Medical Affairs, Mercy Hospital Fort Scott, Fort Scott, KS, p. A235

NICHOLS, Robin, Interim Chief Financial Officer, Dekalb Medical At North Decatur, Decatur, GA, p. A152

NICHOLS, Suzanne, Director Human Resources, Muleshoe Area Medical Center, Muleshoe, TX, p. A625

NICHOLSON, Britain, M.D., Chief Medical Officer, Massgeneral Hospital For Children, MA, p. A297

NICHOLSON, Charles, Vice President, Medical Affairs, Sentara Albemarle Medical Center, Elizabeth City, NC, p. A452

NICHOLSON, Chrissy, Vice President of Human Resources, The King's Daughters Hospital, MS, p. A346

NICHOLSON, Cindy, Director Human Resources, Shelby Baptist Medical Center, Alabaster, AL, p. A13

NICHOLSON, Debra, Manager Finance, Tuskegee Division, AL, p. A21

NICHOLSON, H. Stacy, M.D., M.P.H., Physician in Chief, Phoenix Children's Hospital, Phoenix, AZ, p. A33

NICHOLSON, Jack, Chief Executive Officer, Kindred Hospital Louisville At Jewish Hospital, KY, p. A256

NICHOLSON, Kristin, Coordinator Human Resources, Genesis Medical Center, Dewitt, De Witt, IA, p. A220

NICHOLSON, Molly, MS, R.N.
Chief Nurse Executive, Osf Heart Of Mary Medical Center, Urbana, IL, p. A197
Vice President of Patient Care/Chief Nurse Executive, Osf Sacred Heart Medical Center, Danville, IL, p. A180

NICHOSON, Julia, M.D., Chief Medical Officer, Drew Memorial Health System, Monticello-Drew County, AR, p. A46

NICKEL, Kathleen, Director Communications, Mercy Medical Center, Roseburg, OR, p. A517

NICKELL, Angela, Executive Director, Sequel Pomegranate Health Systems, Columbus, OH, p. A479

NICKELL, Jerry, Vice President Human Resource and Mission, Saint Alphonsus Medical Center - Baker City, Baker City, OR, p. A511

NICKELS, John, M.D., President Medical Staff, Grace Hospital, Cleveland, OH, p. A476

NICKENS, John R., IV, President and Chief Executive Officer, Children's Hospital, New Orleans, LA, p. A275

NICKENS, Wesley, M.D., Chief of Staff, Collingsworth General Hospital, Wellington, TX, p. A643

NICKRAND, Tami, Director Information Technology, Harbor Beach Community Hospital, Harbor Beach, MI, p. A315

NICKS, Bret, M.D., Chief Medical Officer and Chief of Staff, Wake Forest Baptist Health-Davie Medical Center, Bermuda Run, NC, p. A448

NICODEMUS, Lowell, Director Information Systems, Hendricks Regional Health, Danville, IN, p. A202

NICOLAY, Donald, M.D., Chief Medical Officer, Community Hospital, Grand Junction, CO, p. A101

NICOLL, C. Diana, M.D., Ph.D., Chief of Staff, San Francisco Va Medical Center, San Francisco, CA, p. A86

NICOLSON, Lynne T, M.D., Medical Director, Sunnyview Rehabilitation Hospital, Schenectady, NY, p. A442

NICOSIA, Chris, Chief Financial Officer, Corpus Christi Medical Center Bay Area, TX, p. A594

NIECE, Pamela S, Director Human Resources, Orem Community Hospital, Orem, UT, p. A648

NIEDERPRUEM, Mark L., FACHE, Administrator, Shriners Hospitals For Children-Chicago, Chicago, IL, p. A179

NIELSEN, Colleen, Director Operations, Providence St. Joseph Medical Center, Polson, MT, p. A378

NIELSEN, Gwen, Manager Human Resources, Indianhead Medical Center, Shell Lake, WI, p. A703

NIELSEN, Helen V
Director Human Resources, Heart Hospital Of New Mexico, NM, p. A415
Director Human Resources, Lovelace Rehabilitation Hospital, Albuquerque, NM, p. A415

NIELSEN, Kristine, Manager Human Resources, Memorial Community Hospital And Health System, Blair, NE, p. A382

NIELSEN, Randy, Director Information Technology, Morton General Hospital, Morton, WA, p. A673

NIELSEN, Wayne, Director Human Resources, West Marion Community Hospital, FL, p. A133

NIELSON, Curtis, Chief Financial Officer, South Lincoln Medical Center, Kemmerer, WY, p. A708

NIELSON, Lars, M.D., Chief Medical Officer, Weeks Medical Center, Lancaster, NH, p. A399

NIELSON, Lori, Regional Finance Director, Park City Hospital, Park City, UT, p. A649

NIELSON, P Douglas, M.D., Chief of Staff, Kahuku Medical Center, Kahuku, HI, p. A165

NIELSON, Yvonne, Chief Nursing Officer, Director Quality Management and Regulatory Compliance, Mountain West Medical Center, Tooele, UT, p. A651

NIEMALA, Amanda, Director of Information Services, Bigfork Valley Hospital, Bigfork, MN, p. A328

NIEMANN, Lynne, Director Nurses and Patient Care, Community Memorial Hospital, Sumner, IA, p. A230

NIEMUTH, Trisha, Market Chief Executive Officer, Lifecare Hospitals Of Pittsburgh - Suburban, PA, p. A537

NIENHUIS, Jamie, Chief Nursing Officer, Cavalier County Memorial Hospital And Clinics, Langdon, ND, p. A467

NIERMAN, Peter, M.D., Chief Medical Officer, Chicago Lakeshore Hospital, Chicago, IL, p. A176

NIERMAN, Stephen A., President, Winter Haven Hospital, Winter Haven, FL, p. A144

NIERMANN, Michelle, Executive Vice President and Chief Operating Officer, Unitypoint Health - St. Luke's Hospital, Cedar Rapids, IA, p. A218

NIERSTEDT, Kelly
President, Children's Hospital Of Illinois, IL, p. A193
President, Winnie Palmer Hospital For Women And Babies, FL, p. A134

NIES, Lynn, Human Resources Officer, Erie Veterans Affairs Medical Center, Erie, PA, p. A525

NIESE, Mel, Chief Fiscal Service, Veterans Affairs Palo Alto Health Care System, Livermore Division, CA, p. A77

NIESSINK, Henry
Regional Director Information Technology Services, Mercy Medical Center Redding, Redding, CA, p. A79
Senior Manager Information Technology Services, St. Elizabeth Community Hospital, Red Bluff, CA, p. A79

NIEVES, Deborah, Director Management Information Systems, Hospital San Francisco, San Juan, PR, p. A716

NIEVES, Erick, M.D., Medical Director, Hospital San Carlos Borromeo, Moca, PR, p. A714

NIEVES, James F., Executive Director, San Juan City Hospital, San Juan, PR, p. A716

NIGH, Andrew, M.D., Chief of Staff, Indiana University Health West Hospital, Avon, IN, p. A199

NIGHMAN, Mike, Facility Coordinator Information Systems, Shelby Baptist Medical Center, Alabaster, AL, p. A13

NIGHTINGALE, Judi, R.N., Dr.PH, Chief Nursing Officer, Riverside University Health System-Medical Center, Moreno Valley, CA, p. A74

NIGRIN, Daniel, M.D., Vice President Information Services and Chief Information Officer, Boston Children's Hospital, Boston, MA, p. A296

NIGRO, Lee, M.D., Chief Medical Officer, Blue Valley Hospital, Overland Park, KS, p. A243

NIHALANI, Sunil, M.D., Chief Medical Staff, Lake Wales Medical Center, Lake Wales, FL, p. A127

NIJOKA, Monica, Chief Nursing Officer, Baton Rouge General Medical Center-Bluebonnet, LA, p. A263

NIKOLIC, Srbo, Chief Financial Officer, Hartgrove Hospital, Chicago, IL, p. A177

NILES, Heather, Director Human Resources Operations, Mercyhealth Hospital And Medical Center - Harvard, Harvard, IL, p. A184

NILSSON, Keith, Chief Financial Officer, Cleveland Clinic Florida, Weston, FL, p. A144

NIMMO, Ben, M.D., Medical Director, Pinnacle Pointe Hospital, Little Rock-Pulaski County, AR, p. A45

NIMMO, Brian, Director, Huntington Veterans Affairs Medical Center, Huntington, WV, p. A684

NIMS, Carrie, Director of Nursing, Post Acute/Warm Springs Specialty Hospital Of San Antonio, San Antonio, TX, p. A634

NINNEMAN, David, Associate Director, Cincinnati Veterans Affairs Medical Center, Cincinnati, OH, p. A474

NIPPER, Nathan
Chief Operating Officer, Piedmont Fayette Hospital, Fayetteville, GA, p. A153
Vice President and Chief Operating Officer, Piedmont Newnan Hospital, Newnan, GA, p. A158

NIPPERT, Kathi, Acting Chief Human Resources Officer, Kansas City Veterans Affairs Medical Center, Kansas City, MO, p. A361

NISH, Paulette, Chief Nursing Officer, Geisinger Jersey Shore Hospital, Jersey Shore, PA, p. A528

NISKANEN, Grant, M.D., Vice President Medical Affairs, Sky Lakes Medical Center, Klamath Falls, OR, p. A514

NISSEN, Beth, Director Human Resources, Troy Regional Medical Center, Troy, AL, p. A23

NIX, Alisha, Director Human Resources, Wilbarger General Hospital, Vernon, TX, p. A642

NIX, Angela, Administrator, Sam Rayburn Memorial Veterans Center, TX, p. A598

NIX, Bo, Chief Information Officer, Madison Valley Medical Center, Ennis, MT, p. A375

NIX, Julie, Vice President and Administrator, Baptist Health Rehabilitation Institute, Little Rock-Pulaski County, AR, p. A45

NIX, Nikki, Chief Executive Officer, Latimer County General Hospital, Wilburton, OK, p. A510

NIXDORF, David L, Director Support Services, Frances Mahon Deaconess Hospital, Glasgow, MT, p. A375

NIXON, James, Chief Operating Officer, Meadows Regional Medical Center, Vidalia, GA, p. A162

NIXON, Myra, Director Human Resources, Healthsouth Rehabilitation Hospital, Concord, NH, p. A398

NIZAMI, Nassar, Chief Information Officer, Jefferson Methodist Hospital, PA, p. A536

NNAJI, Felix, Chief Medical Staff, Bolivar General Hospital, Bolivar, TN, p. A566

NOAK, Amy, Director Human Resources, St. David's Round Rock Medical Center, Round Rock, TX, p. A631

NOAKES, Timothy J, Chief Financial Officer, Memorial Hospital Los Banos, Los Banos, CA, p. A70

NOBLE, Angela, Director of Nursing, West Feliciana Parish Hospital, Saint Francisville, LA, p. A278

NOBLE, Damien, Director Information Technology and System, Colleton Medical Center, Walterboro, SC, p. A557

NOBLE, Dave, Director of Nursing, Livingston Healthcare, Livingston, MT, p. A377

NOBLE, James D., Chief Executive Officer, Horton Community Hospital, Horton, KS, p. A237

NOBLE, James S, Chief Financial Officer, Huntington Memorial Hospital, Pasadena, CA, p. A78

NOBLE, Kerry L, Chief Financial Officer, Pemiscot Memorial Health System, Hayti, MO, p. A360

NOBLE, Lloyd, Chief Executive Officer, Anchor Hospital, Atlanta, GA, p. A145

NOBLE, Mallie S., Administrator, Mary Breckinridge Arh Hospital, Hyden, KY, p. A254

NOBLES, Diane, Nurse Executive, East Mississippi State Hospital, Meridian, MS, p. A350

NOBLES, Sharon
Chief Financial Officer, North Mississippi Medical Center - Tupelo, Tupelo, MS, p. A353
Interim Chief Financial Officer, Baptist Hospital, Pensacola, FL, p. A136

NOBLES, Trent, Chief Executive Officer, Southside Regional Medical Center, Petersburg, VA, p. A664

NOBLIN, Jeff, FACHE, Chief Executive Officer, Southern Tennessee Regional Health System-Lawrenceburg, Lawrenceburg, TN, p. A573

NOCITA, Suzanne, Senior Vice President and Chief Human Resource Officer, Children's Hospital And Medical Center, Omaha, NE, p. A388

NOCKOWITZ, Richard, M.D., Medical Director, Ohio Hospital For Psychiatry, Columbus, OH, p. A478

NOE, Sharon, Chief Executive Officer, Cobalt Rehabilitation Hospital, Surprise, AZ, p. A36

NOEL, Bill, Chief Operating Officer, Grand River Hospital District, Rifle, CO, p. A105

NOEL, Philip J., III, Chief Executive Officer, Ottumwa Regional Health Center, Ottumwa, IA, p. A228

NOEL, Vicki, Vice President Human Resources, Southern Ohio Medical Center, Portsmouth, OH, p. A489

NOESS, Bobbi, Director of Nursing, Bowdle Hospital, Bowdle, SD, p. A559

NOFFSINGER, Sandy, Executive Assistant, Risk Manager and Director Marketing, Dundy County Hospital, Benkelman, NE, p. A382

NOGLER, Wendy, Director Human Resources, Lincoln County Health System, Fayetteville, TN, p. A569

NOKELS, Kevin J., FACHE, President, Lasting Hope Recovery Center, NE, p. A387

NOKES, Gregory, Vice President Human Resources, Middlesex Hospital, Middletown, CT, p. A109

NOLAN, Douglas, M.D., Medical Director, Cherokee Nation W.W. Hastings Indian Hospital, Tahlequah, OK, p. A507

NOLAN, Heather, Director Information Services, Green Clinic Surgical Hospital, LA, p. A278

NOLAN, Jennifer
President and Chief Executive Officer, Flaget Memorial Hospital, Bardstown, KY, p. A249
President and Chief Executive Officer, Our Lady Of Peace, Louisville, KY, p. A256

NOLAN, Joe, Chief Operating Officer, Saint Clare's Hospital/ Dover, NJ, p. A403

NOLAN, Matthew, Chief Operating Officer, Moses Ludington Hospital, NY, p. A426

NOLAN, Patrick, Vice President Finance and Chief Financial Officer, Gillette Children's Specialty Healthcare, Saint Paul, MN, p. A339

NOLAN, Patrick B, Chief Operating Officer, Inspira Medical Center-Woodbury, Woodbury, NJ, p. A414

NOLAN, Rosemary, R.N., MSN, JD, Chief Operating Officer, Temple University Hospital - Episcopal Division, PA, p. A536

NOLAN, Roz, Interim Chief Nursing Officer, Community Hospital Of San Bernardino, San Bernardino, CA, p. A83

NOLAND, Pam, Director of Nursing, Northern Cochise Community Hospital, Willcox, AZ, p. A38

NOLASCO, Wanda, Chief Nursing Officer, Fairmount Behavioral Health System, Philadelphia, PA, p. A534

NOLD, Pam, Chief Nurse Executive, Northwest Missouri Psychiatric Rehabilitation Center, Saint Joseph, MO, p. A367

NOLEN, Benny, President and Chief Executive Officer, Methodist Hospital, Henderson, KY, p. A253

NOLES, Coy, Chief Financial Officer Consultant, Hamilton Hospital, Olney, TX, p. A626

NOLL, David, Director, Adventist Health St. Helena, Saint Helena, CA, p. A82

NOLL, Gerald A, Chief Financial Officer, Rogers Memorial Hospital-West Allis, WI, p. A700

NOLL, Keith D., President, Wellspan York Hospital, York, PA, p. A546

NOLLETTE, Karen, Chief Financial Officer, West Holt Medical Services, Atkinson, NE, p. A381

NOLLEY, Dexter, Chief Human Resources Officer, Duke Regional Hospital, Durham, NC, p. A451

NOLT, Lori, Director Information Technology, Wellspan Philhaven, Mount Gretna, PA, p. A532

NOLTE, Darlene R, Chief Human Resource Officer, Saint Francis Hospital Vinita, Vinita, OK, p. A509

NONNEMAN, Lisa, Director Information Technology Services, Mary Lanning Healthcare, Hastings, NE, p. A384

NOONAN, Anna T., President and Chief Operating Officer, The University Of Vermont Health Network Central Vermont Medical Center, Berlin, VT, p. A653

NOONAN, Kathryn, Director Information Management, Lemuel Shattuck Hospital, Jamaica Plain, MA, p. A300

NOONE, Thomas, M.D., Chief Medical Officer, Bayfront Health Port Charlotte, Port Charlotte, FL, p. A137

NOPWASKEY, Cristen, Chief Information Officer, Weirton Medical Center, Weirton, WV, p. A687

NORBURY, Denise
Regional Chief Executive Officer, Center For Behavioral Medicine, Kansas City, MO, p. A361
Regional Executive Officer, Northwest Missouri Psychiatric Rehabilitation Center, Saint Joseph, MO, p. A367

NORBY, Michael, Chief Financial Officer, Quentin Mease Hospital, TX, p. A611

NORD, Gay
President, Baylor St. Luke's Medical Center Mcnair Campus, Houston, TX, p. A610
President, Baylor St. Luke's Medical Center, Houston, TX, p. A610

NORD, Stanley K, Chief Financial Officer, West Houston Medical Center, Houston, TX, p. A614

NORDAHL, Richard E, Chief Financial Officer, Sanford Sheldon Medical Center, Sheldon, IA, p. A229

NORDAHL, Richard E., Chief Executive Officer, Sanford Sheldon Medical Center, Sheldon, IA, p. A229

NORDBERG, Traci, Chief Human Resources Officer, Vanderbilt Psychiatric Hospital, TN, p. A578

NORDBY, Betsy, Director of Human Resources, St. Croix Regional Medical Center, St Croix Falls, WI, p. A703

NORDBY, Shawn A, Chief Financial Officer, Mary Lanning Healthcare, Hastings, NE, p. A384

NORDELL, Cindy, Chief Nursing Officer, Healthsouth Rehabilitation Hospital Of Colorado Springs, Colorado Springs, CO, p. A97

NORDENG, Rod, Administrator, Floyd County Medical Center, Charles City, IA, p. A219

NORDIN, Danna, Director Human Resources, Anchor Hospital, Atlanta, GA, p. A145

NORDLAND, Thomas, Chief Medical Officer, Fort Healthcare, Fort Atkinson, WI, p. A692

NORDLUND, Judy, R.N., Chief Nursing Officer, Trinity Hospital, Weaverville, CA, p. A95

NORDLUND, Sarah, Director of Nursing, Garfield County Health Center, Jordan, MT, p. A376

NORDSTROM, Janice, Director Human Resources, Landmark Hospital Of Joplin, Joplin, MO, p. A361

NORDSTROM, Katie, Director Human Resources, Beartooth Billings Clinic, Red Lodge, MT, p. A378

NORDWICK, Thomas, FACHE, Chief Executive Officer, Uvalde Memorial Hospital, Uvalde, TX, p. A641

NORDYKE, Charles, Chief Executive Officer, Clarinda Regional Health Center, Clarinda, IA, p. A219

NORDYKE, Melissa, Chief Financial Officer, Seton Smithville Regional Hospital, Smithville, TX, p. A636

NOREEN, James, M.D., Chief Medical Officer, Regina Hospital, Hastings, MN, p. A332

NORELDIN, Mohsen, M.D., President Medical Staff, Athol Hospital, Athol, MA, p. A295

NORELL, Brett, Interim Chief Executive Officer, Holy Family Memorial, Manitowoc, WI, p. A696

NOREM, Ashley, Chief Information Systems, Starke Hospital, Knox, IN, p. A208

NOREM, Julie, MSN, Chief Nursing Officer, Rochelle Community Hospital, Rochelle, IL, p. A194

NOREN, Tom, M.D., Chief Medical Officer, Up Health System-Marquette, Marquette, MI, p. A318

NORGAARD, Margaret B.
Chief Executive Officer, Poplar Community Hospital, Poplar, MT, p. A378
Chief Executive Officer, Trinity Hospital, Wolf Point, MT, p. A380

NORICK, Laurence, M.D., Clinical Director, U.S. Public Health Service Indian Hospital, Parker, AZ, p. A32

NORKO, Michael A, M.D., Acting Chief Executive Officer, Whiting Forensic Hospital, CT, p. A109

NORMAN, Andrea, Chief Executive Officer, Valley Behavioral Health System, Barling, AR, p. A39

NORMAN, Daniel, Regional Service Manager, Unitypoint Health - Allen Hospital, Waterloo, IA, p. A231

NORMAN, Debbie, MSN, R.N.
Chief Nursing Officer, Elkview General Hospital, Hobart, OK, p. A499
Director Human Resources, Central Louisiana Surgical Hospital, Alexandria, LA, p. A262

NORMAN, Jimmy, Chief Financial Officer, Mountain Lakes Medical Center, Clayton, GA, p. A150

NORMAN, Laura, Chief Development and Information Officer, Windhaven Psychiatric Hospital, Prescott Valley, AZ, p. A35

NORMAN, Lori, Chief Financial Officer, Encompass Health Rehabilitation Hospital Of Gadsden, Gadsden, AL, p. A18

NORMAN, Michael L, Executive Vice President and Chief Operating Officer, Landmark Hospital Of Cape Girardeau, Cape Girardeau, MO, p. A356

NORMAN, Robin, Senior Vice President and Chief Financial Officer, Virginia Hospital Center, Arlington, VA, p. A655

NORMINGTON-SLAY, Jeremy, FACHE
Chief Executive Officer, Ascension Good Samaritan Hospital, Merrill, WI, p. A698
President, North Central Region, Ascension St. Michael's Hospital, Stevens Point, WI, p. A703
President, North Central Region, Ministry Good Samaritan Health Center, Weston, WI, p. A706
President, Ascension Our Lady Of Victory Hospital, Stanley, WI, p. A703

NORQUEST, Cathy, Director Human Resources, York General, York, NE, p. A391

NORRICK, Michael, Director of Campus Operations, Ghs - Laurens County Memorial Hospital, SC, p. A550

NORRIS, David, Chief Medical Staff, Sweetwater Hospital, Sweetwater, TN, p. A580

NORRIS, Lucy, Administrator Interim Chief Nursing Officer, Multicare Good Samaritan Hospital, Puyallup, WA, p. A675

NORRIS, Robert, Chief Executive Officer, Huntington Creek Recovery Center, Shickshinny, PA, p. A541

NORTH, Ralene, Chief Nurse Executive, Massena Memorial Hospital, Massena, NY, p. A430

NORTHCUTT, Lynn, Chief Information Officer, Carolinas Hospital System, Florence, SC, p. A552

NORTHERN, Gail M., Director Human Resources, Blue Mountain Hospital, Blanding, UT, p. A646

NORTHUP, Carol, R.N., Chief Nursing Officer and Chief Operating Officer, J. Arthur Dosher Memorial Hospital, Southport, NC, p. A460

NORTHUP, Jeffrey, D.O., Chief Medical Officer, Knox Community Hospital, Mount Vernon, OH, p. A487

NORTON, Andrew J, M.D.
Chief Medical Officer, Bryn Mawr Hospital, Bryn Mawr, PA, p. A521
Chief Medical Officer, Paoli Hospital, Paoli, PA, p. A533

NORTON, Bill, Chief Nursing Officer, Rehoboth Mckinley Christian Health Care Services, Gallup, NM, p. A417

NORTON, Carole, Chief Nursing Officer, Stonewall Jackson Memorial Hospital, Weston, WV, p. A688

NORTON, Debbie, Chief Financial Officer, Medical Center Barbour, Eufaula, AL, p. A17

NORTON, Julie, Vice President, Operational Finance, Avera Children's Hospital, SD, p. A563

NORTON, Lizette O, Vice President, Human Resources, Loma Linda University Children's Hospital, Loma Linda, CA, p. A64

NORTON, Meg, Executive Vice President and Chief Administrative Officer, Rady Children's Hospital - San Diego, San Diego, CA, p. A84

NORTON, Robert G
President, Salem Campus, MA, p. A304
President, Union Campus, MA, p. A304

NORTON, Susan, Vice President Human Resources, Children's Hospital Of Georgia, GA, p. A147

NORVILLE, Amy, Vice President Support Services, St. Luke's Hospital, Columbus, NC, p. A450

NORWOOD, Lyle, M.D., Chief of Staff, Piedmont Columbus Regional Northside, Columbus, GA, p. A150

NORWOOD, William, Vice President, Human Resources, Brattleboro Memorial Hospital, Brattleboro, VT, p. A653

NOSACKA, David
Chief Financial Officer, Hshs St. Elizabeth's Hospital, O'Fallon, IL, p. A192
Southern Illinois Division Chief Financial Officer, Hshs St. Joseph's Hospital, Highland, IL, p. A185

NOSACKA, Mark, Chief Executive Officer, Piedmont Medical Center, Rock Hill, SC, p. A556

NOSBISCH, Don, Director Human Resources, Floyd County Medical Center, Charles City, IA, p. A219

NOSEWORTHY, Ed, Chief Executive Officer, Florida Hospital-Oceanside, FL, p. A121

NOSKIN, Gary, Senior Vice President and Chief Medical Officer, Northwestern Memorial Hospital, Stone Institute Of Psychiatry, IL, p. A178

NOSKO, Jeannine Burnat, Vice President Patient Care, Aspirus Wausau Hospital, Inc., Wausau, WI, p. A705

NOSTRANT, Hunter, Chief Financial Officer, Helen Newberry Joy Hospital, Newberry, MI, p. A320

NOTEMAN, Laurali, Director Human Resources, Kane County Hospital, Kanab, UT, p. A647

NOTTER, Pat, R.N., Chief Nursing Officer and Director Quality, Melissa Memorial Hospital, Holyoke, CO, p. A102

NOTTINGHAM, Cheryl, Chief Financial Officer, Atlantic General Hospital, Berlin, MD, p. A290

NOUNA, Nabil, M.D., Chief of Staff, Allegan General Hospital, Allegan, MI, p. A307

NOVAK, Charles, M.D., Chief Medical Officer, Intermountain Hospital, Boise, ID, p. A167

NOVAK, Christopher, Chief Operating Officer, Alexian Brothers Behavioral Health Hospital, Hoffman Estates, IL, p. A186

NOVAK, Georgene, Director Human Resources, Littleton Regional Healthcare, Littleton, NH, p. A400

NOVAK, Jerald, Chief People Officer, Vermont Children's Hospital, VT, p. A653

NOVAK, Kristen, Manager Human Resources, River Falls Area Hospital, River Falls, WI, p. A702

NOVAK, Michael, Vice President, Operations and Chief Information Officer, Saint Mary's Hospital, Waterbury, CT, p. A111

NOVELLO, Regina, R.N., Chief Operating Officer, Healdsburg District Hospital, Healdsburg, CA, p. A61

NOVICK, Peggy, Vice President, Clinical Support and Outpatient Services, Whitinsville Medical Center, MA, p. A302

NOVITSKY, Mark, M.D., Sr, Corporate Medical Director, Kirkbride Center, Philadelphia, PA, p. A535

NOVOA LOYOLA, Jose E, M.D., Medical Director, Cardiovascular Center Of Puerto Rico And The Caribbean, San Juan, PR, p. A715

NOVOSEL, Stacie, Vice President, Human Resources, South Bay Hospital, Sun City Center, FL, p. A140

NOWACHEK, Debra S., Director Human Resources, Unitypoint Health - Grinnell Regional Medical Center, Grinnell, IA, p. A223

NOWAK, Kevin, Interim Chief Executive Officer, Hillcrest Hospital - South, Tulsa, OK, p. A508

NOWICKI, Becky, Director Human Resources, Michiana Behavioral Health Center, Plymouth, IN, p. A213

NOWICKI, Michelle, R.N., MSN, Chief Nurse Executive, Kaiser Permanente Baldwin Park Medical Center, Baldwin Park, CA, p. A52

NOWLIN, Angela, R.N., FACHE, Senior VP, Operations, Magnolia Regional Health Center, Corinth, MS, p. A345

NOWLIN, Jeffrey D, President and Chief Operating Officer, St. John Medical Center, Tulsa, OK, p. A509

NOWLIN, Jeffrey D., President and Chief Operating Officer, St. John Medical Center, Tulsa, OK, p. A509

NOWLIN, Patricia
Director Accounting, Cooper County Community Hospital, Boonville, MO, p. A356
Director Human Resources, Cooper County Community Hospital, Boonville, MO, p. A356

NOWLING, Tara, Director Human Resources, Monroe County Hospital, Monroeville, AL, p. A21

NOYES, Vikki, Executive Vice President and Chief Operating Officer, Confluence Health/Central Washington Hospital, Wenatchee, WA, p. A680

NUAKO, Kofi, M.D., President Medical Staff, Baptist Memorial Hospital-Union City, Union City, TN, p. A580

NUDD, Brandon M, Chief Operating Officer, Gordon Hospital, Calhoun, GA, p. A149

NUGENT, Shelly, R.N., Director Nurses and Infection Control, Louisiana Extended Care Hospital West Monroe, West Monroe, LA, p. A281

NUGENT, Victoria, Chief Nursing Officer, Dignity Health Arizona General Hospital, Laveen, AZ, p. A31

NUNEZ, Humberto F., M.D., Chief Medical Officer, Mission Regional Medical Center, Mission, TX, p. A624

NUNEZ, Michael, Chief Financial Officer, University Medical Center Of El Paso, El Paso, TX, p. A603

NUNEZ, Milton, Executive Director, Nyc Health + Hospitals / Lincoln, New York (Includes All Hospitals Located Within The Five Boroughs), NY, p. A436

NUNEZ, Sheila, Director Human Resources, Eastern New Mexico Medical Center, Roswell, NM, p. A419

NUNN, Brian, R.N., Chief Executive Officer, Encompass Health Rehabilitation Hospital Of Florence, Florence, SC, p. A552

NUNN, Chalmers, M.D., Chief Medical Officer and Senior Vice President, Lynchburg General Hospital, VA, p. A660

NUNNELLY, Sarah, Chief Operating Officer, Princeton Baptist Medical Center, Birmingham, AL, p. A15

NURU, Betty, Director Human Resources, Millwood Hospital, Arlington, TX, p. A584

NURY, Alex, Chief Information Officer, Providence Tarzana Medical Center, Los Angeles, CA, p. A69

NUSBAUM, Neil, M.D., Chief of Staff, Veterans Affairs Central Western Massachusetts Healthcare System, Leeds, MA, p. A301

NUSS, Suzanne Langan, M.D., Chief Nursing Officer, Nebraska Medicine - Nebraska Medical Center, Omaha, NE, p. A388

NUSSBAUM, Joseph, M.D., Chief of Staff, California Hospital Medical Center, Los Angeles, CA, p. A66

NUSSBAUM, Mark, Vice President Operations, Marymount Hospital, Garfield Heights, OH, p. A483

NUTTER, Robert, President, Littleton Regional Healthcare, Littleton, NH, p. A400

NWOKIKE, Jerome, M.D., Medical Director, Spring Mountain Treatment Center, Las Vegas, NV, p. A395

NYAMU, Samuel, M.D., Chief Medical Officer, Sanford Aberdeen Medical Center, Aberdeen, SD, p. A559

NYBERG, Becky T, Chief Financial Officer, Bloomington Meadows Hospital, Bloomington, IN, p. A200

NYIKES, Debra, Director Finance and Chief Financial Officer, Cleveland Clinic Children's Hospital For Rehabilitation, Cleveland, OH, p. A476

NYKAMP, Robert, Vice President and Chief Operating Officer, Pine Rest Christian Mental Health Services, Grand Rapids, MI, p. A314

NYLUND, Barbara, M.D., Chief of Staff, Novato Community Hospital, Novato, CA, p. A75

NYMOEN, Gary, Chief Financial Officer, Hialeah Hospital, Hialeah, FL, p. A124

NYSTROM, Dale, M.D., Chief Medical Officer, Physician, Hawarden Regional Healthcare, Hawarden, IA, p. A224

NZERUE, Chike, M.D., Chief Medical Officer, Nashville General Hospital, Nashville, TN, p. A577

O

OAKES, Julie P, R.N., Manager Risk and Quality, Ocean Beach Hospital, Ilwaco, WA, p. A672

OAKES FERRUCCI, Susan, MS, Vice President Patient Services and Chief Nursing Officer, Cobleskill Regional Hospital, Cobleskill, NY, p. A424

OAKLEY, Lisa, Chief Financial Officer, Harper County Community Hospital, Buffalo, OK, p. A496

OAKLEY, Sarah G, Vice President Nursing, North Kansas City Hospital, North Kansas City, MO, p. A365

OAKS, Dana C., Chief Executive Officer, University Pavilion, FL, p. A140

OAXACA, Norma, Director Human Resources, Peak Behavioral Health Services, Santa Teresa, NM, p. A419

OBERHEU, Todd, Administrator, Lincoln County Medical Center, Ruidoso, NM, p. A419

OBERMIER, Jenny, Senior Vice President, Chief Operating Officer and Chief Nursing Officer, York General, York, NE, p. A391

OBERSTAR, Joel V., M.D., Chief Executive Officer and Chief Medical Officer, Prairiecare - Brooklyn Park, Brooklyn Park, MN, p. A329

OBEY, Bianca A., Chief Financial Officer, Alexandria Veterans Affairs Health Care System, Pineville, LA, p. A277

OBORNY, Jane, Chief Financial Officer, Rush County Memorial Hospital, La Crosse, KS, p. A239

O'BRIEN, Daniel R., Vice President and Chief Financial Officer, Community Hospital, Munster, IN, p. A212

O'BRIEN, Elizabeth, Chief Financial Officer, Northern Nevada Adult Mental Health Services, Sparks, NV, p. A397

O'BRIEN, Jane E, M.D., Medical Director, Franciscan Children'S, Brighton, MA, p. A297

O'BRIEN, John, Chief Executive Officer, Manning Regional Healthcare Center, Manning, IA, p. A226

O'BRIEN, Karen, Director Human Resources, Gerald Champion Regional Medical Center, Alamogordo, NM, p. A415

O'BRIEN, Kelly, Chief Operating Officer, Hackensack Meridian Health Riverview Medical Center, Red Bank, NJ, p. A411

O'BRIEN, Kevin, Chief Financial Officer, Share Medical Center, Alva, OK, p. A495

O'BRIEN, Laureen, Chief Information Officer, Providence Newberg Medical Center, Newberg, OR, p. A515

O'BRIEN, Renee, Director Human Resources, Greater Binghamton Health Center, Binghamton, NY, p. A422

O'BRIEN-PARADIS, Katie, M.D., Chief Medical Officer, Chi Oakes Hospital, Oakes, ND, p. A468

O'BRYANT, G. Mark., President and Chief Executive Officer, Tallahassee Memorial Healthcare, Tallahassee, FL, p. A140

OCASIO, J Manuel, Vice President Human Resources, Holy Cross Hospital, Silver Spring, MD, p. A294

OCEGUERA, Louis, M.D., Medical Director, Little Falls Hospital, Little Falls, NY, p. A429

OCHOA, Mark S, M.D., Deputy Commander, Clinical Services, Irwin Army Community Hospital, Junction City, KS, p. A238

OCHOA, Nikki, Interim Chief Financial Officer, St. Joseph's Medical Center, Stockton, CA, p. A91

OCHSENDORF, Derrick, Manager Information Technology and Systems, Johnson Memorial Health Services, Dawson, MN, p. A330

OCKERS, Thomas, Executive Vice President and Chief Administrative Officer, Good Samaritan Hospital Medical Center, West Islip, NY, p. A445

O CONNOR, Joyce, Chief Operating Officer, Taunton State Hospital, Taunton, MA, p. A305

O'CONNELL, Brian, Director Information Services, North Star Behavioral Health, AK, p. A25

O'CONNELL, Melody M, Director Human Resources, St. Bernard Parish Hospital, Chalmette, LA, p. A265

O'CONNELL, Tim, Chief Financial Officer, Lincoln Hospital, Davenport, WA, p. A671

O'CONNOR, Alice M, Chief Executive Officer, Kindred Hospital New Jersey - Wayne, NJ, p. A404

O'CONNOR, Betty, Chief Nursing Officer, Crouse Health, Syracuse, NY, p. A443

O'CONNOR, Colleen, Director Human Resources, Centerstone Hospital, Bradenton, FL, p. A118

O'CONNOR, David, Executive Vice President and Chief Financial Officer, Caromont Regional Medical Center, Gastonia, NC, p. A453

O'CONNOR, Dennis, M.D., Medical Director, Ira Davenport Memorial Hospital, Bath, NY, p. A422

O'CONNOR, James
Chief Administrative Officer, St. Catherine Of Siena Medical Center, Smithtown, NY, p. A443
Executive Vice President and Chief Administrative Officer, St. Charles Hospital, Port Jefferson, NY, p. A440

O'CONNOR, Kathy
Vice President Finance and Controller, St. Joseph Mercy Livingston Hospital, Howell, MI, p. A315
Vice President Finance, St. Joseph Mercy Ann Arbor, Ypsilanti, MI, p. A326

O'CONNOR, Kevin, D.O., President, Medical Staff, Spectrum Health Kelsey Hospital, MI, p. A314

O'CONNOR, Michael F, Senior Vice President Finance, Wellspan York Hospital, York, PA, p. A546

O'CONNOR, Michael P, M.D., Chief Medical Officer, Banner Baywood Medical Center, Mesa, AZ, p. A31

O'CONNOR, Thomas
Interim Chief Executive Officer, Sister Kenny Rehabilitation Institute, MN, p. A335
President, United Hospital, Saint Paul, MN, p. A339

O'CONNOR, Tim, Area Finance Officer, Kaiser Permanente Santa Clara Medical Center, Santa Clara, CA, p. A88

O'CONNOR, Timothy P., Executive Vice President and Chief Financial Officer, Lahey Medical Center, Peabody, MA, p. A298

O'CONNOR-SNYDER, Judy, Chief Nursing Officer, Mercy Hospital Lebanon, Lebanon, MO, p. A363

ODATO, David, Chief Administrative and Chief Human Resources Officer, Ucsf Medical Center Mission Bay, CA, p. A86

O'DEA, Edward
Executive Vice President and Chief Financial Officer, Lehigh Valley Health Network Pediatrics, PA, p. A519
Executive Vice President and Chief Financial Officer, Lehigh Valley Hospital-Muhlenberg, Bethlehem, PA, p. A520

ODEGAARD, Daniel, FACHE, Chief Executive Officer, Caldwell Medical Center, Princeton, KY, p. A260

ODELL, Cheryl, R.N., Chief Nursing Officer, Sharp Mcdonald Center, CA, p. A84

ODELL, Michelle, Director of Public Affairs, Kaiser Permanente South Sacramento Medical Center, Sacramento, CA, p. A82

O'DELL, Darrell, Director Information Services, Good Samaritan Hospital, San Jose, CA, p. A86

O'DELL, Michael, Chief Financial Officer, Sheridan County Health Complex, Hoxie, KS, p. A237

ODEN, Greg, Chief Medical Officer, Merit Health Central, Jackson, MS, p. A348

ODEN, Ryan, D.O., Chief of Staff, Arbuckle Memorial Hospital, Sulphur, OK, p. A507

ODETOYINBO, Adedapo, M.D., Chief Medical Office, Emory Johns Creek Hospital, Johns Creek, GA, p. A155

ODLE, Susan, Administrator, St. Joseph Memorial Hospital, Murphysboro, IL, p. A190

ODOM, Jake, Chief Information Officer, Trinity Hospital, Weaverville, CA, p. A95

ODOM, Jennifer, Interim Director Human Resources, Flowers Hospital, Dothan, AL, p. A17

ODOM, Lee Ann, Division President, Beaumont Hospital - Taylor, MI, p. A324

ODOM, Robbin, Chief Nursing Officer, Christus Ochsner Lake Area Hospital, Lake Charles, LA, p. A272

ODOM, Terry, Chief Executive Officer, Powell Valley Healthcare, Powell, WY, p. A709

O'DONNELL, Jan, Chief Nursing Officer, South Texas Surgical Hospital, Corpus Christi, TX, p. A594

O'DONNELL, John, Director of Information Technology Services, Mary Black Health System-Spartanburg, Spartanburg, SC, p. A557

O'DONNELL, Michael F., CPA, Chief Financial Officer, Peconic Bay Medical Center, Riverhead, NY, p. A441

O'DONNELL, Patrick W., CPA, President and Chief Executive Officer, Chambersburg Hospital, Chambersburg, PA, p. A522

O'DONOGHUE, Brian, M.D., Chief Medical Officer, Breckinridge Memorial Hospital, Hardinsburg, KY, p. A253

ODUWOLE, Adedapo, M.D., Medical Director, Lighthouse Behavioral Health Hospital, Conway, SC, p. A552

OEHL, Varonica, Chief Financial Officer, Fort Lauderdale Hospital, Fort Lauderdale, FL, p. A122

OEHLKE, Tammy, Director Human Resources, St. Mark's Medical Center, La Grange, TX, p. A618

OEHMKE, Brittni, Administrator, Hanover Hospital, Hanover, KS, p. A236

OETTING, Phyllis, Director Human Resources, Mitchell County Hospital Health Systems, Beloit, KS, p. A232

OETZEL, Gerald P, Chief Financial Officer, Temple University Hospital - Episcopal Division, PA, p. A536

OFFUTT, Dan, Manager Finance, Knox County Hospital, Knox City, TX, p. A618

O'FLANAGAN, Jayne, Director Human Resources, Incline Village Community Hospital, Incline Village, NV, p. A393

OFSTEDAL, Jeff, Manager Information Technology, Glacial Ridge Health System, Glenwood, MN, p. A332

OGASAWARA, Keith, M.D., Associate Medical Director and Professional Chief of Staff, Kaiser Permanente Medical Center, Honolulu, HI, p. A164

OGAWA, Quin
Chief Financial Officer, Sutter Health Kahi Mohala, Ewa Beach, HI, p. A164
Vice President Finance and Chief Financial Officer, Kuakini Medical Center, Honolulu, HI, p. A164

OGDEN, Judy, Director Information Technology, Franklin Medical Center, Winnsboro, LA, p. A281

OGDEN, Lesley, M.D.
Chief Executive Officer, Samaritan North Lincoln Hospital, Lincoln City, OR, p. A514
Chief Executive Officer, Samaritan Pacific Communities Hospital, Newport, OR, p. A515

OGDEN, Michael L., President and Chief Executive Officer, Little Falls Hospital, Little Falls, NY, p. A429

OGIER, Katie, Director of Nursing, Rock County Hospital, Bassett, NE, p. A381

OGILVIE, Richard, Chief Information Officer, Southwestern Vermont Medical Center, Bennington, VT, p. A653

OGLESBY, Lorie A., Director of Human Resources, Baptist Health Madisonville, Madisonville, KY, p. A257

OGLESBY, Lorri, Chief Nursing Officer, Encompass Health Rehabilitation Hospital Of Texarkana, Texarkana, TX, p. A639

O'GORMAN, Victoria, Administrator, Kaiser Permanente Fremont Medical Center, Fremont, CA, p. A59

OGORZALEK, Ed, Chief Financial Officer, Rutland Regional Medical Center, Rutland, VT, p. A654

OGRINC, Mary L, R.N., MS, Chief Nursing Officer, Senior Vice President Patient Care Services, Tripoint Medical Center, OH, p. A479

OGROD, Eugene, M.D., Chief Medical Officer, Kingwood Medical Center, Kingwood, TX, p. A618

OH, Christina E., Chief Executive Officer, Placentia-Linda Hospital, Placentia, CA, p. A78

O'HARA, Denise, Vice President Human Resources, Wilson Medical Center, Wilson, NC, p. A462

O'HARA, Gene L., Chief Executive Officer, Colorado Plains Medical Center, Fort Morgan, CO, p. A100

O'HARA, Kathleen, Vice President Human Resources, Erie County Medical Center, Buffalo, NY, p. A423

O'HARA, Michael
Senior Executive Director Human Resources, Houston Medical Center, Warner Robins, GA, p. A163
Senior Executive Director, Perry Hospital, Perry, GA, p. A158

O'HAVER, Tim, Chief Operating Officer, St. Joseph Medical Center, Tacoma, WA, p. A679

OHL, Connie, Acting Chief Human Resources, Veterans Affairs Illiana Health Care System, Danville, IL, p. A180

OHLER, Kevin, Director of Finance, Promise Hospital Of San Diego, San Diego, CA, p. A84

OHMART, Dean, Vice President Financial Services and Chief Financial Officer, Western Missouri Medical Center, Warrensburg, MO, p. A371

OHRT, James M, M.D., Director Medical Staff, Henderson Health Care Services, Henderson, NE, p. A385

OJEDA, Guadalupe, R.N., Chief Nursing Officer, West Covina Medical Center, West Covina, CA, p. A95

OJOMO, Karanita, M.D., Chief of Staff, Lewisgale Hospital Pulaski, Pulaski, VA, p. A664

OKABE, David
Executive Vice President, Chief Financial Officer and Treasurer, Pali Momi Medical Center, Aiea, HI, p. A164
Executive Vice President, Chief Financial Officer and Treasurer, Straub Medical Center, Honolulu, HI, p. A165
Executive Vice President, Chief Financial Officer and Treasurer, Wilcox Medical Center, Lihue, HI, p. A166
Senior Vice President, Chief Financial Officer and Treasurer, Kapiolani Medical Center For Women & Children, Honolulu, HI, p. A164

O'KEEFE, James M., President and Chief Executive Officer, Mile Bluff Medical Center, Mauston, WI, p. A697

O'KEEFE, John
Chief Executive Officer, Select Specialty Hospital-Gulfport, Gulfport, MS, p. A347
Chief Nursing Officer, Day Kimball Hospital, Putnam, CT, p. A110

O'KEEFE, Kathy
Executive Director, Pilgrim Psychiatric Center, Brentwood, NY, p. A423
Interim Executive Director, Sagamore Children's Hospital Psychiatric Center, Dix Hills, NY, p. A425

O'KEEFE, Michael, Interim Chief Executive Officer, Community Memorial Hospital, Redfield, SD, p. A563

O'KEEFE, Sharon L
President, University of Chicago Medical Center, Bernard Mitchell Hospital, IL, p. A180
President, University of Chicago Medical Center, Chicago Lying-In (Cli), IL, p. A180
President, University of Chicago Medical Center, Comer Children's Hospital, IL, p. A180

O'KEEFE, Sharon L., President, Comer Children's Hospital, IL, p. A180

O'KEEFE, Trish, Ph.D., R.N., President, Goryeb Children's Hospital, NJ, p. A408

O'KELLEY, J. Shannon, Chief Operating Officer, Mattel Children's Hospital, CA, p. A69

OKEN, Jeffrey, Vice President of Medical Affairs, Northwestern Medicine Marianjoy Rehabilitation Hospital, Wheaton, IL, p. A198

OKESON, Keith, President and Chief Executive Officer, Lifecare Medical Center, Roseau, MN, p. A338

OKEY, Suzi, Director of Nursing, Southwest Health Center Nursing Home, WI, p. A701

OKONIEWSKI, Susan, M.D., Chief of Staff, Chi St. Gabriel's Health, Little Falls, MN, p. A333

OKSENDAHL, Elaine, Director Human Resources and Risk Management, Schick Shadel Hospital, Seattle, WA, p. A676

OKUHARA, Mary, Chief Human Resource Officer, Lakewood Regional Medical Center, Lakewood, CA, p. A64

OKUNO-JONES, Susan K, Vice President Patient Care Services and Chief Nursing Executive, Advocate Good Samaritan Hospital, Downers Grove, IL, p. A181

O'LAIRE, Beth, Manager Human Resources, Ascension Calumet Hospital, Chilton, WI, p. A691

OLAND, Charisse S., FACHE, President and Chief Executive Officer, Hshs St. Joseph's Hospital, Chippewa Falls, WI, p. A691

OLANDER, Scott, Chief Financial Officer, Evergreenhealth Monroe, Monroe, WA, p. A673

OLASON, Roxanne, R.N., FACHE, Vice President and Chief Nursing Officer, Skagit Regional Health, Mount Vernon, WA, p. A674

OLDER, Michael, M.D., President Medical Staff, Nashoba Valley Medical Center, Ayer, MA, p. A295

OLDHAM, Jennie, Director Human Resources, Goodall-Witcher Hospital Authority, Clifton, TX, p. A593

OLDHAM, Lawrence, Chief Financial Officer, Arise Austin Medical Center, Austin, TX, p. A585

OLDHAM, Marriner, M.D., Chief Medical Officer, U.S. Air Force Regional Hospital, Elmendorf Afb, AK, p. A26

OLDS, Debbie D, R.N., MSN, Director of Nursing, Wk Bossier Health Center, LA, p. A279

O'LEARY, Bill, Chief Executive Officer, Pondera Medical Center, Conrad, MT, p. A374

O'LEARY, Daniel H, M.D., Chief Medical Officer, Umass Memorial Healthalliance-Clinton Hospital, MA, p. A301

O'LEARY, Kevin J, Senior Vice President and Chief Financial Officer, Exeter Hospital, Exeter, NH, p. A399

O'LEARY, Megan A, Vice President Human Resources and Rehabilitation Services, Mckenzie-Willamette Medical Center, Springfield, OR, p. A518

OLEJNICZAK, David R
Chief Operating Officer, Metro Health - University Of Michigan Health, Wyoming, MI, p. A326
Chief Operating Officer, St. John's Children's Hospital, IL, p. A196

OLEKSYK, Mike, M.D., Vice President and Chief Medical Officer, Baptist Hospital, Pensacola, FL, p. A136

OLESTON, Caryn Lynn, FACHE, MSN, R.N.
Chief Nursing Officer, Mercyhealth Hospital And Medical Center - Harvard, Harvard, IL, p. A184
Chief Nursing Officer, Mercyhealth Hospital And Medical Center - Walworth, Lake Geneva, WI, p. A695

OLESZAK, Randy, Director Fiscal Services, Milwaukee County Behavioral Health Division, Milwaukee, WI, p. A699

OLEY, Edwin M., President and Chief Executive Officer, Mercy Regional Medical Center, Lorain, OH, p. A485

OLIGSCHLAEGER, David, Medical Staff President, Hshs Good Shepherd Hospital, Shelbyville, IL, p. A195

OLIND, Shelby
Chief Executive Officer, Platte County Memorial Hospital, Wheatland, WY, p. A710
Interim Chief Executive Officer, Community Hospital, Torrington, WY, p. A710

OLINDE, Chad E., CPA, Administrator and Chief Executive Officer, Pointe Coupee General Hospital, New Roads, LA, p. A276

OLINGER, Richard P, Chief Financial Officer, Lecom Health Millcreek Community Hospital, Erie, PA, p. A525

OLINSKI, Janis, R.N., Vice President Clinical Services, Harrison Community Hospital, Cadiz, OH, p. A473

OLIPHANT, Gerald P, Executive Vice President and Chief Operating Officer, Good Samaritan Hospital, Cincinnati, OH, p. A475

OLIPHANT, Jenny, Executive Vice President and Chief Operating Officer, Bethesda Butler Hospital, OH, p. A474

OLIPHANT, Phillip, Chief Information Officer, U.S. Air Force Regional Hospital, Elmendorf Afb, AK, p. A26

OLIVARES, Rafael, Controller, Starr County Memorial Hospital, Rio Grande City, TX, p. A630

OLIVAREZ, Lorenzo, Senior Vice President and Chief Financial Officer, Bsa Hospital, Llc, Amarillo, TX, p. A583

OLIVAS, Ray, Chief Fiscal Service, West Texas Veterans Affairs Health Care System, Big Spring, TX, p. A589

OLIVE, Alan C., Chief Executive Officer, Northern Nevada Medical Center, Sparks, NV, p. A397

OLIVENCIA, Humberto, M.D., Medical Director, Hospital Perea, Mayaguez, PR, p. A714

OLIVER, David, Director Information Systems, King's Daughters Medical Center, Ashland, KY, p. A249

OLIVER, Diane, R.N., MSN, Chief Nursing Officer, Peninsula Hospital, TN, p. A572

OLIVER, Doug, Chief Financial Officer, Windhaven Psychiatric Hospital, Prescott Valley, AZ, p. A35

OLIVER, Michelle
Chief Nursing Executive, Hshs Good Shepherd Hospital, Shelbyville, IL, p. A195
Chief Nursing Officer, Hshs St. Mary's Hospital, Decatur, IL, p. A181

OLIVER, Rick, Information Technology, Hamilton Hospital, Olney, TX, p. A626

OLIVER, Rosalie
Chief Financial Officer, Florida Hospital Lake Placid, FL, p. A139
Senior Vice President and Chief Financial Officer, Florida Hospital Wauchula, Wauchula, FL, p. A143
OLIVER, Vincent, FACHE, Administrator, Island Hospital, Anacortes, WA, p. A669
OLIVERA, Sue, Vice President, Aultman Hospital Pediatric Services, OH, p. A473
OLIVERAS, Freddy, Chief Information Officer, Martin County Hospital District, Stanton, TX, p. A637
OLIVERAS LAGUNA, Ana, Administrator, Caribbean Medical Center, Fajardo, PR, p. A713
OLIVIER, Athan, III, R.N., FACHE, Administrator and Chief Executive Officer, Iberia Rehabilitation Hospital, New Iberia, LA, p. A275
OLIVIER, Edward
Chief Financial Officer, Charles A. Dean Memorial Hospital, Greenville, ME, p. A284
Chief Financial Officer, Martha's Vineyard Hospital, Oak Bluffs, MA, p. A303
OLLI, Cindy, R.N., Chief Nursing Officer, Schoolcraft Memorial Hospital, Manistique, MI, p. A318
OLLIE, Edwin J, Executive Vice President and Chief Financial Officer, Cape Fear Hospital, NC, p. A462
OLLSON, Joanne, Vice President Human Resources, Baystate Noble Hospital, Westfield, MA, p. A305
OLM-SHIPMAN, Bobby
Chief Executive Officer, Saint Luke's South Hospital, Overland Park, KS, p. A243
President and Chief Executive Officer, Saint Luke's Cushing Hospital, Leavenworth, KS, p. A239
OLMSTEAD, David, Director, Human Resources, City Hospital At White Rock, Dallas, TX, p. A596
OLMSTEAD, Linda, Director, Human Resources, Uw Medicine/Northwest Hospital & Medical Center, Seattle, WA, p. A677
OLNEY, Garry M.
Chief Executive Officer, Providence Little Company Of Mary Medical Center - Torrance, Torrance, CA, p. A92
Chief Executive Officer, Providence Little Company Of Mary Medical Center San Pedro, Los Angeles, CA, p. A69
OLS, Timothy A., FACHE
Chief Executive Officer, Baylor Scott & White Medical Center - Llano, Llano, TX, p. A620
President, Baylor Scott & White Medical Center - Marble Falls, Marble Falls, TX, p. A622
O'LOUGHLIN, James F., Chief Executive Officer, Florida Hospital Ocala, Ocala, FL, p. A133
OLSCAMP, Karen E., President and Chief Executive Officer, University Of Maryland Baltimore Washington Medical Center, Glen Burnie, MD, p. A292
OLSEN, Debbie, Human Resource Partner, Sparrow Ionia Hospital, Ionia, MI, p. A316
OLSEN, Jennifer, M.D., Chief of Staff, North Canyon Medical Center, Gooding, ID, p. A169
OLSEN, Karen M, R.N., Chief Nursing Officer, Mission Hospital, NC, p. A447
OLSEN, Ryan, Chief Operating Officer, Memorialcare, Saddleback Memorial Medical Center, Laguna Hills, CA, p. A63
OLSEN, Sabrina, Chief Financial Officer, Duke Children's Hospital & Health Center, NC, p. A451
OLSON, Cheryl, Vice President, Pomerado Hospital, Poway, CA, p. A79
OLSON, Craig, Director Information Technology, Southwestern Regional Medical Center, Tulsa, OK, p. A509
OLSON, Dave, Director of Nursing, Montana State Hospital, Warm Springs, MT, p. A379
OLSON, Diana
Chief Human Resources Officer, Mercy Health - Willard Hospital, Willard, OH, p. A493
Director Human Resources, Mercy Tiffin Hospital, Tiffin, OH, p. A491
OLSON, Eric, Chief Financial Officer, Providence Portland Medical Center, Portland, OR, p. A516
OLSON, Erik, Chief Executive Officer, Renown Children's Hospital, NV, p. A396
OLSON, Forrest, M.D., Chief Medical Officer, Enloe Medical Center-Cohasset, CA, p. A54
OLSON, John L., M.D., Medical Director, Marshfield Medical Center - Rice Lake, Rice Lake, WI, p. A702
OLSON, Joni, Chief Executive Officer, Gundersen Tri-County Hospital And Clinics, Whitehall, WI, p. A706
OLSON, Kevin, Director Information Systems, Ssm Health St. Anthony South, OK, p. A504
OLSON, Lacey, M.D., Chief Medical Staff, Sanford Chamberlain Medical Center, Chamberlain, SD, p. A560
OLSON, Lynn R, Director Human Resources, Hendricks Community Hospital Association, Hendricks, MN, p. A332

OLSON, Marcia
Business Office Manager, Webster County Community Hospital, Red Cloud, NE, p. A390
Director Finance and Controller, Spearfish Regional Surgery Center, SD, p. A564
OLSON, MariBeth, R.N., Vice President Patient Care Services, Unity Hospital, MN, p. A330
OLSON, Mark, M.D.
Chief of Staff, Lincoln Community Hospital And Nursing Home, Hugo, CO, p. A102
Interim Chief Information Officer, Behavioral Health Network, Natchaug Hospital, Mansfield Center, CT, p. A108
OLSON, Michael R., Chief Executive Officer, Citizens Medical Center, Victoria, TX, p. A642
OLSON, Tim
Senior Vice President Finance, Thedacare Regional Medical Center-Appleton, Appleton, WI, p. A689
Senior Vice President Finance, Thedacare Regional Medical Center-Neenah, Neenah, WI, p. A699
OLSON, Tracy L, Human Resource Officer, Avera St. Luke's Hospital, Aberdeen, SD, p. A559
OLSSON, Dave, Director of Marketing, Aspirus Keweenaw Hospital, Inc., Laurium, MI, p. A318
OLSZYK, Mark, M.D., Vice President Medical Affairs and Chief Medical Officer, Carroll Hospital Center, Westminster, MD, p. A294
O'MALLEY, Constance, President, Beaumont Hospital - Farmington Hills, Farmington Hills, MI, p. A312
O'MALLEY, John F., FACHE, President, St. Joseph Mercy Livingston Hospital, Howell, MI, p. A315
O'MALLEY, Jon P., Chief Executive Officer, Select Specialty Hospital-Macomb County, Mount Clemens, MI, p. A319
O'MALLEY, Mary Jo, R.N., MS, Vice President Diagnostics and Support Services, Oconomowoc Memorial Hospital, Oconomowoc, WI, p. A700
O'MALLEY, Trevor, Site Manager, Presence Saint Joseph Hospital, Elgin, IL, p. A182
OMAN, Michelle, D.O.
Chief Medical Officer, Essentia Health Northern Pines Medical Center, Aurora, MN, p. A327
Chief Medical Officer, Essentia Health-Virginia, Virginia, MN, p. A341
OMOLARA, Khar, M.D., Chief Medical Staff, Jefferson County Hospital, Fayette, MS, p. A345
OMRAN, Yasser, M.D., President Medical Staff, Pomerene Hospital, Millersburg, OH, p. A487
OMTA, Stephen R, Chief Operating Officer, Peacehealth St. Joseph Medical Center, Bellingham, WA, p. A669
OMURA, David
Associate Director, Wm. Jennings Bryan Dorn Veterans Affairs Medical Center, Columbia, SC, p. A552
Interim Director, Wm. Jennings Bryan Dorn Veterans Affairs Medical Center, Columbia, SC, p. A552
ONDRUSEK, Ashley, Chief Executive Officer, Post Acute/Warm Springs Specialty Hospital Of New Braunfels, New Braunfels, TX, p. A625
ONEAL, Karen, Chief Financial Officer, Burke Medical Center, Waynesboro, GA, p. A163
O'NEAL, Charlotte, Vice President Human Resources, Research Psychiatric Center, MO, p. A361
O'NEAL, Jessica, Chief Operating Officer, West Florida Rehabilitation Institute, FL, p. A136
O'NEAL, Lewis Stephen, R.N., MSN, Chief Nursing Officer, Saint Joseph London, London, KY, p. A255
O'NEAL, Michael, Administrator and Chief Executive Officer, George C Grape Community Hospital, Hamburg, IA, p. A223
O'NEIL, Alan, Chief Executive Officer, Unity Medical Center, Grafton, ND, p. A466
O'NEIL, Jeremy, Administrator, Providence Valdez Medical Center, Valdez, AK, p. A27
O'NEIL, John, Chief Executive Officer, Pickens County Medical Center, Carrollton, AL, p. A16
O'NEIL, Patrick, Senior Vice President Medical Affairs, Lake Regional Health System, Osage Beach, MO, p. A365
O'NEIL, Terry, Chief Information Technology, Nazareth Hospital, Philadelphia, PA, p. A535
ONEILL, Steve, Chief Information Officer, Henry J. Carter Specialty Hospital & Nursing Facility, NY, p. A435
O'NEILL, Beth, Chief Nursing Officer, Morgan Memorial Hospital, Madison, GA, p. A157
O'NEILL, Jennifer A, R.N., Chief Nursing Officer, Vice President Patient Care Services, Saint Barnabas Medical Center, Livingston, NJ, p. A406
O'NEILL, Lynn, R.N., Chief Nursing Officer, Medical City Lewisville, Lewisville, TX, p. A619
O'NEILL, Melissa, Vice President Human Resources, Advocate Sherman Hospital, Elgin, IL, p. A182
O'NEILL, Michael, M.D., Chief Medical Officer, Eastside Medical Center, Snellville, GA, p. A161

O'NEILL, Stephan, Vice President Information Services, Institute Of Living, CT, p. A108
O'NEILL, Tana, R.N., Chief Nursing Officer, West Holt Medical Services, Atkinson, NE, p. A381
ONG, Hannah, Director, Medical Affairs, Saint Elizabeths Hospital, Washington, DC, p. A116
ONG, Richard B, Chief Information Officer, Saint Vincent Hospital, Erie, PA, p. A525
ONI, Buki, M.D., Chief Medical Officer, Kenmare Community Hospital, Kenmare, ND, p. A467
ONIFATHER, Jeff, Chief Financial Officer, Cornerstone Of Medical Arts Center Hospital, Fresh Meadows, NY, p. A426
ONO, Craig, M.D., Chief of Staff, Shriners Hospitals For Children-Honolulu, Honolulu, HI, p. A165
ONOFRE, Bonnie, Chief Nursing Officer, South Lake Hospital, Clermont, FL, p. A120
OPBROEK, Steve, Manager Information Technology, Skyline Hospital, White Salmon, WA, p. A680
OPHAUG, Courtney, FACHE, Chief Executive Officer, Banner Estrella Medical Center, Phoenix, AZ, p. A33
OPHEIKENS, Robyn, Assistant Administrator Human Resources, St. Mark's Hospital, Salt Lake City, UT, p. A651
OPPENHEIMER, Steven, Chief Executive Officer, Del Amo Hospital, Torrance, CA, p. A91
OPPONG, Bernard, D.O., Chief of Staff, Madison Health, London, OH, p. A485
OPRANDI, Allison, M.D., Chief Medical Officer, Aultman Hospital Pediatric Services, OH, p. A473
OPRISKO, Judy P
Vice President Human Resources, John Heinz Institute Of Rehabilitation Medicine, Wilkes, PA, p. A544
Vice President, Allied Services Rehabilitation Hospital, Scranton, PA, p. A540
OPSETH, Gregory, Chief Nursing Officer, Guthrie County Hospital, Guthrie Center, IA, p. A223
OPSTEDAHL, DeeAnna, R.N., Vice President Patient Care Services, Chi St. Alexius Health - Dickinson Medical Center, Dickinson, ND, p. A465
OPSUT, Jennifer, Interim Chief Operating Officer, West Valley Medical Center, Caldwell, ID, p. A168
OQUENDO, Tanja, Chief Human Resources Officer, Flaget Memorial Hospital, Bardstown, KY, p. A249
ORAVEC, Jon, Vice President, Human Resources, Howard County General Hospital, Columbia, MD, p. A291
ORAZINE, Jay, Director Information Services, Baptist Health Paducah, Paducah, KY, p. A259
ORCUTT, David, Chief Executive Officer, Lake Granbury Medical Center, Granbury, TX, p. A607
ORDYNA, Daniel, Chief Executive Officer, Portneuf Medical Center, Pocatello, ID, p. A171
ORE, Ruta, Director Human Resources, Pottstown Hospital, Pottstown, PA, p. A539
OREAR, Kathy, Director Human Resources, Newman Regional Health, Emporia, KS, p. A234
O'REAR, Caleb F., Chief Executive Officer, Alta Vista Regional Hospital, Las Vegas, NM, p. A418
OREGEL, Omar, Controller, Kindred Hospital-Ontario, Ontario, CA, p. A76
O'REILLY, Frank, Director, Dr. J. Corrigan Mental Health Center, Fall River, MA, p. A299
ORELLANA, Feliipe, Chief Medical Officer, Barnes-Jewish St. Peters Hospital, Saint Peters, MO, p. A370
OREN, Cole, R.N., Chief Nursing Officer, Select Specialty Hospital-Durham, Durham, NC, p. A451
OREOL, Harry, Acting Chief Executive Officer, Patton State Hospital, Patton, CA, p. A78
ORFANIDIS, Deanna, MS, R.N., Chief Nursing Officer, Mt. Ascutney Hospital And Health Center, Windsor, VT, p. A654
ORIOL, Albert, Vice President Information Management and Chief Information Officer, Rady Children's Hospital - San Diego, San Diego, CA, p. A84
ORLANDI, Mary, Manager Human Resources, Carney Hospital, Boston, MA, p. A296
ORLANDO, Anthony T, Senior Vice President Finance, Englewood Hospital And Medical Center, Englewood, NJ, p. A405
ORLANDO, Kristin, Director Operations, Mid-Hudson Forensic Psychiatric Center, New Hampton, NY, p. A431
ORLANDO, Lorraine, Vice President Human Resources, New York-Presbyterian Queens, New York (Includes All Hospitals Located Within The Five Boroughs), NY, p. A435
ORMAN, Bernard A., Jr, FACHE, Chief Executive Officer, Samaritan Hospital, Macon, MO, p. A364
ORMOND, Evalyn, Chief Executive Officer, Union General Hospital, Farmerville, LA, p. A267
ORMOND, Jack, Chief Financial Officer, Cuba Memorial Hospital, Cuba, NY, p. A425
ORMOND, John (Jack) T., Director Finance and Revenue, Wyoming County Community Hospital, Warsaw, NY, p. A445

ORNELAS, Henry
Chief Operating Officer, Salinas Valley Memorial Healthcare System, Salinas, CA, p. A83
Chief Operating Officer, Women's And Children's Hospital, CA, p. A68
O'ROURKE, Jane, R.N., Chief Nursing Officer, Vice President Operations, St. Peter's Hospital, Albany, NY, p. A421
O'ROURKE, Michael
Regional Human Resource Officer, Presence Mercy Medical Center, Aurora, IL, p. A173
Regional Human Resources Lead, Presence Saint Joseph Hospital, Elgin, IL, p. A182
OROZCO, Jorge, Chief Executive Officer, Rancho Los Amigos National Rehabilitation Center, Downey, CA, p. A56
ORR, Karen
Administrator and Chief Nursing Officer, Providence Medical Center, Kansas City, KS, p. A238
Chief Nursing Officer, Providence Medical Center, Kansas City, KS, p. A238
ORR, Natassia, Chief Operating Officer, Chris Evert Childrens Hospital, FL, p. A122
ORR, Stephanie, Chief Nursing Officer, Steele Memorial Medical Center, Salmon, ID, p. A172
ORRICK, Charles H., Administrator, Donalsonville Hospital, Donalsonville, GA, p. A152
ORSINI, John
Executive Vice President and Chief Financial Officer, Behavioral Health Center, IL, p. A198
Executive Vice President and Chief Financial Officer, Northwestern Medicine Delnor Hospital, Geneva, IL, p. A184
Senior Vice President, Chief Financial Officer, Northwestern Medicine Kishwaukee Hospital, Dekalb, IL, p. A181
ORSINI, Thomas J., President and Chief Executive Officer, Lake Taylor Transitional Care Hospital, Norfolk, VA, p. A662
ORT, Linda, Chief Financial Officer, Piggott Community Hospital, Piggott-Clay County, AR, p. A47
ORTEGA, Becky, Manager Human Resources, Avista Adventist Hospital, Louisville, CO, p. A103
ORTEGA, Cesar, M.D., Chief of Staff, Doctors Hospital Parkway, TX, p. A614
ORTEGA, Debbie, Chief Human Resource Officer and Vice President Administrative Services, Huntington Memorial Hospital, Pasadena, CA, p. A78
ORTEGA, Jose, Chief Operating Officer, Greater El Monte Community Hospital, South El Monte, CA, p. A90
ORTEGO, Ashley, Director Human Resources and Marketing, Springhill Medical Center, Springhill, LA, p. A279
ORTH, Charam, Director Human Resources, Frances Mahon Deaconess Hospital, Glasgow, MT, p. A375
ORTHAUS, Denis, Director Human Resources, Wellspan Philhaven, Mount Gretna, PA, p. A532
ORTIZ, Andrew, Senior Vice President, Human Resources and Organization Development, Cedars-Sinai Medical Center, Los Angeles, CA, p. A66
ORTIZ, Bienvenido, Coordinator Information Systems, Hospital De Damas, Ponce, PR, p. A714
ORTIZ, Blas, Jr, Assistant Superintendent and Public Information Officer, South Texas Health Care System, TX, p. A608
ORTIZ, Edson, Chief Information Officer, Hospital Pavia Yauco, Yauco, PR, p. A717
ORTIZ, Evelyn Padilla
Director Human Resources, Hospital Menonita De Cayey, Cayey, PR, p. A713
Director Human Resources, Mennonite General Hospital, Aibonito, PR, p. A712
ORTIZ, Francisco, M.D., Chief of Staff, Jackson County Hospital District, Edna, TX, p. A601
ORTIZ, Jose O, Chief Financial Officer, Ryder Memorial Hospital, Humacao, PR, p. A714
ORTIZ, Migdalia, Director Human Resources, Hospital San Carlos Borromeo, Moca, PR, p. A714
ORTIZ, Nancy, Director Human Resource and Marketing, Frio Regional Hospital, Pearsall, TX, p. A627
ORTIZ, Norma, M.D., Medical Director, Puerto Rico Children's Hospital, PR, p. A712
ORTIZ BAEZ, Felix, Administrator, I. Gonzalez Martinez Oncologic Hospital, Hato Rey, PR, p. A713
ORTO, Victoria K, R.N., Chief Nursing and Patient Care Services Officer, Duke Regional Hospital, Durham, NC, p. A451
ORTOLANI, Philip A, Vice President Operations, Mid Coast Hospital, Brunswick, ME, p. A283
ORTON, Wendy, Chief Nursing Officer, Alleghany Memorial Hospital, Sparta, NC, p. A461
OSANTOSKI, Tina, Director Human Resources, Harbor Beach Community Hospital, Harbor Beach, MI, p. A315
OSARIO, Cesar, Specialist Information Technology, Cedar Crest Hospital And Residential Treatment Center, Belton, TX, p. A589

OSBAHR, Leah, M.P.H., Chief Executive Officer, Helena Regional Medical Center, Helena-Phillips County, AR, p. A43
OSBERG, Art, M.D., Chief Medical Officer, West Marion Community Hospital, FL, p. A133
OSBORN, Kim, Chief Financial Officer, Sequoia Hospital, Redwood City, CA, p. A80
OSBORN, Melodie
Vice President and Chief Nursing Officer, Transitional Care Services, Renown Rehabilitation Hospital, Reno, NV, p. A396
Vice President and Chief Nursing Officer, Transitional Care Services, Renown South Meadows Medical Center, Reno, NV, p. A396
OSBORN, Tom, D.O., Chief Medical Staff, Holdenville General Hospital, Holdenville, OK, p. A500
OSBORNE, Anna, Chief Human Resources Management Service, West Texas Veterans Affairs Health Care System, Big Spring, TX, p. A589
OSBORNE, Jay, M.D., Senior Vice President Medical Affairs, Northside Medical Center, OH, p. A494
OSBORNE, Phil, Director Information Technology, Bourbon Community Hospital, Paris, KY, p. A259
OSBURN, Jerry, Chief Executive Officer, Yoakum County Hospital, Denver City, TX, p. A599
OSCADAL, Martin
Senior Vice President Human Resources, St. Elizabeth Falmouth, KY, p. A252
Senior Vice President Human Resources, St. Elizabeth Florence, Florence, KY, p. A252
Vice President Human Resources, St. Elizabeth Covington, KY, p. A251
OSE, Peggy, FACHE, MSN, R.N., Chief Nursing Officer, Aspirus Riverview Hospital And Clinics, Inc., Wisconsin Rapids, WI, p. A706
OSEGARD, Jeff, Chief Information Officer, Cass County Memorial Hospital, Atlantic, IA, p. A217
OSEHOBO, Philip, M.D., Chief Medical Officer, Wellstar Spalding Regional Hospital, Griffin, GA, p. A154
OSER, William F., M.D.
Chief Medical Officer, Hackensack Meridian Health Jfk Johnson Rehabilitation Institute, Edison, NJ, p. A404
Senior Vice President and Chief Medical Officer, Hackensack Meridian Health Jfk Medical Center, Edison, NJ, p. A404
O'SHEA, James, Chief Operating Officer, Baton Rouge Behavioral Hospital, Baton Rouge, LA, p. A263
OSINSKI, Kathleen, Chief Human Resources Service, John D. Dingell Veterans Affairs Medical Center, Detroit, MI, p. A311
OSKIN, Jeffrey L., Vice President and Administrator, Camc Memorial Hospital, WV, p. A682
OSLIN, Dave, M.D., Chief of Staff, Philadelphia Veterans Affairs Medical Center, Philadelphia, PA, p. A536
OSOWSKI, Angela, Chief Nursing Officer, Lifecare Hospitals Of Wisconsin, Pewaukee, WI, p. A701
OSSELLO, Susan, Chief Financial Officer, Granite County Medical Center, Philipsburg, MT, p. A378
OSTASZEWSKI, Patricia, MS, Chief Executive Officer, Healthsouth Rehabilitation Hospital Of Toms River, Toms River, NJ, p. A412
OSTBERG, Melissa, Chief Financial Officer, Marias Medical Center, Shelby, MT, p. A379
OSTBLOOM, Jan, Human Resources Consultant, Our Lady Of Peace, Louisville, KY, p. A256
OSTEEN, Tom J, Director Area Technology, Modesto Medical Center, CA, p. A71
O'STEEN, Neil, Director Information Technology, Bacon County Hospital And Health System, Alma, GA, p. A145
OSTENSON, Scott, Chief Financial Officer, Jacobson Memorial Hospital Care Center, Elgin, ND, p. A465
OSTER, Kurt, Human Resources Officer, Carl Vinson Veterans Affairs Medical Center, Dublin, GA, p. A153
OSTERBERG, Valerie, Chief Financial Officer, Sanford Vermillion Medical Center, Vermillion, SD, p. A564
OSTERHOUT, David, Assistant Superintendent and Chief Financial Officer, El Paso Psychiatric Center, El Paso, TX, p. A601
OSTERLY, Eric, Chief Financial Officer, Florida Hospital Fish Memorial, Orange City, FL, p. A133
OSTLIG, Jane, Chief Medical Officer, Sanford Mayville Medical Center, Mayville, ND, p. A467
OSTRANDER, Maria DC, R.N., MSN, Chief Nurse Executive, San Antonio State Hospital, San Antonio, TX, p. A634
OSTREM, Jill, Senior Vice President and Chief Operating Officer, Jefferson Washington Township Hospital, NJ, p. A412
OSTROW, Peter, M.D., President Medical Staff, Beth Israel Deaconess Hospital-Needham Campus, Needham, MA, p. A302

O'SULLIVAN, Barbara, M.D., M.P.H., Medical Director, Rockefeller University Hospital, New York (Includes All Hospitals Located Within The Five Boroughs), NY, p. A437
O'SULLIVAN, Colin, Interim Chief Executive Officer, Cornerstone Hospital Of Houston - Bellaire, TX, p. A643
O'SULLIVAN, Paul, FACHE
Chief Executive Officer, Memorial Hermann Memorial City Medical Center, Houston, TX, p. A612
Chief Executive Officer, Memorial Hermann The Woodlands Hospital, TX, p. A612
OSWAL, Arvind, Interim Chief Financial Officer, Arrowhead Regional Medical Center, Colton, CA, p. A55
OSWALD, Traci L
Vice President of Human Resources, Galion Hospital, Galion, OH, p. A483
Vice President, Chief Human Resources, Avita Ontario Hospital, Ontario, OH, p. A488
OTERO, Jorge Torres., Executive Director, Hospital Del Maestro, San Juan, PR, p. A715
OTHOLE, Jean, Chief Executive Officer, U.S. Public Health Service Indian Hospital, Zuni, NM, p. A420
O'TOOL, Nick, Vice President Operational Finance, Chi Health Lakeside, Omaha, NE, p. A388
OTOTIVO, Brenda, Executive Director, Jim Taliaferro Community Mental Health, Lawton, OK, p. A500
OTOTT, Kelly, R.N., Chief Nursing Officer, Washington County Hospital, Washington, KS, p. A247
OTT, Darin, D.O., Chief of Staff, Kane County Hospital, Kanab, UT, p. A647
OTT, Eugene J., Jr, Chief Operating Officer, Eagleville Hospital, Eagleville, PA, p. A524
OTT, Laurie, Vice President Human Resources and President University Health Care Foundation, University Hospital, Augusta, GA, p. A147
OTT, Mark, M.D., Regional Chief Medical Director, Intermountain Medical Center, Murray, UT, p. A648
OTT, Pamela, Vice President Finance, Aurora Sheboygan Memorial Medical Center, Sheboygan, WI, p. A702
OTT, Ronald H., President, Excela Health Westmoreland Hospital, Greensburg, PA, p. A526
OTTATI, David, Regional Chief Executive Officer, Florida Hospital-Altamonte, FL, p. A134
OTTE, Elaine, Chief Operating Officer, Clarinda Regional Health Center, Clarinda, IA, p. A219
OTTEMAN, Diane, Chief Executive Officer, Kindred Chicago Lakeshore, IL, p. A177
OTTEN, Sharon A., Vice President Nursing, Advocate South Suburban Hospital, Hazel Crest, IL, p. A185
OTTENBACHER, John, Chief of Staff, Bowdle Hospital, Bowdle, SD, p. A559
OTTENS, Mark, Chief Nursing Officer, Baptist Memorial Hospital-North Mississippi, Oxford, MS, p. A351
OTTMAR, Kellie, Manager Information Services, East Adams Rural Healthcare, Ritzville, WA, p. A676
OTTO, Sara, Chief Compliance Officer, North Canyon Medical Center, Gooding, ID, p. A169
OTTO, Steve, Chief Executive Officer, Tristar Skyline Madison Campus, TN, p. A577
OTTOLINO, Joseph
Chief Executive Officer, West Suburban Medical Center, Oak Park, IL, p. A192
Chief Executive Officer, Westlake Hospital, Melrose Park, IL, p. A189
Chief Operating Officer, West Suburban Medical Center, Oak Park, IL, p. A192
OUBRE, Chris, Information Technology Director, Garden Park Medical Center, Gulfport, MS, p. A346
OUELETTE, Lisa, Director Human Resources, Beaumont Hospital - Troy, Troy, MI, p. A325
OUELLETTE, Demetra
Chief Operating Officer, Rehabilitation Hospital Of Rhode Island, North Smithfield, RI, p. A547
President, Roger Williams Medical Center, Providence, RI, p. A548
OUIMET, Mary Elizabeth, MSN, R.N., Senior Vice President and Chief Nursing Officer, Ascension All Saints, Racine, WI, p. A701
OUNGST, Laurie
Vice President and Chief Operating Officer, St. Mary's Hospital, WI, p. A702
Vice President, Operations, Ascension Eagle River Hospital, Eagle River, WI, p. A692
Vice President, Operations, Ascension Sacred Heart Hospital, Tomahawk, WI, p. A704
Vice President, Operations, Howard Young Medical Center, Woodruff, WI, p. A706
OURS, Matt, Chief Executive Officer and Managing Director, Rivendell Behavioral Health, Bowling Green, KY, p. A250
OUSEY, Tracy, Director Human Resources, Washington County Hospital And Clinics, Washington, IA, p. A230

OUTHIER, Amy, Director Health Information Management, Weatherford Regional Hospital, Weatherford, OK, p. A510

OUTLAW, Debbie, R.N., Director Patient Care Services, Coastal Virginia Rehabilitation, Newport News, VA, p. A662

OVANDO, Benjamin, Chief Operations Officer, Rancho Los Amigos National Rehabilitation Center, Downey, CA, p. A56

OVERBEY, William J., Chief Executive Officer, Kansas Rehabilitation Hospital, Topeka, KS, p. A246

OVERBY, Roger, Executive Director Information Systems, Greene County Medical Center, Jefferson, IA, p. A225

OVERCASH, Jenny, Director Human Resources, Healthsouth Huntington Rehabilitation Hospital, Huntington, WV, p. A683

OVERSTREET, Alyson, Chief Financial Officer, Washington County Hospital, Chatom, AL, p. A16

OVERSTREET, Amy, Director Human Resources, Trousdale Medical Center, Hartsville, TN, p. A570

OVERTON, Camie, Chief Executive Officer, Curahealth Tucson, Tucson, AZ, p. A37

OVERTON, Deana, Director Human Resources, Mitchell County Hospital, Colorado City, TX, p. A593

OVERTON, Saundra, R.N., Chief Nursing Officer, Royal Oaks Hospital, Windsor, MO, p. A372

OVESON, Mark, M.D., Chief Medical Staff, Central Valley Medical Center, Nephi, UT, p. A648

OWEN, Sabrina, Human Resources Officer, Knoxville Division, IA, p. A221

OWEN, Sandra, Director Fiscal and Accounting, Hospital District 6 - Anthony Campus, KS, p. A236

OWENS, Beverly, Controller, Rehabilitation Hospital, Navicent Health, Macon, GA, p. A157

OWENS, Brian, Chief Operating Officer, Lindner Center Of Hope, Mason, OH, p. A486

OWENS, Craig A., President, Wellstar Douglas Hospital, Douglasville, GA, p. A152

OWENS, Daniel, Chief Executive Officer, Emory University Hospital Midtown, Atlanta, GA, p. A146

OWENS, Diane, Assistant Administrator, St. David's Rehabilitation Center, TX, p. A586

OWENS, Mark, M.D., Vice President Medical Affairs, Mercy San Juan Medical Center, Carmichael, CA, p. A54

OWENS, Maxwell, FACHE, Chief Financial Officer, Huntsville Memorial Hospital, Huntsville, TX, p. A615

OWENS, Paul, M.D., Chief Medical Officer, Hackettstown Medical Center, Hackettstown, NJ, p. A405

OWENS, Rick, Chief Financial Officer, D. W. Mcmillan Memorial Hospital, Brewton, AL, p. A15

OWENS, Royce Bramer, Chief Operating Officer, Baylor Scott & White Medical Center - Llano, Llano, TX, p. A620

OWENS, Stephanie, Manager Human Resources, Mcdowell Arh Hospital, Mcdowell, KY, p. A258

OWENS, Thomas, M.D., President, Duke Children's Hospital & Health Center, NC, p. A451

OWENSBY, Terri, R.N., Chief Nursing Executive, Kaiser Permanente South Sacramento Medical Center, Sacramento, CA, p. A82

OWINGS, Karen, MSN, Vice President, Patient Care Services, Medstar Union Memorial Hospital, Baltimore, MD, p. A288

OWINGS, Raymond C., Interim Chief Financial Officer, Unc Rockingham Health Care, Eden, NC, p. A451

OWINGS, Thomas, Chief Executive Officer, Wesley Woodlawn Hospital & Er, KS, p. A248

OWREY, Donald R.
President, Shenango Valley Campus, PA, p. A526
President, Upmc Jameson, New Castle, PA, p. A533

OXENDALE, Sharon, President and Chief Operating Officer, Allenmore Hospital, WA, p. A679

OXFORD, Michelle, Chief Operating Officer, Acting Chief Executive Officer, Bakersfield Heart Hospital, Bakersfield, CA, p. A51

OXFORD, Tammy, Director Human Resources, Bob Wilson Memorial Grant County Hospital, Ulysses, KS, p. A247

OXLEY, Dawn, R.N., Associate Director Patient Care Services and Nurse Executive, Iowa City Veterans Affairs Health Care System, Iowa City, IA, p. A224

OXLEY, James, D.O., Vice President Medical Affairs, Orange Regional Medical Center, Middletown, NY, p. A430

OXLEY, Scott, President, The Acadia Hospital, Bangor, ME, p. A282

OXTON, Alice, Director Information Technology, Sentara Obici Hospital, Suffolk, VA, p. A667

OZBURN, Thomas H., Chief Executive Officer, Parkridge West Hospital, TN, p. A567

OZEL, A Deniz, M.D., Chief Medical Officer, Northeast Rehabilitation Hospital, Salem, NH, p. A401

OZMENT, Mary, Chief Nursing Officer, Hillcrest Hospital Pryor, Pryor, OK, p. A506

OZUAH, Philip O., M.D., Ph.D., Executive Vice President and Chief Operating Officer, Montefiore Medical Center - North Division, NY, p. A433

P

PAARLBERG, Ted, Chief Executive Officer, Landmark Hospital Of Salt Lake City, Murray, UT, p. A648

PAASCH, Michael
Regional Chief Information Officer, Ssm Health St. Mary's Hospital - St. Louis, Saint Louis, MO, p. A369
Regional Vice President and Chief Information Officer, Ssm Cardinal Glennon Children's Hospital, Saint Louis, MO, p. A368
Vice President, Regional Chief Information Officer, Ssm Health St. Clare Hospital - Fenton, Fenton, MO, p. A359

PABLO, Gary M., M.D., Chief Medical Officer, Sacred Heart Hospital On The Emerald Coast, Miramar Beach, FL, p. A132

PABON, Jose O, Director Operations, Wilma N. Vazquez Medical Center, Vega Baja, PR, p. A716

PABON-RAMIREZ, Felix, Chief Information Officer, St. Charles Hospital, Port Jefferson, NY, p. A440

PACCA, Richard, M.D., Chief of Staff, Granville Health System, Oxford, NC, p. A458

PACCAPANICCIA, Dominic, Chief Operating Officer, Indiana Regional Medical Center, Indiana, PA, p. A528

PACE, Dewane, President and Chief Executive Officer, Haxtun Hospital District, Haxtun, CO, p. A102

PACE, Kathleen, MSN, R.N., Chief Nursing Officer, Englewood Community Hospital, Englewood, FL, p. A122

PACE, Kelly, Director Human Resource, Strategic Behavioral Health - Wilmington, Leland, NC, p. A456

PACEK, Thomas
Vice President Information Systems and Chief Information Officer, Bridgeton Health Center, NJ, p. A413
Vice President Information Systems and Chief Information Officer, Inspira Medical Center-Elmer, Elmer, NJ, p. A404

PACEY, Amy, Vice President Human Resources, Good Samaritan Medical Center, Lafayette, CO, p. A102

PACHECO, Robert W, Vice President Finance, Women & Infants Hospital Of Rhode Island, Providence, RI, p. A548

PACHUCKI, James J., Jr, Chief Financial Officer, Upmc Susquehanna Sunbury, Sunbury, PA, p. A542

PACINI, Jenna, Human Resources Specialist, Belmont Behavioral Hospital, Philadelphia, PA, p. A533

PACK, Natalie, Chief Financial Officer, St. David's North Austin Medical Center, Austin, TX, p. A586

PACK, William, Chief Financial Officer, Memorial Hermann Orthopedic And Spine Hospital, TX, p. A612

PACKER, Eric, Chief Executive Officer, Cedar City Hospital, Cedar City, UT, p. A646

PACKER, Lee, Administrator, South Florida State Hospital, Hollywood, FL, p. A124

PACKER, Steven J., M.D., President and Chief Executive Officer, Community Hospital Of The Monterey Peninsula, Monterey, CA, p. A73

PACURA, Lori, MSN, R.N., President, Holy Cross Hospital, Chicago, IL, p. A177

PACYNA, Andrew
Acting Director, Veterans Affairs Ann Arbor Healthcare System, Ann Arbor, MI, p. A307
Deputy Director, Louis Stokes Cleveland Veterans Affairs Medical Center, Cleveland, OH, p. A477

PACZKOWSKI, Rick, Chief Operating Officer, Timberlawn Mental Health System, Dallas, TX, p. A598

PADDEN, Ernest C, Chief Financial Officer, Bon Secours Maryview Medical Center, Portsmouth, VA, p. A664

PADDOCK, Steve, Director of Information Services, Gibson General Hospital, Princeton, IN, p. A213

PADEN, Tawnya, Director Human Resources, Weatherford Regional Hospital, Weatherford, OK, p. A510

PADGETT, Martin, President and Chief Executive Officer, Clark Memorial Hospital, Jeffersonville, IN, p. A208

PADGETT, Shirley, Director Human Resources, Cook Medical Center-A Campus Of Tift Regional Medical Center, Adel, GA, p. A145

PADILLA, Ami, Director Human Resources, Arroyo Grande Community Hospital, Arroyo Grande, CA, p. A51

PADILLA, Gregory, Administrator, Coast Plaza Hospital, Norwalk, CA, p. A75

PADILLA, Kathy, Director of Nursing, Marcus Daly Memorial Hospital, Hamilton, MT, p. A376

PADULA, Judy, MSN, R.N., Vice President Patient Care Services and Chief Nursing Officer, St. Joseph's Wayne Hospital, NJ, p. A409

PAFFORD, Roger, M.D., Medical Director, Mineral Community Hospital, Superior, MT, p. A379

PAGANA, Charles C, M.D., Chief Medical Officer, Upmc Susquehanna Sunbury, Sunbury, PA, p. A542

PAGANELLI, Deborah, FACHE, Chief Executive Officer, Lifecare Hospitals Of North Texas-Plano, TX, p. A596

PAGE, Alison, Chief Executive Officer, Western Wisconsin Health, Baldwin, WI, p. A689

PAGE, Bob, Chief Executive Officer, The University Of Kansas Hospital - Indian Creek Campus, KS, p. A238

PAGE, Cynthia, FACHE, Chief Operating Officer, Oss Orthopaedic Hospital, York, PA, p. A545

PAGE, Deborah, Chief Human Resources Officer, Duke Children's Hospital & Health Center, NC, p. A451

PAGE, Heather, MSN, Director of Nursing, Chi St. Joseph Health Burleson Hospital, Caldwell, TX, p. A591

PAGE, Keith Allen., President and Chief Executive Officer, Anderson Hospital, Maryville, IL, p. A188

PAGE, Nancy E., MS, R.N., Chief Nursing Officer, Upstate University Hospital At Community General, NY, p. A444

PAGE, Pattie, Director Marketing and Public Relations, Eastside Medical Center, Snellville, GA, p. A161

PAGE, Robert, III, Chief Information and Technology Officer, Memphis Veterans Affairs Medical Center, Memphis, TN, p. A575

PAGE, Sue, Director Human Resources, Monroe County Medical Center, Tompkinsville, KY, p. A261

PAGE, Susan M., President and Chief Executive Officer, Pratt Regional Medical Center, Pratt, KS, p. A244

PAGE, William E, CPA, Chief Financial Officer, Franklin Medical Center, Winnsboro, LA, p. A281

PAGELER, Robert
Chief Information Officer, Confluence Health/Central Washington Hospital, Wenatchee, WA, p. A680
Chief Information Officer, Confluence Health/Wenatchee Valley Hospital, Wenatchee, WA, p. A680

PAGET, Cindy, Chief Human Resources Officer, Forks Community Hospital, Forks, WA, p. A672

PAGLIUZZA, Greg, Chief Financial Officer, Unitypoint Health - Trinity Bettendorf, Bettendorf, IA, p. A217

PAGNINI, Janie, Administrator Accounting, Atascadero State Hospital, Atascadero, CA, p. A51

PAGUAGA, Ana, Director of Human Resources, Coral Gables Hospital, Coral Gables, FL, p. A120

PAHDE, Carol, R.N., Chief Nursing Officer, Leconte Medical Center, Sevierville, TN, p. A579

PAHE, Gary, Manager Human Resources, Sage Memorial Hospital, Ganado, AZ, p. A29

PAHL, Jodi, Chief Nurse Executive, St. Rita's Medical Center, Lima, OH, p. A485

PAI, Ajith, PharmD, FACHE, President, Texas Health Harris Methodist Hospital Cleburne, Cleburne, TX, p. A592

PAIGE, Peter G, Chief Medical Officer, Jackson South Community Hospital, FL, p. A130

PAINE, Lincoln, M.D., Medical Director, River Oaks Child And Adolescent Hospital, LA, p. A276

PAINE, Russ, Human Resources Officer, Erlanger Murphy Medical Center, Murphy, NC, p. A457

PAINTER, Jeff, Manager Information Technology, Summit Pacific Medical Center, Elma, WA, p. A671

PAIRISH, Katherine, Chief Financial Officer, Eastern Plumas Health Care, Portola, CA, p. A79

PALADINO, James, Controller, New England Rehabilitation Hospital Of Portland, Portland, ME, p. A285

PALAZZOLO, Chris
Health System President and Chief Executive Officer Mid-Michigan, St. Mary's Of Michigan, Saginaw, MI, p. A322
President and Chief Executive Officer, Ascension Crittenton Hospital Medical Center, Rochester, MI, p. A321
President and Chief Executive Officer, Genesys Regional Medical Center, Grand Blanc, MI, p. A313
President and Chief Executive Officer, St. Mary's Of Michigan Standish Hospital, Standish, MI, p. A324

PALERMO, Robert, Vice President Finance, Hackensack Meridian Health Ocean Medical Center, Brick Township, NJ, p. A403

PALETTA, Lisa A., R.N., FACHE
Chief Nursing Officer, Utah Valley Hospital, Provo, UT, p. A649
Chief Executive Officer, Alta View Hospital, Sandy, UT, p. A651

PALICKA, Martha, Director Information Systems, Bartlett Regional Hospital, Juneau, AK, p. A26

PALIGO, Terry, Chief Financial Officer, Union County Hospital, Anna, IL, p. A173

PALKOWSKI, Chris, M.D., Physician in Chief, Kaiser Permanente Sacramento Medical Center, Sacramento, CA, p. A81

PALLIN, Angel, Senior Vice President of Operations, Miami Heart Campus At Mount Sinai Medical Center, FL, p. A131

PALMER, Charles, Director Information Technology, Nanticoke Memorial Hospital, Seaford, DE, p. A114

PALMER, Debra L, MS, R.N., Chief Human Resources Officer and Corporate Compliance Officer, Fairfield Medical Center, Lancaster, OH, p. A484

PALMER, Isaac, Chief Executive Officer, Christus Highland Medical Center, LA, p. A278

PALMER, Janel M, Director Human Resources, Greenwood County Hospital, Eureka, KS, p. A235

PALMER, Justin, Administrator, John C. Stennis Memorial Hospital, De Kalb, MS, p. A345

PALMER, Katie, Manager Human Resources, Sanford Aberdeen Medical Center, Aberdeen, SD, p. A559

PALMER, Keith, Assistant Administrator, Winkler County Memorial Hospital, Kermit, TX, p. A617

PALMER, Kelly, D.O., Medical Director, State Hospital South, Blackfoot, ID, p. A167

PALMER, Stephanie, Chief Nursing Officer, Encompass Health Valley Of The Sun Rehabilitation Hospital, Glendale, AZ, p. A30

PALMER, Trisha, Director, St. James Healthcare, Butte, MT, p. A374

PALMIER, Michael L, Chief Human Resources Management, Overton Brooks Veterans Affairs Medical Center, Shreveport, LA, p. A278

PALMUCCI, Jeffrey, Chief Executive Officer, Vanderbilt Stallworth Rehabilitation Hospital, Nashville, TN, p. A578

PALO, Alan, Chief Financial Officer, Sarah D. Culbertson Memorial Hospital, Rushville, IL, p. A195

PALUMBO, Christopher M., President and Chief Executive Officer, Nebraska Spine Hospital, Omaha, NE, p. A388

PALUMBO, Michael, D.O.
Vice President Medical Affairs and Chief Education, Inland Hospital, Waterville, ME, p. A286
Executive Vice President and Medical Director, White Plains Hospital Center, White Plains, NY, p. A446

PAM, Brower, Chief Financial Officer, Christus Spohn Hospital Corpus Christus South, TX, p. A594

PAMPERIEN, Linda, Chief Financial Officer, Texas County Memorial Hospital, Houston, MO, p. A360

PANDL, Therese B.
President and Chief Executive Officer, Hshs St. Mary's Hospital Medical Center, Green Bay, WI, p. A694
President and Chief Executive Officer, Hshs St. Vincent Hospital, Green Bay, WI, p. A694

PANDO, Terry, R.N., Associate Executive Director and Chief Nursing Officer, Staten Island University Hospital, New York (Includes All Hospitals Located Within The Five Boroughs), NY, p. A437

PANDOLPH, Philip E., FACHE, Chief Executive Officer, Meadville Medical Center, Meadville, PA, p. A531

PANDYA, Kamel, Director Information Services, San Antonio Regional Hospital, Upland, CA, p. A93

PANDYA, Sherrie, Administrator, Kane County Hospital, Kanab, UT, p. A647

PANKEY, De'Niro, Director Information Systems, Corona Regional Medical Center-Rehabilitation, CA, p. A55

PANKEY, Susan Kay, Chief Nursing Officer, Davis County Hospital, Bloomfield, IA, p. A218

PANKOW, Thomas, Chief Information Officer, Jackson Park Hospital And Medical Center, Chicago, IL, p. A177

PANKOWSKI, Charles, Manager Human Resources, Select Specialty Hospital-Columbus, Mount Carmel Campus, OH, p. A479

PANLASIGUI, Bonnie, Chief Operating Officer, St. Mary Medical Center, Long Beach, CA, p. A65

PANNELL, Kenneth
Chief Financial Officer, College Station Medical Center, College Station, TX, p. A593
Chief Financial Officer, Western Arizona Regional Medical Center, Bullhead City, AZ, p. A28

PANNULLO, Ava, M.D., Vice President Medical Services and Physician in Chief, Hebrew Senior Care, West Hartford, CT, p. A112

PANSA, Leonard F, Senior Vice President Human Resources and Administrative Services, Mercy Medical Center, Springfield, MA, p. A304

PANZA, Louis J., Jr, President and Chief Executive Officer, Monongahela Valley Hospital, Monongahela, PA, p. A532

PAOLINELLI, Karen, Chief Executive Officer, Madera Community Hospital, Madera, CA, p. A71

PAOLUCCI, Benjamin, D.O., Chief of Staff, Southeast Michigan Surgical Hospital, Warren, MI, p. A325

PAPA, Alan, President, Cleveland Clinic Akron General, Akron, OH, p. A470

PAPA, AnnMarie, R.N., Vice President and Chief Nursing Officer, Einstein Medical Center Montgomery, East Norriton, PA, p. A524

PAPADAKOS, James, Chief Financial Officer, Signature Healthcare Brockton Hospital, Brockton, MA, p. A298

PAPALIA, Fern, Director of Nursing, Essex County Hospital Center, Cedar Grove, NJ, p. A403

PAPALIA, John, Chief Executive Officer, Healthsouth Rehabilitation Hospital Of Erie, Erie, PA, p. A525

PAPALIA, Mark, President, Upmc Kane, Kane, PA, p. A528

PAPE, Becky A., R.N., Chief Executive Officer, Good Samaritan Regional Medical Center, Corvallis, OR, p. A512

PAPKA, Lauren, Chief Administrative Officer, St. Mary's Sacred Heart Hospital, Lavonia, GA, p. A156

PAPPAN, Clayton, Director Human Resources and Marketing, South Central Kansas Medical Center, Arkansas City, KS, p. A232

PAPPAS, Kirk, M.D., Physician-in-Chief, Kaiser Permanente Santa Rosa Medical Center, Santa Rosa, CA, p. A89

PAPPAS, Michael, Chief Fiscal Service Officer, Louis Stokes Cleveland Veterans Affairs Medical Center, Cleveland, OH, p. A477

PAPPAS, Sheryl L, Chief Financial Officer, Sanford Webster Medical Center, Webster, SD, p. A565

PAPPAS, Theron, Director Management Information Systems, Holy Family Memorial, Manitowoc, WI, p. A696

PAQUETTE, Julie, M.D., Chief Medical Officer, Providence Seaside Hospital, Seaside, OR, p. A518

PARADIS, Brian, Chief Operating Officer, Winter Park Memorial Hospital, FL, p. A134

PARADIS, James, President, Paoli Hospital, Paoli, PA, p. A533

PARADIS, Jeanne, Director Information Services, The Acadia Hospital, Bangor, ME, p. A282

PARAUDA, Martina A, Director, Veterans Affairs New York Harbor Healthcare System - Manhattan Campus, NY, p. A437

PARAUDA, Martina A., Director, Veterans Affairs New York Harbor Healthcare System - Manhattan Campus, NY, p. A437

PARAVATE, Chris, Chief Information Officer, Northeast Georgia Medical Center, Gainesville, GA, p. A154

PARAVISINI, Nilda, Director Human Resources, Hospital Manati Medical Center, Manati, PR, p. A714

PARCEL, Jim, Director Information Technology, Maury Regional Hospital, Columbia, TN, p. A568

PARCHMENT, Deborah, Executive Director, Kingsboro Psychiatric Center, New York (Includes All Hospitals Located Within The Five Boroughs), NY, p. A432

PARDEE, Wendy Ann., President and Chief Executive Officer, The Children's Institute Of Pittsburgh, Pittsburgh, PA, p. A538

PARDUE, Helen, Interim Chief Nursing Officer, Johnson County Community Hospital, Mountain City, TN, p. A576

PAREEK, Yogesh, M.D., Clinical Director, Brown County Community Treatment Center, Green Bay, WI, p. A694

PARENT, Paula A.
Chief Nursing Officer and Director of Human Resources, Cary Medical Center, Caribou, ME, p. A283
Chief Nursing Officer, Cary Medical Center, Caribou, ME, p. A283

PARET, Jason, Chief Executive Officer, Catalina Island Medical Center, Avalon, CA, p. A51

PARHAM, Eva, R.N., Chief Nurse Executive, Central State Hospital, Petersburg, VA, p. A663

PARHAM, Tracy
Chief Information Officer, Unc Lineberger Comprehensive Cancer Center, NC, p. A449
Health Care System Chief Information Officer, Unc Rex Health Care, Raleigh, NC, p. A459

PARIGI, John S, II, Interim Chief Financial Officer, Healdsburg District Hospital, Healdsburg, CA, p. A61

PARIS, David, Chief Executive Officer, Perry County General Hospital, Richton, MS, p. A352

PARIS, Karen, Controller, Crittenden County Hospital, Marion, KY, p. A257

PARIS, Sherri, Chief Operating Officer, Providence Milwaukie Hospital, Milwaukie, OR, p. A515

PARIS, Trevor, M.D., Medical Director, Brooks Rehabilitation Hospital, Jacksonville, FL, p. A125

PARISI, James
Chief Executive Officer, Chi St. Luke's Health-Lakeside Hospital, The Woodlands, TX, p. A639
Chief Executive Officer, Chi St. Luke's Health-The Woodlands Hospital, The Woodlands, TX, p. A639

PARISKY, Yuri, M.D., Chief of Staff, Mammoth Hospital, Mammoth Lakes, CA, p. A71

PARK, Bockhi
Chief Executive Officer, Encino Hospital Medical Center, Los Angeles, CA, p. A66
Chief Executive Officer, Sherman Oaks Hospital, Los Angeles, CA, p. A69

PARK, Denten
Chief Executive Officer, Northwest Medical Center - Bentonville, AR, p. A49
Chief Executive Officer, Physicians' Specialty Hospital, Fayetteville-Washington County, AR, p. A41

Chief Executive Officer, Willow Creek Women's Hospital, AR, p. A49

PARK, Gary L
Chief Executive Officer, Unc Health Care Hillsborough Campus, NC, p. A449
President, N.C. Women's Hospital, NC, p. A449

PARK, Gary L., President, Unc Lineberger Comprehensive Cancer Center, NC, p. A449

PARK, Jessica, Director Accounting, Penn Highlands Brookville, Brookville, PA, p. A521

PARK, Rustin, Director of Nursing, Seven Hills Hospital, Henderson, NV, p. A393

PARK, Theron
Chief Executive Officer, Chi St. Joseph Health Bellville Hospital, Bellville, TX, p. A589
Chief Executive Officer, Chi St. Joseph Health Burleson Hospital, Caldwell, TX, p. A591
Chief Executive Officer, Chi St. Joseph Health Grimes Hospital, Navasota, TX, p. A625
Chief Executive Officer, Chi St. Joseph Health Madison Hospital, Madisonville, TX, p. A622
Chief Executive Officer, Chi St. Joseph Regional Health Center, Bryan, TX, p. A591

PARKE, Carol, Chief Operating Officer, SUN Kentucky, Sun Behavioral Kentucky, Erlanger, KY, p. A251

PARKER, Audrey, Budget Analyst, U.S. Public Health Service Indian Hospital, Winnebago, NE, p. A391

PARKER, Charisse, Director Human Resources, Tennova Healthcare-Shelbyville, Shelbyville, TN, p. A579

PARKER, Cindy, Chief Financial Officer and Director Human Resources, Throckmorton County Memorial Hospital, Throckmorton, TX, p. A640

PARKER, Cynthia, Administrator and Director of Nursing, Carson Tahoe Continuing Care Hospital, Carson City, NV, p. A392

PARKER, David, VP Information Technology, Magnolia Regional Health Center, Corinth, MS, p. A345

PARKER, Deanna, Director Human Resources, J. Arthur Dosher Memorial Hospital, Southport, NC, p. A460

PARKER, Donald J., President and Chief Executive Officer, Carrier Clinic, Belle Mead, NJ, p. A402

PARKER, Janie, Chief Financial Officer, Hardin County General Hospital, Rosiclare, IL, p. A195

PARKER, Jim, FACHE, Chief Executive Officer, Webster County Memorial Hospital, Webster Springs, WV, p. A687

PARKER, Michael, M.D., Chief of Staff, Sharon Hospital, Sharon, CT, p. A110

PARKER, Richard, M.D., President, Hillcrest Hospital, Hillcrest Hospital, Cleveland, OH, p. A476

PARKER, Robert, Chief Executive Officer and Market President, Clark Regional Medical Center, Winchester, KY, p. A261

PARKER, Sandra K, M.D., Chief Medical Officer, Eastpointe Hospital, Daphne, AL, p. A16

PARKER, Theresa M, Regional Finance Director, Transylvania Regional Hospital, Brevard, NC, p. A448

PARKER, Thomas
Chief Executive Officer, Snoqualmie Valley Hospital District, Snoqualmie, WA, p. A677
President, Upper Valley Medical Center, Troy, OH, p. A492

PARKER, Tina, Director Human Resources, Encompass Health Rehabilitation Hospital Midland Odessa, Midland, TX, p. A624

PARKER, Travis, Director Human Resources, Southwest Health System, Cortez, CO, p. A98

PARKER, Valerie, M.D., Clinical Director, U.S. Public Health Service Indian Hospital, Rosebud, SD, p. A563

PARKEY, Kasey, Coordinator Payroll and Benefits, Pam Specialty Hospital Of Corpus Christi South, Corpus Christi, TX, p. A594

PARKHILL, Cherie, Chief Financial Officer, Crosbyton Clinic Hospital, Crosbyton, TX, p. A595

PARKHURST, James E., President and Chief Executive Officer, Newport Bay Hospital, Newport Beach, CA, p. A75

PARKHURST, Jennifer, Chief Financial Officer, City Of Hope's Helford Clinical Research Hospital, Duarte, CA, p. A57

PARKHURST, Phyllis, Vice President Support Services, Newport Bay Hospital, Newport Beach, CA, p. A75

PARKINSON, Justin, M.D., President Medical Staff, Jordan Valley Medical Center West Valley Campus, West Valley City, UT, p. A652

PARKINSON, Michelle A, Director Human Resources, Prairie St. John'S, Fargo, ND, p. A466

PARKS, Amanda, Chief Nursing Officer, Lifebrite Community Hospital Of Stokes, Danbury, NC, p. A450

PARKS, Audrey, Chief Information Officer, Salinas Valley Memorial Healthcare System, Salinas, CA, p. A83

PARKS, Cary, Chief Information Resource Management, Hampton Veterans Affairs Medical Center, Hampton, VA, p. A659

PARKS, Dave, Chief Information Officer, Three Rivers Health, Three Rivers, MI, p. A324

PARKS, Ginger, Director Human Resources, Cape Fear Valley - Bladen County Hospital, Elizabethtown, NC, p. A452

PARKS, Jody, Administrator, Ottawa County Health Center, Minneapolis, KS, p. A241

PARKS, Kathi, Director of Nursing, South Lincoln Medical Center, Kemmerer, WY, p. A708

PARKS, Kelvin L., Interim Director, Veterans Health Care System Of The Ozarks, Fayetteville-Washington County, AR, p. A42

PARKS, Kyle, M.D., Chief of Staff, Evans Memorial Hospital, Claxton, GA, p. A150

PARKS, Michelle, Administrator, Rivervalley Behavioral Health Hospital, Owensboro, KY, p. A259

PARKS, Peggy, R.N., Chief Nursing Officer, Northeast Regional Medical Center, Kirksville, MO, p. A362

PARKS, Sherry, R.N., MS, Chief Nursing Officer, Saint Alphonsus Regional Medical Center, Boise, ID, p. A168

PARKS, Vicki, Chief Financial Officer, Jackson Purchase Medical Center, Mayfield, KY, p. A257

PARMER, David N, FACHE, Chief Executive Officer, Baptist Hospitals Of Southeast Texas Fannin Behavioral Health Center, TX, p. A588

PARMER, David N., FACHE, Chief Executive Officer, Baptist Hospitals Of Southeast Texas Fannin Behavioral Health Center, TX, p. A588

PARMER, Michael, Chief Medical Officer, Carepartners Health Services, Asheville, NC, p. A447

PARNEL, George, Chief Financial Officer, Clifton T. Perkins Hospital Center, Jessup, MD, p. A292

PARNELL, Linda, Chief Nursing Officer, Carolinas Hospital System Marion, Mullins, SC, p. A555

PAROD, Daniel A., President, St. Vincent Evansville, Evansville, IN, p. A203

PAROSKI, Margaret, M.D., Executive Vice President and Chief Medical Officer, Women And Children's Hospital, NY, p. A423

PARR, James
    Chief Financial Officer, Salem Health Rehabilitation Center, OR, p. A517
    Chief Financial Officer, Salem Health West Valley, Dallas, OR, p. A512

PARR, Lynnette, Chief Financial Officer, Down East Community Hospital, Machias, ME, p. A285

PARRA, Kristin, Chief Nursing Officer, Yuma Rehabilitation Hospital, A Partnership Of Encompass Health And Yrmc, Yuma, AZ, p. A38

PARRA, Michelle, Director Human Resources, Kindred Hospital South Bay, Gardena, CA, p. A60

PARRADO, Carlos, M.D., Sr, Chief Medical Officer, Roosevelt Warm Springs Rehabilitation And Specialty Hospitals - Ltac, Warm Springs, GA, p. A162

PARRINELLO, Kathleen M, Ph.D., Chief Operating Officer, Golisano Children's Hospital, NY, p. A441

PARRISH, Becky, Director Human Resources, Southern Virginia Regional Medical Center, Emporia, VA, p. A657

PARRISH, Carl, Chief Fiscal Service, James E. Van Zandt Veterans Affairs Medical Center, Altoona, PA, p. A519

PARRISH, Denise, Interim Chief Administrative Officer, Ascension Northeast Wisconsin Mercy Hospital, Oshkosh, WI, p. A700

PARRISH, James G., FACHE, Chief Executive Officer, Memorial Hospital, Seminole, TX, p. A635

PARRISH, Suann, Chief Financial Officer, Yoakum County Hospital, Denver City, TX, p. A599

PARRISH, Todd, M.D., Chief of Staff, Ut Health Jacksonville, Jacksonville, TX, p. A616

PARROTT, Keith, FACHE, Chief Executive Officer, Brookwood Baptist Medical Center, Birmingham, AL, p. A14

PARRY, Kayla, Manager Human Resources, Ivinson Memorial Hospital, Laramie, WY, p. A708

PARRY, Mary, Vice President Operations and Chief Operating Officer, Oneida Healthcare, Oneida, NY, p. A439

PARRY, Timothy, R.N., Chief Operating Officer, Highland District Hospital, Hillsboro, OH, p. A484

PARSI, Kia, M.D.
    Chief Medical Officer, Chi St. Joseph Regional Health Center, Bryan, TX, p. A591
    Chief Medical Officer, Chi St. Joseph's Health, Park Rapids, MN, p. A337

PARSLEY, George N, Chief Operating Officer, Detar Hospital North, TX, p. A642

PARSON, Charlynne, Nurse Executive, Moccasin Bend Mental Health Institute, Chattanooga, TN, p. A567

PARSONS, Beth, R.N., Administrator, Christus Dubuis Hospital Of Alexandria, Alexandria, LA, p. A262

PARSONS, Brad, FACHE, Administrator and Chief Executive Officer, Nea Baptist Memorial Hospital, Jonesboro-Craighead County, AR, p. A44

PARSONS, Brent, Chief Executive Officer, Bluffton Regional Medical Center, Bluffton, IN, p. A200

PARSONS, John, R.N., Chief Nursing Officer, Trustpoint Rehabilitation Hospital Of Lubbock, Lubbock, TX, p. A621

PARSONS, Terri L., Administrator, Advanced Care Hospital Of White County, Searcy-White County, AR, p. A48

PARTEE, Paris I, Associate Administrator and Director Human Resources, John H. Stroger Jr. Hospital Of Cook County, Chicago, IL, p. A177

PARTENZA, John, Vice President and Treasurer, Northern Westchester Hospital, Mount Kisco, NY, p. A430

PARTHEMORE, Warrenette, Director Human Resources, Promedica Memorial Hospital, Fremont, OH, p. A482

PARTIN, James R, M.D., Chief Medical Director, Hill Country Memorial Hospital, Fredericksburg, TX, p. A606

PARTON, Gerald L., FACHE, Chief Executive Officer, Doctors Hospital Of Jefferson, LA, p. A274

PARTRIDGE, Susan, Director Human Resources, Nantucket Cottage Hospital, Nantucket, MA, p. A302

PARUCH, Randy J, Director, Information Systems, Holland Hospital, Holland, MI, p. A315

PASCASCIO, Dellone, Chief Nursing Officer, Lac-Olive View-Ucla Medical Center, Los Angeles, CA, p. A68

PASCASIO, Robert A., FACHE, Administrator and Chief Executive Officer, Ochiltree General Hospital, Perryton, TX, p. A628

PASCO, Teri, Director Human Resources, East Liverpool City Hospital, East Liverpool, OH, p. A482

PASCOE, John, M.D., Executive Medical Director, Timberlawn Mental Health System, Dallas, TX, p. A598

PASCUAL, Bolivar, M.D., Medical Director, Essex County Hospital Center, Cedar Grove, NJ, p. A403

PASCUZZI, Robert, Chief Financial Officer, Mercy San Juan Medical Center, Carmichael, CA, p. A54

PASQUALE, Mark
    Chief Information Officer, Integris Mental Health System-Spencer, OK, p. A503
    Chief Information Officer, Integris Southwest Medical Center, Oklahoma City, OK, p. A503

PASS, Christian
    Interim Chief Financial Officer, John Muir Medical Center, Concord, Concord, CA, p. A55
    Senior Vice President & Chief Financial Officer, John Muir Medical Center, Walnut Creek, Walnut Creek, CA, p. A94
    Senior Vice President and Chief Financial Officer, John Muir Behavioral Health Center, Concord, CA, p. A55

PASSAFARO, David, Chief Executive Officer, New England Baptist Hospital, Boston, MA, p. A297

PASSANNANTE, Anthony, Jr, M.D., FACC, President, Hackensack Meridian Health Palisades Medical Center, North Bergen, NJ, p. A409

PASSARELLI, Theresa, Human Resources Generalist, Warm Springs Medical Center, Warm Springs, GA, p. A163

PASSMANN, Frederic K, M.D., Chief of Staff, Stonewall Memorial Hospital, Aspermont, TX, p. A584

PASSMORE, Gary, Chief Information Officer, Endless Mountain Health Systems, Montrose, PA, p. A532

PASTIAN, Andre, R.N., MSN, Chief Nursing Officer, Boulder City Hospital, Boulder City, NV, p. A392

PASTOR, Robert, II, R.N., Chief Executive Officer, Rainy Lake Medical Center, International Falls, MN, p. A333

PASTORE, Raymond, M.D., Chief Medical Officer, St. John's Episcopal Hospital-South Shore, New York (Includes All Hospitals Located Within The Five Boroughs), NY, p. A437

PASTRANA, Guillermo, Executive Director, Hospital Pavia-Hato Rey, San Juan, PR, p. A716

PASZTOR, Barbara J., R.N.
    Vice President Nursing and Patient Care Services, Bluffton Hospital, Bluffton, OH, p. A472
    Vice President Patient Care Services and Chief Nursing Officer, Blanchard Valley Hospital, OH, p. A482

PATCHELL, Lee, Lead Human Resources Business Partner, Presbyterian Rust Medical Center, NM, p. A416

PATE, John, M.D., Chief Medical Officer, Tri-County Hospital, Wadena, MN, p. A341

PATE, Lois, R.N., Chief Nursing Officer, Island Hospital, Anacortes, WA, p. A669

PATE, Warren, Chief Financial Officer, South Bay Hospital, Sun City Center, FL, p. A140

PATEL, Amita, M.D., Medical Director, Haven Behavioral Senior Care Of Dayton, Dayton, OH, p. A480

PATEL, Bimal, President, Institute Of Living, CT, p. A108

PATEL, Binesh, M.D., Chief Medical Officer, Mclaren Flint, Flint, MI, p. A312

PATEL, Deepak, M.D., Medical Director, Cumberland Hall Hospital, Hopkinsville, KY, p. A253

PATEL, Dilip, M.D., Chief of Staff, Greater El Monte Community Hospital, South El Monte, CA, p. A90

PATEL, Fatma, M.D., Vice President Medical Affairs, Niagara Falls Memorial Medical Center, Niagara Falls, NY, p. A438

PATEL, Govind, M.D., Medical Director, Healthsouth Mountainview Regional Rehabilitation Hospital, Morgantown, WV, p. A685

PATEL, Hema, Director Medical Records, Riverwoods Behavioral Health System, Riverdale, GA, p. A159

PATEL, Hiral, Interim Chief Executive Officer and Chief Operating Officer, Lakeview Regional Medical Center, LA, p. A276

PATEL, Malini, M.D., Medical Director, Elgin Mental Health Center, Elgin, IL, p. A182

PATEL, Malisha
    Senior Vice President and Chief Executive Officer, Memorial Hermann Southwest Hospital, TX, p. A612
    Senior Vice President and Chief Executive Officer, Memorial Hermann Sugar Land Hospital, Sugar Land, TX, p. A637

PATEL, Natu M, M.D., Chief of Staff, Phoebe Worth Medical Center, Sylvester, GA, p. A161

PATEL, Nirav, M.D.
    Chief of Staff, Los Alamitos Medical Center, Los Alamitos, CA, p. A65
    Interim Chief Medical Officer, Ssm Health Saint Louis University Hospital-South, MO, p. A369

PATEL, Paryus, M.D., Chief Medical Officer, Centinela Hospital Medical Center, Inglewood, CA, p. A62

PATEL, Prakash Chandra, M.D., Chief of Staff, Kindred Hospital Santa Ana, CA, p. A63

PATEL, Pravin, M.D., Acting President and Chief Executive Officer, Southern Virginia Mental Health Institute, Danville, VA, p. A657

PATEL, Pravinchandra, M.D., Chief Medical Officer, Barnes-Kasson County Hospital, Susquehanna, PA, p. A542

PATEL, Raj, M.D., Medical Director, Lifecare Hospitals Of Chester County, West Chester, PA, p. A544

PATEL, Rajesh, M.D., Chief of Staff, Upmc Susquehanna Lock Haven, Lock Haven, PA, p. A530

PATEL, Rakesh, D.O., Medical Director, Healthsouth Rehabilitation Hospital Of Altoona, Altoona, PA, p. A519

PATEL, Shailesh, M.D., Medical Director, Anchor Hospital, Atlanta, GA, p. A145

PATEL, Shalin, M.D., Chief Medical Officer, Memorial Hermann Rehabilitation Hospital - Katy, Katy, TX, p. A616

PATEL, Sharad, M.D., Medical Director, Florida Hospital At Connerton Long Term Acute Care, Land O'Lakes, FL, p. A127

PATEL, Shatish, M.D., Chief Medical Officer, Atrium Medical Center, Stafford, TX, p. A636

PATEL, Tanay M., M.D., Chief of Staff, Golden Plains Community Hospital, Borger, TX, p. A589

PATEL, Viraj, M.D., Chief Medical Officer, Unity Medical & Surgical Hospital, Mishawaka, IN, p. A211

PATER, Tom, Chief Financial Officer, Rml Specialty Hospital, IL, p. A186

PATEY, Jeffrey A, M.D., Chief of Staff, Belmont Community Hospital, Bellaire, OH, p. A472

PATHAK, Ajay, President, Osf Healthcare Saint Clare's Hospital, IL, p. A173

PATHAK, Rajiv, Chief of Staff, Marshall Medical Center, Placerville, CA, p. A78

PATIL, Steve, Chief Financial Officer, W. G. (Bill) Heffner Veterans Affairs Medical Center, Salisbury, NC, p. A460

PATILLO, Laura, Manager Human Resources, Fresno Surgical Hospital, Fresno, CA, p. A59

PATINO, Beth, Chief Information Officer, Dekalb Medical At North Decatur, Decatur, GA, p. A152

PATMAS, Michael, M.D., Chief Medical Officer, Gritman Medical Center, Moscow, ID, p. A170

PATONAI, Steven D., Interim Chief Executive Officer, Lake Chelan Community Hospital And Clinics, Chelan, WA, p. A670

PATRIAS, Thomas, FACHE, Chief Operating Officer, Tulane-Lakeside Hospital, LA, p. A276

PATRICIO, Mars, Jr, Chief Financial Officer, Seven Hills Hospital, Henderson, NV, p. A393

PATRICK, Ann M, Vice President Human Resources, Northwest Community Hospital, Arlington Heights, IL, p. A173

PATRICK, Calvin, II, Director Information Services, Florida Hospital New Smyrna, New Smyrna Beach, FL, p. A132

PATRICK, Chad, President and Chief Executive Officer, Orange Park Medical Center, Orange Park, FL, p. A133

PATRICK, Christian C, M.D., Chief Medical Officer, Baptist Memorial Hospital - Memphis, Memphis, TN, p. A574

PATRICK, Deborah A., Senior Vice President Human Resources, Lehigh Valley Hospital-Muhlenberg, Bethlehem, PA, p. A520

PATRICK, Devin, Manager Human Resources, Utah State Hospital, Provo, UT, p. A649

PATRICK, Lisa, Chief Operating Officer, Caldwell Memorial Hospital, Columbia, LA, p. A265

PATRICK, Ronald, Chief Financial Officer, Northwest Medical Center, Tucson, AZ, p. A37

PATRICK, Sandra, Chief Financial Officer, Three Rivers Hospital, Waverly, TN, p. A580

PATRICK, Sean, Director Information Systems, Gifford Medical Center, Randolph, VT, p. A654

PATRIZIO, Eugene, Chief Executive Officer, Memorial Medical Center, CA, p. A73

PATTEN, William D., Jr, Chief Executive Officer, Holy Cross Hospital, Taos, NM, p. A420

PATTERSON, Anthony, FACHE, Chief Operating Officer, Uab Highlands, AL, p. A15

PATTERSON, Barbara, Chief Financial Officer, Provident Hospital Of Cook County, Chicago, IL, p. A179

PATTERSON, Betsy B, MSN, R.N., Chief Nursing Officer, Baylor Scott & White Medical Center - Llano, Llano, TX, p. A620

PATTERSON, Camie, Chief Operating Officer, Manatee Memorial Hospital, Bradenton, FL, p. A118

PATTERSON, Christina, Chief Financial Officer, Saint Thomas River Park Hospital, Mc Minnville, TN, p. A574

PATTERSON, Dave, Chief Information Officer, Memorial Hospital Of Converse County, Douglas, WY, p. A708

PATTERSON, David, Director Human Resources, Parkside Psychiatric Hospital And Clinic, Tulsa, OK, p. A508

PATTERSON, Debbie, Director Health Information Management, Wesley Rehabilitation Hospital, Wichita, KS, p. A248

PATTERSON, Devasha, Director of Human Resources, Northwest Mississippi Medical Center, Clarksdale, MS, p. A344

PATTERSON, Diane, Senior Vice President, Chief Operating Officer and Chief Nursing Officer, Virginia Mason Memorial, Yakima, WA, p. A680

PATTERSON, Jan, Chief Nursing Officer, Avera St. Luke's Hospital, Aberdeen, SD, p. A559

PATTERSON, Jeff, Chief Executive Officer, Abrazo Arizona Heart Hospital, AZ, p. A30

PATTERSON, Karen, Deputy Director Operations, Elmira Psychiatric Center, Elmira, NY, p. A426

PATTERSON, Larry R., Deputy Commander Administration, Bayne-Jones Army Community Hospital, Fort Polk, LA, p. A267

PATTERSON, Lisa, Director Human Resources, Pointe Coupee General Hospital, New Roads, LA, p. A276

PATTERSON, Marcia, MSN, R.N.
Chief Nursing Officer, Nor-Lea Hospital District, Lovington, NM, p. A418
Chief Financial Officer, Valley Regional Medical Center, Brownsville, TX, p. A590

PATTERSON, Maria, Manager Health Information Management, Canyon Ridge Hospital, Chino, CA, p. A54

PATTERSON, Mark, M.D., Chief Medical Officer, Laughlin Memorial Hospital, Greeneville, TN, p. A570

PATTERSON, Melanie, R.N., Vice President Patient Care Services and Chief Nursing Officer, Children's Hospital Of Orange County, Orange, CA, p. A76

PATTERSON, Michael C., Chief Executive Officer, Flint River Community Hospital, Montezuma, GA, p. A157

PATTERSON, Michael N., Chief Executive Officer, Havasu Regional Medical Center, Lake Havasu City, AZ, p. A30

PATTERSON, Mike, Director of Operations, Northside Hospital-Cherokee, Canton, GA, p. A149

PATTERSON, Philip A., President, Depaul Center, TX, p. A642

PATTERSON, Renee A., Vice President Employment and Training Services, Rogers Memorial Hospital-West Allis, WI, p. A700

PATTERSON, Robert, Vice President Human Resources and Rehabilitation Services, The University Of Vermont Health Network Central Vermont Medical Center, Berlin, VT, p. A653

PATTERSON, Russ
Director Information Technology, St. Rose Dominican Hospitals - Siena Campus, Henderson, NV, p. A393
Site Manager Information Technology, St. Rose Dominican Hospitals - San Martin Campus, Las Vegas, NV, p. A395

PATTERSON, Sam, Chief Financial Officer, Bay Area Hospital, Coos Bay, OR, p. A512

PATTERSON, Steve, Chief Executive Officer, Select Specialty Hospital-Springfield, Springfield, MO, p. A371

PATTERSON, Stuart, M.D., Chief of Staff, Bartow Regional Medical Center, Bartow, FL, p. A117

PATTERSON, Tony, Chief Financial Officer, Ephraim Mcdowell James B. Haggin Memorial Hospital, Harrodsburg, KY, p. A253

PATTI, Rosa, Chief Financial Officer, Cameron Regional Medical Center, Cameron, MO, p. A356

PATTON, Christina, Chief Financial Officer, Colorado Plains Medical Center, Fort Morgan, CO, p. A100

PATTON, Daniel, Director Information Systems, Henrico Doctors' Hospital - Retreat Campus, VA, p. A665

PATTON, David J., President, Upmc St. Margaret, Pittsburgh, PA, p. A538

PATTON, Joy, Director Information Technology, Pampa Regional Medical Center, Pampa, TX, p. A627

PATTON, Kevin, Chief Executive Officer, Old Vineyard Behavioral Health Services, Winston, NC, p. A463

PATTON, Meghan
Vice President Human Resources, Abington Hospital, Abington, PA, p. A519
Vice President Human Resources, Abington-Lansdale Hospital Jefferson Health, Lansdale, PA, p. A529

PATTON, Melissa, MSN, Director of Nursing, Columbus Springs East Hospital, OH, p. A481

PATTON, Pat, Chief Executive Officer, Hospital District 6 - Anthony Campus, KS, p. A236

PATTON, Sally K, R.N., MS, Chief Nursing Officer, New London Hospital, New London, NH, p. A400

PAUL, Adam, Chief Financial Officer, Prairie Lakes Healthcare System, Watertown, SD, p. A565

PAUL, Allison Kay, R.N., Chief Nursing Officer, St. John's Children's Hospital, IL, p. A196

PAUL, Darrick, Chief People Officer, Children's Hospital Of South Carolina At Musc, SC, p. A550

PAUL, Donn, Chief Human Resources, Lackey Memorial Hospital, Forest, MS, p. A346

PAUL, Lise, Vice President Reimbursement and Network Planning, Hebrew Rehabilitation Center, Roslindale, MA, p. A303

PAUL, Mary
Chief Information Officer, Columbia St. Mary's Hospital Ozaukee, Mequon, WI, p. A698
Chief Information Officer, Columbia St. Mary's Milwaukee Hospital, WI, p. A698
Vice President and Chief Information Officer, Columbia St. Mary's Milwaukee Hospital, Milwaukee, WI, p. A698

PAUL, West, M.D., Ph.D.
Senior Vice President and Chief Quality and Medical Staff Officer, Wakemed North Family Health And Women's Hospital, NC, p. A459
Senior Vice President, Chief Quality and Medical Staff Officer, Wakemed Cary Hospital, Cary, NC, p. A449

PAULEY, Clarence, Senior Vice President and Chief Human Resources Officer, University Of Cincinnati Medical Center, Cincinnati, OH, p. A476

PAULS, Scott R, Director Information Technology- HealthNet Connect, Guttenberg Municipal Hospital, Guttenberg, IA, p. A223

PAULSEN, Susan, Director Human Resources, Northridge Hospital Medical Center, Los Angeles, CA, p. A69

PAULSON, Adam, Director Finance, Centracare Health-Melrose, Melrose, MN, p. A334

PAULSON, Erik, Director of Finance, J. D. Mccarty Center For Children With Developmental Disabilities, Norman, OK, p. A502

PAULSON, Gordon, Manager Human Resources, Glacial Ridge Health System, Glenwood, MN, p. A332

PAULSON, Sybil K., Administrator, North Oaks Rehabilitation Hospital, Hammond, LA, p. A268

PAULUS, Terresa Ann
Chief Nursing Officer, Banner Goldfield Medical Center, Apache Junction, AZ, p. A28
Chief Nursing Officer, Banner Ironwood Medical Center, San Tan Valley, AZ, p. A35

PAUTLER, J. Stephen, FACHE, Chief Operating Officer, Peterson Regional Medical Center, Kerrville, TX, p. A617

PAVALONIS, Diane, Chief Nurse Executive, Western State Hospital, Staunton, VA, p. A666

PAVIA, Antoine, M.D., Medical Director, Hospital Pavia Arecibo, Arecibo, PR, p. A712

PAVIK, Sarah, Director Human Resources and Guest Services, Inova Loudoun Hospital, Leesburg, VA, p. A660

PAVILANIS, Charlotte J, R.N., Vice President of Clinical Services and Chief Nursing Officer, Sturgis Hospital, Sturgis, MI, p. A324

PAVLATOS, Thales, Medical Director, Ohio Valley Surgical Hospital, Springfield, OH, p. A490

PAWAR, Ganesh, M.D., Chief of Staff, Marshfield Medical Center - Ladysmith, Ladysmith, WI, p. A695

PAWLEK, Kenny, Chief Operating Officer, Usc Verdugo Hills Hospital, Glendale, CA, p. A60

PAWLOSKI, Paula, Chief Nursing Officer, Lifecare Hospitals Of Pittsburgh - Suburban, PA, p. A537

PAWLOWICZ, James E, Director Human Resources, Shriners Hospitals For Children-Chicago, Chicago, IL, p. A179

PAWLOWSKI, Phil, Chief Financial Officer, Glenbeigh Hospital And Outpatient Centers, Rock Creek, OH, p. A489

PAWOLA, Ken, Chief Operating Officer, Rml Specialty Hospital, IL, p. A186

PAXSON, Gary
Associate Administrator Information Systems, Stone County Medical Center, Mountain View-Stone County, AR, p. A46
Chief Information Officer, White River Medical Center, Batesville, AR, p. A39

PAXTON, Douglas V., Director, Veterans Affairs Roseburg Healthcare System, Roseburg, OR, p. A517

PAYNE, Angel, Clinical Director, Director of Nursing, Sonora Behavioral Health Hospital, Tucson, AZ, p. A38

PAYNE, Ellen, Chief Operating Officer, Georgetown Behavioral Health Institute, Georgetown, TX, p. A607

PAYNE, James, Director Information Systems, Southern Tennessee Regional Health System-Sewanee, TN, p. A581

PAYNE, Jason, Executive Vice President and Chief Operating Officer, Rush Foundation Hospital, Meridian, MS, p. A350

PAYNE, Judy H., Chief Executive Officer, Turning Point Hospital, Moultrie, GA, p. A158

PAYNE, Keela, Director Human Resources, Hamilton General Hospital, Hamilton, TX, p. A608

PAYNE, Kenneth G, Chief Financial Officer, Holzer Medical Center, Gallipolis, OH, p. A483

PAYNE, Michael, M.D., Chief of Staff, Dallas County Medical Center, Fordyce-Dallas County, AR, p. A42

PAYNE, Rick, Director Information Systems, Santa Rosa Medical Center, Milton, FL, p. A131

PAYNE, Steven, Chief Financial Officer, Jordan Valley Medical Center West Valley Campus, West Valley City, UT, p. A652

PAYTON, Becky J, Vice President Human Resources, Mercy Hospital Oklahoma City, Oklahoma City, OK, p. A503

PAZDERNIK, Mary, Chief Financial Officer, Mahnomen Health Center, Mahnomen, MN, p. A334

PEA, Richard, Director Human Resources, Memorial Hospital And Health Care Center, Jasper, IN, p. A208

PEABODY, Kim, Chief Operating Officer, The Brook Hospital - Kmi, Louisville, KY, p. A257

PEACE, Lother E., III, President and Chief Executive Officer, Russell Medical, Alexander City, AL, p. A13

PEACH, Larry, Chief Financial Officer, Jefferson County Health Center, Fairfield, IA, p. A222

PEACH, Susan M., R.N., Chief Executive Officer, Sumner Regional Medical Center, Gallatin, TN, p. A570

PEACOCK, Tammy, Ph.D., Facility Director, Northern Virginia Mental Health Institute, Falls Church, VA, p. A658

PEAL, Chip, Chief Executive Officer, Frankfort Regional Medical Center, Frankfort, KY, p. A252

PEARCE, Charles T, Chief Financial and Information Officer, The Healthcenter, Kalispell, MT, p. A377

PEARCE, Darren
Administrator and Chief Executive Officer, Medical Center Of Peach County, Navicent Health, Bryon, GA, p. A149
Executive Director, Rehabilitation Hospital, Navicent Health, Macon, GA, p. A157

PEARCE, Margaret, R.N., Ph.D., Chief Nursing Officer, University Of Utah Health, Salt Lake City, UT, p. A651

PEARCH, William, Chief Information Officer, Yukon-Kuskokwim Delta Regional Hospital, Bethel, AK, p. A25

PEARCY, Joetta J, Director, Human Resources, Glendive Medical Center, Glendive, MT, p. A375

PEARCY, Steve, Director Human Resources, Community Hospital North, Indianapolis, IN, p. A206

PEARLMAN, Helen, Nurse Executive, Minneapolis Veterans Affairs Health Care System, Minneapolis, MN, p. A335

PEARSON, Bruce, Senior Vice President and Chief Operating Officer, Honorhealth Scottsdale Thompson Peak Medical Center, Scottsdale, AZ, p. A35

PEARSON, Christine, Chief Financial Officer, Anmed Health Women's And Children's Hospital, SC, p. A549

PEARSON, Dawn, Director Human Resources, Healthsouth Rehabilitation Hospital Of Vineland, Vineland, NJ, p. A413

PEARSON, Frank P., Commanding Officer, Naval Hospital Camp Pendleton, Camp Pendleton, CA, p. A54

PEARSON, Gregory, Chief Executive Officer, Minden Medical Center, Minden, LA, p. A274

PEARSON, Jeff
Chief Information Officer, Christus Mother Frances Hospital - Jacksonville, Jacksonville, TX, p. A616
Vice President and Chief Information Officer, Louis & Peaches Owen Heart Hospital, TX, p. A640

PEARSON, Kellie T., Chief Human Resource Officer, St. Christopher's Hospital For Children, Philadelphia, PA, p. A536

PEARSON, Madelyn, R.N., Senior Vice President Patient Care Services and Chief Nursing Officer, Brigham And Women's Hospital, Boston, MA, p. A296

PEARSON, Marshall, Director Management Information Systems, St. David's North Austin Medical Center, Austin, TX, p. A586

PEARSON, Nancy, MSN, R.N., Director, Nursing, Novant Health Thomasville Medical Center, Thomasville, NC, p. A461

PEARSON, Susan, M.D., Chief Medical Officer, Mayo Clinic Health System In Mankato, Mankato, MN, p. A334

PEART, Blake, Administrator, Kindred Hospital-Mansfield, Mansfield, TX, p. A622

PEART, Carol, Chief Financial Officer, Chicago Lakeshore Hospital, Chicago, IL, p. A176

PEBURN, Eric, Chief Financial Officer, Halifax Health Medical Center Of Port Orange, FL, p. A121

PECHOUS, Bryan, M.D., Vice President Medical Affairs, Unitypoint Health - Finley Hospital, Dubuque, IA, p. A222

PECK, Amy, R.N., Chief Nursing Officer, Memorial Regional Health, Craig, CO, p. A98

PECK, Bob, Chief Financial Officer, Wesley Rehabilitation Hospital, Wichita, KS, p. A248

PECK, Charles A., M.D., President and Chief Executive Officer, Piedmont Athens Regional Medical Center, Athens, GA, p. A145

PECK, Darin, M.D., Chief of Staff, Charles A. Dean Memorial Hospital, Greenville, ME, p. A284

PECK, Kay E., Ph.D., Chief Executive Officer, Healthsouth Rehabilitation Hospital Of Modesto, Modesto, CA, p. A72

PECK, Michael D, Assistant Administrator, Caribou Memorial Hospital And Living Center, Soda Springs, ID, p. A172

PECK, Robert C, M.D., Chief Medical Officer, Mayo Clinic Health System In Eau Claire, Eau Claire, WI, p. A692

PECKHAM, Laura D., Chief Executive Officer, Landmark Hospital Of Columbia, Columbia, MO, p. A358

PEDANO, Andrea D, D.O., Chief Medical Officer, Suburban Community Hospital, Norristown, PA, p. A533

PEDERSEN, Darren, Coordinator Information Technology, Weisman Children's Rehabilitation Hospital, Marlton, NJ, p. A407

PEDERSEN, Paul E, M.D., Vice President and Chief Medical Officer, Osf St. Joseph Medical Center, Bloomington, IL, p. A174

PEDERSON, Bryan, Human Resources Manager, Tri-County Hospital, Wadena, MN, p. A341

PEDERSON, Karn, Manager Health Information Management, Mckenzie County Healthcare System, Watford City, ND, p. A469

PEDERSON, Randall K., Chief Executive Officer, Tioga Medical Center, Tioga, ND, p. A468

PEDLEY, Joe, CPA, Vice President and Chief Financial Officer, Lawrence Memorial Hospital, Lawrence, KS, p. A239

PEDLOW, Bernadette R, Senior Vice President Business and Chief Operating Officer, Albany Medical Center South-Clinical Campus, NY, p. A421

PEDRETTI, Jennalee, Vice President Operations, Regional Health Services Of Howard County, Cresco, IA, p. A220

PEDROZA, Fernando, Vice President Information Technology, Mountain Crest Hospital, CO, p. A100

PEEBLES, Wanda V., Chief Nursing Officer, Trinity Springs Pavilion, TX, p. A604

PEEK, Chris, Chief Executive Officer, Caromont Regional Medical Center, Gastonia, NC, p. A453

PEEK, Scott, FACHE, Chief Operating Officer, Karl And Esther Hoblitzelle Memorial Hospital, TX, p. A596

PEELER, Cindy K, R.N., Chief Nursing Officer, Adair County Health System, Greenfield, IA, p. A223

PEEPLES, John, Senior Vice President Human Resources, University Of Maryland Capital Region Health At Laurel Regional Hospital, Laurel, MD, p. A292

PEEPLES, Jonnitra, Chief Human Resource Officer, Vibra Hospital Of Richmond, Richmond, VA, p. A665

PEER, Julianne, President, Penn Highlands Brookville, Brookville, PA, p. A521

PEERY, Lori, Chief Human Resource Management Services, Veterans Affairs Palo Alto Health Care System, Livermore Division, CA, p. A77

PEET, Fred, Chief Information Officer, Yuma Regional Medical Center, Yuma, AZ, p. A38

PEGE, Diane, M.D., Vice President Medical Affairs, Sutter Lakeside Hospital, Lakeport, CA, p. A64

PEIFFER, Paul, Chief Financial Officer and Vice President, Jackson Hospital And Clinic, Montgomery, AL, p. A21

PEIL, Michael, M.D., Chief Medical Director, Kindred Hospital Peoria, Peoria, IL, p. A193

PEIPERT, John, R.N.
Chief Nursing Officer, Hshs St. Francis Hospital, Litchfield, IL, p. A188
Interim President and Chief Executive Officer, Hshs St. Francis Hospital, Litchfield, IL, p. A188

PEKOFSKE, Robert, Vice President Finance, Advocate Hope Children's Hospital, IL, p. A191

PELEUSES, John, Interim Chief Executive Officer, Sonoma West Medical Center, Sebastopol, CA, p. A89

PELFREY, Joy S, R.N., MSN, Vice President and Chief Nursing Officer, Hoops Family Children's Hospital, WV, p. A683

PELHAM, Wesley, Chief Information Officer, Florida State Hospital, Chattahoochee, FL, p. A119

PELKOWSKI, Margaret, R.N., Vice President Patient Care Services, Calvary Hospital, New York (Includes All Hospitals Located Within The Five Boroughs), NY, p. A431

PELLEGRIN, Kimberley, Director, Human Resources, Red River Hospital, Llc, Wichita Falls, TX, p. A644

PELLEGRINO, Ron, Chief Operating Officer, West Virginia University Children's Hospital, WV, p. A685

PELLERIN, Yvonne, Chief Nursing Officer, St. Elizabeth Hospital, Gonzales, LA, p. A268

PELLICONE, John T, M.D., Chief Medical Officer, Nyc Health + Hospitals / Metropolitan, New York (Includes All Hospitals Located Within The Five Boroughs), NY, p. A436

PELOT, Jeff, Interim Chief Information Officer, Denver Health, Denver, CO, p. A98

PELTIER, Glenn, Chief Financial Officer, Christus Mother Frances Hospital - Winnsboro, Winnsboro, TX, p. A644

PELTIER, Robert, M.D.
Chief Medical Officer, North Oaks Medical Center, Hammond, LA, p. A268
Senior Vice President, Chief Medical Officer, North Oaks Health System, North Oaks Rehabilitation Hospital, Hammond, LA, p. A268

PELTON, Ed, Chief of Staff, Chadron Community Hospital And Health Services, Chadron, NE, p. A383

PELUSO, Joseph J., Chief Executive Officer, Tyrone Hospital, Tyrone, PA, p. A542

PEMBERTON, Edith, Chief Financial Officer, East Morgan County Hospital, Brush, CO, p. A97

PEMBERTON, Stacy, Chief Nursing Officer, Grand River Hospital District, Rifle, CO, p. A105

PEMELTON, Debbie, Director Human Resources, Weslaco Regional Rehabilitation Hospital, Weslaco, TX, p. A643

PENA, Carolina, Assistant Director Administrator, Larkin Community Hospital, South Miami, FL, p. A139

PENA, Jessica, Manager Finance, Christus Spohn Hospital Kleberg, Kingsville, TX, p. A617

PENA, Julie, Director Finance, Community Howard Specialty Hospital, Kokomo, IN, p. A209

PENA, Rafael, Chief Executive Officer, Kindred Hospital-Brea, Brea, CA, p. A53

PENA, Terry, Chief Operating Officer and Chief Nursing Officer, San Bernardino Mountains Community Hospital District, Lake Arrowhead, CA, p. A63

PENCO, Kris, Director Information Systems, Coffeyville Regional Medical Center, Coffeyville, KS, p. A233

PENDER, Carol, Assistant Vice President Human Resources, Walden Behavioral Care, Waltham, MA, p. A305

PENDER, Debra, MS, R.N., Vice President Nursing, Mercy Hospital Ardmore, Ardmore, OK, p. A495

PENDERGRAFT, Tina, Chief Nursing Officer, Satanta District Hospital And Long Term Care, Satanta, KS, p. A245

PENDLETON, Gretchen, Director Human Resources, Suburban Community Hospital, Norristown, PA, p. A533

PENDLETON, Timothy, M.D., President Medical Staff, Penn Highlands Brookville, Brookville, PA, p. A521

PENICK, Lisa, R.N., Chief Nursing Officer, Carroll County Memorial Hospital, Carrollton, KY, p. A250

PENLAND, Jennifer, Controller, Kindred Hospital Tarrant County-Arlington, Arlington, TX, p. A584

PENN, Nicholas A., Chief Financial Officer, Hopedale Medical Complex, Hopedale, IL, p. A186

PENN, Shelia, Facility Director, Bryce Hospital, Tuscaloosa, AL, p. A23

PENN, Tripp, Chief Executive Officer, Upson Regional Medical Center, Thomaston, GA, p. A161

PENNACCHIO, Suzanne, Chief Nursing Officer, Nyc Health + Hospitals / Jacobi, New York (Includes All Hospitals Located Within The Five Boroughs), NY, p. A435

PENNER, Jerome, Chief Executive Officer, Murray-Calloway County Hospital, Murray, KY, p. A258

PENNEY, Cindy L, R.N., Vice President Nursing, Mercy Iowa City, Iowa City, IA, p. A224

PENNEY, Jan, R.N., Vice President and Chief Nursing Officer, Midmichigan Medical Center-Midland, Midland, MI, p. A319

PENNINGTON, Brian Keith., President and Chief Executive Officer, Medical West, Bessemer, AL, p. A14

PENNINGTON, Kim, Chief Executive Officer, Select Specialty Hospital-Lexington, Lexington, KY, p. A255

PENNINO, Jackie, Director Human Resources, Old Vineyard Behavioral Health Services, Winston, NC, p. A463

PENNISSON, Jay M., Chief Financial Officer, Brookwood Baptist Medical Center, Birmingham, AL, p. A14

PENOVICH, Carrie L, Chief Clinical Services Officer, Aurora Medical Center - Manitowoc County, Two Rivers, WI, p. A704

PENQUE, Sue, Ph.D., R.N., Senior Vice President and Chief Nursing Officer, South Nassau Communities Hospital, Oceanside, NY, p. A438

PENROD, Kirt, Chief Financial Officer, Shadow Mountain Behavioral Health System, Tulsa, OK, p. A509

PENTZ, Thomas R., Interim Chief Executive Officer, Lewis-Gale Pavilion, VA, p. A666

PENUEL, Jennifer, Director Human Resources, Madison Medical Center, Fredericktown, MO, p. A359

PEOPLES, Kathleen K, R.N., MS, Vice President of Nursing, St. Vincent Kokomo, Kokomo, IN, p. A209

PEOPLES, Kyle, Director Technology Management Services, Springfield Hospital, Springfield, VT, p. A654

PEOPLES, Lynn, Interim Chief Nursing Officer, Person Memorial Hospital, Roxboro, NC, p. A460

PEOPLES, Phyllis L., President and Chief Executive Officer, Terrebonne General Medical Center, Houma, LA, p. A269

PEPE, Joseph, M.D., President and Chief Executive Officer, Catholic Medical Center, Manchester, NH, p. A400

PEPPEL, David
Executive Director, Elmira Psychiatric Center, Elmira, NY, p. A426
Executive Director, Greater Binghamton Health Center, Binghamton, NY, p. A422

PEPPER, L. Douglas, M.D., President, Medical Staff, Monongahela Valley Hospital, Monongahela, PA, p. A532

PEPPLER, Lisa, Financial Manager, Parkview Whitley Hospital, Columbia City, IN, p. A201

PERAL, Sherry, Manager Information Systems, Oak Valley Hospital District, Oakdale, CA, p. A75

PERALTA, Pennie, R.N., VP, Nursing & Chief Nursing Officer, Bon Secours St. Francis Hospital, Charleston, SC, p. A549

PERALTA, Wanda Figuerora, President and Chief Executive Officer, Rivervalley Behavioral Health System, Owensboro, KY, p. A259

PERCELLO, Thomas, Chief Financial Officer, Community Medical Center, Toms River, NJ, p. A412

PEREA, Ely, Director and Chief Executive Officer, Covenant Specialty Hospital, Lubbock, TX, p. A621

PEREACE, Vicki, Manager Human Resources, William Bee Ririe Hospital, Ely, NV, p. A392

PERECKO, Gary L., President, Riddle Hospital, Media, PA, p. A531

PEREIRA, Raul Ramos, M.D., Medical Director, Ryder Memorial Hospital, Humacao, PR, p. A714

PEREL, Michael
Regional Chief Financial Officer, Kauai Veterans Memorial Hospital, Waimea, HI, p. A166
Regional Chief Financial Officer, Samuel Mahelona Memorial Hospital, Kapaa, HI, p. A166

PEREZ, Carmen, Director Human Resources, Doctors' Center Hospital San Juan, San Juan, PR, p. A715

PEREZ, David, Vice President and Chief Information Officer, Eisenhower Medical Center, Rancho Mirage, CA, p. A79

PEREZ, Edwin, M.D., Chief of Medical Staff, Marshall County Hospital, Benton, KY, p. A249

PEREZ, Francisco, Manager Management Information Systems, Hospital De La Universidad De Puerto Rico/Dr. Federico Trilla, Carolina, PR, p. A712

PEREZ, Joe, Associate Director, San Antonio Division, TX, p. A634

PEREZ, Lisa, R.N., Director Nursing, Meadowbrook Rehabilitation Hospital, Gardner, KS, p. A235

PEREZ, Mercedes, Vice President Nursing, Larkin Community Hospital, South Miami, FL, p. A139

PEREZ, Nina, R.N., MSN, Chief Nursing Officer, North Okaloosa Medical Center, Crestview, FL, p. A120

PEREZ, Tony, M.D., President Medical Staff, Jewish Hospital-Shelbyville, Shelbyville, KY, p. A260

PEREZ, III, Miguel, Chief Information Officer, Driscoll Children's Hospital, Corpus Christi, TX, p. A594

PEREZ-GUERRA, Francisco, Chief Executive Officer, Gundersen Moundview Memorial Hospital & Clinics, Friendship, WI, p. A693

PEREZ-MIR, Ernesto, Vice President, Chief Nursing Officer, Newyork-Presbyterian Brooklyn Methodist Hospital, New York (Includes All Hospitals Located Within The Five Boroughs), NY, p. A435

PERI, Gil, President and Chief Operating Officer, Connecticut Children's Medical Center, Hartford, CT, p. A108

PERJON, Cindy, Associate Director, Southwest Connecticut Mental Health System, Bridgeport, CT, p. A107

PERKERSON, Robyn, R.N., Administrator, Lifecare Hospitals Of North Carolina, Rocky Mount, NC, p. A459

PERKES, Neil C, Operations Officer, Logan Regional Hospital, Logan, UT, p. A647

PERKET, William, Vice President Human Resources, North Country Hospital And Health Center, Newport, VT, p. A654

PERKINS, Brett, M.D., Chief Medical Staff, Madison County Memorial Hospital, Madison, FL, p. A128

PERKINS, Chris, Director Information Services, Clinch Valley Medical Center, Richlands, VA, p. A664

PERKINS, Dan
Corporate Director Human Resources, Cornerstone Hospital-West Monroe, West Monroe, LA, p. A280
Vice President of Human Resources, Solara Hospital - Brownsville Campus, TX, p. A609

PERKINS, Jeanne, Vice President Nursing and Interim Manager Human Resources, Bucyrus Hospital, Bucyrus, OH, p. A473

PERKINS, Kathryn, M.D.
Chief Medical Officer, Banner Behavioral Health Center-Thunderbird Campus, AZ, p. A30
Chief Medical Officer, Banner Boswell Medical Center, Sun City, AZ, p. A36

PERKINS, Mike, Vice President and Administrator, Baptist Health Medical Center - North Little Rock, North Little Rock-Pulaski County, AR, p. A47

PERKINS, Richard, Chief Financial Officer, Baylor Scott & White Medical Center - Hillcrest, Waco, TX, p. A642

PERKINS, Sherry B., Ph.D., R.N., President and Chief Executive Officer, University Of Maryland Capital Region Health Prince George's Hospital Center, Cheverly, MD, p. A290

PERKINS, Tom, Chief Information Officer, Shannon Medical Center- St. John's Campus, TX, p. A632

PERKINS-PEPPERS, Andrea, Chief Information Officer, Forks Community Hospital, Forks, WA, p. A672

PERL, Lawrence, M.D., Chief Medical Officer, Columbia Memorial Hospital, Hudson, NY, p. A428

PERLA, Salvatore, President, Norwood Hospital, Norwood, MA, p. A303

PERLICH, Gwynn, Chief Operating Officer, St. Vincent Evansville, Evansville, IN, p. A203

PERLSTEIN, David A., M.D., President and Chief Executive Officer, St. Barnabas Hospital, New York (Includes All Hospitals Located Within The Five Boroughs), NY, p. A437

PERMANN, Darcy, Manager Business Office, Landmann-Jungman Memorial Hospital Avera, Scotland, SD, p. A563

PERMENTER, Ethan, Chief Executive Officer, Parkwood Behavioral Health System, Olive Branch, MS, p. A351

PERNICE, Paul, Vice President Finance, Beebe Healthcare, Lewes, DE, p. A113

PERRA, Scott H., FACHE
Chief Executive Officer, St. Elizabeth Medical Center, Utica, NY, p. A444
President and Chief Executive Officer, St. Luke's Campus, NY, p. A444

PERRAS, Joseph L., President and Chief Executive Officer, Mt. Ascutney Hospital And Health Center, Windsor, VT, p. A654

PERRIGOT, Keri, Manager Human Resources, Cassia Regional Hospital, Burley, ID, p. A168

PERRIN, Cynthia K., FACHE, R.N., President and Chief Executive Officer, Texas Health Presbyterian Hospital Of Rockwall, Rockwall, TX, p. A631

PERRINE, Vicki, FACHE, Chief Operating Officer, Claxton-Hepburn Medical Center, Ogdensburg, NY, p. A439

PERRITT, Daniel, Chief Financial Officer, Sunrise Hospital And Medical Center, Las Vegas, NV, p. A395

PERRON, Kirk, Administrator and Chief Administrative Officer, Jennings Senior Care Hospital, Jennings, LA, p. A269

PERROTTE, Kenneth, Director Operations, Rockland Children's Hospital Psychiatric Center, Orangeburg, NY, p. A439

PERROTTI, Paul R, CPA, Chief Financial Officer, Wellstar West Georgia Medical Center, Lagrange, GA, p. A155

PERRY, Carol, R.N., Vice President and Chief Nursing Officer, Stormont Vail Health, Topeka, KS, p. A246

PERRY, Cheryl
Chief Financial Officer, Integris Mental Health System-Spencer, OK, p. A503
Chief Financial Officer, Vibra Hospital Of Southeastern Massachusetts, New Bedford, MA, p. A302
Executive Director Human Resources, Paris Regional Medical Center, TX, p. A627

PERRY, Cynthia, M.D., Chief of Staff, Stephens Memorial Hospital, Breckenridge, TX, p. A590

PERRY, Darrin Keith, Chief Information Officer and Senior Vice President, St. Jude Children's Research Hospital, Memphis, TN, p. A576

PERRY, Doug, M.D., Chief of Staff, Baptist Medical Center Leake, Carthage, MS, p. A344

PERRY, Faye, Chief Nursing Officer, Tennova Healthcare-Clarksville, Clarksville, TN, p. A568

PERRY, Jan, R.N., Vice President Patient Care Services, Community Medical Center, Missoula, MT, p. A377

PERRY, Jeff
Director Information Technology, St. John's Pleasant Valley Hospital, Camarillo, CA, p. A53

Director Information Technology, St. John's Regional Medical Center, Oxnard, CA, p. A77

PERRY, Karen, Chief Information Resource Management Services, James H. Quillen Veterans Affairs Medical Center, Mountain Home, TN, p. A576

PERRY, Kathleen, Senior Vice President and Chief Information Officer, Mercy Medical Center, Baltimore, MD, p. A288

PERRY, Matthew, Director Information Systems, Andalusia Health, Andalusia, AL, p. A13

PERRY, Matthew J., President and Chief Executive Officer, Good Samaritan Medical And Rehabilitation Center, OH, p. A494

PERRY, Michael, Chief Executive Officer, Michiana Behavioral Health Center, Plymouth, IN, p. A213

PERRY, Nini, Chief Nursing Officer, Georgetown Behavioral Health Institute, Georgetown, TX, p. A607

PERRY, Rhonda S., Chief Financial Officer, Children's Hospital, Navicent Health, GA, p. A156

PERRY, Robert Keith, Senior Vice President, Chief Information Officer, Carilion Franklin Memorial Hospital, Rocky Mount, VA, p. A666

PERRY, Sally, Chief Executive Officer, Coastal Harbor Treatment Center, Savannah, GA, p. A160

PERRY, Shaun, Chief Information Officer, Mcgehee Hospital, Mcgehee-Desha County, AR, p. A46

PERRY, Solette, Regional Director Human Resources, Kauai Veterans Memorial Hospital, Waimea, HI, p. A166

PERRY, Stacey, Director, Nursing, Hamilton County Hospital, Syracuse, KS, p. A246

PERRY, Steve, Chief Executive Officer, Aspen Mountain Medical Center, Rock Springs, WY, p. A709

PERRY, Teresa J, Chief Financial Officer, Up Health System-Bell, Ishpeming, MI, p. A316

PERRY, Tim, Executive Director of Human Resources, Baptist Health Corbin, Corbin, KY, p. A250

PERRY, V Mark, Chief Financial Officer, Adventist Medical Center-Portland, Portland, OR, p. A516

PERRYMAN, Mike, Chief Financial Officer, Baptist Memorial Hospital-Union City, Union City, TN, p. A580

PERSE, David F., M.D., President and Chief Executive Officer, St. Vincent Charity Medical Center, Cleveland, OH, p. A477

PERSILY, Cynthia A., Ph.D., R.N., President and Chief Executive Officer, Highland Hospital, Charleston, WV, p. A682

PERSING, Tamara F., MHA, BSN,, Chief Nursing Officer, Evangelical Community Hospital, Lewisburg, PA, p. A530

PERT, Robert M, Vice President Finance and Chief Financial Officer, United Regional Health Care System-Eleventh Street Campus, TX, p. A644

PERUGINO, Tony, Assistant Vice President Decision Support, Vassar Brothers Medical Center, Poughkeepsie, NY, p. A441

PESCHEL, Colleen, Director Human Resources, Sutter General Hospital, CA, p. A82

PESKIN, Ted, M.D., Acute Care Medical Director, Hilo Medical Center, Hilo, HI, p. A164

PESONEN-JOHNSON, Alice, Chief Nursing Officer, Chi St. Francis Health, Breckenridge, MN, p. A328

PESTLE, Janet K., R.N., MSN, Vice President Nursing and Chief Nursing Officer, Ssm Health St. Joseph Hospital - Lake Saint Louis, Lake Saint Louis, MO, p. A363

PETER, David, M.D.
Senior Vice President Medical Affairs and Chief Medical Director, Cleveland Clinic Akron General, Akron, OH, p. A470
Senior Vice President Medical Affairs and Chief Medical Officer, Cleveland Clinic Akron General Lodi Hospital, Lodi, OH, p. A485

PETER, Douglas G, M.D., Chief Medical Officer, Gallup Indian Medical Center, Gallup, NM, p. A417

PETER, Jan D, Vice President Fiscal Services and Chief Financial Officer, Good Shepherd Health Care System, Hermiston, OR, p. A513

PETER, John, M.D., Vice President Medical Affairs, Ssm Cardinal Glennon Children's Hospital, Saint Louis, MO, p. A368

PETER, Sherma, M.D., Chief of Staff, Optim Medical Center - Screven, Sylvania, GA, p. A161

PETERMAN, John, Vice President and Administrator, Riverside Shore Memorial Hospital, Onancoke, VA, p. A663

PETERMAN, Tammy, R.N., MS, Executive Vice President, Chief Operating Officer and Chief Nursing Officer, The University Of Kansas Hospital - Indian Creek Campus, KS, p. A238

PETERMEIER, Jill, Senior Executive Human Resources, Unitypoint Health - Marshalltown, Marshalltown, IA, p. A226

PETERS, Amy, R.N., Chief Nursing Officer, Truman Medical Center-Lakewood, Kansas City, MO, p. A362

PETERS, Bruce
Chief Executive Officer, Mercy Southwest Hospital, CA, p. A52

Vice President and Chief Operating Officer, Bakersfield Memorial Hospital, Bakersfield, CA, p. A52

PETERS, Candace, R.N., Director of Nursing, Webster County Community Hospital, Red Cloud, NE, p. A390

PETERS, Connie, R.N., President, Chi Health Schuyler, Schuyler, NE, p. A390

PETERS, Dave, Chief Human Resources Officer, Lincoln Division, NE, p. A386

PETERS, Gerald, Vice President Information Technologies and Chief Information Officer, Tripoint Medical Center, OH, p. A479

PETERS, Holli, Director Health Information Management, Holton Community Hospital, Holton, KS, p. A237

PETERS, Jan, Vice President Human Resources, Saint Vincent Hospital, Worcester, MA, p. A306

PETERS, Mary
Chief Information Officer, Womack Army Medical Center, Fort Bragg, NC, p. A452
Chief Nursing Officer, Unitypoint Health - Finley Hospital, Dubuque, IA, p. A222

PETERS, Patrick, Chief Executive Officer, Guthrie County Hospital, Guthrie Center, IA, p. A223

PETERS, Suzanne K, Vice President Human Resources, Munson Medical Center, Traverse City, MI, p. A324

PETERS, Violeta, RN, MA, LNHA, Chief Executive Officer, Specialty Hospital Of Central Jersey, Lakewood, NJ, p. A406

PETERS, Wayne, Administrator, Southern Virginia Mental Health Institute, Danville, VA, p. A657

PETERSEN, Brenda, Human Resources, Sanford Wheaton Medical Center, Wheaton, MN, p. A342

PETERSEN, Debbie, R.N., Chief Operating Officer and Chief Nursing Officer, Spalding Rehabilitation Hospital, Aurora, CO, p. A96

PETERSEN, Julie, CPA, Chief Executive Officer, Kittitas Valley Healthcare, Ellensburg, WA, p. A671

PETERSEN, Richard W
President and Chief Executive Officer, Barbara Bush Children's Hospital, ME, p. A285
President and Chief Executive Officer, Maine Medical Center, Brighton Campus, ME, p. A285

PETERSEN, Richard W., President and Chief Executive Officer, Maine Medical Center, Brighton Campus, ME, p. A285

PETERSEN, Susan, Human Resources, Lincoln Community Hospital And Nursing Home, Hugo, CO, p. A102

PETERSEN, Tina, Chief Nursing Officer, Hillcrest Hospital Cushing, Cushing, OK, p. A497

PETERSON, Alison, Vice President Medical Affairs, United Hospital, Saint Paul, MN, p. A339

PETERSON, Anne, Vice President Human Resources and Support Services, Licking Memorial Hospital, Newark, OH, p. A488

PETERSON, Bill, Director Human Resources, Eastar Health System, East Campus, OK, p. A502

PETERSON, Brent A., Administrator, Cherry County Hospital, Valentine, NE, p. A391

PETERSON, Brett, Director of Information Services, Florida Hospital North Pinellas, Tarpon Springs, FL, p. A142

PETERSON, Carrie, Director of Nursing, Henderson Health Care Services, Henderson, NE, p. A385

PETERSON, Chad, Chief Information Officer, Northwood Deaconess Health Center, Northwood, ND, p. A468

PETERSON, Cheryl, Business Office Manager, Surgical Institute of Reading, Wyomissing, PA, p. A545

PETERSON, Dan, Chief Administrative Officer, Sutter Lakeside Hospital, Lakeport, CA, p. A64

PETERSON, David
Chief Information Officer, University Of Maryland Capital Region Health At Laurel Regional Hospital, Laurel, MD, p. A292
Senior Vice President, Chief Technology Officer, Willie D. Miller Eye Center, TN, p. A567

PETERSON, Denise, R.N., FACHE, President and Chief Executive Officer, Hebrew Senior Care, West Hartford, CT, p. A112

PETERSON, Douglas R., President and Chief Executive Officer, Chippewa Valley Hospital, Durand, WI, p. A691

PETERSON, Eric, Director, Ogden Regional Medical Center, Ogden, UT, p. A648

PETERSON, Erica
Chief Executive Officer and Chief Financial Officer, Sanford Chamberlain Medical Center, Chamberlain, SD, p. A560
Chief Executive Officer, Sanford Chamberlain Medical Center, Chamberlain, SD, p. A560

PETERSON, Gary, M.D., Vice President Medical Affairs and Chief Medical Officer, St. Luke's Hospital, Duluth, MN, p. A331

PETERSON, James Kevin, Human Resources Leader, Kaiser Permanente South Sacramento Medical Center, Sacramento, CA, p. A82

PETERSON, Jeff, M.D., Chief of Staff, Essentia Health Ada, Ada, MN, p. A327

PETERSON, Jeffrey, M.D., Medical Director, Cooperstown Medical Center, Cooperstown, ND, p. A465

PETERSON, Jim, Chief Financial Officer, Steele Memorial Medical Center, Salmon, ID, p. A172

PETERSON, Josilyn, Chief Financial Officer, Ballinger Memorial Hospital, Ballinger, TX, p. A587

PETERSON, Judy, R.N., Chief Nursing Officer, Ut Health Carthage, Carthage, TX, p. A592

PETERSON, Julie, Chief Financial Officer, Sutter Delta Medical Center, Antioch, CA, p. A50

PETERSON, Kathy, Director Information Services, Osf Saint Anthony Medical Center, Rockford, IL, p. A195

PETERSON, Katie, R.N., Chief Nursing Officer, Pender Community Hospital, Pender, NE, p. A389

PETERSON, Larry, Chief Financial Officer, Allen County Regional Hospital, Iola, KS, p. A237

PETERSON, Linda, M.D., Vice President Medical Affairs, Mclaren Orthopedic Hospital, MI, p. A317

PETERSON, Mackenzie, M.D., Chief of Staff, Anderson County Hospital, Garnett, KS, p. A235

PETERSON, Margaret R., Ph.D., R.N., President, California Hospital Medical Center, Los Angeles, CA, p. A66

PETERSON, Michael, FACHE
Chief Operating Officer, Sebasticook Valley Health, Pittsfield, ME, p. A285
President, Androscoggin Valley Hospital, Berlin, NH, p. A398
Chief of Staff, Southeastern Kentucky Medical Center, Pineville, KY, p. A259

PETERSON, Natalie
Director of Human Resources, Optim Medical Center - Jenkins, Millen, GA, p. A157
Director of Human Resources, Optim Medical Center - Screven, Sylvania, GA, p. A161

PETERSON, Randall, President and Chief Executive Officer, Stormont Vail Health, Topeka, KS, p. A246

PETERSON, Robert, I
Chief Executive Officer, Millinocket Regional Hospital, Millinocket, ME, p. A285
Chief Financial Officer, Hackettstown Medical Center, Hackettstown, NJ, p. A405

PETERSON, Ron, FACHE
President and Chief Executive Officer, Baxter Regional Medical Center, Mountain Home-Baxter County, AR, p. A46
Chief Information Officer, Pottstown Hospital, Pottstown, PA, p. A539

PETERSON, Scott, M.D.
President Medical Staff, Avera Flandreau Hospital, Flandreau, SD, p. A561
Vice President of People and Organizational Development, Peninsula Regional Medical Center, Salisbury, MD, p. A294

PETERSON, Scott J., Chief Executive Officer, Healthsouth Rehabilitation Hospital Of Franklin, Franklin, TN, p. A569

PETERSON, Seth, Director Information Services, Coshocton Regional Medical Center, Coshocton, OH, p. A479

PETERSON, Shelley, R.N., Vice President Patient Services and Chief Nursing Officer, St. Mary's Hospital And Medical Center, Grand Junction, CO, p. A101

PETERSON, Steve, M.D., Chief of Staff, Chi Health Plainview, Plainview, NE, p. A390

PETERSON, Steven, Chief Information Officer, Vice President of Operations, Garrett Regional Medical Center, Oakland, MD, p. A293

PETERSON, Tim, M.D., Chief of Staff, Meeker Memorial Hospital, Litchfield, MN, p. A333

PETERSON HALL, Jesse, President, Northshore Glenbrook Hospital, IL, p. A182

PETIK, Jason, Chief Executive Officer, Sidney Regional Medical Center, Sidney, NE, p. A390

PETITT, Michael
Director of Finance, Ascension Southeast Wisconsin Hospital - Elmbrook Campus, Brookfield, WI, p. A690
Director of Finance, Wheaton Franciscan Healthcare - St. Joseph'S, Milwaukee, WI, p. A699

PETRE, Patrick A., Chief Executive Officer, Garfield Medical Center, Monterey Park, CA, p. A73

PETRICK, Teresa G, President, Upmc Passavant Cranberry, PA, p. A538

PETRIK, Jennifer, Interim Chief Nursing Officer, Multicare Deaconess Hospital, Spokane, WA, p. A678

PETRILLO, Mary Ann, R.N., MSN, Acting Associate Director Nursing and Patient Clinical Services, Bedford Veterans Affairs Medical Center, Edith Nourse Rogers Memorial Veterans Hospital, Bedford, MA, p. A295

PETRILLO, Nancy, Director Human Resources, Matheny Medical And Educational Center, Peapack, NJ, p. A409

PETRINA, Robert
Chief Financial Officer, Alta Bates Medical Center-Herrick Campus, CA, p. A52
Interim Chief Financial Officer, Santa Rosa Memorial Hospital, Santa Rosa, CA, p. A89

PETRINI, Julie A., Chief Executive Officer, Alta Bates Medical Center-Herrick Campus, CA, p. A52

PETRINI, Lindsey, Chief Operating Officer, Wellstar North Fulton Hospital, Roswell, GA, p. A159

PETRITZ, Jennifer J, Director Human Resources, University Of Washington Medical Center, Seattle, WA, p. A677

PETROVICH, Lawrence, M.D., Chief Medical Officer, York Hospital, York, ME, p. A286

PETROWER, Stacey, President, New York-Presbyterian/ Hudson Valley Hospital, Cortlandt Manor, NY, p. A425

PETRY, Fernando, M.D., Vice President and Chief Medical Officer, Tradition Medical Center, FL, p. A139

PETRY, Gary, M.D., Chief of Staff, St. Vincent General Hospital District, Leadville, CO, p. A103

PETTEY, Robbie, Chief Financial Officer, National Park Medical Center, Hot Springs-Garland County, AR, p. A43

PETTIGREW, Dennis
Chief Financial Officer, Saint Michael's Medical Center, Newark, NJ, p. A409
Chief Operating Officer, Saint Michael's Medical Center, Newark, NJ, p. A409

PETTIGREW, Rob, Director Information Technology, Wyoming Medical Center, Casper, WY, p. A707

PETTIJOHN, Kim, R.N., MSN, Chief Nursing Officer, Spine Hospital Of Louisiana (Formally The Neuromedical Center Surgical Hospital), Baton Rouge, LA, p. A264

PETTIJOHN, Trent, M.D., Esq
Chief Medical Officer, The Heart Hospital Baylor Denton, Denton, TX, p. A599
Chief Medical Officer, The Heart Hospital Baylor Plano, Plano, TX, p. A629

PETTINATO, Jim, Director Patient Care Services, Wayne Memorial Hospital, Honesdale, PA, p. A527

PETTIT, Amy, R.N., Vice President Nursing Services and Chief Nursing Officer, Schneck Medical Center, Seymour, IN, p. A214

PETTIT, Donny, Chief Financial Officer, Coon Memorial Hospital, Dalhart, TX, p. A595

PETTITE, Shirley F, Chief Human Resources Officer, Nashville Campus, TN, p. A577

PETTREY, Lisa J., MSN, R.N.
Chief Executive Officer, Select Specialty Hospital-Columbus, Mount Carmel Campus, OH, p. A479
Interim Chief Executive Officer, Select Specialty Hospital - Columbus East, OH, p. A479

PETTY, Jane, Director Human Resources, Southern Tennessee Regional Health System-Pulaski, Pulaski, TN, p. A579

PETTY, Russ, M.D., Chief of Staff, Towner County Medical Center, Cando, ND, p. A464

PETULA, Ronald J.
Chief Financial Officer, Good Shepherd Rehabilitation Hospital, Allentown, PA, p. A519
Chief Financial Officer, Good Shepherd Specialty Hospital, Bethlehem, PA, p. A520
Vice President Finance, Good Shepherd Penn Partners Specialty Hospital At Rittenhouse, Philadelphia, PA, p. A534

PEW, Chad, Chief Operating Officer and Senior Vice President, Wyoming Medical Center, Casper, WY, p. A707

PFAFF, Joni, Chief Nursing Officer, Grisell Memorial Hospital District One, Ransom, KS, p. A244

PFAFF, Tony, Chief Executive Officer, Deer Lodge Medical Center, Deer Lodge, MT, p. A375

PFALTZGRAFF, George, Chief Medical Officer, Hansen Family Hospital, Iowa Falls, IA, p. A225

PFAU, Ben, Chief Facility and Information Officer, Bay Area Hospital, Coos Bay, OR, p. A512

PFAU, Beth, M.D., Chief Medical Officer, Larue D. Carter Memorial Hospital, Indianapolis, IN, p. A207

PFEFFER, Amy, Chief Financial Officer, Sturdy Memorial Hospital, Attleboro, MA, p. A295

PFEFFER, Daniel William, Chief Nurse Executive, Weisman Children's Rehabilitation Hospital, Marlton, NJ, p. A407

PFEFFER, Michael, M.D.
Chief Information Officer, Mattel Children's Hospital, CA, p. A69
Chief Medical Informatics Officer, UCLA Health, Stewart & Lynda Resnick Neuropsychiatric Hospital At Ucla, Los Angeles, CA, p. A70

PFEFFER, Stacey, Senior Vice President Human Resources, Children's Medical Center, NY, p. A430

PFEIFER, Bradley D., FACHE, Chief Executive Officer, West Holt Medical Services, Atkinson, NE, p. A381

PFEIFER, Mark P, M.D., Senior Vice President and Chief Medical Officer, University Of Louisville Hospital, Louisville, KY, p. A257

PFEIFFER, James A., FACHE, President and Chief Executive Officer, Self Regional Healthcare, Greenwood, SC, p. A554

PFEIFFER, Margaret, R.N., MSN, Vice President Patient Care Services, Good Samaritan Hospital, Los Angeles, CA, p. A67

PFISTER, Joann M, Director Human Resources, Providence Willamette Falls Medical Center, Oregon City, OR, p. A515

PFISTER, Pam, Chief Executive Officer, Morrison Community Hospital, Morrison, IL, p. A190

PFISTER, Scott, Director Finance, Children At Providence St. Vincent, OR, p. A516

PFLEIGER, Dennis, President and Chief Operating Officer, St. Luke's Hospital - Quakertown Campus, Quakertown, PA, p. A539

PFRANK, Kym, Senior Vice President and Chief Operating Officer, Union Hospital, Terre Haute, IN, p. A215

PHAM, Bong, Chief Medical Officer, Kit Carson County Health Service District, Burlington, CO, p. A97

PHAM, K, M.D., Chief of Staff, Winkler County Memorial Hospital, Kermit, TX, p. A617

PHELAN, Cynthia, Vice President Human Resources, Lawrence General Hospital, Lawrence, MA, p. A300

PHELPS, Britton, Chief Executive Officer, Merit Health Madison, Canton, MS, p. A344

PHELPS, Craig, M.D., Chief of Staff, Great Plains Regional Medical Center, Elk City, OK, p. A498

PHELPS, David E., President and Chief Executive Officer, Hillcrest Hospital, MA, p. A303

PHELPS, Gail, R.N., Chief Nursing Officer, Haxtun Hospital District, Haxtun, CO, p. A102

PHELPS, Joel, Chief Operating Officer, Salina Regional Health Center-Santa Fe Campus, KS, p. A245

PHELPS, Kathleen, Director Human Resources, Treasure Valley Hospital, Boise, ID, p. A168

PHELPS, Lisa, Senior Vice President, Human Resources, Phoenix Children's Hospital, Phoenix, AZ, p. A33

PHELPS, Michael, President and Chief Executive Officer, Ridgeview Medical Center, Waconia, MN, p. A341

PHETTEPLACE, Danial, Director Information Technology, Gundersen St. Joseph's Hospital And Clinics, Hillsboro, WI, p. A694

PHILIP, Neena S., R.N., Assistant Vice President Nursing, Carepoint Health Hoboken University Medical Center, Hoboken, NJ, p. A406

PHILIPS, Grady W., III, President, Winchester Medical Center, Winchester, VA, p. A668

PHILLIPS, Alan M, Controller, Healthsouth Nittany Valley Rehabilitation Hospital, Pleasant Gap, PA, p. A538

PHILLIPS, Barry, Executive Director Human Resources, Camden General Hospital, Camden, TN, p. A566

PHILLIPS, Bill, Vice President Information Services, University Hospital, TX, p. A634

PHILLIPS, Bobby, Chief Nursing Officer, Medical Center Enterprise, Enterprise, AL, p. A17

PHILLIPS, Courtney, Chief Executive Officer, South Sunflower County Hospital, Indianola, MS, p. A347

PHILLIPS, David D., Chief Executive Officer and Administrator, Barnesville Hospital, Barnesville, OH, p. A471

PHILLIPS, David L.
Chief Operating Officer, St. John Broken Arrow, Broken Arrow, OK, p. A496
President and Chief Operating Officer, St. John Owasso, Owasso, OK, p. A505

PHILLIPS, Donna, President, Bryn Mawr Rehabilitation Hospital, Malvern, PA, p. A530

PHILLIPS, Eddie, M.D.
Chief Medical Affairs, Baptist Health Medical Center - North Little Rock, North Little Rock-Pulaski County, AR, p. A47
Chief Medical Officer, Baptist Health Medical Center-Arkadelphia, Arkadelphia, AR, p. A39

PHILLIPS, Frank, M.D., Chief of Staff, Mary Black Health System - Gaffney, Gaffney, SC, p. A553

PHILLIPS, Glenn, Director Information Systems, Gadsden Regional Medical Center, Gadsden, AL, p. A18

PHILLIPS, Heath, Chief Executive Officer, Flowers Hospital, Dothan, AL, p. A17

PHILLIPS, Jan P., R.N., Chief Nursing Officer, Central Carolina Hospital, Sanford, NC, p. A460

PHILLIPS, John, Vice President Information Services, Chi St. Joseph Regional Health Center, Bryan, TX, p. A591

PHILLIPS, John E., FACHE
President, Methodist Dallas Medical Center, Dallas, TX, p. A597
President, Methodist Mansfield Medical Center, Mansfield, TX, p. A622

PHILLIPS, Jonathan, Interim Administrator, University Health Conway, Monroe, LA, p. A274

PHILLIPS, Kelly, M.D., M.P.H., Clinical Director and Chief Staff, Spring Grove Hospital Center, Baltimore, MD, p. A289

PHILLIPS, Kimberly A, Chief Financial Officer, The Children's Home Of Pittsburgh, Pittsburgh, PA, p. A538

PHILLIPS, Lionel J, Vice President Financial Services, Fauquier Hospital, Warrenton, VA, p. A667

PHILLIPS, Michael, Chief Executive Officer, Elkhorn Valley Rehabilitation Hospital, Casper, WY, p. A707

PHILLIPS, Monie, III, Director Clinical Informatics, Jackson Parish Hospital, Jonesboro, LA, p. A269

PHILLIPS, Paul, Chief Financial Officer, Taylor Regional Hospital, Campbellsville, KY, p. A250

PHILLIPS, Robert, M.D., Ph.D., FACC, Executive Vice President and Chief Medical Officer, Houston Methodist Hospital, Houston, TX, p. A611

PHILLIPS, Robert A., Chief Executive Officer, Walker Baptist Medical Center, Jasper, AL, p. A20

PHILLIPS, Sarah, Manager Human Resources, Morgan Memorial Hospital, Madison, GA, p. A157

PHILLIPS, Steve, Information Officer, Greene County General Hospital, Linton, IN, p. A210

PHILLIPS, Tammy, Director, Information Systems, Texas Health Presbyterian Hospital Dallas, Dallas, TX, p. A598

PHILLIPS, Traci, Superintendent, Big Spring State Hospital, Big Spring, TX, p. A589

PHINNEY, Cody, Administrator, Northern Nevada Adult Mental Health Services, Sparks, NV, p. A397

PHIPPS, Emily, Director Human Resources, Oklahoma Center For Orthopedic And Multi-Specialty Surgery, Oklahoma City, OK, p. A504

PHIPPS, Jackie G, Director Human Resources, Johnston Memorial Hospital, Abingdon, VA, p. A655

PHIPPS ADAMS, Holly, Vice President of Human Resources, Carroll Hospital Center, Westminster, MD, p. A294

PIANALTO, Eric, Chief Executive Officer, Mercy Hospital Rogers, Rogers-Benton County, AR, p. A48

PIATKOWSKI, Shannon, Director Information Technology, Blake Medical Center, Bradenton, FL, p. A118

PIATT, Malcolm Keith., M.D., Interim Director, Northern Arizona Veterans Affairs Health Care System, Prescott, AZ, p. A34

PIAZZA, Doreen, Acting Executive Director, South Beach Psychiatric Center, New York (Includes All Hospitals Located Within The Five Boroughs), NY, p. A437

PIAZZA, Kenneth P.
Medical Center Director, Bath Veterans Affairs Medical Center, Bath, NY, p. A422
Medical Center Director, Canandaigua Veterans Affairs Medical Center, Canandaigua, NY, p. A424

PIAZZA, Tony, Director Human Resources, Titus Regional Medical Center, Mount Pleasant, TX, p. A624

PICAZA, Jose, M.D., Chief of Staff, Unicoi County Memorial Hospital, Erwin, TN, p. A569

PICCIONE, Elizabeth, M.D., Chief Medical Officer, Upmc Jameson, New Castle, PA, p. A533

PICCIONE, Jennifer, Chief Nursing and Clinical Services Officer, Madison Health, London, OH, p. A485

PICKARD, Bert, Chief Financial Officer, Gilmore Memorial Hospital, Amory, MS, p. A343

PICKEL, Joseph, Director Resource Management, Walter Reed National Military Medical Center, Bethesda, MD, p. A290

PICKENS, Gayle, Chief Executive Officer, Putnam County Memorial Hospital, Unionville, MO, p. A371

PICKENS, Ramona, Chief Operating Officer, East Cooper Medical Center, Mount Pleasant, SC, p. A555

PICKENS, Regina, Chief Financial Officer, Grafton City Hospital, Grafton, WV, p. A683

PICKER, Josephine, MSN, R.N., Director of Nursing, Asheville Specialty Hospital, Asheville, NC, p. A447

PICKERING, David, System Director, Applications, Linden Oaks Hospital, Naperville, IL, p. A190

PICKETT, C. Judson, Chief of Staff, University Hospital Summerville, Augusta, GA, p. A148

PICKETT, H. Andrew, M.D., Medical Staff President, Excelsior Springs Hospital, Excelsior Springs, MO, p. A359

PICKETT, Lisa C, M.D., Chief Medical Officer, Duke Children's Hospital & Health Center, NC, p. A451

PICKLER, Nancy, Director of Human Resources, Emcompass Health Rehabilitation Hospital Of East, Mesa, AZ, p. A31

PICOU, Timothy, Manager Information Technology, Lower Umpqua Hospital District, Reedsport, OR, p. A517

PIEDRAFITE, JoAnn, R.N., Chief Nursing Officer, Saint Vincent Hospital, Worcester, MA, p. A306

PIEFFER, Paul
Chief Operating Officer, Great River Medical Center, Blytheville-Mississippi County, AR, p. A39
Chief Operating Officer, South Mississippi County Regional Medical Center, Osceola-Mississippi County, AR, p. A47

PIEH, Samuel
Chief Operating Officer, Dmc Huron Valley-Sinai Hospital, Commerce Township, MI, p. A310

Chief Operating Officer, Saint Francis Hospital, Memphis, TN, p. A576

PIEPER, Blaine, Chief Executive Officer, Ohio County Hospital, Hartford, KY, p. A253

PIERCE, Bonnie, MSN, R.N., Associate Director for Patient Care Services, Jack C. Montgomery Veterans Affairs Medical Center, Muskogee, OK, p. A501

PIERCE, Christy, Director of Human Resources, Katherine Shaw Bethea Hospital, Dixon, IL, p. A181

PIERCE, Felicia, R.N.
Chief Nursing Officer, Great River Medical Center, Blytheville-Mississippi County, AR, p. A39
Chief Nursing Officer, South Mississippi County Regional Medical Center, Osceola-Mississippi County, AR, p. A47

PIERCE, James, Administrator, Community Behavioral Health Hospital - Rochester, Rochester, MN, p. A338

PIERCE, Jeff M
Chief Human Resource Officer, Marshall Medical Center, Lewisburg, TN, p. A573
Manager Human Resources, Wayne Medical Center, Waynesboro, TN, p. A581

PIERCE, Jennifer, Administrative Director of Finance, Ssm Health St. Anthony Hospital - Shawnee, Shawnee, OK, p. A506

PIERCE, John, Acting President, Rapid City Regional Hospital, Rapid City, SD, p. A563

PIERCE, Kenneth, Chief Financial Officer, Brookhaven Hospital, Tulsa, OK, p. A508

PIERCE, Laura, Director Human Resources, Memorial Medical Center, Las Cruces, NM, p. A418

PIERCE, Margaret H., Executive Director, Kaiser Permanente Baldwin Park Medical Center, Baldwin Park, CA, p. A52

PIERCE, Pamela, Deputy Chief Executive Officer, Windhaven Psychiatric Hospital, Prescott Valley, AZ, p. A35

PIERCE, Pat, Director Information Systems, Lakewood Regional Medical Center, Lakewood, CA, p. A64

PIERCE, Reid, M.D., Chief Medical Officer, Jefferson Regional Medical Center, Pine Bluff-Jefferson County, AR, p. A47

PIERCE, Sherri, R.N., Chief Nursing Officer, Sweeny Community Hospital, Sweeny, TX, p. A638

PIERCE, Tiffany, Director Human Resources, Wellstone Regional Hospital, Jeffersonville, IN, p. A208

PIERDON, Steven, M.D., Executive Vice President and Chief Medical Officer, Geisinger Wyoming Valley Medical Center, Wilkes Barre, PA, p. A544

PIERESCHI, Giovanni
Vice President Enterprise Information and Chief Information Officer, Hima San Pablo Caguas, Caguas, PR, p. A712
Vice President Management Information Systems, Hospital Hima De Humacao, Humacao, PR, p. A713

PIERLUISI, Guillermo, Vice President of Medical Affairs, Wellstar Paulding Hospital, Hiram, GA, p. A155

PIERRE, Andre, Chief Financial Officer, Forest View Psychiatric Hospital, Grand Rapids, MI, p. A314

PIERRE, Letonia, Coordinator Human Resources, Assumption Community Hospital, Napoleonville, LA, p. A274

PIERSON, Cindy, Interim Chief Nursing Officer, Highlands-Cashiers Hospital, Highlands, NC, p. A455

PIERSON, Jerome, Chief Medical Officer, Mercy Medical Center-Sioux City, Sioux City, IA, p. A229

PIERSON, Kim, R.N., Chief Nursing Officer, Wilbarger General Hospital, Vernon, TX, p. A642

PIERSON, Kyle A., Chief Financial Officer, Roane General Hospital, Spencer, WV, p. A687

PIERSON, Lois K., Chief Financial Officer, University Of Texas Harris County Psychiatric Center, Houston, TX, p. A614

PIETRYKOWSKI, Susan, Commander, U.S. Air Force Hospital, Hampton, VA, p. A659

PIETSCH, Al, CPA, Senior Vice President and Chief Financial Officer, University Of Maryland Baltimore Washington Medical Center, Glen Burnie, MD, p. A292

PIETSCH, Brandon E., Administrator, Centracare Health-Paynesville, Paynesville, MN, p. A337

PIETZ, Gerald, Vice President Finance, Unity Hospital, MN, p. A330

PIFKO, Duane, Interim Director Financial Services, Daniel Drake Center For Post Acute Care, Cincinnati, OH, p. A475

PIGG, Russell, Chief Executive Officer, Eliza Coffee Memorial Hospital, Florence, AL, p. A18

PIGOTT, John, M.D., Chief Medical Officer, Tulane-Lakeside Hospital, LA, p. A276

PIKE, David, Interim Chief Financial Officer, Memorial Hospital Of Carbon County, Rawlins, WY, p. A709

PIKE, Irving, M.D., Senior Vice President and Chief Medical Officer, John Muir Medical Center, Walnut Creek, Walnut Creek, CA, p. A94

PIKE, Pauline, Chief Operating Officer, Addison Gilbert Hospital, MA, p. A295

PIKE, Randi, Director of Nursing, Pioneer Medical Center, Big Timber, MT, p. A373

PIKE, Ronald F, M.D., Medical Director, Adcare Hospital Of Worcester, Worcester, MA, p. A306

PIKE, Tim, M.D., Chief Medical Officer, Portsmouth Regional Hospital, Portsmouth, NH, p. A401

PIKER, John F, M.D., Medical Director, Villa Feliciana Medical Complex, Jackson, LA, p. A269

PIKULA, Shirley, MSN, Associate Director Patient Center Care, San Francisco Va Medical Center, San Francisco, CA, p. A86

PIL, Pieter, M.D., Chief Medical Staff, Martha's Vineyard Hospital, Oak Bluffs, MA, p. A303

PILANT, Jason B., President and Chief Administrative Officer, Roane Medical Center, Harriman, TN, p. A570

PILCHER, Shane, Administrative Director Information Systems, Siskin Hospital For Physical Rehabilitation, Chattanooga, TN, p. A567

PILE, Larry, Director Human Resources, Deaconess Cross Pointe Center, IN, p. A203

PILEGGI, Anne, Administrator and Associate Vice President, Christus Mother Frances Hospital - Jacksonville, Jacksonville, TX, p. A616

PILGRIM, Patti, Chief Financial Officer, Sutter Davis Hospital, Davis, CA, p. A56

PILLION, Scott, Chief Executive Officer, Helen Newberry Joy Hospital, Newberry, MI, p. A320

PILLOT, Juan, M.D., Esq, Medical Director, Hospital Pavia Yauco, Yauco, PR, p. A717

PILNEY, Jeffrey, Chief Medical Officer, Pocahontas Memorial Hospital, Buckeye, WV, p. A681

PILON, Michele, President and Chief Nursing Officer, Transylvania Regional Hospital, Brevard, NC, p. A448

PILONG, Alfred E., Jr, FACHE, President, Munson Medical Center & Chief Operating Officer, Munson Healthcare, Munson Medical Center, Traverse City, MI, p. A324

PILOT, Dave, Chief Financial Officer, Essentia Health St. Joseph's Medical Center, Brainerd, MN, p. A328

PINA, Julie A., Assistant Vice President Patient Care Services and Chief Nursing Officer, Driscoll Children's Hospital, Corpus Christi, TX, p. A594

PINDERSKI, Christopher, M.D., Medical Director of Emergency Room, Black River Medical Center, Poplar Bluff, MO, p. A366

PINE, Richard M., President and Chief Executive Officer, Livengrin Foundation, Bensalem, PA, p. A520

PINEIRO, Carlos M, President, Hospital Hima De Humacao, Humacao, PR, p. A713

PINELLE, Brian, R.N., Chief Nursing Officer, Gulf Coast Regional Medical Center, Panama City, FL, p. A135

PINER, Thomas J., Director for Resources Management, Naval Medical Center San Diego, San Diego, CA, p. A84

PINERO, Efrain, Administrator, Hospital Oriente, Humacao, PR, p. A713

PINETTE, Jameson, Chief Executive Officer, Arbour H. R. I. Hospital, Brookline, MA, p. A298

PINKELMAN, Janet, Director Human Resources, West Campus, NE, p. A387

PINKERTON, Jay, Chief Medical Officer, George Regional Hospital, Lucedale, MS, p. A349

PINKOSKY, Frank
Executive Vice President, Troy Community Hospital, Troy, PA, p. A542
Senior Vice President, Guthrie Robert Packer Hospital, Sayre, PA, p. A540

PINO, Elena, Chief Operating Officer and Chief Nursing Officer, Mesa Hills Specialty Hospital, El Paso, TX, p. A602

PINO, Joseph, M.D., Chief Medical Officer, Regional Medical Center Bayonet Point, Hudson, FL, p. A125

PINON, Richard, Chief Medical Officer, Eastern New Mexico Medical Center, Roswell, NM, p. A419

PINSKY, Karen, M.D., Chief Medical Information Officer, Chester County Hospital, West Chester, PA, p. A544

PINTER, Tabatha, Director of Nursing, George Regional Hospital, Lucedale, MS, p. A349

PINTO, Frank, Chief Information Officer, New Britain General, CT, p. A109

PIO RODA, Claro M, Dr.PH, Vice President, Finance and Chief Financial Officer, Howard County General Hospital, Columbia, MD, p. A291

PIPER, Burt, Chief Operating Officer, Ephraim Mcdowell Regional Medical Center, Danville, KY, p. A251

PIPER, Kevin, Director Information Systems, Florida Hospital Deland, Deland, FL, p. A121

PIPER, Vicky, Vice President Human Resources, Ronald Mcdonald Children's Hospital, IL, p. A189

PIPGRASS, Michele, Chief Fiscal Service, Oklahoma City Veterans Affairs Medical Center, Oklahoma City, OK, p. A504

PIPIA, Paul A., M.D., Interim President and Chief Executive Officer, Nassau University Medical Center, East Meadow, NY, p. A426

PIPKINS, David, Chief Executive Officer and Administrator, Kate Dishman Rehabilitation Hospital, Beaumont, TX, p. A588

PIPPIN, Kim, Chief Nursing Officer, Select Specialty Hospital-Augusta, Augusta, GA, p. A147

PIRKL, Rollie, Chief Financial Officer, Sierra Vista Regional Medical Center, San Luis Obispo, CA, p. A87

PIRO, Michael J, Chief Information Officer, St. John's Episcopal Hospital-South Shore, New York (Includes All Hospitals Located Within The Five Boroughs), NY, p. A437

PIRRI, Christine, Vice President Human Resources, Little Falls Hospital, Little Falls, NY, p. A429

PIRTLE, Kathleen, Director Human Resources, Encompass Health Rehabilitation Hospital Of Wichita Falls, Wichita Falls, TX, p. A644

PIRTLE, Randy B, Chief Financial Officer, King's Daughters Medical Center, Brookhaven, MS, p. A344

PISANO, Thomas, M.D., Chief Professional Services, Whiting Forensic Hospital, CT, p. A109

PISCIOTTA, Michael J., Chief Executive Officer, Southern Surgical Hospital, Slidell, LA, p. A279

PISICOTTA, Robert, Chief Nursing Officer, Baylor Scott And White Continuing Care Hospital, Temple, TX, p. A638

PISPISA, D. Patricia, Senior Vice President, Patient Care Services and Chief Nursing Officer, Eastern Long Island Hospital, Greenport, NY, p. A427

PISTERS, Peter, M.D., President, University Of Texas M.D. Anderson Cancer Center, Houston, TX, p. A614

PISZCZATOSKI, Thomas J, Chief Human Resource Officer, Palm Beach Children's Hospital, FL, p. A143

PITCHER, Ellen, Chief Nursing Officer and Chief Operating Officer, El Paso Children's Hospital, El Paso, TX, p. A601

PITCHFORD, Edward C., President and Chief Executive Officer, Upmc Cole, Coudersport, PA, p. A523

PITMAN, David R, Vice President Finance, Medstar Harbor Hospital, Baltimore, MD, p. A288

PITTMAN, Cyndi, Chief Financial Officer, Baptist Memorial Hospital - Memphis, Memphis, TN, p. A574

PITTMAN, Jennifer, Chief Financial Officer, Shelby Baptist Medical Center, Alabaster, AL, p. A13

PITTMAN, Jeremy, Chief Financial Officer, Castle Rock Adventist Hospital, Castle Rock, CO, p. A97

PITTMAN, Michael, Chief Nursing Officer, Sovah Health-Martinsville, Martinsville, VA, p. A661

PITTMAN, Scott M, Chief Operating Officer, Buchanan General Hospital, Grundy, VA, p. A659

PITTS, Celeste, Chief Financial Officer, Upper Connecticut Valley Hospital, Colebrook, NH, p. A398

PITTS, Lynn, Director Human Resources, Calhoun-Liberty Hospital, Blountstown, FL, p. A118

PITTS, Richard, D.O., Ph.D., Medical Director, Arrowhead Regional Medical Center, Colton, CA, p. A55

PITTS, Robert, Executive Director, Wilmington Treatment Center, Wilmington, NC, p. A462

PITTS, Sherry J., Chief Executive Officer, Merit Health Woman's Hospital, Flowood, MS, p. A346

PITZ, Kenneth, M.D., Chief of Staff, St. Francis Memorial Hospital, West Point, NE, p. A391

PIVONKA, Mary, Director Quality Management, Rockland Children's Hospital Psychiatric Center, Orangeburg, NY, p. A439

PIZ, Tom, Director Human Resources, Fremont Hospital, Fremont, CA, p. A59

PIZARRO, Hugo A, Vice President Human Resources, Terence Cardinal Cooke Health Care Center, New York (Includes All Hospitals Located Within The Five Boroughs), NY, p. A437

PIZZI, Chris, Chief Operating Officer and Chief Financial Officer, Providence Medford Medical Center, Medford, OR, p. A515

PIZZINO, Mary, Chief Information Officer, Effingham Hospital, Springfield, GA, p. A161

PLAGGEMEYER, Rikki, Director Acute Care Nursing, Sturgis Regional Hospital, Sturgis, SD, p. A564

PLAISANCE, Stephen, Chief Financial Officer, Meeker Memorial Hospital, Litchfield, MN, p. A333

PLAMANN, Joy, R.N., Chief Nursing and Operating Officer, St. Cloud Hospital, Saint Cloud, MN, p. A338

PLAMONDON, Richard, Vice President Finance and Chief Financial Officer, St. Joseph Hospital, Nashua, NH, p. A400

PLANO, Crystal, Controller, St. Vincent Dunn Hospital, Bedford, IN, p. A200

PLANT, Steven L, Chief Financial Officer, Cottage Hospital, Woodsville, NH, p. A401

PLASEK, James, M.D., Chief of Staff, Memorial Health Care Systems, Seward, NE, p. A390

PLASKETT, Darice S., R.N., FACHE, Interim Chief Executive Officer, Governor Juan F. Luis Hospital, Christiansted, VI, p. A717

PLASS, Mary Ellen, MS, R.N., Senior Vice President and Chief Nursing Officer, Columbia Memorial Hospital, Hudson, NY, p. A428

PLATE, James, M.D., Chief of Staff, Kimball Health Services, Kimball, NE, p. A385

PLATEL, Raylene, M.D., Chief Medical Officer, Citrus Memorial Health System, Inverness, FL, p. A125

PLATER, Queenie C, Vice President Human Resources for JHM Community Division, Sibley Memorial Hospital, Washington, DC, p. A116

PLATOU, Kenneth E S., President, Mercy Medical Center Mount Shasta, Mount Shasta, CA, p. A74

PLATT, Anne, Chief Executive Officer, Sutter Amador Hospital, Jackson, CA, p. A62

PLATT, Dwayne, M.D., Chief Medical Officer, Conemaugh Meyersdale Medical Center, Meyersdale, PA, p. A532

PLATT, James, Chief Executive Officer, Jackson Hospital, Marianna, FL, p. A129

PLATZ, Scott, Director Finance, University Hospitals Richmond Medical Center, OH, p. A477

PLAUTH, William, M.D., Vice President Operations and Chief Medical Officer, Mercy Regional Medical Center, Durango, CO, p. A99

PLAVIAK, David J, Interim Chief Financial Officer, Novant Health Uva Health System Culpeper Medical Center, Culpeper, VA, p. A657

PLAVIN, Joshua, M.D., Medical Director Medicine Division, Gifford Medical Center, Randolph, VT, p. A654

PLAZA, Marta Rivera., Chief Executive Officer and Managing Director, San Juan Capestrano Hospital, San Juan, PR, p. A716

PLEDGER, Michelle, Coordinator Human Resources, Grady General Hospital, Cairo, GA, p. A149

PLEMEL, Jeff, Director Health Information, Chippewa County-Montevideo Hospital, Montevideo, MN, p. A336

PLEMMONS, Debra, Chief Nursing Officer, Middle Park Medical Center - Granby, CO, p. A102

PLESKOW, Eric D., President and Chief Executive Officer, Brylin Hospitals, Buffalo, NY, p. A423

PLESS, Katy, Director of Human Resources, Carepartners Health Services, Asheville, NC, p. A447

PLETZ, Richard Andrew., Chief Executive Officer, Plaza Specialty Hospital, Houston, TX, p. A613

PLOPPER, Michael, M.D., Chief Medical Officer, Sharp Mcdonald Center, CA, p. A84

PLOSZEK, Judith M., Chief Financial Officer, Tampa General Hospital Children's Medical Center, FL, p. A141

PLOSZEK, Michael, Vice President Physician Strategy and Clinical Operations, Advocate Good Shepherd Hospital, Barrington, IL, p. A174

PLUARD, Dennis, Vice President Finance and Operations, Sarah Bush Lincoln Health Center, Mattoon, IL, p. A188

PLUMLEE, Steve, Chief Executive Officer, Select Specialty Hospital-Knoxville, TN, p. A579

PLUMMER, Debra, Chief Executive Officer, Kindred Hospital-Bay Area St. Petersburg, FL, p. A141

PLUMMER, Doug, Chief Operating Officer, Sabine Medical Center, Many, LA, p. A273

PLUNKETT, Alicia, Chief Nurse Executive, Parkwood Behavioral Health System, Olive Branch, MS, p. A351

PLYMELL, Shane, Chief Executive Officer, Shannon Medical Center- St. John's Campus, TX, p. A632

PLYWACZYNSKI, Russell J., CPA, Director of Finance, St. Joseph's Hospital Of Buckhannon, Buckhannon, WV, p. A682

POBLETE, Ronald, M.D., President Medical and Dental Staff, St. Mary's General Hospital, Passaic, NJ, p. A409

POCCHIARI, Michael, Director Human Resources, Garden Park Medical Center, Gulfport, MS, p. A346

POCOCK, Donald, Vice-President Medical Affairs, Carteret Health Care, Morehead City, NC, p. A457

PODE, Maureen, Co-Interim Executive Director, Nyc Health + Hospitals / North Central Bronx, New York (Includes All Hospitals Located Within The Five Boroughs), NY, p. A436

PODESTA, Charles H, Chief Information Officer, Uc Irvine Medical Center, Orange, CA, p. A76

PODGES, Christopher J, Vice President Outpatient Services and Chief Information Officer, Munson Medical Center, Traverse City, MI, p. A324

PODNOS, Yale D., M.D., Chief Medical Officer, West Hills Hospital And Medical Center, Los Angeles, CA, p. A70

PODOLSKY, Daniel, M.D.
President, University Of Texas Southwestern Medical Center - Zale Lipshy, TX, p. A598
President, William P. Clements, Jr. University Hospital, Dallas, TX, p. A598

PODUSKA, Donna D, MS, R.N., Chief Nursing Officer, Mountain Crest Hospital, CO, p. A100

PODZIMEK, Marcia, Chief Human Resources Officer, Wagner Community Memorial Hospital Avera, Wagner, SD, p. A565

POE, Dale
Vice President and Chief Financial Officer, Hawkins County Memorial Hospital, Rogersville, TN, p. A579

Vice President Finance and Operations, Holston Valley Medical Center, Kingsport, TN, p. A572

POE, Terri Lyn, Interim Chief Nursing Officer, Uab Highlands, AL, p. A15

POEHLER, Kathy, Vice President, Human Resources, University Of Maryland Baltimore Washington Medical Center, Glen Burnie, MD, p. A292

POEST, Scott, Chief Information Officer, Lake Regional Health System, Osage Beach, MO, p. A365

POFAHL, Barnetta, Director Human Resources, Wagoner Community Hospital, Wagoner, OK, p. A510

POFF, Heather, Director Human Resources, Princeton Community Hospital, Princeton, WV, p. A686

POFFENBARGER, John, Director Fiscal Services, Northern Virginia Mental Health Institute, Falls Church, VA, p. A658

POGAS, George, CPA, Senior Vice President and Chief Financial Officer, Witham Health Services, Lebanon, IN, p. A210

POGLIANO, Chris, M.D., Chief Medical Staff, Aspirus Ironwood Hospitals & Clinics, Inc., Ironwood, MI, p. A316

POGUE, Rick, Vice President, Human Resources, Newyork-Presbyterian Brooklyn Methodist Hospital, New York (Includes All Hospitals Located Within The Five Boroughs), NY, p. A435

POHAR, Mark, Executive Director, Margaretville Hospital, Margaretville, NY, p. A429

POHJALA, Eric
Chief Financial Officer, Upmc Susquehanna Soldiers + Sailors, Wellsboro, PA, p. A543
Executive Vice President and Chief Financial Officer, Upmc Susquehanna Muncy, Muncy, PA, p. A532
Executive Vice President and Chief Financial Officer, Upmc Susquehanna Williamsport Regional Medical Center, Williamsport, PA, p. A545

POHL, Ann-Marie J, MSN, R.N., Vice President and Chief Nursing Officer, Lima Memorial Health System, Lima, OH, p. A484

POHL, David F., M.D., Chief of Staff, Cornerstone Hospital Of Round Rock, TX, p. A585

POHL, David L., M.D., Chief of Staff, Hillcrest Hospital - South, Tulsa, OK, p. A508

POHLMAN, John, Vice President Finance and Administration, St. Catherine Of Siena Medical Center, Smithtown, NY, p. A443

POIROT, Diane, Vice President Human Resources, Quentin Mease Hospital, TX, p. A611

POISKER, Karen C, MSN, Vice President Patient Care Services and Chief Nursing Officer, Peninsula Regional Medical Center, Salisbury, MD, p. A294

POISSON, Keith R, Executive Vice President and Chief Operating Officer, Greater Baltimore Medical Center, Baltimore, MD, p. A287

POLAND, David, Chief Financial Officer, Grove City Medical Center, Grove City, PA, p. A526

POLASHEK, Maurene, Chief Financial Officer, Oro Valley Hospital, Oro Valley, AZ, p. A32

POLEGA, Steve, Chief Nursing Officer, Metro Health - University Of Michigan Health, Wyoming, MI, p. A326

POLENZ, Scott, CPA, Chief Administrative Officer, Marshfield Medical Center - Eau Claire Hospital, Eau Claire, WI, p. A692

POLHEBER, Richard, Chief Executive Officer, Benson Hospital, Benson, AZ, p. A28

POLHILL, James, M.D., Chief Medical Officer, Jefferson Hospital, Louisville, GA, p. A156

POLIKAITIS, Audrius, Chief Information Officer, University Of Illinois Hospital & Health Sciences System, Chicago, IL, p. A180

POLING, Rodney, M.D., Medical Director, Unity Psychiatric Care-Columbia, Columbia, TN, p. A568

POLING, Susan, Director Human Resources, King's Daughters' Health, Madison, IN, p. A210

POLIS, Nikki S, Ph.D., Chief Nurse Executive, Methodist Le Bonheur Germantown Hospital, TN, p. A575

POLISKNOWSKI, John, Chief Nursing Officer, Northside Hospital, Saint Petersburg, FL, p. A138

POLITE, Elmer, Chief Financial Officer, Coliseum Northside Hospital, Macon, GA, p. A156

POLITIS, Christos, M.D.
Chief Medical Officer, Memorial Hospital Of Tampa, Tampa, FL, p. A141
Chief Medical Officer, Tampa Community Hospital, Tampa, FL, p. A141

POLITO, Janine, Chief Human Resources Officer, Banner Ironwood Medical Center, San Tan Valley, AZ, p. A35

POLIVKA, Maureen, Chief Nursing Officer, Hill Country Memorial Hospital, Fredericksburg, TX, p. A606

POLIZZI, Arturo
Chief Human Resources Officer, Toledo Children's Hospital, OH, p. A491

President and Chief Executive Officer, Toledo Children's Hospital, OH, p. A491

President, Promedica Bay Park Hospital, Oregon, OH, p. A488

President, Promedica Flower Hospital, Sylvania, OH, p. A491

President, Promedica Wildwood Orthopaedic And Spine Hospital, OH, p. A491

President, Toledo Children's Hospital, OH, p. A491

POLIZZOTTO, Mike, Chief Medical Officer, Swedishamerican - A Division Of Uw Health, Rockford, IL, p. A195

POLK, Brent, M.D., Chair Department of Pediatrics and Vice President Academic Affairs, Children's Hospital Los Angeles, Los Angeles, CA, p. A66

POLK, Claire, Chief Financial Officer, Lake Norman Regional Medical Center, Mooresville, NC, p. A457

POLK, Monica, M.D., Chief Medical Officer, Salt Lake Behavioral Health, Salt Lake City, UT, p. A650

POLKOW, Craig, Vice President, Finance, St. Vincent Evansville, Evansville, IN, p. A203

POLLACK, Neil, Senior Administrator, Terence Cardinal Cooke Health Care Center, New York (Includes All Hospitals Located Within The Five Boroughs), NY, p. A437

POLLAK, Erich, M.D., Chief of Staff, West Covina Medical Center, West Covina, CA, p. A95

POLLARD, Amy, R.N., President and Chief Executive Officer, Nicholas H. Noyes Memorial Hospital, Dansville, NY, p. A425

POLLARD, Anthony, D.O., Chief Medical Officer, Amg Specialty Hospital - Las Vegas, Las Vegas, NV, p. A393

POLLMAN, Brian, Chief Medical Officer, Hutchinson Health, Hutchinson, MN, p. A333

POLLOCK, Jeffrey, Chief Information Officer, Wentworth-Douglass Hospital, Dover, NH, p. A398

POLLOCK, Maureen King., Chief Executive Officer, Eagleville Hospital, Eagleville, PA, p. A524

POLO, James A, M.D., Chief Medical Officer, Western State Hospital, Tacoma, WA, p. A679

POLO, Therese, Medical Staff President, Carlinville Area Hospital, Carlinville, IL, p. A175

POLSELLI, Donna, Chief Operating Officer, Franciscan Children'S, Brighton, MA, p. A297

POLSTER, Peggy, Manager Personnel and Administrative Assistant, Falls Community Hospital And Clinic, Marlin, TX, p. A622

POLTAWSKY, Jeffrey S, Senior Vice President, American Family Children's Hospital, WI, p. A696

POLTAWSKY, Jeffrey S., President and Market Leader, Multicare Mary Bridge Children's Hospital And Health Center, Tacoma, WA, p. A679

POLUNAS, David M., Director, Colorado Mental Health Institute At Fort Logan, Denver, CO, p. A98

POLZIN, Greg

Chief Financial Officer, Iowa Specialty Hospital-Belmond, Belmond, IA, p. A217

Chief Financial Officer, Iowa Specialty Hospital-Clarion, Clarion, IA, p. A219

POMMETT, Francis A, Jr, Chief Operating Officer, Shands Lake Shore Regional Medical Center, Lake City, FL, p. A127

PONCE, Agustin, Supervisor Maintenance, Castaner General Hospital, Castaner, PR, p. A712

PONCE, Joseph A, Chief Information Management, Dwight David Eisenhower Army Medical Center, Fort Gordon, GA, p. A154

PONCE, Martha, Director Information Technologies and Telecommunications, Providence Saint John's Health Center, Santa Monica, CA, p. A89

PONCZOCHA, John, Chief Executive Officer, Select Specialty Hospital-Downriver, Wyandotte, MI, p. A326

POND, Dwight, TIS Boise, Saint Alphonsus Regional Medical Center, Boise, ID, p. A168

POND-BELL, Michele, R.N., Nurse Administrator, Cassia Regional Hospital, Burley, ID, p. A168

PONDER, Beverly K, Executive Assistant and Human Resources Coordinator, Covington County Hospital, Collins, MS, p. A345

PONDER, David, Information Technology Officer, Claremore Indian Hospital, Claremore, OK, p. A497

PONETA, Jan, Director Information Services, Mercy Hospital Jefferson, Crystal City, MO, p. A358

PONOZZO, Nancy Lynn, MSN, R.N., Chief Nursing Officer, Aspirus Iron River Hospitals & Clinics, Inc., Iron River, MI, p. A316

PONTICELLO, Nat, Vice President Human Resources, Valley Children's Healthcare, Madera, CA, p. A71

PONTIOUS, Becky, Human Resources/Accounting, Loring Hospital, Sac City, IA, p. A229

PONTIOUS, Michael, M.D., Chief of Staff, St. Mary's Regional Medical Center, Enid, OK, p. A498

PONTON, Elyonel, Executive Director, Hospital Episcopal San Lucas Guayama, Guayama, PR, p. A713

POOK, Lots, Chief Information Officer, National Jewish Health, Denver, CO, p. A99

POOLE, Andrew J., III, Interim Chief Financial Officer, Oaklawn Hospital, Marshall, MI, p. A319

POOLE, Robert, Chief Executive Officer, Regency Hospital Of Northwest Arkansas - Springdale, Springdale-Washington County, AR, p. A49

POOLE-ADAMS, Veronica, R.N., Vice President, Chief Operating Officer and Chief Nursing Executive, Carolinas Healthcare System Cleveland, Shelby, NC, p. A460

POORE, Justin, D.O., Chief Medical Staff, Cloud County Health Center, Concordia, KS, p. A234

POORE, Luke David., Chief Executive Officer, Kearney County Health Services, Minden, NE, p. A386

POORE, Timothy T., Chief Executive Officer, Encompass Health Rehabilitation Hospital Of Northwest Tucson, Tucson, AZ, p. A37

POOS, Joshua, M.D., President Medical Staff, Community Hospital Of Staunton, Staunton, IL, p. A197

POPE, Alan R, M.D.

Chief Medical Officer, Our Lady Of Lourdes Medical Center, Camden, NJ, p. A403

Vice President, Medical Affairs, Lourdes Medical Center Of Burlington County, Willingboro, NJ, p. A414

POPE, Alice H, Chief Financial Officer, Honorhealth Scottsdale Thompson Peak Medical Center, Scottsdale, AZ, p. A35

POPE, Brad W, Vice President Human Resources, Memorial Hospital Hixson, TN, p. A567

POPE, Eddie, Chief Information Officer, Lackey Memorial Hospital, Forest, MS, p. A346

POPE, James W., FACHE, President and Chief Executive Officer, Van Wert County Hospital, Van Wert, OH, p. A492

POPE, Jayne E., R.N., FACHE, Chief Executive Officer, Hill Country Memorial Hospital, Fredericksburg, TX, p. A606

POPE, Richard, Vice President Human Resources, Jackson County Memorial Hospital, Altus, OK, p. A495

POPE, Robert A., Director I, St. Vincent Anderson, Anderson, IN, p. A199

POPE, Susan, Director Human Resources, Wills Memorial Hospital, Washington, GA, p. A163

POPHAN, Cameron, Chief Financial Officer, Houston Northwest Medical Center, Houston, TX, p. A611

POPKIN, Steven, Chief Executive Officer, Parkview Community Hospital Medical Center, Riverside, CA, p. A81

POPLAWSKI, Christine, Chief Financial Officer, Mary Black Health System - Gaffney, Gaffney, SC, p. A553

POPLI, Anand, Medical Director, Porter-Starke Services, Valparaiso, IN, p. A216

POPOWYCZ, Alex

Chief Information Officer, Health First Viera Hospital, Melbourne, FL, p. A129

Senior Vice President and Chief Information Officer, Health First Cape Canaveral Hospital, Cocoa Beach, FL, p. A120

Senior Vice President and Chief Information Officer, Health First Palm Bay Hospital, Palm Bay, FL, p. A135

POPP, Adam, Director Information Systems, Avera St. Benedict Health Center, Parkston, SD, p. A562

POPP, Jason, Chief of Medical Staff, Rochelle Community Hospital, Rochelle, IL, p. A194

POPP, Susan, Controller, Kindred Hospital Tarrant County-Fort Worth Southwest, TX, p. A604

POPPEN, Jeffrey, Chief Financial Officer, Sanford Aberdeen Medical Center, Aberdeen, SD, p. A559

POPPERT, Dale, M.D., Chief of Staff, Kaiser Permanente Antioch Medical Center, Antioch, CA, p. A50

POPPY, Bill, Chief Information Officer, Virginia Mason Medical Center, Seattle, WA, p. A677

POQUETTE, Gary R., FACHE, Chief Executive Officer, Penobscot Valley Hospital, Lincoln, ME, p. A284

PORADA, John, Chief Financial Officer, Tristar Southern Hills Medical Center, Nashville, TN, p. A578

PORCELLI, Cheri, MSN, R.N., Chief Nursing Officer, Deer's Head Hospital Center, Salisbury, MD, p. A294

PORCO, Albert, Director Management Information Systems, Hackensack Meridian Health Palisades Medical Center, North Bergen, NJ, p. A409

PORTCHY, Mindy, Manager Human Resources, Summit Pacific Medical Center, Elma, WA, p. A671

PORTER, Bruce, Chief Financial Officer, Red River Hospital, Llc, Wichita Falls, TX, p. A644

PORTER, Cedric, M.D., President Medical Staff, Emanuel Medical Center, Swainsboro, GA, p. A161

PORTER, Daniel J., Senior Vice President and Chief Financial Officer, J. Arthur Dosher Memorial Hospital, Southport, NC, p. A460

PORTER, Glen, Vice President Human Resources, St. Mary's Children's Hospital, MN, p. A330

PORTER, Greg, Chief Financial Officer, Rio Grande Hospital, Del Norte, CO, p. A98

PORTER, Heather Renee, Chief Clinical Officer, Newton Medical Center, Newton, KS, p. A242

PORTER, James, Chief Financial Officer, Brookdale Hospital Medical Center, New York (Includes All Hospitals Located Within The Five Boroughs), NY, p. A431

PORTER, James P, Chief Financial Officer, St. Bernard Hospital And Health Care Center, Chicago, IL, p. A179

PORTER, Jim, Chief Financial Officer, Southern Virginia Regional Medical Center, Emporia, VA, p. A657

PORTER, Jody, R.N., Senior Vice President Patient Care Services and Chief Nursing Officer, Greater Baltimore Medical Center, Baltimore, MD, p. A287

PORTER, Lance, Chief Executive Officer, Banner Payson Medical Center, Payson, AZ, p. A32

PORTER, Laura, Executive Director, Good Shepherd Penn Partners Specialty Hospital At Rittenhouse, Philadelphia, PA, p. A534

PORTER, Lisa, Director Human Resources, Leadership and Education, Veterans Affairs Salt Lake City Health Care System, Salt Lake City, UT, p. A651

PORTER, Mary, M.D., Medical Staff President, Grande Ronde Hospital, La Grande, OR, p. A514

PORTER, Sharon, Chief Financial Officer, Pappas Rehabilitation Hospital For Children, Canton, MA, p. A299

PORTER, Stephen D., Chief Executive Officer, Roper St. Francis, Charleston, SC, p. A550

PORTER, T J, Director Human Resources, Bennett County Hospital And Nursing Home, Martin, SD, p. A562

PORTERFIELD, Liza, Chief Financial Officer, Regional Medical Center, Orangeburg, SC, p. A556

PORTMAN, Angela, Chief Executive Officer, Breckinridge Memorial Hospital, Hardinsburg, KY, p. A253

PORTNER, Barry, M.D., Chief of Staff, Prowers Medical Center, Lamar, CO, p. A103

PORWOLL, Amy, Vice President of Information Systems, St. Cloud Hospital, Saint Cloud, MN, p. A338

POSCH, Tim B, Business Manager and Director Personnel, Parsons State Hospital And Training Center, Parsons, KS, p. A244

POSECAI, Scott J, Executive Vice President and Chief Financial Officer, Ochsner Medical Center For Children, LA, p. A276

POSEY, Dawn, Chief Operating Officer, Promise Hospital Of Vicksburg, Vicksburg, MS, p. A354

POSEY, Richard B, Director Human Resources, Baptist Easley Hospital, Easley, SC, p. A552

POSPISIL, Matt E., Vice President Perioperative Services, Nebraska Medicine - Bellevue, Bellevue, NE, p. A382

POST, Daniel J., Interim President, Ronald Mcdonald Children's Hospital, IL, p. A189

POST, Eleanor, R.N., Chief Nursing Officer, Piedmont Rockdale Hospital, Conyers, GA, p. A151

POST, Gwen, R.N., Chief Nursing Officer, Sanford Worthington Medical Center, Worthington, MN, p. A342

POST, John, M.D., Medical Director, Morrill County Community Hospital, Bridgeport, NE, p. A382

POST, Kimberly

Senior Vice President and Chief Clinical Officer, Honorhealth Scottsdale Thompson Peak Medical Center, Scottsdale, AZ, p. A35

Senior Vice President and Chief Executive Officer, Honorhealth Scottsdale Osborn Medical Center, Scottsdale, AZ, p. A35

POST, Michael, Chief Executive Officer, Clarion Psychiatric Center, Clarion, PA, p. A522

POSTERNACK, Charles, M.D., Vice President, Boca Raton Regional Hospital, Boca Raton, FL, p. A118

POSTON, Anne, Director of Human Resources/Compliance, Lake City Community Hospital, Lake City, SC, p. A555

POSTULKA, Carol, Administrative Coordinator, Avera Gregory Hospital, Gregory, SD, p. A561

POTEATE, Kathy, Interim Director Human Resources, Hugh Chatham Memorial Hospital, Elkin, NC, p. A452

POTEETE, Robin, Manager Human Resources, Hawkins County Memorial Hospital, Rogersville, TN, p. A579

POTEMPA, Debra, Vice President, Mercyhealth Hospital And Trauma Center - Janesville, Janesville, WI, p. A695

POTITADKUL, Wendy, Chief Information Officer, Sunrise Canyon Hospital, Lubbock, TX, p. A621

POTTENGER, Jay, Administrator, Montana State Hospital, Warm Springs, MT, p. A379

POTTER, Carolyn

Chief Human Resources Officer, Mclaren Bay Region-West Campus, MI, p. A308

Vice President Human Resources, Mclaren Bay Special Care, Bay City, MI, p. A308

Vice President Human Resources, Mclaren Central Michigan, Mount Pleasant, MI, p. A319

POTTER, Dianne P, Manager Human Resources, Parkview Whitley Hospital, Columbia City, IN, p. A201

POTTER, Val, Director Human Resources, St. Vincent Salem Hospital, Salem, IN, p. A214

POTTORFF, Kelly, Chief Executive Officer, Cheyenne County Hospital, Saint Francis, KS, p. A245

POTTS, Mary Ann, Director Personnel, Montpelier Hospital, OH, p. A473

POULSON, Rhonda, Chief Nursing Officer and Vice President of Clinical Operations, Memorial Hospital Hixson, TN, p. A567

POUND, Steve, Vice President Human Resources, St. Joseph's Hospital, Savannah, GA, p. A160

POUND, Terry, Chief Financial Officer, Hospital District No 1 Of Rice County, Lyons, KS, p. A240

POUND, Veronica, R.N.
    Administrator, Socorro General Hospital, Socorro, NM, p. A420
    Interim Administrator and Director of Patient Care, Socorro General Hospital, Socorro, NM, p. A420

POVICH, Mark, D.O., Medical Director, Osf St. Francis Hospital And Medical Group, Escanaba, MI, p. A312

POWE, Lee, Director Management Information Systems, Hugh Chatham Memorial Hospital, Elkin, NC, p. A452

POWEL, Linda J, M.D., Medical Director, Odessa Memorial Healthcare Center, Odessa, WA, p. A674

POWELL, Adam, Program Manager, Marion Veterans Affairs Medical Center, Marion, IL, p. A188

POWELL, Candy, Administrator, Collingsworth General Hospital, Wellington, TX, p. A643

POWELL, Charles
    Chief Financial Officer, Arkansas Surgical Hospital, North Little Rock-Pulaski County, AR, p. A46
    Interim Chief Executive Officer, Lubbock Heart & Surgical Hospital, Lubbock, TX, p. A621
    President, Sts. Mary & Elizabeth Hospital, Louisville, KY, p. A256

POWELL, D Jerome, M.D., Chief Information Officer, Golisano Children's Hospital, NY, p. A441

POWELL, Hannah, Chief Nursing Officer, Mercy Hospital Kingfisher, Kingfisher, OK, p. A500

POWELL, Holly, Administrator, Continuecare Hospital At Medical Center (Odessa), Odessa, TX, p. A626

POWELL, Jackie, Director Human Resources, Pemiscot Memorial Health System, Hayti, MO, p. A360

POWELL, James R, Associate Administrator, Banner Gateway Medical Center, Gilbert, AZ, p. A29

POWELL, Jimmy, Manager Human Resources, Harry S. Truman Memorial Veterans Hospital, Columbia, MO, p. A358

POWELL, Josh, Facility Controller, Cox Monett Hospital, Monett, MO, p. A365

POWELL, Kay, Director Human Resources, Christus Southeast Texas Jasper Memorial, Jasper, TX, p. A616

POWELL, Michelle, Chief Executive Officer, Select Rehabilitation Hospital Of Denton, Denton, TX, p. A599

POWELL, Parker, Chief Executive Officer, Glendive Medical Center, Glendive, MT, p. A375

POWELL, Tammy, FACHE, M.P.H.
    President, Ssm Health Bone And Joint Hospital At St. Anthony, OK, p. A504
    President, Ssm Health St. Anthony South, OK, p. A504

POWELL, Traci, Director Human Resources, Healthsouth Emerald Coast Rehabilitation Hospital, Panama City, FL, p. A135

POWELL, Virginia, Director Finance, Wilmington Treatment Center, Wilmington, NC, p. A462

POWELL-STAFFORD, Valerie L., Chief Executive Officer, Englewood Community Hospital, Englewood, FL, p. A122

POWER, Bob, Vice President Information Services, Good Samaritan Regional Medical Center, Corvallis, OR, p. A512

POWER, Robert
    Chief Information Officer, Samaritan Pacific Communities Hospital, Newport, OR, p. A515
    Vice President Information Services, Samaritan Lebanon Community Hospital, Lebanon, OR, p. A514

POWERS, Anthony, Interim President and Vice President of Patient Services, Baptist Health Corbin, Corbin, KY, p. A250

POWERS, Barbara, R.N., Chief Nursing Officer, Austin Lakes Hospital, Austin, TX, p. A585

POWERS, Brent, M.D., Vice President/Chief Medical Officer, Lexington Medical Center, West Columbia, SC, p. A558

POWERS, Jamekia, Assistant Director Human Resources, Georgia Regional Hospital At Savannah, Savannah, GA, p. A160

POWERS, Judi, Chief Executive Officer, Advanced Care Hospital Of Montana, Billings, MT, p. A373

POWERS, Kelli, Chief Financial Officer, Madison Hospital, AL, p. A19

POWERS, Mary, R.N., MSN
    Senior Vice President and Chief Nursing Officer, Manchester Memorial Hospital, Manchester, CT, p. A108
    Senior Vice President and Chief Nursing Officer, Rockville General Hospital, Vernon, CT, p. A111

POWERS, Ryan J., Vice President Finance, Spectrum Health Zeeland Community Hospital, Zeeland, MI, p. A326

POWERS, Tim, Chief Executive Officer, North Canyon Medical Center, Gooding, ID, p. A169

POWRIE, Raymond, M.D., Senior Vice President Quality and Clinical Effectiveness, Women & Infants Hospital Of Rhode Island, Providence, RI, p. A548

POYNTER, Carmen, Director Human Resources, Rockcastle Regional Hospital And Respiratory Care Center, Mount Vernon, KY, p. A258

POYTHRESS, Antoine
    Chief Financial Officer, Washington County Regional Medical Center, Sandersville, GA, p. A160
    Interim Chief Executive Officer, Washington County Regional Medical Center, Sandersville, GA, p. A160

PRABHAKARAN, Madhan, M.D., Chief Medical Officer, Palo Alto County Health System, Emmetsburg, IA, p. A222

PRACHEIL, Michael, Chief Financial Officer, Gothenburg Health, Gothenburg, NE, p. A384

PRACHT, Matthew, Vice President Finance, Scotland Health Care System, Laurinburg, NC, p. A456

PRADA, Janina
    Director Information Services, University Medical Center Of El Paso, El Paso, TX, p. A603
    Director Information Technology, El Paso Children's Hospital, El Paso, TX, p. A601

PRAFKA, David, Ed.D., Director of Human Resources, Vidant Edgecombe Hospital, Tarboro, NC, p. A461

PRAKASH, Amitabh, M.D., Chief Medical Officer, Ahmc Anaheim Regional Medical Center, Anaheim, CA, p. A50

PRAKASH, Vijay, Information Technology Officer, Essex County Hospital Center, Cedar Grove, NJ, p. A403

PRANTE, Melissa, Chief Financial Officer, Kimball Health Services, Kimball, NE, p. A385

PRATER, Jeffrey, Chief Executive Officer, Carson Valley Medical Center, Gardnerville, NV, p. A393

PRATER, Judith, Director of Nursing, Pike County Memorial Hospital, Louisiana, MO, p. A363

PRATER, Marsha A, Ph.D., R.N., Senior Vice President and Chief Nursing Officer, Memorial Medical Center, Springfield, IL, p. A196

PRATER, Robin, Director Human Resources, Howard A. Rusk Rehabilitation Center, Columbia, MO, p. A358

PRATHER, Jean, Director of Human Resources, Greene County General Hospital, Linton, IN, p. A210

PRATHER, Rachael, Chief Nursing Officer, Ferrell Hospital, Eldorado, IL, p. A181

PRATT, Audra, Chief Human Resource Officer, St. Vincent Women's Hospital, IN, p. A208

PRATT, Bailey, Chief Financial Officer, Saint Thomas Rutherford Hospital, Murfreesboro, TN, p. A576

PRATT, Dustin, M.D., Chief of Staff, Childress Regional Medical Center, Childress, TX, p. A592

PRATT, Lisa D., Vice President, Human Resources, Mclean Hospital, Belmont, MA, p. A295

PRATT, Mary Ellen., FACHE, Chief Executive Officer, St. James Parish Hospital, Lutcher, LA, p. A273

PRATT, Ramona, Chief Operating Officer, Pih Health Hospital - Downey, Downey, CA, p. A56

PRATT, Timothy J, M.D., Vice President Medical Affairs and Chief Medical Officer, Ssm Health St. Clare Hospital - Fenton, Fenton, MO, p. A359

PRATT, Troy, Information Technology Site Director, Covenant Medical Center-Lakeside, TX, p. A621

PREAU, William, M.D., Medical Director, Avala, Covington, LA, p. A266

PREISINGER, Andrea, Director Human Resources, Menninger Clinic, Houston, TX, p. A612

PREMO, Mark, Senior Director HC Intelligence, Providence Portland Medical Center, Portland, OR, p. A516

PRENTISS, Kristin, Chief Financial Officer, Specialty Hospital Of Central Jersey, Lakewood, NJ, p. A406

PRESCOTT, Tina, Vice President, Hospital Services, West Tennessee Healthcare North Hospital, TN, p. A571

PRESNELL, Elizabeth, Assistant Vice President of Finance, St. Luke's Hospital, Columbus, NC, p. A450

PRESS, Robert, M.D., Senior Vice President, Vice Dean and Chief Hospital Operations, Rusk Institute At Nyu-Hjd, NY, p. A436

PRESSMAN, Sean, Chief Executive Officer, Lewisgale Hospital Pulaski, Pulaski, VA, p. A664

PRESTEGAARD, Benjamin, Chief Medical Officer, Uh Portage Medical Center, Ravenna, OH, p. A489

PRESTON, Tara
    Director Human Resources, Bingham Memorial Hospital, Blackfoot, ID, p. A167
    Director Human Resources, Mountain River Birthing And Surgery Center, Blackfoot, ID, p. A167

PRESTON, Venicea Austin, Administrator, Cypress Grove Behavioral Health, Bastrop, LA, p. A263

PRESTRIDGE, Tim, Interim Chief Financial Officer, Logan Memorial Hospital, Russellville, KY, p. A260

PRETE, Mark, M.D., Vice President Medical Affairs, Charlotte Hungerford Hospital, Torrington, CT, p. A111

PRETTYMAN, Edgar E., PsyD, Chief Executive Officer, Texas Neurorehab Center, Austin, TX, p. A587

PRETZLAFF, Robert, M.D.
    Chief Medical Officer, St. Rose Dominican Hospitals - San Martin Campus, Las Vegas, NV, p. A395
    Chief Medical Officer, St. Rose Dominican Hospitals - Siena Campus, Henderson, NV, p. A393

PREWITT, Connie F, Chief Financial Officer, Billings Clinic, Billings, MT, p. A373

PREWITT, Margaret Elizabeth, Vice President Patient Services and Chief Nursing Officer, St. Catherine Hospital, Garden City, KS, p. A235

PRIBITKIN, Edmund A., M.D., Chief Medical Officer, Jefferson Methodist Hospital, PA, p. A536

PRICE, Bernard J, Chief Human Resources Officer, Children's Hospital, Navicent Health, GA, p. A156

PRICE, Connie, M.D., Chief Medical Officer, Denver Health, Denver, CO, p. A98

PRICE, David
    Chief Executive Officer, Honorhealth Deer Valley Medical Center, Phoenix, AZ, p. A33
    Chief Executive Officer, Honorhealth Scottsdale Thompson Peak Medical Center, Scottsdale, AZ, p. A35

PRICE, Ed, Chief Nurse Officer, Shelby Baptist Medical Center, Alabaster, AL, p. A13

PRICE, Fred, R.N., Chief Executive Officer, Vibra Hospital Of Fort Wayne, Fort Wayne, IN, p. A204

PRICE, James, Hospital Administrator, State Hospital South, Blackfoot, ID, p. A167

PRICE, John, Chief Financial Officer, King's Daughters' Health, Madison, IN, p. A210

PRICE, John Stephen, M.D., Chief of Staff, Fairview Regional Medical Center, Fairview, OK, p. A499

PRICE, Kelley, R.N.
    Chief Nursing Officer, Battle Mountain General Hospital, Battle Mountain, NV, p. A392
    Interim Chief Executive Officer, Battle Mountain General Hospital, Battle Mountain, NV, p. A392

PRICE, Kevin A
    Vice President and Chief Operating Officer, Sparrow Clinton Hospital, Saint Johns, MI, p. A322
    Vice President and Chief Operating Officer, Sparrow Ionia Hospital, Ionia, MI, p. A316

PRICE, Kim, Chief Executive Officer, Franklin General Hospital, Hampton, IA, p. A223

PRICE, Kyle
    Chief Executive Officer, Memorial Hermann Pearland Medical Center, TX, p. A612
    Chief Executive Officer, Memorial Hermann Southeast Hospital, TX, p. A612

PRICE, Larry, Chief Executive Officer, Limestone Medical Center, Groesbeck, TX, p. A608

PRICE, Lori, President, Gottlieb Memorial Hospital, Melrose Park, IL, p. A189

PRICE, Lorraine B, Associate Director, Hampton Veterans Affairs Medical Center, Hampton, VA, p. A659

PRICE, Manuel, Director Information Systems, Brookwood Baptist Medical Center, Birmingham, AL, p. A14

PRICE, Meredith, Vice President Fiscal Services and Chief Financial Officer, St. Joseph's Hospital Health Center, Syracuse, NY, p. A444

PRICE, Norman M., FACHE, Chief Executive Officer, Southwest Mississippi Regional Medical Center, Mccomb, MS, p. A350

PRICE, Sam, Executive Vice President Finance/Chief Financial Officer, East Alabama Medical Center-Lanier, AL, p. A22

PRICE, Shari, Director Information Services, Baptist Health Louisville, Louisville, KY, p. A256

PRICE, Terry, Director Information Technology, Great Plains Regional Medical Center, Elk City, OK, p. A498

PRICE, Tonya, Chief Nursing Officer, Wilson N. Jones Regional Medical Center, Sherman, TX, p. A636

PRICE, Walter, Director Information Technology, Newport Hospital And Health Services, Newport, WA, p. A674

PRICE-YONTS, Melody, Chief Executive Officer, Acoma-Canoncito-Laguna Hospital, Acoma, NM, p. A415

PRICKEL, Trisha, Information Systems Director, Margaret Mary Health, Batesville, IN, p. A199

PRIDDY, Ernest C, III, Chief Financial Officer, Old Vineyard Behavioral Health Services, Winston, NC, p. A463

PRIDDY, Steven, M.D., VP of Physician Affairs/Chief Medical Officer, St. Vincent Carmel Hospital, Carmel, IN, p. A201

PRIDEAUX, Heather, Chief Financial Officer, Rawlins County Health Center, Atwood, KS, p. A232

PRIDGEN, Kim
Chief Financial Officer, Houston County Community Hospital, Erin, TN, p. A569
Chief Financial Officer, Northcrest Medical Center, Springfield, TN, p. A580

PRIDGEN, Parker, Chief Financial Officer, Central Texas Medical Center, San Marcos, TX, p. A635

PRIES, Kathleen M, Director Human Resources, Nazareth Hospital, Philadelphia, PA, p. A535

PRIEST, David, Director Information Systems, Munson Healthcare Charlevoix Hospital, Charlevoix, MI, p. A309

PRIEST, Geoff, M.D., Chief Medical Officer, Unitypoint Health Meriter, Madison, WI, p. A696

PRIEST, Mike, M.D., Chief of Staff, Pawhuska Hospital, Pawhuska, OK, p. A505

PRIESTLEY, Betty, Manager Business Office, Pine Valley Specialty Hospital, Houston, TX, p. A613

PRIETTO, Carlos, President and Chief Executive Officer, Hoag Orthopedic Institute, Irvine, CA, p. A62

PRIHODA, Matt, M.D., Chief of Staff, Washington County Hospital And Clinics, Washington, IA, p. A230

PRILUTSKY, Michael, Chief Operating Officer, Jersey City Medical Center, Jersey City, NJ, p. A406

PRIMACK, Matthew Lee, President, Advocate Hope Children's Hospital, IL, p. A191

PRINCE, Clay, M.D., Chief Medical Officer, Madison Memorial Hospital, Rexburg, ID, p. A171

PRINCE, Kem, Manager of Finance, Parkview Noble Hospital, Kendallville, IN, p. A208

PRINCE, Michele, Chief Operating Officer, Lewis County General Hospital, Lowville, NY, p. A429

PRINCE, Sue, Director Information Systems, Northern Westchester Hospital, Mount Kisco, NY, p. A430

PRINCE, Tina, R.N., Associate Director Patient Care Services, Chief Nursing Officer, New Mexico Veterans Affairs Health Care System - Raymond G. Murphy Medical Center, Albuquerque, NM, p. A416

PRINCIPE, Adam, Chief Executive Officer, Select Specialty Hospital-Pensacola, Pensacola, FL, p. A136

PRINCIPE, Hector Cintron, M.D., Director, Hospital Universitario Dr. Ramon Ruiz Arnau, Bayamon, PR, p. A712

PRINGLE-MILLER, Letitia, Administrative Director, Palmetto Health Tuomey, Sumter, SC, p. A557

PRINTY, Wayne, Chief Financial Officer and Senior Vice President Finance, Lincolnhealth St. Andrews Campus, ME, p. A283

PRIORE, Jacqueline, Chief Nursing Officer, Samaritan Hospital, Troy, NY, p. A444

PRISELAC, Thomas M., President and Chief Executive Officer, Cedars-Sinai Medical Center, Los Angeles, CA, p. A66

PRISTER, James R, President and Chief Executive Officer, Rml Specialty Hospital, IL, p. A186

PRISTER, James R., President and Chief Executive Officer, Rml Specialty Hospital, IL, p. A186

PRITCHARD, Jason, Chief Financial Officer, Hackensack Meridian Health Pascack Valley Medical Center, Westwood, NJ, p. A414

PRITCHARD, Joann, Chief Financial Officer, Erie Veterans Affairs Medical Center, Erie, PA, p. A525

PRITCHETT, Greg, Chief Financial Officer, Cuero Community Hospital, Cuero, TX, p. A595

PRITCHETT, Lynette, Chief Executive Officer, Jamestown Regional Medical Center, Jamestown, TN, p. A571

PRITTS, Robert
Chief Executive Officer and Market Executive, Ssm Health Rehabilitation Hospital - Lake Saint Louis, MO, p. A366
Chief Executive Officer, Ssm Select Rehabilitation Hospital, MO, p. A366

PRIVETT, David, Deputy Director, Western New York Children's Hospital Psychiatric Center, West Seneca, NY, p. A446

PROBASCO, Brent, Chief Financial Officer, Cass Regional Medical Center, Harrisonville, MO, p. A360

PROBST, Nancy, R.N., Chief Nursing Officer, Bigfork Valley Hospital, Bigfork, MN, p. A328

PROBUS, Kimberly, Chief Nursing Officer, Opelousas General Health System-South Campus, LA, p. A277

PROCHASKA, Jodi, Chief Financial Officer, Butler County Health Care Center, David City, NE, p. A383

PROCHILO, John F., Jr, Chief Executive Officer, Northeast Rehabilitation Hospital, Salem, NH, p. A401

PROCHNOW, Bryan
Chief Financial Officer, Matagorda Regional Medical Center, Bay City, TX, p. A587

Interim Chief Executive Officer, Matagorda Regional Medical Center, Bay City, TX, p. A587

PROCTOR, Brandy, Director of Nursing, North Star Behavioral Health, AK, p. A25

PROCTOR, Jason J., Chief Operating Officer, Louis & Peaches Owen Heart Hospital, TX, p. A640

PROCTOR, Quinn, Director Human Resources, Claremore Indian Hospital, Claremore, OK, p. A497

PROCTOR, Sandra, R.N., MS, Chief Nurse Executive, Memorial Medical Center, CA, p. A73

PROCTOR, Scott, Chief Executive Officer, Safe Haven Hospital Of Treasure Valley, Boise, ID, p. A167

PROCTOR, Stephen, Director of Human Resources/Risk, Russellville Hospital, Russellville, AL, p. A23

PROFOTA, Lori, R.N., Chief Nursing Officer, Copley Hospital, Morrisville, VT, p. A654

PRONGER, Derk F, Chief Operating Officer, Munson Medical Center, Traverse City, MI, p. A324

PRONI, John, CPA, Manager Finance and Operations, Baycare Alliant Hospital, Dunedin, FL, p. A122

PROPP, Elizabeth R, Vice President Finance and Chief Financial Officer, Dameron Hospital, Stockton, CA, p. A90

PROSKOCIL, Danielle, Director Human Resources, Valley County Health System, Ord, NE, p. A389

PROSPER, Charles, Chief Executive Officer, Alta Bates Summit Medical Center - Summit Campus, Oakland, CA, p. A75

PROSSER, Alita, Chief Financial Officer, Mclane Children's Hospital Scott & White, TX, p. A638

PROSSER, Edna, Chief Nursing Officer, Ozark Health Medical Center, Clinton-Van Buren County, AR, p. A40

PROSSER, Joseph, M.D., Chief Medical Officer, Texas Health Harris Methodist Hospital Fort Worth, Fort Worth, TX, p. A605

PROUD, James, Vice President Human Resources and Marketing, Uniontown Hospital, Uniontown, PA, p. A542

PROUJANSKY, Roy, M.D., Chief Executive Officer, Alfred I. Dupont Hospital For Children, Wilmington, DE, p. A114

PROVENZANO, Jeff
Vice President and Chief Financial Officer, Midmichigan Medical Center-Clare, Clare, MI, p. A310
Vice President and Chief Financial Officer, Midmichigan Medical Center-Gladwin, Gladwin, MI, p. A313
Vice President and Chief Financial Officer, Midmichigan Medical Center-Gratiot, Alma, MI, p. A307

PROVENZANO, Stacey, Chief Operating Officer, Greystone Park Psychiatric Hospital, Morris Plains, NJ, p. A407

PROVINCE, Steven, President and Chief Executive Officer, Amita Health Adventist Medical Center - Hinsdale, Hinsdale, IL, p. A186

PROVOST, Deborah A, Chief Nursing Officer, Baystate Franklin Medical Center, Greenfield, MA, p. A300

PRUESS, Mark, M.D., Chief Medical Staff, Sparta Community Hospital, Sparta, IL, p. A196

PRUETT-BAER, Karen, Senior Nurse Executive, Naval Hospital Oak Harbor, Oak Harbor, WA, p. A674

PRUITT, Jeffrey, M.D., Chief of Staff, Mercy Hospital Of Defiance, Defiance, OH, p. A481

PRUKOP, Jeff, Director Professional Services, Jackson County Hospital District, Edna, TX, p. A601

PRUNCHUNAS, Edward M, Executive Vice President and Chief Financial Officer, Cedars-Sinai Medical Center, Los Angeles, CA, p. A66

PRUNOSKE, Mark, Chief Financial Officer and Senior Vice President Finance, F. F. Thompson Hospital, Canandaigua, NY, p. A424

PRUSATIS, Michael, Vice President Finance, Dmc - Sinai-Grace Hospital, Detroit, MI, p. A311

PRYBYLO, Mary, President and Chief Executive Officer, St. Joseph Hospital, Bangor, ME, p. A282

PRYOR, David, President, Athens-Limestone Hospital, Athens, AL, p. A13

PRYOR, Jon, M.D., Chief Executive Officer, Hcmc Department Of Pediatrics, MN, p. A335

PRYOR, Vincent, Senior Vice President and Chief Financial Officer, Silver Cross Hospital, New Lenox, IL, p. A191

PRYOR, William B, Chief Human Resources Officer, Cape Fear Valley Rehabilitation Center, NC, p. A452

PRZESTRZELSKI, David, Associate Director, Patient Care Services and Chief Nursing Executive, Charles George Veterans Affairs Medical Center, Asheville, NC, p. A447

PRZYBYLSKI, David, Controller, Sparrow Specialty Hospital, Lansing, MI, p. A317

PSAILA, Justin P, M.D., Vice President Medical Affairs, St. Luke's Hospital - Anderson Campus, Easton, PA, p. A525

PSCODNA, Susan, Director Human Resources, Mercy Hospital Of Defiance, Defiance, OH, p. A481

PU, Steve, D.O., Chief Medical Officer, Poplar Bluff Regional Medical Center-South Campus, MO, p. A366

PUCHBAUER, Aaron, President, Hshs Good Shepherd Hospital, Shelbyville, IL, p. A195

PUCKETT, Clay, Assistant Administrator and Chief Information Officer, Blount Memorial Hospital, Maryville, TN, p. A574

PUCKETT, Kristi, Director Human Resources, Grande Ronde Hospital, La Grande, OR, p. A514

PUCLIK, Becky, Division Chief People Officer, St. John's Children's Hospital, IL, p. A196

PUENTES, Francisco, Human Resource Officer, San Diego County Psychiatric Hospital, San Diego, CA, p. A84

PUFFENBERGER, James, Vice President and Chief Financial Officer, Mercy Hospital Of Defiance, Defiance, OH, p. A481

PUFFENBERGER, Sheila, Manager Information Technology, Hillsdale Hospital, Hillsdale, MI, p. A315

PUGACH, Judy, Chief Nursing Officer, Pih Health Hospital - Downey, Downey, CA, p. A56

PUGH, Larry, Vice President and Chief Financial Officer, Beverly Hospital, Montebello, CA, p. A73

PUGH, Marcia, Chief Executive Officer, Greene County Health System, Eutaw, AL, p. A17

PUGH, Melodee, Director Human Resources, Navarro Regional Hospital, Corsicana, TX, p. A595

PUGH, Ryan, Chief Financial Officer, Western Plains Medical Complex, Dodge City, KS, p. A234

PUGH, William H, Senior Vice President Corporate Finance and Chief Financial Officer, Pinnaclehealth West Shore Hospital, PA, p. A527

PUGSLEY, Tim, Chief Information Officer, Orthonebraska Hospital, Omaha, NE, p. A388

PUHL, Cathy A., Vice President Human Resources, Chambersburg Hospital, Chambersburg, PA, p. A522

PUHY, Dorothy E, Executive VP and Chief Operating Officer, Dana-Farber Cancer Institute, Boston, MA, p. A296

PUKALA, Shirley, R.N., Assistant Administrator Operations, St. Lawrence Rehabilitation Center, Lawrenceville, NJ, p. A406

PULASKI, Jason, Controller, Healthsouth Reading Rehabilitation Hospital, Reading, PA, p. A539

PULEO, Mark, Vice President and Chief Human Resources Officer, Henry Mayo Newhall Hospital, Valencia, CA, p. A93

PULIDO, Michael, Chief Administrative Officer, Mosaic Life Care, Saint Joseph, MO, p. A367

PULLARKAT, Sajit, Chief Executive Officer and Managing Director, Centennial Hills Hospital Medical Center, Las Vegas, NV, p. A393

PULLEN, Connie, R.N., Chief Nursing Officer, Willamette Valley Medical Center, Mcminnville, OR, p. A514

PULLIAM, Elizabeth, Chief Financial Officer, Christus Mother Frances Hospital - Jacksonville, Jacksonville, TX, p. A616

PULLIN, Dennis W., FACHE, President and Chief Executive Officer, Voorhees Pediatric Facility, NJ, p. A413

PULLMAN, Debbie, Director Finance, Avera Hand County Memorial Hospital, Miller, SD, p. A562

PULLMAN, Jayson, Chief Executive Officer, Hawarden Regional Healthcare, Hawarden, IA, p. A224

PULSIPHER, Gary W., President and Chief Executive Officer, St. John's Rehabilitation Center, MO, p. A361

PULVER, Dayna, Director of Nursing, Friend Community Healthcare System, Friend, NE, p. A384

PUMMEL, Keely, Director, Financial Operations, Ohiohealth Dublin Methodist Hospital, Dublin, OH, p. A481

PUMPHREY, Robbin K, Chief Nursing Officer, Jackson Hospital, Marianna, FL, p. A129

PUNG, Margaret, R.N., Chief Nursing Officer, University Of Texas Harris County Psychiatric Center, Houston, TX, p. A614

PUNJABI, Rishab, Chief Financial Officer, Kindred Hospital Santa Ana, CA, p. A63

PUNTEL, Jackie, Senior Director Human Resources, Cleveland Clinic Florida, Weston, FL, p. A144

PUORTO, Charlene, Chief Nursing Officer, Capital District Psychiatric Center, Albany, NY, p. A421

PURCELL, Deborah, Director of Information Technology, Caldwell Unc Health Care, Lenoir, NC, p. A456

PURCELL, Terrance J.
Director Information Services, Lea Regional Medical Center, Hobbs, NM, p. A417
President, St. Luke's - Palmerton Campus, PA, p. A530

PURDY, Bruce, M.D., Chief of Staff, Muleshoe Area Medical Center, Muleshoe, TX, p. A625

PURINGTON, Denise, Vice President and Chief Information Officer, Elliot Hospital, Manchester, NH, p. A400

PURINTON, Sandy, Chief Nursing Officer, Trego County-Lemke Memorial Hospital, Wakeeney, KS, p. A247

PURMONT, Tiffany, Supervisor Medical Records, Monroe County Hospital, Forsyth, GA, p. A153

PUROHIT, Divyesh, M.D., Chief of Staff, Sullivan County Community Hospital, Sullivan, IN, p. A215

PUROHIT, Kumar, Chief Financial Officer, Rockford Center, Newark, DE, p. A113

PUROHIT, Shamb, Chief Financial Officer, Colquitt Regional Medical Center, Moultrie, GA, p. A158

PURRINGTON, Janice, Coordinator Medical Records, Avera Hand County Memorial Hospital, Miller, SD, p. A562

PURSLEY, Roger, Chief Executive Officer, Western Mental Health Institute, Bolivar, TN, p. A566

PURTLE, Mark, M.D.
Vice President Medical Affairs, Unitypoint Health-Iowa Lutheran Hospital, Des Moines, IA, p. A221
Vice President Medical Affairs, Younker Memorial Rehabilitation Center, IA, p. A221

PURUSHOTHAM, Sanjay, Executive Director Information Systems, Bon Secours Baltimore Health System, Baltimore, MD, p. A287

PURVANCE, Clint, M.D., President and Chief Executive Officer, Barton Memorial Hospital, South Lake Tahoe, CA, p. A90

PURVES, Stephen A., FACHE, President and Chief Executive Officer, Arizona Children's Center, AZ, p. A33

PURVIS, Jay, President and Chief Executive Officer, Wabash General Hospital, Mount Carmel, IL, p. A190

PURVIS, Kevin, Chief Information Officer, Community Howard Regional Health, Kokomo, IN, p. A209

PURVIS, Michael L.
Chief Executive Officer, Cook Medical Center-A Campus Of Tift Regional Medical Center, Adel, GA, p. A145
Chief Executive Officer, Novato Community Hospital, Novato, CA, p. A75

PURVIS, Mike, Chief Administrative Officer, Warrack Campus, CA, p. A89

PUSHARD, Roland, Director of Nursing, Riverview Psychiatric Center, Augusta, ME, p. A282

PUSTINA, Karl, Vice President Finance, Upland Hills Health, Dodgeville, WI, p. A691

PUSZKARSKA, Lucyna M., M.D., Medical Director, Riveredge Hospital, Forest Park, IL, p. A183

PUTHOFF, Timothy, Chief Executive Officer, Houston Northwest Medical Center, Houston, TX, p. A611

PUTNAM, Mark, M.D., Medical Director, Haven Behavioral Hospital Of Eastern Pennsylvania, Reading, PA, p. A539

PUTNAM, Maureen M, Director Human Resources, Oss Orthopaedic Hospital, York, PA, p. A545

PUTNAM, Stewart C, Executive Vice President and Chief Operating Officer, Unity Hospital, Rochester, NY, p. A441

PUTNAM, Timothy L., FACHE, President and Chief Executive Officer, Margaret Mary Health, Batesville, IN, p. A199

PUTZ, Kim, R.N., Director, Nursing Hospital, Ridgeview Le Sueur Medical Center, Le Sueur, MN, p. A333

PUVOGEL, LuAnn, R.N., Chief Executive Officer, Salina Surgical Hospital, Salina, KS, p. A245

PUYAU, Susan, M.D., Medical Director, Woman's Hospital, Baton Rouge, LA, p. A264

PUZO, Thomas C., President and Chief Executive Officer, Cornerstone Of Medical Arts Center Hospital, Fresh Meadows, NY, p. A426

PUZZUTO, David, M.D., Vice President Medical Affairs and Chief Medical Officer, Waterbury Hospital, Waterbury, CT, p. A112

PYGON, Bernard, M.D., Chief Medical Officer, University Of Illinois Hospital & Health Sciences System, Chicago, IL, p. A180

PYLE, Diana, Director Human Resources and Executive Assistant to Chief Executive Officer, Cedar County Memorial Hospital, El Dorado Springs, MO, p. A358

PYLE, Julia, R.N., Chief Nursing Officer, Newman Regional Health, Emporia, KS, p. A234

PYLE, Rick, Director Information Systems, Harrisburg Medical Center, Harrisburg, IL, p. A184

PYLE FARRELL, Martha, Vice President Human Resources and General Counsel, Massachusetts Eye And Ear, Boston, MA, p. A296

PYNE, Mel
Chief Executive Officer, Candler County Hospital, Metter, GA, p. A157
Chief Executive Officer, Emanuel Medical Center, Swainsboro, GA, p. A161
Regional Chief Executive Officer, Dorminy Medical Center, Fitzgerald, GA, p. A153

PYRAH, Scott, Director Information Systems, St. Luke's Rehabilitation Hospital, Boise, ID, p. A168

Q

QUACKENBUSH, Kirk, M.D., Chief of Staff, Platte Valley Medical Center, Brighton, CO, p. A97

QUAGLIERI, Mike, Chief Financial Officer, North Central Surgical Center, Dallas, TX, p. A597

QUALLS, Brenda, Chief Financial Officer, Navicent Health Baldwin, Milledgeville, GA, p. A157

QUALLS, Paul E., Chief Executive Officer, Post Acute Medical Specialty Hospital Of Milwaukee, Greenfield, WI, p. A694

QUAMMEN, Becky, Chief Information Officer, Howard University Hospital, Washington, DC, p. A115

QUANCE, Daniel, Chief Financial Officer, Fairmont Regional Medical Center, Fairmont, WV, p. A683

QUARANTE, Dino, CPA, Chief Financial Officer, Oasis Behavioral Health - Chandler, Chandler, AZ, p. A28

QUARLES, Christopher, M.D., Director Medical Services, Naval Hospital Jacksonville, Jacksonville, FL, p. A125

QUATE, Becky, Vice President Nursing and Patient Care Services, Iredell Health System, Statesville, NC, p. A461

QUATROCHE, Thomas J., Jr, Chief Executive Officer, Erie County Medical Center, Buffalo, NY, p. A423

QUATTROCCHI, Robert, President and Chief Executive Officer, Northside Hospital, Atlanta, GA, p. A146

QUEBEDEAUX, Jay, Chief Executive Officer, Mena Regional Health System, Mena-Polk County, AR, p. A46

QUEBODEAUX, Bryce, Chief Executive Officer, Abrom Kaplan Memorial Hospital, Kaplan, LA, p. A270

QUEEN, Sharon H, R.N., Chief Nursing Officer, Piedmont Walton Hospital, Monroe, GA, p. A157

QUENAN, James, M.D., Chief Medical Officer, Amery Hospital And Clinic, Amery, WI, p. A689

QUESNEL, Brenda, R.N., Vice President of Patient Care and Chief Nursing Officer, West Calcasieu Cameron Hospital, Sulphur, LA, p. A280

QUICCI, London, Chief Operating Officer, Dmc - Sinai-Grace Hospital, Detroit, MI, p. A311

QUICHOCHO, Vince, Manager Information Systems, Guam Memorial Hospital Authority, Tamuning, GU, p. A711

QUIGLEY, Stephen J., Chief Executive Officer, Southwood Psychiatric Hospital, Pittsburgh, PA, p. A537

QUILLIN, Gayla, Administrator, Parmer Medical Center, Friona, TX, p. A606

QUIN, Robert, Regional Vice President Finance, and Chief Financial Officer, Unitypoint Health - Peoria, Peoria, IL, p. A193

QUINLAN, Christine, MS, R.N., Chief Nursing Officer, Alexian Brothers Behavioral Health Hospital, Hoffman Estates, IL, p. A186

QUINLAN, Patrick J, M.D., Chief Executive Officer, Ochsner Medical Center For Children, LA, p. A276

QUINLIVAN, John, Chief Executive Officer, Redmond Regional Medical Center, Rome, GA, p. A159

QUINLIVAN, Kathy, Director Management Information Systems, Avera Sacred Heart Hospital, Yankton, SD, p. A565

QUINN, Clifton
Chief Executive Officer, Regency Hospital Of Meridian, Meridian, MS, p. A350
Chief Executive Officer, Select Specialty Hospital-Birmingham, Birmingham, AL, p. A15

QUINN, Donna, Vice President Operations, Driscoll Children's Hospital, Corpus Christi, TX, p. A594

QUINN, Jennifer, Quality and Safety Coordinator, Thedacare Medical Center-Shawano, Shawano, WI, p. A702

QUINN, Judith, Vice President Patient Care Services, Cape Cod Hospital, Hyannis, MA, p. A300

QUINN, Mary Ann
Administrative Assistant, Casey County Hospital, Liberty, KY, p. A255
Administrative Assistant, Jane Todd Crawford Hospital, Greensburg, KY, p. A252

QUINN, Mary Anna, Executive Vice President, Chief Administrative Officer, St. Jude Children's Research Hospital, Memphis, TN, p. A576

QUINN, Paul, Information Systems Manager, Kern Valley Healthcare District, Lake Isabella, CA, p. A63

QUINN, Tim, M.D., Executive Vice President and Chief of Clinical Operations and President Mercy Care Management, Mercy Medical Center, Cedar Rapids, IA, p. A218

QUINONES, Yolanda, Director Finance, I. Gonzalez Martinez Oncologic Hospital, Hato Rey, PR, p. A713

QUINONEZ, Yolanda, Chief Financial Officer, Hospital De La Universidad De Puerto Rico/Dr. Federico Trilla, Carolina, PR, p. A712

QUINTANA, Francisco, Warden, Federal Medical Center, Lexington, KY, p. A255

QUINTANA, Jay, Vice President Operations, Cornerstone Hospital-West Monroe, West Monroe, LA, p. A280

QUINT-BOUZID, Marjorie, Chief Nursing Officer and Vice President Patient Care Services, Fort Washington Medical Center, Oxen Hill, MD, p. A293

QUINTO, Mike, Chief Information Officer, Watauga Medical Center, Boone, NC, p. A448

QUINTON, J Ben., Administrator, William Newton Hospital, Winfield, KS, p. A248

QUINTYNE, Stephen, Chief Executive Officer, The Vines, Ocala, FL, p. A133

QUIRICONI, Stephan F
Chief Financial Officer, Bon Secours St. Mary's Children's Services, VA, p. A664
Vice President Finance, Bon Secours Memorial Regional Medical Center, Mechanicsville, VA, p. A661
Vice President, Finance, Bon Secours St. Francis Medical Center, Midlothian, VA, p. A661

QUIRKE, David, Vice President Information Services, Frederick Regional Health System, Frederick, MD, p. A291

QUITO, Arturo L, M.D., Chief of Staff, Erlanger Bledsoe Hospital, Pikeville, TN, p. A579

QUO, Justin, Chief of Staff, Chi Lakewood Health, Baudette, MN, p. A328

QVISTGAARD, Guy C, Chief Executive Officer, John George Psychiatric Hospital, CA, p. A75

R

RAAUM, Elizabeth, Manger Business Office, Roosevelt Medical Center, Culbertson, MT, p. A374

RABAGO, Janie, Chief Accountant, San Antonio State Hospital, San Antonio, TX, p. A634

RABEL, Jonas, President, Integris Miami Hospital, Miami, OK, p. A501

RABIDEAU, Ray, M.D., Senior Vice President and Chief Medical Officer, Memorial Hospital, North Conway, NH, p. A400

RABIN, Barry, M.D., Regional Medical Director, Linden Oaks Hospital, Naperville, IL, p. A190

RABINE, Traci, Vice President Clinic Operations, Prairie Lakes Healthcare System, Watertown, SD, p. A565

RABINOWITZ, Jordy, Senior Vice President Human Resources Operations, Midhudson Regional Hospital Of Westchester Medical Center, NY, p. A445

RABNER, Barry S., President and Chief Executive Officer, Princeton Healthcare System, Penn Medicine Princeton Medical Center, Plainsboro, NJ, p. A410

RABON, Catherine, M.D., Chief Medical Officer, Mcleod Health Clarendon, Manning, SC, p. A555

RABORN, Janelle, Chief Operating Officer, Lovelace Women's Hospital, Albuquerque, NM, p. A415

RACHAL, Paul, M.D., Chief Medical Officer, Pointe Coupee General Hospital, New Roads, LA, p. A276

RACHUIG, Sue, Director Information Services, Tulane-Lakeside Hospital, LA, p. A276

RACICOT, Mark, Chief Executive Officer, Florida Medical Center - A Campus Of North Shore, FL, p. A130

RACKLIFFE, David, Assistant Vice President Information Services, Bristol Hospital, Bristol, CT, p. A107

RACZEK, James, M.D., Sr. Vice President of Operations and Chief Medical Officer, Eastern Maine Medical Center, Bangor, ME, p. A282

RADANDT, Jeremiah
Chief Financial Officer, Primary Children's Hospital, Salt Lake City, UT, p. A650
President, Children's Medical Center Plano, Plano, TX, p. A628

RADCLIFF, Joey, Chief Financial Officer, Five Rivers Medical Center, Pocahontas-Randolph County, AR, p. A48

RADCLIFFE, Eric, M.D., Medical Director, United Hospital Center, Bridgeport, WV, p. A681

RADEMACHER, Frank
Director, Information Systems, St. Joseph Mercy Livingston Hospital, Howell, MI, p. A315
Senior Director Information Systems, St. Joseph Mercy Ann Arbor, Ypsilanti, MI, p. A326

RADER, Herbert, M.D., Advisor for Medical Affairs, New York Community Hospital, New York (Includes All Hospitals Located Within The Five Boroughs), NY, p. A434

RADFORD, Angie, R.N., Director of Nursing, Wills Memorial Hospital, Washington, GA, p. A163

RADFORD, Jeffrey, Chief Executive Officer, Select Specialty Hospital-Tri Cities, Bristol, TN, p. A566

RADKE, Erma, Director of Operations, Oakleaf Surgical Hospital, Altoona, WI, p. A689

RADKE, Sam, Chief Financial Officer, Southwest Health System, Cortez, CO, p. A98

RADNER, Allen, M.D., Chief Medical Officer, Salinas Valley Memorial Healthcare System, Salinas, CA, p. A83

RADOTICH, Maureen, Director Human Resources, Providence Valdez Medical Center, Valdez, AK, p. A27

RADTKE, Lisa, Chief Administrative Officer, Winneshiek Medical Center, Decorah, IA, p. A221

RADUNSKY, Daniel, M.D., Medical Staff President, Union County General Hospital, Clayton, NM, p. A416

RADZEVICH, Jason, Vice President Finance, Beth Israel Deaconess Hospital Plymouth, Plymouth, MA, p. A303

RAETHEL, Kathryn A., R.N., M.P.H., President and Chief Executive Officer, Adventist Health Castle, Kailua, HI, p. A165

RAETZ, Elizabeth A, R.N., MSN, Vice President Nursing and Chief Nursing Officer, Chi Health St Elizabeth, Lincoln, NE, p. A386

RAFALA, Paula, Director, Human Resources, Memorial Medical Center, CA, p. A73

RAFFERTY, Joyce, Vice President Finance, The University Of Vermont Health Network-Champlain Valley Physicians Hospital, Plattsburgh, NY, p. A440

RAFFERTY, Patrick W, Executive Vice President and Chief Operating Officer, Community Regional Medical Center, Fresno, CA, p. A59

RAFFETY, Leannette, Administrative Generalist, Stroud Regional Medical Center, Stroud, OK, p. A507

RAFFOUL, John, Chief Executive Officer, Adventist Health White Memorial, Los Angeles, CA, p. A66

RAFUS, Matthew, Chief Information Officer, White River Junction Veterans Affairs Medical Center, White River Junction, VT, p. A654

RAGAIN, Michael, M.D., Chief Medical Officer and Senior Vice President, University Medical Center, Lubbock, TX, p. A621

RAGAN, Donna, R.N., Chief Nursing Officer, Shands Live Oak Regional Medical Center, Live Oak, FL, p. A128

RAGAR-THOMAS, Twila, Director Health Information Management and Quality Improvement, Timberlawn Mental Health System, Dallas, TX, p. A598

RAGAS, Rene J., Chief Operating Officer, Bogalusa Community Medical Center, LA, p. A264

RAGER, Claudia, R.N., Vice President Patient Care Services, Memorial Medical Center - Lee Campus, PA, p. A528

RAGGI, Bob, M.D., Chief Medical Officer, Providence Holy Cross Medical Center, Mission Hills, CA, p. A72

RAGGIO, James J., Chief Executive Officer, Lompoc Valley Medical Center, Lompoc, CA, p. A65

RAGGIO, Sharon, President and Chief Executive Officer, West Springs Hospital, Grand Junction, CO, p. A101

RAGLAND, Jane, President Medical Staff, Christus Mother Frances Hospital - Jacksonville, Jacksonville, TX, p. A616

RAGLE, Bertha, Director Personnel, Crossridge Community Hospital, Wynne-Cross County, AR, p. A49

RAGONA, Robert A, Senior Vice President Finance and Chief Financial Officer, Eastern Long Island Hospital, Greenport, NY, p. A427

RAGONESE-GREEN, Virginia, Chief Nursing Officer, Encompass Health Rehabilitation Hospital Of Northwest Tucson, Tucson, AZ, p. A37

RAGSDALE, Sarah, R.N., Chief Nursing Officer, Smith County Memorial Hospital, Smith Center, KS, p. A246

RAGUKAS, Judith, Interim Chief Nursing Officer, Tyler Memorial Hospital, Tunkhannock, PA, p. A542

RAHDERT, Richard, M.D., Medical Director, River Bend Hospital, West Lafayette, IN, p. A216

RAHIJA, David, FACHE, President, Northshore Skokie Hospital, IL, p. A182

RAHMAN, Randy
Chief Information Officer, Miami County Medical Center, Paola, KS, p. A244
Vice President and Chief Information Officer, Olathe Medical Center, Olathe, KS, p. A242

RAHMAN, Syed, M.D., Chief of Staff, Horizon Specialty Hospital, Las Vegas, NV, p. A394

RAHN, Kevin, President Medical Staff, Orthopaedic Hospital Of Lutheran Health Network, Fort Wayne, IN, p. A204

RAINA, Suresh, M.D., Vice President Medical Staff and Chief Medical Officer, Hackensack Meridian Health Palisades Medical Center, North Bergen, NJ, p. A409

RAINBOLT, Mike, Chief Financial Officer, Rivendell Behavioral Health Services Of Arkansas, Benton-Saline County, AR, p. A39

RAINEY, Jackie, Chief Financial Officer, Little River Memorial Hospital, Ashdown, AR, p. A39

RAINEY, Mark J, Director Human Resources, Texas Health Presbyterian Hospital Kaufman, Kaufman, TX, p. A617

RAINEY, Michelle L., Senior Vice President and Chief Nursing Officer, Pikeville Medical Center, Pikeville, KY, p. A259

RAINS, Celeste, D.O., Chief of Staff, Logan County Hospital, Oakley, KS, p. A242

RAINS, Debbie, Coordinator Health Information Management, Erlanger Bledsoe Hospital, Pikeville, TN, p. A579

RAINS, Della, Chief Nursing Officer, Continuecare Hospital At Baptist Health Corbin, Corbin, KY, p. A250

RAINS, Jeff G., Chief Executive Officer, Baptist Medical Center East, Montgomery, AL, p. A21

RAINS, Jon-Michael
Chief Executive Officer, Carrus Rehabilitation Hospital, Sherman, TX, p. A636
Chief Executive Officer, Carrus Specialty Hospital, Sherman, TX, p. A636

RAINS, Paul, R.N., MSN, President, St. Joseph's Behavioral Health Center, Stockton, CA, p. A91

RAINS, Ronald, Chief Executive Officer, University Behavioral Health Of Denton, Denton, TX, p. A599

RAINS, Steve, Director Information Services, Mckee Medical Center, Loveland, CO, p. A104

RAISNER, Gary, Chief Operating Officer, Norristown State Hospital, Norristown, PA, p. A533

RAJEWSKI, Frank A, Chief Financial Officer, Rooks County Health Center, Plainville, KS, p. A244

RAJPARA, Suresh, M.D., Chief Medical Officer, Jerome Golden Center For Behavioral Health, Inc., West Palm Beach, FL, p. A143

RAJU, Vasudeva, M.D., Suffix, Chief, Long Term Acute Care Medicine, Henry J. Carter Specialty Hospital & Nursing Facility, NY, p. A435

RAK, Roger, Director Human Resources, South Shore Hospital, Chicago, IL, p. A179

RAKES, Lori, Chief Operating Officer, Cartersville Medical Center, Cartersville, GA, p. A149

RAKES-STEPHENS, Kim, M.D., Chief Medical Staff, Colleton Medical Center, Walterboro, SC, p. A557

RAKOV, Robert, M.D., Chief Medical Officer, Cogdell Memorial Hospital, Snyder, TX, p. A636

RALSTIN, Char, Director of Nursing, Haven Senior Horizons, Phoenix, AZ, p. A33

RAMA-BANAAG, Gemma, R.N., MSN, Chief Nursing Officer, Bayview Behavioral Health Campus, CA, p. A74

RAMAGE, Gary, M.D., Chief Medical Officer, Mckenzie County Healthcare System, Watford City, ND, p. A469

RAMAN, Jayashree, Vice President and Chief Information Officer, Reading Hospital, West Reading, PA, p. A544

RAMAZANI, Regina
Chief Financial Officer, Garden Park Medical Center, Gulfport, MS, p. A346
Chief Financial Officer, Tulane-Lakeside Hospital, LA, p. A276
Chief Operating Officer, Garden Park Medical Center, Gulfport, MS, p. A346

RAMEY, Rita, Director Information Systems, Buchanan General Hospital, Grundy, VA, p. A659

RAMEY, Robert L., President, Baptist Health Madisonville, Madisonville, KY, p. A257

RAMEY, Steve, Chief Financial Officer, Southampton Memorial Hospital, Franklin, VA, p. A658

RAMIREZ, Ana, Director of Nursing, Mesa Springs, Fort Worth, TX, p. A605

RAMIREZ, Arthur L., M.D.
Medical Director, El Paso Behavioral Health System, El Paso, TX, p. A601
Medical Director, Mesilla Valley Hospital, Las Cruces, NM, p. A418

RAMIREZ, Eddy, Assistant Vice President Business Development, Ochsner Medical Center - Kenner, Kenner, LA, p. A270

RAMIREZ, Harvey, Chief Information Officer, Coleman County Medical Center, Coleman, TX, p. A593

RAMIREZ, Jaime, Chief Executive Officer, Mccamey County Hospital District, Mccamey, TX, p. A623

RAMIREZ, Omar, Chief Executive Officer, Los Angeles Community Hospital Of Norwalk, CA, p. A68

RAMIREZ, Ruben, M.D., Chief of Staff, Monterey Park Hospital, Monterey Park, CA, p. A73

RAMIREZ, Susan, Chief Nursing Officer, Healthsouth Rehabilitation Hospital-Las Vegas, Las Vegas, NV, p. A394

RAMIREZ, Venus V., Executive Director, Hospital San Pablo Del Este, Fajardo, PR, p. A713

RAMIREZ, Willie, Manager Labor Relations, Laguna Honda Hospital And Rehabilitation Center, San Francisco, CA, p. A85

RAMLO, Ricki, Chief Operating Officer and Human Resources, Jamestown Regional Medical Center, Jamestown, ND, p. A467

RAMLOCHAN, Tara, Chief Executive Officer, Meade District Hospital, Meade, KS, p. A241

RAMON, Maggie, Chief Financial Officer, Cochran Memorial Hospital, Morton, TX, p. A624

RAMOS, Eduardo, M.D., Medical Director, Healthsouth Rehabilitation Hospital Of San Juan, San Juan, PR, p. A715

RAMOS, Eric, M.D., Division Chief Medical Officer, Southern Hills Hospital And Medical Center, Las Vegas, NV, p. A394

RAMOS, Gracie, Chief Human Resources Officer, Ogallala Community Hospital, Ogallala, NE, p. A387

RAMOS, Holly, R.N., Chief Clinical Officer, Kindred Hospital-Ontario, Ontario, CA, p. A76

RAMOS, Jessie, Manager Human Resources, Skyline Hospital, White Salmon, WA, p. A680

RAMOS, Jet, Head Staff Administration, Naval Hospital Camp Pendleton, Camp Pendleton, CA, p. A54

RAMOS, Raymond, FACHE, Chief Operating Officer, Doctors Hospital Of Laredo, Laredo, TX, p. A619

RAMPAT, Ananda, Chief Financial Officer, Northwest Medical Center, Margate, FL, p. A129

RAMPP, Randal D, M.D., Chief Medical Officer, Saint Thomas River Park Hospital, Mc Minnville, TN, p. A574

RAMSAMY, Dev, Chief Financial Officer, St. Rose Dominican Hospitals - San Martin Campus, Las Vegas, NV, p. A395

RAMSER, Emmett, Chief Administrative Officer, Norton Children's Hospital, Louisville, KY, p. A256

RAMSEY, Antonina, Senior Vice President and Chief Human Resource Officer, Henry Ford Hospital, Detroit, MI, p. A311

RAMSEY, David L., President and Chief Executive Officer, General Hospital, WV, p. A682

RAMSEY, Kristin, R.N., Senior Vice President and Chief Nursing Executive, Northwestern Memorial Hospital, Stone Institute Of Psychiatry, IL, p. A178

RAMSEY, Lisa, Chief Financial Officer, Prairie View, Newton, KS, p. A242

RAMSEY, Rance, Chief Executive Officer, Martin County Hospital District, Stanton, TX, p. A637

RAMSEY, Rhonda, Controller, Healthsouth Deaconess Rehabilitation Hospital, Evansville, IN, p. A203

RAMSEY, Ross, M.D., Chief of Staff, Scheurer Hospital, Pigeon, MI, p. A320

RAMSEY, Roy M., Executive Director, Bradford Health Services At Warrior Lodge, Warrior, AL, p. A24

RAMSEY, Thomas, Chief Financial Officer, Hancock Medical Center, Bay Saint Louis, MS, p. A343

RAMSEY, Tom, Chief Financial Officer, Morehouse General Hospital, Bastrop, LA, p. A263

RAMTHUN, Jane, Chief Financial Officer, Story County Medical Center, Nevada, IA, p. A227

RANA, Chaula, M.D., Medical Director, Encompass Health Rehabilitation Hospital Of San Antonio, San Antonio, TX, p. A633

RANCK, Sonja, MSN, R.N., Chief Operating Officer and Chief Nursing Officer, Skiff Medical Center, Newton, IA, p. A227

RANCOURT, Lindsay, Director of Nursing, Upper Connecticut Valley Hospital, Colebrook, NH, p. A398

RANDALL, Bryan J
Vice President Finance and Chief Financial Officer, Heritage Valley Health System, Beaver, PA, p. A520
Vice President Finance and Chief Financial Officer, Sewickley Valley Hospital, (A Division Of Valley Medical Facilities), Sewickley, PA, p. A541

RANDALL, Cherry, Business Officer, Greater Binghamton Health Center, Binghamton, NY, p. A422

RANDLE, Emily, Vice President Operations, Memorialcare, Orange Coast Memorial Medical Center, Fountain Valley, CA, p. A58

RANDOLPH, Arianne, Director Human Resources, Pikes Peak Regional Hospital, Woodland Park, CO, p. A106

RANDOLPH, Bonnie, M.D., Chief of Staff, Community Hospital, Torrington, WY, p. A710

RANDOLPH, Joseph, M.D., Chairman Medical Executive Committee, Orthoindy Hospital, Indianapolis, IN, p. A207

RANDOLPH, Karsten, Executive Vice President and Chief Financial Officer, Shawnee Mission Medical Center, Shawnee Mission, KS, p. A246

RANDOLPH, Linda, Director Personnel Services, Washington County Hospital, Chatom, AL, p. A16

RANDOLPH, Mark, President, Children's Hospital Of Shreveport, LA, p. A279

RANEY, Hollie, Director of Nursing, Dallas County Medical Center, Fordyce-Dallas County, AR, p. A42

RANEY, Lance C., Commander, Womack Army Medical Center, Fort Bragg, NC, p. A452

RANG, Robert A., R.N., Chief Executive Officer, Wrangell Medical Center, Wrangell, AK, p. A27

RANGAVIZ, Rassoul, Chief Financial Officer, Copley Hospital, Morrisville, VT, p. A654

RANGE, Bonny, MSN, Chief Nursing Officer, Holy Family Memorial, Manitowoc, WI, p. A696

RANKIN, Charlotte, R.N., Chief Operating Officer, Mercy Hospital Rogers, Rogers-Benton County, AR, p. A48

RANKIN, Cynthia, Chief Nursing Officer, Lovelace Rehabilitation Hospital, Albuquerque, NM, p. A415

RANNEY, Timothy, M.D., Chief Medical Officer, Seton Medical Center, Daly City, CA, p. A56

RANSOM, Natalie
Chief Nursing Officer, Mountainview Hospital, Las Vegas, NV, p. A394
Chief Nursing Officer, North Florida Regional Medical Center, Gainesville, FL, p. A123

RANSOM, Ric A., Chief Operating Officer, Roger C. Peace Rehabilitation Hospital, SC, p. A553

RAO, Gutti, M.D., Medical Director, Amg Specialty Hospital-Greenwood, Greenwood, MS, p. A346

RAO, Kalapala, M.D., Medical Director, Healthsouth Western Hills Regional Rehabilitation Hospital, Parkersburg, WV, p. A686

RAPENSKE, Jennifer, Manager Financial Services, Mercy Medical Center-New Hampton, New Hampton, IA, p. A227

RAPP, Catherine, R.N., MS, Vice President Nursing, Oconomowoc Memorial Hospital, Oconomowoc, WI, p. A700

RAPP, David, Chief Information Officer, Wheeling Hospital, Wheeling, WV, p. A688

RAPP, Ron, Vice President Finance, Upmc Cole, Coudersport, PA, p. A523

RAPPACH, Shannon, Chief Fiscal Services, Dayton Veterans Affairs Medical Center, Dayton, OH, p. A480

RASCHKE, Judy, Director Human Resources, Pipestone County Medical Center Avera, Pipestone, MN, p. A337

RASHFORD, Jennifer, Manager Human Resources, Lifecare Hospitals Of Mechanicsburg, Mechanicsburg, PA, p. A531

RASHID, Harun, Vice President and Chief Information Officer, Akron Children's Hospital, Akron, OH, p. A470

RASHILLA, Matt, Chief Information and Application Officer, Monongahela Valley Hospital, Monongahela, PA, p. A532

RASK, Brenda, Vice President Operations, Chi St Alexius Health Carrington Medical Center, Carrington, ND, p. A464

RASKE, Jamie, Information Technology Lead, Avera St. Mary's Hospital, Pierre, SD, p. A562

RASMUSSEN, Diane, Director Human Resources, Cambridge Medical Center, Cambridge, MN, p. A329

RASMUSSEN, Jeanell, R.N., Vice President Patient Care Services and Chief Nursing Officer, Harrison Medical Center, Bremerton, WA, p. A669

RASMUSSEN, John, Vice President for Information Technology, Medstar Georgetown University Hospital, Washington, DC, p. A115

RASMUSSEN, Rick, Chief Executive Officer, Northwest Specialty Hospital, Post Falls, ID, p. A171

RASMUSSEN, Scott, Director Human Resources, Lincoln Regional Center, Lincoln, NE, p. A386

RASMUSSON, Duane, Vice President Human Resources, St. Cloud Hospital, Saint Cloud, MN, p. A338

RASNICK, Laura Lynn, RN, BSN, CLNC, Administrator, Parkland Health Center-Bonne Terre, Bonne Terre, MO, p. A355

RASOOL, Chaudri, D.O., Chief of Staff, Gundersen Palmer Lutheran Hospital And Clinics, West Union, IA, p. A231

RASOR, Linda, R.N., Chief Executive Officer, Plains Memorial Hospital, Dimmitt, TX, p. A600

RASTER, Robert, M.D., Medical Director, Michiana Behavioral Health Center, Plymouth, IN, p. A213

RATAJ, Marianne, R.N., MS, Chief Nursing Officer, Mercy Orthopedic Hospital Fort Smith, AR, p. A42

RATCLIFF, David, M.D., Chief Medical Affairs, Washington Regional Medical Center, Fayetteville-Washington County, AR, p. A42

RATCLIFF, Paul, Director Information Services, Baylor Scott & White Medical Center - Carrollton, Carrollton, TX, p. A592

RATCLIFFE, Alma, M.D., Executive Vice President Medical Staff and Business Development, Saint Clare's Hospital/Dover, NJ, p. A403

RATH, Kevin, Vice President and Executive Director, Amita Health Women & Children's Hospital, IL, p. A186

RATH, Megan, Chief Financial Officer, Wishek Community Hospital And Clinics, Wishek, ND, p. A469

RATHGABER, Scott W., M.D., Chief Executive Officer, Gundersen Lutheran Medical Center, La Crosse, WI, p. A695

RATLIFF, Ada
Chief Executive Officer, Claiborne County Medical Center, Port Gibson, MS, p. A352
Chief Information Officer, Claiborne County Medical Center, Port Gibson, MS, p. A352

RATLIFF, Bonnie, Chief Information Officer, Columbia Memorial Hospital, Hudson, NY, p. A428

RATLIFF, Kim, Director Health Information Management, Southwestern Virginia Mental Health Institute, Marion, VA, p. A661

RATLIFF, Maggie, Vice President Information Systems, Sarah Bush Lincoln Health Center, Mattoon, IL, p. A188

RATLIFF, Simon, Chief Operating Officer, Logan Regional Medical Center, Logan, WV, p. A684

RATLIFF, Steve, Director Information Technology, Guadalupe Regional Medical Center, Seguin, TX, p. A635

RATNASAMY, Suthanthira M., R.N., FACHE, Chief Executive Officer, Kindred Hospital-Bay Area St. Petersburg, FL, p. A141

RATTLE, John, Chief Financial Officer, West Springs Hospital, Grand Junction, CO, p. A101

RATTRAY, Cindy Stewart, Director Human Resources, Jewish Hospital-Shelbyville, Shelbyville, KY, p. A260

RAU, John, President and Chief Executive Officer, Stevens Community Medical Center, Morris, MN, p. A336

RAU, Robin, Chief Executive Officer, Miller County Hospital, Colquitt, GA, p. A150

RAUB, Jessica, Director Health Information Management, Seven Hills Hospital, Henderson, NV, p. A393

RAUCH, Rhonda, Chief Nursing Officer, Lovelace Regional Hospital - Roswell, Roswell, NM, p. A419

RAUCH, Scott C, Vice President Human Resources, Reid Health, Richmond, IN, p. A214

RAUCH, Scott L., M.D., President and Psychiatrist in Chief, Mclean Hospital, Belmont, MA, p. A295

RAUEN, Rebecca A., Director Human Resources, Maple Grove Hospital, Maple Grove, MN, p. A334

RAUH, Bradley W., Vice President, Chief Operating Officer, Southwest General Health Center, Middleburg Heights, OH, p. A487

RAUH, Cindy, R.N., Vice President and Chief Nursing Officer, Duncan Regional Hospital, Duncan, OK, p. A498

RAUNER, Mary Ellen, R.N., Chief Nursing Officer, Suburban Community Hospital, Norristown, PA, p. A533

RAUPERS, Deb, MSN, R.N.
Chief Nursing Officer, Guthrie Corning Hospital, Corning, NY, p. A425
Vice President Patient Services and Chief Nursing Officer, Cayuga Medical Center At Ithaca, Ithaca, NY, p. A428

RAUTIO, Wendy, Chief Financial Officer, Munising Memorial Hospital, Munising, MI, p. A319

RAVELING, Lynn, Chief Financial Officer, Pocahontas Community Hospital, Pocahontas, IA, p. A228

RAWLEY, Jennifer, PharmD, Chief Executive Officer, Select Specialty Hospital-Durham, Durham, NC, p. A451

RAWLINGS, Linda, Director Human Resources and Personnel, Three Rivers Hospital, Waverly, TN, p. A580

RAWLINGS, Michael, Interim Chief Operating Officer, Nyc Health + Hospitals / Bellevue, New York (Includes All Hospitals Located Within The Five Boroughs), NY, p. A435

RAWLINGS, Patrick
Chief Human Resource Officer, Saint Francis Hospital, Charleston, WV, p. A682
Human Resources Director, Thomas Memorial Hospital, South Charleston, WV, p. A687

RAWLINGS, Sheri, Chief Information Officer, San Juan Regional Medical Center Rehabilitation Hospital, NM, p. A417

RAWSON, Richard, Chief Executive Officer, Fremont Medical Center, CA, p. A72

RAWSON, Richard L, President and Chief Executive Officer, Adventist Medical Center-Selma, CA, p. A61

RAY, Beverly, Director Human Resources, West Tennessee Healthcare Dyersburg Hospital, Dyersburg, TN, p. A569

RAY, Brenda, Director Human Resources, Huntsville Memorial Hospital, Huntsville, TX, p. A615

RAY, Denise, Chief Executive Officer, Piedmont Mountainside Hospital, Jasper, GA, p. A155

RAY, Diane, R.N., FACHE, Vice President and Chief Nursing Officer Patient Services, St. Luke's Hospital, Chesterfield, MO, p. A357

RAY, Donald, Vice President Operations, University Of Maryland Medical Center Midtown Campus, Baltimore, MD, p. A289

RAY, Elaine, Administrator, Choate Mental Health Center, Anna, IL, p. A173

RAY, Evan, FACHE, Chief Executive Officer, St. Vincent's Birmingham, Birmingham, AL, p. A15

RAY, Jerilyn, Manager Human Resources, St. Elizabeth Hospital, Enumclaw, WA, p. A671

RAY, Joel, MSN, Vice President and Chief Nursing Officer, Unc Rex Health Care, Raleigh, NC, p. A459

RAY, Kirk M., President and Chief Executive Officer, Mclaren Orthopedic Hospital, MI, p. A317

RAY, Marge, Director Information Systems, Kimball-Ridge Center, IA, p. A230

RAY, Marilyn, MSN, Chief Nursing Officer, Upson Regional Medical Center, Thomaston, GA, p. A161

RAY, Nancy L, R.N., Executive Vice President, Chief Nursing Executive, University Hospital, TX, p. A634

RAY, Rachel, Chief Financial Officer, Unity Medical Center, Grafton, ND, p. A466

RAY, Roger A, M.D., Executive Vice President and Chief Medical Officer, Levine Children's Hospital, NC, p. A449

RAYBOURN, Gina, Director Health Information, Ellett Memorial Hospital, Appleton City, MO, p. A355

RAYLS, Kim, Director Human Resources, Twin Lakes Regional Medical Center, Leitchfield, KY, p. A254

RAYMER, Chris Lee., R.N., MSN
Chief Executive Officer, Great River Medical Center, Blytheville-Mississippi County, AR, p. A39
Chief Executive Officer, South Mississippi County Regional Medical Center, Osceola-Mississippi County, AR, p. A47

RAYMOND, Greg, Regional Vice President, Southern Colorado, Children's Hospital Of Colorado At Memorial, CO, p. A96

RAYMOND, Heather, Area Public Relations Director, Kaiser Permanente Ontario Medical Center, CA, p. A58

RAYMOND, Jane, Vice President and Chief Operating Officer, Reston Hospital Center, Reston, VA, p. A664

RAYMOND, Katherine, Chief Nursing Officer, St. Rose Dominican Hospitals - San Martin Campus, Las Vegas, NV, p. A395

RAYMOND, Mindy, Vice President Human Resources, Boca Raton Regional Hospital, Boca Raton, FL, p. A118

RAYMOND, Scott, Director Information Systems, Memorialcare, Orange Coast Memorial Medical Center, Fountain Valley, CA, p. A58

RAYNER, Thomas J, Senior Vice President and Chief Operating Officer, South Campus, CA, p. A94

RAYNES, Anthony, M.D., Psychiatrist in Chief, Arbour H. R. I. Hospital, Brookline, MA, p. A298

RAYNES, Scott
President, Baptist Hospital, Pensacola, FL, p. A136
President, Gulf Breeze Hospital, Gulf Breeze, FL, p. A124

RAYNOR, Robert, Human Resources Director, Park Royal Hospital, Fort Myers, FL, p. A123

RAYUDU, Subbu, M.D., Chief of Staff, Alliance Healthcare System, Holly Springs, MS, p. A347

RAZMIC, Tammy, Associate Administrator Finance and Chief Financial Officer, Inova Mount Vernon Hospital, Alexandria, VA, p. A655

RAZO, Virginia, Chief Executive Officer, Curry General Hospital, Gold Beach, OR, p. A513

REA, Jerry A., Ph.D., Superintendent, Parsons State Hospital And Training Center, Parsons, KS, p. A244

READ, Eddie, Interim Chief Financial Officer, Val Verde Regional Medical Center, Del Rio, TX, p. A598

READ, John, Chief Nursing Officer, Allegiance Specialty Hospital Of Greenville, Greenville, MS, p. A346

READ, Paul, R.N., MSN, Vice President and Chief Nursing Officer, Springhill Memorial Hospital, Mobile, AL, p. A20

READ, Richard, Chief Financial Officer, Central Florida Regional Hospital, Sanford, FL, p. A138

READER, G. Whitney, M.D., Chief Medical Officer, Kansas Medical Center, Andover, KS, p. A232

READING, Jared, M.D., Chief of Staff, Uvalde Memorial Hospital, Uvalde, TX, p. A641

READINGER, Phillip, Chief Executive Officer, Select Specialty Hospital - Town And Country, MO, p. A367

REALE, Kelli, Vice President Human Resources, Upmc Mckeesport, Mckeesport, PA, p. A531

REAM, Tom, Regional Chief Information Officer, Sutter Auburn Faith Hospital, Auburn, CA, p. A51

REAMER, Roger J., Chief Executive Officer, Memorial Health Care Systems, Seward, NE, p. A390

REAMES, Jim, Director Human Resources, Bayfront Health St. Petersburg, Saint Petersburg, FL, p. A138

REAMY, Tracy, Administrator, Bozeman Health Big Sky Medical Center, Big Sky, MT, p. A373

REANDEAU, Michael, Chief Information Officer, Mills-Peninsula Medical Center, CA, p. A53

REASER, Michelle, R.N., Chief Nursing Executive, Upmc Pinnacle Lancaster, Lancaster, PA, p. A529

REASONER, Vanessa, Chief Executive Officer, Grace Medical Center, Lubbock, TX, p. A621

REASY, Stephanie
Administrator and Chief Executive Officer, Avera De Smet Memorial Hospital, De Smet, SD, p. A560
Administrator and Chief Executive Officer, Avera Weskota Memorial Hospital, Wessington Springs, SD, p. A565

REBERRY, Darinda, MSN, R.N., President and Chief Executive Officer, Western Missouri Medical Center, Warrensburg, MO, p. A371

REBLOCK, Kimberly, M.D., Chief Operating Officer, The Children's Home Of Pittsburgh, Pittsburgh, PA, p. A538

REBOCK, Michael, Chief Medical Officer, Beaumont Hospital - Farmington Hills, Farmington Hills, MI, p. A312

RECA, Thomas, Sr, Deputy Executive Director and Chief Financial Officer, Staten Island University Hospital, New York (Includes All Hospitals Located Within The Five Boroughs), NY, p. A437

RECHNER, Paula, M.D., Chief Medical Officer, War Memorial Hospital, Sault Sainte Marie, MI, p. A323

REICHERT, James, Chief Medical Officer, Mercer Health, Coldwater, OH, p. A478

REICHFIELD, Michael L., President, Ohiohealth Doctors Hospital, Columbus, OH, p. A478

REICHLE, Paula, Senior Vice President and Chief Operating Officer, Sparrow Children's Center, MI, p. A317

REICHMAN, Joseph, M.D., Vice President Medical Affairs and Clinical Effectiveness, Hackensack Meridian Health Riverview Medical Center, Red Bank, NJ, p. A411

REID, Bernadette, Vice President, Information Technology and Chief Information Officer, Torrance Memorial Medical Center, Torrance, CA, p. A92

REID, Bev, Chief Financial Officer, St. Luke Hospital And Living Center, Marion, KS, p. A241

REID, Dereesa, Administrator, Shriners Hospitals For Children-Portland, Portland, OR, p. A516

REID, Jim, Vice President and Chief Information Officer, Covenant Children's Hospital, Lubbock, TX, p. A620

REID, Kelly, Human Resources Director, South Mississippi State Hospital, Purvis, MS, p. A352

REID, Kenneth G., President and Chief Executive Officer, Carlinville Area Hospital, Carlinville, IL, p. A175

REID, Patricia, Director of Nursing, Marion General Hospital, Columbia, MS, p. A345

REID, Richard, Vice President Chief Finance Officer, Sparrow Carson Hospital, Carson City, MI, p. A309

REID, Stephanie, R.N., Vice President of Patient Care Services and Chief Nursing Officer, Carroll Hospital Center, Westminster, MD, p. A294

REIDER, Rochelle, Vice President Patient Care, Avera Queen Of Peace Hospital, Mitchell, SD, p. A562

REIDY, Margaret, M.D., Vice President Medical Affairs, Western Psychiatric Institute And Clinic, PA, p. A538

REILLY, Brian M, Chief Financial Officer, Bristol-Myers Squibb Children's Hospital, NJ, p. A408

REILLY, Janelle
Chief Executive Officer, Memorial Hospital Hixson, TN, p. A567
Chief Operating Officer, Memorial Hospital Hixson, TN, p. A567

REILLY, Joanne, Administrator, Hudson County Meadowview Psychiatric Hospital, Secaucus, NJ, p. A411

REILLY, John, M.D., Vice President Medical Affairs and Chief Medical Officer, Mercy Medical Center, Rockville Centre, NY, p. A442

REILLY, Richard, Deputy Executive Director, Syosset Hospital, Syosset, NY, p. A443

REILLY, Robert, Vice President and Chief Financial Officer, Anne Arundel Medical Center, Annapolis, MD, p. A287

REILLY, Theresa, MSN, R.N., Senior Vice President Patient Services and Chief Nursing Officer, Abington Hospital, Abington, PA, p. A519

REILLY, Tiffany, Director Human Resources, Lifescape, Sioux Falls, SD, p. A563

REIMER, Arlo, M.D., Chief of Staff, Kearny County Hospital, Lakin, KS, p. A239

REIMER, Randy, Chief Financial Officer, Adventist Behavioral Health And Wellness Services, Rockville, MD, p. A293

REIMER, Ronda, R.N., Chief Nursing Officer and Assistant Administrator, Franklin General Hospital, Hampton, IA, p. A223

REIN, Mitchell S, M.D., Chief Medical Officer, Union Campus, MA, p. A304

REINBOTH, Thomas, Chief Financial Officer, Roxborough Memorial Hospital, Philadelphia, PA, p. A536

REINER, Mark, Chief Medical Office, Executive, St. Anthony's Rehabilitation Hospital, Lauderdale Lakes, FL, p. A128

REINERT, Brenda, Director Human Resources, Tomah Memorial Hospital, Tomah, WI, p. A704

REINERT, Chad, Chief Information Officer, Hamilton General Hospital, Hamilton, TX, p. A608

REINHARD, Diane, R.N., Vice President of Patient Care Services, Craig Hospital, Englewood, CO, p. A100

REINHARD, Russ, Chief Executive, Providence Willamette Falls Medical Center, Oregon City, OR, p. A515

REINKE, Bradley, M.D., Vice President Medical Affairs and Chief Medical Officer, Dameron Hospital, Stockton, CA, p. A90

REINKE, N Sue, Vice President Human Resources, Geisinger-Lewistown Hospital, Lewistown, PA, p. A530

REINKE, Peggy, R.N., Administrator, Chi Lisbon Health, Lisbon, ND, p. A467

REINKING, Cheryl, R.N., MS, Chief Nursing Officer, El Camino Hospital Los Gatos, CA, p. A74

REISELT, Doug
Vice President and Chief Information Officer, Baptist Memorial Hospital - Memphis, Memphis, TN, p. A574
Vice President and Chief Information Officer, Baptist Memorial Hospital-Collierville, Collierville, TN, p. A568

REISING, Robyn, R.N., Chief Nursing Officer, Decatur Memorial Hospital, Decatur, IL, p. A180

REISMAN, Ernestine O, Vice President Human Resources, Down East Community Hospital, Machias, ME, p. A285

REISS, Deanna, Hospital Director of Nursing, Devereux Children's Behavioral Health Center, Malvern, PA, p. A530

REITZ, Brent, President, Adventist Healthcare Physical Health And Rehabilitation, Rockville, MD, p. A293

REITZ, Robert, Ph.D., Chief Executive Officer, Fulton State Hospital, Fulton, MO, p. A359

REITZEL, David, Chief Information Officer, Brookdale Hospital Medical Center, New York (Includes All Hospitals Located Within The Five Boroughs), NY, p. A431

REKOWSKI, Christian
Information Technology Director, Optim Medical Center - Jenkins, Millen, GA, p. A157
Information Technology Manager, Optim Medical Center - Screven, Sylvania, GA, p. A161

RELPH, Daren
Chief Executive Officer, Wayne County Hospital, Corydon, IA, p. A220
Interim Administrator, Decatur County Hospital, Leon, IA, p. A225

REMALEY, Anne, Vice President Human Resources, Acmh Hospital, Kittanning, PA, p. A528

REMARK, Megan, President and Chief Executive Officer, Regions Hospital, Saint Paul, MN, p. A339

REMBIS, Michael A., FACHE, Chief Executive Officer, Maui Memorial Medical Center, Wailuku, HI, p. A166

REMBOLD, Abbey
Human Resources Senior Generalist, Hampshire Memorial Hospital, Romney, WV, p. A686
Human Resources Senior Generalist, War Memorial Hospital, Berkeley Springs, WV, p. A681
Manager, Human Resource Business Partnerships, Valley Health Shenandoah Memorial Hospital, Woodstock, VA, p. A668

REMIGIO, Odalys, Assistant Vice President, Finance, Baptist Health South Florida, West Kendall Baptist Hospital, Miami, FL, p. A130

REMILLARD, John R, President and Chief Executive Officer, Moses Ludington Hospital, NY, p. A426

REMILLARD, John R., President and Chief Executive Officer, Moses Ludington Hospital, NY, p. A426

REMINGTON, Amanda
Director Human Resources, Wellstar Spalding Regional Hospital, Griffin, GA, p. A154
Director Human Resources, Wellstar Sylvan Grove Hospital, Jackson, GA, p. A155

REMLEY, Richard, Chief Executive Officer, Southcoast Behavioral Health, Dartmouth, MA, p. A299

REMSPECHER, Mark, Director Human Resources, Southeast Missouri Mental Health Center, Farmington, MO, p. A359

RENDA, Nick, Chief Financial Officer, Merit Health Woman's Hospital, Flowood, MS, p. A346

RENDER-LEACH, Cynthia, Director Human Resources, Highland Community Hospital, Picayune, MS, p. A352

RENEAU, John D., Medical Director, Healthsouth Rehabilitation Hospital-Las Vegas, Las Vegas, NV, p. A394

RENFREE, Mark, Chief Financial Officer, La Rabida Children's Hospital, Chicago, IL, p. A177

RENIER, Hugh, M.D.
Vice President Medical Affairs, Essentia Health Duluth, Duluth, MN, p. A330
Vice President Medical Affairs, St. Mary's Children's Hospital, MN, p. A330

RENKIEWICZ, Ginger L, Chief Clinical Officer, Chief Nursing Executive, and Chief Quality Officer, Unitypoint Health - Trinity Moline, IL, p. A194

RENN, Amy Katherine, Interim Administrator, Patient Care and Nursing, Via Christi Hospital Pittsburg, Pittsburg, KS, p. A244

RENNEKER, James M, FACHE, MSN, R.N., Vice President and Chief Nursing Officer, Southlake Campus, IN, p. A204

RENNER, Dianne, Director Human Resources, Logansport State Hospital, Logansport, IN, p. A210

RENNING, Kathryn, Director of Nursing, Cherry County Hospital, Valentine, NE, p. A391

RENO, Kelly, R.N., Chief Nursing Officer, Menorah Medical Center, Overland Park, KS, p. A243

RENO, Mike, Chief Operating Officer, Hill Country Memorial Hospital, Fredericksburg, TX, p. A606

RENO, William, M.D., III, President Medical Staff, Merit Health Wesley, Hattiesburg, MS, p. A347

RENSHAW, Dee, Chief Executive Officer, Hillcrest Hospital Henryetta, Henryetta, OK, p. A499

RENTAS, Margarita, R.N., Nursing Director, Castaner General Hospital, Castaner, PR, p. A712

RENTFRO, Donald R., Chief Executive Officer, L. V. Stabler Memorial Hospital, Greenville, AL, p. A19

RENTSCH, Richard E, President, Stroud Regional Medical Center, Stroud, OK, p. A507

REOHR, Sara, Regional Controller, West Gables Rehabilitation Hospital, Miami, FL, p. A131

REPAC, Kimberly S, Senior Vice President and Chief Financial Officer, Western Maryland Regional Medical Center, Cumberland, MD, p. A291

REPASS, Lois, Quality Assurance Specialist and Coordinator Performance Improvement, Northern Nevada Adult Mental Health Services, Sparks, NV, p. A397

REPETTI, Gregory George., III, FACHE, Chief Executive Officer, Multicare Valley Hospital, Spokane Valley, WA, p. A678

REPKO, Keith D., Director, Veterans Affairs St. Louis Health Care System, Saint Louis, MO, p. A370

REPPY, William
President, Lehigh Valley Hospital - Schuylkill East Norwegian Street, Pottsville, PA, p. A539
President, Lehigh Valley Hospital - Schuylkill, Pottsville, PA, p. A539

REPTA, Shirley, Chief Executive Officer, The Pavilion At Williamsburg Place, Williamsburg, VA, p. A668

RESENDEZ, James R., Chief Executive Officer, Doctors Hospital Of Laredo, Laredo, TX, p. A619

RESETAR, Gayle L, Vice President and Chief Operating Officer, Tidelands Georgetown Memorial Hospital, Georgetown, SC, p. A553

RESLER, Lori, R.N., Chief Nurse, Sullivan County Community Hospital, Sullivan, IN, p. A215

RESSLER, David, Chief Executive Officer, Aspen Valley Hospital, Aspen, CO, p. A96

RESSLER, Dennis, Chief Financial Officer, St. Vincent Kokomo, Kokomo, IN, p. A209

RESTREPO, Macarena, Manager Business Office, Sister Emmanuel Hospital, Miami, FL, p. A131

RESTREPO, Nicolas, M.D., Vice President Medical Affairs, Winchester Medical Center, Winchester, VA, p. A668

RESTUCCIA, Michael, Chief Information Officer, Scheie Eye Institute Of The Hospital Of The University Of Pennsylvania, PA, p. A535

RESTUM, William, Chief Executive Officer, Dmc - Rehabilitation Institute Of Michigan, Detroit, MI, p. A311

RETALIC, Tammy B., R.N., MS, Chief Nursing Officer, Hebrew Rehabilitation Center, Roslindale, MA, p. A303

RETHAMEL, Terry, Director of Support Services, Newport News Behavioral Health Center, Newport News, VA, p. A662

RETHORST, Richard, Chief of Medical Staff, Franklin Hospital District, Benton, IL, p. A174

RETTGER, Linda, M.D., President Medical Staff, Upmc Kane, Kane, PA, p. A528

RETTIG, Jeffrey, D.O., Chief of Staff, Limestone Medical Center, Groesbeck, TX, p. A608

RETTIG, Linda, Director Financial Services, Washington County Hospital, Washington, KS, p. A247

REULAND, Charles B., Sc.D.
Executive Vice President and Chief Operating Officer, Johns Hopkins Bayview Medical Center, Baltimore, MD, p. A287
Executive Vice President and Chief Operations Officer, Johns Hopkins Children's Center, MD, p. A287

REUST, Michele, Controller, Memorial Hospital Of Texas County, Guymon, OK, p. A499

REUTTINGER, H. Rex, D.O., Chief Medical Officer, Administration, Garden City Hospital, Garden City, MI, p. A313

REVELS, Beverly, Director Human Resources, Sutter Amador Hospital, Jackson, CA, p. A62

REVELS, Tonya, Senior Strategic Business Partner, Mcdowell Hospital, Marion, NC, p. A456

REVERMAN, Larry, Director Information Systems, Clark Memorial Hospital, Jeffersonville, IN, p. A208

REVIEL, Jackie, R.N., Chief Executive Officer, Allen Parish Hospital, Kinder, LA, p. A270

REWERTS, Karen
System Vice President Finance, Ssm Health St. Joseph - Wentzville, Wentzville, MO, p. A367
System Vice President of Finance, Ssm Cardinal Glennon Children's Hospital, Saint Louis, MO, p. A368
System Vice President of Finance, Ssm Health St. Mary's Hospital - St. Louis, Saint Louis, MO, p. A369

REXFORD, Linda, Director Human Resources, Weeks Medical Center, Lancaster, NH, p. A399

REXWINKLE, Lori
Chief Executive Officer, Coffeyville Regional Medical Center, Coffeyville, KS, p. A233
Chief Nursing Officer, Coffeyville Regional Medical Center, Coffeyville, KS, p. A233

REYES, Anthony, Information Technology Director, Commonwealth Health Center, Saipan, MP, p. A711

REYES, Glenda, Chief Financial Officer, Northwest Medical Center, Winfield, AL, p. A24

REYES, Marco, Executive Director, Hospital Psiquiatrico Metropolitano, Cabo Rojo, PR, p. A712

REYES, Netonua, MSN, Chief Operating Officer and Chief Nursing Officer, Broward Health Imperial Point, Fort Lauderdale, FL, p. A122

REYES, Raul, M.D., Medical Director, San Juan City Hospital, San Juan, PR, p. A716

REYES, Roxanne, Director of Nursing, Cornerstone Regional Hospital, Edinburg, TX, p. A600

REYKA, Michael, Ph.D., Chief Executive Officer, Western Maryland Hospital Center, Hagerstown, MD, p. A292

REYMAN, Reed, President, Chi St. Alexius Health - Dickinson Medical Center, Dickinson, ND, p. A465

REYNA, Krista, Chief Nursing Officer, Mcbride Orthopedic Hospital, Oklahoma City, OK, p. A503

REYNGOUDT, Mark
Chief Financial Officer, Brandywine Hospital, Coatesville, PA, p. A523
Chief Financial Officer, Upmc Pinnacle Carlisle, Carlisle, PA, p. A522

REYNOLDS, Angela D, Chief Financial Officer, Lewis-Gale Pavilion, VA, p. A666

REYNOLDS, Denise, Chief Nursing Officer, Memorial Hospital Miramar, Miramar, FL, p. A132

REYNOLDS, Doug, Area Finance Officer, Kaiser Permanente Redwood City Medical Center, Redwood City, CA, p. A80

REYNOLDS, Hope, Vice President, Human Resources and Service Excellence, Margaret R. Pardee Memorial Hospital, Hendersonville, NC, p. A454

REYNOLDS, Ian, Chief Medical Officer, Advanced Diagnostics Hospital, Houston, TX, p. A610

REYNOLDS, James B, M.D., Medical Director, Northwest Missouri Psychiatric Rehabilitation Center, Saint Joseph, MO, p. A367

REYNOLDS, Jay, M.D., Chief Medical Officer and Chief Clinical Officer, Community General Health Center, ME, p. A286

REYNOLDS, Katelyn, Manager Human Resources, Greeley County Health Services, Tribune, KS, p. A247

REYNOLDS, Lennetta M, Administrative Supervisor, Community Behavioral Health Hospital - Annandale, Annandale, MN, p. A327

REYNOLDS, Mike
Chief Financial Officer, Delta Medical Center, Memphis, TN, p. A575
Chief Financial Officer, Newberry County Memorial Hospital, Newberry, SC, p. A556

REYNOLDS, Paul, M.D., Medical Director, Coleman County Medical Center, Coleman, TX, p. A593

REYNOLDS, Ray, Chief Executive Officer, Glen Rose Medical Center, Glen Rose, TX, p. A607

REYNOLDS, Robert, Director Information Systems, Mary Rutan Hospital, Bellefontaine, OH, p. A472

REYNOLDS, Ronald J., Vice President, Upmc Susquehanna Lock Haven, Lock Haven, PA, p. A530

REYNOLDS, Scott, Vice President Finance, Mercy Orthopedic Hospital Springfield, MO, p. A370

REYNOLDS, Teresa, Chief Operating Officer, Haywood Regional Medical Center, Clyde, NC, p. A450

REYNOLDS, Todd, Chief Information Officer, Memorial Medical Center Of Ashland, Ashland, WI, p. A689

REYNOLDS, Vance V., FACHE, CPA, Chief Executive Officer, Carolinas Hospital System, Florence, SC, p. A552

REYNOLDS-GOSSETTE, Youdie, Controller, Wilma N. Vazquez Medical Center, Vega Baja, PR, p. A716

REZAC, Julie A, R.N., Chief Operating Officer, Saunders Medical Center, Wahoo, NE, p. A391

RHEE, Carolyn F., Chief Executive Officer, Lac-Olive View-Ucla Medical Center, Los Angeles, CA, p. A68

RHEINHEIMER, Rick, Chief Clinical Officer, Kindred Hospital-Chattanooga, Chattanooga, TN, p. A567

RHINE, Kathleen, President and Chief Executive Officer, Mount Nittany Medical Center, State College, PA, p. A541

RHINEHART, Jennie R., Administrator and Chief Executive Officer, Community Hospital, Tallassee, AL, p. A23

RHOADES, Charles E., M.D., Chief Executive Officer, Kansas City Orthopaedic Institute, Leawood, KS, p. A240

RHOADES, Mark, Vice President and Chief Human Resources Officer, Duncan Regional Hospital, Duncan, OK, p. A498

RHOADES, Shelly, Chief Financial Officer, Clarion Psychiatric Center, Clarion, PA, p. A522

RHOADS, Jack, M.D., Medical Director, Landmark Hospital Of Joplin, Joplin, MO, p. A361

RHOADS, Pam, Chief Financial Officer, Fairfax Behavioral Health Everett, WA, p. A673

RHODES, David, M.D., Senior Vice President Medical Affairs and Chief Medical Officer, Rapides Regional Medical Center, Alexandria, LA, p. A262

RHODES, Helen, R.N., Associate Director Operations, Veterans Affairs Northern Indiana Health Care System-Marion Campus, IN, p. A204

RHODES, Tracey, Coordinator Human Resources, Evergreen Medical Center, Evergreen, AL, p. A17

RHONE, Steve, R.N., MS, Vice President Patient Care Services, Beebe Healthcare, Lewes, DE, p. A113

RHYNALDS, Kayla, Interim Chief Financial Officer, Kearney County Health Services, Minden, NE, p. A386

RHYNE, Craig, M.D., FACS
Chief Medical Officer, Covenant Children's Hospital, Lubbock, TX, p. A620
Chief Medical Officer, Covenant Medical Center-Lakeside, TX, p. A621

RHYNE, Dennis, M.D., Acting Medical Director, Fairbanks, Indianapolis, IN, p. A206

RHYNE, Tim, Personnel Officer, Ventura County Medical Center, Ventura, CA, p. A94

RIAL, Joanne, Chief Financial Officer, Cumberland Hospital For Children And Adolescents, New Kent, VA, p. A661

RIALS, Joe, Director Fiscal Services, North Mississippi State Hospital, Tupelo, MS, p. A353

RIALS, Loren
Chief Financial Officer, Carolinas Hospital System Marion, Mullins, SC, p. A555
Chief Financial Officer, Carolinas Hospital System, Florence, SC, p. A552

RIANO, Omaira D., Chief Nursing Officer, Healthsouth Sunrise Rehabilitation Hospital, Sunrise, FL, p. A140

RIBA, Chris, Director Human Resources, Western Wisconsin Health, Baldwin, WI, p. A689

RICARDO, Jennifer, Director of Human Resources, Southern Winds Hospital, FL, p. A131

RICCI, Lynn, President and Chief Executive Officer, Hospital For Special Care, New Britain, CT, p. A109

RICCIARDI, Patrice, Director Human Resources, Columbus Hospital Ltach, Newark, NJ, p. A408

RICCIO, Dustin, M.D.
President Eastern Region, Newark-Wayne Community Hospital, Newark, NY, p. A438
President, Clifton Springs Hospital And Clinic, Clifton Springs, NY, p. A424

RICCIO, John A., M.D., Chief Medical Officer, Auburn Community Hospital, Auburn, NY, p. A422

RICCIONI, Michel
Chief Financial Officer, General Hospital, CA, p. A57
Chief Financial Officer, North Hawaii Community Hospital, Kamuela, HI, p. A165
Chief Financial Officer, Petaluma Valley Hospital, Petaluma, CA, p. A78
Chief Financial Officer, Queen's Medical Center - West Oahu, HI, p. A165
Vice President and Chief Financial Officer, Northern California Region, Queen Of The Valley Medical Center, Napa, CA, p. A74

RICCITELLI, Anthony, Chief Operating Officer, Worcester Recovery Center And Hospital, Worcester, MA, p. A306

RICE, Aimee, Human Resources Manager, Riverview Psychiatric Center, Augusta, ME, p. A282

RICE, Amy, Chief Financial Officer, Helena Regional Medical Center, Helena-Phillips County, AR, p. A43

RICE, Ann Madden, Chief Executive Officer, University Of California Davis Children's Hospital, CA, p. A82

RICE, Ann Madden., Chief Executive Officer, University Of California Davis Children's Hospital, CA, p. A82

RICE, Bernard
Chief Compliance Officer, Rangely District Hospital, Rangely, CO, p. A105
Chief Information Officer, Nemours Children's Hospital, Orlando, FL, p. A134

RICE, Carolyn, M.D., Director Medical Services, Naval Hospital Pensacola, Pensacola, FL, p. A136

RICE, Cathy, Director Support Services, Clifton-Fine Hospital, Star Lake, NY, p. A443

RICE, Craig, Director Information Technology, Schneck Medical Center, Seymour, IN, p. A214

RICE, James W., Director, Oscar G. Johnson Veterans Affairs Medical Center, Iron Mountain, MI, p. A316

RICE, Mark, CPA, Chief Financial Officer, Geisinger Jersey Shore Hospital, Jersey Shore, PA, p. A528

RICE, Mark J., Administrator, Ruston Regional Specialty Hospital, Ruston, LA, p. A278

RICE, Peter, M.D., Medical Director, Peacehealth Ketchikan Medical Center, Ketchikan, AK, p. A26

RICE, Tim, President and Chief Executive Officer, Lakewood Health System, Staples, MN, p. A340

RICH, Anna, Chief Financial Officer, Complex Care Hospital At Tenaya, Las Vegas, NV, p. A394

RICH, Bill, Chief Executive Officer, Tennova Healthcare-Shelbyville, Shelbyville, TN, p. A579

RICH, Judy F., MSN, R.N., President and Chief Executive Officer, Tmc For Children, AZ, p. A38

RICH, Kori, Chief Executive Officer, The Physicians Centre Hospital, Bryan, TX, p. A591

RICH, Philip, M.D., Chief Medical Officer, West Hills Hospital, Reno, NV, p. A396

RICH, Travis, Chief Executive Officer, Highlands Rehabilitation Hospital, El Paso, TX, p. A602

RICHARD, Andrea J., M.D., Chief Medical Officer, Warren State Hospital, Warren, PA, p. A543

RICHARD, Angelique, R.N., Ph.D., Vice President Clinical Nursing, Chief Nursing Officer and Associate Dean for Practice, College of Nursing, Rush Children's Hospital, IL, p. A179

RICHARD, Brandi, Chief Nursing Officer, Michiana Behavioral Health Center, Plymouth, IN, p. A213

RICHARD, Brent, Administrative Director Information Systems, Southern Ohio Medical Center, Portsmouth, OH, p. A489

RICHARD, Christina, Market Chief Executive Officer, Kindred Hospital Tarrant County-Arlington, Arlington, TX, p. A584

RICHARD, Scott, Vice President Finance and Chief Financial Officer, St. Elizabeth Hospital, Gonzales, LA, p. A268

RICHARD, Thomas, Director Budget and Revenue Cycle, Redwood Area Hospital, Redwood Falls, MN, p. A338

RICHARD, Tim, IT Coordinator, Crawford Memorial Hospital, Robinson, IL, p. A194

RICHARDS, Craig A., Chief Executive Officer, Mildred Mitchell-Bateman Hospital, Huntington, WV, p. A684

RICHARDS, Frank
Chief Information Officer, Geisinger Wyoming Valley Medical Center, Wilkes Barre, PA, p. A544
Chief Information Officer, Geisinger-Shamokin Area Community Hospital, PA, p. A523

RICHARDS, Jaena, Chief Financial Officer, Deer Lodge Medical Center, Deer Lodge, MT, p. A375

RICHARDS, Jon, Chief Financial Officer, Tennova Newport Medical Center, Newport, TN, p. A578

RICHARDS, Jonathan, Chief Financial Officer, David Grant Usaf Medical Center, Travis Afb, CA, p. A92

RICHARDS, Judith, Director of Nursing, Adcare Hospital Of Worcester, Worcester, MA, p. A306

RICHARDS, Kelly, MSN
Senior Vice President and Chief Nursing Officer, Kimball-Ridge Center, IA, p. A230
Senior Vice President and Chief Nursing Officer, Mercy Hospital Of Franciscan Sisters, Oelwein, IA, p. A227
Senior Vice President and Chief Nursing Officer, Sartori Memorial Hospital, Cedar Falls, IA, p. A218

RICHARDS, Kyle, Chief Executive Officer, Lake Region Healthcare, Fergus Falls, MN, p. A331

RICHARDS, Mandy, R.N., MSN, Vice President Patient Care, United Hospital, Saint Paul, MN, p. A339

RICHARDS, Nate, Director Information Technology, Mitchell County Hospital Health Systems, Beloit, KS, p. A232

RICHARDS, Sheila K, Human Resources Director, Dallas Medical Center, Dallas, TX, p. A596

RICHARDS, Stanlee, R.N., Chief Nurse Executive, Henry J. Carter Specialty Hospital & Nursing Facility, NY, p. A435

RICHARDS, Suzanne, R.N., M.P.H., FACHE, Chief Executive Officer, Victor Valley Global Medical Center, Victorville, CA, p. A94

RICHARDS, Thom, Director Information Technology, Knoxville Hospital & Clinics, Knoxville, IA, p. A225

RICHARDSON, Crystal, Chief Nursing Officer, Vibra Hospital Of Richmond, Richmond, VA, p. A665

RICHARDSON, David, M.D., Chief of Staff, Delta Medical Center, Memphis, TN, p. A575

RICHARDSON, Denise, R.N., MSN, Senior Vice President and Chief Nursing Officer, St. Barnabas Hospital, New York (Includes All Hospitals Located Within The Five Boroughs), NY, p. A437

RICHARDSON, Dorothy, Director Human Resources, Van Matre Healthsouth Rehabilitation Hospital, Rockford, IL, p. A195

RICHARDSON, Dwayne, Chief Operating Officer, Placentia-Linda Hospital, Placentia, CA, p. A78

RICHARDSON, Greg H, Assistant Administrator Human Resources, Piedmont Newton Hospital, Covington, GA, p. A151

RICHARDSON, Irene, Chief Executive Officer, Memorial Hospital Of Sweetwater County, Rock Springs, WY, p. A709

RICHARDSON, James, Chief Medical Officer, Holy Cross Hospital, Chicago, IL, p. A177

RICHARDSON, Judy, M.D., President Medical Staff, Mid-Columbia Medical Center, The Dalles, OR, p. A518

RICHARDSON, Karen K., Senior Vice President and Chief Financial Officer, Depaul Center, TX, p. A642

RICHARDSON, Keith, President and Chief Executive Officer, East Liverpool City Hospital, East Liverpool, OH, p. A482

RICHARDSON, Kevin, M.D., Chief of Staff, Southwest Mississippi Regional Medical Center, Mccomb, MS, p. A350

RICHARDSON, Kirk, R.N.
Vice President, Chief Operating Officer and Chief Nursing Officer, Bronson South Haven Hospital, South Haven, MI, p. A323
Vice President, Chief Operating Officer, and Chief Nursing Officer, Bronson Lakeview Hospital, Paw Paw, MI, p. A320
RICHARDSON, Kristy, Director of Nursing, De Queen Medical Center, De Queen-Sevier County, AR, p. A41
RICHARDSON, Nathaniel, Jr, President, Decatur Morgan Hospital-West, AL, p. A16
RICHARDSON, Pamela, Business Manager, Central Regional Hospital, Butner, NC, p. A448
RICHARDSON, Paul McKinley, Jr, Vice President, Medical Affairs, Conway Medical Center, Conway, SC, p. A552
RICHARDSON, Robert, Information Technology Administrator, Porter Regional Hospital, Valparaiso, IN, p. A215
RICHARDSON, Rodney, Director of Information Technology, Baptist Health Corbin, Corbin, KY, p. A250
RICHARDSON, Sarah, Director Information Systems, Belton Regional Medical Center, Belton, MO, p. A355
RICHARDSON, Stanley, Coordinator Human Resources and Payroll Benefits, Kindred Hospital-San Antonio, San Antonio, TX, p. A633
RICHARDSON, Terika, MPH, President, Advocate Lutheran General Hospital, Park Ridge, IL, p. A192
RICHARDSON, Terrie, Coordinator Human Resources, Select Specialty Hospital-Augusta, Augusta, GA, p. A147
RICHARDSON, Timothy J, M.D., Chief of Staff, Maine Veterans Affairs Medical Center, Augusta, ME, p. A282
RICHARDSON, Todd, Chief Information Officer, Aspirus Medford Hospital & Clinics, Inc., Medford, WI, p. A697
RICHASON, Amie A
Vice President Human Resources, Leesburg Regional Medical Center, Leesburg, FL, p. A128
Vice President Human Resources, The Villages Regional Hospital, The Villages, FL, p. A142
RICHAUD, Benjamin, Interim Chief Executive Officer, River Region West Campus, MS, p. A354
RICHBOURG, Gail A, Director Human Resources, Mcleod Health Clarendon, Manning, SC, p. A555
RICHBURG, Melanie, Chief Executive Officer, Lynn County Hospital District, Tahoka, TX, p. A638
RICHCREEK, Keith, Manager Technical Services, Lafayette Regional Health Center, Lexington, MO, p. A363
RICHENS, Ken, Chief Information Officer, Central Valley Medical Center, Nephi, UT, p. A648
RICHER, R David, Chief Executive Officer, Cleveland Clinic Rehabilitation Hospital, OH, p. A471
RICHERT, Ed, M.D., Chief of Staff, Modoc Medical Center, Alturas, CA, p. A50
RICHETTI, Michael, Chief Financial Officer, Chilton Medical Center, Pompton Plains, NJ, p. A410
RICHHART, David, Chief Financial Officer, North Valley Hospital, Whitefish, MT, p. A380
RICHMAN, Craig, M.D., Medical Director, Meadows Psychiatric Center, Centre Hall, PA, p. A522
RICHMAN, Jonathan, M.D., Chief of Staff, Chase County Community Hospital, Imperial, NE, p. A385
RICHMAN, Timothy
President and Chief Executive Officer, Ascension Southeast Wisconsin Hospital - Elmbrook Campus, Brookfield, WI, p. A690
President, Wheaton Franciscan Healthcare - St. Joseph'S, Milwaukee, WI, p. A699
RICHMOND, Andy, Director Information Technology, Choctaw Memorial Hospital, Hugo, OK, p. A500
RICHMOND, Brett, Senior Vice President, Chief Operating Officer, Fremont Health, Fremont, NE, p. A384
RICHMOND, Craig, Senior Vice President and Chief Financial Officer, Metrohealth Medical Center, Cleveland, OH, p. A477
RICHMOND, Ira, Associate Director Patient Care Services, Veterans Affairs Medical Center, PA, p. A538
RICHOUX, Jacquelyn, Chief Financial Officer, Lady Of The Sea General Hospital, Cut Off, LA, p. A266
RICHTER, Daniel, M.D., Chief of Staff, Chi Health Missouri Valley, Missouri Valley, IA, p. A226
RICHTER, Karen S., Vice President, Human Resources, Mary Free Bed Rehabilitation Hospital, Grand Rapids, MI, p. A314
RICHTER, Thomas V., Chief Executive Officer, Pioneer Memorial Hospital And Health Services, Viborg, SD, p. A565
RICK, Bob, Vice President Information Technology, Usmd Hospital At Arlington, Arlington, TX, p. A584
RICKARD, Sheryl, Chief Executive Officer, Bonner General Hospital, Sandpoint, ID, p. A172
RICKENS, Chris, R.N., MS, Senior Vice President and Chief Nursing Officer, Upmc Altoona, Altoona, PA, p. A520

RICKS, Edward, Vice President and Chief Information Officer, Beaufort Memorial Hospital, Beaufort, SC, p. A549
RICKS, Loretha, Human Resources Supervisor, Southampton Memorial Hospital, Franklin, VA, p. A658
RICKS, Michael, Chief Operating Officer, Hoag Hospital Irvine, CA, p. A75
RICO, Carrie, Chief Human Resource Officer, Keefe Memorial Hospital, Cheyenne Wells, CO, p. A97
RICO, Richard, Vice President and Chief Financial Officer, Sky Lakes Medical Center, Klamath Falls, OR, p. A514
RIDALL, Jackie, Director Human Resources, Berwick Hospital Center, Berwick, PA, p. A520
RIDDER, Terri, Director Human Resources, St. Francis Memorial Hospital, West Point, NE, p. A391
RIDDLE, Kent, Chief Executive Officer, Mary Free Bed Rehabilitation Hospital, Grand Rapids, MI, p. A314
RIDGE, Frederick R., M.D., Chief of Staff, Greene County General Hospital, Linton, IN, p. A210
RIDGE, Lisa, Chief Executive Officer, Van Diest Medical Center, Webster City, IA, p. A231
RIDGWAY, Diane, President, Methodist Le Bonheur Germantown Hospital, TN, p. A575
RIDLEN, Deborah, CPA, Vice President Finance and Chief Financial Officer, Schneck Medical Center, Seymour, IN, p. A214
RIDLEY, John, Executive Vice President & Chief Operating Officer, Decatur Memorial Hospital, Decatur, IL, p. A180
RIDLEY, Pam, Director Information Systems, Henry County Medical Center, Paris, TN, p. A578
RIDLEY, Zena, Director Human Resources, Harbor Oaks Hospital, New Baltimore, MI, p. A320
RIDNER, Sheila, R.N., Director of Nursing, Unity Psychiatric Care-Columbia, Columbia, TN, p. A568
RIEBER, Dan, Chief Financial Officer, Uchealth Memorial Hospital North, CO, p. A98
RIEBER, Jim, Director Information Systems, Perham Health, Perham, MN, p. A337
RIECHERS, Thomas, M.D., Chief Medical Staff, Mercy Hospital Washington, Washington, MO, p. A372
RIECK, Amy, Human Resources Officer, Greater Regional Medical Center, Creston, IA, p. A220
RIECK MCFARLAND, Anne, President and Chief Executive Officer, Lifescape, Sioux Falls, SD, p. A563
RIEDEL, Sherry, Chief Financial Management Service, John D. Dingell Veterans Affairs Medical Center, Detroit, MI, p. A311
RIEDLINGER, Floyd, Director Human Resources, West Jefferson Medical Center, Marrero, LA, p. A273
RIEDLINGER, Joann, Vice President Nursing and Manager Information Systems, Bucyrus Hospital, Bucyrus, OH, p. A473
RIEG, Kevin, M.D., President Medical Staff, Via Christi Rehabilitation Hospital, Wichita, KS, p. A248
RIEGE, Michael J., Chief Executive Officer, Virginia Gay Hospital, Vinton, IA, p. A230
RIEGER, Bill, Chief Information Officer, Flagler Hospital, Saint Augustine, FL, p. A137
RIEGER, Tim, Chief Financial Officer, St. Rita's Medical Center, Lima, OH, p. A485
RIEGERT, Patricia, Director Fiscal Services, Danville State Hospital, Danville, PA, p. A523
RIEKE, Diane, Director Patient Care Services, Patients' Hospital Of Redding, Redding, CA, p. A80
RIEKS, Katie, Chief Nursing Officer, Hansen Family Hospital, Iowa Falls, IA, p. A225
RIER, Kirk, Chief Operating Officer, Iowa Specialty Hospital-Clarion, Clarion, IA, p. A219
RIES, Heather, MSN, R.N., Chief Nursing Officer, Regional Medical Center, Manchester, IA, p. A226
RIESER, Michael, M.D., Medical Director, Ridge Behavioral Health System, Lexington, KY, p. A255
RIETMAN, Cheryl, Chief Administrative Officer, Deaconess Cross Pointe Center, IN, p. A203
RIETSEMA, Wouter, M.D., Chief Quality and Information Officer, The University Of Vermont Health Network-Champlain Valley Physicians Hospital, Plattsburgh, NY, p. A440
RIEVES, Cheryl, Chief Nurse Executive Lorain Region, Mercy Allen Hospital, Oberlin, OH, p. A488
RIFFLE, Virginia, Vice President Patient Care Services, Samaritan North Lincoln Hospital, Lincoln City, OR, p. A514
RIFKIN, Scott, Chief Executive Officer, Anaheim Global Medical Center, Anaheim, CA, p. A50
RIGAS, Warren Alston, Executive Vice President and Chief Operating Officer, Floyd Medical Center, Rome, GA, p. A159
RIGDON, Alice W., Vice President Finance, Saint Joseph Hospital, Denver, CO, p. A99
RIGDON, Edward, M.D., Chief Medical Officer, Merit Health Rankin, Brandon, MS, p. A344

RIGDON, Pam, Director Nursing, Laird Hospital, Union, MS, p. A353
RIGGIN, Andrew, Chief Executive Officer, Bennett County Hospital And Nursing Home, Martin, SD, p. A562
RIGGLE, Vikki, Director Human Resources, Eastern Louisiana Mental Health System, Jackson, LA, p. A269
RIGGS, Jennifer, R.N., Chief Nurse Officer, Mainegeneral Medical Center-Augusta Campus, ME, p. A282
RIGNEY, Alice, Chief Human Resources Officer, Abbeville Area Medical Center, Abbeville, SC, p. A549
RIGSBEE CARROLL, Cristina, Chief Operating Officer, Granville Health System, Oxford, NC, p. A458
RIGSBY, Diane, Chief Information Officer, Capital Hospice, Arlington, VA, p. A655
RILEY, Colleen, M.D., Medical Director, Laguna Honda Hospital And Rehabilitation Center, San Francisco, CA, p. A85
RILEY, James, Chief Operating Officer, Piedmont Medical Center, Rock Hill, SC, p. A556
RILEY, Jennifer, Vice President Operations, Memorial Regional Health, Craig, CO, p. A98
RILEY, Jim, Director Information Technology, Wagoner Community Hospital, Wagoner, OK, p. A510
RILEY, Joe B., FACHE, President and Chief Executive Officer, Jackson Hospital And Clinic, Montgomery, AL, p. A21
RILEY, Kenneth, Director Information Systems, Baystate Wing Hospital, Palmer, MA, p. A303
RILEY, Linzie, Interim Human Resource Manager, Lifecare Hospitals Of North Texas-Plano, TX, p. A596
RILEY, Mike, President and Chief Operating Officer, Novant Health Huntersville Medical Center, Huntersville, NC, p. A455
RILEY, Randy
Chief Financial Officer, Center For Behavioral Medicine, Kansas City, MO, p. A361
Fiscal and Administrative Manager, Northwest Missouri Psychiatric Rehabilitation Center, Saint Joseph, MO, p. A367
RILEY, Robert, Interim Chief Financial Officer, Doctors Hospital Of Jefferson, LA, p. A274
RILEY, Susan, Director Human Resources, Healthsouth Rehabilitation Hospital Of Miami, Cutler Bay, FL, p. A120
RILEY, Wayne J., M.D., M.P.H., President, University Hospital Of Brooklyn At Long Island College Hospital, NY, p. A437
RILEY, William, M.D., Jr, Chief of Staff, Memorial Hermann Sugar Land Hospital, Sugar Land, TX, p. A637
RILEY-BROWN, Michelle
President, Texas Children's Hospital The Woodlands, TX, p. A613
President, Texas Children's Hospital West Campus, TX, p. A613
RIMOVSKY, A. Jay., Chief Executive Officer, Central Texas Rehabilitation Hospital, Austin, TX, p. A585
RINALDI, Anthony, Executive Vice President, Fairview Hospital, Great Barrington, MA, p. A300
RINALDI, Blythe, Vice President, Mayo Clinic Health System - Northland In Barron, Barron, WI, p. A690
RINDELS, Doris, Vice President Operations, Unitypoint Health - Grinnell Regional Medical Center, Grinnell, IA, p. A223
RINDFLEISCH, Jody, Manager Human Resources, Redwood Area Hospital, Redwood Falls, MN, p. A338
RINDLISBACHER, Diane, Manager Information Systems, Orem Community Hospital, Orem, UT, p. A648
RINEHART, Linda, Director Human Resources, Healthsouth Treasure Coast Rehabilitation Hospital, Vero Beach, FL, p. A142
RINEHART, Rick, Vice President, Chief Information Officer, Carle Foundation Hospital, Urbana, IL, p. A197
RINEY, Jeremy, Chief Executive Officer, Connally Memorial Medical Center, Floresville, TX, p. A603
RING, Brian K, Chief Operating Officer, Henry Community Health, New Castle, IN, p. A212
RING, Caroline A, Chief Nursing Officer, Spectrum Health Big Rapids Hospital, Big Rapids, MI, p. A308
RINGE, Kathy, Director Human Resources, Sage Rehabilitation Hospital, Baton Rouge, LA, p. A264
RINGER, Dave, M.D., Chief of Staff, St. Mary's Good Samaritan Hospital, Greensboro, GA, p. A154
RINGO, Jonathan, M.D., President and Chief Operating Officer, Sinai Hospital Of Baltimore, Baltimore, MD, p. A289
RINKE, Joseph
Director Human Resources, Streamwood Behavioral Health Center, Streamwood, IL, p. A197
Director of Human Resources, Riveredge Hospital, Forest Park, IL, p. A183
RINKENBERGER, Sean, Chief Financial Officer, St. Andrew's Health Center, Bottineau, ND, p. A464
RINKER, John M., Chief Medical Officer, Osf Saint James - John W. Albrecht Medical Center, Pontiac, IL, p. A194

RINKS, Kevin, Chief Executive Officer, West Tennessee Healthcare North Hospital, TN, p. A571

RINTOUL, Alexander M., Chief Executive Officer, The Medical Center At Elizabeth Place, Dayton, OH, p. A481

RION, Trey, Chief Information Officer, West Calcasieu Cameron Hospital, Sulphur, LA, p. A280

RIOS, Cindy, Chief Financial Officer, Alliancehealth Durant, Durant, OK, p. A498

RIOS, Damaris, Executive Nursing Director, Hospital Metropolitano Dr. Susoni, Arecibo, PR, p. A712

RIOS, Jose C, Director Information Services, Murray Medical Center, Chatsworth, GA, p. A150

RIOS, Margot, R.N., Chief Nursing Officer, Christus Spohn Hospital Alice, Alice, TX, p. A582

RIOS, Mary, R.N., Interim Director of Nursing, Cordova Community Medical Center, Cordova, AK, p. A26

RIPPERGER, Ted, Administrative Director Human Resources, Atrium Medical Center, Middletown, OH, p. A487

RIPPEY, Wesley E, M.D., Chief Medical Officer, Adventist Medical Center-Portland, Portland, OR, p. A516

RIPSCH, Sue, Senior Vice President & Chief Operating Officer, Mercyhealth Hospital - Rockton Avenue, Rockford, IL, p. A194

RISBY, Emile, M.D., Clinical Director, Georgia Regional Hospital At Atlanta, Decatur, GA, p. A152

RISHA, Holly, Administrative Director Human Resources, College Hospital Cerritos, Cerritos, CA, p. A54

RISINGER, Jeff, Director Human Resources, Uams Medical Center, Little Rock-Pulaski County, AR, p. A45

RISK, Carl W., II, President, Elkhart General Hospital, Elkhart, IN, p. A202

RISKA, Marilouise, Chief Executive Officer, Select Specialty Hospital-Northwest Detroit, Detroit, MI, p. A311

RISLOW, Deb, Chief Information Officer, Gundersen Lutheran Medical Center, La Crosse, WI, p. A695

RISOVI, Carol, Human Resources, Chi St Alexius Health Carrington Medical Center, Carrington, ND, p. A464

RISSE, Thomas, Chief Financial Officer and Vice President Business Services, Kaiser Permanente Medical Center, Honolulu, HI, p. A164

RITCHEY, Jim, Director Human Resources, Sky Ridge Medical Center, Lone Tree, CO, p. A103

RITCHIE, Bruce, Vice President of Finance and Chief Financial Officer, Peninsula Regional Medical Center, Salisbury, MD, p. A294

RITCHIE, Eric, M.D., Clinical Director, Chinle Comprehensive Health Care Facility, Chinle, AZ, p. A28

RITCHIE, Jill, Director of Nursing, Ellinwood District Hospital, Ellinwood, KS, p. A234

RITCHIE, Jim, Director Management Information Systems, South Shore Hospital, Chicago, IL, p. A179

RITENOUR, Chad W.M., M.D., Chief Medical Officer, Emory Wesley Woods Geriatric Hospital, GA, p. A146

RITON, John, Director Information Services, Memorial Hospital Of Tampa, Tampa, FL, p. A141

RITTENOUR, Melanie, Director Human Resources, Paulding County Hospital, Paulding, OH, p. A489

RITTER, Jane, R.N., Vice President, Patient Care and Clinical Services, United Regional Health Care System-Eleventh Street Campus, TX, p. A644

RITTER, Robert G, FACHE, Associate Director, Harry S. Truman Memorial Veterans Hospital, Columbia, MO, p. A358

RITTMAN, Todd, Director of Nursing, Larue D. Carter Memorial Hospital, Indianapolis, IN, p. A207

RITZUS, Michael, Chief Executive Officer, Elmore Community Hospital, Wetumpka, AL, p. A24

RIVAS, Eloy, Director of Information Systems, Venice Regional Bayfront Health, Venice, FL, p. A142

RIVAS, Jose, M.D., Chief of Staff, Community Hospital Of Huntington Park, Huntington Park, CA, p. A62

RIVAS, Ramon Rodriguez, M.D., Medical Director, Hospital San Cristobal, Coto Laurel, PR, p. A713

RIVERA, Angela, Chief Nursing Officer, Beckley Arh Hospital, Beckley, WV, p. A681

RIVERA, Anthony, Director Human Resources, Hartgrove Hospital, Chicago, IL, p. A177

RIVERA, Ashley, Chief Financial Officer and Chief Executive Officer, Kittson Memorial Healthcare Center, Hallock, MN, p. A332

RIVERA, Christina, Director Human Resources, Southwest General Hospital, San Antonio, TX, p. A634

RIVERA, Cristina, Chief Executive Officer, Rio Grande Regional Hospital, Mcallen, TX, p. A623

RIVERA, Edgar, Chief Information Officer, Brownfield Regional Medical Center, Brownfield, TX, p. A590

RIVERA, Enrique, Chief Financial Officer, Bella Vista Hospital, Mayaguez, PR, p. A714

RIVERA, Ivonne, Director Finance, Hospital Oriente, Humacao, PR, p. A713

RIVERA, Jamie, Chief Financial Officer, Hospital Pavia Arecibo, Arecibo, PR, p. A712

RIVERA, Joe, Chief Information Technology Officer, Laredo Medical Center, Laredo, TX, p. A619

RIVERA, Jose Garcia, Director Human Resources, Hospital Buen Samaritano, Aguadilla, PR, p. A711

RIVERA, Luis, Director Human Resources, San Juan Capestrano Hospital, San Juan, PR, p. A716

RIVERA, Maria, Director Human Resources, Westside Regional Medical Center, Plantation, FL, p. A136

RIVERA, Zamarys, R.N., Chief Nursing Officer, Healthsouth Rehabilitation Hospital Of San Juan, San Juan, PR, p. A715

RIVERA MALDONADO, Luis, Executive Director, Bella Vista Hospital, Mayaguez, PR, p. A714

RIVERA-POL, Noriselle, Vice President Finance, Hospital Manati Medical Center, Manati, PR, p. A714

RIVERS, Eric, Chief Information Officer, Mission Community Hospital, Los Angeles, CA, p. A68

RIVERS, Jan, Director Human Resources, Ochsner Medical Center - Baton Rouge, Baton Rouge, LA, p. A263

RIVERS, Ken, Chief Operating Officer, Fontana Medical Center, Kaiser Permanente Ontario Medical Center, CA, p. A58

RIVERS, Nikki, R.N., Regional Chief Nursing Officer, South Market, Seton Edgar B. Davis Hospital, Luling, TX, p. A622

RIVES, Patricia, R.N., MSN, Chief Executive Officer, Community Hospital Of Huntington Park, Huntington Park, CA, p. A62

RIVOIRE, John, R.N., MSN, Administrator, Louisiana Extended Care Hospital Of Natchitoches, Natchitoches, LA, p. A275

RIZK, Magdy, M.D., Chief of Staff, West Houston Medical Center, Houston, TX, p. A614

RIZK, Norman, M.D., Chief Medical Officer, Stanford Health Care, Palo Alto, CA, p. A77

RIZK, Rob, Director Information Technology, Good Shepherd Health Care System, Hermiston, OR, p. A513

RIZKALLA, Nasseem, M.D., Chief Medical Officer, Aspirus Iron River Hospitals & Clinics, Inc., Iron River, MI, p. A316

RIZZO, Frank, Chief Financial Officer, Central Region, North Shore University Hospital, Manhasset, NY, p. A429

RIZZO, Theresa, Administrator, Franklin County Memorial Hospital, Franklin, NE, p. A383

RIZZUTO, George, CPA, Interim Chief Executive Officer, St. Christopher's Hospital For Children, Philadelphia, PA, p. A536

ROACH, Crystal, Chief Financial Officer, Trustpoint Rehabilitation Hospital Of Lubbock, Lubbock, TX, p. A621

ROACH, David, Vice President Information Systems, Kadlec Regional Medical Center, Richland, WA, p. A676

ROACH, Dee A, M.D., Chief of Staff, Mitchell County Hospital, Colorado City, TX, p. A593

ROACH, Donna
Chief Information Officer, Sacred Heart Hospital Pensacola, Pensacola, FL, p. A136
Chief Information Officer, St. Joseph Campus, KS, p. A248

ROACH, Geoff, Director Human Resources, Barrett Hospital & Healthcare, Dillon, MT, p. A375

ROACH, Maureen, Senior Chief Financial Officer, Kindred Hospital St. Louis-St. Anthony'S, MO, p. A368

ROACH, Renee
System Vice President, Human Resources, Ssm Health St. Clare Hospital - Fenton, Fenton, MO, p. A359
System Vice President, Ssm Health St. Joseph Hospital - Lake Saint Louis, Lake Saint Louis, MO, p. A363

ROACH, Steven P., FACHE, President and Chief Executive Officer, Umass Memorial-Marlborough Hospital, Marlborough, MA, p. A301

ROADER, Charles, Vice President Finance, Edgerton Hospital And Health Services, Edgerton, WI, p. A692

ROAN, Linda Lyn, Chief Nursing Officer, East Morgan County Hospital, Brush, CO, p. A97

ROANHORSE, Anslem, Chief Executive Officer, U.S. Public Health Service Indian Hospital, Crownpoint, NM, p. A416

ROARK, Chris, Chief Information Services, Stillwater Medical Center, Stillwater, OK, p. A507

ROARK, Robert R, Director Human Resources, Laughlin Memorial Hospital, Greeneville, TN, p. A570

ROARTY, Maureen, Executive Vice President Human Resources, Nassau University Medical Center, East Meadow, NY, p. A426

ROB, Lee, Director Human Resources, Monroe Regional Hospital, Aberdeen, MS, p. A343

ROBB, Joy, Vice President Human Resources, Prairie View, Newton, KS, p. A242

ROBBINS, Dan, Information Technology and Account Executive, St. Vincent Medical Center, Los Angeles, CA, p. A70

ROBBINS, Donald, M.D., Jr
Chief Staff, Hills & Dales General Hospital, Cass City, MI, p. A309

Chief Executive Officer, Lawrence County Memorial Hospital, Lawrenceville, IL, p. A187

ROBBINS, Joe, M.D., Vice President Medical Affairs, Sentara Williamsburg Regional Medical Center, Williamsburg, VA, p. A668

ROBBINS, Shannon, Chief Operating Officer, Ohio Hospital For Psychiatry, Columbus, OH, p. A478

ROBEANO, Karen, R.N., Chief Nursing Officer and Vice President Patient Care Services, Firsthealth Moore Regional Hospital - Richmond, NC, p. A458

ROBEL, Susan M, R.N., Executive Vice President and Chief Nursing Officer, Geisinger-Shamokin Area Community Hospital, PA, p. A523

ROBERGE, Jeremy
Chief Financial Officer, Huggins Hospital, Wolfeboro, NH, p. A401
Director Reimbursement, Androscoggin Valley Hospital, Berlin, NH, p. A398
President and Chief Executive Officer, Huggins Hospital, Wolfeboro, NH, p. A401

ROBERSON, Ed, Director Information Systems, Houston Northwest Medical Center, Houston, TX, p. A611

ROBERSON, Joe, Chief Executive Officer, Encompass Health Rehabilitation Hospital Of Abilene, Abilene, TX, p. A582

ROBERSON, Lynda, Senior Program Director, Rusk State Hospital, Rusk, TX, p. A631

ROBERSON, Meika, M.D., Chief Medical Officer, Carepoint Health Hoboken University Medical Center, Hoboken, NJ, p. A406

ROBERSON, Scotty, Assistant Administrator and Chief Nursing Officer, University Of South Alabama Children's And Women's Hospital, Mobile, AL, p. A20

ROBERT, Jeffery, Chief Operaing Officer, Swedish/Issaquah, Issaquah, WA, p. A672

ROBERT, Thomas W., Senior Vice President of Finance and Chief Financial Officer, Mercy Medical Center, Springfield, MA, p. A304

ROBERTS, Allyson, CPA, Chief Financial Officer, Nor-Lea Hospital District, Lovington, NM, p. A418

ROBERTS, Andrew, Interim Chief Human Resources Officer, Veterans Affairs Gulf Coast Veterans Health Care System, Biloxi, MS, p. A343

ROBERTS, Barbara, Chief Financial Officer, Robley Rex Veterans Affairs Medical Center, Louisville, KY, p. A256

ROBERTS, Bert, Controller, Miracle Mile Medical Center, Los Angeles, CA, p. A68

ROBERTS, Brad, Network Administrator, Swisher Memorial Hospital District, Tulia, TX, p. A640

ROBERTS, Cassidi, R.N., Chief Nursing Officer, Wysong Campus, TX, p. A623

ROBERTS, Cathy, Vice President Mission Integration and Human Resources, Mercy Regional Medical Center, Durango, CO, p. A99

ROBERTS, Charles, M.D.
Executive Vice President and Executive Medical Director, Children's Mercy Hospital Kansas City, Kansas City, MO, p. A361
Medical Director, Children's Mercy Hospital Kansas, Overland Park, KS, p. A243

ROBERTS, Curt L., Chief Executive Officer, Cornerstone Hospital Of Round Rock, TX, p. A585

ROBERTS, Cyndi, Director Human Resources, Medical City Fort Worth, Fort Worth, TX, p. A605

ROBERTS, David, M.D., Chief Medical Officer, West Tennessee Healthcare North Hospital, TN, p. A571

ROBERTS, David J., M.D., President, Union Campus, MA, p. A304

ROBERTS, Deborah, R.N., Chief Nursing Officer, The Core Institute Specialty Hospital, Phoenix, AZ, p. A34

ROBERTS, Debra, Director of Human Resources, Chi St. Luke's Health-Lakeside Hospital, The Woodlands, TX, p. A639

ROBERTS, Greg, Superintendent, Oregon State Hospital, Salem, OR, p. A517

ROBERTS, Jason
Director Information System, Carson Valley Medical Center, Gardnerville, NV, p. A393
Director of Information Services, Barton Memorial Hospital, South Lake Tahoe, CA, p. A90

ROBERTS, Jeff, Director Information Technology, Pinckneyville Community Hospital, Pinckneyville, IL, p. A193

ROBERTS, Jeffrey, Chief Executive Officer, Emcompass Health Rehabilitation Hospital Of East, Mesa, AZ, p. A31

ROBERTS, Kathryn, Director Human Resources, Mercy Medical Center-Dubuque, Dubuque, IA, p. A222

ROBERTS, Kenneth D., President, John T. Mather Memorial Hospital, Port Jefferson, NY, p. A440

ROBERTS, Kevin A., FACHE
President and Chief Executive Officer, Metroplex Behavioral Health Center, TX, p. A617
President and Chief Executive Officer, Rollins Brook Community Hospital, Lampasas, TX, p. A619

ROBERTS, Kim, Chief Strategy Officer, Lucile Salter Packard Children's Hospital Stanford, Palo Alto, CA, p. A77

ROBERTS, Krista, Chief Executive Officer, St. Mary's Regional Medical Center, Enid, OK, p. A498

ROBERTS, Laurel, R.N., MSN, Chief Nursing Officer, Rolling Hills Hospital, Franklin, TN, p. A570

ROBERTS, Mark, Chief Operaing Officer, Memorial Satilla Health, Waycross, GA, p. A163

ROBERTS, Matthew S., Chief Executive Officer, Raleigh General Hospital, Beckley, WV, p. A681

ROBERTS, Michael, Chief Information Officer, Highlands Regional Medical Center, Prestonsburg, KY, p. A259

ROBERTS, Nancy, Chief Operating Officer, Children At Providence St. Vincent, OR, p. A516

ROBERTS, Pamela W., Chief Executive Officer, Henderson County Community Hospital, Lexington, TN, p. A573

ROBERTS, Paul L., Director, Cheyenne Veterans Affairs Medical Center, Cheyenne, WY, p. A708

ROBERTS, Paula, Chief Nursing Officer, Cumberland Hospital For Children And Adolescents, New Kent, VA, p. A661

ROBERTS, Phillip G, Vice President Finance and Chief Financial Officer, Columbus Community Hospital, Inc., Columbus, WI, p. A691

ROBERTS, Rob, Director Information Technology, Benson Hospital, Benson, AZ, p. A28

ROBERTS, Robert C
Senior Vice President Financial Services, Baptist Health Medical Center - North Little Rock, North Little Rock-Pulaski County, AR, p. A47
Senior Vice President Financial Services, Baptist Health Medical Center-Little Rock, Little Rock-Pulaski County, AR, p. A45
Senior Vice President, Baptist Health Rehabilitation Institute, Little Rock-Pulaski County, AR, p. A45
Vice President and Chief Financial Officer, Baptist Health Medical Center-Arkadelphia, Arkadelphia, AR, p. A39
Vice President, Baptist Health Extended Care Hospital, Little Rock-Pulaski County, AR, p. A44

ROBERTS, Robin, Executive Director of Patient Services, Takoma Regional Hospital, Greeneville, TN, p. A570

ROBERTS, Roslyn, Manager, Northside Hospital-Cherokee, Canton, GA, p. A149

ROBERTS, Sally, R.N., Director of Nursing, Abrom Kaplan Memorial Hospital, Kaplan, LA, p. A270

ROBERTS, Shayna Brooke, Director Human Resources, Northeastern Health System Sequoyah, Sallisaw, OK, p. A506

ROBERTS, Teresa, Chief Financial Officer, Ringgold County Hospital, Mount Ayr, IA, p. A226

ROBERTSHAW, Hazel, R.N., Ph.D., Chief Nursing Officer, Vice President Patient Services, F. F. Thompson Hospital, Canandaigua, NY, p. A424

ROBERTSON, Carla, Chief Operating Officer and Chief Financial Officer, Saline Memorial Hospital, Benton-Saline County, AR, p. A39

ROBERTSON, Casey, Chief Executive Officer, Longview Regional Medical Center, Longview, TX, p. A620

ROBERTSON, Darcy, Chief Financial Officer, Page Hospital, Page, AZ, p. A32

ROBERTSON, Elizabeth, Area Controller, Encompass Health Rehabilitation Hospital Of Dallas, Dallas, TX, p. A596

ROBERTSON, James A., Jr, President and Chief Executive Officer, Bothwell Regional Health Center, Sedalia, MO, p. A370

ROBERTSON, John L., Administrator, West Central Georgia Regional Hospital, Columbus, GA, p. A151

ROBERTSON, Larry, President, Texas Health Center For Diagnostic & Surgery, Plano, TX, p. A629

ROBERTSON, Laura, R.N., Chief Executive Officer, Samaritan Behavioral Health Center-Desert Samaritan Medical Center, AZ, p. A31

ROBERTSON, Michael, Chief Executive Officer, Piedmont Newnan Hospital, Newnan, GA, p. A158

ROBERTSON, Misty, R.N., Chief Nursing Officer, Bonner General Hospital, Sandpoint, ID, p. A172

ROBERTSON, Pamela, Chief Executive Officer, Pathways Treatment Center, MT, p. A377

ROBERTSON, Steve
Executive Vice President and Chief Information Officer, Straub Medical Center, Honolulu, HI, p. A165
Executive Vice President Revenue Cycle Management and Chief Information Officer, Wilcox Medical Center, Lihue, HI, p. A166
Senior Vice President, Pali Momi Medical Center, Aiea, HI, p. A164
Vice President, Kapiolani Medical Center For Women & Children, Honolulu, HI, p. A164

ROBERTSTAD, John R., FACHE, Chief Executive Officer, Rehabilitation Hospital Of Wisconsin, Waukesha, WI, p. A705

ROBESON, Gail, Vice President Patient Services, Huron Regional Medical Center, Huron, SD, p. A561

ROBICHAUX, Andre'
Interim Administrator, Compass Behavioral Center Of Alexandria, Alexandria, LA, p. A262
Interim Administrator, Compass Behavioral Center Of Houma, Houma, LA, p. A268

ROBICHAUX, Jody, Chief Executive Officer, Amg Specialty Hospital-Houma, Houma, LA, p. A268

ROBICHAUX, Martha, Chief Human Resources Officer, John C. Fremont Healthcare District, Mariposa, CA, p. A71

ROBICHEAUX, James Warren., FACHE, Senior Administrator, Ut Health Pittsburg, Pittsburg, TX, p. A628

ROBINSON, Aaron
Chief Executive Officer, Health First Community Hospitals, Health First Cape Canaveral Hospital, Cocoa Beach, FL, p. A120
Chief Executive Officer, Health First Community Hospitals, Health First Palm Bay Hospital, Palm Bay, FL, p. A135
Chief Executive Officer, Health First Community Hospitals, Health First Viera Hospital, Melbourne, FL, p. A129

ROBINSON, Adam M.
Acting Director, Washington Dc Veterans Affairs Medical Center, Washington, DC, p. A116
Director, Veterans Affairs Maryland Health Care System-Perry Point Division, MD, p. A289

ROBINSON, Alan, Chief Financial Officer, Logan Regional Hospital, Logan, UT, p. A647

ROBINSON, Anitra, Human Resources Director, Healthsouth Rehabilitation Hospital Of Middletown, Middletown, DE, p. A113

ROBINSON, Anthony, Manager, Human Resources, Mercy Hospital Of Folsom, Folsom, CA, p. A58

ROBINSON, Bradley, Chief Financial Officer, Evans U.S. Army Community Hospital, Fort Carson, CO, p. A100

ROBINSON, Cliff, M.D., Chief of Staff, Tuskegee Division, AL, p. A21

ROBINSON, Dakota, Interim Chief Financial Officer and Controller, North Caddo Medical Center, Vivian, LA, p. A280

ROBINSON, David, D.O.
Medical Director, St. Joseph's Behavioral Health Center, Stockton, CA, p. A91
President Medical and Dental Staff, Community Hospital, Munster, IN, p. A212

ROBINSON, Elena, Chief Human Resources Officer, Hima San Pablo Caguas, Caguas, PR, p. A712

ROBINSON, Girard, M.D., Senior Vice President Medical and Clinical Affairs, Spring Harbor Hospital, Westbrook, ME, p. A286

ROBINSON, Glenn A., FACHE, President, Baylor Scott & White Medical Center - Hillcrest, Waco, TX, p. A642

ROBINSON, Herbert, M.D., Vice President, Chief Medical Information Officer, North Oaks Health System, North Oaks Rehabilitation Hospital, Hammond, LA, p. A268

ROBINSON, James L., III, PsyD, President, Presence Saint Joseph Hospital, Chicago, IL, p. A178

ROBINSON, Jeanne, Director Human Resources, Inova Fair Oaks Hospital, Fairfax, VA, p. A657

ROBINSON, Jennifer, Administrator, Unity Psychiatric Care-Clarksville, Clarksville, TN, p. A568

ROBINSON, Jennifer B, Vice President Human Resources, St. Petersburg General Hospital, Saint Petersburg, FL, p. A138

ROBINSON, Mark, FACHE
Chief Executive Officer, St. Mark's Hospital, Salt Lake City, UT, p. A651
Associate Administrator and Chief Financial Officer, William And Inez Mabie Skilled Nursing Facility, CA, p. A61

ROBINSON, Mary, Chief Nursing Officer and Vice President Patient Care Services, Texas Health Hospital Clearfork, TX, p. A605

ROBINSON, Patrick C., M.D., Chief Executive Officer, Oakdale Community Hospital, Oakdale, LA, p. A277

ROBINSON, Paul H, M.D., Medical Director, American Fork Hospital, American Fork, UT, p. A646

ROBINSON, Phil, Chief Financial Officer, Saint Agnes Medical Center, Fresno, CA, p. A59

ROBINSON, Phillip D., President, Lankenau Medical Center, Wynnewood, PA, p. A545

ROBINSON, Raymond, Chief Executive Officer, Pembroke Hospital, Pembroke, MA, p. A303

ROBINSON, Richard H., Chief Executive Officer, Astria Regional Medical Center, Yakima, WA, p. A680

ROBINSON, Stephen, Jr, FACHE, Chief Executive Officer, Ochsner Medical Center - Kenner, Kenner, LA, p. A270

ROBINSON, Susan Beth, Vice President Human Resources, St. Mary's Medical Center, Huntington, WV, p. A684

ROBINSON, Tim, Executive Vice President, Chief Financial and Administrative Officer and Treasurer, Nationwide Children's Hospital, Columbus, OH, p. A478

ROBINSON, Trena, Director, Human Resources, Central Texas Rehabilitation Hospital, Austin, TX, p. A585

ROBINSON, Vance, Chief Information Officer, Iberia Medical Center, New Iberia, LA, p. A275

ROBINSON, William, Director Human Resources, Healthsouth Rehabilitation Hospital Of Erie, Erie, PA, p. A525

ROBISON, Bruce, Vice President and Chief Information Officer, Cox Medical Center South, MO, p. A370

ROBISON, John, Chief Executive Officer, Clifton T. Perkins Hospital Center, Jessup, MD, p. A292

ROBISON, Keith, Chief Information Officer, Upmc Chautauqua Wca, Jamestown, NY, p. A428

ROBISON, Neely, Director Human Resources, The Bridgeway, North Little Rock-Pulaski County, AR, p. A47

ROBISON, Rob, Director Information Technology, Medical Center Of South Arkansas, El Dorado-Union County, AR, p. A41

ROBISON, Ryan, Chief Nursing Officer, Sanpete Valley Hospital, Mount Pleasant, UT, p. A648

ROBISON, Wendell, M.D., Chief of Staff, Sheridan Veterans Affairs Medical Center, Sheridan, WY, p. A709

ROBITAILLE, Mark E, FACHE
President and Chief Executive Officer, Martin Memorial Hospital South, FL, p. A139
President and Chief Executive Officer, Tradition Medical Center, FL, p. A139

ROBL, Chris, Human Resources, Ellinwood District Hospital, Ellinwood, KS, p. A234

ROBLES, Burt, Vice President Information Services, Guthrie Robert Packer Hospital, Sayre, PA, p. A540

ROCA, Robert, M.D., Vice President Medical Affairs, Sheppard Pratt Health System, Baltimore, MD, p. A289

ROCHA, Israel, Jr, Chief Executive Officer, Nyc Health + Hospitals / Elmhurst, New York (Includes All Hospitals Located Within The Five Boroughs), NY, p. A435

ROCHA, Julie, Vice President Human Resources, Mercy Medical Center Merced-Dominican Campus, CA, p. A72

ROCHELEAU, John, Vice President Business Support and Information Technology, Bellin Memorial Hospital, Green Bay, WI, p. A693

ROCHER, Leslie, Senior Vice President and Chief Medical Officer, Beaumont Children's Hospital, MI, p. A322

ROCHESTER, Charmaine, Vice President Finance, Bon Secours-Depaul Medical Center, Norfolk, VA, p. A662

ROCHIER, Dennis, Chief Medical Officer, Renown South Meadows Medical Center, Reno, NV, p. A396

ROCK, Betty Ann, Vice President Nursing and Chief Nursing Officer, Uniontown Hospital, Uniontown, PA, p. A542

ROCK, Brian, Director of Information Systems, Vcu Health Community Memorial Hospital, South Hill, VA, p. A666

ROCK, David, Executive Vice President and Chief Operating Officer, Wyckoff Heights Medical Center, New York (Includes All Hospitals Located Within The Five Boroughs), NY, p. A438

ROCKWELL, Jane, Director Support Services, North Metro Medical Center, Jacksonville-Pulaski County, AR, p. A44

ROCKWELL, Karla, Director of Nursing, Doctors Memorial Hospital, Bonifay, FL, p. A118

ROCKWOOD, John D., President, Medstar National Rehabilitation Hospital, Washington, DC, p. A115

ROCKWOOD, Sylvia, Director Human Resources, Upmc Pinnacle Carlisle, Carlisle, PA, p. A522

RODDEN, Celeste, Chief Information Officer, Hillcrest Hospital Claremore, Claremore, OK, p. A497

RODDY, Thomas, Chief Operating Officer, Saint Thomas Rutherford Hospital, Murfreesboro, TN, p. A576

RODEBUSH, Anthony, Chief Operating Officer, St. Mary's Regional Medical Center, Enid, OK, p. A498

RODEN, George
Vice President Human Resources, Mercy Hospital Aurora, Aurora, MO, p. A355
Vice President Human Resources, Mercy Hospital Cassville, Cassville, MO, p. A357

RODENBAUGH, Cathy, Director Human Resources, Holy Rosary Healthcare, Miles City, MT, p. A377

RODENFELS, Cheryl, System Vice President, IT Operations, Presence Saints Mary & Elizabeth Medical Center, Claremont Avenue, IL, p. A178

RODER, Darla
Chief Operating Officer and Interim Chief Executive Officer, Cavalier County Memorial Hospital And Clinics, Langdon, ND, p. A467
Chief Operating Officer, Cavalier County Memorial Hospital And Clinics, Langdon, ND, p. A467

RODERICK, Travis W., Chief Executive Officer, Premier Surgical Institute, Galena, KS, p. A235

RODERMAN, Nicki, Chief Nursing Officer, Medical City Denton, Denton, TX, p. A599

RODEWALD, Amanda, Interim Chief Financial Officer, Daviess Community Hospital, Washington, IN, p. A216

RODGE, Mark, Director Information Systems, Eaton Rapids Medical Center, Eaton Rapids, MI, p. A312

RODGERS, April, Vice President, Human Resources, Holy Name Medical Center, Teaneck, NJ, p. A412

RODGERS, Bruce C., Chief Administrative Officer, Salem Health West Valley, Dallas, OR, p. A512

RODGERS, Cynthia, Chief Executive Officer, Continuecare Hospital At Midland Memorial, Midland, TX, p. A624

RODGERS, Dondie, Interim Chief Nursing Officer, Memorial Hospital Of Texas County, Guymon, OK, p. A499

RODGERS, Jamie, Interim Chief Executive Officer, Choctaw Regional Medical Center, Ackerman, MS, p. A343

RODGERS, Larry, Chief Executive Officer, Southwestern Medical Center, Lawton, OK, p. A500

RODGERS, Lee, M.D., Vice President Quality, United Regional Health Care System-Eleventh Street Campus, TX, p. A644

RODIER, James Barton, M.D., Chief Quality Officer, Health Central Hospital, Ocoee, FL, p. A133

RODIS, John F., M.D., President, Saint Francis Hospital And Medical Center, Hartford, CT, p. A108

RODOWICZ, Darlene, Chief Financial Officer, Hillcrest Hospital, MA, p. A303

RODRIGUES, Pablo, M.D., Medical Director, Vibra Hospital Of Amarillo, Amarillo, TX, p. A583

RODRIGUEZ, Alex
  Vice President and Chief Information Officer, St. Elizabeth Covington, KY, p. A251
  Vice President and Chief Information Officer, St. Elizabeth Falmouth, KY, p. A252
  Vice President and Chief Information Officer, St. Elizabeth Florence, Florence, KY, p. A252

RODRIGUEZ, Ben A., Chief Executive Officer, Hialeah Hospital, Hialeah, FL, p. A124

RODRIGUEZ, Betsy, Vice President Human Resources, Barnes-Jewish Hospital Psychiatric Support Center, MO, p. A367

RODRIGUEZ, Candie, Director Human Resources, Hospital San Cristobal, Coto Laurel, PR, p. A713

RODRIGUEZ, Edgardo, Director Management Information Systems, Auxilio Mutuo Hospital, San Juan, PR, p. A715

RODRIGUEZ, Heather, Chief Nursing Officer, Fresno Heart And Surgical Hospital, Fresno, CA, p. A59

RODRIGUEZ, Jaime, Chief Financial Officer, San Juan City Hospital, San Juan, PR, p. A716

RODRIGUEZ, Joe, Chief Executive Officer, South Texas Behavioral Health Center, TX, p. A601

RODRIGUEZ, Jose Luis., Chief Executive Officer, Hospital Pavia-Santurce, San Juan, PR, p. A716

RODRIGUEZ, Jose O, M.D., Medical Director, Castaner General Hospital, Castaner, PR, p. A712

RODRIGUEZ, Laura, Director Medical Records, Hospital Del Maestro, San Juan, PR, p. A715

RODRIGUEZ, Leticia, Chief Executive Officer, Ward Memorial Hospital, Monahans, TX, p. A624

RODRIGUEZ, Lizzette, Director Finance, Hospital San Francisco, San Juan, PR, p. A716

RODRIGUEZ, Marco, Chief Financial Officer, Valley Baptist Medical Center-Harlingen, Harlingen, TX, p. A609

RODRIGUEZ, Mario, Chief Executive Officer, New Braunfels Regional Rehabilitation Hospital, New Braunfels, TX, p. A625

RODRIGUEZ, Maritza, Chief Financial Officer, Hospital Metropolitan, San Juan, PR, p. A716

RODRIGUEZ, Miguel, Medical Director, Caribbean Medical Center, Fajardo, PR, p. A713

RODRIGUEZ, Onel, Chief Financial Officer, Broward Health Coral Springs, Coral Springs, FL, p. A120

RODRIGUEZ, Oscar, Chief Fiscal Officer, Veterans Affairs Caribbean Healthcare System, San Juan, PR, p. A716

RODRIGUEZ, Patricia M., Senior Vice President and Area Manager, Kaiser Permanente South Sacramento Medical Center, Sacramento, CA, p. A82

RODRIGUEZ, Ramon J., President and Chief Executive Officer, Wyckoff Heights Medical Center, New York (Includes All Hospitals Located Within The Five Boroughs), NY, p. A438

RODRIGUEZ, Rufus, M.D., Medical Director, Mayo Clinic Health System In Fairmont, Fairmont, MN, p. A331

RODRIGUEZ, Sara
  Chief Financial Officer, Kindred Hospital Sugar Land, Sugar Land, TX, p. A637
  Human Resources, Seton Smithville Regional Hospital, Smithville, TX, p. A636

RODRIGUEZ, Tammy, Vice President of Patient Care Services, Rollins Brook Community Hospital, Lampasas, TX, p. A619

RODRIGUEZ, Tomas, Chief Information Technology Officer, First Hospital Panamericano, Cidra, PR, p. A713

RODRIGUEZ, Tony, Director Human Resources, South Texas Rehabilitation Hospital, Brownsville, TX, p. A590

RODRIGUEZ, Vilma, Director Human Resources, Hospital San Pablo Del Este, Fajardo, PR, p. A713

RODRIGUEZ, Wilfredo, M.D., Chief of Staff, Battle Creek Veterans Affairs Medical Center, Battle Creek, MI, p. A308

RODRIGUEZ, Yelitza Sanchez., Executive Director, Metropolitano De La Montana, Utuado, PR, p. A716

RODRIGUEZ COLLAZO, Jose Luis, Executive Director, Hospital Pavia Arecibo, Arecibo, PR, p. A712

RODRIGUEZ SCHMIDT, Myriam T, Director Human Resources, Cardiovascular Center Of Puerto Rico And The Caribbean, San Juan, PR, p. A715

RODRIQUEZ, Daisy, Director Human Resources, Fort Duncan Regional Medical Center, Eagle Pass, TX, p. A600

RODRIQUEZ, Monica, Director of Human Resources, Stewart & Lynda Resnick Neuropsychiatric Hospital At Ucla, Los Angeles, CA, p. A70

ROE, Daniel, M.D., Chief Operating Officer, Copper Queen Community Hospital, Bisbee, AZ, p. A28

ROE, Timothy J., M.D., President and Chief Executive Officer, Rehabilitation Hospital Of The Pacific, Honolulu, HI, p. A165

ROEBACK, Jason, Chief Operating Officer, Saint Vincent Hospital, Erie, PA, p. A525

ROEBKEN, Curtis, M.D., Chief Medical Staff, Kentfield Rehabilitation And Specialty Hospital, Kentfield, CA, p. A62

ROEBUCK, Amanda
  Director Patient Care Services, Genoa Medical Facilities, Genoa, NE, p. A384
  Interim Chief Executive Officer and Director Patient Care Services, Genoa Medical Facilities, Genoa, NE, p. A384

ROEDER, Donna, Chief Financial Officer, Jackson County Regional Health Center, Maquoketa, IA, p. A226

ROEDERER, Chris, Senior Vice President Human Resources, Tampa General Hospital Children's Medical Center, FL, p. A141

ROEHR, Richard
  Chief Operating Officer, Amita Health Adventist Medical Center Bolingbrook, Bolingbrook, IL, p. A174
  Vice President and Chief Operating Officer, Amita Health Adventist Medical Center Glenoaks, Glendale Heights, IL, p. A184

ROEHRLE, Andreas, Director Finance, Sentara Williamsburg Regional Medical Center, Williamsburg, VA, p. A668

ROESER, William
  Interim President and Chief Executive Officer, Sparrow Carson Hospital, Carson City, MI, p. A309
  President and Chief Executive Officer, Sparrow Ionia Hospital, Ionia, MI, p. A316

ROESLER, Bruce E., FACHE, Chief Executive Officer, Richland Hospital, Richland Center, WI, p. A702

ROETMAN, James D., President and Chief Executive Officer, Pocahontas Community Hospital, Pocahontas, IA, p. A228

ROEVER, Judy, MSN, R.N., Chief Nursing Officer, Scenic Mountain Medical Center, Big Spring, TX, p. A589

ROFFELSEN, Michael S.
  Chief Executive Officer, Healthsouth Sunrise Rehabilitation Hospital, Sunrise, FL, p. A140
  Chief Executive Officer, Kindred Hospital South Florida-Hollywood, FL, p. A123

ROGALSKI, Ted, Administrator, Genesis Medical Center-Aledo, Aledo, IL, p. A173

ROGAN, Edie, Manager Human Resources, Eastern State Hospital, Williamsburg, VA, p. A667

ROGERS, Aaron, Chief Executive Officer, Trinity Hospital, Weaverville, CA, p. A95

ROGERS, B. Carter, Chief of Staff, Piedmont Newton Hospital, Covington, GA, p. A151

ROGERS, Carrie, Chief Nursing Officer, Southern Tennessee Regional Health System-Lawrenceburg, Lawrenceburg, TN, p. A573

ROGERS, Cathy M, Manager Human Resources, Ghs - Laurens County Memorial Hospital, SC, p. A550

ROGERS, David, Chief Executive Officer, Ortonville Area Health Services, Ortonville, MN, p. A337

ROGERS, Doris, Vice President Human Resources, Crittenton Children's Center, MO, p. A362

ROGERS, Eric, Chief Information Officer, Hebrew Rehabilitation Center, Roslindale, MA, p. A303

ROGERS, Gregory H., President, Midmichigan Medical Center-Midland, Midland, MI, p. A319

ROGERS, James H., FACHE, Chief Executive Officer, Cornerstone Hospital Of Little Rock, Little Rock-Pulaski County, AR, p. A45

ROGERS, Jared, M.D.
  President and Chief Executive Officer, Osf Heart Of Mary Medical Center, Urbana, IL, p. A197
  President and Chief Executive Officer, Osf Sacred Heart Medical Center, Danville, IL, p. A180

ROGERS, Jeremy, Chief Financial Officer, St. Francis Medical Center, Monroe, LA, p. A274

ROGERS, Jerry, R.N., Director Nurses and Infection Control, Specialty Hospital, Monroe, LA, p. A274

ROGERS, Joseph J, Vice President and Chief Operating Officer, Redwood Memorial Hospital, Fortuna, CA, p. A58

ROGERS, Kathy, Vice President Marketing, San Luis Valley Health Conejos County Hospital, La Jara, CO, p. A102

ROGERS, LaDonna, Director Human Resources, T. J. Samson Community Hospital, Glasgow, KY, p. A252

ROGERS, Lucy, Chief Information Resource Management Systems, Sam Rayburn Memorial Veterans Center, TX, p. A598

ROGERS, Mark G
  Interim Vice President Finance and Chief Financial Officer, Genesis Medical Center, Silvis, Silvis, IL, p. A196
  Interim Vice President Finance and Chief Financial Officer, Genesis Medical Center-West Campus, IA, p. A220
  Vice President, Finance and Chief Financial Officer, Genesis Medical Center-Aledo, Aledo, IL, p. A173

ROGERS, Matt, Chief Financial Officer, Wellspan Philhaven, Mount Gretna, PA, p. A532

ROGERS, Michael, Vice President Fiscal Services, Brattleboro Memorial Hospital, Brattleboro, VT, p. A653

ROGERS, Patricia, Director of Nursing, Dahl Memorial Healthcare Association, Ekalaka, MT, p. A375

ROGERS, Randy, FACHE, Chief Executive Officer, Garden Park Medical Center, Gulfport, MS, p. A346

ROGERS, Rich, Vice President Information Services, Roger C. Peace Rehabilitation Hospital, SC, p. A553

ROGERS, Robert T, M.D., II, Medical Director, Canton-Potsdam Hospital, Potsdam, NY, p. A440

ROGERS, Seth, Controller, Healthsouth Rehabilitation Hospital Of Modesto, Modesto, CA, p. A72

ROGERS, Sherry L, MS, R.N., Chief Nursing Officer, Redington-Fairview General Hospital, Skowhegan, ME, p. A286

ROGERS, Tammy, Director Human Resources, Mt. San Rafael Hospital, Trinidad, CO, p. A106

ROGERS, Tracy, Chief Executive Officer, North Tampa Behavioral Health, Wesley Chapel, FL, p. A143

ROGERS, Valerie J, Director of Nursing, Cherokee Nation W.W. Hastings Indian Hospital, Tahlequah, OK, p. A507

ROGERS, William, Chief Medical Officer, Gilmore Memorial Hospital, Amory, MS, p. A343

ROGOLS, Kevin L., FACHE, Administrator, Kalkaska Memorial Health Center, Kalkaska, MI, p. A317

ROGOZ, Brian, Vice President Finance and Treasurer, New Britain General, CT, p. A109

ROHAN, Colleen, Director Human Resources, Little Company Of Mary Hospital And Health Care Centers, Evergreen Park, IL, p. A183

ROHAN, Patrick, Chief Operating Officer, Mercy Hospital - A Campus Of Plantation General Hospital, FL, p. A136

ROHLEDER, Scott, Chief Information Officer, Hays Medical Center, Hays, KS, p. A236

ROHLOFF, William A., FACHE, Interim Chief Executive Officer, Reagan Memorial Hospital, Big Lake, TX, p. A589

ROHMAN, Cindy, R.N., MS, Vice President/Chief Nursing Officer, Lexington Medical Center, West Columbia, SC, p. A558

ROHMAN, Ryan, MSN, R.N.
  Chief Operating Officer, Mountain Crest Hospital, CO, p. A100
  Chief Operating Officer, Uchealth Medical Center Of The Rockies, Loveland, CO, p. A104

ROHN, Stephen G., M.D., Vice President and Chief Medical Officer, Hamilton Medical Center, Dalton, GA, p. A152

ROHRBACH, Dan D., President, Southwest Health Center Nursing Home, WI, p. A701

ROHRBACK, Allen, Chief Executive Officer, Madison Valley Medical Center, Ennis, MT, p. A375

ROHRBACK, Jenny, Director Human Resource, Ruby Valley Hospital, Sheridan, MT, p. A379

ROHRER, Harry, Chief Financial Officer, University Of Miami Hospital, FL, p. A131

ROHRER, John J., Director, William S. Middleton Veterans Hospital, Madison, WI, p. A696

ROHRICH, George A., FACHE, Chief Executive Officer, River's Edge Hospital And Clinic, Saint Peter, MN, p. A340

ROIZ, JoAnn, Director Human Resources, Healthsouth Tustin Rehabilitation Hospital, Tustin, CA, p. A92

ROJAS, Anna, Chief Executive Officer, Kindred Hospital Tarrant County-Fort Worth Southwest, TX, p. A604

ROJAS, Curtis, Interim Chief Financial Officer, Connally Memorial Medical Center, Floresville, TX, p. A603

ROKER, Christopher, Chief Executive Officer, Nyc Health + Hospitals / Queens, New York (Includes All Hospitals Located Within The Five Boroughs), NY, p. A436

ROKOSZ, Gregory, D.O., Senior Vice President Medical and Academic Affairs, Saint Barnabas Medical Center, Livingston, NJ, p. A406

ROLAND, Brian, Chief Executive Officer, Muenster Memorial Hospital, Muenster, TX, p. A625

ROLAND, John, R.N., Chief Operating Officer and Chief Nursing Officer, Bleckley Memorial Hospital, Cochran, GA, p. A150

ROLDAN, Lanyce, Chief Nursing Officer, Penn Medicine Lancaster General Hospital, Lancaster, PA, p. A529

ROLEK, Jim, Chief Human Resources Officer, Vice President, Clara Maass Medical Center, Belleville, NJ, p. A402

ROLEY, Margaret, Chief Nursing Officer, South Baldwin Regional Medical Center, Foley, AL, p. A18

ROLFE, David, Chief Information Officer, Madonna Rehabilitation Hospital, Lincoln, NE, p. A386

ROLFF, Christi, Director Business Development, San Joaquin Valley Rehabilitation Hospital, Fresno, CA, p. A59

ROLING, Robin, FACHE, MS, R.N., Chief Operating Officer, Cheyenne Regional Medical Center, Cheyenne, WY, p. A707

ROLLI, Molli Martha, M.D., Medical Director, Mendota Mental Health Institute, Madison, WI, p. A696

ROLLING, Andy, Director of Finance, Regina Hospital, Hastings, MN, p. A332

ROLLINS, David W, Chief Financial Officer, Mt. San Rafael Hospital, Trinidad, CO, p. A106

ROLLINS, James
Chief Financial Officer, Arbour H. R. I. Hospital, Brookline, MA, p. A298
Chief Financial Officer, Arbour-Fuller Hospital, Attleboro, MA, p. A295

ROLLINS, Larry, Supervisor Information Technology, Mccamey County Hospital District, Mccamey, TX, p. A623

ROLLINS, Marlon, Ph.D., Chief Executive Officer, Fremont Hospital, Fremont, CA, p. A59

ROLLINS, Skip, Chief Information Officer, Freeman Hospital East, MO, p. A361

ROLSEN, Timothy, Chief Executive Officer, Regency Hospital Of Cleveland - West, OH, p. A492

ROMAN, Eloy, M.D., Chief of Staff, Palmetto General Hospital, Hialeah, FL, p. A124

ROMAN, Jody, Chief Human Resource Officer, Hillside Rehabilitation Hospital, Warren, OH, p. A492

ROMAN, Linda K, Administrator, Coast Plaza Hospital, Norwalk, CA, p. A75

ROMAN, Marina, M.D., Medical Director, Hospital De La Universidad De Puerto Rico/Dr. Federico Trilla, Carolina, PR, p. A712

ROMANELLO, Marcus, Chief Medical Officer, Fort Hamilton Hospital, Hamilton, OH, p. A483

ROMANIA, Matt, Director of Nursing, Upmc Susquehanna Soldiers + Sailors, Wellsboro, PA, p. A543

ROMANICK, Odile, Chief information Officer, Day Kimball Hospital, Putnam, CT, p. A110

ROMANIELLO, Guy, Director Fiscal Services, Belmont Behavioral Hospital, Philadelphia, PA, p. A533

ROMANO, C. James, M.D., Chief Medical Officer, St. Francis Medical Center, Trenton, NJ, p. A413

ROMANO, Jean, Chief Nursing Officer, Good Shepherd Penn Partners Specialty Hospital At Rittenhouse, Philadelphia, PA, p. A534

ROMANO, Sara, R.N., Vice President, Mountain View Hospital, Gadsden, AL, p. A18

ROMANOWSKI, Ellen, Chief Nursing Officer, Healthsouth Rehabilitation Hospital Of Miami, Cutler Bay, FL, p. A120

ROMANS, Alan, Director Information Technology, Ashland Health Center, Ashland, KS, p. A232

ROMEO, John, Chief Information Officer, Mercy Hospital And Medical Center, Chicago, IL, p. A178

ROMER, Douglas, Executive Director Patient Care Services, Grande Ronde Hospital, La Grande, OR, p. A514

ROMERO, Brenda, Administrator, Presbyterian Espanola Hospital, Espanola, NM, p. A417

ROMERO, Edward, Chief Financial Officer, Rehabilitation Hospital of Fort Wayne, Fort Wayne, IN, p. A204

ROMERO, Frank, M.D.
Chief Medical Officer, Cox Medical Center South, MO, p. A370
Vice President Medical Affairs and Chief Medical Officer, Cox Monett Hospital, Monett, MO, p. A365

ROMERO, Matt, Chief Financial Officer, Oak Hill Hospital, Brooksville, FL, p. A119

ROMIG, Glenn, Chief Financial Officer, Citrus Memorial Health System, Inverness, FL, p. A125

ROMINE, Andrew, Chief Executive Officer, Rockledge Regional Medical Center, Rockledge, FL, p. A137

ROMITO, Edmund J, Chief Information Officer, Good Samaritan Medical And Rehabilitation Center, OH, p. A494

RONAN, Barry P., President and Chief Executive Officer, Western Maryland Regional Medical Center, Cumberland, MD, p. A291

RONAN, John
President, Blue Hill Memorial Hospital, Blue Hill, ME, p. A283

President, Maine Coast Memorial Hospital, Ellsworth, ME, p. A284

RONCA, Cyndi, Director Human Resources, Twin Cities Hospital, Niceville, FL, p. A132

RONDE, Christa, Assistant Chief Financial Officer, Palo Verde Hospital, Blythe, CA, p. A53

RONKE, Lisa, Director Finance, St. Michael's Hospital Avera, Tyndall, SD, p. A564

RONNISCH, Kim, R.N., Vice President Nursing and Operations, St. John River District Hospital, East China, MI, p. A312

ROODMAN, Richard D., Chief Executive Officer, Uw Medicine/ Valley Medical Center, Renton, WA, p. A675

ROOF, Marie, Executive Vice President Information Systems, Vibra Specialty Hospital Of Portland, Portland, OR, p. A517

ROOKER, Mark, Chief Operations and Information Officer, Susan B. Allen Memorial Hospital, El Dorado, KS, p. A234

ROOKS, Tiffany, Interim Chief Nursing Officer, St. Jude Children's Research Hospital, Memphis, TN, p. A576

ROONERY, Nicole, Chief Nursing Officer, Ivinson Memorial Hospital, Laramie, WY, p. A708

ROONEY, Al, Director Information Systems, St. Vincent Healthcare, Billings, MT, p. A373

ROONEY, David, Administrator Operations, Winneshiek Medical Center, Decorah, IA, p. A221

ROONEY, Thomas, Chief Information Resource Management, Veterans Affairs Hudson Valley Health Care System-Montrose Campus, NY, p. A430

ROOP, Terri, Director Patient Care Services, Dickenson Community Hospital, Clintwood, VA, p. A657

ROOS, Joel A., Commanding Officer, Naval Medical Center San Diego, San Diego, CA, p. A84

ROOSA, Carol, Vice President Information Services and Chief Information Officer, Athol Hospital, Athol, MA, p. A295

ROOT, Jim, Vice President Human Resources, Saint Elizabeth's Medical Center, Wabasha, MN, p. A341

ROOT, Rodney Mark, D.O., Vice President Medical Affairs, Bakersfield Memorial Hospital, Bakersfield, CA, p. A52

ROPER, Embra, Chief Medical Officer, Regional Hospital For Respiratory And Complex Care, Burien, WA, p. A670

ROPER, Sandra, Chief Human Resources, General Leonard Wood Army Community Hospital, Fort Leonard Wood, MO, p. A359

ROQUE, Lee Ann, Director of Human Resources, Mary Black Health System-Spartanburg, Spartanburg, SC, p. A557

ROSA-TOLEDO, Luis R, M.D., Medical Director, Hospital Manati Medical Center, Manati, PR, p. A714

ROSAAEN, Nancy, Chief Executive Officer, Mccone County Health Center, Circle, MT, p. A374

ROSADO, Jose S., Executive Director, Hospital Manati Medical Center, Manati, PR, p. A714

ROSALES, Alvina, R.N., Chief Nursing Officer, Tuba City Regional Health Care Corporation, Tuba City, AZ, p. A36

ROSATI, Rosemarie, Chief Operating Officer, University Behavioral Healthcare, Piscataway, NJ, p. A410

ROSBOROUGH, Brian S, M.D., Chief Medical Officer, Osf Saint Elizabeth Medical Center, Ottawa, IL, p. A192

ROSBURG, Deb, Chief Financial Officer, Franklin General Hospital, Hampton, IA, p. A223

ROSCOE, Joan, Chief Information Officer, Winchester Medical Center, Winchester, VA, p. A668

ROSE, Cheryl, Human Resources Director, Fulton County Medical Center, Mc Connellsburg, PA, p. A530

ROSE, Hugh, Vice President Fiscal Management, Palos Health, Palos Heights, IL, p. A192

ROSE, Julia, R.N., Director of Nursing, Braxton County Memorial Hospital, Gassaway, WV, p. A683

ROSE, Kim, Chief Information Technology, Crouse Health, Syracuse, NY, p. A443

ROSE, Laura L, Chief Financial Officer, St. Vincent Anderson, Anderson, IN, p. A199

ROSE, Mary R, R.N., Chief Clinical Officer, Promedica Coldwater Regional Hospital, Coldwater, MI, p. A310

ROSE, May, Director Human Resources, Memorial Hospital, Chester, IL, p. A176

ROSE, Michael S., President and Chief Executive Officer, Southern New Hampshire Medical Center, Nashua, NH, p. A400

ROSE, Michaell, Chief Operating Officer, St. Joseph's Medical Center, Stockton, CA, p. A91

ROSE, Richard T, Associate Director, Manchester Veterans Affairs Medical Center, Manchester, NH, p. A400

ROSE, Robert, M.D., Chief Medical Officer, Upper Connecticut Valley Hospital, Colebrook, NH, p. A398

ROSE, Robin, R.N., Chief Operating and Clinical Officer, Gibson Area Hospital And Health Services, Gibson City, IL, p. A184

ROSE, Silvia, Director Patient Care Services, Vidant Bertie Hospital, Windsor, NC, p. A462

ROSE, Steven A, R.N., President and Chief Executive Officer, Nanticoke Memorial Hospital, Seaford, DE, p. A114

ROSELLO, Patricia M., Chief Executive Officer, Baptist Children's Hospital, FL, p. A129

ROSEMORE, Michael, M.D., Medical Director, Encompass Health Lakeshore Rehabilitation Hospital, Birmingham, AL, p. A14

ROSEN, Barry, M.D., Vice President Medical Management, Advocate Good Shepherd Hospital, Barrington, IL, p. A174

ROSEN, Jules, M.D., Chief Medical Officer, West Springs Hospital, Grand Junction, CO, p. A101

ROSEN, Michael, M.D., Chief Medical Officer, Havasu Regional Medical Center, Lake Havasu City, AZ, p. A30

ROSEN, Raymond, FACHE, Vice President Operations, Wellspan York Hospital, York, PA, p. A546

ROSENA, Robens, Director Information Systems, Pinecrest Rehabilitation Hospital, FL, p. A121

ROSENBALM, Jennifer, Manager Business Office, Veterans Affairs Nebraska-Western Iowa Health Care System, Omaha, NE, p. A389

ROSENBAUM, Robert, Vice President Operations, Vassar Brothers Medical Center, Poughkeepsie, NY, p. A441

ROSENBAUM, Victor, Chief Operating Officer, Alaska Regional Hospital, Anchorage, AK, p. A25

ROSENBERG, Andrew, M.D., Chief Information Officer, C. S. Mott Children's Hospital, MI, p. A307

ROSENBERG, Julie, Administrator, Essentia Health-Graceville, Graceville, MN, p. A332

ROSENBERG, Steven, Chief Financial Officer, New Milford Hospital, CT, p. A107

ROSENBERG, Stuart E., President, Johnson Memorial Medical Center, Stafford Springs, CT, p. A111

ROSENBERGER, Robert, Chief Financial Officer, Adena Medical Center, Chillicothe, OH, p. A474

ROSENBERGER-SLAMPACK, Janie, Chief Executive Officer, Curahealth Heritage Valley, Beaver, PA, p. A520

ROSENBLATT, Michael, M.D., Medical Director, Kindred Rehabilitation Hospital Clear Lake, Webster, TX, p. A643

ROSENBLOOM, Mark, M.D., Vice President of Medical Affairs, Health First Holmes Regional Medical Center, Melbourne, FL, p. A129

ROSENBURG, Deborah L, Vice President Human Resources, Chesapeake Regional Medical Center, Chesapeake, VA, p. A656

ROSENBURG, Jeffrey M., Chief Medical Officer, Sierra Nevada Memorial Hospital, Grass Valley, CA, p. A61

ROSENCRANCE, Daris, Chief Financial Officer, Mon Health Medical Center, Morgantown, WV, p. A685

ROSENDAHL, Lisa, Director Human Resources, St. Cloud Veterans Affairs Health Care System, Saint Cloud, MN, p. A339

ROSENFELD, Merryll, Vice President, Human Resources, Catholic Medical Center, Manchester, NH, p. A400

ROSENSTEIN, Gaynor, Vice President Operations, Bon Secours Community Hospital, Port Jervis, NY, p. A440

ROSENTHAL, Benjamin, Information Systems Director, South Sunflower County Hospital, Indianola, MS, p. A347

ROSENTHAL, Philip P, Executive Director, Manhattan Eye, Ear And Throat Hospital, NY, p. A433

ROSENTHAL, Raul, M.D., Interim Chief of Staff, Cleveland Clinic Florida, Weston, FL, p. A144

ROSEQUIST, Helen, Manager Information Systems, Warren General Hospital, Warren, PA, p. A543

ROSETTA, Kathy, Chief Nursing Officer, Laurel Ridge Treatment Center, San Antonio, TX, p. A633

ROSHAN, Payman
Chief Operating Officer, Kaiser Permanente Baldwin Park Medical Center, Baldwin Park, CA, p. A52
Senior Vice President and Area Manager, Kaiser Permanente Panorama City Medical Center, Los Angeles, CA, p. A62

ROSHETKO, Chet, Chief Nursing Officer, Eastern State Hospital, Medical Lake, WA, p. A673

ROSIAK, Michael, Chief Operating Officer, Weisman Children's Rehabilitation Hospital, Marlton, NJ, p. A407

ROSILES, Nancy, Director Human Resources, Encompass Health Rehabilitation Hospital Of Arlington, Arlington, TX, p. A584

ROSKE, Jeff, D.O., Chief Medical Staff, Community Memorial Hospital, Sumner, IA, p. A230

ROSKOVSKI, Stephanie, Chief Operating Officer, Butler Health System, Butler, PA, p. A521

ROSLER, Andrea P, Vice President Human Resources, Madison Hospital, AL, p. A19

ROSS, Charles, M.D., Vice President Medical Affairs, Chilton Medical Center, Pompton Plains, NJ, p. A410

ROSS, Christopher J., Chief Information Technology Officer, Mayo Eugenio Litta Children's Hospital, MN, p. A338

ROSS, Hoyt, Chief Executive Officer, Promise Hospital Of Florida At The Villages, Oxford, FL, p. A134

ROSS, Jacqueline, Chief Human Resources Officer, Mann-Grandstaff Veterans Affairs Medical Center, Spokane, WA, p. A678

ROSS, James E., President and Chief Executive Officer, West Tennessee Healthcare North Hospital, TN, p. A571

ROSS, Jay
Chief Financial Officer, Chi St. Joseph's Health, Park Rapids, MN, p. A337
Vice President of Finance, Chi Lakewood Health, Baudette, MN, p. A328

ROSS, Jeffrey, M.D.
Chief of Staff, King's Daughters Medical Center, Brookhaven, MS, p. A344
Medical Director, Amg Specialty Hospital-Albuquerque, Albuquerque, NM, p. A415

ROSS, Joan, Senior Vice President and Chief Operating Officer, St. Vincent Charity Medical Center, Cleveland, OH, p. A477

ROSS, John, Vice President, Franciscan Health Mooresville, Mooresville, IN, p. A211

ROSS, Johnny Shane, Executive Medical Director, Encompass Health Rehabilitation Hospital Of Austin, Austin, TX, p. A586

ROSS, Joseph P., President and Chief Executive Officer, Meritus Medical Center, Hagerstown, MD, p. A292

ROSS, Karen, Chief Executive Officer, Allegiance Specialty Hospital Of Kilgore, Kilgore, TX, p. A617

ROSS, Laurie, Chief Nursing Officer, Southampton Memorial Hospital, Franklin, VA, p. A658

ROSS, Phil, Chief Executive Officer, Surgical Hospital Of Oklahoma, Oklahoma City, OK, p. A504

ROSS, Randall W., FACHE, President and Chief Executive Officer, Mercy Hospital Of Folsom, Folsom, CA, p. A58

ROSS, Robert, Chief Operating Officer, Medstar Washington Hospital Center, Washington, DC, p. A116

ROSS, Samuel Lee., M.D., MS, Chief Executive Officer, Bon Secours Baltimore Health System, Baltimore, MD, p. A287

ROSS, Semmes, Jr, Administrator, Lawrence County Hospital, Monticello, MS, p. A351

ROSS, Shana, Vice President Human Resources, Bayhealth Medical Center, Milford Memorial Hospital, DE, p. A113

ROSS, Zeff, FACHE, Executive Vice President and Chief Executive Officer, Memorial Regional Hospital South, FL, p. A124

ROSS-COLE, Melissa, Director Human Resources, Regency Hospital Of Northwest Arkansas - Springdale, Springdale-Washington County, AR, p. A49

ROSS-SPANG, Carol, Chief Human Resources Officer, Methodist Le Bonheur Germantown Hospital, TN, p. A575

ROSSFELD, John, Administrator, Wilson N. Jones Regional Medical Center, Sherman, TX, p. A636

ROSSI, Alfred N., M.D., Chief Executive Officer, Hopedale Medical Complex, Hopedale, IL, p. A186

ROSSI, Coleen, Director Quality Services, Healthsouth Rehabilitation Hospital Of Toms River, Toms River, NJ, p. A412

ROSSI, Lawrence, M.D., Clinical Director, Trenton Psychiatric Hospital, Trenton, NJ, p. A413

ROSSI, Mark F, Chief Operating Officer and General Counsel, Hopedale Medical Complex, Hopedale, IL, p. A186

ROSSMANN, Barbara W., R.N., President and Chief Executive Officer, St. Joseph's Mercy-North, MI, p. A310

ROSSMANN, Samuel H., Chief Executive Officer, Tops Surgical Specialty Hospital, Houston, TX, p. A614

ROSVOLD, Robert, Director Finance, Voorhees Pediatric Facility, NJ, p. A413

ROTENBERRY-BAGGETT, Katie, Administrative Assistant and Human Resources, Yalobusha General Hospital, Water Valley, MS, p. A354

ROTERT, Angela Lynne, Chief Clinical Officer, Kindred Hospital-Indianapolis, Indianapolis, IN, p. A207

ROTGER, Lindsey, Chief Nursing Officer, Spire Cane Creek Rehabilitation Hospital, Martin, TN, p. A574

ROTH, Anna M., R.N., MS, M.P.H., Chief Executive Officer, Contra Costa Regional Medical Center, Martinez, CA, p. A71

ROTH, Chad, Director Information Services, Prairie View, Newton, KS, p. A242

ROTH, Dan, M.D., Vice President Medical Affairs, Mercy Health - Anderson Hospital, Cincinnati, OH, p. A475

ROTH, Diane, Chief Financial Officer, Piedmont Rockdale Hospital, Conyers, GA, p. A151

ROTH, Ed, President, Mercy Allen Hospital, Oberlin, OH, p. A488

ROTH, Edward J., III, President and Chief Executive Officer, Aultman Hospital Pediatric Services, OH, p. A473

ROTH, Eugene, Vice President Information Services, Mercy Children's Hospital St. Louis, MO, p. A368

ROTH, Mark A., Chief Financial Officer, Mountain Valley Regional Rehabilitation Hospital, Prescott Valley, AZ, p. A34

ROTH, Norman G., President, Greenwich Hospital, Greenwich, CT, p. A108

ROTH, Randy, Chief Medical Officer, Singing River Hospital, MS, p. A351

ROTH-MALLEK, Nancy, Vice President of Finance, Aspirus Riverview Hospital And Clinics, Inc., Wisconsin Rapids, WI, p. A706

ROTHBERG, Kathryn, Director Human Resources, Evergreenhealth Monroe, Monroe, WA, p. A673

ROTHBERGER, Richard, Corporate Executive Vice President and Chief Financial Officer, Scripps Green Hospital, La Jolla, CA, p. A62

ROTHENBERGER, David, Chief Financial Officer, Summit Healthcare Regional Medical Center, Show Low, AZ, p. A36

ROTHERMICH, Anthony, Administrator, Mercy Hospital Lincoln, Troy, MO, p. A371

ROTHERMICH, Michael, M.D., Chief of Staff, Hermann Area District Hospital, Hermann, MO, p. A360

ROTHFIELD, Kenneth, M.D., Chief Medical Officer, Medical City Children's Hospital, TX, p. A597

ROTHMAN, Marc, M.D., Medical Director, Friends Hospital, Philadelphia, PA, p. A534

ROTHSCHILD, Marylee, M.D., Chief of Staff, Robley Rex Veterans Affairs Medical Center, Louisville, KY, p. A256

ROTSTED, Scott T., Chief Executive Officer, California Rehabilitation Institute, Los Angeles, CA, p. A66

ROTY, Christopher, Interim President, Baptist Health Paducah, Paducah, KY, p. A259

ROUGH, Vicki, Chief Nursing Officer, Highlands Hospital, Connellsville, PA, p. A523

ROUILLARD, Smita, M.D., Physician in Chief, Kaiser Permanente Fresno Medical Center, Fresno, CA, p. A59

ROULEAU, Greg, Vice President Nursing, Mercy Medical Center Merced-Dominican Campus, CA, p. A72

ROUND, Laurie, MS, R.N., Chief Nurse Executive, Advocate Bromenn Regional Medical Center, IL, p. A191

ROUNDS, Jason
Chief Operating Officer and Administrator, Christus St. Michael Hospital-Atlanta, TX, p. A639
Interim Chief Executive Officer, Christus St. Michael Hospital-Atlanta, TX, p. A639

ROUNDY, Ann, Vice President Employee Services, Columbus Community Hospital, Inc., Columbus, WI, p. A691

ROUNSLEY, Joan, Director Human Resources, Geisinger Jersey Shore Hospital, Jersey Shore, PA, p. A528

ROUNSLEY, Karen, Controller, Healthsouth Chesapeake Rehabilitation Hospital, Salisbury, MD, p. A294

ROUSH, Sharon L., Chief Executive Officer, South Bay Hospital, Sun City Center, FL, p. A140

ROUSSE, Michael, M.D., Vice President of Medical Affairs, Northeastern Vermont Regional Hospital, Saint Johnsbury, VT, p. A654

ROUSSEAU, Mickie, Director Human Resources, Terrebonne General Medical Center, Houma, LA, p. A269

ROUSSEL, Steve
Chief Financial Officer, Baylor Medical Center At Mckinney, Mckinney, TX, p. A623
Vice President Finance, Baylor Scott & White Medical Center-Irving, Irving, TX, p. A615

ROUSSELLE, Karen, Administrator, Omega Hospital, Metairie, LA, p. A274

ROUSSOS, Michael, Administrator, University Hospital, TX, p. A634

ROUTH, Lori, R.N., Nurse Administrator, Mayo Clinic Health System - Albert Lea And Austin, MN, p. A327

ROUX, Roger, Chief Financial Officer, Rady Children's Hospital - San Diego, San Diego, CA, p. A84

ROUZER, Cindy, Director Human Resources, Spooner Health, Spooner, WI, p. A703

ROVITO, Kevin, Chief Financial Officer, Jackson Hospital, Marianna, FL, p. A129

ROW, Tracy, Manager Business Office, Fredonia Regional Hospital, Fredonia, KS, p. A235

ROW, Tyler, Director Information Technology, Fredonia Regional Hospital, Fredonia, KS, p. A235

ROWAN, Cary, Chief Financial Officer, Astria Sunnyside Hospital, Sunnyside, WA, p. A678

ROWAN, Mark, Interim Chief Information Officer, Rome Memorial Hospital, Rome, NY, p. A442

ROWAN, R C, Director Human Resources, Neosho Memorial Regional Medical Center, Chanute, KS, p. A233

ROWE, Chad, Human Resource Director, Aspirus Keweenaw Hospital, Inc., Laurium, MI, p. A318

ROWE, Jeanne M, M.D., Chief Medical Officer, Shore Medical Center, Somers Point, NJ, p. A411

ROWE, Mike, M.D., Chief of Staff, Fayette Regional Health System, Connersville, IN, p. A201

ROWE, Paul W, Director Information Technology, St. Francis Hospital, Wilmington, DE, p. A114

ROWE, Richard M., PharmD

Chief Executive Officer, Garden Grove Hospital And Medical Center, Garden Grove, CA, p. A60
Chief Executive Officer, Huntington Beach Hospital, Huntington Beach, CA, p. A62

ROWE, Scott, Chief Executive Officer, Healthsouth Chattanooga Rehabilitation Hospital, Chattanooga, TN, p. A567

ROWE, Wilma, M.D., Senior Vice President Medical Affairs, Mercy Medical Center, Baltimore, MD, p. A288

ROWELL, Julie, R.N., Chief Nursing Officer, Thomas Hospital, Fairhope, AL, p. A17

ROWEN, Lisa R.N.
Chief Nursing Officer, University Of Maryland Medical Center Midtown Campus, Baltimore, MD, p. A289
Senior Vice President and Chief Nursing Officer, University Of Maryland Hospital For Children, MD, p. A289

ROWLAND, Claire, Director Human Resources, Vermilion Behavioral Health Systems South, LA, p. A271

ROWLAND, Michael, M.D., Vice President Medical Affairs, Franklin Memorial Hospital, Farmington, ME, p. A284

ROWLAND, Nick
Chief Executive Officer, Pushmataha Hospital, Antlers, OK, p. A495
Chief Operating Officer, Pushmataha Hospital, Antlers, OK, p. A495
Interim Chief Executive Officer, Choctaw Memorial Hospital, Hugo, OK, p. A500

ROWLAND, Robert, M.D., Medical Director, Healthsouth Rehabilitation Hospital Of Tallahassee, Tallahassee, FL, p. A140

ROWLAND, Ruby, Strategic Partner, Highlands-Cashiers Hospital, Highlands, NC, p. A455

ROWLAND, Ted, Chief of Medical Staff, Atoka County Medical Center, Atoka, OK, p. A496

ROWLANDS, Dewey R, Vice President and Chief Financial Officer, Rome Memorial Hospital, Rome, NY, p. A442

ROWLEY, Charla, Chief Financial Officer, Southwest Mississippi Regional Medical Center, Mccomb, MS, p. A350

ROWLEY, Mike, Chief Executive Officer, Springbrook Behavioral Health System, Travelers Rest, SC, p. A557

ROY, Joel, Manager Information Systems, The Brook Hospital - Kmi, Louisville, KY, p. A257

ROY, Linda, R.N., Chief Nursing Officer, Walter B. Jones Alcohol And Drug Abuse Treatment Center, Greenville, NC, p. A454

ROY, Rock, Professional Services Director, Power County Hospital District, American Falls, ID, p. A167

ROY, Schindelheim, M.D., Chief of Staff, Mee Memorial Hospital, King City, CA, p. A62

ROYAL, Keli, Chief Human Resources Officer, Shenandoah Medical Center, Shenandoah, IA, p. A229

ROYAL, Shawanna, R.N., Director Nursing, Strategic Behavioral Health - Raleigh, Garner, NC, p. A453

ROYAL, Ty, Executive Director of Human Resources and Support Services, Gibson Area Hospital And Health Services, Gibson City, IL, p. A184

ROYE, G. Dean, M.D., Senior Vice President of Medical Affairs and Chief Medical Officer, Miriam Hospital, Providence, RI, p. A547

ROYNE, Sharon, Senior Vice President: Human Resources, Highline Medical Center, Burien, WA, p. A670

ROYSTER, Kirsten, President and Chief Operating Officer, Novant Health Medical Park Hospital, Winston, NC, p. A463

ROZELL, Becky, Vice President, Human Resources, Madison Health, London, OH, p. A485

ROZENBOOM, Steve, Chief Financial Officer, Holy Cross Hospital, Taos, NM, p. A420

ROZENFELD, Jon, President, Ssm Health St. Mary's Hospital, Madison, WI, p. A696

ROZIER, Derek, Chief Financial Officer, Liberty Regional Medical Center, Hinesville, GA, p. A154

ROZNOVSKY, Karen, Director Human Resources, Yoakum Community Hospital, Yoakum, TX, p. A645

RUBANO, Kathleen A, MSN, R.N., Chief Nursing Officer, Corpus Christi Medical Center Bay Area, TX, p. A594

RUBAR, Jackie, Administrative Assistant and Director Human Resources, Leesville Rehabilitation Hospital, Leesville, LA, p. A272

RUBE, David M, M.D., Clinical Director, Brooklyn Children's Hospital Psychiatric Center, NY, p. A434

RUBEN, Wanda, R.N., Chief Nursing Officer, Garden Grove Hospital And Medical Center, Garden Grove, CA, p. A60

RUBENS, Deborah, Director Human Resources, Shriners Hospitals For Children-Northern California, Sacramento, CA, p. A82

RUBERG, Greg, President and Chief Executive Officer, Lake View Hospital, Two Harbors, MN, p. A341

RUBERTE, Henry, Administrator, Hospital San Gerardo, San Juan, PR, p. A716

RUBERTI, Charlene, Director Information Technology Development, Ancora Psychiatric Hospital, Hammonton, NJ, p. A405

RUBIN, Nancy, Vice President Human Resources, Motion Picture And Television Fund Hospital And Residential Services, Los Angeles, CA, p. A68

RUBIN, Randy, Senior Vice President and Chief Financial Officer, Mercy Medical Center - West Lakes, IA, p. A221

RUBIN, Vincent, Chief Financial Officer, Southern California Hospital At Culver City, Culver City, CA, p. A56

RUBINATE, Donna, R.N., Chief Operating Officer, Good Samaritan Medical Center - Cushing Campus, MA, p. A298

RUBINO, Mark, M.D.
Chief Medical Officer, Forbes Hospital, Monroeville, PA, p. A532
President, Forbes Hospital, Monroeville, PA, p. A532

RUBINSTEIN, Mitchell, M.D.
Chief Medical Officer, Palms Of Pasadena Hospital, Saint Petersburg, FL, p. A138
Chief Medical Officer, St. Petersburg General Hospital, Saint Petersburg, FL, p. A138

RUBIO, Felipe, M.D., Medical Director, Kindred Hospital-Dayton, Dayton, OH, p. A480

RUBLE, Justin
Director Human Resources, Jefferson Medical Center, Ranson, WV, p. A686
Director, Human Resources, Berkeley Medical Center, Martinsburg, WV, p. A684

RUBY, Blaine, M.D., Chief of Staff, Johnson County Healthcare Center, Buffalo, WY, p. A707

RUCH, Jordan, Vice President and Chief Information Officer, Robert Wood Johnson University Hospital Somerset, Somerville, NJ, p. A411

RUCHTI, Robert D., Chief Executive Officer, Buchanan General Hospital, Grundy, VA, p. A659

RUCKER, Alisa, Vice President Finance and Chief Financial Officer, Washington Hospital, Washington, PA, p. A543

RUCKER, Genifer, President, Christus Spohn Hospital Beeville, Beeville, TX, p. A588

RUCKER, Jodi, MSN, R.N., Vice President Patient Care Services and Chief Nursing Officer, Promedica Memorial Hospital, Fremont, OH, p. A482

RUCKER, Rick, Chief Operating Officer, Highland Hospital, Charleston, WV, p. A682

RUCKER, William H., Administrator, Riverland Medical Center, Ferriday, LA, p. A267

RUDBERG, Susan, M.D., Chief Medical Officer, Range Regional Health Services, Hibbing, MN, p. A333

RUDD, Adam, Chief Executive Officer, Southern Hills Hospital And Medical Center, Las Vegas, NV, p. A394

RUDD, Barry, Chief Information Officer, Memorial Satilla Health, Waycross, GA, p. A163

RUDD, Jedd, Director of Ancillary Services and Safety, Mad River Community Hospital, Arcata, CA, p. A51

RUDD, John B., President and Chief Executive Officer, Cayuga Medical Center At Ithaca, Ithaca, NY, p. A428

RUDDEN, Elizabeth, Vice President Human Resources, Connecticut Children's Medical Center, Hartford, CT, p. A108

RUDE, Erik G., Commander, William Beaumont Army Medical Center, El Paso, TX, p. A603

RUDEK, Charles M.
Chief Information Officer, Upmc Jameson, New Castle, PA, p. A533
Chief Information Officer, Upmc St. Margaret, Pittsburgh, PA, p. A538

RUDISILL, Joe, Chief Operating Officer, Regional Medical Center Bayonet Point, Hudson, FL, p. A125

RUDITZ, Bettiann S, MS, R.N., Chief Nursing Officer, Broward Health North, Deerfield Beach, FL, p. A121

RUDOLPH, Dawn, President and Chief Executive Officer, St. Vincent's Behavioral Health, CT, p. A107

RUDQUIST, Debra, FACHE, President and Chief Executive Officer, Amery Hospital And Clinic, Amery, WI, p. A689

RUDY, Bret, M.D., Executive Director and Senior Vice President, Nyu Langone Hospital-Brooklyn, NY, p. A436

RUDZIK, Carrie, Chief Administrative Officer, Eastern State Hospital, Lexington, KY, p. A254

RUDZIK, Donna, Director Human Resources, Christus Mother Frances Hospital - Sulphur Springs, Sulphur Springs, TX, p. A637

RUE, Loring, M.D., Senior Vice President, Quality Patient Safety and Clinical Effectiveness, Uab Highlands, AL, p. A15

RUE, Robert, Chief Financial Officer, Ellenville Regional Hospital, Ellenville, NY, p. A426

RUECKERT, Sebastian, M.D.
Chief Medical Officer, Christian Hospital, Saint Louis, MO, p. A368

Vice President and Chief Medical Officer, Alton Memorial Hospital, Alton, IL, p. A173

RUEDISUELI, Amy, Vice President of Finance, Mckenzie Health System, Sandusky, MI, p. A323

RUEGG, Mary Kaye, Chief Nursing Officer, Mackinac Straits Health System, Inc., Saint Ignace, MI, p. A322

RUELLO, Rocky, Vice President Human Resources, Mercy Children's Hospital St. Louis, MO, p. A368

RUFF, Robin, Chief Financial Officer, Pikes Peak Regional Hospital, Woodland Park, CO, p. A106

RUFF, Victoria, M.D., Medical Director, Select Specialty Hospital-Columbus, Mount Carmel Campus, OH, p. A479

RUFFIN, Marshall, Chief Information Officer, Inova Fair Oaks Hospital, Fairfax, VA, p. A657

RUFFING, Cindy, Director Human Resources, Siloam Springs Regional Hospital, Siloam Springs-Benton County, AR, p. A48

RUFFOLO, Joseph A., President and Chief Executive Officer, Niagara Falls Memorial Medical Center, Niagara Falls, NY, p. A438

RUGE, Randy
Chief Executive Officer, Paulding County Hospital, Paulding, OH, p. A489
Chief Operating Officer, Paulding County Hospital, Paulding, OH, p. A489

RUGGIERO, Taren, R.N., MSN, Vice President and Chief Nursing Officer, Holy Cross Hospital, Fort Lauderdale, FL, p. A122

RUIZ, Irene, Area Human Resources Director, Kaiser Permanente Ontario Medical Center, CA, p. A58

RUIZ, Javier, M.D.
Medical Director, Intracare North Hospital, Houston, TX, p. A611
Medical Director, Kingwood Pines Hospital, Kingwood, TX, p. A618

RUIZ, Kathleen, M.D., Associate Director Patient Care Services, Veterans Affairs Caribbean Healthcare System, San Juan, PR, p. A716

RUIZ, Patricia, R.N., Chief Nursing Officer, Nyc Health + Hospitals / Coney Island, New York (Includes All Hospitals Located Within The Five Boroughs), NY, p. A435

RUIZ, Tony, Senior Vice President, Chief Operating Officer, Medical Center Health System, Odessa, TX, p. A626

RULAND, Jyl
Chief Financial Officer, Clearwater Valley Hospital And Clinics, Orofino, ID, p. A170
Chief Financial Officer, St. Mary's Hospital, Cottonwood, ID, p. A169

RULLI, Sheila, Director Human Resources, Kidspeace Children's Hospital, Orefield, PA, p. A533

RUMMEL, Jennifer
Director Human Resources, Freestone Medical Center, Fairfield, TX, p. A603
Director Human Resources, Ut Health Athens, Athens, TX, p. A585

RUMPH, Jerald W., Chief Executive Officer, Mercy Rehabilitation Hospital St. Louis, Chesterfield, MO, p. A357

RUNKLE, Thomas, MS, Ph.D., Chief Operating Officer, St. Christopher's Hospital For Children, Philadelphia, PA, p. A536

RUNNELS, Clay, Vice President Chief Medical Officer Washington County, Woodridge Hospital, TN, p. A571

RUNYAN, Mark
Director Information Services, Salt Lake Regional Medical Center, Salt Lake City, UT, p. A650
Director Information Systems, Jordan Valley Medical Center West Valley Campus, West Valley City, UT, p. A652

RUNYON, Annette, Vice President and Administrator, Medical Center At Franklin, Franklin, KY, p. A252

RUPA, Maitra, M.D., Acting Medical Director, Chester Mental Health Center, Chester, IL, p. A176

RUPERT, Chris, Chief Executive Officer, Options Behavioral Health System, Indianapolis, IN, p. A207

RUPERT, Duke, Chief Operating Officer, Allegheny General Hospital, Pittsburgh, PA, p. A537

RUPERT, James M., Chief Fiscal Services, Battle Creek Veterans Affairs Medical Center, Battle Creek, MI, p. A308

RUPERT, Michael J, Chief Financial Officer, Va Long Beach Healthcare System, Long Beach, CA, p. A65

RUPP, Connie, MSN, R.N., Executive Vice President and Chief Nursing Officer, Regional West Medical Center, Scottsbluff, NE, p. A390

RUPP, Robert, President, Integris Grove Hospital, Grove, OK, p. A499

RUPPERT, Jennifer, Chief Financial Officer, Iowa City Veterans Affairs Health Care System, Iowa City, IA, p. A224

RUPPERT SCHILLER, Kerri
Senior Vice President and Chief Financial Officer, Children's Hospital Of Orange County, Orange, CA, p. A76

Senior Vice President and Chief Financial Officer, Choc Children's At Mission Hospital, Mission Viejo, CA, p. A72

RUSCH, Brett, M.D., Acting Director, White River Junction Veterans Affairs Medical Center, White River Junction, VT, p. A654

RUSH, Andrew G., Chief Executive Officer, Somerset Hospital, Somerset, PA, p. A541

RUSH, Ann Marie, Chief Financial Officer, Penobscot Valley Hospital, Lincoln, ME, p. A284

RUSH, Christopher, Chief Financial Officer, Specialty Hospital Of Meridian, Meridian, MS, p. A350

RUSH, Cindy, Director Human Resources, Clay County Medical Center, Clay Center, KS, p. A233

RUSH, Ed, President and Chief Executive Officer, Iredell Health System, Statesville, NC, p. A461

RUSH, Jeff, Chief Financial Officer, Rutherford Regional Health System, Rutherfordton, NC, p. A460

RUSH, Matthew, FACHE, President and Chief Executive Officer, Hayes Green Beach Memorial Hospital, Charlotte, MI, p. A309

RUSHIN, Denise, Director Human Resources, Poplar Bluff Regional Medical Center-South Campus, MO, p. A366

RUSHING, Derek
Chief Executive Officer, Uchealth Broomfield Hospital, Broomfield, CO, p. A97
Chief Executive Officer, Uchealth Grandview Hospital, Colorado Springs, CO, p. A98

RUSHING, Heath
Senior Vice President and Chief Executive Officer, Memorial Herman Cypress, TX, p. A612
Senior Vice President and Chief Executive Officer, Memorial Hermann Katy Hospital, Katy, TX, p. A616

RUSHING, R Lynn., Chief Executive Officer, Brook Lane Health Services, Hagerstown, MD, p. A292

RUSHING, Randy, Chief Financial Officer, Massac Memorial Hospital, Metropolis, IL, p. A189

RUSHLOW, David, Vice President Medical Affairs, Mayo Clinic Health System - Franciscan Healthcare In La Crosse, La Crosse, WI, p. A695

RUSK, Scott, M.D., Chief Medical Officer, St. Joseph Hospital, Orange, CA, p. A76

RUSNACZYK, John, Senior Vice President and Chief Financial Officer, St. Vincent Charity Medical Center, Cleveland, OH, p. A477

RUSNAK, Greg, Executive Vice President and Chief Operating Officer, Roger C. Peace Rehabilitation Hospital, SC, p. A553

RUSS, Nicole L, Director Colleague Relations, Alliance Community Hospital, Alliance, OH, p. A470

RUSSELL, Bill, Senior Chief Information Officer, Mission Hospital Laguna Beach, CA, p. A72

RUSSELL, Brant, R.N., Chief Operating Officer, Ascension St. John Hospital, Detroit, MI, p. A310

RUSSELL, Brett, Finance Business Partner Specialist, Eastern State Hospital, Lexington, KY, p. A254

RUSSELL, Dardanella, Chief Human Resources Management Service, Veterans Affairs Hudson Valley Health Care System-Montrose Campus, NY, p. A430

RUSSELL, David, President and Chief Executive Officer, Adventist Medical Center-Portland, Portland, OR, p. A516

RUSSELL, Donald
AMITA Health Senior Vice President and Chief Human Resources Officer, Amita Health Adventist Medical Center Glenoaks, Glendale Heights, IL, p. A184
Senior Vice President and Chief Human Resources Officer, Amita Health Rehabilitation Hospital, IL, p. A182
Senior Vice President and Chief Human Resources Officer, Amita Health Women & Children's Hospital, IL, p. A186

RUSSELL, Erin, Controller, Kindred Hospital-San Antonio, San Antonio, TX, p. A633

RUSSELL, Freda, R.N., Chief Executive Officer and Chief Nursing Officer, Three Rivers Hospital, Waverly, TN, p. A580

RUSSELL, Georgette, Vice President of Talent & Organizational Effectiveness, Sparrow Carson Hospital, Carson City, MI, p. A309

RUSSELL, John D., President and Chief Executive Officer, Columbus Community Hospital, Inc., Columbus, WI, p. A691

RUSSELL, Jon
Senior Vice President & Chief Information Officer, John Muir Medical Center, Walnut Creek, Walnut Creek, CA, p. A94
Senior Vice President and Chief Information Officer, John Muir Medical Center, Concord, Concord, CA, p. A55

RUSSELL, Karen M, Director of Employee Relations, Osf Saint Elizabeth Medical Center, Ottawa, IL, p. A192

RUSSELL, Kathy, R.N., Chief Nursing Officer, Bluegrass Community Hospital, Versailles, KY, p. A261

RUSSELL, Kendrick, Chief Human Resources Officer, Abrazo Scottsdale Campus, Phoenix, AZ, p. A32

RUSSELL, Kimberly, Chief Nursing Officer, Mercy Hospital Booneville, Booneville-Logan County, AR, p. A40

RUSSELL, Laurie, Director Human Resources, Lea Regional Medical Center, Hobbs, NM, p. A417

RUSSELL, Linda, Vice President and Chief Nursing Officer, Self Regional Healthcare, Greenwood, SC, p. A554

RUSSELL, Michelle, Chief Executive Officer, Lafayette Regional Rehabilitation Hospital, Lafayette, IN, p. A209

RUSSELL, Patti, Vice President Nursing, Masonicare Health Center, Wallingford, CT, p. A111

RUSSELL, Ricky, Chief Human Resources Officer, Fountain Valley Regional Hospital And Medical Center, Fountain Valley, CA, p. A58

RUSSELL, Robert, Chief Executive Officer, Encompass Health Rehabilitation Hospital Of Shelby County, Pelham, AL, p. A22

RUSSELL, Robert J, Associate Executive Director Operations, Penn Presbyterian Medical Center, Philadelphia, PA, p. A536

RUSSELL, Shelia, Director Human Resources, Jamestown Regional Medical Center, Jamestown, TN, p. A571

RUSSELL, Shelly
   Chief Executive Officer, Mitchell County Regional Health Center, Osage, IA, p. A227
   Chief Nursing Officer, Mitchell County Regional Health Center, Osage, IA, p. A227

RUSSELL, Sherrie
   AMITA Health Senior Vice President and Chief Information Officer, Amita Health Adventist Medical Center Glenoaks, Glendale Heights, IL, p. A184
   Senior Vice President & Chief Information Officer, Amita Health Rehabilitation Hospital, IL, p. A182
   Senior Vice President and Chief Information Officer, Amita Health Women & Children's Hospital, IL, p. A186
   Vice President and Chief Information Officer, Alexian Brothers Behavioral Health Hospital, Hoffman Estates, IL, p. A186

RUSSELL, Susan
   Chief Financial Officer, Och Regional Medical Center, Starkville, MS, p. A353
   Chief Nursing Officer, Singing River Hospital, MS, p. A351

RUSSELL-COOK, Donna, FACHE, President, Eastern Maine Medical Center, Bangor, ME, p. A282

RUSSELL-JENKINS, Shane, M.D., Medical Director, Windhaven Psychiatric Hospital, Prescott Valley, AZ, p. A35

RUSSO, Arthur, M.D., Director Medical Affairs, Harrington Hospital, Southbridge, MA, p. A304

RUSSO, Kimberly
   Chief Executive Officer, George Washington University Hospital, Washington, DC, p. A115
   Chief Operating Officer, George Washington University Hospital, Washington, DC, p. A115

RUSSO, Mike, Vice President Information Systems, Chi St. Joseph Health Grimes Hospital, Navasota, TX, p. A625

RUSSO, Paul M., FACHE, Director, Miami Veterans Affairs Healthcare System, Miami, FL, p. A130

RUST, Jeff, Information Technology Systems Site Manager, Chi St. Alexius Health - Williston Medical Center, Williston, ND, p. A469

RUST, Steve, Director, Human Resources, Scripps Memorial Hospital-Encinitas, Encinitas, CA, p. A57

RUTH, Daniel R., President and Chief Executive Officer, Jewish Home Of San Francisco, San Francisco, CA, p. A85

RUTH, Joseph, Executive Vice President and Chief Operating Officer, Sparrow Children's Center, MI, p. A317

RUTHERFORD, Eddie, Administrator, Tyler Holmes Memorial Hospital, Winona, MS, p. A354

RUTHERFORD, Jeremiah, Chief Medical Officer, Cornerstone Hospital Of Oklahoma-Broken Arrow, OK, p. A501

RUTHERFORD, Peter, M.D.
   Chief Executive Officer, Confluence Health/Central Washington Hospital, Wenatchee, WA, p. A680
   Chief Executive Officer, Confluence Health/Wenatchee Valley Hospital, Wenatchee, WA, p. A680

RUTHERFORD, Ronald, Chief Information Officer, Beth Israel Deaconess Hospital Plymouth, Plymouth, MA, p. A303

RUTHERFORD, Theresa, R.N., MS, FACHE, President and Chief Executive Officer, Hshs St. Anthony's Memorial Hospital, Effingham, IL, p. A181

RUTHS, Steve, M.D., Chief Medical Officer, Vista Del Mar Hospital, Ventura, CA, p. A94

RUTKOWSKI, Jennifer, R.N., MSN, Vice President Professional Services, Grant Regional Health Center, Lancaster, WI, p. A696

RUTKOWSKI, Jim, Chief Financial Officer, United Hospital Center, Bridgeport, WV, p. A681

RUTLEDGE, Debra K, R.N., Vice President Nursing Services, Chi Health Plainview, Plainview, NE, p. A390

RUTLEDGE, Rebel, Director Human Resources, Grady Memorial Hospital, Chickasha, OK, p. A497

RUWOLDT, Steven T, Chief Operating Officer, Memorial Medical Center, Las Cruces, NM, p. A418

RUYTER, Mary J., Interim Chief Executive Officer, Wheatland Memorial Healthcare, Harlowton, MT, p. A376

RYAN, Chris, Chief Information Officer, Auburn Community Hospital, Auburn, NY, p. A422

RYAN, Christie, Chief Nursing Officer, Healthsouth Rehabilitation Hospital Of Sewickley, Sewickley, PA, p. A541

RYAN, Christina M, R.N., Chief Executive Officer and Chief Nursing Officer, The Women's Hospital, Newburgh, IN, p. A213

RYAN, Christina M., R.N., Chief Executive Officer, The Women's Hospital, Newburgh, IN, p. A213

RYAN, Connie, Chief Nursing Officer, Select Specialty Hospital-Tulsa Midtown, Tulsa, OK, p. A509

RYAN, David P., Vice President Human Resources, Melrose-Wakefield Hospital, MA, p. A301

RYAN, Debora, R.N., Vice President Patient Care, St. Francis Regional Medical Center, Shakopee, MN, p. A340

RYAN, Dennis, Senior Vice President and Chief Financial Officer, Children's Hospital Of The King's Daughters, Norfolk, VA, p. A662

RYAN, Emily, Chief Executive Officer, Medical Behavioral Hospital Of Mishawaka, Knox, IN, p. A208

RYAN, Frank, Chief Financial Officer, Manchester Veterans Affairs Medical Center, Manchester, NH, p. A400

RYAN, Jacqueline, Director Human Resources, Mayo Clinic Health System In Lake City, Lake City, MN, p. A333

RYAN, Jeffrey
   Chief Operating Officer, Cancer Treatment Centers Of America-Eastern Regional Medical Center, Philadelphia, PA, p. A534
   Senior Vice President, Finance and Business Development, Cancer Treatment Centers Of America-Eastern Regional Medical Center, Philadelphia, PA, p. A534

RYAN, John Jack, M.D., Chief Medical Officer, Oakland Regional Hospital, Southfield, MI, p. A323

RYAN, Kimberly, President, Wellstar Atlanta Medical Center - South Campus, GA, p. A147

RYAN, Lisa M, Coordinator Human Resources, Hampstead Hospital, Hampstead, NH, p. A399

RYAN, Maria, Ph.D., Chief Executive Officer, Cottage Hospital, Woodsville, NH, p. A401

RYAN, Mike, Director of Information Services, Gunnison Valley Hospital, Gunnison, UT, p. A647

RYAN, Patrice
   Vice President Human Resources, Cottage Rehabilitation Hospital, CA, p. A88
   Vice President Human Resources, Goleta Valley Cottage Hospital, Santa Barbara, CA, p. A88
   Vice President Human Resources, Santa Ynez Valley Cottage Hospital, Solvang, CA, p. A90

RYAN, Patrick G., Chief Executive Officer, Promise Hospital Of Fort Myers, Fort Myers, FL, p. A123

RYAN, Patrick J., Chief Human Resources Officer, Helen Hayes Hospital, West Haverstraw, NY, p. A445

RYAN, Rebecca, Interim Director Human Resources and Employee Health, Ukiah Valley Medical Center, Ukiah, CA, p. A93

RYAN, Robert, M.D., Chief Medical Officer, Guadalupe Regional Medical Center, Seguin, TX, p. A635

RYAN, Sharon, Regional Controller, Select Specialty Hospital-Macomb County, Mount Clemens, MI, p. A319

RYAN, Tim, Chief Financial Officer, Centennial Peaks Hospital, Louisville, CO, p. A104

RYAN, William, Vice President and Chief Financial Officer, Uf Health Jacksonville, Jacksonville, FL, p. A126

RYBA, Janice L., JD, Chief Executive Officer, St. Mary Medical Center, Hobart, IN, p. A206

RYBA, Thomas L., Chief Executive Officer, Lighthouse Behavioral Health Hospital, Conway, SC, p. A552

RYBICKI, Cathy, Chief Operating Officer, Spectrum Health Reed City Hospital, Reed City, MI, p. A321

RYBOLT, Andrew, Chief Financial Officer, El Paso Children's Hospital, El Paso, TX, p. A601

RYCKMAN, George, D.O., Chief of Staff, Paul Oliver Memorial Hospital, Frankfort, MI, p. A313

RYDER, Doug, President, Holy Cross Germantown Hospital, Germantown, MD, p. A291

RYDER, Jeff, Director Information Systems, Saint Joseph Mount Sterling, Mount Sterling, KY, p. A258

RYDER, Natalie, Chief Administrative Officer, Borgess-Lee Memorial Hospital, Dowagiac, MI, p. A312

RYDER, Ronald, D.O., President of the Medical Staff, Robert Wood Johnson University Hospital At Hamilton, Hamilton, NJ, p. A405

RYERSE, David
   Chief Executive Officer, Daniels Memorial Healthcare Center, Scobey, MT, p. A379

   Chief Executive Officer, Stillwater Billings Clinic, Columbus, MT, p. A374

RYLAND, Jennifer M, R.N., Chief Administrative Officer, Jackson Medical Center, Jackson, AL, p. A19

RYLAND, Jennifer M., R.N., Chief Executive Officer, Jackson Medical Center, Jackson, AL, p. A19

RYLE, Barry W., Chief Information Officer, Oswego Hospital, Oswego, NY, p. A439

RYMER, Brandy, Coordinator Human Resources, Murray Medical Center, Chatsworth, GA, p. A150

RYON, Joel, M.D., Chief of Staff, Henry County Health Center, Mount Pleasant, IA, p. A226

RYS, Jan, R.N., Chief Executive Officer, Straith Hospital For Special Surgery, Southfield, MI, p. A324

RZOMP, Kimberly
   Vice President and Chief Financial Officer, Chambersburg Hospital, Chambersburg, PA, p. A522
   Vice President Finance, Waynesboro Hospital, Waynesboro, PA, p. A543

S

SAAD, Michael, Vice President and Chief Information Officer, University Of Tennessee Medical Center, Knoxville, TN, p. A572

SAADAT, Annette, Human Resources Business Partner, Saint Joseph Mount Sterling, Mount Sterling, KY, p. A258

SAALFELD, Thomas, Senior Vice President and Chief Operating Officer, St. Elizabeth Falmouth, KY, p. A252

SAARI, Heidi L, Director, Human Resources, Upper Connecticut Valley Hospital, Colebrook, NH, p. A398

SAAVEDRA, JayLynn, Chief Information Officer, U.S. Public Health Service Indian Hospital, Parker, AZ, p. A32

SABANDIT, Elizabeth, Director Human Resources, Alhambra Hospital Medical Center, Alhambra, CA, p. A50

SABELLA, Deborah, R.N., Chief Executive Officer, Landmark Hospital Of Cape Girardeau, Cape Girardeau, MO, p. A356

SABHARRWAL, Parajeet, Chief Executive Officer, Minimally Invasive Surgery Hospital, Lenexa, KS, p. A240

SABIA, John, M.D., Vice President Medical Affairs, Northern Dutchess Hospital, Rhinebeck, NY, p. A441

SABLE, Kenneth N., M.D., President, K. Hovnanian Children's Hospital, NJ, p. A408

SABOTTA, John, Director Information Systems, St. Margaret's Hospital, Spring Valley, IL, p. A196

SACHARSKI, Steve, Chief Financial Officer, Havenwyck Hospital, Auburn Hills, MI, p. A307

SACHDEV, Aruna, M.D., Medical Director, Pappas Rehabilitation Hospital For Children, Canton, MA, p. A299

SACHDEV, Vish, M.D., Chief Medical Officer, Brookwood Baptist Medical Center, Birmingham, AL, p. A14

SACHDEVA, Sandeep, M.D., Vice President Medical Affairs, Swedish/Edmonds, Edmonds, WA, p. A671

SACHS, Henry T, M.D., III, Medical Director, Emma Pendleton Bradley Hospital, East Providence, RI, p. A547

SACHTJEN, Mistie, Chief Executive Officer, Community Memorial Hospital, Burke, SD, p. A559

SACHTLEBEN, Michael, President, Medstar Georgetown University Hospital, Washington, DC, p. A115

SACK, Michael V, FACHE, Chief Executive Officer, Melrose-Wakefield Hospital, MA, p. A301

SACKETT, John, President SGMC and Executive Vice President and Chief Operating Officer, Adventist Healthcare Shady Grove Medical Center, Rockville, MD, p. A294

SACKETT, Walter, President, Kettering Behavioral Medical Center, OH, p. A487

SACKMANN, Charles, M.D., Chief of Staff, East Adams Rural Healthcare, Ritzville, WA, p. A676

SACKRISON, Jeffrey
   President, Vidant Bertie Hospital, Windsor, NC, p. A462
   President, Vidant Chowan Hospital, Edenton, NC, p. A452

SADA, Judy, Chief Financial Officer, Memorial Hospital Miramar, Miramar, FL, p. A132

SADLER, Cindy, Chief Nursing Officer, Iron County Medical Center, Pilot Knob, MO, p. A366

SADLER, Donna, Director Human Resources, Arkansas State Hospital, Little Rock-Pulaski County, AR, p. A44

SADLER, Joy, Director Human Resources, Bear River Valley Hospital, Tremonton, UT, p. A651

SADLER BELL, Kelli S, R.N.
   Vice President, Chief Nursing Officer, Novant Health Charlotte Orthopaedic Hospital, Charlotte, NC, p. A450
   Vice President, Chief Nursing Officer, Presbyterian Hemby Children's Hospital, NC, p. A450

SADOFF, Jennifer, Chief Executive Officer, Moab Regional Hospital, Moab, UT, p. A647

SADR, Farrokh, M.D., Chief Medical Officer, St. Luke's Sacred Heart Campus, Allentown, PA, p. A519

SADRO, Cheryl A, Executive Vice President Chief Business and Finance Officer, Angleton Danbury Campus, TX, p. A606

SAENZ, Luis J Rodriguez, M.D., Medical Director, Hospital Menonita De Cayey, Cayey, PR, p. A713

SAENZ, Melanie, Regional Human Resources Officer, Presence Saints Mary & Elizabeth Medical Center, Claremont Avenue, IL, p. A178

SAFFA, Steve, Director Human Resources, University Of Kansas Health System St. Francis Campus, Topeka, KS, p. A246

SAFLEY, Thomas, Chief Financial Officer, St. Joseph Regional Medical Center, Lewiston, ID, p. A170

SAFYER, Steven M., M.D., President and Chief Executive Officer, Montefiore Medical Center - North Division, NY, p. A433

SAGE, Kelly, Chief Nursing Officer, Hshs St. Anthony's Memorial Hospital, Effingham, IL, p. A181

SAGMIT, Rodney, Chief Information Management, Va Long Beach Healthcare System, Long Beach, CA, p. A65

SAHA, Sanjay K, Chief Operating Officer, Sibley Memorial Hospital, Washington, DC, p. A116

SAHLOLBEI, Hossain, M.D., Chief of Staff, Palo Verde Hospital, Blythe, CA, p. A53

SAHLSTROM, Christopher, M.D., Chief of Staff, Mat-Su Regional Medical Center, Palmer, AK, p. A27

SAHMAUNT, Sarabeth, Supervisory Accountant, Lawton Indian Hospital, Lawton, OK, p. A500

SAIA, Carrie L., Chief Executive Officer, Holton Community Hospital, Holton, KS, p. A237

SAINBERT, Wilmino, Chief Human Resources Management Service, Northport Veterans Affairs Medical Center, Northport, NY, p. A438

SAINTZ, Jeffrey, Vice President Human Resources, Titusville Area Hospital, Titusville, PA, p. A542

SAIYED, Ashfaq, M.D., Medical Director, Irwin County Hospital, Ocilla, GA, p. A158

SAIZ, Claudia, Chief Executive Officer, Advanced Care Hospital Of Southern New Mexico, Las Cruces, NM, p. A417

SAJID, Muhammad W., M.D., Medical Director, Lincoln Trail Behavioral Health System, Radcliff, KY, p. A260

SAKALOSKY, Matt, Director Information Services and Chief Information Officer, Fremont Health, Fremont, NE, p. A384

SAKOVITS, Steven, Vice President Information Systems and Chief Information Officer, Stamford Hospital, Stamford, CT, p. A111

SALAKI, Jana, Regional Director Human Resources, Wellspan Ephrata Community Hospital, Ephrata, PA, p. A525

SALAMANCA, Mary, Director Human Resources, Healthsouth Rehabilitation Hospital Of Spring Hill, Brooksville, FL, p. A119

SALAMONE, Joanna, Senior Vice President Clinical Services and Chief Nursing Officer, Southern Maine Health Care - Biddeford Medical Center, ME, p. A283

SALANDI, John, Chief Executive Officer, Landmark Hospital Of Savannah, Savannah, GA, p. A160

SALAS, Dawn, Controller, Healthsouth Rehabilitation Hospital At Martin Health, Stuart, FL, p. A139

SALAS, Victor, M.D., President Medical Staff, Unitypoint Health - Jones Regional Medical Center, Anamosa, IA, p. A217

SALAWAY, Tarek, R.N.
Chief Executive, Mission Hospital Laguna Beach, CA, p. A72
Chief Operating Officer, Usc Norris Comprehensive Cancer Center, Los Angeles, CA, p. A70

SALAZAR, Eloisa, Chief Financial Officer, San Antonio Division, TX, p. A634

SALAZAR, Leanne, Chief Nursing Officer, Oak Hill Hospital, Brooksville, FL, p. A119

SALAZAR, Linda C, Information Technology Leader, Kaiser Permanente Baldwin Park Medical Center, Baldwin Park, CA, p. A52

SALAZAR, Pamela, M.D., Chief of Staff, Walton Rehabilitation Hospital, Augusta, GA, p. A147

SALAZAR, Serafin, M.D., Chief of Staff, Parkview Community Hospital Medical Center, Riverside, CA, p. A81

SALCEDO, Martha, Interim Director Human Resources, Whittier Hospital Medical Center, Whittier, CA, p. A95

SALCEDO, Nydimar, Chief Human Resources Officer, Castaner General Hospital, Castaner, PR, p. A712

SALDANHA, Glenn J., Chief Operating Officer, Palms Of Pasadena Hospital, Saint Petersburg, FL, p. A138

SALDIVAR, Antoninette, Vice President, Human Resources, Bridgepoint Hospital National Harbor, Washington, DC, p. A115

SALDIVAR, Duke, FACHE, Chief Executive Officer, Warm Springs Rehabilitation Hospital Of Kyle, Kyle, TX, p. A618

SALEEBY, Manhal, M.D., Chief of Staff, Vcu Health Community Memorial Hospital, South Hill, VA, p. A666

SALEEM, David, Director Information Technology, Greystone Park Psychiatric Hospital, Morris Plains, NJ, p. A407

SALEM, Gary, M.D., Vice President Medical Affairs, Mclaren Lapeer Region, Lapeer, MI, p. A317

SALEM, Michael, M.D., President and Chief Executive Officer, National Jewish Health, Denver, CO, p. A99

SALGADO, Joe, M.D., Chief of Staff, Artesia General Hospital, Artesia, NM, p. A416

SALIBA, K. Michael, M.D., Medical Director, Shadow Mountain Behavioral Health System, Tulsa, OK, p. A509

SALINAS, Amaro, Assistant Administrator and Human Resource Officer, Starr County Memorial Hospital, Rio Grande City, TX, p. A630

SALINAS, Daniel, M.D., Senior Vice President and Chief Medical Officer, Children's Healthcare Of Atlanta At Scottish Rite, GA, p. A146

SALINAS, Noe
Vice President Information Technology, Nexus Specialty Hospital The Woodlands, The Woodlands, TX, p. A640
Vice President Information Technology, Nexus Specialty Hospital, Shenandoah, TX, p. A635

SALING, Christopher, Manager Human Resources, Park City Hospital, Park City, UT, p. A649

SALISBURY, Dennis, M.D., Vice President for Medical Affairs, St. James Healthcare, Butte, MT, p. A374

SALISBURY, Renee A, Director Human Resources, Osf Saint Luke Medical Center, Kewanee, IL, p. A187

SALISBURY, Tracy
Director Human Resources, Hiram W. Davis Medical Center, Petersburg, VA, p. A663
Regional Manager Human Resources, Central State Hospital, Petersburg, VA, p. A663

SALLER, William, Chief Financial Officer, Rio Grande Regional Hospital, Mcallen, TX, p. A623

SALLEY, Wanda, Vice President Human Resources, West Florida Rehabilitation Institute, FL, p. A136

SALLIS, Tom, Director Information Systems, Sparks Regional Medical Center, Fort Smith-Sebastian County, AR, p. A42

SALLOUM, Fadi, M.D., Medical Director, Select Specialty Hospital-Pontiac, Pontiac, MI, p. A321

SALMAN, Wael, M.D., Vice President Medical Affairs, Memorial Healthcare, Owosso, MI, p. A320

SALMANULLAH, Muhammad, Chief Medical Director, Healthsouth Rehabilitation Hospital, Concord, NH, p. A398

SALNAS, Todd
President, Petaluma Valley Hospital, Petaluma, CA, p. A78
President, Santa Rosa Memorial Hospital, Santa Rosa, CA, p. A89

SALO, Saliba, President, Northridge Hospital Medical Center, Los Angeles, CA, p. A69

SALOM, Ira, M.D., Clinical Director, Northern Navajo Medical Center, Shiprock, NM, p. A420

SALOME, Jenny, Chief Financial Officer and Assistant Administrator, Northwest Hills Surgical Hospital, Austin, TX, p. A586

SALOMON, Kathryn, Director Human Resources, Kona Community Hospital, Kealakekua, HI, p. A166

SALTAFORMAGGIO, Cheri, Chief Executive Officer, St. Charles Surgical Hospital, New Orleans, LA, p. A276

SALTER, Cherry B, Director of Nursing, Hardtner Medical Center, Olla, LA, p. A277

SALTER, Lisa, Chief Executive Officer, Georgetown Behavioral Health Institute, Georgetown, TX, p. A607

SALTONSTALL, Christine, Chief Financial Officer, Kindred Hospital-Baldwin Park, Baldwin Park, CA, p. A52

SALTZGABER, Lee, Chief Medical Officer, Gerald Champion Regional Medical Center, Alamogordo, NM, p. A415

SALVADOR, Ed, Chief Financial Officer, St. Jude Medical Center, Fullerton, CA, p. A60

SALVATI, Mario, Director Fiscal Services, Shriners Hospitals For Children-Philadelphia, Philadelphia, PA, p. A536

SALVI, Donna, Chief Nursing Officer, Watsonville Community Hospital, Watsonville, CA, p. A94

SALVINO, Sonia, Vice President Finance, University Macdonald Women's Hospital, OH, p. A477

SALVITTI, Alfred P, Chief Financial Officer, Eagleville Hospital, Eagleville, PA, p. A524

SALVO, Stephen, Vice President Human Resources, Anna Jaques Hospital, Newburyport, MA, p. A302

SALWAN, Manav, Medical Director, Kindred Hospital-Sycamore, Sycamore, IL, p. A197

SALY, David, Director, Information Services, Largo Medical Center - Indian Rocks, FL, p. A128

SALYER, Steven, Chief Operating Officer, Up Health System-Marquette, Marquette, MI, p. A318

SALZMAN, Shona, Chief Operating Officer, William Newton Hospital, Winfield, KS, p. A248

SAMBASIVAN, Venkataraman, M.D., Chief Medical Officer, Lourdes Medical Center, Pasco, WA, p. A674

SAMILO, Nick, Vice President Fiscal Services and Chief Financial Officer, Carolinas Healthcare System Stanly, Albemarle, NC, p. A447

SAMMARCO, Michael, M.D., Chief Financial Officer, Erie County Medical Center, Buffalo, NY, p. A423

SAMMONS, Craig, Chief Financial Officer, Sky Ridge Medical Center, Lone Tree, CO, p. A103

SAMMONS, Jacquelyn, R.N., Supervisor, Child And Adolescent Behavioral Health Services, Willmar, MN, p. A342

SAMMS, Caswell, Network Chief Financial Officer, Nyc Health + Hospitals / Lincoln, New York (Includes All Hospitals Located Within The Five Boroughs), NY, p. A436

SAMORA, Martha, R.N., FACHE, Chief Executive Officer, Healthsouth Bakersfield Rehabilitation Hospital, Bakersfield, CA, p. A52

SAMPAGA, Arthur, Assistant Director Nursing, Hilo Medical Center, Hilo, HI, p. A164

SAMPSON, Arthur J., FACHE, President, Miriam Hospital, Providence, RI, p. A547

SAMPSON, Bob
Senior Vice President, Human Resources, Evergreenhealth, Kirkland, WA, p. A673
Vice President Human Resources, Redwood Memorial Hospital, Fortuna, CA, p. A58

SAMPSON, Jill, Director Human Resources, Lemuel Shattuck Hospital, Jamaica Plain, MA, p. A300

SAMS, Carla, R.N., Director of Nursing, Cypress Grove Behavioral Health, Bastrop, LA, p. A263

SAMS, James C., Chief of Staff, Mckenzie Health System, Sandusky, MI, p. A323

SAMSON, Ley, Director Management Information Systems, Mainland Medical Center, TX, p. A643

SAMUDRALA, Siresha, M.D., Medical Director, Mercy Rehabilitation Hospital St. Louis, Chesterfield, MO, p. A357

SAMUEL, Nicole, Chief Financial Officer, Sierra Vista Hospital, Sacramento, CA, p. A82

SAMUELS, Christopher, Chief of Staff, Skyline Hospital, White Salmon, WA, p. A680

SAMUELSON, Kimberly, Director of Information Management, Highland-Clarksburg Hospital, Clarksburg, WV, p. A682

SAMUELSON, Melissa A, R.N.
Vice President and Chief Nursing Officer, Mercy Health - Anderson Hospital, Cincinnati, OH, p. A475
Vice President and Chief Nursing Officer, Mercy Health - Clermont Hospital, Batavia, OH, p. A471

SAMYN, Mike, Vice President, Finance and Chief Financial Officer, St. Mary Mercy Hospital, Livonia, MI, p. A318

SAMZ, Jeff, Chief Operating Officer, Madison Hospital, AL, p. A19

SAN FILIPPO, Bruce, M.D., Chief Medical Officer, Memorial Medical Center, Las Cruces, NM, p. A418

SANBORN, Michael, FACHE, MS, President, Baylor All Saints Medical Center At Fort Worth, Fort Worth, TX, p. A604

SANBORN, Randall, Director Information Systems, Garden City Hospital, Garden City, MI, p. A313

SANCHEZ, Alvaro, M.D., Chief Medical Officer, Ridgeview Medical Center, Waconia, MN, p. A341

SANCHEZ, Antonio, M.D.
Acting Director, Veterans Affairs Caribbean Healthcare System, San Juan, PR, p. A716
Chief of Staff, Veterans Affairs Caribbean Healthcare System, San Juan, PR, p. A716

SANCHEZ, Arnaldo Rodriguez, M.D., Chief Operating Officer, Hospital Episcopal San Lucas Guayama, Guayama, PR, p. A713

SANCHEZ, Emalie, Director Human Resources, Baylor Medical Center At Uptown, Dallas, TX, p. A595

SANCHEZ, Esperanza, Chief Clinical Officer, Kindred Hospital Santa Ana, CA, p. A63

SANCHEZ, Freddie, Director Information Systems, Fountain Valley Regional Hospital And Medical Center, Fountain Valley, CA, p. A58

SANCHEZ, John, Vice President Human Resources, White Plains Hospital Center, White Plains, NY, p. A446

SANCHEZ, Jose R., President and Chief Executive Officer, Norwegian American Hospital, Chicago, IL, p. A178

SANCHEZ, Jose', Chief Nursing Officer, Chg Hospital Tucson, Llc, Tucson, AZ, p. A37

SANCHEZ, Nancy, Senior Vice President and Vice Dean Human Resources, Rusk Institute At Nyu-Hjd, NY, p. A436

SANCHEZ, Rebecca, R.N., M.P.H., Director of Nursing, Texas Center For Infectious Disease, San Antonio, TX, p. A634

SANCHEZ-BICKLEY, Michelle

Vice President Human Resources, Renown Children's Hospital, NV, p. A396

Vice President Human Resources, Renown Rehabilitation Hospital, Reno, NV, p. A396

Vice President Human Resources, Renown South Meadows Medical Center, Reno, NV, p. A396

SANCHEZ-RICO, Gloria, Chief Nursing Officer and Vice President, Huntington Memorial Hospital, Pasadena, CA, p. A78

SAND, Michelle, R.N., MSN, Vice President and Chief Nursing Officer, Cascade Valley Hospital, Arlington, WA, p. A669

SANDAGER, Brian, Chief Information Officer, Lowell General Hospital, Saints Campus, MA, p. A301

SANDBERG, Sue, R.N., Chief Operating Officer, Unc Rex Health Care, Raleigh, NC, p. A459

SANDBERG, Susan, R.N., Chief Executive Officer, Melrose-Wakefield Hospital, MA, p. A301

SANDBERG, Todd, Chief Executive Officer, Riverwood Healthcare Center, Aitkin, MN, p. A327

SANDBULTE, Nyla H, R.N., Director of Nursing, Sanford Luverne Medical Center, Luverne, MN, p. A334

SANDEFUR, Gwen, President, Spectrum Health Hospital Group, Spectrum Health, MI, p. A314

SANDER, Cindy, Coordinator Human Resources, Kindred Hospital St. Louis-St. Anthony'S, MO, p. A368

SANDERS, Amy, Chief Human Resources, Captain James A. Lovell Federal Health Care Center, North Chicago, IL, p. A191

SANDERS, Carolyn Lucey, Senior Vice President Patient Services and Chief Nursing Officer, University Of Colorado Hospital, Aurora, CO, p. A96

SANDERS, David, Chief Financial Officer, Springhill Medical Center, Springhill, LA, p. A279

SANDERS, David S., Chief Executive Officer, Fannin Regional Hospital, Blue Ridge, GA, p. A148

SANDERS, Gale H, Director, Gadsden Regional Medical Center, Gadsden, AL, p. A18

SANDERS, Harv, Chief Financial Officer, Rhea Medical Center, Dayton, TN, p. A569

SANDERS, Jeff, Senior Vice President, Chief Operating Officer, Maine Medical Center, Brighton Campus, ME, p. A285

SANDERS, Jeffrey, M.D., Chief of Staff, Sierra Surgery Hospital, NV, p. A392

SANDERS, Kelly B., Vice President Human Resources, Good Shepherd Health Care System, Hermiston, OR, p. A513

SANDERS, Kenneth, Administrator and Chief Executive Officer, Dallas County Medical Center, Fordyce-Dallas County, AR, p. A42

SANDERS, Kimberly, Chief Nursing Officer, Baptist Memorial Hospital-Huntingdon, Huntingdon, TN, p. A571

SANDERS, Kris, Chief Financial Officer, Methodist Healthcare Olive Branch Hospital, Olive Branch, MS, p. A351

SANDERS, Kyle, Chief Financial Officer, Nea Baptist Memorial Hospital, Jonesboro-Craighead County, AR, p. A44

SANDERS, Michael B., President and Chief Executive Officer, Monroe Clinic, Monroe, WI, p. A699

SANDERS, Michael R, MS, Chief Operating Officer, Promise Hospital Baton Rouge - Main Campus, Baton Rouge, LA, p. A264

SANDERS, R. Bradley, D.O., Executive Medical Director, Alvarado Parkway Institute Behavioral Health System, La Mesa, CA, p. A63

SANDERS, Robert, M.D., Chief Medical Officer, Tmc Behavioral Health Center, TX, p. A599

SANDERS, Sheila M, Chief Information Officer, Emory Wesley Woods Geriatric Hospital, GA, p. A146

SANDERS, Steve, Chief Financial Officer, Washington County Hospital And Clinics, Washington, IA, p. A230

SANDERS, Susie Sherrod, Chief Financial Officer, Cherry Hospital, Goldsboro, NC, p. A453

SANDERS, Victoria Odom., FACHE, Chief Executive Officer, Baylor Institute For Rehabilitation At Fort Worth, Fort Worth, TX, p. A604

SANDHU, Rohinder, M.D., President of the Medical Staff, San Antonio Regional Hospital, Upland, CA, p. A93

SANDIFER, Ron, Chief Information Officer, Community Memorial Hospital, CA, p. A94

SANDIN, James H, M.D., Assistant Administrator Medical Affairs, Hunt Regional Medical Center, Greenville, TX, p. A608

SANDLES, Christopher R., FACHE
Director, Central Texas Veterans Affairs Health Care System, Olin E. Teague Veterans Medical Center, TX, p. A638

Director, Central Texas Veterans Health Care System, Doris Miller Veterans Medical Center, TX, p. A638

Medical Center Director and Chief Executive Officer, Central Texas Veterans Health Care System, Doris Miller Veterans Medical Center, TX, p. A638

SANDLIN, Michael, M.D., Chief of Staff, Muscogee Creek Nation Medical Center, Okmulgee, OK, p. A505

SANDMANN, Patty, Senior Director of Nursing, Burgess Health Center, Onawa, IA, p. A227

SANDS, Dennis, Chief Medical Officer, Osf Healthcare Saint Clare's Hospital, IL, p. A173

SANDS, Naomi, Administrative Assistant and Manager Human Resources, Swift County - Benson Health Services, Benson, MN, p. A328

SANDS, Sherry, R.N., Chief Nursing Officer, Southern Tennessee Regional Health System-Pulaski, Pulaski, TN, p. A579

SANDS, Tiffany, Manager Health Information, Arbuckle Memorial Hospital, Sulphur, OK, p. A507

SANDS, Tom, Interim Chief Executive Officer, Carney Hospital, Boston, MA, p. A296

SANDSTROM, C Bruce, Vice President and Chief Financial Officer, Community General Health Center, ME, p. A286

SANDUJA, Sourabh, Administrator, Altus Baytown Hospital, Baytown, TX, p. A587

SANFORD, Debbie F, R.N., MS, Administrator, Pine Grove Behavioral Health And Addiction Services, MS, p. A347

SANFORD, Lisa
Chief Nursing Officer, St. Luke's Elmore, Mountain Home, ID, p. A170

VP Patient Care/CNO, Holy Rosary Healthcare, Miles City, MT, p. A377

SANFORD, Ricca, Director Human Resources, Regional West Garden County, Oshkosh, NE, p. A389

SANFORD, Sharon K, Director Human Resources, Jersey Community Hospital, Jerseyville, IL, p. A186

SANFORD, Stacy, Chief Executive Officer, Oceans Behavioral Hospital Abilene, Abilene, TX, p. A582

SANGER, David, M.D., Chief Medical Officer, Pawnee Valley Community Hospital, Larned, KS, p. A239

SANGER, Ken, R.N., Chief Nursing Officer and Chief Operations Officer, Lake Huron Medical Center, Port Huron, MI, p. A321

SANGER, Neal, Vice President Information Services, Mayo Clinic Health System - Franciscan Healthcare In La Crosse, La Crosse, WI, p. A695

SANGHI, Harishankar, M.D., Clinical Director, St. Lawrence Psychiatric Center, Ogdensburg, NY, p. A439

SANKARAN, Jaya, M.D., Chief of Staff, St. Mary's Of Michigan Standish Hospital, Standish, MI, p. A324

SANKE, Kristina, Chief Financial Officer, Orchard Hospital, Gridley, CA, p. A61

SANKOORIKAL, Joseph, M.D., Chief Medical Staff, Kansas Rehabilitation Hospital, Topeka, KS, p. A246

SANKS, Claude, Chief Medical Staff, Effingham Hospital, Springfield, GA, p. A161

SANNUTO, John
Chief Executive Officer, Clearvista Health And Wellness, Lorain, OH, p. A485

Chief Executive Officer, Wellbridge Healthcare Greater Dallas, Plano, TX, p. A629

SANSOM, Christine R, Chief Nursing Officer, Mclaren Port Huron, Port Huron, MI, p. A321

SANSONE, John, Vice President, Human Resources, Monadnock Community Hospital, Peterborough, NH, p. A401

SANTA ANA, Coleen F., President, Sentara Albemarle Medical Center, Elizabeth City, NC, p. A452

SANTANA, Leticia, Administrator Medical Records, Puerto Rico Children's Hospital, PR, p. A712

SANTANGELO, Craig, Director Information Services, Medical City Arlington, Arlington, TX, p. A584

SANTANGELO, Joe, M.D., Vice President of Medical Affairs, Munson Healthcare Cadillac Hospital, Cadillac, MI, p. A309

SANTANGELO, John, Director Information Technology, Cleveland Clinic Florida, Weston, FL, p. A144

SANTARELLI, James, M.D., President Medical Staff, Aurora Medical Center Kenosha, Kenosha, WI, p. A695

SANTIAGO, Alejandro, Director Finance, Doctors' Center Hospital San Juan, San Juan, PR, p. A715

SANTIAGO, Julio, M.D., Chief of Staff, Genesis Medical Center-Aledo, Aledo, IL, p. A173

SANTIAGO, Manuel, Chief Information Officer, Hospital Metropolitan, San Juan, PR, p. A716

SANTIAGO, Orlando, Human Resources Officer, Hospital Del Maestro, San Juan, PR, p. A715

SANTIAGO, Sugehi, Director, Hospital San Francisco, San Juan, PR, p. A716

SANTIAGO, Ubaldo, M.D., Chairman, Doctors' Center Hospital San Juan, San Juan, PR, p. A715

SANTIESTEBAN, Nancy, Director Patient Care Services, Presbyterian Espanola Hospital, Espanola, NM, p. A417

SANTILLI, Robert J., Chief Executive Officer, Gunnison Valley Hospital, Gunnison, CO, p. A101

SANTINA, Ray, Director Information Systems, Psychiatric Institute Of Washington, Washington, DC, p. A116

SANTISTEVAN, Vivian, Chief Human Resources, Tsehootsooi Medical Center, Fort Defiance, AZ, p. A29

SANTMAN, Kim D, Vice President Finance, St. Margaret's Hospital, Spring Valley, IL, p. A196

SANTOPIETRO, John, M.D., President and Medical Director, Silver Hill Hospital, New Canaan, CT, p. A109

SANTORA, Judith
Chief Human Resource Officer, Lutheran Hospital, Cleveland, OH, p. A477

Human Resources Business Partner, Marymount Hospital, Garfield Heights, OH, p. A483

SANTOS, Alfred, Chief Executive Officer, Encompass Health Rehabilitation Hospital Of Northern Virginia, Aldie, VA, p. A655

SANTOS, Daniel, Director Ancillary Services, Pacifica Hospital Of The Valley, Los Angeles, CA, p. A69

SANTOS, David
President and Chief Executive Officer, Adventist Health Clear Lake, Clearlake, CA, p. A54

President and Chief Executive Officer, Adventist Health Clear Lake, Clearlake, CA, p. A54

SANTOS, Deborah, R.N., Chief Nursing Officer, Healthsouth Rehabilitation Hospital Of Western Massachusetts, Ludlow, MA, p. A301

SANTOS, Gloria N, R.N., MS
Chief Nursing Officer, Florida Hospital Lake Placid, FL, p. A139

Vice President and Chief Nursing Officer, Florida Hospital Wauchula, Wauchula, FL, p. A143

SANTOS, Ismael, Director Human Resources, Valle Vista Hospital, Greenwood, IN, p. A205

SANTOS, Lori
Chief Financial Officer, St. Peter's Hospital, Albany, NY, p. A421

Vice President Finance, Albany Memorial Hospital, Albany, NY, p. A421

SANTUCCI, James, Chief Operating Officer, Desert Regional Medical Center, Palm Springs, CA, p. A77

SANTULLI, Patricia, Director Human Resources, Elmira Psychiatric Center, Elmira, NY, p. A426

SANVILLE, David, Chief Financial Officer, Mt. Ascutney Hospital And Health Center, Windsor, VT, p. A654

SANWARI, Murtaza, Chief Operating Officer, Kaiser Permanente Panorama City Medical Center, Los Angeles, CA, p. A67

SANZONE, Frank, Manager Information Technology, Brighton Center For Recovery, Brighton, MI, p. A308

SAPMAZ, Cagri, Information Technology Director, Bolivar Medical Center, Cleveland, MS, p. A345

SAPORITO, Angie, Administrator, Mercy Hospital Columbus, Columbus, KS, p. A233

SAPORITO, Joann L., R.N., Vice President Nursing Services, Oak Valley Hospital District, Oakdale, CA, p. A75

SAPP, Tracy, Director Human Resources, Healthsouth Rehabilitation Hospital Of Ocala, Ocala, FL, p. A133

SAPPENFIELD, Debra, R.N., Chief Nursing Officer, Hemphill County Hospital, Canadian, TX, p. A591

SAPPINGTON-CRITTENDEN, Shana, Chief Operating Officer, Westside Regional Medical Center, Plantation, FL, p. A136

SARBACHER, James, Chief Information Officer, State Hospital North, Orofino, ID, p. A171

SARDANA, Sadhana, M.D., Clinical Director, Rockland Children's Hospital Psychiatric Center, Orangeburg, NY, p. A439

SARDELLA, Jeff, Director Information Technology, Terrebonne General Medical Center, Houma, LA, p. A269

SARDONE, Frank J, President and Chief Executive Officer, Bronson Vicksburg Hospital, MI, p. A317

SARDONE, Frank J.
President and Chief Executive Officer, Children's Hospital At Bronson, MI, p. A317

President and Chief Executive Officer, Main Campus, MI, p. A308

SARDUY, Innette Mary, M.P.H., R.N., Associate Director Patient Care Services and Nurse Executive, Louis Stokes Cleveland Veterans Affairs Medical Center, Cleveland, OH, p. A477

SARGENT, Kimberly, Vice President Patient Services, St. Luke's Hospital - Miners Campus, Coaldale, PA, p. A523

SARGENT, Kurt, CPA
Vice President Operational Finance, Chi St. Alexius Health Devils Lake Hospital, Devils Lake, ND, p. A465

Vice President, Operational Finance, Chi St Alexius Health Carrington Medical Center, Carrington, ND, p. A464

SARGENT, Reed
Assistant Administrator Finance, Cedar City Hospital, Cedar City, UT, p. A646

Assistant Administrator Finance, Garfield Memorial Hospital, Panguitch, UT, p. A649

SCHALES, Marion, Chief Financial Officer, John George Psychiatric Hospital, CA, p. A75

SCHALL, Dee, R.N., Chief Nursing Officer, Baptist Health Medical Center-Hot Spring County, Malvern-Hot Spring County, AR, p. A45

SCHALSKI, Paula, Director Human Resources, Pushmataha Hospital, Antlers, OK, p. A495

SCHALTZ, Linda, MSN, R.N., Chief Nursing Officer, Spectrum Health Kelsey Hospital, MI, p. A314

SCHAMP, Cindy K., FACHE, President, Baylor Scott & White Medical Center-Irving, Irving, TX, p. A615

SCHANDL, Brian, Chief Information Officer, Marshall Browning Hospital, Du Quoin, IL, p. A181

SCHANEL, Judith A, R.N., MSN, FACHE, Chief Operating Officer, Cone Health, NC, p. A453

SCHANWALD, Pamela R., Chief Executive Officer, The Children's Home Of Pittsburgh, Pittsburgh, PA, p. A538

SCHAPP, Susan, Vice President Finance and Treasurer, Charlotte Hungerford Hospital, Torrington, CT, p. A111

SCHARBER, Laurel, Administrative Assistant and Coordinator Human Resources, Kindred Hospital-Ontario, Ontario, CA, p. A76

SCHARENBROCK, Chris, M.D., Chief Medical Staff, David Grant Usaf Medical Center, Travis Afb, CA, p. A92

SCHARFF, Tom, Director Information Services, University Pavilion, FL, p. A140

SCHARNBERG, Cathi Rae, R.N., M.P.H., Vice President Patient Services, Avera Holy Family Hospital, Estherville, IA, p. A222

SCHARNHORST, Alicia, Human Resources and Administrative Assistant, Garfield County Public Hospital District, Pomeroy, WA, p. A674

SCHARR, Vickie, Chief Financial Officer, Bakersfield Heart Hospital, Bakersfield, CA, p. A51

SCHATTSCHNEIDER, Tami, Chief Nursing Officer, St. Agnes Hospital, Fond Du Lac, WI, p. A692

SCHAUF, Jeffrey, Director Information Systems, Wesley Woodlawn Hospital & Er, KS, p. A248

SCHAUF, Kyle, M.D., President Medical Staff, Integris Grove Hospital, Grove, OK, p. A499

SCHAWL, Bud, Chief Executive Officer, Kindred Hospital-Albuquerque, Albuquerque, NM, p. A415

SCHEAFFEL, Margaret M.
Chief Nursing Officer, Carilion Franklin Memorial Hospital, Rocky Mount, VA, p. A666
Chief Nursing Officer, Roanoke Memorial Rehabilitation Center, VA, p. A665

SCHEERER, Dan, M.D., Chief Medical Officer, Good Samaritan Medical And Rehabilitation Center, OH, p. A494

SCHEETZ, Allison, M.D., Medical Director, Rehabilitation Hospital, Navicent Health, Macon, GA, p. A157

SCHEFFLER, Tom, Chief Fiscal Officer, Veterans Affairs Maryland Health Care System-Perry Point Division, MD, p. A289

SCHEINBART, Lee, M.D.
Vice President Medical Affairs, Health First Community Hospitals, Health First Cape Canaveral Hospital, Cocoa Beach, FL, p. A120
Vice President Medical Affairs, Health First Community Hospitals, Health First Palm Bay Hospital, Palm Bay, FL, p. A135

SCHEINBLUM, Richard, Chief Financial Officer, Monadnock Community Hospital, Peterborough, NH, p. A401

SCHELBAR, E Joe, M.D., Medical Director, Select Specialty Hospital-Tulsa Midtown, Tulsa, OK, p. A509

SCHELL, James, M.D., Vice President Medical Affairs, Saint Francis Medical Center, Cape Girardeau, MO, p. A356

SCHELL, Jonathan, Chief Nursing Officer, Drew Memorial Health System, Monticello-Drew County, AR, p. A46

SCHEMER, Tonia, Interim Chief Human Resources, St. Joseph Mercy Livingston Hospital, Howell, MI, p. A315

SCHENKER, Amy, Human Resources Director, Shriners Hospitals For Children-Tampa, Tampa, FL, p. A141

SCHEPICI, Denise, M.P.H., Chief Executive Officer and President, Martha's Vineyard Hospital, Oak Bluffs, MA, p. A303

SCHEPMANN, Jane, Vice President and Chief Nursing Officer, Clara Barton Hospital, Hoisington, KS, p. A236

SCHEPPERS, Levi, Chief Executive Officer, Orthonebraska Hospital, Omaha, NE, p. A388

SCHEPPERS, Lisa, Chief Medical Officer, Regional West Medical Center, Scottsbluff, NE, p. A390

SCHER, Kathleen, Ed.D., R.N., Chief Nursing Officer, Jamaica Hospital Medical Center, New York (Includes All Hospitals Located Within The Five Boroughs), NY, p. A432

SCHERER, Timothy, M.D., Chief Medical Officer, Southern New Hampshire Medical Center, Nashua, NH, p. A400

SCHERLER, Jay, Vice President Finance and Chief Information Officer, Depaul Center, TX, p. A642

SCHERLING, Adam, President and Chief Executive Officer, Grundy County Memorial Hospital, Grundy Center, IA, p. A223

SCHERNECK, Michael D., President and Chief Executive Officer, Southeast Georgia Health System Brunswick Campus, Brunswick, GA, p. A149

SCHEVING, Travis, Chief Financial Officer, Holy Rosary Healthcare, Miles City, MT, p. A377

SCHEXNAYDER, Glenn, M.D., Chief of Staff, Prevost Memorial Hospital, Donaldsonville, LA, p. A267

SCHEY, David, Chief Financial Officer, Brook Lane Health Services, Hagerstown, MD, p. A292

SCHICK, Eric
Chief Financial Officer, Saint Francis Hospital South, Tulsa, OK, p. A509
Senior Vice President and Chief Financial Officer, Saint Francis Health System, Saint Francis Heart Hospital, OK, p. A509
Senior Vice President, Chief Administrative Officer and Chief Financial Officer, Laureate Psychiatric Clinic And Hospital, Tulsa, OK, p. A508

SCHIEBER, Steven M, MBA, FACMPE, FACHE, Chief Executive Officer, Wright Memorial Hospital, Trenton, MO, p. A371

SCHIEBER, Steven M., FACHE, Chief Executive Officer, Hedrick Medical Center, Chillicothe, MO, p. A357

SCHIEFELBEIN, Shelia, Coordinator Human Resources, Northwest Florida Community Hospital, Chipley, FL, p. A119

SCHIERECK, Stacie, Director Management Services, Mendota Mental Health Institute, Madison, WI, p. A696

SCHIESL, Troy, Director Information Services, Bellin Psychiatric Center, Green Bay, WI, p. A693

SCHIESLER, Hannah, Interim Assistant Director Human Resources, Baptist Hospitals Of Southeast Texas Fannin Behavioral Health Center, TX, p. A588

SCHILLER, Ann Mattia, Vice President Human Resources, College Medical Center, Long Beach, CA, p. A65

SCHILLER, Jonathan, Chief Executive Officer, Catskill Regional Medical Center, Harris, NY, p. A427

SCHILLING, Helen, M.D., Medical Director, Kindred Rehabilitation Hospital Northeast Houston, Humble, TX, p. A615

SCHIMEROWSKI, Deb
Regional Chief Financial Officer, Presence St. Mary's Hospital, Kankakee, IL, p. A187
Regional Finance Officer, Presence Saint Joseph Medical Center, Joliet, IL, p. A187

SCHIMMING, Christopher, M.D., Medical Director, Mayo Clinic Health System In Waseca, Waseca, MN, p. A342

SCHIMMING, Michael B
Director Financial Services, Shriners Hospitals For Children-Galveston, Galveston, TX, p. A606
Director Fiscal Services, Shriners Hospitals For Children-Houston, Houston, TX, p. A613

SCHIPPER, Brad J., Chief Operating Officer, Sanford Children's Hospital, SD, p. A564

SCHIPPER, Jody, Director of Nursing, Grundy County Memorial Hospital, Grundy Center, IA, p. A223

SCHIRALLI, Rocco, President and Chief Executive Officer, Porter-Starke Services, Valparaiso, IN, p. A216

SCHLABACH, Michael, M.D., Chief Medical Officer, Scott & White Hospital - Brenham, Brenham, TX, p. A590

SCHLADER, Rod G., Interim Chief Executive Officer, Mercy Medical Center-North Iowa, Mason City, IA, p. A226

SCHLAGER, Robert, M.D., Chief Medical Officer, Sebasticook Valley Health, Pittsfield, ME, p. A285

SCHLAGGER, Bradley, M.D., President and Chief Executive Officer, Kennedy Krieger Institute, Baltimore, MD, p. A287

SCHLANGEN, Greg, R.N., Chief Operating Officer, Carolina Center For Behavioral Health, Greer, SC, p. A554

SCHLATTER, Christina, Chief Financial Officer, Oswego Community Hospital, Oswego, KS, p. A243

SCHLECHTER, Sandy, Chief Executive Officer, Bowdle Hospital, Bowdle, SD, p. A559

SCHLEETER, Larry C, Chief Human Resources Officer, Memorial Health, Marysville, OH, p. A486

SCHLEGEL, Patricia, Executive Director Finance, Ridgeview Le Sueur Medical Center, Le Sueur, MN, p. A333

SCHLEICHER, Larry, Manager Information Services, Warner Hospital And Health Services, Clinton, IL, p. A180

SCHLEIF, John V, Senior Vice President and Chief Operating Officer, Henry Mayo Newhall Hospital, Valencia, CA, p. A93

SCHLENKER, Jim, Chief Operating Officer, Good Shepherd Health Care System, Hermiston, OR, p. A513

SCHLESKE, Brenda, Administrator, Community Behavioral Health Hospital - Fergus Falls, Fergus Falls, MN, p. A331

SCHLESSMAN, Alissa, Administrator, Beaver County Memorial Hospital, Beaver, OK, p. A496

SCHLEY, Kurt, Market Chief Executive Officer, Chi St. Alexius Health, Bismarck, ND, p. A464

SCHLICHTMAN, Beth A, Manager Human Resources, Brodstone Memorial Hospital, Superior, NE, p. A390

SCHLICHTMANN, Phyllis J., BSN, RN, MBA, Chief Executive Officer, Kessler Marlton Rehabilitation, Marlton, NJ, p. A407

SCHLIECH, Roxane K, Chief Financial Officer, Gundersen Tri-County Hospital And Clinics, Whitehall, WI, p. A706

SCHLUETER, Ann, Chief Operating Officer, Community Hospital-Fairfax, Fairfax, MO, p. A359

SCHLUNTZ, Ana, Director of Human Resources, Harlan County Health System, Alma, NE, p. A381

SCHLUTER, Robin M., Chief Executive Officer, Regional Health Services Of Howard County, Cresco, IA, p. A220

SCHMACKER, Eric, President, Mission Trail Baptist Hospital, TX, p. A632

SCHMAEDECKE, Dena, Vice President Human Resources, North Suburban Medical Center, Thornton, CO, p. A105

SCHMEDEMANN, Isabel, R.N., Chief Executive Officer and Administrator, Herington Municipal Hospital, Herington, KS, p. A236

SCHMID, Nancy A, R.N., MS, Associate Director Patient Care Services, Coatesville Veterans Affairs Medical Center, Coatesville, PA, p. A523

SCHMIDT, Allen J, M.D., President, Medical Staff, Decatur Morgan Hospital-West, AL, p. A16

SCHMIDT, Anne, Vice President of Patient Care Services and Chief Nursing Officer, South County Hospital, Wakefield, RI, p. A548

SCHMIDT, Barbara, Chief Executive Officer, Mesa Springs, Fort Worth, TX, p. A605

SCHMIDT, Bobbi, Chief Nursing Officer, Select Specialty Hospital-Cincinnati, Cincinnati, OH, p. A475

SCHMIDT, Constance, FACHE, R.N., Vice President Patient Care Services and Chief Nursing Officer, St. Mary-Corwin Medical Center, Pueblo, CO, p. A105

SCHMIDT, Harry M., President and Chief Executive Officer, Passavant Area Hospital, Jacksonville, IL, p. A186

SCHMIDT, Janie, Director of Nursing, Greeley County Health Services, Tribune, KS, p. A247

SCHMIDT, Joan E, Director Human Resources, Elmwood Healthcare Center At The Springs, Green Springs, OH, p. A483

SCHMIDT, Jodi A., Interim Chief Executive Officer, University Of Kansas Health System Great Bend Campus, Great Bend, KS, p. A236

SCHMIDT, Mark C.
President, Custer Regional Hospital, Custer, SD, p. A560
President, Lead-Deadwood Regional Hospital, Deadwood, SD, p. A560

SCHMIDT, Milan, Medical Director, North Shore Health, Grand Marais, MN, p. A332

SCHMIDT, Richard O, Jr, President and Chief Executive Officer, Froedtert South - St. Catherine's Medical Center, WI, p. A695

SCHMIDT, Richard O., Jr, President and Chief Executive Officer, Froedtert South - St. Catherine's Medical Center, WI, p. A695

SCHMIDT, Robert F, Director Human Resources, Hocking Valley Community Hospital, Logan, OH, p. A485

SCHMIDT, Rosanne, R.N., Chief Nursing Officer, Chi St. Alexius Health, Bismarck, ND, p. A464

SCHMIDT, Steve, Director Information Systems, Evans Memorial Hospital, Claxton, GA, p. A150

SCHMIDT, Veronica, Chief Executive Officer, Jennie M. Melham Memorial Medical Center, Broken Bow, NE, p. A382

SCHMIDT, William
Chief Executive Officer, Thedacare Medical Center-Shawano, Shawano, WI, p. A702
President and Chief Executive Officer, Thedacare Medical Center-New London, New London, WI, p. A700

SCHMIDTBERGER, Sheryl, Chief Financial Officer, Alliancehealth Ponca City, Ponca City, OK, p. A505

SCHMIEDT, Jason, Chief Financial Officer, Clinch Valley Medical Center, Richlands, VA, p. A664

SCHMIER, Joseph, Interim Director Human Resources, North Valley Hospital, Whitefish, MT, p. A380

SCHMIESING, Karee, Director of Nursing, Sleepy Eye Medical Center, Sleepy Eye, MN, p. A340

SCHMITS, Peggy, Director, Nursing Operations, New Braunfels Regional Rehabilitation Hospital, New Braunfels, TX, p. A625

SCHMITT, John, Senior Vice President and Chief Financial Officer, Kingsbrook Jewish Medical Center, New York (Includes All Hospitals Located Within The Five Boroughs), NY, p. A433

SCHMITT, Joseph, III
Senior Vice President Finance and Chief Financial Officer, Henry Ford Hospital, Detroit, MI, p. A311
Chief Financial Officer, Va Greater Los Angeles Healthcare System, Los Angeles, CA, p. A70
Chief Information Officer, St. Elizabeth's Medical Center, Brighton, MA, p. A297
SCHMITT, Karl, M.D., Chief of Staff, St. Elizabeth Covington, KY, p. A251
SCHMITT, Peggy, President and Chief Executive Officer, North Kansas City Hospital, North Kansas City, MO, p. A365
SCHMITT, Robert C., II, CPA, FACHE, Chief Executive Officer, Gibson Area Hospital And Health Services, Gibson City, IL, p. A184
SCHMITT, Thomas M., Chief Executive Officer, Kansas Spine And Specialty Hospital, Wichita, KS, p. A247
SCHMITT, Zach, Chief Financial Officer, Red Bud Regional Hospital, Red Bud, IL, p. A194
SCHMITZ, Bonnie
Chief Financial Officer, Ripon Medical Center, Ripon, WI, p. A702
Chief Financial Officer, Waupun Memorial Hospital, Waupun, WI, p. A705
Vice President and Chief Financial Officer, St. Agnes Hospital, Fond Du Lac, WI, p. A692
SCHMITZ, Christopher, Associate Vice President, Director Human Resources, Stoughton Hospital Association, Stoughton, WI, p. A703
SCHMITZ, Douglas, Director of Nursing, Long-Term Acute Care Hospital, Mosaic Life Care At St. Joseph, Saint Joseph, MO, p. A367
SCHMITZ, Jessica, Director of Nursing, Roosevelt Medical Center, Culbertson, MT, p. A374
SCHMITZ, Joseph, Chief Financial Officer, St. Cloud Veterans Affairs Health Care System, Saint Cloud, MN, p. A339
SCHMOTZER, Dave, Chief Financial Officer, Bryn Mawr Rehabilitation Hospital, Malvern, PA, p. A530
SCHMOYER, Leah, Human Resources Director, Buffalo Hospital, Buffalo, MN, p. A329
SCHMUS, Angie, Chief Information Technology, Aleda E. Lutz Veterans Affairs Medical Center, Saginaw, MI, p. A322
SCHNABEL, Annette, FACHE, President and Chief Executive Officer, Perry Memorial Hospital, Princeton, IL, p. A194
SCHNACK, Tim H.
Chief Financial Officer, Chi Health Immanuel, Omaha, NE, p. A388
Chief Financial Officer, Chi Health Plainview, Plainview, NE, p. A390
Chief Financial Officer, Chi Health Schuyler, Schuyler, NE, p. A390
Vice President Financial Services, Lasting Hope Recovery Center, NE, p. A387
Vice President Operations Finance, Chi Health St. Mary'S, Nebraska City, NE, p. A387
SCHNEDLER, Lisa W., FACHE, President and Chief Executive Officer, Upland Hills Health, Dodgeville, WI, p. A691
SCHNEIDER, Barbara, R.N., Chief Executive Officer, Foothill Regional Medical Center, Tustin, CA, p. A92
SCHNEIDER, Brenda, Chief Financial Officer, Skyline Hospital, White Salmon, WA, p. A680
SCHNEIDER, Brian, Chief Financial Officer, Dupont Hospital, Fort Wayne, IN, p. A203
SCHNEIDER, Carol L., President and Chief Executive Officer, Mercy Hospital And Medical Center, Chicago, IL, p. A178
SCHNEIDER, Frank, FACHE, Chief Executive Officer, Gateway Rehabilitation Hospital, Florence, KY, p. A251
SCHNEIDER, Gina, Director Human Resources, Northwest Specialty Hospital, Post Falls, ID, p. A171
SCHNEIDER, Jennifer S., Vice President of Finance, Saint Francis Hospital And Medical Center, Hartford, CT, p. A108
SCHNEIDER, Jessie, Director Human Resources, Community Memorial Healthcare, Marysville, KS, p. A241
SCHNEIDER, John, M.D.
Medical Director, Milwaukee County Behavioral Health Division, Milwaukee, WI, p. A699
Human Resources Director, Putnam Community Medical Center, Palatka, FL, p. A134
SCHNEIDER, Shanon, Chief Information Officer, Greeley County Health Services, Tribune, KS, p. A247
SCHNEIDER, Stacie A, Director Human Resources, Aurora Sheboygan Memorial Medical Center, Sheboygan, WI, p. A702
SCHNEIDER, Stephen, Manager Information Services, Alaska Psychiatric Institute, Anchorage, AK, p. A25
SCHNEIDER, Steve, Manager Behavioral Services and Director Operations, New Ulm Medical Center, New Ulm, MN, p. A336
SCHNEIDER, Steven E., M.D., President, Saint Mary's Hospital, Waterbury, CT, p. A111

SCHNEIDER, Thomas D, D.O., Chief of Staff, Jack C. Montgomery Veterans Affairs Medical Center, Muskogee, OK, p. A501
SCHNEIDER, Valerie, Director Human Resources, Gove County Medical Center, Quinter, KS, p. A244
SCHNELL, Dawn
Chief Nursing Officer and Interim Senior Director, Sanford Jackson Medical Center, Jackson, MN, p. A333
Chief Nursing Officer, Sanford Jackson Medical Center, Jackson, MN, p. A333
SCHNIEDERS, Michael H., FACHE, President, Richard H. Young Behavioral Health Center, NE, p. A385
SCHNIER, Martin, D.O., Chief of Staff, West Texas Veterans Affairs Health Care System, Big Spring, TX, p. A589
SCHNITTKER, Kira, Director of Nursing, St. Vincent's Blount, Oneonta, AL, p. A22
SCHNOOR, Jeff, Director Information Systems, Swedish Medical Center, Englewood, CO, p. A100
SCHOELLER, Betsy V, Director Human Resources and Education, Mary Greeley Medical Center, Ames, IA, p. A217
SCHOEN, Greg, M.D., Regional Medical Director, Fairview Northland Medical Center, Princeton, MN, p. A337
SCHOENDALER, Hannah, Chief Nursing Officer, Sheridan County Health Complex, Hoxie, KS, p. A237
SCHOENECKER, Perry L, M.D., Chief of Staff, Shriners Hospitals For Children-St. Louis, Saint Louis, MO, p. A368
SCHOENER, Timothy E
Chief Information Officer, Upmc Susquehanna Muncy, Muncy, PA, p. A532
Senior Vice President and Chief Information Officer, Upmc Susquehanna Soldiers + Sailors, Wellsboro, PA, p. A543
Vice President and Chief Information Officer, Upmc Susquehanna Williamsport Regional Medical Center, Williamsport, PA, p. A545
SCHOENIG, Thomas
Chief Information Officer, Amita Health Adventist La Grange Medical Center, La Grange, IL, p. A187
Chief Information Officer, Jupiter Medical Center, Jupiter, FL, p. A126
Regional Chief Information Officer, Texas Health Huguley Hospital Fort Worth South, Burleson, TX, p. A591
SCHOENIG, Tom, Regional Director Information Services, Valley Hospital Medical Center, Las Vegas, NV, p. A395
SCHOETTLE, Steve, M.D., Chief Medical Staff, Ozark Health Medical Center, Clinton-Van Buren County, AR, p. A40
SCHOFIELD, Joseph, Chief Operating Officer, Suburban Community Hospital, Norristown, PA, p. A533
SCHOFIELD, Sherry, Director Human Resources, Sovah Health-Martinsville, Martinsville, VA, p. A661
SCHOLEFIELD, Robert, MS, R.N., Executive Vice President and Chief Operating Officer, St. Luke's Campus, NY, p. A444
SCHOLL, Shyanne, Interim Human Resources Director, Friend Community Healthcare System, Friend, NE, p. A384
SCHOLZ, Suzanne, Director Medical Records, Horsham Clinic, Ambler, PA, p. A520
SCHOMER, Steve, M.D., Interim Chief Executive Officer, Washington County Hospital And Clinics, Washington, IA, p. A230
SCHON, John, Administrator and Chief Executive Officer, Dickinson County Healthcare System, Iron Mountain, MI, p. A316
SCHONEBERY, Jeremy, Director Information Technology, Heart Of America Medical Center, Rugby, ND, p. A468
SCHONLAU, Dan
Chief Financial Officer and Vice President of Finance, Chi Health St Elizabeth, Lincoln, NE, p. A386
Vice President Operational Finance, Chi Health Nebraska Heart, Lincoln, NE, p. A386
SCHONS, Jeri, R.N., Chief Nursing Officer, Sanford Tracy Medical Center, Tracy, MN, p. A341
SCHOOL, Peggy, Director of Nursing, Thedacare Medical Center-New London, New London, WI, p. A700
SCHOOLER, Rick, Vice President and Chief Information Officer, Winnie Palmer Hospital For Women And Babies, FL, p. A134
SCHOPP, Mary Ellen, Senior Vice President Human Resources, Rush Children's Hospital, IL, p. A179
SCHOR, Mark, Chief Executive Officer, Belmont Behavioral Hospital, Philadelphia, PA, p. A533
SCHORER, Emily
Senior Vice President Human Resources, Cape Cod Hospital, Hyannis, MA, p. A300
Vice President, Human Resources, Falmouth Hospital, Falmouth, MA, p. A299
SCHOTT, Connie, Vice President, Human Resources, Ozarks Medical Center, West Plains, MO, p. A372
SCHOTTEL, Roxanne, Chief Executive Officer, Washington County Hospital, Washington, KS, p. A247

SCHOWENGERDT, Daniel, M.D., Chief of Staff, Comanche County Hospital, Coldwater, KS, p. A233
SCHRADER, Guillermo, M.D., Acting Medical Director, Eastern State Hospital, Williamsburg, VA, p. A667
SCHRAEDER, David, Director Information Systems, Russell Regional Hospital, Russell, KS, p. A245
SCHRAMM, Michael, Chief Executive Officer, Rice Memorial Hospital, Willmar, MN, p. A342
SCHRAMM, Steven R, Chief Financial Officer, Mountain View Hospital, Payson, UT, p. A649
SCHRANK, Kenton, M.D., President Medical Staff, Wilson N. Jones Regional Medical Center, Sherman, TX, p. A636
SCHRANT, Benjamin, M.D., Chief of Staff, Northeast Regional Medical Center, Kirksville, MO, p. A362
SCHREFFLER, Mary Jane, Director Human Resources, Meadows Psychiatric Center, Centre Hall, PA, p. A522
SCHREIBER, Anne, Manager Human Resources, Fairfax Behavioral Health Everett, WA, p. A673
SCHREIBER, Elizabeth, R.N., Director Patient Care Services, Flambeau Hospital, Park Falls, WI, p. A701
SCHREIER, Garett E., R.N., Associate Director, Nursing and Patient Care Services, Ralph H. Johnson Veterans Affairs Medical Center, Charleston, SC, p. A550
SCHREINER, David L., FACHE, President and Chief Executive Officer, Katherine Shaw Bethea Hospital, Dixon, IL, p. A181
SCHREINER, Jim, Chief Information Officer, Graham Hospital Association, Canton, IL, p. A175
SCHRIER, Erick, Supervisor Information Technology, Van Diest Medical Center, Webster City, IA, p. A231
SCHROCK, Bonnie W, FACHE, Chief Operating Officer, Baptist Health Paducah, Paducah, KY, p. A259
SCHRODER, Loren D, Chief Financial Officer, Phelps Memorial Health Center, Holdrege, NE, p. A385
SCHROEDER, Brian D., M.D., Senior Vice President and Chief Medical Officer, Sparrow Children's Center, MI, p. A317
SCHROEDER, Catherine, Deputy Chief Information Officer, Brigham And Women's Faulkner Hospital, Boston, MA, p. A296
SCHROEDER, Cygnet, D.O., Medical Director, Healthsouth Rehabilitation Hospital Of Fort Smith, Fort Smith-Sebastian County, AR, p. A42
SCHROEDER, Destiny, Information Systems Director, Rawlins County Health Center, Atwood, KS, p. A232
SCHROEDER, Heather, R.N., Vice President Nursing, Aurora Baycare Medical Center, Green Bay, WI, p. A693
SCHROEDER, Joanne, President, Munson Healthcare Charlevoix Hospital, Charlevoix, MI, p. A309
SCHROEDER, Rick, Chief Executive Officer, North Big Horn Hospital District, Lovell, WY, p. A709
SCHROEDL, Greg, M.D., Vice President, Medical and Chief Medical Officer, Uw Medicine/Northwest Hospital & Medical Center, Seattle, WA, p. A677
SCHROEPPEL, Stacie, Director of Human Resources, Baptist Memorial Rehabilitation Hospital, Germantown, TN, p. A570
SCHROYER, Mike K., FACHE, MSN, R.N., President, St. Vincent Anderson, Anderson, IN, p. A199
SCHRUMPF, Jason, President, Missouri Delta Medical Center, Sikeston, MO, p. A370
SCHUBACH, Michael, Chief People Officer, Carroll County Memorial Hospital, Carrollton, MO, p. A357
SCHUCK, Eric, M.D., Chief Medical Officer, Tristar Southern Hills Medical Center, Nashville, TN, p. A578
SCHUCK, Jennifer, Associate Administrator, Emory Wesley Woods Geriatric Hospital, GA, p. A146
SCHUCKMAN, Tim, Chief Financial Officer, Jennie M. Melham Memorial Medical Center, Broken Bow, NE, p. A382
SCHUE, Janine
Executive Vice President, Chief Human Resources Officer, Rochester Regional Health, Newark-Wayne Community Hospital, Newark, NY, p. A438
Senior Vice President Human Resources, Rochester General Hospital, Rochester, NY, p. A441
SCHUELER, Joe, Chief Financial Officer, Morrow County Hospital, Mount Gilead, OH, p. A487
SCHUERCH, Timothy, President and Chief Executive Officer, Maniilaq Health Center, Kotzebue, AK, p. A26
SCHUESSLER, Dwight, Chief Information Officer, Iowa City Veterans Affairs Health Care System, Iowa City, IA, p. A224
SCHUITEMAN, Jackson, Chief Financial Officer, Sioux Center Health, Sioux Center, IA, p. A229
SCHULER, Allison, R.N., Chief Nursing Officer, Baptist Medical Center Attala, Kosciusko, MS, p. A349
SCHULER, Kathy, R.N., MS, Chief Operating Officer and Chief Nursing Officer, Winchester Hospital, Winchester, MA, p. A306
SCHULHOF, Alicia, President and Chief Executive Officer, Indiana University Health Saxony Hospital, IN, p. A207
SCHULMAN, Joseph, Interim Chief Executive Officer, Staten Island University Hospital, New York (Includes All Hospitals Located Within The Five Boroughs), NY, p. A437

SCHULTE, Mark, FACHE, President, Sturgis Regional Hospital, Sturgis, SD, p. A564

SCHULTES, Jeremy, Administrator and Chief Executive Officer, Philip Health Services, Philip, SD, p. A562

SCHULTHEIS, Hal, Director Information Systems, Tristar Hendersonville Medical Center, Hendersonville, TN, p. A570

SCHULTZ, Bradley, Chief Financial Officer, Wesley Woodlawn Hospital & Er, KS, p. A248

SCHULTZ, David W., FACHE
President, Peninsula Region, Harrison Medical Center, Bremerton, WA, p. A669
President, Peninsula Region, St. Anthony Hospital, Gig Harbor, WA, p. A672

SCHULTZ, Jacky, MSN, R.N., President, Suburban Hospital, Bethesda, MD, p. A290

SCHULTZ, Jim, Chief Executive Officer, Edgerton Hospital And Health Services, Edgerton, WI, p. A692

SCHULTZ, Kurt
Chief Financial Officer, Cornerstone Hospital-West Monroe, West Monroe, LA, p. A280
Chief Financial Officer, Solara Hospital - Brownsville Campus, TX, p. A609
Group Chief Financial Officer, Chg Hospital Tucson, Llc, Tucson, AZ, p. A37

SCHULTZ, Mary Kay, Director Human Resources, Sturgis Hospital, Sturgis, MI, p. A324

SCHULTZ, Merrilee, Chief Finance, Sanford Children's Hospital, SD, p. A564

SCHULTZ, Rachelle H., Ed.D., President and Chief Executive Officer, Winona Health, Winona, MN, p. A342

SCHULTZ, Sharon A, MSN, R.N., M.P.H., Chief Nurse Executive and Vice President, Tri-City Medical Center, Oceanside, CA, p. A76

SCHULTZ, Teresa L, R.N., Vice President of Patient Care, Rogers Memorial Hospital-West Allis, WI, p. A700

SCHULTZ, Vince, M.D., Chief Medical Officer, Munson Healthcare Grayling Hospital, Grayling, MI, p. A314

SCHULZ, Ken, Chief Operating Officer, North Dakota State Hospital, Jamestown, ND, p. A467

SCHULZ, Leah, Director of Nursing, North Dakota State Hospital, Jamestown, ND, p. A467

SCHULZ, Marcie, Director Patient Care, Sakakawea Medical Center, Hazen, ND, p. A466

SCHULZ, Susan G, Director Patient Care Services, Beaumont Hospital - Trenton, Trenton, MI, p. A324

SCHUMACHER, Ann, R.N., MSN, FACHE, President, Chi Health Immanuel, Omaha, NE, p. A388

SCHUMACHER, Debbie
Chief Human Resource Officer, Clearwater Valley Hospital And Clinics, Orofino, ID, p. A170
Chief Human Resource Officer, St. Mary's Hospital, Cottonwood, ID, p. A169

SCHUMACHER, Kevin, Director of Information Systems, Lifecare Medical Center, Roseau, MN, p. A338

SCHUMACHER, Larry P, R.N., MSN, Chief Executive Officer, Memorial Hospital Hixson, TN, p. A567

SCHUMACHER, Paul, Chief Operating Officer, Mcleod Health Clarendon, Manning, SC, p. A555

SCHUMANN, Vera, Director of Finance and Controller, North Shore Health, Grand Marais, MN, p. A332

SCHURKAMP, Christine, Senior Human Resources Business Partner, Spectrum Health Gerber Memorial, Fremont, MI, p. A313

SCHUSTER, Carol E, R.N., Chief Nursing Officer and Vice President Patient Care Services, Franciscan Health Crown Point, Crown Point, IN, p. A202

SCHUSTER, Christine C., R.N., President and Chief Executive Officer, Emerson Hospital, Concord, MA, p. A299

SCHUSTER, Janet, Chief Nursing Officer, Lutheran Hospital, Cleveland, OH, p. A477

SCHUSTER, Jolene, Chief Financial Officer, Grisell Memorial Hospital District One, Ransom, KS, p. A244

SCHUSTER, Lexie, Vice President Human Resources, Good Samaritan Hospital, Los Angeles, CA, p. A67

SCHUSTER, Todd, Administrator, Saint Francis Hospital Vinita, Vinita, OK, p. A509

SCHUSTER, Tony, M.D.
Vice President of Physician Services, Mease Countryside Hospital, Safety Harbor, FL, p. A137
Vice President of Physician Services, Mease Dunedin Hospital, Dunedin, FL, p. A122

SCHWAB, Bob, M.D., Chief Medical Officer, Texas Health Presbyterian Hospital Allen, Allen, TX, p. A582

SCHWAB, Caryn A, Executive Director, Mount Sinai Queens, NY, p. A434

SCHWAB, Eric, Chief Executive Officer, Select Specialty Hospital-Laurel Highlands, Latrobe, PA, p. A529

SCHWABENBAUER, Mary Ann, Director Information Technology, Penn Highlands Elk, Saint Marys, PA, p. A540

SCHWAEGEL, Glen
Chief Financial Officer, Progress West Hospital, O'Fallon, MO, p. A365
Vice President and Chief Financial Officer, Barnes-Jewish St. Peters Hospital, Saint Peters, MO, p. A370

SCHWAGER, Mary A, Director Human Resources, Antelope Memorial Hospital, Neligh, NE, p. A387

SCHWALL, Garry, Chief Operating Officer, Children's Medical Center, NY, p. A430

SCHWAN, Joni, Director Human Resources, Excelsior Springs Hospital, Excelsior Springs, MO, p. A359

SCHWAN, Karin, Chief Nursing Officer, Vice President Patient Care Services, University Hospitals Samaritan Medical Center, Ashland, OH, p. A470

SCHWANER, Charles, III, Chief Financial Officer, Doctors Hospital Of Sarasota, Sarasota, FL, p. A138

SCHWANKE, Daniel, President, Promedica Monroe Regional Hospital, Monroe, MI, p. A319

SCHWARM, Tony, President, Missouri Baptist Sullivan Hospital, Sullivan, MO, p. A371

SCHWARTZ, Ave, Chief Information Officer, Austen Riggs Center, Stockbridge, MA, p. A305

SCHWARTZ, David, M.D.
Chief Medical Officer, Saint Francis Hospital-Bartlett, Bartlett, TN, p. A566
Chief Medical Officer, Saint Francis Hospital, Memphis, TN, p. A576

SCHWARTZ, David M, D.O., Vice President, Medical Affairs, Sentara Northern Virginia Medical Center, Woodbridge, VA, p. A668

SCHWARTZ, Jack, Director Information Technology, Kittitas Valley Healthcare, Ellensburg, WA, p. A671

SCHWARTZ, Jonathon, M.D., Chief Medical Officer, Spaulding Hospital For Continuing Medical Care Cambridge, Cambridge, MA, p. A298

SCHWARTZ, Kenneth V, M.D., Medical Director, Griffin Hospital, Derby, CT, p. A107

SCHWARTZ, Kim, Assistant Administrator Human Resources and Operations, Boone County Hospital, Boone, IA, p. A218

SCHWARTZ, Michael, M.D., Chief of Staff, College Hospital Costa Mesa, Costa Mesa, CA, p. A55

SCHWARTZ, Mitchell B, M.D., Chief Medical Officer, Anne Arundel Medical Center, Annapolis, MD, p. A287

SCHWARTZ, Peggy, Vice President Human Resources, Wayne Healthcare, Greenville, OH, p. A483

SCHWARTZ, Peter
Director Information Systems, East Mountain Hospital, Belle Mead, NJ, p. A402
Director of Information Systems, Carrier Clinic, Belle Mead, NJ, p. A402

SCHWARTZ, Roberta, Ph.D., Executive Vice President, Houston Methodist Hospital, Houston, TX, p. A611

SCHWARTZ, Ronald, M.D., Medical Director, Masonicare Health Center, Wallingford, CT, p. A111

SCHWARTZ, Sharon, Director Medical Records, Scott & White Hospital - Brenham, Brenham, TX, p. A590

SCHWARTZ, Stephanie L, FACHE, MA, Vice President AHS and President CMC, Chilton Medical Center, Pompton Plains, NJ, p. A410

SCHWARZ, John, Vice President Administration, Lankenau Medical Center, Wynnewood, PA, p. A545

SCHWARZBACH, Jerry, M.D., Medical Director, Ut Health Rehabilitation Hospital, Tyler, TX, p. A641

SCHWARZKOPF, Ruth, R.N., Chief Nursing Officer, West Boca Medical Center, Boca Raton, FL, p. A118

SCHWEBLER, Michael W., President and Chief Executive Officer, Highpoint Health, Lawrenceburg, IN, p. A210

SCHWECHHEIMER, Betsy L, Chief Operating Officer, Tewksbury Hospital, Tewksbury, MA, p. A305

SCHWEICKHARDT, Mary Jo, Vice President Human Resources, Medstar Georgetown University Hospital, Washington, DC, p. A115

SCHWEIGERT, Nicole, Director Human Resources, Texas Health Presbyterian Hospital Flower Mound, Flower Mound, TX, p. A603

SCHWEIGHART, Karen, R.N., MS, Administrator, Andrew Mcfarland Mental Health Center, Springfield, IL, p. A196

SCHWEIKART, Jay
Chief Financial Officer, Kindred Hospital Chicago-Northlake, Northlake, IL, p. A191
Chief Financial Officer, Kindred Hospital-Sycamore, Sycamore, IL, p. A197

SCHWEITZER, Michael, M.D., Chief Medical Officer, St. Vincent Healthcare, Billings, MT, p. A373

SCHWIEGER, Kay, Chief Human Resources Officer, Clement J. Zablocki Veterans Affairs Medical Center, Milwaukee, WI, p. A698

SCHWIND, David, Chief Financial Officer, Capital Hospice, Arlington, VA, p. A655

SCHWINGLER, Joyce, Chief Financial Officer, Eureka Community Health Services Avera, Eureka, SD, p. A560

SCIARRA, Michael, M.D., Chief Medical Officer, Hudson Regional Hospital, Secaucus, NJ, p. A411

SCIARRO, Jason
President and Chief Operating Officer, Centegra Hospital - Woodstock, Woodstock, IL, p. A198
President and Chief Operating Officer, Centegra Hospital-Huntley, IL, p. A189

SCIMECA, Paul, Senior Vice President Operations and Chief Operating Officer, Glens Falls Hospital, Glens Falls, NY, p. A427

SCIONTI, Jeff, Chief Executive Officer, Parkland Medical Center, Derry, NH, p. A398

SCIOSCIA, Angela, M.D., Chief Medical Officer, Uc San Diego Shiley Eye Institute, CA, p. A84

SCLAMA, Tony, M.D., Vice President Medical Affairs, Medstar Franklin Square Medical Center, Baltimore, MD, p. A288

SCOFIELD, Mark, M.D., Chief Medical Officer, Shelby Baptist Medical Center, Alabaster, AL, p. A13

SCOGGIN, Terry
Chief Financial Officer, Titus Regional Medical Center, Mount Pleasant, TX, p. A624
Interim Chief Executive Officer, Titus Regional Medical Center, Mount Pleasant, TX, p. A624

SCOGGINS, James, Director of Nursing, Arkansas State Hospital, Little Rock-Pulaski County, AR, p. A44

SCOGGINS, Mib, Chief Executive Officer, Mcleod Health Cheraw, Cheraw, SC, p. A550

SCOGNA, Stephen, President and Chief Executive Officer, Northwest Community Hospital, Arlington Heights, IL, p. A173

SCORZELLI, Gerard, Chief Financial Officer, Albany Stratton Veterans Affairs Medical Center, Albany, NY, p. A421

SCOTFORD, Lucrecia, Executive Vice President and Chief Operations Officer, Bristol Bay Area Health Corporation, Dillingham, AK, p. A26

SCOTT, Colleen M, Vice President Finance, Waterbury Hospital, Waterbury, CT, p. A112

SCOTT, Cullen, Chief Executive Officer, Northwest Hills Surgical Hospital, Austin, TX, p. A586

SCOTT, Damien, Chief Information Officer, Emanuel Medical Center, Swainsboro, GA, p. A161

SCOTT, Daniel, Director of Information Systems, Good Samaritan Hospital, Vincennes, IN, p. A216

SCOTT, David W., President and Chief Executive Officer, Ohio Valley Hospital, Mckees Rocks, PA, p. A531

SCOTT, Doug, Corporate Director Human Resources, Rmc Anniston, Anniston, AL, p. A13

SCOTT, Ernie, Director Human Resources, Natchitoches Regional Medical Center, Natchitoches, LA, p. A275

SCOTT, Henry, Executive Director, Technical Services, Piedmont Newnan Hospital, Newnan, GA, p. A158

SCOTT, James, M.D.
Vice President Medical Affairs, Candler Hospital, Savannah, GA, p. A160
Vice President Medical Affairs, St. Joseph's Hospital, Savannah, GA, p. A160

SCOTT, Jeffrey, Chief Information Officer, St. Vincent Kokomo, Kokomo, IN, p. A209

SCOTT, Jennifer, Director of Informatics, Carepartners Health Services, Asheville, NC, p. A447

SCOTT, Jo Ellen, R.N., MS, Senior Vice President of Patient Care Services and Chief Nursing Officer, Indiana University Health Tipton Hospital, Tipton, IN, p. A215

SCOTT, Joseph F., FACHE, President and Chief Executive Officer, Jersey City Medical Center, Jersey City, NJ, p. A406

SCOTT, Julie, Chief Nursing Officer, Healthsouth Rehabilitation Hospital Of York, York, PA, p. A545

SCOTT, Karen M, Vice President Patient Care, Adventist Health Howard Memorial, Willits, CA, p. A95

SCOTT, Lincoln, Vice President Human Resources, Southeast Hospital, Cape Girardeau, MO, p. A357

SCOTT, M Daryl, Assistant Vice President, Jefferson Regional Medical Center, Pine Bluff-Jefferson County, AR, p. A47

SCOTT, Margie A., M.D., Director, North Little Rock Division, AR, p. A45

SCOTT, Martha Lynn, Chief Patient Care Officer, Covington County Hospital, Collins, MS, p. A345

SCOTT, Monica, Chief Financial Officer, Great Plains Regional Medical Center, Elk City, OK, p. A498

SCOTT, Paul, M.D., Chief of Staff, Hudson Hospital And Clinic, Hudson, WI, p. A694

SCOTT, Rhonda A, Ph.D., R.N., Chief Operating Officer, Grady Memorial Hospital, Atlanta, GA, p. A146

SCOTT, Robert F, Vice President and Chief Human Resources Officer, Memorial Medical Center, Springfield, IL, p. A196

SCOTT, Sam, Vice President Financial Services, St. Dominic-Jackson Memorial Hospital, Jackson, MS, p. A348

SCOTT, Sharon, Health Information Director, Allegiance Specialty Hospital Of Greenville, Greenville, MS, p. A346

SCOTT, Steve, Chief Operating Officer, Sheridan Community Hospital, Sheridan, MI, p. A323

SCOTT, Susan, Chief Nurse Executive, Ventura County Medical Center, Ventura, CA, p. A94

SCOTT, Thomas W., Senior Vice President and Chief Operating Officer, Centrastate Healthcare System, Freehold, NJ, p. A405

SCOTT, Tina, Acting Health Director, Choctaw Health Center, Philadelphia, MS, p. A352

SCOTT, Todd, Chief Financial Officer, Vibra Hospital Of Sacramento, Folsom, CA, p. A58

SCOTT, Travis
Chief Executive Officer, Lawton Indian Hospital, Lawton, OK, p. A500
Service Unit Director, U.S. Public Health Service Indian Hospital, Pine Ridge, SD, p. A562

SCOTT, Veronica, Business Office Manager, Midwest City Specialty Hospital, Midwest City, OK, p. A501

SCOTT, William, M.D.
Vice President Medical Affairs, Regional Medical Center Of San Jose, San Jose, CA, p. A86
Chief Financial Officer, Promise Hospital Of Overland Park, Overland Park, KS, p. A243

SCOTT, William P, M.D., Chief of Staff, River Valley Medical Center, Dardanelle-Yell County, AR, p. A41

SCOTTO, Dan, Director Information Technology, Eastern Long Island Hospital, Greenport, NY, p. A427

SCOUFOS, Jennifer, M.D., Chief of Staff, Northeastern Health System Sequoyah, Sallisaw, OK, p. A506

SCOVILL, Terry, Chief Executive Officer, Intracare North Hospital, Houston, TX, p. A611

SCOWN, Kent, Director Operations and Information Services, Jerold Phelps Community Hospital, Garberville, CA, p. A60

SCREMIN, Karen, Vice President Finance, Exempla West Pines, CO, p. A106

SCRIVO, Joseph A, Jr, Director Human Resources, Mercy Hospital, Buffalo, NY, p. A423

SCROGGIN, Christy, Chief Operating Officer, Conway Regional Rehabilitation Hospital, Conway-Faulkner County, AR, p. A40

SCROGGINS, Todd, Chief Financial Officer, Wise Regional Health System, West Campus Decatur, TX, p. A598

SCROGGS, Amy, Chief Nursing Officer, Delano Regional Medical Center, Delano, CA, p. A56

SCRUGGS, Sherry, Administrator, Milan General Hospital, Milan, TN, p. A576

SCUDDER, Angela K., MSN, R.N., Vice President Patient Care Services, Highpoint Health, Lawrenceburg, IN, p. A210

SCUDERI, Denise, Vice President Patient Care Services, Mayo Regional Hospital, Dover, ME, p. A284

SCULL, Stephen W, Vice President Ethics and Compliance officer, Rapides Regional Medical Center, Alexandria, LA, p. A262

SCULLY, Charles
Chief Information Officer, Honorhealth Scottsdale Thompson Peak Medical Center, Scottsdale, AZ, p. A35
Chief Information Officer, Renown Children's Hospital, NV, p. A396

SCULLY, Kem, Chief Executive Officer and Chief Nursing Officer, Purcell Municipal Hospital, Purcell, OK, p. A506

SCULLY, Trish
Director Human Resources, Taunton State Hospital, Taunton, MA, p. A305
Manager Employment Services, Pappas Rehabilitation Hospital For Children, Canton, MA, p. A299

SCZYGELSKI, Sidney C, Senior Vice President Finance and Chief Financial Officer, Aspirus Wausau Hospital, Inc., Wausau, WI, p. A705

SEAGER, Jerry, Assistant Vice President and Chief Financial Officer, Inova Fair Oaks Hospital, Fairfax, VA, p. A657

SEAGO, Terri, Chief Financial Officer, Baptist Memorial Hospital-Collierville, Collierville, TN, p. A568

SEAGRAM, Patricia, Vice President Human Resources, Henry Ford Allegiance Health, Jackson, MI, p. A316

SEAGROVES, Matthew, Chief Financial Officer, Bayfront Health Spring Hill, FL, p. A119

SEAHORN, Martha, Chief Nursing Officer, Gadsden Regional Medical Center, Gadsden, AL, p. A18

SEAL, John, Director Human Resources, Riverside Medical Center, Franklinton, LA, p. A267

SEAL, Ronald T., Chief Executive Officer, Tmc Behavioral Health Center, TX, p. A599

SEALE, Corey A, Chief Operating Officer, Kaiser Permanente Moreno Valley Medical Center, Moreno Valley, CA, p. A73

SEALE, Jonathan, Chief Information Officer, Erie Veterans Affairs Medical Center, Erie, PA, p. A525

SEALE, Julie, Administrator, Christus Santa Rosa Hospital - Alamo Heights, TX, p. A632

SEALS, Robert, D.O., Medical Director, Sparrow Carson Hospital, Carson City, MI, p. A309

SEAMON, Robert L., Chief Executive Officer, Copper Queen Community Hospital, Bisbee, AZ, p. A28

SEARLE, Anne, Chief Information Officer, Penn Medicine Princeton Medical Center, Plainsboro, NJ, p. A410

SEARLS, Barbara, Chief Financial Officer, Searhc Mt. Edgecumbe Hospital, Sitka, AK, p. A27

SEARLS, Gary, Chief Financial Officer, Brandon Regional Hospital, Brandon, FL, p. A119

SEARS, Erin Clare, Associate Director of Operations, Providence Veterans Affairs Medical Center, Providence, RI, p. A547

SEARS, Marilyn, Chief Financial Officer, Hshs Good Shepherd Hospital, Shelbyville, IL, p. A195

SEARS, Tina, Director Patient Care Services, Sullivan County Memorial Hospital, Milan, MO, p. A364

SEASE, Peggy, Vice President Human Resources, Northport Medical Center, AL, p. A24

SEATON, Tracy, Director of Nursing, Taylorville Memorial Hospital, Taylorville, IL, p. A197

SEAVER, Roger E., President and Chief Executive Officer, Henry Mayo Newhall Hospital, Valencia, CA, p. A93

SEBEK, Brenda Jean, R.N., Administrator, Chi Health St. Mary'S, Nebraska City, NE, p. A387

SEBENALER, Ginette, Associate Chief Financial Officer, Aspen Valley Hospital, Aspen, CO, p. A96

SECKINGER, Mark R., President, O'Bleness Memorial Hospital, Athens, OH, p. A471

SECOR, April, R.N., Chief Nursing Officer, Hillcrest Hospital Henryetta, Henryetta, OK, p. A499

SECOR, Diane K, Director Human Resources, Lawrence Medical Center, Moulton, AL, p. A21

SECURRO, Matthew J., Vice President, Human Resources, Conway Medical Center, Conway, SC, p. A552

SEDA, Jolene R., Vice President People and Culture, Virginia Mason Memorial, Yakima, WA, p. A680

SEDMINIK, Vince, Chief Executive Officer, Springhill Medical Center, Springhill, LA, p. A279

SEEDER, Rachael, Controller, Santiam Hospital, Stayton, OR, p. A518

SEELEY, Kevin, Chief Information Officer, Mike O'Callaghan Federal Hospital, Nellis Afb, NV, p. A395

SEELEY, Pam, Chief Nursing Officer, Elmira Psychiatric Center, Elmira, NY, p. A426

SEELEY, Steven, Vice President, Chief Operating Officer, Chief Nursing Officer, Jupiter Medical Center, Jupiter, FL, p. A126

SEELY, Paula, Manager Human Resources, Kossuth Regional Health Center, Algona, IA, p. A217

SEEMS, Steven, Director of Information Technology, Phillips County Hospital, Phillipsburg, KS, p. A244

SEESE, Rebecca, Chief Operating Officer, U.S. Air Force Regional Hospital, Elmendorf Afb, AK, p. A26

SEESEE, Alan, Chief Executive Officer, Capital Regional Medical Center, Tallahassee, FL, p. A140

SEEVER, Jennifer, Regional Chief Financial Officer, Sedan City Hospital, Sedan, KS, p. A245

SEGAL, Jonathan, Chief Financial Officer, New York State Psychiatric Institute, New York (Includes All Hospitals Located Within The Five Boroughs), NY, p. A434

SEGAL, Rebecca, Chief Executive Officer, Rutherford Regional Health System, Rutherfordton, NC, p. A460

SEGAL, Stanton, M.D., Chief Medical Officer, Frankford Campus, PA, p. A535

SEGAL, Tanya, Director, Easton Hospital, Easton, PA, p. A524

SEGALLA, Domenic, Chief Operating Officer and Chief Financial Officer, Clara Maass Medical Center, Belleville, NJ, p. A402

SEGAWA, Lance
Chief Executive Officer, Kauai Veterans Memorial Hospital, Waimea, HI, p. A166
Chief Executive Officer, Samuel Mahelona Memorial Hospital, Kapaa, HI, p. A166

SEGER, LaDonna, Director Information Services, Saint Luke's North Hospital-Smithville Campus, MO, p. A362

SEGIN, Robert
Chief Financial Officer, Virtua Memorial, Mount Holly, NJ, p. A408
Executive Vice President & Chief Financial Officer, Virtua Marlton, Marlton, NJ, p. A407

SEGUR, Jennifer, Chief Nursing Officer and Chief Clinical Officer, Florida Hospital North Pinellas, Tarpon Springs, FL, p. A142

SEGURA, Ezra, Chief Executive Officer, Utah Valley Specialty Hospital, Provo, UT, p. A649

SEGURA, Mario, Director of Nursing, Starr County Memorial Hospital, Rio Grande City, TX, p. A630

SEHRT, Lori
Associate Chief Financial Officer Northern Colorado, Banner Fort Collins Medical Center, Fort Collins, CO, p. A100

Chief Financial Officer, Mckee Medical Center, Loveland, CO, p. A104

SEIBERT, Jenee, Chief Finance Officer, Fulton County Health Center, Wauseon, OH, p. A493

SEIBOLD, Spencer Garrett, M.D., Chief of Medical Staff, Power County Hospital District, American Falls, ID, p. A167

SEID, Lynette, Area Chief Financial Officer, Kaiser Permanente San Diego Medical Center, CA, p. A83

SEIDL, Doris A, Vice President Human Resources, Mclaren Port Huron, Port Huron, MI, p. A321

SEIDLER, Richard A., FACHE
President and Chief Executive Officer, Unitypoint Health - Trinity Bettendorf, Bettendorf, IA, p. A217
President and Chief Executive Officer, Unitypoint Health - Trinity Moline, IL, p. A194

SEIDMAN, Robert
Chief Operating Officer, Health Alliance Hospital - Broadway Campus, Kingston, NY, p. A428
Chief Operating Officer, Health Alliance Hospital - Mary's Avenue Campus, Kingston, NY, p. A428

SEIFER, Jill, Vice President Human Resources, Oaklawn Psychiatric Center, Goshen, IN, p. A205

SEIFERT, Debra A, Director Human Resources, Lake Huron Medical Center, Port Huron, MI, p. A321

SEILER, Gregory A, Chief Executive Officer, Metropolitan Methodist Hospital, TX, p. A633

SEIM, Kay E., Chief Executive Officer, Aurora Santa Rosa Hospital, Santa Rosa, CA, p. A89

SEIM, Lori, R.N., Director Nursing Services, First Care Health Center, Park River, ND, p. A468

SEIP, Jeffrey, M.D., Chief Medical Staff, Hi-Desert Medical Center, Joshua Tree, CA, p. A62

SEIPLE, Donald, President, St. Luke's Monroe, Stroudsburg, PA, p. A542

SEIRER, Jeff, Interim Chief Financial Officer, St. Joseph Campus, KS, p. A248

SEITZ, Kimberly A, Area Human Resources Leader, Kaiser Permanente Redwood City Medical Center, Redwood City, CA, p. A80

SEITZ, Stewart R., Chief Executive Officer, Gladys Spellman Specialty Hospital And Nursing Center, Cheverly, MD, p. A290

SEITZ, Tawnya, Chief Financial Officer, Lincoln County Hospital, Lincoln, KS, p. A240

SELBY, Eric, R.N., Chief Nursing Officer, Chicot Memorial Medical Center, Lake Village-Chicot County, AR, p. A44

SELBY, Victoria, MHA, BSN,, Vice President, Ancillary and Support Services, Community Hospital Of San Bernardino, San Bernardino, CA, p. A83

SELF, Chris, Chief Operating Officer, Manchester Memorial Hospital, Manchester, KY, p. A257

SELF, Joshua, Chief Executive Officer, Mary Black Health System - Gaffney, Gaffney, SC, p. A553

SELFRIDGE, Tara, Manager Human Resources, Purcell Municipal Hospital, Purcell, OK, p. A506

SELHORST, Sonya, R.N., Administrator and Chief Nursing Officer, Mercy Hospital Of Defiance, Defiance, OH, p. A481

SELIG, Doug R, MSN, R.N., Vice President of Patient Services, Parkview Huntington Hospital, Huntington, IN, p. A206

SELIGA, Patricia, R.N., Chief Nursing Officer, Moses Taylor Hospital, Scranton, PA, p. A540

SELIGMAN, Joel, President and Chief Executive Officer, Northern Westchester Hospital, Mount Kisco, NY, p. A430

SELIGMAN, Morris H, M.D., Chief Medical Officer and Chief Medical Information Officer, Sycamore Shoals Hospital, Elizabethton, TN, p. A569

SELL, Paula, Director Human Resources, Allen County Regional Hospital, Iola, KS, p. A237

SELL, Teri, Payroll and Personnel Coordinator, Jennie M. Melham Memorial Medical Center, Broken Bow, NE, p. A382

SELLARDS, Michael G., President and Chief Executive Officer, St. Mary's Medical Center, Huntington, WV, p. A684

SELLE, Ginger, Vice President Patient Care Services, Ssm Health St. Clare Hospital-Baraboo, Baraboo, WI, p. A689

SELLE, Justin, Chief Executive Officer, Hshs St. Nicholas Hospital, Sheboygan, WI, p. A703

SELLERS, Laura, Director Information Systems, Youth Villages Inner Harbour Campus, Douglasville, GA, p. A152

SELLERS, Mary, Chief Information Officer, Navos, Seattle, WA, p. A676

SELLERS, Robert R.
Chief Executive Officer, Optim Medical Center - Jenkins, Millen, GA, p. A157
Chief Executive Officer, Optim Medical Center - Screven, Sylvania, GA, p. A161

SELLHEIM, Kevin, Administrator, Sleepy Eye Medical Center, Sleepy Eye, MN, p. A340

SELLS, Matt, Chief Executive Officer, Shenandoah Medical Center, Shenandoah, IA, p. A229

SELMAN, David, Chief Executive Officer, Select Specialty Hospital-Phoenix Downtown, Phoenix, AZ, p. A34

SELMAN, J Peter., FACHE, Chief Executive Officer, Baptist Medical Center South, Montgomery, AL, p. A21

SELMON, Patricia, Director Public Relations and Chief Human Resources, Jefferson County Hospital, Fayette, MS, p. A345

SELNER, Ralph, Chief Executive Officer, Kindred Hospital Central Tampa, Tampa, FL, p. A141

SELPH, Wendy, Director Human Resources, Dodge County Hospital, Eastman, GA, p. A153

SELSOR, Doug, Director Finance, Select Rehabilitation Hospital Of Denton, Denton, TX, p. A599

SELTZER, Paul, M.D., Chief of Staff, Jfk Medical Center North Campus, West Palm Beach, FL, p. A143

SELVAM, A Panneer, M.D., Chief of Staff, Northern Arizona Veterans Affairs Health Care System, Prescott, AZ, p. A34

SELVIDGE, Sandra, Chief Fiscal Service, Cincinnati Veterans Affairs Medical Center, Cincinnati, OH, p. A474

SELZ, Timothy P, Vice President, Orange Regional Medical Center, Middletown, NY, p. A430

SELZER, Stephen R., Market Chief Executive Officer, Providence Hospital Northeast, SC, p. A551

SEMAR, Dale, Controller, Pauls Valley General Hospital, Pauls Valley, OK, p. A505

SEMELSBERGER, Kimberly, CPA, Chief Financial Officer, Conemaugh Nason Medical Center, Roaring Spring, PA, p. A540

SEMERDJIAN, Nancy, R.N., Chief Nursing Officer, Northshore Skokie Hospital, IL, p. A182

SEMERE, Jana
Chief Nursing Officer, Leonard J. Chabert Medical Center, Houma, LA, p. A269
Chief Nursing Officer, Ochsner St. Anne General Hospital, Raceland, LA, p. A277

SEMEYN, Janice, D.O., President, Medical Staff, Clarion Hospital, Clarion, PA, p. A522

SEMINARO, Anthony J.
Chief Financial Officer, Mercy Health - St. Elizabeth Youngstown Hospital, Youngstown, OH, p. A494
Chief Financial Youngstown, Mercy Health - St. Elizabeth Boardman Hospital, Boardman, OH, p. A472

SEMINGSON, John H., Chief Executive Officer, Ruby Valley Hospital, Sheridan, MT, p. A379

SEMRAD, Louis, Chief Executive Officer, Jefferson Hospital, Louisville, GA, p. A156

SEMRAU, Clint, Chief of Staff, Western Wisconsin Health, Baldwin, WI, p. A689

SENDAYDIEGO, Fe, Director Information Services, Sonoma Valley Hospital, Sonoma, CA, p. A90

SENGER, Joshua
Chief Financial Officer, Chi St. Francis Health, Breckenridge, MN, p. A328
Vice President, Operational Finance, Chi Mercy Health, Valley City, ND, p. A468

SENGER, Richard, Chief Financial Officer, Portsmouth Regional Hospital, Portsmouth, NH, p. A401

SENGER, Tricia, Chief Financial Officer, St. Luke's Elmore, Mountain Home, ID, p. A170

SENKER, Margaret, Chief Information Officer, Veterans Affairs Western New York Healthcare System-Buffalo Division, Buffalo, NY, p. A424

SENKER, Thomas, Interim Chief Executive Officer, Mon Health Medical Center, Morgantown, WV, p. A685

SENKER, Thomas J., FACHE, President, Medstar Montgomery Medical Center, Olney, MD, p. A293

SENN, Sheila, PsyD, Chief Clinical and Administrative Officer, Community First Medical Center, Chicago, IL, p. A176

SENNEFF, Robert G., FACHE, President and Chief Executive Officer, Graham Hospital Association, Canton, IL, p. A175

SENNETT, Paul, Chief Financial Officer, Centinela Hospital Medical Center, Inglewood, CA, p. A62

SENNISH, James, Vice President Human Resources, Firelands Regional Medical Center South Campus, OH, p. A490

SENSAT, Marsha, R.N., Chief Nursing Officer, Pikes Peak Regional Hospital, Woodland Park, CO, p. A106

SEPP, Howard W., Jr, Vice-President and Administrator, Southeast Georgia Health System Camden Campus, Saint Marys, GA, p. A159

SEQUIN, Shannon, MSN, Chief Nursing Officer, Select Specialty Hospital-Saginaw, Saginaw, MI, p. A322

SERENO, Joseph, Chief Financial Officer, Lovelace Women's Hospital, Albuquerque, NM, p. A415

SERFLING, G Aubrey., President and Chief Executive Officer, Eisenhower Medical Center, Rancho Mirage, CA, p. A79

SERGEANT, Lindy, Medical Staff President, Community Hospital Of Bremen, Bremen, IN, p. A200

SERKETICH, Steve, Manager Information Services, Aurora Sheboygan Memorial Medical Center, Sheboygan, WI, p. A702

SERLE, John, FACHE, President and Chief Executive Officer, Lourdes Medical Center, Pasco, WA, p. A674

SERNYAK, Michael, M.D., Director, Connecticut Mental Health Center, New Haven, CT, p. A109

SERRANO, Jorge L Matta., Administrator, Auxilio Mutuo Hospital, San Juan, PR, p. A715

SERRANO, Lorenzo, Chief Executive Officer, Winkler County Memorial Hospital, Kermit, TX, p. A617

SERZAN, Megan, Director of Quality, Compliance, Risk & Safety, Asheville Specialty Hospital, Asheville, NC, p. A447

SESSIONS, Jerry W., M.D., Chief Medical Staff, Springhill Medical Center, Springhill, LA, p. A279

SESSLER, Connie, Director Human Resources, St. Luke's Hospital, Maumee, OH, p. A486

SESTERHENN, Steven, Vice President, Unitypoint Health - Allen Hospital, Waterloo, IA, p. A231

SETHI, Sanjiv, M.D., Medical Director, Fulton State Hospital, Fulton, MO, p. A359

SETHNEY, Julie, R.N., Vice President Patient Care, Fairview Ridges Hospital, Burnsville, MN, p. A329

SETLIFF, Chad
President and Chief Operating Officer, Kernersville Medical Center, NC, p. A462
President and Chief Operating Officer, Novant Health Clemmons Medical Center, NC, p. A462

SETO, Colbert, Chief Information Officer, Rehabilitation Hospital Of The Pacific, Honolulu, HI, p. A165

SETTLE, Andrea, Director Human Resources, Taylor Regional Hospital, Campbellsville, KY, p. A250

SETTLES, Allicia, Chief Nursing Officer, Ut Health Quitman, Quitman, TX, p. A629

SETTLES, April, Chief Financial Officer, Greene County General Hospital, Linton, IN, p. A210

SETZER, Jeffery, Administrator Information Systems, J. D. Mccarty Center For Children With Developmental Disabilities, Norman, OK, p. A502

SETZER, Randy R, Financial Services Manager, Waukesha County Mental Health Center, Waukesha, WI, p. A705

SETZKORN-MEYER, Marsha, Director Public Relations and Marketing, Hillsboro Community Hospital, Hillsboro, KS, p. A236

SEVCO, Mark
President, Upmc East, Monroeville, PA, p. A532
President, Upmc Mckeesport, Mckeesport, PA, p. A531

SEVILLA, Mark, Executive Director, Yale-New Haven Psychiatric Hospital, CT, p. A110

SEVILLIAN, Clarence, President and Chief Executive Officer, Mclaren Bay Region-West Campus, MI, p. A308

SEWATSKY, Mary, M.D., Chief Medical Officer, Moses Taylor Hospital, Scranton, PA, p. A540

SEWELL, Lance, Chief Financial Officer, South Lake Hospital, Clermont, FL, p. A120

SEWICK, Alayne, Vice President Human Resources, Wysong Campus, TX, p. A623

SEXTON, Charles, Manager Human Resources, Cumberland Medical Center, Crossville, TN, p. A569

SEXTON, Cindy, Director Information Systems, St. David's Round Rock Medical Center, Round Rock, TX, p. A631

SEXTON, Kevin, Director Information Systems, Raleigh General Hospital, Beckley, WV, p. A681

SEXTON, William P., Chief Executive Officer, Crossing Rivers Health Medical Center, Prairie Du Chien, WI, p. A701

SEYMOUR, Barbara, Vice President of Nursing, Health First Holmes Regional Medical Center, Melbourne, FL, p. A129

SEYMOUR, Claudette, Director Personnel, Memphis Mental Health Institute, Memphis, TN, p. A575

SEYMOUR, Jose, Chief Information Resource Management, James A. Haley Veterans' Hospital-Tampa, Tampa, FL, p. A141

SEYMOUR, Robert, Chief Financial Officer/Senior Director Finance, Grande Ronde Hospital, La Grande, OR, p. A514

SEYMOUR, Ryan, Chief Executive Officer, Baylor Institute For Rehabilitation At Frisco, Frisco, TX, p. A606

SEYMOUR, Sally, Chief Operating Officer, Medical Center Of Trinity, Trinity, FL, p. A142

SGARLATA, Lisa, MSN
Chief Patient Care Officer, Cape Coral Hospital, Cape Coral, FL, p. A119
Chief Patient Care Officer, Gulf Coast Medical Center, Fort Myers, FL, p. A123

SHACKELFORD, Gerald, Staff Support Specialist, Texas Center For Infectious Disease, San Antonio, TX, p. A634

SHACKELFORD, J. Larry., President and Chief Executive Officer, Washington Regional Medical Center, Fayetteville-Washington County, AR, p. A42

SHACKELFORD, Paul, M.D., Chief Medical Officer, University Health Systems Children's Hospital, NC, p. A454

SHACKLETON, Carol, M.D., Medical Director, Gothenburg Health, Gothenburg, NE, p. A384

SHADENSACK, Don, Vice President Clinical Services, Osf St. Mary Medical Center, Galesburg, IL, p. A183

SHADOWENS, Karen, Director Finance and Chief Financial Officer, West Chester Hospital Surgical Center, OH, p. A493

SHAFER, Kenny, Chief Operating Officer, Woodridge Hospital, TN, p. A571

SHAFER, Robert
Vice President Finance, Mercy Medical Center-Dubuque, Dubuque, IA, p. A222
Vice President Finance, Mercy Medical Center-Dyersville, Dyersville, IA, p. A222

SHAFER, Timothy, M.D., Medical Director, Grace Cottage Hospital, Townshend, VT, p. A654

SHAFFER, Jeraldene, MSN, Chief Nursing Officer, Roseland Community Hospital, Chicago, IL, p. A179

SHAFFER, Lana, Chief Executive Officer, Harper County Community Hospital, Buffalo, OK, p. A496

SHAFICI, Khaled, M.D., President Medical Staff, Cornerstone Hospital-West Monroe, West Monroe, LA, p. A280

SHAFIU, Mohamed, M.D., Chief of Staff, Val Verde Regional Medical Center, Del Rio, TX, p. A598

SHAH, Beena, M.D., Chief of Staff and Chief Medical Officer, Anaheim Global Medical Center, Anaheim, CA, p. A50

SHAH, Jayendra H, M.D., Chief Medical Officer, Southern Arizona Veterans Affairs Health Care System, Tucson, AZ, p. A38

SHAH, Ketan, M.D., Acting Director, Battle Creek Veterans Affairs Medical Center, Battle Creek, MI, p. A308

SHAH, Paresh, Director Information Systems, Reston Hospital Center, Reston, VA, p. A664

SHAH, Syed, M.D., Chief of Staff, Pioneer Memorial Hospital And Health Services, Viborg, SD, p. A565

SHAH, Vital, M.D., Associate Director and Chief Medical Officer, Central State Hospital, Louisville, KY, p. A256

SHAHAN, Matthew, Chief Executive Officer, West River Regional Medical Center, Hettinger, ND, p. A467

SHAHI, Niloo, Chief Operating Officer, Lac-Olive View-Ucla Medical Center, Los Angeles, CA, p. A68

SHAHNAM, Melissa Shreves, Director Human Resources, Mon Health Medical Center, Morgantown, WV, p. A685

SHAHRYAR, Syed, M.D., Medical Director, Promise Hospital Of Phoenix, Mesa, AZ, p. A31

SHAHZADA, Kamran, M.D., Chief Medical Staff, South Central Kansas Medical Center, Arkansas City, KS, p. A232

SHAIFFER, Mandy, Chief Nursing Officer, Mt. San Rafael Hospital, Trinidad, CO, p. A106

SHAKOOR, Arif, Chief of Staff, Raulerson Hospital, Okeechobee, FL, p. A133

SHALLOCK, James R, Chief Financial Officer, Memorial Hermann The Woodlands Hospital, TX, p. A467

SHAMBURG, Steffen, M.D., Chief of Staff, Hiawatha Community Hospital, Hiawatha, KS, p. A236

SHAMMAS, Karen, Chief Executive Officer, Curahealth Phoenix, AZ, p. A33

SHANAHAN, Thomas
Chief Financial Officer and Senior Vice President, Perth Amboy Division, NJ, p. A410
Chief Operating Officer, Perth Amboy Division, NJ, p. A410
Vice President, Human Resources, Children's Hospital Of Wisconsin-Fox Valley, Neenah, WI, p. A699
Vice President, Human Resources, Children's Hospital Of Wisconsin, Milwaukee, WI, p. A698

SHAND, Natalie, M.D., Vice President Integrative Medicine and Chief Medical Officer, Scottsdale Liberty Hospital, Scottsdale, AZ, p. A35

SHANLEY, Diane, Deputy Service Unit Director, U.S. Public Health Service Indian Hospital-Sells, Sells, AZ, p. A36

SHANLEY, Linda L., Vice President, Chief Information Officer, Saint Francis Hospital And Medical Center, Hartford, CT, p. A108

SHANNON, David A., Interim Chief Executive Officer, Three Rivers Health, Three Rivers, MI, p. A324

SHANNON, Greg
Chief Executive Officer, Two Rivers Behavioral Health System, Kansas City, MO, p. A362
Chief Human Resources Officer, Golden Valley Memorial Healthcare, Clinton, MO, p. A357

SHANNON, John Jay., M.D.
Chief Executive Officer, John H. Stroger Jr. Hospital Of Cook County, Chicago, IL, p. A177
Chief Executive Officer, Provident Hospital Of Cook County, Chicago, IL, p. A179

SHANNON, Lori, Chief Nursing Officer, St. Vincent Heart Center, Indianapolis, IN, p. A208

SHANNON, Patrick, Chief Operating Officer, Baptist Hospitals Of Southeast Texas Fannin Behavioral Health Center, TX, p. A588

SHANNON, Richard, M.D., Chief of Staff, Montrose Memorial Hospital, Montrose, CO, p. A104

SHANNON, Scott, Director Finance, Socorro General Hospital, Socorro, NM, p. A420

SHAPE, Amy, Information Technology, North Dakota State Hospital, Jamestown, ND, p. A467

SHAPIRO, David, M.D.
Vice President Medical Affairs and Chief Medical Officer, Columbia St. Mary's Hospital Ozaukee, Mequon, WI, p. A698
Vice President Medical Affairs and Chief Medical Officer, Columbia St. Mary's Milwaukee Hospital, Milwaukee, WI, p. A698
Vice President Medical Affairs and Chief Medical Officer, Columbia St. Mary's Milwaukee Hospital, WI, p. A698

SHAPIRO, Louis A., President and Chief Executive Officer, Hospital For Special Surgery, New York (Includes All Hospitals Located Within The Five Boroughs), NY, p. A432

SHAPIRO, Marc, M.D., Chief Medical Officer, Adventist Health Clear Lake, Clearlake, CA, p. A54

SHAPIRO, Steven D, M.D.
Chief Medical Officer, Bon Secours St. Francis Hospital, Charleston, SC, p. A549
Chief Medical Officer, Roper St. Francis Mount Pleasant Hospital, Mount Pleasant, SC, p. A555
Vice President Medical Affairs, Roper St. Francis, Charleston, SC, p. A550

SHAPPLEY, Robert, Chief Operating Officer, Lakewood Regional Medical Center, Lakewood, CA, p. A64

SHARANGPANI, Rojesh, M.D., Chief of Staff, Capital Medical Center, Olympia, WA, p. A674

SHARBER-HOWELL, Sheryl, Administrator, Creek Nation Community Hospital, Okemah, OK, p. A502

SHARKEY, Linda, R.N., MSN, Vice President Patient Care Services and Chief Nurse Executive, Fauquier Hospital, Warrenton, VA, p. A667

SHARLOW, Joseph, M.D., Chief of Staff, Ste. Genevieve County Memorial Hospital, Ste Genevieve, MO, p. A371

SHARMA, Adhi, M.D., Senior Vice President, Medical Affairs and Chief Medical Officer, South Nassau Communities Hospital, Oceanside, NY, p. A438

SHARMA, Aika, M.D., President Medical Staff, Alameda Hospital, Alameda, CA, p. A50

SHARMA, Chandra, M.D., Chief of Staff, Welch Community Hospital, Welch, WV, p. A687

SHARMA, Roger, Executive Vice President/Chief Financial Officer, Citrus Valley Medical Center-Queen Of The Valley Campus, CA, p. A56

SHARMA, Satish C, M.D., Chief of Staff, Providence Veterans Affairs Medical Center, Providence, RI, p. A547

SHARON, Joesph P., Associate Director, Wilkes-Barre Veterans Affairs Medical Center, Wilkes, PA, p. A544

SHARON, Sandy, Senior Vice President and Area Manager, Kaiser Permanente Sacramento Medical Center, Sacramento, CA, p. A81

SHARP, Alan
Chief Financial Officer, Saint Thomas Dekalb Hospital, Smithville, TN, p. A580
Chief Financial Officer, Saint Thomas Stones River Hospital, Woodbury, TN, p. A581

SHARP, Cheryl, Chief Financial Office, Miami County Medical Center, Paola, KS, p. A244

SHARP, Cindy, M.D., Chief Medical Officer, Madison Valley Medical Center, Ennis, MT, p. A375

SHARP, Gina, FACHE, President and Chief Executive Officer, Linden Oaks Hospital, Naperville, IL, p. A190

SHARP, John K, Chief Financial Officer, Seton Medical Center Harker Heights, Harker Heights, TX, p. A608

SHARP, Julie, Supervisor Human Resources, Chase County Community Hospital, Imperial, NE, p. A385

SHARP, Mike, Interim Director, Wellstar Atlanta Medical Center - South Campus, GA, p. A147

SHARP, Rebecca, Chief Financial Officer, Wagoner Community Hospital, Wagoner, OK, p. A510

SHARP, Richard, M.D., Medical Director, Christus St. Michael Rehabilitation Hospital, Texarkana, TX, p. A639

SHARP, Stacy, Coordinator Human Resources, Atoka County Medical Center, Atoka, OK, p. A496

SHARP, Tanya, President and Chief Executive Officer, Boone County Health Center, Albion, NE, p. A381

SHARP, Tony, Supervisor Information System, Sweetwater Hospital, Sweetwater, TN, p. A580

SHARPE, Deborah, R.N., Director of Nursing, West Springs Hospital, Grand Junction, CO, p. A101

SHARPTON, Debra, Director of Nursing, Devereux Advanced Behavioral Health Georgia, Kennesaw, GA, p. A155

SHARUM, Melinda
Director Human Resources, Mercy Hospital Ardmore, Ardmore, OK, p. A495

Director Human Resources, Mercy Hospital Healdton, Healdton, OK, p. A499

SHATRAW, Thomas, Director Human Resources, Samaritan Medical Center, Watertown, NY, p. A445

SHAUGHNESSY, John, Chief Financial Officer, Mcleod Health Clarendon, Manning, SC, p. A555

SHAUGHNESSY, Mary
Vice President Finance, Spaulding Hospital For Continuing Medical Care Cambridge, Cambridge, MA, p. A298
Vice President Finance, Spaulding Rehabilitation Hospital Cape Cod, East Sandwich, MA, p. A299
Vice President Finance, Spaulding Rehabilitation Hospital, Charlestown, MA, p. A299

SHAUINGER, Beckie, Chief Executive Officer, Fairfax Behavioral Health Everett, WA, p. A673

SHAULL, Heather, Chief Financial Officer, Adair County Health System, Greenfield, IA, p. A223

SHAULL, Ty, President and Chief Executive Officer, Wyandot Memorial Hospital, Upper Sandusky, OH, p. A492

SHAUNESSY, Celia, Vice President Human Resources, Ascension St. Michael's Hospital, Stevens Point, WI, p. A703

SHAVER, Chris
Vice President Human Resources, Covenant Children's Hospital, Lubbock, TX, p. A620
Vice President Human Resources, Covenant Medical Center-Lakeside, TX, p. A621
Vice President Human Resources, Covenant Specialty Hospital, Lubbock, TX, p. A621

SHAVER, Jennifer
Director of Nursing, Gouverneur Hospital, Gouverneur, NY, p. A427
Director of Nursing, Lewis County General Hospital, Lowville, NY, p. A429

SHAVER, John, Chief Financial Officer, Baystate Noble Hospital, Westfield, MA, p. A305

SHAVER, Robert D, M.D., Vice President Medical Affairs, Wellspan Good Samaritan Hospital, Lebanon, PA, p. A529

SHAW, David, Director Information Technology, Forrest City Medical Center, Forrest City-St. Francis County, AR, p. A42

SHAW, David B., Chief Executive Officer and Administrator, Nor-Lea Hospital District, Lovington, NM, p. A418

SHAW, Douglas A., Chief Executive Officer, Mad River Community Hospital, Arcata, CA, p. A51

SHAW, Gary, President, Cambridge Medical Center, Cambridge, MN, p. A329

SHAW, Greg, Vice President, Finance, Aspirus Medford Hospital & Clinics, Inc., Medford, WI, p. A697

SHAW, Howard, M.D., Chief Medical Officer, Medical City Denton, Denton, TX, p. A599

SHAW, Jan, Director Personnel, River Bend Hospital, West Lafayette, IN, p. A216

SHAW, Jean, Chief Financial Officer, Valley Regional Hospital, Claremont, NH, p. A398

SHAW, John C, M.D., Medical Director, Southern Indiana Rehabilitation Hospital, New Albany, IN, p. A212

SHAW, Kendra, Chief Information Officer, Western Wisconsin Health, Baldwin, WI, p. A689

SHAW, Kimberly
Chief Operating Officer, St. Rose Dominican Hospitals - Siena Campus, Henderson, NV, p. A393
Vice President Patient Care and Chief Nursing Executive, Mercy Medical Center Redding, Redding, CA, p. A79

SHAW, Mandy, M.D., Chief of Staff, Sidney Regional Medical Center, Sidney, NE, p. A390

SHAW, Patrick D., Chief Executive Officer, Grafton City Hospital, Grafton, WV, p. A683

SHAW, Violet, R.N., Director of Nursing, Grafton City Hospital, Grafton, WV, p. A683

SHAWAN, Christy, Chief Executive Officer, Black River Medical Center, Poplar Bluff, MO, p. A366

SHAWGO, Darla, Director Human Resources, Sparta Community Hospital, Sparta, IL, p. A196

SHAWN, D.J., Director Human Resources, Alliancehealth Madill, Madill, OK, p. A500

SHEA, Drew, Chief Financial Officer, City Hospital At White Rock, Dallas, TX, p. A596

SHEA, Natalie, Chief Nursing Officer, Central Community Hospital, Elkader, IA, p. A222

SHEAR, Larry, Administrative Assistant, Norwood Health Center, Marshfield, WI, p. A697

SHEARER, Christopher, M.D., Chief Medical Officer, Honorhealth John C. Lincoln Medical Center, Phoenix, AZ, p. A33

SHEARER, Laura, R.N., MSN, Senior Vice President and Chief Nursing Officer, Phoebe North, GA, p. A145

SHEARER, Ron, M.D., Regional Medical Director, Peacehealth Peace Harbor Medical Center, Florence, OR, p. A512

SHEARS, Ann Marie, Vice President Patient Care Services, Robert Wood Johnson University Hospital Rahway, Rahway, NJ, p. A411

SHECKLER, Robert L., Administrator, Avera Gettysburg Hospital, Gettysburg, SD, p. A561

SHEEHAN, Karen, Vice President and Chief Information Officer, Swedish Covenant Hospital, Chicago, IL, p. A180

SHEEHAN, T J, Chief Financial Officer, Lauderdale Community Hospital, Ripley, TN, p. A579

SHEEHAN, Terrence P, M.D., Medical Director, Adventist Healthcare Physical Health And Rehabilitation, Rockville, MD, p. A293

SHEEHY, Earl Nielsen., Chief Executive Officer, Ray County Memorial Hospital, Richmond, MO, p. A366

SHEERIN, Rick
Chief Financial Officer, Polk Medical Center, Cedartown, GA, p. A150
Vice President Fiscal Services, Floyd Medical Center, Rome, GA, p. A159

SHEETS, Cindy, Vice President Information Systems and Chief Information Officer, Mansfield Hospital, OH, p. A485

SHEETS, Jim, Chief Executive Officer and Administrator, Lds Hospital, Salt Lake City, UT, p. A650

SHEFFIELD, Aubrey, Administrative Assistant Human Resources and Public Relations, Grove Hill Memorial Hospital, Grove Hill, AL, p. A19

SHEFFIELD, Nichol, Chief Executive Officer, Pacific Grove Hospital, Riverside, CA, p. A81

SHEFIELD, Jennifer, M.D., Chief of Staff, West River Regional Medical Center, Hettinger, ND, p. A467

SHEFTE, David H., Chief Executive Officer, Healthsouth Rehabilitation Hospital Of Littleton, Littleton, CO, p. A103

SHEGOLEV, Igor, Vice President Human Resources, Carondelet St. Joseph's Hospital, Tucson, AZ, p. A37

SHEHAN, Mary, R.N., MSN, Chief Executive Officer, Louis A. Weiss Memorial Hospital, Chicago, IL, p. A177

SHEHATA, Nady, M.D., Vice President Medical Affairs, St. Joseph Hospital, NY, p. A424

SHEHI, G Michael, M.D., Medical Director, Mountain View Hospital, Gadsden, AL, p. A18

SHEHI, G Michael., M.D., Chief Executive Officer, Mountain View Hospital, Gadsden, AL, p. A18

SHEHI, Jay, Chief Executive Officer, Alliance Health Center, Meridian, MS, p. A350

SHEIKH, Arsalan, Chief of Medicine, Bon Secours Baltimore Health System, Baltimore, MD, p. A287

SHEIKH, Azad, Chief Medical Officer, Fremont Medical Center, CA, p. A72

SHEINBEIN, David, Chief Medical Officer, Banner - University Medical Center South, Tucson, AZ, p. A36

SHELAK, Matt, Chief Executive Officer, Roxborough Memorial Hospital, Philadelphia, PA, p. A536

SHELBURNE, John D, M.D., Chief of Staff, Durham Veterans Affairs Medical Center, Durham, NC, p. A451

SHELBY, Dennis R., Chief Executive Officer, Wilson Medical Center, Neodesha, KS, p. A241

SHELBY, Joyce, Manager Human Resources, Hardin County General Hospital, Rosiclare, IL, p. A195

SHELDEN, Diana, Chief Nursing Officer, Stone County Medical Center, Mountain View-Stone County, AR, p. A46

SHELDON, Lyle Ernest., FACHE
President and Chief Executive Officer, University Of Maryland Harford Memorial Hospital, Havre De Grace, MD, p. A292
President and Chief Executive Officer, University Of Maryland Upper Chesapeake Medical Center, Bel Air, MD, p. A289

SHELDON, Mo P., FACHE, Chief Executive Officer and Administrator, Odessa Memorial Healthcare Center, Odessa, WA, p. A674

SHELFORD, Dave, Assistant Superintendent, Richmond State Hospital, Richmond, IN, p. A214

SHELL, John, M.D., Chief Medical Officer, Coffey County Hospital, Burlington, KS, p. A233

SHELL, Steve, Chief Executive Officer, Desert Parkway Behavioral Healthcare Hospital, Las Vegas, NV, p. A394

SHELLENBERGER, David, President, St. John Vianney Hospital, Downingtown, PA, p. A524

SHELLS, Tammy, Chief Nursing Officer, Belmont Pines Hospital, Youngstown, OH, p. A494

SHELT, Elizabeth, Civilian Personnel Officer, Dwight David Eisenhower Army Medical Center, Fort Gordon, GA, p. A154

SHELTON, Amy, Chief Nursing Officer, St. Vincent's East, Birmingham, AL, p. A15

SHELTON, Angela, Chief Financial Officer, Jack Hughston Memorial Hospital, Phenix City, AL, p. A22

SHELTON, Carol, Director Human Resources, Lovelace Women's Hospital, Albuquerque, NM, p. A415

SHELTON, Darlene, Coordinator Team Resources, Baycare Alliant Hospital, Dunedin, FL, p. A122

SHELTON, Jared, Chief Executive Officer, Texas Health Presbyterian Hospital Allen, Allen, TX, p. A582

SHELTON, Jeffrey, Chief Executive Officer, Hiawatha Community Hospital, Hiawatha, KS, p. A236

SHELTON, Kathy, Director Human Resources, Ut Health Pittsburg, Pittsburg, TX, p. A628

SHELTON, Mark, Chief of Staff, Winn Parish Medical Center, Winnfield, LA, p. A281

SHELTON, Richard, M.D., Chief Medical Officer, Baptist Health Richmond, Richmond, KY, p. A260

SHELTON, Tom, Coordinator of Nursing Services, Porterville Developmental Center, Porterville, CA, p. A79

SHENDELL-FALIK, Nancy, R.N.
President, Baystate Children's Hospital, MA, p. A304
Senior Vice President, Chief Operating Officer and Chief Nursing Officer, Baystate Children's Hospital, MA, p. A304

SHENEFIELD, Jason, Senior Vice President and Chief Operating Officer, Phelps County Regional Medical Center, Rolla, MO, p. A366

SHENGLE, Lori, Director Information Technology, Morrill County Community Hospital, Bridgeport, NE, p. A382

SHEPARD, Bridget, Vice President Human Resources, Wabash General Hospital, Mount Carmel, IL, p. A190

SHEPARD, Karen, Senior Vice President and Chief Financial Officer, St. Charles Prineville, Prineville, OR, p. A517

SHEPARD, Megan, Director Clinical Services, Odessa Memorial Healthcare Center, Odessa, WA, p. A674

SHEPARD, Sheila, Controller, Encompass Health Rehabilitation Hospital Of Humble, Humble, TX, p. A614

SHEPARDSON, Dean, Chief Financial Officer, Banner Estrella Medical Center, Phoenix, AZ, p. A33

SHEPARDSON, Heather S, Vice President Human Resources, Roanoke Memorial Rehabilitation Center, VA, p. A665

SHEPHARD, Bryan, Chief Financial Officer, Tristar Summit Medical Center, Hermitage, TN, p. A570

SHEPHARD, Russ, Senior Systems Analyst, West Tennessee Healthcare Dyersburg Hospital, Dyersburg, TN, p. A569

SHEPHERD, Laura, Director Human Resources, Texas Health Huguley Hospital Fort Worth South, Burleson, TX, p. A591

SHEPHERD, Linda M., Chief Nursing Officer, Johnston Memorial Hospital, Abingdon, VA, p. A655

SHEPHERD, Lisa, M.D., Chief of Staff, Buena Vista Regional Medical Center, Storm Lake, IA, p. A230

SHEPHERD, Thomas, Executive Vice President and Chief Operating Officer, Gwinnett Medical Center, GA, p. A156

SHEPLER, Mary, R.N., Vice President and Chief Nursing Officer, Saint Joseph Hospital, Denver, CO, p. A99

SHEPPARD, Ballard, Chief Executive Officer, Rivendell Behavioral Health Services Of Arkansas, Benton-Saline County, AR, p. A39

SHEPPARD, Sandy, Vice President Patient Services, Wake Forest Baptist Health - Wilkes Medical Center, North Wilkesboro, NC, p. A458

SHEPPARD, Sharon, Manager Human Resources, Sycamore Shoals Hospital, Elizabethton, TN, p. A569

SHEPPARD, Varinya, R.N., Chief Nursing Officer, St. Elizabeth Medical Center, Utica, NY, p. A444

SHERBONDY, Beverly, Assistant Vice President, Human Resources, Jeanes Hospital, Philadelphia, PA, p. A535

SHERBONDY, Lori, Director Human Resources, Battle Mountain General Hospital, Battle Mountain, NV, p. A392

SHERER, Janet, Chief of Patient Care Services, Springfield Hospital, Springfield, VT, p. A654

SHERER, Susan, Chief Information Resource Management, Dayton Veterans Affairs Medical Center, Dayton, OH, p. A480

SHERIDAN, Cheryl, R.N., Senior Vice President Patient Care Services, Rochester General Hospital, Rochester, NY, p. A441

SHERIDAN, Elizabeth
Chief Operating Officer and Chief Nursing Executive, Bridgeton Health Center, NJ, p. A413
Chief Operating Officer and Chief Nursing Executive, Inspira Medical Center-Elmer, Elmer, NJ, p. A404

SHERIDAN, Kolbe, Chief Operating Officer, Heartland Regional Medical Center, Marion, IL, p. A188

SHERIDAN, Phil, Chief Executive Officer, Beckett Springs, West Chester, OH, p. A493

SHERIF, Ali, M.D., Chief of Staff, Lea Regional Medical Center, Hobbs, NM, p. A417

SHERMAN, Angelina, R.N., MSN, Chief Nursing Officer, The Rehabilitation Institute Of St. Louis, Saint Louis, MO, p. A369

SHERMAN, Frederick C, M.D., Chief Medical Officer, The Children's Home Of Pittsburgh, Pittsburgh, PA, p. A538

SHERMAN, Sheila, Vice President Patient Care Services, Vail Health, Vail, CO, p. A106

SHERMAN, Stephanie, Chief Human Resources Officer, West Boca Medical Center, Boca Raton, FL, p. A118

SHERON, William E., Chief Executive Officer, Wooster Community Hospital, Wooster, OH, p. A494

SHERRILL, Angela
Chief Information Officer, Laird Hospital, Union, MS, p. A353
Corporate Director Information System, Rush Foundation Hospital, Meridian, MS, p. A350
Corporate Director Information System, Specialty Hospital Of Meridian, Meridian, MS, p. A350

SHERROD, Michael, Chief Executive Officer, Tristar Greenview Regional Hospital, Bowling Green, KY, p. A250

SHERROD, Rhonda Kay., R.N., MSN
Chief Executive Officer, Shands Lake Shore Regional Medical Center, Lake City, FL, p. A127
Chief Executive Officer, Shands Live Oak Regional Medical Center, Live Oak, FL, p. A128

SHERRON, Tammy M., Vice President Finance, Carolinaeast Health System, New Bern, NC, p. A458

SHERRY, Bernie, President, Ascension Wisconsin, Midwest Orthopedic Specialty Hospital, Franklin, WI, p. A692

SHERRY, Mark A., Regional Director Human Resource Strategic Services, Austin/Round Rock Region, Baylor Scott & White Medical Center - Lakeway, TX, p. A631

SHERWIN, Charles H., President, Midmichigan Medical Center - Alpena, Alpena, MI, p. A307

SHERWOOD, Edward J, M.D., Chief Executive Officer, Cornerstone Hospital Of Austin, TX, p. A585

SHERWOOD, Jennifer L, Division, Human Resource Business Partner, Banner - University Medical Center South, Tucson, AZ, p. A36

SHERWOOD, Matthew M, Chief Financial Officer, Unity Medical & Surgical Hospital, Mishawaka, IN, p. A211

SHETTLESWORTH, Amanda, Director Human Resources, Bloomington Meadows Hospital, Bloomington, IN, p. A200

SHETTY, Atul, Chief of Staff, Weirton Medical Center, Weirton, WV, p. A687

SHEW, Angel, Director Area Technology, Kaiser Permanente South San Francisco, South San Francisco, CA, p. A90

SHEWBRIDGE, Richard K., President, Cleveland Clinic, Medina Hospital, Medina, OH, p. A486

SHEYKA, Patricia, Chief Nursing Officer, Gila Regional Medical Center, Silver City, NM, p. A420

SHIBINETTE, Lori, Chief Executive Officer, New Hampshire Hospital, Concord, NH, p. A398

SHICKOLOVICH, William, Chief Information Officer, Tufts Medical Center, Boston, MA, p. A297

SHIELDS, Charlie, President and Chief Executive Officer, Truman Medical Center-Hospital Hill, Kansas City, MO, p. A362

SHIELDS, Diane, Chief Human Resources Officer, Midmichigan Medical Center - Alpena, Alpena, MI, p. A307

SHIELDS, Stuart, Director, G. Werber Bryan Psychiatric Hospital, Columbia, SC, p. A551

SHIFF, Mary Treacy, Chief Financial Officer, Kindred Hospital Chicago North, IL, p. A177

SHIFFERMILLER, William, M.D., Vice President Medical Affairs, Methodist Women's Hospital, NE, p. A388

SHIHADY, Sharon, Director Human Resources, Spire Cane Creek Rehabilitation Hospital, Martin, TN, p. A574

SHIKIAR, Mindy, MSN, Chief Operating Officer, Boca Raton Regional Hospital, Boca Raton, FL, p. A118

SHILKAITIS, Mary, Vice President Patient Care and Chief Nursing Officer, Rush-Copley Medical Center, Aurora, IL, p. A174

SHILLING, Stacy, Controller, St. Vincent Rehabilitation Hospital, Sherwood-Pulaski County, AR, p. A48

SHIM, Eunmee, R.N., MSN, Vice President Operations, Adventist Healthcare Shady Grove Medical Center, Rockville, MD, p. A294

SHIMAMOTO, Kevin, Vice President and Chief Informational Officer, Valley Children's Healthcare, Madera, CA, p. A71

SHIMP, David, Chief Executive Officer, Del Sol Medical Center, TX, p. A602

SHINAGAWA, Nathan, Chief Operating Officer, Banner Del E. Webb Medical Center, Sun City West, AZ, p. A36

SHINER, Cindy, Manager Human Resources, Lebanon Veterans Affairs Medical Center, Lebanon, PA, p. A529

SHINGLETON, Kathy J., Ed.D., Vice President, Human Resources, Virginia Mason Medical Center, Seattle, WA, p. A677

SHINICK, Mary K, Vice President Human Resources, Nyack Hospital, Nyack, NY, p. A438

SHININGER, Kimberly R, Manger, Human Resources, Parkview Wabash County Hospital, Wabash, IN, p. A216

SHIPLEY, Carolyn, Chief Nursing Officer, Roane Medical Center, Harriman, TN, p. A570

SHIPLEY, Janice, M.D., Chief Medical Officer, Cibola General Hospital, Grants, NM, p. A417

SHIPLEY, Kurt, Chief Financial Officer, Mountain Point Medical Center, UT, p. A652

SHIPP, Geraldine H, Director of Risk Management, Sampson Regional Medical Center, Clinton, NC, p. A450

SHIRAH, Anita, Director Human Resources, Usa Health University Hospital, Mobile, AL, p. A21

SHIRLEY, Christian, Director Human Resources, Geisinger Healthsouth Rehabilitation Hospital, Danville, PA, p. A523

SHIRLEY, Douglas E., Senior Executive Vice President and Chief Financial Officer, Childen's Regional Hospital At Cooper, NJ, p. A403

SHIRLEY, Steve, Chief Information Officer, Parkview Medical Center, Pueblo, CO, p. A104

SHIVELY, Lori, Vice President of Finance, Munson Healthcare Grayling Hospital, Grayling, MI, p. A314

SHIVERY, Toni M
Vice President Human Resources, University Of Maryland Harford Memorial Hospital, Havre De Grace, MD, p. A292
Vice President Human Resources, University Of Maryland Upper Chesapeake Medical Center, Bel Air, MD, p. A289

SHMERLING, James E., President and Chief Executive Officer, Connecticut Children's Medical Center, Hartford, CT, p. A108

SHOBE, Franklin, Administrator and Chief Executive Officer, Black Hills Surgical Hospital, Rapid City, SD, p. A563

SHOBE, Susan, Director Administration and Support Services, Alton Mental Health Center, Alton, IL, p. A173

SHOCK, Ernest, Chief Nursing Officer, Abbeville Area Medical Center, Abbeville, SC, p. A549

SHOCKEY, Kathryn L, Director Human Resources, Lead-Deadwood Regional Hospital, Deadwood, SD, p. A560

SHOCKLEY, Mary, Human Resources Director, Russell Medical, Alexander City, AL, p. A13

SHOCKNEY, Brian T, FACHE, Chief Operating Officer, Indiana University Health Bloomington Hospital, Bloomington, IN, p. A200

SHOCKNEY, Brian T., FACHE, Interim President, Indiana University Health Bloomington Hospital, Bloomington, IN, p. A200

SHOEMAKER, Matt, D.O., Vice President and Chief Medical Officer, Southeast Hospital, Cape Girardeau, MO, p. A357

SHOENER, Carl, Chief Information Officer, Lehigh Valley Hospital - Hazleton, Hazleton, PA, p. A527

SHOFNER, Connie, Chief Nursing Officer, Carlsbad Medical Center, Carlsbad, NM, p. A416

SHOLTIS, Bridget, Chief Financial Officer, Mclaren Port Huron, Port Huron, MI, p. A321

SHOMAKER, Susan, Director Information Management Systems, J. Arthur Dosher Memorial Hospital, Southport, NC, p. A460

SHOOK, Susan, Interim Chief Executive officer, Murray Medical Center, Chatsworth, GA, p. A150

SHOR, Joel, M.D., Chief of Staff, Bluefield Regional Medical Center, Bluefield, WV, p. A681

SHORES, Larry, M.D., Executive Medical Director, Cedar Springs Hospital, Colorado Springs, CO, p. A97

SHORT, M Andrew, Vice President Information Services, Samaritan Medical Center, Watertown, NY, p. A445

SHORT, Penny, R.N., Chief Operating Officer, Nanticoke Memorial Hospital, Seaford, DE, p. A114

SHORT, Peter H, M.D., Senior Vice President Medical Affairs, Addison Gilbert Hospital, MA, p. A295

SHORT, Ted, Chief Financial Officer, Fairview Park Hospital, Dublin, GA, p. A153

SHORT, W L, M.D., Chief Medical Officer, Memorial Health System, Abilene, KS, p. A232

SHOUKAIR, Sami, M.D., Chief Medical Officer, La Palma Intercommunity Hospital, La Palma, CA, p. A63

SHOUP, Barbara, R.N., Chief Nursing Officer, Brighton Center For Recovery, Brighton, MI, p. A308

SHOUP, Emily, Director Nursing Services, Roundup Memorial Healthcare, Roundup, MT, p. A378

SHOUSE, Shellie, Chief Financial Officer, Bluegrass Community Hospital, Versailles, KY, p. A261

SHOWALTER, Amy J, R.N.
Chief Operating Officer, Sheltering Arms Hospital South, Midlothian, VA, p. A661
Chief Operating Officer, Sheltering Arms Rehabilitation Hospital, Mechanicsville, VA, p. A661

SHOWALTER, Will, Senior Vice President Information Technology, Holston Valley Medical Center, Kingsport, TN, p. A572

SHOWALTER, William, Senior Vice President and Chief Information Officer, Information Technology Services, Wake Forest Baptist Health-Davie Medical Center, Bermuda Run, NC, p. A448

SHOWS, Carla
Human Resource and Payroll Clerk, George Regional Hospital, Lucedale, MS, p. A349
Payroll Clerk, Greene County Hospital, Leakesville, MS, p. A349

SHREEVE, Susan, Chief Financial Officer, Research Psychiatric Center, MO, p. A361

SHRESTHA, Sanjeeb, M.D., Chief Medical Staff, Medical City Weatherford, Weatherford, TX, p. A643

SHREVE, Susan, Executive Director Information Technology, Boone Memorial Hospital, Madison, WV, p. A684

SHREWSBURY, Kim, Vice President and Chief Financial Officer, Decatur Morgan Hospital-West, AL, p. A16

SHRIDE, Chris, President, Presence St. Mary's Hospital, Kankakee, IL, p. A187

SHRIVASTAVA, Rakesh, M.D., Chief Medical Officer, Cornerstone Hospital Of Oklahoma-Shawnee, Shawnee, OK, p. A506

SHRIVER, Debra, R.N., MSN, Chief Nurse Executive, Unitypoint Health - Trinity Regional Medical Center, Fort Dodge, IA, p. A222

SHRIVER, Kren K, M.D., Clinical Director, Capital District Psychiatric Center, Albany, NY, p. A421

SHROADES, David W, Vice President Technology Services, Alliance Community Hospital, Alliance, OH, p. A470

SHROCK, Lynda J, Vice President Human Resources, Logansport Memorial Hospital, Logansport, IN, p. A210

SHROFF, Divya, Chief Medical Officer, Tristar Ashland City Medical Center, Ashland City, TN, p. A566

SHROFF, Rajendra, M.D., Administrative Medical Director, Ssm Health St. Mary's Hospital Centralia, Centralia, IL, p. A175

SHUART, Jeffery, M.D., Chief of Staff, Blackwell Regional Hospital, Blackwell, OK, p. A496

SHUFFLEBARGER, Tom, Chief Operating Officer, Children's Of Alabama, Birmingham, AL, p. A14

SHUFORD, Little, Health Information Manager, Kindred Hospital-Greensboro, Greensboro, NC, p. A453

SHUGARMAN, Mark D., Administrator, Shriners Hospitals For Children - Cincinnati, Cincinnati, OH, p. A475

SHUGART, Susan C, Chief Operating Officer, Carolina Pines Regional Medical Center, Hartsville, SC, p. A554

SHUGHART, Deborah A, Chief Financial Officer, Fulton County Medical Center, Mc Connellsburg, PA, p. A530

SHUGRUE, Dianne, President and Chief Executive Officer, Glens Falls Hospital, Glens Falls, NY, p. A427

SHULER, Conrad K, M.D., Chief Medical Officer, Oconee Memorial Hospital, Seneca, SC, p. A556

SHULIK, David, Vice President and Chief Financial Officer, Shenango Valley Campus, PA, p. A526

SHULL, Jennifer, R.N., Chief Nursing Officer, Florida Hospital Fish Memorial, Orange City, FL, p. A133

SHULTS, Randi L., Chief Executive Officer, North Carolina Specialty Hospital, Durham, NC, p. A451

SHUMAKER, Bradley, Chief Medical Officer, Kendall Regional Medical Center, Miami, FL, p. A130

SHUMAN, Betty, Director Human Resources, Wesley Rehabilitation Hospital, Wichita, KS, p. A248

SHUMAN, Daniel, D.O., Chief Medical Officer, Ashland Health Center, Ashland, KS, p. A232

SHUMATE, Karen J, R.N., Chief Operating Officer, Lawrence Memorial Hospital, Lawrence, KS, p. A239

SHUMATE, Kim, Human Resources Officer, Ohio State University Hospitals East, OH, p. A478

SHUMWAY, Barbara, Director Human Resources, North Big Horn Hospital District, Lovell, WY, p. A709

SHUPERT, Charlene
Director Staff Services, Carrus Rehabilitation Hospital, Sherman, TX, p. A636
Director Staff Services, Carrus Specialty Hospital, Sherman, TX, p. A636

SHUPP, Susan, Chief Human Resources Officer, Nemaha County Hospital, Auburn, NE, p. A381

SHUSHTARI, J. Kevin, M.D., Chief Medical Officer, Hospital For Special Care, New Britain, CT, p. A109

SHUTE, Keith M, M.D., Senior Vice President Medical Affairs and Clinical Services, Androscoggin Valley Hospital, Berlin, NH, p. A398

SHYSHKA, Susan, Associate Director, Va Greater Los Angeles Healthcare System, Los Angeles, CA, p. A70

SIAL, Ajay, Chief Financial Officer, UC Irvine Health, Uc Irvine Medical Center, Orange, CA, p. A76

SIAL, Jay, Chief Financial Officer, Ronald Mcdonald Children's Hospital, IL, p. A189

SIBBITT, Stephen, M.D., Chief Medical Officer, Mclane Children's Hospital Scott & White, TX, p. A638

SIBLEY, Beth, Director of Nursing, Sage Rehabilitation Hospital, Baton Rouge, LA, p. A264

SIBLEY, Jeri, Director Revenue Cycle, Riverside Tappahannock Hospital, Tappahannock, VA, p. A667

SICA, Vincent A., President and Chief Executive Officer, Desoto Memorial Hospital, Arcadia, FL, p. A117

SICHTS, Pam, Director Human Resources, Sycamore Springs Hospital, Lafayette, IN, p. A209

SICILIA, Bruce, M.D., Medical Director, Healthsouth Rehabilitation Hospital Of York, York, PA, p. A545

SIDDIQI, Ather, M.D.
Medical Director, Nexus Specialty Hospital The Woodlands, The Woodlands, TX, p. A640
Medical Director, Nexus Specialty Hospital, Shenandoah, TX, p. A635

SIDDIQI, Syed, M.D., President Medical Staff, Raleigh General Hospital, Beckley, WV, p. A681

SIDDIQUI, Joseph, Vice President Human Resources, Community General Health Center, ME, p. A286

SIDES, Tim, Chief Financial Officer, Valle Vista Hospital, Greenwood, IN, p. A205

SIDMAN, Robert, M.D., Regional Vice President, Medical Affairs, The William W. Backus Hospital, Norwich, CT, p. A110

SIDONE, LeighAnn, MSN, R.N., Chief Nursing Officer, Suburban Hospital, Bethesda, MD, p. A290

SIEBENALER, Christopher, Regional Senior Vice President and Chief Executive Officer, Houston Methodist Sugar Land Hospital, Sugar Land, TX, p. A637

SIEBERT, Matt, Assistant Administrator Ancillary Services, Hermann Area District Hospital, Hermann, MO, p. A360

SIEDLECKI, Cathy, Director Human Resources, Carthage Area Hospital, Carthage, NY, p. A424

SIEG, Greg, Director Information Technology, Healthsource Saginaw, Inc., Saginaw, MI, p. A322

SIEGEL, Fredric, M.D., Chief of Staff, Desert View Hospital, Pahrump, NV, p. A396

SIEGEL, Lesley, M.D., Medical Director, Albert J. Solnit Psychiatric Center - South Campus, Middletown, CT, p. A109

SIEGEL, Tiffany, Chief Nursing Officer, Fulton County Health Center, Wauseon, OH, p. A493

SIEGELMAN, Gary M, M.D., MSC, Senior Vice President and Chief Medical Officer, Bayhealth Medical Center, Milford Memorial Hospital, DE, p. A113

SIEGFRIED, Carole A, MSN, R.N., Campus Nurse Executive, Palmetto Health Children's Hospital, SC, p. A551

SIEGLE, Lora, M.D., Chief Medical Officer, Morris County Hospital, Council Grove, KS, p. A234

SIEGLEN, Linda, M.D., Chief Medical Officer, Mission Hospital Laguna Beach, CA, p. A72

SIEGMAN, Ira, M.D., Chief Medical Officer, Northside Hospital, Saint Petersburg, FL, p. A138

SIEGRIST, Steve, Director of Human Resources, Mesa View Regional Hospital, Mesquite, NV, p. A395

SIEK, Terry, MSN, R.N., Chief Nursing Officer, Hays Medical Center, Hays, KS, p. A236

SIEMERS, Thomas R., Chief Executive Officer, J. Arthur Dosher Memorial Hospital, Southport, NC, p. A460

SIEWERT, Charles
Director Human Resources, Buffalo Psychiatric Center, Buffalo, NY, p. A423
Director Human Resources, Western New York Children's Hospital Psychiatric Center, West Seneca, NY, p. A446

SIFERS, Carl, Director Information Technology and System Services, Centerpoint Medical Center, Independence, MO, p. A360

SIFFRING, Connie K., Chief Executive Officer, Select Specialty Hospital - Lincoln, Lincoln, NE, p. A386

SIFRI, Christi, Chief Nursing Executive, Regional Hospital For Respiratory And Complex Care, Burien, WA, p. A670

SIGEL, Heather, Director of Clinical Services, War Memorial Hospital, Berkeley Springs, WV, p. A681

SIGLER, Wes
Chief Executive Officer, University Of Mississippi Medical Center Grenada, Grenada, MS, p. A346
Chief Executive Officer, University Of Mississippi Medical Center Holmes County, Lexington, MS, p. A349

SIGNOR, Kristin, Director Finance, Sunnyview Rehabilitation Hospital, Schenectady, NY, p. A442

SIGREST, Marion, M.D., Chief of Staff, Baptist Medical Center Yazoo, Yazoo City, MS, p. A354

SILARD, Kathleen A, R.N., MS, FACHE, Executive Vice President Operations and Chief Operating Officer, Stamford Hospital, Stamford, CT, p. A111

SILAS, Maria, Manager Human Resources, University Hospital Of Brooklyn At Long Island College Hospital, NY, p. A437

SILBER, Steven, M.D., Senior Vice President Medical Affairs, Newyork-Presbyterian Brooklyn Methodist Hospital, New York (Includes All Hospitals Located Within The Five Boroughs), NY, p. A435

SILLS, Doug, Chief Executive Officer, Santa Rosa Medical Center, Milton, FL, p. A131

SILLS, John T, Chief Information Officer, Health Central Hospital, Ocoee, FL, p. A133

SILLYMAN, Bryce, Chief Operating Officer, Pottstown Hospital, Pottstown, PA, p. A539

SILSBEE, Dave, Chief Information Officer, Cary Medical Center, Caribou, ME, p. A283

SILVA, Carmen, R.N., Chief Operating Officer, Doctors Hospital Of Manteca, Manteca, CA, p. A71

SILVA, Francisco, Financial Director, Hospital Metropolitano Dr. Susoni, Arecibo, PR, p. A712

SILVA, Shawn, Chief Executive Officer, Heritage Oaks Hospital, Sacramento, CA, p. A81

SILVA-STEELE, Jamie A., FACHE, R.N., President and Chief Executive Officer, Unm Sandoval Regional Medical Center, Inc., Rio Rancho, NM, p. A419

SILVEIRA, Mike, Suffix, Human Resources Leader, Kaiser Permanente Fresno Medical Center, Fresno, CA, p. A59

SILVER, Michael R., M.D.
Chief Information Officer, Rush Oak Park Hospital, Oak Park, IL, p. A191
Vice President Medical Affairs, Rush Oak Park Hospital, Oak Park, IL, p. A191

SILVER, Timothy, M.D., Medical Director, SAH-S, Sheltering Arms Hospital South, Midlothian, VA, p. A661

SILVERIA, Rich, Executive Vice President and Chief Financial Officer, Comer Children's Hospital, IL, p. A180

SILVERMAN, Daniel C, M.D.
Chief Medical Officer, Acute Care Troy, Samaritan Hospital, Troy, NY, p. A444
Chief Medical Officer, Seton Health System-St. Mary's Hospital, NY, p. A444
Vice President and Chief Medical Officer, Sinai Hospital Of Baltimore, Baltimore, MD, p. A289

SILVERSTEIN, Douglas M, President, Northshore Evanston Hospital, IL, p. A182

SILVERSTEIN, Joel, M.D., Chief Medical Officer, Copley Hospital, Morrisville, VT, p. A654

SILVERSTEIN, Kenneth L, M.D., Chief Clinical Officer, Christiana Care Health System, Newark, DE, p. A113

SILVERTHORNE, Samuel, Chief Information Officer, U.S. Air Force Medical Center Keesler, Keesler Afb, MS, p. A348

SILVESTRI, Scott, Chief Financial Officer, Hospital Financial Operations, Guthrie Robert Packer Hospital, Sayre, PA, p. A540

SILVEUS, Patrick, M.D., Medical Director, Kosciusko Community Hospital, Warsaw, IN, p. A216

SILVEY, Christie, Director People Services, Hshs St. Joseph's Hospital, Highland, IL, p. A185

SILVIA, Charles B, M.D., Chief Medical Officer and Vice President Medical Affairs, Peninsula Regional Medical Center, Salisbury, MD, p. A294

SIM, Carol, President and Chief Executive Officer, Siskin Hospital For Physical Rehabilitation, Chattanooga, TN, p. A567

SIM, Edward H., Chief Executive Officer, St. Anthony Hospital, Lakewood, CO, p. A103

SIMCHUK, Cathy J, Chief Operating Officer, Providence Holy Family Hospital, Spokane, WA, p. A678

SIMIA, Greg
Chief Financial Officer, Hshs St. Clare Memorial Hospital, Oconto Falls, WI, p. A700
Chief Financial Officer, Hshs St. Mary's Hospital Medical Center, Green Bay, WI, p. A694
Chief Financial Officer, Hshs St. Nicholas Hospital, Sheboygan, WI, p. A703
Chief Financial Officer, Hshs St. Vincent Hospital, Green Bay, WI, p. A694

SIMKINS, Palma, Chief Human Resources Management Services, Battle Creek Veterans Affairs Medical Center, Battle Creek, MI, p. A308

SIMMONS, Angela L., Chief Executive Officer, Encompass Health Rehabilitation Hospital Of Humble, Humble, TX, p. A614

SIMMONS, Barbara, R.N.
Chief Executive Officer, Mercy Hospital - A Campus Of Plantation General Hospital, FL, p. A136
Chief Executive Officer, Westside Regional Medical Center, Plantation, FL, p. A136

SIMMONS, Brad
Chief Operating Officer, Crittenton Children's Center, MO, p. A362
Chief Operating Officer, University Of California Davis Children's Hospital, CA, p. A82

SIMMONS, Daniel F, Senior Vice President and Treasurer, Monongahela Valley Hospital, Monongahela, PA, p. A532

SIMMONS, Dorlynn, Chief Executive Officer, Mescalero Public Health Service Indian Hospital, Mescalero, NM, p. A418

SIMMONS, Dwayne, Interim Chief Information Officer, St. Luke's Cornwall Hospital - Newburgh Campus, NY, p. A438

SIMMONS, Eileen
Chief Financial Officer, UPMC Hospital Network, Upmc Mercy, Pittsburgh, PA, p. A538
Chief Financial Officer, Magee-Womens Hospital Of Upmc, Pittsburgh, PA, p. A537

Chief Financial Officer, Western Psychiatric Institute And Clinic, PA, p. A538

SIMMONS, Iman
Chief Operating Officer and Interim President, St. Charles Bend, Bend, OR, p. A511
Chief Operating Officer and Interim President, St. Charles Redmond, Redmond, OR, p. A517

SIMMONS, Jeanette, Chief Operating Officer, Center For Behavioral Medicine, Kansas City, MO, p. A361

SIMMONS, Jodi, Chief Nursing Officer, Hillcrest Medical Center, Tulsa, OK, p. A508

SIMMONS, Leslie, FACHE, R.N., President, Carroll Hospital Center, Westminster, MD, p. A294

SIMMONS, Randy, Chief Executive Officer, Cooper County Community Hospital, Boonville, MO, p. A356

SIMMONS, Rickie, Controller, Kindred Hospital North Florida, Green Cove Springs, FL, p. A124

SIMMS, Miquel Noelani, R.N., Chief Nursing Officer, North Hawaii Community Hospital, Kamuela, HI, p. A165

SIMODEJKA, John E, Marketing Chief Executive Officer, Select Specialty Hospital-Harrisburg, PA, p. A522

SIMON, Anha, Director Human Resources, Riceland Medical Center, Winnie, TX, p. A644

SIMON, Ashley, Chief Financial Officer, Kansas Surgery And Recovery Center, Wichita, KS, p. A248

SIMON, Daniel I., M.D., President, University Macdonald Women's Hospital, OH, p. A477

SIMON, Deborah R., R.N.
President and Chief Executive Officer, Unitypoint Health - Proctor, Peoria, IL, p. A193
Regional Chief Executive Officer, Unitypoint Health - Peoria, Peoria, IL, p. A193
Regional Chief Executive Officer, Unitypoint Health-Pekin Hospital, Pekin, IL, p. A193

SIMON, Joan M., R.N., FACHE, Chief Nursing Officer, Kootenai Behavioral Health, ID, p. A169

SIMON, Kareen, Vice President of Operations, Wheeling Hospital, Wheeling, WV, p. A688

SIMON, Kenneth B, M.D., Chief of Staff, Veterans Affairs Gulf Coast Veterans Health Care System, Biloxi, MS, p. A343

SIMON, Keri, Executive Director, Women's And Children's Hospital, MO, p. A358

SIMON, Lisa M.
Senior Vice President and Chief Financial Officer, Ohio Valley Medical Center, Wheeling, WV, p. A688
Senior Vice President Chief Financial Officer, East Ohio Regional Hospital, Martins Ferry, OH, p. A486

SIMON, Lloyd, M.D., Medical Director, Eastern Long Island Hospital, Greenport, NY, p. A427

SIMON, Mark, System Chief Information Officer, Benefis Health Care-West Campus, MT, p. A376

SIMON, Patricia, Chief Nursing Officer, Encompass Health Rehabilitation Hospital Of Charleston, Charleston, SC, p. A550

SIMON, Richard, M.D., Chief of Staff, Uconn, John Dempsey Hospital, Farmington, CT, p. A108

SIMON, Stuart, M.D., Medical Director, North Central Surgical Center, Dallas, TX, p. A597

SIMON, Teresa, Director Information Systems, Nacogdoches Medical Center, Nacogdoches, TX, p. A625

SIMON, Thresa, M.D., Medical Director, Poplar Springs Hospital, Petersburg, VA, p. A663

SIMONEAUX, Katherine
Administrator, Oceans Behavioral Hospital Of Crowley, Rayne, LA, p. A278
Administrator, Oceans Behavioral Hospital Of Opelousas, Opelousas, LA, p. A277

SIMONIN, Steven J., President and Chief Executive Officer, Iowa Specialty Hospital-Clarion, Clarion, IA, p. A219

SIMONS, Janice, FACHE, Chief Executive Officer, Medina Regional Hospital, Hondo, TX, p. A609

SIMONS, Preston, Chief Information Officer, Aurora Medical Center - Manitowoc County, Two Rivers, WI, p. A704

SIMONSON, John F, M.D., President Medical Staff, Memorial Community Hospital And Health System, Blair, NE, p. A382

SIMONSON, Paul, Vice President, Trinity Hospital-St. Joseph'S, ND, p. A468

SIMPSON, Brenda, R.N.
Chief Nursing Officer, Largo Medical Center - Indian Rocks, FL, p. A128
Chief Nursing Officer, Northeast Georgia Medical Center, Gainesville, GA, p. A154

SIMPSON, Chris, Chief Executive Officer, Cornerstone Hospital-West Monroe, West Monroe, LA, p. A280

SIMPSON, Greg, Chief Nursing Officer, St. Joseph Medical Center, Kansas City, MO, p. A362

SIMPSON, Joan W., Manager Human Resources, Lauderdale Community Hospital, Ripley, TN, p. A579

SIMPSON, Julie, Vice President Human Resources, University Of Tennessee Medical Center, Knoxville, TN, p. A572

SIMPSON, Keith J, Chief Operating Officer, Jennings American Legion Hospital, Jennings, LA, p. A269

SIMPSON, Laura, Director Human Resources, Sabine County Hospital, Hemphill, TX, p. A609

SIMPSON, Mark, Chief Executive Officer, Welch Community Hospital, Welch, WV, p. A687

SIMPSON, Michelle, Chief Nursing Officer and Quality Leader, Lauderdale Community Hospital, Ripley, TN, p. A579

SIMPSON, Rae, R.N., Chief Nursing Officer, Western State Hospital, Tacoma, WA, p. A679

SIMPSON, Robert, Vice President Operations, Methodist Richardson Medical Center, Richardson, TX, p. A630

SIMPSON, Shannon, Director Information Services, St. Elizabeth Hospital, Gonzales, LA, p. A268

SIMPSON, Shawndra, Interim Chief Executive Officer, Sutter Surgical Hospital - North Valley, Yuba City, CA, p. A95

SIMPSON, Sheila, Vice President Human Resources, Palmetto Lowcountry Behavioral Health, Charleston, SC, p. A550

SIMPSON, Steve, Chief Executive Officer, Northeastern Nevada Regional Hospital, Elko, NV, p. A392

SIMPSON-TUGGLE, Deloris, Vice President Human Resources and Organizational Development and Chief Human Resources Officer, Greater Baltimore Medical Center, Baltimore, MD, p. A287

SIMS, Anthony, M.D., Chief of Staff, Dekalb Regional Medical Center, Fort Payne, AL, p. A18

SIMS, Brian, Chief Executive Officer, Lucas County Health Center, Chariton, IA, p. A219

SIMS, Charles, M.D., Chief of Staff, Chi St. Luke's Health-The Woodlands Hospital, The Woodlands, TX, p. A639

SIMS, Jason, M.D.
Chief Medical Officer, Cleveland Area Hospital, Cleveland, OK, p. A497
Facility Information Security Officer, Medical City North Hills, North Richland Hills, TX, p. A626

SIMS, Jeffrey, Chief Executive Officer, Heartland Behavioral Healthcare, Massillon, OH, p. A486

SIMS, Jyric, FACHE, Chief Executive Officer, Medical City Fort Worth, Fort Worth, TX, p. A605

SIMS, Mark E., Chief Executive Officer, Grand Strand Regional Medical Center, Myrtle Beach, SC, p. A556

SIMS, William, M.D., Medical Director, Elkview General Hospital, Hobart, OK, p. A499

SIMZYK, Monica
Regional Chief Human Resources Officer, Presence St. Mary's Hospital, Kankakee, IL, p. A187
Regional Human Resource Officer, Presence Saint Joseph Medical Center, Joliet, IL, p. A187

SINCICH, Robert, Vice President Human Resources, Trumbull Memorial Hospital, Warren, OH, p. A492

SINCLAIR, Brad, Chief Financial Officer, Merit Health River Oaks, Flowood, MS, p. A345

SINCLAIR, Elyria, Director Human Resources, Crestwood Medical Center, Huntsville, AL, p. A19

SINCLAIR, Kathy, Vice President Human Resources, Spartanburg Medical Center, Spartanburg, SC, p. A557

SINCLAIR, Laura, Director Human Resources, Kansas City Orthopaedic Institute, Leawood, KS, p. A240

SINCLAIR, Noreen, Human Resources Administrator, Connecticut Veterans Home And Hospital, Rocky Hill, CT, p. A110

SINCLAIR-CHUNG, Opal, R.N., MS, Chief Nursing Officer, Deputy Executive Director, Nyc Health + Hospitals / Kings County, New York (Includes All Hospitals Located Within The Five Boroughs), NY, p. A436

SINCOCK, Gregory M, Information Technology Leader, Kaiser Permanente West Los Angeles Medical Center, Los Angeles, CA, p. A67

SINDELAR, Michael, Vice President and Chief Financial Officer, Fremont Health, Fremont, NE, p. A384

SINDLINGER, Julie A, Director of Human Resources, Weston County Health Services, Newcastle, WY, p. A709

SINEK, James J., FACHE, President, Boone Hospital Center, Columbia, MO, p. A358

SINGER, John, IV, Chief Operating Officer, Munson Healthcare Charlevoix Hospital, Charlevoix, MI, p. A309

SINGH, Amandeep, Chief Medical Officer, Monroe Hospital, Bloomington, IN, p. A200

SINGH, Amarjit, M.D., President and Chief Executive Officer, Brunswick Psych Center, Amityville, NY, p. A421

SINGH, Brij, Medical Staff Director, Kindred Hospital Rome, Rome, GA, p. A159

SINGH, Gagandeep, M.D., Chief Medical Officer Behavioral Health, Banner Behavioral Health Hospital - Scottsdale, Scottsdale, AZ, p. A35

SINGH, Gurmant, Chief of Staff, Good Samaritan Hospital, Bakersfield, CA, p. A52

SINGH, Himanshu, M.D., Associate Director, Veterans Affairs Ann Arbor Healthcare System, Ann Arbor, MI, p. A307

SINGH, Vijayant, M.D., Chief Medical Officer, Carepoint Health Bayonne Medical Center, Bayonne, NJ, p. A402

SINGLES, James L, Chief Financial Officer, Marlette Regional Hospital, Marlette, MI, p. A318

SINGLETARY-TWYMAN, Michelle, Chief Nursing Officer, Rockford Center, Newark, DE, p. A113

SINGLETON, Al, M.D., Chief Psychiatry and Chief Medical Staff, Colorado Mental Health Institute At Pueblo, Pueblo, CO, p. A104

SINGLETON, Doris, Chief Executive Officer, Conway Behavioral Health Hospital, Conway-Faulkner County, AR, p. A40

SINGLETON, Roy, Director Computer Information Systems, Palmdale Regional Medical Center, Palmdale, CA, p. A77

SINHA, Sunil K., M.D., FACHE, Chief Medical Officer, Bon Secours Memorial Regional Medical Center, Mechanicsville, VA, p. A661

SINIARD, Sandra, Vice President of Patient Care Services, Chi Memorial Hospital - Georgia, Fort Oglethorpe, GA, p. A154

SINICKAS, Robert, Director Information Services, Northwestern Medicine Marianjoy Rehabilitation Hospital, Wheaton, IL, p. A198

SINICROPE, Frank J, Jr, Vice President Financial Services, Princeton Community Hospital, Princeton, WV, p. A686

SINISI, Albert, Director Information Systems, Doctors' Hospital Of Michigan, Pontiac, MI, p. A321

SINK, Kristi M., President, University Hospitals Elyria Medical Center, Elyria, OH, p. A482

SINNOTT, Daniel J., President and Chief Executive Officer, St. Francis Hospital, Wilmington, DE, p. A114

SINNOTT, James, M.D., Chief Medical Staff, Coquille Valley Hospital, Coquille, OR, p. A512

SINNOTT, Lisa M, Director Human Resources, Acuity Specialty Hospital Of Southern New Jersey, Willingboro, NJ, p. A414

SINOPOLI, Angelo, M.D., Vice President Clinical Integration and Chief Medical Officer, Roger C. Peace Rehabilitation Hospital, SC, p. A553

SINOTTE, Brian, Chief Executive Officer, Up Health System-Marquette, Marquette, MI, p. A318

SINYARD, Robert, M.D.
Chief Medical Officer, Piedmont Athens Regional Medical Center, Athens, GA, p. A145
Chief Medical Officer, Piedmont Walton Hospital, Monroe, GA, p. A157

SIOSON, Stephanie
Director Human Resources, Garden Grove Hospital And Medical Center, Garden Grove, CA, p. A60
Director Human Resources, Huntington Beach Hospital, Huntington Beach, CA, p. A62
Director Human Resources, La Palma Intercommunity Hospital, La Palma, CA, p. A63
Director Human Resources, West Anaheim Medical Center, Anaheim, CA, p. A50

SIOUFI, Habib, M.D., Chief Medical Officer, Umass Memorial-Marlborough Hospital, Marlborough, MA, p. A301

SIPEK, John, Supervisor Client Services, Aurora Medical Center In Washington County, Hartford, WI, p. A694

SIREK, David, Chief Information Officer, Myrtue Medical Center, Harlan, IA, p. A224

SIRK, Donald, Director Information Systems, Medstar St. Mary's Hospital, Leonardtown, MD, p. A292

SIROIS, Peter, Chief Executive Officer, Northern Maine Medical Center, Fort Kent, ME, p. A284

SIROTTA, Ted
Chief Financial Officer, Vail Health, Vail, CO, p. A106
Senior Vice President and Chief Financial Officer, Henry Mayo Newhall Hospital, Valencia, CA, p. A93

SISILLO, Sabato, M.D.
Chief Medical Officer, Providence Medical Center, Kansas City, KS, p. A238
Chief Medical Officer, Saint John Hospital, Leavenworth, KS, p. A239

SISK, Bryan W., Associate Director Patient and Nursing Services, Central Texas Veterans Health Care System, Doris Miller Veterans Medical Center, TX, p. A638

SISK, Glenn C., President, Coosa Valley Medical Center, Sylacauga, AL, p. A23

SISK, Jack, Chief Financial Officer, Punxsutawney Area Hospital, Punxsutawney, PA, p. A539

SISK, Lori, R.N.
Chief Executive Officer, Sanford Canby Medical Center, Canby, MN, p. A329
Chief Executive Officer, Sanford Clear Lake Medical Center, Clear Lake, SD, p. A560

SISK, Rodney, Chief Financial Officer, University Hospital Summerville, Augusta, GA, p. A148

SISK, Susan, Chief Financial Officer, Chi St. Alexius Health, Bismarck, ND, p. A464

SISLER, Debbie, Director, Human Resource, Vidant Roanoke-Chowan Hospital, Ahoskie, NC, p. A447

SISON, Joseph, M.D., Medical Director, Heritage Oaks Hospital, Sacramento, CA, p. A81

SISSON, Travis, Chief Executive Officer, Panola Medical Center, Batesville, MS, p. A343

SISSON, William G., FACHE, President, Baptist Health Lexington, Lexington, KY, p. A254

SISTO, Steven A., Senior Vice President and Chief Operating Officer, Methodist Hospital Of Southern California, Arcadia, CA, p. A51

SISTRUNK, Heather, MHSA, RN, BSN
Chief Executive Officer, Merit Health Rankin, Brandon, MS, p. A344
Chief Operating Officer, Merit Health River Oaks, Flowood, MS, p. A345

SITLINGER, James, Chief Human Resources Management, Charles George Veterans Affairs Medical Center, Asheville, NC, p. A447

SITTIG, Kevin, M.D., Senior Associate Dean and Chief Medical Officer, Children's Hospital Of Shreveport, LA, p. A279

SIU, Max, Chief Information Officer, Hackensack Meridian Health Mountainside Medical Center, Montclair, NJ, p. A407

SIVAK, Steven, M.D., Chief Medical Officer, Einstein Physicians Philadelphia, Einstein Medical Center Elkins Park, PA, p. A534

SIVEK, Carla, Director, Coatesville Veterans Affairs Medical Center, Coatesville, PA, p. A523

SIVLEY, Susanna S, Chief Personnel Officer, Highlands Medical Center, Scottsboro, AL, p. A23

SIWEK, Steven M., M.D., President and Chief Executive Officer, Scottsdale Liberty Hospital, Scottsdale, AZ, p. A35

SIX, Deborah, Coordinator Data Processing, Wayne Memorial Hospital, Jesup, GA, p. A155

SIX, Stephanie, Chief Executive Officer, Northeastern Health System Sequoyah, Sallisaw, OK, p. A506

SJOBERG, Rochelle, Director Human Resources, Ely-Bloomenson Community Hospital, Ely, MN, p. A331

SKABELUND, Hoyt, Chief Executive Officer, Sterling Regional Medcenter, Sterling, CO, p. A105

SKAGGS, Lynda, Chief Nursing Officer, Fleming County Hospital, Flemingsburg, KY, p. A251

SKALA, Pat, Chief Information Officer, Laguna Honda Hospital And Rehabilitation Center, San Francisco, CA, p. A85

SKALSKI, Eileen, Chief Nursing Officer, Healthsouth Harmarville Rehabilitation Hospital, Pittsburgh, PA, p. A537

SKARKA, Kathy, MSN, R.N., Executive Vice President Patient Care Services, Nassau University Medical Center, East Meadow, NY, p. A426

SKARULIS, Patricia, Senior Vice President and Chief Information Systems Officer, Memorial Sloan-Kettering Cancer Center, New York (Includes All Hospitals Located Within The Five Boroughs), NY, p. A433

SKARZYNSKI, Joseph, M.D., Medical Director, Nyc Health + Hospitals / North Central Bronx, New York (Includes All Hospitals Located Within The Five Boroughs), NY, p. A436

SKEEN, Steven, R.N., Chief Nursing Officer, Mizell Memorial Hospital, Opp, AL, p. A22

SKEENS, Henrietta, Cheif Financial Officer, De Poo Hospital, FL, p. A126

SKELDON, Timothy
Chief Financial Officer, Thomas Memorial Hospital, South Charleston, WV, p. A687
Senior Vice President and Chief Financial Officer, Parrish Medical Center, Titusville, FL, p. A142

SKELTON, Jenny, System Integration Manager, The Women's Hospital, Newburgh, IN, p. A213

SKELTON, Katie, MSN, R.N., Vice President Nursing and Chief Nursing Officer, St. Joseph Hospital, Orange, CA, p. A76

SKIBBA, Joshua, Chief Medical Officer, Ohio County Hospital, Hartford, KY, p. A253

SKIDMORE, Jocelyn, Director Finance, Ssm Health St. Francis Hospital - Maryville, Maryville, MO, p. A364

SKIDMORE, Kim, Chief Executive Officer, Izard County Medical Center, Calico Rock-Logan County, AR, p. A40

SKIEM, Paul, Senior Vice President Human Resources, Presence Saint Francis Hospital, Evanston, IL, p. A182

SKILLINGS, Charles E., President and Chief Executive Officer, Ssm Health St. Anthony Hospital - Shawnee, Shawnee, OK, p. A506

SKILLINGS, Lois N., R.N., MSN, President and Chief Executive Officer, Mid Coast Hospital, Brunswick, ME, p. A283

SKILLINGS, Michelle, Chief Nursing Officer, Franklin Foundation Hospital, Franklin, LA, p. A267

SKINNER, Christopher, Chief of Staff, Spectrum Health Big Rapids Hospital, Big Rapids, MI, p. A308

SKINNER, Eileen F., FACHE, Administrator, Shriners Hospitals For Children-Boston, Boston, MA, p. A297

SKINNER, Gary, Director Information Technology, Rehabilitation Hospital Of Indiana, Indianapolis, IN, p. A207

SKINNER, Gwendolyn, Operational Vice President, Devereux Advanced Behavioral Health Georgia, Kennesaw, GA, p. A155

SKINNER, Kellcie, Controller, Newman Memorial Hospital, Shattuck, OK, p. A506

SKINNER, Kristina, Director Quality, Sanpete Valley Hospital, Mount Pleasant, UT, p. A648

SKINNER, Marjorie, Director Finance, Pershing General Hospital, Lovelock, NV, p. A395

SKINNER, Richard, Chief Information Technology Officer, University Of Virginia Children's Hospital, VA, p. A656

SKIPPER, Kymberli, Manager Human Resources, Prattville Baptist Hospital, Prattville, AL, p. A22

SKIPPER, Michelle, Director Human Resources, Kaiser Permanente Riverside Medical Center, Riverside, CA, p. A81

SKJOLDEN, Jessica, M.D., Chief of Staff, St. Andrew's Health Center, Bottineau, ND, p. A464

SKLAMBERG, Todd, President, Sunrise Hospital And Medical Center, Las Vegas, NV, p. A395

SKLAR, Joel, M.D., Chief Medical Officer, Marin General Hospital, Greenbrae, CA, p. A61

SKLIRIS, Demetre, Chief Medical Officer, Avera Dells Area Hospital, Dell Rapids, SD, p. A560

SKOWRON, Paul, Chief Executive Officer, Warner Hospital And Health Services, Clinton, IL, p. A180

SKRINDE, Tracie, Senior Human Resources Partner, Peacehealth United General Medical Center, Sedro, WA, p. A677

SKRIPPS, Michele M., R.N., Chief Executive Officer, Encompass Health Rehabilitation Hospital Of Charleston, Charleston, SC, p. A550

SKULA, Erika
President and Chief Executive Officer, Florida Hospital Carrollwood, Tampa, FL, p. A140
President and Chief Executive Officer, Manchester Memorial Hospital, Manchester, KY, p. A257

SKULA, Joe, Director Human Resources, Manchester Memorial Hospital, Manchester, KY, p. A257

SKVARENINA, Michael, Assistant Vice President Information Systems, Holy Name Medical Center, Teaneck, NJ, p. A412

SLABA, Bryan, Chief Executive Officer, Wagner Community Memorial Hospital Avera, Wagner, SD, p. A565

SLABIK, Shauna, Chief Financial Officer, Sanford Mayville Medical Center, Mayville, ND, p. A467

SLACK, Randy, Chief Financial Officer, Nacogdoches Medical Center, Nacogdoches, TX, p. A625

SLADKY, Todd J., Chief Financial Officer and Vice President Finance, Great River Medical Center, West Burlington, IA, p. A231

SLAGLE, Julie A, R.N., MSN, Vice President Patient Care Services, Sidney Regional Medical Center, Sidney, NE, p. A390

SLATE, Sonny, Chief Operating Officer, Georgia Regional Hospital At Atlanta, Decatur, GA, p. A152

SLATER, Craig M, M.D., Chief Medical Officer, Carolinas Healthcare System Union, Monroe, NC, p. A457

SLATER, Mark, Director Information Systems, Baylor Scott & White Medical Center - Lake Pointe, Rowlett, TX, p. A631

SLATER-NESUOLD, Stephanie, Director of Nursing, Landmark Hospital Of Joplin, Joplin, MO, p. A361

SLATON, Brenda, Superintendent, Rusk State Hospital, Rusk, TX, p. A631

SLATTERY, Greg, Vice President Information, Montpelier Hospital, OH, p. A473

SLATTERY, Robert, Vice President of Operations, Bridgton Hospital, Bridgton, ME, p. A283

SLATTERY, Susan L, Director Human Resources, Unitypoint Health - St. Luke's Hospital, Cedar Rapids, IA, p. A218

SLATTMAN, Robin, Chief Nursing Officer, Memorial Health, Marysville, OH, p. A486

SLAVIN, Kevin J, FACHE, President and Chief Executive Officer, St. Joseph's Children's Hospital, NJ, p. A409

SLAVIN, Kevin J., FACHE, President and Chief Executive Officer, St. Joseph's Wayne Hospital, NJ, p. A409

SLAVIN, Peter L., M.D., President, Massgeneral Hospital For Children, MA, p. A297

SLAWITSKY, Bruce, Vice President Human Resources, Hospital For Special Surgery, New York (Includes All Hospitals Located Within The Five Boroughs), NY, p. A432

SLAYMAN, Aubree, Director Patient Services, Miami County Medical Center, Paola, KS, p. A244

SLAYTON, Val, M.D., Vice President Medical Affairs, Sts. Mary & Elizabeth Hospital, Louisville, KY, p. A256

SLEDGE, Cynthia Moore, M.D., Medical Director, Bryce Hospital, Tuscaloosa, AL, p. A23

SLEDGE, Tasha, Director Human Resources, Texas Health Harris Methodist Hospital Southlake, Southlake, TX, p. A636

SLEDGE, Thomas, Chief Executive Officer, North Texas Medical Center, Gainesville, TX, p. A606

SLEDGE, Tom, Chief Operating Officer, Willow Creek Women's Hospital, AR, p. A49

SLEE, Kim, Chief Operating Officer, Fulton County Medical Center, Mc Connellsburg, PA, p. A530

SLEEPER, Justin, Vice President Clinical Operations, Behavioral Health Network, Natchaug Hospital, Mansfield Center, CT, p. A108

SLEIME, Melanie, Director Human Resources, Memorial Hospital, North Conway, NH, p. A400

SLEITER, Michelle, Chief Executive Officer, Humboldt County Memorial Hospital, Humboldt, IA, p. A224

SLESSOR, Steve Robert., Chief Executive Officer, Buchanan County Health Center, Independence, IA, p. A224

SLICK, Lois, Director Human Resources, Lifecare Medical Center, Roseau, MN, p. A338

SLIDER, Carol, Chief Nursing Officer, Titus Regional Medical Center, Mount Pleasant, TX, p. A624

SLIGER, Susan, Director Human Resources, War Memorial Hospital, Sault Sainte Marie, MI, p. A323

SLITER, Elizabeth, M.D., Chairman Medical Staff, Decatur Health Systems, Oberlin, KS, p. A242

SLIVA, Paul, Chief Information Officer, Boone County Hospital, Boone, IA, p. A218

SLIWA, James, M.D., Chief Medical Officer, Shirley Ryan Abilitylab, Chicago, IL, p. A179

SLIWINSKI, Jeff, Chief Financial Officer, Mainland Medical Center, TX, p. A643

SLIWINSKI, Ron, Chief of Hospital Division, American Family Children's Hospital, WI, p. A696

SLOAN, Brian, Chief Operating Officer, Duke Raleigh Hospital, Raleigh, NC, p. A459

SLOAN, Patrick, Chief Financial Officer, Memorial Satilla Health, Waycross, GA, p. A163

SLOAN, Prudence, Coordinator Human Resources, Select Specialty Hospital-Pittsburgh/Upmc, Pittsburgh, PA, p. A537

SLOAN, Ronald A., FACHE, President, The Outer Banks Hospital, Nags Head, NC, p. A458

SLOAN, Steve, Chief Financial Officer, Lake Cumberland Regional Hospital, Somerset, KY, p. A260

SLOCUM, Brandon H, Senior Vice President and Chief Financial Officer, Medical West, Bessemer, AL, p. A14

SLOCUM, Gregg Y, Chief Financial Officer, Valley Forge Medical Center And Hospital, Norristown, PA, p. A533

SLONIM, Sheryl A, Executive Vice President and Chief Nursing Officer, Holy Name Medical Center, Teaneck, NJ, p. A412

SLONINA, Marrianne, Director Human Resources, Georgetown Community Hospital, Georgetown, KY, p. A252

SLOPER, Carol, Manager Information Technology, Cheyenne County Hospital, Saint Francis, KS, p. A245

SLUCK, Jeana, R.N., Executive Director Nursing Clinical Inpatient Departments, Allied Services Rehabilitation Hospital, Scranton, PA, p. A540

SLUSHER, Carlene, Director Finance, Seneca Healthcare District, Chester, CA, p. A54

SLUSHER, Michael, Community Chief Executive Officer, Middlesboro Arh Hospital, Middlesboro, KY, p. A258

SLUSHER, W. James (Jamie), M.D., Chief of Staff, Jackson Parish Hospital, Jonesboro, LA, p. A269

SLUTSKER, Vladimir, Medical Director, Encompass Health Rehabilitation Hospital Of Gadsden, Gadsden, AL, p. A18

SLYTER, Mark F., FACHE, President and Chief Executive Officer, East Valley, Dignity Health Arizona General Hospital, Laveen, AZ, p. A31

SMAJSTRLA, Julie, Director Nursing, Seymour Hospital, Seymour, TX, p. A635

SMALE, Cindy, Director, Human Resources, Iredell Health System, Statesville, NC, p. A461

SMALL, Becky
Chief Human Resources Officer, Kindred Hospital-Aurora, Aurora, CO, p. A96
Chief Nursing Officer, North Texas Medical Center, Gainesville, TX, p. A606

SMALL, Brenda, Chief Clinical Officer, Amg Specialty Hospital-Greenwood, Greenwood, MS, p. A346

SMALL, David R., FACHE, Interim Chief Executive Officer, Hahnemann University Hospital, Philadelphia, PA, p. A534

SMALL, Donna, R.N., Chief Nursing Officer, Palm Beach Children's Hospital, FL, p. A143

SMALL, Jonathan, Chief Operations Information and Technology, John D. Dingell Veterans Affairs Medical Center, Detroit, MI, p. A311

SMALL, Terry L., Assistant Chief Executive Officer, William R. Sharpe, Jr. Hospital, Weston, WV, p. A688

SMALLEY, Ben, Administrator, Cassia Regional Hospital, Burley, ID, p. A168

SMALLWOOD, Ravae, IS Coordinator, Chi Health Missouri Valley, Missouri Valley, IA, p. A226

SMARR, Susan, M.D., Physician-in-Chief, Kaiser Permanente Santa Clara Medical Center, Santa Clara, CA, p. A88

SMART, Dan, Chief Information Management Officer, Permian Regional Medical Center, Andrews, TX, p. A583

SMART, George J, Vice President Finance and Information Technology, Midmichigan Medical Center - Alpena, Alpena, MI, p. A307

SMART, Joanne F, M.D., Director Medical Affairs, Indiana University Health Bedford Hospital, Bedford, IN, p. A199

SMART, Melissa, Communication ad Public Relations Specialist, Texas Health Presbyterian Hospital Denton, Denton, TX, p. A599

SMART, Paul, CPA, Chief Financial Officer, Franklin County Medical Center, Preston, ID, p. A171

SMART, Robert M., Chief Executive Officer, Encompass Health Rehabilitation Hospital Of The Mid-Cities, Bedford, TX, p. A588

SMART, Stephanie, Chief Nursing Officer, United Hospital Center, Bridgeport, WV, p. A681

SMELTZER, Sharon, Chief Executive Officer, Mercy Rehabilitation Hospital Oklahoma City, Oklahoma City, OK, p. A503

SMENDIK, Douglas, M.D., Hospital Medical Director, Spectrum Health Pennock, Hastings, MI, p. A315

SMIDT, Jessica, R.N., Director of Nursing, Pipestone County Medical Center Avera, Pipestone, MN, p. A337

SMIGA, Lance, Chief Financial Officer, Jackson County Hospital District, Edna, TX, p. A601

SMILEY, Christy, Leader Human Resources, Ssm Health St. Mary's Hospital - Audrain, Mexico, MO, p. A364

SMITH, Agnes A, MSN, R.N., Chief Nursing Officer, Twin County Regional Healthcare, Galax, VA, p. A658

SMITH, Alan H
Chief Financial Officer, Huntington Beach Hospital, Huntington Beach, CA, p. A62
Chief Financial Officer, La Palma Intercommunity Hospital, La Palma, CA, p. A63

SMITH, Andrew
Chief Financial Officer, Blake Medical Center, Bradenton, FL, p. A118
Chief Information Management, Madigan Army Medical Center, Tacoma, WA, p. A679

SMITH, Anton C., Administrator, Shriners Hospitals For Children-Honolulu, Honolulu, HI, p. A165

SMITH, Barbara H, Senior Vice President & Chief Operating Officer, Robert Wood Johnson University Hospital At Hamilton, Hamilton, NJ, p. A405

SMITH, Bennie
Chief Information Officer, Lady Of The Sea General Hospital, Cut Off, LA, p. A266
Director Human Resources and Risk Management, Lady Of The Sea General Hospital, Cut Off, LA, p. A266

SMITH, Bernie, Chief Financial Officer, Troy Community Hospital, Troy, PA, p. A542

SMITH, Bethany
Controller, Spire Cane Creek Rehabilitation Hospital, Martin, TN, p. A574
Director of Finance, Chi Oakes Hospital, Oakes, ND, p. A468

SMITH, Betsy, Chief Nursing Officer, Effingham Hospital, Springfield, GA, p. A161

SMITH, Beverly Bzdek, Chief Nursing Officer, Southside Regional Medical Center, Petersburg, VA, p. A664

SMITH, Blythe, Administrative Assistant, Faulkton Area Medical Center, Faulkton, SD, p. A560

SMITH, Bobby, Vice President Physician Services and Quality, Illinois Valley Community Hospital, Peru, IL, p. A193

SMITH, Bradley, President and Chief Executive Officer, Rush Memorial Hospital, Rushville, IN, p. A214

SMITH, Brenda, Director Financial Services, Alliance Health Center, Meridian, MS, p. A350

SMITH, Brent, Chief Executive Officer, Comanche County Memorial Hospital, Lawton, OK, p. A500

SMITH, Brian
Chief Financial Officer, Beth Israel Deaconess Hospital-Needham Campus, Needham, MA, p. A302
Director of Operations, Wamego Health Center, Wamego, KS, p. A247

SMITH, C David, M.D., Chief Medical Officer, Jay Hospital, Jay, FL, p. A126

SMITH, Candace Susan, Chief Nursing Officer, Manatee Memorial Hospital, Bradenton, FL, p. A118

SMITH, Carl, Director Information Systems, King's Daughters Medical Center, Brookhaven, MS, p. A344

SMITH, Carol, Vice President Patient Care and Chief Nursing Officer, Tift Regional Medical Center, Tifton, GA, p. A162

SMITH, Carol A, R.N., Director Operations and Nursing, Novant Health Medical Park Hospital, Winston, NC, p. A463

SMITH, Carole, Senior Human Resource Business Partner, Banner Del E. Webb Medical Center, Sun City West, AZ, p. A36

SMITH, Cheryl, Manager Human Resources, New Braunfels Regional Rehabilitation Hospital, New Braunfels, TX, p. A625

SMITH, Chris, Chief Information Officer, Falls Community Hospital And Clinic, Marlin, TX, p. A622

SMITH, Connie, FACHE, MSN, R.N., Chief Executive Officer, Medical Center At Bowling Green, Bowling Green, KY, p. A250

SMITH, Dan
Director Human Resources, Austin Lakes Hospital, Austin, TX, p. A585
Director Human Resources, Memorial Hospital, Carthage, IL, p. A175

SMITH, Daniel
Chief Financial Officer, Palo Pinto General Hospital, Mineral Wells, TX, p. A624
Chief Financial Officer, Tops Surgical Specialty Hospital, Houston, TX, p. A614
Interim Chief Executive Officer, Palo Pinto General Hospital, Mineral Wells, TX, p. A624

SMITH, Daniel B
Chief Financial Officer, Samaritan Pacific Communities Hospital, Newport, OR, p. A515
Vice President Finance, Good Samaritan Regional Medical Center, Corvallis, OR, p. A512
Vice President Finance, Samaritan Albany General Hospital, Albany, OR, p. A511
Vice President Finance, Samaritan Lebanon Community Hospital, Lebanon, OR, p. A514

SMITH, Darrin, Vice President Human Resources, Parkview Medical Center, Pueblo, CO, p. A104

SMITH, Darwin K, Vice President Human Resources, Cleveland Clinic Union Hospital, Dover, OH, p. A481

SMITH, David, D.O.
Chief of Staff, Madison County Health Care System, Winterset, IA, p. A231
Chief Executive Officer, Baylor Institute For Rehabilitation, Dallas, TX, p. A595

SMITH, Debra, Chief Nursing Officer, Healthsouth Rehabilitation Hospital, Kingsport, TN, p. A572

SMITH, Denise
Director Health Information, Healthsouth Chattanooga Rehabilitation Hospital, Chattanooga, TN, p. A567
Director People Services, Hshs St. Mary's Hospital, Decatur, IL, p. A181

SMITH, Diana B, Chief Financial Officer, Promise Hospital Of Dallas, Dallas, TX, p. A597

SMITH, Dianne, Director Personnel and Human Resources, Potomac Valley Hospital, Keyser, WV, p. A684

SMITH, Dick, Director Human Resources, West Park Hospital, Cody, WY, p. A708

SMITH, Dirkland T., Chief Executive Officer, Faulkton Area Medical Center, Faulkton, SD, p. A560

SMITH, Donald, President Medical Staff, Bellevue Hospital, Bellevue, OH, p. A472

SMITH, Donna M, Chief Nursing Officer, Barstow Community Hospital, Barstow, CA, p. A52

SMITH, Donna P, R.N., Vice President Chief Operating Officer and Chief Nursing Officer, Clifton Springs Hospital And Clinic, Clifton Springs, NY, p. A424

SMITH, Donnie
Chief Human Resources Officer, Laird Hospital, Union, MS, p. A353
Director Human Resources, Rush Foundation Hospital, Meridian, MS, p. A350
Director of Human Resources, Specialty Hospital Of Meridian, Meridian, MS, p. A350

SMITH, Doug
Chief Financial Officer, Mckay-Dee Hospital, Ogden, UT, p. A648
Chief Financial Officer, Sun Behavioral Houston, Houston, TX, p. A613

SMITH, Edward, Chief of Staff, Mackinac Straits Health System, Inc., Saint Ignace, MI, p. A322

SMITH, Edward H., President and Chief Executive Officer, St. Anthony Regional Hospital, Carroll, IA, p. A218

SMITH, Eric, Chief Financial Officer, Bayfront Health St. Petersburg, Saint Petersburg, FL, p. A138

SMITH, Ericka, Chief Operating Officer, Monterey Park Hospital, Monterey Park, CA, p. A73

SMITH, Erin, Chief Operating Officer, East Georgia Regional Medical Center, Statesboro, GA, p. A161

SMITH, Eugene, Chief Information Officer, Maniilaq Health Center, Kotzebue, AK, p. A26

SMITH, G. Todd., Chief Executive Officer, Mercy Medical Center Redding, Redding, CA, p. A79

SMITH, Gary, Chief Operating Officer, Aurelia Osborn Fox Memorial Hospital, Oneonta, NY, p. A439

SMITH, Gene, Chief Executive Officer, North Alabama Specialty Hospital, Athens, AL, p. A13

SMITH, Geoffrey, Chief Financial Officer, Lebanon Veterans Affairs Medical Center, Lebanon, PA, p. A529

SMITH, Gia, Chief Executive Officer, Central Valley Specialty Hospital, Modesto, CA, p. A72

SMITH, Greg, Chief Medical Officer, Lake Region Healthcare, Fergus Falls, MN, p. A331

SMITH, Gregory, M.D.
Chief Executive Officer, Fort Belknap Service Unit, Harlem, MT, p. A376
Senior Vice President and Chief Information Officer, Midwest Orthopedic Specialty Hospital, Franklin, WI, p. A692
Senior Vice President and Chief Information Officer, Wheaton Franciscan Healthcare - Franklin, Franklin, WI, p. A693
Senior Vice President and Chief Information Officer, Wheaton Franciscan Healthcare - St. Francis, Milwaukee, WI, p. A699

SMITH, Gretchen, Vice President of Operations, Risk and Compliance, and Chief Operating Officer, Rush Memorial Hospital, Rushville, IN, p. A214

SMITH, Harley, Chief Executive Officer, Tmc Bonham Hospital, Bonham, TX, p. A589

SMITH, Heather
Chief Operating Officer, Welch Community Hospital, Welch, WV, p. A687
President, Conemaugh Meyersdale Medical Center, Meyersdale, PA, p. A532

SMITH, Holt, Chief Financial Officer, Springs Memorial Hospital, Lancaster, SC, p. A555

SMITH, Jack, Acting Chief Information Resources Management Service, Veterans Affairs Sierra Nevada Health Care System, Reno, NV, p. A396

SMITH, Jackie, R.N., Chief Nursing Officer, Holdenville General Hospital, Holdenville, OK, p. A500

SMITH, James E.
Superintendent, North Texas State Hospital, Wichita Falls Campus, Wichita Falls, TX, p. A644
Superintendent, North Texas State Hospital, Vernon, TX, p. A642

SMITH, Jameson, President, Saint Joseph Hospital, Denver, CO, p. A99

SMITH, Jamie, Supervisor Health Information Management Systems, Healthsouth Rehabilitation Hospital Of Sewickley, Sewickley, PA, p. A541

SMITH, Janet, Chief Financial Officer, Troy Regional Medical Center, Troy, AL, p. A23

SMITH, Jared M., Chief Executive Officer, Broward Health Coral Springs, Coral Springs, FL, p. A120

SMITH, Jason
Chief Medical Officer, Beaver Dam Community Hospitals, Beaver Dam, WI, p. A690
Chief Operating Officer, Piedmont Athens Regional Medical Center, Athens, GA, p. A145

SMITH, Jay, Director Information Systems, Brownwood Regional Medical Center, Brownwood, TX, p. A590

SMITH, Jeanna, Administrative Assistant and Human Resources Officer, Polk Medical Center, Cedartown, GA, p. A150

SMITH, Jeff, Chief Information Officer, Holy Cross Hospital, Fort Lauderdale, FL, p. A122

SMITH, Jeffrey A., M.D.
Executive Vice President Hospital Operations and Chief Operating Officer, Cedars-Sinai Medical Center, Los Angeles, CA, p. A66
Senior Vice President and Chief Medical Officer, Aurora St. Luke's South Shore, WI, p. A698

SMITH, Jesse, Director of Nursing, Keefe Memorial Hospital, Cheyenne Wells, CO, p. A97

SMITH, Jim, Director Information Systems, Washington County Memorial Hospital, Potosi, MO, p. A366

SMITH, Jo Beth
Chief Operating Officer, Medical Arts Hospital, Lamesa, TX, p. A618
Vice President Human Resources, Decatur County Hospital, Leon, IA, p. A225

SMITH, JoAnn P., R.N., Chief Nursing Officer, and Vice President Patient Care Services, Unc Rockingham Health Care, Eden, NC, p. A451

SMITH, Joanne C., M.D., President and Chief Executive Officer, Shirley Ryan Abilitylab, Chicago, IL, p. A179

SMITH, Jodi, Administrative Assistant Human Resources, Eureka Springs Hospital, Eureka Springs-Carroll County, AR, p. A41

SMITH, Jon, Chief Financial Officer, Lost Rivers Medical Center, Arco, ID, p. A167

SMITH, Jonathan, Assistant Administrator and Chief Financial Officer, Blount Memorial Hospital, Maryville, TN, p. A574

SMITH, Joseph S., Chief Executive Officer, Boone County Hospital, Boone, IA, p. A218

SMITH, Julia
Chief Financial Officer, Kindred Hospital Rome, Rome, GA, p. A159
Chief Financial Officer, Kindred Hospital-Chattanooga, Chattanooga, TN, p. A567
Chief Financial Officer, Vibra Hospital Of Charleston, Mt. Pleasant, SC, p. A555

SMITH, Julie, R.N., MSN
Director of Nursing, Jersey Community Hospital, Jerseyville, IL, p. A186
Director Human Resources, Encompass Health Lakeshore Rehabilitation Hospital, Birmingham, AL, p. A14
Senior Human Resources Strategic Partner, Providence Milwaukie Hospital, Milwaukie, OR, p. A515

SMITH, Karen S, Director Information Services, Chilton Medical Center, Pompton Plains, NJ, p. A410

SMITH, Karla, Director Human Resources, St. Peter's Hospital, Helena, MT, p. A376

SMITH, Karyl, Director Human Resources, Harbor-Ucla Medical Center, Torrance, CA, p. A91

SMITH, Kathy A., MSN, R.N., Nurse Executive, Summit Behavioral Healthcare, Cincinnati, OH, p. A475

SMITH, Kelli, M.D., Chief of Staff, Magee General Hospital, Magee, MS, p. A349

SMITH, Kenneth P, Chief of Staff, John C. Fremont Healthcare District, Mariposa, CA, p. A71

SMITH, Kevin, D.O., Chief of Staff, Munson Healthcare Otsego Memorial Hospital, Gaylord, MI, p. A313

SMITH, Kevin L, Area Finance Officer, Kaiser Permanente South Sacramento Medical Center, Sacramento, CA, p. A82

SMITH, Kevin M, Director Human Resources, Indian Path Medical Center, Kingsport, TN, p. A572

SMITH, Kim, Director Business Office, Doctor's Hospital Of Deer Creek, Leesville, LA, p. A272

SMITH, Kris, Controller, Chi St. Joseph Health Rehabilitation Hospital, An Affiliate Of Encompass Health, Bryan, TX, p. A591

SMITH, Kyle, Director Information Systems, Iredell Health System, Statesville, NC, p. A461

SMITH, Lana, Human Resources Director, Ashe Memorial Hospital, Jefferson, NC, p. A455

SMITH, Larry, Senior Vice President and Chief Financial Officer, Uw Medicine/Valley Medical Center, Renton, WA, p. A675

SMITH, Laura
Chief Nursing Officer and Director of Infection Control, Ellett Memorial Hospital, Appleton City, MO, p. A355
Vice President Finance and Chief Financial Officer, Milford Hospital, Milford, CT, p. A109

SMITH, LaVonne, Director Health Information Technology, Tomah Memorial Hospital, Tomah, WI, p. A704

SMITH, Leanne, Chief Financial Officer, Windsor-Laurelwood Center For Behavioral Medicine, Willoughby, OH, p. A493

SMITH, Leighton, M.D., Chief Medical Officer, Florida Hospital Fish Memorial, Orange City, FL, p. A133

SMITH, Leora, Information System and Health Information Management Team Leader, Phelps Memorial Health Center, Holdrege, NE, p. A385

SMITH, Linda C, M.D., Medical Director, Pam Rehabilitation Hospital Of Beaumont, Beaumont, TX, p. A588

SMITH, Linda T, Director Human Resources, Clay County Hospital, Ashland, AL, p. A13

SMITH, Linda V, Vice President Human Resources, Central Florida Regional Hospital, Sanford, FL, p. A138

SMITH, Lori, Chief Financial Officer, North Big Horn Hospital District, Lovell, WY, p. A709

SMITH, Lori J., Vice President Human Resources, St. Bernards Medical Center, Jonesboro-Craighead County, AR, p. A44

SMITH, Lorie, Director Human Resources, Conemaugh Nason Medical Center, Roaring Spring, PA, p. A540

SMITH, Lorraine, Chief Executive Officer, Monroe County Hospital, Forsyth, GA, p. A153

SMITH, Lory Beth, Manager Human Resource, South Texas Surgical Hospital, Corpus Christi, TX, p. A594

SMITH, M. Scott, President, St. Anthony's Hospital, Saint Petersburg, FL, p. A138

SMITH, Marisa, Director, Kindred Hospital The Heights, TX, p. A640

SMITH, Mark, M.D.
Chief Medical Officer, Methodist Richardson Medical Center, Richardson, TX, p. A630
Director Human Resources, Providence Holy Family Hospital, Spokane, WA, p. A678

Director Human Resources, Sacred Heart Children's Hospital, WA, p. A678

Director Nursing Operations, Northern Colorado Rehabilitation Hospital, Johnstown, CO, p. A102

SMITH, Mark T., JD, CPA, President and Chief Operating Officer, Multicare Auburn Medical Center, Auburn, WA, p. A669

SMITH, Marsh, Manager Health Information, University Behavioral Health Of Denton, Denton, TX, p. A599

SMITH, Martha, R.N.
Chief Nursing Officer, New Orleans East Hospital, New Orleans, LA, p. A275
Chief Executive Officer, Kapiolani Medical Center For Women & Children, Honolulu, HI, p. A164

SMITH, Mary Clare.
Director, Western State Hospital, Staunton, VA, p. A666
Acting Facility Director, Commonwealth Center For Children And Adolescents, Staunton, VA, p. A666

SMITH, Mary Jo, Chief Human Resources Officer, University Of Illinois Hospital & Health Sciences System, Chicago, IL, p. A180

SMITH, Matt, Interim Chief Executive Officer, Bourbon Community Hospital, Paris, KY, p. A259

SMITH, Matthew, M.D., Vice President Medical Affairs and Chief Medical Officer, Baylor Scott & White Medical Center - Carrollton, Carrollton, TX, p. A592

SMITH, Megan, M.D., Chief Medical Staff, Community Memorial Hospital, Burke, SD, p. A559

SMITH, Melinda, Chief Information Systems, H. C. Watkins Memorial Hospital, Quitman, MS, p. A352

SMITH, Melissa
Controller, Select Specialty Hospital-Jackson, Jackson, MS, p. A348
Interim Vice President Human Resources, North Memorial Health Hospital, Robbinsdale, MN, p. A338

SMITH, Michael, Director of Nursing, Cypress Creek Hospital, Houston, TX, p. A610

SMITH, Michelle, Coordinator Human Resources, Baton Rouge Rehabilitation Hospital, Baton Rouge, LA, p. A263

SMITH, Michelle T, R.N., MSN, FACHE, Vice President Nursing Chief Nursing Officer Chief Experience Officer, Roger C. Peace Rehabilitation Hospital, SC, p. A553

SMITH, Mickey, Chief Executive Officer, Oak Hill Hospital, Brooksville, FL, p. A119

SMITH, Mike
Chief Information Officer, Cape Coral Hospital, Cape Coral, FL, p. A119
Chief Information Officer, Gulf Coast Medical Center, Fort Myers, FL, p. A123
Chief Information Officer, The Rehabilitation Hospital, FL, p. A123

SMITH, Missy, Coordinator Human Resources, Scotland County Hospital, Memphis, MO, p. A364

SMITH, Mona R., Chief Nursing Officer, Santa Cruz Valley Regional Hospital, Green Valley, AZ, p. A30

SMITH, Moneca, Chief Nursing Officer, The University Of Toledo Medical Center, Toledo, OH, p. A492

SMITH, Nadine, Director Human Resources, Reeves County Hospital, Pecos, TX, p. A628

SMITH, Neil, D.O., President, Cleveland Clinic Fairview Hospital, Cleveland, OH, p. A476

SMITH, Nekisha, Director Health Information Systems, Riverland Medical Center, Ferriday, LA, p. A267

SMITH, Nelson, Chief Executive Officer, Poplar Springs Hospital, Petersburg, VA, p. A663

SMITH, Nicholas T., Chief Executive Officer, Palm Springs General Hospital, Hialeah, FL, p. A124

SMITH, Nicole, Director Human Resources, Hi-Desert Medical Center, Joshua Tree, CA, p. A62

SMITH, Norine, Chief Executive Officer, Red Lake Indian Health Service Hospital, Red Lake, MN, p. A337

SMITH, Oliver, President and Chief Executive Officer, Paris Community Hospital, Paris, IL, p. A192

SMITH, Pam, Chief Nursing Officer, Encompass Health Rehabilitation Hospital Of Richardson, Richardson, TX, p. A630

SMITH, Pamela, Commander, U.S. Air Force Regional Hospital, Eglin Afb, FL, p. A122

SMITH, Patricia, Chief Nursing Officer, Oconee Memorial Hospital, Seneca, SC, p. A556

SMITH, Patrick, M.D.
Chief Medical Officer, Abrazo Arizona Heart Hospital, AZ, p. A30
Director Information Technology, Clay County Hospital, Ashland, AL, p. A13

SMITH, Peg, Vice President and Chief Nursing Officer, Chandler Regional Medical Center, Chandler, AZ, p. A28

SMITH, Phyllis, Vice President Human Resources, Northeastern Health System, Tahlequah, OK, p. A507

SMITH, Phyllis J., Associate Director, Birmingham Veterans Affairs Medical Center, Birmingham, AL, p. A14

SMITH, Randall, Executive Vice President, Jackson Park Hospital And Medical Center, Chicago, IL, p. A177

SMITH, Rebecca T, Chief Operating Officer and Chief Nursing Officer, Caldwell Unc Health Care, Lenoir, NC, p. A456

SMITH, Rhonda
Applications Support Manager, Uh Portage Medical Center, Ravenna, OH, p. A489
Chief Nursing Officer, Benewah Community Hospital, Saint Maries, ID, p. A171
Director Human Resources, Shriners Hospitals For Children-Portland, Portland, OR, p. A516

SMITH, Rich
Vice President Human Resources, Kaiser Foundation Hospital Westside Medical Center, Hillsboro, OR, p. A513
Vice President Human Resources, Kaiser Sunnyside Medical Center, Clackamas, OR, p. A512

SMITH, Richard, Chief of Staff, Carroll County Memorial Hospital, Carrollton, MO, p. A357

SMITH, Richard C.
Chief Financial Officer, Hackensack Meridian Health Jfk Johnson Rehabilitation Institute, Edison, NJ, p. A404
Senior Vice President and Chief Financial Officer, Hackensack Meridian Health Jfk Medical Center, Edison, NJ, p. A404
Senior Vice President Finance, Hackensack Meridian Health Shore Rehabilitation Institute, Brick, NJ, p. A402

SMITH, Rick
Chief Financial Officer, Mason General Hospital And Family Of Clinics, Shelton, WA, p. A677
Chief Operating Officer, Health Central Hospital, Ocoee, FL, p. A133
Director Information Services, Cibola General Hospital, Grants, NM, p. A417
Director Information Systems, Jamestown Regional Medical Center, Jamestown, TN, p. A571
Senior Vice President Human Resources and Chief Administrative Officer, Vail Health, Vail, CO, p. A106

SMITH, Robert M., M.D., Director, Va San Diego Healthcare System, San Diego, CA, p. A84

SMITH, Robert T., M.D.
Chief Medical Officer, Kettering Behavioral Medical Center, OH, p. A487
Chief Medical Officer, Kettering Medical Center, Kettering, OH, p. A484

SMITH, Robin C, Chief Nursing Officer, Indiana University Health White Memorial Hospital, Monticello, IN, p. A211

SMITH, Rodney, Vice President and Administrator, Herrin Hospital, Herrin, IL, p. A185

SMITH, Roy, Chief Financial Officer, Onslow Memorial Hospital, Jacksonville, NC, p. A455

SMITH, Ruth, Division Human Resources Business Partner, Banner Lassen Medical Center, Susanville, CA, p. A91

SMITH, Ryan K, Senior Vice President Information Technology, Banner - University Medical Center South, Tucson, AZ, p. A36

SMITH, Ryan K., Chief Executive Officer, Memorial Hospital Of Converse County, Douglas, WY, p. A708

SMITH, Scott, M.D.
Chief Medical Officer, Adams Memorial Hospital, Decatur, IN, p. A202
President, St. Joseph's Hospital-South, FL, p. A141

SMITH, Scott M., Interim Chief Executive Officer, Western Plains Medical Complex, Dodge City, KS, p. A234

SMITH, Sherry, Manager Human Resources, Dallas County Hospital, Perry, IA, p. A228

SMITH, Shirley M, Chief Financial Officer, Andalusia Health, Andalusia, AL, p. A13

SMITH, Sid, Director Information Resources, Larned State Hospital, Larned, KS, p. A239

SMITH, Skip, Vice President Finance, Iredell Health System, Statesville, NC, p. A461

SMITH, Stacey, R.N., Director of Nursing, Jefferson Hospital, Louisville, GA, p. A156

SMITH, Stephen, President, Selby General Hospital, Marietta, OH, p. A486

SMITH, Steve, M.D.
Chief of Staff, Providence Kodiak Island Medical Center, Kodiak, AK, p. A26
Assistant Vice President Finance, Chi St. Gabriel's Health, Little Falls, MN, p. A333
Chief Financial Officer, Kansas Heart Hospital, Wichita, KS, p. A247

SMITH, Steven, Chief Information Officer, Northshore Skokie Hospital, IL, p. A182

SMITH, Stormy, Chief Nursing Officer, Chillicothe Hospital District, Chillicothe, TX, p. A592

SOLBERG, Bradley V., FACHE, President, Osf Saint James - John W. Albrecht Medical Center, Pontiac, IL, p. A194

SOLBERG, Don, M.D., Chief Medical Officer, Kittitas Valley Healthcare, Ellensburg, WA, p. A671

SOLCHER, Barry, M.D., Chief of Staff, The Physicians Centre Hospital, Bryan, TX, p. A591

SOLDO, Stephen, M.D., Chief Medical Officer, Saint Agnes Medical Center, Fresno, CA, p. A59

SOLE, Kelly, Chief Operating Officer, Appalachian Behavioral Healthcare, Athens, OH, p. A471

SOLER, Eddie, Chief Financial Officer, Winter Park Memorial Hospital, FL, p. A134

SOLES, Jason, Manager Information Systems, St. James Mercy Hospital, Hornell, NY, p. A427

SOLHEIM, John H., Chief Executive Officer, Trios Health, Kennewick, WA, p. A672

SOLIE, Carol M., M.D., Chief Medical Officer, Wyoming Medical Center, Casper, WY, p. A707

SOLIMAN, Russell, Director Information Services, Presence St. Mary's Hospital, Kankakee, IL, p. A187

SOLIN, Andrea
    Chief Financial Officer, Lovelace Rehabilitation Hospital, Albuquerque, NM, p. A415
    Chief Financial Officer, Lovelace Westside Hospital, Albuquerque, NM, p. A415

SOLINSKI, Ruth, Senior Director Human Resources, Up Health System-Marquette, Marquette, MI, p. A318

SOLIS, Gloria, R.N., MSN, Chief Nursing Officer, Saint Luke's East Hospital, Lee's Summit, MO, p. A363

SOLIVAN, Jose E
    Chief Financial Officer, Hospital Menonita De Cayey, Cayey, PR, p. A713
    Chief Financial Officer, Mennonite General Hospital, Aibonito, PR, p. A712

SOLIZ, Mindy
    Director Human Resource Strategy, Christus Spohn Hospital Kleberg, Kingsville, TX, p. A617
    Director Human Resources, Christus Spohn Hospital Alice, Alice, TX, p. A582

SOLLENBERGER, Donna K, Executive Vice President and Chief Executive Officer, Angleton Danbury Campus, TX, p. A606

SOLLENBERGER, Donna K., Executive Vice President and Chief Executive Officer, Angleton Danbury Campus, TX, p. A606

SOLLIS, Jeff, Chief Executive Officer, Eastern Idaho Regional Medical Center, Idaho Falls, ID, p. A169

SOLOMON, John, M.D., Director, South Carolina Department Of Corrections Hospital, Columbia, SC, p. A551

SOLOMON, Oliver, M.D., Chief Medical Officer, Glendora Community Hospital, Glendora, CA, p. A61

SOLOMON, Tina, Executive Director Finance, Winter Haven Hospital, Winter Haven, FL, p. A144

SOLOMON-OWENS, Felicia, Director Human Resources, Fayette Medical Center, Fayette, AL, p. A18

SOLORIO, Roberta, Vice President, Chief Human Resource Officer, Midland Memorial Hospital, TX, p. A624

SOLORZANO, Rosa, Interim Director Human Resources, Astria Toppenish Hospital, Toppenish, WA, p. A679

SOLOW, Jodie Sartor, Director of Human Resources, Chatham Hospital, Siler City, NC, p. A460

SOLTIS, Les, Director - Human Resources, St. Francis Hospital, Federal Way, WA, p. A672

SOMERS, Tyrel, M.D., Chief Medical Officer, Russell Regional Hospital, Russell, KS, p. A245

SOMMERS, Belinda, Chief Information Officer, Lake Charles Memorial Hospital For Women, LA, p. A272

SOMMERS, Dorene M., Associate Director Patient Care Services, Erie Veterans Affairs Medical Center, Erie, PA, p. A525

SONATORE, Carol, D.O., Medical Director, Healthsouth Rehabilitation Hospital Of Toms River, Toms River, NJ, p. A412

SONDAG, Timothy, Senior Nursing Officer, Hopedale Medical Complex, Hopedale, IL, p. A186

SONDERMAN, Betty, Manager Human Resources, Ridgeview Institute, Smyrna, GA, p. A160

SONDERMAN, Thomas, M.D., Vice President and Chief Medical Officer, Columbus Regional Hospital, Columbus, IN, p. A201

SONEL, Ali, M.D., Chief of Staff, Veterans Affairs Medical Center, PA, p. A538

SONENREICH, Steven D., President and Chief Executive Officer, Miami Heart Campus At Mount Sinai Medical Center, FL, p. A131

SONES, Eric B., Commander, Keller Army Community Hospital, West Point, NY, p. A446

SONG, Daniel, Chief Financial Officer, Monterey Park Hospital, Monterey Park, CA, p. A73

SONGER, Lucille, Chief Nursing Officer, Athol Hospital, Athol, MA, p. A295

SONGY, David, President and Chief Executive Officer, Saint Luke Institute, Silver Spring, MD, p. A294

SONI, Anita, M.D., Chief Medical Officer, Nyc Health + Hospitals / Lincoln, New York (Includes All Hospitals Located Within The Five Boroughs), NY, p. A436

SONNENBERG, Martha, M.D., Chief of Staff, Southern California Hospital At Culver City, Culver City, CA, p. A56

SONNENBERG, Stephanie
    Director Information Technology, Promedica Bixby Hospital, Adrian, MI, p. A307
    Director Information Technology, Promedica Herrick Hospital, Tecumseh, MI, p. A324

SONNENBERG, William, M.D., President Medical Staff, Titusville Area Hospital, Titusville, PA, p. A542

SONNENSCHEIN, Silvia, M.D., Chief of Staff, Kohala Hospital, Kohala, HI, p. A166

SONTZ, Jennifer
    Director Human Resources, Evansville Psychiatric Children Center, Evansville, IN, p. A203
    Director Human Resources, Evansville State Hospital, Evansville, IN, p. A203

SOOHOO, Richard, Chief Financial Officer, Sutter General Hospital, CA, p. A82

SOPER, Brent, Chief Financial Officer, Adventist Health Bakersfield, Bakersfield, CA, p. A51

SOPIARZ, Ed, Chief Financial Officer, University Behavioral Health Of Denton, Denton, TX, p. A599

SOPKO, Joseph A., M.D., Chief Medical Officer, St. Vincent Charity Medical Center, Cleveland, OH, p. A477

SOPT, Michael, M.D., Chief of Staff, Brooks County Hospital, Quitman, GA, p. A158

SORBELLO, Bud, Director Management Information Systems, New York-Presbyterian/Hudson Valley Hospital, Cortlandt Manor, NY, p. A425

SORENSEN, Bonny
    Chief Financial Officer, Wadley Regional Medical Center At Hope, Hope-Hempstead County, AR, p. A43
    Chief Financial Officer, Wadley Regional Medical Center, Texarkana, TX, p. A639

SORENSEN, Damon, Chief Financial Officer, Mclaren Bay Region-West Campus, MI, p. A308

SORENSEN, Joanne L., R.N., FACHE, MS, Vice President Patient Care Services, Upmc Northwest, Seneca, PA, p. A541

SORENSEN, Vanessa, Chief Nursing Officer, Summit Medical Center, Casper, WY, p. A707

SORENSON, Chris
    Chief Health Information Officer, Sheltering Arms Hospital South, Midlothian, VA, p. A661
    Chief Information Officer, Sheltering Arms Rehabilitation Hospital, Mechanicsville, VA, p. A661

SORENSON, Dennis, Supervisor Information Technology, Bronson South Haven Hospital, South Haven, MI, p. A323

SORENSON, Eric C, Chief Financial Officer, Veterans Affairs Loma Linda Healthcare System, Loma Linda, CA, p. A64

SORENSON, Sheri, Manager Business Office, Highland Ridge Hospital, Midvale, UT, p. A647

SORENSON, Tawnya, Director of Nursing, Kittson Memorial Healthcare Center, Hallock, MN, p. A332

SORRELL, Dierdra, R.N., Interim Chief Executive Officer, Clifton-Fine Hospital, Star Lake, NY, p. A443

SORRELL, Rachel, Chief Financial Officer, Tsehootsooi Medical Center, Fort Defiance, AZ, p. A29

SORRELL, Ralph W, Sr, Chief Financial Officer, Adena Greenfield Medical Center, Greenfield, OH, p. A483

SORRELLS, Dwane, Chief Information Officer, Choctaw Nation Health Care Center, Talihina, OK, p. A507

SOSA, Phillip
    Chief Financial Officer, El Paso Behavioral Health System, El Paso, TX, p. A601
    Interim Chief Executive Officer, El Paso Behavioral Health System, El Paso, TX, p. A601

SOSA-GUERRERO, Sandra, Chief Executive Officer, Larkin Community Hospital, South Miami, FL, p. A139

SOSNOW, Peter L, Medical Director, O'Connor Hospital, Delhi, NY, p. A425

SOTERAKIS, Jack, M.D., Executive Vice President Medical Affairs, St. Francis Hospital, The Heart Center, Roslyn, NY, p. A442

SOTO, Ciria, Director Human Resources, Sonora Behavioral Health Hospital, Tucson, AZ, p. A38

SOTO, Itza, MSN, Nursing Executive, Ashford Presbyterian Community Hospital, San Juan, PR, p. A715

SOTO, Juan Carlos, Director Information Systems, Hospital San Carlos Borromeo, Moca, PR, p. A714

SOTOIZAGUIRRE, Felix, Chief Financial Officer, Wellstar North Fulton Hospital, Roswell, GA, p. A159

SOTOS, Steven, M.D., President Medical Staff, Lifecare Hospitals Of Pittsburgh - Suburban, PA, p. A537

SOUDERS, Stuart, Chief, Human Resources, William S. Middleton Memorial Veterans Hospital, Madison, WI, p. A696

SOUKUP, Paul, Chief Financial Officer, St. Luke Community Healthcare, Ronan, MT, p. A378

SOULAR, Dan, M.D., Vice President, Medical Affairs, Grand Itasca Clinic And Hospital, Grand Rapids, MN, p. A332

SOULE, Joyce M, R.N., MSN, Chief Nursing Officer, Medical City Children's Hospital, TX, p. A597

SOURBEER, Jay C., Commanding Officer, Robert E. Bush Naval Hospital, Twentynine Palms, CA, p. A92

SOUTHER, Geoffrey C, Chief Operating Officer, New Hampshire Hospital, Concord, NH, p. A398

SOUTHERN, Joel, R.N., MSN, Chief Executive Officer, Northwest Mississippi Medical Center, Clarksdale, MS, p. A344

SOUTHWICK, Mitch, Chief Operating Officer, Mclaren Bay Region-West Campus, MI, p. A308

SOUTHWICK, William, R.N., Chief Executive Officer, Banner Behavioral Health Hospital - Scottsdale, Scottsdale, AZ, p. A35

SOUTHWORTH, Scott, M.D., Medical Director, South Davis Community Hospital, Bountiful, UT, p. A646

SOUZA, Beatrix, Chief Executive Officer, Buffalo Psychiatric Center, Buffalo, NY, p. A423

SOUZA, Darlene, Vice President, St. Joseph Hospital For Specialty Care, RI, p. A547

SOUZA, Greg, Vice President Human Resources, Lucile Salter Packard Children's Hospital Stanford, Palo Alto, CA, p. A77

SOUZA, Jim, Chief Medical Officer, St. Luke's Meridian Medical Center, ID, p. A168

SOUZA, Liz, Coordinator Nursing Services, Atascadero State Hospital, Atascadero, CA, p. A51

SOUZA, Michael
    Chief Executive Officer, Landmark Medical Center-Woonsocket Unit, RI, p. A548
    Chief Executive Officer, Rehabilitation Hospital Of Rhode Island, North Smithfield, RI, p. A547

SOVETSKHY, Ed, Director Information Services, Portsmouth Regional Hospital, Portsmouth, NH, p. A401

SOWDERS, Dale, President and Chief Executive Officer, Holland Hospital, Holland, MI, p. A315

SOWELL, Ronald G., FACHE
    Chief Financial Officer, Medical Center At Scottsville, Scottsville, KY, p. A260
    Executive Vice President and Chief Financial Officer, The Medical Center At Caverna, Horse Cave, KY, p. A253
    Executive Vice President, Chief Financial Officer, The Medical Center Albany, Albany, KY, p. A249
    Executive Vice President, Commonwealth Regional Specialty Hospital, Bowling Green, KY, p. A249
    Executive Vice President, Medical Center At Bowling Green, Bowling Green, KY, p. A250
    Executive Vice President, Medical Center At Franklin, Franklin, KY, p. A252

SOWELL, Vincent, Chief Nursing Officer, Otto Kaiser Memorial Hospital, Kenedy, TX, p. A617

SOWERS, Chuck, Vice President Finance and Chief Financial Officer, Mercy Gilbert Medical Center, Gilbert, AZ, p. A29

SOWIZRAL, Shirley, Chief Executive Officer, Wernersville State Hospital, Wernersville, PA, p. A543

SPACK, Paula, R.N., MSN, Vice President Nursing, Punxsutawney Area Hospital, Punxsutawney, PA, p. A539

SPACKMAN, Jared
    Chief Financial Officer, Davis Hospital And Medical Center, Layton, UT, p. A647
    Chief Operating Officer, Davis Hospital And Medical Center, Layton, UT, p. A647

SPACONE, Celia, M.D., Director Operations, Buffalo Psychiatric Center, Buffalo, NY, p. A423

SPADE, Ann M., Chief Nursing Executive, Upmc Pinnacle Carlisle, Carlisle, PA, p. A522

SPADONI, Robert S, Vice President of Hospital Operations, Rush Oak Park Hospital, Oak Park, IL, p. A191

SPAGNA, Lauren, Marketing Director, West Boca Medical Center, Boca Raton, FL, p. A118

SPAHLINGER, David, M.D., President, C. S. Mott Children's Hospital, MI, p. A307

SPAHR, Kristen, Director of Marketing, Desoto Memorial Hospital, Arcadia, FL, p. A117

SPAIN, Jeanine R R.N., MS, Chief Operating Office, UnityPoint Health - Pekin, Regional Chief Nursing Officer, Unitypoint Health - Peoria, Peoria, IL, p. A193

SPAIN, Steve, Chief Operating Officer, Larned State Hospital, Larned, KS, p. A239

SPAIN, Tom, Director Operations Finance, Community Memorial Hospital, Turtle Lake, ND, p. A468

SPALDING, Cathy, Vice President of Operations, Frazier Rehab Institute, KY, p. A256

SPANBAUER, Lisa, Financial Program Supervisor, Winnebago Mental Health Institute, Winnebago, WI, p. A706

SPANGHER, Guido, M.D., Clinical Director, Big Spring State Hospital, Big Spring, TX, p. A589

SPANGLER, Mark, M.D., Chief Medical Officer, Gibson Area Hospital And Health Services, Gibson City, IL, p. A184

SPANGLER, Michael, Health Information Management Services Supervisor, Healthsouth Rehabilitation Hospital Of Tallahassee, Tallahassee, FL, p. A140

SPANGLER, Wendell J, M.D., Chief of Staff, Paulding County Hospital, Paulding, OH, p. A489

SPANN, Debbie, Director Human Resources, Morehouse General Hospital, Bastrop, LA, p. A263

SPANN, Lori, Director Human Resources, Iberia Medical Center, New Iberia, LA, p. A275

SPANO, Dennis, M.D., Medical Director, Mayo Clinic Health System In Lake City, Lake City, MN, p. A333

SPANO, Jason, Director of Information Technology, Prowers Medical Center, Lamar, CO, p. A103

SPARE, John, Accountant, Parsons State Hospital And Training Center, Parsons, KS, p. A244

SPARER, Cynthia, Senior Vice President and Executive Director Women's & Children, Yale-New Haven Children's Hospital, CT, p. A110

SPARGER, Kathy, R.N., MSN, Chief Nursing Officer, Baptist Health South Florida, South Miami Hospital, Miami, FL, p. A130

SPARKMAN, Dena C., FACHE, Community Chief Executive Officer, Whitesburg Arh Hospital, Whitesburg, KY, p. A261

SPARKMAN, Jill, Director Human Resources, Odessa Regional Medical Center, Odessa, TX, p. A626

SPARKS, Dennis W.
Vice President Human Resources, Saint Michael's Medical Center, Newark, NJ, p. A409
Vice President of Human Resources, Saint Francis Hospital And Medical Center, Hartford, CT, p. A108

SPARKS, Gary R.
Administrator, Crossridge Community Hospital, Wynne-Cross County, AR, p. A49
Interim President, Lawrence Memorial Hospital, Walnut Ridge-Lawrence County, AR, p. A49

SPARKS, Holly H., Chief Clinical Officer, South Sunflower County Hospital, Indianola, MS, p. A347

SPARKS, Jason, Director, Human Resources, Healthsouth Rehabilitation Hospital Of Cincinnati At Norwood, OH, p. A475

SPARKS, Jennifer, Human Resources Generalist, Complex Care Hospital At Ridgelake, Sarasota, FL, p. A138

SPARKS, Lisa, R.N., Chief Nursing Officer and Vice President Patient Care Services, Indiana University Health West Hospital, Avon, IN, p. A199

SPARKS, Wendy, Chief Operating Officer, North Colorado Medical Center, Greeley, CO, p. A101

SPARLING, Nicki, Manager Human Resources, Major Hospital, Shelbyville, IN, p. A214

SPARROW, Francis D, M.D., Medical Director, Wellspan Philhaven, Mount Gretna, PA, p. A532

SPARROW, Robert T., M.D., Vice President, Chief Medical Officer, Children's Hospital Of Illinois, IL, p. A193

SPARTZ, Dale A, Chief Human Resources Officer, University Of Utah Health, Salt Lake City, UT, p. A651

SPARZO, John, M.D., Vice President Medical Affairs, Hendricks Regional Health, Danville, IN, p. A202

SPATH, Deborah, R.N., MSN, Associate Director Patient and Nurses Services, Albany Stratton Veterans Affairs Medical Center, Albany, NY, p. A421

SPEARE, Mark, Senior Associate Director Patient Relations and Human Resources, Ucla Medical Center-Santa Monica, Santa Monica, CA, p. A89

SPEARS, David, D.O., Chief of Staff, Selby General Hospital, Marietta, OH, p. A486

SPEARS, Gina, Chief Financial Officer, Thomas B. Finan Center, Cumberland, MD, p. A291

SPEARS, Kevin, Chief Executive Officer, Stone County Medical Center, Mountain View-Stone County, AR, p. A46

SPEARS, LaLana, Supervisor Accounting, Claremore Indian Hospital, Claremore, OK, p. A497

SPEARS, Michael, Human Resource Leader, Ssm Health St. Anthony Hospital - Shawnee, Shawnee, OK, p. A506

SPEAS, Ryan, Director Finance, Livingston Healthcare, Livingston, MT, p. A377

SPEASE, Dorothy, Manager Business Office, Douglas County Memorial Hospital, Armour, SD, p. A559

SPECK, Michelle, Senior Vice President Human Resources, Usmd Hospital At Fort Worth, Fort Worth, TX, p. A605

SPECK, Michelle A
Vice President Human Resources, Upmc Altoona, Altoona, PA, p. A520

Vice President Human Resources, Upmc Bedford Memorial, Everett, PA, p. A526

SPECKMAN, Kelly Ann, Chief Financial Officer, Kearny County Hospital, Lakin, KS, p. A239

SPEECH, Thomas, Ph.D., Director, Winnebago Mental Health Institute, Winnebago, WI, p. A706

SPEEK, Timothy, I, Director of Nursing, Glenn Medical Center, Willows, CA, p. A95

SPEELMAN, Steven, Director Information Systems, Novant Health Uva Health System Culpeper Medical Center, Culpeper, VA, p. A657

SPEER, Kevin, Chief Executive Officer, Hendricks Regional Health, Danville, IN, p. A202

SPEER-SMITH, Carol, R.N., Chief Nursing Officer, Oroville Hospital, Oroville, CA, p. A77

SPEES, M. Shane., Chief Executive Officer, North Mississippi Medical Center - Tupelo, Tupelo, MS, p. A353

SPEIER, Ryan, Vice President Administration, Kvc Prairie Ridge Psychiatric Hospital, Kansas City, KS, p. A238

SPEIGHT, Marianne, Vice President Information System and Chief Information Officer, Children's Hospital, OH, p. A474

SPELL, Kenneth R, Vice President Operations, Baptist Health South Florida, Homestead Hospital, Homestead, FL, p. A125

SPELL, Nicole
Director Human Resources, Vidant Bertie Hospital, Windsor, NC, p. A462
Director Human Resources, Vidant Chowan Hospital, Edenton, NC, p. A452

SPELLBERG, Brad, M.D., Chief Medical Officer, Women's And Children's Hospital, CA, p. A68

SPELLMAN, Warren K., Chief Executive Officer, Grady Memorial Hospital, Chickasha, OK, p. A497

SPELLMEIER, Rhonda, R.N., Director of Nursing, Sabetha Community Hospital, Sabetha, KS, p. A245

SPELLS-WILSON, Debbie, R.N., Chief Operating Officer and Chief Nursing Officer, Conemaugh Miners Medical Center, Hastings, PA, p. A527

SPENCE, Andre, Chief Medical Staff, Sanford Bagley Medical Center, Bagley, MN, p. A328

SPENCE, Ben
Chief Financial Officer, Cape Coral Hospital, Cape Coral, FL, p. A119
Chief Financial Officer, Gulf Coast Medical Center, Fort Myers, FL, p. A123
Chief Financial Officer, The Rehabilitation Hospital, FL, p. A123

SPENCE, Karie, Director Human Resources, Miller County Hospital, Colquitt, GA, p. A150

SPENCE, Karla, Director of Nursing, St. Andrew's Health Center, Bottineau, ND, p. A464

SPENCE, Monte, Chief Operating Officer, Rehabilitation Hospital Of Indiana, Indianapolis, IN, p. A207

SPENCE, Sheldon, Director of Revenue Cycle, IT, Memorial Hospital Of Texas County, Guymon, OK, p. A499

SPENCE, Steven Walter, M.D., Chief Medical Officer, Jackson Hospital, Marianna, FL, p. A129

SPENCE, Terri
Chief Information Officer, Bon Secours Maryview Medical Center, Portsmouth, VA, p. A664
Chief Information Officer, Bon Secours St. Mary's Children's Services, VA, p. A664
Vice President and Regional Chief Information Officer, Bon Secours St. Francis Medical Center, Midlothian, VA, p. A661
Vice President Information Services, Bon Secours Mary Immaculate Hospital, Newport News, VA, p. A662

SPENCER, Erich, Chief Human Resource Officer, Fairview Northland Medical Center, Princeton, MN, p. A337

SPENCER, Jim, Director Information System, Mcleod Health Cheraw, Cheraw, SC, p. A550

SPENCER, Marie, Chief Nursing Officer and Senior Administrator, Burke Rehabilitation Hospital, White Plains, NY, p. A446

SPENCER, Mike, Chief Information Officer, Henry Community Health, New Castle, IN, p. A212

SPENCER, Misti, Director Inpatient Services, Selby General Hospital, Marietta, OH, p. A486

SPENCER, Sarah, M.D., Chief of Staff, South Peninsula Hospital, Homer, AK, p. A26

SPENCER, Scott, Chief Financial Officer, South Shore Hospital, Chicago, IL, p. A179

SPENCER, Susan, Chief Financial Officer, Samaritan Hospital, Macon, MO, p. A364

SPENCER, Todd, M.D., Chief Medical Staff, Adventist Medical Center-Reedley, Reedley, CA, p. A80

SPENST, Brett, Chief Executive Officer, Littleton Adventist Hospital, Littleton, CO, p. A103

SPERDUTI, Karen, Chief Operating Officer, Saint Camillus Medical Center, Hurst, TX, p. A615

SPERLING, Deanna, R.N., President and Chief Executive Officer, Barnabas Health Behavioral Health Center, Toms River, NJ, p. A412

SPERLING, Louis J, Vice President Human Resources, Hasbro Children's Hospital, RI, p. A548

SPERLING, Walter, M.D., Medical Director, Ellenville Regional Hospital, Ellenville, NY, p. A426

SPERRAZZA, John, Chief Operating Officer, St. Joseph Hospital, NY, p. A424

SPERRING, Jeff, M.D., Chief Executive Officer, Seattle Children's Hospital, Seattle, WA, p. A676

SPICER, Joan G, R.N., Chief Nursing Officer, San Mateo Medical Center, San Mateo, CA, p. A87

SPICER, Michael J., President and Chief Executive Officer, Saint Joseph's Medical Center, Yonkers, NY, p. A446

SPICER, Randy, Information Technology Supervisor, Central State Hospital, Louisville, KY, p. A256

SPICER, Sam, M.D., Vice President Medical Affairs, Cape Fear Hospital, NC, p. A462

SPIDLE, Tara, Chief Financial Officer, Decatur County Hospital, Leon, IA, p. A225

SPIEGEL, Kevin M., Chief Executive Officer, Willie D. Miller Eye Center, TN, p. A567

SPIER, Deborah, Administrator, Oceans Behavioral Hospital Of Greater New Orleans, Kenner, LA, p. A270

SPIGEL, Michael, Executive Vice President & Chief Operating Officer, Brooks Rehabilitation Hospital, Jacksonville, FL, p. A125

SPIGNER, Jason, Vice President Human Resources, Advocate Good Shepherd Hospital, Barrington, IL, p. A174

SPIKE, Jennifer, Director Human Resources, St. James Mercy Hospital, Hornell, NY, p. A427

SPILLERS, David S., Chief Executive Officer, Madison Hospital, AL, p. A19

SPILSBURY, Lauren, R.N., MSN, Vice President for Patient Care Services, Redlands Community Hospital, Redlands, CA, p. A80

SPINA, Lori, Vice President Human Resources, Good Samaritan Hospital Medical Center, West Islip, NY, p. A445

SPINALE, Joseph W, D.O., Chief Medical Officer, St. Joseph's Hospital Health Center, Syracuse, NY, p. A444

SPINGOS, Maria, Director of Nursing, Fort Lauderdale Hospital, Fort Lauderdale, FL, p. A122

SPISSO, Johnese, Chief Executive Officer, Mattel Children's Hospital, CA, p. A69

SPITSER, Christy
Vice President Finance and Business Development, Saint Joseph London, London, KY, p. A255
Vice President Finance, Saint Joseph Berea, Berea, KY, p. A249

SPIVEY, Amy, Chief Medical Officer, Mccullough-Hyde Memorial Hospital/Trihealth, Oxford, OH, p. A489

SPIVEY, Courtney, Chief Nursing Officer, Hardin County General Hospital, Rosiclare, IL, p. A195

SPIVEY, David A., President and Chief Executive Officer, St. Mary Mercy Hospital, Livonia, MI, p. A318

SPLITT, Richie, FACHE
President and Chief Executive Office, Norman Regional Hospital, OK, p. A502
President and Chief Executive Officer, Norman Regional Moore, OK, p. A502

SPOELMA, Susan G, MSN, R.N., Chief Nursing Officer, Healdsburg District Hospital, Healdsburg, CA, p. A61

SPONSLER, Betsy A, Chief Financial Officer, Valley Hospital Medical Center, Las Vegas, NV, p. A395

SPOON, Barry, M.D., Chief of Staff, Mercy St. Francis Hospital, Mountain View, MO, p. A365

SPOONER, Allan M, President and Chief Executive Officer, St. James Hospital And Health Centers - Chicago Heights Campus, IL, p. A192

SPOONER, Allan M., President and Chief Executive Officer, St. James Hospital And Health Centers - Chicago Heights Campus, IL, p. A192

SPOONER, Jennifer, Controller, Healthsouth Rehabilitation Hospital Of Tallahassee, Tallahassee, FL, p. A140

SPOOR, David, R.N., Vice President, Patient Care Services and Chief Nursing Officer, Sturdy Memorial Hospital, Attleboro, MA, p. A295

SPORE, Larry, Chief Financial Officer, Lawrence County Memorial Hospital, Lawrenceville, IL, p. A187

SPRADLIN, John, Information Systems Director, Franklin Foundation Hospital, Franklin, LA, p. A267

SPRAGUE, F. Remington, M.D., Chief Medical Officer, Mercy Health, Mercy Campus, MI, p. A319

SPRAKER, Larissa, Vice President Business Development and Chief Strategy Officer, Mercy Gilbert Medical Center, Gilbert, AZ, p. A29

SPRANGER, Lance, Chief Information Officer, St. John's Medical Center And Living Center, Jackson, WY, p. A708

SPRAY, William R, Interim Chief Executive Officer, Southern Tennessee Regional Health System-Sewanee, TN, p. A581

SPRAY, William R., Chief Executive Officer, Southern Tennessee Regional Health System-Sewanee, TN, p. A581

SPREER-ALBERT, Frances, Chief Financial Officer and Executive Vice President, Albany Medical Center South-Clinical Campus, NY, p. A421

SPRIGGS, Larry Floyd, CPA, Controller, Encompass Health Rehabilitation Hospital Of San Antonio, San Antonio, TX, p. A633

SPRINGATE, Brian, Chief Executive Officer, Fleming County Hospital, Flemingsburg, KY, p. A251

SPRINGER, Amy, Medical Director, Webster County Community Hospital, Red Cloud, NE, p. A390

SPRINGER, Madge, Director Human Resources, Florida Hospital Waterman, Tavares, FL, p. A142

SPRINGER, Rebecca, MSN, R.N., Chief Nursing Officer, Hendry Regional Medical Center, Clewiston, FL, p. A120

SPRINGER, Sharon, Chief Nursing Officer, Cameron Memorial Community Hospital, Angola, IN, p. A199

SPRINGER, Theresa, Chief Financial Officer, Osf Holy Family Medical Center, Monmouth, IL, p. A189

SPRINGMANN, Tressa
  Vice President and Chief Information Officer, Levindale Hebrew Geriatric Center And Hospital, Baltimore, MD, p. A288
  Vice President and Chief Information Officer, Northwest Hospital, Randallstown, MD, p. A293

SPRINKEL, George, Chief Financial Officer, Tennova Healthcare-Clarksville, Clarksville, TN, p. A568

SPRINKLE, Patricia, Vice President, Human Resources, Bluffton Regional Medical Center, Bluffton, IN, p. A200

SPROTT, Kendell R., M.D., JD, Chief Executive Officer, Matheny Medical And Educational Center, Peapack, NJ, p. A409

SPROUT, Merry, R.N., Chief Nursing Officer, Antelope Memorial Hospital, Neligh, NE, p. A387

SPROWL, Chris, M.D., Vice President, Peacehealth St. Joseph Medical Center, Bellingham, WA, p. A669

SPRUYT, Jim, Chief Executive Officer, Rolling Hills Hospital, Franklin, TN, p. A570

SPRYS, Michael, D.O., Chief of Staff, Medical Arts Hospital, Lamesa, TX, p. A618

SPUHLER, Richard, Chief Executive Officer, Brigham City Community Hospital, Brigham City, UT, p. A646

SPURLOCK, James, D.O., Chief of Staff, Saint Thomas Stones River Hospital, Woodbury, TN, p. A581

SPURLOCK, Steve, Director Information Systems, Buena Vista Regional Medical Center, Storm Lake, IA, p. A230

SPYKERMAN, Connie, Chief Nursing Officer, Pelham Medical Center, Greer, SC, p. A554

SPYROW, Florence (Flo)., Chief Administrative Officer, Flagstaff Medical Center, Flagstaff, AZ, p. A29

SQUIRES, Danny
  Chief Financial Officer, Wake Forest Baptist Health-Davie Medical Center, Bermuda Run, NC, p. A448
  Vice President and Chief Financial Officer, Wake Forest Baptist Health-Lexington Medical Center, Lexington, NC, p. A456

SQUIRES, Elizabeth, R.N., Chief Nursing Officer, Healthsouth Rehabilitation Hospital Of Tallahassee, Tallahassee, FL, p. A140

SQUIRES, Paula C, Senior Vice President, Chief Human Resources Officer and Chief Human Resources Officer, Baystate Children's Hospital, MA, p. A304

SQUIRES, Teresa, R.N., Chief Nursing Officer, Lake District Hospital, Lakeview, OR, p. A514

SRAON, Karandeep, Interim Director, Aleda E. Lutz Veterans Affairs Medical Center, Saginaw, MI, p. A322

SREBINSKI, Ron, Chief Financial Officer, Mclaren Caro Region, Caro, MI, p. A309

SRIBNICK, Wayne, M.D., Senior Vice President and Chief Medical Officer, Providence Hospital Northeast, SC, p. A551

SRINIVASAN, Parthasarathy, M.D., President Medical Staff, Galesburg Cottage Hospital, Galesburg, IL, p. A183

SRIPADA, Subra
  Exec. Vice President, Chief Transformation Officer and Chief Information Officer, Beaumont Hospital - Taylor, Taylor, MI, p. A324
  Executive Vice President, Chief Transformation Officer and Chief Information Officer, Beaumont Hospital - Dearborn, Dearborn, MI, p. A310
  Executive Vice President, Chief Transformation Officer and Chief Information Officer, Beaumont Hospital - Trenton, Trenton, MI, p. A324
  Executive Vice President, Chief Transformation Officer and Chief Information Officer, Beaumont Hospital, Wayne, Wayne, MI, p. A325

Executive Vice President, Chief Transportation Officer and Chief Information Officer, Beaumont Children's Hospital, MI, p. A322

Executive Vice President, Chief Transportation Officer and Chief Information Officer, Beaumont Hospital - Farmington Hills, Farmington Hills, MI, p. A312

Executive Vice President, Chief Transportation Officer and Chief Information Officer, Beaumont Hospital - Grosse Pointe, Grosse Pointe, MI, p. A315

Executive Vice President, Chief Transportation Officer and Chief Information Officer, Beaumont Hospital - Troy, Troy, MI, p. A325

SRIVASTAVA, Mohit, M.D., Chief of Staff, Bunkie General Hospital, Bunkie, LA, p. A265

ST CLAIR, Jeffery M., President and Chief Executive Officer, Springhill Memorial Hospital, Mobile, AL, p. A20

ST PIERRE, Jay, Chief Financial Officer, North Florida Regional Medical Center, Gainesville, FL, p. A123

ST. AUBYN, Lisa, Chief Executive Officer, Signature Psychiatric Hospital, Kansas City, MO, p. A362

ST. GERMAIN, Jackie, Chief Executive Officer, Rock Prairie Behavioral Health, College Station, TX, p. A593

ST. LOUIS, Charles, Director of Patient Care Services, Sutter Health Kahi Mohala, Ewa Beach, HI, p. A164

ST. PE', Laurin, Administrator - Singing River Hospital, Singing River Hospital, MS, p. A351

ST. PETER, Colette, Senior Manager Human Resources, Mercy Hospital Carthage, Carthage, MO, p. A357

ST. PIERRE, Fran, Chief Nursing Officer, Hood Memorial Hospital, Amite, LA, p. A262

STAATS, Jason, Chief Executive Officer, Cumberland Hall Hospital, Hopkinsville, KY, p. A253

STABRYLA, Della, Director of Nursing, Ellwood City Medical Center, Ellwood City, PA, p. A525

STACEY, Brian, Chief Financial Officer, Nyc Health + Hospitals / Queens, New York (Includes All Hospitals Located Within The Five Boroughs), NY, p. A436

STACEY, Susan, Chief Nursing Officer, Sacred Heart Children's Hospital, WA, p. A678

STACIE, Beverly, Director Human Resources, Clifton T. Perkins Hospital Center, Jessup, MD, p. A292

STACKHOUSE, Jenni, Chief Financial Officer, River Point Behavioral Health, Jacksonville, FL, p. A125

STACKHOUSE, Rebecca J., Medical Center Director, Salem Veterans Affairs Medical Center, Salem, VA, p. A666

STACKHOUSE, Sharon, Assistant Administrator and Director Risk Management, Peachford Behavioral Health System, Atlanta, GA, p. A146

STACY, Doug, Director Information Technology, Up Health System-Marquette, Marquette, MI, p. A318

STADHEIM, Barbara, Chief Nursing Officer, West River Regional Medical Center, Hettinger, ND, p. A467

STADHEIM, Nathan, Chief Financial Officer, West River Regional Medical Center, Hettinger, ND, p. A467

STADLER, James J, M.D., Associate Administrator Medical Services, Guam Memorial Hospital Authority, Tamuning, GU, p. A711

STADLER, Thomas, M.D., Vice President Medical Affairs and Chief Medical Officer, Madonna Rehabilitation Hospital, Lincoln, NE, p. A386

STAFFORD, Tom, Chief Information Officer, Halifax Health Medical Center Of Port Orange, FL, p. A121

STAFFORD, Walt, Director Information Technology, Chatuge Regional Hospital And Nursing Home, Hiawassee, GA, p. A154

STAGG, Kevin, Executive Vice President Finance and Chief Financial Officer, Christian Health Care Center, Wyckoff, NJ, p. A414

STAGGS, Nathan, Chief Executive Officer, Pauls Valley General Hospital, Pauls Valley, OK, p. A505

STAHL, Anthony, Ph.D., FACHE
  Chief Executive Officer, Central Texas Medical Center, San Marcos, TX, p. A635
  Vice President, Florida Hospital Lake Placid, FL, p. A139

STAHL, Daniel, D.O., Chief Medical Officer, Rush Memorial Hospital, Rushville, IN, p. A214

STAHL, Kathy, Chief Nursing Officer, Wheeling Hospital, Wheeling, WV, p. A688

STAHL, Pam, Regional Chief Human Resources Officer, Providence Holy Cross Medical Center, Mission Hills, CA, p. A72

STAHL, Sherri, R.N., Senior Vice President Hospital Services, Chambersburg Hospital, Chambersburg, PA, p. A522

STAHL, Steven J, Director Human Resources, Columbia County Health System, Dayton, WA, p. A671

STAHL, William D, Chief Operating Officer, Rooks County Health Center, Plainville, KS, p. A244

STAHLKUPPE, Robert F, M.D., Chief of Staff, Chatuge Regional Hospital And Nursing Home, Hiawassee, GA, p. A154

STAHULAK, Brian M, R.N., Chief Nursing Officer, Ann & Robert H. Lurie Children's Hospital Of Chicago, Chicago, IL, p. A176

STAIGER, Tom, Medical Director, University Of Washington Medical Center, Seattle, WA, p. A677

STAIGL, Chris, Chief Nursing Officer, Tristar Southern Hills Medical Center, Nashville, TN, p. A578

STALCUP, Connie, Manager Information Systems, Erlanger Murphy Medical Center, Murphy, NC, p. A457

STALCUP, Linda, Chief Executive Officer, Stevens County Hospital, Hugoton, KS, p. A237

STALKER, Neil, M.D., Chief of Staff, Dukes Memorial Hospital, Peru, IN, p. A213

STALL, Kristi, Chief Human Resources Officer, Mahnomen Health Center, Mahnomen, MN, p. A334

STALLINGS, Jay, Chief Executive Officer, Washakie Medical Center, Worland, WY, p. A710

STALLINGS, Terry, M.D., Chief Medical Officer, West Florida Rehabilitation Institute, FL, p. A136

STALLINGS-SICARD, Lori, R.N., Chief Nursing Officer, Dmc Huron Valley-Sinai Hospital, Commerce Township, MI, p. A310

STALLWORTH, David, M.D., Chief of Staff, Monroe County Hospital, Monroeville, AL, p. A21

STALLWORTH, Monica, M.D., Chief of Staff, Western Maryland Hospital Center, Hagerstown, MD, p. A292

STALLWORTH, Terresa, M.D., Clinical Director, San Antonio State Hospital, San Antonio, TX, p. A634

STALNAKER, Avah, Chief Executive Officer, Stonewall Jackson Memorial Hospital, Weston, WV, p. A688

STALNAKER, Kevin P, CPA, Assistant Chief Executive Officer, Stonewall Jackson Memorial Hospital, Weston, WV, p. A688

STAMAS, Peter, M.D., Vice President Medical Affairs, Marshfield Childen's Hospital, WI, p. A697

STAMBAUGH, Lynn E., R.N., Chief Executive Officer, Sarah D. Culbertson Memorial Hospital, Rushville, IL, p. A195

STAMM, Pam, Chief Nursing Officer, Throckmorton County Memorial Hospital, Throckmorton, TX, p. A640

STAMOPOULOS, Marion, Vice President Human Resouces, Deborah Heart And Lung Center, Browns Mills, NJ, p. A403

STAMOS, George D., M.D., Chief Medical Officer, Overland Park Regional Medical Center, Overland Park, KS, p. A243

STANBRO, Dave
  Director Human Resources, Arnot Ogden Medical Center, Elmira, NY, p. A426
  Director Human Resources, Ira Davenport Memorial Hospital, Bath, NY, p. A422
  Director Human Resources, St. Joseph's Hospital, Elmira, NY, p. A426

STANDARD, Heather, Chief Nursing Officer, Northeast Georgia Medical Center Barrow, Winder, GA, p. A163

STANDEFFER, Luke, Administrator, Northport Medical Center, AL, p. A24

STANDER, Paul, M.D., Chief Medical Officer, Banner - University Medical Center Phoenix, Phoenix, AZ, p. A33

STANDIFORD, Steven B., M.D., Chief of Staff, Cancer Treatment Centers Of America-Eastern Regional Medical Center, Philadelphia, PA, p. A534

STANDLEE, Cynthia, R.N., Chief Nursing Officer, Estes Park Medical Center, Estes Park, CO, p. A100

STANEK, Janet, Senior Vice President and Chief Operating Officer, Stormont Vail Health, Topeka, KS, p. A246

STANFORD, Brion, Director Human Resources, New Orleans East Hospital, New Orleans, LA, p. A275

STANFORD, Tracy
  Director Human Resources, Baylor All Saints Medical Center At Fort Worth, Fort Worth, TX, p. A604
  Director Human Resources, The Heart Hospital Baylor Denton, Denton, TX, p. A599
  Director Human Resources, The Heart Hospital Baylor Plano, Plano, TX, p. A629

STANGE, Della G, Director Human Resources, Rancho Springs Medical Center, CA, p. A74

STANGE KOLO, Tracey
  Vice President Human Resources, Upmc St. Margaret, Pittsburgh, PA, p. A538
  Vice President, Human Resources, Upmc Mercy, Pittsburgh, PA, p. A538

STANGL, Abbey, Chief Financial Officer, Cass County Memorial Hospital, Atlantic, IA, p. A217

STANHILL, Keith, Chief Human Resources Officer, Saint Francis Hospital, Memphis, TN, p. A576

STANIC, Steve M
  Vice President and Chief Information Officer, Mississippi Baptist Medical Center, Jackson, MS, p. A348
  Vice President and Chief Information Officer, Select Specialty Hospital - Belhaven, Jackson, MS, p. A348

STANKO, Shelley, M.D., Chief Medical Officer, Saint Joseph London, London, KY, p. A255

STANLEY, Cassandra, Director Personnel, Eastern Shore Hospital Center, Cambridge, MD, p. A290

STANLEY, Donna K, R.N., Chief Nursing Officer, Ut Health Henderson, Henderson, TX, p. A609

STANLEY, James, Interim Chief Operating Officer, Galesburg Cottage Hospital, Galesburg, IL, p. A183

STANLEY, Jennifer, M.D., Chief Medical Officer, St. Vincent Jennings Hospital, North Vernon, IN, p. A213

STANLEY, Mark, Director Fiscal Services, Middle Tennessee Mental Health Institute, Nashville, TN, p. A577

STANSBERY, Shawn, M.D., Chief of Staff, Wood County Hospital, Bowling Green, OH, p. A472

STANSBURY, Bill, Chief Financial Officer, Jackson Parish Hospital, Jonesboro, LA, p. A269

STANSBURY, Kevin M., Chief Executive Officer, Lincoln Community Hospital And Nursing Home, Hugo, CO, p. A102

STANSKI, Vickie, Financial Manager, Parkview Lagrange Hospital, Lagrange, IN, p. A210

STANTON, Lowell, Chief Financial Officer, Houston Methodist Sugar Land Hospital, Sugar Land, TX, p. A637

STANTON, Melanie, R.N.
Chief Nursing Officer, Sycamore Shoals Hospital, Elizabethton, TN, p. A569
Chief Nursing Officer, Unicoi County Memorial Hospital, Erwin, TN, p. A569

STANTON, Mike, D.O., Medical Director, Baylor Medical Center At Trophy Club, Trophy Club, TX, p. A640

STANUSH, Chris, Director Information Management, San Antonio State Hospital, San Antonio, TX, p. A634

STANZIONE, Dominick, President and Chief Executive Officer, Brookdale Hospital Medical Center, New York (Includes All Hospitals Located Within The Five Boroughs), NY, p. A431

STAPLES, Janet, Vice President Human Resources, South Central Regional Medical Center, Laurel, MS, p. A349

STAPLES-EVANS, Helen, Chief Nursing Officer, LLUCH, Loma Linda University Children's Hospital, Loma Linda, CA, p. A64

STAPLETON, Carla J., Director Human Resources, Paul B. Hall Regional Medical Center, Paintsville, KY, p. A259

STAPLETON, Kathleen, Chief Financial Officer, Baptist Easley Hospital, Easley, SC, p. A552

STAPLETON, Michael, President and Chief Executive Officer, F. F. Thompson Hospital, Canandaigua, NY, p. A424

STAPLETON, Robert, Director Administration, Richard H. Hutchings Psychiatric Center, Syracuse, NY, p. A443

STARA, Jeanne, R.N., MSN, Chief Nursing Officer, Alliancehealth Ponca City, Ponca City, OK, p. A505

STARCK, Rebecca, M.D., Chief, Cleveland Clinic Avon Hospital, Avon, OH, p. A471

STARK, David, Chief Financial Officer, Lancaster Rehabilitation Hospital, Lancaster, PA, p. A528

STARK, David A., FACHE
President and Chief Executive Officer, Unitypoint Health - Methodist West Hospital, IA, p. A221
President and Chief Executive Officer, Unitypoint Health-Iowa Lutheran Hospital, Des Moines, IA, p. A221
President and Chief Executive Officer, Younker Memorial Rehabilitation Center, IA, p. A221

STARK, Donna, Director Human Resources, Baylor Regional Medical Center At Grapevine, Grapevine, TX, p. A607

STARK, Patricia Ann, R.N., CNO, Florida Hospital Deland, Deland, FL, p. A121

STARK, Sharon, R.N., Manager Clinical Information Systems, Methodist Mckinney Hospital, Mckinney, TX, p. A623

STARK, Steve, Chief Executive Officer, Orchard Hospital, Gridley, CA, p. A61

STARKEBAUM, Gordon, M.D., Chief of Staff, Veterans Affairs Puget Sound Health Care System-American Lake Division, WA, p. A677

STARKES, Henry, M.D., Medical Director, Orchard Hospital, Gridley, CA, p. A61

STARLING, James F, M.D., Chief Medical Officer, Sovah Health-Danville, Danville, VA, p. A657

STARLING, Susan, President and Chief Executive Officer, Mercy Health - Marcum And Wallace, Irvine, KY, p. A254

STARNES, Gregory D., Chief Executive Officer, Fayette County Hospital, Vandalia, IL, p. A197

STARR, Candie, Chief Executive Officer, Lincoln County Health System, Fayetteville, TN, p. A569

STARR, Kay, Manager Human Resources, Vernon Memorial Healthcare, Viroqua, WI, p. A704

STASI, Joseph P, Chief Financial Officer, Saint Luke's East Hospital, Lee's Summit, MO, p. A363

STASKIN, David, Director Human Resources, Healthsouth Rehabilitation Hospital Of Mechanicsburg, Mechanicsburg, PA, p. A531

STASNEY, Amy, R.N., Chief Executive Officer, Cornerstone Hospital Of Houston - Bellaire, TX, p. A643

STASTNY, Mark, Vice President and Chief Information Officer, Children's Hospital And Medical Center, Omaha, NE, p. A388

STATEN, Gary L., Chief Executive Officer, Trace Regional Hospital, Houston, MS, p. A347

STATES, Chuck, Director Information Systems, Punxsutawney Area Hospital, Punxsutawney, PA, p. A539

STATON, Donna, Chief Information Officer, Fauquier Hospital, Warrenton, VA, p. A667

STATON, John, Senior Vice President Operations, Olathe Medical Center, Olathe, KS, p. A242

STATON, Paul
Chief Financial Officer, Mattel Children's Hospital, CA, p. A69
Chief Financial Officer, Ucla Medical Center-Santa Monica, Santa Monica, CA, p. A89

STATZ, Chris, Chief Financial Officer, Lincoln Prairie Behavioral Health Center, Springfield, IL, p. A196

STATZ, Linda Taplin, System Director, Employee Experience, Ssm Health St. Mary's Hospital, Madison, WI, p. A696

STAUB, David, M.D., Chief of Staff, Coteau Des Prairies Hospital, Sisseton, SD, p. A564

STAUB, Julie, Chief Human Resources Officer, Jackson South Community Hospital, FL, p. A130

STAUDINGER, Michael, M.D., Chief of Staff, Theda Care Medical Center - Wild Rose, Wild Rose, WI, p. A706

STAUFFER, Karla, Executive Director People Resources, Billings Clinic, Billings, MT, p. A373

STAUFFER, Keith, Regional Chief Information Officer, Chi St Alexius Health Carrington Medical Center, Carrington, ND, p. A464

STAUSS, Laura, Director of Human Resources, Huggins Hospital, Wolfeboro, NH, p. A401

STAVELEY, Melinda, President and Chief Executive Officer, Cottage Rehabilitation Hospital, CA, p. A88

STAWNIAK, Laura, R.N., Chief Nursing Executive, Memorial Community Hospital And Health System, Blair, NE, p. A382

STEAD, William, Associate Vice Chancellor Health Affairs, Director Informatics Center and Chief Strategy and Information Officer, Vanderbilt Psychiatric Hospital, TN, p. A578

STEADHAM, Emily, Administrator, Grove Hill Memorial Hospital, Grove Hill, AL, p. A19

STEADHAM, Mark B., President and Chief Executive Officer, Morris Hospital & Healthcare Centers, Morris, IL, p. A190

STEAGALL, Susan, Vice President Information Services, Children's Hospital Of Richmond At Vcu, VA, p. A665

STEARNS, Charles, Area Information Officer, Kaiser Foundation Hospital Westside Medical Center, Hillsboro, OR, p. A513

STEARNS, Zebediah, M.D., Chief of Staff, Acadian Medical Center, LA, p. A280

STEC, Julianne, Chief Operating Officer, Mercy Orthopedic Hospital Fort Smith, AR, p. A42

STECKEL, Cindy, Ph.D., R.N., Vice President Chief Nurse and Operations Executive, Scripps Memorial Hospital-La Jolla, La Jolla, CA, p. A63

STECKER, Tim, Chief Financial Officer, Kindred Hospital-Denver, Denver, CO, p. A99

STEED, Robert A, Director Information Systems, Capital Regional Medical Center, Tallahassee, FL, p. A140

STEEL, Diana, Vice President Human Resources, West Hills Hospital And Medical Center, Los Angeles, CA, p. A70

STEELE, Anthony, M.D., Chief Medical Officer, Witham Health Services, Lebanon, IN, p. A210

STEELE, Chrys, Director Information Systems, Springs Memorial Hospital, Lancaster, SC, p. A555

STEELE, David, Vice President Chief Information Officer, Leesburg Regional Medical Center, Leesburg, FL, p. A128

STEELE, Erik N, D.O., Senior Vice President and Chief Medical Officer, Summa Saint Thomas Hospital, OH, p. A470

STEELE, Mark, M.D.
Chief Medical Officer, Truman Medical Center-Hospital Hill, Kansas City, MO, p. A362
Chief Medical Officer, Truman Medical Center-Lakewood, Kansas City, MO, p. A362

STEELE, Michael, M.D., Chief of Staff, Perry County Memorial Hospital, Perryville, MO, p. A366

STEELE, Robert, M.D., President, Mercy Orthopedic Hospital Springfield, MO, p. A370

STEELE, Sherri, Chief Nursing Officer, Providence Medford Medical Center, Medford, OR, p. A515

STEELE, Terry L, Vice President Finance and Chief Financial Officer, Holland Hospital, Holland, MI, p. A315

STEELE, Tina, Chief Executive Officer and Chief Financial Officer, Fairfax Community Hospital, Fairfax, OK, p. A499

STEELE, Wes, M.D., Chief of Staff, Fairmont Regional Medical Center, Fairmont, WV, p. A683

STEELMAN, Jeffrey, Director Information Systems, Lewisgale Hospital Alleghany, Low Moor, VA, p. A660

STEELY, Karen, Administrator, Murray Medical Center, Chatsworth, GA, p. A150

STEEN, Jon, Director Human Resources, Davis Medical Center, Elkins, WV, p. A682

STEENPORT, John, Information Systems Manager, Aspirus Ironwood Hospitals & Clinics, Inc., Ironwood, MI, p. A316

STEFFEN, Elizabeth, Director Information Technology, Seneca Healthcare District, Chester, CA, p. A54

STEFFEN, Lorri, Director of Nursing, Osage Beach Center For Cognitive Disorders, Osage Beach, MO, p. A366

STEFFENS, Aaron, Chief Operating Officer, Mercy Hospital Oklahoma City, Oklahoma City, OK, p. A503

STEFFIN, Renee, Chief Nursing Officer, Cuyuna Regional Medical Center, Crosby, MN, p. A330

STEFL, William, Director Information Systems, Mercy Health, Mercy Campus, MI, p. A319

STEGALL, Christopher A, Regional Chief Financial Officer and Chief Operating Officer, Promise Hospital Of Vicksburg, Vicksburg, MS, p. A354

STEGER, Elizabeth, FACHE, R.N., Chief Nursing Officer, Seton Medical Center Austin, Austin, TX, p. A586

STEGGE, Sherri, Director Human Resources, Kaiser Permanente Vallejo Medical Center, Vallejo, CA, p. A93

STEHMER, Marie F, Senior Director of Human Resources, Peacehealth Sacred Heart Medical Center At Riverbend, Springfield, OR, p. A518

STEICHEN, Barry L
Executive Vice President and Chief Operating Officer, Saint Francis Health System, Saint Francis Heart Hospital, OK, p. A509
Executive Vice President and Chief Operating Officer, Saint Francis Hospital South, Tulsa, OK, p. A509

STEICHEN, Elizabeth, Human Resources, Lewis And Clark Specialty Hospital, Yankton, SD, p. A565

STEICHEN, Terry, Business Officer, Lewis And Clark Specialty Hospital, Yankton, SD, p. A565

STEIGMAN, Don S
Chief Executive Officer, Holtz Children's Hospital, FL, p. A130
Chief Operating Officer, Jackson South Community Hospital, FL, p. A130

STEIGMEYER, Robert P., President and Chief Executive Officer, Concord Hospital, Concord, NH, p. A398

STEIMEL, Ronald, Executive Vice President and Chief Administrative Officer, Mercy Medical Center, Rockville Centre, NY, p. A442

STEIN, Brad, Chief Financial Officer, Wysong Campus, TX, p. A623

STEIN, Cathy, Chief Inpatient Services, Sagamore Children's Hospital Psychiatric Center, Dix Hills, NY, p. A425

STEIN, Eric H., FACHE, President, Cobleskill Regional Hospital, Cobleskill, NY, p. A424

STEIN, Keith L, M.D.
Chief Medical Officer, Baptist Medical Center Beaches, Jacksonville Beach, FL, p. A126
Senior Vice President Medical Affairs and Chief Medical Officer, Wolfson Children's Hospital, FL, p. A125

STEIN, Patrick, M.D., Clinical Director, Western New York Children's Hospital Psychiatric Center, West Seneca, NY, p. A446

STEIN, Paul, Chief Operating Officer, Mainegeneral Medical Center-Augusta Campus, ME, p. A282

STEIN, Richard, M.D., Chief Medical Officer, Bay Area Medical Center, Marinette, WI, p. A697

STEIN, Robert, M.D.
Vice President Medical Management, Advocate Hope Children's Hospital, IL, p. A191
Chief Executive Officer, Kindred Hospital Houston Medical Center, Houston, TX, p. A611

STEIN, Sandra, Chief Human Resources Management, Veterans Affairs Central California Health Care System, Fresno, CA, p. A60

STEIN, Sheldon J., President and Chief Executive Officer, Mt. Washington Pediatric Hospital, Baltimore, MD, p. A288

STEINBERG, James P, M.D., Chief Medical Officer, Emory University Hospital Midtown, Atlanta, GA, p. A146

STEINBLOCK, Matthew, Director Information Systems, Community Memorial Hospital, Syracuse, NE, p. A390

STEINER, Jeffrey T, Vice President Finance, Memorial Behavioral Health, MS, p. A346

STEINER, Scott, FACHE
Chief Executive Officer, Dmc - Detroit Receiving Hospital, Detroit, MI, p. A311
Chief Executive Officer, Dmc Hutzel Women's Hospital, MI, p. A311

STEINER, Thomas K., Interim Chief Executive Officer, Burke Medical Center, Waynesboro, GA, p. A163

STEINES, Brian D, Chief Financial Officer, Northeast Georgia Medical Center, Gainesville, GA, p. A154

STEINES, Jeanne, D.O., Medical Director, Connecticut Mental Health Center, New Haven, CT, p. A109

STEINGALL, Patricia, MS, R.N., R.N., MS, Vice President, Patient Care Services, Hunterdon Medical Center, Flemington, NJ, p. A405

STEINHART, Curt, M.D., Chief Medical Officer, Presbyterian Tower, OK, p. A504

STEINKE, Paul, D.O.
President and Chief Executive Officer, Cgh Medical Center, Sterling, IL, p. A197
Chief Financial Officer, Providence Holy Cross Medical Center, Mission Hills, CA, p. A72

STEINKRUGER, Roger W., Chief Executive Officer, Community Hospital-Fairfax, Fairfax, MO, p. A359

STEINMANN, Robin, Administrative Director Human Resources, Anderson Hospital, Maryville, IL, p. A188

STEINSICK, Bill, M.D., Chief Medical Staff, Asante Ashland Community Hospital, Ashland, OR, p. A511

STEINWACHS, Lynn R., Vice President and Administrator, Methodist Hospital Union County, Morganfield, KY, p. A258

STELL, G Max, M.D., Medical Director, Minden Medical Center, Minden, LA, p. A274

STELLER, Wayne, Vice President Chief Nursing Officer, The Acadia Hospital, Bangor, ME, p. A282

STELLING, Jonathan, M.D., Vice President Medical Affairs, Chi Health St. Mary'S, Nebraska City, NE, p. A387

STELTENPOHL, Robert, Vice President, Southern Indiana Rehabilitation Hospital, New Albany, IN, p. A212

STELTER, Carolyn, M.D., Chief of Staff, Ridgeview Le Sueur Medical Center, Le Sueur, MN, p. A333

STELZER, Jason, Director Human Resources, Ssm Health St. Clare Hospital-Baraboo, Baraboo, WI, p. A689

STENCEL, Lindsay, Chief Administrative Officer, Baptist Memorial Hospital-Collierville, Collierville, TN, p. A568

STENDEL-FREELS, Robin, Coordinator Human Resources, Amg Specialty Hospital-Albuquerque, Albuquerque, NM, p. A415

STENERSON, David, Vice President and Chief Financial Officer, Osf Saint Anthony Medical Center, Rockford, IL, p. A195

STENGER, George S., D.O., Chief of Staff, Okeene Municipal Hospital, Okeene, OK, p. A502

STENGER, John D, Acting Associate Director, Charlie Norwood Veterans Affairs Medical Center, Augusta, GA, p. A147

STENGER, Mike, Interim Chief Executive Officer, Western Arizona Regional Medical Center, Bullhead City, AZ, p. A28

STENGER, Sandra, Acting Chief Human Resources, Cincinnati Veterans Affairs Medical Center, Cincinnati, OH, p. A474

STENNETT, Kevin T, M.D., Chief of Staff, W. J. Mangold Memorial Hospital, Lockney, TX, p. A620

STENSON, James, Chief Information Officer, Syracuse Veterans Affairs Medical Center, Syracuse, NY, p. A444

STENSRUD, Kirk A., Chief Executive Officer, Glacial Ridge Health System, Glenwood, MN, p. A332

STEPANSKY, David, M.D., Chief Medical Officer, Phoenixville Hospital, Phoenixville, PA, p. A537

STEPHENS, Carrie, Director Information Technology, Saunders Medical Center, Wahoo, NE, p. A391

STEPHENS, Debra, Director Personnel, Riverland Medical Center, Ferriday, LA, p. A267

STEPHENS, Eddy, Vice President Information Technology, Rotary Rehabilitation Hospital, AL, p. A20

STEPHENS, Ellen, Vice President Information Services, Mercy Hospital Oklahoma City, Oklahoma City, OK, p. A503

STEPHENS, Heather, Director of Information Health Technology, Ssm Health St. Clare Hospital-Baraboo, Baraboo, WI, p. A689

STEPHENS, Jeremy, Vice President and Chief Human Resources Officer, St. Joseph Mercy Chelsea, Chelsea, MI, p. A309

STEPHENS, Kathy, Vice President of Patient Care, Decatur County Memorial Hospital, Greensburg, IN, p. A205

STEPHENS, Larry
Chief Financial Officer, Collingsworth General Hospital, Wellington, TX, p. A643
Chief Financial Officer, Kimble Hospital, Junction, TX, p. A616
Chief Financial Officer, Sabine County Hospital, Hemphill, TX, p. A609
Chief Financial Officer, Schleicher County Medical Center, Eldorado, TX, p. A603

STEPHENS, Linda, R.N., Chief Nursing Officer, Memorial Hermann Northeast, Humble, TX, p. A615

STEPHENS, Maria, Director Human Resources, Education and Occupational Health and Wellness, Vcu Health Community Memorial Hospital, South Hill, VA, p. A666

STEPHENS, Mike, Chief Financial Officer, Nch North Naples Hospital, FL, p. A132

STEPHENS, Norman F.
Interim Chief Executive Officer, Vista Medical Center East, Waukegan, IL, p. A198
Interim Chief Executive Officer, Vista Medical Center West, Waukegan, IL, p. A198

STEPHENS, Peggy, M.D., Superintendent and Medical Director, Madison State Hospital, Madison, IN, p. A210

STEPHENS, Royce
Chief Financial Officer, Riverton Hospital, Riverton, UT, p. A650
Director Finance, Intermountain Medical Center, Murray, UT, p. A648

STEPHENS, Ruth M., MSN, R.N., Chief Executive Officer, Pawnee County Memorial Hospital And Rural Health Clinic, Pawnee City, NE, p. A389

STEPHENS, Terry A., Chief Executive Officer, River Park Hospital, Huntington, WV, p. A684

STEPHENSON, Ben, M.D., Chief of Staff, Phillips County Hospital, Phillipsburg, KS, p. A244

STEPHENSON, Darlene
Chief Executive Officer, Bon Secours Mary Immaculate Hospital, Newport News, VA, p. A662
Vice President Operations, Bon Secours Mary Immaculate Hospital, Newport News, VA, p. A662

STEPHENSON, Melinda, Chief Executive Officer, Kingwood Medical Center, Kingwood, TX, p. A618

STEPHENSON, Michelle, R.N., Executive Vice President & Chief Operations Officer, Ann & Robert H. Lurie Children's Hospital Of Chicago, Chicago, IL, p. A176

STEPHENSON, Ron, Chief Operating Officer, Long Island Community Hospital, Patchogue, NY, p. A440

STEPHENSON, Steve R., M.D., President and Chief Operating Officer, Unitypoint Health - Blank Children's Hospital, IA, p. A221

STEPP, Dana, Human Resources Officer, Mercy Health - Marcum And Wallace, Irvine, KY, p. A254

STEPP, Keri, Human Resources Director, Mckenzie Regional Hospital, Mckenzie, TN, p. A574

STERBACH, Maureen, Vice President Human Resources, St. Joseph's Westgate Medical Center, AZ, p. A34

STERN, Barry, President and Chief Executive Officer, New York Community Hospital, New York (Includes All Hospitals Located Within The Five Boroughs), NY, p. A434

STERNBERG, Paul, M.D., Professor and Chairman, Vanderbilt Psychiatric Hospital, TN, p. A578

STERUD, Brian, Chief Information Officer, West Campus, NE, p. A387

STESNEY-RIDENOUR, Christine, FACHE, President, Beaumont Hospital - Trenton, Trenton, MI, p. A324

STETTHEIMER, Timothy, Vice President and Chief Information Officer, St. Vincent's Birmingham, Birmingham, AL, p. A15

STEVEN, Eva, Chief Financial Officer, Roosevelt General Hospital, Portales, NM, p. A418

STEVENS, Ann Marie., R.N., Chief Executive Officer, Tyler Memorial Hospital., Tunkhannock, PA, p. A542

STEVENS, Belinda, Chief Executive Officer, Access Hospital Dayton, Dayton, OH, p. A480

STEVENS, Ben, Chief Financial Officer, Buchanan County Health Center, Independence, IA, p. A224

STEVENS, Bryan N
Chief Financial Officer, Field Memorial Community Hospital, Centreville, MS, p. A344
Interim Chief Financial Officer, Copiah County Medical Center, Hazlehurst, MS, p. A347

STEVENS, Chris E, Chief Information Officer, Billings Clinic, Billings, MT, p. A373

STEVENS, Dori, Chief Executive Officer, Sutter Delta Medical Center, Antioch, CA, p. A50

STEVENS, Emily, Chief Nursing Officer, Mat-Su Regional Medical Center, Palmer, AK, p. A27

STEVENS, Eric, Chief Executive Officer, Florida Hospital Lake Placid, FL, p. A139

STEVENS, Jeffrey, Executive Vice President and Chief Human Resource Officer, Jefferson Methodist Hospital, PA, p. A536

STEVENS, Kelly, Manager Human Resources, St. Joseph Memorial Hospital, Murphysboro, IL, p. A190

STEVENS, Lisa, Chief Clinical Officer and Chief Operating Officer, Vibra Hospital Of Northern California, Redding, CA, p. A80

STEVENS, Lori A, MSN, R.N., Interim Chief Nursing Officer, Verde Valley Medical Center, Cottonwood, AZ, p. A29

STEVENS, Mark, M.D.
Chief Medical Staff, Marion General Hospital, Columbia, MS, p. A345
Director Human Resources, St. Luke's Jerome, Jerome, ID, p. A169

Senior Director Human Resources, St. Luke's Magic Valley Medical Center, Twin Falls, ID, p. A172

STEVENS, Rick, President, Christian Hospital, Saint Louis, MO, p. A368

STEVENS, Rodney, East Central Region Director of Nursing Practice, Indiana University Health Blackford Hospital, Hartford City, IN, p. A206

STEVENS, Scot, Assistant Administrator, Salt Lake Regional Medical Center, Salt Lake City, UT, p. A650

STEVENS, Shelbourn, President and Chief Operating Officer, Novant Health Brunswick Medical Center, Bolivia, NC, p. A448

STEVENS, Susan
Director Human Resources, The Healthcenter, Kalispell, MT, p. A377
Human Resources Strategic Business Partner, Transylvania Regional Hospital, Brevard, NC, p. A448
Information Technology Specialist, Fallon Medical Complex, Baker, MT, p. A373

STEVENS, Tammy, Chief Executive Officer, Madison County Memorial Hospital, Madison, FL, p. A128

STEVENS, Tom, Director Personnel, Unc Rockingham Health Care, Eden, NC, p. A451

STEVENS, Vicki, Human Resources Executive, Northfield Hospital And Clinics, Northfield, MN, p. A336

STEVENSON, Angelia, Manager Finance, Tuscaloosa Veterans Affairs Medical Center, Tuscaloosa, AL, p. A24

STEVENSON, Brett, Controller, Kindred Hospital Northland, Kansas City, MO, p. A361

STEVENSON, John, M.D., Senior Vice President and Chief Medical Officer, South Shore Hospital, South Weymouth, MA, p. A304

STEVERSON, Denise, Director Human Resources, Dorminy Medical Center, Fitzgerald, GA, p. A153

STEVES, Sonja
Senior Vice President Human Resources and Marketing, Randall Children's Hospital, OR, p. A516
Senior Vice President Human Resources, Legacy Mount Hood Medical Center, Gresham, OR, p. A513
Senior Vice President Human Resources, Legacy Salmon Creek Medical Center, Vancouver, WA, p. A679
Vice President Human Resources and Marketing, Legacy Meridian Park Medical Center, Tualatin, OR, p. A518
Vice President Marketing, Rehabilitation Institute Of Oregon, OR, p. A516

STEWARD, Rachel, Director Human Resources, Hillcrest Hospital - South, Tulsa, OK, p. A508

STEWARD, Todd E., FACHE, Chief Executive Officer, St. David's South Austin Medical Center, Austin, TX, p. A587

STEWART, Anne, Vice President and Chief Nursing Officer, Beaumont Hospital - Grosse Pointe, Grosse Pointe, MI, p. A315

STEWART, Brandi, R.N., Vice President and Chief Nursing Officer, Integris Grove Hospital, Grove, OK, p. A499

STEWART, Caroline, Chief Nursing Officer, Citrus Memorial Health System, Inverness, FL, p. A125

STEWART, Christine R., FACHE, Chief Executive Officer, Russellville Hospital, Russellville, AL, p. A23

STEWART, Clint
Chief Financial Officer, Blue Ridge Medical Center - Yancey Campus, NC, p. A461
Regional Director of Finance East, Mcdowell Hospital, Marion, NC, p. A456

STEWART, Daniel, M.D., Vice President Medical Affairs, Main Campus, MI, p. A308

STEWART, David K, Senior Vice President and Chief Financial Officer, Mercy Medical Center, Canton, OH, p. A473

STEWART, Douglas, PsyD, President, Unity Hospital, Rochester, NY, p. A441

STEWART, Greg, Chief Executive Officer, Wellstone Regional Hospital, Jeffersonville, IN, p. A208

STEWART, Hedda, Director Human Resources, Neshoba County General Hospital, Philadelphia, MS, p. A352

STEWART, Inez, Vice President, Boston Children's Hospital, Boston, MA, p. A296

STEWART, Jane, Director Information Services, Jfk Medical Center, Atlantis, FL, p. A117

STEWART, Jessi, Director Human Resources, Rockford Center, Newark, DE, p. A113

STEWART, John, Director Finance, Burke Rehabilitation Hospital, White Plains, NY, p. A446

STEWART, Kelly, Director of Human Resources, Community Mental Health Center, Lawrenceburg, IN, p. A210

STEWART, Kendall, M.D., Chief Medical Officer, Southern Ohio Medical Center, Portsmouth, OH, p. A489

STEWART, Larry D., Jr, Chief Medical Officer and Vice President, Medical Affairs, Perry Hospital, Perry, GA, p. A158

STEWART, Marc, M.D., Vice President and Medical Director, Seattle Cancer Care Alliance, Seattle, WA, p. A676

STEWART, Marty, Chief Information Officer, Anmed Health Women's And Children's Hospital, SC, p. A549

STEWART, Michael K., Chief Executive Officer, Navarro Regional Hospital, Corsicana, TX, p. A595

STEWART, Michele, R.N., Chief Operating Officer, St. John's Rehabilitation Center, MO, p. A361

STEWART, Pamela, Director of Nursing, Washington County Regional Medical Center, Sandersville, GA, p. A160

STEWART, Patty, Chief Financial Officer, Gonzales Healthcare Systems, Gonzales, TX, p. A607

STEWART, Paul, M.D., Medical Director, Kindred Hospital-Flamingo, NV, p. A393

STEWART, Paul R., President and Chief Executive Officer, Sky Lakes Medical Center, Klamath Falls, OR, p. A514

STEWART, Ronnelle, Chief Human Resources Officer, Brookwood Baptist Medical Center, Birmingham, AL, p. A14

STEWART, Roxane, Chief Financial Officer, Magnolia Regional Medical Center, Magnolia-Columbia County, AR, p. A45

STEWART, Russell L, D.O., Medical Director, Braxton County Memorial Hospital, Gassaway, WV, p. A683

STEWART, Scott, M.D.
Vice President Medical Management, Good Samaritan Medical Center - Cushing Campus, MA, p. A298
Manager Information Services, Rochelle Community Hospital, Rochelle, IL, p. A194

STEWART, Stephen, M.D., Vice President Medical Affairs, Ssm Health St. Mary's Hospital - Jefferson City, Jefferson City, MO, p. A360

STEWART, Tim, Chief Information Officer, Abbeville Area Medical Center, Abbeville, SC, p. A549

STIEKES, Robert, Chief Operating Officer, Wilkes-Barre General Hospital, PA, p. A544

STIFF, Patrick, Coordinator Information Technology, Madison County Memorial Hospital, Madison, FL, p. A128

STIFFARM, Garland, Chief Executive Officer, Blackfeet Community Hospital, Saint Mary, MT, p. A379

STIFFARM, Kevin J., Chief Executive Officer, Indian Health Service Hospital, Rapid City, SD, p. A563

STIKELEATHER, Janie, Director Marketing and Community Relations, Davis Regional Medical Center, Statesville, NC, p. A461

STILES, Geoffrey, M.D., Chief Medical Officer, Sharp Memorial Hospital, San Diego, CA, p. A84

STILGENBAUER, Mike, Director Finance, Marymount Hospital, Garfield Heights, OH, p. A483

STILLER, Brian G., Director Medical Center, Veterans Affairs Western New York Healthcare System-Buffalo Division, Buffalo, NY, p. A424

STILLWELL, Michelle, Chief Financial Officer, Claiborne Memorial Medical Center, Homer, LA, p. A268

STILSON, Dwain, Chief Financial Officer, Mosaic Life Care, Saint Joseph, MO, p. A367

STILTNER, Wanda B., Director Human Resources, Buchanan General Hospital, Grundy, VA, p. A659

STIMPSON, Dan, Chief Financial Officer, Banner Del E. Webb Medical Center, Sun City West, AZ, p. A36

STIMPSON, Jared, Chief Financial Officer, Central Carolina Hospital, Sanford, NC, p. A460

STIMSON, Judi
Chief Financial Officer, Desert Regional Medical Center, Palm Springs, CA, p. A77
Chief Financial Officer, Palm Beach Gardens Medical Center, Palm Beach Gardens, FL, p. A135

STIMSON, Michael, Chief Nursing Officer, Florida Hospital Waterman, Tavares, FL, p. A142

STINGLEY, Susan D, Chief Nursing Officer, Kearny County Hospital, Lakin, KS, p. A239

STINNETT, Thomas, M.D., Chief Medical Officer, Conway Behavioral Health Hospital, Conway-Faulkner County, AR, p. A40

STINSON, Katy, Director Information Services, Alliancehealth Durant, Durant, OK, p. A498

STINSON, Martha, Director of Information Technology, Palms West Hospital, Loxahatchee, FL, p. A128

STINSON, Michael, Human Resources Coordinator, Select Specialty Hospital-Durham, Durham, NC, p. A451

STIPE, Christopher R., FACHE, Chief Executive Officer, Manhattan Surgical, Manhattan, KS, p. A240

STITH, Melanie
Vice President Human Resources, Roper St. Francis Mount Pleasant Hospital, Mount Pleasant, SC, p. A555
Vice President Human Resources, Roper St. Francis, Charleston, SC, p. A550

STITT, Bobby, R.N., Administrator, Mercy Hospital Logan County, Guthrie, OK, p. A499

STOBER, Karick, Chief Financial Officer, Pam Specialty Hospital Of Covington, Covington, LA, p. A266

STOCK, Constance, M.D., Chief Medical Officer, Sturgis Regional Hospital, Sturgis, SD, p. A564

STOCK, Greg K., FACHE, Chief Executive Officer, Thibodaux Regional Medical Center, Thibodaux, LA, p. A280

STOCK, Lesa, R.N., Chief Clinical Officer, Citizens Memorial Hospital, Bolivar, MO, p. A355

STOCK, Neil, Director Technology and Facilities, Mercy Regional Medical Center, Durango, CO, p. A99

STOCKARD, Herbert, M.D., Chief Medical Officer, Mercy St. Anne Hospital, Toledo, OH, p. A491

STOCKER, Trena, Chief Nursing Executive, Mercy Health - Marcum And Wallace, Irvine, KY, p. A254

STOCKHAUSEN, Christopher, Chief Financial Officer, Upmc Mckeesport, Mckeesport, PA, p. A531

STOCKS, Gregory, M.D., Chief of Staff, Texas Orthopedic Hospital, Houston, TX, p. A613

STOCKSTILL, Mark, R.N., Administrator, Highland Community Hospital, Picayune, MS, p. A352

STOCKTON, David Bradley, Chief Operating Officer, Redmond Regional Medical Center, Rome, GA, p. A159

STOCKTON, Kevin, Chief Executive Officer, Northwest Medical Center, Tucson, AZ, p. A37

STOCKTON, Linda, Interim Chief Executive Officer, Seven Rivers Regional Medical Center, Crystal River, FL, p. A120

STOCKTON, Rick, Chief Executive Officer, Promise Hospital Of Louisiana - Bossier City Campus, LA, p. A278

STODDARD, Mark R., Chief Executive Officer, Central Valley Medical Center, Nephi, UT, p. A648

STOFFERSON, Laura, Chief Nursing Officer, Shenandoah Medical Center, Shenandoah, IA, p. A229

STOGSDILL, Don, Chief Medical Officer, St. Vincent Heart Center, Indianapolis, IN, p. A208

STOGSDILL, Vicki, R.N., MSN, Chief Nursing Officer, Healthpark, KY, p. A258

STOJAKOVICH, Edward R
Chief Financial Officer, Dominion Hospital, Falls Church, VA, p. A657
Chief Financial Officer, Reston Hospital Center, Reston, VA, p. A664

STOKER, Rick, Director Management Information Systems, Tristar Horizon Medical Center, Dickson, TN, p. A569

STOKER, Vicki, Chief Nursing Officer, University Behavioral Health Of Denton, Denton, TX, p. A599

STOKES, Elia, Chief Financial Officer, Medical City Fort Worth, Fort Worth, TX, p. A605

STOKES, Eric, Vice President of Operations, Decatur County Memorial Hospital, Greensburg, IN, p. A205

STOKES, Jeb, Chief Executive Officer, Crestwyn Behavioral Health, Memphis, TN, p. A575

STOKES, Laura
Director Human Resources, Roosevelt Warm Springs Rehabilitation And Specialty Hospitals - Ltac, Warm Springs, GA, p. A162
Director Human Resources, Roosevelt Warm Springs Rehabilitation Hospital - Rehab, Warm Springs, GA, p. A162

STOKES, Letha, Chief Executive Officer, Medical Arts Hospital, Lamesa, TX, p. A618

STOKES, Priscilla, MS, R.N., Vice President Patient Care and Hospital Operations, Unitypoint Health - St. Lukes's Sioux City, Sioux City, IA, p. A230

STOKES, Richard W, CPA, Jr, Chief Financial Officer, Gila Regional Medical Center, Silver City, NM, p. A420

STOKES, Tina, Manager Human Resources, Regency Hospital Of Florence, Florence, SC, p. A553

STOKOE, Shelby
Chief Financial Officer, Providence Holy Family Hospital, Spokane, WA, p. A678
Senior Director Finance, Sacred Heart Children's Hospital, WA, p. A678

STOLDT, Garrick J, Vice President and Chief Financial Officer, The Children's Hospital At Saint Peter's University, NJ, p. A408

STOLLAR, Joseph Randall, Chief Information Officer, Johnson County Hospital, Tecumseh, NE, p. A391

STOLLER, Theo, Chief Executive Officer, Jacobson Memorial Hospital Care Center, Elgin, ND, p. A465

STOLS, Natalie, Interim Chief Executive Officer, Amg Physical Rehabilitation Hospital, Covington, LA, p. A266

STOLTMAN, Erin, Administrator, Essentia Health Ada, Ada, MN, p. A327

STOLTZ, Kyla, Vice President Human Resources, Centerpoint Medical Center, Independence, MO, p. A360

STOLYAR, Edward B., D.O., Divisional Chief Informational Officer, New York Community Hospital, New York (Includes All Hospitals Located Within The Five Boroughs), NY, p. A434

STOMBERG, LeAnn, Chief Financial Officer, Minneapolis Veterans Affairs Health Care System, Minneapolis, MN, p. A335

STONE, Connie, R.N., Chief Nursing Officer, Medstar Montgomery Medical Center, Olney, MD, p. A293

STONE, Dan, Senior Community Chief Executive Officer, Hazard Arh Regional Medical Center, Hazard, KY, p. A253

STONE, Darlene, Vice President Human Resources, Baptist Hospital, Pensacola, FL, p. A136

STONE, Duncan, D.D.S., Chief Medical Staff, Whitfield Medical Surgical Hospital, MS, p. A354

STONE, Jeanette, Vice President Operations, Baptist Health South Florida, South Miami Hospital, Miami, FL, p. A130

STONE, Jill, Manager Human Resources, Lynn County Hospital District, Tahoka, TX, p. A638

STONE, Joanna, Chief Nursing Officer, Livingston Hospital And Healthcare Services, Salem, KY, p. A260

STONE, Levi Ross, R.N., Chief Nursing Officer and Chief Operating Officer, Odessa Regional Medical Center, Odessa, TX, p. A626

STONE, Loren, Chief Executive Officer, Endless Mountain Health Systems, Montrose, PA, p. A532

STONE, Matt, President and Chief Executive Officer, St. Luke's Baptist Hospital, TX, p. A632

STONE, Patricia, R.N., MSN, Senior Vice President Operations and Chief Nursing Officer, Adventist Health White Memorial, Los Angeles, CA, p. A66

STONE, Richard, Manager, Technical Services, Uhs Chenango Memorial Hospital, Norwich, NY, p. A438

STONE, Robert, President and Chief Executive Officer, City Of Hope's Helford Clinical Research Hospital, Duarte, CA, p. A57

STONE, Ronald W, Regional Chief Human Resource Officer, Zucker Hillside Hospital, NY, p. A433

STONE, Sam, Operations Administrator, Essentia Health-Virginia, Virginia, MN, p. A341

STONE, Susan, R.N., Ph.D.
Senior Vice President and Chief Executive Officer, Sharp Coronado Hospital And Healthcare Center, Coronado, CA, p. A55
Director Human Resources, Claiborne Medical Center, Tazewell, TN, p. A580

STONE, Terry, Chief Financial Officer and Chief Information Officer, Willapa Harbor Hospital, South Bend, WA, p. A678

STONE, Thomas J., FACHE, Chief Executive Officer, Doctor's Memorial Hospital, Perry, FL, p. A136

STONE, Timothy D., Jr, President and Chief Executive Officer, Decatur Memorial Hospital, Decatur, IL, p. A180

STONEBURNER, Marianna, R.N., Chief Nursing Officer, Upmc Jameson, New Castle, PA, p. A533

STONER, Jamey, Chief Financial Officer, Frye Regional Medical Center-South Campus, NC, p. A454

STONER, Steve, Chief Information Officer, Richard L. Roudebush Veterans Affairs Medical Center, Indianapolis, IN, p. A207

STONESTREET, Jana S, R.N., Ph.D., Chief Nursing Officer, Tulane-Lakeside Hospital, LA, p. A276

STOOPS, Stephens, M.D., Chief Medical Officer, Osceola Regional Medical Center, Kissimmee, FL, p. A126

STOPPER, Jim, CPA, Chief Financial Officer, Evangelical Community Hospital, Lewisburg, PA, p. A530

STOPPLER, Maria, Chief Executive Officer, Granite County Medical Center, Philipsburg, MT, p. A378

STOREY, Kam, Director Human Resources, Sebastian River Medical Center, Sebastian, FL, p. A139

STOREY, Kevin L., Vice President and Administrator, Baptist Health Medical Center-Stuttgart, Stuttgart-Arkansas County, AR, p. A49

STOREY, Paul, FACHE, President and Chief Executive Officer, Helen Keller Hospital, Sheffield, AL, p. A23

STORFJELL, Judith, Ph.D., R.N., Senior Vice President and Chief Nursing Officer, Loma Linda University Heart & Surgical Hospital, CA, p. A64

STORM, Dave, Director Business Support, Hshs St. Anthony's Memorial Hospital, Effingham, IL, p. A181

STORR, Katie, Director of Human Resources, Whitfield Medical Surgical Hospital, MS, p. A354

STORRS, Elaine, Chief Nursing Officer, Springfield Regional Medical Center, Springfield, OH, p. A490

STORTO, David E., President, Spaulding Rehabilitation Hospital, Charlestown, MA, p. A299

STOTLER, Sherry, R.N., MSN, Chief Nursing Officer, Arizona Children's Center, AZ, p. A33

STOTTLEMYRE, Georgan L., Chief Human Relations Officer, Northern Inyo Hospital, Bishop, CA, p. A53

STOTTS, Vicki, Coordinator Human Resources, Flint River Community Hospital, Montezuma, GA, p. A157

STOUGH, Joe, Interim President, Rotary Rehabilitation Hospital, AL, p. A20

STOUT, Amanda, Chief Nursing Officer, Minneola District Hospital, Minneola, KS, p. A241

STOUT, Bess, Director Human Resources, Tennova Healthcare-Lafollette Medical Center, La Follette, TN, p. A573

STOUT, Cindy, R.N., Chief Executive Officer, El Paso Children's Hospital, El Paso, TX, p. A601

STOUT, Deana
Vice President Financial Services, Medstar Good Samaritan Hospital, Baltimore, MD, p. A288
Vice President, Finance, Medstar Union Memorial Hospital, Baltimore, MD, p. A288

STOUT, Jeffrey, MSN, R.N., Chief Operating Officer, St. Francis Medical Center, Lynwood, CA, p. A70

STOUT, Kimberly Dawn, CPHRM, Chief Nursing Officer and Chief Operating Officer, Mcalester Regional Health Center, Mcalester, OK, p. A501

STOUT, Patsy, Director Personnel, Richland Parish Hospital, Delhi, LA, p. A267

STOUT-TORRES, Sherri, R.N., Chief Nursing Executive, Sutter Maternity And Surgery Center Of Santa Cruz, Santa Cruz, CA, p. A89

STOVALL, Henry, President, Sacred Heart Hospital Pensacola, Pensacola, FL, p. A136

STOVALL, Richard G, Senior Vice President Fiscal Services and Chief Financial Officer, Southern Regional Medical Center, Riverdale, GA, p. A159

STOVALL, Shella D., R.N., Acting Director, Veterans Affairs Salt Lake City Health Care System, Salt Lake City, UT, p. A651

STOVER, Benny, Vice President Finance, Mercy Hospital Rogers, Rogers-Benton County, AR, p. A48

STOVER, George M., Chief Executive Officer, Hospital District No 1 Of Rice County, Lyons, KS, p. A240

STOVER, Nick, Director Information Systems, Plateau Medical Center, Oak Hill, WV, p. A685

STOVER, Patricia A, Administrator Nursing, Doylestown Hospital, Doylestown, PA, p. A524

STOVER, Raymond
President and Chief Executive Officer, Midmichigan Medical Center-Clare, Clare, MI, p. A310
President and Chief Executive Officer, Midmichigan Medical Center-Gladwin, Gladwin, MI, p. A313

STOVER, Theresa, Chief Human Resource Officer, Edgefield County Hospital, Edgefield, SC, p. A552

STOVER, Tim, M.D., Interim Chief Executive Officer, Borgess-Pipp Hospital, MI, p. A316

STOWE, Mary
Senior Vice President and Chief Nursing Officer, Children's Medical Center Dallas, Dallas, TX, p. A596
Senior Vice President and Chief Nursing Officer, Children's Medical Center Plano, Plano, TX, p. A628

STOWELL, Dana A, Chief Information Officer, Mccurtain Memorial Hospital, Idabel, OK, p. A500

STOWMAN, Amber, Controller, Chi Lisbon Health, Lisbon, ND, p. A467

STOY, Gale, Manager Information Systems, Mid Coast Hospital, Brunswick, ME, p. A283

STOYANOFF, Pamela
Executive Vice President and Chief Operating Officer, Methodist Charlton Medical Center, Dallas, TX, p. A597
Executive Vice President and Chief Operating Officer, Methodist Dallas Medical Center, Dallas, TX, p. A597

STRABEL, Elizabeth, M.D., Chief Medical Staff, Divine Savior Healthcare, Portage, WI, p. A701

STRACHAN, Ronald
Chief Information Officer, Mclaren Bay Region-West Campus, MI, p. A308
Chief Information Officer, Mclaren Flint, Flint, MI, p. A312

STRACK, Kirk, Vice President and Chief Financial Officer, Clark Memorial Hospital, Jeffersonville, IN, p. A208

STRADER, Lynn, Chief Financial Officer, Johnston-Willis Hospital, VA, p. A664

STRADER, Yvonne M, Chief Nursing Officer, Providence St. Mary Medical Center, Walla Walla, WA, p. A680

STRADI, Silvia, Chief Nursing Officer, Palms West Hospital, Loxahatchee, FL, p. A128

STRADTMAN, Jackie, Director Human Resources, Chi St. Joseph Health Burleson Hospital, Caldwell, TX, p. A591

STRAHAN, Greg
Chief Operating Officer, Healthpark, KY, p. A258
Interim Chief Executive Officer, Healthpark, KY, p. A258

STRAIN, Donna, Director Human Resources, Ray County Memorial Hospital, Richmond, MO, p. A366

STRAIN, Lynn, R.N., MSN, Chief Nursing Officer, Slidell Memorial Hospital, Slidell, LA, p. A279

STRAMOWSKI, Mallary, Chief Human Resources Officer, Select Specialty Hospital-Madison, Madison, WI, p. A696

STRAND, Eric, Director Information Services, North Florida Regional Medical Center, Gainesville, FL, p. A123

STRANGE, John, President and Chief Executive Officer, St. Luke's Hospital, Duluth, MN, p. A331

STRASH, Shawn G., Chief Executive Officer, Arise Austin Medical Center, Austin, TX, p. A585

STRASSER, Michael, Vice President and Chief Financial Officer, Mercy Medical Center Merced-Dominican Campus, CA, p. A72

STRASSNER III, Lawrence F, Ph.D., FACHE, R.N., MS, Senior Vice President Operations and Chief Nursing Officer, Medstar Franklin Square Medical Center, Baltimore, MD, p. A288

STRATON, Sam, Chief Nursing Officer, Saint Thomas West Hospital, Nashville, TN, p. A577

STRATTON, James
Regional Vice President Finance, Ssm Health St. Mary's Hospital - Audrain, Mexico, MO, p. A364
Vice President Finance, Ssm Health St. Mary's Hospital - Jefferson City, Jefferson City, MO, p. A360

STRATTON, Joseph, FACHE, Chief Executive Officer, Geary Community Hospital, Junction City, KS, p. A238

STRATTON, Mary, Director Human Resources, River Park Hospital, Huntington, WV, p. A684

STRATTON, Tracie, Chief Nursing Officer, Los Alamos Medical Center, Los Alamos, NM, p. A418

STRAUGHAN, Janet, Manager Human Resources, Highlands Rehabilitation Hospital, El Paso, TX, p. A602

STRAUGHAN, John, Director Information Technology, Wallowa Memorial Hospital, Enterprise, OR, p. A512

STRAUMAN, Karen S, R.N., Chief Nurse Executive, Kaiser Permanente Fresno Medical Center, Fresno, CA, p. A59

STRAUMANIS, John P., M.D., Vice President Medical Affairs and Chief Medical Officer, University Of Maryland Rehabilitation & Orthopaedic Institute, Baltimore, MD, p. A289

STRAUSBAUGH, Andrew, Chief Administrative Officer, Norton Brownsboro Hospital, KY, p. A256

STRAUSS, Alan
Chief Financial Officer, Carondelet Holy Cross Hospital, Nogales, AZ, p. A32
Chief Financial Officer, Carondelet St. Joseph's Hospital, Tucson, AZ, p. A37

STRAUSS, Karen, Chief Human Resources Officer, Promedica Flower Hospital, Sylvania, OH, p. A491

STRAWN, Keith A, Vice President Human Resources, Cape Fear Hospital, NC, p. A462

STRAWSER, Debbie A, Director Human Resources, Lindner Center Of Hope, Mason, OH, p. A486

STRAYHORN, Shelly, R.N.
Chief Nursing Officer, Wadley Regional Medical Center At Hope, Hope-Hempstead County, AR, p. A43
Chief Nursing Officer, Wadley Regional Medical Center, Texarkana, TX, p. A639

STRBICH, Steve, D.O., Chief of Staff, Spectrum Health Ludington Hospital, Ludington, MI, p. A318

STREATER, Vivian
Chief Nursing Officer and Co-Acting Chief Executive Officer, Broughton Hospital, Morganton, NC, p. A457
Co-Acting Chief Executive Officer, Broughton Hospital, Morganton, NC, p. A457

STRECKER, Kevin, President, St. Joseph Campus, KS, p. A248

STRECKER, Robert, M.D., Chief of Staff, Colorado River Medical Center, Needles, CA, p. A75

STREDNEY, Thomas, Chief Human Resources Management Service, Aleda E. Lutz Veterans Affairs Medical Center, Saginaw, MI, p. A322

STREET, Rex, Senior Vice President and Chief Financial Officer, Alamance Regional Medical Center, Burlington, NC, p. A448

STREET, Scott, Chief Executive Officer, Medical Center Of South Arkansas, El Dorado-Union County, AR, p. A41

STREETER, Alan W, Chief Financial Officer, Beatrice Community Hospital And Health Center, Beatrice, NE, p. A382

STREETER, Matthew, Chief Financial Officer, Southwest Health Center Nursing Home, WI, p. A701

STREETER, Maxine, Administrator, Reception And Medical Center, Lake Butler, FL, p. A127

STREETER, Robert, M.D., Vice President Medical Affairs, Mercy Medical Center Merced-Dominican Campus, CA, p. A72

STREICH, Rebecca, Manager Human Resources and Education Manager, Hutchinson Health, Hutchinson, MN, p. A333

STREIT, Loren, Director Human Resources, Geary Community Hospital, Junction City, KS, p. A238

STREJC, Irene T, M.P.H., R.N., Vice President, Nursing, Methodist Richardson Medical Center, Richardson, TX, p. A630

STRICKER, Sean, Chief Executive Officer, Regency Hospital Of Minneapolis, Golden Valley, MN, p. A332

STRICKER, Steven, M.D., Physician in Chief, Kaiser Permanente Vallejo Medical Center, Vallejo, CA, p. A93

STRICKLAND, Barrie, Chief Financial Officer, Ucsf Medical Center Mission Bay, CA, p. A86

STRICKLAND, David, Area Information Officer, Kaiser Foundation Mental Health Center, CA, p. A67

STRICKLAND, Lee, Regional Director Information Technology, Park Ridge Health, Hendersonville, NC, p. A454

STRICKLAND, Morris S, Chief Financial Officer, Helen Keller Hospital, Sheffield, AL, p. A23

STRICKLER, David
Chief Financial Officer, Nexus Specialty Hospital The Woodlands, The Woodlands, TX, p. A640
Chief Financial Officer, Nexus Specialty Hospital, Shenandoah, TX, p. A635

STRICKLER, Stephen Todd, Director of Nursing, Sistersville General Hospital, Sistersville, WV, p. A687

STRICKLING, Keith
Chief Accountant, Jay Hospital, Jay, FL, p. A126
Chief Financial Officer, Atmore Community Hospital, Atmore, AL, p. A14

STRIEBICH, Shannon, Chief Executive Officer, St. Joseph Mercy Oakland, Pontiac, MI, p. A321

STRIKE, Helen J, R.N., President, Unity Hospital, MN, p. A330

STRING, Sherrie
Senior Vice President Human Resources, Hackensack Meridian Health Bayshore Community Hospital, Holmdel, NJ, p. A406
Senior Vice President Human Resources, Hackensack Meridian Health Ocean Medical Center, Brick Township, NJ, p. A403
Senior Vice President Human Resources, Hackensack Meridian Health Riverview Medical Center, Red Bank, NJ, p. A411

STRINGFELLOW, Grace, M.D., Chief of Staff, Veterans Affairs Nebraska-Western Iowa Health Care System, Omaha, NE, p. A389

STRINGOS, Gust, M.D., Medical Staff Director, Redington-Fairview General Hospital, Skowhegan, ME, p. A286

STRIPLIN, Elizabeth, Chief Financial Officer, Rehabilitation Hospital Of Southern New Mexico, Las Cruces, NM, p. A418

STRITTMATTER, Julie, Director Human Resources, Karl And Esther Hoblitzelle Memorial Hospital, TX, p. A596

STROBEL, Deb, R.N., Chief Nursing Officer, Russell Regional Hospital, Russell, KS, p. A245

STROBEL, Jane, Vice President and Chief Financial Officer, Mercy Regional Medical Center, Durango, CO, p. A99

STROBEL, Rand
Regional Chief Information Officer, Information Technology Services, Harrison Medical Center, Bremerton, WA, p. A669
Regional Chief Information Officer, St. Francis Hospital, Federal Way, WA, p. A672
Vice President Information Technology and Compliance, St. Joseph Medical Center, Tacoma, WA, p. A679

STRODE, Marc, Chief Executive Officer, Methodist Stone Oak Hospital, San Antonio, TX, p. A633

STROH, Rhonda, Chief Human Resources Officer, Community Memorial Hospital, Redfield, SD, p. A563

STROHECKER, Sharon, R.N., MSN, Vice President Clinical Operations and Chief Nursing Officer, Penn State Health St. Joseph - Downtown Campus, PA, p. A539

STROHLA, Patti, R.N., Chief Nursing Officer, Franklin Regional Hospital, Franklin, NH, p. A399

STROM, Lisa, Director Information Systems, North Big Horn Hospital District, Lovell, WY, p. A709

STROMBERG, Audrey, Administrator, Roosevelt Medical Center, Culbertson, MT, p. A374

STRONG, David, Chief Financial Officer/Vice President Finance, Cox Medical Center Branson, Branson, MO, p. A356

STRONG, Melissa D, Chief Nursing Officer, Mason General Hospital And Family Of Clinics, Shelton, WA, p. A677

STRONG, Patricia, Chief Financial Officer, Cumberland River Hospital, Celina, TN, p. A566

STRONG, Tanya, Manager Information Technology, Harney District Hospital, Burns, OR, p. A511

STROSS, Daniel
Chief Information Officer, Genesys Regional Medical Center, Grand Blanc, MI, p. A313
Chief Information Officer, St. Joseph Health System, Tawas City, MI, p. A324
Chief Information Officer, St. Mary's Of Michigan, Saginaw, MI, p. A322

STROTHER, James, Site Director Information Technology Systems, Mercy Medical Center - West Lakes, IA, p. A221

STROTHKAMP, Brad, Chief Information Systems, Lakeland Behavioral Health System, Springfield, MO, p. A370

STROUCKEN, Christian, Chief Operating Officer, Carney Hospital, Boston, MA, p. A296

STROUD, Justin, Chief Financial Officer, Merit Health Central, Jackson, MS, p. A348

STROUD, Teresa, Chief Financial Officer, Salem Township Hospital, Salem, IL, p. A195

STROUP, Jeff, Chief Operating Officer, Oklahoma State University Medical Center, Tulsa, OK, p. A508

STROUSE, Thomas, M.D., Medical Director and Professor of Clinical Psych, Stewart & Lynda Resnick Neuropsychiatric Hospital At Ucla, Los Angeles, CA, p. A70

STRUB, Lisa, Chief Operating Officer, Centennial Peaks Hospital, Louisville, CO, p. A104

STRUYK, Douglas A., CPA, President and Chief Executive Officer, Christian Health Care Center, Wyckoff, NJ, p. A414

STRZELECKI, Sarah, Ed.D., R.N., Chief Nursing Officer, Phoenixville Hospital, Phoenixville, PA, p. A537

STRZEMPKO, Stanley, M.D., Vice President Medical Affairs and Chief Medical Officer, Baystate Noble Hospital, Westfield, MA, p. A305

STUART, Danna, M.D., Chief Medical Officer, Newman Memorial Hospital, Shattuck, OK, p. A506

STUART, Jimmy D., Chief Executive Officer, Cornerstone Hospital Of Oklahoma-Shawnee, Shawnee, OK, p. A506

STUART, Philip J., Administrator and Chief Executive Officer, Tomah Memorial Hospital, Tomah, WI, p. A704

STUART, Robin, Chief Executive Officer, Morrill County Community Hospital, Bridgeport, NE, p. A382

STUBBS, Don, Vice President Human Resources, Candler Hospital, Savannah, GA, p. A160

STUBBS, Kay, Chief Nursing Officer, Northwest Medical Center, Tucson, AZ, p. A37

STUBITSCH, Brian, M.D., Chief Medical Officer, Edgerton Hospital And Health Services, Edgerton, WI, p. A692

STUCKY, Nancy, Director Human Resources and Public Relations, Kingman Community Hospital, Kingman, KS, p. A238

STUCZYNSKI, Joseph, Assistant Administrator Finance and Support, Memorial Hospital Pembroke, Pembroke Pines, FL, p. A135

STUDEBAKER, Shelly
Director Management Information Systems, Clinch Memorial Hospital, Homerville, GA, p. A155
Manager Human Resources, Clinch Memorial Hospital, Homerville, GA, p. A155

STUDER, Tim, President Medical Staff, Perham Health, Perham, MN, p. A337

STUDLEY, Jason A., FACHE, President, Sentara Halifax Regional Hospital, South Boston, VA, p. A666

STUENKEL, Kurt, FACHE, President and Chief Executive Officer, Floyd Medical Center, Rome, GA, p. A159

STUEVE, Angela, M.D., Chief Medical Officer, Nemaha Valley Community Hospital, Seneca, KS, p. A245

STUEVE, Jo W.
Executive Vice President and Co-Chief Operating Officer, Children's Mercy Hospital Kansas City, Kansas City, MO, p. A361
Executive Vice President and Co-Chief Operating Officer, Children's Mercy Hospital Kansas, Overland Park, KS, p. A243
Interim Chief Executive Officer, Children's Mercy Hospital Kansas City, Kansas City, MO, p. A361

STUHLMILLER, Michael, Chief Financial Officer, Mann-Grandstaff Veterans Affairs Medical Center, Spokane, WA, p. A678

STULTS, Cynthia S., Executive Assistant and Human Resources Director, Rangely District Hospital, Rangely, CO, p. A105

STULTS, Kim, Director, Information Systems, Bellevue Hospital, Bellevue, OH, p. A472

STUMBO, Kathy, President, Arh Our Lady Of The Way, Martin, KY, p. A257

STUMME, Sarah, Director Human Resources, Owatonna Hospital, Owatonna, MN, p. A337

STUMP, Lisa, Interim Chief Information Officer, Yale-New Haven Psychiatric Hospital, CT, p. A110

STUMP, Tammie, R.N., Chief Executive Officer, Union County General Hospital, Clayton, NM, p. A416

STUMP, Veronica, Director of Nursing, Carilion Giles Community Hospital, Pearisburg, VA, p. A663

STUMPO, Barbara J, R.N., Vice President Patient Care Services, Griffin Hospital, Derby, CT, p. A107

STUNKARD, Jill, R.N., MSN, Associate Chief Nurse Executive and Interim Chief Nursing Officer, Einstein Medical Center Elkins Park, PA, p. A534

STURGEON, Jim, Area Director Human Resources, Kindred Hospital-Flamingo, NV, p. A393

STURGILL, Lori
Vice President Business Partnership, Mercy Hospital Fort Scott, Fort Scott, KS, p. A235
Vice President Business Partnership, Mercy Orthopedic Hospital Springfield, MO, p. A370

STURGIS, Gayle, R.N., Nurse Administrator, Heber Valley Medical Center, Heber City, UT, p. A647

STURGIS, Jonathan, Chief Financial Officer, Houston Methodist San Jacinto Hospital - Alexander, TX, p. A587

STURGIS, Paul
Chief Human Resource Officer, Sparrow Specialty Hospital, Lansing, MI, p. A317
Director Human Resources, Dmc - Rehabilitation Institute Of Michigan, Detroit, MI, p. A311
Vice President and Chief Human Resources Officer, Sparrow Children's Center, MI, p. A317

STURLER, Kelly, Chief Nursing Officer, Mckee Medical Center, Loveland, CO, p. A104

STURSA, Robin, Chief Information Officer, St. Vincent Charity Medical Center, Cleveland, OH, p. A477

STUWE, Shannon, Director of Nursing, Faulkton Area Medical Center, Faulkton, SD, p. A560

STYER, Brent
Chief Information Officer, Summers County Arh Hospital, Hinton, WV, p. A683
Director Information Technology, Whitesburg Arh Hospital, Whitesburg, KY, p. A261

STYLES, Kelly R, Vice President and Chief Information Officer, Connecticut Children's Medical Center, Hartford, CT, p. A108

STYRON, Stacie, Chief Nursing Officer, Lamb Healthcare Center, Littlefield, TX, p. A620

SUAREZ, Irma, Deputy Executive Director, Nyc Health + Hospitals / Woodhull, New York (Includes All Hospitals Located Within The Five Boroughs), NY, p. A436

SUAREZ, Lauren, Chief Executive Officer, Kentfield Rehabilitation And Specialty Hospital, Kentfield, CA, p. A62

SUAREZ, Orlando, Director Information Technology, Larkin Community Hospital, South Miami, FL, p. A139

SUBIA, Corina, Director Human Resources, Ward Memorial Hospital, Monahans, TX, p. A624

SUBLER, Jeffrey R., Vice President Support Services, Wayne Healthcare, Greenville, OH, p. A483

SUBLETTE, Elizabeth, Director Finance, Providence Willamette Falls Medical Center, Oregon City, OR, p. A515

SUBRAMANIAN, Aarti, Vice President and Chief Financial Officer, Psychiatric Institute Of Washington, Washington, DC, p. A116

SUCATO, Daniel J, M.D., MS, Chief of Staff, Texas Scottish Rite Hospital For Children, Dallas, TX, p. A598

SUCHER, Therese O, Senior Vice President Operations, Southern Regional Medical Center, Riverdale, GA, p. A159

SUDAK, Mariellena, R.N., MSN, Vice President and Chief Nursing Officer, Palomar Medical Center, Escondido, CA, p. A57

SUDBURY, Russ, M.D., President Medical Staff, Ascension Sacred Heart Hospital, Tomahawk, WI, p. A704

SUDDUTH, Anthony G., CPA, Interim Chief Executive Officer, Southwest Health System, Cortez, CO, p. A98

SUDICKY, Mary, Chief Financial Officer, St. Mary Medical Center, Hobart, IN, p. A206

SUDOLCAN, Joseph, M.D., Medical Director, Reagan Memorial Hospital, Big Lake, TX, p. A589

SUEHS, JoAnne, Manager Human Resources, Chapman Global Medical Center, Orange, CA, p. A76

SUGAR, Bev, Associate Administrator and Director Human Resources, Inova Mount Vernon Hospital, Alexandria, VA, p. A655

SUGDEN, Elizabeth, M.D., Chief Medical Officer, St. Luke's Jerome, Jerome, ID, p. A169

SUGG, Amy, Director Human Resources, Scott Regional Hospital, Morton, MS, p. A351

SUGGS, Heather, Manager Human Resources, Jay Hospital, Jay, FL, p. A126

SUHR, Nancy, Manager Human Resources, Pender Community Hospital, Pender, NE, p. A389

SUITTER, Marie, Chief Financial Officer, The Acadia Hospital, Bangor, ME, p. A282

SUKENIK, Richard, CPA, Vice President Finance and Chief Financial Officer, Chan Soon-Shiong Medical Center, Windber, PA, p. A545

SUKIN, Debra F., Ph.D., Regional Senior Vice President and Chief Executive Officer, Houston Methodist The Woodlands Hospital, The Woodlands, TX, p. A640

SUKSI, Eugene, Chief Executive Officer, Adventist Health Medical Center - Tehachapi Valley, Tehachapi, CA, p. A91

SULIT, Teresa, Director of Human Resources, Seven Hills Hospital, Henderson, NV, p. A393

SULLIVAN, Christopher, M.D., Chief Medical Officer, Centerpoint Medical Center, Independence, MO, p. A360

SULLIVAN, Daniel, D.O., Chief Medical Officer, Vice President Medical Administration, Elmhurst Hospital, Elmhurst, IL, p. A182

SULLIVAN, Danita S, R.N., Chief Nursing Officer, Touro Rehabilitation Center, LA, p. A276

SULLIVAN, David, Director Human Resources, Ohiohealth Doctors Hospital, Columbus, OH, p. A478

SULLIVAN, Denis, Chief Human Resources Management, Veterans Affairs Medical Center Hot Springs Campus, SD, p. A561

SULLIVAN, Donald, M.D., Medical Director, Healthsouth Rehabilitation Hospital Memphis-North, Memphis, TN, p. A575

SULLIVAN, Gregory, Manager Human Resources, Girard Medical Center, Girard, KS, p. A235

SULLIVAN, James, M.D., Chief Medical Officer, Butler Hospital, Providence, RI, p. A547

SULLIVAN, Jennie, Chief Executive Officer, Wray Community District Hospital, Wray, CO, p. A106

SULLIVAN, John, M.D., Chief Medical Officer, St. Clair Hospital, Pittsburgh, PA, p. A537

SULLIVAN, Katherine, Director, Human Resources, Moab Regional Hospital, Moab, UT, p. A647

SULLIVAN, Kathleen, M.D., Chief of Staff, Memorialcare, Saddleback Memorial Medical Center, Laguna Hills, CA, p. A63

SULLIVAN, Lowery, M.D., Chief Medical Officer, Northwestern Medical Center, Saint Albans, VT, p. A654

SULLIVAN, Martha, Chief Information Officer, Harrison Memorial Hospital, Cynthiana, KY, p. A251

SULLIVAN, Mary Patricia, R.N., MSN, Chief Nursing Officer, Overlook Medical Center, Summit, NJ, p. A412

SULLIVAN, Michael, M.D.
Chief Medical Officer, Northern Maine Medical Center, Fort Kent, ME, p. A284
Medical Director Emergency Services, Peacehealth Peace Island Medical Center, Friday Harbor, WA, p. A672

SULLIVAN, Michael Dean, M.D., Chief of Staff, Mercy Hospital El Reno, El Reno, OK, p. A498

SULLIVAN, Patrick L, Chief Operating Officer, St. John's Episcopal Hospital-South Shore, New York (Includes All Hospitals Located Within The Five Boroughs), NY, p. A437

SULLIVAN, Peter, Chief Executive Officer, Riverside Medical Center, Franklinton, LA, p. A267

SULLIVAN, Rita
Vice President Operations, Mayo Clinic Health System - Chippewa Valley In Bloomer, Bloomer, WI, p. A690
Vice President Operations, Mayo Clinic Health System - Northland In Barron, Barron, WI, p. A690

SULLIVAN, Staci, R.N., Chief Nursing Officer, Lane Regional Medical Center, Zachary, LA, p. A281

SULLIVAN, Theresa, Chief Executive Officer, Samaritan Healthcare, Moses Lake, WA, p. A673

SULLIVAN, Thomas, Vice President Fiscal Services, Harrington Hospital, Southbridge, MA, p. A304

SULLIVAN, William, Chief Financial Officer, Mount Auburn Hospital, Cambridge, MA, p. A298

SULLIVAN SMITH, Mary, R.N., MS, Senior Vice President, Chief Operating Officer and Chief Nursing Officer, New England Baptist Hospital, Boston, MA, p. A297

SULLIVANT, Laura, Area Chief Information Officer, Kaiser Permanente San Diego Medical Center, CA, p. A83

SULSER, Jamey, Director Human Resources, South Davis Community Hospital, Bountiful, UT, p. A646

SULU, Dorothy, Budget Analyst, Hopi Health Care Center, Keams Canyon, AZ, p. A30

SULZEN, Jessica, Director Human Resources, Belton Regional Medical Center, Belton, MO, p. A355

SUMMERLIN, Craig, Chief Human Resources Officer, Singing River Hospital, MS, p. A351

SUMMERLIN, Valerie, R.N., MS, Chief Nursing Officer, Adventist Healthcare Physical Health And Rehabilitation, Rockville, MD, p. A293

SUMMERS, Barbara L., Ph.D., R.N., Vice President Nursing Practice and Chief Nursing Officer, University Of Texas M.D. Anderson Cancer Center, Houston, TX, p. A614

SUMMERS, Curtis, Chief Executive Officer, Summit Medical Center, Edmond, OK, p. A498

SUMMERS, David A, Chief Financial Officer, Tristar Centennial Women's & Children'S, TN, p. A577

SUMMERS, Debra, Chief Nursing Officer, Calhoun-Liberty Hospital, Blountstown, FL, p. A118

SUMMERS, Jeff, M.D., Medical Director, Select Specialty Hospital-Knoxville, TN, p. A579

SUMMERS, Kelly, Chief Information Officer, Arizona Children's Center, AZ, p. A33

SUMMERS, Paul
Interim Chief Financial Officer, Uhs Delaware Valley Hospital, Walton, NY, p. A445
President and Chief Executive Officer, Uhs Delaware Valley Hospital, Walton, NY, p. A445

SUMMERS-MAIN, Theresa, R.N., Interim President, Genesis Medical Center, Silvis, Silvis, IL, p. A196

SUMMERSETT, James A., III, FACHE, Interim Chief Executive Officer, Nix Health Care System, San Antonio, TX, p. A633

SUMMERSON, Tonya, Chief Clinical Officer, Dallas County Hospital, Perry, IA, p. A228

SUMMERVILLE, Wendell, Chief Financial Officer, Bryce Hospital, Tuscaloosa, AL, p. A23

SUMNER, Donna, Director, Human Resources and Organizational Development, St. Joseph Medical Center, Kansas City, MO, p. A362

SUMNER, Jack R, Assistant Administrator Finance, Providence Newberg Medical Center, Newberg, OR, p. A515

SUMNER, John, Chief Executive Officer, Trigg County Hospital, Cadiz, KY, p. A250

SUMPTER, Nikki, Senior Vice President Human Resources, Trinity Springs Pavilion, TX, p. A604

SUMRA, K S, M.D., Chief of Staff, Pembina County Memorial Hospital And Wedgewood Manor, Cavalier, ND, p. A465

SUMRALL, Mary Ellen, Chief Nursing Officer, Baptist Memorial Hospital-Golden Triangle, Columbus, MS, p. A345

SUMTER, Rob
   Executive Vice President and Chief Operating Officer, Regional One Health, Memphis, TN, p. A575
   Executive Vice President and Chief Operation Officer, Regional One Health, Memphis, TN, p. A575

SUN RHODES, Neil, M.D., Chief Medical Officer, Blackfeet Community Hospital, Saint Mary, MT, p. A379

SUND, Lynn A.
   Chief Nurse Executive and Administrator, Saint Francis Heart Hospital, OK, p. A509
   Chief Nursing Executive, Saint Francis Hospital South, Tulsa, OK, p. A509
   Senior Vice President, Administrator and Chief Nursing Executive, Laureate Psychiatric Clinic And Hospital, Tulsa, OK, p. A508
   Senior Vice President, Chief Nurse Executive, Saint Francis Health System and Administrator, Saint Francis Hospital, Saint Francis Heart Hospital, OK, p. A509

SUNDARAMOORTHY, Abirammy, M.D., Chief Medical Officer, University Hospitals Conneaut Medical Center, Conneaut, OH, p. A479

SUNDBERG, Nita, Director Human Resources, Three Rivers Behavioral Health, West Columbia, SC, p. A558

SUNDBLOM, Karin, MSN, R.N., Chief Nursing Officer, Saint Luke's Cushing Hospital, Leavenworth, KS, p. A239

SUNDERLIN, Tammy, Director of Nursing, Auburn Community Hospital, Auburn, NY, p. A422

SUNDIN, Jon, M.D., Medical Director, The Orthopedic Specialty Hospital, Murray, UT, p. A648

SUNDRUD, Diane
   Director Human Resources, Essentia Health Fosston, Fosston, MN, p. A331
   Human Resource Service Partner, Essentia Health St. Mary's - Detroit Lakes, Detroit Lakes, MN, p. A330

SUNGA, Marcos N, M.D., Chief of Staff, Hardin County General Hospital, Rosiclare, IL, p. A195

SUNKAVALLE, Krishna, M.D., Chief Medical Officer, Hamlin Memorial Hospital, Hamlin, TX, p. A608

SUNQUIST, Joanne
   Chief Information Officer East Region, St. Joseph's Hospital, Saint Paul, MN, p. A339
   Chief Information Officer, Woodwinds Health Campus, Woodbury, MN, p. A342

SUNTAY, Renato, Chief Financial Officer, Meadville Medical Center, Meadville, PA, p. A531

SUNTHA, Mohan, M.D.
   President and Chief Executive Officer, University Of Maryland Hospital For Children, MD, p. A289
   President and Chief Executive Officer, University Of Maryland Medical Center Midtown Campus, Baltimore, MD, p. A289

SUNTRAPAK, Todd A., President and Chief Executive Officer, Valley Children's Healthcare, Madera, CA, p. A71

SUPPLEE, Linda, Chief Executive Officer, Select Specialty Hospital Of Southeast Ohio, Newark, OH, p. A488

SURBER, Randy, Chief Executive Officer, Florida Hospital Lake Placid, FL, p. A139

SURBER, Shannon, Chief Operating Officer, Peacehealth Sacred Heart Medical Center At Riverbend, Springfield, OR, p. A518

SURCOUF, Shelli, Chief Financial Officer, Georgetown Behavioral Health Institute, Georgetown, TX, p. A607

SURESH, Srinivasan, M.D., Chief Medical Information Officer, Children's Hospital Of Pittsburgh Of Upmc, Pittsburgh, PA, p. A537

SURGUY, Jean, Vice President, Chief Nursing Officer, Mile Bluff Medical Center, Mauston, WI, p. A697

SURL, Deepak, Chief Information Officer, Eastern New Mexico Medical Center, Roswell, NM, p. A419

SURO, Marta R Mercado, Chief Operating Officer, Mennonite General Hospital, Aibonito, PR, p. A712

SUROWITZ, Dale, Chief Executive, Providence Tarzana Medical Center, Los Angeles, CA, p. A69

SURRATT, Shawn, M.D., Chief of Staff, Memorial Hospital And Manor, Bainbridge, GA, p. A148

SURROCK, Lester, Chief Financial Officer, Mission Regional Medical Center, Mission, TX, p. A624

SUSI, Jeffrey L, President and Chief Executive Officer, Behavioral Health Center, FL, p. A143

SUSICK, Nancy, MSN, President, Beaumont Hospital - Troy, Troy, MI, p. A325

SUSIE-LATTNER, Debra, M.D., Vice President Medical Management, Advocate Condell Medical Center, Libertyville, IL, p. A188

SUSSMAN, Andrew, M.D., Chief Operating Officer, University Campus, MA, p. A306

SUSSMAN, Howard, M.D., Chief Medical Officer, St. Joseph Hospital, Bethpage, NY, p. A422

SUSTERICH, Tim, Chief Financial Officer and Chief Operating Officer, Memorial Healthcare, Owosso, MI, p. A320

SUTER, Brian, Chief Financial Officer, Mayo Clinic Health System In Fairmont, Fairmont, MN, p. A331

SUTER, Lorenzo, Chief Executive Officer, Dupont Hospital, Fort Wayne, IN, p. A203

SUTER, Mia, Chief Administration Officer, Healthpark, KY, p. A258

SUTHERLAND, Shea, Chief Financial Officer, Merit Health Madison, Canton, MS, p. A344

SUTIKA, John, President, Penn Highlands Dubois, Dubois, PA, p. A524

SUTKUS, Amy, M.D., Medical Staff President, Santiam Hospital, Stayton, OR, p. A518

SUTTLES, Mary Anne, Chief Nursing Officer, St. Francis Medical Center, Trenton, NJ, p. A413

SUTTON, Andrew
   Chief Human Resources Officer, Coatesville Veterans Affairs Medical Center, Coatesville, PA, p. A523
   Chief, Human Resources Management Service, James A. Haley Veterans' Hospital-Tampa, Tampa, FL, p. A141

SUTTON, Angie, Chief Financial Officer, Genoa Medical Facilities, Genoa, NE, p. A384

SUTTON, Elaine, Chief Information Officer, Pershing Memorial Hospital, Brookfield, MO, p. A356

SUTTON, Fred, M.D., Chief Medical Officer, Quentin Mease Hospital, TX, p. A611

SUTTON, Janet, D.O., Medical Director, Mclaren Bay Special Care, Bay City, MI, p. A308

SUTTON, Jeffrey, Chief Information Officer, Lexington Veterans Affairs Medical Center, Lexington, KY, p. A255

SUTTON, Jesse, Senior Vice President and Chief Financial Officer, Texas Health Huguley Hospital Fort Worth South, Burleson, TX, p. A591

SUTTON, Julie, Director Performance Improvement, State Hospital South, Blackfoot, ID, p. A167

SUTTON, Michele K., FACHE, President and Chief Executive Officer, North Oaks Medical Center, Hammond, LA, p. A268

SUTTON, Rhonda, Director Human Resources, Richland Hospital, Richland Center, WI, p. A702

SUTTON, Richard O., FACHE, Chief Executive Officer, Southeast Alabama Medical Center, Dothan, AL, p. A17

SUTTON, Thomas, Associate Director, Lake City Veterans Affairs Medical Center, FL, p. A123

SUTTON-WALLACE, Pamela, Chief Executive Officer, University Of Virginia Children's Hospital, VA, p. A656

SUVER, James A., FACHE, Chief Executive Officer, Ridgecrest Regional Hospital, Ridgecrest, CA, p. A80

SUZUKI, Daniel, M.D., Medical Director, Las Encinas Hospital, Pasadena, CA, p. A78

SVARC, Mackenzie, Finance Director, Friend Community Healthcare System, Friend, NE, p. A384

SVEC, David, M.D., Chief Medical Officer, Valley Memorial, CA, p. A78

SVENDSEN, Mark Deyo, M.D., Medical Director, Mayo Clinic Health System - Red Cedar In Menomonie, Menomonie, WI, p. A697

SWAGERTY, Jill, Director Human Resources, Union County General Hospital, Clayton, NM, p. A416

SWAIN, Art, Vice President Support Services, Joint Township District Memorial Hospital, Saint Marys, OH, p. A490

SWAINE, Richard P., President, Beaumont Hospital - Grosse Pointe, Grosse Pointe, MI, p. A315

SWANDAL, Dianne, R.N., MSN, Vice President Patient Care, St. Joseph Hospital, Bangor, ME, p. A282

SWANGER, Cae, Chief Information Officer, Riverside Community Hospital, Riverside, CA, p. A81

SWANGER, Carol, Chief Nursing Officer, Kansas Rehabilitation Hospital, Topeka, KS, p. A246

SWANK, Colleen, Chief Medical Officer, Altru Rehabilitation Center, ND, p. A466

SWANK, Georgia, Chief Nursing Officer, Ridge Behavioral Health System, Lexington, KY, p. A255

SWANSON, Julie, Coordinator Human Resources, Healthsouth Western Hills Regional Rehabilitation Hospital, Parkersburg, WV, p. A686

SWANSON, Kerry, Regional President, President Good Samaritan, Good Samaritan Regional Health Center, Mount Vernon, IL, p. A190

SWARTOUT, Paula, Human Resources Manager, Dickinson County Healthcare System, Iron Mountain, MI, p. A316

SWARTWOOD, Peggy, Assistant Vice President, Finance and Controller, Uhs Chenango Memorial Hospital, Norwich, NY, p. A438

SWARTWOOD, Philip, Director Information Systems, Grove City Medical Center, Grove City, PA, p. A526

SWARTZ, Edward, Chief Financial Officer, Spring Grove Hospital Center, Baltimore, MD, p. A289

SWARTZ, Michael J., FACHE, Interim Director, Veterans Affairs Western New York Healthcare System-Batavia Division, Batavia, NY, p. A422

SWAYNE, Angela, M.D., Chief Medical Officer, Piedmont Fayette Hospital, Fayetteville, GA, p. A153

SWEARINGEN, Angela, Vice President Finance, St. Mary's Medical Center, Huntington, WV, p. A684

SWEAT, Holli, Associate Administrator and Chief Nursing Officer, Memorial Satilla Health, Waycross, GA, p. A163

SWEAT, Kendra, Director Human Resources, Power County Hospital District, American Falls, ID, p. A167

SWEENEY, Janey, Chief Nursing Officer, Suncoast Behavioral Health Center, Bradenton, FL, p. A119

SWEENEY, Karen, MSN, R.N., Vice President, Chief Nursing Officer, Mercy Hospital Ada, Ada, OK, p. A495

SWEENEY, Michael
   Chief Informatics Officer, Jeanes Hospital, Philadelphia, PA, p. A535
   Chief Information Officer, Fox Chase Cancer Center-American Oncologic Hospital, Philadelphia, PA, p. A534

SWEENEY, Shaun, Vice President Patient Care Services, Carrier Clinic, Belle Mead, NJ, p. A402

SWEET, Mary, Administrator, Kiowa County Memorial Hospital, Greensburg, KS, p. A236

SWEET, Renae, Chief Financial Officer, Surprise Valley Health Care District, Cedarville, CA, p. A54

SWEET, Terrance J., Director Information Technology, Winnebago Mental Health Institute, Winnebago, WI, p. A706

SWEETAPPLE, Carolyn, Ph.D., R.N., CPA, Executive Director, South Oaks Hospital, Amityville, NY, p. A421

SWEHA, Amir, M.D., Vice President Medical Administration, Methodist Hospital Of Sacramento, Sacramento, CA, p. A82

SWEITZER, Gregory, Chief Medical Officer, Wright Patterson Medical Center, Wright, OH, p. A494

SWENSON, Daniel J., FACHE, Administrator, Centracare Health-Long Prairie, Long Prairie, MN, p. A333

SWENSON, Jennifer, President and Chief Executive Officer, Simi Valley Hospital, Simi Valley, CA, p. A90

SWENSON, Nena, Financial Manager, Tahoe Pacific Hospitals, NV, p. A397

SWENSON, Nina, Director Business Services, Newport Bay Hospital, Newport Beach, CA, p. A75

SWENSON, Paula C, R.N., Vice President and Chief Nursing Officer, St. Catherine Hospital, East Chicago, IN, p. A202

SWENSON, Warren, Chief Financial Officer, United Medical Rehabilitation Hospital - Gonzales, LA, p. A268

SWICK, Michael D., President and Chief Executive Officer, Lima Memorial Health System, Lima, OH, p. A484

SWIDERSKI, Tom, Chief Financial Officer, Orthopaedic Hospital Of Wisconsin - Glendale, Glendale, WI, p. A693

SWIFT, Brian M, Senior Administrator Plant Operations, Burke Rehabilitation Hospital, White Plains, NY, p. A446

SWIFT, David, Chief Human Resources Officer, Penn State Children's Hospital, PA, p. A527

SWIFT, Diane, Director Medical Records, I-70 Community Hospital, Sweet Springs, MO, p. A371

SWIFT, Kyle, Chief Executive Officer, Woodland Heights Medical Center, Lufkin, TX, p. A622

SWIFT, Nick, Chief Financial Officer, Maury Regional Hospital, Columbia, TN, p. A568

SWIFT, Patrick T., PhD, MBA, FACHE, Chief Executive Officer, Select Specialty Hospital-Northeast New Jersey, Rochelle Park, NJ, p. A411

SWIGER, Jared, Director Information Systems, Ashtabula County Medical Center, Ashtabula, OH, p. A471

SWIM, Doug, Chief Executive Officer, Memorial Hospital Of Texas County, Guymon, OK, p. A499

SWINDELL, Terry
   Chief Financial Officer, Camden General Hospital, Camden, TN, p. A566
   Controller, Bolivar General Hospital, Bolivar, TN, p. A566

SWINDLE, Patrick, Administrator, Ut Health Quitman, Quitman, TX, p. A629

SWINDLER, Diana, Chief Financial Officer, Tri Valley Health System, Cambridge, NE, p. A382

SWINGLE, Dale, Vice President Information Services, Troy Community Hospital, Troy, PA, p. A542

SWINT, Ken
Director Finance, Promedica Defiance Regional Hospital, Defiance, OH, p. A481
Vice President Finance and Chief Financial Officer, Promedica Fostoria Community Hospital, Fostoria, OH, p. A482

SWINT, Patricia
Director Information Management Systems, Promedica Defiance Regional Hospital, Defiance, OH, p. A481
Director Information Technology, St. Luke's Hospital, Maumee, OH, p. A486

SWISHER, Kay, Chief Nursing Officer, Ghs - Laurens County Memorial Hospital, SC, p. A550

SWISSHELM, Patricia, Acting Chief Fiscal Service, Lexington Veterans Affairs Medical Center, Lexington, KY, p. A255

SWOFFORD, William, M.D., Chief of Staff, Miller County Hospital, Colquitt, GA, p. A150

SWOPE, Jon D., Interim President, Mercy Orthopedic Hospital Springfield, MO, p. A370

SY, Annette
Chief Nursing Officer, Keck Hospital Of Usc, Los Angeles, CA, p. A68
Chief Nursing Officer, Usc Norris Comprehensive Cancer Center, Los Angeles, CA, p. A70

SYED, Imran, Manager Technology Information Services, Spectrum Health Zeeland Community Hospital, Zeeland, MI, p. A326

SYED, Mamoon
Vice President Human Resources, Children's Hospital Of Orange County, Orange, CA, p. A76
Vice President Human Resources, Rady Children's Hospital - San Diego, San Diego, CA, p. A84

SYKES, Angel, Director Human Resources, Memorial Hospital And Manor, Bainbridge, GA, p. A148

SYKES, Christina, Director Human Resources, Labette Health, Parsons, KS, p. A244

SYKES, Lee, Human Resources Director, Lifebrite Community Hospital Of Stokes, Danbury, NC, p. A450

SYKES, Lisa
Director Information Services, Carolinas Healthcare System Union, Monroe, NC, p. A457
IS/Communications Director, Carolinas Healthcare System Anson, Wadesboro, NC, p. A461
Manager, Information Services, Carolinas Healthcare System Northeast, Concord, NC, p. A450

SYKES, Rebecca S
Chief Information Officer, Mercy Health - Fairfield Hospital, Fairfield, OH, p. A482
Chief Information Officer, Mercy St. Anne Hospital, Toledo, OH, p. A491
Senior Vice President Resource Management, Chief Information Officer, Mercy Health - St. Charles Hospital, Oregon, OH, p. A488

SYLSBERRY, Angelia, Chief Nursing Officer, Pam Rehabilitation Hospital Of Tulsa, Tulsa, OK, p. A508

SYLVESTER, Joy L., Administrator, People Services, South Lake Hospital, Clermont, FL, p. A120

SYLVIA-HUTCHINSON, Doreen M, Vice President Operations and Chief Nurse Executive, Fairview Hospital, Great Barrington, MA, p. A300

SYNDERGAARD, Christy, Vice President Nursing, Cherokee Regional Medical Center, Cherokee, IA, p. A219

SYNNESTVEDT, Eric, Director Information Technology, Southside Regional Medical Center, Petersburg, VA, p. A664

SYPIEN, Troy
Director Information Technology and Systems, Medical City Children's Hospital, TX, p. A597
Director Information Technology and Systems, Tristar Skyline Madison Campus, TN, p. A577

SZABO, Sandor, M.D., Ph.D., M.P.H., Chief of Staff, Va Long Beach Healthcare System, Long Beach, CA, p. A65

SZAPOR, Ann, Vice President and Chief Nursing Officer, Memorial Hermann The Woodlands Hospital, TX, p. A612

SZCZEPANSKI, Bernadette S
Senior Vice President Human Resources, Centegra Hospital - Woodstock, Woodstock, IL, p. A198
Senior Vice President, Human Resources, Centegra Hospital-Huntley, IL, p. A189

SZCZUROWSKI, Richard, Director Human Resources, Norristown State Hospital, Norristown, PA, p. A533

SZEKELY, Lauraine, R.N., Senior Vice President, Patient Care, Northern Westchester Hospital, Mount Kisco, NY, p. A430

SZEWCZYK, Edwin, Chief Financial Officer, Wetzel County Hospital, New Martinsville, WV, p. A685

SZKLANY, Chelsea, Hospital Administrator, Southern Nevada Adult Mental Health Services, Las Vegas, NV, p. A394

SZOSTEK, Joshua, Chief Financial Officer, Specialty Hospital Jacksonville, Jacksonville, FL, p. A126

SZUMEL, Richard C., M.D., Chief Executive Officer, Union Hospital, Elkton, MD, p. A291

SZURA, Kathleen, R.N., Chief Nursing Officer, Healthsouth Bakersfield Rehabilitation Hospital, Bakersfield, CA, p. A52

SZYMANSKI, Michael, Chief Financial Officer, Doctors Hospital Of Manteca, Manteca, CA, p. A71

SZYSKA, Julie, Chief Executive Officer and Managing Director, Havenwyck Hospital, Auburn Hills, MI, p. A307

T

TAAFFE, Janette, Vice President, Human Resource, St. Luke's Hospital, Chesterfield, MO, p. A357

TABAK, Jeremy, M.D., President Medical Staff, Baptist Health South Florida, South Miami Hospital, Miami, FL, p. A130

TABB, Kevin, M.D., Chief Executive Officer, Beth Israel Deaconess Medical Center, Boston, MA, p. A296

TABIBI, Wasae S, M.D., President Medical Staff, Plaza Specialty Hospital, Houston, TX, p. A613

TABOADO, Ketty, Chief Financial Officer, Gladys Spellman Specialty Hospital And Nursing Center, Cheverly, MD, p. A290

TABOR, J. Britton, Executive Vice President, Chief Financial Officer, Willie D. Miller Eye Center, TN, p. A567

TABOR, Jeffrey, Director Human Resources, Jackson General Hospital, Ripley, WV, p. A686

TABOR, Susan, Interim Chief Executive Officer, Red River Behavioral Health System, Grand Forks, ND, p. A466

TABOR, Tammie, Chief Executive Officer, Vibra Rehabilitation Hospital Of Amarillo, Amarillo, TX, p. A583

TABORA, Knaya, Chief Operating Officer and Chief Nursing Officer, Colorado River Medical Center, Needles, CA, p. A75

TABUENCA, Arnold, M.D., Medical Director, Riverside University Health System-Medical Center, Moreno Valley, CA, p. A74

TACHIBANA, Charleen, R.N., Senior Vice President and Chief Nursing Officer, Virginia Mason Medical Center, Seattle, WA, p. A677

TACKITT, Sue, Chief Nursing Officer, Connally Memorial Medical Center, Floresville, TX, p. A603

TADURAN, Virgilio, M.D., Chief Medical Officer, Satanta District Hospital And Long Term Care, Satanta, KS, p. A245

TADYCH, Michael C., FACHE, Director, Veterans Affairs Puget Sound Health Care System-American Lake Division, WA, p. A677

TAFFE, Patrick, Vice President Information Services, North Memorial Health Hospital, Robbinsdale, MN, p. A338

TAFOYA, Debbie, Vice President and Chief Information Officer, Huntington Memorial Hospital, Pasadena, CA, p. A78

TAFT, Kenneth L, Executive Vice President and Chief Operating Officer, Children's Hospital At Bronson, MI, p. A317

TAFUR, Mario, M.D., Chief of Staff, St. Luke's Behavioral Health Center, Phoenix, AZ, p. A34

TAGGART, Travis, Director Information Technology, Rivervalley Behavioral Health Hospital, Owensboro, KY, p. A259

TAGGE, Gordon, M.D., President Medical Staff, Three Rivers Hospital, Brewster, WA, p. A670

TAHAN, Pamela S, Chief Operating Officer, Wellington Regional Medical Center, Wellington, FL, p. A143

TAHBO, Robin, Financial Management Officer, U.S. Public Health Service Indian Hospital, Parker, AZ, p. A32

TAHIR, Fahad
Chief Executive Officer, Saint Thomas Midtown Hospital, Nashville, TN, p. A577
Chief Executive Officer, Saint Thomas West Hospital, Nashville, TN, p. A577

TAILLEFER, Marguerite, M.D., Acting President Medical Staff, Sarah D. Culbertson Memorial Hospital, Rushville, IL, p. A195

TAKACS, Susan, Market Chief Operating Officer, Physicians Regional, FL, p. A132

TAKES, Kay, R.N.
President, Mercy Medical Center-Dubuque, Dubuque, IA, p. A222
President, Mercy Medical Center-Dyersville, Dyersville, IA, p. A222

TAKEUCHI, Susi, Chief Human Resources and Organization Development Officer, Mattel Children's Hospital, CA, p. A69

TALBERT, Adrienne, Interim Administrator, North Greenville Hospital, Travelers Rest, SC, p. A557

TALBERT, Bradley S., FACHE, President and Chief Executive Officer, Memorial Hospital Jacksonville, Jacksonville, FL, p. A125

TALBOT, Angela, Manager Human Resources, Hamilton County Hospital, Syracuse, KS, p. A246

TALBOT, Jack, Director, Human Resources, West Chester Hospital Surgical Center, OH, p. A493

TALBOT, Lisa, Director Human Resources, St. David's South Austin Medical Center, Austin, TX, p. A587

TALBOT, Tom, Chief Executive Officer, Community Mental Health Center, Lawrenceburg, IN, p. A210

TALBOTT, Ellen E, MSN, R.N., Vice President Patient Care Services, Mclaren Bay Region-West Campus, MI, p. A308

TALBOTT, Sarah, Chief Nursing Officer, Sanford Chamberlain Medical Center, Chamberlain, SD, p. A560

TALENTO, Rick, Senior Vice President and Chief Financial Officer, Providence Hospital, Washington, DC, p. A116

TALLEY, Cyndi, Director Information Systems, Tristar Greenview Regional Hospital, Bowling Green, KY, p. A250

TALLEY, Linda, MS, R.N., Vice President and Chief Nursing Officer, Children's National Health System, Washington, DC, p. A115

TALLEY, Rockey, M.D., Chief Medical Officer, Alliancehealth Midwest, Midwest City, OK, p. A501

TALLEY, Stephanie S.
Chief Human Resource Officer, The Hospitals Of Providence Sierra Campus, El Paso, TX, p. A602
Chief Human Resource Officer, The Hospitals Of Providence Transmountain Campus, El Paso, TX, p. A602
Director Human Resources, Baylor Scott & White Medical Center - Centennial, Frisco, TX, p. A606
Market Chief Human Resource Officer, Providence Children's Hospital, TX, p. A602

TALLEY, Tracey, Chief Financial and Information Officer, Pathways Treatment Center, MT, p. A377

TALLON, Joe, Vice President Finance, Salina Regional Health Center-Santa Fe Campus, KS, p. A245

TALLON, Richard, Chief Financial Officer, Jefferson County Hospital, Waurika, OK, p. A510

TAM, David A, M.D., FACHE, Chief Operating Officer, Providence Saint John's Health Center, Santa Monica, CA, p. A89

TAM, Paulina, Vice President of Operations, Tampa Community Hospital, Tampa, FL, p. A141

TAMANAHA, Nona, Vice President Human Resources, Queen's Medical Center - West Oahu, HI, p. A165

TAMAYO, Loree, Chief Executive Officer, Coon Memorial Hospital, Dalhart, TX, p. A595

TAMBURELLO, Leonardo, Chief Financial Officer, New York Community Hospital, New York (Includes All Hospitals Located Within The Five Boroughs), NY, p. A434

TAMMARO, Vincent, Chief Financial Officer, Yale-New Haven Psychiatric Hospital, CT, p. A110

TAMMINEN, John, M.D., President Medical Staff, Carilion Giles Community Hospital, Pearisburg, VA, p. A663

TAN, Bradford, M.D., Chief Medical Officer, Midwestern Regional Medical Center, Zion, IL, p. A198

TANAKA, Steven, Chief Information Officer, Pomerado Hospital, Poway, CA, p. A79

TANCREDO, Beth, Director Operations, South Florida Baptist Hospital, Plant City, FL, p. A136

TANDE, Brett, Chief Financial Officer, Santa Ynez Valley Cottage Hospital, Solvang, CA, p. A90

TANDON, Satwant, M.D., Director of Clinical Services, Oklahoma Forensic Center, Vinita, OK, p. A509

TANDY, Gary R, Chief Financial Officer, Pershing Memorial Hospital, Brookfield, MO, p. A356

TANDY, William C., Chief Information Officer, Upmc Pinnacle Hanover, Hanover, PA, p. A526

TANEBAUM, Cynthia, Director Information Services, Medstar Harbor Hospital, Baltimore, MD, p. A288

TANEJA, K. Singh, Chief Operating Officer, Saint Elizabeths Hospital, Washington, DC, p. A116

TANEY, Amy, Chief Human Resource Officer, Highland Hospital, Rochester, NY, p. A441

TANG, Francis, Chief Information Officer, Rancho Los Amigos National Rehabilitation Center, Downey, CA, p. A56

TANG, Shirley, R.N., Chief Nursing Officer, Monterey Park Hospital, Monterey Park, CA, p. A73

TANGEMAN, Todd
Chief Operating Officer and Chief Human Resource Officer, Newton Medical Center, Newton, KS, p. A242
Chief Operating Officer, Newton Medical Center, Newton, KS, p. A242

TANGUAY, Denis, Chief Information Officer, Central Maine Medical Center, Lewiston, ME, p. A284

TANJUAKIO, Robert, Chief Information Resources Management, Edward Hines, Jr. Veterans Affairs Hospital, Hines, IL, p. A185

TANKEL, Nancy, R.N., Chief Nurse Executive, Kaiser Permanente Woodland Hills Medical Center, Los Angeles, CA, p. A67

TANNENBAUM, Scott, M.D., Medical Director, Healthsouth Sunrise Rehabilitation Hospital, Sunrise, FL, p. A140

TANNER, Ashley, Director of Nursing, Wiregrass Medical Center, Geneva, AL, p. A18

TANNER, Douglas, President, Atmore Community Hospital, Atmore, AL, p. A14

TANNER, James, M.D., Chief Medical Officer, Willow Creek Women's Hospital, AR, p. A49

TANNOS, Paul, Chief Financial Officer, The Physicians Centre Hospital, Bryan, TX, p. A591

TANTHOREY, Geoff, Director, Information Systems, Granville Health System, Oxford, NC, p. A458

TANZELLA, Richard, Chief Executive Officer, Piedmont Rockdale Hospital, Conyers, GA, p. A151

TAPLETT, Dean, Controller, Quincy Valley Medical Center, Quincy, WA, p. A675

TAPLIN, Tyrrell, Chief Executive Officer, Encompass Health Rehabilitation Hospital Of Arlington, Arlington, TX, p. A584

TAPP, Gina
　Director Human Resources, Samaritan North Lincoln Hospital, Lincoln City, OR, p. A514
　Director Human Resources, Samaritan Pacific Communities Hospital, Newport, OR, p. A515

TAPPER, Shane, Director Management Information Systems, Fort Madison Community Hospital, Fort Madison, IA, p. A223

TARAR, Ahmad, M.D., Medical Director, Heartland Behavioral Health Services, Nevada, MO, p. A365

TARASOVICH, James
　Chief Financial Officer, Mayo Clinic Health System In Saint James, Saint James, MN, p. A339
　Chief Financial Officer, Mayo Clinic Health System In Springfield, Springfield, MN, p. A340

TARBAY, Amy, Director Nursing Services, Naval Hospital Pensacola, Pensacola, FL, p. A136

TARBET, Joyce, M.D., Chief Medical Officer, Murray County Medical Center, Slayton, MN, p. A340

TARDIF, Kathleen, Director of Human Resources, Central Regional Hospital, Butner, NC, p. A448

TAROLA, Robert, Chief Financial Officer, Little Company Of Mary Hospital And Health Care Centers, Evergreen Park, IL, p. A183

TARRANT, Jeffrey S., FACHE
　Chief Executive Officer, Alliancehealth Durant, Durant, OK, p. A498
　Chief Executive Officer, Alliancehealth Madill, Madill, OK, p. A500

TARRANT, Maureen, President and Chief Executive Officer, Rocky Mountain Hospital For Children, CO, p. A99

TARULLI, Pamela, Senior Vice President Human Resources, Good Samaritan Regional Medical Center, Suffern, NY, p. A443

TARVER, Dennis, Director Information Technology, Elkview General Hospital, Hobart, OK, p. A499

TARVER, Jeanette, Director of Finance, Sonoma Valley Hospital, Sonoma, CA, p. A90

TARVER, Rebecca, Chief Nursing Officer, Bates County Memorial Hospital, Butler, MO, p. A356

TASSEY, Karen, FACHE, Chief Operating Officer, Columbia Memorial Hospital, Hudson, NY, p. A428

TASSIN, Bruce J., President, Saint Joseph Hospital, Lexington, KY, p. A255

TASSO, Tina, Manager Human Resources, The Orthopedic Specialty Hospital, Murray, UT, p. A648

TATE, Charlene, M.D., Chief Medical Staff and Clinical Services, Eleanor Slater Hospital, Cranston, RI, p. A547

TATE, Charles, Director Information Technology, Lallie Kemp Medical Center, Independence, LA, p. A269

TATE, James, M.D., Chief of Staff, Patients' Hospital Of Redding, Redding, CA, p. A80

TATE, Jean, Vice President Human Resources, Riverview Health, Crookston, MN, p. A330

TATE, Joel W., FACHE, Chief Executive Officer, Clay County Hospital, Ashland, AL, p. A13

TATE, Mary Lou, Chief Financial Officer, Morris Hospital & Healthcare Centers, Morris, IL, p. A190

TATRO, Chad, Supervisor Information Systems, Northeast Regional Medical Center, Kirksville, MO, p. A362

TATRO, Mary, Esq, Chief Nursing Officer, Millinocket Regional Hospital, Millinocket, ME, p. A285

TATU, Ryan, Chief Executive Officer, Tmc Behavioral Health Center, TX, p. A599

TATUM, Monica, Administrator, Oceans Behavioral Hospital Of Lake Charles, Lake Charles, LA, p. A272

TAUL, Kelly, Business Manager, Meadowbrook Rehabilitation Hospital, Gardner, KS, p. A235

TAUNER, Gary, Chief Operating Officer, St. John's Medical Center And Living Center, Jackson, WY, p. A708

TAUNTON, David, M.D., Chief of Staff, Texas Health Harris Methodist Hospital Southlake, Southlake, TX, p. A636

TAUPIN, Michel, M.D., Chief Medical Officer, Abington-Lansdale Hospital Jefferson Health, Lansdale, PA, p. A529

TAUTZ, Linda, Chief Executive Officer, Vibra Hospital Of Denver, Thornton, CO, p. A106

TAVARY, James, Chief Executive Officer, Wickenburg Community Hospital, Wickenburg, AZ, p. A38

TAVELLA, Christopher
　Acting Executive Director, Rockland Children's Hospital Psychiatric Center, Orangeburg, NY, p. A439
　Executive Director, Rockland Psychiatric Center, Orangeburg, NY, p. A439

TAWNEY, Michael W, D.O., Vice President Medical Affairs, Mclaren Port Huron, Port Huron, MI, p. A321

TAYLOR, Adam, Manager Information Technology, Northern Inyo Hospital, Bishop, CA, p. A53

TAYLOR, Adrienne, Director of Health Information Management, Northwest Mississippi Medical Center, Clarksdale, MS, p. A344

TAYLOR, Al
　Interim Chief Executive Officer, Clarion Hospital, Clarion, PA, p. A522
　Vice President and Administrator, Memorial Hospital Of Carbondale, Carbondale, IL, p. A175

TAYLOR, Alice, R.N., MSN, Chief Executive Officer, Broward Health North, Deerfield Beach, FL, p. A121

TAYLOR, Allison H, R.N., Chief Nursing Officer and Vice President Clinical Services, Sampson Regional Medical Center, Clinton, NC, p. A450

TAYLOR, Amy, Chief Financial Officer, Oklahoma Center For Orthopedic And Multi-Specialty Surgery, Oklahoma City, OK, p. A504

TAYLOR, Anthony, Manager Information Technology, Cherokee Indian Hospital, Cherokee, NC, p. A450

TAYLOR, Beth, Vice President, Human Resources, Massgeneral For Children At Newton-Wellesley Hospital, MA, p. A302

TAYLOR, Brenda, Director Information Systems, Texas Health Harris Methodist Hospital Cleburne, Cleburne, TX, p. A592

TAYLOR, Brett, Manager Information, Van Wert County Hospital, Van Wert, OH, p. A492

TAYLOR, Carol M., R.N., Regional Director Clinical Operations, Kaiser Permanente Capitol Hill Campus, Seattle, WA, p. A676

TAYLOR, Cecilia, Chief Financial Officer, Midwestern Regional Medical Center, Zion, IL, p. A198

TAYLOR, Cherie, Chief Executive Officer, Northern Rockies Medical Center, Cut Bank, MT, p. A374

TAYLOR, Cheryl, R.N., Director of Nursing, Henry Ford Kingswood Hospital, Ferndale, MI, p. A312

TAYLOR, Christina, Director Human Resources, The Brook Hospital - Kmi, Louisville, KY, p. A257

TAYLOR, Dana Shantel, Director Organizational Development, Fairfield Memorial Hospital, Fairfield, IL, p. A183

TAYLOR, Deborah, Chief Information Officer, Chatham Hospital, Siler City, NC, p. A460

TAYLOR, Debra, Chief Nursing Officer, Paris Regional Medical Center, TX, p. A627

TAYLOR, Dwayne, Chief Executive Officer, Sycamore Shoals Hospital, Elizabethton, TN, p. A569

TAYLOR, Ernest Lee, M.D., Vice President Medical Affairs, St. Mary's Medical Center, Huntington, WV, p. A684

TAYLOR, Eulon Ross, Clinical Director, North Texas State Hospital, Wichita Falls Campus, Wichita Falls, TX, p. A644

TAYLOR, Faye M, R.N., Director of Nursing, Stephens County Hospital, Toccoa, GA, p. A162

TAYLOR, Gregory W, M.D., Vice President and Chief Operating Officer, High Point Regional Health System, High Point, NC, p. A454

TAYLOR, Heather, Human Resources Manager, Tippah County Hospital, Ripley, MS, p. A353

TAYLOR, Heidi, Chief Financial Officer, Morton Hospital And Medical Center, Taunton, MA, p. A305

TAYLOR, Janey, Chief Information and Technology, Overton Brooks Veterans Affairs Medical Center, Shreveport, LA, p. A278

TAYLOR, Jay, M.D., Chief of Medical Staff, Pondera Medical Center, Conrad, MT, p. A374

TAYLOR, Jeff, Vice President Finance, St. Luke's Meridian Medical Center, ID, p. A168

TAYLOR, Jeremy, Director Information Services, Saint Francis Hospital, Charleston, WV, p. A682

TAYLOR, Jim, Chief Business Office, Lake City Veterans Affairs Medical Center, FL, p. A123

TAYLOR, Joel
　Chief Executive Officer, Coastal Carolina Hospital, Hardeeville, SC, p. A554
　Chief Information Officer, Carepoint Health Bayonne Medical Center, Bayonne, NJ, p. A402
　Chief Information Officer, Carepoint Health Hoboken University Medical Center, Hoboken, NJ, p. A406

TAYLOR, Judd
　Chief Financial Officer, Eastern Idaho Regional Medical Center, Idaho Falls, ID, p. A169
　Chief Financial Officer, Ogden Regional Medical Center, Ogden, UT, p. A648

TAYLOR, Julia, Area Director Human Resources, Vibra Hospital Of Charleston, Mt. Pleasant, SC, p. A555

TAYLOR, Julie, FACHE, Chief Executive Officer, Alaska Regional Hospital, Anchorage, AK, p. A25

TAYLOR, Kendra, MSN, R.N.
　President and Chief Executive Officer, Salem Township Hospital, Salem, IL, p. A195
　President and Chief Executive Officer, Salem Township Hospital, Salem, IL, p. A195

TAYLOR, Konnie, Chief Financial Officer, Carl Albert Community Mental Health Center, Mcalester, OK, p. A501

TAYLOR, Kristie, Chief Financial Officer, Southern Tennessee Regional Health System-Lawrenceburg, Lawrenceburg, TN, p. A573

TAYLOR, Linda, Chief Human Resources Officer, Goodland Regional Medical Center, Goodland, KS, p. A235

TAYLOR, Lora, Director Human Resources and Compliance Officer, Unitypoint Health-Keokuk, Keokuk, IA, p. A225

TAYLOR, Marc, IS Director, Mountain West Medical Center, Tooele, UT, p. A651

TAYLOR, Marcia, Chief Executive Officer, Select Specialty Hospital-Memphis, Memphis, TN, p. A576

TAYLOR, Meredith, Controller, South Sunflower County Hospital, Indianola, MS, p. A347

TAYLOR, Merle, Vice President Operations, Upmc St. Margaret, Pittsburgh, PA, p. A538

TAYLOR, Michael
　Chief Information Officer, Bon Secours St. Francis Hospital, Charleston, SC, p. A549
　Vice President Finance, Northridge Hospital Medical Center, Los Angeles, CA, p. A69
　Vice President Financial Services and Chief Financial Officer, St. Rose Hospital, Hayward, CA, p. A61

TAYLOR, Michael V
　Senior Vice President Human Resources, Sentara Leigh Hospital, Norfolk, VA, p. A662
　Vice President Human Resources, Sentara Princess Anne Hospital, Virginia Beach, VA, p. A667

TAYLOR, Mimi
　Corporate Vice President Information Technology, Baptist Children's Hospital, FL, p. A129
　Corporate Vice President Information Technology, Baptist Health South Florida, Homestead Hospital, Homestead, FL, p. A125
　Vice President Information Technology, Baptist Health South Florida, Mariners Hospital, Tavernier, FL, p. A142
　Vice President Information Technology, Baptist Health South Florida, South Miami Hospital, Miami, FL, p. A130

TAYLOR, Nathan, Director of Nursing, Heartland Behavioral Health Services, Nevada, MO, p. A365

TAYLOR, Nick, Chief Executive Officer, Baylor Medical Center At Uptown, Dallas, TX, p. A595

TAYLOR, Patrick, M.D., President and Chief Executive Officer, Holy Cross Hospital, Fort Lauderdale, FL, p. A122

TAYLOR, Paul, Administrator, Ozarks Community Hospital, Gravette-Benton County, AR, p. A43

TAYLOR, Randy, Chief Information Technology Officer, Perry Memorial Hospital, Perry, OK, p. A505

TAYLOR, Renae, Chief Nursing Officer, Southeastern Health, Lumberton, NC, p. A456

TAYLOR, Richard, Chief Financial Officer, Western Mental Health Institute, Bolivar, TN, p. A566

TAYLOR, Robbie, Director Human Resources, North Sunflower Medical Center, Ruleville, MS, p. A353

TAYLOR, Robert, Director Information Services, St. Christopher's Hospital For Children, Philadelphia, PA, p. A536

TAYLOR, Ross, M.D., Clinical Director, Austin State Hospital, Austin, TX, p. A585

TAYLOR, Sarah, Chief Human Resources, National Jewish Health, Denver, CO, p. A99

TAYLOR, Scott J., President and Chief Executive Officer, St. Catherine Hospital, Garden City, KS, p. A235

TAYLOR, Scotty, Information Technology Director, East Mississippi State Hospital, Meridian, MS, p. A350

TAYLOR, Sharon, Human Resources Director, Allegiance Specialty Hospital Of Greenville, Greenville, MS, p. A346

TAYLOR, Sheri, Director Human Resources, Union General Hospital, Farmerville, LA, p. A267

TAYLOR, Stacy, Chief Financial Officer, Nemaha County Hospital, Auburn, NE, p. A381

TAYLOR, Steve, Chief Information Officer, Anderson Regional Health System South, Meridian, MS, p. A350

TAYLOR, Steven E.
Chief Executive Officer, Blackwell Regional Hospital, Blackwell, OK, p. A496
Chief Executive Officer, Perry Memorial Hospital, Perry, OK, p. A505

TAYLOR, Steven L., Chief Executive Officer, Harrison County Hospital, Corydon, IN, p. A201

TAYLOR, Sue O., Vice President Nursing, Vidant Duplin Hospital, Kenansville, NC, p. A455

TAYLOR, Susan L., JD, Chief Executive Officer, College Hospital Costa Mesa, Costa Mesa, CA, p. A55

TAYLOR, Todd, Chief Executive Officer, Stafford County Hospital, Stafford, KS, p. A246

TAYLOR, Tracy, Chief Nurse Executive, Fairfield Memorial Hospital, Fairfield, IL, p. A183

TAYLOR, Tyler, Chief Executive Officer, Wayne Medical Center, Waynesboro, TN, p. A581

TAYLOR, Tyrone, Chief Financial Officer, Lyons Division, NJ, p. A404

TAYLOR, Venus, Director Human Resources, Bhc Alhambra Hospital, Rosemead, CA, p. A81

TAYLOR, Wes, Chief Operating Officer, Havasu Regional Medical Center, Lake Havasu City, AZ, p. A30

TEAFF, Sarah, Chief Operating Officer, St. Luke Community Healthcare, Ronan, MT, p. A378

TEAGUE, Dean, FACHE, Chief Executive Officer, Calverthealth Medical Center, Prince Frederick, MD, p. A293

TEAGUE, Lara Ellen, R.N., Chief Nursing Officer, Lillian M. Hudspeth Memorial Hospital, Sonora, TX, p. A636

TEAHL, Bradley, Director Human Resources, Healthsouth Rehabilitation Hospital Of York, York, PA, p. A545

TEAL, Amy, Chief Executive Officer, Healthsouth Reading Rehabilitation Hospital, Reading, PA, p. A539

TEAL, Barbara, R.N., Associate Director Patient Care Services and Nurse Executive, Sioux Falls Veterans Affairs Health Care System, Sioux Falls, SD, p. A564

TEAL, Cydney, M.D., Vice President Medical Affairs, Union Hospital, Elkton, MD, p. A291

TEAS, Gregory, M.D., Chief Medical Officer, Alexian Brothers Behavioral Health Hospital, Hoffman Estates, IL, p. A186

TEASDALE, Peggy, Director Human Resources, Southeast Health Center Of Ripley County, Doniphan, MO, p. A358

TEATER, Phyllis, Chief Information Officer, Ohio State University Hospitals East, OH, p. A478

TEATSORTH, Neil, Vice President Human Resources, Norwegian American Hospital, Chicago, IL, p. A178

TEBBE, James, M.D., Vice President Medical Affairs, Ochsner Medical Center - Kenner, Kenner, LA, p. A270

TEDDER, Cookie, Human Resources Manager, Texas Health Center For Diagnostic & Surgery, Plano, TX, p. A629

TEDESCO, Art, Interim Chief Financial Officer, Gaylord Hospital, Wallingford, CT, p. A111

TEEL, David R., Financial Officer, Terrell State Hospital, Terrell, TX, p. A639

TEETER, Stephen, Business Manager, Hawaii State Hospital, Kaneohe, HI, p. A166

TEFFETELLER, Scott L., Senior Vice President and President of East Region, Community Heart And Vascular Hospital, IN, p. A206

TEICHMEIER, Laura, Director Human Resources, Memorial Community Health, Aurora, NE, p. A381

TEIGEN, Seth, President, Wheaton Franciscan Healthcare - St. Francis, Milwaukee, WI, p. A699

TEITELBAUM, Karen
Chief Executive Officer, Schwab Rehabilitation Hospital, Chicago, IL, p. A179
President and Chief Executive Officer, Sinai Children's Hospital, IL, p. A178

TEJADA, Vanessa, Director Human Resources, Encompass Health Rehabilitation Hospital Of San Antonio, San Antonio, TX, p. A633

TEJEDA, Nicholas R, FACHE, Market Chief Executive Officer, Providence Children's Hospital, TX, p. A602

TEJEDA, Nicholas R., FACHE
Chief Executive Officer, The Hospitals Of Providence Sierra Campus, El Paso, TX, p. A602
Market Chief Executive Officer, Providence Children's Hospital, TX, p. A602

TELHIARD, Nicole, MSN, Chief Nursing Officer, Our Lady Of The Lake Children's Hospital, LA, p. A264

TELITZ, Rita, Chief Administrative Officer, Marshfield Medical Center - Ladysmith, Ladysmith, WI, p. A695

TELL, Marjorie, Vice President Information Technology, Aspirus Riverview Hospital And Clinics, Inc., Wisconsin Rapids, WI, p. A706

TELLOR, Tammy, Acting Director Human Resources, Choate Mental Health Center, Anna, IL, p. A173

TELLY, Joel, Chief Executive Officer, Healthbridge Children's Hospital Of Houston, Houston, TX, p. A611

TELTHORSTER, M.ED, Marcia M, Vice President Human Resources, Penn Medicine Princeton Medical Center, Plainsboro, NJ, p. A410

TEMPELMEYER, Zak, M.D., Chief Medical Staff, Community Memorial Hospital, Syracuse, NE, p. A390

TEMPEST, Wendy, Director Human Resources, Vibra Hospital Of Northern California, Redding, CA, p. A80

TEMPLE, Amber L, Director Human Resources, Morrison Community Hospital, Morrison, IL, p. A190

TEMPLE, Gina, Chief Nurse Executive, Sutter Auburn Faith Hospital, Auburn, CA, p. A51

TEMPLE, Richard, Chief Information Officer, Deborah Heart And Lung Center, Browns Mills, NJ, p. A403

TEMPLETON, Gary, M.D., Medical Director, Regency Hospital Of Northwest Arkansas - Springdale, Springdale-Washington County, AR, p. A49

TEMPLETON, Parker A., FACHE, Chief Executive Officer, Iberia Medical Center, New Iberia, LA, p. A275

TEMPLETON, Sheryl, Chief Financial Officer, Scotland County Hospital, Memphis, MO, p. A364

TEMPLETON, William, M.D., III, Medical Director, Clark Memorial Hospital, Jeffersonville, IN, p. A208

TEMPLIN, Nancy, Vice President Finance and Chief Financial Officer, Johns Hopkins All Children's Hospital, Saint Petersburg, FL, p. A138

TENEWITZ, Edward, M.D., Chief of Staff, Healthmark Regional Medical Center, Defuniak Springs, FL, p. A121

TENGERES, Michael A.
Chief Financial Officer, Crouse Health, Syracuse, NY, p. A443
Corporate Vice President and Chief Financial Officer, Bassett Medical Center, Cooperstown, NY, p. A425

TENHENGEL-DEVILLE, Michelle, Chief Executive Officer, Regency Hospital Of South Atlanta, East Point, GA, p. A153

TENHOUSE, Steven D., FACHE, Chief Executive Officer, Kirby Medical Center, Monticello, IL, p. A190

TENNEY, Ralph
Chief Information Officer, Ascension Crittenton Hospital Medical Center, Rochester, MI, p. A321
Chief Information Officer, Ascension St. John Hospital, Detroit, MI, p. A310
Chief Information Officer, St. John Macomb-Oakland Hospital, Warren Campus, MI, p. A325

TENNISON, Gary, M.D., Chief of Staff, Crawford Memorial Hospital, Robinson, IL, p. A194

TENNYSON, Ruby, Director Administration, Naval Hospital Jacksonville, Jacksonville, FL, p. A125

TENREIRO, Edgardo J, Chief Executive Officer and Chief Operating Officer, Baton Rouge General Medical Center-Bluebonnet, LA, p. A263

TENREIRO, Edgardo J., Chief Executive Officer and Chief Operating Officer, Baton Rouge General Medical Center-Bluebonnet, LA, p. A263

TEPEDINO, Miguel, M.D., Chief Medicine, Lake City Medical Center, Lake City, FL, p. A127

TEPPER, Gil, M.D.
Chief Executive Officer, Miracle Mile Medical Center, Los Angeles, CA, p. A68
Chief of Staff, Miracle Mile Medical Center, Los Angeles, CA, p. A68

TER HORST, Thomas C, Vice President Human Resources, Aurora St. Luke's South Shore, WI, p. A698

TERBUSH, Jennifer, Vice President, Patient Services, Hills & Dales General Hospital, Cass City, MI, p. A309

TERI, Anthony, Director Information Technology, Hackensack Meridian Health Pascack Valley Medical Center, Westwood, NJ, p. A414

TERPSTRA, Kelli, R.N., Senior Director, Our Children's House, Dallas, TX, p. A597

TERRELL, Jay, Manager Management Information Systems, Riverview Regional Medical Center, Gadsden, AL, p. A18

TERRESON, Gregg, Chief Financial Officer, Cascade Behavioral Hospital, Tukwila, WA, p. A679

TERRINONI, Gary G., President and Chief Executive Officer, Brooklyn Hospital Center, New York (Includes All Hospitals Located Within The Five Boroughs), NY, p. A431

TERRY, Darrell K., Sr, M.P.H., FACHE, President and Chief Executive Officer, Children's Hospital Of New Jersey, NJ, p. A408

TERRY, Micheal, President and Chief Executive Officer, Salina Regional Health Center-Santa Fe Campus, KS, p. A245

TERRY, Randi, Site Director Management Information Systems, Munson Healthcare Cadillac Hospital, Cadillac, MI, p. A309

TERRY, Richard, Vice President & Chief Information Officer, Sparrow Carson Hospital, Carson City, MI, p. A309

TERRY, Teresa, Director Human Resource, Payroll, Fisher County Hospital District, Rotan, TX, p. A631

TERRY-WILLIAMS, Teresa, R.N., Chief Nursing Officer, Pennsylvania Psychiatric Institute, Harrisburg, PA, p. A526

TERSHAKOVEC, George R., M.D., President Medical Staff, Baptist Health South Florida, Homestead Hospital, Homestead, FL, p. A125

TERTEL, Jenifer K, Director Human Resources, Medical City Children's Hospital, TX, p. A597

TERWILLIGER, Michael, Chief Financial Officer, Friends Hospital, Philadelphia, PA, p. A534

TERZANO, Valerie, MSN, R.N., Senior Vice President Nursing, Children's Medical Center, NY, p. A430

TESKE, Mark, Chief Financial Officer, Hill Crest Behavioral Health Services, Birmingham, AL, p. A14

TESSARZIK, Connie, Business Manager, Albert J. Solnit Psychiatric Center - South Campus, Middletown, CT, p. A109

TESSLER, Nicolette B, Chief Executive Officer of Behavioral Health Hospital, Jackson Behavioral Health Hospital, FL, p. A130

TESTA, Nick, M.D., Chief Medical Officer, Providence Saint Joseph Medical Center, Burbank, CA, p. A53

TETZ, Warren, Senior Vice President and Chief Operating Officer, Adventist Health Glendale, Los Angeles, CA, p. A66

TEUBNER, Sandra, Chief Financial Officer, St. Aloisius Medical Center, Harvey, ND, p. A466

TEUFEL, George, Vice President Finance, Advocate Good Shepherd Hospital, Barrington, IL, p. A174

TEVES, Alicia, Coordinator Human Resources, Molokai General Hospital, Kaunakakai, HI, p. A166

TEW, Brian, Chief Information Officer, Catskill Regional Medical Center, Harris, NY, p. A427

TEWARI, Arun, M.D., Chief Medical Officer, Henry Community Health, New Castle, IN, p. A212

TEWKSBURY, Randy E, Senior Vice President Finance and Chief Financial Officer, Mount Nittany Medical Center, State College, PA, p. A541

THACKER, Adam, Chief Operating Officer, Good Samaritan Hospital, Vincennes, IN, p. A216

THACKER, Roland, Chief Financial Officer, Piedmont Columbus Regional Northside, Columbus, GA, p. A150

THAKOR, Pratapji, M.D., Chief of Staff, South Mississippi County Regional Medical Center, Osceola-Mississippi County, AR, p. A47

THAKUR, Abhash, M.D., Chief of Staff, Greenwood Leflore Hospital, Greenwood, MS, p. A346

THALER, Klaus, FACS, M.D., Chief Medical Officer, Houston Methodist San Jacinto Hospital - Alexander, TX, p. A587

THAMA, Todd, Chief Operating Officer, Fairfax Behavioral Health Everett, WA, p. A673

THAMES, Stephen, Chief Financial Officer, Allen Parish Hospital, Kinder, LA, p. A270

THAMES, Thomas B., M.D., President, Sentara Princess Anne Hospital, Virginia Beach, VA, p. A667

THARP, Beth S., R.N., President and Chief Executive Officer, Community Hospital Of Anderson & Madison County, Anderson, IN, p. A199

THARP, Stephen
Medical Director, Indiana University Health Frankfort, Frankfort, IN, p. A204
Regional Chief Medical Officer, St. Vincent Clay Hospital, Brazil, IN, p. A200

THAUNG, Htin, M.D., Chief Medical Officer, Ward Memorial Hospital, Monahans, TX, p. A624

THAYER, Charles, M.D., Chief Medical Officer, Morton Hospital And Medical Center, Taunton, MA, p. A305

THAYER, Gilbert M., M.D., Chief Medical Staff, Hardin Medical Center, Savannah, TN, p. A579

THAYER, Kendra, MSN, R.N., Chief Nursing Officer, Vice President Clinical Services, Garrett Regional Medical Center, Oakland, MD, p. A293

THEIRING, James, Chief Executive Officer, Mission Community Hospital, Los Angeles, CA, p. A68

THEISEN, Janet
Chief Information Officer, Sanford Tracy Medical Center, Tracy, MN, p. A341
Chief Information Officer, Sanford Westbrook Medical Center, Westbrook, MN, p. A342

THELEN, Raymond Scott, Vice President and Chief Financial Officer, Masonicare Health Center, Wallingford, CT, p. A111

THEOBALD, Terry, Chief Information Officer, Ventura County Medical Center, Ventura, CA, p. A94

THEODOROU, Andreas, Chief Medical Officer, Diamond Children's Hospital, AZ, p. A37

THEOHARES, Nick, Executive Director, Operations, St. Vincent Anderson, Anderson, IN, p. A199

THERADY, Agnes, MSN, FACHE
Vice President and Chief Nursing Officer, Franciscan Health Carmel, Carmel, IN, p. A201
Vice President and Chief Nursing Officer, Franciscan Health Indianapolis, Indianapolis, IN, p. A206
Vice President and Chief Nursing Officer, Franciscan Health Mooresville, Mooresville, IN, p. A211

THERIAC, Gary, Director Information Technology, Lawrence County Memorial Hospital, Lawrenceville, IL, p. A187

THERIOT, Paul, Chief Executive Officer, East Georgia Regional Medical Center, Statesboro, GA, p. A161

THERRIEN, Charles D., President, Mercy Hospital Of Portland, Portland, ME, p. A285

THERRIEN, Tinna, R.N., Chief Information Officer and Senior Director Ancillary Services, Gothenburg Health, Gothenburg, NE, p. A384

THETFORD, Carol, Chief Nursing Officer, Baptist Memorial Hospital For Women, Memphis, TN, p. A574

THEUS, Will, M.D., Chief of Staff, Gordon Hospital, Calhoun, GA, p. A149

THIBERT, Kimberly, R.N., MSN, Vice President Patient Care Services and Chief Nursing Officer, Samaritan Medical Center, Watertown, NY, p. A445

THIBODEAU, Helene, R.N., MSN, Vice President Patient Care Services, Northeast Rehabilitation Hospital, Salem, NH, p. A401

THIBODEAU, Jan, Director Human Resources, Healthsouth Southern Hills Rehabilitation Hospital, Princeton, WV, p. A686

THIBODEAUX, Anita, Chief Nursing Officer, Beauregard Health System, De Ridder, LA, p. A266

THIBODEAUX, Annette, Director Human Resources, Savoy Medical Center, Mamou, LA, p. A273

THIBODEAUX, Douglas, M.D., Chief Medical Officer, Oakbend Medical Center Williams Way Campus, TX, p. A630

THIBODEAUX, Traci, Chief Operating Officer, Doctor's Hospital Of Deer Creek, Leesville, LA, p. A272

THIEL, David, M.D., Medical Director, Mayo Clinic Hospital In Florida, Jacksonville, FL, p. A125

THIEL, Stefanie
Senior Human Resources Business Partner, Saint Alphonsus Medical Center - Nampa, Nampa, ID, p. A170
Senior Human Resources Business Partner, Saint Alphonsus Medical Center - Ontario, Ontario, OR, p. A515

THIELEMIER, Kevin, Director Human Resources, Arkansas Methodist Medical Center, Paragould-Greene County, AR, p. A47

THIELEN, Kurt, Associate Director, Minneapolis Veterans Affairs Health Care System, Minneapolis, MN, p. A335

THIELK, Colleen, MSN, R.N., Chief Nursing Officer, Palms Of Pasadena Hospital, Saint Petersburg, FL, p. A138

THIELKE, Jayne, Chief Financial Officer, Swift County - Benson Health Services, Benson, MN, p. A328

THIEME, Ron, Ph.D., Chief Knowledge and Information Officer, Community Hospital North, Indianapolis, IN, p. A206

THIES, Dana, Director of Nursing, Meadows Psychiatric Center, Centre Hall, PA, p. A522

THILGES, Michael, Chief Financial Officer, Clarke County Hospital, Osceola, IA, p. A228

THILL, Jennifer, Chief of Staff, Mid-Valley Hospital, Omak, WA, p. A674

THIRUMALAREDDY, Joseph, M.D., Chief of Staff, Wishek Community Hospital And Clinics, Wishek, ND, p. A469

THOELE, Theresa, Director Human Resources, Coffey County Hospital, Burlington, KS, p. A233

THOENDEL, Victor, M.D., Chief Medical Officer, Butler County Health Care Center, David City, NE, p. A383

THOMAN, Dawn, Vice President Human Resources, Cloud County Health Center, Concordia, KS, p. A234

THOMAN, Michele, R.N., Chief Nursing Officer, Nch North Naples Hospital, FL, p. A132

THOMAS, Andrea, Chief Operating Officer, St. Cloud Regional Medical Center, Saint Cloud, FL, p. A138

THOMAS, Andrew, M.D., Chief Medical Officer, Ohio State University Hospitals East, OH, p. A478

THOMAS, Anthony, Chief Executive Officer, Rooks County Health Center, Plainville, KS, p. A244

THOMAS, Brian E., Administrator, Alton Mental Health Center, Alton, IL, p. A173

THOMAS, Brian N., President and Chief Executive Officer, Jefferson Regional Medical Center, Pine Bluff-Jefferson County, AR, p. A47

THOMAS, Brook, Chief Financial Officer, West Boca Medical Center, Boca Raton, FL, p. A118

THOMAS, Calvin, IV, Chief Operating Officer, St. Lucie Medical Center, Port St Lucie, FL, p. A137

THOMAS, Chris, FACHE, President and Chief Executive Officer, Community Hospital, Grand Junction, CO, p. A101

THOMAS, Christina, MHA, RN, FACHE, Chief Executive Officer, Caribou Memorial Hospital And Living Center, Soda Springs, ID, p. A172

THOMAS, Clay, Chief Operating Officer, Covenant Children's Hospital, Lubbock, TX, p. A620

THOMAS, Curt, Administrator, Ness County Hospital District No 2, Ness City, KS, p. A242

THOMAS, David, President Medical Staff, Riddle Hospital, Media, PA, p. A531

THOMAS, Deana, Vice President Finance and Chief Financial Officer, North Arkansas Regional Medical Center, Harrison-Boone County, AR, p. A43

THOMAS, Debora, Chief Financial Officer, Florida Hospital-Oceanside, FL, p. A121

THOMAS, Debra A., Vice President of Patient Care Services and Chief Nursing Officer, Penn Highlands Brookville, Brookville, PA, p. A521

THOMAS, Denise, Chief Financial Officer, Spring View Hospital, Lebanon, KY, p. A254

THOMAS, Dennis, Chief Nursing Officer, Hardeman County Memorial Hospital, Quanah, TX, p. A629

THOMAS, Frank D., Chief Executive Officer, Citizens Baptist Medical Center, Talladega, AL, p. A23

THOMAS, Gene, Vice President, Information Systems, Chief Information Officer, Memorial Behavioral Health, MS, p. A346

THOMAS, George, M.D., Chief of Staff, Palo Pinto General Hospital, Mineral Wells, TX, p. A624

THOMAS, Gina, Chief Nursing Officer & Director of Patient Care Services, Carle Richland Memorial Hospital, Olney, IL, p. A192

THOMAS, Jayne
Chief Nursing Officer, Integris Deaconess, Oklahoma City, OK, p. A502
Chief Nursing Officer, Southwestern Medical Center, Lawton, OK, p. A500

THOMAS, Jeff, Chief Financial Officer, Heartland Regional Medical Center, Marion, IL, p. A188

THOMAS, Jennifer, Chief Operating Officer and Director of Public Relations, Lake Butler Hospital Hand Surgery Center, Lake Butler, FL, p. A127

THOMAS, Jill, Director of Nursing, Western State Hospital, Hopkinsville, KY, p. A253

THOMAS, John, Chief Operating Officer, San Mateo Medical Center, San Mateo, CA, p. A87

THOMAS, John A., M.D., Chief Medical Staff, Culberson Hospital, Van Horn, TX, p. A641

THOMAS, Keith, M.D., Chief of Staff, Blue Mountain Hospital, John Day, OR, p. A514

THOMAS, Kirk E, MHA, Chief Administrative Officer, Geisinger-Lewistown Hospital, Lewistown, PA, p. A530

THOMAS, Maggie, Vice President Human Resources and Practice Management, South County Hospital, Wakefield, RI, p. A548

THOMAS, Michael
Associate Administrator, Wayne County Hospital, Corydon, IA, p. A220
Chief Executive Officer, Encompass Health Rehabilitation Hospital Of San Antonio, San Antonio, TX, p. A633

THOMAS, Michael S, President and Chief Administrative Officer, John Muir Medical Center, Concord, Concord, CA, p. A55

THOMAS, Michael S., President and Chief Administrative Officer, John Muir Medical Center, Concord, Concord, CA, p. A55

THOMAS, Nicky, Director Human Resources, Baptist Memorial Hospital-Union City, Union City, TN, p. A580

THOMAS, Nicole B., President, Baptist Medical Center South, FL, p. A125

THOMAS, Patricia F, Chief Nursing Officer, Sentara Halifax Regional Hospital, South Boston, VA, p. A666

THOMAS, Paula, R.N., MSN, Vice President Patient Services, Upmc Bedford Memorial, Everett, PA, p. A526

THOMAS, Phillip, Jr, Director Human Resources, Jackson Parish Hospital, Jonesboro, LA, p. A269

THOMAS, Ron, M.D., Chief Medical Officer, Florida Hospital Flagler, Palm Coast, FL, p. A135

THOMAS, Russell, M.D., Chief of Staff, Rice Medical Center, Eagle Lake, TX, p. A600

THOMAS, Ruth, Chief Operating Officer, Mercy Philadelphia Hospital, PA, p. A524

THOMAS, Sarah, Director of Human Resources, Healthsouth Rehabilitation Hospital Of Littleton, Littleton, CO, p. A103

THOMAS, Scott, Administrative Director Human Resources and Communications, Granville Health System, Oxford, NC, p. A458

THOMAS, Shawn M., Director Human Resources, Banner Payson Medical Center, Payson, AZ, p. A32

THOMAS, Spencer, Chief Executive Officer, Central Carolina Hospital, Sanford, NC, p. A460

THOMAS, Sue, Manager Human Resources, Beckley Arh Hospital, Beckley, WV, p. A681

THOMAS, Sylvia, Chief Nursing Officer, Jack Hughston Memorial Hospital, Phenix City, AL, p. A22

THOMAS, Twilla, Chief Nursing Officer, Pampa Regional Medical Center, Pampa, TX, p. A627

THOMAS, William, M.D., Jr, Medical Director Clinical and Internal Affairs, Molokai General Hospital, Kaunakakai, HI, p. A166

THOMAS, Wilson A., Chief Executive Officer, Southern Virginia Regional Medical Center, Emporia, VA, p. A657

THOMAS-BOYD, Sharon, Chief Operating Officer, Oaklawn Hospital, Marshall, MI, p. A319

THOMAS-FOLDS, Lana, System Director Human Resources, Jack Hughston Memorial Hospital, Phenix City, AL, p. A22

THOMASON, Scott, Chief Nursing Officer, Lakeside Behavioral Health System, Memphis, TN, p. A575

THOMMAN, Connie, Director of Nursing, Covenant Hospital-Levelland, Levelland, TX, p. A619

THOMPSON, Aaron, M.D., Chief of Staff, Arkansas Methodist Medical Center, Paragould-Greene County, AR, p. A47

THOMPSON, Alan, M.D., President Medical Staff, Warm Springs Medical Center, Warm Springs, GA, p. A163

THOMPSON, Amy, M.D., Chief Executive Officer, Covenant Children's Hospital, Lubbock, TX, p. A620

THOMPSON, Becki, President, Chi Oakes Hospital, Oakes, ND, p. A468

THOMPSON, Belinda, Coordinator Human Resources, Healthsouth Chesapeake Rehabilitation Hospital, Salisbury, MD, p. A294

THOMPSON, Bobby, Director Information Technology, Stephens Memorial Hospital, Breckenridge, TX, p. A590

THOMPSON, Cathy, Manager Human Resources, Paris Community Hospital, Paris, IL, p. A192

THOMPSON, Chad
Administrator, Hamilton County Hospital, Syracuse, KS, p. A246
Chief Financial Officer, Lallie Kemp Medical Center, Independence, LA, p. A269
President and Chief Executive Officer, Friend Community Healthcare System, Friend, NE, p. A384

THOMPSON, Charles, M.D., Chief Medical Officer, Nacogdoches Medical Center, Nacogdoches, TX, p. A625

THOMPSON, Charolette, Chief Financial Officer, Reeves Memorial Medical Center, Bernice, LA, p. A264

THOMPSON, Cheryl
Chief Nursing Officer, Garden Park Medical Center, Gulfport, MS, p. A346
Facility Director Human Resources, Whiting Forensic Hospital, CT, p. A109

THOMPSON, Chris
Chief Financial Officer, Delta Community Medical Center, Delta, UT, p. A646
Chief Financial Officer, Fillmore Community Hospital, Fillmore, UT, p. A646
Chief Financial Officer, Sanpete Valley Hospital, Mount Pleasant, UT, p. A648
Chief Financial Officer, Sevier Valley Hospital, Richfield, UT, p. A649

THOMPSON, Cindy, Chief Financial Officer, Northwest Surgical Hospital, Oklahoma City, OK, p. A503

THOMPSON, Craig, Chief Executive Officer, Golden Valley Memorial Healthcare, Clinton, MO, p. A357

THOMPSON, Craig B., M.D., President and Chief Executive Officer, Memorial Sloan-Kettering Cancer Center, New York (Includes All Hospitals Located Within The Five Boroughs), NY, p. A433

THOMPSON, Dale, Chief Financial Officer, Mclaren Orthopedic Hospital, MI, p. A317

THOMPSON, David, M.D.
Chief of Staff, Richardson Medical Center, Rayville, LA, p. A278
Chief Financial Officer, Central Maine Medical Center, Lewiston, ME, p. A284

THOMPSON, David M., Chief Executive Officer, Sutter Tracy Community Hospital, Tracy, CA, p. A92

THOMPSON, Debbie, Chief Financial Officer, Sweetwater Hospital, Sweetwater, TN, p. A580

THOMPSON, Douglas, Chief Information Officer, Upson Regional Medical Center, Thomaston, GA, p. A161

THOMPSON, Dwight, Chief Financial Officer, Altru Rehabilitation Center, ND, p. A466

THOMPSON, Greg
Chief Medical Officer, Gundersen Lutheran Medical Center, La Crosse, WI, p. A695
Corporate Director, Human Resources, Winnie Palmer Hospital For Women And Babies, FL, p. A134

THOMPSON, Heath, R.N., Administrator, Ocean Springs Hospital, MS, p. A351

THOMPSON, Ian, Jr, M.D., President, Christus Santa Rosa-Medical Center, TX, p. A632

THOMPSON, Ivan, Vice President, Chief Human Resource Officer, University Of Texas Southwestern Medical Center - Zale Lipshy, TX, p. A598

THOMPSON, James H., Ph.D., FACHE, Owner and Chief Executive Officer, Healthmark Regional Medical Center, Defuniak Springs, FL, p. A121

THOMPSON, John W, M.D., Chief of Staff, Eastern Louisiana Mental Health System, Jackson, LA, p. A269

THOMPSON, Julie
   Chief Operating Officer and Chief Nursing Officer, Bluffton Regional Medical Center, Bluffton, IN, p. A200
   Manager Personnel and Payroll, Mayers Memorial Hospital District, Fall River Mills, CA, p. A58

THOMPSON, Kim, Vice President and Chief Financial Officer, Ozarks Medical Center, West Plains, MO, p. A372

THOMPSON, Lennis, II, Vice President and Chief Financial Officer, Hardin Memorial Health, Elizabethtown, KY, p. A251

THOMPSON, Linda
   Chief Operating Officer, Fairfax Community Hospital, Fairfax, OK, p. A499
   Senior Vice President, Human Resources and Service Excellence, New England Baptist Hospital, Boston, MA, p. A297

THOMPSON, Lisa, MSN, R.N., Director of Nursing, Hiawatha Community Hospital, Hiawatha, KS, p. A236

THOMPSON, Lori L, Manager Human Resources, Orthonebraska Hospital, Omaha, NE, p. A388

THOMPSON, Marion A., FACHE, Chief Executive Officer, Allen County Regional Hospital, Iola, KS, p. A237

THOMPSON, Mark, M.D.
   Chief Medical Officer, Monroe Clinic, Monroe, WI, p. A699
   Market Chief Financial Officer Northern Region and Chief Financial Officer, Mercy Health - St. Charles Hospital, Oregon, OH, p. A488
   Vice President Financial Services, Rapid City Regional Hospital, Rapid City, SD, p. A563

THOMPSON, Nate, Chief Executive Officer, Story County Medical Center, Nevada, IA, p. A227

THOMPSON, Ormand P., President, Thomas Hospital, Fairhope, AL, p. A17

THOMPSON, Pamela, Chief Operations Officer, Huhukam Memorial Hospital, Sacaton, AZ, p. A35

THOMPSON, Patti, Chief Operating Officer, San Luis Valley Health, Alamosa, CO, p. A96

THOMPSON, Patty, Area Compliance Officer, Kaiser Permanente Fresno Medical Center, Fresno, CA, p. A59

THOMPSON, Randell, Chief Nursing Officer, Plateau Medical Center, Oak Hill, WV, p. A685

THOMPSON, Randy, Chief Executive Officer, Encompass Health Rehabilitation Hospital Of Montgomery, Montgomery, AL, p. A21

THOMPSON, Reanna, R.N., Chief Operating Officer and Chief Nursing Officer, Pih Health Hospital - Whittier, Whittier, CA, p. A95

THOMPSON, Ronnie, Chief Financial Officer, Belton Regional Medical Center, Belton, MO, p. A355

THOMPSON, Sarah, Director Health Information Management, Hardtner Medical Center, Olla, LA, p. A277

THOMPSON, Scott, Chief Executive Officer, Russell County Hospital, Russell Springs, KY, p. A260

THOMPSON, Selva, R.N., Chief Nurse Executive, Gallup Indian Medical Center, Gallup, NM, p. A417

THOMPSON, Sheila, Director Human Resources, Hamilton Memorial Hospital District, Mcleansboro, IL, p. A189

THOMPSON, Stuart, Vice President Human Resources, Memorial Hospital Jacksonville, Jacksonville, FL, p. A125

THOMPSON, Susan K., RN, Interim President and Chief Executive Officer, Unitypoint Health - Trinity Regional Medical Center, Fort Dodge, IA, p. A222

THOMPSON, Thomas R., President, Regina Hospital, Hastings, MN, p. A332

THOMPSON, Tim
   Senior Vice President and Chief Informatics Officer, St. Anthony's Hospital, Saint Petersburg, FL, p. A138
   Senior Vice President, Chief Information Officer, South Florida Baptist Hospital, Plant City, FL, p. A136
   Senior Vice President, Informant Services and Chief Information Officer, Mease Countryside Hospital, Safety Harbor, FL, p. A137
   Senior Vice President, Information Services and Chief Information Officer, Mease Dunedin Hospital, Dunedin, FL, p. A122

THOMPSON, Timothy
   Senior Vice President and Chief Information Officer, Morton Plant Hospital, Clearwater, FL, p. A119

   Senior Vice President and Chief Information Officer, Morton Plant North Bay Hospital, New Port Richey, FL, p. A132

THOMPSON, Tina H, Coordinator Human Resources, Firsthealth Montgomery Memorial Hospital, Troy, NC, p. A461

THOMPSON, Trinise, Director Human Resources, Tempe St. Luke's Hospital, AZ, p. A34

THOMPSON, Vera, Director Human Resources, Kingsboro Psychiatric Center, New York (Includes All Hospitals Located Within The Five Boroughs), NY, p. A432

THOMPSON, Wayne, Executive Vice President and Chief Information Officer, Mount Nittany Medical Center, State College, PA, p. A541

THOMPSON, Wesley, M.D., President Medical Staff, Fairfield Memorial Hospital, Fairfield, IL, p. A183

THOMPSON, William, M.D.
   Chief Medical Officer, Saint Thomas Midtown Hospital, Nashville, TN, p. A577
   Chief Financial Officer, Mississippi Baptist Medical Center, Jackson, MS, p. A348

THOMPSON-COOK, Timothy, Chief Operating Officer, Contra Costa Regional Medical Center, Martinez, CA, p. A71

THOMSEN, Sue, Chief Financial Officer, New Braunfels Regional Rehabilitation Hospital, New Braunfels, TX, p. A625

THOMSEN, Vicki
   Director Human Resources, Aurora Behavioral Health System East, Tempe, AZ, p. A36
   Director Human Resources, Aurora Behavioral Health System West, Glendale, AZ, p. A30

THOMSON, Doug, M.D., Chief Medical Officer, Commonwealth Regional Specialty Hospital, Bowling Green, KY, p. A249

THOMSON, Nicole, Chief Financial Officer, Saint Louise Regional Hospital, Gilroy, CA, p. A60

THOMSON, Steven, M.D., Medical Director, Heartland Behavioral Healthcare, Massillon, OH, p. A486

THORDARSON, Heidar, Chief Financial Officer, Adventist Health Castle, Kailua, HI, p. A165

THORE, Joe, Chief Operating Officer, Ashe Memorial Hospital, Jefferson, NC, p. A455

THORELL, Nicole, R.N., MSN, Chief Nursing Officer, Lexington Regional Health Center, Lexington, NE, p. A385

THORESON, Scott D., FACHE
   Administrator, Mayo Clinic Health System In Saint James, Saint James, MN, p. A339
   Administrator, Mayo Clinic Health System In Springfield, Springfield, MN, p. A340

THORN, Eugene A, III, Vice President Finance and Chief Financial Officer, Cleveland Clinic Union Hospital, Dover, OH, p. A481

THORN, Margaret, Interim Director of Nursing, Red Bay Hospital, Red Bay, AL, p. A23

THORN, Mark, FACHE, Executive Director, Finance, Mercy Hospital Lincoln, Troy, MO, p. A371

THORN, Robert, FACHE, Interim Chief Executive Officer, Sedgwick County Health Center, Julesburg, CO, p. A102

THORNBRUGH, Mitchell
   Acting Chief Information Officer, Cherokee Nation W.W. Hastings Indian Hospital, Tahlequah, OK, p. A507
   Administrative Officer, Cherokee Nation W.W. Hastings Indian Hospital, Tahlequah, OK, p. A507

THORNBURY, Neil
   Chief Executive Officer, T. J. Samson Community Hospital, Glasgow, KY, p. A252
   Chief Executive Officer, T.J. Health Columbia, Columbia, KY, p. A250

THORNE, Dana, Administrator Human Resources, Valley Hospital Medical Center, Las Vegas, NV, p. A395

THORNELL, Louise, Chief Nursing Officer, Christus St. Michael Hospital-Atlanta, TX, p. A639

THORNELL, Timothy, FACHE, Chief Executive Officer, Lea Regional Medical Center, Hobbs, NM, p. A417

THORNSBERRY, Michael, M.D., Chief Medical Officer, Texas Health Specialty Hospital, Fort Worth, TX, p. A605

THORNTON, Carol, Director Human Resources, Cherry Hospital, Goldsboro, NC, p. A453

THORNTON, Cayetano, Chief Information Officer, Walter Reed National Military Medical Center, Bethesda, MD, p. A290

THORNTON, Daryl W, Chief Operating Officer, Kansas Medical Center, Andover, KS, p. A232

THORNTON, Jan, Chief Nursing Officer, Bay Medical Sacred Heart, Panama City, FL, p. A135

THORNTON, Jillisa, Director of Nursing, Coastal Harbor Treatment Center, Savannah, GA, p. A160

THORNTON, Laird, Director Information Systems, Alta Vista Regional Hospital, Las Vegas, NM, p. A418

THORNTON, Matt, Chief Executive Officer, Liberty Dayton Regional Medical Center, Liberty, TX, p. A619

THORPE, Judith, R.N., MSN, Vice President and Chief Nursing Officer, Umass Memorial Healthalliance-Clinton Hospital, MA, p. A301

THORPE, Linda, Chief Executive Officer, East Morgan County Hospital, Brush, CO, p. A97

THORPE, Wendy, Area Director Information Systems, General Hospital, CA, p. A57

THORSEN, Erik, Chief Executive Officer, Columbia Memorial Hospital, Astoria, OR, p. A511

THORWALD, Robert, Chief Information Officer, Washington Hospital Healthcare System, Fremont, CA, p. A59

THOTAKURA, Raj, M.D., Medical Director, Old Vineyard Behavioral Health Services, Winston, NC, p. A463

THRASHER, Amanda, Director Nursing, Ellsworth County Medical Center, Ellsworth, KS, p. A234

THRASHER, Kimberly, Controller, Encompass Health Lakeshore Rehabilitation Hospital, Birmingham, AL, p. A14

THRASHER, Sherri, Executive Human Resources Partner, Spectrum Health Pennock, Hastings, MI, p. A315

THREEWITS, Sheree, Director Human Resources, Manatee Memorial Hospital, Bradenton, FL, p. A118

THRIFT, William Kyle, Chief Nursing Officer, Brandon Regional Hospital, Brandon, FL, p. A119

THULI, Karen, Information Systems Coordinator, Upland Hills Health, Dodgeville, WI, p. A691

THUN, Todd, Director Human Resources, Montana State Hospital, Warm Springs, MT, p. A379

THUN, Tracey, Director Business and Support Services, Montana State Hospital, Warm Springs, MT, p. A379

THUNELL, Adam, Chief Operating Officer and Vice President Operations, Community Memorial Hospital, CA, p. A94

THURBER, Joe, Director Information Technology, Central Regional Hospital, Butner, NC, p. A448

THURMER, DeAnn
   Chief Nursing Officer, Waupun Memorial Hospital, Waupun, WI, p. A705
   Chief Operating Officer, Waupun Memorial Hospital, Waupun, WI, p. A705
   Interim Chief Operating Officer and Chief Nursing Officer, Ripon Medical Center, Ripon, WI, p. A702

THURSTON, Thomas, M.D., Medical Director, J. D. Mccarty Center For Children With Developmental Disabilities, Norman, OK, p. A502

THYGESON, Cindy, M.D., Director Medical Affairs, Sutter Center For Psychiatry, Sacramento, CA, p. A82

THYNE, Shannon, Chief Medical Officer, Lac-Olive View-Ucla Medical Center, Los Angeles, CA, p. A68

TIBBITS, Dick, Vice President and Chief Operating Officer, Florida Hospital Tampa, Tampa, FL, p. A140

TIBBITS, Richard M, Vice President and Chief Operating Officer, Loma Linda University Medical Center-Murrieta, Murrieta, CA, p. A74

TIBBS, E W., President and Chief Executive Officer, Lynchburg General Hospital, VA, p. A660

TICE, Evan, Director Information Technology and Systems, Sky Ridge Medical Center, Lone Tree, CO, p. A103

TICE, Heidi, Chief Financial Officer, Cheyenne County Hospital, Saint Francis, KS, p. A245

TICE, Kirk C., President and Chief Executive Officer, Robert Wood Johnson University Hospital Rahway, Rahway, NJ, p. A411

TICE, Linda, Director Information Systems, Sagewest Health Care At Lander, WY, p. A709

TICHENOR, John, Chief Financial Officer, Ohio County Hospital, Hartford, KY, p. A253

TICHENOR, Rick, Chief Executive Officer, Accel Rehabilitation Hospital Of Plano, Plano, TX, p. A628

TIDWELL, Jan, Chief Nursing Officer, Cartersville Medical Center, Cartersville, GA, p. A149

TIDWELL, Tim, Human Resources Director, Wiregrass Medical Center, Geneva, AL, p. A18

TIDWELL, Wesley, Chief Operating Officer, Memorial Hermann The Woodlands Hospital, TX, p. A612

TIEDE, Brad, Director Information Systems, Memorial Community Health, Aurora, NE, p. A381

TIEDT, Douglas, M.D., Chief of Staff, Springs Memorial Hospital, Lancaster, SC, p. A555

TIEDT, Jerry, Director Information Systems, Waverly Health Center, Waverly, IA, p. A231

TIEFENTHALER, Brenda Marie, R.N., MSN, Vice President Patient Care and Informatics, Spencer Hospital, Spencer, IA, p. A230

TIEMENS, Linda, Chief Executive Officer, Vibra Hospital Of Richmond, Richmond, VA, p. A665

TIERNAN, Kelley, Chief Financial Officer, Claxton-Hepburn Medical Center, Ogdensburg, NY, p. A439

TIERNEY, Gregory, M.D., President, BMG and BHS Chief Medical Officer, Benefis Health Care-West Campus, MT, p. A376

TIERNEY, Mark A, Chief Financial Officer, Manatee Memorial Hospital, Bradenton, FL, p. A118

TIETJEN, Patricia, M.D., Vice President, Medical Affairs, New Milford Hospital, CT, p. A107

TIGGELAAR, Tom
Vice President Finance ad Chief Financial Officer, Mayo Clinic Health System - Franciscan Healthcare In Sparta, Sparta, WI, p. A703
Vice President Finance, Mayo Clinic Health System - Franciscan Healthcare In La Crosse, La Crosse, WI, p. A695

TILGHMAN, Bradley, Controller, Healthsouth Emerald Coast Rehabilitation Hospital, Panama City, FL, p. A135

TILLER, Debra, Director Personnel and Administrative Secretary, Healthmark Regional Medical Center, Defuniak Springs, FL, p. A121

TILLER, Jaconna Joni**, Chief Nursing Officer, Alliancehealth Midwest, Midwest City, OK, p. A501

TILLETT, Grant, Chief Information Officer, Prairie Lakes Healthcare System, Watertown, SD, p. A565

TILLMAN, Jill, Assistant Chief Executive Officer, Brandywine Hospital, Coatesville, PA, p. A523

TILLMAN, Kanner
Chief Financial Officer, Corona Regional Medical Center-Rehabilitation, CA, p. A55
Chief Financial Officer, Encino Hospital Medical Center, Los Angeles, CA, p. A66

TILLMAN, Michael C., President and Chief Executive Officer, United Hospital Center, Bridgeport, WV, p. A681

TILLMAN, Pamela P., Administrator, Lifebrite Community Hospital Of Stokes, Danbury, NC, p. A450

TILLMAN, Randy, M.D., Chief Medical Staff, Promise Hospital Of Miss Lou, Vidalia, LA, p. A280

TILLMAN-TAYLOR, Susan, Manager Human Resources, Hackensack Meridian Health Southern Ocean Medical Center, Manahawkin, NJ, p. A407

TILSON, Natalie, Controller, Healthsouth Rehabilitation Hospital, Kingsport, TN, p. A572

TIMANUS, Anthony, Chief Executive Officer, Avera Gregory Hospital, Gregory, SD, p. A561

TIMBERS, Christopher, Vice President and Chief Information Officer, Northbay Vacavalley Hospital, CA, p. A57

TIMBERS, Christopher T, Chief Information Officer, Sibley Memorial Hospital, Washington, DC, p. A116

TIMLIN, Marie, R.N., Chief Nursing Officer, Uchealth Yampa Valley Medical Center, Steamboat Springs, CO, p. A105

TIMM, Doreen, MSN, Senior Director and Chief Nursing Officer, Mercyhealth Hospital - Rockton Avenue, Rockford, IL, p. A194

TIMM, Karen, R.N., MSN, Vice President Patient Services, St. Anthony Regional Hospital, Carroll, IA, p. A218

TIMM, Mark, Executive Director Human Resources, Yavapai Regional Medical Center - East, AZ, p. A34

TIMM, Matt, M.D., Medical Director, Pender Community Hospital, Pender, NE, p. A389

TIMMER, Kari, Chief Financial Officer, Hegg Health Center Avera, Rock Valley, IA, p. A229

TIMMERMAN, Jo, Manager Accounting, Norwood Health Center, Marshfield, WI, p. A697

TIMMONS, William
Chief Executive Officer, Los Ninos Hospital, Phoenix, AZ, p. A33
President and Chief Executive Officer, Hacienda Children's Hospital, Mesa, AZ, p. A31

TIMPE, Ron, Chief Financial Officer, Floyd County Medical Center, Charles City, IA, p. A219

TINAGERO, Doris, Executive Director, Carrie Tingley Hospital, NM, p. A416

TINCH, Roberta, Chief Operations Officer, Spotsylvania Regional Medical Center, Fredericksburg, VA, p. A658

TINCHER, Pat, Director Finance, Aspirus Langlade Hospital, Antigo, WI, p. A689

TINDALL, Shedale, Chief Nursing Officer, The Pavilion At Williamsburg Place, Williamsburg, VA, p. A668

TINDLE, Jeff A., Chief Executive Officer, Carroll County Memorial Hospital, Carrollton, MO, p. A357

TINDLE, Tim, Chief Information Officer, Quentin Mease Hospital, TX, p. A611

TINGSTAD, Jonathan, Vice President and Chief Financial Officer, Seattle Cancer Care Alliance, Seattle, WA, p. A676

TINNERELLO, Jeremy, MSN, R.N., Chief Executive Officer, Chief Operating Officer, Glenwood Surgery Center, LA, p. A280

TINNERELLO, Jeremy M., CEN, MSN, RN, President, Glenwood Surgery Center, LA, p. A280

TINNESZ, Thomas, M.D., Chief Medical Officer, Chambers Memorial Hospital, Danville-Yell County, AR, p. A41

TINNEY, Sean, FACHE, Chief Operating Officer, Medical West, Bessemer, AL, p. A14

TINSA, Udom, M.D., Medical Director, Ashley Medical Center, Ashley, ND, p. A464

TINSLEY, Cassie, Director, Human Resources, Powell Valley Healthcare, Powell, WY, p. A709

TINSLEY, Edward D., III, Regional Administrator, Mcleod Seacoast, SC, p. A555

TINSLEY, Nancy M., R.N.
President, Rochester General Hospital, Rochester, NY, p. A441
President, Advocate Good Samaritan Hospital, Downers Grove, IL, p. A181

TIPPIN, Russell, Chief Executive Officer and Administrator, Permian Regional Medical Center, Andrews, TX, p. A583

TIPPS, Linda, Director Human Resources, Southern Tennessee Regional Health System-Sewanee, TN, p. A581

TIPTON, Gina, Director of Operations, Rehabilitation Hospital, Navicent Health, Macon, GA, p. A157

TIPTON, Maggie, Chief Information Officer, Unicoi County Memorial Hospital, Erwin, TN, p. A569

TIPTON, Peggy, Chief Operating Officer and Chief Nursing Officer, Oklahoma Heart Hospital, Oklahoma City, OK, p. A504

TIRA, Cheryl, Director Information Systems, Columbus Community Hospital, Columbus, NE, p. A383

TIRADO, Norma, Vice President, Human Resources and Health Information Technology, Lakeland Hospital, Watervliet, Watervliet, MI, p. A325

TISCHER, Jesse G.
Interim President, Aspirus Ontonagon Hospital, Inc., Ontonagon, MI, p. A320
Interim Presidnet, Aspirus Keweenaw Hospital, Inc., Laurium, MI, p. A318

TISDALE, Willis E, Director Human Resources, Shriners Hospitals For Children-Greenville, Greenville, SC, p. A554

TISDALL, Renae, Chief Financial Officer, Mobridge Regional Hospital, Mobridge, SD, p. A562

TISSIER, Becky, Chief Fiscal Service, Veterans Affairs Illiana Health Care System, Danville, IL, p. A180

TITO, David, M.D., President Medical Staff, Riverside Community Hospital, Riverside, CA, p. A81

TITSWORTH, Sue, Director Human Resources, Coleman County Medical Center, Coleman, TX, p. A593

TITTLE, JoDee, Chief Executive Officer, Southern Coos Hospital And Health Center, Bandon, OR, p. A511

TITUS, Monica B., BSN, MBA, RN
Regional Chief Executive Officer, Acuity Specialty Hospital Of New Jersey, Atlantic City, NJ, p. A402
Regional Chief Executive Officer, Acuity Specialty Hospital Of Southern New Jersey, Willingboro, NJ, p. A414

TOALSON, Jason, Chief Executive Officer, Cottonwood Springs Hospital, Olathe, KS, p. A242

TOBEY, Shelley R, R.N., MS, Chief Operating Officer and Chief Nursing Officer, Texas Health Presbyterian Hospital Flower Mound, Flower Mound, TX, p. A603

TOBIN, Hugh, Chief Financial Officer, Davis Regional Medical Center, Statesville, NC, p. A461

TOBIN, Ryan, President and Chief Executive Officer, Rose Medical Center, Denver, CO, p. A99

TOBIN-PAYNE, Cindy, Director, Magee Rehabilitation Hospital, Philadelphia, PA, p. A535

TOBLER, Randy, M.D.
Chief Executive Officer, Scotland County Hospital, Memphis, MO, p. A364
Chief Medical Officer, Scotland County Hospital, Memphis, MO, p. A364

TOCCO-BRADLEY, Rosalie, Ph.D., M.D.
Chief Medical Officer, St. Joseph Mercy Ann Arbor, Ypsilanti, MI, p. A326
Chief Medical Officer, St. Joseph Mercy Livingston Hospital, Howell, MI, p. A315

TODD, David, M.D., President Medical Staff, Chi St. Luke's Health Memorial Specialty Hospital, Lufkin, TX, p. A621

TODD, Kimberly, Chief Nursing Officer, Alliancehealth Clinton, Clinton, OK, p. A497

TODD, Mark, Senior Systems Administrator, Hamilton Memorial Hospital District, Mcleansboro, IL, p. A189

TODD, Nate, Chief Financial Officer, North Little Rock Division, AR, p. A45

TODD, Robbie, Director Information Technology, Horn Memorial Hospital, Ida Grove, IA, p. A224

TODD, Shawn, Chief Executive Officer, Pam Rehabilitation Hospital Of Victoria, Victoria, TX, p. A642

TODD, Steve J., Chief Executive Officer, St. Luke Community Healthcare, Ronan, MT, p. A378

TODOROW, Thomas, Chief Financial Officer and Executive Vice President, Children's Hospital Of Philadelphia, Philadelphia, PA, p. A534

TOEDT, Michael E, M.D., Director Clinical Services, Cherokee Indian Hospital, Cherokee, NC, p. A450

TOFANI, Barbara F., R.N., MSN, Senior Vice President and Chief Nursing Officer, Children's Hospital, OH, p. A474

TOJINO, Allan, Director, Information Systems, Bayview Behavioral Health Campus, CA, p. A74

TOKAR, Andrew, Chief Financial Officer, Overlake Medical Center, Bellevue, WA, p. A669

TOL, Daryl, President and Chief Executive Officer, Winter Park Memorial Hospital, FL, p. A134

TOLBERT, James, Director Information Systems, Eastar Health System, East Campus, OK, p. A502

TOLEDO, Iris, Chief Nursing Officer, Hospital Pavia Arecibo, Arecibo, PR, p. A712

TOLINE, Tyler, FACHE, Chief Executive Officer, Saunders Medical Center, Wahoo, NE, p. A391

TOLLEFSON, Sue, Coordinator Payroll Personnel, Granite Falls Health, Granite Falls, MN, p. A332

TOLLEY, Cherie, Chief Executive Officer, Willingway Hospital, Statesboro, GA, p. A161

TOLLIVER, Amy, Administrator, Magee General Hospital, Magee, MS, p. A349

TOLSON, Rick
Chief Administrative Officer and Chief Human Resources Officer, Christ Hospital, Cincinnati, OH, p. A474
Divisional Chief People Officer, Hshs St. Joseph's Hospital, Chippewa Falls, WI, p. A691

TOMAS, George, Director Information Services, Griffin Hospital, Derby, CT, p. A107

TOMASESKI, Gina, Chief Executive Officer, Icare Rehabilitation Hospital, Flower Mound, TX, p. A603

TOMASO, Nancy, Vice President, Patient Care Services, Whitinsville Medical Center, MA, p. A302

TOME, Michael, M.D., Medical Director, Kaiser Foundation Mental Health Center, CA, p. A67

TOMLIN, Jeff, M.D., Chief Medical and Quality Officer, Evergreenhealth, Kirkland, WA, p. A673

TOMLIN, Kerry W, Associate Administrator, Clay County Hospital, Ashland, AL, p. A13

TOMLINSON, Charles M, M.D., Chief Medical Officer, Carolinas Healthcare System Cleveland, Shelby, NC, p. A460

TOMLINSON, David
Executive Vice President Chief Financial Officer and Chief Information Officer, Centegra Hospital - Woodstock, Woodstock, IL, p. A198
Executive Vice President Chief Financial Officer and Chief Information Officer, Centegra Hospital-Huntley, IL, p. A189
Senior Vice President, Chief Information Officer, Centegra Hospital - Woodstock, Woodstock, IL, p. A198

TOMLINSON, Sallie, Manager Human Resources, Arbuckle Memorial Hospital, Sulphur, OK, p. A507

TOMORY, Gerald, M.D.
Regional Medical Director, Kauai Veterans Memorial Hospital, Waimea, HI, p. A166
Regional Medical Director, Samuel Mahelona Memorial Hospital, Kapaa, HI, p. A166

TOMPKINS, Charles, M.D., Chief of Staff, Crenshaw Community Hospital, Luverne, AL, p. A20

TOMPKINS, Kim, Director Information Services, Detar Hospital North, TX, p. A642

TOMPKINS, Misti, Employee Relations Director, Osf St. Joseph Medical Center, Bloomington, IL, p. A174

TOMPKINS, Tommy, Vice President, Finance and Chief Financial Officer, Yukon-Kuskokwim Delta Regional Hospital, Bethel, AK, p. A25

TOMSU, Karen, MSN, R.N., Chief Nursing Officer, Baptist Hospitals Of Southeast Texas Fannin Behavioral Health Center, TX, p. A588

TONER, Tina, Director of Nursing, North Big Horn Hospital District, Lovell, WY, p. A709

TONEY, Patty, R.N., MSN, Chief Nurse Executive, Christus Santa Rosa-Medical Center, TX, p. A632

TONG, Cheryl, Corporate Chief Financial Officer, Community Hospital Of Huntington Park, Huntington Park, CA, p. A62

TONGATE, Scott A., Chief Financial Officer, Macon Community Hospital, Lafayette, TN, p. A573

TONJES, Ken, Chief Financial Officer, Peacehealth Ketchikan Medical Center, Ketchikan, AK, p. A26

TONN, Deb L, Vice President Patient Care, Campbell County Health, Gillette, WY, p. A708

TONNU, Lannie, Senior Vice President and Chief Financial Officer, Children's Hospital Los Angeles, Los Angeles, CA, p. A66

TOOKE, Ryan, Chief Executive Officer, Dahl Memorial Healthcare Association, Ekalaka, MT, p. A375

TOOLE, LaDon, Vice President Network Operations, Mitchell County Hospital, Camilla, GA, p. A149

TOOLE, Patricia, Vice President Human Resources, East Mountain Hospital, Belle Mead, NJ, p. A402

TOOLE, Trish, Vice President Administrative Services, Carrier Clinic, Belle Mead, NJ, p. A402

TOON, William, Chief Information Officer, Baptist Hospitals Of Southeast Texas Fannin Behavioral Health Center, TX, p. A588

TOPOLEWSKI, Ted, Chief Executive Officer, Madison Parish Hospital, Tallulah, LA, p. A280

TOPPEN, Jacki, Director of Nursing, Prairie St. John'S, Fargo, ND, p. A466

TORBETT, Russell B, Director Human Resources, Creek Nation Community Hospital, Okemah, OK, p. A502

TORCHIA, Jude, Chief Executive Officer, Orthocolorado Hospital, Lakewood, CO, p. A102

TORCHIA NEA-BC, Lisa F, MSN, R.N., Vice President and Chief Nursing Officer, Geisinger Holy Spirit, Camp Hill, PA, p. A521

TORGE, Andrew, Director Human Resources, Shasta Regional Medical Center, Redding, CA, p. A80

TORMANEN, John, Director Mission and Human Resources, Chi St. Joseph's Health, Park Rapids, MN, p. A337

TORO PALACIOS, Belinda L., Executive Director, Doctors Center, Manati, PR, p. A714

TORONTOW, R. John, M.D., Chief Medical Staff, Cedar County Memorial Hospital, El Dorado Springs, MO, p. A358

TOROSSIAN, Lynn M., President and Chief Executive Officer, Henry Ford West Bloomfield Hospital, West Bloomfield, MI, p. A325

TORRES, Anthony, M.D.
Chief Medical Officer, Yavapai Regional Medical Center - East, AZ, p. A34
Manager Information Technology, Blue Mountain Hospital, Blanding, UT, p. A646

TORRES, Jose M., Executive Director, St. Luke's Episcopal Hospital, Ponce, PR, p. A714

TORRES, Maribel, Chief Nursing Officer, Hialeah Hospital, Hialeah, FL, p. A124

TORRES, Mayra, CPA, Chief Financial Officer, Ashford Presbyterian Community Hospital, San Juan, PR, p. A715

TORRES, Tammy, R.N., MSN, Chief Executive Officer, Memorial Hospital Of Salem County, Salem, NJ, p. A411

TORRES, Victor, Information Technology Specialist Administrator, El Paso Behavioral Health System, El Paso, TX, p. A601

TORRES AYALA, Eugenio, Director Information Systems, Cardiovascular Center Of Puerto Rico And The Caribbean, San Juan, PR, p. A715

TORRICO, Pat, Chief Nursing Officer, Osf Saint Elizabeth Medical Center, Ottawa, IL, p. A192

TORSCH, Peter, Chief Financial Officer, St. Charles Parish Hospital, Luling, LA, p. A273

TORTELLA, Anthony, Chief Financial Officer, Fairmount Behavioral Health System, Philadelphia, PA, p. A534

TOSTEBERG, Chris, Superintendent, Mental Health Institute, Cherokee, IA, p. A219

TOSTENSON, Brad, Chief Information Officer, Essentia Health-Graceville, Graceville, MN, p. A332

TOSTI, Debra, Chief Executive Officer, Tewksbury Hospital, Tewksbury, MA, p. A305

TOTAH, Sam, Chief Operating Officer, Kaiser Permanente San Diego Medical Center, CA, p. A83

TOUCHSTONE, Pat, Chief Nursing Officer, Crane Memorial Hospital, Crane, TX, p. A595

TOUPS, Sharon A, Senior Vice President and Chief Operating Officer, St. Tammany Parish Hospital, Covington, LA, p. A266

TOURE', Joahd, M.D., Chief Medical Officer, Adirondack Health, Saranac Lake, NY, p. A442

TOURIGNY, Barry
Human Resources Director, Woodridge Hospital, TN, p. A571
Vice President Human Resources and Organizational Development, Hoops Family Children's Hospital, WV, p. A683

TOUSIGNANT, Grace, R.N., MSN
Chief Nursing Officer, Aspirus Ironwood Hospitals & Clinics, Inc., Ironwood, MI, p. A316
Chief Nursing Officer, Aspirus Keweenaw Hospital, Inc., Laurium, MI, p. A318

TOUVELLE, Cynthia, R.N., Senior Director Care Management and Chief Nursing Officer, Barnesville Hospital, Barnesville, OH, p. A471

TOWERY, O B, M.D., Chief of Staff, John Muir Behavioral Health Center, Concord, CA, p. A55

TOWLE, Sonya, Director Human Resources, Mercy Hospital, Moose Lake, MN, p. A336

TOWN, Alex
Chief Financial Officer, Samaritan Healthcare, Moses Lake, WA, p. A673
Vice President Finance, Tri-State Memorial Hospital, Clarkston, WA, p. A670

TOWNDROW, Geraldine, R.N., Senior Vice President Nursing, Exempla West Pines, CO, p. A106

TOWNE, Jana, Nurse Executive, U.S. Public Health Service Indian Hospital-Whiteriver, Whiteriver, AZ, p. A38

TOWNER, Chad, Chief Executive Officer, Saint Joseph Health System, Mishawaka, IN, p. A211

TOWNES, Tim, Director Information Systems, Grandview Medical Center, Birmingham, AL, p. A14

TOWNLEY, Nancy, R.N., Senior Vice President Operations, United Regional Health Care System-Eleventh Street Campus, TX, p. A644

TOWNLEY, Patricia, Director Operations, Lasting Hope Recovery Center, NE, p. A387

TOWNSEND, Alan, Interim Chief Financial Officer, Trinity Springs Pavilion, TX, p. A604

TOWNSEND, Cathy, Chief Nursing Officer, Banner - University Medical Center South, Tucson, AZ, p. A36

TOWNSEND, Dona E, Chief Nursing Officer, Navarro Regional Hospital, Corsicana, TX, p. A595

TOWNSEND, Gary, Chief Information Officer, Hurley Children's Hospital, MI, p. A312

TOWNSEND, Michael, Chief Information Officer, James Cancer Hospital And Solove Research Institute, Columbus, OH, p. A478

TOWNSEND, Mike, Interim Director Health Information Systems, Grady Memorial Hospital, Chickasha, OK, p. A497

TOWNSEND, Sammuel, LAN Administrator, University Of Mississippi Medical Center Holmes County, Lexington, MS, p. A349

TOWNSEND, Tanya, Senior Vice President, Chief Information Officer (part of LCMC), Children's Hospital, New Orleans, LA, p. A275

TOWNSEND, Theodore E., FACHE
Interim Chief Executive Officer, Unitypoint Health - Finley Hospital, Dubuque, IA, p. A222
President and Chief Executive Officer, Unitypoint Health - St. Luke's Hospital, Cedar Rapids, IA, p. A218

TOY, Linda, Director Information Systems, Havasu Regional Medical Center, Lake Havasu City, AZ, p. A30

TOY, Stanley, Jr, M.D., Chief Executive Officer, Greater El Monte Community Hospital, South El Monte, CA, p. A90

TRABAL, Milton, Chief Financial Officer, Clarinda Regional Health Center, Clarinda, IA, p. A219

TRAC, Vincent, Chief Executive Officer, Kindred Hospital-Ontario, Ontario, CA, p. A76

TRACEY, Karen, Chief Human Resources, Select Specialty Hospital-Greensboro, Greensboro, NC, p. A453

TRACY, Allen R, Senior Vice President and Chief Financial Officer, St. John Medical Center, Westlake, OH, p. A493

TRACY, Larry A., Jr, FACHE, President, Beacon Children's Hospital, IN, p. A215

TRACY, Pat, Administrator, Ridgeview Behavioral Hospital, Middle Point, OH, p. A487

TRACY, Thomas, Jr, Chief Medical Officer, Penn State Children's Hospital, PA, p. A527

TRACY, Timothy J., Senior Director, Sanford Vermillion Medical Center, Vermillion, SD, p. A564

TRACZ, Robert B, CPA, Senior Vice President and Chief Financial Officer, Tripoint Medical Center, OH, p. A479

TRAHAN, Jennifer Lynch, Assistant Vice President Human Resources, Our Lady Of Lourdes Regional Medical Center, Lafayette, LA, p. A271

TRAHAN, John, Director Information Systems, Women's And Children's Hospital, Lafayette, LA, p. A272

TRAHAN, Leslie, Chief Executive Officer, Calcasieu Oaks Geriatric Psychiatric Hospital, LA, p. A265

TRAHAN, Thomas, M.D., Chief of Medical Staff, Lane Regional Medical Center, Zachary, LA, p. A281

TRAHERN, Sheri, CPA, FACHE, Chief Executive Officer, St. Thomas More Hospital, Canon City, CO, p. A97

TRAIL, Alan, Director Information Systems, Owensboro Health Muhlenberg Community Hospital, Greenville, KY, p. A252

TRAINER, Michael, Chief Financial Officer, Akron Children's Hospital, Akron, OH, p. A470

TRAINOR, Karyn, Director Human Resources, St. Patrick Hospital, Missoula, MT, p. A378

TRAINOR, Paul, Senior Vice President Finance and Chief Financial Officer, Southern New Hampshire Medical Center, Nashua, NH, p. A400

TRAISTER, Lynne, Controller, Healthsouth Rehabilitation Hospital Of Tinton Falls, Tinton Falls, NJ, p. A412

TRAMMELL, Patrick, Chief Executive Officer, Dekalb Regional Medical Center, Fort Payne, AL, p. A18

TRAMP, Francis G., President, Burgess Health Center, Onawa, IA, p. A227

TRAN, Ann, Chief Financial Officer, Pike County Memorial Hospital, Louisiana, MO, p. A363

TRAN, Khiem, M.D., Acting Chief of Staff, Veterans Affairs Illiana Health Care System, Danville, IL, p. A180

TRAN, Lac, Senior Vice President Information Services, Rush Children's Hospital, IL, p. A179

TRAN, Richard, Director Information Technology, Galesburg Cottage Hospital, Galesburg, IL, p. A183

TRAN, Thanh, FACHE, Chief Executive Officer, North Central Surgical Center, Dallas, TX, p. A597

TRANCHINA, Scott, R.N., MSN, Administrator, Cobalt Rehabilitation Hospital Of New Orleans, New Orleans, LA, p. A275

TRANSIER, Rhonda, Financial Officer, Rusk State Hospital, Rusk, TX, p. A631

TRANTALIS, Carolyn, R.N., MSN
Chief Operating Officer, East Region, Windham Hospital, Willimantic, CT, p. A112
Regional Vice President, Clinical Services and Operations, The William W. Backus Hospital, Norwich, CT, p. A110

TRANTHAM, Susan, Director Human Resources, Encompass Health Rehabilitation Hospital Of Florence, Florence, SC, p. A552

TRAPNELL, Kerry A., Chief Executive Officer, Elbert Memorial Hospital, Elberton, GA, p. A153

TRAPP, John, Vice President Medical Affairs, Bryan Medical Center-West, NE, p. A385

TRAUTMAN, Bob, Chief Executive Officer, Saline Memorial Hospital, Benton-Saline County, AR, p. A39

TRAVIS, Calee, R.N., Chief Nursing Officer, Baylor Scott & White Medical Center - Centennial, Frisco, TX, p. A606

TRAVIS, David A
Chief Financial Officer, Freestone Medical Center, Fairfield, TX, p. A603
Chief Financial Officer, Ut Health Athens, Athens, TX, p. A585

TRAVIS, Dee Dee, Vice President Community Relations, Calais Regional Hospital, Calais, ME, p. A283

TRAVIS, Sara, Chief Nursing Officer and Assistant Administrator, Palo Alto County Health System, Emmetsburg, IA, p. A222

TRAXLER, Martin J., Chief Executive Officer, Robley Rex Veterans Affairs Medical Center, Louisville, KY, p. A256

TRAYLOR, Desiree, Chief Information Officer, Chickasaw Nation Medical Center, Ada, OK, p. A495

TRAYLOR, Jerri Sue, Director Human Resources, The Women's Hospital, Newburgh, IN, p. A213

TRAYNOR, Karen, Chief Financial Officer, Richland Hospital, Richland Center, WI, p. A702

TRCZINSKI, Judi, Vice President and Chief Human Resources Officer, Hospital For Special Care, New Britain, CT, p. A109

TREACY, Nancy, Director Finance, Cambridge Medical Center, Cambridge, MN, p. A329

TREACY-SHIFF, Mary, Vice President Finance, Advocate Good Samaritan Hospital, Downers Grove, IL, p. A181

TREADWAY, Michael G, Controller, Christus Trinity Mother Frances Rehabilitation Hospital, A Partner Of Encompass Health, Tyler, TX, p. A641

TREADWELL, Karen, Director Human Resources, Lake Martin Community Hospital, Dadeville, AL, p. A16

TREASE, Kevin, Chief Information Officer, Antelope Memorial Hospital, Neligh, NE, p. A387

TREASURE, Angela, Chief Nursing Officer, Portneuf Medical Center, Pocatello, ID, p. A171

TREASURE, Jeffrey
Chief Financial Officer, Northern Arizona Healthcare, Flagstaff Medical Center, Flagstaff, AZ, p. A29
Chief Financial Officer, Northern Arizona Healthcare, Verde Valley Medical Center, Cottonwood, AZ, p. A29

TREASURE, Martin, Director Human Resources, Lehigh Valley Hospital - Schuylkill, Pottsville, PA, p. A539

TREECE, Amy, M.D., Medical Director, North Greenville Hospital, Travelers Rest, SC, p. A557

TREGLOWN, Brad, Director Information Systems, Redmond Regional Medical Center, Rome, GA, p. A159

TREHAN, Rajeev, M.D., M.P.H., Chief of Staff, Veterans Affairs Eastern Kansas Health Care System-Dwight D. Eisenhower Veterans Affairs Medical Center, KS, p. A246

TREITLER, Scot, Chief Operating Officer, Cypress Pointe Surgical Hospital, Hammond, LA, p. A268

TREMAINE, Lisa, Manager Human Resources, Carson Valley Medical Center, Gardnerville, NV, p. A393

TREMBLE, Nakia, Chief Executive Officer, Kindred Hospital Indianapolis North, Indianapolis, IN, p. A207

TREMONTI, Carl
Chief Financial Officer, Mease Countryside Hospital, Safety Harbor, FL, p. A137
Chief Financial Officer, Mease Dunedin Hospital, Dunedin, FL, p. A122
Chief Financial Officer, Morton Plant Hospital, Clearwater, FL, p. A119
Chief Financial Officer, Morton Plant North Bay Hospital, New Port Richey, FL, p. A132
Chief Financial Officer, South Florida Baptist Hospital, Plant City, FL, p. A136
Chief Financial Officer, St. Anthony's Hospital, Saint Petersburg, FL, p. A138

TREMONTI, Yvette, Chief Financial Officer, H. Lee Moffitt Cancer Center And Research Institute, Tampa, FL, p. A140

TRENDE, Gary D, FACHE, Associate Director, Tuscaloosa Veterans Affairs Medical Center, Tuscaloosa, AL, p. A24

TRENSCHEL, Robert, D.O., FACHE, M.P.H., President and Chief Executive Officer, Yuma Regional Medical Center, Yuma, AZ, p. A38

TRENT, Cindy, Manager Personnel, Fall River Hospital, Hot Springs, SD, p. A561

TRESSLER, Carrie, Vice President of Nursing and Chief Nursing Officer, Rush Memorial Hospital, Rushville, IN, p. A214

TRETINA, Mike, Senior Vice President and Chief Financial Officer, Bayhealth Medical Center, Milford Memorial Hospital, DE, p. A113

TRETTER, Stan, M.D., Chief Medical Officer, Memorial Hospital And Health Care Center, Jasper, IN, p. A208

TREVATHAN, Dave, Director Information Systems, Rose Medical Center, Denver, CO, p. A99

TREVINO, Chris, M.D., Chief Medical Officer, St. Elizabeth Hospital, Gonzales, LA, p. A268

TREVINO, Jorge, Chief Executive Officer, City Hospital At White Rock, Dallas, TX, p. A596

TREVINO, Malissa, Director Human Resources, Pecos County Memorial Hospital, Fort Stockton, TX, p. A604

TREVINO, Paul, Chief Executive Officer, Christus Southeast Texas Hospital-St. Mary, TX, p. A588

TREVISANI, Michael F, M.D., Senior Vice President and Chief Medical Officer, St. Luke's Campus, NY, p. A444

TRIANA, Rudy, M.D., Chief of Staff, Jackson Purchase Medical Center, Mayfield, KY, p. A257

TRICKEY, Donna, R.N., Chief Nursing Officer, Fairview Park Hospital, Dublin, GA, p. A153

TRIEBES, David G., Chief Executive Officer, Samaritan Albany General Hospital, Albany, OR, p. A511

TRIGG, Terry, Director Human Resources, Merit Health Wesley, Hattiesburg, MS, p. A347

TRIMBLE, Deborah, R.N., Chief Executive Officer, Paul B. Hall Regional Medical Center, Paintsville, KY, p. A259

TRIMBLE, Donald, CPA, Chief Financial Officer, Vibra Specialty Hospital At Desoto, Desoto, TX, p. A600

TRIMBLE, Lisa, Controller, Healthsouth Rehabilitation Hospital Of Middletown, Middletown, DE, p. A113

TRIMM, Robert, Administrator, North Mississippi Medical Center-Hamilton, Hamilton, AL, p. A19

TRIMMER, Mary R, Interim Chief Operating Officer, Mount Carmel West Hospital, OH, p. A478

TRIMMER, Matthew, Director Information Services, Holy Cross Hospital, Silver Spring, MD, p. A294

TRINCHETTO, Thomas, M.D., Chief Medical Officer, Doctors Hospital Of Sarasota, Sarasota, FL, p. A138

TRINH, Khiet, M.D., Chief Medical Officer, Bon Secours St. Mary's Children's Services, VA, p. A664

TRIPLETT, Daniel, Acting Chief Operating Officer, Springfield Hospital Center, Sykesville, MD, p. A294

TRIPLETT, John, D.O., President Medical Staff, Arh Our Lady Of The Way, Martin, KY, p. A257

TRIPLETT, Robin, Chief Financial Officer, Southern Coos Hospital And Health Center, Bandon, OR, p. A511

TRIPP, Gina, Director Information Systems, Tirr Memorial Hermann, Houston, TX, p. A614

TRIPP, Kelly, Chief Executive Officer, Ten Broeck Tennessee Treatment Facility, Cookeville, TN, p. A568

TRIPPEL, Donald E, Chief Financial Officer, Hugh Chatham Memorial Hospital, Elkin, NC, p. A452

TRITTIN, Kim, Manager Human Resources, Mayo Clinic Health System In Red Wing, Red Wing, MN, p. A338

TRIVEDI, Harsh, M.D., President and Chief Executive Officer, Sheppard Pratt Health System, Baltimore, MD, p. A289

TRIVETTE, Chastity, Chief Executive Officer, Johnson County Community Hospital, Mountain City, TN, p. A576

TRIVETTE, Theresa, R.N., Chief Nursing Officer, Florida Hospital Tampa, Tampa, FL, p. A140

TROCINO, Mark, Chief Information Officer, Dekalb Medical At Hillandale, Lithonia, GA, p. A156

TROGMAN, Richard, FACHE, Chief Operating Officer, Kaiser Permanente Woodland Hills Medical Center, Los Angeles, CA, p. A67

TROLLOPE, Grant, Chief Financial Officer, Northeastern Nevada Regional Hospital, Elko, NV, p. A392

TROMBATORE, Beverly, R.N., Director Managed Information Systems, Matagorda Regional Medical Center, Bay City, TX, p. A587

TROMBLEE, Julie, R.N., Chief Nursing Officer, Moses Ludington Hospital, NY, p. A426

TROMPETER, Dawn, President, Osf Saint Paul Medical Center, Mendota, IL, p. A189

TRONCONE, Michael T, Chief Human Resources Officer, Calvary Hospital, New York (Includes All Hospitals Located Within The Five Boroughs), NY, p. A431

TROSCLAIR, Andree, Vice President Human Resources, Arkansas Children's Hospital, Little Rock-Pulaski County, AR, p. A44

TROSIN, Jill A., R.N., MSN, Vice President Patient Care Services, Chief Nursing Officer, St. Luke's Hospital, Maumee, OH, p. A486

TROTTER, Wally, Director Human Resources, Mountain View Hospital, Payson, UT, p. A649

TROTTIER, Timothy R., Chief Executive Officer, Spring View Hospital, Lebanon, KY, p. A254

TROUBLEFIELD, David, Chief Communications Officer, Hemphill County Hospital, Canadian, TX, p. A591

TROUP, Bill, M.D., Chief of Staff, Stanton County Hospital, Johnson, KS, p. A237

TROUP, Matthew, President and Chief Executive Officer, Conway Regional Medical Center, Conway-Faulkner County, AR, p. A40

TROUT, Gene, Chief Financial Officer, Weirton Medical Center, Weirton, WV, p. A687

TROUTMAN, Gary, CPA, Chief Financial Officer, Baptist Hospitals Of Southeast Texas Fannin Behavioral Health Center, TX, p. A588

TROWHILL, Jan, Director Health Information Management Systems, Spire Cane Creek Rehabilitation Hospital, Martin, TN, p. A574

TROXELL, Larry, Chief Executive Officer, Comanche County Medical Center, Comanche, TX, p. A593

TROY, Patrick J, R.N., MSN, Associate Director Patient Care Services, Lyons Division, NJ, p. A404

TROY, Peggy N.
President and Chief Executive Officer, Children's Hospital Of Wisconsin-Fox Valley, Neenah, WI, p. A699
President and Chief Executive Officer, Children's Hospital Of Wisconsin, Milwaukee, WI, p. A698

TROYER, David, Chief Information Officer, Veterans Affairs Northern Indiana Health Care System-Marion Campus, IN, p. A204

TROYER, Devin, M.D., Medical Director, Encompass Health Rehabilitation Hospital Of Columbia, Columbia, SC, p. A551

TROYO-SAUVIAC, Glynda, Chief Executive Officer, Vibra Hospital Of Central Dakotas, Mandan, ND, p. A467

TRUE, Terry, M.D., Chief of Staff, Shoals Hospital, Muscle Shoals, AL, p. A22

TRUEBLOOD, Susan
Chief Executive Officer, Georgia Regional Hospital At Atlanta, Decatur, GA, p. A152
Regional Hospital Administrator, Central State Hospital, Milledgeville, GA, p. A157

TRUELOVE, Lynn, Chief Executive Officer, Stone County Hospital, Wiggins, MS, p. A354

TRUESDALE, Fred A, Jr, Administrator, North Mississippi Medical Center-Iuka, Iuka, MS, p. A347

TRUESDALE, Fred A., Jr, Administrator, North Mississippi Medical Center-Iuka, Iuka, MS, p. A347

TRUESDELL, Shannon, Chief Operating Officer, Marshall Medical Center, Placerville, CA, p. A78

TRUITT, Louise
Human Resource Director, Coliseum Northside Hospital, Macon, GA, p. A156
Vice President Human Resources, Capital Regional Medical Center, Tallahassee, FL, p. A140

TRUJILLO, Jesse, Chief Information Officer, St. Mark's Hospital, Salt Lake City, UT, p. A651

TRUMAN, Julia
Chief Operating Officer, Allenmore Hospital, WA, p. A679
Vice President Human Resources, Fort Walton Beach Medical Center, Fort Walton Beach, FL, p. A123

TRUMAN, Lisa, Chief Nursing Officer, Sea Pines Rehabilitation Hospital, Melbourne, FL, p. A129

TRUMAN, Mark, Vice President of Operations, Baptist Health Floyd, New Albany, IN, p. A212

TRYON, Ellen, R.N., Chief Nursing Officer, Adventist Medical Center-Portland, Portland, OR, p. A516

TSAI, James, M.D., President, New York Eye And Ear Infirmary Of Mount Sinai, New York (Includes All Hospitals Located Within The Five Boroughs), NY, p. A434

TSALATE, Cynthia, Human Resource Specialist, U.S. Public Health Service Indian Hospital, Zuni, NM, p. A420

TSAMBIRAS, Petros, M.D., Chief of Staff, Florida Hospital Dade City, Dade City, FL, p. A121

TSAO, Sean, Director Information Technology, Blue Mountain Hospital, John Day, OR, p. A514

TSE, Graham, M.D., Chief Medical Officer, Memorialcare, Miller Children's & Women's Hospital Long Beach, Long Beach, CA, p. A65

TSENG, Allen, Chief Operations Officer, Memorial Hermann Memorial City Medical Center, Houston, TX, p. A612

TSO, Ron, Chief Executive Officer, Chinle Comprehensive Health Care Facility, Chinle, AZ, p. A28

TSUNEISHI, Lani, Nursing Services Manager, Hawaii State Hospital, Kaneohe, HI, p. A166

TUAZON, Nelson, R.N., Chief Nursing Officer, St. Luke's Baptist Hospital, TX, p. A632

TUBBS, John, M.D.
Chief of Staff, Rock County Hospital, Bassett, NE, p. A381
Chief of Staff, West Holt Medical Services, Atkinson, NE, p. A381

TUBBS, Mary Beth, Chief Nursing Officer, Astria Sunnyside Hospital, Sunnyside, WA, p. A678

TUBERVILLE, Abby, Human Resource Manager, Fillmore County Hospital, Geneva, NE, p. A384

TUCK, Greg, Area Information Officer, Kaiser Permanente San Jose Medical Center, San Jose, CA, p. A86

TUCKER, Albert, Chief Financial Officer, Miami Veterans Affairs Healthcare System, Miami, FL, p. A130

TUCKER, Amy, MD, Interim Chief Medical Officer, Upstate University Hospital At Community General, NY, p. A444

TUCKER, Andy, Chief Financial Officer, South Mississippi State Hospital, Purvis, MS, p. A352

TUCKER, Cathy, Director Human Resources, Iraan General Hospital, Iraan, TX, p. A615

TUCKER, Denis, Chief Information Officer, Wilkes-Barre General Hospital, PA, p. A544

TUCKER, Gary C., President and Chief Executive Officer, Mount St. Mary's Hospital And Health Center, Lewiston, NY, p. A429

TUCKER, Ian, M.D., Vice President Medical Affairs, Johnson Memorial Medical Center, Stafford Springs, CT, p. A111

TUCKER, Jessie Lee, Ph.D., III, Senior Vice President and Chief Operating Officer, Bristol-Myers Squibb Children's Hospital, NJ, p. A408

TUCKER, John
Chief Executive Officer, Mt. San Rafael Hospital, Trinidad, CO, p. A106
Chief Nursing Executive, Center For Behavioral Medicine, Kansas City, MO, p. A361

TUCKER, Joseph B, Senior Vice President and Chief Financial Officer, Fort Washington Medical Center, Oxen Hill, MD, p. A293

TUCKER, Joseph B., Acting President and Chief Executive Officer, Fort Washington Medical Center, Oxen Hill, MD, p. A293

TUCKER, Meagan, Director Human Resources, Black River Medical Center, Poplar Bluff, MO, p. A366

TUCKER, Mona, Director Human Resources, Seton Medical Center Harker Heights, Harker Heights, TX, p. A608

TUCKER, Rebecca
Chief Financial Officer, Memorial Hermann Northeast, Humble, TX, p. A615
President, Texas Health Hospital Clearfork, TX, p. A605

TUCKER, Ron, Business Office Manager, Kiowa County Memorial Hospital, Greensburg, KS, p. A236

TUCKER, Sarah, Chief Nursing Officer, Bradley County Medical Center, Warren-Bradley County, AR, p. A49

TUCKER, Steven E, Chief Executive Officer, Memorial Medical Center - Lee Campus, PA, p. A528

TUCKER, Steven E., Chief Executive Officer, Memorial Medical Center - Lee Campus, PA, p. A528

TUCKER, Theresa, Human Resources Officer, Sioux Center Health, Sioux Center, IA, p. A229

TUCKER, Tom, Chief Executive Officer, Valir Rehabilitation Hospital, Oklahoma City, OK, p. A505

TUDELA, John M, M.D., Director of Medical Affairs, Commonwealth Health Center, Saipan, MP, p. A711

TUDOR, Brandon, Chief Executive Officer, Encompass Health Rehabilitation Hospital Of Plano, Plano, TX, p. A628

TUDOR, Nathan, Chief Executive Officer, El Campo Memorial Hospital, El Campo, TX, p. A601

TULLIER, Debbie, Chief Executive Officer, Lake Pines Hospital, Kenner, LA, p. A270

TULLIS, Bea, Chief Financial Officer and Budget Officer, Broughton Hospital, Morganton, NC, p. A457

TULLMAN, Stephen M., Chief Executive Officer, Phoenixville Hospital, Phoenixville, PA, p. A537

TUMA, Bonnie, Human Resources Team Lead, Children's Inn At Nih, MD, p. A290

TUMA, Roman, Chief Medical Officer, Easton Hospital, Easton, PA, p. A524

TUMLIN, Richard, Chief Administrative Officer, Saint Thomas Highlands Hospital, Sparta, TN, p. A580

TUMMONS, Coleen, Chief Executive Officer, Gove County Medical Center, Quinter, KS, p. A244

TUMMURU, Ramireddy K, M.D., Chief Medical Officer, Porter Regional Hospital, Valparaiso, IN, p. A215

TUNGATE, Rex A.
Chief Executive Officer, Casey County Hospital, Liberty, KY, p. A255
Chief Executive Officer, Jane Todd Crawford Hospital, Greensburg, KY, p. A252

TUNNELL, Richard, Chief Information Officer, University Hospital, Newark, NJ, p. A409

TUNSON, Lynn, Manager Medical Records, Complex Care Hospital At Tenaya, Las Vegas, NV, p. A394

TUPPONCE, David, M.D., President, Central Maine Medical Center, Lewiston, ME, p. A284

TURBAK, Shelly, R.N., Chief Nursing Officer, Prairie Lakes Healthcare System, Watertown, SD, p. A565

TUREK, Beth, Site Manager Information Systems, Advocate South Suburban Hospital, Hazel Crest, IL, p. A185

TUREK, Derrill Kent, R.N., Chief Nursing Officer, Blue Mountain Hospital, Blanding, UT, p. A646

TURK, Edward, Vice President Finance, Scripps Mercy Hospital Chula Vista, CA, p. A84

TURK, Jan, Administrator, Extended Care Hospital, Kenner, LA, p. A270

TURKAL-BARRETT, Kari, Flight Commander Resource Management Officer, Mike O'Callaghan Federal Hospital, Nellis Afb, NV, p. A395

TURKEL, Brooks, Chief Executive Officer, Upmc Pinnacle Lancaster, Lancaster, PA, p. A529

TURLEY, Mary Ann, D.O., Medical Director, Honorhealth Deer Valley Medical Center, Phoenix, AZ, p. A33

TURLEY, Matt, Interim Director Information Systems, Greenbrier Valley Medical Center, Ronceverte, WV, p. A687

TURLEY, Susan S.
Chief Financial Officer, Doctor's Hospital At Renaissance, Edinburg, TX, p. A600
President, Doctor's Hospital At Renaissance, Edinburg, TX, p. A600

TURMAN, Anna, Chief Executive Officer, Chadron Community Hospital And Health Services, Chadron, NE, p. A383

TURNA, Tarlochan, M.D., Medical Director, Mayo Clinic Health System In Cannon Falls, Cannon Falls, MN, p. A329

TURNAGE, Richard, M.D., Chief Executive Officer, Uams Medical Center, Little Rock-Pulaski County, AR, p. A45

TURNBULL, James, Chief Information Officer, University Of Utah Health, Salt Lake City, UT, p. A651

TURNBULL, Rosie, Director Human Resources, St. Lawrence Psychiatric Center, Ogdensburg, NY, p. A439

TURNER, Barbara, Director of Nursing, Austen Riggs Center, Stockbridge, MA, p. A305

TURNER, Bill, Vice President Human Resources, Valir Rehabilitation Hospital, Oklahoma City, OK, p. A505

TURNER, Brenda C
Chief Human Resources Officer, Palomar Medical Center, Escondido, CA, p. A57
Chief Human Resources Officer, Pomerado Hospital, Poway, CA, p. A79

TURNER, Chad, Chief Financial Officer, Star Valley Medical Center, Afton, WY, p. A707

TURNER, Cindy R, Chief Executive Officer, Bacon County Hospital And Health System, Alma, GA, p. A145

TURNER, Cindy R., Chief Executive Officer, Bacon County Hospital And Health System, Alma, GA, p. A145

TURNER, Dale, Chief Operating Officer, Reedsburg Area Medical Center, Reedsburg, WI, p. A702

TURNER, Howard D., Chief Executive Officer, Abbeville Area Medical Center, Abbeville, SC, p. A549

TURNER, Jeff, FACHE, Chief Executive Officer, Moore County Hospital District, Dumas, TX, p. A600

TURNER, Karen, Chief Nursing Officer, Seneca Healthcare District, Chester, CA, p. A54

TURNER, Karissa, Vice President Operations, Wabash General Hospital, Mount Carmel, IL, p. A190

TURNER, Kelly, Senior Vice President Finance and Chief Financial Officer, Adventist Health Glendale, Los Angeles, CA, p. A66

TURNER, Kevin, M.D., Medical Director, Pathways Of Tennessee, Jackson, TN, p. A571

TURNER, Laurie, Chief Nursing Officer, Tristar Skyline Madison Campus, TN, p. A577

TURNER, Mark
Director Information Systems, Beverly Hospital, Montebello, CA, p. A73
Manager Information Technology, Ojai Valley Community Hospital, Ojai, CA, p. A76

TURNER, Mark J., FACHE
President, Memorial Hospital East, Shiloh, IL, p. A196
President, Memorial Hospital, Belleville, IL, p. A174

TURNER, Mark S., Chief Executive Officer, Capital Medical Center, Olympia, WA, p. A674

TURNER, Marquita, Chief Operating Officer and Chief Nursing Officer, Atrium Medical Center, Middletown, OH, p. A487

TURNER, Maurita, Team Leader Health Information Systems Services, Chi St. Joseph Health Madison Hospital, Madisonville, TX, p. A622

TURNER, Melissa, Senior Vice President Human Resources, Bridgeport Hospital, Bridgeport, CT, p. A107

TURNER, Michael
Chief Information Officer, Plaza Specialty Hospital, Houston, TX, p. A613
Director Human Resources, Moberly Regional Medical Center, Moberly, MO, p. A364

TURNER, Nancy, Director Communications, Sutter Roseville Medical Center, Roseville, CA, p. A81

TURNER, Peggy, Assistant Vice President and Director of Nursing, Unity Health Specialty Care, AR, p. A48

TURNER, Randy, Chief Human Resource Management Services, Boise Veterans Affairs Medical Center, Boise, ID, p. A167

TURNER, Robert A., Chief Executive Officer, Ad Hospital East, Houston, TX, p. A609

TURNER, Sara, Director Human Resources, Alvarado Hospital Medical Center, San Diego, CA, p. A83

TURNER, Saundra G, Director Human Resources, Mercy Hospital Jefferson, Crystal City, MO, p. A358

TURNER, Scott, Chief Operating Officer, University Of Iowa Stead Family Children's Hospital, IA, p. A224

TURNER, Sherrilyn, Director Human Resources, Southeast Colorado Hospital District, Springfield, CO, p. A105

TURNER, Spencer, FACHE, President, Texas Health Presbyterian Hospital Flower Mound, Flower Mound, TX, p. A603

TURNER, Steve, Director Information Technology, Salem Township Hospital, Salem, IL, p. A195

TURNER, Teri, Chief Nursing Officer, Haskell Memorial Hospital, Haskell, TX, p. A609

TURNER, Tiffany, MSN, R.N., Vice President of Nursing and Chief Nursing Officer, Paris Community Hospital, Paris, IL, p. A192

TURNEY, Amanda, Director Human Resources, Cochran Memorial Hospital, Morton, TX, p. A624

TURNEY, Brian, Chief Executive Officer, Kingman Regional Medical Center, Kingman, AZ, p. A30

TURNEY, David, Chief Information Officer, Cochran Memorial Hospital, Morton, TX, p. A624

TURNEY, Larry, Administrator, Cochran Memorial Hospital, Morton, TX, p. A624

TURNQUIST, Carrie, Director Human Resources, Buena Vista Regional Medical Center, Storm Lake, IA, p. A230

TURO, Albert, Vice President Human Resources, St. Mary's Healthcare, NY, p. A421

TURPEN, Brad, FACHE, Interim Chief Executive Officer, Valor Health, Emmett, ID, p. A169

TURPIN, Debra, R.N., MSN, Vice President Patient Care Services and Chief Nursing Officer, Alton Memorial Hospital, Alton, IL, p. A173

TURPIN, James
Chief of Staff, Ephraim Mcdowell Fort Logan Hospital, Stanford, KY, p. A261
Human Resources, Breckinridge Memorial Hospital, Hardinsburg, KY, p. A253

TURQUEZA, Sandra
Human Resources Business Partner, Saint Joseph Berea, Berea, KY, p. A249
Senior Human Resources Business Partner, Saint Joseph London, London, KY, p. A255

TURSKY, Martin, President and Chief Executive Officer, Mclaren Central Michigan, Mount Pleasant, MI, p. A319

TURSO, Janet, Controller, Healthsouth Rehabilitation Hospital Of Toms River, Toms River, NJ, p. A412

TURTON, Jonathan, FACHE, Chief Executive Officer, Chris Evert Childrens Hospital, FL, p. A122

TUSA, Edward A, Chief Financial Officer, Mayo Clinic Health System In Cannon Falls, Cannon Falls, MN, p. A329

TUSCANY, Joanne E
Director Human Resources, Ascension St. John Hospital, Detroit, MI, p. A310
Senior Director Human Resources, St. John Macomb-Oakland Hospital, Warren Campus, MI, p. A325

TUSTEN, Jay, Chief Executive Officer, Stanton County Hospital, Johnson, KS, p. A237

TUTT, Michael, M.D., Chief Medical Officer, Tsehootsooi Medical Center, Fort Defiance, AZ, p. A29

TUTTLE, Casey, Director Information Technology, Sistersville General Hospital, Sistersville, WV, p. A687

TUTTLE, Kathryn, R.N., Director of Nursing, Memorial Medical Center Of Ashland, Ashland, WI, p. A689

TVEIT, Charles B., Chief Executive Officer, Lake District Hospital, Lakeview, OR, p. A514

TWARDY, Cindi, Manager Human Resources, Meeker Memorial Hospital, Litchfield, MN, p. A333

TWEED, Frances, R.N., Executive Director and Administrator, New Mexico Behavioral Health Institute At Las Vegas, Las Vegas, NM, p. A418

TWEHOUS, Debra, Medical Director, Fairlawn Rehabilitation Hospital, Worcester, MA, p. A306

TWIDWELL, Lisa, Administrator, Madison Medical Center, Fredericktown, MO, p. A359

TWIGG, Nicole, Director Human Resources, Brook Lane Health Services, Hagerstown, MD, p. A292

TYE, Angie, Director Human Resources, Waverly Health Center, Waverly, IA, p. A231

TYK, Robert C., Interim Chief Executive Officer, Artesia General Hospital, Artesia, NM, p. A416

TYLER, Holley, R.N., Chief Nursing Officer, Woman's Hospital Of Texas, Houston, TX, p. A614

TYLER, James E., Chief Executive Officer, Smyth County Community Hospital, Marion, VA, p. A661

TYLER, Kevin L, M.D., President Medical Staff, Penn Highlands Clearfield, Clearfield, PA, p. A522

TYLER, Philene, Chief Finance Officer, Chinle Comprehensive Health Care Facility, Chinle, AZ, p. A28

TYLER, Richard, Corporate Director Human Resources, Conway Regional Medical Center, Conway-Faulkner County, AR, p. A40

TYLER, Rick, M.D., Vice President Medical Affairs, Christus Southeast Texas Hospital-St. Mary, TX, p. A588

TYLER, Rob, Chief Financial Officer, West Oaks Hospital, Houston, TX, p. A614

TYLER, Tanya, Vice President Human Resources, Chi St. Luke's Health Memorial Lufkin, Lufkin, TX, p. A621

TYNES, L Lee, M.D., Ph.D., Jr, Medical Director, Central Louisiana State Hospital, Pineville, LA, p. A277

TYO, Joanne, Chief Financial Officer, Carolinas Continuecare Hospital At Pineville, Charlotte, NC, p. A449

TYRA, Diana, Director Health Information, Kentucky River Medical Center, Jackson, KY, p. A254

TYRA, J Allen., Chief Executive, Gilmore Memorial Hospital, Amory, MS, p. A343

TYRER, Andrew, Chief Operating Officer, Tristar Stonecrest Medical Center, Smyrna, TN, p. A580

TYRRELL, Wade Alan, RN, Chief Nursing Officer, Sterling Regional Medcenter, Sterling, CO, p. A105

TYSLAND, Tanya, Chief Executive Officer, Gundersen Palmer Lutheran Hospital And Clinics, West Union, IA, p. A231

TYSON, Rhoda, Chief Information Officer, Tuskegee Division, AL, p. A21

U

UBER, Charlotte M., Chief Executive Officer, Warren State Hospital, Warren, PA, p. A543

UDALL, Ben, M.D., Chief of Staff, Kimble Hospital, Junction, TX, p. A616

UDOVICH, Christopher, M.D., Chief of Staff, Silver Cross Hospital, New Lenox, IL, p. A191

UFFER, Mark H., Chief Executive Officer, Corona Regional Medical Center-Rehabilitation, CA, p. A55

UGHOUWA, Ejiro, M.D., Chief of Staff, Allen Parish Hospital, Kinder, LA, p. A270

UGWUEKE, Michael, President and Chief Executive Officer, Methodist Le Bonheur Germantown Hospital, TN, p. A575

UHARRIET, Bart, Director Information Services, Whitfield Medical Surgical Hospital, MS, p. A354

UHL, Michael, President, Atrium Medical Center, Middletown, OH, p. A487

UHLIR, Tricia, Chief Executive Officer, Fall River Hospital, Hot Springs, SD, p. A561

ULERY, Brian
Chief Operating Officer, Thomas Memorial Hospital, South Charleston, WV, p. A687
Senior Vice President and Chief Operating Officer, Saint Francis Hospital, Charleston, WV, p. A682

ULETT, John, Vice President and Chief Information Officer, Centrastate Healthcare System, Freehold, NJ, p. A405

ULFERTS, Wendy, Vice President and Chief Nursing Officer, Maple Grove Hospital, Maple Grove, MN, p. A334

ULI, James
Chief Financial Officer, Loma Linda University Medical Center-Murrieta, Murrieta, CA, p. A74
Chief Financial Officer, Providence Saint John's Health Center, Santa Monica, CA, p. A89

ULIBARRI, Laura, M.D., Chief of Staff, Catalina Island Medical Center, Avalon, CA, p. A51

ULLRICH, John, M.D., Chief of Staff, Ivinson Memorial Hospital, Laramie, WY, p. A708

ULMER, Becky, R.N., Director of Nursing, Jasper General Hospital, Bay Springs, MS, p. A343

ULMER, Carlton, President and Chief Executive Officer, West Florida Rehabilitation Institute, FL, p. A136

ULMER, Carol, Chief Executive Officer, Select Specialty Hospital-Sioux Falls, Sioux Falls, SD, p. A564

ULREICH, Shawn, R.N., MSN, Vice President Clinical Operations and Chief Nursing Executive, Spectrum Health, MI, p. A314

ULREY, Chris, Director Management Information Systems, St. Luke's Behavioral Health Center, Phoenix, AZ, p. A34

ULRICH, Alan
Chief Financial Officer, Bartlett Regional Hospital, Juneau, AK, p. A26
Chief Financial Officer, Guam Memorial Hospital Authority, Tamuning, GU, p. A711

ULRICH, James P., Jr, Chief Executive Officer, York General, York, NE, p. A391

ULSETH, Randy, Chief Executive Officer, Firstlight Health System, Mora, MN, p. A336

ULVELING, Kyle, M.D., Chief of Staff, St. Anthony Regional Hospital, Carroll, IA, p. A218

UMHAU, John, M.D., Clinical Director, U.S. Public Health Service Indian Hospital-Whiteriver, Whiteriver, AZ, p. A38

UNDERDAHL, Steve, President and Chief Executive Officer, Northfield Hospital And Clinics, Northfield, MN, p. A336

UNDERHILL, Robert, Director of Business Services, Central State Hospital, Louisville, KY, p. A256

UNDERWOOD, Debbie, Manager Human Resources, Plains Memorial Hospital, Dimmitt, TX, p. A600

UNDERWOOD, Jerri C, R.N., Chief Nursing Officer, Parkridge West Hospital, TN, p. A567

UNDERWOOD, Kelsey N, Director of Nursing, Gundersen Tri-County Hospital And Clinics, Whitehall, WI, p. A706

UNDERWOOD, Ken, Chief Executive Officer, William And Inez Mabie Skilled Nursing Facility, CA, p. A61

UNDERWOOD, Martha, Chief Human Resources Officer, Saint Thomas Midtown Hospital, Nashville, TN, p. A577

UNDERWOOD, Phillip, Chief Executive Officer, Kindred Hospital-Dayton, Dayton, OH, p. A480

UNDERWOOD, Vickie, Director Human Resources, Wyandot Memorial Hospital, Upper Sandusky, OH, p. A492

UNDERWOOD, Virgil, Chief Executive Officer, Boone Memorial Hospital, Madison, WV, p. A684

UNDLIN, Cassie, Chief Operating Officer, Navos, Seattle, WA, p. A676

UNELL, Deonna, Chief Executive Officer, Baylor Surgical Hospital At Las Colinas, Irving, TX, p. A615

UNG, David
Director, Information Technology, California Hospital Medical Center, Los Angeles, CA, p. A66
Site Director, St. Mary Medical Center, Long Beach, CA, p. A65

UNGER, Henry D., M.D., Senior Vice President and Chief Medical Officer, Holy Redeemer Hospital, Meadowbrook, PA, p. A531

UNGER, Kevin L., Ph.D., FACHE
President and Chief Executive Officer, Mountain Crest Hospital, CO, p. A100
President and Chief Executive Officer, Uchealth Medical Center Of The Rockies, Loveland, CO, p. A104

UNHEE, Kim, President, Mount Carmel St. Ann'S, Westerville, OH, p. A493

UNITAN, Carol, M.D., Chief Medical Officer, Kaiser Foundation Hospital Westside Medical Center, Hillsboro, OR, p. A513

UNRUH, Greg, Chief Executive Officer, Citizens Medical Center, Colby, KS, p. A233

UNZEN, John, Chief Financial Officer, Mille Lacs Health System, Onamia, MN, p. A336

UPCHURCH, Jim, M.D., Chief Medical Officer, Crow/Northern Cheyenne Hospital, Crow Agency, MT, p. A374

UPCRAFT, Jeffrey, Director Information Services, Rancho Springs Medical Center, CA, p. A74

UPFIELD, Jaclyn, Chief Operating Officer, G. Werber Bryan Psychiatric Hospital, Columbia, SC, p. A551

UPSHAW, Joy, Chief Nursing Officer, Oklahoma State University Medical Center, Tulsa, OK, p. A508

UPTON, Carol
Interim Chief Executive Officer, Merit Health Wesley, Hattiesburg, MS, p. A347
Regional Area Practice Manager, Gilmore Memorial Hospital, Amory, MS, p. A343

UPTON, Daniel, Vice President and Chief Financial Officer, Doylestown Hospital, Doylestown, PA, p. A524

UPTON, Matthew
Chief Medical Information Officer, Thomas Memorial Hospital, South Charleston, WV, p. A687
Chief Medical Officer and Chief Medical Information Officer, Saint Francis Hospital, Charleston, WV, p. A682

URADNIK, Michael, Chief Executive Officer, Cascade Behavioral Hospital, Tukwila, WA, p. A679

URAIZEE, Rizwan A., Chief Financial Officer, Kedren Community Mental Health Center, Los Angeles, CA, p. A68

URBAN, Frank, Chief Financial Officer, Southwood Psychiatric Hospital, Pittsburgh, PA, p. A537

URBAN, Josh, Chief Executive Officer, Memorial Hermann Northeast, Humble, TX, p. A615

URBAN, Louise, R.N.
President and Chief Executive Officer, Canonsburg Hospital, Canonsburg, PA, p. A522
President and Chief Executive Officer, Jefferson Hospital, Jefferson Hills, PA, p. A528

URBAN, Thomas S., FACHE, President and Chief Executive Officer, Mercy Health - Fairfield Hospital, Fairfield, OH, p. A482

URBANCSIK, Don
Director Finance, Euclid Hospital, Euclid, OH, p. A482
Director Finance, Lutheran Hospital, Cleveland, OH, p. A477

URBANSKI, Pamela A, R.N., MSN, Chief Nursing Officer, Senior Vice President, Patient Care Services, Promedica Monroe Regional Hospital, Monroe, MI, p. A319

URBINA, Ana, Chief Financial Officer, Atrium Medical Center, Stafford, TX, p. A636

URBISTONDO, Lisa, Chief Financial Officer, Medical Center Of Peach County, Navicent Health, Bryon, GA, p. A149

URDANETA, Alfonso, M.D., President Medical Staff, Washington County Hospital, Nashville, IL, p. A191

URISH, Abigail R., M.D., Chief of Staff, Rangely District Hospital, Rangely, CO, p. A105

URLAUB, Charles J., President and Chief Executive Officer, Mercy Hospital, Buffalo, NY, p. A423

URQUHART, Mary, R.N., Vice President Patient Care, Brattleboro Memorial Hospital, Brattleboro, VT, p. A653

URQUHART, Mary Beth, Vice President Patient Care Services and Director of Quality, New England Sinai Hospital And Rehabilitation Center, Stoughton, MA, p. A305

URQUHART, Mary Beth., Interim President, Vice President Patient Care Services and Chief Nursing Officer, New England Sinai Hospital And Rehabilitation Center, Stoughton, MA, p. A305

URQUHART, Teresa C., Chief Operating Officer, Pinecrest Rehabilitation Hospital, FL, p. A121

URSIN, Ronnie, FACHE, President and Chief Executive Officer, Jennersville Hospital, West Grove, PA, p. A544

USELMAN, Krista, Chief Executive Officer, Encompass Health Rehabilitation Hospital The Vintage, Houston, TX, p. A610

USELMAN, Melissa, Chief Financial Officer, Gundersen Boscobel Area Hospital And Clinics, Boscobel, WI, p. A690

USHIJIMA, Arthur A., FACHE, President, Queen's Medical Center - West Oahu, HI, p. A165

UTECHT, Tom, M.D.
Chief Medical and Quality Officer, Community Regional Medical Center, Fresno, CA, p. A59
Corporate Chief Quality Officer, Fresno Heart And Surgical Hospital, Fresno, CA, p. A59
Senior Vice President and Chief Quality Officer, Community Behavioral Health Center, Fresno, CA, p. A59

UTLEY, Donna, Vice President Human Resources, Mercy San Juan Medical Center, Carmichael, CA, p. A54

UTLEY, Renee, Chief Financial Officer, Hamilton Center, Terre Haute, IN, p. A215

UTTENDORFSKY, Rob, Director Information Management, Lewis County General Hospital, Lowville, NY, p. A429

UTTER, Camille, R.N., Chief Nursing Officer, Scotland Health Care System, Laurinburg, NC, p. A456

UTTERBACK, Julie, Chief Financial Officer, Roane Medical Center, Harriman, TN, p. A570

UYEMURA, Monte, M.D., Chief of Staff, Wray Community District Hospital, Wray, CO, p. A106

V

VAAGENES, Carl P., Chief Executive Officer, Alomere Health, Alexandria, MN, p. A327

VAALER, Mark, M.D.
Chief Medical Officer, South Florida Baptist Hospital, Plant City, FL, p. A136
Vice President Medical Staff Affairs, St. Joseph's Women's Hospital, FL, p. A141

VACCARO, Stacey, Chief Operating Officer, The Children's Institute Of Pittsburgh, Pittsburgh, PA, p. A538

VACHON, Scott, Director Information Technology, Littleton Regional Healthcare, Littleton, NH, p. A400

VADEN, Jim, Director Information Systems, Lauderdale Community Hospital, Ripley, TN, p. A579

VADYAK, Karen, Chief Nursing Officer, Easton Hospital, Easton, PA, p. A524

VAEZAZIZI, Reza, M.D., Chief of Staff, Rancho Springs Medical Center, CA, p. A74

VAGUE, Jeff, Regional Manager Information Systems, Mercy Southwest Hospital, CA, p. A52

VAHLBERG, Susan, Director Employee and Community Relations, Valor Health, Emmett, ID, p. A169

VAIL, B J, Director Information Systems, Morehouse General Hospital, Bastrop, LA, p. A263

VAIL, Bryan, Chief Information Officer, Clement J. Zablocki Veterans Affairs Medical Center, Milwaukee, WI, p. A698

VAIL, Lisa M, R.N., Chief Nursing Officer and Vice President of Patient Care Services, Bryan Medical Center-West, NE, p. A385

VAIL, Ronald, M.D., Chief of Staff, Lower Umpqua Hospital District, Reedsport, OR, p. A517

VAILLANCOURT, Alex, Chief Information Officer, Christ Hospital, Cincinnati, OH, p. A474

VAILLANCOURT, Stacy, Vice President Marketing, Communications, Advocacy and Human Resources, Saint Agnes Medical Center, Fresno, CA, p. A59

VALBUENA, Richard, M.D., Medical Director, Latimer County General Hospital, Wilburton, OK, p. A510

VALDENEGRO, Maria, Chief Financial Officer, Meadow Wood Behavioral Health System, New Castle, DE, p. A113

VALDERAZ, Leonard, Administrator, Sunrise Canyon Hospital, Lubbock, TX, p. A621

VALDESPINO, Gustavo A., President and Chief Executive Officer, Valley Presbyterian Hospital, Los Angeles, CA, p. A70

VALDEZ, J. Alex, JD, President and Chief Executive Officer, Christus St. Vincent Physicians Medical Center, NM, p. A419

VALENCERINA, Madeline, Chief Operating Officer, Kedren Community Mental Health Center, Los Angeles, CA, p. A68

VALENTE, Anthony, M.D., Vice President Medical Affairs, Lehigh Valley Hospital - Hazleton, Hazleton, PA, p. A527

VALENTE, T. J., M.D., Medical Director, Lifestream Behavioral Center, Leesburg, FL, p. A128

VALENTIN, Carlos, Chief Financial Officer, St. Luke's Episcopal Hospital, Ponce, PR, p. A714

VALENTIN, Leonardo, Chief Executive Officer, Professional Hospital Guaynabo, Guaynabo, PR, p. A713

VALENTINE, Mark
President, The Heart Hospital Baylor Denton, Denton, TX, p. A599
President, The Heart Hospital Baylor Plano, Plano, TX, p. A629

VALENTINE, Robert A., President, Chi Health Missouri Valley, Missouri Valley, IA, p. A226

VALENTINI, Rudolph, M.D., Chief Medical Officer, Dmc - Children's Hospital Of Michigan, Detroit, MI, p. A310

VALENTO, Jessica, Director Information Systems, Range Regional Health Services, Hibbing, MN, p. A333

VALLA, Nancy, R.N., Chief Nursing Officer, St. Mary Medical Center, Long Beach, CA, p. A65

VALLE, Bernardo, Vice President Human Resources, Usmd Hospital At Arlington, Arlington, TX, p. A584

VALLE, David, Chief Information Officer, Hospital Pavia Arecibo, Arecibo, PR, p. A712

VALLE, Karla, Area Chief Financial Officer, Kaiser Permanente Panorama City Medical Center, Los Angeles, CA, p. A67

VALLELY, Ian, Information Technology Site Leader, Sequoia Hospital, Redwood City, CA, p. A80

VALLIDO, Gabe, Chief Information Officer, Naval Hospital Camp Pendleton, Camp Pendleton, CA, p. A54

VALLIERE, George, Chief Executive Officer, Claremore Indian Hospital, Claremore, OK, p. A497

VAN BOENING, Jon, President and Chief Executive Officer, Bakersfield Memorial Hospital, Bakersfield, CA, p. A52

VAN BREE, Margaret M., Dr.PH, President, Hasbro Children's Hospital, RI, p. A548

VAN BUSKIRK, George F, M.D., Chief of Staff, Bay Pines Veterans Affairs Healthcare System, Bay Pines, FL, p. A117

VAN BUSKIRK, Kryder, III, Medical Staff President at EMRMC, Ephraim Mcdowell Regional Medical Center, Danville, KY, p. A251

VAN CAMP, Keith, Vice President Information Services, St. Dominic-Jackson Memorial Hospital, Jackson, MS, p. A348

VAN CLEAVE, Bruce L, M.D., Senior Vice President and Chief Medical Officer, Aurora Medical Center Of Oshkosh, Oshkosh, WI, p. A700

VAN CLEAVE, Chad, Chief Financial Officer, Columbus Community Hospital, Columbus, NE, p. A383

VAN DECAR, Tama, M.D., Chief Medical Officer, Fort Walton Beach Medical Center, Fort Walton Beach, FL, p. A123

VAN DER VEER, Jon, D.O., Vice President Medical Affairs, Greene County Medical Center, Jefferson, IA, p. A225

VAN DRIEL, Allen, FACHE, Administrator, Smith County Memorial Hospital, Smith Center, KS, p. A246

VAN DYK, Holly, M.D., Interim Chief Medical Officer, Tuba City Regional Health Care Corporation, Tuba City, AZ, p. A36

VAN EECKHOUT, Barbara, M.D., Chief of Staff, Los Alamos Medical Center, Los Alamos, NM, p. A418

VAN EPERN, Keri, Manager Human Resources, Aspirus Ironwood Hospitals & Clinics, Inc., Ironwood, MI, p. A316

VAN ESSENDELFT, Seth
Vice President and Chief Financial Officer, Lawrence + Memorial Hospital, New London, CT, p. A110
Vice President and Chief Financial Officer, Westerly Hospital, Westerly, RI, p. A548

VAN ETTEN, Mark, M.D., Chief of Staff, Spooner Health, Spooner, WI, p. A703

VAN GENDEREN, Nathan, Executive Vice President and Chief Financial Officer, Mercy Medical Center, Cedar Rapids, IA, p. A218

VAN HOET, Jim, Chief Financial Officer, Coffey County Hospital, Burlington, KS, p. A233

VAN HOUDEN, Charles, M.D., Chief Medical Officer, Neosho Memorial Regional Medical Center, Chanute, KS, p. A233

VAN HYNING, Jill, Director Human Resources, Carle Richland Memorial Hospital, Olney, IL, p. A192

VAN KAMPEN, Cindy, Chief Nursing Officer, North Ottawa Community Hospital, Grand Haven, MI, p. A313

VAN LEEUWE, Matthew, Chief Operating Officer, Abilene Regional Medical Center, Abilene, TX, p. A582

VAN MEETEREN, Robert, President and Chief Executive Officer, Reedsburg Area Medical Center, Reedsburg, WI, p. A702

VAN NATTA, Timothy, M.D., Chief Medical Officer, Harbor-Ucla Medical Center, Torrance, CA, p. A91

VAN NORMAN, Steven, M.D., Medical Director, Dixie Regional Medical Center, UT, p. A650

VAN RYBROEK, Greg, Chief Executive Officer, Mendota Mental Health Institute, Madison, WI, p. A696

VAN SCOYK, Mitch, Manager Information Systems, Delta County Memorial Hospital, Delta, CO, p. A98

VAN VICKLE, Robin, Chief Financial Officer, Bristow Medical Center, Bristow, OK, p. A496

VAN VOLKENBURG, Mark, Chief Executive Officer, Healthsouth Harmarville Rehabilitation Hospital, Pittsburgh, PA, p. A537

VAN VRANKEN, Arthur, M.D., Chief Medical Officer, Essentia Health-Graceville, Graceville, MN, p. A332

VAN VRANKEN, Ross, Executive Director, University Of Utah Neuropsychiatric Institute, Salt Lake City, UT, p. A651

VAN WHY, Susan, Director Human Resources, St. Luke's Hospital - Miners Campus, Coaldale, PA, p. A523

VAN WINKLE, James, M.D., Chief of Staff, Unity Medical Center, Manchester, TN, p. A574

VAN WINKLE, Melanie, Chief Financial Officer, Mammoth Hospital, Mammoth Lakes, CA, p. A71

VAN ZANTEN, Lorinda, MSN, Chief Executive, Providence Newberg Medical Center, Newberg, OR, p. A515

VANATOR, John, CPA
Chief Financial Officer, Indiana University Health Ball Memorial Hospital, Muncie, IN, p. A212
Chief Financial Officer, Indiana University Health Blackford Hospital, Hartford City, IN, p. A206

VANBOEKEL, Tony, Director Information Systems, Shasta Regional Medical Center, Redding, CA, p. A80

VANCE, Derek
President, Chi Health Nebraska Heart, Lincoln, NE, p. A386
President, Chi Health St Elizabeth, Lincoln, NE, p. A386

VANCE, Ellen B
Chief Human Resource Officer, Sheltering Arms Rehabilitation Hospital, Mechanicsville, VA, p. A661
Chief Human Resources Officer, Sheltering Arms Hospital South, Midlothian, VA, p. A661

VANCE, Mark, M.D., Chief Medical Officer, Quincy Valley Medical Center, Quincy, WA, p. A675

VANCE, Ruth, Director Information Systems, Quincy Valley Medical Center, Quincy, WA, p. A675

VANCE, Stacie
Chief Nursing Officer and Chief Operations Officer, Orthoindy Hospital, Indianapolis, IN, p. A207
Chief Nursing Officer and Vice President Operations, Orthoindy Hospital, Indianapolis, IN, p. A207
Chief Nursing Officer and, Orthoindy Hospital, Indianapolis, IN, p. A207

VANCE, Steven
Chief Financial Officer, Dixie Regional Medical Center, UT, p. A650
Information Technology Director, Lake District Hospital, Lakeview, OR, p. A514

VANCOURT, Bernie
Chief Operating Officer, Bay Area Medical Center, Marinette, WI, p. A697
Interim Chief Nursing Officer, Bay Area Medical Center, Marinette, WI, p. A697

VANDENBARK, Heather, Human Resources Specialist, State Hospital North, Orofino, ID, p. A171

VANDENBERG, Andra, Director Human Resources, Butler County Health Care Center, David City, NE, p. A383

VANDENBOSCH, Dan, Chief Information Officer, Madison County Health Care System, Winterset, IA, p. A231

VANDER, Allen, M.D., Chief Medical Staff, Thibodaux Regional Medical Center, Thibodaux, LA, p. A280

VANDER KOLK, Keith, President and Chief Executive Officer, Saint Agnes Healthcare, Baltimore, MD, p. A288

VANDERBEEK, Sam, Chief Information Officer, W. J. Mangold Memorial Hospital, Lockney, TX, p. A620

VANDERHOOFT, J Eric, M.D., President Medical Staff, St. Mark's Hospital, Salt Lake City, UT, p. A651

VANDERLINDEN, Mark A, Chief Financial Officer, Greene County Medical Center, Jefferson, IA, p. A225

VANDERMARK, Jay H, Chief Financial Officer, Veterans Affairs Northern Indiana Health Care System-Marion Campus, IN, p. A204

VANDERMEER, Nick, Director Information Systems, Banner Payson Medical Center, Payson, AZ, p. A32

VANDERPOL, Antoinette, Chief of Staff, Avera St. Benedict Health Center, Parkston, SD, p. A562

VANDERPOOL, Lee, Vice President, Dominican Hospital, Santa Cruz, CA, p. A88

VANDERSCHAAFF, Trixie, Chief Nursing Officer, St. Anthony Summit Medical Center, Frisco, CO, p. A100

VANDERSLICE, Douglas M, Senior Vice President and Chief Financial Officer, Boston Children's Hospital, Boston, MA, p. A296

VANDERSTEK, Eliott R, Chief Fiscal Service, Veterans Affairs Eastern Colorado Health Care System, Denver, CO, p. A99

VANDERSTOUW, Karl, Vice President Information Systems, Unc Lenoir Healthcare, Kinston, NC, p. A456

VANDERVLIET, William, M.D., Vice President Medical Affairs, Holland Hospital, Holland, MI, p. A315

VANDERWEGE, Larry, Administrator, Lindsborg Community Hospital, Lindsborg, KS, p. A240

VANDEUSEN, Leya, Interim Chief Financial Officer, Hillsdale Hospital, Hillsdale, MI, p. A315

VANDEWEGE, Dana, Director Human Resources, Capital Medical Center, Olympia, WA, p. A674

VANDONKELAAR, Rodney
Chief Financial Officer, Carolina Pines Regional Medical Center, Hartsville, SC, p. A554
Chief Financial Officer, Saint Thomas Highlands Hospital, Sparta, TN, p. A580

VANDORT, Patti J, MSN, R.N., Vice President Nursing/Chief Nursing Officer, Holland Hospital, Holland, MI, p. A315

VANDRIEL, Mary Kay
President, Spectrum Health Big Rapids Hospital, Big Rapids, MI, p. A308
President, Spectrum Health Reed City Hospital, Reed City, MI, p. A321

VANDRUFF, John, M.D., Chief of Staff, Banner Payson Medical Center, Payson, AZ, p. A32

VANDYKE, Yvonne, R.N., MSN, Chief Nursing Officer, Texas Market, Seton Northwest Hospital, Austin, TX, p. A586

VANEK, James, Chief Executive Officer, Columbus Community Hospital, Columbus, TX, p. A593

VANES, Wendell, Chief Financial Officer, Saint Mary's Regional Medical Center, Russellville-Pope County, AR, p. A48

VANHAREN, James, M.D., Medical Director, Forest View Psychiatric Hospital, Grand Rapids, MI, p. A314

VANHORN, Jeffrey, Chief Executive Officer, Star Medical Center, Plano, TX, p. A629

VANHOUWELING, Mason, Chief Executive Officer, Children's Hospital Of Nevada At Umc, NV, p. A395

VANHOY, Michael, Director of Quality, Uva-Healthsouth Rehabilitation Hospital, Charlottesville, VA, p. A656

VANMETER, David, Interim Director, Carl Vinson Veterans Affairs Medical Center, Dublin, GA, p. A153

VANNATTER, Mistie, Chief Nursing Officer, Advanced Care Hospital Of White County, Searcy-White County, AR, p. A48

VANNETT, Vince, Director Human Resources, Jellico Community Hospital, Jellico, TN, p. A571

VANO, Ann
Vice President Human Resources, Providence - Providence Park Hospital, Novi Campus, MI, p. A323
Vice President, Human Resources, Ascension Crittenton Hospital Medical Center, Rochester, MI, p. A321

VANOSDOL, Thomas J.
Chief Executive Officer, St. Vincent's Medical Center Riverside, Jacksonville, FL, p. A126
Chief Executive Officer, St. Vincent's Medical Center Southside, Jacksonville, FL, p. A126

VANSANT, Scott, M.D., Chief Medical Officer, Central State Hospital, Milledgeville, GA, p. A157

VANSTRIEN, Amy, Director Talent Operations, Midwestern Regional Medical Center, Zion, IL, p. A198

VANTONGEREN, Teri, Director Information Services, Spectrum Health Pennock, Hastings, MI, p. A315

VANWALLAGHEN, Brenda, Interim Chief Nursing Officer, Dmc - Children's Hospital Of Michigan, Detroit, MI, p. A310

VANWICHEN, Ward C., Chief Executive Officer, Phillips County Hospital, Malta, MT, p. A377

VANWYHE, Brenda, Senior Vice President Finance and Chief Financial Officer, Rush-Copley Medical Center, Aurora, IL, p. A174

VARELA, Alberto M., M.D., President, Inspira Ponce, Ponce, PR, p. A714

VARELA, Nancy, Director Human Resources, Patton State Hospital, Patton, CA, p. A78

VARGA, Patrick, Chief Operating Officer, Mercy Medical Center Redding, Redding, CA, p. A79

VARGAS, Idelfonso, Executive Director, Dr. Ramon E. Betances Hospital-Mayaguez Medical Center Branch, Mayaguez, PR, p. A714

VARGAS, Jose L, M.D., Medical Director, West Gables Rehabilitation Hospital, Miami, FL, p. A131

VARGAS, Margie, Chief Human Resources Officer, Memorial Regional Hospital South, FL, p. A124

VARGAS, Marisol, Director Finance, Hospital Del Maestro, San Juan, PR, p. A715

VARGAS, Nancy
Chief Human Resources, St. Joseph's Behavioral Health Center, Stockton, CA, p. A91
Director Human Resources, Mark Twain Medical Center, San Andreas, CA, p. A83
Vice President Human Resources, St. Joseph's Medical Center, Stockton, CA, p. A91

VARGAS-MAHAR, Monica, FACHE, Chief Executive Officer, The Hospitals Of Providence East Campus, El Paso, TX, p. A602

VARGHESE, Roy, M.D., Chief of Staff, Mary Breckinridge Arh Hospital, Hyden, KY, p. A254

VARGHESE, Shibu, Vice President Human Resources, University Of Texas M.D. Anderson Cancer Center, Houston, TX, p. A614

VARIALE, Vincenzo, Chief Executive Officer, North Vista Hospital, North Las Vegas, NV, p. A396

VARIAN, Grant, M.D., Medical Director, Mary Rutan Hospital, Bellefontaine, OH, p. A472

VARK, Lawrence, M.D., Chief Medical Officer, Creek Nation Community Hospital, Okemah, OK, p. A502

VARLEY, Kevin
Chief Financial Officer, Curahealth Heritage Valley, Beaver, PA, p. A520
Chief Financial Officer, Curahealth Pittsburgh, Oakdale, PA, p. A533
Chief Financial Officer, Kindred Hospital South Philadelphia, Philadelphia, PA, p. A535

VARNADO, Anjanette, M.D., Chief Medical Officer, St. Helena Parish Hospital, Greensburg, LA, p. A268

VARNADO, Darryl, Executive Vice President and Chief People Officer, Children's National Health System, Washington, DC, p. A115

VARNADO, Donna, Vice President Finance, Cypress Pointe Surgical Hospital, Hammond, LA, p. A268

VARNADO, Kim, R.N., Chief Nursing Officer, Highland Community Hospital, Picayune, MS, p. A352

VARNADOE, Milo, Director Information Systems, Warm Springs Medical Center, Warm Springs, GA, p. A163

VARNADORE, Jennifer, Administrator, Christus Bossier Emergency Hospital, LA, p. A278

VARNAM, Jessica, Chief of Staff, Grant Regional Health Center, Lancaster, WI, p. A696

VARNER, Terry, Administrator, Yalobusha General Hospital, Water Valley, MS, p. A354

VARNEY, Tim, R.N., Chief Nursing Officer, Select Specialty Hospital-Ann Arbor, Ypsilanti, MI, p. A326

VARTANIAN, Sarkis, Chief Nursing Officer, Whittier Hospital Medical Center, Whittier, CA, p. A95

VARTELAS, Helene M., MSN, Chief Executive Officer, Whiting Forensic Hospital, CT, p. A109

VASCONCELLOS, Jacques, Director, Operations, Winter Haven Hospital, Winter Haven, FL, p. A144

VASEK, Barbara, Director Information Technology, Yoakum Community Hospital, Yoakum, TX, p. A645

VASHISHTA, Ashok, M.D., Vice President Medical Affairs, Mclaren Central Michigan, Mount Pleasant, MI, p. A319

VASIL, Kathleen, Vice President Finance, St. Charles Hospital, Port Jefferson, NY, p. A440

VASILE, Ann, M.D., Medical Director, Healthsouth Tustin Rehabilitation Hospital, Tustin, CA, p. A92

VASQUEZ, Alberto, Administrator, Garfield Memorial Hospital, Panguitch, UT, p. A649

VASQUEZ, Arthur, President, Indiana University Health West Hospital, Avon, IN, p. A199

VASQUEZ, Christann
Executive Vice President and Chief Operating Officer, University Hospital, TX, p. A634
President and Chief Executive Officer, Seton Medical Center Austin, Austin, TX, p. A586
President and Chief Executive Officer, Seton Shoal Creek Hospital, Austin, TX, p. A586
President, Dell Seton Medical Center At The University Of Texas, Austin, TX, p. A586

VASQUEZ, George
Chief Technology Officer, Clovis Community Medical Center, Clovis, CA, p. A55
Corporate Chief Information Officer, Fresno Heart And Surgical Hospital, Fresno, CA, p. A59
Vice President Information Services, Community Behavioral Health Center, Fresno, CA, p. A59

VASQUEZ, Jill, Manager Human Resources, Spectrum Health Ludington Hospital, Ludington, MI, p. A318

VASQUEZ, Kenneth, Associate Director, Jfk Medical Center North Campus, West Palm Beach, FL, p. A143

VASQUEZ, Miguel
Chief Executive Officer, Sister Emmanuel Hospital, Miami, FL, p. A131
Chief Financial Officer, Sister Emmanuel Hospital, Miami, FL, p. A131

VASQUEZ, Nelson, Vice President Finance, Jackson Park Hospital And Medical Center, Chicago, IL, p. A177

VASQUEZ, Stacy J., Director, Beckley Veterans Affairs Medical Center, Beckley, WV, p. A681

VASS, Paula, Vice President Clinical Operations, Walden Behavioral Care, Waltham, MA, p. A305

VASTOLA, David, Medical Director, Searhc Mt. Edgecumbe Hospital, Sitka, AK, p. A27

VASUNAGA, Amy, Chief Nurse Executive, Leahi Hospital, Honolulu, HI, p. A164

VATH, Richard, M.D., Vice President Medical Affairs, Our Lady Of The Lake Children's Hospital, LA, p. A264

VATSAVAI, Sundararama R, M.D., Medical Director, Baton Rouge Rehabilitation Hospital, Baton Rouge, LA, p. A263

VAUGHAN, Alan, Director Information Technology, Share Medical Center, Alva, OK, p. A495

VAUGHAN, Amanda
Chief Financial Officer, Bob Wilson Memorial Grant County Hospital, Ulysses, KS, p. A247
Chief Financial Officer, St. Catherine Hospital, Garden City, KS, p. A235
Interim Administrator, Bob Wilson Memorial Grant County Hospital, Ulysses, KS, p. A247

VAUGHAN, Brandon, Chief Financial Officer and Vice President Finance, Jamestown Regional Medical Center, Jamestown, ND, p. A467

VAUGHAN, Page H.
Chief Executive Officer, Chester Regional Medical Center, Chester, SC, p. A550
Chief Executive Officer, Springs Memorial Hospital, Lancaster, SC, p. A555

VAUGHAN, Peggy, M.D.
Senior Vice President Medical Affairs, University Of Maryland Harford Memorial Hospital, Havre De Grace, MD, p. A292
Senior Vice President Medical Affairs, University Of Maryland Upper Chesapeake Medical Center, Bel Air, MD, p. A289

VAUGHAN, Rob, Chief Financial Officer, Carilion Clinic Saint Albans Hospital, VA, p. A656

VAUGHN, Barbara, R.N., Chief Nursing Officer, Baylor Scott & White Medical Center - Carrollton, Carrollton, TX, p. A592

VAUGHN, Debbie, Chief Nursing Officer, The Medical Center Of Southeast Texas, Port Arthur, TX, p. A629

VAUGHN, Joseph, Director, W. G. (Bill) Heffner Veterans Affairs Medical Center, Salisbury, NC, p. A460

VAUGHN, Kerry, Chief Information Officer, St. Mary's Health Care System, Athens, GA, p. A145

VAUGHN, Kevin P, Chief Financial Officer, Kansas Spine And Specialty Hospital, Wichita, KS, p. A247

VAUGHN, Michael, Director of Nursing, Southeast Rehabilitation Hospital, Lake Village-Chicot County, AR, p. A44

VAUGHN, Sandy
Director Information Services, Baylor All Saints Medical Center At Fort Worth, Fort Worth, TX, p. A604
Director Information Systems, Baylor Regional Medical Center At Grapevine, Grapevine, TX, p. A607

VAUGHN, Sharma, Esq, Chief Nursing Officer, Rangely District Hospital, Rangely, CO, p. A105

VAUGHN, Ted W, Director Human Resources, Unitypoint Health - Trinity Regional Medical Center, Fort Dodge, IA, p. A222

VAUGHN, Vickie, Chief Nursing Officer, Tennova Healthcare-Shelbyville, Shelbyville, TN, p. A579

VAUTER, Rebecca, PsyD, Facility Director, Central State Hospital, Petersburg, VA, p. A663

VAVARUTSOS, Tony, Director Information Systems, Thorek Memorial Hospital, Chicago, IL, p. A180

VAZIRI, H Kevin., President, Woodland Healthcare, Woodland, CA, p. A95

VAZQUEZ, Barbara
Chief Nursing Officer, Palmetto General Hospital, Hialeah, FL, p. A124
Chief Nursing Officer, Providence Children's Hospital, TX, p. A602

VAZQUEZ, Brunilda, Medical Director, Hospital De Psiquiatria, San Juan, PR, p. A715

VAZQUEZ, Emilio, M.D., Chief Medical Officer, Dekalb Health, Auburn, IN, p. A199

VAZQUEZ, Francisco, Director, Michael E. Debakey Veterans Affairs Medical Center, Houston, TX, p. A612

VEACH, Jamie, Chief Operating Officer, Clay County Hospital, Flora, IL, p. A183

VEAL, Bonita Wells, Chief Nursing Officer, Anaheim Global Medical Center, Anaheim, CA, p. A50

VEDRAL-BARON, Jennifer, Health System Director, Nashville Campus, TN, p. A577

VEERAMACHANENI, Harish, M.D., Chief of Staff, Wayne Medical Center, Waynesboro, TN, p. A581

VEESER, Tom, Chief Nursing Officer, Ascension St. Michael's Hospital, Stevens Point, WI, p. A703

VEGA, James, Director Information Systems, Palm Beach Gardens Medical Center, Palm Beach Gardens, FL, p. A135

VEGA, Jane, Executive Director, Industrial Hospital, San Juan, PR, p. A716

VEGA, Maria, Director Human Resources, Auxilio Mutuo Hospital, San Juan, PR, p. A715

VEGA, Mary, R.N., MSN, Vice President Nursing, St. Margaret's Hospital, Spring Valley, IL, p. A196

VEGA, Oscar, M.D., Chief Medical Officer, Las Palmas Rehabilitation Hospital, TX, p. A602

VEGA, Zoraida, MSN, R.N., Chief Nursing Officer, St. Luke's Episcopal Hospital, Ponce, PR, p. A714

VEILLETTE, Michael D.
Senior Vice President and Chief Financial Officer, Manchester Memorial Hospital, Manchester, CT, p. A108
Senior Vice President and Chief Financial Officer, Rockville General Hospital, Vernon, CT, p. A111

VEILLEUX, Jeffrey
Executive Vice President and Chief Financial Officer, Swedish Medical Center-Ballard, WA, p. A676
Senior Vice President and Chief Financial Officer, Swedish Medical Center-Cherry Hill Campus, Seattle, WA, p. A676

VEILLON, Paul, CPA
Chief Financial Officer, Christus Dubuis Hospital Of Fort Smith, Fort Smith-Sebastian County, AR, p. A42
Chief Financial Officer, Christus Dubuis Hospital Of Hot Springs, Hot Springs National Park-Garland County, AR, p. A43

VEIT, Amanda, R.N., Chief Nursing Officer, Rocky Mountain Hospital For Children, CO, p. A99

VELA, Javier, Director Information Technology, Baylor Medical Center At Uptown, Dallas, TX, p. A595

VELA, Manuel, President and Chief Executive Officer, Valley Baptist Medical Center-Harlingen, Harlingen, TX, p. A609

VELASCO, Paul, IT Manager, Kit Carson County Health Service District, Burlington, CO, p. A97

VELASQUEZ, Alfred T
Area Information Officer, Kaiser Permanente Moreno Valley Medical Center, Moreno Valley, CA, p. A73
Area Information Officer, Kaiser Permanente Riverside Medical Center, Riverside, CA, p. A81

VELASQUEZ, Lin, Vice President Human Resources, Saint Louise Regional Hospital, Gilroy, CA, p. A60

VELEZ, Luz M, Director-Administration of Nursing Services, Hospital San Carlos Borromeo, Moca, PR, p. A714

VELEZ, Pablo, R.N., Ph.D., Chief Executive Officer, Sharp Chula Vista Medical Center, Chula Vista, CA, p. A54

VELEZ, Raul
Director Information Systems, Huntsville Memorial Hospital, Huntsville, TX, p. A615
Information Technology Director, Eliza Coffee Memorial Hospital, Florence, AL, p. A18

VENABLE, Mark, Interim Director Human Resources, Shriners Hospitals For Children-St. Louis, Saint Louis, MO, p. A368

VENABLE, Robert, M.D., Chief Medical Staff, Washington County Hospital, Plymouth, NC, p. A458

VENDETTI, Marilouise, M.D., Chief Medical Officer, Atlanticare Regional Medical Center-Mainland Division, NJ, p. A402

VENEZIANO, Terri, Interim Chief Nursing Officer, Columbus Regional Healthcare System, Whiteville, NC, p. A462

VENGCO, Joel L., MS, Vice President, Chief Information Officer, Baystate Children's Hospital, MA, p. A304

VENHUIZEN, Pamela, Chief Human Resources Officer, Cooperstown Medical Center, Cooperstown, ND, p. A465

VENOIT, Jon-Paul
Chief Operating Officer, Masonicare Health Center, Wallingford, CT, p. A111
President and Chief Executive Officer, Masonicare Health Center, Wallingford, CT, p. A111

VENTURA, Rosemary, M.D., Chief Nursing Informatics Officer, The Allen Pavilion, NY, p. A434

VENTURA, Sylvia A, R.N., MS, Chief Nursing Officer, Olympia Medical Center, Los Angeles, CA, p. A69

VENTURELLA, James, Vice President Information Technology, West Virginia University Children's Hospital, WV, p. A685

VENUTO, Frank, Chief Human Capital Officer, Nebraska Medicine—Nebraska Medical Center, Omaha, NE, p. A388

VENZANT, Shamada, Manager Health Information, Specialty Hospital Of Winnfield, Winnfield, LA, p. A281

VERA, Luis F, M.D., Medical Director, Kensington Hospital, Philadelphia, PA, p. A535

VERAGIWALA, Jignesh, Chief of Staff, Mercy Hospital Logan County, Guthrie, OK, p. A499

VERBEKE, Lori, Chief Financial Officer, Timberlawn Mental Health System, Dallas, TX, p. A598

VERBUS, John R, Senior Vice President and Chief Operating Officer, Frederick Regional Health System, Frederick, MD, p. A291

VERCHER, Gretchen, Chief Nursing Officer, Encompass Health Rehabilitation Hospital Of Montgomery, Montgomery, AL, p. A21

VERDEJA, Juan-Carlos, M.D., President of Medical Staff, Baptist Health South Florida, West Kendall Baptist Hospital, Miami, FL, p. A130

VERDON, Chris, Director Finance, Phillips Eye Institute, Minneapolis, MN, p. A335

VERFURTH, Larry, D.O., Executive Vice President and Chief Medical Officer, Christus Good Shepherd Medical Center, TX, p. A622

VERGA, Joseph P., FACHE, Chief Executive Officer, Guam Memorial Hospital Authority, Tamuning, GU, p. A711

VERGARA, Aimee, Chief Executive Officer, Hospital For Extended Recovery, Norfolk, VA, p. A662

VERGONIO, Merlinda, Chief Information Management and Technology, U.S. Air Force Hospital, Hampton, VA, p. A659

VERGOS, Katherine, President, St. Agnes Hospital, Fond Du Lac, WI, p. A692

VERINDER, David, President and Chief Executive Officer, Sarasota Memorial Health Care System, Sarasota, FL, p. A139

VERMA, Virendar, M.D., Medical Director, Healthsouth Rehabilitation Hospital Of Jonesboro, Jonesboro-Craighead County, AR, p. A44

VERMILLION, Kerry, Senior Vice President Finance and Chief Financial Officer, Gulf Breeze Hospital, Gulf Breeze, FL, p. A124

VERMULEN, Peter, Director Information Technology, Schick Shadel Hospital, Seattle, WA, p. A676

VERRET, Dean, Vice President Financial Services, Terrebonne General Medical Center, Houma, LA, p. A269

VERRETTE, Paul, M.D., Chief Medical Officer, St. Bernard Parish Hospital, Chalmette, LA, p. A265

VERRETTE, Paula, M.D., Senior Vice President Quality and Physician Services and Chief Medical Officer, Huntington Memorial Hospital, Pasadena, CA, p. A78

VERRILL, Alan, M.D., President Medical Staff, Bridgton Hospital, Bridgton, ME, p. A283

VERTIN, Amy, M.D., Chief of Staff, Crete Area Medical Center, Crete, NE, p. A383

VETTER, Norman, Chief Executive Officer, Division of Substance Abuse and Mental Health, Delaware Psychiatric Center, New Castle, DE, p. A113

VETTER, Rich, M.D., Associate Chief, Essentia Health St. Mary's - Detroit Lakes, Detroit Lakes, MN, p. A330

VIALL, John, M.D., Vice President Medical Affairs, Holzer Medical Center, Gallipolis, OH, p. A483

VIATOR, Dionne, CPA, FACHE, Chief Financial Officer, Iberia Medical Center, New Iberia, LA, p. A275

VIBETO, Brett, M.D., Chief of Staff, Chi St. Alexius Health - Williston Medical Center, Williston, ND, p. A469

VIBHAKAR, Neel, M.D., Senior Vice President and Chief Medical Officer, University Of Maryland Baltimore Washington Medical Center, Glen Burnie, MD, p. A292

VICE, Jeff
Chief Operating Officer and Interim Chief Executive Officer, Starke Hospital, Knox, IN, p. A208
Chief Operating Officer, Starke Hospital, Knox, IN, p. A208

VICENS-RIVERA, Enrique A., Jr, JD, Chief Executive Officer, Healthsouth Rehabilitation Hospital Of Miami, Cutler Bay, FL, p. A120

VICENT, Leonardo, III, Executive Director, Highbridge Woodycrest Center, NY, p. A431

VICENTE, Oscar, Chief Financial Officer, Palmetto General Hospital, Hialeah, FL, p. A124

VICENTI, Darren, M.D., Clinical Director, Hopi Health Care Center, Keams Canyon, AZ, p. A30

VICK, Dan J., M.D., Vice President of Medical Affairs and Chief Medical Officer, Oneida Healthcare, Oneida, NY, p. A439

VICKERS, Cynthia, R.N., Assistant Administrator for Nursing Services, Memorial Hospital And Manor, Bainbridge, GA, p. A148

VICKERS, Dave, Chief Financial Officer, Los Alamitos Medical Center, Los Alamitos, CA, p. A65

VICKERS, Don
Chief Executive Officer, Cleveland Emergency Hospital, Cleveland, TX, p. A592
Chief Executive Officer, Woodlands Specialty Hospital, The Woodlands, TX, p. A640

VICKERS, Kathy, Director Human Resources, Vantage Point Of Northwest Arkansas, Fayetteville-Washington County, AR, p. A42

VICKERY, Ian, Director Information Technology, D. W. Mcmillan Memorial Hospital, Brewton, AL, p. A15

VICKERY, Tim, Chief Information Officer, St. Mary's Sacred Heart Hospital, Lavonia, GA, p. A156

VICKROY, Joseph, M.D., Medical Director, Healthsouth Rehabilitation Hospital Of Utah, Sandy, UT, p. A651

VICKS, Ray, Senior Vice President, Finance and Chief Financial Officer, The Hsc Pediatric Center, Washington, DC, p. A116

VICTORIA, Mario, M.D., Vice President, Medical Affairs, Samaritan Medical Center, Watertown, NY, p. A445

VIDONI-CLARK, Clotilde, Ph.D., R.N., Chief Nursing Executive, Saint Elizabeths Hospital, Washington, DC, p. A116

VIEIRA, Jeanette, Chief Executive, Providence Hood River Memorial Hospital, Hood River, OR, p. A513

VIEIRA, Terri
President and Chief Executive Officer, Sebasticook Valley Health, Pittsfield, ME, p. A285
President, Charles A. Dean Memorial Hospital, Greenville, ME, p. A284

VIELKIND, James
Chief Financial Officer, Cobleskill Regional Hospital, Cobleskill, NY, p. A424
Chief Financial Officer, Little Falls Hospital, Little Falls, NY, p. A429

VIENNEAU, Marie E., FACHE, President and Chief Executive Officer, Mayo Regional Hospital, Dover, ME, p. A284

VIERLING, Taryn, Chief Nursing Officer, Select Specialty Hospital Of Southeast Ohio, Newark, OH, p. A488

VIG, Vibha, Chief of Staff, Merit Health Madison, Canton, MS, p. A344

VIGIL, Kevin, Director Information Systems, Los Alamos Medical Center, Los Alamos, NM, p. A418

VIGILANTE, Sarah, Manager Human Resources, Mammoth Hospital, Mammoth Lakes, CA, p. A71

VIGNA, Greg A., M.D., Medical Director, Healthsouth Rehabilitation Hospital Of Modesto, Modesto, CA, p. A72

VIGNERI, Joseph, M.D., Chief Medical Officer, Summit Medical Center, Casper, WY, p. A707

VILANOVA, Lynda, Director Patient Care Services, Shriners Hospitals For Children-Spokane, Spokane, WA, p. A678

VILAR, Ramon J., Administrator, Wilma N. Vazquez Medical Center, Vega Baja, PR, p. A716

VILHAUER, Beverly, Chief Executive Officer, Wishek Community Hospital And Clinics, Wishek, ND, p. A469

VILLA, Alex, Chief Executive Officer, Tennova Healthcare-Clarksville, Clarksville, TN, p. A568

VILLA, Maria, Interim Chief Nursing Officer, Kendall Regional Medical Center, Miami, FL, p. A130

VILLAFRANCO, Brenda
Administrator, Memorial Hermann First Colony Hospital, Sugar Land, TX, p. A637
Administrator, Memorial Hermann Tomball Hospital, Tomball, TX, p. A640

VILLAFUERTE, Herbert
Chief Operating Officer and Chief Nursing Officer, Garfield Medical Center, Monterey Park, CA, p. A73
Chief Operating Officer/Chief Nursing Officer, Garfield Medical Center, Monterey Park, CA, p. A73

VILLANI, Travis A., FACHE, Chief Executive Officer and Administrator, Physicians' Hospital In Anadarko, Anadarko, OK, p. A495

VILLANO, Jeremi, M.D., Chief of Staff, Crook County Medical Services District, Sundance, WY, p. A710

VILLANUEVA, Andrew, M.D., Interim Chief Medical Officer, Lahey Medical Center, Peabody, MA, p. A298

VILLARREAL, Xavier, FACHE, Chief Executive Officer, Medical City North Hills, North Richland Hills, TX, p. A626

VILLARRUZ, Alex, Chief Executive Officer, Healthbridge Children's Hospital, Orange, CA, p. A76

VILLEGAS, Lorraine, Manager Human Resources, Bayview Behavioral Health Campus, CA, p. A74

VILLEGAS, William, Vice President Finance, Fort Hamilton Hospital, Hamilton, OH, p. A483

VILUMS, Karlis, Chief Financial Officer, Broadlawns Medical Center, Des Moines, IA, p. A221

VINAS, Elmo, Director Human Resources, Franklin Foundation Hospital, Franklin, LA, p. A267

VINCENT, Ben, FACHE, Chief Executive Officer, Braxton County Memorial Hospital, Gassaway, WV, p. A683

VINCENT, Cynthia, Vice President Finance and Operations, St. Francis Regional Medical Center, Shakopee, MN, p. A340

VINCENT, David, Director Information Systems, Canonsburg Hospital, Canonsburg, PA, p. A522

VINCENT, Joan M, MSN, MS, R.N., Vice President Patient Care Services and Chief Nurse Executive, Adventist Healthcare Shady Grove Medical Center, Rockville, MD, p. A294

VINCENT, Julie S., R.N., MSN, Chief Nursing Officer, Kettering Behavioral Medical Center, OH, p. A487

VINCENT, Larry, Director Human Resources, Delta County Memorial Hospital, Delta, CO, p. A98

VINCENT, Laurence Marie, Chief Nursing Officer, University Hospital And Clinics, Lafayette, LA, p. A271

VINCENT, Mitchell S, Vice President Organizational Support, Range Regional Health Services, Hibbing, MN, p. A333

VINCENT, Paula, MSN, President and Chief Operating Officer, Presbyterian Hemby Children's Hospital, NC, p. A450

VINCENT, Shawn, Interim Chief Operating Officer, Children's Hospital Of Georgia, GA, p. A147

VINCENZ, Felix T, Chief Operating Officer, St. Louis Psychiatric Rehabilitation Center, Saint Louis, MO, p. A369

VINCIFORA, Teresa, Chief Operating Officer, Benson Hospital, Benson, AZ, p. A28

VINCIGUERRA, Tracy, Chief Executive Officer, Healthsouth Mountainview Regional Rehabilitation Hospital, Morgantown, WV, p. A685

VINSANT, George O'Neal, M.D., Chief Medical Officer, Tennova Healthcare-Lafollette Medical Center, La Follette, TN, p. A573

VIOLETTE, Brenda, M.D., Director Medical Staff, Firelands Regional Medical Center South Campus, OH, p. A490

VIOLI, Ronald L., Chief Executive Officer, Wheeling Hospital, Wheeling, WV, p. A688

VIRGEN, Tomas, R.N., MSN, Chief Operating Officer, El Centro Regional Medical Center, El Centro, CA, p. A57

VIRGIL, Cindy L, MSN, R.N., Senior Vice President Patient Care Services, Indiana Regional Medical Center, Indiana, PA, p. A528

VIRJI, Ayaz, M.D., Chief of Staff, Johnson Memorial Health Services, Dawson, MN, p. A330

VIRKLER, Joe, Chief Information Officer, Carthage Area Hospital, Carthage, NY, p. A424

VISCONI, Deborah D., President and Chief Executive Officer, New Bridge Medical Center, Paramus, NJ, p. A409

VISH, Nancy, Ph.D., FACHE, R.N., President, Baylor Jack And Jane Hamilton Heart And Vascular Hospital, Dallas, TX, p. A595

VISSER, Jessica, R.N., Vice President Patient Care Services and Chief Nursing Officer, Mount St. Mary's Hospital And Health Center, Lewiston, NY, p. A429

VISSERS, Robert, M.D., President and Chief Executive Officer, Boulder Community Foothills Hospital, CO, p. A96

VITAL, Dale, Chief Nursing Officer, Memorialcare, Orange Coast Memorial Medical Center, Fountain Valley, CA, p. A58

VITALE-NOLEN, Roberta A, Administrator, Patient Care Services, New Hampshire Hospital, Concord, NH, p. A398

VITALI, Joe, Director Information Technology, Parkside Psychiatric Hospital And Clinic, Tulsa, OK, p. A508

VITALI, Vincent S, Chief Information Officer, Rml Specialty Hospital, IL, p. A186

VITIELLO, Jon, Senior Vice President, Finance Operations and Analytics, Mercy Hospital Oklahoma City, Oklahoma City, OK, p. A503

VITOLAS, Victor, Acting Chief Information Technology Services, Central Texas Veterans Health Care System, Doris Miller Veterans Medical Center, TX, p. A638

VIVIANO, Paul S., President and Chief Executive Officer, Children's Hospital Los Angeles, Los Angeles, CA, p. A66

VIVIT, Romeo, Chief Surgeon, U.S. Public Health Service Indian Hospital, Rosebud, SD, p. A563

VIVODA, Michael
Senior Vice President Human Resources, Northwestern Medicine Valley West Hospital, Sandwich, IL, p. A195
Senior Vice President, Administration, Stone Institute Of Psychiatry, IL, p. A178
Senior Vice President, Human Resources, Northwestern Medicine Kishwaukee Hospital, Dekalb, IL, p. A181

VIZCARRA, Edred T., M.D., Chief of Staff, St. Luke Community Healthcare, Ronan, MT, p. A378

VLAHAVAS, Beth, R.N., MSN, Vice President Patient Care Services and Chief Nursing Officer, Mercy Medical Center, Rockville Centre, NY, p. A442

VLARS, Scott, Chief Information Technology Services, Wilmington Veterans Affairs Medical Center, Wilmington, DE, p. A114

VLODARCHYK, Coreen, R.N., Vice President, Patient Care Services and Chief Nursing Officer, Barnes-Jewish Hospital Psychiatric Support Center, MO, p. A367

VLOSICH, Kristopher Wade., Director, Oklahoma City Veterans Affairs Medical Center, Oklahoma City, OK, p. A504

VOCCA, Lori A, Vice President Human Resources, Providence Everett Medical Center - Pacific Campus, WA, p. A671

VOECKS, Barbara, Chief Information Officer, Ortonville Area Health Services, Ortonville, MN, p. A337

VOELKEL, Jill, Chief Nursing Officer, Pinnacle Specialty Hospital, Tulsa, OK, p. A508

VOELKEL, Jonathon, Administrator, Culberson Hospital, Van Horn, TX, p. A641

VOELKER, Justin, Chief Financial Officer, Multicare Valley Hospital, Spokane Valley, WA, p. A678

VOELKER, Thomas, M.D., Chief Medical Officer, Aspirus Riverview Hospital And Clinics, Inc., Wisconsin Rapids, WI, p. A706

VOGE, Chris, Chief of Staff, French Hospital Medical Center, San Luis Obispo, CA, p. A87

VOGEL, Clay, Administrator and Chief Executive Officer, Coleman County Medical Center, Coleman, TX, p. A593

VOGELSANG, Mark, Director Information Services, Providence Holy Family Hospital, Spokane, WA, p. A678

VOGENTIZ, William, M.D., Medical Director, Anmed Health Rehabilitation Hospital, Anderson, SC, p. A549

VOGT, Dennis, Director Information Technology, Madison Health, London, OH, p. A485

VOGT, Sam, Manager Human Resources, Hebrew Senior Care, West Hartford, CT, p. A112

VOHS, Lester, Manager Information Systems, Cass Regional Medical Center, Harrisonville, MO, p. A360

VOIGT, Jordan, Administrator, Genesis Medical Center-West Campus, IA, p. A220

VOISARD, Victor, Director Human Resources, San Gabriel Valley Medical Center, San Gabriel, CA, p. A86

VOISELLE, Dana, Director Human Resources and Community Relations, Baptist Medical Center Beaches, Jacksonville Beach, FL, p. A126

VOKOUN, Cory, Chief Nursing Officer, Nevada Regional Medical Center, Nevada, MO, p. A365

VOLANTO, John, Vice President, Chief Operating Officer, Nyack Hospital, Nyack, NY, p. A438

VOLINSKI, Douglas R, Vice President and Chief Financial Officer, Duncan Regional Hospital, Duncan, OK, p. A498

VOLK, Charles T., M.D., Regional Chief Medical Officer, Christus Spohn Hospital Corpus Christus South, TX, p. A594

VOLKERDING, Elizabeth, Director Workforce Excellence, San Juan Regional Medical Center Rehabilitation Hospital, NM, p. A417

VOLKERT, Brent, Director Information Technology, Ferrell Hospital, Eldorado, IL, p. A181

VOLLER, Kristi, Director of Nursing, Mobridge Regional Hospital, Mobridge, SD, p. A562

VOLLMER, Kris, Director Patient Care Services, Avera Tyler Hospital, Tyler, MN, p. A341

VOLOCH, Bill, President and Chief Executive Officer, Wesley Woodlawn Hospital & Er, KS, p. A248

VOLOVIC, Mark, Vice President and Chief Information Officer, Indiana Regional Medical Center, Indiana, PA, p. A528

VOLPE, Buddy, Director Human Resources, Peterson Regional Medical Center, Kerrville, TX, p. A617

VOLPE, Michele M., Chief Executive Officer, Penn Presbyterian Medical Center, Philadelphia, PA, p. A536

VON ARX, Michelle, Chief Executive Officer, Penn State Hershey Rehabilitation Hospital, Hummelstown, PA, p. A527

VON BEHREN, Rachel, Director Financial Services, Unitypoint Health - Jones Regional Medical Center, Anamosa, IA, p. A217

VONACHEN, April, Chief Financial Officer and Vice President Financial Services, Cumberland Medical Center, Crossville, TN, p. A569

VONK, Brandon, Nurse Administrator, Lds Hospital, Salt Lake City, UT, p. A650

VOORHEES, Michael, MS, Executive Director, East Mountain Hospital, Belle Mead, NJ, p. A402

VOOYS, Nathan, Chief Executive Officer, Terre Haute Regional Hospital, Terre Haute, IN, p. A215

VOS, Helen, R.N., Interim Chief Nursing Officer, Vancouver Memorial Campus, WA, p. A680

VOSHELL, Shane, Director Human Resources, Adventist Medical Center-Portland, Portland, OR, p. A516

VOSS, Daryle, FACHE, President and Chief Executive Officer, Mercy Hospital Ardmore, Ardmore, OK, p. A495

VOSS, Peter, M.D., Chief Medical Officer, Indiana University Health Ball Memorial Hospital, Muncie, IN, p. A212

VOSS, Robert, Chief Financial Officer, Laredo Specialty Hospital, Laredo, TX, p. A619

VOSS, Stacie, Executive Assistant, Meeker Memorial Hospital, Litchfield, MN, p. A333

VOSS, Wayne M., Chief Executive Officer, Houston Methodist West Hospital, Houston, TX, p. A611

VOSSBERG, Brad, M.D., Chief Rehabilitation, Community Howard Specialty Hospital, Kokomo, IN, p. A209

VOSSLER, Jeffrey W, Chief Financial Officer, Joint Township District Memorial Hospital, Saint Marys, OH, p. A490

VOWELL, Christy, D.O., Chief of Staff, North Mississippi Medical Center-Eupora, Eupora, MS, p. A345

VOZOS, Frank J., M.D., FACS, Chief Executive Officer, MMC Southern Campus, Monmouth Medical Center, Southern Campus, Lakewood, NJ, p. A406

VRANA, Daniel A
    Area Controller, Healthsouth Rehabilitation Hospital Of Sewickley, Sewickley, PA, p. A541
    Controller, Healthsouth Harmarville Rehabilitation Hospital, Pittsburgh, PA, p. A537

VRBA, Frank, Chief Information Officer, Annie Jeffrey Memorial County Health Center, Osceola, NE, p. A389

VRBAS, Laken, R.N., Director of Nursing, Dundy County Hospital, Benkelman, NE, p. A382

VROBEL, Matthew, Vice President, Medical Operations, Cleveland Clinic, Medina Hospital, Medina, OH, p. A486

VRONKO, Jeremy, Manager, Information Services, Spectrum Health Ludington Hospital, Ludington, MI, p. A318

VROTSOS, Darlene, R.N., Senior Vice President and Chief Nursing Officer, Virginia Hospital Center, Arlington, VA, p. A655

VUCHAK, Jerry
    Vice President Healthcare Delivery, Barnes-Jewish Hospital Psychiatric Support Center, MO, p. A367
    Vice President Information Systems, Barnes-Jewish West County Hospital, Saint Louis, MO, p. A367

VUKICH, David, M.D., Senior Vice President, Chief Medical Officer and Chief Quality Officer, Uf Health Jacksonville, Jacksonville, FL, p. A126

VUKSTA, Jeanne, Chief Financial Officer, Bacharach Institute For Rehabilitation, Pomona, NJ, p. A410

VUTRANO, Frank A, Chief Financial Officer, Wyckoff Heights Medical Center, New York (Includes All Hospitals Located Within The Five Boroughs), NY, p. A438

VYZOUREK, Treg, Chief Executive Officer, Brodstone Memorial Hospital, Superior, NE, p. A390

W

WAALA, Shelly, Vice President Patient Care Services and Chief Nursing Officer, St. Joseph's Hospital, West Bend, WI, p. A706

WABAUNSEE, Gary, Service Unit Director, U.S. Public Health Service Indian Hospital, Winnebago, NE, p. A391

WACHOWIAK, Darrell, Associate Vice President Operations, Promedica Bay Park Hospital, Oregon, OH, p. A488

WACK, Mark, Senior Vice President and Chief Financial Officer, Touro Rehabilitation Center, LA, p. A276

WADDELL, Kathy, Administrator, Wayne General Hospital, Waynesboro, MS, p. A354

WADDELL, Lesa, Director Human Resources, Compass Memorial Healthcare, Marengo, IA, p. A226

WADE, Bruce, Vice President Human Resources, Indiana University Health Bedford Hospital, Bedford, IN, p. A199

WADE, Cynthia, R.N., RN, BSN,, Executive Vice President and Chief Operating Officer, Lincolnhealth St. Andrews Campus, ME, p. A283

WADE, Donald Lee, Chief Financial Officer, Goodland Regional Medical Center, Goodland, KS, p. A235

WADE, Donna, Senior Director Human Resources, Comanche County Memorial Hospital, Lawton, OK, p. A500

WADE, Glenn, Director Information Systems, Saint Thomas Highlands Hospital, Sparta, TN, p. A580

WADE, Hong, Chief Financial Officer, Sweeny Community Hospital, Sweeny, TX, p. A638

WADE, Jacqueline, Ph.D., Director, Desert Willow Treatment Center, Las Vegas, NV, p. A394

WADE, Jonathan O., Chief Executive Officer, Jersey Community Hospital, Jerseyville, IL, p. A186

WADE, Kathy, Chief Human Resource Officer, Winona Health, Winona, MN, p. A342

WADE, Susan, Vice President, Hendrick Health System, Abilene, TX, p. A582

WADEWITZ, Martin, Chief Operations Officer/ Vice President, Operations, Angel Medical Center, Franklin, NC, p. A452

WADLE, Don
    Interim Director Human Resources, Portneuf Medical Center, Pocatello, ID, p. A171
    Vice President Clinical and Support Services, Portneuf Medical Center, Pocatello, ID, p. A171

WADSWORTH, Barbara A, MSN, R.N., FACHE, Chief Nursing Officer, Bryn Mawr Hospital, Bryn Mawr, PA, p. A521

WAFFORD, Marty, Under Secretary of Support and Programs, Chickasaw Nation Medical Center, Ada, OK, p. A495

WAFLE, Sue, Director, Human Resources, Mile Bluff Medical Center, Mauston, WI, p. A697

WAGERS, Rick, Senior Executive Vice President and Chief Financial Officer, Regional One Health, Memphis, TN, p. A575

WAGGENER, Yvonne, Chief Financial Officer, San Bernardino Mountains Community Hospital District, Lake Arrowhead, CA, p. A63

WAGGONER, Jeff, M.D., Chief of Staff, Weisbrod Memorial County Hospital, Eads, CO, p. A100

WAGGONER, Michelle, Chief Executive Officer, Community Memorial Hospital, Hicksville, OH, p. A484

WAGLE, Roberta, Director Human Resources, Pinnacle Specialty Hospital, Tulsa, OK, p. A508

WAGLEY, Ronnie, Market Chief Executive Officer, Select Specialty Hospital-Gainesville, Gainesville, FL, p. A123

WAGMEISTER, Lee, M.D., President Medical Staff, The Heart Hospital At Deaconess Gateway, Newburgh, IN, p. A212

WAGNER, Dale, Chief Financial Officer, Kindred Hospital-Westminster, Westminster, CA, p. A95

WAGNER, David, South Florida Market Chief Executive Officer, Kindred Hospital South Florida-Hollywood, FL, p. A123

WAGNER, David D, Chief Information Management Service, Veterans Affairs Gulf Coast Veterans Health Care System, Biloxi, MS, p. A343

WAGNER, David S., FACHE, Chief Executive Officer, Pearland Medical Center, Pearland, TX, p. A627

WAGNER, Elaina, Director Human Resources, Astria Sunnyside Hospital, Sunnyside, WA, p. A678

WAGNER, Fred, Chief Financial Officer, Osf St. Francis Hospital And Medical Group, Escanaba, MI, p. A312

WAGNER, Gwendolyn Dianne, R.N., MSN, Chief Nursing Officer, Mission Community Hospital, Los Angeles, CA, p. A68

WAGNER, Janet, R.N.
    Chief Executive Officer, Mills Health Center, CA, p. A53
    Chief Executive Officer, Mills-Peninsula Medical Center, CA, p. A53

WAGNER, Jefferey, Director, Information Technology, Lake Huron Medical Center, Port Huron, MI, p. A321

WAGNER, Linda, Chief Financial Officer, Sanford Worthington Medical Center, Worthington, MN, p. A342

WAGNER, Linda S., R.N., MSN, FACHE, Chief Executive Officer, Seneca Healthcare District, Chester, CA, p. A54

WAGNER, Lynne, R.N., Chief Nursing Officer, Rose Medical Center, Denver, CO, p. A99

WAGNER, Randall J, Chief Operating Officer, Mercy Health Rockford, MI, p. A314

WAGNER, Renee, M.D., Chief Medical Officer, Fairfield Medical Center, Lancaster, OH, p. A484

WAGNER, Russell R, Executive Vice President and Chief Financial Officer, Holy Redeemer Hospital, Meadowbrook, PA, p. A531

WAGNER, Sarah, Human Resources Officer, Memorial Hospital Of Texas County, Guymon, OK, p. A499

WAGNER, Sherrie A, Manager Human Resources, The Core Institute Specialty Hospital, Phoenix, AZ, p. A34

WAGNER, Suzie, Director Human Resources, Healthsouth Rehabilitation Hospital Of Alexandria, Alexandria, LA, p. A262

WAGNER, Terry, R.N.
    Chief Operating Officer, Pocahontas Memorial Hospital, Buckeye, WV, p. A681
    Chief Information Officer, Upstate University Hospital At Community General, NY, p. A444

WAGNER, Timothy, M.D., Chief Medical Staff, Yoakum Community Hospital, Yoakum, TX, p. A645

WAGNER, Tom, Interim Vice President Finance, Avera St. Mary's Hospital, Pierre, SD, p. A562

WAGNER, Vanessa, Chief Financial Officer, Lawrence Memorial Hospital, Walnut Ridge-Lawrence County, AR, p. A49

WAGNON, LaNell, Director Medical Records, Comanche County Hospital, Coldwater, KS, p. A233

WAGNON, William, Chief Executive Officer, Henrico Doctors' Hospital - Retreat Campus, VA, p. A665

WAGONER, Craig
    Chief Executive Officer, Community Behavioral Health Center, Fresno, CA, p. A59
    Chief Executive Officer, Community Regional Medical Center, Fresno, CA, p. A59

WAGONER, Dean, Director Human Resources, Good Samaritan Hospital, Vincennes, IN, p. A216

WAGONER, Renee, R.N., Director of Nursing, Gove County Medical Center, Quinter, KS, p. A244

WAHAB, Amir J., M.D., Medical Staff President, Abraham Lincoln Memorial Hospital, Lincoln, IL, p. A188

WAHL, Josephine Sclafani, R.N., MS, FACHE, VP, Patient Care Services & CNO, Henry Ford Wyandotte Hospital, Wyandotte, MI, p. A326

WAHL, Tony, Chief Executive Officer, Baylor Scott & White Texas Spine & Joint Hospital, Tyler, TX, p. A641

WAHLERS, Brenda, M.D., Chief of Staff, Upmc Cole, Coudersport, PA, p. A523

WAHLUND, Keith, Vice President Human Resources, Essentia Health Fargo, Fargo, ND, p. A465

WAIBEL, David, M.D., Medical Director, Clarks Summit State Hospital, Clarks Summit, PA, p. A522

WAIDE, Mary Beth, JD, MS, R.N., Chief Executive Officer, Deer's Head Hospital Center, Salisbury, MD, p. A294

WAIN, Matthew, Chief Operating Officer, Children's Hospital Of South Carolina At Musc, SC, p. A550

WAIND, Mark, Chief Information Officer, Altru Rehabilitation Center, ND, p. A466

WAIT, Wendy, Chief Financial Officer, Montgomery County Emergency Service, Norristown, PA, p. A533

WAITE, Douglas, M.D., Chief Medical Officer, Saint Vincent Hospital, Worcester, MA, p. A306

WAITE, Douglas D
    Senior Vice President and Chief Financial Officer, Seton Highland Lakes, Burnet, TX, p. A591
    Senior Vice President and Chief Financial Officer, Seton Medical Center Williamson, Round Rock, TX, p. A631

WAITES, Alan, Chief Financial Officer, Gove County Medical Center, Quinter, KS, p. A244

WAJDA, David, Chief Financial Officer, Nazareth Hospital, Philadelphia, PA, p. A535

WAKEFIELD, Brett
    Director Human Resources, Thorek Memorial Hospital, Chicago, IL, p. A180
    Vice President Human Resources, Gottlieb Memorial Hospital, Melrose Park, IL, p. A189

WAKEFIELD, Jeff, CPA, Chief Financial Officer, Marion General Hospital, Marion, IN, p. A211

WAKEFIELD, Mamie
    Chief Financial Officer, Miriam Hospital, Providence, RI, p. A547
    Senior Vice President and Chief Financial Officer, Hasbro Children's Hospital, RI, p. A548
    Vice President Finance and Chief Financial Officer, Emma Pendleton Bradley Hospital, East Providence, RI, p. A547

WAKEM, Jennifer, Chief Financial Officer, Children's Hospital Of Nevada At Umc, NV, p. A395

WAKEMAN, Daniel L., President, St. Luke's Hospital, Maumee, OH, p. A486

WAKIM, Tina, Vice President Information, Northside Hospital, Atlanta, GA, p. A146

WALAS, Steven, Chief Executive Officer, Healthsouth Chesapeake Rehabilitation Hospital, Salisbury, MD, p. A294

WALCEK, Peter, Vice President Finance, Wentworth-Douglass Hospital, Dover, NH, p. A398

WALCH, Tina, M.D., Medical Director, South Oaks Hospital, Amityville, NY, p. A421

WALCZAK, Laura, President, Ssm Health St. Clare Hospital-Baraboo, Baraboo, WI, p. A689

WALCZYK-JOERS, Barbara, President and Chief Executive Officer, Gillette Children's Specialty Healthcare, Saint Paul, MN, p. A339

WALD, Barry, Chief Financial Officer, Wake Forest Baptist Health - Wilkes Medical Center, North Wilkesboro, NC, p. A458

WALDBART, Andy, Department Manager, Heart Of The Rockies Regional Medical Center, Salida, CO, p. A105

WALDBILLIG, Karla, Director Human Resources, Unitypoint Health - Finley Hospital, Dubuque, IA, p. A222

WALDBILLIG, Kurt, Chief Executive Officer, Swift County - Benson Health Services, Benson, MN, p. A328

WALDEN, Anita, Vice President and Chief Nursing Officer, Decatur Morgan Hospital-West, AL, p. A16

WALDERA, John, Director Information Technology, Gundersen Tri-County Hospital And Clinics, Whitehall, WI, p. A706

WALDO, Bruce
    Chief Executive Officer, Aurora Behavioral Health System East, Tempe, AZ, p. A36
    Chief Executive Officer, Aurora Behavioral Health System West, Glendale, AZ, p. A30

WALDO, Gail, Director Information Technology, Piedmont Rockdale Hospital, Conyers, GA, p. A151

WALDRON, Michele, Senior Vice President and Chief Financial Officer, Valley Children's Healthcare, Madera, CA, p. A71

WALDRON, Ray, Director Information Technology, Gordon Memorial Health Services, Gordon, NE, p. A384

WALDRON, Sheila, Finance Manager, Providence Milwaukie Hospital, Milwaukie, OR, p. A515

WALDROP, Catherine M.
  Administrator, Southeast Rehabilitation Hospital, Lake Village-Chicot County, AR, p. A44
  Administrator, Sterlington Rehabilitation Hospital, Bastrop, LA, p. A263

WALDROP, Cathy, Director, Hospital Nursing Services, North Mississippi Medical Center-Pontotoc, Pontotoc, MS, p. A352

WALI, Jyotika, M.D., Chief of Staff, Kindred Hospital-Brea, Brea, CA, p. A53

WALIGURA, R Curtis, D.O., Vice President Medical Affairs, Chief Medical Officer, Upmc Mckeesport, Mckeesport, PA, p. A531

WALK, Rex D., Chief Executive Officer, Phillips County Hospital, Phillipsburg, KS, p. A244

WALKENHORST, Debbie G
  Network Vice President, Ssm Cardinal Glennon Children's Hospital, Saint Louis, MO, p. A368
  System Vice President Talent Management, Ssm Health St. Joseph - Wentzville, MO, p. A367

WALKER, Alene, Director Human Resources, Quincy Valley Medical Center, Quincy, WA, p. A675

WALKER, Alexander J., Executive Vice President Operations and Strategic Development, Catholic Medical Center, Manchester, NH, p. A400

WALKER, Amy, MSN, Chief Nursing Officer, The King's Daughters Hospital, MS, p. A346

WALKER, Angela, M.D.
  Medical Director, Healthsouth Rehabilitation Hospital Of New Mexico, Albuquerque, NM, p. A415
  Manager Human Resources, Aspire Hospital, Conroe, TX, p. A593

WALKER, Annette
  Associate Director, John D. Dingell Veterans Affairs Medical Center, Detroit, MI, p. A311
  Director, Atlanta Veterans Affairs Medical Center, Decatur, GA, p. A152

WALKER, Beth, R.N.
  President, Firsthealth Montgomery Memorial Hospital, Troy, NC, p. A461
  Chief Information Officer, Emanuel Medical Center, Turlock, CA, p. A92

WALKER, C O, M.D., Chief of Staff, Donalsonville Hospital, Donalsonville, GA, p. A152

WALKER, Candace, Chief Financial Officer, East Central Regional Hospital, GA, p. A147

WALKER, Carol, Chief Financial Officer, Oklahoma Heart Hospital, Oklahoma City, OK, p. A504

WALKER, Cass
  Vice President Administrative & Support Services, Franklin Regional Hospital, Franklin, NH, p. A399
  Vice President Administrative & Support Services, Lakes Region General Hospital, Laconia, NH, p. A399

WALKER, Charles, Director Information Technology, Kimball Health Services, Kimball, NE, p. A385

WALKER, Cheri, R.N., Chief Nursing Officer, King's Daughters Medical Center, Brookhaven, MS, p. A344

WALKER, Christopher, Chief Nursing Officer and Operating Officer, Sharp Coronado Hospital And Healthcare Center, Coronado, CA, p. A55

WALKER, Codie, Chief Financial Officer, Salem Veterans Affairs Medical Center, Salem, VA, p. A666

WALKER, Dan, Chief Nursing Officer, Lincoln Community Hospital And Nursing Home, Hugo, CO, p. A102

WALKER, David M., M.D., Medical Center Director, G.V. (Sonny) Montgomery Veterans Affairs Medical Center, Jackson, MS, p. A348

WALKER, Donna, Chief Nurse Executive, Weeks Medical Center, Lancaster, NH, p. A399

WALKER, Durwin, M.D., Chief Medical Officer, Sage Specialty Hospital (Ltac), Denham Springs, LA, p. A267

WALKER, Gerri H., President and Chief Executive Officer, Girard Medical Center, PA, p. A536

WALKER, Gregory J., Chief Executive Officer, Wentworth-Douglass Hospital, Dover, NH, p. A398

WALKER, Imani, M.D., Medical Director, Gateways Hospital And Mental Health Center, Los Angeles, CA, p. A67

WALKER, Jan
  Director Human Resources, Glenwood Surgery Center, LA, p. A280
  Director Human Resources, Lynchburg General Hospital, VA, p. A660

WALKER, Janice L., R.N., Chief Operating Officer, Baylor All Saints Medical Center At Fort Worth, Fort Worth, TX, p. A604

WALKER, Jeff E., Chief Operating Officer, City Of Hope's Helford Clinical Research Hospital, Duarte, CA, p. A57

WALKER, Jeremy Tyler, Vice President and Chief Financial Officer, Hendrick Health System, Abilene, TX, p. A582

WALKER, John, Chief Operating Officer, Medical City Denton, Denton, TX, p. A599

WALKER, Jon W., M.D., Chief Medical Officer, Wise Regional Health System, West Campus Decatur, TX, p. A598

WALKER, Karen, Chief Executive Officer, Oakwood Springs, Oklahoma City, OK, p. A503

WALKER, Kathy, Chief Financial Officer, Trinity Hospital, Weaverville, CA, p. A95

WALKER, Kimberly, Director of Human Resources, Northcrest Medical Center, Springfield, TN, p. A580

WALKER, Kristie E, M.P.H., Director of Human Resources, Wythe County Community Hospital, Wytheville, VA, p. A668

WALKER, LeRoy, Vice President Human Resources, Dekalb Medical At North Decatur, Decatur, GA, p. A152

WALKER, Lynette, R.N., Ph.D., Vice President Human Resources, Baptist Health Lexington, Lexington, KY, p. A254

WALKER, Mary, Manager Information Technology, Encompass Health Rehabilitation Hospital Of Wichita Falls, Wichita Falls, TX, p. A644

WALKER, Matthew, Chief Executive Officer and Administrator, William Bee Ririe Hospital, Ely, NV, p. A392

WALKER, Melissa, CPA, Chief Financial Officer, North Texas Medical Center, Gainesville, TX, p. A606

WALKER, Nicole, Chief Executive Officer, Hermann Drive Surgical Hospital, Houston, TX, p. A611

WALKER, Pandora, Director, Human Resources, Beaumont Hospital - Grosse Pointe, Grosse Pointe, MI, p. A315

WALKER, Randy
  Chief Nursing Officer, Hillcrest Hospital Claremore, Claremore, OK, p. A497
  Director Nursing Services, State Hospital South, Blackfoot, ID, p. A167
  Vice President, Methodist Dallas Medical Center, Dallas, TX, p. A597

WALKER, Robert, M.D., Medical Director, Healthsouth Southern Hills Rehabilitation Hospital, Princeton, WV, p. A686

WALKER, Robert L., FACHE, President and Chief Executive Officer, Texas Scottish Rite Hospital For Children, Dallas, TX, p. A598

WALKER, Robin, Chief Nursing Officer, Field Memorial Community Hospital, Centreville, MS, p. A344

WALKER, Samuel, Director of IT, Pocahontas Memorial Hospital, Buckeye, WV, p. A681

WALKER, Scott, Chief Financial Officer, Southeastern Regional Medical Center, Newnan, GA, p. A158

WALKER, Tim, Manager Information Services, Peacehealth Ketchikan Medical Center, Ketchikan, AK, p. A26

WALKER, Todd, President, Baptist Easley Hospital, Easley, SC, p. A552

WALKER, Troy, Director Finance, Ssm Health St. Clare Hospital-Baraboo, Baraboo, WI, p. A689

WALKER, Tyree, Chief Human Resources Officer, University Health Systems Children's Hospital, NC, p. A454

WALKER, Virginia, Vice President Nursing Services and Chief Nursing Officer, Kuakini Medical Center, Honolulu, HI, p. A164

WALL, Daniel J., President and Chief Executive Officer, Emma Pendleton Bradley Hospital, East Providence, RI, p. A547

WALL, Debbie, Chief Nursing Officer, Cherry Hospital, Goldsboro, NC, p. A453

WALL, Doug, M.D.
  Vice President Medical Affairs, Novant Health Uva Health System Prince William Medical Center, Manassas, VA, p. A661
  Vice President of Medical Affairs, Novant Health Uva Health System Haymarket Medical Center, Haymarket, VA, p. A659

WALL, Heather, Chief Nursing Officer, Peacehealth Sacred Heart Medical Center At Riverbend, Springfield, OR, p. A518

WALL, Kathryn S
  Executive Vice President Human Resources and Organizational Development, Stafford Hospital, Stafford, VA, p. A666
  Executive Vice President, Human Resources and Organizational Development, Snowden At Fredericksburg, VA, p. A658

WALL, Lorraine, Chief Nursing Officer and Chief Operating Officer, Olympic Medical Center, Port Angeles, WA, p. A675

WALL, Michael L., FACHE, President and Chief Executive Officer, Antelope Valley Hospital, Lancaster, CA, p. A64

WALLACE, Brad, Director Information Services, Grays Harbor Community Hospital, Aberdeen, WA, p. A669

WALLACE, Carolyn, Director Human Resources, Connecticut Mental Health Center, New Haven, CT, p. A109

WALLACE, Cynthia, M.D., Medical Director, Vibra Specialty Hospital Of Portland, Portland, OR, p. A517

WALLACE, David, Chief Executive Officer, Mat-Su Regional Medical Center, Palmer, AK, p. A27

WALLACE, Dianne, County Information Manager, Douglas County Community Mental Health Center, Omaha, NE, p. A388

WALLACE, Donna Geiken, Chief Operating Officer and Chief Financial Officer, Christus Mother Frances Hospital - Sulphur Springs, Sulphur Springs, TX, p. A637

WALLACE, Glenn, Chief Executive Officer, Medical City Alliance, Fort Worth, TX, p. A605

WALLACE, Jennifer, Chief Executive Officer, Amg Specialty Hospital-Greenwood, Greenwood, MS, p. A346

WALLACE, Kathleen, R.N., MSN, Administrator and Chief Executive Officer, Lifecare Hospitals Of North Texas-Plano, TX, p. A596

WALLACE, Kent, Chief Operating Officer, Kindred Hospital New Jersey - Wayne, NJ, p. A404

WALLACE, Kristina, R.N., Chief Executive Officer, Presbyterian Tower, OK, p. A504

WALLACE, Mark, Chief Financial Officer, Cumberland Hall Hospital, Hopkinsville, KY, p. A253

WALLACE, Mark A., FACHE, President and Chief Executive Officer, Texas Children's Hospital West Campus, TX, p. A613

WALLACE, Mark T, Director Human Resources, Lodi Memorial Hospital West, CA, p. A64

WALLACE, Martha, Administrator, California Mens Colony Correctional Treatment Center, San Luis Obispo, CA, p. A87

WALLACE, Matthew, Manager Information Technology, Biomed, Black River Medical Center, Poplar Bluff, MO, p. A366

WALLACE, Melanie, Manager Human Resources, Sutter Tracy Community Hospital, Tracy, CA, p. A92

WALLACE, Michael S., President and Chief Executive Officer, Fort Healthcare, Fort Atkinson, WI, p. A692

WALLACE, Nancy
  Division Senior Vice President, Chief Human Resource Officer, Chi Health Lakeside, Omaha, NE, p. A388
  Division Senior Vice President, Chief Human Resource Officer, Chi Health Midlands, Papillion, NE, p. A389
  Senior Vice President Human Resources, Chi Health Mercy Council Bluffs, Council Bluffs, IA, p. A220
  Senior Vice President, Chief Human Resources Officer, Chi Health St Elizabeth, Lincoln, NE, p. A386
  Vice President Human Resources, CHI Health, St. Francis Medical Plaza, NE, p. A384
  Vice President Human Resources, Chi Health Immanuel, Omaha, NE, p. A388
  Vice President Human Resources, Chi Health Schuyler, Schuyler, NE, p. A390
  Vice President Human Resources, Lasting Hope Recovery Center, NE, p. A387

WALLACE, Penny, Chief Financial Officer, Guadalupe Regional Medical Center, Seguin, TX, p. A635

WALLACE, Tabatha, Director Human Resources, Florida Hospital Dade City, Dade City, FL, p. A121

WALLACE-MOORE, Patrice, Chief Executive Officer and Executive Director, Arms Acres, Carmel, NY, p. A424

WALLEN, Carla, Manager Human Resources, Cass Regional Medical Center, Harrisonville, MO, p. A360

WALLENTINE, Jeffrey, Chief of Staff, Mountain View Hospital, Payson, UT, p. A649

WALLER, Ernie, Director Information Technology, Ed Fraser Memorial Hospital And Baker Community Health Center, Macclenny, FL, p. A128

WALLER, Kenneth, Fiscal Administrator, Deer's Head Hospital Center, Salisbury, MD, p. A294

WALLER, Matthew, Chief Executive Officer, Liberty Medical Center, Chester, MT, p. A374

WALLER, Raymond A., Director, Brighton Center For Recovery, Brighton, MI, p. A308

WALLINE, Linda K, R.N., Ph.D., MSN, Vice President Nursing, Columbus Community Hospital, Columbus, NE, p. A383

WALLING, Vernon, M.D.
  Chief Medical Officer, Sun Behavioral Houston, Houston, TX, p. A613
  Executive Medical Director, West Oaks Hospital, Houston, TX, p. A614

WALLINGA, Joel, Chief Financial Officer, Veterans Affairs Ann Arbor Healthcare System, Ann Arbor, MI, p. A307

WALLINGA, Melvin, M.D., Medical Director, St. Michael's Hospital Avera, Tyndall, SD, p. A564

WALLIS, Pam B, MSN, Vice President Nursing Services, Magnolia Regional Health Center, Corinth, MS, p. A345

WALLMAN, Gerald H., Administrator, West Covina Medical Center, West Covina, CA, p. A95

WALLS, Craig, M.D., Ph.D., Chief Medical Officer, Natividad Medical Center, Salinas, CA, p. A83

WALLS, Martha Delaney, R.N., MSN, Chief Nursing Officer, Crestwood Medical Center, Huntsville, AL, p. A19

WALLS, Randy, Manager Information Services, Fairbanks, Indianapolis, IN, p. A206

WALLS, Ron, M.D., Executive Vice President and Chief Operating Officer, Brigham And Women's Hospital, Boston, MA, p. A296

WALLSCHLAEGER, Erich, Chief Financial Officer, Cedar Park Regional Medical Center, Cedar Park, TX, p. A592

WALRATH, Andrea, Chief Operating Officer, Forest Health Medical Center, Ypsilanti, MI, p. A326

WALRAVEN, Jeff, Chief Executive Officer, Lindsay Municipal Hospital, Lindsay, OK, p. A500

WALSER, Bill, Coordinator Technology, Cameron Regional Medical Center, Cameron, MO, p. A356

WALSH, Brad, M.D., Chief of Staff, Ashley County Medical Center, Crossett-Ashley County, AR, p. A40

WALSH, Catherine, Interim Nursing Executive, Mercy Regional Medical Center, Lorain, OH, p. A485

WALSH, Daniel P., Vice President, Information Systems and Technology Northern Division, Abington Hospital, Abington, PA, p. A519

WALSH, Debbie, MSN, Chief Operating Officer, Maui Memorial Medical Center, Wailuku, HI, p. A166

WALSH, Gerard W., Chief Executive Officer, St. John's Episcopal Hospital-South Shore, New York (Includes All Hospitals Located Within The Five Boroughs), NY, p. A437

WALSH, John, Chief Fiscal Services, Veterans Affairs Hudson Valley Health Care System-Montrose Campus, NY, p. A430

WALSH, Kate, M.P.H., President and Chief Executive Officer, Boston Medical Center, Boston, MA, p. A296

WALSH, Katherine, MS, R.N., Dr.PH, Vice President and Chief Nursing Officer, Houston Methodist Hospital, Houston, TX, p. A611

WALSH, Ken, Chief Financial Officer, Tempe St. Luke's Hospital, AZ, p. A34

WALSH, Kim, Chief Nursing Officer, Signature Healthcare Brockton Hospital, Brockton, MA, p. A298

WALSH, Len, Executive Vice President and Chief Operating Officer, St. Barnabas Hospital, New York (Includes All Hospitals Located Within The Five Boroughs), NY, p. A437

WALSH, Linda, R.N., MSN, Vice President Chief Nursing Executive, Hackensack Meridian Health Bayshore Community Hospital, Holmdel, NJ, p. A406

WALSH, Marcia S, M.P.H., Chief Operating Officer, Community Healthcare System, Onaga, KS, p. A242

WALSH, Marilyn J, Vice President Human Resources, Kent County Memorial Hospital, Warwick, RI, p. A548

WALSH, Mary, R.N., MSN
Vice President Patient Care Services and Chief Nursing Officer, Mount Sinai Beth Israel Brooklyn, NY, p. A434
Vice President Patient Care Services and Chief Nursing Officer, Mount Sinai West Hospital, NY, p. A434

WALSH, Michael
Senior Vice President Finance and Chief Financial Officer, Abington Hospital, Abington, PA, p. A519
Senior Vice President Finance and Chief Financial Officer, Abington-Lansdale Hospital Jefferson Health, Lansdale, PA, p. A529

WALSH, Michele M, Chief Nursing Officer, St. Mary's Healthcare, NY, p. A421

WALSTON, John, Chief Information Officer, Southern Arizona Veterans Affairs Health Care System, Tucson, AZ, p. A38

WALTER, Gayle, Director of Nursing, Thomas B. Finan Center, Cumberland, MD, p. A291

WALTER, Melissa, Director Human Resources, Clarinda Regional Health Center, Clarinda, IA, p. A219

WALTER, Stephen
Senior Vice President and Chief Financial Officer, Community Behavioral Health Center, Fresno, CA, p. A59
Senior Vice President and Chief Financial Officer, Community Regional Medical Center, Fresno, CA, p. A59

WALTERS, Cindy, Chief Executive Officer, Acadia-St. Landry Hospital, Church Point, LA, p. A265

WALTERS, Jane, Director of Nursing, Mendota Mental Health Institute, Madison, WI, p. A696

WALTERS, Julie, Chief Nursing Officer, Hillsdale Hospital, Hillsdale, MI, p. A315

WALTERS, Kevin, Chief Financial Officer, St. Rose Dominican Hospitals - Rose De Lima Campus, Henderson, NV, p. A393

WALTERS, Leah, R.N., Director of Nursing, Mountain Valley Regional Rehabilitation Hospital, Prescott Valley, AZ, p. A34

WALTERS, Leslie, MSN, Chief Nursing Officer, Clarion Hospital, Clarion, PA, p. A522

WALTERS, Todd, Director of UHC Information Technology Services, University Health Conway, Monroe, LA, p. A274

WALTHALL, Wayne, Vice President and Chief Financial Officer, St. John Medical Center, Tulsa, OK, p. A509

WALTHER, Diane, Controller, Henry County Hospital, Napoleon, OH, p. A487

WALTON, Amy E., M.D., Chief Medical Officer, Seton Shoal Creek Hospital, Austin, TX, p. A586

WALTON, Dawn, Chief Financial Officer, Children's Of Alabama, Birmingham, AL, p. A14

WALTON, Gary, M.D., Chief Medical Officer, Hill Hospital Of Sumter County, York, AL, p. A24

WALTON, Georgian, Director Human Resources, Elbert Memorial Hospital, Elberton, GA, p. A153

WALTON, Linda, R.N., MSN, Chief Nursing Officer, Behavioral Health Center, FL, p. A143

WALTON, Robert M., Healthcare System Director, San Antonio Division, TX, p. A634

WALTZ, Dan, Vice President and Chief Information Officer, Midmichigan Medical Center-Gladwin, Gladwin, MI, p. A313

WALZ, Rachel A, Director Patient Care, Centracare Health-Paynesville, Paynesville, MN, p. A337

WAMPLER, Andrew
Chief Financial Officer, Franklin Woods Community Hospital, Johnson City, TN, p. A571
Chief Financial Officer, Margaret R. Pardee Memorial Hospital, Hendersonville, NC, p. A454

WAMPLER, Beth A, R.N., Chief Nursing Officer, Fayette Regional Health System, Connersville, IN, p. A201

WAMSLEY, Marie, Chief Financial Officer, Memorial Hospital Of Lafayette County, Darlington, WI, p. A691

WANG, William Norberto, M.D., Chief Operating Officer, Nyc Health + Hospitals / Metropolitan, New York (Includes All Hospitals Located Within The Five Boroughs), NY, p. A436

WANG, Shu-Ming, MD, Vice President Medical Affairs, St. Francis Medical Plaza, NE, p. A384

WANGSMO, Gary L, Chief Financial Officer, Mee Memorial Hospital, King City, CA, p. A62

WANGSNESS, Erik, President, Adventist Healthcare Washington Adventist Hospital, Takoma Park, MD, p. A294

WANLY, Bahaa, Interim Chief Operating Officer, Salem Health Rehabilitation Center, OR, p. A517

WANNER, David
Chief Information Officer, Trinity Hospital-St. Joseph'S, ND, p. A468
Director Information Technology, Kenmare Community Hospital, Kenmare, ND, p. A467

WAPPELHORST, Andrea, Chief Nursing Officer, Tops Surgical Specialty Hospital, Houston, TX, p. A614

WAR, Melissa, Chief Executive Officer, Mountain's Edge Hospital, Las Vegas, NV, p. A394

WARBURTON, John B., Chief Executive Officer, Riverwoods Behavioral Health System, Riverdale, GA, p. A159

WARD, Brook, Executive Vice President, Washington Hospital, Washington, PA, p. A543

WARD, Celia F, Controller and Chief Financial Officer, Doctors Memorial Hospital, Bonifay, FL, p. A118

WARD, Charlotte, Entity Financial Officer, Texas Health Hospital Clearfork, TX, p. A605

WARD, Chris
Chief Nursing Officer, Comanche County Memorial Hospital, Lawton, OK, p. A500
Director Management Information Systems, Dorminy Medical Center, Fitzgerald, GA, p. A153

WARD, David M, Chief Financial Officer and Chief Acquisition Officer, Hoops Family Children's Hospital, WV, p. A683

WARD, Dillon, Management Information Systems Specialist, Tennova Healthcare-Lafollette Medical Center, La Follette, TN, p. A573

WARD, Elizabeth S.
Chief Financial Officer, Tidelands Georgetown Memorial Hospital, Georgetown, SC, p. A553
Chief Financial Officer, Tidelands Waccamaw Community Hospital, Murrells Inlet, SC, p. A556

WARD, Jeffery, Director Human Resources, Cedar Park Regional Medical Center, Cedar Park, TX, p. A592

WARD, Julie, MSN, R.N.
Chief Nursing Officer, St. Joseph's Westgate Medical Center, AZ, p. A34
Vice President Finance, Northeastern Health System, Tahlequah, OK, p. A507

WARD, Julie R., MSN, R.N., Vice President Patient Care Services, Hutchinson Regional Medical Center, Hutchinson, KS, p. A237

WARD, Kevin, Chief Operating Officer, Jewish Home Of San Francisco, San Francisco, CA, p. A85

WARD, Kevin J, Vice President and Chief Financial Officer, New York-Presbyterian Queens, New York (Includes All Hospitals Located Within The Five Boroughs), NY, p. A435

WARD, Kimberly J, Chief Nurse Officer, St. Luke's Rehabilitation Institute, Spokane, WA, p. A678

WARD, Lesli, Vice President Human Resources, Uf Health Jacksonville, Jacksonville, FL, p. A126

WARD, Lisa, Director Information Systems, Columbus Regional Healthcare System, Whiteville, NC, p. A462

WARD, Lorna J, MSN, R.N., Chief Nursing Officer, Novant Health Brunswick Medical Center, Bolivia, NC, p. A448

WARD, Louis James, Chief Operating Officer, Mayers Memorial Hospital District, Fall River Mills, CA, p. A58

WARD, Louis James., Interim Chief Executive Officer, Mayers Memorial Hospital District, Fall River Mills, CA, p. A58

WARD, Mark, M.D., Chief of Staff, Roundup Memorial Healthcare, Roundup, MT, p. A378

WARD, Michael
Chief Executive Officer, Healthsouth Rehabilitation Hospital-Las Vegas, Las Vegas, NV, p. A394
Director Information Services, Anderson Hospital, Maryville, IL, p. A188

WARD, Mike
Chief Information Officer, Morristown-Hamblen Healthcare System, Morristown, TN, p. A576
Covenant Health, Senior Vice President and Chief Information Officer, Methodist Medical Center Of Oak Ridge, Oak Ridge, TN, p. A578
Senior Vice President Chief Information Officer, Roane Medical Center, Harriman, TN, p. A570

WARD, Rhonda, R.N., MSN, Chief Nursing Officer, Littleton Adventist Hospital, Littleton, CO, p. A103

WARD, Robert, Chief Executive Officer, Select Rehabilitation Hospital Of San Antonio, San Antonio, TX, p. A634

WARD, Rory, Chief Financial Officer, Pushmataha Hospital, Antlers, OK, p. A495

WARD, Silva, Director Human Resources, Center For Behavioral Medicine, Kansas City, MO, p. A361

WARD, Stormy, Chief Nurse Executive, Big Spring State Hospital, Big Spring, TX, p. A589

WARD, Virginia, Human Resources Officer, Robert E. Bush Naval Hospital, Twentynine Palms, CA, p. A92

WARD, Wendy, Director Human Resources, Mercy Hospital El Reno, El Reno, OK, p. A498

WARDA, Paul, Chief Financial Officer, Medstar Georgetown University Hospital, Washington, DC, p. A115

WARDELL, Patrick R., Chief Executive Officer, Whidden Memorial Hospital, MA, p. A298

WARDEN, Michael S, Senior Vice President Information Technology, Banner - University Medical Center Phoenix, Phoenix, AZ, p. A33

WARDLOW, Marlon, Chief Operating Officer, Parkview Hospital Randallia, IN, p. A204

WARDROP, Daniel, M.D., Medical Director, Heart Of The Rockies Regional Medical Center, Salida, CO, p. A105

WARE, Bobbie K., MHS, BSN, RN, FACHE
Chief Executive Officer, Select Specialty Hospital - Belhaven, Jackson, MS, p. A348
Chief Executive Officer, Mississippi Baptist Medical Center, Jackson, MS, p. A348
Vice President Patient Care and Chief Nursing Officer, Mississippi Baptist Medical Center, Jackson, MS, p. A348

WARE, Dana, M.D., Chief of Staff, Seneca Healthcare District, Chester, CA, p. A54

WARE, John, Director of Human Resources, Venice Regional Bayfront Health, Venice, FL, p. A142

WARE, Judy
Chief Financial Officer, Putnam General Hospital, Eatonton, GA, p. A153
Director Human Resources, Johnson Memorial Hospital, Franklin, IN, p. A204

WARE, Judy King, Chief Financial Officer, Monroe County Hospital, Forsyth, GA, p. A153

WARE, Kathy, Director of Nursing, Daniels Memorial Healthcare Center, Scobey, MT, p. A379

WARE, Risa, Commander, Irwin Army Community Hospital, Junction City, KS, p. A238

WAREING, Colleen, Vice President Patient Care Services, Atlantic General Hospital, Berlin, MD, p. A290

WARFIELD, William, Chief Human Resources Management, Veterans Affairs Boston Healthcare System, West Roxbury, MA, p. A305

WARING, Lance, Director Human Resources, Texas Health Harris Methodist Hospital Azle, Azle, TX, p. A587

WARLICK, Mark
Chief Information Officer, Beacon Children's Hospital, IN, p. A215
Chief Information Officer, Elkhart General Hospital, Elkhart, IN, p. A202

WARLITNER, Todd, Vice President Business Operations, The Outer Banks Hospital, Nags Head, NC, p. A458

WARM, Ira, Senior Vice President Human Resources, Brooklyn Hospital Center, New York (Includes All Hospitals Located Within The Five Boroughs), NY, p. A431

WARMAN, Debbie, Vice President Human Resources, Metrohealth Medical Center, Cleveland, OH, p. A477

WARMAN, Harold C., Jr, FACHE, President and Chief Executive Officer, Highlands Regional Medical Center, Prestonsburg, KY, p. A259

WARMBOLD, Steve, Director Information Management Service Line, Veterans Affairs St. Louis Health Care System, Saint Louis, MO, p. A370

WARMERDAM, David, Chief Financial Officer, Brynn Marr Hospital, Jacksonville, NC, p. A455

WARNER, Grady, Director of Information Technology, Burgess Health Center, Onawa, IA, p. A227

WARNER, John, M.D.
Chief Executive Officer, Interim Chief Medical Officer, University Of Texas Southwestern Medical Center - Zale Lipshy, TX, p. A598
Chief Executive Officer, University Of Texas Southwestern Medical Center - Zale Lipshy, TX, p. A598

WARNER, Norma, Area Director Health Information Management, Kindred Hospital Tarrant County-Fort Worth Southwest, TX, p. A604

WARNER, Petra, Chief of Staff, Shriners Hospitals For Children - Cincinnati, Cincinnati, OH, p. A475

WARNER-PACHECO, Paula, Chief Human Resources, Rio Grande Hospital, Del Norte, CO, p. A98

WARNING, Kendra, Chief Financial Officer, Davis County Hospital, Bloomfield, IA, p. A218

WARNOCK, Dawn, Director Medical Records, Taylor Regional Hospital, Hawkinsville, GA, p. A154

WARREN, Brent, President Medical Staff, Iredell Health System, Statesville, NC, p. A461

WARREN, Charlene, R.N., Chief Nursing Officer, Greenbrier Valley Medical Center, Ronceverte, WV, p. A687

WARREN, Danny, Chief Financial Officer, Lake Wales Medical Center, Lake Wales, FL, p. A127

WARREN, Denise Wilder, R.N.
Executive Vice President and Chief Operating Officer, Wakemed Cary Hospital, Cary, NC, p. A449
Executive Vice President and Chief Operating Officer, Wakemed North Family Health And Women's Hospital, NC, p. A459

WARREN, Gidgett, Director of Nursing, T.J. Health Columbia, Columbia, KY, p. A250

WARREN, Jana, Human Resources Business Partner, Piedmont Henry Hospital, Stockbridge, GA, p. A161

WARREN, Karen, Fiscal Officer, Porterville Developmental Center, Porterville, CA, p. A79

WARREN, Linda, Director Human Resources, Cogdell Memorial Hospital, Snyder, TX, p. A636

WARREN, Lynn, Interim Chief Executive Officer, Group Vice President NueHealth, Methodist Hospital For Surgery, Addison, TX, p. A582

WARREN, Sarah, Coordinator Human Resources, Hickory Trail Hospital, Desoto, TX, p. A600

WARREN, Seth, President and Chief Executive Officer, Riverview Health, Noblesville, IN, p. A213

WARREN, Shanna, Director Human Resources, Medical City Frisco, TX, p. A628

WARREN, Wm. Michael., Jr, President and Chief Executive Officer, Children's Of Alabama, Birmingham, AL, p. A14

WARRENER, Gerald, M.D., Chief Medical Officer, Parkview Noble Hospital, Kendallville, IN, p. A208

WARRIN, Richard, Chief Operating Officer, Springs Memorial Hospital, Lancaster, SC, p. A555

WARRINER, Ken, Market Chief Financial Officer, Physicians Regional, FL, p. A132

WARRNER, Judy, Chief Operating Officer, Northridge Medical Center, Commerce, GA, p. A151

WARSING, Tracy, M.D., Site Leader Chief of Staff, Mayo Clinic Health System - Franciscan Healthcare In Sparta, Sparta, WI, p. A703

WAS, Gregory J., CPA, Chief Executive Officer, White Mountain Regional Medical Center, Springerville, AZ, p. A36

WASEK, Arthur A, Director Human Resources, Panola Medical Center, Batesville, MS, p. A343

WASHBURN, Geoff, Vice President Human Resources, Thousand Oaks Surgical Hospital, CA, p. A91

WASHBURN, Geoffrey A., Vice President, Regional Medical Center Bayonet Point, Hudson, FL, p. A125

WASHBURN, Kimberly D, Director Human Resources, Snoqualmie Valley Hospital District, Snoqualmie, WA, p. A677

WASHBURN, Tonya, M.D., Medical Director, Valir Rehabilitation Hospital, Oklahoma City, OK, p. A505

WASHECKA, James, Chief Financial Officer, Hillcrest Hospital - South, Tulsa, OK, p. A508

WASHINGTON, Carolyn, Director of Human Resources, Doctors Hospital Parkway, TX, p. A614

WASHINGTON, Glen A., Chief Executive Officer, Pleasant Valley Hospital, Point Pleasant, WV, p. A686

WASHINGTON, Stephanie
Director Community Relations and Human Resources, Baptist Medical Center Yazoo, Yazoo City, MS, p. A354
Human Resources Director, Baptist Medical Center Attala, Kosciusko, MS, p. A349

WASHINGTON, Tarra, Chief Executive Officer, Kindred Hospital New Jersey - Wayne, NJ, p. A404

WASHINGTON, Vindell, M.D., Vice President Performance Excellence and Technology, Our Lady Of The Lake Children's Hospital, LA, p. A264

WASILICK, Tamara, Director Operations, Kidspeace Children's Hospital, Orefield, PA, p. A533

WATERBURY, Brad, Director Human Resources, Bonner General Hospital, Sandpoint, ID, p. A172

WATERS, Bill, M.D., Chief Medical Officer, Higgins General Hospital, Bremen, GA, p. A148

WATERS, Danny, Director, Information Services, Palms Of Pasadena Hospital, Saint Petersburg, FL, p. A138

WATERS, Eric, Vice President Operations, Pen Bay Medical Center, Rockport, ME, p. A286

WATERS, Gina, Director Human Resources, Evans Memorial Hospital, Claxton, GA, p. A150

WATERS, Jerod, Chief Nursing Officer, Chickasaw Nation Medical Center, Ada, OK, p. A495

WATERS, Karen, Chief Nursing Officer, St. Vincent Warrick Hospital, Boonville, IN, p. A200

WATERS, Laura M, Vice President Human Resources, Garrett Regional Medical Center, Oakland, MD, p. A293

WATERS, Nancy, Interim Chief Information Officer, High Point Regional Health System, High Point, NC, p. A454

WATERS, Stephen F, M.D., Medical Director, Atlantic General Hospital, Berlin, MD, p. A290

WATERS, William, M.D., IV
Chief Medical Officer, Tanner Medical Center-Carrollton, Carrollton, GA, p. A149
Executive Vice President, Willowbrooke At Tanner, GA, p. A162

WATHEN, Cheryl A, Interim Chief Financial Officer, Deaconess Cross Pointe Center, IN, p. A203

WATHEN, Susan R, Vice President Human Resources, Hannibal Regional Hospital, Hannibal, MO, p. A360

WATKINS, Anne Marie, Chief Nurse Executive, Kaiser Permanente San Diego Medical Center, CA, p. A83

WATKINS, Chris, Director of Information Technology, Craig Hospital, Englewood, CO, p. A100

WATKINS, James, M.D., President Medical Staff, Providence Willamette Falls Medical Center, Oregon City, OR, p. A515

WATKINS, Jonathan, Chief Executive Officer, Broward Health Imperial Point, Fort Lauderdale, FL, p. A122

WATKINS, Joycelyn, R.N., Chief Nursing Officer, Magnolia Regional Medical Center, Magnolia-Columbia County, AR, p. A45

WATKINS, Michael, Chief Operating Officer, North Oaks Medical Center, Hammond, LA, p. A268

WATKINS, Michelle, Human Resources Manager, Greenwood Regional Rehabilitation Hospital, Greenwood, SC, p. A554

WATKINS, Pamela, Chief Financial Officer, Atlanta Veterans Affairs Medical Center, Decatur, GA, p. A152

WATKINS, Paul, JD, Chief Administrative Officer, Ucla Medical Center-Santa Monica, Santa Monica, CA, p. A89

WATKINS, Rolanda, Chief Human Resources Management Service, Dayton Veterans Affairs Medical Center, Dayton, OH, p. A480

WATRIDGE, Donna, R.N.
Chief Nursing Officer, Hackettstown Medical Center, Hackettstown, NJ, p. A405
Director of Operations, Hackettstown Medical Center, Hackettstown, NJ, p. A405

WATRY, Margaret, Director of Patient Care Services and Nurse Executive, Phillips Eye Institute, Minneapolis, MN, p. A335

WATSON, B Keith, M.D., Chief Medical Staff, North Mississippi Medical Center-West Point, West Point, MS, p. A354

WATSON, Barbara K, Chief Nursing Officer, Osceola Regional Medical Center, Kissimmee, FL, p. A126

WATSON, Betty A, Chief Financial Officer, Syringa Hospital And Clinics, Grangeville, ID, p. A169

WATSON, Cheryl, Chief Information Officer, Howard County Medical Center, Saint Paul, NE, p. A390

WATSON, Dalph, Director of Human Resources, Beaumont Hospital - Farmington Hills, Farmington Hills, MI, p. A312

WATSON, Deagan, Chief Executive Officer, River Oaks Child And Adolescent Hospital, LA, p. A276

WATSON, Dean, M.D., Chief Medical Officer, Tallahassee Memorial Healthcare, Tallahassee, FL, p. A140

WATSON, Deborah, R.N.
Chief Nursing Officer, Providence Mount Carmel Hospital, Colville, WA, p. A670
Chief Nursing Officer, Providence St. Joseph's Hospital, Chewelah, WA, p. A670
Senior Vice President and Chief Operating Officer, Bayhealth Medical Center, Milford Memorial Hospital, DE, p. A113

WATSON, Deidre L, Director Human Resources, Belmont Pines Hospital, Youngstown, OH, p. A494

WATSON, Dolores, Director Health Information Management, Arms Acres, Carmel, NY, p. A424

WATSON, H Alan., FACHE, Chief Executive Officer, Maury Regional Hospital, Columbia, TN, p. A568

WATSON, Heath
Controller, Encompass Health Rehabilitation Hospital Of Dothan, Dothan, AL, p. A17
Controller, Encompass Health Rehabilitation Hospital Of Montgomery, Montgomery, AL, p. A21

WATSON, James B., President, Schuyler Hospital, Montour Falls, NY, p. A430

WATSON, Kathy, R.N., Administrator and Chief Nursing Officer, Saint Thomas Hospital For Spinal Surgery, Nashville, TN, p. A577

WATSON, Lisa, Chief Executive Officer, St. Vincent Rehabilitation Hospital, Sherwood-Pulaski County, AR, p. A48

WATSON, Luke, M.D., Chief of Staff, College Medical Center, Long Beach, CA, p. A65

WATSON, Lynn, Interim Chief Nursing Officer, Presence Saint Joseph Medical Center, Joliet, IL, p. A187

WATSON, Margie, MSN, RN-B, Chief Nursing Officer, Sabine County Hospital, Hemphill, TX, p. A609

WATSON, Michael, M.D., Chief of Staff, Memorial Hospital, Seminole, TX, p. A635

WATSON, Nancy, Director Human Resources, Unity Hospital, MN, p. A330

WATSON, Nathan, M.D., Jr, Chief of Staff, Carrus Specialty Hospital, Sherman, TX, p. A636

WATSON, Rob, M.D., Chief Medical Officer, Baylor Scott & White Medical Center - Lakeway, TX, p. A631

WATSON, Scott, Administrator, Mercy Hospital Carthage, Carthage, MO, p. A357

WATSON, Shane, Chief Executive Officer, Red Bud Regional Hospital, Red Bud, IL, p. A194

WATSON, Susan, MSN, R.N., Vice President, Main Campus, MI, p. A308

WATSON, Teresa C, Vice President Administration, Carolinas Healthcare System Lincoln, Lincolnton, NC, p. A456

WATSON, Thelma Ruth, M.D., Medical Director, Schneider Regional Medical Center, Saint Thomas, VI, p. A717

WATSON, Thomas, M.D., Chief of Staff, Mayers Memorial Hospital District, Fall River Mills, CA, p. A58

WATSON, Trey, Network Administrator, Sumner County Hospital District One, Caldwell, KS, p. A233

WATSON, Vicki, Manager Human Resources, Select Specialty Hospital-Jackson, Jackson, MS, p. A348

WATT, Andrew, M.D., Vice President, Information Technology & Services, Chief Information Officer, Chief Medical Information Officer, Southern New Hampshire Medical Center, Nashua, NH, p. A400

WATT, Ella, Chief Financial Officer, Unm Children's Hospital, NM, p. A416

WATTENBARGER, J. Michael, M.D., Chief of Staff, Shriners Hospitals For Children-Greenville, Greenville, SC, p. A554

WATTENBARGER, Mike
Chief Information Officer, Lifecare Hospitals Of Pittsburgh - Suburban, PA, p. A537
Chief Information Officer, Lifecare Hospitals Of San Antonio, San Antonio, TX, p. A633

WATTERS, Greg, Chief Financial Officer, El Paso Specialty Hospital, El Paso, TX, p. A601

WATTOO, Dost, M.D., Chief of Staff, Valley Hospital Medical Center, Las Vegas, NV, p. A395

WATTS, Blake, Chief Operating Officer, Piedmont Rockdale Hospital, Conyers, GA, p. A151

WATTS, Chris
President, Barnes-Jewish St. Peters Hospital, Saint Peters, MO, p. A370
President, Progress West Hospital, O'Fallon, MO, p. A365

WATTS, Dawn, Chief Executive Officer, Healthsouth Rehabilitation Hospital Of Fort Smith, Fort Smith-Sebastian County, AR, p. A42

WATTS, Gail, Director, St. Vincent Medical Center, Los Angeles, CA, p. A70

WATTS, Lynda, R.N., Vice President, Chief Nursing Officer, Fort Sanders Regional Medical Center, Knoxville, TN, p. A572

WATTS-JOHNSON, Christine M, Assistant Vice President, Madera Community Hospital, Madera, CA, p. A71

WAY, Dee, Director Human Resources, Jerold Phelps Community Hospital, Garberville, CA, p. A60

WAYNE, Ann, Chief Executive Officer, Meadows Psychiatric Center, Centre Hall, PA, p. A522

WAYNE, Denise, Chief Executive Officer, Pioneer Specialty Hospital, Pontiac, MI, p. A321

WAYNE, Jason, Network Administrator, Suburban Community Hospital, Norristown, PA, p. A533

WAYTULA, Elizabeth, Chief Executive Officer, Cornerstone Hospital Of Oklahoma-Broken Arrow, OK, p. A501

WEAKHEE, Michael, Chief Executive Officer, U.S. Public Health Service Phoenix Indian Medical Center, Phoenix, AZ, p. A34

WEATHERFORD, Cynthia, Administrator and Director of Nursing, Mercy St. Francis Hospital, Mountain View, MO, p. A365

WEATHERFORD, Dennis, Chief Executive Officer, Putnam County Hospital, Greencastle, IN, p. A205

WEATHERLY, Daniel R, Chief Operating Officer, Cape Fear Valley Rehabilitation Center, NC, p. A452

WEATHERSBY, Mae C, R.N., Chief Clinical Officer, Vibra Specialty Hospital At Desoto, Desoto, TX, p. A600

WEATHERWAX, Lisa, R.N., Chief Nursing Officer, Iowa Specialty Hospital-Belmond, Belmond, IA, p. A217

WEATHERWAX, Marlene, Vice President and Chief Financial Officer, Columbus Regional Hospital, Columbus, IN, p. A201

WEAVER, Angie L, Director Human Resources, Gilmore Memorial Hospital, Amory, MS, p. A343

WEAVER, Daryl W., Chief Executive Officer, Baptist Medical Center Leake, Carthage, MS, p. A344

WEAVER, Douglas K., FACHE, Chief Executive Officer, Hillcrest Hospital Pryor, Pryor, OK, p. A506

WEAVER, Greg
Chief Operating Officer, Coteau Des Prairies Hospital, Sisseton, SD, p. A564
Interim Chief Executive Officer and Chief Operating Officer, Coteau Des Prairies Hospital, Sisseton, SD, p. A564

WEAVER, Harry, M.D., Chief of Staff, Covenant Hospital-Levelland, Levelland, TX, p. A619

WEAVER, Jason, Director Information Systems, Southern Tennessee Regional Health System-Lawrenceburg, Lawrenceburg, TN, p. A573

WEAVER, Jeff, Chief Financial Officer, Medical Arts Hospital, Lamesa, TX, p. A618

WEAVER, Joe, Chief Executive Officer, Rmc-Stringfellow Memorial Hospital, Anniston, AL, p. A13

WEAVER, Judy K., MS, Chief Executive Officer, Acuity Specialty Hospitals Ohio Valley At Belmont, OH, p. A490

WEAVER, Kimberli, Chief Nursing Officer, L. V. Stabler Memorial Hospital, Greenville, AL, p. A19

WEAVER, Rudolph D, Vice President Human Resources, Southwestern Vermont Medical Center, Bennington, VT, p. A653

WEAVER, Rusty, Manager Information Technology, Pauls Valley General Hospital, Pauls Valley, OK, p. A505

WEAVER, Sabrina, Director of Human Resources, Marshall Medical Center North, Guntersville, AL, p. A19

WEAVER, William, Chief Executive Officer, Brentwood Hospital, Shreveport, LA, p. A278

WEBB, Amy, Chief Operating Officer, Cascade Medical Center, Leavenworth, WA, p. A673

WEBB, Charles L., Jr, Chief Executive Officer, Lincoln Trail Behavioral Health System, Radcliff, KY, p. A260

WEBB, Darrallyn, R.N., Chief Nursing Officer, Conway Regional Rehabilitation Hospital, Conway-Faulkner County, AR, p. A40

WEBB, David, Chief Financial Officer, Baptist Memorial Hospital-Golden Triangle, Columbus, MS, p. A345

WEBB, Dee, Vice President Human Resources, St. Bernardine Medical Center, San Bernardino, CA, p. A83

WEBB, Donald, Chief Executive Officer, Williamson Medical Center, Franklin, TN, p. A570

WEBB, Glenn T., M.D., Medical Director, Ten Broeck Tennessee Treatment Facility, Cookeville, TN, p. A568

WEBB, Jeffrey D, CPA, Chief Financial Officer, Franciscan Health Rensselear, Rensselaer, IN, p. A214

WEBB, Joseph, Chief Executive Officer, Nashville General Hospital, Nashville, TN, p. A577

WEBB, Kimberly, Chief Financial Officer, Kootenai Behavioral Health, ID, p. A169

WEBB, Linda, R.N., Chief Nursing Executive, Pulaski Memorial Hospital, Winamac, IN, p. A216

WEBB, Lisa
Vice President for Operational Finance, Richard H. Young Behavioral Health Center, NE, p. A385
Vice President Operational Finance, St. Francis Medical Plaza, NE, p. A384

WEBB, Melanie R
Vice President Human Resources, Houston Northwest Medical Center, Houston, TX, p. A611
Vice President Human Resources, Park Plaza Hospital, Houston, TX, p. A612

WEBB, Paula, Chief Financial Officer and Compliance Officer, Lake Butler Hospital Hand Surgery Center, Lake Butler, FL, p. A127

WEBB, Renick, M.D., Chief Medical Director, Central Louisiana Surgical Hospital, Alexandria, LA, p. A262

WEBB, Rhonda, M.D., Chief Executive Officer, Pagosa Springs Medical Center, Pagosa Springs, CO, p. A104

WEBB, Steven B., FACHE, President and Chief Executive Officer, Unity Health Specialty Care, AR, p. A48

WEBB, William, Assistant Superintendent, Eastern Shore Hospital Center, Cambridge, MD, p. A290

WEBBER, Cathy, Director of Health Information Management, Franklin County Memorial Hospital, Franklin, NE, p. A383

WEBBER, Denise, President and Chief Executive Officer, Stillwater Medical Center, Stillwater, OK, p. A507

WEBBER, Joyce, Chief Financial Officer, Spalding Rehabilitation Hospital, Aurora, CO, p. A96

WEBER, Andrew, Vice President and Administrator, Camc Women And Children's Hospital, WV, p. A682

WEBER, Ann, M.D., Chief Medical Officer, North Florida Regional Medical Center, Gainesville, FL, p. A123

WEBER, Carmen, Administrator, Eureka Community Health Services Avera, Eureka, SD, p. A560

WEBER, Deborah, Chief Human Resource Officer, Northeast Georgia Medical Center, Gainesville, GA, p. A154

WEBER, Frank, Chief Executive Officer, Select Specialty Hospital-Charleston, Charleston, WV, p. A682

WEBER, Gordon, Chief Operating Officer, Clarks Summit State Hospital, Clarks Summit, PA, p. A522

WEBER, Lauren, Administrator, Oceans Behavioral Hospital Longview, Longview, TX, p. A620

WEBER, Mark, M.D., President Medical Staff, Midmichigan Medical Center - West Branch, West Branch, MI, p. A326

WEBER, Pete M., President and Chief Executive Officer, Gordon Hospital, Calhoun, GA, p. A149

WEBER, Rebecca
Senior Vice President and Chief Information Officer, Hackensack Meridian Health Bayshore Community Hospital, Holmdel, NJ, p. A406
Senior Vice President and Chief Information Officer, Hackensack Meridian Health Ocean Medical Center, Brick Township, NJ, p. A403
Senior Vice President and Chief Information Officer, Hackensack Meridian Health Southern Ocean Medical Center, Manahawkin, NJ, p. A407
Senior Vice President and Chief Information Officer, K. Hovnanian Children's Hospital, NJ, p. A408
Senior Vice President Information Technology, Hackensack Meridian Health Riverview Medical Center, Red Bank, NJ, p. A411

WEBER, Stephen, M.D., Chief Medical Officer, Comer Children's Hospital, IL, p. A180

WEBER, Tiffany, Chief Financial Officer, Sterling Regional Medcenter, Sterling, CO, p. A105

WEBER, Trish, R.N., FACHE, Vice President Operations and Chief Nursing Officer, Franciscan Health Michigan City, Michigan City, IN, p. A211

WEBER, Wilson, Chief Operating Officer, Continuecare Hospital At Baptist Health Corbin, Corbin, KY, p. A250

WEBSTER, Cindy, Vice President Financial Services, Licking Memorial Hospital, Newark, OH, p. A488

WEBSTER, Gwen, M.D., President Medical Staff, Texas Health Presbyterian Hospital Plano, Plano, TX, p. A629

WEBSTER, Janice, Director Human Resources, West Oaks Hospital, Houston, TX, p. A614

WEBSTER, Jeffrey, Administrator, Quentin Mease Hospital, TX, p. A611

WEBSTER, Kathleen, R.N., MSN, Vice President Patient Services, New York-Presbyterian/Hudson Valley Hospital, Cortlandt Manor, NY, p. A425

WEBSTER, Mark
President and Chief Executive Officer, Cortland Regional Medical Center, Cortland, NY, p. A425
Vice President Finance, New York-Presbyterian/Hudson Valley Hospital, Cortlandt Manor, NY, p. A425

WEBSTER, Nancy, Administrator and Chief Operating Officer, St. Luke's Rehabilitation Institute, Spokane, WA, p. A678

WEBSTER, Richard, R.N., President, Jefferson Methodist Hospital, PA, p. A536

WECKENBORG, Janet, Vice President Operations, Capital Region Medical Center, Jefferson City, MO, p. A360

WECKESSER, Kim, Director Human Resources, Munson Healthcare Manistee Hospital, Manistee, MI, p. A318

WEDDLE, Chari, Chief Human Resource Management Service, Richard L. Roudebush Veterans Affairs Medical Center, Indianapolis, IN, p. A207

WEDDLE, Lynn, Interim Chief Executive Officer, Providence St. Joseph Medical Center, Polson, MT, p. A378

WEDGEWORTH, Joyce, Financial Clerk, Hill Hospital Of Sumter County, York, AL, p. A24

WEE, Donald, Chief Executive Officer, Tri-State Memorial Hospital, Clarkston, WA, p. A670

WEED, John, M.D., III, Medical Director, Rockdale Hospital, Rockdale, TX, p. A630

WEED, Warren
Director Associate Relations, Merit Health Woman's Hospital, Flowood, MS, p. A346
Director Human Resources, Merit Health River Oaks, Flowood, MS, p. A345

WEEDEN, Gerard, Chief Medical Officer, Vibra Hospital Of Richmond, Richmond, VA, p. A665

WEEKS, Doug, Executive Vice President and Chief Operations Officer, Baptist Health Medical Center - North Little Rock, North Little Rock-Pulaski County, AR, p. A47

WEEKS, Ed, Manager Information Services, Paris Community Hospital, Paris, IL, p. A192

WEELDREYER, Jim, Manager Information Technology, Pershing General Hospital, Lovelock, NV, p. A395

WEEMS, Reva S, Director Human Resources, Gateway Regional Medical Center, Granite City, IL, p. A184

WEEMS, Taylor, Vice President, Chief Information Officer, Midland Memorial Hospital, TX, p. A624

WEG, Jennifer, MS, R.N., Executive Director, Sanford Worthington Medical Center, Worthington, MN, p. A342

WEGHORST, George, M.D., Chief Medical Officer, Providence Newberg Medical Center, Newberg, OR, p. A515

WEGLARZ, Ron, Chief Executive Officer and Managing Director, Streamwood Behavioral Health Center, Streamwood, IL, p. A197

WEGLEITNER, Theodore, Chief Executive Officer and President, Lakeview Hospital, Stillwater, MN, p. A340

WEHBEH, Wehbeh, M.D., Chief Medical Officer, Nyc Health + Hospitals / Coney Island, New York (Includes All Hospitals Located Within The Five Boroughs), NY, p. A435

WEHE, Brad, Chief Operating Officer, Altru Rehabilitation Center, ND, p. A466

WEHLING, Ed, Chief Medical Staff, Decatur County Hospital, Leon, IA, p. A225

WEHLING, Robert D, Interim Chief Financial Officer, Saint Alphonsus Medical Center - Baker City, Baker City, OR, p. A511

WEHMEYER, Jeffrey, Director Information Technology, Hermann Area District Hospital, Hermann, MO, p. A360

WEHNER, Jill, Vice President Financial Services, Harbor Beach Community Hospital, Harbor Beach, MI, p. A315

WEHRMEISTER, Erica, Chief Operating Officer, St. Vincent Women's Hospital, IN, p. A208

WEIDER, Will
Chief Information Officer, Ascension Calumet Hospital, Chilton, WI, p. A691
Chief Information Officer, Ascension Northeast Wisconsin Mercy Hospital, Oshkosh, WI, p. A700
Chief Information Officer, Ascension Northeast Wisconsin St. Elizabeth Hospital, Appleton, WI, p. A689
Chief Information Officer, Ascension St. Michael's Hospital, Stevens Point, WI, p. A703
Chief Information Officer, Marshfield Childen's Hospital, WI, p. A697

WEIDNER, Deborah, Medical Director, Natchaug Hospital, Mansfield Center, CT, p. A108

WEIDNER, Peter, Director Information Technology, St. John's Riverside Hospital - Dobbs Ferry Pavilion, NY, p. A446

WEIER, Jeffrey Paul., Chief Executive Officer, Vibra Hospital Of Springfield, Springfield, IL, p. A196

WEIGEL, Cherry, Director Health Information Management, Rc Hospital And Clinics, Olivia, MN, p. A336

WEIL, David S., Senior Vice President and Administrator, Saint Francis Hospital South, Tulsa, OK, p. A509

WEILAND, David, M.D., Chief Medical Officer, Largo Medical Center - Indian Rocks, FL, p. A128

WEIMER, Linn, Chief Information Officer, Adena Medical Center, Chillicothe, OH, p. A474

WEINER, Gary
Chief Information Officer, St. Catherine Hospital, East Chicago, IN, p. A202
Vice President Information Technology and Chief Information Officer, St. Mary Medical Center, Hobart, IN, p. A206
Vice President Information Technology, Chief Information Officer, Community Hospital, Munster, IN, p. A212

WEINER, Jerome, M.D., Senior Vice President Medical Affairs, Good Samaritan Hospital Medical Center, West Islip, NY, p. A445

WEINER, Richard I., M.D., Chief Executive Officer and Chief Medical Officer, Winchester Hospital, Winchester, MA, p. A306

WEINGART, Steve, Chief Financial Officer, Los Alamos Medical Center, Los Alamos, NM, p. A418

WEINGARTNER, Ronald, Vice President Administration, St. Charles Hospital, Port Jefferson, NY, p. A440

WEINKRANTZ, Alan, Chief Financial Officer, Finance, University Behavioral Healthcare, Piscataway, NJ, p. A410

WEINMANN, Shannon, Human Resources Manager, Community Medical Center, Inc., Falls City, NE, p. A383

WEINREIS, Brian, Vice President Operations and Finance, Sister Kenny Rehabilitation Institute, MN, p. A335

WEINSTEIN, Barry S, Chief Financial Officer, Four Winds Hospital, Katonah, NY, p. A428

WEINSTEIN, Brian, M.D., Chief of Staff, Westside Regional Medical Center, Plantation, FL, p. A136

WEINSTEIN, Freddie, M.D., Chief Medical Officer, Dominican Hospital, Santa Cruz, CA, p. A88

WEINSTEIN, Gary B., President and Chief Executive Officer, Washington Hospital, Washington, PA, p. A543

WEINSTEIN, Todd S, M.D., Chief of Staff, Logansport Memorial Hospital, Logansport, IN, p. A210

WEIR, Elizabeth, MSN, R.N., Chief Executive Officer, Ira Davenport Memorial Hospital, Bath, NY, p. A422

WEIR, Tim W., FACHE, Chief Executive Officer, Olmsted Medical Center, Rochester, MN, p. A338

WEIS, Brian, M.D., Chief Medical Officer, Northwest Texas Surgery Center, TX, p. A583

WEIS, Charles
  Chief Financial Officer, Schwab Rehabilitation Hospital, Chicago, IL, p. A179
  Chief Financial Officer, Sinai Children's Hospital, IL, p. A178
  Executive Vice President and Chief Financial Officer, Holy Cross Hospital, Chicago, IL, p. A177

WEIS, Harry, Chief Executive Officer, Tahoe Forest Hospital District, Truckee, CA, p. A92

WEIS, Maurine, MSN, R.N., Vice President Nursing and Chief Nursing Officer, Promedica Flower Hospital, Sylvania, OH, p. A491

WEIS, Robert
  Director Information Systems, Bingham Memorial Hospital, Blackfoot, ID, p. A167
  Director Information Technology, Mountain River Birthing And Surgery Center, Blackfoot, ID, p. A167

WEISENBERGER, Scott, Chief Executive Officer, Malvern Institute, Malvern, PA, p. A530

WEISENFREUND, Jochanan, M.D., Senior Vice President Academic and Medical Affairs, Interfaith Medical Center, New York (Includes All Hospitals Located Within The Five Boroughs), NY, p. A432

WEISER, Marcus, D.O., Chief of Staff, Community Healthcare System, Onaga, KS, p. A242

WEISFIELD, Phyllis, Chief Executive Officer and Managing Director, Horsham Clinic, Ambler, PA, p. A520

WEISHAPL, Natasha, Manager Business Office and Human Resources, Decatur Health Systems, Oberlin, KS, p. A242

WEISKITTEL, Scott, Chief Operating Officer, Summerville Medical Center, SC, p. A550

WEISNER, Brad, Executive Vice President and Chief Operating Officer, Nash Health Care Systems, Rocky Mount, NC, p. A459

WEISS, Allen S., M.D., President and Chief Executive Officer, Nch North Naples Hospital, FL, p. A132

WEISS, Anthony, M.D., Chief Medical Officer, Beth Israel Deaconess Medical Center, Boston, MA, p. A296

WEISS, David, M.D., Vice President, Medical Operations, Peninsula Region, Harrison Medical Center, Bremerton, WA, p. A669

WEISS, Gary, Chief Financial Officer, Northshore Skokie Hospital, IL, p. A182

WEISS, Jeffrey, Interim Director, Community Howard Specialty Hospital, Kokomo, IN, p. A209

WEISS, Patrice M, Executive Vice President, Administration, Carilion Franklin Memorial Hospital, Rocky Mount, VA, p. A666

WEISS, Phyllis, Director Human Resources, Alameda Hospital, Alameda, CA, p. A50

WEISS, Terri, Chief Financial Officer, Encompass Health Rehabilitation Hospital Vision Park, Shenandoah, TX, p. A635

WEISSENBERGER, Ralf, Director Information Systems, Adventist Health White Memorial, Los Angeles, CA, p. A66

WEISSER, Lisa, Supervisor Finance, Wagner Community Memorial Hospital Avera, Wagner, SD, p. A565

WEISSINGER, Drew, Chief Financial Officer, North Sunflower Medical Center, Ruleville, MS, p. A353

WEISSLER, Jonathan, M.D., Chief Medical Officer, Lifecare Hospitals Of North Texas-Plano, TX, p. A596

WEISTREICH, Tracy, Ph.D., R.N., Associate Director Patient Care Services/Nurse Executive, Veterans Affairs Roseburg Healthcare System, Roseburg, OR, p. A517

WEISUL, Jonathan, M.D., Vice President Medical Affairs and Chief Medical Officer, Christus Coushatta Health Care Center, Coushatta, LA, p. A266

WELANDER, Jennifer, CPA
  Senior Vice President Finance and Chief Financial Officer, St. Charles Bend, Bend, OR, p. A511
  Senior Vice President Finance and Chief Financial Officer, St. Charles Redmond, Redmond, OR, p. A517

WELCH, Abbey, Director Human Resources, Harmon Memorial Hospital, Hollis, OK, p. A500

WELCH, Andrew
  Director, New Mexico Veterans Affairs Health Care System - Raymond G. Murphy Medical Center, Albuquerque, NM, p. A416
  Interim Director, Veterans Affairs Loma Linda Healthcare System, Loma Linda, CA, p. A64

WELCH, Bryant, Chief Human Resources, Washington Hospital Healthcare System, Fremont, CA, p. A59

WELCH, David, M.D.
  Medical Director, Clifton-Fine Hospital, Star Lake, NY, p. A443
  Director Information Technology, Simpson General Hospital, Mendenhall, MS, p. A350

WELCH, Denise, Chief Financial Officer, Arbuckle Memorial Hospital, Sulphur, OK, p. A507

WELCH, Donald E, Chief Operating Officer, Florida Hospital Zephyrhills, Zephyrhills, FL, p. A144

WELCH, Douglas, Chief Executive Officer, Doctors Hospital, Augusta, GA, p. A147

WELCH, Gary A., Assistant to the Chief Executive Officer and Administrative Director Support Systems, Bon Secours Memorial Regional Medical Center, Mechanicsville, VA, p. A661

WELCH, Nicole, Chief Human Resources Officer, Fairbanks Memorial Hospital, Fairbanks, AK, p. A26

WELCH, Rosemary C, R.N., Vice President and Chief Nursing Officer, Medstar National Rehabilitation Hospital, Washington, DC, p. A115

WELCH, Sherri, R.N., Chief Nursing Officer, College Station Medical Center, College Station, TX, p. A593

WELCH, Thomas, M.D., Chief Medical Officer, Mercy Children's Hospital, OH, p. A491

WELCH, Tony, Vice President Human Resources, Southeast Alabama Medical Center, Dothan, AL, p. A17

WELDAY, Doug, Senior Vice President Finance, Spectrum Health, MI, p. A314

WELDON, James, Chief Information Officer, North Mississippi Medical Center - Tupelo, Tupelo, MS, p. A353

WELDY, Alan, Vice President Human Resources, Compliance and Legal Services, Goshen Health, Goshen, IN, p. A205

WELKIE, Katy, MBA, R.N., Chief Executive Officer, Primary Children's Hospital, Salt Lake City, UT, p. A650

WELLBROCK, Jenna, Chief Nursing Officer, Gateway Rehabilitation Hospital, Florence, KY, p. A251

WELLING, Lynn, M.D., Chief Medical Officer, Sharp Chula Vista Medical Center, Chula Vista, CA, p. A54

WELLING, Michele, M.D., Chief of Staff, Bluegrass Community Hospital, Versailles, KY, p. A261

WELLMAN, Amanda, MSN, R.N., Chief Nursing Officer, Select Specialty Hospital-Omaha, Omaha, NE, p. A388

WELLMAN, James, Senior Director Information Services, Comanche County Memorial Hospital, Lawton, OK, p. A500

WELLMAN, Sonia I., Chief Executive Officer, Memorial Hospital Of Tampa, Tampa, FL, p. A141

WELLMANN, Jane, Chief Financial Officer, Scott & White Hospital - Brenham, Brenham, TX, p. A590

WELLS, A Shane, Chief Financial Officer, Cornerstone Hospital Of Houston - Bellaire, TX, p. A643

WELLS, Carol, R.N., MSN, Chief Nursing Officer, Central Louisiana Surgical Hospital, Alexandria, LA, p. A262

WELLS, Craig, Chief Information Officer, George C Grape Community Hospital, Hamburg, IA, p. A223

WELLS, Crystal, Administrator, Grady General Hospital, Cairo, GA, p. A149

WELLS, Dale W., Chief Financial and Operating Officer, Alliance Community Hospital, Alliance, OH, p. A470

WELLS, James, R.N.
  Chief Nursing Officer, Eastar Health System, East Campus, OK, p. A502
  Chief Nursing Officer, Merit Health Biloxi, Biloxi, MS, p. A343

WELLS, Jason
  Chief Human Resources Management Service, Fargo Veterans Affairs Health Care System, Fargo, ND, p. A465
  President and Chief Executive Officer, Adventist Health Howard Memorial, Willits, CA, p. A95

WELLS, Jimmy, Chief Nursing and Administrative Officer, Westside Surgical Hospital, Houston, TX, p. A614

WELLS, Jonathan, Supervisor Information Technology, Kansas Surgery And Recovery Center, Wichita, KS, p. A248

WELLS, Mallory Gulley, CPA, Chief Financial Officer, Richardson Medical Center, Rayville, LA, p. A278

WELLS, Mary Ellen, FACHE, Administrator, Centracare Health-Monticello, Monticello, MN, p. A336

WELLS, Michelle, Director of Nursing, River Oaks Child And Adolescent Hospital, LA, p. A276

WELLS, Pamela, R.N., MSN, Chief Nursing Officer, Sharp Memorial Hospital, San Diego, CA, p. A84

WELLS, Robert, M.D., Chief Medical Officer, Providence Portland Medical Center, Portland, OR, p. A516

WELLS, Roxie Cannon., M.D.
  Chief Executive Officer, Cape Fear Valley - Bladen County Hospital, Elizabethtown, NC, p. A452
  President, Hoke Hospital, Raeford, NC, p. A458

WELLS, Scott E, MSN, R.N., Vice President Patient Care Services, Caromont Regional Medical Center, Gastonia, NC, p. A453

WELLS, Todd
  Chief Executive Officer, Blue Valley Hospital, Overland Park, KS, p. A243
  Chief Operating Officer, Blue Valley Hospital, Overland Park, KS, p. A243

WELLS, Valerie, Manager Human Resources, Encompass Health Rehabilitation Hospital The Woodlands, Conroe, TX, p. A594

WELSER, Jeremy, Director Information Systems, Bonner General Hospital, Sandpoint, ID, p. A172

WELSH, Dennis, President and CEO, Down East Community Hospital, Machias, ME, p. A285

WELSH, J. Luckey., Jr, Chief Executive Officer, Cherry Hospital, Goldsboro, NC, p. A453

WELSH, Joyce, R.N., MS, Vice President of Clinical Services and Chief Nursing Officer, Emerson Hospital, Concord, MA, p. A299

WELTER, Matt, Chief Medical Officer, Cache Valley Hospital, North Logan, UT, p. A648

WELTON, George, Chief Executive Officer, Healthsouth Rehabilitation Hospital Of Altamonte Springs, Altamonte Springs, FL, p. A117

WELTON, Jill, President and Chief Executive Officer, Glendale Memorial Hospital And Health Center, Glendale, CA, p. A60

WELTON, Mark, M.D.
  Chief Medical Officer, Bethesda Hospital, Saint Paul, MN, p. A339
  Chief Medical Officer, St. John's Hospital, Maplewood, MN, p. A334

WEMPE, John M, M.D., Chief of Staff, Sioux Falls Veterans Affairs Health Care System, Sioux Falls, SD, p. A564

WENDELL, David, Manager, Information Systems, St. Mary's Medical Center, Huntington, WV, p. A684

WENDELL, Sean, Chief Executive Officer, Beacon Behavioral Hospital, Lutcher, LA, p. A273

WENGER, Cheryl, Manager Health Information and Quality Assurance, Hiawatha Community Hospital, Hiawatha, KS, p. A232

WENGER, Jill, Director Human Resources, Atchison Hospital, Atchison, KS, p. A232

WENGER-KELLER, David, M.D., Chief of Staff, Fort Madison Community Hospital, Fort Madison, IA, p. A223

WENTWORTH, Cynthia, Chief Human Resource Officer, East Morgan County Hospital, Brush, CO, p. A97

WENTZ, Amber, Director of Clinical Information Systems & Clinical Informatics, Skiff Medical Center, Newton, IA, p. A227

WENTZ, Jim, Chief Financial Officer, Flaget Memorial Hospital, Bardstown, KY, p. A249

WENTZ, Robert J., President and Chief Executive Officer, Oroville Hospital, Oroville, CA, p. A77

WENTZEL, Chris, M.D., Interim Medical Director, Guthrie Corning Hospital, Corning, NY, p. A425

WENZEL, Matthew, President and Chief Executive Officer, Great River Medical Center, West Burlington, IA, p. A231

WERFT, Ronald C.
  President and Chief Executive Officer, Cottage Rehabilitation Hospital, CA, p. A88
  President and Chief Executive Officer, Goleta Valley Cottage Hospital, Santa Barbara, CA, p. A88
  President and Chief Executive Officer, Santa Ynez Valley Cottage Hospital, Solvang, CA, p. A90

WERKIN, Dave, Vice President Finance and Chief Financial Officer, Trinity Medical Center West, OH, p. A491

WERNER, John W., Chief Executive Officer, Brown County Hospital, Ainsworth, NE, p. A381

WERNER, Kurt, M.D., Chief of Staff, Veterans Affairs Montana Health Care System, Fort Harrison, MT, p. A375

WERNER, Tiffany
Senior Human Resource Business Partner, Banner Baywood Medical Center, Mesa, AZ, p. A31
Senior Human Resource Business Partner, Banner Heart Hospital, Mesa, AZ, p. A31

WERNICK, Joel, President and Chief Executive Officer, Phoebe North, GA, p. A145

WERNKE, Chris, Chief Operating Officer, Dominican Hospital, Santa Cruz, CA, p. A88

WERRBACH, John P., President and Chief Executive Officer, Amita Health Rehabilitation Hospital, IL, p. A182

WERTH-SWEENEY, Stacey, Facility Operating Officer, Lincoln Regional Center, Lincoln, NE, p. A386

WERTHMAN, Ronald J, Senior Vice President Finance, Chief Financial Officer and Treasurer, Johns Hopkins Children's Center, MD, p. A287

WERTZ, Jackie, Director Human Resources, George C Grape Community Hospital, Hamburg, IA, p. A223

WESCOATT, Sampson, Manager Information Technology, Molokai General Hospital, Kaunakakai, HI, p. A166

WESCOTT, Lisle
President, Ssm Health St. Joseph - Wentzville, MO, p. A367
President, Ssm Health St. Joseph Hospital - Lake Saint Louis, Lake Saint Louis, MO, p. A363

WESENER DIECK, Jill, Human Resources Operations Manager, Gundersen Tri-County Hospital And Clinics, Whitehall, WI, p. A706

WESLEY, Deb, MSN, Chief Nursing Officer, Children's Of Alabama, Birmingham, AL, p. A14

WESLEY, Jim, Senior Vice President and Chief Information Officer, John Muir Behavioral Health Center, Concord, CA, p. A55

WESLEY, Mary Lou, R.N., Senior Vice President and Chief Nursing Officer, Sparrow Children's Center, MI, p. A317

WESOLOWSKI, Paul J, Chief Operating Officer, Children's Hospital Of Richmond At Vcu, VA, p. A665

WESP, Clyde, M.D., Chief Medical Officer, Valley Presbyterian Hospital, Los Angeles, CA, p. A70

WESSELS, Jana, Associate Vice President Human Resources, University Of Iowa Stead Family Children's Hospital, IA, p. A224

WESSELS, William, M.D., Chief Medical Officer, Aspirus Wausau Hospital, Inc., Wausau, WI, p. A705

WESSON, Jim D, President and Administrator, Christus Santa Rosa Hospital - New Braunfels, TX, p. A632

WEST, Andrea, MS, Vice President of Human Resources, Columbus Regional Healthcare System, Whiteville, NC, p. A462

WEST, Brenda, R.N., MSN
Chief Nursing Officer, Evergreenhealth Monroe, Monroe, WA, p. A673
Vice President, Information Services and Interim Chief Information Officer, Einstein Medical Center Elkins Park, PA, p. A534

WEST, Bridgette, Director Patient Access Services, Cobleskill Regional Hospital, Cobleskill, NY, p. A424

WEST, Charles, M.D., Chief Medical Officer, Randolph Hospital, Asheboro, NC, p. A447

WEST, Christopher, Chief Executive Officer, Seven Hills Hospital, Henderson, NV, p. A393

WEST, Darren, M.D., Interim Chief Medical Officer, Banner Ironwood Medical Center, San Tan Valley, AZ, p. A35

WEST, James R.
President and Chief Executive Officer, Pih Health Hospital - Downey, Downey, CA, p. A56
President and Chief Executive Officer, Pih Health Hospital - Whittier, Whittier, CA, p. A95

WEST, Jennifer, R.N., Chief Nursing Officer, South Texas Spine And Surgical Hospital, San Antonio, TX, p. A634

WEST, Judith M, Senior Vice President Human Resources and Chief Human Resources Officer, Maine Medical Center, Brighton Campus, ME, p. A285

WEST, Melissa, Chief Financial Officer, Cedar Crest Hospital And Residential Treatment Center, Belton, TX, p. A589

WEST, Michael, Manager Systems Account, New England Sinai Hospital And Rehabilitation Center, Stoughton, MA, p. A305

WEST, Michael C, M.D., Chief of Staff, Mccurtain Memorial Hospital, Idabel, OK, p. A500

WEST, Steve, M.D., Chief Medical Officer, Capital Regional Medical Center, Tallahassee, FL, p. A140

WEST, Tamara, R.N., MSN, Vice President Patient Care, Nicholas H. Noyes Memorial Hospital, Dansville, NY, p. A425

WESTENFELDER, Grant, M.D., Chief Medical Officer, Midwest Medical Center, Galena, IL, p. A183

WESTENHOFER, Steve, Interim Chief Executive Officer, Mimbres Memorial Hospital, Deming, NM, p. A417

WESTER, K Scott., FACHE, President and Chief Executive Officer, Our Lady Of The Lake Children's Hospital, LA, p. A264

WESTERCHIL, Beth, Chief Nursing Officer, Byrd Regional Hospital, Leesville, LA, p. A272

WESTERFIELD, Jerry D., M.D., Chief of Medical Staff, Russell County Hospital, Russell Springs, KY, p. A260

WESTERHEIDE, Karen, Chief Financial Officer, Veterans Affairs St. Louis Health Care System, Saint Louis, MO, p. A370

WESTERMAN, Mandy, Chief Executive Officer, West Oaks Hospital, Houston, TX, p. A614

WESTFALL, Gay, Senior Vice President Human Resources, Kaiser Permanente Sacramento Medical Center, Sacramento, CA, p. A81

WESTFALL, Roger, Director, Western State Hospital, Hopkinsville, KY, p. A253

WESTIN, Robert, M.D., Chief Medical Officer, Cuyuna Regional Medical Center, Crosby, MN, p. A330

WESTMAN, Ken, Chief Executive Officer, Barrett Hospital & Healthcare, Dillon, MT, p. A375

WESTMORELAND, Penny
Chief Financial Officer, Lakeland Community Hospital, Haleyville, AL, p. A19
Chief Financial Officer, Red Bay Hospital, Red Bay, AL, p. A23
Chief Financial Officer, Russellville Hospital, Russellville, AL, p. A23

WESTON, Betty, Chief Human Resources Officer, U.S. Public Health Service Phoenix Indian Medical Center, Phoenix, AZ, p. A34

WESTON, Dana, Chief Executive Officer, Unc Rockingham Health Care, Eden, NC, p. A451

WESTON, Susan, CPA, Chief Financial Officer, Mountrail County Medical Center, Stanley, ND, p. A468

WESTON, Terry, M.D., Vice President Physician Services, Mansfield Hospital, OH, p. A485

WESTON-HALL, Patricia, Chief Executive Officer, Glenbeigh Hospital And Outpatient Centers, Rock Creek, OH, p. A489

WESTOVER, Teresa, Director Human Resources, North Texas Medical Center, Gainesville, TX, p. A606

WESTPHAL, Chris, Chief Information Technology Officer, Southeast Colorado Hospital District, Springfield, CO, p. A105

WESTPHAL, James, M.D., AMHD Medical Director, Hawaii State Hospital, Kaneohe, HI, p. A166

WESTPHAL, Laura R., R.N., Vice President Patient Care Services, Adventist Health Castle, Kailua, HI, p. A165

WESTPHAL, Susan, Assistant Administrator, Patient Care Services, Fairchild Medical Center, Yreka, CA, p. A95

WESTRUM, Jennifer, Administrator, Community Behavioral Health Hospital - Alexandria, Alexandria, MN, p. A327

WESTRY, Tanza, Chief Financial Officer, Hunter Holmes Mcguire Veterans Affairs Medical Center-Richmond, Richmond, VA, p. A665

WESTWOOD, Denise P, Chief Nursing Officer, Weirton Medical Center, Weirton, WV, p. A687

WETHAL, Robert, R.N., Vice President and Chief Nursing Officer, Mercy Medical Center-Dubuque, Dubuque, IA, p. A222

WETMORE, Melanie, MSN, R.N., Chief Nursing Officer, Regional Medical Center Bayonet Point, Hudson, FL, p. A125

WETTON, Darlene, R.N., Chief Executive Officer, Temecula Valley Hospital, Temecula, CA, p. A91

WETZ, Staci, Chief Financial Officer, Shannon Medical Center-St. John's Campus, TX, p. A632

WETZEL, James L, M.D., Senior Vice President, Chief Medical Officer, Olathe Medical Center, Olathe, KS, p. A242

WETZEL, Lou, M.D., Chief of Staff, The University Of Kansas Hospital - Indian Creek Campus, KS, p. A238

WEYMOUTH, Deborah K, FACHE, President and Chief Executive Officer, Umass Memorial Healthalliance-Clinton Hospital, MA, p. A301

WEYMOUTH, Deborah K., FACHE, President and Chief Executive Officer, Umass Memorial Healthalliance-Clinton Hospital, MA, p. A301

WEYMOUTH, Linda, Chief Financial Officer, Suncoast Behavioral Health Center, Bradenton, FL, p. A119

WHALEN, David, Chief Executive Officer, Twin Cities Hospital, Niceville, FL, p. A132

WHALEN, Eileen, R.N., President and Chief Operating Officer, Vermont Children's Hospital, VT, p. A653

WHALEN, Patti, Manager Human Resources, Wichita County Health Center, Leoti, KS, p. A240

WHALEN, Thomas, Vice President Finance, Good Samaritan Medical Center - Cushing Campus, MA, p. A298

WHALEN, Thomas V., M.D.
Chief Medical Officer, Lehigh Valley Health Network Pediatrics, PA, p. A519

Executive Vice President and Chief Medical Officer, Lehigh Valley Hospital-Muhlenberg, Bethlehem, PA, p. A520

WHALEY, Joseph, Chief, Human Resources Management Service, Fayetteville Veterans Affairs Medical Center, Fayetteville, NC, p. A452

WHALEY, Mary, Director of Acute Care, Johnson County Healthcare Center, Buffalo, WY, p. A707

WHARTON, Joe H, M.D., Chief of Staff, Bradley County Medical Center, Warren-Bradley County, AR, p. A49

WHEAT, Ken, Senior Vice President and Chief Financial Officer, Eisenhower Medical Center, Rancho Mirage, CA, p. A79

WHEAT, Terry, R.N., M.P.H., Director of Patient Care Services, Shriners Hospitals For Children-Chicago, Chicago, IL, p. A179

WHEATLEY, Bernard, FACHE, Chief Executive Officer, Schneider Regional Medical Center, Saint Thomas, VI, p. A717

WHEATLEY, Jane, Chief Executive Officer, Taylor Regional Hospital, Campbellsville, KY, p. A250

WHEATLEY, Richard, Chief Information Officer, Cape Regional Health System, Cape May Court House, NJ, p. A403

WHEATLEY, Samuel N, Chief Medical Officer, Columbus Regional Healthcare System, Whiteville, NC, p. A462

WHEATLEY, Sonya, Human Resources Manager, Central State Hospital, Louisville, KY, p. A256

WHEATLEY, Stephen J., Director of Operations, Franciscan Health Carmel, Carmel, IN, p. A201

WHEATON, David, Director Human Resources, Blue Hill Memorial Hospital, Blue Hill, ME, p. A283

WHEATON, Tammy H., Interim Chief Nursing Officer, Union County Hospital, Anna, IL, p. A173

WHEELAN, Kevin, M.D., Medical Director, Baylor Jack And Jane Hamilton Heart And Vascular Hospital, Dallas, TX, p. A595

WHEELER, Brent, Vice President of Operations, Mclaren Flint, Flint, MI, p. A312

WHEELER, Cambria, Communications and Marketing, Adventist Health Clear Lake, Clearlake, CA, p. A54

WHEELER, Dane, Chief Financial Officer, Adams Memorial Hospital, Decatur, IN, p. A202

WHEELER, Dawne, Chief Executive Officer, Select Specialty Hospital-Canton, Canton, OH, p. A474

WHEELER, Frankie, Director, Human Resources, Saint Elizabeths Hospital, Washington, DC, p. A116

WHEELER, James A, Vice President Human Relations and Community Development, Androscoggin Valley Hospital, Berlin, NH, p. A398

WHEELER, Kim, R.N., Director of Nursing, Kingwood Pines Hospital, Kingwood, TX, p. A618

WHEELER, Lynette, MSN, Chief Operating Officer, Truman Medical Center-Lakewood, Kansas City, MO, p. A362

WHEELER, Newman, Chief Financial Officer and Chief Operating Officer, Covenant Hospital-Levelland, Levelland, TX, p. A619

WHEELER, Pamela R, Director Human Resources, Scott County Hospital, Scott City, KS, p. A245

WHEELER, Penny Ann, M.D., President and Chief Medical Officer, Sister Kenny Rehabilitation Institute, MN, p. A335

WHEELER, Philip, Director Finance, Mercy Health - Clermont Hospital, Batavia, OH, p. A471

WHEELER, Rebecca, Director Finance, Kaiser Permanente Baldwin Park Medical Center, Baldwin Park, CA, p. A52

WHEELER, Robert
Controller, Encompass Health Rehabilitation Hospital Of Florence, Florence, SC, p. A552
Vice President Human Resources, South Shore Hospital, South Weymouth, MA, p. A304

WHEELER, Tina, R.N., MSN, Director Nursing, William Newton Hospital, Winfield, KS, p. A248

WHEELER, William, M.D., Chief of Staff, Benewah Community Hospital, Saint Maries, ID, p. A171

WHEELER, Zachariah P, Senior Vice President Human Resources, John D. Archbold Memorial Hospital, Thomasville, GA, p. A161

WHEELER-MOORE, Juanita, Director Financial Services, Four Winds Hospital, Saratoga Springs, NY, p. A442

WHEELES, Locke, Information Technology Manager, Field Memorial Community Hospital, Centreville, MS, p. A344

WHEELUS, Matthew
Chief Operating Officer, Spring Valley Hospital Medical Center, Las Vegas, NV, p. A395
Vice President, Chief Operating Officer, Harrison Medical Center, Bremerton, WA, p. A669

WHELAN, Laurie A, Senior Vice President Finance and Chief Financial Officer, Hospital For Special Care, New Britain, CT, p. A109

WHELAN, Thomas, Chief Executive Officer, Cibola General Hospital, Grants, NM, p. A417

WHERRY, Robin, Risk Manager and Director Quality Assurance and Health Information Management, Healthsouth

WHITNUM, Rhonda, Director Health Improvement Management, Prague Community Hospital, Prague, OK, p. A506

WHITSON, Charles P, CPA, Senior Vice President Finance, Lake Charles Memorial Hospital For Women, LA, p. A272

WHITT, Alicia, R.N., Chief Nursing Officer, Stephens Memorial Hospital, Breckenridge, TX, p. A590

WHITT, Horace, Chief Executive Officer and Chief Operating Officer, Refugio County Memorial Hospital, Refugio, TX, p. A630

WHITT, Stevan, M.D., Chief Medical Officer, Women's And Children's Hospital, MO, p. A358

WHITTAKER, Kelly, Vice President Nursing, Mclaren Caro Region, Caro, MI, p. A309

WHITTAKER, Shawn, Chief Nursing Officer, Miller County Hospital, Colquitt, GA, p. A150

WHITTAKER, Sheena, M.D., Chief Medical Officer, Maine Coast Memorial Hospital, Ellsworth, ME, p. A284

WHITTEMORE, Marjorie, Director Human Resources, Rio Grande Regional Hospital, Mcallen, TX, p. A623

WHITTEMORE, Scott
Chief Financial Officer and Chief of Ancillary Services, Springfield Hospital, Springfield, VT, p. A654
Chief Financial Officer, University Of Mississippi Medical Center Grenada, Grenada, MS, p. A346
Chief Financial Officer, University Of Mississippi Medical Center Holmes County, Lexington, MS, p. A349

WHITTEN, Jacquelyn, MSN, RN, Chief Executive Nurse, Advocate Trinity Hospital, Chicago, IL, p. A176

WHITTINGTON, Bruce, Vice President Human Resources, Pawnee Valley Community Hospital, Larned, KS, p. A239

WHITTINGTON, Dorothy, Chief Financial Officer, University Health Conway, Monroe, LA, p. A274

WHITTINGTON, Hilary, Chief Financial Officer, Jefferson Healthcare, Port Townsend, WA, p. A675

WHITTINGTON, Laurie A, Chief Operating Officer, Memorial Health, Marysville, OH, p. A486

WHITTINGTON, Shane, Chief Financial Officer, Caldwell Medical Center, Princeton, KY, p. A260

WHITTINGTON-GEPPERT, Kelley, Director Human Resources, Munson Healthcare Cadillac Hospital, Cadillac, MI, p. A309

WHITTON, Beth, Director Human Resources, Ocean Beach Hospital, Ilwaco, WA, p. A672

WHOLLEY, Diane, Director Fiscal Services, Bridgewater State Hospital, Bridgewater, MA, p. A297

WHORLEY, Chris, Chief Information Officer, Nashville General Hospital, Nashville, TN, p. A577

WHYBROW, Peter, M.D., Chief Executive Officer, Stewart & Lynda Resnick Neuropsychiatric Hospital At Ucla, Los Angeles, CA, p. A70

WHYTE, Brett, M.D., Chief of Medical Staff, Winona Health, Winona, MN, p. A342

WIATREK, Joseph, Director Information Technology, Otto Kaiser Memorial Hospital, Kenedy, TX, p. A617

WIBBENMEYER, Christopher, Director Human Resources, Perry County Memorial Hospital, Perryville, MO, p. A366

WIBBENS, Cheryl, M.D., Vice President Medical Staff Affairs, Beacon Children's Hospital, IN, p. A215

WIBBLESMAN, Christopher, M.D., Chief of Staff, Colorado Canyons Hospital And Medical Center, Fruita, CO, p. A101

WIBORG, Shelley, MS, R.N.
Chief Nursing Officer, Osf Saint Luke Medical Center, Kewanee, IL, p. A187
Director of Nursing, Osf Holy Family Medical Center, Monmouth, IL, p. A189

WICKE, Julius, III, Vice President Finance and Hospital Financial Officer, Baylor Jack And Jane Hamilton Heart And Vascular Hospital, Dallas, TX, p. A595

WICKE, Regina, Chief Financial Officer, Columbus Community Hospital, Columbus, TX, p. A593

WICKENS, Amy Lynn, Executive Director Human Resources, Decatur County Memorial Hospital, Greensburg, IN, p. A205

WICKER, Kenneth R., Chief Executive Officer, Bayfront Health Spring Hill, FL, p. A119

WICKIZER, Boyd, M.D., Jr, Chief Medical Officer, Southside Regional Medical Center, Petersburg, VA, p. A664

WICKLANDER, Jeff, President, North Memorial Health Hospital, Robbinsdale, MN, p. A338

WICKLINE, Melissa, Director Marketing, Greenbrier Valley Medical Center, Ronceverte, WV, p. A687

WICKLUND, Grant, President and Chief Executive Officer, Exempla West Pines, CO, p. A106

WIDEMAN, Jeff, Director Information Systems, Gilmore Memorial Hospital, Amory, MS, p. A343

WIDGER, Judy, M.D., Chief of Staff, Healdsburg District Hospital, Healdsburg, CA, p. A61

WIDICK, Brent, Superintendent, Kansas Neurological Institute, Topeka, KS, p. A246

WIDNER, Eric W., FACHE, Division President, Beaumont Hospital, Wayne, Wayne, MI, p. A325

WIDRA, Linda S, FACHE, Ph.D., R.N., Chief Operating Officer, Lakewood Ranch Medical Center, Bradenton, FL, p. A118

WIECZOREK, Pawel, Director Information Technology, Brylin Hospitals, Buffalo, NY, p. A423

WIEMAN, Jason S., Director, Fort Belvoir Community Hospital, Fort Belvoir, VA, p. A658

WIENS, Ron, Chief Financial Officer, Shodair Children's Hospital, Helena, MT, p. A376

WIENTJES, Keri, Director Human Resources, Mobridge Regional Hospital, Mobridge, SD, p. A562

WIERZBICKI, Barb, Manager Human Resources, Select Specialty Hospital-Downriver, Wyandotte, MI, p. A326

WIESMAN, David H, Interim Chief Financial Officer, Fayette County Hospital, Vandalia, IL, p. A197

WIESMANN, Marie, Vice President of Nursing and Chief Nursing Officer, Fort Healthcare, Fort Atkinson, WI, p. A692

WIESNER, Jerry, Administrator and Chief Executive Officer, Southwest Healthcare Services, Bowman, ND, p. A464

WIEWORA, Ron, M.D., Chief Medical Officer, Lakeside Medical Center, Belle Glade, FL, p. A117

WIGGINS, Carla, Director Human Resources, Livingston Hospital And Healthcare Services, Salem, KY, p. A260

WIGGINS, John, Chief Financial Officer, Evans Memorial Hospital, Claxton, GA, p. A150

WIGGINS, Marjorie, Senior Vice President, Chief Nursing Officer, Maine Medical Center, Brighton Campus, ME, p. A285

WIGHTMAN, Lori, R.N., MSN, FACHE, President, Mercy Hospital Ada, Ada, OK, p. A495

WIGINGTON, Yvonne, Vice President, Chief Financial Officer, Wyoming Medical Center, Casper, WY, p. A707

WIGMAN, Cathryn, Director Human Resources, Healthsouth Braintree Rehabilitation Hospital, Braintree, MA, p. A297

WIIK, Jennifer, Chief Nursing Officer, Ortonville Area Health Services, Ortonville, MN, p. A337

WIJAYA, Joanne, MSN, R.N., Chief Operating Officer and Risk Manager, Hampton Behavioral Health Center, Westampton, NJ, p. A414

WIJEWARDANE, Chamath, Chief Information Technology Officer, Och Regional Medical Center, Starkville, MS, p. A353

WILBANKS, John F, FACHE
Chief Operating Officer, Baptist Medical Center Beaches, Jacksonville Beach, FL, p. A126
Chief Operating Officer, Wolfson Children's Hospital, FL, p. A125

WILBUR, Bruce, M.D., Chief Medical Officer, Good Samaritan Hospital, San Jose, CA, p. A86

WILBUR, Thomas W., Chief Executive Officer and Superintendent, Newport Hospital And Health Services, Newport, WA, p. A674

WILBURN, Matt, Chief Executive Officer, Highland Ridge Hospital, Midvale, UT, p. A647

WILBURN, Sue, Vice President Human Resources and Organizational Development, East Tennessee Children's Hospital, Knoxville, TN, p. A572

WILCHER, Greta
Senior Vice President and Chief Financial Officer, Mercy Hospital Waldron, Waldron-Scott County, AR, p. A49
Senior Vice President and Chief Financial Officer, Mercy Orthopedic Hospital Fort Smith, AR, p. A42

WILCOX, Bill, Chief Information Technology Officer, Bristol Bay Area Health Corporation, Dillingham, AK, p. A26

WILCOX, Byron, Chief Financial Management Officer, Standing Rock Service Unit, Fort Yates Hospital, Indian Health Service, Dhhs, Fort Yates, ND, p. A466

WILCOX, David, Chief Financial Officer, L. V. Stabler Memorial Hospital, Greenville, AL, p. A19

WILCOX, Jack
Chief Financial Officer, Ennis Regional Medical Center, Ennis, TX, p. A603
Chief Financial Officer, Parkview Regional Hospital, Mexia, TX, p. A624

WILCOX, James, Chief Executive Officer, El Paso Specialty Hospital, El Paso, TX, p. A601

WILCOX, John, Chief Information Officer, Ozarks Medical Center, West Plains, MO, p. A372

WILCOX, Kyle M, Vice President Finance, Unitypoint Health - Grinnell Regional Medical Center, Grinnell, IA, p. A223

WILCOX, Robert, Chief Financial Officer, Munson Healthcare Charlevoix Hospital, Charlevoix, MI, p. A309

WILCZEK, Joseph, Chief Executive Officer, St. Elizabeth Hospital, Enumclaw, WA, p. A671

WILCZEK, Vincent Scot, Controller, Pratt Regional Medical Center, Pratt, KS, p. A244

WILDA, Joshua, Chief Information Officer, Metro Health - University Of Michigan Health, Wyoming, MI, p. A326

WILDE, Gary, President and Chief Executive Officer, Community Memorial Hospital, CA, p. A94

WILDE, Kathy R, R.N., Chief Nursing Officer, Hcmc Department Of Pediatrics, MN, p. A335

WILDER, Janet, Director Human Resources, Barbourville Arh Hospital, Barbourville, KY, p. A249

WILDER, Susan
Director Financial Services, Roosevelt Warm Springs Rehabilitation And Specialty Hospitals - Ltac, Warm Springs, GA, p. A162
Director Financial Services, Roosevelt Warm Springs Rehabilitation Hospital - Rehab, Warm Springs, GA, p. A162

WILDHAGEN, Quentin, Systems Administrator, Izard County Medical Center, Calico Rock-Logan County, AR, p. A40

WILEY, Chuck, Manager Information Systems, Harrison County Hospital, Corydon, IN, p. A201

WILEY, Donald J., President and Chief Executive Officer, St. Joseph's Medical Center, Stockton, CA, p. A91

WILEY, George, Chief Financial Officer, Desert Springs Hospital Medical Center, Las Vegas, NV, p. A394

WILEY, Mark, Manager Information Systems Development, Upmc Bedford Memorial, Everett, PA, p. A526

WILEY, Ronette, R.N., Executive Vice President and Chief Operating Officer, Bassett Medical Center, Cooperstown, NY, p. A425

WILFER, James, Chief Executive Officer, Red River Hospital, Llc, Wichita Falls, TX, p. A644

WILFONG, Mario, Vice President Finance and Administration, Upmc Bedford Memorial, Everett, PA, p. A526

WILHELM, Connie, Chief Financial Officer, Swisher Memorial Hospital District, Tulia, TX, p. A640

WILHELM, Paul, M.D., Chief of Staff, Kiowa District Healthcare, Kiowa, KS, p. A238

WILHITE, James, Director Systems Information, North Mississippi State Hospital, Tupelo, MS, p. A353

WILHITE, Jerald, Administrator Human Resources, Heartland Behavioral Healthcare, Massillon, OH, p. A486

WILHOITE, David, CPA, Senior Vice President Finance and Chief Financial Officer, Trousdale Medical Center, Hartsville, TN, p. A570

WILK, Leonard, President and Chief Executive Officer, Amita Health Women & Children's Hospital, IL, p. A186

WILKE, Kris, Manager Health Information, Granite Falls Health, Granite Falls, MN, p. A332

WILKEN, Thomas
Senior Vice President and Chief Human Resources Officer, Louis & Peaches Owen Heart Hospital, TX, p. A640
Vice President Human Resources, Seton Medical Center Williamson, Round Rock, TX, p. A631

WILKENS, Gregory, M.D., Chief of Staff, Jellico Community Hospital, Jellico, TN, p. A571

WILKENS, Katy, Chief Nursing Officer and Vice President, Northern Arizona Healthcare, Flagstaff Medical Center, Flagstaff, AZ, p. A29

WILKER, Johnathan, Vice President Finance and Chief Financial Officer, West Campus, NE, p. A387

WILKERSON, Donald H., FACHE, Chief Executive Officer, St. David's Rehabilitation Center, TX, p. A586

WILKERSON, Jacquelyn, R.N., Chief Nursing Officer, Conway Regional Medical Center, Conway-Faulkner County, AR, p. A40

WILKERSON-UDDYBACK, Patricia, M.D.
Chief Medical Officer, Dmc - Detroit Receiving Hospital, Detroit, MI, p. A311
Chief Medical Officer, Dmc Hutzel Women's Hospital, MI, p. A311

WILKES, Chris, MS, Director Human Resources, Blount Memorial Hospital, Maryville, TN, p. A574

WILKES, Margaret, Chief Fiscal Officer, Charles George Veterans Affairs Medical Center, Asheville, NC, p. A447

WILKIE, Chance, Information Technology Specialist, Indian Health Service - Quentin N. Burdick Memorial Health Care Facility, Belcourt, ND, p. A464

WILKIE, Paula, Chief Financial Officer, Presentation Medical Center, Rolla, ND, p. A468

WILKINS, Joseph, Chief Executive Officer, Wythe County Community Hospital, Wytheville, VA, p. A668

WILKINS, Michael, Chief Operating Officer, Advocate Hope Children's Hospital, IL, p. A191

WILKINSON, Kyle, Chief Financial Officer, Morgan Memorial Hospital, Madison, GA, p. A157

WILKINSON, Mark, M.D., Chief Medical Officer, Indian Path Medical Center, Kingsport, TN, p. A572

WILKINSON, Steven D., Interim Chief Executive Officer, St. Mary's Medical Center, Blue Springs, MO, p. A355

WILKS, Angela, Finance Director, Missouri Baptist Sullivan Hospital, Sullivan, MO, p. A371

WILL, DeDe, Director Finance, Douglas County Community Mental Health Center, Omaha, NE, p. A388

WILL, Nicole, Human Resources Officer, Herington Municipal Hospital, Herington, KS, p. A236

WILLAMS, Mike, Chief Information Officer, Fhn Memorial Hospital, Freeport, IL, p. A183

WILLARD, Cheri, R.N., Chief Nursing Officer, Evanston Regional Hospital, Evanston, WY, p. A708

WILLARD, Craig, Director Information Technology and Systems, Frankfort Regional Medical Center, Frankfort, KY, p. A252

WILLCOXON, Phil, Chief Executive Officer, Delta Medical Center, Memphis, TN, p. A575

WILLE, Lesley A., Executive Director, Kaiser Permanente South Bay Medical Center, Los Angeles, CA, p. A67

WILLEMSEN, Jane, President and Chief Administrative Officer, John Muir Medical Center, Walnut Creek, Walnut Creek, CA, p. A94

WILLERT, Todd, Chief Executive Officer, Community Healthcare System, Onaga, KS, p. A242

WILLET, Terry, Chief Financial Officer, Allen Parish Hospital, Kinder, LA, p. A270

WILLETT, Richard, Chief Executive Officer, Redington-Fairview General Hospital, Skowhegan, ME, p. A286

WILLETT, Simon, Director Administrative Operations, San Antonio Division, TX, p. A634

WILLETT, Vita M.
Executive Director, Kaiser Permanente Riverside Medical Center, Riverside, CA, p. A81
Senior Vice President, Area Manager, Kaiser Permanente Moreno Valley Medical Center, Moreno Valley, CA, p. A73

WILLEY, Randy, Business Manager, Lincoln Regional Center, Lincoln, NE, p. A386

WILLHITE, Jean, Director Human Resources, Sutter Solano Medical Center, Vallejo, CA, p. A93

WILLIAMS, Adrian, Chief Executive Officer, Serenity Springs Specialty Hospital, Ruston, LA, p. A278

WILLIAMS, Alec, Chief Information Officer, Southwest General Health Center, Middleburg Heights, OH, p. A487

WILLIAMS, Amber, Vice President and Chief Financial Officer, Southwest Medical Center, Liberal, KS, p. A240

WILLIAMS, Andrew G., Chief Executive Officer, Frio Regional Hospital, Pearsall, TX, p. A627

WILLIAMS, Antoinette, Chief Nursing Officer, John H. Stroger Jr. Hospital Of Cook County, Chicago, IL, p. A177

WILLIAMS, Arthur, M.D., Medical Director, Healthsouth Braintree Rehabilitation Hospital, Braintree, MA, p. A297

WILLIAMS, Avilla, MS, President, Integris Health Edmond, Edmond, OK, p. A498

WILLIAMS, Bernett, Interim Chief Human Resource Officer, Akron Children's Hospital, Akron, OH, p. A470

WILLIAMS, Beth, R.N., Chief Nursing Officer, Conway Behavioral Health Hospital, Conway-Faulkner County, AR, p. A40

WILLIAMS, Beverly, R.N., Chief Nursing Officer, Washington County Memorial Hospital, Potosi, MO, p. A366

WILLIAMS, Bob, President and Chief Executive Officer, Bsa Hospital, Llc, Amarillo, TX, p. A583

WILLIAMS, Brian, M.D.
Chief of Medical Staff, Florida Hospital North Pinellas, Tarpon Springs, FL, p. A142
Web Services and Information Technology Manager, St. Joseph's Hospital Of Buckhannon, Buckhannon, WV, p. A682

WILLIAMS, Brian A., Chief Executive Officer, Labette Health, Parsons, KS, p. A244

WILLIAMS, Brit, M.D., President Medical Staff, Warner Hospital And Health Services, Clinton, IL, p. A180

WILLIAMS, Bryan, R.N., Vice President Patient Care Services, Chi St. Vincent Hot Springs, Hot Springs-Garland County, AR, p. A43

WILLIAMS, CarolAnn, Chief Financial Officer, Massachusetts Eye And Ear, Boston, MA, p. A296

WILLIAMS, Catherine, M.D., Medical Director, Lewis County General Hospital, Lowville, NY, p. A429

WILLIAMS, Cecille, Assistant Administrator, Shamrock General Hospital, Shamrock, TX, p. A635

WILLIAMS, Charles E., FACHE, President and Chief Executive Officer, Regional Medical Center, Orangeburg, SC, p. A556

WILLIAMS, Chris J., FACHE, Vice President Operations, Perry Memorial Hospital, Princeton, IL, p. A194

WILLIAMS, Christine, Chief Financial Officer, University Medical Center, New Orleans, LA, p. A276

WILLIAMS, Christopher, M.D., Chief of Staff, Pioneers Medical Center, Meeker, CO, p. A104

WILLIAMS, Craig T., President, St. Elizabeth's Medical Center, Brighton, MA, p. A297

WILLIAMS, Damita, Ed.D., R.N., MSN, Chief Nursing Officer, Medical City Fort Worth, Fort Worth, TX, p. A605

WILLIAMS, Dan, Vice President Finance and Support, Liberty Hospital, Liberty, MO, p. A363

WILLIAMS, Dana, Chief Financial Officer, Baptist Memorial Hospital-North Mississippi, Oxford, MS, p. A351

WILLIAMS, Dana D., Chief Executive Officer, Jennings American Legion Hospital, Jennings, LA, p. A269

WILLIAMS, Danielle, Administrator, Caldwell Memorial Hospital, Columbia, LA, p. A265

WILLIAMS, Darek, Director Human Resources, Elgin Mental Health Center, Elgin, IL, p. A182

WILLIAMS, Darlene, R.N.
Administrator, Chi St. Luke's Health Memorial San Augustine, San Augustine, TX, p. A635
Administrator, Chi St. Luke's Health Memorial Specialty Hospital, Lufkin, TX, p. A621

WILLIAMS, David, Director Information Technology, Franklin Hospital District, Benton, IL, p. A174

WILLIAMS, David L., M.D., Chief Medical Officer, St. Vincent Kokomo, Kokomo, IN, p. A209

WILLIAMS, Dionne, Director Human Resources, Vaughan Regional Medical Center, Selma, AL, p. A23

WILLIAMS, Douglas, Vice President, Saint Francis Heart Hospital, Saint Francis Heart Hospital, OK, p. A509

WILLIAMS, Erica, Assistant Chief Executive Officer, Calcasieu Oaks Geriatric Psychiatric Hospital, LA, p. A265

WILLIAMS, Frank L., Executive Vice President/ Medical Director, Kedren Community Mental Health Center, Los Angeles, CA, p. A68

WILLIAMS, Greg
Chief Financial Officer, Pih Health Hospital - Downey, Downey, CA, p. A56
Chief Financial Officer, Pih Health Hospital - Whittier, Whittier, CA, p. A95

WILLIAMS, Jackie, Director Human Resources, Merit Health Madison, Canton, MS, p. A344

WILLIAMS, James, M.D.
Chief of Staff, Thedacare Medical Center-Waupaca, Waupaca, WI, p. A705
Chief Executive Officer, Pearl River County Hospital, Poplarville, MS, p. A352
Vice President and Chief Nursing Officer, Mclaren Flint, Flint, MI, p. A312

WILLIAMS, James R.
Chief Financial Officer, Louisiana Market, Teche Regional Medical Center, Morgan City, LA, p. A274
Chief Financial Officer, Minden Medical Center, Minden, LA, p. A274

WILLIAMS, Jason, Director Information Systems, Olympia Medical Center, Los Angeles, CA, p. A69

WILLIAMS, Jeanette, Chief Executive Officer, Kindred Hospital-Aurora, Aurora, CO, p. A96

WILLIAMS, Jeremy, Chief Financial Officer, Banner Boswell Medical Center, Sun City, AZ, p. A36

WILLIAMS, Joan, Administrative Assistant/Human Resources, Lamb Healthcare Center, Littlefield, TX, p. A620

WILLIAMS, John
Administrator and Chief Executive Officer, Nell J. Redfield Memorial Hospital, Malad City, ID, p. A170
Chief Financial Officer, Upson Regional Medical Center, Thomaston, GA, p. A161
Chief Information Officer, Bay Pines Veterans Affairs Healthcare System, Bay Pines, FL, p. A117

WILLIAMS, John D, Jr, Chief Financial Officer, Veterans Affairs Gulf Coast Veterans Health Care System, Biloxi, MS, p. A343

WILLIAMS, Joyce, Consultant Human Resources and Organizational Development, Memorial Hermann Rehabilitation Hospital - Katy, Katy, TX, p. A616

WILLIAMS, Julie
Chief Financial Officer, Muenster Memorial Hospital, Muenster, TX, p. A625
Chief Financial Officer, Smith County Memorial Hospital, Smith Center, KS, p. A246

WILLIAMS, Kathy, Chief Nursing Officer, Eastern New Mexico Medical Center, Roswell, NM, p. A419

WILLIAMS, Kenneth, Chief Information Officer, Fayetteville Veterans Affairs Medical Center, Fayetteville, NC, p. A452

WILLIAMS, Kim, R.N., MS, Chief Executive Officer, Providence Everett Medical Center - Pacific Campus, WA, p. A671

WILLIAMS, Kristy, Manager Finance, John J. Pershing Veterans Affairs Medical Center, Poplar Bluff, MO, p. A366

WILLIAMS, L Dale, M.D., Vice President and Chief Medical Director, High Point Regional Health System, High Point, NC, p. A454

WILLIAMS, Laci, Director Human Resources, Kearny County Hospital, Lakin, KS, p. A239

WILLIAMS, Lana T., Chief Nursing Officer, Arkansas Methodist Medical Center, Paragould-Greene County, AR, p. A47

WILLIAMS, Linda, Director of Nursing, Villa Feliciana Medical Complex, Jackson, LA, p. A269

WILLIAMS, Lorie, R.N., Vice President Nursing, Samaritan Pacific Communities Hospital, Newport, OR, p. A515

WILLIAMS, Lynn
Vice President Human Resources, Commonwealth Regional Specialty Hospital, Bowling Green, KY, p. A249
Vice President Human Resources, Medical Center At Bowling Green, Bowling Green, KY, p. A250
Vice President Human Resources, Medical Center At Scottsville, Scottsville, KY, p. A260
Vice President, Human Resources, The Medical Center Albany, Albany, KY, p. A249
Vice President, Human Resources, The Medical Center At Caverna, Horse Cave, KY, p. A253

WILLIAMS, Margaret, Chief Financial Officer, Baptist Memorial Hospital For Women, Memphis, TN, p. A574

WILLIAMS, Margo L., R.N., Chief Nursing Officer, Anderson County Hospital, Garnett, KS, p. A235

WILLIAMS, Mary, Director Human Resources, Medina Memorial Hospital, Medina, NY, p. A430

WILLIAMS, Matthew, R.N.
Chief Executive Officer, Olympia Medical Center, Los Angeles, CA, p. A69
Chief Financial Officer, Olympia Medical Center, Los Angeles, CA, p. A69

WILLIAMS, Michael, Chief Information Officer, Lawrence Memorial Hospital, Lawrence, KS, p. A239

WILLIAMS, Michael D, Vice President and Administrator, General Hospital, WV, p. A682

WILLIAMS, Michael F., Chief Financial Officer, Limestone Medical Center, Groesbeck, TX, p. A608

WILLIAMS, Michael L, FACHE, Vice President Human Resources, Community Howard Regional Health, Kokomo, IN, p. A209

WILLIAMS, Michelle, Administrator, Sedan City Hospital, Sedan, KS, p. A245

WILLIAMS, Mickey, Manager Information Technology, Moccasin Bend Mental Health Institute, Chattanooga, TN, p. A567

WILLIAMS, Nancy M., R.N., Administrator, Brooks County Hospital, Quitman, GA, p. A158

WILLIAMS, Nicole
Chief Operating Officer, Columbia Memorial Hospital, Astoria, OR, p. A511
Director of Human Resources Operations, Dmc Huron Valley-Sinai Hospital, Commerce Township, MI, p. A310

WILLIAMS, Pamela, Vice President, Ridgeview Le Sueur Medical Center, Le Sueur, MN, p. A333

WILLIAMS, Pamela G, Director Human Resources, Unity Health Specialty Care, AR, p. A48

WILLIAMS, Perry E., Sr, Administrator and Chief Executive Officer, Alliance Healthcare System, Holly Springs, MS, p. A347

WILLIAMS, Qiana, Director, Human Resource Business Partner, Grant, Ohiohealth Grant Medical Center, Columbus, OH, p. A478

WILLIAMS, R D, Chief Executive Officer, Hendry Regional Medical Center, Clewiston, FL, p. A120

WILLIAMS, Randy, Director Management Information Systems, Maria Parham Medical Center, Henderson, NC, p. A454

WILLIAMS, Reginald, M.D., Medical Staff President, Curry General Hospital, Gold Beach, OR, p. A513

WILLIAMS, Rich, Director Human Resources, Upson Regional Medical Center, Thomaston, GA, p. A161

WILLIAMS, Richard, Chief Operating Officer, Southwest Mississippi Regional Medical Center, Mccomb, MS, p. A350

WILLIAMS, Robert, M.D.
Chief Medical Officer, Arkansas Children's Hospital, Little Rock-Pulaski County, AR, p. A44
Chief Executive Officer, Healthsouth Southern Hills Rehabilitation Hospital, Princeton, WV, p. A686

WILLIAMS, Robert D., Chief Executive Officer, Upmc Susquehanna Sunbury, Sunbury, PA, p. A542

WILLIAMS, Robert J., M.D., Chief Medical Staff, Wills Memorial Hospital, Washington, GA, p. A163

WILLIAMS, Roberta A, Director of Nursing, U.S. Public Health Service Indian Hospital, Cass Lake, MN, p. A329

WILLIAMS, Roby D., Administrator, Hardin County General Hospital, Rosiclare, IL, p. A195

WILLIAMS, Rodney W, M.D., JD, MS, Vice President Medical Affairs, Good Samaritan Regional Medical Center, Suffern, NY, p. A443

WILLIAMS, Ronald G., Administrator, Central Louisiana State Hospital, Pineville, LA, p. A277

WILLIAMS, Sabrina, Interm Vice President Human Resources, Brigham And Women's Hospital, Boston, MA, p. A296

WILLIAMS, Sandra, Chief Financial Officer, Cape Fear Valley Rehabilitation Center, NC, p. A452

WILLIAMS, Scott
Chief Executive Officer, Centerpointe Hospital, Saint Charles, MO, p. A367
Chief Executive Officer, Rehabilitation Hospital Of Northwest Ohio, Toledo, OH, p. A491
Chief Operating Officer, Cookeville Regional Medical Center, Cookeville, TN, p. A568

WILLIAMS, Sean J., President and Chief Executive Officer, Mercy Iowa City, Iowa City, IA, p. A224

WILLIAMS, Shane, Director Information Systems, Davis Hospital And Medical Center, Layton, UT, p. A647

WILLIAMS, Sharon, Vice President Finance and Information Technology, Avera Marshall Regional Medical Center, Marshall, MN, p. A334

WILLIAMS, Sheila, Vice President and Administrator, Baptist Health Medical Center-Hot Spring County, Malvern-Hot Spring County, AR, p. A45

WILLIAMS, Sheri, Chief Operating Officer, Guadalupe Regional Medical Center, Seguin, TX, p. A635

WILLIAMS, Stephanie, R.N.
Chief Nursing Officer, Washington Hospital Healthcare System, Fremont, CA, p. A59
Coordinator Human Resources, Kindred Rehabilitation Hospital Northeast Houston, Humble, TX, p. A615
Market Director Human Resources, Lake Norman Regional Medical Center, Mooresville, NC, p. A457

WILLIAMS, Sue Ann, Chief Executive Officer, Southeast Health Center Of Stoddard County, Dexter, MO, p. A358

WILLIAMS, Susan, M.D.
Chief Medical Officer, Conemaugh Miners Medical Center, Hastings, PA, p. A527
Chief Medical Officer, Memorial Medical Center - Lee Campus, PA, p. A528
Chief Nursing Officer, Baptist Health Medical Center-Stuttgart, Stuttgart-Arkansas County, AR, p. A49

WILLIAMS, Teresa, BSN, R.N.
Regional Administrator, Mercy Hospital Ozark, Ozark-Franklin County, AR, p. A47
Regional Administrator, Mercy Hospital Paris, Paris-Logan County, AR, p. A47
Regional Administrator, Mercy Hospital Booneville, Booneville-Logan County, AR, p. A40
Regional Administrator, Mercy Hospital Waldron, Waldron-Scott County, AR, p. A49

WILLIAMS, Thaddeus, Controller, Healthsouth Rehabilitation Hospital Memphis-North, Memphis, TN, p. A575

WILLIAMS, Todd, Chief Financial Officer, Siloam Springs Regional Hospital, Siloam Springs-Benton County, AR, p. A48

WILLIAMS, Tom, Vice President Employee and Community Development, Lake Regional Health System, Osage Beach, MO, p. A365

WILLIAMS, Wade, Chief Information Officer, Unc Rockingham Health Care, Eden, NC, p. A451

WILLIAMS, Wendell H, M.D., Jr, Medical Director, Specialty Hospital Jacksonville, Jacksonville, FL, p. A126

WILLIAMSON, Alan, M.D., Chief Medical Officer, Eisenhower Medical Center, Rancho Mirage, CA, p. A79

WILLIAMSON, Barry, President Medical Staff, Southeastern Health, Lumberton, NC, p. A456

WILLIAMSON, John, Human Resources Site Manager, Baptist Health South Florida, Mariners Hospital, Tavernier, FL, p. A142

WILLIAMSON, Johnny, M.D., Chief Medical Officer, Hartgrove Hospital, Chicago, IL, p. A177

WILLIAMSON, Sharon, Chief Information Technology, Robert J. Dole Veterans Affairs Medical Center, Wichita, KS, p. A248

WILLIE, David, Chief Financial Officer, Yuma Regional Medical Center, Yuma, AZ, p. A38

WILLIFORD, Sandy, Chief Health Information Management and Revenue Administration, Charlie Norwood Veterans Affairs Medical Center, Augusta, GA, p. A147

WILLINGHAM, John, Chief Executive Officer and Managing Director, Carolina Center For Behavioral Health, Greer, SC, p. A554

WILLIS, Bill, Director Information Technology, River Point Behavioral Health, Jacksonville, FL, p. A125

WILLIS, Brenda, Director of Nursing, Doctor's Hospital Of Deer Creek, Leesville, LA, p. A272

WILLIS, Darrell, M.D., Chief of Staff, Dr. Dan C. Trigg Memorial Hospital, Tucumcari, NM, p. A420

WILLIS, Jayne, Vice President Nursing and Chief Nursing Officer, Winnie Palmer Hospital For Women And Babies, FL, p. A134

WILLIS, Jonathon, Director Information Services, Tennova Healthcare-Shelbyville, Shelbyville, TN, p. A579

WILLIS, Joshua, Chief Executive Officer, West Florida Community Care Center, Milton, FL, p. A131

WILLIS, Joy, Acting Chief Fiscal Service, G.V. (Sonny) Montgomery Veterans Affairs Medical Center, Jackson, MS, p. A348

WILLIS, Kathy, M.D., Medical Director, Lallie Kemp Medical Center, Independence, LA, p. A269

WILLIS, Raymond, IT Manager, Choctaw Health Center, Philadelphia, MS, p. A352

WILLIS, Robert, Director Human Resources, North Shore Health, Grand Marais, MN, p. A332

WILLIS, Sandra, Director of Human Resources, Citizens Baptist Medical Center, Talladega, AL, p. A23

WILLIS, Toni, M.D., Medical Director, Encompass Health Rehabilitation Hospital Of The Mid-Cities, Bedford, TX, p. A588

WILLIS, Wendy L, Vice President Human Resources, Children's Hospital, New Orleans, LA, p. A275

WILLMANN, Adam, President and Chief Executive Officer, Goodall-Witcher Hospital Authority, Clifton, TX, p. A593

WILLMON, Brian, M.D., Medical Director, Plains Regional Medical Center, Clovis, NM, p. A416

WILLMORE, Lois, Supervisor Health Information Management, Cedar County Memorial Hospital, El Dorado Springs, MO, p. A358

WILLOUGHBY, Kirsten, Director of Nursing, Big Horn County Memorial Hospital, Hardin, MT, p. A376

WILLS, Andrea, R.N., Chief Nursing Executive, Munising Memorial Hospital, Munising, MI, p. A319

WILLS, Andy, M.D., Medical Director, Colquitt Regional Medical Center, Moultrie, GA, p. A158

WILLS, Kim, Chief Operating Officer, Cook Medical Center-A Campus Of Tift Regional Medical Center, Adel, GA, p. A145

WILLS, Laura S.
Administrator, Noland Hospital Birmingham, Birmingham, AL, p. A14
Administrator, Noland Hospital Shelby, Alabaster, AL, p. A13

WILLS, Michele, Registered Health Information Administrator, Caro Center, Caro, MI, p. A309

WILLS, Robert, M.D., Chief Medical Officer, Arise Austin Medical Center, Austin, TX, p. A585

WILLS, Shannon, Director Human Resources, Pinecrest Rehabilitation Hospital, FL, p. A121

WILLSHER, Jay, Chief Operating Officer, Unitypoint Health - Trinity Bettendorf, Bettendorf, IA, p. A217

WILLSIE, Brett, Vice President Human Resources, Sentara Northern Virginia Medical Center, Woodbridge, VA, p. A668

WILLWERTH, Deborah J., R.N., MSN, Chief Executive Officer, Upmc Pinnacle Lititz, Lititz, PA, p. A530

WILLYARD, Deborah, R.N., MSN, Chief Nursing Officer, Pella Regional Health Center, Pella, IA, p. A228

WILMOT, Joan, Chief Finance Officer, White River Junction Veterans Affairs Medical Center, White River Junction, VT, p. A654

WILMOTH, Donna, Vice President Patient Care Services and Chief Nursing Officer, Sentara Williamsburg Regional Medical Center, Williamsburg, VA, p. A668

WILMS, Mike, Director Information Systems, Regional Medical Center Bayonet Point, Hudson, FL, p. A125

WILSON, Ada, R.N., Interim Chief Executive Officer, Jefferson County Hospital, Fayette, MS, p. A345

WILSON, Alice, FACHE, Vice President Administration, St. Luke's Hospital - Warren Campus, Phillipsburg, NJ, p. A410

WILSON, Amy, M.D., Medical Director, Baylor Institute For Rehabilitation, Dallas, TX, p. A595

WILSON, Bill, Chief Financial Officer, North Carolina Specialty Hospital, Durham, NC, p. A451

WILSON, Bobbie, Director Human Resources, Crete Area Medical Center, Crete, NE, p. A383

WILSON, Brent, Chief Executive Officer, Marian Center, Salt Lake City, UT, p. A650

WILSON, Carolyn, R.N.
Chief Operating Officer, Beaumont Children's Hospital, MI, p. A322
Chief Operating Officer, Beaumont Hospital - Farmington Hills, Farmington Hills, MI, p. A312
Chief Operating Officer, Beaumont Hospital - Grosse Pointe, Grosse Pointe, MI, p. A315
Chief Operating Officer, Beaumont Hospital - Taylor, Taylor, MI, p. A324
Chief Operating Officer, Beaumont Hospital - Trenton, Trenton, MI, p. A324
Chief Operating Officer, Beaumont Hospital - Troy, Troy, MI, p. A325
Chief Operating Officer, Beaumont Hospital, Wayne, Wayne, MI, p. A325
Chief Operating Officer, Beaumont Hospital - Dearborn, Dearborn, MI, p. A310

WILSON, Charlene J, Vice President Human Resources, St. Francis Hospital, Wilmington, DE, p. A114

WILSON, Chase, Chief Financial Officer, Sycamore Shoals Hospital, Elizabethton, TN, p. A569

WILSON, Christopher, M.D., Inpatient Medical Director, South Texas Rehabilitation Hospital, Brownsville, TX, p. A590

WILSON, Christy, Chief Financial Officer, Merit Health Rankin, Brandon, MS, p. A344

WILSON, Clifford, Chief Operating Officer, Southern Tennessee Regional Health System-Sewanee, TN, p. A581

WILSON, Colleen, Chief Nursing Officer, Southern Inyo Healthcare District, Lone Pine, CA, p. A65

WILSON, Craig, Chief Medical Officer, St. Vincent Fishers Hospital, Fishers, IN, p. A203

WILSON, David R, M.D., Chief of Staff, St. Vincent's Blount, Oneonta, AL, p. A22

WILSON, Deanna, VP Patient Care Services/Site Manager, Aspirus Ontonagon Hospital, Inc., Ontonagon, MI, p. A320

WILSON, Deb, Director Human Resources, Pathways Treatment Center, MT, p. A377

WILSON, Debra, Vice President and Chief Nursing Officer, Crittenton Children's Center, MO, p. A362

WILSON, Dottie D, Director Human Resources, Pickens County Medical Center, Carrollton, AL, p. A16

WILSON, Eleanor, R.N., MSN, Vice President and Chief Operating Officer, Doylestown Hospital, Doylestown, PA, p. A524

WILSON, Elizabeth M, Coordinator Human Resources, Select Specialty Hospital - Cincinnati North, Cincinnati, OH, p. A475

WILSON, Erin, Human Resource Director, Bear Valley Community Hospital, Big Bear Lake, CA, p. A53

WILSON, Fiore, Director Information Systems, Castleview Hospital, Price, UT, p. A649

WILSON, Hamlin J
Senior Vice President Human Resources, Bristol Regional Medical Center, Bristol, TN, p. A566
Senior Vice President Human Resources, Holston Valley Medical Center, Kingsport, TN, p. A572

WILSON, Jason, Administrator and Chief Executive Officer, American Fork Hospital, American Fork, UT, p. A646

WILSON, Jeffrey, Chief Executive Officer, Methodist Specialty And Transplant Hospital, TX, p. A633

WILSON, Jim, Vice President Information Technology, Promise Hospital Of San Diego, San Diego, CA, p. A84

WILSON, Jodi, President and Chief Operating Officer, Diley Ridge Medical Center, Canal Winchester, OH, p. A473

WILSON, John R
Chief Operating Officer, Murray-Calloway County Hospital, Murray, KY, p. A258
Vice President, Human Resources, Murray-Calloway County Hospital, Murray, KY, p. A258

WILSON, Kari, MHA, FNP, RN, Chief Nursing Officer, Ssm Health St. Mary's Hospital - Audrain, Mexico, MO, p. A364

WILSON, Kathey, Acting Chief Executive Officer, U.S. Public Health Service Indian Hospital, Rosebud, SD, p. A563

WILSON, Kim, Human Resources Coordinator, Cordova Community Medical Center, Cordova, AK, p. A26

WILSON, Kimberly P, Director Human Resources, Uk Healthcare Good Samaritan Hospital, KY, p. A255

WILSON, Lawrence, M.D., Vice President, Chief Medical Officer, Midland Memorial Hospital, TX, p. A624

WILSON, Lerae, Vice President Patient Services and Chief Nursing Officer, St. Claire Healthcare, Morehead, KY, p. A258

WILSON, Loretta, Administrator, Hill Hospital Of Sumter County, York, AL, p. A24

WILSON, Mallory, Administrative Assistant and Human Resources Coordinator, Select Specialty Hospital-Knoxville, TN, p. A576

WILSON, Margaret G., R.N., MSN, Acting Director, Lebanon Veterans Affairs Medical Center, Lebanon, PA, p. A529

WILSON, Monte, President, Wellstar Windy Hill Hospital, Marietta, GA, p. A157

WILSON, Nadine, Manager, Human Resources, Jerome Golden Center For Behavioral Health, Inc., West Palm Beach, FL, p. A143

WILSON, Nancy, Chief Financial Officer, Parkview Community Hospital Medical Center, Riverside, CA, p. A81

WILSON, Nathan, R.N., Vice President and Chief Nursing Officer, Baptist Health La Grange, La Grange, KY, p. A254

WILSON, Nicole, Manager Human Resources, St. Theresa Specialty Hospital, Kenner, LA, p. A270

WILSON, Patricia, Senior Vice President Human Resources, Englewood Hospital And Medical Center, Englewood, NJ, p. A405

WILSON, Regina, R.N., Director of Nursing, Share Medical Center, Alva, OK, p. A495

WILSON, Robert, D.O., Director Medical Services, Eagleville Hospital, Eagleville, PA, p. A524

WILSON, Robert E
Vice President and Chief Information Officer, Delaware County Memorial Hospital, Drexel Hill, PA, p. A524
Vice President and Chief Information Officer, Taylor Hospital, PA, p. A543

WILSON, Robert E., Esq
Chief Executive Officer, Dekalb Medical At Downtown Decatur, Decatur, GA, p. A152
Chief Executive Officer, Dekalb Medical At Hillandale, Lithonia, GA, p. A156
Chief Executive Officer, Dekalb Medical At North Decatur, Decatur, GA, p. A152

WILSON, Roy, M.D., Medical Director, St. Louis Psychiatric Rehabilitation Center, Saint Louis, MO, p. A369

WILSON, Sara, Director Human Resources, Cheyenne County Hospital, Saint Francis, KS, p. A245

WILSON, Shea, Chief Nursing Officer, T. J. Samson Community Hospital, Glasgow, KY, p. A252

WILSON, Sherry, R.N., Chief Nursing Officer, Mayers Memorial Hospital District, Fall River Mills, CA, p. A58

WILSON, Sondra Dianne, Chief Executive Officer, Tyler County Hospital, Woodville, TX, p. A645

WILSON, Stephan A, Chief Financial Officer, Montrose Memorial Hospital, Montrose, CO, p. A104

WILSON, Stephan A., Chief Financial Officer, Lifescape, Sioux Falls, SD, p. A563

WILSON, Tammie, R.N., MSN, Chief Nursing Officer, Fayette County Memorial Hospital, Washington Court House, OH, p. A493

WILSON, Terrance E, President and Chief Executive Officer, Franciscan Health Lafayette Central, IN, p. A209

WILSON, Terrance E.
President and Chief Executive Officer, Franciscan Health Lafayette Central, IN, p. A209
President and Chief Executive Officer, Franciscan Health Rensselaer, Rensselaer, IN, p. A214

WILSON, Tracy, Chief Executive Officer, Kindred Rehabilitation Hospital Northeast Houston, Humble, TX, p. A615

WILSON, Vicki, Human Resources Director, Dixie Regional Medical Center, UT, p. A650

WILSON, William, M.D., Chief Medical Officer, Uc Irvine Medical Center, Orange, CA, p. A76

WILSON RN, MSN,CEN, Sondra Dianne, R.N., MSN, Assistant Administrator and Chief Nursing Officer, Tyler County Hospital, Woodville, TX, p. A645

WILSON-NEIL, Carla, FACHE, Chief Operating Officer, Spectrum Health Pennock, Hastings, MI, p. A315

WILSON-STUBBS, Yolande, President, Presence Holy Family Medical Center, Des Plaines, IL, p. A181

WILTERMOOD, Michael C., President and Chief Executive Officer, Enloe Medical Center-Cohasset, CA, p. A54

WILTROUT, Kristy, R.N., Chief Operating Officer, Vernon Memorial Healthcare, Viroqua, WI, p. A704

WILTROUT, Terry, President, Washington Health System Greene, Waynesburg, PA, p. A543

WILVER, Donald, Jr
Vice President Human Resources, Upmc Susquehanna Muncy, Muncy, PA, p. A532
Vice President Human Resources, Upmc Susquehanna Williamsport Regional Medical Center, Williamsport, PA, p. A545

WIMMER, Keri, R.N., Patient Care Director, Centracare Health-Melrose, Melrose, MN, p. A334

WIMSATT, Michael, Director Human Resources, Piedmont Geriatric Hospital, Burkeville, VA, p. A656

WINBERY, Ben, Chief Financial Officer, Vantage Point Of Northwest Arkansas, Fayetteville-Washington County, AR, p. A42

WINBUSH, Joyce O., Chief Nursing Officer, Star Medical Center, Plano, TX, p. A629

WINCHESTER, Matthew, Chief Executive Officer, Highland Springs Hospital, Highland Hills, OH, p. A484

WINDAS, Allison Leigh, Director of Patient Care Services-Nurse Executive, Shriners Hospitals For Children-Greenville, Greenville, SC, p. A554

WINDHAM, Joel
Vice President Human Resources, Anderson Regional Health System South, Meridian, MS, p. A350
Vice President Human Resources, Anderson Regional Health System, Meridian, MS, p. A350

WINDHAM, Michael D., Chief Executive Officer, Northwest Medical Center, Winfield, AL, p. A24

WINDHAM, William, Chief Executive Officer, Lewisgale Hospital Alleghany, Low Moor, VA, p. A660

WINDLAND, J Michael, M.D., Chief of Staff, Southern Tennessee Regional Health System-Pulaski, Pulaski, TN, p. A579

WINDOLOVICH, Winona, Associate Chief Information Officer, Zuckerberg San Francisco General Hospital And Trauma Center, San Francisco, CA, p. A86

WINDROW, Matthew, M.D., Chief of Staff, Medina Regional Hospital, Hondo, TX, p. A609

WINDSOR, Bonnie, Senior Vice President Human Resources, Johns Hopkins Children's Center, MD, p. A287

WINEGARNER, Rodney, Chief Financial Officer, Mercy Southwest Hospital, CA, p. A52

WINEKAUF, Glen, Chief Executive Officer, Horn Memorial Hospital, Ida Grove, IA, p. A224

WINFREE, Kersey, M.D., Chief Medical Officer, Ssm Health St. Anthony South, OK, p. A504

WING, Lilly, Chief Nursing Officer, Three Rivers Behavioral Health, West Columbia, SC, p. A558

WING, Yakesun, Business Strategy and Finance Leader, Kaiser Foundation Hospital, CA, p. A94

WINGATE, Phyllis A., FACHE, President, Carolinas Healthcare System Northeast, Concord, NC, p. A450

WINGER, Ronald C, President, Heart Hospital Of New Mexico, NM, p. A415

WINGET, Mary, Director Human Resources, Minden Medical Center, Minden, LA, p. A274

WINGFIELD, Gena, Senior Vice President and Chief Financial Officer, Arkansas Children's Hospital, Little Rock-Pulaski County, AR, p. A44

WINIGER, Cecilia, Community Outreach and Communication Manager, Adventist Health Howard Memorial, Willits, CA, p. A95

WINK, Jeri, Director Human Resources, Grandview Medical Center, Birmingham, AL, p. A14

WINKELMAN, Dan, President and Chief Executive Officer, Yukon-Kuskokwim Delta Regional Hospital, Bethel, AK, p. A25

WINKLER, Gordon W., Administrator and Chief Executive Officer, Ringgold County Hospital, Mount Ayr, IA, p. A226

WINN, Ann M, M.D., R.N., FACHE, Chief Nursing Officer, Methodist Stone Oak Hospital, San Antonio, TX, p. A633

WINN, Cameron, Director Information Services, Ashley Regional Medical Center, Vernal, UT, p. A651

WINN, Eleyce, Chief Executive Officer, Regency Hospital Of Porter County, IN, p. A202

WINN, Holly, FACHE, Chief Operating Officer, Black River Memorial Hospital, Black River Falls, WI, p. A690

WINNER, Douglas, Chief Financial Officer, Acute Care Operations, Providence - Providence Park Hospital, Novi Campus, MI, p. A323

WINNETT, Steve, Chief Executive Officer, Advanced Diagnostics Hospital, Houston, TX, p. A610

WINNIK, Mitchell, Chief Operating Officer, Corona Regional Medical Center-Rehabilitation, CA, p. A55

WINSETT, Gracia, Chief Financial Officer, Wellstone Regional Hospital, Jeffersonville, IN, p. A208

WINSTON, Bob, M.D., Medical Director, Vermilion Behavioral Health Systems South, LA, p. A271

WINSTON, Patricia A, FACHE, MS, R.N., Vice President, Chief Administrative Officer and Chief Operating Officer, University Hospital Of Brooklyn At Long Island College Hospital, NY, p. A437

WINT, Jesse, Director of Nursing, Hardin Medical Center, Savannah, TN, p. A579

WINTER, Jon R., D.O., Chief of Staff, Camden General Hospital, Camden, TN, p. A566

WINTER, Melissa, R.N., MSN, Chief Operating Officer and Chief Nursing Officer, Baylor Medical Center At Mckinney, Mckinney, TX, p. A623

WINTER-CLARK, Jan, Chief Executive Officer, Bristow Medical Center, Bristow, OK, p. A496

WINTERS, Gene, Chief Financial Officer, Northwest Texas Surgery Center, TX, p. A583

WINTERS, Heidi, Business Partner Human Resources, Chi Health Missouri Valley, Missouri Valley, IA, p. A226

WINTERS, Janice, Controller, Pickens County Medical Center, Carrollton, AL, p. A16

WINTERS, Mary, Interim Chief Nursing Officer, St. James Healthcare, Butte, MT, p. A374

WINTERS, Shane, Chief Information Officer, Jersey Community Hospital, Jerseyville, IL, p. A186

WINTHROP, Michael, President, Bellevue Hospital, Bellevue, OH, p. A472

WIRJO, Jonathan, M.D., Medical Director, Seven Hills Hospital, Henderson, NV, p. A393

WIRTHGEN, Doug
Chief Information Officer, Veterans Affairs Palo Alto Health Care System, Livermore Division, CA, p. A77
Facility Information Officer, Veterans Affairs Loma Linda Healthcare System, Loma Linda, CA, p. A64

WIRTZ, David
Senior LAN Administrator, Evansville State Hospital, Evansville, IN, p. A203
Supervisor Information Technology, Evansville Psychiatric Children Center, Evansville, IN, p. A203

WISE, Dan, Manager Information Technology, Sarah D. Culbertson Memorial Hospital, Rushville, IL, p. A195

WISE, Elizabeth, R.N., MS
Chief Nursing Officer and Vice President, Patient Care Services, The Children's Hospital At Saint Peter's University, NJ, p. A408
President and Chief Executive Officer, Lehigh Valley Hospital - Pocono, East Stroudsburg, PA, p. A524

WISE, Josh, Director Information Technology, Lawrence Memorial Hospital, Walnut Ridge-Lawrence County, AR, p. A49

WISE, Kim, Director Human Resources, Bronson South Haven Hospital, South Haven, MI, p. A323

WISE, Teresa, R.N., Chief Nursing Officer, Mena Regional Health System, Mena-Polk County, AR, p. A46

WISE, Toby, Chief Nursing Officer, Winn Parish Medical Center, Winnfield, LA, p. A281

WISEMAN, Josh, Chief Financial Officer, Va Portland Healthcare System, Portland, OR, p. A517

WISEMANN, Jacob, Chief Financial Officer, Parkland Medical Center, Derry, NH, p. A398

WISEMORE, Donna S, R.N., Vice President and Chief Nursing Officer, Dekalb Health, Auburn, IN, p. A199

WISLER, Tam, Director Human Resources, Columbus Springs East Hospital, OH, p. A481

WISMANN, Andrea, M.D., Chief of Staff, Southeast Colorado Hospital District, Springfield, CO, p. A105

WISMER, Doug, Chief Financial Officer, Thayer County Health Services, Hebron, NE, p. A384

WISNER, Donna, Chief Financial Officer, Warner Hospital And Health Services, Clinton, IL, p. A180

WISNIESKI, Thomas, FACHE, Director, Lake City Veterans Affairs Medical Center, FL, p. A123

WISNIEWSKI, Cass, Interim Chief Financial Officer, Hurley Children's Hospital, MI, p. A312

WISNOSKI, Joseph, Chief Financial Officer, John T. Mather Memorial Hospital, Port Jefferson, NY, p. A440

WISSMAN, Sheryl, M.D., Chief Medical Officer, Ascension Crittenton Hospital Medical Center, Rochester, MI, p. A321

WISWELL, Ashleigh, Chief Operations Officer, Moore County Hospital District, Dumas, TX, p. A600

WITCHER-BOATENG, Bernetta, Ph.D., Director Quality Improvement Services and Compliance, Southwest Connecticut Mental Health System, Bridgeport, CT, p. A107

WITENSKE, James, Chief Information Officer, Jefferson Hospital, Jefferson Hills, PA, p. A528

WITHAM, Val
Director Health Information, Avera Flandreau Hospital, Flandreau, SD, p. A561
Director of Health Information, Avera Dells Area Hospital, Dell Rapids, SD, p. A560

WITHERELL, Jodi, Vice President Patient Care and Quality, Tlc Health Network - Lake Shore Hospital, NY, p. A425

WITHERSPOON, Lynn, Vice President and Chief Information Officer, Ochsner Medical Center For Children, LA, p. A276

WITHINGTON, Amber, RN, Chief Clinical Officer, Rawlins County Health Center, Atwood, KS, p. A232

WITKOWICZ, Victor J, Senior Vice President and Chief Financial Officer, Madonna Rehabilitation Hospital, Lincoln, NE, p. A386

WITMER, Bruce, M.D., Medical Director, Fresno Surgical Hospital, Fresno, CA, p. A59

WITT, Cheryl M, Human Resources Director, Kaiser Permanente Moreno Valley Medical Center, Moreno Valley, CA, p. A73

WITT, David, Chief Financial Officer, Meadows Psychiatric Center, Centre Hall, PA, p. A522

WITT, David A, Vice President Finances, Houston Methodist Clear Lake Hospital, Nassau Bay, TX, p. A625

WITT, Jana, Chief Executive Officer, Cedar County Memorial Hospital, El Dorado Springs, MO, p. A358

WITT, Laura, Administrator Human Resources, Banner Behavioral Health Center-Thunderbird Campus, AZ, p. A30

WITT, Lori, Site Finance Director, Mercy Health - Marcum And Wallace, Irvine, KY, p. A254

WITT, Sarah, Director Human Resources, Richmond State Hospital, Richmond, IN, p. A214

WITT, Stephen, President and Chief Executive Officer, College Hospital Cerritos, Cerritos, CA, p. A54

WITT, Ty, M.D., Chief Medical Officer, Lake Chelan Community Hospital And Clinics, Chelan, WA, p. A670

WITTE, Kari, Director Patient Care, Windom Area Hospital, Windom, MN, p. A342

WITTE, Russell, Director Information Technology, Citizens Medical Center, Victoria, TX, p. A642

WITTENSTEIN, Robin D., Ed.D., Chief Executive Officer, Denver Health, Denver, CO, p. A98

WITTHAUS, Patricia, Director Information Services, Valley Regional Hospital, Claremont, NH, p. A398

WITTMAN, Thomas, Chief Information Officer, Frazier Rehab Institute, KY, p. A256

WITTWER, Julie, Chief Financial Officer, South Texas Surgical Hospital, Corpus Christi, TX, p. A594

WLEKLINSKI, Maria, Chief Nursing Officer, Siloam Springs Regional Hospital, Siloam Springs-Benton County, AR, p. A48

WODARZ, Christopher A., Chief, Resource Management Division, Tripler Army Medical Center, Honolulu, HI, p. A165

WODICKA, Mary Jo, Vice President Human Resources, Ascension All Saints, Racine, WI, p. A701

WOELKERS, Joe, Executive Vice President and Chief Staff, Ut Health North Campus Tyler, Tyler, TX, p. A641

WOELTJEN, Bill, Chief Financial Officer, Sarasota Memorial Health Care System, Sarasota, FL, p. A139

WOEN, Linda, Director Human Resources, Yuma Rehabilitation Hospital, A Partnership Of Encompass Health And Yrmc, Yuma, AZ, p. A38

WOHLFARDT, Diana, Director Human Resources, Nashville General Hospital, Nashville, TN, p. A577

WOHLFORD, Steve, Chief Operating Officer, Johnson Memorial Hospital, Franklin, IN, p. A204

WOHLMAN, John, Manager Information Systems, Shoshone Medical Center, Kellogg, ID, p. A169

WOISKE, Edward, M.D., Chief Medical Officer, Avera Marshall Regional Medical Center, Marshall, MN, p. A334

WOITALEWICZ, Rebecca, Chief Financial Officer, Children's Hospitals And Clinics Of Minnesota, MN, p. A335

WOJNO, Kathy, R.N., MSN
Administrator, Memorial Hospital Of Gardena, Gardena, CA, p. A60
Vice President Nursing Services and Chief Nursing Officer, Beverly Hospital, Montebello, CA, p. A73

WOJTALEWICZ, Jeanette, Chief Financial Officer, Chi Health Mercy Council Bluffs, Council Bluffs, IA, p. A220

WOLAK, Robert, Chief Information Resource Management Service, G.V. (Sonny) Montgomery Veterans Affairs Medical Center, Jackson, MS, p. A348

WOLCOTT, Daniel, President and Chief Executive Officer, Lodi Memorial Hospital West, CA, p. A64

WOLD, Lynn
Chief Operation Officer, Unitypoint Health - St. Lukes's Sioux City, Sioux City, IA, p. A230
President and Chief Executive Officer, Unitypoint Health - St. Lukes's Sioux City, Sioux City, IA, p. A230

WOLESKE, Chris, Chief Operating Officer, Bellin Psychiatric Center, Green Bay, WI, p. A693

WOLF, Brenda J., President and Chief Executive Officer, La Rabida Children's Hospital, Chicago, IL, p. A177

WOLF, Chris, Director Information Technology, Clay County Medical Center, Clay Center, KS, p. A233

WOLF, Gregory A, Director Information Systems, Shriners Hospitals For Children-Honolulu, Honolulu, HI, p. A165

WOLF, Heather, Human Resources Business Partner, Skiff Medical Center, Newton, IA, p. A227

WOLF, Jack, Vice President Information Systems, Montefiore Medical Center - North Division, NY, p. A433

WOLF, Manuela, R.N., President and Chief Executive Officer, Memorial Community Hospital And Health System, Blair, NE, p. A382

WOLF, Marc, Assistant Vice President Human Resources, St. Barnabas Hospital, New York (Includes All Hospitals Located Within The Five Boroughs), NY, p. A437

WOLF, Ned H., Chief Administrative Officer, Marshfield Childen's Hospital, WI, p. A697

WOLF, Randall, Vice President Finance, Perry County Memorial Hospital, Perryville, MO, p. A366

WOLF, Robin, Chief Nursing Officer, Complex Care Hospital At Tenaya, Las Vegas, NV, p. A394

WOLF, Sherry L., M.D., Chief of Medical Staff, Chillicothe Hospital District, Chillicothe, TX, p. A592

WOLF, Stephanne, Chief Nursing Officer, Morris County Hospital, Council Grove, KS, p. A234

WOLF, Tricia, Director Information Technology, Oss Orthopaedic Hospital, York, PA, p. A545

WOLFE, Anita, Chief Nurse Executive, Allenmore Hospital, WA, p. A679

WOLFE, Brian, Chief of Staff, Allen County Regional Hospital, Iola, KS, p. A237

WOLFE, Cathy Allyson, Chief Nursing Officer, Parkview Wabash County Hospital, Wabash, IN, p. A216

WOLFE, Darryl, Chief Financial Officer, Olympic Medical Center, Port Angeles, WA, p. A675

WOLFE, John, Chief Financial Officer, Saint Elizabeth's Medical Center, Wabasha, MN, p. A341

WOLFE, Lisa, President, Chi Health Mercy Corning, Corning, IA, p. A219

WOLFE, Lois, Director Human Resources, Geisinger-Community Medical Center, Scranton, PA, p. A540

WOLFE, Philip R., President and Chief Executive Officer, Gwinnett Medical Center, GA, p. A156

WOLFE, Phillip, Vice President of Professional Operations, Good Samaritan Hospital, Los Angeles, CA, p. A67

WOLFE, Phillip R., Chief Executive Officer, Kindred Hospital-Los Angeles, Los Angeles, CA, p. A68

WOLFE, Scott A., Chief Financial Officer, Piedmont Fayette Hospital, Fayetteville, GA, p. A153

WOLFE, Scott R., CPA, President, St. Luke's Hospital - Warren Campus, Phillipsburg, NJ, p. A410

WOLFE, Sean, Vice President Finance and Chief Financial Officer, Community Hospital, Mccook, NE, p. A386

WOLFE, Stephen A., President and Chief Executive Officer, Indiana Regional Medical Center, Indiana, PA, p. A528

WOLFE, Teresa E, Manager Human Resources, Kansas Heart Hospital, Wichita, KS, p. A247

WOLFENBARGER, Carol C., FACHE, MSN, President, Mcdowell Hospital, Marion, NC, p. A456

WOLFF, David, Director Information Technology, Newberry County Memorial Hospital, Newberry, SC, p. A556

WOLFF, Holly, Chief Executive Officer, Ashley Medical Center, Ashley, ND, p. A464

WOLFF, Patrice P
Director Information Services, Westfields Hospital And Clinic, New Richmond, WI, p. A700
Director Management Information Systems, Amery Hospital And Clinic, Amery, WI, p. A689

WOLFGANG, Tony, Chief Financial Officer, Coatesville Veterans Affairs Medical Center, Coatesville, PA, p. A523

WOLKART, Kristin, R.N., President and Chief Executive Officer, St. Francis Medical Center, Monroe, LA, p. A274

WOLOSZYN, Daniel B., Chief Executive Officer, Rehabilitation Hospital Of Indiana, Indianapolis, IN, p. A207

WOLOWITZ, Julie, Vice President, Imaging, Lab, Spectrum Health - Blodgett Campus, MI, p. A314

WOLTEMATH, Kelli, D.O., Chief Medical Staff, George C Grape Community Hospital, Hamburg, IA, p. A223

WOLTERMAN, Robert K., Chief Executive Officer, Ochsner Medical Center For Children, LA, p. A276

WOLTHER, Eunice, Public Information Officer, Colorado Mental Health Institute At Pueblo, Pueblo, CO, p. A104

WOLTHUIZEN, Dianne, Director Human Resources, Sanford Sheldon Medical Center, Sheldon, IA, p. A229

WOLZ, John, M.D., Chief Medical Staff, Yuma District Hospital, Yuma, CO, p. A106

WOMACK, James, Administrator, Mitchell County Hospital, Camilla, GA, p. A149

WONG, Anne Marie, M.D., Chief Medical Officer, Grays Harbor Community Hospital, Aberdeen, WA, p. A669

WONG, Art, Chief Financial Officer, Heritage Oaks Hospital, Sacramento, CA, p. A81

WONG, Bryan, M.D., Medical Director, Ventura County Medical Center, Ventura, CA, p. A94

WONG, Davies, M.D., Medical Director, Kindred Hospital-San Diego, San Diego, CA, p. A83

WONG, Dionne, Vice President and Chief Human Resources Officer, Chris Evert Childrens Hospital, FL, p. A122

WONG, Karen, Chief Human Resources Officer, Mee Memorial Hospital, King City, CA, p. A62

WONG, Lily, Director Psychiatry, Trinity Springs Pavilion, TX, p. A604

WONG, Philip, PsyD
Chief Executive Officer, Gateways Hospital And Mental Health Center, Los Angeles, CA, p. A67
Chief Operating Officer, Gateways Hospital And Mental Health Center, Los Angeles, CA, p. A67

WONG, Wesley, M.D., Acting Vice President Medical and Academic Affairs, Community Hospital North, Indianapolis, IN, p. A206

WONSER, Matt, Director, Information Services, Providence Everett Medical Center - Pacific Campus, WA, p. A671

WOOD, Aaron C., Chief Executive Officer and Administrator, Sanpete Valley Hospital, Mount Pleasant, UT, p. A648

WOOD, Brian, Director Human Resources, Southern Hills Hospital And Medical Center, Las Vegas, NV, p. A394

WOOD, Bud, Chief Human Resources Officer, Saint Thomas West Hospital, Nashville, TN, p. A577

WOOD, Cathy, Vice President, Human Resources, Memorial Behavioral Health, MS, p. A346

WOOD, Clyde, Chief Executive Officer, Tennova North Knoxville Medical Center, TN, p. A572

WOOD, David P., FACHE, Director, Boise Veterans Affairs Medical Center, Boise, ID, p. A167

WOOD, Drew, Director Information Technology, Eureka Springs Hospital, Eureka Springs-Carroll County, AR, p. A41

WOOD, Gregory C., President and Chief Executive Officer, Scotland Health Care System, Laurinburg, NC, p. A456

WOOD, Jim
Chief Administrative Officer, Confluence Health/Central Washington Hospital, Wenatchee, WA, p. A680
Chief Human Resources Officer, Confluence Health/Wenatchee Valley Hospital, Wenatchee, WA, p. A680

WOOD, Joann, M.D., Chief Medical Officer, Baptist Memorial Hospital-Desoto, Southaven, MS, p. A353

WOOD, Joseph, Vice President and Chief Information Officer, Long Island Community Hospital, Patchogue, NY, p. A440

WOOD, Joyce, Vice President Organizational Improvement and Chief Nursing Officer, Riverview Health, Noblesville, IN, p. A213

WOOD, Kevin, Interim Chief Clinical Officer, Promise Hospital Of San Diego, San Diego, CA, p. A84

WOOD, Lawrence, M.D., Chief Medical Officer, Littleton Adventist Hospital, Littleton, CO, p. A103

WOOD, Lisa, Chief Financial Officer, Brown County Hospital, Ainsworth, NE, p. A381

WOOD, Phillip E., Jr, Chief Information Officer, Cape Fear Valley Rehabilitation Center, NC, p. A452

WOOD, Richard, Chief Financial Officer, Seton Medical Center, Daly City, CA, p. A56

WOOD, Sandy, MSN, R.N., Vice President Patient Services and Chief Nursing Officer, O'Bleness Memorial Hospital, Athens, OH, p. A471

WOOD, Thomas, M.D., Chief Medical Officer, Page Hospital, Page, AZ, p. A32

WOOD, Tina
Chief Operating Officer, Dmc Hutzel Women's Hospital, MI, p. A311
Chief Operations Officer, Dmc - Detroit Receiving Hospital, Detroit, MI, p. A311

WOOD, Troy, Chief Executive Officer, Lakeview Hospital, Bountiful, UT, p. A646

WOOD, William, M.D., Vice President Medical Affairs, St. Joseph Hospital, Bangor, ME, p. A282

WOODALL, Jay, FACHE, Chief Executive Officer, Corpus Christi Medical Center Bay Area, TX, p. A594

WOODALL, Lois, Director Human Resources, Lighthouse Behavioral Health Hospital, Conway, SC, p. A552

WOODARD, James, Chief Nursing Officer, St. Thomas More Hospital, Canon City, CO, p. A97

WOODARD, Victor, Manager Information Technology, Dodge County Hospital, Eastman, GA, p. A153

WOODCOCK, Lisa, Director Human Resources, Gordon Memorial Health Services, Gordon, NE, p. A384

WOODDELL, Mike, Director Information Services, Fairmont Regional Medical Center, Fairmont, WV, p. A683

WOODHOUSE, Janice, Director of Nursing, Missouri River Medical Center, Fort Benton, MT, p. A375

WOODIN, Joseph L., Chief Executive Officer, South Peninsula Hospital, Homer, AK, p. A26

WOODRICH, John T., President and Chief Operating Officer, Bryan Medical Center-West, NE, p. A385

WOODROW, Victoria, Chief Executive Officer, Hamilton Memorial Hospital District, Mcleansboro, IL, p. A189

WOODRUFF, Kathy, R.N., MSN, Chief Nursing Officer, Marshall Medical Center North, Guntersville, AL, p. A19

WOODRUFF, Stephen, M.D., Chief Medical Officer, Nea Baptist Memorial Hospital, Jonesboro-Craighead County, AR, p. A44

WOODS, Bob, Chief Information Officer, Valley Memorial, CA, p. A78

WOODS, Brian, Human Resources Director, Andalusia Health, Andalusia, AL, p. A13

WOODS, Cheryl, Chief Nursing Officer, Ochsner Medical Center - North Shore, Slidell, LA, p. A279

WOODS, Dan, Chief Executive Officer, El Camino Hospital Los Gatos, CA, p. A78

WOODS, Duane L, Jr, Chief Financial Officer, Fisher-Titus Medical Center, Norwalk, OH, p. A488

WOODS, Fred, Chief Financial Officer, The Bridgeway, North Little Rock-Pulaski County, AR, p. A47

WOODS, Jennifer, R.N., MSN, Chief Nursing Officer, Mclaren Northern Michigan, Petoskey, MI, p. A320

WOODS, Josh, Director Information Systems, Camden Clark Medical Center, Parkersburg, WV, p. A685

WOODS, Julia, R.N., MSN, Vice President and Chief Nursing Officer, Saint Luke's South Hospital, Overland Park, KS, p. A243

WOODS, Marc Anthony, Assistant Chief Nurse Executive, Eastern State Hospital, Lexington, KY, p. A254

WOODS, Matthew, Vice President Finance, Winchester Hospital, Winchester, MA, p. A306

WOODS, Rashawn, Vice President Human Resources, Barlow Respiratory Hospital, Los Angeles, CA, p. A66

WOODS, Rebecca, Chief Information Officer, Porter Medical Center, Middlebury, VT, p. A653

WOODS, Regetta, Chief Nursing Officer and Chief Clinical Officer, Promise Hospital Of Miss Lou, Vidalia, LA, p. A280

WOODS, Suzanne
Chief Executive Officer, Medical Center Enterprise, Enterprise, AL, p. A17
Senior Vice President of Nursing, Memorial Hospital Jacksonville, Jacksonville, FL, p. A125

WOODS, Theresa L, MSN, R.N., FACHE, Chief Nursing Officer, Jennings American Legion Hospital, Jennings, LA, p. A269

WOODS, Trina, Administrator, Noland Hospital Anniston, Anniston, AL, p. A13

WOODS, Willard, M.D., Chief Medical Officer, Platte County Memorial Hospital, Wheatland, WY, p. A710

WOODSON, Joshua, Chief Executive Officer, Cedar Crest Hospital And Residential Treatment Center, Belton, TX, p. A589

WOODSON, Leslie, Chief Nursing Officer, Mesa View Regional Hospital, Mesquite, NV, p. A395

WOODSON, Stephen, D.O., Chief of Staff, Haskell County Community Hospital, Stigler, OK, p. A507

WOODWARD, Ashley, Director Financial Services, Valley County Health System, Ord, NE, p. A389

WOODWARD, David E., Executive Director, Devereux Children's Behavioral Health Center, Malvern, PA, p. A530

WOODWARD, James L., President and Chief Executive Officer, St. Mary Medical Center, Langhorne, PA, p. A529

WOODWARD, Martin D, Director Acute Care Services, Larry B. Zieverink, Sr. Alcoholism Treatment Center, Raleigh, NC, p. A459

WOODWARD, Martin D., Director Acute Care Services, Larry B. Zieverink, Sr. Alcoholism Treatment Center, Raleigh, NC, p. A459

WOODWARD, Russell, M.D., Chief Medical Officer, Northeast Methodist Hospital, TX, p. A633

WOODYARD, Nancy, Chief Financial Officer, Neosho Memorial Regional Medical Center, Chanute, KS, p. A233

WOOLDRIDGE, Joseph, Chief Financial Officer, Brownwood Regional Medical Center, Brownwood, TX, p. A590

WOOLLEY, Diane, Vice President Human Resources, Waterbury Hospital, Waterbury, CT, p. A112

WOOLLEY, Jacqueline
Vice President Human Resources, Southern New Hampshire Medical Center, Nashua, NH, p. A400
Vice President Human Resources, St. Joseph Hospital, Nashua, NH, p. A400

WOOLLEY, Russell, Chief Operating Officer, Highline Medical Center, Burien, WA, p. A670

WOOLLEY, Sheila, R.N., M.P.H., Vice President, Patient Care Services, Wentworth-Douglass Hospital, Dover, NH, p. A398

WOOLSTENHULME, Daren, Chief Financial Officer, Salt Lake Behavioral Health, Salt Lake City, UT, p. A650

WOOTEN, Scott
Senior Vice President and Chief Financial Officer, Baptist Medical Center Beaches, Jacksonville Beach, FL, p. A126
Senior Vice President and Chief Financial Officer, Wolfson Children's Hospital, FL, p. A125

WOOTEN, Terrence, Vice President of Operations, Support Services, Mission Hospital Laguna Beach, CA, p. A72

WOOTON, Lore, M.D., Chief of Medical Staff, Weiser Memorial Hospital, Weiser, ID, p. A172

WOOTTON, Aaron, Vice President, Health Information Systems and Chief Information Officer, Henry Ford Allegiance Health, Jackson, MI, p. A316

WORATSCHEK, Alan, System Director of Information Services, Desert Springs Hospital Medical Center, Las Vegas, NV, p. A394

WORD, Jenni, R.N., Chief Nursing Officer, Wallowa Memorial Hospital, Enterprise, OR, p. A512

WORDEKEMPER, Jerry, President and Chief Executive Officer, St. Francis Memorial Hospital, West Point, NE, p. A391

WORDEN, Beth, Director Nursing Services, Mcpherson Hospital, Mcpherson, KS, p. A241

WORDEN, Donza T., M.D., Chief Clinical Officer, Unitypoint Health-Keokuk, Keokuk, IA, p. A225

WORDEN, Kieth Anne, Director Human Resources, Mildred Mitchell-Bateman Hospital, Huntington, WV, p. A684

WORKMAN, Donovan, Director Human Capital Management, Appalachian Behavioral Healthcare, Athens, OH, p. A471

WORKMAN, Jessika M, Chief Nursing Officer, Wesley Rehabilitation Hospital, Wichita, KS, p. A248

WORKMAN, Madison, Chief Operating Officer, Coral Gables Hospital, Coral Gables, FL, p. A120

WORLEY, John C., III, Chief Executive Officer, Cache Valley Hospital, North Logan, UT, p. A648

WORLEY, Stella
Director of Finance, Keefe Memorial Hospital, Cheyenne Wells, CO, p. A97
Interim Chief Executive Officer, Keefe Memorial Hospital, Cheyenne Wells, CO, p. A97

WORMAN, Scott, Chief of Staff, Tri-City Medical Center, Oceanside, CA, p. A76

WORRELL, James W, Chief Financial Officer, Pioneers Medical Center, Meeker, CO, p. A104

WORRICK, Gerald M., President and Chief Executive Officer, Door County Medical Center, Sturgeon Bay, WI, p. A704

WORSLEY, Thomas, Chief Executive Officer, Spearfish Regional Surgery Center, SD, p. A564

WORSOWICZ, Gregory, M.D., Medical Director, Howard A. Rusk Rehabilitation Center, Columbia, MO, p. A358

WORTHAM, Christopher, Chief Executive Officer, Encompass Health Rehabilitation Hospital Midland Odessa, Midland, TX, p. A624

WORTHAM, Turner, Chief Financial Officer, Grand Strand Regional Medical Center, Myrtle Beach, SC, p. A556

WORTHY, David, M.D., Vice President and Chief Medical Officer, Baptist Health Corbin, Corbin, KY, p. A250

WOZNIKAITIS, Linda, Chief Financial Officer, Southwest Connecticut Mental Health System, Bridgeport, CT, p. A107

WRAALSTAD, Kimber L., FACHE, Administrator, North Shore Health, Grand Marais, MN, p. A332

WRAGGE, Jean, Chief Nursing Officer, Limestone Medical Center, Groesbeck, TX, p. A608

WRATCHFORD, R. Austin, Chief Operating Officer, Parkview Regional Hospital, Mexia, TX, p. A624

WRAY, Christine R.
President, Medstar Southern Maryland Hospital Center, Clinton, MD, p. A290
President, Medstar St. Mary's Hospital, Leonardtown, MD, p. A292

WRAY, Dean, Vice President Finance, Southern Ohio Medical Center, Portsmouth, OH, p. A489

WRAY, Thomas, Director Information, Geisinger-Bloomsburg Hospital, Bloomsburg, PA, p. A521

WREN, Jason
Chief Executive Officer, Wise Regional Health System, West Campus Decatur, TX, p. A598
President and Chief Executive Officer, Wise Health Surgical Hospital At Argyle, TX, p. A598
President and Chief Executive Officer, Wise Health Surgical Hospital At Parkway, TX, p. A598
President and Chief Executive Officer, Wise Regional Health System, West Campus Decatur, TX, p. A598

WREN, Mark A, M.D., Medical Director, Encompass Health Rehabilitation Hospital Of Texarkana, Texarkana, TX, p. A639

WREN, Timothy, Chief Financial Officer, Abbeville Area Medical Center, Abbeville, SC, p. A549

WRIGHT, Albert L., Jr, PharmD, President and Chief Executive Officer, West Virginia University Children's Hospital, WV, p. A685

WRIGHT, Ann L, R.N., MSN, Assistant Central Delivery System CNO, Presbyterian Rust Medical Center, NM, p. A416

WRIGHT, April, Human Resources Officer, Collingsworth General Hospital, Wellington, TX, p. A643

WRIGHT, Betsy T., President and Chief Executive Officer, Upmc Chautauqua Wca, Jamestown, NY, p. A428

WRIGHT, Brady, Information Technology Network Administrator, Washington County Hospital, Chatom, AL, p. A16

WRIGHT, Calvin, Chief Information Officer, Hutchinson Regional Medical Center, Hutchinson, KS, p. A237

WRIGHT, Carlene, Chief Financial Officer, Vibra Hospital Of Amarillo, Amarillo, TX, p. A583

WRIGHT, Carol, Chief Nursing Officer, Alliancehealth Madill, Madill, OK, p. A500

WRIGHT, Charles, Chief Financial Officer, Ashe Memorial Hospital, Jefferson, NC, p. A455

WRIGHT, Coleby, Chief Executive Officer, Cross Creek Hospital, Austin, TX, p. A585

WRIGHT, Connie, Vice President Human Resources, Texas Scottish Rite Hospital For Children, Dallas, TX, p. A598

WRIGHT, Creighton, M.D., Vice President Medical Administration, Mercy Health - West Hospital, Cincinnati, OH, p. A475

WRIGHT, Dan, Vice President Human Resources, Children's Mercy Hospital Kansas, Overland Park, KS, p. A243

WRIGHT, Daniel, Director Information Technology, Saint Alphonsus Medical Center - Nampa, Nampa, ID, p. A170

WRIGHT, Debra J., R.N., Chief Executive Officer, Howard Memorial Hospital, Nashville-Howard County, AR, p. A46

WRIGHT, Dustin, Vice President of Operations, Unitypoint Health - Marshalltown, Marshalltown, IA, p. A226

WRIGHT, Fran, Director of Nursing, Broadwater Health Center, Townsend, MT, p. A379

WRIGHT, James, M.D., Chief Financial Officer, Cypress Fairbanks Medical Center, Houston, TX, p. A610

WRIGHT, Jennifer
Vice President Human Resources, Christus St. Michael Rehabilitation Hospital, Texarkana, TX, p. A639
Vice President Regional Human Resources, Christus St. Michael Hospital-Atlanta, TX, p. A639

WRIGHT, Joe, Chief Financial Officer, Mitchell County Hospital, Colorado City, TX, p. A593

WRIGHT, Jordan, Chief Executive Officer, St. Elizabeth Community Hospital, Red Bluff, CA, p. A79

WRIGHT, Julie M, Director Human Resources, Ridgeview Psychiatric Hospital And Center, Oak Ridge, TN, p. A578

WRIGHT, Krista, Director Human Resources, Indiana University Health Frankfort, Frankfort, IN, p. A204

WRIGHT, Linda
Chief Financial Officer, Healthsouth Rehabilitation Hospital Of Alexandria, Alexandria, LA, p. A262
Director Information, Ottawa County Health Center, Minneapolis, KS, p. A241

WRIGHT, Mark
Chief Financial Officer, Aultman Specialty Hospital, Canton, OH, p. A473
Vice President, Aultman Hospital Pediatric Services, OH, p. A473

WRIGHT, Mark J., Chief Financial Officer, Aurelia Osborn Fox Memorial Hospital, Oneonta, NY, p. A439

WRIGHT, Mary, Vice President Nursing Services and Chief Nursing Officer, Cortland Regional Medical Center, Cortland, NY, p. A425

WRIGHT, Mary Lynne, R.N., President, Madison Hospital, AL, p. A19

WRIGHT, Maura, Chief Nursing Officer, Southern Hills Hospital And Medical Center, Las Vegas, NV, p. A394

WRIGHT, Nancy, M.D., Chief Medical Staff, Alta Vista Regional Hospital, Las Vegas, NM, p. A418

WRIGHT, Peter J., FACHE, Chief Executive Officer, Valley Regional Hospital, Claremont, NH, p. A398

WRIGHT, Phillip L., FACHE, Chief Executive Officer, Select Specialty Hospital Hampton Roads, Newport News, VA, p. A662

WRIGHT, Philoron A., FACHE, II, Chief Operating Officer, Florida Hospital Ocala, Ocala, FL, p. A133

WRIGHT, Robert
Senior Human Resource Advisor, East Ohio Regional Hospital, Martins Ferry, OH, p. A486
Senior Human Resource Advisor, Ohio Valley Medical Center, Wheeling, WV, p. A688

WRIGHT, Robert N., Chief Executive Officer, Newman Regional Health, Emporia, KS, p. A234

WRIGHT, Rory, M.D., President Medical Staff, Orthopaedic Hospital Of Wisconsin - Glendale, Glendale, WI, p. A693

WRIGHT, Sharon, R.N., Vice President and Chief Nursing Officer, Hardin Memorial Health, Elizabethtown, KY, p. A251

WRIGHT, Stephanie, Director Human Resources Management, Va San Diego Healthcare System, San Diego, CA, p. A84

WRIGHT, Stuart M, CPA, Chief Financial Officer, Upstate University Hospital At Community General, NY, p. A444

WRIGHT, Terri, Vice President and Chief Nursing Officer, Warren Memorial Hospital, Front Royal, VA, p. A658

WRIGHT, Tom, Director Human Resources, Kindred Hospital Riverside, Perris, CA, p. A78

WRIGHT, Trevor
Chief Operating Officer, Loma Linda University Children's Hospital, Loma Linda, CA, p. A64
Chief Operating Officer, Loma Linda University Heart & Surgical Hospital, CA, p. A64

WRIGHT-WHITAKER, Ruth, Director Information Services, Chi Memorial Hospital - Georgia, Fort Oglethorpe, GA, p. A154

WRINN, Denise, Vice President Finance and Chief Financial Officer, Cortland Regional Medical Center, Cortland, NY, p. A425

WROBBEL, Patricia A., Senior Vice President and Chief Nurse Executive, Midhudson Regional Hospital Of Westchester Medical Center, NY, p. A445

WROBLEWSKI, Edmund, M.D.
Vice President Medical Affairs and Chief Medical Officer, Cottage Rehabilitation Hospital, CA, p. A88
Vice President Medical Affairs and Chief Medical Officer, Goleta Valley Cottage Hospital, Santa Barbara, CA, p. A88
Vice President Medical Affairs and Chief Medical Officer, Santa Ynez Valley Cottage Hospital, Solvang, CA, p. A90

WROGG, Frank, Director Information Technology, Mayo Clinic Health System - Red Cedar In Menomonie, Menomonie, WI, p. A697

WU, Kenneth, M.D., Medical Director, Kessler Marlton Rehabilitation, Marlton, NJ, p. A407

WUCHTER, Greg, R.N., MSN, Chief Executive Officer, Select Specialty Hospital-Savannah, Savannah, GA, p. A160

WUENSCHEL, Diedra, D.O., President Medical Staff, Coryell Memorial Hospital, Gatesville, TX, p. A607

WUNDERWALD, Wendie, R.N., Vice President Patient Care Services, Samaritan Lebanon Community Hospital, Lebanon, OR, p. A514

WURGLER, Brad D, Chief Financial Officer, Perham Health, Perham, MN, p. A337

WURTZEL, Leann, Director Human Resources, Mayo Clinic Health System - Red Cedar In Menomonie, Menomonie, WI, p. A697

WYATT, Christy, R.N., Interim Chief Nursing Officer, Jackson Parish Hospital, Jonesboro, LA, p. A269

WYATT, Jana, Chief Executive Officer, Mizell Memorial Hospital, Opp, AL, p. A22

WYBLE, Karen O., R.N., Chief Executive Officer, St. Martin Hospital, Breaux Bridge, LA, p. A265

WYDICK, Sue, Director Human Resources, Ohio County Hospital, Hartford, KY, p. A253

WYDRA, Lana, Vice President Human Resources, Nathan Littauer Hospital And Nursing Home, Gloversville, NY, p. A427

WYER, Jolena, R.N., Chief Nursing Officer, Oklahoma Center For Orthopedic And Multi-Specialty Surgery, Oklahoma City, OK, p. A504

WYERS, Michael, Chief Financial Officer, Medical Center Of Trinity, Trinity, FL, p. A142

WYLER, Allyson, Vice President, Operations, Advocate Lutheran General Hospital, Park Ridge, IL, p. A192

WYLIE, Eugene, Chief Human Resources Officer, Veterans Affairs Loma Linda Healthcare System, Loma Linda, CA, p. A64

WYLIE, Patrick, Director Information Systems, Petaluma Valley Hospital, Petaluma, CA, p. A78

WYMAN, Alan, Chief Information Officer, Providence Hospital, Washington, DC, p. A116

WYMAN, David, President and Chief Executive Officer, Gracie Square Hospital, New York (Includes All Hospitals Located Within The Five Boroughs), NY, p. A432

WYMER, Melanie, Director Human Resources, Highland District Hospital, Hillsboro, OH, p. A484

WYNN, Katherine, Director Human Resource, Oklahoma Heart Hospital, Oklahoma City, OK, p. A504

WYNN, Paige
Administrator, Irwin County Hospital, Ocilla, GA, p. A158
Chief Financial Officer, Dorminy Medical Center, Fitzgerald, GA, p. A153

WYNNE, Scott, Chief Information Officer Director, Bleckley Memorial Hospital, Cochran, GA, p. A150

WYPYSKI, Jeanne, Chief Executive Officer, Shadow Mountain Behavioral Health System, Tulsa, OK, p. A509

WYSE, Debbie, Controller, Quillen Rehabilitation Hospital, Johnson City, TN, p. A572

WYSOCKI, Greg, Chief Financial Officer, Austin Lakes Hospital, Austin, TX, p. A585

WYSONG-HARDER, Alyson, Chief Executive Officer, Heartland Behavioral Health Services, Nevada, MO, p. A365

Y

YABUT, Eduardo, M.D., Medical Director, North Dakota State Hospital, Jamestown, ND, p. A467

YAEGER, Eric, M.D.
Chief Medical Officer, Kindred Hospital-Aurora, Aurora, CO, p. A96
Medical Director, Kindred Hospital-Denver, Denver, CO, p. A99

YAHNER, Michael, Chief Financial Officer, Torrance State Hospital, Torrance, PA, p. A542

YAKE, Laurie B., Vice President Finance, Aurora Medical Center Kenosha, Kenosha, WI, p. A695

YAKLIN, Shelleye, President and Chief Executive Officer, North Ottawa Community Hospital, Grand Haven, MI, p. A313

YAKOVENKO, Gene, Director of Finance, Presence Holy Family Medical Center, Des Plaines, IL, p. A181

YAKULIS, Paul, MS, R.N., Senior Vice President Human Resources, Lankenau Medical Center, Wynnewood, PA, p. A545

YALLOWITZ, Joseph, M.D., Vice President and Chief Medical Officer, Valley Hospital, Ridgewood, NJ, p. A411

YAMADA, Jeff, Vice President, Virginia Mason Memorial, Yakima, WA, p. A680

YANCY, Daniel, Chief Executive Officer, Riceland Medical Center, Winnie, TX, p. A644

YANES, John C., Chief Executive Officer, Andalusia Health, Andalusia, AL, p. A13

YANEZ, Maria J, Chief Financial Officer, Baptist Health South Florida, Doctors Hospital, Coral Gables, FL, p. A120

YANGA, Ismael David, M.D., Chief Medical Officer, Brighton Center For Recovery, Brighton, MI, p. A308

YANIK, Sahin, M.D.
Vice President Medical Administration, St. John's Regional Medical Center, Oxnard, CA, p. A77
Vice President Medical Associate, St. John's Pleasant Valley Hospital, Camarillo, CA, p. A53

YANKTON, Nikki, Director Human Resources, Oakleaf Surgical Hospital, Altoona, WI, p. A689

YANNI, Anthony, M.D., Vice President Medical Affairs, Regional Hospital Of Scranton, Scranton, PA, p. A540

YAP, Elvy, Director of Finance, Rush Oak Park Hospital, Oak Park, IL, p. A191

YAP, Eric, Chief Executive Officer, Ohiohealth Rehabilitation Hospital, Columbus, OH, p. A478

YAP, Winston, M.D., Chief Medical Officer, Carroll County Memorial Hospital, Carrollton, KY, p. A250

YARBOROUGH, Dianne, Director of Information Technology, Baylor Scott & White Medical Center - Centennial, Frisco, TX, p. A606

YARBROUGH, Michelle, Coordinator Human Resources, Allegiance Specialty Hospital Of Kilgore, Kilgore, TX, p. A617

YARBROUGH, Ruth, Vice President, Mercyhealth Hospital - Rockton Avenue, Rockford, IL, p. A194

YARLING, John, M.D., Medical Director, Four County Counseling Center, Logansport, IN, p. A210

YARMEL, Jeffrey N, Chief Operating Officer, St. Mary Medical Center, Langhorne, PA, p. A529

YARN, Jayce, Director Information Technology, Marias Medical Center, Shelby, MT, p. A379

YAROCH, Julie, D.O.
President, Promedica Bixby Hospital, Adrian, MI, p. A307
President, Promedica Herrick Hospital, Tecumseh, MI, p. A324

YARRISH, Barbara, R.N., President, Wellspan Surgery And Rehabilitation Hospital, York, PA, p. A546

YATES, Ann C, R.N., MSN, Chief Nursing Officer, St. Vincent Mercy Hospital, Elwood, IN, p. A203

YATES, Ann C., R.N., MSN, Administrator and Chief Nursing Officer, St. Vincent Mercy Hospital, Elwood, IN, p. A203

YATES, Brent, Chief Executive Officer, Encompass Health Rehabilitation Hospital Of Richardson, Richardson, TX, p. A630

YATES, Jackie, R.N., Nurse Executive, Whitfield Medical Surgical Hospital, MS, p. A354

YATES, Jeremy, Chief Executive Officer, Healthsouth Northern Kentucky Rehabilitation Hospital, Edgewood, KY, p. A251

YATES, Katie, Chief Financial Officer, South Sunflower County Hospital, Indianola, MS, p. A347

YATES, Ralph, D.O.
Chief Medical Officer, Salem Health Rehabilitation Center, OR, p. A517
Chief Medical Officer, Salem Health West Valley, Dallas, OR, p. A512

YATES, Randy, M.D., Chief Medical Officer, Straub Medical Center, Honolulu, HI, p. A165

YATSATTIE, Clyde, Administrative Officer, U.S. Public Health Service Indian Hospital, Zuni, NM, p. A420

YAWORSKY, Jason
Chief Information Officer, Bradford Regional Medical Center, Bradford, PA, p. A521
Senior Vice President Information Systems and Chief Information Officer, Olean General Hospital, Olean, NY, p. A439

YAZAWA, Albert, M.D., Regional Medical Director, Leahi Hospital, Honolulu, HI, p. A164

YBARRA, Farra, R.N., Chief Nursing Officer, Coal County General Hospital, Coalgate, OK, p. A497

YEAGER, Angela, Director Information Technology, Palacios Community Medical Center, Palacios, TX, p. A626

YEAGER, Dianne, Chief Executive Officer, Crane Memorial Hospital, Crane, TX, p. A595

YEAGER, Kerry, Director Information Technology, Berwick Hospital Center, Berwick, PA, p. A520

YEAGER, Kevin, Vice President Fiscal Services, Holzer Medical Center - Jackson, Jackson, OH, p. A484

YEARY, John M., FACHE, Chief Executive Officer, Freestone Medical Center, Fairfield, TX, p. A603

YEATES, Alan H, Vice President Fiscal Services, Wyandot Memorial Hospital, Upper Sandusky, OH, p. A492

YEATES, Diane, Chief Operating Officer, Terrebonne General Medical Center, Houma, LA, p. A269

YEATS, Melania, M.D., Chief Medical Officer, San Juan Regional Medical Center Rehabilitation Hospital, NM, p. A417

YEE, Martin, M.D., Medical Director, Emcompass Health Rehabilitation Hospital Of East, Mesa, AZ, p. A31

YEH, Ada
Chief Executive Officer, Chapman Global Medical Center, Orange, CA, p. A76
Chief Executive Officer, South Coast Global Medical Center, Santa Ana, CA, p. A88
Chief Operating Officer and Chief Nursing Officer, Chapman Global Medical Center, Orange, CA, p. A76

YEHL, Warren
Chief Operating Officer, Mountainview Regional Medical Center, Las Cruces, NM, p. A418
Interim Chief Executive Officer, Eastern New Mexico Medical Center, Roswell, NM, p. A419

YEHLEN, Lorraine, R.N., Vice President Patient Care Services, Northport Medical Center, AL, p. A24

YELENICK, Lori, Chief Financial Officer, Iroquois Memorial Hospital And Resident Home, Watseka, IL, p. A197

YELKEN, Kari, R.N., Director of Nursing, Franklin County Memorial Hospital, Franklin, NE, p. A383

YELVINGTON, Fleury, Administrator, Shriners Hospitals For Children-Tampa, Tampa, FL, p. A141

YETMAN, Robert, M.D., Medical Director, Healthbridge Children's Hospital Of Houston, Houston, TX, p. A611

YETTER, Tad A., M.D., President Medical Staff, Mason District Hospital, Havana, IL, p. A185

YEUNG, Christopher A., M.D., Chief of Staff, The Core Institute Specialty Hospital, Phoenix, AZ, p. A34

YHLEN, David, Chief Operating Officer, Inspira Medical Center-Elmer, Elmer, NJ, p. A404

YI, Brenda, Director Medical Resource Management and Chief Financial Officer, U.S. Air Force Medical Center Keesler, Keesler Afb, MS, p. A348

YIM, Janet, Director Information Services, St. Mary Mercy Hospital, Livonia, MI, p. A318

YIN, Khin, Medical Director, Rehabilitation Hospital Of Rhode Island, North Smithfield, RI, p. A547

YINGLING, Barbara, R.N., Vice President Patient Care Services and Chief Nursing Officer, Mercy Medical Center, Canton, OH, p. A473

YITTA, Prasad, M.D., Medical Director, River Hospital, Alexandria Bay, NY, p. A421

YOCHELSON, Michael R, M.D., Vice President and Medical Director, Medstar National Rehabilitation Hospital, Washington, DC, p. A115

YOCHUM, Richard E., FACHE, President and Chief Executive Officer, Pomona Valley Hospital Medical Center, Pomona, CA, p. A79

YODER, Cathy, Chief Financial Officer, St. Joseph's Women's Hospital, FL, p. A141

YODER, Lamont M., R.N., MSN, FACHE
Chief Executive Officer, Banner Baywood Medical Center, Mesa, AZ, p. A31
Chief Executive Officer, Banner Gateway Medical Center, Gilbert, AZ, p. A29
Chief Executive Officer, Banner Heart Hospital, Mesa, AZ, p. A31

YODER, Leslie, Executive Director, Finance, Community Hospital South, Indianapolis, IN, p. A206

YOE, Adam, Chief Executive Officer, Healthsouth Rehabilitation Hospital Memphis-North, Memphis, TN, p. A575

YOGEL, Louis, M.D., Chief of Staff, Chris Evert Childrens Hospital, FL, p. A122

YOO, George, M.D., Chief Medical Officer, Karmanos Cancer Center, Detroit, MI, p. A311

YOON, Chris, M.D., Medical Director, Healthsouth Bakersfield Rehabilitation Hospital, Bakersfield, CA, p. A52

YORK, Christopher, FACHE
President, Baylor Regional Medical Center At Grapevine, Grapevine, TX, p. A607
President, Baylor Scott & White Medical Center At Waxahachie, Waxahachie, TX, p. A642

YORK, Don, Vice President and Chief Human Resource Officer, Sky Lakes Medical Center, Klamath Falls, OR, p. A514

YORK, Linda, Director Human Resource, Memorial Hospital Of Converse County, Douglas, WY, p. A708

YORK, Russell W, Vice President and Chief Financial Officer, Select Specialty Hospital - Belhaven, Jackson, MS, p. A348

YOSHII, Brian, Vice President Information Technology and Chief Information Officer, Queen's Medical Center - West Oahu, HI, p. A165

YOUNADAM, Sandro, M.D., Chief Medical Officer, Ottumwa Regional Health Center, Ottumwa, IA, p. A228

YOUNG, Aaron, Chief Information Officer, Summit Healthcare Regional Medical Center, Show Low, AZ, p. A36

YOUNG, Abby, Chief Nursing Officer, Iowa Specialty Hospital-Clarion, Clarion, IA, p. A219

YOUNG, Angela, Human Resources Officer, Chillicothe Veterans Affairs Medical Center, Chillicothe, OH, p. A474

YOUNG, Anita, Chief Operating Officer, Florida Hospital Waterman, Tavares, FL, p. A142

YOUNG, Ann, Interim President, Mercy Medical Center-Centerville, Centerville, IA, p. A218

YOUNG, Anthony, Information Services Specialist, Chester Mental Health Center, Chester, IL, p. A176

YOUNG, Anthony R., Chief Executive Officer, Eastar Health System, East Campus, OK, p. A502

YOUNG, Barry, Director Human Resources, Western Mental Health Institute, Bolivar, TN, p. A566

YOUNG, Bev, Director Human Resources, Frankfort Regional Medical Center, Frankfort, KY, p. A252

YOUNG, Bryce A
Chief Operating Officer, Hays Medical Center, Hays, KS, p. A236
Chief Operating Officer, Pawnee Valley Community Hospital, Larned, KS, p. A239

YOUNG, C. Ray, M.D., Chief Medical Officer, Bourbon Community Hospital, Paris, KY, p. A259

YOUNG, Chris, Chief Executive Officer, Allegiance Health Center Of Ruston, LA, p. A280

YOUNG, Christine, MSN, R.N., Vice President of Patient Services and Chief Nursing Officer, Akron Children's Hospital, Akron, OH, p. A470

YOUNG, David, Senior Vice President Planning and Technology, Trousdale Medical Center, Hartsville, TN, p. A570

YOUNG, Debra, R.N., MSN, Vice President, Patient Services and Chief Nursing Officer, Up Health System-Portage, Hancock, MI, p. A315

YOUNG, Eric, M.D.
Chief of Staff, Veterans Affairs Ann Arbor Healthcare System, Ann Arbor, MI, p. A307
Director Information Technology and Systems, South Bay Hospital, Sun City Center, FL, p. A140

YOUNG, Eric L
Chief Financial Officer, Selby General Hospital, Marietta, OH, p. A486
Vice President Finance and Chief Financial Officer, Marietta Memorial Hospital, Marietta, OH, p. A485

YOUNG, Gladys, M.D., Chief of Staff, Liberty Medical Center, Chester, MT, p. A374

YOUNG, J Phillip, FACHE, Chief Executive Officer, Northeast Baptist Hospital, TX, p. A632

YOUNG, James, M.D., Chief of Staff, Mcgehee Hospital, Mcgehee-Desha County, AR, p. A46

YOUNG, Jeffrey, Chief Human Resource Officer, San Antonio Division, TX, p. A634

YOUNG, Jeffrey D, Chief Information Officer, Children's Hospitals And Clinics Of Minnesota, MN, p. A335

YOUNG, Jeremie, M.D., Chief of Staff, Regional General Hospital, Williston, FL, p. A144

YOUNG, John E., Interim Chief Executive Officer, Columbus Regional Healthcare System, Whiteville, NC, p. A462

YOUNG, Joyce, Ph.D., R.N.
Vice President, Patient Services and Chief Nursing Officer, St. Joseph Mercy Ann Arbor, Ypsilanti, MI, p. A326
Vice President, Patient Services and Chief Nursing Officer, St. Joseph Mercy Livingston Hospital, Howell, MI, p. A315

YOUNG, Kevin, FACHE, President, Adventist Behavioral Health And Wellness Services, Rockville, MD, p. A293

YOUNG, Lisa, CPA
Chief Financial Officer, Carolinas Continuecare Hospital At Kings Mountain, Kings Mountain, NC, p. A455
Chief Financial Officer, Continuecare Hospital At Baptist Health Corbin, Corbin, KY, p. A250
Chief Financial Officer, Continuecare Hospital At Hendrick Medical Center, Abilene, TX, p. A582

YOUNG, Martha, Director Human Resources, Cumberland County Hospital, Burkesville, KY, p. A250

YOUNG, Mary, Director Human Resources, Colorado Mental Health Institute At Pueblo, Pueblo, CO, p. A104

YOUNG, Mary C., Chief Executive Officer, Moccasin Bend Mental Health Institute, Chattanooga, TN, p. A567

YOUNG, Mary Lou, Chief Nursing Officer, Continuecare Hospital At Baptist Health Paducah, Paducah, KY, p. A259

YOUNG, Michael, Chief Financial Officer, Mad River Community Hospital, Arcata, CA, p. A51

YOUNG, Pam, Director Human Resources, Davis County Hospital, Bloomfield, IA, p. A218

YOUNG, Patty, R.N., Chief Nursing Officer, Ashland Health Center, Ashland, KS, p. A232

YOUNG, Rhonda, Human Resource Director, Encompass Health Rehabilitation Hospital Of Gadsden, Gadsden, AL, p. A18

YOUNG, Richard T., FACHE, Director, Walter P. Reuther Psychiatric Hospital, Westland, MI, p. A326

YOUNG, Roberta, Vice President Nursing, Sanford South University, ND, p. A466

YOUNG, Sabrina
Administrative Support Director, South Mississippi State Hospital, Purvis, MS, p. A352
Director, South Mississippi State Hospital, Purvis, MS, p. A352

YOUNG, Shalen, Chief Financial Officer, Arizona Orthopedic Surgical Hospital, Chandler, AZ, p. A28

YOUNG, Sheila, Vice President Human Resources, Rotary Rehabilitation Hospital, AL, p. A20

YOUNG, Stephanie, Associate Director, Aleda E. Lutz Veterans Affairs Medical Center, Saginaw, MI, p. A322

YOUNG, Steve, Chief Operating Officer, Oak Hill Hospital, Brooksville, FL, p. A119

YOUNG, Terry, Chief Information Officer, Plains Memorial Hospital, Dimmitt, TX, p. A600

YOUNG, Theresa M, Senior Vice President Human Resources, Nemours Children's Hospital, Orlando, FL, p. A134

YOUNG, William, Chief Information Officer, Hillcrest Hospital, MA, p. A303

YOUNG, William A., Jr, President and Chief Executive Officer, Southwest General Health Center, Middleburg Heights, OH, p. A487

YOUNGBLOOD, Carrie, Director of Human Resources, Kittitas Valley Healthcare, Ellensburg, WA, p. A671

YOUNGBLOOD, Erin R, Chief Human Resources Officer, Behavioral Center Of Michigan, Warren, MI, p. A325

YOUNGMAN, Darrell, D.O., Chief Medical Officer, St. Joseph Campus, KS, p. A248

YOUNGS, Patsy, President, Texas Health Presbyterian Hospital Kaufman, Kaufman, TX, p. A617

YOUREE, Ben, Chief Executive Officer, Tennova Turkey Creek Medical Center, TN, p. A572

YOURTEE, Edward, M.D., Chief Medical Officer, Parkland Medical Center, Derry, NH, p. A398

YOURZEK, Tari, Chief Nursing Officer, Boundary Community Hospital, Bonners Ferry, ID, p. A168

YOUSAITIS, Zoe, Director Human Resources, Eagleville Hospital, Eagleville, PA, p. A524

YOUSSEF, Moudy, M.D., Chief Medical Officer, Fairchild Medical Center, Yreka, CA, p. A95

YOUSUF, Faraaz, President and Chief Operating Officer, Northwest Hospital, Randallstown, MD, p. A293

YU, Henry
Vice President Finance and Chief Financial Officer, California Pacific Medical Center-St. Luke's Campus, San Francisco, CA, p. A85
Vice President Finance and Chief Financial Officer, California Pacific Medical Center, San Francisco, CA, p. A85

YUHAS, Joel P., FACHE, President and Chief Executive Officer, Uchealth Memorial Hospital North, CO, p. A98

YUHAS, John, D.O., Medical Director, Elmwood Healthcare Center At The Springs, Green Springs, OH, p. A483

YUNGMANN, Michael, President and Chief Executive Officer, Lourdes Hospital, Paducah, KY, p. A259

YUNUSOV, Ed
Chief Information Officer, Creedmoor Psychiatric Center, New York (Includes All Hospitals Located Within The Five Boroughs), NY, p. A432
Coordinator Facility Information Center, Brooklyn Children's Hospital Psychiatric Center, NY, p. A434

YUST, Randall C
Chief Financial Officer NCR, Indiana University Health Tipton Hospital, Tipton, IN, p. A215
Chief Operating Officer and Chief Financial Officer, Indiana University Health North Hospital, Carmel, IN, p. A201

YUST, Randall C., Interim President, Indiana University Health North Hospital, Carmel, IN, p. A201

Z

ZAAS, David William., M.D., Chief Executive Officer, Duke Raleigh Hospital, Raleigh, NC, p. A459

ZABAWSKI, Denise, Vice President Information Services and Chief Information Officer, Nationwide Children's Hospital, Columbus, OH, p. A478

ZABEL, Sarah, Vice President, Operations, Swedish/Edmonds, Edmonds, WA, p. A671

ZABIELSKI, Gerald C, M.D., Chief Medical Staff, Wright Memorial Hospital, Trenton, MO, p. A371

ZACHARIASEN, Keith, Chief Financial Officer, Wamego Health Center, Wamego, KS, p. A247

ZACHARY, Kevin, Chief Executive Officer, Logan Regional Medical Center, Logan, WV, p. A684

ZACHRY, Jan, R.N., Vice President Administrator and Chief Operations Executive, Scripps Memorial Hospital-Encinitas, Encinitas, CA, p. A57

ZACIEWSKI, Gary, Chief Executive Officer, Regency Hospital Of Toledo, Sylvania, OH, p. A491

ZAFEREO, Carolyn, Chief Accounting Officer, Citizens Medical Center, Victoria, TX, p. A642

ZAFONTE, Ross, D.O., Chief, Physical Medicine and Rehabilitation and Vice President Medical Affairs, Research and Education, Spaulding Rehabilitation Hospital, Charlestown, MA, p. A299

ZAGERMAN, Robert, Chief Financial Officer, Brooke Glen Behavioral Hospital, Fort Washington, PA, p. A526

ZAHN, Chip, Chief Operating Officer, Medical City Las Colinas, Irving, TX, p. A615

ZAID, Ahmad, Chief Executive Officer, Atrium Medical Center, Stafford, TX, p. A636

ZAIDI, Syed A., M.D., Chief of Staff, Lauderdale Community Hospital, Ripley, TN, p. A579

ZAJEC, Doris A., Director Human Resources, South Pointe Hospital, Warrensville Heights, OH, p. A492

ZAJIC, Holly, Chief Operating Officer, Ivinson Memorial Hospital, Laramie, WY, p. A708

ZAJICEK, Tammy, Director of Nursing, Jackson County Hospital District, Edna, TX, p. A601

ZAKAI, Aminadav, M.D., Medical Director, Arbour-Fuller Hospital, Attleboro, MA, p. A295

ZAKHARY, M. George, M.D., Chief of Staff, Jackson County Memorial Hospital, Altus, OK, p. A495

ZALDIVAR, Rogelio, M.D., Medical Director, Southern Winds Hospital, FL, p. A131

ZALESKI, Theodore, M.D., Vice President Clinical Effectiveness, Hackensack Meridian Health Southern Ocean Medical Center, Manahawkin, NJ, p. A407

ZALUD, Nicolette, Customer Site Manager, Mclaren Central Michigan, Mount Pleasant, MI, p. A319

ZALUSKI, Heather, M.D., President Medical Staff, Shodair Children's Hospital, Helena, MT, p. A376

ZAMBITO, John, M.D., Chief of Staff, Astria Regional Medical Center, Yakima, WA, p. A680

ZAMBRANA, David, Ph.D., R.N., Senior Vice President and Chief Executive Officer, Jackson Memorial Hospital, FL, p. A130

ZAMBRELLO, Sally, Chief Information Officer, Carondelet St. Joseph's Hospital, Tucson, AZ, p. A37

ZAMORA DE AGUERO, Hilde, Human Resources Site Director, Baptist Health South Florida, West Kendall Baptist Hospital, Miami, FL, p. A130

ZAMPINI, Maria, Chief Operating Officer, University Medical Center Of El Paso, El Paso, TX, p. A603

ZANE, Kristi, Chief Human Resources Officer, Crawford Memorial Hospital, Robinson, IL, p. A194

ZANI, Carl, Chief Technology Director, Memorial Health, Marysville, OH, p. A486

ZANIS, Tina, Director Information Systems, Lehigh Valley Hospital - Schuylkill, Pottsville, PA, p. A539

ZANNI, David M., Administrator, Adena Pike Medical Center, Waverly, OH, p. A493

ZANT, Dan, M.D., Chief of Staff, Morgan Memorial Hospital, Madison, GA, p. A157

ZARAK, Tamie, Director Human Resources, Memorial Medical Center - Neillsville, Neillsville, WI, p. A699

ZARECKY, Dan, Chief Executive Officer, Peak View Behavioral Health, Colorado Springs, CO, p. A97

ZAREMA, Claudette A., M.D., Medical Officer, Alaska Psychiatric Institute, Anchorage, AK, p. A25

ZAREN, Douglas, FACHE, Administrator and CEO, Memorial Regional Hospital South, FL, p. A124

ZASTOUPIL, Rockford, Administrator, Mountrail County Medical Center, Stanley, ND, p. A468

ZAUNER, Janiece, R.N.
Chief Nursing Officer, Providence Seaside Hospital, Seaside, OR, p. A518
Chief Operating Officer, Providence Seaside Hospital, Seaside, OR, p. A518

ZAUNER, Mike, Chief Executive Officer, Sierra Vista Hospital, Sacramento, CA, p. A82

ZAVATCHEN, Nancy, Director Information Technology, Cullman Regional Medical Center, Cullman, AL, p. A16

ZAVODNICK, Jacquelyn, M.D., Medical Director, Devereux Children's Behavioral Health Center, Malvern, PA, p. A530

ZAWACKI, Brenda, Chief Operating Manager, Providence Kodiak Island Medical Center, Kodiak, AK, p. A26

ZDEBLICK, Mick, Chief Executive Officer, Asante Rogue Regional Medical Center, Medford, OR, p. A515

ZDRODOWSKI, Michael, Vice President of Operations and Ambulatory Services, Munson Healthcare Cadillac Hospital, Cadillac, MI, p. A309

ZECHMAN, David M., FACHE, President and Chief Executive Officer, Mclaren Northern Michigan, Petoskey, MI, p. A320

ZEDNICEK, Allison, Chief Executive Officer, West Hills Hospital, Reno, NV, p. A396

ZEHM, Laura, Vice President and Chief Financial Officer, Community Hospital Of The Monterey Peninsula, Monterey, CA, p. A73

ZEHNER, Douglas A, Chief Financial Officer, Children's Hospital Of New Jersey, NJ, p. A408

ZEIGLER, Michele
Vice President and Chief Information Officer, Chambersburg Hospital, Chambersburg, PA, p. A522
Vice President Information Services, Waynesboro Hospital, Waynesboro, PA, p. A543

ZEISEL, Henry
Chief Financial Officer, Northern Region, Amita Health Rehabilitation Hospital, IL, p. A182
Chief Financial Officer, Northern Region, Amita Health Women & Children's Hospital, IL, p. A186

ZEITLER, Irvin, D.O., Vice President Medical Affairs, Shannon Medical Center- St. John's Campus, TX, p. A632

ZEITLER, Jenny, Network Administrator, North Okaloosa Medical Center, Crestview, FL, p. A120

ZELENKA, Anthony, President and Chief Operating Officer, Berkeley Medical Center, Martinsburg, WV, p. A684

ZELIN, Mira, D.O., Medical Director, Healthsouth Rehabilitation Hospital Of Spring Hill, Brooksville, FL, p. A119

ZELL, John R, Chief Financial Officer, Osf St. Joseph Medical Center, Bloomington, IL, p. A174

ZELLER, Brad, Vice President Operations, Hayward Area Memorial Hospital And Water's Edge, Hayward, WI, p. A694

ZELLER, Paul, Vice President Human Resources, Medstar Southern Maryland Hospital Center, Clinton, MD, p. A290

ZELLER, Sonya M., R.N., Vice President, Chief Operating Officer and Chief Nursing Officer, Indiana University Health Paoli Hospital, Paoli, IN, p. A213

ZEMAN, Brian, Chief Human Resources, Salem Veterans Affairs Medical Center, Salem, VA, p. A666

ZENDER, Dale, President Hospital Services NW, Peacehealth St. Joseph Medical Center, Bellingham, WA, p. A669

ZENGOTITA, Jamie, M.D., Chief Medical Staff, Mercy Hospital Cassville, Cassville, MO, p. A357

ZENN, Michael B., Chief Executive Officer, University Of Illinois Hospital & Health Sciences System, Chicago, IL, p. A180

ZENNA, Rita, R.N., Vice President Patient Care Services, Deborah Heart And Lung Center, Browns Mills, NJ, p. A403

ZENONE, Michael J, Chief Financial Officer, Emerald Coast Behavioral Hospital, Panama City, FL, p. A135

ZEPHIER, Michelle, Human Resource Specialist, U.S. Public Health Service Indian Hospital, Rosebud, SD, p. A563

ZEPS, Joseph, Vice President Finance, Tomah Memorial Hospital, Tomah, WI, p. A704

ZERINGUE, Rhonda, R.N., Chief Nursing Officer, St. James Parish Hospital, Lutcher, LA, p. A273

ZERRER, Lana, M.D., Chief of Staff, Harry S. Truman Memorial Veterans Hospital, Columbia, MO, p. A358

ZEVENBERGEN, Glenn, Chief Executive Officer, Hegg Health Center Avera, Rock Valley, IA, p. A229

ZEWE, Jeff S, R.N.
Chief Operating Officer, Bradford Regional Medical Center, Bradford, PA, p. A521
Senior Vice President, Chief Operating Officer, Olean General Hospital, Olean, NY, p. A439

ZEYNELOGLU, Nejat, Vice President and Chief Quality Medical Officer, Long Island Community Hospital, Patchogue, NY, p. A440

ZHANG, Jian Q, MSN, Chief Operating Officer, Chinese Hospital, San Francisco, CA, p. A85

ZHANG, Jian Q., MSN, Chief Executive Officer, Chinese Hospital, San Francisco, CA, p. A85

ZHIRKIN, Georgii, Chief Financial Officer, Community Mental Health Center, Lawrenceburg, IN, p. A210

ZIEGLER, John C, FACHE
Vice President Human Resources, Memorial Hospital East, Shiloh, IL, p. A196
Vice President Human Resources, Memorial Hospital, Belleville, IL, p. A174

ZIELAZINSKI, Mark, Chief Information and Technology Integration Officer, Marin General Hospital, Greenbrae, CA, p. A61

ZIELINSKI, Sharon
Chief Information Resource Officer, Veterans Affairs Maryland Health Care System-Perry Point Division, MD, p. A289
Manager Health Information, Healthsouth Rehabilitation Hospital Of Erie, Erie, PA, p. A525

ZIEMAN, Michael A, FACHE, Administrator, Memorial Behavioral Health, MS, p. A346

ZIEMER, Patrick C., Chief Executive Officer, Alvarado Parkway Institute Behavioral Health System, La Mesa, CA, p. A63

ZIEMIANSKI, Karen, R.N., MS, Senior Vice President Nursing, Erie County Medical Center, Buffalo, NY, p. A423

ZIENIEWICZ, Stephen P., FACHE, President and Chief Executive Officer, Saint Barnabas Medical Center, Livingston, NJ, p. A406

ZIEROLD, Bob, Senior Vice President Human Resources, Christian Health Care Center, Wyckoff, NJ, p. A414

ZIGLOR, Danyale
Assistant Director Human Resources, Wellstar Douglas Hospital, Douglasville, GA, p. A152
Assistant Vice President Human Resources, Wellstar Cobb Hospital, Austell, GA, p. A148

ZILE, Ron, M.D., Chief of Staff, Highland District Hospital, Hillsboro, OH, p. A484

ZILKOW, Jon, Chief Financial Officer, Rancho Springs Medical Center, CA, p. A74

ZILLER, Andrew, M.D., Chief Medical Officer, Rose Medical Center, Denver, CO, p. A99

ZILLMAN, Sally E., Interim Vice President, Patient Care Services, Ministry Good Samaritan Health Center, Weston, WI, p. A706

ZIMA, Cheryl F, Vice President Human Resources Ministry Health Care, Marshfield Childen's Hospital, WI, p. A697

ZIMMEL, Robert, Senior Vice President Human Resources, St Luke's Hospital - Allentown Campus, PA, p. A521

ZIMMER, Jan, R.N., MSN, R.N., MS, Chief Nursing Officer, West Tennessee Healthcare Dyersburg Hospital, Dyersburg, TN, p. A569

ZIMMERLY, Kara, Manager Human Resources, Promedica Bay Park Hospital, Oregon, OH, p. A488

ZIMMERMAN, Aimee, R.N., Chief Operations Officer, Logan County Hospital, Oakley, KS, p. A242

ZIMMERMAN, Anne, Senior Director Patient Care Services and Chief Nursing Officer, Mercy Tiffin Hospital, Tiffin, OH, p. A491

ZIMMERMAN, David, M.D., Chief of Staff, Swain Community Hospital, Bryson City, NC, p. A448

ZIMMERMAN, Don, Director Human Resources, Morris County Hospital, Council Grove, KS, p. A234

ZIMMERMAN, Joanna, Regional Chief Financial Officer, Monmouth Medical Center, Southern Campus, Lakewood, NJ, p. A406

ZIMMERMAN, Keith, Chief Executive Officer, Medical City Arlington, Arlington, TX, p. A584

ZIMMERMAN, Michael
Human Resource Officer, Osf Heart Of Mary Medical Center, Urbana, IL, p. A197
Human Resource Officer, Osf Sacred Heart Medical Center, Danville, IL, p. A180

ZIMMERMAN, Nancy, R.N., Administrator, Comanche County Hospital, Coldwater, KS, p. A233

ZIMMERMANN, Deb, R.N., Chief Nursing Officer and Vice President Patient Care Services, Children's Hospital Of Richmond At Vcu, VA, p. A665

ZIMMERMANN, Wayne, Chief Operating Officer, Nyc Health + Hospitals / Elmhurst, New York (Includes All Hospitals Located Within The Five Boroughs), NY, p. A435

ZINAMAN, Michael, M.D., Acting Chief Medical Officer, Nyc Health + Hospitals / Jacobi, New York (Includes All Hospitals Located Within The Five Boroughs), NY, p. A435

ZINK, Jayne, Director of Nursing, Ohio Hospital For Psychiatry, Columbus, OH, p. A478

ZINK, Summer, Chief Financial Officer, Ellinwood District Hospital, Ellinwood, KS, p. A234

ZINKER, Dena, MSN, R.N., Vice President Patient Services, Colquitt Regional Medical Center, Moultrie, GA, p. A158

ZINKULA, Lisa, Chief Financial Officer, Grundy County Memorial Hospital, Grundy Center, IA, p. A223

ZINN, David, M.D., Vice President Medical Affairs, Rmc Anniston, Anniston, AL, p. A13

ZINN, Troy, Chief Executive Officer, Cameron Hospital, Cameron, TX, p. A591

ZINNER, Barbara, Chief Nursing Officer, Marymount Hospital, Garfield Heights, OH, p. A483

ZINNI, Melissa, Chief Financial Officer, Hampton Behavioral Health Center, Westampton, NJ, p. A414

ZINSMEISTER, Mary Sue, MSN, R.N., Chief Nursing Officer, Rockledge Regional Medical Center, Rockledge, FL, p. A137

ZIOBRO, Ron, Chief Operating Officer, Easton Hospital, Easton, PA, p. A524

ZIOBRO, Ronald, Interim Chief Executive Officer, Regional Hospital Of Scranton, Scranton, PA, p. A540

ZIOLKOWSKI, David, Chief Executive Officer, Person Memorial Hospital, Roxboro, NC, p. A460

ZIRBSER, Glenn, Senior Vice President Finance and Chief Financial Officer, Jefferson Washington Township Hospital, NJ, p. A412

ZIRGER, Marion, Chief Financial Officer, Minneola District Hospital, Minneola, KS, p. A241

ZIRKELBACH, Mark
Chief Information Officer, Loma Linda University Children's Hospital, Loma Linda, CA, p. A64
Chief Information Officer, Loma Linda University Heart & Surgical Hospital, CA, p. A64

ZIRKELBACK, Mark, Chief Information Officer, Loma Linda University Behavioral Medicine Center, Redlands, CA, p. A80

ZIRKLE, William, Manager Information Systems, Sentara Halifax Regional Hospital, South Boston, VA, p. A666

ZISKIN, Robert, Chief Information Officer, Northport Veterans Affairs Medical Center, Northport, NY, p. A438

ZOCH, Jeremy
Chief Executive, St. Joseph Hospital, Orange, CA, p. A76
Executive Vice President and Chief Operating Officer, St. Joseph Hospital, Orange, CA, p. A76

ZOESCH, Jim, Information Technology Director, Pmh Medical Center, Prosser, WA, p. A675

ZOGELMAN, Sharon, Director Human Resources, St. Luke Hospital And Living Center, Marion, KS, p. A241

ZOLKIWSKY, Walter R, M.D.
Chief Medical Officer, Reston Hospital Center, Reston, VA, p. A664
Chief Medical Officer, Stonesprings Hospital Center, Dulles, VA, p. A657

ZOMCHECK, Daniel, Interim Director, Captain James A. Lovell Federal Health Care Center, North Chicago, IL, p. A191

ZOMCHECK, Daniel, Ph.D., Chief Executive Officer and Medical Center Director, Clement J. Zablocki Veterans Affairs Medical Center, Milwaukee, WI, p. A698

ZOOK, Danette, Chief Financial Officer, Mercy Medical Center-North Iowa, Mason City, IA, p. A226

ZOOK, Lori, Chief Financial Officer, River's Edge Hospital And Clinic, Saint Peter, MN, p. A340

ZORZA, Elizabeth, Assistant Administrator, Osf St. Francis Hospital And Medical Group, Escanaba, MI, p. A312

ZOUCHA, Larry, Chief Information Officer, Boone County Health Center, Albion, NE, p. A381

ZUANICH, Elizabeth
Chief Financial Officer, Providence Little Company Of Mary Medical Center - Torrance, Torrance, CA, p. A92
Chief Financial Officer, Providence Little Company Of Mary Medical Center San Pedro, Los Angeles, CA, p. A69

ZUBER, Steven, Vice President, Methodist Jennie Edmundson Hospital, Council Bluffs, IA, p. A220

ZUEL, Sally, Vice President Human Resources, Union Hospital, Terre Haute, IN, p. A215

ZUHD, Dajani, M.D., President Medical Staff, Punxsutawney Area Hospital, Punxsutawney, PA, p. A539

ZUKOWSKI, Andrew, Chief Financial Officer, Unc Rex Health Care, Raleigh, NC, p. A459

ZULIANI, Michael E., Chief Executive Officer, Healthsouth Huntington Rehabilitation Hospital, Huntington, WV, p. A683

ZULTANKY, Lynne, Director Corporate Communications and Media Relations, Bon Secours-Depaul Medical Center, Norfolk, VA, p. A662

ZUMPANO, Anthony, Chief Financial Officer, Penn Presbyterian Medical Center, Philadelphia, PA, p. A536

ZUMSTEIN, James F., M.D., Chief of Medicine, Jack Hughston Memorial Hospital, Phenix City, AL, p. A22

ZUTZ-WICZEK, Sandy, Chief Operating Officer, Firstlight Health System, Mora, MN, p. A336

ZVANUT, Michelle, Vice President Human Resources, Boone Hospital Center, Columbia, MO, p. A358

ZWANZIGER, Marcia, Vice President Finance, Huron Regional Medical Center, Huron, SD, p. A561

ZWEIFEL, Mary A., MS
President and Chief Executive Officer, Sheltering Arms Hospital South, Midlothian, VA, p. A661
President and Chief Executive Officer, Sheltering Arms Rehabilitation Hospital, Mechanicsville, VA, p. A661

ZWENG, Thomas
Executive Vice President and Chief Medical Officer, Novant Health Brunswick Medical Center, Bolivia, NC, p. A448
Executive Vice President and Chief Medical Officer, Novant Health Charlotte Orthopaedic Hospital, Charlotte, NC, p. A450
Executive Vice President and Chief Medical Officer, Novant Health Clemmons Medical Center, NC, p. A462
Executive Vice President and Chief Medical Officer, Novant Health Huntersville Medical Center, Huntersville, NC, p. A455
Executive Vice President and Chief Medical Officer, Novant Health Matthews Medical Center, Matthews, NC, p. A457
Executive Vice President and Chief Medical Officer, Novant Health Medical Park Hospital, Winston, NC, p. A463
Executive Vice President and Chief Medical Officer, Novant Health Rowan Medical Center, Salisbury, NC, p. A460
Executive Vice President and Chief Medical Officer, Novant Health Thomasville Medical Center, Thomasville, NC, p. A461
Executive Vice President and Chief Medical Officer, Presbyterian Hemby Children's Hospital, NC, p. A450

ZWICKER, Mike, Chief Executive Officer, St. Aloisius Medical Center, Harvey, ND, p. A466

ZWIEFEL, Laura, Chief Executive Officer, Hancock County Health System, Britt, IA, p. A218

ZWIEG, Faye, Vice President and Chief Nursing Officer, Aurora St. Luke's South Shore, WI, p. A698

ZWINGER, Glenn, Manager Information Systems Services, Veterans Affairs Puget Sound Health Care System-American Lake Division, WA, p. A677

ZYCH, Anita, Director of Nursing, Arrowhead Behavioral Health Hospital, Maumee, OH, p. A486

ZYLA, Jeffrey, Chief Financial Officer, Abrazo Scottsdale Campus, Phoenix, AZ, p. A32

AHA Membership Categories

The American Hospital Association is primarily an organization of hospitals and related institutions. Its object, according to its bylaws, is "to promote high–quality health care and health services for all the people through leadership in the development of public policy, leadership in the representation and advocacy of hospital and health care organization interests, and leadership in the provision of services to assist hospitals and health care organizations in meeting the health care needs of their communities."

Institutional Members

Hospitals or health services organizations or systems which provide a continuum of integrated, community health resources and which include at least one licensed hospital that is owned, leased, managed or religiously sponsored

Institutional members include hospitals, health care systems, integrated delivery systems, and physician hospital organizations (PHOs) and health maintenance organizations (HMOs) wholly or partially owned by or owning a member hospital or system. An Institutional member hospital, health care system or integrated delivery system may, at its discretion and upon approval of a membership application by the Association chief executive officer, extend membership to the health care provider organizations, other than a hospital that it owns, leases, or fully controls.

Freestanding Health Care Provider Organizations

These are health provider organizations, other than registered hospitals, that provide patient care services, including, but not limited to, ambulatory, preventive, rehabilitative, specialty, post–acute and continuing care, as well as physician groups, health insurance services, and staff and group model health maintenance organizations without a hospital component. Freestanding Health Care Provider Organizations members are not owned or controlled by an Institutional member hospital, health care system or integrated delivery system member. They may, however, be part of an organization eligible for, but not holding, Institutional membership.

Other Organizations

This category includes organizations interested in the objectives of the American Hospital Association, but not eligible for Institutional or Freestanding Health Care Provider Organization Membership. Organizations eligible for Other membership shall include, but not be limited to, associations, societies, foundations, corporations, educational and academic institutions, companies, government agencies, international health providers, and organizations having an interest in and a desire to support the objectives of the Association.

Provisional Members

Hospitals that are in the planning or construction stage and that, on completion, will be eligible for institutional membership. Provisional membership may also be granted to applicant institutions that cannot, at present, meet the requirements of Institutional or Freestanding Health Care Provider Organization membership.

Government Institution Group Members

Groups of government hospitals operated by the same unit of government may obtain institutional membership under a group plan. Membership dues are based on a special schedule set forth in the bylaws of the AHA.

Other Institutional Members

Hospitals

U.S. hospitals and hospitals in areas associated with the U.S. that are Institutional members of the American Hospital Association are included in the list of hospitals in section A. Canadian Institutional members of the American Hospital Association are listed below.

Canada

ALBERTA

Lamont: LAMONT HEALTH CARE CENTRE, P O Bag 10, Zip T0B 2R0; tel. 780/895–2211; Harold James, Executive Director

MANITOBA

Winnipeg: RIVERVIEW HEALTH CENTRE, 1 Morley Avenue East, Zip R3L 2P4; tel. 204/452–3411; Norman R. Kasian, President and Chief Executive Officer

ONTARIO

Renfrew: RENFREW VICTORIA HOSPITAL, 499 Raglan Street North, Zip K7V 1P6, tel. 613/432–4851; Randy V. Penney, President and Chief Executive Officer

Thornhill: SHOULDICE HOSPITAL, 7750 Bayview Avenue, Zip L3T 4A3; tel. 905/889–1125; John Hughes, Chief Administrative Officer

Associated University Programs in Health Administration

IOWA

Iowa City: DEPARTMENT OF HEALTH MANAGEMENT AND POLICY, UNIVERSITY OF IOWA, 105 River Street, N232A CPHB, Zip 52246; tel. 319/384–3830; Keith Mueller, Professor and Head

MARYLAND

Bethesda: NAVY MEDICINE PROFESSIONAL DEVELOPMENT CENTER, Naval Medicine, Education and Training Command, 8901 Wisconsin Avenue, Building 1, Zip 20889-5611; tel. 301/295–1251; Commander DuWayne Griepentrog, Director Administration

MISSOURI

Columbia: UNIVERSITY OF MISSOURI, HEALTH MANAGEMENT AND INFORMATICS, CE707 Clinical Support and Education Building, DC 00600, One Hospital Drive, Zip 65212; tel. 573/882–6179; Eduardo Simoes; Chair

TEXAS

San Antonio: ARMY-BAYLOR UNIVERSITY PROGRAM IN HEALTH CARE ADMINISTRATION, 3151 Scott Road, Bldg 2841, Zip 78234–6135; tel. 210/221–6443; Lieutenant Colonel M Nicholas Coppola, Program Director

Sheppard AFB: U.S. AIR FORCE SCHOOL OF HEALTH CARE SCIENCES, Building 1900, MST/114, Academic Library, Zip 76311; tel. 817/851–2511

PUERTO RICO

San Juan: SCHOOL OF PUBLIC HEALTH, P O Box 5067, Zip 00936; tel. 809/767–9626; Orlando Nieves, Dean

Hospital Schools of Nursing

PENNSYLVANIA
New Castle: JAMESON HOSPITAL School of Nursing

Nonhospital Preacute and Postacute Care Facilities

CALIFORNIA

Winterhaven: U. S. PUBLIC HEALTH SERVICE INDIAN HOSPITAL, P O Box 1368, Zip 85366–1368; tel. 760/572–0217; Geniel Harrison, Clinic Director

DELAWARE

Newark: HEALTH CARE CENTER AT CHRISTIANA, 200 Hygeia Drive, Zip 19714; tel. 302/623–0100; Douglas P. Azar, Senior Vice President, Medical Group

FLORIDA

Jacksonville: NEMOURS CHILDREN'S CLINIC, 807 Children's Way, Zip 32207; tel. 904/390–3600; William A. Cover, Administrator

GEORGIA

Calhoun: ALLIANT HEALTH PLANS, INC., 401 South Wall Street, Ste 201, Zip 30701; tel. 706/629–8848; Judy Pair, Chief Executive Officer

GEORGIA HEALTH PLUS, 401 South Wall Street, Ste 201, Zip 30701; tel. 706/629–1833;

Rome: CENTREX, 420 East Second Avenue, Zip 30161; tel. 706/235–1006; Dee B. Russell, Chief Executive Officer

COMMUNITY HOSPICECARE, P O Box 233, Zip 30162–0233; tel. 706/232–0807; Kurt Stuenkel, President and Chief Executive Officer

FLOYD HOME HEALTH AGENCY, P O Box 6248, Zip 30162–6248; tel. 706/802–4600; Kurt Stuenkel, President and Chief Executive Officer

FLOYD MEDICAL OUTPATIENT SURGERY, P O Box 233, Zip 30162–0233; tel. 706/802–2070; Kurt Stuenkel, President and Chief Executive Officer

FLOYD REHABILITATION CENTER, P O Box 233, Zip 30162–0233; tel. 706/802–2091; Kurt Stuenkel, President and Chief Executive Officer

HAWAII

Honolulu: MALUHIA HOSPITAL, 1027 Hala Drive, Zip 96817; tel. 808/832–5874; Derek Akiyoshi, Chief Executive Officer

ILLINOIS

Oak Forest: OAK FOREST HEALTH CENTER OF COOK COUNTY, 15900 South Cicero Avenue, Zip 60452–4006; tel. 708/687–7200;

MAINE

Damariscotta: COVE'S EDGE, 26 Schooner Street, Zip 4543; tel. 207/563–4645; Judy McGuire, Administrator

MILES MEDICAL GROUP, INC., 35 Miles Street, Zip 4543; tel. 207/563–1234; Stacey Miller-Friant, Vice President, Physician Services

Kennebunk: SOUTHERN MAINE HEALTH AND HOME SERVICES, P O Box 739, Zip 4043; tel. 207/985–4767; Elaine Brady, Executive Director

MARYLAND

Baltimore: ST. AGNES HEALTH SERVICES, 900 Caton Avenue, Zip 21229; tel. 410/368–2945; Peter Clay, Senior Vice President Managed Care

ST. AGNES HOME CARE AND HOSPICE, 3421 Benson Avenue, Suite G100, Zip 21227; tel. 410/368–2825; Robin Dowell, Director

Ellicott City: ST. AGNES NURSING AND REHABILITATION CENTER, 3000 North Ridge Road, Zip 21043; tel. 410/461–7577; Barbara A. Gustke, Administrator Extended Care Facility

MASSACHUSETTS

Boston: JOSLIN DIABETES CENTER, One Joslin Place, Zip 2215; tel. 617/732–2400; John L. Brooks, President and Chief Executive Officer

Springfield: BAY STATE VISITING NURSE ASSOCIATION AND HOSPICE, 50 Maple Street, Zip 1105; tel. 413/781–5070; Ruth Odgren, President

MICHIGAN

Big Rapids: MECOSTA HEALTH SERVICES, 650 Linden Street, Zip 49307; tel. 231/796–3200; Gail Bullard, Director

Sault Sainte Marie: SAULT SAINTE MARIE TRIBAL HEALTH AND HUMAN SERVICES CENTER, 2864 Ashmun Street, Zip 49783; tel. 906/495–5651; Russell Vizina, Division Director Health

MISSOURI

Independence: SURGI-CARE CENTER OF INDEPENDENCE, 2311 Redwood Avenue, Zip 64057; tel. 816/373–7995;

NEBRASKA

North Platte: GREAT PLAINS PHO, INC., P O Box 1167, Zip 69103; tel. 308/535–7496; Todd Hlavaty, Chairman

NEW JERSEY

Jersey City: ST. FRANCIS HOSPITAL, 25 McWilliams Place, Zip 07302–1698; tel. 201/418–1000;

Millburn: ATLANTIC HOME CARE AND HOSPICE, 33 Bleeker Street, Zip 7041; tel. 973/379–8400; Susan Quinn, Administrator

Morristown: ALLIANCE IMAGING CENTER, 65 Maple Street, Zip 7960; tel. 973/267–5700; Barbara Picorale, Administrator

Succasunna: DIALYSIS CENTER OF NORTHWEST NEW JERSEY, 170 Righter Road, Zip 7876; tel. 973/584–1117; Carol Cahill, Administrator

NEW MEXICO

Albuquerque: ALBUQUERQUE IHS HEALTH CENTER, 801 Vassar Drive NE, Zip 87106–2799; tel. 505/248–4000; Maria Rickert, Chief Executive Officer

NEW YORK

Tuckahoe: HOME NURSING ASSOCIATION OF WESTCHESTER, 69 Main Street, Zip 10707; tel. 919/961–2818; Mary Wehrberger, Director

NORTH CAROLINA

Jefferson: AMH SEGRAVES CARE CENTER, 200 Hospital Avenue, Zip 28640; tel. 336/246–7101;

Wilson: WILMED NURSING CARE CENTER, 1705 Tarboro Street SW, Zip 27893–3428; tel. 252/399–8998; Randy Smithey, Administrator

OHIO

Cleveland: METROHEALTH CENTER FOR SKILLED NURSING CARE, 4229 Pearl Road, Zip 44109; tel. 216/957–3675; Yvette Bozman, Administrator

OKLAHOMA

Clinton: U. S. PUBLIC HEALTH SERVICE INDIAN HOSPITAL, Route 1, Box 3060, Zip 73601–9303; tel. 580/323–2884;

Eufaula: EUFALA INDIAN HEALTH CENTER, 800 Forest Avenue, Zip 74432; tel. 918/689–2547; Shelly Crow, Health System Administrator

Okmulgee: OKMULGEE INDIAN HEALTH SYSTEM, 1313 East 20th, Zip 74447; tel. 918/758–1926; Kara Lee, Administrator

Sapulpa: SAPULPA INDIAN HEALTH CENTER, 1125 East Cleveland, Zip 74066; tel. 918/224–9310; Sid Daniels, Acting Administrator

PENNSYLVANIA

Warminster: ABINGTON MEMORIAL HEALTH CENTER - WARMINSTER CAMPUS, 225 Newtown Road, Zip 18974–5221; tel. 215/441–6600; Kathleen Farrell, Executive Director

TEXAS

Dallas: SURGICARE OF TRAVIS CENTER, INC., 13355 Noel Road, Suite 650, Zip 75240–6694; tel. 713/520–1782;

Houston: GRAMERCY OUTPATIENT SURGERY CENTER. LTD., 2727 Gramercy, Zip 77025; tel. 713/660–6900; Hamel Patel, Administrator

Houston: WEST HOUSTON SURGICARE, 970 Campbell Road, Zip 77024; tel. 713/461–3547;

Webster: BAY AREA SURGICARE CENTER, 502 Medical Center Boulevard, Zip 77598; tel. 281/332–2433; Carol Simons, Administrator

WISCONSIN

Green Bay: UNITY HOSPICE, P O Box 28345, Zip 54324–8345; tel. 920/494–0225; Donald Seibel, Executive Director

Provisional Hospitals

This listing includes organizations that, as of September 16, 2015, were in the planning or construction stage and that, on completion, will be eligible for Institutional membership. Some hospitals are granted provisional membership for reasons related to other Association requirements. Hospitals classified as provisional members for reasons other than being under construction are indicated by a bullet (•).

TEXAS

Houston: BAYLOR ST. LUKE'S MEDICAL CENTER MCNAIR CAMPUS, One Baylor Plaza, BCM 100, Zip 77030–3411; tel. 713/798–4951; Paul Klotman, M.D., President

Marble Falls: WAYNE & EILEEN HURD REGIONAL MEDICAL CENTER – SCOTT & WHITE, 800 West Highway 71, Zip 78654; tel. 830/598–1204; Eric N. Looper, Chief Executive Officer

GUAM

Dededo: GUAM REGIONAL MEDICAL CITY, P.O. Box 3830, Zip 96932; tel. 671/649–4764; Gloria Long, Chief Operating Officer

Associate Members

Ambulatory Centers and Home Care Agencies

UNITED STATES

NEW YORK

MIDTOWN SURGERY CENTER, 305 East 47th Street, Zip 10017–2303; tel. 212/751–2100; Julia Ferguson, Director, Operations

PENNSYLVANIA

WILLS EYE HOSPITAL, 840 Walnut Street, Philadelphia, Zip 19107–5109; tel. 215/928–3000; Joseph P. Bilson, Executive Director

Blue Cross Plans

UNITED STATES

ARIZONA

BLUE CROSS AND BLUE SHIELD OF ARIZONA, Box 13466, Phoenix, Zip 85002–3466; tel. 602/864–4541; Vishu Jhaveri; Senior Vice President and Chief Medical Officer

Other Members

UNITED STATES

Architecture

DEVENNEY GROUP ARCHITECTS, 201 West Indian School Road, Phoenix, Arizona Zip 85013–3203; tel: 602/943–8950; Julie Barkenbush, Chief Executive Officer; devenneygroup.com

MATTHEI AND COLIN ASSOCIATES, 332 South Michigan Avenue, Suite 614, Chicago, Illinois Zip 60604; tel: 312/939–4002; Randall Bacidore, Principal; mca-architecture.com/

MESSER CONSTRUCTION COMPANY, 5158 Fishwick Drive, Cincinnati, Ohio Zip 45216; tel: 513/242–1541; Nick Apanius, Health Care Vice President; messer.com

Bank

HEALTHCARE ASSOCIATES CREDIT UNION, 1151 East Warrenville Road, Naperville, Illinois Zip 60563; tel: 630/276–5771; Jennifer Kleinhenz, Senior Vice President Strategic Initiatives; hacu.org

TD BANK, 2130 Centre Park West Drive, 2nd Floor, West Palm Beach, Florida Zip 33409–6411; tel: 561/352–2086; Colleen Mullaney, Senior Vice President; tdbank.com

Communication Systems Org

AVAILITY, LLC, 750 Old Hickory Boulevard, Building 2 Suite 270, Brentwood, Tennessee Zip 37027–4528; tel: 615/760–3361; Ashleigh Eisinger, Events and Social Media Specialist; availity.com

Construction Firm

POETTKER CONSTRUCTION COMPANY, 308 South Germantown Road, Breese, Illinois Zip 62230; tel: 618/526–7213; Curtis C. Rommerskirchen, Brand Ambassador for Healthcare Facility Services; poettkerconstruction.com

AON RISK SOLUTIONS, 5600 West 83rd Street, 8200 Tower, Suite 1000, Minneapolis, Minnesota Zip 55402–3721; tel: 952/807–0768; James Craig Nelson, Senior Vice President; stratford360.com

ARAMARK, 10510 Twin Lakes Boulevard, Charlotte, North Carolina Zip 28269–7658; tel: 704/948–4774; Tom Elmore, Director, Industry Relations; aramark.com

AVIVA HEALTHCARE SOLUTIONS, 98 Golden Eye Lane, Port Monmouth, New Jersey Zip 07758–1647; tel: 800/530–5728; Thomas Bojko, President and Managing Partner; avivahealthsolutions.com

CARE TECH SOLUTIONS, 901 Wilshire Drive, Suite 100, Troy, Michigan Zip 48084; tel: 248/823–0950; Jody Meehan, Vice President, Marketing, Communications, and Government Affairs; caretech.com/

CARERISE|CARERISE INDEX, PO Box 880, Mandeville, Louisiana Zip 70470–0880; tel: 985/727–4740; Tim G. Goux, Founder; carerise.com

CLEARWATER COMPLIANCE LLC, 106 Windward Point, Hendersonville, Tennessee Zip 37075–5108; tel: 615/800–7988; Kathy S. Ebbert, Chief Operating Officer; clearwatercompliance.com

CONIFER HEALTH SOLUTIONS, 2401 Internet Boulevard, Suite 201, Frisco, Texas Zip 75034–5977; tel: 972/335–6120; Vanessa Harris, Senior Market Research Specialist; coniferhealth.com

CREATE PPO, 317 6th Avenue, Suite 1440, Des Moines, Iowa Zip 50309–4131; tel: 515/657–4888; Clayton R. Copple, President and Chief Executive Officer; createppo.com

EASTER HEALTHCARE CONSULTING, 518 Neilwood Drive, Nashville, Tennessee Zip 37205–3026; tel: 615/424–3642; James G. Easter Jr., Principal and Chief Executive Officer; easterhealthcare.com

EIDE BAILLY, LLP, 800 Nicollet Mall, Suite 1300, Minneapolis, Minnesota Zip 55402–7033; tel: 612/253–6582; Jen Dreis, Marketing Manager; eidebailly.com/healthcare

ERNST & YOUNG, 150 Fourth Avenue North, Suite 1400, Nashville, Tennessee Zip 37219–2409; tel: 615/252–8254; Chris Barber, US Health Brand, Marketing and Communications Leader; ey.com

GOLDMAN, SACHS AND COMPANY, 200 West Street, New York, New York Zip 10282–2198; Cynthia Rivera, Public Sector and Infrastructure Banking;

HEALTHCARE CHAPLAINCY NETWORK, INC., 65 Broadway, 12th Floor, New York, New York Zip 10010; tel: 212/644–1111; Eric J. Hall, President and Chief Executive Officer; healthcarechaplaincy.org

HEALTHCARE MANAGEMENT PARTNERS, LLC, 1515 Market Street, Suite 1200, Philadelphia, Pennsylvania Zip 19102–1932; tel: 215/854–4086; Scott K. Phillips, Managing Director; hcmpllc.com

HEALTHCARESOURCE, 100 Sylvan Road, Suite 100, Woburn, Massachusetts Zip 01801–1851; tel: 800/691–3737; Sean Parlin, Strategic Alliances Manager; healthcaresource.com

HEALTHEQUITY, INC., 15 West Scenic Pointe Drive, Suite 100, Draper, Utah Zip 84020–6120; tel: 801/727–1000; Stephen Neeleman, Founder and Vice Chairman; healthequity.com

HEALTHPORT, 925 North Point Parkway, Alpharetta, Georgia Zip 30005–5210; tel: 770/360–1700; Catherine Valyi, Vice President Marketing; healthport.com

INGENIOUS MED, 400 Galleria Parkway, SE Suite 1600, Atlanta, Georgia Zip 30339; tel: 678/486–4256; J. Scott McClintock, Chief Marketing Officer; ingeniousmed.com

KAUFMAN HALL, 5202 Old Orchard Road, Suite N700, Skokie, Illinois Zip 60077; tel: 847/441–8780; Jason H. Sussman, Partner; kaufmanhall.com

LATHAM AND WATKINS, LLP, 633 West 5th Street, Ste 4000, Los Angeles, California Zip 90071; tel: 213/485–1234; Daniel K. Settelmayer, Partner; lw.com

MCDONALD HOPKINS, LLC, 600 Superior Avenue East, Suite 2100, Cleveland, Ohio Zip 44114–2690; tel: 216/348–5400; Richard S. Cooper, Member; mcdonaldhopkins.com

MCKESSON CORPORATION, 1 Post Street, 33rd Floor, San Francisco, California Zip 94104–5203; tel: 404/338–2985; Anastasia Agapoff, Assistant Manager, Library Operations; mckesson.com/

MEDASSETS, 100 North Pointe Center East, Suite 200, Alpharetta, Georgia Zip 30022–1506; tel: 314/579–1896; Ron DeCarlo, Senior Vice President; medassets.com

MILESTONE HEALTHCARE, LLC, 275 West Campbell Road, Suite 300, Richardson, Texas Zip 75080–3560; tel: 800/926–2388; George Thompson, General Manager; milestonehealth.com

NATIONAL CENTER FOR HEALTH STATISTICS, 3311 Toledo Road, Hyattsville, Maryland Zip 20782–2064; tel: 800/232–4636; Monica Deckers, Lead Admin Officer; cdc.gov

NAVEX GLOBAL, 6000 Meadows Road, Suite 200, Lake Oswego, Oregon Zip 97035–3172; tel: 503/924–1640; Stephen J. Molen, Vice President Strategic Solutions; navexglobal.com

NEWRISTICS, 8777 East Via de Ventura #188, Scottsdale, Arizona Zip 85258; tel: 480/947–8078; Sheryl Bronkesh, President; hsmgroup.com

PROTIVITI, INC., 13727 Noel Road, Suite 800, Dallas, Texas Zip 75240–1336; tel: 214/395–1662; Richard Williams, Managing Director and Global Healthcare Industry Practice; protiviti.com

RYCAN, P O Box 306, Marshall, Minnesota Zip 56258–0306; tel: 800/201–3324; Marg Louwagie, Administrative Assistant; rycan.com

STRATA DECISION TECHNOLOGY, tel: 312/726–1227; Dan Michelson, Chief Executive Officer; stratadecision.com

STROUDWATER ASSOCIATES, 50 Sewall Street, Suite 102, Portland, Maine Zip 04102–2646; tel: 207/221–8255; Marc Voyvodich, Chief Executive Officer; stroudwater.com/

SULLIVAN COTTER & ASSOCIATES, INC, 200 West Madison Street, Suite 2450, Chicago, Illinois Zip 60606–3499; tel: 312/564–5883; Deana Kraft, Director of External Affairs; sullivancotter.com

SYMPLR, 315 Capitol Street, Suite 100, Houston, Texas Zip 77002–2826; tel: 281/863–9500; Rick Pleczko, Chief Executive Officer; vcsdatabase.com

TEAMHEALTH, 265 Brookview Centre Way, Suite 400, Knoxville, Tennessee Zip 37919; tel: 865/293–5486; Leif Murphy, Chief Executive Officer; teamhealth.com

THE CHARTIS GROUP, 220 West Kinzie Street, 5th Floor, Chicago, Illinois Zip 60654–4912; tel: 312/932–3068; Celine White, Manager of Financial Operations; chartis.com

THE QUAMMEN GROUP, INC., 151 Southhall Lane, Suite 168, Maitland, Florida Zip 32751–7486; tel: 407/539–2015; Alexandra Robertson, Director of Marketing; quammengroup.com

VERRAS HEALTHCARE INTERNATIONAL , tel: 888/791–5556; Robert T. Langston, Partner; verras.com/

VIIAD SYSTEMS LLC, 1170 Wheeler Way, Suite 200, Langhorne, Pennsylvania Zip 19047–3243; tel: 866/498–4423; Tricia Bradley, Director, Sales and Marketing Support; viiad.com

WESTERN HEALTHCARE ALLIANCE, 715 Horizon Drive, Suite 401, Grand Junction, Colorado Zip 81506–8731; tel: 970/683–5223; Carolyn Bruce, Chief Executive Officer; wha1.org

XANITOS, INC., 3809 West Chester Pike, Suite 210, Newtown Square, Pennsylvania Zip 19073–2304; tel: 484/654–2300; Graeme A. Crothall, Chairman and Chief Executive Officer; xanitos.com

Educational Services

NATIONAL RURAL HEALTH RESOURCE CENTER, 525 South Lake Avenue, Suite 320, Duluth, Minnesota Zip 55802; tel: 218/727–9390; Sally Buck, Chief Executive Officer; ruralcenter.org

Hospice

HOSPICE OF THE VALLEY, 1510 East Flower Street, Phoenix, Arizona Zip 85014–5698; tel: 602/530–6900; Rachel Behrendt, Senior Vice President, Operations; hov.org

Information Systems

CERNER CORPORATION, 2800 Rockcreek Parkway, Kansas City, Missouri Zip 64117; tel: 816/221–1024; Laurel Vine, Program Manager, Industry Events; cerner.com

EVOLENT, 540 West Madison Street, Suite 1500, Chicago, Illinois Zip 60661; tel: 312/273–6623; Kevin Weinstein, Chief Marketing Officer; valencehealth.com

FLEMING AOD, INC., 816 Thayer Avenue, Floor 3rd, Silver Spring, Maryland Zip 20910–4508; tel: 202/872–1033; Mary Dalrymple, Managing Director; aod.cx

IMPRIVATA, INC., 10 Maguire Road Building 4, Lexington, Massachusetts Zip 02421–3110; tel: 781/674–2700; Ed Gaudel, Chief Marketing Officer; imprivata.com

KPMG LLP, 200 East Randolph Street, Suite 5500, Chicago, Illinois Zip 60601–6607; tel: 312/665–2073; Edward J. Giniat, National Line of Business Leader, Healthcare and Pharmaceuticals Practice; https://home.kpmg.com/us/en/home.html?cid=M-00002211&gclid=CKfszoeUrtACFZSFaQod82wE4g

MEDHOST, 6100 West Plano Parkway, Suite 3100, Plano, Texas Zip 75093–8342; tel: 888/218–4678; Leslie LaFon, Departmental Segment Manager; medhost.com

*The members listed in **bold** are Associate Advantage members*

Insurance Broker

BOSTON MUTUAL LIFE INSURANCE COMPANY, 120 Royall Street, Canton, Massachusetts Zip 2021; tel: 781/828–7000; Peter Tillson, Vice President; bostonmutual.com

IRONSHORE, 300 South Wacker Drive, Chicago, Illinois Zip 60606–6680; tel: 312/496–7535; Daniel R. Nash, Senior Vice President Field Operations and Business Development; ironshore.com

LTC SOLUTIONS, 14715 North East 95th Street, Suite 200, Redmond, Washington Zip 98052; tel: 877/286–2852; Christine McCullugh, President ; ltc-solutions.com

THE ALLEN J. FLOOD COMPANIES, INC., 2 Madison Avenue, Larchmont, New York Zip 10538; tel: 914/834–9326; Allen J. Flood, President; ajfusa.com

Managed Care/Utilization

CENTENE CORPORATION, 111 East Capitol Street, Suite 500, Jackson, Mississippi Zip 39201; tel: 601/863–0835; K. Michael Bailey, Vice President; centene.com

Manufacturer/Supplier

3M, 3M Center, Building 275-4E-01, Saint Paul, Minnesota Zip 55144–1000; tel: 612/733–8183; Donald R. Brewer, Director Medical-Surgical Markets; 3m.com

GE HEALTHCARE , 9900 West Innovation Drive, RP-2177, Wauwatosa, Wisconsin Zip 53226–4856; tel: 262/290–8769; Kimberly Rutherford, Business Partner and Director, Advertising & Promotion US-Canada Region; www3.gehealthcare.com

HILL-ROM, 1069 State Route 46 East, Batesville, Indiana Zip 47006–9167; tel: 812/934–7958; Thomas J. Jeffers, Director Government Relations; hill-rom.com

Metro Hospital Assn

HOSPITAL ASSOCIATION OF SOUTHERN CALIFORNIA, 515 South Figueroa Street, Suite 1300, Los Angeles, California Zip 90071–3300; tel: 213/538–0700; George W. Greene, President and Chief Executive Officer; hasc.org

Other

A3-ASHLEY ADVERTISING AGENCY, 2825 Soni Drive, Trooper, Pennsylvania Zip 19403–1275; tel: 610/631–5500; Frank Gussoni, President; ashleyadvertising.com

ACADEMIC PARTNERSHIP LLC, 600 North Pearl Street, Suite 900, Dallas, Texas Zip 75201; tel: 682/305–3063; Nimisha Savani, Vertical Chief Healthcare; aphealthcareedge.com

AIR METHODS CORPORATION, 7211 South Peoria Street, Englewood, Colorado Zip 80112–4133; tel: 303/792–7565; Carolyn Hicks-Mayle, Vice President, Government Affairs; airmethods.com

AMBIUS, 1125 Berkshire Boulevard, Suite 150, Reading, Pennsylvania Zip 19610–1211; tel: 610/372–9700; Cathy Hoffman, Marketing Assistant; ambius.com

AMC HEALTH, INC., 39 Broadway, Suite 540, New York, New York Zip 10006; tel: 877/776–1746; Joanna Haskin, Vice President Partner Development; amchealth.com

AMERICAN ASSOCIATION FOR WOUND CARE MANAGEMENT, 4109 Glenrose Street, Kensington, Maryland Zip 20895–3718; tel: 301/933–2200; Jule Crider, Executive Director; aawcm.org

AMERICAN ASSOCIATION OF NURSE ANESTHETISTS, 222 South Prospect Avenue, Park Ridge, Illinois Zip 60068–4001; tel: 847/655–1100; Randall Moore, Chief Executive Officer; aana.com

AMERICAN BOARD OF MEDICAL SPECIALTIES, 353 North Clark Street, Suite 1400, Chicago, Illinois Zip 60654–3454; tel: 312/436–2626; Lois Margaret Nora, President and Chief Executive Officer; abms.org

AMERICAN COLLEGE OF HEALTHCARE EXECUTIVES, 300 South Riverside Plaza, Suite 1900, Chicago, Illinois Zip 60606–6613; tel: 312/424–2800; Deborah Bowen, President and Chief Executive Officer; ache.org

AMERICAN HEALTH INFORMATION MANAGEMENT ASSOCIATION, 233 North Michigan Avenue, Suite 2150, Chicago, Illinois Zip 60601–5806; tel: 312/233–1100; David A. Sweet, Director Library Services; ahima.org

AMERICAN SOCIETY OF ANESTHESIOLOGISTS, 1061 American Lane, Schaumburg, Illinois Zip 60173; tel: 847/268–9160; Paul Pomerantz, Chief Executive Officer; asahq.org

AMN HEALTHCARE, INC., 12400 High Bluff Drive, Suite 100, San Diego, California Zip 92130–3581; tel: 866/871–8519; Steve Wehn, Senior Vice President of Corporate Development; amnhealthcare.com

APOGEE PHYSICIANS, 15059 North Scottsdale Road, Suite 600, Scottsdale, Arizona Zip 85254–2685; tel: 602/778–3600; Michael Gregory, Chairman; apogeephysicians.com

ARENA, 502 South Sharp Street, Suite 2300, Baltimore, Maryland Zip 21201–2445; tel: 888/444–0693; Michael Finn, Vice President, Marketing; arena.io

ARIS RADIOLOGY, 5655 Hudson Drive, Suite 210, Hudson, Ohio Zip 44236; tel: 330/655–3800; Stacey Christofferson, Sales and Marketing; arisradiology.com

ASSOCIATION OF PERIOPERATIVE REGISTERED NURSES, 2170 South Parker Road, Suite 400, Denver, Colorado Zip 80231; tel: 303/755–6304; Linda Kay Groah, Executive Director and Chief Executive Officer; aorn.org

AVATAR SOLUTIONS, 25 East Washington Street, Suite 600, Chicago, Illinois Zip 60602; tel: 312/236–7170; Jeffrey Brady, Chief Executive Officer; hrsolutionsinc.com

BACTES, 8344 Clairemont Mesa Boulevard, Suite 201, San Diego, California Zip 92111–1327; tel: 858/244–1811; Rae Danell, Marketing Coordinator; bactes.com

BFB GALLAGHER , 6525 Morrison Boulevard, Suite 200, Charlotte, North Carolina Zip 28211–3532; tel: 877/332–2265; James Craig Nelson, Senior Vice President; bfbgallagher.com

BLUE CROSS AND BLUE SHIELD ASSOCIATION, 225 North Michigan Avenue, Chicago, Illinois Zip 60601–7680; tel: 312/297–6000; Scott P. Serota, President and Chief Executive Officer ; bcbs.com

BOARDVANTAGE, 4300 Bohannon Drive, Suite 110, Menlo Park, California Zip 94025; tel: 650/330–2444; Virginia Portillo, Conference and Events Coordinator; boardvantage.com

BUREAU OF MEDICINE AND SURGERY, DEPARTMENT OF THE NAVY, 7700 Arlington Boulevard, Suite 5126, Falls Church, Virginia Zip 22042; tel: 703/681–8489; Bryce H.P. Mendez, Healthcare Policy Analyst; med.navy.mil

CANON SOLUTIONS AMERICA, INC., 300 Commerce Square Boulevard, Burlington, New Jersey Zip 08016–1270; tel: 847/706–3411; Paul T. Murphy, Director Strategic Contract Support; solutions.canon.com

CAPROCK EMERGENCY HOSPITAL, 1630 Briarcrest Drive, Suite 100, Bryan, Texas Zip 77802–2709; tel: 979/314–2323; Lon Young, Chief Medical Officer; caprocker.com

CARECENTRIX, 20 Church Street, Floor 12th, Hartford, Connecticut Zip 06103–1246; tel: 800/808–1902; Sherl Brand, Senior Vice President Strategic Solutions; carecentrix.com

CERTIPHI SCREENING, INC., 1105 Industrial Highway, Southampton, Pennsylvania Zip 18966; tel: 888/260–1370; Tony D'Orazio, President; certiphi.com

CHANGE HEALTHCARE, 3535 Piedmont Road, Suite 800, Atlanta, Georgia Zip 30305–1543; tel: 404/279–5029; Kim R. Williams, Chief Financial Officer; changehealthcare.com

CISCO SYSTEMS, 165 Needletree Lane, Glastonbury, Connecticut Zip 6033; tel: 860/657–8127; Michael Haymaker, Director Healthcare Industry Marketing; cisco.com

COMPREHENSIVE PHARMACY SERVICES, 6409 North Quail Hollow Road, Memphis, Tennessee Zip 38120–1414; tel: 901/748–0470; Walker Upshaw, Chief Development Officer; cpspharm.com

CROSS COUNTRY HEALTHCARE, 5201 Congress Avenue, Boca Raton, Florida Zip 33487–3629; tel: 800/347–2264; Robert Murphy, President Workforce Solutions; crosscountryhealthcare.com

CYRACOM, 5780 North Swan Road, Tucson, Arizona Zip 85718–4527; tel: 800/713–4950; Jeremy Woan, President and Chief Executive Officer; cyracom.com

DEPARTMENT OF AIR FORCE MEDICAL SERVICE, HQ USAF/SG, Bolling AFB, District of Columbia Zip 20332–6188; tel: 202/545–6700; Mark A. Ediger, Surgeon General; airforcemedicine.af.mil

DEPARTMENT OF THE ARMY, OFFICE OF THE SURGEON GENERAL, 5109 Leesburg Pike, Falls Church, Virginia Zip 22041–3258; tel: 202/690–6467; Nadja West, Surgeon General and Commanding General; armymedicine.mil

DISH, PO Box 5096524, Englewood, Colorado Zip 80112–5905; tel: 720/514–6019; Steven Wilson, Manager; dish.com

DNV HEALTHCARE, INC., 400 Techne Center Drive, Suite 100, Milford, Ohio Zip 45150–2792; tel: 513/388–4863; Shannon Walker, Team Operator and Planner; dnvhealthcareinc.com

EVICORE, 730 Cool Springs Boulevard, Suite 800, Franklin, Tennessee Zip 37067–7289; tel: 615/468–4116; Laura Lee, Marketing Project Manager, Providers; medsolutions.com

FIRST AMERICAN EQUIPMENT FINANCE, 255 Woodcliff Drive, Fairport, New York Zip 14450–4219; tel: 585/643–3266; Lori Dennis, Senior Vice President; faef.com

FIRST DATA USA, 5565 Glenridge Connector NE, Atlanta, Georgia Zip 30342; tel: 914/450–4545; Andrew Finck, Vice President Healthcare Segment; firstdata.com

GOZIO HEALTH, 75 5th Street NW, Suite 2220, Atlanta, Georgia Zip 30308–1019; tel: 772/444–6946; Barbara Kragor, Vice President Sales and Customer Experience; goziohealth.com

HEALTHCARE REVENUE SOLUTIONS, 4851 Keller Springs Road, Suite 228, Addison, Texas Zip 75001; tel: 972/546–6491; Andre Kus, Chief Executive Officer; healthcarerevenuesolutions.org

HEALTHGRID, 4203 Vineland Road, Suite K6, Orlando, Florida Zip 32811; tel: 855/624–2844; Raj Toleti, Founder and Chief Executive Officer; healthgrid.com

HEALTHTRUST PURCHASING GROUP INC, 155 Franklin Road, Suite 400, Brentwood, Tennessee Zip 37027–4693; tel: 615/344–3030; Beverly Wallace, President; healthtrustpg.com

HEALTHWAYS, INC, 701 Cool Springs Boulevard, Franklin, Tennessee Zip 37067–2697; tel: 800/327–3822; Karen Meyer, Principal; healthways.com

HMS, 355 Quartermaster Court, Jeffersonville, Indiana Zip 47130–3670; tel: 812/704–5747; Rich Flaherty, Vice President Sales and Marketing; hms.com

HOOPER, LUNDY & BOOKMAN, INC., 1875 Century Park East, Suite 1600, Los Angeles, California Zip 90067; tel: 310/551–8111; Lloyd Bookman, Partner; health-law.com

HOSPITALRECRUITING.COM, 899 South College Mall Road, Suite 395, Bloomington, Indiana Zip 47401–6301; tel: 800/244–7236; Michael Jones, Managing Partner; hospitalrecruiting.com

HQ ACC/SGMS, 162 Dodd, Suite 100, Langley AFB, Virginia Zip 23665–1995; military.com/base-guide/langley-air-force-base

HQ AETC/SGAL, 63 Main Circle, Suite 3, Randolph AFB, Texas Zip 78150–4549; military.com/base-guide/randolph-air-force-base

HQ AFMC/SGAR, 4225 Logistics Avenue, N-209, Dayton, Ohio Zip 45433–5761; tel: 937/656–3655; Alice Rohrbach, wpafb.af.mil/

HQ AFSPC/SGAL, 150 Vandenberg Street, Suite 1105, Peterson AFB, Colorado Zip 80914–4550; tel: 719/556–6141; peterson.af.mil/

HQ AMC/SGSL, 203 West Losey Street, Room 1180, Scott AFB, Illinois Zip 62225–5219; airforcemedicine.af.mil/MTF/Scott/About-Us/

HQ PACAF/SGAL, 25 E Street, Suite D1, Hickam AFB, Hawaii Zip 96853–5418; tel: 808/449–7110; Gary North, Commander; 15wing.af.mil/

HQ USAFA/SGAL, Pinion Drive, Building 4102, Suite 3, USAF Academy, Colorado Zip 80840; tel: 719/524–2273; airforcemedicine.af.mil/MTF/Air-Force-Academy/

HYLAND SOFTWARE, INC., 28500 Clemens Road, Westlake, Ohio Zip 44145; tel: 440/788–5814; Michael Kortan, Director Health Care Solutions; onbase.com

IMALOGIX, 1150 First Avenue, Suite 450, King Of Prussia, Pennsylvania Zip 19406–1363; tel: 855/681–9100; David Steigerwalt, Product Manager; imalogix.com

INDATATECH, 85 NE Loop 410, Suite 405, San Antonio, Texas Zip 78216–5829; tel: 210/344–3540; Bede Ramcharan, President and Chief Executive Officer; indatatech.com

INNOVATIVE CAPITAL LLC, 1489 Baltimore Pike, Building 400, Springfield, Pennsylvania Zip 19064–3958; tel: 610/543–2490; Alan P. Richman, President and Chief Executive Officer; innovativecapital.com

INTALERE, 500 Commonwealth Drive, Warrendale, Pennsylvania Zip 15086–7516; tel: 877/711–5700; Laurie McGrath, Vice President Marketing; amerinet-gpo.com

INTERACTIVE HEALTH SOLUTIONS, 3800 North Wilke Road, Suite 155, Arlington Heights, Illinois Zip 60004–1278; tel: 847/754–2698; Joseph O'Brien, President; interactivesolutions.com

IP SERVICES, 2896 Crescent Avenue, Suite 201, Eugene, Oregon Zip 97408–7422; tel: 541/343–5974; Mark Allers, Vice President Business Development; ipservices.com

JANI-KING, 16885 Dallas Parkway, Addison, Texas Zip 75001; tel: 972/991–0900; Bob Carabajal, Director Healthcare Services; janiking.com

JEWISH GUILD HEALTHCARE, 15 West 65th Street, New York, New York Zip 10023; tel: 212/769–6200; Alan R. Morse, President and Chief Executive Officer; jgb.org

LANGUAGE LINE SOLUTIONS, One Lower Ragsdale Drive, Building 2, Monterey, California Zip 93940; tel: 800/752–6096; Suzanne duMont-Perez, Government Relations and Channel Manager; languageline.com

LITTLER MENDELSON, P.C., 1100 Superior Avenue, 20th Floor, Cleveland, Ohio Zip 44114–2530; tel: 216/623–6104; Angela Lupardus, Manager, Regional Business Development and Marketing; littler.com

MEDICAL INFORMATION TECHNOLOGY, INC., tel: 781/821–3000; Lynn Robblee, Supervisor of Event Coordination and Memberships; meditech.com

MEDISOLV, INC., 10440 Little Patuxent Parkway, Suite 1000, Columbia, Maryland Zip 21044–3630; tel: 443/539–0505; Erin Heilman, Marketing Specialist; medisolv.com

MEDNAX SERVICES INC., 1301 Concord Terrace, Sunrise, Florida Zip 33323–2843; tel: 954/384–0175; Roger J. Medel, President; mednax.com

MODERN HEALTHCARE, 150 North Michigan Avenue, 17th Floor, Chicago, Illinois Zip 60601–3806; tel: 312/649–5491; Fawn Lopez, Publisher; modernhealthcare.com

MUCH SHELIST, 191 North Wacker Drive, Chicago, Illinois Zip 60606–1615; tel: 312/521–2000; Ned Milenkovich, Partner; muchshelist.com

NATIONAL COUNCIL OF STATE BOARDS OF NURSING, 111 East Wacker Drive, 29th Floor, Chicago, Illinois Zip 60601–4277; tel: 312/525–3600; David Charles Benton, Chief Executive Officer; ncsbn.org

OB HOSPITALIST GROUP, tel: 800/967–2289; Guy Kohn, Director, Marketing; obhg.com

PLANON CORPORATION, 45 Braintree Hill Office Park, Suite 400, Braintree, Massachusetts Zip 02184–8730; tel: 781/356–0999; Ellen Schwier, Marketing Manager; planonsoftware.com

PROASSURANCE , 100 Brookwood Place, Birmingham, Alabama Zip 35209–6811; tel: 205/877–4400; W. Stancil Starnes, Chairman, Chief Executive Officer; proassurance.com

PROMED HEALTHCARE FINANCING, 1001 Woodward Avenue, Suite 1700, Detroit, Michigan Zip 48226–1904; tel: 631/707–4347; Dan De Chiaro, Director of Operations; promedhcf.com

QUARLES AND BRADY LLP, 300 North LaSalle Street, Suite 4000, Chicago, Illinois Zip 60654–3422; tel: 312/715–2751; Susan Stewart, Director, Client Relations; quarles.com

RENTOKIL STERITECH, 1125 Berkshire Boulevard, Suite 150, Reading, Pennsylvania Zip 19610–1211; tel: 610/372–9700; Audrey Napoleon, Marketing Manager; rentokil-steritech.com

RRS, 416 Longshore Drive, Ann Arbor, Michigan Zip 48103; tel: 800/517–9634; Nicole Chardoul, Partner and Vice President; recycle.com

SENTRY DATA SYSTEMS, INC., 800 Fairway Drive, Suite 400, Deerfield Beach, Florida Zip 33441–1830; tel: 806/411–4566; Tim Lantz, Senior Vice President, Data Next; sentryds.com

SIMPLEX GRINNELL, 50 Technology Drive, Westminster, Massachusetts Zip 1441; tel: 978/731–8486; Suzanne Rahall, Marketing Manager, Healthcare Communications; simplexgrinnell.com

SUBWAY, 325 Bic Drive, Milford, Connecticut Zip 6461; tel: 800/888–4848; Joanne Kilgore, Global Account Manager; subway.com

TANDEM HOSPITAL PARTNERS, 1415 Louisiana Street, Houston, Texas Zip 77002–7360; tel: 713/999–0837; Debora Simmons, Chief Quality Officer and Chief Nursing Officer; tandemhospitalpartners.com

THE AMERICAN COLLEGE OF OBSTETRICIANS AND GYNECOLOGISTS, 409 12th Street, SW, Washington, District of Columbia Zip 20024–2188; tel: 202/638–5577; Hal Lawrence, Executive Vice President; acog.org

THE CPI GROUP, 7400 East Orchard Road, Suite 270, Englewood, Colorado Zip 80111; tel: 303/504–9999; John Van Gulik, Business Development Manager; thecpigroup.net

THE WALKER COMPANY, 31090 SW Boones Bend Road, Wilsonville, Oregon Zip 97070–6412; tel: 503/694–8539; Larry W. Walker, Principal; walkercompany.com

TRACE SECURITY, 6300 Corporate Boulevard, Baton Rouge, Louisiana Zip 70809–1097; tel: 877/275–3009; Marissa Adams, Marketing Coordinator; tracesecurity.com

TRANSAMERICA RETIREMENT SOLUTIONS, 4 Manhattanville Road, Purchase, New York Zip 10577; tel: 914/697–8952; Peter Kunkel, President and Chief Executive Officer; https://www.trsretire.com

TRAPOLLO, 13900 Lincoln Park Drive, 5th Floor, Herndon, Virginia Zip 20171; tel: 866/807–5047; Lisa Majdi, Marketing Director; trapollo.com

TRAVELERS INSURANCE COMPANY, One Tower Square, 6th Floor, Hartford, Connecticut Zip 06183–1134; tel: 860/277–9830; John Truhan, Operations Manager; travelers.com

U. S. ARMY MEDICAL COMMAND, 2050 Worth Road, Suite 10, San Antonio, Texas Zip 78234–6010; tel: 210/221–2212; Ann Russell Potter,

UBS, 315 Deaderick Street, Nashville, Tennessee Zip 37238–3000; tel: 615/393–7549; Whit Mayo, Managing Director; ubs.com

UNIFORM DATA SYSTEM FOR MEDICAL REHABILITATION, 270 Northpointe Parkway, Suite 300, Amherst, New York Zip 14228; tel: 716/817–7800; Troy Hillman, Manager, Analytical Services Group; udsmr.org

USDTL, 1700 South Mount Prospect Road, Des Plaines, Illinois Zip 60018–1804; tel: 847/375–0770; Catharine Steccato, Vice President Business Development; usdtl.com

VANGUARD MODULAR BUILDING SYSTEMS, LLC, 3 Great Valley Parkway, Suite 170, Malvern, Pennsylvania Zip 19355–1417; tel: 610/240–8686; Mark Meyers, Vice President, Marketing Services; vanguardmodular.com

VERISYS CORPORATION, 1001 North Fairfax Avenue, Suite 640, Alexandria, Virginia Zip 22314–1798; tel: 703/535–1471; John Benson, Chief Operating Officer; verisys.com/

VESTAGEN TECHNICAL TEXTILES, INC., tel: 407/781–2395; Brian Crawford, Chief Business Officer; vestagen.com

VIGILANZ CORPORATION , 5775 Wayzata Boulevard, Suite 970, Minneapolis, Minnesota Zip 55416–2669; tel: 855/525–9078; David Goldsteen, Chairman and Chief Executive Officer; vigilanzcorp.com

VITAS HEALTHCARE, 201 South Biscayne Boulevard, Suite 400, Miami, Florida Zip 33131; tel: 305/374–4143; Drew Landmeier, Chief Marketing Officer; vistas.com

VIZIENT, 799 9th Street Northwest, Suite 210, Washington, District of Columbia Zip 20001–5325; tel: 202/354–2600; Shoshana Krilow, Vice President Public Policy and Government Relations; https://www.vizientinc.com/

WELLTOWER, INC., 4500 Dorr Street, Toledo, Ohio Zip 43615–4040; tel: 419/247–2800; Rachel Watson, Assistant Vice President; welltower.com

WITT/KIEFFER, 2015 Spring Rd, Ste 510, Oak Brook, Illinois Zip 60523; tel: 630/990–1370; James Gauss, Chairman of Board Services; wittkieffer.com/

YOURCARE UNIVERSE, INC, 6550 Carothers Parkway, Suite 100, Franklin, Tennessee Zip 37067; tel: 844/641–6800; Lauren Douglass, Brand Manager; yourcareuniverse.com

Other Health Related

CENTER FOR MEDICAL INTEROPERABILITY, 618 Church Street Suite 220, Nashville, Tennessee Zip 37219–2453; tel: 202/617–6009; Kerry McDermott, Vice President for Public Policy and Communications; medicalinteroperability.org

Recruitment Services

DOCCAFE.COM, tel: 574/453–3131; Briana Wick, Digital Marketing Director; doccafe.com

Regional Health Care Assn

TEXAS ORGANIZATION OF RURAL & COMMUNITY HOSPITALS, P O Box 203878, Austin, Texas Zip 78720–3878; tel: 512/873–0045; John Henderson, Chief Executive Officer; torchnet.org

CANADA

Other

HALOGEN SOFTWARE CORPORATION, 495 March Road, Suite 500, Ottawa, Ontario Zip K2K 3G1; tel: 613/270–1011; Lorna Daly, Channel Manager Healthcare; halogensoftware.com

Provincial Hospital Assn

ONTARIO HOSPITAL ASSOCIATION, 200 Front Street West, Suite 2800, Toronto, Ontario Zip M5V 3L1; tel: 416/205–1300; Hazim Hassan, Vice President, Business Planning and Strategy; oha.com

BAHAMAS

BAHAMAS

Other

PRINCESS MARGARET HOSPITAL, P O Box N-8200, Nassau tel: 242/322–2861; Mary Elizabeth Lightbourne-Walker, Hospital Administrator; phabahamas.org

BAHRAIN

Other

INTERNATIONAL HOSPITAL OF BAHRAIN, P O Box 1084, Manama tel: 11/759–8222; F.S. Zeerah, President; ihb.net/

BRAZIL

Other

HOSPITAL SAMARITANO, Rua Conselheiro Brotero, 1486, Sao Paulo Zip 01232–010; tel: 551/821–5300; Luiz Alberto Oliveira De Luca, Corporate Superintendent; samaritano.com.br

COLOMBIA

Other

ASOCIACION COLOMBIANA DE HOSPITALES Y CLINICAS, Carrera 4, No 73–15, Bogota Juan Carlos Giraldo Valencia, Director General; achc.org.co

DOMINICAN REPUBLIC

Other

UNITED TELEMEDICINE NETWORK-HOSPITAL CHARLES DE GAULLE, Av Charles de Gaulle #43, Santo Domingo Zip 11509; tel: 829/345–9335; Horacio Stagno, Commercial Director; hospitalunited.com

GEORGIA

Other

BOKHUA MEMORIAL CARDIOVASCULAR CENTER, Chachava 1 Street, Tbilisi Zip 159; Giorgi Kipiani, Director;

INNOVA MEDICAL CENTER, 7A Sandra Euli Street, Tbilisi Zip 105; Giorgi Kipiani, Director; innovamedical.ge

MARITIME HOSPITAL JSC, Melikishrin 102B, Batumi Zip 60100; Tamari Kachlishvili, Medical Director; mh.com.ge

MEDI CLUB GEORGIA, 22A, Tashkenti Street, Tbilisi Zip 160; tel: 995/225–1991; Nugzar Abramishvili, General Director; mediclubgeorgia.ge

TBILISI CENTRAL HOSPITAL, Chachava Street 1, Tbilisi Zip 159; Ivane Martiashuili, Co-founder; tch.ge

ZHORDANIA CLINIC, Chachava N1, Tbilisi Zip 159; Tamar Kobiashvili, Director;

GERMANY

Other

HQ USAFE/SGPXL, Unit 3050, Box 130, Ramstein AB, Armed Forces Africa, Canada, E Zip 09094–5001; ramstein.af.mil/

JAPAN

Other

U.S. NAVAL HOSPITAL OKINAWA, U S Naval Base, FPO Zip 96362; tel: 11/743–7555; Martin Kerr, med.navy.mil/sites/nhoki/Pages/default.aspx

JORDAN

Other

SPECIALTY HOSPITAL, P O Box 930186, Amman Zip 11193; Fawzi Al-Hammouri, General Manager; specialty-hospital.com

LEBANON

Other

SAINT GEORGE HOSPITAL UNIVERSITY MEDICAL CENTER, P O Box 166378, Beirut Zip 1100–2807; tel: 961/158–5700; Dimitri Haddad, Director; stgeorgehospital.org

MEXICO

Other

SHRINERS HOSPITAL FOR CHILDREN, Av Del Iman 257, Col Pedregal de Santa Ursula, Delegacion Coyoacan, Mexico City Zip 4600; Mariano Gonzalez Lugo, Administrator; shrinershospitalsforchildren.org/locations/mexicocity

MYANMAR

Other

ASIA ROYAL GENERAL HOSPITAL, 14 Baho Street, Sanchaung Township, Yangon Zip 11162; tel: 951/153–8055; Myat Thu, Managing Director; asiaroyalmedical.com

NIGERIA

Consulting Firm

PETALICE MEDICAL CENTRE, 5/7 Marickson Hospital Way, Uyo, Akwa Ibom State Zip 520241; Cletus Bassey, Archbishop;

PANAMA

Other

CLINICA HOSPITAL SAN FERNANDO, S. A., Dept PTY 1663, P O Box 25207, Miami, Florida Zip 33102–5207; tel: 507/305–6399; Edgardo Fernandez, Medical Director; hospitalsanfernando.com

PERU

Other

BRITISH AMERICAN HOSPITAL, Avenue Alfredo Salazar 3 Era, Lima 27 tel: 511/712–3000; Gonzalo Garrido-Lecca, Director; angloamericana.com.pe

PHILIPPINES

Ambulatory Care Center

DEPARTMENT OF VETERANS AFFAIRS, OUTPATIENT CLINIC, Pasay City, APO Zip 96440; tel: 632/833–4566; Artemio Arugay, Commander; va.gov

Other

ST. LUKE'S MEDICAL CENTER, 279 East Rodriguez Sr Boulevard, Quezon City tel: 632/723–0101; Edgardo R. Cortez, President and Chief Executive Officer; stluke.com.ph/home

SAUDI ARABIA

Other

ABDUL RAHMAN AL MISHARI GENERAL HOSPITAL, Olaya, P.O. Box 56929, Riyadh Zip 11564; tel: 11/465–7700; Abdul Rahman Al Mishari, President; drabdulrahmanalmishari.com.sa/

MUHAMMAD SALEH BASHARAHIL HOSPITAL, P O Box 10505, Madinah Road, Omora Gadida, Makkah tel: 9/520–4444; Turki M. Basharahil, General Manager; msbasharahil.com/

NABIL AL KADI CONSULTANT ENGINEERS, Dammam, Damman Taufik Ridani, Chief Executive Officer;

SPAIN

Information Systems

SIGESA, S.A., Calle Guatemala, 14, 4b, Madrid Zip 28016; tel: 349/345–4018; Francisco Alvarez, Chief Financial Officer; sigesa.com

TURKEY

Other

ARTE CERRAHI HASTENESI, 1920 Cad. No:61 Cayyolu, Ankara Zip 6810; tel: 903/236–1001; Oguz Engiz, Chief Executive Officer; artesaglik.com

UNITED ARAB EMIRATES

Other

AMERICAN HOSPITAL-DUBAI, Oud Metha Road, P.O. Box 5566, Dubai tel: 11/336–7777; Saeed M. Almulla, Chairman; https://www.ahdubai.com/en/

UNITED KINGDOM

Consulting Firm

I.G. ADVISORS, 201 Borough High Street, London Zip SE11JA; tel: 440/234–0389; Carlos Miranda, Chief Executive Officer; impactandgrowth.com

Other

FINANSCO HEALTHCARE, 11A Blacka Moor Road, Sheffield 0 tel: 448/225–3844; Rukhsar Khan, Chief Executive Officer; finansco.com

B

**Health Care Systems,
Networks
and Alliances**

Section B

Introduction

This section includes listings for networks, health care systems and alliances.

Health Care Systems

To reflect the diversity that exists among health care organizations, this publication uses the term health care system to identify both multihospital and diversified single hospital systems.

Multihospital Systems

A multihospital health care system is two or more hospitals owned, leased, sponsored, or contract managed by a central organization.

Single Hospital Systems

Single, freestanding member hospitals may be categorized as health care systems by bringing into membership three or more, and at least 25 percent, of their owned or leased non–hospital preacute and postacute health care organizations. (For purposes of definition, health care delivery is the availability of professional healthcare staff during all hours of the organization's operations). Organizations provide, or provide and finance, diagnostic, therapeutic, and/or consultative patient or client services that normally precede or follow acute, inpatient, hospitalization; or that serve to prevent or substitute for such hospitalization. These services are provided in either a freestanding facility not eligible for licensure as a hospital under state statue or through one that is a subsidiary of a hospital.

The first part of this section is an alphabetical list of health care systems which are listed under the system by state. Data for this section were compiled from the 2017 *Annual Survey* and the membership information base as published in section A of the *AHA Guide*.

One of the following codes appears after the name of each system listed to indicate the type of organizational control reported by that system:

CC   Catholic (Roman) church–related system, not–for–profit

CO   Other church–related system, not–for–profit

NP   Other not–for–profit system, including nonfederal, governmental systems

IO   Investor–owned, for profit system

FG   Federal Government

One of the following codes appears after the name of each hospital to indicate how that hospital is related to the system:

O   Owned

L   Leased

S   Sponsored

CM   Contract–managed

Health System Classification System

An identification system for Health Systems was developed jointly by the American Hospital Association's Health Research and Education Trust and Health Forum, and the University of California-Berkeley.[1] A health system is assigned to one of five categories based on how much they differentiate and centralized their hospital services, physician arrangements, and provider-based insurance products. Differentiation refers to the number of different products or services that the organization offers. Centralization refers to whether decision-making and service delivery emanate from the system level more so than individual hospitals.

Categories:

Centralized Health System: A delivery system in which the system centrally organizes individual hospital service delivery, physician arrangements, and insurance product development. The number of different products/services that are offered across the system is moderate.

Centralized Physician/Insurance Health System: A delivery system with highly centralized physician arrangements and insurance product development. Within this group, hospital services are relatively decentralized with individual hospitals having discretion over the array of services they offer. The number of different products/services that are offered across the system is moderate.

Moderately Centralized Health System: A delivery system that is distinguished by the presence of both centralized and decentralized activity for hospital services, physician arrangements, and insurance product development. For example, a system within this group may have centralized care of expensive, high technology services, such as open heart surgery, but allows individual hospitals to provide an array of other health services based on local needs. The number of different products/services that are offered across the system is moderate.

Decentralized Health System: A delivery system with a high degree of decentralized of hospital services, physician arrangements, and insurance product development. Within this group, systems may lack an overarching structure for coordination. Service and product differentiation is high, which may explain why centralization is hard to achieve. In this group, the system may simply service a role in sharing information and providing administrative support to highly developed local delivery systems centered around hospitals.

Independent Hospital System: A delivery system with limited differentiation in hospital services, physician arrangements, and insurance product development. These systems are largely horizontal affiliations of autonomous hospitals.

No Assignment: For some systems sufficient data from the Annual Survey were not available to determine a cluster assignment.

The second part of this section lists health care systems indexed geographically by state and city. Every effort has been made to be as inclusive and accurate as possible. However, as in all efforts of this type, there may be omissions. For further information, write to the Section for Health Care Systems, American Hospital Association, 155 N. Wacker Drive, Chicago, IL 60606.

Networks

The *AHA Guide* shows listings of networks. A network is defined as a group of hospitals, physicians, other providers, insurers and/or community agencies that work together to coordinate and deliver a broad spectrum of services to their community. Organizations listed represent the lead or hub of the network activity. Networks are listed by state, then alphabetically by name including participating partners.

The network identification process has purposely been designed to capture networks of varying organization type. Sources include but are not limited to the following: *AHA Annual Survey*, national, state and metropolitan associations, national news and periodical searches, and the networks and their health care providers themselves. Therefore, networks are included regardless of whether a hospital or healthcare system is the network lead. When an individual hospital does appear in the listing, it is indicative of the role the hospital plays as the network lead. In addition, the network listing is not mutually exclusive of the hospital, health care system or alliance listings within this publication.

Networks are very fluid in their composition as goals evolve and partners change. Therefore, some of the networks included in this listing may have dissolved, reformed, or simply been renamed as this section was being produced for publication.

The network identification process is an ongoing and responsive initiative. As more information is collected and validated, it will be made available in other venues, in addition to the *AHA Guide*. For more information concerning the network identification process, please contact The American Hospital Association Resource Center at 312/422–2050.

Alliances

An alliance is a formal organization, usually owned by shareholders/members, that works on behalf of its individual members in the provision of services and products and in the promotion of activities and ventures. The organization functions under a set of bylaws or other written rules to which each member agrees to abide.

Alliances are listed alphabetically by name. Its members are listed alphabetically by state, city, and then by member name.

[1]Bazzoli, CJ; Shortell, SM; Dubbs, N; Chan, C; and Kralovec, P; "A Taxonomy of Health networks and Systems: Bringing Order Out of Chaos" *Health Services Research*, February; 1999

Statistics for Health Care Systems and their Hospitals

The following tables describing health care systems refers to information in section B of the 2019 *AHA Guide*.

Table 1 shows the number of health care systems by type of control. Table 2 provides a breakdown of the number of systems that own, lease, sponsor or contract manage hospitals within each control category. Table 3 gives the number of hospitals and beds in each control category as well as total hospitals and beds. Finally, Table 4 shows the percentage of hospitals and beds in each control category.

For more information on health care systems, please write to the Section for Health Care Systems, 155 N. Wacker Drive, Chicago, Illinois 60606 or call 312/422–3000.

Table 1. Multihospital Health Care Systems, by Type of Organizaton Control

Type of Control	Code	Number of Systems
Catholic (Roman) church–related	CC	27
Other church–related	CO	7
Subtotal, church–related		34
Other not–for–profit	NP	309
Subtotal, not–for–profit		343
Investor Owned	IO	77
Federal Government	FG	5
Total		425

Table 2. Multihospital Health Care Systems, by Type of Ownership and Control

Type of Ownership	Catholic Church–Related (CC)	Other Church–Related (CO)	Total Church–Related (CC + CO)	Other Not–for–Profit (NP)	Total Not–for–Profit (CC, CO, + NP)	Investor–Owned (IO)	Federal Government (FG)	All Systems
Systems that only own, lease or sponsor	21	6	27	188	215	17	4	236
Systems that only contract–manage	0	0	0	12	12	4	0	16
Systems that manage, own, lease, or sponsor	6	1	7	109	116	56	1	173
Total	27	7	34	309	343	77	5	425

Table 3. Hospitals and Beds in Multihospital Health Care Systems, by Type of Ownership and Control

Type of Ownership	Catholic Church–Related (CC) H	B	Other Church–Related (CO) H	B	Total Church–Related (CC + CO) H	B	Other Not–for–Profit (NP) H	B	Total Not–for–Profit (CC, CO, + NP) H	B	Investor–Owned (IO) H	B	Federal Government (FG) H	B	All Systems H	B
Owned, leased or sponsored	580	105,725	76	17,639	656	123,364	1,659	350,107	2,315	473,471	1,374	164,789	204	40,232	3,893	678,492
Contract–managed	44	2,494	3	485	47	2,979	120	9,233	167	12,212	88	4,623	0	0	255	16,835
Total	624	108,219	79	18,124	703	126,343	3,318	359,340	4,021	485,683	1,462	169,412	204	40,232	5,687	695,327

H = hospitals; **B** = beds.

Table 4. Hospitals and Beds in Multihospital Health Care Systems, by Type of Ownership and Control as a Percentage of All Systems

Type of Ownership	Catholic Church–Related (CC) H	B	Other Church–Related (CO) H	B	Total Church–Related (CC + CO) H	B	Other Not–for–Profit (NP) H	B	Total Not–for–Profit (CC, CO, + NP) H	B	Investor–Owned (IO) H	B	Federal Government (FG) H	B	All Systems H	B
Owned, leased or sponsored	14.9	15.6	1.9	2.6	16.9	18.2	42.6	51.6	59.5	69.8	35.3	24.3	5.2	5.9	99.9	100
Contract managed	17.3	14.8	1.2	2.9	18.4	17.7	47.1	51.6	65.5	72.5	34.5	24.3	0	5.9	100.1	99.5
Total	10.9	15.6	1.4	2.6	12.4	18.2	58.3	51.6	70.7	69.9	25.7	24.3	3.6	5.9	99.9	100

H = hospitals; **B** = beds.
*Please note that figures may not always equal the provided subtotal or total percentages due to rounding.

0091: ACADIA HEALTHCARE COMPANY, INC. (IO)
830 Crescent Centre Drive, Suite 610, Franklin, TN, Zip 37067–7323; tel. 615/861–6000; Joey Jacobs, Chairman and Chief Executive Officer

(Decentralized Health System)

ARIZONA: OASIS BEHAVIORAL HEALTH – CHANDLER (O, 146 beds) 2190 North Grace Boulevard, Chandler, AZ, Zip 85225–3416; tel. 480/917–9301; James Gallagher, Chief Executive Officer

SONORA BEHAVIORAL HEALTH HOSPITAL (O, 106 beds) 6050 North Corona Road, #3, Tucson, AZ, Zip 85704–1096; tel. 520/469–8700; Edeli Kinsala, Chief Executive Officer

ARKANSAS: CONWAY BEHAVIORAL HEALTH HOSPITAL (O, 80 beds) 2255 Sturgis Road, Conway, AR, Zip 72034–8029; tel. 501/858–3048; Doris Singleton, Chief Executive Officer
Web address: www.conwaybh.com

RIVERVIEW BEHAVIORAL HEALTH (O, 62 beds) 701 Arkansas Boulevard, Texarkana, AR, Zip 71854–2105; tel. 870/772–5028; Sherrie James, R.N., Chief Executive Officer
Web address: www.riverviewbehavioralhealth.com

VALLEY BEHAVIORAL HEALTH SYSTEM (O, 114 beds) 10301 Mayo Drive, Barling, AR, Zip 72923–1660; tel. 479/494–5700; Andrea Norman, Chief Executive Officer

VANTAGE POINT OF NORTHWEST ARKANSAS (O, 114 beds) 4253 North Crossover Road, Fayetteville, AR, Zip 72703–4596; tel. 479/521–5731; Connie Borengasser, Chief Executive Officer
Web address: www.vantagepointnwa.com

CALIFORNIA: PACIFIC GROVE HOSPITAL (O, 68 beds) 5900 Brockton Avenue, Riverside, CA, Zip 92506–1862; tel. 951/275–8400; Nichol Sheffield, Chief Executive Officer
Web address: www.pacificgrovehospital.com

SAN JOSE BEHAVORIAL HEALTH (O, 80 beds) 455 Silicon Valley Boulevard, San Jose, CA, Zip 95138–1858; tel. 888/210–2484; Rob Marsh, Chief Executive Officer

DELAWARE: MEADOW WOOD BEHAVIORAL HEALTH SYSTEM (O, 53 beds) 575 South Dupont Highway, New Castle, DE, Zip 19720–4606; tel. 302/328–3330; Bill A. Mason, Chief Executive Officer
Web address: www.meadowwoodhospital.com

FLORIDA: NORTH TAMPA BEHAVIORAL HEALTH (O, 75 beds) 29910 State Road 56, Wesley Chapel, FL, Zip 33543–8800; tel. 813/922–3300; Tracy Rogers, Chief Executive Officer
Web address: www.northtampabehavioralhealth.com

PARK ROYAL HOSPITAL (O, 103 beds) 9241 Park Royal Drive, Fort Myers, FL, Zip 33908–9204; tel. 239/985–2700; Michael Ham, Chief Executive Officer
Web address: www.ParkRoyalHospital.com

GEORGIA: GREENLEAF BEHAVIORAL HEALTH HOSPITAL (O, 103 beds) 2209 Pineview Drive, Valdosta, GA, Zip 31602–7316; tel. 229/247–4357; Stephen Register, Chief Executive Officer

LAKEVIEW BEHAVIORAL HEALTH (O, 70 beds) 1 Technology Parkway South, Norcross, GA, Zip 30092–2928; tel. 678/713–2600; Bill Anderson, Chief Executive Officer
Web address: www.lakeviewbehavioralhealth.com

RIVERWOODS BEHAVIORAL HEALTH SYSTEM (O, 75 beds) 233 Medical Center Drive, Riverdale, GA, Zip 30274–2640; tel. 770/991–8500; John B. Warburton, Chief Executive Officer

INDIANA: OPTIONS BEHAVIORAL HEALTH SYSTEM (O, 84 beds) 5602 Caito Drive, Indianapolis, IN, Zip 46226–1346; tel. 317/544–4340; Chris Rupert, Chief Executive Officer
Web address: www.optionsbehavioralhealthsystem.com/

LOUISIANA: COVINGTON BEHAVIOR HEALTH (O, 60 beds) 201 Greenbrier Boulevard, Covington, LA, Zip 70433–7236; tel. 985/893–2970; Wes Crawford, Chief Executive Officer
Web address: www.greenbrierhospital.com/

LONGLEAF HOSPITAL (O, 92 beds) 44 Versailles Boulevard, Alexandria, LA, Zip 71303–3960; tel. 318/445–5111; Claire Hick, Chief Executive Officer
Web address: www.longleafhospital.com/

RIVER PLACE BEHAVIORAL HEALTH (O, 82 beds) 500 Rue De Sante, La Place, LA, Zip 70068–5418; tel. 985/303–2327; Rick Bennett, Chief Executive Officer
Web address: www.riverplacebh.com

VERMILION BEHAVIORAL HEALTH SYSTEMS (O, 78 beds) 2520 North University Avenue, Lafayette, LA, Zip 70507–5306; tel. 337/234–5614; Stephanie Hrdlicka, Chief Executive Officer

MASSACHUSETTS: SOUTHCOAST BEHAVIORAL HEALTH (O, 120 beds) 581 Faunce Corner Road, Dartmouth, MA, Zip 02747–1242; tel. 888/210–2475; Richard Remley, Chief Executive Officer
Web address: www.southcoastbehavioral.com

MICHIGAN: HARBOR OAKS HOSPITAL (O, 99 beds) 35031 23 Mile Road, New Baltimore, MI, Zip 48047–3649; tel. 586/725–5777; Sari Abromovich, Chief Executive Officer

STONECREST CENTER (O, 134 beds) 15000 Gratiot Avenue, Detroit, MI, Zip 48205–1973; tel. 313/245–0600; Steve Savage, Chief Executive Officer
Web address: www.stonecrestcenter.com

MISSOURI: LAKELAND BEHAVIORAL HEALTH SYSTEM (O, 100 beds) 440 South Market Street, Springfield, MO, Zip 65806–2026; tel. 417/865–5581; Nathan Duncan, Chief Executive Officer
Web address: www.lakeland–hospital.com

NEVADA: SEVEN HILLS HOSPITAL (O, 94 beds) 3021 West Horizon Ridge Parkway, Henderson, NV, Zip 89052–3990; tel. 702/646–5000; Christopher West, Chief Executive Officer

OHIO: OHIO HOSPITAL FOR PSYCHIATRY (O, 90 beds) 880 Greenlawn Avenue, Columbus, OH, Zip 43223–2616; tel. 614/449–9664; Stanley Frank, Chief Executive Officer
Web address: www.ohiohospitalforpsychiatry.com/

TEN LAKES CENTER (O, 16 beds) 819 North First Street, 3rd Floor, Dennison, OH, Zip 44621–1003; tel. 740/922–7499; Debra C. Gardner, R.N., MSN, Administrator

OKLAHOMA: ROLLING HILLS HOSPITAL (O, 108 beds) 1000 Rolling Hills Lane, Ada, OK, Zip 74820–9415; tel. 580/436–3600; Anthony Guild, Chief Executive Officer
Web address: www.rollinghillshospital.com

PENNSYLVANIA: BELMONT BEHAVIORAL HOSPITAL (O, 171 beds) 4200 Monument Road, Philadelphia, PA, Zip 19131–1625; tel. 215/877–2000; Mark Schor, Chief Executive Officer

SOUTHWOOD PSYCHIATRIC HOSPITAL (O, 156 beds) 2575 Boyce Plaza Road, Pittsburgh, PA, Zip 15241–3925; tel. 412/257–2290; Stephen J. Quigley, Chief Executive Officer
Web address: www.southwoodhospital.com

PUERTO RICO: SAN JUAN CAPESTRANO HOSPITAL (O, 108 beds) Rural Route 2, Box 11, San Juan, PR, Zip 926; tel. 787/625–2900; Marta Rivera. Plaza, Chief Executive Officer and Managing Director
Web address: www.sjcapestrano.com

SOUTH CAROLINA: REBOUND BEHAVIORAL HEALTH (O, 42 beds) 134 East Rebound Road, Lancaster, SC, Zip 29720–7712; tel. 877/959–5063; Patricia Hamilton, Chief Executive Officer
Web address: www.reboundbehavioralhealth.com

TENNESSEE: CRESTWYN BEHAVIORAL HEALTH (O, 60 beds) 9485 Crestwyn Hills Cove, Memphis, TN, Zip 38125–8515; tel. 901/248–1500; Jeb Stokes, Chief Executive Officer

DELTA MEDICAL CENTER (O, 179 beds) 3000 Getwell Road, Memphis, TN, Zip 38118–2299; tel. 901/369–8100; Phil Willcoxon, Chief Executive Officer
Web address: www.deltamedcenter.com

TRUSTPOINT HOSPITAL (O, 101 beds) 1009 North Thompson Lane, Murfreesboro, TN, Zip 37129–4351; tel. 615/867–1111; Beth Goodner, Chief Executive Officer
Web address: www.trustpointhospital.com

For explanation of codes following names, see page B2.
★ Indicates Type III membership in the American Hospital Association.

TEXAS: CROSS CREEK HOSPITAL (O, 90 beds) 8402 Cross Park Drive, Austin, TX, Zip 78754; tel. 512/215–3900; Coleby Wright, Chief Executive Officer
Web address: www.cornerstonehealthcaregroup.com

RED RIVER HOSPITAL, LLC (O, 96 beds) 1505 Eighth Street, Wichita Falls, TX, Zip 76301–3106; tel. 940/322–3171; James Wilfer, Chief Executive Officer

UTAH: HIGHLAND RIDGE HOSPITAL (O, 83 beds) 7309 South 180 West, Midvale, UT, Zip 84047–3769; tel. 801/569–2153; Matt Wilburn, Chief Executive Officer
Web address: www.highlandridgehospital.com

WASHINGTON: CASCADE BEHAVIORAL HOSPITAL (O, 63 beds) 12844 Military Road South, Tukwila, WA, Zip 98168–3045; tel. 206/244–0180; Michael Uradnik, Chief Executive Officer

Owned, leased, sponsored:	38 hospitals	3555 beds
Contract–managed:	0 hospitals	0 beds
Totals:	38 hospitals	3555 beds

★**0640: ACUITYHEALTHCARE, LP** (IO)
10200 Mallard Creek Road, Suite 300, Charlotte, NC, Zip 28262–9705; tel. 704/887–7280; Edwin H. Cooper Jr, President and Chief Executive Officer
(Independent Hospital System)

NEW JERSEY: ACUITY SPECIALTY HOSPITAL OF NEW JERSEY (O, 30 beds) 1925 Pacific Avenue, 7th Floor, 5 Wellness, Atlantic City, NJ, Zip 08401–6713; tel. 609/441–2122; Monica B. Titus, BSN, MBA, RN, Regional Chief Executive Officer
Web address: www.acuityhealthcare.net

ACUITY SPECIALTY HOSPITAL OF SOUTHERN NEW JERSEY (O, 53 beds) 218 A Sunset Road, Willingboro, NJ, Zip 08046–1110, Mailing Address: 220 Sunset Road, Zip 08046–1110, tel. 609/835–3650; Monica B. Titus, R.N., Regional Chief Executive Officer
Web address: www.willingboro.acuityhealthcare.net

OHIO: ACUITY SPECIALTY HOSPITALS OHIO VALLEY (O, 52 beds) 380 Summit Avenue, 3rd Floor, Steubenville, OH, Zip 43952–2667; tel. 740/283–7600; Judy K. Weaver, MS, Chief Executive Officer

TEXAS: ACUITY HOSPITAL OF SOUTH TEXAS (O, 30 beds) 718 Lexington Avenue, San Antonio, TX, Zip 78212–4768; tel. 210/572–4600
Web address: www.southtexas.acuityhealthcare.net/

Owned, leased, sponsored:	4 hospitals	165 beds
Contract–managed:	0 hospitals	0 beds
Totals:	4 hospitals	165 beds

0895: ADENA HEALTH SYSTEM (NP)
272 Hospital Road, Chillicothe, OH, Zip 45601–9031, Mailing Address: PO Box 802846, Kansas City, MO, Zip 64180–2846, tel. 740/779–7500; Jeff Graham, President and Chief Executive Officer
(Independent Hospital System)

OHIO: ADENA GREENFIELD MEDICAL CENTER (O, 25 beds) 550 Mirabeau Street, Greenfield, OH, Zip 45123–1617; tel. 937/981–9400; Josh McCoy, Administrator
Web address: www.adena.org

ADENA MEDICAL CENTER (O, 192 beds) 272 Hospital Road, Chillicothe, OH, Zip 45601–9031; tel. 740/779–7500; Jeff Graham, President and Chief Executive Officer

ADENA PIKE MEDICAL CENTER (O, 25 beds) 100 Dawn Lane, Waverly, OH, Zip 45690–9138; tel. 740/947–2186; David M. Zanni, Administrator
Web address: www.adena.org

Owned, leased, sponsored:	3 hospitals	242 beds
Contract–managed:	0 hospitals	0 beds
Totals:	3 hospitals	242 beds

★**0235: ADVENTIST HEALTH** (CO)
2100 Douglas Boulevard, Roseville, CA, Zip 95661–3898, Mailing Address: P.O. Box 619002, Zip 95661–9002, tel. 916/781–2000; Scott Reiner, Chief Executive Officer
(Decentralized Health System)

CALIFORNIA: ADVENTIST HEALTH BAKERSFIELD (O, 254 beds) 2615 Chester Avenue, Bakersfield, CA, Zip 93301–2014, Mailing Address: P.O. Box 2615, Zip 93303–2615, tel. 661/395–3000; Sharlet Briggs, Ph.D., Market Chief Executive Officer and President
Web address: www.sanjoaquinhospital.org

ADVENTIST HEALTH CLEAR LAKE (O, 25 beds) 15630 18th Avenue, Clearlake, CA, Zip 95422–9336, Mailing Address: P.O. Box 6710, Zip 95422, tel. 707/994–6486; David Santos, President and Chief Executive Officer
Web address: www.adventisthealth.org

ADVENTIST HEALTH FEATHER RIVER (O, 54 beds) 5974 Pentz Road, Paradise, CA, Zip 95969–5593; tel. 530/877–9361; Monty E. Knittel, Chief Executive Officer

ADVENTIST HEALTH GLENDALE (O, 462 beds) 8700 Beverly Blvd, NT–3138, Los Angeles, CA, Zip 90048, Mailing Address: 1509 Wilson Terrace, Glendale, Zip 91206–4098, tel. 818/409–8000; Alice H. Issai, President
Web address: www.glendaleadventist.com

ADVENTIST HEALTH HOWARD MEMORIAL (L, 25 beds) One Marcela Drive, Willits, CA, Zip 95490–4298; tel. 707/459–6801; Jason Wells, President and Chief Executive Officer
Web address: www.howardhospital.com

ADVENTIST HEALTH LODI MEMORIAL (O, 190 beds) 975 South Fairmont Avenue, Lodi, CA, Zip 95240–5118, Mailing Address: P.O. Box 3004, Zip 95241–1908, tel. 209/334–3411; Daniel Wolcott, President and Chief Executive Officer
Web address: www.lodihealth.org

ADVENTIST HEALTH MEDICAL CENTER – TEHACHAPI VALLEY (C, 24 beds) 115 West 'E' Street, Tehachapi, CA, Zip 93561–1607, Mailing Address: P.O. Box 1900, Zip 93581–1900, tel. 661/823–3000; Eugene Suksi, Chief Executive Officer

ADVENTIST HEALTH SONORA (O, 152 beds) 1000 Greenley Road, Sonora, CA, Zip 95370–4819; tel. 209/536–5000; Michelle Fuentes, President
Web address: www.sonoramedicalcenter.org/

ADVENTIST HEALTH ST. HELENA (O, 116 beds) 10 Woodland Road, Saint Helena, CA, Zip 94574–9554; tel. 707/963–3611; Steven Herber, M.D., FACS, President and Chief Executive Officer
Web address: www.sthelenahospital.org

ADVENTIST HEALTH ST. HELENA (O, 61 beds) 525 Oregon Street, Vallejo, CA, Zip 94590–3201; tel. 707/648–2200; Steven Herber, M.D., FACS, President and Chief Executive Officer
Web address: www.sthelenahospitals.org/location/center–for–behavioral–health

ADVENTIST HEALTH WHITE MEMORIAL (O, 353 beds) 1720 Cesar Chavez Avenue, Los Angeles, CA, Zip 90033–2414; tel. 323/268–5000; John Raffoul, Chief Executive Officer

ADVENTIST MEDICAL CENTER – HANFORD (O, 199 beds) 115 Mall Drive, Hanford, CA, Zip 93230–3513; tel. 559/582–9000; Wayne Ferch, President and Chief Executive Officer
Web address: www.adventisthealthcv.com/hospital_newhanfordhospital.aspx

ADVENTIST MEDICAL CENTER–REEDLEY (L, 49 beds) 372 West Cypress Avenue, Reedley, CA, Zip 93654–2199; tel. 559/638–8155; Wayne Ferch, President and Chief Executive Officer

CENTRAL VALLEY GENERAL HOSPITAL (O, 49 beds) 1025 North Douty Street, Hanford, CA, Zip 93230–3722, Mailing Address: P.O. Box 480, Zip 93232–2113, tel. 559/583–2100; Wayne Ferch, President and Chief Executive Officer
Web address: www.hanfordhealth.com

SIMI VALLEY HOSPITAL (O, 144 beds) 2975 North Sycamore Drive, Simi Valley, CA, Zip 93065–1277; tel. 805/955–6000; Jennifer Swenson, President and Chief Executive Officer

UKIAH VALLEY MEDICAL CENTER (O, 50 beds) 275 Hospital Drive, Ukiah, CA, Zip 95482–4531; tel. 707/462–3111; Gwen Matthews, R.N., MSN, Chief Executive Officer
Web address: www.adventisthealth.org

HAWAII: ADVENTIST HEALTH CASTLE (O, 160 beds) 640 Ulukahiki Street, Kailua, HI, Zip 96734–4454; tel. 808/263–5500; Kathryn A. Raethel, R.N., M.P.H., President and Chief Executive Officer
Web address: www.castlemed.org

OREGON: ADVENTIST MEDICAL CENTER–PORTLAND (O, 199 beds) 10123 SE Market Street, Portland, OR, Zip 97216–2599; tel. 503/257–2500; David Russell, President and Chief Executive Officer

For explanation of codes following names, see page B2.
★ Indicates Type III membership in the American Hospital Association.

Section B

TILLAMOOK REGIONAL MEDICAL CENTER (L, 25 beds) 1000 Third Street, Tillamook, OR, Zip 97141–3430; tel. 503/842–4444; David Butler, President and Chief Executive Officer

Web address: www.tillamookregionalmc.com

Owned, leased, sponsored:	18 hospitals	2567 beds
Contract–managed:	1 hospitals	24 beds
Totals:	19 hospitals	2591 beds

★**4165: ADVENTIST HEALTH SYSTEM SUNBELT HEALTH CARE CORPORATION** (CO)

900 Hope Way, Altamonte Springs, FL, Zip 32714–1502; tel. 407/357–1000; Terry Shaw, President and Chief Executive Officer

(Decentralized Health System)

COLORADO: AVISTA ADVENTIST HOSPITAL (O, 108 beds) 100 Health Park Drive, Louisville, CO, Zip 80027–9583; tel. 303/673–1000; Jillyan McKinney, Chief Executive Officer

CASTLE ROCK ADVENTIST HOSPITAL (O, 53 beds) 2350 Meadows Boulevard, Castle Rock, CO, Zip 80109–8405; tel. 720/455–5000; Todd Folkenberg, Chief Executive Officer
Web address: www.castlerockhospital.org

LITTLETON ADVENTIST HOSPITAL (O, 176 beds) 7700 South Broadway Street, Littleton, CO, Zip 80122–2628; tel. 303/730–8900; Brett Spenst, Chief Executive Officer

PARKER ADVENTIST HOSPITAL (O, 167 beds) 9395 Crown Crest Boulevard, Parker, CO, Zip 80138–8573; tel. 303/269–4000; Michael Goebel, Chief Executive Officer
Web address: www.parkerhospital.org

PORTER ADVENTIST HOSPITAL (O, 250 beds) 2525 South Downing Street, Denver, CO, Zip 80210–5876; tel. 303/778–1955; Morre Dean, Chief Executive Officer
Web address: www.porterhospital.org/poh/home/

FLORIDA: FLORIDA HOSPITAL CARROLLWOOD (O, 96 beds) 7171 North Dale Mabry Highway, Tampa, FL, Zip 33614–2665; tel. 813/932–2222; Erika Skula, President and Chief Executive Officer
Web address: https://www.floridahospital.com/carrollwood

FLORIDA HOSPITAL DADE CITY (O, 120 beds) 13100 Fort King Road, Dade City, FL, Zip 33525–5294; tel. 352/521–1100; Amanda Maggard, Chief Executive Officer
Web address: www.floridahospital.com/dade–city

FLORIDA HOSPITAL DELAND (O, 156 beds) 701 West Plymouth Avenue, DeLand, FL, Zip 32720–3236; tel. 386/943–4522; Lorenzo Brown, Chief Executive Officer

FLORIDA HOSPITAL FISH MEMORIAL (O, 175 beds) 1055 Saxon Boulevard, Orange City, FL, Zip 32763–8468; tel. 386/917–5000; Robert Deininger, Chief Executive Officer
Web address: www.fhfishmemorial.org

FLORIDA HOSPITAL FLAGLER (O, 99 beds) 60 Memorial Medical Parkway, Palm Coast, FL, Zip 32164–5980; tel. 386/586–2000; Ronald Jimenez, M.D., Chief Executive Officer

FLORIDA HOSPITAL HEARTLAND MEDICAL CENTER (O, 197 beds) 4200 Sun'n Lake Boulevard, Sebring, FL, Zip 33872–1986, Mailing Address: P.O. Box 9400, Zip 33871–9400, tel. 863/314–4466; Randy Surber, Chief Executive Officer
Web address: www.floridahospital.com/heartland/our–location

FLORIDA HOSPITAL MEMORIAL MEDICAL CENTER (O, 326 beds) 301 Memorial Medical Parkway, Daytona Beach, FL, Zip 32117–5167; tel. 386/676–6000; Ed Noseworthy, Chief Executive Officer

FLORIDA HOSPITAL NEW SMYRNA (O, 112 beds) 401 Palmetto Street, New Smyrna Beach, FL, Zip 32168–7399; tel. 386/424–5000; Kenneth R. Mattison, Chief Executive Officer
Web address: https://www.floridahospital.com/new–smyrna

FLORIDA HOSPITAL NORTH PINELLAS (O, 187 beds) 1395 South Pinellas Avenue, Tarpon Springs, FL, Zip 34689–3790; tel. 727/942–5000; Jason Dunkel, President and Chief Executive Officer

FLORIDA HOSPITAL TAMPA (O, 536 beds) 3100 East Fletcher Avenue, Tampa, FL, Zip 33613–4688; tel. 813/971–6000; Brian Adams, President and Chief Executive Officer
Web address: www.floridahospital.com/tampa

FLORIDA HOSPITAL WATERMAN (O, 269 beds) 1000 Waterman Way, Tavares, FL, Zip 32778–5266; tel. 352/253–3333; Abel Biri, Chief Executive Officer
Web address: www.fhwat.org

FLORIDA HOSPITAL WAUCHULA (O, 25 beds) 533 West Carlton Street, Wauchula, FL, Zip 33873–3407; tel. 863/773–3101; Denise Grimsley, R.N., Vice President and Administrator

FLORIDA HOSPITAL WESLEY CHAPEL (O, 145 beds) 2600 Bruce B Downs Bouelvard, Wesley Chapel, FL, Zip 33544–9207; tel. 813/929–5000; Denyse Bales–Chubb, President and Chief Executive Officer
Web address: https://www.floridahospital.com/wesley–chapel

FLORIDA HOSPITAL ZEPHYRHILLS (O, 139 beds) 7050 Gall Boulevard, Zephyrhills, FL, Zip 33541–1399; tel. 813/788–0411; Amanda Maggard, Chief Executive Officer
Web address: www.fhzeph.org

FLORIDA HOSPITAL AT CONNERTON LONG TERM ACUTE CARE (O, 50 beds) 9441 Health Center Drive, Land O'Lakes, FL, Zip 34637–5837; tel. 813/903–3701; Brian Adams, President and Chief Executive Officer

FLORIDA HOSPITAL (O, 2877 beds) 601 East Rollins Street, Orlando, FL, Zip 32803–1248; tel. 407/303–6611; Daryl Tol, President and Chief Executive Officer
Web address: www.floridahospital.com/orlando

MUNROE REGIONAL MEDICAL CENTER (O, 420 beds) 1500 SW 1st Avenue, Ocala, FL, Zip 34471–6504, Mailing Address: P.O. Box 6000, Zip 34478–6000, tel. 352/351–7200; James F. O'Loughlin, Chief Executive Officer
Web address: www.munroeregional.com

GEORGIA: GORDON HOSPITAL (O, 83 beds) 1035 Red Bud Road, Calhoun, GA, Zip 30701–2082, Mailing Address: P.O. Box 12938, Zip 30703–7013, tel. 706/629–2895; Pete M. Weber, President and Chief Executive Officer
Web address: www.gordonhospital.com

MURRAY MEDICAL CENTER (O, 12 beds) 707 Old Dalton Ellijay Road, Chatsworth, GA, Zip 30705–2060, Mailing Address: P.O. Box 1406, Zip 30705–1406, tel. 706/695–4564; Karen Steely, Administrator

ILLINOIS: AMITA HEALTH ADVENTIST LA GRANGE MEDICAL CENTER (O, 191 beds) 5101 South Willow Spring Road, La Grange, IL, Zip 60525–2600; tel. 708/245–9000; Michael Murrill, President and Chief Executive Officer
Web address: www.keepingyouwell.com

AMITA HEALTH ADVENTIST MEDICAL CENTER – HINSDALE (O, 261 beds) 120 North Oak Street, Hinsdale, IL, Zip 60521–3890; tel. 630/856–6001; Steven Province, President and Chief Executive Officer

AMITA HEALTH ADVENTIST MEDICAL CENTER BOLINGBROOK (O, 136 beds) 500 Remington Boulevard, Bolingbrook, IL, Zip 60440–4906; tel. 630/312–5000; Bruce C. Christian, Chief Executive Officer
Web address: www.keepingyouwell.com/abh/

AMITA HEALTH ADVENTIST MEDICAL CENTER GLENOAKS (O, 123 beds) 701 Winthrop Avenue, Glendale Heights, IL, Zip 60139–1403; tel. 630/545–8000; Bruce C. Christian, President and Chief Executive Officer

KANSAS: SHAWNEE MISSION MEDICAL CENTER (O, 397 beds) 9100 West 74th Street, Shawnee Mission, KS, Zip 66204–4004, Mailing Address: Box 2923, Zip 66201–1323, tel. 913/676–2000; Sam D. Huenergardt, Chief Executive Officer
Web address: www.shawneemission.org

KENTUCKY: MANCHESTER MEMORIAL HOSPITAL (O, 49 beds) 210 Marie Langdon Drive, Manchester, KY, Zip 40962–6388; tel. 606/598–5104; Erika Skula, President and Chief Executive Officer
Web address: www.manchestermemorial.org

NORTH CAROLINA: PARK RIDGE HEALTH (O, 87 beds) 100 Hospital Drive, Hendersonville, NC, Zip 28792–5272; tel. 828/684–8501; Jimm Bunch, President and Chief Executive Officer

TEXAS: CENTRAL TEXAS MEDICAL CENTER (O, 111 beds) 1301 Wonder World Drive, San Marcos, TX, Zip 78666–7544; tel. 512/353–8979; Anthony Stahl, Ph.D., FACHE, Chief Executive Officer
Web address: www.ctmc.org

For explanation of codes following names, see page B2.
★ Indicates Type III membership in the American Hospital Association.

METROPLEX ADVENTIST HOSPITAL (O, 177 beds) 2201 South Clear Creek Road, Killeen, TX, Zip 76549–4110; tel. 254/526–7523; Kevin A. Roberts, FACHE, President and Chief Executive Officer
Web address: www.mplex.org

ROLLINS BROOK COMMUNITY HOSPITAL (O, 35 beds) 608 North Key Avenue, Lampasas, TX, Zip 76550–1106, Mailing Address: P.O. Box 589, Zip 76550–0032, tel. 512/556–3682; Kevin A. Roberts, FACHE, President and Chief Executive Officer
Web address: www.mplex.org

TEXAS HEALTH HUGULEY HOSPITAL FORT WORTH SOUTH (C, 193 beds) 11801 South Freeway, Burleson, TX, Zip 76028–7021, Mailing Address: P.O. Box 6337, Fort Worth, Zip 76115–0337, tel. 817/293–9110; Kenneth A. Finch, President and Chief Executive Officer

WISCONSIN: CHIPPEWA VALLEY HOSPITAL (O, 25 beds) 1220 Third Avenue West, Durand, WI, Zip 54736–1600, Mailing Address: P.O. Box 224, Zip 54736–0224, tel. 715/672–4211; Douglas R. Peterson, President and Chief Executive Officer
Web address: www.chippewavalleyhospital.com/

Owned, leased, sponsored:	35 hospitals	8370 beds
Contract–managed:	1 hospitals	193 beds
Totals:	36 hospitals	8563 beds

0214: ADVENTIST HEALTHCARE (NP)
820 West Diamond Avenue, Suite 600, Gaithersburg, MD, Zip 20878–1419; tel. 301/315–3185; Terry Forde, President and Chief Executive Officer
(Independent Hospital System)

MARYLAND: ADVENTIST BEHAVIORAL HEALTH AND WELLNESS SERVICES (O, 220 beds) 14901 Broschart Road, Rockville, MD, Zip 20850–3318; tel. 301/251–4500; Kevin Young, FACHE, President
Web address: www.adventistbehavioralhealth.com

ADVENTIST HEALTHCARE PHYSICAL HEALTH AND REHABILITATION (O, 77 beds) 9909 Medical Center Drive, Rockville, MD, Zip 20850–6361; tel. 240/864–6000; Brent Reitz, President

ADVENTIST HEALTHCARE SHADY GROVE MEDICAL CENTER (O, 315 beds) 9901 Medical Center Drive, Rockville, MD, Zip 20850–3395; tel. 240/826–6000; John Sackett , President SGMC and Executive Vice President and Chief Operating Officer
Web address: www.adventisthealthcare.com

ADVENTIST HEALTHCARE WASHINGTON ADVENTIST HOSPITAL (O, 230 beds) 7600 Carroll Avenue, Takoma Park, MD, Zip 20912–6392; tel. 301/891–7600; Erik Wangsness, President
Web address: www.adventisthealthcare.com

Owned, leased, sponsored:	4 hospitals	842 beds
Contract–managed:	0 hospitals	0 beds
Totals:	4 hospitals	842 beds

★1032: ADVOCATE AURORA HEALTH (NP)
3075 Highland Parkway, Suite 600, Downers Grove, IL, Zip 60515–5563; tel. 630/929–8700; Jim Skogsbergh, Chief Executive Officer

ILLINOIS: ADVOCATE BROMENN MEDICAL CENTER (O, 198 beds) 1304 Franklin Avenue, Normal, IL, Zip 61761–3558, Mailing Address: P.O. Box 2850, Bloomington, Zip 61702–2850, tel. 309/454–1400; Colleen Kannaday, FACHE, President

ADVOCATE CHRIST MEDICAL CENTER (O, 778 beds) 4440 West 95th Street, Oak Lawn, IL, Zip 60453–2699; tel. 708/684–8000; Matthew Lee Primack, President
Web address: www.advocatehealth.com/christ

ADVOCATE CONDELL MEDICAL CENTER (O, 283 beds) 801 South Milwaukee Avenue, Libertyville, IL, Zip 60048–3199; tel. 847/362–2900; Karen A. Lambert, President
Web address: www.advocatehealth.com/condell/

ADVOCATE EUREKA HOSPITAL (O, 11 beds) 101 South Major Street, Eureka, IL, Zip 61530–1246; tel. 309/467–2371; Colleen Kannaday, FACHE, President

ADVOCATE GOOD SAMARITAN HOSPITAL (O, 278 beds) 3815 Highland Avenue, Downers Grove, IL, Zip 60515–1590; tel. 630/275–5900; Nancy M. Tinsley, RN, MBA, FACHE, President
Web address: www.advocatehealth.com/gsam

ADVOCATE GOOD SHEPHERD HOSPITAL (O, 176 beds) 450 West Highway 22, Barrington, IL, Zip 60010–1919; tel. 847/381–0123; Karen A. Lambert, President

ADVOCATE ILLINOIS MASONIC MEDICAL CENTER (O, 334 beds) 836 West Wellington Avenue, Chicago, IL, Zip 60657–5147; tel. 773/975–1600; Susan Nordstrom. Lopez, President
Web address: www.advocatehealth.com/masonic

ADVOCATE LUTHERAN GENERAL HOSPITAL (O, 623 beds) 1775 Dempster Street, Park Ridge, IL, Zip 60068–1174; tel. 847/723–2210; Terika Richardson, MPH, President

ADVOCATE SHERMAN HOSPITAL (O, 255 beds) 1425 North Randall Road , Elgin, IL, Zip 60123–2300; tel. 847/742–9800; Linda Deering, MSN, R.N., President
Web address: www.advocatehealth.com/sherman

ADVOCATE SOUTH SUBURBAN HOSPITAL (O, 215 beds) 17800 South Kedzie Avenue, Hazel Crest, IL, Zip 60429–0989; tel. 708/799–8000; Rashard Johnson, President
Web address: www.advocatehealth.com/ssub/

ADVOCATE TRINITY HOSPITAL (O, 174 beds) 2320 East 93rd Street, Chicago, IL, Zip 60617–3909; tel. 773/967–2000; Rashard Johnson, President
Web address: https://www.advocatehealth.com/trin/

WISCONSIN: AURORA BAYCARE MEDICAL CENTER (O, 167 beds) 2845 Greenbrier Road, Green Bay, WI, Zip 54311–6519, Mailing Address: P.O. Box 8900, Zip 54308–8900, tel. 920/288–8000; Daniel T. Meyer, President

AURORA LAKELAND MEDICAL CENTER (O, 67 beds) W3985 County Road NN, Elkhorn, WI, Zip 53121–4389; tel. 262/741–2000; Bob Miller, President
Web address: www.aurorahealthcare.org

AURORA MEDICAL CENTER – MANITOWOC COUNTY (O, 62 beds) 5000 Memorial Drive, Two Rivers, WI, Zip 54241–3900; tel. 920/794–5000; Cathie A. Kocourek, President

AURORA MEDICAL CENTER GRAFTON (O, 127 beds) 975 Port Washington Road, Grafton, WI, Zip 53024–9201; tel. 262/329–1000; David Graebner, Interim President
Web address: www.aurorahealthcare.org

AURORA MEDICAL CENTER KENOSHA (O, 79 beds) 10400 75th Street, Kenosha, WI, Zip 53142–7884; tel. 262/948–5600; Douglas E. Koch, Market President

AURORA MEDICAL CENTER SUMMIT (O, 91 beds) 36500 Aurora Drive, Summit, WI, Zip 53066–4899; tel. 262/434–1000; Michael Bergmann, President
Web address: www.aurorahealthcare.org

AURORA MEDICAL CENTER IN WASHINGTON COUNTY (O, 34 beds) 1032 East Sumner Street, Hartford, WI, Zip 53027–1698; tel. 262/673–2300; David Graebner, President
Web address: www.aurorahealthcare.org

AURORA MEDICAL CENTER OF OSHKOSH (O, 61 beds) 855 North Westhaven Drive, Oshkosh, WI, Zip 54904–7668; tel. 920/456–6000; Jeffrey Bard, President
Web address: www.aurorahealthcare.com

AURORA MEMORIAL HOSPITAL OF BURLINGTON (O, 55 beds) 252 McHenry Street, Burlington, WI, Zip 53105–1828; tel. 262/767–6000; Bob Miller, President

AURORA PSYCHIATRIC HOSPITAL (O, 91 beds) 1220 Dewey Avenue, Wauwatosa, WI, Zip 53213–2598; tel. 414/454–6600; Peter Carlson, President, Behavioral Health Services
Web address: www.aurorahealthcare.org

AURORA SHEBOYGAN MEMORIAL MEDICAL CENTER (O, 136 beds) 2629 North Seventh Street, Sheboygan, WI, Zip 53083–4998; tel. 920/451–5000; David Graebner, President
Web address: www.aurorahealthcare.org

AURORA SINAI MEDICAL CENTER (O, 202 beds) 945 North 12th Street, Milwaukee, WI, Zip 53233–1337, Mailing Address: P.O. Box 342, Zip 53201–0342, tel. 414/219–2000; Jessica Bauer, President
Web address: www.aurorahealthcare.org

For explanation of codes following names, see page B2.
★ Indicates Type III membership in the American Hospital Association.

AURORA ST. LUKE'S MEDICAL CENTER (O, 711 beds) 2900 West Oklahoma Avenue, Milwaukee, WI, Zip 53215–4330, Mailing Address: P.O. Box 2901, Zip 53201–2901, tel. 414/649–6000; Marie Golanowski, R.N., MS, President **Web address**: www.aurorahealthcare.org

AURORA WEST ALLIS MEDICAL CENTER (O, 218 beds) 8901 West Lincoln Avenue, West Allis, WI, Zip 53227–2409, Mailing Address: P.O. Box 27901, Zip 53227–0901, tel. 414/328–6000; Richard A. Kellar, President **Web address**: www.aurorahealthcare.org

Owned, leased, sponsored:	25 hospitals	5426 beds
Contract–managed:	0 hospitals	0 beds
Totals:	25 hospitals	5426 beds

0312: AHMC & HEALTHCARE, INC. (IO)

55 South Raymond Avenue, Suite 105, Alhambra, CA, Zip 91801–7101; tel. 626/457–9600; Jonathan Wu, M.D., President and Chairman
(Independent Hospital System)

CALIFORNIA: AHMC ANAHEIM REGIONAL MEDICAL CENTER (O, 223 beds) 1111 West La Palma Avenue, Anaheim, CA, Zip 92801–2881; tel. 714/774–1450; Richard Castro, Chief Executive Officer

ALHAMBRA HOSPITAL MEDICAL CENTER (O, 144 beds) 100 South Raymond Avenue, Alhambra, CA, Zip 91801–3199, Mailing Address: P.O. Box 510, Zip 91802–2510, tel. 626/570–1606; Iris Lai, Chief Executive Officer
Web address: www.alhambrahospital.com

GARFIELD MEDICAL CENTER (O, 195 beds) 525 North Garfield Avenue, Monterey Park, CA, Zip 91754–1205; tel. 626/573–2222; Patrick A. Petre, Chief Executive Officer

GREATER EL MONTE COMMUNITY HOSPITAL (O, 117 beds) 1701 Santa Anita Avenue, South El Monte, CA, Zip 91733–3411; tel. 626/579–7777; Stanley Toy Jr, M.D., Chief Executive Officer
Web address: www.greaterelmonte.com

MONTEREY PARK HOSPITAL (O, 101 beds) 900 South Atlantic Boulevard, Monterey Park, CA, Zip 91754–4780; tel. 626/570–9000; Philip A. Cohen, Chief Executive Officer

SAN GABRIEL VALLEY MEDICAL CENTER (O, 273 beds) 438 West Las Tunas Drive, San Gabriel, CA, Zip 91776–1216, Mailing Address: P.O. Box 1507, Zip 91778–1507, tel. 626/289–5454; Jonathon F. Aquino, Chief Executive Officer
Web address: www.sgvmc.org

WHITTIER HOSPITAL MEDICAL CENTER (O, 100 beds) 9080 Colima Road, Whittier, CA, Zip 90605–1600; tel. 562/945–3561; Richard Castro, Chief Executive Officer
Web address: www.whittierhospital.com

Owned, leased, sponsored:	7 hospitals	1153 beds
Contract–managed:	0 hospitals	0 beds
Totals:	7 hospitals	1153 beds

0225: ALAMEDA HEALTH SYSTEM (NP)

15400 Foothill Boulevard, San Leandro, CA, Zip 94578–1009; tel. 510/677–7920; Delvecchio Finley, Chief Executive Officer
(Moderately Centralized Health System)

CALIFORNIA: ALAMEDA HOSPITAL (O, 247 beds) 2070 Clinton Avenue, Alameda, CA, Zip 94501–4397; tel. 510/522–3700; John Chapman, Chief Administrative Officer
Web address: www.alamedahealthsystem.org

HIGHLAND HOSPITAL (O, 382 beds) 1411 East 31st Street, Oakland, CA, Zip 94602–1018; tel. 510/437–4800; Delvecchio Finley, Chief Executive Officer
Web address: www.alamedahealthsystem.org

SAN LEANDRO HOSPITAL (O, 45 beds) 13855 East 14th Street, San Leandro, CA, Zip 94578–2600; tel. 510/357–6500; James E T. Jackson, M.P.H., Chief Administrative Officer

Owned, leased, sponsored:	3 hospitals	674 beds
Contract–managed:	0 hospitals	0 beds
Totals:	3 hospitals	674 beds

1020: ALECTO HEALTHCARE (IO)

16310 Bake Parkway, Suite 200, Irvine, CA, Zip 92618–4684; tel. 323/932–5963; Lex Reddy, Chief Executive Officer
(Moderately Centralized Health System)

CALIFORNIA: OLYMPIA MEDICAL CENTER (O, 204 beds) 5900 West Olympic Boulevard, Los Angeles, CA, Zip 90036–4671; tel. 310/657–5900; Matthew Williams, R.N., Chief Executive Officer
Web address: www.olympiamc.com

ST. ROSE HOSPITAL (C, 150 beds) 27200 Calaroga Avenue, Hayward, CA, Zip 94545–4383; tel. 510/264–4000; Aman Dhuper, President and Chief Executive Officer

OHIO: EAST OHIO REGIONAL HOSPITAL (O, 139 beds) 90 North Fourth Street, Martins Ferry, OH, Zip 43935–1648; tel. 740/633–1100; Bernie Albertini, Chief Administrative Officer
Web address: www.ovmc-eorh.com

TEXAS: WILSON N. JONES REGIONAL MEDICAL CENTER (O, 108 beds) 500 North Highland Avenue, Sherman, TX, Zip 75092–7354; tel. 903/870–4611; John Rossfeld, Administrator

WEST VIRGINIA: FAIRMONT REGIONAL MEDICAL CENTER (O, 144 beds) 1325 Locust Avenue, Fairmont, WV, Zip 26554–1435; tel. 304/367–7100; Robert S. Adcock, Chief Executive Officer
Web address: www.frmcwv.com

OHIO VALLEY MEDICAL CENTER (O, 189 beds) 2000 Eoff Street, Wheeling, WV, Zip 26003–3870; tel. 304/234–0123; Daniel C. Dunmyer, Chief Executive Officer
Web address: www.ovmc-eorh.com

Owned, leased, sponsored:	5 hospitals	784 beds
Contract–managed:	1 hospitals	150 beds
Totals:	6 hospitals	934 beds

★0199: ALLEGHENY HEALTH NETWORK (NP)

30 Isabella Street, Suite 300, Pittsburgh, PA, Zip 15212–5862; tel. 412/359–3131; Cynthia Hundorfean, President and Chief Executive Officer
(Independent Hospital System)

NEW YORK: WESTFIELD MEMORIAL HOSPITAL (O, 4 beds) 189 East Main Street, Westfield, NY, Zip 14787–1195; tel. 716/326–4921; Valarie Jackson, President
Web address: www.wmhinc.org

PENNSYLVANIA: ALLEGHENY GENERAL HOSPITAL (O, 531 beds) 320 East North Avenue, Pittsburgh, PA, Zip 15212–4756; tel. 412/359–3131; Jeffrey Cohen, M.D., President

ALLEGHENY VALLEY HOSPITAL (O, 121 beds) 1301 Carlisle Street, Natrona Heights, PA, Zip 15065–1152; tel. 724/224–5100; William Englert, Chief Executive Officer
Web address: www.wpahs.org

CANONSBURG HOSPITAL (O, 87 beds) 100 Medical Boulevard, Canonsburg, PA, Zip 15317–9762; tel. 724/745–6100; Louise Urban, R.N., President and Chief Executive Officer

FORBES HOSPITAL (O, 315 beds) 2570 Haymaker Road, Monroeville, PA, Zip 15146–3513; tel. 412/858–2000; Mark Rubino, M.D., President
Web address: www.ahn.org

JEFFERSON HOSPITAL (O, 341 beds) 565 Coal Valley Road, Jefferson Hills, PA, Zip 15025–3703, Mailing Address: Box 18119, Pittsburgh, Zip 15236–0119, tel. 412/469–5000; Louise Urban, R.N., President and Chief Executive Officer
Web address: www.jeffersonregional.com

SAINT VINCENT HOSPITAL (O, 371 beds) 232 West 25th Street, Erie, PA, Zip 16544–0002; tel. 814/452–5000; Christopher Clark, D.O., President and Chief Executive Officer

WEST PENN HOSPITAL (O, 309 beds) 4800 Friendship Avenue, Pittsburgh, PA, Zip 15224–1722; tel. 412/578–5000; Ronald J. Andro, R.N., MS, President and Chief Executive Officer
Web address: www.wpahs.org

Owned, leased, sponsored:	8 hospitals	2079 beds
Contract–managed:	0 hospitals	0 beds
Totals:	8 hospitals	2079 beds

For explanation of codes following names, see page B2.
★ Indicates Type III membership in the American Hospital Association.

0413: ALLEGIANCE HEALTH MANAGEMENT (IO)
504 Texas Street, Suite 200, Shreveport, LA, Zip 71101–3526; tel. 318/226–8202; Rock Bordelon, President and Chief Executive Officer
(Independent Hospital System)

ARKANSAS: EUREKA SPRINGS HOSPITAL (O, 15 beds) 24 Norris Street, Eureka Springs, AR, Zip 72632–3541; tel. 479/253–7400; Vicki Andert, Chief Executive Officer
Web address: www.eurekaspringshospital.com

NORTH METRO MEDICAL CENTER (O, 113 beds) 1400 West Braden Street, Jacksonville, AR, Zip 72076–3788; tel. 501/985–7000; Dale Anderson, RN, Chief Executive Officer

RIVER VALLEY MEDICAL CENTER (O, 35 beds) 200 North Third Street, Dardanelle, AR, Zip 72834–3802, Mailing Address: P.O. Box 578, Zip 72834–0578, tel. 479/229–4677; Vicki Andert, Chief Executive Officer
Web address: www.rivervalleymedicalcenter.com/

LOUISIANA: BIENVILLE MEDICAL CENTER (O, 21 beds) 1175 Pine Street, Suite 200, Arcadia, LA, Zip 71001–3122; tel. 318/263–4700; Kirk Lemoine, Chief Executive Officer
Web address: www.bienvillemedicalcenter.net/

BYRD REGIONAL HOSPITAL (O, 60 beds) 1020 West Fertitta Boulevard, Leesville, LA, Zip 71446–4645; tel. 337/239–9041; F. Peter. Savoy III, Chief Executive Officer
Web address: www.byrdregional.com

MERCY REGIONAL MEDICAL CENTER (O, 109 beds) 800 East Main Street, Ville Platte, LA, Zip 70586–4618; tel. 337/363–5684; Calvin Green, Chief Executive Officer
Web address: www.mercyregionalmedicalcenter.com

MINDEN MEDICAL CENTER (O, 161 beds) 1 Medical Plaza, Minden, LA, Zip 71055–3330, Mailing Address: P.O. Box 5003, Zip 71058–5003, tel. 318/377–2321; Gregory Pearson, Chief Executive Officer

SABINE MEDICAL CENTER (O, 24 beds) 240 Highland Drive, Many, LA, Zip 71449–3718; tel. 318/256–5691
Web address: www.sabinemedicalcenter.net

MISSISSIPPI: ALLEGIANCE SPECIALTY HOSPITAL OF GREENVILLE (O, 39 beds) 300 South Washington Avenue, 3rd Floor, Greenville, MS, Zip 38701–4719; tel. 662/332–7344; Vearnail Herzog, Chief Executive Officer

TEXAS: ALLEGIANCE BEHAVIORAL HEALTH CENTER OF PLAINVIEW (O, 20 beds) 2601 Dimmit Road, Suite 400, Suite 400, Plainview, TX, Zip 79072–1833; tel. 806/296–9191; Angie Alexander, Chief Executive Officer
Web address: www.ahmgt.com

ALLEGIANCE SPECIALTY HOSPITAL OF KILGORE (O, 60 beds) 1612 South Henderson Boulevard, Kilgore, TX, Zip 75662–3594; tel. 903/984–3505; Karen Ross, Chief Executive Officer
Web address: www.ahmgt.com

Owned, leased, sponsored:	11 hospitals	657 beds
Contract–managed:	0 hospitals	0 beds
Totals:	11 hospitals	657 beds

0317: ALLIANT MANAGEMENT SERVICES (IO)
2650 Eastpoint Parkway, Suite 300, Louisville, KY, Zip 40223–5164; tel. 502/992–3525; Stephen E. Fischer, Regional Vice President, Finance
(Moderately Centralized Health System)

FLORIDA: CALHOUN–LIBERTY HOSPITAL (C, 25 beds) 20370 NE Burns Avenue, Blountstown, FL, Zip 32424–1045, Mailing Address: P.O. Box 419, Zip 32424–0419, tel. 850/674–5411; Charles E. Durant Jr, FACHE, Chief Executive Officer

NORTHWEST FLORIDA COMMUNITY HOSPITAL (C, 59 beds) 1360 Brickyard Road, Chipley, FL, Zip 32428–6303, Mailing Address: P.O. Box 889, Zip 32428–0889, tel. 850/638–1610; Michael A. Kozar, Chief Executive Officer
Web address: www.nfch.org

ILLINOIS: FAYETTE COUNTY HOSPITAL (O, 110 beds) 650 West Taylor Street, Vandalia, IL, Zip 62471–1296; tel. 618/283–1231; Gregory D. Starnes, Chief Executive Officer

GIBSON AREA HOSPITAL AND HEALTH SERVICES (C, 67 beds) 1120 North Melvin Street, Gibson City, IL, Zip 60936–1477, Mailing Address: P.O. Box 429, Zip 60936–0429, tel. 217/784–4251; Robert C. Schmitt II, CPA, FACHE, Chief Executive Officer
Web address: www.gibsonhospital.org

PARIS COMMUNITY HOSPITAL (C, 25 beds) 721 East Court Street, Paris, IL, Zip 61944–2460; tel. 217/465–4141; Oliver Smith, President and Chief Executive Officer
Web address: www.pariscommunityhospital.com

WABASH GENERAL HOSPITAL (C, 25 beds) 1418 College Drive, Mount Carmel, IL, Zip 62863–2638; tel. 618/262–8621; Jay Purvis, President and Chief Executive Officer
Web address: www.wabashgeneral.com

INDIANA: PERRY COUNTY MEMORIAL HOSPITAL (C, 25 beds) 8885 State Road 237, Tell City, IN, Zip 47586–2750; tel. 812/547–7011; Brian J. Herwig, Chief Executive Officer

KENTUCKY: BRECKINRIDGE MEMORIAL HOSPITAL (C, 43 beds) 1011 Old Highway 60, Hardinsburg, KY, Zip 40143–2597; tel. 270/756–7000; Angela Portman, Chief Executive Officer
Web address: www.breckinridgehealth.org/

CARROLL COUNTY MEMORIAL HOSPITAL (C, 25 beds) 309 11th Street, Carrollton, KY, Zip 41008–1400; tel. 502/732–4321; Harry Hays, Chief Executive Officer
Web address: www.ccmhosp.com

TWIN LAKES REGIONAL MEDICAL CENTER (C, 75 beds) 910 Wallace Avenue, Leitchfield, KY, Zip 42754–2414; tel. 270/259–9400; Wayne Meriwether, Chief Executive Officer

Owned, leased, sponsored:	1 hospitals	110 beds
Contract–managed:	9 hospitals	369 beds
Totals:	10 hospitals	479 beds

★0041: ALLINA HEALTH (NP)
2925 Chicago Avenue, Minneapolis, MN, Zip 55407–1321, Mailing Address: P.O. Box 43, Zip 55440–0043, tel. 612/262–5000; Penny Ann. Wheeler, M.D., Chief Executive Officer
(Moderately Centralized Health System)

MINNESOTA: ABBOTT NORTHWESTERN HOSPITAL (O, 679 beds) 800 East 28th Street, Minneapolis, MN, Zip 55407–3799; tel. 612/863–4000; Thomas O'Connor, Interim Chief Executive Officer

BUFFALO HOSPITAL (O, 44 beds) 303 Catlin Street, Buffalo, MN, Zip 55313–1947; tel. 763/682–1212; Jennifer Myster, President
Web address: www.buffalohospital.org

CAMBRIDGE MEDICAL CENTER (O, 73 beds) 701 South Dellwood Street, Cambridge, MN, Zip 55008–1920; tel. 763/689–7700; Gary Shaw, President
Web address: www.allina.com/ahs/cambridge.nsf

DISTRICT ONE HOSPITAL (O, 42 beds) 200 State Avenue, Faribault, MN, Zip 55021–6345; tel. 507/334–6451; David L. Albrecht, President
Web address: www.allinahealth.org/District–One–Hospital/

MERCY HOSPITAL (O, 412 beds) 4050 Coon Rapids Boulevard, Coon Rapids, MN, Zip 55433–2586; tel. 763/236–6000; Sara J. Criger, President

NEW ULM MEDICAL CENTER (O, 45 beds) 1324 Fifth Street North, New Ulm, MN, Zip 56073–1553; tel. 507/217–5000; Toby Freier, President
Web address: www.newulmmedicalcenter.com

OWATONNA HOSPITAL (O, 43 beds) 2250 NW 26th Street, Owatonna, MN, Zip 55060–5503; tel. 507/451–3850; David L. Albrecht, President

PHILLIPS EYE INSTITUTE (O, 8 beds) 2215 Park Avenue, Minneapolis, MN, Zip 55404–3756; tel. 612/775–8800; Daniel S. Conrad, M.D., President
Web address: www.allinahealth.org/ahs/pei.nsf/

REGINA HOSPITAL (O, 43 beds) 1175 Nininger Road, Hastings, MN, Zip 55033–1098; tel. 651/480–4100; Thomas R. Thompson, President
Web address: www.reginamedical.org

ST. FRANCIS REGIONAL MEDICAL CENTER (O, 85 beds) 1455 St Francis Avenue, Shakopee, MN, Zip 55379–3380; tel. 952/428–3000; Mike McMahan, President

Section B

For explanation of codes following names, see page B2.
★ Indicates Type III membership in the American Hospital Association.

UNITED HOSPITAL (O, 377 beds) 333 North Smith Avenue, Saint Paul, MN, Zip 55102–2389; tel. 651/241–8000; Thomas O'Connor, President
Web address: www.allina.com

WISCONSIN: RIVER FALLS AREA HOSPITAL (O, 18 beds) 1629 East Division Street, River Falls, WI, Zip 54022–1571; tel. 715/425–6155; David R. Miller, President
Web address: www.allina.com

Owned, leased, sponsored:	12 hospitals	1869 beds
Contract–managed:	0 hospitals	0 beds
Totals:	12 hospitals	1869 beds

0877: ALTAPOINTE HEALTH SYSTEMS (IO)

5750–A Southland Drive, Mobile, AL, Zip 36693–3316; tel. 251/473–4423; J. Tuerk. Schlesinger, Chief Executive Officer

ALABAMA: BAYPOINTE BEHAVIORAL HEALTH (O, 60 beds) 5800 Southland Drive, Mobile, AL, Zip 36693–3313; tel. 251/661–0153; Jarett Crum, Hospital Director
Web address: www.altapointe.org

EASTPOINTE HOSPITAL (O, 50 beds) 7400 Roper Lane, Daphne, AL, Zip 36526–5274; tel. 251/378–6500; Philip L. Cusa, Hospital Director

Owned, leased, sponsored:	2 hospitals	110 beds
Contract–managed:	0 hospitals	0 beds
Totals:	2 hospitals	110 beds

2295: AMERICAN PROVINCE OF LITTLE COMPANY OF MARY SISTERS (CO)

9350 South California Avenue, Evergreen Park, IL, Zip 60805–2595; tel. 708/229–5491; Sister, Kathleen McIntyre, Province Leader
(Moderately Centralized Health System)

ILLINOIS: LITTLE COMPANY OF MARY HOSPITAL AND HEALTH CARE CENTERS (O, 254 beds) 2800 West 95th Street, Evergreen Park, IL, Zip 60805–2795; tel. 708/422–6200; John Hanlon, MD, President and Chief Executive Officer
Web address: www.lcmh.org

INDIANA: MEMORIAL HOSPITAL AND HEALTH CARE CENTER (O, 143 beds) 800 West Ninth Street, Jasper, IN, Zip 47546–2516; tel. 812/996–2345; E Kyle. Bennett, President and Chief Executive Officer

Owned, leased, sponsored:	2 hospitals	397 beds
Contract–managed:	0 hospitals	0 beds
Totals:	2 hospitals	397 beds

0644: AMG INTEGRATED HEALTHCARE MANAGEMENT (IO)

101 La Rue France, Suite 500, Lafayette, LA, Zip 70508–3144; tel. 337/269–9828; Timothy W. Howard, Chief Executive Officer
(Independent Hospital System)

KANSAS: AMG SPECIALTY HOSPITAL–WICHITA (O, 26 beds) 8080 East Pawnee Street, Wichita, KS, Zip 67207–5475; tel. 316/682–0004; Robert A. Loepp Jr, FACHE, Chief Executive Officer
Web address: www.amgwichita.com/

LOUISIANA: AMG PHYSICAL REHABILITATION HOSPITAL (O, 24 beds) 5025 Keystone Boulevard, Suite 200, Covington, LA, Zip 70433; tel. 985/888–0301; Natalie Stols, Interim Chief Executive Officer

AMG SPECIALTY HOSPITAL–HOUMA (O, 40 beds) 629 Dunn Street, Houma, LA, Zip 70360–4707; tel. 985/274–0001; Jody Robichaux, Chief Executive Officer
Web address: www.amghouma.com/

AMG SPECIALTY HOSPITAL–LAFAYETTE (O, 58 beds) 310 Youngsville Highway, Lafayette, LA, Zip 70508–4524; tel. 337/839–9880; Rachel Mayeaux, Chief Executive Officer
Web address: www.amglafayette.com

AMG SPECIALTY HOSPITAL–ZACHARY (O, 16 beds) 4601 McHugh Road, Zachary, LA, Zip 70791–5348; tel. 225/683–1600; April Ebeling, Chief Executive Officer

LAFAYETTE PHYSICAL REHABILITATION HOSPITAL (O, 32 beds) 307 Polly Lane, Lafayette, LA, Zip 70508–4960; tel. 337/314–1111; Bruce J. Bartels, Interim Chief Executive Officer
Web address: www.lafayettephysicalrehab.com/

THE NEUROMEDICAL CENTER REHABILITATION HOSPITAL (O, 23 beds) 10101 Park Rowe Avenue, Suite 500, Baton Rouge, LA, Zip 70810–1685; tel. 225/906–2999; Sherry Mix, Chief Executive Officer and Administrator

MISSISSIPPI: AMG SPECIALTY HOSPITAL–GREENWOOD (O, 40 beds) 1401 River Road Floor 2, Greenwood, MS, Zip 38930–4030; tel. 662/459–2681; Jennifer Wallace, Chief Executive Officer
Web address: www.amggreenwood.com/

NEVADA: AMG SPECIALTY HOSPITAL – LAS VEGAS (O, 24 beds) 4015 Mcleod Drive, Las Vegas, NV, Zip 89121–4305; tel. 702/433–2200; William Fox, Chief Executive Officer

NEW MEXICO: AMG SPECIALTY HOSPITAL–ALBUQUERQUE (O, 24 beds) 235 Elm Street NE, Albuquerque, NM, Zip 87102–3672; tel. 505/842–5550; Kendra Camp, R.N., Chief Executive Officer
Web address: www.amgalbuquerque.com/

OKLAHOMA: AMG SPECIALTY HOSPITAL AT MERCY (O, 30 beds) 4300 West Memorial Road, 2nd Floor, Oklahoma City, OK, Zip 73120–8304; tel. 405/936–5822; Keith Carruth, Chief Executive Officer

TEXAS: AMG SPECIALTY HOSPITAL (O, 30 beds) 718 Lexington Avenue, San Antonio, TX, Zip 78212–4768; tel. 210/572–4600; Melissa Low, Chief Executive Officer

Owned, leased, sponsored:	12 hospitals	367 beds
Contract–managed:	0 hospitals	0 beds
Totals:	12 hospitals	367 beds

★0389: ANMED HEALTH (NP)

800 North Fant Street, Anderson, SC, Zip 29621–5793; tel. 864/512–1000; William T. Manson III, FACHE, Chief Executive Officer
(Independent Hospital System)

SOUTH CAROLINA: ANMED HEALTH CANNON (O, 24 beds) 123 W G Acker Drive, Pickens, SC, Zip 29671–2739, Mailing Address: P.O. Box 188, Zip 29671–0188, tel. 864/878–4791; Brandon Clary, President and Chief Executive Officer
Web address: www.cannonhospital.org

ANMED HEALTH MEDICAL CENTER (O, 394 beds) 800 North Fant Street, Anderson, SC, Zip 29621–5793; tel. 864/512–1000; William T. Manson III, FACHE, Chief Executive Officer

Owned, leased, sponsored:	2 hospitals	418 beds
Contract–managed:	0 hospitals	0 beds
Totals:	2 hospitals	418 beds

★0866: APPALACHIAN REGIONAL HEALTHCARE SYSTEM (NP)

336 Deerfield Road, Boone, NC, Zip 28607–5008, Mailing Address: P.O. Box 2600, Zip 28607–2600, tel. 828/262–4100; Charles Mantooth, President and Chief Executive Officer
(Independent Hospital System)

NORTH CAROLINA: BLOWING ROCK REHABILITATION & DAVANT EXTENDED CARE CENTER (C, 72 beds) 418 Chestnut Street, Blowing Rock, NC, Zip 28605–0148, Mailing Address: P.O. Box 148, Zip 28605–0148, tel. 828/295–3136; Elizabeth Hayes, R.N., Interim Administrator

CHARLES A. CANNON MEMORIAL HOSPITAL (C, 35 beds) 434 Hospital Drive, Newland, NC, Zip 28646, Mailing Address: P.O. Box 767, Linville, Zip 28646–0767, tel. 828/737–7000; Carmen Lacey, MSN, R.N., President
Web address: www.https://apprhs.org/locations/cannon–memorial–hospital

---

For explanation of codes following names, see page B2.
★ Indicates Type III membership in the American Hospital Association.

Section B

WATAUGA MEDICAL CENTER (C, 99 beds) 336 Deerfield Road, Boone, NC, Zip 28607–5008, Mailing Address: P.O. Box 2600, Zip 28607–2600, tel. 828/262–4100; Charles Mantooth, President and Chief Executive Officer
Web address: www.https://apprhs.org/contact–us

Owned, leased, sponsored:	0 hospitals	0 beds
Contract–managed:	3 hospitals	206 beds
Totals:	3 hospitals	206 beds

0145: APPALACHIAN REGIONAL HEALTHCARE, INC. (NP)

2260 Executive Drive, Lexington, KY, Zip 40505–4810, Mailing Address: P.O. Box 8086, Zip 40533–8086, tel. 859/226–2440; Joseph Grossman, President and Chief Executive Officer
(Decentralized Health System)

KENTUCKY: HARLAN ARH HOSPITAL (O, 103 beds) 81 Ball Park Road, Harlan, KY, Zip 40831–1792; tel. 606/573–8100; Donald R. Fields, Community Chief Executive Officer
Web address: www.arh.org

HAZARD ARH REGIONAL MEDICAL CENTER (O, 358 beds) 100 Medical Center Drive, Hazard, KY, Zip 41701–9421; tel. 606/439–6600; Dan Stone, Senior Community Chief Executive Officer

MARY BRECKINRIDGE ARH HOSPITAL (O, 25 beds) 130 Kate Ireland Drive, Hyden, KY, Zip 41749–9071, Mailing Address: P.O. Box 447–A, Zip 41749–0717, tel. 606/672–2901; Mallie S. Noble, Administrator
Web address: www.frontiernursing.org

MCDOWELL ARH HOSPITAL (O, 25 beds) Route 122, McDowell, KY, Zip 41647, Mailing Address: P.O. Box 247, Zip 41647–0247, tel. 606/377–3400; Russell Barker, Community Chief Executive Officer

MIDDLESBORO ARH HOSPITAL (O, 73 beds) 3600 West Cumberland Avenue, Middlesboro, KY, Zip 40965–2614, Mailing Address: P.O. Box 340, Zip 40965–0340, tel. 606/242–1100; Michael Slusher, Community Chief Executive Officer
Web address: www.arh.org/middlesboro

MORGAN COUNTY ARH HOSPITAL (L, 25 beds) 476 Liberty Road, West Liberty, KY, Zip 41472–2049, Mailing Address: P O Box 579, Zip 41472–0579, tel. 606/743–3186; Stephen M. Gavalchik, FACHE, Community Chief Executive Officer
Web address: www.arh.org

TUG VALLEY ARH REGIONAL MEDICAL CENTER (O, 141 beds) 260 Hospital Drive, South Williamson, KY, Zip 41503–4072; tel. 606/237–1710; Timothy A. Hatfield, Community Chief Executive Officer

WHITESBURG ARH HOSPITAL (O, 89 beds) 240 Hospital Road, Whitesburg, KY, Zip 41858–7627; tel. 606/633–3500; Dena C. Sparkman, FACHE, Community Chief Executive Officer
Web address: www.arh.org/whitesburg

WEST VIRGINIA: BECKLEY ARH HOSPITAL (O, 160 beds) 306 Stanaford Road, Beckley, WV, Zip 25801–3142; tel. 304/255–3000; Rocco K. Massey, Community Chief Executive Officer

SUMMERS COUNTY ARH HOSPITAL (L, 25 beds) Terrace Street, Hinton, WV, Zip 25951–2407, Mailing Address: Drawer 940, Zip 25951–0940, tel. 304/466–1000; Wesley Dangerfield, Community Chief Executive Officer
Web address: www.arh.org

Owned, leased, sponsored:	10 hospitals	1024 beds
Contract–managed:	0 hospitals	0 beds
Totals:	10 hospitals	1024 beds

★0104: ARCHBOLD MEDICAL CENTER (NP)

910 South Broad Street, Thomasville, GA, Zip 31792–6113; tel. 229/228–2739; J Perry. Mustian, President
(Moderately Centralized Health System)

GEORGIA: BROOKS COUNTY HOSPITAL (L, 25 beds) 903 North Court Street, Quitman, GA, Zip 31643–1315, Mailing Address: P.O. Box 5000, Zip 31643–5000, tel. 229/263–4171; Nancy M. Williams, R.N., Administrator
Web address: www.archbold.org

GRADY GENERAL HOSPITAL (L, 39 beds) 1155 Fifth Street SE, Cairo, GA, Zip 39828–3142, Mailing Address: P.O. Box 360, Zip 39828–0360, tel. 229/377–1150; Crystal Wells, Administrator

JOHN D. ARCHBOLD MEMORIAL HOSPITAL (O, 306 beds) 915 Gordon Avenue, Thomasville, GA, Zip 31792–6614, Mailing Address: P.O. Box 1018, Zip 31799–1018, tel. 229/228–2000; J Perry. Mustian, President and Chief Executive Officer
Web address: www.archbold.org

MITCHELL COUNTY HOSPITAL (L, 181 beds) 90 East Stephens Street, Camilla, GA, Zip 31730–1836, Mailing Address: P.O. Box 639, Zip 31730–0639, tel. 229/336–5284; James Womack, Administrator
Web address: www.archbold.org

Owned, leased, sponsored:	4 hospitals	551 beds
Contract–managed:	0 hospitals	0 beds
Totals:	4 hospitals	551 beds

★0069: ARDENT HEALTH SERVICES (IO)

1 Burton Hills Boulevard, Suite 250, Nashville, TN, Zip 37215–6195; tel. 615/296–3000; David T. Vandewater, President and Chief Executive Officer
(Moderately Centralized Health System)

FLORIDA: BAY MEDICAL SACRED HEART (O, 273 beds) 615 North Bonita Avenue, Panama City, FL, Zip 32401–3600, Mailing Address: P.O. Box 59515, Zip 32412–0515, tel. 850/769–1511; Scott Campbell, Chief Executive Officer
Web address: www.baymedical.org

IDAHO: PORTNEUF MEDICAL CENTER (O, 175 beds) 777 Hospital Way, Pocatello, ID, Zip 83201–5175; tel. 208/239–1000; Daniel Ordyna, Chief Executive Officer
Web address: www.portmed.org

KANSAS: UNIVERSITY OF KANSAS HEALTH SYSTEM ST. FRANCIS CAMPUS (O, 259 beds) 1700 SW 7th Street, Topeka, KS, Zip 66606–1690; tel. 785/295–8000; Steven Anderson, Chief Executive Officer
Web address: www.stfrancistopeka.org

NEW JERSEY: HACKENSACK MERIDIAN HEALTH MOUNTAINSIDE MEDICAL CENTER (O, 202 beds) 1 Bay Avenue, Montclair, NJ, Zip 07042–4898; tel. 973/429–6000; John A Fromhold, FACHE, President and Chief Executive Officer

HACKENSACK MERIDIAN HEALTH PASCACK VALLEY MEDICAL CENTER (O, 128 beds) 250 Old Hook Road, Westwood, NJ, Zip 07675–3123; tel. 201/383–1035; Emily L. Holliman, Chief Executive Officer
Web address: www.hackensackumcpv.com/

NEW MEXICO: LOVELACE MEDICAL CENTER (O, 263 beds) 601 Martin Luther King Avenue NE, Albuquerque, NM, Zip 87102–3619; tel. 505/727–8000; Troy Greer, Chief Executive Officer
Web address: www.lovelace.com/albuquerque–hospital/lovelace–medical–center#.UDZ1laDhf48

LOVELACE REGIONAL HOSPITAL – ROSWELL (O, 26 beds) 117 East 19th Street, Roswell, NM, Zip 88201–5151; tel. 575/627–7000; Heather L. Harper, FACHE, Chief Executive Officer

LOVELACE REHABILITATION HOSPITAL (O, 52 beds) 505 Elm Street NE, Albuquerque, NM, Zip 87102–2500; tel. 505/727–4700; Derrick Jones, Chief Executive Officer
Web address: www.lovelace.com

LOVELACE WESTSIDE HOSPITAL (O, 80 beds) 10501 Golf Course Road NW, Albuquerque, NM, Zip 87114–5000, Mailing Address: P.O. Box 25555, Zip 87125–0555, tel. 505/727–8000; Amy Blasing, Chief Executive Officer

LOVELACE WOMEN'S HOSPITAL (O, 78 beds) 4701 Montgomery Boulevard NE, Albuquerque, NM, Zip 87109–1251, Mailing Address: P.O. Box 25555, Zip 87125–0555, tel. 505/727–7800; Sheri Milone, Chief Executive Officer and Administrator
Web address: www.lovelace.com/albuquerque–hospital/lovelace–womens–hospital#.UDZ17KDhf48

OKLAHOMA: BAILEY MEDICAL CENTER (O, 37 beds) 10502 North 110th East Avenue, Owasso, OK, Zip 74055–6655; tel. 918/376–8000; Keith Mason, Chief Executive Officer
Web address: www.baileymedicalcenter.com

For explanation of codes following names, see page B2.
★ Indicates Type III membership in the American Hospital Association.

HILLCREST HOSPITAL – SOUTH (O, 161 beds) 8801 South 101st East Avenue, Tulsa, OK, Zip 74133–5716; tel. 918/294–4000; Kevin Nowak, Interim Chief Executive Officer
Web address: www.southcresthospital.com

HILLCREST HOSPITAL CLAREMORE (O, 67 beds) 1202 North Muskogee Place, Claremore, OK, Zip 74017–3036; tel. 918/341–2556; David Chaussard, Chief Executive Officer

HILLCREST HOSPITAL CUSHING (O, 99 beds) 1027 East Cherry Street, Cushing, OK, Zip 74023–4101; tel. 918/225–2915; Kevin Hawk, Chief Executive Officer
Web address: www.hillcrestcushing.com/

HILLCREST HOSPITAL HENRYETTA (O, 37 beds) 2401 West Main Street, Henryetta, OK, Zip 74437–3893, Mailing Address: P.O. Box 1269, Zip 74437–1269, tel. 918/650–1100; Dee Renshaw, Chief Executive Officer
Web address: www.hillcresthenryetta.com/

HILLCREST HOSPITAL PRYOR (O, 22 beds) 111 North Bailey Street, Pryor, OK, Zip 74361–4201; tel. 918/825–1600; Douglas K. Weaver, FACHE, Chief Executive Officer

HILLCREST MEDICAL CENTER (O, 508 beds) 1120 South Utica Avenue, Tulsa, OK, Zip 74104–4090; tel. 918/579–1000; Kevin J. Gross, FACHE, Chief Executive Officer
Web address: www.hillcrestmedicalcenter.com

TULSA SPINE AND SPECIALTY HOSPITAL (O, 38 beds) 6901 South Olympia Avenue, Tulsa, OK, Zip 74132–1843; tel. 918/388–5701; Trent Gastineau, Chief Executive Officer

TEXAS: BSA HOSPITAL, LLC (O, 355 beds) 1600 Wallace Boulevard, Amarillo, TX, Zip 79106–1799; tel. 806/212–2000; Bob Williams, President and Chief Executive Officer
Web address: www.bsahs.org

PHYSICIANS SURGICAL HOSPITAL – QUAIL CREEK (O, 41 beds) 6819 Plum Creek, Amarillo, TX, Zip 79124–1602; tel. 806/354–6100; Todd Greene, Chief Executive Officer

SETON MEDICAL CENTER HARKER HEIGHTS (O, 83 beds) 850 West Central Texas Expressway, Harker Heights, TX, Zip 76548–1890; tel. 254/690–0900; Zachary K. Dietze, Chief Executive Officer
Web address: www.setonharkerheights.net

UT HEALTH ATHENS (O, 127 beds) 2000 South Palestine Street, Athens, TX, Zip 75751–5610; tel. 903/676–1000; Jack A. Endres, FACHE, JD, Administrator
Web address: www.https://uthealthathens.com/

UT HEALTH CARTHAGE (O, 23 beds) 409 Cottage Road, Carthage, TX, Zip 75633–1466; tel. 903/693–3841; Gary Mikeal. Hudson, Administrator

UT HEALTH HENDERSON (O, 41 beds) 300 Wilson Street, Henderson, TX, Zip 75652–5956; tel. 903/657–7541; Mark Leitner, FACHE, Administrator
Web address: www.https://uthealthhenderson.com/

UT HEALTH JACKSONVILLE (O, 38 beds) 501 South Ragsdale Street, Jacksonville, TX, Zip 75766–2413; tel. 903/541–5000; DeLeigh Haley, Chief Executive Officer

UT HEALTH PITTSBURG (O, 25 beds) 2701 Highway 271 North, Pittsburg, TX, Zip 75686–1032; tel. 903/946–5000; James Warren. Robicheaux, FACHE, Senior Administrator
Web address: www.https://uthealthpittsburg.com/

UT HEALTH QUITMAN (O, 25 beds) 117 Winnsboro Street, Quitman, TX, Zip 75783–2144, Mailing Address: P.O. Box 1000, Zip 75783–1000, tel. 903/763–6300; Patrick Swindle, Administrator
Web address: www.https://uthealthquitman.com/

UT HEALTH REHABILITATION HOSPITAL (O, 49 beds) 701 Olympic Plaza Circle, Tyler, TX, Zip 75701–1950, Mailing Address: P.O. Box 7530, Zip 75711–7530, tel. 903/596–3000; Laurie Lehnhof–Watts, Administrator and Chief Nursing Officer

UT HEALTH SPECIALTY HOSPITAL (O, 36 beds) 1000 South Beckham, 5th Floor, Tyler, TX, Zip 75701–1908, Mailing Address: P.O. Box 7018, Zip 75711–7018, tel. 903/596–3600; Laurie Lehnhof–Watts, Administrator and Chief Nursing Officer
Web address: www.https://uthealtheasttexas.com/locations/ut–health–east–texas–specialty–hospital

UT HEALTH TYLER (O, 399 beds) 1000 South Beckham Street, Tyler, TX, Zip 75701–1908, Mailing Address: Box 6400, Zip 75711–6400, tel. 903/597–0351; Vicki R. Briggs, Chief Executive Officer
Web address: www.https://uthealthtylerhospital.com/

Owned, leased, sponsored:	30 hospitals	3747 beds
Contract–managed:	0 hospitals	0 beds
Totals:	30 hospitals	3747 beds

0809: ARNOT HEALTH (NP)
600 Roe Avenue, Elmira, NY, Zip 14905–1629; tel. 607/737–4100; Jonathan I. Lawrence, President and Chief Executive Officer **(Independent Hospital System)**

NEW YORK: ARNOT OGDEN MEDICAL CENTER (O, 266 beds) 600 Roe Avenue, Elmira, NY, Zip 14905–1629; tel. 607/737–4100; Jonathan I. Lawrence, System Chief Operating Officer
Web address: www.arnothealth.org

IRA DAVENPORT MEMORIAL HOSPITAL (O, 132 beds) 7571 State Route 54, Bath, NY, Zip 14810–9590; tel. 607/776–8500; Elizabeth Weir, MSN, R.N., Chief Executive Officer

ST. JOSEPH'S HOSPITAL (O, 141 beds) 555 St. Joseph's Boulevard, Elmira, NY, Zip 14901–3223; tel. 607/733–6541; Jonathan I. Lawrence, President and Chief Executive Officer
Web address: www.arnothealth.org

Owned, leased, sponsored:	3 hospitals	539 beds
Contract–managed:	0 hospitals	0 beds
Totals:	3 hospitals	539 beds

★0094: ASANTE HEALTH SYSTEM (NP)
2650 Siskiyou Boulevard, Suite 200, Medford, OR, Zip 97504–8170; tel. 541/789–4100; Roy G. Vinyard, FACHE, President and Chief Executive Officer **(Moderately Centralized Health System)**

OREGON: ASANTE ASHLAND COMMUNITY HOSPITAL (O, 36 beds) 280 Maple Street, Ashland, OR, Zip 97520–1593; tel. 541/201–4000; Sheila Clough, Chief Executive Officer

ASANTE ROGUE REGIONAL MEDICAL CENTER (O, 320 beds) 2825 East Barnett Road, Medford, OR, Zip 97504–8332; tel. 541/789–7000; Mick Zdeblick, Chief Executive Officer
Web address: www.asante.org

ASANTE THREE RIVERS MEDICAL CENTER (O, 111 beds) 500 SW Ramsey Avenue, Grants Pass, OR, Zip 97527–5554; tel. 541/472–7000; Win Howard, Chief Executive Officer

Owned, leased, sponsored:	3 hospitals	467 beds
Contract–managed:	0 hospitals	0 beds
Totals:	3 hospitals	467 beds

★0198: ASCENSION HEALTHCARE (CO)
101 South Hanley Road, Suite 450, Saint Louis, MO, Zip 63105–3406; tel. 314/733–8000; Patricia A. Maryland, Dr.PH, President and Chief Executive Officer **(Decentralized Health System)**

ALABAMA: PROVIDENCE HOSPITAL (S, 305 beds) 6801 Airport Boulevard, Mobile, AL, Zip 36608–3785, Mailing Address: P.O. Box 850429, Zip 36685–0429, tel. 251/633–1000; Todd S. Kennedy, President and Chief Executive Officer
Web address: www.providencehospital.org

ST. VINCENT'S BIRMINGHAM (S, 409 beds) 810 St Vincent's Drive, Birmingham, AL, Zip 35205–1695, Mailing Address: P.O. Box 12407, Zip 35202–2407, tel. 205/939–7000; Evan Ray, FACHE, Chief Executive Officer

ST. VINCENT'S BLOUNT (S, 25 beds) 150 Gilbreath, Oneonta, AL, Zip 35121–2827, Mailing Address: P.O. Box 1000, Zip 35121–0013, tel. 205/274–3000; Greg Brown, Administrator
Web address: www.stvhs.com

ST. VINCENT'S CHILTON HOSPITAL (L, 36 beds) 2030 Lay Dam Road, Clanton, AL, Zip 35045; tel. 205/258–4400; Suzannah Campbell, Administrator

ST. VINCENT'S EAST (S, 362 beds) 50 Medical Park East Drive, Birmingham, AL, Zip 35235–9987; tel. 205/838–3000; Andrew Gnann, Vice President Operations
Web address: www.stvhs.com

ST. VINCENT'S ST. CLAIR (S, 40 beds) 7063 Veterans Parkway, Pell City, AL, Zip 35125–1499; tel. 205/814–2105; Lisa Nichols, R.N., Administrator

---

For explanation of codes following names, see page B2.
★ Indicates Type III membership in the American Hospital Association.

CONNECTICUT: ST. VINCENT'S MEDICAL CENTER (S, 343 beds) 2800 Main Street, Bridgeport, CT, Zip 06606–4292; tel. 203/576–6000; Dawn Rudolph, President and Chief Executive Officer
Web address: www.stvincents.org

DISTRICT OF COLUMBIA: PROVIDENCE HOSPITAL (S, 447 beds) 1150 Varnum Street NE, Washington, DC, Zip 20017–2104; tel. 202/269–7000; Darcy Burthay, MSN, R.N., President and Chief Executive Officer
Web address: www.provhosp.org

FLORIDA: SACRED HEART HOSPITAL PENSACOLA (S, 440 beds) 5151 North Ninth Avenue, Pensacola, FL, Zip 32504–8795, Mailing Address: P.O. Box 2700, Zip 32513–2700, tel. 850/416–7000; Henry Stovall, President

SACRED HEART HOSPITAL ON THE EMERALD COAST (S, 58 beds) 7800 Highway 98 West, Miramar Beach, FL, Zip 32550; tel. 850/278–3000; Roger L. Hall, President
Web address: www.sacredheartemerald.org

SACRED HEART HOSPITAL ON THE GULF (S, 19 beds) 3801 East Highway 98, Port St Joe, FL, Zip 32456–5318; tel. 850/229–5600; Roger L. Hall, President

ST. VINCENT'S MEDICAL CENTER CLAY COUNTY (O, 106 beds) 1670 St. Vincent's Way, Middleburg, FL, Zip 32068–8427, Mailing Address: 1670 St. Vincents Way, Zip 32068–8447, tel. 904/602–1000; James Machado, President
Web address: www.jaxhealth.com/

ST. VINCENT'S MEDICAL CENTER RIVERSIDE (S, 482 beds) 1 Shircliff Way, Jacksonville, FL, Zip 32204–4748, Mailing Address: P.O. Box 2982, Zip 32203–2982, tel. 904/308–7300; Thomas J. VanOsdol, Chief Executive Officer
Web address: www.jaxhealth.com

ST. VINCENT'S MEDICAL CENTER SOUTHSIDE (S, 289 beds) 4201 Belfort Road, Jacksonville, FL, Zip 32216–1431; tel. 904/296–3700; Thomas J. VanOsdol, Chief Executive Officer

ILLINOIS: AMITA HEALTH ELK GROVE VILLAGE (O, 380 beds) 800 Biesterfield Road, Elk Grove Village, IL, Zip 60007–3397; tel. 847/437–5500; John P. Werrbach, President and Chief Executive Officer
Web address: www.AMITAHealth.org

AMITA HEALTH HOFFMAN ESTATES (O, 290 beds) 1555 Barrington Road, Hoffman Estates, IL, Zip 60169–1019; tel. 847/843–2000; Leonard Wilk, President and Chief Executive Officer
Web address: www.AMITAHealth.org

ALEXIAN BROTHERS BEHAVIORAL HEALTH HOSPITAL (O, 141 beds) 1650 Moon Lake Boulevard, Hoffman Estates, IL, Zip 60169–1010; tel. 847/882–1600; Clayton Ciha, President and Chief Executive Officer

OUR LADY OF THE RESURRECTION–LONG TERM CARE (O, 50 beds) 5645 West Addison Street, Chicago, IL, Zip 60634

PRESENCE HOLY FAMILY MEDICAL CENTER (O, 178 beds) 100 North River Road, Des Plaines, IL, Zip 60016–1255; tel. 847/297–1800; Yolande Wilson–Stubbs, President
Web address: www.presencehealth.org

PRESENCE MERCY MEDICAL CENTER (O, 242 beds) 1325 North Highland Avenue, Aurora, IL, Zip 60506–1449; tel. 630/859–2222; Michael L. Brown, Regional President and Chief Executive Officer

PRESENCE RESURRECTION MEDICAL CENTER (O, 337 beds) 7435 West Talcott Avenue, Chicago, IL, Zip 60631–3746; tel. 773/774–8000; Robert Dahl, President and Chief Executive Officer
Web address: www.presencehealth.org

PRESENCE SAINT FRANCIS HOSPITAL (O, 189 beds) 355 Ridge Avenue, Evanston, IL, Zip 60202–3399; tel. 847/316–4000; Kenneth Jones, President

PRESENCE SAINT JOSEPH HOSPITAL (O, 361 beds) 2900 North Lake Shore Drive, Chicago, IL, Zip 60657–6274; tel. 773/665–3000; James L. Robinson III, PsyD, President
Web address: www.reshealth.org

PRESENCE SAINT JOSEPH HOSPITAL (O, 184 beds) 77 North Airlite Street, Elgin, IL, Zip 60123–4912; tel. 847/695–3200; Michael L. Brown, Regional President and Chief Executive Officer

PRESENCE SAINT JOSEPH MEDICAL CENTER (O, 460 beds) 333 North Madison Street, Joliet, IL, Zip 60435–8200; tel. 815/725–7133; Robert J. Erickson, President
Web address: www.presencehealth.org/stjoes

PRESENCE SAINTS MARY & ELIZABETH MEDICAL CENTER (O, 495 beds) 2233 West Division Street, Chicago, IL, Zip 60622–3086; tel. 312/770–2000; Martin H. Judd, Regional President and Chief Executive Officer

PRESENCE ST. MARY'S HOSPITAL (O, 156 beds) 500 West Court Street, Kankakee, IL, Zip 60901–3661; tel. 815/937–2400; Chris Shride, President
Web address: www.presencehealth.org/presence–st–marys–hospital–kankakee

RESURRECTION NURSING PAVILION (O, 295 beds) 1001 North Greenwood, Park Ridge, IL, Zip 60068, Patricia Tiernan, Administrator

INDIANA: DAVIESS COMMUNITY HOSPITAL (C, 72 beds) 1314 East Walnut Street, Washington, IN, Zip 47501–2860, Mailing Address: P.O. Box 760, Zip 47501–0760, tel. 812/254–2760; Tracy Conroy, Chief Executive Officer
Web address: www.dchosp.org

ST. VINCENT ANDERSON (S, 141 beds) 2015 Jackson Street, Anderson, IN, Zip 46016–4339; tel. 765/649–2511; Mike K. Schroyer, FACHE, MSN, R.N., President

ST. VINCENT CARMEL HOSPITAL (S, 121 beds) 13500 North Meridian Street, Carmel, IN, Zip 46032–1456; tel. 317/582–7000; Gary Fammartino, Regional President
Web address: https://www.stvincent.org

ST. VINCENT CLAY HOSPITAL (S, 25 beds) 1206 East National Avenue, Brazil, IN, Zip 47834–2797, Mailing Address: 1206 East National Ave , Zip 47834–0489, tel. 812/442–2500; Jerry Laue, Administrator

ST. VINCENT DUNN HOSPITAL (S, 25 beds) 1600 23rd Street, Bedford, IN, Zip 47421–4704; tel. 812/275–3331; Jerry Laue, Administrator
Web address: www.stvincent.org/St-Vincent-Dunn/Default.aspx

ST. VINCENT EVANSVILLE (S, 436 beds) 3700 Washington Avenue, Evansville, IN, Zip 47714–0541; tel. 812/485–4000; Daniel A. Parod, President

ST. VINCENT FISHERS HOSPITAL (S, 46 beds) 13861 Olio Road, Fishers, IN, Zip 46037–3487; tel. 317/415–9000; Gary Fammartino, Regional President
Web address: www.stvincent.org

ST. VINCENT HEART CENTER (S, 80 beds) 10580 North Meridian Street, Indianapolis, IN, Zip 46290–1028; tel. 317/583–5000; Blake A. Dye, FACHE, President

ST. VINCENT INDIANAPOLIS HOSPITAL (S, 832 beds) 2001 West 86th Street, Indianapolis, IN, Zip 46260–1991, Mailing Address: P.O. Box 40970, Zip 46240–0970, tel. 317/338–2345; Joel Feldman, Regional President
Web address: www.stvincent.org

ST. VINCENT JENNINGS HOSPITAL (S, 17 beds) 301 Henry Street, North Vernon, IN, Zip 47265–1097; tel. 812/352–4200; Christina Crank, Chief Nursing Officer

ST. VINCENT KOKOMO (S, 129 beds) 1907 West Sycamore Street, Kokomo, IN, Zip 46901–4197; tel. 765/452–5611; Margaret M. Johnson, President, St. Vincent Northwest Region
Web address: www.stvincent.org/stjoseph

ST. VINCENT MERCY HOSPITAL (S, 12 beds) 1331 South 'A' Street, Elwood, IN, Zip 46036–1942; tel. 765/552–4600; Ann C. Yates, R.N., MSN, Administrator and Chief Nursing Officer

ST. VINCENT RANDOLPH HOSPITAL (S, 18 beds) 473 Greenville Avenue, Winchester, IN, Zip 47394–9436; tel. 765/584–0004; Carla Fouse, Administrator and Chief Nursing Officer
Web address: www.stvincent.org

ST. VINCENT SALEM HOSPITAL (S, 25 beds) 911 North Shelby Street, Salem, IN, Zip 47167–1694; tel. 812/883–5881; Dana M. Muntz, Chief Executive Officer

ST. VINCENT SETON SPECIALTY HOSPITAL (S, 74 beds) 8050 Township Line Road, Indianapolis, IN, Zip 46260–2478; tel. 317/415–8500; Joel Feldman, Regional President
Web address: www.stvincent.org/

ST. VINCENT WARRICK HOSPITAL (S, 35 beds) 1116 Millis Avenue, Boonville, IN, Zip 47601–2204; tel. 812/897–4800; Kathy J. Hall, Administrator
Web address: www.stmarys.org/warrick

ST. VINCENT WILLIAMSPORT HOSPITAL (S, 16 beds) 412 North Monroe Street, Williamsport, IN, Zip 47993–1049; tel. 765/762–4000; Jane Craigin, Chief Executive Officer

KANSAS: VIA CHRISTI HOSPITAL MANHATTAN, INC. (O, 96 beds) 1823 College Avenue, Manhattan, KS, Zip 66502–3346; tel. 785/776–3322; Robert C. Copple, FACHE, Senior Administrator
Web address: https://www.viachristi.org/manhattan

For explanation of codes following names, see page B2.
★ Indicates Type III membership in the American Hospital Association.

Section B

VIA CHRISTI HOSPITAL PITTSBURG (O, 89 beds) 1 Mt. Carmel Way, Pittsburg, KS, Zip 66762–7587; tel. 620/231–6100; Randall R. Cason, FACHE, Senior Administrator

VIA CHRISTI HOSPITAL ON ST. FRANCIS (O, 675 beds) 929 North St Francis Street, Wichita, KS, Zip 67214–3882; tel. 316/268–5000; Kevin Strecker, President
Web address: www.via-christi.org

VIA CHRISTI HOSPITAL ON ST. TERESA (O, 48 beds) 14800 West St. Teresa, Wichita, KS, Zip 67235–9602; tel. 316/796–7000Robyn Chadwick, President
Web address: www.via-christi.org/st-teresa

VIA CHRISTI REHABILITATION HOSPITAL (O, 58 beds) 1151 North Rock Road, Wichita, KS, Zip 67206–1262; tel. 316/634–3400

MARYLAND: SAINT AGNES HEALTHCARE (S, 367 beds) 900 Caton Avenue, Baltimore, MD, Zip 21229–5201; tel. 667/234–6000; Keith Vander Kolk, President and Chief Executive Officer
Web address: www.stagnes.org

MICHIGAN: ASCENSION CRITTENTON HOSPITAL MEDICAL CENTER (O, 226 beds) 1101 West University Drive, Rochester, MI, Zip 48307–1831; tel. 248/652–5000; Chris Palazzolo, President and Chief Executive Officer
Web address: www.crittenton.com

ASCENSION ST. JOHN HOSPITAL (S, 621 beds) 22101 Moross Road, Detroit, MI, Zip 48236–2148; tel. 313/343–4000; Robert E. Hoban, President

BORGESS MEDICAL CENTER (S, 422 beds) 1521 Gull Road, Kalamazoo, MI, Zip 49048–1640; tel. 269/226–7000; Tim Stover, M.D., Interim Chief Executive Officer
Web address: www.borgess.com

BORGESS–LEE MEMORIAL HOSPITAL (S, 25 beds) 420 West High Street, Dowagiac, MI, Zip 49047–1943; tel. 269/782–8681; Natalie Ryder, Chief Administrative Officer
Web address: www.borgess.com

BRIGHTON CENTER FOR RECOVERY (S, 99 beds) 12851 Grand River Road, Brighton, MI, Zip 48116–8506; tel. 810/227–1211; Raymond A. Waller, Director

GENESYS REGIONAL MEDICAL CENTER (S, 427 beds) One Genesys Parkway, Grand Blanc, MI, Zip 48439–8066; tel. 810/606–5000; Chris Palazzolo, President and Chief Executive Officer
Web address: www.genesys.org

PROVIDENCE–PROVIDENCE PARK HOSPITALS (S, 635 beds) 16001 West Nine Mile Road, Southfield, MI, Zip 48075; tel. 248/849–3400; Joseph R. Hurshe, President
Web address: www.https://ascension.org/michigan

ST. JOHN MACOMB–OAKLAND HOSPITAL (S, 535 beds) 11800 East 12 Mile Road, Warren, MI, Zip 48093–3472; tel. 586/573–5000; Terry Hamilton, President
Web address: www.stjohnprovidence.org/macomb–oakland/

ST. JOHN RIVER DISTRICT HOSPITAL (S, 68 beds) 4100 River Road, East China, MI, Zip 48054–2909; tel. 810/329–7111; Robert E. Hoban, President

ST. JOSEPH HEALTH SYSTEM (S, 20 beds) 200 Hemlock Street, Tawas City, MI, Zip 48763–9237, Mailing Address: P.O. Box 659, Zip 48764–0659, tel. 989/362–3411; Jan Jacob, R.N., Interim Administrator
Web address: www.sjhsys.org

ST. MARY'S OF MICHIGAN STANDISH HOSPITAL (S, 25 beds) 805 West Cedar Street, Standish, MI, Zip 48658–9526; tel. 989/846–4521; Chris Palazzolo, President and Chief Executive Officer
Web address: www.stmarysofmichigan.org/standish

ST. MARY'S OF MICHIGAN (S, 286 beds) 800 South Washington Avenue, Saginaw, MI, Zip 48601–2594; tel. 989/907–8000; Chris Palazzolo, Health System President and Chief Executive Officer Mid–Michigan
Web address: www.stmarysofmichigan.org

MINNESOTA: SAINT ELIZABETH'S MEDICAL CENTER (O, 153 beds) 1200 Grant Boulevard West, Wabasha, MN, Zip 55981–1042; tel. 651/565–4531; Thomas Crowley, President and Chief Executive Officer

NEW YORK: OUR LADY OF LOURDES MEMORIAL HOSPITAL, INC. (S, 154 beds) 169 Riverside Drive, Binghamton, NY, Zip 13905–4246; tel. 607/798–5111; Kathryn Connerton, President and Chief Executive Officer
Web address: www.lourdes.com

ST. MARY'S HEALTHCARE (S, 290 beds) 427 Guy Park Avenue, Amsterdam, NY, Zip 12010–1054; tel. 518/842–1900; Victor Giulianelli, FACHE, President and Chief Executive Officer

OKLAHOMA: JANE PHILLIPS MEDICAL CENTER (O, 114 beds) 3500 East Frank Phillips Boulevard, Bartlesville, OK, Zip 74006–2411; tel. 918/333–7200; Mike Moore, President and Chief Operating Officer
Web address: www.jpmc.org

JANE PHILLIPS NOWATA HEALTH CENTER (O, 15 beds) 237 South Locust Street, Nowata, OK, Zip 74048–3660; tel. 918/273–3102; Jason McCauley, Administrator

ST. JOHN BROKEN ARROW (O, 44 beds) 1000 West Boise Circle, Broken Arrow, OK, Zip 74012–4900; tel. 918/994–8100; David L. Phillips, Chief Operating Officer
Web address: www.stjohnbrokenarrow.com

ST. JOHN MEDICAL CENTER (O, 523 beds) 1923 South Utica Avenue, Tulsa, OK, Zip 74104–6502; tel. 918/744–2345; Jeffrey D. Nowlin, President and Chief Operating Officer
Web address: www.sjmc.org

ST. JOHN OWASSO (O, 45 beds) 12451 East 100th Street North, Owasso, OK, Zip 74055–4600; tel. 918/274–5000; David L. Phillips, President and Chief Operating Officer

ST. JOHN SAPULPA (O, 25 beds) 1004 East Bryan Avenue, Sapulpa, OK, Zip 74066–4513, Mailing Address: P.O. Box 1368, Zip 74067–1368, tel. 918/224–4280; Michael Christian, Chief Operating Officer
Web address: www.stjohnhealthsystem.com/sapulpa

TENNESSEE: SAINT THOMAS DEKALB HOSPITAL (O, 56 beds) 520 West Main Street, Smithville, TN, Zip 37166–1138, Mailing Address: P.O. Box 640, Zip 37166–0640, tel. 615/215–5000; Bradley Mullinax, Chief Administrative Officer

SAINT THOMAS HICKMAN HOSPITAL (S, 65 beds) 135 East Swan Street, Centerville, TN, Zip 37033–1417; tel. 931/729–4271; Kevin Campbell, Chief Executive Officer
Web address: www.sths.com/hickman

SAINT THOMAS HIGHLANDS HOSPITAL (O, 60 beds) 401 Sewell Road, Sparta, TN, Zip 38583–1299; tel. 931/738–9211; Richard Tumlin, Chief Administrative Officer
Web address: www.whitecountyhospital.com

SAINT THOMAS HOSPITAL FOR SPINAL SURGERY (S, 23 beds) 2011 Murphy Avenue, Suite 400, Nashville, TN, Zip 37203–2065; tel. 615/341–7500; Kathy Watson, R.N., Administrator and Chief Nursing Officer

SAINT THOMAS MIDTOWN HOSPITAL (S, 425 beds) 2000 Church Street, Nashville, TN, Zip 37236–0002; tel. 615/284–5555; Fahad Tahir, Chief Executive Officer
Web address: www.sths.com

SAINT THOMAS RIVER PARK HOSPITAL (O, 85 beds) 1559 Sparta Street, Mc Minnville, TN, Zip 37110–1316; tel. 931/815–4000; Dale Humphrey, Chief Executive Officer
Web address: www.riverparkhospital.com

SAINT THOMAS RUTHERFORD HOSPITAL (S, 286 beds) 1700 Medical Center Parkway, Murfreesboro, TN, Zip 37129–2245; tel. 615/396–4100; Gordon B. Ferguson, President and Chief Executive Officer

SAINT THOMAS STONES RIVER HOSPITAL (O, 60 beds) 324 Doolittle Road, Woodbury, TN, Zip 37190–1139; tel. 615/563–4001; Brian Gill, Chief Administrative Officer
Web address: www.stonesriverhospital.com

SAINT THOMAS WEST HOSPITAL (S, 395 beds) 4220 Harding Road, Nashville, TN, Zip 37205–2095, Mailing Address: P.O. Box 380, Zip 37202–0380, tel. 615/222–2111; Fahad Tahir, Chief Executive Officer

TEXAS: DELL CHILDREN'S MEDICAL CENTER OF CENTRAL TEXAS (S, 189 beds) 4900 Mueller Boulevard, Austin, TX, Zip 78723–3079; tel. 512/324–0000; Debra M. Brown, Vice President, Chief Nursing Officer and Chief Operating Officer
Web address: www.dellchildrens.net

DELL SETON MEDICAL CENTER AT THE UNIVERSITY OF TEXAS (O, 211 beds) 1500 Red River Street, Austin, TX, Zip 78701; tel. 512/324–7000; Christann Vasquez, President
Web address: www.seton.net/locations/dell–seton/

PROVIDENCE HEALTHCARE NETWORK (S, 284 beds) 6901 Medical Parkway, Waco, TX, Zip 76712–7998, Mailing Address: P.O. Box 2589, Zip 76702–2589, tel. 254/751–4000; Philip A. Patterson, President

For explanation of codes following names, see page B2.
★ Indicates Type III membership in the American Hospital Association.

SETON EDGAR B. DAVIS HOSPITAL (S, 25 beds) 130 Hays Street, Luling, TX, Zip 78648–3207; tel. 830/875–7000; Scott O. Fuller, President and Chief Executive Officer
Web address: www.seton.net/locations/edgar_davis/

SETON HIGHLAND LAKES (S, 19 beds) 3201 South Water Street, Burnet, TX, Zip 78611–4510, Mailing Address: P.O. Box 1219, Zip 78611–7219, tel. 512/715–3000; Scott O. Fuller, President and Chief Executive Officer

SETON MEDICAL CENTER AUSTIN (S, 382 beds) 1201 West 38th Street, Austin, TX, Zip 78705–1006; tel. 512/324–1000; Christann Vasquez, President and Chief Executive Officer
Web address: www.seton.net/locations/smc/

SETON MEDICAL CENTER HAYS (O, 142 beds) 6001 Kyle Parkway, Kyle, TX, Zip 78640–6112; tel. 512/504–5000; Katherine Henderson, President and Chief Executive Officer
Web address: www.seton.net/locations/seton_medical_center_hays/

SETON MEDICAL CENTER WILLIAMSON (S, 126 beds) 201 Seton Parkway, Round Rock, TX, Zip 78665–8000; tel. 512/324–4000; Katherine Henderson, President and Chief Executive Officer

SETON NORTHWEST HOSPITAL (S, 117 beds) 11113 Research Boulevard, Austin, TX, Zip 78759–5236; tel. 512/324–6000; Katherine Henderson, President and Chief Executive Officer
Web address: www.seton.net

SETON SHOAL CREEK HOSPITAL (S, 94 beds) 3501 Mills Avenue, Austin, TX, Zip 78731–6391; tel. 512/324–2000; Christann Vasquez, President and Chief Executive Officer
Web address: www.seton.net

SETON SMITHVILLE REGIONAL HOSPITAL (O, 5 beds) 1201 Hill Road, Smithville, TX, Zip 78957; tel. 512/237–3214; Scott O. Fuller, President and Chief Executive Officer
Web address: www.seton.org

SETON SOUTHWEST HOSPITAL (S, 11 beds) 7900 F M 1826, Building 1, Austin, TX, Zip 78737–1407; tel. 512/324–9000; Katherine Henderson, President and Chief Executive Officer
Web address: www.seton.net

WISCONSIN: ASCENSION ALL SAINTS (O, 338 beds) 3801 Spring Street, Racine, WI, Zip 53405–1690; tel. 262/687–4011; Kristin McManmon, President

ASCENSION CALUMET HOSPITAL (O, 15 beds) 614 Memorial Drive, Chilton, WI, Zip 53014–1597; tel. 920/849–2386; Jenny Derks, Chief Administrative Officer
Web address: www.affinityhealth.org

ASCENSION EAGLE RIVER HOSPITAL (O, 14 beds) 201 Hospital Road, Eagle River, WI, Zip 54521–8835; tel. 715/479–7411; Sandra L. Anderson, President

ASCENSION GOOD SAMARITAN HOSPITAL (O, 10 beds) 601 South Center Avenue, Merrill, WI, Zip 54452–3404; tel. 715/536–5511; Jeremy Normington–Slay, FACHE, Chief Executive Officer
Web address: www.ministryhealth.org

ASCENSION MERCY HOSPITAL (O, 120 beds) 500 South Oakwood Road, Oshkosh, WI, Zip 54904–7944; tel. 920/223–2000; Denise Parrish, Interim Chief Administrative Officer
Web address: www.affinityhealth.org

ASCENSION OUR LADY OF VICTORY HOSPITAL (O, 5 beds) 1120 Pine Street, Stanley, WI, Zip 54768–1297; tel. 715/644–5571; Jeremy Normington–Slay, FACHE, President
Web address: www.ministryhealth.org

ASCENSION SACRED HEART HOSPITAL (O, 8 beds) 401 West Mohawk Drive, Tomahawk, WI, Zip 54487–2274; tel. 715/453–7700; Sandra L. Anderson, President and Chief Executive Officer

ASCENSION SAINT MARY'S HOSPITALS (O, 64 beds) 2251 North Shore Drive, Rhinelander, WI, Zip 54501–6710; tel. 715/361–2000; Sandra L. Anderson, President
Web address: www.ministryhealth.org

ASCENSION ST. ELIZABETH HOSPITAL (O, 190 beds) 1506 South Oneida Street, Appleton, WI, Zip 54915–1305; tel. 920/738–2000; Monica Hilt, President and Regional Vice President
Web address: www.affinityhealth.org

ASCENSION ST. MICHAEL'S HOSPITAL (O, 50 beds) 900 Illinois Avenue, Stevens Point, WI, Zip 54481–3196; tel. 715/346–5000; Jeremy Normington–Slay, FACHE, President, North Central Region

COLUMBIA ST. MARY'S HOSPITAL MILWAUKEE (S, 277 beds) 2301 North Lake Drive, Milwaukee, WI, Zip 53211–4508; tel. 414/291–1000; Travis Andersen, Chief Executive Officer
Web address: www.columbia–stmarys.org

COLUMBIA ST. MARY'S HOSPITAL OZAUKEE (S, 112 beds) 13111 North Port Washington Road, Mequon, WI, Zip 53097–2416; tel. 262/243–7300; Travis Andersen, President and Chief Executive Officer

COLUMBIA ST. MARY'S MILWAUKEE HOSPITAL (S, 31 beds) 2323 North Lake Drive, Milwaukee, WI, Zip 53211–4508, Mailing Address: 2301 North Lake Drive, Zip 53211–4508, tel. 414/585–1000; Kelly Elkins, President and Chief Executive Officer
Web address: www.columbia–stmarys.org/SHRI

HOWARD YOUNG MEDICAL CENTER (O, 50 beds) 240 Maple Street, Woodruff, WI, Zip 54568–9190, Mailing Address: P.O. Box 470, Zip 54568–0470, tel. 715/356–8000; Sandra L. Anderson, President and Chief Executive Officer
Web address: www.ministryhealth.org

MIDWEST ORTHOPEDIC SPECIALTY HOSPITAL (O, 16 beds) 10101 South 27th Street, 2nd Floor, Franklin, WI, Zip 53132–7209; tel. 414/817–5800; Bernie Sherry, President, Ascension Wisconsin

MINISTRY GOOD SAMARITAN HEALTH CENTER (O, 99 beds) 3400 Ministry Parkway, Weston, WI, Zip 54476–5220; tel. 715/393–3000; Jeremy Normington–Slay, FACHE, President, North Central Region
Web address: www.ministryhealth.org

WHEATON FRANCISCAN – ELMBROOK MEMORIAL CAMPUS (O, 122 beds) 19333 West North Avenue, Brookfield, WI, Zip 53045–4198; tel. 262/785–2000; Timothy Richman, President and Chief Executive Officer
Web address: www.wfhealthcare.org

WHEATON FRANCISCAN HEALTHCARE – FRANKLIN (O, 44 beds) 10101 South 27th Street, Franklin, WI, Zip 53132–7209; tel. 414/325–4700; Sheila Gansemer, R.N., Vice President Patient Care Services and Chief Nursing Officer

WHEATON FRANCISCAN HEALTHCARE – ST. FRANCIS (O, 161 beds) 3237 South 16th Street, Milwaukee, WI, Zip 53215; tel. 414/647–5000; Seth Teigen, President
Web address: www.mywheaton.org/stfrancis

WHEATON FRANCISCAN HEALTHCARE – ST. JOSEPH'S (O, 197 beds) 5000 West Chambers Street, Milwaukee, WI, Zip 53210–1650; tel. 414/447–2000; Timothy Richman, President
Web address: www.mywheaton.org/stjoseph

Owned, leased, sponsored:	112 hospitals	20219 beds
Contract–managed:	1 hospitals	72 beds
Totals:	113 hospitals	20291 beds

★**0519: ASPIRUS, INC.** (NP)
425 Pine Ridge Boulevard, Wausau, WI, Zip 54401–4123; tel. 715/847–2118; Matthew Heywood, Chief Executive Officer
(Moderately Centralized Health System)

MICHIGAN: ASPIRUS IRON RIVER HOSPITALS & CLINICS, INC. (O, 12 beds) 1400 West Ice Lake Road, Iron River, MI, Zip 49935–9526; tel. 906/265–6121; Connie L. Koutouzos, R.N., MSN, Chief Executive Officer
Web address: www.aspirus.org

ASPIRUS IRONWOOD HOSPITALS & CLINICS, INC. (O, 25 beds) N10561 Grand View Lane, Ironwood, MI, Zip 49938–9622; tel. 906/932–2525; Paula L. Chermside, Chief Executive Officer
Web address: www.aspirus.org

ASPIRUS KEWEENAW HOSPITAL, INC. (O, 25 beds) 205 Osceola Street, Laurium, MI, Zip 49913–2134; tel. 906/337–6500; Jesse G. Tischer, Interim Presidnet

ASPIRUS ONTONAGON HOSPITAL, INC. (O, 64 beds) 601 South Seventh Street, Ontonagon, MI, Zip 49953–1459; tel. 906/884–8000; Jesse G. Tischer, Interim President
Web address: www.aspirus.org

WISCONSIN: ASPIRUS LANGLADE HOSPITAL (O, 22 beds) 112 East Fifth Avenue, Antigo, WI, Zip 54409–2796; tel. 715/623–2331; Andrew J. Barth, Executive Director

For explanation of codes following names, see page B2.
★ Indicates Type III membership in the American Hospital Association.

Section B

ASPIRUS MEDFORD HOSPITAL & CLINICS, INC. (O, 124 beds) 135 South Gibson Street, Medford, WI, Zip 54451; tel. 715/748–8100; Dale Hustedt, Chief Executive Officer
Web address: www.aspirus.org

ASPIRUS RIVERVIEW HOSPITAL AND CLINICS, INC. (O, 75 beds) 410 Dewey Street, Wisconsin Rapids, WI, Zip 54494–4715, Mailing Address: P.O. Box 8080, Zip 54495–8080, tel. 715/423–6060; Todd Burch, Chief Executive Officer
Web address: www.aspirus.org

ASPIRUS WAUSAU HOSPITAL, INC. (O, 263 beds) 333 Pine Ridge Boulevard, Wausau, WI, Zip 54401–4187; tel. 715/847–2121; Darrell Lentz, President

Owned, leased, sponsored:	8 hospitals	610 beds
Contract–managed:	0 hospitals	0 beds
Totals:	8 hospitals	610 beds

1031: ASTRIA HEALTH (NP)

1016 Tacoma Ave, Sunnyside, WA, Zip 98944–2263, Mailing Address: P.O. Box 979, Zip 98944, tel. 509/837–1330; John Gallagher, President and Chief Executive Officer

WASHINGTON: ASTRIA REGIONAL MEDICAL CENTER (O, 167 beds) 110 South Ninth Avenue, Yakima, WA, Zip 98902–3315; tel. 509/575–5000; Richard H. Robinson, Chief Executive Officer

ASTRIA SUNNYSIDE HOSPITAL (O, 25 beds) 1016 Tacoma Avenue, Sunnyside, WA, Zip 98944–2263, Mailing Address: P.O. Box 719, Zip 98944–0719, tel. 509/837–1500; Brian P. Gibbons Jr, Chief Executive Officer
Web address: www.astria.health/

ASTRIA TOPPENISH HOSPITAL (O, 48 beds) 502 West Fourth Avenue, Toppenish, WA, Zip 98948–1616, Mailing Address: P.O. Box 672, Zip 98948–0672, tel. 509/865–3105; Eric P. Jensen, Chief Executive Officer
Web address: www.astria.health/

Owned, leased, sponsored:	3 hospitals	240 beds
Contract–managed:	0 hospitals	0 beds
Totals:	3 hospitals	240 beds

★**0865: ATLANTIC HEALTH SYSTEM** (NP)

475 South Street, Morristown, NJ, Zip 07960–6459, Mailing Address: P.O. Box 1905, Zip 07962–1905, tel. 973/660–3270; Brian A. Gragnolati, FACHE, President and Chief Executive Officer
(Decentralized Health System)

NEW JERSEY: CHILTON MEDICAL CENTER (O, 131 beds) 97 West Parkway, Pompton Plains, NJ, Zip 07444–1696; tel. 973/831–5000; Stephanie L. Schwartz, FACHE, Vice President AHS and President CMC
Web address: www.chiltonmemorial.org

HACKETTSTOWN MEDICAL CENTER (O, 80 beds) 651 Willow Grove Street, Hackettstown, NJ, Zip 07840–1799; tel. 908/852–5100; Joseph DiPaolo, FACHE, President

MORRISTOWN MEDICAL CENTER (O, 727 beds) 100 Madison Avenue, Morristown, NJ, Zip 07960–6136; tel. 973/971–5000; Trish O'Keefe, Ph.D., R.N., President
Web address: www.atlantichealth.org/Morristown/

NEWTON MEDICAL CENTER (O, 148 beds) 175 High Street, Newton, NJ, Zip 07860–1004; tel. 973/383–2121; Joseph DiPaolo, FACHE, President

OVERLOOK MEDICAL CENTER (O, 384 beds) 99 Beauvoir Avenue, Summit, NJ, Zip 07901–3533; tel. 908/522–2000; Alan R. Lieber, President
Web address: www.atlantichealth.org/Overlook

Owned, leased, sponsored:	5 hospitals	1470 beds
Contract–managed:	0 hospitals	0 beds
Totals:	5 hospitals	1470 beds

★**0705: ATRIUM HEALTH** (NP)

1000 Blythe Boulevard, Charlotte, NC, Zip 28203–5871, Mailing Address: PO Box 32861, Zip 28232–2861, tel. 704/355–2000; Eugene A. Woods, FACHE, President and Chief Executive Officer
(Moderately Centralized Health System)

NORTH CAROLINA: CAROLINAS HEALTHCARE SYSTEM ANSON (O, 15 beds) 2301 US Highway 74 W, Wadesboro, NC, Zip 28170–7554, Mailing Address: 2301 U.S Highway 74 West, Zip 28170, tel. 704/994–4500; Dave Anderson, FACHE, Vice President and Administrator
Web address: www.carolinashealthcare.org/anson

CAROLINAS HEALTHCARE SYSTEM BLUE RIDGE (C, 156 beds) 2201 South Sterling Street, Morganton, NC, Zip 28655–4058; tel. 828/580–5000; Kathy C. Bailey, Ph.D., FACHE, President and Chief Executive Officer

CAROLINAS HEALTHCARE SYSTEM CLEVELAND (L, 161 beds) 201 East Grover Street, Shelby, NC, Zip 28150–3917; tel. 980/487–3000; Brian Gwyn, President and Chief Executive Officer
Web address: www.clevelandregional.org

CAROLINAS HEALTHCARE SYSTEM KINGS MOUNTAIN (O, 59 beds) 706 West King Street, Kings Mountain, NC, Zip 28086–2708; tel. 980/487–5000; Brian Gwyn, President and Chief Executive Officer
Web address: www.clevelandregional.org/kings–mountain–hospital.html

CAROLINAS HEALTHCARE SYSTEM LINCOLN (O, 101 beds) 433 McAlister Road, Lincolnton, NC, Zip 28092–4147, Mailing Address: PO Box 677, Zip 28093–0677, tel. 980/212–2000; Peter W. Acker, President and Chief Executive Officer

CAROLINAS HEALTHCARE SYSTEM NORTHEAST (O, 455 beds) 920 Church Street North, Concord, NC, Zip 28025–2983; tel. 704/403–3000; Phyllis A. Wingate, FACHE, President
Web address: www.carolinashealthcare.org/northeast

CAROLINAS HEALTHCARE SYSTEM STANLY (C, 109 beds) 301 Yadkin Street, Albemarle, NC, Zip 28001–3441, Mailing Address: P.O. Box 1489, Zip 28002–1489, tel. 704/984–4000; Brian Freeman, President

CAROLINAS HEALTHCARE SYSTEM UNIVERSITY (O, 100 beds) 8800 North Tryon Street, Charlotte, NC, Zip 28262–3300, Mailing Address: P.O. Box 560727, Zip 28256–0727, tel. 704/863–6000; William H. Leonard, President
Web address: www.carolinashealthcare.org/university

CAROLINAS HEALTHCARE SYSTEM PINEVILLE (O, 235 beds) 10628 Park Road, Charlotte, NC, Zip 28210–8407; tel. 704/667–1000; Christopher R. Hummer, President
Web address: www.carolinashealthcare.org/pineville

CAROLINAS HEALTHCARE SYSTEM UNION (L, 228 beds) 600 Hospital Drive, Monroe, NC, Zip 28112–6000, Mailing Address: P.O. Box 5003, Zip 28111–5003, tel. 980/993–3100; Michael Lutes, President

CAROLINAS MEDICAL CENTER (O, 1246 beds) 1000 Blythe Boulevard, Charlotte, NC, Zip 28203–5871, Mailing Address: P.O. Box 32861, Zip 28232–2861, tel. 704/355–2000; Christopher Bowe, FACHE, Interim Chief Executive Officer
Web address: www.carolinashealthcare.org/cmc

CAROLINAS REHABILITATION (O, 150 beds) 1100 Blythe Boulevard, Charlotte, NC, Zip 28203–5864; tel. 704/355–4300; Robert G. Larrison Jr, President
Web address: www.carolinashealthcare.org/rehabilitation

COLUMBUS REGIONAL HEALTHCARE SYSTEM (C, 85 beds) 500 Jefferson Street, Whiteville, NC, Zip 28472–3634; tel. 910/642–8011; John E. Young, Interim Chief Executive Officer
Web address: www.crhealthcare.org/

SCOTLAND HEALTH CARE SYSTEM (C, 104 beds) 500 Lauchwood Drive, Laurinburg, NC, Zip 28352–5599; tel. 910/291–7000; Gregory C. Wood, President and Chief Executive Officer

ST. LUKE'S HOSPITAL (C, 35 beds) 101 Hospital Drive, Columbus, NC, Zip 28722–6418; tel. 828/894–3311; James B. Bross, President
Web address: www.saintlukeshospital.com

SOUTH CAROLINA: BON SECOURS ST. FRANCIS HOSPITAL (C, 160 beds) 2095 Henry Tecklenburg Drive, Charleston, SC, Zip 29414–5733; tel. 843/402–1000; Anthony Jackson, Chief Executive Officer
Web address: www.rsfh.com/

ROPER ST. FRANCIS MOUNT PLEASANT HOSPITAL (C, 73 beds) 3500 Highway 17 North, Mount Pleasant, SC, Zip 29466–9123, Mailing Address: 3500 North Highway 17, Zip 29466–9123, tel. 843/606–7000; Anthony Jackson, Chief Executive Officer
Web address: www.rsfh.com/mount–pleasant–hospital

ROPER ST. FRANCIS (C, 292 beds) 316 Calhoun Street, Charleston, SC, Zip 29401–1125; tel. 843/724–2000; Stephen D. Porter, Chief Executive Officer

Owned, leased, sponsored:	10 hospitals	2750 beds
Contract–managed:	8 hospitals	1014 beds
Totals:	18 hospitals	3764 beds

For explanation of codes following names, see page B2.
★ Indicates Type III membership in the American Hospital Association.

0859: AULTMAN HEALTH FOUNDATION (NP)

2600 Sixth Street SW, Canton, OH, Zip 44710–1702;
tel. 330/363–6192; Edward J. Roth III, President and Chief
Executive Officer
(Moderately Centralized Health System)

OHIO: ALLIANCE COMMUNITY HOSPITAL (O, 202 beds) 200 East State Street,
Alliance, OH, Zip 44601–4936; tel. 330/596–6000; Ryan Jones, Chief
Executive Officer
Web address: www.achosp.org

AULTMAN HOSPITAL (O, 532 beds) 2600 Sixth Street SW, Canton, OH,
Zip 44710–1702; tel. 330/452–9911; Edward J. Roth III, President and Chief
Executive Officer

AULTMAN ORRVILLE HOSPITAL (O, 25 beds) 832 South Main Street, Orrville, OH,
Zip 44667–2208; tel. 330/682–3010; Jennifer Kessel, Chief Executive Officer
Web address: www.aultmanorrville.org

AULTMAN SPECIALTY HOSPITAL (O, 16 beds) 2600 Sixth Street, SW, Canton,
OH, Zip 44710–1702; tel. 330/363–4000; Ryan J. Kuharich, Chief Executive
Officer
Web address: www.aultman.org

Owned, leased, sponsored:	4 hospitals	775 beds
Contract–managed:	0 hospitals	0 beds
Totals:	4 hospitals	775 beds

0869: AVANTI HOSPITALS (IO)

222 North Sepulveda Boulevard, Suite 950, El Segundo, CA,
Zip 90245–5614; tel. 310/356–0550; Michael A. Rembis,
FACHE, Corporate Chief Executive Officer
(Independent Hospital System)

CALIFORNIA: COAST PLAZA HOSPITAL (O, 123 beds) 13100 Studebaker
Road, Norwalk, CA, Zip 90650–2500; tel. 562/868–3751; Gregory Padilla,
Administrator
Web address: www.avantihospitals.com/coast–plaza–hospital

COMMUNITY HOSPITAL OF HUNTINGTON PARK (O, 81 beds) 2623 East
Slauson Avenue, Huntington Park, CA, Zip 90255–2926; tel. 323/583–1931;
Patricia Rives, R.N., MSN, Chief Executive Officer
Web address: www.avantihospitals.com/community–hospital–of–huntington–
park

EAST LOS ANGELES DOCTORS HOSPITAL (O, 127 beds) 4060 Whittier
Boulevard, Los Angeles, CA, Zip 90023–2526; tel. 323/268–5514; Gerald B.
Clute, Chief Executive Officer
Web address: www.avantihospitals.com

MEMORIAL HOSPITAL OF GARDENA (O, 172 beds) 1145 West Redondo Beach
Boulevard, Gardena, CA, Zip 90247–3528; tel. 310/532–4200; Kathy Wojno,
R.N., MSN, Administrator

Owned, leased, sponsored:	4 hospitals	503 beds
Contract–managed:	0 hospitals	0 beds
Totals:	4 hospitals	503 beds

★5255: AVERA HEALTH (CO)

3900 West Avera Drive, Suite 300, Sioux Falls, SD, Zip 57108–
5721; tel. 605/322–4700; Bob Sutton, President and Chief
Executive Officer
(Decentralized Health System)

IOWA: AVERA HOLY FAMILY HOSPITAL (O, 25 beds) 826 North Eighth Street,
Estherville, IA, Zip 51334–1598; tel. 712/362–2631; Kayleen R. Lee,
Interim Chief Executive Officer

FLOYD VALLEY HEALTHCARE (C, 25 beds) 714 Lincoln Street NE, Le
Mars, IA, Zip 51031–3314; tel. 712/546–7871; Michael T. Donlin, FACHE,
Administrator
Web address: www.floydvalley.org

HEGG MEMORIAL HEALTH CENTER AVERA (C, 85 beds) 1202 21st Avenue,
Rock Valley, IA, Zip 51247–1497; tel. 712/476–8000; Glenn Zevenbergen,
Chief Executive Officer
Web address: www.hegghc.org

LAKES REGIONAL HEALTHCARE (C, 30 beds) 2301 Highway 71 South, Spirit
Lake, IA, Zip 51360–0159, Mailing Address: P.O. Box AB, Zip 51360–0159,
tel. 712/336–1230; Jason Harrington, FACHE, President and Chief Executive
Officer

OSCEOLA COMMUNITY HOSPITAL (C, 25 beds) 600 Ninth Avenue North,
Sibley, IA, Zip 51249–1012, Mailing Address: P.O. Box 258, Zip 51249–0258,
tel. 712/754–2574; Ben Davis, Chief Executive Officer
Web address: www.osceolacommunityhospital.org

SIOUX CENTER HEALTH (C, 88 beds) 1101 9th Street SE, Sioux Center, IA,
Zip 51250; tel. 712/722–8107; Cory D. Nelson, Administrator

MINNESOTA: AVERA MARSHALL REGIONAL MEDICAL CENTER (O, 111 beds)
300 South Bruce Street, Marshall, MN, Zip 56258–3900; tel. 507/532–
9661; Mary B. Maertens, FACHE, President and Chief Executive Officer
Web address: www.avera.org

AVERA TYLER HOSPITAL (C, 25 beds) 240 Willow Street, Tyler, MN,
Zip 56178–1166; tel. 507/247–5521; Allen Anderson, Administrator

PIPESTONE COUNTY MEDICAL CENTER AVERA (C, 18 beds) 916 4th Avenue
SW, Pipestone, MN, Zip 56164–1890; tel. 507/825–5811; Bradley D. Burris,
Chief Executive Officer
Web address: www.pcmchealth.org

NEBRASKA: AVERA CREIGHTON HOSPITAL (O, 64 beds) 1503 Main Street,
Creighton, NE, Zip 68729–3007, Mailing Address: P.O. Box 186, Zip 68729–
0186, tel. 402/358–5700; Todd Consbruck, Chief Executive Officer
Web address: www.avera.org/creighton/

AVERA ST. ANTHONY'S HOSPITAL (O, 25 beds) 300 North Second Street,
O'Neill, NE, Zip 68763–1514, Mailing Address: P.O. Box 270, Oneill,
Zip 68763–0270, tel. 402/336–2611; Todd Consbruck, President and Chief
Executive Officer

SOUTH DAKOTA: AVERA DE SMET MEMORIAL HOSPITAL (L, 6 beds) 306
Prairie Avenue SW, De Smet, SD, Zip 57231–2285, Mailing Address:
P.O. Box 160, Zip 57231–0160, tel. 605/854–6100; Stephanie Reasy,
Administrator and Chief Executive Officer
Web address: www.avera.org

AVERA DELLS AREA HOSPITAL (L, 23 beds) 909 North Iowa Avenue, Dell
Rapids, SD, Zip 57022–1231; tel. 605/428–5431; Scott James. Hargens,
Administrator and Chief Executive Officer

AVERA FLANDREAU HOSPITAL (L, 18 beds) 214 North Prairie Street,
Flandreau, SD, Zip 57028–1243; tel. 605/997–2433; Scott James. Hargens,
Administrator and Chief Executive Officer
Web address: www.avera.org/flandreau–medical/

AVERA GETTYSBURG HOSPITAL (O, 55 beds) 606 East Garfield Avenue,
Gettysburg, SD, Zip 57442–1398; tel. 605/765–2480; Robert L. Sheckler,
Administrator

AVERA GREGORY HOSPITAL (O, 65 beds) 400 Park Avenue, Gregory,
SD, Zip 57533–1302, Mailing Address: P.O. Box 408, Zip 57533–0408,
tel. 605/835–8394; Anthony Timanus, Chief Executive Officer
Web address: www.gregoryhealthcare.org

AVERA HAND COUNTY MEMORIAL HOSPITAL (L, 9 beds) 300 West Fifth
Street, Miller, SD, Zip 57362–1238; tel. 605/853–2421; Bryan Breitling,
Administrator
Web address: www.avera.org

AVERA HEART HOSPITAL OF SOUTH DAKOTA (O, 53 beds) 4500 West 69th
Street, Sioux Falls, SD, Zip 57108–8148; tel. 605/977–7000; Michael Gibbs,
President

AVERA MCKENNAN HOSPITAL AND UNIVERSITY HEALTH CENTER (O, 485
beds) 1325 South Cliff Avenue, Sioux Falls, SD, Zip 57105–1007, Mailing
Address: P.O. Box 5045, Zip 57117–5045, tel. 605/322–8000; David Flicek,
President and Chief Executive Officer
Web address: www.averamckennan.org

AVERA QUEEN OF PEACE HOSPITAL (O, 159 beds) 525 North Foster, Mitchell,
SD, Zip 57301–2999; tel. 605/995–2000; Thomas A. Clark, Regional
President and Chief Executive Officer

AVERA SACRED HEART HOSPITAL (O, 286 beds) 501 Summit Avenue,
Yankton, SD, Zip 57078–3855; tel. 605/668–8000; Douglas R. Ekeren,
Regional President and Chief Executive Officer
Web address: www.averasacredheart.com

AVERA ST. BENEDICT HEALTH CENTER (O, 99 beds) 401 West Glynn Drive,
Parkston, SD, Zip 57366–9605; tel. 605/928–3311; Rita Blasius, President
and Chief Executive Officer

Section B

For explanation of codes following names, see page B2.
★ Indicates Type III membership in the American Hospital Association.

AVERA ST. LUKE'S HOSPITAL (O, 222 beds) 305 South State Street, Aberdeen, SD, Zip 57401–4527; tel. 605/622–5000; Todd Forkel, President and Chief Executive Officer
Web address: www.avera.org/st-lukes-hospital/

AVERA ST. MARY'S HOSPITAL (O, 110 beds) 801 East Sioux Avenue, Pierre, SD, Zip 57501–3323; tel. 605/224–3100; Todd Forkel, Interim Chief Executive Officer

AVERA WESKOTA MEMORIAL HOSPITAL (L, 23 beds) 604 First Street NE, Wessington Springs, SD, Zip 57382–2166; tel. 605/539–1201; Stephanie Reasy, Administrator and Chief Executive Officer
Web address: www.averaweskota.org

EUREKA COMMUNITY HEALTH SERVICES AVERA (C, 6 beds) 410 Ninth Street, Eureka, SD, Zip 57437–2182, Mailing Address: P.O. Box 517, Zip 57437–0517, tel. 605/284–2661; Carmen Weber, Administrator
Web address: www.avera.org

LANDMANN–JUNGMAN MEMORIAL HOSPITAL AVERA (C, 25 beds) 600 Billars Street, Scotland, SD, Zip 57059–2026; tel. 605/583–2226; Melissa Gale, Chief Executive Officer

MARSHALL COUNTY HEALTHCARE CENTER AVERA (C, 18 beds) 413 Ninth Street, Britton, SD, Zip 57430–2274; tel. 605/448–2253; Nick Fosness, Chief Executive Officer
Web address: www.avera.org

MILBANK AREA HOSPITAL AVERA (L, 25 beds) 301 Flynn Drive, Milbank, SD, Zip 57252–1508; tel. 605/432–4538; Natalie Gauer, Administrator
Web address: www.averamilbank.org

PLATTE HEALTH CENTER AVERA (C, 59 beds) 601 East Seventh, Platte, SD, Zip 57369–2123, Mailing Address: P.O. Box 200, Zip 57369–0200, tel. 605/337–3364; Mark Burket, Chief Executive Officer
Web address: www.phcavera.org

ST. MICHAEL'S HOSPITAL AVERA (C, 25 beds) 410 West 16th Avenue, Tyndall, SD, Zip 57066–2318; tel. 605/589–2152; Carol Deurmier, Chief Executive Officer

WAGNER COMMUNITY MEMORIAL HOSPITAL AVERA (C, 20 beds) 513 Third Street SW, Wagner, SD, Zip 57380–9675, Mailing Address: P.O. Box 280, Zip 57380–0280, tel. 605/384–3611; Bryan Slaba, Chief Executive Officer
Web address: www.avera.org/wagnerhospital

Owned, leased, sponsored:	19 hospitals	1863 beds
Contract–managed:	13 hospitals	449 beds
Totals:	32 hospitals	2312 beds

★0633: AVITA HEALTH SYSTEM (NP)
269 Portland Way South, Galion, OH, Zip 44833–2399; tel. 419/468–4841; Jerome Morasko, President and Chief Executive Officer
(Independent Hospital System)

OHIO: AVITA ONTARIO HOSPITAL (O, 26 beds) 715 Richland Mall, Ontario, OH, Zip 44906–3802; tel. 567/307–7666; Jerome Morasko, President and Chief Executive Officer

BUCYRUS HOSPITAL (O, 25 beds) 629 North Sandusky Avenue, Bucyrus, OH, Zip 44820–1821; tel. 419/562–4677; Jerome Morasko, Chief Executive Officer
Web address: www.bchonline.org

GALION HOSPITAL (O, 35 beds) 269 Portland Way South, Galion, OH, Zip 44833–2399; tel. 419/468–4841; Jerome Morasko, President and Chief Executive Officer

Owned, leased, sponsored:	3 hospitals	86 beds
Contract–managed:	0 hospitals	0 beds
Totals:	3 hospitals	86 beds

1033: BALLAD HEALTH (NP)
303 Med Tech Parkway, Johnson City, TN, Zip 37604–2391; tel. 833/822–5523; Alan M. Levine, President and Chief Executive Officer

TENNESSEE: BRISTOL REGIONAL MEDICAL CENTER (O, 314 beds) 1 Medical Park Boulevard, Bristol, TN, Zip 37620–7430; tel. 423/844–1121; Greg Neal, FACHE, President

FRANKLIN WOODS COMMUNITY HOSPITAL (O, 80 beds) 300 MedTech Parkway, Johnson City, TN, Zip 37604–2277; tel. 423/302–1000; Patricia Baise, R.N., FACHE, Chief Executive Officer
Web address: www.msha.com

HANCOCK COUNTY HOSPITAL (O, 10 beds) 1519 Main Street, Sneedville, TN, Zip 37869–3657; tel. 423/733–5000; Rebecca Beck, President
Web address: www.wellmont.org/Hospitals/Hancock-County-Hospital.aspx

HAWKINS COUNTY MEMORIAL HOSPITAL (O, 22 beds) 851 Locust Street, Rogersville, TN, Zip 37857–2407, Mailing Address: P.O. Box 130, Zip 37857–0130, tel. 423/921–7000; Regina Day, Chief Executive Officer

HOLSTON VALLEY MEDICAL CENTER (O, 345 beds) 130 West Ravine Street, Kingsport, TN, Zip 37660–3837, Mailing Address: P.O. Box 238, Zip 37662–0238, tel. 423/224–4000; Monty E. McLaurin, Interim Chief Executive Officer
Web address: www.wellmont.org

INDIAN PATH MEDICAL CENTER (O, 160 beds) 2000 Brookside Drive, Kingsport, TN, Zip 37660–4627; tel. 423/857–7000; Monty E. McLaurin, Chief Executive Officer, Northwest Market

JOHNSON CITY MEDICAL CENTER (O, 585 beds) 400 North State of Franklin Road, Johnson City, TN, Zip 37604–6094; tel. 423/431–6111; Stan Hickson, FACHE, Chief Executive Officer
Web address: www.msha.com

JOHNSON COUNTY COMMUNITY HOSPITAL (O, 2 beds) 1901 South Shady Street, Mountain City, TN, Zip 37683–2271; tel. 423/727–1100; Chastity Trivette, Chief Executive Officer
Web address: www.msha.com

LAUGHLIN MEMORIAL HOSPITAL (O, 143 beds) 1420 Tusculum Boulevard, Greeneville, TN, Zip 37745–5825; tel. 423/787–5000; Charles H. Whitfield Jr, President and Chief Executive Officer

SYCAMORE SHOALS HOSPITAL (O, 74 beds) 1501 West Elk Avenue, Elizabethton, TN, Zip 37643–2874; tel. 423/542–1300; Dwayne Taylor, Chief Executive Officer
Web address: www.msha.com

TAKOMA REGIONAL HOSPITAL (O, 92 beds) 401 Takoma Avenue, Greeneville, TN, Zip 37743–4647; tel. 423/639–3151; Tammy Albright, President

UNICOI COUNTY MEMORIAL HOSPITAL (O, 94 beds) 100 Greenway Circle, Erwin, TN, Zip 37650–2196, Mailing Address: P.O. Box 802, Zip 37650–0802, tel. 423/743–3141; Eric Carroll, Chief Executive Officer
Web address: www.msha.com

VIRGINIA: DICKENSON COMMUNITY HOSPITAL (O, 11 beds) 312 Hospital Drive, Clintwood, VA, Zip 24228, Mailing Address: P.O. Box 1440, Zip 24228–1440, tel. 276/926–0300; Mark T. Leonard, Chief Executive Officer

JOHNSTON MEMORIAL HOSPITAL (O, 116 beds) 16000 Johnston Memorial Drive, Abingdon, VA, Zip 24211–7659; tel. 276/258–1000; John Jeter, Chief Executive Officer
Web address: www.jmh.org

LONESOME PINE HOSPITAL (O, 32 beds) 1990 Holton Avenue East, Big Stone Gap, VA, Zip 24219–3350; tel. 276/523–3111; Mark T. Leonard, Interim Chief Executive Officer

MOUNTAIN VIEW REGIONAL MEDICAL CENTER (O, 70 beds) 310 Third Street NE, Norton, VA, Zip 24273–1137; tel. 276/679–9100; Dale Clark, President
Web address: www.wellmont.org

NORTON COMMUNITY HOSPITAL (O, 70 beds) 100 15th Street NW, Norton, VA, Zip 24273–1616; tel. 276/679–9600; Mark T. Leonard, Chief Executive Officer
Web address: www.msha.com/nch

RUSSELL COUNTY MEDICAL CENTER (O, 78 beds) 58 Carroll Street, Lebanon, VA, Zip 24266, Mailing Address: P.O. Box 3600, Zip 24266–0200, tel. 276/883–8000; Stephen K. Givens, Assistant Vice President and Administrator
Web address: www.mountainstateshealth.com/rcmc

For explanation of codes following names, see page B2.
★ Indicates Type III membership in the American Hospital Association.

SMYTH COUNTY COMMUNITY HOSPITAL (O, 153 beds) 245 Medical Park Drive, Marion, VA, Zip 24354, Mailing Address: P.O. Box 880, Zip 24354–0880, tel. 276/378–1000; James E. Tyler, Chief Executive Officer
Web address: www.msha.com/scch

Owned, leased, sponsored:	19 hospitals	2451 beds
Contract-managed:	0 hospitals	0 beds
Totals:	19 hospitals	2451 beds

★**0194: BANNER HEALTH** (NP)

2872 E. Fruitvale Ave, Gilbert, AZ, Zip 85297, Mailing Address: P.O. Box 25489, Phoenix, Zip 85002–5489, tel. 602/747–4000; Peter S. Fine, FACHE, President and Chief Executive Officer
(Centralized Health System)

ARIZONA: BANNER – UNIVERSITY MEDICAL CENTER PHOENIX (O, 685 beds) 1111 East McDowell Road, Phoenix, AZ, Zip 85006–2666, Mailing Address: P.O. Box 2989, Zip 85062–2989, tel. 602/239–2000; Steve Narang, M.D., Chief Executive Officer
Web address: www.bannerhealth.com/Locations/Arizona/Banner+Good+Samaritan+Medical+Center

BANNER – UNIVERSITY MEDICAL CENTER SOUTH (O, 167 beds) 2800 East Ajo Way, Tucson, AZ, Zip 85713–6289; tel. 520/874–2000; Sarah Frost, Chief Executive Officer
Web address: www.bannerhealth.com

BANNER – UNIVERSITY MEDICAL CENTER TUCSON (O, 439 beds) 1501 North Campbell Avenue, Tucson, AZ, Zip 85724–5128; tel. 520/694–0111; Sarah Frost, Chief Executive Officer
Web address: https://www.bannerhealth.com/locations/tucson/banner–university–medical–center–tucson

BANNER BAYWOOD MEDICAL CENTER (O, 359 beds) 6644 East Baywood Avenue, Mesa, AZ, Zip 85206–1797; tel. 480/321–2000; Lamont M. Yoder, R.N., MSN, FACHE, Chief Executive Officer

BANNER BEHAVIORAL HEALTH HOSPITAL – SCOTTSDALE (O, 104 beds) 7575 East Earll Drive, Scottsdale, AZ, Zip 85251–6915; tel. 480/941–7500; William Southwick, R.N., Chief Executive Officer
Web address: https://www.bannerhealth.com/locations/scottsdale/banner–behavioral–health–hospital

BANNER BOSWELL MEDICAL CENTER (O, 429 beds) 10401 West Thunderbird Blvd, Sun City, AZ, Zip 85351–3004, Mailing Address: P.O. Box 1690, Zip 85372–1690, tel. 623/832–4000; Debbie Flores, Interim Chief Executive Officer

BANNER CASA GRANDE MEDICAL CENTER (O, 84 beds) 1800 East Florence Boulevard, Casa Grande, AZ, Zip 85122–5399; tel. 520/381–6300; Rona Curphy, President and Chief Executive Officer
Web address: https://www.bannerhealth.com/Locations/Arizona/Banner+Casa+Grande+Medical+Center/_Banner+Casa+Grande+Medical+Center.htm

BANNER DEL E. WEBB MEDICAL CENTER (O, 390 beds) 14502 West Meeker Boulevard, Sun City West, AZ, Zip 85375–5299; tel. 623/524–4000; Debbie Flores, Chief Executive Officer

BANNER DESERT MEDICAL CENTER (O, 595 beds) 1400 South Dobson Road, Mesa, AZ, Zip 85202–4707; tel. 480/412–3000; Laura Robertson, R.N., Chief Executive Officer
Web address: www.bannerhealth.com/Locations/Arizona/Banner+Desert+Medical+Center

BANNER ESTRELLA MEDICAL CENTER (O, 278 beds) 9201 West Thomas Road, Phoenix, AZ, Zip 85037–3332; tel. 623/327–4000; Courtney Ophaug, FACHE, Chief Executive Officer
Web address: www.bannerhealth.com/Locations/Arizona/Banner+Estrella+Medical+Center/

BANNER GATEWAY MEDICAL CENTER (O, 177 beds) 1900 North Higley Road, Gilbert, AZ, Zip 85234–1604; tel. 480/543–2000; Lamont M. Yoder, R.N., MSN, FACHE, Chief Executive Officer
Web address: www.bannerhealth.com/Locations/Arizona/Banner+Gateway+Medical+Center/

BANNER GOLDFIELD MEDICAL CENTER (O, 20 beds) 2050 West Southern Avenue, Apache Junction, AZ, Zip 85120–7305; tel. 480/733–3300; Sharon Lind, MSN, FACHE, Chief Executive Officer

BANNER HEART HOSPITAL (O, 111 beds) 6750 East Baywood Avenue, Mesa, AZ, Zip 85206–1749; tel. 480/854–5000; Lamont M. Yoder, R.N., MSN, FACHE, Chief Executive Officer
Web address: www.bannerhealth.com/Locations/Arizona/Banner+Heart+Hospital/

BANNER IRONWOOD MEDICAL CENTER (O, 53 beds) 37000 North Gantzel Road, San Tan Valley, AZ, Zip 85140–7303; tel. 480/394–4000; Sharon Lind, MSN, FACHE, Chief Executive Officer
Web address: www.bannerhealth.com/Locations/Arizona/Banner+Ironwood/

BANNER PAYSON MEDICAL CENTER (O, 25 beds) 807 South Ponderosa Street, Payson, AZ, Zip 85541–5599; tel. 928/474–3222; Lance Porter, Chief Executive Officer
Web address: www.paysonhospital.com

BANNER THUNDERBIRD MEDICAL CENTER (O, 458 beds) 5555 West Thunderbird Road, Glendale, AZ, Zip 85306–4696; tel. 602/865–5555; Debra J. Krmpotic, R.N., Chief Executive Officer

PAGE HOSPITAL (C, 25 beds) 501 North Navajo Drive, Page, AZ, Zip 86040, Mailing Address: P.O. Box 1447, Zip 86040–1447, tel. 928/645–2424; Brian Kellar, Chief Executive Officer
Web address: www.bannerhealth.com/Locations/Arizona/Page+Hospital

CALIFORNIA: BANNER LASSEN MEDICAL CENTER (O, 25 beds) 1800 Spring Ridge Drive, Susanville, CA, Zip 96130–6100; tel. 530/252–2000; Catherine S. Harshbarger, R.N., Chief Executive Officer

COLORADO: BANNER FORT COLLINS MEDICAL CENTER (O, 23 beds) 4700 Lady Moon Drive, Fort Collins, CO, Zip 80528–4426; tel. 970/821–4000; Margo Karsten, Ph.D., MSN, Chief Executive Officer
Web address: www.bannerhealth.com/Locations/Colorado/Banner+Fort+Collins+Medical+Center

EAST MORGAN COUNTY HOSPITAL (L, 19 beds) 2400 West Edison Street, Brush, CO, Zip 80723–1640; tel. 970/842–6200; Linda Thorpe, Chief Executive Officer
Web address: www.emchbrush.com

MCKEE MEDICAL CENTER (O, 96 beds) 2000 Boise Avenue, Loveland, CO, Zip 80538–4281; tel. 970/669–4640; Margo Karsten, Ph.D., MSN, Chief Executive Officer

NORTH COLORADO MEDICAL CENTER (L, 236 beds) 1801 16th Street, Greeley, CO, Zip 80631–5154; tel. 970/352–4121; Margo Karsten, Ph.D., MSN, Chief Executive Officer
Web address: www.ncmcgreeley.com

STERLING REGIONAL MEDCENTER (O, 25 beds) 615 Fairhurst Street, Sterling, CO, Zip 80751–4523; tel. 970/522–0122; Hoyt Skabelund, Chief Executive Officer

NEBRASKA: OGALLALA COMMUNITY HOSPITAL (L, 18 beds) 2601 North Spruce Street, Ogallala, NE, Zip 69153–2465; tel. 308/284–4011; Drew H. Dostal, R.N., FACHE, Chief Executive Officer
Web address: https://www.bannerhealth.com/locations/ogallala/ogallala–community–hospital

NEVADA: BANNER CHURCHILL COMMUNITY HOSPITAL (O, 25 beds) 801 East Williams Avenue, Fallon, NV, Zip 89406–3052; tel. 775/423–3151; Robert H. Carnahan II, R.N., Chief Executive Officer

WYOMING: COMMUNITY HOSPITAL (O, 20 beds) 2000 Campbell Drive, Torrington, WY, Zip 82240–1597; tel. 307/532–4181; Shelby Olind, Interim Chief Executive Officer
Web address: www.bannerhealth.com/Locations/Wyoming/Community+Hospital/

PLATTE COUNTY MEMORIAL HOSPITAL (L, 25 beds) 201 14th Street, Wheatland, WY, Zip 82201–3201, Mailing Address: P.O. Box 848, Zip 82201–0848, tel. 307/322–3636; Shelby Olind, Chief Executive Officer

WASHAKIE MEDICAL CENTER (L, 18 beds) 400 South 15th Street, Worland, WY, Zip 82401–3531, Mailing Address: P.O. Box 700, Zip 82401–0700, tel. 307/347–3221; Jay Stallings, Chief Executive Officer
Web address: www.washakiemedicalcenter.com

Owned, leased, sponsored:	27 hospitals	4904 beds
Contract-managed:	1 hospitals	25 beds
Totals:	28 hospitals	4929 beds

For explanation of codes following names, see page B2.
★ Indicates Type III membership in the American Hospital Association.

★0005: BAPTIST HEALTH (NP)
841 Prudential Drive, Suite 1601, Jacksonville, FL, Zip 32207–8202; tel. 904/202–2000; Hugh Greene, President and Chief Executive Officer
(Moderately Centralized Health System)

FLORIDA: BAPTIST MEDICAL CENTER BEACHES (O, 135 beds) 1350 13th Avenue South, Jacksonville Beach, FL, Zip 32250–3205; tel. 904/627–2900; Joseph M. Mitrick, FACHE, President
Web address: www.community.e–baptisthealth.com/bmc/beaches/index.html

BAPTIST MEDICAL CENTER JACKSONVILLE (O, 941 beds) 800 Prudential Drive, Jacksonville, FL, Zip 32207–8202; tel. 904/202–2000; Michael A. Mayo, FACHE, President
Web address: www.e–baptisthealth.com

BAPTIST MEDICAL CENTER NASSAU (O, 52 beds) 1250 South 18th Street, Fernandina Beach, FL, Zip 32034–3098; tel. 904/321–3500; Edward T. Hubel, FACHE, President

Owned, leased, sponsored:	3 hospitals	1128 beds
Contract–managed:	0 hospitals	0 beds
Totals:	3 hospitals	1128 beds

0150: BAPTIST HEALTH (NP)
301 Brown Springs Road, Montgomery, AL, Zip 36117–7005; tel. 334/273–4400; W Russell. Tyner, President and Chief Executive Officer
(Independent Hospital System)

ALABAMA: BAPTIST MEDICAL CENTER EAST (O, 164 beds) 400 Taylor Road, Montgomery, AL, Zip 36117–3512, Mailing Address: P.O. Box 241267, Zip 36124–1267, tel. 334/277–8330; Jeff G. Rains, Chief Executive Officer
Web address: www.baptistfirst.org

BAPTIST MEDICAL CENTER SOUTH (O, 389 beds) 2105 East South Boulevard, Montgomery, AL, Zip 36116–2409, Mailing Address: Box 11010, Zip 36111–0010, tel. 334/288–2100; J Peter. Selman, FACHE, Chief Executive Officer
Web address: www.baptistfirst.org

PRATTVILLE BAPTIST HOSPITAL (O, 55 beds) 124 South Memorial Drive, Prattville, AL, Zip 36067–3619, Mailing Address: P.O. Box 681630, Zip 36068–1638, tel. 334/365–0651; Eric Morgan, Chief Executive Officer

Owned, leased, sponsored:	3 hospitals	608 beds
Contract–managed:	0 hospitals	0 beds
Totals:	3 hospitals	608 beds

★0315: BAPTIST HEALTH (CO)
2701 Eastpoint Parkway, Louisville, KY, Zip 40223; tel. 502/896–5000; Gerard Colman, Ph.D., Chief Executive Officer
(Centralized Physician/Insurance Health System)

INDIANA: BAPTIST HEALTH FLOYD (O, 216 beds) 1850 State Street, New Albany, IN, Zip 47150–4997; tel. 812/949–5500; Daniel J. Eichenberger, M.D., President and Chief Executive Officer

KENTUCKY: BAPTIST HEALTH CORBIN (O, 273 beds) 1 Trillium Way, Corbin, KY, Zip 40701–8420; tel. 606/528–1212; Anthony Powers, Interim President and Vice President of Patient Services
Web address: www.baptisthealth.com/corbin

BAPTIST HEALTH LA GRANGE (O, 65 beds) 1025 New Moody Lane, La Grange, KY, Zip 40031–9154; tel. 502/222–5388; Clint Kaho, President
Web address: www.baptisthealthlagrange.com

BAPTIST HEALTH LEXINGTON (O, 391 beds) 1740 Nicholasville Road, Lexington, KY, Zip 40503–1499; tel. 859/260–6100; William G. Sisson, FACHE, President

BAPTIST HEALTH LOUISVILLE (O, 500 beds) 4000 Kresge Way, Louisville, KY, Zip 40207–4676; tel. 502/897–8100; Larry W. Gray, President
Web address: www.baptisthealthlouisville.com

BAPTIST HEALTH MADISONVILLE (O, 175 beds) 900 Hospital Drive, Madisonville, KY, Zip 42431–1694; tel. 270/825–5100; Robert L. Ramey, President
Web address: www.baptisthealthmadisonville.com

BAPTIST HEALTH PADUCAH (O, 210 beds) 2501 Kentucky Avenue, Paducah, KY, Zip 42003–3200; tel. 270/575–2100; Christopher Roty, Interim President

BAPTIST HEALTH RICHMOND (O, 60 beds) 801 Eastern Bypass, Richmond, KY, Zip 40475–2405, Mailing Address: P.O. Box 1600, Zip 40476–2603, tel. 859/623–3131; Greg Donavan. Gerard, President
Web address: www.baptisthealthrichmond.com

HARDIN MEMORIAL HEALTH (C, 268 beds) 913 North Dixie Avenue, Elizabethtown, KY, Zip 42701–2503; tel. 270/737–1212; Dennis B. Johnson, President and Chief Executive Officer
Web address: www.hmh.net

Owned, leased, sponsored:	8 hospitals	1890 beds
Contract–managed:	1 hospitals	268 beds
Totals:	9 hospitals	2158 beds

★0355: BAPTIST HEALTH (NP)
9601 Baptist Health Drive, Little Rock, AR, Zip 72205–6321; tel. 501/202–2000; Troy R. Wells, Chief Executive Officer
(Centralized Physician/Insurance Health System)

ARKANSAS: BAPTIST HEALTH EXTENDED CARE HOSPITAL (O, 55 beds) 9601 Baptist Health Drive, Little Rock, AR, Zip 72205–7202; tel. 501/202–1070; Lee Gentry, FACHE, Vice President and Administrator
Web address: www.baptist–health.com/maps-directions/bh_extended_care/default.aspx

BAPTIST HEALTH MEDICAL CENTER – CONWAY (O, 111 beds) 1555 Exchange Avenue, Conway, AR, Zip 72032–7824; tel. 501/585–2000; Tim Bowen, Administrator

BAPTIST HEALTH MEDICAL CENTER – NORTH LITTLE ROCK (O, 177 beds) 3333 Springhill Drive, North Little Rock, AR, Zip 72117–2922; tel. 501/202–3000; Mike Perkins, Vice President and Administrator
Web address: https://www.baptist–health.com/location/baptist–health–medical–center–north–little–rock–north–little–rock

BAPTIST HEALTH MEDICAL CENTER–ARKADELPHIA (L, 25 beds) 3050 Twin Rivers Drive, Arkadelphia, AR, Zip 71923–4299; tel. 870/245–2622; Tony Hardage, Assistant Vice President and Administrator

BAPTIST HEALTH MEDICAL CENTER–HEBER SPRINGS (O, 25 beds) 1800 Bypass Road, Heber Springs, AR, Zip 72543–9135; tel. 501/887–3000; Edward L. Lacy, FACHE, Vice President and Administrator
Web address: www.baptist–health.com/maps-directions/bhmc–heber–springs

BAPTIST HEALTH MEDICAL CENTER–HOT SPRING COUNTY (L, 72 beds) 1001 Schneider Drive, Malvern, AR, Zip 72104–4811; tel. 501/332–1000; Sheila Williams, Vice President and Administrator

BAPTIST HEALTH MEDICAL CENTER–LITTLE ROCK (O, 682 beds) 9601 Baptist Health Drive, Little Rock, AR, Zip 72205–7299; tel. 501/202–2000; Greg Crain, FACHE, Senior Vice President and Administrator
Web address: www.baptist–health.org/maps-directions/bhmc–lr

BAPTIST HEALTH MEDICAL CENTER–STUTTGART (L, 49 beds) 1703 North Buerkle Road, Stuttgart, AR, Zip 72160–1905, Mailing Address: P.O. Box 1905, Zip 72160–1905, tel. 870/673–3511; Kevin L. Storey, Vice President and Administrator

BAPTIST HEALTH REHABILITATION INSTITUTE (O, 120 beds) 9501 Baptist Health Drive, Little Rock, AR, Zip 72205–6225; tel. 501/202–7000; Julie Nix, Vice President and Administrator
Web address: www.baptist–health.com/locations/accesspoint.aspx?accessPointID=202

Owned, leased, sponsored:	9 hospitals	1316 beds
Contract–managed:	0 hospitals	0 beds
Totals:	9 hospitals	1316 beds

★0185: BAPTIST HEALTH CARE CORPORATION (NP)
1717 North 'E' Street, Suite 402, Pensacola, FL, Zip 32501–6377, Mailing Address: P.O. Box 17500, Zip 32522–7500, tel. 850/434–4011; Mark T. Faulkner, President
(Centralized Physician/Insurance Health System)

FLORIDA: BAPTIST HOSPITAL (O, 340 beds) 1000 West Moreno Street, Pensacola, FL, Zip 32501–2316, Mailing Address: P.O. Box 17500, Zip 32522–7500, tel. 850/434–4011; Scott Raynes, President

For explanation of codes following names, see page B2.
★ Indicates Type III membership in the American Hospital Association.

GULF BREEZE HOSPITAL (O, 65 beds) 1110 Gulf Breeze Parkway, Gulf Breeze, FL, Zip 32561–4884; tel. 850/934–2000; Scott Raynes, President
Web address: www.ebaptisthealthcare.org/GulfBreezeHospital/

JAY HOSPITAL (L, 21 beds) 14114 South Alabama Street, Jay, FL, Zip 32565–1219; tel. 850/675–8000; Michael T. Hutchins, Administrator
Web address: www.bhcpns.org/jayhospital/

Owned, leased, sponsored:	3 hospitals	426 beds
Contract–managed:	0 hospitals	0 beds
Totals:	3 hospitals	426 beds

★0122: BAPTIST HEALTH SOUTH FLORIDA (NP)
6855 Red Road, Suite 600, Coral Gables, FL, Zip 33143–3632; tel. 786/662–7111; Brian E. Keeley, President and Chief Executive Officer
(Centralized Health System)

FLORIDA: BAPTIST HEALTH SOUTH FLORIDA, BAPTIST HOSPITAL OF MIAMI (O, 720 beds) 8900 North Kendall Drive, Miami, FL, Zip 33176–2197; tel. 786/596–1960; Patricia M. Rosello, Chief Executive Officer
Web address: www.baptisthealth.net

BAPTIST HEALTH SOUTH FLORIDA, DOCTORS HOSPITAL (O, 126 beds) 5000 University Drive, Coral Gables, FL, Zip 33146–2094; tel. 786/308–3000; Nelson Lazo, Chief Executive Officer
Web address: www.baptisthealth.net

BAPTIST HEALTH SOUTH FLORIDA, HOMESTEAD HOSPITAL (O, 142 beds) 975 Baptist Way, Homestead, FL, Zip 33033–7600; tel. 786/243–8000; William M. Duquette, Chief Executive Officer

BAPTIST HEALTH SOUTH FLORIDA, MARINERS HOSPITAL (O, 25 beds) 91500 Overseas Highway, Tavernier, FL, Zip 33070–2547; tel. 305/434–3000; Rick Freeburg, Chief Executive Officer
Web address: www.baptisthealth.net/en/facilities/mariners–hospital/Pages/default.aspx

BAPTIST HEALTH SOUTH FLORIDA, SOUTH MIAMI HOSPITAL (O, 336 beds) 6200 SW 73rd Street, Miami, FL, Zip 33143–4679; tel. 786/662–4000; Lincoln S. Mendez, Chief Executive Officer

BAPTIST HEALTH SOUTH FLORIDA, WEST KENDALL BAPTIST HOSPITAL (O, 133 beds) 9555 SW 162nd Avenue, Miami, FL, Zip 33196–6408; tel. 786/467–2000; Javier Hernandez–Lichtl, Chief Executive Officer
Web address: www.baptisthealth.net/en/facilities/West–Kendall–Baptist–Hospital/Pages/default.aspx

BETHESDA HOSPITAL EAST (O, 481 beds) 2815 South Seacrest Boulevard, Boynton Beach, FL, Zip 33435–7995; tel. 561/737–7733; Roger L. Kirk, President and Chief Executive Officer

Owned, leased, sponsored:	7 hospitals	1963 beds
Contract–managed:	0 hospitals	0 beds
Totals:	7 hospitals	1963 beds

★1625: BAPTIST MEMORIAL HEALTH CARE CORPORATION (NP)
350 North Humphreys Boulevard, Memphis, TN, Zip 38120–2177; tel. 901/227–5117; Jason Little, President and Chief Executive Officer
(Moderately Centralized Health System)

ARKANSAS: NEA BAPTIST MEMORIAL HOSPITAL (O, 228 beds) 4800 East Johnson Avenue, Jonesboro, AR, Zip 72401–8413; tel. 870/936–1000; Brad Parsons, FACHE, Administrator and Chief Executive Officer
Web address: www.neabaptist.com

MISSISSIPPI: BAPTIST MEDICAL CENTER ATTALA (O, 25 beds) 220 Highway 12 West, Kosciusko, MS, Zip 39090–3208, Mailing Address: P.O. Box 887, Zip 39090–0887, tel. 662/289–4311; Robert Coleman, Chief Executive Officer

BAPTIST MEDICAL CENTER LEAKE (O, 25 beds) 1100 Highway 16 E, Carthage, MS, Zip 39051–3809, Mailing Address: P.O. Box 909, Zip 39051–0909, tel. 601/267–1100; Daryl W. Weaver, Chief Executive Officer
Web address: www.mbhs.com/locations/baptist–medical–center–leake/

BAPTIST MEDICAL CENTER YAZOO (O, 25 beds) 823 Grand Avenue, Yazoo City, MS, Zip 39194–3233; tel. 662/746–2261; Robert Coleman, Chief Executive Officer
Web address: www.kdhyazoo.com

BAPTIST MEMORIAL HOSPITAL – CALHOUN (L, 145 beds) 140 Burke–Calhoun City Road, Calhoun City, MS, Zip 38916–9690; tel. 662/628–6611; Collin Cheek, Administrator

BAPTIST MEMORIAL HOSPITAL–BOONEVILLE (L, 63 beds) 100 Hospital Street, Booneville, MS, Zip 38829–3359; tel. 662/720–5000; James Grantham, Administrator and Chief Executive Officer
Web address: www.bmhcc.org/booneville

BAPTIST MEMORIAL HOSPITAL–DESOTO (O, 339 beds) 7601 Southcrest Parkway, Southaven, MS, Zip 38671–4742; tel. 662/772–4000; James Huffman, Chief Executive Officer and Administrator

BAPTIST MEMORIAL HOSPITAL–GOLDEN TRIANGLE (O, 236 beds) 2520 Fifth Street North, Columbus, MS, Zip 39705–2095, Mailing Address: P.O. Box 1307, Zip 39703–1307, tel. 662/244–1000; Paul Cade, Administrator and Chief Executive Officer
Web address: www.baptistonline.org/golden–triangle/

BAPTIST MEMORIAL HOSPITAL–NORTH MISSISSIPPI (O, 172 beds) 2301 South Lamar Boulevard, Oxford, MS, Zip 38655–5373, Mailing Address: P.O. Box 946, Zip 38655–6002, tel. 662/232–8100; William C. Henning, Administrator and Chief Executive Officer
Web address: www.baptistonline.org/north–mississippi/

BAPTIST MEMORIAL HOSPITAL–UNION COUNTY (L, 153 beds) 200 Highway 30 West, New Albany, MS, Zip 38652–3112; tel. 662/538–7631; Walter Grace, Chief Executive Officer and Administrator
Web address: www.baptistonline.org/union–county/

MISSISSIPPI BAPTIST MEDICAL CENTER (O, 450 beds) 1225 North State Street, Jackson, MS, Zip 39202–2064; tel. 601/968–1000; Bobbie K. Ware, R.N., FACHE, Chief Executive Officer

TENNESSEE: BAPTIST MEMORIAL HOSPITAL – MEMPHIS (O, 563 beds) 6019 Walnut Grove Road, Memphis, TN, Zip 38120–2173; tel. 901/226–5000; Dana Dye, R.N., Vice President, Administrator and Chief Executive Officer
Web address: www.baptistonline.org/memphis/

BAPTIST MEMORIAL HOSPITAL FOR WOMEN (O, 140 beds) 6225 Humphreys Boulevard, Memphis, TN, Zip 38120–2373; tel. 901/227–9000; Kevin R. Hammeran, Chief Executive Officer and Administrator

BAPTIST MEMORIAL HOSPITAL–COLLIERVILLE (O, 51 beds) 1500 West Poplar Avenue, Collierville, TN, Zip 38017–0601; tel. 901/861–9400; Lindsay Stencel, Chief Administrative Officer
Web address: www.baptistonline.org/collierville/

BAPTIST MEMORIAL HOSPITAL–HUNTINGDON (O, 35 beds) 631 R.B. Wilson Drive, Huntingdon, TN, Zip 38344–1727; tel. 731/986–4461; Susan M. Breeden, Administrator and Chief Executive Officer

BAPTIST MEMORIAL HOSPITAL–TIPTON (O, 50 beds) 1995 Highway 51 South, Covington, TN, Zip 38019–3635; tel. 901/476–2621; Samuel Lynd, Administrator and Chief Executive Officer
Web address: www.baptistonline.org/tipton/

BAPTIST MEMORIAL HOSPITAL–UNION CITY (O, 63 beds) 1201 Bishop Street, Union City, TN, Zip 38261–5403, Mailing Address: P.O. Box 310, Zip 38281–0310, tel. 731/885–2410; Barry Bondurant, Administrator and Chief Executive Officer

BAPTIST MEMORIAL REHABILITATION HOSPITAL (O, 49 beds) 1240 South Germantown Road, Germantown, TN, Zip 38138–2226; tel. 901/275–3300; Christopher L. Bariola, Chief Executive Officer
Web address: www.baptistrehab.com

BAPTIST MEMORIAL RESTORATIVE CARE HOSPITAL (O, 30 beds) 6019 Walnut Grove Road, Memphis, TN, Zip 38120–2113; tel. 901/226–4200; Janice Hill, R.N., Administrator

Owned, leased, sponsored:	19 hospitals	2842 beds
Contract–managed:	0 hospitals	0 beds
Totals:	19 hospitals	2842 beds

★0528: BASSETT HEALTHCARE NETWORK (NP)
1 Atwell Road, Cooperstown, NY, Zip 13326–1301; tel. 607/547–3456; William F. Streck, M.D., President and Chief Executive Officer
(Independent Hospital System)

For explanation of codes following names, see page B2.
★ Indicates Type III membership in the American Hospital Association.

© 2018 AHA Guide

Health Care Systems, Networks and Alliances **B21**

Section B

NEW YORK: AURELIA OSBORN FOX MEMORIAL HOSPITAL (O, 184 beds) 1 Norton Avenue, Oneonta, NY, Zip 13820–2629; tel. 607/432–2000; Jeff Joyner, President
Web address: www.bassett.org/ao-fox-hospital/

BASSETT MEDICAL CENTER (O, 152 beds) One Atwell Road, Cooperstown, NY, Zip 13326–1394; tel. 607/547–3456; William W. LeCates, M.D., President
Web address: www.bassett.org

COBLESKILL REGIONAL HOSPITAL (O, 40 beds) 178 Grandview Drive, Cobleskill, NY, Zip 12043–5144; tel. 518/254–3456; Eric H. Stein, FACHE, President

LITTLE FALLS HOSPITAL (O, 25 beds) 140 Burwell Street, Little Falls, NY, Zip 13365–1725; tel. 315/823–1000; Michael L. Ogden, President and Chief Executive Officer
Web address: www.bassett.org

O'CONNOR HOSPITAL (O, 16 beds) 460 Andes Road, State Route 28, Delhi, NY, Zip 13753–7407; tel. 607/746–0300; Scott Bonderoff, President

Owned, leased, sponsored:	5 hospitals	417 beds
Contract–managed:	0 hospitals	0 beds
Totals:	5 hospitals	417 beds

★0918: BAYLOR SCOTT & WHITE HEALTH (NP)
4005 Crutcher Street, Suite 310, Dallas, TX, Zip 75246–1779; tel. 214/820–0111; James H. Hinton, Chief Executive Officer
(Centralized Physician/Insurance Health System)

TEXAS: BAYLOR ALL SAINTS MEDICAL CENTER AT FORT WORTH (O, 360 beds) 1400 Eighth Avenue, Fort Worth, TX, Zip 76104–4192; tel. 817/926–2544; Michael Sanborn, FACHE, MS, President
Web address: www.baylorhealth.com/PhysiciansLocations/AllSaints/Pages/Default.aspx

BAYLOR MEDICAL CENTER AT MCKINNEY (O, 143 beds) 5252 West University Drive, McKinney, TX, Zip 75071–7822; tel. 469/764–1000; Kyle Armstrong, President

BAYLOR REGIONAL MEDICAL CENTER AT GRAPEVINE (O, 270 beds) 1650 West College Street, Grapevine, TX, Zip 76051–3565; tel. 817/481–1588; Christopher York, FACHE, President
Web address: https://www.baylorhealth.com/PhysiciansLocations/Grapevine/Pages/Default.aspx

BAYLOR REGIONAL MEDICAL CENTER AT PLANO (O, 124 beds) 4700 Alliance Boulevard, Plano, TX, Zip 75093–5323; tel. 469/814–2000; Jerri Garison, R.N., President
Web address: www.baylorhealth.com/PhysiciansLocations/Plano/Pages/Default.aspx

BAYLOR SCOTT & WHITE MEDICAL CENTER – CARROLLTON (L, 120 beds) 4343 North Josey Lane, Carrollton, TX, Zip 75010–4691; tel. 972/394–1010; Jerri Garison, R.N., Interim Chief Executive Officer and Chief Operating Officer

BAYLOR SCOTT & WHITE MEDICAL CENTER – CENTENNIAL (O, 106 beds) 12505 Lebanon Road, Frisco, TX, Zip 75035–8298; tel. 972/963–3333; Jaikumar Krishnaswamy, President
Web address: www.centennialmedcenter.com

BAYLOR SCOTT & WHITE MEDICAL CENTER – HILLCREST (C, 226 beds) 100 Hillcrest Medical Boulevard, Waco, TX, Zip 76712–8897; tel. 254/202–2000; Glenn A. Robinson, FACHE, President
Web address: www.sw.org/hillcrest-medical-center

BAYLOR SCOTT & WHITE MEDICAL CENTER – LAKE POINTE (O, 112 beds) 6800 Scenic Drive, Rowlett, TX, Zip 75088–4552, Mailing Address: P.O. Box 1550, Zip 75030–1550, tel. 972/412–2273; Donas Cole, FACHE, President

BAYLOR SCOTT & WHITE MEDICAL CENTER – LLANO (O, 10 beds) 200 West Ollie Street, Llano, TX, Zip 78643–2628; tel. 325/247–5040; Timothy A. Ols, FACHE, Chief Executive Officer
Web address: www.bwshealth.com

BAYLOR SCOTT & WHITE MEDICAL CENTER – MARBLE FALLS (O, 46 beds) 800 West Highway 71, Marble Falls, TX, Zip 78654; tel. 830/201–8000; Timothy A. Ols, FACHE, President

BAYLOR SCOTT & WHITE MEDICAL CENTER – ROUND ROCK (O, 173 beds) 300 University Boulevard, Round Rock, TX, Zip 78665–1032; tel. 512/509–0100; Jay Fox, President
Web address: www.sw.org

BAYLOR SCOTT & WHITE MEDICAL CENTER – TAYLOR (O, 25 beds) 305 Mallard Lane, Taylor, TX, Zip 76574–1208; tel. 512/352–7611; Jay Fox, Director Operations

BAYLOR SCOTT & WHITE MEDICAL CENTER AT WAXAHACHIE (O, 104 beds) 2400 North I–35E, Waxahachie, TX, Zip 75165; tel. 469/843–4000; Christopher York, FACHE, President
Web address: www.baylorhealth.com/PhysiciansLocations/Waxahachie/Pages/Default.aspx

BAYLOR SCOTT & WHITE MEDICAL CENTER–IRVING (L, 233 beds) 1901 North MacArthur Boulevard, Irving, TX, Zip 75061–2220; tel. 972/579–8100; Cindy K. Schamp, FACHE, President
Web address: www.bswhealth.com

BAYLOR SCOTT AND WHITE CONTINUING CARE HOSPITAL (O, 48 beds) 546 North Kegley Road, Temple, TX, Zip 76502–4069; tel. 254/215–0900; Shahin Motakef, FACHE, President

BAYLOR UNIVERSITY MEDICAL CENTER (O, 863 beds) 3500 Gaston Avenue, Dallas, TX, Zip 75246–2088; tel. 214/820–0111; Steven R. Newton, FACHE, President
Web address: www.baylorhealth.com/PhysiciansLocations/Dallas/Pages/Default.aspx

SCOTT & WHITE HOSPITAL – BRENHAM (O, 56 beds) 700 Medical Parkway, Brenham, TX, Zip 77833–5498; tel. 979/337–5000; Jason Jennings, FACHE, President

SCOTT & WHITE HOSPITAL – COLLEGE STATION (O, 119 beds) 700 Scott & White Drive, College Station, TX, Zip 77845; tel. 979/207–0100; Jason Jennings, FACHE, President
Web address: www.sw.org/location/college-station-hospital

SCOTT & WHITE MEDICAL CENTER – TEMPLE (O, 647 beds) 2401 South 31st Street, Temple, TX, Zip 76508–0002; tel. 254/724–2111; Shahin Motakef, FACHE, President

Owned, leased, sponsored:	18 hospitals	3559 beds
Contract–managed:	1 hospitals	226 beds
Totals:	19 hospitals	3785 beds

★1095: BAYSTATE HEALTH, INC. (NP)
280 Chestnut Street, Springfield, MA, Zip 01199–0001; tel. 413/794–0000; Mark A. Keroack, M.D., M.P.H., President and Chief Executive Officer
(Centralized Physician/Insurance Health System)

MASSACHUSETTS: BAYSTATE FRANKLIN MEDICAL CENTER (O, 89 beds) 164 High Street, Greenfield, MA, Zip 01301–2613; tel. 413/773–0211; Ronald Bryant, President
Web address: www.baystatehealth.org

BAYSTATE MEDICAL CENTER (O, 720 beds) 759 Chestnut Street, Springfield, MA, Zip 01199–0001; tel. 413/794–0000; Nancy Shendell–Falik, R.N., President

BAYSTATE NOBLE HOSPITAL (O, 97 beds) 115 West Silver Street, Westfield, MA, Zip 01085–3628; tel. 413/568–2811; Ronald Bryant, President
Web address: www.baystatehealth.org/locations/noble-hospital

BAYSTATE WING HOSPITAL (O, 74 beds) 40 Wright Street, Palmer, MA, Zip 01069–1138; tel. 413/283–7651; Michael Francis. Moran, President and Chief Administrative Officer
Web address: www.baystatewinghospital.org/

Owned, leased, sponsored:	4 hospitals	980 beds
Contract–managed:	0 hospitals	0 beds
Totals:	4 hospitals	980 beds

★0940: BEACON HEALTH SYSTEM (NP)
615 North Michigan Street, South Bend, IN, Zip 46601–1033; tel. 574/647–1000; Kreg Gruber, Chief Executive Officer
(Centralized Physician/Insurance Health System)

INDIANA: ELKHART GENERAL HOSPITAL (O, 230 beds) 600 East Boulevard, Elkhart, IN, Zip 46514–2499, Mailing Address: P.O. Box 1329, Zip 46515–1329, tel. 574/294–2621; Carl W. Risk II, President
Web address: www.egh.org

For explanation of codes following names, see page B2.
★ Indicates Type III membership in the American Hospital Association.

MEMORIAL HOSPITAL OF SOUTH BEND (O, 445 beds) 615 North Michigan Street, South Bend, IN, Zip 46601–1033; tel. 574/647–1000; Larry A. Tracy Jr, FACHE, President
Web address: www.beaconhealthsystem.org

LOUISIANA: BEACON BEHAVIORAL HOSPITAL (O, 17 beds) 323 Evergreen Street, Bunkie, LA, Zip 71322–1307; tel. 318/346–3143; Randall Johnson, Administrator
Web address: www.beaconbh.com

Owned, leased, sponsored:	3 hospitals	692 beds
Contract–managed:	0 hospitals	0 beds
Totals:	3 hospitals	692 beds

★0953: BEAUMONT HEALTH (NP)

2000 Town Center, Suite 1200, Southfield, MI, Zip 48075–1145, fraser, tel. 248/898–5000; John T. Fox, President and Chief Executive Officer
(Centralized Health System)

MICHIGAN: BEAUMONT HOSPITAL – DEARBORN (O, 632 beds) 18101 Oakwood Boulevard, Dearborn, MI, Zip 48124–4089, Mailing Address: P.O. Box 2500, Zip 48123–2500, tel. 313/593–7000; David Claeys, FACHE, Chief Executive Officer
Web address: www.beaumont.org

BEAUMONT HOSPITAL – FARMINGTON HILLS (O, 330 beds) 28050 Grand River Avenue, Farmington Hills, MI, Zip 48336–5933; tel. 248/471–8000; Constance O'Malley, President

BEAUMONT HOSPITAL – GROSSE POINTE (O, 280 beds) 468 Cadieux Road, Grosse Pointe, MI, Zip 48230–1507; tel. 313/473–1000; Richard P. Swaine, President
Web address: www.beaumont.org

BEAUMONT HOSPITAL – ROYAL OAK (O, 1100 beds) 3601 West Thirteen Mile Road, Royal Oak, MI, Zip 48073–6712; tel. 248/898–5000; Rosanna Morris, R.N., President Royal Oak Hospital

BEAUMONT HOSPITAL – TAYLOR (O, 189 beds) 10000 Telegraph Road, Taylor, MI, Zip 48180–3330; tel. 313/295–5000; Lee Ann Odom, Division President
Web address: www.beaumont.org

BEAUMONT HOSPITAL – TRENTON (O, 173 beds) 5450 Fort Street, Trenton, MI, Zip 48183–4625; tel. 734/671–3800; Christine Stesney–Ridenour, FACHE, President

BEAUMONT HOSPITAL – TROY (O, 520 beds) 44201 Dequindre Road, Troy, MI, Zip 48085–1117; tel. 248/964–5000; Nancy Susick, MSN, President
Web address: www.beaumont.org

BEAUMONT HOSPITAL, WAYNE (O, 185 beds) 33155 Annapolis Street, Wayne, MI, Zip 48184–2405; tel. 734/467–4000; Eric W. Widner, FACHE, Division President
Web address: www.beaumont.org

Owned, leased, sponsored:	8 hospitals	3409 beds
Contract–managed:	0 hospitals	0 beds
Totals:	8 hospitals	3409 beds

0538: BENEFIS HEALTH SYSTEM (NP)

1101 26th Street South, Great Falls, MT, Zip 59405–5161; tel. 406/455–5000; John H. Goodnow, Chief Executive Officer
(Moderately Centralized Health System)

MONTANA: BENEFIS HEALTH SYSTEM (O, 502 beds) 1101 26th Street South, Great Falls, MT, Zip 59405–5104; tel. 406/455–5000; John H. Goodnow, Chief Executive Officer

BENEFIS TETON MEDICAL CENTER (O, 46 beds) 915 4th Street North West, Choteau, MT, Zip 59422–9123; tel. 406/466–5763; Louie King, Chief Executive Officer
Web address: www.tetonmedicalcenter.net

MISSOURI RIVER MEDICAL CENTER (C, 25 beds) 1501 St Charles Street, Fort Benton, MT, Zip 59442–0249, Mailing Address: P.O. Box 249, Zip 59442–0249, tel. 406/622–3331; Louie King, President, Harry Bold Nursing Home Administrator

Owned, leased, sponsored:	2 hospitals	548 beds
Contract–managed:	1 hospitals	25 beds
Totals:	3 hospitals	573 beds

★2435: BERKSHIRE HEALTH SYSTEMS, INC. (NP)

725 North Street, Pittsfield, MA, Zip 01201–4124; tel. 413/447–2750; David E. Phelps, President and Chief Executive Officer
(Moderately Centralized Health System)

MASSACHUSETTS: BERKSHIRE MEDICAL CENTER (O, 275 beds) 725 North ST, Pittsfield, MA, Zip 01201–4124, Mailing Address: 725 North Street, Zip 01201–4124, tel. 413/447–2000; David E. Phelps, President and Chief Executive Officer
Web address: www.berkshirehealthsystems.org

FAIRVIEW HOSPITAL (O, 25 beds) 29 Lewis Avenue, Great Barrington, MA, Zip 01230–1713; tel. 413/528–0790; Eugene A. Dellea, President

Owned, leased, sponsored:	2 hospitals	300 beds
Contract–managed:	0 hospitals	0 beds
Totals:	2 hospitals	300 beds

★0051: BJC HEALTHCARE (NP)

4901 Forest Park Avenue, Suite 1200, Saint Louis, MO, Zip 63108–1402; tel. 314/286–2000; Richard J. Liekweg, President and Chief Executive Officer
(Centralized Health System)

ILLINOIS: ALTON MEMORIAL HOSPITAL (O, 258 beds) One Memorial Drive, Alton, IL, Zip 62002–6722; tel. 618/463–7311; David A. Braasch, President
Web address: www.altonmemorialhospital.org

MEMORIAL HOSPITAL EAST (O, 68 beds) 1404 Cross Street, Shiloh, IL, Zip 62269–2988; tel. 618/607–1000; Mark J. Turner, FACHE, President

MEMORIAL HOSPITAL (O, 302 beds) 4500 Memorial Drive, Belleville, IL, Zip 62226–5399; tel. 618/233–7750; Mark J. Turner, FACHE, President
Web address: www.memhosp.com

MISSOURI: BARNES–JEWISH HOSPITAL (O, 1396 beds) 1 Barnes–Jewish Hospital Plaza, Saint Louis, MO, Zip 63110–1003; tel. 314/747–3000; Robert W. Cannon, President
Web address: www.barnesjewish.org

BARNES–JEWISH ST. PETERS HOSPITAL (O, 101 beds) 10 Hospital Drive, Saint Peters, MO, Zip 63376–1659; tel. 636/916–9000; Chris Watts, President

BARNES–JEWISH WEST COUNTY HOSPITAL (O, 77 beds) 12634 Olive Boulevard, Saint Louis, MO, Zip 63141–6337; tel. 314/996–8000; Trisha Lollo, President
Web address: www.barnesjewishwestcounty.org

BOONE HOSPITAL CENTER (L, 311 beds) 1600 East Broadway, Columbia, MO, Zip 65201–5844; tel. 573/815–8000; James J. Sinek, FACHE, President
Web address: www.boone.org

CHRISTIAN HOSPITAL (O, 220 beds) 11133 Dunn Road, Saint Louis, MO, Zip 63136–6119; tel. 314/653–5000; Rick Stevens, President

MISSOURI BAPTIST MEDICAL CENTER (O, 443 beds) 3015 North Ballas Road, Saint Louis, MO, Zip 63131–2329; tel. 314/996–5000; John Antes, President
Web address: www.missouribaptist.org

MISSOURI BAPTIST SULLIVAN HOSPITAL (O, 35 beds) 751 Sappington Bridge Road, Sullivan, MO, Zip 63080–2354; tel. 573/468–4186; Tony Schwarm, President
Web address: www.missouribaptistsullivan.org

PARKLAND HEALTH CENTER – FARMINGTON COMMUNITY (O, 103 beds) 1101 West Liberty Street, Farmington, MO, Zip 63640–1921; tel. 573/756–6451; Thomas P. Karl, President
Web address: www.parklandhealthcenter.org

PARKLAND HEALTH CENTER–BONNE TERRE (O, 3 beds) 7245 Raider Road, Bonne Terre, MO, Zip 63628, Mailing Address: 1101 West Liberty Street, Farmington, Zip 63640, tel. 573/358–1400; Laura Lynn Rasnick, RN, BSN, CLNC, Administrator

PROGRESS WEST HOSPITAL (O, 74 beds) Two Progress Point Parkway, O'Fallon, MO, Zip 63368–2208; tel. 636/344–1000; Chris Watts, President
Web address: www.progresswest.org

For explanation of codes following names, see page B2.
★ Indicates Type III membership in the American Hospital Association.

Section B

ST. LOUIS CHILDREN'S HOSPITAL (O, 274 beds) One Children's Place, Saint Louis, MO, Zip 63110–1002; tel. 314/454–6000; Joan Magruder, President
Web address: www.stlouischildrens.org

Owned, leased, sponsored:	14 hospitals	3665 beds
Contract–managed:	0 hospitals	0 beds
Totals:	14 hospitals	3665 beds

★0852: BLANCHARD VALLEY HEALTH SYSTEM (NP)
1900 South Main Street, Findlay, OH, Zip 45840–1214; tel. 419/423–4500; Scott C. Malaney, FACHE, President and Chief Executive Officer
(Centralized Physician/Insurance Health System)

OHIO: BLANCHARD VALLEY HOSPITAL (O, 159 beds) 1900 South Main Street, Findlay, OH, Zip 45840–1214; tel. 419/423–4500; Scott C. Malaney, FACHE, President and Chief Executive Officer
Web address: www.bvhealthsystem.org

BLUFFTON HOSPITAL (O, 25 beds) 139 Garau Street, Bluffton, OH, Zip 45817–1027; tel. 419/358–9010; Christine Keller, Chief Administrative Officer
Web address: www.bvhealthsystem.org/

Owned, leased, sponsored:	2 hospitals	184 beds
Contract–managed:	0 hospitals	0 beds
Totals:	2 hospitals	184 beds

★5085: BON SECOURS HEALTH SYSTEM, INC. (CO)
1505 Marriottsville Road, Marriottsville, MD, Zip 21104–1399; tel. 410/442–5511; Richard Statuto, President and Chief Executive Officer
(Moderately Centralized Health System)

KENTUCKY: OUR LADY OF BELLEFONTE HOSPITAL (O, 140 beds) St Christopher Drive, Ashland, KY, Zip 41101, Mailing Address: P.O. Box 789, Zip 41105–0789, tel. 606/833–3333; Kevin Halter, Chief Executive Officer
Web address: www.olbh.com

MARYLAND: BON SECOURS BALTIMORE HEALTH SYSTEM (O, 69 beds) 2000 West Baltimore Street, Baltimore, MD, Zip 21223–1558; tel. 410/362–3000; Samuel Lee. Ross, M.D., MS, Chief Executive Officer
Web address: www.bonsecoursbaltimore.com

SOUTH CAROLINA: BON SECOURS ST. FRANCIS HEALTH SYSTEM (O, 352 beds) One St Francis Drive, Greenville, SC, Zip 29601–3207; tel. 864/255–1000; Craig McCoy, Chief Executive Officer

VIRGINIA: BON SECOURS MARY IMMACULATE HOSPITAL (O, 238 beds) 2 Bernardine Drive, Newport News, VA, Zip 23602–4499; tel. 757/886–6000; Darlene Stephenson, Chief Executive Officer
Web address: www.bonsecourshamptonroads.com

BON SECOURS MARYVIEW MEDICAL CENTER (O, 466 beds) 3636 High Street, Portsmouth, VA, Zip 23707–3270; tel. 757/398–2200; Paul Gaden, Chief Executive Officer
Web address: www.bonsecourshamptonroads.com

BON SECOURS MEMORIAL REGIONAL MEDICAL CENTER (O, 225 beds) 8260 Atlee Road, Mechanicsville, VA, Zip 23116–1844; tel. 804/764–6000; Mark M. Gordon, Chief Executive Officer

BON SECOURS ST. FRANCIS MEDICAL CENTER (O, 124 beds) 13710 St Francis Boulevard, Midlothian, VA, Zip 23114–3267; tel. 804/594–7300; Chris Accashian, Chief Executive Officer
Web address: www.bonsecours.com/sfmc/default.asp

BON SECOURS ST. MARY'S HOSPITAL (O, 391 beds) 5801 Bremo Road, Richmond, VA, Zip 23226–1907; tel. 804/285–2011; Francine Barr, R.N., MS, Chief Executive Officer
Web address: www.bonsecours.com

BON SECOURS–DEPAUL MEDICAL CENTER (O, 204 beds) 150 Kingsley Lane, Norfolk, VA, Zip 23505–4650; tel. 757/889–5000; Paul Gaden, Chief Executive Officer
Web address: www.bonsecourshamptonroads.com

BON SECOURS–RICHMOND COMMUNITY HOSPITAL (O, 85 beds) 1500 North 28th Street, Richmond, VA, Zip 23223–5396, Mailing Address: P.O. Box 27184, Zip 23261–7184, tel. 804/225–1700; Mark M. Gordon, Chief Executive Officer

RAPPAHANNOCK GENERAL HOSPITAL (O, 35 beds) 101 Harris Drive, Kilmarnock, VA, Zip 22482–3880, Mailing Address: P.O. Box 1449, Zip 22482–1449, tel. 804/435–8000; Chris Accashian, Chief Executive Officer
Web address: www.https://bonsecours.com/richmond/find–a–facility/rappahannock–general–hospital

Owned, leased, sponsored:	11 hospitals	2329 beds
Contract–managed:	0 hospitals	0 beds
Totals:	11 hospitals	2329 beds

2455: BRADFORD HEALTH SERVICES (IO)
2101 Magnolia Avenue South, Suite 518, Birmingham, AL, Zip 35205–2853; tel. 205/251–7753; Jerry W. Crowder, President and Chief Executive Officer

ALABAMA: BRADFORD HEALTH SERVICES AT HUNTSVILLE (O, 84 beds) 1600 Browns Ferry Road, Madison, AL, Zip 35758–9601, Mailing Address: P.O. Box 1488, Zip 35758–0176, tel. 256/461–7272; Bob Hinds, Executive Director
Web address: www.bradfordhealth.com

BRADFORD HEALTH SERVICES AT WARRIOR LODGE (O, 100 beds) 1189 Allbritt Road, Warrior, AL, Zip 35180, Mailing Address: P.O. Box 129, Zip 35180–0129, tel. 205/647–1945; Roy M. Ramsey, Executive Director
Web address: www.bradfordhealth.com

Owned, leased, sponsored:	2 hospitals	184 beds
Contract–managed:	0 hospitals	0 beds
Totals:	2 hospitals	184 beds

0352: BRIDGEPOINT HEALTHCARE (IO)
155 Fleet Street, Portsmouth, NH, Zip 03801–4050; tel. 603/570–4888; Marc C. Ferrell, President and Chief Executive Officer
(Independent Hospital System)

DISTRICT OF COLUMBIA: BRIDGEPOINT HOSPITAL CAPITOL HILL (O, 177 beds) 700 Constitution Avenue NE, Washington, DC, Zip 20002–6058; tel. 202/546–5700; James Linhares, Chief Executive Officer

BRIDGEPOINT HOSPITAL NATIONAL HARBOR (O, 82 beds) 4601 Martin Luther King Jr Avenue, SW, Washington, DC, Zip 20032–1131; tel. 202/574–5700; Swenda Moreh, Interim Chief Executive Officer
Web address: www.bridgepointhealthcare.com/

Owned, leased, sponsored:	2 hospitals	259 beds
Contract–managed:	0 hospitals	0 beds
Totals:	2 hospitals	259 beds

★0595: BRONSON HEALTHCARE GROUP (NP)
301 John Street, Kalamazoo, MI, Zip 49007–5295; tel. 269/341–6000; Frank J. Sardone, President and Chief Executive Officer
(Moderately Centralized Health System)

MICHIGAN: BRONSON BATTLE CREEK HOSPITAL (O, 198 beds) 300 North Avenue, Battle Creek, MI, Zip 49017–3307; tel. 269/245–8000; Frank J. Sardone, President and Chief Executive Officer
Web address: www.bronsonhealth.com

BRONSON LAKEVIEW HOSPITAL (O, 35 beds) 408 Hazen Street, Paw Paw, MI, Zip 49079–1019, Mailing Address: P.O. Box 209, Zip 49079–0209, tel. 269/657–3141; Kirk Richardson, R.N., Vice President, Chief Operating Officer, and Chief Nursing Officer
Web address: www.bronsonhealth.com/lakeview

BRONSON METHODIST HOSPITAL (O, 415 beds) 601 John Street, Kalamazoo, MI, Zip 49007–5346; tel. 269/341–6000; Frank J. Sardone, President and Chief Executive Officer
Web address: www.bronsonhealth.com

For explanation of codes following names, see page B2.
★ Indicates Type III membership in the American Hospital Association.

BRONSON SOUTH HAVEN HOSPITAL (O, 49 beds) 955 South Bailey Avenue, South Haven, MI, Zip 49090–6743; tel. 269/637–5271; Kirk Richardson, R.N., Vice President, Chief Operating Officer and Chief Nursing Officer

Owned, leased, sponsored:	4 hospitals	697 beds
Contract–managed:	0 hospitals	0 beds
Totals:	4 hospitals	697 beds

★3115: BROWARD HEALTH (NP)

1800 NW 49th Street, Fort Lauderdale, FL, Zip 33309–3092; tel. 954/355–4400; Beverly Capasso, President and Chief Executive Officer

FLORIDA: BROWARD HEALTH CORAL SPRINGS (O, 196 beds) 3000 Coral Hills Drive, Coral Springs, FL, Zip 33065–4108; tel. 954/344–3000; Jared M. Smith, Chief Executive Officer
Web address: www.browardhealth.org

BROWARD HEALTH IMPERIAL POINT (O, 180 beds) 6401 North Federal Highway, Fort Lauderdale, FL, Zip 33308–1495; tel. 954/776–8500; Jonathan Watkins, Chief Executive Officer
Web address: www.browardhealth.org

BROWARD HEALTH MEDICAL CENTER (O, 656 beds) 1600 South Andrews Avenue, Fort Lauderdale, FL, Zip 33316–2510; tel. 954/355–4400; Jonathan Turton, FACHE, Chief Executive Officer

BROWARD HEALTH NORTH (O, 344 beds) 201 East Sample Road, Deerfield Beach, FL, Zip 33064–3502; tel. 954/941–8300; Alice Taylor, R.N., MSN, Chief Executive Officer
Web address: www.browardhealth.org

Owned, leased, sponsored:	4 hospitals	1376 beds
Contract–managed:	0 hospitals	0 beds
Totals:	4 hospitals	1376 beds

★0400: BRYAN HEALTH (NP)

1600 South 48th Street, Lincoln, NE, Zip 68506–1283, Mailing Address: 1600 S 48th ST, Zip 68506–1283, tel. 402/481–1111; Kimberly A. Russel, FACHE, President and Chief Executive Officer
(Moderately Centralized Health System)

IOWA: CLARINDA REGIONAL HEALTH CENTER (C, 25 beds) 220 Essie Davison Drive, Clarinda, IA, Zip 51632–2915, Mailing Address: P.O. Box 217, Zip 51632–0217, tel. 712/542–2176; Charles Nordyke, Chief Executive Officer
Web address: www.clarindahealth.com

NEBRASKA: BRYAN MEDICAL CENTER (O, 540 beds) 1600 South 48th Street, Lincoln, NE, Zip 68506–1299; tel. 402/481–1111; John T. Woodrich, President and Chief Operating Officer
Web address: www.bryanhealth.org

CRETE AREA MEDICAL CENTER (O, 24 beds) 2910 Betten Drive, Crete, NE, Zip 68333–3084, Mailing Address: P.O. Box 220, Zip 68333–0220, tel. 402/826–2102; Rebekah Mussman, Chief Executive Officer

MERRICK MEDICAL CENTER (O, 65 beds) 1715 26th Street, Central City, NE, Zip 68826–9620; tel. 308/946–3015; Julie Murray, Chief Executive Officer
Web address: https://www.bryanhealth.com

SAUNDERS MEDICAL CENTER (C, 16 beds) 1760 County Road J, Wahoo, NE, Zip 68066–4152; tel. 402/443–4191; Tyler Toline, FACHE, Chief Executive Officer

Owned, leased, sponsored:	3 hospitals	629 beds
Contract–managed:	2 hospitals	41 beds
Totals:	5 hospitals	670 beds

9655: BUREAU OF MEDICINE AND SURGERY, DEPARTMENT OF THE NAVY (FG)

7700 Arlington Boulevard, Suite 5126, Falls Church, VA, Zip 22042; tel. 202/762–3701; Bryce H.P. Mendez, Healthcare Policy Analyst
(Independent Hospital System)

CALIFORNIA: NAVAL HOSPITAL CAMP PENDLETON (O, 72 beds) 200 Mercy Circle, Camp Pendleton, CA, Zip 92055–5191, Mailing Address: P.O. Box 555191, Zip 92055–5191, tel. 760/725–1304; Captain, Frank P. Pearson, Commanding Officer
Web address: www.cpen.med.navy.mil/

NAVAL HOSPITAL LEMOORE (O, 16 beds) 937 Franklin Avenue, Lemoore, CA, Zip 93246–0001; tel. 559/998–4481; Captain, Kristen Attenbury, Commanding Officer

NAVAL MEDICAL CENTER SAN DIEGO (O, 285 beds) 34800 Bob Wilson Drive, San Diego, CA, Zip 92134–5000; tel. 619/532–6400; Captain, Joel A. Roos, Commanding Officer
Web address: www.med.navy.mil/sites/nmcsd/Pages/default.aspx

ROBERT E. BUSH NAVAL HOSPITAL (O, 29 beds) 1145 Sturgis Road, Twentynine Palms, CA, Zip 92278, Mailing Address: Box 788250, MCAGCC, Zip 92278–8250, tel. 760/830–2190; Captain, Jay C. Sourbeer, Commanding Officer

FLORIDA: NAVAL HOSPITAL JACKSONVILLE (O, 64 beds) 2080 Child Street, Jacksonville, FL, Zip 32214–5000; tel. 904/542–7300; Commander, Darryl Green, Director Administration
Web address: www.med.navy.mil/SITES/NAVALHOSPITALJAX/Pages/default.aspx

NAVAL HOSPITAL PENSACOLA (O, 28 beds) 6000 West Highway 98, Pensacola, FL, Zip 32512–0003; tel. 850/505–6601; Commander, Devin Morrison, Director Administration

GUAM: U.S. NAVAL HOSPITAL GUAM (O, 55 beds) Building #50 Farenholt Avenue, Agana, GU, Zip 96910, Mailing Address: PSC 490, Box 208, FPO, Zip 96540, tel. 671/344–9340; Captain, Daniel Cornwell, Command Officer
Web address: www.med.navy.mil/sites/usnhguam/Pages/default.aspx

MARYLAND: WALTER REED NATIONAL MILITARY MEDICAL CENTER (O, 247 beds) 8901 Wisconsin Avenue, Bethesda, MD, Zip 20889–5600; tel. 301/295–4611; Colonel, CAPT Mark A. Kobelja, MC, USN, Director
Web address: www.wrnmmc.capmed.mil/SitePages/home.aspx

NORTH CAROLINA: NAVAL HOSPITAL CAMP LEJEUNE (O, 117 beds) 100 Brewster Boulevard, Camp Lejeune, NC, Zip 28547–2538, Mailing Address: P.O. Box 10100, Zip 28547–0100, tel. 910/450–4300; Captain, Rick Freedman, Commanding Officer

SOUTH CAROLINA: NAVAL HOSPITAL BEAUFORT (O, 20 beds) 1 Pinckney Boulevard, Beaufort, SC, Zip 29902–6122; tel. 843/228–5301; Lieutenant Commander, Willie Brown, Director Administration
Web address: www.med.navy.mil/sites/nhbeaufort/Pages/Welcome_Page.aspx

VIRGINIA: NAVAL MEDICAL CENTER (O, 274 beds) 620 John Paul Jones Circle, Portsmouth, VA, Zip 23708–2197; tel. 757/953–1980; Captain, Matthew Case, MSC, USN, Executive Officer

WASHINGTON: NAVAL HOSPITAL BREMERTON (O, 23 beds) One Boone Road, Bremerton, WA, Zip 98312–1898; tel. 360/475–4000; Captain, Jeffrey Bitterman, Commanding Officer
Web address: www.med.navy.mil/sites/nhbrem/Pages/default.aspx

NAVAL HOSPITAL OAK HARBOR (O, 29 beds) 3475 North Saratoga Street, Oak Harbor, WA, Zip 98278–8800; tel. 360/257–9500; Commander, Frederick Joseph. McDonald, Commanding Officer
Web address: www.med.navy.mil/sites/nhoh/Pages/default.aspx

Owned, leased, sponsored:	13 hospitals	1259 beds
Contract–managed:	0 hospitals	0 beds
Totals:	13 hospitals	1259 beds

0113: CANCER TREATMENT CENTERS OF AMERICA (IO)

1336 Basswood Road, Schaumburg, IL, Zip 60173–4544; tel. 847/342–7400; Rajesh K. Garg, M.D., JD, President and Chief Executive Officer

ARIZONA: WESTERN REGIONAL MEDICAL CENTER (O, 12 beds) 14200 West Celebrate Life way, Goodyear, AZ, Zip 85338–3005; tel. 623/207–3000; Robert Gould, President and Chief Executive Officer
Web address: www.cancercenter.com/western–hospital.cfm

For explanation of codes following names, see page B2.
★ Indicates Type III membership in the American Hospital Association.

GEORGIA: SOUTHEASTERN REGIONAL MEDICAL CENTER (O, 50 beds) 600 Celebrate Life Parkway, Newnan, GA, Zip 30265–8000; tel. 770/400–6000; Anne Meisner, MSN, President and Chief Executive Officer
Web address: www.cancercenter.com/southeastern–hospital.cfm

ILLINOIS: MIDWESTERN REGIONAL MEDICAL CENTER (O, 72 beds) 2520 Elisha Avenue, Zion, IL, Zip 60099–2587; tel. 847/872–4561; Scott Jones, President and Chief Executive Officer

OKLAHOMA: SOUTHWESTERN REGIONAL MEDICAL CENTER (O, 40 beds) 10109 East 79th Street, Tulsa, OK, Zip 74133–4564; tel. 918/286–5000; Jay Foley, President and Chief Executive Officer
Web address: www.cancercenter.com

PENNSYLVANIA: CANCER TREATMENT CENTERS OF AMERICA–EASTERN REGIONAL MEDICAL CENTER (O, 56 beds) 1331 East Wyoming Avenue, Philadelphia, PA, Zip 19124–3808; tel. 215/537–7400; Nancy Hesse, MSN, R.N., President and Chief Executive Officer

Owned, leased, sponsored:	5 hospitals	230 beds
Contract–managed:	0 hospitals	0 beds
Totals:	5 hospitals	230 beds

★0124: CAPE COD HEALTHCARE, INC. (NP)
27 Park Street, Hyannis, MA, Zip 02601–5230; tel. 508/862–5121; Michael K. Lauf, President and Chief Executive Officer
(Centralized Health System)

MASSACHUSETTS: CAPE COD HOSPITAL (O, 259 beds) 27 Park Street, Hyannis, MA, Zip 02601–5230; tel. 508/771–1800; Michael K. Lauf, President and Chief Executive Officer

FALMOUTH HOSPITAL (O, 95 beds) 100 Ter Heun Drive, Falmouth, MA, Zip 02540–2599; tel. 508/548–5300; Lori Jewett, R.N., Chief Executive Officer
Web address: www.capecodhealth.org

Owned, leased, sponsored:	2 hospitals	354 beds
Contract–managed:	0 hospitals	0 beds
Totals:	2 hospitals	354 beds

0835: CAPE FEAR VALLEY HEALTH SYSTEM (NP)
1638 Owen Drive, Fayetteville, NC, Zip 28304–3424, Mailing Address: P.O. Box 2000, Zip 28302–2000, tel. 910/615–4000; Michael Nagowski, President and Chief Executive Officer
(Independent Hospital System)

NORTH CAROLINA: CAPE FEAR VALLEY – BLADEN COUNTY HOSPITAL (O, 25 beds) 501 South Poplar Street, Elizabethtown, NC, Zip 28337–9375, Mailing Address: P.O. Box 398, Zip 28337–0398, tel. 910/862–5100; Roxie Cannon. Wells, M.D., Chief Executive Officer

CAPE FEAR VALLEY MEDICAL CENTER (O, 608 beds) 1638 Owen Drive, Fayetteville, NC, Zip 28304–3431, Mailing Address: P.O. Box 2000, Zip 28302–2000, tel. 910/615–4000; Michael Nagowski, Chief Executive Officer
Web address: www.capefearvalley.com

HARNETT HEALTH SYSTEM (C, 105 beds) 800 Tilghman Drive, Dunn, NC, Zip 28334–5599, Mailing Address: P.O. Box 1706, Zip 28335–1706, tel. 910/892–1000; Kevin Jackson, Interim Chief Executive Officer

HIGHSMITH–RAINEY SPECIALTY HOSPITAL (O, 66 beds) 150 Robeson Street, Fayetteville, NC, Zip 28301–5570; tel. 910/615–1000; Kevin Jackson, On Site Administrator
Web address: www.capefearvalley.com

HOKE HOSPITAL (O, 41 beds) 210 Medical Pavilion Drive, Raeford, NC, Zip 28376–9111; tel. 910/904–8000; Roxie Cannon. Wells, M.D., President
Web address: www.capefearvalley.com

Owned, leased, sponsored:	4 hospitals	740 beds
Contract–managed:	1 hospitals	105 beds
Totals:	5 hospitals	845 beds

★0297: CAPITAL HEALTH (NP)
750 Brunswick Avenue, Trenton, NJ, Zip 08638–4143; tel. 609/394–6000; Al Maghazehe, Ph.D., FACHE, President and Chief Executive Officer
(Independent Hospital System)

NEW JERSEY: CAPITAL HEALTH MEDICAL CENTER–HOPEWELL (O, 170 beds) 1 Capital Way, Pennington, NJ, Zip 08534–2520; tel. 609/303–4000; Al Maghazehe, Ph.D., FACHE, President and Chief Executive Officer
Web address: www.capitalhealth.org

CAPITAL HEALTH REGIONAL MEDICAL CENTER (O, 167 beds) 750 Brunswick Avenue, Trenton, NJ, Zip 08638–4143; tel. 609/394–6000; Al Maghazehe, Ph.D., FACHE, President and Chief Executive Officer

Owned, leased, sponsored:	2 hospitals	337 beds
Contract–managed:	0 hospitals	0 beds
Totals:	2 hospitals	337 beds

★0099: CARE NEW ENGLAND HEALTH SYSTEM (NP)
45 Willard Avenue, Providence, RI, Zip 02905–3218; tel. 401/453–7900; James E. Fanale, M.D., President, Chief Executive Officer and Chief Clinical Officer
(Moderately Centralized Health System)

RHODE ISLAND: BUTLER HOSPITAL (O, 143 beds) 345 Blackstone Boulevard, Providence, RI, Zip 02906–4829; tel. 401/455–6200; Mary Marran, MS, President and Chief Operating Officer
Web address: www.butler.org

KENT COUNTY MEMORIAL HOSPITAL (O, 317 beds) 455 Tollgate Road, Warwick, RI, Zip 02886–2770; tel. 401/737–7000; Robert Haffey, R.N., President and Chief Operating Officer
Web address: www.kentri.org

WOMEN & INFANTS HOSPITAL OF RHODE ISLAND (O, 247 beds) 101 Dudley Street, Providence, RI, Zip 02905–2499; tel. 401/274–1100; Rick Majzun, FACHE, President and Chief Operating Officer

Owned, leased, sponsored:	3 hospitals	707 beds
Contract–managed:	0 hospitals	0 beds
Totals:	3 hospitals	707 beds

0931: CAREPOINT HEALTH (IO)
10 Exchange Place, 15th Floor, Jersey City, NJ, Zip 07302–3918; tel. 877/791–7000; Natasha Deckmann, Chief Executive Officer

NEW JERSEY: CAREPOINT HEALTH BAYONNE MEDICAL CENTER (O, 178 beds) 29th Street & Avenue E, Bayonne, NJ, Zip 07002–4699, Mailing Address: 29 East 29 Street, Zip 07002–4699, tel. 201/858–5000; W. Peter Daniels, FACHE, Executive Vice President and Chief Operating Officer

CAREPOINT HEALTH CHRIST HOSPITAL (O, 376 beds) 176 Palisade Avenue, Jersey City, NJ, Zip 07306–1196, Mailing Address: 176 Palisades Avenue, Zip 07306–1196, tel. 201/795–8200; Marie Theresa Duffy, Chief Operating Officer
Web address: www.carepointhealth.org

CAREPOINT HEALTH HOBOKEN UNIVERSITY MEDICAL CENTER (O, 228 beds) 308 Willow Avenue, Hoboken, NJ, Zip 07030–3889; tel. 201/418–1000; Ann P. Logan, R.N., Ph.D., Chief Operating Officer

Owned, leased, sponsored:	3 hospitals	782 beds
Contract–managed:	0 hospitals	0 beds
Totals:	3 hospitals	782 beds

★0070: CARILION CLINIC (NP)
1906 Belleview Avenue SE, Roanoke, VA, Zip 24014–1838, Mailing Address: P.O. Box 13727, Zip 24036–3727, tel. 540/981–7000; Nancy Howell. Agee, President and Chief Executive Officer
(Moderately Centralized Health System)

VIRGINIA: CARILION FRANKLIN MEMORIAL HOSPITAL (O, 14 beds) 180 Floyd Avenue, Rocky Mount, VA, Zip 24151–1389; tel. 540/483–5277; William D. Jacobsen, FACHE, Administrator and Hospital Vice President

For explanation of codes following names, see page B2.
★ Indicates Type III membership in the American Hospital Association.

CARILION GILES COMMUNITY HOSPITAL (O, 10 beds) 159 Hartley Way, Pearisburg, VA, Zip 24134–2471; tel. 540/921–6000; William Flattery, Vice President and Administrator Western Division
Web address: https://www.carilionclinic.org

CARILION NEW RIVER VALLEY MEDICAL CENTER (O, 88 beds) 2900 Lamb Circle, Christiansburg, VA, Zip 24073–6344, Mailing Address: P.O. Box 5, Radford, Zip 24143–0005, tel. 540/731–2000; William Flattery, Vice President and Administrator Western Division

CARILION ROANOKE MEMORIAL HOSPITAL (O, 620 beds) 1906 Belleview Avenue Southeast, Roanoke, VA, Zip 24014–1838, Mailing Address: P.O. Box 13367, Zip 24033–3367, tel. 540/981–7000; Steven C. Arner, President
Web address: www.carilionclinic.org

CARILION STONEWALL JACKSON HOSPITAL (O, 12 beds) 1 Health Circle, Lexington, VA, Zip 24450–2492; tel. 540/458–3300; Greg T. Madsen, Chief Executive Officer

CARILION TAZEWELL COMMUNITY HOSPITAL (O, 5 beds) 141 Ben Bolt Avenue, Tazewell, VA, Zip 24651–9700, Mailing Address: 388 Ben Bolt Avenue, Zip 24651, tel. 276/988–8700; Kathren Dowdy, MSN, Regional Hospital Senior Director
Web address: www.carilionclinic.org

Owned, leased, sponsored:	6 hospitals	749 beds
Contract–managed:	0 hospitals	0 beds
Totals:	6 hospitals	749 beds

★**2575: CARLE FOUNDATION** (NP)
611 West Park Street, Urbana, IL, Zip 61801–2595; tel. 217/383–3311; James C. Leonard, M.D., President and Chief Executive Officer **(Centralized Physician/Insurance Health System)**

ILLINOIS: CARLE FOUNDATION HOSPITAL (O, 391 beds) 611 West Park Street, Urbana, IL, Zip 61801–2529; tel. 217/383–3311; James C. Leonard, M.D., President and Chief Executive Officer
Web address: www.carle.org

CARLE HOOPESTON REGIONAL HEALTH CENTER (O, 13 beds) 701 East Orange Street, Hoopeston, IL, Zip 60942–1801; tel. 217/283–5531; Harry Brockus, Chief Executive Officer
Web address: www.carle.org

CARLE RICHLAND MEMORIAL HOSPITAL (O, 74 beds) 800 East Locust Street, Olney, IL, Zip 62450–2553; tel. 618/395–2131; Jennifer Emmons, Interim Chief Executive Officer

Owned, leased, sponsored:	3 hospitals	478 beds
Contract–managed:	0 hospitals	0 beds
Totals:	3 hospitals	478 beds

0656: CARRUS HOSPITALS (IO)
1810 West US Highway 82, Sherman, TX, Zip 75092–7069; tel. 903/870–2600; Ronald E. Dorris, Chief Executive Officer **(Independent Hospital System)**

TEXAS: CARRUS REHABILITATION HOSPITAL (O, 24 beds) 1810 West US Highway 82, Suite 100, Sherman, TX, Zip 75092–7069; tel. 903/870–2600; Jon–Michael Rains, Chief Executive Officer
Web address: www.carrushospital.com

CARRUS SPECIALTY HOSPITAL (O, 16 beds) 1810 West US Highway 82, Sherman, TX, Zip 75092–7069; tel. 903/870–2600; Jon–Michael Rains, Chief Executive Officer

Owned, leased, sponsored:	2 hospitals	40 beds
Contract–managed:	0 hospitals	0 beds
Totals:	2 hospitals	40 beds

★**0092: CATHOLIC HEALTH INITIATIVES** (CO)
198 Inverness Drive West, Suite 800, Englewood, CO, Zip 80112–5202; tel. 303/298–9100; Kevin E. Lofton, FACHE, Chief Executive Officer **(Decentralized Health System)**

ARKANSAS: CHI ST. VINCENT HOT SPRINGS (O, 241 beds) 300 Werner Street, Hot Springs, AR, Zip 71913–6406; tel. 501/622–1000; Anthony Houston, FACHE, President
Web address: www.chistvincent.com/Hospitals/st-vincent–hot–springs

CHI ST. VINCENT INFIRMARY MEDICAL CENTER (S, 423 beds) Two St Vincent Circle, Little Rock, AR, Zip 72205–5499; tel. 501/552–3000; Polly J. Davenport, FACHE, R.N., President
Web address: www.chistvincent.com/

CHI ST. VINCENT MEDICAL CENTER–NORTH (S, 69 beds) 2215 Wildwood Avenue, Sherwood, AR, Zip 72120–5089; tel. 501/552–7100; Polly J Davenport, BSN, DSC, FACHE, President
Web address: www.stvincenthealth.com

CHI ST. VINCENT MORRILTON (S, 25 beds) 4 Hospital Drive, Morrilton, AR, Zip 72110–4510; tel. 501/977–2300; Leslie Arnold, Chief Executive Officer and Administrator
Web address: www.chistvincent.com/Hospitals/st-vincent–morrilton

COLORADO: LONGMONT UNITED HOSPITAL (S, 146 beds) 1950 West Mountain View Avenue, Longmont, CO, Zip 80501–3162, Mailing Address: P.O. Box 1659, Zip 80502–1659, tel. 303/651–5111; Christina Johnson, M.D., Chief Executive Officer

MERCY REGIONAL MEDICAL CENTER (S, 82 beds) 1010 Three Springs Boulevard, Durango, CO, Zip 81301–8296; tel. 970/247–4311; William McConnell, Ph.D., President and Chief Executive Officer
Web address: www.mercydurango.org

ORTHOCOLORADO HOSPITAL (O, 48 beds) 11650 West 2nd Place, Lakewood, CO, Zip 80228–1527; tel. 720/321–5000; Jude Torchia, Chief Executive Officer

PENROSE–ST. FRANCIS HEALTH SERVICES (S, 444 beds) 2222 North Nevada Avenue, Colorado Springs, CO, Zip 80907–6799; tel. 719/776–5000; Brian Erling, Interim Chief Executive Officer
Web address: www.penrosestfrancis.org

ST. ANTHONY HOSPITAL (S, 219 beds) 11600 West Second Place, Lakewood, CO, Zip 80228–1527; tel. 720/321–0000; Edward H. Sim, Chief Executive Officer
Web address: www.stanthonyhosp.org

ST. ANTHONY NORTH HEALTH CAMPUS (S, 97 beds) 14300 Orchard Parkway, Westminster, CO, Zip 80023–9206; tel. 720/627–0000; Kevin Jenkins, President and Chief Executive Officer
Web address: www.stanthonynorth.org

ST. ANTHONY SUMMIT MEDICAL CENTER (S, 34 beds) 340 Peak One Drive, Frisco, CO, Zip 80443, Mailing Address: P.O. Box 738, Zip 80443–0738, tel. 970/668–3300; Marshall Denkinger, M.D., Interim Chief Executive Officer
Web address: www.summitmedicalcenter.org

ST. MARY–CORWIN MEDICAL CENTER (S, 125 beds) 1008 Minnequa Avenue, Pueblo, CO, Zip 81004–3798; tel. 719/557–4000; Michael Cafasso, Chief Executive Officer

ST. THOMAS MORE HOSPITAL (S, 25 beds) 1338 Phay Avenue, Canon City, CO, Zip 81212–2302; tel. 719/285–2000; Sheri Trahern, CPA, FACHE, Chief Executive Officer
Web address: www.stmhospital.org

GEORGIA: CHI MEMORIAL HOSPITAL – GEORGIA (O, 179 beds) 100 Gross Crescent Circle, Fort Oglethorpe, GA, Zip 30742–3669; tel. 706/858–2000; Angie Hullander, Administrator and Special Operations
Web address: www.memorial.org/chi–memorial–hospital–georgia

IOWA: CHI HEALTH MERCY CORNING (S, 22 beds) 603 Rosary Drive, Corning, IA, Zip 50841–1683; tel. 641/322–3121; Lisa Wolfe, President

CHI HEALTH MERCY COUNCIL BLUFFS (S, 148 beds) 800 Mercy Drive, Council Bluffs, IA, Zip 51503–3128; tel. 712/328–5000; Marie E. Knedler, R.N., FACHE, President
Web address: www.chihealth.com/chi–health–mercy–council–bluffs

CHI HEALTH MISSOURI VALLEY (S, 16 beds) 631 North Eighth Street, Missouri Valley, IA, Zip 51555–1102; tel. 712/642–2784; Robert A. Valentine, President
Web address: www.chihealth.com/chi–health–missouri–valley

KNOXVILLE HOSPITAL & CLINICS (C, 25 beds) 1002 South Lincoln Street, Knoxville, IA, Zip 50138–3155; tel. 641/842–2151; Kevin Kincaid, Chief Executive Officer

For explanation of codes following names, see page B2.
★ Indicates Type III membership in the American Hospital Association.

MADISON COUNTY HEALTH CARE SYSTEM (C, 25 beds) 300 West Hutchings Street, Winterset, IA, Zip 50273–2109; tel. 515/462–2373; Marcia Hendricks, FACHE, R.N., Chief Executive Officer
Web address: www.madisonhealth.com

MERCY MEDICAL CENTER–CENTERVILLE (S, 45 beds) 1 St Joseph's Drive, Centerville, IA, Zip 52544–8055; tel. 641/437–4111; Ann Young, Interim President

MERCY MEDICAL CENTER–DES MOINES (S, 539 beds) 1111 6th Avenue, Des Moines, IA, Zip 50314–2611; tel. 515/247–3121; Karl Keeler, President
Web address: www.mercydesmoines.org

SKIFF MEDICAL CENTER (O, 26 beds) 204 North Fourth Avenue East, Newton, IA, Zip 50208–3100; tel. 641/792–1273; Laurie A. Conner, FACHE, Chief Executive Officer

KANSAS: BOB WILSON MEMORIAL GRANT COUNTY HOSPITAL (O, 26 beds) 415 North Main Street, Ulysses, KS, Zip 67880–2133; tel. 620/356–1266; Amanda Vaughan, Interim Administrator
Web address: www.bwmgch.com

ST. CATHERINE HOSPITAL (S, 104 beds) 401 East Spruce Street, Garden City, KS, Zip 67846–5679; tel. 620/272–2561; Scott J. Taylor, President and Chief Executive Officer

KENTUCKY: CONTINUING CARE HOSPITAL (S, 23 beds) 1 Saint Joseph Drive, Lexington, KY, Zip 40504–3742; tel. 859/967–5744; Robert C. Desotelle, President and Chief Executive Officer
Web address: www.kentuckyonehealth.org

FLAGET MEMORIAL HOSPITAL (S, 42 beds) 4305 New Shepherdsville Road, Bardstown, KY, Zip 40004–9019; tel. 502/350–5000; Jennifer Nolan, President and Chief Executive Officer
Web address: www.kentuckyonehealth.org/flaget

JEWISH HOSPITAL–SHELBYVILLE (O, 30 beds) 727 Hospital Drive, Shelbyville, KY, Zip 40065–1699; tel. 502/647–4000; Annessa Baker, Site Executive and Chief Nursing Officer

JEWISH HOSPITAL (O, 321 beds) 200 Abraham Flexner Way, Louisville, KY, Zip 40202–1886; tel. 502/587–4011; Charles W. Neumann, President and Chief Medical Officer
Web address: www.kentuckyonehealth.org/jewish–hospital

OUR LADY OF PEACE (O, 220 beds) 2020 Newburg Road, Louisville, KY, Zip 40205–1879; tel. 502/479–4500; Jennifer Nolan, President and Chief Executive Officer

SAINT JOSEPH LONDON (S, 116 beds) 1001 Saint Joseph Lane, London, KY, Zip 40741–8345; tel. 606/330–6000; Terrence G. Deis, CPA, FACHE, President
Web address: www.saintjosephhealthsystem.org

SAINT JOSEPH – MARTIN (S, 25 beds) 11203 Main Street, Martin, KY, Zip 41649; tel. 606/285–6400; Kathy Stumbo, President

SAINT JOSEPH BEREA (S, 25 beds) 305 Estill Street, Berea, KY, Zip 40403–1909; tel. 859/986–3151; Terrence G. Deis, CPA, FACHE, President
Web address: www.kentuckyonehealth.org/berea

SAINT JOSEPH EAST (S, 150 beds) 150 North Eagle Creek Drive, Lexington, KY, Zip 40509–1805; tel. 859/967–5000; Eric Gilliam, President

SAINT JOSEPH HOSPITAL (S, 307 beds) One St Joseph Drive, Lexington, KY, Zip 40504–3754; tel. 859/278–3436; Bruce J. Tassin, President
Web address: www.sjhlex.org

SAINT JOSEPH MOUNT STERLING (S, 42 beds) 225 Falcon Drive, Mount Sterling, KY, Zip 40353–1158, Mailing Address: P.O. Box 7, Zip 40353–0007, tel. 859/497–5000; Terrence G. Deis, CPA, FACHE, President
Web address: www.sjhlex.org

STS. MARY & ELIZABETH HOSPITAL (O, 173 beds) 1850 Bluegrass Avenue, Louisville, KY, Zip 40215–1199; tel. 502/361–6000; Charles Powell, President

TAYLOR REGIONAL HOSPITAL (C, 90 beds) 1700 Old Lebanon Road, Campbellsville, KY, Zip 42718–9600; tel. 270/465–3561; Jane Wheatley, Chief Executive Officer
Web address: www.trhosp.org

UNIVERSITY OF LOUISVILLE HOSPITAL (C, 329 beds) 530 South Jackson Street, Louisville, KY, Zip 40202–3611; tel. 502/562–3000; Kenneth P. Marshall, President and Chief Executive Officer

MINNESOTA: CHI LAKEWOOD HEALTH (S, 55 beds) 600 Main Avenue South, Baudette, MN, Zip 56623–2855; tel. 218/634–2120; Benjamin Koppelman, Interim President
Web address: www.lakewoodhealthcenter.org

CHI ST. FRANCIS HEALTH (S, 105 beds) 2400 St Francis Drive, Breckenridge, MN, Zip 56520–1025; tel. 218/643–3000; David A. Nelson, President and Chief Executive Officer

CHI ST. GABRIEL'S HEALTH (S, 25 beds) 815 Second Street SE, Little Falls, MN, Zip 56345–3596; tel. 320/632–5441; Lee Boyles, President
Web address: www.stgabriels.com

CHI ST. JOSEPH'S HEALTH (S, 25 beds) 600 Pleasant Avenue, Park Rapids, MN, Zip 56470–1431; tel. 218/732–3311; Benjamin Koppelman, President

NEBRASKA: CHI HEALTH CREIGHTON UNIVERSITY MEDICAL CENTER – BERGAN MERCY (S, 336 beds) 7500 Mercy Road, Omaha, NE, Zip 68124–2319; tel. 402/398–6060; Kevin J. Nokels, FACHE, President
Web address: www.chihealth.com/chi–health–bergan–mercy

CHI HEALTH GOOD SAMARITAN (S, 217 beds) 10 East 31st Street, Kearney, NE, Zip 68847–2926, Mailing Address: P.O. Box 1990, Zip 68848–1990, tel. 308/865–7100; Michael H. Schnieders, FACHE, President

CHI HEALTH IMMANUEL (S, 272 beds) 6901 North 72nd Street, Omaha, NE, Zip 68122–1799; tel. 402/572–2121; Ann Schumacher, R.N., MSN, FACHE, President
Web address: www.alegent.com/immanuel

CHI HEALTH LAKESIDE (S, 128 beds) 16901 Lakeside Hills Court, Omaha, NE, Zip 68130–2318; tel. 402/717–8000; Kevin Miller, President
Web address: www.CHIhealth.com

CHI HEALTH MIDLANDS (S, 28 beds) 11111 South 84th Street, Papillion, NE, Zip 68046–4122; tel. 402/593–3000; Kevin Miller, President
Web address: www.CHIhealth.com

CHI HEALTH NEBRASKA HEART (S, 63 beds) 7500 South 91st Street, Lincoln, NE, Zip 68526–9437; tel. 402/327–2700; Derek Vance, President
Web address: www.CHIhealthNebraskaHeart.com

CHI HEALTH PLAINVIEW (S, 15 beds) 704 North Third Street, Plainview, NE, Zip 68769–2047, Mailing Address: P.O. Box 489, Zip 68769–0489, tel. 402/582–4245; Gregory Beckmann, Chief Executive Officer

CHI HEALTH SAINT FRANCIS (S, 159 beds) 2620 West Faidley Avenue, Grand Island, NE, Zip 68803–4297, Mailing Address: P.O. Box 9804, Zip 68802–9804, tel. 308/384–4600; Edward J. Hannon, FACHE, President
Web address: www.saintfrancisgi.org

CHI HEALTH SCHUYLER (S, 25 beds) 104 West 17th Street, Schuyler, NE, Zip 68661–1304; tel. 402/352–2441; Connie Peters, R.N., President

CHI HEALTH ST ELIZABETH (S, 260 beds) 555 South 70th Street, Lincoln, NE, Zip 68510–2494; tel. 402/219–8000; Derek Vance, President
Web address: www.saintelizabethonline.com

CHI HEALTH ST. MARY'S (S, 18 beds) 1301 Grundman Boulevard, Nebraska City, NE, Zip 68410; tel. 402/873–3321; Daniel DeFreece, M.D., Interim President
Web address: www.chihealthstmarys.com

NORTH DAKOTA: CHI LISBON HEALTH (S, 25 beds) 905 Main Street, Lisbon, ND, Zip 58054–4334, Mailing Address: P.O. Box 353, Zip 58054–0353, tel. 701/683–6400; Peggy Reinke, R.N., Administrator
Web address: www.lisbonhospital.com

CHI MERCY HEALTH (S, 19 beds) 570 Chautauqua Boulevard, Valley City, ND, Zip 58072–3199; tel. 701/845–6400; Keith E. Heuser, Market President

CHI OAKES HOSPITAL (S, 20 beds) 1200 North Seventh Street, Oakes, ND, Zip 58474–2502; tel. 701/742–3291; Becki Thompson, President
Web address: www.oakeshospital.com

CHI ST ALEXIUS HEALTH CARRINGTON MEDICAL CENTER (S, 25 beds) 800 North Fourth Street, Carrington, ND, Zip 58421–1217, Mailing Address: P.O. Box 461, Zip 58421–0461, tel. 701/652–3141; Mariann Doeling, R.N., President
Web address: www.carringtonhealthcenter.org

CHI ST. ALEXIUS HEALTH – DICKINSON MEDICAL CENTER (S, 25 beds) 2500 Fairway Street, Dickinson, ND, Zip 58601–4399; tel. 701/456–4000; Reed Reyman, President

CHI ST. ALEXIUS HEALTH – WILLISTON MEDICAL CENTER (S, 25 beds) 1301 15th Avenue West, Williston, ND, Zip 58801–3896; tel. 701/774–7400; Dan Bjerknes, Market Leader
Web address: www.mercy–williston.org

For explanation of codes following names, see page B2.
★ Indicates Type III membership in the American Hospital Association.

Section B

CHI ST. ALEXIUS HEALTH DEVILS LAKE HOSPITAL (S, 25 beds) 1031 Seventh Street NE, Devils Lake, ND, Zip 58301–2798; tel. 701/662–2131; Andrew Lankowicz, FACHE, President
Web address: www.mercyhospitaldl.com

CHI ST. ALEXIUS HEALTH GARRISON (O, 50 beds) 407 Third Avenue SE, Garrison, ND, Zip 58540–7235; tel. 701/463–2275; Tod Graeber, Administrator

CHI ST. ALEXIUS HEALTH (O, 237 beds) 900 East Broadway, Bismarck, ND, Zip 58501–4586, Mailing Address: P.O. Box 5510, Zip 58506–5510, tel. 701/530–7000; Kurt Schley, Market Chief Executive Officer
Web address: www.st.alexius.org

COMMUNITY MEMORIAL HOSPITAL (O, 25 beds) 220 Fifth Avenue, Turtle Lake, ND, Zip 58575–4005, Mailing Address: P.O. Box 280, Zip 58575–0280, tel. 701/448–2331; Tod Graeber, Administrator

OHIO: GOOD SAMARITAN HOSPITAL (S, 438 beds) 375 Dixmyth Avenue, Cincinnati, OH, Zip 45220–2489; tel. 513/862–1400; Jamie Easterling, Executive Director, Operations
Web address: www.trihealth.com

PROVIDENCE CARE CENTER (O, 138 beds) 2025 Hayes Avenue, Sandusky, OH, Zip 44870, Rick G. Ryan, Administrator and Chief Executive Officer

TRINITY HEALTH SYSTEM (O, 320 beds) 380 Summit Avenue, Steubenville, OH, Zip 43952–2699; tel. 740/283–7000; Matthew Grimshaw, Market Chief Executive Officer
Web address: www.trinityhealth.com

TRINITY HOSPITAL TWIN CITY (O, 25 beds) 819 North First Street, Dennison, OH, Zip 44621–1098; tel. 740/922–2800; Teresa Gagliardi, R.N., Vice President of Hospital Operations and Site Administrator

OREGON: CHI ST. ANTHONY HOSPITAL (S, 25 beds) 2801 St Anthony Way, Pendleton, OR, Zip 97801–3800; tel. 541/276–5121; Harold S. Geller, Chief Executive Officer
Web address: www.sahpendleton.org

MERCY MEDICAL CENTER (S, 140 beds) 2700 Stewart Parkway, Roseburg, OR, Zip 97471–1281; tel. 541/673–0611; Kelly C. Morgan, President and Chief Executive Officer

TENNESSEE: CHI MEMORIAL (S, 405 beds) 2525 De Sales Avenue, Chattanooga, TN, Zip 37404–1161; tel. 423/495–2525; Janelle Reilly, Chief Executive Officer
Web address: www.memorial.org

TEXAS: BAYLOR ST. LUKE'S MEDICAL CENTER MCNAIR CAMPUS (O, 256 beds) One Baylor Plaza, BCM 100, Houston, TX, Zip 77030–3411; tel. 713/798–4951; Gay Nord, President
Web address: www.bcm.edu

BAYLOR ST. LUKE'S MEDICAL CENTER (O, 615 beds) 6720 Bertner Avenue, Houston, TX, Zip 77030–2697, Mailing Address: P.O. Box 20269, Zip 77225–0269, tel. 832/355–1000; Gay Nord, President
Web address: www.stlukestexas.com

CHI ST. JOSEPH HEALTH BELLVILLE HOSPITAL (O, 10 beds) 44 North Cummings Street, Bellville, TX, Zip 77418–1347, Mailing Address: P.O. Box 977, Zip 77418–0977, tel. 979/413–7400; Theron Park, Chief Executive Officer

CHI ST. JOSEPH HEALTH BURLESON HOSPITAL (O, 12 beds) 1101 Woodson Drive, Caldwell, TX, Zip 77836–1052, Mailing Address: P.O. Box 360, Zip 77836–0360, tel. 979/567–3245; Theron Park, Chief Executive Officer
Web address: www.chistjoseph.org/

CHI ST. JOSEPH HEALTH GRIMES HOSPITAL (O, 18 beds) 210 South Judson Street, Navasota, TX, Zip 77868–3704; tel. 936/825–6585; Theron Park, Chief Executive Officer
Web address: www.st–joseph.org

CHI ST. JOSEPH HEALTH MADISON HOSPITAL (O, 25 beds) 100 West Cross Street, Madisonville, TX, Zip 77864–2432, Mailing Address: Box 698, Zip 77864–0698, tel. 936/348–2631; Theron Park, Chief Executive Officer

CHI ST. JOSEPH REGIONAL HEALTH CENTER (O, 222 beds) 2801 Franciscan Drive, Bryan, TX, Zip 77802–2599; tel. 979/776–3777; Theron Park, Chief Executive Officer
Web address: www.st–joseph.org

CHI ST. LUKE'S HEALTH – PATIENTS MEDICAL CENTER (O, 61 beds) 4600 East Sam Houston Parkway South, Pasadena, TX, Zip 77505–3948; tel. 713/948–7000; Steven Foster, Chief Executive Officer

CHI ST. LUKE'S HEALTH BRAZOSPORT (O, 103 beds) 100 Medical Drive, Lake Jackson, TX, Zip 77566–5674; tel. 979/297–4411; Al Guevara Jr, FACHE, President
Web address: www.chistlukesbrazosport.org

CHI ST. LUKE'S HEALTH MEMORIAL LIVINGSTON (O, 66 beds) 1717 Highway 59 Bypass, Livingston, TX, Zip 77351–1257, Mailing Address: P.O. Box 1257, Zip 77351–0022, tel. 936/329–8700; Kristi Froese, R.N., Vice President Clinical Operations

CHI ST. LUKE'S HEALTH MEMORIAL LUFKIN (O, 194 beds) 1201 West Frank Avenue, Lufkin, TX, Zip 75904–3357, Mailing Address: P.O. Box 1447, Zip 75902–1447, tel. 936/634–8111; Monte J. Bostwick, Market Chief Executive Officer
Web address: www.memorialhealth.us/centers/lufkin

CHI ST. LUKE'S HEALTH MEMORIAL SAN AUGUSTINE (O, 9 beds) 511 East Hospital Street, San Augustine, TX, Zip 75972–2121, Mailing Address: P.O. Box 658, Zip 75972–0658, tel. 936/275–3446; Darlene Williams, R.N., Administrator

CHI ST. LUKE'S HEALTH MEMORIAL SPECIALTY HOSPITAL (O, 20 beds) 1201 West Frank Avenue, D5, Lufkin, TX, Zip 75904–3357, Mailing Address: P.O. Box 1447, Zip 75902–1447, tel. 936/639–7530; Darlene Williams, R.N., Administrator
Web address: www.memorialhealth.org

CHI ST. LUKE'S HEALTH–LAKESIDE HOSPITAL (O, 30 beds) 17400 St. Luke's Way, The Woodlands, TX, Zip 77384–8036; tel. 936/266–9000; James Parisi, Chief Executive Officer

CHI ST. LUKE'S HEALTH–THE WOODLANDS HOSPITAL (O, 207 beds) 17200 St. Luke's Way, The Woodlands, TX, Zip 77384–8007; tel. 936/266–2000; James Parisi, Chief Executive Officer
Web address: www.stlukeswoodlands.com

CHI ST. LUKE'S HOSPITAL – THE VINTAGE HOSPITAL (O, 78 beds) 20171 Chasewood Park Drive, Houston, TX, Zip 77070–1437; tel. 832/534–5000; Roland Cruickshank, President

ST. LUKE'S SUGAR LAND HOSPITAL (O, 96 beds) 1317 Lake Pointe Parkway, Sugar Land, TX, Zip 77478–3997; tel. 281/637–7000; Robert A. Heifner, FACHE, Chief Executive Officer
Web address: www.stlukessugarland.com

WASHINGTON: HARRISON MEDICAL CENTER (O, 260 beds) 2520 Cherry Avenue, Bremerton, WA, Zip 98310–4229; tel. 360/744–3911; David W. Schultz, FACHE, President, Peninsula Region

HIGHLINE MEDICAL CENTER (O, 128 beds) 16251 Sylvester Road SW, Burien, WA, Zip 98166–3052; tel. 206/244–9970; Anthony McLean, President
Web address: https://www.chifranciscan.org/highline–medical–center.html

REGIONAL HOSPITAL FOR RESPIRATORY AND COMPLEX CARE (O, 26 beds) 16251 Sylvester Road SW, Burien, WA, Zip 98166–3017; tel. 206/248–4548; Anne McBride, Chief Executive Officer

ST. ANTHONY HOSPITAL (O, 80 beds) 11567 Canterwood Boulevard NW, Gig Harbor, WA, Zip 98332–5812; tel. 253/530–2000; David W. Schultz, FACHE, President, Peninsula Region
Web address: www.chifranciscan.org/

ST. CLARE HOSPITAL (S, 103 beds) 11315 Bridgeport Way SW, Lakewood, WA, Zip 98499–3004; tel. 253/985–1711; Syd Bersante, R.N., President
Web address: www.fhshealth.org

ST. ELIZABETH HOSPITAL (S, 25 beds) 1455 Battersby Avenue, Enumclaw, WA, Zip 98022–3634, Mailing Address: P.O. Box 218, Zip 98022–0218, tel. 360/802–8800; Syd Bersante, R.N., Market President

ST. FRANCIS HOSPITAL (S, 124 beds) 34515 Ninth Avenue South, Federal Way, WA, Zip 98003–6799; tel. 253/944–8100; Anthony McLean, Market President
Web address: www.fhshealth.org

ST. JOSEPH MEDICAL CENTER (S, 366 beds) 1717 South 'J' Street, Tacoma, WA, Zip 98405–3004, Mailing Address: P.O. Box 2197, Zip 98401–2197, tel. 253/426–4101; Syd Bersante, R.N., President
Web address: www.chifranciscan.org

Owned, leased, sponsored:	91 hospitals	11389 beds
Contract–managed:	4 hospitals	469 beds
Totals:	95 hospitals	11858 beds

0903: CATHOLIC HEALTH SERVICES (CO)
4790 North State Road 7, Lauderdale Lakes, FL, Zip 33319–5860; tel. 954/484–1515; Joseph M. Catania, President and Chief Executive Officer

For explanation of codes following names, see page B2.
★ Indicates Type III membership in the American Hospital Association.

FLORIDA: ST. ANTHONY'S REHABILITATION HOSPITAL (S, 26 beds) 3485 NW 30th Street, Lauderdale Lakes, FL, Zip 33311–1890; tel. 954/739–6233; Joseph M. Catania, Chief Executive Officer
Web address: www.catholichealthservices.org

ST. CATHERINE'S REHABILITATION HOSPITAL (S, 60 beds) 1050 NE 125th Street, North Miami, FL, Zip 33161–5881; tel. 305/357–1735; Jaime Gonzalez, Administrator

Owned, leased, sponsored:	2 hospitals	86 beds
Contract–managed:	0 hospitals	0 beds
Totals:	2 hospitals	86 beds

0233: CATHOLIC HEALTH SERVICES OF LONG ISLAND (CO)
992 North Village Avenue, 1st Floor, Rockville Centre, NY, Zip 11570–1002; tel. 516/705–3700; Alan D. Guerci, M.D., President and Chief Executive Officer
(Centralized Physician/Insurance Health System)

NEW YORK: GOOD SAMARITAN HOSPITAL MEDICAL CENTER (O, 522 beds) 1000 Montauk Highway, West Islip, NY, Zip 11795–4927; tel. 631/376–3000; Thomas Ockers, Executive Vice President and Chief Administrative Officer
Web address: www.good–samaritan–hospital.org

MERCY MEDICAL CENTER (O, 191 beds) 1000 North Village Avenue, Rockville Centre, NY, Zip 11570–1000; tel. 516/705–2525; Ronald Steimel, Executive Vice President and Chief Administrative Officer

ST. CATHERINE OF SIENA MEDICAL CENTER (O, 503 beds) 50 Route 25–A, Smithtown, NY, Zip 11787–1348; tel. 631/862–3000; James O'Connor, Chief Administrative Officer
Web address: www.stcatherines.chsli.org/

ST. CHARLES HOSPITAL (O, 243 beds) 200 Belle Terre Road, Port Jefferson, NY, Zip 11777–1928; tel. 631/474–6000; James O'Connor, Executive Vice President and Chief Administrative Officer
Web address: www.stcharleshospital.chsli.org

ST. FRANCIS HOSPITAL, THE HEART CENTER (O, 320 beds) 100 Port Washington Boulevard, Roslyn, NY, Zip 11576–1353; tel. 516/562–6000; Ruth Hennessey, Executive Vice President and Chief Administrative Officer

ST. JOSEPH HOSPITAL (S, 128 beds) 4295 Hempstead Turnpike, Bethpage, NY, Zip 11714–5769; tel. 516/579–6000; Peter Scaminaci, Executive Vice President and Chief Administrative Officer
Web address: www.stjosephhospital.chsli.org/

Owned, leased, sponsored:	6 hospitals	1907 beds
Contract–managed:	0 hospitals	0 beds
Totals:	6 hospitals	1907 beds

★0234: CATHOLIC HEALTH SYSTEM (CO)
144 Genesee Street, Buffalo, NY, Zip 14203–1560; tel. 716/862–2410; Mark A. Sullivan, FACHE, President and Chief Executive Officer
(Centralized Health System)

NEW YORK: FATHER BAKER MANOR (O, 160 beds) 6400 Powers Road, Orchard Park, NY, Zip 14127; tel. 716/667–0001; Christine Kluckhohn, President, Continuing Care

KENMORE MERCY HOSPITAL (O, 329 beds) 2950 Elmwood Avenue, Kenmore, NY, Zip 14217–1390, Mailing Address: 2950 Elmwood Avenue, Room 4024, Zip 14217–1390, tel. 716/447–6100; Walter Ludwig, President and Chief Executive Officer
Web address: www.chsbuffalo.org

MCAULEY RESIDENCE (O, 160 beds) 1503 Military Road, Kenmore, NY, Zip 14217; tel. 716/447–6600; Christine Kluckhohn, President, Continuing Care

MERCY HOSPITAL (O, 420 beds) 565 Abbott Road, Buffalo, NY, Zip 14220–2095; tel. 716/826–7000; Charles J. Urlaub, President and Chief Executive Officer
Web address: www.chsbuffalo.org

MERCY NURSING FACILITY (O, 74 beds) 565 Abbott Road, Buffalo, NY, Zip 14220; tel. 716/828–2301; Christine Kluckhohn, President, Continuing Care

MOUNT ST. MARY'S HOSPITAL AND HEALTH CENTER (O, 145 beds) 5300 Military Road, Lewiston, NY, Zip 14092–1903; tel. 716/297–4800; Gary C. Tucker, President and Chief Executive Officer
Web address: www.msmh.org

NAZARETH HOME (O, 125 beds) 291 West North Street, Buffalo, NY, Zip 14201; tel. 716/881–2323; Christine Kluckhohn, President, Continuing Care

SISTERS OF CHARITY HOSPITAL OF BUFFALO (O, 378 beds) 2157 Main Street, Buffalo, NY, Zip 14214–2692; tel. 716/862–1000; Martin Boryszak, President and Chief Executive Officer
Web address: www.chsbuffalo.org

ST. CATHERINE LABOURE (O, 80 beds) 2157 Main Street, Buffalo, NY, Zip 14214; tel. 716/862–1451; Christine Kluckhohn, President, Continuing Care

ST. ELIZABETH'S HOME (O, 117 beds) 5539 Broadway, Lancaster, NY, Zip 14086; tel. 716/683–5150; Christine Kluckhohn, President, Continuing Care

ST. FRANCIS OF BUFFALO (O, 120 beds) 34 Benwood Avenue, Buffalo, NY, Zip 14214; tel. 716/862–2500; Christine Kluckhohn, President, Continuing Care

ST. FRANCIS OF WILLIAMSVILLE (O, 142 beds) 147 Reist Street, Williamsville, NY, Zip 14221; tel. 716/633–5400; Christine Kluckhohn, President, Continuing Care

ST. JOSEPH MANOR (O, 22 beds) 2211 West State Street, Olean, NY, Zip 14760; tel. 716/372–7810; Christine Kluckhohn, President, Continuing Care

Owned, leased, sponsored:	13 hospitals	2272 beds
Contract–managed:	0 hospitals	0 beds
Totals:	13 hospitals	2272 beds

★0991: CAYUGA HEALTH SYSTEM (NP)
101 Dates Drive, Ithaca, NY, Zip 14850–1342; tel. 607/274–4011; John B. Rudd, President and Chief Executive Officer
(Independent Hospital System)

NEW YORK: CAYUGA MEDICAL CENTER AT ITHACA (O, 193 beds) 101 Dates Drive, Ithaca, NY, Zip 14850–1342; tel. 607/274–4011; John B. Rudd, President and Chief Executive Officer
Web address: www.cayugamed.org

SCHUYLER HOSPITAL (O, 145 beds) 220 Steuben Street, Montour Falls, NY, Zip 14865–9709; tel. 607/535–7121; James B. Watson, President

Owned, leased, sponsored:	2 hospitals	338 beds
Contract–managed:	0 hospitals	0 beds
Totals:	2 hospitals	338 beds

★0984: CEDARS–SINAI HEALTH SYSTEM (NP)
8700 Beverly Boulevard, West Hollywood, CA, Zip 90048–1865, Mailing Address: Box 48750, Los Angeles, Zip 90048–0750, tel. 310/423–5000; Thomas M. Priselac, President and Chief Executive Officer
(Independent Hospital System)

CALIFORNIA: CEDARS–SINAI MEDICAL CENTER (O, 885 beds) 8700 Beverly Boulevard, Los Angeles, CA, Zip 90048–1865; tel. 310/423–5000; Thomas M. Priselac, President and Chief Executive Officer
Web address: www.cedars–sinai.edu

MARINA DEL REY HOSPITAL (O, 145 beds) 4650 Lincoln Boulevard, Marina Del Rey, CA, Zip 90292–6306; tel. 310/823–8911; Paulette Heitmeyer, Administrator and Chief Operating Officer

TORRANCE MEMORIAL MEDICAL CENTER (O, 444 beds) 3330 Lomita Boulevard, Torrance, CA, Zip 90505–5073; tel. 310/325–9110; Craig Leach, President and Chief Executive Officer
Web address: www.torrancememorial.org

Owned, leased, sponsored:	3 hospitals	1474 beds
Contract–managed:	0 hospitals	0 beds
Totals:	3 hospitals	1474 beds

★0298: CENTEGRA HEALTH SYSTEM (NP)
385 Millennium Drive, Crystal Lake, IL, Zip 60012–3761; tel. 815/788–5800; Michael S. Eesley, Chief Executive Officer
(Independent Hospital System)

For explanation of codes following names, see page B2.
★ Indicates Type III membership in the American Hospital Association.

ILLINOIS: CENTEGRA HOSPITAL – MCHENRY (O, 296 beds) 4201 Medical Center Drive, McHenry, IL, Zip 60050–8409; tel. 815/344–5000; Michael S. Eesley, Chief Executive Officer
Web address: www.centegra.org

CENTEGRA HOSPITAL – WOODSTOCK (O, 104 beds) 3701 Doty Road, Woodstock, IL, Zip 60098–7509, Mailing Address: P.O. Box 1990, Zip 60098–1990, tel. 815/338–2500; Michael S. Eesley, Chief Executive Officer

Owned, leased, sponsored:	2 hospitals	400 beds
Contract–managed:	0 hospitals	0 beds
Totals:	2 hospitals	400 beds

★2265: CENTRA HEALTH, INC. (NP)
1901 Tate Springs Road, Lynchburg, VA, Zip 24501–1109; tel. 434/200–3000; E W. Tibbs, President and Chief Executive Officer
(Moderately Centralized Health System)

VIRGINIA: CENTRA LYNCHBURG GENERAL HOSPITAL (O, 1029 beds) 1901 Tate Springs Road, Lynchburg, VA, Zip 24501–1109; tel. 434/200–4700; E W. Tibbs, President and Chief Executive Officer
Web address: www.centrahealth.com

CENTRA SOUTHSIDE COMMUNITY HOSPITAL (O, 86 beds) 800 Oak Street, Farmville, VA, Zip 23901–1199; tel. 434/392–8811; Thomas Angelo, Chief Executive Officer
Web address: www.sch.centrahealth.com/

Owned, leased, sponsored:	2 hospitals	1115 beds
Contract–managed:	0 hospitals	0 beds
Totals:	2 hospitals	1115 beds

★0184: CENTRACARE HEALTH (NP)
1406 Sixth Avenue North, Saint Cloud, MN, Zip 56303–1900; tel. 320/251–2700; Kenneth D. Holmen, M.D., President and Chief Executive Officer
(Moderately Centralized Health System)

MINNESOTA: CENTRACARE HEALTH–LONG PRAIRIE (O, 20 beds) 20 Ninth Street SE, Long Prairie, MN, Zip 56347–1404; tel. 320/732–2141; Daniel J. Swenson, FACHE, Administrator
Web address: www.centracare.com

CENTRACARE HEALTH–MELROSE (O, 93 beds) 525 Main Street West, Melrose, MN, Zip 56352–1043; tel. 320/256–4231; Gerry Gilbertson, FACHE, Administrator
Web address: www.centracare.com

CENTRACARE HEALTH–MONTICELLO (O, 126 beds) 1013 Hart Boulevard, Monticello, MN, Zip 55362–8230; tel. 763/295–2945; Mary Ellen Wells, FACHE, Administrator
Web address: www.centracare.com

CENTRACARE HEALTH–PAYNESVILLE (O, 67 beds) 200 West 1st Street, Paynesville, MN, Zip 56362–1496; tel. 320/243–3767; Brandon E. Pietsch, Administrator

CENTRACARE HEALTH–SAUK CENTRE (O, 85 beds) 425 North Elm Street, Sauk Centre, MN, Zip 56378–1010; tel. 320/352–2221; Delano Christianson, Administrator
Web address: www.centracare.com/hospitals/sauk_centre/index.html

RICE MEMORIAL HOSPITAL (L, 164 beds) 301 Becker Avenue SW, Willmar, MN, Zip 56201–3395; tel. 320/235–4543; Michael Schramm, Chief Executive Officer

ST. CLOUD HOSPITAL (O, 487 beds) 1406 Sixth Avenue North, Saint Cloud, MN, Zip 56303–1901; tel. 320/251–2700; Craig J. Broman, FACHE, President
Web address: www.centracare.com

Owned, leased, sponsored:	7 hospitals	1042 beds
Contract–managed:	0 hospitals	0 beds
Totals:	7 hospitals	1042 beds

0856: CENTRAL FLORIDA HEALTH (NP)
600 East Dixie Avenue, Leesburg, FL, Zip 34748–5925; tel. 352/323–5762; Donald G. Henderson, FACHE, Chief Executive Officer

FLORIDA: LEESBURG REGIONAL MEDICAL CENTER (O, 330 beds) 600 East Dixie Avenue, Leesburg, FL, Zip 34748–5999; tel. 352/323–5762; Donald G. Henderson, FACHE, President and Chief Executive Officer

THE VILLAGES REGIONAL HOSPITAL (O, 297 beds) 1451 El Camino Real, The Villages, FL, Zip 32159–0041; tel. 352/751–8000; Donald G. Henderson, FACHE, President and Chief Executive Officer
Web address: www.cfhalliance.org

Owned, leased, sponsored:	2 hospitals	627 beds
Contract–managed:	0 hospitals	0 beds
Totals:	2 hospitals	627 beds

1007: CENTRAL MAINE HEALTHCARE (NP)
300 Main Street, Lewiston, ME, Zip 04240–7027; tel. 207/795–0111; Jeffrey L. Brickman, FACHE, Chief Executive Officer
(Independent Hospital System)

MAINE: BRIDGTON HOSPITAL (O, 22 beds) 10 Hospital Drive, Bridgton, ME, Zip 04009–1148; tel. 207/647–6000; R David. Frum, President

CENTRAL MAINE MEDICAL CENTER (O, 190 beds) 300 Main Street, Lewiston, ME, Zip 04240–7027; tel. 207/795–0111; David Tupponce, M.D., President
Web address: www.cmmc.org

RUMFORD HOSPITAL (O, 25 beds) 420 Franklin Street, Rumford, ME, Zip 04276–2145; tel. 207/369–1000; R David. Frum, President

Owned, leased, sponsored:	3 hospitals	237 beds
Contract–managed:	0 hospitals	0 beds
Totals:	3 hospitals	237 beds

1039: CHILDREN'S HEALTH (NP)
1935 Medical District Drive, Dallas, TX, Zip 75235–7701; tel. 214/456–7000; Christopher J. Durovich, President and Chief Executive Officer

TEXAS: CHILDREN'S MEDICAL CENTER DALLAS (O, 362 beds) 1935 Medical District Drive, Pavilion, 3rd Floor, Dallas, TX, Zip 75235–7701; tel. 214/456–7000; Christopher J. Durovich, President and Chief Executive Officer
Web address: www.childrens.com

CHILDREN'S MEDICAL CENTER PLANO (O, 72 beds) 7601 Preston Road, Plano, TX, Zip 75024–3214; tel. 469/303–7000; Jeremiah Radandt, President

OUR CHILDREN'S HOUSE (O, 39 beds) 1340 Empire Central Drive, Dallas, TX, Zip 75247–4022; tel. 214/867–6700; David T. Berry, President, Children's Health Clinical Operations
Web address: https://www.childrens.com/och

Owned, leased, sponsored:	3 hospitals	473 beds
Contract–managed:	0 hospitals	0 beds
Totals:	3 hospitals	473 beds

0407: CHILDREN'S HOSPITAL AND HEALTH SYSTEM (NP)
9000 West Wisconsin Avenue, Milwaukee, WI, Zip 53226–4810, Mailing Address: P.O. Box 1997, Zip 53201–1997, tel. 414/226–2000; Peggy N. Troy, President and Chief Executive Officer
(Independent Hospital System)

WISCONSIN: CHILDREN'S HOSPITAL OF WISCONSIN–FOX VALLEY (O, 14 beds) 130 Second Street, Neenah, WI, Zip 54956–2883; tel. 920/969–7900; Peggy N. Troy, President and Chief Executive Officer
Web address: www.chw.org

For explanation of codes following names, see page B2.
★ Indicates Type III membership in the American Hospital Association.

Section B

CHILDREN'S HOSPITAL OF WISCONSIN (O, 193 beds) 9000 West Wisconsin Avenue, Milwaukee, WI, Zip 53226–4810, Mailing Address: P.O. Box 1997, Zip 53201–1997, tel. 414/266–2000; Peggy N. Troy, President and Chief Executive Officer

Owned, leased, sponsored:	2 hospitals	207 beds
Contract–managed:	0 hospitals	0 beds
Totals:	2 hospitals	207 beds

★0131: CHRISTIANA CARE HEALTH SYSTEM (NP)

501 West 14th Street, Wilmington, DE, Zip 19801–1013, Mailing Address: P.O. Box 1668, Zip 19899–1668, tel. 302/733–1000; Janice E. Nevin, M.D., M.P.H., Chief Executive Officer

(Independent Hospital System)

DELAWARE: CHRISTIANA CARE HEALTH SYSTEM (O, 1080 beds) 4755 Ogletown–Stanton Road, Newark, DE, Zip 19718–0002, Mailing Address: P.O. Box 6001, Zip 19718, tel. 302/733–1000; Janice E. Nevin, M.D., M.P.H., Chief Executive Officer
Web address: www.christianacare.org

Owned, leased, sponsored:	1 hospitals	1080 beds
Contract–managed:	0 hospitals	0 beds
Totals:	1 hospitals	1080 beds

★0192: CHRISTUS HEALTH (CO)

919 Hidden Ridge Drive, Irving, TX, Zip 75038; tel. 469/282–2000; Ernie W. Sadau, Chief Executive Officer

(Moderately Centralized Health System)

LOUISIANA: CHRISTUS COUSHATTA HEALTH CARE CENTER (O, 25 beds) 1635 Marvel Street, Coushatta, LA, Zip 71019–9022, Mailing Address: P.O. Box 589, Zip 71019–0589, tel. 318/932–2000; Brandon Hillman, Interim Administrator, Director of Hospital Services
Web address: www.christuscoushatta.org

CHRISTUS HEALTH SHREVEPORT–BOSSIER (O, 185 beds) 1453 East Bert Kouns Industrial Loop, Shreveport, LA, Zip 71105–6800; tel. 318/681–5000; Isaac Palmer, Chief Executive Officer

CHRISTUS LAKE AREA HOSPITAL (O, 88 beds) 4200 Nelson Road, Lake Charles, LA, Zip 70605–4118; tel. 337/474–6370; Robbin Odom, R.N., MSN, Interim Chief Executive Officer and Chief Nursing Officer
Web address: www.Lakeareamc.com

CHRISTUS ST. FRANCES CABRINI HOSPITAL (O, 281 beds) 3330 Masonic Drive, Alexandria, LA, Zip 71301–3899; tel. 318/487–1122; Chris Karam, FACHE, Chief Executive Officer
Web address: www.cabrini.org/

CHRISTUS ST. PATRICK HOSPITAL OF LAKE CHARLES (O, 160 beds) 524 Dr Michael Debakey Drive, Lake Charles, LA, Zip 70601–5799, Mailing Address: P.O. Box 3401, Zip 70602–3401, tel. 337/436–2511; Donald H. Lloyd II, Chief Executive Officer

NATCHITOCHES REGIONAL MEDICAL CENTER (C, 91 beds) 501 Keyser Avenue, Natchitoches, LA, Zip 71457–6036, Mailing Address: P.O. Box 2009, Zip 71457–2009, tel. 318/214–4200; D. Kirk. Soileau, FACHE, Chief Executive Officer
Web address: www.nrmchospital.org

SAVOY MEDICAL CENTER (C, 172 beds) 801 Poinciana Avenue, Mamou, LA, Zip 70554–2298; tel. 337/468–5261; Eugene H. Burge, Chief Executive Officer
Web address: www.savoymedical.com/

NEW MEXICO: CHRISTUS ST. VINCENT REGIONAL MEDICAL CENTER (O, 219 beds) 455 Saint Michaels Drive, Santa Fe, NM, Zip 87505–7601, Mailing Address: P.O. Box 2107, Zip 87505, tel. 505/983–3361; Lillian Montoya, President and Chief Executive Officer

TEXAS: CHRISTUS GOOD SHEPHERD MEDICAL CENTER–MARSHALL (O, 891 beds) 811 South Washington Avenue, Marshall, TX, Zip 75670–5336, Mailing Address: P.O. Box 1599, Zip 75671–1599, tel. 903/927–6000; Todd Hancock, President and Chief Executive Officer
Web address: https://www.christushealth.org/good-shepherd/marshall

CHRISTUS MOTHER FRANCES HOSPITAL – JACKSONVILLE (O, 23 beds) 2026 South Jackson, Jacksonville, TX, Zip 75766–5822; tel. 903/541–4500; Anne Pileggi, Administrator and Associate Vice President

CHRISTUS MOTHER FRANCES HOSPITAL – SULPHUR SPRINGS (O, 56 beds) 115 Airport Road, Sulphur Springs, TX, Zip 75482–2105; tel. 903/885–7671; Paul Harvey, President and Chief Executive Officer
Web address: www.tmfhc.org/maps–and–locations/locations–profile/?id=72&searchId=8bcb329f–a152–e611–b37f–2c768a4e1b84&sort=11&page=1&pageSize=10

CHRISTUS MOTHER FRANCES HOSPITAL – TYLER (O, 466 beds) 800 East Dawson Street, Tyler, TX, Zip 75701–2036; tel. 903/593–8441; Jason J. Proctor, Chief Operating Officer

CHRISTUS MOTHER FRANCES HOSPITAL – WINNSBORO (O, 25 beds) 719 West Coke Road, Winnsboro, TX, Zip 75494–3011; tel. 903/342–5227; Paul Harvey, Chief Executive Officer
Web address: www.tmfhs.org

CHRISTUS SANTA ROSA HEALTH SYSTEM (O, 766 beds) 333 North Santa Rosa Street, San Antonio, TX, Zip 78207–3108, Mailing Address: 100 NE Loop 410 Suite 800, Zip 78216–4749, tel. 210/704–2000; Dean Alexander, President and Chief Executive Officer
Web address: www.christussantarosa.org

CHRISTUS SOUTHEAST TEXAS HOSPITAL – ST. ELIZABETH (O, 370 beds) 2830 Calder Avenue, Beaumont, TX, Zip 77702–1809, Mailing Address: P.O. Box 5405, Zip 77726–5405, tel. 409/892–7171; Paul Trevino, Chief Executive Officer

CHRISTUS SOUTHEAST TEXAS JASPER MEMORIAL (O, 40 beds) 1275 Marvin Hancock Drive, Jasper, TX, Zip 75951–4995; tel. 409/384–5461; Wayne Moore, Interim Administrator
Web address: www.christusjasper.org

CHRISTUS SPOHN HOSPITAL ALICE (O, 74 beds) 2500 East Main Street, Alice, TX, Zip 78332–4169; tel. 361/661–8000; Thomas McKinney, President
Web address: www.christusspohn.org/locations_alice.htm

CHRISTUS SPOHN HOSPITAL BEEVILLE (O, 49 beds) 1500 East Houston Street, Beeville, TX, Zip 78102–5312; tel. 361/354–2000; Genifer Rucker, President

CHRISTUS SPOHN HOSPITAL CORPUS CHRISTI MEMORIAL (O, 572 beds) 2606 Hospital Boulevard, Corpus Christi, TX, Zip 78405–1804, Mailing Address: P.O. Box 5280, Zip 78405, tel. 361/902–4000; Brian Connor, FACHE, President
Web address: www.christusspohn.org

CHRISTUS SPOHN HOSPITAL KLEBERG (O, 50 beds) 1311 General Cavazos Boulevard, Kingsville, TX, Zip 78363–7130; tel. 361/595–1661; Thomas McKinney, President
Web address: www.christusspohn.org

CHRISTUS ST. MICHAEL HEALTH SYSTEM (O, 354 beds) 2600 St Michael Drive, Texarkana, TX, Zip 75503–5220; tel. 903/614–1000; Jason Rounds, Interim Chief Executive Officer

CHRISTUS ST. MICHAEL REHABILITATION HOSPITAL (O, 50 beds) 2400 St Michael Drive, Texarkana, TX, Zip 75503–2374; tel. 903/614–4000; Patrick Flannery, Administrator
Web address: www.christusstmichael.org/rehab

KATE DISHMAN REHABILITATION HOSPITAL (O, 27 beds) 2830 Calder Street, 6th Floor, Beaumont, TX, Zip 77702–1809; tel. 409/899–8380; David Pipkins, Chief Executive Officer and Administrator

Owned, leased, sponsored:	21 hospitals	4771 beds
Contract–managed:	2 hospitals	263 beds
Totals:	23 hospitals	5034 beds

★0101: CITRUS VALLEY HEALTH PARTNERS (NP)

210 West San Bernardino Road, Covina, CA, Zip 91723–1515; tel. 626/331–7331; Robert H. Curry, President and Chief Executive Officer

CALIFORNIA: CITRUS VALLEY MEDICAL CENTER–INTER COMMUNITY CAMPUS (O, 320 beds) 210 West San Bernadino Road, Covina, CA, Zip 91723–1515, Mailing Address: P.O. Box 6108, Zip 91722–5108, tel. 626/331–7331; Robert H. Curry, President and Chief Executive Officer
Web address: www.cvhp.org

For explanation of codes following names, see page B2.
★ Indicates Type III membership in the American Hospital Association.

FOOTHILL PRESBYTERIAN HOSPITAL (O, 72 beds) 250 South Grand Avenue, Glendora, CA, Zip 91741–4218; tel. 626/963–8411; Robert H. Curry, President and Chief Executive Officer

Owned, leased, sponsored:	2 hospitals	392 beds
Contract–managed:	0 hospitals	0 beds
Totals:	2 hospitals	392 beds

★0212: CLEVELAND CLINIC HEALTH SYSTEM (NP)
9500 Euclid, Cleveland, OH, Zip 44195–5108; tel. 216/444–2200; Tomislav Mihaljevic, M.D., Chief Executive Officer and President
(Centralized Health System)

FLORIDA: CLEVELAND CLINIC FLORIDA (O, 155 beds) 2950 Cleveland Clinic Boulevard, Weston, FL, Zip 33331–3602; tel. 954/659–5000; Wael Barsoum, M.D., President
Web address: www.clevelandclinic.org/florida

OHIO: CLEVELAND CLINIC AKRON GENERAL LODI HOSPITAL (O, 20 beds) 225 Elyria Street, Lodi, OH, Zip 44254–1096; tel. 330/948–1222; Dana Kocsis, Vice President, Nursing and Operations
Web address: www.lodihospital.org

CLEVELAND CLINIC AKRON GENERAL (O, 450 beds) 1 Akron General Avenue, Akron, OH, Zip 44307–2433; tel. 330/344–6000; Alan Papa, President

CLEVELAND CLINIC AVON HOSPITAL (O, 126 beds) 33300 Cleveland Clinic Boulevard, Avon, OH, Zip 44011; tel. 440/695–5000; Rebecca Starck, M.D., President
Web address: www.my.clevelandclinic.org

CLEVELAND CLINIC CHILDREN'S HOSPITAL FOR REHABILITATION (O, 25 beds) 2801 Martin Luther King Jr Drive, Cleveland, OH, Zip 44104–3865; tel. 216/448–6400; Michelle Marks, D.O., Medical Director
Web address: www.my.clevelandclinic.org/childrens–hospital/default.aspx

CLEVELAND CLINIC FAIRVIEW HOSPITAL (O, 460 beds) 18101 Lorain Avenue, Cleveland, OH, Zip 44111–5656; tel. 216/476–7000; Neil Smith, D.O., President

CLEVELAND CLINIC UNION HOSPITAL (O, 159 beds) 659 Boulevard, Dover, OH, Zip 44622–2077; tel. 330/343–3311; Bruce James, President and Chief Executive Officer
Web address: www.unionhospital.org

CLEVELAND CLINIC, MEDINA HOSPITAL (O, 121 beds) 1000 East Washington Street, Medina, OH, Zip 44256–2170; tel. 330/725–1000; Richard K. Shewbridge, President

CLEVELAND CLINIC (O, 1275 beds) 9500 Euclid Avenue, Cleveland, OH, Zip 44195–5108; tel. 216/444–2200; Tomislav Mihaljevic, M.D., President and Chief Executive Officer
Web address: www.clevelandclinic.org

EDWIN SHAW REHAB (O, 35 beds) 330 Broadway Street East, Cuyahoga Falls, OH, Zip 44221–3312; tel. 330/436–0910; Geoffrey Hall, Chief Executive Officer
Web address: www.edwinshaw.com

EUCLID HOSPITAL (O, 165 beds) 18901 Lake Shore Boulevard, Euclid, OH, Zip 44119–1090; tel. 216/531–9000; Daniel Napierkowski, M.D., President

HILLCREST HOSPITAL (O, 440 beds) 6780 Mayfield Road, Cleveland, OH, Zip 44124–2203; tel. 440/312–4500; Richard Parker, M.D., President, Hillcrest Hospital
Web address: www.hillcresthospital.org

LUTHERAN HOSPITAL (O, 194 beds) 1730 West 25th Street, Cleveland, OH, Zip 44113–3170; tel. 216/696–4300; Donald A. Malone Jr, President

MARYMOUNT HOSPITAL (O, 277 beds) 12300 McCracken Road, Garfield Heights, OH, Zip 44125–2975; tel. 216/581–0500; Daniel Napierkowski, M.D., President
Web address: www.marymount.org

SOUTH POINTE HOSPITAL (O, 139 beds) 20000 Harvard Road, Warrensville Heights, OH, Zip 44122–6805; tel. 216/491–6000; Margaret McKenzie, M.D., President

Owned, leased, sponsored:	15 hospitals	4041 beds
Contract–managed:	0 hospitals	0 beds
Totals:	15 hospitals	4041 beds

0076: COLLEGE HEALTH ENTERPRISES (IO)
11627 Telegraph Road, Suite 200, Santa Fe Springs, CA, Zip 90670–6814; tel. 562/923–9449; Barry J. Weiss, Chairman of the Board

CALIFORNIA: COLLEGE HOSPITAL CERRITOS (O, 187 beds) 10802 College Place, Cerritos, CA, Zip 90703–1579; tel. 562/924–9581; Stephen Witt, President and Chief Executive Officer
Web address: www.collegehospitals.com

COLLEGE HOSPITAL COSTA MESA (O, 122 beds) 301 Victoria Street, Costa Mesa, CA, Zip 92627–7131; tel. 949/642–2734; Susan L. Taylor, JD, Chief Executive Officer

Owned, leased, sponsored:	2 hospitals	309 beds
Contract–managed:	0 hospitals	0 beds
Totals:	2 hospitals	309 beds

0161: COLUMBUS REGIONAL HEALTHCARE SYSTEM (NP)
707 Center Street, Suite 400, Columbus, GA, Zip 31901–1575; tel. 706/660–6100; M. Scott. Hill, Chief Executive Officer
(Independent Hospital System)

GEORGIA: AZALEA TRACE (O, 110 beds) 910 Talbotton Road, Columbus, GA, Zip 31901; tel. 706/323–9513; Todd West, Administrator

HAMILTON HOUSE NURSING CENTER/ADULT LIVING CENTER (O, 128 beds) 1911 Hamilton Road, Columbus, GA, Zip 31901; tel. 706/571–1850; John Sims, Administrator

MARION MEMORIAL NURSING HOME (O, 70 beds) Highway 41, Buena Vista, GA, Zip 31803, Mailing Address: P.O. Box 197, Zip 31803, tel. 229/649–7100; Barbara Mitchell, Administrator

PIEDMONT COLUMBUS REGIONAL NORTHSIDE (O, 100 beds) 100 Frist Court, Columbus, GA, Zip 31909–3578, Mailing Address: P.O. Box 7188, Zip 31908–7188, tel. 706/494–2100; M. Scott. Hill, President and Chief Executive Officer
Web address: www.columbusregional.com

Owned, leased, sponsored:	4 hospitals	408 beds
Contract–managed:	0 hospitals	0 beds
Totals:	4 hospitals	408 beds

★0401: COMMUNITY HEALTH NETWORK (NP)
7330 Shadeland Station, Indianapolis, IN, Zip 46256–3957; tel. 317/355–1411; Bryan A. Mills, President and Chief Executive Officer
(Moderately Centralized Health System)

INDIANA: COMMUNITY HOSPITAL EAST (O, 337 beds) 1500 North Ritter Avenue, Indianapolis, IN, Zip 46219–3095; tel. 317/355–1411; Scott L. Teffeteller, Senior Vice President and President of East Region
Web address: www.ecommunity.com/east/

COMMUNITY HOSPITAL NORTH (O, 308 beds) 7150 Clearvista Drive, Indianapolis, IN, Zip 46256–1695, Mailing Address: 7250 Clearvista Drive, Suite 200, Zip 46256–1695, tel. 317/355–2469; Kathleen R. Krusie, FACHE, President

COMMUNITY HOSPITAL SOUTH (O, 167 beds) 1402 East County Line Road South, Indianapolis, IN, Zip 46227–0963; tel. 317/887–7000; David Kiley, M.D., Vice President
Web address: www.ecommunity.com

COMMUNITY HOSPITAL OF ANDERSON & MADISON COUNTY (O, 140 beds) 1515 North Madison Avenue, Anderson, IN, Zip 46011–3453; tel. 765/298–4242; Beth S. Tharp, R.N., President and Chief Executive Officer

COMMUNITY HOWARD REGIONAL HEALTH (O, 137 beds) 3500 South Lafountain Street, Kokomo, IN, Zip 46902–3803, Mailing Address: P.O. Box 9011, Zip 46904–9011, tel. 765/453–0702; Joseph Hooper, President and Chief Executive Officer
Web address: www.howardregional.org

For explanation of codes following names, see page B2.
★ Indicates Type III membership in the American Hospital Association.

COMMUNITY HOWARD SPECIALTY HOSPITAL (O, 30 beds) 829 North Dixon Road, Kokomo, IN, Zip 46901–7709; tel. 765/452–6700; Jeffrey Weiss, Interim Director

Owned, leased, sponsored:	6 hospitals	1119 beds
Contract–managed:	0 hospitals	0 beds
Totals:	6 hospitals	1119 beds

★0080: COMMUNITY HEALTH SYSTEMS, INC. (IO)

4000 Meridian Boulevard, Franklin, TN, Zip 37067–6325, Mailing Address: P.O. Box 689020, Zip 37068–9020, tel. 615/465–7000; Wayne T. Smith, Chairman, President and Chief Executive Officer

(Decentralized Health System)

ALABAMA: CRESTWOOD MEDICAL CENTER (O, 147 beds) One Hospital Drive, Huntsville, AL, Zip 35801–3403; tel. 256/429–4000; Pamela Hudson, M.D., Chief Executive Officer
Web address: www.crestwoodmedcenter.com

FLOWERS HOSPITAL (O, 147 beds) 4370 West Main Street, Dothan, AL, Zip 36305–4000, Mailing Address: P.O. Box 6907, Zip 36302–6907, tel. 334/793–5000; Heath Phillips, Chief Executive Officer
Web address: www.flowershospital.com

GADSDEN REGIONAL MEDICAL CENTER (O, 279 beds) 1007 Goodyear Avenue, Gadsden, AL, Zip 35903–1195; tel. 256/494–4000; Corey Ewing, Chief Executive Officer
Web address: www.gadsdenregional.com

GRANDVIEW MEDICAL CENTER (O, 379 beds) 3690 Grandview Parkway, Birmingham, AL, Zip 35243–3326; tel. 205/971–1000; Drew Mason, Chief Executive Officer

MEDICAL CENTER ENTERPRISE (O, 117 beds) 400 North Edwards Street, Enterprise, AL, Zip 36330–2510; tel. 334/347–0584; Suzanne Woods, Chief Executive Officer
Web address: www.mcehospital.com

SOUTH BALDWIN REGIONAL MEDICAL CENTER (L, 112 beds) 1613 North McKenzie Street, Foley, AL, Zip 36535–2299; tel. 251/949–3400; Daniel McKinney, Chief Executive Officer
Web address: www.southbaldwinrmc.com

ALASKA: MAT–SU REGIONAL MEDICAL CENTER (O, 74 beds) 2500 South Woodworth Loop, Palmer, AK, Zip 99645–8984, Mailing Address: P.O. Box 1687, Zip 99645–1687, tel. 907/861–6000; David Wallace, Chief Executive Officer

ARIZONA: NORTHWEST MEDICAL CENTER (O, 270 beds) 6200 North La Cholla Boulevard, Tucson, AZ, Zip 85741–3599; tel. 520/742–9000; Kevin Stockton, Chief Executive Officer
Web address: www.northwestmedicalcenter.com

ORO VALLEY HOSPITAL (O, 144 beds) 1551 East Tangerine Road, Oro Valley, AZ, Zip 85755–6213; tel. 520/901–3500; Jae Dale, Chief Executive Officer

WESTERN ARIZONA REGIONAL MEDICAL CENTER (O, 139 beds) 2735 Silver Creek Road, Bullhead City, AZ, Zip 86442–8303; tel. 928/763–2273; Mike Stenger, Interim Chief Executive Officer
Web address: www.warmc.com

ARKANSAS: MEDICAL CENTER OF SOUTH ARKANSAS (L, 117 beds) 700 West Grove Street, El Dorado, AR, Zip 71730–4416; tel. 870/863–2000; Scott Street, Chief Executive Officer

NORTHWEST MEDICAL CENTER – SPRINGDALE (O, 323 beds) 609 West Maple Avenue, Springdale, AR, Zip 72764–5394, Mailing Address: P.O. Box 47, Zip 72765–0047, tel. 479/751–5711; Denten Park, Chief Executive Officer
Web address: www.northwesthealth.com

PHYSICIANS' SPECIALTY HOSPITAL (O, 21 beds) 3873 North Parkview Drive, Fayetteville, AR, Zip 72703–6286; tel. 479/571–7070; Denten Park, Chief Executive Officer
Web address: www.pshfay.com

SILOAM SPRINGS REGIONAL HOSPITAL (O, 44 beds) 603 North Progress Avenue, Siloam Springs, AR, Zip 72761–4352; tel. 479/215–3000; Patrick Kerrwood, Chief Executive Officer
Web address: www.ssrh.net

SPARKS MEDICAL CENTER – VAN BUREN (L, 33 beds) East Main and South 20th Streets, Van Buren, AR, Zip 72956–5715, Mailing Address: P.O. Box 409, Zip 72957–0409, tel. 479/474–3401; Brandon Bullard, Interim Chief Executive Officer

SPARKS REGIONAL MEDICAL CENTER (O, 303 beds) 1001 Towson Avenue, Fort Smith, AR, Zip 72901–4921, Mailing Address: P.O. Box 2406, Zip 72917–7006, tel. 479/441–4000; Brandon Bullard, Interim Chief Executive Officer
Web address: https://www.sparkshealth.com/

FLORIDA: BAYFRONT HEALTH BROOKSVILLE (L, 120 beds) 17240 Cortez Boulevard, Brooksville, FL, Zip 34601–8921, Mailing Address: P.O. Box 37, Zip 34605–0037, tel. 352/796–5111; Kenneth R. Wicker, Chief Executive Officer

BAYFRONT HEALTH PORT CHARLOTTE (O, 254 beds) 2500 Harbor Boulevard, Port Charlotte, FL, Zip 33952–5000; tel. 941/766–4122; Timothy J. Cerullo, Chief Executive Officer
Web address: www.bayfrontcharlotte.com

BAYFRONT HEALTH PUNTA GORDA (O, 190 beds) 809 East Marion Avenue, Punta Gorda, FL, Zip 33950–3819, Mailing Address: P.O. Box 51–1328, Zip 33951–1328, tel. 941/639–3131; Andrew Emery, Chief Executive Officer

BAYFRONT HEALTH ST. PETERSBURG (O, 480 beds) 701 Sixth Street South, Saint Petersburg, FL, Zip 33701–4891; tel. 727/823–1234; John R. McLain, President and Chief Executive Officer
Web address: www.bayfrontstpete.com

HEART OF FLORIDA REGIONAL MEDICAL CENTER (O, 193 beds) 40100 Highway 27, Davenport, FL, Zip 33837–5906; tel. 863/422–4971; Ann Barnhart, Chief Executive Officer

LAKE WALES MEDICAL CENTER (O, 131 beds) 410 South 11th Street, Lake Wales, FL, Zip 33853–4256; tel. 863/676–1433; Rebecca Brewer, FACHE, Chief Executive Officer
Web address: www.lakewalesmedicalcenter.com

LOWER KEYS MEDICAL CENTER (L, 90 beds) 5900 College Road, Key West, FL, Zip 33040–4396, Mailing Address: P.O. Box 9107, Zip 33041–9107, tel. 305/294–5531; David Clay, Chief Executive Officer
Web address: www.lkmc.com

NORTH OKALOOSA MEDICAL CENTER (O, 110 beds) 151 Redstone Avenue SE, Crestview, FL, Zip 32539–6026; tel. 850/689–8100; Ronnie Daves, Chief Executive Officer
Web address: www.northokaloosa.com

PHYSICIANS REGIONAL – PINE RIDGE (O, 201 beds) 6101 Pine Ridge Road, Naples, FL, Zip 34119–3900; tel. 239/348–4000; Scott Lowe, Interim Market Chief Executive Officer

SANTA ROSA MEDICAL CENTER (L, 68 beds) 6002 Berryhill Road, Milton, FL, Zip 32570–5062; tel. 850/626–7762; Doug Sills, Chief Executive Officer
Web address: www.santarosamedicalcenter.org

SEVEN RIVERS REGIONAL MEDICAL CENTER (O, 128 beds) 6201 North Suncoast Boulevard, Crystal River, FL, Zip 34428–6712; tel. 352/795–6560; Linda Stockton, Interim Chief Executive Officer

SHANDS LAKE SHORE REGIONAL MEDICAL CENTER (O, 85 beds) 368 NE Franklin Street, Lake City, FL, Zip 32055–3047; tel. 386/292–8000; Rhonda Kay. Sherrod, R.N., MSN, Chief Executive Officer
Web address: www.shandslakeshore.com

SHANDS LIVE OAK REGIONAL MEDICAL CENTER (O, 25 beds) 1100 SW 11th Street, Live Oak, FL, Zip 32064–3608; tel. 386/362–0800; Rhonda Kay. Sherrod, R.N., MSN, Chief Executive Officer
Web address: www.shandsliveoak.com/

SHANDS STARKE REGIONAL MEDICAL CENTER (O, 49 beds) 922 East Call Street, Starke, FL, Zip 32091–3699; tel. 904/368–2300; John Emery, Chief Executive Officer

ST. CLOUD REGIONAL MEDICAL CENTER (O, 84 beds) 2906 17th Street, Saint Cloud, FL, Zip 34769–6099; tel. 407/892–2135; Brent Burish, Chief Executive Officer
Web address: www.stcloudregional.com

VENICE REGIONAL BAYFRONT HEALTH (O, 221 beds) 540 The Rialto, Venice, FL, Zip 34285–2900; tel. 941/485–7711; Karen Fordham, Chief Executive Officer
Web address: www.veniceregional.com

GEORGIA: EAST GEORGIA REGIONAL MEDICAL CENTER (O, 149 beds) 1499 Fair Road, Statesboro, GA, Zip 30458–1683, Mailing Address: P.O. Box 1048, Zip 30459–1048, tel. 912/486–1000; Paul Theriot, Chief Executive Officer

---

For explanation of codes following names, see page B2.
★ Indicates Type III membership in the American Hospital Association.

INDIANA: BLUFFTON REGIONAL MEDICAL CENTER (O, 54 beds) 303 South Main Street, Bluffton, IN, Zip 46714–2503; tel. 260/824–3210; Brent Parsons, Chief Executive Officer
Web address: www.blufftonregional.com

DUKES MEMORIAL HOSPITAL (O, 25 beds) 275 West 12th Street, Peru, IN, Zip 46970–1638; tel. 765/472–8000; Debra Close, Chief Executive Officer
Web address: www.dukesmemorialhosp.com

DUPONT HOSPITAL (O, 131 beds) 2520 East Dupont Road, Fort Wayne, IN, Zip 46825–1675; tel. 260/416–3000; Lorenzo Suter, Chief Executive Officer

KOSCIUSKO COMMUNITY HOSPITAL (O, 72 beds) 2101 East Dubois Drive, Warsaw, IN, Zip 46580–3288; tel. 574/267–3200; Kim Finch, Interim Chief Executive Officer Chief Nursing Officer
Web address: www.kch.com

LA PORTE HOSPITAL (O, 129 beds) 1007 Lincolnway, La Porte, IN, Zip 46350–3201, Mailing Address: P.O. Box 250, Zip 46352–0250, tel. 219/326–1234; Ashley Dickinson, Chief Executive Officer
Web address: www.iuhealth.org

LUTHERAN HOSPITAL OF INDIANA (O, 407 beds) 7950 West Jefferson Boulevard, Fort Wayne, IN, Zip 46804–4140; tel. 260/435–7001; Paula R. Autry, FACHE, Chief Executive Officer

ORTHOPAEDIC HOSPITAL OF LUTHERAN HEALTH NETWORK (O, 43 beds) 7952 West Jefferson Boulevard, Fort Wayne, IN, Zip 46804–4140; tel. 260/435–2999; Lorie Ailor, Chief Executive Officer
Web address: www.theorthohospital.com

PORTER REGIONAL HOSPITAL (O, 276 beds) 85 East U.S. Highway 6, Valparaiso, IN, Zip 46383–8947; tel. 219/983–8300; Sean T. Dardeau, FACHE, Chief Executive Officer

REHABILITATION HOSPITAL OF FORT WAYNE (O, 36 beds) 7970 West Jefferson Boulevard, Fort Wayne, IN, Zip 46804–4140; tel. 260/435–6100; Ryan Cassedy, Chief Administrative Officer
Web address: www.rehabhospital.com

ST. JOSEPH HOSPITAL (O, 182 beds) 700 Broadway, Fort Wayne, IN, Zip 46802–1493; tel. 260/425–3000; Lisa Dolan, Interim Chief Executive Officer
Web address: www.stjoehospital.com

STARKE HOSPITAL (O, 15 beds) 102 East Culver Road, Knox, IN, Zip 46534–2216, Mailing Address: P.O. Box 339, Zip 46534–0339, tel. 574/772–6231; Jeff Vice, Chief Operating Officer and Interim Chief Executive Officer

LOUISIANA: NORTHERN LOUISIANA MEDICAL CENTER (O, 104 beds) 401 East Vaughn Avenue, Ruston, LA, Zip 71270–5950; tel. 318/254–2100; Keith Newton, Interim Chief Executive Officer
Web address: www.northernlouisianamedicalcenter.com

MISSISSIPPI: MERIT HEALTH BILOXI (L, 198 beds) 150 Reynoir Street, Biloxi, MS, Zip 39530–4199, Mailing Address: P.O. Box 128, Zip 39533–0128, tel. 228/432–1571; Robert Calhoun, Chief Executive Officer
Web address: www.merithealthbiloxi.com

MERIT HEALTH CENTRAL (L, 319 beds) 1850 Chadwick Drive, Jackson, MS, Zip 39204–3479, Mailing Address: P.O. Box 59001, Zip 39284–9001, tel. 601/376–1000; Barry Moss, Chief Executive Officer

MERIT HEALTH MADISON (L, 43 beds) 161 River Oaks Drive, Canton, MS, Zip 39046–5375, Mailing Address: PO Box 1607, Zip 39046–5375, tel. 601/855–4000; Britton Phelps, Chief Executive Officer
Web address: www.merithealthmadison.com

MERIT HEALTH NATCHEZ (O, 136 beds) 54 Seargent 'S' Prentiss Drive, Natchez, MS, Zip 39120–4726; tel. 601/443–2100; Lance Boyd, Chief Executive Officer
Web address: www.natchezregional.com

MERIT HEALTH RANKIN (L, 134 beds) 350 Crossgates Boulevard, Brandon, MS, Zip 39042–2698; tel. 601/825–2811; Heather Sistrunk, MHSA, RN, BSN, Chief Executive Officer

MERIT HEALTH RIVER OAKS (O, 158 beds) 1030 River Oaks Drive, Flowood, MS, Zip 39232–9553, Mailing Address: P.O. Box 5100, Jackson, Zip 39296–5100, tel. 601/932–1030; L Dwayne. Blaylock, Chief Executive Officer
Web address: www.riveroakshosp.com

MERIT HEALTH RIVER REGION (O, 361 beds) 2100 Highway 61 North, Vicksburg, MS, Zip 39183–8211, Mailing Address: P.O. Box 590, Zip 39181–0590, tel. 601/883–5000; Benjamin Richaud, Interim Chief Executive Officer
Web address: www.riverregion.com

MERIT HEALTH WESLEY (O, 211 beds) 5001 Hardy Street, Hattiesburg, MS, Zip 39402–1308, Mailing Address: P.O. Box 16509, Zip 39404–6509, tel. 601/268–8000; Carol Upton, Interim Chief Executive Officer

MERIT HEALTH WOMAN'S HOSPITAL (O, 60 beds) 1026 North Flowood Drive, Flowood, MS, Zip 39232–9532, Mailing Address: 1026 North Flowood Drive, Zip 39232, tel. 601/932–1000; Sherry J. Pitts, Chief Executive Officer
Web address: www.merithealthwomanshospital.com

MISSOURI: MOBERLY REGIONAL MEDICAL CENTER (O, 100 beds) 1515 Union Avenue, Moberly, MO, Zip 65270–9449; tel. 660/263–8400; Ranee C. Brayton, FACHE, MSN, R.N., Chief Executive Officer

NORTHEAST REGIONAL MEDICAL CENTER (L, 76 beds) 315 South Osteopathy, Kirksville, MO, Zip 63501–6401, Mailing Address: P.O. Box C8502, Zip 63501–8599, tel. 660/785–1000; Ranee C. Brayton, FACHE, MSN, R.N., Chief Executive Officer
Web address: www.nermc.com

POPLAR BLUFF REGIONAL MEDICAL CENTER (O, 296 beds) 3100 Oak Grove Road, Poplar Bluff, MO, Zip 63901, Mailing Address: P.O. Box 88, Zip 63902–0088, tel. 573/776–2000; Bryan Bateman, Chief Executive Officer

NEW JERSEY: MEMORIAL HOSPITAL OF SALEM COUNTY (O, 110 beds) 310 Woodstown Road, Salem, NJ, Zip 08079–2080; tel. 856/935–1000; Tammy Torres, R.N., MSN, Chief Executive Officer
Web address: www.salemhospitalnj.org

NEW MEXICO: CARLSBAD MEDICAL CENTER (O, 130 beds) 2430 West Pierce Street, Carlsbad, NM, Zip 88220–3597; tel. 575/887–4100; Cathy Hibbs, Chief Executive Officer

EASTERN NEW MEXICO MEDICAL CENTER (O, 149 beds) 405 West Country Club Road, Roswell, NM, Zip 88201–5209; tel. 575/622–8170; Warren Yehl, Interim Chief Executive Officer
Web address: www.enmmc.com

LEA REGIONAL MEDICAL CENTER (O, 195 beds) 5419 North Lovington Highway, Hobbs, NM, Zip 88240–9125, Mailing Address: P.O. Box 3000, Zip 88241–9501, tel. 575/492–5000; Timothy Thornell, FACHE, Chief Executive Officer

MOUNTAINVIEW REGIONAL MEDICAL CENTER (O, 142 beds) 4311 East Lohman Avenue, Las Cruces, NM, Zip 88011–8255; tel. 575/556–7600; Derrick Cuenca, Chief Executive Officer
Web address: www.mountainviewregional.com

NORTH CAROLINA: DAVIS REGIONAL MEDICAL CENTER (O, 130 beds) 218 Old Mocksville Road, Statesville, NC, Zip 28625–1930, Mailing Address: P.O. Box 1823, Zip 28687–1823, tel. 704/873–0281; Matthew Banks, Chief Executive Officer

LAKE NORMAN REGIONAL MEDICAL CENTER (O, 123 beds) 171 Fairview Road, Mooresville, NC, Zip 28117–9500, Mailing Address: P.O. Box 3250, Zip 28117–3250, tel. 704/660–4000; Stephen L. Midkiff, Chief Executive Officer
Web address: www.lnrmc.com

OKLAHOMA: ALLIANCEHEALTH CLINTON (O, 49 beds) 100 North 30th Street, Clinton, OK, Zip 73601–3117; tel. 580/323–2363; Landon E. Hise, Chief Executive Officer

ALLIANCEHEALTH DEACONESS (O, 141 beds) 5501 North Portland Avenue, Oklahoma City, OK, Zip 73112–2099; tel. 405/604–6000; Damon Brown, Interim Chief Executive Officer
Web address: www.deaconessokc.com

ALLIANCEHEALTH DURANT (O, 140 beds) 1800 University Boulevard, Durant, OK, Zip 74701–3006, Mailing Address: P.O. Box 1207, Zip 74702–1207, tel. 580/924–3080; Jeffrey S. Tarrant, FACHE, Chief Executive Officer

ALLIANCEHEALTH MADILL (O, 21 beds) 901 South Fifth Avenue, Madill, OK, Zip 73446–3640, Mailing Address: P.O. Box 827, Zip 73446–0827, tel. 580/795–3384; Jeffrey S. Tarrant, FACHE, Chief Executive Officer
Web address: www.myalliancehealth.com

ALLIANCEHEALTH MIDWEST (L, 255 beds) 2825 Parklawn Drive, Midwest City, OK, Zip 73110–4258; tel. 405/610–4411; Clay Franklin, Chief Executive Officer
Web address: www.myalliancehealth.com

ALLIANCEHEALTH PONCA CITY (O, 74 beds) 1900 North 14th Street, Ponca City, OK, Zip 74601–2099; tel. 580/765–3321; Christopher Mendoza, Chief Executive Officer

Section B

For explanation of codes following names, see page B2.
★ Indicates Type III membership in the American Hospital Association.

ALLIANCEHEALTH SEMINOLE (O, 32 beds) 2401 Wrangler Boulevard, Seminole, OK, Zip 74868–1917; tel. 405/303–4000; Adam Bracks, Chief Executive Officer
Web address: www.alliancehealthseminole.com/

ALLIANCEHEALTH WOODWARD (L, 40 beds) 900 17th Street, Woodward, OK, Zip 73801–2448; tel. 580/256–5511; Ross Korkmas, Chief Executive Officer

PENNSYLVANIA: BERWICK HOSPITAL CENTER (O, 101 beds) 701 East 16th Street, Berwick, PA, Zip 18603–2397; tel. 570/759–5000; Thomas Neal, Chief Executive Officer
Web address: www.berwick–hospital.com

FIRST HOSPITAL WYOMING VALLEY (O, 127 beds) 562 Wyoming Avenue, Kingston, PA, Zip 18704–3721; tel. 570/552–3900; James Gallagher, Chief Executive Officer

MOSES TAYLOR HOSPITAL (O, 213 beds) 700 Quincy Avenue, Scranton, PA, Zip 18510–1724; tel. 570/770–5000
Web address: www.mth.org

REGIONAL HOSPITAL OF SCRANTON (O, 186 beds) 746 Jefferson Avenue, Scranton, PA, Zip 18510–1624; tel. 570/348–7100; Ronald Ziobro, Interim Chief Executive Officer
Web address: www.regionalhospitalofscranton.net

TYLER MEMORIAL HOSPITAL (O, 44 beds) 5950 State Route 6, Tunkhannock, PA, Zip 18657–7905; tel. 570/836–2161; Ann Marie. Stevens, R.N., Chief Executive Officer

WILKES–BARRE GENERAL HOSPITAL (O, 374 beds) 575 North River Street, Wilkes–Barre, PA, Zip 18764–0001; tel. 570/829–8111; Cornelio R. Catena, President and Chief Executive Officer
Web address: www.wvhc.org

SOUTH CAROLINA: CAROLINAS HOSPITAL SYSTEM MARION (O, 216 beds) 2829 East Highway 76, Mullins, SC, Zip 29574–6035, Mailing Address: P O Drawer 1150, Marion, Zip 29571–1150, tel. 843/431–2000

CAROLINAS HOSPITAL SYSTEM (O, 416 beds) 805 Pamplico Highway, Florence, SC, Zip 29505–6050, Mailing Address: P.O. Box 100550, Zip 29502–0550, tel. 843/674–5000; Vance V. Reynolds, FACHE, CPA, Chief Executive Officer
Web address: www.carolinashospital.com

CHESTER REGIONAL MEDICAL CENTER (L, 36 beds) 1 Medical Park Drive, Chester, SC, Zip 29706–9769; tel. 803/581–3151; Page H. Vaughan, Chief Executive Officer
Web address: www.chesterregional.com

MARY BLACK HEALTH SYSTEM – GAFFNEY (O, 125 beds) 1530 North Limestone Street, Gaffney, SC, Zip 29340–4738; tel. 864/487–4271; Joshua Self, Chief Executive Officer

MARY BLACK HEALTH SYSTEM–SPARTANBURG (O, 176 beds) 1700 Skylyn Drive, Spartanburg, SC, Zip 29307–1061, Mailing Address: P.O. Box 3217, Zip 29304–3217, tel. 864/573–3000; Parkes Coggins, Chief Executive Officer
Web address: www.maryblackhealthsystem.com

SPRINGS MEMORIAL HOSPITAL (O, 162 beds) 800 West Meeting Street, Lancaster, SC, Zip 29720–2298; tel. 803/286–1214; Page H. Vaughan, Chief Executive Officer

TENNESSEE: LAKEWAY REGIONAL HOSPITAL (O, 135 beds) 726 McFarland Street, Morristown, TN, Zip 37814–3990; tel. 423/586–2302; Tammy White, Interim Chief Executive Officer
Web address: www.tennova.com

TENNOVA HEALTHCARE – CLEVELAND (O, 187 beds) 2305 Chambliss Avenue NW, Cleveland, TN, Zip 37311–3847, Mailing Address: P.O. Box 3060, Zip 37320–3060, tel. 423/559–6000; R Coleman. Foss, Chief Executive Officer
Web address: www.skyridgemedicalcenter.net

TENNOVA HEALTHCARE–CLARKSVILLE (O, 247 beds) 651 Dunlop Lane, Clarksville, TN, Zip 37040–5015, Mailing Address: P.O. Box 31629, Zip 37040–0028, tel. 931/502–1000; Alex Villa, Chief Executive Officer
Web address: www.tennova.com/

TENNOVA HEALTHCARE–HARTON (O, 135 beds) 1801 North Jackson Street, Tullahoma, TN, Zip 37388–8259; tel. 931/393–3000; Richard Ellis, Chief Executive Officer
Web address: www.hartonmedicalcenter.com

TENNOVA HEALTHCARE–JEFFERSON MEMORIAL HOSPITAL (L, 54 beds) 110 Hospital Drive, Jefferson City, TN, Zip 37760–5281; tel. 865/471–2500; Colin McRae, Chief Executive Officer

TENNOVA HEALTHCARE–LAFOLLETTE MEDICAL CENTER (O, 164 beds) 923 East Central Avenue, La Follette, TN, Zip 37766–2768, Mailing Address: P.O. Box 1301, Zip 37766–1301, tel. 423/907–1200; Mark Cain, Chief Executive Officer
Web address: www.tennova.com

TENNOVA HEALTHCARE–LEBANON (O, 245 beds) 1411 Baddour Parkway, Lebanon, TN, Zip 37087–2513; tel. 615/444–8262; Jay Hinesley, FACHE, Chief Executive Officer
Web address: www.universitymedicalcenter.com

TENNOVA HEALTHCARE–SHELBYVILLE (O, 49 beds) 2835 Highway 231 North, Shelbyville, TN, Zip 37160–7327; tel. 931/685–5433; Bill Rich, Chief Executive Officer
Web address: www.Tennova.com

TENNOVA NEWPORT MEDICAL CENTER (O, 47 beds) 435 Second Street, Newport, TN, Zip 37821–3799; tel. 423/625–2200; Pamela Beck, Interim Chief Executive Officer

TENNOVA PHYSICIANS REGIONAL MEDICAL CENTER (O, 220 beds) 900 East Oak Hill Avenue, Knoxville, TN, Zip 37917–4556; tel. 865/545–8000; Pamela Beck, Interim Chief Executive Officer
Web address: www.hma.com/content/physicians–regional–medical–center

TEXAS: ABILENE REGIONAL MEDICAL CENTER (O, 205 beds) 6250 US Highway 83, Abilene, TX, Zip 79606–5299; tel. 325/428–1000; Michael D. Murphy, FACHE, Chief Executive Officer
Web address: www.abileneregional.com

BROWNWOOD REGIONAL MEDICAL CENTER (O, 188 beds) 1501 Burnet Road, Brownwood, TX, Zip 76801–8520, Mailing Address: P.O. Box 760, Zip 76804–0760, tel. 325/646–8541; Claude E Chip"". Camp III, FACHE, Chief Executive Officer

CEDAR PARK REGIONAL MEDICAL CENTER (O, 108 beds) 1401 Medical Parkway, Cedar Park, TX, Zip 78613–7763; tel. 512/528–7000; Brad D. Holland, Chief Executive Officer
Web address: www.cedarparkregional.com

COLLEGE STATION MEDICAL CENTER (O, 160 beds) 1604 Rock Prairie Road, College Station, TX, Zip 77845–8345; tel. 979/764–5100; America S. Farrell, FACHE, Chief Executive Officer
Web address: www.csmedcenter.com

DETAR HEALTHCARE SYSTEM (O, 225 beds) 506 East San Antonio Street, Victoria, TX, Zip 77901–6060, Mailing Address: P.O. Box 2089, Zip 77902–2089, tel. 361/575–7441; Gary Malaer, Chief Executive Officer

HILL REGIONAL HOSPITAL (O, 66 beds) 101 Circle Drive, Hillsboro, TX, Zip 76645–2670; tel. 254/580–8500; Michael J. Ellis, FACHE, Chief Executive Officer
Web address: www.chs.net

LAKE GRANBURY MEDICAL CENTER (L, 73 beds) 1310 Paluxy Road, Granbury, TX, Zip 76048–5655; tel. 817/573–2273; David Orcutt, Chief Executive Officer
Web address: www.lakegranburymedicalcenter.com

LAREDO MEDICAL CENTER (O, 326 beds) 1700 East Saunders Avenue, Laredo, TX, Zip 78041–5474, Mailing Address: P.O. Box 2068, Zip 78044–2068, tel. 956/796–5000; Enrique Gallegos, Chief Executive Officer

LONGVIEW REGIONAL MEDICAL CENTER (O, 224 beds) 2901 North Fourth Street, Longview, TX, Zip 75605–5191, Mailing Address: P.O. Box 14000, Zip 75607–4000, tel. 903/758–1818; Casey Robertson, Chief Executive Officer
Web address: www.longviewregional.com

NAVARRO REGIONAL HOSPITAL (O, 49 beds) 3201 West State Highway 22, Corsicana, TX, Zip 75110–2469; tel. 903/654–6800; Michael K. Stewart, Chief Executive Officer

SAN ANGELO COMMUNITY MEDICAL CENTER (O, 131 beds) 3501 Knickerbocker Road, San Angelo, TX, Zip 76904–7698; tel. 325/949–9511; Buddy Daniels, Chief Executive Officer
Web address: www.sacmc.com

WOODLAND HEIGHTS MEDICAL CENTER (O, 124 beds) 505 South John Redditt Drive, Lufkin, TX, Zip 75904–3157, Mailing Address: P.O. Box 150610, Zip 75904, tel. 936/634–8311; Kyle Swift, Chief Executive Officer
Web address: www.woodlandheights.net

VIRGINIA: SOUTHAMPTON MEMORIAL HOSPITAL (O, 72 beds) 100 Fairview Drive, Franklin, VA, Zip 23851–1238, Mailing Address: P.O. Box 817, Zip 23851–0817, tel. 757/569–6100; Kimberly W. Marks, Chief Executive Officer
Web address: www.smhfranklin.com

SOUTHERN VIRGINIA REGIONAL MEDICAL CENTER (O, 80 beds) 727 North Main Street, Emporia, VA, Zip 23847–1274; tel. 434/348–4400; Wilson A. Thomas, Chief Executive Officer

For explanation of codes following names, see page B2.
★ Indicates Type III membership in the American Hospital Association.

SOUTHSIDE REGIONAL MEDICAL CENTER (O, 294 beds) 200 Medical Park Boulevard, Petersburg, VA, Zip 23805–9274; tel. 804/765–5000; Trent Nobles, Chief Executive Officer
Web address: www.srmconline.com

WEST VIRGINIA: BLUEFIELD REGIONAL MEDICAL CENTER (O, 92 beds) 500 Cherry Street, Bluefield, WV, Zip 24701–3390; tel. 304/327–1100; Derek W. Cimala, Interim Chief Executive Officer

GREENBRIER VALLEY MEDICAL CENTER (O, 113 beds) 202 Maplewood Avenue, Ronceverte, WV, Zip 24970–1334, Mailing Address: P.O. Box 497, Zip 24970–0497, tel. 304/647–4411; Jim Hobson, Chief Executive Officer
Web address: www.gvmc.com

PLATEAU MEDICAL CENTER (O, 25 beds) 430 Main Street, Oak Hill, WV, Zip 25901–3455; tel. 304/469–8600; Derek W. Cimala, Interim Chief Executive Officer

WILLIAMSON MEMORIAL HOSPITAL (O, 76 beds) 859 Alderson Street, Williamson, WV, Zip 25661–3215, Mailing Address: P.O. Box 1980, Zip 25661–1980, tel. 304/235–2500; Michael D. Makosky, Interim Chief Executive Officer
Web address: www.williamsonmemorial.net

Owned, leased, sponsored:	113 hospitals	16814 beds
Contract–managed:	0 hospitals	0 beds
Totals:	113 hospitals	16814 beds

0249: COMMUNITY HEALTHCARE SYSTEM (NP)
901 MacArthur Boulevard, Hammond, IN, Zip 46321–2959; tel. 219/836–1600; Donald P. Fesko, President and Chief Executive Officer
(Independent Hospital System)

INDIANA: COMMUNITY HOSPITAL (O, 510 beds) 901 Macarthur Boulevard, Munster, IN, Zip 46321–2959; tel. 219/836–1600; Luis F. Molina, Chief Executive Officer and Administrator

ST. CATHERINE HOSPITAL (O, 220 beds) 4321 Fir Street, East Chicago, IN, Zip 46312–3097; tel. 219/392–1700; Leo Correa, Chief Executive Officer and Administrator
Web address: www.stcatherinehospital.org

ST. MARY MEDICAL CENTER (O, 200 beds) 1500 South Lake Park Avenue, Hobart, IN, Zip 46342–6699; tel. 219/942–0551; Janice L. Ryba, JD, Chief Executive Officer
Web address: www.comhs.org

Owned, leased, sponsored:	3 hospitals	930 beds
Contract–managed:	0 hospitals	0 beds
Totals:	3 hospitals	930 beds

★0384: COMMUNITY HOSPITAL CORPORATION (NP)
7800 North Dallas Parkway, Suite 200, Plano, TX, Zip 75024–6116; tel. 972/943–6400; Jim R. Kendrick, President and Chief Executive Officer
(Moderately Centralized Health System)

KENTUCKY: CONTINUECARE HOSPITAL AT BAPTIST HEALTH CORBIN (O, 32 beds) 1 Trillium Way, Lower Level, Corbin, KY, Zip 40701–8727; tel. 606/523–5150; Tuan Le, Chief Executive Officer

CONTINUECARE HOSPITAL AT BAPTIST HEALTH PADUCAH (O, 37 beds) 2501 Kentucky Avenue, 5th Floor, Paducah, KY, Zip 42003–3813; tel. 270/575–2598; Len McDade, Chief Executive Officer
Web address: www.continuecare.org/paducah//

CONTINUECARE HOSPITAL AT MADISONVILLE (O, 35 beds) 900 Hospital Drive, 4th Floor, Madisonville, KY, Zip 42431–1644; tel. 270/825–5450; Lea Ann H. Klarner, Chief Executive Officer
Web address: www.continuecare.org/madisonville/

LOUISIANA: MOREHOUSE GENERAL HOSPITAL (C, 49 beds) 323 West Walnut Avenue, Bastrop, LA, Zip 71220–4521, Mailing Address: P.O. Box 1060, Zip 71221–1060, tel. 318/283–3600; Derrick A. Frazier, FACHE, Chief Executive Officer

NEW MEXICO: UNION COUNTY GENERAL HOSPITAL (C, 21 beds) 300 Wilson Street, Clayton, NM, Zip 88415–3304, Mailing Address: P.O. Box 489, Zip 88415–0489, tel. 575/374–2585; Tammie Stump, R.N., Chief Executive Officer
Web address: www.ucgh.net/

NORTH CAROLINA: CAROLINAS CONTINUECARE HOSPITAL AT KINGS MOUNTAIN (O, 28 beds) 706 West King Street, 2nd Floor, Kings Mountain, NC, Zip 28086–2708, Mailing Address: P.O. Box 159, Zip 28086–0159, tel. 980/487–5520; Derek Murzyn, Chief Executive Officer
Web address: www.continuecare.org/kings–mountain/

CAROLINAS CONTINUECARE HOSPITAL AT PINEVILLE (O, 40 beds) 10648 Park Road, Charlotte, NC, Zip 28210; tel. 704/667–8050; Derek Murzyn, Market Chief Executive Officer
Web address: www.continuecare.org/pineville/

CAROLINAS CONTINUECARE HOSPITAL AT UNIVERSITY (O, 35 beds) 8800 North Tryon Street, Charlotte, NC, Zip 28262–3300; tel. 704/863–8300; Derek Murzyn, Chief Executive Officer
Web address: www.continuecare.org/charlotte//

SOUTH CAROLINA: CONTINUECARE HOSPITAL AT PALMETTO HEALTH BAPTIST (O, 35 beds) Taylor at Marion Street, Columbia, SC, Zip 29220, Mailing Address: PO BOX 11069, Zip 29211–1069, tel. 803/296–3757; Thomas P. Harlan, Chief Executive Officer
Web address: www.continuecare.org/palmetto//

TENNESSEE: JELLICO COMMUNITY HOSPITAL (O, 47 beds) 188 Hospital Lane, Jellico, TN, Zip 37762–4400; tel. 423/784–7252; Gene Miller, Interim Chief Executive Officer
Web address: www.jellicohospital.com

TEXAS: BAPTIST HOSPITALS OF SOUTHEAST TEXAS (O, 323 beds) 3080 College Street, Beaumont, TX, Zip 77701–4689, Mailing Address: P.O. Box 1591, Zip 77704–1591, tel. 409/212–5000; David N. Parmer, FACHE, Chief Executive Officer

CONTINUECARE HOSPITAL AT HENDRICK MEDICAL CENTER (O, 23 beds) 1900 Pine Street, 7th Floor, Jones Building, Abilene, TX, Zip 79601–2432; tel. 325/670–6251; Billy Blasingame, Chief Executive Officer
Web address: www.continuecare.org/hendrick/

CONTINUECARE HOSPITAL AT MEDICAL CENTER (ODESSA) (O, 25 beds) 500 West Fourth Street, 4th Floor, Odessa, TX, Zip 79761–5001; tel. 432/640–4380; Holly Powell, Administrator

CONTINUECARE HOSPITAL AT MIDLAND MEMORIAL (O, 29 beds) 4214 Andrews Highway, 3rd Floor, Midland, TX, Zip 79703–4822; tel. 432/221–3044; Cynthia Rodgers, Chief Executive Officer
Web address: www.continuecare.org/midland/

FREESTONE MEDICAL CENTER (C, 37 beds) 125 Newman Street, Fairfield, TX, Zip 75840–1499; tel. 903/389–2121; John M. Yeary, FACHE, Chief Executive Officer

ST. MARK'S MEDICAL CENTER (O, 65 beds) One St Mark's Place, La Grange, TX, Zip 78945; tel. 979/242–2200; Rick J. Montelongo, Chief Executive Officer
Web address: www.smmctx.org

TYLER CONTINUECARE HOSPITAL (O, 51 beds) 800 East Dawson, 4th Floor, Tyler, TX, Zip 75701–2036; tel. 903/531–4080; Stephanie Hyde, R.N., MSN, Chief Executive Officer
Web address: www.continuecare.org

YOAKUM COMMUNITY HOSPITAL (O, 25 beds) 1200 Carl Ramert Drive, Yoakum, TX, Zip 77995–4868; tel. 361/293–2321; Karen Barber, R.N., Chief Executive Officer

Owned, leased, sponsored:	15 hospitals	830 beds
Contract–managed:	3 hospitals	107 beds
Totals:	18 hospitals	937 beds

1085: COMMUNITY MEDICAL CENTERS (NP)
Fresno and Maddy Drive, Fresno, CA, Zip 93721, Mailing Address: P.O. Box 1232, Zip 93715–1232, tel. 559/459–6000; Tim A. Joslin, President and Chief Executive Officer
(Moderately Centralized Health System)

CALIFORNIA: CLOVIS COMMUNITY MEDICAL CENTER (O, 109 beds) 2755 Herndon Avenue, Clovis, CA, Zip 93611–6801; tel. 559/324–4000; Craig Castro, Chief Executive Officer
Web address: www.communitymedical.org

For explanation of codes following names, see page B2.
★ Indicates Type III membership in the American Hospital Association.

Section B

COMMUNITY BEHAVIORAL HEALTH CENTER (O, 61 beds) 7171 North Cedar Avenue, Fresno, CA, Zip 93720–3311; tel. 559/449–8000; Craig Wagoner, Chief Executive Officer
Web address: www.communitymedical.org

COMMUNITY REGIONAL MEDICAL CENTER (O, 808 beds) 2823 Fresno Street, Fresno, CA, Zip 93721–1324, Mailing Address: P.O. Box 1232, Zip 93715–1232, tel. 559/459–6000; Craig Wagoner, Chief Executive Officer

FRESNO HEART AND SURGICAL HOSPITAL (O, 60 beds) 15 East Audubon Drive, Fresno, CA, Zip 93720–1542; tel. 559/433–8000; Ben Armfield, Associate Administrator
Web address: www.fresnoheartandsurgical.org

Owned, leased, sponsored:	4 hospitals	1038 beds
Contract–managed:	0 hospitals	0 beds
Totals:	4 hospitals	1038 beds

0990: COMMUNITY MEMORIAL HEALTH SYSTEM (NP)
147 North Brent Street, Ventura, CA, Zip 93003–2809; tel. 805/652–5011; Gary Wilde, President and Chief Executive Officer
(Independent Hospital System)

CALIFORNIA: COMMUNITY MEMORIAL HOSPITAL (O, 284 beds) 147 North Brent Street, Ventura, CA, Zip 93003–2809; tel. 805/652–5011; Gary Wilde, President and Chief Executive Officer
Web address: www.cmhshealth.org

OJAI VALLEY COMMUNITY HOSPITAL (O, 96 beds) 1306 Maricopa Highway, Ojai, CA, Zip 93023–3163; tel. 805/646–1401; Haady Lashkari, Chief Administrative Officer

Owned, leased, sponsored:	2 hospitals	380 beds
Contract–managed:	0 hospitals	0 beds
Totals:	2 hospitals	380 beds

0909: COMPASS HEALTH (NP)
713 North Avenue L, Crowley, LA, Zip 70526–3832; tel. 337/788–3330; Aimee Monaghan, Chief Executive Officer
(Independent Hospital System)

LOUISIANA: COMPASS BEHAVIORAL CENTER OF ALEXANDRIA (O, 16 beds) 6410 Masonic Drve, Alexandria, LA, Zip 71301–2319; tel. 318/442–3163; Andre' Robichaux, Interim Administrator
Web address: www.compasshealthcare.com/site191.php

COMPASS BEHAVIORAL CENTER OF HOUMA (O, 20 beds) 4701 West Park Avenue, Houma, LA, Zip 70364–4426; tel. 985/876–1715; Andre' Robichaux, Interim Administrator

COMPASS BEHAVIORAL CENTER OF LAFAYETTE (O, 16 beds) 312 Youngsville Highway, Lafayette, LA, Zip 70508; tel. 337/534–4655; Jason Branson, Administrator
Web address: www.compasshealthcare.com/site184.php

Owned, leased, sponsored:	3 hospitals	52 beds
Contract–managed:	0 hospitals	0 beds
Totals:	3 hospitals	52 beds

0999: CONCORD HEALTHCARE GROUP (IO)
111 Clifton AVenue, Lakewood, NJ, Zip 8701; tel. 214/396–3462; Joe Neuman, Chief Executive Officer
(Independent Hospital System)

OKLAHOMA: MIDWEST CITY SPECIALTY HOSPITAL (O, 31 beds) 8210 National Avenue, Midwest City, OK, Zip 73110–8518; tel. 405/739–0800; Bobby Snyder, Chief Executive Officer

TEXAS: MESA HILLS SPECIALTY HOSPITAL (O, 32 beds) 2311 North Oregon Street, 5th Floor, El Paso, TX, Zip 79902–3216; tel. 915/545–1823; Jose Huerta, Chief Executive Officer
Web address: www.specialtyhospitalmesahills.com/

PINE VALLEY SPECIALTY HOSPITAL (O, 35 beds) 6160 South Loop East, Houston, TX, Zip 77087–1010; tel. 713/640–2400
Web address: www.pinevalleyspecialtyhospital.com/wp–pine/

PLANO SPECIALTY HOSPITAL (O, 43 beds) 1621 Coit Road, Plano, TX, Zip 75075–6141; tel. 972/758–5200; Wayne Cook, Chief Executive Officer

Owned, leased, sponsored:	4 hospitals	141 beds
Contract–managed:	0 hospitals	0 beds
Totals:	4 hospitals	141 beds

0950: CONE HEALTH (NP)
1200 North Elm Street, Greensboro, NC, Zip 27401–1004; tel. 336/832–7000; Terry Akin, President and Chief Executive Officer
(Independent Hospital System)

NORTH CAROLINA: ALAMANCE REGIONAL MEDICAL CENTER (O, 200 beds) 1240 Huffman Mill Road, Burlington, NC, Zip 27215–8700, Mailing Address: P.O. Box 202, Zip 27216–0202, tel. 336/538–7000; Preston W. Hammock, President
Web address: www.armc.com

MOSES H. CONE MEMORIAL HOSPITAL (O, 921 beds) 1200 North Elm Street, Greensboro, NC, Zip 27401–1020; tel. 336/832–7000; Mickey Foster, President

Owned, leased, sponsored:	2 hospitals	1121 beds
Contract–managed:	0 hospitals	0 beds
Totals:	2 hospitals	1121 beds

0014: CONNECTICUT DEPARTMENT OF MENTAL HEALTH AND ADDICTION SERVICES (NP)
410 Capitol Avenue, Hartford, CT, Zip 06106–1367, Mailing Address: P.O. Box 341431, Zip 06134–1431, tel. 860/418–7000; Miriam Delphin–Rittmon, Ph.D., Commissioner
(Independent Hospital System)

CONNECTICUT: CONNECTICUT MENTAL HEALTH CENTER (O, 32 beds) 34 Park Street, New Haven, CT, Zip 06519–1109, Mailing Address: P.O. Box 1842, Zip 06508–1842, tel. 203/974–7144; Michael Sernyak, M.D., Director
Web address: www.ct.gov/dmhas/cwp/view.asp?a=2906&q=334596

CONNECTICUT VALLEY HOSPITAL (O, 596 beds) 1000 Silver Street, Middletown, CT, Zip 06457–3947; tel. 860/262–5000; Helene M. Vartelas, MSN, Chief Executive Officer
Web address: www.ct.gov/dmhas/cwp/view.asp?a=3519&q=416778

SOUTHWEST CONNECTICUT MENTAL HEALTH SYSTEM (O, 62 beds) 1635 Central Avenue, Bridgeport, CT, Zip 06610–2717; tel. 203/551–7400; Alicia Feller, Chief Executive Officer

Owned, leased, sponsored:	3 hospitals	690 beds
Contract–managed:	0 hospitals	0 beds
Totals:	3 hospitals	690 beds

★0016: COOK COUNTY HEALTH AND HOSPITALS SYSTEM (NP)
1900 West Polk Street, Suite 220, Chicago, IL, Zip 60612–3723; tel. 312/864–6820; John Jay. Shannon, M.D., Chief Executive Officer
(Independent Hospital System)

ILLINOIS: JOHN H. STROGER JR. HOSPITAL OF COOK COUNTY (O, 450 beds) 1969 West Ogden Avenue, Chicago, IL, Zip 60612–3714; tel. 312/864–6000; John Jay. Shannon, M.D., Chief Executive Officer
Web address: www.cookcountyhealth.net

PROVIDENT HOSPITAL OF COOK COUNTY (O, 25 beds) 500 East 51st Street, Chicago, IL, Zip 60615–2494; tel. 312/572–2000; John Jay. Shannon, M.D., Chief Executive Officer
Web address: www.ccbhs.org/pages/ProvidentHospitalofCookCounty.htm

Owned, leased, sponsored:	2 hospitals	475 beds
Contract–managed:	0 hospitals	0 beds
Totals:	2 hospitals	475 beds

For explanation of codes following names, see page B2.
★ Indicates Type III membership in the American Hospital Association.

0905: CORNERSTONE HEALTHCARE GROUP (IO)
2200 Ross Avenue, Suite 5400, Dallas, TX, Zip 75201–7984; tel. 469/621–6700; Steve Jakubcanin, President and Chief Executive Officer
(Independent Hospital System)

ARIZONA: CHG HOSPITAL TUCSON, LLC (O, 34 beds) 7220 East Rosewood Drive, Tucson, AZ, Zip 85710–1350; tel. 520/546–4595; Vanessa Acevedo, Interim Chief Executive Officer
Web address: www.chghospitals.com

ARKANSAS: CORNERSTONE HOSPITAL OF LITTLE ROCK (O, 30 beds) 2 Saint Vincent Circle, 6th Floor, Little Rock, AR, Zip 72205–5423; tel. 501/265–0600; James H. Rogers, FACHE, Chief Executive Officer

LOUISIANA: CORNERSTONE HOSPITAL OF BOSSIER CITY (O, 54 beds) 4900 Medical Drive, Bossier City, LA, Zip 71112–4521; tel. 318/747–9500; Sheri Burnette, R.N., Chief Executive Officer and Administrator
Web address: www.chghospitals.com/

CORNERSTONE HOSPITAL OF SOUTHWEST LOUISIANA (O, 30 beds) 703 Cypress Street, Sulphur, LA, Zip 70663–5053; tel. 337/310–6000; Jeffrey Clark, Chief Executive Officer

CORNERSTONE HOSPITAL–WEST MONROE (O, 40 beds) 6198 Cypress Street, West Monroe, LA, Zip 71291–9010; tel. 318/396–5600; Chris Simpson, Chief Executive Officer
Web address: www.chghospitals.com/chwm.html

OKLAHOMA: CORNERSTONE HOSPITAL OF OKLAHOMA–MUSKOGEE (O, 41 beds) 351 South 40th Street, Muskogee, OK, Zip 74401–4916; tel. 918/682–6161; Elizabeth Waytula, Chief Executive Officer

CORNERSTONE HOSPITAL OF OKLAHOMA–SHAWNEE (O, 34 beds) 1900 Gordon Cooper Drive, 2nd Floor, Shawnee, OK, Zip 74801–8603, Mailing Address: P.O. Box 1245, Zip 74802–1245, tel. 405/395–5800; Jimmy D. Stuart, Chief Executive Officer
Web address: www.chghospitals.com/shawnee/

TEXAS: CHG CORNERSTONE HOSPITAL CONROE (O, 41 beds) 1500 Grand Lake Drive, Conroe, TX, Zip 77304–2891; tel. 936/523–1800; Suzanne Kretschmer, Chief Executive Officer
Web address: www.chghospitals.com/conroe/

CORNERSTONE HOSPITAL OF AUSTIN (O, 86 beds) 4207 Burnet Road, Austin, TX, Zip 78756–3396; tel. 512/706–1900; Curt L. Roberts, Chief Executive Officer

CORNERSTONE HOSPITAL OF HOUSTON AT CLEARLAKE (O, 148 beds) 709 Medical Center Boulevard, Webster, TX, Zip 77598; tel. 281/332–3322; Amy Stasney, R.N., Chief Executive Officer
Web address: www.cornerstonehealthcaregroup.com

CORNERSTONE HOSPITAL–MEDICAL CENTER OF HOUSTON (O, 35 beds) 2001 Hermann Drive, Houston, TX, Zip 77004; tel. 832/649–6200; Michael Higginbotham, Chief Executive Officer

SOLARA HOSPITAL HARLINGEN (O, 82 beds) 508 Victoria Lane, Harlingen, TX, Zip 78550–3225; tel. 956/425–9600; Cary L. Montalvo, Chief Executive Officer
Web address: www.chghospitals.com/harlingen/

SOLARA HOSPITAL MCALLEN (O, 78 beds) 301 West Expressway 83, 8th Floor, McAllen, TX, Zip 78503–3045; tel. 956/632–4880; Austin B. Cleveland, Chief Executive Officer
Web address: www.chghospitals.com/mcallen/

WEST VIRGINIA: CORNERSTONE HOSPITAL OF HUNTINGTON (O, 28 beds) 2900 First Avenue, Two East, Huntington, WV, Zip 25702–1241; tel. 304/399–2600; Cynthia Isaacs, Chief Executive Officer

Owned, leased, sponsored:	14 hospitals	761 beds
Contract-managed:	0 hospitals	0 beds
Totals:	14 hospitals	761 beds

★0103: COTTAGE HEALTH (NP)
400 West Pueblo Street, Santa Barbara, CA, Zip 93105–4353, Mailing Address: P.O. Box 689, Zip 93102–0689, tel. 805/569–7290; Ronald C. Werft, President and Chief Executive Officer
(Independent Hospital System)

CALIFORNIA: GOLETA VALLEY COTTAGE HOSPITAL (O, 28 beds) 351 South Patterson Avenue, Santa Barbara, CA, Zip 93111–2496, Mailing Address: Box 6306, Zip 93160–6306, tel. 805/967–3411; Ronald C. Werft, President and Chief Executive Officer
Web address: www.sbch.org

SANTA BARBARA COTTAGE HOSPITAL (O, 363 beds) 400 West Pueblo Street, Santa Barbara, CA, Zip 93105–4390, Mailing Address: P.O. Box 689, Zip 93102–0689, tel. 805/682–7111; Ronald C. Werft, President and Chief Executive Officer
Web address: www.cottagehealthsystem.org

SANTA YNEZ VALLEY COTTAGE HOSPITAL (O, 11 beds) 2050 Viborg Road, Solvang, CA, Zip 93463–2295; tel. 805/688–6431; Ronald C. Werft, President and Chief Executive Officer
Web address: www.cottagehealthsystem.org

Owned, leased, sponsored:	3 hospitals	402 beds
Contract-managed:	0 hospitals	0 beds
Totals:	3 hospitals	402 beds

★0123: COVENANT HEALTH (NP)
100 Fort Sanders West Boulevard, Knoxville, TN, Zip 37922–3353; tel. 865/531–5555; James VanderSteeg, President and Chief Executive Officer
(Centralized Health System)

TENNESSEE: CLAIBORNE MEDICAL CENTER (L, 132 beds) 1850 Old Knoxville Road, Tazewell, TN, Zip 37879–3625; tel. 423/626–4211; Patricia P. Ketterman, R.N., President and Chief Administrative Officer
Web address: www.claibornehospital.org

CUMBERLAND MEDICAL CENTER (O, 85 beds) 421 South Main Street, Crossville, TN, Zip 38555–5031; tel. 931/484–9511; David V. Bunch, President and Chief Administrative Officer
Web address: www.cmchealthcare.org

FORT LOUDOUN MEDICAL CENTER (L, 30 beds) 550 Fort Loudoun Medical Center Drive, Lenoir City, TN, Zip 37772–5673; tel. 865/271–6000; Jeffrey Feike, President and Chief Administrative Officer
Web address: www.covenanthealth.com

FORT SANDERS REGIONAL MEDICAL CENTER (O, 384 beds) 1901 West Clinch Avenue , Knoxville, TN, Zip 37916–2307; tel. 865/541–1111; Keith Altshuler, President and Chief Administrative Officer

LECONTE MEDICAL CENTER (O, 131 beds) 742 Middle Creek Road, Sevierville, TN, Zip 37862–5019, Mailing Address: P.O. Box 8005, Zip 37864–8005, tel. 865/446–7000; Gaye Jolly, FACHE, President and Chief Administrative Officer
Web address: www.lecontemedicalcenter.com

METHODIST MEDICAL CENTER OF OAK RIDGE (O, 210 beds) 990 Oak Ridge Turnpike, Oak Ridge, TN, Zip 37830–6976, Mailing Address: P.O. Box 2529, Zip 37831–2529, tel. 865/835–1000; Jeremy Biggs, President and Chief Administrative Officer
Web address: www.mmcoakridge.com

MORRISTOWN–HAMBLEN HEALTHCARE SYSTEM (O, 131 beds) 908 West Fourth North Street, Morristown, TN, Zip 37814–3894, Mailing Address: P.O. Box 1178, Zip 37816–1178, tel. 423/492–9000; Gordon Lintz, President and Chief Administrative Officer
Web address: www.morristownhamblen.com

PARKWEST MEDICAL CENTER (O, 297 beds) 9352 Park West Boulevard, Knoxville, TN, Zip 37923–4325, Mailing Address: P.O. Box 22993, Zip 37933–0993, tel. 865/373–1000; Neil Heatherly, President and Chief Administrative Officer

ROANE MEDICAL CENTER (O, 52 beds) 8045 Roane Medical Center Dr, Harriman, TN, Zip 37748–8333; tel. 865/316–1000; Jason B. Pilant, President and Chief Administrative Officer
Web address: www.roanemedical.com

Owned, leased, sponsored:	9 hospitals	1452 beds
Contract-managed:	0 hospitals	0 beds
Totals:	9 hospitals	1452 beds

★5885: COVENANT HEALTH (CO)
100 Ames Pond Drive, Suite 102, Tewksbury, MA, Zip 01876–1240; tel. 978/654–6363; David R. Lincoln, FACHE, President and Chief Executive Officer
(Moderately Centralized Health System)

For explanation of codes following names, see page B2.
★ Indicates Type III membership in the American Hospital Association.

MAINE: ST. JOSEPH HOSPITAL (O, 84 beds) 360 Broadway, Bangor, ME, Zip 04401–3979, Mailing Address: P.O. Box 403, Zip 04402–0403, tel. 207/262–1000; Mary Prybylo, President and Chief Executive Officer

ST. MARY'S REGIONAL MEDICAL CENTER (O, 350 beds) 93 Campus Avenue, Lewiston, ME, Zip 04240–6030, Mailing Address: P.O. Box 291, Zip 04243–0291, tel. 207/777–8100; Steven C. Jorgensen, Chief Executive Officer
Web address: www.stmarysmaine.com

NEW HAMPSHIRE: ST. JOSEPH HOSPITAL (O, 135 beds) 172 Kinsley Street, Nashua, NH, Zip 03060–3648; tel. 603/882–3000; John A. Jurczyk, FACHE, Senior Vice President and President

Owned, leased, sponsored:	3 hospitals	569 beds
Contract–managed:	0 hospitals	0 beds
Totals:	3 hospitals	569 beds

★0036: COVENANT HEALTH SYSTEM (NP)

3615 19th Street, Lubbock, TX, Zip 79410–1203; tel. 806/725–0447; Richard H. Parks, FACHE, President and Chief Executive Officer

TEXAS: COVENANT CHILDREN'S HOSPITAL (O, 269 beds) 4015 22nd Place, Lubbock, TX, Zip 79410; tel. 806/725–1011; Amy Thompson, M.D., Chief Executive Officer
Web address: www.covenanthealth.org/About–Us/Facilities/Childrens–Hospital.aspx

COVENANT HOSPITAL PLAINVIEW (L, 68 beds) 2601 Dimmitt Road, Plainview, TX, Zip 79072–1833; tel. 806/296–5531; Clay Taylor, Chief Executive Officer
Web address: www.covenantplainview.org

COVENANT HOSPITAL–LEVELLAND (L, 26 beds) 1900 South College Avenue, Levelland, TX, Zip 79336–6508; tel. 806/894–4963; Bruce White, Administrator
Web address: www.covenanthospitallevelland.com/

COVENANT MEDICAL CENTER (O, 394 beds) 3615 19th Street, Lubbock, TX, Zip 79410–1203, Mailing Address: P.O. Box 1201, Zip 79408–1201, tel. 806/725–0000; Walt Cathey, Chief Executive Officer
Web address: www.covenanthealth.org

COVENANT SPECIALTY HOSPITAL (O, 56 beds) 3815 20th Street, Lubbock, TX, Zip 79410–1235; tel. 806/725–9200; Ely Perea, Director and Chief Executive Officer

GRACE MEDICAL CENTER (O, 43 beds) 2412 50th Street, Lubbock, TX, Zip 79412–2494; tel. 806/788–4100; Vanessa Reasoner, Chief Executive Officer
Web address: www.gracehealthsystem.com

Owned, leased, sponsored:	6 hospitals	856 beds
Contract–managed:	0 hospitals	0 beds
Totals:	6 hospitals	856 beds

0179: COXHEALTH (NP)

1423 North Jefferson Avenue, Springfield, MO, Zip 65802–1988; tel. 417/269–3108; Steven D. Edwards, President and Chief Executive Officer
(Centralized Physician/Insurance Health System)

MISSOURI: COX BARTON COUNTY MEMORIAL HOSPITAL (O, 25 beds) 29 NW First Lane, Lamar, MO, Zip 64759–8105; tel. 417/681–5100; Wendy Duvall, Chief Executive Officer
Web address: www.bcmh.net

COX MEDICAL CENTER BRANSON (O, 120 beds) 251 Skaggs Road, Branson, MO, Zip 65616–2031, Mailing Address: P.O. Box 650, Zip 65615–0650, tel. 417/335–7000; William K. Mahoney, FACHE, President and Chief Executive Officer

COX MEDICAL CENTERS (O, 640 beds) 1423 North Jefferson Street, Springfield, MO, Zip 65802–1988; tel. 417/269–3000; Steven D. Edwards, President and Chief Executive Officer
Web address: www.coxhealth.com

COX MONETT HOSPITAL (O, 25 beds) 801 North Lincoln Avenue, Monett, MO, Zip 65708–1641; tel. 417/235–3144; Darren Bass, President
Web address: www.coxhealth.com

Owned, leased, sponsored:	4 hospitals	810 beds
Contract–managed:	0 hospitals	0 beds
Totals:	4 hospitals	810 beds

0930: CRC HEALTH GROUP, INC. (IO)

20400 Stevens Creek Boulevard, Suite 600, Cupertino, CA, Zip 95014–2217; tel. 866/540–5240; Jerome E. Rhodes, Chief Executive Officer
(Independent Hospital System)

ARIZONA: SIERRA TUCSON (O, 139 beds) 39580 South Lago Del Oro Parkway, Tucson, AZ, Zip 85739–1091; tel. 520/624–4000; Stephen P. Fahey, Executive Director
Web address: www.sierratucson.com

NORTH CAROLINA: WILMINGTON TREATMENT CENTER (O, 44 beds) 2520 Troy Drive, Wilmington, NC, Zip 28401–7643; tel. 910/762–2727; Robert Pitts, Executive Director
Web address: www.wilmtreatment.com

Owned, leased, sponsored:	2 hospitals	183 beds
Contract–managed:	0 hospitals	0 beds
Totals:	2 hospitals	183 beds

0960: CURAE HEALTH (NP)

121 Leinart Street, Clinton, TN, Zip 37716–3632, Mailing Address: P.O. Box 358, Zip 37717–0358, tel. 865/269–4074; Steve Clapp, President and Chief Executive Officer
(Moderately Centralized Health System)

ALABAMA: NORTHWEST MEDICAL CENTER (O, 43 beds) 1530 U S Highway 43, Winfield, AL, Zip 35594–5056; tel. 205/487–7000; Michael D. Windham, Chief Executive Officer
Web address: www.northwestmedcenter.com

RUSSELLVILLE HOSPITAL (O, 92 beds) 15155 Highway 43, Russellville, AL, Zip 35653–1975, Mailing Address: P.O. Box 1089, Zip 35653–1089, tel. 256/332–1611; Christine R. Stewart, FACHE, Chief Executive Officer

FLORIDA: SPECIALTY HOSPITAL JACKSONVILLE (O, 62 beds) 4901 Richard Street, Jacksonville, FL, Zip 32207–7328; tel. 904/737–3120; Barbara McCarthy, Chief Executive Officer
Web address: www.specialtyhospitaljax.com

MISSISSIPPI: GILMORE MEMORIAL HOSPITAL (O, 95 beds) 1105 Earl Frye Boulevard, Amory, MS, Zip 38821–5500, Mailing Address: P.O. Box 459, Zip 38821–0459, tel. 662/256–7111; J Allen. Tyra, Chief Executive

NORTHWEST MISSISSIPPI MEDICAL CENTER (O, 181 beds) 1970 Hospital Drive, Clarksdale, MS, Zip 38614–7202, Mailing Address: P.O. Box 1218, Zip 38614–1218, tel. 662/627–3211; Joel Southern, R.N., MSN, Chief Executive Officer
Web address: www.merithealthnorthwestms.com

PANOLA MEDICAL CENTER (O, 112 beds) 303 Medical Center Drive, Batesville, MS, Zip 38606–8608; tel. 662/563–5611; Travis Sisson, Chief Executive Officer
Web address: www.panolamedicalcenter.org/

Owned, leased, sponsored:	6 hospitals	585 beds
Contract–managed:	0 hospitals	0 beds
Totals:	6 hospitals	585 beds

1013: CURAHEALTH HOSPITALS (IO)

650 Beebalm Lane, Suite 220, Garland, TX, Zip 75040–2955; tel. 972/414–0070; Ken McGee, President and Chief Operating Officer
(Independent Hospital System)

ARIZONA: CURAHEALTH PHOENIX (O, 58 beds) 40 East Indianola Avenue, Phoenix, AZ, Zip 85012–2059; tel. 602/280–7000; Karen Cawley, Chief Executive Officer
Web address: www.curahealth.com

CURAHEALTH TUCSON (O, 51 beds) 355 North Wilmot Road, Tucson, AZ, Zip 85711–2601; tel. 520/584–4500; Camie Overton, Chief Executive Officer

LOUISIANA: CURAHEALTH NEW ORLEANS (O, 80 beds) 3601 Coliseum Street, New Orleans, LA, Zip 70115–3606; tel. 504/899–1555; Richard Daughdrill, R.N., Chief Executive Officer
Web address: www.curahealth.com

For explanation of codes following names, see page B2.
★ Indicates Type III membership in the American Hospital Association.

MASSACHUSETTS: CURAHEALTH HOSPITAL STOUGHTON (O, 111 beds) 909 Sumner Street, 1st Floor, Stoughton, MA, Zip 02072–3396; tel. 781/297–8200; MacGregor Morgan, R.N., Chief Executive Officer

OKLAHOMA: CURAHEALTH HOSPITAL OKLAHOMA CITY (O, 93 beds) 1407 North Robinson Avenue, Oklahoma City, OK, Zip 73103–4823; tel. 405/232–8000; Brenda Hood, Chief Executive Officer
Web address: www.curahealth.com

PENNSYLVANIA: CURAHEALTH HERITAGE VALLEY (O, 35 beds) 1000 Dutch Ridge Road, Beaver, PA, Zip 15009–9727; tel. 724/773–8480; Janie Rosenberger–Slampack, Chief Executive Officer
Web address: www.curahealth.com

CURAHEALTH PITTSBURGH (O, 31 beds) 7777 Steubenville Pike, Oakdale, PA, Zip 15071–3409; tel. 412/494–5500; Carol Falo, RN, BSN, MBA, Chief Executive Officer

TENNESSEE: CURAHEALTH NASHVILLE (O, 58 beds) 1412 County Hospital Road, Nashville, TN, Zip 37218–3007; tel. 615/687–2600; Timothy C. Deaton, Chief Executive Officer
Web address: www.curahealth.com

Owned, leased, sponsored:	8 hospitals	517 beds
Contract–managed:	0 hospitals	0 beds
Totals:	8 hospitals	517 beds

★0864: DAVIS HEALTH SYSTEM (NP)
Reed Street and Gorman Avenue, Elkins, WV, Zip 26241, Mailing Address: P.O. Box 1697, Zip 26241–1697, tel. 304/636–3300; Vance Jackson, FACHE, President and Chief Executive Officer
(Independent Hospital System)

WEST VIRGINIA: BROADDUS HOSPITAL (O, 72 beds) 1 Healthcare Drive, Philippi, WV, Zip 26416–9405, Mailing Address: P.O. Box 930, Zip 26416–0930, tel. 304/457–1760; Dana L. Gould, Chief Executive Officer
Web address: www.davishealthsystem.org/

DAVIS MEDICAL CENTER (O, 80 beds) Gorman Avenue and Reed Street, Elkins, WV, Zip 26241, Mailing Address: P.O. Box 1484, Zip 26241–1484, tel. 304/636–3300; Vance Jackson, FACHE, Chief Executive Officer

Owned, leased, sponsored:	2 hospitals	152 beds
Contract–managed:	0 hospitals	0 beds
Totals:	2 hospitals	152 beds

1825: DCH HEALTH SYSTEM (NP)
809 University Boulevard East, Tuscaloosa, AL, Zip 35401–2029; tel. 205/759–7111; Bryan N. Kindred, FACHE, President and Chief Executive Officer
(Moderately Centralized Health System)

ALABAMA: DCH REGIONAL MEDICAL CENTER (O, 583 beds) 809 University Boulevard East, Tuscaloosa, AL, Zip 35401–2029; tel. 205/759–7111; Paul Betz, FACHE, Administrator

FAYETTE MEDICAL CENTER (L, 167 beds) 1653 Temple Avenue North, Fayette, AL, Zip 35555–1314, Mailing Address: P O Drawer 710, Zip 35555–0710, tel. 205/932–5966; Donald J. Jones, FACHE, Administrator
Web address: www.dchsystem.com

Owned, leased, sponsored:	2 hospitals	750 beds
Contract–managed:	0 hospitals	0 beds
Totals:	2 hospitals	750 beds

★0313: DEACONESS HEALTH SYSTEM (NP)
600 Mary Street, Evansville, IN, Zip 47710–1658; tel. 812/450–5000; Shawn W. McCoy, Chief Executive Officer
(Moderately Centralized Health System)

INDIANA: DEACONESS HOSPITAL (O, 483 beds) 600 Mary Street, Evansville, IN, Zip 47710–1658; tel. 812/450–5000; Shawn W. McCoy, Chief Executive Officer

GIBSON GENERAL HOSPITAL (C, 70 beds) 1808 Sherman Drive, Princeton, IN, Zip 47670–1043; tel. 812/385–3401; Mike Carney, Interim President and Chief Executive Officer
Web address: www.gibsongeneral.com

THE HEART HOSPITAL AT DEACONESS GATEWAY (O, 24 beds) 4007 Gateway Boulevard, Newburgh, IN, Zip 47630–8947; tel. 812/842–4784; Rebecca Malotte, Executive Director and Chief Nursing Officer

THE WOMEN'S HOSPITAL (O, 74 beds) 4199 Gateway Boulevard, Newburgh, IN, Zip 47630–8940; tel. 812/842–4200; Christina M. Ryan, R.N., Chief Executive Officer
Web address: www.deaconess.com

Owned, leased, sponsored:	3 hospitals	581 beds
Contract–managed:	1 hospitals	70 beds
Totals:	4 hospitals	651 beds

9495: DEPARTMENT OF THE AIR FORCE (FG)
1420 Pentagon, Room 4E1084, Washington, DC, Zip 20330–1420; tel. 202/767–4765; Lieutenant General, Thomas Travis, Surgeon General
(Independent Hospital System)

ALASKA: U.S. AIR FORCE REGIONAL HOSPITAL (O, 64 beds) 5955 Zeamer Avenue, Elmendorf AFB, AK, Zip 99506–3702; tel. 907/580–3006; Major, Mark Lamey, Commander

CALIFORNIA: DAVID GRANT USAF MEDICAL CENTER (O, 116 beds) 101 Bodin Circle, Travis AFB, CA, Zip 94535–1809; tel. 707/423–7300; Lieutenant, Michael Higgins, Commander
Web address: www.travis.af.mil/units/dgmc/index.asp

FLORIDA: U.S. AIR FORCE REGIONAL HOSPITAL (O, 57 beds) 307 Boatner Road, Suite 114, Eglin AFB, FL, Zip 32542–1282; tel. 850/883–8221; Colonel, Pamela Smith, Commander

MISSISSIPPI: U.S. AIR FORCE MEDICAL CENTER KEESLER (O, 56 beds) 301 Fisher Street, Room 1A132, Keesler AFB, MS, Zip 39534–2519; tel. 228/376–2550; Colonel, Thomas Harrell, M.D., Commander
Web address: www.keesler.af.mil

NEVADA: MIKE O'CALLAGHAN FEDERAL HOSPITAL (O, 46 beds) 4700 Las Vegas Boulevard North, Suite 2419, Nellis AFB, NV, Zip 89191–6600; tel. 702/653–2000; Colonel, Christian Benjamin, USAF, MC, Commander

OHIO: WRIGHT PATTERSON MEDICAL CENTER (O, 62 beds) 4881 Sugar Maple Drive, Wright–Patterson AFB, OH, Zip 45433–5529; tel. 937/257–9144; Colonel, Brent J. Erickson, Administrator
Web address: www.wpafb.af.mil/units/wpmc/

VIRGINIA: U.S. AIR FORCE HOSPITAL (O, 60 beds) 77 Nealy Avenue, Hampton, VA, Zip 23665–2040; tel. 757/764–6969; Colonel, Susan Pietrykowski, Commander
Web address: www.jble.af.mil

Owned, leased, sponsored:	7 hospitals	461 beds
Contract–managed:	0 hospitals	0 beds
Totals:	7 hospitals	461 beds

9395: DEPARTMENT OF THE ARMY, OFFICE OF THE SURGEON GENERAL (FG)
5109 Leesburg Pike, Falls Church, VA, Zip 22041–3215; tel. 703/681–3000; Lieutenant General, Eric B. Schoomaker, Surgeon General
(Moderately Centralized Health System)

ALASKA: BASSETT ARMY COMMUNITY HOSPITAL (O, 21 beds) 1060 Gaffney Road, Box 7400, Fort Wainwright, AK, Zip 99703–5001, Mailing Address: 1060 Gaffney Road, Box 7440, Zip 99703–5001, tel. 907/361–4000; Timothy Bergeron, Deputy Commander, Administration

CALIFORNIA: WEED ARMY COMMUNITY HOSPITAL (O, 27 beds) Inner Loop Road and 4th Street, Building 166, Fort Irwin, CA, Zip 92310–5065, Mailing Address: P.O. Box 105109, Zip 92310–5109, tel. 760/380–3108; Colonel, Martin Doperak, Commander
Web address: www.irwin.amedd.army.mil

For explanation of codes following names, see page B2.
★ Indicates Type III membership in the American Hospital Association.

Section B

COLORADO: EVANS U.S. ARMY COMMUNITY HOSPITAL (O, 69 beds) 1650 Cochrane Circle, Building 7500, Fort Carson, CO, Zip 80913–4613; tel. 719/526–7200; Colonel, Patrick M. Garman, Commander

GEORGIA: DWIGHT DAVID EISENHOWER ARMY MEDICAL CENTER (O, 107 beds) 300 West Hospital Road, Fort Gordon, GA, Zip 30905–5741; tel. 706/787–5811; Colonel, John P. Lamoureux, Commander
Web address: www.ddeamc.amedd.army.mil

MARTIN ARMY COMMUNITY HOSPITAL (O, 57 beds) 7950 Martin Loop, Fort Benning, GA, Zip 31905–5648, Mailing Address: 7950 Martin Loop, B9200, Room 010, Zip 31905–5648, tel. 706/544–2516; Colonel, Marie Dominguez, Commander
Web address: www.martin.amedd.army.mil

WINN ARMY COMMUNITY HOSPITAL (O, 37 beds) 1061 Harmon Avenue, Hinesville, GA, Zip 31314–5641, Mailing Address: 1061 Harmon Avenue, Suite 2311B, Zip 31314–5641, tel. 912/435–6965; Colonel, Kirk W. Eggleston, Commanding Officer
Web address: www.winn.amedd.army.mil/

HAWAII: TRIPLER ARMY MEDICAL CENTER (O, 194 beds) 1 Jarret White Road, Honolulu, HI, Zip 96859–5001; tel. 808/433–6661; Colonel, Mary Krueger, Commanding Officer

KANSAS: IRWIN ARMY COMMUNITY HOSPITAL (O, 44 beds) 600 Caisson Hill Road, Junction City, KS, Zip 66442–7037; tel. 785/239–7000; Colonel, Risa Ware, Commander
Web address: www.iach.amedd.army.mil

KENTUCKY: COLONEL FLORENCE A. BLANCHFIELD ARMY COMMUNITY HOSPITAL (O, 66 beds) 650 Joel Drive, Fort Campbell, KY, Zip 42223–5318; tel. 270/798–8040; Colonel, Telita Crosland, Commander
Web address: www.campbell.amedd.army.mil/

LOUISIANA: BAYNE–JONES ARMY COMMUNITY HOSPITAL (O, 13 beds) 1585 3rd Street, Fort Polk, LA, Zip 71459–5102; tel. 337/531–3928; Colonel, Marla J. Ferguson, Commanding Officer

MARSHALL ISLANDS: KWAJALEIN HOSPITAL (O, 14 beds) U S Army Kwajalein Atoll, Kwajalein Island, MH, Zip 96960, Mailing Address: Box 1702, APO, UNIT, Zip 96555–5000, tel. 805/355–2225; Elaine McMahon, Administrator

MISSOURI: GENERAL LEONARD WOOD ARMY COMMUNITY HOSPITAL (O, 46 beds) 4430 Missouri Avenue, Fort Leonard Wood, MO, Zip 65473–8952, Mailing Address: PO Box 4430, Zip 65473–8952, tel. 573/596–0414; Colonel, Kimberlie Biever, Hospital Commander
Web address: www.glwach.amedd.army.mil/

NEW YORK: KELLER ARMY COMMUNITY HOSPITAL (O, 16 beds) 900 Washington Road, West Point, NY, Zip 10996–1197, Mailing Address: U S Military Academy, Building 900, Zip 10996–1197, tel. 845/938–5169; Colonel, Eric B. Sones, Commander

NORTH CAROLINA: WOMACK ARMY MEDICAL CENTER (O, 156 beds) 2817 Reilly Road, Fort Bragg, NC, Zip 28310–7302; tel. 910/907–6000; Colonel, Lance C. Raney, Commander
Web address: www.wamc.amedd.army.mil/

SOUTH CAROLINA: MONCRIEF ARMY COMMUNITY HOSPITAL (O, 60 beds) 4500 Stuart Street, Fort Jackson, SC, Zip 29207–5700; tel. 803/751–2160; Colonel, Traci Crawford, R.N., Commander
Web address: www.moncrief.amedd.army.mil

TEXAS: BROOKE ARMY MEDICAL CENTER (O, 226 beds) 3851 Roger Brookes Drive, Fort Sam Houston, TX, Zip 78234–4501; tel. 210/916–4141; Brigadier General, Jeffrey Johnson, Commander
Web address: www.bamc.amedd.army.mil

CARL R. DARNALL ARMY MEDICAL CENTER (O, 109 beds) 36000 Darnall Loop, Fort Hood, TX, Zip 76544–5095; tel. 254/288–8000; Colonel, David R. Gibson, Chief Executive Officer

WILLIAM BEAUMONT ARMY MEDICAL CENTER (O, 209 beds) 5005 North Piedras Street, El Paso, TX, Zip 79920–5001; tel. 915/742–2121; Colonel, Erik G. Rude, Commander
Web address: https://www.wbamc.amedd.army.mil/NewPersonnel/CDR.aspx

VIRGINIA: FORT BELVOIR COMMUNITY HOSPITAL (O, 46 beds) 9300 Dewitt Loop, Fort Belvoir, VA, Zip 22060–5285; tel. 571/231–3224; Colonel, Jason S. Wieman, Director

WASHINGTON: MADIGAN ARMY MEDICAL CENTER (O, 200 beds) Fitzsimmons Drive, Building 9040, Tacoma, WA, Zip 98431–1100; tel. 253/968–1110; Colonel, Thomas S. Bundt, Commanding Officer
Web address: www.mamc.health.mil/

Owned, leased, sponsored:	20 hospitals	1717 beds
Contract–managed:	0 hospitals	0 beds
Totals:	20 hospitals	1717 beds

9295: DEPARTMENT OF VETERANS AFFAIRS (FG)
P.O. Box 1000, Bldg 101, Room 41, Perry Point, MD, Zip 21902, Mailing Address: 810 Vermont Avenue NW, Washington, DC, Zip 20420, tel. 202/273–5781; Honorable, Robert Wilkie, Secretary

(Decentralized Health System)

ALABAMA: BIRMINGHAM VETERANS AFFAIRS MEDICAL CENTER (O, 151 beds) 700 South 19th Street, Birmingham, AL, Zip 35233–1927; tel. 205/933–8101; Thomas C. Smith III, FACHE, Director
Web address: www.birmingham.va.gov/

CENTRAL ALABAMA VETERANS HEALTH CARE SYSTEM (O, 245 beds) 215 Perry Hill Road, Montgomery, AL, Zip 36109–3798; tel. 334/272–4670; Linda Lake . Boyle, R.N., MSN, Director
Web address: www.centralalabama.va.gov/

TUSCALOOSA VETERANS AFFAIRS MEDICAL CENTER (O, 305 beds) 3701 Loop Road East, Tuscaloosa, AL, Zip 35404–5015; tel. 205/554–2000; John F. Merkle, Medical Center Director
Web address: www.tuscaloosa.va.gov

ARIZONA: NORTHERN ARIZONA VETERANS AFFAIRS HEALTH CARE SYSTEM (O, 147 beds) 500 Highway 89 North, Prescott, AZ, Zip 86313–5000; tel. 928/445–4860; Malcolm Keith. Piatt, M.D., Interim Director

PHOENIX VETERANS AFFAIRS HEALTH CARE SYSTEM (O, 197 beds) 650 East Indian School Road, Phoenix, AZ, Zip 85012–1892; tel. 602/277–5551; RimaAnn O. Nelson, R.N., Director
Web address: www.phoenix.va.gov/

SOUTHERN ARIZONA VETERANS AFFAIRS HEALTH CARE SYSTEM (O, 328 beds) 3601 Sout 6th Avenue, Tucson, AZ, Zip 85723–0002, Mailing Address: 3601 South 6th Avenue, Zip 85723–0002, tel. 520/792–1450; William J. Caron, Director
Web address: www.tucson.va.gov

ARKANSAS: CENTRAL ARKANSAS VETERANS HEALTHCARE SYSTEM (O, 637 beds) 4300 West Seventh Street, Little Rock, AR, Zip 72205–5446; tel. 501/257–1000; Margie A. Scott, M.D., Director

VETERANS HEALTH CARE SYSTEM OF THE OZARKS (O, 72 beds) 1100 North College Avenue, Fayetteville, AR, Zip 72703–1944; tel. 479/443–4301; Kelvin L. Parks, Interim Director
Web address: www.fayettevillear.va.gov

CALIFORNIA: SAN FRANCISCO VA MEDICAL CENTER (O, 241 beds) 4150 Clement Street, San Francisco, CA, Zip 94121–1545; tel. 415/221–4810; Bonnie S. Graham, Director

VA GREATER LOS ANGELES HEALTHCARE SYSTEM (O, 1087 beds) 11301 Wilshire Boulevard, Los Angeles, CA, Zip 90073–1003; tel. 310/478–3711; Ann R. Brown, M.D., Director
Web address: www.losangeles.va.gov/

VA LONG BEACH HEALTHCARE SYSTEM (O, 358 beds) 5901 East 7th Street, Long Beach, CA, Zip 90822–5201; tel. 562/826–8000; Walt Dannenberg, Director

VA PALO ALTO HEALTH CARE SYSTEM (O, 808 beds) 3801 Miranda Avenue, Palo Alto, CA, Zip 94304–1207; tel. 650/493–5000; Thomas J. Fitzgerald III, Interim Director
Web address: www.paloalto.va.gov/

VA SAN DIEGO HEALTHCARE SYSTEM (O, 248 beds) 3350 LaJolla Village Drive, San Diego, CA, Zip 92161–0002; tel. 858/552–8585; Robert M. Smith, M.D., Director
Web address: www.sandiego.va.gov

VETERANS AFFAIRS CENTRAL CALIFORNIA HEALTH CARE SYSTEM (O, 117 beds) 2615 East Clinton Avenue, Fresno, CA, Zip 93703–2223; tel. 559/225–6100; Stephen R. Bauman, Medical Center Director

---

For explanation of codes following names, see page B2.
★ Indicates Type III membership in the American Hospital Association.

VETERANS AFFAIRS LOMA LINDA HEALTHCARE SYSTEM (O, 268 beds) 11201 Benton Street, Loma Linda, CA, Zip 92357–1000; tel. 909/825–7084; Andrew Welch, Interim Director
Web address: www.lomalinda.va.gov

COLORADO: GRAND JUNCTION VETERANS HEALTH CARE SYSTEM (O, 23 beds) 2121 North Avenue, Grand Junction, CO, Zip 81501–6428; tel. 970/242–0731; Michael T. Kilmer, DirectorSOUTHERN COLORADO HEALTHCARE SYSTEM (O, 299 beds)Las AnimasCO81054–0390719456–1260StuartCCollyer5139873Director

VETERANS AFFAIRS EASTERN COLORADO HEALTH CARE SYSTEM (O, 271 beds) 1055 Clermont Street, Denver, CO, Zip 80220–3877; tel. 303/399–8020; Sallie Houser-Hanfelder, FACHE, Director
Web address: www.denver.va.gov/

CONNECTICUT: VETERANS AFFAIRS CONNECTICUT HEALTHCARE SYSTEM (O, 197 beds) 950 Campbell Avenue, West Haven, CT, Zip 06516–2770; tel. 203/932–5711; Gerald F. Culliton, Medical Center Director
Web address: www.connecticut.va.gov

DELAWARE: WILMINGTON VETERANS AFFAIRS MEDICAL CENTER (O, 60 beds) 1601 Kirkwood Highway, Wilmington, DE, Zip 19805–4989; tel. 302/994–2511; Robert W. Callahan Jr, Interim Director

DISTRICT OF COLUMBIA: WASHINGTON DC VETERANS AFFAIRS MEDICAL CENTER (O, 291 beds) 50 Irving Street NW, Washington, DC, Zip 20422–0002; tel. 202/745–8000; Adam M. Robinson, Acting Director
Web address: www.washingtondc.va.gov/

FLORIDA: BAY PINES VETERANS AFFAIRS HEALTHCARE SYSTEM (O, 396 beds) 10000 Bay Pines Boulevard, Bay Pines, FL, Zip 33744–8200, Mailing Address: P.O. Box 5005, Zip 33744–5005, tel. 727/398–6661; Suzanne M. Klinker, Director

JAMES A. HALEY VETERANS' HOSPITAL–TAMPA (O, 499 beds) 13000 Bruce B Downs Boulevard, Tampa, FL, Zip 33612–4745; tel. 813/972–2000; Joe Battle, Director
Web address: www.tampa.va.gov/

MIAMI VETERANS AFFAIRS HEALTHCARE SYSTEM (O, 401 beds) 1201 NW 16th Street, Miami, FL, Zip 33125–1624; tel. 305/575–7000; Paul M. Russo, FACHE, Director

NORTH FLORIDA/SOUTH GEORGIA VETERAN'S HEALTH SYSTEM (O, 623 beds) 1601 SW Archer Road, Gainesville, FL, Zip 32608–1135; tel. 352/376–1611; Thomas Wisnieski, FACHE, Director
Web address: www.northflorida.va.gov

WEST PALM BEACH VETERANS AFFAIRS MEDICAL CENTER (O, 300 beds) 7305 North Military Trail, West Palm Beach, FL, Zip 33410–6400; tel. 561/422–8262; Donna Katen-Bahensky, Director
Web address: www.westpalmbeach.va.gov/

GEORGIA: ATLANTA VETERANS AFFAIRS MEDICAL CENTER (O, 239 beds) 1670 Clairmont Road, Decatur, GA, Zip 30033–4004; tel. 404/321–6111; Annette Walker, Director
Web address: www.atlanta.va.gov/

CARL VINSON VETERANS AFFAIRS MEDICAL CENTER (O, 178 beds) 1826 Veterans Boulevard, Dublin, GA, Zip 31021–3620; tel. 478/272–1210; David VanMeter, Interim Director
Web address: www.dublin.va.gov/

CHARLIE NORWOOD VETERANS AFFAIRS MEDICAL CENTER (O, 338 beds) 1 Freedom Way, Augusta, GA, Zip 30904–6285; tel. 706/733–0188; Robin E. Jackson, Ph.D., Interim Acting Director
Web address: www.augusta.va.gov/

HAWAII: VETERANS AFFAIRS PACIFIC ISLANDS HEALTH CARE SYSTEM (O, 80 beds) 459 Patterson Road, Honolulu, HI, Zip 96819–1522; tel. 808/433–0600; Jennifer S. Gutowski, FACHE, Director

IDAHO: BOISE VETERANS AFFAIRS MEDICAL CENTER (O, 100 beds) 500 West Fort Street, Boise, ID, Zip 83702–4598; tel. 208/422–1000; David P. Wood, FACHE, Director
Web address: www.boise.va.gov/

ILLINOIS: CAPTAIN JAMES A. LOVELL FEDERAL HEALTH CARE CENTER (O, 314 beds) 3001 Green Bay Road, North Chicago, IL, Zip 60064–3049; tel. 847/688–1900; Daniel Zomcheck, Interim Director
Web address: www.lovell.fhcc.va.gov

EDWARD HINES, JR. VETERANS AFFAIRS HOSPITAL (O, 485 beds) 5000 South Fifth Avenue, Hines, IL, Zip 60141–3030, Mailing Address: P.O. Box 5000, Zip 60141–5000, tel. 708/202–8387; Steven E. Braverman, M.D., Director

JESSE BROWN VETERANS AFFAIRS MEDICAL CENTER (O, 207 beds) 820 South Damen, Chicago, IL, Zip 60612–3776; tel. 312/569–8387; Marc Magill, MS, Medical Center Director
Web address: www.chicago.va.gov/

MARION VETERANS AFFAIRS MEDICAL CENTER (O, 99 beds) 2401 West Main Street, Marion, IL, Zip 62959–1188; tel. 618/997–5311; Jo-Ann M. Ginsberg, R.N., MSN, Director

VETERANS AFFAIRS ILLIANA HEALTH CARE SYSTEM (O, 221 beds) 1900 East Main Street, Danville, IL, Zip 61832–5198; tel. 217/554–3000; Diana Carranza, Interim Director
Web address: www.danville.va.gov/

INDIANA: RICHARD L. ROUDEBUSH VETERANS AFFAIRS MEDICAL CENTER (O, 209 beds) 1481 West Tenth Street, Indianapolis, IN, Zip 46202–2884; tel. 317/554–0000; Brian Hancock, M.D., Director
Web address: www.indianapolis.va.gov

VETERANS AFFAIRS NORTHERN INDIANA HEALTH CARE SYSTEM (O, 217 beds) 2121 Lake Avenue, Fort Wayne, IN, Zip 46805–5100; tel. 260/426–5431; Michael Hershmann, Medical Center Director

IOWA: IOWA CITY VETERANS AFFAIRS HEALTH CARE SYSTEM (O, 78 beds) 601 Highway 6 West, Iowa City, IA, Zip 52246–2208; tel. 319/338–0581; Judith Johnson-Mekota, Director
Web address: www.iowacity.va.gov/

VETERANS AFFAIRS CENTRAL IOWA HEALTH CARE SYSTEM (O, 220 beds) 3600 30th Street, Des Moines, IA, Zip 50310–5753; tel. 515/699–5999; Gail L. Graham, Director
Web address: www.centraliowa.va.gov/

KANSAS: ROBERT J. DOLE VETERANS AFFAIRS MEDICAL CENTER (O, 41 beds) 5500 East Kellogg, Wichita, KS, Zip 67218–1607; tel. 316/685–2221; Rick Ament, Chief Executive Officer

VETERANS AFFAIRS EASTERN KANSAS HEALTH CARE SYSTEM (O, 213 beds) 2200 South West Gage Boulevard, Topeka, KS, Zip 66622–0002; tel. 785/350–3111; Anthony Rudy. Klopfer, FACHE, Director
Web address: www.topeka.va.gov/

KENTUCKY: LEXINGTON VETERANS AFFAIRS MEDICAL CENTER (O, 168 beds) 1101 Veterans Drive, Lexington, KY, Zip 40502–2235; tel. 859/281–4901; Emma Metcalf, MSN, R.N., Director
Web address: www.lexington.va.gov/

ROBLEY REX VETERANS AFFAIRS MEDICAL CENTER (O, 116 beds) 800 Zorn Avenue, Louisville, KY, Zip 40206–1499; tel. 502/287–4000; Marylee Rothschild, MD, Chief of Staff

LOUISIANA: ALEXANDRIA VETERANS AFFAIRS HEALTH CARE SYSTEM (O, 143 beds) 2495 Shreveport Highway, 71 N, Pineville, LA, Zip 71360–4044, Mailing Address: P.O. Box 69004, Alexandria, Zip 71306–9004, tel. 318/473–0010; Peter C. Dancy Jr, Director
Web address: www.alexandria.va.gov/

OVERTON BROOKS VETERANS AFFAIRS MEDICAL CENTER (O, 100 beds) 510 East Stoner Avenue, Shreveport, LA, Zip 71101–4295; tel. 318/221–8411; Richard Crockett, Director
Web address: www.shreveport.va.gov/

MAINE: MAINE VETERANS AFFAIRS MEDICAL CENTER (O, 167 beds) 1 VA Center, Augusta, ME, Zip 04330–6719; tel. 207/623–8411; Ryan S. Lilly, Director

MARYLAND: VETERANS AFFAIRS MARYLAND HEALTH CARE SYSTEM–BALTIMORE DIVISION (O, 727 beds) 10 North Greene Street, Baltimore, MD, Zip 21201–1524; tel. 410/605–7001; Adam M. Robinson, Director
Web address: www.maryland.va.gov/

MASSACHUSETTS: BEDFORD VETERANS AFFAIRS MEDICAL CENTER, EDITH NOURSE ROGERS MEMORIAL VETERANS HOSPITAL (O, 461 beds) 200 Springs Road, Bedford, MA, Zip 01730–1198; tel. 781/687–2000; Joan Clifford, R.N., FACHE, Director

VETERANS AFFAIRS BOSTON HEALTHCARE SYSTEM BROCKTON DIVISION (O, 375 beds) 940 Belmont Street, Brockton, MA, Zip 02301–5596; tel. 508/583–4500; Vincent Ng, Director
Web address: www.boston.va.gov/

For explanation of codes following names, see page B2.
★ Indicates Type III membership in the American Hospital Association.

VETERANS AFFAIRS BOSTON HEALTHCARE SYSTEM (O, 361 beds) 1400 VFW Parkway, West Roxbury, MA, Zip 02132–4927; tel. 617/323–7700; Vincent Ng, Director
Web address: www.boston.va.gov/

VETERANS AFFAIRS CENTRAL WESTERN MASSACHUSETTS HEALTHCARE SYSTEM (O, 117 beds) 421 North Main Street, Leeds, MA, Zip 01053–9764; tel. 413/582–3000; John P. Collins, FACHE, Medical Center Director

MICHIGAN: ALEDA E. LUTZ VETERANS AFFAIRS MEDICAL CENTER (O, 89 beds) 1500 Weiss Street, Saginaw, MI, Zip 48602–5298; tel. 989/497–2500; Karandeep Sraon, Interim Director
Web address: www.saginaw.va.gov/

BATTLE CREEK VETERANS AFFAIRS MEDICAL CENTER (O, 242 beds) 5500 Armstrong Road, Battle Creek, MI, Zip 49037–7314; tel. 269/966–5600; Ketan Shah, M.D., Acting Director

JOHN D. DINGELL VETERANS AFFAIRS MEDICAL CENTER (O, 216 beds) 4646 John 'R' Street, Detroit, MI, Zip 48201–1932; tel. 313/576–1000; Pamela J. Reeves, M.D., Director
Web address: www.detroit.va.gov/

OSCAR G. JOHNSON VETERANS AFFAIRS MEDICAL CENTER (O, 17 beds) 325 East 'H' Street, Iron Mountain, MI, Zip 49801–4792; tel. 906/774–3300; James W. Rice, Director

VETERANS AFFAIRS ANN ARBOR HEALTHCARE SYSTEM (O, 109 beds) 2215 Fuller Road, Ann Arbor, MI, Zip 48105–2399; tel. 734/769–7100; Andrew Pacyna, Acting Director
Web address: www.annarbor.va.gov

MINNESOTA: MINNEAPOLIS VETERANS AFFAIRS HEALTH CARE SYSTEM (O, 309 beds) One Veterans Drive, Minneapolis, MN, Zip 55417–2399; tel. 612/725–2000; Patrick J. Kelly, FACHE, Director

ST. CLOUD VETERANS AFFAIRS HEALTH CARE SYSTEM (O, 388 beds) 4801 Veterans Drive, Saint Cloud, MN, Zip 56303–2099; tel. 320/252–1670; Stephen Black, MS, Health Care System Director
Web address: www.stcloud.va.gov

MISSISSIPPI: G.V. (SONNY) MONTGOMERY VETERANS AFFAIRS MEDICAL CENTER (O, 323 beds) 1500 East Woodrow Wilson Drive, Jackson, MS, Zip 39216–5199; tel. 601/362–4471; David M. Walker, M.D., Medical Center Director
Web address: www.jackson.va.gov/

VETERANS AFFAIRS GULF COAST VETERANS HEALTH CARE SYSTEM (O, 392 beds) 400 Veterans Avenue, Biloxi, MS, Zip 39531–2410; tel. 228/523–5000; Christopher M. Saslo, Acting Director

MISSOURI: HARRY S. TRUMAN MEMORIAL VETERANS HOSPITAL (O, 126 beds) 800 Hospital Drive, Columbia, MO, Zip 65201–5275; tel. 573/814–6000; David Isaacks, Director
Web address: www.columbiamo.va.gov

JOHN J. PERSHING VETERANS AFFAIRS MEDICAL CENTER (O, 58 beds) 1500 North Westwood Boulevard, Poplar Bluff, MO, Zip 63901–3318; tel. 573/686–4151; Patricia Hall, MSN, Ph.D., R.N., Director

KANSAS CITY VETERANS AFFAIRS MEDICAL CENTER (O, 157 beds) 4801 East Linwood Boulevard, Kansas City, MO, Zip 64128–2226; tel. 816/861–4700; Kathleen R. Fogarty, MS, Director
Web address: www.kansascity.va.gov/

VETERANS AFFAIRS ST. LOUIS HEALTH CARE SYSTEM (O, 356 beds) 915 North Grand, Saint Louis, MO, Zip 63106–1621; tel. 314/652–4100; Keith D. Repko, Director

MONTANA: VETERANS AFFAIRS MONTANA HEALTH CARE SYSTEM (O, 94 beds) 3687 Veterans Drive, Fort Harrison, MT, Zip 59636–9703, Mailing Address: P.O. Box 1500, Zip 59636–1500, tel. 406/442–6410; Kathy Berger, R.N., Director
Web address: www.montana.va.gov/

NEBRASKA: VETERANS AFFAIRS NEBRASKA–WESTERN IOWA HEALTH CARE SYSTEM – LINCOLN (O, 132 beds) 600 South 70th Street, Lincoln, NE, Zip 68510–2493; tel. 402/489–3802; Don Burman, Director
Web address: www.nebraska.va.gov/

VETERANS AFFAIRS NEBRASKA–WESTERN IOWA HEALTH CARE SYSTEM (O, 137 beds) 4101 Woolworth Avenue, Omaha, NE, Zip 68105–1873; tel. 402/346–8800; Don Burman, Director
Web address: www.nebraska.va.gov/

NEVADA: VETERANS AFFAIRS SIERRA NEVADA HEALTH CARE SYSTEM (O, 124 beds) 975 Kirman Avenue, Reno, NV, Zip 89502–0993; tel. 775/786–7200; Lisa M. Howard, Director
Web address: www.reno.va.gov/

VETERANS AFFAIRS SOUTHERN NEVADA HEALTHCARE SYSTEM (O, 90 beds) 6900 North Pecos Road, North Las Vegas, NV, Zip 89086–4400; tel. 702/791–9000; Peggy W. Kearns, MS, FACHE, Executive Director

NEW HAMPSHIRE: MANCHESTER VETERANS AFFAIRS MEDICAL CENTER (O, 41 beds) 718 Smyth Road, Manchester, NH, Zip 03104–4098; tel. 603/624–4366; Alfred Montoya, Director
Web address: www.manchester.va.gov/

NEW JERSEY: VETERANS AFFAIRS NEW JERSEY HEALTH CARE SYSTEM (O, 429 beds) 385 Tremont Avenue, East Orange, NJ, Zip 07018–1095; tel. 973/676–1000; Vincent F. Immiti, FACHE, Director
Web address: www.newjersey.va.gov/

NEW MEXICO: NEW MEXICO VETERANS AFFAIRS HEALTH CARE SYSTEM – RAYMOND G. MURPHY MEDICAL CENTER (O, 203 beds) 1501 San Pedro SE, Albuquerque, NM, Zip 87108–5153; tel. 505/265–1711; Andrew Welch, Director
Web address: www.albuquerque.va.gov/

NEW YORK: ALBANY STRATTON VETERANS AFFAIRS MEDICAL CENTER (O, 121 beds) 113 Holland Avenue, Albany, NY, Zip 12208–3473; tel. 518/626–5000; Darlene DeLancey, Interim Director
Web address: www.albany.va.gov/

BATH VETERANS AFFAIRS MEDICAL CENTER (O, 274 beds) 76 Veterans Avenue, Bath, NY, Zip 14810–0842; tel. 607/664–4000; Kenneth P. Piazza, Medical Center Director

CANANDAIGUA VETERANS AFFAIRS MEDICAL CENTER (O, 196 beds) 400 Fort Hill Avenue, Canandaigua, NY, Zip 14424–1159; tel. 585/394–2000; Kenneth P. Piazza, Medical Center Director
Web address: www.canandaigua.va.gov/

JAMES J. PETERS VETERANS AFFAIRS MEDICAL CENTER (O, 378 beds) 130 West Kingsbridge Road, Bronx, NY, Zip 10468–3904; tel. 718/584–9000; Erik Langhoff, M.D., Ph.D., Director

NORTHPORT VETERANS AFFAIRS MEDICAL CENTER (O, 254 beds) 79 Middleville Road, Northport, NY, Zip 11768–2200; tel. 631/261–4400; D. Scott. Guermonprez, FACHE, Director
Web address: www.northport.va.gov/index.asp

SYRACUSE VETERANS AFFAIRS MEDICAL CENTER (O, 160 beds) 800 Irving Avenue, Syracuse, NY, Zip 13210–2716; tel. 315/425–4400; Judy A. Hayman, Ph.D., Director

VETERANS AFFAIRS HUDSON VALLEY HEALTH CARE SYSTEM (O, 272 beds) 2094 Albany Post Road, Montrose, NY, Zip 10548–1454, Mailing Address: P.O. Box 100, Zip 10548–0100, tel. 914/737–4400; Margaret B. Caplan, Director
Web address: www.hudsonvalley.va.gov/

VETERANS AFFAIRS NEW YORK HARBOR HEALTHCARE SYSTEM (O, 522 beds) 800 Poly Place, Brooklyn, NY, Zip 11209–7104; tel. 718/630–3500; Martina A. Parauda, Director

VETERANS AFFAIRS WESTERN NEW YORK HEALTHCARE SYSTEM–BATAVIA DIVISION (O, 128 beds) 222 Richmond Avenue, Batavia, NY, Zip 14020–1288; tel. 585/297–1000; Michael J. Swartz, FACHE, Interim Director
Web address: www.buffalo.va.gov/batavia.asp

VETERANS AFFAIRS WESTERN NEW YORK HEALTHCARE SYSTEM–BUFFALO DIVISION (O, 113 beds) 3495 Bailey Avenue, Buffalo, NY, Zip 14215–1129; tel. 716/834–9200; Brian G. Stiller, Director Medical Center

NORTH CAROLINA: CHARLES GEORGE VETERANS AFFAIRS MEDICAL CENTER (O, 174 beds) 1100 Tunnel Road, Asheville, NC, Zip 28805–2087; tel. 828/298–7911; Cynthia Breyfogle, FACHE, Director
Web address: www.asheville.va.gov/

DURHAM VETERANS AFFAIRS MEDICAL CENTER (O, 251 beds) 508 Fulton Street, Durham, NC, Zip 27705–3897; tel. 919/286–0411; Paul Crews, Director
Web address: www.durham.va.gov/

FAYETTEVILLE VETERANS AFFAIRS MEDICAL CENTER (O, 58 beds) 2300 Ramsey Street, Fayetteville, NC, Zip 28301–3899; tel. 910/488–2120; Elizabeth Goolsby, Director
Web address: www.fayettevillenc.va.gov

W. G. (BILL) HEFFNER VETERANS AFFAIRS MEDICAL CENTER (O, 171 beds) 1601 Brenner Avenue, Salisbury, NC, Zip 28144–2559; tel. 704/638–9000; Joseph Vaughn, Director
Web address: www.salisbury.va.gov

For explanation of codes following names, see page B2.
★ Indicates Type III membership in the American Hospital Association.

NORTH DAKOTA: FARGO VETERANS AFFAIRS HEALTH CARE SYSTEM (O, 72 beds) 2101 Elm Street North, Fargo, ND, Zip 58102; tel. 701/232–3241; Lavonne Liversage, Director

OHIO: CHILLICOTHE VETERANS AFFAIRS MEDICAL CENTER (O, 295 beds) 17273 State Route 104, Chillicothe, OH, Zip 45601–9718; tel. 740/773–1141; Mark Murdock, FACHE, Director
Web address: www.chillicothe.va.gov/

CINCINNATI VETERANS AFFAIRS MEDICAL CENTER (O, 268 beds) 3200 Vine Street, Cincinnati, OH, Zip 45220–2288; tel. 513/475–6300; Colonel, Vivian T. Hutson, Director
Web address: www.cincinnati.va.gov/

DAYTON VETERANS AFFAIRS MEDICAL CENTER (O, 486 beds) 4100 West Third Street, Dayton, OH, Zip 45428–9000; tel. 937/268–6511; James Hardy, D.O., Chief Executive Officer
Web address: www.dayton.va.gov/

LOUIS STOKES CLEVELAND VETERANS AFFAIRS MEDICAL CENTER (O, 578 beds) 10701 East Boulevard, Cleveland, OH, Zip 44106–1702; tel. 216/791–3800; Susan Fuehrer, Director

OKLAHOMA: JACK C. MONTGOMERY VETERANS AFFAIRS MEDICAL CENTER (O, 99 beds) 1011 Honor Heights Drive, Muskogee, OK, Zip 74401–1318; tel. 918/577–3000; Mark E. Morgan, Medical Center Director
Web address: www.muskogee.va.gov

OKLAHOMA CITY VETERANS AFFAIRS MEDICAL CENTER (O, 192 beds) 921 NE 13th Street, Oklahoma City, OK, Zip 73104–5028; tel. 405/456–1000; Kristopher Wade. Vlosich, Director
Web address: www.oklahoma.va.gov

OREGON: SOUTHERN OREGON–WHITE CITY VETERANS AFFAIRS REHABILITATION CENTER AND CLINICS (O, 1075 beds) 8495 Crater Lake Highway, White City, OR, Zip 97503; tel. 503/826–2111; Frank A. Drake, Director

VA PORTLAND HEALTHCARE SYSTEM (O, 303 beds) 3710 SW U S Veterans Hospital Road, Portland, OR, Zip 97239–2964, Mailing Address: 3710 SW US Veterans Hospital Road, Zip 97207–1034, tel. 503/220–8262; Michael W. Fisher, Director
Web address: www.portland.va.gov/

VETERANS AFFAIRS ROSEBURG HEALTHCARE SYSTEM (O, 88 beds) 913 NW Garden Valley Boulevard, Roseburg, OR, Zip 97471–6513; tel. 541/440–1000; Douglas V. Paxton, Director

PENNSYLVANIA: COATESVILLE VETERANS AFFAIRS MEDICAL CENTER (O, 118 beds) 1400 Black Horse Hill Road, Coatesville, PA, Zip 19320–2040; tel. 610/384–7711; Carla Sivek, Director
Web address: www.coatesville.va.gov/

ERIE VETERANS AFFAIRS MEDICAL CENTER (O, 52 beds) 135 East 38th Street, Erie, PA, Zip 16504–1559; tel. 814/860–2576; John Gennaro, FACHE, Director

JAMES E. VAN ZANDT VETERANS AFFAIRS MEDICAL CENTER (O, 68 beds) 2907 Pleasant Valley Boulevard, Altoona, PA, Zip 16602–4305; tel. 877/626–2500; Sigrid Andrew, Director
Web address: www.altoona.va.gov/

LEBANON VETERANS AFFAIRS MEDICAL CENTER (O, 213 beds) 1700 South Lincoln Avenue, Lebanon, PA, Zip 17042–7529; tel. 717/272–6621; Margaret G. Wilson, R.N., MSN, Acting Director
Web address: www.lebanon.va.gov

PHILADELPHIA VETERANS AFFAIRS MEDICAL CENTER (O, 317 beds) 3900 Woodland Avenue, Philadelphia, PA, Zip 19104–4594; tel. 215/823–5800; Daniel Hendee, Director
Web address: www.philadelphia.va.gov/

VETERANS AFFAIRS PITTSBURGH HEALTHCARE SYSTEM (O, 549 beds) University Drive, Pittsburgh, PA, Zip 15240–1001; tel. 866/482–7488; Karin L. McGraw, MSN, FACHE, Director

WILKES–BARRE VETERANS AFFAIRS MEDICAL CENTER (O, 146 beds) 1111 East End Boulevard, Wilkes-Barre, PA, Zip 18711–0030; tel. 570/824–3521; Russell E. Lloyd, Director
Web address: www.va.gov/vamcwb

PUERTO RICO: VETERANS AFFAIRS CARIBBEAN HEALTHCARE SYSTEM (O, 330 beds) 10 Casia Street, San Juan, PR, Zip 00921–3201; tel. 787/641–7582; Antonio Sanchez, M.D., Acting Director
Web address: www.caribbean.va.gov/

RHODE ISLAND: PROVIDENCE VETERANS AFFAIRS MEDICAL CENTER (O, 73 beds) 830 Chalkstone Avenue, Providence, RI, Zip 02908–4799; tel. 401/273–7100; Susan Mackenzie, Ph.D., Medical Center Director

SOUTH CAROLINA: RALPH H. JOHNSON VETERANS AFFAIRS MEDICAL CENTER (O, 98 beds) 109 Bee Street, Charleston, SC, Zip 29401–5799; tel. 843/577–5011; Scott R. Isaacks, FACHE, Director and Chief Executive Officer
Web address: www.charleston.va.gov/

WM. JENNINGS BRYAN DORN VETERANS AFFAIRS MEDICAL CENTER (O, 216 beds) 6439 Garners Ferry Road, Columbia, SC, Zip 29209–1639; tel. 803/776–4000; David Omura, Interim Director

SOUTH DAKOTA: SIOUX FALLS VETERANS AFFAIRS HEALTH CARE SYSTEM (O, 92 beds) 2501 West 22nd Street, Sioux Falls, SD, Zip 57105–1305, Mailing Address: P.O. Box 5046, Zip 57117–5046, tel. 605/336–3230; Darwin Goodspeed, Director
Web address: www.siouxfalls.va.gov

VETERANS AFFAIRS BLACK HILLS HEALTH CARE SYSTEM (O, 247 beds) 113 Comanche Road, Fort Meade, SD, Zip 57741–1099; tel. 605/347–2511; Sandra Horsman, Director

TENNESSEE: JAMES H. QUILLEN VETERANS AFFAIRS MEDICAL CENTER (O, 98 beds) Corner of Lamont & Veterans Way, Mountain Home, TN, Zip 37684, Mailing Address: P.O. Box 4000, Zip 37684–4000, tel. 423/926–1171; Dean B. Borsos, Medical Center Director
Web address: www.mountainhome.va.gov/

MEMPHIS VETERANS AFFAIRS MEDICAL CENTER (O, 251 beds) 1030 Jefferson Avenue, Memphis, TN, Zip 38104–2193; tel. 901/523–8990; David K. Dunning, Medical Center Director and Chief Executive Officer
Web address: www.memphis.va.gov/

TENNESSEE VALLEY HEALTHCARE SYSTEM (O, 437 beds) 1310 24th Avenue South, Nashville, TN, Zip 37212–2637; tel. 615/327–4751; Captain, Jennifer Vedral-Baron, Health System Director

TEXAS: AMARILLO VETERANS AFFAIRS HEALTH CARE SYSTEM (O, 55 beds) 6010 West Amarillo Boulevard, Amarillo, TX, Zip 79106–1992; tel. 806/355–9703; Elizabeth Lowery, Interim Director
Web address: www.amarillo.va.gov/

CENTRAL TEXAS VETERANS HEALTH CARE SYSTEM (O, 1532 beds) 1901 Veterans Memorial Drive, Temple, TX, Zip 76504–7493; tel. 254/778–4811; Christopher R. Sandles, FACHE, Medical Center Director and Chief Executive Officer

MICHAEL E. DEBAKEY VETERANS AFFAIRS MEDICAL CENTER (O, 479 beds) 2002 Holcombe Boulevard, Houston, TX, Zip 77030–4298; tel. 713/791–1414; Francisco Vazquez, Director
Web address: www.houston.va.gov

SOUTH TEXAS VETERANS HEALTH CARE SYSTEM (O, 838 beds) 7400 Merton Minter Boulevard, San Antonio, TX, Zip 78229–4404; tel. 210/617–5300; Robert M. Walton, Healthcare System Director
Web address: www.southtexas.va.gov/

VETERANS AFFAIRS NORTH TEXAS HEALTH CARE SYSTEM (O, 875 beds) 4500 South Lancaster Road, Dallas, TX, Zip 75216–7167; tel. 214/742–8387; Stephen R. Holt, M.D., Director
Web address: www.northtexas.va.gov/

WEST TEXAS VETERANS AFFAIRS HEALTH CARE SYSTEM (O, 149 beds) 300 Veterans Boulevard, Big Spring, TX, Zip 79720–5500, Big Springs, tel. 432/263–7361; Kalautie JangDhari, Director

UTAH: VETERANS AFFAIRS SALT LAKE CITY HEALTH CARE SYSTEM (O, 130 beds) 500 Foothill Drive, Salt Lake City, UT, Zip 84148–0002; tel. 801/582–1565; Shella D. Stovall, R.N., Acting Director
Web address: www.saltlakecity.va.gov/

VERMONT: WHITE RIVER JUNCTION VETERANS AFFAIRS MEDICAL CENTER (O, 74 beds) 215 North Main Street, White River Junction, VT, Zip 05009–0001; tel. 802/295–9363; Brett Rusch, M.D., Acting Director

VIRGINIA: HAMPTON VETERANS AFFAIRS MEDICAL CENTER (O, 451 beds) 100 Emancipation Drive, Hampton, VA, Zip 23667–0001; tel. 757/722–9961; J. Ronald. Johnson, Medical Center Director
Web address: www.hampton.va.gov/

For explanation of codes following names, see page B2.
★ Indicates Type III membership in the American Hospital Association.

Section B

HUNTER HOLMES MCGUIRE VETERANS AFFAIRS MEDICAL CENTER–RICHMOND (O, 381 beds) 1201 Broad Rock Boulevard, Richmond, VA, Zip 23249–0002; tel. 804/675–5000; John A. Brandecker, M.P.H., Director
Web address: www.richmond.va.gov/

SALEM VETERANS AFFAIRS MEDICAL CENTER (O, 212 beds) 1970 Roanoke Boulevard, Salem, VA, Zip 24153–6478; tel. 540/982–2463; Rebecca J. Stackhouse, Medical Center Director

WASHINGTON: MANN–GRANDSTAFF VETERANS AFFAIRS MEDICAL CENTER (O, 70 beds) 4815 North Assembly Street, Spokane, WA, Zip 99205–6197; tel. 509/434–7000; Tracey B. Davis, Interim Medical Center Director
Web address: www.spokane.va.gov/

VETERANS AFFAIRS PUGET SOUND HEALTH CARE SYSTEM (O, 358 beds) 1660 South Columbian Way, Seattle, WA, Zip 98108–1597; tel. 206/762–1010; Michael C. Tadych, FACHE, Director

WEST VIRGINIA: BECKLEY VETERANS AFFAIRS MEDICAL CENTER (O, 173 beds) 200 Veterans Avenue, Beckley, WV, Zip 25801–6499; tel. 304/255–2121; Stacy J. Vasquez, Director
Web address: www.beckley.va.gov/

HUNTINGTON VETERANS AFFAIRS MEDICAL CENTER (O, 80 beds) 1540 Spring Valley Drive, Huntington, WV, Zip 25704–9300; tel. 304/429–6741; Brian Nimmo, Director

LOUIS A. JOHNSON VETERANS AFFAIRS MEDICAL CENTER (O, 71 beds) 1 Medical Center Drive, Clarksburg, WV, Zip 26301–4199; tel. 304/623–3461; Glenn R. Snider, M.D., Interim Director
Web address: www.clarksburg.va.gov

MARTINSBURG VETERANS AFFAIRS MEDICAL CENTER (O, 487 beds) 510 Butler Avenue, Martinsburg, WV, Zip 25405–9990; tel. 304/263–0811; Timothy J. Cooke, Medical Center Director and Chief Executive Officer
Web address: www.martinsburg.va.gov/

WISCONSIN: CLEMENT J. ZABLOCKI VETERANS AFFAIRS MEDICAL CENTER (O, 637 beds) 5000 West National Avenue, Milwaukee, WI, Zip 53295–0001; tel. 414/384–2000; Daniel Zomchek, Ph.D., Chief Executive Officer and Medical Center Director
Web address: www.milwaukee.va.gov/

VA MEDICAL CENTER (O, 71 beds) 500 East Veterans Street, Tomah, WI, Zip 54660–3105; tel. 608/372–3971; Victoria Brahm, R.N., MSN, Medical Center Director

WILLIAM S. MIDDLETON MEMORIAL VETERANS HOSPITAL (O, 87 beds) 2500 Overlook Terrace, Madison, WI, Zip 53705–2286; tel. 608/256–1901; John J. Rohrer, Director
Web address: www.madison.va.gov

WYOMING: CHEYENNE VETERANS AFFAIRS MEDICAL CENTER (O, 61 beds) 2360 East Pershing Boulevard, Cheyenne, WY, Zip 82001–5392; tel. 307/778–7550; Paul L. Roberts, Director
Web address: www.cheyenne.va.gov/

SHERIDAN VETERANS AFFAIRS MEDICAL CENTER (O, 145 beds) 1898 Fort Road, Sheridan, WY, Zip 82801–8320; tel. 307/672–3473; Pamela Crowell, Director
Web address: www.sheridan.va.gov/

Owned, leased, sponsored:	135 hospitals	35824 beds
Contract–managed:	0 hospitals	0 beds
Totals:	135 hospitals	35824 beds

0845: DEVEREUX (NP)
444 Devereux Drive, Villanova, PA, Zip 19085–1932, Mailing Address: P.O. Box 638, Zip 19085–0638, tel. 610/520–3000; Robert Q. Kreider, President and Chief Executive Officer
(Independent Hospital System)

FLORIDA: DEVEREUX HOSPITAL AND CHILDREN'S CENTER OF FLORIDA (O, 100 beds) 8000 Devereux Drive, Melbourne, FL, Zip 32940–7907; tel. 321/242–9100; Steven Murphy, Executive Director

GEORGIA: DEVEREUX ADVANCED BEHAVIORAL HEALTH GEORGIA (O, 100 beds) 1291 Stanley Road NW, Kennesaw, GA, Zip 30152–4359; tel. 770/427–0147; Gwendolyn Skinner, Operational Vice President
Web address: www.devereuxga.org

PENNSYLVANIA: DEVEREUX CHILDREN'S BEHAVIORAL HEALTH CENTER (O, 49 beds) 655 Sugartown Road, Malvern, PA, Zip 19355–3303, Mailing Address: 655 Sugartown Rd, Zip 19355–3303, tel. 800/345–1292; David E. Woodward, Executive Director
Web address: www.devereux.org

TEXAS: DEVEREUX TEXAS TREATMENT NETWORK (O, 47 beds) 1150 Devereux Drive, League City, TX, Zip 77573–2043; tel. 281/335–1000; Pamela E. Helm, Executive Director

Owned, leased, sponsored:	4 hospitals	296 beds
Contract–managed:	0 hospitals	0 beds
Totals:	4 hospitals	296 beds

★5205: DIGNITY HEALTH (CO)
185 Berry Street, Suite 300, San Francisco, CA, Zip 94107–1773; tel. 415/438–5500; Lloyd H. Dean, President and Chief Executive Officer
(Decentralized Health System)

ARIZONA: CHANDLER REGIONAL MEDICAL CENTER (O, 338 beds) 1955 West Frye Road, Chandler, AZ, Zip 85224–6282; tel. 480/728–3000; Jane E. Hanson, R.N., Interim Chief Executive Officer
Web address: www.chandlerregional.com

MERCY GILBERT MEDICAL CENTER (S, 198 beds) 3555 South Val Vista Road, Gilbert, AZ, Zip 85297–7323; tel. 480/728–8000; Jane E. Hanson, R.N., Interim President and Chief Executive Officer

ST. JOSEPH'S HOSPITAL AND MEDICAL CENTER (S, 577 beds) 350 West Thomas Road, Phoenix, AZ, Zip 85013–4496, Mailing Address: P.O. Box 2071, Zip 85001–2071, tel. 602/406–3000; Patty White, R.N., MS, President
Web address: www.stjosephs–phx.org

CALIFORNIA: BAKERSFIELD MEMORIAL HOSPITAL (O, 401 beds) 420 34th Street, Bakersfield, CA, Zip 93301–2237; tel. 661/327–1792; Jon Van Boening, President and Chief Executive Officer
Web address: www.bakersfieldmemorial.org

CALIFORNIA HOSPITAL MEDICAL CENTER (O, 318 beds) 1401 South Grand Avenue, Los Angeles, CA, Zip 90015–3010; tel. 213/748–2411; Margaret R. Peterson, Ph.D., R.N., President

COMMUNITY HOSPITAL OF SAN BERNARDINO (O, 379 beds) 1805 Medical Center Drive, San Bernardino, CA, Zip 92411–1214; tel. 909/887–6333; June Collison, President
Web address: www.dignityhealth.org/san–bernardino

DOMINICAN HOSPITAL (S, 223 beds) 1555 Soquel Drive, Santa Cruz, CA, Zip 95065–1794; tel. 831/462–7700; Nanette Mickiewicz, M.D., President

FRENCH HOSPITAL MEDICAL CENTER (O, 72 beds) 1911 Johnson Avenue, San Luis Obispo, CA, Zip 93401–4197; tel. 805/543–5353; Alan Iftiniuk, Chief Executive Officer
Web address: www.frenchmedicalcenter.org

GLENDALE MEMORIAL HOSPITAL AND HEALTH CENTER (O, 334 beds) 1420 South Central Avenue, Glendale, CA, Zip 91204–2594; tel. 818/502–1900; Jill Welton, President and Chief Executive Officer
Web address: www.glendalememorial.com

MARIAN REGIONAL MEDICAL CENTER (S, 286 beds) 1400 East Church Street, Santa Maria, CA, Zip 93454–5906; tel. 805/739–3000; Kerin A. Mase, President and Chief Executive Officer

MARK TWAIN MEDICAL CENTER (O, 25 beds) 768 Mountain Ranch Road, San Andreas, CA, Zip 95249–9998; tel. 209/754–3521; Robert Diehl, President
Web address: www.marktwainhospital.com

MERCY GENERAL HOSPITAL (S, 305 beds) 4001 'J' Street, Sacramento, CA, Zip 95819–3600; tel. 916/453–4545; Edmundo Castaneda, President
Web address: www.mercygeneral.org

MERCY HOSPITAL OF FOLSOM (S, 106 beds) 1650 Creekside Drive, Folsom, CA, Zip 95630–3400; tel. 916/983–7400; Randall W. Ross, FACHE, President and Chief Executive Officer
Web address: www.mercyfolsom.org

MERCY HOSPITALS OF BAKERSFIELD (S, 200 beds) 2215 Truxtun Avenue, Bakersfield, CA, Zip 93301–3698, Mailing Address: P.O. Box 119, Zip 93302–0119, tel. 661/632–5000; Bruce Peters, Chief Executive Officer

For explanation of codes following names, see page B2.
★ Indicates Type III membership in the American Hospital Association.

MERCY MEDICAL CENTER MERCED (S, 186 beds) 333 Mercy Avenue, Merced, CA, Zip 95340–8319; tel. 209/564–5000; Charles Kassis, President
Web address: www.mercymercedcares.org

MERCY MEDICAL CENTER MOUNT SHASTA (S, 33 beds) 914 Pine Street, Mount Shasta, CA, Zip 96067–2143; tel. 530/926–6111; Kenneth E S. Platou, President

MERCY MEDICAL CENTER REDDING (S, 267 beds) 2175 Rosaline Avenue, Redding, CA, Zip 96001–2549, Mailing Address: P.O. Box 496009, Zip 96049–6009, tel. 530/225–6000; G. Todd. Smith, Chief Executive Officer
Web address: www.mercy.org

MERCY SAN JUAN MEDICAL CENTER (S, 340 beds) 6501 Coyle Avenue, Carmichael, CA, Zip 95608–0306; tel. 916/537–5000; Michael Korpiel, FACHE, Chief Executive Officer
Web address: www.mercysanjuan.org

METHODIST HOSPITAL OF SACRAMENTO (O, 281 beds) 7500 Hospital Drive, Sacramento, CA, Zip 95823–5477; tel. 916/423–3000; Phyllis Baltz, Chief Executive Officer
Web address: www.methodistsacramento.org

NORTHRIDGE HOSPITAL MEDICAL CENTER (O, 371 beds) 18300 Roscoe Boulevard, Northridge, CA, Zip 91328–4167; tel. 818/885–8500; Saliba Salo, President
Web address: www.northridgehospital.org

SAINT FRANCIS MEMORIAL HOSPITAL (O, 239 beds) 900 Hyde Street, San Francisco, CA, Zip 94109–4899, Mailing Address: P.O. Box 7726, Zip 94120–7726, tel. 415/353–6000; David G. Klein, M.D., President

SEQUOIA HOSPITAL (O, 131 beds) 170 Alameda De Las Pulgas, Redwood City, CA, Zip 94062–2799; tel. 650/369–5811; Bill Graham, President
Web address: www.sequoiahospital.org

SIERRA NEVADA MEMORIAL HOSPITAL (O, 104 beds) 155 Glasson Way, Grass Valley, CA, Zip 95945–5723, Mailing Address: P.O. Box 1029, Zip 95945–1029, tel. 530/274–6000; Katherine A. Medeiros, President and Chief Executive Officer

ST. BERNARDINE MEDICAL CENTER (S, 342 beds) 2101 North Waterman Avenue, San Bernardino, CA, Zip 92404–4855; tel. 909/883–8711; Douglas V. Kleam, President
Web address: www.stbernardinemedicalcenter.com

ST. ELIZABETH COMMUNITY HOSPITAL (S, 65 beds) 2550 Sister Mary Columba Drive, Red Bluff, CA, Zip 96080–4397; tel. 530/529–8000; Jordan Wright, Chief Executive Officer

ST. JOHN'S PLEASANT VALLEY HOSPITAL (S, 127 beds) 2309 Antonio Avenue, Camarillo, CA, Zip 93010–1414; tel. 805/389–5800; Darren W. Lee, President and Chief Executive Officer
Web address: www.dignityhealth.org/pleasantvalley

ST. JOHN'S REGIONAL MEDICAL CENTER (S, 139 beds) 1600 North Rose Avenue, Oxnard, CA, Zip 93030–3723; tel. 805/988–2500; Darren W. Lee, President and Chief Executive Officer

ST. JOSEPH'S BEHAVIORAL HEALTH CENTER (S, 35 beds) 2510 North California Street, Stockton, CA, Zip 95204–5568; tel. 209/461–2000; Paul Rains, R.N., MSN, President
Web address: www.stjosephscanhelp.org

ST. JOSEPH'S MEDICAL CENTER (S, 273 beds) 1800 North California Street, Stockton, CA, Zip 95204–6019, Mailing Address: P.O. Box 213008, Zip 95213–9008, tel. 209/943–2000; Donald J. Wiley, President and Chief Executive Officer

ST. MARY MEDICAL CENTER (S, 302 beds) 1050 Linden Avenue, Long Beach, CA, Zip 90813–3321, Mailing Address: P.O. Box 887, Zip 90801–0887, tel. 562/491–9000; Carolyn P. Caldwell, FACHE, President and Chief Executive Officer
Web address: www.stmarymedicalcenter.org

ST. MARY'S MEDICAL CENTER (S, 232 beds) 450 Stanyan Street, San Francisco, CA, Zip 94117–1079; tel. 415/668–1000; John P. Allen, President

WOODLAND HEALTHCARE (O, 108 beds) 1325 Cottonwood Street, Woodland, CA, Zip 95695–5199; tel. 530/662–3961; H Kevin. Vaziri, President
Web address: www.woodlandhealthcare.org

NEVADA: ST. ROSE DOMINICAN HOSPITALS – ROSE DE LIMA CAMPUS (S, 110 beds) 102 East Lake Mead Parkway, Henderson, NV, Zip 89015–5524; tel. 702/616–5000; Teressa Conley, President and Chief Executive Officer

ST. ROSE DOMINICAN HOSPITALS – SAN MARTIN CAMPUS (O, 147 beds) 8280 West Warm Springs Road, Las Vegas, NV, Zip 89113–3612; tel. 702/492–8000; Lawrence Barnard, President and Chief Executive Officer
Web address: www.strosehospitals.org

ST. ROSE DOMINICAN HOSPITALS – SIENA CAMPUS (S, 326 beds) 3001 St Rose Parkway, Henderson, NV, Zip 89052; tel. 702/616–5000; Eugene Bassett, President and Chief Executive Officer

Owned, leased, sponsored:	35 hospitals	7920 beds
Contract–managed:	0 hospitals	0 beds
Totals:	35 hospitals	7920 beds

0010: DIVISION OF MENTAL HEALTH AND ADDICTION SERVICES, DEPARTMENT OF HUMAN SERVICES, STATE OF NEW JERSEY (NP)

222 South Warren Street, Trenton, NJ, Zip 08608–2306, Mailing Address: P.O. Box 700, Zip 08625–0700, tel. 609/777–0702; Lynn Kovich, Assistant Commissioner
(Independent Hospital System)

NEW JERSEY: ANCORA PSYCHIATRIC HOSPITAL (O, 449 beds) 301 Spring Garden Road, Hammonton, NJ, Zip 08037–9699; tel. 609/561–1700; Christopher Morrison, Chief Executive Officer
Web address: www.state.nj.us/humanservices/dmhs/oshm/aph/

ARTHUR BRISBANE CHILDREN TREATMENT CENTER (O, 92 beds) County Road 524, Farmingdale, NJ, Zip 7727, Mailing Address: P.O. Box 625, Zip 7727, Vincent Giampeitro, Chief Executive Officer

GREYSTONE PARK PSYCHIATRIC HOSPITAL (O, 468 beds) 59 Koch Avenue, Morris Plains, NJ, Zip 07950–4400; tel. 973/538–1800; Tomika Carter, Deputy Chief Executive Officer
Web address: www.state.nj.us/humanservices/dmhs/oshm/gpph/

TRENTON PSYCHIATRIC HOSPITAL (O, 431 beds) Route 29 and Sullivan Way, Trenton, NJ, Zip 08628–3425, Mailing Address: P.O. Box 7500, West Trenton, Zip 08628–0500, tel. 609/633–1500; Robyn Caporoso, Chief Executive Officer
Web address: www.state.nj.us/humanservices/dmhs/oshm/tph/

Owned, leased, sponsored:	4 hospitals	1440 beds
Contract–managed:	0 hospitals	0 beds
Totals:	4 hospitals	1440 beds

0536: DIVISION OF MENTAL HEALTH, DEPARTMENT OF HUMAN SERVICES (NP)

319 East Madison Street, S–3B, Springfield, IL, Zip 62701–1035; tel. 217/785–6023; Lorrie Rickman. Jones, Ph.D., Director
(Independent Hospital System)

ILLINOIS: ALTON MENTAL HEALTH CENTER (O, 125 beds) 4500 College Avenue, Alton, IL, Zip 62002–5099; tel. 618/474–3800; Brian E. Thomas, Administrator

ANDREW MCFARLAND MENTAL HEALTH CENTER (O, 118 beds) 901 East Southwind Road, Springfield, IL, Zip 62703–5125; tel. 217/786–6994; Karen Schweighart, R.N., MS, Administrator

CHESTER MENTAL HEALTH CENTER (O, 245 beds) Chester Road, Chester, IL, Zip 62233–0031, Mailing Address: Box 31, Zip 62233–0031, tel. 618/826–4571; Leah Hammel, Acting Administrator

CHICAGO–READ MENTAL HEALTH CENTER (O, 200 beds) 4200 North Oak Park Avenue, Chicago, IL, Zip 60634–1457; tel. 773/794–4000; Richard Carmik, Facility Director and Hospital Administrator

CHOATE MENTAL HEALTH CENTER (O, 79 beds) 1000 North Main Street, Anna, IL, Zip 62906–1699; tel. 618/833–5161; Elaine Ray, Administrator

ELGIN MENTAL HEALTH CENTER (O, 383 beds) 750 South State Street, Elgin, IL, Zip 60123–7692; tel. 847/742–1040; Meredith Kiss, Administrator
Web address: www.dhs.state.il.us

JOHN J. MADDEN MENTAL HEALTH CENTER (O, 125 beds) 1200 South First Avenue, Hines, IL, Zip 60141–0800; tel. 708/338–7202; Edith Newman, Interim Administrator

Owned, leased, sponsored:	7 hospitals	1275 beds
Contract–managed:	0 hospitals	0 beds
Totals:	7 hospitals	1275 beds

For explanation of codes following names, see page B2.
★ Indicates Type III membership in the American Hospital Association.

Section B

★0861: DUKE LIFEPOINT HEALTHCARE (IO)

330 Seven Springs Way, Brentwood, TN, Zip 37027–5098; tel. 615/920–7000; Jeffrey G. Seraphine, FACHE, President

(Moderately Centralized Health System)

MICHIGAN: UP HEALTH SYSTEM–MARQUETTE (O, 260 beds) 580 West College Avenue, Marquette, MI, Zip 49855–2736; tel. 906/228–9440; Brian Sinotte, Chief Executive Officer
Web address: www.mgh.org

NORTH CAROLINA: CENTRAL CAROLINA HOSPITAL (O, 137 beds) 1135 Carthage Street, Sanford, NC, Zip 27330–4162; tel. 919/774–2100; Spencer Thomas, Chief Executive Officer

FRYE REGIONAL MEDICAL CENTER (O, 271 beds) 420 North Center Street, Hickory, NC, Zip 28601–5049; tel. 828/315–5000; Garfield Atchison, Chief Executive Officer
Web address: www.fryemedctr.com

HARRIS REGIONAL HOSPITAL (O, 86 beds) 68 Hospital Road, Sylva, NC, Zip 28779–2722; tel. 828/586–7000; Steve Heatherly, Chief Executive Officer

HAYWOOD REGIONAL MEDICAL CENTER (O, 146 beds) 262 Leroy George Drive, Clyde, NC, Zip 28721–7430; tel. 828/456–7311; Rod Harkleroad, R.N., Chief Executive Officer
Web address: www.haymed.org

MARIA PARHAM MEDICAL CENTER (O, 102 beds) 566 Ruin Creek Road, Henderson, NC, Zip 27536–2927; tel. 252/438–4143; Bert Beard, Chief Executive Officer

PERSON MEMORIAL HOSPITAL (O, 98 beds) 615 Ridge Road, Roxboro, NC, Zip 27573–4629; tel. 336/599–2121; David Ziolkowski, Chief Executive Officer
Web address: www.personhospital.com

RUTHERFORD REGIONAL HEALTH SYSTEM (O, 112 beds) 288 South Ridgecrest Avenue, Rutherfordton, NC, Zip 28139–2838; tel. 828/286–5000; Rebecca Segal, Chief Executive Officer
Web address: www.rutherfordhosp.org

SWAIN COMMUNITY HOSPITAL (O, 25 beds) 45 Plateau Street, Bryson City, NC, Zip 28713–4200; tel. 828/488–2155; Steve Heatherly, Chief Executive Officer

WILSON MEDICAL CENTER (O, 244 beds) 1705 Tarboro Street, SW, Wilson, NC, Zip 27893–3428; tel. 252/399–8040; William E. Caldwell Jr, FACHE, Chief Executive Officer
Web address: www.wilmed.org

PENNSYLVANIA: CONEMAUGH MEMORIAL MEDICAL CENTER (O, 539 beds) 1086 Franklin Street, Johnstown, PA, Zip 15905–4398; tel. 814/534–9000; Steven E. Tucker, Chief Executive Officer

CONEMAUGH MEYERSDALE MEDICAL CENTER (O, 20 beds) 200 Hospital Drive, Meyersdale, PA, Zip 15552–1249; tel. 814/634–5911; Heather Smith, President
Web address: www.conemaugh.org

CONEMAUGH MINERS MEDICAL CENTER (O, 30 beds) 290 Haida Avenue, Hastings, PA, Zip 16646–5610, Mailing Address: P.O. Box 689, Zip 16646–0689, tel. 814/247–3100; Timothy Harclerode, Chief Executive Officer

VIRGINIA: TWIN COUNTY REGIONAL HEALTHCARE (O, 86 beds) 200 Hospital Drive, Galax, VA, Zip 24333–2227; tel. 276/236–8181; Dale Alward, Chief Executive Officer
Web address: www.tcrh.org

Owned, leased, sponsored:	14 hospitals	2156 beds
Contract–managed:	0 hospitals	0 beds
Totals:	14 hospitals	2156 beds

★0190: DUKE UNIVERSITY HEALTH SYSTEM (NP)

201 Trent Drive, Durham, NC, Zip 27710–3037, Mailing Address: P.O. Box 3701, Zip 27710–3701, tel. 919/684–2255; A. Eugene. Washington, M.D., President and Chief Executive Officer

(Centralized Health System)

NORTH CAROLINA: DUKE RALEIGH HOSPITAL (O, 171 beds) 3400 Wake Forest Road, Raleigh, NC, Zip 27609–7373; tel. 919/954–3000; David William. Zaas, M.D., Chief Executive Officer
Web address: www.dukehealthraleigh.org

DUKE REGIONAL HOSPITAL (L, 214 beds) 3643 North Roxboro Street, Durham, NC, Zip 27704–2763; tel. 919/470–4000; Kathleen B. Galbraith, FACHE, President

DUKE UNIVERSITY HOSPITAL (O, 962 beds) 2301 Erwin Road, DUMC Box # 3814, Durham, NC, Zip 27705–4699, Mailing Address: P.O. Box 3814, Zip 27710–3708, tel. 919/684–8111; Thomas Owens, M.D., President
Web address: www.dukehealth.org

Owned, leased, sponsored:	3 hospitals	1347 beds
Contract–managed:	0 hospitals	0 beds
Totals:	3 hospitals	1347 beds

1027: DUNCAN REGIONAL HOSPITAL (NP)

1407 North Whisenant Drive, Duncan, OK, Zip 73533–1650; tel. 580/252–5300; Jay R. Johnson, FACHE, President and Chief Executive Officer

(Independent Hospital System)

OKLAHOMA: DUNCAN REGIONAL HOSPITAL (O, 117 beds) 1407 North Whisenant Drive, Duncan, OK, Zip 73533–1650, Mailing Address: P.O. Box 2000, Zip 73534–2000, tel. 580/252–5300; Jay R. Johnson, FACHE, President and Chief Executive Officer
Web address: www.duncanregional.com

JEFFERSON COUNTY HOSPITAL (L, 25 beds) Highway 70 and 81, Waurika, OK, Zip 73573–3075, Mailing Address: P.O. Box 90, Zip 73573–0090, tel. 580/228–2344; Richard Gillespie, Chief Executive Officer

Owned, leased, sponsored:	2 hospitals	142 beds
Contract–managed:	0 hospitals	0 beds
Totals:	2 hospitals	142 beds

★0926: EDWARD–ELMHURST HEALTHCARE (NP)

801 South Washington Street, Naperville, IL, Zip 60540–7430; tel. 630/527–3000; Mary Lou Mastro, FACHE, MS, R.N., System Chief Executive Officer

(Independent Hospital System)

ILLINOIS: EDWARD HOSPITAL (O, 350 beds) 801 South Washington Street, Naperville, IL, Zip 60540–7499; tel. 630/527–3000; Bill Kottmann, President and Chief Executive Officer
Web address: www.eehealth.org

ELMHURST HOSPITAL (O, 267 beds) 155 East Brush Hill Road, Elmhurst, IL, Zip 60126–5658; tel. 331/221–1000; Pamela L. Dunley, MS, R.N., Chief Executive Officer

LINDEN OAKS HOSPITAL (O, 108 beds) 852 South West Street, Naperville, IL, Zip 60540–6400; tel. 630/305–5500; Gina Sharp, FACHE, President and Chief Executive Officer
Web address: https://www.eehealth.org/services/behavioral–health

Owned, leased, sponsored:	3 hospitals	725 beds
Contract–managed:	0 hospitals	0 beds
Totals:	3 hospitals	725 beds

1685: EINSTEIN HEALTHCARE NETWORK (NP)

5501 Old York Road, Philadelphia, PA, Zip 19141–3098; tel. 215/456–7890; Barry R. Freedman, President and Chief Executive Officer

PENNSYLVANIA: EINSTEIN MEDICAL CENTER MONTGOMERY (O, 171 beds) 559 West Germantown Pike, East Norriton, PA, Zip 19403–4250; tel. 484/622–1000; Beth Duffy, Chief Operating Officer

EINSTEIN MEDICAL CENTER PHILADELPHIA (O, 472 beds) 5501 Old York Road, Philadelphia, PA, Zip 19141–3098; tel. 215/456–7890; Barry R. Freedman, President and Chief Executive Officer
Web address: www.einstein.edu

Owned, leased, sponsored:	2 hospitals	643 beds
Contract–managed:	0 hospitals	0 beds
Totals:	2 hospitals	643 beds

For explanation of codes following names, see page B2.
★ Indicates Type III membership in the American Hospital Association.

Section B

0879: EMERUS (IO)

10077 Grogan's Mill, Suite 100, The Woodlands, TX, Zip 77380–1022; tel. 281/292–2450; Craig Goguen, Chief Executive Officer

TEXAS: BAPTIST EMERGENCY HOSPITAL (O, 30 beds) 16088 San Pedro, San Antonio, TX, Zip 78232–2249; tel. 210/402–4092; David Mitchell, Interim Chief Executive Officer
Web address: www.baptistemergencyhospital.com

BAYLOR EMERGENCY MEDICAL CENTER AT AUBREY (O, 32 beds) 26791 Highway 380, Aubrey, TX, Zip 76227; tel. 972/347–2525; Kyle Kirkpatrick, Chief Executive Officer

BAYLOR EMERGENCY MEDICAL CENTERS – BURLESON (O, 24 beds) 12500 South Freeway Suite 100, Burleson, TX, Zip 76028–7128; tel. 214/294–6250; Kyle Kirkpatrick, Chief Executive Officer
Web address: www.bayloremc.com/burleson

BAYLOR EMERGENCY MEDICAL CENTERS – ROCKWALL (O, 8 beds) 1975 Alpha Drive Suite 100, Rockwall, TX, Zip 75087–4951; tel. 214/294–6200; Kyle Kirkpatrick, Chief Executive Officer
Web address: www.bayloremc.com/rockwall

EMERUS HOSPITAL – SUGAR LAND (O, 7 beds) 16000 Southwest Freeway, Suite 100, Sugar Land, TX, Zip 77479–2674; tel. 281/277–0911; Mike Kohler, Chief Executive Officer

MEMORIAL HERMANN TOMBALL HOSPITAL (O, 8 beds) 24429 State Highway 249, Tomball, TX, Zip 77375–8214; tel. 281/516–0911; Brenda Villafranco, Administrator
Web address: www.emerus.com/tomball/

Owned, leased, sponsored:	6 hospitals	109 beds
Contract–managed:	0 hospitals	0 beds
Totals:	6 hospitals	109 beds

★0256: EMORY HEALTHCARE (NP)

1440 Clifton Road NE, Suite 400, Atlanta, GA, Zip 30322–1102; tel. 404/778–5000; Jonathan S. Lewin, M.D., President
(Centralized Health System)

GEORGIA: DEKALB MEDICAL AT DOWNTOWN DECATUR (O, 44 beds) 450 North Candler Street, Decatur, GA, Zip 30030–2671; tel. 404/501–6700; Robert E. Wilson Esq, Chief Executive Officer

DEKALB MEDICAL AT HILLANDALE (O, 80 beds) 2801 DeKalb Medical Parkway, Lithonia, GA, Zip 30058–4996; tel. 404/501–8000; Robert E. Wilson Esq, Chief Executive Officer
Web address: www.dekalbmedical.org

DEKALB MEDICAL AT NORTH DECATUR (O, 417 beds) 2701 North Decatur Road, Decatur, GA, Zip 30033–5995; tel. 404/501–1000; Robert E. Wilson Esq, Chief Executive Officer
Web address: www.dekalbmedical.org

EMORY JOHNS CREEK HOSPITAL (O, 113 beds) 6325 Hospital Parkway, Johns Creek, GA, Zip 30097–5775; tel. 678/474–7000; Marilyn Margolis, MSN, Chief Executive Officer

EMORY REHABILITATION HOSPITAL (O, 46 beds) 1441 Clifton Road NE, Atlanta, GA, Zip 30322–1004; tel. 404/712–5512; Michael Eric. Garrard, FACHE, Chief Executive Officer
Web address: www.emoryhealthcare.org/rehabilitation

EMORY SAINT JOSEPH'S HOSPITAL OF ATLANTA (O, 273 beds) 5665 Peachtree Dunwoody Road NE, Atlanta, GA, Zip 30342–1701; tel. 678/843–7001; Heather Dexter, Chief Executive Officer

EMORY UNIVERSITY HOSPITAL MIDTOWN (O, 459 beds) 550 Peachtree Street NE, Atlanta, GA, Zip 30308–2247; tel. 404/686–4411; Daniel Owens, Chief Executive Officer
Web address: www.emoryhealthcare.org

EMORY UNIVERSITY HOSPITAL (O, 563 beds) 1364 Clifton Road NE, Atlanta, GA, Zip 30322; tel. 404/712–2000; Bryce D. Gartland, M.D., Chief Executive Officer
Web address: www.emoryhealthcare.org

Owned, leased, sponsored:	8 hospitals	1995 beds
Contract–managed:	0 hospitals	0 beds
Totals:	8 hospitals	1995 beds

★0023: ENCOMPASS HEALTH CORPORATION (IO)

3660 Grandview Parkway, Suite 200, Birmingham, AL, Zip 35243–3332; tel. 205/967–7116; Mark J. Tarr, President and Chief Executive Officer
(Independent Hospital System)

ALABAMA: ENCOMPASS HEALTH LAKESHORE REHABILITATION HOSPITAL (O, 100 beds) 3800 Ridgeway Drive, Birmingham, AL, Zip 35209–5599; tel. 205/868–2000; Michael Bartell, Chief Executive Officer

ENCOMPASS HEALTH REHABILITATION HOSPITAL OF DOTHAN (O, 51 beds) 1736 East Main Street, Dothan, AL, Zip 36301–3040, Mailing Address: P.O. Box 6708, Zip 36302–6708, tel. 334/712–6333; Margaret A. Futch, Chief Executive Officer
Web address: www.encompasshealth.com/dothanrehab

ENCOMPASS HEALTH REHABILITATION HOSPITAL OF GADSDEN (O, 44 beds) 801 Goodyear Avenue, Gadsden, AL, Zip 35903–1133; tel. 256/439–5000; Kayla Feazell, Chief Executive Officer

ENCOMPASS HEALTH REHABILITATION HOSPITAL OF MONTGOMERY (O, 70 beds) 4465 Narrow Lane Road, Montgomery, AL, Zip 36116–2900; tel. 334/284–7700; Randy Thompson, Chief Executive Officer
Web address: www.encompasshealth.com/montgomeryrehab

ENCOMPASS HEALTH REHABILITATION HOSPITAL OF SHELBY COUNTY (O, 35 beds) 900 Oak Mountain Commons Lane, Pelham, AL, Zip 35124; tel. 205/216–7600; Robert Russell, Chief Executive Officer
Web address: www.encompasshealth.com/shelbycountyrehab

ENCOMPASS REHABILITATION HOSPITAL OF NORTH ALABAMA (O, 70 beds) 107 Governors Drive SW, Huntsville, AL, Zip 35801–4326; tel. 256/535–2300; Douglas H. Beverly, Chief Executive Officer
Web address: www.encompasshealth.com/huntsvillerehab

REGIONAL REHABILITATION HOSPITAL (O, 48 beds) 3715 Highway 280/431 North, Phenix City, AL, Zip 36867; tel. 334/732–2200; Lora Davis, FACHE, Chief Executive Officer

ARIZONA: EMCOMPASS HEALTH REHABILITATION HOSPITAL OF EAST (O, 60 beds) 5652 East Baseline Road, Mesa, AZ, Zip 85206–4713; tel. 480/567–0350; Jeffrey Roberts, Chief Executive Officer
Web address: www.healthsoutheastvalley.com

ENCOMPASS HEALTH REHABILITATION HOSPITAL OF NORTHWEST TUCSON (O, 60 beds) 1921 West Hospital Way, Tucson, AZ, Zip 85704–7806; tel. 520/742–2800; Timothy T. Poore, Chief Executive Officer
Web address: https://www.encompasshealth.com/northwesttucsonrehab

ENCOMPASS HEALTH REHABILITATION HOSPITAL OF SCOTTSDALE (O, 60 beds) 9630 East Shea Boulevard, Scottsdale, AZ, Zip 85260–6267; tel. 480/551–5400; Kenneth Bell, Chief Executive Officer
Web address: https://www.encompasshealth.com/locations/scottsdalerehab

ENCOMPASS HEALTH REHABILITATION INSTITUTE OF TUCSON (O, 80 beds) 2650 North Wyatt Drive, Tucson, AZ, Zip 85712–6108; tel. 520/325–1300; Jeffrey Christensen, Chief Executive Officer

ENCOMPASS HEALTH VALLEY OF THE SUN REHABILITATION HOSPITAL (O, 75 beds) 13460 North 67th Avenue, Glendale, AZ, Zip 85304–1042; tel. 623/878–8800; Beth Bacher, Chief Executive Officer
Web address: https://www.encompasshealth.com/valleyofthesunrehab

YUMA REHABILITATION HOSPITAL, A PARTNERSHIP OF ENCOMPASS HEALTH AND YRMC (O, 41 beds) 901 West 24th Street, Yuma, AZ, Zip 85364–6384; tel. 928/726–5000; Ian Hodge, Chief Executive Officer

ARKANSAS: HEALTHSOUTH REHABILITATION HOSPITAL OF FORT SMITH (O, 60 beds) 1401 South 'J' Street, Fort Smith, AR, Zip 72901–5155; tel. 479/785–3300; Dawn Watts, Chief Executive Officer
Web address: www.healthsouthfortsmith.com

HEALTHSOUTH REHABILITATION HOSPITAL OF JONESBORO (O, 67 beds) 1201 Fleming Avenue, Jonesboro, AR, Zip 72401–4311, Mailing Address: P.O. Box 1680, Zip 72403–1680, tel. 870/932–0440; Donna Harris, Chief Executive Officer

HEALTHSOUTH REHABILITATION HOSPITAL (O, 80 beds) 153 East Monte Painter Drive, Fayetteville, AR, Zip 72703–4002; tel. 479/444–2200; Jack C. Mitchell, FACHE, Chief Executive Officer
Web address: www.healthsouthfayetteville.com

ST. VINCENT REHABILITATION HOSPITAL (O, 80 beds) 2201 Wildwood Avenue, Sherwood, AR, Zip 72120–5074; tel. 501/834–1800; Lisa Watson, Chief Executive Officer

For explanation of codes following names, see page B2.
★ Indicates Type III membership in the American Hospital Association.

Section B

CALIFORNIA: HEALTHSOUTH BAKERSFIELD REHABILITATION HOSPITAL (O, 66 beds) 5001 Commerce Drive, Bakersfield, CA, Zip 93309–0689; tel. 661/323–5500; Martha Samora, R.N., FACHE, Chief Executive Officer
Web address: www.healthsouthbakersfield.com

HEALTHSOUTH TUSTIN REHABILITATION HOSPITAL (O, 48 beds) 14851 Yorba Street, Tustin, CA, Zip 92780–2925; tel. 714/832–9200; Diana Hanyak, Chief Executive Officer
Web address: www.tustinrehab.com

COLORADO: HEALTHSOUTH REHABILITATION HOSPITAL OF COLORADO SPRINGS (O, 60 beds) 325 Parkside Drive, Colorado Springs, CO, Zip 80910–3134; tel. 719/630–8000; Stephen Schaefer, Chief Executive Officer
Web address: www.healthsouthcoloradosprings.com

HEALTHSOUTH REHABILITATION HOSPITAL OF LITTLETON (O, 28 beds) 1001 West Mineral Avenue, Littleton, CO, Zip 80120–4507; tel. 303/334–1100; David H. Shefte, Chief Executive Officer
Web address: www.healthsouthdenver.com

DELAWARE: HEALTHSOUTH REHABILITATION HOSPITAL OF MIDDLETOWN (O, 37 beds) 250 East Hampden Road, Middletown, DE, Zip 19709–5303; tel. 302/464–3400; Mathew Gooch, Chief Executive Officer
Web address: www.healthsouthmiddletown.com

FLORIDA: HEALTHSOUTH EMERALD COAST REHABILITATION HOSPITAL (O, 75 beds) 1847 Florida Avenue, Panama City, FL, Zip 32405–4640; tel. 850/914–8600; Tony N. Bennett, Chief Executive Officer

HEALTHSOUTH REHABILITATION HOSPITAL AT MARTIN HEALTH (O, 54 beds) 5850 SE Community Drive, Stuart, FL, Zip 34997–6420; tel. 772/324–3500; Ivette Miranda, Chief Executive Officer
Web address: www.healthsouthmartin.com

HEALTHSOUTH REHABILITATION HOSPITAL OF LARGO (O, 70 beds) 901 North Clearwater–Largo Road, Largo, FL, Zip 33770–4126; tel. 727/586–2999; Tripp Smith, Chief Executive Officer

HEALTHSOUTH REHABILITATION HOSPITAL OF MIAMI (O, 60 beds) 20601 Old Cutler Road, Cutler Bay, FL, Zip 33189–2400; tel. 305/251–3800; Enrique A. Vicens–Rivera Jr, JD, Chief Executive Officer
Web address: www.healthsouthmiami.com

HEALTHSOUTH REHABILITATION HOSPITAL OF OCALA (O, 40 beds) 2275 SW 22nd Lane, Ocala, FL, Zip 34471–7710; tel. 352/282–4000; Karthik Muthu, Chief Executive Officer

HEALTHSOUTH REHABILITATION HOSPITAL OF SARASOTA (O, 96 beds) 6400 Edgelake Drive, Sarasota, FL, Zip 34240–8813; tel. 941/921–8600; Marcus Braz, Chief Executive Officer
Web address: www.healthsouthsarasota.com

HEALTHSOUTH REHABILITATION HOSPITAL OF SPRING HILL (O, 80 beds) 12440 Cortez Boulevard, Brooksville, FL, Zip 34613–2628; tel. 352/592–4250; Jeffrey Alexander, Chief Executive Officer
Web address: www.healthsouthspringhill.com

HEALTHSOUTH SEA PINES REHABILITATION HOSPITAL (O, 90 beds) 101 East Florida Avenue, Melbourne, FL, Zip 32901–8301; tel. 321/984–4600; Denise B. McGrath, Chief Executive Officer
Web address: www.healthsouthseapines.com

HEALTHSOUTH SUNRISE REHABILITATION HOSPITAL (O, 126 beds) 4399 North Nob Hill Road, Sunrise, FL, Zip 33351–5899; tel. 954/749–0300; Michael S. Roffelsen, Chief Executive Officer
Web address: www.healthsouthsunrise.com

HEALTHSOUTH TREASURE COAST REHABILITATION HOSPITAL (O, 80 beds) 1600 37th Street, Vero Beach, FL, Zip 32960–4863; tel. 772/778–2100; Michael Kissner, Chief Executive Officer

HEALTHSOUTH REHABILITATION HOSPITAL OF TALLAHASSEE (O, 76 beds) 1675 Riggins Road, Tallahassee, FL, Zip 32308–5315; tel. 850/656–4800; K. Dale. Neely, FACHE, Chief Executive Officer
Web address: www.healthsouthtallahassee.com

HEALTHSOUTH REHABILITATION HOSPITAL OF ALTAMONTE SPRINGS (O, 50 beds) 831 South State Road 434, Altamonte Springs, FL, Zip 32714–3502; tel. 407/587–8600; George Welton, Chief Executive Officer
Web address: www.healthsouthaltamontesprings.com

GEORGIA: HEALTHSOUTH WALTON REHABILITATION HOSPITAL (O, 58 beds) 1355 Independence Drive, Augusta, GA, Zip 30901–1037; tel. 706/724–7746; Eric Crossan, Chief Executive Officer

REHABILITATION HOSPITAL OF SAVANNAH (O, 50 beds) 6510 Seawright DR, Savannah, GA, Zip 31406–2752; tel. 800/622–7269; Kathy Kleinsteuber, Chief Executive Officer
Web address: www.rehabilitationhospitalsavannah.com

ILLINOIS: VAN MATRE HEALTHSOUTH REHABILITATION HOSPITAL (O, 61 beds) 950 South Mulford Road, Rockford, IL, Zip 61108–4274; tel. 815/381–8500; Jeffrey Reese, Chief Executive Officer
Web address: www.healthsouth.com

INDIANA: HEALTHSOUTH DEACONESS REHABILITATION HOSPITAL (O, 103 beds) 4100 Covert Avenue, Evansville, IN, Zip 47714–5567, Mailing Address: P.O. Box 5349, Zip 47716–5349, tel. 812/476–9983; Blake Bunner, Chief Executive Officer

KANSAS: KANSAS REHABILITATION HOSPITAL (O, 57 beds) 1504 SW Eighth Avenue, Topeka, KS, Zip 66606–1632; tel. 785/235–6600; William J. Overbey, Chief Executive Officer
Web address: www.kansasrehabhospital.com

MID–AMERICA REHABILITATION HOSPITAL (O, 98 beds) 5701 West 110th Street, Shawnee Mission, KS, Zip 66211–2503, Overland Park, tel. 913/491–2400; Tiffany Kiehl, Chief Executive Officer

WESLEY REHABILITATION HOSPITAL (O, 65 beds) 8338 West 13th Street North, Wichita, KS, Zip 67212–2984; tel. 316/729–9999; James F. Grocholski, FACHE, Chief Executive Officer
Web address: www.wesleyrehabhospital.com

KENTUCKY: CARDINAL HILL REHABILITATION HOSPITAL (O, 232 beds) 2050 Versailles Road, Lexington, KY, Zip 40504–1405; tel. 859/254–5701; Tara Diebling, Chief Executive Officer
Web address: www.cardinalhillhealthsouth.com

HEALTHSOUTH LAKEVIEW REHABILITATION HOSPITAL (O, 40 beds) 134 Heartland Drive, Elizabethtown, KY, Zip 42701–2778; tel. 270/769–3100; Lori Jarboe, Chief Executive Officer

HEALTHSOUTH NORTHERN KENTUCKY REHABILITATION HOSPITAL (O, 40 beds) 201 Medical Village Drive, Edgewood, KY, Zip 41017–3407; tel. 859/341–2044; Jeremy Yates, Chief Executive Officer
Web address: www.healthsouthkentucky.com

LOUISIANA: HEALTHSOUTH REHABILITATION HOSPITAL OF ALEXANDRIA (O, 47 beds) 104 North Third Street, Alexandria, LA, Zip 71301–8581; tel. 318/449–1370; James W. McClung, Chief Executive Officer

MAINE: NEW ENGLAND REHABILITATION HOSPITAL OF PORTLAND (O, 90 beds) 335 Brighton Avenue, Portland, ME, Zip 04102–2363; tel. 207/775–4000; Jeanine Chesley, Chief Executive Officer
Web address: www.nerhp.org

MARYLAND: HEALTHSOUTH CHESAPEAKE REHABILITATION HOSPITAL (O, 54 beds) 220 Tilghman Road, Salisbury, MD, Zip 21804–1921; tel. 410/546–4600; Steven Walas, Chief Executive Officer
Web address: www.healthsouthchesapeake.com

MASSACHUSETTS: FAIRLAWN REHABILITATION HOSPITAL (O, 110 beds) 189 May Street, Worcester, MA, Zip 01602–4339; tel. 508/791–6351; William P. Johnson, Interim Chief Executive Officer

HEALTHSOUTH BRAINTREE REHABILITATION HOSPITAL (O, 187 beds) 250 Pond Street, Braintree, MA, Zip 02184–5351; tel. 781/348–2500; Randy Doherty, CPA, Chief Executive Officer
Web address: www.braintreerehabhospital.com

HEALTHSOUTH NEW ENGLAND REHABILITATION HOSPITAL (O, 210 beds) Two Rehabilitation Way, Woburn, MA, Zip 01801–6098; tel. 781/935–5050; David Coggins, MS, Chief Executive Officer
Web address: www.newenglandrehab.com

HEALTHSOUTH REHABILITATION HOSPITAL OF WESTERN MASSACHUSETTS (O, 53 beds) 222 State Street, Ludlow, MA, Zip 01056–3437; tel. 413/308–3300; John R. Hunt, Chief Executive Officer

MISSISSIPPI: HEALTHSOUTH REHABILITATION OF GULFPORT (O, 33 beds) 4500 13th Street, Suite 900, Gulfport, MS, Zip 39501–2515; tel. 228/822–6965; Amber Hester, Chief Executive Officer
Web address: www.healthsouthgulfport.com

MISSOURI: HOWARD A. RUSK REHABILITATION CENTER (O, 60 beds) 315 Business Loop 70 West, Columbia, MO, Zip 65203–3248; tel. 573/817–2703; John M. Dawes, FACHE, Chief Executive Officer
Web address: www.ruskrehab.com

For explanation of codes following names, see page B2.
★ Indicates Type III membership in the American Hospital Association.

Section B

THE REHABILITATION INSTITUTE OF ST. LOUIS (O, 131 beds) 4455 Duncan Avenue, Saint Louis, MO, Zip 63110–1111; tel. 314/658–3800; Mark Dwyer, Chief Executive Officer

NEVADA: HEALTHSOUTH DESERT CANYON REHABILITATION HOSPITAL (O, 50 beds) 9175 West Oquendo Road, Las Vegas, NV, Zip 89148–1234; tel. 702/252–7342; Andrea Davis, Chief Executive Officer
Web address: www.healthsouthdesertcanyon.com

HEALTHSOUTH REHABILITATION HOSPITAL – HENDERSON (O, 90 beds) 10301 Jeffreys Street, Henderson, NV, Zip 89052–3922; tel. 702/939–9400; Samantha Billig, Chief Executive Officer

HEALTHSOUTH REHABILITATION HOSPITAL–LAS VEGAS (O, 79 beds) 1250 South Valley View Boulevard, Las Vegas, NV, Zip 89102–1861; tel. 702/877–8898; Michael Ward, Chief Executive Officer
Web address: www.healthsouthlasvegas.com

NEW HAMPSHIRE: HEALTHSOUTH REHABILITATION HOSPITAL (O, 50 beds) 254 Pleasant Street, Concord, NH, Zip 03301–2508; tel. 603/226–9800; Diana Lachapelle, CPA, Chief Executive Officer
Web address: www.healthsouthrehabconcordnh.com

NEW JERSEY: HEALTHSOUTH REHABILITATION HOSPITAL OF TINTON FALLS (O, 60 beds) 2 Centre Plaza, Tinton Falls, NJ, Zip 07724–9744; tel. 732/460–5320; Jason Dan. Hudson RN, BSN,, R.N., Chief Executive Officer

HEALTHSOUTH REHABILITATION HOSPITAL OF TOMS RIVER (O, 92 beds) 14 Hospital Drive, Toms River, NJ, Zip 08755–6470; tel. 732/244–3100; Patricia Ostaszewski, MS, Chief Executive Officer
Web address: www.rehabnjtomsriver.com/

HEALTHSOUTH REHABILITATION HOSPITAL OF VINELAND (O, 41 beds) 1237 West Sherman Avenue, Vineland, NJ, Zip 08360–6920; tel. 856/696–7100; Tammy Feuer, Chief Executive Officer
Web address: www.healthsouthvineland.com

NEW MEXICO: HEALTHSOUTH REHABILITATION HOSPITAL OF NEW MEXICO (O, 87 beds) 7000 Jefferson Street NE, Albuquerque, NM, Zip 87109–4313; tel. 505/344–9478; David S. Nevill, Chief Executive Officer

OHIO: HEALTHSOUTH REHABILITATION HOSPITAL AT DRAKE (O, 100 beds) 151 West Galbraith Road, Cincinnati, OH, Zip 45216–1015; tel. 513/418–5600; Ryan Smokovitz, Chief Executive Officer
Web address: www.healthsouthatdrake.com

HEALTHSOUTH REHABILITATION HOSPITAL OF DAYTON (O, 50 beds) One Elizabeth Place, Dayton, OH, Zip 45417–3445; tel. 937/424–8200; Lynne Blinco, Chief Executive Officer
Web address: www.reliantdayton.com

OKLAHOMA: ST. JOHN REHABILITATION HOSPITAL (O, 22 beds) 1200 West Albany Drive, Broken Arrow, OK, Zip 74012–8146; tel. 918/744–2338; David Nicholas, Chief Executive Officer

PENNSYLVANIA: GEISINGER HEALTHSOUTH REHABILITATION HOSPITAL (O, 42 beds) 2 Rehab Lane, Danville, PA, Zip 17821–8498; tel. 570/271–6733; Lorie Dillon, Chief Executive Officer
Web address: www.geisingerhealthsouth.com

HEALTHSOUTH HARMARVILLE REHABILITATION HOSPITAL (O, 162 beds) 320 Guys Run Road, Pittsburgh, PA, Zip 15238–0460, Mailing Address: P.O. Box 11460, Zip 15238–0460, tel. 412/828–1300; Mark Van Volkenburg, Chief Executive Officer
Web address: www.healthsouthharmarville.com

HEALTHSOUTH NITTANY VALLEY REHABILITATION HOSPITAL (O, 73 beds) 550 West College Avenue, Pleasant Gap, PA, Zip 16823–7401; tel. 814/359–3421; Susan Hartman, Chief Executive Officer

HEALTHSOUTH READING REHABILITATION HOSPITAL (O, 60 beds) 1623 Morgantown Road, Reading, PA, Zip 19607–9455; tel. 610/796–6000; Amy Teal, Chief Executive Officer
Web address: www.healthsouthreading.com

HEALTHSOUTH REHABILITATION HOSPITAL OF ALTOONA (O, 80 beds) 2005 Valley View Boulevard, Altoona, PA, Zip 16602–4598; tel. 814/944–3535; Scott Filler, Chief Executive Officer
Web address: www.healthsouthaltoona.com

HEALTHSOUTH REHABILITATION HOSPITAL OF ERIE (O, 100 beds) 143 East Second Street, Erie, PA, Zip 16507–1501; tel. 814/878–1200; John Papalia, Chief Executive Officer

HEALTHSOUTH REHABILITATION HOSPITAL OF MECHANICSBURG (O, 75 beds) 175 Lancaster Boulevard, Mechanicsburg, PA, Zip 17055–3562; tel. 717/691–3700; Josette M. Myers, Chief Executive Officer
Web address: www.healthsouthpa.com

HEALTHSOUTH REHABILITATION HOSPITAL OF SEWICKLEY (O, 44 beds) 303 Camp Meeting Road, Sewickley, PA, Zip 15143–8322; tel. 412/741–9500; Leah Laffey, R.N., Chief Executive Officer

HEALTHSOUTH REHABILITATION HOSPITAL OF YORK (O, 90 beds) 1850 Normandie Drive, York, PA, Zip 17408–1534; tel. 717/767–6941; Steven Alwine, Chief Executive Officer
Web address: www.healthsouthyork.com

PUERTO RICO: HEALTHSOUTH HOSPITAL OF MANATI (O, 40 beds) Carretera 2, Kilometro 47 7, Manati, PR, Zip 674; tel. 787/621–3800; Enid Y. Gonzalez, Chief Executive Officer
Web address: www.healthsouth.com

HEALTHSOUTH REHABILITATION HOSPITAL OF SAN JUAN (O, 32 beds) University Hospital, 3rd Floor, San Juan, PR, Zip 923, Mailing Address: P.O. Box 70344, Zip 923, tel. 787/274–5100; Daniel Del Castillo, Chief Executive Officer
Web address: www.healthsouthsanjuan.com

SOUTH CAROLINA: ANMED HEALTH REHABILITATION HOSPITAL (O, 60 beds) 1 Spring Back Way, Anderson, SC, Zip 29621–2676; tel. 864/716–2600; Denise R. Murray, Chief Executive Officer
Web address: www.anmedrehab.com

ENCOMPASS HEALTH REHABILITATION HOSPITAL OF CHARLESTON (O, 49 beds) 9181 Medcom Street, Charleston, SC, Zip 29406–9168; tel. 843/820–7777; Michele M. Skripps, R.N., Chief Executive Officer

ENCOMPASS HEALTH REHABILITATION HOSPITAL OF COLUMBIA (O, 96 beds) 2935 Colonial Drive, Columbia, SC, Zip 29203–6811; tel. 803/254–7777; Chris Daughtry, Chief Executive Officer
Web address: www.healthsouthcolumbia.com

ENCOMPASS HEALTH REHABILITATION HOSPITAL OF FLORENCE (O, 88 beds) 900 East Cheves Street, Florence, SC, Zip 29506–2704; tel. 843/679–9000; Brian Nunn, R.N., Chief Executive Officer

ENCOMPASS HEALTH REHABILITATION HOSPITAL OF ROCK HILL (O, 50 beds) 1795 Dr. Frank Gaston Boulevard, Rock Hill, SC, Zip 29732–1190; tel. 803/326–3500; Deanna Martin, Chief Executive Officer
Web address: www.healthsouthrockhill.com

TENNESSEE: HEALTHSOUTH CHATTANOOGA REHABILITATION HOSPITAL (O, 69 beds) 2412 McCallie Avenue, Chattanooga, TN, Zip 37404–3398; tel. 423/698–0221; Scott Rowe, Chief Executive Officer

HEALTHSOUTH REHABILITATION HOSPITAL MEMPHIS–NORTH (O, 50 beds) 4100 Austin Peay Highway, Memphis, TN, Zip 38128–2502; tel. 901/213–5400; Adam Yoe, Chief Executive Officer
Web address: www.healthsouthnorthmemphis.com

HEALTHSOUTH REHABILITATION HOSPITAL OF FRANKLIN (O, 40 beds) 1000 Physicians Way, Franklin, TN, Zip 37067–1471; tel. 615/721–4000; Scott J. Peterson, Chief Executive Officer

HEALTHSOUTH REHABILITATION HOSPITAL OF MEMPHIS (O, 72 beds) 1282 Union Avenue, Memphis, TN, Zip 38104–3414; tel. 901/722–2000; Stephanie Bridges, Chief Executive Officer
Web address: www.healthsouthmemphis.com

HEALTHSOUTH REHABILITATION HOSPITAL (O, 50 beds) 113 Cassel Drive, Kingsport, TN, Zip 37660–3775; tel. 423/246–7240; Troy Clark, Chief Executive Officer

QUILLEN REHABILITATION HOSPITAL (O, 31 beds) 2511 Wesley Street, Johnson City, TN, Zip 37601–1723; tel. 423/952–1700; Brian Luff, Chief Executive Officer
Web address: www.quillenrehabilitationhospital.com/

SPIRE CANE CREEK REHABILITATION HOSPITAL (O, 40 beds) 180 Mount Pelia Road, Martin, TN, Zip 38237–3812; tel. 731/587–4231; Rick Johnson, Chief Executive Officer
Web address: www.healthsouthcanecreek.com

VANDERBILT STALLWORTH REHABILITATION HOSPITAL (O, 70 beds) 2201 Childrens Way, Nashville, TN, Zip 37212–3165; tel. 615/320–7600; Jeffrey Palmucci, Chief Executive Officer

Section B

For explanation of codes following names, see page B2.
★ Indicates Type III membership in the American Hospital Association.

TEXAS: CHI ST. JOSEPH HEALTH REHABILITATION HOSPITAL, AN AFFILIATE OF ENCOMPASS HEALTH (O, 49 beds) 1600 Joseph Drive, Suite 2000, Bryan, TX, Zip 77802–1502; tel. 979/213–4300; Amy Gray, Chief Executive Officer
Web address: www.encompasshealth.com/locations/stjrehab

CHRISTUS TRINITY MOTHER FRANCES REHABILITATION HOSPITAL, A PARTNER OF ENCOMPASS HEALTH (O, 94 beds) 3131 Troup Highway, Tyler, TX, Zip 75701–8352; tel. 903/510–7000; Sharla Anderson, Chief Executive Officer
Web address: www.tmfrehabhospital.com

ENCOMPASS HEALTH REHABILITATION HOSPITAL MIDLAND ODESSA (O, 80 beds) 1800 Heritage Boulevard, Midland, TX, Zip 79707–9750; tel. 432/520–1600; Christopher Wortham, Chief Executive Officer
Web address: www.healthsouthmidland.com

ENCOMPASS HEALTH REHABILITATION HOSPITAL THE VINTAGE (O, 39 beds) 20180 Chasewood Park Drive, Houston, TX, Zip 77070–1436; tel. 281/205–5100; Krista Uselman, Chief Executive Officer

ENCOMPASS HEALTH REHABILITATION HOSPITAL THE WOODLANDS (O, 84 beds) 18550 'IH' 45 South, Conroe, TX, Zip 77384; tel. 281/364–2000; Jennifer Brewer, Chief Executive Officer
Web address: www.healthssouththewoodlands.com

ENCOMPASS HEALTH REHABILITATION HOSPITAL VISION PARK (O, 60 beds) 117 Vision Park Boulevard, Shenandoah, TX, Zip 77384–3001; tel. 936/444–1700; Jennifer Brewer, Chief Executive Officer
Web address: www.healthsouthvisionpark.com/

ENCOMPASS HEALTH REHABILITATION HOSPITAL OF ABILENE (O, 60 beds) 6401 Directors Parkway, Abilene, TX, Zip 79606–5869; tel. 325/691–1600; Joe Roberson, Chief Executive Officer

ENCOMPASS HEALTH REHABILITATION HOSPITAL OF ARLINGTON (O, 85 beds) 3200 Matlock Road, Arlington, TX, Zip 76015–2911; tel. 817/468–4000; Tyrrell Taplin, Chief Executive Officer
Web address: www.healthsoutharlington.com

ENCOMPASS HEALTH REHABILITATION HOSPITAL OF AUSTIN (O, 40 beds) 330 West Ben White Boulevard, Austin, TX, Zip 78704; tel. 512/730–4800; Brad Dinsmore, Chief Executive Officer

ENCOMPASS HEALTH REHABILITATION HOSPITAL OF CITY VIEW (O, 62 beds) 6701 Oakmont Boulevard, Fort Worth, TX, Zip 76132–2957; tel. 817/370–4700; Janell Briscoe, Chief Executive Officer
Web address: www.healthsouthcityview.com

ENCOMPASS HEALTH REHABILITATION HOSPITAL OF CYPRESS (O, 60 beds) 13031 Wortham Center Drive, Houston, TX, Zip 77065–5662; tel. 832/280–2500; Sheila A. Bollier, Chief Executive Officer

ENCOMPASS HEALTH REHABILITATION HOSPITAL OF DALLAS (O, 60 beds) 7930 Northaven Road, Dallas, TX, Zip 75230–3331; tel. 214/706–8200; Daniel MacNicol, Chief Executive Officer
Web address: www.healthsouthdallas.com

ENCOMPASS HEALTH REHABILITATION HOSPITAL OF FORT WORTH (O, 60 beds) 1212 West Lancaster Avenue, Fort Worth, TX, Zip 76102–4510; tel. 817/870–2336; Janell Briscoe, Chief Executive Officer

ENCOMPASS HEALTH REHABILITATION HOSPITAL OF HUMBLE (O, 60 beds) 19002 McKay Drive, Humble, TX, Zip 77338–5701; tel. 281/446–6148; Angela L. Simmons, Chief Executive Officer
Web address: www.healthsouthhumble.com

ENCOMPASS HEALTH REHABILITATION HOSPITAL OF PEARLAND (O, 40 beds) 2121 Business Center Drive, Pearland, TX, Zip 77584–2153; tel. 346/907–3000; Michael Cabiro, Chief Executive Officer
Web address: https://www.encompasshealth.com/locations/pearlandrehab

ENCOMPASS HEALTH REHABILITATION HOSPITAL OF PLANO (O, 83 beds) 2800 West 15th Street, Plano, TX, Zip 75075–7526; tel. 972/612–9000; Brandon Tudor, Chief Executive Officer

ENCOMPASS HEALTH REHABILITATION HOSPITAL OF RICHARDSON (O, 50 beds) 3351 Waterview Parkway, Richardson, TX, Zip 75080–1449; tel. 972/398–5700; Brent Yates, Chief Executive Officer
Web address: www.relianthcp.com

ENCOMPASS HEALTH REHABILITATION HOSPITAL OF ROUND ROCK (O, 75 beds) 1400 Hester's Crossing, Round Rock, TX, Zip 78681–8025; tel. 512/244–4400; Jack Boggess, Chief Executive Officer

ENCOMPASS HEALTH REHABILITATION HOSPITAL OF SAN ANTONIO (O, 96 beds) 9119 Cinnamon Hill, San Antonio, TX, Zip 78240–5401; tel. 210/691–0737; Michael Thomas, Chief Executive Officer
Web address: www.hsriosa.com

ENCOMPASS HEALTH REHABILITATION HOSPITAL OF SUGAR LAND (O, 50 beds) 1325 Highway 6, Sugar Land, TX, Zip 77478–4906; tel. 281/276–7574; Nicholas Hardin, FACHE, Chief Executive Officer

ENCOMPASS HEALTH REHABILITATION HOSPITAL OF TEXARKANA (O, 60 beds) 515 West 12th Street, Texarkana, TX, Zip 75501–4416; tel. 903/735–5000; Harlo McCall, Chief Executive Officer
Web address: www.healthsouthtexarkana.com

ENCOMPASS HEALTH REHABILITATION HOSPITAL OF WICHITA FALLS (O, 63 beds) 3901 Armory Road, Wichita Falls, TX, Zip 76302–2204; tel. 940/720–5700; Robbi Hudson, Chief Executive Officer
Web address: www.healthsouthwichitafalls.com

ENCOMPASS HEALTH REHABILITATION HOSPITAL OF THE MID–CITIES (O, 60 beds) 2304 State Highway 121, Bedford, TX, Zip 76021–5985; tel. 817/684–2000; Robert M. Smart, Chief Executive Officer

UTAH: HEALTHSOUTH REHABILITATION HOSPITAL OF UTAH (O, 105 beds) 8074 South 1300 East, Sandy, UT, Zip 84094–0743; tel. 801/561–3400; Jeff Frandsen, Chief Executive Officer
Web address: www.healthsouthutah.com

VIRGINIA: EMCOMPASS HEALTH REHABILITATION HOSPITAL OF VIRGINIA (O, 28 beds) 5700 Fitzhugh Avenue, Richmond, VA, Zip 23226–1800; tel. 804/288–5700; Dan Gaskell, Chief Executive Officer

ENCOMPASS HEALTH REHABILITATION HOSPITAL OF FREDERICKSBURG (O, 40 beds) 300 Park Hill Drive, Fredericksburg, VA, Zip 22401–3387; tel. 540/368–7300; David Cashwell, Chief Executive Officer
Web address: www.fredericksburgrehabhospital.com

ENCOMPASS HEALTH REHABILITATION HOSPITAL OF NORTHERN VIRGINIA (O, 60 beds) 24430 Millstream Drive, Aldie, VA, Zip 20105–3098; tel. 703/957–2000; Alfred Santos, Chief Executive Officer

ENCOMPASS HEALTH REHABILITATION HOSPITAL OF PETERSBURG (O, 53 beds) 95 Medical Park Boulevard, Petersburg, VA, Zip 23805–9233; tel. 804/504–8100; Louis Collier, Chief Executive Officer
Web address: https://www.encompasshealth.com

REHABILITATION HOSPITAL OF SOUTHWEST VIRGINIA (O, 25 beds) 103 North Street, Bristol, VA, Zip 24201–3201; tel. 276/642–7900; Georgeanne Cole, Chief Executive Officer

UVA–HEALTHSOUTH REHABILITATION HOSPITAL (O, 50 beds) 515 Ray C Hunt Drive, Charlottesville, VA, Zip 22903–2981; tel. 434/244–2000; Barbara Adcock Mohr, Chief Executive Officer
Web address: www.uvahealthsouth.com

WEST VIRGINIA: HEALTHSOUTH HUNTINGTON REHABILITATION HOSPITAL (O, 62 beds) 6900 West Country Club Drive, Huntington, WV, Zip 25705–2000; tel. 304/733–1060; Michael E. Zuliani, Chief Executive Officer
Web address: www.healthsouthhuntington.com

HEALTHSOUTH MOUNTAINVIEW REGIONAL REHABILITATION HOSPITAL (O, 96 beds) 1160 Van Voorhis Road, Morgantown, WV, Zip 26505–3437; tel. 304/598–1100; Tracy Vinciguerra, Chief Executive Officer

HEALTHSOUTH SOUTHERN HILLS REHABILITATION HOSPITAL (O, 45 beds) 120 Twelfth Street, Princeton, WV, Zip 24740–2352; tel. 304/487–8000; Robert Williams, Chief Executive Officer
Web address: www.healthsouthsouthernhills.com

HEALTHSOUTH WESTERN HILLS REGIONAL REHABILITATION HOSPITAL (O, 40 beds) 3 Western Hills Drive, Parkersburg, WV, Zip 26105–8122; tel. 304/420–1300; Alvin R. Lawson, FACHE, JD, Chief Executive Officer

Owned, leased, sponsored:	123 hospitals	8354 beds
Contract–managed:	0 hospitals	0 beds
Totals:	123 hospitals	8354 beds

0959: EPHRAIM MCDOWELL HEALTH (NP)
217 South Third Street, Danville, KY, Zip 40422–1823; tel. 859/239–1000; Daniel E. McKay, Chief Executive Officer
(Independent Hospital System)

KENTUCKY: EPHRAIM MCDOWELL FORT LOGAN HOSPITAL (O, 25 beds) 110 Metker Trail, Stanford, KY, Zip 40484–1020; tel. 606/365–4600; Ina Louise . Glass, Administrator
Web address: www.fortloganhospital.org

For explanation of codes following names, see page B2.
★ Indicates Type III membership in the American Hospital Association.

Section B

EPHRAIM MCDOWELL JAMES B. HAGGIN MEMORIAL HOSPITAL (O, 25 beds) 464 Linden Avenue, Harrodsburg, KY, Zip 40330–1862; tel. 859/734–5441; Lynne Warner Lynn, R.N., Administrator

EPHRAIM MCDOWELL REGIONAL MEDICAL CENTER (O, 159 beds) 217 South Third Street, Danville, KY, Zip 40422–1823; tel. 859/239–1000; Daniel E. McKay, Chief Executive Officer
Web address: www.emrmc.org

Owned, leased, sponsored:	3 hospitals	209 beds
Contract–managed:	0 hospitals	0 beds
Totals:	3 hospitals	209 beds

0525: ERLANGER HEALTH SYSTEM (NP)
975 East Third Street, Chattanooga, TN, Zip 37403–2147; tel. 423/778–7000; Kevin M. Spiegel, President and Chief Executive Officer
(Centralized Health System)

NORTH CAROLINA: ERLANGER MURPHY MEDICAL CENTER (O, 191 beds) 3990 U S Highway 64 East Alt, Murphy, NC, Zip 28906–7917; tel. 828/837–8161; Mark E. Kimball, Chief Executive Officer
Web address: www.murphymedical.org

TENNESSEE: ERLANGER BLEDSOE HOSPITAL (C, 25 beds) 71 Wheeler Avenue, Pikeville, TN, Zip 37367, Mailing Address: P.O. Box 699, Zip 37367–0699, tel. 423/447–2112; Stephanie Boynton, Administrator
Web address: www.erlanger.org

ERLANGER MEDICAL CENTER (O, 688 beds) 975 East Third Street, Chattanooga, TN, Zip 37403–2147; tel. 423/778–7000; Kevin M. Spiegel, Chief Executive Officer

Owned, leased, sponsored:	2 hospitals	879 beds
Contract–managed:	1 hospitals	25 beds
Totals:	3 hospitals	904 beds

0382: ERNEST HEALTH, INC. (IO)
7770 Jefferson Street NE, Suite 320, Albuquerque, NM, Zip 87109–4386; tel. 505/856–5300; Darby Brockette, Chief Executive Officer
(Independent Hospital System)

ARIZONA: MOUNTAIN VALLEY REGIONAL REHABILITATION HOSPITAL (O, 16 beds) 3700 North Windsong Drive, Prescott Valley, AZ, Zip 86314–1253; tel. 928/759–8800; Judy Baum, Chief Executive Officer

COLORADO: NORTHERN COLORADO LONG TERM ACUTE HOSPITAL (O, 40 beds) 4401 Union Street, Johnstown, CO, Zip 80534; tel. 970/619–3663; Lamar McBride, Chief Executive Officer
Web address: www.ncltah.ernesthealth.com/

NORTHERN COLORADO REHABILITATION HOSPITAL (O, 40 beds) 4401 Union Street, Johnstown, CO, Zip 80534–2800; tel. 970/619–3400; Elizabeth Bullard, Chief Executive Officer

IDAHO: NORTHERN IDAHO ADVANCED CARE HOSPITAL (O, 40 beds) 600 North Cecil Road, Post Falls, ID, Zip 83854–6200; tel. 208/262–2800; Una Alderman, Chief Executive Officer
Web address: www.niach.ernesthealth.com

REHABILITATION HOSPITAL OF THE NORTHWEST (O, 25 beds) 3372 East Jenalan Avenue, Post Falls, ID, Zip 83854–7787; tel. 208/262–8700; Darby Brockette, Chief Executive Officer
Web address: www.ernesthealth.com

INDIANA: LAFAYETTE REGIONAL REHABILITATION HOSPITAL (O, 40 beds) 950 Park East Boulevard, Lafayette, IN, Zip 47905–0792; tel. 765/447–4040; Michelle Russell, Chief Executive Officer

MONTANA: ADVANCED CARE HOSPITAL OF MONTANA (O, 40 beds) 3528 Gabel Road, Billings, MT, Zip 59102–7307; tel. 406/373–8000; Judi Powers, Chief Executive Officer
Web address: www.achm.ernesthealth.com

NEW MEXICO: ADVANCED CARE HOSPITAL OF SOUTHERN NEW MEXICO (O, 40 beds) 4451 East Lohman Avenue, Las Cruces, NM, Zip 88011–8267; tel. 575/521–6600; Claudia Saiz, Chief Executive Officer

REHABILITATION HOSPITAL OF SOUTHERN NEW MEXICO (O, 40 beds) 4441 East Lohman Avenue, Las Cruces, NM, Zip 88011–8267; tel. 575/521–6400; Sabrina Martin, Chief Executive Officer
Web address: www.rhsnm.ernesthealth.com

OHIO: REHABILITATION HOSPITAL OF NORTHWEST OHIO (O, 40 beds) 1455 West Medical Loop, Toledo, OH, Zip 43614; tel. 419/214–6600; Scott Williams, Chief Executive Officer

SOUTH CAROLINA: GREENWOOD REGIONAL REHABILITATION HOSPITAL (O, 54 beds) 1530 Parkway, Greenwood, SC, Zip 29646–4027; tel. 864/330–1800; Kristin Manske, Chief Executive Officer
Web address: www.grrh.ernesthealth.com

TEXAS: LAREDO REHABILITATION HOSPITAL (O, 20 beds) 2005a East Bustamante Street, Laredo, TX, Zip 78041; tel. 956/764–8555; Larisa Higgins, Administrator and Chief Operating Officer

LAREDO SPECIALTY HOSPITAL (O, 40 beds) 2005 Bustamante Street, Laredo, TX, Zip 78041–5470; tel. 956/753–5353; Hanna Huang, Chief Executive Officer
Web address: www.lsh.ernesthealth.com

MESQUITE REHABILITATION INSTITUTE (O, 20 beds) 1023 North Belt Line Road, Mesquite, TX, Zip 75149–1788; tel. 972/216–2400; Brian Abraham, Chief Executive Officer
Web address: www.mesquiterehab.ernesthealth.com/

MESQUITE SPECIALTY HOSPITAL (O, 40 beds) 1024 North Galloway Avenue, Mesquite, TX, Zip 75149–2434; tel. 972/216–2300; Louis Bradley, Chief Executive Officer
Web address: www.msh.ernesthealth.com

NEW BRAUNFELS REGIONAL REHABILITATION HOSPITAL (O, 40 beds) 2041 Sundance Parkway, New Braunfels, TX, Zip 78130–2779; tel. 830/625–6700; Mario Rodriguez, Chief Executive Officer

SOUTH TEXAS REHABILITATION HOSPITAL (O, 40 beds) 425 East Alton Gloor Boulevard, Brownsville, TX, Zip 78526–3361; tel. 956/554–6000; Leo Garza, Chief Executive Officer
Web address: www.strh.ernesthealth.com

TRUSTPOINT REHABILITATION HOSPITAL OF LUBBOCK (O, 66 beds) 4302A Princeton Street, Lubbock, TX, Zip 79415–1304; tel. 806/749–2222; Craig Bragg, Chief Executive Officer
Web address: www.trustpointhospital.com/

UTAH: NORTHERN UTAH REHABILITATION HOSPITAL (O, 40 beds) 5825 Harrison Boulevard, South Ogden, UT, Zip 84403–4316; tel. 801/475–5254; Ryan Keele, Chief Executive Officer

UTAH VALLEY SPECIALTY HOSPITAL (O, 40 beds) 306 River Bend Lane, Provo, UT, Zip 84604–5625; tel. 801/226–8880; Ezra Segura, Chief Executive Officer
Web address: www.uvsh.ernesthealth.com

WYOMING: ELKHORN VALLEY REHABILITATION HOSPITAL (O, 40 beds) 5715 East 2nd Street, Casper, WY, Zip 82609–4322; tel. 307/265–0005; Michael Phillips, Chief Executive Officer
Web address: www.evrh.ernesthealth.com/

Owned, leased, sponsored:	21 hospitals	801 beds
Contract–managed:	0 hospitals	0 beds
Totals:	21 hospitals	801 beds

★0396: ESSENTIA HEALTH (NP)
502 East Second Street, Duluth, MN, Zip 55805–1913; tel. 218/786–8376; David C. Herman, M.D., Chief Executive Officer
(Moderately Centralized Health System)

IDAHO: CLEARWATER VALLEY HOSPITAL AND CLINICS (O, 23 beds) 301 Cedar, Orofino, ID, Zip 83544–9029; tel. 208/476–4555; Lenne Bonner, President

ST. MARY'S HOSPITAL (O, 28 beds) 701 Lewiston Street , Cottonwood, ID, Zip 83522–9750, Mailing Address: P.O. Box 137, Zip 83522–0137, tel. 208/962–3251; Lenne Bonner, President
Web address: www.smh–cvhc.org/getpage.php?name=index

For explanation of codes following names, see page B2.
★ Indicates Type III membership in the American Hospital Association.

Section B

MINNESOTA: ESSENTIA HEALTH ADA (O, 14 beds) 201 9th Street West, Ada, MN, Zip 56510–1279; tel. 218/784–5000; Erin Stoltman, Administrator
Web address: www.essentiahealth.org

ESSENTIA HEALTH DULUTH (O, 154 beds) 502 East Second Street, Duluth, MN, Zip 55805–1982; tel. 218/727–8762; James Garvey, Hospital Operations

ESSENTIA HEALTH FOSSTON (O, 74 beds) 900 Hilligoss Boulevard SE, Fosston, MN, Zip 56542–1599; tel. 218/435–1133; Kevin Gish, Administrator and Vice President
Web address: www.essentiahealth.org

ESSENTIA HEALTH NORTHERN PINES MEDICAL CENTER (O, 58 beds) 5211 Highway 110, Aurora, MN, Zip 55705–1599; tel. 218/229–2211; Laura Ackman, Chief Operating Officer and Administrator
Web address: www.essentiahealth.org/NorthernPines/FindaClinic/Essentia-HealthNorthern-Pines-36.aspx

ESSENTIA HEALTH SANDSTONE (O, 31 beds) 705 Lundorff Drive, Sandstone, MN, Zip 55072–5009; tel. 320/245–2212; Michael D. Hedrix, Administrator and President
Web address: www.pinemedicalcenter.org

ESSENTIA HEALTH ST. JOSEPH'S MEDICAL CENTER (O, 136 beds) 523 North Third Street, Brainerd, MN, Zip 56401–3098; tel. 218/829–2861; Adam Rees, President

ESSENTIA HEALTH ST. MARY'S – DETROIT LAKES (O, 132 beds) 1027 Washington Avenue, Detroit Lakes, MN, Zip 56501–3409; tel. 218/847–5611; Peter Jacobson, President
Web address: www.essentiahealth.org

ESSENTIA HEALTH ST. MARY'S MEDICAL CENTER (O, 310 beds) 407 East Third Street, Duluth, MN, Zip 55805–1984; tel. 218/786–4000; James Garvey, Senior Vice President Hospital Practice, Essentia Health East
Web address: www.essentiahealth.org/StMarysMedicalCenter/FindaClinic/Essentia-HealthSt-Marys-Medical-Center-46.aspx

ESSENTIA HEALTH–DEER RIVER (O, 52 beds) 115 10th Avenue NE , Deer River, MN, Zip 56636–8795; tel. 218/246–2900; Marsha Green, Administrator and Chief Operating Officer

ESSENTIA HEALTH–GRACEVILLE (O, 60 beds) 115 West Second Street, Graceville, MN, Zip 56240–4845, Mailing Address: P.O. Box 157, Zip 56240–0157, tel. 320/748–7223; Julie Rosenberg, Administrator
Web address: www.essentiahealth.org/HolyTrinityHospital/FindaClinic/Essentia-HealthHoly-Trinity-Hospital-96.aspx

ESSENTIA HEALTH–VIRGINIA (L, 144 beds) 901 Ninth Street North, Virginia, MN, Zip 55792–2398; tel. 218/741–3340; Sam Stone, Operations Administrator
Web address: www.essentiahealth.org

NORTH DAKOTA: ESSENTIA HEALTH FARGO (O, 137 beds) 3000 32nd Avenue South, Fargo, ND, Zip 58103–6132; tel. 701/364–8000; Timothy Sayler, Chief Operating Officer

WISCONSIN: ESSENTIA HEALTH ST. MARY'S HOSPITAL OF SUPERIOR (O, 25 beds) 3500 Tower Avenue, Superior, WI, Zip 54880–5395; tel. 715/817–7000; Terry Jacobson, Administrator and Chief Executive Officer
Web address: www.essentiahealth.org/EssentiaHealthStMarysHospitalofSuperiorFoundation/overview.aspx

Owned, leased, sponsored:	15 hospitals	1378 beds
Contract–managed:	0 hospitals	0 beds
Totals:	15 hospitals	1378 beds

2395: EXCELA HEALTH (NP)

532 West Pittsburgh Street, Greensburg, PA, Zip 15601, Mailing Address: 134 Industrial Park Road, Zip 15601–7328, tel. 724/832–5050; Robert Rogalski, Chief Executive Officer
(Centralized Health System)

PENNSYLVANIA: EXCELA FRICK HOSPITAL (O, 33 beds) 508 South Church Street, Mount Pleasant, PA, Zip 15666–1790; tel. 724/547–1500; Michael D. Busch, Executive Vice President and Chief Operating Officer
Web address: www.excelahealth.org/PatientsandVisitors/HospitalsFacilities/Hospitals/Frick.aspx

EXCELA HEALTH WESTMORELAND HOSPITAL (O, 270 beds) 532 West Pittsburgh Street, Greensburg, PA, Zip 15601–2282; tel. 724/832–4000; Ronald H. Ott, President

EXCELA LATROBE AREA HOSPITAL (O, 114 beds) One Mellon Way, Latrobe, PA, Zip 15650–1096; tel. 724/537–1000; Michael D. Busch, Executive Vice President and Chief Operating Officer
Web address: www.excelahealth.org

Owned, leased, sponsored:	3 hospitals	417 beds
Contract–managed:	0 hospitals	0 beds
Totals:	3 hospitals	417 beds

★1325: FAIRVIEW HEALTH SERVICES (NP)

2450 Riverside Avenue, Minneapolis, MN, Zip 55454–1400; tel. 612/672–6141; James Hereford, President and Chief Executive Officer
(Centralized Health System)

MINNESOTA: BETHESDA HOSPITAL (O, 114 beds) 559 Capitol Boulevard, Saint Paul, MN, Zip 55103–2101; tel. 651/232–2000; Patrick Belland, Chief Operating Officer, Acute Care Services

FAIRVIEW LAKES HEALTH SERVICES (O, 34 beds) 5200 Fairview Boulevard, Wyoming, MN, Zip 55092–8013; tel. 651/982–7000; Lia Christiansen, Chief Operating Officer, Acute Care Hospitals
Web address: www.fairview.org/

FAIRVIEW NORTHLAND MEDICAL CENTER (O, 23 beds) 911 Northland Drive, Princeton, MN, Zip 55371–2173; tel. 763/389–1313; Lia Christiansen, Chief Operating Officer, Acute Care Hospitals
Web address: www.northland.fairview.org

FAIRVIEW RIDGES HOSPITAL (O, 150 beds) 201 East Nicollet Boulevard, Burnsville, MN, Zip 55337–5799; tel. 952/892–2000; Patrick Belland, Chief Operating Officer, Acute Care Services

FAIRVIEW SOUTHDALE HOSPITAL (O, 316 beds) 6401 France Avenue South, Edina, MN, Zip 55435–2199; tel. 952/924–5000; Patrick Belland, Chief Operating Officer, Acute Care Services
Web address: www.fairview.org

GRAND ITASCA CLINIC AND HOSPITAL (O, 31 beds) 1601 Golf Course Road, Grand Rapids, MN, Zip 55744–8648; tel. 218/326–5000; Laura Reed, R.N., President, Acute Care Hospitals

RANGE REGIONAL HEALTH SERVICES (O, 73 beds) 750 East 34th Street, Hibbing, MN, Zip 55746–4600; tel. 218/262–4881; Laura Reed, R.N., President, Acute Care Hospitals
Web address: www.range.fairview.org

ST. JOHN'S HOSPITAL (O, 192 beds) 1575 Beam Avenue, Maplewood, MN, Zip 55109–1126; tel. 651/232–7000; Lia Christiansen, Chief Operating Officer, Acute Care Hospitals

ST. JOSEPH'S HOSPITAL (O, 237 beds) 45 West 10th Street, Saint Paul, MN, Zip 55102–1053; tel. 651/232–3000; Lia Christiansen, Chief Operating Officer, Acute Care Hospitals
Web address: www.healtheast.org

UNIVERSITY OF MINNESOTA MEDICAL CENTER, FAIRVIEW (O, 860 beds) 2450 Riverside Avenue, Minneapolis, MN, Zip 55454–1400; tel. 612/672–6000; John Doherty, Co–President, M Health
Web address: www.fairview.org

WOODWINDS HEALTH CAMPUS (O, 86 beds) 1925 Woodwinds Drive, Woodbury, MN, Zip 55125–4445; tel. 651/232–0228; Lia Christiansen, Chief Operating Officer, Acute Care Hospitals

Owned, leased, sponsored:	11 hospitals	2116 beds
Contract–managed:	0 hospitals	0 beds
Totals:	11 hospitals	2116 beds

0814: FAITH REGIONAL HEALTH SERVICES (NP)

2700 West Norfolk Avenue, Norfolk, NE, Zip 68701–4438, Mailing Address: P.O. Box 869, Zip 68702–0869, tel. 402/371–4880; Kelly Driscoll, RN, Chief Executive Officer
(Independent Hospital System)

NEBRASKA: FAITH REGIONAL HEALTH SERVICES (O, 136 beds) 2700 West Norfolk Avenue, Norfolk, NE, Zip 68701–4438, Mailing Address: P.O. Box 869, Zip 68702–0869, tel. 402/371–4880; Kelly Driscoll, R.N., Interim President and Chief Executive Officer
Web address: www.frhs.org

For explanation of codes following names, see page B2.
★ Indicates Type III membership in the American Hospital Association.

NIOBRARA VALLEY HOSPITAL (C, 20 beds) 401 South Fifth Street, Lynch, NE, Zip 68746–0118, Mailing Address: P.O. Box 118, Zip 68746–0118, tel. 402/569–2451; Kelly Kalkowski, Chief Executive Officer

WEST HOLT MEDICAL SERVICES (C, 17 beds) 406 West Neely Street, Atkinson, NE, Zip 68713–4801; tel. 402/925–2811; Bradley D. Pfeifer, FACHE, Chief Executive Officer
Web address: www.westholtmed.org

Owned, leased, sponsored:	1 hospitals	136 beds
Contract–managed:	2 hospitals	37 beds
Totals:	3 hospitals	173 beds

0397: FINGER LAKES HEALTH (NP)

196 North Street, Geneva, NY, Zip 14456–1651; tel. 315/787–4000; Jose Acevedo, M.D., President and Chief Executive Officer
(Independent Hospital System)

NEW YORK: FINGER LAKES HOSPITAL (O, 132 beds) 196 North Street, Geneva, NY, Zip 14456–1694; tel. 315/787–4000; Frank Korich, FACHE, Senior Vice President, Operations
Web address: www.flhealth.org

SOLDIERS AND SAILORS MEMORIAL HOSPITAL OF YATES COUNTY (O, 186 beds) 418 North Main Street, Penn Yan, NY, Zip 14527–1085; tel. 315/531–2000; Frank Korich, FACHE, Senior Vice President, Operations

Owned, leased, sponsored:	2 hospitals	318 beds
Contract–managed:	0 hospitals	0 beds
Totals:	2 hospitals	318 beds

1010: FIRST PHYSICIANS CAPITAL GROUP, INC. (IO)

4323 NW 63rd Street Suite 140, Oklahoma City, OK, Zip 73116–1513; tel. 405/246–0218; Sean Kirrane, Chief Executive Officer

OKLAHOMA: CARNEGIE TRI–COUNTY MUNICIPAL HOSPITAL (C, 17 beds) 102 North Broadway, Carnegie, OK, Zip 73015, Mailing Address: P.O. Box 97, Zip 73015–0097, tel. 580/654–1050; Thomas Henton, Chief Executive Officer

PHYSICIANS' HOSPITAL IN ANADARKO (C, 25 beds) 1002 Central Boulevard East, Anadarko, OK, Zip 73005–4496; tel. 405/247–2551; Travis A. Villani, FACHE, Chief Executive Officer and Administrator
Web address: www.anadarkohospital.com

STROUD REGIONAL MEDICAL CENTER (C, 24 beds) Highway 66 West, Stroud, OK, Zip 74079, Mailing Address: P.O. Box 530, Zip 74079–0530, tel. 918/968–3571; Ed Dyer, Chief Executive Officer

Owned, leased, sponsored:	0 hospitals	0 beds
Contract–managed:	3 hospitals	66 beds
Totals:	3 hospitals	66 beds

★0243: FIRSTHEALTH OF THE CAROLINAS (NP)

155 Memorial Drive, Pinehurst, NC, Zip 28374–8710, Mailing Address: P.O. Box 3000, Zip 28374–3000, tel. 910/715–1000; David J. Kilarski, FACHE, Chief Executive Officer
(Independent Hospital System)

NORTH CAROLINA: FIRSTHEALTH MONTGOMERY MEMORIAL HOSPITAL (O, 5 beds) 520 Allen Street, Troy, NC, Zip 27371–2802; tel. 910/571–5000; Beth Walker, R.N., President
Web address: www.firsthealth.org

FIRSTHEALTH MOORE REGIONAL HOSPITAL (O, 376 beds) 155 Memorial Drive, Pinehurst, NC, Zip 28374–8710, Mailing Address: P.O. Box 3000, Zip 28374–3000, tel. 910/715–1000; David J. Kilarski, FACHE, Chief Executive Officer
Web address: www.firsthealth.org

Owned, leased, sponsored:	2 hospitals	381 beds
Contract–managed:	0 hospitals	0 beds
Totals:	2 hospitals	381 beds

1016: FLOYD HEALTHCARE MANAGEMENT (NP)

304 Turner McCall Boulevard, Rome, GA, Zip 30165–5621, Mailing Address: P.O. Box 233, Zip 30162–0233, tel. 706/509–5000; Kurt Stuenkel, FACHE, President and Chief Executive Officer

ALABAMA: FLOYD CHEROKEE MEDICAL CENTER (O, 45 beds) 400 Northwood Drive, Centre, AL, Zip 35960–1023; tel. 256/927–5531; Brandon Reece, Chief Executive Officer

GEORGIA: FLOYD MEDICAL CENTER (O, 327 beds) 304 Turner McCall Boulevard, Rome, GA, Zip 30165–5621, Mailing Address: P.O. Box 233, Zip 30162–0233, tel. 706/509–5000; Kurt Stuenkel, FACHE, President and Chief Executive Officer
Web address: www.floyd.org

POLK MEDICAL CENTER (O, 25 beds) 2360 Rockmart Highway, Cedartown, GA, Zip 30125–6029; tel. 770/748–2500; Tifani Kinard, Administrator and Chief Nursing Officer
Web address: www.polkhospital.org

Owned, leased, sponsored:	3 hospitals	397 beds
Contract–managed:	0 hospitals	0 beds
Totals:	3 hospitals	397 beds

0900: FOUNDATION SURGICAL HOSPITAL AFFILIATES (IO)

14000 North Portland Avenue, Suite 204, Oklahoma City, OK, Zip 73134–4002; tel. 405/608–1700; Thomas A. Michaud, Chief Executive Officer
(Independent Hospital System)

TEXAS: BAYLOR SCOTT & WHITE SURGICAL HOSPITAL AT SHERMAN (O, 12 beds) 3601 North Calais Street, Sherman, TX, Zip 75090–1785; tel. 903/870–0999; Marc Devorsetz, Chief Executive Officer
Web address: www.heritageparksurgicalhospital.com

FOUNDATION SURGICAL HOSPITAL OF EL PASO (O, 20 beds) 1416 George Dieter Drive, El Paso, TX, Zip 79936–7601; tel. 915/598–4240; Don Burris, Chief Executive Officer
Web address: www.foundationhospitals.com/elpaso/

Owned, leased, sponsored:	2 hospitals	32 beds
Contract–managed:	0 hospitals	0 beds
Totals:	2 hospitals	32 beds

5345: FRANCISCAN HEALTH (CO)

1515 Dragoon Trail, Mishawaka, IN, Zip 46544–4710, Mailing Address: P.O. Box 1290, Zip 46546–1290, tel. 574/256–3935; Kevin D. Leahy, President and Chief Executive Officer
(Moderately Centralized Health System)

ILLINOIS: FRANCISCAN HEALTH OLYMPIA FIELDS (O, 329 beds) 20201 South Crawford Avenue, Olympia Fields, IL, Zip 60461–1010; tel. 708/747–4000; Allan M. Spooner, President and Chief Executive Officer

INDIANA: FRANCISCAN HEALTH CARMEL (O, 6 beds) 12188B North Meridian Street, Carmel, IN, Zip 46032–4840; tel. 317/705–4500; Stephen J. Wheatley, Director of Operations
Web address: www.franciscanalliance.org/hospitals/carmel/Pages/default.aspx

FRANCISCAN HEALTH CRAWFORDSVILLE (O, 40 beds) 1710 Lafayette Road, Crawfordsville, IN, Zip 47933–1099; tel. 765/362–2800; Terrence Klein, Ph.D., Vice President and Chief Operating Officer
Web address: www.stclaremedical.org

FRANCISCAN HEALTH CROWN POINT (O, 254 beds) 1201 South Main Street, Crown Point, IN, Zip 46307–8483; tel. 219/738–2100; Daniel McCormick, M.D., President and Chief Executive Officer

FRANCISCAN HEALTH DYER (O, 341 beds) 24 Joliet Street, Dyer, IN, Zip 46311–1799; tel. 219/865–2141; Patrick J. Maloney, Chief Executive Officer

FRANCISCAN HEALTH HAMMOND (O, 406 beds) 5454 Hohman Avenue, Hammond, IN, Zip 46320–1999; tel. 219/932–2300; Patrick J. Maloney, Chief Executive Officer
Web address: https://www.franciscanhealth.org/healthcare–facilities/franciscan–health–hammond–18

For explanation of codes following names, see page B2.
★ Indicates Type III membership in the American Hospital Association.

Section B

FRANCISCAN HEALTH INDIANAPOLIS (O, 485 beds) 8111 South Emerson Avenue, Indianapolis, IN, Zip 46237–8601; tel. 317/528–5000; James Callaghan III, M.D., President and Chief Executive Officer
Web address: www.stfrancishospitals.org

FRANCISCAN HEALTH LAFAYETTE EAST (O, 187 beds) 1701 South Creasy Lane, Lafayette, IN, Zip 47905–4972; tel. 765/502–4000; Terrance E. Wilson, President and Chief Executive Officer

FRANCISCAN HEALTH MICHIGAN CITY (O, 171 beds) 301 West Homer Street, Michigan City, IN, Zip 46360–4358; tel. 219/879–8511; Dean Mazzoni, President and Chief Executive Officer
Web address: www.franciscanalliance.org

FRANCISCAN HEALTH MOORESVILLE (O, 115 beds) 1201 Hadley Road, Mooresville, IN, Zip 46158–1789; tel. 317/831–1160; Peter J. Murphy, Senior Vice President and Chief Operating Officer

FRANCISCAN HEALTH RENSSELEAR (O, 46 beds) 1104 East Grace Street, Rensselaer, IN, Zip 47978–3296; tel. 219/866–5141; Terrance E. Wilson, President and Chief Executive Officer
Web address: www.franciscanhealth.org

FRANCISCAN HEALTHCARE MUNSTER (O, 32 beds) 701 Superior Avenue, Munster, IN, Zip 46321–4037; tel. 219/924–1300; Patrick J. Maloney, Chief Executive Officer
Web address: www.franciscanphysicianshospital.org

Owned, leased, sponsored:	12 hospitals	2412 beds
Contract–managed:	0 hospitals	0 beds
Totals:	12 hospitals	2412 beds

★1475: FRANCISCAN MISSIONARIES OF OUR LADY HEALTH SYSTEM, INC. (CO)

4200 Essen Lane, Baton Rouge, LA, Zip 70809–2158; tel. 225/923–2701; Michael McBride, President and Chief Executive Officer

(Moderately Centralized Health System)

LOUISIANA: ASSUMPTION COMMUNITY HOSPITAL (O, 6 beds) 135 Highway 402, Napoleonville, LA, Zip 70390–2217; tel. 985/369–3600; Christina Hockaday, FACHE, Chief Executive Officer
Web address: www.https://ololrmc.com

OUR LADY OF LOURDES REGIONAL MEDICAL CENTER (O, 186 beds) 4801 Ambassador Caffery Parkway, Lafayette, LA, Zip 70508–6917; tel. 337/470–2000; W. Bryan. Lee, Chief Executive Officer
Web address: www.lourdesrmc.com

OUR LADY OF THE ANGELS HOSPITAL (O, 57 beds) 433 Plaza Street, Bogalusa, LA, Zip 70427–3793; tel. 985/730–6700; Rene J. Ragas, Chief Operating Officer

OUR LADY OF THE LAKE REGIONAL MEDICAL CENTER (O, 1219 beds) 5000 Hennessy Boulevard, Baton Rouge, LA, Zip 70808–4375; tel. 225/765–6565; K Scott. Wester, FACHE, President and Chief Executive Officer
Web address: www.ololrmc.com

ST. ELIZABETH HOSPITAL (O, 57 beds) 1125 West Highway 30, Gonzales, LA, Zip 70737–5004; tel. 225/647–5000; Robert L. Burgess, President and Chief Executive Officer

ST. FRANCIS MEDICAL CENTER (O, 365 beds) 309 Jackson Street, Monroe, LA, Zip 71201–7407, Mailing Address: P.O. Box 1901, Zip 71210–1901, tel. 318/966–4000; Kristin Wolkart, R.N., President and Chief Executive Officer
Web address: www.stfran.com

Owned, leased, sponsored:	6 hospitals	1890 beds
Contract–managed:	0 hospitals	0 beds
Totals:	6 hospitals	1890 beds

★1455: FRANCISCAN SISTERS OF CHRISTIAN CHARITY SPONSORED MINISTRIES, INC. (CO)

1415 South Rapids Road, Manitowoc, WI, Zip 54220–9302; tel. 920/684–7071; Scott McConnaha, FACHE, Acting Chief Executive Officer and Vice President, Mission and Strategy
(Moderately Centralized Health System)

NEBRASKA: ST. FRANCIS MEMORIAL HOSPITAL (O, 88 beds) 430 North Monitor Street, West Point, NE, Zip 68788–1555; tel. 402/372–2404; Jerry Wordekemper, President and Chief Executive Officer
Web address: www.fcswp.org

OHIO: GENESIS HEALTHCARE SYSTEM (O, 321 beds) 2951 Maple Avenue, Zanesville, OH, Zip 43701–1406; tel. 740/454–5000; Matthew J. Perry, President and Chief Executive Officer

WISCONSIN: HOLY FAMILY MEMORIAL (O, 67 beds) 2300 Western Avenue, Manitowoc, WI, Zip 54220–3712, Mailing Address: P.O. Box 1450, Zip 54221–1450, tel. 920/320–2011; Brett Norell, Interim Chief Executive Officer
Web address: www.hfmhealth.org

Owned, leased, sponsored:	3 hospitals	476 beds
Contract–managed:	0 hospitals	0 beds
Totals:	3 hospitals	476 beds

★0271: FREEMAN HEALTH SYSTEM (NP)

1102 West 32nd Street, Joplin, MO, Zip 64804–3503; tel. 417/347–1111; Paula F. Baker, President and Chief Executive Officer

(Centralized Health System)

MISSOURI: FREEMAN HEALTH SYSTEM (O, 381 beds) 1102 West 32nd Street, Joplin, MO, Zip 64804–3503; tel. 417/347–1111; Paula F. Baker, President and Chief Executive Officer
Web address: www.freemanhealth.com

FREEMAN NEOSHO HOSPITAL (O, 25 beds) 113 West Hickory Street, Neosho, MO, Zip 64850–1705; tel. 417/455–4352; Renee Denton, Chief Operating Officer

NEVADA REGIONAL MEDICAL CENTER (C, 71 beds) 800 South Ash Street, Nevada, MO, Zip 64772–3223; tel. 417/667–3355; Wes Braman, Chief Executive Officer
Web address: www.nrmchealth.com

Owned, leased, sponsored:	2 hospitals	406 beds
Contract–managed:	1 hospitals	71 beds
Totals:	3 hospitals	477 beds

0924: FROEDTERT HEALTH (NP)

9200 West Wisconsin Avenue, Milwaukee, WI, Zip 53226–3596, Mailing Address: P.O. Box 26099, Zip 53226–0099, tel. 414/805–3000; Catherine A. Jacobson, President and Chief Executive Officer

WISCONSIN: COMMUNITY MEMORIAL HOSPITAL (O, 202 beds) W180 N8085 Town Hall Road, Menomonee Falls, WI, Zip 53051–3518, Mailing Address: P.O. Box 408, Zip 53052–0408, tel. 262/251–1000; Teresa M. Lux, President and Chief Operating Officer
Web address: www.communitymemorial.com

FROEDTERT AND THE MEDICAL COLLEGE OF WISCONSIN FROEDTERT HOSPITAL (O, 585 beds) 9200 West Wisconsin Avenue, Milwaukee, WI, Zip 53226–3596, Mailing Address: P.O. Box 26099, Zip 53226–0099, tel. 414/805–3000; Catherine Buck, MSN, R.N., President
Web address: www.froedtert.com

ST. JOSEPH'S HOSPITAL (O, 70 beds) 3200 Pleasant Valley Road, West Bend, WI, Zip 53095–9274; tel. 262/836–5533; Allen Ericson, President
Web address: www.froedtert.com

Owned, leased, sponsored:	3 hospitals	857 beds
Contract–managed:	0 hospitals	0 beds
Totals:	3 hospitals	857 beds

0182: FUNDAMENTAL LONG TERM CARE HOLDINGS, LLC (IO)

930 Ridgebrook Road, Sparks Glencoe, MD, Zip 21152–9390; tel. 410/773–1000; W Bradley. Bennett, President and Chief Executive Officer

(Independent Hospital System)

For explanation of codes following names, see page B2.
★ Indicates Type III membership in the American Hospital Association.

NEVADA: HARMON MEDICAL AND REHABILITATION HOSPITAL (O, 118 beds) 2170 East Harmon Avenue, Las Vegas, NV, Zip 89119–7840; tel. 702/794–0100; Bonnie Essex. Hillegass, Chief Executive Officer

HORIZON SPECIALTY HOSPITAL (O, 49 beds) 640 Desert Lane, Las Vegas, NV, Zip 89106–4207; tel. 702/382–3155; Darrin Cook, Chief Executive Officer and Administrator
Web address: www.horizonspecialtyhosp.com/

SOUTHERN NEVADA MEDICAL AND REHABILITATION CENTER (O, 100 beds) 2945 Casa Vegas, Las Vegas, NV, Zip 89169–2248; tel. 702/735–7179; Maureen Davis, Administrator

Owned, leased, sponsored:	3 hospitals	267 beds
Contract–managed:	0 hospitals	0 beds
Totals:	3 hospitals	267 beds

★5570: GEISINGER (NP)
100 North Academy Avenue, Danville, PA, Zip 17822–9800; tel. 570/271–6211; David T. Feinberg, M.D., President and Chief Executive Officer
(Centralized Physician/Insurance Health System)

NEW JERSEY: ATLANTICARE REGIONAL MEDICAL CENTER (O, 533 beds) 1925 Pacific Avenue, Atlantic City, NJ, Zip 08401–6713; tel. 609/441–8994; Lori S. Herndon, R.N., President and Chief Executive Officer
Web address: www.atlanticare.org

PENNSYLVANIA: GEISINGER HOLY SPIRIT (O, 295 beds) 503 North 21st Street, Camp Hill, PA, Zip 17011–2204; tel. 717/763–2100; Kyle C. Snyder, Chief Administrative Officer
Web address: www.hsh.org

GEISINGER JERSEY SHORE HOSPITAL (O, 25 beds) 1020 Thompson Street, Jersey Shore, PA, Zip 17740–1794; tel. 570/398–0100; Tammy Anderer, Acting President

GEISINGER MEDICAL CENTER (O, 540 beds) 100 North Academy Avenue, Danville, PA, Zip 17822–2201; tel. 570/271–6211; Thomas P. Sokola, Chief Administrative Officer
Web address: www.geisinger.org

GEISINGER WYOMING VALLEY MEDICAL CENTER (O, 268 beds) 1000 East Mountain Boulevard, Wilkes Barre, PA, Zip 18711–0027; tel. 570/808–7300; Ronald R Beer, FACHE, Chief Administrative Officer

GEISINGER–BLOOMSBURG HOSPITAL (O, 76 beds) 549 Fair Street, Bloomsburg, PA, Zip 17815–1419; tel. 570/387–2100; Lissa Bryan–Smith, Chief Administrative Officer
Web address: www.bloomhealth.net

GEISINGER–COMMUNITY MEDICAL CENTER (O, 182 beds) 1800 Mulberry Street, Scranton, PA, Zip 18510–2369; tel. 570/703–8000; Ronald R Beer, FACHE, Chief Administrative Officer

GEISINGER–LEWISTOWN HOSPITAL (O, 123 beds) 400 Highland Avenue, Lewistown, PA, Zip 17044–1198; tel. 717/248–5411; Kirk E. Thomas, Vice President Operations
Web address: www.geisinger.org

Owned, leased, sponsored:	8 hospitals	2042 beds
Contract–managed:	0 hospitals	0 beds
Totals:	8 hospitals	2042 beds

★0311: GENESIS HEALTH SYSTEM (NP)
1227 East Rusholme Street, Davenport, IA, Zip 52803–2498; tel. 563/421–1000; Douglas P. Cropper, President and Chief Executive Officer
(Centralized Physician/Insurance Health System)

ILLINOIS: GENESIS MEDICAL CENTER, SILVIS (O, 135 beds) 801 Illini Drive, Silvis, IL, Zip 61282–1893; tel. 309/281–4000; Theresa Summers–Main, R.N., Interim President
Web address: www.genesishealth.com

GENESIS MEDICAL CENTER–ALEDO (O, 22 beds) 409 NW Ninth Avenue, Aledo, IL, Zip 61231–1296; tel. 309/582–9100; Ted Rogalski, Administrator
Web address: www.genesishealth.com

IOWA: GENESIS MEDICAL CENTER, DAVENPORT (O, 368 beds) 1227 East Rusholme Street, Davenport, IA, Zip 52803–2498; tel. 563/421–1000; Jordan Voigt, Administrator

GENESIS MEDICAL CENTER, DEWITT (O, 88 beds) 1118 11th Street, De Witt, IA, Zip 52742–1296; tel. 563/659–4200; Curt Coleman, FACHE, Chief Executive Officer
Web address: www.genesishealth.com

JACKSON COUNTY REGIONAL HEALTH CENTER (C, 12 beds) 700 West Grove Street, Maquoketa, IA, Zip 52060–2163; tel. 563/652–2474; Curt Coleman, FACHE, Administrator
Web address: www.jcrhc.org

Owned, leased, sponsored:	4 hospitals	613 beds
Contract–managed:	1 hospitals	12 beds
Totals:	5 hospitals	625 beds

0283: GILLIARD HEALTH SERVICES (IO)
3091 Carter Hill Road, Montgomery, AL, Zip 36111–1801; tel. 334/265–5009; William G. McKenzie, President, Chief Executive Officer and Chairman

ALABAMA: EVERGREEN MEDICAL CENTER (O, 39 beds) 101 Crestview Avenue, Evergreen, AL, Zip 36401–3333, Mailing Address: P.O. Box 706, Zip 36401–0706, tel. 251/578–2480; Tom McLendon, Administrator
Web address: www.evergreenmedical.org

JACKSON MEDICAL CENTER (O, 26 beds) 220 Hospital Drive, Jackson, AL, Zip 36545–2459, Mailing Address: P.O. Box 428, Zip 36545–0428, tel. 251/246–9021; Jennifer M. Ryland, R.N., Chief Executive Officer
Web address: www.jacksonmedicalcenter.org

Owned, leased, sponsored:	2 hospitals	65 beds
Contract–managed:	0 hospitals	0 beds
Totals:	2 hospitals	65 beds

0648: GOOD SHEPHERD REHABILITATION NETWORK (IO)
850 South Fifth Street, Allentown, PA, Zip 18103–3308; tel. 610/776–3100; John Kristel, President and Chief Executive Officer
(Independent Hospital System)

PENNSYLVANIA: GOOD SHEPHERD REHABILITATION HOSPITAL (O, 106 beds) 850 South 5th Street, Allentown, PA, Zip 18103–3308; tel. 610/776–3299; John Kristel, President and Chief Executive Officer

GOOD SHEPHERD SPECIALTY HOSPITAL (O, 32 beds) 2545 Schoenersville Road, 4th Floor, Bethlehem, PA, Zip 18017–7300; tel. 484/884–5051; Andrew Shane. Martin, Administrator
Web address: www.goodshepherdrehab.org

Owned, leased, sponsored:	2 hospitals	138 beds
Contract–managed:	0 hospitals	0 beds
Totals:	2 hospitals	138 beds

★1535: GREAT PLAINS HEALTH ALLIANCE, INC. (NP)
250 North Rock Road, Suite 160, Wichita, KS, Zip 67206–2241; tel. 316/685–1523; Dave Dellasega, President and Chief Executive Officer
(Decentralized Health System)

KANSAS: ASHLAND HEALTH CENTER (C, 25 beds) 709 Oak Street, Ashland, KS, Zip 67831–0188, Mailing Address: P.O. Box 188, Zip 67831–0188, tel. 620/635–2241; Michael Mages, Chief Executive Officer
Web address: www.ashlandhc.org

CHEYENNE COUNTY HOSPITAL (L, 16 beds) 210 West First Street, Saint Francis, KS, Zip 67756–3540, Mailing Address: P.O. Box 547, Zip 67756–0547, tel. 785/332–2104; Kelly Pottorff, Chief Executive Officer
Web address: www.cheyennecountyhospital.com

COMANCHE COUNTY HOSPITAL (C, 12 beds) 202 South Frisco Street, Coldwater, KS, Zip 67029–9101, Mailing Address: HC 65, Box 8A, Zip 67029–9500, tel. 620/582–2144; Nancy Zimmerman, R.N., Administrator

For explanation of codes following names, see page B2.
★ Indicates Type III membership in the American Hospital Association.

ELLINWOOD DISTRICT HOSPITAL (L, 25 beds) 605 North Main Street, Ellinwood, KS, Zip 67526–1440; tel. 620/564–2548; Kile Magner, Administrator
Web address: www.ellinwooddistricthospital.org

FREDONIA REGIONAL HOSPITAL (C, 34 beds) 1527 Madison Street, Fredonia, KS, Zip 66736–1751, Mailing Address: P.O. Box 579, Zip 66736–0579, tel. 620/378–2121; Johnathan Durrett, Chief Executive Officer

GRISELL MEMORIAL HOSPITAL DISTRICT ONE (C, 42 beds) 210 South Vermont Avenue, Ransom, KS, Zip 67572–9525; tel. 785/731–2231; David Caudill, Administrator
Web address: www.grisellmemorialhospital.org

KIOWA COUNTY MEMORIAL HOSPITAL (L, 15 beds) 721 West Kansas Avenue, Greensburg, KS, Zip 67054–1633; tel. 620/723–3341; Mary Sweet, Administrator

LANE COUNTY HOSPITAL (C, 25 beds) 235 West Vine, Dighton, KS, Zip 67839–0969, Mailing Address: P.O. Box 969, Zip 67839–0969, tel. 620/397–5321; Brian Sarpy, Chief Executive Officer
Web address: www.lanecountyhospital.com/

MEDICINE LODGE MEMORIAL HOSPITAL (C, 25 beds) 710 North Walnut Street, Medicine Lodge, KS, Zip 67104–1019; tel. 620/886–3771; Kevin A. White, Administrator

MINNEOLA DISTRICT HOSPITAL (C, 54 beds) 212 Main Street, Minneola, KS, Zip 67865–8511, Mailing Address: P.O. Box 127, Zip 67865–0127, tel. 620/885–4264; Deborah Bruner, Chief Executive Officer and Administrator
Web address: www.minneolahealthcare.com

OSBORNE COUNTY MEMORIAL HOSPITAL (C, 25 beds) 424 West New Hampshire Street, Osborne, KS, Zip 67473–2314, Mailing Address: P.O. Box 70, Zip 67473–0070, tel. 785/346–2121; Marianna Harris, Administrator
Web address: www.ocmh.org

OTTAWA COUNTY HEALTH CENTER (L, 45 beds) 215 East Eighth, Minneapolis, KS, Zip 67467–1902, Mailing Address: P.O. Box 290, Zip 67467–0290, tel. 785/392–2122; Jody Parks, Administrator

PHILLIPS COUNTY HOSPITAL (L, 25 beds) 1150 State Street, Phillipsburg, KS, Zip 67661–1743, Mailing Address: P.O. Box 607, Zip 67661–0607, tel. 785/543–5226; Rex D. Walk, Chief Executive Officer
Web address: www.phillipshospital.org

REPUBLIC COUNTY HOSPITAL (L, 63 beds) 2420 'G' Street, Belleville, KS, Zip 66935–2400; tel. 785/527–2254; David–Paul Cavazos, Chief Executive Officer

SABETHA COMMUNITY HOSPITAL (L, 25 beds) 14th and Oregon Streets, Sabetha, KS, Zip 66534–0229, Mailing Address: P.O. Box 229, Zip 66534–0229, tel. 785/284–2121; Lora Key, Chief Executive Officer
Web address: www.sabethahospital.com

SATANTA DISTRICT HOSPITAL AND LONG TERM CARE (C, 57 beds) 401 South Cheyenne Street, Satanta, KS, Zip 67870–0159, Mailing Address: P.O. Box 159, Zip 67870–0159, tel. 620/649–2761; Jeremy Clingenpeel, Administrator

SMITH COUNTY MEMORIAL HOSPITAL (L, 53 beds) 614 South Main Street, Smith Center, KS, Zip 66967–3001; tel. 785/282–6845; Allen Van Driel, FACHE, Administrator
Web address: www.gpha.com

TREGO COUNTY–LEMKE MEMORIAL HOSPITAL (C, 62 beds) 320 North 13th Street, Wakeeney, KS, Zip 67672–2099; tel. 785/743–2182; David Augustine, Chief Executive Officer

WICHITA COUNTY HEALTH CENTER (C, 42 beds) 211 East Earl Street, Leoti, KS, Zip 67861–9620; tel. 620/375–2233; Teresa Clark, Chief Executive Officer and Administrator
Web address: www.wichitacountyhealthcenter.com

NEBRASKA: HARLAN COUNTY HEALTH SYSTEM (C, 19 beds) 717 North Brown Street, Alma, NE, Zip 68920–2132, Mailing Address: P.O. Box 836, Zip 68920–0836, tel. 308/928–2151; Mark A. Miller, FACHE, Interim Chief Executive Officer
Web address: www.harlancountyhealth.com

Owned, leased, sponsored:	8 hospitals	267 beds
Contract–managed:	12 hospitals	422 beds
Totals:	20 hospitals	689 beds

★0144: GREATER HUDSON VALLEY HEALTH SYSTEM (NP)
707 East Main Street, Middletown, NY, Zip 10940–2650; tel. 845/333–1000; Scott Batulis, President and Chief Executive Officer
(Centralized Physician/Insurance Health System)

NEW YORK: CATSKILL REGIONAL MEDICAL CENTER (O, 119 beds) 68 Harris Bushville Road, Harris, NY, Zip 12742–5030, Mailing Address: P.O. Box 800, Zip 12742–0800, tel. 845/794–3300; Jonathan Schiller, Chief Executive Officer
Web address: www.crmcny.org

GROVER M. HERMANN HOSPITAL (O, 10 beds) 8881 Route 97, Callicoon, NY, Zip 12723; tel. 845/887–5530; Rolland Bojo, R.N., Administrator
Web address: www.crmcny.org

ORANGE REGIONAL MEDICAL CENTER (O, 340 beds) 707 East Main Street, Middletown, NY, Zip 10940–2650; tel. 845/333–1000; Scott Batulis, President and Chief Executive Officer
Web address: www.ormc.org

Owned, leased, sponsored:	3 hospitals	469 beds
Contract–managed:	0 hospitals	0 beds
Totals:	3 hospitals	469 beds

★1555: GREENVILLE HEALTH SYSTEM (NP)
701 Grove Road, Greenville, SC, Zip 29605–5611; tel. 864/455–7000; Spence Taylor, M.D., President and Chief Executive Officer
(Centralized Health System)

SOUTH CAROLINA: GHS GREENVILLE MEMORIAL HOSPITAL (O, 822 beds) 701 Grove Road, Greenville, SC, Zip 29605–4295; tel. 864/455–7000; Ric A. Ransom, Chief Operating Officer

GHS GREER MEMORIAL HOSPITAL (O, 70 beds) 830 South Buncombe Road, Greer, SC, Zip 29650–2400; tel. 864/797–8000; John F. Mansure, FACHE, President
Web address: www.ghs.org

GHS HILLCREST MEMORIAL HOSPITAL (O, 43 beds) 729 SE Main Street, Simpsonville, SC, Zip 29681–3280; tel. 864/454–6100; Scott R. Jones, FACHE, Chief Operating Officer

GREENVILLE HEALTH SYSTEM – LAURENS COUNTY MEMORIAL HOSPITAL (L, 71 beds) 22725 Highway 76 East, Clinton, SC, Zip 29325–7527, Mailing Address: P O Drawer 976, Zip 29325–0976, tel. 864/833–9100; Justin Benfield, Southern Region Chief Operating Officer
Web address: www.ghs.org/laurens

OCONEE MEMORIAL HOSPITAL (L, 252 beds) 298 Memorial Drive, Seneca, SC, Zip 29672–9499; tel. 864/882–3351; Hunter Kome, Campus President

PATEWOOD MEMORIAL HOSPITAL (O, 72 beds) 175 Patewood Drive, Greenville, SC, Zip 29615–3570; tel. 864/797–1000; Tim Brookshire, Chief Operating Officer
Web address: www.ghs.org/patewood

Owned, leased, sponsored:	6 hospitals	1330 beds
Contract–managed:	0 hospitals	0 beds
Totals:	6 hospitals	1330 beds

★0675: GUTHRIE CLINIC (NP)
One Guthrie Square, Sayre, PA, Zip 18840–1625; tel. 570/888–5858; Joseph A. Scopelliti, M.D., President and Chief Executive Officer
(Moderately Centralized Health System)

NEW YORK: GUTHRIE CORNING HOSPITAL (O, 65 beds) One Guthrie Drive, Corning, NY, Zip 14830–3696; tel. 607/937–7200; Garrett W. Hoover, FACHE, President
Web address: www.corninghospital.com

PENNSYLVANIA: GUTHRIE ROBERT PACKER HOSPITAL (O, 254 beds) 1 Guthrie Square, Sayre, PA, Zip 18840–1698; tel. 570/888–6666; Joseph T. Sawyer Jr, President
Web address: https://www.guthrie.org/location/robert–packer–hospital

GUTHRIE TOWANDA MEMORIAL HOSPITAL (O, 195 beds) 91 Hospital Drive, Towanda, PA, Zip 18848–9702; tel. 570/265–2191; Staci Covey, R.N., MS, President

TROY COMMUNITY HOSPITAL (O, 25 beds) 275 Guthrie Drive, Troy, PA, Zip 16947; tel. 570/297–2121; Staci Covey, R.N., MS, President
Web address: www.guthrie.org

Owned, leased, sponsored:	4 hospitals	539 beds
Contract–managed:	0 hospitals	0 beds
Totals:	4 hospitals	539 beds

For explanation of codes following names, see page B2.
★ Indicates Type III membership in the American Hospital Association.

Section B

★1003: HACKENSACK MERIDIAN HEALTH (NP)

343 Thornall Street, 8th Floor, Edison, NJ, Zip 08837–2206, Mailing Address: 343 Thornall Street, Zip 08837–2206, tel. 844/464–9355; Robert C. Garrett, FACHE, Co–Chief Executive Officer
(Centralized Health System)

NEW JERSEY: HACKENSACK MERIDIAN HEALTH BAYSHORE COMMUNITY HOSPITAL (O, 160 beds) 727 North Beers Street, Holmdel, NJ, Zip 07733–1598; tel. 732/739–5900; Timothy J. Hogan, FACHE, President, RMC and BMC

HACKENSACK MERIDIAN HEALTH HACKENSACK UNIVERSITY MEDICAL CENTER (O, 737 beds) 30 Prospect Avenue, Hackensack, NJ, Zip 07601–1914; tel. 201/996–2000; Ihor S. Sawczuk, M.D., FACS, President
Web address: www.hackensackumc.org

HACKENSACK MERIDIAN HEALTH JERSEY SHORE UNIVERSITY MEDICAL CENTER (O, 579 beds) 1945 Route 33, Neptune, NJ, Zip 07754–0397; tel. 732/775–5500; Kenneth N. Sable, M.D., President

HACKENSACK MERIDIAN HEALTH OCEAN MEDICAL CENTER (O, 317 beds) 425 Jack Martin Boulevard, Brick Township, NJ, Zip 08724–7732; tel. 732/840–2200; Dean Q. Lin, FACHE, Regional President
Web address: www.meridianhealth.com

HACKENSACK MERIDIAN HEALTH PALISADES MEDICAL CENTER (O, 228 beds) 7600 River Road, North Bergen, NJ, Zip 07047–6217; tel. 201/854–5000; Anthony Passannante Jr, M.D., FACC, President

HACKENSACK MERIDIAN HEALTH RARITAN BAY MEDICAL CENTER (O, 282 beds) 530 New Brunswick Avenue, Perth Amboy, NJ, Zip 08861–3654; tel. 732/442–3700; Thomas Shanahan, Chief Operating Officer
Web address: www.rbmc.org

HACKENSACK MERIDIAN HEALTH RIVERVIEW MEDICAL CENTER (O, 321 beds) 1 Riverview Plaza, Red Bank, NJ, Zip 07701–1864; tel. 732/741–2700; Timothy J. Hogan, FACHE, President, RMC and BMC
Web address: www.riverviewmedicalcenter.com

HACKENSACK MERIDIAN HEALTH SHORE REHABILITATION INSTITUTE (O, 40 beds) 425 Jack Martin Boulevard, Brick, NJ, Zip 08724–7732; tel. 732/836–4500; Kerri Fitzgerald, Executive Director
Web address: www.shorerehabilitationinstitute.com

HACKENSACK MERIDIAN HEALTH SOUTHERN OCEAN MEDICAL CENTER (O, 172 beds) 1140 Route 72 West, Manahawkin, NJ, Zip 08050–2499; tel. 609/597–6011; Regina Foley, R.N., FACHE, Chief Operating Officer

Owned, leased, sponsored:	9 hospitals	2836 beds
Contract–managed:	0 hospitals	0 beds
Totals:	9 hospitals	2836 beds

★0541: HARTFORD HEALTHCARE (NP)

One State Street, 19th Floor, Hartford, CT, Zip 6103; tel. 860/263–4100; Elliot T. Joseph, Chief Executive Officer
(Centralized Health System)

CONNECTICUT: CHARLOTTE HUNGERFORD HOSPITAL (O, 66 beds) 540 Litchfield Street, Torrington, CT, Zip 06790–6679, Mailing Address: P.O. Box 988, Zip 06790–0988, tel. 860/496–6666; Daniel J. McIntyre, President
Web address: www.charlottehungerford.org

HARTFORD HOSPITAL (O, 900 beds) 80 Seymour Street, Hartford, CT, Zip 06102–8000, Mailing Address: P.O. Box 5037, Zip 06102–5037, tel. 860/545–5000; Bimal Patel, President

MIDSTATE MEDICAL CENTER (O, 85 beds) 435 Lewis Avenue, Meriden, CT, Zip 06451–2101; tel. 203/694–8200; Gary C. Havican, President
Web address: www.midstatemedical.org

NATCHAUG HOSPITAL (O, 57 beds) 189 Storrs Road, Mansfield Center, CT, Zip 06250–1683; tel. 860/456–1311; Patricia Rehmer, MSN, FACHE, President

THE HOSPITAL OF CENTRAL CONNECTICUT (O, 173 beds) 100 Grand Street, New Britain, CT, Zip 06052–2017, Mailing Address: P.O. Box 100, Zip 06052–2017, tel. 860/224–5011; Gary C. Havican, President
Web address: www.thocc.org

THE WILLIAM W. BACKUS HOSPITAL (O, 184 beds) 326 Washington Street, Norwich, CT, Zip 06360–2740; tel. 860/889–8331; Donna Handley, President

WINDHAM HOSPITAL (O, 99 beds) 112 Mansfield Avenue, Willimantic, CT, Zip 06226–2040; tel. 860/456–9116; Donna Handley, President
Web address: www.windhamhospital.org

Owned, leased, sponsored:	7 hospitals	1564 beds
Contract–managed:	0 hospitals	0 beds
Totals:	7 hospitals	1564 beds

0637: HAVEN BEHAVIORAL HEALTHCARE (IO)

652 West Iris Drive, Nashville, TN, Zip 37204–3191; tel. 615/250–9500; Michael Lindley, Chief Executive Officer

ARIZONA: HAVEN SENIOR HORIZONS (O, 45 beds) 1201 South 7th Avenue, Suite 200, Phoenix, AZ, Zip 85007–4076; tel. 623/236–2000; Ashley Ellis, Chief Executive Officer
Web address: www.havenbehavioral.com

OHIO: HAVEN BEHAVIORAL SENIOR CARE OF DAYTON (O, 32 beds) One Elizabeth Place, 4th Floor Southwest Tower, Dayton, OH, Zip 45417–3445; tel. 937/234–0100; Keith Kuhn, Chief Executive Officer

PENNSYLVANIA: HAVEN BEHAVIORAL HOSPITAL OF EASTERN PENNSYLVANIA (O, 48 beds) 145 North 6th Street, 3rd Floor, Reading, PA, Zip 19601–3096; tel. 610/406–4340; Bryan W. Lett, Chief Executive Officer
Web address: www.https://havenbehavioral.com/

HAVEN BEHAVIORAL HOSPITAL OF PHILADELPHIA (O, 36 beds) Four Falls Building, 3301 Scotts Lane, Philadelphia, PA, Zip 19129–1121; tel. 215/791–6821; Abigail Halloran, Chief Executive Officer

Owned, leased, sponsored:	4 hospitals	161 beds
Contract–managed:	0 hospitals	0 beds
Totals:	4 hospitals	161 beds

★3555: HAWAII HEALTH SYSTEMS CORPORATION (NP)

3675 Kilauea Avenue, Honolulu, HI, Zip 96816–2333; tel. 808/733–4151; Linda Rosen, M.D., Chief Executive Officer
(Independent Hospital System)

HAWAII: HALE HO'OLA HAMAKUA (O, 77 beds) 45–547 Plumeria Street, Honokaa, HI, Zip 96727–6902; tel. 808/932–4100; Denise Mackey, Administrator
Web address: www.halehoolahamakua.org

HILO MEDICAL CENTER (O, 199 beds) 1190 Waianuenue Avenue, Hilo, HI, Zip 96720–2089; tel. 808/932–3000; Dan Brinkman, R.N., Chief Executive Officer

KA'U HOSPITAL (O, 21 beds) 1 Kamani Street, Pahala, HI, Zip 96777, Mailing Address: P.O. Box 40, Zip 96777–0040, tel. 808/932–4200; Merilyn Harris, Administrator
Web address: www.hhsc.org

KAUAI VETERANS MEMORIAL HOSPITAL (O, 45 beds) 4643 Waimea Canyon Road, Waimea, HI, Zip 96796, Mailing Address: P.O. Box 337, Zip 96796–0337, tel. 808/338–9431; Lance Segawa, Chief Executive Officer

KOHALA HOSPITAL (O, 28 beds) 54–383 Hospital Road, Kohala, HI, Zip 96755, Mailing Address: P.O. Box 10, Kapaau, Zip 96755–0010, tel. 808/889–6211; Eugene Amar Jr, Administrator
Web address: www.koh.hhsc.org

KONA COMMUNITY HOSPITAL (O, 94 beds) 79–1019 Haukapila Street, Kealakekua, HI, Zip 96750–7920; tel. 808/322–9311; Jay E. Kreuzer, FACHE, Chief Executive Officer

LEAHI HOSPITAL (O, 164 beds) 3675 Kilauea Avenue, Honolulu, HI, Zip 96816–2398; tel. 808/733–8000; Derek Akiyoshi, Chief Executive Officer
Web address: www.hhsc.org

MALUHIA HOSPITAL (O, 146 beds) 1027 Hala Drive, Honolulu, HI, Zip 96817; tel. 808/832–5874; Derek Akiyoshi, Chief Executive Officer

SAMUEL MAHELONA MEMORIAL HOSPITAL (O, 80 beds) 4800 Kawaihau Road, Kapaa, HI, Zip 96746–1971; tel. 808/822–4961; Lance Segawa, Chief Executive Officer
Web address: www.smmh.hhsc.org

Owned, leased, sponsored:	9 hospitals	854 beds
Contract–managed:	0 hospitals	0 beds
Totals:	9 hospitals	854 beds

For explanation of codes following names, see page B2.
★ Indicates Type III membership in the American Hospital Association.

0266: HAWAII PACIFIC HEALTH (NP)

55 Merchant Street, Honolulu, HI, Zip 96813–4306; tel. 808/949–9355; Raymond P. Vara Jr, President and Chief Executive Officer
(Centralized Health System)

HAWAII: KAPIOLANI MEDICAL CENTER FOR WOMEN & CHILDREN (O, 185 beds) 1319 Punahou Street, Honolulu, HI, Zip 96826–1001; tel. 808/983–6000; Martha Smith, Chief Executive Officer

PALI MOMI MEDICAL CENTER (O, 118 beds) 98–1079 Moanalua Road, Aiea, HI, Zip 96701–4713; tel. 808/486–6000; Art Gladstone, R.N., Chief Executive Officer
Web address: www.palimomi.org

STRAUB MEDICAL CENTER (O, 118 beds) 888 South King Street, Honolulu, HI, Zip 96813–3097; tel. 808/522–4000; Art Gladstone, R.N., Chief Executive Officer

WILCOX MEDICAL CENTER (O, 65 beds) 3–3420 Kuhio Highway, Lihue, HI, Zip 96766–1099; tel. 808/245–1100; Jen Chahanovich, President and Chief Executive Officer
Web address: www.wilcoxhealth.org

Owned, leased, sponsored:	4 hospitals	486 beds
Contract–managed:	0 hospitals	0 beds
Totals:	4 hospitals	486 beds

★0048: HCA HEALTHCARE (IO)

One Park Plaza, Nashville, TN, Zip 37203–1548; tel. 615/344–5248; R Milton. Johnson, President and Chief Executive Officer
(Decentralized Health System)

ALASKA: ALASKA REGIONAL HOSPITAL (O, 132 beds) 2801 Debarr Road, Anchorage, AK, Zip 99508–2997; tel. 907/264–1754; Julie Taylor, FACHE, Chief Executive Officer
Web address: www.alaskaregional.com

CALIFORNIA: GOOD SAMARITAN HOSPITAL (O, 349 beds) 2425 Samaritan Drive, San Jose, CA, Zip 95124–3997, Mailing Address: P.O. Box 240002, Zip 95154–2402, tel. 408/559–2011; Joseph DeSchryver, Chief Executive Officer

LOS ROBLES HOSPITAL AND MEDICAL CENTER (O, 325 beds) 215 West Janss Road, Thousand Oaks, CA, Zip 91360–1899; tel. 805/370–4421; Natalie Mussi, President and Chief Executive Officer
Web address: www.losrobleshospital.com

REGIONAL MEDICAL CENTER OF SAN JOSE (O, 247 beds) 225 North Jackson Avenue, San Jose, CA, Zip 95116–1603; tel. 408/259–5000; Michael T. Johnson, FACHE, President and Chief Executive Officer
Web address: www.regionalmedicalsanjose.com

RIVERSIDE COMMUNITY HOSPITAL (O, 373 beds) 4445 Magnolia Avenue, Riverside, CA, Zip 92501–4199; tel. 951/788–3000; Patrick D. Brilliant, President and Chief Executive Officer
Web address: www.riversidecommunityhospital.com

WEST HILLS HOSPITAL AND MEDICAL CENTER (O, 225 beds) 7300 Medical Center Drive, West Hills, CA, Zip 91307–1900; tel. 818/676–4000; Douglas Long, President and Chief Executive Officer

COLORADO: MEDICAL CENTER OF AURORA (O, 340 beds) 1501 South Potomac Street, Aurora, CO, Zip 80012–5411; tel. 303/695–2600; Daniel Miller, FACHE, President and Chief Executive Officer
Web address: www.auroramed.com

NORTH SUBURBAN MEDICAL CENTER (O, 139 beds) 9191 Grant Street, Thornton, CO, Zip 80229–4341; tel. 303/451–7800; Daphne G. David, President and Chief Executive Officer

PRESBYTERIAN–ST. LUKE'S MEDICAL CENTER (O, 374 beds) 1719 East 19th Avenue, Denver, CO, Zip 80218–1281; tel. 303/839–6000; Maureen Tarrant, President and Chief Executive Officer
Web address: www.pslmc.com

ROSE MEDICAL CENTER (O, 282 beds) 4567 East Ninth Avenue, Denver, CO, Zip 80220–3941; tel. 303/320–2121; Ryan Tobin, President and Chief Executive Officer

SKY RIDGE MEDICAL CENTER (O, 274 beds) 10101 Ridge Gate Parkway, Lone Tree, CO, Zip 80124–5522; tel. 720/225–1000; Susan Hicks, Chief Executive Officer
Web address: www.skyridgemedcenter.com

SPALDING REHABILITATION HOSPITAL (O, 40 beds) 900 Potomac Steet, Aurora, CO, Zip 80011–6716; tel. 303/367–1166; Daniel Miller, FACHE, President and Chief Executive Officer

SWEDISH MEDICAL CENTER (O, 361 beds) 501 East Hampden Avenue, Englewood, CO, Zip 80113–2702; tel. 303/788–5000; Richard A. Hammett, President and Chief Executive Officer
Web address: www.swedishhospital.com

FLORIDA: AVENTURA HOSPITAL AND MEDICAL CENTER (O, 359 beds) 20900 Biscayne Boulevard, Aventura, FL, Zip 33180–1407; tel. 305/682–7000; Lee B. Chaykin, Chief Executive Officer

BLAKE MEDICAL CENTER (O, 383 beds) 2020 59th Street West, Bradenton, FL, Zip 34209–4669; tel. 941/792–6611; Randy Currin, Chief Executive Officer
Web address: www.blakemedicalcenter.com

BRANDON REGIONAL HOSPITAL (O, 407 beds) 119 Oakfield Drive, Brandon, FL, Zip 33511–5779; tel. 813/681–5551; Bland Eng, Chief Executive Officer

CAPITAL REGIONAL MEDICAL CENTER (O, 198 beds) 2626 Capital Medical Boulevard, Tallahassee, FL, Zip 32308–4499; tel. 850/325–5000; Alan Seesee, Chief Executive Officer
Web address: www.capitalregionalmedicalcenter.com

CENTRAL FLORIDA REGIONAL HOSPITAL (O, 226 beds) 1401 West Seminole Boulevard, Sanford, FL, Zip 32771–6764; tel. 407/321–4500; Wendy H. Brandon, Chief Executive Officer

CITRUS MEMORIAL HEALTH SYSTEM (O, 204 beds) 502 West Highland Boulevard, Inverness, FL, Zip 34452–4754; tel. 352/726–1551; Ralph A. Aleman, President and Chief Executive Officer
Web address: www.citrusmh.com

DOCTORS HOSPITAL OF SARASOTA (O, 168 beds) 5731 Bee Ridge Road, Sarasota, FL, Zip 34233–5056; tel. 941/342–1100; Robert C. Meade, Chief Executive Officer

ENGLEWOOD COMMUNITY HOSPITAL (O, 100 beds) 700 Medical Boulevard, Englewood, FL, Zip 34223–3978; tel. 941/475–6571; Valerie L. Powell–Stafford, Chief Executive Officer
Web address: www.englewoodcommunityhospital.com

FAWCETT MEMORIAL HOSPITAL (O, 237 beds) 21298 Olean Boulevard, Port Charlotte, FL, Zip 33952–6765; tel. 941/629–1181; William Hawley, President and Chief Executive Officer
Web address: www.fawcetthospital.com

FORT WALTON BEACH MEDICAL CENTER (O, 257 beds) 1000 Mar–Walt Drive, Fort Walton Beach, FL, Zip 32547–6795; tel. 850/862–1111; Mitchell P. Mongell, FACHE, Chief Executive Officer
Web address: www.fwbmc.com

GULF COAST REGIONAL MEDICAL CENTER (O, 176 beds) 449 West 23rd Street, Panama City, FL, Zip 32405–4593, Mailing Address: P.O. Box 15309, Zip 32406–5309, tel. 850/769–8341; Brad Griffin, Chief Executive Officer

HIGHLANDS REGIONAL MEDICAL CENTER (O, 80 beds) 3600 South Highlands Avenue, Sebring, FL, Zip 33870–5495, Mailing Address: Drawer 2066, Zip 33871–2066, tel. 863/385–6101; John D. Montois, Interim Chief Executive Officer
Web address: www.highlandsregional.com

JFK MEDICAL CENTER NORTH CAMPUS (O, 245 beds) 2201 45th Street, West Palm Beach, FL, Zip 33407–2047; tel. 561/842–6141; Patricia Burns, Chief Executive Officer
Web address: www.westpalmhospital.com

JFK MEDICAL CENTER (O, 424 beds) 5301 South Congress Avenue, Atlantis, FL, Zip 33462–1197; tel. 561/965–7300; Gina Melby, Chief Executive Officer

KENDALL REGIONAL MEDICAL CENTER (O, 300 beds) 11750 Bird Road, Miami, FL, Zip 33175–3530; tel. 305/223–3000; Brandon Haushalter, Chief Executive Officer
Web address: www.kendallmed.com

LAKE CITY MEDICAL CENTER (O, 67 beds) 340 NW Commerce Drive, Lake City, FL, Zip 32055–4709; tel. 386/719–9000; Rick Naegler, Chief Executive Officer

LARGO MEDICAL CENTER (O, 243 beds) 201 14th Street SW, Largo, FL, Zip 33770–3133; tel. 727/588–5200; Anthony M Degina, President and Chief Executive Officer
Web address: www.largomedical.com

For explanation of codes following names, see page B2.
★ Indicates Type III membership in the American Hospital Association.

LAWNWOOD REGIONAL MEDICAL CENTER & HEART INSTITUTE (O, 331 beds) 1700 South 23rd Street, Fort Pierce, FL, Zip 34950–4803; tel. 772/461–4000; Eric Goldman, Chief Executive Officer
Web address: www.lawnwoodmed.com

MEDICAL CENTER OF TRINITY (O, 276 beds) 9330 State Road 54, Trinity, FL, Zip 34655–1808; tel. 727/834–4900; Leigh Massengill, Chief Executive Officer

MEMORIAL HOSPITAL JACKSONVILLE (O, 418 beds) 3625 University Boulevard South, Jacksonville, FL, Zip 32216–4207; tel. 904/702–6111; Bradley S. Talbert, FACHE, President and Chief Executive Officer
Web address: www.memorialhospitaljax.com

MEMORIAL HOSPITAL OF TAMPA (O, 139 beds) 2901 Swann Avenue, Tampa, FL, Zip 33609–4057; tel. 813/873–6400; Sonia I. Wellman, Chief Executive Officer
Web address: www.memorialhospitaltampa.com

NORTH FLORIDA REGIONAL MEDICAL CENTER (O, 432 beds) 6500 Newberry Road, Gainesville, FL, Zip 32605–4392, Mailing Address: P.O. Box 147006, Zip 32614–7006, tel. 352/333–4000; Eric Lawson, Chief Executive Officer

NORTHSIDE HOSPITAL (O, 217 beds) 6000 49th Street North, Saint Petersburg, FL, Zip 33709–2145; tel. 727/521–4411; Dia Nichols, Chief Executive Officer
Web address: www.northsidehospital.com

NORTHWEST MEDICAL CENTER (O, 228 beds) 2801 North State Road 7, Margate, FL, Zip 33063–5727; tel. 954/974–0400; Erica Gulrich, Chief Executive Officer
Web address: www.northwestmed.com

OAK HILL HOSPITAL (O, 262 beds) 11375 Cortez Boulevard, Brooksville, FL, Zip 34613–5409; tel. 352/596–6632; Mickey Smith, Chief Executive Officer

OCALA REGIONAL MEDICAL CENTER (O, 270 beds) 1431 SW First Avenue, Ocala, FL, Zip 34471–6500, Mailing Address: P.O. Box 2200, Zip 34478–2200, tel. 352/401–1000; Chad Christianson, Chief Executive Officer
Web address: www.ocalaregional.com

ORANGE PARK MEDICAL CENTER (O, 297 beds) 2001 Kingsley Avenue, Orange Park, FL, Zip 32073–5156; tel. 904/639–8500; Chad Patrick, President and Chief Executive Officer
Web address: www.opmedical.com

OSCEOLA REGIONAL MEDICAL CENTER (O, 235 beds) 700 West Oak Street, Kissimmee, FL, Zip 34741–4996; tel. 407/846–2266; Davide M. Carbone, FACHE, Chief Executive Officer

OVIEDO MEDICAL CENTER (O, 64 beds) 8300 Red Bug Lake Road, Oviedo, FL, Zip 32765–6801; tel. 407/890–2273; Kenneth C. Donahey, Chief Executive Officer
Web address: www.oviedomedicalcenter.com

PALMS WEST HOSPITAL (O, 204 beds) 13001 Southern Boulevard, Loxahatchee, FL, Zip 33470–9203; tel. 561/798–3300; Joshua DeTillio, Chief Executive Officer

PALMS OF PASADENA HOSPITAL (O, 187 beds) 1501 Pasadena Avenue South, Saint Petersburg, FL, Zip 33707–3798; tel. 727/381–1000; Jacob Fisher, Chief Executive Officer
Web address: www.palmspasadena.com

PLANTATION GENERAL HOSPITAL (O, 264 beds) 401 NW 42nd Avenue, Plantation, FL, Zip 33317–2882; tel. 954/587–5010; Madeline Nava, Chief Executive Officer

POINCIANA MEDICAL CENTER (O, 24 beds) 325 Cypress Parkway, Kissimmee, FL, Zip 34758; tel. 407/530–2000; Christopher Cosby, Chief Executive Officer
Web address: www.poincianamedicalcenter.com

PUTNAM COMMUNITY MEDICAL CENTER (O, 99 beds) 611 Zeagler Drive, Palatka, FL, Zip 32177–3810; tel. 386/328–5711; Mark J. Dooley, Chief Executive Officer

RAULERSON HOSPITAL (O, 100 beds) 1796 Highway 441 North, Okeechobee, FL, Zip 34972–1918, Mailing Address: P.O. Box 1307, Zip 34973–1307, tel. 863/763–2151; Brian Melear, Chief Executive Officer
Web address: www.raulersonhospital.com

REGIONAL MEDICAL CENTER BAYONET POINT (O, 290 beds) 14000 Fivay Road, Hudson, FL, Zip 34667–7199; tel. 727/869–5400; Thomas Lawhorne, Interim Chief Executive Officer

SOUTH BAY HOSPITAL (O, 138 beds) 4016 Sun City Center Blvd, Sun City Center, FL, Zip 33573–5298; tel. 813/634–3301; Sharon L. Roush, Chief Executive Officer
Web address: www.southbayhospital.com/

ST. LUCIE MEDICAL CENTER (O, 194 beds) 1800 SE Tiffany Avenue, Port St Lucie, FL, Zip 34952–7521; tel. 772/335–4000; Jay Finnegan, Chief Executive Officer

ST. PETERSBURG GENERAL HOSPITAL (O, 219 beds) 6500 38th Avenue North, Saint Petersburg, FL, Zip 33710–1629; tel. 727/384–1414; Janice Balzano, President and Chief Executive Officer
Web address: www.stpetegeneral.com

TAMPA COMMUNITY HOSPITAL (O, 201 beds) 6001 Webb Road, Tampa, FL, Zip 33615–3291; tel. 813/888–7060
Web address: www.tampacommunityhospital.com/

TWIN CITIES HOSPITAL (O, 65 beds) 2190 Highway 85 North, Niceville, FL, Zip 32578–1045; tel. 850/678–4131; David Whalen, Chief Executive Officer
Web address: www.tchealthcare.com

UNIVERSITY HOSPITAL AND MEDICAL CENTER (O, 317 beds) 7201 North University Drive, Tamarac, FL, Zip 33321–2996; tel. 954/721–2200; Dana C. Oaks, Chief Executive Officer

WEST FLORIDA HOSPITAL (O, 339 beds) 8383 North Davis Highway, Pensacola, FL, Zip 32514–6088; tel. 850/494–4000; Carlton Ulmer, President and Chief Executive Officer
Web address: www.westfloridahospital.com

WESTSIDE REGIONAL MEDICAL CENTER (O, 215 beds) 8201 West Broward Boulevard, Plantation, FL, Zip 33324–2701; tel. 954/473–6600; Barbara Simmons, R.N., Chief Executive Officer

GEORGIA: CARTERSVILLE MEDICAL CENTER (O, 80 beds) 960 Joe Frank Harris Parkway, Cartersville, GA, Zip 30120–2129; tel. 770/382–1530; J. Christopher. Mosley, Chief Executive Officer
Web address: www.cartersvillemedical.com

COLISEUM MEDICAL CENTERS (O, 227 beds) 350 Hospital Drive, Macon, GA, Zip 31217–3871; tel. 478/765–7000; Stephen J. Daugherty, Chief Executive Officer

COLISEUM NORTHSIDE HOSPITAL (O, 103 beds) 400 Charter Boulevard, Macon, GA, Zip 31210–4853, Mailing Address: P.O. Box 4627, Zip 31208–4627, tel. 478/757–8200; Greg Caples, Chief Executive Officer
Web address: www.coliseumhealthsystem.com

DOCTORS HOSPITAL (O, 307 beds) 3651 Wheeler Road, Augusta, GA, Zip 30909–6426; tel. 706/651–3232; Douglas Welch, Chief Executive Officer
Web address: www.doctors–hospital.net

EASTSIDE MEDICAL CENTER (O, 294 beds) 1700 Medical Way, Snellville, GA, Zip 30078–2195; tel. 770/979–0200; Trent Lind, Chief Executive Officer

FAIRVIEW PARK HOSPITAL (O, 168 beds) 200 Industrial Boulevard, Dublin, GA, Zip 31021–2997, Mailing Address: P.O. Box 1408, Zip 31040–1408, tel. 478/275–2000; Donald R. Avery, FACHE, President and Chief Executive Officer
Web address: www.fairviewparkhospital.com

MEMORIAL HEALTH (O, 523 beds) 4700 Waters Avenue, Savannah, GA, Zip 31404–6283, Mailing Address: P.O. Box 23089, Zip 31403–3089, tel. 912/350–8000; Shayne George, Chief Executive Officer

MEMORIAL SATILLA HEALTH (O, 199 beds) 1900 Tebeau Street, Waycross, GA, Zip 31501–6357, Mailing Address: P.O. Box 139, Zip 31502–0139, tel. 912/283–3030; Bobby McCullough, Chief Executive Officer
Web address: www.memorialsatillahealth.com/

REDMOND REGIONAL MEDICAL CENTER (O, 230 beds) 501 Redmond Road, Rome, GA, Zip 30165–1415, Mailing Address: P.O. Box 107001, Zip 30164–7001, tel. 706/291–0291; John Quinlivan, Chief Executive Officer

IDAHO: EASTERN IDAHO REGIONAL MEDICAL CENTER (O, 293 beds) 3100 Channing Way, Idaho Falls, ID, Zip 83404–7533, Mailing Address: P.O. Box 2077, Zip 83403–2077, tel. 208/529–6111; Jeff Sollis, Chief Executive Officer
Web address: www.eirmc.com

WEST VALLEY MEDICAL CENTER (O, 105 beds) 1717 Arlington, Caldwell, ID, Zip 83605–4802; tel. 208/459–4641; Elizabeth Hunsicker, Chief Executive Officer

INDIANA: TERRE HAUTE REGIONAL HOSPITAL (O, 208 beds) 3901 South Seventh Street, Terre Haute, IN, Zip 47802–5709; tel. 812/232–0021; Nathan Vooys, Chief Executive Officer
Web address: www.regionalhospital.com

For explanation of codes following names, see page B2.
★ Indicates Type III membership in the American Hospital Association.

KANSAS: MENORAH MEDICAL CENTER (O, 158 beds) 5721 West 119th Street, Overland Park, KS, Zip 66209–3722; tel. 913/498–6000; Charles Laird, Chief Executive Officer

OVERLAND PARK REGIONAL MEDICAL CENTER (O, 275 beds) 10500 Quivira Road, Overland Park, KS, Zip 66215–2306, Mailing Address: P.O. Box 15959, Zip 66215–5959, tel. 913/541–5000; Matt Sogard, Chief Executive Officer
Web address: www.oprmc.com

WESLEY HEALTHCARE CENTER (O, 562 beds) 550 North Hillside, Wichita, KS, Zip 67214–4976; tel. 316/962–2000; Bill Voloch, President and Chief Executive Officer

KENTUCKY: FRANKFORT REGIONAL MEDICAL CENTER (O, 116 beds) 299 King's Daughters Drive, Frankfort, KY, Zip 40601–4186; tel. 502/875–5240; Chip Peal, Chief Executive Officer
Web address: www.frankfortregional.com

TRISTAR GREENVIEW REGIONAL HOSPITAL (O, 167 beds) 1801 Ashley Circle, Bowling Green, KY, Zip 42104–3362; tel. 270/793–1000; Michael Sherrod, Chief Executive Officer

LOUISIANA: RAPIDES REGIONAL MEDICAL CENTER (O, 357 beds) 211 4th ST, Alexandria, LA, Zip 71301–8421, Mailing Address: 211 Fourth Street, Zip 71301–8421, tel. 318/769–3000; Jason E. Cobb, FACHE, Chief Executive Officer
Web address: www.rapidesregional.com

TULANE MEDICAL CENTER (O, 552 beds) 1415 Tulane Avenue, New Orleans, LA, Zip 70112–2600; tel. 504/988–5263; William Lunn, M.D., Chief Executive Officer

WOMEN'S AND CHILDREN'S HOSPITAL (O, 161 beds) 4600 Ambassador Caffery Parkway, Lafayette, LA, Zip 70508–6923, Mailing Address: P.O. Box 88030, Zip 70598–8030, tel. 337/521–9100; Leona Boullion, R.N., Interim Chief Executive Officer
Web address: www.womens–childrens.com

MISSISSIPPI: GARDEN PARK MEDICAL CENTER (O, 130 beds) 15200 Community Road, Gulfport, MS, Zip 39503–3085, Mailing Address: P.O. Box 1240, Zip 39502–1240, tel. 228/575–7000; Randy Rogers, FACHE, Chief Executive Officer

MISSOURI: BELTON REGIONAL MEDICAL CENTER (O, 48 beds) 17065 South 71 Highway, Belton, MO, Zip 64012–4631; tel. 816/348–1200; Todd Krass, Chief Executive Officer
Web address: www.beltonregionalmedicalcenter.com

CENTERPOINT MEDICAL CENTER (O, 221 beds) 19600 East 39th Street, Independence, MO, Zip 64057–2301; tel. 816/698–7000; Bret Kolman, CPA, FACHE, Chief Executive Officer

LAFAYETTE REGIONAL HEALTH CENTER (O, 25 beds) 1500 State Street, Lexington, MO, Zip 64067–1107; tel. 660/259–2203; Darrel Box, Chief Executive Officer
Web address: www.lafayetteregionalhealthcenter.com

LEE'S SUMMIT MEDICAL CENTER (O, 64 beds) 2100 SE Blue Parkway, Lee's Summit, MO, Zip 64063–1007; tel. 816/282–5000; Patrick Kueny, Interim Chief Executive Officer
Web address: www.leessummitmedicalcenter.com

RESEARCH MEDICAL CENTER (O, 463 beds) 2316 East Meyer Boulevard, Kansas City, MO, Zip 64132–1136; tel. 816/276–4000; Jacqueline DeSouza, Chief Executive Officer

NEVADA: MOUNTAINVIEW HOSPITAL (O, 340 beds) 3100 North Tenaya Way, Las Vegas, NV, Zip 89128–0436; tel. 702/255–5000; Jeremy Bradshaw, Chief Executive Officer
Web address: www.mountainview–hospital.com

SOUTHERN HILLS HOSPITAL AND MEDICAL CENTER (O, 134 beds) 9300 West Sunset Road, Las Vegas, NV, Zip 89148–4844; tel. 702/880–2100; Adam Rudd, Chief Executive Officer

SUNRISE HOSPITAL AND MEDICAL CENTER (O, 668 beds) 3186 South Maryland Parkway, Las Vegas, NV, Zip 89109–2306, Mailing Address: P.O. Box 98530, Zip 89193, tel. 702/731–8000; Todd Sklamberg, President
Web address: www.sunrisehospital.com

NEW HAMPSHIRE: PARKLAND MEDICAL CENTER (O, 82 beds) One Parkland Drive, Derry, NH, Zip 03038–2750; tel. 603/432–1500; Jeff Scionti, Chief Executive Officer
Web address: www.parklandmedicalcenter.com

PORTSMOUTH REGIONAL HOSPITAL (O, 165 beds) 333 Borthwick Avenue, Portsmouth, NH, Zip 03801–7128; tel. 603/436–5110; Dean Carucci, Chief Executive Officer
Web address: www.portsmouthhospital.com

SOUTH CAROLINA: COLLETON MEDICAL CENTER (O, 131 beds) 501 Robertson Boulevard, Walterboro, SC, Zip 29488–5714; tel. 843/782–2000; Jimmy O. Hiott III, Chief Executive Officer

GRAND STRAND REGIONAL MEDICAL CENTER (O, 303 beds) 809 82nd Parkway, Myrtle Beach, SC, Zip 29572–4607; tel. 843/692–1000; Mark E. Sims, Chief Executive Officer
Web address: www.grandstrandmed.com

TRIDENT MEDICAL CENTER (O, 421 beds) 9330 Medical Plaza Drive, Charleston, SC, Zip 29406–9195; tel. 843/797–7000; Todd Gallati, FACHE, President and Chief Executive Officer

TENNESSEE: PARKRIDGE MEDICAL CENTER (O, 472 beds) 2333 McCallie Avenue, Chattanooga, TN, Zip 37404–3258; tel. 423/698–6061; Thomas H. Ozburn, Chief Executive Officer
Web address: www.parkridgemedicalcenter.com

TRISTAR ASHLAND CITY MEDICAL CENTER (O, 12 beds) 313 North Main Street, Ashland City, TN, Zip 37015–1347; tel. 615/792–3030; Darrell White, R.N., Administrator and Chief Nursing Officer

TRISTAR CENTENNIAL MEDICAL CENTER (O, 650 beds) 2300 Patterson Street, Nashville, TN, Zip 37203–1528; tel. 615/342–1000; Scott A. Cihak, President and Chief Executive Officer
Web address: www.tristarcentennial.com

TRISTAR HENDERSONVILLE MEDICAL CENTER (O, 96 beds) 355 New Shackle Island Road, Hendersonville, TN, Zip 37075–2479; tel. 615/338–1000; Regina Bartlett, Chief Executive Officer
Web address: www.hendersonvillemedicalcenter.com

TRISTAR HORIZON MEDICAL CENTER (O, 130 beds) 111 Highway 70 East, Dickson, TN, Zip 37055–2080; tel. 615/446–0446; Dustin Greene, Chief Executive Officer
Web address: www.horizonmedicalcenter.com

TRISTAR SKYLINE MEDICAL CENTER (O, 579 beds) 3441 Dickerson Pike, Nashville, TN, Zip 37207–2539; tel. 615/769–2000; Steve Otto, Chief Executive Officer
Web address: www.tristarskyline.com

TRISTAR SOUTHERN HILLS MEDICAL CENTER (O, 87 beds) 391 Wallace Road, Nashville, TN, Zip 37211–4859; tel. 615/781–4000; Joanna J. Conley, FACHE, Chief Executive Officer

TRISTAR STONECREST MEDICAL CENTER (O, 101 beds) 200 StoneCrest Boulevard, Smyrna, TN, Zip 37167–6810; tel. 615/768–2000; Louis Caputo, Chief Executive Officer
Web address: www.stonecrestmedical.com

TRISTAR SUMMIT MEDICAL CENTER (O, 200 beds) 5655 Frist Boulevard, Hermitage, TN, Zip 37076–2053; tel. 615/316–3000; Brian Marger, Chief Executive Officer
Web address: www.summitmedctr.com

TEXAS: BAYSHORE MEDICAL CENTER (O, 286 beds) 4000 Spencer Highway, Pasadena, TX, Zip 77504–1202; tel. 713/359–2000; Jeanna Barnard, FACHE, Chief Executive Officer
Web address: www.bayshoremedical.com

CLEAR LAKE REGIONAL MEDICAL CENTER (O, 589 beds) 500 Medical Center Boulevard, Webster, TX, Zip 77598–4220; tel. 281/332–2511; Todd Caliva, FACHE, Chief Executive Officer

CONROE REGIONAL MEDICAL CENTER (O, 301 beds) 504 Medical Boulevard, Conroe, TX, Zip 77304, Mailing Address: P.O. Box 1538, Zip 77305–1538, tel. 936/539–1111; Matt Davis, FACHE, Chief Executive Officer
Web address: www.conroeregional.com/

CORPUS CHRISTI MEDICAL CENTER (O, 416 beds) 3315 South Alameda Street, Corpus Christi, TX, Zip 78411–1883, Mailing Address: P.O. Box 8991, Zip 78468–8991, tel. 361/761–1400; Jay Woodall, FACHE, Chief Executive Officer

CYPRESS FAIRBANKS MEDICAL CENTER (O, 155 beds) 10655 Steepletop Drive, Houston, TX, Zip 77065–4297; tel. 281/890–4285; Naman Mahajan, Chief Executive Officer
Web address: www.cyfairhospital.com

HOUSTON NORTHWEST MEDICAL CENTER (O, 339 beds) 710 Cypress Creek Parkway, Houston, TX, Zip 77090–3402; tel. 281/440–1000; Timothy Puthoff, Chief Executive Officer
Web address: www.hnmc.com

KINGWOOD MEDICAL CENTER (O, 358 beds) 22999 U S Highway 59 North, Kingwood, TX, Zip 77339; tel. 281/348–8000; Melinda Stephenson, Chief Executive Officer

For explanation of codes following names, see page B2.
★ Indicates Type III membership in the American Hospital Association.

LAS PALMAS MEDICAL CENTER (O, 509 beds) 1801 North Oregon Street, El Paso, TX, Zip 79902–3591; tel. 915/521–1200; Don Karl, Interim Chief Executive Officer
Web address: www.laspalmashealth.com

MEDICAL CITY ALLIANCE (O, 75 beds) 3101 North Tarrant Parkway, Fort Worth, TX, Zip 76177; tel. 817/639–1000; Glenn Wallace, Chief Executive Officer
Web address: www.baylorhealth.com/PhysiciansLocations/BIR/Pages/Default.aspx

MEDICAL CITY ARLINGTON (O, 309 beds) 3301 Matlock Road, Arlington, TX, Zip 76015–2908; tel. 817/465–3241; Keith Zimmerman, Chief Executive Officer

MEDICAL CITY DALLAS (O, 607 beds) 7777 Forest Lane, Dallas, TX, Zip 75230–2598; tel. 972/566–7000; Chris Mowan, Chief Executive Officer
Web address: www.medicalcityhospital.com

MEDICAL CITY DENTON (O, 185 beds) 3535 South 1–35 East, Denton, TX, Zip 76210; tel. 940/384–3535; Steven Edgar, FACHE, President and Chief Executive Officer
Web address: www.dentonregional.com

MEDICAL CITY FORT WORTH (O, 212 beds) 900 Eighth Avenue, Fort Worth, TX, Zip 76104–3902; tel. 817/336–2100; Jyric Sims, FACHE, Chief Executive Officer

MEDICAL CITY GREEN OAKS HOSPITAL (O, 124 beds) 7808 Clodus Fields Drive, Dallas, TX, Zip 75251–2206; tel. 972/991–9504; Thomas M. Collins, President, Chairman and Chief Executive Officer
Web address: www.greenoakspsych.com

MEDICAL CITY LAS COLINAS (O, 90 beds) 6800 North MacArthur Boulevard, Irving, TX, Zip 75039–2422; tel. 972/969–2000; Daniela Decell, Chief Executive Officer

MEDICAL CITY LEWISVILLE (O, 166 beds) 500 West Main, Lewisville, TX, Zip 75057–3699; tel. 972/420–1000; LaSharndra Barbarin, Chief Executive Officer
Web address: www.lewisvillemedical.com

MEDICAL CITY MCKINNEY (O, 222 beds) 4500 Medical Center Drive, McKinney, TX, Zip 75069–1650; tel. 972/547–8000; Ernest C. Lynch III, FACHE, President and Chief Executive Officer
Web address: www.medicalcenterofmckinney.com

MEDICAL CITY NORTH HILLS (O, 137 beds) 4401 Booth Calloway Road, North Richland Hills, TX, Zip 76180–7399; tel. 817/255–1000; Xavier Villarreal, FACHE, Chief Executive Officer
Web address: www.northhillshospital.com

MEDICAL CITY PLANO (O, 442 beds) 3901 West 15th Street, Plano, TX, Zip 75075–7738; tel. 972/596–6800; Charles Gressle, Chief Executive Officer
Web address: www.medicalcenterplano.com

MEDICAL CITY WEATHERFORD (O, 92 beds) 713 East Anderson Street, Weatherford, TX, Zip 76086–5705; tel. 682/582–1000; Sean Kamber, Chief Executive Officer

METHODIST AMBULATORY SURGERY HOSPITAL – NORTHWEST (O, 21 beds) 9150 Huebner Road, Suite 100, San Antonio, TX, Zip 78240–1545; tel. 210/575–5000; Scott Davis, Chief Executive Officer

METHODIST HOSPITAL SOUTH (O, 67 beds) 1905 Highway 97 East, Jourdanton, TX, Zip 78026–1504; tel. 830/769–3515; Pamela Guillory, Interim Chief Executive Officer

METHODIST HOSPITAL (O, 1599 beds) 7700 Floyd Curl Drive, San Antonio, TX, Zip 78229–3993; tel. 210/575–4000; Allen Harrison, Chief Executive Officer
Web address: www.sahealth.com

METHODIST STONE OAK HOSPITAL (O, 242 beds) 1139 E Sonterra Boulevard, San Antonio, TX, Zip 78258–4347, Mailing Address: 1139 East Sonterra Boulevard, Zip 78258–4347, tel. 210/638–2100; Marc Strode, Chief Executive Officer

PARK PLAZA HOSPITAL (O, 139 beds) 1313 Hermann Drive, Houston, TX, Zip 77004–7092; tel. 713/527–5000; Peyton Elliott, Chief Executive Officer
Web address: www.parkplazahospital.com

PEARLAND MEDICAL CENTER (O, 30 beds) 11100 Shadow Creek Parkway, Pearland, TX, Zip 77584–7285; tel. 713/770–7000; David S. Wagner, FACHE, Chief Executive Officer
Web address: www.pearlandmc.com

PLAZA SPECIALTY HOSPITAL (O, 46 beds) 1300 Binz Street, Houston, TX, Zip 77004–7016; tel. 713/285–1000; Richard Andrew. Pletz, Chief Executive Officer

RIO GRANDE REGIONAL HOSPITAL (O, 320 beds) 101 East Ridge Road, McAllen, TX, Zip 78503–1299; tel. 956/632–6000; Cristina Rivera, Chief Executive Officer
Web address: www.riohealth.com

ST. DAVID'S MEDICAL CENTER (O, 595 beds) 919 East 32nd Street, Austin, TX, Zip 78705–2709, Mailing Address: P.O. Box 4039, Zip 78765–4039, tel. 512/476–7111; Donald H. Wilkerson, FACHE, Chief Executive Officer
Web address: www.stdavids.com

ST. DAVID'S NORTH AUSTIN MEDICAL CENTER (O, 398 beds) 12221 North MoPac Expressway, Austin, TX, Zip 78758–2496; tel. 512/901–1000; Thomas W. Jackson, Chief Executive Officer

ST. DAVID'S ROUND ROCK MEDICAL CENTER (O, 171 beds) 2400 Round Rock Avenue, Round Rock, TX, Zip 78681–4097; tel. 512/341–1000; Jeremy Barclay, Chief Executive Officer
Web address: www.stdavids.com

ST. DAVID'S SOUTH AUSTIN MEDICAL CENTER (O, 290 beds) 901 West Ben White Boulevard, Austin, TX, Zip 78704–6903; tel. 512/447–2211; Todd E. Steward, FACHE, Chief Executive Officer
Web address: www.southaustinmc.com

TEXAS ORTHOPEDIC HOSPITAL (O, 49 beds) 7401 South Main Street, Houston, TX, Zip 77030–4509; tel. 713/799–8600; Eric Becker, Chief Executive Officer
Web address: www.texasorthopedic.com

TOMBALL REGIONAL MEDICAL CENTER (O, 191 beds) 605 Holderrieth Street, Tomball, TX, Zip 77375–6445; tel. 281/401–7500; Eric Evans, Chief Executive Officer

VALLEY REGIONAL MEDICAL CENTER (O, 214 beds) 100A Alton Gloor Boulevard, Brownsville, TX, Zip 78526–3354; tel. 956/350–7101; Art Garza, FACHE, Chief Executive Officer
Web address: www.valleyregionalmedicalcenter.com

WEST HOUSTON MEDICAL CENTER (O, 264 beds) 12141 Richmond Avenue, Houston, TX, Zip 77082–2499; tel. 281/558–3444; Megan Marietta, Chief Executive Officer

WOMAN'S HOSPITAL OF TEXAS (O, 367 beds) 7600 Fannin Street, Houston, TX, Zip 77054–1906; tel. 713/790–1234; Ashley McClellan, FACHE, Chief Executive Officer
Web address: www.womanshospital.com

UTAH: BRIGHAM CITY COMMUNITY HOSPITAL (O, 39 beds) 950 South Medical Drive, Brigham City, UT, Zip 84302–4724; tel. 435/734–9471; Richard Spuhler, Chief Executive Officer
Web address: www.brighamcityhospital.com

CACHE VALLEY HOSPITAL (O, 22 beds) 2380 North 400 East, North Logan, UT, Zip 84341–6000; tel. 435/713–9700; John C. Worley III, Chief Executive Officer
Web address: www.cachevalleyhospital.com/

LAKEVIEW HOSPITAL (O, 119 beds) 630 East Medical Drive, Bountiful, UT, Zip 84010–4908; tel. 801/299–2200; Troy Wood, Chief Executive Officer
Web address: www.lakeviewhospital.com

LONE PEAK HOSPITAL (O, 32 beds) 1925 South State Street, Draper, UT, Zip 84020; tel. 801/545–8000; Mark Meadows, Chief Executive Officer

MOUNTAIN VIEW HOSPITAL (O, 114 beds) 1000 East 100 North, Payson, UT, Zip 84651–1600; tel. 801/465–7000; Kevin Johnson, Chief Executive Officer
Web address: www.mvhpayson.com

OGDEN REGIONAL MEDICAL CENTER (O, 167 beds) 5475 South 500 East, Ogden, UT, Zip 84405–6905; tel. 801/479–2111; Mark B. Adams, Chief Executive Officer

ST. MARK'S HOSPITAL (O, 277 beds) 1200 East 3900 South, Salt Lake City, UT, Zip 84124–1390; tel. 801/268–7111; Mark Robinson, FACHE, Chief Executive Officer
Web address: www.stmarkshospital.com

TIMPANOGOS REGIONAL HOSPITAL (O, 105 beds) 750 West 800 North, Orem, UT, Zip 84057–3660; tel. 801/714–6000; Kimball S. Anderson, FACHE, Chief Executive Officer
Web address: www.timpanogosregionalhospital.com

VIRGINIA: CHIPPENHAM HOSPITAL (O, 765 beds) 7101 Jahnke Road, Richmond, VA, Zip 23225–4044; tel. 804/320–3911; Greg Lowe, Chief Executive Officer
Web address: www.cjwmedical.com

For explanation of codes following names, see page B2.
★ Indicates Type III membership in the American Hospital Association.

DOMINION HOSPITAL (O, 100 beds) 2960 Sleepy Hollow Road, Falls Church, VA, Zip 22044–2030; tel. 703/536–2000; Lee Higginbotham, Chief Executive Officer
Web address: www.dominionhospital.com

HENRICO DOCTORS' HOSPITAL (O, 560 beds) 1602 Skipwith Road, Richmond, VA, Zip 23229–5205; tel. 804/289–4500; William Wagnon, Chief Executive Officer

JOHN RANDOLPH MEDICAL CENTER (O, 112 beds) 411 West Randolph Road, Hopewell, VA, Zip 23860–2938; tel. 804/541–1600; Joseph Mazzo, Chief Executive Officer
Web address: www.johnrandolphmed.com

LEWIS–GALE MEDICAL CENTER (O, 521 beds) 1900 Electric Road, Salem, VA, Zip 24153–7494; tel. 540/776–4000; Thomas R. Pentz, Interim Chief Executive Officer

LEWISGALE HOSPITAL ALLEGHANY (O, 146 beds) One ARH Lane, Low Moor, VA, Zip 24457, Mailing Address: P.O. Box 7, Zip 24457–0007, tel. 540/862–6011; William Windham, Chief Executive Officer
Web address: www.alleghanyregional.com

LEWISGALE HOSPITAL MONTGOMERY (O, 89 beds) 3700 South Main Street, Blacksburg, VA, Zip 24060–7081, Mailing Address: P.O. Box 90004, Zip 24062–9004, tel. 540/951–1111; Alan J. Fabian, Chief Executive Officer
Web address: www.lewisgale.com

LEWISGALE HOSPITAL PULASKI (O, 54 beds) 2400 Lee Highway, Pulaski, VA, Zip 24301–2326, Mailing Address: P.O. Box 759, Zip 24301–0759, tel. 540/994–8100; Sean Pressman, Chief Executive Officer

RESTON HOSPITAL CENTER (O, 199 beds) 1850 Town Center Parkway, Reston, VA, Zip 20190–3219; tel. 703/689–9000; John A. Deardorff, President and Chief Executive, Northern Virginia Market
Web address: www.restonhospital.com

SPOTSYLVANIA REGIONAL MEDICAL CENTER (O, 100 beds) 4600 Spotsylvania Parkway, Fredericksburg, VA, Zip 22408–7762; tel. 540/498–4000; David McKnight, CPA, Chief Executive Officer
Web address: www.spotsrmc.com

STONESPRINGS HOSPITAL CENTER (O, 124 beds) 24440 Stone Spring Boulevard, Dulles, VA, Zip 20166–2247; tel. 571/349–4000; Lance Jones, Chief Executive Officer

Owned, leased, sponsored:	156 hospitals	38429 beds
Contract–managed:	0 hospitals	0 beds
Totals:	156 hospitals	38429 beds

0328: HEALTH FIRST, INC. (NP)

6450 US Highway 1, Rockledge, FL, Zip 32955–5747; tel. 321/434–7000; Steven P. Johnson, Ph.D., President and Chief Executive Officer
(Centralized Health System)

FLORIDA: HEALTH FIRST CAPE CANAVERAL HOSPITAL (O, 144 beds) 701 West Cocoa Beach Causeway, Cocoa Beach, FL, Zip 32931–5595, Mailing Address: P.O. Box 320069, Zip 32932–0069, tel. 321/799–7111; Aaron Robinson, Chief Executive Officer, Health First Community Hospitals

HEALTH FIRST HOLMES REGIONAL MEDICAL CENTER (O, 514 beds) 1350 South Hickory Street, Melbourne, FL, Zip 32901–3224; tel. 321/434–7000; Brett A. Esrock, FACHE, Chief Executive Officer
Web address: www.health–first.org

HEALTH FIRST PALM BAY HOSPITAL (O, 138 beds) 1425 Malabar Road NE, Palm Bay, FL, Zip 32907–2506; tel. 321/434–8000; Aaron Robinson, Chief Executive Officer, Health First Community Hospitals

HEALTH FIRST VIERA HOSPITAL (O, 84 beds) 8745 North Wickham Road, Melbourne, FL, Zip 32940–5997; tel. 321/434–9164; Aaron Robinson, Chief Executive Officer, Health First Community Hospitals
Web address: www.vierahospital.org

Owned, leased, sponsored:	4 hospitals	880 beds
Contract–managed:	0 hospitals	0 beds
Totals:	4 hospitals	880 beds

0307: HEALTH QUEST SYSTEMS, INC. (NP)

1351 Route 55 Ste 200, LaGrangeville, NY, Zip 12540–5108, Mailing Address: 1351 Route 55, Zip 12540–5108, tel. 845/475–9500; Robert Friedberg, President and Chief Executive Officer
(Independent Hospital System)

CONNECTICUT: SHARON HOSPITAL (O, 57 beds) 50 Hospital Hill Road, Sharon, CT, Zip 06069–2096, Mailing Address: P.O. Box 789, Zip 06069–0789, tel. 860/364–4000; Peter Cordeau, Chief Executive Officer

NEW YORK: NORTHERN DUTCHESS HOSPITAL (O, 68 beds) 6511 Springbrook Avenue, Rhinebeck, NY, Zip 12572–3709, Mailing Address: P.O. Box 5002, Zip 12572–5002, tel. 845/876–3001; Denise George, R.N., President
Web address: www.health–quest.org/home_nd.cfm?id=9

PUTNAM HOSPITAL CENTER (O, 164 beds) 670 Stoneleigh Avenue, Carmel, NY, Zip 10512–3997; tel. 845/279–5711; Peter Kelly, President

VASSAR BROTHERS MEDICAL CENTER (O, 365 beds) 45 Reade Place, Poughkeepsie, NY, Zip 12601–3947; tel. 845/454–8500; Ann McMackin, President
Web address: www.health–quest.org

Owned, leased, sponsored:	4 hospitals	654 beds
Contract–managed:	0 hospitals	0 beds
Totals:	4 hospitals	654 beds

0342: HEALTHPARTNERS (NP)

8170 33rd Avenue South, Bloomington, MN, Zip 55425–4516; tel. 952/883–7600; Andrea Walsh, President and Chief Executive Officer
(Moderately Centralized Health System)

MINNESOTA: GLENCOE REGIONAL HEALTH SERVICES (C, 135 beds) 1805 Hennepin Avenue North, Glencoe, MN, Zip 55336–1416; tel. 320/864–3121; Jeffrey Mason, President and Chief Executive Officer
Web address: www.grhsonline.org

HUTCHINSON HEALTH (O, 49 beds) 1095 Highway 15 South, Hutchinson, MN, Zip 55350–3182; tel. 320/234–5000; Steven Mulder, M.D., President and Chief Executive Officer

LAKEVIEW HOSPITAL (O, 67 beds) 927 Churchill Street West, Stillwater, MN, Zip 55082–6605; tel. 651/439–5330; Theodore Wegleitner, Chief Executive Officer and President
Web address: www.lakeview.org

PARK NICOLLET METHODIST HOSPITAL (O, 420 beds) 6500 Excelsior Boulevard, Saint Louis Park, MN, Zip 55426–4702, Minneapolis, tel. 952/993–5000; Roxanna L. Gapstur, Ph.D., R.N., President
Web address: www.parknicollet.com

REGIONS HOSPITAL (O, 463 beds) 640 Jackson Street, Saint Paul, MN, Zip 55101–2595; tel. 651/254–3456; Megan Remark, President and Chief Executive Officer

WISCONSIN: AMERY HOSPITAL AND CLINIC (O, 11 beds) 265 Griffin Street East, Amery, WI, Zip 54001–1439; tel. 715/268–8000; Debra Rudquist, FACHE, President and Chief Executive Officer
Web address: www.amerymedicalcenter.org

HUDSON HOSPITAL AND CLINIC (O, 24 beds) 405 Stageline Road, Hudson, WI, Zip 54016–7848; tel. 715/531–6000; Thomas Borowski, FACHE, President

WESTFIELDS HOSPITAL AND CLINIC (O, 25 beds) 535 Hospital Road, New Richmond, WI, Zip 54017–1449; tel. 715/243–2600; Steven Massey, President and Chief Executive Officer
Web address: www.westfieldshospital.com

Owned, leased, sponsored:	7 hospitals	1059 beds
Contract–managed:	1 hospitals	135 beds
Totals:	8 hospitals	1194 beds

★0585: HEALTHTECH MANAGEMENT SERVICES (IO)

5110 Maryland Way Suite 200, Brentwood, TN, Zip 37027–2307; tel. 615/309–6053; Derek Morkel, Chief Executive Officer
(Moderately Centralized Health System)

For explanation of codes following names, see page B2.
★ Indicates Type III membership in the American Hospital Association.

ARIZONA: COBRE VALLEY REGIONAL MEDICAL CENTER (C, 25 beds) 5880 South Hospital Drive, Globe, AZ, Zip 85501–9454; tel. 928/425–3261; Neal Jensen, Chief Executive Officer

GEORGIA: UPSON REGIONAL MEDICAL CENTER (C, 81 beds) 801 West Gordon Street, Thomaston, GA, Zip 30286–3426, Mailing Address: P.O. Box 1059, Zip 30286–0027, tel. 706/647–8111; Tripp Penn, Chief Executive Officer
Web address: www.urmc.org

ILLINOIS: CARLINVILLE AREA HOSPITAL (C, 25 beds) 20733 North Broad Street, Carlinville, IL, Zip 62626–1499; tel. 217/854–3141; Kenneth G. Reid, President and Chief Executive Officer
Web address: www.cahcare.com

HAMMOND–HENRY HOSPITAL (C, 61 beds) 600 North College Avenue, Geneseo, IL, Zip 61254–1099; tel. 309/944–6431; Mark Kuhn, Chief Executive Officer

HILLSBORO AREA HOSPITAL (C, 25 beds) 1200 East Tremont Street, Hillsboro, IL, Zip 62049–1900; tel. 217/532–6111; Rex H. Brown, President and Chief Executive Officer
Web address: www.hillsborohealth.org

LOUISIANA: IBERIA MEDICAL CENTER (C, 123 beds) 2315 East Main Street, New Iberia, LA, Zip 70560–4031, Mailing Address: P.O. Box 13338, Zip 70562–3338, tel. 337/364–0441; Parker A. Templeton, FACHE, Chief Executive Officer
Web address: www.iberiamedicalcenter.com

MONTANA: BARRETT HOSPITAL & HEALTHCARE (C, 18 beds) 600 Mt Highway 91 South, Dillon, MT, Zip 59725–7379; tel. 406/683–3000; Ken Westman, Chief Executive Officer

OREGON: BLUE MOUNTAIN HOSPITAL (C, 62 beds) 170 Ford Road, John Day, OR, Zip 97845–2009; tel. 541/575–1311; Derek Daly, Chief Executive Officer
Web address: www.bluemountainhospital.org

WISCONSIN: GRANT REGIONAL HEALTH CENTER (C, 4 beds) 507 South Monroe Street, Lancaster, WI, Zip 53813–2054; tel. 608/723–2143; Nicole Clapp, R.N., MSN, FACHE, President and Chief Executive Officer

SPOONER HEALTH (C, 20 beds) 1280 Chandler Drive, Spooner, WI, Zip 54801–1299; tel. 715/635–2111; Michael Schafer, Chief Executive Officer and Administrator
Web address: www.spoonerhealth.com

TOMAH MEMORIAL HOSPITAL (C, 25 beds) 321 Butts Avenue, Tomah, WI, Zip 54660–1412; tel. 608/372–2181; Philip J. Stuart, Administrator and Chief Executive Officer
Web address: www.tomahhospital.org

WYOMING: HOT SPRINGS COUNTY MEMORIAL HOSPITAL (C, 25 beds) 150 East Arapahoe Street, Thermopolis, WY, Zip 82443–2498; tel. 307/864–3121; Margie Molitor, FACHE, R.N., Chief Executive Officer

Owned, leased, sponsored:	0 hospitals	0 beds
Contract–managed:	12 hospitals	494 beds
Totals:	12 hospitals	494 beds

★9505: HENRY FORD HEALTH SYSTEM (NP)
One Ford Place, Detroit, MI, Zip 48202–3450; tel. 313/876–8708; Wright L. Lassiter III, President and Chief Executive Officer
(Centralized Health System)

MICHIGAN: HENRY FORD ALLEGIANCE HEALTH (O, 401 beds) 205 North East Avenue, Jackson, MI, Zip 49201–1753; tel. 517/205–4800; Georgia R. Fojtasek, President and Chief Executive Officer
Web address: www.allegiancehealth.org

HENRY FORD ALLEGIANCE SPECIALTY HOSPITAL (O, 44 beds) 110 North Elm Avenue, Jackson, MI, Zip 49202–3595; tel. 517/205–4463; J Mark. Fall, Chief Executive Officer

HENRY FORD HOSPITAL (O, 725 beds) 2799 West Grand Boulevard, Detroit, MI, Zip 48202–2608; tel. 313/916–2600; Veronica Hall, RN, Chief Operating Officer, Henry Ford Hospital and Chief Nursing Officer, Henry Ford Health System
Web address: www.henryfordhealth.org

HENRY FORD KINGSWOOD HOSPITAL (O, 91 beds) 10300 West Eight Mile Road, Ferndale, MI, Zip 48220–2100; tel. 248/398–3200; Cathrine Frank, M.D., Chairperson

HENRY FORD MACOMB HOSPITALS (O, 415 beds) 15855 19 Mile Road, Clinton Township, MI, Zip 48038–6324; tel. 586/263–2300; Barbara W. Rossmann, R.N., President and Chief Executive Officer
Web address: www.henryfordmacomb.com

HENRY FORD WEST BLOOMFIELD HOSPITAL (O, 212 beds) 6777 West Maple Road, West Bloomfield, MI, Zip 48322–3013; tel. 248/661–4100; Lynn M. Torossian, President and Chief Executive Officer

HENRY FORD WYANDOTTE HOSPITAL (O, 345 beds) 2333 Biddle Avenue, Wyandotte, MI, Zip 48192–4668; tel. 734/246–6000; Denise Brooks–Williams, President and Chief Executive Officer
Web address: www.henryfordhealth.org

Owned, leased, sponsored:	7 hospitals	2233 beds
Contract–managed:	0 hospitals	0 beds
Totals:	7 hospitals	2233 beds

0309: HERITAGE VALLEY HEALTH SYSTEM (NP)
1000 Dutch Ridge Road, Beaver, PA, Zip 15009–9727; tel. 724/773–2024; Norman F. Mitry, President and Chief Executive Officer
(Independent Hospital System)

PENNSYLVANIA: HERITAGE VALLEY HEALTH SYSTEM (O, 271 beds) 1000 Dutch Ridge Road, Beaver, PA, Zip 15009–9727; tel. 724/728–7000; Norman F. Mitry, President and Chief Executive Officer
Web address: www.heritagevalley.org

SEWICKLEY VALLEY HOSPITAL, (A DIVISION OF VALLEY MEDICAL FACILITIES) (O, 179 beds) 720 Blackburn Road, Sewickley, PA, Zip 15143–1459; tel. 412/741–6600; Norman F. Mitry, President and Chief Executive Officer

Owned, leased, sponsored:	2 hospitals	450 beds
Contract–managed:	0 hospitals	0 beds
Totals:	2 hospitals	450 beds

1024: HEYWOOD HEALTHCARE (NP)
242 Green Street, Gardner, MA, Zip 01440–1336; tel. 978/632–3420; Winfield S. Brown, FACHE, Chief Executive Officer
(Independent Hospital System)

MASSACHUSETTS: ATHOL HOSPITAL (O, 25 beds) 2033 Main Street, Athol, MA, Zip 01331–3598; tel. 978/249–3511; Winfield S. Brown, FACHE, President and Chief Executive Officer
Web address: www.atholhospital.org

HEYWOOD HOSPITAL (O, 93 beds) 242 Green Street, Gardner, MA, Zip 01440–1373; tel. 978/632–3420; Winfield S. Brown, FACHE, President and Chief Executive Officer
Web address: www.heywood.org

Owned, leased, sponsored:	2 hospitals	118 beds
Contract–managed:	0 hospitals	0 beds
Totals:	2 hospitals	118 beds

1014: HOLZER HEALTH SYSTEM (NP)
500 Burlington Road, Jackson, OH, Zip 45640–9360; tel. 855/446–5937; Michael Canady, M.D., Chief Executive Officer
(Independent Hospital System)

OHIO: HOLZER MEDICAL CENTER – JACKSON (O, 24 beds) 500 Burlington Road, Jackson, OH, Zip 45640–9360; tel. 740/288–4625; Michael Canady, M.D., Chief Executive Officer

HOLZER MEDICAL CENTER (O, 194 beds) 100 Jackson Pike, Gallipolis, OH, Zip 45631–1563; tel. 740/446–5000; Michael Canady, M.D., Interim Chief Executive Officer
Web address: www.holzer.org

Owned, leased, sponsored:	2 hospitals	218 beds
Contract–managed:	0 hospitals	0 beds
Totals:	2 hospitals	218 beds

For explanation of codes following names, see page B2.
★ Indicates Type III membership in the American Hospital Association.

Section B

★0963: HONORHEALTH (NP)

8125 North Hayden Road, Scottsdale, AZ, Zip 85258–2463; tel. 623/580–5800; Todd LaPorte, Chief Executive Officer
(Independent Hospital System)

ARIZONA: HONORHEALTH DEER VALLEY MEDICAL CENTER (O, 204 beds) 19829 North 27th Avenue, Phoenix, AZ, Zip 85027–4002; tel. 623/879–6100; David Price, Chief Executive Officer
Web address: www.jcl.com

HONORHEALTH JOHN C. LINCOLN MEDICAL CENTER (O, 262 beds) 250 East Dunlap Avenue, Phoenix, AZ, Zip 85020–2825; tel. 602/943–2381; Margaret Elizabeth. Griffin, Chief Executive Officer

HONORHEALTH SCOTTSDALE OSBORN MEDICAL CENTER (O, 347 beds) 7400 East Osborn Road, Scottsdale, AZ, Zip 85251–6403; tel. 480/882–4000; Kimberly Post, Senior Vice President and Chief Executive Officer
Web address: www.shc.org

HONORHEALTH SCOTTSDALE SHEA MEDICAL CENTER (O, 409 beds) 9003 East Shea Boulevard, Scottsdale, AZ, Zip 85260–6771; tel. 480/323–3000; Gary E. Baker, Senior Vice President and Chief Executive Officer

HONORHEALTH SCOTTSDALE THOMPSON PEAK MEDICAL CENTER (O, 92 beds) 7400 East Thompson Peak Parkway, Scottsdale, AZ, Zip 85255–4109; tel. 480/324–7000; David Price, Chief Executive Officer
Web address: www.shc.org

Owned, leased, sponsored:	5 hospitals	1314 beds
Contract–managed:	0 hospitals	0 beds
Totals:	5 hospitals	1314 beds

★0642: HOUSTON HEALTHCARE SYSTEM (NP)

1601 Watson Boulevard, Warner Robins, GA, Zip 31093–3431, Mailing Address: P.O. Box 2886, Zip 31099–2886, tel. 478/922–4281; Cary Martin, Chief Executive Officer
(Independent Hospital System)

GEORGIA: HOUSTON MEDICAL CENTER (O, 237 beds) 1601 Watson Boulevard, Warner Robins, GA, Zip 31093–3431, Mailing Address: P.O. Box 2886, Zip 31099–2886, tel. 478/922–4281; Cary Martin, Chief Executive Officer

PERRY HOSPITAL (O, 39 beds) 1120 Morningside Drive, Perry, GA, Zip 31069–2906; tel. 478/987–3600; David Campbell, Administrator
Web address: www.hhc.org

Owned, leased, sponsored:	2 hospitals	276 beds
Contract–managed:	0 hospitals	0 beds
Totals:	2 hospitals	276 beds

★7235: HOUSTON METHODIST (CO)

6565 Fannin Street, D–200, Houston, TX, Zip 77030–2707; tel. 713/441–2221; Marc L. Boom, M.D., Chief Executive Officer
(Centralized Health System)

TEXAS: HOUSTON METHODIST BAYTOWN HOSPITAL (O, 257 beds) 4401 Garth Road, Administration Department, Baytown, TX, Zip 77521–2122; tel. 281/420–8600; David P. Bernard, FACHE, Chief Executive Officer

HOUSTON METHODIST CLEAR LAKE HOSPITAL (O, 113 beds) 18300 St John Drive, Nassau Bay, TX, Zip 77058–6302; tel. 281/333–5503; Dan Newman, Chief Executive Officer
Web address: www.houstonmethodist.org/st-john–clear–lake

HOUSTON METHODIST CONTINUING CARE HOSPITAL (O, 58 beds) 701 Fry Road, Katy, TX, Zip 77450–2255; tel. 281/599–5700; Gary L. Kempf, R.N., Administrator

HOUSTON METHODIST HOSPITAL (O, 933 beds) 6565 Fannin Street, D200, Houston, TX, Zip 77030–2707; tel. 713/790–3311; Roberta Schwartz, Ph.D., Executive Vice President
Web address: www.methodisthealth.com

HOUSTON METHODIST SUGAR LAND HOSPITAL (O, 305 beds) 16655 SW Freeway, Sugar Land, TX, Zip 77479–2329; tel. 281/274–7000; Christopher Siebenaler, Regional Senior Vice President and Chief Executive Officer

HOUSTON METHODIST THE WOODLANDS HOSPITAL (O, 101 beds) 17201 Interstate 45 South, The Woodlands, TX, Zip 77385; tel. 713/790–3333; Debra F. Sukin, Ph.D., Regional Senior Vice President and Chief Executive Officer
Web address: www.houstonmethodist.org/locations/the-woodlands/

HOUSTON METHODIST WEST HOSPITAL (O, 193 beds) 18500 Katy Freeway, Houston, TX, Zip 77094–1110; tel. 832/522–1000; Wayne M. Voss, Chief Executive Officer

HOUSTON METHODIST WILLOWBROOK HOSPITAL (O, 312 beds) 18220 State Highway 249, Houston, TX, Zip 77070–4347; tel. 281/477–1000; Keith Barber, CPA, Chief Executive Officer
Web address: www.houstonmethodist.org/locations/willowbrook/

Owned, leased, sponsored:	8 hospitals	2272 beds
Contract–managed:	0 hospitals	0 beds
Totals:	8 hospitals	2272 beds

★5355: HSHS HOSPITAL SISTERS HEALTH SYSTEM (CO)

4936 LaVerna Road, Springfield, IL, Zip 62707–9797, Mailing Address: P.O. Box 19456, Zip 62794–9456, tel. 217/523–4747; Mary Starmann–Harrison, FACHE, R.N., President and Chief Executive Officer
(Decentralized Health System)

ILLINOIS: HSHS GOOD SHEPHERD HOSPITAL (O, 30 beds) 200 South Cedar Street, Shelbyville, IL, Zip 62565–1838; tel. 217/774–3961; Aaron Puchbauer, President

HSHS HOLY FAMILY HOSPITAL IN GREENVILLE (O, 42 beds) 200 Healthcare Drive, Greenville, IL, Zip 62246–1154; tel. 618/664–1230; James F. Dover, FACHE, Interim Chief Executive Officer
Web address: www.greenvilleregionalhospital.com

HSHS ST. ANTHONY'S MEMORIAL HOSPITAL (O, 123 beds) 503 North Maple Street, Effingham, IL, Zip 62401–2099; tel. 217/342–2121; Theresa Rutherford, R.N., MS, FACHE, President and Chief Executive Officer
Web address: www.stanthonyshospital.org

HSHS ST. ELIZABETH'S HOSPITAL (O, 260 beds) One St. Elizabeth's Boulevard, O'Fallon, IL, Zip 62269; tel. 618/234–2120; Patricia Fischer, FACHE, R.N., President and Chief Executive Officer
Web address: www.steliz.org

HSHS ST. FRANCIS HOSPITAL (O, 25 beds) 1215 Franciscan Drive, Litchfield, IL, Zip 62056–1799, Mailing Address: P.O. Box 1215, Zip 62056–0999, tel. 217/324–2191; John Peipert, R.N., Interim President and Chief Executive Officer

HSHS ST. JOHN'S HOSPITAL (O, 402 beds) 800 East Carpenter Street, Springfield, IL, Zip 62769–0002; tel. 217/544–6464; Charles Lucore, M.D., President and Chief Executive Officer
Web address: www.st-johns.org

HSHS ST. JOSEPH'S HOSPITAL (O, 65 beds) 9515 Holy Cross Lane, Breese, IL, Zip 62230–3618, Mailing Address: PO Box 99, Zip 62230–0099, tel. 618/526–4511; Chris Klay, President and Chief Executive Officer

HSHS ST. JOSEPH'S HOSPITAL (O, 25 beds) 12866 Troxler Avenue, Highland, IL, Zip 62249–1698; tel. 618/651–2600; John A. Ludwig, President and Chief Operating Officer
Web address: www.stjosephshighland.com

HSHS ST. MARY'S HOSPITAL (O, 230 beds) 1800 East Lake Shore Drive, Decatur, IL, Zip 62521–3883; tel. 217/464–2966; Evert J. Kuiper, Interim President and Chief Executive Officer

WISCONSIN: HSHS SACRED HEART HOSPITAL (O, 216 beds) 900 West Clairemont Avenue, Eau Claire, WI, Zip 54701–6122; tel. 715/717–4121; Andrew Bagnall, President and Chief Executive Officer
Web address: www.sacredhearteauclaire.org

HSHS ST. CLARE MEMORIAL HOSPITAL (O, 20 beds) 855 South Main Street, Oconto Falls, WI, Zip 54154–1296; tel. 920/846–3444; Christopher Brabant, President and Chief Executive Officer
Web address: www.stclarememorial.org

HSHS ST. JOSEPH'S HOSPITAL (O, 102 beds) 2661 County Highway I, Chippewa Falls, WI, Zip 54729–5407; tel. 715/723–1811; Charisse S. Oland, FACHE, President and Chief Executive Officer

HSHS ST. MARY'S HOSPITAL MEDICAL CENTER (O, 83 beds) 1726 Shawano Avenue, Green Bay, WI, Zip 54303–3282; tel. 920/498–4200; Therese B. Pandl, President and Chief Executive Officer
Web address: www.stmgb.org

HSHS ST. NICHOLAS HOSPITAL (O, 46 beds) 3100 Superior Avenue, Sheboygan, WI, Zip 53081–1948; tel. 920/459–8300; Justin Selle, Chief Executive Officer
Web address: www.stnicholashospital.org

For explanation of codes following names, see page B2.
★ Indicates Type III membership in the American Hospital Association.

HSHS ST. VINCENT HOSPITAL (O, 255 beds) 835 South Van Buren Street, Green Bay, WI, Zip 54301–3526, Mailing Address: P.O. Box 13508, Zip 54307–3508, tel. 920/433–0111; Therese B. Pandl, President and Chief Executive Officer
Web address: www.stvincenthospital.org

Owned, leased, sponsored:	15 hospitals	1924 beds
Contract–managed:	0 hospitals	0 beds
Totals:	15 hospitals	1924 beds

0907: HUNT REGIONAL HEALTHCARE (NP)

4215 Joe Ramsey Boulevard, Greenville, TX, Zip 75401–7852, Mailing Address: P.O. Box 1059, Zip 75403–1059, tel. 903/408–5000; Richard Carter, Chief Executive Officer
(Independent Hospital System)

TEXAS: HUNT REGIONAL MEDICAL CENTER (O, 167 beds) 4215 Joe Ramsey Boulevard, Greenville, TX, Zip 75401–7899, Mailing Address: P.O. Box 1059, Zip 75403–1059, tel. 903/408–5000; Richard Carter, District Chief Executive Officer
Web address: www.huntregional.org

Owned, leased, sponsored:	1 hospitals	167 beds
Contract–managed:	0 hospitals	0 beds
Totals:	1 hospitals	167 beds

0117: HUNTSVILLE HOSPITAL HEALTH SYSTEM (NP)

101 Sivley Road SW, Huntsville, AL, Zip 35801–4421; tel. 265/256–1000; David S. Spillers, Chief Executive Officer
(Moderately Centralized Health System)

ALABAMA: ATHENS–LIMESTONE HOSPITAL (C, 71 beds) 700 West Market Street, Athens, AL, Zip 35611–2457, Mailing Address: P.O. Box 999, Zip 35612–0999, tel. 256/233–9292; David Pryor, President
Web address: www.athenslimestonehospital.com

DECATUR MORGAN HOSPITAL (O, 127 beds) 1201 Seventh Street SE, Decatur, AL, Zip 35601–3303, Mailing Address: P.O. Box 2239, Zip 35609–2239, tel. 256/341–2000; Nathaniel Richardson Jr, President

HELEN KELLER HOSPITAL (C, 145 beds) 1300 South Montgomery Avenue, Sheffield, AL, Zip 35660–6334, Mailing Address: P.O. Box 610, Zip 35660–0610, tel. 256/386–4196; Paul Storey, FACHE, President and Chief Executive Officer
Web address: www.helenkeller.com

HUNTSVILLE HOSPITAL (O, 927 beds) 101 Sivley Road SW, Huntsville, AL, Zip 35801–4470; tel. 256/265–1000; David S. Spillers, Chief Executive Officer
Web address: www.huntsvillehospital.org

LAWRENCE MEDICAL CENTER (C, 43 beds) 202 Hospital Street, Moulton, AL, Zip 35650–1218, Mailing Address: P.O. Box 39, Zip 35650–0039, tel. 256/974–2200; Dean A. Griffin, Chief Executive Officer

RED BAY HOSPITAL (C, 25 beds) 211 Hospital Road, Red Bay, AL, Zip 35582–3858, Mailing Address: P.O. Box 490, Zip 35582–0490, tel. 256/356–9532; Sherry Jolley, Director of Operations and Nursing
Web address: www.redbayhospital.com

Owned, leased, sponsored:	2 hospitals	1054 beds
Contract–managed:	4 hospitals	284 beds
Totals:	6 hospitals	1338 beds

★0231: INDIANA UNIVERSITY HEALTH (NP)

340 West 10th Street, Suite 6100, Indianapolis, IN, Zip 46202–3082, Mailing Address: P.O. Box 1367, Zip 46206–1367, tel. 317/962–5900; Dennis M. Murphy, President and Chief Executive Officer
(Centralized Physician/Insurance Health System)

INDIANA: INDIANA UNIVERSITY HEALTH ARNETT HOSPITAL (O, 187 beds) 5165 McCarty Lane, Lafayette, IN, Zip 47905–8764, Mailing Address: P.O. Box 5545, Zip 47903–5545, tel. 765/448–8000; Daniel Neufelder, President
Web address: www.iuhealth.org

INDIANA UNIVERSITY HEALTH BALL MEMORIAL HOSPITAL (O, 346 beds) 2401 University Avenue, Muncie, IN, Zip 47303–3499; tel. 765/747–3111; Jeffrey C. Bird, M.D., President
Web address: www.iuhealth.org

INDIANA UNIVERSITY HEALTH BEDFORD HOSPITAL (O, 25 beds) 2900 West 16th Street, Bedford, IN, Zip 47421–3583; tel. 812/275–1200; Bradford W. Dykes, President and Chief Executive Officer
Web address: www.iuhealth.org

INDIANA UNIVERSITY HEALTH BLACKFORD HOSPITAL (O, 15 beds) 410 Pilgrim Boulevard, Hartford City, IN, Zip 47348–1897; tel. 765/348–0300; David W. Hyatt, President

INDIANA UNIVERSITY HEALTH BLOOMINGTON HOSPITAL (O, 274 beds) 601 West Second Street, Bloomington, IN, Zip 47403–2317, Mailing Address: P.O. Box 1149, Zip 47402–1149, tel. 812/336–6821; Brian T. Shockney, FACHE, Interim President
Web address: www.iuhealth.org

INDIANA UNIVERSITY HEALTH FRANKFORT (C, 25 beds) 1300 South Jackson Street, Frankfort, IN, Zip 46041–3313; tel. 765/656–3000; Kelly Braverman, President

INDIANA UNIVERSITY HEALTH JAY HOSPITAL (C, 35 beds) 500 West Votaw Street, Portland, IN, Zip 47371–1322; tel. 260/726–7131; David W. Hyatt, President
Web address: www.jaycountyhospital.com

INDIANA UNIVERSITY HEALTH NORTH HOSPITAL (O, 161 beds) 11700 North Meridian Avenue, Carmel, IN, Zip 46032–4656; tel. 317/688–2000; Randall C. Yust, Interim President
Web address: www.iuhealth.org/north

INDIANA UNIVERSITY HEALTH PAOLI HOSPITAL (O, 25 beds) 642 West Hospital Road, Paoli, IN, Zip 47454–9672, Mailing Address: P.O. Box 499, Zip 47454–0499, tel. 812/723–2811; Larry Bailey, President

INDIANA UNIVERSITY HEALTH TIPTON HOSPITAL (O, 25 beds) 1000 South Main Street, Tipton, IN, Zip 46072–9799; tel. 765/675–8500; Michael Harlowe, President and Chief Executive Officer
Web address: www.iuhealth.org

INDIANA UNIVERSITY HEALTH UNIVERSITY HOSPITAL (O, 1282 beds) 550 University Boulevard, Indianapolis, IN, Zip 46202–5149, Mailing Address: P.O. Box 1367, Zip 46206–1367, tel. 317/944–5000; Ryan Nagy, M.D., Interim President and Chief Medical Officer

INDIANA UNIVERSITY HEALTH WEST HOSPITAL (O, 127 beds) 1111 North Ronald Reagan Parkway, Avon, IN, Zip 46123–7085; tel. 317/217–3000; Arthur Vasquez, President
Web address: www.iuhealth.org

INDIANA UNIVERSITY HEALTH WHITE MEMORIAL HOSPITAL (O, 25 beds) 720 South Sixth Street, Monticello, IN, Zip 47960–8182; tel. 574/583–7111; Mary Minier, President

REHABILITATION HOSPITAL OF INDIANA (O, 83 beds) 4141 Shore Drive, Indianapolis, IN, Zip 46254–2607; tel. 317/329–2000; Daniel B. Woloszyn, Chief Executive Officer
Web address: www.rhin.com

Owned, leased, sponsored:	12 hospitals	2575 beds
Contract–managed:	2 hospitals	60 beds
Totals:	14 hospitals	2635 beds

2025: INFIRMARY HEALTH SYSTEM (NP)

5 Mobile Infirmary Circle, Mobile, AL, Zip 36607–3513; tel. 251/435–5500; D Mark. Nix, President and Chief Executive Officer
(Moderately Centralized Health System)

ALABAMA: ATMORE COMMUNITY HOSPITAL (O, 33 beds) 401 Medical Park Drive, Atmore, AL, Zip 36502–3091; tel. 251/368–2500; Douglas Tanner, President

INFIRMARY LONG TERM ACUTE CARE HOSPITAL (L, 38 beds) 5 Mobile Infirmary Circle, Mobile, AL, Zip 36607–3513, Mailing Address: P.O. Box 2226, Zip 36652–2226, tel. 251/660–5239; Susanne Marmande, Administrator
Web address: www.theinfirmary.com/

For explanation of codes following names, see page B2.
★ Indicates Type III membership in the American Hospital Association.

Section B

MOBILE INFIRMARY MEDICAL CENTER (O, 526 beds) 5 Mobile Infirmary Drive North, Mobile, AL, Zip 36607–3513, Mailing Address: P.O. Box 2144, Zip 36652–2144, tel. 251/435–2400; Joe Stough, Interim President
Web address: www.infirmaryhealth.org

NORTH BALDWIN INFIRMARY (L, 50 beds) 1815 Hand Avenue, Bay Minette, AL, Zip 36507–4110, Mailing Address: P.O. Box 1409, Zip 36507–1409, tel. 251/937–5521; Benjamin K. Hansert, Administrator
Web address: www.mobileinfirmary.org

THOMAS HOSPITAL (L, 136 beds) 750 Morphy Avenue, Fairhope, AL, Zip 36532–1812, Mailing Address: P.O. Box 929, Zip 36533–0929, tel. 251/928–2375; Ormand P. Thompson, President

Owned, leased, sponsored:	5 hospitals	783 beds
Contract–managed:	0 hospitals	0 beds
Totals:	5 hospitals	783 beds

★1305: INOVA HEALTH SYSTEM (NP)

8110 Gatehouse Road, Suite 200 East, Falls Church, VA, Zip 22042–1252; tel. 703/289–2069; J Stephen. Jones, M.D., Chief Executive Officer
(Centralized Health System)

VIRGINIA: INOVA ALEXANDRIA HOSPITAL (O, 334 beds) 4320 Seminary Road, Alexandria, VA, Zip 22304–1535; tel. 703/504–3167; Susan Carroll, Chief Executive Officer

INOVA FAIR OAKS HOSPITAL (O, 201 beds) 3600 Joseph Siewick Drive, Fairfax, VA, Zip 22033–1798; tel. 703/391–3600; John L. Fitzgerald, Chief Executive Officer
Web address: www.inova.org

INOVA FAIRFAX HOSPITAL (O, 1002 beds) 3300 Gallows Road, Falls Church, VA, Zip 22042–3300; tel. 703/776–4001; Patrick Christiansen, Ph.D., Chief Executive Officer
Web address: www.inova.org

INOVA LOUDOUN HOSPITAL (O, 279 beds) 44045 Riverside Parkway, Leesburg, VA, Zip 20176–5101, Mailing Address: P.O. Box 6000, Zip 20177–0600, tel. 703/858–6000; Deborah Addo, Chief Executive Officer

INOVA MOUNT VERNON HOSPITAL (O, 237 beds) 2501 Parker's Lane, Alexandria, VA, Zip 22306–3209; tel. 703/664–7000; Donald Brideau, M.D., Chief Executive Officer
Web address: www.inova.org

Owned, leased, sponsored:	5 hospitals	2053 beds
Contract–managed:	0 hospitals	0 beds
Totals:	5 hospitals	2053 beds

★0151: INSPIRA HEALTH NETWORK (NP)

165 Bridgeton Pike, Mullica Hill, NJ, Zip 8062; tel. 856/641–8000; John A. DiAngelo, President and Chief Executive Officer
(Moderately Centralized Health System)

NEW JERSEY: INSPIRA MEDICAL CENTER–ELMER (O, 96 beds) 501 West Front Street, Elmer, NJ, Zip 08318–2101; tel. 856/363–1000; John A. DiAngelo, President and Chief Executive Officer
Web address: www.inspirahealthnetwork.org/?id=5281&sid=1

INSPIRA MEDICAL CENTER–VINELAND (O, 335 beds) 1505 West Sherman Avenue, Vineland, NJ, Zip 08360–6912; tel. 856/641–8000; John A. DiAngelo, President and Chief Executive Officer
Web address: www.inspirahealthnetwork.org/?id=5280&sid=1

INSPIRA MEDICAL CENTER–WOODBURY (O, 261 beds) 509 North Broad Street, Woodbury, NJ, Zip 08096–1697; tel. 856/845–0100; John A. DiAngelo, President and Chief Executive Officer

Owned, leased, sponsored:	3 hospitals	692 beds
Contract–managed:	0 hospitals	0 beds
Totals:	3 hospitals	692 beds

★0305: INTEGRIS HEALTH (NP)

3366 NW Expressway, Suite 800, Oklahoma City, OK, Zip 73112–9756; tel. 405/949–6066; Timothy T. Pehrson, President and Chief Executive Officer
(Moderately Centralized Health System)

OKLAHOMA: INTEGRIS BAPTIST MEDICAL CENTER (O, 597 beds) 3300 NW Expressway, Oklahoma City, OK, Zip 73112–4418; tel. 405/949–3011; Timothy J. Johnsen, MS, President

INTEGRIS CANADIAN VALLEY HOSPITAL (O, 58 beds) 1201 Health Center Parkway, Yukon, OK, Zip 73099–6381; tel. 405/717–6800; Teresa Gray, President
Web address: www.integris–health.com

INTEGRIS DEACONESS (O, 141) 5501 North Portland Avenue, Oklahoma City, OK, Zip 73112–2099; tel. 405/604–6000; Rex Van Meter, President

INTEGRIS GROVE HOSPITAL (O, 58 beds) 1001 East 18th Street, Grove, OK, Zip 74344–2907; tel. 918/786–2243; Robert Rupp, President

INTEGRIS HEALTH EDMOND (O, 40 beds) 4801 Integris Parkway, Edmond, OK, Zip 73034–8864; tel. 405/657–3000; Avilla Williams, MS, President
Web address: www.integrisok.com/edmond

INTEGRIS MIAMI HOSPITAL (O, 84 beds) 200 Second Avenue SW, Miami, OK, Zip 74354–6830; tel. 918/542–6611; Jonas Rabel, President
Web address: www.integrisok.com/miami–hospital

INTEGRIS SOUTHWEST MEDICAL CENTER (O, 275 beds) 4401 South Western, Oklahoma City, OK, Zip 73109–3413; tel. 405/636–7000; Jordan Cash, President

INTEGRIS BASS BAPTIST HEALTH CENTER (O, 167 beds) 600 South Monroe Street, Enid, OK, Zip 73701–7211, Mailing Address: P.O. Box 3168, Zip 73702–3168, tel. 580/233–2300; Finny Mathew, President
Web address: www.integris–health.com

LAKESIDE WOMEN'S HOSPITAL (O, 23 beds) 11200 North Portland Avenue, Oklahoma City, OK, Zip 73120–5045; tel. 405/936–1500; Kelley Brewer, R.N., MSN, President
Web address: www.lakeside–wh.net

Owned, leased, sponsored:	9 hospitals	1443 beds
Contract–managed:	0 hospitals	0 beds
Totals:	9 hospitals	1443 beds

★1815: INTERMOUNTAIN HEALTHCARE, INC. (NP)

36 South State Street, 22nd Floor, Salt Lake City, UT, Zip 84111–1453; tel. 801/442–2000; A. Marc. Harrison, M.D., President and Chief Executive Officer
(Decentralized Health System)

IDAHO: CASSIA REGIONAL HOSPITAL (O, 25 beds) 1501 Hiland Avenue, Burley, ID, Zip 83318–2688; tel. 208/678–4444; Ben Smalley, Administrator
Web address: www.cassiaregional.org

UTAH: ALTA VIEW HOSPITAL (O, 66 beds) 9660 South 1300 East, Sandy, UT, Zip 84094–3793; tel. 801/501–2600; Lisa A. Paletta, RN, MPA, NEA–BC, Chief Executive Officer

AMERICAN FORK HOSPITAL (O, 89 beds) 170 North 1100 East, American Fork, UT, Zip 84003–2096; tel. 801/855–3300; Jason Wilson, Administrator and Chief Executive Officer
Web address: www.intermountainhealthcare.org

BEAR RIVER VALLEY HOSPITAL (O, 14 beds) 905 North 1000 West, Tremonton, UT, Zip 84337–2497; tel. 435/207–4500; James Montgomery, Interim Chief Executive Officer
Web address: www.https://intermountainhealthcare.org/locations/bear–river–valley–hospital/

CEDAR CITY HOSPITAL (O, 48 beds) 1303 North Main Street, Cedar City, UT, Zip 84721–9746; tel. 435/868–5000; Eric Packer, Chief Executive Officer

DELTA COMMUNITY MEDICAL CENTER (O, 15 beds) 126 South White Sage Avenue, Delta, UT, Zip 84624–8937; tel. 435/864–5591; Lenny Lyons, Administrator
Web address: www.ihc.com

DIXIE REGIONAL MEDICAL CENTER (O, 245 beds) 1380 East Medical Center Drive, Saint George, UT, Zip 84790–2123; tel. 435/251–1000; Mitchell Cloward, Administrator
Web address: www.intermountainhealthcare.org

FILLMORE COMMUNITY HOSPITAL (O, 19 beds) 674 South Highway 99, Fillmore, UT, Zip 84631–5013; tel. 435/743–5591; Lenny Lyons, Administrator
Web address: www.ihc.com

For explanation of codes following names, see page B2.
★ Indicates Type III membership in the American Hospital Association.

© 2018 AHA Guide

GARFIELD MEMORIAL HOSPITAL (C, 15 beds) 200 North 400 East, Panguitch, UT, Zip 84759, Mailing Address: P.O. Box 389, Zip 84759–0389, tel. 435/676–8811; Alberto Vasquez, Administrator

HEBER VALLEY MEDICAL CENTER (O, 19 beds) 1485 South Highway 40, Heber City, UT, Zip 84032–3522; tel. 435/654–2500; Shawn Morrow, Administrator
Web address: www.intermountainhealthcare.org

INTERMOUNTAIN MEDICAL CENTER (O, 510 beds) 5121 South Cottonwood Street, Murray, UT, Zip 84107–5701; tel. 801/507–7000; Joseph Mott, Chief Executive Officer

LDS HOSPITAL (O, 243 beds) Eighth Avenue and 'C' Street, Salt Lake City, UT, Zip 84143–0001; tel. 801/408–1100; Jim Sheets, Chief Executive Officer and Administrator
Web address: www.intermountainhealthcare.org

LOGAN REGIONAL HOSPITAL (O, 128 beds) 1400 North 500 East, Logan, UT, Zip 84341–2455; tel. 435/716–1000; Kyle A. Hansen, Chief Executive Officer
Web address: www.loganregionalhospital.org

MCKAY-DEE HOSPITAL (O, 312 beds) 4401 Harrison Boulevard, Ogden, UT, Zip 84403–3195; tel. 801/387–2800; Michael A. Clark, Administrator

OREM COMMUNITY HOSPITAL (O, 18 beds) 331 North 400 West, Orem, UT, Zip 84057–1999; tel. 801/224–4080; J. Francis. Gibson, Administrator and Chief Executive Officer
Web address: www.intermountainhealthcare.org

PARK CITY HOSPITAL (O, 37 beds) 900 Round Valley Drive, Park City, UT, Zip 84060–7552; tel. 435/658–7000; Si William. Hutt, Administrator

PRIMARY CHILDREN'S HOSPITAL (O, 289 beds) 100 North Mario Capecchi Drive, Salt Lake City, UT, Zip 84113–1100; tel. 801/662–1000; Katy Welkie MBA, R.N., Chief Executive Officer
Web address: www.intermountainhealthcare.org

RIVERTON HOSPITAL (O, 88 beds) 3741 West 12600 South, Riverton, UT, Zip 84065–7215; tel. 801/285–4000; Todd Neubert, Chief Executive Officer

SANPETE VALLEY HOSPITAL (O, 18 beds) 1100 South Medical Drive, Mount Pleasant, UT, Zip 84647–2222; tel. 435/462–2441; Aaron C. Wood, Chief Executive Officer and Administrator
Web address: www.intermountainhealthcare.com

SEVIER VALLEY HOSPITAL (O, 29 beds) 1000 North Main Street, Richfield, UT, Zip 84701–1857; tel. 435/893–4100; Gary E. Beck, Administrator

THE ORTHOPEDIC SPECIALTY HOSPITAL (O, 40 beds) 5848 South 300 East, Murray, UT, Zip 84107–6121; tel. 801/314–4100; Lisa Bagley, Nurse Administrator
Web address: www.intermountainhealthcare.org

UTAH VALLEY HOSPITAL (O, 359 beds) 1034 North 500 West, Provo, UT, Zip 84604–3337; tel. 801/357–7850; Kevin Brooks, Hospital Administrator
Web address: www.utahvalleyregional.org

Owned, leased, sponsored:	21 hospitals	2611 beds
Contract–managed:	1 hospitals	15 beds
Totals:	22 hospitals	2626 beds

★0902: IOWA SPECIALTY HOSPITALS (NP)
1316 South Main Street, Clarion, IA, Zip 50525–2019; tel. 515/532–2811; Steven J. Simonin, Chief Executive Officer
(Independent Hospital System)

IOWA: IOWA SPECIALTY HOSPITAL–BELMOND (C, 22 beds) 403 1st Street SE, Belmond, IA, Zip 50421–1201; tel. 641/444–3223; Amy McDaniel, Chief Executive Officer

IOWA SPECIALTY HOSPITAL–CLARION (C, 25 beds) 1316 South Main Street, Clarion, IA, Zip 50525–2019; tel. 515/532–2811; Steven J. Simonin, President and Chief Executive Officer
Web address: www.iowaspecialtyhospital.com

Owned, leased, sponsored:	0 hospitals	0 beds
Contract–managed:	2 hospitals	47 beds
Totals:	2 hospitals	47 beds

★7775: JEFFERSON HEALTH (NP)
925 Chestnut Street, Suite 110, Philadelphia, PA, Zip 19107–4216; tel. 610/225–6200; Stephen K. Klasko, M.D., Chief Executive Officer
(Moderately Centralized Health System)

NEW JERSEY: JEFFERSON STRATFORD HOSPITAL (O, 527 beds) 18 East Laurel Road, Stratford, NJ, Zip 08084–1327; tel. 856/346–6000; Jill Ostrem, Senior Vice President and Chief Operating Officer

PENNSYLVANIA: ABINGTON HOSPITAL (O, 613 beds) 1200 Old York Road, Abington, PA, Zip 19001–3720; tel. 215/481–2000; Margaret M. McGoldrick, President
Web address: www.abingtonhealth.org

ABINGTON–LANSDALE HOSPITAL JEFFERSON HEALTH (O, 127 beds) 100 Medical Campus Drive, Lansdale, PA, Zip 19446–1200; tel. 215/368–2100; Kathleen Farrell, Chief Administrative Officer
Web address: www.abingtonhealth.org/find–a–location/abington–lansdale–hospital/#.V5dyWL9yk4

JEFFERSON HEALTH NORTHEAST (O, 464 beds) 10800 Knights Road, Mansion House, Philadelphia, PA, Zip 19114–4200; tel. 215/612–4000; Kathleen Kinslow, Ed.D., Chief Executive Officer
Web address: www.ariahealth.org

THOMAS JEFFERSON UNIVERSITY HOSPITALS (O, 899 beds) 111 South 11th Street, Philadelphia, PA, Zip 19107–5084; tel. 215/955–6000; Richard Webster, R.N., President

Owned, leased, sponsored:	5 hospitals	2630 beds
Contract–managed:	0 hospitals	0 beds
Totals:	5 hospitals	2630 beds

★8855: JFK HEALTH (NP)
80 James Street, 2nd Floor, Edison, NJ, Zip 08820–3938; tel. 732/632–1503; Raymond F. Fredericks, President and Chief Executive Officer

NEW JERSEY: HACKENSACK MERIDIAN HEALTH JFK JOHNSON REHABILITATION INSTITUTE (O, 94 beds) 65 James Street, Edison, NJ, Zip 8818; tel. 732/321–7050; Anthony Cuzzola, Vice President and Administrator
Web address: www.njrehab.org

HACKENSACK MERIDIAN HEALTH JFK MEDICAL CENTER (O, 388 beds) 65 James Street, Edison, NJ, Zip 8818; tel. 732/321–7000; Raymond F. Fredericks, Central Regional President
Web address: www.jfkmc.org

Owned, leased, sponsored:	2 hospitals	482 beds
Contract–managed:	0 hospitals	0 beds
Totals:	2 hospitals	482 beds

★0324: JOHN MUIR HEALTH (NP)
1400 Treat Boulevard, Walnut Creek, CA, Zip 94597–2142; tel. 925/941–2100; Calvin K. Knight, President and Chief Executive Officer
(Independent Hospital System)

CALIFORNIA: JOHN MUIR BEHAVIORAL HEALTH CENTER (O, 73 beds) 2740 Grant Street, Concord, CA, Zip 94520–2265; tel. 925/674–4100; Cindy Bolter, Chief Nursing and Operations Officer
Web address: www.johnmuirhealth.com

JOHN MUIR MEDICAL CENTER, CONCORD (O, 207 beds) 2540 East Street, Concord, CA, Zip 94520–1906; tel. 925/682–8200; Michael S. Thomas, President and Chief Administrative Officer

JOHN MUIR MEDICAL CENTER, WALNUT CREEK (O, 425 beds) 1601 Ygnacio Valley Road, Walnut Creek, CA, Zip 94598–3194; tel. 925/939–3000; Jane Willemsen, President and Chief Administrative Officer
Web address: https://www.johnmuirhealth.com/

Owned, leased, sponsored:	3 hospitals	705 beds
Contract–managed:	0 hospitals	0 beds
Totals:	3 hospitals	705 beds

★1015: JOHNS HOPKINS HEALTH SYSTEM (NP)
733 North Broadway, BRB 104, Baltimore, MD, Zip 21205–1832; tel. 410/955–5000; Kevin W. Sowers, MSN, R.N., President
(Centralized Physician/Insurance Health System)

For explanation of codes following names, see page B2.
★ Indicates Type III membership in the American Hospital Association.

Section B

DISTRICT OF COLUMBIA: SIBLEY MEMORIAL HOSPITAL (O, 258 beds) 5255 Loughboro Road NW, Washington, DC, Zip 20016–2633; tel. 202/537–4000; Richard O. Davis, Ph.D., President

FLORIDA: JOHNS HOPKINS ALL CHILDREN'S HOSPITAL (O, 259 beds) 501 6th Avenue South, Saint Petersburg, FL, Zip 33701–4634; tel. 727/898–7451; Jonathan M. Ellen, M.D., President
Web address: www.allkids.org

MARYLAND: HOWARD COUNTY GENERAL HOSPITAL (O, 262 beds) 5755 Cedar Lane, Columbia, MD, Zip 21044–2999; tel. 410/740–7890; Steven C. Snelgrove, President

JOHNS HOPKINS BAYVIEW MEDICAL CENTER (O, 420 beds) 4940 Eastern Avenue, Baltimore, MD, Zip 21224–2780; tel. 410/550–0100; Richard G. Bennett, M.D., President
Web address: www.hopkinsbayview.org

JOHNS HOPKINS HOSPITAL (O, 976 beds) 600 North Wolfe Street, Admin 104, Baltimore, MD, Zip 21287–1629; tel. 410/955–5000; Redonda G. Miller, M.D., President

SUBURBAN HOSPITAL (O, 208 beds) 8600 Old Georgetown Road, Bethesda, MD, Zip 20814–1497; tel. 301/896–3100; Jacky Schultz, MSN, R.N., President
Web address: www.suburbanhospital.org

Owned, leased, sponsored:	6 hospitals	2383 beds
Contract–managed:	0 hospitals	0 beds
Totals:	6 hospitals	2383 beds

★2105: KAISER FOUNDATION HOSPITALS (NP)
One Kaiser Plaza, Oakland, CA, Zip 94612–3600; tel. 510/271–5910; Bernard J. Tyson, Chairman and Chief Executive Officer
(Decentralized Health System)

CALIFORNIA: KAISER PERMANENTE ANTIOCH MEDICAL CENTER (O, 150 beds) 4501 Sand Creek Road, Antioch, CA, Zip 94531–8687; tel. 925/813–6500; Colleen McKeown, Senior Vice President and Area Manager

KAISER PERMANENTE BALDWIN PARK MEDICAL CENTER (O, 257 beds) 1011 Baldwin Park Boulevard, Baldwin Park, CA, Zip 91706–5806; tel. 626/851–1011; Margaret H. Pierce, Executive Director
Web address: www.kp.org

KAISER PERMANENTE DOWNEY MEDICAL CENTER (O, 409 beds) 9333 Imperial Highway, Downey, CA, Zip 90242–2812; tel. 562/657–9000; James Branchick, R.N., MS, Senior Vice President and Area Manager
Web address: www.kaiserpermanente.org

KAISER PERMANENTE FONTANA MEDICAL CENTER (O, 490 beds) 9961 Sierra Avenue, Fontana, CA, Zip 92335–6794; tel. 909/427–5000; Greg Christian, Senior Vice President, Area Manager – San Bernardino County Area

KAISER PERMANENTE FREMONT MEDICAL CENTER (O, 76 beds) 39400 Paseo Padre Parkway, Fremont, CA, Zip 94538–2310; tel. 510/248–3000; Victoria O'Gorman, Administrator
Web address: www.kp.org

KAISER PERMANENTE FRESNO MEDICAL CENTER (O, 169 beds) 7300 North Fresno Street, Fresno, CA, Zip 93720–2942; tel. 559/448–4500; Debbie Hemker, Senior Vice President and Area Manager
Web address: www.kaiserpermanente.org

KAISER PERMANENTE LOS ANGELES MEDICAL CENTER (O, 528 beds) 4867 Sunset Boulevard, Los Angeles, CA, Zip 90027–5961; tel. 323/783–4011; William N. Grice, Executive Director
Web address: www.kaiserpermanente.org

KAISER PERMANENTE MANTECA MEDICAL CENTER (O, 251 beds) 1777 West Yosemite Avenue, Manteca, CA, Zip 95337–5187; tel. 209/825–3700; Corwin N. Harper, Senior Vice President and Area Manager

KAISER PERMANENTE MORENO VALLEY MEDICAL CENTER (O, 94 beds) 27300 Iris Avenue, Moreno Valley, CA, Zip 92555–4800; tel. 951/243–0811; Vita M. Willett, Senior Vice President, Area Manager

KAISER PERMANENTE OAKLAND MEDICAL CENTER (O, 297 beds) 3600 Broadway, Oakland, CA, Zip 94611–5693; tel. 510/752–1000; Jeffrey A. Collins, M.D., Senior Vice President and Area Manager
Web address: www.kaiserpermanente.org

KAISER PERMANENTE ORANGE COUNTY ANAHEIM MEDICAL CENTER (O, 436 beds) 3440 East La Palma Avenue, Anaheim, CA, Zip 92806–2020; tel. 714/644–2000; Mark E. Costa, Executive Director

KAISER PERMANENTE PANORAMA CITY MEDICAL CENTER (O, 115 beds) 13652 Cantara Street, Panorama City, CA, Zip 91402–5497; tel. 818/375–2000; Payman Roshan, Senior Vice President and Area Manager
Web address: www.kaiserpermanente.org

KAISER PERMANENTE REDWOOD CITY MEDICAL CENTER (O, 145 beds) 1100 Veterans Boulevard, Redwood City, CA, Zip 94063–2087; tel. 650/299–2000; Michelle Gaskill–Hames, R.N., Senior Vice President & Area Manager
Web address: www.kaiserpermanente.org

KAISER PERMANENTE RIVERSIDE MEDICAL CENTER (O, 226 beds) 10800 Magnolia Avenue, Riverside, CA, Zip 92505–3000; tel. 951/353–2000; Vita M. Willett, Executive Director

KAISER PERMANENTE ROSEVILLE MEDICAL CENTER (O, 340 beds) 1600 Eureka Road, Roseville, CA, Zip 95661–3027; tel. 916/784–4000; Jordan Herget, Senior Vice President and Manager
Web address: www.kp.org

KAISER PERMANENTE SACRAMENTO MEDICAL CENTER (O, 200 beds) 2025 Morse Avenue, Sacramento, CA, Zip 95825–2100; tel. 916/973–5000; Sandy Sharon, Senior Vice President and Area Manager
Web address: www.kp.org

KAISER PERMANENTE SAN DIEGO MEDICAL CENTER (O, 541 beds) 4647 Zion Avenue, San Diego, CA, Zip 92120–2507; tel. 619/528–5000; Jane Finley, Senior Vice President & Area Manager
Web address: www.kaiserpermanente.org

KAISER PERMANENTE SAN FRANCISCO MEDICAL CENTER (O, 239 beds) 2425 Geary Boulevard, San Francisco, CA, Zip 94115–3358; tel. 415/833–2000; Ronald Groepper, Senior Vice President and Area Manager

KAISER PERMANENTE SAN JOSE MEDICAL CENTER (O, 222 beds) 250 Hospital Parkway, San Jose, CA, Zip 95119–1199; tel. 408/972–7000; Irene Chavez, Senior Vice President and Area Manager
Web address: www.kaiserpermanente.org

KAISER PERMANENTE SAN LEANDRO MEDICAL CENTER (O, 184 beds) 2500 Merced Street, San Leandro, CA, Zip 94577–4201; tel. 510/454–1000; Thomas S. Hanenburg, Senior Vice President and Area Manager
Web address: www.kaiserpermanente.org

KAISER PERMANENTE SAN RAFAEL MEDICAL CENTER (O, 116 beds) 99 Montecillo Road, San Rafael, CA, Zip 94903–3397; tel. 415/444–2000; Judy Coffey, R.N., Senior Vice President and Area Manager

KAISER PERMANENTE SANTA CLARA MEDICAL CENTER (O, 327 beds) 700 Lawrence Expressway, Santa Clara, CA, Zip 95051–5173; tel. 408/851–1000; Christopher L. Boyd, Senior Vice President and Area Manager
Web address: www.kaiserpermanente.org

KAISER PERMANENTE SANTA ROSA MEDICAL CENTER (O, 173 beds) 401 Bicentennial Way, Santa Rosa, CA, Zip 95403–2192; tel. 707/393–4000; Judy Coffey, R.N., Senior Vice President and Area Manager
Web address: www.kaiserpermanente.org

KAISER PERMANENTE SOUTH BAY MEDICAL CENTER (O, 172 beds) 25825 Vermont Avenue, Harbor City, CA, Zip 90710–3599; tel. 310/325–5111; Lesley A. Wille, Executive Director
Web address: www.kaiserpermanente.org

KAISER PERMANENTE SOUTH SACRAMENTO MEDICAL CENTER (O, 217 beds) 6600 Bruceville Road, Sacramento, CA, Zip 95823–4691; tel. 916/688–2430; Patricia M. Rodriguez, Senior Vice President and Area Manager

KAISER PERMANENTE SOUTH SAN FRANCISCO (O, 120 beds) 1200 El Camino Real, South San Francisco, CA, Zip 94080–3208; tel. 650/742–2000; Ronald Groepper, Senior Vice President and Area Manager
Web address: www.kaiserpermanente.org

KAISER PERMANENTE VACAVILLE MEDICAL CENTER (O, 140 beds) 1 Quality Drive, Vacaville, CA, Zip 95688–9494; tel. 707/624–4000; Norair Jemjemian, Senior Vice President and Area Manager

KAISER PERMANENTE VALLEJO MEDICAL CENTER (O, 248 beds) 975 Sereno Drive, Vallejo, CA, Zip 94589–2441; tel. 707/651–1000; Corwin N. Harper, Senior Vice President and Area Manager
Web address: www.kaiserpermanente.org

KAISER PERMANENTE WALNUT CREEK MEDICAL CENTER (O, 233 beds) 1425 South Main Street, Walnut Creek, CA, Zip 94596–5300; tel. 925/295–4000; Colleen McKeown, Senior Vice President and Area Manager

For explanation of codes following names, see page B2.
★ Indicates Type III membership in the American Hospital Association.

KAISER PERMANENTE WEST LOS ANGELES MEDICAL CENTER (O, 118 beds) 6041 Cadillac Avenue, Los Angeles, CA, Zip 90034–1700; tel. 323/857–2201; Georgina R. Garcia, R.N., Executive Director
Web address: www.kaiserpermanente.org

KAISER PERMANENTE WOODLAND HILLS MEDICAL CENTER (O, 138 beds) 5601 DeSoto Avenue, Woodland Hills, CA, Zip 91367–6798; tel. 818/719–2000; Dennis C. Benton, Senior Vice President and Area Manager

HAWAII: KAISER PERMANENTE MEDICAL CENTER (O, 193 beds) 3288 Moanalua Road, Honolulu, HI, Zip 96819–1469; tel. 808/432–0000; James Y. Lee, Hospital Administrator
Web address: www.kaiserpermanente.org

KULA HOSPITAL (C, 6 beds) 100 Keokea Place, Kula, HI, Zip 96790–7450; tel. 808/878–1221; Paul Harper–O'Connor, Interim Chief Executive Officer

LANAI COMMUNITY HOSPITAL (C, 24 beds) 628 Seventh Street, Lanai City, HI, Zip 96763–0650, Mailing Address: P.O. Box 630650, Zip 96763–0650, tel. 808/565–8450; Paul Harper–O'Connor, Interim Administrator
Web address: https://www.mauihealthsystem.org/lanai–hospital/

MAUI MEMORIAL MEDICAL CENTER (C, 213 beds) 221 Mahalani Street, Wailuku, HI, Zip 96793–2581; tel. 808/244–9056; Michael A. Rembis, FACHE, Chief Executive Officer

OREGON: KAISER FOUNDATION HOSPITAL WESTSIDE MEDICAL CENTER (O, 122 beds) 2875 NW Stucki Avenue, Hillsboro, OR, Zip 97124–5806; tel. 971/310–1000; Brantley Dettmer, Administrator and Chief Operating Officer
Web address: www.kp.org

KAISER SUNNYSIDE MEDICAL CENTER (O, 301 beds) 10180 SE Sunnyside Road, Clackamas, OR, Zip 97015–8970; tel. 503/652–2880; Justin N. Evander, Administrator and Chief Operating Officer

Owned, leased, sponsored:	34 hospitals	7987 beds
Contract–managed:	3 hospitals	243 beds
Totals:	37 hospitals	8230 beds

0954: KECK MEDICINE OF USC (NP)
1510 San Pablo Street, Suite 600, Los Angeles, CA, Zip 90033–5405; tel. 323/442–8500; Thomas E. Jackiewicz, Senior Vice President and Chief Executive Officer
(Independent Hospital System)

CALIFORNIA: KECK HOSPITAL OF USC (O, 401 beds) 1500 San Pablo Street, Los Angeles, CA, Zip 90033–5313; tel. 323/442–8500; Rodney B. Hanners, Chief Executive Officer
Web address: www.keckhospitalofusc.org

USC NORRIS COMPREHENSIVE CANCER CENTER (O, 60 beds) 1441 Eastlake Avenue, Los Angeles, CA, Zip 90089–0112; tel. 323/865–3000; Rodney B. Hanners, Chief Executive Officer

USC VERDUGO HILLS HOSPITAL (O, 156 beds) 1812 Verdugo Boulevard, Glendale, CA, Zip 91208–1409; tel. 818/790–7100; Keith Hobbs, Chief Executive Officer
Web address: www.uscvhh.org

Owned, leased, sponsored:	3 hospitals	617 beds
Contract–managed:	0 hospitals	0 beds
Totals:	3 hospitals	617 beds

★0258: KETTERING HEALTH NETWORK (NP)
3965 Southern Boulevard, Dayton, OH, Zip 45429–1229; tel. 937/395–8150; Fred M. Manchur, Chief Executive Officer
(Independent Hospital System)

OHIO: FORT HAMILTON HOSPITAL (O, 164 beds) 630 Eaton Avenue, Hamilton, OH, Zip 45013–2770; tel. 513/867–2000; Michael Mewhirter, President

GRANDVIEW MEDICAL CENTER (O, 282 beds) 405 West Grand Avenue, Dayton, OH, Zip 45405–4796; tel. 937/723–3200; Rebecca Lewis, President
Web address: www.ketteringhealth.org/grandview/

GREENE MEMORIAL HOSPITAL (O, 49 beds) 1141 North Monroe Drive, Xenia, OH, Zip 45385–1600; tel. 937/352–2000; Rick A. Dodds, President

KETTERING MEDICAL CENTER (O, 391 beds) 3535 Southern Boulevard, Kettering, OH, Zip 45429–1221; tel. 937/298–4331; Terry M. Burns, President
Web address: www.ketteringhealth.org/kettering

SOIN MEDICAL CENTER (O, 133 beds) 3535 Pentagon Boulevard, Beavercreek, OH, Zip 45431–1705; tel. 937/702–4000; Rick A. Dodds, President
Web address: www.khnetwork.org/soin

SYCAMORE MEDICAL CENTER (O, 202 beds) 4000 Miamisburg–Centerville Road, Miamisburg, OH, Zip 45342–7615; tel. 937/866–0551; Walter Sackett, President
Web address: www.khnetwork.org/sycamore

Owned, leased, sponsored:	6 hospitals	1221 beds
Contract–managed:	0 hospitals	0 beds
Totals:	6 hospitals	1221 beds

★0026: KINDRED HEALTHCARE (IO)
680 South Fourth Street, Louisville, KY, Zip 40202–2412; tel. 502/596–7300; Kent Wallace, Chief Operating Officer
(Independent Hospital System)

CALIFORNIA: KINDRED HOSPITAL RANCHO (O, 55 beds) 10841 White Oak Avenue, Rancho Cucamonga, CA, Zip 91730–3811; tel. 909/581–6400; Victor Carrasco, Chief Executive Officer
Web address: www.khrancho.com

KINDRED HOSPITAL RIVERSIDE (O, 40 beds) 2224 Medical Center Drive, Perris, CA, Zip 92571–2638; tel. 951/436–3535; William Mitchell, Chief Executive Officer and Administrator
Web address: www.khriverside.com

KINDRED HOSPITAL SOUTH BAY (O, 84 beds) 1246 West 155th Street, Gardena, CA, Zip 90247–4062; tel. 310/323–5330; Michael D. Kerr, Chief Executive Officer
Web address: www.khsouthbay.com/

KINDRED HOSPITAL–BALDWIN PARK (C, 91 beds) 14148 Francisquito Avenue, Baldwin Park, CA, Zip 91706–6120; tel. 626/388–2700; Fiona Basa–Reyes, Chief Executive Officer

KINDRED HOSPITAL–BREA (O, 48 beds) 875 North Brea Boulevard, Brea, CA, Zip 92821–2699; tel. 714/529–6842; Rafael Pena, Chief Executive Officer
Web address: www.kindredhospitalbrea.com/

KINDRED HOSPITAL–LA MIRADA (O, 216 beds) 14900 East Imperial Highway, La Mirada, CA, Zip 90638–2172; tel. 562/944–1900; David Kowalski, Chief Executive Officer

KINDRED HOSPITAL–LOS ANGELES (O, 81 beds) 5525 West Slauson Avenue, Los Angeles, CA, Zip 90056–1067; tel. 310/642–0325; Phillip R. Wolfe, Chief Executive Officer
Web address: www.kindredhospitalla.com/

KINDRED HOSPITAL–ONTARIO (O, 81 beds) 550 North Monterey Avenue, Ontario, CA, Zip 91764–3399; tel. 909/391–0333; Vincent Trac, Chief Executive Officer
Web address: www.khontario.com/

KINDRED HOSPITAL–SAN DIEGO (O, 58 beds) 1940 El Cajon Boulevard, San Diego, CA, Zip 92104–1096; tel. 619/543–4500; Kerry Ashment, Chief Executive Officer
Web address: www.kindredsandiego.com

KINDRED HOSPITAL–SAN FRANCISCO BAY AREA (O, 99 beds) 2800 Benedict Drive, San Leandro, CA, Zip 94577–6840; tel. 510/357–8300; Jacob M. McCarty, Chief Executive Officer

KINDRED HOSPITAL–WESTMINSTER (O, 109 beds) 200 Hospital Circle, Westminster, CA, Zip 92683–3910; tel. 714/893–4541; Julie Myers, Chief Executive Officer
Web address: www.khwestminster.com/

COLORADO: KINDRED HOSPITAL DENVER SOUTH (O, 28 beds) 2525 South Downing Street, 3 South, Denver, CO, Zip 80210–5817; tel. 303/715–7373; Marc Lemon, Chief Executive Officer
Web address: www.kindreddenversouth.com/

KINDRED HOSPITAL–AURORA (O, 37 beds) 700 Potomac Street 2nd Floor, Aurora, CO, Zip 80011–6844; tel. 720/857–8333; Jeanette Williams, Chief Executive Officer

For explanation of codes following names, see page B2.
★ Indicates Type III membership in the American Hospital Association.

Section B

KINDRED HOSPITAL–DENVER (O, 68 beds) 1920 High Street, Denver, CO, Zip 80218–1213; tel. 303/320–5871; Janelle Kircher, R.N., MSN, Chief Executive Officer
Web address: www.kh-denver.com

FLORIDA: KINDRED HOSPITAL BAY AREA–TAMPA (O, 73 beds) 4555 South Manhattan Avenue, Tampa, FL, Zip 33611–2397; tel. 813/839–6341; Suthanthira M. Ratnasamy, R.N., FACHE, Chief Executive Officer
Web address: www.khtampa.com/

KINDRED HOSPITAL CENTRAL TAMPA (O, 102 beds) 4801 North Howard Avenue, Tampa, FL, Zip 33603–1411; tel. 813/874–7575; Ralph Selner, Chief Executive Officer

KINDRED HOSPITAL MELBOURNE (O, 60 beds) 765 West Nasa Boulevard, Melbourne, FL, Zip 32901–1815; tel. 321/733–5725; Pamela R. Reed, Chief Executive Officer
Web address: www.khmelbourne.com

KINDRED HOSPITAL NORTH FLORIDA (O, 80 beds) 801 Oak Street, Green Cove Springs, FL, Zip 32043–4317; tel. 904/284–9230; Patrick McVey, Chief Executive Officer
Web address: www.khnorthflorida.com

KINDRED HOSPITAL OCALA (O, 31 beds) 1500 SW 1st Avenue, Ocala, FL, Zip 34471–6504; tel. 352/369–0513; Merlene Bhoorasingh , Administrator

KINDRED HOSPITAL SOUTH FLORIDA–FORT LAUDERDALE (O, 123 beds) 1516 East Las Olas Boulevard, Fort Lauderdale, FL, Zip 33301–2399; tel. 954/764–8900; Michael S. Roffelsen, Chief Executive Officer
Web address: www.khfortlauderdale.com/

KINDRED HOSPITAL THE PALM BEACHES (O, 70 beds) 5555 West Blue Heron Boulevard, Riviera Beach, FL, Zip 33418–7813; tel. 561/840–0754; Elayne Lopreato, Chief Executive Officer
Web address: www.khthepalmbeaches.com/

GEORGIA: KINDRED HOSPITAL ROME (O, 45 beds) 304 Turner McCall Boulevard, Rome, GA, Zip 30165–5621; tel. 706/378–6800; Al Diaz, M.D., Chief Executive Officer
Web address: www.kindredrome.com

ILLINOIS: KINDRED CHICAGO–CENTRAL HOSPITAL (O, 187 beds) 4058 West Melrose Street, Chicago, IL, Zip 60641–4797; tel. 773/736–7000

KINDRED HOSPITAL CHICAGO–NORTHLAKE (O, 94 beds) 365 East North Avenue, Northlake, IL, Zip 60164–2628; tel. 708/345–8100; Beverly Foster, Chief Executive Officer
Web address: www.kindrednorthlake.com/

KINDRED HOSPITAL PEORIA (O, 50 beds) 500 West Romeo B Garrett Avenue, Peoria, IL, Zip 61605–2301; tel. 309/680–1500; Christopher Curry, Chief Executive Officer

KINDRED HOSPITAL–SYCAMORE (O, 69 beds) 225 Edward Street, Sycamore, IL, Zip 60178–2137; tel. 815/895–2144; Jim Cohick, Chief Executive Officer
Web address: www.kindredhospitalsyc.com/

INDIANA: KINDRED HOSPITAL INDIANAPOLIS NORTH (O, 45 beds) 8060 Knue Road, Indianapolis, IN, Zip 46250–1976; tel. 317/813–8900; Nakia Tremble, Chief Executive Officer
Web address: www.kindredindynorth.com/

KINDRED HOSPITAL NORTHWEST INDIANA (O, 70 beds) 5454 Hohman Avenue, 5th Floor, Hammond, IN, Zip 46320–1931; tel. 219/937–9900; Frank A. Solare, Chief Executive Officer

KINDRED HOSPITAL–INDIANAPOLIS (O, 59 beds) 1700 West 10th Street, Indianapolis, IN, Zip 46222–3802; tel. 317/636–4400; Bryan Chatterton, Chief Executive Officer
Web address: www.kindredhospitalindy.com/

KENTUCKY: KINDRED HOSPITAL–LOUISVILLE (O, 117 beds) 1313 Saint Anthony Place, Louisville, KY, Zip 40204–1740; tel. 502/587–7001; Jack Nicholson, Chief Executive Officer

MISSOURI: KINDRED HOSPITAL NORTHLAND (O, 35 beds) 500 Northwest 68th Street, Kansas City, MO, Zip 64118–2455; tel. 816/420–6300; Laura Inge, Chief Executive Officer
Web address: www.khnorthland.com

KINDRED HOSPITAL–ST. LOUIS (O, 98 beds) 4930 Lindell Boulevard, Saint Louis, MO, Zip 63108–1510; tel. 314/361–8700; Lourene Money, R.N., Resource Chief Executive Officer
Web address: www.kindredstlouis.com/

MERCY REHABILITATION HOSPITAL ST. LOUIS (O, 90 beds) 14561 North Outer Forty Road, Chesterfield, MO, Zip 63017; tel. 314/881–4000; Jerald W. Rumph, Chief Executive Officer

NEVADA: KINDRED HOSPITAL LAS VEGAS–SAHARA (O, 238 beds) 102 East Mead Parkway, 3rd Floor, Henderson, NV, Zip 89015; tel. 702/871–1418; Doug McCoy, Chief Executive Officer
Web address: www.kindredhospitallvs.com/

NEW JERSEY: KINDRED HOSPITAL–NEW JERSEY MORRIS COUNTY (O, 117 beds) 400 West Blackwell Street, Dover, NJ, Zip 07801–2525; tel. 973/537–3818; Tarra Washington, Chief Executive Officer

NEW MEXICO: KINDRED HOSPITAL–ALBUQUERQUE (O, 61 beds) 700 High Street NE, Albuquerque, NM, Zip 87102–2565; tel. 505/242–4444; Bud Schawl, Chief Executive Officer
Web address: www.kindredalbuquerque.com/

NORTH CAROLINA: KINDRED HOSPITAL–GREENSBORO (O, 101 beds) 2401 Southside Boulevard, Greensboro, NC, Zip 27406–3311; tel. 336/271–2800; Chad Lovett, Chief Executive Officer

OHIO: KINDRED HOSPITAL LIMA (O, 26 beds) 730 West Market Street, 6th Floor, Lima, OH, Zip 45801–4602; tel. 419/224–1888; Susan Krinke, Chief Executive Officer
Web address: www.khlima.com

KINDRED HOSPITAL–DAYTON (O, 67 beds) 707 South Edwin C Moses Boulevard, Dayton, OH, Zip 45417–3462; tel. 937/222–5963; Phillip Underwood, Chief Executive Officer
Web address: www.khdayton.com

UH AVON REHABILITATION HOSPITAL (O, 50 beds) 37900 Chester Road, Avon, OH, Zip 44011–1044; tel. 440/695–7100; Andrew Goldfrach, Chief Executive Officer

UH REHABILITATION HOSPITAL (O, 50 beds) 23333 Harvard Road, Beachwood, OH, Zip 44122–6232; tel. 216/593–2200; Mirza Baig, M.D., Medical Director
Web address: www.uhhospitals.org

PENNSYLVANIA: KINDRED HOSPITAL SOUTH PHILADELPHIA (O, 58 beds) 1930 South Broad Street, Philadelphia, PA, Zip 19145–2328; tel. 267/570–5200; Michele S. Basile, Chief Executive Officer
Web address: www.khsouthphilly.com

KINDRED HOSPITAL–PHILADELPHIA (O, 52 beds) 6129 Palmetto Street, Philadelphia, PA, Zip 19111–5729; tel. 215/722–8555; Michael Bass, M.D., Chief Executive Officer

ST. MARY REHABILITATION HOSPITAL (O, 50 beds) 1201 Langhorne Newtown Road, Langhorne, PA, Zip 19047–1201, Mailing Address: 1208 Langhorne Newtown Road, Zip 19047–1234, tel. 267/560–1111; Lisa Haney, Chief Executive Officer
Web address: www.stmaryhealthcare.org

TENNESSEE: KINDRED HOSPITAL–CHATTANOOGA (O, 44 beds) 709 Walnut Street, Chattanooga, TN, Zip 37402–1916; tel. 423/266–7721; Andrea White, Chief Executive Officer

TEXAS: KINDRED HOSPITAL CLEAR LAKE (O, 110 beds) 350 Blossom Street, Webster, TX, Zip 77598; tel. 281/316–7800; Angel Gradney, Chief Executive Officer
Web address: www.khclearlake.com

KINDRED HOSPITAL DALLAS CENTRAL (O, 60 beds) 8050 Meadow Road, Dallas, TX, Zip 75231–3406; tel. 469/232–6500; Kyron J. Kooken, MS, Chief Executive Officer

KINDRED HOSPITAL EL PASO (O, 57 beds) 1740 Curie Drive, El Paso, TX, Zip 79902–2901; tel. 915/351–9044; America Jones, R.N., Chief Executive Officer
Web address: www.khelpaso.com

KINDRED HOSPITAL HOUSTON MEDICAL CENTER (O, 105 beds) 6441 Main Street, Houston, TX, Zip 77030–1596; tel. 713/790–0500; Robert Stein, Chief Executive Officer

KINDRED HOSPITAL SAN ANTONIO CENTRAL (O, 44 beds) 111 Dallas Street, 4th Floor, San Antonio, TX, Zip 78205–1201; tel. 210/297–7185; Abiola Anyebe, Interim Chief Executive Officer
Web address: www.kindredsanantoniocentral.com/

KINDRED HOSPITAL SUGAR LAND (O, 105 beds) 1550 First Colony Boulevard, Sugar Land, TX, Zip 77479–4000; tel. 281/275–6000; John D. Cross, Chief Executive Officer

For explanation of codes following names, see page B2.
★ Indicates Type III membership in the American Hospital Association.

KINDRED HOSPITAL TARRANT COUNTY–ARLINGTON (O, 55 beds) 1000 North Cooper Street, Arlington, TX, Zip 76011–5540; tel. 817/548–3400; Christina Richard, Market Chief Executive Officer
Web address: www.kindredhospitalarl.com/

KINDRED HOSPITAL TOMBALL (O, 258 beds) 505 Graham Drive, Tomball, TX, Zip 77375–3368; tel. 281/255–5600; Tracy Kohler, Chief Executive Officer

KINDRED HOSPITAL–DALLAS (O, 50 beds) 9525 Greenville Avenue, Dallas, TX, Zip 75243–4116; tel. 214/355–2600; Kyron J. Kooken, MS, Chief Executive Officer
Web address: www.khdallas.com

KINDRED HOSPITAL–FORT WORTH (O, 156 beds) 815 Eighth Avenue, Fort Worth, TX, Zip 76104–2609; tel. 817/332–4812; Susan Schaetti, Chief Executive Officer

KINDRED HOSPITAL–HOUSTON NORTHWEST (O, 84 beds) 11297 Fallbrook Drive, Houston, TX, Zip 77065–4292; tel. 281/897–8114; Tracy Kohler, Chief Executive Officer
Web address: www.khhoustonnw.com/

KINDRED HOSPITAL–MANSFIELD (O, 55 beds) 1802 Highway 157 North, Mansfield, TX, Zip 76063–3923; tel. 817/473–6101; Blake Peart, Administrator
Web address: www.kindredmansfield.com

KINDRED HOSPITAL–SAN ANTONIO (O, 59 beds) 3636 Medical Drive, San Antonio, TX, Zip 78229–2183; tel. 210/616–0616; Abiola Anyebe, Interim Chief Executive Officer

TEXAS REHABILITATION HOSPITAL OF FORT WORTH (O, 66 beds) 425 Alabama Avenue, Fort Worth, TX, Zip 76104–1022; tel. 817/820–3400; Jake Daggett, Chief Executive Officer
Web address: www.texasrehabhospital.com/

WASHINGTON: KINDRED HOSPITAL SEATTLE–NORTHGATE (O, 80 beds) 10631 8th Avenue NE, Seattle, WA, Zip 98125–7213; tel. 206/364–2050; Lerenda Johnson, Interim Chief Executive Officer

WISCONSIN: REHABILITATION HOSPITAL OF WISCONSIN (O, 40 beds) 1625 Coldwater Creek Drive, Waukesha, WI, Zip 53188–8028; tel. 262/521–8800; John R. Robertstad, FACHE, Chief Executive Officer
Web address: www.rehabhospitalwi.com

Owned, leased, sponsored:	60 hospitals	4800 beds
Contract–managed:	1 hospitals	91 beds
Totals:	61 hospitals	4891 beds

0333: KPC HEALTHCARE, INC. (IO)
1301 North Tustin Avenue, Santa Ana, CA, Zip 92705–8619; tel. 714/953–3652; Suzanne Richards, R.N., M.P.H., FACHE, Chief Executive Officer
(Independent Hospital System)

CALIFORNIA: ANAHEIM GLOBAL MEDICAL CENTER (O, 188 beds) 1025 South Anaheim Boulevard, Anaheim, CA, Zip 92805–5806; tel. 714/533–6220; Scott Rifkin, Chief Executive Officer

CHAPMAN GLOBAL MEDICAL CENTER (O, 100 beds) 2601 East Chapman Avenue, Orange, CA, Zip 92869–3296; tel. 714/633–0011; Ada Yeh, Chief Executive Officer
Web address: www.Chapman-GMC.com

ORANGE COUNTY GLOBAL MEDICAL CENTER, INC. (O, 282 beds) 1001 North Tustin Avenue, Santa Ana, CA, Zip 92705–3577; tel. 714/953–3500; Ann Abe, Interim Chief Executive Officer
Web address: www.orangecounty-gmc.com

SOUTH COAST GLOBAL MEDICAL CENTER (O, 178 beds) 2701 South Bristol Street, Santa Ana, CA, Zip 92704–6278; tel. 714/754–5454; Ada Yeh, Chief Executive Officer

Owned, leased, sponsored:	4 hospitals	748 beds
Contract–managed:	0 hospitals	0 beds
Totals:	4 hospitals	748 beds

0911: LAFAYETTE GENERAL HEALTH (NP)
920 West Pinhook Road, Lafayette, LA, Zip 70503–2455; tel. 337/289–7991; David L. Callecod, President and Chief Executive Officer
(Independent Hospital System)

LOUISIANA: ABROM KAPLAN MEMORIAL HOSPITAL (C, 35 beds) 1310 West Seventh Street, Kaplan, LA, Zip 70548–2910; tel. 337/643–8300; Bryce Quebodeaux, Chief Executive Officer

ACADIA GENERAL HOSPITAL (C, 140 beds) 1305 Crowley Rayne Highway, Crowley, LA, Zip 70526–8202; tel. 337/783–3222; Joe J. Mitchell, Chief Executive Officer
Web address: www.acadiageneral.com

LAFAYETTE GENERAL MEDICAL CENTER (O, 420 beds) 1214 Coolidge Avenue, Lafayette, LA, Zip 70503–2696, Mailing Address: P.O. Box 52009 OCS, Zip 70505–2009, tel. 337/289–7991; Patrick W. Gandy Jr, CPA, Executive Vice President and Chief Executive Officer
Web address: www.lafayettegeneral.com

LAFAYETTE GENERAL SURGICAL HOSPITAL (C, 10 beds) 1000 West Pinhook Road, Lafayette, LA, Zip 70503–2460; tel. 337/289–8088; Kimberly H. Dooley, Administrator
Web address: www.lafayettegeneral.com/our_facilities/main_facilities/ lafayette_general_surgical_hospital.aspx

ST. MARTIN HOSPITAL (C, 25 beds) 210 Champagne Boulevard, Breaux Bridge, LA, Zip 70517–3700, Mailing Address: P.O. Box 357, Zip 70517–0357, tel. 337/332–2178; Karen O. Wyble, R.N., Chief Executive Officer
Web address: www.stmartinhospital.org

UNIVERSITY HOSPITAL AND CLINICS (L, 52 beds) 2390 West Congress Street, Lafayette, LA, Zip 70506–4298; tel. 337/261–6000; Katherine D. Hebert, Chief Executive Officer
Web address: www.lafayettegeneral.com

Owned, leased, sponsored:	2 hospitals	472 beds
Contract–managed:	4 hospitals	210 beds
Totals:	6 hospitals	682 beds

★0891: LAHEY HEALTH (NP)
41 Mall Road, Burlington, MA, Zip 01805–0001; tel. 781/744–7100; Howard R. Grant, M.D., President and Chief Executive Officer
(Centralized Physician/Insurance Health System)

MASSACHUSETTS: BEVERLY HOSPITAL (O, 320 beds) 85 Herrick Street, Beverly, MA, Zip 01915–1777; tel. 978/922–3000; Philip M. Cormier, Chief Executive Officer

LAHEY HOSPITAL & MEDICAL CENTER, BURLINGTON (O, 345 beds) 41 Mall Road, Burlington, MA, Zip 01805–0001; tel. 781/744–5100; David L. Longworth, MD, Chief Executive Officer
Web address: www.lahey.org

WINCHESTER HOSPITAL (O, 197 beds) 41 Highland Avenue, Winchester, MA, Zip 01890–1496; tel. 781/729–9000; Richard I. Weiner, M.D., Chief Executive Officer and Chief Medical Officer

Owned, leased, sponsored:	3 hospitals	862 beds
Contract–managed:	0 hospitals	0 beds
Totals:	3 hospitals	862 beds

★0056: LAKELAND HEALTH (NP)
1234 Napier Avenue, Saint Joseph, MI, Zip 49085–2158; tel. 269/983–8300; Loren Hamel, M.D., President and Chief Executive Officer
(Independent Hospital System)

MICHIGAN: LAKELAND HOSPITAL, WATERVLIET (O, 44 beds) 400 Medical Park Drive, Watervliet, MI, Zip 49098–9225; tel. 269/463–3111; Ray Cruse, Chief Executive Officer

LAKELAND MEDICAL CENTER, ST. JOSEPH (O, 300 beds) 1234 Napier Avenue, Saint Joseph, MI, Zip 49085–2158; tel. 269/983–8300; Loren Hamel, M.D., President and Chief Executive Officer
Web address: www.lakelandhealth.org

Owned, leased, sponsored:	2 hospitals	344 beds
Contract–managed:	0 hospitals	0 beds
Totals:	2 hospitals	344 beds

Section B

For explanation of codes following names, see page B2.
★ Indicates Type III membership in the American Hospital Association.

0393: LANDMARK HOSPITALS (IO)
3255 Independence Street, Cape Girardeau, MO, Zip 63701–4914; tel. 573/335–1091; William K. Kapp III, M.D., President and Chief Executive Officer
(Independent Hospital System)

FLORIDA: LANDMARK HOSPITAL OF SOUTHWEST FLORIDA (O, 50 beds) 1285 Creekside Boulevard East, Naples, FL, Zip 34108; tel. 239/529–1800; James Whitacre, Chief Executive Officer
Web address: www.landmarkhospitals.com/our–hospitals/southwest–florida/

GEORGIA: LANDMARK HOSPITAL OF ATHENS (O, 42 beds) 775 Sunset Drive, Athens, GA, Zip 30606–2211; tel. 706/425–1500; Vivian Goff, R.N., Chief Executive Officer
Web address: www.landmarkhospitals.com

LANDMARK HOSPITAL OF SAVANNAH (O, 50 beds) 800 East 68th Street, Savannah, GA, Zip 31405–4710; tel. 912/298–1000; John Salandi, Chief Executive Officer

MISSOURI: LANDMARK HOSPITAL OF CAPE GIRARDEAU (O, 30 beds) 3255 Independence Street, Cape Girardeau, MO, Zip 63701–4914; tel. 573/335–1091; Deborah Sabella, R.N., Chief Executive Officer
Web address: www.landmarkhospitals.com

LANDMARK HOSPITAL OF COLUMBIA (O, 42 beds) 604 Old 63 North, Columbia, MO, Zip 65201–6308; tel. 573/499–6600; Laura D. Peckham, Chief Executive Officer

LANDMARK HOSPITAL OF JOPLIN (O, 30 beds) 2040 West 32nd Street, Joplin, MO, Zip 64804–3512; tel. 417/627–1300; Kevin J. Clement, Chief Executive Officer
Web address: www.landmarkhospitals.com

UTAH: LANDMARK HOSPITAL OF SALT LAKE CITY (O, 38 beds) 4252 South Birkhill Boulevard, Murray, UT, Zip 84107–5715; tel. 801/268–5400; Ted Paarlberg, Chief Executive Officer
Web address: www.landmarkhospitals.com/utah.aspx

Owned, leased, sponsored:	7 hospitals	282 beds
Contract–managed:	0 hospitals	0 beds
Totals:	7 hospitals	282 beds

0932: LCMC HEALTH (NP)
200 Henry Clay Avenue, New Orleans, LA, Zip 70118–5720; tel. 504/899–9511; Greg Feirn, CPA, President and Chief Executive Officer
(Moderately Centralized Health System)

LOUISIANA: CHILDREN'S HOSPITAL (O, 177 beds) 200 Henry Clay Avenue, New Orleans, LA, Zip 70118–5720; tel. 504/899–9511; John R. Nickens IV, President and Chief Executive Officer
Web address: www.chnola.org

NEW ORLEANS EAST HOSPITAL (C, 34 beds) 5620 Read Boulevard, New Orleans, LA, Zip 70127–3106, Mailing Address: 5620 Read Blvd, Zip 70127–3106, tel. 504/592–6600; Takeisha C. Davis, M.D., M.P.H., President and Chief Executive Officer
Web address: www.noehospital.org

TOURO INFIRMARY (O, 280 beds) 1401 Foucher Street, New Orleans, LA, Zip 70115–3593; tel. 504/897–7011; Susan E. Andrews, Chief Executive Officer
Web address: www.touro.com

UNIVERSITY MEDICAL CENTER (O, 298 beds) 2000 Canal Street, New Orleans, LA, Zip 70112–3018; tel. 504/903–3000; William J. Masterton, President and Chief Executive Officer

WEST JEFFERSON MEDICAL CENTER (C, 243 beds) 1101 Medical Center Boulevard, Marrero, LA, Zip 70072–3191; tel. 504/347–5511; Nancy R. Cassagne, FACHE, Chief Executive Officer
Web address: www.wjmc.org

Owned, leased, sponsored:	3 hospitals	755 beds
Contract–managed:	2 hospitals	277 beds
Totals:	5 hospitals	1032 beds

★**0369: LEE HEALTH** (NP)
2776 Cleveland Avenue, Fort Myers, FL, Zip 33901–5864, Mailing Address: P.O. Box 2218, Zip 33902–2218, tel. 239/343–2000; Lawrence Antonucci, M.D., President and Chief Executive Officer
(Independent Hospital System)

FLORIDA: CAPE CORAL HOSPITAL (O, 291 beds) 636 Del Prado Boulevard, Cape Coral, FL, Zip 33990–2695; tel. 239/424–2000; Lawrence Antonucci, M.D., President and Chief Executive Officer

GULF COAST MEDICAL CENTER (O, 349 beds) 13681 Doctor's Way, Fort Myers, FL, Zip 33912–4300; tel. 239/343–1000; Lawrence Antonucci, M.D., President and Chief Executive Officer
Web address: www.leememorial.org

LEE MEMORIAL HOSPITAL (O, 812 beds) 2776 Cleveland Avenue, Fort Myers, FL, Zip 33901–5855, Mailing Address: P.O. Box 2218, Zip 33902–2218, tel. 239/343–2000; Lawrence Antonucci, M.D., President and Chief Executive Officer

Owned, leased, sponsored:	3 hospitals	1452 beds
Contract–managed:	0 hospitals	0 beds
Totals:	3 hospitals	1452 beds

★**2755: LEGACY HEALTH** (NP)
1919 NW Lovejoy Street, Portland, OR, Zip 97209–1503; tel. 503/415–5600; Kathryn G. Correia, President and Chief Executive Officer
(Moderately Centralized Health System)

OREGON: LEGACY EMANUEL MEDICAL CENTER (O, 518 beds) 2801 North Gantenbein Avenue, Portland, OR, Zip 97227–1674; tel. 503/413–2200; Trent Green, President
Web address: www.legacyhealth.org

LEGACY GOOD SAMARITAN MEDICAL CENTER (O, 222 beds) 1015 NW 22nd Avenue, Portland, OR, Zip 97210–3099; tel. 503/413–7711; Jonathan Avery, Chief Administrative Officer
Web address: www.legacyhealth.org

LEGACY MERIDIAN PARK MEDICAL CENTER (O, 134 beds) 19300 SW 65th Avenue, Tualatin, OR, Zip 97062–9741; tel. 503/692–1212; Allyson Anderson, President

LEGACY MOUNT HOOD MEDICAL CENTER (O, 97 beds) 24800 SE Stark, Gresham, OR, Zip 97030–3378; tel. 503/667–1122; Gretchen Nichols, R.N., President
Web address: www.legacyhealth.org

LEGACY SILVERTON MEDICAL CENTER (O, 48 beds) 342 Fairview Street, Silverton, OR, Zip 97381–1993; tel. 503/873–1500; Sarah Fronza, President
Web address: www.legacyhealth.org/locations/hospitals/legacy–silverton–medical–center.aspx

WASHINGTON: LEGACY SALMON CREEK MEDICAL CENTER (O, 211 beds) 2211 NE 139th Street, Vancouver, WA, Zip 98686–2742; tel. 360/487–1000; Bryce R. Helgerson, Chief Administrative Officer

Owned, leased, sponsored:	6 hospitals	1230 beds
Contract–managed:	0 hospitals	0 beds
Totals:	6 hospitals	1230 beds

★**0370: LEHIGH VALLEY HEALTH NETWORK** (NP)
1200 South Cedar Crest Boulevard, Allentown, PA, Zip 18103–6202, Mailing Address: P.O. Box 689, Zip 18105–1556, tel. 610/402–8000; Brian A. Nester, D.O., President and Chief Executive Officer
(Moderately Centralized Health System)

PENNSYLVANIA: LEHIGH VALLEY HOSPITAL – HAZLETON (O, 120 beds) 700 East Broad Street, Hazleton, PA, Zip 18201–6897; tel. 570/501–4000; John R. Fletcher, President
Web address: www.lvhn.org/hazleton/

LEHIGH VALLEY HOSPITAL – POCONO (O, 235 beds) 206 East Brown Street, East Stroudsburg, PA, Zip 18301–3006; tel. 570/421–4000; Elizabeth Wise, President and Chief Executive Officer
Web address: www.pmchealthsystem.org

For explanation of codes following names, see page B2.
★ Indicates Type III membership in the American Hospital Association.

LEHIGH VALLEY HOSPITAL – SCHUYLKILL SOUTH JACKSON STREET (O, 67 beds) 420 South Jackson Street, Pottsville, PA, Zip 17901–3625; tel. 570/621–5000; William Reppy, President

LEHIGH VALLEY HOSPITAL–MUHLENBERG (O, 186 beds) 2545 Schoenersville Road, Bethlehem, PA, Zip 18017–7300; tel. 484/884–2200; Brian A. Nester, D.O., President and Chief Executive Officer

Web address: www.lvhn.org

LEHIGH VALLEY HOSPITAL (O, 863 beds) 1200 South Cedar Crest Boulevard, Allentown, PA, Zip 18103–6248, Mailing Address: P.O. Box 689, Zip 18105–1556, tel. 610/402–8000; Brian A. Nester, D.O., President and Chief Executive Officer

Owned, leased, sponsored:	5 hospitals	1471 beds
Contract–managed:	0 hospitals	0 beds
Totals:	5 hospitals	1471 beds

0632: LHC GROUP (IO)

420 West Pinhook Road, Lafayette, LA, Zip 70503–2131; tel. 337/233–1307; Keith G. Myers, Chairman and Chief Executive Officer
(Independent Hospital System)

ARKANSAS: CHRISTUS DUBUIS HOSPITAL OF FORT SMITH (O, 25 beds) 7301 Rogers Avenue, 4th Floor, Fort Smith, AR, Zip 72903–4100; tel. 479/314–4900; Julie Cormack, Administrator

Web address: www.christusdubuis.org/fortsmith

CHRISTUS DUBUIS HOSPITAL OF HOT SPRINGS (O, 26 beds) 300 Werner Street, 3rd Floor East, Hot Springs National Park, AR, Zip 71913–6406; tel. 501/609–4300; Kenneth Costello, Administrator
Web address: www.christusdubuis.org/hotsprings

GEORGIA: SOUTHERN CRESCENT HOSPITAL FOR SPECIALTY CARE (O, 30 beds) 11 Upper Riverdale Road SW, 6th Floor, Riverdale, GA, Zip 30274–2615; tel. 770/897–7600; Ulysses Fisher, Administrator

LOUISIANA: CHRISTUS DUBUIS HOSPITAL OF ALEXANDRIA (O, 25 beds) 3330 Masonic Drive, 4th Floor, Alexandria, LA, Zip 71301–3841; tel. 318/448–4938; Beth Parsons, R.N., Administrator
Web address: www.christusdubuis.org/CHRISTUSDubuisHospitalofAlexandriaLA

LOUISIANA EXTENDED CARE HOSPITAL WEST MONROE (O, 18 beds) 503 McMillan Road, 3rd Floor, West Monroe, LA, Zip 71291–5327; tel. 318/329–4378; Cleta Munholland, Administrator

LOUISIANA EXTENDED CARE HOSPITAL OF LAFAYETTE (O, 42 beds) 1214 Coolidge Boulevard, Floors 9 & 10, Lafayette, LA, Zip 70503–2621; tel. 337/289–8180; Kevin Frank, Administrator
Web address: www.lhcgroup.com

LOUISIANA EXTENDED CARE HOSPITAL OF NATCHITOCHES (O, 21 beds) 501 Keyser Avenue, Natchitoches, LA, Zip 71457–6018; tel. 318/354–2044; John Rivoire, R.N., MSN, Administrator

OCHSNER EXTENDED CARE HOSPITAL OF KENNER (O, 32 beds) 180 West Esplanade Avenue, 5th Floor, Kenner, LA, Zip 70065–2467; tel. 504/464–8658; Jan Turk, Administrator
Web address: www.lhcgroup.com/

SPECIALTY HOSPITAL (O, 32 beds) 309 Jackson Street, 7th Floor, Monroe, LA, Zip 71201–7407, Mailing Address: P.O. Box 1532, Zip 71210–1532, tel. 318/966–7045; Cleta Munholland, Administrator

ST. LANDRY EXTENDED CARE HOSPITAL (O, 41 beds) 3983 1–49 South Service Road, 2nd Floor, Opelousas, LA, Zip 70570; tel. 337/948–2251; Biff David, R.N., Administrator
Web address: www.lhcgroup.com

TEXAS: CHRISTUS DUBUIS HOSPITAL OF BEAUMONT (O, 51 beds) 2830 Calder Avenue, 4th Floor, Beaumont, TX, Zip 77702–1809; tel. 409/899–7680; William E. Klamfoth, Administrator
Web address: www.christusdubuis.org/BeaumontandPortArthurSystem–CHRISTUSDubuisHospitalofBeaumont

CHRISTUS DUBUIS HOSPITAL OF PARIS (O, 25 beds) 820 Clarksville Street, 6th Floor, Paris, TX, Zip 75460–6027; tel. 903/737–3600; Kathie Reese, R.N., Regional Administrator and Chief Executive Officer
Web address: www.christusdubuis.org

Owned, leased, sponsored:	12 hospitals	368 beds
Contract–managed:	0 hospitals	0 beds
Totals:	12 hospitals	368 beds

0158: LIFEBRIDGE HEALTH (NP)

2401 West Belvedere Avenue, Baltimore, MD, Zip 21215–5216; tel. 410/601–5134; Neil M. Meltzer, President and Chief Executive Officer
(Moderately Centralized Health System)

MARYLAND: CARROLL HOSPITAL CENTER (O, 143 beds) 200 Memorial Avenue, Westminster, MD, Zip 21157–5799; tel. 410/848–3000; Leslie Simmons, FACHE, R.N., President

LEVINDALE HEBREW GERIATRIC CENTER AND HOSPITAL (O, 490 beds) 2434 West Belvedere Avenue, Baltimore, MD, Zip 21215–5267; tel. 410/601–2400; Idriz Limaj, Chief Operating Officer and Executive Director
Web address: www.sinai–balt.com

NORTHWEST HOSPITAL (O, 253 beds) 5401 Old Court Road, Randallstown, MD, Zip 21133–5185; tel. 410/521–2200; Faraaz Yousuf, President and Chief Operating Officer
Web address: www.lifebridgehealth.org

SINAI HOSPITAL OF BALTIMORE (O, 378 beds) 2401 West Belvedere Avenue, Baltimore, MD, Zip 21215–5271; tel. 410/601–9000; Jonathan Ringo, M.D., President and Chief Operating Officer

Owned, leased, sponsored:	4 hospitals	1264 beds
Contract–managed:	0 hospitals	0 beds
Totals:	4 hospitals	1264 beds

★0191: LIFECARE MANAGEMENT SERVICES (IO)

5340 Legacy Drive, Suite 150, Plano, TX, Zip 75024–3131; tel. 469/241–2100; James E. Murray, Chief Executive Officer
(Independent Hospital System)

COLORADO: COLORADO ACUTE LONG TERM HOSPITAL (O, 63 beds) 1690 North Meade Street, Denver, CO, Zip 80204–1552; tel. 303/264–6900; Craig Bailey, MS, Chief Executive Officer and Administrator
Web address: www.lifecare–hospitals.com/hospital/colorado

FLORIDA: COMPLEX CARE HOSPITAL AT RIDGELAKE (O, 40 beds) 6150 Edgelake Drive, Sarasota, FL, Zip 34240–8803; tel. 941/342–3000; Robert E. Mallicoat, Chief Executive Officer

NEVADA: COMPLEX CARE HOSPITAL AT TENAYA (O, 70 beds) 2500 North Tenaya, Las Vegas, NV, Zip 89128–0482; tel. 702/562–2021; Matt Archer, Chief Executive Officer
Web address: www.lifecare–hospitals.com

TAHOE PACIFIC HOSPITALS (O, 60 beds) 2375 East Prater Way, Sparks, NV, Zip 89434; tel. 775/355–5600; Matt Archer, Chief Executive Officer

NORTH CAROLINA: LIFECARE HOSPITALS OF NORTH CAROLINA (O, 43 beds) 1051 Noell Lane, Rocky Mount, NC, Zip 27804–1761; tel. 252/451–2300; Robyn Perkerson, R.N., Administrator
Web address: www.lifecare–hospitals.com

OHIO: LIFECARE HOSPITAL OF DAYTON (O, 44 beds) 4000 Miamisburg–Centerville Road, Miamisburg, OH, Zip 45342–7615; tel. 937/384–8300; William Bryant, Chief Executive Officer

PENNSYLVANIA: LIFECARE HOSPITALS OF CHESTER COUNTY (O, 39 beds) 400 East Marshall Street, West Chester, PA, Zip 19380–5412; tel. 484/826–0400; Janet Biedron, R.N., Chief Executive Officer
Web address: www.lifecare–hospitals.com

LIFECARE HOSPITALS OF MECHANICSBURG (O, 68 beds) 4950 Wilson Lane, Mechanicsburg, PA, Zip 17055–4442; tel. 717/697–7706; Jacob McGuirt, Chief Executive Officer

---

For explanation of codes following names, see page B2.
★ Indicates Type III membership in the American Hospital Association.

LIFECARE HOSPITALS OF PITTSBURGH (O, 196 beds) 225 Penn Avenue, Pittsburgh, PA, Zip 15221–2148; tel. 469/241–2100; Jennifer Malko, Market Chief Executive Officer
Web address: www.lifecare–hospitals.com

TEXAS: LIFECARE HOSPITALS OF DALLAS (O, 113 beds) 1950 Record Crossing Road, Dallas, TX, Zip 75235–6223; tel. 214/640–9600; Deborah Paganelli, FACHE, Chief Executive Officer

LIFECARE HOSPITALS OF SAN ANTONIO (O, 62 beds) 8902 Floyd Curl Drive, San Antonio, TX, Zip 78240–1681; tel. 210/690–7000; Michelle Lozano, Chief Executive Officer
Web address: www.lifecare–hospitals.com

WISCONSIN: LIFECARE HOSPITALS OF WISCONSIN (O, 30 beds) 2400 Golf Road, Pewaukee, WI, Zip 53072–5590; tel. 262/524–2600; David Chaudier, Chief Executive Officer

Owned, leased, sponsored:	12 hospitals	828 beds
Contract–managed:	0 hospitals	0 beds
Totals:	12 hospitals	828 beds

★**0180: LIFEPOINT HEALTH** (IO)
330 Seven Springs Way, Brentwood, TN, Zip 37027–4536; tel. 615/920–7000; William F. Carpenter III, Chairman and Chief Executive Officer
(Decentralized Health System)

ALABAMA: ANDALUSIA HEALTH (O, 88 beds) 849 South Three Notch Street, Andalusia, AL, Zip 36420–5325, Mailing Address: P.O. Box 760, Zip 36420–1214, tel. 334/222–8466; John C. Yanes, Chief Executive Officer

VAUGHAN REGIONAL MEDICAL CENTER (O, 149 beds) 1015 Medical Center Parkway, Selma, AL, Zip 36701–6352; tel. 334/418–4100; J. David. McCormack, Chief Executive Officer
Web address: www.vaughanregional.com

ARIZONA: HAVASU REGIONAL MEDICAL CENTER (O, 162 beds) 101 Civic Center Lane, Lake Havasu City, AZ, Zip 86403–5683; tel. 928/855–8185; Michael N. Patterson, Chief Executive Officer
Web address: www.havasuregional.com

VALLEY VIEW MEDICAL CENTER (O, 84 beds) 5330 South Highway 95, Fort Mohave, AZ, Zip 86426–9225; tel. 928/788–2273; Feliciano Jiron, Executive Officer
Web address: www.valleyviewmedicalcenter.net

COLORADO: COLORADO PLAINS MEDICAL CENTER (L, 50 beds) 1000 Lincoln Street, Fort Morgan, CO, Zip 80701–3298; tel. 970/867–3391; Gene L. O'Hara, Chief Executive Officer

GEORGIA: ST. FRANCIS HOSPITAL (O, 302 beds) 2122 Manchester Expressway, Columbus, GA, Zip 31904–6878, Mailing Address: P.O. Box 7000, Zip 31908–7000, tel. 706/596–4000; Danny L. Jones Jr, FACHE, Chief Executive Officer
Web address: www.mystfrancis.com

INDIANA: CLARK MEMORIAL HOSPITAL (O, 185 beds) 1220 Missouri Avenue, Jeffersonville, IN, Zip 47130–3743, Mailing Address: P.O. Box 69, Zip 47131–0600, tel. 812/282–6631; Martin Padgett, President and Chief Executive Officer

SCOTT MEMORIAL HOSPITAL (O, 25 beds) 1415 North Gardner Street, Scottsburg, IN, Zip 47170, Mailing Address: Box 430, Zip 47170–0430, tel. 812/752–3456; Michael Everett, Chief Executive Officer
Web address: www.scottmemorial.com

KANSAS: WESTERN PLAINS MEDICAL COMPLEX (O, 45 beds) 3001 Avenue 'A', Dodge City, KS, Zip 67801–6508, Mailing Address: P.O. Box 1478, Zip 67801–1478, tel. 620/225–8400; Scott M. Smith, Interim Chief Executive Officer
Web address: www.westernplainsmc.com

KENTUCKY: BLUEGRASS COMMUNITY HOSPITAL (O, 16 beds) 360 Amsden Avenue, Versailles, KY, Zip 40383–1286; tel. 859/873–3111; Tommy Haggard, Chief Executive Officer

BOURBON COMMUNITY HOSPITAL (O, 58 beds) 9 Linville Drive, Paris, KY, Zip 40361–2196; tel. 859/987–3600; Matt Smith, Interim Chief Executive Officer
Web address: www.bourbonhospital.com

CLARK REGIONAL MEDICAL CENTER (O, 79 beds) 175 Hospital Drive, Winchester, KY, Zip 40391–9591; tel. 859/745–3500; Robert Parker, Chief Executive Officer and Market President

FLEMING COUNTY HOSPITAL (O, 52 beds) 55 Foundation Drive, Flemingsburg, KY, Zip 41041–9815, Mailing Address: P.O. Box 388, Zip 41041–0388, tel. 606/849–5000; Brian Springate, Chief Executive Officer
Web address: www.flemingcountyhospital.org

GEORGETOWN COMMUNITY HOSPITAL (O, 58 beds) 1140 Lexington Road, Georgetown, KY, Zip 40324–9362; tel. 502/868–1100; William Haugh, Administrator
Web address: www.georgetowncommunityhospital.com

JACKSON PURCHASE MEDICAL CENTER (O, 227 beds) 1099 Medical Center Circle, Mayfield, KY, Zip 42066–1159; tel. 270/251–4100; David Anderson, Chief Executive Officer
Web address: www.jacksonpurchase.com

LAKE CUMBERLAND REGIONAL HOSPITAL (O, 295 beds) 305 Langdon Street, Somerset, KY, Zip 42503–2750, Mailing Address: P.O. Box 620, Zip 42502–0620, tel. 606/679–7441; Elizabeth Jones, Interim Chief Executive Officer

LOGAN MEMORIAL HOSPITAL (O, 30 beds) 1625 South Nashville Road, Russellville, KY, Zip 42276–8834, Mailing Address: P.O. Box 10, Zip 42276–0010, tel. 270/726–4011; James Bills, Chief Executive Officer
Web address: www.loganmemorial.com

MEADOWVIEW REGIONAL MEDICAL CENTER (O, 100 beds) 989 Medical Park Drive, Maysville, KY, Zip 41056–8750; tel. 606/759–5311; Joseph G. Koch, Chief Executive Officer

SPRING VIEW HOSPITAL (O, 60 beds) 320 Loretto Road, Lebanon, KY, Zip 40033–1300; tel. 270/692–3161; Timothy R. Trottier, Chief Executive Officer
Web address: www.springviewhospital.com

LOUISIANA: TECHE REGIONAL MEDICAL CENTER (L, 164 beds) 1125 Marguerite Street, Morgan City, LA, Zip 70380–1855, Mailing Address: P.O. Box 2308, Zip 70381–2308, tel. 985/384–2200; Aphreikah DuHaney–West, Chief Executive Officer

MICHIGAN: UP HEALTH SYSTEM–BELL (O, 25 beds) 901 Lakeshore Drive, Ishpeming, MI, Zip 49849–1367; tel. 906/486–4431; Mitchell D. Leckelt, Chief Executive Officer
Web address: www.bellhospital.org

UP HEALTH SYSTEM–PORTAGE (O, 96 beds) 500 Campus Drive, Hancock, MI, Zip 49930–1569; tel. 906/483–1000; Randy Neiswonger, Chief Executive Officer
Web address: www.portagehealth.org

MISSISSIPPI: BOLIVAR MEDICAL CENTER (L, 129 beds) 901 East Sunflower Road, Cleveland, MS, Zip 38732–2833, Mailing Address: P.O. Box 1380, Zip 38732–1380, tel. 662/846–0061; Robert L. Marshall Jr, FACHE, Chief Executive Officer

NEVADA: NORTHEASTERN NEVADA REGIONAL HOSPITAL (O, 50 beds) 2001 Errecart Boulevard, Elko, NV, Zip 89801–8333; tel. 775/738–5151; Steve Simpson, Chief Executive Officer
Web address: www.nnrhospital.com

NEW MEXICO: LOS ALAMOS MEDICAL CENTER (O, 29 beds) 3917 West Road, Los Alamos, NM, Zip 87544–2293; tel. 505/661–9500; John Whiteside, Chief Executive Officer

MEMORIAL MEDICAL CENTER (L, 173 beds) 2450 South Telshor Boulevard, Las Cruces, NM, Zip 88011–5076; tel. 575/522–8641; John Harris, Chief Executive Officer
Web address: www.mmclc.org

PENNSYLVANIA: CONEMAUGH NASON MEDICAL CENTER (O, 45 beds) 105 Nason Drive, Roaring Spring, PA, Zip 16673–1202; tel. 814/224–2141; Timothy Harclerode, Chief Executive Officer
Web address: www.nasonhospital.com

SOUTH CAROLINA: PROVIDENCE HOSPITAL (O, 247 beds) 2435 Forest Drive, Columbia, SC, Zip 29204–2098; tel. 803/865–4500; Stephen R. Selzer, Market Chief Executive Officer
Web address: www.sistersofcharityhealth.org/health–care/providence–hospitals/

TENNESSEE: LIVINGSTON REGIONAL HOSPITAL (O, 114 beds) 315 Oak Street, Livingston, TN, Zip 38570–1728, Mailing Address: P.O. Box 550, Zip 38570–0550, tel. 931/823–5611; Timothy W. McGill, Chief Executive Officer
Web address: www.MyLivingstonHospital.com

RIVERVIEW REGIONAL MEDICAL CENTER (O, 35 beds) 158 Hospital Drive, Carthage, TN, Zip 37030–1096; tel. 615/735–1560; Michael Herman, Chief Executive Officer

For explanation of codes following names, see page B2.
★ Indicates Type III membership in the American Hospital Association.

SOUTHERN TENNESSEE REGIONAL HEALTH SYSTEM–LAWRENCEBURG (O, 99 beds) 1607 South Locust Avenue, Lawrenceburg, TN, Zip 38464–4011, Mailing Address: P.O. Box 847, Zip 38464–0847, tel. 931/762–6571; Jeff Noblin, FACHE, Chief Executive Officer
Web address: www.crocketthospital.com

SOUTHERN TENNESSEE REGIONAL HEALTH SYSTEM–PULASKI (O, 59 beds) 1265 East College Street, Pulaski, TN, Zip 38478–4541; tel. 931/363–7531; James H. Edmondson, Chief Executive Officer

SOUTHERN TENNESSEE REGIONAL HEALTH SYSTEM–WINCHESTER (O, 142 beds) 185 Hospital Road, Winchester, TN, Zip 37398–2404; tel. 931/967–8200; William R. Spray, Chief Executive Officer
Web address: www.southerntennessee.com

STARR REGIONAL MEDICAL CENTER (O, 63 beds) 1114 West Madison Avenue, Athens, TN, Zip 37303–4150, Mailing Address: P.O. Box 250, Zip 37371–0250, tel. 423/745–1411; Mark Nichols, FACHE, Chief Executive Officer

SUMNER REGIONAL MEDICAL CENTER (O, 155 beds) 555 Hartsville Pike, Gallatin, TN, Zip 37066–2400, Mailing Address: P.O. Box 1558, Zip 37066–1558, tel. 615/452–4210; Susan M. Peach, R.N., Chief Executive Officer
Web address: www.mysumnermedical.com

TROUSDALE MEDICAL CENTER (O, 25 beds) 500 Church Street, Hartsville, TN, Zip 37074–1744; tel. 615/374–2221; Michael Herman, Chief Executive Officer

TEXAS: ENNIS REGIONAL MEDICAL CENTER (L, 58 beds) 2201 West Lampasas Street, Ennis, TX, Zip 75119–5644; tel. 972/875–0900; Robert C. Honeycutt, Chief Executive Officer
Web address: www.ennisregional.com

PALESTINE REGIONAL MEDICAL CENTER–EAST (O, 120 beds) 2900 South Loop 256, Palestine, TX, Zip 75801–6958; tel. 903/731–1000; Roy Finch, Chief Executive Officer

PALESTINE REGIONAL MEDICAL CENTER (O, 12 beds) 2900 S Loop 256, Palestine, TX, Zip 75801–6958; tel. 903/731–1000; Roy Finch, Chief Executive Officer
Web address: www.palestineregional.com

PARKVIEW REGIONAL HOSPITAL (L, 58 beds) 600 South Bonham, Mexia, TX, Zip 76667–3603; tel. 254/562–5332; Robert C. Honeycutt, Chief Executive Officer

UTAH: ASHLEY REGIONAL MEDICAL CENTER (O, 39 beds) 150 West 100 North, Vernal, UT, Zip 84078–2036; tel. 435/789–3342; Ben Cluff, Chief Executive Officer
Web address: www.ashleyregional.com

CASTLEVIEW HOSPITAL (O, 49 beds) 300 North Hospital Drive, Price, UT, Zip 84501–4200; tel. 435/637–4800; Jerry Dooley, Interim Chief Executive Officer
Web address: www.castleviewhospital.net

VIRGINIA: CLINCH VALLEY MEDICAL CENTER (O, 111 beds) 6801 Governor G C Peery Highway, Richlands, VA, Zip 24641–2194; tel. 276/596–6000; Peter Mulkey, Chief Executive Officer
Web address: www.clinchvalleymedicalcenter.com

FAUQUIER HOSPITAL (O, 86 beds) 500 Hospital Drive, Warrenton, VA, Zip 20186–3099; tel. 540/316–5000; Chad Melton, Chief Executive Officer

SOVAH HEALTH–DANVILLE (O, 250 beds) 142 South Main Street, Danville, VA, Zip 24541–2922; tel. 434/799–2100; Alan Larson, Chief Executive Officer
Web address: www.danvilleregional.com/

SOVAH HEALTH–MARTINSVILLE (O, 150 beds) 320 Hospital Drive, Martinsville, VA, Zip 24112–1981, Mailing Address: P.O. Box 4788, Zip 24115–4788, tel. 276/666–7200; Michael Ehrat, Chief Executive Officer

WYTHE COUNTY COMMUNITY HOSPITAL (L, 70 beds) 600 West Ridge Road, Wytheville, VA, Zip 24382–1099; tel. 276/228–0200; Joseph Wilkins, Chief Executive Officer
Web address: www.wcchcares.com

WEST VIRGINIA: LOGAN REGIONAL MEDICAL CENTER (O, 129 beds) 20 Hospital Drive, Logan, WV, Zip 25601–3452; tel. 304/831–1101; Kevin Zachary, Chief Executive Officer
Web address: www.loganregionalmedicalcenter.com

RALEIGH GENERAL HOSPITAL (O, 229 beds) 1710 Harper Road, Beckley, WV, Zip 25801–3397; tel. 304/256–4100; Matthew S. Roberts, Chief Executive Officer

WISCONSIN: WATERTOWN REGIONAL MEDICAL CENTER (O, 56 beds) 125 Hospital Drive, Watertown, WI, Zip 53098–3303; tel. 920/261–4210; David Critchlow, Senior Vice President, Government Relations, LifePoint Health
Web address: www.watertownregional.com/Main/Home.aspx

WYOMING: SAGEWEST HEALTH CARE AT RIVERTON (O, 71 beds) 2100 West Sunset Drive, Riverton, WY, Zip 82501–2274; tel. 307/856–4161; Robert Alan. Daugherty, Chief Executive Officer
Web address: www.sagewesthealthcare.com

Owned, leased, sponsored:	51 hospitals	5203 beds
Contract–managed:	0 hospitals	0 beds
Totals:	51 hospitals	5203 beds

0060: LIFESPAN CORPORATION (NP)
167 Point Street, Providence, RI, Zip 02903–4771; tel. 401/444–3500; Timothy J. Babineau, M.D., President and Chief Executive Officer
(Centralized Health System)

RHODE ISLAND: EMMA PENDLETON BRADLEY HOSPITAL (O, 70 beds) 1011 Veterans Memorial Parkway, East Providence, RI, Zip 02915–5099; tel. 401/432–1000; Daniel J. Wall, President and Chief Executive Officer

MIRIAM HOSPITAL (O, 247 beds) 164 Summit Avenue, Providence, RI, Zip 02906–2853; tel. 401/793–2500; Arthur J. Sampson, FACHE, President
Web address: www.lifespan.org

NEWPORT HOSPITAL (O, 119 beds) 11 Friendship Street, Newport, RI, Zip 02840–2299; tel. 401/846–6400; Crista F. Durand, President

RHODE ISLAND HOSPITAL (O, 679 beds) 593 Eddy Street, Providence, RI, Zip 02903–4900; tel. 401/444–4000; Margaret M. Van Bree, Dr.PH, President
Web address: www.rhodeislandhospital.org/

Owned, leased, sponsored:	4 hospitals	1115 beds
Contract–managed:	0 hospitals	0 beds
Totals:	4 hospitals	1115 beds

2175: LOMA LINDA UNIVERSITY ADVENTIST HEALTH SCIENCES CENTER (NP)
11175 Campus Street, Loma Linda, CA, Zip 92350–1700; tel. 909/558–7572; Richard H. Hart, President and Chief Executive Officer
(Centralized Health System)

CALIFORNIA: LOMA LINDA UNIVERSITY BEHAVIORAL MEDICINE CENTER (O, 89 beds) 1710 Barton Road, Redlands, CA, Zip 92373–5304; tel. 909/558–9200; Edward Field, Administrator
Web address: www.llu.edu

LOMA LINDA UNIVERSITY CHILDREN'S HOSPITAL (O, 337 beds) 11234 Anderson Street, Loma Linda, CA, Zip 92354–2804; tel. 909/558–8000; Kerry Heinrich, JD, Chief Executive Officer
Web address: www.llu.edu/lluch

LOMA LINDA UNIVERSITY MEDICAL CENTER–MURRIETA (O, 106 beds) 28062 Baxter Road , Murrieta, CA, Zip 92563–1401; tel. 951/290–4000; Peter Baker, Senior Vice President and Administrator

LOMA LINDA UNIVERSITY MEDICAL CENTER (O, 538 beds) 11234 Anderson Street, Loma Linda, CA, Zip 92354–2804, Mailing Address: P.O. Box 2000, Zip 92354–0200, tel. 909/558–4000; Kerry Heinrich, JD, Chief Executive Officer
Web address: www.llumc.edu

Owned, leased, sponsored:	4 hospitals	1070 beds
Contract–managed:	0 hospitals	0 beds
Totals:	4 hospitals	1070 beds

5755: LOS ANGELES COUNTY–DEPARTMENT OF HEALTH SERVICES (NP)
313 North Figueroa Street, Room 912, Los Angeles, CA, Zip 90012–2691; tel. 213/240–8101; Mitchell H. Katz, M.D., Director
(Moderately Centralized Health System)

For explanation of codes following names, see page B2.
★ Indicates Type III membership in the American Hospital Association.

Section B

CALIFORNIA: HARBOR–UCLA MEDICAL CENTER (O, 397 beds) 1000 West Carson Street, Torrance, CA, Zip 90502–2059; tel. 310/222–2345; Kimberly McKenzie, R.N., MSN, Interim Chief Executive Officer

LAC+USC MEDICAL CENTER (O, 538 beds) 2051 Marengo Street, Los Angeles, CA, Zip 90033–1352; tel. 323/409–1000; Dan A. Castillo, FACHE, Chief Executive Officer
Web address: www.lacusc.org

LAC–OLIVE VIEW–UCLA MEDICAL CENTER (O, 198 beds) 14445 Olive View Drive, Sylmar, CA, Zip 91342–1438; tel. 818/364–1555; Carolyn F. Rhee, Chief Executive Officer
Web address: www.ladhs.org

RANCHO LOS AMIGOS NATIONAL REHABILITATION CENTER (O, 207 beds) 7601 East Imperial Highway, Downey, CA, Zip 90242–3496; tel. 562/401–7111; Jorge Orozco, Chief Executive Officer
Web address: www.rancho.org

Owned, leased, sponsored:	4 hospitals	1340 beds
Contract–managed:	0 hospitals	0 beds
Totals:	4 hospitals	1340 beds

0047: LOUISIANA STATE HOSPITALS (NP)
628 North 4th Street, Baton Rouge, LA, Zip 70802–5342, Mailing Address: P.O. Box 629, Zip 70821–0628, tel. 225/342–9500; Shelby Price, Chief Executive Officer
(Independent Hospital System)

LOUISIANA: CENTRAL LOUISIANA STATE HOSPITAL (O, 120 beds) 242 West Shamrock Avenue, Pineville, LA, Zip 71360–6439, Mailing Address: P.O. Box 5031, Zip 71361–5031, tel. 318/484–6200; Ronald G. Williams, Administrator
Web address: www.dhh.louisiana.gov/index.cfm/directory/detail/217

EASTERN LOUISIANA MENTAL HEALTH SYSTEM (O, 473 beds) 4502 Highway 951, Jackson, LA, Zip 70748–5842, Mailing Address: P.O. Box 498, Zip 70748–0498, tel. 225/634–0100; Hampton P S. Lea, Acting Chief Executive Officer

Owned, leased, sponsored:	2 hospitals	593 beds
Contract–managed:	0 hospitals	0 beds
Totals:	2 hospitals	593 beds

★0320: LRGHEALTHCARE (NP)
80 Highland Street, Laconia, NH, Zip 03246–3298; tel. 603/524–3211; Kevin Donovan, FACHE, President and Chief Executive Officer
(Independent Hospital System)

NEW HAMPSHIRE: FRANKLIN REGIONAL HOSPITAL (O, 31 beds) 15 Aiken Avenue, Franklin, NH, Zip 03235–1299; tel. 603/934–2060; Kevin Donovan, FACHE, President and Chief Executive Officer
Web address: www.lrgh.org

LAKES REGION GENERAL HOSPITAL (O, 96 beds) 80 Highland Street, Laconia, NH, Zip 03246–3298; tel. 603/524–3211; Kevin Donovan, FACHE, President and Chief Executive Officer
Web address: www.lrgh.org

Owned, leased, sponsored:	2 hospitals	127 beds
Contract–managed:	0 hospitals	0 beds
Totals:	2 hospitals	127 beds

0614: MAINEHEALTH (NP)
110 Free Street, Portland, ME, Zip 04101–3537; tel. 207/661–7001; William L. Caron Jr, President
(Moderately Centralized Health System)

MAINE: LINCOLNHEALTH (O, 91 beds) 35 Miles Street, Damariscotta, ME, Zip 04543–4047; tel. 207/563–1234; James W. Donovan, President and Chief Executive Officer
Web address: www.lchcare.org

MAINE MEDICAL CENTER (O, 637 beds) 22 Bramhall Street, Portland, ME, Zip 04102–3175; tel. 207/662–0111; Richard W. Petersen, President and Chief Executive Officer

PEN BAY MEDICAL CENTER (O, 165 beds) 6 Glen Cove Drive, Rockport, ME, Zip 04856–4240; tel. 207/921–8000; Mark Fourre, President and Chief Executive Officer
Web address: www.penbayhealthcare.org

SPRING HARBOR HOSPITAL (O, 88 beds) 123 Andover Road, Westbrook, ME, Zip 04092–3850; tel. 207/761–2200; Mary Jane Krebs, FACHE, President

STEPHENS MEMORIAL HOSPITAL (O, 25 beds) 181 Main Street, Norway, ME, Zip 04268–5664; tel. 207/743–5933; Timothy A. Churchill, President
Web address: www.wmhcc.com

WALDO COUNTY GENERAL HOSPITAL MAINE HEALTH (O, 25 beds) 118 Northport Avenue, Belfast, ME, Zip 04915–6072, Mailing Address: P.O. Box 287, Zip 04915–0287, tel. 207/338–2500; Mark Fourre, Chief Executive Officer

NEW HAMPSHIRE: MEMORIAL HOSPITAL (O, 70 beds) 3073 White Mountain Highway, North Conway, NH, Zip 03860–7101; tel. 603/356–5461; Scott McKinnon, President and Chief Executive Officer
Web address: www.memorialhospitalnh.org

Owned, leased, sponsored:	7 hospitals	1101 beds
Contract–managed:	0 hospitals	0 beds
Totals:	7 hospitals	1101 beds

1975: MARSHALL HEALTH SYSTEM (NP)
227 Britany Road, Guntersville, AL, Zip 35976–5766; tel. 256/894–6615; Gary R. Gore, Chief Executive Officer
(Independent Hospital System)

ALABAMA: MARSHALL MEDICAL CENTER NORTH (O, 90 beds) 8000 Alabama Highway 69, Guntersville, AL, Zip 35976; tel. 256/753–8000; Cheryl M. Hays, FACHE, Administrator and Chief Operating Officer
Web address: www.mmcenters.com

MARSHALL MEDICAL CENTER SOUTH (O, 114 beds) U S Highway 431 North, Boaz, AL, Zip 35957–0999, Mailing Address: P.O. Box 758, Zip 35957–0758, tel. 256/593–8310; John D. Anderson, FACHE, Administrator
Web address: www.mmcenters.com//index.php/facilities/marshall_south

Owned, leased, sponsored:	2 hospitals	204 beds
Contract–managed:	0 hospitals	0 beds
Totals:	2 hospitals	204 beds

★1022: MARSHFIELD CLINIC HEALTH SYSTEM (NP)
1000 North Oak Avenue, Marshfield, WI, Zip 54449–5703; tel. 800/782–8581; Susan Turney, M.D., MS, Chief Executive Officer
(Moderately Centralized Health System)

WISCONSIN: FLAMBEAU HOSPITAL (O, 25 beds) 98 Sherry Avenue, Park Falls, WI, Zip 54552–1467, Mailing Address: P.O. Box 310, Zip 54552–0310, tel. 715/762–2484; James R. Braun, Chief Administrative Officer and Chief Financial Officer
Web address: www.flambeauhospital.org

LAKEVIEW MEDICAL CENTER (O, 40 beds) 1700 West Stout Street, Rice Lake, WI, Zip 54868–5000; tel. 715/234–1515; Bradley D. Groseth, Chief Administrative Officer

MARSHFIELD MEDICAL CENTER – EAU CLAIRE HOSPITAL (O, 44 beds) 2310 Craig Road, Eau Claire, WI, Zip 54701–6128; tel. 715/858–8100; Scott Polenz, CPA, Chief Administrative Officer

MARSHFIELD MEDICAL CENTER (O, 176 beds) 611 St Joseph Avenue, Marshfield, WI, Zip 54449–1898; tel. 715/387–1713; Ned H. Wolf, Chief Administrative Officer
Web address: www.stjosephs-marshfield.org

Owned, leased, sponsored:	4 hospitals	285 beds
Contract–managed:	0 hospitals	0 beds
Totals:	4 hospitals	285 beds

★0523: MARY WASHINGTON HEALTHCARE (NP)
1001 Sam Perry Boulevard, Fredericksburg, VA, Zip 22401–4453; tel. 540/741–3100; Michael P. McDermott, M.D., President and Chief Executive Officer
(Centralized Health System)

For explanation of codes following names, see page B2.
★ Indicates Type III membership in the American Hospital Association.

VIRGINIA: MARY WASHINGTON HOSPITAL (O, 451 beds) 1001 Sam Perry Boulevard, Fredericksburg, VA, Zip 22401–3354; tel. 540/741–1100; Michael P. McDermott, M.D., President and Chief Executive Officer
Web address: www.marywashingtonhealthcare.com

STAFFORD HOSPITAL (O, 82 beds) 101 Hospital Center Boulevard, Stafford, VA, Zip 22554–6200; tel. 540/741–9000; Michael P. McDermott, M.D., President and Chief Executive Officer

Owned, leased, sponsored:	2 hospitals	533 beds
Contract–managed:	0 hospitals	0 beds
Totals:	2 hospitals	533 beds

0013: MASSACHUSETTS DEPARTMENT OF MENTAL HEALTH (NP)
25 Staniford Street, Boston, MA, Zip 02114–2575; tel. 617/626–8123; Joan Mikula, Interim Commissioner

MASSACHUSETTS: DR. J. CORRIGAN MENTAL HEALTH CENTER (O, 16 beds) 49 Hillside Street, Fall River, MA, Zip 02720–5266; tel. 508/235–7200; Frank O'Reilly, Director

TAUNTON STATE HOSPITAL (O, 45 beds) 60 Hodges Avenue Extension, Taunton, MA, Zip 02780–3034, Mailing Address: PO Box 4007, Zip 02780–0997, tel. 508/977–3000; Joyce O Connor, Chief Operating Officer

WORCESTER RECOVERY CENTER AND HOSPITAL (O, 126 beds) 309 Belmont Street, Worcester, MA, Zip 01604–1695; tel. 508/368–3300; Anthony Riccitelli, Chief Operating Officer

Owned, leased, sponsored:	3 hospitals	187 beds
Contract–managed:	0 hospitals	0 beds
Totals:	3 hospitals	187 beds

0280: MASSACHUSETTS DEPARTMENT OF PUBLIC HEALTH (NP)
250 Washington Street, Boston, MA, Zip 02108–4619; tel. 617/624–6000; Sandra Akers, Bureau Director, Public Health Hospitals
(Independent Hospital System)

MASSACHUSETTS: LEMUEL SHATTUCK HOSPITAL (O, 260 beds) 170 Morton Street, Jamaica Plain, MA, Zip 02130–3735; tel. 617/522–8110; Rosette Martinez, Acting Chief Executive Officer
Web address: www.mass.gov/shattuckhospital

PAPPAS REHABILITATION HOSPITAL FOR CHILDREN (O, 80 beds) 3 Randolph Street, Canton, MA, Zip 02021–2351; tel. 781/828–2440; Brian V. Devin, Chief Executive Officer

TEWKSBURY HOSPITAL (O, 381 beds) 365 East Street, Tewksbury, MA, Zip 01876–1998; tel. 978/851–7321; Debra Tosti, Chief Executive Officer
Web address: www.mass.gov

WESTERN MASSACHUSETTS HOSPITAL (O, 80 beds) 91 East Mountain Road, Westfield, MA, Zip 01085–1801; tel. 413/562–4131; Valenda M. Liptak, Chief Executive Officer

Owned, leased, sponsored:	4 hospitals	801 beds
Contract–managed:	0 hospitals	0 beds
Totals:	4 hospitals	801 beds

★0882: MAURY REGIONAL HEALTH SYSTEM (NP)
1224 Trotwood Avenue, Columbia, TN, Zip 38401–4802; tel. 931/381–1111; H Alan. Watson, FACHE, Chief Executive Officer
(Independent Hospital System)

TENNESSEE: MARSHALL MEDICAL CENTER (O, 12 beds) 1080 North Ellington Parkway, Lewisburg, TN, Zip 37091–2227, Mailing Address: P.O. Box 1609, Zip 37091–1609, tel. 931/359–6241; Phyllis Brown, Chief Executive Officer

MAURY REGIONAL HOSPITAL (O, 209 beds) 1224 Trotwood Avenue, Columbia, TN, Zip 38401–4802; tel. 931/381–1111; H Alan. Watson, FACHE, Chief Executive Officer
Web address: www.mauryregional.com

WAYNE MEDICAL CENTER (L, 25 beds) 103 J V Mangubat Drive, Waynesboro, TN, Zip 38485–2440, Mailing Address: P.O. Box 580, Zip 38485–0580, tel. 931/722–5411; Tyler Taylor, Chief Executive Officer
Web address: www.mauryregional.com

Owned, leased, sponsored:	3 hospitals	246 beds
Contract–managed:	0 hospitals	0 beds
Totals:	3 hospitals	246 beds

★1875: MAYO CLINIC (NP)
200 First Street SW, Rochester, MN, Zip 55905–0002; tel. 507/284–2511; John H. Noseworthy, MD, President and Chief Executive Officer
(Decentralized Health System)

ARIZONA: MAYO CLINIC HOSPITAL (O, 280 beds) 5777 East Mayo Boulevard, Phoenix, AZ, Zip 85054–4502; tel. 480/342–2000; Wyatt Decker, Chief Executive Officer, Mayo Clinic in Arizona
Web address: www.mayoclinic.org/arizona/

FLORIDA: MAYO CLINIC HOSPITAL IN FLORIDA (O, 263 beds) 4500 San Pablo Road South, Jacksonville, FL, Zip 32224–1865; tel. 904/953–2000; Gianrico Farrugia, M.D., Vice President and Chief Executive Officer
Web address: www.mayoclinic.org/jacksonville/

IOWA: FLOYD COUNTY MEDICAL CENTER (C, 25 beds) 800 Eleventh Street, Charles City, IA, Zip 50616–3499; tel. 641/228–6830; Rod Nordeng, Administrator

WINNESHIEK MEDICAL CENTER (C, 25 beds) 901 Montgomery Street, Decorah, IA, Zip 52101–2325; tel. 563/382–2911; Lisa Radtke, Chief Administrative Officer
Web address: www.winmedical.org

MINNESOTA: MAYO CLINIC HEALTH SYSTEM – ALBERT LEA AND AUSTIN (O, 69 beds) 404 West Fountain Street, Albert Lea, MN, Zip 56007–2473; tel. 507/373–2384; Mark Ciota, M.D., Chief Executive Officer

MAYO CLINIC HEALTH SYSTEM IN CANNON FALLS (O, 15 beds) 32021 County Road 24 Boulevard, Cannon Falls, MN, Zip 55009–1898; tel. 507/263–4221; Brian Whited, M.D., Vice Chair Mayo Clinic Health System
Web address: www.mayoclinichealthsystem.org/locations/cannon–falls

MAYO CLINIC HEALTH SYSTEM IN FAIRMONT (O, 23 beds) 800 Medical Center Drive, Fairmont, MN, Zip 56031–4575; tel. 507/238–8100; Amy Long, Administrator

MAYO CLINIC HEALTH SYSTEM IN LAKE CITY (O, 105 beds) 500 West Grant Street, Lake City, MN, Zip 55041–1143; tel. 651/345–3321; Brian Whited, M.D., President and Chief Executive Officer
Web address: www.lakecitymedicalcenter.org

MAYO CLINIC HEALTH SYSTEM IN MANKATO (O, 145 beds) 1025 Marsh Street, Mankato, MN, Zip 56001–4752; tel. 507/625–4031; James Hebl, M.D., Regional Vice President
Web address: www.mayoclinichealthsystem.org

MAYO CLINIC HEALTH SYSTEM IN NEW PRAGUE (O, 20 beds) 301 Second Street NE, New Prague, MN, Zip 56071–1799; tel. 952/758–4431; Mary J. Klimp, FACHE, Interim Administrator

MAYO CLINIC HEALTH SYSTEM IN RED WING (O, 22 beds) 701 Hewitt Boulevard, Red Wing, MN, Zip 55066–2848, Mailing Address: P.O. Box 95, Zip 55066–0095, tel. 651/267–5000; Brian Whited, M.D., President and Chief Executive Officer
Web address: www.mayoclinichealthsystem.org/locations/red–wing

MAYO CLINIC HEALTH SYSTEM IN SAINT JAMES (O, 13 beds) 1101 Moulton and Parsons Drive, Saint James, MN, Zip 56081–5550; tel. 507/375–3261; Scott D. Thoreson, FACHE, Administrator
Web address: www.mayoclinichealthsystem.org/locations/st–james

MAYO CLINIC HEALTH SYSTEM IN SPRINGFIELD (O, 10 beds) 625 North Jackson Avenue, Springfield, MN, Zip 56087–1714, Mailing Address: P.O. Box 146, Zip 56087–0146, tel. 507/723–6201; Scott D. Thoreson, FACHE, Administrator
Web address: www.mayoclinichealthsystem.org

MAYO CLINIC HEALTH SYSTEM IN WASECA (O, 12 beds) 501 North State Street, Waseca, MN, Zip 56093–2811; tel. 507/835–1210; April Lanz, Interim Administrator

For explanation of codes following names, see page B2.
★ Indicates Type III membership in the American Hospital Association.

MAYO CLINIC HOSPITAL – ROCHESTER (O, 1287 beds) 1216 Second Street SW, Rochester, MN, Zip 55902–1906; tel. 507/255–5123; F. Kenneth. Ackerman, FACHE, Hospital Administrator
Web address: www.mayoclinic.org

WISCONSIN: MAYO CLINIC HEALTH SYSTEM – CHIPPEWA VALLEY IN BLOOMER (O, 21 beds) 1501 Thompson Street, Bloomer, WI, Zip 54724–1299; tel. 715/568–2000; Rita Sullivan, Vice President Operations
Web address: www.bloomermedicalcenter.org

MAYO CLINIC HEALTH SYSTEM – FRANCISCAN HEALTHCARE IN LA CROSSE (O, 91 beds) 700 West Avenue South, La Crosse, WI, Zip 54601–4783; tel. 608/785–0940; Timothy Johnson, M.D., President and Chief Executive Officer

MAYO CLINIC HEALTH SYSTEM – FRANCISCAN HEALTHCARE IN SPARTA (O, 12 beds) 310 West Main Street, Sparta, WI, Zip 54656–2171; tel. 608/269–2132; Kimberly Hawthorne, Administrator
Web address: www.mayoclinichealthsystem.org

MAYO CLINIC HEALTH SYSTEM – NORTHLAND IN BARRON (O, 20 beds) 1222 East Woodland Avenue, Barron, WI, Zip 54812–1798; tel. 715/537–3186; Rita Sullivan, Vice President Operations

MAYO CLINIC HEALTH SYSTEM – OAKRIDGE IN OSSEO (O, 16 beds) 13025 Eighth Street, Osseo, WI, Zip 54758–7634, Mailing Address: P.O. Box 70, Zip 54758–0070, tel. 715/597–3121; Dean Eide, Vice President
Web address: www.mayoclinichealthsystem.org/locations/osseo

MAYO CLINIC HEALTH SYSTEM – RED CEDAR IN MENOMONIE (O, 25 beds) 2321 Stout Road, Menomonie, WI, Zip 54751–2397; tel. 715/235–5531; Steven Lindberg, Chief Administrative Officer

MAYO CLINIC HEALTH SYSTEM IN EAU CLAIRE (O, 185 beds) 1221 Whipple Street, Eau Claire, WI, Zip 54703–5270, Mailing Address: P.O. Box 4105, Zip 54702, tel. 715/838–3311; Richard Helmers, M.D., Regional Vice President
Web address: www.mhs.mayo.edu

Owned, leased, sponsored:	20 hospitals	2634 beds
Contract–managed:	2 hospitals	50 beds
Totals:	22 hospitals	2684 beds

0252: MCLAREN HEALTH CARE CORPORATION (NP)

3373 Regency Park Drive, Grand Blanc, MI, Zip 48439, Mailing Address: One McLaren Parkway, Zip 48439, tel. 810/342–1100; Philip A. Incarnati, President and Chief Executive Officer
(Centralized Physician/Insurance Health System)

MICHIGAN: MARWOOD MANOR NURSING HOME (O, 106 beds) 1300 Beard Street, Port Huron, MI, Zip 48060; tel. 818/982–2594; Brian Oberly, Administrator

MCLAREN BAY REGION (O, 338 beds) 1900 Columbus Avenue, Bay City, MI, Zip 48708–6831; tel. 989/894–3000; Clarence Sevillian, President and Chief Executive Officer
Web address: www.mclaren.org/bayregion

MCLAREN BAY SPECIAL CARE (O, 10 beds) 3250 East Midland Road, Suite 1, Bay City, MI, Zip 48706–2835; tel. 989/667–6851; Monica Baranski, MS, R.N., President
Web address: www.mclaren/bayspecialcare

MCLAREN CARO REGION (O, 25 beds) 401 North Hooper Street, Caro, MI, Zip 48723–1476, Mailing Address: P.O. Box 435, Zip 48723–0435, tel. 989/673–3141; Marc Augsburger, R.N., President and Chief Executive Officer
Web address: www.cch–mi.org

MCLAREN CENTRAL MICHIGAN (O, 78 beds) 1221 South Drive, Mount Pleasant, MI, Zip 48858–3257; tel. 989/772–6700; Martin Tursky, President and Chief Executive Officer

MCLAREN FLINT (O, 358 beds) 401 South Ballenger Highway, Flint, MI, Zip 48532–3685; tel. 810/342–2000; Chad M. Grant, President and Chief Executive Officer
Web address: www.mclaren.org/flint

MCLAREN GREATER LANSING (O, 321 beds) 401 West Greenlawn Avenue, Lansing, MI, Zip 48910–2819; tel. 517/975–6000; Kirk M. Ray, President and Chief Executive Officer

MCLAREN LAPEER REGION (O, 159 beds) 1375 North Main Street, Lapeer, MI, Zip 48446–1350; tel. 810/667–5500; Chris Candela, President and Chief Executive Officer
Web address: www.lapeerregional.org

MCLAREN MACOMB (O, 288 beds) 1000 Harrington Boulevard, Mount Clemens, MI, Zip 48043–2992; tel. 586/493–8000; Thomas M. Brisse, President and Chief Executive Officer

MCLAREN NORTHERN MICHIGAN (O, 188 beds) 416 Connable Avenue, Petoskey, MI, Zip 49770–2297; tel. 231/487–4000; David M. Zechman, FACHE, President and Chief Executive Officer
Web address: www.northernhealth.org

MCLAREN OAKLAND (O, 263 beds) 50 North Perry Street, Pontiac, MI, Zip 48342–2253; tel. 248/338–5000; Margaret Dimond, Ph.D., President and Chief Executive Officer

MCLAREN PORT HURON (O, 186 beds) 1221 Pine Grove Avenue, Port Huron, MI, Zip 48060–3511; tel. 810/987–5000; Jennifer Montgomery, FACHE, R.N., President and Chief Executive Officer
Web address: www.porthuronhospital.org

MCLAREN THUMB REGION (O, 46 beds) 1100 South Van Dyke Road, Bad Axe, MI, Zip 48413–9615; tel. 989/269–9521; Michael Eric. Johnston, President and Chief Executive Officer
Web address: www.huronmedicalcenter.org

Owned, leased, sponsored:	13 hospitals	2366 beds
Contract–managed:	0 hospitals	0 beds
Totals:	13 hospitals	2366 beds

0874: MCLEOD HEALTH (NP)

555 East Cheves Street, Florence, SC, Zip 29506–2617, Mailing Address: P.O. Box 100551, Zip 29502–0551, tel. 843/777–2000; Robert L. Colones, President and Chief Executive Officer
(Centralized Health System)

SOUTH CAROLINA: MCLEOD HEALTH CHERAW (O, 52 beds) 711 Chesterfield Highway, Cheraw, SC, Zip 29520–7002; tel. 843/537–7881; Mib Scoggins, Chief Executive Officer
Web address: www.chesterfieldgeneral.com

MCLEOD HEALTH CLARENDON (C, 64 beds) 10 Hospital Street, Manning, SC, Zip 29102–3153, Mailing Address: P.O. Box 550, Zip 29102–0550, tel. 803/433–3000; Rachel Gainey, Administrator

MCLEOD LORIS SEACOAST HOSPITAL (O, 155 beds) 3655 Mitchell Street, Loris, SC, Zip 29569–2827; tel. 843/716–7000; Edward D. Tinsley III, Regional Administrator
Web address: www.mcleodhealth.org

MCLEOD MEDICAL CENTER DARLINGTON (O, 40 beds) 701 Cashua Ferry Road, Darlington, SC, Zip 29532–8488, Mailing Address: P.O. Box 1859, Zip 29540, tel. 843/395–1100; Tim Smoak, Administrator
Web address: www.mcleodhealth.org

MCLEOD MEDICAL CENTER DILLON (O, 34 beds) 301 East Jackson Street, Dillon, SC, Zip 29536–2509, Mailing Address: P.O. Box 1327, Zip 29536–1327, tel. 843/774–4111; Joan Ervin, Administrator

MCLEOD REGIONAL MEDICAL CENTER (O, 466 beds) 555 East Cheves Street, Florence, SC, Zip 29506–2617, Mailing Address: P.O. Box 100551, Zip 29502–0551, tel. 843/777–2000; Robert L. Colones, President and Chief Executive Officer
Web address: www.mcleodhealth.org

Owned, leased, sponsored:	5 hospitals	747 beds
Contract–managed:	1 hospitals	64 beds
Totals:	6 hospitals	811 beds

★1001: MEADVILLE MEDICAL CENTER (NP)

751 Liberty Street, Meadville, PA, Zip 16335–2559; tel. 814/333–5000; Philip E. Pandolph, FACHE, Chief Executive Officer
(Independent Hospital System)

PENNSYLVANIA: MEADVILLE MEDICAL CENTER (O, 234 beds) 751 Liberty Street, Meadville, PA, Zip 16335–2559; tel. 814/333–5000; Philip E. Pandolph, FACHE, Chief Executive Officer
Web address: www.mmchs.org

For explanation of codes following names, see page B2.
★ Indicates Type III membership in the American Hospital Association.

TITUSVILLE AREA HOSPITAL (O, 25 beds) 406 West Oak Street, Titusville, PA, Zip 16354–1404; tel. 814/827–1851; Lee Clinton, FACHE, Chief Executive Officer

Owned, leased, sponsored:	2 hospitals	259 beds
Contract–managed:	0 hospitals	0 beds
Totals:	2 hospitals	259 beds

0520: MED CENTER HEALTH (NP)

800 Park Street, Bowling Green, KY, Zip 42101–2356; tel. 270/745–1500; Connie Smith, FACHE, MSN, R.N., President and Chief Executive Officer
(Independent Hospital System)

KENTUCKY: COMMONWEALTH REGIONAL SPECIALTY HOSPITAL (O, 28 beds) 250 Park Drive, 6th Floor, Bowling Green, KY, Zip 42101–1760, Mailing Address: P.O. Box 90010, Zip 42102–9010, tel. 270/796–6200; Christa Atkins, Administrator
Web address: www.commonwealthregionalspecialtyhospital.org

MEDICAL CENTER AT BOWLING GREEN (O, 337 beds) 250 Park Street, Bowling Green, KY, Zip 42101–1795, Mailing Address: P.O. Box 90010, Zip 42102–9010, tel. 270/745–1000; Connie Smith, FACHE, MSN, R.N., Chief Executive Officer
Web address: www.themedicalcenter.org

MEDICAL CENTER AT FRANKLIN (O, 25 beds) 1100 Brookhaven Road, Franklin, KY, Zip 42134–2746; tel. 270/598–4800; Annette Runyon, Vice President and Administrator
Web address: www.themedicalcenterfranklin.org

MEDICAL CENTER AT SCOTTSVILLE (O, 135 beds) 456 Burnley Road, Scottsville, KY, Zip 42164–6355; tel. 270/622–2800; Eric Hagan, R.N., Executive Vice President and Administrator

THE MEDICAL CENTER ALBANY (C, 42 beds) 723 Burkesville Road, Albany, KY, Zip 42602–1654; tel. 606/387–8000; Laura Belcher, Administrator
Web address: www.chc.net/services/hospitals/the_medical_center_at_albany.aspx

THE MEDICAL CENTER AT CAVERNA (O, 25 beds) 1501 South Dixie Street, Horse Cave, KY, Zip 42749–1477; tel. 270/786–2191; Alan B. Alexander, FACHE, Vice President and Administrator

Owned, leased, sponsored:	5 hospitals	550 beds
Contract–managed:	1 hospitals	42 beds
Totals:	6 hospitals	592 beds

★0971: MEDISYS HEALTH NETWORK (NP)

8900 Van Wyck Expressway, Jamaica, NY, Zip 11418–2832; tel. 718/206–6000; Bruce J. Flanz, President and Chief Executive Officer
(Moderately Centralized Health System)

NEW YORK: FLUSHING HOSPITAL MEDICAL CENTER (C, 299 beds) 4500 Parsons Boulevard, Flushing, NY, Zip 11355–2205; tel. 718/670–5000; Bruce J. Flanz, President and Chief Executive Officer
Web address: www.flushinghospital.org

JAMAICA HOSPITAL MEDICAL CENTER (C, 632 beds) 8900 Van Wyck Expressway, Jamaica, NY, Zip 11418–2832; tel. 718/206–6000; Bruce J. Flanz, President and Chief Executive Officer

Owned, leased, sponsored:	0 hospitals	0 beds
Contract–managed:	2 hospitals	931 beds
Totals:	2 hospitals	931 beds

★0154: MEDSTAR HEALTH (NP)

10980 Grantchester Way, Columbia, MD, Zip 21044–2665; tel. 410/772–6500; Kenneth A. Samet, President and Chief Executive Officer
(Centralized Health System)

DISTRICT OF COLUMBIA: MEDSTAR GEORGETOWN UNIVERSITY HOSPITAL (O, 409 beds) 3800 Reservoir Road NW, Washington, DC, Zip 20007–2197; tel. 202/444–2000; Michael Sachtleben, President
Web address: www.georgetownuniversityhospital.org

MEDSTAR NATIONAL REHABILITATION HOSPITAL (O, 137 beds) 102 Irving Street NW, Washington, DC, Zip 20010–2949; tel. 202/877–1000; John D. Rockwood, President
Web address: www.medstarnrh.org

MEDSTAR WASHINGTON HOSPITAL CENTER (O, 763 beds) 110 Irving Street NW, Washington, DC, Zip 20010–3017; tel. 202/877–7000; Gregory J. Argyros, M.D., Senior Vice President and President

MARYLAND: MEDSTAR FRANKLIN SQUARE MEDICAL CENTER (O, 373 beds) 9000 Franklin Square Drive, Baltimore, MD, Zip 21237–3901; tel. 443/777–7000; Samuel E. Moskowitz, President
Web address: www.medstarfranklin.org

MEDSTAR GOOD SAMARITAN HOSPITAL (O, 230 beds) 5601 Loch Raven Boulevard, Baltimore, MD, Zip 21239–2995; tel. 443/444–8000; Bradley Chambers, President and Senior Vice President, MedStar Health
Web address: www.goodsam–md.org

MEDSTAR HARBOR HOSPITAL (O, 127 beds) 3001 South Hanover Street, Baltimore, MD, Zip 21225–1290; tel. 410/350–3200; Stuart M. Levine, M.D., President and Chief Medical Officer

MEDSTAR MONTGOMERY MEDICAL CENTER (O, 147 beds) 18101 Prince Philip Drive, Olney, MD, Zip 20832–1512; tel. 301/774–8882; Thomas J. Senker, FACHE, President
Web address: www.medstarmontgomery.org

MEDSTAR SOUTHERN MARYLAND HOSPITAL CENTER (O, 216 beds) 7503 Surratts Road, Clinton, MD, Zip 20735–3358; tel. 301/868–8000; Christine R. Wray, President
Web address: www.medstarsouthernmaryland.org

MEDSTAR ST. MARY'S HOSPITAL (O, 103 beds) 25500 Point Lookout Road, Leonardtown, MD, Zip 20650–2015, Mailing Address: PO Box 527, Zip 20650–0527, tel. 301/475–6001; Christine R. Wray, President

MEDSTAR UNION MEMORIAL HOSPITAL (O, 199 beds) 201 East University Parkway, Baltimore, MD, Zip 21218–2895; tel. 410/554–2000; Bradley Chambers, President
Web address: www.medstarunionmemorial.org

Owned, leased, sponsored:	10 hospitals	2704 beds
Contract–managed:	0 hospitals	0 beds
Totals:	10 hospitals	2704 beds

★0086: MEMORIAL HEALTH SYSTEM (NP)

701 North First Street, Springfield, IL, Zip 62781–0001; tel. 217/788–3000; Edgar J. Curtis, FACHE, President and Chief Executive Officer
(Centralized Health System)

ILLINOIS: ABRAHAM LINCOLN MEMORIAL HOSPITAL (O, 25 beds) 200 Stahlhut Drive, Lincoln, IL, Zip 62656–5066; tel. 217/732–2161; Dolan Dalpoas, President and Chief Executive Officer
Web address: www.almh.org

MEMORIAL MEDICAL CENTER (O, 475 beds) 701 North First Street, Springfield, IL, Zip 62781–0001; tel. 217/788–3000; Edgar J. Curtis, FACHE, President and Chief Executive Officer
Web address: www.memorialmedical.com

PASSAVANT AREA HOSPITAL (O, 118 beds) 1600 West Walnut Street, Jacksonville, IL, Zip 62650–1136; tel. 217/245–9541; Harry M. Schmidt, President and Chief Executive Officer
Web address: www.passavanthospital.com

TAYLORVILLE MEMORIAL HOSPITAL (O, 25 beds) 201 East Pleasant Street, Taylorville, IL, Zip 62568–1597; tel. 217/824–3331; Kimberly L. Bourne, Chief Executive Officer
Web address: www.taylorvillememorial.org

Owned, leased, sponsored:	4 hospitals	643 beds
Contract–managed:	0 hospitals	0 beds
Totals:	4 hospitals	643 beds

0998: MEMORIAL HEALTH SYSTEM (NP)

401 Matthew Street, Marietta, OH, Zip 45750–1635; tel. 740/374–1400; J Scott. Cantley, President and Chief Executive Officer
(Independent Hospital System)

For explanation of codes following names, see page B2.
★ Indicates Type III membership in the American Hospital Association.

Section B

OHIO: MARIETTA MEMORIAL HOSPITAL (O, 218 beds) 401 Matthew Street, Marietta, OH, Zip 45750–1699; tel. 740/374–1400; J Scott. Cantley, President and Chief Executive Officer
Web address: www.mhsystem.org

SELBY GENERAL HOSPITAL (O, 25 beds) 1106 Colegate Drive, Marietta, OH, Zip 45750–1323; tel. 740/568–2000; Stephen Smith, President
Web address: www.selbygeneral.org

Owned, leased, sponsored:	2 hospitals	243 beds
Contract–managed:	0 hospitals	0 beds
Totals:	2 hospitals	243 beds

★0083: MEMORIAL HEALTHCARE SYSTEM (NP)
3501 Johnson Street, Hollywood, FL, Zip 33021–5421; tel. 954/987–2000; Aurelio Fernandez, Chief Executive Officer
(Centralized Health System)

FLORIDA: MEMORIAL HOSPITAL MIRAMAR (O, 178 beds) 1901 SW 172nd Avenue, Miramar, FL, Zip 33029–5592; tel. 954/538–5000; Grisel Fernandez–Bravo, R.N., Administrator and Chief Executive Officer
Web address: www.mhs.net

MEMORIAL HOSPITAL PEMBROKE (L, 157 beds) 7800 Sheridan Street, Pembroke Pines, FL, Zip 33024–2536; tel. 954/883–8482; Mark Doyle, Administrator and Chief Executive Officer

MEMORIAL HOSPITAL WEST (O, 382 beds) 703 North Flamingo Road, Pembroke Pines, FL, Zip 33028–1014; tel. 954/436–5000; Leah A. Carpenter, Administrator and Chief Executive Officer
Web address: www.mhs.net

MEMORIAL REGIONAL HOSPITAL (O, 1064 beds) 3501 Johnson Street, Hollywood, FL, Zip 33021–5421; tel. 954/987–2000; Zeff Ross, FACHE, Executive Vice President and Chief Executive Officer
Web address: www.mhs.net

Owned, leased, sponsored:	4 hospitals	1781 beds
Contract–managed:	0 hospitals	0 beds
Totals:	4 hospitals	1781 beds

★2645: MEMORIAL HERMANN HEALTH SYSTEM (NP)
929 Gessner, Suite 2700, Houston, TX, Zip 77024–2593; tel. 713/338–5555; Charles D. Stokes, FACHE, President and Chief Executive Officer
(Centralized Health System)

TEXAS: MEMORIAL HERMANN – TEXAS MEDICAL CENTER (O, 1042 beds) 6411 Fannin Street, Houston, TX, Zip 77030–1501; tel. 713/704–4000; Gregory Haralson, FACHE, Senior Vice President and Chief Executive Officer
Web address: www.mhhs.org

MEMORIAL HERMANN GREATER HEIGHTS HOSPITAL (O, 1379 beds) 1635 North Loop West, Houston, TX, Zip 77008–1532; tel. 713/867–3380; Paul O'Sullivan, FACHE, Chief Executive Officer

MEMORIAL HERMANN KATY HOSPITAL (O, 208 beds) 23900 Katy Freeway, Katy, TX, Zip 77494–1323; tel. 281/644–7000; Heath Rushing, Senior Vice President and Chief Executive Officer
Web address: www.memorialhermann.org/locations/katy/

MEMORIAL HERMANN MEMORIAL CITY MEDICAL CENTER (L, 421 beds) 921 Gessner Road, Houston, TX, Zip 77024–2501; tel. 713/242–3000; Paul O'Sullivan, FACHE, Chief Executive Officer
Web address: www.memorialhermann.org

MEMORIAL HERMANN NORTHEAST (O, 217 beds) 18951 North Memorial Drive, Humble, TX, Zip 77338–4297; tel. 281/540–7700; Josh Urban, Chief Executive Officer

MEMORIAL HERMANN REHABILITATION HOSPITAL – KATY (O, 35 beds) 21720 Kingsland Boulevard, 2nd Floor, Katy, TX, Zip 77450–2550, Jerry Ashworth, Interim Chief Executive Officer
Web address: www.memorialhermann.org/locations/katy–rehab/

MEMORIAL HERMANN SUGAR LAND HOSPITAL (O, 149 beds) 17500 West Grand Parkway South, Sugar Land, TX, Zip 77479–2562; tel. 281/725–5000; Malisha Patel, Senior Vice President and Chief Executive Officer
Web address: www.memorialhermann.org

MEMORIAL HERMANN TOMBALL HOSPITAL (O, 8 beds) 24429 State Highway 249, Tomball, TX, Zip 77375–8214; tel. 281/516–0911; Brenda Villafranco, Administrator
Web address: www.emerus.com/tomball/

TIRR MEMORIAL HERMANN (O, 134 beds) 1333 Moursund Street, Houston, TX, Zip 77030–3405; tel. 713/799–5000; Jerry Ashworth, Interim Chief Executive Officer

Owned, leased, sponsored:	9 hospitals	3593 beds
Contract–managed:	0 hospitals	0 beds
Totals:	9 hospitals	3593 beds

0084: MEMORIALCARE (NP)
17360 Brookhurst Street, Fountain Valley, CA, Zip 92708–3720, Mailing Address: P.O. Box 1428, Long Beach, Zip 90801–1428, tel. 714/377–2900; Barry S. Arbuckle, Ph.D., President and Chief Executive Officer
(Centralized Health System)

CALIFORNIA: MEMORIALCARE, LONG BEACH MEMORIAL MEDICAL CENTER (O, 458 beds) 2801 Atlantic Avenue, Long Beach, CA, Zip 90806–1701, Mailing Address: P.O. Box 1428, Zip 90801–1428, tel. 562/933–2000; John Bishop, Chief Executive Officer
Web address: www.memorialcare.org/LongBeach

MEMORIALCARE, MILLER CHILDREN'S & WOMEN'S HOSPITAL LONG BEACH (O, 371 beds) 2801 Atlantic Avenue, Long Beach, CA, Zip 90806–1701; tel. 562/933–5437; John Bishop, Chief Executive Officer
Web address: www.memorialcare.org

MEMORIALCARE, ORANGE COAST MEMORIAL MEDICAL CENTER (O, 218 beds) 9920 Talbert Avenue, Fountain Valley, CA, Zip 92708–5115; tel. 714/378–7000; Marcia Manker, Chief Executive Officer
Web address: www.memorialcare.org

MEMORIALCARE, SADDLEBACK MEMORIAL MEDICAL CENTER (O, 313 beds) 24451 Health Center Drive, Laguna Hills, CA, Zip 92653–3689; tel. 949/837–4500; Marcia Manker, Chief Executive Officer

Owned, leased, sponsored:	4 hospitals	1360 beds
Contract–managed:	0 hospitals	0 beds
Totals:	4 hospitals	1360 beds

★5185: MERCY (CO)
14528 South Outer 40, Suite 100, Chesterfield, MO, Zip 63017–5743; tel. 314/579–6100; Lynn Britton, President and Chief Executive Officer
(Decentralized Health System)

ARKANSAS: MERCY HOSPITAL BERRYVILLE (O, 25 beds) 214 Carter Street, Berryville, AR, Zip 72616–4303; tel. 870/423–3355; VonDa Moore, Administrator
Web address: www.mercy.net/berryvillear

MERCY HOSPITAL BOONEVILLE (O, 25 beds) 880 West Main Street, Booneville, AR, Zip 72927–3443; tel. 479/675–2800; Teresa Williams, R.N., Regional Administrator
Web address: www.mercy.net

MERCY HOSPITAL FORT SMITH (O, 352 beds) 7301 Rogers Avenue, Fort Smith, AR, Zip 72903–4189, Mailing Address: P.O. Box 17000, Zip 72917–7000, tel. 479/314–6000; Ryan Gehrig, President
Web address: www.mercy.net/fortsmithar

MERCY HOSPITAL OZARK (O, 25 beds) 801 West River Street, Ozark, AR, Zip 72949–3023; tel. 479/667–4138; Teresa Williams, BSN, RN, Regional Administrator

MERCY HOSPITAL PARIS (O, 16 beds) 500 East Academy, Paris, AR, Zip 72855–4040; tel. 479/963–6101; Teresa Williams, BSN, RN, Regional Administrator
Web address: www.mercy.net/fortsmithar

MERCY HOSPITAL ROGERS (O, 191 beds) 2710 Rife Medical Lane, Rogers, AR, Zip 72758–1452; tel. 479/338–8000; Eric Pianalto, President

MERCY HOSPITAL WALDRON (O, 24 beds) 1341 West 6th Street, Waldron, AR, Zip 72958–7642; tel. 479/637–4135; Teresa Williams, R.N., Regional Administrator
Web address: https://www.mercy.net/practice/mercy–hospital–waldron/

For explanation of codes following names, see page B2.
★ Indicates Type III membership in the American Hospital Association.

KANSAS: MERCY HOSPITAL COLUMBUS (O, 18 beds) 220 North Pennsylvania Avenue, Columbus, KS, Zip 66725–1110; tel. 620/429–2545; Angie Saporito, Administrator

MERCY HOSPITAL FORT SCOTT (O, 46 beds) 401 Woodland Hills Boulevard, Fort Scott, KS, Zip 66701–8797; tel. 620/223–2200; Reta K. Baker, President
Web address: www.mercykansas.com

MISSOURI: MERCY HOSPITAL AURORA (L, 25 beds) 500 Porter Street, Aurora, MO, Zip 65605–2365; tel. 417/678–2122; Nicki Gamet, R.N., Administrator
Web address: www.stjohns.com/aboutus/aurora.aspx

MERCY HOSPITAL CARTHAGE (L, 13 beds) 3125 Dr Russell Smith Way, Carthage, MO, Zip 64836–7402; tel. 417/358–8121; Scott Watson, Administrator
Web address: www.mercy.net

MERCY HOSPITAL CASSVILLE (L, 18 beds) 94 Main Street, Cassville, MO, Zip 65625–1610; tel. 417/847–6000; Nicki Gamet, R.N., Administrator

MERCY HOSPITAL JEFFERSON (O, 205 beds) Highway 61 South, Crystal City, MO, Zip 63019, Mailing Address: P.O. Box 350, Zip 63019–0350, tel. 636/933–1000; Eric Ammons, President
Web address: www.mercy.net/crystalcitymo

MERCY HOSPITAL JOPLIN (O, 229 beds) 100 Mercy Way, Joplin, MO, Zip 64804–1626; tel. 417/781–2727; Gary W. Pulsipher, President and Chief Executive Officer

MERCY HOSPITAL LEBANON (O, 58 beds) 100 Hospital Drive, Lebanon, MO, Zip 65536–9210; tel. 417/533–6100; Scott W. Childers, Administrator
Web address: www.mercy.net/practice/mercy–hospital–lebanon

MERCY HOSPITAL LINCOLN (L, 25 beds) 1000 East Cherry Street, Troy, MO, Zip 63379–1513; tel. 636/528–8551; Anthony Rothermich, Administrator

MERCY HOSPITAL SPRINGFIELD (O, 744 beds) 1235 East Cherokee Street, Springfield, MO, Zip 65804–2263; tel. 417/820–2000; Brent Hubbard, FACHE, Chief Operating Officer
Web address: www.mercy.net/springfieldmo

MERCY HOSPITAL ST. LOUIS (O, 859 beds) 615 South New Ballas Road, Saint Louis, MO, Zip 63141–8277; tel. 314/251–6000; Stephen Mackin, President
Web address: www.mercy.net/stlouismo

MERCY HOSPITAL WASHINGTON (O, 148 beds) 901 East Fifth Street, Washington, MO, Zip 63090–3127; tel. 636/239–8000; Eric J. Eoloff, President

MERCY ST. FRANCIS HOSPITAL (O, 20 beds) 100 West Highway 60, Mountain View, MO, Zip 65548–7125; tel. 417/934–7000; Cynthia Weatherford, Administrator and Director of Nursing
Web address: www.stjohns.com/aboutus/stfrancis.aspx

ST. ANTHONY'S MERCY (O, 520 beds) 10010 Kennerly Road, Saint Louis, MO, Zip 63128–2106; tel. 314/525–1000; Sean Hogan, FACHE, President

OKLAHOMA: ARBUCKLE MEMORIAL HOSPITAL (C, 15 beds) 2011 West Broadway Street, Sulphur, OK, Zip 73086–4221, Mailing Address: P.O. Box 1109, Zip 73086–8109, tel. 580/622–2161; Jeremy A. Jones, Chief Executive Officer
Web address: www.arbucklehospital.com/

MERCY HEALTH LOVE COUNTY (C, 25 beds) 300 Wanda Street, Marietta, OK, Zip 73448–1200; tel. 580/276–3347; Richard Barker, Administrator and Chief Executive Officer
Web address: www.mercyhealthlovecounty.com

MERCY HOSPITAL ADA (L, 156 beds) 430 North Monte Vista, Ada, OK, Zip 74820–4610; tel. 580/332–2323; Lori Wightman, R.N., MSN, FACHE, President

MERCY HOSPITAL ARDMORE (O, 190 beds) 1011 14th Avenue NW, Ardmore, OK, Zip 73401–1828; tel. 580/223–5400; Daryle Voss, FACHE, President and Chief Executive Officer
Web address: www.mercyok.net

MERCY HOSPITAL EL RENO (L, 48 beds) 2115 Parkview Drive, El Reno, OK, Zip 73036–2199; tel. 405/262–2640; Cindy Carmichael, Administrator
Web address: www.mercyok.net

MERCY HOSPITAL HEALDTON (L, 22 beds) 3462 Hospital Road, Healdton, OK, Zip 73438–6124, Mailing Address: P.O. Box 928, Zip 73438–0928, tel. 580/229–0701; Nichole Barrett, R.N., Interim Administrator
Web address: www.mercyok.com

MERCY HOSPITAL KINGFISHER (L, 25 beds) 1000 Hospital Cirle, Kingfisher, OK, Zip 73750–5002, Mailing Address: P.O. Box 59, Zip 73750–0059, tel. 405/375–3141; Brian Denton, Administrator

MERCY HOSPITAL LOGAN COUNTY (O, 25 beds) 200 South Academy Road, Guthrie, OK, Zip 73044–8727, Mailing Address: P.O. Box 1017, Zip 73044–1017, tel. 405/282–6700; Bobby Stitt, R.N., Administrator
Web address: www.mercy.net

MERCY HOSPITAL OKLAHOMA CITY (O, 369 beds) 4300 West Memorial Road, Oklahoma City, OK, Zip 73120–8362; tel. 405/755–1515; Jim Gebhart Jr, FACHE, President

MERCY HOSPITAL TISHOMINGO (L, 25 beds) 1000 South Byrd Street, Tishomingo, OK, Zip 73460–3299; tel. 580/371–2327; Lori McMillin, Administrator
Web address: www.mercy.net/

MERCY HOSPITAL WATONGA (L, 25 beds) 500 North Clarence Nash Boulevard, Watonga, OK, Zip 73772–2845, Mailing Address: P.O. Box 370, Zip 73772–0370, tel. 580/623–7211; Cindy Carmichael, Administrator

Owned, leased, sponsored:	30 hospitals	4471 beds
Contract–managed:	2 hospitals	40 beds
Totals:	32 hospitals	4511 beds

★5155: MERCY HEALTH (CO)
1701 Mercy Health Place, Cincinnati, OH, Zip 45237; tel. 513/639–2800; John M. Starcher, President and Chief Executive Officer
(Moderately Centralized Health System)

KENTUCKY: LOURDES HOSPITAL (O, 281 beds) 1530 Lone Oak Road, Paducah, KY, Zip 42003–7900, Mailing Address: P.O. Box 7100, Zip 42002–7100, tel. 270/444–2444; Michael Yungmann, President and Chief Executive Officer
Web address: www.lourdes–pad.org

MERCY HEALTH – MARCUM AND WALLACE (O, 25 beds) 60 Mercy Court, Irvine, KY, Zip 40336–1331; tel. 606/723–2115; Susan Starling, President and Chief Executive Officer

OHIO: INSTITUTE FOR ORTHOPAEDIC SURGERY (O, 3 beds) 801 Medical Drive, Suite B, Lima, OH, Zip 45804–4030; tel. 419/224–7586; Mark McDonald, M.D., President and Chief Executive Officer
Web address: www.ioshospital.com

MERCY ALLEN HOSPITAL (O, 25 beds) 200 West Lorain Street, Oberlin, OH, Zip 44074–1077; tel. 440/775–1211; Ed Roth, President
Web address: www.mercyonline.org/mercy_allen_hospital.aspx

MERCY HEALTH – ST. CHARLES HOSPITAL (O, 279 beds) 2600 Navarre Avenue, Oregon, OH, Zip 43616–3297; tel. 419/696–7200; Craig Albers, President and Chief Operating Officer

MERCY HEALTH – ANDERSON HOSPITAL (O, 281 beds) 7500 State Road, Cincinnati, OH, Zip 45255–2492; tel. 513/624–4500; Ken James, President and Chief Executive Officer of East Market
Web address: www.e-mercy.com

MERCY HEALTH – CLERMONT HOSPITAL (O, 147 beds) 3000 Hospital Drive, Batavia, OH, Zip 45103–1921; tel. 513/732–8200; Justin Krueger, FACHE, President
Web address: www.e-mercy.com

MERCY HEALTH – FAIRFIELD HOSPITAL (O, 236 beds) 3000 Mack Road, Fairfield, OH, Zip 45014–5335; tel. 513/870–7000; Thomas S. Urban, FACHE, President and Chief Executive Officer

MERCY HEALTH – ST. ELIZABETH BOARDMAN HOSPITAL (O, 217 beds) 8401 Market Street, Boardman, OH, Zip 44512–6777; tel. 330/729–2929; Eugenia Aubel, President, St. Elizabeth Boardman Hospital
Web address: https://www.mercy.com/youngstown

MERCY HEALTH – ST. ELIZABETH YOUNGSTOWN HOSPITAL (O, 396 beds) 1044 Belmont Avenue, Youngstown, OH, Zip 44504–1096, Mailing Address: P.O. Box 1790, Zip 44501–1790, tel. 330/746–7211; Donald E. Kline, President and Chief Executive Officer

MERCY HEALTH – ST. JOSEPH WARREN HOSPITAL (O, 136 beds) 667 Eastland Avenue SE, Warren, OH, Zip 44484–4531, Mailing Address: 627 Eastland Avenue , Zip 44484–4531, tel. 330/841–4000; Kathy Cook, FACHE, MSN, President
Web address: www.hmpartners.org

For explanation of codes following names, see page B2.
★ Indicates Type III membership in the American Hospital Association.

MERCY HEALTH – WEST HOSPITAL (O, 250 beds) 3300 Mercy Health Boulevard, Cincinnati, OH, Zip 45211–1103; tel. 513/215–5000; Michael Kramer, Chief Executive Officer

MERCY HEALTH – WILLARD HOSPITAL (O, 20 beds) 1100 Neal Zick Road, Willard, OH, Zip 44890–9287; tel. 419/964–5000; B Lynn. Detterman, President and Chief Executive Officer
Web address: www.mercyweb.org

MERCY HOSPITAL OF DEFIANCE (O, 23 beds) 1404 East Second Street, Defiance, OH, Zip 43512–2440; tel. 419/782–8444; B Lynn. Detterman, President and Chief Executive Officer

MERCY MEMORIAL HOSPITAL (O, 25 beds) 904 Scioto Street, Urbana, OH, Zip 43078–2200; tel. 937/653–5231; Matthew T. Caldwell, President and Chief Executive Officer
Web address: www.health–partners.org

MERCY REGIONAL MEDICAL CENTER (O, 259 beds) 3700 Kolbe Road, Lorain, OH, Zip 44053–1697; tel. 440/960–4000; Edwin M. Oley, President and Chief Executive Officer

MERCY ST. ANNE HOSPITAL (O, 96 beds) 3404 West Sylvania Avenue, Toledo, OH, Zip 43623–4467; tel. 419/407–2663; Bradley J. Bertke, President and Chief Operating Officer
Web address: www.mercyweb.org

MERCY ST. VINCENT MEDICAL CENTER (O, 350 beds) 2213 Cherry Street, Toledo, OH, Zip 43608–2691; tel. 419/251–3232; Jeffrey Dempsey, President

MERCY TIFFIN HOSPITAL (O, 45 beds) 45 St Lawrence Drive, Tiffin, OH, Zip 44883–8310; tel. 419/455–7000; B Lynn. Detterman, President and Chief Executive Officer
Web address: www.mercyweb.org

SPRINGFIELD REGIONAL MEDICAL CENTER (O, 259 beds) 100 Medical Center Drive, Springfield, OH, Zip 45504–2687; tel. 937/523–1000; Matthew T. Caldwell, President and Chief Executive Officer

ST. RITA'S MEDICAL CENTER (O, 271 beds) 730 West Market Street, Lima, OH, Zip 45801–4602; tel. 419/227–3361; Robert O. Baxter, Regional Chief Executive Officer, Lima
Web address: www.stritas.org

THE JEWISH HOSPITAL – MERCY HEALTH (O, 209 beds) 4777 East Galbraith Road, Cincinnati, OH, Zip 45236–2725; tel. 513/686–3000; Patricia Davis–Hagens, R.N., Central Market Leader and President

Owned, leased, sponsored:	22 hospitals	3833 beds
Contract–managed:	0 hospitals	0 beds
Totals:	22 hospitals	3833 beds

0649: MERCY HEALTH SYSTEM (NP)
1000 Mineral Point Avenue, Janesville, WI, Zip 53548–2940, Mailing Address: P.O. Box 5003, Zip 53547–5003, tel. 608/756–6000; Javon R. Bea, President and Chief Executive Officer
(Centralized Physician/Insurance Health System)

ILLINOIS: MERCYHEALTH HOSPITAL – ROCKTON AVENUE (O, 288 beds) 2400 North Rockton Avenue, Rockford, IL, Zip 61103–3655; tel. 815/971–5000; Javon R. Bea, President and Chief Executive Officer

MERCYHEALTH HOSPITAL AND MEDICAL CENTER – HARVARD (O, 50 beds) 901 Grant Street, Harvard, IL, Zip 60033–1898, Mailing Address: P.O. Box 850, Zip 60033–0850, tel. 815/943–5431; Javon R. Bea, Chief Executive Officer
Web address: www.mercyhealthsystem.org

WISCONSIN: MERCYHEALTH HOSPITAL AND MEDICAL CENTER – WALWORTH (O, 17 beds) N2950 State Road 67, Lake Geneva, WI, Zip 53147–2655; tel. 262/245–0535; Javon R. Bea, President and Chief Executive Officer
Web address: www.mercyhealthsystem.org

MERCYHEALTH HOSPITAL AND TRAUMA CENTER – JANESVILLE (O, 135 beds) 1000 Mineral Point Avenue, Janesville, WI, Zip 53548–2982, Mailing Address: P.O. Box 5003, Zip 53547–5003, tel. 608/756–6000; Javon R. Bea, President and Chief Executive Officer

Owned, leased, sponsored:	4 hospitals	490 beds
Contract–managed:	0 hospitals	0 beds
Totals:	4 hospitals	490 beds

★**2735: METHODIST HEALTH SYSTEM** (NP)
1441 North Beckley Avenue, Dallas, TX, Zip 75203–1201, Mailing Address: P.O. Box 655999, Zip 75265–5999, tel. 214/947–8181; Stephen L. Mansfield, Ph.D., FACHE, President and Chief Executive Officer
(Centralized Physician/Insurance Health System)

TEXAS: METHODIST CHARLTON MEDICAL CENTER (O, 292 beds) 3500 West Wheatland Road, Dallas, TX, Zip 75237–3460, Mailing Address: P.O. Box 225357, Zip 75222–5357, tel. 214/947–7777; Fran Laukaitis, R.N., FACHE, President
Web address: www.methodisthealthsystem.org/charlton

METHODIST DALLAS MEDICAL CENTER (O, 390 beds) 1441 North Beckley Avenue, Dallas, TX, Zip 75203–1201, Mailing Address: P.O. Box 655999, Zip 75265–5999, tel. 214/947–8181; John E. Phillips, FACHE, President
Web address: www.methodisthealthsystem.org/Dallas

METHODIST MANSFIELD MEDICAL CENTER (O, 221 beds) 2700 East Broad Street, Mansfield, TX, Zip 76063–5899; tel. 682/622–2000; Jary Ganske, Chief Financial Officer

METHODIST RICHARDSON MEDICAL CENTER (O, 266 beds) 2831 East President George Bush Highway, Richardson, TX, Zip 75082–3561; tel. 469/204–1000; E. Kenneth. Hutchenrider Jr, FACHE, President
Web address: www.methodisthealthsystem.org/richardson

METHODIST SOUTHLAKE HOSPITAL (O, 12 beds) 421 East State Highway 114, Southlake, TX, Zip 76092; tel. 817/865–4400; John McGreevy, FACHE, President

Owned, leased, sponsored:	5 hospitals	1181 beds
Contract–managed:	0 hospitals	0 beds
Totals:	5 hospitals	1181 beds

★**9345: METHODIST LE BONHEUR HEALTHCARE** (CO)
1211 Union Avenue, Suite 700, Memphis, TN, Zip 38104–6600; tel. 901/516–0791; Michael Ugwueke, President and Chief Executive Officer
(Centralized Physician/Insurance Health System)

MISSISSIPPI: METHODIST HEALTHCARE OLIVE BRANCH HOSPITAL (O, 69 beds) 4250 Bethel Road, Olive Branch, MS, Zip 38654–8737; tel. 662/932–9000; David G. Baytos, President

TENNESSEE: METHODIST HEALTHCARE MEMPHIS HOSPITALS (O, 1384 beds) 1265 Union Avenue, Memphis, TN, Zip 38104–3415; tel. 901/516–7000; Michael Ugwueke, President and Chief Executive Officer
Web address: www.methodisthealth.org

Owned, leased, sponsored:	2 hospitals	1453 beds
Contract–managed:	0 hospitals	0 beds
Totals:	2 hospitals	1453 beds

★**0001: MIDMICHIGAN HEALTH** (NP)
4000 Wellness Drive, Midland, MI, Zip 48670–0001; tel. 989/839–3000; Diane Postler–Slattery, Ph.D., President and Chief Executive Officer
(Centralized Physician/Insurance Health System)

MICHIGAN: MIDMICHIGAN MEDICAL CENTER – ALPENA (O, 125 beds) 1501 West Chisholm Street, Alpena, MI, Zip 49707–1401; tel. 989/356–7000; Charles H. Sherwin, President
Web address: www.alpenaregionalmedicalcenter.org

MIDMICHIGAN MEDICAL CENTER – WEST BRANCH (O, 88 beds) 2463 South M–30, West Branch, MI, Zip 48661–1199; tel. 989/345–3660; Robert McGrail, Chief Executive Officer
Web address: www.wbrmc.com

MIDMICHIGAN MEDICAL CENTER–CLARE (O, 49 beds) 703 North McEwan Street, Clare, MI, Zip 48617–1440; tel. 989/802–5000; Raymond Stover, President and Chief Executive Officer

MIDMICHIGAN MEDICAL CENTER–GLADWIN (O, 25 beds) 515 Quarter Street, Gladwin, MI, Zip 48624–1959; tel. 989/426–9286; Raymond Stover, President and Chief Executive Officer
Web address: www.midmichigan.org

For explanation of codes following names, see page B2.
★ Indicates Type III membership in the American Hospital Association.

MIDMICHIGAN MEDICAL CENTER–GRATIOT (O, 96 beds) 300 East Warwick Drive, Alma, MI, Zip 48801–1014; tel. 989/463–1101; Marita Hattem–Schiffman, President

MIDMICHIGAN MEDICAL CENTER–MIDLAND (O, 304 beds) 4000 Wellness Drive, Midland, MI, Zip 48670–2000; tel. 989/839–3000; Gregory H. Rogers, President
Web address: www.midmichigan.org

Owned, leased, sponsored:	6 hospitals	687 beds
Contract–managed:	0 hospitals	0 beds
Totals:	6 hospitals	687 beds

0368: MINNESOTA DEPARTMENT OF HUMAN SERVICES (NP)
540 Cedar Street, Saint Paul, MN, Zip 55101–2208, Mailing Address: P.O. Box 64998, Zip 55164–0998, tel. 651/431–3212; Anne Barry, Deputy Commissioner
(Independent Hospital System)

MINNESOTA: ANOKA–METROPOLITAN REGIONAL TREATMENT CENTER (O, 200 beds) 3301 Seventh Avenue, Anoka, MN, Zip 55303–4516, Mailing Address: 3301 Seventh Avenue North, Zip 55303–4516, tel. 651/431–5000; Wade Brost, Executive Director

COMMUNITY BEHAVIORAL HEALTH HOSPITAL – ALEXANDRIA (O, 16 beds) 1610 8th Avenue East, Alexandria, MN, Zip 56308–2472; tel. 320/335–6201; Jennifer Westrum, Administrator
Web address: www.health.state.mn.us

COMMUNITY BEHAVIORAL HEALTH HOSPITAL – ANNANDALE (O, 16 beds) 400 Annandale Boulevard, Annandale, MN, Zip 55302–3141; tel. 651/259–3850; James P. Kelly, FACHE, Administrator
Web address: www.health.state.mn.us

COMMUNITY BEHAVIORAL HEALTH HOSPITAL – BAXTER (O, 16 beds) 14241 Grand Oaks Drive, Baxter, MN, Zip 56425–8749; tel. 218/316–3101; James Coughenour, Administrator
Web address: www.business.explorebrainerdlakes.com/list/member/community–behavioral–health–hospital–baxter–8647

COMMUNITY BEHAVIORAL HEALTH HOSPITAL – BEMIDJI (O, 16 beds) 800 Bemidji Avenue North, Bemidji, MN, Zip 56601–3054; tel. 218/308–2400; Larry A. Laudon, Administrator

COMMUNITY BEHAVIORAL HEALTH HOSPITAL – FERGUS FALLS (O, 16 beds) 1801 West Alcott Avenue, Fergus Falls, MN, Zip 56537–2661, Mailing Address: P.O. Box 478, Zip 56538–0478, tel. 218/332–5001; Brenda Schleske, Administrator

COMMUNITY BEHAVIORAL HEALTH HOSPITAL – ROCHESTER (O, 8 beds) 251 Wood Lake Drive SE, Rochester, MN, Zip 55904–5530; tel. 507/206–2561; James Pierce, Administrator
Web address: www.health.state.mn.us

Owned, leased, sponsored:	7 hospitals	288 beds
Contract–managed:	0 hospitals	0 beds
Totals:	7 hospitals	288 beds

★0143: MISSION HEALTH SYSTEM (NP)
509 Biltmore Avenue, Asheville, NC, Zip 28801–4601; tel. 828/213–1111; Ronald A. Paulus, M.D., President and Chief Executive Officer
(Centralized Physician/Insurance Health System)

NORTH CAROLINA: ANGEL MEDICAL CENTER (O, 36 beds) 120 Riverview Street, Franklin, NC, Zip 28734–2612, Mailing Address: P.O. Box 1209, Zip 28744–0569, tel. 828/524–8411; Karen S. Gorby, R.N., MSN, FACHE, President and Chief Nursing Officer
Web address: www.angelmed.org

ASHEVILLE SPECIALTY HOSPITAL (O, 34 beds) 428 Biltmore Avenue, 4th Floor, Asheville, NC, Zip 28801–4502; tel. 828/213–5400; Julie A. Dikos, MSN, R.N., President and Chief Executive Officer

BLUE RIDGE REGIONAL HOSPITAL (O, 25 beds) 125 Hospital Drive, Spruce Pine, NC, Zip 28777–3035; tel. 828/765–4201; Rebecca W. Carter, MSN, R.N., FACHE, Chief Executive Officer and Chief Nursing Officer
Web address: www.spchospital.org

CAREPARTNERS HEALTH SERVICES (O, 80 beds) 68 Sweeten Creek Road, Asheville, NC, Zip 28803–2318, Mailing Address: P.O. Box 15025, Zip 28813–0025, tel. 828/277–4800; Tracy Buchanan, Chief Executive Officer and President

HIGHLANDS–CASHIERS HOSPITAL (O, 104 beds) 190 Hospital Drive, Highlands, NC, Zip 28741–7600, Mailing Address: P O Drawer 190, Zip 28741–0190, tel. 828/526–1200; Jacqueline Medland, MS, Ph.D., President and Chief Nursing Officer
Web address: www.hchospital.org

MCDOWELL HOSPITAL (O, 49 beds) 430 Rankin Drive, Marion, NC, Zip 28752–6568, Mailing Address: P.O. Box 730, Zip 28752–0730, tel. 828/659–5000; Carol C. Wolfenbarger, FACHE, MSN, President
Web address: www.mission–health.org

MISSION HOSPITAL (O, 763 beds) 509 Biltmore Avenue, Asheville, NC, Zip 28801–4690; tel. 828/213–1111; Jill Hoggard Green, Ph.D., R.N., President
Web address: www.mission–health.org

TRANSYLVANIA REGIONAL HOSPITAL (O, 40 beds) 260 Hospital Drive, Brevard, NC, Zip 28712–3378; tel. 828/884–9111; Michele Pilon, President and Chief Nursing Officer

Owned, leased, sponsored:	8 hospitals	1131 beds
Contract–managed:	0 hospitals	0 beds
Totals:	8 hospitals	1131 beds

★2475: MISSISSIPPI COUNTY HOSPITAL SYSTEM (NP)
1520 North Division Street, Blytheville, AR, Zip 72315–1448, Mailing Address: P.O. Box 108, Zip 72316–0108, tel. 870/838–7300; Chris Lee. Raymer, R.N., MSN, Chief Executive Officer

ARKANSAS: GREAT RIVER MEDICAL CENTER (O, 73 beds) 1520 North Division Street, Blytheville, AR, Zip 72315–1448, Mailing Address: P.O. Box 108, Zip 72316–0108, tel. 870/838–7300; Chris Lee. Raymer, R.N., MSN, Chief Executive Officer

SOUTH MISSISSIPPI COUNTY REGIONAL MEDICAL CENTER (O, 25 beds) 611 West Lee Avenue, Osceola, AR, Zip 72370–3001, Mailing Address: P.O. Box 108, Blytheville, Zip 72316–0108, tel. 870/563–7000; Chris Lee. Raymer, R.N., MSN, Chief Executive Officer
Web address: www.mchsys.org

Owned, leased, sponsored:	0 hospitals	0 beds
Contract–managed:	2 hospitals	98 beds
Totals:	2 hospitals	98 beds

0017: MISSISSIPPI STATE DEPARTMENT OF MENTAL HEALTH (NP)
1101 Robert E Lee Building, 239 North Lamar Street, Jackson, MS, Zip 39201–1101; tel. 601/359–1288; Edwin C. LeGrand III, Executive Director
(Independent Hospital System)

MISSISSIPPI: EAST MISSISSIPPI STATE HOSPITAL (O, 310 beds) 1818 College Drive, Meridian, MS, Zip 39307, Mailing Address: Box 4128, West Station, Zip 39304–4128, tel. 601/482–6186; Charles Carlisle, Director

MISSISSIPPI STATE HOSPITAL (O, 395 beds) 3550 Highway 468 West, Whitfield, MS, Zip 39193–5529, Mailing Address: P.O. Box 157–A, Zip 39193–0157, tel. 601/351–8000; James G. Chastain, FACHE, Director
Web address: www.msh.state.ms.us

NORTH MISSISSIPPI STATE HOSPITAL (O, 50 beds) 1937 Briar Ridge Road, Tupelo, MS, Zip 38804–5963; tel. 662/690–4200; Paul A. Callens, Ph.D., Director
Web address: www.nmsh.state.ms.us

SOUTH MISSISSIPPI STATE HOSPITAL (O, 50 beds) 823 Highway 589, Purvis, MS, Zip 39475–4194; tel. 601/794–0100; Sabrina Young, Director
Web address: www.smsh.ms.gov/

Owned, leased, sponsored:	4 hospitals	805 beds
Contract–managed:	0 hospitals	0 beds
Totals:	4 hospitals	805 beds

★0970: MON HEALTH SYSTEM (NP)
1200 J. D. Anderson Drive, Morgantown, WV, Zip 26505–3494; tel. 304/598–1200; Thomas Senker, Interim Chief Executive Officer
(Independent Hospital System)

For explanation of codes following names, see page B2.
★ Indicates Type III membership in the American Hospital Association.

WEST VIRGINIA: MON HEALTH MEDICAL CENTER (O, 185 beds) 1200 J D Anderson Drive, Morgantown, WV, Zip 26505–3486; tel. 304/598–1200; Thomas Senker, Interim Chief Executive Officer

PRESTON MEMORIAL HOSPITAL (O, 25 beds) 150 Memorial Drive, Kingwood, WV, Zip 26537–1495; tel. 304/329–1400; Melissa Lockwood, Chief Executive Officer
Web address: www.prestonmemorial.org

STONEWALL JACKSON MEMORIAL HOSPITAL (O, 70 beds) 230 Hospital Plaza, Weston, WV, Zip 26452–8558; tel. 304/269–8000; Avah Stalnaker, Chief Executive Officer

Owned, leased, sponsored:	3 hospitals	280 beds
Contract–managed:	0 hospitals	0 beds
Totals:	3 hospitals	280 beds

0343: MONTEFIORE HEALTH SYSTEM (NP)

111 East 210th Street, Bronx, NY, Zip 10467–2490; tel. 718/920–4321; Steven M. Safyer, M.D., President and CEO
(Centralized Physician/Insurance Health System)

NEW YORK: BURKE REHABILITATION HOSPITAL (O, 150 beds) 785 Mamaroneck Avenue, White Plains, NY, Zip 10605–2523; tel. 914/597–2500; Jeffrey Menkes, President and Chief Executive Officer

MONTEFIORE MEDICAL CENTER (O, 1519 beds) 111 East 210th Street, Bronx, NY, Zip 10467–2401; tel. 718/920–4321; Steven M. Safyer, M.D., President and Chief Executive Officer
Web address: www.montefiore.org

MONTEFIORE MOUNT VERNON (O, 63 beds) 12 North Seventh Avenue, Mount Vernon, NY, Zip 10550–2098; tel. 914/664–8000; Jaccel Kouns, R.N., MS, Vice President and Executive Director
Web address: www.montefiorehealthsystem.org/landing.cfm?id=17

MONTEFIORE NEW ROCHELLE (O, 301 beds) 16 Guion Place, New Rochelle, NY, Zip 10801–5502; tel. 914/632–5000; Anthony Alfano, Vice President Executive Director
Web address: www.montefiorehealthsystem.org

NYACK HOSPITAL (O, 245 beds) 160 North Midland Avenue, Nyack, NY, Zip 10960–1998; tel. 845/348–2000; Mark Geller, M.D., President and Chief Executive Officer
Web address: www.nyackhospital.org

ST. LUKE'S CORNWALL HOSPITAL (O, 128 beds) 70 Dubois Street, Newburgh, NY, Zip 12550–4851; tel. 845/561–4400; Joan Cusack–McGuirk, President and Chief Executive Officer

WHITE PLAINS HOSPITAL CENTER (O, 292 beds) 41 East Post Road, White Plains, NY, Zip 10601–4699; tel. 914/681–0600; Susan Fox, President and Chief Executive Officer
Web address: www.wphospital.org

Owned, leased, sponsored:	7 hospitals	2698 beds
Contract–managed:	0 hospitals	0 beds
Totals:	7 hospitals	2698 beds

1335: MORTON PLANT MEASE HEALTH CARE (NP)

300 Pinellas Street, Clearwater, FL, Zip 33756–3804, Mailing Address: P.O. Box 210, Zip 33757–0210, tel. 727/462–7000; Glenn D. Waters, FACHE, President

FLORIDA: MORTON PLANT HOSPITAL (O, 710 beds) 300 Pinellas Street, Clearwater, FL, Zip 33756–3804, Mailing Address: P.O. Box 210, Zip 33757–0210, tel. 727/462–7000; N. Kristopher. Hoce, President
Web address: www.mortonplant.com

MORTON PLANT NORTH BAY HOSPITAL (O, 222 beds) 6600 Madison Street, New Port Richey, FL, Zip 34652–1900; tel. 727/842–8468; Sarah Naumowich, Interim President
Web address: www.mpmhealth.com

MORTON PLANT REHABILITATION CENTER (O, 126 beds) 400 Corbett Street, Belleair, FL, Zip 34640; tel. 813/462–7600; Linda A. Kirk, Administrator

Owned, leased, sponsored:	3 hospitals	1058 beds
Contract–managed:	0 hospitals	0 beds
Totals:	3 hospitals	1058 beds

★0917: MOUNT SINAI HEALTH SYSTEM (NP)

One Gustave L. Levy Place, New York, NY, Zip 10029; tel. 212/659–8888; Kenneth L. Davis, M.D., President and Chief Executive
(Centralized Health System)

NEW YORK: MOUNT SINAI BETH ISRAEL (O, 649 beds) First Avenue and 16th Street, New York, NY, Zip 10003–3803; tel. 212/420–2000; Jeremy Boal, M.D., President
Web address: www.bethisraelny.org

MOUNT SINAI HOSPITAL (O, 1113 beds) One Gustave L Levy Place, P.O. Box 1068, New York, NY, Zip 10029–0310; tel. 212/241–6500; David L. Reich, M.D., President and Chief Operating Officer

MOUNT SINAI WEST (O, 672 beds) 1111 Amsterdam Avenue, New York, NY, Zip 10025–1716; tel. 212/523–4000; Arthur A. Gianelli, M.P.H., President
Web address: www.stlukeshospitalnyc.org

NEW YORK EYE AND EAR INFIRMARY OF MOUNT SINAI (O, 32 beds) 310 East 14th Street, New York, NY, Zip 10003–4201; tel. 212/979–4000; James Tsai, M.D., President
Web address: www.nyee.edu

Owned, leased, sponsored:	4 hospitals	2466 beds
Contract–managed:	0 hospitals	0 beds
Totals:	4 hospitals	2466 beds

6555: MULTICARE HEALTH SYSTEM (NP)

315 Martin Luther King Jr Way, Tacoma, WA, Zip 98405–4234, Mailing Address: P.O. Box 5299, Zip 98415–0299, tel. 253/403–1000; William G. Robertson, President and Chief Executive Officer
(Centralized Physician/Insurance Health System)

WASHINGTON: MULTICARE AUBURN MEDICAL CENTER (O, 153 beds) 202 North Division, Plaza One, Auburn, WA, Zip 98001–4908; tel. 253/833–7711; Mark T. Smith, JD, CPA, President and Chief Operating Officer
Web address: https://www.multicare.org/auburn–medical–center/

MULTICARE DEACONESS HOSPITAL (O, 352 beds) 800 West Fifth Avenue, Spokane, WA, Zip 99204–2803, Mailing Address: P.O. Box 248, Zip 99210–0248, tel. 509/458–5800; Laureen Driscoll, President

MULTICARE GOOD SAMARITAN HOSPITAL (O, 287 beds) 401 15th Avenue SE, Puyallup, WA, Zip 98372–3770, Mailing Address: P.O. Box 1247, Zip 98371–0192, tel. 253/697–4000; Christopher Bredeson, President and Chief Operating Officer
Web address: www.multicare.org/good–samaritan–hospital/

MULTICARE MARY BRIDGE CHILDREN'S HOSPITAL AND HEALTH CENTER (O, 75 beds) 317 Martin Luther King Jr Way, Tacoma, WA, Zip 98405–4234, Mailing Address: P.O. Box 5299, Zip 98415–0299, tel. 253/403–1400; Jeffrey S. Poltawsky, President and Market Leader

MULTICARE TACOMA GENERAL HOSPITAL (O, 457 beds) 315 Martin Luther King Jr Way, Tacoma, WA, Zip 98405–4234, Mailing Address: P.O. Box 5299, Zip 98415–0299, tel. 253/403–1000; Sharon Oxendale, President and Chief Operating Officer
Web address: www.multicare.org

MULTICARE VALLEY HOSPITAL (O, 92 beds) 12606 East Mission Avenue, Spokane Valley, WA, Zip 99216–1090; tel. 509/924–6650; Gregory George. Repetti III, FACHE, Chief Executive Officer
Web address: www.valleyhospital.org

Owned, leased, sponsored:	6 hospitals	1416 beds
Contract–managed:	0 hospitals	0 beds
Totals:	6 hospitals	1416 beds

For explanation of codes following names, see page B2.
★ Indicates Type III membership in the American Hospital Association.

★1465: MUNSON HEALTHCARE (NP)

1105 Sixth Street, Traverse City, MI, Zip 49684–2386; tel. 231/935–6703; Edwin Ness, President and Chief Executive Officer **(Centralized Health System)**

MICHIGAN: KALKASKA MEMORIAL HEALTH CENTER (C, 112 beds) 419 South Coral Street, Kalkaska, MI, Zip 49646–2503; tel. 231/258–7500; Kevin L. Rogols, FACHE, Administrator
Web address: www.munsonhealthcare.org

MUNSON HEALTHCARE CADILLAC HOSPITAL (O, 49 beds) 400 Hobart Street, Cadillac, MI, Zip 49601–2389; tel. 231/876–7200; Tonya Smith, President
Web address: www.mercyhealthcadillac.com/welcome–cadillac

MUNSON HEALTHCARE CHARLEVOIX HOSPITAL (O, 25 beds) 14700 Lake Shore Drive, Charlevoix, MI, Zip 49720–1999; tel. 231/547–4024; Joanne Schroeder, President

MUNSON HEALTHCARE GRAYLING HOSPITAL (O, 110 beds) 1100 East Michigan Avenue, Grayling, MI, Zip 49738–1312; tel. 989/348–5461; Kirsten Korth–White, Interim President
Web address: www.mercygrayling.munsonhealthcare.org/

MUNSON HEALTHCARE MANISTEE HOSPITAL (O, 45 beds) 1465 East Parkdale Avenue, Manistee, MI, Zip 49660–9709; tel. 231/398–1000; James Barker, Chief Executive Officer
Web address: www.westshoremedcenter.org

MUNSON HEALTHCARE OTSEGO MEMORIAL HOSPITAL (O, 80 beds) 825 North Center Avenue, Gaylord, MI, Zip 49735–1592; tel. 989/731–2100; Thomas R. Lemon, Chief Executive Officer

MUNSON MEDICAL CENTER (O, 439 beds) 1105 Sixth Street, Traverse City, MI, Zip 49684–2386; tel. 231/935–5000; Alfred E. Pilong Jr, FACHE, President, Munson Medical Center & Chief Operating Officer, Munson Healthcare
Web address: www.munsonhealthcare.org

PAUL OLIVER MEMORIAL HOSPITAL (O, 47 beds) 224 Park Avenue, Frankfort, MI, Zip 49635–9658; tel. 231/352–2200; Peter Marinoff, President

Owned, leased, sponsored:	7 hospitals	795 beds
Contract–managed:	1 hospitals	112 beds
Totals:	8 hospitals	907 beds

0261: NATIONAL SURGICAL HEALTHCARE (IO)

250 South Wacker Drive, Suite 500, Chicago, IL, Zip 60606–5897; tel. 312/627–8400; David Crane, Chief Executive Officer **(Independent Hospital System)**

ARIZONA: ARIZONA SPINE AND JOINT HOSPITAL (O, 23 beds) 4620 East Baseline Road, Mesa, AZ, Zip 85206–4624; tel. 480/832–4770; Todd Greene, Chief Executive Officer
Web address: www.azspineandjoint.com

GEORGIA: OPTIM MEDICAL CENTER – JENKINS (O, 25 beds) 931 East Winthrope Avenue, Millen, GA, Zip 30442–1839; tel. 478/982–4221; Robert R. Sellers, Chief Executive Officer
Web address: www.optimhealth.com

OPTIM MEDICAL CENTER – SCREVEN (O, 25 beds) 215 Mims Road, Sylvania, GA, Zip 30467–2097; tel. 912/564–7426; Robert R. Sellers, Chief Executive Officer

OPTIM MEDICAL CENTER – TATTNALL (O, 25 beds) 247 South Main Street, Reidsville, GA, Zip 30453–4605; tel. 912/557–1000; Rob Snipes, Administrator
Web address: www.optimmedicalcenter.com

IDAHO: NORTHWEST SPECIALTY HOSPITAL (O, 34 beds) 1593 East Polston Avenue, Post Falls, ID, Zip 83854–5326; tel. 208/262–2300; Rick Rasmussen, Chief Executive Officer
Web address: www.northwestspecialtyhospital.com

LOUISIANA: LAFAYETTE SURGICAL SPECIALTY HOSPITAL (O, 20 beds) 1101 Kaliste Saloom Road, Lafayette, LA, Zip 70508–5705; tel. 337/769–4100; Buffy Domingue, Chief Executive Officer

MICHIGAN: SOUTHEAST MICHIGAN SURGICAL HOSPITAL (O, 13 beds) 21230 Dequindre, Warren, MI, Zip 48091–2287; tel. 586/427–1000; Barry Cullen, Chief Executive Officer
Web address: www.nshinc.com

NORTH CAROLINA: NORTH CAROLINA SPECIALTY HOSPITAL (O, 18 beds) 3916 Ben Franklin Boulevard, Durham, NC, Zip 27704–2383, Mailing Address: PO Box 15819, Zip 27704–2383, tel. 919/956–9300; Randi L. Shults, Chief Executive Officer
Web address: www.ncspecialty.com

TEXAS: EL PASO SPECIALTY HOSPITAL (O, 20 beds) 1755 Curie Drive, El Paso, TX, Zip 79902–2919; tel. 915/544–3636; James Wilcox, Chief Executive Officer

SOUTH TEXAS SPINE AND SURGICAL HOSPITAL (O, 30 beds) 18600 Hardy Oak Boulevard, San Antonio, TX, Zip 78258–4206; tel. 210/507–4090; Angie Kauffman, Chief Executive Officer
Web address: www.southtexassurgical.com

SOUTH TEXAS SURGICAL HOSPITAL (O, 20 beds) 6130 Parkway Drive, Corpus Christi, TX, Zip 78414–2455; tel. 361/993–2000; David G. Covert, Chief Executive Officer
Web address: www.southtexassurgicalhospital.com

WISCONSIN: OAKLEAF SURGICAL HOSPITAL (O, 13 beds) 1000 OakLeaf Way, Altoona, WI, Zip 54701–3016; tel. 715/831–8130; Anne Hargrave–Thomas, Chief Executive Officer

WYOMING: MOUNTAIN VIEW REGIONAL HOSPITAL (O, 23 beds) 6550 East Second Street, Casper, WY, Zip 82609–4321, Mailing Address: P.O. Box 51888, Zip 82605–1888, tel. 307/995–8100; Thomas Kopitnik, Acting Chief Executive Officer
Web address: www.mountainviewregionalhospital.com

Owned, leased, sponsored:	13 hospitals	289 beds
Contract–managed:	0 hospitals	0 beds
Totals:	13 hospitals	289 beds

0923: NAVICENT HEALTH (NP)

777 Hemlock Street, MSC 105, Macon, GA, Zip 31201–2155, Mailing Address: 777 Hemlock Street, Zip 31201–2155, tel. 478/633–1000; Ninfa M. Saunders, Chief Executive Officer **(Moderately Centralized Health System)**

GEORGIA: MEDICAL CENTER OF PEACH COUNTY, NAVICENT HEALTH (O, 25 beds) 1960 Highway 247 Connector, Bryon, GA, Zip 31008; tel. 478/654–2000; Darren Pearce, Administrator and Chief Executive Officer

MEDICAL CENTER, NAVICENT HEALTH (O, 627 beds) 777 Hemlock Street, Macon, GA, Zip 31201–2155; tel. 478/633–1000; Ninfa M. Saunders, Chief Executive Officer
Web address: https://www.navicenthealth.org/

NAVICENT HEALTH BALDWIN (O, 90 beds) 821 North Cobb Street, Milledgeville, GA, Zip 31061–2351, Mailing Address: P.O. Box 690, Zip 31059–0690, tel. 478/454–3505; Todd Dixon, R.N., Chief Executive Officer

REHABILITATION HOSPITAL, NAVICENT HEALTH (O, 58 beds) 3351 Northside Drive, Macon, GA, Zip 31210–2587; tel. 478/201–6500; Gina Tipton, Director of Operations
Web address: www.navicenthealth.org/service–center/rehabilitation–hospital–navicent–health

Owned, leased, sponsored:	4 hospitals	800 beds
Contract–managed:	0 hospitals	0 beds
Totals:	4 hospitals	800 beds

★9265: NEBRASKA METHODIST HEALTH SYSTEM, INC. (CO)

8511 West Dodge Road, Omaha, NE, Zip 68114–3403; tel. 402/354–5411; Stephen L. Goeser, FACHE, President and Chief Executive Officer **(Centralized Physician/Insurance Health System)**

IOWA: METHODIST JENNIE EDMUNDSON HOSPITAL (O, 114 beds) 933 East Pierce Street, Council Bluffs, IA, Zip 51503–4652, Mailing Address: P.O. Box 2C, Zip 51502–3002, tel. 712/396–6000; Steven P. Baumert, President and Chief Executive Officer
Web address: www.bestcare.org

For explanation of codes following names, see page B2.
★ Indicates Type III membership in the American Hospital Association.

Section B

NEBRASKA: NEBRASKA METHODIST HOSPITAL (O, 400 beds) 8303 Dodge Street, Omaha, NE, Zip 68114–4199; tel. 402/354–4000; Stephen L. Goeser, FACHE, President and Chief Executive Officer

Owned, leased, sponsored:	2 hospitals	514 beds
Contract–managed:	0 hospitals	0 beds
Totals:	2 hospitals	514 beds

0892: NEMOURS (NP)

10140 Centurion Parkway North, Jacksonville, FL, Zip 32256–0532; tel. 904/697–4100; R. Lawrence Moss, President and Chief Executive Officer

(Independent Hospital System)

DELAWARE: ALFRED I. DUPONT HOSPITAL FOR CHILDREN (O, 200 beds) 1600 Rockland Road, Wilmington, DE, Zip 19803–3616, Mailing Address: Box 269, Zip 19899–0269, tel. 302/651–4000; Roy Proujansky, M.D., Chief Executive Officer
Web address: www.nemours.org

FLORIDA: NEMOURS CHILDREN'S HOSPITAL (O, 92 beds) 13535 Nemours Parkway, Orlando, FL, Zip 32827–7402; tel. 407/567–4000; Dana Bledsoe, MS, R.N., President

Owned, leased, sponsored:	2 hospitals	292 beds
Contract–managed:	0 hospitals	0 beds
Totals:	2 hospitals	292 beds

0620: NEUROPSYCHIATRIC HOSPITALS (IO)

1625 East Jefferson Boulevard, Mishawaka, IN, Zip 46545–7103; tel. 574/255–1400; Cameron R. Gilbert, Ph.D., President and Chief Executive Officer

INDIANA: DOCTORS NEUROPSYCHIATRIC HOSPITAL AND RESEARCH INSTITUTE (O, 20 beds) 417 South Whitlock Street, Bremen, IN, Zip 46506–1626; tel. 574/546–0330; Christy Gilbert, Interim Chief Executive Officer

MEDICAL BEHAVIORAL HOSPITAL OF MISHAWAKA (O, 30 beds) 5985 E 200 S , Knox, IN, Zip 46534, Mailing Address: 1625 East Jefferson Boulevard, Mishawaka, Zip 46545–7103, tel. 574/255–1400; Emily Ryan, Chief Executive Officer
Web address: www.physicianshospitalsystem.net/

NEUROPSYCHIATRIC HOSPITAL OF INDIANAPOLIS (O, 50 beds) 6720 Parkdale Place, Indianapolis, IN, Zip 46254–4668; tel. 317/744–9200; Tracy Davis, Chief Executive Officer
Web address: https://www.neuropsychichospitals.net

Owned, leased, sponsored:	3 hospitals	100 beds
Contract–managed:	0 hospitals	0 beds
Totals:	3 hospitals	100 beds

★**0213: NEW HANOVER REGIONAL MEDICAL CENTER** (NP)

2131 South 17th Street, Wilmington, NC, Zip 28401–7407; tel. 910/343–7040; John H. Gizdic, President and Chief Executive Officer
(Moderately Centralized Health System)

NORTH CAROLINA: NEW HANOVER REGIONAL MEDICAL CENTER (O, 711 beds) 2131 South 17th Street, Wilmington, NC, Zip 28401–7483, Mailing Address: P.O. Box 9000, Zip 28402–9000, tel. 910/343–7000; Andre Boyd Sr, Executive Vice President, Hospital Division
Web address: www.nhrmc.org

PENDER MEMORIAL HOSPITAL (C, 68 beds) 507 East Freemont Street, Burgaw, NC, Zip 28425–5131; tel. 910/259–5451; Ruth Glaser, President

Owned, leased, sponsored:	1 hospitals	711 beds
Contract–managed:	1 hospitals	68 beds
Totals:	2 hospitals	779 beds

0009: NEW YORK STATE OFFICE OF MENTAL HEALTH (NP)

44 Holland Avenue, Albany, NY, Zip 12208–3411; tel. 518/474–7056; Kristin M. Woodlock, R.N., Acting Commissioner
(Independent Hospital System)

NEW YORK: BRONX PSYCHIATRIC CENTER (O, 450 beds) 1500 Waters Place, Bronx, NY, Zip 10461–2796; tel. 718/931–0600; Anita Daniels, Director
Web address: www.omh.ny.gov

BUFFALO PSYCHIATRIC CENTER (O, 240 beds) 400 Forest Avenue, Buffalo, NY, Zip 14213–1298; tel. 716/885–2261; Beatrix Souza, Chief Executive Officer

CAPITAL DISTRICT PSYCHIATRIC CENTER (O, 200 beds) 75 New Scotland Avenue, Albany, NY, Zip 12208–3474; tel. 518/549–6000; William Dickson, Executive Director
Web address: www.omh.ny.gov/omhweb/facilities/cdpc/facility.htm

CENTRAL NEW YORK PSYCHIATRIC CENTER (O, 226 beds) 9005 Old River Road, Marcy, NY, Zip 13403–3000, Mailing Address: P.O. Box 300, Zip 13403–0300, tel. 315/765–3600; Maureen Bosco, Executive Director
Web address: www.omh.ny.gov

CREEDMOOR PSYCHIATRIC CENTER (O, 322 beds) 79–25 Winchester Boulevard, Jamaica, NY, Zip 11427–2128; tel. 718/264–3600; Ann Marie. Barbarotta, Executive Director
Web address: www.omh.ny.gov

ELMIRA PSYCHIATRIC CENTER (O, 60 beds) 100 Washington Street, Elmira, NY, Zip 14901–2898; tel. 607/737–4739; David Peppel, Executive Director

GREATER BINGHAMTON HEALTH CENTER (O, 86 beds) 425 Robinson Street, Binghamton, NY, Zip 13904–1735; tel. 607/724–1391; David Peppel, Executive Director
Web address: www.omh.ny.gov/omhweb/facilities/bipc/facility.htm

KINGSBORO PSYCHIATRIC CENTER (O, 290 beds) 681 Clarkson Avenue, Brooklyn, NY, Zip 11203–2125; tel. 718/221–7395; Deborah Parchment, Executive Director
Web address: www.omh.ny.gov/omhweb/facilities/kbpc/facility/htm

KIRBY FORENSIC PSYCHIATRIC CENTER (O, 193 beds) 600 East 125th Street, New York, NY, Zip 10035–6000; tel. 646/672–5800; Vincent Miccoli, Executive Director

MANHATTAN PSYCHIATRIC CENTER–WARD'S ISLAND (O, 745 beds) 600 East 125th Street, New York, NY, Zip 10035–6000; tel. 646/672–6767; Vincent Miccoli, Executive Director
Web address: www.omh.ny.gov

MID–HUDSON FORENSIC PSYCHIATRIC CENTER (O, 285 beds) Route 17M, New Hampton, NY, Zip 10958, Mailing Address: P.O. Box 158, Zip 10958–0158, tel. 845/374–8700; Joseph Freebern, Executive Director

MOHAWK VALLEY PSYCHIATRIC CENTER (O, 614 beds) 1400 Noyes Street, Utica, NY, Zip 13502–3854; tel. 315/738–3800; Colleen A. Sawyer, R.N., MSN, Executive Director
Web address: www.omh.ny.gov/omhweb/facilities/mvpc/facility.htm

NEW YORK CITY CHILDREN'S CENTER (O, 102 beds) 74–03 Commonwealth Boulevard, Jamaica, NY, Zip 11426–1890; tel. 718/264–4506; Kanika Jefferies, Executive Director

NEW YORK STATE PSYCHIATRIC INSTITUTE (O, 58 beds) 1051 Riverside Drive, New York, NY, Zip 10032–1007; tel. 646/774–5000; Jeffrey A. Lieberman, M.D., Executive Director
Web address: www.nyspi.org

PILGRIM PSYCHIATRIC CENTER (O, 569 beds) 998 Crooked Hill Road, Brentwood, NY, Zip 11717–1019; tel. 631/761–3500; Kathy O'Keefe, Executive Director

RICHARD H. HUTCHINGS PSYCHIATRIC CENTER (O, 131 beds) 620 Madison Street, Syracuse, NY, Zip 13210–2319; tel. 315/426–3632; Colleen A. Sawyer, R.N., MSN, Executive Director
Web address: www.omh.ny.gov

ROCHESTER PSYCHIATRIC CENTER (O, 180 beds) 1111 Elmwood Avenue, Rochester, NY, Zip 14620–3005; tel. 585/241–1200; Philip Griffin, Director of Operations

ROCKLAND CHILDREN'S PSYCHIATRIC CENTER (O, 54 beds) 599 Convent Road, Orangeburg, NY, Zip 10962–1162; tel. 845/359–7400; Christopher Tavella, Acting Executive Director
Web address: www.omh.ny.gov/

ROCKLAND PSYCHIATRIC CENTER (O, 525 beds) 140 Old Orangeburg Road, Orangeburg, NY, Zip 10962–1157; tel. 845/359–1000; Christopher Tavella, Executive Director

For explanation of codes following names, see page B2.
★ Indicates Type III membership in the American Hospital Association.

Section B

SAGAMORE CHILDREN'S PSYCHIATRIC CENTER (O, 69 beds) 197 Half Hollow Road, Dix Hills, NY, Zip 11746–5861; tel. 631/370–1700; Kathy O'Keefe, Interim Executive Director
Web address: www.omh.ny.gov

SOUTH BEACH PSYCHIATRIC CENTER (O, 340 beds) 777 Seaview Avenue, Staten Island, NY, Zip 10305–3409; tel. 718/667–2300; Doreen Piazza, Acting Executive Director
Web address: www.omh.ny.gov/omhweb/facilities/sbpc/facility.htm

ST. LAWRENCE PSYCHIATRIC CENTER (O, 146 beds) 1 Chimney Point Drive, Ogdensburg, NY, Zip 13669–2291; tel. 315/541–2001; Timothy Farrell, Executive Director

WESTERN NEW YORK CHILDREN'S PSYCHIATRIC CENTER (O, 46 beds) 1010 East and West Road, West Seneca, NY, Zip 14224–3602; tel. 716/677–7000; Kathe Hayes, Executive Director
Web address: www.omh.ny.gov

Owned, leased, sponsored:	23 hospitals	5931 beds
Contract–managed:	0 hospitals	0 beds
Totals:	23 hospitals	5931 beds

★0142: NEWYORK–PRESBYTERIAN (NP)
525 East 68th Street, Box 182, New York, NY, Zip 10065; tel. 212/746–3745; Steven J. Corwin, M.D., President and Chief Executive Officer
(Moderately Centralized Health System)

NEW YORK: NEW YORK–PRESBYTERIAN HOSPITAL (O, 2540 beds) 525 East 68th Street, New York, NY, Zip 10065–4870; tel. 212/746–5454; Steven J. Corwin, M.D., President and Chief Executive Officer
Web address: www.nyp.org

NEW YORK–PRESBYTERIAN QUEENS (O, 482 beds) 56–45 Main Street, Flushing, NY, Zip 11355–5045; tel. 718/670–1231; Jaclyn Mucaria, President
Web address: www.nyhq.org

NEW YORK–PRESBYTERIAN/HUDSON VALLEY HOSPITAL (O, 128 beds) 1980 Crompond Road, Cortlandt Manor, NY, Zip 10567–4182; tel. 914/737–9000; Stacey Petrower, President

NEWYORK–PRESBYTERIAN BROOKLYN METHODIST HOSPITAL (O, 591 beds) 506 Sixth Street, Brooklyn, NY, Zip 11215–3609; tel. 718/780–3000; Robert Guimento, President
Web address: www.nym.org

Owned, leased, sponsored:	4 hospitals	3741 beds
Contract–managed:	0 hospitals	0 beds
Totals:	4 hospitals	3741 beds

0353: NEXUS HEALTH SYSTEMS (IO)
One Riverway, Suite 600, Houston, TX, Zip 77056–1993; tel. 713/355–6111; John W. Cassidy, M.D., President, Chief Executive Officer and Chief Medical Officer
(Independent Hospital System)

CALIFORNIA: HEALTHBRIDGE CHILDREN'S HOSPITAL (O, 27 beds) 393 South Tustin Street, Orange, CA, Zip 92866–2501; tel. 714/289–2400; Alex Villarruz, Chief Executive Officer
Web address: www.HealthBridgeOrange.com

TEXAS: HEALTHBRIDGE CHILDREN'S HOSPITAL OF HOUSTON (O, 40 beds) 2929 Woodland Park Drive, Houston, TX, Zip 77082–2687; tel. 281/293–7774; Joel Telly, Chief Executive Officer

NEXUS SPECIALTY HOSPITAL (O, 76 beds) 123 Vision Park Boulevard, Shenandoah, TX, Zip 77384–3001; tel. 281/364–0317; Eric Cantrell, Chief Executive Officer
Web address: www.nexusspecialty.com

Owned, leased, sponsored:	3 hospitals	143 beds
Contract–managed:	0 hospitals	0 beds
Totals:	3 hospitals	143 beds

1021: NOBILIS HEALTH CORPORATION (IO)
11700 Katy Freeway Suite 300, Houston, TX, Zip 77079–1218; tel. 713/355–8614; Harry Fleming, Chief Executive Officer
(Independent Hospital System)

ARIZONA: SCOTTSDALE LIBERTY HOSPITAL (O, 12 beds) 17500 North Perimeter Drive, Scottsdale, AZ, Zip 85255–7808; tel. 480/586–2300; Steven M. Siwek, M.D., President and Chief Executive Officer

TEXAS: FIRST SURGICAL HOSPITAL (O, 19 beds) 4801 Bissonnet, Bellaire, TX, Zip 77401–4028; tel. 713/275–1111; Susan Bosnick–Sinift, Chief Executive Officer
Web address: www.firststreethospital.com

HERMANN DRIVE SURGICAL HOSPITAL (O, 25 beds) 2001 Hermann Drive, Houston, TX, Zip 77004–7643; tel. 713/285–5500; Nicole Walker, Chief Executive Officer
Web address: www.nobilishealth.com/our–facilities/houston/

PLANO SURGICAL HOSPITAL (O, 26 beds) 2301 Marsh Lane, Plano, TX, Zip 75093–8497; tel. 972/820–2600; Jay Lindsey, Chief Executive Officer

Owned, leased, sponsored:	4 hospitals	82 beds
Contract–managed:	0 hospitals	0 beds
Totals:	4 hospitals	82 beds

0349: NOLAND HEALTH SERVICES, INC. (NP)
600 Corporate Parkway, Suite 100, Birmingham, AL, Zip 35242–5451; tel. 205/783–8484; Gary M. Glasscock, President and Chief Executive Officer

ALABAMA: NOLAND HOSPITAL ANNISTON (O, 38 beds) 400 East 10th Street, 4th Fl, Anniston, AL, Zip 36207–4716; tel. 256/741–6141; Trina Woods, Administrator
Web address: www.nolandhealth.com

NOLAND HOSPITAL BIRMINGHAM (O, 45 beds) 50 Medical Park East Drive, 8th Floor, Birmingham, AL, Zip 35235; tel. 205/808–5100; Laura S. Wills, Administrator

NOLAND HOSPITAL DOTHAN (O, 38 beds) 1108 Ross Clark Circle, 4th Floor, Dothan, AL, Zip 36301–3022; tel. 334/699–4300; Kaye Burk, Administrator
Web address: www.nolandhealth.com

NOLAND HOSPITAL MONTGOMERY (O, 65 beds) 1725 Pine Street, 5 North, Montgomery, AL, Zip 36106–1109; tel. 334/240–0532; Dale Jones, Administrator
Web address: www.nolandhealth.com

NOLAND HOSPITAL SHELBY (O, 15 beds) 1000 First Street North, 3rd Floor, Alabaster, AL, Zip 35007–8703; tel. 205/620–8641; Laura S. Wills, Administrator

NOLAND HOSPITAL TUSCALOOSA (O, 32 beds) 809 University Blvd E, 4th Fl, Tuscaloosa, AL, Zip 35401–2029; tel. 205/759–7241; Jack Gibson, Administrator
Web address: www.nolandhealth.com

Owned, leased, sponsored:	6 hospitals	233 beds
Contract–managed:	0 hospitals	0 beds
Totals:	6 hospitals	233 beds

1030: NORTH COUNTRY HEALTHCARE (NP)
600 Saint Johnsbury Road, Littleton, NH, Zip 03561–3442; tel. 603/444–9000; Edward L. Duffy, M.D., Interim Chief Executive Officer

NEW HAMPSHIRE: ANDROSCOGGIN VALLEY HOSPITAL (C, 25 beds) 59 Page Hill Road, Berlin, NH, Zip 03570–3531; tel. 603/752–2200; Michael Peterson, FACHE, President
Web address: www.avhnh.org

LITTLETON REGIONAL HEALTHCARE (C, 25 beds) 600 Saint Johnsbury Road, Littleton, NH, Zip 03561–3442; tel. 603/444–9000; Robert Nutter, President

UPPER CONNECTICUT VALLEY HOSPITAL (C, 12 beds) 181 Corliss Lane, Colebrook, NH, Zip 03576–3207; tel. 603/237–4971; Scott Colby, President
Web address: www.ucvh.org

For explanation of codes following names, see page B2.
★ Indicates Type III membership in the American Hospital Association.

Section B

WEEKS MEDICAL CENTER (C, 25 beds) 173 Middle Street, Lancaster, NH, Zip 03584–3508; tel. 603/788–4911; Michael Lee, President
Web address: www.weeksmedical.org

Owned, leased, sponsored:	0 hospitals	0 beds
Contract–managed:	4 hospitals	87 beds
Totals:	4 hospitals	87 beds

0887: NORTH MEMORIAL HEALTH CARE (NP)

3300 Oakdale Avenue North, Robbinsdale, MN, Zip 55422–2926; tel. 763/520–5200; J. Kevin. Croston, M.D., Chief Executive Officer
(Centralized Physician/Insurance Health System)

MINNESOTA: MAPLE GROVE HOSPITAL (C, 108 beds) 9875 Hospital Drive, Maple Grove, MN, Zip 55369–4648; tel. 763/581–1000; Andrew S. Cochrane, Chief Executive Officer

NORTH MEMORIAL HEALTH HOSPITAL (O, 358 beds) 3300 Oakdale Avenue North, Robbinsdale, MN, Zip 55422–2926; tel. 763/520–5200; Jeff Wicklander, President
Web address: www.northmemorial.com

Owned, leased, sponsored:	1 hospitals	358 beds
Contract–managed:	1 hospitals	108 beds
Totals:	2 hospitals	466 beds

★0032: NORTH MISSISSIPPI HEALTH SERVICES, INC. (NP)

830 South Gloster Street, Tupelo, MS, Zip 38801–4996; tel. 662/377–3136; M. Shane. Spees, President and Chief Executive Officer
(Centralized Physician/Insurance Health System)

ALABAMA: NORTH MISSISSIPPI MEDICAL CENTER–HAMILTON (O, 15 beds) 1256 Military Street South, Hamilton, AL, Zip 35570–5003; tel. 205/921–6200; Robert Trimm, Administrator

MISSISSIPPI: NORTH MISSISSIPPI MEDICAL CENTER – TUPELO (O, 747 beds) 830 South Gloster Street, Tupelo, MS, Zip 38801–4934; tel. 662/377–3000; M. Shane. Spees, Chief Executive Officer
Web address: www.nmhs.net

NORTH MISSISSIPPI MEDICAL CENTER–EUPORA (O, 73 beds) 70 Medical Plaza, Eupora, MS, Zip 39744–4018; tel. 662/258–6221; Robin Mixon, Interim Chief Executive Officer

NORTH MISSISSIPPI MEDICAL CENTER–IUKA (O, 48 beds) 1777 Curtis Drive, Iuka, MS, Zip 38852–1001, Mailing Address: P.O. Box 860, Zip 38852–0860, tel. 662/423–6051; Fred A. Truesdale Jr, Administrator
Web address: www.nmhs.net

NORTH MISSISSIPPI MEDICAL CENTER–PONTOTOC (L, 69 beds) 176 South Main Street, Pontotoc, MS, Zip 38863–3311, Mailing Address: P.O. Box 790, Zip 38863–0790, tel. 662/488–7640; Leslia Carter, Administrator
Web address: www.nmhs.net

NORTH MISSISSIPPI MEDICAL CENTER–WEST POINT (O, 49 beds) 835 Medical Center Drive, West Point, MS, Zip 39773–9320; tel. 662/495–2300; Barry L. Keel, Administration

Owned, leased, sponsored:	6 hospitals	1001 beds
Contract–managed:	0 hospitals	0 beds
Totals:	6 hospitals	1001 beds

0867: NORTH OAKS HEALTH SYSTEM (NP)

15790 Paul Vega MD Drive, Hammond, LA, Zip 70403–1436, Mailing Address: P.O. Box 2668, Zip 70404–2668, tel. 985/345–2700; Michele K. Sutton, FACHE, President and Chief Executive Officer
(Independent Hospital System)

LOUISIANA: NORTH OAKS MEDICAL CENTER (O, 231 beds) 15790 Paul Vega, MD, Drive, Hammond, LA, Zip 70403–1436, Mailing Address: P.O. Box 2668, Zip 70404–2668, tel. 985/345–2700; Michele K. Sutton, FACHE, President and Chief Executive Officer

NORTH OAKS REHABILITATION HOSPITAL (O, 27 beds) 1900 South Morrison Boulevard, Hammond, LA, Zip 70403–5742; tel. 985/542–7777; Sybil K. Paulson, Administrator
Web address: www.northoaks.org

Owned, leased, sponsored:	2 hospitals	258 beds
Contract–managed:	0 hospitals	0 beds
Totals:	2 hospitals	258 beds

1018: NORTHEAST GEORGIA HEALTH SYSTEM (NP)

743 Spring Street NE, Gainesville, GA, Zip 30501–3715; tel. 770/219–9000; Carol H. Burrell, President and Chief Executive Officer
(Moderately Centralized Health System)

GEORGIA: NORTHEAST GEORGIA MEDICAL CENTER BARROW (O, 30 beds) 316 North Broad Street, Winder, GA, Zip 30680–2150, Mailing Address: P.O. Box 688, Zip 30680–0688, tel. 770/867–3400; Chad Hatfield, Chief Executive Officer

NORTHEAST GEORGIA MEDICAL CENTER BRASELTON (O, 100 beds) 1400 River Place, Braselton, GA, Zip 30517–5600; tel. 770/219–9000; Carol H. Burrell, Chief Executive Officer
Web address: www.nghs.com/locations/braselton

NORTHEAST GEORGIA MEDICAL CENTER (O, 906 beds) 743 Spring Street NE, Gainesville, GA, Zip 30501–3899; tel. 770/219–3553; Carol H. Burrell, Chief Executive Officer

Owned, leased, sponsored:	3 hospitals	1036 beds
Contract–managed:	0 hospitals	0 beds
Totals:	3 hospitals	1036 beds

★0281: NORTHERN ARIZONA HEALTHCARE (NP)

1200 North Beaver Street, Flagstaff, AZ, Zip 86001–3118; tel. 928/779–3366; Florence (Flo). Spyrow, Interim President and Chief Executive Officer
(Independent Hospital System)

ARIZONA: FLAGSTAFF MEDICAL CENTER (O, 264 beds) 1200 North Beaver Street, Flagstaff, AZ, Zip 86001–3118; tel. 928/779–3366; Florence (Flo). Spyrow, Chief Administrative Officer
Web address: www.nahealth.com

VERDE VALLEY MEDICAL CENTER (O, 98 beds) 269 South Candy Lane, Cottonwood, AZ, Zip 86326–4170; tel. 928/639–6000; Barbara Firminger, Chief Administrative Officer

Owned, leased, sponsored:	2 hospitals	362 beds
Contract–managed:	0 hospitals	0 beds
Totals:	2 hospitals	362 beds

★0555: NORTHERN LIGHT HEALTH (NP)

43 Whiting Hill Road, Brewer, ME, Zip 04412–1005; tel. 207/973–7045; M. Michelle. Hood, FACHE, President and Chief Executive Officer
(Moderately Centralized Health System)

MAINE: BLUE HILL MEMORIAL HOSPITAL (O, 23 beds) 57 Water Street, Blue Hill, ME, Zip 04614–5231, Mailing Address: P.O. Box 1029, Zip 04614–1029, tel. 207/374–3400; John Ronan, President
Web address: www.bhmh.org

CHARLES A. DEAN MEMORIAL HOSPITAL (O, 23 beds) 364 Pritham Avenue, Greenville, ME, Zip 04441–1395, Mailing Address: P.O. Box 1129, Zip 04441–1129, tel. 207/695–5200; Terri Vieira, President
Web address: www.cadean.org

EASTERN MAINE MEDICAL CENTER (O, 385 beds) 489 State Street, Bangor, ME, Zip 04401–6674, Mailing Address: P.O. Box 404, Zip 04402–0404, tel. 207/973–7000; Donna Russell-Cook, FACHE, President
Web address: www.emh.org

For explanation of codes following names, see page B2.
★ Indicates Type III membership in the American Hospital Association.

INLAND HOSPITAL (O, 29 beds) 200 Kennedy Memorial Drive, Waterville, ME, Zip 04901-4595; tel. 207/861-3000; John Dalton, President
Web address: www.inlandhospital.org

MAINE COAST MEMORIAL HOSPITAL (O, 48 beds) 50 Union Street, Ellsworth, ME, Zip 04605-1599; tel. 207/664-5311; John Ronan, President

MERCY HOSPITAL OF PORTLAND (O, 104 beds) 144 State Street, Portland, ME, Zip 04101-3795; tel. 207/879-3000; Charles D. Therrien, President
Web address: www.mercyhospital.org

SEBASTICOOK VALLEY HEALTH (O, 25 beds) 447 North Main Street, Pittsfield, ME, Zip 04967-3707; tel. 207/487-4000; Terri Vieira, President
Web address: www.sebasticookvalleyhealth.org

THE ACADIA HOSPITAL (O, 68 beds) 268 Stillwater Avenue, Bangor, ME, Zip 04401-3945, Mailing Address: P.O. Box 422, Zip 04402-0422, tel. 207/973-6100; Scott Oxley, President

THE AROOSTOOK MEDICAL CENTER (O, 115 beds) 140 Academy Street, Presque Isle, ME, Zip 04769-3171, Mailing Address: P.O. Box 151, Zip 04769-0151, tel. 207/768-4000; Gregory LaFrancois, President
Web address: www.tamc.org

Owned, leased, sponsored:	9 hospitals	820 beds
Contract-managed:	0 hospitals	0 beds
Totals:	9 hospitals	820 beds

★**0410: NORTHSIDE HEALTHCARE SYSTEM** (NP)

1000 Johnson Ferry Road NE, Atlanta, GA, Zip 30342-1611; tel. 404/851-8000; Robert Quattrocchi, President and Chief Executive Officer

GEORGIA: NORTHSIDE HOSPITAL–CHEROKEE (O, 109 beds) 450 Northside Cherokee Boulevard, Canton, GA, Zip 30115-8015, Mailing Address: P.O. Box 906, Zip 30169-0906, tel. 770/720-5100; William M. Hayes, Chief Executive Officer
Web address: www.northside.com

NORTHSIDE HOSPITAL–FORSYTH (O, 289 beds) 1200 Northside Forsyth Drive, Cumming, GA, Zip 30041-7659; tel. 770/844-3200; Lynn Jackson, Administrator
Web address: www.northside.com

NORTHSIDE HOSPITAL (O, 603 beds) 1000 Johnson Ferry Road NE, Atlanta, GA, Zip 30342-1611; tel. 404/851-8000; Robert Quattrocchi, President and Chief Executive Officer

Owned, leased, sponsored:	3 hospitals	1001 beds
Contract-managed:	0 hospitals	0 beds
Totals:	3 hospitals	1001 beds

★**0062: NORTHWELL HEALTH** (NP)

2000 Marcus Avenue, New Hyde Park, NY, Zip 11042; tel. 516/465-8100; Michael J. Dowling, President and Chief Executive Officer
(Centralized Health System)

NEW YORK: GLEN COVE HOSPITAL (O, 119 beds) 101 St Andrews Lane, Glen Cove, NY, Zip 11542-2254; tel. 516/674-7300; Susan Kwiatek, R.N., Executive Director

HUNTINGTON HOSPITAL (O, 290 beds) 270 Park Avenue, Huntington, NY, Zip 11743-2799; tel. 631/351-2000; Gerard Brogan Jr, M.D., Executive Director
Web address: www.northwell.edu

JOHN T. MATHER MEMORIAL HOSPITAL (O, 248 beds) 75 North Country Road, Port Jefferson, NY, Zip 11777-2190; tel. 631/473-1320; Kenneth D. Roberts, President

LENOX HILL HOSPITAL (O, 440 beds) 100 East 77th Street, New York, NY, Zip 10075-1850; tel. 212/434-2000; Jill Kalman, Executive Director
Web address: www.lenoxhillhospital.org

LONG ISLAND JEWISH MEDICAL CENTER (O, 1211 beds) 270-05 76th Avenue, New Hyde Park, NY, Zip 11040-1496; tel. 718/470-7000; Michael Goldberg, Executive Director
Web address: www.lij.edu

NORTH SHORE UNIVERSITY HOSPITAL (O, 738 beds) 300 Community Drive, Manhasset, NY, Zip 11030-3816; tel. 516/562-0100; Alessandro Bellucci, M.D., Executive Director

NORTHERN WESTCHESTER HOSPITAL (O, 195 beds) 400 East Main Street, Mount Kisco, NY, Zip 10549-3477, Mailing Address: 400 East Main Street, G-02, Zip 10549-3477, tel. 914/666-1200; Joel Seligman, President and Chief Executive Officer
Web address: www.nwhc.net

PECONIC BAY MEDICAL CENTER (O, 101 beds) 1300 Roanoke Avenue, Riverhead, NY, Zip 11901-2031; tel. 631/548-6000; Andrew J. Mitchell, President and Chief Executive Officer
Web address: www.pbmchealth.org

PHELPS MEMORIAL HOSPITAL CENTER (O, 158 beds) 701 North Broadway, Sleepy Hollow, NY, Zip 10591-1020; tel. 914/366-3000; Daniel Blum, President
Web address: www.phelpshospital.org

PLAINVIEW HOSPITAL (O, 150 beds) 888 Old Country Road, Plainview, NY, Zip 11803-4978; tel. 516/719-3000; Michael Fener, Executive Director

SOUTH OAKS HOSPITAL (O, 258 beds) 400 Sunrise Highway, Amityville, NY, Zip 11701-2508; tel. 631/264-4000; Carolyn Sweetapple, Ph.D., R.N., CPA, Executive Director
Web address: www.longislandhome.org

SOUTHSIDE HOSPITAL (O, 275 beds) 301 East Main Street, Bay Shore, NY, Zip 11706-8458; tel. 631/968-3000; Donna Moravick, R.N., MSN, Executive Director
Web address: https://www.northwell.edu/find-care/locations/southside-hospital

STATEN ISLAND UNIVERSITY HOSPITAL (O, 634 beds) 475 Seaview Avenue, Staten Island, NY, Zip 10305-3436; tel. 718/226-9000; Joseph Schulman, Interim Chief Executive Officer

SYOSSET HOSPITAL (O, 75 beds) 221 Jericho Turnpike, Syosset, NY, Zip 11791-4515; tel. 516/496-6500; Michael Fener, Executive Director
Web address: www.northshorelij.com

Owned, leased, sponsored:	14 hospitals	4892 beds
Contract-managed:	0 hospitals	0 beds
Totals:	14 hospitals	4892 beds

★**0024: NORTHWESTERN MEMORIAL HEALTHCARE** (NP)

251 East Huron Street, Chicago, IL, Zip 60611-2908; tel. 312/926-2000; Dean M. Harrison, President and Chief Executive Officer
(Centralized Health System)

ILLINOIS: NORTHWESTERN MEDICINE CENTRAL DUPAGE HOSPITAL (O, 413 beds) 25 North Winfield Road, Winfield, IL, Zip 60190; tel. 630/933-1600; Brian J. Lemon, President
Web address: www.nm.org

NORTHWESTERN MEDICINE DELNOR HOSPITAL (O, 154 beds) 300 Randall Road, Geneva, IL, Zip 60134-4200; tel. 630/208-3000; Maureen A. Bryant, FACHE, President

NORTHWESTERN MEDICINE KISHWAUKEE HOSPITAL (O, 98 beds) 1 Kish Hospital Drive, DeKalb, IL, Zip 60115-9602, Mailing Address: P.O. Box 707, Zip 60115-0707, tel. 815/756-1521; Jay Anderson, President
Web address: www.nm.org

NORTHWESTERN MEDICINE LAKE FOREST HOSPITAL (O, 123 beds) 1000 North Westmoreland Road, Lake Forest, IL, Zip 60045-1696, Mailing Address: 660 North Westmoreland Road, Zip 60045-1696, tel. 847/234-5600; Thomas J. McAfee, President, North Region

NORTHWESTERN MEDICINE MARIANJOY REHABILITATION HOSPITAL (O, 127 beds) 26 West 171 Roosevelt Road, Wheaton, IL, Zip 60187-0795, Mailing Address: P.O. Box 795, Zip 60187-0795, tel. 630/909-8000; Brian J. Lemon, President
Web address: www.marianjoy.org

NORTHWESTERN MEDICINE VALLEY WEST HOSPITAL (O, 25 beds) 1302 North Main Street, Sandwich, IL, Zip 60548-2587; tel. 815/786-8484; Jay Anderson, President
Web address: www.nm.org

For explanation of codes following names, see page B2.
★ Indicates Type III membership in the American Hospital Association.

NORTHWESTERN MEMORIAL HOSPITAL (O, 894 beds) 251 East Huron Street, Chicago, IL, Zip 60611–2908; tel. 312/926–2000; Julie L. Creamer, President, Northwestern Memorial Hospital and Senior Vice President Northwestern Memorial HealthCare

Owned, leased, sponsored:	7 hospitals	1834 beds
Contract–managed:	0 hospitals	0 beds
Totals:	7 hospitals	1834 beds

★2285: NORTON HEALTHCARE (NP)
4967 US Highway 42, Suite 100, Louisville, KY, Zip 40222–6363, Mailing Address: P.O. Box 35070, Zip 40232–5070, tel. 502/629–8000; Russell Cox, President and Chief Executive Officer
(Centralized Health System)

KENTUCKY: NORTON CHILDREN'S HOSPITAL (O, 267 beds) 231 East Chestnut Street, Louisville, KY, Zip 40202–1821; tel. 502/629–6000; Emmett Ramser, Chief Administrative Officer

NORTON HOSPITAL (O, 383 beds) 200 East Chestnut Street, Louisville, KY, Zip 40202–1800, Mailing Address: P.O. Box 35070, Zip 40232–5070, tel. 502/629–8000; Matthew Ayers, Chief Administrative Officer
Web address: www.nortonhealthcare.com/nortonhospital

Owned, leased, sponsored:	2 hospitals	650 beds
Contract–managed:	0 hospitals	0 beds
Totals:	2 hospitals	650 beds

★0139: NOVANT HEALTH (NP)
2085 Frontis Plaza Boulevard, Winston Salem, NC, Zip 27103–5614; tel. 336/718–5600; Carl S. Armato, President and Chief Executive Officer
(Moderately Centralized Health System)

NORTH CAROLINA: ASHE MEMORIAL HOSPITAL (C, 25 beds) 200 Hospital Avenue, Jefferson, NC, Zip 28640–9244; tel. 336/846–7101; Laura Lambeth, Chief Executive Officer
Web address: www.ashememorial.org

HALIFAX REGIONAL MEDICAL CENTER (C, 142 beds) 250 Smith Church Road, Roanoke Rapids, NC, Zip 27870–4914, Mailing Address: P.O. Box 1089, Zip 27870–1089, tel. 252/535–8011; William Mahone, President and Chief Executive Officer
Web address: www.halifaxmedicalcenter.org

NOVANT HEALTH BRUNSWICK MEDICAL CENTER (O, 53 beds) 240 Hospital Drive NE, Bolivia, NC, Zip 28422–8346; tel. 910/721–1000; Shelbourn Stevens, President and Chief Operating Officer
Web address: https://www.novanthealth.org

NOVANT HEALTH CHARLOTTE ORTHOPAEDIC HOSPITAL (O, 33 beds) 1901 Randolph Road, Charlotte, NC, Zip 28207–1195; tel. 704/316–2000; Jason Bernd, Vice President
Web address: www.novanthealth.org

NOVANT HEALTH FORSYTH MEDICAL CENTER (O, 706 beds) 3333 Silas Creek Parkway, Winston–Salem, NC, Zip 27103–3090; tel. 336/718–5000; Chad Setliff, President and Chief Operating Officer

NOVANT HEALTH HUNTERSVILLE MEDICAL CENTER (O, 78 beds) 10030 Gilead Road, Huntersville, NC, Zip 28078–7545, Mailing Address: P.O. Box 3508, Zip 28070–3508, tel. 704/316–4000; Mike Riley, President and Chief Operating Officer
Web address: www.novanthealth.org

NOVANT HEALTH MATTHEWS MEDICAL CENTER (O, 111 beds) 1500 Matthews Township Parkway, Matthews, NC, Zip 28105–4656; tel. 704/384–6500; Roland R. Bibeau, President and Chief Operating Officer

NOVANT HEALTH MEDICAL PARK HOSPITAL (O, 14 beds) 1950 South Hawthorne Road, Winston–Salem, NC, Zip 27103–3993; tel. 336/718–0600; Kirsten Royster, President and Chief Operating Officer
Web address: www.novanthealth.org

NOVANT HEALTH PRESBYTERIAN MEDICAL CENTER (O, 419 beds) 200 Hawthorne Lane, Charlotte, NC, Zip 28204–2528, Mailing Address: P.O. Box 33549, Zip 28233–3549, tel. 704/384–4000; Paula Vincent, MSN, President and Chief Operating Officer

NOVANT HEALTH ROWAN MEDICAL CENTER (O, 147 beds) 612 Mocksville Avenue, Salisbury, NC, Zip 28144–2799; tel. 704/210–5000; Dari Caldwell, R.N., Ph.D., FACHE, President and Chief Operating Officer
Web address: https://www.novanthealth.org/rowan–medical–center.aspx

NOVANT HEALTH THOMASVILLE MEDICAL CENTER (O, 80 beds) 207 Old Lexington Road, Thomasville, NC, Zip 27360–3428, Mailing Address: P.O. Box 789, Zip 27361–0789, tel. 336/472–2000; Jon D. Applebaum, President and Chief Operating Officer
Web address: www.thomasvillemedicalcenter.org

VIRGINIA: NOVANT HEALTH UVA HEALTH SYSTEM CULPEPER MEDICAL CENTER (O, 68 beds) 501 Sunset Lane, Culpeper, VA, Zip 22701–3917, Mailing Address: P.O. Box 592, Zip 22701–0500, tel. 540/829–4100; Jeff Hetmanski, President and Chief Executive Officer

NOVANT HEALTH UVA HEALTH SYSTEM HAYMARKET MEDICAL CENTER (O, 18 beds) 15225 Heathcote Boulevard, Haymarket, VA, Zip 20155–4023, Mailing Address: 14535 John Marshall Hwy, Gainesville, Zip 20155–4023, tel. 571/284–1000; Greg Napps, President
Web address: www.novanthealth.org

NOVANT HEALTH UVA HEALTH SYSTEM PRINCE WILLIAM MEDICAL CENTER (O, 90 beds) 8700 Sudley Road, Manassas, VA, Zip 20110–4418, Mailing Address: P.O. Box 2610, Zip 20108–0867, tel. 703/369–8000; Greg Napps, President
Web address: www.pwhs.org

Owned, leased, sponsored:	12 hospitals	1817 beds
Contract–managed:	2 hospitals	167 beds
Totals:	14 hospitals	1984 beds

★3075: NYC HEALTH + HOSPITALS (NP)
125 Worth Street, Room 514, New York, NY, Zip 10013–4006; tel. 212/788–3321; Mitchell H. Katz, M.D., Chief Executive Officer
(Moderately Centralized Health System)

NEW YORK: NYC HEALTH + HOSPITALS / BELLEVUE (O, 719 beds) 462 First Avenue, New York, NY, Zip 10016–9198; tel. 212/562–4141; William Hicks, Chief Executive Officer
Web address: www.nyc.gov/bellevue

NYC HEALTH + HOSPITALS / CONEY ISLAND (O, 371 beds) 2601 Ocean Parkway, Brooklyn, NY, Zip 11235–7795; tel. 718/616–3000; William A. Brown, FACHE, Chief Executive Officer
Web address: www.nyc.gov/html/hhc/html/facilities/coneyisland.shtml

NYC HEALTH + HOSPITALS / ELMHURST (O, 506 beds) 79–01 Broadway, Elmhurst, NY, Zip 11373–1329; tel. 718/334–4000; Israel Rocha Jr, Chief Executive Officer

NYC HEALTH + HOSPITALS / GOUVERNEUR (O, 196 beds) 227 Madison Street, New York, NY, Zip 10002; tel. 212/238–7000; Martha Adams Sullivan, Chief Executive Officer

NYC HEALTH + HOSPITALS / HARLEM (O, 252 beds) 506 Lenox Avenue, New York, NY, Zip 10037–1802; tel. 212/939–1000; Ebone' Carrington, Chief Executive Officer and Chief Operating Officer
Web address: www.nyc.gov/html/hhc/harlem

NYC HEALTH + HOSPITALS / HENRY J CARTER SPECIALTY HOSPITAL AND MEDICAL CENTER (O, 365 beds) 1752 Park Avenue, New York, NY, Zip 10035; tel. 646/686–0000; Robert K. Hughes, Chief Executive Officer

NYC HEALTH + HOSPITALS / JACOBI (O, 457 beds) 1400 Pelham Parkway South, Bronx, NY, Zip 10461–1197; tel. 718/918–5000; Christopher Mastromanno, Interim Chief Executive Officer
Web address: www.nyc.gov/html/hhc/jacobi/home.html

NYC HEALTH + HOSPITALS / KINGS COUNTY (O, 589 beds) 451 Clarkson Avenue, Brooklyn, NY, Zip 11203–2054; tel. 718/245–3131; Sheldon Mcleod, Chief Executive Officer

NYC HEALTH + HOSPITALS / LINCOLN (O, 367 beds) 234 East 149th Street, Bronx, NY, Zip 10451–5504, Mailing Address: 234 East 149th Street, Room 923, Zip 10451–5504, tel. 718/579–5700; Milton Nunez, Executive Director
Web address: www.nyc.gov/html/hhc/lincoln/

NYC HEALTH + HOSPITALS / METROPOLITAN (O, 302 beds) 1901 First Avenue, New York, NY, Zip 10029–7404; tel. 212/423–6262; Alina Moran, Chief Executive Officer

---

For explanation of codes following names, see page B2.
★ Indicates Type III membership in the American Hospital Association.

NYC HEALTH + HOSPITALS / NORTH CENTRAL BRONX (O, 232 beds) 3424 Kossuth Avenue, Bronx, NY, Zip 10467–2489; tel. 718/519–3500; Maureen Pode, Co–Interim Executive Director
Web address: www.nyc.gov/html/hhc/ncbh/html/home/home.shtml

NYC HEALTH + HOSPITALS / QUEENS (O, 259 beds) 82–68 164th Street, Jamaica, NY, Zip 11432–1104; tel. 718/883–3000; Christopher Roker, Chief Executive Officer
Web address: www.nyc.gov/html/hhc/qhc/html/home/home.shtml

NYC HEALTH + HOSPITALS / SEA VIEW (O, 304 beds) 460 Brielle Avenue, Staten Island, NY, Zip 10314; tel. 212/390–8181; Jane M. Lyons, Executive Director

NYC HEALTH + HOSPITALS / WOODHULL (O, 272 beds) 760 Broadway, Brooklyn, NY, Zip 11206–5383; tel. 718/963–8000; Gregory Calliste, Ph.D., FACHE, Chief Executive Officer
Web address: www.nyc.gov/html/hhc

Owned, leased, sponsored:	14 hospitals	5191 beds
Contract–managed:	0 hospitals	0 beds
Totals:	14 hospitals	5191 beds

1026: NYU LANGONE HEALTH (NP)

550 First Avenue, New York, NY, Zip 10016–6402; tel. 646/929–7870; Robert I. Grossman, M.D., Chief Executive Officer
(Moderately Centralized Health System)

NEW YORK: NYU LANGONE HOSPITALS (O, 1096 beds) 550 First Avenue, New York, NY, Zip 10016–6402; tel. 212/263–7300; Robert I. Grossman, M.D., Chief Executive Officer

NYU WINTHROP HOSPITAL (O, 511 beds) 259 First Street, Mineola, NY, Zip 11501–3957; tel. 516/663–0333; John F. Collins, President and Chief Executive Officer
Web address: www.winthrop.org

Owned, leased, sponsored:	2 hospitals	1607 beds
Contract–managed:	0 hospitals	0 beds
Totals:	2 hospitals	1607 beds

0616: OCEANS HEALTHCARE (IO)

2720 Rue de Jardin, Suite 100, Lake Charles, LA, Zip 70605–4050; tel. 337/721–1900; Jason Reed, President and Chief Executive Officer
(Independent Hospital System)

LOUISIANA: OCEANS BEHAVIORAL HOSPITAL OF ALEXANDRIA (O, 24 beds) 2621 North Bolton Avenue, Alexandria, LA, Zip 71303–4506; tel. 318/448–8473; Ben Cooper, Administrator

OCEANS BEHAVIORAL HOSPITAL OF BATON ROUGE (O, 20 beds) 11135 Florida Boulevard, Baton Rouge, LA, Zip 70815–2013; tel. 225/356–7030; Valerie Dalton, R.N., Administrator
Web address: www.obhbr.info/

OCEANS BEHAVIORAL HOSPITAL OF BROUSSARD (O, 38 beds) 418 Albertson Parkway, Broussard, LA, Zip 70518–4971; tel. 337/237–6444; Amy Dysart–Credeur, Administrator
Web address: www.obhb.info/

OCEANS BEHAVIORAL HOSPITAL OF DE RIDDER (O, 20 beds) 1420 Blankenship Drive, Deridder, LA, Zip 70634–4604; tel. 337/460–9472; Stuart Archer, Chief Executive Officer

OCEANS BEHAVIORAL HOSPITAL OF GREATER NEW ORLEANS (O, 30 beds) 716 Village Road, Kenner, LA, Zip 70065–2751; tel. 504/464–8895; Deborah Spier, Administrator
Web address: www.obhgno.info/

OCEANS BEHAVIORAL HOSPITAL OF KENTWOOD (O, 16 beds) 921 Avenue G, Kentwood, LA, Zip 70444–2636; tel. 985/229–0717; Frederick Nelson, MA, Administrator
Web address: www.obhk.info/

OCEANS BEHAVIORAL HOSPITAL OF LAKE CHARLES (O, 40 beds) 302 West Mcneese Street, Lake Charles, LA, Zip 70605–5604; tel. 337/474–7581; Monica Tatum, Administrator
Web address: www.obhlc.info/

OCEANS BEHAVIORAL HOSPITAL OF OPELOUSAS (O, 20 beds) 1310 Heather Drive, Opelousas, LA, Zip 70570–7714; tel. 337/948–8820; Katherine Simoneaux, Administrator
Web address: www.obho.info/

TEXAS: OCEANS BEHAVIORAL HEALTH CENTER PERMIAN BASIN (O, 58 beds) 3300 South FM 1788, Midland, TX, Zip 79706–2601; tel. 432/561–5915; Lorie Dunnam, Chief Executive Officer

OCEANS BEHAVIORAL HOSPITAL ABILENE (O, 90 beds) 4225 Woods Place, Abilene, TX, Zip 79602–7991; tel. 325/691–0030; Stacy Sanford, Chief Executive Officer
Web address: www.oceansabilene.com

OCEANS BEHAVIORAL HOSPITAL KATY (O, 48 beds) 455 Park Grove Lane, Katy, TX, Zip 77450–1572; tel. 281/492–8888; Stuart Archer, Chief Executive Officer
Web address: www.memorialhermann.org/locations/katy–rehab/

OCEANS BEHAVIORAL HOSPITAL LONGVIEW (O, 24 beds) 615 Clinic Drive, Longview, TX, Zip 75605–5172; tel. 903/212–3105; Lauren Weber, Administrator

OCEANS BEHAVIORAL HOSPITAL LUFKIN (O, 24 beds) 302 Gobblers Knob Road, Lufkin, TX, Zip 75904–5419; tel. 936/632–2276; Laci Laird, Chief Executive Officer
Web address: www.oceanslufkin.com/

Owned, leased, sponsored:	13 hospitals	452 beds
Contract–managed:	0 hospitals	0 beds
Totals:	13 hospitals	452 beds

★0359: OCHSNER HEALTH SYSTEM (NP)

1514 Jefferson Highway, New Orleans, LA, Zip 70121–2429; tel. 800/874–8984; Warner L. Thomas, FACHE, President and Chief Executive Officer
(Centralized Health System)

LOUISIANA: LEONARD J. CHABERT MEDICAL CENTER (C, 72 beds) 1978 Industrial Boulevard, Houma, LA, Zip 70363–7094; tel. 985/873–2200; Timothy J. Allen, FACHE, Chief Executive Officer

OCHSNER MEDICAL CENTER – BATON ROUGE (O, 154 beds) 17000 Medical Center Drive, Baton Rouge, LA, Zip 70816–3224; tel. 225/752–2470; Eric McMillen, Chief Executive Officer
Web address: www.ochsner.org/page.cfm?id=103

OCHSNER MEDICAL CENTER – KENNER (O, 110 beds) 180 West Esplanade Avenue, Kenner, LA, Zip 70065–6001; tel. 504/468–8600; Stephen Robinson Jr, FACHE, Chief Executive Officer
Web address: https://www.ochsner.org/locations/ochsner–medical–center–kenner/

OCHSNER MEDICAL CENTER – NORTH SHORE (L, 168 beds) 100 Medical Center Drive, Slidell, LA, Zip 70461–5520; tel. 985/649–7070; John William Bill"". Davis, Chief Executive Officer

OCHSNER MEDICAL CENTER (O, 823 beds) 1514 Jefferson Highway, New Orleans, LA, Zip 70121–2429; tel. 504/842–3000; Robert K. Wolterman, Chief Executive Officer
Web address: www.ochsner.org

OCHSNER ST. ANNE GENERAL HOSPITAL (O, 35 beds) 4608 Highway 1, Raceland, LA, Zip 70394–2623; tel. 985/537–6841; Timothy J. Allen, FACHE, Chief Executive Officer
Web address: www.ochsner.org/locations/ochsner–st–anne

SLIDELL MEMORIAL HOSPITAL (C, 175 beds) 1001 Gause Boulevard, Slidell, LA, Zip 70458–2987; tel. 985/280–2200; John William Bill"". Davis, Chief Executive Officer

ST. CHARLES PARISH HOSPITAL (C, 59 beds) 1057 Paul Maillard Road, Luling, LA, Zip 70070–4349, Mailing Address: P.O. Box 87, Zip 70070–0087; tel. 985/785–6242; Austin Reeder, Chief Executive Officer
Web address: https://www.ochsner.org/locations/st–charles–parish–hospital/

MISSISSIPPI: HANCOCK MEDICAL CENTER (C, 102 beds) 149 Drinkwater Boulevard, Bay Saint Louis, MS, Zip 39520–1658, Bay St Louis, tel. 228/467–8600; Alan Hodges, Chief Executive Officer
Web address: www.hmc.org

Owned, leased, sponsored:	5 hospitals	1290 beds
Contract–managed:	4 hospitals	408 beds
Totals:	9 hospitals	1698 beds

For explanation of codes following names, see page B2.
★ Indicates Type III membership in the American Hospital Association.

Section B

0537: OHIO DEPARTMENT OF MENTAL HEALTH (NP)

30 East Broad Street, 8th Floor, Columbus, OH, Zip 43215–3430; tel. 614/466–2297; Tracy Plouck, Director
(Independent Hospital System)

OHIO: APPALACHIAN BEHAVIORAL HEALTHCARE (O, 224 beds) 100 Hospital Drive, Athens, OH, Zip 45701–2301; tel. 740/594–5000; Jane E. Krason, R.N., Chief Executive Officer
Web address: www.mh.state.oh.us

HEARTLAND BEHAVIORAL HEALTHCARE (O, 152 beds) 3000 Erie Stree South, Massillon, OH, Zip 44646–7993, Mailing Address: 3000 Erie Street South, Zip 44646–7976, tel. 330/833–3135; Jeffrey Sims, Chief Executive Officer
Web address: www.mh.state.oh.us/ibhs/bhos/hoh.html

NORTHCOAST BEHAVIORAL HEALTHCARE (O, 260 beds) 1756 Sagamore Road, Northfield, OH, Zip 44067–1086; tel. 330/467–7131; Douglas W. Kern, Chief Executive Officer

NORTHWEST OHIO PSYCHIATRIC HOSPITAL (O, 114 beds) 930 Detroit Avenue, Toledo, OH, Zip 43614–2701; tel. 419/381–1881; Brett M. Johnson, Chief Executive Officer
Web address: www.mh.state.oh.us/

SUMMIT BEHAVIORAL HEALTHCARE (O, 291 beds) 1101 Summit Road, Cincinnati, OH, Zip 45237–2652; tel. 513/948–3600; Elizabeth Banks, Chief Executive Officer

TWIN VALLEY BEHAVIORAL HEALTHCARE (O, 178 beds) 2200 West Broad Street, Columbus, OH, Zip 43223–1297; tel. 614/752–0333; Veronica Lofton, Acting Chief Executive Officer
Web address: www.mh.state.oh.us/ibhs/bhos/tvbh.html

Owned, leased, sponsored:	6 hospitals	1219 beds
Contract–managed:	0 hospitals	0 beds
Totals:	6 hospitals	1219 beds

★0251: OHIO STATE UNIVERSITY HEALTH SYSTEM (NP)

370 West Ninth Avenue, Columbus, OH, Zip 43210–1238; tel. 614/685–9015; David P. McQuaid, FACHE, Chief Executive Officer
(Centralized Physician/Insurance Health System)

OHIO: JAMES CANCER HOSPITAL AND SOLOVE RESEARCH INSTITUTE (O, 308 beds) 460 West Tenth Avenue, Columbus, OH, Zip 43210–1240; tel. 614/293–3300; William Farrar, M.D., Interim Chief Executive Officer

OHIO STATE UNIVERSITY WEXNER MEDICAL CENTER (O, 1057 beds) 410 West 10th Avenue, Columbus, OH, Zip 43210–1240; tel. 614/293–8000; David P. McQuaid, FACHE, Chief Operating Officer
Web address: www.medicalcenter.osu.edu

Owned, leased, sponsored:	2 hospitals	1365 beds
Contract–managed:	0 hospitals	0 beds
Totals:	2 hospitals	1365 beds

★0162: OHIOHEALTH (NP)

180 East Broad Street, Columbus, OH, Zip 43215–3707; tel. 614/544–4455; David P. Blom, President and Chief Executive Officer
(Moderately Centralized Health System)

OHIO: MORROW COUNTY HOSPITAL (C, 22 beds) 651 West Marion Road, Mount Gilead, OH, Zip 43338–1027; tel. 419/946–5015; Chad J. Miller, President and Chief Executive Officer

O'BLENESS MEMORIAL HOSPITAL (O, 64 beds) 55 Hospital Drive, Athens, OH, Zip 45701–2302; tel. 740/593–5551; Mark R. Seckinger, President
Web address: www.obleness.org

OHIOHEALTH DOCTORS HOSPITAL (O, 195 beds) 5100 West Broad Street, Columbus, OH, Zip 43228–1607; tel. 614/544–1000; Michael L. Reichfield, President
Web address: www.ohiohealth.com

OHIOHEALTH DUBLIN METHODIST HOSPITAL (O, 120 beds) 7500 Hospital Drive, Dublin, OH, Zip 43016–8518; tel. 614/544–8000; Steve Bunyard, President
Web address: www.ohiohealth.com

OHIOHEALTH GRADY MEMORIAL HOSPITAL (O, 59 beds) 561 West Central Avenue, Delaware, OH, Zip 43015–1410; tel. 740/615–1000; Steve Bunyard, President

OHIOHEALTH GRANT MEDICAL CENTER (O, 425 beds) 111 South Grant Avenue, Columbus, OH, Zip 43215–1898; tel. 614/566–9000; Michael Lawson, President and Chief Operating Officer
Web address: www.ohiohealth.com

OHIOHEALTH HARDIN MEMORIAL HOSPITAL (O, 25 beds) 921 East Franklin Street, Kenton, OH, Zip 43326–2099; tel. 419/673–0761; Ron Snyder, Chief Operating Officer
Web address: www.hardinmemorial.org

OHIOHEALTH MARION GENERAL HOSPITAL (O, 174 beds) 1000 McKinley Park Drive, Marion, OH, Zip 43302–6397; tel. 740/383–8400; Bruce P. Hagen, President

OHIOHEALTH MEDCENTRAL MANSFIELD HOSPITAL (O, 253 beds) 335 Glessner Avenue, Mansfield, OH, Zip 44903–2265; tel. 419/526–8000; Jean Halpin, President
Web address: www.medcentral.org

OHIOHEALTH MEDCENTRAL SHELBY HOSPITAL (O, 25 beds) 199 West Main Street, Shelby, OH, Zip 44875–1490; tel. 419/342–5015; Jean Halpin, President

OHIOHEALTH RIVERSIDE METHODIST HOSPITAL (O, 754 beds) 3535 Olentangy River Road, Columbus, OH, Zip 43214–3998; tel. 614/566–5000; Brian Jepson, President
Web address: www.ohiohealth.com

Owned, leased, sponsored:	10 hospitals	2094 beds
Contract–managed:	1 hospitals	22 beds
Totals:	11 hospitals	2116 beds

0018: OKLAHOMA DEPARTMENT OF MENTAL HEALTH AND SUBSTANCE ABUSE SERVICES (NP)

1200 NE 13th Street, Oklahoma City, OK, Zip 73117–1022, Mailing Address: P.O. Box 53277, Zip 73152–3277, tel. 405/522–3908; Terri White, Commissioner
(Independent Hospital System)

OKLAHOMA: GRIFFIN MEMORIAL HOSPITAL (O, 120 beds) 900 East Main Street, Norman, OK, Zip 73071–5305, Mailing Address: P.O. Box 151, Zip 73070–0151, tel. 405/573–6600; Henry Hartsell, Ph.D., Executive Director

NORTHWEST CENTER FOR BEHAVIORAL HEALTH (O, 24 beds) 1 Mi East Highway 270, Fort Supply, OK, Zip 73841, Mailing Address: 1222 10th Street, Suite 211, Woodward, Zip 73801–3156, tel. 580/766–2311; Trudy Hoffman, Executive Director
Web address: www.ncbhok.org/

OKLAHOMA FORENSIC CENTER (O, 200 beds) 24800 South 4420 Road, Vinita, OK, Zip 74301–5544, Mailing Address: P.O. Box 69, Zip 74301–0069, tel. 918/256–7841; Kevan Finley, Chief Executive Officer
Web address: www.odmhsas.org

Owned, leased, sponsored:	3 hospitals	344 beds
Contract–managed:	0 hospitals	0 beds
Totals:	3 hospitals	344 beds

3355: ORLANDO HEALTH (NP)

1414 Kuhl Avenue, Orlando, FL, Zip 32806–2093; tel. 321/843–7000; David W. Strong, President and Chief Executive Officer
(Centralized Physician/Insurance Health System)

FLORIDA: HEALTH CENTRAL HOSPITAL (O, 439 beds) 10000 West Colonial Drive, Ocoee, FL, Zip 34761–3499; tel. 407/296–1000; Mark A. Marsh, President
Web address: www.healthcentral.org

LAKELAND REGIONAL HEALTH MEDICAL CENTER (O, 849 beds) 1324 Lakeland Hills Blvd, Lakeland, FL, Zip 33805–4543, Mailing Address: P.O. Box 95448, Zip 33804–5448, tel. 863/687–1100; Timothy Regan, M.D., President and Chief Medical Officer
Web address: www.mylrh.org

For explanation of codes following names, see page B2.
★ Indicates Type III membership in the American Hospital Association.

ORLANDO REGIONAL MEDICAL CENTER (O, 1203 beds) 52 West Underwood Street, Orlando, FL, Zip 32806; tel. 407/841–5111; Mark A. Jones, President
Web address: www.orlandohealth.com/facilities/orlando–regional–medical–center

SOUTH LAKE HOSPITAL (O, 170 beds) 1900 Don Wickham Drive, Clermont, FL, Zip 34711–1979; tel. 352/394–4071; John Moore, President

Owned, leased, sponsored:	4 hospitals	2661 beds
Contract–managed:	0 hospitals	0 beds
Totals:	4 hospitals	2661 beds

★**5335: OSF HEALTHCARE** (CO)
800 NE Glen Oak Avenue, Peoria, IL, Zip 61603–3200; tel. 309/655–2850; Robert Sehring, Chief Executive Officer
(Moderately Centralized Health System)

ILLINOIS: OSF HEALTHCARE SAINT ANTHONY'S HEALTH CENTER (O, 140 beds) 1 Saint Anthony's Way, Alton, IL, Zip 62002–4579, Mailing Address: PO Box 340, Zip 62002–0340, tel. 618/465–2571; Ajay Pathak, President
Web address: www.osfsaintanthonys.org

OSF HEART OF MARY MEDICAL CENTER (O, 181 beds) 1400 West Park Street, Urbana, IL, Zip 61801–2396, Mailing Address: P.O. Box 6259, Peoria, Zip 61601, tel. 217/337–2000; Jared Rogers, M.D., President and Chief Executive Officer
Web address: www.presencehealth.org/covenant

OSF HOLY FAMILY MEDICAL CENTER (O, 23 beds) 1000 West Harlem Avenue, Monmouth, IL, Zip 61462–1007; tel. 309/734–3141; Patricia A. Luker, President

OSF SACRED HEART MEDICAL CENTER (O, 117 beds) 812 North Logan, Danville, IL, Zip 61832–3788; tel. 217/443–5000; Jared Rogers, M.D., President and Chief Executive Officer
Web address: www.presencehealth.org/usmc

OSF SAINT ANTHONY MEDICAL CENTER (O, 235 beds) 5666 East State Street, Rockford, IL, Zip 61108–2425; tel. 815/226–2000; Paula A. Carynski, MS, R.N., President
Web address: www.osfhealth.com

OSF SAINT ELIZABETH MEDICAL CENTER (O, 87 beds) 1100 East Norris Drive, Ottawa, IL, Zip 61350–1687; tel. 815/433–3100; Kenneth Beutke, President

OSF SAINT FRANCIS MEDICAL CENTER (O, 629 beds) 530 NE Glen Oak Avenue, Peoria, IL, Zip 61637–0001; tel. 309/655–2000; Robert G. Anderson Jr, President
Web address: www.osfsaintfrancis.org

OSF SAINT JAMES – JOHN W. ALBRECHT MEDICAL CENTER (O, 42 beds) 2500 West Reynolds, Pontiac, IL, Zip 61764–9774; tel. 815/842–2828; Bradley V. Solberg, FACHE, President

OSF SAINT LUKE MEDICAL CENTER (O, 25 beds) 1051 West South Street, Kewanee, IL, Zip 61443–8354, Mailing Address: P.O. Box 747, Zip 61443–0747, tel. 309/852–7500; Jacqueline D. Kernan, President
Web address: www.osfsaintluke.org

OSF SAINT PAUL MEDICAL CENTER (O, 25 beds) 1401 East 12th Street, Mendota, IL, Zip 61342–9216; tel. 815/539–7461; Dawn Trompeter, President
Web address: https://www.osfhealthcare.org/saint–paul

OSF ST. JOSEPH MEDICAL CENTER (O, 149 beds) 2200 East Washington Street, Bloomington, IL, Zip 61701–4323; tel. 309/662–3311; Lynn Fulton, President

OSF ST. MARY MEDICAL CENTER (O, 81 beds) 3333 North Seminary Street, Galesburg, IL, Zip 61401–1299; tel. 309/344–3161; Jennifer Junis, MSN, R.N., President
Web address: www.osfstmary.org

SAINT CLARE HOME (O, 0 beds) 5533 North Galena Road, Peoria Heights, IL, Zip 61614–4499; tel. 309/682–5428; Candy Conover, Administrator

ST. ANTHONY'S CONTINUING CARE CENTER (O, 179 beds) 767 30th Street, Rock Island, IL, Zip 61201; Sister, Mary Anthony. Mazzaferri, Administrator

MICHIGAN: OSF ST. FRANCIS HOSPITAL AND MEDICAL GROUP (O, 25 beds) 3401 Ludington Street, Escanaba, MI, Zip 49829–1377; tel. 906/786–3311; David Lord, President
Web address: www.osfstfrancis.org

Owned, leased, sponsored:	15 hospitals	1938 beds
Contract–managed:	0 hospitals	0 beds
Totals:	15 hospitals	1938 beds

0982: OWENSBORO HEALTH (NP)
1201 Pleasant Valley Road, Owensboro, KY, Zip 42303–9811; tel. 270/417–2000; Greg Strahan, Interim Chief Executive Officer
(Moderately Centralized Health System)

KENTUCKY: OWENSBORO HEALTH MUHLENBERG COMMUNITY HOSPITAL (O, 105 beds) 440 Hopkinsville Street, Greenville, KY, Zip 42345–1172, Mailing Address: P.O. Box 387, Zip 42345–0378, tel. 270/338–8000; Ed Heath, FACHE, Chief Executive Officer
Web address: www.mchky.org

OWENSBORO HEALTH REGIONAL HOSPITAL (O, 360 beds) 1201 Pleasant Valley Road, Owensboro, KY, Zip 42303; tel. 270/417–2000; Greg Strahan, Interim Chief Executive Officer

Owned, leased, sponsored:	2 hospitals	465 beds
Contract–managed:	0 hospitals	0 beds
Totals:	2 hospitals	465 beds

0367: PACER HEALTH CORPORATION (IO)
14100 Palmetto Frontage Road, Suite 110, Miami Lakes, FL, Zip 33016; tel. 305/828–7660; Rainier Gonzalez, Chairman and Chief Executive Officer

KENTUCKY: BARBOURVILLE ARH HOSPITAL (O, 25 beds) 80 Hospital Drive, Barbourville, KY, Zip 40906–7363, Mailing Address: P.O. Box 10, Zip 40906–0010, tel. 606/546–4175; Charles D. Lovell Jr, FACHE, Chief Executive Officer
Web address: www.knoxcohospital.com

Owned, leased, sponsored:	1 hospitals	25 beds
Contract–managed:	0 hospitals	0 beds
Totals:	1 hospitals	25 beds

★**5235: PALLOTTINE HEALTH SERVICES** (CO)
2900 First Avenue, Huntington, WV, Zip 25702–1241; tel. 304/526–1234; Michael G. Sellards, Chief Executive Officer
(Independent Hospital System)

WEST VIRGINIA: ST. MARY'S MEDICAL CENTER (O, 393 beds) 2900 First Avenue, Huntington, WV, Zip 25702–1272; tel. 304/526–1234; Michael G. Sellards, President and Chief Executive Officer
Web address: www.st–marys.org

Owned, leased, sponsored:	1 hospitals	393 beds
Contract–managed:	0 hospitals	0 beds
Totals:	1 hospitals	393 beds

★**4155: PALMETTO HEALTH** (NP)
1301 Taylor Street, Suite 9–A, Columbia, SC, Zip 29201–2942, Mailing Address: P.O. Box 2266, Zip 29202–2266, tel. 803/296–2100; Charles D. Beaman Jr, Chief Executive Officer
(Centralized Health System)

SOUTH CAROLINA: PALMETTO HEALTH BAPTIST PARKRIDGE (O, 76 beds) 400 Palmetto Health Parkway, Columbia, SC, Zip 29212–1760, Mailing Address: P.O. Box 2266, Zip 29202–2266, tel. 803/907–7000; Emilie Keene, Interim Chief Operating Officer

PALMETTO HEALTH BAPTIST (O, 400 beds) Taylor at Marion Street, Columbia, SC, Zip 29220–0001; tel. 803/296–5010; Gregory B. Gattman, Chief Operating Officer
Web address: www.palmettohealth.org

Section B

PALMETTO HEALTH RICHLAND (O, 671 beds) Five Richland Medical Park Drive, Columbia, SC, Zip 29203–6897; tel. 803/434–7000; Jay Hamm, R.N., FACHE, Chief Operating Officer

PALMETTO HEALTH TUOMEY (O, 238 beds) 129 North Washington Street, Sumter, SC, Zip 29150–4983; tel. 803/774–9000; Michelle Logan–Owens, Ph.D., R.N., Chief Operating Officer
Web address: www.tuomey.com

Owned, leased, sponsored:	4 hospitals	1385 beds
Contract–managed:	0 hospitals	0 beds
Totals:	4 hospitals	1385 beds

★7555: PALOMAR HEALTH (NP)
456 East Grand Avenue, Escondido, CA, Zip 92025–3319; tel. 760/740–6393; Diane Hansen, Chief Executive Officer
(Moderately Centralized Health System)

CALIFORNIA: PALOMAR MEDICAL CENTER (O, 344 beds) 2185 West Citracado Parkway, Escondido, CA, Zip 92029–4159; tel. 760/739–3000; Mariellena Sudak, R.N., MSN, Vice President and Chief Nursing Officer

POMERADO HOSPITAL (O, 201 beds) 15615 Pomerado Road, Poway, CA, Zip 92064–2460; tel. 858/613–4000; Cheryl Olson, Vice President
Web address: www.pph.org

Owned, leased, sponsored:	2 hospitals	545 beds
Contract–managed:	0 hospitals	0 beds
Totals:	2 hospitals	545 beds

★0159: PARKVIEW HEALTH (NP)
10501 Corporate Drive, Fort Wayne, IN, Zip 46845–1700; tel. 260/373–7001; Michael J. Packnett, President and Chief Executive Officer
(Centralized Physician/Insurance Health System)

INDIANA: PARKVIEW ORTHO HOSPITAL (O, 37 beds) 11130 Parkview Circle Drive, Fort Wayne, IN, Zip 46845–1735; tel. 260/672–5000; Julie Fleck, Chief Operating Officer
Web address: www.parkview.com

PARKVIEW HUNTINGTON HOSPITAL (O, 36 beds) 2001 Stults Road, Huntington, IN, Zip 46750–1291; tel. 260/355–3000; Juli Johnson, MSN, R.N., President

PARKVIEW LAGRANGE HOSPITAL (O, 25 beds) 207 North Townline Road, LaGrange, IN, Zip 46761–1325; tel. 260/463–9000; Jordi K. Disler, President
Web address: www.parkview.com

PARKVIEW NOBLE HOSPITAL (O, 31 beds) 401 Sawyer Road, Kendallville, IN, Zip 46755–2568; tel. 260/347–8700; Gary W. Adkins, President

PARKVIEW REGIONAL MEDICAL CENTER (O, 732 beds) 11109 Parkview Plaza Drive, Fort Wayne, IN, Zip 46845–1701; tel. 260/266–1000; Ben Miles, President
Web address: www.parkview.com

PARKVIEW WABASH COUNTY HOSPITAL (O, 25 beds) 710 North East Street, Wabash, IN, Zip 46992–1924; tel. 260/563–3131; Marilyn J. Custer–Mitchell, President

PARKVIEW WHITLEY HOSPITAL (O, 30 beds) 1260 East State Road 205, Columbia City, IN, Zip 46725–9492; tel. 260/248–9000; Scott F. Gabriel, President
Web address: www.parkview.com

Owned, leased, sponsored:	7 hospitals	916 beds
Contract–managed:	0 hospitals	0 beds
Totals:	7 hospitals	916 beds

★1785: PARTNERS HEALTHCARE SYSTEM, INC. (NP)
800 Boylston Street, Suite 1150, Boston, MA, Zip 02199–8123; tel. 617/278–1004; David Torchiana, M.D., Chief Executive Officer
(Decentralized Health System)

MASSACHUSETTS: BRIGHAM AND WOMEN'S FAULKNER HOSPITAL (O, 144 beds) 1153 Centre Street, Boston, MA, Zip 02130–3446; tel. 617/983–7000; David O. McCready, President
Web address: www.brighamandwomensfaulkner.org/index.asp

BRIGHAM AND WOMEN'S HOSPITAL (O, 761 beds) 75 Francis Street, Boston, MA, Zip 02115–6110; tel. 617/732–5500; Elizabeth Nabel, M.D., President
Web address: www.brighamandwomens.org

COOLEY DICKINSON HOSPITAL (O, 86 beds) 30 Locust Street, Northampton, MA, Zip 01060–2093, Mailing Address: P.O. Box 5001, Zip 01061–5001, tel. 413/582–2000; Joanne Marqusee, President and Chief Executive Officer

MARTHA'S VINEYARD HOSPITAL (O, 25 beds) One Hospital Road, Oak Bluffs, MA, Zip 2557, Mailing Address: P.O. Box 1477, Zip 02557–1477, tel. 508/693–0410; Denise Schepici, M.P.H., Chief Executive Officer and President
Web address: www.mvhospital.com/

MASSACHUSETTS EYE AND EAR (O, 41 beds) 243 Charles Street, Boston, MA, Zip 02114–3002; tel. 617/523–7900; John R. Fernandez, President and Chief Executive Officer
Web address: www.masseyeandear.org

MASSACHUSETTS GENERAL HOSPITAL (O, 1032 beds) 55 Fruit Street, Boston, MA, Zip 02114–2696; tel. 617/726–2000; Peter L. Slavin, M.D., President
Web address: www.massgeneral.org

MCLEAN HOSPITAL (O, 217 beds) 115 Mill Street, Belmont, MA, Zip 02478–1064; tel. 617/855–2000; Scott L. Rauch, M.D., President and Psychiatrist in Chief

NANTUCKET COTTAGE HOSPITAL (O, 19 beds) 57 Prospect Street, Nantucket, MA, Zip 02554–2799; tel. 508/825–8100; Margot Hartmann, M.D., Ph.D., President and Chief Executive Officer
Web address: www.nantuckethospital.org

NEWTON–WELLESLEY HOSPITAL (O, 220 beds) 2014 Washington Street, Newton Lower Falls, MA, Zip 02462–1699; tel. 617/243–6000; Michael R. Jaff, D.O., President
Web address: www.nwh.org

NORTH SHORE MEDICAL CENTER (O, 408 beds) 81 Highland Avenue, Salem, MA, Zip 01970–2714; tel. 978/741–1200; David J. Roberts, M.D., President

SPAULDING HOSPITAL FOR CONTINUING MEDICAL CARE CAMBRIDGE (O, 128 beds) 1575 Cambridge Street, Cambridge, MA, Zip 02138–4308; tel. 617/876–4344; Maureen Banks, FACHE, MS, R.N., President
Web address: www.spauldingnetwork.org

SPAULDING REHABILITATION HOSPITAL CAPE COD (O, 60 beds) 311 Service Road, East Sandwich, MA, Zip 02537–1370; tel. 508/833–4000; Maureen Banks, FACHE, MS, R.N., President

SPAULDING REHABILITATION HOSPITAL (O, 132 beds) 300 First Avenue, Charlestown, MA, Zip 02129–3109; tel. 617/952–5000; David E. Storto, President
Web address: www.spauldingrehab.org

NEW HAMPSHIRE: WENTWORTH–DOUGLASS HOSPITAL (O, 148 beds) 789 Central Avenue, Dover, NH, Zip 3820; tel. 603/742–5252; Gregory J. Walker, Chief Executive Officer
Web address: www.wdhospital.com

Owned, leased, sponsored:	14 hospitals	3421 beds
Contract–managed:	0 hospitals	0 beds
Totals:	14 hospitals	3421 beds

★5415: PEACEHEALTH (CO)
1115 SE 164th Avenue, Vancouver, WA, Zip 98683; tel. 360/729–1000; Elizabeth Dunne, President and Chief Executive Officer
(Moderately Centralized Health System)

ALASKA: PEACEHEALTH KETCHIKAN MEDICAL CENTER (L, 50 beds) 3100 Tongass Avenue, Ketchikan, AK, Zip 99901–5746; tel. 907/225–5171; Edward E. Freysinger, Chief Administrative Officer
Web address: www.peacehealth.org

OREGON: PEACEHEALTH COTTAGE GROVE COMMUNITY MEDICAL CENTER (O, 14 beds) 1515 Village Drive, Cottage Grove, OR, Zip 97424–9700; tel. 541/942–0511; Tim Herrmann, R.N., Administrator
Web address: www.peacehealth.org

For explanation of codes following names, see page B2.
★ Indicates Type III membership in the American Hospital Association.

PEACEHEALTH PEACE HARBOR MEDICAL CENTER (O, 21 beds) 400 Ninth Street, Florence, OR, Zip 97439–7398; tel. 541/997–8412; Jason F. Hawkins, Chief Administrative Officer

PEACEHEALTH SACRED HEART MEDICAL CENTER UNIVERSITY DISTRICT (O, 104 beds) 1255 Hilyard Street, Eugene, OR, Zip 97401–3700, Mailing Address: P.O. Box 10905, Zip 97440–2905, tel. 541/686–7300; Mary Anne McMurren, R.N., Chief Administrative Officer
Web address: www.peacehealth.org

PEACEHEALTH SACRED HEART MEDICAL CENTER AT RIVERBEND (O, 379 beds) 3333 Riverbend Drive, Springfield, OR, Zip 97477–8800; tel. 541/222–7300; Mary E. Kingston, FACHE, R.N., Chief Executive
Web address: www.peacehealth.org

WASHINGTON: PEACEHEALTH PEACE ISLAND MEDICAL CENTER (O, 10 beds) 1117 Spring Street, Friday Harbor, WA, Zip 98250–9782; tel. 360/378–2141; Merry Ann Keane, Chief Administrative Officer

PEACEHEALTH SOUTHWEST MEDICAL CENTER (O, 412 beds) 400 NE Mother Joseph Place, Vancouver, WA, Zip 98664–3200, Mailing Address: P.O. Box 1600, Zip 98668–1600, tel. 360/256–2000; Sean Gregory, Chief Executive
Web address: www.peacehealth.org

PEACEHEALTH ST. JOHN MEDICAL CENTER (O, 180 beds) 1615 Delaware Street, Longview, WA, Zip 98632–2367, Mailing Address: P.O. Box 3002, Zip 98632–0302, tel. 360/414–2000; Cherelle Montanye–Ireland, Chief Administrative Officer

PEACEHEALTH ST. JOSEPH MEDICAL CENTER (O, 225 beds) 2901 Squalicum Parkway, Bellingham, WA, Zip 98225–1851; tel. 360/734–5400; Dale Zender, President Hospital Services NW
Web address: www.peacehealth.org

PEACEHEALTH UNITED GENERAL MEDICAL CENTER (C, 25 beds) 2000 Hospital Drive, Sedro–Woolley, WA, Zip 98284–4327; tel. 360/856–6021; Christopher Johnston, Chief Administrative Officer
Web address: www.peacehealth.org/united–general

Owned, leased, sponsored:	9 hospitals	1395 beds
Contract–managed:	1 hospitals	25 beds
Totals:	10 hospitals	1420 beds

0989: PENN STATE HERSHEY HEALTH SYSTEM (NP)
500 University Drive, Hershey, PA, Zip 17033–2360; tel. 717/531–8521; A. Craig. Hillemeier, M.D., Chief Executive Officer
(Independent Hospital System)

PENNSYLVANIA: PENN STATE HEALTH ST. JOSEPH (O, 144 beds) 2500 Bernville Road, Reading, PA, Zip 19605–9453, Mailing Address: P.O. Box 316, Zip 19603–0316, tel. 610/378–2000; John R. Morahan, President and Chief Executive Officer
Web address: www.thefutureofhealthcare.org

PENN STATE MILTON S. HERSHEY MEDICAL CENTER (O, 530 beds) 500 University Drive, Hershey, PA, Zip 17033–2360, Mailing Address: P.O. Box 850, Zip 17033–0850, tel. 717/531–8521; A. Craig. Hillemeier, M.D., Chief Executive Officer

Owned, leased, sponsored:	2 hospitals	674 beds
Contract–managed:	0 hospitals	0 beds
Totals:	2 hospitals	674 beds

★0314: PHOEBE PUTNEY HEALTH SYSTEM (NP)
417 Third Avenue, Albany, GA, Zip 31701–1943; tel. 229/312–1000; Joel Wernick, President and Chief Executive Officer
(Independent Hospital System)

GEORGIA: PHOEBE PUTNEY MEMORIAL HOSPITAL (O, 449 beds) 417 West Third Avenue, Albany, GA, Zip 31701–1943, Mailing Address: P.O. Box 3770, Zip 31706–3770, tel. 229/312–4100; Joel Wernick, President and Chief Executive Officer

PHOEBE SUMTER MEDICAL CENTER (O, 44 beds) 126 Highway, 280 West, Americus, GA, Zip 31719, Mailing Address: 126 Highway 280 West, Zip 31719, tel. 229/924–6011; Brandi Lunneborg, Chief Executive Officer
Web address: www.phoebesumter.org

PHOEBE WORTH MEDICAL CENTER (O, 18 beds) 807 South Isabella Street, Sylvester, GA, Zip 31791–7554, Mailing Address: P.O. Box 545, Zip 31791–0545, tel. 229/776–6961; Kim Gilman, Chief Executive Officer

SOUTHWEST GEORGIA REGIONAL MEDICAL CENTER (O, 25 beds) 361 Randolph Street, Cuthbert, GA, Zip 39840–6127; tel. 229/732–2181; Kim Gilman, Chief Executive Officer and Chief Nursing Officer
Web address: www.phoebeputney.com/

Owned, leased, sponsored:	4 hospitals	536 beds
Contract–managed:	0 hospitals	0 beds
Totals:	4 hospitals	536 beds

0043: PHYSICIANS FOR HEALTHY HOSPITALS (IO)
1117 East Devonshire Avenue, Hemet, CA, Zip 92543–3083; tel. 951/652–2811; Joel M. Bergenfeld, Chief Executive Officer

CALIFORNIA: HEMET VALLEY MEDICAL CENTER (O, 238 beds) 1117 East Devonshire Avenue, Hemet, CA, Zip 92543–3083; tel. 951/652–2811; Dan C. McLaughlin, Chief Hospital Executive Officer
Web address: www.physiciansforhealthyhospitals.com

MENIFEE VALLEY MEDICAL CENTER (O, 74 beds) 28400 McCall Boulevard, Sun City, CA, Zip 92585–9537; tel. 951/679–8888; Dan C. McLaughlin, Chief Executive Officer

Owned, leased, sponsored:	2 hospitals	312 beds
Contract–managed:	0 hospitals	0 beds
Totals:	2 hospitals	312 beds

0310: PIEDMONT HEALTHCARE (NP)
1800 Howell Mill Road NW, Suite 850, Roswell, GA, Zip 30076, Atlanta, tel. 404/425–1314; Kevin Brown, President and Chief Executive Officer
(Moderately Centralized Health System)

GEORGIA: PIEDMONT ATHENS REGIONAL MEDICAL CENTER (O, 343 beds) 1199 Prince Avenue, Athens, GA, Zip 30606–2797; tel. 706/475–7000; Charles A. Peck, M.D., President and Chief Executive Officer
Web address: https://www.piedmont.org/locations/piedmont–athens

PIEDMONT COLUMBUS REGIONAL MIDTOWN (O, 550 beds) 710 Center Street, Columbus, GA, Zip 31901–1527, Mailing Address: P.O. Box 951, Zip 31902–0951, tel. 706/571–1000; M. Scott. Hill, President and Chief Executive Officer

PIEDMONT FAYETTE HOSPITAL (O, 210 beds) 1255 Highway 54 West, Fayetteville, GA, Zip 30214–4526; tel. 770/719–7000; Michael Burnett, Chief Executive Officer
Web address: www.piedmont.org

PIEDMONT HENRY HOSPITAL (L, 214 beds) 1133 Eagle's Landing Parkway, Stockbridge, GA, Zip 30281–5099; tel. 678/604–1000; Deborah Armstrong, Chief Executive Officer

PIEDMONT HOSPITAL (O, 510 beds) 1968 Peachtree Road NW, Atlanta, GA, Zip 30309–1281; tel. 404/605–5000; Patrick M. Battey, FACS, M.D., Chief Executive Officer
Web address: www.piedmont.org

PIEDMONT MOUNTAINSIDE HOSPITAL (O, 52 beds) 1266 Highway 515 South, Jasper, GA, Zip 30143–4872; tel. 706/692–2441; Denise Ray, Chief Executive Officer

PIEDMONT NEWNAN HOSPITAL (O, 146 beds) 745 Poplar Road, Newnan, GA, Zip 30265–1618; tel. 770/400–1000; Michael Robertson, Chief Executive Officer
Web address: www.piedmont.org/locations/piedmont–newnan/pnh–home

PIEDMONT NEWTON HOSPITAL (O, 103 beds) 5126 Hospital Drive, Covington, GA, Zip 30014–2567; tel. 770/786–7053; Eric Bour, M.D., FACS, Chief Executive Officer
Web address: www.newtonmedical.com

PIEDMONT ROCKDALE HOSPITAL (O, 138 beds) 1412 Milstead Avenue NE, Conyers, GA, Zip 30012–3877; tel. 770/918–3000; Richard Tanzella, Chief Executive Officer
Web address: www.rockdalemedicalcenter.org

For explanation of codes following names, see page B2.
★ Indicates Type III membership in the American Hospital Association.

© 2018 AHA Guide　　　　　Health Care Systems, Networks and Alliances　**B97**

Section B

PIEDMONT WALTON HOSPITAL (O, 77 beds) 2151 West Spring Street, Monroe, GA, Zip 30655–3115, Mailing Address: PO BOX 1346, Zip 30655–1346, tel. 770/267–8461; Michael Johnson, Chief Executive Officer

Owned, leased, sponsored:	10 hospitals	2343 beds
Contract–managed:	0 hospitals	0 beds
Totals:	10 hospitals	2343 beds

★0958: PIH HEALTH (NP)

12401 Washington Boulevard, Whittier, CA, Zip 90602–1006; tel. 562/698–0811; James R. West, President and Chief Executive Officer

(Moderately Centralized Health System)

CALIFORNIA: PIH HEALTH HOSPITAL – DOWNEY (O, 181 beds) 11500 Brookshire Avenue, Downey, CA, Zip 90241–4917; tel. 562/904–5000; James R. West, President and Chief Executive Officer
Web address: www.PIHHealth.org

PIH HEALTH HOSPITAL – WHITTIER (O, 212 beds) 12401 Washington Boulevard, Whittier, CA, Zip 90602–1099; tel. 562/698–0811; James R. West, President and Chief Executive Officer

Owned, leased, sponsored:	2 hospitals	393 beds
Contract–managed:	0 hospitals	0 beds
Totals:	2 hospitals	393 beds

★0617: POST ACUTE MEDICAL, LLC (IO)

1828 Good Hope Road, Suite 102, Enola, PA, Zip 17025–1233; tel. 717/731–9660; Anthony F. Misitano, President and Chief Executive Officer

(Independent Hospital System)

LOUISIANA: PAM SPECIALTY HOSPITAL OF COVINGTON (O, 58 beds) 20050 Crestwood Boulevard, Covington, LA, Zip 70433–5207; tel. 985/875–7525; J Cullen. Meyers, Chief Executive Officer

PAM SPECIALTY HOSPITAL OF HAMMOND (O, 40 beds) 42074 Veterans Avenue, Hammond, LA, Zip 70403–1408; tel. 985/902–8148; Nicholas Paul. Mendez, Chief Executive Officer
Web address: www.postacutemedical.com

OKLAHOMA: PAM REHABILITATION HOSPITAL OF TULSA (O, 41 beds) 10020 East 91st Street, Tulsa, OK, Zip 74133; tel. 918/893–2400; Thomas Biby, Chief Executive Officer

POST ACUTE MEDICAL SPECIALTY HOSPITAL OF TULSA (O, 60 beds) 3219 South 79th East Avenue, Tulsa, OK, Zip 74145–1343; tel. 918/663–8183; Kristopher Karns, Chief Executive Officer
Web address: www.postacutetulsa.com

PENNSYLVANIA: PAM SPECIALTY HOSPITAL OF WILKES–BARRE (O, 36 beds) 575 North River Street, 7th Floor, Wilkes Barre, PA, Zip 18702–2634; tel. 570/208–3310; Salvatore Aquilina, Chief Executive Officer
Web address: www.warmsprings.org/our–facilities/hospitals/post–acute–medical–specialty–hospital–wilkes–barre/

TEXAS: CUMBERLAND SURGICAL HOSPITAL (O, 9 beds) 5330 N. Loop 1604 W, San Antonio, TX, Zip 78249; tel. 210/877–8000; Paul B. Abraham, FACHE, Chief Executive Officer

PAM REHABILITATION HOSPITAL OF BEAUMONT (O, 61 beds) 3340 Plaza 10 Boulevard, Beaumont, TX, Zip 77707–2551; tel. 409/835–0835; Todd Lorenz, Chief Executive Officer
Web address: www.postacutemedical.com/our–facilities/outpatient–rehabilitation/rehabilitation–hospital–beaumont/

PAM REHABILITATION HOSPITAL OF VICTORIA (O, 26 beds) 101 James Coleman Drive, Victoria, TX, Zip 77904–3147; Shawn Todd, Chief Executive Officer
Web address: www.warmsprings.org/our–facilities/outpatient–rehabilitation/warm–springs–rehabilitation–center–victoria/

PAM SPECIALTY HOSPITAL OF CORPUS CHRISTI SOUTH (O, 74 beds) 6226 Saratoga Boulevard, Corpus Christi, TX, Zip 78414–3421; tel. 361/986–1600; Hector Bernal, Chief Executive Officer
Web address: www.postacutemedical.com

PAM SPECIALTY HOSPITAL OF VICTORIA NORTH (O, 26 beds) 102 Medical Drive, Victoria, TX, Zip 77904–3101; tel. 361/576–6200; Christina Adrean, Chief Executive Officer
Web address: www.warmsprings.org

PAM SPECIALTY HOSPITAL OF VICTORIA SOUTH (O, 23 beds) 506 East San Antonio Street, 3rd Floor, Victoria, TX, Zip 77901–6060; tel. 361/575–1445; Christina Adrean, Chief Executive Officer
Web address: www.warmsprings.org/our–facilities/hospitals/post–acute–medical–specialty–hospital–victoria/

POST ACUTE MEDICAL SPECIALTY HOSPITAL OF CORPUS CHRISTI – NORTH (O, 22 beds) 600 Elizabeth Street, 3rd Floor, Corpus Christi, TX, Zip 78404–2235; tel. 361/881–3223; Hector Bernal, Chief Executive Officer

POST ACUTE MEDICAL SPECIALTY HOSPITAL OF TEXARKANA – NORTH (O, 49 beds) 2400 St Michael Drive, 2nd Floor, Texarkana, TX, Zip 75503–2372; tel. 903/614–7600; Lorraine Murray, Chief Executive Officer
Web address: www.postacutemedical.com

POST ACUTE/WARM SPRINGS REHABILITATION HOSPITAL OF ALLEN (O, 39 beds) 1001 Raintree Circle, Allen, TX, Zip 75013–4912; tel. 972/908–2015; Bill Kaupas, Chief Executive Officer
Web address: www.warmsprings.org

POST ACUTE/WARM SPRINGS SPECIALTY HOSPITAL OF LULING (O, 34 beds) 200 Memorial Drive, Luling, TX, Zip 78648–3213; tel. 830/875–8400; Jana Kuykendall, Chief Executive Officer
Web address: www.warmsprings.org

POST ACUTE/WARM SPRINGS SPECIALTY HOSPITAL OF NEW BRAUNFELS (O, 40 beds) 1445 Hanz Drive, New Braunfels, TX, Zip 78130–2567; tel. 830/627–7600; Ashley Ondrusek, Chief Executive Officer
Web address: www.warmsprings.org/locations/hos/h1/

POST ACUTE/WARM SPRINGS SPECIALTY HOSPITAL OF SAN ANTONIO (O, 26 beds) 5418 N Loop 1604 W, San Antonio, TX, Zip 78247; tel. 210/921–3550; Kristen Lowe, Chief Executive Officer

WARM SPRINGS REHABILITATION HOSPITAL OF KYLE (O, 40 beds) 5980 Kyle Parkway, Kyle, TX, Zip 78640–2400; tel. 512/262–0821; Duke Saldivar, FACHE, Chief Executive Officer
Web address: www.warmsprings.org/our–facilities/outpatient–rehabilitation/warm–springs–rehabilitation–center–kyle/

WARM SPRINGS REHABILITATION HOSPITAL OF SAN ANTONIO (O, 139 beds) 5101 Medical Drive, San Antonio, TX, Zip 78229–4801; tel. 210/616–0100; Debra Bornmann, Chief Executive Officer

WISCONSIN: POST ACUTE MEDICAL SPECIALTY HOSPITAL OF MILWAUKEE (O, 56 beds) 5017 South 110Th Street, Greenfield, WI, Zip 53228–3131; tel. 414/427–8282; Paul E. Qualls, Chief Executive Officer
Web address: www.postacutemedical.com/

Owned, leased, sponsored:	20 hospitals	899 beds
Contract–managed:	0 hospitals	0 beds
Totals:	20 hospitals	899 beds

0240: PREFERRED MANAGEMENT CORPORATION (IO)

120 West MacArthur, Suite 121, Shawnee, OK, Zip 74804–2005; tel. 405/878–0202; Donald Freeman, President and Chief Executive Officer

(Independent Hospital System)

TEXAS: COLEMAN COUNTY MEDICAL CENTER (L, 25 beds) 310 South Pecos Street, Coleman, TX, Zip 76834–4159; tel. 325/625–2135; Clay Vogel, Administrator and Chief Executive Officer
Web address: www.colemantexas.org/hospital.html

COLLINGSWORTH GENERAL HOSPITAL (L, 13 beds) 1013 15th Street, Wellington, TX, Zip 79095–3703, Mailing Address: P.O. Box 1112, Zip 79095–1112, tel. 806/447–2521; Candy Powell, Administrator

CULBERSON HOSPITAL (L, 14 beds) Eisenhower–Farm Market Road 2185, Van Horn, TX, Zip 79855, Mailing Address: P.O. Box 609, Zip 79855–0609, tel. 432/283–2760; Jonathon Voelkel, Administrator
Web address: www.culbersonhospital.org

KIMBLE HOSPITAL (O, 15 beds) 349 Reid Road, Junction, TX, Zip 76849–3049; tel. 325/446–3321; William Barnes, FACHE, Administrator

MULESHOE AREA MEDICAL CENTER (L, 25 beds) 708 South First Street, Muleshoe, TX, Zip 79347–3627; tel. 806/272–4524; Dennis Fleenor, R.N., Administrator
Web address: www.mahdtx.org

PARMER MEDICAL CENTER (C, 15 beds) 1307 Cleveland Street, Friona, TX, Zip 79035–1121; tel. 806/250–2754; Gayla Quillin, Administrator
Web address: www.parmermedicalcenter.com

SABINE COUNTY HOSPITAL (L, 25 beds) 2301 Worth Street, Hemphill, TX, Zip 75948–7216, Mailing Address: P.O. Box 750, Zip 75948–0750, tel. 409/787–3300; Jerry Howell, Administrator

SCHLEICHER COUNTY MEDICAL CENTER (L, 14 beds) 102 North US Highway 277, Eldorado, TX, Zip 76936–4010; tel. 325/853–2507; Paul Burke, Administrator
Web address: www.scmc.us

Owned, leased, sponsored:	7 hospitals	131 beds
Contract–managed:	1 hospitals	15 beds
Totals:	8 hospitals	146 beds

★0977: PREMIER HEALTH (NP)

110 North Main Street Suite 390, Dayton, OH, Zip 45402–3720; tel. 937/499–9401; Mary H. Boosalis, President
(Centralized Physician/Insurance Health System)

OHIO: ATRIUM MEDICAL CENTER (O, 284 beds) One Medical Center Drive, Middletown, OH, Zip 45005–1066; tel. 513/424–2111; Michael Uhl, President
Web address: www.PremierHealth.com

MIAMI VALLEY HOSPITAL (O, 598 beds) One Wyoming Street, Dayton, OH, Zip 45409–2793; tel. 937/208–8000; Michael J. Maiberger, President
Web address: www.miamivalleyhospital.org

UPPER VALLEY MEDICAL CENTER (O, 93 beds) 3130 North County Road 25A, Troy, OH, Zip 45373–1309; tel. 937/440–4000; Thomas Parker, President
Web address: www.uvmc.com

Owned, leased, sponsored:	3 hospitals	975 beds
Contract–managed:	0 hospitals	0 beds
Totals:	3 hospitals	975 beds

★3505: PRESBYTERIAN HEALTHCARE SERVICES (NP)

9521 San Mateo Blvd. NE, Albuquerque, NM, Zip 87113, Mailing Address: P.O. Box 26666, Zip 87125–6666, tel. 505/841–1234; Dale Maxwell, Chief Executive Officer
(Centralized Physician/Insurance Health System)

NEW MEXICO: DR. DAN C. TRIGG MEMORIAL HOSPITAL (L, 10 beds) 301 East Miel De Luna Avenue, Tucumcari, NM, Zip 88401–3810, Mailing Address: P.O. Box 608, Zip 88401–0608, tel. 575/461–7000; Troy Clark, Interim Administrator
Web address: www.phs.org

LINCOLN COUNTY MEDICAL CENTER (L, 25 beds) 211 Sudderth Drive, Ruidoso, NM, Zip 88345–6043, Mailing Address: P.O. Box 8000, Zip 88355–8000, tel. 575/257–8200; Todd Oberheu, Administrator

PLAINS REGIONAL MEDICAL CENTER (O, 60 beds) 2100 North Doctor Martin Luther King Boulevard, Clovis, NM, Zip 88101–9412, Mailing Address: P.O. Box 1688, Zip 88102–1688, tel. 575/769–2141; Troy Clark, Interim Administrator
Web address: www.phs.org

PRESBYTERIAN ESPANOLA HOSPITAL (O, 46 beds) 1010 Spruce Street, Espanola, NM, Zip 87532–2746; tel. 505/753–7111; Brenda Romero, Administrator

PRESBYTERIAN HOSPITAL (O, 616 beds) 1100 Central Avenue SE, Albuquerque, NM, Zip 87106–4934, Mailing Address: P.O. Box 26666, Zip 87125–6666, tel. 505/841–1234; Devon Hyde, Vice President, Chief Administrative Officer
Web address: www.phs.org

SOCORRO GENERAL HOSPITAL (O, 19 beds) 1202 Highway 60 West, Socorro, NM, Zip 87801–3914, Mailing Address: P.O. Box 1009, Zip 87801–1009, tel. 575/835–1140; Veronica Pound, R.N., Administrator
Web address: www.phs.org

Owned, leased, sponsored:	6 hospitals	776 beds
Contract–managed:	0 hospitals	0 beds
Totals:	6 hospitals	776 beds

★0357: PRIME HEALTHCARE (IO)

3300 East Guasti Road, Ontario, CA, Zip 91761–8655; tel. 909/235–4400; Prem Reddy, M.D., Chairman, President and Chief Executive Officer
(Moderately Centralized Health System)

ALABAMA: RIVERVIEW REGIONAL MEDICAL CENTER (O, 280 beds) 600 South Third Street, Gadsden, AL, Zip 35901–5399; tel. 256/543–5200; John Langlois, Chief Executive Officer

CALIFORNIA: ALVARADO HOSPITAL MEDICAL CENTER (O, 306 beds) 6655 Alvarado Road, San Diego, CA, Zip 92120–5208; tel. 619/287–3270; Robin Gomez, R.N., MSN, Administrator
Web address: www.alvaradohospital.com

CENTINELA HOSPITAL MEDICAL CENTER (O, 369 beds) 555 East Hardy Street, Inglewood, CA, Zip 90301–4011, Mailing Address: P.O. Box 720, Zip 90312–6720, tel. 310/673–4660; Linda Bradley, Chief Executive Officer

CHINO VALLEY MEDICAL CENTER (O, 112 beds) 5451 Walnut Avenue, Chino, CA, Zip 91710–2672; tel. 909/464–8600; James M. Lally, D.O., President and Chief Medical Officer
Web address: www.cvmc.com

DESERT VALLEY HOSPITAL (O, 110 beds) 16850 Bear Valley Road, Victorville, CA, Zip 92395–5795; tel. 760/241–8000; Fred Hunter, R.N., Chief Executive Officer
Web address: www.dvmc.com

ENCINO HOSPITAL MEDICAL CENTER (O, 80 beds) 16237 Ventura Boulevard, Encino, CA, Zip 91436–2272; tel. 818/995–5000; Bockhi Park, Chief Executive Officer

GARDEN GROVE HOSPITAL AND MEDICAL CENTER (O, 167 beds) 12601 Garden Grove Boulevard, Garden Grove, CA, Zip 92843–1959; tel. 714/537–5160; Richard M. Rowe, PharmD, Chief Executive Officer
Web address: www.gardengrovehospital.com

GLENDORA COMMUNITY HOSPITAL (O, 128 beds) 150 West Route 66, Glendora, CA, Zip 91740–6207; tel. 626/852–5000; Sofia Abrina, R.N., Chief Executive Officer
Web address: www.evhmc.com

HUNTINGTON BEACH HOSPITAL (O, 102 beds) 17772 Beach Boulevard, Huntington Beach, CA, Zip 92647–6896; tel. 714/843–5000; Richard M. Rowe, PharmD, Chief Executive Officer

LA PALMA INTERCOMMUNITY HOSPITAL (O, 140 beds) 7901 Walker Street, La Palma, CA, Zip 90623–1764; tel. 714/670–7400; Edward Mirzabegian, Chief Executive Officer
Web address: www.lapalmaintercommunityhospital.com

MONTCLAIR HOSPITAL MEDICAL CENTER (O, 102 beds) 5000 San Bernardino Street, Montclair, CA, Zip 91763–2326; tel. 909/625–5411; Sofia Abrina, R.N., Administrator

PARADISE VALLEY HOSPITAL (O, 256 beds) 2400 East Fourth Street, National City, CA, Zip 91950–2099; tel. 619/470–4321; Neerav Jadeja, Administrator
Web address: www.paradisevalleyhospital.org

SAN DIMAS COMMUNITY HOSPITAL (O, 101 beds) 1350 West Covina Boulevard, San Dimas, CA, Zip 91773–3219; tel. 909/599–6811; Parrish Scarboro, Chief Executive Officer
Web address: www.sandimashospital.com/

SHASTA REGIONAL MEDICAL CENTER (O, 113 beds) 1100 Butte Street, Redding, CA, Zip 96001–0853, Mailing Address: P.O. Box 496072, Zip 96049–6072, tel. 530/244–5400; Casey Fatch, Chief Executive Officer

SHERMAN OAKS HOSPITAL (O, 90 beds) 4929 Van Nuys Boulevard, Sherman Oaks, CA, Zip 91403–1777; tel. 818/981–7111; Bockhi Park, Chief Executive Officer
Web address: www.shermanoakshospital.com

For explanation of codes following names, see page B2.
★ Indicates Type III membership in the American Hospital Association.

Section B

WEST ANAHEIM MEDICAL CENTER (O, 219 beds) 3033 West Orange Avenue, Anaheim, CA, Zip 92804–3183; tel. 714/827–3000; Edward Mirzabegian, Chief Executive Officer
Web address: www.westanaheimmedctr.com

FLORIDA: LEHIGH REGIONAL MEDICAL CENTER (O, 88 beds) 1500 Lee Boulevard, Lehigh Acres, FL, Zip 33936–4835; tel. 239/369–2101; Gary C. Bell, LFACHE, Chief Executive Officer
Web address: www.lehighregional.com

GEORGIA: SOUTHERN REGIONAL MEDICAL CENTER (O, 331 beds) 11 Upper Riverdale Road SW, Riverdale, GA, Zip 30274–2615; tel. 770/991–8000; Charlotte W. Dupre, Chief Executive Officer

INDIANA: MONROE HOSPITAL (O, 32 beds) 4011 South Monroe Medical Park Boulevard, Bloomington, IN, Zip 47424; tel. 812/825–1111; Nancy Bakewell, Administrator
Web address: www.monroehospital.com

KANSAS: PROVIDENCE MEDICAL CENTER (O, 215 beds) 8929 Parallel Parkway, Kansas City, KS, Zip 66112–1689; tel. 913/596–4000; Karen Orr, Administrator and Chief Nursing Officer
Web address: www.providencekc.com

SAINT JOHN HOSPITAL (O, 58 beds) 3500 South Fourth Street, Leavenworth, KS, Zip 66048–5043; tel. 913/680–6000; Paula Ellis, Administrator

MICHIGAN: GARDEN CITY HOSPITAL (O, 164 beds) 6245 Inkster Road, Garden City, MI, Zip 48135–4001; tel. 734/421–3300; Saju George, Chief Executive Officer
Web address: www.gch.org

LAKE HURON MEDICAL CENTER (O, 119 beds) 2601 Electric Avenue, Port Huron, MI, Zip 48060–6518; tel. 810/985–1500; Jay De los Reyes, Chief Executive Officer
Web address: www.mymercy.us

MISSOURI: ST. JOSEPH MEDICAL CENTER (O, 116 beds) 1000 Carondelet Drive, Kansas City, MO, Zip 64114–4673; tel. 816/942–4400; Jodi Fincher, Administrator
Web address: www.stjosephkc.com/

ST. MARY'S MEDICAL CENTER (O, 83 beds) 201 Northwest R D Mize Road, Blue Springs, MO, Zip 64014–2518; tel. 816/228–5900; Steven D. Wilkinson, Interim Chief Executive Officer

NEVADA: NORTH VISTA HOSPITAL (O, 177 beds) 1409 East Lake Mead Boulevard, North Las Vegas, NV, Zip 89030–7197; tel. 702/649–7711; Vincenzo Variale, Chief Executive Officer
Web address: www.northvistahospital.com

SAINT MARY'S REGIONAL MEDICAL CENTER (O, 281 beds) 235 West Sixth Street, Reno, NV, Zip 89503–4548; tel. 775/770–3000; Helen Lidholm, Chief Executive Officer
Web address: www.saintmarysreno.org

NEW JERSEY: SAINT CLARE'S DENVILLE HOSPITAL (O, 412 beds) 25 Pocono Road, Denville, NJ, Zip 07834–2954; tel. 973/625–6000; Brian Finestein, Chief Executive Officer
Web address: www.saintclares.org

SAINT MICHAEL'S MEDICAL CENTER (O, 162 beds) 111 Central Avenue, Newark, NJ, Zip 07102–1909; tel. 973/877–5350; Robert C. Iannaccone, JD, Chief Executive Officer
Web address: www.smmcnj.org

ST. MARY'S GENERAL HOSPITAL (O, 287 beds) 350 Boulevard, Passaic, NJ, Zip 07055–2840; tel. 973/365–4300; Edward Condit, President and Chief Executive Officer

OHIO: COSHOCTON REGIONAL MEDICAL CENTER (O, 44 beds) 1460 Orange Street, Coshocton, OH, Zip 43812–2229, Mailing Address: P.O. Box 1330, Zip 43812–6330, tel. 740/622–6411; Stephanie Conn, Administrator and Chief Nursing Officer
Web address: https://www.coshoctonhospital.org

EAST LIVERPOOL CITY HOSPITAL (O, 120 beds) 425 West Fifth Street, East Liverpool, OH, Zip 43920–2498; tel. 330/385–7200; Keith Richardson, President and Chief Executive Officer
Web address: www.elch.org

PENNSYLVANIA: LOWER BUCKS HOSPITAL (O, 104 beds) 501 Bath Road, Bristol, PA, Zip 19007–3190; tel. 215/785–9200; Kelly M. Lorah, FACHE, Chief Executive Officer

ROXBOROUGH MEMORIAL HOSPITAL (O, 131 beds) 5800 Ridge Avenue, Philadelphia, PA, Zip 19128–1737; tel. 215/483–9900; Matt Shelak, Chief Executive Officer
Web address: www.roxboroughmemorial.com

SUBURBAN COMMUNITY HOSPITAL (O, 126 beds) 2701 DeKalb Pike, Norristown, PA, Zip 19401–1820; tel. 610/278–2000; Mark McLoone, Chief Executive Officer

RHODE ISLAND: LANDMARK MEDICAL CENTER (O, 140 beds) 115 Cass Avenue, Woonsocket, RI, Zip 02895–4731; tel. 401/769–4100; Michael Souza, Chief Executive Officer
Web address: www.landmarkmedcenter.com

REHABILITATION HOSPITAL OF RHODE ISLAND (O, 70 beds) 116 Eddie Dowling Highway, North Smithfield, RI, Zip 02896–7327; tel. 401/766–0800; Michael Souza, Chief Executive Officer

TEXAS: DALLAS MEDICAL CENTER (O, 71 beds) Seven Medical Parkway, Dallas, TX, Zip 75234–7823, Mailing Address: P.O. Box 819094, Zip 75381–9094, tel. 972/247–1000; J. T. Barnhart, Chief Executive Officer
Web address: www.dallasmedcenter.com

DALLAS REGIONAL MEDICAL CENTER (O, 127 beds) 1011 North Galloway Avenue, Mesquite, TX, Zip 75149–2433; tel. 214/320–7000; Glenda Newby, Chief Executive Officer

HARLINGEN MEDICAL CENTER (O, 88 beds) 5501 South Expressway 77, Harlingen, TX, Zip 78550–3213; tel. 956/365–1000; Brenda Ivory, Chief Executive Officer
Web address: www.harlingenmedicalcenter.com

KNAPP MEDICAL CENTER (O, 196 beds) 1401 East Eighth Street, Weslaco, TX, Zip 78596–6640, Mailing Address: P.O. Box 1110, Zip 78599–1110, tel. 956/968–8567; Rene Lopez, Chief Executive Officer
Web address: www.knappmed.org

MISSION REGIONAL MEDICAL CENTER (O, 228 beds) 900 South Bryan Road, Mission, TX, Zip 78572–6613; tel. 956/323–9103; Kane A. Dawson, Chief Executive Officer

PAMPA REGIONAL MEDICAL CENTER (O, 72 beds) One Medical Plaza, Pampa, TX, Zip 79065; tel. 806/665–3721; Edwin Leon, Chief Executive Officer
Web address: www.prmctx.com

Owned, leased, sponsored:	43 hospitals	6717 beds
Contract-managed:	0 hospitals	0 beds
Totals:	43 hospitals	6717 beds

★0153: PROHEALTH CARE, INC. (NP)
N17 W24100 Riverwood Drive, Suite 130, Waukesha, WI, Zip 53188; tel. 262/928–2242; Susan A. Edwards, President and Chief Executive Officer
(Centralized Health System)

WISCONSIN: OCONOMOWOC MEMORIAL HOSPITAL (O, 58 beds) 791 Summit Avenue, Oconomowoc, WI, Zip 53066–3896; tel. 262/569–9400; Susan A. Edwards, President and Chief Executive Officer
Web address: www.prohealthcare.org/locations/locations-v2-detail/?id=1123

WAUKESHA MEMORIAL HOSPITAL (O, 262 beds) 725 American Avenue, Waukesha, WI, Zip 53188–5099; tel. 262/928–1000; Susan A. Edwards, Chief Executive Officer

Owned, leased, sponsored:	2 hospitals	320 beds
Contract-managed:	0 hospitals	0 beds
Totals:	2 hospitals	320 beds

★0197: PROMEDICA HEALTH SYSTEM (NP)
100 Madison Avenue, Toledo, OH, Zip 43604–1516; tel. 567/585–9601; Randall D. Oostra, FACHE, President and Chief Executive Officer
(Centralized Health System)

For explanation of codes following names, see page B2.
★ Indicates Type III membership in the American Hospital Association.

Section B

MICHIGAN: PROMEDICA BIXBY HOSPITAL (O, 66 beds) 818 Riverside Avenue, Adrian, MI, Zip 49221–1446; tel. 517/265–0900; Julie Yaroch, D.O., President
Web address: www.promedica.org

PROMEDICA COLDWATER REGIONAL HOSPITAL (O, 62 beds) 274 East Chicago Street, Coldwater, MI, Zip 49036–2041; tel. 517/279–5400; Randy DeGroot, President and Chief Executive Officer

PROMEDICA HERRICK HOSPITAL (O, 25 beds) 500 East Pottawatamie Street, Tecumseh, MI, Zip 49286–2018; tel. 517/424–3000; Julie Yaroch, D.O., President
Web address: www.promedica.org

PROMEDICA MONROE REGIONAL HOSPITAL (O, 100 beds) 718 North Macomb Street, Monroe, MI, Zip 48162–7815; tel. 734/240–8400; Daniel Schwanke, President
Web address: www.promedica.org

OHIO: PROMEDICA BAY PARK HOSPITAL (O, 44 beds) 2801 Bay Park Drive, Oregon, OH, Zip 43616–4920; tel. 419/690–7900; Arturo Polizzi, President

PROMEDICA DEFIANCE REGIONAL HOSPITAL (O, 35 beds) 1200 Ralston Avenue, Defiance, OH, Zip 43512–1396; tel. 419/783–6955; Doug Bush, President
Web address: www.promedica.org

PROMEDICA FLOWER HOSPITAL (O, 295 beds) 5200 Harroun Road, Sylvania, OH, Zip 43560–2196; tel. 419/824–1444; Arturo Polizzi, President

PROMEDICA FOSTORIA COMMUNITY HOSPITAL (O, 25 beds) 501 Van Buren Street, Fostoria, OH, Zip 44830–1534, Mailing Address: P.O. Box 907, Zip 44830–0907, tel. 419/435–7734; Pamela M. Jensen, FACHE, President
Web address: www.promedica.org

PROMEDICA MEMORIAL HOSPITAL (O, 76 beds) 715 South Taft Avenue, Fremont, OH, Zip 43420–3237; tel. 419/332–7321; Pamela M. Jensen, FACHE, President

PROMEDICA TOLEDO HOSPITAL (O, 595 beds) 2142 North Cove Boulevard, Toledo, OH, Zip 43606–3896; tel. 419/291–4000; Arturo Polizzi, President
Web address: www.promedica.org

Owned, leased, sponsored:	10 hospitals	1323 beds
Contract–managed:	0 hospitals	0 beds
Totals:	10 hospitals	1323 beds

0230: PROMISE HEALTHCARE (IO)

999 Yamato Road, 3rd Floor, Boca Raton, FL, Zip 33431–4477; tel. 561/869–3100; Peter R. Baronoff, Chief Executive Officer
(Independent Hospital System)

ARIZONA: PROMISE HOSPITAL OF PHOENIX (L, 40 beds) 433 East 6th Street, Mesa, AZ, Zip 85203–7104; tel. 480/427–3000; Wayne Kinsey, Chief Executive Officer
Web address: www.promise–phoenix.com

CALIFORNIA: PROMISE HOSPITAL OF EAST LOS ANGELES (L, 177 beds) 443 South Soto Street, Los Angeles, CA, Zip 90033–4398; tel. 323/261–1181; Michael D. Kerr, Chief Executive Officer

PROMISE HOSPITAL OF SAN DIEGO (O, 100 beds) 5550 University Avenue, San Diego, CA, Zip 92105–2307; tel. 619/582–3800
Web address: www.promisesandiego.com

FLORIDA: PROMISE HOSPITAL OF FLORIDA AT THE VILLAGES (O, 40 beds) 5050 County Road 472, Oxford, FL, Zip 34484; tel. 352/689–6400; Hoyt Ross, Chief Executive Officer

PROMISE HOSPITAL OF FORT MYERS (O, 60 beds) 3050 Champion Ring Road, Fort Myers, FL, Zip 33905–5599; tel. 239/313–2900; Patrick G. Ryan, Chief Executive Officer
Web address: www.promisefortmyers.om

PROMISE HOSPITAL OF MIAMI (O, 60 beds) 14001 NW 82nd Avenue, Miami, FL, Zip 33158; tel. 786/609–9200; Charles Doten, Chief Executive Officer
Web address: www.promise–miami.com

KANSAS: PROMISE HOSPITAL OF OVERLAND PARK (O, 104 beds) 6509 West 103rd Street, Overland Park, KS, Zip 66212–1728; tel. 913/649–3701; Kristen Barrett, Chief Executive Officer
Web address: www.promise–overlandpark.com

LOUISIANA: PROMISE HOSPITAL BATON ROUGE – MAIN CAMPUS (L, 54 beds) 5130 Mancuso Lane, Baton Rouge, LA, Zip 70809–3583; tel. 225/490–9600; Kiley P. Cedotal, FACHE, Chief Executive Officer

PROMISE HOSPITAL OF BATON ROUGE – OCHSNER CAMPUS (O, 86 beds) 17000 Medical Center Drive, 3rd Floor, Baton Rouge, LA, Zip 70816–3246; tel. 225/236–5440; Kiley P. Cedotal, FACHE, Chief Executive Officer
Web address: www.promise–batonrougeochsner.com

PROMISE HOSPITAL OF LOUISIANA – SHREVEPORT CAMPUS (O, 146 beds) 1800 Irving Place, Shreveport, LA, Zip 71101–4608; tel. 318/425–4096; Rick Stockton, Chief Executive Officer

PROMISE HOSPITAL OF MISS LOU (O, 40 beds) 209 Front Street, Vidalia, LA, Zip 71373–2837; tel. 318/336–6500; Michael Harrell, R.N., Chief Executive Officer
Web address: www.promise–misslou.com

MISSISSIPPI: PROMISE HOSPITAL OF VICKSBURG (L, 33 beds) 1111 North Frontage Road, 2nd Floor, Vicksburg, MS, Zip 39180–5102; tel. 601/619–3526; Michael Harrell, R.N., Chief Executive Officer
Web address: www.promise–vicksburg.com

TEXAS: PROMISE HOSPITAL OF DALLAS (O, 62 beds) 7955 Harry Hines Boulevard, Dallas, TX, Zip 75235–3305; tel. 214/637–0000; Louis P. Bradley Jr, Chief Executive Officer

PROMISE HOSPITAL OF WICHITA FALLS (O, 31 beds) 1103 Grace Street, Wichita Falls, TX, Zip 76301–4414; tel. 940/720–6633; Louis P. Bradley Jr, Chief Executive Officer
Web address: www.promise–wichitafalls.com

UTAH: PROMISE HOSPITAL OF SALT LAKE (O, 41 beds) 8 Avenue, C Street, Salt Lake City, UT, Zip 84143; tel. 801/408–7110; Wayne Kinsey, Chief Executive Officer

Owned, leased, sponsored:	15 hospitals	1074 beds
Contract–managed:	0 hospitals	0 beds
Totals:	15 hospitals	1074 beds

1012: PROSPECT MEDICAL HOLDINGS (IO)

10780 California Route 2 #400, Los Angeles, CA, Zip 90025; tel. 714/796–5900; Mitchell Lew, M.D., President
(Moderately Centralized Health System)

CALIFORNIA: FOOTHILL REGIONAL MEDICAL CENTER (O, 80 beds) 14662 Newport Avenue, Tustin, CA, Zip 92780–6064; tel. 714/838–9600; Barbara Schneider, R.N., Chief Executive Officer
Web address: www.hfcis.cdph.ca.gov/longtermcare/Facility.aspx?fac=060000013

LOS ANGELES COMMUNITY HOSPITAL AT LOS ANGELES (O, 180 beds) 4081 East Olympic Boulevard, Los Angeles, CA, Zip 90023–3330; tel. 323/267–0477; Omar Ramirez, Chief Executive Officer
Web address: www.altacorp.com/altacorp/our–hospitals/lach–menu.html

SOUTHERN CALIFORNIA HOSPITAL AT CULVER CITY (O, 239 beds) 3828 Delmas Terrace, Culver City, CA, Zip 90232–6806; tel. 310/836–7000; Sean Fowler, Chief Executive Officer
Web address: www.sch–culvercity.com

SOUTHERN CALIFORNIA HOSPITAL AT HOLLYWOOD (O, 45 beds) 6245 De Longpre Avenue, Los Angeles, CA, Zip 90028–9001; tel. 323/462–2271; Bruce P. Grimshaw, FACHE, Chief Executive Officer

CONNECTICUT: MANCHESTER MEMORIAL HOSPITAL (O, 156 beds) 71 Haynes Street, Manchester, CT, Zip 06040–4188; tel. 860/646–1222; Michael F. Collins, Chief Executive Officer
Web address: www.echn.org

ROCKVILLE GENERAL HOSPITAL (O, 47 beds) 31 Union Street, Vernon, CT, Zip 06066–3160; tel. 860/872–0501; Michael F. Collins, Chief Executive Officer

WATERBURY HOSPITAL (O, 183 beds) 64 Robbins Street, Waterbury, CT, Zip 06708–2600; tel. 203/573–6000; Peter J. Adamo, President and Chief Executive Officer
Web address: www.waterburyhospital.org

Section B

For explanation of codes following names, see page B2.
★ Indicates Type III membership in the American Hospital Association.

NEW JERSEY: EAST ORANGE GENERAL HOSPITAL (O, 186 beds) 300 Central Avenue, East Orange, NJ, Zip 07018–2897; tel. 973/672–8400; Paige Dworak, FACHE, Chief Executive Officer
Web address: www.evh.org

PENNSYLVANIA: CROZER–CHESTER MEDICAL CENTER (O, 384 beds) One Medical Center Boulevard, Upland, PA, Zip 19013–3995; tel. 610/447–2000; Michael Curran, President

DELAWARE COUNTY MEMORIAL HOSPITAL (O, 168 beds) 501 North Lansdowne Avenue, Drexel Hill, PA, Zip 19026–1114; tel. 610/284–8100; Robert Haffey, R.N., President
Web address: www.crozer.org

RHODE ISLAND: ROGER WILLIAMS MEDICAL CENTER (O, 86 beds) 825 Chalkstone Avenue, Providence, RI, Zip 02908–4735; tel. 401/456–2000; Demetra Ouellette, President
Web address: www.rwmc.org/

ST. JOSEPH HEALTH SERVICES OF RHODE ISLAND (O, 125 beds) 200 High Service Avenue, North Providence, RI, Zip 02904–5199; tel. 401/456–3000; John J. Holiver, Chief Executive Officer

TEXAS: NIX HEALTH CARE SYSTEM (O, 246 beds) 414 Navarro Street, San Antonio, TX, Zip 78205–2516; tel. 210/271–1800; James A. Summersett III, FACHE, Interim Chief Executive Officer
Web address: www.nixhealth.com

Owned, leased, sponsored:	13 hospitals	2125 beds
Contract–managed:	0 hospitals	0 beds
Totals:	13 hospitals	2125 beds

★1006: PROVIDENCE ST. JOSEPH HEALTH (CO)
1801 Lind Avenue Southwest, 9016, Renton, WA, Zip 98057–9016, Mailing Address: 181 Lind Avenue Southwest, 9016, Zip 98057–9016, tel. 425/525–3698; Rodney F. Hochman, M.D., President and Chief Executive Officer
(Decentralized Health System)

ALASKA: PROVIDENCE ALASKA MEDICAL CENTER (O, 401 beds) 3200 Providence Drive, Anchorage, AK, Zip 99508–4615, Mailing Address: P.O. Box 196604, Zip 99519–6604, tel. 907/562–2211; Ella M. Goss, MSN, R.N., Chief Executive Officer
Web address: www.alaska.providence.org/locations/p/pamc

PROVIDENCE KODIAK ISLAND MEDICAL CENTER (L, 6 beds) 1915 East Rezanof Drive, Kodiak, AK, Zip 99615–6602; tel. 907/486–3281; Regina L. Bishop, Administrator

PROVIDENCE SEWARD MEDICAL CENTER (C, 46 beds) 417 First Avenue, Seward, AK, Zip 99664, Mailing Address: P.O. Box 365, Zip 99664–0365, tel. 907/224–5205; Joseph Fong, Administrator
Web address: www.providence.org

PROVIDENCE VALDEZ MEDICAL CENTER (C, 21 beds) 911 Meals Avenue, Valdez, AK, Zip 99686–0550, Mailing Address: P.O. Box 550, Zip 99686–0550, tel. 907/835–2249; Jeremy O'Neil, Administrator
Web address: www.providence.org/alaska

CALIFORNIA: HOAG MEMORIAL HOSPITAL PRESBYTERIAN (O, 470 beds) One Hoag Drive, Newport Beach, CA, Zip 92663–4120, Mailing Address: P.O. Box 6100, Zip 92658–6100, tel. 949/764–4624; Robert Braithwaite, President and Chief Executive Officer

MISSION HOSPITAL (O, 257 beds) 27700 Medical Center Road, Mission Viejo, CA, Zip 92691–6474; tel. 949/364–1400; Tarek Salaway, R.N., Chief Executive
Web address: www.mission4health.com

PROVIDENCE HOLY CROSS MEDICAL CENTER (O, 377 beds) 15031 Rinaldi Street, Mission Hills, CA, Zip 91345–1207; tel. 818/365–8051; Bernard Klein, M.D., Chief Executive
Web address: www.https://california.providence.org/holy–cross/Pages/default.aspx

PROVIDENCE LITTLE COMPANY OF MARY MEDICAL CENTER – TORRANCE (O, 386 beds) 4101 Torrance Boulevard, Torrance, CA, Zip 90503–4664; tel. 310/540–7676; Garry M. Olney, Chief Executive Officer

PROVIDENCE LITTLE COMPANY OF MARY MEDICAL CENTER SAN PEDRO (O, 318 beds) 1300 West Seventh Street, San Pedro, CA, Zip 90732–3505; tel. 310/832–3311; Garry M. Olney, Chief Executive Officer
Web address: www.https://california.providence.org/san–pedro

PROVIDENCE SAINT JOHN'S HEALTH CENTER (O, 228 beds) 2121 Santa Monica Boulevard, Santa Monica, CA, Zip 90404–2091; tel. 310/829–5511; Marcel C. Loh, FACHE, Chief Executive Officer

PROVIDENCE SAINT JOSEPH MEDICAL CENTER (O, 383 beds) 501 South Buena Vista Street, Burbank, CA, Zip 91505–4866; tel. 818/843–5111; Kelly Linden, Chief Executive Officer
Web address: www.providence.org

PROVIDENCE TARZANA MEDICAL CENTER (O, 249 beds) 18321 Clark Street, Tarzana, CA, Zip 91356–3521; tel. 818/881–0800; Dale Surowitz, Chief Executive

QUEEN OF THE VALLEY MEDICAL CENTER (O, 120 beds) 1000 Trancas Street, Napa, CA, Zip 94558–2906, Mailing Address: P.O. Box 2340, Zip 94558–0688, tel. 707/252–4411; Larry Coomes, Chief Executive Officer
Web address: www.thequeen.org

REDWOOD MEMORIAL HOSPITAL (O, 25 beds) 3300 Renner Drive, Fortuna, CA, Zip 95540–3198; tel. 707/725–3361; Roberta Luskin–Hawk, M.D., Chief Executive

SANTA ROSA MEMORIAL HOSPITAL (O, 278 beds) 1165 Montgomery Drive, Santa Rosa, CA, Zip 95405–4897, Mailing Address: P.O. Box 522, Zip 95402–0522, tel. 707/546–3210; Todd Salnas, President
Web address: www.stjosephhealth.org

ST. JOSEPH HOSPITAL (O, 153 beds) 2700 Dolbeer Street, Eureka, CA, Zip 95501–4799; tel. 707/445–8121; Roberta Luskin–Hawk, M.D., Chief Executive

ST. JOSEPH HOSPITAL (O, 379 beds) 1100 West Stewart Drive, Orange, CA, Zip 92868–3849, Mailing Address: P.O. Box 5600, Zip 92863–5600, tel. 714/633–9111; Jeremy Zoch, Chief Executive
Web address: www.sjo.org

ST. JUDE MEDICAL CENTER (O, 320 beds) 101 East Valencia Mesa Drive, Fullerton, CA, Zip 92835–3875; tel. 714/992–3000; Brian Helleland, Chief Executive Officer

ST. MARY MEDICAL CENTER (O, 212 beds) 18300 Highway 18, Apple Valley, CA, Zip 92307–2206, Mailing Address: P.O. Box 7025, Zip 92307–0725, tel. 760/242–2311; Alan H. Garrett, President and Chief Executive Officer
Web address: www.stmaryapplevalley.com/

MONTANA: GRANITE COUNTY MEDICAL CENTER (C, 25 beds) 310 Sansome Street, Philipsburg, MT, Zip 59858–0729, Mailing Address: P.O. Box 729, Zip 59858–0729, tel. 406/859–3271; Maria Stoppler, Chief Executive Officer
Web address: www.gcmedcenter.org/

PROVIDENCE ST. JOSEPH MEDICAL CENTER (O, 22 beds) 6 Thirteenth Avenue East, Polson, MT, Zip 59860–5315, Mailing Address: P.O. Box 1010, Zip 59860–1010, tel. 406/883–5377; Lynn Weddle, Interim Chief Executive Officer
Web address: www.saintjoes.org

ST. PATRICK HOSPITAL (O, 180 beds) 500 West Broadway, Missoula, MT, Zip 59802–4096, Mailing Address: P.O. Box 4587, Zip 59806–4587, tel. 406/543–7271; Joyce Dombrouski, R.N., Chief Executive Officer
Web address: www.montana.providence.org

OREGON: PROVIDENCE HOOD RIVER MEMORIAL HOSPITAL (O, 25 beds) 810 12th Street, Hood River, OR, Zip 97031–1587, Mailing Address: P.O. Box 149, Zip 97031–0055, tel. 541/386–3911; Jeanette Vieira, Chief Executive

PROVIDENCE MEDFORD MEDICAL CENTER (O, 138 beds) 1111 Crater Lake Avenue, Medford, OR, Zip 97504–6241; tel. 541/732–5000; Cindy Mayo, R.N., FACHE, Chief Executive
Web address: www.providence.org

PROVIDENCE MILWAUKIE HOSPITAL (O, 59 beds) 10150 SE 32nd Avenue, Milwaukie, OR, Zip 97222–6516; tel. 503/513–8300; Keith Hyde, Chief Executive

PROVIDENCE NEWBERG MEDICAL CENTER (O, 40 beds) 1001 Providence Drive, Newberg, OR, Zip 97132–7485; tel. 503/537–1555; Lorinda Van Zanten, MSN, Chief Executive
Web address: www.phsor.org

PROVIDENCE PORTLAND MEDICAL CENTER (O, 427 beds) 4805 NE Glisan Street, Portland, OR, Zip 97213–2933; tel. 503/215–5526; Krista Farnham, Chief Executive
Web address: www.providence.org

For explanation of codes following names, see page B2.
★ Indicates Type III membership in the American Hospital Association.

PROVIDENCE SEASIDE HOSPITAL (O, 25 beds) 725 South Wahanna Road, Seaside, OR, Zip 97138–7735; tel. 503/717–7000; Kendall Sawa, R.N., Chief Executive Officer
Web address: www.providence.org

PROVIDENCE ST. VINCENT MEDICAL CENTER (O, 487 beds) 9205 SW Barnes Road, Portland, OR, Zip 97225–6661; tel. 503/216–1234; Janice Burger, Chief Executive

PROVIDENCE WILLAMETTE FALLS MEDICAL CENTER (O, 111 beds) 1500 Division Street, Oregon City, OR, Zip 97045–1597; tel. 503/656–1631; Russ Reinhard, Chief Executive
Web address: www.providence.org/pwfmc

TEXAS: COVENANT CHILDREN'S HOSPITAL (O, 269 beds) 4015 22nd Place, Lubbock, TX, Zip 79410; tel. 806/725–1011; Amy Thompson, M.D., Chief Executive Officer
Web address: www.covenanthealth.org/About–Us/Facilities/Childrens–Hospital.aspx

COVENANT HOSPITAL PLAINVIEW (O, 68 beds) 2601 Dimmitt Road, Plainview, TX, Zip 79072–1833; tel. 806/296–5531; Robert Copeland, Interim Chief Executive Officer
Web address: www.covenantplainview.org

COVENANT HOSPITAL–LEVELLAND (L, 26 beds) 1900 South College Avenue, Levelland, TX, Zip 79336–6508; tel. 806/894–4963; Bruce White, Administrator

COVENANT MEDICAL CENTER (O, 394 beds) 3615 19th Street, Lubbock, TX, Zip 79410–1203, Mailing Address: P.O. Box 1201, Zip 79408–1201, tel. 806/725–0000; Walt Cathey, Chief Executive Officer
Web address: www.covenanthealth.org

COVENANT SPECIALTY HOSPITAL (O, 56 beds) 3815 20th Street, Lubbock, TX, Zip 79410–1235; tel. 806/725–9200; Ely Perea, Director and Chief Executive Officer

GRACE MEDICAL CENTER (O, 43 beds) 2412 50th Street, Lubbock, TX, Zip 79412–2494; tel. 806/788–4100; Vanessa Reasoner, Chief Executive Officer
Web address: www.gracehealthsystem.com

WASHINGTON: KADLEC REGIONAL MEDICAL CENTER (O, 260 beds) 888 Swift Boulevard, Richland, WA, Zip 99352–3514; tel. 509/946–4611; Reza Kaleel, Chief Administrative Officer
Web address: https://www.kadlec.org

PROVIDENCE CENTRALIA HOSPITAL (O, 91 beds) 914 S Scheuber RD, Centralia, WA, Zip 98531–9027, Mailing Address: 914 South Scheuber Road, Zip 98531–9027, tel. 360/736–2803; Medrice Coluccio, R.N., Southwest Region Chief Executive
Web address: www.providence.org

PROVIDENCE HOLY FAMILY HOSPITAL (O, 191 beds) 5633 North Lidgerwood Street, Spokane, WA, Zip 99208–1224; tel. 509/482–0111; Peggy M. Currie, R.N., Chief Operating Officer

PROVIDENCE MOUNT CARMEL HOSPITAL (O, 25 beds) 982 East Columbia Avenue, Colville, WA, Zip 99114–3352; tel. 509/685–5100; Ronald G. Rehn, Chief Executive Officer
Web address: www.mtcarmelhospital.org

PROVIDENCE REGIONAL MEDICAL CENTER EVERETT (O, 530 beds) 1321 Colby Avenue, Everett, WA, Zip 98201–1665, Mailing Address: P.O. Box 1147, Zip 98206–1147, tel. 425/261–2000; Kim Williams, R.N., MS, Chief Executive Officer

PROVIDENCE SACRED HEART MEDICAL CENTER & CHILDREN'S HOSPITAL (O, 719 beds) 101 West Eighth Avenue, Spokane, WA, Zip 99204–2364, Mailing Address: P.O. Box 2555, Zip 99220–2555, tel. 509/474–3131; Peggy M. Currie, R.N., Chief Operating Officer
Web address: www.shmc.org

PROVIDENCE ST. JOSEPH'S HOSPITAL (O, 55 beds) 500 East Webster Street, Chewelah, WA, Zip 99109–9523; tel. 509/935–8211; Ronald G. Rehn, Chief Executive Officer
Web address: www.washington.providence.org/hospitals/st-josephs–hospital/

PROVIDENCE ST. MARY MEDICAL CENTER (O, 92 beds) 401 West Poplar Street, Walla Walla, WA, Zip 99362–2846, Mailing Address: P.O. Box 1477, Zip 99362–0312, tel. 509/897–3320; Susan Blackburn, Chief Administrative Officer
Web address: www.washington.providence.org/hospitals/st-mary/

PROVIDENCE ST. PETER HOSPITAL (O, 350 beds) 413 Lilly Road NE, Olympia, WA, Zip 98506–5166; tel. 360/491–9480; Medrice Coluccio, R.N., Chief Executive Officer

ST. LUKE'S REHABILITATION INSTITUTE (O, 78 beds) 711 South Cowley Street, Spokane, WA, Zip 99202–1388; tel. 509/473–6000; Nancy Webster, Administrator and Chief Operating Officer
Web address: www.st-lukes.org

SWEDISH MEDICAL CENTER–CHERRY HILL CAMPUS (O, 227 beds) 500 17th Avenue, Seattle, WA, Zip 98122–5711; tel. 206/320–2000; June Altaras, R.N., Chief Executive Officer
Web address: www.swedish.org

SWEDISH MEDICAL CENTER–FIRST HILL (O, 659 beds) 747 Broadway, Seattle, WA, Zip 98122–4307; tel. 206/386–6000; June Altaras, R.N., Chief Executive Officer

SWEDISH/EDMONDS (O, 186 beds) 21601 76th Avenue West, Edmonds, WA, Zip 98026–7506; tel. 425/640–4000; Sarah Zabel, Vice President, Operations
Web address: www.swedish.org

SWEDISH/ISSAQUAH (O, 134 beds) 751 NE Blakely Drive, Issaquah, WA, Zip 98029–6201; tel. 425/313–4000; Guy Hudson, Chief Executive Officer

WHITMAN HOSPITAL AND MEDICAL CENTER (C, 25 beds) 1200 West Fairview Street, Colfax, WA, Zip 99111–9579; tel. 509/397–3435; Hank Hanigan, FACHE, Chief Executive Officer
Web address: www.whitmanhospital.org

Owned, leased, sponsored:	47 hospitals	10529 beds
Contract–managed:	4 hospitals	117 beds
Totals:	51 hospitals	10646 beds

★0011: PUERTO RICO DEPARTMENT OF HEALTH (NP)
Building 'A' – Medical Center, San Juan, PR, Zip 936, Mailing Address: Call Box 70184, Zip 936, tel. 787/765–2929; Rafael Rodriguez. Mercado, Secretary of Health
(Independent Hospital System)

PUERTO RICO: CARDIOVASCULAR CENTER OF PUERTO RICO AND THE CARIBBEAN (O, 154 beds) Americo Miranda Centro Medico, San Juan, PR, Zip 936, Mailing Address: P.O. Box 366528, Zip 00936–6528, tel. 787/754–8500; Carlos Cabrera, Executive Director

HOSPITAL UNIVERSITARIO DR. RAMON RUIZ ARNAU (O, 101 beds) Avenue Laurel #100, Santa Juanita, Bayamon, PR, Zip 956; tel. 787/787–5151; Prudencio A. Laureano, Chief Executive Officer
Web address: www.salud.gov.pr/Dept–de–Salud/Pages/Nuestros–Hospitales.aspx

UNIVERSITY HOSPITAL (O, 220 beds) Nineyas 869 Rio Piedras, San Juan, PR, Zip 922, Mailing Address: P.O. Box 2116, Zip 922, tel. 787/754–0101; Jorge Matta. Gonzalez, Executive Director

UNIVERSITY PEDIATRIC HOSPITAL (O, 145 beds) Barrio Monacenno, Carretera 22, Rio Piedras, PR, Zip 935, Mailing Address: P.O. Box 191079, San Juan, Zip 00910–1070, tel. 787/777–3535; Gloria Hernandez, Executive Director
Web address: www.md.rcm.upr.edu/pediatrics/university_pediatric_hospital.php

Owned, leased, sponsored:	4 hospitals	620 beds
Contract–managed:	0 hospitals	0 beds
Totals:	4 hospitals	620 beds

★0002: QHR (IO)
1573 Mallory Lane, Suite 200, Brentwood, TN, Zip 37027, Mailing Address: 1573 Mallory Lane, Suite 200, Zip 37027, tel. 800/233–1470; Bob Vento, President and Chief Executive Officer
(Decentralized Health System)

ARKANSAS: GREAT RIVER MEDICAL CENTER (C, 73 beds) 1520 North Division Street, Blytheville, AR, Zip 72315–1448, Mailing Address: P.O. Box 108, Zip 72316–0108, tel. 870/838–7300; Chris Lee. Raymer, R.N., MSN, Chief Executive Officer

SOUTH MISSISSIPPI COUNTY REGIONAL MEDICAL CENTER (C, 25 beds) 611 West Lee Avenue, Osceola, AR, Zip 72370–3001, Mailing Address: P.O. Box 108, Blytheville, Zip 72316–0108, tel. 870/563–7000; Chris Lee. Raymer, R.N., MSN, Chief Executive Officer
Web address: www.mchsys.org

For explanation of codes following names, see page B2.
★ Indicates Type III membership in the American Hospital Association.

CALIFORNIA: BEAR VALLEY COMMUNITY HOSPITAL (C, 30 beds) 41870 Garstin Drive, Big Bear Lake, CA, Zip 92315, Mailing Address: P.O. Box 1649, Zip 92315-1649, tel. 909/866-6501; John P. Friel, Chief Executive Officer
Web address: www.bvchd.com

COLORADO: ARKANSAS VALLEY REGIONAL MEDICAL CENTER (C, 106 beds) 1100 Carson Avenue, La Junta, CO, Zip 81050-2799; tel. 719/383-6000; Lynn Crowell, Chief Executive Officer

COMMUNITY HOSPITAL (C, 78 beds) 2351 G Road, Grand Junction, CO, Zip 81505; tel. 970/242-0920; Chris Thomas, FACHE, President and Chief Executive Officer
Web address: www.yourcommunityhospital.com

MONTROSE MEMORIAL HOSPITAL (C, 60 beds) 800 South Third Street, Montrose, CO, Zip 81401-4212; tel. 970/249-2211; James R. Kiser II, Chief Executive Officer

PIONEERS MEDICAL CENTER (C, 40 beds) 100 Pioneers Medical Center Drive, Meeker, CO, Zip 81641-3181; tel. 970/878-5047; Kenneth Harman, Chief Executive Officer
Web address: www.pioneershospital.org

PROWERS MEDICAL CENTER (C, 25 beds) 401 Kendall Drive, Lamar, CO, Zip 81052-3993; tel. 719/336-4343; Craig Loveless, Chief Executive Officer

FLORIDA: HENDRY REGIONAL MEDICAL CENTER (C, 25 beds) 524 West Sagamore Avenue, Clewiston, FL, Zip 33440-3514; tel. 863/902-3000; R D Williams, Chief Executive Officer
Web address: www.hendryregional.org

JACKSON HOSPITAL (C, 68 beds) 4250 Hospital Drive, Marianna, FL, Zip 32446-1917, Mailing Address: P.O. Box 1608, Zip 32447-5608, tel. 850/526-2200; James Platt, Chief Executive Officer

IDAHO: GRITMAN MEDICAL CENTER (C, 25 beds) 700 South Main Street, Moscow, ID, Zip 83843-3056; tel. 208/882-4511; Kara Besst, President and Chief Executive Officer
Web address: www.gritman.org

STEELE MEMORIAL MEDICAL CENTER (C, 18 beds) 203 South Daisy Street, Salmon, ID, Zip 83467-4709; tel. 208/756-5600; Jeanine Gentry, Chief Executive Officer

ILLINOIS: CRAWFORD MEMORIAL HOSPITAL (C, 63 beds) 1000 North Allen Street, Robinson, IL, Zip 62454-1167; tel. 618/544-3131; Douglas Florkowski, Chief Executive Officer
Web address: www.crawfordmh.net

LAWRENCE COUNTY MEMORIAL HOSPITAL (C, 25 beds) 2200 West State Street, Lawrenceville, IL, Zip 62439-1852; tel. 618/943-1000; Donald Robbins, Chief Executive Officer

INDIANA: SULLIVAN COUNTY COMMUNITY HOSPITAL (C, 25 beds) 2200 North Section Street, Sullivan, IN, Zip 47882-7523, Mailing Address: P.O. Box 10, Zip 47882-0010, tel. 812/268-4311; Michelle Franklin, Chief Executive Officer
Web address: www.schosp.com

IOWA: BOONE COUNTY HOSPITAL (C, 25 beds) 1015 Union Street, Boone, IA, Zip 50036-4821; tel. 515/432-3140; Joseph S. Smith, Chief Executive Officer
Web address: www.boonehospital.com

FORT MADISON COMMUNITY HOSPITAL (C, 50 beds) 5445 Avenue 'O', Fort Madison, IA, Zip 52627-9611, Mailing Address: P.O. Box 174, Zip 52627-0174, tel. 319/372-6530; Jeremy Alexander, Chief Executive Officer
Web address: www.fmchosp.com

KANSAS: GREELEY COUNTY HEALTH SERVICES (C, 50 beds) 506 Third Street, Tribune, KS, Zip 67879-9684, Mailing Address: P.O. Box 338, Zip 67879-0338, tel. 620/376-4221; Burke Kline, Chief Executive Officer

NEOSHO MEMORIAL REGIONAL MEDICAL CENTER (C, 25 beds) 629 South Plummer, Chanute, KS, Zip 66720-1928, Mailing Address: P.O. Box 426, Zip 66720-0426, tel. 620/431-4000; Dennis Franks, FACHE, Chief Executive Officer
Web address: www.nmrmc.com

WILSON MEDICAL CENTER (C, 15 beds) 2600 Ottawa Road, Neodesha, KS, Zip 66757-1897, Mailing Address: P.O. Box 360, Zip 66757-0360, tel. 620/325-2611; Dennis R. Shelby, Chief Executive Officer
Web address: www.wilsonmedical.org

KENTUCKY: CALDWELL MEDICAL CENTER (C, 25 beds) 100 Medical Center Drive, Princeton, KY, Zip 42445-2430, Mailing Address: P.O. Box 410, Zip 42445-0410, tel. 270/365-0300; Daniel Odegaard, FACHE, Chief Executive Officer
Web address: www.caldwellhosp.org

JENNIE STUART MEDICAL CENTER (C, 139 beds) 320 West 18th Street, Hopkinsville, KY, Zip 42240-1965, Mailing Address: P.O. Box 2400, Zip 42241-2400, tel. 270/887-0100; Eric A. Lee, President and Chief Executive Officer

MONROE COUNTY MEDICAL CENTER (C, 49 beds) 529 Capp Harlan Road, Tompkinsville, KY, Zip 42167-1840; tel. 270/487-9231; Vicky McFall, Chief Executive Officer
Web address: www.mcmccares.com

OHIO COUNTY HOSPITAL (C, 30 beds) 1211 Main Street, Hartford, KY, Zip 42347-1619; tel. 270/298-7411; Blaine Pieper, Chief Executive Officer

LOUISIANA: FRANKLIN FOUNDATION HOSPITAL (C, 22 beds) 1097 Northwest Boulevard, Franklin, LA, Zip 70538-3407, Mailing Address: P.O. Box 577, Zip 70538-0577, tel. 337/828-0760; Stephanie Guidry, Chief Executive Officer
Web address: www.franklinfoundation.org

MAINE: CARY MEDICAL CENTER (C, 49 beds) 163 Van Buren Road, Suite 1, Caribou, ME, Zip 04736-3567; tel. 207/498-3111; Kris A. Doody, R.N., Chief Executive Officer

PENOBSCOT VALLEY HOSPITAL (C, 25 beds) 7 Transalpine Road, Lincoln, ME, Zip 04457-4222, Mailing Address: P.O. Box 368, Zip 04457-0368, tel. 207/794-3321; Gary R. Poquette, FACHE, Chief Executive Officer
Web address: www.pvhme.org

MICHIGAN: ALLEGAN GENERAL HOSPITAL (C, 25 beds) 555 Linn Street, Allegan, MI, Zip 49010-1524; tel. 269/673-8424; Gerald J. Barbini, President and Chief Executive Officer
Web address: www.aghosp.org

HAYES GREEN BEACH MEMORIAL HOSPITAL (C, 25 beds) 321 East Harris Street, Charlotte, MI, Zip 48813-1629; tel. 517/543-1050; Matthew Rush, FACHE, President and Chief Executive Officer

STURGIS HOSPITAL (C, 49 beds) 916 Myrtle Street, Sturgis, MI, Zip 49091-2326; tel. 269/651-7824; Robert J. LaBarge, President and Chief Executive Officer
Web address: www.sturgishospital.com

THREE RIVERS HEALTH (C, 60 beds) 701 South Health Parkway, Three Rivers, MI, Zip 49093-8352; tel. 269/278-1145; David A. Shannon, Interim Chief Executive Officer

MISSISSIPPI: KING'S DAUGHTERS MEDICAL CENTER (C, 79 beds) 427 Highway 51 North, Brookhaven, MS, Zip 39601-2350, Mailing Address: P.O. Box 948, Zip 39602-0948, tel. 601/833-6011; Alvin Hoover, FACHE, Chief Executive Officer
Web address: www.kdmc.org

NEBRASKA: PHELPS MEMORIAL HEALTH CENTER (C, 25 beds) 1215 Tibbals Street, Holdrege, NE, Zip 68949-1255; tel. 308/995-2211; Mark Harrel, Chief Executive Officer
Web address: www.phelpsmemorial.com

NEW MEXICO: CIBOLA GENERAL HOSPITAL (C, 25 beds) 1016 East Roosevelt Avenue, Grants, NM, Zip 87020-2118; tel. 505/287-4446; Thomas Whelan, Chief Executive Officer

HOLY CROSS HOSPITAL (C, 29 beds) 1397 Weimer Road, Taos, NM, Zip 87571-6253; tel. 575/758-8883; William D. Patten Jr, Chief Executive Officer
Web address: www.taoshospital.org

SIERRA VISTA HOSPITAL (C, 15 beds) 800 East Ninth Avenue, Truth or Consequences, NM, Zip 87901-1961; tel. 575/894-2111; David Faulkner, Interim Chief Executive Officer

NORTH CAROLINA: NORTHERN HOSPITAL OF SURRY COUNTY (C, 108 beds) 830 Rockford Street, Mount Airy, NC, Zip 27030-5365, Mailing Address: P.O. Box 1101, Zip 27030-1101, tel. 336/719-7000; Chris A. Lumsden, President and Chief Executive Officer
Web address: www.northernhospital.com

OHIO: KNOX COMMUNITY HOSPITAL (C, 65 beds) 1330 Coshocton Road, Mount Vernon, OH, Zip 43050-1495; tel. 740/393-9000; Bruce D. White, Chief Executive Officer
Web address: www.kch.org

WOOSTER COMMUNITY HOSPITAL (C, 152 beds) 1761 Beall Avenue, Wooster, OH, Zip 44691-2342; tel. 330/263-8100; William E. Sheron, Chief Executive Officer

OKLAHOMA: PERRY MEMORIAL HOSPITAL (C, 26 beds) 501 North 14th Street, Perry, OK, Zip 73077-5099; tel. 580/336-3541; Steven E. Taylor, Chief Executive Officer
Web address: www.pmh-ok.org

For explanation of codes following names, see page B2.
★ Indicates Type III membership in the American Hospital Association.

PENNSYLVANIA: CLARION HOSPITAL (C, 66 beds) One Hospital Drive, Clarion, PA, Zip 16214–8501; tel. 814/226–9500; Al Taylor, Interim Chief Executive Officer

SOUTH CAROLINA: ABBEVILLE AREA MEDICAL CENTER (C, 25 beds) 420 Thomson Circle, Abbeville, SC, Zip 29620–5656, Mailing Address: P.O. Box 887, Zip 29620–0887, tel. 864/366–5011; Howard D. Turner, Chief Executive Officer
Web address: www.abbevilleareamc.com

NEWBERRY COUNTY MEMORIAL HOSPITAL (C, 54 beds) 2669 Kinard Street, Newberry, SC, Zip 29108–2911, Mailing Address: P.O. Box 497, Zip 29108–0497, tel. 803/276–7570; Bruce A. Baldwin, Chief Executive Officer
Web address: www.newberryhospital.org

REGIONAL MEDICAL CENTER (C, 283 beds) 3000 St Matthews Road, Orangeburg, SC, Zip 29118–1442; tel. 803/395–2200; Charles E. Williams, FACHE, President and Chief Executive Officer
Web address: www.trmchealth.org

TIDELANDS GEORGETOWN MEMORIAL HOSPITAL (C, 136 beds) 606 Black River Road, Georgetown, SC, Zip 29440–3368, Mailing Address: Drawer 421718, Zip 29442–4203, tel. 843/527–7000; Bruce P. Bailey, Chief Executive Officer

TIDELANDS WACCAMAW COMMUNITY HOSPITAL (C, 169 beds) 4070 Highway 17 Bypass, Murrells Inlet, SC, Zip 29576–5033, Mailing Address: P O Drawer 3350, Zip 29576–2673, tel. 843/652–1000; Bruce P. Bailey, Chief Executive Officer
Web address: www.tidelandswaccamawcommunity.org

SOUTH DAKOTA: HURON REGIONAL MEDICAL CENTER (C, 30 beds) 172 Fourth Street SE, Huron, SD, Zip 57350–2590; tel. 605/353–6200; David Dick, Chief Executive Officer

TENNESSEE: MACON COMMUNITY HOSPITAL (C, 25 beds) 204 Medical Drive, Lafayette, TN, Zip 37083–1799, Mailing Address: P.O. Box 378, Zip 37083–0378, tel. 615/666–2147; Thomas J. Kidd, CPA, Chief Executive Officer
Web address: www.mcgh.net

RHEA MEDICAL CENTER (C, 25 beds) 9400 Rhea County Highway, Dayton, TN, Zip 37321–7922; tel. 423/775–1121; David Bixler, Chief Executive Officer
Web address: www.rheamedical.org

TEXAS: FIRST BAPTIST MEDICAL CENTER (C, 18 beds) 8111 Meadow Road, Dallas, TX, Zip 75231; tel. 469/329–3700; Harold Gaskill III, M.D., Chief Executive Officer

GONZALES HEALTHCARE SYSTEMS (C, 33 beds) 1110 Sarah Dewitt Drive, Gonzales, TX, Zip 78629–3311, Mailing Address: P.O. Box 587, Zip 78629–0587, tel. 830/672–7581; John R. Hughson, Chief Executive Officer
Web address: www.gonzaleshealthcare.com

MATAGORDA REGIONAL MEDICAL CENTER (C, 58 beds) 104 7th Street, Bay City, TX, Zip 77414–4853; tel. 979/245–6383; Bryan Prochnow, Interim Chief Executive Officer
Web address: www.matagordaregional.org

VERMONT: NORTHWESTERN MEDICAL CENTER (C, 70 beds) 133 Fairfield Street, Saint Albans, VT, Zip 05478–1726; tel. 802/524–5911; Jill Berry. Bowen, Chief Executive Officer

WASHINGTON: TRIOS HEALTH (C, 111 beds) 900 South Auburn Street, Kennewick, WA, Zip 99336–5621, Mailing Address: P.O. Box 6128, Zip 99336–0128, tel. 509/586–6111; John H. Solheim, Chief Executive Officer
Web address: www.trioshealth.org

WEST VIRGINIA: SUMMERSVILLE REGIONAL MEDICAL CENTER (C, 153 beds) 400 Fairview Heights Road, Summersville, WV, Zip 26651–9308; tel. 304/872–2891; Karen A. Fiducia, FACHE, President and Chief Executive Officer

WYOMING: MEMORIAL HOSPITAL OF CARBON COUNTY (C, 25 beds) 2221 West Elm Street, Rawlins, WY, Zip 82301–5108, Mailing Address: P.O. Box 460, Zip 82301–0460, tel. 307/324–2221; Dana Barnett, Chief Executive Officer
Web address: www.imhcc.com

WEST PARK HOSPITAL (C, 112 beds) 707 Sheridan Avenue, Cody, WY, Zip 82414–3409; tel. 307/527–7501; Douglas A. McMillan, Administrator and Chief Executive Officer
Web address: www.westparkhospital.org

Owned, leased, sponsored:	0 hospitals	0 beds
Contract–managed:	57 hospitals	3266 beds
Totals:	57 hospitals	3266 beds

★**0040: QUEEN'S HEALTH SYSTEMS** (NP)
1301 Punchbowl Street, Honolulu, HI, Zip 96813–2402; tel. 808/535–5448; Arthur A. Ushijima, FACHE, President and Chief Executive Officer
(Moderately Centralized Health System)

HAWAII: MOLOKAI GENERAL HOSPITAL (O, 15 beds) 280 Home Olu Place, Kaunakakai, HI, Zip 96748–0408, Mailing Address: P.O. Box 408, Zip 96748–0408, tel. 808/553–5331; Janice Kalanihuia, President
Web address: www.queens.org

NORTH HAWAII COMMUNITY HOSPITAL (O, 35 beds) 67–1125 Mamalahoa Highway, Kamuela, HI, Zip 96743–8496; tel. 808/885–4444; Cynthia Kamikawa, R.N., MSN, President
Web address: www.nhch.com

THE QUEEN'S MEDICAL CENTER (O, 517 beds) 1301 Punchbowl Street, Honolulu, HI, Zip 96813–2499; tel. 808/691–5100; Arthur A. Ushijima, FACHE, President
Web address: www.queensmedicalcenter.org

Owned, leased, sponsored:	3 hospitals	567 beds
Contract–managed:	0 hospitals	0 beds
Totals:	3 hospitals	567 beds

★**0981: QUORUM HEALTH** (IO)
1573 Mallory Lane, Suite 100, Brentwood, TN, Zip 37027; tel. 615/221–1400; Robert D. Fish, Chief Executive Officer
(Moderately Centralized Health System)

ALABAMA: DEKALB REGIONAL MEDICAL CENTER (O, 115 beds) 200 Medical Center Drive, Fort Payne, AL, Zip 35968–3458, Mailing Address: P.O. Box 680778, Zip 35968–1608, tel. 256/845–3150; Patrick Trammell, Chief Executive Officer
Web address: www.dekalbregional.com

ARKANSAS: FORREST CITY MEDICAL CENTER (L, 55 beds) 1601 Newcastle Road, Forrest City, AR, Zip 72335–2218; tel. 870/261–0000; Kevin Decker, Chief Executive Officer

HELENA REGIONAL MEDICAL CENTER (L, 105 beds) 1801 Martin Luther King Drive, Helena, AR, Zip 72342, Mailing Address: P.O. Box 788, Zip 72342–0788, tel. 870/338–5800; Leah Osbahr, M.P.H., Chief Executive Officer
Web address: www.helenarmc.com

CALIFORNIA: BARSTOW COMMUNITY HOSPITAL (L, 30 beds) 820 East Mountain View Street, Barstow, CA, Zip 92311–3004; tel. 760/256–1761; Matthew H. Blevins, Chief Executive Officer
Web address: www.barstowhospital.com

BEAR VALLEY COMMUNITY HOSPITAL (O, 30 beds) 41870 Garstin Drive, Big Bear Lake, CA, Zip 92315, Mailing Address: P.O. Box 1649, Zip 92315–1649, tel. 909/866–6501; John P. Friel, Chief Executive Officer

WATSONVILLE COMMUNITY HOSPITAL (O, 106 beds) 75 Nielson Street, Watsonville, CA, Zip 95076–2468; tel. 831/724–4741; Audra Earle, FACHE, Chief Executive Officer
Web address: www.watsonvillehospital.com

COLORADO: ARKANSAS VALLEY REGIONAL MEDICAL CENTER (O, 106 beds) 1100 Carson Avenue, La Junta, CO, Zip 81050–2799; tel. 719/383–6000; Lynn Crowell, Chief Executive Officer

GEORGIA: FANNIN REGIONAL HOSPITAL (O, 50 beds) 2855 Old Highway 5, Blue Ridge, GA, Zip 30513–6248; tel. 706/632–3711; David S. Sanders, Chief Executive Officer
Web address: www.fanninregionalhospital.com

ILLINOIS: CROSSROADS COMMUNITY HOSPITAL (O, 47 beds) 8 Doctors Park Road, Mount Vernon, IL, Zip 62864–6224; tel. 618/244–5500; Amanda J. Basso, Chief Executive Officer

GALESBURG COTTAGE HOSPITAL (O, 119 beds) 695 North Kellogg Street, Galesburg, IL, Zip 61401–2885; tel. 309/343–8131; James Flynn, Chief Executive Officer
Web address: www.cottagehospital.com

GATEWAY REGIONAL MEDICAL CENTER (O, 268 beds) 2100 Madison Avenue, Granite City, IL, Zip 62040–4799; tel. 618/798–3000; M Edward. Cunningham, Chief Executive Officer

For explanation of codes following names, see page B2.
★ Indicates Type III membership in the American Hospital Association.

HEARTLAND REGIONAL MEDICAL CENTER (O, 92 beds) 3333 West DeYoung, Marion, IL, Zip 62959–5884; tel. 618/998–7000; Melisa Adkins, Chief Executive Officer
Web address: www.heartlandregional.com

METROSOUTH MEDICAL CENTER (O, 285 beds) 12935 South Gregory Street, Blue Island, IL, Zip 60406–2470; tel. 708/597–2000; John D. Baird, Chief Executive Officer

RED BUD REGIONAL HOSPITAL (O, 140 beds) 325 Spring Street, Red Bud, IL, Zip 62278–1105; tel. 618/282–3831; Shane Watson, Chief Executive Officer
Web address: www.redbudregional.com

UNION COUNTY HOSPITAL (L, 47 beds) 517 North Main Street, Anna, IL, Zip 62906–1696; tel. 618/833–4511; James R. Farris, FACHE, Chief Executive Officer
Web address: www.unioncountyhospital.com

VISTA MEDICAL CENTER EAST (O, 190 beds) 1324 North Sheridan Road, Waukegan, IL, Zip 60085–2161; tel. 847/360–3000; Norman F. Stephens, Interim Chief Executive Officer
Web address: www.vistahealth.com

KENTUCKY: KENTUCKY RIVER MEDICAL CENTER (L, 54 beds) 540 Jett Drive, Jackson, KY, Zip 41339–9622; tel. 606/666–6000; John Ballard, Ph.D., Chief Executive Officer
Web address: www.kentuckyrivermc.com

PAUL B. HALL REGIONAL MEDICAL CENTER (O, 72 beds) 625 James S. Trimble Boulevard, Paintsville, KY, Zip 41240–0000; tel. 606/789–3511; Deborah Trimble, R.N., Chief Executive Officer

THREE RIVERS MEDICAL CENTER (O, 90 beds) 2485 Highway 644, Louisa, KY, Zip 41230–9242, Mailing Address: P.O. Box 769, Zip 41230–0769, tel. 606/638–9451; Greg Kiser, Chief Executive Officer
Web address: www.threeriversmedicalcenter.com

MICHIGAN: ALLEGAN GENERAL HOSPITAL (O, 25 beds) 555 Linn Street, Allegan, MI, Zip 49010–1524; tel. 269/673–8424; Gerald J. Barbini, President and Chief Executive Officer
Web address: www.aghosp.org

NEVADA: MESA VIEW REGIONAL HOSPITAL (O, 25 beds) 1299 Bertha Howe Avenue, Mesquite, NV, Zip 89027–7500; tel. 702/346–8040; Ned Hill, Chief Executive Officer
Web address: www.mesaviewhospital.com

NEW MEXICO: ALTA VISTA REGIONAL HOSPITAL (O, 54 beds) 104 Legion Drive, Las Vegas, NM, Zip 87701–4804; tel. 505/426–3500; Caleb F. O'Rear, Chief Executive Officer

MIMBRES MEMORIAL HOSPITAL (O, 25 beds) 900 West Ash Street, Deming, NM, Zip 88030–4098, Mailing Address: P.O. Box 710, Zip 88031–0710, tel. 575/546–5800; Steve Westenhofer, Interim Chief Executive Officer
Web address: www.mimbresmemorial.com

NORTH CAROLINA: MARTIN GENERAL HOSPITAL (L, 49 beds) 310 South McCaskey Road, Williamston, NC, Zip 27892–2150, Mailing Address: P.O. Box 1128, Zip 27892–1128, tel. 252/809–6300; John Jacobson, Interim Chief Executive Officer
Web address: www.martingeneral.com

OREGON: MCKENZIE–WILLAMETTE MEDICAL CENTER (O, 113 beds) 1460 'G' Street, Springfield, OR, Zip 97477–4197; tel. 541/726–4400; David Elgarico, Chief Executive Officer

SOUTH CAROLINA: ABBEVILLE AREA MEDICAL CENTER (O, 25 beds) 420 Thomson Circle, Abbeville, SC, Zip 29620–5656, Mailing Address: P.O. Box 887, Zip 29620–0887, tel. 864/366–5011; Howard D. Turner, Chief Executive Officer
Web address: www.abbevilleareamc.com

TENNESSEE: HENDERSON COUNTY COMMUNITY HOSPITAL (O, 45 beds) 200 West Church Street, Lexington, TN, Zip 38351–2038; tel. 731/968–3646; Pamela W. Roberts, Chief Executive Officer
Web address: www.hendersoncchospital.com

MCKENZIE REGIONAL HOSPITAL (O, 35 beds) 161 Hospital Drive, McKenzie, TN, Zip 38201–1636; tel. 731/352–5344; Michael Morrical, Chief Executive Officer

TEXAS: BIG BEND REGIONAL MEDICAL CENTER (O, 25 beds) 2600 Highway 118 North, Alpine, TX, Zip 79830–2002; tel. 432/837–3447; Rick Flores, Interim Chief Executive Officer
Web address: www.bigbendhealthcare.com

SCENIC MOUNTAIN MEDICAL CENTER (O, 82 beds) 1601 West 11th Place, Big Spring, TX, Zip 79720–4198; tel. 432/263–1211; Emma Krabill, Chief Executive Officer
Web address: www.smmccares.com

UTAH: MOUNTAIN WEST MEDICAL CENTER (O, 44 beds) 2055 North Main Street, Tooele, UT, Zip 84074–9819; tel. 435/843–3600; Philip Eaton, Interim Chief Executive Officer

WYOMING: EVANSTON REGIONAL HOSPITAL (O, 42 beds) 190 Arrowhead Drive, Evanston, WY, Zip 82930–9266; tel. 307/789–3636; Jeremy Davis, Chief Executive Officer
Web address: www.evanstonregionalhospital.com

Owned, leased, sponsored:	32 hospitals	2590 beds
Contract-managed:	0 hospitals	0 beds
Totals:	32 hospitals	2590 beds

0996: RCCH HEALTHCARE PARTNERS (IO)
103 Continental Place Ste 200, Brentwood, TN, Zip 37027–1042; tel. 615/844–9800; Martin S. Rash, Chief Executive Officer
(Moderately Centralized Health System)

ALABAMA: ELIZA COFFEE MEMORIAL HOSPITAL (O, 278 beds) 205 Marengo Street, Florence, AL, Zip 35630–6033, Mailing Address: P.O. Box 818, Zip 35631–0818, tel. 256/768–9191; Russell Pigg, Chief Executive Officer
Web address: www.chgroup.org

SHOALS HOSPITAL (O, 137 beds) 201 Avalon Avenue, Muscle Shoals, AL, Zip 35661–2805, Mailing Address: P.O. Box 3359, Zip 35662–3359, tel. 256/386–1600; Kidada Hawkins, Chief Executive Officer
Web address: www.shoalshospital.com

ARIZONA: CANYON VISTA MEDICAL CENTER (L, 100 beds) 5700 East Highway 90, Sierra Vista, AZ, Zip 85635–9110; tel. 520/263–2000; Bob Gomes, FACHE, President and Chief Executive Officer

ARKANSAS: NATIONAL PARK MEDICAL CENTER (O, 208 beds) 1910 Malvern Avenue, Hot Springs, AR, Zip 71901–7799; tel. 501/321–1000; Jerry D. Mabry, FACHE, Chief Executive Officer
Web address: www.nationalparkmedical.com

SAINT MARY'S REGIONAL MEDICAL CENTER (O, 141 beds) 1808 West Main Street, Russellville, AR, Zip 72801–2724; tel. 479/968–2841; James Davidson, Chief Executive Officer

IDAHO: ST. JOSEPH REGIONAL MEDICAL CENTER (O, 123 beds) 415 Sixth Street, Lewiston, ID, Zip 83501–2431; tel. 208/743–2511; Blain Claypool, Chief Executive Officer
Web address: www.sjrmc.org

IOWA: OTTUMWA REGIONAL HEALTH CENTER (O, 101 beds) 1001 Pennsylvania Avenue, Ottumwa, IA, Zip 52501–2186; tel. 641/684–2300; Philip J. Noel III, Chief Executive Officer
Web address: www.ottumwaregionalhealth.com

MONTANA: COMMUNITY MEDICAL CENTER (O, 135 beds) 2827 Fort Missoula Road, Missoula, MT, Zip 59804–7408; tel. 406/728–4100; Dean French, M.D., Chief Executive Officer
Web address: www.communitymed.org

OHIO: CMH REGIONAL HEALTH SYSTEM (O, 119 beds) 610 West Main Street, Wilmington, OH, Zip 45177–2125; tel. 937/382–6611; Lance Beus, Chief Executive Officer

OKLAHOMA: SOUTHWESTERN MEDICAL CENTER (O, 178 beds) 5602 SW Lee Boulevard, Lawton, OK, Zip 73505–9635; tel. 580/531–4700; Larry Rodgers, Chief Executive Officer
Web address: www.swmconline.com

OREGON: WILLAMETTE VALLEY MEDICAL CENTER (O, 88 beds) 2700 SE Stratus Avenue, McMinnville, OR, Zip 97128–6255; tel. 503/472–6131; Peter A. Hofstetter, Chief Executive Officer
Web address: www.willamettevalleymedical.com/

SOUTH CAROLINA: CAROLINA PINES REGIONAL MEDICAL CENTER (O, 105 beds) 1304 West Bobo Newsom Highway, Hartsville, SC, Zip 29550–4710; tel. 843/339–2100; William Little, Chief Executive Officer

---

For explanation of codes following names, see page B2.
★ Indicates Type III membership in the American Hospital Association.

B106 Health Care Systems, Networks and Alliances

© 2018 AHA Guide

KERSHAWHEALTH (O, 119 beds) 1315 Roberts Street, Camden, SC, Zip 29020–3737, Mailing Address: P.O. Box 7003, Zip 29021–7003, tel. 803/432–4311; Terry Gunn, FACHE, Chief Executive Officer
Web address: www.kershawhealth.com

TEXAS: PARIS REGIONAL MEDICAL CENTER (O, 165 beds) 865 Deshong Drive, Paris, TX, Zip 75460–9313, Mailing Address: P.O. Box 9070, Zip 75461–9070, tel. 903/785–4521; Steve Hyde, Chief Executive Officer
Web address: www.https://parisregionalmedical.com/

WASHINGTON: CAPITAL MEDICAL CENTER (O, 85 beds) 3900 Capital Mall Drive SW, Olympia, WA, Zip 98502–5026; tel. 360/754–5858; Mark S. Turner, Chief Executive Officer

LOURDES COUNSELING CENTER (O, 20 beds) 1175 Carondelet Drive, Richland, WA, Zip 99354–3300; tel. 509/943–9104; Mark Gregson, Interim Chief Executive Officer
Web address: www.lourdeshealth.net

LOURDES MEDICAL CENTER (O, 53 beds) 520 North Fourth Avenue, Pasco, WA, Zip 99301–5257; tel. 509/547–7704; John Serle, FACHE, President and Chief Executive Officer
Web address: www.lourdeshealth.net

Owned, leased, sponsored:	17 hospitals	2155 beds
Contract–managed:	0 hospitals	0 beds
Totals:	17 hospitals	2155 beds

★8495: REGIONAL HEALTH (NP)
353 Fairmont Boulevard, Rapid City, SD, Zip 57701–7375, Mailing Address: P.O. Box 6000, Zip 57709–6000, tel. 605/719–1000; Paulette Davidson, FACHE, President and Chief Executive Officer
(Moderately Centralized Health System)

SOUTH DAKOTA: CUSTER REGIONAL HOSPITAL (L, 87 beds) 1039 Montgomery Street, Custer, SD, Zip 57730–1397; tel. 605/673–2229; Mark C. Schmidt, President
Web address: www.regionalhealth.com

LEAD–DEADWOOD REGIONAL HOSPITAL (O, 9 beds) 61 Charles Street, Deadwood, SD, Zip 57732–1303; tel. 605/717–6000; Mark C. Schmidt, President
Web address: www.regionalhealth.com

PHILIP HEALTH SERVICES (C, 48 beds) 503 West Pine Street, Philip, SD, Zip 57567–3300, Mailing Address: P.O. Box 790, Zip 57567–0790, tel. 605/859–2511; Jeremy Schultes, Administrator and Chief Executive Officer

RAPID CITY REGIONAL HOSPITAL (O, 366 beds) 353 Fairmont Boulevard, Rapid City, SD, Zip 57701–7393, Mailing Address: P.O. Box 6000, Zip 57709–6000, tel. 605/755–1000; John Pierce, Acting President
Web address: www.regionalhealth.com

SPEARFISH REGIONAL HOSPITAL (O, 35 beds) 1440 North Main Street, Spearfish, SD, Zip 57783–1504; tel. 605/644–4000; Thomas Worsley, Chief Executive Officer
Web address: www.regionalhealth.com/Our-Locations/Regional-Hospitals/Spearfish-Regional-Hospital.aspx

STURGIS REGIONAL HOSPITAL (O, 109 beds) 949 Harmon Street, Sturgis, SD, Zip 57785–2452; tel. 605/720–2400; Mark Schulte, FACHE, President

WYOMING: CROOK COUNTY MEDICAL SERVICES DISTRICT (C, 16 beds) 713 Oak Street, Sundance, WY, Zip 82729, Mailing Address: P.O. Box 517, Zip 82729–0517, tel. 307/283–3501; Nathan Hough, Chief Executive Officer
Web address: www.ccmsd.org/

WESTON COUNTY HEALTH SERVICES (C, 66 beds) 1124 Washington Boulevard, Newcastle, WY, Zip 82701–2972; tel. 307/746–4491; Maureen K. Cadwell, Chief Executive Officer
Web address: www.wchs-wy.org

Owned, leased, sponsored:	5 hospitals	606 beds
Contract–managed:	3 hospitals	130 beds
Totals:	8 hospitals	736 beds

1019: REGIONAL MEDICAL CENTER (NP)
400 East 10th Street, Anniston, AL, Zip 36207–4716; tel. 256/235–5121; Louis A. Bass, President and Chief Executive Officer
(Independent Hospital System)

ALABAMA: RMC ANNISTON (O, 276 beds) 400 East Tenth Street, Anniston, AL, Zip 36207–4716; Mailing Address: P.O. Box 2208, Zip 36202–2208, tel. 256/235–5121; Louis A. Bass, Chief Executive Officer
Web address: www.rmccares.org

RMC–STRINGFELLOW MEMORIAL HOSPITAL (O, 29 beds) 301 East 18th Street, Anniston, AL, Zip 36207–3952; tel. 256/235–8900; Joe Weaver, Chief Executive Officer

Owned, leased, sponsored:	2 hospitals	305 beds
Contract–managed:	0 hospitals	0 beds
Totals:	2 hospitals	305 beds

★2625: RENOWN HEALTH (NP)
50 West Liberty Street, Suite 1100, Reno, NV, Zip 89501–1951; tel. 775/982–5529; Anthony D. Slonim, M.D., Dr.PH, President and Chief Executive Officer
(Centralized Health System)

NEVADA: RENOWN REGIONAL MEDICAL CENTER (O, 661 beds) 1155 Mill Street, Reno, NV, Zip 89502–1576; tel. 775/982–4100; Erik Olson, Chief Executive Officer
Web address: www.renown.org

RENOWN REHABILITATION HOSPITAL (O, 62 beds) 1495 Mill Street, Reno, NV, Zip 89502–1479; tel. 775/982–3500; Chris Nicholas, Administrator of Rehabilitation Hospital
Web address: www.renown.org

RENOWN SOUTH MEADOWS MEDICAL CENTER (O, 76 beds) 10101 Double 'R' Boulevard, Reno, NV, Zip 89521–5931; tel. 775/982–7000; Siri Nelson, Chief Executive Officer

Owned, leased, sponsored:	3 hospitals	799 beds
Contract–managed:	0 hospitals	0 beds
Totals:	3 hospitals	799 beds

★0964: RIDGEVIEW MEDICAL CENTER (IO)
500 South Maple Street, Waconia, MN, Zip 55387–1752; tel. 952/442–2191; Michael Phelps, President and Chief Executive Officer
(Independent Hospital System)

MINNESOTA: RIDGEVIEW LE SUEUR MEDICAL CENTER (O, 9 beds) 621 South Fourth Street, Le Sueur, MN, Zip 56058–2298; tel. 507/665–3375; Pamela Williams, Vice President
Web address: www.mvhc.org

RIDGEVIEW MEDICAL CENTER (O, 108 beds) 500 South Maple Street, Waconia, MN, Zip 55387–1791; tel. 952/442–2191; Michael Phelps, President and Chief Executive Officer

RIDGEVIEW SIBLEY MEDICAL CENTER (L, 16 beds) 601 West Chandler Street, Arlington, MN, Zip 55307–2127; tel. 507/964–2271
Web address: www.sibleymedical.org

Owned, leased, sponsored:	3 hospitals	133 beds
Contract–managed:	0 hospitals	0 beds
Totals:	3 hospitals	133 beds

4810: RIVERSIDE HEALTH SYSTEM (NP)
701 Town Center Drive, Suite 1000, Newport News, VA, Zip 23606–4286; tel. 757/534–7000; William B. Downey, President and Chief Executive Officer
(Centralized Health System)

VIRGINIA: RIVERSIDE DOCTORS' HOSPITAL WILLIAMSBURG (O, 14 beds) 1500 Commonwealth Avenue, Williamsburg, VA, Zip 23185–5229; tel. 757/585–2200; Steve C. McCary, Administrator

RIVERSIDE REGIONAL MEDICAL CENTER (O, 307 beds) 500 J Clyde Morris Boulevard, Newport News, VA, Zip 23601–1929; tel. 757/594–2000; Michael J. Doucette, Senior Vice President and Administrator
Web address: https://www.riversideonline.com/rrmc/index.cfm

For explanation of codes following names, see page B2.
★ Indicates Type III membership in the American Hospital Association.

Section B

RIVERSIDE SHORE MEMORIAL HOSPITAL (O, 24 beds) 204800 Market Street, Onancoke, VA, Zip 23417, Mailing Address: P.O. Box 17, Nassawadox, Zip 23413–0017, tel. 757/302–2100; John Peterman, Vice President and Administrator

RIVERSIDE TAPPAHANNOCK HOSPITAL (O, 18 beds) 618 Hospital Road, Tappahannock, VA, Zip 22560–5000; tel. 804/443–3311; Esther Muscari. Desimini, Administrator
Web address: www.riverside–online.com

RIVERSIDE WALTER REED HOSPITAL (O, 30 beds) 7519 Hospital Drive, Gloucester, VA, Zip 23061–4178, Mailing Address: P.O. Box 1130, Zip 23061–1130, tel. 804/693–8800; Esther Muscari. Desimini, Interim Administrator

Owned, leased, sponsored:	5 hospitals	393 beds
Contract-managed:	0 hospitals	0 beds
Totals:	5 hospitals	393 beds

★0046: ROCHESTER REGIONAL HEALTH (NP)
1425 Portland Avenue, 5th Floor, Rochester, NY, Zip 14621–3001; tel. 585/922–4000; Eric Bieber, M.D., President and Chief Executive Officer
(Centralized Health System)

NEW YORK: CLIFTON SPRINGS HOSPITAL AND CLINIC (O, 181 beds) 2 Coulter Road, Clifton Springs, NY, Zip 14432–1189; tel. 315/462–9561; Dustin Riccio, M.D., President
Web address: www.cliftonspringshospital.org

NEWARK–WAYNE COMMUNITY HOSPITAL (O, 289 beds) 1200 Driving Park Avenue, Newark, NY, Zip 14513–1057, Mailing Address: P.O. Box 111, Zip 14513–0111, tel. 315/332–2022; Dustin Riccio, M.D., President Eastern Region

ROCHESTER GENERAL HOSPITAL (O, 528 beds) 1425 Portland Avenue, Rochester, NY, Zip 14621–3099; tel. 585/922–4000; Nancy M. . Tinsley, R.N., President
Web address: www.rochestergeneral.org

UNITED MEMORIAL MEDICAL CENTER (O, 133 beds) 127 North Street, Batavia, NY, Zip 14020–1631; tel. 585/343–6030; Daniel P. Ireland, FACHE, President

UNITY HOSPITAL (O, 454 beds) 1555 Long Pond Road, Rochester, NY, Zip 14626–4182; tel. 585/723–7000; Douglas Stewart, PsyD, President
Web address: www.unityhealth.org

Owned, leased, sponsored:	5 hospitals	1585 beds
Contract-managed:	0 hospitals	0 beds
Totals:	5 hospitals	1585 beds

0348: RURAL COMMUNITY HOSPITALS OF AMERICA (IO)
1100 Main Street, Suite 2350, Kansas City, MO, Zip 64105–5186; tel. 816/474–7800; Lawrence J. Arthur, President
(Independent Hospital System)

KANSAS: HILLSBORO COMMUNITY HOSPITAL (O, 10 beds) 701 South Main Street, Hillsboro, KS, Zip 67063–1553; tel. 620/947–3114; Marion Regier, Chief Executive Officer

HORTON COMMUNITY HOSPITAL (O, 25 beds) 240 West 18th Street, Horton, KS, Zip 66439–1245; tel. 785/486–2642; James D. Noble, Chief Executive Officer
Web address: www.horton–hospital.com

OSWEGO COMMUNITY HOSPITAL (O, 12 beds) 800 Barker Drive, Oswego, KS, Zip 67356–9014; tel. 620/795–2921; Bill Cochran, Interim Chief Executive Officer

MISSOURI: COOPER COUNTY COMMUNITY HOSPITAL (C, 32 beds) 17651 'B' Highway, Boonville, MO, Zip 65233–2839, Mailing Address: P.O. Box 88, Zip 65233–0088, tel. 660/882–7461; Randy Simmons, Chief Executive Officer
Web address: www.coopercmh.com

I–70 COMMUNITY HOSPITAL (O, 11 beds) 105 Hospital Drive, Sweet Springs, MO, Zip 65351–2229; tel. 660/335–4700; Jeff Bloemker, Chief Executive Officer
Web address: www.i70medcenter.com

NORTH CAROLINA: WASHINGTON COUNTY HOSPITAL (O, 25 beds) 958 U S Highway 64 East, Plymouth, NC, Zip 27962–9591, Mailing Address: PO Box 707, Zip 27962–9591, tel. 252/793–4135; Al Arrowood, Interim President

OKLAHOMA: DRUMRIGHT REGIONAL HOSPITAL (O, 15 beds) 610 West Bypass , Drumright, OK, Zip 74030–5957; tel. 918/382–2300; Tracy Byers, Chief Executive Officer
Web address: www.drumrighthospital.com/

FAIRFAX COMMUNITY HOSPITAL (O, 15 beds) 40 Hospital Road, Fairfax, OK, Zip 74637–5084; tel. 918/642–3291; Tina Steele, Chief Executive Officer and Chief Financial Officer

HASKELL COUNTY COMMUNITY HOSPITAL (O, 18 beds) 401 Northwest 'H' Street, Stigler, OK, Zip 74462–1625; tel. 918/967–4682; Donald E. Buchanan, Chief Executive Officer
Web address: www.haskellhospital.com

PRAGUE COMMUNITY HOSPITAL (O, 15 beds) 1322 Klabzuba Avenue, Prague, OK, Zip 74864–9005, Mailing Address: P.O. Box S, Zip 74864–1090, tel. 405/567–4922; Shelly Dyer, Interim Chief Executive Officer
Web address: www.praguehospital.com

TENNESSEE: LAUDERDALE COMMUNITY HOSPITAL (O, 25 beds) 326 Asbury Avenue, Ripley, TN, Zip 38063–5577; tel. 731/221–2200; Michael G. Layfield, Interim Chief Executive Officer

Owned, leased, sponsored:	10 hospitals	171 beds
Contract-managed:	1 hospitals	32 beds
Totals:	11 hospitals	203 beds

★0109: RURAL HEALTH GROUP (IO)
48 West 1500 North, Nephi, UT, Zip 84648–8900; tel. 435/623–4924; Mark R. Stoddard, President and Chairman
(Independent Hospital System)

UTAH: CENTRAL VALLEY MEDICAL CENTER (L, 27 beds) 48 West 1500 North, Nephi, UT, Zip 84648–8900; tel. 435/623–3000; Mark R. Stoddard, Chief Executive Officer

Owned, leased, sponsored:	1 hospitals	27 beds
Contract-managed:	0 hospitals	0 beds
Totals:	1 hospitals	27 beds

★0220: RUSH HEALTH SYSTEMS (NP)
1314 19th Avenue, Meridian, MS, Zip 39301–4116; tel. 601/483–0011; Larkin Kennedy, President and Chief Executive Officer
(Centralized Physician/Insurance Health System)

ALABAMA: CHOCTAW GENERAL HOSPITAL (O, 25 beds) 401 Vanity Fair Avenue, Butler, AL, Zip 36904–3032; tel. 205/459–9100; J W. Cowan, Administrator
Web address: www.choctawgeneral.com/cgh/

MISSISSIPPI: H. C. WATKINS MEMORIAL HOSPITAL (O, 25 beds) 605 South Archusa Avenue, Quitman, MS, Zip 39355–2331; tel. 601/776–6925; Michael Nester, Administrator

JOHN C. STENNIS MEMORIAL HOSPITAL (O, 25 beds) 14365 Highway 16 West, De Kalb, MS, Zip 39328–7974; tel. 769/486–1000; Justin Palmer, Administrator
Web address: www.johncstennismemorialhospital.com/jcsmh/

LAIRD HOSPITAL (O, 25 beds) 25117 Highway 15, Union, MS, Zip 39365–9099; tel. 601/774–8214; Thomas G. Bartlett III, Administrator

RUSH FOUNDATION HOSPITAL (O, 182 beds) 1314 19th Avenue, Meridian, MS, Zip 39301–4195; tel. 601/483–0011; Larkin Kennedy, Chief Executive Officer
Web address: www.rushhealthsystems.org/rfh/

SCOTT REGIONAL HOSPITAL (O, 25 beds) 317 Highway 13 South, Morton, MS, Zip 39117–3353, Mailing Address: P.O. Box 259, Zip 39117–0259, tel. 601/732–6301; Heather Davis, Administrator
Web address: www.scottregional.org/srh/

SPECIALTY HOSPITAL OF MERIDIAN (O, 49 beds) 1314 19th Avenue, Meridian, MS, Zip 39301–4116; tel. 601/703–4211; Elizabeth C. Mitchell, Chief Executive Officer and Chief Operating Officer

Owned, leased, sponsored:	7 hospitals	356 beds
Contract-managed:	0 hospitals	0 beds
Totals:	7 hospitals	356 beds

For explanation of codes following names, see page B2.
★ Indicates Type III membership in the American Hospital Association.

★**3855: RUSH UNIVERSITY MEDICAL CENTER** (NP)

1653 West Congress Parkway, Chicago, IL, Zip 60612–3864; tel. 312/942–5000; Larry J. Goodman, M.D., Chief Executive Officer

(Moderately Centralized Health System)

ILLINOIS: RUSH OAK PARK HOSPITAL (O, 127 beds) 520 South Maple Avenue, Oak Park, IL, Zip 60304–1097; tel. 708/383–9300; Bruce M. Elegant, FACHE, President and Chief Executive Officer
Web address: www.roph.org

RUSH UNIVERSITY MEDICAL CENTER (O, 673 beds) 1653 West Congress Parkway, Chicago, IL, Zip 60612–3833; tel. 312/942–5000; Larry J. Goodman, M.D., Chief Executive Officer

RUSH–COPLEY MEDICAL CENTER (O, 210 beds) 2000 Ogden Avenue, Aurora, IL, Zip 60504–7222; tel. 630/978–6200; Barry C. Finn, President and Chief Executive Officer
Web address: www.rushcopley.com

Owned, leased, sponsored:	3 hospitals	1010 beds
Contract–managed:	0 hospitals	0 beds
Totals:	3 hospitals	1010 beds

★**0994: RWJBARNABAS HEALTH** (NP)

95 Old Short Hills Road, West Orange, NJ, Zip 07052–1008; tel. 973/322–4000; Barry Ostrowsky, President and Chief Executive Officer

(Moderately Centralized Health System)

NEW JERSEY: BARNABAS HEALTH BEHAVIORAL HEALTH CENTER (O, 40 beds) 1691 Highway 9, Toms River, NJ, Zip 8754; tel. 732/914–1688; Deanna Sperling, R.N., President and Chief Executive Officer
Web address: www.barnabashealth.org/hospitals/psychiatric/index.html

CHILDREN'S SPECIALIZED HOSPITAL (O, 140 beds) 200 Somerset Street, New Brunswick, NJ, Zip 08901–1942; tel. 732/258–7000; Warren E. Moore, FACHE, President and Chief Executive Officer
Web address: www.childrens–specialized.org

CLARA MAASS MEDICAL CENTER (O, 364 beds) One Clara Maass Drive, Belleville, NJ, Zip 07109–3557; tel. 973/450–2000; Mary Ellen Clyne, Ph.D., President and Chief Executive Officer

COMMUNITY MEDICAL CENTER (O, 338 beds) 99 Route 37 West, Toms River, NJ, Zip 08755–6423; tel. 732/557–8000; Michael Mimoso, FACHE, President and Chief Executive Officer
Web address: www.barnabashealth.org/hospitals/community_medical/index.html

JERSEY CITY MEDICAL CENTER (O, 316 beds) 355 Grand Street, Jersey City, NJ, Zip 07302–4321; tel. 201/915–2000; Joseph F. Scott, FACHE, President and Chief Executive Officer

MONMOUTH MEDICAL CENTER, LONG BRANCH CAMPUS (O, 296 beds) 300 Second Avenue, Long Branch, NJ, Zip 07740–6303; tel. 732/222–5200; Bill Arnold, President and Chief Executive Officer
Web address: www.barnabashealth.org/hospitals/monmouth_medical/index.html

MONMOUTH MEDICAL CENTER, SOUTHERN CAMPUS (O, 124 beds) 600 River Avenue, Lakewood, NJ, Zip 08701–5237; tel. 732/363–1900; Frank J. Vozos, M.D., FACS, Chief Executive Officer, MMC Southern Campus
Web address: www.rwjbarnabashealth.org/monmouth–medical–center–southern–campus.aspx

NEWARK BETH ISRAEL MEDICAL CENTER (O, 333 beds) 201 Lyons Avenue at Osborne Terrace, Newark, NJ, Zip 07112–2027; tel. 973/926–7000; Darrell K. Terry Sr, M.P.H., FACHE, President and Chief Executive Officer
Web address: www.barnabashealth.org/hospitals/newark_beth_israel/index.html

ROBERT WOOD JOHNSON UNIVERSITY HOSPITAL RAHWAY (O, 106 beds) 865 Stone Street, Rahway, NJ, Zip 07065–2797; tel. 732/381–4200; Kirk C. Tice, President and Chief Executive Officer
Web address: www.rwjuhr.com

ROBERT WOOD JOHNSON UNIVERSITY HOSPITAL SOMERSET (O, 285 beds) 110 Rehill Avenue, Somerville, NJ, Zip 08876–2598; tel. 908/685–2200; Anthony V. Cava, MS, FACHE, President

ROBERT WOOD JOHNSON UNIVERSITY HOSPITAL AT HAMILTON (O, 164 beds) One Hamilton Health Place, Hamilton, NJ, Zip 08690–3599; tel. 609/586–7900; Richard Freeman, President and Chief Executive Officer
Web address: www.rwjhamilton.org

ROBERT WOOD JOHNSON UNIVERSITY HOSPITAL (O, 610 beds) 1 Robert Wood Johnson Place, New Brunswick, NJ, Zip 08901–1928; tel. 732/828–3000; John J. Gantner, President and Chief Executive Officer
Web address: www.rwjuh.edu

SAINT BARNABAS MEDICAL CENTER (O, 553 beds) 94 Old Short Hills Rd, Livingston, NJ, Zip 07039–5672; tel. 973/322–5000; Stephen P. Zieniewicz, FACHE, President and Chief Executive Officer
Web address: www.barnabashealth.org/hospitals/saint_barnabas/index.html

Owned, leased, sponsored:	13 hospitals	3669 beds
Contract–managed:	0 hospitals	0 beds
Totals:	13 hospitals	3669 beds

0912: SAFE HAVEN HEALTH CARE (IO)

2520 South 5th Avenue, Pocatello, ID, Zip 83204–1923; tel. 800/261–2443; Scott Burpee, President

IDAHO: SAFE HAVEN HOSPITAL OF POCATELLO (O, 87 beds) 1200 Hospital Way, Pocatello, ID, Zip 83201–2708; tel. 208/232–2570; Karen Neilson, Administrator

SAFE HAVEN HOSPITAL OF TREASURE VALLEY (O, 22 beds) 8050 Northview Street, Boise, ID, Zip 83704–7126; tel. 208/327–0504; Scott Proctor, Chief Executive Officer
Web address: www.boisepsychhospital.com

Owned, leased, sponsored:	2 hospitals	109 beds
Contract–managed:	0 hospitals	0 beds
Totals:	2 hospitals	109 beds

★**0254: SAINT FRANCIS HEALTH SYSTEM** (NP)

6161 South Yale Avenue, Tulsa, OK, Zip 74136–1902; tel. 918/494–8454; Jake Henry Jr, President and Chief Executive Officer

(Centralized Health System)

OKLAHOMA: LAUREATE PSYCHIATRIC CLINIC AND HOSPITAL (O, 106 beds) 6655 South Yale Avenue, Tulsa, OK, Zip 74136–3329; tel. 918/481–4000; Michele A. Keeling, Senior Vice President and Administrator
Web address: www.laureate.com

OKLAHOMA STATE UNIVERSITY MEDICAL CENTER (C, 191 beds) 744 West Ninth Street, Tulsa, OK, Zip 74127–9020; tel. 918/599–1000; Matthew Adams, Administrator
Web address: www.osumc.net

SAINT FRANCIS HOSPITAL MUSKOGEE (O, 160 beds) 300 Rockefeller Drive, Muskogee, OK, Zip 74401–5081; tel. 918/682–5501; Anthony R. Young, Chief Executive Officer
Web address: https://www.saintfrancis.com/muskogee/Pages/default.aspx

SAINT FRANCIS HOSPITAL SOUTH (O, 90 beds) 10501 East 91st Street, Tulsa, OK, Zip 74133–5790; tel. 918/307–6010; David S. Weil, Senior Vice President and Administrator

SAINT FRANCIS HOSPITAL VINITA (O, 70 beds) 735 North Foreman Street, Vinita, OK, Zip 74301–1418, Mailing Address: P.O. Box 326, Zip 74301–0326, tel. 918/256–7551; Todd Schuster, Administrator
Web address: https://www.saintfrancis.com/vinita/Pages/default.aspx

SAINT FRANCIS HOSPITAL (O, 842 beds) 6161 South Yale Avenue, Tulsa, OK, Zip 74136–1902; tel. 918/494–2200; Lynn A. Sund, Chief Nurse Executive and Administrator
Web address: www.saintfrancis.com

Owned, leased, sponsored:	5 hospitals	1268 beds
Contract–managed:	1 hospitals	191 beds
Totals:	6 hospitals	1459 beds

For explanation of codes following names, see page B2.
★ Indicates Type III membership in the American Hospital Association.

★0120: SAINT LUKE'S HEALTH SYSTEM (NP)
901 East 104th Street, Mailstop 900N, Kansas City, MO, Zip 64131–4517, Mailing Address: 901 East 104th Street, Zip 64131–4517, tel. 816/932–2000; Melinda Estes, M.D., President and Chief Executive Officer
(Centralized Health System)

KANSAS: ANDERSON COUNTY HOSPITAL (L, 48 beds) 421 South Maple, Garnett, KS, Zip 66032–1334, Mailing Address: P.O. Box 309, Zip 66032–0309, tel. 785/448–3131; Rick McKain, Chief Executive Officer
Web address: www.saint–lukes.org

SAINT LUKE'S COMMUNITY HOSPITAL AT LEAWOOD (O, 8 beds) 13200 State Line Road, Leawood, KS, Zip 66209; tel. 913/222–8380; Teresa Collins, R.N., Chief Executive Officer and Chief Nursing Officer

SAINT LUKE'S CUSHING HOSPITAL (O, 25 beds) 711 Marshall Street, Leavenworth, KS, Zip 66048–3235; tel. 913/684–1100; Bobby Olm–Shipman, President and Chief Executive Officer
Web address: www.saintlukeshealthsystem.org/locations/saint–lukes–cushing–hospital

SAINT LUKE'S SOUTH HOSPITAL (O, 104 beds) 12300 Metcalf Avenue, Overland Park, KS, Zip 66213–1324; tel. 913/317–7000; Bobby Olm–Shipman, Chief Executive Officer
Web address: www.saintlukeshealthsystem.org/south

MISSOURI: HEDRICK MEDICAL CENTER (L, 25 beds) 2799 North Washington Street, Chillicothe, MO, Zip 64601–2902; tel. 660/646–1480; Steven M. Schieber, FACHE, Chief Executive Officer
Web address: www.saintlukeskc.org

SAINT LUKE'S EAST HOSPITAL (O, 203 beds) 100 NE Saint Luke's Boulevard, Lee's Summit, MO, Zip 64086–6000; tel. 816/347–5000; Ron Baker, FACHE, Chief Executive Officer
Web address: www.saintlukeskc.org

SAINT LUKE'S HOSPITAL OF KANSAS CITY (O, 478 beds) 4401 Wornall Road, Kansas City, MO, Zip 64111–3220; tel. 816/932–3800; Jani L. Johnson, R.N., MSN, Chief Executive Officer

SAINT LUKE'S NORTH HOSPITAL – BARRY ROAD (O, 137 beds) 5830 NW Barry Road, Kansas City, MO, Zip 64154–2778; tel. 816/891–6000; Adele Ducharme, MSN, R.N., Chief Executive Officer
Web address: www.saint–lukes.org

WRIGHT MEMORIAL HOSPITAL (L, 15 beds) 191 Iowa Boulevard, Trenton, MO, Zip 64683–8343; tel. 660/358–5700; Steven M Schieber, MBA, FACMPE, FACHE, Chief Executive Officer

Owned, leased, sponsored:	9 hospitals	1043 beds
Contract–managed:	0 hospitals	0 beds
Totals:	9 hospitals	1043 beds

0403: SALEM HEALTH (NP)
890 Oak Street Bldg B POB 14001, Salem, OR, Zip 97309–5014; tel. 503/561–5200; Norman F. Gruber, President and Chief Executive Officer
(Independent Hospital System)

OREGON: SALEM HEALTH WEST VALLEY (O, 6 beds) 525 SE Washington Street, Dallas, OR, Zip 97338–2834, Mailing Address: P.O. Box 378, Zip 97338–0378, tel. 503/623–8301; Bruce C. Rodgers, Chief Administrative Officer
Web address: www.salemhealth.org/wvh/

SALEM HOSPITAL (O, 424 beds) 890 Oak Street SE, Salem, OR, Zip 97301–3959, Mailing Address: P.O. Box 14001, Zip 97309–5014, tel. 503/561–5200; Cheryl R. Nester Wolfe, President and Chief Executive Officer

Owned, leased, sponsored:	2 hospitals	430 beds
Contract–managed:	0 hospitals	0 beds
Totals:	2 hospitals	430 beds

1002: SALINA REGIONAL HEALTH CENTER (NP)
400 South Santa Fe Avenue, Salina, KS, Zip 67401–4198, Mailing Address: PO Box 5080, Zip 67402–5080, tel. 785/452–7000; Micheal Terry, President and Chief Executive Officer
(Moderately Centralized Health System)

KANSAS: CLOUD COUNTY HEALTH CENTER (C, 25 beds) 1100 Highland Drive, Concordia, KS, Zip 66901–3923; tel. 785/243–1234; David Garnas, Administrator
Web address: www.cchc.com

LINDSBORG COMMUNITY HOSPITAL (C, 21 beds) 605 West Lincoln Street, Lindsborg, KS, Zip 67456–2328; tel. 785/227–3308; Larry VanDerWege, Administrator

SALINA REGIONAL HEALTH CENTER (O, 205 beds) 400 South Santa Fe Avenue, Salina, KS, Zip 67401–4198, Mailing Address: P.O. Box 5080, Zip 67402–5080, tel. 785/452–7000; Micheal Terry, President and Chief Executive Officer
Web address: www.srhc.com

Owned, leased, sponsored:	1 hospitals	205 beds
Contract–managed:	2 hospitals	46 beds
Totals:	3 hospitals	251 beds

★0186: SAMARITAN HEALTH SERVICES (NP)
3600 NW Samaritan Drive, Corvallis, OR, Zip 97330–3737, Mailing Address: P.O. Box 1068, Zip 97339–1068, tel. 541/768–5001; Doug Boysen, President and Chief Executive Officer
(Centralized Physician/Insurance Health System)

OREGON: GOOD SAMARITAN REGIONAL MEDICAL CENTER (O, 182 beds) 3600 NW Samaritan Drive, Corvallis, OR, Zip 97330–3737, Mailing Address: P.O. Box 1068, Zip 97339–1068, tel. 541/768–5111; Becky A. Pape, R.N., Chief Executive Officer
Web address: www.samhealth.org

SAMARITAN ALBANY GENERAL HOSPITAL (O, 70 beds) 1046 Sixth Avenue, SW, Albany, OR, Zip 97321–1999; tel. 541/812–4000; David G. Triebes, Chief Executive Officer
Web address: www.samhealth.org

SAMARITAN LEBANON COMMUNITY HOSPITAL (O, 25 beds) 525 North Santiam Highway, Lebanon, OR, Zip 97355–4363, Mailing Address: P.O. Box 739, Zip 97355–0739, tel. 541/258–2101; Marty Cahill, Chief Executive Officer

SAMARITAN NORTH LINCOLN HOSPITAL (C, 25 beds) 3043 NE 28th Street, Lincoln City, OR, Zip 97367–4518, Mailing Address: P.O. Box 767, Zip 97367–0767, tel. 541/994–3661; Lesley Ogden, M.D., Chief Executive Officer
Web address: www.samhealth.org

SAMARITAN PACIFIC COMMUNITIES HOSPITAL (C, 25 beds) 930 SW Abbey Street, Newport, OR, Zip 97365–4820, Mailing Address: P.O. Box 945, Zip 97365–0072, tel. 541/265–2244; Lesley Ogden, M.D., Chief Executive Officer

Owned, leased, sponsored:	3 hospitals	277 beds
Contract–managed:	2 hospitals	50 beds
Totals:	5 hospitals	327 beds

★0914: SAN LUIS VALLEY HEALTH (NP)
106 Blanca Avenue, Alamosa, CO, Zip 81101–2340; tel. 719/589–2511; Konnie Martin, Chief Executive Officer
(Independent Hospital System)

COLORADO: SAN LUIS VALLEY HEALTH CONEJOS COUNTY HOSPITAL (O, 17 beds) 19021 U S Highway 285, La Jara, CO, Zip 81140–0639, Mailing Address: P.O. Box 639, Zip 81140–0639, tel. 719/274–5121; Kelly Gallegos, Administrator

SAN LUIS VALLEY HEALTH (O, 44 beds) 106 Blanca Avenue, Alamosa, CO, Zip 81101–2393; tel. 719/589–2511; Konnie Martin, Chief Executive Officer
Web address: www.sanluisvalleyhealth.org

Owned, leased, sponsored:	2 hospitals	61 beds
Contract–managed:	0 hospitals	0 beds
Totals:	2 hospitals	61 beds

★0530: SANFORD HEALTH (NP)
2301 East 60th Street North, Sioux Falls, SD, Zip 57104–0569, Mailing Address: PO Box 5039, Zip 57117–5039, tel. 605/333–1000; Kelby K. Krabbenhoft, President and Chief Executive Officer
(Decentralized Health System)

For explanation of codes following names, see page B2.
★ Indicates Type III membership in the American Hospital Association.

IOWA: ORANGE CITY AREA HEALTH SYSTEM (C, 114 beds) 1000 Lincoln Circle SE, Orange City, IA, Zip 51041–1862; tel. 712/737–4984; Martin W. Guthmiller, Chief Executive Officer
Web address: www.ochealthsystem.org

SANFORD ROCK RAPIDS MEDICAL CENTER (L, 14 beds) 801 South Greene Street, Rock Rapids, IA, Zip 51246–1998; tel. 712/472–2591; Tammy Loosbrock, Chief Executive Officer
Web address: www.sanfordrockrapids.org

SANFORD SHELDON MEDICAL CENTER (O, 95 beds) 118 North Seventh Avenue, Sheldon, IA, Zip 51201–1235, Mailing Address: P.O. Box 250, Zip 51201–0250, tel. 712/324–5041; Richard E. Nordahl, Chief Executive Officer

MINNESOTA: ARNOLD MEMORIAL HEALTH CARE CENTER (L, 50 beds) 601 Louisiana Avenue, Adrian, MN, Zip 56110–0279, Mailing Address: P.O. Box 279, Zip 56110–0279, tel. 507/483–2668; Michele Roban, Administrator

MAHNOMEN HEALTH CENTER (C, 56 beds) 414 West Jefferson Avenue, Mahnomen, MN, Zip 56557–4912, Mailing Address: P.O. Box 396, Zip 56557–0396, tel. 218/935–2511; Dale K. Kruger, Chief Executive Officer
Web address: www.mahnomenhealthcenter.com

MURRAY COUNTY MEDICAL CENTER (C, 18 beds) 2042 Juniper Avenue, Slayton, MN, Zip 56172–1017; tel. 507/836–6111; Dennis Goebel, Chief Executive Officer

ORTONVILLE AREA HEALTH SERVICES (C, 90 beds) 450 Eastvold Avenue, Ortonville, MN, Zip 56278–1133; tel. 320/839–2502; David Rogers, Chief Executive Officer
Web address: www.oahs.us

PERHAM HEALTH (C, 121 beds) 1000 Coney Street West, Perham, MN, Zip 56573–1108; tel. 218/347–4500; Chuck Hofius, Chief Executive Officer

SANFORD BAGLEY MEDICAL CENTER (O, 8 beds) 203 Fourth Street NW, Bagley, MN, Zip 56621–8307; tel. 218/694–6501; Robert Belanger, Administrator Director
Web address: www.sanfordhealth.org

SANFORD BEMIDJI MEDICAL CENTER (O, 196 beds) 1300 Anne Street NW, Bemidji, MN, Zip 56601–5103; tel. 218/751–5430; Bryan Nermoe, Executive Vice President
Web address: www.sanfordhealth.org/bemidji

SANFORD CANBY MEDICAL CENTER (L, 83 beds) 112 St Olaf Avenue South, Canby, MN, Zip 56220–1433; tel. 507/223–7277; Lori Sisk, R.N., Chief Executive Officer

SANFORD JACKSON MEDICAL CENTER (O, 14 beds) 1430 North Highway, Jackson, MN, Zip 56143–1093; tel. 507/847–2420; Dawn Schnell, Chief Nursing Officer and Interim Senior Director
Web address: www.sanfordjackson.org

SANFORD LUVERNE MEDICAL CENTER (O, 25 beds) 1600 North Kniss Avenue, Luverne, MN, Zip 56156–1067; tel. 507/283–2321; Tammy Loosbrock, Senior Director

SANFORD MEDICAL CENTER THIEF RIVER FALLS (O, 25 beds) 3001 Sanford Parkway, Thief River Falls, MN, Zip 56701–2700; tel. 218/681–4747; Brian J. Carlson, FACHE, Executive Director
Web address: www.sanfordhealth.org

SANFORD THIEF RIVER FALLS BEHAVIORAL HEALTH CENTER (O, 16 beds) 120 LaBree Avenue South, Thief River Falls, MN, Zip 56701–2819, Mailing Address: 3001 Sanford Parkway, Zip 56701–2819, tel. 218/683–4349; Brian J. Carlson, FACHE, Chief Executive Officer
Web address: www.sanfordhealth.org/Locations/1766896362

SANFORD TRACY MEDICAL CENTER (O, 25 beds) 251 Fifth Street East, Tracy, MN, Zip 56175–1536; tel. 507/629–8400; Stacy Barstad, Chief Executive Officer

SANFORD WESTBROOK MEDICAL CENTER (L, 6 beds) 920 Bell Avenue, Westbrook, MN, Zip 56183–9669, Mailing Address: P.O. Box 188, Zip 56183–0188, tel. 507/274–6121; Stacy Barstad, Chief Executive Officer
Web address: www.sanfordwestbrook.org

SANFORD WHEATON MEDICAL CENTER (O, 15 beds) 401 12th Street North, Wheaton, MN, Zip 56296–1099; tel. 320/563–8226; JoAnn M. Foltz, R.N., Chief Executive Officer
Web address: www.sanfordhealth.org

SANFORD WORTHINGTON MEDICAL CENTER (O, 48 beds) 1018 Sixth Avenue, Worthington, MN, Zip 56187–2202, Mailing Address: P.O. Box 997, Zip 56187–0997, tel. 507/372–2941; Jennifer . Weg, MS, R.N., Executive Director

WINDOM AREA HOSPITAL (C, 18 beds) 2150 Hospital Drive, Windom, MN, Zip 56101–0339, Mailing Address: P.O. Box 339, Zip 56101–0339, tel. 507/831–2400; Shelby Medina, Chief Executive Officer
Web address: www.windomareahospital.com

NORTH DAKOTA: NORTHWOOD DEACONESS HEALTH CENTER (O, 57 beds) 4 North Park Street, Northwood, ND, Zip 58267–4102, Mailing Address: P.O. Box 190, Zip 58267–0190, tel. 701/587–6060; Pete Antonson, Chief Executive Officer
Web address: www.ndhc.net

SANFORD BISMARCK (O, 208 beds) 300 North Seventh Street, Bismarck, ND, Zip 58501–4439, Mailing Address: P.O. Box 5525, Zip 58506–5525, tel. 701/323–6000; Craig Lambrecht, M.D., President
Web address: www.bismarck.sanfordhealth.org/

SANFORD HILLSBORO MEDICAL CENTER (C, 52 beds) 12 Third Street SE, Hillsboro, ND, Zip 58045–4840, Mailing Address: P.O. Box 609, Zip 58045–0609, tel. 701/636–3200; Jac McTaggart, Chief Executive Officer

SANFORD MAYVILLE MEDICAL CENTER (O, 18 beds) 42 Sixth Avenue SE, Mayville, ND, Zip 58257–1598; tel. 701/786–3800; Jac McTaggart, Chief Executive Officer
Web address: www.unionhospital.com

SANFORD MEDICAL CENTER FARGO (O, 490 beds) 801 Broadway North, Fargo, ND, Zip 58122–3641; tel. 701/234–2000; Nate White, Executive Vice President

SOUTH DAKOTA: COMMUNITY MEMORIAL HOSPITAL (C, 16 beds) 809 Jackson Street, Burke, SD, Zip 57523–2065, Mailing Address: P.O. Box 319, Zip 57523–0319, tel. 605/775–2621; Mistie Sachtjen, Chief Executive Officer
Web address: www.sanfordhealth.org

PIONEER MEMORIAL HOSPITAL AND HEALTH SERVICES (C, 64 beds) 315 North Washington Street, Viborg, SD, Zip 57070–2002, Mailing Address: P.O. Box 368, Zip 57070–0368, tel. 605/326–5161; Thomas V. Richter, Chief Executive Officer
Web address: www.pioneermemorial.org

SANFORD ABERDEEN MEDICAL CENTER (O, 16 beds) 2905 3rd Avenue SE, Aberdeen, SD, Zip 57401–5420; tel. 605/626–4200; Ashley M. Erickson, Chief Executive Officer

SANFORD CANTON–INWOOD MEDICAL CENTER (O, 11 beds) 440 North Hiawatha Drive, Canton, SD, Zip 57013–5800; tel. 605/764–1400; Scott C. Larson, Chief Executive Officer
Web address: www.sanfordcantoninwood.org

SANFORD CHAMBERLAIN MEDICAL CENTER (O, 69 beds) 300 South Byron Boulevard, Chamberlain, SD, Zip 57325–9741; tel. 605/234–5511; Erica Peterson, Chief Executive Officer
Web address: www.sanfordchamberlain.org

SANFORD CLEAR LAKE MEDICAL CENTER (L, 10 beds) 701 Third Avenue South, Clear Lake, SD, Zip 57226–2016; tel. 605/874–2141; Lori Sisk, R.N., Chief Executive Officer
Web address: www.sanforddeuelcounty.org

SANFORD USD MEDICAL CENTER (O, 500 beds) 1305 West 18th Street, Sioux Falls, SD, Zip 57105–0496, Mailing Address: P.O. Box 5039, Zip 57117–5039, tel. 605/333–1000; Paul A. Hanson, FACHE, President

SANFORD VERMILLION MEDICAL CENTER (L, 120 beds) 20 South Plum Street, Vermillion, SD, Zip 57069–3346; tel. 605/677–3500; Timothy J. Tracy, Senior Director
Web address: www.sanfordvermillion.org

SANFORD WEBSTER MEDICAL CENTER (L, 20 beds) 1401 West 1st Street, Webster, SD, Zip 57274–1054, Mailing Address: P.O. Box 489, Zip 57274–0489, tel. 605/345–3336; Isaac Gerdes, Chief Executive Officer

WINNER REGIONAL HEALTHCARE CENTER (C, 104 beds) 745 East Eighth Street, Winner, SD, Zip 57580–2631; tel. 605/842–7100; Kevin Coffey, Chief Executive Officer
Web address: www.winnerregional.org

Owned, leased, sponsored:	25 hospitals	2139 beds
Contract–managed:	10 hospitals	653 beds
Totals:	35 hospitals	2792 beds

For explanation of codes following names, see page B2.
★ Indicates Type III membership in the American Hospital Association.

★**5095: SCL HEALTH** (CO)

500 Eldorado Boulevard, Suite 4300, Broomfield, CO, Zip 80021; tel. 303/813–5180; Lydia Jumonville, President and Chief Executive Officer

(Moderately Centralized Health System)

COLORADO: GOOD SAMARITAN MEDICAL CENTER (S, 185 beds) 200 Exempla Circle, Lafayette, CO, Zip 80026–3370; tel. 303/689–4000; Jennifer Alderfer, President

Web address: www.goodsamaritancolorado.org/

LUTHERAN MEDICAL CENTER (S, 518 beds) 8300 West 38th Avenue, Wheat Ridge, CO, Zip 80033–6005; tel. 303/425–4500; Grant Wicklund, President and Chief Executive Officer

Web address: https://www.sclhealth.org/locations/lutheran–medical–center/

PLATTE VALLEY MEDICAL CENTER (C, 70 beds) 1600 Prairie Center Parkway, Brighton, CO, Zip 80601–4006; tel. 303/498–1600; John R. Hicks, President and Chief Executive Officer

SAINT JOSEPH HOSPITAL (O, 379 beds) 1375 East 19th Avenue, Denver, CO, Zip 80218–1126; tel. 303/837–7111; Jameson Smith, President

Web address: www.saintjosephdenver.org/

ST. MARY'S HOSPITAL AND MEDICAL CENTER (O, 315 beds) 2635 North 7th Street, Grand Junction, CO, Zip 81501–8209, Mailing Address: P.O. Box 1628, Zip 81502–1628, tel. 970/298–2273; Brian Davidson, M.D., President and Chief Medical Officer

MONTANA: HOLY ROSARY HEALTHCARE (O, 90 beds) 2600 Wilson Street, Miles City, MT, Zip 59301–5094; tel. 406/233–2600; Paul Lewis, Chief Executive Officer

Web address: www.holyrosaryhealthcare.org

ST. JAMES HEALTHCARE (O, 67 beds) 400 South Clark Street, Butte, MT, Zip 59701–2328; tel. 406/723–2500; Jay Doyle, President and Chief Executive Officer

ST. VINCENT HEALTHCARE (O, 221 beds) 1233 North 30th Street, Billings, MT, Zip 59101–0165, Mailing Address: P.O. Box 35200, Zip 59107–5200, tel. 406/237–7000; Steve Loveless, President and Chief Executive Officer

Web address: www.svh–mt.org

Owned, leased, sponsored:	7 hospitals	1775 beds
Contract–managed:	1 hospitals	70 beds
Totals:	8 hospitals	1845 beds

★**1505: SCRIPPS HEALTH** (NP)

4275 Campus Point Court CP112, San Diego, CA, Zip 92121–1513, Mailing Address: 4275 Campus Point Court, Zip 92121–1513, tel. 858/678–7200; Chris D. Van Gorder, FACHE, President and Chief Executive Officer

(Centralized Health System)

CALIFORNIA: SCRIPPS GREEN HOSPITAL (O, 173 beds) 10666 North Torrey Pines Road, La Jolla, CA, Zip 92037–1093; tel. 858/455–9100; Carl J. Etter, Chief Executive Officer

SCRIPPS MEMORIAL HOSPITAL–ENCINITAS (O, 155 beds) 354 Santa Fe Drive, Encinitas, CA, Zip 92024–5182, Mailing Address: P.O. Box 230817, Zip 92023–0817, tel. 760/633–6501; Carl J. Etter, Chief Executive and Senior Vice President

Web address: www.scripps.org

SCRIPPS MEMORIAL HOSPITAL–LA JOLLA (O, 302 beds) 9888 Genesee Avenue, La Jolla, CA, Zip 92037–1200, Mailing Address: P.O. Box 28, Zip 92038–0028, tel. 858/626–4123; Carl J. Etter, Chief Executive Officer

SCRIPPS MERCY HOSPITAL (O, 392 beds) 4077 Fifth Avenue, San Diego, CA, Zip 92103–2105; tel. 619/294–8111; Thomas A. Gammiere, Chief Executive, Senior Vice President

Web address: www.scrippshealth.org

Owned, leased, sponsored:	4 hospitals	1022 beds
Contract–managed:	0 hospitals	0 beds
Totals:	4 hospitals	1022 beds

★**0181: SELECT MEDICAL CORPORATION** (IO)

4714 Gettysburg Road, Mechanicsburg, PA, Zip 17055–4325; tel. 717/972–1100; David S. Chernow, President and Chief Executive Officer

(Independent Hospital System)

ALABAMA: SELECT SPECIALTY HOSPITAL–BIRMINGHAM (O, 38 beds) 2010 Brookwood Medical Center Drive, 3rd Floor, Birmingham, AL, Zip 35209–6804; tel. 205/599–4600; Clifton Quinn, Chief Executive Officer

Web address: www.birmingham.selectspecialtyhospitals.com

ARIZONA: HONORHEALTH REHABILITATION HOSPITAL (O, 50 beds) 8850 East Pima Center Parkway, Scottsdale, AZ, Zip 85258–4619; tel. 480/800–3900; Scott R. Keen, Chief Executive Officer

SELECT SPECIALTY HOSPITAL–PHOENIX DOWNTOWN (O, 33 beds) 1012 East Wiletta Street, 4th Floor, Phoenix, AZ, Zip 85006; tel. 602/839–6550; David Selman, Chief Executive Officer

Web address: www.selectmedicalcorp.com

SELECT SPECIALTY HOSPITAL–PHOENIX (O, 48 beds) 350 West Thomas Road, 3rd Floor Main, Phoenix, AZ, Zip 85013–4409; tel. 602/406–6810; Karen Crowley, Chief Executive Officer

Web address: www.https://phoenix.selectspecialtyhospitals.com

ARKANSAS: REGENCY HOSPITAL OF NORTHWEST ARKANSAS – SPRINGDALE (O, 25 beds) 609 West Maple Avenue, 6th Fl, Springdale, AR, Zip 72764; tel. 479/757–2600; Robert Poole, Chief Executive Officer

SELECT SPECIALTY HOSPITAL–FORT SMITH (O, 34 beds) 1001 Towson Avenue, 6 Central, Fort Smith, AR, Zip 72901–4921; tel. 479/441–3960; Shannon Grams, Chief Executive Officer

Web address: www.https://fortsmith.selectspecialtyhospitals.com/

CALIFORNIA: CALIFORNIA REHABILITATION INSTITUTE (O, 138 beds) 2070 Century Park East, Los Angeles, CA, Zip 90067–1907; tel. 424/363–1000; Scott T. Rotsted, Chief Executive Officer

DELAWARE: SELECT SPECIALTY HOSPITAL–WILMINGTON (O, 35 beds) 701 North Clayton Street, 5th Floor, Wilmington, DE, Zip 19805–3948; tel. 302/421–4545; Donna Gares, R.N., FACHE, MSN, Chief Executive Officer

Web address: www.wilmington.selectspecialtyhospitals.com

FLORIDA: SELECT SPECIALTY HOSPITAL DAYTONA BEACH (O, 34 beds) 301 Memorial Medical Parkway, 11th Floor, Daytona Beach, FL, Zip 32117–5167; tel. 386/231–3436; Adrianne Lutes, Chief Executive Officer

Web address: www.daytonabeach.selectspecialtyhospitals.com

SELECT SPECIALTY HOSPITAL–GAINESVILLE (O, 44 beds) 2708 SW Archer Road, Gainesville, FL, Zip 32608–1316; tel. 352/337–3240; Ronnie Wagley, Market Chief Executive Officer

SELECT SPECIALTY HOSPITAL–MIAMI (O, 47 beds) 955 NW 3rd Street, Miami, FL, Zip 33128–1274; tel. 305/416–5700; Dionisio Bencomo, Chief Executive Officer

Web address: www.selectspecialtyhospitals.com/company/locations/miami.aspx

SELECT SPECIALTY HOSPITAL–ORLANDO (O, 75 beds) 2250 Bedford Road, Orlando, FL, Zip 32803–1443; tel. 407/303–7869; Theodore Mena, Chief Executive Officer

Web address: www.selectspecialtyhospitals.com/company/locations/orlando.aspx

SELECT SPECIALTY HOSPITAL–PALM BEACH (O, 60 beds) 3060 Melaleuca Lane, Lake Worth, FL, Zip 33461–5174; tel. 561/357–7200; Larry Melby, Chief Executive Officer

SELECT SPECIALTY HOSPITAL–PANAMA CITY (O, 30 beds) 615 North Bonita Avenue, 3rd Floor, Panama City, FL, Zip 32401–3623; tel. 850/767–3180; Randal S. Hamilton, Chief Executive Officer

Web address: www.selectspecialtyhospitals.com/company/locations/panamacity.aspx

SELECT SPECIALTY HOSPITAL–PENSACOLA (O, 75 beds) 7000 Cobble Creek Drive, Pensacola, FL, Zip 32504–8638; tel. 850/473–4800; Adam Principe, Chief Executive Officer

SELECT SPECIALTY HOSPITAL–TALLAHASSEE (O, 29 beds) 1554 Surgeons Drive, Tallahassee, FL, Zip 32308–4631; tel. 850/219–6950; Jay Faherty, Chief Executive Officer

Web address: www.tallahassee.selectspecialtyhospitals.com/

For explanation of codes following names, see page B2.
★ Indicates Type III membership in the American Hospital Association.

WEST GABLES REHABILITATION HOSPITAL (O, 60 beds) 2525 SW 75th Avenue, Miami, FL, Zip 33155-2800; tel. 305/262-6800; Walter Concepcion, Chief Executive Officer
Web address: www.westgablesrehabhospital.com/

GEORGIA: REGENCY HOSPITAL OF CENTRAL GEORGIA (O, 60 beds) 535 Coliseum Drive, Macon, GA, Zip 31217-0104; tel. 478/803-7300; Wayne B. Boutwell, Chief Executive Officer

REGENCY HOSPITAL OF SOUTH ATLANTA (O, 40 beds) 1170 Cleveland Avenue, 4th Floor, East Point, GA, Zip 30344-3615; tel. 404/466-6250; Michelle Tenhengel-deVille, Chief Executive Officer
Web address: www.regencyhospital.com

SELECT SPECIALTY HOSPITAL MIDTOWN ATLANTA (O, 72 beds) 705 Juniper Street NE, Atlanta, GA, Zip 30308-1307; tel. 404/873-2871; Adriene Kinnaird, Chief Executive Officer

SELECT SPECIALTY HOSPITAL-AUGUSTA (O, 80 beds) 1537 Walton Way, Augusta, GA, Zip 30904-3764; tel. 706/731-1200; E Rick. Lowe, FACHE, Chief Executive Officer
Web address: www.augusta.selectspecialtyhospitals.com

SELECT SPECIALTY HOSPITAL-SAVANNAH (O, 40 beds) 5353 Reynolds Street, 4 South, Savannah, GA, Zip 31405-6015; tel. 912/819-7972; Greg Wuchter, R.N., MSN, Chief Executive Officer

INDIANA: REGENCY HOSPITAL OF NORTHWEST INDIANA (O, 61 beds) 4321 Fir Street, 4th Floor, East Chicago, IN, Zip 46312-3049; tel. 219/392-7799; Eleyce Winn, Chief Executive Officer
Web address: www.regencyhospital.com/company/locations/indiana-northwest-indiana.aspx

SELECT SPECIALTY HOSPITAL-EVANSVILLE (O, 51 beds) 400 SE 4th Street, Evansville, IN, Zip 47713-1206; tel. 812/421-2500; Scott A. Butler, Chief Executive Officer

IOWA: SELECT SPECIALTY HOSPITAL-DES MOINES (O, 30 beds) 1111 6th Avenue, 4th Floor Main, Des Moines, IA, Zip 50314-2610; tel. 515/247-4400; Glen Griesheim, Chief Executive Officer
Web address: www.selectspecialtyhospitals.com

SELECT SPECIALTY HOSPITAL-QUAD CITIES (O, 50 beds) 1111 West Kimberly Road, Davenport, IA, Zip 52806-5711; tel. 563/468-2000; Codie Dillie, Chief Executive Officer

KANSAS: SELECT SPECIALTY HOSPITAL-KANSAS CITY (O, 40 beds) 1731 North 90th Street, Kansas City, KS, Zip 66112-1515; tel. 913/732-5900; Bridgette Hunter, Chief Executive Officer
Web address: www.selectspecialtyhospitals.com

SELECT SPECIALTY HOSPITAL-WICHITA (O, 48 beds) 929 North St Francis Street, Wichita, KS, Zip 67214-3821; tel. 316/261-8303; Christopher Keith, Chief Executive Officer
Web address: www.selectspecialtyhospitals.com/company/locations/wichita.aspx

KENTUCKY: SELECT SPECIALTY HOSPITAL-LEXINGTON (O, 41 beds) 310 South Limestone Street, 3rd Floor, Lexington, KY, Zip 40508-3008; tel. 859/226-7096; Kim Pennington, Chief Executive Officer
Web address: www.lexington.selectspecialtyhospitals.com/

SELECT SPECIALTY HOSPITAL-NORTHERN KENTUCKY (O, 33 beds) 85 North Grand Avenue, Fort Thomas, KY, Zip 41075-1793; tel. 859/572-3880; Mavis Bechtle, MSN, R.N., FACHE, Chief Executive Officer

MICHIGAN: SELECT SPECIALTY HOSPITAL - SPECTRUM HEALTH (O, 36 beds) 1840 Wealthy Street, Southeast, Grand Rapids, MI, Zip 49506-2921; tel. 616/774-3800; Jim Aldrich, Chief Executive Officer
Web address: www.https://grandrapids.selectspecialtyhospitals.com

SELECT SPECIALTY HOSPITAL-ANN ARBOR (O, 36 beds) 5301 East Huron River Drive, 7th Floor, Ypsilanti, MI, Zip 48197-1051; tel. 734/712-6751; Bryan Cutliff, Chief Executive Officer
Web address: www.annarbor.selectspecialtyhospitals.com/

SELECT SPECIALTY HOSPITAL-BATTLE CREEK (O, 25 beds) 300 North Avenue, Battle Creek, MI, Zip 49017-3307; tel. 269/245-4675; Robert Mach, Chief Executive Officer

SELECT SPECIALTY HOSPITAL-DOWNRIVER (O, 35 beds) 2333 Biddle Avenue, 8th Floor, Wyandotte, MI, Zip 48192-4668; tel. 734/246-5500; John Ponczocha, Chief Executive Officer
Web address: www.downriver.selectspecialtyhospitals.com/

SELECT SPECIALTY HOSPITAL-FLINT (O, 26 beds) 401 South Ballenger Highway, 5th Floor Central, Flint, MI, Zip 48532-3638; tel. 810/342-4545; Christina DeBlouw, Chief Executive Officer

SELECT SPECIALTY HOSPITAL-GROSSE POINTE (O, 30 beds) 468 Cadieux Road, 3 North East, Grosse Pointe, MI, Zip 48230-1507, Mailing Address: 22101 Moross Road, 6th Floor, Detroit, Zip 48236, tel. 313/473-6131; Zaahra Butt, Chief Executive Officer
Web address: www.grossepointe.selectspecialtyhospitals.com/

SELECT SPECIALTY HOSPITAL-MACOMB COUNTY (O, 36 beds) 215 North Avenue, Mount Clemens, MI, Zip 48043-1700; tel. 586/307-9000; Jon P. O'Malley, Chief Executive Officer

SELECT SPECIALTY HOSPITAL-MUSKEGON (O, 31 beds) 1700 Clinton Street, 3 South, Muskegon, MI, Zip 49442-5502; tel. 231/728-5811; Kerry McLane, Chief Executive Officer
Web address: www.greatlakesspecialtyhospital.com

SELECT SPECIALTY HOSPITAL-NORTHWEST DETROIT (O, 36 beds) 6071 West Outer Drive, Detroit, MI, Zip 48235-2624; tel. 313/966-4747; Marilouise Riska, Chief Executive Officer

SELECT SPECIALTY HOSPITAL-PONTIAC (O, 30 beds) 44405 Woodward Avenue, 8th Floor, Pontiac, MI, Zip 48341-5023; tel. 248/452-5252; Peggy Kingston, Chief Executive Officer
Web address: www.selectspecialtyhospitals.com/company/locations/pontiac.aspx

SELECT SPECIALTY HOSPITAL-SAGINAW (O, 32 beds) 1447 North Harrison Street, 8th Floor, Saginaw, MI, Zip 48602-4785; tel. 989/583-4235; Matthew J. Campbell Esq, Chief Executive Officer

MINNESOTA: REGENCY HOSPITAL OF MINNEAPOLIS (O, 92 beds) 1300 Hidden Lakes Parkway, Golden Valley, MN, Zip 55422-4286; tel. 763/588-2750; Sean Stricker, Chief Executive Officer
Web address: www.regencyhospital.com

MISSISSIPPI: REGENCY HOSPITAL OF MERIDIAN (O, 40 beds) 1102 Constitution Avenue, 2nd Floor, Meridian, MS, Zip 39301-4001; tel. 601/484-7900; Clifton Quinn, Chief Executive Officer
Web address: www.regencyhospital.com

SELECT SPECIALTY HOSPITAL – BELHAVEN (O, 25 beds) 1225 North State Street, Jackson, MS, Zip 39202-2097, Mailing Address: P.O. Box 23695, Zip 39225-3695, tel. 601/968-1000; Bobbie K. Ware, MHS, BSN, RN, FACHE, Chief Executive Officer

SELECT SPECIALTY HOSPITAL-GULFPORT (O, 61 beds) 1520 Broad Avenue, Suite 300, Gulfport, MS, Zip 39501-3601; tel. 228/575-7500; John O'Keefe, Chief Executive Officer
Web address: www.selectspecialtyhospitals.com/company/locations/gulfcoast.aspx

SELECT SPECIALTY HOSPITAL-JACKSON (O, 53 beds) 5903 Ridgewood Road, Suite 100, Jackson, MS, Zip 39211-3700; tel. 601/899-3800; Chandler Ewing, Chief Executive Officer
Web address: www.selectspecialtyhospitals.com/company/locations/jackson.aspx

MISSOURI: SSM SELECT REHABILITATION HOSPITAL (O, 125 beds) 1027 Bellevue Avenue, 3rd Floor, Richmond Heights, MO, Zip 63117-1851, Mailing Address: 1027 Bellevue Avenue, Zip 63117-1851, tel. 314/768-5300; Robert Pritts, Chief Executive Officer

SELECT SPECIALTY HOSPITAL-SPRINGFIELD (O, 44 beds) 1630 East Primrose Street, Springfield, MO, Zip 65804-7929; tel. 417/885-4700; Steve Patterson, Chief Executive Officer
Web address: www.selectspecialtyhospitals.com/company/locations/springfield.aspx

SELECT SPECIALTY HOSPITAL-ST. LOUIS (O, 33 beds) 300 First Capitol Drive, Unit 1, Saint Charles, MO, Zip 63301-2844; tel. 636/947-5010; Phillip Readinger, Chief Executive Officer

NEBRASKA: SELECT SPECIALTY HOSPITAL – LINCOLN (O, 24 beds) 2300 South 16th Street, 7th Floor, Lincoln, NE, Zip 68502-3704; tel. 402/483-8444; Connie K. Siffring, Chief Executive Officer
Web address: www.selectmedical.com

SELECT SPECIALTY HOSPITAL-OMAHA (O, 52 beds) 1870 South 75th Street, Omaha, NE, Zip 68124-1700; tel. 402/361-5700; Nancy Laughlin Wagner, R.N., Chief Executive Officer
Web address: www.https://omaha.selectspecialtyhospitals.com

Section B

For explanation of codes following names, see page B2.
★ Indicates Type III membership in the American Hospital Association.

NEW JERSEY: KESSLER INSTITUTE FOR REHABILITATION (O, 336 beds) 1199 Pleasant Valley Way, West Orange, NJ, Zip 07052–1424; tel. 973/731–3600; Sue Kida, President
Web address: www.kessler-rehab.com

KESSLER MARLTON REHABILITATION (O, 61 beds) 92 Brick Road, Marlton, NJ, Zip 08053–2177; tel. 856/988–8778; Phyllis J. Schlichtmann, R.N., Chief Executive Officer

SELECT SPECIALTY HOSPITAL–NORTHEAST NEW JERSEY (O, 62 beds) 96 Parkway, Rochelle Park, NJ, Zip 07662–4200; tel. 201/221–2352; Patrick T. Swift, Chief Executive Officer
Web address: www.northeastnewjersey.selectspecialtyhospitals.com/about/

NORTH CAROLINA: SELECT SPECIALTY HOSPITAL–DURHAM (O, 30 beds) 3643 North Roxboro Road, 6th Floor, Durham, NC, Zip 27704–2702; tel. 919/470–9159; Jennifer Rawley, PharmD, Chief Executive Officer

SELECT SPECIALTY HOSPITAL–GREENSBORO (O, 30 beds) 1200 North Elm Street, 5th Floor, Greensboro, NC, Zip 27401–1004; tel. 336/832–8571; Deana Knight, Chief Executive Officer
Web address: www.selectspecialtyhospitals.com/company/locations/greensboro.aspx

OHIO: CLEVELAND CLINIC REHABILITATION HOSPITAL (O, 120 beds) 33355 Health Campus Boulevard, Avon, OH, Zip 44011; tel. 440/937–9099; Sam Bayoumy, Chief Executive Officer

OHIOHEALTH REHABILITATION HOSPITAL (O, 44 beds) 1087 Dennison Avenue, 4th Floor, Columbus, OH, Zip 43201–3201; tel. 614/484–9600; Eric Yap, Chief Executive Officer
Web address: www.ohiohealth-rehab.com

REGENCY HOSPITAL CLEVELAND EAST (O, 87 beds) 4200 Interchange Corporate Center Road, Warrensville Heights, OH, Zip 44128–5631; tel. 216/910–3800; Lisa Deering, Chief Executive Officer

REGENCY HOSPITAL OF COLUMBUS (O, 66 beds) 1430 South High Street, Columbus, OH, Zip 43207–1045; tel. 614/456–0300; Kindra Marks, Chief Executive Officer
Web address: www.regencyhospital.com/

REGENCY HOSPITAL OF TOLEDO (O, 45 beds) 5220 Alexis Road, Sylvania, OH, Zip 43560–2504; tel. 419/318–5700; Gary Zaciewski, Chief Executive Officer
Web address: www.regencyhospital.com

SELECT SPECIALTY HOSPITAL – BOARDMAN (O, 24 beds) 8401 Market Street, 7 South, Boardman, OH, Zip 44512–6725; tel. 330/729–1750; Varun Chauhan, Chief Executive Officer
Web address: www.selectspecialtyhospitals.com/

SELECT SPECIALTY HOSPITAL – CINCINNATI NORTH (O, 41 beds) 10500 Montgomery Road, Cincinnati, OH, Zip 45242–4402; tel. 513/865–5300; Raymond Carnevale, Interim Chief Executive Officer

SELECT SPECIALTY HOSPITAL – CLEVELAND GATEWAY (O, 143 beds) 2351 East 22nd Street, 7th Floor, Cleveland, OH, Zip 44115–3111; tel. 216/363–2671; Julie Idoine–Fries, Chief Executive Officer
Web address: www.selectspecialtyhospitals.com/

SELECT SPECIALTY HOSPITAL OF SOUTHEAST OHIO (O, 35 beds) 2000 Tamarack Road, Newark, OH, Zip 43055; tel. 740/588–7888; Linda Supplee, Chief Executive Officer
Web address: www.selectspecialtyhospitals.com/company/locations/zanesville.aspx

SELECT SPECIALTY HOSPITAL–AKRON (O, 60 beds) 200 East Market Street, Akron, OH, Zip 44308–2015; tel. 330/761–7500; Sonda Burns, Chief Executive Officer
Web address: www.selectspecialtyhospitals.com/company/locations/akron.aspx

SELECT SPECIALTY HOSPITAL–CANTON (O, 30 beds) 1320 Mercy Drive NW, 6th Floor, Canton, OH, Zip 44708–2614; tel. 330/489–8189; Dawne Wheeler, Chief Executive Officer
Web address: www.selectspecialtyhospitals.com/company/locations/canton.aspx

SELECT SPECIALTY HOSPITAL–CINCINNATI (O, 30 beds) 375 Dixmyth Avenue, 15th Floor, Cincinnati, OH, Zip 45220–2475; tel. 513/862–4444; David D. Muggli, FACHE, Chief Executive Officer

SELECT SPECIALTY HOSPITAL–COLUMBUS (O, 186 beds) 1087 Dennison Avenue, Columbus, OH, Zip 43201–3201; tel. 614/458–9000; Lisa J. Pettrey, MSN, R.N., Chief Executive Officer
Web address: www.selectspecialtyhospitals.com/company/locations/columbus.aspx

SELECT SPECIALTY HOSPITAL–YOUNGSTOWN (O, 56 beds) 1044 Belmont Avenue, Youngstown, OH, Zip 44504–1006; tel. 330/480–2349; Jodi Costello, Chief Executive Officer

TRIHEALTH REHABILITATION HOSPITAL (O, 60 beds) 2155 Dana Avenue, Cincinnati, OH, Zip 45207; tel. 513/601–0600; Daphne Glenn, Chief Executive Officer
Web address: www.trihealthrehab.com

OKLAHOMA: SELECT SPECIALTY HOSPITAL–OKLAHOMA CITY (O, 72 beds) 3524 NW 56th Street, Oklahoma City, OK, Zip 73112–4518; tel. 405/606–6700; Zackary L. Dawson, Chief Executive Officer
Web address: www.https://oklahomacity.selectspecialtyhospitals.com/

SELECT SPECIALTY HOSPITAL–TULSA MIDTOWN (O, 56 beds) 1125 South Trenton Avenue, 3rd Floor, Tulsa, OK, Zip 74120–5418; tel. 918/579–7300; Raymond Carnevale, Interim Chief Executive Officer

PENNSYLVANIA: HELEN M. SIMPSON REHABILITATION HOSPITAL (C, 55 beds) 4300 Londonderry Road, Harrisburg, PA, Zip 17109–5317; tel. 717/920–4300; Mark Freeburn, Chief Executive Officer
Web address: www.simpson-rehab.com/

PENN STATE HERSHEY REHABILITATION HOSPITAL (O, 76 beds) 1135 Old West Chocolate Avenue, Hummelstown, PA, Zip 17036; tel. 717/832–2600; Michelle Von Arx, Chief Executive Officer

SELECT SPECIALTY HOSPITAL–CAMP HILL (O, 92 beds) 503 North 21st Street, 5th Floor, Camp Hill, PA, Zip 17011–2204; tel. 717/972–4575; Pat Alexander, Chief Executive Officer
Web address: www.camphill.selectspecialtyhospitals.com/

SELECT SPECIALTY HOSPITAL–DANVILLE (O, 30 beds) 100 North Academy Avenue, 3rd Floor, Danville, PA, Zip 17822–3050; tel. 570/214–9653; Brian Mann, Chief Executive Officer

SELECT SPECIALTY HOSPITAL–ERIE (O, 50 beds) 252 West 11th Street, Erie, PA, Zip 16501–1702; tel. 814/874–5300; Thomas Fucci, FACHE, Chief Executive Officer
Web address: www.erie.selectspecialtyhospitals.com/

SELECT SPECIALTY HOSPITAL–JOHNSTOWN (O, 39 beds) 320 Main Street, 3rd Floor, Johnstown, PA, Zip 15901–1601; tel. 814/534–7300; Kelly Blake, Chief Executive Officer
Web address: www.selectspecialtyhospitals.com/company/locations/johnstown.aspx

SELECT SPECIALTY HOSPITAL–LAUREL HIGHLANDS (O, 40 beds) One Mellon Way, 3rd Floor, Latrobe, PA, Zip 15650–1197; tel. 724/539–3870; Eric Schwab, Chief Executive Officer

SELECT SPECIALTY HOSPITAL–MCKEESPORT (O, 30 beds) 1500 Fifth Avenue, 6th Floor, McKeesport, PA, Zip 15132–2422; tel. 412/664–2900; Angela Merryman, Chief Executive Officer
Web address: www.mckeesport.selectspecialtyhospitals.com/

SELECT SPECIALTY HOSPITAL–PITTSBURGH/UPMC (O, 32 beds) 200 Lothrop Street, E824, Pittsburgh, PA, Zip 15213–2536; tel. 412/586–9800; Yvonne Kughn, Chief Executive Officer
Web address: www.pittsburghupmc.selectspecialtyhospitals.com/

SOUTH CAROLINA: REGENCY HOSPITAL OF FLORENCE (O, 40 beds) 121 East Cedar Street, 4th Floor, Florence, SC, Zip 29506–2576; tel. 843/661–3471; Amy Metz, Chief Executive Officer
Web address: www.regencyhospital.com

REGENCY HOSPITAL OF GREENVILLE (O, 32 beds) One St Francis Drive, 4th Floor, Greenville, SC, Zip 29601–3955; tel. 864/255–1438; Paige Beauregard, Chief Executive Officer

SOUTH DAKOTA: SELECT SPECIALTY HOSPITAL–SIOUX FALLS (O, 24 beds) 1305 West 18th Street, Sioux Falls, SD, Zip 57105–0401; tel. 605/312–9500; Carol Ulmer, Chief Executive Officer
Web address: www.selectspecialtyhospitals.com/company/locations/siouxfalls.aspx

TENNESSEE: SELECT SPECIALTY HOSPITAL–MEMPHIS (O, 39 beds) 5959 Park Avenue, 12th Floor, Memphis, TN, Zip 38119–5200; tel. 901/765–1245; Marcia Taylor, Chief Executive Officer

For explanation of codes following names, see page B2.
★ Indicates Type III membership in the American Hospital Association.

Section B

SELECT SPECIALTY HOSPITAL–NASHVILLE (O, 70 beds) 2000 Hayes Street, Nashville, TN, Zip 37203–2318; tel. 615/284–4599; Jennifer Causey, Chief Executive Officer
Web address: www.selectspecialtyhospitals.com/company/locations/nashville.aspx

SELECT SPECIALTY HOSPITAL–NORTH KNOXVILLE (O, 68 beds) 7557B Dannaher Drive, Suite 145, Powell, TN, Zip 37849–3568; tel. 865/512–2450; Steve Plumlee, Chief Executive Officer
Web address: www.northknoxville.selectspecialtyhospitals.com/

SELECT SPECIALTY HOSPITAL–TRI CITIES (O, 33 beds) One Medical Park Boulevard, 5th Floor, Bristol, TN, Zip 37620–8964; tel. 423/844–5900; Jeffrey Radford, Chief Executive Officer

TEXAS: BAYLOR INSTITUTE FOR REHABILITATION AT FORT WORTH (C, 42 beds) 6601 Harris Parkway, Fort Worth, TX, Zip 76132–6108, Victoria Odom. Sanders, FACHE, Chief Executive Officer
Web address: www.baylorhealth.com/PhysiciansLocations/BIR/Pages/Default.aspx

BAYLOR INSTITUTE FOR REHABILITATION AT FRISCO (O, 44 beds) 2990 Legacy Drive, Frisco, TX, Zip 75034–6066; tel. 469/888–5100; Ryan Seymour, Chief Executive Officer

SELECT REHABILITATION HOSPITAL OF DENTON (O, 44 beds) 2620 Scripture Street, Denton, TX, Zip 76201–4315; tel. 940/297–6500; Michelle Powell, Chief Executive Officer
Web address: www.selectrehab–denton.com/

SELECT REHABILITATION HOSPITAL OF SAN ANTONIO (O, 42 beds) 19126 Stonehue Road, San Antonio, TX, Zip 78258–3490; tel. 210/482–3400; Robert Ward, Chief Executive Officer

SELECT SPECIALTY HOSPITAL – DALLAS DOWNTOWN (O, 26 beds) 3500 Gaston Avenue, Floors 3&4 Jonsson, Dallas, TX, Zip 75246–2017; tel. 469/801–4500; Michael McAlister, Chief Executive Officer
Web address: www.dallasdowntown.selectspecialtyhospitals.com/

SELECT SPECIALTY HOSPITAL–DALLAS (O, 60 beds) 2329 West Parker Road, Carrollton, TX, Zip 75010–4713, Ty Burgess, Chief Executive Officer

SELECT SPECIALTY HOSPITAL–LONGVIEW (O, 32 beds) 700 East Marshall Avenue, 1st Floor, Longview, TX, Zip 75601–5580; tel. 903/315–1100; Andrew Meade, Chief Executive Officer
Web address: www.longview.selectspecialtyhospitals.com/

VIRGINIA: COASTAL VIRGINIA REHABILITATION (C, 35 beds) 245 Chesapeake Avenue, Newport News, VA, Zip 23607–6038; tel. 757/928–8000; Daniel Ballin, Administrator

SELECT SPECIALTY HOSPITAL HAMPTON ROADS (O, 25 beds) 245 Chesapeake Avenue, Newport News, VA, Zip 23607–6038; tel. 757/534–5000; Phillip L. Wright, FACHE, Chief Executive Officer
Web address: www.hamptonroadsspecialtyhospital.com

WEST VIRGINIA: SELECT SPECIALTY HOSPITAL–CHARLESTON (O, 32 beds) 333 Laidley Street, 3rd Floor East, Charleston, WV, Zip 25301–1614; tel. 304/720–7234; Frank Weber, Chief Executive Officer

WISCONSIN: SELECT SPECIALTY HOSPITAL–MADISON (O, 58 beds) 801 Braxton Place, Madison, WI, Zip 53715–1415; tel. 608/260–2700; Mary Kay. Diderrich, R.N., Chief Executive Officer
Web address: www.madison.selectspecialtyhospitals.com

SELECT SPECIALTY HOSPITAL–MILWAUKEE (O, 63 beds) 8901 West Lincoln Avenue, 2nd Floor, Milwaukee, WI, Zip 53227–2409, West Allis, tel. 414/328–7700; Mary Kay. Diderrich, R.N., Chief Executive Officer
Web address: www.selectspecialtyhospitals.com/company/locations/milwaukee.aspx

Owned, leased, sponsored:	98 hospitals	5198 beds
Contract–managed:	3 hospitals	132 beds
Totals:	101 hospitals	5330 beds

★2565: SENTARA HEALTHCARE (NP)

6015 Poplar Hall Drive, Norfolk, VA, Zip 23502–3819; tel. 757/455–7000; Howard P. Kern, Chief Executive Officer
(Centralized Physician/Insurance Health System)

NORTH CAROLINA: SENTARA ALBEMARLE MEDICAL CENTER (L, 109 beds) 1144 North Road Street, Elizabeth City, NC, Zip 27909–3473, Mailing Address: P.O. Box 1587, Zip 27906–1587, tel. 252/335–0531; Coleen F. Santa Ana, President
Web address: www.albemarlehealth.org

VIRGINIA: SENTARA CAREPLEX HOSPITAL (O, 169 beds) 3000 Coliseum Drive, Hampton, VA, Zip 23666–5963; tel. 757/736–1000; Kirkpatrick Conley, President

SENTARA HALIFAX REGIONAL HOSPITAL (O, 456 beds) 2204 Wilborn Avenue, South Boston, VA, Zip 24592–1638; tel. 434/517–3100; Jason A. Studley, FACHE, President
Web address: www.hrhs.org

SENTARA LEIGH HOSPITAL (O, 250 beds) 830 Kempsville Road, Norfolk, VA, Zip 23502–3920; tel. 757/261–6000; Joanne Inman, President
Web address: www.sentara.com

SENTARA MARTHA JEFFERSON HOSPITAL (O, 144 beds) 500 Martha Jefferson Drive, Charlottesville, VA, Zip 22911–4668; tel. 434/654–7000; Jonathan S. Davis, FACHE, President
Web address: www.marthajefferson.org

SENTARA NORFOLK GENERAL HOSPITAL (O, 495 beds) 600 Gresham Drive, Norfolk, VA, Zip 23507–1904; tel. 757/388–3000; Kurt T. Hofelich, President
Web address: www.sentara.com

SENTARA NORTHERN VIRGINIA MEDICAL CENTER (O, 183 beds) 2300 Opitz Boulevard, Woodbridge, VA, Zip 22191–3399; tel. 703/523–1000; Katherine Johnson, Ph.D., President

SENTARA OBICI HOSPITAL (O, 178 beds) 2800 Godwin Boulevard, Suffolk, VA, Zip 23434–8038; tel. 757/934–4000; Steve Julian, M.D., President
Web address: www.sentara.com

SENTARA PRINCESS ANNE HOSPITAL (O, 160 beds) 2025 Glenn Mitchell Drive, Virginia Beach, VA, Zip 23456–0178; tel. 757/507–1000; Thomas B. Thames, M.D., President
Web address: www.sentara.com

SENTARA RMH MEDICAL CENTER (O, 244 beds) 2010 Health Campus Drive, Harrisonburg, VA, Zip 22801–3293; tel. 540/689–1000; Douglas J. Moyer, President

SENTARA VIRGINIA BEACH GENERAL HOSPITAL (O, 259 beds) 1060 First Colonial Road, Virginia Beach, VA, Zip 23454–3002; tel. 757/395–8000; Elwood Bernard. Boone III, FACHE, President
Web address: www.sentara.com

SENTARA WILLIAMSBURG REGIONAL MEDICAL CENTER (O, 145 beds) 100 Sentara Circle, Williamsburg, VA, Zip 23188–5713; tel. 757/984–6000; David J. Masterson, President

Owned, leased, sponsored:	12 hospitals	2792 beds
Contract–managed:	0 hospitals	0 beds
Totals:	12 hospitals	2792 beds

★2065: SHARP HEALTHCARE (NP)

8695 Spectrum Center Boulevard, San Diego, CA, Zip 92123–1489; tel. 858/499–4000; Michael Murphy, CPA, President & Chief Executive Officer
(Centralized Health System)

CALIFORNIA: SHARP CHULA VISTA MEDICAL CENTER (O, 339 beds) 751 Medical Center Court, Chula Vista, CA, Zip 91911–6699; tel. 619/502–5800; Pablo Velez, R.N., Ph.D., Chief Executive Officer
Web address: www.sharp.com

SHARP CORONADO HOSPITAL AND HEALTHCARE CENTER (L, 181 beds) 250 Prospect Place, Coronado, CA, Zip 92118–1999; tel. 619/522–3600; Susan Stone, R.N., Ph.D., Senior Vice President and Chief Executive Officer
Web address: www.sharp.com

SHARP GROSSMONT HOSPITAL (L, 509 beds) 5555 Grossmont Center Drive, La Mesa, CA, Zip 91942–3019, Mailing Address: PO Box 158, Zip 91944–0158, tel. 619/740–6000; Scott Evans, PharmD, FACHE, Senior Vice President and Chief Executive Officer

SHARP MEMORIAL HOSPITAL (O, 450 beds) 7901 Frost Street, San Diego, CA, Zip 92123–2701; tel. 858/939–3400; Tim Smith, Senior Vice President and Chief Executive Officer
Web address: www.sharp.com

For explanation of codes following names, see page B2.
★ Indicates Type III membership in the American Hospital Association.

Section B

SHARP MESA VISTA HOSPITAL (O, 168 beds) 7850 Vista Hill Avenue, San Diego, CA, Zip 92123–2717; tel. 858/278–4110; Trisha Khaleghi, Senior Vice President and Chief Executive Officer
Web address: www.sharp.com

Owned, leased, sponsored:	5 hospitals	1647 beds
Contract–managed:	0 hospitals	0 beds
Totals:	5 hospitals	1647 beds

4125: SHRINERS HOSPITALS FOR CHILDREN (NP)
2900 North Rocky Point Drive, Tampa, FL, Zip 33607–1435, Mailing Address: P.O. Box 31356, Zip 33631–3356, tel. 813/281–0300; John P. McCabe, Executive Vice President
(Independent Hospital System)

CALIFORNIA: SHRINERS HOSPITALS FOR CHILDREN–NORTHERN CALIFORNIA (O, 70 beds) 2425 Stockton Boulevard, Sacramento, CA, Zip 95817–2215; tel. 916/453–2000; Margaret Bryan, Administrator
Web address: www.shrinershospitalsforchildren.org/Hospitals/Locations/NorthernCalifornia.aspx

FLORIDA: SHRINERS HOSPITALS FOR CHILDREN–TAMPA (O, 60 beds) 12502 USF Pine Drive, Tampa, FL, Zip 33612–9499; tel. 813/972–2250; Fleury Yelvington, Administrator

HAWAII: SHRINERS HOSPITALS FOR CHILDREN–HONOLULU (O, 16 beds) 1310 Punahou Street, Honolulu, HI, Zip 96826–1099; tel. 808/941–4466; Anton C. Smith, Administrator
Web address: www.shrinershospitalsforchildren.org/honolulu

ILLINOIS: SHRINERS HOSPITALS FOR CHILDREN–CHICAGO (O, 36 beds) 2211 North Oak Park Avenue, Chicago, IL, Zip 60707–3392; tel. 773/622–5400; Mark L. Niederpruem, FACHE, Administrator
Web address: www.shrinershospitalsforchildren.org/Hospitals/Locations/Chicago.aspx

LOUISIANA: SHRINERS HOSPITALS FOR CHILDREN–SHREVEPORT (O, 45 beds) 3100 Samford Avenue, Shreveport, LA, Zip 71103–4289; tel. 318/222–5704; Garry Kim. Green, FACHE, Administrator
Web address: www.shrinershospitalsforchildren.org/Hospitals/Locations/Shreveport.aspx

MASSACHUSETTS: SHRINERS HOSPITALS FOR CHILDREN–BOSTON (O, 14 beds) 51 Blossom Street, Boston, MA, Zip 02114–2601; tel. 617/722–3000; Eileen F. Skinner, FACHE, Administrator

SHRINERS HOSPITALS FOR CHILDREN–SPRINGFIELD (O, 10 beds) 516 Carew Street, Springfield, MA, Zip 01104–2396; tel. 413/787–2000; H Lee. Kirk Jr, FACHE, Administrator
Web address: www.shrinershospitalsforchildren.org/Hospitals/Locations/Springfield.aspx

MINNESOTA: SHRINERS HOSPITALS FOR CHILDREN–TWIN CITIES (O, 40 beds) 2025 East River Parkway, Minneapolis, MN, Zip 55414–3696; tel. 612/596–6100; Charles C. Lobeck, Administrator

MISSOURI: SHRINERS HOSPITALS FOR CHILDREN–ST. LOUIS (O, 12 beds) 4400 Clayton Avenue, Saint Louis, MO, Zip 63110–1624; tel. 314/432–3600; Phillip L. Grady, Administrator
Web address: https://www.shrinershospitalsforchildren.org

OHIO: SHRINERS HOSPITALS FOR CHILDREN – CINCINNATI (O, 30 beds) 3229 Burnet Avenue, Cincinnati, OH, Zip 45229–3095; tel. 513/872–6000; Mark D. Shugarman, Administrator
Web address: www.shrinershospitalsforchildren.org/Hospitals/Locations/Cincinnati.aspx

OREGON: SHRINERS HOSPITALS FOR CHILDREN–PORTLAND (O, 12 beds) 3101 SW Sam Jackson Park Road, Portland, OR, Zip 97239–3009; tel. 503/241–5090; Dereesa Reid, Administrator

PENNSYLVANIA: SHRINERS HOSPITALS FOR CHILDREN–PHILADELPHIA (O, 39 beds) 3551 North Broad Street, Philadelphia, PA, Zip 19140–4160; tel. 215/430–4000; Ed Myers, Administrator
Web address: www.shrinershospitalsforchildren.org/Hospitals/Locations/Philadelphia.aspx

SOUTH CAROLINA: SHRINERS HOSPITALS FOR CHILDREN–GREENVILLE (O, 15 beds) 950 West Faris Road, Greenville, SC, Zip 29605–4277; tel. 864/271–3444; Bill Munley, Administrator

TEXAS: SHRINERS HOSPITALS FOR CHILDREN–GALVESTON (O, 15 beds) 815 Market Street, Galveston, TX, Zip 77550–2725; tel. 409/770–6600; Mary Jaco, Administrator
Web address: www.shrinershospitalsforchildren.org/Hospitals/Locations/Galveston.aspx

SHRINERS HOSPITALS FOR CHILDREN–HOUSTON (O, 40 beds) 6977 Main Street, Houston, TX, Zip 77030–3701; tel. 713/797–1616; Cathy Moniaci, R.N., MS, Administrator

UTAH: SHRINERS HOSPITALS FOR CHILDREN–SALT LAKE CITY (O, 45 beds) 1275 East Fairfax Road, Salt Lake City, UT, Zip 84103–4399; tel. 801/536–3500; Kevin Martin, M.P.H., R.N., FACHE, Administrator
Web address: www.shrinershospitalsforchildren.org/Hospitals/Locations/SaltLakeCity.aspx

WASHINGTON: SHRINERS HOSPITALS FOR CHILDREN–SPOKANE (O, 30 beds) 911 West Fifth Avenue, Spokane, WA, Zip 99204–2901, Mailing Address: P.O. Box 2472, Zip 99210–2472, tel. 509/455–7844; Peter G. Brewer, Administrator
Web address: www.shrinershospitalsforchildren.org/Hospitals/Locations/Spokane.aspx

Owned, leased, sponsored:	17 hospitals	529 beds
Contract–managed:	0 hospitals	0 beds
Totals:	17 hospitals	529 beds

0360: SIGNATURE HEALTHCARE SERVICES (IO)
4238 Green River Road, Corona, CA, Zip 92880–1669; tel. 951/549–8032; Soon K. Kim, M.D., President and Chief Executive Officer
(Independent Hospital System)

ARIZONA: AURORA BEHAVIORAL HEALTH SYSTEM EAST (O, 70 beds) 6350 South Maple Street, Tempe, AZ, Zip 85283–2857; tel. 480/345–5400; Bruce Waldo, Chief Executive Officer

AURORA BEHAVIORAL HEALTH SYSTEM WEST (O, 80 beds) 6015 West Peoria Avenue, Glendale, AZ, Zip 85302–1213; tel. 623/344–4400; Bruce Waldo, Chief Executive Officer
Web address: www.aurorabehavioral.com

CALIFORNIA: AURORA BEHAVIORAL HEALTHCARE SAN DIEGO (O, 80 beds) 11878 Avenue of Industry, San Diego, CA, Zip 92128–3490; tel. 858/487–3200; Alain Azcona, Chief Executive Officer
Web address: www.sandiego.aurorabehavioral.com/

AURORA CHARTER OAK HOSPITAL (O, 146 beds) 1161 East Covina Boulevard, Covina, CA, Zip 91724–1599; tel. 626/966–1632; Todd A. Smith, Chief Executive Officer

LAS ENCINAS HOSPITAL (O, 138 beds) 2900 East Del Mar Boulevard, Pasadena, CA, Zip 91107–4399; tel. 626/795–9901; Thomas J. Mahle, Chief Executive Officer
Web address: www.lasencinashospital.com

VISTA DEL MAR HOSPITAL (O, 87 beds) 801 Seneca Street, Ventura, CA, Zip 93001–1411; tel. 805/653–6434; Mayla Krebsbach, Chief Executive Officer

ILLINOIS: CHICAGO LAKESHORE HOSPITAL (O, 161 beds) 4840 North Marine Drive, Chicago, IL, Zip 60640–4296; tel. 773/878–9700; David Fletcher–Janzen, Chief Executive Officer
Web address: www.chicagolakeshorehospital.com

NEVADA: DESERT PARKWAY BEHAVIORAL HEALTHCARE HOSPITAL (O, 83 beds) 3247 South Maryland Parkway, Las Vegas, NV, Zip 89109–2412; tel. 702/776–3500; Steve Shell, Chief Executive Officer

TEXAS: DALLAS BEHAVIORAL HEALTHCARE HOSPITAL (O, 116 beds) 800 Kirnwood Drive, Desoto, TX, Zip 75115–2000; tel. 855/982–0897; Selene Q. Hammon, Chief Executive Officer
Web address: www.dallasbehavioral.com

GEORGETOWN BEHAVIORAL HEALTH INSTITUTE (O, 118 beds) 3101 South Austin Avenue, Georgetown, TX, Zip 78626–7541; tel. 512/819–1100; Lisa Salter, Chief Executive Officer

HOUSTON BEHAVIORAL HEALTHCARE HOSPITAL (O, 25 beds) 2801 Gessner Road, Houston, TX, Zip 77080–2503; tel. 832/834–7710; Roy Hollis, Chief Executive Officer
Web address: www.houstonbehavioralhealth.com/

For explanation of codes following names, see page B2.
★ Indicates Type III membership in the American Hospital Association.

SAN ANTONIO BEHAVIORAL HEALTHCARE HOSPITAL (O, 108 beds) 8550 Huebner Road, San Antonio, TX, Zip 78240–1803; tel. 877/514–0010; Aleen D. Arabit, Chief Executive Officer

Owned, leased, sponsored:	12 hospitals	1212 beds
Contract–managed:	0 hospitals	0 beds
Totals:	12 hospitals	1212 beds

★0284: SINAI HEALTH SYSTEM (NP)

1500 South Fairfield Avenue, Chicago, IL, Zip 60608–1782; tel. 773/542–2000; Karen Teitelbaum, President and Chief Executive Officer
(Centralized Health System)

ILLINOIS: HOLY CROSS HOSPITAL (O, 298 beds) 2701 West 68th Street, Chicago, IL, Zip 60629–1882; tel. 773/884–9000; Lori Pacura, MSN, R.N., President

MOUNT SINAI HOSPITAL (O, 288 beds) 1500 South Fairfield Avenue, Chicago, IL, Zip 60608–1729; tel. 773/542–2000; Loren Chandler, President

Web address: www.sinai.org

SCHWAB REHABILITATION HOSPITAL (O, 83 beds) 1401 South California Avenue, Chicago, IL, Zip 60608–1858; tel. 773/522–2010; Karen Teitelbaum, Chief Executive Officer

Owned, leased, sponsored:	3 hospitals	669 beds
Contract–managed:	0 hospitals	0 beds
Totals:	3 hospitals	669 beds

5125: SISTERS OF CHARITY HEALTH SYSTEM (CO)

2475 East 22nd Street, Cleveland, OH, Zip 44115–3221; tel. 216/363–2797; Thomas J. Strauss, Chief Executive Officer
(Moderately Centralized Health System)

OHIO: MERCY MEDICAL CENTER (O, 304 beds) 1320 Mercy Drive NW, Canton, OH, Zip 44708–2641; tel. 330/489–1000; Paul C. Hiltz, FACHE, Interim Chief Executive Officer

Web address: www.cantonmercy.org

ST. VINCENT CHARITY MEDICAL CENTER (O, 199 beds) 2351 East 22nd Street, Cleveland, OH, Zip 44115–3111; tel. 216/861–6200; David F. Perse, M.D., President and Chief Executive Officer

Owned, leased, sponsored:	2 hospitals	503 beds
Contract–managed:	0 hospitals	0 beds
Totals:	2 hospitals	503 beds

5805: SISTERS OF MARY OF THE PRESENTATION HEALTH SYSTEM (CO)

1202 Page Drive SW, Fargo, ND, Zip 58103–2340, Mailing Address: P.O. Box 10007, Zip 58106–0007, tel. 701/237–9290; Aaron K. Alton, President and Chief Executive Officer
(Moderately Centralized Health System)

ILLINOIS: ST. MARGARET'S HOSPITAL (O, 41 beds) 600 East First Street, Spring Valley, IL, Zip 61362–1512; tel. 815/664–5311; Tim Muntz, President and Chief Executive Officer

NORTH DAKOTA: PRESENTATION MEDICAL CENTER (O, 25 beds) 213 Second Avenue NE, Rolla, ND, Zip 58367–7153, Mailing Address: P.O. Box 759, Zip 58367–0759, tel. 701/477–3161; Chris Albertson, Chief Executive Officer

Web address: www.pmc-rolla.com

ST. ALOISIUS MEDICAL CENTER (O, 116 beds) 325 East Brewster Street, Harvey, ND, Zip 58341–1653; tel. 701/324–4651; Mike Zwicker, Chief Executive Officer

ST. ANDREW'S HEALTH CENTER (O, 25 beds) 316 Ohmer Street, Bottineau, ND, Zip 58318–1045; tel. 701/228–9300; Jodi Atkinson, President and Chief Executive Officer

Web address: www.standrewshealth.com

Owned, leased, sponsored:	4 hospitals	207 beds
Contract–managed:	0 hospitals	0 beds
Totals:	4 hospitals	207 beds

0997: SKAGIT REGIONAL HEALTH (NP)

1415 E Kincaid Street, Mount Vernon, WA, Zip 98274–4126; tel. 360/424–4111; Gregg Agustin. Davidson, FACHE, President and Chief Executive Officer
(Independent Hospital System)

WASHINGTON: CASCADE VALLEY HOSPITAL (L, 48 beds) 330 South Stillaguamish Avenue, Arlington, WA, Zip 98223–1642; tel. 360/435–2133; Brian K. Ivie, President and Chief Executive Officer

SKAGIT REGIONAL HEALTH (O, 137 beds) 1415 East Kincaid, Mount Vernon, WA, Zip 98274–4126, Mailing Address: P.O. Box 1376, Zip 98273–1376, tel. 360/424–4111; Brian K. Ivie, President and Chief Executive Officer

Web address: www.skagitregionalhealth.org

Owned, leased, sponsored:	2 hospitals	185 beds
Contract–managed:	0 hospitals	0 beds
Totals:	2 hospitals	185 beds

1034: SOUTH GEORGIA MEDICAL CENTER (NP)

2501 North Patterson Street, Valdosta, GA, Zip 31602–1735, Mailing Address: P.O. Box 1727, Zip 31603–1727, tel. 229/333–1000; Bill Forbes, Interim Chief Executive Officer

GEORGIA: SOUTH GEORGIA MEDICAL CENTER BERRIEN CAMPUS (O, 39 beds) 1221 East McPherson Avenue, Nashville, GA, Zip 31639–2326; tel. 229/433–8600; Richard Huth, Administrator

SOUTH GEORGIA MEDICAL CENTER LANIER CAMPUS (O, 87 beds) 116 West Thigpen Avenue, Lakeland, GA, Zip 31635–1011; tel. 229/482–3110; Richard Huth, Administrator

Web address: www.sgmc.org

SOUTH GEORGIA MEDICAL CENTER (O, 302 beds) 2501 North Patterson Street, Valdosta, GA, Zip 31602–1735, Mailing Address: P.O. Box 1727, Zip 31603–1727, tel. 229/333–1000; Bill Forbes, Interim Chief Executive Officer

Owned, leased, sponsored:	3 hospitals	428 beds
Contract–managed:	0 hospitals	0 beds
Totals:	3 hospitals	428 beds

★0253: SOUTHEAST GEORGIA HEALTH SYSTEM (NP)

2415 Parkwood Drive, Brunswick, GA, Zip 31520–4722, Mailing Address: P.O. Box 1518, Zip 31521–1518, tel. 912/466–7000; Michael D. Scherneck, President and Chief Executive Officer

GEORGIA: SOUTHEAST GEORGIA HEALTH SYSTEM BRUNSWICK CAMPUS (O, 532 beds) 2415 Parkwood Drive, Brunswick, GA, Zip 31520–4722, Mailing Address: P.O. Box 1518, Zip 31521–1518, tel. 912/466–7000; Michael D. Scherneck, President and Chief Executive Officer

Web address: www.sghs.org

SOUTHEAST GEORGIA HEALTH SYSTEM CAMDEN CAMPUS (O, 40 beds) 2000 Dan Proctor Drive, Saint Marys, GA, Zip 31558–3810; tel. 912/576–6200; Howard W. Sepp Jr, Vice–President and Administrator

Owned, leased, sponsored:	2 hospitals	572 beds
Contract–managed:	0 hospitals	0 beds
Totals:	2 hospitals	572 beds

For explanation of codes following names, see page B2.
★ Indicates Type III membership in the American Hospital Association.

Section B

0628: SOUTHEASTHEALTH (NP)

1701 Lacey Street, Cape Girardeau, MO, Zip 63701–5230;
tel. 573/334–4822; Kenneth Bateman, CPA, Chief Executive Officer
(Moderately Centralized Health System)

MISSOURI: SOUTHEAST HEALTH CENTER OF RIPLEY COUNTY (L, 8 beds) 109 Plum Street, Doniphan, MO, Zip 63935–1299; tel. 573/996–2141; Cheryl Lynne. Barton, R.N., Chief Executive Officer
Web address: www.sehealth.org/southeast–health–center–of–ripley–county/SoutheastHEALTH.aspx?nd=41

SOUTHEAST HEALTH CENTER OF STODDARD COUNTY (L, 16 beds) 1200 North One Mile Road, Dexter, MO, Zip 63841–1000; tel. 573/624–5566; Sue Ann Williams, Chief Executive Officer
Web address: www.sehealth.org

SOUTHEAST HOSPITAL (O, 209 beds) 1701 Lacey Street, Cape Girardeau, MO, Zip 63701–5230; tel. 573/334–4822; Kenneth Bateman, CPA, President and Chief Executive Officer

Owned, leased, sponsored:	3 hospitals	233 beds
Contract–managed:	0 hospitals	0 beds
Totals:	3 hospitals	233 beds

4175: SOUTHERN ILLINOIS HEALTHCARE (NP)

1239 East Main Street, Carbondale, IL, Zip 62901–3114, Mailing Address: P.O. Box 3988, Zip 62902–3988, tel. 618/457–5200; Rex P. Budde, President and Chief Executive Officer
(Independent Hospital System)

ILLINOIS: HERRIN HOSPITAL (O, 114 beds) 201 South 14th Street, Herrin, IL, Zip 62948–3631; tel. 618/942–2171; Rodney Smith, Vice President and Administrator
Web address: www.sih.net

MEMORIAL HOSPITAL OF CARBONDALE (O, 167 beds) 405 West Jackson Street, Carbondale, IL, Zip 62901–1467, Mailing Address: P.O. Box 10000, Zip 62902–9000, tel. 618/549–0721; Al Taylor, Vice President and Administrator

ST. JOSEPH MEMORIAL HOSPITAL (O, 25 beds) 2 South Hospital Drive, Murphysboro, IL, Zip 62966–3333; tel. 618/684–3156; Susan Odle, Administrator
Web address: www.sih.net

Owned, leased, sponsored:	3 hospitals	306 beds
Contract–managed:	0 hospitals	0 beds
Totals:	3 hospitals	306 beds

0652: SOUTHWEST HEALTH SYSTEMS (NP)

215 Marion Avenue, Mccomb, MS, Zip 39648–2705, Mailing Address: P.O. Box 1307, Zip 39649–1307, tel. 601/249–5500; Norman M. Price, FACHE, Chief Executive Officer and Administrator
(Independent Hospital System)

MISSISSIPPI: LAWRENCE COUNTY HOSPITAL (O, 25 beds) Highway 84 East, Monticello, MS, Zip 39654–0788, Mailing Address: P.O. Box 788, Zip 39654–0788, tel. 601/587–4051; Semmes Ross Jr, Administrator
Web address: www.smrmc.com

SOUTHWEST MISSISSIPPI REGIONAL MEDICAL CENTER (O, 145 beds) 215 Marion Avenue, McComb, MS, Zip 39648–2705, Mailing Address: P.O. Box 1307, Zip 39649–1307, tel. 601/249–5500; Norman M. Price, FACHE, Chief Executive Officer

Owned, leased, sponsored:	2 hospitals	170 beds
Contract–managed:	0 hospitals	0 beds
Totals:	2 hospitals	170 beds

0164: SOUTHWEST HEALTHCARE SYSTEM (IO)

7025 N Scottsdale Road Suite 9347, Scottsdale, AZ, Zip 85253–3675, Mailing Address: 7025 North Scottsdale Road, Suite 9347, Zip 85251–3331, tel. 480/518–5444; Paul R. Tuft, President
(Independent Hospital System)

CALIFORNIA: PACIFICA HOSPITAL OF THE VALLEY (O, 231 beds) 9449 San Fernando Road, Sun Valley, CA, Zip 91352–1489; tel. 818/767–3310; Ayman Mousa, R.N., Ph.D., Chief Executive Officer

Owned, leased, sponsored:	1 hospitals	231 beds
Contract–managed:	0 hospitals	0 beds
Totals:	1 hospitals	231 beds

★1245: SPARROW HEALTH SYSTEM (NP)

1215 East Michigan Avenue, Lansing, MI, Zip 48912–1811; tel. 517/364–1000; Dennis A. Swan, JD, FACHE, President and Chief Executive Officer
(Centralized Physician/Insurance Health System)

MICHIGAN: SPARROW CARSON HOSPITAL (O, 48 beds) 406 East Elm Street, Carson City, MI, Zip 48811–9693, Mailing Address: P.O. Box 879, Zip 48811–0879, tel. 989/584–3131; William Roeser, Interim President and Chief Executive Officer

SPARROW CLINTON HOSPITAL (O, 25 beds) 805 South Oakland Street, Saint Johns, MI, Zip 48879–2253; tel. 989/227–3400; Edward Bruun, President and Chief Executive Officer
Web address: www.sparrowclinton.org

SPARROW HOSPITAL (O, 631 beds) 1215 East Michigan Avenue, Lansing, MI, Zip 48912–1811; tel. 517/364–1000; Mark Brett, Chief Executive Officer
Web address: www.sparrow.org

SPARROW IONIA HOSPITAL (O, 22 beds) 3565 South State Road, Ionia, MI, Zip 48846–1870; tel. 616/523–1400; William Roeser, President and Chief Executive Officer

SPARROW SPECIALTY HOSPITAL (O, 30 beds) 8 West Sparrow Hospital Tower, 1215 East Michigan Avenue, Lansing, MI, Zip 48912; tel. 517/364–4840; Lou Little, President and Chief Executive Officer
Web address: www.sparrowspecialty.org

Owned, leased, sponsored:	5 hospitals	756 beds
Contract–managed:	0 hospitals	0 beds
Totals:	5 hospitals	756 beds

★4195: SPARTANBURG REGIONAL HEALTHCARE SYSTEM (NP)

101 East Wood Street, Spartanburg, SC, Zip 29303–3040; tel. 864/560–6000; Bruce Holstien, President and Chief Executive Officer
(Centralized Health System)

SOUTH CAROLINA: PELHAM MEDICAL CENTER (O, 48 beds) 250 Westmoreland Road, Greer, SC, Zip 29651–9013; tel. 864/530–6000; Anthony Kouskolekas, FACHE, President

SPARTANBURG HOSPITAL FOR RESTORATIVE CARE (O, 116 beds) 389 Serpentine Drive, Spartanburg, SC, Zip 29303–3026; tel. 864/560–3280; Anita M. Butler, Chief Executive Officer
Web address: www.srhs.com

SPARTANBURG MEDICAL CENTER (O, 514 beds) 101 East Wood Street, Spartanburg, SC, Zip 29303–3040; tel. 864/560–6000; J Philip. Feisal, President and Chief Executive Officer

UNION MEDICAL CENTER (O, 50 beds) 322 West South Street, Union, SC, Zip 29379–2857, Mailing Address: P.O. Box 789, Zip 29379–0789, tel. 864/301–2000; Paul R. Newhouse, President
Web address: https://www.spartanburgregional.com/locations/union–medical–center/

Owned, leased, sponsored:	4 hospitals	728 beds
Contract–managed:	0 hospitals	0 beds
Totals:	4 hospitals	728 beds

★0177: SPECTRUM HEALTH (NP)

100 Michigan Street NE, Grand Rapids, MI, Zip 49503–2551, Mailing Address: 444 Michigan Street Northeast | MC065, Zip 49503–2551, tel. 616/391–1774; Christina Freese Decker, FACHE, MSIE, MHA, President and Chief Executive Officer
(Centralized Physician/Insurance Health System)

For explanation of codes following names, see page B2.
★ Indicates Type III membership in the American Hospital Association.

MICHIGAN: SPECTRUM HEALTH – BUTTERWORTH HOSPITAL (O, 1126 beds) 100 Michigan Street NE, Grand Rapids, MI, Zip 49503–2560; tel. 616/391–1774; Gwen Sandefur, President, Spectrum Health Hospital Group

SPECTRUM HEALTH BIG RAPIDS HOSPITAL (O, 48 beds) 605 Oak Street, Big Rapids, MI, Zip 49307–2099; tel. 231/796–8691; Mary Kay VanDriel, President
Web address: www.spectrumhealth.org

SPECTRUM HEALTH GERBER MEMORIAL (O, 25 beds) 212 South Sullivan Avenue, Fremont, MI, Zip 49412–1548; tel. 231/924–3300; Randall Kelley, FACHE, President
Web address: www.spectrumhealth.org

SPECTRUM HEALTH LUDINGTON HOSPITAL (O, 41 beds) One Atkinson Drive, Ludington, MI, Zip 49431–1906, Mailing Address: PO Box 2408, Grand Rapids, Zip 49501–2408, tel. 231/843–2591; Randall Kelley, FACHE, President
Web address: www.mmcwm.com

SPECTRUM HEALTH PENNOCK (O, 39 beds) 1009 West Green Street, Hastings, MI, Zip 49058–1710; tel. 269/945–3451; Sheryl Lewis. Blake, FACHE, President

SPECTRUM HEALTH REED CITY HOSPITAL (O, 72 beds) 300 North Patterson Road, Reed City, MI, Zip 49677–8041, Mailing Address: P.O. Box 75, Zip 49677–0075, tel. 231/832–3271; Mary Kay VanDriel, President
Web address: www.spectrumhealth.org/reedcity

SPECTRUM HEALTH UNITED HOSPITAL (O, 116 beds) 615 South Bower Street, Greenville, MI, Zip 48838–2614; tel. 616/754–4691; Andrea M. Leslie, MSN, R.N., President
Web address: www.spectrumhealth.org

SPECTRUM HEALTH ZEELAND COMMUNITY HOSPITAL (O, 50 beds) 8333 Felch Street, Zeeland, MI, Zip 49464–2608; tel. 616/772–4644; Ron Lewis, President

Owned, leased, sponsored:	8 hospitals	1517 beds
Contract–managed:	0 hospitals	0 beds
Totals:	8 hospitals	1517 beds

1037: SPRINGSTONE (IO)

101 South Fifth Street, Suite 3850, Louisville, KY, Zip 40202–3127; tel. 855/595–2292; Robert Maha, M.D., President and Chief Executive Officer

COLORADO: DENVER SPRINGS (O, 96 beds) 8835 American Way, Englewood, CO, Zip 80112–7056; tel. 720/643–4300; David Morris, Chief Executive Officer
Web address: www.denversprings.com/

INDIANA: BRENTWOOD SPRINGS (O, 48 beds) 4455 Roslin Road, Newburgh, IN, Zip 47630; tel. 812/858–7200; Jessica Black, Chief Executive Officer

SYCAMORE SPRINGS HOSPITAL (O, 48 beds) 833 Park East Boulevard, Lafayette, IN, Zip 47905–0785; tel. 765/743–4400; Zoe Frantz, Chief Executive Officer
Web address: www.sycamorespringshealth.com

KANSAS: COTTONWOOD SPRINGS HOSPITAL (O, 72 beds) 13351 South Arapaho Drive, Olathe, KS, Zip 66062–1520; tel. 913/353–3000; Jason Toalson, Chief Executive Officer
Web address: www.cottonwoodsprings.com

NORTH CAROLINA: TRIANGLE SPRINGS HOSPITAL (O, 77 beds) 10901 World Trade Boulevard, Raleigh, NC, Zip 27617–4203; tel. 919/372–4408; Carla Hollis, Chief Executive Officer

OHIO: BECKETT SPRINGS (O, 48 beds) 8614 Shepherd Farm Drive, West Chester, OH, Zip 45069; tel. 513/942–9500; Phil Sheridan, Chief Executive Officer
Web address: www.springstone.com/hospitals.stmhl

COLUMBUS DUBLIN SPRINGS (O, 144 beds) 7625 Hospital Drive, Dublin, OH, Zip 43016–9649; tel. 614/717–1800; Garry W. Hoyes, Chief Executive Officer
Web address: www.dublinsprings.com

HIGHLAND SPRINGS HOSPITAL (O, 72 beds) 4199 Mill Pond Drive, Highland Hills, OH, Zip 44122–5731; tel. 602/314–7800; Matthew Winchester, Chief Executive Officer

OKLAHOMA: OAKWOOD SPRINGS (O, 72 beds) 13101 Memorial Springs Court, Oklahoma City, OK, Zip 73114–2226; tel. 405/438–3000; Karen Walker, Chief Executive Officer
Web address: www.oakwoodsprings.com/

TEXAS: CARROLLTON SPRINGS (O, 53 beds) 2225 Parker Road, Carrollton, TX, Zip 75010–4711; tel. 972/242–4114; Samantha Castle, Chief Executive Officer
Web address: www.carrolltonsprings.com

MESA SPRINGS (O, 72 beds) 5560 Mesa Springs Drive, Fort Worth, TX, Zip 76123; tel. 817/292–4600; Barbara Schmidt, Chief Executive Officer
Web address: www.springstone.com/hospitals.stmhl

ROCK SPRINGS (O, 72 beds) 700 Southeast Inner Loop, Georgetown, TX, Zip 78626; tel. 512/819–9400; Jason McPherson, Chief Executive Officer

WESTPARK SPRINGS (O, 72 beds) 6902 South Peek Road, Richmond, TX, Zip 77407; tel. 832/532–8107; Colleen McCammon, Chief Executive Officer
Web address: www.westparksprings.com/why–westpark–springs/

WOODLAND SPRINGS HOSPITAL (O, 96 beds) 15680 Old Conroe Road, Conroe, TX, Zip 77384; tel. 936/270–7520; Dustin Davis, Chief Executive Officer
Web address: https://www.woodlandspringshealth.com/

Owned, leased, sponsored:	14 hospitals	1042 beds
Contract–managed:	0 hospitals	0 beds
Totals:	14 hospitals	1042 beds

★**5455: SSM HEALTH** (CO)

10101 Woodfield Lane, Saint Louis, MO, Zip 63132–2937; tel. 314/994–7800; Laura Kaiser, President and Chief Executive Officer

(Decentralized Health System)

ILLINOIS: CLAY COUNTY HOSPITAL (C, 22 beds) 911 Stacy Burk Drive, Flora, IL, Zip 62839–3241, Mailing Address: P.O. Box 280, Zip 62839–0280, tel. 618/662–2131; Chris Hunt, President
Web address: www.claycountyhospital.org

GOOD SAMARITAN REGIONAL HEALTH CENTER (O, 134 beds) 1 Good Samaritan Way, Mount Vernon, IL, Zip 62864–2402; tel. 618/242–4600; Kerry Swanson, Regional President, President Good Samaritan

SSM HEALTH ST. MARY'S HOSPITAL CENTRALIA (O, 124 beds) 400 North Pleasant Avenue, Centralia, IL, Zip 62801–3056; tel. 618/436–8000; Damon R. Harbison, President
Web address: https://www.ssmhealth.com/locations/st–marys–hospital–centralia

MISSOURI: SSM CARDINAL GLENNON CHILDREN'S HOSPITAL (O, 176 beds) 1465 South Grand Boulevard, Saint Louis, MO, Zip 63104–1095; tel. 314/577–5600; Steven Burghart, President
Web address: www.cardinalglennon.com

SSM HEALTH DEPAUL HOSPITAL – ST. LOUIS (O, 529 beds) 12303 De Paul Drive, Bridgeton, MO, Zip 63044–2512; tel. 314/344–6000; Ellis Hawkins, President

SSM HEALTH SAINT LOUIS UNIVERSITY HOSPITAL (O, 356 beds) 3635 Vista at Grand Boulevard, Saint Louis, MO, Zip 63110–0250, Mailing Address: P.O. Box 15250, Zip 63110–0250, tel. 314/577–8000; Patti Kelley, Vice President, Nurisng and Chief Nursing Officer
Web address: www.sluhospital.com

SSM HEALTH ST. CLARE HOSPITAL – FENTON (O, 184 beds) 1015 Bowles Avenue, Fenton, MO, Zip 63026–2394; tel. 636/496–2000; Tina Garrison, President

SSM HEALTH ST. FRANCIS HOSPITAL – MARYVILLE (O, 52 beds) 2016 South Main Street, Maryville, MO, Zip 64468–2655; tel. 660/562–2600; Michael A. Baumgartner, President
Web address: www.ssmhealthstfrancis.com

SSM HEALTH ST. JOSEPH – ST. CHARLES (O, 341 beds) 300 First Capitol Drive, Saint Charles, MO, Zip 63301–2844; tel. 636/947–5000; Lisle Wescott, President
Web address: www.ssmstjoseph.com

SSM HEALTH ST. JOSEPH HOSPITAL – LAKE SAINT LOUIS (O, 215 beds) 100 Medical Plaza, Lake Saint Louis, MO, Zip 63367–1366; tel. 636/625–5200; Lisle Wescott, President

Section B

For explanation of codes following names, see page B2.
★ Indicates Type III membership in the American Hospital Association.

SSM HEALTH ST. MARY'S HOSPITAL – AUDRAIN (O, 57 beds) 620 East Monroe Street, Mexico, MO, Zip 65265–2919; tel. 573/582–5000; Donna K. Jacobs, FACHE, President
Web address: www.ssmhealthmidmo.com

SSM HEALTH ST. MARY'S HOSPITAL – JEFFERSON CITY (O, 95 beds) 2505 Mission Drive, Jefferson City, MO, Zip 65109; tel. 573/681–3000; Philip P. Gustafson, Interim President

SSM HEALTH ST. MARY'S HOSPITAL – ST. LOUIS (O, 394 beds) 6420 Clayton Road, Saint Louis, MO, Zip 63117–1811, Richmond Heights, tel. 314/768–8000; Travis Capers, FACHE, President
Web address: www.stmarys–stlouis.com

OKLAHOMA: SSM HEALTH ST. ANTHONY HOSPITAL – OKLAHOMA CITY (O, 625 beds) 1000 North Lee Street, Oklahoma City, OK, Zip 73102–1080, Mailing Address: P.O. Box 205, Zip 73101–0205, tel. 405/272–7000; Tammy Powell, FACHE, M.P.H., President

SSM HEALTH ST. ANTHONY HOSPITAL – SHAWNEE (O, 70 beds) 1102 West MacArthur Street, Shawnee, OK, Zip 74804–1744; tel. 405/273–2270; Charles E. Skillings, President and Chief Executive Officer
Web address: www.stanthonyshawnee.com

WISCONSIN: MONROE CLINIC (O, 58 beds) 515 22nd Avenue, Monroe, WI, Zip 53566–1598; tel. 608/324–2000; Michael B. Sanders, President and Chief Executive Officer
Web address: www.monroeclinic.org

RIPON MEDICAL CENTER (O, 18 beds) 845 Parkside Street, Ripon, WI, Zip 54971–8505, Mailing Address: P.O. Box 390, Zip 54971–0390, tel. 920/748–3101; DeAnn Thurmer, Interim Chief Operating Officer and Chief Nursing Officer

SSM HEALTH ST. CLARE HOSPITAL–BARABOO (O, 43 beds) 707 14th Street, Baraboo, WI, Zip 53913–1597; tel. 608/356–1400; Laura Walczak, President
Web address: www.stclare.com

SSM HEALTH ST. MARY'S HOSPITAL JANESVILLE (O, 50 beds) 3400 East Racine Steeet, Janesville, WI, Zip 53546–2344; tel. 608/373–8000; Benjamin Layman, President

SSM HEALTH ST. MARY'S HOSPITAL (O, 362 beds) 700 South Park Street, Madison, WI, Zip 53715–1830; tel. 608/251–6100; Jon Rozenfeld, President
Web address: www.stmarysmadison.com

ST. AGNES HOSPITAL (O, 140 beds) 430 East Division Street, Fond Du Lac, WI, Zip 54935–4560, Mailing Address: P.O. Box 385, Zip 54936–0385, tel. 920/929–2300; Katherine Vergos, President
Web address: www.agnesian.com

WAUPUN MEMORIAL HOSPITAL (O, 25 beds) 620 West Brown Street, Waupun, WI, Zip 53963–1799; tel. 920/324–5581; DeAnn Thurmer, Chief Operating Officer

Owned, leased, sponsored:	21 hospitals	4048 beds
Contract–managed:	1 hospitals	22 beds
Totals:	22 hospitals	4070 beds

★0250: ST. CHARLES HEALTH SYSTEM, INC. (NP)
2500 NE Neff Road, Bend, OR, Zip 97701–6015; tel. 541/382–4321; Joseph Sluka, President and Chief Executive Officer
(Centralized Physician/Insurance Health System)

OREGON: ST. CHARLES BEND (O, 259 beds) 2500 NE Neff Road, Bend, OR, Zip 97701–6015; tel. 541/382–4321; Iman Simmons, Chief Operating Officer and Interim President

ST. CHARLES MADRAS (O, 25 beds) 470 NE 'A' Street, Madras, OR, Zip 97741–1844; tel. 541/475–3882; John Bishop, President
Web address: www.stcharleshealthcare.org/Our–Locations/Madras

ST. CHARLES PRINEVILLE (O, 20 beds) 384 SE Combs Flat Road, Prineville, OR, Zip 97754–1206; tel. 541/447–6254; John Bishop, President

ST. CHARLES REDMOND (O, 48 beds) 1253 NW Canal Boulevard, Redmond, OR, Zip 97756–1395; tel. 541/548–8131; Iman Simmons, Chief Operating Officer and Interim President
Web address: www.stcharleshealthcare.org

Owned, leased, sponsored:	4 hospitals	352 beds
Contract–managed:	0 hospitals	0 beds
Totals:	4 hospitals	352 beds

0618: ST. ELIZABETH HEALTHCARE (NP)
1 Medical Village Drive, Edgewood, KY, Zip 41017–3403; tel. 859/301–2000; Garren Colvin, Chief Executive Officer
(Centralized Physician/Insurance Health System)

KENTUCKY: ST. ELIZABETH EDGEWOOD (O, 508 beds) 1 Medical Village Drive, Edgewood, KY, Zip 41017–3403; tel. 859/301–2000; Garren Colvin, Chief Executive Officer
Web address: www.stelizabeth.com

ST. ELIZABETH FLORENCE (O, 169 beds) 4900 Houston Road, Florence, KY, Zip 41042–4824; tel. 859/212–5200; Garren Colvin, Chief Executive Officer

ST. ELIZABETH FORT THOMAS (O, 171 beds) 85 North Grand Avenue, Fort Thomas, KY, Zip 41075–1796; tel. 859/572–3100; Garren Colvin, Chief Executive Officer
Web address: www.stelizabeth.com

ST. ELIZABETH GRANT (O, 16 beds) 238 Barnes Road, Williamstown, KY, Zip 41097–9482; tel. 859/824–8240; Garren Colvin, Chief Executive Officer

Owned, leased, sponsored:	4 hospitals	864 beds
Contract–managed:	0 hospitals	0 beds
Totals:	4 hospitals	864 beds

0928: ST. LAWRENCE HEALTH SYSTEM (NP)
50 Leroy Street, Potsdam, NY, Zip 13676–1799; tel. 315/265–3300; David B. Acker, FACHE, President and CEO
(Independent Hospital System)

NEW YORK: CANTON–POTSDAM HOSPITAL (O, 87 beds) 50 Leroy Street, Potsdam, NY, Zip 13676–1799; tel. 315/265–3300; David B. Acker, FACHE, President and Chief Executive Officer

GOUVERNEUR HOSPITAL (O, 25 beds) 77 West Barney Street, Gouverneur, NY, Zip 13642–1040; tel. 315/287–1000; David Bender, Chief Executive Officer
Web address: www.gvnrhospital.org

Owned, leased, sponsored:	2 hospitals	112 beds
Contract–managed:	0 hospitals	0 beds
Totals:	2 hospitals	112 beds

★0356: ST. LUKE'S HEALTH SYSTEM (NP)
190 East Bannock Street, Boise, ID, Zip 83712–6241; tel. 208/381–4200; David C. Pate, M.D., JD, President and Chief Executive Officer
(Moderately Centralized Health System)

IDAHO: ST. LUKE'S ELMORE (L, 56 beds) 895 North Sixth East Street, Mountain Home, ID, Zip 83647–2207, Mailing Address: P.O. Box 1270, Zip 83647–1270, tel. 208/587–8401; Michael Blauer, Administrator
Web address: www.stlukesonline.org/elmore/

ST. LUKE'S JEROME (O, 25 beds) 709 North Lincoln Street, Jerome, ID, Zip 83338–1851, Mailing Address: 709 North Lincoln Avenue, Zip 83338–1851, tel. 208/814–9500; Curtis Maier, Administrator
Web address: www.stlukesonline.org/jerome/

ST. LUKE'S MAGIC VALLEY MEDICAL CENTER (O, 224 beds) 801 Pole Line Road West, Twin Falls, ID, Zip 83301–5810, Mailing Address: P.O. Box 409, Zip 83303–0409, tel. 208/814–1000; Michael A. Fenello, Administrator and West Region Chief Executive Officer

---

For explanation of codes following names, see page B2.
★ Indicates Type III membership in the American Hospital Association.

ST. LUKE'S MCCALL (L, 15 beds) 1000 State Street, McCall, ID, Zip 83638–3704; tel. 208/634–2221; Sean McCallister, Administrator
Web address: https://www.stlukesonline.org/communities–and–locations/facilities/hospitals–and–medical–centers/st–lukes–mccall–medical–center

ST. LUKE'S NAMPA (O, 87 beds) 9850 West St.Luke's Drive, Nampa, ID, Zip 83687; tel. 208/505–2000; Ed Castledine, Chief Executive Officer

ST. LUKE'S REGIONAL MEDICAL CENTER (O, 604 beds) 190 East Bannock Street, Boise, ID, Zip 83712–6241; tel. 208/381–2222; David M. McFadyen, Administrator
Web address: www.stlukesonline.org/boise

ST. LUKE'S REHABILITATION HOSPITAL (O, 31 beds) 600 North Robbins Road, Boise, ID, Zip 83702–4565, Mailing Address: P.O. Box 1100, Zip 83701–1100, tel. 208/489–4444; Nolan Hoffer, Senior Director
Web address: www.idahoelksrehab.org

ST. LUKE'S WOOD RIVER MEDICAL CENTER (O, 25 beds) 100 Hospital Drive, Ketchum, ID, Zip 83340, Mailing Address: P.O. Box 100, Zip 83340–0100, tel. 208/727–8800; Cody Langbehn, Administrator

WEISER MEMORIAL HOSPITAL (C, 18 beds) 645 East Fifth Street, Weiser, ID, Zip 83672–2202; tel. 208/549–0370; Steven D. Hale, FACHE, Chief Executive Officer
Web address: www.weisermemorialhospital.org

Owned, leased, sponsored:	8 hospitals	1067 beds
Contract–managed:	1 hospitals	18 beds
Totals:	9 hospitals	1085 beds

0862: ST. LUKE'S UNIVERSITY HEALTH NETWORK (NP)
801 Ostrum Street, Bethlehem, PA, Zip 18015–1000; tel. 610/954–4000; Richard A. Anderson, President and Chief Executive Officer
(Centralized Health System)

NEW JERSEY: ST. LUKE'S HOSPITAL – WARREN CAMPUS (O, 103 beds) 185 Roseberry Street, Phillipsburg, NJ, Zip 08865–1690; tel. 908/859–6700; Scott R. Wolfe, CPA, President

PENNSYLVANIA: ST. LUKE'S – GNADEN HUETTEN CAMPUS (O, 250 beds) 211 North 12th Street, Lehighton, PA, Zip 18235–1138; tel. 610/377–1300; Terrance J. Purcell, President
Web address: www.blmtn.org

ST. LUKE'S HOSPITAL – ANDERSON CAMPUS (O, 108 beds) 1872 Riverside Circle, Easton, PA, Zip 18045–5669; tel. 484/503–3000; Edward Nawrocki, President
Web address: www.mystlukesonline.org

ST. LUKE'S HOSPITAL – MINERS CAMPUS (O, 92 beds) 360 West Ruddle Street, Coaldale, PA, Zip 18218–1027; tel. 570/645–2131; Wendy Lazo, President

ST. LUKE'S HOSPITAL – QUAKERTOWN CAMPUS (O, 57 beds) 1021 Park Avenue, Quakertown, PA, Zip 18951–1573; tel. 215/538–4500; Dennis Pfleiger, President and Chief Operating Officer
Web address: www.slhhn.org

ST. LUKE'S SACRED HEART CAMPUS (O, 112 beds) 421 West Chew Street, Allentown, PA, Zip 18102–3490; tel. 610/776–4500; John L. Nespoli, Chief Executive Officer
Web address: www.shh.org

ST. LUKE'S UNIVERSITY HOSPITAL – BETHLEHEM CAMPUS (O, 540 beds) 801 Ostrum Street, Bethlehem, PA, Zip 18015–1065; tel. 484/526–4000; Carol Kuplen, R.N., MSN, President and Chief Executive Officer
Web address: www.slhn–lehighvalley.org

Owned, leased, sponsored:	7 hospitals	1262 beds
Contract–managed:	0 hospitals	0 beds
Totals:	7 hospitals	1262 beds

★**0156: STANFORD HEALTH CARE** (NP)
300 Pasteur Drive, Palo Alto, CA, Zip 94304–2299; tel. 650/723–4000; David Entwistle, President and Chief Executive Officer
(Centralized Physician/Insurance Health System)

CALIFORNIA: STANFORD HEALTH CARE – VALLEYCARE (O, 193 beds) 5555 West Las Positas Boulevard, Pleasanton, CA, Zip 94588–4000; tel. 925/847–3000; Scott Gregerson, President and Chief Executive Officer
Web address: www.valleycare.com

STANFORD HEALTH CARE (O, 477 beds) 300 Pasteur Drive, Suite H3200, Palo Alto, CA, Zip 94304–2203; tel. 650/723–4000; David Entwistle, President and Chief Executive Officer

Owned, leased, sponsored:	2 hospitals	670 beds
Contract–managed:	0 hospitals	0 beds
Totals:	2 hospitals	670 beds

0141: STEWARD HEALTH CARE SYSTEM, LLC (IO)
1900 North Pearl Street, Suite 2400, Dallas, TX, Zip 75201; tel. 617/419–4700; Ralph de la Torre, M.D., Chairman and Chief Executive Officer
(Moderately Centralized Health System)

ARIZONA: MOUNTAIN VISTA MEDICAL CENTER (O, 178 beds) 1301 South Crismon Road, Mesa, AZ, Zip 85209–3767; tel. 480/358–6100; Jacob Golich, Chief Executive Officer
Web address: www.mvmedicalcenter.com

ST. LUKE'S BEHAVIORAL HEALTH CENTER (O, 85 beds) 1800 East Van Buren, Phoenix, AZ, Zip 85006–3742; tel. 602/251–8546; Gregory L. Jahn, R.N., Chief Executive Officer

ST. LUKE'S MEDICAL CENTER (O, 284 beds) 1800 East Van Buren Street, Phoenix, AZ, Zip 85006–3742; tel. 602/251–8100; James Flinn, JD, FACHE, Chief Executive Officer
Web address: www.stlukesmedcenter.com

ARKANSAS: WADLEY REGIONAL MEDICAL CENTER AT HOPE (O, 79 beds) 2001 South Main Street, Hope, AR, Zip 71801–8194; tel. 870/722–3800; Thomas D. Gilbert, FACHE, Chief Executive Officer
Web address: www.wadleyhealthathope.com

COLORADO: PIKES PEAK REGIONAL HOSPITAL (O, 15 beds) 16420 West Highway 24, Woodland Park, CO, Zip 80863; tel. 719/687–9999; Kimberly Monjesky, Chief Executive Officer

FLORIDA: MELBOURNE REGIONAL MEDICAL CENTER (O, 119 beds) 250 North Wickham Road, Melbourne, FL, Zip 32935–8625; tel. 321/752–1200; Ron Gicca, Chief Executive Officer
Web address: www.wuesthoff.com/locations/wuesthoff–medical–center–melbourne

ROCKLEDGE REGIONAL MEDICAL CENTER (O, 215 beds) 110 Longwood Avenue, Rockledge, FL, Zip 32955–2887, Mailing Address: P.O. Box 565002, Mail Stop 1, Zip 32956–5002, tel. 321/636–2211; Andrew Romine, Chief Executive Officer

SEBASTIAN RIVER MEDICAL CENTER (O, 187 beds) 13695 North U S Hwy 1, Sebastian, FL, Zip 32958–3230, Mailing Address: Box 780838, Zip 32978–0838, tel. 772/589–3186; Kelly Enriquez, Chief Executive Officer
Web address: www.sebastianrivermedical.com

LOUISIANA: GLENWOOD REGIONAL MEDICAL CENTER (O, 278 beds) 503 McMillan Road, West Monroe, LA, Zip 71291–5327; tel. 318/329–4200; Jeremy M. Tinnerello, CEN, MSN, RN, President
Web address: www.grmc.com

MASSACHUSETTS: CARNEY HOSPITAL (O, 81 beds) 2100 Dorchester Avenue, Boston, MA, Zip 02124–5615; tel. 617/296–4000; Tom Sands, Interim Chief Executive Officer
Web address: www.carneyhospital.org

GOOD SAMARITAN MEDICAL CENTER (O, 190 beds) 235 North Pearl Street, Brockton, MA, Zip 02301–1794; tel. 508/427–3000; Harrison Bane, President
Web address: www.goodsamaritanmedical.org

HOLY FAMILY HOSPITAL (O, 329 beds) 70 East Street, Methuen, MA, Zip 01844–4597; tel. 978/687–0151; Craig A. Jesiolowski, FACHE, President

MORTON HOSPITAL AND MEDICAL CENTER (O, 153 beds) 88 Washington Street, Taunton, MA, Zip 02780–2465; tel. 508/828–7000; Deborah Bitsoli, CPA, President
Web address: www.mortonhospital.org

For explanation of codes following names, see page B2.
★ Indicates Type III membership in the American Hospital Association.

Section B

NASHOBA VALLEY MEDICAL CENTER (O, 48 beds) 200 Groton Road, Ayer, MA, Zip 01432–3300; tel. 978/784–9000; Korry Dow, Interim President
Web address: https://www.nashobamed.org

NEW ENGLAND SINAI HOSPITAL AND REHABILITATION CENTER (O, 212 beds) 150 York Street, Stoughton, MA, Zip 02072–1881; tel. 781/344–0600; Mary Beth. Urquhart, Interim President, Vice President Patient Care Services and Chief Nursing Officer

NORWOOD HOSPITAL (O, 188 beds) 800 Washington Street, Norwood, MA, Zip 02062–3487; tel. 781/769–4000; Salvatore Perla, President
Web address: www.norwood–hospital.org

SAINT ANNE'S HOSPITAL (O, 160 beds) 795 Middle Street, Fall River, MA, Zip 02721–1798; tel. 508/674–5741; Michael Bushell, President

ST. ELIZABETH'S MEDICAL CENTER (O, 338 beds) 736 Cambridge Street, Brighton, MA, Zip 02135–2997; tel. 617/789–3000; Craig T. Williams, President
Web address: www.semc.org/

OHIO: HILLSIDE REHABILITATION HOSPITAL (O, 65 beds) 8747 Squires Lane NE, Warren, OH, Zip 44484–1649; tel. 330/841–3700; Krista McFadden, Interim Chief Executive Officer

NORTHSIDE MEDICAL CENTER (O, 373 beds) 500 Gypsy Lane, Youngstown, OH, Zip 44504–1315; tel. 330/884–1000; Linda J. Grass, Chief Executive Officer
Web address: www.northsidemedicalcenter.net

TRUMBULL MEMORIAL HOSPITAL (O, 292 beds) 1350 East Market Street, Warren, OH, Zip 44483–6628; tel. 330/841–9011; Ronald L. Bierman, Chief Executive Officer
Web address: www.https://trumbullmemorial.org/?_ga=2.209137234.1564767671.1497292183–315051339.1497292183

PENNSYLVANIA: EASTON HOSPITAL (O, 196 beds) 250 South 21st Street, Easton, PA, Zip 18042–3892; tel. 610/250–4000; Jeffery Snyder, Chief Executive Officer

SHARON REGIONAL MEDICAL CENTER (O, 218 beds) 740 East State Street, Sharon, PA, Zip 16146–3395; tel. 724/983–3911; Joseph G. . Hugar, President
Web address: https://www.sharonregionalmedical.org

TEXAS: MEDICAL CENTER OF SOUTHEAST TEXAS (O, 17 beds) 6025 Metropolitan Drive, Beaumont, TX, Zip 77706–2407; tel. 409/617–7700; Becky Ames, Chief Executive Officer

ODESSA REGIONAL MEDICAL CENTER (O, 213 beds) 520 East Sixth Street, Odessa, TX, Zip 79761–4565, Mailing Address: P.O. Box 4859, Zip 79760–4859, tel. 432/582–8000; Stacey L. Gerig, Chief Executive Officer
Web address: www.odessaregionalmedicalcenter.com

SOUTHWEST GENERAL HOSPITAL (O, 253 beds) 7400 Barlite Boulevard, San Antonio, TX, Zip 78224–1399; tel. 210/921–2000; P Craig. Desmond, Chief Executive Officer
Web address: www.swgeneralhospital.com

ST. JOSEPH MEDICAL CENTER (O, 463 beds) 1401 St Joseph Parkway, Houston, TX, Zip 77002–8301; tel. 713/757–1000; Kimberly S. Bassett, R.N., President

THE MEDICAL CENTER OF SOUTHEAST TEXAS (O, 172 beds) 2555 Jimmy Johnson Boulevard, Port Arthur, TX, Zip 77640–2007; tel. 409/724–7389; Carl Bo"". Beaudry, President
Web address: www.medicalcentersetexas.com

WADLEY REGIONAL MEDICAL CENTER (O, 179 beds) 1000 Pine Street, Texarkana, TX, Zip 75501–5170; tel. 903/798–8000; Thomas D. Gilbert, FACHE, Chief Executive Officer

UTAH: DAVIS HOSPITAL AND MEDICAL CENTER (O, 221 beds) 1600 West Antelope Drive, Layton, UT, Zip 84041–1142; tel. 801/807–1000; Michael Jensen, Chief Executive Officer
Web address: www.davishospital.com

JORDAN VALLEY MEDICAL CENTER WEST VALLEY CAMPUS (O, 101 beds) 3460 South Pioneer Parkway, West Valley City, UT, Zip 84120–2049; tel. 801/561–8888; Jon R. Butterfield, Administrator and Chief Executive Officer
Web address: https://www.jordanwestvalley.org

JORDAN VALLEY MEDICAL CENTER (O, 183 beds) 3580 West 9000 South, West Jordan, UT, Zip 84088–8812; tel. 801/561–8888
Web address: www.jordanvalleymc.com

SALT LAKE REGIONAL MEDICAL CENTER (O, 132 beds) 1050 East South Temple, Salt Lake City, UT, Zip 84102–1507; tel. 801/350–4111; Dale Johns, FACHE, Chief Executive Officer

Owned, leased, sponsored:	33 hospitals	6217 beds
Contract–managed:	0 hospitals	0 beds
Totals:	33 hospitals	6217 beds

0858: STRATEGIC BEHAVIORAL HEALTH, LLC (IO)
8295 Tournament Drive, Suite 201, Memphis, TN, Zip 38125–8913; tel. 901/969–3100; Jim Shaheen, President

COLORADO: PEAK VIEW BEHAVIORAL HEALTH (O, 112 beds) 7353 Sisters Grove, Colorado Springs, CO, Zip 80923–2615; tel. 719/444–8484; Dan Zarecky, Chief Executive Officer
Web address: www.strategicbh.com/peakview.html

NEVADA: MONTEVISTA HOSPITAL (O, 202 beds) 5900 West Rochelle Avenue, Las Vegas, NV, Zip 89103–3327; tel. 702/364–1111; Richard Failla, Chief Executive Officer
Web address: www.montevistahospital.com

RED ROCK BEHAVIORAL HOSPITAL (O, 21 beds) 5975 West Twain Avenue, Las Vegas, NV, Zip 89103–1237; tel. 702/214–8099; Richard Failla, Chief Executive Officer
Web address: www.redrockhospital.com

NEW MEXICO: PEAK BEHAVIORAL HEALTH SERVICES (O, 36 beds) 5065 McNutt Road, Santa Teresa, NM, Zip 88008–9442; tel. 575/589–3000; Peggy Cunningham, Chief Executive Officer

NORTH CAROLINA: STRATEGIC BEHAVIORAL HEALTH – CHARLOTTE (O, 60 beds) 1715 Sharon Road West, Charlotte, NC, Zip 28210–5663; tel. 704/944–0650; George G. Boykin, Chief Executive Officer
Web address: www.sbccharlotte.com/

STRATEGIC BEHAVIORAL HEALTH – RALEIGH (O, 50 beds) 3200 Waterfield Drive, Garner, NC, Zip 27529–7727; tel. 919/800–4400; Matt Doyle, Chief Executive Officer

STRATEGIC BEHAVIORAL HEALTH – WILMINGTON (O, 112 beds) 2050 Mercantile Drive, Leland, NC, Zip 28451–4053; tel. 910/371–2500; Daniel Kern, Chief Executive Officer
Web address: www.sbcwilmington.com/

TEXAS: ROCK PRAIRIE BEHAVIORAL HEALTH (O, 72 beds) 3550 Normand Drive, College Station, TX, Zip 77845–6399; tel. 979/703–8848; Jackie St. Germain, Chief Executive Officer

WISCONSIN: WILLOW CREEK BEHAVIORAL HEALTH (O, 72 beds) 1351 Ontario Road, Green Bay, WI, Zip 54311–8302; tel. 920/328–1220; Teena Ahuja, Interim Chief Executive Officer and Regional Vice President of Operations
Web address: www.willowcreekbh.com

Owned, leased, sponsored:	9 hospitals	737 beds
Contract–managed:	0 hospitals	0 beds
Totals:	9 hospitals	737 beds

0517: SUCCESS HEALTHCARE (IO)
999 Yamato Road, 3rd Floor, Boca Raton, FL, Zip 33431–4477; tel. 561/869–6300; Peter R. Baronoff, President and Chief Executive Officer
(Independent Hospital System)

CALIFORNIA: SILVER LAKE MEDICAL CENTER (O, 175 beds) 1711 West Temple Street, Los Angeles, CA, Zip 90026–5421; tel. 213/989–6100; Brent A. Cope, Chief Executive Officer
Web address: www.silverlakemc.com

MISSOURI: ST. ALEXIUS HOSPITAL – BROADWAY CAMPUS (O, 190 beds) 3933 South Broadway, Saint Louis, MO, Zip 63118–4601; tel. 314/865–7000; Michael J. Motte, Chief Executive Officer

Owned, leased, sponsored:	2 hospitals	365 beds
Contract–managed:	0 hospitals	0 beds
Totals:	2 hospitals	365 beds

For explanation of codes following names, see page B2.
★ Indicates Type III membership in the American Hospital Association.

0399: SUMMA HEALTH (NP)

1077 Gorge Boulevard, Akron, OH, Zip 44310; tel. 330/375–3000; T. Clifford Deveny, M.D., Interim Chief Executive Officer
(Centralized Physician/Insurance Health System)

OHIO: SUMMA HEALTH SYSTEM (O, 639 beds) 525 East Market Street, Akron, OH, Zip 44304–1619; tel. 330/375–3000; David Custodio, M.D., President Summa Health System Akron
Web address: www.summahealth.org

SUMMA REHAB HOSPITAL (O, 60 beds) 29 North Adams Street, Akron, OH, Zip 44304–1641; tel. 330/572–7300; Cheryl Henthorn, Chief Executive Officer

Owned, leased, sponsored:	2 hospitals	699 beds
Contract-managed:	0 hospitals	0 beds
Totals:	2 hospitals	699 beds

★0189: SUMMIT HEALTH (NP)

112 North Seventh Street, Chambersburg, PA, Zip 17201–1720; tel. 717/267–7138; Patrick W. O'Donnell, CPA, President and Chief Executive Officer
(Independent Hospital System)

PENNSYLVANIA: CHAMBERSBURG HOSPITAL (O, 271 beds) 112 North Seventh Street, Chambersburg, PA, Zip 17201–1720; tel. 717/267–3000; Patrick W. O'Donnell, CPA, President and Chief Executive Officer
Web address: www.summithealth.org

WAYNESBORO HOSPITAL (O, 56 beds) 501 East Main Street, Waynesboro, PA, Zip 17268–2394; tel. 717/765–4000; Melissa Dubrow, Chief Operating Officer

Owned, leased, sponsored:	2 hospitals	327 beds
Contract-managed:	0 hospitals	0 beds
Totals:	2 hospitals	327 beds

★8795: SUTTER HEALTH (NP)

2200 River Plaza Drive, Sacramento, CA, Zip 95833–4134; tel. 916/733–8800; Sarah Krevans, President and Chief Executive Officer
(Centralized Health System)

CALIFORNIA: ALTA BATES SUMMIT MEDICAL CENTER – SUMMIT CAMPUS (O, 427 beds) 350 Hawthorne Avenue, Oakland, CA, Zip 94609–3100; tel. 510/655–4000; Charles Prosper, Chief Executive Officer
Web address: www.altabatessummit.com

ALTA BATES SUMMIT MEDICAL CENTER (O, 416 beds) 2450 Ashby Avenue, Berkeley, CA, Zip 94705–2067; tel. 510/204–4444; Julie A. Petrini, Chief Executive Officer
Web address: www.altabatessummit.org/

CALIFORNIA PACIFIC MEDICAL CENTER–DAVIES CAMPUS (O, 154 beds) Castro and Duboce Streets, San Francisco, CA, Zip 94114; tel. 415/600–6000; Mary Lanier, Vice President, Post Acute Services and Site Administrator

CALIFORNIA PACIFIC MEDICAL CENTER–ST. LUKE'S CAMPUS (O, 165 beds) 3555 Cesar Chavez Street, San Francisco, CA, Zip 94110–4403; tel. 415/600–6000; Warren S. Browner, M.D., M.P.H., Chief Executive Officer
Web address: www.stlukes-sf.org

CALIFORNIA PACIFIC MEDICAL CENTER (O, 640 beds) 2333 Buchanan Street, San Francisco, CA, Zip 94115–1925, Mailing Address: P.O. Box 7999, Zip 94120–7999, tel. 415/600–6000; Warren S. Browner, M.D., M.P.H., Chief Executive Officer

EDEN MEDICAL CENTER (O, 130 beds) 20103 Lake Chabot Road, Castro Valley, CA, Zip 94546–5305; tel. 510/537–1234; Stephen Gray, Chief Executive Officer
Web address: www.edenmedcenter.org

MEMORIAL HOSPITAL LOS BANOS (O, 44 beds) 520 West 'I' Street, Los Banos, CA, Zip 93635–3498; tel. 209/826–0591; Doug Archer, Administrator

MEMORIAL MEDICAL CENTER (O, 220 beds) 1700 Coffee Road, Modesto, CA, Zip 95355–2869, Mailing Address: P.O. Box 942, Zip 95353–0942, tel. 209/526–4500; Eugene Patrizio, Chief Executive Officer
Web address: www.memorialmedicalcenter.org

MENLO PARK SURGICAL HOSPITAL (O, 16 beds) 570 Willow Road, Menlo Park, CA, Zip 94025–2617; tel. 650/324–8500; Jeanette Engle–Ramirez, Chief Executive Officer
Web address: www.pamf.org/mpsh

MILLS–PENINSULA HEALTH SERVICES (O, 266 beds) 1501 Trousdale Drive, Burlingame, CA, Zip 94010–3282; tel. 650/696–5400; Janet Wagner, R.N., Chief Executive Officer

NOVATO COMMUNITY HOSPITAL (O, 40 beds) 180 Rowland Way, Novato, CA, Zip 94945–5009, Mailing Address: P.O. Box 1108, Zip 94948–1108, tel. 415/209–1300; Michael L. Purvis, Chief Executive Officer
Web address: www.novatocommunity.sutterhealth.org

STANISLAUS SURGICAL HOSPITAL (O, 23 beds) 1421 Oakdale Road, Modesto, CA, Zip 95355–3356; tel. 209/572–2700; Douglas V. Johnson, Chief Executive Officer

SUTTER AMADOR HOSPITAL (O, 52 beds) 200 Mission Boulevard, Jackson, CA, Zip 95642–2564; tel. 209/223–7500; Anne Platt, Chief Executive Officer
Web address: www.sutteramador.org

SUTTER AUBURN FAITH HOSPITAL (O, 72 beds) 11815 Education Street, Auburn, CA, Zip 95602–2410; tel. 530/888–4500; Mitchell J. Hanna, Chief Executive Officer

SUTTER CENTER FOR PSYCHIATRY (O, 71 beds) 7700 Folsom Boulevard, Sacramento, CA, Zip 95826–2608; tel. 916/386–3000; John W. Boyd, PsyD, Chief Executive Officer
Web address: www.sutterpsychiatry.org

SUTTER COAST HOSPITAL (O, 49 beds) 800 East Washington Boulevard, Crescent City, CA, Zip 95531–8359; tel. 707/464–8511; Mitchell J. Hanna, Chief Executive Officer
Web address: www.sutterhealth.org

SUTTER DAVIS HOSPITAL (O, 48 beds) 2000 Sutter Place, Davis, CA, Zip 95616–6201, Mailing Address: P.O. Box 1617, Zip 95617–1617, tel. 530/756–6440; Rachael McKinney, FACHE, Chief Executive Officer

SUTTER DELTA MEDICAL CENTER (O, 132 beds) 3901 Lone Tree Way, Antioch, CA, Zip 94509–6253; tel. 925/779–7200; Dori Stevens, Chief Executive Officer
Web address: www.sutterdelta.org

SUTTER LAKESIDE HOSPITAL (O, 25 beds) 5176 Hill Road East, Lakeport, CA, Zip 95453–6300; tel. 707/262–5000; Dan Peterson, Chief Administrative Officer
Web address: www.sutterlakeside.org

SUTTER MATERNITY AND SURGERY CENTER OF SANTA CRUZ (O, 30 beds) 2900 Chanticleer Avenue, Santa Cruz, CA, Zip 95065–1816; tel. 831/477–2200; Trina White, President and Chief Executive Officer

SUTTER MEDICAL CENTER, SACRAMENTO (O, 523 beds) 2801 'L' Street, Sacramento, CA, Zip 95816–5680; tel. 916/454–3333; David Cheney, Chief Executive Officer
Web address: www.sutterhealth.org

SUTTER OAKS NURSING CENTER (O, 100 beds) 2600 L Street, Sacramento, CA, Zip 95816–5612; tel. 916/552–2200; John W. Boyd, PsyD, Chief Administrative Officer

SUTTER ROSEVILLE MEDICAL CENTER (O, 328 beds) One Medical Plaza Drive, Roseville, CA, Zip 95661–3037; tel. 916/781–1000; Brian Alexander, Chief Executive Officer
Web address: www.sutterroseville.org

SUTTER SANTA ROSA REGIONAL HOSPITAL (O, 84 beds) 30 Mark West Springs Road, Santa Rosa, CA, Zip 95403; tel. 707/576–4000; Mike Purvis, Chief Administrative Officer
Web address: www.sutterhealth.org

SUTTER SOLANO MEDICAL CENTER (O, 108 beds) 300 Hospital Drive, Vallejo, CA, Zip 94589–2574, Mailing Address: P.O. Box 3189, Zip 94590–0669, tel. 707/554–4444; Abhishek Dosi, Chief Executive Officer

SUTTER SURGICAL HOSPITAL – NORTH VALLEY (O, 14 beds) 455 Plumas Boulevard, Yuba City, CA, Zip 95991–5074; tel. 530/749–5700; Shawndra Simpson, Interim Chief Executive Officer
Web address: www.sshnv.org

SUTTER TRACY COMMUNITY HOSPITAL (O, 33 beds) 1420 North Tracy Boulevard, Tracy, CA, Zip 95376–3497; tel. 209/835–1500; David M. Thompson, Chief Executive Officer

For explanation of codes following names, see page B2.
★ Indicates Type III membership in the American Hospital Association.

© 2018 AHA Guide   Health Care Systems, Networks and Alliances   **B123**

HAWAII: SUTTER HEALTH KAHI MOHALA (O, 76 beds) 91–2301 Old Fort Weaver Road, Ewa Beach, HI, Zip 96706–3602; tel. 808/671–8511; Leonard Licina, Chief Executive Officer
Web address: www.kahimohala.org

Owned, leased, sponsored:	28 hospitals	4286 beds
Contract–managed:	0 hospitals	0 beds
Totals:	28 hospitals	4286 beds

★0871: SWEDISH HEALTH SERVICES (NP)

747 Broadway, Seattle, WA, Zip 98122–4379; tel. 206/386–6000; R. Guy. Hudson, Chief Executive Officer
(Independent Hospital System)

WASHINGTON: SWEDISH MEDICAL CENTER–CHERRY HILL CAMPUS (O, 227 beds) 500 17th Avenue, Seattle, WA, Zip 98122–5711; tel. 206/320–2000; June Altaras, R.N., Chief Executive Officer
Web address: www.swedish.org

SWEDISH MEDICAL CENTER–FIRST HILL (O, 659 beds) 747 Broadway, Seattle, WA, Zip 98122–4307; tel. 206/386–6000; June Altaras, R.N., Chief Executive Officer

SWEDISH/EDMONDS (O, 186 beds) 21601 76th Avenue West, Edmonds, WA, Zip 98026–7506; tel. 425/640–4000; Sarah Zabel, Vice President, Operations
Web address: www.swedish.org

SWEDISH/ISSAQUAH (O, 134 beds) 751 NE Blakely Drive, Issaquah, WA, Zip 98029–6201; tel. 425/313–4000; Guy Hudson, Chief Executive Officer

Owned, leased, sponsored:	4 hospitals	1206 beds
Contract–managed:	0 hospitals	0 beds
Totals:	4 hospitals	1206 beds

★0379: TAHOE FOREST HEALTH SYSTEM (NP)

10121 Pine Avenue, Truckee, CA, Zip 96161–4835; tel. 530/587–6011; Harry Weis, Chief Executive Officer

CALIFORNIA: TAHOE FOREST HOSPITAL DISTRICT (O, 62 beds) 10121 Pine Avenue, Truckee, CA, Zip 96161–4856, Mailing Address: P.O. Box 759, Zip 96160–0759, tel. 530/587–6011; Harry Weis, Chief Executive Officer
Web address: www.tfhd.com

NEVADA: INCLINE VILLAGE COMMUNITY HOSPITAL (O, 6 beds) 880 Alder Avenue, Incline Village, NV, Zip 89451–8335; tel. 775/833–4100; Judy Newland, R.N., Chief Nursing Officer

Owned, leased, sponsored:	2 hospitals	68 beds
Contract–managed:	0 hospitals	0 beds
Totals:	2 hospitals	68 beds

★0341: TANNER HEALTH SYSTEM (NP)

705 Dixie Street, Carrollton, GA, Zip 30117–3818; tel. 770/836–9580; Loy M. Howard, President and Chief Executive Officer

ALABAMA: TANNER MEDICAL CENTER/EAST ALABAMA (O, 26 beds) 1032 South Main Street, Wedowee, AL, Zip 36278–7428; tel. 256/357–2111; Jerry Morris, Administrator
Web address: www.tanner.org/eastalabama

GEORGIA: TANNER HIGGINS GENERAL HOSPITAL (O, 23 beds) 200 Allen Memorial Drive, Bremen, GA, Zip 30110–2012; tel. 770/824–2000; Jerry Morris, Administrator

TANNER MEDICAL CENTER–CARROLLTON (O, 142 beds) 705 Dixie Street, Carrollton, GA, Zip 30117–3818; tel. 770/836–9666; Loy M. Howard, Chief Operating Officer
Web address: www.tanner.org

TANNER MEDICAL CENTER–VILLA RICA (O, 118 beds) 601 Dallas Highway, Villa Rica, GA, Zip 30180–1202; tel. 770/456–3000; Eric Dalton, Administrator

Owned, leased, sponsored:	4 hospitals	309 beds
Contract–managed:	0 hospitals	0 beds
Totals:	4 hospitals	309 beds

★0169: TEMPLE UNIVERSITY HEALTH SYSTEM (NP)

3509 North Broad Street, 9th Floor, Philadelphia, PA, Zip 19140–4105; tel. 215/707–0900; Larry Kaiser, M.D., President and Chief Executive Officer
(Centralized Physician/Insurance Health System)

PENNSYLVANIA: FOX CHASE CANCER CENTER–AMERICAN ONCOLOGIC HOSPITAL (O, 67 beds) 333 Cottman Avenue, Philadelphia, PA, Zip 19111–2434; tel. 215/728–6900; Richard Fisher, M.D., President and Chief Executive Officer
Web address: www.fccc.org

JEANES HOSPITAL (O, 146 beds) 7600 Central Avenue, Philadelphia, PA, Zip 19111–2499; tel. 215/728–2000; Marc P. Hurowitz, D.O., President and Chief Executive Officer
Web address: www.jeanes.com

TEMPLE UNIVERSITY HOSPITAL (O, 732 beds) 3401 North Broad Street, Philadelphia, PA, Zip 19140–5103; tel. 215/707–2000; Verdi Disesa, M.D., President and Chief Executive Officer
Web address: www.tuh.templehealth.org/content/default.htm

Owned, leased, sponsored:	3 hospitals	945 beds
Contract–managed:	0 hospitals	0 beds
Totals:	3 hospitals	945 beds

★0919: TENET HEALTHCARE CORPORATION (IO)

1445 Ross Avenue, Suite 1400, Dallas, TX, Zip 75202–2703, Mailing Address: P.O. Box 1390369, Zip 75313–9036, tel. 469/893–2200; J. Eric. Evans, President, Hospital Operations
(Decentralized Health System)

ALABAMA: BROOKWOOD BAPTIST MEDICAL CENTER (O, 607 beds) 2010 Brookwood Medical Center Drive, Birmingham, AL, Zip 35209–6875; tel. 205/877–1000; Keith Parrott, FACHE, President and Chief Executive Officer
Web address: https://www.brookwoodbaptisthealth.com/

CITIZENS BAPTIST MEDICAL CENTER (O, 72 beds) 604 Stone Avenue, Talladega, AL, Zip 35160–2217, Mailing Address: P.O. Box 978, Zip 35161–0978, tel. 256/362–8111; Frank D. Thomas, Chief Executive Officer
Web address: www.brookwoodbaptisthealth.org

PRINCETON BAPTIST MEDICAL CENTER (O, 315 beds) 701 Princeton Avenue SW, Birmingham, AL, Zip 35211–1303; tel. 205/783–3000; Michael Neuendorf, Chief Executive Officer

SHELBY BAPTIST MEDICAL CENTER (O, 231 beds) 1000 First Street North, Alabaster, AL, Zip 35007–8703; tel. 205/620–8100; Daniel Listi, Chief Executive Officer
Web address: www.brookwoodbaptisthealth.com

WALKER BAPTIST MEDICAL CENTER (O, 158 beds) 3400 Highway 78 East, Jasper, AL, Zip 35501–8907, Mailing Address: P.O. Box 3547, Zip 35502–3547, tel. 205/387–4000; Robert A. Phillips, Chief Executive Officer
Web address: www.bhsala.com

ARIZONA: ABRAZO ARROWHEAD CAMPUS (O, 234 beds) 18701 North 67th Avenue, Glendale, AZ, Zip 85308–7100; tel. 623/561–1000; Jeff Patterson, Chief Executive Officer

ABRAZO CENTRAL CAMPUS (O, 215 beds) 2000 West Bethany Home Road, Phoenix, AZ, Zip 85015–2443; tel. 602/249–0212; Frank L. Molinaro, Chief Executive Officer
Web address: www.abrazohealth.com

ABRAZO SCOTTSDALE CAMPUS (O, 142 beds) 3929 East Bell Road, Phoenix, AZ, Zip 85032–2196; tel. 602/923–5000; Frank L. Molinaro, Chief Executive Officer

---

For explanation of codes following names, see page B2.
★ Indicates Type III membership in the American Hospital Association.

ABRAZO WEST CAMPUS (O, 106 beds) 13677 West McDowell Road, Goodyear, AZ, Zip 85395–2635; tel. 623/882–1500; Stan Holm, Chief Executive Officer
Web address: www.abrazohealth.com

CARONDELET HOLY CROSS HOSPITAL (O, 25 beds) 1171 West Target Range Road, Nogales, AZ, Zip 85621–2415; tel. 520/285–3000; Debbie Knapheide, MSN, Site Administrator, Chief Nursing Officer and Chief Operating Officer

CARONDELET ST. JOSEPH'S HOSPITAL (O, 486 beds) 350 North Wilmot Road, Tucson, AZ, Zip 85711–2678; tel. 520/873–3000; Mark A. Benz, President and Chief Executive Officer
Web address: www.carondelet.org

CARONDELET ST. MARY'S HOSPITAL (O, 300 beds) 1601 West St Mary's Road, Tucson, AZ, Zip 85745–2682; tel. 520/872–3000; Mark A. Benz, President and Chief Executive Officer
Web address: www.carondelet.org

CALIFORNIA: DESERT REGIONAL MEDICAL CENTER (L, 382 beds) 1150 North Indian Canyon Drive, Palm Springs, CA, Zip 92262–4872; tel. 760/323–6511; Michele Finney, Chief Executive Officer

DOCTORS HOSPITAL OF MANTECA (O, 56 beds) 1205 East North Street, Manteca, CA, Zip 95336–4900; tel. 209/823–3111; Brandon May, Chief Executive Officer
Web address: www.doctorsmanteca.com

DOCTORS MEDICAL CENTER OF MODESTO (O, 461 beds) 1441 Florida Avenue, Modesto, CA, Zip 95350–4418, Mailing Address: P.O. Box 4138, Zip 95352–4138, tel. 209/578–1211; Warren J. Kirk, Chief Executive Officer
Web address: www.dmc-modesto.com

EMANUEL MEDICAL CENTER (O, 104 beds) 825 Delbon Avenue, Turlock, CA, Zip 95382–2016, Mailing Address: P.O. Box 819005, Zip 95382, tel. 209/667–4200; Lani Dickinson, Chief Executive Officer

FOUNTAIN VALLEY REGIONAL HOSPITAL AND MEDICAL CENTER (O, 243 beds) 17100 Euclid Street, Fountain Valley, CA, Zip 92708–4043; tel. 714/966–7200; Kenneth D. McFarland, Chief Executive Officer
Web address: www.fountainvalleyhospital.com

HI–DESERT MEDICAL CENTER (L, 179 beds) 6601 White Feather Road, Joshua Tree, CA, Zip 92284; tel. 760/366–3711; Karen Faulis, Chief Executive Officer
Web address: www.hdmc.org

JOHN F. KENNEDY MEMORIAL HOSPITAL (O, 145 beds) 47111 Monroe Street, Indio, CA, Zip 92201–6799; tel. 760/347–6191; Gary Honts, Chief Executive Officer

LAKEWOOD REGIONAL MEDICAL CENTER (O, 153 beds) 3700 East South Street, Lakewood, CA, Zip 90712–1498, Mailing Address: P.O. Box 6070, Zip 90712, tel. 562/531–2550; John A. Grah, FACHE, Chief Executive Officer
Web address: www.lakewoodregional.com

LOS ALAMITOS MEDICAL CENTER (O, 167 beds) 3751 Katella Avenue, Los Alamitos, CA, Zip 90720–3164; tel. 562/598–1311; Kent G. Clayton, Chief Executive Officer
Web address: www.losalamitosmedctr.com

PLACENTIA–LINDA HOSPITAL (O, 114 beds) 1301 North Rose Drive, Placentia, CA, Zip 92870–3899; tel. 714/993–2000; Christina E. Oh, Chief Executive Officer
Web address: www.placentialinda.com

SAN RAMON REGIONAL MEDICAL CENTER (O, 123 beds) 6001 Norris Canyon Road, San Ramon, CA, Zip 94583–5400; tel. 925/275–9200; Ann Lucena, Chief Executive Officer

SIERRA VISTA REGIONAL MEDICAL CENTER (O, 164 beds) 1010 Murray Avenue, San Luis Obispo, CA, Zip 93405–1806, Mailing Address: P.O. Box 1367, Zip 93405, tel. 805/546–7600; Mark P. Lisa, FACHE, Chief Executive Officer
Web address: www.sierravistaregional.com

TWIN CITIES COMMUNITY HOSPITAL (O, 89 beds) 1100 Las Tablas Road, Templeton, CA, Zip 93465–9796; tel. 805/434–3500; Mark P. Lisa, FACHE, Chief Executive Officer
Web address: www.twincitieshospital.com

FLORIDA: CORAL GABLES HOSPITAL (O, 256 beds) 3100 Douglas Road, Coral Gables, FL, Zip 33134–6914; tel. 305/445–8461; Cristina Jimenez, Chief Executive Officer

DELRAY MEDICAL CENTER (O, 536 beds) 5352 Linton Boulevard, Delray Beach, FL, Zip 33484–6580; tel. 561/498–4440; Margaret Gill, Chief Executive Officer
Web address: www.delraymedicalctr.com

GOOD SAMARITAN MEDICAL CENTER (O, 174 beds) 1309 North Flagler Drive, West Palm Beach, FL, Zip 33401–3499; tel. 561/655–5511; Tara McCoy, Chief Executive Officer

HIALEAH HOSPITAL (O, 191 beds) 651 East 25th Street, Hialeah, FL, Zip 33013–3878; tel. 305/693–6100; Ben A. Rodriguez, Chief Executive Officer
Web address: www.hialeahhosp.com

NORTH SHORE MEDICAL CENTER (O, 816 beds) 1100 NW 95th Street, Miami, FL, Zip 33150–2098; tel. 305/835–6000; Mark Racicot, Chief Executive Officer

PALM BEACH GARDENS MEDICAL CENTER (L, 199 beds) 3360 Burns Road, Palm Beach Gardens, FL, Zip 33410–4323; tel. 561/622–1411; Trey Abshier, Chief Executive Officer
Web address: www.pbgmc.com

PALMETTO GENERAL HOSPITAL (O, 360 beds) 2001 West 68th Street, Hialeah, FL, Zip 33016–1898; tel. 305/823–5000; Ana J. Mederos, Chief Executive Officer

ST. MARY'S MEDICAL CENTER (O, 464 beds) 901 45th Street, West Palm Beach, FL, Zip 33407–2495; tel. 561/844–6300; Gabrielle Finley–Hazle, Chief Executive Officer
Web address: www.stmarysmc.com

WEST BOCA MEDICAL CENTER (O, 195 beds) 21644 State Road 7, Boca Raton, FL, Zip 33428–1899; tel. 561/488–8000; Mitchell S. Feldman, Chief Executive Officer

ILLINOIS: LOUIS A. WEISS MEMORIAL HOSPITAL (O, 153 beds) 4646 North Marine Drive, Chicago, IL, Zip 60640–5759; tel. 773/878–8700; Mary Shehan, R.N., MSN, Chief Executive Officer
Web address: www.weisshospital.com

WEST SUBURBAN MEDICAL CENTER (O, 172 beds) 3 Erie Court, Oak Park, IL, Zip 60302–2599; tel. 708/383–6200; Joseph Ottolino, Chief Executive Officer

WESTLAKE HOSPITAL (O, 181 beds) 1225 Lake Street, Melrose Park, IL, Zip 60160–4000; tel. 708/681–3000; Joseph Ottolino, Chief Executive Officer
Web address: www.westlakehosp.com

MASSACHUSETTS: METROWEST MEDICAL CENTER (O, 160 beds) 115 Lincoln Street, Framingham, MA, Zip 01702–6342; tel. 508/383–1000; Andrew D. Harding, R.N., Interim Chief Executive Officer
Web address: www.mwmc.com

SAINT VINCENT HOSPITAL (O, 283 beds) 123 Summer Street, Worcester, MA, Zip 01608–1216; tel. 508/363–5000; Ava Jo. Collins, FACHE, Interim Chief Executive Officer

MICHIGAN: DMC – CHILDREN'S HOSPITAL OF MICHIGAN (O, 227 beds) 3901 Beaubien Street, Detroit, MI, Zip 48201–2119; tel. 313/745–5852; Monique Butler, MD, Chief Operaitng Officer
Web address: www.chmkids.org

DMC – DETROIT RECEIVING HOSPITAL (O, 187 beds) 4201 Saint Antoine Street, Detroit, MI, Zip 48201–2153; tel. 313/745–3000; Scott Steiner, FACHE, Chief Executive Officer
Web address: www.dmc.org

DMC – REHABILITATION INSTITUTE OF MICHIGAN (O, 69 beds) 261 Mack Avenue, Detroit, MI, Zip 48201–2495; tel. 313/745–1203; William Restum, Chief Executive Officer
Web address: www.rimrehab.org

DMC – SINAI–GRACE HOSPITAL (O, 301 beds) 6071 West Outer Drive, Detroit, MI, Zip 48235–2679; tel. 313/966–3300; Conrad L. Mallett Jr, Chief Executive Officer

DMC HARPER UNIVERSITY HOSPITAL (O, 364 beds) 3990 John 'R' Street, Detroit, MI, Zip 48201–2018; tel. 313/745–8040; Scott Steiner, FACHE, Chief Executive Officer
Web address: www.harperhospital.org

DMC HURON VALLEY–SINAI HOSPITAL (O, 156 beds) 1 William Carls Drive, Commerce Township, MI, Zip 48382–2201; tel. 248/937–3300; Karima Bentounsi, Chief Executive Officer

SOUTH CAROLINA: COASTAL CAROLINA HOSPITAL (O, 35 beds) 1000 Medical Center Drive, Hardeeville, SC, Zip 29927–3446; tel. 843/784–8000; Joel Taylor, Chief Executive Officer
Web address: www.coastalhospital.com

For explanation of codes following names, see page B2.
★ Indicates Type III membership in the American Hospital Association.

EAST COOPER MEDICAL CENTER (O, 140 beds) 2000 Hospital Drive, Mount Pleasant, SC, Zip 29464–3764; tel. 843/881–0100; Patrick Downes, Chief Executive Officer
Web address: www.eastcoopermedctr.com

HILTON HEAD HOSPITAL (O, 93 beds) 25 Hospital Center Boulevard, Hilton Head Island, SC, Zip 29926–2738; tel. 843/681–6122; Jeremy L. Clark, Market Chief Executive Officer

PIEDMONT MEDICAL CENTER (O, 276 beds) 222 Herlong Avenue, Rock Hill, SC, Zip 29732; tel. 803/329–1234; Mark Nosacka, Chief Executive Officer
Web address: www.piedmontmedicalcenter.com

TENNESSEE: SAINT FRANCIS HOSPITAL–BARTLETT (O, 156 beds) 2986 Kate Bond Road, Bartlett, TN, Zip 38133–4003; tel. 901/820–7000; Christopher Locke, Chief Executive Officer

SAINT FRANCIS HOSPITAL (O, 415 beds) 5959 Park Avenue, Memphis, TN, Zip 38119–5198; tel. 901/765–1000; Audrey Gregory, R.N., MSN, Chief Executive Officer
Web address: www.saintfrancishosp.com

TEXAS: BAPTIST MEDICAL CENTER (O, 1580 beds) 111 Dallas Street, San Antonio, TX, Zip 78205–1230; tel. 210/297–7000; Matt Stone, President and Chief Executive Officer
Web address: www.baptisthealthsystem.com

BAYLOR SCOTT & WHITE MEDICAL CENTER – SUNNYVALE (O, 70 beds) 231 South Collins Road, Sunnyvale, TX, Zip 75182–4624; tel. 972/892–3000; Jon Duckert, FACHE, Chief Executive Officer

NACOGDOCHES MEDICAL CENTER (O, 109 beds) 4920 NE Stallings Drive, Nacogdoches, TX, Zip 75965–1200; tel. 936/569–9481; Philip Koovakada, Chief Executive Officer
Web address: www.nacmedicalcenter.com

RESOLUTE HEALTH (O, 70 beds) 555 Creekside Crossing, New Braunfels, TX, Zip 78130–2594; tel. 830/500–6000; Mark L. Bernard, Chief Executive Officer
Web address: www.resolutehealth.com

THE HOSPITALS OF PROVIDENCE EAST CAMPUS (O, 182 beds) 3280 Joe Battle Boulevard, El Paso, TX, Zip 79938–2622; tel. 915/832–2000; Monica Vargas–Mahar, FACHE, Chief Executive Officer
Web address: www.sphn.com

THE HOSPITALS OF PROVIDENCE MEMORIAL CAMPUS (O, 382 beds) 2001 North Oregon Street, El Paso, TX, Zip 79902–3368; tel. 915/577–6625; Nicholas R. Tejeda, FACHE, Market Chief Executive Officer

THE HOSPITALS OF PROVIDENCE SIERRA CAMPUS (O, 297 beds) 1625 Medical Center Drive, El Paso, TX, Zip 79902–5005; tel. 915/747–4000; Nicholas R. Tejeda, FACHE, Chief Executive Officer
Web address: www.thehospitalsofprovidence.com

THE HOSPITALS OF PROVIDENCE TRANSMOUNTAIN CAMPUS (O, 106 beds) 2000 Transmountain Road, El Paso, TX, Zip 79911; tel. 915/877–8300; Tasha Hopper, Chief Executive Officer
Web address: https://www.thehospitalsofprovidence.com/our–locations/transmountain

VALLEY BAPTIST MEDICAL CENTER–BROWNSVILLE (O, 262 beds) 1040 West Jefferson Street, Brownsville, TX, Zip 78520–6338, Mailing Address: P.O. Box 3590, Zip 78523–3590, tel. 956/698–5400; Leslie Bingham, Senior Vice President and Chief Executive Officer

VALLEY BAPTIST MEDICAL CENTER–HARLINGEN (O, 428 beds) 2101 Pease Street, Harlingen, TX, Zip 78550–8307, Mailing Address: P O Drawer 2588, Zip 78551–2588, tel. 956/389–1100; Manuel Vela, President and Chief Executive Officer
Web address: www.valleybaptist.net/harlingen/index.htm

Owned, leased, sponsored:	61 hospitals	15316 beds
Contract–managed:	0 hospitals	0 beds
Totals:	61 hospitals	15316 beds

0876: TENNESSEE HEALTH MANAGEMENT (IO)

52 West Eighth Street, Parsons, TN, Zip 38363–4656, Mailing Address: PO Box 10, Zip 38363–0010, tel. 731/847–6343; Dennis Berry, Chief Executive Officer

ALABAMA: UNITY PSYCHIATRIC CARE–HUNTSVILLE (O, 20 beds) 5315 Millennium Drive NW, Huntsville, AL, Zip 35806–2458; tel. 256/964–6700; Bradley Moss, Administrator

TENNESSEE: UNITY PSYCHIATRIC CARE–CLARKSVILLE (O, 26 beds) 930 Professional Park Drive, Clarksville, TN, Zip 37040–5136; tel. 931/538–6420; Jennifer Robinson, Administrator
Web address: www.unitypsych.com

UNITY PSYCHIATRIC CARE–COLUMBIA (O, 16 beds) 1400 Rosewood Drive, Columbia, TN, Zip 38401–4878; tel. 931/388–6573; Paula Chennault, Administrator
Web address: www.unitypsych.com

UNITY PSYCHIATRIC CARE–MARTIN (O, 16 beds) 458 Hannings Lane, Martin, TN, Zip 38237–3308; tel. 731/588–2830; Carrie Brawley, Administrator

Owned, leased, sponsored:	4 hospitals	78 beds
Contract–managed:	0 hospitals	0 beds
Totals:	4 hospitals	78 beds

0020: TEXAS DEPARTMENT OF STATE HEALTH SERVICES (NP)

1100 West 49th Street, Austin, TX, Zip 78756–3199; tel. 512/458–7111; Kirk Cole, Interim Commissioner
(Independent Hospital System)

TEXAS: AUSTIN STATE HOSPITAL (O, 252 beds) 4110 Guadalupe Street, Austin, TX, Zip 78751–4296; tel. 512/452–0381; Alan Isaacson, Superintendent

BIG SPRING STATE HOSPITAL (O, 200 beds) 1901 North Highway 87, Big Spring, TX, Zip 79720–0283; tel. 432/267–8216; Traci Phillips, Superintendent
Web address: www.dshs.state.tx.us/mhhospitals/BigSpringSH/default.shtm

EL PASO PSYCHIATRIC CENTER (O, 74 beds) 4615 Alameda Avenue, El Paso, TX, Zip 79905–2702; tel. 915/532–2202; Zulema Carrillo, Superintendent
Web address: www.dshs.state.tx.us/mhhospitals/ElPasoPC/default.shtm

KERRVILLE STATE HOSPITAL (O, 202 beds) 721 Thompson Drive, Kerrville, TX, Zip 78028–5154; tel. 830/896–2211; Leigh Ann Fitzpatrick, Superintendent

NORTH TEXAS STATE HOSPITAL (O, 641 beds) Highway 70 Northwest, Vernon, TX, Zip 76384, Mailing Address: P.O. Box 2231, Zip 76385–2231, tel. 940/552–9901; James E. Smith, Superintendent
Web address: www.online.dshs.state.tx.us/northtexassh/default.htm

RIO GRANDE STATE CENTER/SOUTH TEXAS HEALTH CARE SYSTEM (O, 55 beds) 1401 South Rangerville Road, Harlingen, TX, Zip 78552–7638; tel. 956/364–8000; Sonia Hernandez–Keeble, Superintendent
Web address: www.dshs.state.tx.us/mhhospitals/RioGrandeSC/default.shtm

RUSK STATE HOSPITAL (O, 262 beds) 805 North Dickinson, Rusk, TX, Zip 75785–2333, Mailing Address: P.O. Box 318, Zip 75785–0318, tel. 903/683–3421; Brenda Slaton, Superintendent

SAN ANTONIO STATE HOSPITAL (O, 278 beds) 6711 South New Braunfels, Suite 100, San Antonio, TX, Zip 78223–3006; tel. 210/531–7711; Robert C. Arizpe, Superintendent
Web address: www.dshs.state.tx.us/mhhospitals/SanAntonioSH/default.shtm

TERRELL STATE HOSPITAL (O, 288 beds) 1200 East Brin Street, Terrell, TX, Zip 75160–2938, Mailing Address: P.O. Box 70, Zip 75160–9000, tel. 972/524–6452; Dorothy Floyd, Ph.D., Superintendent
Web address: www.dshs.state.tx.us/mhhospitals/terrellsh

TEXAS CENTER FOR INFECTIOUS DISEASE (O, 31 beds) 2303 SE Military Drive, San Antonio, TX, Zip 78223–3597; tel. 210/534–8857; James N. Elkins, FACHE, Director

Owned, leased, sponsored:	10 hospitals	2283 beds
Contract–managed:	0 hospitals	0 beds
Totals:	10 hospitals	2283 beds

★0129: TEXAS HEALTH RESOURCES (NP)

612 East Lamar Boulevard, Suite 900, Arlington, TX, Zip 76011–4130; tel. 682/236–7900; Barclay E. Berdan, FACHE, Chief Executive Officer
(Centralized Physician/Insurance Health System)

For explanation of codes following names, see page B2.
★ Indicates Type III membership in the American Hospital Association.

TEXAS: TEXAS HEALTH ARLINGTON MEMORIAL HOSPITAL (O, 269 beds) 800 West Randol Mill Road, Arlington, TX, Zip 76012–2503; tel. 817/548–6100; Blake Kretz, FACHE, President

TEXAS HEALTH HARRIS METHODIST HOSPITAL ALLIANCE (O, 101 beds) 10864 Texas Health Trail, Fort Worth, TX, Zip 76244–4897; tel. 682/212–2000; Clint Abernathy, President and Chief Operating Officer
Web address: https://www.texashealth.org/alliance/Pages/default.aspx

TEXAS HEALTH HARRIS METHODIST HOSPITAL AZLE (O, 31 beds) 108 Denver Trail, Azle, TX, Zip 76020–3614; tel. 817/444–8600; Bob S. Ellzey, FACHE, President

TEXAS HEALTH HARRIS METHODIST HOSPITAL CLEBURNE (O, 92 beds) 201 Walls Drive, Cleburne, TX, Zip 76033–4007; tel. 817/641–2551; Ajith Pai, PharmD, FACHE, President
Web address: www.texashealth.org

TEXAS HEALTH HARRIS METHODIST HOSPITAL FORT WORTH (O, 639 beds) 1301 Pennsylvania Avenue, Fort Worth, TX, Zip 76104–2122; tel. 817/250–2000; Joseph DeLeon, President

TEXAS HEALTH HARRIS METHODIST HOSPITAL HURST–EULESS–BEDFORD (O, 285 beds) 1600 Hospital Parkway, Bedford, TX, Zip 76022–6913; tel. 817/685–4000; Fraser Hay, President
Web address: www.texashealth.org

TEXAS HEALTH HARRIS METHODIST HOSPITAL SOUTHWEST FORT WORTH (O, 247 beds) 6100 Harris Parkway, Fort Worth, TX, Zip 76132–4199; tel. 817/433–5000; Rebecca Tucker, President
Web address: www.texashealth.org

TEXAS HEALTH HARRIS METHODIST HOSPITAL STEPHENVILLE (O, 54 beds) 411 North Belknap Street, Stephenville, TX, Zip 76401–3415; tel. 254/965–1500; Christopher Leu, President
Web address: www.texashealth.org/landing.cfm?id=108

TEXAS HEALTH PRESBYTERIAN HOSPITAL ALLEN (O, 68 beds) 1105 Central Expressway North, Suite 140, Allen, TX, Zip 75013–6103; tel. 972/747–1000; Jared Shelton, Chief Executive Officer

TEXAS HEALTH PRESBYTERIAN HOSPITAL DALLAS (O, 611 beds) 8200 Walnut Hill Lane, Dallas, TX, Zip 75231–4426; tel. 214/345–6789; James Berg, FACHE, President
Web address: www.texashealth.org

TEXAS HEALTH PRESBYTERIAN HOSPITAL DENTON (O, 197 beds) 3000 North I–35, Denton, TX, Zip 76201–5119; tel. 940/898–7000; Jeff Reecer, FACHE, Chief Executive Officer
Web address: www.dentonhospital.com

TEXAS HEALTH PRESBYTERIAN HOSPITAL KAUFMAN (O, 37 beds) 850 Ed Hall Drive, Kaufman, TX, Zip 75142–1861, Mailing Address: P.O. Box 1108, Zip 75142–5401, tel. 972/932–7200; Patsy Youngs, President

TEXAS HEALTH PRESBYTERIAN HOSPITAL PLANO (O, 361 beds) 6200 West Parker Road, Plano, TX, Zip 75093–8185; tel. 972/981–8000; Joshua Floren, President
Web address: www.texashealth.org

TEXAS HEALTH SPECIALTY HOSPITAL (O, 10 beds) 1301 Pennsylvania Avenue, 4th Floor, Fort Worth, TX, Zip 76104–2190; tel. 817/250–5500; Pam Duffey, MSN, R.N., Interim Chief Executive Officer

Owned, leased, sponsored:	14 hospitals	3002 beds
Contract–managed:	0 hospitals	0 beds
Totals:	14 hospitals	3002 beds

1038: THE CARPENTER HEALTH NETWORK (IO)

10615 Jefferson Highway, Baton Rouge, LA, Zip 70809–7230; tel. 225/769–4180; Pat Mitchell, Chief Executive Officer

LOUISIANA: SAGE REHABILITATION HOSPITAL (O, 42 beds) 8000 Summa Avenue, Baton Rouge, LA, Zip 70809–3423, Mailing Address: P.O. Box 82681, Zip 70884–2681, tel. 225/819–0703; Scott McClelland, Administrator

SAGE SPECIALTY HOSPITAL (LTAC) (O, 117 beds) 8375 Florida Boulevard, Denham Springs, LA, Zip 70726–7806; tel. 225/665–2664; Sharon Faulkner, Administrator
Web address: www.amgdenham.com/

Owned, leased, sponsored:	2 hospitals	159 beds
Contract–managed:	0 hospitals	0 beds
Totals:	2 hospitals	159 beds

1040: THE UNIVERSITY OF KANSAS HEALTH SYSTEM (NP)

4000 Cambridge Street, Kansas City, KS, Zip 66160–0001; tel. 913/588–1227; Bob Page, President and Chief Executive Officer

KANSAS: HAYS MEDICAL CENTER (O, 127 beds) 2220 Canterbury Drive, Hays, KS, Zip 67601–2370, Mailing Address: P.O. Box 8100, Zip 67601–8100, tel. 785/623–5000; Edward Herrman, R.N., FACHE, President and Chief Executive Officer
Web address: www.haysmed.com

PAWNEE VALLEY COMMUNITY HOSPITAL (O, 22 beds) 923 Carroll Avenue, Larned, KS, Zip 67550–2429; tel. 620/285–3161; Kendra Barker, Administrator

THE UNIVERSITY OF KANSAS HOSPITAL (O, 792 beds) 4000 Cambridge Street, MS 3011, Kansas City, KS, Zip 66160; tel. 913/588–5000; Bob Page, Chief Executive Officer
Web address: www.kumed.com

UNIVERSITY OF KANSAS HEALTH SYSTEM GREAT BEND CAMPUS (O, 33 beds) 514 Cleveland Street, Great Bend, KS, Zip 67530–3562; tel. 620/792–8833; Jodi A. Schmidt, Interim Chief Executive Officer
Web address: www.gbregional.com

Owned, leased, sponsored:	4 hospitals	974 beds
Contract–managed:	0 hospitals	0 beds
Totals:	4 hospitals	974 beds

2445: THEDACARE, INC. (NP)

122 East College Avenue, Appleton, WI, Zip 54911–5794, Mailing Address: P.O. Box 8025, Zip 54912–8025, tel. 920/830–5889; Imran A. Andrabi, M.D., President and Chief Executive Officer
(Moderately Centralized Health System)

WISCONSIN: THEDA CARE MEDICAL CENTER – WILD ROSE (O, 25 beds) 601 Grove Avenue, Wild Rose, WI, Zip 54984–6903, Mailing Address: P.O. Box 243, Zip 54984–0243, tel. 920/622–3257; Craig A. Kantos, Chief Executive Officer
Web address: www.wildrosehospital.org

THEDACARE MEDICAL CENTER–BERLIN (O, 25 beds) 225 Memorial Drive, Berlin, WI, Zip 54923–1295; tel. 920/361–1313; Tammy Bending, Vice President, Critical Access Hospital

THEDACARE MEDICAL CENTER–NEW LONDON (O, 25 beds) 1405 Mill Street, New London, WI, Zip 54961–0307, Mailing Address: P.O. Box 307, Zip 54961–0307, tel. 920/531–2000; William Schmidt, President and Chief Executive Officer
Web address: www.thedacare.org

THEDACARE MEDICAL CENTER–SHAWANO (O, 22 beds) 100 County Road B, Shawano, WI, Zip 54166–2127; tel. 715/526–2111; William Schmidt, Chief Executive Officer
Web address: www.shawanomed.org

THEDACARE MEDICAL CENTER–WAUPACA (O, 25 beds) 800 Riverside Drive, Waupaca, WI, Zip 54981–1999; tel. 715/258–1000; Craig A. Kantos, Chief Executive Officer

THEDACARE REGIONAL MEDICAL CENTER–APPLETON (O, 147 beds) 1818 North Meade Street, Appleton, WI, Zip 54911–3496; tel. 920/731–4101; Brian Burmeister, Senior Vice President, ThedaCare Medical Centers
Web address: www.thedacare.org

THEDACARE REGIONAL MEDICAL CENTER–NEENAH (O, 164 beds) 130 Second Street, Neenah, WI, Zip 54956–2883, Mailing Address: P.O. Box 2021, Zip 54957–2021, tel. 920/729–3100; Brian Burmeister, Senior Vice President, ThedaCare Medical Centers

Owned, leased, sponsored:	7 hospitals	433 beds
Contract–managed:	0 hospitals	0 beds
Totals:	7 hospitals	433 beds

★0643: THOMAS HEALTH SYSTEM, INC. (NP)

4605 MacCorkle Avenue SW, South Charleston, WV, Zip 25309–1311; tel. 304/766–3600; Daniel Lauffer, FACHE, President and Chief Executive Officer
(Centralized Health System)

For explanation of codes following names, see page B2.
★ Indicates Type III membership in the American Hospital Association.

Section B

WEST VIRGINIA: SAINT FRANCIS HOSPITAL (O, 65 beds) 333 Laidley Street, Charleston, WV, Zip 25301–1628, Mailing Address: P.O. Box 471, Zip 25322–0471, tel. 304/347–6500; Daniel Lauffer, FACHE, President and Chief Executive Officer

Web address: www.stfrancishospital.com

THOMAS MEMORIAL HOSPITAL (O, 211 beds) 4605 MacCorkle Avenue SW, South Charleston, WV, Zip 25309–1398; tel. 304/766–3600; Daniel Lauffer, FACHE, President and Chief Executive Officer

Owned, leased, sponsored:	2 hospitals	276 beds
Contract–managed:	0 hospitals	0 beds
Totals:	2 hospitals	276 beds

★0812: TIDELANDS HEALTH (NP)

606 Black River Road, Georgetown, SC, Zip 29440–3304, Mailing Address: P.O. Box 421718, Zip 29442–4203, tel. 843/527–7000; Bruce P. Bailey, President and Chief Executive Officer

SOUTH CAROLINA: TIDELANDS GEORGETOWN MEMORIAL HOSPITAL (O, 136 beds) 606 Black River Road, Georgetown, SC, Zip 29440–3368, Mailing Address: Drawer 421718, Zip 29442–4203, tel. 843/527–7000; Bruce P. Bailey, Chief Executive Officer

TIDELANDS WACCAMAW COMMUNITY HOSPITAL (O, 169 beds) 4070 Highway 17 Bypass, Murrells Inlet, SC, Zip 29576–5033, Mailing Address: P O Drawer 3350, Zip 29576–2673, tel. 843/652–1000; Bruce P. Bailey, Chief Executive Officer

Web address: www.tidelandswaccamawcommunity.org

Owned, leased, sponsored:	0 hospitals	0 beds
Contract–managed:	2 hospitals	305 beds
Totals:	2 hospitals	305 beds

★0910: TIFT REGIONAL HEALTH SYSTEM (NP)

901 East 18th Street, Tifton, GA, Zip 31794–3648; tel. 229/353–6100; Christopher Dorman, President and Chief Executive Officer
(Independent Hospital System)

GEORGIA: COOK MEDICAL CENTER–A CAMPUS OF TIFT REGIONAL MEDICAL CENTER (O, 155 beds) 706 North Parrish Avenue, Adel, GA, Zip 31620–1511; tel. 229/896–8000; Michael L. Purvis, Chief Executive Officer

TIFT REGIONAL MEDICAL CENTER (O, 181 beds) 901 East 18th Street, Tifton, GA, Zip 31794–3648, Mailing Address: Drawer 747, Zip 31793–0747, tel. 229/382–7120; Christopher Dorman, President and Chief Executive Officer

Web address: www.tiftregional.com

Owned, leased, sponsored:	2 hospitals	336 beds
Contract–managed:	0 hospitals	0 beds
Totals:	2 hospitals	336 beds

1029: TOWER HEALTH (NP)

Sixth Avenue and Spruce Street, West Reading, PA, Zip 19611; tel. 610/988–8000; Clinton Matthews, President and Chief Executive Officer

PENNSYLVANIA: BRANDYWINE HOSPITAL (O, 169 beds) 201 Reeceville Road, Coatesville, PA, Zip 19320–1536; tel. 610/383–8000; W. Jeffrey. Hunt, Chief Executive Officer

Web address: www.https://brandywine.towerhealth.org/

CHESTNUT HILL HOSPITAL (O, 212 beds) 8835 Germantown Avenue, Philadelphia, PA, Zip 19118–2718; tel. 215/248–8200; John D. . Cacciamani, M.D., Chief Executive Officer

JENNERSVILLE HOSPITAL (O, 63 beds) 1015 West Baltimore Pike, West Grove, PA, Zip 19390–9459; tel. 610/869–1000; Ronnie Ursin, FACHE, President and Chief Executive Officer

Web address: www.jennersville.com

PHOENIXVILLE HOSPITAL (O, 139 beds) 140 Nutt Road, Phoenixville, PA, Zip 19460–3900, Mailing Address: P.O. Box 3001, Zip 19460–0916, tel. 610/983–1000; Stephen M. Tullman, Chief Executive Officer
Web address: www.https://phoenixville.towerhealth.org

POTTSTOWN HOSPITAL (O, 232 beds) 1600 East High Street, Pottstown, PA, Zip 19464–5093; tel. 610/327–7000; Richard Newell, Chief Executive Officer
Web address: www.pottstownmemorial.com

READING HOSPITAL (O, 732 beds) Sixth Avenue and Spruce Street, West Reading, PA, Zip 19611–1428, Mailing Address: P.O. Box 16052, Zip 19612–6052, tel. 610/988–8000; Clinton Matthews, President and Chief Executive Officer
Web address: www.readinghospital.org

Owned, leased, sponsored:	6 hospitals	1547 beds
Contract–managed:	0 hospitals	0 beds
Totals:	6 hospitals	1547 beds

★0906: TRINITY HEALTH (CO)

20555 Victor Parkway, Livonia, MI, Zip 48152–7031; tel. 734/343–1000; Richard J. Gilfillan, M.D., Chief Executive Officer
(Decentralized Health System)

CALIFORNIA: SAINT AGNES MEDICAL CENTER (O, 436 beds) 1303 East Herndon Avenue, Fresno, CA, Zip 93720–3397; tel. 559/450–3000; Nancy Hollingsworth, R.N., MSN, President and Chief Executive Officer
Web address: www.samc.com

CONNECTICUT: JOHNSON MEMORIAL MEDICAL CENTER (O, 88 beds) 201 Chestnut Hill Road, Stafford Springs, CT, Zip 06076–4005; tel. 860/684–4251; Stuart E. Rosenberg, President

MOUNT SINAI REHABILITATION HOSPITAL (O, 32 beds) 490 Blue Hills Avenue, Hartford, CT, Zip 06112–1513; tel. 860/714–3500; Robert J. Krug, M.D., Chief Executive Officer
Web address: www.stfranciscare.org

SAINT FRANCIS HOSPITAL AND MEDICAL CENTER (O, 456 beds) 114 Woodland Street, Hartford, CT, Zip 06105–1208; tel. 860/714–4000; John F. Rodis, M.D., President
Web address: www.saintfranciscare.com

SAINT MARY'S HOSPITAL (O, 187 beds) 56 Franklin Street, Waterbury, CT, Zip 06706–1281; tel. 203/709–6000; Steven E. Schneider, M.D., President

DELAWARE: ST. FRANCIS HOSPITAL (O, 214 beds) 701 North Clayton Street, Wilmington, DE, Zip 19805, Mailing Address: P.O. Box 2500, Zip 19805–0500, tel. 302/421–4100; Daniel J. Sinnott, President and Chief Executive Officer
Web address: www.stfrancishealthcare.org

FLORIDA: BARTOW REGIONAL MEDICAL CENTER (O, 72 beds) 2200 Osprey Boulevard, Bartow, FL, Zip 33830–3308; tel. 863/533–8111; Philip Minden, Chief Executive Officer

BAYCARE ALLIANT HOSPITAL (S, 35 beds) 601 Main Street, MS#402, Dunedin, FL, Zip 34698–5848; tel. 727/736–9991; Jacqueline Arocho, Administrator
Web address: www.baycare.org

HOLY CROSS HOSPITAL (O, 367 beds) 4725 North Federal Highway, Fort Lauderdale, FL, Zip 33308–4668, Mailing Address: P.O. Box 23460, Zip 33307–3460, tel. 954/771–8000; Patrick Taylor, M.D., President and Chief Executive Officer

MEASE COUNTRYSIDE HOSPITAL (C, 311 beds) 3231 McMullen Booth Road, Safety Harbor, FL, Zip 34695–6607; tel. 727/725–6111; Lou Galdieri, R.N., President
Web address: www.mpmhealth.com

MEASE DUNEDIN HOSPITAL (C, 120 beds) 601 Main Street, Dunedin, FL, Zip 34698–5891; tel. 727/733–1111; Lou Galdieri, R.N., President

SOUTH FLORIDA BAPTIST HOSPITAL (S, 133 beds) 301 North Alexander Street, Plant City, FL, Zip 33563–4303; tel. 813/757–1200; Karen Kerr, R.N., President
Web address: www.https://baycare.org/sfbh

ST. ANTHONY'S HOSPITAL (S, 393 beds) 1200 Seventh Avenue North, Saint Petersburg, FL, Zip 33705–1388, Mailing Address: P.O. Box 12588, Zip 33733–2588, tel. 727/825–1100; M. Scott Smith, President

---

For explanation of codes following names, see page B2.
★ Indicates Type III membership in the American Hospital Association.

ST. JOSEPH'S HOSPITAL (S, 1049 beds) 3001 West Martin Luther King Jr. Boulevard, Tampa, FL, Zip 33607–6387, Mailing Address: P.O. Box 4227, Zip 33677–4227, tel. 813/870–4000; Kimberly Guy, President
Web address: www.sjbhealth.org

WINTER HAVEN HOSPITAL (S, 361 beds) 200 Avenue F NE, Winter Haven, FL, Zip 33881–4193; tel. 863/293–1121; Stephen A. Nierman, President

GEORGIA: ST. MARY'S GOOD SAMARITAN HOSPITAL (O, 25 beds) 5401 Lake Oconee Parkway, Greensboro, GA, Zip 30642–4232; tel. 706/453–7331; Tanya M. Adcock, President
Web address: www.stmarysgoodsam.org

ST. MARY'S HEALTH CARE SYSTEM (O, 174 beds) 1230 Baxter Street, Athens, GA, Zip 30606–3791; tel. 706/389–3000; D. Montez. Carter, Chief Executive Officer

ST. MARY'S SACRED HEART HOSPITAL (O, 41 beds) 367 Clear Creek Parkway, Lavonia, GA, Zip 30553–4173; tel. 706/356–7800; Jeff English, President
Web address: www.stmaryssacredheart.org/

IDAHO: SAINT ALPHONSUS MEDICAL CENTER – NAMPA (O, 106 beds) 4300 East Flamingo Avenue, Nampa, ID, Zip 83686–6008; tel. 208/205–1000; Travis Leach, President

SAINT ALPHONSUS REGIONAL MEDICAL CENTER (O, 399 beds) 1055 N Curtis Rd , Boise, ID, Zip 83706–1309, Mailing Address: 1055 North Curtis Road, Zip 83706–1309, tel. 208/367–2121; Odette Bolano, Interim Chief Executive Officer
Web address: www.saintalphonsus.org

ILLINOIS: GOTTLIEB MEMORIAL HOSPITAL (O, 171 beds) 701 West North Avenue, Melrose Park, IL, Zip 60160–1612; tel. 708/681–3200; Lori Price, President
Web address: www.gottliebhospital.org

LOYOLA UNIVERSITY MEDICAL CENTER (O, 524 beds) 2160 South First Avenue, Maywood, IL, Zip 60153–3328; tel. 708/216–9000; Daniel J. Post, Interim President
Web address: www.loyolamedicine.org/Medical_Services/index.cfm

MACNEAL HOSPITAL (O, 358 beds) 3249 South Oak Park Avenue, Berwyn, IL, Zip 60402–0715; tel. 708/783–9100; Mary Elizabeth. Cleary, President

MERCY HOSPITAL AND MEDICAL CENTER (O, 354 beds) 2525 South Michigan Avenue, Chicago, IL, Zip 60616–2333; tel. 312/567–2000; Carol L. Schneider, President and Chief Executive Officer
Web address: www.mercy–chicago.org

INDIANA: PLYMOUTH MEDICAL CENTER (O, 48 beds) 1915 Lake Avenue, Plymouth, IN, Zip 46563–9366, Mailing Address: P.O. Box 670, Zip 46563–0670, tel. 574/948–4000; Christopher J. Karam, President

SAINT JOSEPH HEALTH SYSTEM (O, 300 beds) 5215 Holy Cross Parkway, Mishawaka, IN, Zip 46545–1469; tel. 574/335–5000; Chad Towner, Chief Executive Officer
Web address: www.sjmed.com

IOWA: BAUM HARMON MERCY HOSPITAL (O, 11 beds) 255 North Welch Avenue, Primghar, IA, Zip 51245–7765, Mailing Address: P.O. Box 528, Zip 51245–0528, tel. 712/957–2300; Misty Dulin, CAH, Director

CENTRAL COMMUNITY HOSPITAL (C, 15 beds) 901 Davidson Street NW, Elkader, IA, Zip 52043–9015; tel. 563/245–7000; Brooke Kensinger, Chief Executive Officer
Web address: www.centralcommunityhospital.com

COVENANT MEDICAL CENTER (C, 229 beds) 3421 West Ninth Street, Waterloo, IA, Zip 50702–5401; tel. 319/272–8000; Jack Dusenbery, President and Chief Executive Officer
Web address: www.wheatoniowa.org

FRANKLIN GENERAL HOSPITAL (C, 77 beds) 1720 Central Avenue East, Suite A, Hampton, IA, Zip 50441–1867; tel. 641/456–5000; Kim Price, Chief Executive Officer
Web address: www.franklingeneral.com

HANCOCK COUNTY HEALTH SYSTEM (C, 25 beds) 532 First Street NW, Britt, IA, Zip 50423–1227; tel. 641/843–5000; Laura Zwiefel, Chief Executive Officer
Web address: www.trusthchs.com/hancock–county–health–system

HANSEN FAMILY HOSPITAL (C, 21 beds) 920 South Oak, Iowa Falls, IA, Zip 50126–9506; tel. 641/648–4631; Douglas E. Morse, Chief Executive Officer

HAWARDEN REGIONAL HEALTHCARE (C, 18 beds) 1111 11th Street, Hawarden, IA, Zip 51023–1999; tel. 712/551–3100; Jayson Pullman, Chief Executive Officer
Web address: www.hawardenregionalhealthcare.com/

KOSSUTH REGIONAL HEALTH CENTER (C, 23 beds) 1515 South Phillips Street, Algona, IA, Zip 50511–3649; tel. 515/295–2451; Scott A. Curtis, Administrator and Chief Executive Officer

MERCY HOSPITAL OF FRANCISCAN SISTERS (C, 64 beds) 201 Eighth Avenue SE, Oelwein, IA, Zip 50662–2447; tel. 319/283–6000; Terri Derflinger, Site Administrator
Web address: www.wheatoniowa.org

MERCY MEDICAL CENTER–CLINTON (O, 290 beds) 1410 North Fourth Street, Clinton, IA, Zip 52732–2940; tel. 563/244–5555; Amy Berentes, R.N., MSN, Executive Vice President and Chief Operating Officer
Web address: www.mercyclinton.com

MERCY MEDICAL CENTER–DUBUQUE (O, 231 beds) 250 Mercy Drive, Dubuque, IA, Zip 52001–7360; tel. 563/589–8000; Kay Takes, R.N., President

MERCY MEDICAL CENTER–DYERSVILLE (O, 20 beds) 1111 Third Street SW, Dyersville, IA, Zip 52040–1725; tel. 563/875–7101; Kay Takes, R.N., President
Web address: www.mercydubuque.com/mercy–dyersville

MERCY MEDICAL CENTER–NEW HAMPTON (O, 18 beds) 308 North Maple Avenue, New Hampton, IA, Zip 50659–1142; tel. 641/394–4121; Aaron Flugum, Chief Executive Officer
Web address: www.mercynewhampton.com

MERCY MEDICAL CENTER–NORTH IOWA (O, 205 beds) 1000 Fourth Street SW, Mason City, IA, Zip 50401–2800; tel. 641/428–7000; Rod G. Schlader, Interim Chief Executive Officer
Web address: www.mercynorthiowa.com

MERCY MEDICAL CENTER–SIOUX CITY (O, 186 beds) 801 Fifth Street, Sioux City, IA, Zip 51101–1326, Mailing Address: P.O. Box 3168, Zip 51102–3168, tel. 712/279–2010; Beth Hughes, President

MITCHELL COUNTY REGIONAL HEALTH CENTER (C, 25 beds) 616 North Eighth Street, Osage, IA, Zip 50461–1498; tel. 641/732–6000; Shelly Russell, Chief Executive Officer
Web address: www.mitchellcohospital–clinics.com

PALO ALTO COUNTY HEALTH SYSTEM (C, 47 beds) 3201 First Street, Emmetsburg, IA, Zip 50536–2516; tel. 712/852–5500; Brett Antczak, Chief Executive Officer

REGIONAL HEALTH SERVICES OF HOWARD COUNTY (C, 19 beds) 235 Eighth Avenue West, Cresco, IA, Zip 52136–1098; tel. 563/547–2101; Robin M. Schluter, Chief Executive Officer
Web address: www.rhshc.com

SARTORI MEMORIAL HOSPITAL (C, 50 beds) 515 College Street, Cedar Falls, IA, Zip 50613–2500; tel. 319/268–3000; MaryJo Kavalier, Administrator

MARYLAND: HOLY CROSS GERMANTOWN HOSPITAL (O, 101 beds) 19801 Observation Drive, Germantown, MD, Zip 20876–4070; tel. 301/754–7000; Doug Ryder, President
Web address: www.holycrosshealth.org/germantown

HOLY CROSS HOSPITAL (O, 415 beds) 1500 Forest Glen Road, Silver Spring, MD, Zip 20910–1487; tel. 301/754–7000; Louis Damiano, MD, President
Web address: www.holycrosshealth.org

MASSACHUSETTS: FARREN CARE CENTER (O, 72 beds) 340 Montague City Road, Turners Falls, MA, Zip 01376–9983; tel. 413/774–3111; James Clifford, Administrator

MERCY MEDICAL CENTER (O, 336 beds) 271 Carew Street, Springfield, MA, Zip 01104–2398, Mailing Address: P.O. Box 9012, Zip 01102–9012, tel. 413/748–9000; Mark M. Fulco, President
Web address: www.mercycares.com

MICHIGAN: MERCY HEALTH HACKLEY CAMPUS (O, 401 beds) 1700 Clinton Street, Muskegon, MI, Zip 49442–5502, Mailing Address: P.O. Box 3302, Zip 49443–3302, tel. 231/726–3511; Gary Allore, President
Web address: www.mercyhealthmuskegon.com

MERCY HEALTH SAINT MARY'S (O, 371 beds) 200 Jefferson Avenue Southeast, Grand Rapids, MI, Zip 49503–4598, Mailing Address: 200 Jefferson Avenue SE, Zip 49503–4598, tel. 616/685–5000; Bill Manns, President

For explanation of codes following names, see page B2.
★ Indicates Type III membership in the American Hospital Association.

MERCY HEALTH, LAKESHORE CAMPUS (O, 24 beds) 72 South State Street, Shelby, MI, Zip 49455–1299; tel. 231/861–2156; Jay Bryan, President and Chief Executive Officer
Web address: www.mercyhealthmuskegon.com

ST. JOSEPH MERCY ANN ARBOR (O, 483 beds) 5301 Mcauley Drive, Ypsilanti, MI, Zip 48197–1051, Mailing Address: P.O. Box 995, Ann Arbor, Zip 48106–0995, tel. 734/712–3456; David Brooks, President

ST. JOSEPH MERCY CHELSEA (O, 96 beds) 775 South Main Street, Chelsea, MI, Zip 48118–1383; tel. 734/593–6000; Nancy Kay. Graebner, President and Chief Executive Officer
Web address: www.cch.org

ST. JOSEPH MERCY LIVINGSTON HOSPITAL (O, 38 beds) 620 Byron Road, Howell, MI, Zip 48843–1093; tel. 517/545–6000; John F. O'Malley, FACHE, President
Web address: www.stjoeslivingston.org/livingston

ST. JOSEPH MERCY OAKLAND (O, 411 beds) 44405 Woodward Avenue, Pontiac, MI, Zip 48341–5023; tel. 248/858–3000; Shannon Striebich, Chief Executive Officer
Web address: www.stjoesoakland.com

ST. MARY MERCY HOSPITAL (O, 303 beds) 36475 Five Mile Road, Livonia, MI, Zip 48154–1988; tel. 734/655–4800; David A. Spivey, President and Chief Executive Officer

NEBRASKA: OAKLAND MERCY HOSPITAL (O, 18 beds) 601 East Second Street, Oakland, NE, Zip 68045–1499; tel. 402/685–5601; Laura Gamble, Director of Critical Access Hospitals
Web address: www.oaklandhospital.org

PENDER COMMUNITY HOSPITAL (C, 61 beds) 100 Hospital Drive , Pender, NE, Zip 68047–0100, Mailing Address: P.O. Box 100, Zip 68047–0100, tel. 402/385–3083; Melissa Kelly, Chief Executive Officer and Chief Financial Officer
Web address: www.pendercommunityhospital.com

NEW JERSEY: LOURDES MEDICAL CENTER OF BURLINGTON COUNTY (O, 169 beds) 218–A Sunset Road, Willingboro, NJ, Zip 08046–1162; tel. 609/835–2900; Mark Nessel, Executive Vice President and Chief Operating Officer

OUR LADY OF LOURDES MEDICAL CENTER (O, 340 beds) 1600 Haddon Avenue, Camden, NJ, Zip 08103–3117; tel. 856/757–3500; Reginald Blaber, M.D., FACC, President
Web address: www.lourdesnet.org

ST. FRANCIS MEDICAL CENTER (O, 142 beds) 601 Hamilton Avenue, Trenton, NJ, Zip 08629–1986; tel. 609/599–5000; Daniel P. Moen, President
Web address: www.stfrancismedical.org/

NEW YORK: ALBANY MEMORIAL HOSPITAL (O, 74 beds) 600 Northern Boulevard, Albany, NY, Zip 12204–1083; tel. 518/471–3221; James K. Reed, M.D., Chief Executive Officer
Web address: www.nehealth.com

BURDETT BIRTH CENTER (O, 15 beds) 2215 Burdett Avenue, Suite 200, Troy, NY, Zip 12180–2466; tel. 518/271–3393

SAMARITAN HOSPITAL (O, 183 beds) 2215 Burdett Avenue, Troy, NY, Zip 12180–2475; tel. 518/271–3300; James K. Reed, M.D., Chief Executive Officer
Web address: www.nehealth.com

SETON HEALTH ST. MARY'S HOSPITAL (O, 20 beds) 1300 Massachusetts Avenue, Troy, NY, Zip 12180–1695; tel. 518/268–5000; James K. Reed, M.D., Chief Executive Officer

ST. JOSEPH'S HOSPITAL HEALTH CENTER (O, 451 beds) 301 Prospect Avenue, Syracuse, NY, Zip 13203–1807; tel. 315/448–5111; Leslie Paul. Luke, President and Chief Executive Officer
Web address: www.sjhsyr.org

ST. PETER'S HOSPITAL (O, 442 beds) 315 South Manning Boulevard, Albany, NY, Zip 12208–1789; tel. 518/525–1550; James K. Reed, M.D., Chief Executive Officer
Web address: www.sphcs.org

SUNNYVIEW REHABILITATION HOSPITAL (O, 115 beds) 1270 Belmont Avenue, Schenectady, NY, Zip 12308–2104; tel. 518/382–4500; Edward Eisenman, Chief Executive Officer

NORTH CAROLINA: ST. JOSEPH OF THE PINES HOSPITAL (O, 204 beds) 590 Central Drive, Southern Pines, NC, Zip 28387; tel. 910/246–1000; Ken Cormier, President and Chief Executive Officer

OHIO: MOUNT CARMEL NEW ALBANY SURGICAL HOSPITAL (O, 60 beds) 7333 Smith's Mill Road, New Albany, OH, Zip 43054–9291; tel. 614/775–6600; Diane Doucette, R.N., President
Web address: www.mountcarmelhealth.com

MOUNT CARMEL ST. ANN'S (O, 305 beds) 500 South Cleveland Avenue, Westerville, OH, Zip 43081–8998; tel. 614/898–4000; Kim Unhee, President

MOUNT CARMEL (O, 685 beds) 793 West State Street, Columbus, OH, Zip 43222–1551; tel. 614/234–5000; Sean McKibben, President and Chief Operating Officer
Web address: www.mountcarmelhealth.com

OREGON: SAINT ALPHONSUS MEDICAL CENTER – BAKER CITY (S, 25 beds) 3325 Pocahontas Road, Baker City, OR, Zip 97814–1464; tel. 541/523–6461; Charles Davis, President
Web address: https://www.saintalphonsus.org/bakercity

SAINT ALPHONSUS MEDICAL CENTER – ONTARIO (S, 36 beds) 351 SW Ninth Street, Ontario, OR, Zip 97914–2693; tel. 541/881–7000; Kenneth Hart, President
Web address: www.saintalphonsus.org/ontario

PENNSYLVANIA: MERCY FITZGERALD HOSPITAL (O, 340 beds) 1500 Lansdowne Avenue, Suite 100, Darby, PA, Zip 19023–1200; tel. 610/237–4000; Susan Cusack, Executive Director

NAZARETH HOSPITAL (O, 162 beds) 2601 Holme Avenue, Philadelphia, PA, Zip 19152–2096; tel. 215/335–6000; Nancy Cherone, Executive Director and Administrator
Web address: www.nazarethhospital.org

ST. MARY MEDICAL CENTER (O, 353 beds) 1201 Langhorne–Newtown Road, Langhorne, PA, Zip 19047–1201; tel. 215/710–2000; James L. Woodward, President and Chief Executive Officer
Web address: www.stmaryhealthcare.org

Owned, leased, sponsored:	63 hospitals	14474 beds
Contract–managed:	15 hospitals	1105 beds
Totals:	78 hospitals	15579 beds

★**9255: TRUMAN MEDICAL CENTERS** (NP)
2301 Holmes Street, Kansas City, MO, Zip 64108–2677; tel. 816/404–1000; Charlie Shields, Chief Executive Officer
(Moderately Centralized Health System)

MISSOURI: TRUMAN MEDICAL CENTER–HOSPITAL HILL (O, 249 beds) 2301 Holmes Street, Kansas City, MO, Zip 64108–2640; tel. 816/404–1000; Charlie Shields, President and Chief Executive Officer
Web address: www.trumed.org

TRUMAN MEDICAL CENTER–LAKEWOOD (O, 298 beds) 7900 Lee's Summit Road, Kansas City, MO, Zip 64139–1236; tel. 816/404–7000; Lynette Wheeler, MSN, Chief Operating Officer
Web address: www.trumed.org

Owned, leased, sponsored:	2 hospitals	547 beds
Contract–managed:	0 hospitals	0 beds
Totals:	2 hospitals	547 beds

★**9105: UAB HEALTH SYSTEM** (NP)
500 22nd Street South, Suite 408, Birmingham, AL, Zip 35233–3110; tel. 205/975–5362; William Ferniany, Ph.D., Chief Executive Officer
(Centralized Physician/Insurance Health System)

ALABAMA: BRYAN W. WHITFIELD MEMORIAL HOSPITAL (C, 82 beds) 105 U S Highway 80 East, Demopolis, AL, Zip 36732–3616, Mailing Address: P.O. Box 890, Zip 36732–0890, tel. 334/289–4000; Douglas L. Brewer, Chief Executive Officer

MEDICAL WEST (O, 231 beds) 995 Ninth Avenue SW, Bessemer, AL, Zip 35022–4527; tel. 205/481–7000; Brian Keith. Pennington, President and Chief Executive Officer
Web address: www.medicalwesthospital.org

For explanation of codes following names, see page B2.
★ Indicates Type III membership in the American Hospital Association.

UNIVERSITY OF ALABAMA HOSPITAL (O, 1191 beds) 619 19th Street South, Birmingham, AL, Zip 35249–1900; tel. 205/934–4011; Reid F. Jones, Chief Executive Officer

Owned, leased, sponsored:	2 hospitals	1422 beds
Contract–managed:	1 hospitals	82 beds
Totals:	3 hospitals	1504 beds

★0082: UC HEALTH (NP)

3200 Burnet Avenue, Cincinnati, OH, Zip 45229–3019; tel. 513/585–6000; Richard P. Lofgren, M.D., M.P.H., President and CEO
(Moderately Centralized Health System)

OHIO: DANIEL DRAKE CENTER FOR POST ACUTE CARE (O, 202 beds) 151 West Galbraith Road, Cincinnati, OH, Zip 45216–1015; tel. 513/418–2500; Lafe Bauer, Vice President, Post Acute Care Services and Chief Administrative Officer

UNIVERSITY OF CINCINNATI MEDICAL CENTER (O, 555 beds) 234 Goodman Street, Cincinnati, OH, Zip 45219–2316; tel. 513/584–1000; Beverly A. Bokovitz, R.N., Chief Nursing Officer
Web address: www.uchealth.com/university–of–cincinnati–medical–center/

WEST CHESTER HOSPITAL (O, 182 beds) 7700 University Drive, West Chester, OH, Zip 45069–2505; tel. 513/298–3000; Tom G. Daskalakis, Chief Administrative Officer

Owned, leased, sponsored:	3 hospitals	939 beds
Contract–managed:	0 hospitals	0 beds
Totals:	3 hospitals	939 beds

★0381: UCHEALTH (NP)

2315 East Harmony Road, Suite 200, Fort Collins, CO, Zip 80528–8620; tel. 970/495–7000; Elizabeth B. Concordia, President and Chief Executive Officer
(Moderately Centralized Health System)

COLORADO: UCHEALTH BROOMFIELD HOSPITAL (O, 22 beds) 11820 Destination Drive, Broomfield, CO, Zip 80021; tel. 303/460–6000; Derek Rushing, Chief Executive Officer
Web address: www.uchealth.org/pages/OHAM/OrgUnitDetails.aspx?

UCHEALTH GRANDVIEW HOSPITAL (O, 22 beds) 5623 Pulpit Peak View, Colorado Springs, CO, Zip 80918; tel. 719/272–3600; Derek Rushing, Chief Executive Officer
Web address: https://www.uchealth.org/Pages/OHAM/OrgUnitDetails.aspx?OrganizationalUnitId=514

UCHEALTH MEDICAL CENTER OF THE ROCKIES (O, 187 beds) 2500 Rocky Mountain Avenue, Loveland, CO, Zip 80538–9004; tel. 970/624–2500; Kevin L. Unger, Ph.D., FACHE, President and Chief Executive Officer
Web address: www.medctrrockies.org

UCHEALTH MEMORIAL HOSPITAL (L, 509 beds) 1400 East Boulder Street, Colorado Springs, CO, Zip 80909–5599; tel. 719/365–5000; Joel P. Yuhas, FACHE, President and Chief Executive Officer

UCHEALTH POUDRE VALLEY HOSPITAL (O, 275 beds) 1024 South Lemay Avenue, Fort Collins, CO, Zip 80524–3998, Mailing Address: 2315 East Harmony Road, Suite 200, Zip 80528, tel. 970/495–7000; Kevin L. Unger, Ph.D., FACHE, President and Chief Executive Officer
Web address: www.uchealth.org

UCHEALTH YAMPA VALLEY MEDICAL CENTER (O, 39 beds) 1024 Central Park Drive, Steamboat Springs, CO, Zip 80487–8813; tel. 970/879–1322; Frank May, Chief Executive Officer

UNIVERSITY OF COLORADO HOSPITAL (O, 673 beds) 12401 East 17th Avenue, MS F417, Aurora, CO, Zip 80045–2545; tel. 720/848–0000; William Cook, President and Chief Executive Officer
Web address: www.uchealth.org

Owned, leased, sponsored:	7 hospitals	1727 beds
Contract–managed:	0 hospitals	0 beds
Totals:	7 hospitals	1727 beds

★0111: UF HEALTH SHANDS (NP)

1600 SW Archer Road, Gainesville, FL, Zip 32610–0326; tel. 352/733–1500; Edward Jimenez, Chief Executive Officer
(Moderately Centralized Health System)

FLORIDA: UF HEALTH JACKSONVILLE (O, 585 beds) 655 West Eighth Street, Jacksonville, FL, Zip 32209–6595; tel. 904/244–0411; Leon L. Haley Jr, M.D., Chief Executive Officer
Web address: www.ufhealthjax.org/

UF HEALTH SHANDS HOSPITAL (O, 986 beds) 1600 SW Archer Road, Gainesville, FL, Zip 32610–3003, Mailing Address: PO Box 100326, Zip 32610–0326, tel. 352/265–0111; Edward Jimenez, Chief Executive Officer

Owned, leased, sponsored:	2 hospitals	1571 beds
Contract–managed:	0 hospitals	0 beds
Totals:	2 hospitals	1571 beds

★0224: UMASS MEMORIAL HEALTH CARE, INC. (NP)

1 Biotech Park, Worcester, MA, Zip 01605–2982; tel. 508/334–0100; Eric Dickson, M.D., President and Chief Executive Officer
(Centralized Physician/Insurance Health System)

MASSACHUSETTS: UMASS MEMORIAL HEALTHALLIANCE–CLINTON HOSPITAL (O, 103 beds) 60 Hospital Road, Leominster, MA, Zip 01453–2205; tel. 978/466–2000; Deborah K. Weymouth, FACHE, President and Chief Executive Officer
Web address: www.healthalliance.com

UMASS MEMORIAL MEDICAL CENTER (O, 654 beds) 119 Belmont Street, Worcester, MA, Zip 01605–2982; tel. 508/334–1000; Michael Gustafson, M.D., President
Web address: www.umassmemorial.org

UMASS MEMORIAL–MARLBOROUGH HOSPITAL (O, 67 beds) 157 Union ST, Marlborough, MA, Zip 01752–1297; tel. 508/481–5000; Steven P. Roach, FACHE, President and Chief Executive Officer

Owned, leased, sponsored:	3 hospitals	824 beds
Contract–managed:	0 hospitals	0 beds
Totals:	3 hospitals	824 beds

★0901: UNC HEALTH CARE (NP)

101 Manning Drive, Chapel Hill, NC, Zip 27514–4220; tel. 919/966–4131; William L. Roper, M.D., M.P.H., Chief Executive Officer
(Moderately Centralized Health System)

NORTH CAROLINA: CALDWELL UNC HEALTH CARE (O, 82 beds) 321 Mulberry Street SW, Lenoir, NC, Zip 28645–5720, Mailing Address: P.O. Box 1890, Zip 28645–1890, tel. 828/757–5100; Laura J. Easton, President and Chief Executive Officer

CHATHAM HOSPITAL (O, 25 beds) 475 Progress Boulevard, Siler City, NC, Zip 27344–6787, Mailing Address: P.O. Box 649, Zip 27344–0649, tel. 919/799–4000; Robert A. Enders Jr, President
Web address: www.chathamhospital.org

HIGH POINT REGIONAL HEALTH SYSTEM (O, 297 beds) 601 North Elm Street, High Point, NC, Zip 27262–4398, Mailing Address: P.O. Box HP–5, Zip 27261–1899, tel. 336/878–6000; Ernest L. Bovio Jr, Chief Executive Officer
Web address: www.highpointregional.com

JOHNSTON HEALTH (C, 153 beds) 509 North Bright Leaf Blvd, Smithfield, NC, Zip 27577–4407, Mailing Address: P.O. Box 1376, Zip 27577–1376, tel. 919/934–8171; Charles W. Elliott Jr, Chief Executive Officer

MARGARET R. PARDEE MEMORIAL HOSPITAL (C, 160 beds) 800 North Justice Street, Hendersonville, NC, Zip 28791–3410; tel. 828/696–1000; James M. Kirby II, President and Chief Executive Officer
Web address: www.pardeehospital.org

NASH HEALTH CARE SYSTEMS (C, 273 beds) 2460 Curtis Ellis Drive, Rocky Mount, NC, Zip 27804–2237; tel. 252/962–8000; L Lee. Isley, FACHE, Ph.D., President and Chief Executive Officer
Web address: www.nhcs.org

For explanation of codes following names, see page B2.
★ Indicates Type III membership in the American Hospital Association.

UNC LENOIR HEALTHCARE (C, 155 beds) 100 Airport Road, Kinston, NC, Zip 28501–1634, Mailing Address: P.O. Box 1678, Zip 28503–1678, tel. 252/522–7000; Gary E. Black, President and Chief Executive Officer
Web address: www.lenoirmemorial.org

UNC REX HEALTH CARE (O, 666 beds) 4420 Lake Boone Trail, Raleigh, NC, Zip 27607–6599; tel. 919/784–3100; Stephen W. Burriss, President

UNC ROCKINGHAM HEALTH CARE (O, 188 beds) 117 East King's Highway, Eden, NC, Zip 27288–5201; tel. 336/623–9711; Dana Weston, Chief Executive Officer
Web address: www.morehead.org

UNIVERSITY OF NORTH CAROLINA HOSPITALS (O, 929 beds) 101 Manning Drive, Chapel Hill, NC, Zip 27514–4220; tel. 984/974–1000; Gary L. Park, President

WAYNE UNC HEALTH CARE (C, 274 beds) 2700 Wayne Memorial Drive, Goldsboro, NC, Zip 27534–9494, Mailing Address: P.O. Box 8001, Zip 27533–8001, tel. 919/736–1110; Janie Jaberg, FACHE, President and Chief Executive Officer
Web address: www.waynehealth.org

Owned, leased, sponsored:	6 hospitals	2187 beds
Contract–managed:	5 hospitals	1015 beds
Totals:	11 hospitals	3202 beds

0922: UNION GENERAL HOSPITAL, INC. (NP)
35 Hospital Road, Blairsville, GA, Zip 30512–3139; tel. 706/745–2111; Mike Gowder, Chief Executive Officer

GEORGIA: CHATUGE REGIONAL HOSPITAL AND NURSING HOME (O, 150 beds) 110 Main Street, Hiawassee, GA, Zip 30546–3408, Mailing Address: P.O. Box 509, Zip 30546–0509, tel. 706/896–2222; Ryan Snow, Administrator
Web address: www.chatugeregionalhospital.org

UNION GENERAL HOSPITAL (O, 195 beds) 35 Hospital Road, Blairsville, GA, Zip 30512–3139; tel. 706/745–2111; Lewis Kelley, Interim Chief Executive Officer
Web address: www.uniongeneralhospital.com

Owned, leased, sponsored:	2 hospitals	345 beds
Contract–managed:	0 hospitals	0 beds
Totals:	2 hospitals	345 beds

0288: UNITED HEALTH SERVICES (NP)
10–42 Mitchell Avenue, Binghamton, NY, Zip 13903–1617; tel. 607/762–2200; John M. Carrigg, President and Chief Executive Officer
(Independent Hospital System)

NEW YORK: UHS CHENANGO MEMORIAL HOSPITAL (O, 138 beds) 179 North Broad Street, Norwich, NY, Zip 13815–1097; tel. 607/337–4111; Drake M. Lamen, M.D., President, Chief Executive Officer and Chief Medical Officer
Web address: www.uhs.net/cmh

UHS DELAWARE VALLEY HOSPITAL (O, 25 beds) 1 Titus Place, Walton, NY, Zip 13856–1498; tel. 607/865–2100; Paul Summers, President and Chief Executive Officer

UNITED HEALTH SERVICES HOSPITALS–BINGHAMTON (O, 464 beds) 10–42 Mitchell Avenue, Binghamton, NY, Zip 13903–1678; tel. 607/763–6000; John M. Carrigg, President and Chief Executive Officer
Web address: www.uhs.net

Owned, leased, sponsored:	3 hospitals	627 beds
Contract–managed:	0 hospitals	0 beds
Totals:	3 hospitals	627 beds

9605: UNITED MEDICAL CORPORATION (IO)
603 Main Street, Windermere, FL, Zip 34786–3548, Mailing Address: P.O. Box 1100, Zip 34786–1100, tel. 407/876–2200; Donald R. Dizney, Chairman and Chief Executive Officer

PUERTO RICO: HOSPITAL PAVIA–HATO REY (O, 180 beds) 435 Ponce De Leon Avenue, San Juan, PR, Zip 00917–3428, Mailing Address: PO Box 190828, Zip 00917–3428, tel. 787/641–2323; Guillermo Pastrana, Executive Director

HOSPITAL PAVIA–SANTURCE (O, 197 beds) 1462 Asia Street, San Juan, PR, Zip 00909–2143, Mailing Address: Box 11137, Santurce Station, Zip 00910–1137, tel. 787/727–6060; Jose Luis. Rodriguez, Chief Executive Officer
Web address: www.paviahealth.com

HOSPITAL PEREA (O, 103 beds) 15 Basora Street, Mayaguez, PR, Zip 681, Mailing Address: P.O. Box 170, Zip 681, tel. 787/834–0101; Jorge I. Martinez, Executive Director
Web address: www.paviahealth.com/perea_hospital.htm

HOSPITAL SAN FRANCISCO (O, 148 beds) 371 Avenida De Diego, San Juan, PR, Zip 00923–1711, Mailing Address: P.O. Box 29025, Zip 00929–0025, tel. 787/767–5100; Marcos Aguila, Chief Executive Officer
Web address: www.metropavia.com/SanFrancisco.cfm

SAN JORGE CHILDREN'S HOSPITAL (O, 125 beds) 258 San Jorge Street, Santurce, Santurce, PR, Zip 00912–3310, Mailing Address: PO Box 6308, San Juan, Zip 00912–3310, tel. 787/727–1000; Domingo Cruz, Senior Vice President Operations

TENNESSEE: TEN BROECK TENNESSEE TREATMENT FACILITY (O, 38 beds) 1 Medical Center Boulevard, 5 West, Cookeville, TN, Zip 38501; tel. 931/783–2570; Kelly Tripp, Chief Executive Officer
Web address: www.tenbroeck.com

Owned, leased, sponsored:	6 hospitals	791 beds
Contract–managed:	0 hospitals	0 beds
Totals:	6 hospitals	791 beds

0937: UNITED MEDICAL REHABILITATION HOSPITALS (IO)
3201 Wall Boulevard, Suite B, Gretna, LA, Zip 70056–7755; tel. 504/433–5551; John E.H. Mills, President and Chief Executive Officer

LOUISIANA: UNITED MEDICAL REHABILITATION HOSPITAL (O, 21 beds) 3201 Wall Boulevard, Suite B, Gretna, LA, Zip 70056–7755; tel. 504/433–5551; Jerry Deller, Administrator
Web address: www.umrhospital.com/

UNITED MEDICAL REHABILITATION HOSPITAL (O, 20 beds) 15717 Belle Drive, Hammond, LA, Zip 70403–1439; tel. 985/340–5998; Jonathan Landreth, Administrator

Owned, leased, sponsored:	2 hospitals	41 beds
Contract–managed:	0 hospitals	0 beds
Totals:	2 hospitals	41 beds

0322: UNITED SURGICAL PARTNERS INTERNATIONAL (IO)
15305 Dallas Parkway, Suite 1600, Addison, TX, Zip 75001–6491; tel. 972/713–3500; William H. Wilcox, President and Chief Executive Officer
(Independent Hospital System)

ARIZONA: ARIZONA ORTHOPEDIC SURGICAL HOSPITAL (O, 24 beds) 2905 West Warner Road, Suite 1, Chandler, AZ, Zip 85224–1674; tel. 480/603–9000; Patricia K. Alice, Chief Executive Officer

OKLAHOMA: OKLAHOMA CENTER FOR ORTHOPEDIC AND MULTI–SPECIALTY SURGERY (O, 10 beds) 8100 South Walker, Suite C, Oklahoma City, OK, Zip 73139–9402, Mailing Address: P.O. Box 890609, Zip 73189–0609, tel. 405/602–6500; Mike Kimzey, Chief Executive Officer and Administrator
Web address: www.ocomhospital.com

TEXAS: BAYLOR MEDICAL CENTER AT FRISCO (O, 68 beds) 5601 Warren Parkway, Frisco, TX, Zip 75034–4069; tel. 214/407–5000; Trevor Castaneda, Chief Executive Officer

BAYLOR MEDICAL CENTER AT UPTOWN (O, 24 beds) 2727 East Lemmon Avenue, Dallas, TX, Zip 75204–2895; tel. 214/443–3000; Nick Taylor, Chief Executive Officer
Web address: www.bmcuptown.com

For explanation of codes following names, see page B2.
★ Indicates Type III membership in the American Hospital Association.

BAYLOR SURGICAL HOSPITAL AT LAS COLINAS (O, 12 beds) 400 West Interstate 635, Irving, TX, Zip 75063; tel. 972/868–4000; Deonna Unell, Chief Executive Officer
Web address: www.baylorhealth.com/About/Community/Assessments/West/ICSH/Pages/Default.aspx

TOPS SURGICAL SPECIALTY HOSPITAL (O, 15 beds) 17080 Red Oak Drive, Houston, TX, Zip 77090–2602; tel. 281/539–2900; Samuel H. Rossmann, Chief Executive Officer

Owned, leased, sponsored:	6 hospitals	153 beds
Contract–managed:	0 hospitals	0 beds
Totals:	6 hospitals	153 beds

★0061: UNITYPOINT HEALTH (NP)
1776 West Lakes Parkway, Suite 400, West Des Moines, IA, Zip 50266–8393; tel. 515/241–6161; Kevin Vermeer, President and Chief Executive Officer
(Decentralized Health System)

ILLINOIS: MEMORIAL HOSPITAL (O, 18 beds) 1454 North County Road 2050, Carthage, IL, Zip 62321–3551, Mailing Address: P.O. Box 160, Zip 62321–0160, tel. 217/357–8500; Ada Bair, Chief Executive Officer
Web address: www.mhtlc.org

UNITYPOINT HEALTH – PEORIA (O, 262 beds) 221 NE Glen Oak Avenue, Peoria, IL, Zip 61636–4310; tel. 309/672–5522; Deborah R. Simon, R.N., Regional Chief Executive Officer

UNITYPOINT HEALTH – PROCTOR (O, 125 beds) 5409 North Knoxville Avenue, Peoria, IL, Zip 61614–5069; tel. 309/691–1000; Deborah R. Simon, R.N., President and Chief Executive Officer
Web address: www.proctor.org

UNITYPOINT HEALTH – TRINITY ROCK ISLAND (O, 343 beds) 2701 17th Street, Rock Island, IL, Zip 61201–5393; tel. 309/779–5000; Richard A. Seidler, FACHE, President and Chief Executive Officer
Web address: www.trinityqc.com

UNITYPOINT HEALTH–PEKIN HOSPITAL (O, 107 beds) 600 South 13th Street, Pekin, IL, Zip 61554–4936; tel. 309/347–1151; Bob J. Haley, Chief Executive Officer
Web address: www.pekinhospital.org

IOWA: BUCHANAN COUNTY HEALTH CENTER (O, 58 beds) 1600 First Street East, Independence, IA, Zip 50644–3155; tel. 319/332–0999; Steve Robert. Slessor, Chief Executive Officer

BUENA VISTA REGIONAL MEDICAL CENTER (C, 35 beds) 1525 West Fifth Street, Storm Lake, IA, Zip 50588–3027, Mailing Address: P.O. Box 309, Zip 50588–0309, tel. 712/732–4030; Steven Colerick, Chief Executive Officer
Web address: www.bvrmc.org

CHEROKEE REGIONAL MEDICAL CENTER (O, 25 beds) 300 Sioux Valley Drive, Cherokee, IA, Zip 51012–1205; tel. 712/225–5101; Matthew Johnson, Chief Executive Officer and President
Web address: www.cherokeermc.org

CLARKE COUNTY HOSPITAL (C, 25 beds) 800 South Fillmore Street, Osceola, IA, Zip 50213–1619; tel. 641/342–2184; Brian G. Evans, FACHE, Chief Executive Officer
Web address: www.clarkehosp.org

COMMUNITY MEMORIAL HOSPITAL (C, 16 beds) 909 West First Street, Sumner, IA, Zip 50674–1203, Mailing Address: P.O. Box 148, Zip 50674–0148, tel. 563/578–3275; Dawn Everding, President and Chief Financial Officer

COMPASS MEMORIAL HEALTHCARE (O, 25 beds) 300 West May Street, Marengo, IA, Zip 52301–1261; tel. 319/642–5543; Barry Goettsch, FACHE, Chief Executive Officer
Web address: www.compassmemorial.org

GREATER REGIONAL MEDICAL CENTER (C, 25 beds) 1700 West Townline Street Suite 3, Creston, IA, Zip 50801–1099; tel. 641/782–7091; Monte Neitzel, Chief Executive Officer
Web address: www.greaterregional.org

GREENE COUNTY MEDICAL CENTER (C, 85 beds) 1000 West Lincolnway, Jefferson, IA, Zip 50129–1645; tel. 515/386–2114; Carl P. Behne, Chief Executive Officer

GRUNDY COUNTY MEMORIAL HOSPITAL (C, 80 beds) 201 East 'J' Avenue, Grundy Center, IA, Zip 50638–2096; tel. 319/824–5421; Adam Scherling, President and Chief Executive Officer
Web address: www.grundycountyhospital.com

GUTHRIE COUNTY HOSPITAL (C, 17 beds) 710 North 12th Street, Guthrie Center, IA, Zip 50115–1544; tel. 641/332–2201; Patrick Peters, Chief Executive Officer

HUMBOLDT COUNTY MEMORIAL HOSPITAL (C, 49 beds) 1000 North 15th Street, Humboldt, IA, Zip 50548–1008; tel. 515/332–4200; Michelle Sleiter, Chief Executive Officer
Web address: www.humboldthospital.org

LORING HOSPITAL (C, 25 beds) 211 Highland Avenue, Sac City, IA, Zip 50583–2424; tel. 712/662–7105; Brian Martin, Chief Executive Officer
Web address: www.loringhospital.org

LUCAS COUNTY HEALTH CENTER (C, 25 beds) 1200 North Seventh Street, Chariton, IA, Zip 50049–1258; tel. 641/774–3000; Brian Sims, Chief Executive Officer

POCAHONTAS COMMUNITY HOSPITAL (C, 20 beds) 606 NW Seventh Street, Pocahontas, IA, Zip 50574–1099; tel. 712/335–3501; James D. Roetman, President and Chief Executive Officer
Web address: www.pocahontashospital.org

STEWART MEMORIAL COMMUNITY HOSPITAL (C, 25 beds) 1301 West Main, Lake City, IA, Zip 51449–1585; tel. 712/464–3171; Cynthia L. Carstens, R.N., President and Chief Executive Officer

STORY COUNTY MEDICAL CENTER (C, 82 beds) 640 South 19th Street, Nevada, IA, Zip 50201–2902; tel. 515/382–2111; Nate Thompson, Chief Executive Officer
Web address: www.storymedical.org

UNITYPOINT HEALTH – ALLEN HOSPITAL (O, 201 beds) 1825 Logan Avenue, Waterloo, IA, Zip 50703–1916; tel. 319/235–3941; Pamela K. Delagardelle, President and Chief Executive Officer
Web address: www.unitypoint.org/waterloo

UNITYPOINT HEALTH – FINLEY HOSPITAL (O, 109 beds) 350 North Grandview Avenue, Dubuque, IA, Zip 52001–6393; tel. 563/582–1881; Theodore E. Townsend, FACHE, Interim Chief Executive Officer

UNITYPOINT HEALTH – GRINNELL REGIONAL MEDICAL CENTER (O, 49 beds) 210 Fourth Avenue, Grinnell, IA, Zip 50112–1898; tel. 641/236–7511; Jennifer Havens, Chief Executive Officer
Web address: www.grmc.us

UNITYPOINT HEALTH – IOWA METHODIST MEDICAL CENTER (O, 448 beds) 1200 Pleasant Street, Des Moines, IA, Zip 50309–1406; tel. 515/241–6212; David A. Stark, FACHE, President and Chief Executive Officer
Web address: www.unitypoint.org

UNITYPOINT HEALTH – JONES REGIONAL MEDICAL CENTER (O, 22 beds) 1795 Highway 64 East, Anamosa, IA, Zip 52205–2112; tel. 319/462–6131; Eric Briesemeister, Chief Executive Officer

UNITYPOINT HEALTH – MARSHALLTOWN (O, 34 beds) 3 South Fourth Avenue, Marshalltown, IA, Zip 50158–2998; tel. 641/754–5151; Jennifer Friedly, President
Web address: www.https://marshalltown.unitypoint.org

UNITYPOINT HEALTH – ST. LUKE'S HOSPITAL (O, 348 beds) 1026 'A' Avenue NE, Cedar Rapids, IA, Zip 52402–3026, Mailing Address: P.O. Box 3026, Zip 52406–3026, tel. 319/369–7211; Theodore E. Townsend, FACHE, President and Chief Executive Officer
Web address: www.unitypoint.org

UNITYPOINT HEALTH – ST. LUKES'S SIOUX CITY (O, 150 beds) 2720 Stone Park Boulevard, Sioux City, IA, Zip 51104–3734; tel. 712/279–3500; Lynn Wold, President and Chief Executive Officer

UNITYPOINT HEALTH – TRINITY BETTENDORF (O, 86 beds) 4500 Utica Ridge Road, Bettendorf, IA, Zip 52722–1626; tel. 563/742–5000; Richard A. Seidler, FACHE, President and Chief Executive Officer
Web address: www.trinityqc.com

UNITYPOINT HEALTH – TRINITY MUSCATINE (O, 45 beds) 1518 Mulberry Avenue, Muscatine, IA, Zip 52761–3499; tel. 563/264–9100; Angela Johnson, Executive Director
Web address: www.unitypoint.org/quadcities/trinity–muscatine.aspx

UNITYPOINT HEALTH – TRINITY REGIONAL MEDICAL CENTER (O, 49 beds) 802 Kenyon Road, Fort Dodge, IA, Zip 50501–5795; tel. 515/573–3101; Susan K. Thompson, RN, Interim President and Chief Executive Officer

For explanation of codes following names, see page B2.
★ Indicates Type III membership in the American Hospital Association.

UNITYPOINT HEALTH–IOWA LUTHERAN HOSPITAL (O, 206 beds) 700 East University Avenue, Des Moines, IA, Zip 50316–2392; tel. 515/263–5612; David A. Stark, FACHE, President and Chief Executive Officer
Web address: www.unitypoint.org

UNITYPOINT HEALTH–KEOKUK (O, 42 beds) 1600 Morgan Street, Keokuk, IA, Zip 52632–3456; tel. 319/524–7150; Donza T. Worden, M.D., Chief Clinical Officer
Web address: www.keokukhealthsystems.org

WISCONSIN: MEMORIAL HOSPITAL OF LAFAYETTE COUNTY (O, 25 beds) 800 Clay Street, Darlington, WI, Zip 53530–1228, Mailing Address: P.O. Box 70, Zip 53530–0070, tel. 608/776–4466; Julie Chikowski, Administrator

UNITYPOINT HEALTH MERITER (O, 217 beds) 202 South Park Street, Madison, WI, Zip 53715–1507; tel. 608/417–6000; Sue Erickson, President and Chief Executive Officer
Web address: www.meriter.com

Owned, leased, sponsored:	23 hospitals	2994 beds
Contract–managed:	13 hospitals	509 beds
Totals:	36 hospitals	3503 beds

9555: UNIVERSAL HEALTH SERVICES, INC. (IO)
367 South Gulph Road, King of Prussia, PA, Zip 19406–3121, Mailing Address: P.O. Box 61558, Zip 19406–0958, tel. 610/768–3300; Alan B. Miller, Chairman and Chief Executive Officer

(Decentralized Health System)

ALABAMA: HILL CREST BEHAVIORAL HEALTH SERVICES (O, 94 beds) 6869 Fifth Avenue South, Birmingham, AL, Zip 35212–1866; tel. 205/833–9000; Steve McCabe, Chief Executive Officer
Web address: www.hillcrestbhs.com

LAUREL OAKS BEHAVIORAL HEALTH CENTER (O, 38 beds) 700 East Cottonwood Road, Dothan, AL, Zip 36301–3644; tel. 334/794–7373; Derek Johnson, Chief Executive Officer

ALASKA: NORTH STAR BEHAVIORAL HEALTH SYSTEM (O, 200 beds) 2530 DeBarr Circle, Anchorage, AK, Zip 99508–2948; tel. 907/258–7575; Andrew Mayo, Ph.D., Chief Executive Officer and Managing Director
Web address: www.northstarbehavioral.com

ARIZONA: PALO VERDE BEHAVIORAL HEALTH (O, 48 beds) 2695 North Craycroft Road, Tucson, AZ, Zip 85712–2244; tel. 520/322–2888; Melissa Eckstein, Chief Executive Officer

VALLEY HOSPITAL PHOENIX (O, 122 beds) 3550 East Pinchot Avenue, Phoenix, AZ, Zip 85018–7434; tel. 602/957–4000; Michelle David, Chief Executive Officer
Web address: www.valleyhospital–phoenix.com

ARKANSAS: PINNACLE POINTE HOSPITAL (O, 127 beds) 11501 Financial Center Parkway, Little Rock, AR, Zip 72211–3715; tel. 501/223–3322; Shane Frazier, Chief Executive Officer
Web address: www.pinnaclepointehospital.com

RIVENDELL BEHAVIORAL HEALTH SERVICES OF ARKANSAS (O, 77 beds) 100 Rivendell Drive, Benton, AR, Zip 72019–9100; tel. 501/316–1255; Ballard Sheppard, Chief Executive Officer

SPRINGWOODS BEHAVIORAL HEALTH HOSPITAL (O, 80 beds) 1955 West Truckers Drive, Fayetteville, AR, Zip 72704–5637; tel. 479/973–6000; Jordon Babcock, Interim Chief Executive Officer
Web address: www.springwoodsbehavioral.com

THE BRIDGEWAY (L, 127 beds) 21 Bridgeway Road, North Little Rock, AR, Zip 72113–9516; tel. 501/771–1500; Jonathon Gammon, Interim Chief Executive Officer

CALIFORNIA: BHC ALHAMBRA HOSPITAL (O, 97 beds) 4619 North Rosemead Boulevard, Rosemead, CA, Zip 91770–1478, Mailing Address: P.O. Box 369, Zip 91770–0369, tel. 626/286–1191; Peggy Minnick, R.N., Chief Executive Officer
Web address: www.bhcalhambra.com

CANYON RIDGE HOSPITAL (O, 106 beds) 5353 'G' Street, Chino, CA, Zip 91710–5250; tel. 909/590–3700; Burt Harris, Acting Chief Executive Officer
Web address: www.canyonridgehospital.com

CORONA REGIONAL MEDICAL CENTER (O, 238 beds) 800 South Main Street, Corona, CA, Zip 92882–3400; tel. 951/737–4343; Mark H. Uffer, Chief Executive Officer
Web address: www.coronaregional.com

DEL AMO HOSPITAL (O, 70 beds) 23700 Camino Del Sol, Torrance, CA, Zip 90505–5000; tel. 310/530–1151; Steven Oppenheimer, Chief Executive Officer

FREMONT HOSPITAL (O, 148 beds) 39001 Sundale Drive, Fremont, CA, Zip 94538–2005; tel. 510/796–1100; Marlon Rollins, Ph.D., Chief Executive Officer
Web address: www.fremonthospital.com

HERITAGE OAKS HOSPITAL (O, 120 beds) 4250 Auburn Boulevard, Sacramento, CA, Zip 95841–4164; tel. 916/489–3336; Shawn Silva, Chief Executive Officer
Web address: www.heritageoakshospital.com

PALMDALE REGIONAL MEDICAL CENTER (O, 184 beds) 38600 Medical Center Drive, Palmdale, CA, Zip 93551–4483; tel. 661/382–5000; Richard Allen, Chief Executive Officer

SIERRA VISTA HOSPITAL (O, 120 beds) 8001 Bruceville Road, Sacramento, CA, Zip 95823–2329; tel. 916/288–0300; Mike Zauner, Chief Executive Officer
Web address: www.sierravistahospital.com

SOUTHWEST HEALTHCARE SYSTEM (O, 240 beds) 25500 Medical Center Drive, Murrieta, CA, Zip 92562–5965; tel. 951/696–6000; Bradley D. Neet, FACHE, Chief Executive Officer

TEMECULA VALLEY HOSPITAL (O, 140 beds) 31700 Temecula Parkway, Temecula, CA, Zip 92592–5896; tel. 951/331–2216; Darlene Wetton, R.N., Chief Executive Officer
Web address: www.temeculavalleyhospital.com

COLORADO: CEDAR SPRINGS HOSPITAL (O, 110 beds) 2135 Southgate Road, Colorado Springs, CO, Zip 80906–2693; tel. 719/633–4114; Christopher D. Burke, Ph.D., Chief Executive Officer

CENTENNIAL PEAKS HOSPITAL (O, 104 beds) 2255 South 88th Street, Louisville, CO, Zip 80027–9716; tel. 303/673–9990; Elicia Bunch, Chief Executive Officer
Web address: www.centennialpeaks.com

HIGHLANDS BEHAVIORAL HEALTH SYSTEM (O, 86 beds) 8565 South Poplar Way, Littleton, CO, Zip 80130–3602; tel. 720/348–2800; Elicia Bunch, Chief Executive Officer
Web address: www.highlandsbhs.com

DELAWARE: DOVER BEHAVIORAL HEALTH SYSTEM (O, 72 beds) 725 Horsepond Road, Dover, DE, Zip 19901–7232; tel. 302/741–0140; Jean–Charles Constant, Administrator

ROCKFORD CENTER (O, 128 beds) 100 Rockford Drive, Newark, DE, Zip 19713–2121; tel. 302/996–5480; John F. McKenna, Chief Executive Officer and Managing Director
Web address: www.rockfordcenter.com

DISTRICT OF COLUMBIA: GEORGE WASHINGTON UNIVERSITY HOSPITAL (O, 385 beds) 900 23rd Street NW, Washington, DC, Zip 20037–2342; tel. 202/715–4000; Kimberly Russo, Chief Executive Officer

FLORIDA: CENTRAL FLORIDA BEHAVIORAL HOSPITAL (O, 126 beds) 6601 Central Florida Parkway, Orlando, FL, Zip 32821–8064; tel. 407/370–0111; Vickie Lewis, Chief Executive Officer
Web address: www.centralfloridabehavioral.com

EMERALD COAST BEHAVIORAL HOSPITAL (O, 86 beds) 1940 Harrison Avenue, Panama City, FL, Zip 32405–4542; tel. 850/763–0017; Tim Bedford, Chief Executive Officer
Web address: www.emeraldcoastbehavioral.com

FORT LAUDERDALE HOSPITAL (L, 100 beds) 1601 East Las Olas Boulevard, Fort Lauderdale, FL, Zip 33301–2393; tel. 954/463–4321; Manuel R. Llano, Chief Executive Officer
Web address: www.fortlauderdalehospital.org

LAKEWOOD RANCH MEDICAL CENTER (O, 120 beds) 8330 Lakewood Ranch Boulevard, Bradenton, FL, Zip 34202–5174; tel. 941/782–2100; Andrew Guz, Chief Executive Officer

MANATEE MEMORIAL HOSPITAL (O, 319 beds) 206 Second Street East, Bradenton, FL, Zip 34208–1000; tel. 941/746–5111; Kevin DiLallo, Chief Executive Officer
Web address: www.manateememorial.com

For explanation of codes following names, see page B2.
★ Indicates Type III membership in the American Hospital Association.

RIVER POINT BEHAVIORAL HEALTH (O, 92 beds) 6300 Beach Boulevard, Jacksonville, FL, Zip 32216–2782; tel. 904/724–9202; Kevin McGee, Chief Executive Officer

SUNCOAST BEHAVIORAL HEALTH CENTER (O, 80 beds) 4480 51st Street West, Bradenton, FL, Zip 34210–2855; tel. 941/251–5000; Brandy Hamilton, Chief Executive Officer
Web address: www.suncoastbhc.com

THE VINES (O, 98 beds) 3130 SW 27th Avenue, Ocala, FL, Zip 34471–4306; tel. 352/671–3130; Stephen Quintyne, Chief Executive Officer
Web address: www.thevineshospital.com

WEKIVA SPRINGS (O, 60 beds) 3947 Salisbury Road, Jacksonville, FL, Zip 32216–6115; tel. 904/296–3533; Sheila Carr, Chief Executive Officer

WELLINGTON REGIONAL MEDICAL CENTER (L, 233 beds) 10101 Forest Hill Boulevard, Wellington, FL, Zip 33414–6199; tel. 561/798–8500; Robbin Lee, Chief Executive Officer
Web address: www.wellingtonregional.com

WINDMOOR HEALTHCARE OF CLEARWATER (O, 100 beds) 11300 U S 19 North, Clearwater, FL, Zip 33764; tel. 727/541–2646; Wendy Merson, Chief Executive Officer

GEORGIA: ANCHOR HOSPITAL (O, 122 beds) 5454 Yorktowne Drive, Atlanta, GA, Zip 30349–5317; tel. 770/991–6044; Lloyd Noble, Chief Executive Officer
Web address: www.anchorhospital.com

COASTAL HARBOR TREATMENT CENTER (O, 191 beds) 1150 Cornell Avenue, Savannah, GA, Zip 31406–2702; tel. 912/354–3911; Sally Perry, Chief Executive Officer

PEACHFORD BEHAVIORAL HEALTH SYSTEM (O, 246 beds) 2151 Peachford Road, Atlanta, GA, Zip 30338–6599; tel. 770/455–3200; Matthew Crouch, Chief Executive Officer and Managing Director
Web address: www.peachfordhospital.com

SAINT SIMONS BY-THE-SEA HOSPITAL (O, 101 beds) 2927 Demere Road, Saint Simons Island, GA, Zip 31522–1620; tel. 912/638–1999; Chuck Flavio, Chief Executive Officer

TURNING POINT HOSPITAL (O, 59 beds) 3015 Veterans Parkway South, Moultrie, GA, Zip 31788–6705, Mailing Address: P.O. Box 1177, Zip 31776–1177, tel. 229/985–4815; Judy H. Payne, Chief Executive Officer
Web address: www.turningpointcare.com

IDAHO: INTERMOUNTAIN HOSPITAL (O, 140 beds) 303 North Allumbaugh Street, Boise, ID, Zip 83704–9208; tel. 208/377–8400; Jeffrey F. Morrell, Chief Executive Officer

ILLINOIS: GARFIELD PARK HOSPITAL (O, 88 beds) 520 North Ridgeway Avenue, Chicago, IL, Zip 60624–1232; tel. 773/265–3700; Steven Airhart, Chief Executive Officer
Web address: www.garfieldparkhospital.com

HARTGROVE HOSPITAL (O, 128 beds) 5730 West Roosevelt Road, Chicago, IL, Zip 60644–1580; tel. 773/413–1700; Steven Airhart, Chief Executive Officer

LINCOLN PRAIRIE BEHAVIORAL HEALTH CENTER (O, 97 beds) 5230 South Sixth Street, Springfield, IL, Zip 62703–5128; tel. 217/585–1180; Mark Littrell, Chief Executive Officer
Web address: www.lincolnprairiebhc.com/

RIVEREDGE HOSPITAL (O, 210 beds) 8311 West Roosevelt Road, Forest Park, IL, Zip 60130–2500; tel. 708/771–7000; Carey Carlock, Chief Executive Officer
Web address: www.riveredgehospital.com

STREAMWOOD BEHAVIORAL HEALTH CENTER (O, 178 beds) 1400 East Irving Park Road, Streamwood, IL, Zip 60107–3203; tel. 630/837–9000; Ron Weglarz, Chief Executive Officer and Managing Director
Web address: www.streamwoodhospital.com

THE PAVILION (O, 106 beds) 809 West Church Street, Champaign, IL, Zip 61820–3399; tel. 217/373–1700; Mark Littrell, Group Director

INDIANA: BLOOMINGTON MEADOWS HOSPITAL (O, 71 beds) 3600 North Prow Road, Bloomington, IN, Zip 47404–1616; tel. 812/331–8000; Christopher Downers, Chief Executive Officer
Web address: www.bloomingtonmeadows.com

MICHIANA BEHAVIORAL HEALTH CENTER (O, 75 beds) 1800 North Oak Drive, Plymouth, IN, Zip 46563–3492; tel. 574/936–3784; Michael Perry, Chief Executive Officer
Web address: www.michianabhc.com

VALLE VISTA HOSPITAL (O, 102 beds) 898 East Main Street, Greenwood, IN, Zip 46143–1400; tel. 317/887–1348; Sherri R. Jewett, Chief Executive Officer

WELLSTONE REGIONAL HOSPITAL (O, 100 beds) 2700 Vissing Park Road, Jeffersonville, IN, Zip 47130–5989; tel. 812/284–8000; Greg Stewart, Chief Executive Officer
Web address: www.wellstonehospital.com

KENTUCKY: CUMBERLAND HALL HOSPITAL (O, 97 beds) 270 Walton Way, Hopkinsville, KY, Zip 42240–6808; tel. 270/886–1919; Jason Staats, Chief Executive Officer

LINCOLN TRAIL BEHAVIORAL HEALTH SYSTEM (O, 140 beds) 3909 South Wilson Road, Radcliff, KY, Zip 40160–8944, Mailing Address: P.O. Box 369, Zip 40159–0369, tel. 270/351–9444; Charles L. Webb Jr, Chief Executive Officer
Web address: www.lincolnbehavioral.com

RIDGE BEHAVIORAL HEALTH SYSTEM (O, 110 beds) 3050 Rio Dosa Drive, Lexington, KY, Zip 40509–1540; tel. 859/269–2325; Nina W. Eisner, Chief Executive Officer and Managing Director

RIVENDELL BEHAVIORAL HEALTH (O, 125 beds) 1035 Porter Pike, Bowling Green, KY, Zip 42103–9581; tel. 270/843–1199; Matt Ours, Chief Executive Officer and Managing Director
Web address: www.rivendellbehavioral.com

THE BROOK HOSPITAL – KMI (O, 110 beds) 8521 Old LaGrange Road, Louisville, KY, Zip 40242–3800; tel. 502/426–6380; Paul Andrews, Chief Executive Officer
Web address: www.thebrookhospitals.com

THE BROOK AT DUPONT (O, 88 beds) 1405 Browns Lane, Louisville, KY, Zip 40207–4608; tel. 502/896–0495; Paul Andrews, Chief Executive Officer

LOUISIANA: BRENTWOOD HOSPITAL (O, 176 beds) 1006 Highland Avenue, Shreveport, LA, Zip 71101–4103; tel. 318/678–7500; William Weaver, Chief Executive Officer
Web address: www.brentwoodbehavioral.com

RIVER OAKS HOSPITAL (O, 126 beds) 1525 River Oaks Road West, New Orleans, LA, Zip 70123–2162; tel. 504/734–1740; Deagan Watson, Chief Executive Officer
Web address: www.riveroakshospital.com

MASSACHUSETTS: ARBOUR H. R. I. HOSPITAL (O, 76 beds) 227 Babcock Street, Brookline, MA, Zip 02446–6799; tel. 617/731–3200; Jameson Pinette, Chief Executive Officer

ARBOUR HOSPITAL (O, 118 beds) 49 Robinwood Avenue, Boston, MA, Zip 02130–2156; tel. 617/522–4400; Eric Kennedy, Chief Executive Officer
Web address: www.arbourhealth.com

ARBOUR–FULLER HOSPITAL (O, 46 beds) 200 May Street, Attleboro, MA, Zip 02703–5520; tel. 508/761–8500; Rachel Legend, Chief Executive Officer
Web address: www.arbourhealth.com

PEMBROKE HOSPITAL (O, 115 beds) 199 Oak Street, Pembroke, MA, Zip 02359–1953; tel. 781/829–7000; Raymond Robinson, Chief Executive Officer

MICHIGAN: FOREST VIEW PSYCHIATRIC HOSPITAL (O, 108 beds) 1055 Medical Park Drive SE, Grand Rapids, MI, Zip 49546–3607; tel. 616/942–9610; Andrew Hotaling, Chief Executive Officer
Web address: www.forestviewhospital.com

HAVENWYCK HOSPITAL (O, 243 beds) 1525 University Drive, Auburn Hills, MI, Zip 48326–2673; tel. 248/373–9200; Julie Szyska, Chief Executive Officer and Managing Director

MISSISSIPPI: ALLIANCE HEALTH CENTER (O, 154 beds) 5000 Highway 39 North, Meridian, MS, Zip 39301–1021; tel. 601/483–6211; Jay Shehi, Chief Executive Officer
Web address: www.alliancehealthcenter.com

BRENTWOOD BEHAVIORAL HEALTHCARE OF MISSISSIPPI (O, 105 beds) 3531 East Lakeland Drive, Jackson, MS, Zip 39232–8839; tel. 601/936–2024; Michael J. Carney, Chief Executive Officer
Web address: www.brentwoodjackson.com

PARKWOOD BEHAVIORAL HEALTH SYSTEM (O, 148 beds) 8135 Goodman Road, Olive Branch, MS, Zip 38654–2103; tel. 662/895–4900; Ethan Permenter, Chief Executive Officer

For explanation of codes following names, see page B2.
★ Indicates Type III membership in the American Hospital Association.

Section B

MISSOURI: HEARTLAND BEHAVIORAL HEALTH SERVICES (O, 69 beds) 1500 West Ashland Street, Nevada, MO, Zip 64772–1710; tel. 417/667–2666; Alyson Wysong–Harder, Chief Executive Officer
Web address: www.heartlandbehavioral.com

TWO RIVERS BEHAVIORAL HEALTH SYSTEM (O, 105 beds) 5121 Raytown Road, Kansas City, MO, Zip 64133–2141; tel. 816/382–6300; Greg Shannon, Chief Executive Officer
Web address: www.tworivershospital.com

NEVADA: CENTENNIAL HILLS HOSPITAL MEDICAL CENTER (O, 165 beds) 6900 North Durango Drive, Las Vegas, NV, Zip 89149–4409; tel. 702/835–9700; Sajit Pullarkat, Chief Executive Officer and Managing Director

DESERT SPRINGS HOSPITAL MEDICAL CENTER (O, 293 beds) 2075 East Flamingo Road, Las Vegas, NV, Zip 89119–5121; tel. 702/733–8800; Ryan Jensen, Chief Executive Officer
Web address: www.desertspringshospital.com

DESERT VIEW HOSPITAL (O, 25 beds) 360 South Lola Lane, Pahrump, NV, Zip 89048–0884; tel. 775/751–7500; Susan Davila, Chief Executive Officer
Web address: www.desertviewhospital.com

HENDERSON HOSPITAL (O, 145 beds) 1050 West Galleria Drive, Henderson, NV, Zip 89011; tel. 702/963–7000; Samuel Kaufman, Chief Executive Officer
Web address: www.hendersonhospital.com/

NORTHERN NEVADA MEDICAL CENTER (O, 108 beds) 2375 East Prater Way, Sparks, NV, Zip 89434–9641; tel. 775/331–7000; Alan C. Olive, Chief Executive Officer

SPRING MOUNTAIN SAHARA (O, 30 beds) 5460 West Sahara, Las Vegas, NV, Zip 89146–3307; tel. 702/216–8900; Darryl S. Dubroca, Chief Executive Officer and Managing Director
Web address: www.springmountainsahara.com

SPRING MOUNTAIN TREATMENT CENTER (L, 110 beds) 7000 West Spring Mountain Road, Las Vegas, NV, Zip 89117–3816; tel. 702/873–2400; C. Alan. Eaks, Chief Executive Officer and Managing Director
Web address: www.springmountaintreatmentcenter.com/

SPRING VALLEY HOSPITAL MEDICAL CENTER (O, 169 beds) 5400 South Rainbow Boulevard, Las Vegas, NV, Zip 89118–1859; tel. 702/853–3000; Leonard Freehof, Chief Executive Officer and Managing Director

SUMMERLIN HOSPITAL MEDICAL CENTER (O, 148 beds) 657 Town Center Drive, Las Vegas, NV, Zip 89144–6367; tel. 702/233–7000; Robert S. Freymuller, Chief Executive Officer
Web address: www.summerlinhospital.com

VALLEY HOSPITAL MEDICAL CENTER (O, 365 beds) 620 Shadow Lane, Las Vegas, NV, Zip 89106–4119; tel. 702/388–4000; Elaine Glaser, Chief Executive Officer

WEST HILLS HOSPITAL (O, 190 beds) 1240 East Ninth Street, Reno, NV, Zip 89512–2964; tel. 775/323–0478; Allison Zednicek, Chief Executive Officer
Web address: www.westhillshospital.net

NEW JERSEY: HAMPTON BEHAVIORAL HEALTH CENTER (O, 120 beds) 650 Rancocas Road, Westampton, NJ, Zip 08060–5613; tel. 609/267–7000; Craig Hilton, Chief Executive Officer and Managing Director
Web address: www.hamptonhospital.com

SUMMIT OAKS HOSPITAL (O, 90 beds) 19 Prospect Street, Summit, NJ, Zip 07901–2530; tel. 908/522–7000; Ross Friedman, Chief Executive Officer

NEW MEXICO: MESILLA VALLEY HOSPITAL (O, 120 beds) 3751 Del Rey Boulevard, Las Cruces, NM, Zip 88012–8526; tel. 575/382–3500; Anna Laliotis, Chief Executive Officer
Web address: www.mesillavalleyhospital.com

NORTH CAROLINA: BRYNN MARR HOSPITAL (O, 99 beds) 192 Village Drive, Jacksonville, NC, Zip 28546–7299; tel. 910/577–1400; Jay Kortemeyer, Chief Executive Officer

HOLLY HILL HOSPITAL (O, 228 beds) 3019 Falstaff Road, Raleigh, NC, Zip 27610–1812; tel. 919/250–7000; Amanda Johanson, Chief Executive Officer
Web address: www.hollyhillhospital.com

OLD VINEYARD BEHAVIORAL HEALTH SERVICES (O, 148 beds) 3637 Old Vineyard Road, Winston–Salem, NC, Zip 27104–4842; tel. 336/794–3550; Kevin Patton, Chief Executive Officer

NORTH DAKOTA: PRAIRIE ST. JOHN'S (O, 94 beds) 510 4th Street South, Fargo, ND, Zip 58103–1914; tel. 701/476–7200; Jeff Herman, Chief Executive Officer
Web address: www.prairie–stjohns.com

OHIO: ARROWHEAD BEHAVIORAL HEALTH HOSPITAL (O, 48 beds) 1725 Timber Line Road, Maumee, OH, Zip 43537–4015; tel. 419/891–9333; Joseph Denicola, Chief Executive Officer and Managing Director
Web address: www.arrowheadbehavioral.com

BELMONT PINES HOSPITAL (O, 96 beds) 615 Churchill–Hubbard Road, Youngstown, OH, Zip 44505–1379; tel. 330/759–2700; Lisa Cocca, Chief Executive Officer

WINDSOR–LAURELWOOD CENTER FOR BEHAVIORAL MEDICINE (O, 159 beds) 35900 Euclid Avenue, Willoughby, OH, Zip 44094–4648; tel. 440/953–3000; Ric McAllister, Chief Executive Officer
Web address: www.windsorlaurelwood.com

OKLAHOMA: CEDAR RIDGE HOSPITAL (O, 172 beds) 6501 NE 50th Street, Oklahoma City, OK, Zip 73141–9118; tel. 405/605–6111; Heather Joseph, Chief Executive Officer

SHADOW MOUNTAIN BEHAVIORAL HEALTH SYSTEM (O, 238 beds) 6262 South Sheridan Road, Tulsa, OK, Zip 74133–4055; tel. 918/492–8200; Jeanne Wypyski, Chief Executive Officer
Web address: www.shadowmountainbhs.com

ST. MARY'S REGIONAL MEDICAL CENTER (O, 154 beds) 305 South Fifth Street, Enid, OK, Zip 73701–5899, Mailing Address: P.O. Box 232, Zip 73702–0232, tel. 580/233–6100; Krista Roberts, Chief Executive Officer

OREGON: CEDAR HILLS HOSPITAL (O, 78 beds) 10300 SW Eastridge Street, Portland, OR, Zip 97225–5004; tel. 503/944–5000; Elizabeth Hutter, Chief Executive Officer
Web address: www.cedarhillshospital.com

PENNSYLVANIA: BROOKE GLEN BEHAVIORAL HOSPITAL (O, 146 beds) 7170 Lafayette Avenue, Fort Washington, PA, Zip 19034–2301; tel. 215/641–5300; Neil Callahan, Chief Executive Officer
Web address: www.brookeglenhospital.com

CLARION PSYCHIATRIC CENTER (O, 74 beds) 2 Hospital Drive, Clarion, PA, Zip 16214–8502; tel. 814/226–9545; Michael Post, Chief Executive Officer

FAIRMOUNT BEHAVIORAL HEALTH SYSTEM (O, 235 beds) 561 Fairthorne Avenue, Philadelphia, PA, Zip 19128–2499; tel. 215/487–4000; Lisa M. McConlogue, MSN, Ph.D., Chief Executive Officer and Managing Director
Web address: www.fairmountbhs.com

FOUNDATIONS BEHAVIORAL HEALTH (O, 58 beds) 833 East Butler Avenue, Doylestown, PA, Zip 18901–2280; tel. 215/345–0444; Gina Fusco, Chief Executive Officer

FRIENDS HOSPITAL (O, 192 beds) 4641 Roosevelt Boulevard, Philadelphia, PA, Zip 19124–2343; tel. 215/831–4600; Michael S. McDonald Jr, Chief Executive Officer
Web address: www.friendshospital.com

HORSHAM CLINIC (O, 138 beds) 722 East Butler Pike, Ambler, PA, Zip 19002–2310; tel. 215/643–7800; Phyllis Weisfield, Chief Executive Officer and Managing Director
Web address: www.horshamclinic.com

MEADOWS PSYCHIATRIC CENTER (O, 117 beds) 132 The Meadows Drive, Centre Hall, PA, Zip 16828–9231; tel. 814/364–2161; Ann Wayne, Chief Executive Officer

ROXBURY TREATMENT CENTER (O, 94 beds) 601 Roxbury Road, Shippensburg, PA, Zip 17257–9302; tel. 800/648–4673; Shauna Mogerman, Chief Executive Officer
Web address: www.roxburyhospital.com

PUERTO RICO: FIRST HOSPITAL PANAMERICANO (O, 153 beds) State Road 787 KM 1 5, Cidra, PR, Zip 739, Mailing Address: P.O. Box 1400, Zip 739, tel. 787/739–5555; Astro Munoz, Executive Director
Web address: www.hospitalpanamericano.com

SOUTH CAROLINA: AIKEN REGIONAL MEDICAL CENTERS (O, 285 beds) 302 University Parkway, Aiken, SC, Zip 29801–6302; tel. 803/641–5000; Matt Merrifield, Interim Chief Executive Officer

CAROLINA CENTER FOR BEHAVIORAL HEALTH (O, 130 beds) 2700 East Phillips Road, Greer, SC, Zip 29650–4816; tel. 864/235–2335; John Willingham, Chief Executive Officer and Managing Director
Web address: www.thecarolinacenter.com

For explanation of codes following names, see page B2.
★ Indicates Type III membership in the American Hospital Association.

LIGHTHOUSE BEHAVIORAL HEALTH HOSPITAL (O, 87 beds) 152 Waccamaw Medical Park Drive, Conway, SC, Zip 29526–8901; tel. 843/347–8871; Thomas L. Ryba, Chief Executive Officer
Web address: www.lighthousecarecenterofconway.com/

PALMETTO LOWCOUNTRY BEHAVIORAL HEALTH (O, 100 beds) 2777 Speissegger Drive, Charleston, SC, Zip 29405–8229; tel. 843/747–5830; Clint Hauger, Chief Executive Officer
Web address: www.palmettobehavioralhealth.com

THREE RIVERS BEHAVIORAL HEALTH (O, 122 beds) 2900 Sunset Boulevard, West Columbia, SC, Zip 29169–3422; tel. 803/796–9911; Nannette M. Lewis, Chief Executive Officer
Web address: www.threeriversbehavioral.org

TENNESSEE: LAKESIDE BEHAVIORAL HEALTH SYSTEM (O, 345 beds) 2911 Brunswick Road, Memphis, TN, Zip 38133–4199; tel. 901/377–4700; Joy Golden, Chief Executive Officer

ROLLING HILLS HOSPITAL (O, 130 beds) 2014 Quail Hollow Circle, Franklin, TN, Zip 37067–5967; tel. 615/628–5700; Jim Spruyt, Chief Executive Officer
Web address: www.RollingHillsHospital.org/

TEXAS: AUSTIN LAKES HOSPITAL (O, 58 beds) 1025 East 32nd Street, Austin, TX, Zip 78705–2714; tel. 512/544–5253; Robert J. Lerma, MS, Chief Executive Officer
Web address: www.austinlakeshospital.com

AUSTIN OAKS HOSPITAL (O, 80 beds) 1407 West Stassney Lane, Austin, TX, Zip 78745–2947; tel. 512/440–4800; Steve Kelly, Interim Chief Executive Officer

BEHAVIORAL HOSPITAL OF BELLAIRE (O, 122 beds) 5314 Dashwood Drive, Houston, TX, Zip 77081–4603; tel. 713/600–9500; Dhruv Narielwala, Interim Chief Executive Officer
Web address: www.bhbhospital.com

CORNERSTONE REGIONAL HOSPITAL (L, 14 beds) 2302 Cornerstone Boulevard, Edinburg, TX, Zip 78539–8471; tel. 956/618–4444; Roxanna M. Godinez, Chief Executive Officer

CYPRESS CREEK HOSPITAL (O, 96 beds) 17750 Cali Drive, Houston, TX, Zip 77090–2700; tel. 281/586–7600; Phuong Cardoza, Interim Chief Executive Officer
Web address: www.cypresscreekhospital.com

DOCTORS HOSPITAL OF LAREDO (O, 183 beds) 10700 McPherson Road, Laredo, TX, Zip 78045–6268; tel. 956/523–2000; James R. Resendez, Chief Executive Officer
Web address: www.doctorshoslaredo.com

EL PASO BEHAVIORAL HEALTH SYSTEM (O, 163 beds) 1900 Denver Avenue, El Paso, TX, Zip 79902–3008; tel. 915/544–4000; Phillip Sosa, Interim Chief Executive Officer
Web address: www.ubhelpaso.com/

FORT DUNCAN REGIONAL MEDICAL CENTER (O, 101 beds) 3333 North Foster Maldonado Boulevard, Eagle Pass, TX, Zip 78852–5893; tel. 830/773–5321; Eladio Montalvo, Chief Executive Officer
Web address: www.fortduncanmedicalcenter.com

GARLAND BEHAVIORAL HOSPITAL (O, 72 beds) 2300 Marie Curie Boulevard, 5th Floor, Garland, TX, Zip 75402; tel. 972/487–5309; Kristin Harris, Chief Executive Officer

GLEN OAKS HOSPITAL (O, 54 beds) 301 Division Street, Greenville, TX, Zip 75401–4101; tel. 903/454–6000; Jonathon Gammon, Interim Chief Executive Officer
Web address: www.glenoakshospital.com

HICKORY TRAIL HOSPITAL (O, 86 beds) 2000 Old Hickory Trail, Desoto, TX, Zip 75115–2242; tel. 972/298–7323; Kay McKennery, Interim Chief Executive Officer

KINGWOOD PINES HOSPITAL (O, 65 beds) 2001 Ladbrook Drive, Kingwood, TX, Zip 77339–3004; tel. 281/404–1001; Shanti Carter, Chief Executive Officer
Web address: www.kingwoodpines.com

LAUREL RIDGE TREATMENT CENTER (O, 208 beds) 17720 Corporate Woods Drive, San Antonio, TX, Zip 78259–3500; tel. 210/491–9400; Jacob Cuellar, M.D., Chief Executive Officer

MAYHILL HOSPITAL (O, 59 beds) 2809 South Mayhill Road, Denton, TX, Zip 76208–5910; tel. 940/239–3000; Nichol Attar, Chief Executive Officer
Web address: www.mayhillhospital.com

MILLWOOD HOSPITAL (O, 128 beds) 1011 North Cooper Street, Arlington, TX, Zip 76011–5517; tel. 817/261–3121; Dwight A. Lacy, Chief Executive Officer

NORTHWEST TEXAS HEALTHCARE SYSTEM (O, 424 beds) 1501 South Coulter Avenue, Amarillo, TX, Zip 79106–1770, Mailing Address: P.O. Box 1110, Zip 79105–1110, tel. 806/354–1000; Ryan Chandler, Chief Executive Officer
Web address: www.nwtexashealthcare.com

RIVER CREST HOSPITAL (O, 80 beds) 1636 Hunters Glen Road, San Angelo, TX, Zip 76901–5016; tel. 325/949–5722; Juana Giralt, Interim Chief Executive Officer
Web address: www.rivercresthospital.com

SOUTH TEXAS HEALTH SYSTEM (O, 810 beds) 1400 West Trenton Road, Edinburg, TX, Zip 78539–9105, Mailing Address: 1102 West Trenton Road, Zip 78539–9105, tel. 956/388–6000; Lance Ames, Interim Chief Executive Officer

TEXAS NEUROREHAB CENTER (O, 47 beds) 1106 West Dittmar Road, Building 9, Austin, TX, Zip 78745–6328, Mailing Address: P.O. Box 150459, Zip 78715–0459, tel. 512/444–4835; Edgar E. Prettyman, PsyD, Chief Executive Officer
Web address: www.texasneurorehab.com

TEXOMA MEDICAL CENTER (O, 326 beds) 5016 South US Highway 75 , Denison, TX, Zip 75020–4584, Mailing Address: P.O. Box 890, Zip 75021–0890, tel. 903/416–4000; Ronald T. Seal, Chief Executive Officer

TIMBERLAWN MENTAL HEALTH SYSTEM (O, 57 beds) 4600 Samuell Boulevard, Dallas, TX, Zip 75228–6800; tel. 214/381–7181; Shelah Adams, Chief Executive Officer
Web address: www.timberlawn.com

UNIVERSITY BEHAVIORAL HEALTH OF DENTON (O, 104 beds) 2026 West University Drive, Denton, TX, Zip 76201–0644; tel. 940/320–8100; Ronald Rains, Chief Executive Officer

WEST OAKS HOSPITAL (O, 144 beds) 6500 Hornwood Drive, Houston, TX, Zip 77074–5095; tel. 713/995–0909; Mandy Westerman, Chief Executive Officer
Web address: www.westoakshospital.com

UTAH: PROVO CANYON BEHAVIORAL HOSPITAL (O, 80 beds) 1350 East 750 North, Orem, UT, Zip 84097–4345; tel. 801/852–2273; Jeremy Cottle, Ph.D., Chief Executive Officer

SALT LAKE BEHAVIORAL HEALTH (O, 118 beds) 3802 South 700 East, Salt Lake City, UT, Zip 84106–1182; tel. 801/264–6000; Kreg Gillman, Chief Executive Officer
Web address: www.saltlakebehavioralhealth.com

VIRGINIA: CUMBERLAND HOSPITAL FOR CHILDREN AND ADOLESCENTS (O, 118 beds) 9407 Cumberland Road, New Kent, VA, Zip 23124–2029; tel. 804/966–2242; Patrice Gay. Brooks, Chief Executive Officer
Web address: www.cumberlandhospital.com

POPLAR SPRINGS HOSPITAL (O, 180 beds) 350 Poplar Drive, Petersburg, VA, Zip 23805–9367; tel. 804/733–6874; Nelson Smith, Chief Executive Officer

VIRGINIA BEACH PSYCHIATRIC CENTER (O, 100 beds) 1100 First Colonial Road, Virginia Beach, VA, Zip 23454–2403; tel. 757/496–6000; Jennifer Kelly, Chief Executive Officer
Web address: www.vbpcweb.com

WASHINGTON: FAIRFAX BEHAVIORAL HEALTH (O, 221 beds) 10200 NE 132nd Street, Kirkland, WA, Zip 98034–2899; tel. 425/821–2000; Beckie Shauinger, Chief Executive Officer
Web address: www.fairfaxhospital.com

WEST VIRGINIA: RIVER PARK HOSPITAL (O, 175 beds) 1230 Sixth Avenue, Huntington, WV, Zip 25701–2312, Mailing Address: P.O. Box 1875, Zip 25719–1875, tel. 304/526–9111; Terry A. Stephens, Chief Executive Officer
Web address: www.riverparkhospital.net

WYOMING: WYOMING BEHAVIORAL INSTITUTE (O, 129 beds) 2521 East 15th Street, Casper, WY, Zip 82609–4126; tel. 307/237–7444; Joseph Gallagher, Chief Executive Officer
Web address: www.wbihelp.com

Owned, leased, sponsored:	143 hospitals	19548 beds
Contract-managed:	0 hospitals	0 beds
Totals:	143 hospitals	19548 beds

For explanation of codes following names, see page B2.
★ Indicates Type III membership in the American Hospital Association.

Section B

★0896: UNIVERSITY HEALTH CARE SYSTEM (NP)

1350 Walton Way, Augusta, GA, Zip 30901–2629; tel. 706/722–9011; James R. Davis, President and Chief Executive Officer
(Independent Hospital System)

GEORGIA: UNIVERSITY HOSPITAL MCDUFFIE (O, 22 beds) 2460 Washington Road, NE, Thomson, GA, Zip 30824; tel. 706/595–1411; Bob Kepshire, R.N., MS, Administrator and Chief Nursing Officer

UNIVERSITY HOSPITAL SUMMERVILLE (O, 105 beds) 2260 Wrightsboro Road, Augusta, GA, Zip 30904–4726; tel. 706/481–7000; James R. Davis, Chief Executive Officer
Web address: www.universityhealth.org/summerville/

UNIVERSITY HOSPITAL (O, 554 beds) 1350 Walton Way, Augusta, GA, Zip 30901–2629; tel. 706/722–9011; James R. Davis, Chief Executive Officer

Owned, leased, sponsored:	3 hospitals	681 beds
Contract–managed:	0 hospitals	0 beds
Totals:	3 hospitals	681 beds

0961: UNIVERSITY HEALTH SYSTEM (NP)

1501 Kings Highway, Shreveport, LA, Zip 71103–4228; tel. 318/675–5000; Daniel J. Snyder, Chief Executive Officer
(Moderately Centralized Health System)

LOUISIANA: UNIVERSITY HEALTH CONWAY (O, 123 beds) 4864 Jackson Street, Monroe, LA, Zip 71202–6497, Mailing Address: P.O. Box 1881, Zip 71210–8005, tel. 318/330–7000; Jonathan Phillips, Interim Administrator

UNIVERSITY HEALTH SHREVEPORT (O, 386 beds) 1501 Kings Highway, Shreveport, LA, Zip 71103–4228, Mailing Address: P.O. Box 33932, Zip 71130–3932, tel. 318/675–5000; Mark Randolph, President
Web address: www.lsuhscshreveport.edu

Owned, leased, sponsored:	2 hospitals	509 beds
Contract–managed:	0 hospitals	0 beds
Totals:	2 hospitals	509 beds

★0112: UNIVERSITY HOSPITALS (NP)

11100 Euclid Avenue, Cleveland, OH, Zip 44106–5000; tel. 216/844–1000; Thomas F. Zenty III, President and Chief Executive Officer
(Centralized Health System)

OHIO: ST. JOHN MEDICAL CENTER (O, 176 beds) 29000 Center Ridge Road, Westlake, OH, Zip 44145–5293; tel. 440/835–8000; Robert G. David, President
Web address: www.sjws.net

UH PORTAGE MEDICAL CENTER (O, 127 beds) 6847 North Chestnut Street, Ravenna, OH, Zip 44266–3929, Mailing Address: P.O. Box 1204, Zip 44266–1204, tel. 330/297–0811; M Steven. Jones, President

UH REGIONAL HOSPITALS (O, 101 beds) 27100 Chardon Road, Cleveland, OH, Zip 44143–1116; tel. 440/585–6500; Brian Monter, MSN, R.N., President
Web address: www.uhhospitals.org

UNIVERSITY HOSPITALS AHUJA MEDICAL CENTER (O, 138 beds) 3999 Richmond Road, Beachwood, OH, Zip 44122–6046; tel. 216/593–5500; Susan V. Juris, President
Web address: www.uhhospitals.org/ahuja/tabid/7051/uhahujamedicalcenter.aspx

UNIVERSITY HOSPITALS CLEVELAND MEDICAL CENTER (O, 871 beds) 11100 Euclid Avenue, Cleveland, OH, Zip 44106–1716; tel. 216/844–1000; Daniel I. Simon, M.D., President

UNIVERSITY HOSPITALS CONNEAUT MEDICAL CENTER (O, 25 beds) 158 West Main Road, Conneaut, OH, Zip 44030–2039; tel. 440/593–1131; M Steven. Jones, President
Web address: www.uhhospitals.org

UNIVERSITY HOSPITALS ELYRIA MEDICAL CENTER (O, 202 beds) 630 East River Street, Elyria, OH, Zip 44035–5902; tel. 440/329–7500; Kristi M. Sink, President

UNIVERSITY HOSPITALS GEAUGA MEDICAL CENTER (O, 142 beds) 13207 Ravenna Road, Chardon, OH, Zip 44024–7032; tel. 440/269–6000; M Steven. Jones, President
Web address: www.uhhospitals.org/geauga/

UNIVERSITY HOSPITALS GENEVA MEDICAL CENTER (O, 25 beds) 870 West Main Street, Geneva, OH, Zip 44041–1295; tel. 440/466–1141; M Steven. Jones, President
Web address: www.uhhs.com

UNIVERSITY HOSPITALS PARMA MEDICAL CENTER (O, 266 beds) 7007 Powers Boulevard, Parma, OH, Zip 44129–5495; tel. 440/743–3000; Peter U. Bergmann, President

UNIVERSITY HOSPITALS SAMARITAN MEDICAL CENTER (O, 39 beds) 1025 Center Street, Ashland, OH, Zip 44805–4011; tel. 419/289–0491; Karen McNeil, President
Web address: www.samaritanhospital.org

Owned, leased, sponsored:	11 hospitals	2112 beds
Contract–managed:	0 hospitals	0 beds
Totals:	11 hospitals	2112 beds

★0915: UNIVERSITY HOSPITALS AND HEALTH SYSTEM (NP)

2500 North State Street, Jackson, MS, Zip 39216–4500; tel. 601/984–1000; Kevin S. Cook, Chief Executive Officer
(Decentralized Health System)

MISSISSIPPI: UNIVERSITY OF MISSISSIPPI MEDICAL CENTER GRENADA (C, 58 beds) 960 Avent Drive, Grenada, MS, Zip 38901–5230; tel. 662/227–7000; Wes Sigler, Chief Executive Officer
Web address: www.glmc.net/

UNIVERSITY OF MISSISSIPPI MEDICAL CENTER HOLMES COUNTY (O, 25 beds) 239 Bowling Green Road, Lexington, MS, Zip 39095–5167; tel. 601/496–5200; Wes Sigler, Chief Executive Officer
Web address: www.ummchealth.com/holmes/

UNIVERSITY OF MISSISSIPPI MEDICAL CENTER (O, 680 beds) 2500 North State Street, Jackson, MS, Zip 39216–4505; tel. 601/984–1000; Kevin S. Cook, Chief Executive Officer

Owned, leased, sponsored:	2 hospitals	705 beds
Contract–managed:	1 hospitals	58 beds
Totals:	3 hospitals	763 beds

★6405: UNIVERSITY OF CALIFORNIA SYSTEMWIDE ADMINISTRATION (NP)

1111 Franklin Street, 11th Floor, Oakland, CA, Zip 94607–5200; tel. 510/987–9071; John D. Stobo, M.D., Executive Vice President and Chief Executive Officer
(Moderately Centralized Health System)

CALIFORNIA: RONALD REAGAN UCLA MEDICAL CENTER (O, 445 beds) 757 Westwood Plaza, Los Angeles, CA, Zip 90095–8358; tel. 310/825–9111; Johnese Spisso, Chief Executive Officer
Web address: www.uclahealth.org

STEWART & LYNDA RESNICK NEUROPSYCHIATRIC HOSPITAL AT UCLA (O, 74 beds) 150 UCLA Medical Plaza, Los Angeles, CA, Zip 90095–8353; tel. 310/825–9989; Peter Whybrow, M.D., Chief Executive Officer
Web address: www.semel.ucla.edu/resnick

UC IRVINE MEDICAL CENTER (O, 417 beds) 101 The City Drive South, Orange, CA, Zip 92868–3298; tel. 714/456–6011; Richard Gannotta, Chief Executive Officer

UC SAN DIEGO HEALTH (O, 664 beds) 200 West Arbor Drive, San Diego, CA Zip 92103–9000; tel. 619/543–6222; Patty Maysent, Chief Executive Officer
Web address: www.health.ucsd.edu

UCLA MEDICAL CENTER–SANTA MONICA (O, 265 beds) 1250 16th Street, Santa Monica, CA, Zip 90404–1249; tel. 310/319–4000; Paul Watkins, JD, Chief Administrative Officer

For explanation of codes following names, see page B2.
★ Indicates Type III membership in the American Hospital Association.

UCSF MEDICAL CENTER (O, 978 beds) 500 Parnassus Avenue, San Francisco, CA, Zip 94143–0296, Mailing Address: 500 Parnassus Avenue, Box 0296, Zip 94143–0296, tel. 415/476–1000; Mark R. Laret, Chief Executive Officer
Web address: www.ucsfhealth.org

UNIVERSITY OF CALIFORNIA, DAVIS MEDICAL CENTER (O, 601 beds) 2315 Stockton Boulevard, Sacramento, CA, Zip 95817–2282; tel. 916/734–2011; Brad Simmons, Chief Operating Officer

Owned, leased, sponsored:	7 hospitals	3444 beds
Contract–managed:	0 hospitals	0 beds
Totals:	7 hospitals	3444 beds

★0058: UNIVERSITY OF CHICAGO MEDICINE (NP)

5841 South Maryland Avenue, Chicago, IL, Zip 60637–1447; tel. 773/702–6240; Sharon L. O'Keefe, President
(Moderately Centralized Health System)

ILLINOIS: INGALLS MEMORIAL HOSPITAL (O, 199 beds) One Ingalls Drive, Harvey, IL, Zip 60426–3591; tel. 708/333–2300; Jonathan R. Goble, FACHE, Interim President

UNIVERSITY OF CHICAGO MEDICAL CENTER (O, 650 beds) 5841 South Maryland Avenue, Chicago, IL, Zip 60637–1443; tel. 773/702–1000; Sharon L. O'Keefe, President
Web address: www.uchospitals.edu

Owned, leased, sponsored:	2 hospitals	849 beds
Contract–managed:	0 hospitals	0 beds
Totals:	2 hospitals	849 beds

★0216: UNIVERSITY OF MARYLAND MEDICAL SYSTEM (NP)

250 West Pratt Street, 24th Floor, Baltimore, MD, Zip 21201–1595; tel. 410/328–8667; Robert A. Chrencik, President and Chief Executive Officer
(Centralized Physician/Insurance Health System)

MARYLAND: MT. WASHINGTON PEDIATRIC HOSPITAL (O, 61 beds) 1708 West Rogers Avenue, Baltimore, MD, Zip 21209–4545; tel. 410/578–8600; Sheldon J. Stein, President and Chief Executive Officer
Web address: www.mwph.org

UNIVERSITY OF MARYLAND BALTIMORE WASHINGTON MEDICAL CENTER (O, 326 beds) 301 Hospital Drive, Glen Burnie, MD, Zip 21061–5899; tel. 410/787–4000; Karen E. Olscamp, President and Chief Executive Officer

UNIVERSITY OF MARYLAND CAPITAL REGION HEALTH PRINCE GEORGE'S HOSPITAL CENTER (O, 227 beds) 3001 Hospital Drive, Cheverly, MD, Zip 20785–1189; tel. 301/618–2000; Sherry B. Perkins, Ph.D., R.N., President and Chief Executive Officer
Web address: www.princegeorgeshospital.org

UNIVERSITY OF MARYLAND CAPITAL REGION HEALTH AT LAUREL REGIONAL HOSPITAL (O, 70 beds) 7300 Van Dusen Road, Laurel, MD, Zip 20707–9463; tel. 301/725–4300; Trudy Hall, M.D., Vice President Medical Affairs and Interim Chief Executive Officer

UNIVERSITY OF MARYLAND CHARLES REGIONAL MEDICAL CENTER (O, 89 beds) 5 Garrett Avenue, La Plata, MD, Zip 20646–5960, Mailing Address: P.O. Box 1070, Zip 20646–1070, tel. 301/609–4000; Noel A. Cervino, President and Chief Executive Officer
Web address: www.charlesregional.org

UNIVERSITY OF MARYLAND HARFORD MEMORIAL HOSPITAL (O, 85 beds) 501 South Union Avenue, Havre De Grace, MD, Zip 21078–3493; tel. 443/843–5000; Lyle Ernest. Sheldon, FACHE, President and Chief Executive Officer

UNIVERSITY OF MARYLAND MEDICAL CENTER MIDTOWN CAMPUS (O, 170 beds) 827 Linden Avenue, Baltimore, MD, Zip 21201–4606; tel. 410/225–8000; Mohan Suntha, M.D., President and Chief Executive Officer
Web address: www.ummidtown.org/

UNIVERSITY OF MARYLAND MEDICAL CENTER (O, 680 beds) 22 South Greene Street, Baltimore, MD, Zip 21201–1595; tel. 410/328–9199; Mohan Suntha, M.D., President and Chief Executive Officer

UNIVERSITY OF MARYLAND REHABILITATION & ORTHOPAEDIC INSTITUTE (O, 141 beds) 2200 Kernan Drive, Baltimore, MD, Zip 21207–6697; tel. 410/448–2500; Cynthia Kelleher, M.P.H., President and Chief Executive Officer
Web address: www.umrehabortho.org

UNIVERSITY OF MARYLAND SHORE MEDICAL CENTER AT CHESTERTOWN (O, 124 beds) 100 Brown Street, Chestertown, MD, Zip 21620–1499; tel. 410/778–3300; Kenneth D. Kozel, FACHE, President and Chief Executive Officer
Web address: www.umms.org/hospitals/shore–health–system.htm

UNIVERSITY OF MARYLAND SHORE MEDICAL CENTER AT DORCHESTER (O, 47 beds) 300 Byrn Street, Cambridge, MD, Zip 21613–1908; tel. 410/228–5511; Kenneth D. Kozel, FACHE, President and Chief Executive Officer

UNIVERSITY OF MARYLAND SHORE MEDICAL CENTER AT EASTON (O, 132 beds) 219 South Washington Street, Easton, MD, Zip 21601–2996; tel. 410/822–1000; Kenneth D. Kozel, FACHE, President and Chief Executive Officer
Web address: www.shorehealth.org

UNIVERSITY OF MARYLAND ST. JOSEPH MEDICAL CENTER (O, 287 beds) 7601 Osler Drive, Towson, MD, Zip 21204–7582; tel. 410/337–1000; Thomas Smyth, President and Chief Executive Officer
Web address: www.stjosephtowson.com/home.aspx

UNIVERSITY OF MARYLAND UPPER CHESAPEAKE MEDICAL CENTER (O, 170 beds) 500 Upper Chesapeake Drive, Bel Air, MD, Zip 21014–4324; tel. 443/643–1000; Lyle Ernest. Sheldon, FACHE, President and Chief Executive Officer

Owned, leased, sponsored:	14 hospitals	2609 beds
Contract–managed:	0 hospitals	0 beds
Totals:	14 hospitals	2609 beds

★0227: UNIVERSITY OF MISSOURI HEALTH CARE (NP)

One Hospital Drive, DC 031, Columbia, MO, Zip 65212–0001; tel. 573/882–4141; Jonathan W. Curtright, Chief Executive Officer and Chief Operating Officer
(Moderately Centralized Health System)

MISSOURI: CAPITAL REGION MEDICAL CENTER (O, 114 beds) 1125 Madison Street, Jefferson City, MO, Zip 65101–5200, Mailing Address: P.O. Box 1128, Zip 65102–1128, tel. 573/632–5000; Gaspare Calvaruso, President
Web address: www.crmc.org

UNIVERSITY OF MISSOURI HEALTH CARE (O, 595 beds) One Hospital Drive, Columbia, MO, Zip 65212–0001; tel. 573/882–4141; Jonathan W. Curtright, Chief Executive Officer and Chief Operating Officer
Web address: www.muhealth.org

Owned, leased, sponsored:	2 hospitals	709 beds
Contract–managed:	0 hospitals	0 beds
Totals:	2 hospitals	709 beds

0021: UNIVERSITY OF NEW MEXICO HOSPITALS (NP)

915 Camino De Salud, Albuquerque, NM, Zip 87131–0001; tel. 505/272–5849; Michael Chicarelli, R.N., Interim Chief Executive Officer
(Moderately Centralized Health System)

NEW MEXICO: UNM SANDOVAL REGIONAL MEDICAL CENTER, INC. (O, 60 beds) 3001 Broadmoor Boulevard NE, Rio Rancho, NM, Zip 87131; tel. 505/994–7000; Jamie A. Silva-Steele, FACHE, R.N., President and Chief Executive Officer
Web address: www.hsc.unm.edu/health/locations/sandoval–regional–medical–center.html

UNIVERSITY OF NEW MEXICO HOSPITALS (O, 537 beds) 2211 Lomas Boulevard NE, Albuquerque, NM, Zip 87106–2745; tel. 505/272–2111; Kathleen R. Becker, M.P.H., JD, Chief Executive Officer
Web address: www.unm.edu

Owned, leased, sponsored:	2 hospitals	597 beds
Contract–managed:	0 hospitals	0 beds
Totals:	2 hospitals	597 beds

For explanation of codes following names, see page B2.
★ Indicates Type III membership in the American Hospital Association.

Section B

★0168: UNIVERSITY OF PENNSYLVANIA HEALTH SYSTEM (NP)

3400 Civic Center Bouelvard, Philadelphia, PA, Zip 19104–5127; tel. 215/662–2203; Ralph W. Muller, President and Chief Executive Officer

(Moderately Centralized Health System)

NEW JERSEY: PENN MEDICINE PRINCETON MEDICAL CENTER (O, 355 beds) One Plainsboro Road, Plainsboro, NJ, Zip 08536–1913; tel. 609/853–7100; Barry S. Rabner, President and Chief Executive Officer, Princeton Healthcare System
Web address: www.princetonhcs.org

PENNSYLVANIA: CHESTER COUNTY HOSPITAL (O, 248 beds) 701 East Marshall Street, West Chester, PA, Zip 19380–4412; tel. 610/431–5000; Michael J. Duncan, President and Chief Executive Officer

HOSPITAL OF THE UNIVERSITY OF PENNSYLVANIA (O, 797 beds) 3400 Spruce Street, Philadelphia, PA, Zip 19104–4206; tel. 215/662–4000; Regina Cunningham, Ph.D., R.N., Chief Executive Officer
Web address: www.pennmedicine.org

PENN MEDICINE LANCASTER GENERAL HOSPITAL (O, 604 beds) 555 North Duke Street, Lancaster, PA, Zip 17602–2250; tel. 717/544–5511; Jan L. Bergen, President and Chief Executive Officer

PENN PRESBYTERIAN MEDICAL CENTER (O, 375 beds) 51 North 39th Street, Philadelphia, PA, Zip 19104–2699; tel. 215/662–8000; Michele M. Volpe, Chief Executive Officer
Web address: www.pennmedicine.org/pmc/

PENNSYLVANIA HOSPITAL (O, 475 beds) 800 Spruce Street, Philadelphia, PA, Zip 19107–6192; tel. 215/829–3000; Theresa M. . Larivee, Chief Executive Officer

Owned, leased, sponsored:	6 hospitals	2854 beds
Contract–managed:	0 hospitals	0 beds
Totals:	6 hospitals	2854 beds

★0223: UNIVERSITY OF ROCHESTER MEDICAL CENTER (NP)

601 Elmwood Ave Box 623, Rochester, NY, Zip 14642–0002, Mailing Address: 601 Elmwood Avenue, Zip 14642–0002, tel. 585/275–2100; Mark B. Taubman, M.D., Chief Executive Officer

(Moderately Centralized Health System)

NEW YORK: F. F. THOMPSON HOSPITAL (O, 291 beds) 350 Parrish Street, Canandaigua, NY, Zip 14424–1731; tel. 585/396–6000; Michael Stapleton, President and Chief Executive Officer
Web address: www.thompsonhealth.com

HIGHLAND HOSPITAL (O, 261 beds) 1000 South Avenue, Rochester, NY, Zip 14620–2733; tel. 585/473–2200; Steven I. Goldstein, President and Chief Executive Officer

JONES MEMORIAL HOSPITAL (O, 33 beds) 191 North Main Street, Wellsville, NY, Zip 14895–1150, Mailing Address: P.O. Box 72, Zip 14895–0072, tel. 585/593–1100; Eva Benedict, R.N., President and Chief Executive Officer
Web address: www.jmhny.org

NICHOLAS H. NOYES MEMORIAL HOSPITAL (O, 40 beds) 111 Clara Barton Street, Dansville, NY, Zip 14437–9503; tel. 585/335–6001; Amy Pollard, R.N., President and Chief Executive Officer
Web address: www.noyes–health.org

ST. JAMES MERCY HOSPITAL (O, 222 beds) 411 Canisteo Street, Hornell, NY, Zip 14843–2197; tel. 607/324–8000; Leo P. Brideau, FACHE, Interim President and Chief Executive Officer

STRONG MEMORIAL HOSPITAL OF THE UNIVERSITY OF ROCHESTER (O, 835 beds) 601 Elmwood Avenue, Rochester, NY, Zip 14642–0002, Mailing Address: 601 Elmwood Avenue, Box 612, Zip 14642–0002, tel. 585/275–2100; Steven I. Goldstein, President and Chief Executive Officer
Web address: www.urmc.rochester.edu

Owned, leased, sponsored:	6 hospitals	1682 beds
Contract–managed:	0 hospitals	0 beds
Totals:	6 hospitals	1682 beds

★0057: UNIVERSITY OF SOUTH ALABAMA HEALTH SYSTEM (NP)

2451 Fillingim Street, Mobile, AL, Zip 36617–2238; tel. 251/471–7000; Owen Bailey, FACHE, Chief Executive Officer and Senior Associate Vice President for Medical Affairs

(Independent Hospital System)

ALABAMA: USA HEALTH UNIVERSITY HOSPITAL (O, 142 beds) 2451 USA Medical Center Drive, Mobile, AL, Zip 36617–2293; tel. 251/471–7000; Sam Dean, Administrator
Web address: www.usahealthsystem.com/usamc

UNIVERSITY OF SOUTH ALABAMA CHILDREN'S AND WOMEN'S HOSPITAL (O, 172 beds) 1700 Center Street, Mobile, AL, Zip 36604–3301; tel. 251/415–1000; Chris Jett, Administrator
Web address: www.usahealthsystem.com/usacwh

Owned, leased, sponsored:	2 hospitals	314 beds
Contract–managed:	0 hospitals	0 beds
Totals:	2 hospitals	314 beds

★0033: UNIVERSITY OF TEXAS SYSTEM (NP)

601 Colorado Street, Suite 205, Austin, TX, Zip 78701–2904; tel. 512/499–4224; Raymond Greenberg, M.D., Executive Vice Chancellor

(Moderately Centralized Health System)

TEXAS: UT HEALTH NORTH CAMPUS TYLER (O, 130 beds) 11937 Highway 271, Tyler, TX, Zip 75708–3154; tel. 903/877–7777; Kirk A. Calhoun, M.D., President
Web address: www.https://uthealthnorth.com/

UNIVERSITY OF TEXAS HARRIS COUNTY PSYCHIATRIC CENTER (C, 206 beds) 2800 South MacGregor Way, Houston, TX, Zip 77021–1000, Mailing Address: P.O. Box 20249, Zip 77225–0249, tel. 713/741–7870; Jair C. Soares, M.D., Executive Director
Web address: www.hcpc.uth.tmc.edu

UNIVERSITY OF TEXAS M.D. ANDERSON CANCER CENTER (O, 658 beds) 1515 Holcombe Boulevard, Unit 1491, Houston, TX, Zip 77030–4000; tel. 713/792–2121; Peter Pisters, M.D., President
Web address: www.mdanderson.org

UNIVERSITY OF TEXAS MEDICAL BRANCH (O, 456 beds) 301 University Boulevard, Galveston, TX, Zip 77555–0128; tel. 409/772–1011; Donna K. Sollenberger, Executive Vice President and Chief Executive Officer

Owned, leased, sponsored:	3 hospitals	1244 beds
Contract–managed:	1 hospitals	206 beds
Totals:	4 hospitals	1450 beds

0137: UPMC (NP)

600 Grant Street, US Steel Tower, Suite 6262, Pittsburgh, PA, Zip 15219–2702; tel. 412/647–8762; Jeffrey A. Romoff, President and Chief Executive Officer

(Decentralized Health System)

NEW YORK: UPMC CHAUTAUQUA WCA (O, 111 beds) 207 Foote Avenue, Jamestown, NY, Zip 14701–7077, Mailing Address: P.O. Box 840, Zip 14702–0840, tel. 716/487–0141; Betsy T. Wright, President and Chief Executive Officer

PENNSYLVANIA: CHILDREN'S HOSPITAL OF PITTSBURGH OF UPMC (O, 305 beds) One Children's Hospital Drive, 4401 Penn Avenue, Pittsburgh, PA, Zip 15224–1334; tel. 412/692–5325; Christopher A. Gessner, President
Web address: www.chp.edu

MAGEE–WOMENS HOSPITAL OF UPMC (O, 321 beds) 300 Halket Street, Pittsburgh, PA, Zip 15213–3108; tel. 412/641–1000; Leslie C. Davis, President

UPMC ALTOONA (O, 346 beds) 620 Howard Avenue, Altoona, PA, Zip 16601–4804; tel. 814/889–2011; Gerald Murray, President
Web address: www.altoonaregional.org

UPMC BEDFORD MEMORIAL (O, 27 beds) 10455 Lincoln Highway, Everett, PA, Zip 15537–7046; tel. 814/623–6161; Gerald Murray, President

For explanation of codes following names, see page B2.
★ Indicates Type III membership in the American Hospital Association.

UPMC EAST (O, 155 beds) 2775 Mosside Boulevard, Monroeville, PA, Zip 15146–2760; tel. 412/357–3000; Mark Sevco, President
Web address: www.upmc.com/locations/hospitals/east/Pages/default.aspx

UPMC HAMOT (O, 327 beds) 201 State Street, Erie, PA, Zip 16550–0002; tel. 814/877–6000; David Gibbons, President

UPMC HORIZON (O, 121 beds) 2200 Memorial Drive, Farrell, PA, Zip 16121–1357; tel. 724/588–2100; Donald R. Owrey, President
Web address: www.upmc.com

UPMC JAMESON (O, 102 beds) 1211 Wilmington Avenue, New Castle, PA, Zip 16105–2516; tel. 724/658–9001; Donald R. Owrey, President
Web address: www.upmcjameson.com

UPMC KANE (O, 31 beds) 4372 Route 6, Kane, PA, Zip 16735–3060; tel. 814/837–8585; Mark Papalia, President

UPMC MCKEESPORT (O, 181 beds) 1500 Fifth Avenue, McKeesport, PA, Zip 15132–2422; tel. 412/664–2000; Mark Sevco, President
Web address: www.mckeesport.upmc.com

UPMC MERCY (O, 453 beds) 1400 Locust Street, Pittsburgh, PA, Zip 15219–5166; tel. 412/232–8111; Michael A. Grace, President

UPMC NORTHWEST (O, 128 beds) 100 Fairfield Drive, Seneca, PA, Zip 16346–2130; tel. 814/676–7600; Brian Durniok, President
Web address: www.upmc.com/locations/hospitals/northwest/Pages/default.aspx

UPMC PASSAVANT (O, 286 beds) 9100 Babcock Boulevard, Pittsburgh, PA, Zip 15237–5815; tel. 412/748–6700; David T. Martin, President
Web address: www.upmc.edu/passavant

UPMC PINNACLE CARLISLE (O, 65 beds) 361 Alexander Spring Road, Carlisle, PA, Zip 17015–6940; tel. 717/249–1212; Christian H. . Caicedo, President

UPMC PINNACLE HANOVER (O, 93 beds) 300 Highland Avenue, Hanover, PA, Zip 17331–2297; tel. 717/316–3711; Michael W. Gaskins, President
Web address: www.hanoverhospital.org

UPMC PINNACLE HARRISBURG (O, 659 beds) 111 South Front Street, Harrisburg, PA, Zip 17101–2010, Mailing Address: P.O. Box 8700, Zip 17105–8700, tel. 717/231–8900; Philip Guarneschelli, Interim Chief Executive Officer
Web address: www.pinnaclehealth.org

UPMC PINNACLE LANCASTER (O, 150 beds) 250 College Avenue, Lancaster, PA, Zip 17603–3363, Mailing Address: P.O. Box 3434, Zip 17604–3434, tel. 717/291–8211; Brooks Turkel, Chief Executive Officer

UPMC PINNACLE LITITZ (O, 90 beds) 1500 Highlands Drive, Lititz, PA, Zip 17543–7694; tel. 717/625–5000; Deborah J. Willwerth, R.N., MSN, Chief Executive Officer
Web address: www.heartoflancaster.com

UPMC PINNACLE MEMORIAL (O, 100 beds) 325 South Belmont Street, York, PA, Zip 17403–2609, Mailing Address: P.O. Box 15118, Zip 17405–7118, tel. 717/843–8623; Curtis Herrin, Chief Financial Officer

UPMC PRESBYTERIAN (O, 1378 beds) 200 Lothrop Street, Pittsburgh, PA, Zip 15213–2536; tel. 412/647–2345; John Innocenti Sr, President and Chief Executive Officer
Web address: www.upmc.edu

UPMC ST. MARGARET (O, 208 beds) 815 Freeport Road, Pittsburgh, PA, Zip 15215–3301; tel. 412/784–4000; David J. Patton, President

Owned, leased, sponsored:	22 hospitals	5637 beds
Contract-managed:	0 hospitals	0 beds
Totals:	22 hospitals	5637 beds

★0066: UPMC SUSQUEHANNA (NP)
700 High Street , Williamsport, PA, Zip 17701–3100; tel. 570/321–1000; Steven P. Johnson, FACHE, President and Chief Executive Officer
(Centralized Health System)

PENNSYLVANIA: DIVINE PROVIDENCE HOSPITAL (O, 31 beds) 1100 Grampian Boulevard, Williamsport, PA, Zip 17701–1995; tel. 570/326–8000; Robert E. Kane, Chief Administrative Officer

UPMC SUSQUEHANNA LOCK HAVEN (O, 83 beds) 24 Cree Drive, Lock Haven, PA, Zip 17745–2699; tel. 570/893–5000; Ronald J. Reynolds, Vice President
Web address: www.lockhavenhospital.com

UPMC SUSQUEHANNA MUNCY (O, 156 beds) 215 East Water Street, Muncy, PA, Zip 17756–8700; tel. 570/546–8282; Matthew McLaughlin, President and Chief Executive Officer
Web address: www.susquehannahealth.org

UPMC SUSQUEHANNA SOLDIERS + SAILORS (O, 25 beds) 32–36 Central Avenue, Wellsboro, PA, Zip 16901–1899; tel. 570/724–1631; Janie Hilfiger, Chief Administrative Officer
Web address: www.susquehannahealth.org

UPMC SUSQUEHANNA SUNBURY (O, 70 beds) 350 North Eleventh Street, Sunbury, PA, Zip 17801–1611; tel. 570/286–3333; Robert D. Williams, Chief Executive Officer

UPMC SUSQUEHANNA WILLIAMSPORT REGIONAL MEDICAL CENTER (O, 220 beds) 700 High Street, Williamsport, PA, Zip 17701–3100; tel. 570/321–1000; Steven P. Johnson, FACHE, President
Web address: www.susquehannahealth.org

Owned, leased, sponsored:	6 hospitals	585 beds
Contract-managed:	0 hospitals	0 beds
Totals:	6 hospitals	585 beds

0816: UPPER ALLEGHENY HEALTH SYSTEM (NP)
130 South Union Street, Suite 300, Olean, NY, Zip 14760–3676; tel. 716/375–6190; Timothy J. Finan, FACHE, President and Chief Executive Officer
(Independent Hospital System)

NEW YORK: OLEAN GENERAL HOSPITAL (O, 186 beds) 515 Main Street, Olean, NY, Zip 14760–1513; tel. 716/373–2600; Timothy J. Finan, FACHE, President and Chief Executive Officer
Web address: www.ogh.org

PENNSYLVANIA: BRADFORD REGIONAL MEDICAL CENTER (O, 202 beds) 116 Interstate Parkway, Bradford, PA, Zip 16701–1036; tel. 814/368–4143; Timothy J. Finan, FACHE, President and Chief Executive Officer
Web address: www.brmc.com

Owned, leased, sponsored:	2 hospitals	388 beds
Contract-managed:	0 hospitals	0 beds
Totals:	2 hospitals	388 beds

9195: U.S. INDIAN HEALTH SERVICE (FG)
801 Thompson Avenue, Rockville, MD, Zip 20852–1627; tel. 301/443–1083; Yvette Roubideaux, M.D., M.P.H., Director
(Independent Hospital System)

ARIZONA: CHINLE COMPREHENSIVE HEALTH CARE FACILITY (O, 60 beds) Highway 191, Hospital Road, Chinle, AZ, Zip 86503, Mailing Address: P O Drawer PH, Zip 86503–8000, tel. 928/674–7001; Ron Tso, Chief Executive Officer
Web address: www.ihs.gov

HOPI HEALTH CARE CENTER (O, 15 beds) Highway 264 Mile Marker 388, Keams Canyon, AZ, Zip 86042, Mailing Address: P.O. Box 4000, Polacca, Zip 86042–4000, tel. 928/737–6000; Mose Herne, Chief Executive Officer

SAN CARLOS APACHE HEALTHCARE CORPORATION (O, 8 beds) 103 Medicine Way Road, Peridot, AZ, Zip 85542; tel. 928/475–1400; Victoria D. Began, R.N., MS, President and Chief Executive Officer
Web address: www.ihs.gov

U.S. PUBLIC HEALTH SERVICE INDIAN HOSPITAL–SELLS (O, 12 beds) Highway 86 & Topawa Road, Sells, AZ, Zip 85634, Mailing Address: P.O. Box 548, Zip 85634–0548, tel. 520/383–7251; Angela Fallon, Acting Chief Executive Officer

U.S. PUBLIC HEALTH SERVICE INDIAN HOSPITAL–WHITERIVER (O, 35 beds) 200 West Hospital Drive, Whiteriver, AZ, Zip 85941–0860, Mailing Address: State Route 73, Box 860, Zip 85941–0860, tel. 928/338–4911; Michelle Martinez, Chief Executive Officer
Web address: www.ihs.gov

U.S. PUBLIC HEALTH SERVICE INDIAN HOSPITAL (O, 20 beds) 12033 Agency Road, Parker, AZ, Zip 85344–7718; tel. 928/669–2137; Elizabeth Helsel, Chief Executive Officer
Web address: www.ihs.gov

For explanation of codes following names, see page B2.
★ Indicates Type III membership in the American Hospital Association.

U.S. PUBLIC HEALTH SERVICE PHOENIX INDIAN MEDICAL CENTER (O, 127 beds) 4212 North 16th Street, Phoenix, AZ, Zip 85016–5389; tel. 602/263–1200; Rear Admiral, Michael Weakhee, Chief Executive Officer

MARYLAND: NATIONAL INSTITUTES OF HEALTH CLINICAL CENTER (O, 121 beds) 9000 Rockville Pike, Building 10, Room 6–2551, Bethesda, MD, Zip 20892–1504; tel. 301/496–4000; James K. Gilman, M.D., Chief Executive Officer
Web address: www.clinicalcenter.nih.gov

MINNESOTA: RED LAKE INDIAN HEALTH SERVICE HOSPITAL (O, 19 beds) 24760 Hospital Drive, Red Lake, MN, Zip 56671, Mailing Address: P.O. Box 497, Zip 56671–0497, tel. 218/679–3912; Norine Smith, Chief Executive Officer
Web address: www.rlnnredlakehospital.com/

U.S. PUBLIC HEALTH SERVICE INDIAN HOSPITAL (O, 9 beds) 425 7th Street North West, Cass Lake, MN, Zip 56633; tel. 218/335–3200; Louis P. Erdrich, Acting Chief Executive Officer

MONTANA: BLACKFEET COMMUNITY HOSPITAL (O, 25 beds) 760 New Hospital Circle, Saint Mary, MT, Zip 59417–0760, Mailing Address: P.O. Box 760, Browning, Zip 59417–0760, tel. 406/338–6100; Garland Stiffarm, Chief Executive Officer
Web address: www.ihs.gov

CROW/NORTHERN CHEYENNE HOSPITAL (O, 24 beds) 10110 South 7650 East, Crow Agency, MT, Zip 59022–0009, Mailing Address: P.O. Box 9, Zip 59022–0009, tel. 406/638–2626; Darren Crowe, Chief Executive Officer
Web address: https://www.ihs.gov/billings/healthcarefacilities/crow/

FORT BELKNAP SERVICE UNIT (O, 6 beds) 669 Agency Main Street, Harlem, MT, Zip 59526–9455; tel. 406/353–3100; Gregory Smith, M.D., Chief Executive Officer

NEBRASKA: U.S. PUBLIC HEALTH SERVICE INDIAN HOSPITAL (O, 30 beds) Highway 7577, Winnebago, NE, Zip 68071; tel. 402/878–2231; Gary Wabaunsee, Service Unit Director
Web address: www.ihs.gov

NEW MEXICO: ACOMA–CANONCITO–LAGUNA HOSPITAL (O, 6 beds) 80B Veterans Boulevard, Acoma, NM, Zip 87034, Mailing Address: P.O. Box 130, San Fidel, Zip 87049–0130, tel. 505/552–5300; Melody Price–Yonts, Chief Executive Officer

GALLUP INDIAN MEDICAL CENTER (O, 57 beds) 516 East Nizhoni Boulevard, Gallup, NM, Zip 87301–5748, Mailing Address: P.O. Box 1337, Zip 87305–1337, tel. 505/722–1000; John Meese, Acting Director
Web address: www.ihs.gov/navajo/index.cfm?module=nao_hcc_gallup

MESCALERO PUBLIC HEALTH SERVICE INDIAN HOSPITAL (O, 13 beds) 318 Abalone Loop, Mescalero, NM, Zip 88340, Mailing Address: Box 210, Zip 88340–0210, tel. 505/464–3801; Dorlynn Simmons, Chief Executive Officer

NORTHERN NAVAJO MEDICAL CENTER (O, 68 beds) Highway 491 North, Shiprock, NM, Zip 87420–0160, Mailing Address: P.O. Box 160, Zip 87420–0160, tel. 505/368–6001; Fannessa Comer, Chief Executive Officer
Web address: www.ihs.gov/

PHS SANTA FE INDIAN HOSPITAL (O, 4 beds) 1700 Cerrillos Road, Santa Fe, NM, Zip 87505–3554; tel. 505/988–9821; Leslie Dye, Chief Executive Officer

U.S. PUBLIC HEALTH SERVICE INDIAN HOSPITAL (O, 12 beds) Route 9 and State Road 371, Crownpoint, NM, Zip 87313, Mailing Address: P.O. Box 358, Zip 87313–0358, tel. 505/786–5291; Anslem Roanhorse, Chief Executive Officer
Web address: www.ihs.gov

U.S. PUBLIC HEALTH SERVICE INDIAN HOSPITAL (O, 32 beds) Route 301 North B Street, Zuni, NM, Zip 87327, Mailing Address: P.O. Box 467, Zip 87327–0467, tel. 505/782–4431; Jean Othole, Chief Executive Officer
Web address: www.ihs.gov

NORTH DAKOTA: INDIAN HEALTH SERVICE – QUENTIN N. BURDICK MEMORIAL HEALTH CARE FACILITY (O, 29 beds) 1300 Hospital Loop, Belcourt, ND, Zip 58316, Mailing Address: P.O. Box 160, Zip 58316–0160, tel. 701/477–6111; Shelly Harris, Chief Executive Officer
Web address: www.ihs.gov

STANDING ROCK SERVICE UNIT, FORT YATES HOSPITAL, INDIAN HEALTH SERVICE, DHHS (O, 14 beds) 10 North River Road, Fort Yates, ND, Zip 58538, Mailing Address: P.O. Box 'J', Zip 58538, tel. 701/854–3831; Jana Gipp, Chief Executive Officer

OKLAHOMA: CLAREMORE INDIAN HOSPITAL (O, 44 beds) 101 South Moore Avenue, Claremore, OK, Zip 74017–5091; tel. 918/342–6200; George Valliere, Chief Executive Officer
Web address: www.ihs.gov

LAWTON INDIAN HOSPITAL (O, 26 beds) 1515 Lawrie Tatum Road, Lawton, OK, Zip 73507–3099; tel. 580/353–0350; Travis Scott, Chief Executive Officer

SOUTH DAKOTA: INDIAN HEALTH SERVICE HOSPITAL (O, 9 beds) 3200 Canyon Lake Drive, Rapid City, SD, Zip 57702–8197; tel. 605/355–2280; Kevin J. Stiffarm, Chief Executive Officer
Web address: www.ihs.gov

U.S. PUBLIC HEALTH SERVICE INDIAN HOSPITAL (O, 8 beds) 317 Main Street, Eagle Butte, SD, Zip 57625–1012, Mailing Address: P.O. Box 1012, Zip 57625–1012, tel. 605/964–7724; Charles Fisher, Chief Executive Officer

U.S. PUBLIC HEALTH SERVICE INDIAN HOSPITAL (O, 45 beds) East Highway 18, Pine Ridge, SD, Zip 57770, Mailing Address: P.O. Box 1201, Zip 57770–1201, tel. 605/867–5131; Travis Scott, Service Unit Director
Web address: www.ihs.gov

U.S. PUBLIC HEALTH SERVICE INDIAN HOSPITAL (O, 35 beds) Highway 18, Soldier Creek Road, Rosebud, SD, Zip 57570; tel. 605/747–2231; Kathey Wilson, Acting Chief Executive Officer

Owned, leased, sponsored:	29 hospitals	913 beds
Contract–managed:	0 hospitals	0 beds
Totals:	29 hospitals	913 beds

0868: USMD HEALTH SYSTEM (IO)
6333 North State Highway 161 Suite 200, Irving, TX, Zip 75038–2229; tel. 214/493–4000; Mike Bukosky, President, Hospital Division
(Independent Hospital System)

TEXAS: USMD HOSPITAL AT ARLINGTON (O, 34 beds) 801 West Interstate 20, Arlington, TX, Zip 76017–5851; tel. 817/472–3400; Marcia Crim, R.N., MSN, Chief Executive Officer
Web address: www.usmdarlington.com

USMD HOSPITAL AT FORT WORTH (O, 8 beds) 5900 Altamesa Boulevard, Fort Worth, TX, Zip 76132–5473; tel. 817/433–9100; Kathy L Early, CPHRM, Chief Executive Officer and Chief Nursing Officer

Owned, leased, sponsored:	2 hospitals	42 beds
Contract–managed:	0 hospitals	0 beds
Totals:	2 hospitals	42 beds

★0860: UVA HEALTH SYSTEM (NP)
1215 Lee Street, Charlottesville, VA, Zip 22908–0816; tel. 434/924–0211; Richard Shannon, M.D., Executive Vice President for Health Affairs
(Centralized Health System)

VIRGINIA: UVA TRANSITIONAL CARE HOSPITAL (O, 40 beds) 2965 Ivy Rd (250 West), Charlottesville, VA, Zip 22903–9330; tel. 434/924–8245; Christine K. Matt, Interim Associate Chief

UNIVERSITY OF VIRGINIA MEDICAL CENTER (O, 596 beds) 1215 Lee Street, Charlottesville, VA, Zip 22908–0001, Mailing Address: P.O. Box 800809, Zip 22908–0809, tel. 434/924–0211; Pamela Sutton–Wallace, Chief Executive Officer
Web address: www.healthsystem.virginia.edu

Owned, leased, sponsored:	2 hospitals	636 beds
Contract–managed:	0 hospitals	0 beds
Totals:	2 hospitals	636 beds

1009: UW HEALTH SYSTEM (IO)
600 Highland Avenue, Madison, WI, Zip 53792–0001; tel. 608/263–6400; Alan Kaplan, M.D., Chief Executive Officer
(Moderately Centralized Health System)

For explanation of codes following names, see page B2.
★ Indicates Type III membership in the American Hospital Association.

WISCONSIN: UW HEALTH REHABILITATION HOSPITAL (O, 25 beds) 5115 North Biltmore Lane, Madison, WI, Zip 53718–2161; tel. 608/592–8100; Gregory A. Banaszynski, Chief Executive Officer
Web address: www.uwhealth.org

UNIVERSITY HOSPITAL (O, 621 beds) 600 Highland Avenue, Madison, WI, Zip 53792–0002; tel. 608/263–6400; Alan Kaplan, M.D., Chief Executive Officer
Web address: www.uwhealth.org

Owned, leased, sponsored:	2 hospitals	646 beds
Contract–managed:	0 hospitals	0 beds
Totals:	2 hospitals	646 beds

★6415: UW MEDICINE (NP)

1959 NE Pacific Street, Seattle, WA, Zip 98195–0001, Mailing Address: P.O. Box 356350, Zip 98195–6350, tel. 206/543–7718; Paul G. Ramsey, M.D., Chief Executive Officer
(Independent Hospital System)

WASHINGTON: UW MEDICINE/HARBORVIEW MEDICAL CENTER (C, 413 beds) 325 Ninth Avenue, Seattle, WA, Zip 98104–2499, Mailing Address: P.O. Box 359717, Zip 98195–9717, tel. 206/744–3000; Paul Hayes, R.N., Executive Director
Web address: www.uwmedicine.org/Patient–Care/Locations/HMC/Pages/default.aspx

UW MEDICINE/NORTHWEST HOSPITAL & MEDICAL CENTER (O, 197 beds) 1550 North 115th Street, Seattle, WA, Zip 98133–8401; tel. 206/364–0500; Cynthia Hecker, R.N., Executive Director
Web address: www.uwmedicine.org/Patient–Care/Locations/nwh/Pages/default.aspx

UW MEDICINE/VALLEY MEDICAL CENTER (C, 295 beds) 400 South 43rd Street, Renton, WA, Zip 98055–5714, Mailing Address: P.O. Box 50010, Zip 98058–5010, tel. 425/228–3450; Richard D. Roodman, Chief Executive Officer

UNIVERSITY OF WASHINGTON MEDICAL CENTER (O, 452 beds) 1959 NE Pacific Street, Seattle, WA, Zip 98195–6151; tel. 206/598–3300; Geoff Austin, Executive Director
Web address: www.uwmedicine.org/uw–medical–center

Owned, leased, sponsored:	2 hospitals	649 beds
Contract–managed:	2 hospitals	708 beds
Totals:	4 hospitals	1357 beds

★0128: VALLEY HEALTH SYSTEM (NP)

220 Campus Boulevard, Suite 420, Winchester, VA, Zip 22601–2889, Mailing Address: P.O. Box 3340, Zip 22604–2540, tel. 540/536–8024; Mark H. Merrill, President and Chief Executive Officer
(Moderately Centralized Health System)

VIRGINIA: PAGE MEMORIAL HOSPITAL (O, 25 beds) 200 Memorial Drive, Luray, VA, Zip 22835–1005; tel. 540/743–4561; N Travis. Clark, President

VALLEY HEALTH SHENANDOAH MEMORIAL HOSPITAL (O, 25 beds) 759 South Main Street, Woodstock, VA, Zip 22664–1127; tel. 540/459–1100; N Travis. Clark, President
Web address: www.valleyhealthlink.com/shenandoah

WARREN MEMORIAL HOSPITAL (O, 164 beds) 1000 North Shenandoah Avenue, Front Royal, VA, Zip 22630–3598; tel. 540/636–0300; Floyd Heater, President
Web address: www.valleyhealthlink.com/WMH

WINCHESTER MEDICAL CENTER (O, 485 beds) 1840 Amherst Street, Winchester, VA, Zip 22601–2808, Mailing Address: P.O. Box 3340, Zip 22604–2540, tel. 540/536–8000; Grady W. Philips III, President

WEST VIRGINIA: HAMPSHIRE MEMORIAL HOSPITAL (O, 44 beds) 363 Sunrise Boulevard, Romney, WV, Zip 26757–4607; tel. 304/822–4561; Thomas S. Kluge, President
Web address: www.valleyhealthlink.com/hampshire

WAR MEMORIAL HOSPITAL (O, 41 beds) One Healthy Way, Berkeley Springs, WV, Zip 25411–7463; tel. 304/258–1234; Thomas S. Kluge, President
Web address: www.valleyhealthlink.com/war

Owned, leased, sponsored:	6 hospitals	784 beds
Contract–managed:	0 hospitals	0 beds
Totals:	6 hospitals	784 beds

★0387: VANDERBILT HEALTH (NP)

1211 22nd Avenue South, Nashville, TN, Zip 37232; tel. 615/322–5000; Charles Wright. Pinson, M.D., Deputy Vice Chancellor for Health Affairs and Chief Executive Officer of Vanderbilt Health System
(Moderately Centralized Health System)

TENNESSEE: VANDERBILT UNIVERSITY MEDICAL CENTER (O, 1011 beds) 1211 Medical Center Drive, Nashville, TN, Zip 37232–2102; tel. 615/322–5000; Jeffrey R. Balsar, President and Chief Executive Officer Vanderbilt Medical Center and Dean, Vanderbilt University School of Medicine
Web address: www.mc.vanderbilt.edu

Owned, leased, sponsored:	1 hospitals	1011 beds
Contract–managed:	0 hospitals	0 beds
Totals:	1 hospitals	1011 beds

★0939: VCU HEALTH SYSTEM (NP)

1250 East Marshall Street, Richmond, VA, Zip 23298–5051, Mailing Address: P.O. Box 980510, Zip 23298–0510, tel. 804/828–9000; Marsha Rappley, M.D., Chief Executive Officer and Vice President for Health Sciences
(Moderately Centralized Health System)

VIRGINIA: CHILDREN'S HOSPITAL OF RICHMOND AT VCU–BROOK ROAD CAMPUS (O, 36 beds) 2924 Brook Road, Richmond, VA, Zip 23220–1298; tel. 804/321–7474; Elias Neujahr, Chief Executive Officer
Web address: www.chrichmond.org

VCU HEALTH COMMUNITY MEMORIAL HOSPITAL (O, 178 beds) 125 Buena Vista Circle, South Hill, VA, Zip 23970–1431, Mailing Address: P.O. Box 90, Zip 23970–0090, tel. 434/447–3151; W Scott. Burnette, Chief Executive Officer
Web address: www.cmh-sh.org

VCU MEDICAL CENTER (O, 802 beds) 1250 East Marshall Street, Richmond, VA, Zip 23298–5051, Mailing Address: P.O. Box 980510, Zip 23298–0510, tel. 804/828–9000; Deborah W. Davis, Chief Executive Officer and Vice President Clinical Services

Owned, leased, sponsored:	3 hospitals	1016 beds
Contract–managed:	0 hospitals	0 beds
Totals:	3 hospitals	1016 beds

1041: VERITAS COLLABORATIVE (IO)

4024 Stirrup Creek Drive, Durham, NC, Zip 27703–9464; tel. 855/875–5812; Stacie McEntyre, Chief Executive Officer

NORTH CAROLINA: VERITAS COLLABORATIVE (L, 40 beds) 4024 Stirrup Creek Drive, Durham, NC, Zip 27703–9464; tel. 919/908–9730; Sara Hofmeier, Executive Director
Web address: www.https://veritascollaborative.com

VERITAS COLLABORATIVE (L, 25 beds) 615 Douglas Street, Suite 500, Durham, NC, Zip 27705–6616; tel. 919/908–9730; Becca Eckstein, Executive Director

Owned, leased, sponsored:	2 hospitals	65 beds
Contract–managed:	0 hospitals	0 beds
Totals:	2 hospitals	65 beds

1075: VERITY HEALTH SYSTEM (NP)

2200 West Third Street, Suite 200, Los Angeles, CA, Zip 90057–1935, Mailing Address: 203 Redwood Shores Parkway, Suite 800, Redwood City, Zip 94065, tel. 650/551–6650; Richard Adcock, President and Chief Executive Officer
(Independent Hospital System)

CALIFORNIA: O'CONNOR HOSPITAL (O, 202 beds) 2105 Forest Avenue, San Jose, CA, Zip 95128–1471; tel. 408/947–2500; Jordan Herget, President and Chief Executive Officer
Web address: www.oconnorhospital.org

Section B

For explanation of codes following names, see page B2.
★ Indicates Type III membership in the American Hospital Association.

SAINT LOUISE REGIONAL HOSPITAL (O, 93 beds) 9400 No Name Uno, Gilroy, CA, Zip 95020–3528; tel. 408/848–2000; John Hennelly, Chief Executive Officer

SETON MEDICAL CENTER COASTSIDE (O, 116 beds) 600 Marine Boulevard, Moss Beach, CA, Zip 94038–9641; tel. 650/563–7100; John Ferrelli, Chief Executive Officer

SETON MEDICAL CENTER (O, 393 beds) 1900 Sullivan Avenue, Daly City, CA, Zip 94015–2229; tel. 650/992–4000; Mark Fratzke, R.N., President and Chief Executive Officer
Web address: www.setonmedicalcenter.org

ST. FRANCIS MEDICAL CENTER (O, 323 beds) 3630 East Imperial Highway, Lynwood, CA, Zip 90262–2636; tel. 310/900–8900; Gerald T. Kozai, PharmD, President and Chief Executive Officer
Web address: www.dochs.org

ST. VINCENT MEDICAL CENTER (O, 271 beds) 2131 West Third Street, Los Angeles, CA, Zip 90057–1901, Mailing Address: P.O. Box 57992, Zip 90057–0992, tel. 213/484–7111; Frank J. Cracolici, President and Chief Executive Officer

Owned, leased, sponsored:	6 hospitals	1398 beds
Contract–managed:	0 hospitals	0 beds
Totals:	6 hospitals	1398 beds

★0299: VIBRA HEALTHCARE (IO)

4550 Lena Drive, Suite 225, Mechanicsburg, PA, Zip 17055–4920; tel. 717/591–5700; Brad Hollinger, Chairman and Chief Executive Officer
(Independent Hospital System)

CALIFORNIA: BALLARD REHABILITATION HOSPITAL (O, 55 beds) 1760 West 16th Street, San Bernardino, CA, Zip 92411–1160; tel. 909/473–1200; Mary Miles. Hunt, Chief Executive Officer
Web address: www.ballardrehab.com

KENTFIELD REHABILITATION AND SPECIALTY HOSPITAL (O, 60 beds) 1125 Sir Francis Drake Boulevard, Kentfield, CA, Zip 94904–1455; tel. 415/456–9680; Lauren Suarez, Chief Executive Officer

SAN JOAQUIN VALLEY REHABILITATION HOSPITAL (O, 62 beds) 7173 North Sharon Avenue, Fresno, CA, Zip 93720–3329; tel. 559/436–3600; Mary Jo Jacobson, Chief Executive Officer
Web address: www.sanjoaquinrehab.com

VIBRA HOSPITAL OF NORTHERN CALIFORNIA (O, 88 beds) 2801 Eureka Way, Redding, CA, Zip 96001–0222; tel. 530/246–9000; Chris Jones, Chief Executive Officer

VIBRA HOSPITAL OF SACRAMENTO (O, 58 beds) 330 Montrose Drive, Folsom, CA, Zip 95630–2720; tel. 916/351–9151; Kimberly Horton, R.N., MSN, Chief Executive Officer
Web address: www.vhsacramento.com

VIBRA HOSPITAL OF SAN DIEGO (O, 110 beds) 555 Washington Street, San Diego, CA, Zip 92103–2294; tel. 619/260–8300; Yameeka Jones, Chief Executive Officer

COLORADO: VIBRA HOSPITAL OF DENVER (O, 71 beds) 8451 Pearl Street, Thornton, CO, Zip 80229–4804; tel. 303/288–3000; Linda Tautz, Chief Executive Officer
Web address: www.vhdenver.com

IDAHO: VIBRA HOSPITAL OF BOISE (O, 60 beds) 6651 West Franklin Road, Boise, ID, Zip 83709–0914; tel. 877/801–2244; Cynthia Newsom, Chief Executive Officer
Web address: www.vhboise.com

ILLINOIS: VIBRA HOSPITAL OF SPRINGFIELD (O, 50 beds) 701 North Walnut Street, Springfield, IL, Zip 62702–4931; tel. 217/528–1217; Jeffrey Paul. Weier, Chief Executive Officer
Web address: www.vhspringfield.com

INDIANA: SOUTHERN INDIANA REHABILITATION HOSPITAL (O, 60 beds) 3104 Blackiston Boulevard, New Albany, IN, Zip 47150–9579; tel. 812/941–8300; William Boso, Executive Director, Administrator
Web address: www.sirh.org

VIBRA HOSPITAL OF FORT WAYNE (O, 24 beds) 2200 Randallia Drive, Fort Wayne, IN, Zip 46805–4638; tel. 260/399–2900; Fred Price, R.N., Chief Executive Officer

VIBRA HOSPITAL OF NORTHWESTERN INDIANA (O, 40 beds) 9509 Georgia Street, Crown Point, IN, Zip 46307–6518; tel. 219/472–2200; Larry Deal, R.N., Chief Executive Officer
Web address: www.vhnwindiana.com/

KENTUCKY: GATEWAY REHABILITATION HOSPITAL (C, 40 beds) 5940 Merchant Street, Florence, KY, Zip 41042–1158; tel. 859/426–2400; Frank Schneider, FACHE, Chief Executive Officer

SOUTHERN KENTUCKY REHABILITATION HOSPITAL (O, 60 beds) 1300 Campbell Lane, Bowling Green, KY, Zip 42104–4162; tel. 270/782–6900; Stuart Locke, Chief Executive Officer
Web address: www.skyrehab.com

MASSACHUSETTS: VIBRA HOSPITAL OF SOUTHEASTERN MASSACHUSETTS (O, 90 beds) 4499 Acushnet Avenue, New Bedford, MA, Zip 02745–4707; tel. 508/995–6900; Edward B. Leary, Chief Executive Officer
Web address: www.newbedfordrehab.com

VIBRA HOSPITAL OF WESTERN MASSACHUSETTS (O, 155 beds) 1400 State Street, Springfield, MA, Zip 01109–2550; tel. 413/726–6700; Edward B. Leary, Interim Chief Executive Officer

MICHIGAN: VIBRA HOSPITAL OF SOUTHEASTERN MICHIGAN, LLC (O, 220 beds) 26400 West Outer Drive, Lincoln Park, MI, Zip 48146–2088; tel. 313/386–2000; Reginald Lee, Chief Executive Officer
Web address: www.vhsemichigan.com/

NORTH DAKOTA: VIBRA HOSPITAL OF CENTRAL DAKOTAS (O, 41 beds) 1000 18th Street NW, Mandan, ND, Zip 58554–1612; tel. 701/667–2000; Glynda Troyo–Sauviac, Chief Executive Officer
Web address: www.vhcentraldakotas.com

VIBRA HOSPITAL OF FARGO (O, 31 beds) 1720 University Drive South, Fargo, ND, Zip 58103–4940; tel. 701/241–9099; Custer Huseby, Chief Executive Officer
Web address: www.vhfargo.com

OHIO: VIBRA HOSPITAL OF MAHONING VALLEY (O, 42 beds) 8049 South Avenue, Boardman, OH, Zip 44512–6154; tel. 330/726–5000; Nathan Mast, Chief Executive Officer

OREGON: VIBRA SPECIALTY HOSPITAL OF PORTLAND (O, 68 beds) 10300 NE Hancock Street, Portland, OR, Zip 97220–3831; tel. 503/257–5500; Victor Jackson, Chief Executive Officer
Web address: www.vshportland.com

SOUTH CAROLINA: VIBRA HOSPITAL OF CHARLESTON (O, 94 beds) 1200 Hospital Drive, Mt. Pleasant, SC, Zip 29464; tel. 843/375–4000; J. Scott Broome, Chief Executive Officer

TEXAS: HIGHLANDS REHABILITATION HOSPITAL (O, 41 beds) 1395 George Dieter Drive, El Paso, TX, Zip 79936–7410; tel. 915/298–7222; Travis Rich, Chief Executive Officer
Web address: www.vrhhighlands.com/

VIBRA HOSPITAL OF AMARILLO (O, 72 beds) 7501 Wallace Boulevard, Amarillo, TX, Zip 79124–2150; tel. 806/467–7000; Becky Burton, R.N., Chief Executive Officer and Market Chief Executive Officer

VIBRA REHABILITATION HOSPITAL LAKE TRAVIS (O, 36 beds) 2000 Medical Drive, Lakeway, TX, Zip 78734–4200; tel. 512/263–4500; Deborah Hopps, R.N., FACHE, Chief Executive Officer
Web address: www.vrhlaketravis.com

VIBRA REHABILITATION HOSPITAL OF AMARILLO (O, 44 beds) 7200 West 9th Avenue, Amarillo, TX, Zip 79106–1703; tel. 806/468–2900; Tammie Tabor, Chief Executive Officer

VIBRA SPECIALTY HOSPITAL AT DESOTO (O, 40 beds) 2700 Walker Way, Desoto, TX, Zip 75115–2088; tel. 972/298–1100; Thomas Alexander, Chief Executive Officer
Web address: www.vshdesoto.com

VIRGINIA: VIBRA HOSPITAL OF RICHMOND (O, 60 beds) 2220 Edward Holland Drive, Richmond, VA, Zip 23230–2519; tel. 804/678–7000; Linda Tiemens, Chief Executive Officer
Web address: www.vhrichmond.com

Owned, leased, sponsored:	27 hospitals	1832 beds
Contract–managed:	1 hospitals	40 beds
Totals:	28 hospitals	1872 beds

For explanation of codes following names, see page B2.
★ Indicates Type III membership in the American Hospital Association.

★0217: VIDANT HEALTH (NP)
2100 Stantonsburg Road, Greenville, NC, Zip 27834–2818, Mailing Address: P.O. Box 6028, Zip 27835–6028, tel. 252/847–4100; Michael Waldrum, M.D., Chief Executive Officer
(Moderately Centralized Health System)

NORTH CAROLINA: THE OUTER BANKS HOSPITAL (O, 21 beds) 4800 South Croatan Highway, Nags Head, NC, Zip 27959–9704; tel. 252/449–4500; Ronald A. Sloan, FACHE, President
Web address: www.theouterbankshospital.com

VIDANT BEAUFORT HOSPITAL (L, 142 beds) 628 East 12th Street, Washington, NC, Zip 27889–3409; tel. 252/975–4100; Harvey Case, President
Web address: www.vidanthealth.com

VIDANT BERTIE HOSPITAL (L, 6 beds) 1403 South King Street, P.O. Box 40, Windsor, NC, Zip 27983–9666, Mailing Address: P.O. Box 40, Zip 27983–0040, tel. 252/794–6600; Jeffrey Sackrison, President
Web address: www.vidanthealth.com

VIDANT CHOWAN HOSPITAL (L, 19 beds) 211 Virginia Road, Edenton, NC, Zip 27932–9668, Mailing Address: P.O. Box 629, Zip 27932–0629, tel. 252/482–8451; Jeffrey Sackrison, President

VIDANT DUPLIN HOSPITAL (L, 42 beds) 401 North Main Street, Kenansville, NC, Zip 28349–8801, Mailing Address: P.O. Box 278, Zip 28349–0278, tel. 910/296–0941; Jay Briley, President
Web address: www.vidanthealth.com

VIDANT EDGECOMBE HOSPITAL (O, 94 beds) 111 Hospital Drive, Tarboro, NC, Zip 27886–2011; tel. 252/641–7700; Wendell H. Baker Jr, President

VIDANT MEDICAL CENTER (O, 974 beds) 2100 Stantonsburg Road, Greenville, NC, Zip 27834–2818, Mailing Address: P.O. Box 6028, Zip 27835–6028, tel. 252/847–4100; William Brian. Floyd, President
Web address: https://www.vidanthealth.com/

VIDANT ROANOKE–CHOWAN HOSPITAL (L, 71 beds) 500 South Academy Street, Ahoskie, NC, Zip 27910–3261, Mailing Address: P.O. Box 1385, Zip 27910–1385, tel. 252/209–3000; Patrick Heins, President

Owned, leased, sponsored:	8 hospitals	1369 beds
Contract–managed:	0 hospitals	0 beds
Totals:	8 hospitals	1369 beds

0012: VIRGINIA DEPARTMENT OF MENTAL HEALTH (NP)
1220 Bank Street, Richmond, VA, Zip 23219–3645, Mailing Address: P.O. Box 1797, Zip 23218–1797, tel. 804/786–3921; James S. Reinhard, M.D., Commissioner
(Independent Hospital System)

VIRGINIA: CATAWBA HOSPITAL (O, 110 beds) 5525 Catawba Hospital Drive, Catawba, VA, Zip 24070–2115, Mailing Address: P.O. Box 200, Zip 24070–0200, tel. 540/375–4200; Walton F. Mitchell III, Director
Web address: www.catawba.dbhds.virginia.gov

CENTRAL STATE HOSPITAL (O, 277 beds) 26317 West Washington Street, Petersburg, VA, Zip 23803–2727, Mailing Address: P.O. Box 4030, Zip 23803–0030, tel. 804/524–7000; Rebecca Vauter, PsyD, Facility Director

CENTRAL VIRGINIA TRAINING CENTER (O, 1112 beds) 210 East Colony Road, Madison Heights, VA, Zip 24572–2005, Mailing Address: P.O. Box 1098, Lynchburg, Zip 24505–1098, tel. 434/947–6326; David Cole, Assistant Director of Administration, Chief Financial Officer, Department of Behavioral Health and Developmental Service
Web address: www.cvtc.dmhrsas.virginia.gov/

COMMONWEALTH CENTER FOR CHILDREN AND ADOLESCENTS (O, 60 beds) 1355 Richmond Road, Staunton, VA, Zip 24401–9146, Mailing Address: Box 4000, Zip 24402–4000, tel. 540/332–2100; Mary Clare. Smith, Acting Facility Director
Web address: www.ccca.dbhds.virginia.gov

EASTERN STATE HOSPITAL (O, 300 beds) 4601 Ironbound Road, Williamsburg, VA, Zip 23188–2652; tel. 757/253–5161; John M. Favret, Director
Web address: www.esh.dmhrsas.virginia.gov/

HIRAM W. DAVIS MEDICAL CENTER (O, 10 beds) 26317 West Washington Street, Petersburg, VA, Zip 23803–2727, Mailing Address: P.O. Box 4030, Zip 23803–0030, tel. 804/524–7344; Brenda Buenvenida, Director

NORTHERN VIRGINIA MENTAL HEALTH INSTITUTE (O, 134 beds) 3302 Gallows Road, Falls Church, VA, Zip 22042–3398; tel. 703/207–7100; Tammy Peacock, Ph.D., Facility Director
Web address: www.nvmhi.dbhds.virginia.gov

PIEDMONT GERIATRIC HOSPITAL (O, 135 beds) 5001 East Patrick Henry Hwy, Burkeville, VA, Zip 23922–3460, Mailing Address: P.O. Box 427, Zip 23922–0427, tel. 434/767–4401; Hilton McDaniel, President
Web address: www.pgh.dmhmrsas.virginia.gov

SOUTHERN VIRGINIA MENTAL HEALTH INSTITUTE (O, 72 beds) 382 Taylor Drive, Danville, VA, Zip 24541–4023; tel. 434/799–6220; William Cook, Director
Web address: www.svmhi.dbhds.virginia.gov

SOUTHWESTERN VIRGINIA MENTAL HEALTH INSTITUTE (O, 166 beds) 340 Bagley Circle, Marion, VA, Zip 24354–3390; tel. 276/783–1200; Cynthia McClaskey, Ph.D., Director

WESTERN STATE HOSPITAL (O, 246 beds) 103 Valley Center Drive, Staunton, VA, Zip 24401–9146, Mailing Address: P.O. Box 2500, Zip 24402–2500, tel. 540/332–8000; Mary Clare. Smith, Director
Web address: www.dbhds.virginia.gov

Owned, leased, sponsored:	11 hospitals	2622 beds
Contract–managed:	0 hospitals	0 beds
Totals:	11 hospitals	2622 beds

0986: VIRGINIA MASON HEALTH SYSTEM (NP)
1100 Ninth Avenue, Seattle, WA, Zip 98101–2756, Mailing Address: P.O. Box 900, Zip 98111–0900, tel. 206/223–6600; Gary Kaplan, M.D., FACHE, Chief Executive Officer
(Moderately Centralized Health System)

WASHINGTON: VIRGINIA MASON MEDICAL CENTER (O, 232 beds) 1100 Ninth Avenue, Seattle, WA, Zip 98101–2756, Mailing Address: P.O. Box 900, Zip 98111–0900, tel. 206/223–6600; Gary Kaplan, M.D., FACHE, Chairman and Chief Executive Officer
Web address: www.VirginiaMason.org

VIRGINIA MASON MEMORIAL (O, 220 beds) 2811 Tieton Drive, Yakima, WA, Zip 98902–3761; tel. 509/575–8000; Russ Myers, Chief Executive Officer

Owned, leased, sponsored:	2 hospitals	452 beds
Contract–managed:	0 hospitals	0 beds
Totals:	2 hospitals	452 beds

★6725: VIRTUA HEALTH (NP)
303 Lippincott Drive, 4th Floor, Marlton, NJ, Zip 08053–4160; tel. 856/355–0010; Dennis W. Pullin, FACHE, President and Chief Executive Officer
(Centralized Health System)

NEW JERSEY: VIRTUA MARLTON (O, 187 beds) 90 Brick Road, Marlton, NJ, Zip 08053–2177; tel. 856/355–6000; Lisa Ferraro, Senior Vice President and Chief Operating Officer

VIRTUA MEMORIAL (O, 334 beds) 175 Madison Avenue, Mount Holly, NJ, Zip 08060–2099; tel. 609/267–0700; John Kirby, Senior Vice President and Chief Operating Officer
Web address: www.virtua.org

VIRTUA VOORHEES (O, 402 beds) 100 Bowman Drive, Voorhees, NJ, Zip 08043–9612; tel. 856/325–3000; Dennis W. Pullin, FACHE, President and Chief Executive Officer
Web address: www.virtua.org

Owned, leased, sponsored:	3 hospitals	923 beds
Contract–managed:	0 hospitals	0 beds
Totals:	3 hospitals	923 beds

★0221: WAKE FOREST BAPTIST HEALTH (NP)
One Medical Center Boulevard, Winston–Salem, NC, Zip 27157; tel. 336/716–2011; Julie Ann . Freischlag, M.D., Chief Executive Officer
(Centralized Health System)

Section B

For explanation of codes following names, see page B2.
★ Indicates Type III membership in the American Hospital Association.

NORTH CAROLINA: WAKE FOREST BAPTIST HEALTH – WILKES MEDICAL CENTER (L, 92 beds) 1370 West 'D' Street, North Wilkesboro, NC, Zip 28659–3506, Mailing Address: P.O. Box 609, Zip 28659–0609, tel. 336/651–8100; J Gene. Faile, Chief Executive Officer and President
Web address: www.wilkesregional.com/

WAKE FOREST BAPTIST HEALTH–DAVIE MEDICAL CENTER (O, 50 beds) 329 NC Highway 801 North, Bermuda Run, NC, Zip 27006; tel. 336/998–1300; Chad J. Brown, M.P.H., President

WAKE FOREST BAPTIST HEALTH–LEXINGTON MEDICAL CENTER (O, 85 beds) 250 Hospital Drive, Lexington, NC, Zip 27292–6728, Mailing Address: P.O. Box 1817, Zip 27293–1817, tel. 336/248–5161; William B. James, FACHE, President
Web address: www.lexington.wakehealth.edu

WAKE FOREST BAPTIST MEDICAL CENTER (O, 798 beds) Medical Center Boulevard, Winston–Salem, NC, Zip 27157–0001; tel. 336/716–2011; Julie Ann . Freischlag, M.D., Chief Executive Officer

Owned, leased, sponsored:	4 hospitals	1025 beds
Contract–managed:	0 hospitals	0 beds
Totals:	4 hospitals	1025 beds

★6705: WAKEMED HEALTH & HOSPITALS (NP)

3000 New Bern Avenue, Raleigh, NC, Zip 27610–1231; tel. 919/350–8000; Donald R. Gintzig, President and Chief Executive Officer
(Moderately Centralized Health System)

NORTH CAROLINA: WAKEMED CARY HOSPITAL (O, 156 beds) 1900 Kildaire Farm Road, Cary, NC, Zip 27518–6616; tel. 919/350–8000; Donald R. Gintzig, President and Chief Executive Officer

WAKEMED RALEIGH CAMPUS (O, 695 beds) 3000 New Bern Avenue, Raleigh, NC, Zip 27610–1295; tel. 919/350–8000; Donald R. Gintzig, President and Chief Executive Officer
Web address: www.wakemed.org

Owned, leased, sponsored:	2 hospitals	851 beds
Contract–managed:	0 hospitals	0 beds
Totals:	2 hospitals	851 beds

★0979: WASHINGTON HEALTH SYSTEM (NP)

155 Wilson Avenue, Washington, PA, Zip 15301–3336; tel. 724/225–7000; Gary B. Weinstein, Chief Executive Officer
(Independent Hospital System)

PENNSYLVANIA: WASHINGTON HEALTH SYSTEM GREENE (O, 49 beds) 350 Bonar Avenue, Waynesburg, PA, Zip 15370–1608; tel. 724/627–3101; Terry Wiltrout, President
Web address: www.southwestregionalmedical.com/

WASHINGTON HOSPITAL (O, 206 beds) 155 Wilson Avenue, Washington, PA, Zip 15301–3398; tel. 724/225–7000; Gary B. Weinstein, President and Chief Executive Officer

Owned, leased, sponsored:	2 hospitals	255 beds
Contract–managed:	0 hospitals	0 beds
Totals:	2 hospitals	255 beds

★0068: WELLSPAN HEALTH (NP)

45 Monument Road, Suite 200, York, PA, Zip 17403–5071; tel. 717/851–2121; Kevin H. Mosser, M.D., President and Chief Executive Officer
(Centralized Physician/Insurance Health System)

PENNSYLVANIA: WELLSPAN EPHRATA COMMUNITY HOSPITAL (O, 130 beds) 169 Martin Avenue, Ephrata, PA, Zip 17522–1724, Mailing Address: P.O. Box 1002, Zip 17522–1002, tel. 717/733–0311

WELLSPAN GETTYSBURG HOSPITAL (O, 76 beds) 147 Gettys Street, Gettysburg, PA, Zip 17325–2534; tel. 717/334–2121; Jane E. Hyde, President
Web address: www.wellspan.org

WELLSPAN GOOD SAMARITAN HOSPITAL (O, 162 beds) Fourth and Walnut Streets, Lebanon, PA, Zip 17042–1281, Mailing Address: P.O. Box 1281, Zip 17042–1281, tel. 717/270–7500; Thomas R. Harlow, FACHE, President
Web address: www.gshleb.org

WELLSPAN PHILHAVEN (O, 103 beds) 283 South Butler Road, Mount Gretna, PA, Zip 17064–6085, Mailing Address: P.O. Box 550, Zip 17064–0550, tel. 717/273–8871; Phil Hess, Chief Executive Officer
Web address: www.philhaven.org

WELLSPAN SURGERY AND REHABILLITATION HOSPITAL (O, 73 beds) 55 Monument Road, York, PA, Zip 17403–5023; tel. 717/812–6100; Barbara Yarrish, R.N., President
Web address: www.wellspan.org

WELLSPAN YORK HOSPITAL (O, 564 beds) 1001 South George Street, York, PA, Zip 17403–3645; tel. 717/851–2345; Keith D. Noll, President

Owned, leased, sponsored:	6 hospitals	1108 beds
Contract–managed:	0 hospitals	0 beds
Totals:	6 hospitals	1108 beds

★0995: WELLSTAR HEALTH SYSTEM (NP)

793 Sawyer Road, Marietta, GA, Zip 30062; tel. 770/792–5012; Candice Saunders, President and Chief Executive Officer
(Centralized Health System)

GEORGIA: WELLSTAR COBB HOSPITAL (O, 370 beds) 3950 Austell Road, Austell, GA, Zip 30106–1121; tel. 470/732–4000; Callie Andrews, President

WELLSTAR DOUGLAS HOSPITAL (O, 108 beds) 8954 Hospital Drive, Douglasville, GA, Zip 30134–2282; tel. 770/949–1500; Craig A. Owens, President
Web address: www.wellstar.org

WELLSTAR KENNESTONE HOSPITAL (O, 657 beds) 677 Church Street, Marietta, GA, Zip 30060–1148; tel. 770/793–5000; Mary Chatman, Ph.D., Chief Executive Officer
Web address: www.wellstar.org

WELLSTAR PAULDING HOSPITAL (O, 294 beds) 2518 Jimmy Lee Smith Parkway, Hiram, GA, Zip 30141; tel. 470/644–7000; John Kueven, Senior Vice President and President

WELLSTAR WINDY HILL HOSPITAL (O, 55 beds) 2540 Windy Hill Road, Marietta, GA, Zip 30067–8632; tel. 770/644–1000; Monte Wilson, President
Web address: www.wellstar.org

WELLSTAR ATLANTA MEDICAL CENTER (O, 494 beds) 303 Parkway Drive NE, Atlanta, GA, Zip 30312–1212; tel. 404/265–4000; Kimberly Ryan, President
Web address: www.atlantamedcenter.com

WELLSTAR NORTH FULTON HOSPITAL (O, 173 beds) 3000 Hospital Boulevard, Roswell, GA, Zip 30076–3899; tel. 770/751–2500; Jon–Paul Croom, President

WELLSTAR SPALDING REGIONAL HOSPITAL (O, 160 beds) 601 South Eighth Street, Griffin, GA, Zip 30224–4294, Mailing Address: P O Drawer 'V', Zip 30224–1168, tel. 770/228–2721; Tamara Ison, Senior Vice President and President
Web address: www.spaldingregional.com

WELLSTAR SYLVAN GROVE HOSPITAL (O, 24 beds) 1050 McDonough Road, Jackson, GA, Zip 30233–1599; tel. 770/775–7861; Tamara Ison, Senior Vice President and President
Web address: www.sylvangrovehospital.com

WEST GEORGIA HEALTH (O, 390 beds) 1514 Vernon Road, Lagrange, GA, Zip 30240–4131; tel. 706/882–1411; Gerald N. Fulks, President

Owned, leased, sponsored:	10 hospitals	2725 beds
Contract–managed:	0 hospitals	0 beds
Totals:	10 hospitals	2725 beds

For explanation of codes following names, see page B2.
★ Indicates Type III membership in the American Hospital Association.

Section B

★0004: WEST TENNESSEE HEALTHCARE (NP)

620 Skyline Drive, Jackson, TN, Zip 38301–3923; tel. 731/541–5000; James E. Ross, President and Chief Executive Officer
(Centralized Physician/Insurance Health System)

TENNESSEE: BOLIVAR GENERAL HOSPITAL (O, 21 beds) 650 Nuckolls Road, Bolivar, TN, Zip 38008–1532, Mailing Address: PO Box 509, Zip 38008–0509, tel. 731/658–3100; Ruby Kirby, Administrator

CAMDEN GENERAL HOSPITAL (O, 25 beds) 175 Hospital Drive, Camden, TN, Zip 38320–1617; tel. 731/593–6300; Scott Barber, Vice President
Web address: www.wth.net

JACKSON–MADISON COUNTY GENERAL HOSPITAL (O, 690 beds) 620 Skyline Drive, Jackson, TN, Zip 38301–3923; tel. 731/541–5000; James E. Ross, President and Chief Executive Officer

MILAN GENERAL HOSPITAL (O, 28 beds) 4039 Highland Street, Milan, TN, Zip 38358–3483; tel. 731/686–1591; Sherry Scruggs, Administrator
Web address: www.wth.org

PATHWAYS OF TENNESSEE (O, 25 beds) 238 Summar Drive, Jackson, TN, Zip 38301–3906; tel. 731/541–8200; Pam Henson, Executive Director
Web address: www.wth.net/pathways

WEST TENNESSEE HEALTHCARE DYERSBURG HOSPITAL (O, 120 beds) 400 East Tickle Street, Dyersburg, TN, Zip 38024–3120; tel. 731/285–2410; Reba Celsor, Chief Executive Officer
Web address: www.wth.org/locations/west–tennessee–healthcare–dyersburg–hospital

WEST TENNESSEE HEALTHCARE VOLUNTEER HOSPITAL (O, 65 beds) 161 Mount Pelia Road, Martin, TN, Zip 38237–3811; tel. 731/587–4261; Darrell Blaylock, Chief Executive Officer

Owned, leased, sponsored:	7 hospitals	974 beds
Contract–managed:	0 hospitals	0 beds
Totals:	7 hospitals	974 beds

★0119: WEST VIRGINIA UNIVERSITY HEALTH SYSTEM (NP)

One Medical Center, Box 8136, Morgantown, WV, Zip 26506–8136; tel. 304/285–7150; Albert L. Wright Jr, PharmD, President and Chief Executive Officer
(Moderately Centralized Health System)

WEST VIRGINIA: BERKELEY MEDICAL CENTER (O, 195 beds) 2500 Hospital Drive, Martinsburg, WV, Zip 25401–3402; tel. 304/264–1000; Anthony Zelenka, President and Chief Operating Officer

CAMDEN CLARK MEDICAL CENTER (O, 240 beds) 800 Garfield Avenue, Parkersburg, WV, Zip 26101–5378, Mailing Address: P.O. Box 718, Zip 26102–0718, tel. 304/424–2111; Steve Altmiller, President and Chief Executive Officer
Web address: www.camdenclark.org

JEFFERSON MEDICAL CENTER (O, 25 beds) 300 South Preston Street, Ranson, WV, Zip 25438–1631; tel. 304/728–1600; Neil R. McLaughlin, R.N., Administrator and Vice President, Operations

POTOMAC VALLEY HOSPITAL (O, 25 beds) 100 Pin Oak Lane, Keyser, WV, Zip 26726–5908; tel. 304/597–3500; Mark G. Boucot, FACHE, President and Chief Executive Officer
Web address: www.potomacvalleyhospital.com

REYNOLDS MEMORIAL HOSPITAL (O, 90 beds) 800 Wheeling Avenue, Glen Dale, WV, Zip 26038–1697; tel. 304/845–3211; David F. Hess, M.D., Chief Executive Officer

ST. JOSEPH'S HOSPITAL OF BUCKHANNON (O, 51 beds) 1 Amalia Drive, Buckhannon, WV, Zip 26201–2276; tel. 304/473–2000; Skip Gjolberg, FACHE, Administrator
Web address: www.stj.net

UNITED HOSPITAL CENTER (O, 264 beds) 327 Medical Park Drive, Bridgeport, WV, Zip 26330–9006; tel. 681/342–1000; Michael C. Tillman, President and Chief Executive Officer

WEST VIRGINIA UNIVERSITY HOSPITALS (O, 631 beds) 1 Medical Center Drive, Morgantown, WV, Zip 26506–4749; tel. 304/598–4000; Albert L. Wright Jr, PharmD, President and Chief Executive Officer
Web address: www.health.wvu.edu

Owned, leased, sponsored:	8 hospitals	1521 beds
Contract–managed:	0 hospitals	0 beds
Totals:	8 hospitals	1521 beds

★0811: WESTERN CONNECTICUT HEALTH NETWORK (NP)

24 Hospital Avenue, Danbury, CT, Zip 06810–6099; tel. 203/739–7066; John M. Murphy, M.D., President and Chief Executive Officer
(Moderately Centralized Health System)

CONNECTICUT: DANBURY HOSPITAL (O, 265 beds) 24 Hospital Avenue, Danbury, CT, Zip 06810–6099; tel. 203/739–7000; John M. Murphy, M.D., President

NORWALK HOSPITAL (O, 150 beds) 34 Maple Street, Norwalk, CT, Zip 06850–3894; tel. 203/852–2000; Michael Daglio, President
Web address: www.norwalkhospital.org

Owned, leased, sponsored:	2 hospitals	415 beds
Contract–managed:	0 hospitals	0 beds
Totals:	2 hospitals	415 beds

★0468: WHITE RIVER HEALTH SYSTEM (NP)

1710 Harrison Street, Batesville, AR, Zip 72501–7303; tel. 870/262–1200; Gary Bebow, FACHE, Administrator and Chief Executive Officer
(Independent Hospital System)

ARKANSAS: STONE COUNTY MEDICAL CENTER (O, 25 beds) 2106 East Main Street, Mountain View, AR, Zip 72560–6439, Mailing Address: P.O. Box 510, Zip 72560–0510, tel. 870/269–4361; Kevin Spears, Chief Executive Officer

WHITE RIVER MEDICAL CENTER (O, 210 beds) 1710 Harrison Street, Batesville, AR, Zip 72501–7303, Mailing Address: P.O. Box 2197, Zip 72503–2197, tel. 870/262–1200; Gary Bebow, FACHE, Administrator and Chief Executive Officer
Web address: www.whiteriverhealthsystem.com

Owned, leased, sponsored:	2 hospitals	235 beds
Contract–managed:	0 hospitals	0 beds
Totals:	2 hospitals	235 beds

0646: WHITTIER HEALTH NETWORK (IO)

25 Railroad Square, Haverhill, MA, Zip 01832–5721; tel. 978/556–5858; Alfred L. Arcidi, M.D., President
(Independent Hospital System)

MASSACHUSETTS: WHITTIER PAVILION (O, 65 beds) 76 Summer Street, Haverhill, MA, Zip 01830–5814; tel. 978/373–8222; Alfred L. Arcidi, M.D., Chief Executive Officer
Web address: www.whittierhealth.com

WHITTIER REHABILITATION HOSPITAL (O, 60 beds) 150 Flanders Road, Westborough, MA, Zip 01581–1017; tel. 508/871–2000; Alfred J. Arcidi, M.D., Senior Vice President

WHITTIER REHABILITATION HOSPITAL (O, 60 beds) 145 Ward Hill Avenue, Bradford, MA, Zip 01835–6928; tel. 978/372–8000; Alfred J. Arcidi, M.D., Senior Vice President
Web address: www.whittierhealth.com

Owned, leased, sponsored:	3 hospitals	185 beds
Contract–managed:	0 hospitals	0 beds
Totals:	3 hospitals	185 beds

1945: WILLIS–KNIGHTON HEALTH SYSTEM (NP)

2600 Greenwood Road, Shreveport, LA, Zip 71103–3908; tel. 318/212–4000; James K. Elrod, FACHE, President and Chief Executive Officer
(Moderately Centralized Health System)

For explanation of codes following names, see page B2.
★ Indicates Type III membership in the American Hospital Association.

Section B

LOUISIANA: DE SOTO REGIONAL HEALTH SYSTEM (C, 10 beds) 207 Jefferson Street, Mansfield, LA, Zip 71052–2603, Mailing Address: P.O. Box 1636, Zip 71052–1636, tel. 318/872–4610; Todd Eppler, FACHE, Chief Executive Officer
Web address: www.desotoregional.com

SPRINGHILL MEDICAL CENTER (C, 32 beds) 2001 Doctors Drive, Springhill, LA, Zip 71075–4526, Mailing Address: P.O. Box 920, Zip 71075–0920, tel. 318/539–1000; Vince Sedminik, Chief Executive Officer
Web address: www.smccare.com

WILLIS–KNIGHTON MEDICAL CENTER (O, 799 beds) 2600 Greenwood Road, Shreveport, LA, Zip 71103–3908, Mailing Address: P.O. Box 32600, Zip 71130–2600, tel. 318/212–4600; James K. Elrod, FACHE, Chief Executive Officer

Owned, leased, sponsored:	1 hospitals	799 beds
Contract–managed:	2 hospitals	42 beds
Totals:	3 hospitals	841 beds

1004: WMCHEALTH (NP)

100 Woods Road, Valhalla, NY, Zip 10595–1530; tel. 914/493–7000; Michael D. Israel, President and Chief Executive Officer
(Moderately Centralized Health System)

NEW YORK: BON SECOURS COMMUNITY HOSPITAL (O, 189 beds) 160 East Main Street, Port Jervis, NY, Zip 12771–2245, Mailing Address: P.O. Box 1014, Zip 12771–0268, tel. 845/858–7000; Mary Leahy, M.D., Chief Executive Officer
Web address: www.bonsecourscommunityhosp.org

GOOD SAMARITAN REGIONAL MEDICAL CENTER (O, 308 beds) 255 Lafayette Avenue, Suffern, NY, Zip 10901–4869; tel. 845/368–5000; Mary Leahy, M.D., Chief Executive Officer
Web address: www.goodsamhosp.org

HEALTH ALLIANCE HOSPITAL – BROADWAY CAMPUS (O, 150 beds) 396 Broadway, Kingston, NY, Zip 12401–4692; tel. 845/331–3131; David Scarpino, President and Chief Executive Officer

HEALTH ALLIANCE HOSPITAL – MARY'S AVENUE CAMPUS (O, 105 beds) 105 Marys Avenue, Kingston, NY, Zip 12401–5894; tel. 845/338–2500; David Scarpino, President and Chief Executive Officer
Web address: www.hahv.org

MARGARETVILLE HOSPITAL (O, 15 beds) 42084 State Highway 28, Margaretville, NY, Zip 12455–2820; tel. 845/586–2631; Mark Pohar, Executive Director
Web address: www.margaretvillehospital.org

ST. ANTHONY COMMUNITY HOSPITAL (O, 60 beds) 15 Maple Avenue, Warwick, NY, Zip 10990–1028; tel. 845/986–2276; Mary Leahy, M.D., Chief Executive Officer

WESTCHESTER MEDICAL CENTER (O, 872 beds) 100 Woods Road, Valhalla, NY, Zip 10595–1530; tel. 914/493–7000; Michael D. Israel, President and Chief Executive Officer
Web address: www.wmchealth.org

Owned, leased, sponsored:	7 hospitals	1699 beds
Contract–managed:	0 hospitals	0 beds
Totals:	7 hospitals	1699 beds

★0157: YALE NEW HAVEN HEALTH (NP)

789 Howard Avenue, New Haven, CT, Zip 06519–1304; tel. 203/688–4608; Marna P. Borgstrom, President and Chief Executive Officer
(Centralized Physician/Insurance Health System)

CONNECTICUT: BRIDGEPORT HOSPITAL (O, 358 beds) 267 Grant Street, Bridgeport, CT, Zip 06610–2805, Mailing Address: P.O. Box 5000, Zip 06610–0120, tel. 203/384–3000; Michael Ivy, MD, Interim Chief Executive Officer
Web address: www.bridgeporthospital.org

GREENWICH HOSPITAL (O, 174 beds) 5 Perryridge Road, Greenwich, CT, Zip 06830–4697; tel. 203/863–3000; Norman G. Roth, President

LAWRENCE + MEMORIAL HOSPITAL (O, 251 beds) 365 Montauk Avenue, New London, CT, Zip 06320–4769; tel. 860/442–0711; Patrick Green, FACHE, President and Chief Executive Officer
Web address: www.lmhospital.org

YALE–NEW HAVEN HOSPITAL (O, 1389 beds) 20 York Street, New Haven, CT, Zip 06510–3202; tel. 203/688–4242; Marna P. Borgstrom, Chief Executive Officer

RHODE ISLAND: WESTERLY HOSPITAL (O, 41 beds) 25 Wells Street, Westerly, RI, Zip 02891–2934; tel. 401/596–6000; Patrick Green, FACHE, President and Chief Executive Officer
Web address: www.westerlyhospital.org

Owned, leased, sponsored:	5 hospitals	2213 beds
Contract–managed:	0 hospitals	0 beds
Totals:	5 hospitals	2213 beds

Section B

Geographically

United States

ALABAMA

Anniston: REGIONAL MEDICAL CENTER 400 East 10th Street, Zip 36207–4716; tel. 256/235–5121; Louis A. Bass, President and Chief Executive Officer, p. B107

Birmingham: BRADFORD HEALTH SERVICES 2101 Magnolia Avenue South, Suite 518, Zip 35205–2853; tel. 205/251–7753; Jerry W. Crowder, President and Chief Executive Officer, p. B24

★ ENCOMPASS HEALTH CORPORATION 3660 Grandview Parkway, Suite 200, Zip 35243–3332; tel. 205/967–7116; Mark J. Tarr, President and Chief Executive Officer, p. B49

NOLAND HEALTH SERVICES, INC. 600 Corporate Parkway, Suite 100, Zip 35242–5451; tel. 205/783–8484; Gary M. Glasscock, President and Chief Executive Officer, p. B89

★ UAB HEALTH SYSTEM 500 22nd Street South, Suite 408, Zip 35233–3110; tel. 205/975–5362; William Ferniany, Chief Executive Officer, p. B130

Guntersville: MARSHALL HEALTH SYSTEM 227 Britany Road, Zip 35976–5766; tel. 256/894–6615; Gary R. Gore, Chief Executive Officer, p. B78

Huntsville: HUNTSVILLE HOSPITAL HEALTH SYSTEM 101 Sivley Road SW, Zip 35801–4421; tel. 265/256–1000; David S. Spillers, Chief Executive Officer, p. B67

Mobile: ALTAPOINTE HEALTH SYSTEMS 5750-A Southland Drive, Zip 36693–3316; tel. 251/473–4423; J. Tuerk. Schlesinger, Chief Executive Officer, p. B10

INFIRMARY HEALTH SYSTEM 5 Mobile Infirmary Circle, Zip 36607–3513; tel. 251/435–5500; D Mark. Nix, President and Chief Executive Officer, p. B67

★ UNIVERSITY OF SOUTH ALABAMA HEALTH SYSTEM 2451 Fillingim Street, Zip 36617–2238; tel. 251/471–7000; Owen Bailey, Chief Executive Officer and Senior Associate Vice President for Medical Affairs, p. B140

Montgomery: BAPTIST HEALTH 301 Brown Springs Road, Zip 36117–7005; tel. 334/273–4400; W Russell. Tyner, President and Chief Executive Officer, p. B20

GILLIARD HEALTH SERVICES 3091 Carter Hill Road, Zip 36111–1801; tel. 334/265–5009; William G. McKenzie, President, Chief Executive Officer and Chairman, p. B57

Tuscaloosa: DCH HEALTH SYSTEM 809 University Boulevard East, Zip 35401–2029; tel. 205/759–7111; Bryan N. Kindred, President and Chief Executive Officer, p. B41

ARIZONA

Flagstaff: ★ NORTHERN ARIZONA HEALTHCARE 1200 North Beaver Street, Zip 86001–3118; tel. 928/779–3366; Florence (Flo). Spyrow, Interim President and Chief Executive Officer, p. B90

Gilbert: ★ BANNER HEALTH 2872 E. Fruitvale Ave, Zip 85297, Mailing Address: P.O. Box 25489, Phoenix, Zip 85002–5489, tel. 602/747–4000; Peter S. Fine, President and Chief Executive Officer, p. B19

Scottsdale: ★ HONORHEALTH 8125 North Hayden Road, Zip 85258–2463; tel. 623/580–5800; Todd LaPorte, Chief Executive Officer, p. B66

SOUTHWEST HEALTHCARE SYSTEM 7025 N Scottsdale Road Suite 9347, Zip 85253–3675, Mailing Address: 7025 North Scottsdale Road, Suite 9347, Zip 85251–3331, tel. 480/518–5444; Paul R. Tuft, President, p. B118

ARKANSAS

Batesville: ★ WHITE RIVER HEALTH SYSTEM 1710 Harrison Street, Zip 72501–7303; tel. 870/262–1200; Gary Bebow, Administrator and Chief Executive Officer, p. B147

Blytheville: ★ MISSISSIPPI COUNTY HOSPITAL SYSTEM 1520 North Division Street, Zip 72315–1448, Mailing Address: P.O. Box 108, Zip 72316–0108, tel. 870/838–7300; Chris Lee. Raymer, Chief Executive Officer, p. B85

Little Rock: ★ BAPTIST HEALTH 9601 Baptist Health Drive, Zip 72205–6321; tel. 501/202–2000; Troy R. Wells, Chief Executive Officer, p. B20

CALIFORNIA

Alhambra: AHMC & HEALTHCARE, INC. 55 South Raymond Avenue, Suite 105, Zip 91801–7101; tel. 626/457–9600; Jonathan Wu, President and Chairman, p. B8

Corona: SIGNATURE HEALTHCARE SERVICES 4238 Green River Road, Zip 92880–1669; tel. 951/549–8032; Soon K. Kim, President and Chief Executive Officer, p. B116

Covina: ★ CITRUS VALLEY HEALTH PARTNERS 210 West San Bernardino Road, Zip 91723–1515; tel. 626/331–7331; Robert H. Curry, President and Chief Executive Officer, p. B32

Cupertino: CRC HEALTH GROUP, INC. 20400 Stevens Creek Boulevard, Suite 600, Zip 95014–2217; tel. 866/540–5240; Jerome E. Rhodes, Chief Executive Officer, p. B40

El Segundo: AVANTI HOSPITALS 222 North Sepulveda Boulevard, Suite 950, Zip 90245–5614; tel. 310/356–0550; Michael A. Rembis, Corporate Chief Executive Officer, p. B17

Escondido: ★ PALOMAR HEALTH 456 East Grand Avenue, Zip 92025–3319; tel. 760/740–6393; Diane Hansen, Chief Executive Officer, p. B96

Fountain Valley: MEMORIALCARE 17360 Brookhurst Street, Zip 92708–3720, Mailing Address: P.O. Box 1428, Long Beach, Zip 90801–1428, tel. 714/377–2900; Barry S. Arbuckle, President and Chief Executive Officer, p. B82

Fresno: COMMUNITY MEDICAL CENTERS Fresno and Maddy Drive, Zip 93721, Mailing Address: P.O. Box 1232, Zip 93715–1232, tel. 559/459–6000; Tim A. Joslin, President and Chief Executive Officer, p. B37

Hemet: PHYSICIANS FOR HEALTHY HOSPITALS 1117 East Devonshire Avenue, Zip 92543–3083; tel. 951/652–2811; Joel M. Bergenfeld, Chief Executive Officer, p. B97

Irvine: ALECTO HEALTHCARE 16310 Bake Parkway, Suite 200, Zip 92618–4684; tel. 323/932–5963; Lex Reddy, Chief Executive Officer, p. B8

Loma Linda: LOMA LINDA UNIVERSITY ADVENTIST HEALTH SCIENCES CENTER 11175 Campus Street, Zip 92350–1700; tel. 909/558–7572; Richard H. Hart, President and Chief Executive Officer, p. B77

Los Angeles: KECK MEDICINE OF USC 1510 San Pablo Street, Suite 600, Zip 90033–5405; tel. 323/442–8500; Thomas E. Jackiewicz, Senior Vice President and Chief Executive Officer, p. B71

LOS ANGELES COUNTY-DEPARTMENT OF HEALTH SERVICES 313 North Figueroa Street, Room 912, Zip 90012–2691; tel. 213/240–8101; Mitchell H. Katz, Director, p. B77

PROSPECT MEDICAL HOLDINGS 10780 California Route 2 #400, Zip 90025; tel. 714/796–5900; Mitchell Lew, President, p. B101

VERITY HEALTH SYSTEM 2200 West Third Street, Suite 200, Zip 90057–1935, Mailing Address: 203 Redwood Shores Parkway, Suite 800, Redwood City, Zip 94065, tel. 650/551–6650; Richard Adcock, President and Chief Executive Officer, p. B143

Oakland: ★ KAISER FOUNDATION HOSPITALS One Kaiser Plaza, Zip 94612–3600; tel. 510/271–5910; Bernard J. Tyson, Chairman and Chief Executive Officer, p. B70

★ UNIVERSITY OF CALIFORNIA SYSTEMWIDE ADMINISTRATION 1111 Franklin Street, 11th Floor, Zip 94607–5200; tel. 510/987–9071; John D. Stobo, Executive Vice President and Chief Executive Officer, p. B138

Ontario: ★ PRIME HEALTHCARE 3300 East Guasti Road, Zip 91761–8655; tel. 909/235–4400; Prem Reddy, Chairman, President and Chief Executive Officer, p. B99

Palo Alto: ★ STANFORD HEALTH CARE 300 Pasteur Drive, Zip 94304–2299; tel. 650/723–4000; David Entwistle, President and Chief Executive Officer, p. B121

Roseville: ★ ADVENTIST HEALTH 2100 Douglas Boulevard, Zip 95661–3898, Mailing Address: P.O. Box 619002, Zip 95661–9002, tel. 916/781–2000; Scott Reiner, Chief Executive Officer, p. B5

Sacramento: ★ SUTTER HEALTH 2200 River Plaza Drive, Zip 95833–4134; tel. 916/733–8800; Sarah Krevans, President and Chief Executive Officer, p. B123

San Diego: ★ SCRIPPS HEALTH 4275 Campus Point Court CP112, Zip 92121–1513, Mailing Address: 4275 Campus Point Court, Zip 92121–1513, tel. 858/678–7200; Chris D. Van Gorder, President and Chief Executive Officer, p. B112

★ SHARP HEALTHCARE 8695 Spectrum Center Boulevard, Zip 92123–1489; tel. 858/499–4000; Michael Murphy, President & Chief Executive Officer, p. B115

San Francisco: ★ DIGNITY HEALTH 185 Berry Street, Suite 300, Zip 94107–1773; tel. 415/438–5500; Lloyd H. Dean, President and Chief Executive Officer, p. B46

San Leandro: ALAMEDA HEALTH SYSTEM 15400 Foothill Boulevard, Zip 94578–1009; tel. 510/677–7920; Delvecchio Finley, Chief Executive Officer, p. B8

Santa Ana: KPC HEALTHCARE, INC. 1301 North Tustin Avenue, Zip 92705–8619; tel. 714/953–3652; Suzanne Richards, Chief Executive Officer, p. B73

Santa Barbara: ★ COTTAGE HEALTH 400 West Pueblo Street, Zip 93105–4353, Mailing Address: P.O. Box 689, Zip 93102–0689, tel. 805/569–7290; Ronald C. Werft, President and Chief Executive Officer, p. B39

Santa Fe Springs: COLLEGE HEALTH ENTERPRISES 11627 Telegraph Road, Suite 200, Zip 90670–6814; tel. 562/923–9449; Barry J. Weiss, Chairman of the Board, p. B33

Truckee: ★ TAHOE FOREST HEALTH SYSTEM 10121 Pine Avenue, Zip 96161–4835; tel. 530/587–6011; Harry Weis, Chief Executive Officer, p. B124

Ventura: COMMUNITY MEMORIAL HEALTH SYSTEM 147 North Brent Street, Zip 93003–2809; tel. 805/652–5011; Gary Wilde, President and Chief Executive Officer, p. B38

Walnut Creek: ★ JOHN MUIR HEALTH 1400 Treat Boulevard, Zip 94597–2142; tel. 925/941–2100; Calvin K. Knight, President and Chief Executive Officer, p. B69

West Hollywood: ★ CEDARS-SINAI HEALTH SYSTEM 8700 Beverly Boulevard, Zip 90048–1865, Mailing Address: Box 48750, Los Angeles, Zip 90048–0750, tel. 310/423–5000; Thomas M. Priselac, President and Chief Executive Officer, p. B30

Whittier: ★ PIH HEALTH 12401 Washington Boulevard, Zip 90602–1006; tel. 562/698–0811; James R. West, President and Chief Executive Officer, p. B98

COLORADO

Alamosa: ★ SAN LUIS VALLEY HEALTH 106 Blanca Avenue, Zip 81101–2340; tel. 719/589–2511; Konnie Martin, Chief Executive Officer, p. B110

Broomfield: ★ SCL HEALTH 500 Eldorado Boulevard, Suite 4300, Zip 80021; tel. 303/813–5180; Lydia Jumonville, President and Chief Executive Officer, p. B112

Englewood: ★ CATHOLIC HEALTH INITIATIVES 198 Inverness Drive West, Suite 800, Zip 80112–5202; tel. 303/298–9100; Kevin E. Lofton, Chief Executive Officer, p. B27

Fort Collins: ★ UCHEALTH 2315 East Harmony Road, Suite 200, Zip 80528–8620; tel. 970/495–7000; Elizabeth B. Concordia, President and Chief Executive Officer, p. B131

CONNECTICUT

Danbury: ★ WESTERN CONNECTICUT HEALTH NETWORK 24 Hospital Avenue, Zip 06810–6099; tel. 203/739–7066; John M. Murphy, President and Chief Executive Officer, p. B147

Hartford: CONNECTICUT DEPARTMENT OF MENTAL HEALTH AND ADDICTION SERVICES 410 Capitol Avenue, Zip 06106–1367, Mailing Address: P.O. Box 341431, Zip 06134–1431, tel. 860/418–7000; Miriam Delphin-Rittmon, Commissioner, p. B38

★ HARTFORD HEALTHCARE One State Street, 19th Floor, Zip 6103; tel. 860/263–4100; Elliot T. Joseph, Chief Executive Officer, p. B59

New Haven: ★ YALE NEW HAVEN HEALTH 789 Howard Avenue, Zip 06519–1304; tel. 203/688–4608; Marna P. Borgstrom, President and Chief Executive Officer, p. B148

DELAWARE

Wilmington: ★ CHRISTIANA CARE HEALTH SYSTEM 501 West 14th Street, Zip 19801–1013, Mailing Address: P.O. Box 1668, Zip 19899–1668, tel. 302/733–1000; Janice E. Nevin, Chief Executive Officer, p. B32

DISTRICT OF COLUMBIA

Washington: DEPARTMENT OF THE AIR FORCE 1420 Pentagon, Room 4E1084, Zip 20330–1420; tel. 202/767–4765, Lieutenant General, Thomas Travis, Surgeon General, p. B41

FLORIDA

Altamonte Springs: ★ ADVENTIST HEALTH SYSTEM SUNBELT HEALTH CARE CORPORATION 900 Hope Way, Zip 32714–1502; tel. 407/357–1000; Terry Shaw, President and Chief Executive Officer, p. B6

Boca Raton: PROMISE HEALTHCARE 999 Yamato Road, 3rd Floor, Zip 33431–4477; tel. 561/869–3100; Peter R. Baronoff, Chief Executive Officer, p. B101

SUCCESS HEALTHCARE 999 Yamato Road, 3rd Floor, Zip 33431–4477; tel. 561/869–6300; Peter R. Baronoff, President and Chief Executive Officer, p. B122

Clearwater: MORTON PLANT MEASE HEALTH CARE 300 Pinellas Street, Zip 33756–3804, Mailing Address: P.O. Box 210, Zip 33757–0210, tel. 727/462–7000; Glenn D. Waters, President, p. B86

Coral Gables: ★ BAPTIST HEALTH SOUTH FLORIDA 6855 Red Road, Suite 600, Zip 33143–3632; tel. 786/662–7111; Brian E. Keeley, President and Chief Executive Officer, p. B21

Fort Lauderdale: ★ BROWARD HEALTH 1800 NW 49th Street, Zip 33309–3092; tel. 954/355–4400; Beverly Capasso, President and Chief Executive Officer, p. B25

Fort Myers: ★ LEE HEALTH 2776 Cleveland Avenue, Zip 33901–5864, Mailing Address: P.O. Box 2218, Zip 33902–2218, tel. 239/343–2000; Lawrence Antonucci, President and Chief Executive Officer, p. B74

Gainesville: ★ UF HEALTH SHANDS 1600 SW Archer Road, Zip 32610–0326; tel. 352/733–1500; Edward Jimenez, Chief Executive Officer, p. B131

Hollywood: ★ MEMORIAL HEALTHCARE SYSTEM 3501 Johnson Street, Zip 33021–5421; tel. 954/987–2000; Aurelio Fernandez, Chief Executive Officer, p. B82

Jacksonville: ★ BAPTIST HEALTH 841 Prudential Drive, Suite 1601, Zip 32207–8202; tel. 904/202–2000; Hugh Greene, President and Chief Executive Officer, p. B20

NEMOURS 10140 Centurion Parkway North, Zip 32256–0532; tel. 904/697–4100; David J. Bailey, President and Chief Executive Officer, p. B88

Lauderdale Lakes: CATHOLIC HEALTH SERVICES 4790 North State Road 7, Zip 33319–5860; tel. 954/484–1515; Joseph M. Catania, President and Chief Executive Officer, p. B29

Leesburg: CENTRAL FLORIDA HEALTH 600 East Dixie Avenue, Zip 34748–5925; tel. 352/323–5762; Donald G. Henderson, Chief Executive Officer, p. B31

Miami Lakes: PACER HEALTH CORPORATION 14100 Palmetto Frontage Road, Suite 110, Zip 33016; tel. 305/828–7660; Rainier Gonzalez, Chairman and Chief Executive Officer, p. B95

Orlando: ORLANDO HEALTH 1414 Kuhl Avenue, Zip 32806–2093; tel. 321/843–7000; David W. Strong, President and Chief Executive Officer, p. B94

Pensacola: ★ BAPTIST HEALTH CARE CORPORATION 1717 North 'E' Street, Suite 402, Zip 32501–6377, Mailing Address: P.O. Box 17500, Zip 32522–7500, tel. 850/434–4011; Mark T. Faulkner, President, p. B20

Rockledge: HEALTH FIRST, INC. 6450 US Highway 1, Zip 32955–5747; tel. 321/434–7000; Steven P. Johnson, President and Chief Executive Officer, p. B64

Tampa: SHRINERS HOSPITALS FOR CHILDREN 2900 North Rocky Point Drive, Zip 33607–1435, Mailing Address: P.O. Box 31356, Zip 33631–3356, tel. 813/281–0300; John P. McCabe, Executive Vice President, p. B116

Windermere: UNITED MEDICAL CORPORATION 603 Main Street, Zip 34786–3548, Mailing Address: P.O. Box 1100, Zip 34786–1100, tel. 407/876–2200; Donald R. Dizney, Chairman and Chief Executive Officer, p. B132

GEORGIA

Albany: ★ PHOEBE PUTNEY HEALTH SYSTEM 417 Third Avenue, Zip 31701–1943; tel. 229/312–1000; Joel Wernick, President and Chief Executive Officer, p. B97

Atlanta: ★ EMORY HEALTHCARE 1440 Clifton Road NE, Suite 400, Zip 30322–1102; tel. 404/778–5000; Jonathan S. Lewin, President, p. B49

★ NORTHSIDE HEALTHCARE SYSTEM 1000 Johnson Ferry Road NE, Zip 30342–1611; tel. 404/851–8000; Robert Quattrocchi, President and Chief Executive Officer, p. B91

Augusta: ★ UNIVERSITY HEALTH CARE SYSTEM 1350 Walton Way, Zip 30901–2629; tel. 706/722–9011; James R. Davis, President and Chief Executive Officer, p. B138

Blairsville: UNION GENERAL HOSPITAL, INC. 35 Hospital Road, Zip 30512–3139; tel. 706/745–2111; Mike Gowder, Chief Executive Officer, p. B132

Brunswick: ★ SOUTHEAST GEORGIA HEALTH SYSTEM 2415 Parkwood Drive, Zip 31520–4722, Mailing Address: P.O. Box 1518, Zip 31521–1518, tel. 912/466–7000; Michael D. Scherneck, President and Chief Executive Officer, p. B117

Carrollton: ★ TANNER HEALTH SYSTEM 705 Dixie Street, Zip 30117–3818; tel. 770/836–9580; Loy M. Howard, President and Chief Executive Officer, p. B124

Columbus: COLUMBUS REGIONAL HEALTHCARE SYSTEM 707 Center Street, Suite 400, Zip 31901–1575; tel. 706/660–6100; M. Scott. Hill, Chief Executive Officer, p. B33

Gainesville: NORTHEAST GEORGIA HEALTH SYSTEM 743 Spring Street NE, Zip 30501–3715; tel. 770/219–9000; Carol H. Burrell, President and Chief Executive Officer, p. B90

Macon: NAVICENT HEALTH 777 Hemlock Street, MSC 105, Zip 31201–2155, Mailing Address: 777 Hemlock Street, Zip 31201–2155, tel. 478/633–1000; Ninfa M. Saunders, Chief Executive Officer, p. B87

Marietta: ★ WELLSTAR HEALTH SYSTEM 793 Sawyer Road, Zip 30062; tel. 770/792–5012; Candice Saunders, President and Chief Executive Officer, p. B146

Rome: FLOYD HEALTHCARE MANAGEMENT 304 Turner McCall Boulevard, Zip 30165–5621, Mailing Address: P.O. Box 233, Zip 30162–0233, tel. 706/509–5000; Kurt Stuenkel, President and Chief Executive Officer, p. B55

Roswell: PIEDMONT HEALTHCARE 1800 Howell Mill Road NW, Suite 850, Zip 30076, Atlanta, tel. 404/425–1314; Kevin Brown, President and Chief Executive Officer, p. B97

Thomasville: ★ ARCHBOLD MEDICAL CENTER 910 South Broad Street, Zip 31792–6113; tel. 229/228–2739; J Perry. Mustian, President, p. B11

Tifton: ★ TIFT REGIONAL HEALTH SYSTEM 901 East 18th Street, Zip 31794–3648; tel. 229/353–6100; Christopher Dorman, President and Chief Executive Officer, p. B128

Valdosta: SOUTH GEORGIA MEDICAL CENTER 2501 North Patterson Street, Zip 31602–1735, Mailing Address: P.O. Box 1727, Zip 31603–1727, tel. 229/333–1000; Bill Forbes, Interim Chief Executive Officer, p. B117

Warner Robins: ★ HOUSTON HEALTHCARE SYSTEM 1601 Watson Boulevard, Zip 31093–3431, Mailing Address: P.O. Box 2886, Zip 31099–2886, tel. 478/922–4281; Cary Martin, Chief Executive Officer, p. B66

HAWAII

Honolulu: ★ HAWAII HEALTH SYSTEMS CORPORATION 3675 Kilauea Avenue, Zip 96816–2333; tel. 808/733–4151; Linda Rosen, Chief Executive Officer, p. B59

HAWAII PACIFIC HEALTH 55 Merchant Street, Zip 96813–4306; tel. 808/949–9355; Raymond P. Vara Jr, President and Chief Executive Officer, p. B60

★ QUEEN'S HEALTH SYSTEMS 1301 Punchbowl Street, Zip 96813–2402; tel. 808/535–5448; Arthur A. Ushijima, President and Chief Executive Officer, p. B105

IDAHO

Boise: ★ ST. LUKE'S HEALTH SYSTEM 190 East Bannock Street, Zip 83712–6241; tel. 208/381–4200; David C. Pate, President and Chief Executive Officer, p. B120

Pocatello: SAFE HAVEN HEALTH CARE 2520 South 5th Avenue, Zip 83204–1923; tel. 800/261–2443; Scott Burpee, President, p. B109

ILLINOIS

Carbondale: SOUTHERN ILLINOIS HEALTHCARE 1239 East Main Street, Zip 62901–3114, Mailing Address: P.O. Box 3988, Zip 62902–3988, tel. 618/457–5200; Rex P. Budde, President and Chief Executive Officer, p. B118

Chicago: ★ COOK COUNTY HEALTH AND HOSPITALS SYSTEM 1900 West Polk Street, Suite 220, Zip 60612–3723; tel. 312/864–6820; John Jay. Shannon, Chief Executive Officer, p. B38

NATIONAL SURGICAL HEALTHCARE 250 South Wacker Drive, Suite 500, Zip 60606–5897; tel. 312/627–8400; David Crane, Chief Executive Officer, p. B87

★ NORTHWESTERN MEMORIAL HEALTHCARE 251 East Huron Street, Zip 60611–2908; tel. 312/926–2000; Dean M. Harrison, President and Chief Executive Officer, p. B91

★ RUSH UNIVERSITY MEDICAL CENTER 1653 West Congress Parkway, Zip 60612–3864; tel. 312/942–5000; Larry J. Goodman, Chief Executive Officer, p. B109

★ SINAI HEALTH SYSTEM 1500 South Fairfield Avenue, Zip 60608–1782; tel. 773/542–2000; Karen Teitelbaum, President and Chief Executive Officer, p. B117

★ UNIVERSITY OF CHICAGO MEDICINE 5841 South Maryland Avenue, Zip 60637–1447; tel. 773/702–6240; Sharon L. O'Keefe, President, p. B139

Crystal Lake: ★ CENTEGRA HEALTH SYSTEM 385 Millennium Drive, Zip 60012–3761; tel. 815/788–5800; Michael S. Eesley, Chief Executive Officer, p. B30

Downers Grove: ★ ADVOCATE AURORA HEALTH 3075 Highland Parkway, Suite 600, Zip 60515–5563; tel. 630/929–8700; Jim Skogsbergh, Chief Executive Officer, p. B7

Evergreen Park: AMERICAN PROVINCE OF LITTLE COMPANY OF MARY SISTERS 9350 South California Avenue, Zip 60805–2595; tel. 708/229–5491, Sister, Kathleen McIntyre, Province Leader, p. B10

Naperville: ★ EDWARD-ELMHURST HEALTHCARE 801 South Washington Street, Zip 60540–7430; tel. 630/527–3000; Mary Lou Mastro, System Chief Executive Officer, p. B48

Peoria: ★ OSF HEALTHCARE 800 NE Glen Oak Avenue, Zip 61603–3200; tel. 309/655–2850; Robert Sehring, Chief Executive Officer, p. B95

Schaumburg: CANCER TREATMENT CENTERS OF AMERICA 1336 Basswood Road, Zip 60173–4544; tel. 847/342–7400; Rajesh K. Garg, President and Chief Executive Officer, p. B25

Springfield: DIVISION OF MENTAL HEALTH, DEPARTMENT OF HUMAN SERVICES 319 East Madison Street, S-3B, Zip 62701–1035; tel. 217/785–6023; Lorrie Rickman. Jones, Director, p. B47

★ HSHS HOSPITAL SISTERS HEALTH SYSTEM 4936 LaVerna Road, Zip 62707–9797, Mailing Address: P.O. Box 19456, Zip 62794–9456, tel. 217/523–4747; Mary Starmann-Harrison, President and Chief Executive Officer, p. B66

★ MEMORIAL HEALTH SYSTEM 701 North First Street, Zip 62781–0001; tel. 217/788–3000; Edgar J. Curtis, President and Chief Executive Officer, p. B81

Urbana: ★ CARLE FOUNDATION 611 West Park Street, Zip 61801–2595; tel. 217/383–3311; James C. Leonard, President and Chief Executive Officer, p. B27

INDIANA

Evansville: ★ DEACONESS HEALTH SYSTEM 600 Mary Street, Zip 47710–1658; tel. 812/450–5000; Shawn W. McCoy, Chief Executive Officer, p. B41

Fort Wayne: ★ PARKVIEW HEALTH 10501 Corporate Drive, Zip 46845–1700; tel. 260/373–7001; Michael J. Packnett, President and Chief Executive Officer, p. B96

Hammond: COMMUNITY HEALTHCARE SYSTEM 901 MacArthur Boulevard, Zip 46321–2959; tel. 219/836–1600; Donald P. Fesko, President and Chief Executive Officer, p. B37

Indianapolis: ★ COMMUNITY HEALTH NETWORK 7330 Shadeland Station, Zip 46256–3957; tel. 317/355–1411; Bryan A. Mills, President and Chief Executive Officer, p. B33

★ INDIANA UNIVERSITY HEALTH 340 West 10th Street, Suite 6100, Zip 46202–3082, Mailing Address: P.O. Box 1367, Zip 46206–1367, tel. 317/962–5900; Dennis M. Murphy, President and Chief Executive Officer, p. B67

Mishawaka: FRANCISCAN HEALTH 1515 Dragoon Trail, Zip 46544–4710, Mailing Address: P.O. Box 1290, Zip 46546–1290, tel. 574/256–3935; Kevin D. Leahy, President and Chief Executive Officer, p. B55

NEUROPSYCHIATRIC HOSPITALS 1625 East Jefferson Boulevard, Zip 46545–7103; tel. 574/255–1400; Cameron R. Gilbert, President and Chief Executive Officer, p. B88

South Bend: ★ BEACON HEALTH SYSTEM 615 North Michigan Street, Zip 46601–1033; tel. 574/647–1000; Kreg Gruber, Chief Executive Officer, p. B22

IOWA

Clarion: ★ IOWA SPECIALTY HOSPITALS 1316 South Main Street, Zip 50525–2019; tel. 515/532–2811; Steven J. Simonin, Chief Executive Officer, p. B69

Davenport: ★ GENESIS HEALTH SYSTEM 1227 East Rusholme Street, Zip 52803–2498; tel. 563/421–1000; Douglas P. Cropper, President and Chief Executive Officer, p. B57

West Des Moines: ★ UNITYPOINT HEALTH 1776 West Lakes Parkway, Suite 400, Zip 50266–8393; tel. 515/241–6161; Kevin Vermeer, President and Chief Executive Officer, p. B133

KANSAS

Kansas City: THE UNIVERSITY OF KANSAS HEALTH SYSTEM 4000 Cambridge Street, Zip 66160–0001; tel. 913/588–1227; Bob Page, President and Chief Executive Officer, p. B127

Salina: SALINA REGIONAL HEALTH CENTER 400 South Santa Fe Avenue, Zip 67401–4198, Mailing Address: PO Box 5080, Zip 67402–5080, tel. 785/452–7000; Micheal Terry, President and Chief Executive Officer, p. B110

Wichita: ★ GREAT PLAINS HEALTH ALLIANCE, INC. 250 North Rock Road, Suite 160, Zip 67206–2241; tel. 316/685–1523; Dave Dellasega, President and Chief Executive Officer, p. B57

KENTUCKY

Bowling Green: MED CENTER HEALTH 800 Park Street, Zip 42101–2356; tel. 270/745–1500; Connie Smith, President and Chief Executive Officer, p. B81

Danville: EPHRAIM MCDOWELL HEALTH 217 South Third Street, Zip 40422–1823; tel. 859/239–1000; Daniel E. McKay, Chief Executive Officer, p. B52

Edgewood: ST. ELIZABETH HEALTHCARE 1 Medical Village Drive, Zip 41017–3403; tel. 859/301–2000; Garren Colvin, Chief Executive Officer, p. B120

Lexington: APPALACHIAN REGIONAL HEALTHCARE, INC. 2260 Executive Drive, Zip 40505–4810, Mailing Address: P.O. Box 8086, Zip 40533–8086, tel. 859/226–2440; Joseph Grossman, President and Chief Executive Officer, p. B11

Louisville: ALLIANT MANAGEMENT SERVICES 2650 Eastpoint Parkway, Suite 300, Zip 40223–5164; tel. 502/992–3525; Stephen E. Fischer, Regional Vice President, Finance, p. B9

★ BAPTIST HEALTH 2701 Eastpoint Parkway, Zip 40223; tel. 502/896–5000; Gerard Colman, Chief Executive Officer, p. B20

★ KINDRED HEALTHCARE 680 South Fourth Street, Zip 40202–2412; tel. 502/596–7300; Kent Wallace, Chief Operating Officer, p. B71

★ NORTON HEALTHCARE 4967 US Highway 42, Suite 100, Zip 40222–6363, Mailing Address: P.O. Box 35070, Zip 40232–5070, tel. 502/629–8000; Russell Cox, President and Chief Executive Officer, p. B92

SPRINGSTONE 101 South Fifth Street, Suite 3850, Zip 40202–3127; tel. 855/595–2292; Robert Maha, President and Chief Executive Officer, p. B119

Owensboro: OWENSBORO HEALTH 1201 Pleasant Valley Road, Zip 42303–9811; tel. 270/417–2000; Greg Strahan, Interim Chief Executive Officer, p. B95

LOUISIANA

Baton Rouge: ★ FRANCISCAN MISSIONARIES OF OUR LADY HEALTH SYSTEM, INC. 4200 Essen Lane, Zip 70809–2158; tel. 225/923–2701; Michael McBride, President and Chief Executive Officer, p. B56

LOUISIANA STATE HOSPITALS 628 North 4th Street, Zip 70802–5342, Mailing Address: P.O. Box 629, Zip 70821–0628, tel. 225/342–9500; Shelby Price, Chief Executive Officer , p. B78

THE CARPENTER HEALTH NETWORK 10615 Jefferson Highway, Zip 70809–7230; tel. 225/769–4180; Pat Mitchell, Chief Executive Officer, p. B127

Crowley: COMPASS HEALTH 713 North Avenue L, Zip 70526–3832; tel. 337/788–3330; Aimee Monaghan, Chief Executive Officer, p. B38

Gretna: UNITED MEDICAL REHABILITATION HOSPITALS 3201 Wall Boulevard, Suite B, Zip 70056–7755; tel. 504/433–5551; John E.H. Mills, President and Chief Executive Officer, p. B132

Hammond: NORTH OAKS HEALTH SYSTEM 15790 Paul Vega MD Drive, Zip 70403–1436, Mailing Address: P.O. Box 2668, Zip 70404–2668, tel. 985/345–2700; Michele K. Sutton, President and Chief Executive Officer, p. B90

Lafayette: AMG INTEGRATED HEALTHCARE MANAGEMENT 101 La Rue France, Suite 500, Zip 70508–3144; tel. 337/269–9828; Timothy W. Howard, Chief Executive Officer, p. B10

LAFAYETTE GENERAL HEALTH 920 West Pinhook Road, Zip 70503–2455; tel. 337/289–7991; David L. Callecod, President and Chief Executive Officer, p. B73

LHC GROUP 420 West Pinhook Road, Zip 70503–2131; tel. 337/233–1307; Keith G. Myers, Chairman and Chief Executive Officer, p. B75

Lake Charles: OCEANS HEALTHCARE 2720 Rue de Jardin, Suite 100, Zip 70605–4050; tel. 337/721–1900; Jason Reed, President and Chief Executive Officer, p. B93

New Orleans: LCMC HEALTH 200 Henry Clay Avenue, Zip 70118–5720; tel. 504/899–9511; Greg Feirn, President and Chief Executive Officer, p. B74

★ OCHSNER HEALTH SYSTEM 1514 Jefferson Highway, Zip 70121–2429; tel. 800/874–8984; Warner L. Thomas, President and Chief Executive Officer, p. B93

Shreveport: ALLEGIANCE HEALTH MANAGEMENT 504 Texas Street, Suite 200, Zip 71101–3526; tel. 318/226–8202; Rock Bordelon, President and Chief Executive Officer, p. B9

UNIVERSITY HEALTH SYSTEM 1501 Kings Highway, Zip 71103–4228; tel. 318/675–5000; Daniel J. Snyder, Chief Executive Officer, p. B138

WILLIS-KNIGHTON HEALTH SYSTEM 2600 Greenwood Road, Zip 71103–3908; tel. 318/212–4000; James K. Elrod, President and Chief Executive Officer, p. B147

MAINE

Brewer: ★ EASTERN MAINE HEALTHCARE SYSTEMS 43 Whiting Hill Road, Zip 04412–1005; tel. 207/973–7045; M. Michelle. Hood, President and Chief Executive Officer

Lewiston: CENTRAL MAINE HEALTHCARE 300 Main Street, Zip 04240–7027; tel. 207/795–0111; Jeffrey L. Brickman, Chief Executive Officer, p. B31

Portland: MAINEHEALTH 110 Free Street, Zip 04101–3537; tel. 207/661–7001; William L. Caron Jr, President, p. B78

MARYLAND

Baltimore: ★ JOHNS HOPKINS HEALTH SYSTEM 733 North Broadway, BRB 104, Zip 21205–1832; tel. 410/955–5000; Kevin W. Sowers, President, p. B69

LIFEBRIDGE HEALTH 2401 West Belvedere Avenue, Zip 21215–5216; tel. 410/601–5134; Neil M. Meltzer, President and Chief Executive Officer, p. B75

★ UNIVERSITY OF MARYLAND MEDICAL SYSTEM 250 West Pratt Street, 24th Floor, Zip 21201–1595; tel. 410/328–8667; Robert A. Chrencik, President and Chief Executive Officer, p. B139

Columbia: ★ MEDSTAR HEALTH 10980 Grantchester Way, Zip 21044–2665; tel. 410/772–6500; Kenneth A. Samet, President and Chief Executive Officer, p. B81

Gaithersburg: ADVENTIST HEALTHCARE 820 West Diamond Avenue, Suite 600, Zip 20878–1419; tel. 301/315–3185; Terry Forde, President and Chief Executive Officer, p. B7

Marriottsville: ★ BON SECOURS HEALTH SYSTEM, INC. 1505 Marriottsville Road, Zip 21104–1399; tel. 410/442–5511; Richard Statuto, President and Chief Executive Officer, p. B24

Perry Point: DEPARTMENT OF VETERANS AFFAIRS P.O. Box 1000, Bldg 101, Room 41, Zip 21902, Mailing Address: 810 Vermont Avenue NW, Washington, DC, Zip 20420, tel. 202/273–5781; Honorable, Robert Wilkie, Secretary, p. B42

Rockville: U. S. INDIAN HEALTH SERVICE 801 Thompson Avenue, Zip 20852–1627; tel. 301/443–1083; Yvette Roubideaux, Director, p. B141

Sparks Glencoe: FUNDAMENTAL LONG TERM CARE HOLDINGS, LLC 930 Ridgebrook Road, Zip 21152–9390; tel. 410/773–1000; W Bradley. Bennett, President and Chief Executive Officer, p. B56

MASSACHUSETTS

Boston: MASSACHUSETTS DEPARTMENT OF MENTAL HEALTH 25 Staniford Street, Zip 02114–2575; tel. 617/626–8123; Joan Mikula, Interim Commissioner, p. B79

MASSACHUSETTS DEPARTMENT OF PUBLIC HEALTH 250 Washington Street, Zip 02108–4619; tel. 617/624–6000; Sandra Akers, Bureau Director, Public Health Hospitals, p. B79

★ PARTNERS HEALTHCARE SYSTEM, INC. 800 Boylston Street, Suite 1150, Zip 02199–8123; tel. 617/278–1004; David Torchiana, Chief Executive Officer, p. B96

Burlington: ★ LAHEY HEALTH 41 Mall Road, Zip 01805–0001; tel. 781/744–7100; Howard R. Grant, President and Chief Executive Officer, p. B73

Gardner: HEYWOOD HEALTHCARE 242 Green Street, Zip 01440–1336; tel. 978/632–3420; Winfield S. Brown, Chief Executive Officer, p. B65

Haverhill: WHITTIER HEALTH NETWORK 25 Railroad Square, Zip 01832–5721; tel. 978/556–5858; Alfred L. Arcidi, President, p. B147

Hyannis: ★ CAPE COD HEALTHCARE, INC. 27 Park Street, Zip 02601–5230; tel. 508/862–5121; Michael K. Lauf, President and Chief Executive Officer, p. B26

Pittsfield: ★ BERKSHIRE HEALTH SYSTEMS, INC. 725 North Street, Zip 01201–4124; tel. 413/447–2750; David E. Phelps, President and Chief Executive Officer, p. B23

Springfield: ★ BAYSTATE HEALTH, INC. 280 Chestnut Street, Zip 01199–0001; tel. 413/794–0000; Mark A. Keroack, President and Chief Executive Officer, p. B22

Tewksbury: ★ COVENANT HEALTH 100 Ames Pond Drive, Suite 102, Zip 01876–1240; tel. 978/654–6363; David R. Lincoln, President and Chief Executive Officer, p. B39

Worcester: ★ UMASS MEMORIAL HEALTH CARE, INC. 1 Biotech Park, Zip 01605–2982; tel. 508/334–0100; Eric Dickson, President and Chief Executive Officer, p. B131

MICHIGAN

Detroit: ★ HENRY FORD HEALTH SYSTEM One Ford Place, Zip 48202–3450; tel. 313/876–8708; Wright L. Lassiter III, President and Chief Executive Officer, p. B65

Grand Blanc: MCLAREN HEALTH CARE CORPORATION 3373 Regency Park Drive, Zip 48439, Mailing Address: One McLaren Parkway, Zip 48439, tel. 810/342–1100; Philip A. Incarnati, President and Chief Executive Officer, p. B80

Grand Rapids: ★ SPECTRUM HEALTH 100 Michigan Street NE, Zip 49503–2551, Mailing Address: 444 Michigan Street Northeast | MC065, Zip 49503–2551, tel. 616/391–1774; Richard C. Breon, President and Chief Executive Officer, p. B118

Kalamazoo: ★ BRONSON HEALTHCARE GROUP 301 John Street, Zip 49007–5295; tel. 269/341–6000; Frank J. Sardone, President and Chief Executive Officer, p. B24

Lansing: ★ SPARROW HEALTH SYSTEM 1215 East Michigan Avenue, Zip 48912–1811; tel. 517/364–1000; Dennis A. Swan, President and Chief Executive Officer, p. B118

Livonia: ★ TRINITY HEALTH 20555 Victor Parkway, Zip 48152–7031; tel. 734/343–1000; Richard J. Gilfillan, Chief Executive Officer, p. B128

Midland: ★ MIDMICHIGAN HEALTH 4000 Wellness Drive, Zip 48670–0001; tel. 989/839–3000; Diane Postler-Slattery, President and Chief Executive Officer, p. B84

Saint Joseph: ★ LAKELAND HEALTH 1234 Napier Avenue, Zip 49085–2158; tel. 269/983–8300; Loren Hamel, President and Chief Executive Officer, p. B73

Southfield: ★ BEAUMONT HEALTH 2000 Town Center, Suite 1200, Zip 48075–1145, fraser, tel. 248/898–5000; John T. Fox, President and Chief Executive Officer, p. B23

Traverse City: ★ MUNSON HEALTHCARE 1105 Sixth Street, Zip 49684–2386; tel. 231/935–6703; Edwin Ness, President and Chief Executive Officer, p. B87

MINNESOTA

Bloomington: HEALTHPARTNERS 8170 33rd Avenue South, Zip 55425–4516; tel. 952/883–7600; Andrea Walsh, President and Chief Executive Officer, p. B64

Duluth: ★ ESSENTIA HEALTH 502 East Second Street, Zip 55805–1913; tel. 218/786–8376; David C. Herman, Chief Executive Officer, p. B53

Minneapolis: ★ ALLINA HEALTH 2925 Chicago Avenue, Zip 55407–1321, Mailing Address: P.O. Box 43, Zip 55440–0043, tel. 612/262–5000; Penny Ann. Wheeler, Chief Executive Officer, p. B9

★ FAIRVIEW HEALTH SERVICES 2450 Riverside Avenue, Zip 55454–1400; tel. 612/672–6141; James Hereford, President and Chief Executive Officer, p. B54

Robbinsdale: NORTH MEMORIAL HEALTH CARE 3300 Oakdale Avenue North, Zip 55422–2926; tel. 763/520–5200; J. Kevin Croston, Chief Executive Officer, p. B90

Rochester: ★ MAYO CLINIC 200 First Street SW, Zip 55905–0002; tel. 507/284–2511; John H. Noseworthy, MD, President and Chief Executive Officer, p. B79

Saint Cloud: ★ CENTRACARE HEALTH 1406 Sixth Avenue North, Zip 56303–1900; tel. 320/251–2700; Kenneth D. Holmen, President and Chief Executive Officer, p. B31

Saint Paul: MINNESOTA DEPARTMENT OF HUMAN SERVICES 540 Cedar Street, Zip 55101–2208, Mailing Address: P.O. Box 64998, Zip 55164–0998, tel. 651/431–3212; Anne Barry, Deputy Commissioner, p. B85

Waconia: ★ RIDGEVIEW MEDICAL CENTER 500 South Maple Street, Zip 55387–1752; tel. 952/442–2191; Michael Phelps, President and Chief Executive Officer, p. B107

MISSISSIPPI

Jackson: MISSISSIPPI STATE DEPARTMENT OF MENTAL HEALTH 1101 Robert E Lee Building, 239 North Lamar Street, Zip 39201–1101; tel. 601/359–1288; Edwin C. LeGrand III, Executive Director, p. B85

★ UNIVERSITY HOSPITALS AND HEALTH SYSTEM 2500 North State Street, Zip 39216–4500; tel. 601/984–1000; Kevin S. Cook, Chief Executive Officer, p. B138

Mccomb: SOUTHWEST HEALTH SYSTEMS 215 Marion Avenue, Zip 39648–2705, Mailing Address: P.O. Box 1307, Zip 39649–1307, tel. 601/249–5500; Norman M. Price, Chief Executive Officer and Administrator, p. B118

Meridian: ★ RUSH HEALTH SYSTEMS 1314 19th Avenue, Zip 39301–4116; tel. 601/483–0011; Larkin Kennedy, President and Chief Executive Officer, p. B108

Tupelo: ★ NORTH MISSISSIPPI HEALTH SERVICES, INC. 830 South Gloster Street, Zip 38801–4996; tel. 662/377–3136; M. Shane. Spees, President and Chief Executive Officer, p. B90

MISSOURI

Cape Girardeau: LANDMARK HOSPITALS 3255 Independence Street, Zip 63701–4914; tel. 573/335–1091; William K. Kapp III, President and Chief Executive Officer, p. B74

SOUTHEASTHEALTH 1701 Lacey Street, Zip 63701–5230; tel. 573/334–4822; Kenneth Bateman, Chief Executive Officer, p. B118

Chesterfield: ★ MERCY 14528 South Outer 40, Suite 100, Zip 63017–5743; tel. 314/579–6100; Lynn Britton, President and Chief Executive Officer, p. B82

Columbia: ★ UNIVERSITY OF MISSOURI HEALTH CARE One Hospital Drive, DC 031, Zip 65212–0001; tel. 573/882–4141; Jonathan W. Curtright, Chief Executive Officer and Chief Operating Officer, p. B139

Joplin: ★ FREEMAN HEALTH SYSTEM 1102 West 32nd Street, Zip 64804–3503; tel. 417/347–1111; Paula F. Baker, President and Chief Executive Officer, p. B56

Kansas City: RURAL COMMUNITY HOSPITALS OF AMERICA 1100 Main Street, Suite 2350, Zip 64105–5186; tel. 816/474–7800; Lawrence J. Arthur, President, p. B108

★ SAINT LUKE'S HEALTH SYSTEM 901 East 104th Street, Mailstop 900N, Zip 64131–4517, Mailing Address: 901 East 104th Street, Zip 64131–4517, tel. 816/932–2000; Melinda Estes, President and Chief Executive Officer, p. B110

★ TRUMAN MEDICAL CENTERS 2301 Holmes Street, Zip 64108–2677; tel. 816/404–1000; Charlie Shields, Chief Executive Officer, p. B130

Saint Louis: ★ ASCENSION HEALTHCARE 101 South Hanley Road, Suite 450, Zip 63105–3406; tel. 314/733–8000; Patricia A. Maryland, President and Chief Executive Officer, p. B12

★ BJC HEALTHCARE 4901 Forest Park Avenue, Suite 1200, Zip 63108–1402; tel. 314/286–2000; Richard J. Liekweg, President and Chief Executive Officer, p. B23

★ SSM HEALTH 10101 Woodfield Lane, Zip 63132–2937; tel. 314/994–7800; Laura Kaiser, President and Chief Executive Officer, p. B119

Springfield: COXHEALTH 1423 North Jefferson Avenue, Zip 65802–1988; tel. 417/269–3108; Steven D. Edwards, President and Chief Executive Officer, p. B40

MONTANA

Great Falls: BENEFIS HEALTH SYSTEM 1101 26th Street South, Zip 59405–5161; tel. 406/455–5000; John H. Goodnow, Chief Executive Officer, p. B23

NEBRASKA

Lincoln: ★ BRYAN HEALTH 1600 South 48th Street, Zip 68506–1283, Mailing Address: 1600 S 48th ST, Zip 68506–1283, tel. 402/481–1111; Kimberly A. Russel, President and Chief Executive Officer, p. B25

Norfolk: FAITH REGIONAL HEALTH SERVICES 2700 West Norfolk Avenue, Zip 68701–4438, Mailing Address: P.O. Box 869, Zip 68702–0869, tel. 402/371–4880; Kelly Driscoll, Interim President and Chief Executive Officer, p. B54

Omaha: ★ NEBRASKA METHODIST HEALTH SYSTEM, INC. 8511 West Dodge Road, Zip 68114–3403; tel. 402/354–5411; Stephen L. Goeser, President and Chief Executive Officer, p. B87

NEVADA

Reno: ★ RENOWN HEALTH 50 West Liberty Street, Suite 1100, Zip 89501–1951; tel. 775/982–5529; Anthony D. Slonim, President and Chief Executive Officer, p. B107

NEW HAMPSHIRE

Laconia: ★ LRGHEALTHCARE 80 Highland Street, Zip 03246–3298; tel. 603/524–3211; Kevin Donovan, President and Chief Executive Officer, p. B78

Littleton: NORTH COUNTRY HEALTHCARE 600 Saint Johnsbury Road, Zip 03561–3442; tel. 603/444–9000; Edward L. Duffy, Interim Chief Executive Officer, p. B89

Portsmouth: BRIDGEPOINT HEALTHCARE 155 Fleet Street, Zip 03801–4050; tel. 603/570–4888; Marc C. Ferrell, President and Chief Executive Officer, p. B24

NEW JERSEY

Edison: ★ HACKENSACK MERIDIAN HEALTH 343 Thornall Street, 8th Floor, Zip 08837–2206, Mailing Address: 343 Thornall Street, Zip 08837–2206, tel. 844/464–9355; Robert C. Garrett, Co-Chief Executive Officer, p. B59

★ JFK HEALTH 80 James Street, 2nd Floor, Zip 08820–3938; tel. 732/632–1503; Raymond F. Fredericks, President and Chief Executive Officer, p. B69

Jersey City: CAREPOINT HEALTH 10 Exchange Place, 15th Floor, Zip 07302–3918; tel. 877/791–7000; Natasha Deckmann, Chief Executive Officer, p. B26

Lakewood: CONCORD HEALTHCARE GROUP 111 Clifton AVenue, Zip 8701; tel. 214/396–3462; Joe Neuman, Chief Executive Officer, p. B38

Marlton: ★ VIRTUA HEALTH 303 Lippincott Drive, 4th Floor, Zip 08053–4160; tel. 856/355–0010; Dennis W. Pullin, President and Chief Executive Officer, p. B145

Morristown: ★ ATLANTIC HEALTH SYSTEM 475 South Street, Zip 07960–6459, Mailing Address: P.O. Box 1905, Zip 07962–1905, tel. 973/660–3270; Brian A. Gragnolati, President and Chief Executive Officer, p. B16

Mullica Hill: ★ INSPIRA HEALTH NETWORK 165 Bridgeton Pike, Zip 8062; tel. 856/641–8000; John A. DiAngelo, President and Chief Executive Officer, p. B68

Trenton: ★ CAPITAL HEALTH 750 Brunswick Avenue, Zip 08638–4143; tel. 609/394–6000; Al Maghazehe, President and Chief Executive Officer, p. B26

DIVISION OF MENTAL HEALTH AND ADDICTION SERVICES, DEPARTMENT OF HUMAN SERVICES, STATE OF NEW JERSEY 222 South Warren Street, Zip 08608–2306, Mailing Address: P.O. Box 700, Zip 08625–0700, tel. 609/777–0702; Lynn Kovich, Assistant Commissioner, p. B47

West Orange: ★ RWJBARNABAS HEALTH 95 Old Short Hills Road, Zip 07052–1008; tel. 973/322–4000; Barry Ostrowsky, President and Chief Executive Officer, p. B109

NEW MEXICO

Albuquerque: ERNEST HEALTH, INC. 7770 Jefferson Street NE, Suite 320, Zip 87109–4386; tel. 505/856–5300; Darby Brockette, Chief Executive Officer, p. B53

★ PRESBYTERIAN HEALTHCARE SERVICES 9521 San Mateo Blvd. NE, Zip 87113, Mailing Address: P.O. Box 26666, Zip 87125–6666, tel. 505/841–1234; Dale Maxwell, Chief Executive Officer, p. B99

UNIVERSITY OF NEW MEXICO HOSPITALS 915 Camino De Salud, Zip 87131–0001; tel. 505/272–5849; Michael Chicarelli, Interim Chief Executive Officer, p. B139

NEW YORK

Albany: NEW YORK STATE OFFICE OF MENTAL HEALTH 44 Holland Avenue, Zip 12208–3411; tel. 518/474–7056; Kristin M. Woodlock, Acting Commissioner, p. B88

Binghamton: UNITED HEALTH SERVICES 10–42 Mitchell Avenue, Zip 13903–1617; tel. 607/762–2200; John M. Carrigg, President and Chief Executive Officer, p. B132

Bronx: MONTEFIORE HEALTH SYSTEM 111 East 210th Street, Zip 10467–2490; tel. 718/920–4321; Steven M. Safyer, President and CEO, p. B86

Buffalo: ★ CATHOLIC HEALTH SYSTEM 144 Genesee Street, Zip 14203–1560; tel. 716/862–2410; Mark A. Sullivan, President and Chief Executive Officer, p. B30

Cooperstown: ★ BASSETT HEALTHCARE NETWORK 1 Atwell Road, Zip 13326–1301; tel. 607/547–3456; William F. Streck, President and Chief Executive Officer, p. B21

Elmira: ARNOT HEALTH 600 Roe Avenue, Zip 14905–1629; tel. 607/737–4100; Jonathan I. Lawrence, President and Chief Executive Officer, p. B12

Geneva: FINGER LAKES HEALTH 196 North Street, Zip 14456–1651; tel. 315/787–4000; Jose Acevedo, President and Chief Executive Officer, p. B55

Ithaca: ★ CAYUGA HEALTH SYSTEM 101 Dates Drive, Zip 14850–1342; tel. 607/274–4011; John B. Rudd, President and Chief Executive Officer, p. B30

Jamaica: ★ MEDISYS HEALTH NETWORK 8900 Van Wyck Expressway, Zip 11418–2832; tel. 718/206–6000; Bruce J. Flanz, President and Chief Executive Officer, p. B81

LaGrangeville: HEALTH QUEST SYSTEMS, INC. 1351 Route 55 Ste 200, Zip 12540–5108, Mailing Address: 1351 Route 55, Zip 12540–5108, tel. 845/475–9500; Robert Friedberg, President and Chief Executive Officer, p. B64

Middletown: ★ GREATER HUDSON VALLEY HEALTH SYSTEM 707 East Main Street, Zip 10940–2650; tel. 845/333–1000; Scott Batulis, President and Chief Executive Officer, p. B58

New Hyde Park: ★ NORTHWELL HEALTH 2000 Marcus Avenue, Zip 11042; tel. 516/465–8100; Michael J. Dowling, President and Chief Executive Officer, p. B91

New York: ★ MOUNT SINAI HEALTH SYSTEM One Gustave L. Levy Place, Zip 10029; tel. 212/659–8888; Kenneth L. Davis, President and Chief Executive, p. B86

★ NEWYORK-PRESBYTERIAN 525 East 68th Street, Box 182, Zip 10065; tel. 212/746–3745; Steven J. Corwin, President and Chief Executive Officer, p. B89

★ NYC HEALTH + HOSPITALS 125 Worth Street, Room 514, Zip 10013–4006; tel. 212/788–3321; Mitchell H. Katz, Chief Executive Officer, p. B92

NYU LANGONE HEALTH 550 First Avenue, Zip 10016–6402; tel. 646/929–7870; Robert I. Grossman, Chief Executive Officer, p. B93

Olean: UPPER ALLEGHENY HEALTH SYSTEM 130 South Union Street, Suite 300, Zip 14760–3676; tel. 716/375–6190; Timothy J. Finan, President and Chief Executive Officer, p. B141

Potsdam: ST. LAWRENCE HEALTH SYSTEM 50 Leroy Street, Zip 13676–1799; tel. 315/265–3300; David B. Acker, President and CEO, p. B120

Rochester: ★ ROCHESTER REGIONAL HEALTH 1425 Portland Avenue, 5th Floor, Zip 14621–3001; tel. 585/922–4000; Eric Bieber, President and Chief Executive Officer, p. B108

★ UNIVERSITY OF ROCHESTER MEDICAL CENTER 601 Elmwood Ave Box 623, Zip 14642–0002, Mailing Address: 601 Elmwood Avenue, Zip 14642–0002, tel. 585/275–2100; Mark B. Taubman, Chief Executive Officer, p. B140

Rockville Centre: CATHOLIC HEALTH SERVICES OF LONG ISLAND 992 North Village Avenue, 1st Floor, Zip 11570–1002; tel. 516/705–3700; Alan D. Guerci, President and Chief Executive Officer, p. B30

Valhalla: WMCHEALTH 100 Woods Road, Zip 10595–1530; tel. 914/493–7000; Michael D. Israel, President and Chief Executive Officer, p. B148

NORTH CAROLINA

Asheville: ★ MISSION HEALTH SYSTEM 509 Biltmore Avenue, Zip 28801–4601; tel. 828/213–1111; Ronald A. Paulus, President and Chief Executive Officer, p. B85

Boone: ★ APPALACHIAN REGIONAL HEALTHCARE SYSTEM 336 Deerfield Road, Zip 28607–5008, Mailing Address: P.O. Box 2600, Zip 28607–2600, tel. 828/262–4100; Charles Mantooth, President and Chief Executive Officer, p. B10

Chapel Hill: ★ UNC HEALTH CARE 101 Manning Drive, Zip 27514–4220; tel. 919/966–4131; William L. Roper, Chief Executive Officer, p. B131

Charlotte: ★ ACUITYHEALTHCARE, LP 10200 Mallard Creek Road, Suite 300, Zip 28262–9705; tel. 704/887–7280; Edwin H. Cooper Jr, President and Chief Executive Officer, p. B5

★ ATRIUM HEALTH 1000 Blythe Boulevard, Zip 28203–5871, Mailing Address: PO Box 32861, Zip 28232–2861, tel. 704/355–2000; Eugene A. Woods, President and Chief Executive Officer, p. B16

Durham: ★ DUKE UNIVERSITY HEALTH SYSTEM 201 Trent Drive, Zip 27710–3037, Mailing Address: P.O. Box 3701, Zip 27710–3701, tel. 919/684–2255; A. Eugene. Washington, President and Chief Executive Officer, p. B48

VERITAS COLLABORATIVE 4024 Stirrup Creek Drive, Zip 27703–9464; tel. 855/875–5812; Stacie McEntyre, Chief Executive Officer, p. B143

Fayetteville: CAPE FEAR VALLEY HEALTH SYSTEM 1638 Owen Drive, Zip 28304–3424, Mailing Address: P.O. Box 2000, Zip 28302–2000, tel. 910/615–4000; Michael Nagowski, President and Chief Executive Officer, p. B26

Greensboro: CONE HEALTH 1200 North Elm Street, Zip 27401–1004; tel. 336/832–7000; Terry Akin, President and Chief Executive Officer, p. B38

Greenville: ★ VIDANT HEALTH 2100 Stantonsburg Road, Zip 27834–2818, Mailing Address: P.O. Box 6028, Zip 27835–6028, tel. 252/847–4100; Michael Waldrum, Chief Executive Officer, p. B145

Pinehurst: ★ FIRSTHEALTH OF THE CAROLINAS 155 Memorial Drive, Zip 28374–8710, Mailing Address: P.O. Box 3000, Zip 28374–3000, tel. 910/715–1000; David J. Kilarski, Chief Executive Officer, p. B55

Raleigh: ★ WAKEMED HEALTH & HOSPITALS 3000 New Bern Avenue, Zip 27610–1231; tel. 919/350–8000; Donald R. Gintzig, President and Chief Executive Officer, p. B146

Wilmington: ★ NEW HANOVER REGIONAL MEDICAL CENTER 2131 South 17th Street, Zip 28401–7407; tel. 910/343–7040; John H. Gizdic, President and Chief Executive Officer, p. B88

Winston Salem: ★ NOVANT HEALTH 2085 Frontis Plaza Boulevard, Zip 27103–5614; tel. 336/718–5600; Carl S. Armato, President and Chief Executive Officer, p. B92

Winston-Salem: ★ WAKE FOREST BAPTIST HEALTH One Medical Center Boulevard, Zip 27157; tel. 336/716–2011; Julie Ann . Freischlag, Chief Executive Officer, p. B145

NORTH DAKOTA

Fargo: SISTERS OF MARY OF THE PRESENTATION HEALTH SYSTEM 1202 Page Drive SW, Zip 58103–2340, Mailing Address: P.O. Box 10007, Zip 58106–0007, tel. 701/237–9290; Aaron K. Alton, President and Chief Executive Officer, p. B117

OHIO

Akron: SUMMA HEALTH 1077 Gorge Boulevard, Zip 44310; tel. 330/375–3000; T. Clifford Deveny, Interim Chief Executive Officer, p. B123

Canton: AULTMAN HEALTH FOUNDATION 2600 Sixth Street SW, Zip 44710–1702; tel. 330/363–6192; Edward J. Roth III, President and Chief Executive Officer, p. B17

Chillicothe: ADENA HEALTH SYSTEM 272 Hospital Road, Zip 45601–9031, Mailing Address: PO Box 802846, Kansas City, MO, Zip 64180–2846, tel. 740/779–7500; Jeff Graham, President and Chief Executive Officer, p. B5

Cincinnati: ★ MERCY HEALTH 1701 Mercy Health Place, Zip 45237; tel. 513/639–2800; John M. Starcher, President and Chief Executive Officer, p. B83

★ UC HEALTH 3200 Burnet Avenue, Zip 45229–3019; tel. 513/585–6000; Richard P. Lofgren, President and CEO, p. B131

Cleveland: ★ CLEVELAND CLINIC HEALTH SYSTEM 9500 Euclid, Zip 44195–5108; tel. 216/444–2200; Tomislav Mihaljevic, Chief Executive Officer and President, p. B33

SISTERS OF CHARITY HEALTH SYSTEM 2475 East 22nd Street, Zip 44115–3221; tel. 216/363–2797; Thomas J. Strauss, Chief Executive Officer, p. B117

★ UNIVERSITY HOSPITALS 11100 Euclid Avenue, Zip 44106–5000; tel. 216/844–1000; Thomas F. Zenty III, President and Chief Executive Officer, p. B138

Columbus: OHIO DEPARTMENT OF MENTAL HEALTH 30 East Broad Street, 8th Floor, Zip 43215–3430; tel. 614/466–2297; Tracy Plouck, Director, p. B94

★ OHIO STATE UNIVERSITY HEALTH SYSTEM 370 West Ninth Avenue, Zip 43210–1238; tel. 614/685–9015; David P. McQuaid, Chief Executive Officer, p. B94

★ OHIOHEALTH 180 East Broad Street, Zip 43215–3707; tel. 614/544–4455; David P. Blom, President and Chief Executive Officer, p. B94

Dayton: ★ KETTERING HEALTH NETWORK 3965 Southern Boulevard, Zip 45429–1229; tel. 937/395–8150; Fred M. Manchur, Chief Executive Officer, p. B71

★ PREMIER HEALTH 110 North Main Street Suite 390, Zip 45402–3720; tel. 937/499–9401; Mary H. Boosalis, President, p. B99

Findlay: ★ BLANCHARD VALLEY HEALTH SYSTEM 1900 South Main Street, Zip 45840–1214; tel. 419/423–4500; Scott C. Malaney, President and Chief Executive Officer, p. B24

Galion: ★ AVITA HEALTH SYSTEM 269 Portland Way South, Zip 44833–2399; tel. 419/468–4841; Jerome Morasko, President and Chief Executive Officer, p. B18

Jackson: HOLZER HEALTH SYSTEM 500 Burlington Road, Zip 45640–9360; tel. 855/446–5937; Michael Canady, Chief Executive Officer, p. B65

Marietta: MEMORIAL HEALTH SYSTEM 401 Matthew Street, Zip 45750–1635; tel. 740/374–1400; J Scott. Cantley, President and Chief Executive Officer, p. B81

Toledo: ★ PROMEDICA HEALTH SYSTEM 100 Madison Avenue, Zip 43604–1516; tel. 567/585–9601; Randall D. Oostra, President and Chief Executive Officer, p. B100

OKLAHOMA

Duncan: DUNCAN REGIONAL HOSPITAL 1407 North Whisenant Drive, Zip 73533–1650; tel. 580/252–5300; Jay R. Johnson, President and Chief Executive Officer, p. B48

Oklahoma City: FIRST PHYSICIANS CAPITAL GROUP, INC. 4323 NW 63rd Street Suite 140, Zip 73116–1513; tel. 405/246–0218; Sean Kirrane, Chief Executive Officer, p. B55

FOUNDATION SURGICAL HOSPITAL AFFILIATES 14000 North Portland Avenue, Suite 204, Zip 73134–4002; tel. 405/608–1700; Thomas A. Michaud, Chief Executive Officer, p. B55

★ INTEGRIS HEALTH 3366 NW Expressway, Suite 800, Zip 73112–9756; tel. 405/949–6066; Timothy T. Pehrson, President and Chief Executive Officer, p. B68

OKLAHOMA DEPARTMENT OF MENTAL HEALTH AND SUBSTANCE ABUSE SERVICES 1200 NE 13th Street, Zip 73117–1022, Mailing Address: P.O. Box 53277, Zip 73152–3277, tel. 405/522–3908; Terri White, Commissioner, p. B94

Shawnee: PREFERRED MANAGEMENT CORPORATION 120 West MacArthur, Suite 121, Zip 74804–2005; tel. 405/878–0202; Donald Freeman, President and Chief Executive Officer, p. B98

Tulsa: ★ SAINT FRANCIS HEALTH SYSTEM 6161 South Yale Avenue, Zip 74136–1902; tel. 918/494–8454; Jake Henry Jr, President and Chief Executive Officer, p. B109

OREGON

Bend: ★ ST. CHARLES HEALTH SYSTEM, INC. 2500 NE Neff Road, Zip 97701–6015; tel. 541/382–4321; Joseph Sluka, President and Chief Executive Officer, p. B120

Corvallis: ★ SAMARITAN HEALTH SERVICES 3600 NW Samaritan Drive, Zip 97330–3737, Mailing Address: P.O. Box 1068, Zip 97339–1068, tel. 541/768–5001; Doug Boysen, President and Chief Executive Officer, p. B110

Medford: ★ ASANTE HEALTH SYSTEM 2650 Siskiyou Boulevard, Suite 200, Zip 97504–8170; tel. 541/789–4100; Roy G. Vinyard, President and Chief Executive Officer, p. B12

Portland: ★ LEGACY HEALTH 1919 NW Lovejoy Street, Zip 97209–1503; tel. 503/415–5600; Kathryn G. Correia, President and Chief Executive Officer, p. B74

Salem: SALEM HEALTH 890 Oak Street Bldg B POB 14001, Zip 97309–5014; tel. 503/561–5200; Norman F. Gruber, President and Chief Executive Officer, p. B110

PENNSYLVANIA

Allentown: GOOD SHEPHERD REHABILITATION NETWORK 850 South Fifth Street, Zip 18103–3308; tel. 610/776–3100; John Kristel, President and Chief Executive Officer, p. B57

★ LEHIGH VALLEY HEALTH NETWORK 1200 South Cedar Crest Boulevard, Zip 18103–6202, Mailing Address: P.O. Box 689, Zip 18105–1556, tel. 610/402–8000; Brian A. Nester, President and Chief Executive Officer, p. B74

Beaver: HERITAGE VALLEY HEALTH SYSTEM 1000 Dutch Ridge Road, Zip 15009–9727; tel. 724/773–2024; Norman F. Mitry, President and Chief Executive Officer, p. B65

Bethlehem: ST. LUKE'S UNIVERSITY HEALTH NETWORK 801 Ostrum Street, Zip 18015–1000; tel. 610/954–4000; Richard A. Anderson, President and Chief Executive Officer, p. B121

Chambersburg: ★ SUMMIT HEALTH 112 North Seventh Street, Zip 17201–1720; tel. 717/267–7138; Patrick W. O'Donnell, President and Chief Executive Officer, p. B123

Danville: ★ GEISINGER 100 North Academy Avenue, Zip 17822–9800; tel. 570/271–6211; David T. Feinberg, President and Chief Executive Officer, p. B57

Enola: ★ POST ACUTE MEDICAL, LLC 1828 Good Hope Road, Suite 102, Zip 17025–1233; tel. 717/731–9660; Anthony F. Misitano, President and Chief Executive Officer, p. B98

Greensburg: EXCELA HEALTH 532 West Pittsburgh Street, Zip 15601, Mailing Address: 134 Industrial Park Road, Zip 15601–7328, tel. 724/832–5050; Robert Rogalski, Chief Executive Officer, p. B54

Hershey: PENN STATE HERSHEY HEALTH SYSTEM 500 University Drive, Zip 17033–2360; tel. 717/531–8521; A. Craig. Hillemeier, Chief Executive Officer, p. B97

King of Prussia: UNIVERSAL HEALTH SERVICES, INC. 367 South Gulph Road, Zip 19406–3121, Mailing Address: P.O. Box 61558, Zip 19406–0958, tel. 610/768–3300; Alan B. Miller, Chairman and Chief Executive Officer, p. B134

Meadville: ★ MEADVILLE MEDICAL CENTER 751 Liberty Street, Zip 16335–2559; tel. 814/333–5000; Philip E. Pandolph, Chief Executive Officer, p. B80

Mechanicsburg: ★ SELECT MEDICAL CORPORATION 4714 Gettysburg Road, Zip 17055–4325; tel. 717/972–1100; David S. Chernow, President and Chief Executive Officer, p. B112

★ VIBRA HEALTHCARE 4550 Lena Drive, Suite 225, Zip 17055–4920; tel. 717/591–5700; Brad Hollinger, Chairman and Chief Executive Officer, p. B144

Philadelphia: EINSTEIN HEALTHCARE NETWORK 5501 Old York Road, Zip 19141–3098; tel. 215/456–7890; Barry R. Freedman, President and Chief Executive Officer, p. B48

★ JEFFERSON HEALTH 925 Chestnut Street, Suite 110, Zip 19107–4216; tel. 610/225–6200; Stephen K. Klasko, Chief Executive Officer, p. B69

★ TEMPLE UNIVERSITY HEALTH SYSTEM 3509 North Broad Street, 9th Floor, Zip 19140–4105; tel. 215/707–0900; Larry Kaiser, President and Chief Executive Officer, p. B124

★ UNIVERSITY OF PENNSYLVANIA HEALTH SYSTEM 3400 Civic Center Boulevard, Zip 19104–5127; tel. 215/662–2203; Ralph W. Muller, President and Chief Executive Officer, p. B140

Pittsburgh: ★ ALLEGHENY HEALTH NETWORK 30 Isabella Street, Suite 300, Zip 15212–5862; tel. 412/359–3131; Cynthia Hundorfean, President and Chief Executive Officer, p. B8

UPMC 600 Grant Street, US Steel Tower, Suite 6262, Zip 15219–2702; tel. 412/647–8762; Jeffrey A. Romoff, President and Chief Executive Officer, p. B140

Sayre: ★ GUTHRIE CLINIC One Guthrie Square, Zip 18840–1625; tel. 570/888–5858; Joseph A. Scopelliti, President and Chief Executive Officer, p. B58

Villanova: ★ DEVEREUX 444 Devereux Drive, Zip 19085–1932, Mailing Address: P.O. Box 638, Zip 19085–0638, tel. 610/520–3000; Robert Q. Kreider, President and Chief Executive Officer, p. B46

Washington: ★ WASHINGTON HEALTH SYSTEM 155 Wilson Avenue, Zip 15301–3336; tel. 724/225–7000; Gary B. Weinstein, Chief Executive Officer, p. B146

West Reading: TOWER HEALTH Sixth Avenue and Spruce Street, Zip 19611; tel. 610/988–8000; Clinton Matthews, President and Chief Executive Officer, p. B128

Williamsport: ★ UPMC SUSQUEHANNA 700 High Street , Zip 17701–3100; tel. 570/321–1000; Steven P. Johnson, President and Chief Executive Officer, p. B141

York: ★ WELLSPAN HEALTH 45 Monument Road, Suite 200, Zip 17403–5071; tel. 717/851–2121; Kevin H. Mosser, President and Chief Executive Officer, p. B146

PUERTO RICO

San Juan: ★ PUERTO RICO DEPARTMENT OF HEALTH Building 'A' - Medical Center, Zip 936, Mailing Address: Call Box 70184, Zip 936, tel. 787/765–2929; Rafael Rodriguez. Mercado, Secretary of Health, p. B103

RHODE ISLAND

Providence: ★ CARE NEW ENGLAND HEALTH SYSTEM 45 Willard Avenue, Zip 02905–3218; tel. 401/453–7900; James E. Fanale, President, Chief Executive Officer and Chief Clinical Officer, p. B26

LIFESPAN CORPORATION 167 Point Street, Zip 02903–4771; tel. 401/444–3500; Timothy J. Babineau, President and Chief Executive Officer, p. B77

SOUTH CAROLINA

Anderson: ★ ANMED HEALTH 800 North Fant Street, Zip 29621–5793; tel. 864/512–1000; William T. Manson III, Chief Executive Officer, p. B10

Columbia: ★ PALMETTO HEALTH 1301 Taylor Street, Suite 9-A, Zip 29201–2942, Mailing Address: P.O. Box 2266, Zip 29202–2266, tel. 803/296–2100; Charles D. Beaman Jr, Chief Executive Officer, p. B95

Florence: MCLEOD HEALTH 555 East Cheves Street, Zip 29506–2617, Mailing Address: P.O. Box 100551, Zip 29502–0551, tel. 843/777–2000; Robert L. Colones, President and Chief Executive Officer, p. B80

Georgetown: ★ TIDELANDS HEALTH 606 Black River Road, Zip 29440–3304, Mailing Address: P.O. Box 421718, Zip 29442–4203, tel. 843/527–7000; Bruce P. Bailey, President and Chief Executive Officer, p. B128

Greenville: ★ GREENVILLE HEALTH SYSTEM 701 Grove Road, Zip 29605–5611; tel. 864/455–7000; Spence Taylor, President and Chief Executive Officer, p. B58

Spartanburg: ★ SPARTANBURG REGIONAL HEALTHCARE SYSTEM 101 East Wood Street, Zip 29303–3040; tel. 864/560–6000; Bruce Holstien, President and Chief Executive Officer, p. B118

SOUTH DAKOTA

Rapid City: ★ REGIONAL HEALTH 353 Fairmont Boulevard, Zip 57701–7375, Mailing Address: P.O. Box 6000, Zip 57709–6000, tel. 605/719–1000; Paulette Davidson, President and Chief Executive Officer , p. B107

Sioux Falls: ★ AVERA HEALTH 3900 West Avera Drive, Suite 300, Zip 57108–5721; tel. 605/322–4700; Bob Sutton, President and Chief Executive Officer, p. B17

★ SANFORD HEALTH 2301 East 60th Street North, Zip 57104–0569, Mailing Address: PO Box 5039, Zip 57117–5039, tel. 605/333–1000; Kelby K. Krabbenhoft, President and Chief Executive Officer, p. B110

TENNESSEE

Brentwood: ★ DUKE LIFEPOINT HEALTHCARE 330 Seven Springs Way, Zip 37027–5098; tel. 615/920–7000; Jeffrey G. Seraphine, President, p. B48

★ HEALTHTECH MANAGEMENT SERVICES 5110 Maryland Way Suite 200, Zip 37027–2307; tel. 615/309–6053; Derek Morkel, Chief Executive Officer, p. B64

★ LIFEPOINT HEALTH 330 Seven Springs Way, Zip 37027–4536; tel. 615/920–7000; William F. Carpenter III, Chairman and Chief Executive Officer, p. B76

★ QHR 1573 Mallory Lane, Suite 200, Zip 37027, Mailing Address: 1573 Mallory Lane, Suite 200, Zip 37027, tel. 800/233–1470; Bob Vento, President and Chief Executive Officer, p. B103

★ QUORUM HEALTH 1573 Mallory Lane, Suite 100, Zip 37027; tel. 615/221–1400; Robert D. Fish, Chief Executive Officer, p. B105

RCCH HEALTHCARE PARTNERS 103 Continental Place Ste 200, Zip 37027–1042; tel. 615/844–9800; Martin S. Rash, Chief Executive Officer, p. B106

Chattanooga: ERLANGER HEALTH SYSTEM 975 East Third Street, Zip 37403–2147; tel. 423/778–7000; Kevin M. Spiegel, President and Chief Executive Officer, p. B53

Clinton: CURAE HEALTH 121 Leinart Street, Zip 37716–3632, Mailing Address: P.O. Box 358, Zip 37717–0358, tel. 865/269–4074; Steve Clapp, President and Chief Executive Officer, p. B40

Columbia: ★ MAURY REGIONAL HEALTH SYSTEM 1224 Trotwood Avenue, Zip 38401–4802; tel. 931/381–1111; H Alan. Watson, Chief Executive Officer, p. B79

Franklin: ACADIA HEALTHCARE COMPANY, INC. 830 Crescent Centre Drive, Suite 610, Zip 37067–7323; tel. 615/861–6000; Joey Jacobs, Chairman and Chief Executive Officer, p. B4

★ COMMUNITY HEALTH SYSTEMS, INC. 4000 Meridian Boulevard, Zip 37067–6325, Mailing Address: P.O. Box 689020, Zip 37068–9020, tel. 615/465–7000; Wayne T. Smith, Chairman, President and Chief Executive Officer, p. B34

Jackson: ★ WEST TENNESSEE HEALTHCARE 620 Skyline Drive, Zip 38301–3923; tel. 731/541–5000; James E. Ross, President and Chief Executive Officer, p. B147

Johnson City: BALLAD HEALTH 303 Med Tech Parkway, Zip 37604–2391; tel. 833/822–5523; Alan M. Levine, President and Chief Executive Officer, p. B18

Knoxville: ★ COVENANT HEALTH 100 Fort Sanders West Boulevard, Zip 37922–3353; tel. 865/531–5555; James VanderSteeg, President and Chief Executive Officer, p. B39

Memphis: ★ BAPTIST MEMORIAL HEALTH CARE CORPORATION 350 North Humphreys Boulevard, Zip 38120–2177; tel. 901/227–5117; Jason Little, President and Chief Executive Officer, p. B21

★ METHODIST LE BONHEUR HEALTHCARE 1211 Union Avenue, Suite 700, Zip 38104–6600; tel. 901/516–0791; Michael Ugwueke, President and Chief Executive Officer, p. B84

STRATEGIC BEHAVIORAL HEALTH, LLC 8295 Tournament Drive, Suite 201, Zip 38125–8913; tel. 901/969–3100; Jim Shaheen, President, p. B122

Nashville: ★ ARDENT HEALTH SERVICES 1 Burton Hills Boulevard, Suite 250, Zip 37215–6195; tel. 615/296–3000; David T. Vandewater, President and Chief Executive Officer, p. B11

HAVEN BEHAVIORAL HEALTHCARE 652 West Iris Drive, Zip 37204–3191; tel. 615/250–9500; Michael Lindley, Chief Executive Officer, p. B59

★ HCA HEALTHCARE One Park Plaza, Zip 37203–1548; tel. 615/344–5248; R Milton. Johnson, President and Chief Executive Officer, p. B60

★ VANDERBILT HEALTH 1211 22nd Avenue South, Zip 37232; tel. 615/322–5000; Charles Wright. Pinson, Deputy Vice Chancellor for Health Affairs and Chief Executive Officer of Vanderbilt Health System, p. B143

Parsons: TENNESSEE HEALTH MANAGEMENT 52 West Eighth Street, Zip 38363–4656, Mailing Address: PO Box 10, Zip 38363–0010, tel. 731/847–6343; Dennis Berry, Chief Executive Officer, p. B126

TEXAS

Addison: UNITED SURGICAL PARTNERS INTERNATIONAL 15305 Dallas Parkway, Suite 1600, Zip 75001–6491; tel. 972/713–3500; William H. Wilcox, President and Chief Executive Officer, p. B132

Arlington: ★ TEXAS HEALTH RESOURCES 612 East Lamar Boulevard, Suite 900, Zip 76011–4130; tel. 682/236–7900; Barclay E. Berdan, Chief Executive Officer, p. B126

Austin: TEXAS DEPARTMENT OF STATE HEALTH SERVICES 1100 West 49th Street, Zip 78756–3199; tel. 512/458–7111; Kirk Cole, Interim Commissioner, p. B126

★ UNIVERSITY OF TEXAS SYSTEM 601 Colorado Street, Suite 205, Zip 78701–2904; tel. 512/499–4224; Raymond Greenberg, Executive Vice Chancellor, p. B140

Dallas: ★ BAYLOR SCOTT & WHITE HEALTH 4005 Crutcher Street, Suite 310, Zip 75246–1779; tel. 214/820–0111; James H. Hinton, Chief Executive Officer, p. B22

CHILDREN'S HEALTH 1935 Medical District Drive, Zip 75235–7701; tel. 214/456–7000; Christopher J. Durovich, President and Chief Executive Officer, p. B31

CORNERSTONE HEALTHCARE GROUP 2200 Ross Avenue, Suite 5400, Zip 75201–7984; tel. 469/621–6700; Steve Jakubcanin, President and Chief Executive Officer, p. B39

★ METHODIST HEALTH SYSTEM 1441 North Beckley Avenue, Zip 75203–1201, Mailing Address: P.O. Box 655999, Zip 75265–5999, tel. 214/947–8181; Stephen L. Mansfield, President and Chief Executive Officer, p. B84

STEWARD HEALTH CARE SYSTEM, LLC 1900 North Pearl Street, Suite 2400, Zip 75201; tel. 617/419–4700; Ralph de la Torre, Chairman and Chief Executive Officer, p. B121

★ TENET HEALTHCARE CORPORATION 1445 Ross Avenue, Suite 1400, Zip 75202–2703, Mailing Address: P.O. Box 1390369, Zip 75313–9036, tel. 469/893–2200; J. Eric. Evans, President, Hospital Operations, p. B124

Garland: CURAHEALTH HOSPITALS 650 Beebalm Lane, Suite 220, Zip 75040–2955; tel. 972/414–0070; Ken McGee, President and Chief Operating Officer, p. B40

Greenville: HUNT REGIONAL HEALTHCARE 4215 Joe Ramsey Boulevard, Zip 75401–7852, Mailing Address: P.O. Box 1059, Zip 75403–1059, tel. 903/408–5000; Richard Carter, Chief Executive Officer, p. B67

Houston: ★ HOUSTON METHODIST 6565 Fannin Street, D-200, Zip 77030–2707; tel. 713/441–2221; Marc L. Boom, Chief Executive Officer, p. B66

★ MEMORIAL HERMANN HEALTH SYSTEM 929 Gessner, Suite 2700, Zip 77024–2593; tel. 713/338–5555; Charles D. Stokes, President and Chief Executive Officer, p. B82

NEXUS HEALTH SYSTEMS One Riverway, Suite 600, Zip 77056–1993; tel. 713/355–6111; John W. Cassidy, President, Chief Executive Officer and Chief Medical Officer, p. B89

NOBILIS HEALTH CORPORATION 11700 Katy Freeway Suite 300, Zip 77079–1218; tel. 713/355–8614; Harry Fleming, Chief Executive Officer, p. B89

Irving: ★ CHRISTUS HEALTH 919 Hidden Ridge Drive, Zip 75038; tel. 469/282–2000; Ernie W. Sadau, Chief Executive Officer, p. B32

USMD HEALTH SYSTEM 6333 North State Highway 161 Suite 200, Zip 75038–2229; tel. 214/493–4000; Mike Bukosky, President, Hospital Division, p. B142

Lubbock: ★ COVENANT HEALTH SYSTEM 3615 19th Street, Zip 79410–1203; tel. 806/725–0447; Richard H. Parks, President and Chief Executive Officer, p. B40

Plano: ★ COMMUNITY HOSPITAL CORPORATION 7800 North Dallas Parkway, Suite 200, Zip 75024–6116; tel. 972/943–6400; Jim R. Kendrick, President and Chief Executive Officer, p. B37

★ LIFECARE MANAGEMENT SERVICES 5340 Legacy Drive, Suite 150, Zip 75024–3131; tel. 469/241–2100; James E. Murray, Chief Executive Officer, p. B75

Sherman: CARRUS HOSPITALS 1810 West US Highway 82, Zip 75092–7069; tel. 903/870–2600; Ronald E. Dorris, Chief Executive Officer, p. B27

The Woodlands: EMERUS 10077 Grogan's Mill, Suite 100, Zip 77380–1022; tel. 281/292–2450; Craig Goguen, Chief Executive Officer, p. B49

UTAH

Nephi: ★ RURAL HEALTH GROUP 48 West 1500 North, Zip 84648–8900; tel. 435/623–4924; Mark R. Stoddard, President and Chairman, p. B108

Salt Lake City: ★ INTERMOUNTAIN HEALTHCARE, INC. 36 South State Street, 22nd Floor, Zip 84111–1453; tel. 801/442–2000; A. Marc. Harrison, President and Chief Executive Officer, p. B68

VIRGINIA

Charlottesville: ★ UVA HEALTH SYSTEM 1215 Lee Street, Zip 22908–0816; tel. 434/924–0211; Richard Shannon, Executive Vice President for Health Affairs, p. B142

Falls Church: BUREAU OF MEDICINE AND SURGERY, DEPARTMENT OF THE NAVY 7700 Arlington Boulevard, Suite 5126, Zip 22042; tel. 202/762–3701; Bryce H.P. Mendez, Healthcare Policy Analyst, p. B25

DEPARTMENT OF THE ARMY, OFFICE OF THE SURGEON GENERAL 5109 Leesburg Pike, Zip 22041–3215; tel. 703/681–3000; Lieutenant General, Eric B. Schoomaker, Surgeon General, p. B41

★ INOVA HEALTH SYSTEM 8110 Gatehouse Road, Suite 200 East, Zip 22042–1252; tel. 703/289–2069; J Stephen. Jones, Chief Executive Officer, p. B68

Fredericksburg: ★ MARY WASHINGTON HEALTHCARE 1001 Sam Perry Boulevard, Zip 22401–4453; tel. 540/741–3100; Michael P. McDermott, President and Chief Executive Officer, p. B78

Lynchburg: ★ CENTRA HEALTH, INC. 1901 Tate Springs Road, Zip 24501–1109; tel. 434/200–3000; E W. Tibbs, President and Chief Executive Officer, p. B31

Newport News: RIVERSIDE HEALTH SYSTEM 701 Town Center Drive, Suite 1000, Zip 23606–4286; tel. 757/534–7000; William B. Downey, President and Chief Executive Officer, p. B107

Norfolk: ★ SENTARA HEALTHCARE 6015 Poplar Hall Drive, Zip 23502–3819; tel. 757/455–7000; Howard P. Kern, Chief Executive Officer, p. B115

Richmond: ★ VCU HEALTH SYSTEM 1250 East Marshall Street, Zip 23298–5051, Mailing Address: P.O. Box 980510, Zip 23298–0510, tel. 804/828–9000; Marsha Rappley, Chief Executive Officer and Vice President for Health Sciences, p. B143

VIRGINIA DEPARTMENT OF MENTAL HEALTH 1220 Bank Street, Zip 23219–3645, Mailing Address: P.O. Box 1797, Zip 23218–1797, tel. 804/786–3921; James S. Reinhard, Commissioner, p. B145

Roanoke: ★ CARILION CLINIC 1906 Belleview Avenue SE, Zip 24014–1838, Mailing Address: P.O. Box 13727, Zip 24036–3727, tel. 540/981–7000; Nancy Howell. Agee, President and Chief Executive Officer, p. B26

Winchester: ★ VALLEY HEALTH SYSTEM 220 Campus Boulevard, Suite 420, Zip 22601–2889, Mailing Address: P.O. Box 3340, Zip 22604–2540, tel. 540/536–8024; Mark H. Merrill, President and Chief Executive Officer, p. B143

WASHINGTON

Mount Vernon: SKAGIT REGIONAL HEALTH 1415 E Kincaid Street, Zip 98274–4126; tel. 360/424–4111; Gregg Agustin. Davidson, President and Chief Executive Officer, p. B117

Renton: ★ PROVIDENCE ST. JOSEPH HEALTH 1801 Lind Avenue Southwest, 9016, Zip 98057–9016, Mailing Address: 181 Lind Avenue Southwest, 9016, Zip 98057–9016, tel. 425/525–3698; Rodney F. Hochman, President and Chief Executive Officer, p. B102

Seattle: ★ SWEDISH HEALTH SERVICES 747 Broadway, Zip 98122–4379; tel. 206/386–6000; R. Guy. Hudson, Chief Executive Officer, p. B124

★ UW MEDICINE 1959 NE Pacific Street, Zip 98195–0001, Mailing Address: P.O. Box 356350, Zip 98195–6350, tel. 206/543–7718; Paul G. Ramsey, Chief Executive Officer, p. B143

VIRGINIA MASON HEALTH SYSTEM 1100 Ninth Avenue, Zip 98101–2756, Mailing Address: P.O. Box 900, Zip 98111–0900, tel. 206/223–6600; Gary Kaplan, Chief Executive Officer, p. B145

Sunnyside: ASTRIA HEALTH 1016 Tacoma Ave, Zip 98944–2263, Mailing Address: P.O. Box 979, Zip 98944, tel. 509/837–1330; John Gallagher, President and Chief Executive Officer, p. B16

Tacoma: MULTICARE HEALTH SYSTEM 315 Martin Luther King Jr Way, Zip 98405–4234, Mailing Address: P.O. Box 5299, Zip 98415–0299, tel. 253/403–1000; William G. Robertson, President and Chief Executive Officer, p. B86

Vancouver: ★ PEACEHEALTH 1115 SE 164th Avenue, Zip 98683; tel. 360/729–1000; Elizabeth Dunne, President and Chief Executive Officer, p. B96

WEST VIRGINIA

Elkins: ★ DAVIS HEALTH SYSTEM Reed Street and Gorman Avenue, Zip 26241, Mailing Address: P.O. Box 1697, Zip 26241–1697, tel. 304/636–3300; Vance Jackson, President and Chief Executive Officer, p. B41

Huntington: ★ PALLOTTINE HEALTH SERVICES 2900 First Avenue, Zip 25702–1241; tel. 304/526–1234; Michael G. Sellards, Chief Executive Officer, p. B95

Morgantown: ★ MON HEALTH SYSTEM 1200 J. D. Anderson Drive, Zip 26505–3494; tel. 304/598–1200; Thomas Senker, Interim Chief Executive Officer, p. B85

★ WEST VIRGINIA UNIVERSITY HEALTH SYSTEM One Medical Center, Box 8136, Zip 26506–8136; tel. 304/285–7150; Albert L. Wright Jr, President and Chief Executive Officer, p. B147

South Charleston: ★ THOMAS HEALTH SYSTEM, INC. 4605 MacCorkle Avenue SW, Zip 25309–1311; tel. 304/766–3600; Daniel Lauffer, President and Chief Executive Officer, p. B127

WISCONSIN

Appleton: THEDACARE, INC. 122 East College Avenue, Zip 54911–5794, Mailing Address: P.O. Box 8025, Zip 54912–8025, tel. 920/830–5889; Imran A. Andrabi, President and Chief Executive Officer, p. B127

Janesville: MERCY HEALTH SYSTEM 1000 Mineral Point Avenue, Zip 53548–2940, Mailing Address: P.O. Box 5003, Zip 53547–5003, tel. 608/756–6000; Javon R. Bea, President and Chief Executive Officer, p. B84

Madison: UW HEALTH SYSTEM 600 Highland Avenue, Zip 53792–0001; tel. 608/263–6400; Alan Kaplan, Chief Executive Officer, p. B142

Manitowoc: ★ FRANCISCAN SISTERS OF CHRISTIAN CHARITY SPONSORED MINISTRIES, INC. 1415 South Rapids Road, Zip 54220–9302; tel. 920/684–7071; Scott McConnaha, FACHE, Acting Chief Executive Officer and Vice President, Mission and Strategy, p. B56

Marshfield: ★ MARSHFIELD CLINIC HEALTH SYSTEM 1000 North Oak Avenue, Zip 54449–5703; tel. 800/782–8581; Susan Turney, Chief Executive Officer, p. B78

Milwaukee: CHILDREN'S HOSPITAL AND HEALTH SYSTEM 9000 West Wisconsin Avenue, Zip 53226–4810, Mailing Address: P.O. Box 1997, Zip 53201–1997, tel. 414/226–2000; Peggy N. Troy, President and Chief Executive Officer, p. B31

FROEDTERT HEALTH 9200 West Wisconsin Avenue, Zip 53226–3596, Mailing Address: P.O. Box 26099, Zip 53226–0099, tel. 414/805–3000; Catherine A. Jacobson, President and Chief Executive Officer, p. B56

Waukesha: ★ PROHEALTH CARE, INC. N17 W24100 Riverwood Drive, Suite 130, Zip 53188; tel. 262/928–2242; Susan A. Edwards, President and Chief Executive Officer, p. B100

Wausau: ★ ASPIRUS, INC. 425 Pine Ridge Boulevard, Zip 54401–4123; tel. 715/847–2118; Matthew Heywood, Chief Executive Officer, p. B15

Health Care Systems Index

Networks and their Hospitals

ARIZONA

HONORHEALTH
8125 North Hayden Road, Scottsdale, AZ, Zip 85258–2463; tel. 480/882–4000; Todd LaPorte, Chief Executive Officer

HONORHEALTH DEER VALLEY MEDICAL CENTER, 19829 North 27th Avenue, Phoenix, AZ, Zip 85027–4002; tel. 623/879–6100; David Price, Chief Executive Officer

HONORHEALTH JOHN C. LINCOLN MEDICAL CENTER, 250 East Dunlap Avenue, Phoenix, AZ, Zip 85020–2825; tel. 602/943–2381; Margaret Elizabeth. Griffin, Chief Executive Officer

HONORHEALTH REHABILITATION HOSPITAL, 8850 East Pima Center Parkway, Scottsdale, AZ, Zip 85258–4619; tel. 480/800–3900; Scott R. Keen, Chief Executive Officer

HONORHEALTH SCOTTSDALE OSBORN MEDICAL CENTER, 7400 East Osborn Road, Scottsdale, AZ, Zip 85251–6403; tel. 480/882–4000; Kimberly Post, Senior Vice President and Chief Executive Officer

HONORHEALTH SCOTTSDALE SHEA MEDICAL CENTER, 9003 East Shea Boulevard, Scottsdale, AZ, Zip 85260–6771; tel. 480/323–3000; Gary E. Baker, Senior Vice President and Chief Executive Officer

HONORHEALTH SCOTTSDALE THOMPSON PEAK MEDICAL CENTER, 7400 East Thompson Peak Parkway, Scottsdale, AZ, Zip 85255–4109; tel. 480/324–7000; David Price, Chief Executive Officer

NORTHERN ARIZONA HEALTHCARE
1200 North Beaver Street, Flagstaff, AZ, Zip 86001–3118; tel. 928/779–3366; Robert P. Thames, President and Chief Executive Officer

FLAGSTAFF MEDICAL CENTER, 1200 North Beaver Street, Flagstaff, AZ, Zip 86001–3118; tel. 928/779–3366; Florence (Flo). Spyrow, Chief Administrative Officer

VERDE VALLEY MEDICAL CENTER, 269 South Candy Lane, Cottonwood, AZ, Zip 86326–4170; tel. 928/639–6000; Barbara Firminger, Chief Administrative Officer

CALIFORNIA

ADVENTIST HEALTH NORTHERN CALIFORNIA NETWORK
463 Aviation Boulevard, Santa Rosa, CA, Zip 95403–1079; tel. 707/571–2893; Jeff Eller, FACHE, President and Chief Executive Officer

ADVENTIST HEALTH CLEAR LAKE, 15630 18th Avenue, Clearlake, CA, Zip 95422–9336, Mailing Address: P.O. Box 6710, Zip 95422, tel. 707/994–6486; David Santos, President and Chief Executive Officer

ADVENTIST HEALTH HOWARD MEMORIAL, One Marcela Drive, Willits, CA, Zip 95490–4298; tel. 707/459–6801; Jason Wells, President and Chief Executive Officer

ADVENTIST HEALTH ST. HELENA, 10 Woodland Road, Saint Helena, CA, Zip 94574–9554; tel. 707/963–3611; Steven Herber, M.D., FACS, President and Chief Executive Officer

ADVENTIST HEALTH ST. HELENA, 525 Oregon Street, Vallejo, CA, Zip 94590–3201; tel. 707/648–2200; Steven Herber, M.D., FACS, President and Chief Executive Officer

UKIAH VALLEY MEDICAL CENTER, 275 Hospital Drive, Ukiah, CA, Zip 95482–4531; tel. 707/462–3111; Gwen Matthews, R.N., MSN, Chief Executive Officer

PROVIDENCE HEALTH AND SERVICES - SOUTHERN CALIFORNIA
Regional Administration, 20555 Earl Street, Torrance, CA, Zip 90503–3006; tel. 310/793–8087; Erik G. Wexler, Chief Executive Officer

PROVIDENCE HOLY CROSS MEDICAL CENTER, 15031 Rinaldi Street, Mission Hills, CA, Zip 91345–1207; tel. 818/365–8051; Bernard Klein, M.D., Chief Executive

PROVIDENCE LITTLE COMPANY OF MARY MEDICAL CENTER - TORRANCE, 4101 Torrance Boulevard, Torrance, CA, Zip 90503–4664; tel. 310/540–7676; Garry M. Olney, Chief Executive Officer

PROVIDENCE LITTLE COMPANY OF MARY MEDICAL CENTER SAN PEDRO, 1300 West Seventh Street, San Pedro, CA, Zip 90732–3505; tel. 310/832–3311; Garry M. Olney, Chief Executive Officer

PROVIDENCE SAINT JOHN'S HEALTH CENTER, 2121 Santa Monica Boulevard, Santa Monica, CA, Zip 90404–2091; tel. 310/829–5511; Marcel C. Loh, FACHE, Chief Executive Officer

PROVIDENCE SAINT JOSEPH MEDICAL CENTER, 501 South Buena Vista Street, Burbank, CA, Zip 91505–4866; tel. 818/843–5111; Kelly Linden, Chief Executive Officer

PROVIDENCE TARZANA MEDICAL CENTER, 18321 Clark Street, Tarzana, CA, Zip 91356–3521; tel. 818/881–0800; Dale Surowitz, Chief Executive

ST. JOSEPH HOAG HEALTH
3345 Michelson Drive, Suite 100, Irvine, CA, Zip 92612–0693; tel. 949/381–4019; Richard Afable, M.D., M.P.H., President and Chief Executive Officer

HOAG MEMORIAL HOSPITAL PRESBYTERIAN, One Hoag Drive, Newport Beach, CA, Zip 92663–4120, Mailing Address: P.O. Box 6100, Zip 92658–6100, tel. 949/764–4624; Robert Braithwaite, President and Chief Executive Officer

MISSION HOSPITAL, 27700 Medical Center Road, Mission Viejo, CA, Zip 92691–6474; tel. 949/364–1400; Tarek Salaway, R.N., Chief Executive

ST. JOSEPH HOSPITAL, 1100 West Stewart Drive, Orange, CA, Zip 92868–3849, Mailing Address: P.O. Box 5600, Zip 92863–5600, tel. 714/633–9111; Jeremy Zoch, Chief Executive

ST. MARY MEDICAL CENTER, 18300 Highway 18, Apple Valley, CA, Zip 92307–2206, Mailing Address: P.O. Box 7025, Zip 92307–0725, tel. 760/242–2311; Alan H. Garrett, President and Chief Executive Officer

COLORADO

CENTURA HEALTH
188 Inverness Drive West, Suite 500, Englewood, CO, Zip 80112–5204; tel. 303/290–6500; Peter D. Banko, FACHE, President and Chief Executive Officer

AVISTA ADVENTIST HOSPITAL, 100 Health Park Drive, Louisville, CO, Zip 80027–9583; tel. 303/673–1000; Jillyan McKinney, Chief Executive Officer

CASTLE ROCK ADVENTIST HOSPITAL, 2350 Meadows Boulevard, Castle Rock, CO, Zip 80109–8405; tel. 720/455–5000; Todd Folkenberg, Chief Executive Officer

LITTLETON ADVENTIST HOSPITAL, 7700 South Broadway Street, Littleton, CO, Zip 80122–2628; tel. 303/730–8900; Brett Spenst, Chief Executive Officer

PARKER ADVENTIST HOSPITAL, 9395 Crown Crest Boulevard, Parker, CO, Zip 80138–8573; tel. 303/269–4000; Michael Goebel, Chief Executive Officer

PENROSE-ST. FRANCIS HEALTH SERVICES, 2222 North Nevada Avenue, Colorado Springs, CO, Zip 80907–6799; tel. 719/776–5000; Brian Erling, Interim Chief Executive Officer

PORTER ADVENTIST HOSPITAL, 2525 South Downing Street, Denver, CO, Zip 80210–5876; tel. 303/778–1955; Morre Dean, Chief Executive Officer

RAWLINS COUNTY HEALTH CENTER, 707 Grant Street, Atwood, KS, Zip 67730–1526, Mailing Address: P.O. Box 47, Zip 67730–0047, tel. 785/626–3211; Sharon K. Cox, FACHE, Chief Executive Officer

ST. ANTHONY HOSPITAL, 11600 West Second Place, Lakewood, CO, Zip 80228–1527; tel. 720/321–0000; Edward H. Sim, Chief Executive Officer

ST. ANTHONY NORTH HEALTH CAMPUS, 14300 Orchard Parkway, Westminster, CO, Zip 80023–9206; tel. 720/627–0000; Kevin Jenkins, President and Chief Executive Officer

ST. ANTHONY SUMMIT MEDICAL CENTER, 340 Peak One Drive, Frisco, CO, Zip 80443, Mailing Address: P.O. Box 738, Zip 80443–0738, tel. 970/668–3300; Marshall Denkinger, M.D., Interim Chief Executive Officer

ST. MARY-CORWIN MEDICAL CENTER, 1008 Minnequa Avenue, Pueblo, CO, Zip 81004–3798; tel. 719/557–4000; Michael Cafasso, Chief Executive Officer

ST. THOMAS MORE HOSPITAL, 1338 Phay Avenue, Canon City, CO, Zip 81212–2302; tel. 719/285–2000; Sheri Trahern, CPA, FACHE, Chief Executive Officer

ST. VINCENT GENERAL HOSPITAL DISTRICT, 822 West 4th Street, Leadville, CO, Zip 80461–3897; tel. 719/486–0230; Gary Campbell, Chief Executive Officer

COMMUNITY HEALTH PROVIDERS ORGANIZATION
2021 North 12th Street, Grand Junction, CO, Zip 81501–2980; tel. 970/256–6200; Chris Thomas, FACHE, President and Chief Executive Officer

COMMUNITY HOSPITAL, 2351 G Road, Grand Junction, CO, Zip 81505; tel. 970/242–0920; Chris Thomas, FACHE, President and Chief Executive Officer

HCA HEALTHONE, LLC
4900 South Monaco Street, Suite 380, Denver, CO, Zip 80237–3487; tel. 303/788–2500; Sylvia Young, President

MEDICAL CENTER OF AURORA, 1501 South Potomac Street, Aurora, CO, Zip 80012–5411; tel. 303/695–2600; Daniel Miller, FACHE, President and Chief Executive Officer

NORTH SUBURBAN MEDICAL CENTER, 9191 Grant Street, Thornton, CO, Zip 80229–4341; tel. 303/451–7800; Daphne G. David, President and Chief Executive Officer

PRESBYTERIAN-ST. LUKE'S MEDICAL CENTER, 1719 East 19th Avenue, Denver, CO, Zip 80218–1281; tel. 303/839–6000; Maureen Tarrant, President and Chief Executive Officer

ROSE MEDICAL CENTER, 4567 East Ninth Avenue, Denver, CO, Zip 80220–3941; tel. 303/320–2121; Ryan Tobin, President and Chief Executive Officer

SKY RIDGE MEDICAL CENTER, 10101 Ridge Gate Parkway, Lone Tree, CO, Zip 80124–5522; tel. 720/225–1000; Susan Hicks, Chief Executive Officer

SPALDING REHABILITATION HOSPITAL, 900 Potomac Steet, Aurora, CO, Zip 80011–6716; tel. 303/367–1166; Daniel Miller, FACHE, President and Chief Executive Officer

SWEDISH MEDICAL CENTER, 501 East Hampden Avenue, Englewood, CO, Zip 80113–2702; tel. 303/788–5000; Richard A. Hammett, President and Chief Executive Officer

CONNECTICUT

EASTERN CONNECTICUT HEALTH NETWORK
71 Haynes Street, Manchester, CT, Zip 06040–4131; tel. 860/533–3400; Michael F. Collins, Interim President and Chief Executive Officer

MANCHESTER MEMORIAL HOSPITAL, 71 Haynes Street, Manchester, CT, Zip 06040–4188; tel. 860/646–1222; Michael F. Collins, Chief Executive Officer

ROCKVILLE GENERAL HOSPITAL, 31 Union Street, Vernon, CT, Zip 06066–3160; tel. 860/872–0501; Michael F. Collins, Chief Executive Officer

FLORIDA

BAYCARE HEALTH SYSTEM
2985 Drew Street, Clearwater, FL, Zip 33759–3012; tel. 877/692–2922; Tommy Inzina, President and Chief Executive Officer

BARTOW REGIONAL MEDICAL CENTER, 2200 Osprey Boulevard, Bartow, FL, Zip 33830–3308; tel. 863/533–8111; Philip Minden, Chief Executive Officer

BAYCARE ALLIANT HOSPITAL, 601 Main Street, MS#402, Dunedin, FL, Zip 34698–5848; tel. 727/736–9991; Jacqueline Arocho, Administrator

MEASE COUNTRYSIDE HOSPITAL, 3231 McMullen Booth Road, Safety Harbor, FL, Zip 34695–6607; tel. 727/725–6111; Lou Galdieri, R.N., President

MEASE DUNEDIN HOSPITAL, 601 Main Street, Dunedin, FL, Zip 34698–5891; tel. 727/733–1111; Lou Galdieri, R.N., President

MORTON PLANT HOSPITAL, 300 Pinellas Street, Clearwater, FL, Zip 33756–3804, Mailing Address: P.O. Box 210, Zip 33757–0210, tel. 727/462–7000; N. Kristopher. Hoce, President

MORTON PLANT NORTH BAY HOSPITAL, 6600 Madison Street, New Port Richey, FL, Zip 34652–1900; tel. 727/842–8468; Sarah Naumowich, Interim President

SOUTH FLORIDA BAPTIST HOSPITAL, 301 North Alexander Street, Plant City, FL, Zip 33563–4303; tel. 813/757–1200; Karen Kerr, R.N., President

ST. ANTHONY'S HOSPITAL, 1200 Seventh Avenue North, Saint Petersburg, FL, Zip 33705–1388, Mailing Address: P.O. Box 12588, Zip 33733–2588, tel. 727/825–1100; M. Scott Smith, President

ST. JOSEPH'S HOSPITAL, 3001 West Martin Luther King Jr. Boulevard, Tampa, FL, Zip 33607–6387, Mailing Address: P.O. Box 4227, Zip 33677–4227, tel. 813/870–4000; Kimberly Guy, President

WINTER HAVEN HOSPITAL, 200 Avenue F NE, Winter Haven, FL, Zip 33881–4193; tel. 863/293–1121; Stephen A. Nierman, President

GEORGIA

ST. JOSEPH'S/CANDLER HEALTH SYSTEM, INC.
5353 Reynolds Street, Savannah, GA, Zip 31405–6015; tel. 912/819–6000; Paul P. Hinchey, President and Chief Executive Officer

APPLING HEALTHCARE SYSTEM, 163 East Tollison Street, Baxley, GA, Zip 31513–0120; tel. 912/367–9841; Raymond J. Leadbetter, Jr., Interim Chief Executive Officer

CANDLER HOSPITAL, 5353 Reynolds Street, Savannah, GA, Zip 31405–6015; tel. 912/819–6000; Paul P. Hinchey, President and Chief Executive Officer

EFFINGHAM HOSPITAL, 459 Highway 119 South, Springfield, GA, Zip 31329–3021, Mailing Address: P.O. Box 386, Zip 31329–0386, tel. 912/754–6451; Francine Baker-Witt, R.N., Chief Executive Officer

EMORY UNIVERSITY HOSPITAL, 1364 Clifton Road NE, Atlanta, GA, Zip 30322; tel. 404/712–2000; Bryce D. Gartland, M.D., Chief Executive Officer

LIBERTY REGIONAL MEDICAL CENTER, 462 Elma G Miles Parkway, Hinesville, GA, Zip 31313–4000, Mailing Address: P.O. Box 919, Zip 31310–0919, tel. 912/369–9400; Michael Hester, Chief Executive Officer

MEADOWS REGIONAL MEDICAL CENTER, One Meadows Parkway, Vidalia, GA, Zip 30474–8759, Mailing Address: P.O. Box 1048, Zip 30475–1048, tel. 912/535–5555; Alan Kent, Chief Executive Officer

ST. JOSEPH'S HOSPITAL, 11705 Mercy Boulevard, Savannah, GA, Zip 31419–1791; tel. 912/819–4100; Paul P. Hinchey, President and Chief Executive Officer

IDAHO

THE HOSPITAL COOPERATIVE
500 South 11th Avenue Suite 503, Pocatello, ID, Zip 83201–4881; tel. 208/239–1951; Jon Smith, Executive Director

BEAR LAKE MEMORIAL HOSPITAL, 164 South Fifth Street, Montpelier, ID, Zip 83254–1597; tel. 208/847–1630; Dennis Carlson, Chief Executive Officer

BINGHAM MEMORIAL HOSPITAL, 98 Poplar Street, Blackfoot, ID, Zip 83221–1799; tel. 208/785–4100; Jake Erickson, Chief Executive Officer

CARIBOU MEMORIAL HOSPITAL AND LIVING CENTER, 300 South Third West, Soda Springs, ID, Zip 83276–1598; tel. 208/547–3341; Christina Thomas, R.N., FACHE, Chief Executive Officer

EASTERN IDAHO REGIONAL MEDICAL CENTER, 3100 Channing Way, Idaho Falls, ID, Zip 83404–7533, Mailing Address: P.O. Box 2077, Zip 83403–2077, tel. 208/529–6111; Jeff Sollis, Chief Executive Officer

FRANKLIN COUNTY MEDICAL CENTER, 44 North First East Street, Preston, ID, Zip 83263–1399; tel. 208/852–0137; Darin Dransfield, Chief Executive Officer

LOST RIVERS MEDICAL CENTER, 551 Highland Drive, Arco, ID, Zip 83213–9771, Mailing Address: P.O. Box 145, Zip 83213–0145, tel. 208/527–8206; Brad Huerta, Chief Executive Officer and Administrator

MADISON MEMORIAL HOSPITAL, 450 East Main Street, Rexburg, ID, Zip 83440–2048, Mailing Address: P.O. Box 310, Zip 83440–0310, tel. 208/359–6900; Rachel Ann. Gonzales, Chief Executive Officer

MINIDOKA MEMORIAL HOSPITAL, 1224 Eighth Street, Rupert, ID, Zip 83350–1599; tel. 208/436–0481; Tom Murphy, Chief Executive Officer

NELL J. REDFIELD MEMORIAL HOSPITAL, 150 North 200 West, Malad City, ID, Zip 83252–1239, Mailing Address: Box 126, Zip 83252–0126, tel. 208/766–2231; John Williams, Administrator and Chief Executive Officer

PORTNEUF MEDICAL CENTER, 777 Hospital Way, Pocatello, ID, Zip 83201–5175; tel. 208/239–1000; Daniel Ordyna, Chief Executive Officer

POWER COUNTY HOSPITAL DISTRICT, 510 Roosevelt Street, American Falls, ID, Zip 83211–1362, Mailing Address: P.O. Box 420, Zip 83211–0420, tel. 208/226–3200; Dallas Clinger, Administrator

STAR VALLEY MEDICAL CENTER, 901 Adams Street, Afton, WY, Zip 83110–9621, Mailing Address: P.O. Box 579, Zip 83110–0579, tel. 307/885–5800; Mike Hunsaker, Interim President and Chief Executive Officer

STEELE MEMORIAL MEDICAL CENTER, 203 South Daisy Street, Salmon, ID, Zip 83467–4709; tel. 208/756–5600; Jeanine Gentry, Chief Executive Officer

TETON VALLEY HEALTH CARE, 120 East Howard Street, Driggs, ID, Zip 83422–5112; tel. 208/354–2383; Keith Gnagey, Chief Executive Officer

ILLINOIS

AMITA HEALTH
120 North Oak Street, Hinsdale, IL, Zip 60521–3829; tel. 630/856–9000

AMITA HEALTH ADVENTIST LA GRANGE MEDICAL CENTER, 5101 South Willow Spring Road, La Grange, IL, Zip 60525–2600; tel. 708/245–9000; Michael Murrill, President and Chief Executive Officer

AMITA HEALTH ADVENTIST MEDICAL CENTER - HINSDALE, 120 North Oak Street, Hinsdale, IL, Zip 60521–3890; tel. 630/856–6001; Steven Province, President and Chief Executive Officer

AMITA HEALTH ADVENTIST MEDICAL CENTER BOLINGBROOK , 500 Remington Boulevard, Bolingbrook, IL, Zip 60440–4906; tel. 630/312–5000; Bruce C. Christian, Chief Executive Officer

AMITA HEALTH ADVENTIST MEDICAL CENTER GLENOAKS, 701 Winthrop Avenue, Glendale Heights, IL, Zip 60139–1403; tel. 630/545–8000; Bruce C. Christian, President and Chief Executive Officer

ALEXIAN BROTHERS BEHAVIORAL HEALTH HOSPITAL, 1650 Moon Lake Boulevard, Hoffman Estates, IL, Zip 60169–1010; tel. 847/882–1600; Clayton Ciha, President and Chief Executive Officer

MERCY HEALTH CORPORATION
2400 North Rockton Avenue, Rockford, IL, Zip 61103–3655; tel. 608/756–6000; Javon R. Bea, President and Chief Executive Officer

MERCYHEALTH HOSPITAL - ROCKTON AVENUE, 2400 North Rockton Avenue, Rockford, IL, Zip 61103–3655; tel. 815/971–5000; Javon R. Bea, President and Chief Executive Officer

MERCYHEALTH HOSPITAL AND MEDICAL CENTER - HARVARD, 901 Grant Street, Harvard, IL, Zip 60033–1898, Mailing Address: P.O. Box 850, Zip 60033–0850, tel. 815/943–5431; Javon R. Bea, Chief Executive Officer

MERCYHEALTH HOSPITAL AND MEDICAL CENTER - WALWORTH, N2950 State Road 67, Lake Geneva, WI, Zip 53147–2655; tel. 262/245–0535; Javon R. Bea, President and Chief Executive Officer

MERCYHEALTH HOSPITAL AND TRAUMA CENTER - JANESVILLE, 1000 Mineral Point Avenue, Janesville, WI, Zip 53548–2982, Mailing Address: P.O. Box 5003, Zip 53547–5003, tel. 608/756–6000; Javon R. Bea, President and Chief Executive Officer

INDIANA

LUTHERAN HEALTH NETWORK
7950 West Jefferson Boulevard, Fort Wayne, IN, Zip 46804–4140; tel. 260/435–7001; Michael Poore, Chief Executive Officer and Regional President

BLUFFTON REGIONAL MEDICAL CENTER, 303 South Main Street, Bluffton, IN, Zip 46714–2503; tel. 260/824–3210; Brent Parsons, Chief Executive Officer

DUKES MEMORIAL HOSPITAL, 275 West 12th Street, Peru, IN, Zip 46970–1638; tel. 765/472–8000; Debra Close, Chief Executive Officer

DUPONT HOSPITAL, 2520 East Dupont Road, Fort Wayne, IN, Zip 46825–1675; tel. 260/416–3000; Lorenzo Suter, Chief Executive Officer

KOSCIUSKO COMMUNITY HOSPITAL, 2101 East Dubois Drive, Warsaw, IN, Zip 46580–3288; tel. 574/267–3200; Kim Finch, Interim Chief Executive Officer Chief Nursing Officer

LUTHERAN HOSPITAL OF INDIANA, 7950 West Jefferson Boulevard, Fort Wayne, IN, Zip 46804–4140; tel. 260/435–7001; Paula R. Autry, FACHE, Chief Executive Officer

ORTHOPAEDIC HOSPITAL OF LUTHERAN HEALTH NETWORK, 7952 West Jefferson Boulevard, Fort Wayne, IN, Zip 46804–4140; tel. 260/435–2999; Lorie Ailor, Chief Executive Officer

REHABILITATION HOSPITAL OF FORT WAYNE, 7970 West Jefferson Boulevard, Fort Wayne, IN, Zip 46804–4140; tel. 260/435–6100; Ryan Cassedy, Chief Administrative Officer

ST. JOSEPH HOSPITAL, 700 Broadway, Fort Wayne, IN, Zip 46802–1493; tel. 260/425–3000; Lisa Dolan, Interim Chief Executive Officer

ST. VINCENT HEALTH
10330 North Meridian Street, Indianapolis, IN, Zip 46290; tel. 317/338–2273; Jonathan Nalli, Senior Vice President, Ascension Health and Indiana Ministry Market Executive

ST. VINCENT ANDERSON , 2015 Jackson Street, Anderson, IN, Zip 46016–4339; tel. 765/649–2511; Mike K. Schroyer, FACHE, MSN, R.N., President

ST. VINCENT CARMEL HOSPITAL, 13500 North Meridian Street, Carmel, IN, Zip 46032–1456; tel. 317/582–7000; Gary Fammartino, Regional President

ST. VINCENT CLAY HOSPITAL, 1206 East National Avenue, Brazil, IN, Zip 47834–2797, Mailing Address: 1206 East National Ave , Zip 47834–0489, tel. 812/442–2500; Jerry Laue, Administrator

ST. VINCENT DUNN HOSPITAL, 1600 23rd Street, Bedford, IN, Zip 47421–4704; tel. 812/275–3331; Jerry Laue, Administrator

ST. VINCENT EVANSVILLE, 3700 Washington Avenue, Evansville, IN, Zip 47714–0541; tel. 812/485–4000; Daniel A. Parod, President

ST. VINCENT FISHERS HOSPITAL, 13861 Olio Road, Fishers, IN, Zip 46037–3487; tel. 317/415–9000; Gary Fammartino, Regional President

ST. VINCENT HEART CENTER, 10580 North Meridian Street, Indianapolis, IN, Zip 46290–1028; tel. 317/583–5000; Blake A. Dye, FACHE, President

ST. VINCENT INDIANAPOLIS HOSPITAL, 2001 West 86th Street, Indianapolis, IN, Zip 46260–1991, Mailing Address: P.O. Box 40970, Zip 46240–0970, tel. 317/338–2345; Joel Feldman, Regional President

ST. VINCENT JENNINGS HOSPITAL, 301 Henry Street, North Vernon, IN, Zip 47265–1097; tel. 812/352–4200; Christina Crank, Chief Nursing Officer

ST. VINCENT MERCY HOSPITAL, 1331 South 'A' Street, Elwood, IN, Zip 46036–1942; tel. 765/552–4600; Ann C. Yates, R.N., MSN, Administrator and Chief Nursing Officer

ST. VINCENT RANDOLPH HOSPITAL, 473 Greenville Avenue, Winchester, IN, Zip 47394–9436; tel. 765/584–0004; Carla Fouse, Administrator and Chief Nursing Officer

ST. VINCENT SALEM HOSPITAL, 911 North Shelby Street, Salem, IN, Zip 47167–1694; tel. 812/883–5881; Dana M. Muntz, Chief Executive Officer

ST. VINCENT SETON SPECIALTY HOSPITAL, 8050 Township Line Road, Indianapolis, IN, Zip 46260–2478; tel. 317/415–8500; Joel Feldman, Regional President

ST. VINCENT WARRICK HOSPITAL, 1116 Millis Avenue, Boonville, IN, Zip 47601–2204; tel. 812/897–4800; Kathy J. Hall, Administrator

ST. VINCENT WILLIAMSPORT HOSPITAL, 412 North Monroe Street, Williamsport, IN, Zip 47993–1049; tel. 765/762–4000; Jane Craigin, Chief Executive Officer

SUBURBAN HEALTH ORGANIZATION
2780 Waterfront Parkway East Drive, Suite 300, Indianapolis, IN, Zip 46214; tel. 317/692–5222; Dave Lippincott, President

GOSHEN HEALTH, 200 High Park Avenue, Goshen, IN, Zip 46526–4899, Mailing Address: P.O. Box 139, Zip 46527–0139, tel. 574/533–2141; Randal Christophel, President and Chief Executive Officer

HANCOCK REGIONAL HOSPITAL, 801 North State Street, Greenfield, IN, Zip 46140–1270, Mailing Address: P.O. Box 827, Zip 46140–0827, tel. 317/462–5544; Steven V. Long, FACHE, President and Chief Executive Officer

HENDRICKS REGIONAL HEALTH, 1000 East Main Street, Danville, IN, Zip 46122–1948, Mailing Address: P.O. Box 409, Zip 46122–0409, tel. 317/745–4451; Kevin Speer, Chief Executive Officer

HENRY COMMUNITY HEALTH, 1000 North 16th Street, New Castle, IN, Zip 47362–4319, Mailing Address: P.O. Box 490, Zip 47362–0490, tel. 765/521–0890; Paul Janssen, President and Chief Executive Officer

JOHNSON MEMORIAL HOSPITAL, 1125 West Jefferson Street, Franklin, IN, Zip 46131–2140, Mailing Address: P.O. Box 549, Zip 46131–0549, tel. 317/736–3300; Larry Heydon, President and Chief Executive Officer

MAJOR HOSPITAL, 150 West Washington Street, Shelbyville, IN, Zip 46176–1236, Mailing Address: 2451 Intelliplex Drive, Zip 46176, tel. 317/392–3211; John M. Horner, President and Chief Executive Officer

MARGARET MARY HEALTH, 321 Mitchell Avenue, Batesville, IN, Zip 47006–8909, Mailing Address: P.O. Box 226, Zip 47006–0226, tel. 812/934–6624; Timothy L. Putnam, FACHE, President and Chief Executive Officer

RIVERVIEW HEALTH, 395 Westfield Road, Noblesville, IN, Zip 46060–1425, Mailing Address: P.O. Box 220, Zip 46061–0220, tel. 317/773–0760; Seth Warren, President and Chief Executive Officer

RUSH MEMORIAL HOSPITAL, 1300 North Main Street, Rushville, IN, Zip 46173–1198; tel. 765/932–4111; Bradley Smith, President and Chief Executive Officer

WITHAM HEALTH SERVICES, 2605 North Lebanon Street, Lebanon, IN, Zip 46052–1476, Mailing Address: P.O. Box 1200, Zip 46052–3005, tel. 765/485–8000; Raymond V. Ingham, Ph.D., President and Chief Executive Officer

IOWA

GENESIS HEALTH SYSTEM
1227 East Rusholme Street, Davenport, IA, Zip 52803–2459; tel. 563/421–1000; Douglas P. Cropper, President and Chief Executive Officer

GENESIS MEDICAL CENTER, DAVENPORT, 1227 East Rusholme Street, Davenport, IA, Zip 52803–2498; tel. 563/421–1000; Jordan Voigt, Administrator

GENESIS MEDICAL CENTER, DEWITT, 1118 11th Street, De Witt, IA, Zip 52742–1296; tel. 563/659–4200; Curt Coleman, FACHE, Chief Executive Officer

GENESIS MEDICAL CENTER, SILVIS, 801 Illini Drive, Silvis, IL, Zip 61282–1893; tel. 309/281–4000; Theresa Summers-Main, R.N., Interim President

GENESIS MEDICAL CENTER-ALEDO, 409 NW Ninth Avenue, Aledo, IL, Zip 61231–1296; tel. 309/582–9100; Ted Rogalski, Administrator

MERCY HEALTH NETWORK
1449 NW 128th Street, Building 5, Suite 200, Clive, IA, Zip 50325; tel. 515/358–9200; Robert P. Ritz, Chief Executive Officer

ADAIR COUNTY HEALTH SYSTEM, 609 SE Kent Street, Greenfield, IA, Zip 50849–9454; tel. 641/743–2123; Marcia Hendricks, FACHE, R.N., Chief Executive Officer

BAUM HARMON MERCY HOSPITAL, 255 North Welch Avenue, Primghar, IA, Zip 51245–7765, Mailing Address: P.O. Box 528, Zip 51245–0528, tel. 712/957–2300; Misty Dulin, CAH, Director

BOONE COUNTY HOSPITAL, 1015 Union Street, Boone, IA, Zip 50036–4821; tel. 515/432–3140; Joseph S. Smith, Chief Executive Officer

KANSAS

HEALTH INNOVATIONS NETWORK OF KANSAS
1500 SW 10th Avenue, Topeka, KS, Zip 66604–1301; tel. 785/354–6137; Kristi Gosser, Network Operations Director

ATCHISON HOSPITAL, 800 Raven Hill Drive, Atchison, KS, Zip 66002–9204; tel. 913/367–2131; John L. Jacobson, Chief Executive Officer

CLAY COUNTY MEDICAL CENTER, 617 Liberty Street, Clay Center, KS, Zip 67432–1564, Mailing Address: P.O. Box 512, Zip 67432–0512, tel. 785/632–2144; Austin M. Gillard, Chief Executive Officer

COFFEY COUNTY HOSPITAL, 801 North 4th Street, Burlington, KS, Zip 66839–2602; tel. 620/364–2121; Leonard Hernandez, Chief Executive Officer

COMMUNITY HEALTHCARE SYSTEM, 120 West Eighth Street, Onaga, KS, Zip 66521–9574; tel. 785/889–4272; Todd Willert, Chief Executive Officer

F. W. HUSTON MEDICAL CENTER, 408 Delaware Street, Winchester, KS, Zip 66097–4003; tel. 913/774–4340; LaMont Cook, Administrator

GEARY COMMUNITY HOSPITAL, 1102 St Mary's Road, Junction City, KS, Zip 66441–4196, Mailing Address: P.O. Box 490, Zip 66441–0490, tel. 785/238–4131; Joseph Stratton, FACHE, Chief Executive Officer

HERINGTON MUNICIPAL HOSPITAL, 100 East Helen Street, Herington, KS, Zip 67449–1606; tel. 785/258–2207; Isabel Schmedemann, R.N., Chief Executive Officer and Administrator

HIAWATHA COMMUNITY HOSPITAL, 300 Utah Street, Hiawatha, KS, Zip 66434–2314; tel. 785/742–2131; Jeffrey Shelton, Chief Executive Officer

HORTON COMMUNITY HOSPITAL, 240 West 18th Street, Horton, KS, Zip 66439–1245; tel. 785/486–2642; James D. Noble, Chief Executive Officer

IRWIN ARMY COMMUNITY HOSPITAL, 600 Caisson Hill Road, Junction City, KS, Zip 66442–7037; tel. 785/239–7000, Colonel, Risa Ware, Commander

KANSAS REHABILITATION HOSPITAL, 1504 SW Eighth Avenue, Topeka, KS, Zip 66606–1632; tel. 785/235–6600; William J. Overbey, Chief Executive Officer

MORRIS COUNTY HOSPITAL, 600 North Washington Street, Council Grove, KS, Zip 66846–1422; tel. 620/767–6811; Kevin Leeper, Chief Executive Officer

NEMAHA VALLEY COMMUNITY HOSPITAL, 1600 Community Drive, Seneca, KS, Zip 66538–9739; tel. 785/336–6181; Kiley Floyd, Chief Executive Officer

NEWMAN REGIONAL HEALTH, 1201 West 12th Avenue, Emporia, KS, Zip 66801–2597; tel. 620/343–6800; Robert N. Wright, Chief Executive Officer

SABETHA COMMUNITY HOSPITAL, 14th and Oregon Streets, Sabetha, KS, Zip 66534–0229, Mailing Address: P.O. Box 229, Zip 66534–0229, tel. 785/284–2121; Lora Key, Chief Executive Officer

STORMONT VAIL HEALTH, 1500 SW Tenth Avenue, Topeka, KS, Zip 66604–1353; tel. 785/354–6000; Randall Peterson, President and Chief Executive Officer

VIA CHRISTI HOSPITAL MANHATTAN, INC., 1823 College Avenue, Manhattan, KS, Zip 66502–3346; tel. 785/776–3322; Robert C. Copple, FACHE, Senior Administrator

WAMEGO HEALTH CENTER, 711 Genn Drive, Wamego, KS, Zip 66547–1179; tel. 785/456–2295; Steve Land, Senior Administrator

WASHINGTON COUNTY HOSPITAL, 304 East Third Street, Washington, KS, Zip 66968–2033; tel. 785/325–2211; Roxanne Schottel, Chief Executive Officer

MED-OP, INC.
220 Canterbury Drive, Hays, KS, Zip 67601; tel. 785/623–2301; Shae Veach, Executive Director

CITIZENS MEDICAL CENTER, 100 East College Drive, Colby, KS, Zip 67701–3799; tel. 785/462–7511; Greg Unruh, Chief Executive Officer

CLARA BARTON HOSPITAL, 250 West Ninth Street, Hoisington, KS, Zip 67544–1706; tel. 620/653–2114; James Blackwell, President and Chief Executive Officer

GOODLAND REGIONAL MEDICAL CENTER, 220 West Second Street, Goodland, KS, Zip 67735–1602; tel. 785/890–3625; Chris Smolik, Chief Executive Officer

GOVE COUNTY MEDICAL CENTER, 520 West Fifth Street, Quinter, KS, Zip 67752–0129, Mailing Address: P.O. Box 129, Zip 67752–0129, tel. 785/754–3341; Coleen Tummons, Chief Executive Officer

GRAHAM COUNTY HOSPITAL, 304 West Prout Street, Hill City, KS, Zip 67642–1435; tel. 785/421–2121; Melissa Atkins, CPA, Chief Executive Officer

HAYS MEDICAL CENTER, 2220 Canterbury Drive, Hays, KS, Zip 67601–2370, Mailing Address: P.O. Box 8100, Zip 67601–8100, tel. 785/623–5000; Edward Herrman, R.N., FACHE, President and Chief Executive Officer

LOGAN COUNTY HOSPITAL, 211 Cherry Street, Oakley, KS, Zip 67748–1201; tel. 785/672–3211; Meldon L. Snow, Chief Executive Officer

NESS COUNTY HOSPITAL DISTRICT NO 2, 312 Custer Street, Ness City, KS, Zip 67560–1654; tel. 785/798–2291; Curt Thomas, Administrator

NORTON COUNTY HOSPITAL, 102 East Holme, Norton, KS, Zip 67654–1406, Mailing Address: P.O. Box 250, Zip 67654–0250, tel. 785/877–3351; Gina Frack, Chief Executive Officer

PAWNEE VALLEY COMMUNITY HOSPITAL, 923 Carroll Avenue, Larned, KS, Zip 67550–2429; tel. 620/285–3161; Kendra Barker, Administrator

ROOKS COUNTY HEALTH CENTER, 1210 North Washington Street, Plainville, KS, Zip 67663–1632, Mailing Address: P.O. Box 389, Zip 67663–0389, tel. 785/434–4553; Anthony Thomas, Chief Executive Officer

RUSH COUNTY MEMORIAL HOSPITAL, 801 Locust Street, La Crosse, KS, Zip 67548–9673, Mailing Address: P.O. Box 520, Zip 67548–0520, tel. 785/222–2545; Brenda Legleiter, R.N., Chief Executive Officer

RUSSELL REGIONAL HOSPITAL, 200 South Main Street, Russell, KS, Zip 67665–2920; tel. 785/483–3131; Sharon Collins, Interim Chief Executive Officer

SCOTT COUNTY HOSPITAL, 201 East Albert Avenue, Scott City, KS, Zip 67871–1203; tel. 620/872–5811; Mark Burnett, President and Chief Executive Officer

SHERIDAN COUNTY HEALTH COMPLEX, 826 18th Street, Hoxie, KS, Zip 67740–0167, Mailing Address: P.O. Box 167, Zip 67740–0167, tel. 785/675–3281; Niceta Farber, Chief Executive Officer

PIONEER HEALTH NETWORK, INC.
310 East Walnut Street, Suite 210, Garden City, KS, Zip 67846–5565; tel. 620/276–6100; Mary Adam, Executive Director

BOB WILSON MEMORIAL GRANT COUNTY HOSPITAL, 415 North Main Street, Ulysses, KS, Zip 67880–2133; tel. 620/356–1266; Amanda Vaughan, Interim Administrator

CITIZENS MEDICAL CENTER, 100 East College Drive, Colby, KS, Zip 67701–3799; tel. 785/462–7511; Greg Unruh, Chief Executive Officer

EDWARDS COUNTY MEDICAL CENTER, 620 West Eighth Street, Kinsley, KS, Zip 67547–2329, Mailing Address: P.O. Box 99, Zip 67547–0099, tel. 620/659–3621; Jimmie W. Hansel, Ph.D., Chief Executive Officer

GREELEY COUNTY HEALTH SERVICES, 506 Third Street, Tribune, KS, Zip 67879–9684, Mailing Address: P.O. Box 338, Zip 67879–0338, tel. 620/376–4221; Burke Kline, Chief Executive Officer

HAMILTON COUNTY HOSPITAL, 700 North Huser Street, Syracuse, KS, Zip 67878–0948, Mailing Address: P.O. Box 948, Zip 67878–0948, tel. 620/384–7461; Chad Thompson, Administrator

HODGEMAN COUNTY HEALTH CENTER, 809 Bramley Street, Jetmore, KS, Zip 67854–9320, Mailing Address: P.O. Box 310, Zip 67854–0310, tel. 620/357–8361; Phil Ginder, Chief Executive Officer

KEARNY COUNTY HOSPITAL, 500 Thorpe Street, Lakin, KS, Zip 67860–9625; tel. 620/355–7111; Benjamin Anderson, Chief Executive Officer and Administrator

LANE COUNTY HOSPITAL, 235 West Vine, Dighton, KS, Zip 67839–0969, Mailing Address: P.O. Box 969, Zip 67839–0969, tel. 620/397–5321; Brian Sarpy, Chief Executive Officer

LOGAN COUNTY HOSPITAL, 211 Cherry Street, Oakley, KS, Zip 67748–1201; tel. 785/672–3211; Meldon L. Snow, Chief Executive Officer

MEADE DISTRICT HOSPITAL, 510 East Carthage Street, Meade, KS, Zip 67864–6401, Mailing Address: P.O. Box 820, Zip 67864–0820, tel. 620/873–2141; Tara Ramlochan, Chief Executive Officer

MINNEOLA DISTRICT HOSPITAL, 212 Main Street, Minneola, KS, Zip 67865–8511, Mailing Address: P.O. Box 127, Zip 67865–0127, tel. 620/885–4264; Deborah Bruner, Chief Executive Officer and Administrator

MORTON COUNTY HEALTH SYSTEM, 445 Hilltop Street, Elkhart, KS, Zip 67950–0937, Mailing Address: P.O. Box 937, Zip 67950–0937, tel. 620/697–2141; Richard Q. Bergling, Chief Executive Officer

SATANTA DISTRICT HOSPITAL AND LONG TERM CARE, 401 South Cheyenne Street, Satanta, KS, Zip 67870–0159, Mailing Address: P.O. Box 159, Zip 67870–0159, tel. 620/649–2761; Jeremy Clingenpeel, Administrator

SCOTT COUNTY HOSPITAL, 201 East Albert Avenue, Scott City, KS, Zip 67871–1203; tel. 620/872–5811; Mark Burnett, President and Chief Executive Officer

SOUTHWEST MEDICAL CENTER, 315 West 15th Street, Liberal, KS, Zip 67901–2455, Mailing Address: Box 1340, Zip 67905–1340, tel. 620/624–1651; William Ermann, President and Chief Executive Officer

ST. CATHERINE HOSPITAL, 401 East Spruce Street, Garden City, KS, Zip 67846–5679; tel. 620/272–2561; Scott J. Taylor, President and Chief Executive Officer

STANTON COUNTY HOSPITAL, 404 North Chestnut Street, Johnson, KS, Zip 67855–5001, Mailing Address: P.O. Box 779, Zip 67855–0779, tel. 620/492–6250; Jay Tusten, Chief Executive Officer

STEVENS COUNTY HOSPITAL, 1006 South Jackson Street, Hugoton, KS, Zip 67951–2858, Mailing Address: P.O. Box 10, Zip 67951–0010, tel. 620/544–8511; Linda Stalcup, Chief Executive Officer

WICHITA COUNTY HEALTH CENTER, 211 East Earl Street, Leoti, KS, Zip 67861–9620; tel. 620/375–2233; Teresa Clark, Chief Executive Officer and Administrator

SUNFLOWER HEALTH NETWORK
400 South Santa Fe Avenue, Salina, KS, Zip 67401–4144; tel. 785/452–6102; Heather Fuller, Executive Director

CLAY COUNTY MEDICAL CENTER, 617 Liberty Street, Clay Center, KS, Zip 67432–1564, Mailing Address: P.O. Box 512, Zip 67432–0512, tel. 785/632–2144; Austin M. Gillard, Chief Executive Officer

CLOUD COUNTY HEALTH CENTER, 1100 Highland Drive, Concordia, KS, Zip 66901–3923; tel. 785/243–1234; David Garnas, Administrator

ELLSWORTH COUNTY MEDICAL CENTER, 1604 Aylward Street, Ellsworth, KS, Zip 67439–0087, Mailing Address: P.O. Box 87, Zip 67439–0087, tel. 785/472–3111; John R. Broberg, FACHE, Interim Chief Executive Officer

HERINGTON MUNICIPAL HOSPITAL, 100 East Helen Street, Herington, KS, Zip 67449–1606; tel. 785/258–2207; Isabel Schmedemann, R.N., Chief Executive Officer and Administrator

HILLSBORO COMMUNITY HOSPITAL, 701 South Main Street, Hillsboro, KS, Zip 67063–1553; tel. 620/947–3114; Marion Regier, Chief Executive Officer

HOSPITAL DISTRICT NO 1 OF RICE COUNTY, 619 South Clark Street, Lyons, KS, Zip 67554–3003, Mailing Address: P.O. Box 828, Zip 67554–0828, tel. 620/257–5173; George M. Stover, Chief Executive Officer

JEWELL COUNTY HOSPITAL, 100 Crestvue Avenue, Mankato, KS, Zip 66956–2407, Mailing Address: P.O. Box 327, Zip 66956–0327, tel. 785/378–3137; Doyle L. McKimmy, FACHE, Chief Executive Officer

LINCOLN COUNTY HOSPITAL, 624 North Second Street, Lincoln, KS, Zip 67455–1738, Mailing Address: P.O. Box 406, Zip 67455–0406, tel. 785/524–4403; Steven L. Granzow, Chief Executive Officer

LINDSBORG COMMUNITY HOSPITAL, 605 West Lincoln Street, Lindsborg, KS, Zip 67456–2328; tel. 785/227–3308; Larry VanDerWege, Administrator

MEMORIAL HEALTH SYSTEM, 511 NE Tenth Street, Abilene, KS, Zip 67410–2153; tel. 785/263–2100; Harold Courtois, Chief Executive Officer

MITCHELL COUNTY HOSPITAL HEALTH SYSTEMS, 400 West Eighth, Beloit, KS, Zip 67420–1605, Mailing Address: P.O. Box 399, Zip 67420–0399, tel. 785/738–2266; Jeremy Armstrong, FACHE, Chief Executive Officer

OSBORNE COUNTY MEMORIAL HOSPITAL, 424 West New Hampshire Street, Osborne, KS, Zip 67473–2314, Mailing Address: P.O. Box 70, Zip 67473–0070, tel. 785/346–2121; Marianna Harris, Administrator

OTTAWA COUNTY HEALTH CENTER, 215 East Eighth, Minneapolis, KS, Zip 67467–1902, Mailing Address: P.O. Box 290, Zip 67467–0290, tel. 785/392–2122; Jody Parks, Administrator

REPUBLIC COUNTY HOSPITAL, 2420 'G' Street, Belleville, KS, Zip 66935–2400; tel. 785/527–2254; David-Paul Cavazos, Chief Executive Officer

SALINA REGIONAL HEALTH CENTER, 400 South Santa Fe Avenue, Salina, KS, Zip 67401–4198, Mailing Address: P.O. Box 5080, Zip 67402–5080, tel. 785/452–7000; Micheal Terry, President and Chief Executive Officer

SMITH COUNTY MEMORIAL HOSPITAL, 614 South Main Street, Smith Center, KS, Zip 66967–3001; tel. 785/282–6845; Allen Van Driel, FACHE, Administrator

KENTUCKY

COMMONWEALTH HEALTH CORPORATION
800 Park Street, Bowling Green, KY, Zip 42101–2356; tel. 270/745–1500; Connie Smith, FACHE, MSN, R.N., Chief Executive Officer

COMMONWEALTH REGIONAL SPECIALTY HOSPITAL, 250 Park Drive, 6th Floor, Bowling Green, KY, Zip 42101–1760, Mailing Address: P.O. Box 90010, Zip 42102–9010, tel. 270/796–6200; Christa Atkins, Administrator

MEDICAL CENTER AT BOWLING GREEN, 250 Park Street, Bowling Green, KY, Zip 42101–1795, Mailing Address: P.O. Box 90010, Zip 42102–9010, tel. 270/745–1000; Connie Smith, FACHE, MSN, R.N., Chief Executive Officer

MEDICAL CENTER AT FRANKLIN, 1100 Brookhaven Road, Franklin, KY, Zip 42134–2746; tel. 270/598–4800; Annette Runyon, Vice President and Administrator

MEDICAL CENTER AT SCOTTSVILLE, 456 Burnley Road, Scottsville, KY, Zip 42164–6355; tel. 270/622–2800; Eric Hagan, R.N., Executive Vice President and Administrator

COMMUNITY CARE NETWORK
110 A Second Street, Henderson, KY, Zip 42420; tel. 619/278–2273; Roberta Alexander, Director

BAPTIST HEALTH MADISONVILLE, 900 Hospital Drive, Madisonville, KY, Zip 42431–1694; tel. 270/825–5100; Robert L. Ramey, President

BAPTIST HEALTH PADUCAH, 2501 Kentucky Avenue, Paducah, KY, Zip 42003–3200; tel. 270/575–2100; Christopher Roty, Interim President

CALDWELL MEDICAL CENTER, 100 Medical Center Drive, Princeton, KY, Zip 42445–2430, Mailing Address: P.O. Box 410, Zip 42445–0410, tel. 270/365–0300; Daniel Odegaard, FACHE, Chief Executive Officer

CRITTENDEN COUNTY HOSPITAL, 520 West Gum Street, Marion, KY, Zip 42064–1516, Mailing Address: P.O. Box 386, Zip 42064–0386, tel. 270/965–5281; Daniel Hiben, Chief Executive Officer

HEALTHSOUTH DEACONESS REHABILITATION HOSPITAL, 4100 Covert Avenue, Evansville, IN, Zip 47714–5567, Mailing Address: P.O. Box 5349, Zip 47716–5349, tel. 812/476–9983; Blake Bunner, Chief Executive Officer

JENNIE STUART MEDICAL CENTER, 320 West 18th Street, Hopkinsville, KY, Zip 42240–1965, Mailing Address: P.O. Box 2400, Zip 42241–2400, tel. 270/887–0100; Eric A. Lee, President and Chief Executive Officer

LINCOLN TRAIL BEHAVIORAL HEALTH SYSTEM, 3909 South Wilson Road, Radcliff, KY, Zip 40160–8944, Mailing Address: P.O. Box 369, Zip 40159–0369, tel. 270/351–9444; Charles L. Webb, Jr., Chief Executive Officer

LIVINGSTON HOSPITAL AND HEALTHCARE SERVICES, 131 Hospital Drive, Salem, KY, Zip 42078–8043; tel. 270/988–2299; Elizabeth Snodgrass, Chief Executive Officer

MEDICAL CENTER AT FRANKLIN, 1100 Brookhaven Road, Franklin, KY, Zip 42134–2746; tel. 270/598–4800; Annette Runyon, Vice President and Administrator

METHODIST HOSPITAL UNION COUNTY, 4604 Highway 60 West, Morganfield, KY, Zip 42437–9570; tel. 270/389–5000; Lynn R. Steinwachs, Vice President and Administrator

METHODIST HOSPITAL, 1305 North Elm Street, Henderson, KY, Zip 42420–2775, Mailing Address: P.O. Box 48, Zip 42419–0048, tel. 270/827–7700; Benny Nolen, President and Chief Executive Officer

MURRAY-CALLOWAY COUNTY HOSPITAL, 803 Poplar Street, Murray, KY, Zip 42071–2432; tel. 270/762–1100; Colonel, Jerome Penner, Chief Executive Officer

NORTON CHILDREN'S HOSPITAL, 231 East Chestnut Street, Louisville, KY, Zip 40202–1821; tel. 502/629–6000; Emmett Ramser, Chief Administrative Officer

NORTON HOSPITAL, 200 East Chestnut Street, Louisville, KY, Zip 40202–1800, Mailing Address: P.O. Box 35070, Zip 40232–5070, tel. 502/629–8000; Matthew Ayers, Chief Administrative Officer

OHIO COUNTY HOSPITAL, 1211 Main Street, Hartford, KY, Zip 42347–1619; tel. 270/298–7411; Blaine Pieper, Chief Executive Officer

OWENSBORO HEALTH MUHLENBERG COMMUNITY HOSPITAL, 440 Hopkinsville Street, Greenville, KY, Zip 42345–1172, Mailing Address: P.O. Box 387, Zip 42345–0378, tel. 270/338–8000; Ed Heath, FACHE, Chief Executive Officer

RIVERVALLEY BEHAVIORAL HEALTH HOSPITAL, 1000 Industrial Drive, Owensboro, KY, Zip 42301–8715; tel. 270/689–6500; Wanda Figuerora Peralta, President and Chief Executive Officer

SAINT THOMAS WEST HOSPITAL, 4220 Harding Road, Nashville, TN, Zip 37205–2095, Mailing Address: P.O. Box 380, Zip 37202–0380, tel. 615/222–2111; Fahad Tahir, Chief Executive Officer

ST. VINCENT EVANSVILLE, 3700 Washington Avenue, Evansville, IN, Zip 47714–0541; tel. 812/485–4000; Daniel A. Parod, President

STS. MARY & ELIZABETH HOSPITAL, 1850 Bluegrass Avenue, Louisville, KY, Zip 40215–1199; tel. 502/361–6000; Charles Powell, President

TRIGG COUNTY HOSPITAL, 254 Main Street, Cadiz, KY, Zip 42211–9153, Mailing Address: P.O. Box 312, Zip 42211–0312, tel. 270/522–3215; John Sumner, Chief Executive Officer

KENTUCKYONE
200 Abraham Flexner Way, Louisville, KY, Zip 40202–2877; tel. 502/587–4011; Charles W. Neumann, Interim President and Chief Executive Officer

CONTINUING CARE HOSPITAL, 1 Saint Joseph Drive, Lexington, KY, Zip 40504–3742; tel. 859/967–5744; Robert C. Desotelle, President and Chief Executive Officer

FLAGET MEMORIAL HOSPITAL, 4305 New Shepherdsville Road, Bardstown, KY, Zip 40004–9019; tel. 502/350–5000; Jennifer Nolan, President and Chief Executive Officer

JEWISH HOSPITAL-SHELBYVILLE, 727 Hospital Drive, Shelbyville, KY, Zip 40065–1699; tel. 502/647–4000; Annessa Baker, Site Executive and Chief Nursing Officer

JEWISH HOSPITAL, 200 Abraham Flexner Way, Louisville, KY, Zip 40202–1886; tel. 502/587–4011; Charles W. Neumann, President and Chief Medical Officer

OUR LADY OF PEACE, 2020 Newburg Road, Louisville, KY, Zip 40205–1879; tel. 502/479–4500; Jennifer Nolan, President and Chief Executive Officer

SAINT JOSEPH LONDON, 1001 Saint Joseph Lane, London, KY, Zip 40741–8345; tel. 606/330–6000; Terrence G. Deis, CPA, FACHE, President

SAINT JOSEPH BEREA, 305 Estill Street, Berea, KY, Zip 40403–1909; tel. 859/986–3151; Terrence G. Deis, CPA, FACHE, President

SAINT JOSEPH EAST, 150 North Eagle Creek Drive, Lexington, KY, Zip 40509–1805; tel. 859/967–5000; Eric Gilliam, President

SAINT JOSEPH HOSPITAL, One St Joseph Drive, Lexington, KY, Zip 40504–3754; tel. 859/278–3436; Bruce J. Tassin, President

SAINT JOSEPH MOUNT STERLING, 225 Falcon Drive, Mount Sterling, KY, Zip 40353–1158, Mailing Address: P.O. Box 7, Zip 40353–0007, tel. 859/497–5000; Terrence G. Deis, CPA, FACHE, President

STS. MARY & ELIZABETH HOSPITAL, 1850 Bluegrass Avenue, Louisville, KY, Zip 40215–1199; tel. 502/361–6000; Charles Powell, President

ST. ELIZABETH HEALTHCARE
1 Medical Village Drive, Edgewood, KY, Zip 41017–3403; tel. 859/301–2000; Garren Colvin, Chief Executive Officer

ST. ELIZABETH EDGEWOOD, 1 Medical Village Drive, Edgewood, KY, Zip 41017–3403; tel. 859/301–2000; Garren Colvin, Chief Executive Officer

ST. ELIZABETH FLORENCE, 4900 Houston Road, Florence, KY, Zip 41042–4824; tel. 859/212–5200; Garren Colvin, Chief Executive Officer

ST. ELIZABETH FORT THOMAS, 85 North Grand Avenue, Fort Thomas, KY, Zip 41075–1796; tel. 859/572–3100; Garren Colvin, Chief Executive Officer

ST. ELIZABETH GRANT , 238 Barnes Road, Williamstown, KY, Zip 41097–9482; tel. 859/824–8240; Garren Colvin, Chief Executive Officer

MASSACHUSETTS

LAHEY HEALTH
41 Mall Road, Burlington, MA, Zip 01805–0001; tel. 781/744–7100; Howard R. Grant, M.D., President and Chief Executive Officer

BEVERLY HOSPITAL, 85 Herrick Street, Beverly, MA, Zip 01915–1777; tel. 978/922–3000; Philip M. Cormier, Chief Executive Officer

LAHEY HOSPITAL & MEDICAL CENTER, BURLINGTON, 41 Mall Road, Burlington, MA, Zip 01805–0001; tel. 781/744–5100; David L. Longworth, MD, Chief Executive Officer

WINCHESTER HOSPITAL, 41 Highland Avenue, Winchester, MA, Zip 01890–1496; tel. 781/729–9000; Richard I. Weiner, M.D., Chief Executive Officer and Chief Medical Officer

WELLFORCE
1600 District Avenue, Suite 125, Burlington, MA, Zip 01803–5217; tel. 978/942–2220; Normand E. Deschene, FACHE, Chief Executive Officer

LOWELL GENERAL HOSPITAL, 295 Varnum Avenue, Lowell, MA, Zip 01854–2134; tel. 978/937–6000; Joseph White, FACHE, President and Chief Executive Officer

MELROSEWAKEFIELD HEALTHCARE, 585 Lebanon Street, Melrose, MA, Zip 02176–3225; tel. 781/979–3000; Susan Sandberg, R.N., Chief Executive Officer

TUFTS MEDICAL CENTER, 800 Washington Street, Boston, MA, Zip 02111–1552; tel. 617/636–5000; Michael Apkon, MD, PhD, Chief Executive Officer

MICHIGAN

GENESYS HEALTH SYSTEM
1 Genesys Parkway, Grand Blanc, MI, Zip 48439–8065; tel. 810/606–5000; Elizabeth Aderholdt, Chief Executive Officer

ST. JOHN MACOMB-OAKLAND HOSPITAL, 11800 East 12 Mile Road, Warren, MI, Zip 48093–3472; tel. 586/573–5000; Terry Hamilton, President

ST. JOSEPH HEALTH SYSTEM, 200 Hemlock Street, Tawas City, MI, Zip 48763–9237, Mailing Address: P.O. Box 659, Zip 48764–0659, tel. 989/362–3411; Jan Jacob, R.N., Interim Administrator

ST. MARY'S OF MICHIGAN, 800 South Washington Avenue, Saginaw, MI, Zip 48601–2594; tel. 989/907–8000; Chris Palazzolo, Health System President and Chief Executive Officer Mid-Michigan

LAKELAND REGIONAL HEALTH SYSTEM
1234 Napier Avenue, Saint Joseph, MI, Zip 49085–2112; tel. 269/983–8300; Loren Hamel, M.D., President and Chief Executive Officer

LAKELAND HOSPITAL, WATERVLIET, 400 Medical Park Drive, Watervliet, MI, Zip 49098–9225; tel. 269/463–3111; Ray Cruse, Chief Executive Officer

LAKELAND MEDICAL CENTER, ST. JOSEPH, 1234 Napier Avenue, Saint Joseph, MI, Zip 49085–2158; tel. 269/983–8300; Loren Hamel, M.D., President and Chief Executive Officer

ST. JOHN PROVIDENCE HEALTH SYSTEM
28000 Dequindre Drive, Warren, MI, Zip 48092; tel. 866/501–3627; Jean Meyer, President and Chief Executive Officer

ASCENSION ST. JOHN HOSPITAL, 22101 Moross Road, Detroit, MI, Zip 48236–2148; tel. 313/343–4000; Robert E. Hoban, President

BRIGHTON CENTER FOR RECOVERY, 12851 Grand River Road, Brighton, MI, Zip 48116–8506; tel. 810/227–1211; Raymond A. Waller, Director

PROVIDENCE-PROVIDENCE PARK HOSPITALS, 16001 West Nine Mile Road, Southfield, MI, Zip 48075; tel. 248/849–3400; Joseph R. Hurshe, President

ST. JOHN MACOMB-OAKLAND HOSPITAL, 11800 East 12 Mile Road, Warren, MI, Zip 48093–3472; tel. 586/573–5000; Terry Hamilton, President

ST. JOHN RIVER DISTRICT HOSPITAL, 4100 River Road, East China, MI, Zip 48054–2909; tel. 810/329–7111; Robert E. Hoban, President

UPPER PENINSULA HEALTH CARE NETWORK (UPHCN)
228 West Washington Street, Marquette, MI, Zip 49855–4330; tel. 906/225–3146; Dennis Smith, Chief Executive Officer

ASPIRUS IRON RIVER HOSPITALS & CLINICS, INC., 1400 West Ice Lake Road, Iron River, MI, Zip 49935–9526; tel. 906/265–6121; Connie L. Koutouzos, R.N., MSN, Chief Executive Officer

ASPIRUS IRONWOOD HOSPITALS & CLINICS, INC., N10561 Grand View Lane, Ironwood, MI, Zip 49938–9622; tel. 906/932–2525; Paula L. Chermside, Chief Executive Officer

ASPIRUS KEWEENAW HOSPITAL, INC., 205 Osceola Street, Laurium, MI, Zip 49913–2134; tel. 906/337–6500; Jesse G. Tischer, Interim Presidnet

ASPIRUS ONTONAGON HOSPITAL, INC., 601 South Seventh Street, Ontonagon, MI, Zip 49953–1459; tel. 906/884–8000; Jesse G. Tischer, Interim President

BARAGA COUNTY MEMORIAL HOSPITAL, 18341 U.S. Highway 41, L'Anse, MI, Zip 49946–8024; tel. 906/524–3300; Margie Hale, R.N., MSN, Chief Executive Officer

DICKINSON COUNTY HEALTHCARE SYSTEM, 1721 South Stephenson Avenue, Iron Mountain, MI, Zip 49801–3637; tel. 906/774–1313; John Schon, Administrator and Chief Executive Officer

HELEN NEWBERRY JOY HOSPITAL, Helen Newberry Joy Hospital Annex, 502 West Harrie Street, Newberry, MI, Zip 49868–1209; tel. 906/293–9200; Scott Pillion, Chief Executive Officer

MACKINAC STRAITS HEALTH SYSTEM, INC., 1140 North State Street, Saint Ignace, MI, Zip 49781–1048; tel. 906/643–8585; Karen Cheeseman, Chief Executive Officer

MUNISING MEMORIAL HOSPITAL, 1500 Sand Point Road, Munising, MI, Zip 49862–1406; tel. 906/387–4110; Melissa Hall, Chief Executive Officer

SCHOOLCRAFT MEMORIAL HOSPITAL, 7870W US Highway 2, Manistique, MI, Zip 49854–8992; tel. 906/341–3200; Robert Crumb, MS, Chief Executive Officer

UP HEALTH SYSTEM-BELL , 901 Lakeshore Drive, Ishpeming, MI, Zip 49849–1367; tel. 906/486–4431; Mitchell D. Leckelt, Chief Executive Officer

UP HEALTH SYSTEM-PORTAGE, 500 Campus Drive, Hancock, MI, Zip 49930–1569; tel. 906/483–1000; Randy Neiswonger, Chief Executive Officer

WAR MEMORIAL HOSPITAL, 500 Osborn Boulevard, Sault Sainte Marie, MI, Zip 49783–1884; tel. 906/635–4460; David B. Jahn, President and Chief Executive Officer

MINNESOTA

NORTHWEST METRO ALLIANCE
c/O Mercy Hospital, 4050 Coon Rapids Boulevard, Coon Rapids, MN, Zip 55433–2586; tel. 763/236–6000; Sara J. Criger, President

MERCY HOSPITAL, 4050 Coon Rapids Boulevard, Coon Rapids, MN, Zip 55433–2586; tel. 763/236–6000; Sara J. Criger, President

MISSOURI

HEALTH NETWORK OF MISSOURI
One Hospital Drive, Room C1213, DC 079.00, Columbia, MO, Zip 65212; tel. 573/815–8000; Marty McCormick, Chief Executive Officer

BOTHWELL REGIONAL HEALTH CENTER, 601 East 14th Street, Sedalia, MO, Zip 65301–5972, Mailing Address: P.O. Box 1706, Zip 65302–1706, tel. 660/826–8833; James A. Robertson, Jr., President and Chief Executive Officer

CAPITAL REGION MEDICAL CENTER, 1125 Madison Street, Jefferson City, MO, Zip 65101–5200, Mailing Address: P.O. Box 1128, Zip 65102–1128, tel. 573/632–5000; Gaspare Calvaruso, President

HANNIBAL REGIONAL HOSPITAL, 6000 Hospital Drive, Hannibal, MO, Zip 63401–6887, Mailing Address: P.O. Box 551, Zip 63401–0551, tel. 573/248–1300; C Todd. Ahrens, President and Chief Executive Officer

LAKE REGIONAL HEALTH SYSTEM, 54 Hospital Drive, Osage Beach, MO, Zip 65065–3050; tel. 573/348–8000; Dane W. Henry, Chief Executive Officer

SAINT FRANCIS MEDICAL CENTER, 211 St Francis Drive, Cape Girardeau, MO, Zip 63703–5049; tel. 573/331–3000; Maryann Reese, R.N., FACHE, President and Chief Executive Officer

UNIVERSITY OF MISSOURI HEALTH CARE, One Hospital Drive, Columbia, MO, Zip 65212–0001; tel. 573/882–4141; Jonathan W. Curtright, Chief Executive Officer and Chief Operating Officer

MERCY HEALTH EAST
615 South New Ballas Road, Saint Louis, MO, Zip 63141–8221; tel. 314/364–3000; Donn Sorensen, Regional President, West Communities

MERCY HOSPITAL JEFFERSON, Highway 61 South, Crystal City, MO, Zip 63019, Mailing Address: P.O. Box 350, Zip 63019–0350, tel. 636/933–1000; Eric Ammons, President

MERCY HOSPITAL ST. LOUIS , 615 South New Ballas Road, Saint Louis, MO, Zip 63141–8277; tel. 314/251–6000; Stephen Mackin, President

MERCY HOSPITAL WASHINGTON, 901 East Fifth Street, Washington, MO, Zip 63090–3127; tel. 636/239–8000; Eric J. Eoloff, President

MOSAIC LIFE CARE
5325 Faraon Street, Saint Joseph, MO, Zip 64506–3488; tel. 816/271–6000; Brady Dubois, President

LONG-TERM ACUTE CARE HOSPITAL, MOSAIC LIFE CARE AT ST. JOSEPH, 5325 Faraon Street, Saint Joseph, MO, Zip 64506–3488; tel. 816/271–6000; Dana Anderson, Administrator

MOSAIC LIFE CARE , 5325 Faraon Street, Saint Joseph, MO, Zip 64506–3488; tel. 816/271–6000; Samuel Mark. Laney, M.D., Chief Executive Officer

NORTHWEST MEDICAL CENTER, 705 North College Street, Albany, MO, Zip 64402–1433; tel. 660/726–3941; Jon D. Doolittle, Regional President

MONTANA

MONTANA HEALTH NETWORK
519 Pleasant Street, Miles City, MT, Zip 59301–3030; tel. 406/234–1420; Janet Bastian, Chief Executive Officer

BILLINGS CLINIC, 2800 10th Avenue North, Billings, MT, Zip 59101–0703, Mailing Address: P.O. Box 37000, Zip 59107–7000, tel. 406/657–4000; Randall K. Gibb, M.D., Chief Executive Officer

CENTRAL MONTANA MEDICAL CENTER, 408 Wendell Avenue, Lewistown, MT, Zip 59457–2261; tel. 406/535–7711; Michael Dowdy, Chief Executive Officer

DAHL MEMORIAL HEALTHCARE ASSOCIATION, 215 Sandy Street, Ekalaka, MT, Zip 59324, Mailing Address: P.O. Box 46, Zip 59324–0046, tel. 406/775–8730; Ryan Tooke, Chief Executive Officer

DANIELS MEMORIAL HEALTHCARE CENTER, 105 Fifth Avenue East, Scobey, MT, Zip 59263, Mailing Address: P.O. Box 400, Zip 59263–0400, tel. 406/487–2296; David Ryerse, Chief Executive Officer

FALLON MEDICAL COMPLEX, 202 South 4th Street West, Baker, MT, Zip 59313–9156, Mailing Address: P.O. Box 820, Zip 59313–0820, tel. 406/778–3331; David Espeland, Chief Executive Officer

FRANCES MAHON DEACONESS HOSPITAL, 621 Third Street South, Glasgow, MT, Zip 59230–2699; tel. 406/228–3500; Randall G. Holom, Chief Executive Officer

GLENDIVE MEDICAL CENTER, 202 Prospect Drive, Glendive, MT, Zip 59330–1999; tel. 406/345–3306; Parker Powell, Chief Executive Officer

HOLY ROSARY HEALTHCARE, 2600 Wilson Street, Miles City, MT, Zip 59301–5094; tel. 406/233–2600; Paul Lewis, Chief Executive Officer

MCCONE COUNTY HEALTH CENTER, 605 Sullivan Avenue, Circle, MT, Zip 59215, Mailing Address: P.O. Box 48, Zip 59215–0048, tel. 406/485–3381; Nancy Rosaaen, Chief Executive Officer

PHILLIPS COUNTY HOSPITAL, 311 South 8th Avenue East, Malta, MT, Zip 59538–0640, Mailing Address: P.O. Box 640, Zip 59538–0640, tel. 406/654–1100; Ward C. VanWichen, Chief Executive Officer

ROOSEVELT MEDICAL CENTER, 818 Second Avenue East, Culbertson, MT, Zip 59218, Mailing Address: P.O. Box 419, Zip 59218–0419, tel. 406/787–6401; Audrey Stromberg, Administrator

SHERIDAN MEMORIAL HOSPITAL, 440 West Laurel Avenue, Plentywood, MT, Zip 59254–1596; tel. 406/765–3700; Gregory L. Maurer, Chief Executive Officer

SIDNEY HEALTH CENTER, 216 14th Avenue SW, Sidney, MT, Zip 59270–3586; tel. 406/488–2100; Richard Haraldson, Chief Executive Officer

STILLWATER BILLINGS CLINIC, 44 West Fourth Avenue North, Columbus, MT, Zip 59019–0959, Mailing Address: P.O. Box 959, Zip 59019–0959, tel. 406/322–5316; David Ryerse, Chief Executive Officer

WHEATLAND MEMORIAL HEALTHCARE, 530 Third Street North West, Harlowton, MT, Zip 59036, Mailing Address: P.O. Box 287, Zip 59036–0287, tel. 406/632–4351; Mary J. Ruyter, Interim Chief Executive Officer

NEBRASKA

CHI HEALTH
12809 West Dodge Road, Omaha, NE, Zip 68154–2155; tel. 402/343–4300; Cliff Robertson, M.D., President and Chief Executive Officer

CHI HEALTH CREIGHTON UNIVERSITY MEDICAL CENTER - BERGAN MERCY, 7500 Mercy Road, Omaha, NE, Zip 68124–2319; tel. 402/398–6060; Kevin J. Nokels, FACHE, President

CHI HEALTH GOOD SAMARITAN , 10 East 31st Street, Kearney, NE, Zip 68847–2926, Mailing Address: P.O. Box 1990, Zip 68848–1990, tel. 308/865–7100; Michael H. Schnieders, FACHE, President

Health Care Systems, Networks and Alliances

CHI HEALTH IMMANUEL, 6901 North 72nd Street, Omaha, NE, Zip 68122–1799; tel. 402/572–2121; Ann Schumacher, R.N., MSN, FACHE, President

CHI HEALTH LAKESIDE , 16901 Lakeside Hills Court, Omaha, NE, Zip 68130–2318; tel. 402/717–8000; Kevin Miller, President

CHI HEALTH MERCY CORNING, 603 Rosary Drive, Corning, IA, Zip 50841–1683; tel. 641/322–3121; Lisa Wolfe, President

CHI HEALTH MERCY COUNCIL BLUFFS, 800 Mercy Drive, Council Bluffs, IA, Zip 51503–3128; tel. 712/328–5000; Marie E. Knedler, R.N., FACHE, President

CHI HEALTH MIDLANDS , 11111 South 84th Street, Papillion, NE, Zip 68046–4122; tel. 402/593–3000; Kevin Miller, President

CHI HEALTH MISSOURI VALLEY, 631 North Eighth Street, Missouri Valley, IA, Zip 51555–1102; tel. 712/642–2784; Robert A. Valentine, President

CHI HEALTH NEBRASKA HEART , 7500 South 91st Street, Lincoln, NE, Zip 68526–9437; tel. 402/327–2700; Derek Vance, President

CHI HEALTH PLAINVIEW , 704 North Third Street, Plainview, NE, Zip 68769–2047, Mailing Address: P.O. Box 489, Zip 68769–0489, tel. 402/582–4245; Gregory Beckmann, Chief Executive Officer

CHI HEALTH SAINT FRANCIS, 2620 West Faidley Avenue, Grand Island, NE, Zip 68803–4297, Mailing Address: P.O. Box 9804, Zip 68802–9804, tel. 308/384–4600; Edward J. Hannon, FACHE, President

CHI HEALTH SCHUYLER, 104 West 17th Street, Schuyler, NE, Zip 68661–1304; tel. 402/352–2441; Connie Peters, R.N., President

CHI HEALTH ST ELIZABETH , 555 South 70th Street, Lincoln, NE, Zip 68510–2494; tel. 402/219–8000; Derek Vance, President

CHI HEALTH ST. MARY'S , 1301 Grundman Boulevard, Nebraska City, NE, Zip 68410; tel. 402/873–3321; Daniel DeFreece, M.D., Interim President

NEBRASKA MEDICINE
987400 Nebraska Medical Center, Omaha, NE, Zip 68198–7400; tel. 877/763–0000; James Linder, M.D., Chief Executive Officer

NEBRASKA MEDICINE - BELLEVUE, 2500 Bellevue Medical Center Drive, Bellevue, NE, Zip 68123–1591; tel. 402/763–3000; Matt E. Pospisil, Vice President Perioperative Services

NEBRASKA MEDICINE - NEBRASKA MEDICAL CENTER, 987400 Nebraska Medical Center, Omaha, NE, Zip 68198–7400; tel. 402/552–2000; James Linder, M.D., Chief Executive Officer

NORTHEAST HEALTH SERVICES
704 North Third Street, c/o CHI Plainview, Plainview, NE, Zip 68769–2047; tel. 402/358–5700; Gregory Beckmann, Chief Executive Officer

AVERA CREIGHTON HOSPITAL, 1503 Main Street, Creighton, NE, Zip 68729–3007, Mailing Address: P.O. Box 186, Zip 68729–0186, tel. 402/358–5700; Todd Consbruck, Chief Executive Officer

CHI HEALTH PLAINVIEW , 704 North Third Street, Plainview, NE, Zip 68769–2047, Mailing Address: P.O. Box 489, Zip 68769–0489, tel. 402/582–4245; Gregory Beckmann, Chief Executive Officer

OSMOND GENERAL HOSPITAL, 402 North Maple Street, Osmond, NE, Zip 68765–5726, Mailing Address: P.O. Box 429, Zip 68765–0429, tel. 402/748–3393; Lon Knievel, Chief Executive Officer

NEW HAMPSHIRE

CARING COMMUNITY NETWORK OF THE TWIN RIVERS
c/o First Health, 841 Central Street, Franklin, NH, Zip 03235–2026; tel. 603/934–0177; Rick Silverberg, Managing Director

FRANKLIN REGIONAL HOSPITAL, 15 Aiken Avenue, Franklin, NH, Zip 03235–1299; tel. 603/934–2060; Kevin Donovan, FACHE, President and Chief Executive Officer

NEW JERSEY

QUALCARE, INC.
242 Old New Brunswick Road, Piscataway, NJ, Zip 08854–3754; tel. 732/562–2800; Jerry Eisenberg, Network Contact

CAPITAL HEALTH MEDICAL CENTER-HOPEWELL, 1 Capital Way, Pennington, NJ, Zip 08534–2520; tel. 609/303–4000; Al Maghazehe, Ph.D., FACHE, President and Chief Executive Officer

CAREPOINT HEALTH CHRIST HOSPITAL, 176 Palisade Avenue, Jersey City, NJ, Zip 07306–1196, Mailing Address: 176 Palisades Avenue, Zip 07306–1196, tel. 201/795–8200; Marie Theresa Duffy, Chief Operating Officer

CHILTON MEDICAL CENTER, 97 West Parkway, Pompton Plains, NJ, Zip 07444–1696; tel. 973/831–5000; Stephanie L. Schwartz, FACHE, Vice President AHS and President CMC

CLARA MAASS MEDICAL CENTER, One Clara Maass Drive, Belleville, NJ, Zip 07109–3557; tel. 973/450–2000; Mary Ellen Clyne, Ph.D., President and Chief Executive Officer

DEBORAH HEART AND LUNG CENTER, 200 Trenton Road, Browns Mills, NJ, Zip 08015–1705; tel. 609/893–6611; Joseph Chirichella, President and Chief Executive Officer

ENGLEWOOD HOSPITAL AND MEDICAL CENTER, 350 Engle Street, Englewood, NJ, Zip 07631–1898; tel. 201/894–3000; Warren Geller, President and Chief Executive Officer

HACKENSACK MERIDIAN HEALTH HACKENSACK UNIVERSITY MEDICAL CENTER, 30 Prospect Avenue, Hackensack, NJ, Zip 07601–1914; tel. 201/996–2000; Ihor S. Sawczuk, M.D., FACS, President

HACKENSACK MERIDIAN HEALTH JFK MEDICAL CENTER, 65 James Street, Edison, NJ, Zip 8818; tel. 732/321–7000; Raymond F. Fredericks, Central Regional President

HACKENSACK MERIDIAN HEALTH OCEAN MEDICAL CENTER, 425 Jack Martin Boulevard, Brick Township, NJ, Zip 08724–7732; tel. 732/840–2200; Dean Q. Lin, FACHE, Regional President

HACKENSACK MERIDIAN HEALTH RARITAN BAY MEDICAL CENTER, 530 New Brunswick Avenue, Perth Amboy, NJ, Zip 08861–3654; tel. 732/442–3700; Thomas Shanahan, Chief Operating Officer

HACKENSACK MERIDIAN HEALTH RIVERVIEW MEDICAL CENTER, 1 Riverview Plaza, Red Bank, NJ, Zip 07701–1864; tel. 732/741–2700; Timothy J. Hogan, FACHE, President, RMC and BMC

HACKETTSTOWN MEDICAL CENTER, 651 Willow Grove Street, Hackettstown, NJ, Zip 07840–1799; tel. 908/852–5100; Joseph DiPaolo, FACHE, President

INSPIRA MEDICAL CENTER-VINELAND, 1505 West Sherman Avenue, Vineland, NJ, Zip 08360–6912; tel. 856/641–8000; John A. DiAngelo, President and Chief Executive Officer

MEMORIAL HOSPITAL OF SALEM COUNTY, 310 Woodstown Road, Salem, NJ, Zip 08079–2080; tel. 856/935–1000; Tammy Torres, R.N., MSN, Chief Executive Officer

PENN MEDICINE PRINCETON MEDICAL CENTER, One Plainsboro Road, Plainsboro, NJ, Zip 08536–1913; tel. 609/853–7100; Barry S. Rabner, President and Chief Executive Officer, Princeton Healthcare System

PIEDMONT MOUNTAINSIDE HOSPITAL, 1266 Highway 515 South, Jasper, GA, Zip 30143–4872; tel. 706/692–2441; Denise Ray, Chief Executive Officer

ROBERT WOOD JOHNSON UNIVERSITY HOSPITAL, 1 Robert Wood Johnson Place, New Brunswick, NJ, Zip 08901–1928; tel. 732/828–3000; John J. Gantner, President and Chief Executive Officer

SAINT MICHAEL'S MEDICAL CENTER, 111 Central Avenue, Newark, NJ, Zip 07102–1909; tel. 973/877–5350; Robert C. Iannaccone, JD, Chief Executive Officer

ST. MARY'S GENERAL HOSPITAL, 350 Boulevard, Passaic, NJ, Zip 07055–2840; tel. 973/365–4300; Edward Condit, President and Chief Executive Officer

UNIVERSITY HOSPITAL, 150 Bergen Street, Newark, NJ, Zip 07103–2496; tel. 973/972–4300; John N. Kastanis, FACHE, President and Chief Executive Officer

VIRTUA MARLTON, 90 Brick Road, Marlton, NJ, Zip 08053–2177; tel. 856/355–6000; Lisa Ferraro, Senior Vice President and Chief Operating Officer

NEW MEXICO

NEW MEXICO RURAL HOSPITAL NETWORK
7471 Pan American Freeway NE, Albuquerque, NM, Zip 87109; tel. 505/346–0216; Stephen Stoddard, FACHE, Executive Director

ARTESIA GENERAL HOSPITAL, 702 North 13th Street, Artesia, NM, Zip 88210–1199; tel. 575/748–3333; Robert C. Tyk, Interim Chief Executive Officer

CIBOLA GENERAL HOSPITAL, 1016 East Roosevelt Avenue, Grants, NM, Zip 87020–2118; tel. 505/287–4446; Thomas Whelan, Chief Executive Officer

GUADALUPE COUNTY HOSPITAL, 117 Camino de Vida, Santa Rosa, NM, Zip 88435–2267; tel. 575/472–3417; Christina Campos, Administrator

HOLY CROSS HOSPITAL, 1397 Weimer Road, Taos, NM, Zip 87571–6253; tel. 575/758–8883; William D. Patten, Jr., Chief Executive Officer

MINERS' COLFAX MEDICAL CENTER, 200 Hospital Drive, Raton, NM, Zip 87740–2099; tel. 575/445–7700; Bo Beames, Interim Chief Executive Officer

NOR-LEA HOSPITAL DISTRICT, 1600 North Main Avenue, Lovington, NM, Zip 88260–2871; tel. 575/396–6611; David B. Shaw, Chief Executive Officer and Administrator

REHOBOTH MCKINLEY CHRISTIAN HEALTH CARE SERVICES, 1901 Red Rock Drive, Gallup, NM, Zip 87301–5683; tel. 505/863–7000; David Conejo, Chief Executive Officer

ROOSEVELT GENERAL HOSPITAL, 42121 U S Highway 70, Portales, NM, Zip 88130, Mailing Address: P.O. Box 868, Zip 88130–0868, tel. 575/359–1800; Kaye Green, FACHE, Chief Executive Officer

SIERRA VISTA HOSPITAL, 800 East Ninth Avenue, Truth or Consequences, NM, Zip 87901–1961; tel. 575/894–2111; David Faulkner, Interim Chief Executive Officer

UNION COUNTY GENERAL HOSPITAL, 300 Wilson Street, Clayton, NM, Zip 88415–3304, Mailing Address: P.O. Box 489, Zip 88415–0489, tel. 575/374–2585; Tammie Stump, R.N., Chief Executive Officer

NEW YORK

ARDENT SOLUTIONS, INC.
85 North Main Street, Suite 4, Wellsville, NY, Zip 14895–1254; tel. 585/593–5223; Carrie Whitwood, Executive Director

JONES MEMORIAL HOSPITAL, 191 North Main Street, Wellsville, NY, Zip 14895–1150, Mailing Address: P.O. Box 72, Zip 14895–0072, tel. 585/593–1100; Eva Benedict, R.N., President and Chief Executive Officer

ARNOT HEALTH
600 Roe Avenue, Elmira, NY, Zip 14905–1629; tel. 607/737–4100; Robert K. Lambert, M.D., FACHE, President and Chief Executive Officer

ARNOT OGDEN MEDICAL CENTER, 600 Roe Avenue, Elmira, NY, Zip 14905–1629; tel. 607/737–4100; Jonathan I. Lawrence, System Chief Operating Officer

IRA DAVENPORT MEMORIAL HOSPITAL, 7571 State Route 54, Bath, NY, Zip 14810–9590; tel. 607/776–8500; Elizabeth Weir, MSN, R.N., Chief Executive Officer

ST. JOSEPH'S HOSPITAL, 555 St. Joseph's Boulevard, Elmira, NY, Zip 14901–3223; tel. 607/733–6541; Jonathan I. Lawrence, President and Chief Executive Officer

BASSETT HEALTHCARE NETWORK
1 Atwell Road, Cooperstown, NY, Zip 13326–1301; tel. 607/547–3456; William F. Streck, M.D., President and Chief Executive Officer

AURELIA OSBORN FOX MEMORIAL HOSPITAL, 1 Norton Avenue, Oneonta, NY, Zip 13820–2629; tel. 607/432–2000; Jeff Joyner, President

BASSETT MEDICAL CENTER, One Atwell Road, Cooperstown, NY, Zip 13326–1394; tel. 607/547–3456; William W. LeCates, M.D., President

COBLESKILL REGIONAL HOSPITAL, 178 Grandview Drive, Cobleskill, NY, Zip 12043–5144; tel. 518/254–3456; Eric H. Stein, FACHE, President

LITTLE FALLS HOSPITAL, 140 Burwell Street, Little Falls, NY, Zip 13365–1725; tel. 315/823–1000; Michael L. Ogden, President and Chief Executive Officer

O'CONNOR HOSPITAL, 460 Andes Road, State Route 28, Delhi, NY, Zip 13753–7407; tel. 607/746–0300; Scott Bonderoff, President

GREAT LAKES HEALTH SYSTEM OF WESTERN NEW YORK
726 Exchange Street, Suite 522, Buffalo, NY, Zip 14210–1485; tel. 716/859–8820; Jody Lomeo, Interim Chief Executive Officer

ERIE COUNTY MEDICAL CENTER, 462 Grider Street, Buffalo, NY, Zip 14215–3098; tel. 716/898–3000; Thomas J. Quatroche, Jr., Chief Executive Officer

KALEIDA HEALTH, 100 High Street, Buffalo, NY, Zip 14203–1154; tel. 716/859–5600; Jody Lomeo, Chief Executive Officer

LAKE ERIE REGIONAL HEALTH SYSTEM OF NEW YORK
529 Central Avenue, Dunkirk, NY, Zip 14048–2514; tel. 716/366–1111; J. Gary Rhodes, FACHE, Interim Chief Executive Officer

BROOKS MEMORIAL HOSPITAL, 529 Central Avenue, Dunkirk, NY, Zip 14048–2599; tel. 716/366–1111; Mary E. LaRowe, FACHE, President and Chief Executive Officer

MOHAWK VALLEY HEALTH SYSTEM (MVHS)
1656 Champlin Avenue, Utica, NY, Zip 13502–4830; tel. 315/624–6002; Scott H. Perra, FACHE, President and Chief Executive Officer

FAXTON ST. LUKE'S HEALTHCARE, 1656 Champlin Avenue, Utica, NY, Zip 13502–4830, Mailing Address: P.O. Box 479, Zip 13503–0479, tel. 315/624–6000; Scott H. Perra, FACHE, President and Chief Executive Officer

ST. ELIZABETH MEDICAL CENTER, 2209 Genesee Street, Utica, NY, Zip 13501–5999; tel. 315/798–8100; Scott H. Perra, FACHE, Chief Executive Officer

MOUNT SINAI NYU HEALTH NETWORK
One Gustave L. Levy Place, New York, NY, Zip 10029; tel. 212/659–8888; Arthur A. Klein, M.D., President

ENGLEWOOD HOSPITAL AND MEDICAL CENTER, 350 Engle Street, Englewood, NJ, Zip 07631–1898; tel. 201/894–3000; Warren Geller, President and Chief Executive Officer

HUDSON REGIONAL HOSPITAL, 55 Meadowlands Parkway, Secaucus, NJ, Zip 07094–2977; tel. 201/392–3100; Felicia Karsos, R.N., President and Chief Executive Officer

JAMES J. PETERS VETERANS AFFAIRS MEDICAL CENTER, 130 West Kingsbridge Road, Bronx, NY, Zip 10468–3904; tel. 718/584–9000; Erik Langhoff, M.D., Ph.D., Director

JERSEY CITY MEDICAL CENTER, 355 Grand Street, Jersey City, NJ, Zip 07302–4321; tel. 201/915–2000; Joseph F. Scott, FACHE, President and Chief Executive Officer

MORRISTOWN MEDICAL CENTER, 100 Madison Avenue, Morristown, NJ, Zip 07960–6136; tel. 973/971–5000; Trish O'Keefe, Ph.D., R.N., President

MOUNT SINAI HOSPITAL, One Gustave L Levy Place, P.O. Box 1068, New York, NY, Zip 10029–0310; tel. 212/241–6500; David L. Reich, M.D., President and Chief Operating Officer

NYC HEALTH + HOSPITALS / ELMHURST, 79–01 Broadway, Elmhurst, NY, Zip 11373–1329; tel. 718/334–4000; Israel Rocha, Jr., Chief Executive Officer

NYC HEALTH + HOSPITALS / QUEENS , 82–68 164th Street, Jamaica, NY, Zip 11432–1104; tel. 718/883–3000; Christopher Roker, Chief Executive Officer

OVERLOOK MEDICAL CENTER, 99 Beauvoir Avenue, Summit, NJ, Zip 07901–3533; tel. 908/522–2000; Alan R. Lieber, President

PHELPS MEMORIAL HOSPITAL CENTER, 701 North Broadway, Sleepy Hollow, NY, Zip 10591–1020; tel. 914/366–3000; Daniel Blum, President

ST. JOHN'S RIVERSIDE HOSPITAL, 967 North Broadway, Yonkers, NY, Zip 10701–1399; tel. 914/964–4444; Ronald J. Corti, President and Chief Executive Officer

ST. JOSEPH'S UNIVERSITY MEDICAL CENTER, 703 Main Street, Paterson, NJ, Zip 07503–2691; tel. 973/754–2000; Kevin J. Slavin, FACHE, President and Chief Executive Officer

ST. LUKE'S CORNWALL HOSPITAL, 70 Dubois Street, Newburgh, NY, Zip 12550–4851; tel. 845/561–4400; Joan Cusack-McGuirk, President and Chief Executive Officer

VASSAR BROTHERS MEDICAL CENTER, 45 Reade Place, Poughkeepsie, NY, Zip 12601–3947; tel. 845/454–8500; Ann McMackin, President

NEW YORK PRESBYTERIAN REGIONAL HOSPITAL NETWORK
525 East 68th Street, Box 182, New York, NY, Zip 10065–4870; tel. 212/746–3745; Steven J. Corwin, M.D., President and Chief Executive Officer

GRACIE SQUARE HOSPITAL, 420 East 76th Street, New York, NY, Zip 10021–3396; tel. 212/988–4400; David Wyman, President and Chief Executive Officer

NEW YORK COMMUNITY HOSPITAL, 2525 Kings Highway, Brooklyn, NY, Zip 11229–1705; tel. 718/692–5300; Barry Stern, President and Chief Executive Officer

NEWYORK-PRESBYTERIAN BROOKLYN METHODIST HOSPITAL, 506 Sixth Street, Brooklyn, NY, Zip 11215–3609; tel. 718/780–3000; Robert Guimento, President

RURAL HEALTH NETWORK OF OSWEGO COUNTY
10 George Street, Oswego, NY, Zip 13126; tel. 315/592–0827; Brian Coleman, Coordinator

OSWEGO HOSPITAL, 110 West Sixth Street, Oswego, NY, Zip 13126–2507; tel. 315/349–5511; Michael Harlovic, R.N., President and Chief Executive Officer

STELLARIS HEALTH
135 Bedford Rd, Armonk, NY, Zip 10504–1945; tel. 914/273–5454; Sharon A. Lucian, President and Chief Executive Officer

NORTHERN WESTCHESTER HOSPITAL, 400 East Main Street, Mount Kisco, NY, Zip 10549–3477, Mailing Address: 400 East Main Street, G-02, Zip 10549–3477, tel. 914/666–1200; Joel Seligman, President and Chief Executive Officer

PHELPS MEMORIAL HOSPITAL CENTER, 701 North Broadway, Sleepy Hollow, NY, Zip 10591–1020; tel. 914/366–3000; Daniel Blum, President

WHITE PLAINS HOSPITAL CENTER, 41 East Post Road, White Plains, NY, Zip 10601–4699; tel. 914/681–0600; Susan Fox, President and Chief Executive Officer

NORTH CAROLINA

COASTAL CAROLINAS HEALTH ALLIANCE
5305-M Wrightsville Avenue, Wilmington, NC, Zip 28403; tel. 910/332–8012; Yvonne Hughes, Chief Executive Officer

CAPE FEAR VALLEY - BLADEN COUNTY HOSPITAL, 501 South Poplar Street, Elizabethtown, NC, Zip 28337–9375, Mailing Address: P.O. Box 398, Zip 28337–0398, tel. 910/862–5100; Roxie Cannon. Wells, M.D., Chief Executive Officer

COLUMBUS REGIONAL HEALTHCARE SYSTEM, 500 Jefferson Street, Whiteville, NC, Zip 28472–3634; tel. 910/642–8011; John E. Young, Interim Chief Executive Officer

J. ARTHUR DOSHER MEMORIAL HOSPITAL, 924 North Howe Street, Southport, NC, Zip 28461–3099; tel. 910/457–3800; Thomas R. Siemers, Chief Executive Officer

MCLEOD LORIS SEACOAST HOSPITAL, 3655 Mitchell Street, Loris, SC, Zip 29569–2827; tel. 843/716–7000; Edward D. Tinsley, III., Regional Administrator

MCLEOD REGIONAL MEDICAL CENTER, 555 East Cheves Street, Florence, SC, Zip 29506–2617, Mailing Address: P.O. Box 100551, Zip 29502–0551, tel. 843/777–2000; Robert L. Colones, President and Chief Executive Officer

NEW HANOVER REGIONAL MEDICAL CENTER, 2131 South 17th Street, Wilmington, NC, Zip 28401–7483, Mailing Address: P.O. Box 9000, Zip 28402–9000, tel. 910/343–7000; Andre Boyd, Sr., Executive Vice President, Hospital Division

PENDER MEMORIAL HOSPITAL, 507 East Freemont Street, Burgaw, NC, Zip 28425–5131; tel. 910/259–5451; Ruth Glaser, President

SAMPSON REGIONAL MEDICAL CENTER, 607 Beaman Street, Clinton, NC, Zip 28328–2697, Mailing Address: P.O. Box 260, Zip 28329–0260, tel. 910/592–8511; Shawn Howerton, M.D., Chief Executive Officer and President, Medical Staff

SCOTLAND HEALTH CARE SYSTEM, 500 Lauchwood Drive, Laurinburg, NC, Zip 28352–5599; tel. 910/291–7000; Gregory C. Wood, President and Chief Executive Officer

SOUTHEASTERN HEALTH, 300 West 27th Street, Lumberton, NC, Zip 28358–3075, Mailing Address: P.O. Box 1408, Zip 28359–1408, tel. 910/671–5000; Joann Anderson, President and Chief Executive Officer

VIDANT DUPLIN HOSPITAL, 401 North Main Street, Kenansville, NC, Zip 28349–8801, Mailing Address: P.O. Box 278, Zip 28349–0278, tel. 910/296–0941; Jay Briley, President

VIDANT MEDICAL CENTER, 2100 Stantonsburg Road, Greenville, NC, Zip 27834–2818, Mailing Address: P.O. Box 6028, Zip 27835–6028, tel. 252/847–4100; William Brian. Floyd, President

MISSION HEALTH SYSTEM
509 Biltmore Avenue, Asheville, NC, Zip 28801–4601; tel. 828/213–1111; Ronald A. Paulus, M.D., President and Chief Executive Officer

ANGEL MEDICAL CENTER, 120 Riverview Street, Franklin, NC, Zip 28734–2612, Mailing Address: P.O. Box 1209, Zip 28744–0569, tel. 828/524–8411; Karen S. Gorby, R.N., MSN, FACHE, President and Chief Nursing Officer

ASHEVILLE SPECIALTY HOSPITAL, 428 Biltmore Avenue, 4th Floor, Asheville, NC, Zip 28801–4502; tel. 828/213–5400; Julie A. Dikos, MSN, R.N., President and Chief Executive Officer

BLUE RIDGE REGIONAL HOSPITAL, 125 Hospital Drive, Spruce Pine, NC, Zip 28777–3035; tel. 828/765–4201; Rebecca W. Carter, MSN, R.N., FACHE, Chief Executive Officer and Chief Nursing Officer

CAREPARTNERS HEALTH SERVICES, 68 Sweeten Creek Road, Asheville, NC, Zip 28803–2318, Mailing Address: P.O. Box 15025, Zip 28813–0025, tel. 828/277–4800; Tracy Buchanan, Chief Executive Officer and President

HIGHLANDS-CASHIERS HOSPITAL, 190 Hospital Drive, Highlands, NC, Zip 28741–7600, Mailing Address: P O Drawer 190, Zip 28741–0190, tel. 828/526–1200; Jacqueline Medland, MS, Ph.D., President and Chief Nursing Officer

MCDOWELL HOSPITAL, 430 Rankin Drive, Marion, NC, Zip 28752–6568, Mailing Address: P.O. Box 730, Zip 28752–0730, tel. 828/659–5000; Carol C. Wolfenbarger, FACHE, MSN, President

MISSION HOSPITAL, 509 Biltmore Avenue, Asheville, NC, Zip 28801–4690; tel. 828/213–1111; Jill Hoggard Green, Ph.D., R.N., President

TRANSYLVANIA REGIONAL HOSPITAL, 260 Hospital Drive, Brevard, NC, Zip 28712–3378; tel. 828/884–9111; Michele Pilon, President and Chief Nursing Officer

WNC HEALTH NETWORK, INC.
1200 Ridgefield Boulevard Suite 200, Asheville, NC, Zip 28806–2280; tel. 828/667–8220; Heather Gates, Executive Director

ANGEL MEDICAL CENTER, 120 Riverview Street, Franklin, NC, Zip 28734–2612, Mailing Address: P.O. Box 1209, Zip 28744–0569, tel. 828/524–8411; Karen S. Gorby, R.N., MSN, FACHE, President and Chief Nursing Officer

BLUE RIDGE REGIONAL HOSPITAL, 125 Hospital Drive, Spruce Pine, NC, Zip 28777–3035; tel. 828/765–4201; Rebecca W. Carter, MSN, R.N., FACHE, Chief Executive Officer and Chief Nursing Officer

CAREPARTNERS HEALTH SERVICES, 68 Sweeten Creek Road, Asheville, NC, Zip 28803–2318, Mailing Address: P.O. Box 15025, Zip 28813–0025, tel. 828/277–4800; Tracy Buchanan, Chief Executive Officer and President

CHARLES GEORGE VETERANS AFFAIRS MEDICAL CENTER, 1100 Tunnel Road, Asheville, NC, Zip 28805–2087; tel. 828/298–7911; Cynthia Breyfogle, FACHE, Director

CHEROKEE INDIAN HOSPITAL, 1 Hospital Road, Cherokee, NC, Zip 28719; tel. 828/497–9163; Casey Cooper, Chief Executive Officer

ERLANGER MURPHY MEDICAL CENTER, 3990 U S Highway 64 East Alt, Murphy, NC, Zip 28906–7917; tel. 828/837–8161; Mark E. Kimball, Chief Executive Officer

HARRIS REGIONAL HOSPITAL, 68 Hospital Road, Sylva, NC, Zip 28779–2722; tel. 828/586–7000; Steve Heatherly, Chief Executive Officer

HAYWOOD REGIONAL MEDICAL CENTER, 262 Leroy George Drive, Clyde, NC, Zip 28721–7430; tel. 828/456–7311; Rod Harkleroad, R.N., Chief Executive Officer

HIGHLANDS-CASHIERS HOSPITAL, 190 Hospital Drive, Highlands, NC, Zip 28741–7600, Mailing Address: P O Drawer 190, Zip 28741–0190, tel. 828/526–1200; Jacqueline Medland, MS, Ph.D., President and Chief Nursing Officer

MARGARET R. PARDEE MEMORIAL HOSPITAL, 800 North Justice Street, Hendersonville, NC, Zip 28791–3410; tel. 828/696–1000; James M. Kirby, II., President and Chief Executive Officer

MCDOWELL HOSPITAL, 430 Rankin Drive, Marion, NC, Zip 28752–6568, Mailing Address: P.O. Box 730, Zip 28752–0730, tel. 828/659–5000; Carol C. Wolfenbarger, FACHE, MSN, President

MISSION HOSPITAL, 509 Biltmore Avenue, Asheville, NC, Zip 28801–4690; tel. 828/213–1111; Jill Hoggard Green, Ph.D., R.N., President

PARK RIDGE HEALTH, 100 Hospital Drive, Hendersonville, NC, Zip 28792–5272; tel. 828/684–8501; Jimm Bunch, President and Chief Executive Officer

RUTHERFORD REGIONAL HEALTH SYSTEM, 288 South Ridgecrest Avenue, Rutherfordton, NC, Zip 28139–2838; tel. 828/286–5000; Rebecca Segal, Chief Executive Officer

ST. LUKE'S HOSPITAL, 101 Hospital Drive, Columbus, NC, Zip 28722–6418; tel. 828/894–3311; James B. Bross, President

SWAIN COMMUNITY HOSPITAL, 45 Plateau Street, Bryson City, NC, Zip 28713–4200; tel. 828/488–2155; Steve Heatherly, Chief Executive Officer

TRANSYLVANIA REGIONAL HOSPITAL, 260 Hospital Drive, Brevard, NC, Zip 28712–3378; tel. 828/884–9111; Michele Pilon, President and Chief Nursing Officer

NORTH DAKOTA

NORTHLAND HEALTHCARE ALLIANCE
2223 East Rosser Avenue, Bismarck, ND, Zip 58501–4949; tel. 701/250–0709; Timothy Cox, President

ASHLEY MEDICAL CENTER, 612 North Center Avenue, Ashley, ND, Zip 58413–7013, Mailing Address: P.O. Box 450, Zip 58413–0450, tel. 701/288–3433; Holly Wolff, Chief Executive Officer

CHI ST. ALEXIUS HEALTH - DICKINSON MEDICAL CENTER, 2500 Fairway Street, Dickinson, ND, Zip 58601–4399; tel. 701/456–4000; Reed Reyman, President

CHI ST. ALEXIUS HEALTH GARRISON, 407 Third Avenue SE, Garrison, ND, Zip 58540–7235; tel. 701/463–2275; Tod Graeber, Administrator

CHI ST. ALEXIUS HEALTH, 900 East Broadway, Bismarck, ND, Zip 58501–4586, Mailing Address: P.O. Box 5510, Zip 58506–5510, tel. 701/530–7000; Kurt Schley, Market Chief Executive Officer

COMMUNITY MEMORIAL HOSPITAL, 220 Fifth Avenue, Turtle Lake, ND, Zip 58575–4005, Mailing Address: P.O. Box 280, Zip 58575–0280, tel. 701/448–2331; Tod Graeber, Administrator

LINTON HOSPITAL, 518 North Broadway, Linton, ND, Zip 58552–7308, Mailing Address: P.O. Box 850, Zip 58552–0850, tel. 701/254–4511; Robert O. Black, Chief Executive Officer

MCKENZIE COUNTY HEALTHCARE SYSTEM, 516 North Main Street, Watford City, ND, Zip 58854–7310; tel. 701/842–3000; Daniel R. Kelly, Chief Executive Officer

MOBRIDGE REGIONAL HOSPITAL, 1401 Tenth Avenue West, Mobridge, SD, Zip 57601–1106, Mailing Address: P.O. Box 580, Zip 57601–0580, tel. 605/845–3692; John J. Ayoub, FACHE, Chief Executive Officer

PRESENTATION MEDICAL CENTER, 213 Second Avenue NE, Rolla, ND, Zip 58367–7153, Mailing Address: P.O. Box 759, Zip 58367–0759, tel. 701/477–3161; Chris Albertson, Chief Executive Officer

SAKAKAWEA MEDICAL CENTER, 510 Eighth Avenue NE, Hazen, ND, Zip 58545–4637; tel. 701/748–2225; Darrold Bertsch, Chief Executive Officer

SOUTHWEST HEALTHCARE SERVICES, 802 2nd Street Northwest, Bowman, ND, Zip 58623–4483, Mailing Address: P O Drawer 'C', Zip 58623, tel. 701/523–5265; Jerry Wiesner, Administrator and Chief Executive Officer

WEST RIVER REGIONAL MEDICAL CENTER, 1000 Highway 12, Hettinger, ND, Zip 58639–7530; tel. 701/567–4561; Matthew Shahan, Chief Executive Officer

WISHEK COMMUNITY HOSPITAL AND CLINICS, 1007 Fourth Avenue South, Wishek, ND, Zip 58495–7527, Mailing Address: P.O. Box 647, Zip 58495–0647, tel. 701/452–2326; Beverly Vilhauer, Chief Executive Officer

SANFORD HEALTH NETWORK - FARGO MARKET
736 Broadway North, Route 1000, Fargo, ND, Zip 58102–4421; tel. 701/234–6951; Bruce Viessman, Vice President Operations

BOZEMAN HEALTH DEACONESS HOSPITAL, 915 Highland Boulevard, Bozeman, MT, Zip 59715–6902; tel. 406/585–5000; John Hill, President and Chief Executive Officer

JAMESTOWN REGIONAL MEDICAL CENTER, 2422 20th Street SW, Jamestown, ND, Zip 58401–6201; tel. 701/252–1050; Trisha Jungels, R.N., Interim Chief Executive Officer

KITTSON MEMORIAL HEALTHCARE CENTER, 1010 South Birch Street, Hallock, MN, Zip 56728–4215, Mailing Address: P.O. Box 700, Zip 56728–0700, tel. 218/843–3612; Ashley Rivera, Chief Financial Officer and Chief Executive Officer

LIBERTY MEDICAL CENTER, 315 West Madison Avenue, Chester, MT, Zip 59522, Mailing Address: P.O. Box 705, Zip 59522–0705, tel. 406/759–5181; Matthew Waller, Chief Executive Officer

MAHNOMEN HEALTH CENTER, 414 West Jefferson Avenue, Mahnomen, MN, Zip 56557–4912, Mailing Address: P.O. Box 396, Zip 56557–0396, tel. 218/935–2511; Dale K. Kruger, Chief Executive Officer

MCKENZIE COUNTY HEALTHCARE SYSTEM, 516 North Main Street, Watford City, ND, Zip 58854–7310; tel. 701/842–3000; Daniel R. Kelly, Chief Executive Officer

NORTHWOOD DEACONESS HEALTH CENTER, 4 North Park Street, Northwood, ND, Zip 58267–4102, Mailing Address: P.O. Box 190, Zip 58267–0190, tel. 701/587–6060; Pete Antonson, Chief Executive Officer

PERHAM HEALTH, 1000 Coney Street West, Perham, MN, Zip 56573–1108; tel. 218/347–4500; Chuck Hofius, Chief Executive Officer

RIVERVIEW HEALTH, 323 South Minnesota Street, Crookston, MN, Zip 56716–1601; tel. 218/281–9200; Carrie Michalski, President and Chief Executive Officer

SANFORD BAGLEY MEDICAL CENTER, 203 Fourth Street NW, Bagley, MN, Zip 56621–8307; tel. 218/694–6501; Robert Belanger, Administrator Director

SANFORD BEMIDJI MEDICAL CENTER, 1300 Anne Street NW, Bemidji, MN, Zip 56601–5103; tel. 218/751–5430; Bryan Nermoe, Executive Vice President

SANFORD BISMARCK, 300 North Seventh Street, Bismarck, ND, Zip 58501–4439, Mailing Address: P.O. Box 5525, Zip 58506–5525, tel. 701/323–6000; Craig Lambrecht, M.D., President

SANFORD MAYVILLE MEDICAL CENTER, 42 Sixth Avenue SE, Mayville, ND, Zip 58257–1598; tel. 701/786–3800; Jac McTaggart, Chief Executive Officer

SANFORD MEDICAL CENTER THIEF RIVER FALLS, 3001 Sanford Parkway, Thief River Falls, MN, Zip 56701–2700; tel. 218/681–4747; Brian J. Carlson, FACHE, Executive Director

SANFORD THIEF RIVER FALLS BEHAVIORAL HEALTH CENTER, 120 LaBree Avenue South, Thief River Falls, MN, Zip 56701–2819, Mailing Address: 3001 Sanford Parkway, Zip 56701–2819, tel. 218/683–4349; Brian J. Carlson, FACHE, Chief Executive Officer

SANFORD WHEATON MEDICAL CENTER, 401 12th Street North, Wheaton, MN, Zip 56296–1099; tel. 320/563–8226; JoAnn M. Foltz, R.N., Chief Executive Officer

SIDNEY HEALTH CENTER, 216 14th Avenue SW, Sidney, MT, Zip 59270–3586; tel. 406/488–2100; Richard Haraldson, Chief Executive Officer

OHIO

CLEVELAND HEALTH NETWORK
6000 West Creek Road, Suite 20, Independence, OH, Zip 44131–2139; tel. 216/986–1100; Fred M. DeGrandis, President

AKRON CHILDREN'S HOSPITAL, One Perkins Square, Akron, OH, Zip 44308–1063; tel. 330/543–1000; William H. Considine, President

ASHTABULA COUNTY MEDICAL CENTER, 2420 Lake Avenue, Ashtabula, OH, Zip 44004–4954; tel. 440/997–2262; Michael J. Habowski, President and Chief Executive Officer

CLEVELAND CLINIC CHILDREN'S HOSPITAL FOR REHABILITATION, 2801 Martin Luther King Jr Drive, Cleveland, OH, Zip 44104–3865; tel. 216/448–6400; Michelle Marks, D.O., Medical Director

CLEVELAND CLINIC FAIRVIEW HOSPITAL, 18101 Lorain Avenue, Cleveland, OH, Zip 44111–5656; tel. 216/476–7000; Neil Smith, D.O., President

CLEVELAND CLINIC, MEDINA HOSPITAL, 1000 East Washington Street, Medina, OH, Zip 44256–2170; tel. 330/725–1000; Richard K. Shewbridge, President

CLEVELAND CLINIC, 9500 Euclid Avenue, Cleveland, OH, Zip 44195–5108; tel. 216/444–2200; Tomislav Mihaljevic, M.D., President and Chief Executive Officer

EUCLID HOSPITAL, 18901 Lake Shore Boulevard, Euclid, OH, Zip 44119–1090; tel. 216/531–9000; Daniel Napierkowski, M.D., President

FIRELANDS REGIONAL HEALTH SYSTEM, 1111 Hayes Avenue, Sandusky, OH, Zip 44870–3323; tel. 419/557–7400; Daniel J. Moncher, Interim President and Chief Executive Officer

FISHER-TITUS MEDICAL CENTER, 272 Benedict Avenue, Norwalk, OH, Zip 44857–2374; tel. 419/668–8101; Matthew Gross, Chief Executive Officer

HILLCREST HOSPITAL, 6780 Mayfield Road, Cleveland, OH, Zip 44124–2203; tel. 440/312–4500; Richard Parker, M.D., President, Hillcrest Hospital

LUTHERAN HOSPITAL, 1730 West 25th Street, Cleveland, OH, Zip 44113–3170; tel. 216/696–4300; Donald A. Malone, Jr., President

MARYMOUNT HOSPITAL, 12300 McCracken Road, Garfield Heights, OH, Zip 44125–2975; tel. 216/581–0500; Daniel Napierkowski, M.D., President

METROHEALTH MEDICAL CENTER, 2500 MetroHealth Drive, Cleveland, OH, Zip 44109–1998; tel. 216/778–7800; Akram Boutros, M.D., FACHE, President and Chief Executive Officer

SOUTH POINTE HOSPITAL, 20000 Harvard Road, Warrensville Heights, OH, Zip 44122–6805; tel. 216/491–6000; Margaret McKenzie, M.D., President

SUMMA HEALTH SYSTEM, 525 East Market Street, Akron, OH, Zip 44304–1619; tel. 330/375–3000; David Custodio, M.D., President Summa Health System Akron

UNIVERSITY HOSPITALS ELYRIA MEDICAL CENTER, 630 East River Street, Elyria, OH, Zip 44035–5902; tel. 440/329–7500; Kristi M. Sink, President

UNIVERSITY HOSPITALS PARMA MEDICAL CENTER, 7007 Powers Boulevard, Parma, OH, Zip 44129–5495; tel. 440/743–3000; Peter U. Bergmann, President

WESTERN RESERVE HOSPITAL, 1900 23rd Street, Cuyahoga Falls, OH, Zip 44223–1499; tel. 330/971–7000; Robert Kent, D.O., President and Chief Executive Officer

MERCY HEALTH - SOUTHWEST OHIO
4600 McAuley Place, Cincinnati, OH, Zip 45242; tel. 513/981–6000; John M. Starcher, President and Chief Executive Officer

MERCY HEALTH - ANDERSON HOSPITAL, 7500 State Road, Cincinnati, OH, Zip 45255–2492; tel. 513/624–4500; Ken James, President and Chief Executive Officer of East Market

MERCY HEALTH - CLERMONT HOSPITAL, 3000 Hospital Drive, Batavia, OH, Zip 45103–1921; tel. 513/732–8200; Justin Krueger, FACHE, President

MERCY HEALTH - FAIRFIELD HOSPITAL, 3000 Mack Road, Fairfield, OH, Zip 45014–5335; tel. 513/870–7000; Thomas S. Urban, FACHE, President and Chief Executive Officer

MERCY HEALTH - WEST HOSPITAL, 3300 Mercy Health Boulevard, Cincinnati, OH, Zip 45211–1103; tel. 513/215–5000; Michael Kramer, Chief Executive Officer

THE JEWISH HOSPITAL - MERCY HEALTH, 4777 East Galbraith Road, Cincinnati, OH, Zip 45236–2725; tel. 513/686–3000; Patricia Davis-Hagens, R.N., Central Market Leader and President

PREMIER HEALTH
110 North Main Street, Suite 390, Dayton, OH, Zip 45402–3720; tel. 937/499–9401; Mary H. Boosalis, President and Chief Executive Officer

ATRIUM MEDICAL CENTER, One Medical Center Drive, Middletown, OH, Zip 45005–1066; tel. 513/424–2111; Michael Uhl, President

MIAMI VALLEY HOSPITAL, One Wyoming Street, Dayton, OH, Zip 45409–2793; tel. 937/208–8000; Michael J. Maiberger, President

UPPER VALLEY MEDICAL CENTER, 3130 North County Road 25A, Troy, OH, Zip 45373–1309; tel. 937/440–4000; Thomas Parker, President

THE OHIO STATE HEALTH NETWORK
660 Ackerman Road, Suite 601F, Columbus, OH, Zip 43202–4500; tel. 614/293–4425; Thomas Blincoe, Executive Director

AVITA ONTARIO HOSPITAL, 715 Richland Mall, Ontario, OH, Zip 44906–3802; tel. 567/307–7666; Jerome Morasko, President and Chief Executive Officer

BARNESVILLE HOSPITAL, 639 West Main Street, Barnesville, OH, Zip 43713–1039, Mailing Address: P.O. Box 309, Zip 43713–0309, tel. 740/425–3941; David D. Phillips, Chief Executive Officer and Administrator

BUCYRUS HOSPITAL, 629 North Sandusky Avenue, Bucyrus, OH, Zip 44820–1821; tel. 419/562–4677; Jerome Morasko, Chief Executive Officer

FAYETTE COUNTY MEMORIAL HOSPITAL, 1430 Columbus Avenue, Washington Court House, OH, Zip 43160–1791; tel. 740/335–1210; D Michael. Diener, Chief Executive Officer

GALION HOSPITAL, 269 Portland Way South, Galion, OH, Zip 44833–2399; tel. 419/468–4841; Jerome Morasko, President and Chief Executive Officer

HIGHLAND DISTRICT HOSPITAL, 1275 North High Street, Hillsboro, OH, Zip 45133–8273; tel. 937/393–6100; Randal P. Lennartz, CPA, President and Chief Executive Officer

HOCKING VALLEY COMMUNITY HOSPITAL, 601 State Route 664 North, Logan, OH, Zip 43138–8541, Mailing Address: P.O. Box 966, Zip 43138–0966, tel. 740/380–8000; Stacey Gabriel, R.N., President and Chief Executive Officer

MADISON HEALTH, 210 North Main Street, London, OH, Zip 43140–1115; tel. 740/845–7000; Dana E. Engle, Chief Executive Officer

MARY RUTAN HOSPITAL, 205 Palmer Avenue, Bellefontaine, OH, Zip 43311–2281; tel. 937/592–4015; Mandy C. Goble, President and Chief Executive Officer

MERCER HEALTH, 800 West Main Street, Coldwater, OH, Zip 45828–1698; tel. 419/678–2341; Lisa R. Klenke, R.N., Chief Executive Officer

OHIO STATE UNIVERSITY WEXNER MEDICAL CENTER, 410 West 10th Avenue, Columbus, OH, Zip 43210–1240; tel. 614/293–8000; David P. McQuaid, FACHE, Chief Operating Officer

WAYNE HEALTHCARE, 835 Sweitzer Street, Greenville, OH, Zip 45331–1077; tel. 937/548–1141; Wayne G. Deschambeau, President and Chief Executive Officer

WILSON MEMORIAL HOSPITAL, 915 West Michigan Street, Sidney, OH, Zip 45365–2491; tel. 937/498–2311; Duane Francis, Interim Chief Executive Officer

WYANDOT MEMORIAL HOSPITAL, 885 North Sandusky Avenue, Upper Sandusky, OH, Zip 43351–1098; tel. 419/294–4991; Ty Shaull, President and Chief Executive Officer

TRIHEALTH
619 Oak Street, Cincinnati, OH, Zip 45206; tel. 513/569–6507; Mark C. Clement, President and Chief Executive Officer

BETHESDA NORTH HOSPITAL, 10500 Montgomery Road, Cincinnati, OH, Zip 45242–4402; tel. 513/865–1111; Barbara Boyne, Executive Director, Operations

GOOD SAMARITAN HOSPITAL, 375 Dixmyth Avenue, Cincinnati, OH, Zip 45220–2489; tel. 513/862–1400; Jamie Easterling, Executive Director, Operations

MCCULLOUGH-HYDE MEMORIAL HOSPITAL/TRIHEALTH, 110 North Poplar Street, Oxford, OH, Zip 45056–1292; tel. 513/523–2111; Brett Kirkpatrick, Executive Director

TRIHEALTH EVENDALE HOSPITAL, 3155 Glendale Milford Road, Cincinnati, OH, Zip 45241–3134; tel. 513/454–2222; Kelvin Hanger, Chief Executive Officer

OKLAHOMA

ALLIANCEHEALTH OKLAHOMA
5300 North Grand Boulevard, Oklahoma City, OK, Zip 73112–5647; tel. 405/815–3900; Clay Franklin, Market Chief Executive Officer

ALLIANCEHEALTH CLINTON, 100 North 30th Street, Clinton, OK, Zip 73601–3117; tel. 580/323–2363; Landon E. Hise, Chief Executive Officer

ALLIANCEHEALTH DURANT, 1800 University Boulevard, Durant, OK, Zip 74701–3006, Mailing Address: P.O. Box 1207, Zip 74702–1207, tel. 580/924–3080; Jeffrey S. Tarrant, FACHE, Chief Executive Officer

ALLIANCEHEALTH MADILL, 901 South Fifth Avenue, Madill, OK, Zip 73446–3640, Mailing Address: P.O. Box 827, Zip 73446–0827, tel. 580/795–3384; Jeffrey S. Tarrant, FACHE, Chief Executive Officer

ALLIANCEHEALTH MIDWEST, 2825 Parklawn Drive, Midwest City, OK, Zip 73110–4258; tel. 405/610–4411; Clay Franklin, Chief Executive Officer

ALLIANCEHEALTH PONCA CITY, 1900 North 14th Street, Ponca City, OK, Zip 74601–2099; tel. 580/765–3321; Christopher Mendoza, Chief Executive Officer

ALLIANCEHEALTH SEMINOLE, 2401 Wrangler Boulevard, Seminole, OK, Zip 74868–1917; tel. 405/303–4000; Adam Bracks, Chief Executive Officer

ALLIANCEHEALTH WOODWARD, 900 17th Street, Woodward, OK, Zip 73801–2448; tel. 580/256–5511; Ross Korkmas, Chief Executive Officer

INTEGRIS DEACONESS, 5501 North Portland Avenue, Oklahoma City, OK, Zip 73112–2099; tel. 405/604–6000; Rex Van Meter, President

MERCY HEALTH SYSTEM OF OKLAHOMA
 4300 West Memorial Road, Oklahoma City, OK, Zip 73120–8304; tel. 405/752–3756; Diana Smalley, President and Chief Executive Officer

ARBUCKLE MEMORIAL HOSPITAL, 2011 West Broadway Street, Sulphur, OK, Zip 73086–4221, Mailing Address: P.O. Box 1109, Zip 73086–8109, tel. 580/622–2161; Jeremy A. Jones, Chief Executive Officer

MERCY HEALTH LOVE COUNTY, 300 Wanda Street, Marietta, OK, Zip 73448–1200; tel. 580/276–3347; Richard Barker, Administrator and Chief Executive Officer

MERCY HOSPITAL ADA, 430 North Monte Vista, Ada, OK, Zip 74820–4610; tel. 580/332–2323; Lori Wightman, R.N., MSN, FACHE, President

MERCY HOSPITAL ARDMORE, 1011 14th Avenue NW, Ardmore, OK, Zip 73401–1828; tel. 580/223–5400; Daryle Voss, FACHE, President and Chief Executive Officer

MERCY HOSPITAL EL RENO, 2115 Parkview Drive, El Reno, OK, Zip 73036–2199; tel. 405/262–2640; Cindy Carmichael, Administrator

MERCY HOSPITAL HEALDTON, 3462 Hospital Road, Healdton, OK, Zip 73438–6124, Mailing Address: P.O. Box 928, Zip 73438–0928, tel. 580/229–0701; Nichole Barrett, R.N., Interim Administrator

MERCY HOSPITAL KINGFISHER, 1000 Hospital Cirle, Kingfisher, OK, Zip 73750–5002, Mailing Address: P.O. Box 59, Zip 73750–0059, tel. 405/375–3141; Brian Denton, Administrator

MERCY HOSPITAL LOGAN COUNTY, 200 South Academy Road, Guthrie, OK, Zip 73044–8727, Mailing Address: P.O. Box 1017, Zip 73044–1017, tel. 405/282–6700; Bobby Stitt, R.N., Administrator

MERCY HOSPITAL OKLAHOMA CITY, 4300 West Memorial Road, Oklahoma City, OK, Zip 73120–8362; tel. 405/755–1515; Jim Gebhart, Jr., FACHE, President

MERCY HOSPITAL TISHOMINGO, 1000 South Byrd Street, Tishomingo, OK, Zip 73460–3299; tel. 580/371–2327; Lori McMillin, Administrator

MERCY HOSPITAL WATONGA, 500 North Clarence Nash Boulevard, Watonga, OK, Zip 73772–2845, Mailing Address: P.O. Box 370, Zip 73772–0370, tel. 580/623–7211; Cindy Carmichael, Administrator

MERCY REHABILITATION HOSPITAL OKLAHOMA CITY, 5401 West Memorial Rd, Oklahoma City, OK, Zip 73142–2026; tel. 405/752–3935; Sharon Smeltzer, Chief Executive Officer

OKLAHOMA HEART HOSPITAL SOUTH CAMPUS, 5200 East I-240 Service Road, Oklahoma City, OK, Zip 73135; tel. 405/628–6000; John Harvey, M.D., Chief Executive Officer

OKLAHOMA HEART HOSPITAL, 4050 West Memorial Road, Oklahoma City, OK, Zip 73120–8382; tel. 405/608–3200; John Harvey, M.D., Chief Executive Officer

OKLAHOMA STATE UNIVERSITY MEDICAL CENTER, 744 West Ninth Street, Tulsa, OK, Zip 74127–9020; tel. 918/599–1000; Matthew Adams, Administrator

SEILING REGIONAL MEDICAL CENTER, Highway 60 NE, Seiling, OK, Zip 73663, Mailing Address: P.O. Box 720, Zip 73663–0720, tel. 580/922–7361; Jennifer Coons, Chief Executive Officer

PENNSYLVANIA

ALLEGHENY HEALTH NETWORK
 30 Isabella Street, Suite 300, Pittsburgh, PA, Zip 15212–5862; tel. 412/330–2400; Cynthia Hundorfean, President and Chief Executive Officer

ALLEGHENY GENERAL HOSPITAL, 320 East North Avenue, Pittsburgh, PA, Zip 15212–4756; tel. 412/359–3131; Jeffrey Cohen, M.D., President

ALLEGHENY VALLEY HOSPITAL , 1301 Carlisle Street, Natrona Heights, PA, Zip 15065–1152; tel. 724/224–5100; William Englert, Chief Executive Officer

CANONSBURG HOSPITAL, 100 Medical Boulevard, Canonsburg, PA, Zip 15317–9762; tel. 724/745–6100; Louise Urban, R.N., President and Chief Executive Officer

FORBES HOSPITAL, 2570 Haymaker Road, Monroeville, PA, Zip 15146–3513; tel. 412/858–2000; Mark Rubino, M.D., President

JEFFERSON HOSPITAL, 565 Coal Valley Road, Jefferson Hills, PA, Zip 15025–3703, Mailing Address: Box 18119, Pittsburgh, Zip 15236–0119, tel. 412/469–5000; Louise Urban, R.N., President and Chief Executive Officer

SAINT VINCENT HOSPITAL, 232 West 25th Street, Erie, PA, Zip 16544–0002; tel. 814/452–5000; Christopher Clark, D.O., President and Chief Executive Officer

WEST PENN HOSPITAL, 4800 Friendship Avenue, Pittsburgh, PA, Zip 15224–1722; tel. 412/578–5000; Ronald J. Andro, R.N., MS, President and Chief Executive Officer

WESTFIELD MEMORIAL HOSPITAL, 189 East Main Street, Westfield, NY, Zip 14787–1195; tel. 716/326–4921; Valarie Jackson, President

BRIDGES HEALTH PARTNERS
 500 Commonwealth Drive, Warrendale, PA, Zip 15086–7516; tel. 724/300–8105

BUTLER HEALTH SYSTEM, 1 Hospital Way, Butler, PA, Zip 16001–4697; tel. 724/283–6666; Ken DeFurio, President and Chief Executive Officer

EXCELA FRICK HOSPITAL, 508 South Church Street, Mount Pleasant, PA, Zip 15666–1790; tel. 724/547–1500; Michael D. Busch, Executive Vice President and Chief Operating Officer

EXCELA HEALTH WESTMORELAND HOSPITAL, 532 West Pittsburgh Street, Greensburg, PA, Zip 15601–2282; tel. 724/832–4000; Ronald H. Ott, President

EXCELA LATROBE AREA HOSPITAL, One Mellon Way, Latrobe, PA, Zip 15650–1096; tel. 724/537–1000; Michael D. Busch, Executive Vice President and Chief Operating Officer

ST. CLAIR HOSPITAL, 1000 Bower Hill Road, Pittsburgh, PA, Zip 15243–1873; tel. 412/942–4000; James M. Collins, President and Chief Executive Officer

WASHINGTON HEALTH SYSTEM GREENE, 350 Bonar Avenue, Waynesburg, PA, Zip 15370–1608; tel. 724/627–3101; Terry Wiltrout, President

WASHINGTON HOSPITAL, 155 Wilson Avenue, Washington, PA, Zip 15301–3398; tel. 724/225–7000; Gary B. Weinstein, President and Chief Executive Officer

COMMONWEALTH HEALTH
 575 North River Street, Wilkes Barre, PA, Zip 18764–0999; tel. 570/829–8111; Cornelio R. Catena, Market President and Chief Executive Officer, Wilkes-Barre General Hospital

BERWICK HOSPITAL CENTER, 701 East 16th Street, Berwick, PA, Zip 18603–2397; tel. 570/759–5000; Thomas Neal, Chief Executive Officer

FIRST HOSPITAL WYOMING VALLEY, 562 Wyoming Avenue, Kingston, PA, Zip 18704–3721; tel. 570/552–3900; James Gallagher, Chief Executive Officer

MOSES TAYLOR HOSPITAL, 700 Quincy Avenue, Scranton, PA, Zip 18510–1724; tel. 570/770–5000

REGIONAL HOSPITAL OF SCRANTON, 746 Jefferson Avenue, Scranton, PA, Zip 18510–1624; tel. 570/348–7100; Ronald Ziobro, Interim Chief Executive Officer

TYLER MEMORIAL HOSPITAL, 5950 State Route 6, Tunkhannock, PA, Zip 18657–7905; tel. 570/836–2161; Ann Marie. Stevens, R.N., Chief Executive Officer

WILKES-BARRE GENERAL HOSPITAL, 575 North River Street, Wilkes-Barre, PA, Zip 18764–0001; tel. 570/829–8111; Cornelio R. Catena, President and Chief Executive Officer

PENN HIGHLANDS HEALTHCARE
 204 Hospital Avenue, DuBois, PA, Zip 15801–0447; tel. 814/375–6430; Steven M. Fontaine, System Chief Executive Officer

PENN HIGHLANDS BROOKVILLE , 100 Hospital Road, Brookville, PA, Zip 15825–1367; tel. 814/849–2312; Julianne Peer, President

PENN HIGHLANDS CLEARFIELD, 809 Turnpike Avenue, Clearfield, PA, Zip 16830–1232, Mailing Address: P.O. Box 992, Zip 16830–0992, tel. 814/765–5341; Rhonda Halstead, President

PENN HIGHLANDS DUBOIS, 100 Hospital Avenue, DuBois, PA, Zip 15801–1440, Mailing Address: P.O. Box 447, Zip 15801–0447, tel. 814/371–2200; John Sutika, President

PENN HIGHLANDS ELK, 763 Johnsonburg Road, Saint Marys, PA, Zip 15857–3498; tel. 814/788–8000; Bradley Chapman, President

VANTAGE HEALTHCARE NETWORK, INC.
 18282 Technology Drive, Suite 202, Meadville, PA, Zip 16335–8378; tel. 814/337–0000; David Petrarca, Director Retail Operations

BRADFORD REGIONAL MEDICAL CENTER, 116 Interstate Parkway, Bradford, PA, Zip 16701–1036; tel. 814/368–4143; Timothy J. Finan, FACHE, President and Chief Executive Officer

CLARION HOSPITAL, One Hospital Drive, Clarion, PA, Zip 16214–8501; tel. 814/226–9500; Al Taylor, Interim Chief Executive Officer

MEADVILLE MEDICAL CENTER, 751 Liberty Street, Meadville, PA, Zip 16335–2559; tel. 814/333–5000; Philip E. Pandolph, FACHE, Chief Executive Officer

PENN HIGHLANDS BROOKVILLE , 100 Hospital Road, Brookville, PA, Zip 15825–1367; tel. 814/849–2312; Julianne Peer, President

PENN HIGHLANDS ELK, 763 Johnsonburg Road, Saint Marys, PA, Zip 15857–3498; tel. 814/788–8000; Bradley Chapman, President

PUNXSUTAWNEY AREA HOSPITAL, 81 Hillcrest Drive, Punxsutawney, PA, Zip 15767–2616; tel. 814/938–1800; Daniel D. Blough, Jr., Chief Executive Officer

TITUSVILLE AREA HOSPITAL, 406 West Oak Street, Titusville, PA, Zip 16354–1404; tel. 814/827–1851; Lee Clinton, FACHE, Chief Executive Officer

UPMC BEDFORD MEMORIAL, 10455 Lincoln Highway, Everett, PA, Zip 15537–7046; tel. 814/623–6161; Gerald Murray, President

UPMC HAMOT, 201 State Street, Erie, PA, Zip 16550–0002; tel. 814/877–6000; David Gibbons, President

UPMC JAMESON , 1211 Wilmington Avenue, New Castle, PA, Zip 16105–2516; tel. 724/658–9001; Donald R. Owrey, President

UPMC KANE, 4372 Route 6, Kane, PA, Zip 16735–3060; tel. 814/837–8585; Mark Papalia, President

UPMC MCKEESPORT, 1500 Fifth Avenue, McKeesport, PA, Zip 15132–2422; tel. 412/664–2000; Mark Sevco, President

UPMC NORTHWEST, 100 Fairfield Drive, Seneca, PA, Zip 16346–2130; tel. 814/676–7600; Brian Durniok, President

UPMC PASSAVANT, 9100 Babcock Boulevard, Pittsburgh, PA, Zip 15237–5815; tel. 412/748–6700; David T. Martin, President

UPMC ST. MARGARET, 815 Freeport Road, Pittsburgh, PA, Zip 15215–3301; tel. 412/784–4000; David J. Patton, President

WARREN GENERAL HOSPITAL, Two Crescent Park West, Warren, PA, Zip 16365–0068, Mailing Address: P.O. Box 68, Zip 16365–0068, tel. 814/723–4973; Richard Allen, Chief Executive Officer

SOUTH DAKOTA

REGIONAL HEALTH
353 Fairmont Boulevard, Rapid City, SD, Zip 57701–7375; tel. 605/719–1000; Brent R. Phillips, President and Chief Executive Officer

CUSTER REGIONAL HOSPITAL, 1039 Montgomery Street, Custer, SD, Zip 57730–1397; tel. 605/673–2229; Mark C. Schmidt, President

LEAD-DEADWOOD REGIONAL HOSPITAL, 61 Charles Street, Deadwood, SD, Zip 57732–1303; tel. 605/717–6000; Mark C. Schmidt, President

PHILIP HEALTH SERVICES, 503 West Pine Street, Philip, SD, Zip 57567–3300, Mailing Address: P.O. Box 790, Zip 57567–0790, tel. 605/859–2511; Jeremy Schultes, Administrator and Chief Executive Officer

RAPID CITY REGIONAL HOSPITAL, 353 Fairmont Boulevard, Rapid City, SD, Zip 57701–7393, Mailing Address: P.O. Box 6000, Zip 57709–6000, tel. 605/755–1000; John Pierce, Acting President

SPEARFISH REGIONAL HOSPITAL, 1440 North Main Street, Spearfish, SD, Zip 57783–1504; tel. 605/644–4000; Thomas Worsley, Chief Executive Officer

STURGIS REGIONAL HOSPITAL, 949 Harmon Street, Sturgis, SD, Zip 57785–2452; tel. 605/720–2400; Mark Schulte, FACHE, President

WESTON COUNTY HEALTH SERVICES, 1124 Washington Boulevard, Newcastle, WY, Zip 82701–2972; tel. 307/746–4491; Maureen K. Cadwell, Chief Executive Officer

SANFORD HEALTH NETWORK - SIOUX FALLS MARKET
1305 West 18th Street, Route 6145, Sioux Falls, SD, Zip 57105–0401; tel. 605/328–5513; Eric C. Hilmoe, Vice President Operations

COMMUNITY MEMORIAL HOSPITAL, 809 Jackson Street, Burke, SD, Zip 57523–2065, Mailing Address: P.O. Box 319, Zip 57523–0319, tel. 605/775–2621; Mistie Sachtjen, Chief Executive Officer

DOUGLAS COUNTY MEMORIAL HOSPITAL, 708 Eighth Street, Armour, SD, Zip 57313–2102; tel. 605/724–2159; Heath Brouwer, Administrator

MURRAY COUNTY MEDICAL CENTER, 2042 Juniper Avenue, Slayton, MN, Zip 56172–1017; tel. 507/836–6111; Dennis Goebel, Chief Executive Officer

ORANGE CITY AREA HEALTH SYSTEM, 1000 Lincoln Circle SE, Orange City, IA, Zip 51041–1862; tel. 712/737–4984; Martin W. Guthmiller, Chief Executive Officer

ORTONVILLE AREA HEALTH SERVICES, 450 Eastvold Avenue, Ortonville, MN, Zip 56278–1133; tel. 320/839–2502; David Rogers, Chief Executive Officer

PIONEER MEMORIAL HOSPITAL AND HEALTH SERVICES, 315 North Washington Street, Viborg, SD, Zip 57070–2002, Mailing Address: P.O. Box 368, Zip 57070–0368, tel. 605/326–5161; Thomas V. Richter, Chief Executive Officer

SANFORD ABERDEEN MEDICAL CENTER, 2905 3rd Avenue SE, Aberdeen, SD, Zip 57401–5420; tel. 605/626–4200; Ashley M. Erickson, Chief Executive Officer

SANFORD CANBY MEDICAL CENTER, 112 St Olaf Avenue South, Canby, MN, Zip 56220–1433; tel. 507/223–7277; Lori Sisk, R.N., Chief Executive Officer

SANFORD CANTON-INWOOD MEDICAL CENTER, 440 North Hiawatha Drive, Canton, SD, Zip 57013–5800; tel. 605/764–1400; Scott C. Larson, Chief Executive Officer

SANFORD CHAMBERLAIN MEDICAL CENTER, 300 South Byron Boulevard, Chamberlain, SD, Zip 57325–9741; tel. 605/234–5511; Erica Peterson, Chief Executive Officer

SANFORD CLEAR LAKE MEDICAL CENTER, 701 Third Avenue South, Clear Lake, SD, Zip 57226–2016; tel. 605/874–2141; Lori Sisk, R.N., Chief Executive Officer

SANFORD HILLSBORO MEDICAL CENTER, 12 Third Street SE, Hillsboro, ND, Zip 58045–4840, Mailing Address: P.O. Box 609, Zip 58045–0609, tel. 701/636–3200; Jac McTaggart, Chief Executive Officer

SANFORD JACKSON MEDICAL CENTER, 1430 North Highway, Jackson, MN, Zip 56143–1093; tel. 507/847–2420; Dawn Schnell, Chief Nursing Officer and Interim Senior Director

SANFORD LUVERNE MEDICAL CENTER, 1600 North Kniss Avenue, Luverne, MN, Zip 56156–1067; tel. 507/283–2321; Tammy Loosbrock, Senior Director

SANFORD ROCK RAPIDS MEDICAL CENTER, 801 South Greene Street, Rock Rapids, IA, Zip 51246–1998; tel. 712/472–2591; Tammy Loosbrock, Chief Executive Officer

SANFORD SHELDON MEDICAL CENTER, 118 North Seventh Avenue, Sheldon, IA, Zip 51201–1235, Mailing Address: P.O. Box 250, Zip 51201–0250, tel. 712/324–5041; Richard E. Nordahl, Chief Executive Officer

SANFORD TRACY MEDICAL CENTER, 251 Fifth Street East, Tracy, MN, Zip 56175–1536; tel. 507/629–8400; Stacy Barstad, Chief Executive Officer

SANFORD USD MEDICAL CENTER, 1305 West 18th Street, Sioux Falls, SD, Zip 57105–0496, Mailing Address: P.O. Box 5039, Zip 57117–5039, tel. 605/333–1000; Paul A. Hanson, FACHE, President

SANFORD VERMILLION MEDICAL CENTER, 20 South Plum Street, Vermillion, SD, Zip 57069–3346; tel. 605/677–3500; Timothy J. Tracy, Senior Director

SANFORD WESTBROOK MEDICAL CENTER, 920 Bell Avenue, Westbrook, MN, Zip 56183–9669, Mailing Address: P.O. Box 188, Zip 56183–0188, tel. 507/274–6121; Stacy Barstad, Chief Executive Officer

SANFORD WORTHINGTON MEDICAL CENTER, 1018 Sixth Avenue, Worthington, MN, Zip 56187–2202, Mailing Address: P.O. Box 997, Zip 56187–0997, tel. 507/372–2941; Jennifer . Weg, MS, R.N., Executive Director

WEST HOLT MEDICAL SERVICES, 406 West Neely Street, Atkinson, NE, Zip 68713–4801; tel. 402/925–2811; Bradley D. Pfeifer, FACHE, Chief Executive Officer

WINDOM AREA HOSPITAL, 2150 Hospital Drive, Windom, MN, Zip 56101–0339, Mailing Address: P.O. Box 339, Zip 56101–0339, tel. 507/831–2400; Shelby Medina, Chief Executive Officer

WINNER REGIONAL HEALTHCARE CENTER, 745 East Eighth Street, Winner, SD, Zip 57580–2631; tel. 605/842–7100; Kevin Coffey, Chief Executive Officer

TENNESSEE

TRISTAR HEALTH
110 Winners Circle, First Floor, Brentwood, TN, Zip 37027–5070; tel. 615/886–4900; Stephen Corbeil, President

CARTERSVILLE MEDICAL CENTER, 960 Joe Frank Harris Parkway, Cartersville, GA, Zip 30120–2129; tel. 770/382–1530; J. Christopher. Mosley, Chief Executive Officer

EASTSIDE MEDICAL CENTER, 1700 Medical Way, Snellville, GA, Zip 30078–2195; tel. 770/979–0200; Trent Lind, Chief Executive Officer

PARKRIDGE MEDICAL CENTER, 2333 McCallie Avenue, Chattanooga, TN, Zip 37404–3258; tel. 423/698–6061; Thomas H. Ozburn, Chief Executive Officer

REDMOND REGIONAL MEDICAL CENTER, 501 Redmond Road, Rome, GA, Zip 30165–1415, Mailing Address: P.O. Box 107001, Zip 30164–7001, tel. 706/291–0291; John Quinlivan, Chief Executive Officer

TRISTAR ASHLAND CITY MEDICAL CENTER, 313 North Main Street, Ashland City, TN, Zip 37015–1347; tel. 615/792–3030; Darrell White, R.N., Administrator and Chief Nursing Officer

TRISTAR CENTENNIAL MEDICAL CENTER, 2300 Patterson Street, Nashville, TN, Zip 37203–1528; tel. 615/342–1000; Scott A. Cihak, President and Chief Executive Officer

TRISTAR GREENVIEW REGIONAL HOSPITAL, 1801 Ashley Circle, Bowling Green, KY, Zip 42104–3362; tel. 270/793–1000; Michael Sherrod, Chief Executive Officer

TRISTAR HENDERSONVILLE MEDICAL CENTER, 355 New Shackle Island Road, Hendersonville, TN, Zip 37075–2479; tel. 615/338–1000; Regina Bartlett, Chief Executive Officer

TRISTAR HORIZON MEDICAL CENTER, 111 Highway 70 East, Dickson, TN, Zip 37055–2080; tel. 615/446–0446; Dustin Greene, Chief Executive Officer

TRISTAR SKYLINE MEDICAL CENTER, 3441 Dickerson Pike, Nashville, TN, Zip 37207–2539; tel. 615/769–2000; Steve Otto, Chief Executive Officer

TRISTAR SOUTHERN HILLS MEDICAL CENTER, 391 Wallace Road, Nashville, TN, Zip 37211–4859; tel. 615/781–4000; Joanna J. Conley, FACHE, Chief Executive Officer

TRISTAR STONECREST MEDICAL CENTER, 200 StoneCrest Boulevard, Smyrna, TN, Zip 37167–6810; tel. 615/768–2000; Louis Caputo, Chief Executive Officer

TRISTAR SUMMIT MEDICAL CENTER, 5655 Frist Boulevard, Hermitage, TN, Zip 37076–2053; tel. 615/316–3000; Brian Marger, Chief Executive Officer

TEXAS

LITTLE RIVER HEALTHCARE
1700 Brazos Avenue, Rockdale, TX, Zip 76567–2517; tel. 512/446–4500; Jeffrey Madison, FACHE, Chief Executive Officer

CAMERON HOSPITAL, 806 North Crockett Avenue, Cameron, TX, Zip 76520–2553; tel. 254/605–1300; Troy Zinn, Chief Executive Officer

ROCKDALE HOSPITAL, 1700 Brazos Street, Rockdale, TX, Zip 76567–2517, Mailing Address: Drawer 1010, Zip 76567–1010, tel. 512/446–4500; Jeffrey Madison, FACHE, Chief Executive Officer

METHODIST HEALTHCARE SYSTEM
8109 Fredericksburg Road, San Antonio, TX, Zip 78229–3311; tel. 210/575–0355; Allen Harrison, Chief Executive Officer

METHODIST AMBULATORY SURGERY HOSPITAL - NORTHWEST, 9150 Huebner Road, Suite 100, San Antonio, TX, Zip 78240–1545; tel. 210/575–5000; Scott Davis, Chief Executive Officer

METHODIST HOSPITAL, 7700 Floyd Curl Drive, San Antonio, TX, Zip 78229–3993; tel. 210/575–4000; Allen Harrison, Chief Executive Officer

METHODIST STONE OAK HOSPITAL, 1139 E Sonterra Boulevard, San Antonio, TX, Zip 78258–4347, Mailing Address: 1139 East Sonterra Boulevard, Zip 78258–4347, tel. 210/638–2100; Marc Strode, Chief Executive Officer

REGIONAL HEALTHCARE ALLIANCE
530 South Beckham Avenue, Tyler, TX, Zip 75702–8310; tel. 903/531–4449; John Webb, President

ALLEGIANCE SPECIALTY HOSPITAL OF KILGORE, 1612 South Henderson Boulevard, Kilgore, TX, Zip 75662–3594; tel. 903/984–3505; Karen Ross, Chief Executive Officer

BAYLOR UNIVERSITY MEDICAL CENTER, 3500 Gaston Avenue, Dallas, TX, Zip 75246–2088; tel. 214/820–0111; Steven R. Newton, FACHE, President

CHRISTUS MOTHER FRANCES HOSPITAL - JACKSONVILLE, 2026 South Jackson, Jacksonville, TX, Zip 75766–5822; tel. 903/541–4500; Anne Pileggi, Administrator and Associate Vice President

CHRISTUS MOTHER FRANCES HOSPITAL - SULPHUR SPRINGS, 115 Airport Road, Sulphur Springs, TX, Zip 75482–2105; tel. 903/885–7671; Paul Harvey, President and Chief Executive Officer

CHRISTUS MOTHER FRANCES HOSPITAL - TYLER, 800 East Dawson Street, Tyler, TX, Zip 75701–2036; tel. 903/593–8441; Jason J. Proctor, Chief Operating Officer

CHRISTUS TRINITY MOTHER FRANCES REHABILITATION HOSPITAL, A PARTNER OF ENCOMPASS HEALTH, 3131 Troup Highway, Tyler, TX, Zip 75701–8352; tel. 903/510–7000; Sharla Anderson, Chief Executive Officer

CHILDREN'S MEDICAL CENTER DALLAS, 1935 Medical District Drive, Pavilion, 3rd Floor, Dallas, TX, Zip 75235–7701; tel. 214/456–7000; Christopher J. Durovich, President and Chief Executive Officer

NACOGDOCHES MEDICAL CENTER, 4920 NE Stallings Drive, Nacogdoches, TX, Zip 75965–1200; tel. 936/569–9481; Philip Koovakada, Chief Executive Officer

PALESTINE REGIONAL MEDICAL CENTER-EAST, 2900 South Loop 256, Palestine, TX, Zip 75801–6958; tel. 903/731–1000; Roy Finch, Chief Executive Officer

PARIS REGIONAL MEDICAL CENTER, 865 Deshong Drive, Paris, TX, Zip 75460–9313, Mailing Address: P.O. Box 9070, Zip 75461–9070, tel. 903/785–4521; Steve Hyde, Chief Executive Officer

TITUS REGIONAL MEDICAL CENTER, 2001 North Jefferson Avenue, Mount Pleasant, TX, Zip 75455–2398; tel. 903/577–6000; Terry Scoggin, Interim Chief Executive Officer

TYLER CONTINUECARE HOSPITAL, 800 East Dawson, 4th Floor, Tyler, TX, Zip 75701–2036; tel. 903/531–4080; Stephanie Hyde, R.N., MSN, Chief Executive Officer

UT HEALTH HENDERSON, 300 Wilson Street, Henderson, TX, Zip 75652–5956; tel. 903/657–7541; Mark Leitner, FACHE, Administrator

UT HEALTH NORTH CAMPUS TYLER, 11937 Highway 271, Tyler, TX, Zip 75708–3154; tel. 903/877–7777; Kirk A. Calhoun, M.D., President

ST. DAVID'S HEALTH NETWORK
98 San Jacinto Boulevard, Austin, TX, Zip 78701–4082; tel. 512/708–9700; David Huffstutler, President and Chief Executive Officer

ST. DAVID'S MEDICAL CENTER, 919 East 32nd Street, Austin, TX, Zip 78705–2709, Mailing Address: P.O. Box 4039, Zip 78765–4039, tel. 512/476–7111; Donald H. Wilkerson, FACHE, Chief Executive Officer

ST. DAVID'S NORTH AUSTIN MEDICAL CENTER, 12221 North MoPac Expressway, Austin, TX, Zip 78758–2496; tel. 512/901–1000; Thomas W. Jackson, Chief Executive Officer

ST. DAVID'S ROUND ROCK MEDICAL CENTER, 2400 Round Rock Avenue, Round Rock, TX, Zip 78681–4097; tel. 512/341–1000; Jeremy Barclay, Chief Executive Officer

ST. DAVID'S SOUTH AUSTIN MEDICAL CENTER, 901 West Ben White Boulevard, Austin, TX, Zip 78704–6903; tel. 512/447–2211; Todd E. Steward, FACHE, Chief Executive Officer

THE HOSPITALS OF PROVIDENCE
2001 North Oregon Street, El Paso, TX, Zip 79902–3320; tel. 915/577–6625; Nicholas R. Tejeda, FACHE, Market Chief Executive Officer

THE HOSPITALS OF PROVIDENCE EAST CAMPUS, 3280 Joe Battle Boulevard, El Paso, TX, Zip 79938–2622; tel. 915/832–2000; Monica Vargas-Mahar, FACHE, Chief Executive Officer

THE HOSPITALS OF PROVIDENCE MEMORIAL CAMPUS, 2001 North Oregon Street, El Paso, TX, Zip 79902–3368; tel. 915/577–6625; Nicholas R. Tejeda, FACHE, Market Chief Executive Officer

THE HOSPITALS OF PROVIDENCE SIERRA CAMPUS, 1625 Medical Center Drive, El Paso, TX, Zip 79902–5005; tel. 915/747–4000; Nicholas R. Tejeda, FACHE, Chief Executive Officer

THE HOSPITALS OF PROVIDENCE TRANSMOUNTAIN CAMPUS, 2000 Transmountain Road, El Paso, TX, Zip 79911; tel. 915/877–8300; Tasha Hopper, Chief Executive Officer

VERMONT

THE UNIVERSITY OF VERMONT HEALTH NETWORK
111 Colchester Avenue, Burlington, VT, Zip 05401–1473; tel. 802/847–3983; John R. Brumsted, M.D., President and Chief Executive Officer

THE UNIVERSITY OF VERMONT HEALTH NETWORK CENTRAL VERMONT MEDICAL CENTER, 130 Fisher Road, Berlin, VT, Zip 05602–9516, Mailing Address: P.O. Box 547, Barre, Zip 05641–0547, tel. 802/371–4100; Anna T. Noonan, President and Chief Operating Officer

THE UNIVERSITY OF VERMONT HEALTH NETWORK ELIZABETHTOWN COMMUNITY HOSPITAL, 75 Park Street, Elizabethtown, NY, Zip 12932, Mailing Address: P.O. Box 277, Zip 12932–0277, tel. 518/873–6377; John R. Remillard, President and Chief Executive Officer

THE UNIVERSITY OF VERMONT HEALTH NETWORK-CHAMPLAIN VALLEY PHYSICIANS HOSPITAL, 75 Beekman Street, Plattsburgh, NY, Zip 12901–1438; tel. 518/561–2000; Michelle Lebeau, President and Chief Operating Officer

UNIVERSITY OF VERMONT MEDICAL CENTER, 111 Colchester Avenue, Burlington, VT, Zip 05401–1473; tel. 802/847–0000; Eileen Whalen, R.N., President and Chief Operating Officer

VIRGINIA

VIRGINIA HEALTH NETWORK
7400 Beaufont Springs Drive, Suite 505, Richmond, VA, Zip 23225–5521; tel. 804/320–3837; James Brittain, President

AUGUSTA HEALTH, 78 Medical Center Drive, Fishersville, VA, Zip 22939–2332, Mailing Address: P.O. Box 1000, Zip 22939–1000, tel. 540/932–4000; Mary N. Mannix, FACHE, President and Chief Executive Officer

BATH COMMUNITY HOSPITAL, 106 Park Drive, Hot Springs, VA, Zip 24445–2921, Mailing Address: P.O. Box Z, Zip 24445–0750, tel. 540/839–7000; Kathy Landreth, Chief Executive Officer

BON SECOURS MARY IMMACULATE HOSPITAL, 2 Bernardine Drive, Newport News, VA, Zip 23602–4499; tel. 757/886–6000; Darlene Stephenson, Chief Executive Officer

BON SECOURS MARYVIEW MEDICAL CENTER, 3636 High Street, Portsmouth, VA, Zip 23707–3270; tel. 757/398–2200; Paul Gaden, Chief Executive Officer

BON SECOURS MEMORIAL REGIONAL MEDICAL CENTER, 8260 Atlee Road, Mechanicsville, VA, Zip 23116–1844; tel. 804/764–6000; Mark M. Gordon, Chief Executive Officer

BON SECOURS ST. FRANCIS MEDICAL CENTER, 13710 St Francis Boulevard, Midlothian, VA, Zip 23114–3267; tel. 804/594–7300; Chris Accashian, Chief Executive Officer

BON SECOURS ST. MARY'S HOSPITAL, 5801 Bremo Road, Richmond, VA, Zip 23226–1907; tel. 804/285–2011; Francine Barr, R.N., MS, Chief Executive Officer

BON SECOURS-DEPAUL MEDICAL CENTER, 150 Kingsley Lane, Norfolk, VA, Zip 23505–4650; tel. 757/889–5000; Paul Gaden, Chief Executive Officer

BON SECOURS-RICHMOND COMMUNITY HOSPITAL, 1500 North 28th Street, Richmond, VA, Zip 23223–5396, Mailing Address: P.O. Box 27184, Zip 23261–7184, tel. 804/225–1700; Mark M. Gordon, Chief Executive Officer

BUCHANAN GENERAL HOSPITAL, 1535 Slate Creek Road, Grundy, VA, Zip 24614–6974; tel. 276/935–1000; Robert D. Ruchti, Chief Executive Officer

CARILION FRANKLIN MEMORIAL HOSPITAL, 180 Floyd Avenue, Rocky Mount, VA, Zip 24151–1389; tel. 540/483–5277; William D. Jacobsen, FACHE, Administrator and Hospital Vice President

CARILION GILES COMMUNITY HOSPITAL, 159 Hartley Way, Pearisburg, VA, Zip 24134–2471; tel. 540/921–6000; William Flattery, Vice President and Administrator Western Division

CARILION NEW RIVER VALLEY MEDICAL CENTER, 2900 Lamb Circle, Christiansburg, VA, Zip 24073–6344, Mailing Address: P.O. Box 5, Radford, Zip 24143–0005, tel. 540/731–2000; William Flattery, Vice President and Administrator Western Division

CARILION ROANOKE MEMORIAL HOSPITAL, 1906 Belleview Avenue Southeast, Roanoke, VA, Zip 24014–1838, Mailing Address: P.O. Box 13367, Zip 24033–3367, tel. 540/981–7000; Steven C. Arner, President

CARILION STONEWALL JACKSON HOSPITAL, 1 Health Circle, Lexington, VA, Zip 24450–2492; tel. 540/458–3300; Greg T. Madsen, Chief Executive Officer

CARILION TAZEWELL COMMUNITY HOSPITAL, 141 Ben Bolt Avenue, Tazewell, VA, Zip 24651–9700, Mailing Address: 388 Ben Bolt Avenue, Zip 24651, tel. 276/988–8700; Kathren Dowdy, MSN, Regional Hospital Senior Director

CENTRA BEDFORD MEMORIAL HOSPITAL, 1613 Oakwood Street, Bedford, VA, Zip 24523–1213; tel. 540/586–2441; Patti Jurkus, Vice President and Chief Executive Officer

CENTRA SOUTHSIDE COMMUNITY HOSPITAL, 800 Oak Street, Farmville, VA, Zip 23901–1199; tel. 434/392–8811; Thomas Angelo, Chief Executive Officer

CHESAPEAKE REGIONAL MEDICAL CENTER, 736 Battlefield Boulevard North, Chesapeake, VA, Zip 23320–4941, Mailing Address: P.O. Box 2028, Zip 23327–2028, tel. 757/312–8121; Reese Jackson, President and Chief Executive Officer

CHILDREN'S HOSPITAL OF RICHMOND AT VCU-BROOK ROAD CAMPUS, 2924 Brook Road, Richmond, VA, Zip 23220–1298; tel. 804/321–7474; Elias Neujahr, Chief Executive Officer

CHILDREN'S HOSPITAL OF THE KING'S DAUGHTERS, 601 Children's Lane, Norfolk, VA, Zip 23507–1910; tel. 757/668–7000; James D. Dahling, President and Chief Executive Officer

CHIPPENHAM HOSPITAL, 7101 Jahnke Road, Richmond, VA, Zip 23225–4044; tel. 804/320–3911; Greg Lowe, Chief Executive Officer

CLINCH VALLEY MEDICAL CENTER, 6801 Governor G C Peery Highway, Richlands, VA, Zip 24641–2194; tel. 276/596–6000; Peter Mulkey, Chief Executive Officer

COASTAL VIRGINIA REHABILITATION, 245 Chesapeake Avenue, Newport News, VA, Zip 23607–6038; tel. 757/928–8000; Daniel Ballin, Administrator

DOMINION HOSPITAL, 2960 Sleepy Hollow Road, Falls Church, VA, Zip 22044–2030; tel. 703/536–2000; Lee Higginbotham, Chief Executive Officer

EMCOMPASS HEALTH REHABILITATION HOSPITAL OF VIRGINIA, 5700 Fitzhugh Avenue, Richmond, VA, Zip 23226–1800; tel. 804/288–5700; Dan Gaskell, Chief Executive Officer

FAUQUIER HOSPITAL, 500 Hospital Drive, Warrenton, VA, Zip 20186–3099; tel. 540/316–5000; Chad Melton, Chief Executive Officer

HENRICO DOCTORS' HOSPITAL, 1602 Skipwith Road, Richmond, VA, Zip 23229–5205; tel. 804/289–4500; William Wagnon, Chief Executive Officer

INOVA ALEXANDRIA HOSPITAL, 4320 Seminary Road, Alexandria, VA, Zip 22304–1535; tel. 703/504–3167; Susan Carroll, Chief Executive Officer

INOVA FAIR OAKS HOSPITAL, 3600 Joseph Siewick Drive, Fairfax, VA, Zip 22033–1798; tel. 703/391–3600; John L. Fitzgerald, Chief Executive Officer

INOVA FAIRFAX HOSPITAL, 3300 Gallows Road, Falls Church, VA, Zip 22042–3300; tel. 703/776–4001; Patrick Christiansen, Ph.D., Chief Executive Officer

INOVA LOUDOUN HOSPITAL, 44045 Riverside Parkway, Leesburg, VA, Zip 20176–5101; Mailing Address: P.O. Box 6000, Zip 20177–0600, tel. 703/858–6000; Deborah Addo, Chief Executive Officer

INOVA MOUNT VERNON HOSPITAL, 2501 Parker's Lane, Alexandria, VA, Zip 22306–3209; tel. 703/664–7000; Donald Brideau, M.D., Chief Executive Officer

JOHN RANDOLPH MEDICAL CENTER, 411 West Randolph Road, Hopewell, VA, Zip 23860–2938; tel. 804/541–1600; Joseph Mazzo, Chief Executive Officer

JOHNSTON MEMORIAL HOSPITAL, 16000 Johnston Memorial Drive, Abingdon, VA, Zip 24211–7659; tel. 276/258–1000; John Jeter, Chief Executive Officer

LEWISGALE HOSPITAL ALLEGHANY, One ARH Lane, Low Moor, VA, Zip 24457, Mailing Address: P.O. Box 7, Zip 24457–0007, tel. 540/862–6011; William Windham, Chief Executive Officer

LEWISGALE HOSPITAL PULASKI, 2400 Lee Highway, Pulaski, VA, Zip 24301–2326, Mailing Address: P.O. Box 759, Zip 24301–0759, tel. 540/994–8100; Sean Pressman, Chief Executive Officer

MARY WASHINGTON HOSPITAL, 1001 Sam Perry Boulevard, Fredericksburg, VA, Zip 22401–3354; tel. 540/741–1100; Michael P. McDermott, M.D., President and Chief Executive Officer

MOUNTAIN VIEW REGIONAL MEDICAL CENTER, 310 Third Street NE, Norton, VA, Zip 24273–1137; tel. 276/679–9100; Dale Clark, President

NORTHERN HOSPITAL OF SURRY COUNTY, 830 Rockford Street, Mount Airy, NC, Zip 27030–5365, Mailing Address: P.O. Box 1101, Zip 27030–1101, tel. 336/719–7000; Chris A. Lumsden, President and Chief Executive Officer

NOVANT HEALTH UVA HEALTH SYSTEM CULPEPER MEDICAL CENTER, 501 Sunset Lane, Culpeper, VA, Zip 22701–3917, Mailing Address: P.O. Box 592, Zip 22701–0500, tel. 540/829–4100; Jeff Hetmanski, President and Chief Operating Officer

NOVANT HEALTH UVA HEALTH SYSTEM PRINCE WILLIAM MEDICAL CENTER, 8700 Sudley Road, Manassas, VA, Zip 20110–4418, Mailing Address: P.O. Box 2610, Zip 20108–0867, tel. 703/369–8000; Greg Napps, President

RAPPAHANNOCK GENERAL HOSPITAL, 101 Harris Drive, Kilmarnock, VA, Zip 22482–3880, Mailing Address: P.O. Box 1449, Zip 22482–1449, tel. 804/435–8000; Chris Accashian, Chief Executive Officer

RESTON HOSPITAL CENTER, 1850 Town Center Parkway, Reston, VA, Zip 20190–3219; tel. 703/689–9000; John A. Deardorff, President and Chief Executive, Northern Virginia Market

RIVERSIDE REGIONAL MEDICAL CENTER, 500 J Clyde Morris Boulevard, Newport News, VA, Zip 23601–1929; tel. 757/594–2000; Michael J. Doucette, Senior Vice President and Administrator

RIVERSIDE SHORE MEMORIAL HOSPITAL, 204800 Market Street, Onancoke, VA, Zip 23417, Mailing Address: P.O. Box 17, Nassawadox, Zip 23413–0017, tel. 757/302–2100; John Peterman, Vice President and Administrator

RIVERSIDE TAPPAHANNOCK HOSPITAL, 618 Hospital Road, Tappahannock, VA, Zip 22560–5000; tel. 804/443–3311; Esther Muscari. Desimini, Administrator

RIVERSIDE WALTER REED HOSPITAL, 7519 Hospital Drive, Gloucester, VA, Zip 23061–4178, Mailing Address: P.O. Box 1130, Zip 23061–1130, tel. 804/693–8800; Esther Muscari. Desimini, Interim Administrator

RUSSELL COUNTY MEDICAL CENTER, 58 Carroll Street, Lebanon, VA, Zip 24266, Mailing Address: P.O. Box 3600, Zip 24266–0200, tel. 276/883–8000; Stephen K. Givens, Assistant Vice President and Administrator

SOVAH HEALTH-MARTINSVILLE, 320 Hospital Drive, Martinsville, VA, Zip 24112–1981, Mailing Address: P.O. Box 4788, Zip 24115–4788, tel. 276/666–7200; Michael Ehrat, Chief Executive Officer

SENTARA CAREPLEX HOSPITAL, 3000 Coliseum Drive, Hampton, VA, Zip 23666–5963; tel. 757/736–1000; Kirkpatrick Conley, President

SENTARA LEIGH HOSPITAL, 830 Kempsville Road, Norfolk, VA, Zip 23502–3920; tel. 757/261–6000; Joanne Inman, President

SENTARA MARTHA JEFFERSON HOSPITAL, 500 Martha Jefferson Drive, Charlottesville, VA, Zip 22911–4668; tel. 434/654–7000; Jonathan S. Davis, FACHE, President

SENTARA NORFOLK GENERAL HOSPITAL, 600 Gresham Drive, Norfolk, VA, Zip 23507–1904; tel. 757/388–3000; Kurt T. Hofelich, President

SENTARA NORTHERN VIRGINIA MEDICAL CENTER, 2300 Opitz Boulevard, Woodbridge, VA, Zip 22191–3399; tel. 703/523–1000; Katherine Johnson, Ph.D., President

SENTARA OBICI HOSPITAL, 2800 Godwin Boulevard, Suffolk, VA, Zip 23434–8038; tel. 757/934–4000; Steve Julian, M.D., President

SENTARA PRINCESS ANNE HOSPITAL, 2025 Glenn Mitchell Drive, Virginia Beach, VA, Zip 23456–0178; tel. 757/507–1000; Thomas B. Thames, M.D., President

SENTARA VIRGINIA BEACH GENERAL HOSPITAL, 1060 First Colonial Road, Virginia Beach, VA, Zip 23454–3002; tel. 757/395–8000; Elwood Bernard. Boone, III., FACHE, President

SENTARA WILLIAMSBURG REGIONAL MEDICAL CENTER, 100 Sentara Circle, Williamsburg, VA, Zip 23188–5713; tel. 757/984–6000; David J. Masterson, President

SHELTERING ARMS REHABILITATION HOSPITAL, 8254 Atlee Road, Mechanicsville, VA, Zip 23116–1844; tel. 804/764–1000; Mary A. Zweifel, MS, President and Chief Executive Officer

SMYTH COUNTY COMMUNITY HOSPITAL , 245 Medical Park Drive, Marion, VA, Zip 24354, Mailing Address: P.O. Box 880, Zip 24354–0880, tel. 276/378–1000; James E. Tyler, Chief Executive Officer

SOUTHAMPTON MEMORIAL HOSPITAL, 100 Fairview Drive, Franklin, VA, Zip 23851–1238, Mailing Address: P.O. Box 817, Zip 23851–0817, tel. 757/569–6100; Kimberly W. Marks, Chief Executive Officer

SOUTHERN VIRGINIA REGIONAL MEDICAL CENTER, 727 North Main Street, Emporia, VA, Zip 23847–1274; tel. 434/348–4400; Wilson A. Thomas, Chief Executive Officer

SOUTHSIDE REGIONAL MEDICAL CENTER, 200 Medical Park Boulevard, Petersburg, VA, Zip 23805–9274; tel. 804/765–5000; Trent Nobles, Chief Executive Officer

TWIN COUNTY REGIONAL HEALTHCARE, 200 Hospital Drive, Galax, VA, Zip 24333–2227; tel. 276/236–8181; Dale Alward, Chief Executive Officer

UVA-HEALTHSOUTH REHABILITATION HOSPITAL, 515 Ray C Hunt Drive, Charlottesville, VA, Zip 22903–2981; tel. 434/244–2000; Barbara Adcock Mohr, Chief Executive Officer

UNIVERSITY OF VIRGINIA MEDICAL CENTER, 1215 Lee Street, Charlottesville, VA, Zip 22908–0001, Mailing Address: P.O. Box 800809, Zip 22908–0809, tel. 434/924–0211; Pamela Sutton-Wallace, Chief Executive Officer

VCU HEALTH COMMUNITY MEMORIAL HOSPITAL, 125 Buena Vista Circle, South Hill, VA, Zip 23970–1431, Mailing Address: P.O. Box 90, Zip 23970–0090, tel. 434/447–3151; W Scott. Burnette, Chief Executive Officer

VCU MEDICAL CENTER, 1250 East Marshall Street, Richmond, VA, Zip 23298–5051, Mailing Address: P.O. Box 980510, Zip 23298–0510, tel. 804/828–9000; Deborah W. Davis, Chief Executive Officer and Vice President Clinical Services

VIRGINIA HOSPITAL CENTER, 1701 North George Mason Drive, Arlington, VA, Zip 22205–3698; tel. 703/558–5000; James B. Cole, President and Chief Executive Officer

WYTHE COUNTY COMMUNITY HOSPITAL, 600 West Ridge Road, Wytheville, VA, Zip 24382–1099; tel. 276/228–0200; Joseph Wilkins, Chief Executive Officer

WASHINGTON

GROUP HEALTH COOPERATIVE
320 Westlake Avenue North, Suite 100, Seattle, WA, Zip 98109–5233; tel. 206/448–5083; Scott Armstrong, Chief Executive Officer

ASTRIA REGIONAL MEDICAL CENTER, 110 South Ninth Avenue, Yakima, WA, Zip 98902–3315; tel. 509/575–5000; Richard H. Robinson, Chief Executive Officer

ASTRIA SUNNYSIDE HOSPITAL, 1016 Tacoma Avenue, Sunnyside, WA, Zip 98944–2263, Mailing Address: P.O. Box 719, Zip 98944–0719, tel. 509/837–1500; Brian P. Gibbons, Jr., Chief Executive Officer

ASTRIA TOPPENISH HOSPITAL, 502 West Fourth Avenue, Toppenish, WA, Zip 98948–1616, Mailing Address: P.O. Box 672, Zip 98948–0672, tel. 509/865–3105; Eric P. Jensen, Chief Executive Officer

CASCADE VALLEY HOSPITAL , 330 South Stillaguamish Avenue, Arlington, WA, Zip 98223–1642; tel. 360/435–2133; Brian K. Ivie, President and Chief Executive Officer

COLUMBIA COUNTY HEALTH SYSTEM, 1012 South Third Street, Dayton, WA, Zip 99328–1696; tel. 509/382–2531; Shane McGuire, Chief Executive Officer

HARRISON MEDICAL CENTER, 2520 Cherry Avenue, Bremerton, WA, Zip 98310–4229; tel. 360/744–3911; David W. Schultz, FACHE, President, Peninsula Region

ISLAND HOSPITAL, 1211 24th Street, Anacortes, WA, Zip 98221–2562; tel. 360/299–1300; Vincent Oliver, FACHE, Administrator

KADLEC REGIONAL MEDICAL CENTER, 888 Swift Boulevard, Richland, WA, Zip 99352–3514; tel. 509/946–4611; Reza Kaleel, Chief Administrative Officer

KAISER PERMANENTE CAPITOL HILL CAMPUS, 201 16th Avenue East, Seattle, WA, Zip 98112–5226; tel. 206/326–3000; Carol M. Taylor, R.N., Regional Director Clinical Operations

KITTITAS VALLEY HEALTHCARE, 603 South Chestnut Street, Ellensburg, WA, Zip 98926–3875; tel. 509/962–7302; Julie Petersen, CPA, Chief Executive Officer

KOOTENAI HEALTH, 2003 Kootenai Health Way, Coeur D'Alene, ID, Zip 83814–2677; tel. 208/625–4000; Jon Ness, Chief Executive Officer

LOURDES MEDICAL CENTER, 520 North Fourth Avenue, Pasco, WA, Zip 99301–5257; tel. 509/547–7704; John Serle, FACHE, President and Chief Executive Officer

MULTICARE DEACONESS HOSPITAL, 800 West Fifth Avenue, Spokane, WA, Zip 99204–2803, Mailing Address: P.O. Box 248, Zip 99210–0248, tel. 509/458–5800; Laureen Driscoll, President

MULTICARE MARY BRIDGE CHILDREN'S HOSPITAL AND HEALTH CENTER, 317 Martin Luther King Jr Way, Tacoma, WA, Zip 98405–4234, Mailing Address: P.O. Box 5299, Zip 98415–0299, tel. 253/403–1400; Jeffrey S. Poltawsky, President and Market Leader

MULTICARE VALLEY HOSPITAL , 12606 East Mission Avenue, Spokane Valley, WA, Zip 99216–1090; tel. 509/924–6650; Gregory George. Repetti, III., FACHE, Chief Executive Officer

NORTHWEST SPECIALTY HOSPITAL, 1593 East Polston Avenue, Post Falls, ID, Zip 83854–5326; tel. 208/262–2300; Rick Rasmussen, Chief Executive Officer

OVERLAKE MEDICAL CENTER, 1035 116th Avenue NE, Bellevue, WA, Zip 98004–4604; tel. 425/688–5000; J. Michael. Marsh, President and Chief Executive Officer

PMH MEDICAL CENTER, 723 Memorial Street, Prosser, WA, Zip 99350–1524; tel. 509/786–2222; Craig J. Marks, FACHE, Chief Executive Officer

PEACEHEALTH ST. JOSEPH MEDICAL CENTER, 2901 Squalicum Parkway, Bellingham, WA, Zip 98225–1851; tel. 360/734–5400; Dale Zender, President Hospital Services NW

PEACEHEALTH UNITED GENERAL MEDICAL CENTER, 2000 Hospital Drive, Sedro-Woolley, WA, Zip 98284–4327; tel. 360/856–6021; Christopher Johnston, Chief Administrative Officer

PROVIDENCE CENTRALIA HOSPITAL, 914 S Scheuber RD, Centralia, WA, Zip 98531–9027, Mailing Address: 914 South Scheuber Road, Zip 98531–9027, tel. 360/736–2803; Medrice Coluccio, R.N., Southwest Region Chief Executive

PROVIDENCE HOLY FAMILY HOSPITAL, 5633 North Lidgerwood Street, Spokane, WA, Zip 99208–1224; tel. 509/482–0111; Peggy M. Currie, R.N., Chief Operating Officer

PROVIDENCE REGIONAL MEDICAL CENTER EVERETT, 1321 Colby Avenue, Everett, WA, Zip 98201–1665, Mailing Address: P.O. Box 1147, Zip 98206–1147, tel. 425/261–2000; Kim Williams, R.N., MS, Chief Executive Officer

PROVIDENCE SACRED HEART MEDICAL CENTER & CHILDREN'S HOSPITAL, 101 West Eighth Avenue, Spokane, WA, Zip 99204–2364, Mailing Address: P.O. Box 2555, Zip 99220–2555, tel. 509/474–3131; Peggy M. Currie, R.N., Chief Operating Officer

PROVIDENCE ST. MARY MEDICAL CENTER, 401 West Poplar Street, Walla Walla, WA, Zip 99362–2846, Mailing Address: P.O. Box 1477, Zip 99362–0312, tel. 509/897–3320; Susan Blackburn, Chief Administrative Officer

PULLMAN REGIONAL HOSPITAL, 835 SE Bishop Boulevard, Pullman, WA, Zip 99163–5512; tel. 509/332–2541; Scott K. Adams, FACHE, Chief Executive Officer

SEATTLE CHILDREN'S HOSPITAL, 4800 Sand Point Way NE, Seattle, WA, Zip 98105–3901, Mailing Address: P.O. Box 5371, Zip 98145–5005, tel. 206/987–2000; Jeff Sperring, M.D., Chief Executive Officer

SKAGIT REGIONAL HEALTH, 1415 East Kincaid, Mount Vernon, WA, Zip 98274–4126, Mailing Address: P.O. Box 1376, Zip 98273–1376, tel. 360/424–4111; Brian K. Ivie, President and Chief Executive Officer

ST. FRANCIS HOSPITAL, 34515 Ninth Avenue South, Federal Way, WA, Zip 98003–6799; tel. 253/944–8100; Anthony McLean, Market President

ST. JOSEPH MEDICAL CENTER, 1717 South 'J' Street, Tacoma, WA, Zip 98405–3004, Mailing Address: P.O. Box 2197, Zip 98401–2197, tel. 253/426–4101; Syd Bersante, R.N., President

TRIOS HEALTH, 900 South Auburn Street, Kennewick, WA, Zip 99336–5621, Mailing Address: P.O. Box 6128, Zip 99336–0128, tel. 509/586–6111; John H. Solheim, Chief Executive Officer

VIRGINIA MASON MEDICAL CENTER, 1100 Ninth Avenue, Seattle, WA, Zip 98101–2756, Mailing Address: P.O. Box 900, Zip 98111–0900, tel. 206/223–6600; Gary Kaplan, M.D., FACHE, Chairman and Chief Executive Officer

VIRGINIA MASON MEMORIAL, 2811 Tieton Drive, Yakima, WA, Zip 98902–3761; tel. 509/575–8000; Russ Myers, Chief Executive Officer

WHIDBEYHEALTH, 101 North Main Street, Coupeville, WA, Zip 98239–3413; tel. 360/678–5151; Geri Forbes, Chief Executive Officer

WHITMAN HOSPITAL AND MEDICAL CENTER, 1200 West Fairview Street, Colfax, WA, Zip 99111–9579; tel. 509/397–3435; Hank Hanigan, FACHE, Chief Executive Officer

LINCOLN COUNTY HEALTH DEPARTMENT
90 Nichols Street, Davenport, WA, Zip 99122–9729; tel. 509/725–1001; Ed Dzedzy, Public Health Administration

LINCOLN HOSPITAL, 10 Nicholls Street, Davenport, WA, Zip 99122–9729; tel. 509/725–7101; Tyson Lacy, Chief Executive Officer and Superintendent

ODESSA MEMORIAL HEALTHCARE CENTER, 502 East Amende Drive, Odessa, WA, Zip 99159–7003, Mailing Address: P.O. Box 368, Zip 99159–0368, tel. 509/982–2611; Mo P. Sheldon, FACHE, Chief Executive Officer and Administrator

WEST VIRGINIA

HEALTH PARTNERS NETWORK, INC.
1000 Technology Drive, Suite 2320, Fairmont, WV, Zip 26554–8834; tel. 304/368–2740; William G. MacLean, Executive Director

BROADDUS HOSPITAL, 1 Healthcare Drive, Philippi, WV, Zip 26416–9405, Mailing Address: P.O. Box 930, Zip 26416–0930, tel. 304/457–1760; Dana L. Gould, Chief Executive Officer

CAMDEN CLARK MEDICAL CENTER, 800 Garfield Avenue, Parkersburg, WV, Zip 26101–5378, Mailing Address: P.O. Box 718, Zip 26102–0718, tel. 304/424–2111; Steve Altmiller, President and Chief Executive Officer

DAVIS MEDICAL CENTER, Gorman Avenue and Reed Street, Elkins, WV, Zip 26241, Mailing Address: P.O. Box 1484, Zip 26241–1484, tel. 304/636–3300; Vance Jackson, FACHE, Chief Executive Officer

GRAFTON CITY HOSPITAL, 1 Hospital Plaza, Grafton, WV, Zip 26354–1283; tel. 304/265–0400; Patrick D. Shaw, Chief Executive Officer

HEALTHSOUTH MOUNTAINVIEW REGIONAL REHABILITATION HOSPITAL, 1160 Van Voorhis Road, Morgantown, WV, Zip 26505–3437; tel. 304/598–1100; Tracy Vinciguerra, Chief Executive Officer

MINNIE HAMILTON HEALTHCARE CENTER, 186 Hospital Drive, Grantsville, WV, Zip 26147–7100; tel. 304/354–9244; Steve Whited, Chief Executive Officer

ST. JOSEPH'S HOSPITAL OF BUCKHANNON, 1 Amalia Drive, Buckhannon, WV, Zip 26201–2276; tel. 304/473–2000; Skip Gjolberg, FACHE, Administrator

STONEWALL JACKSON MEMORIAL HOSPITAL, 230 Hospital Plaza, Weston, WV, Zip 26452–8558; tel. 304/269–8000; Avah Stalnaker, Chief Executive Officer

UNITED HOSPITAL CENTER, 327 Medical Park Drive, Bridgeport, WV, Zip 26330–9006; tel. 681/342–1000; Michael C. Tillman, President and Chief Executive Officer

WEBSTER COUNTY MEMORIAL HOSPITAL, 324 Miller Mountain Drive, Webster Springs, WV, Zip 26288–1087, Mailing Address: P.O. Box 312, Zip 26288–0312, tel. 304/847–5682; Jim Parker, FACHE, Chief Executive Officer

WEST VIRGINIA UNIVERSITY HOSPITALS, 1 Medical Center Drive, Morgantown, WV, Zip 26506–4749; tel. 304/598–4000; Albert L. Wright, Jr., PharmD, President and Chief Executive Officer

PARTNERS IN HEALTH NETWORK, INC.
405 Capitol Street, Suite 505, Charleston, WV, Zip 25301–1783; tel. 304/388–7385; Robert D. Whitler, Executive Director

BOONE MEMORIAL HOSPITAL, 701 Madison Avenue, Madison, WV, Zip 25130–1699; tel. 304/369–1230; Virgil Underwood, Chief Executive Officer

BRAXTON COUNTY MEMORIAL HOSPITAL, 100 Hoylman DR, Gassaway, WV, Zip 26624–9318, Mailing Address: 100 Hoylman Drive, Zip 26624–9318, tel. 304/364–5156; Ben Vincent, FACHE, Chief Executive Officer

CHARLESTON AREA MEDICAL CENTER, 501 Morris Street, Charleston, WV, Zip 25301–1300, Mailing Address: P.O. Box 1547, Zip 25326–1547, tel. 304/388–5432; David L. Ramsey, President and Chief Executive Officer

CHARLESTON SURGICAL HOSPITAL, 1306 Kanawha Boulevard East, Charleston, WV, Zip 25301–3001, Mailing Address: P.O. Box 2271, Zip 25328–2271, tel. 304/343–4371; Christina Arvon, Administrator and Chief Executive Officer

HIGHLAND HOSPITAL, 300 56th Street SE, Charleston, WV, Zip 25304–2361, Mailing Address: P.O. Box 4107, Zip 25364–4107, tel. 304/926–1600; Cynthia A. Persily, Ph.D., R.N., President and Chief Executive Officer

JACKSON GENERAL HOSPITAL, 122 Pinnell Street, Ripley, WV, Zip 25271–9101, Mailing Address: P.O. Box 720, Zip 25271–0720, tel. 304/372–2731; Stephanie McCoy, President and Chief Executive Officer

MINNIE HAMILTON HEALTHCARE CENTER, 186 Hospital Drive, Grantsville, WV, Zip 26147–7100; tel. 304/354–9244; Steve Whited, Chief Executive Officer

MONTGOMERY GENERAL HOSPITAL, 401 Sixth Avenue, Montgomery, WV, Zip 25136–2116, Mailing Address: P.O. Box 270, Zip 25136–0270, tel. 304/442–5151; Vickie Gay, Chief Executive Officer

POCAHONTAS MEMORIAL HOSPITAL, 150 Duncan Road, Buckeye, WV, Zip 24924; tel. 304/799–7400; Barbara Lay, Chief Executive Officer

ROANE GENERAL HOSPITAL, 200 Hospital Drive, Spencer, WV, Zip 25276–1050; tel. 304/927–4444; Douglas E. Bentz, Chief Executive Officer

STONEWALL JACKSON MEMORIAL HOSPITAL, 230 Hospital Plaza, Weston, WV, Zip 26452–8558; tel. 304/269–8000; Avah Stalnaker, Chief Executive Officer

SUMMERSVILLE REGIONAL MEDICAL CENTER, 400 Fairview Heights Road, Summersville, WV, Zip 26651–9308; tel. 304/872–2891; Karen A. Fiducia, FACHE, President and Chief Executive Officer

WEBSTER COUNTY MEMORIAL HOSPITAL, 324 Miller Mountain Drive, Webster Springs, WV, Zip 26288–1087, Mailing Address: P.O. Box 312, Zip 26288–0312, tel. 304/847–5682; Jim Parker, FACHE, Chief Executive Officer

WISCONSIN

ASCENSION WISCONSIN
1506 South Oneida Street, Appleton, WI, Zip 54915–1305; tel. 920/831–8912; Monica Hilt, President and Chief Executive Officer

ASCENSION CALUMET HOSPITAL, 614 Memorial Drive, Chilton, WI, Zip 53014–1597; tel. 920/849–2386; Jenny Derks, Chief Administrative Officer

ASCENSION NORTHEAST WISCONSIN MERCY HOSPITAL, 500 South Oakwood Road, Oshkosh, WI, Zip 54904–7944; tel. 920/223–2000; Denise Parrish, Interim Chief Administrative Officer

ASCENSION NORTHEAST WISCONSIN ST. ELIZABETH HOSPITAL, 1506 South Oneida Street, Appleton, WI, Zip 54915–1305; tel. 920/738–2000; Monica Hilt, President and Regional Vice President

ASPIRUS, INC.
 2200 Westwood Drive, Wausau, WI, Zip 54401–7806; tel. 715/847–2118; Matthew Heywood, President and Chief Executive Officer

ASPIRUS IRON RIVER HOSPITALS & CLINICS, INC., 1400 West Ice Lake Road, Iron River, MI, Zip 49935–9526; tel. 906/265–6121; Connie L. Koutouzos, R.N., MSN, Chief Executive Officer

ASPIRUS IRONWOOD HOSPITALS & CLINICS, INC., N10561 Grand View Lane, Ironwood, MI, Zip 49938–9622; tel. 906/932–2525; Paula L. Chermside, Chief Executive Officer

ASPIRUS KEWEENAW HOSPITAL, INC., 205 Osceola Street, Laurium, MI, Zip 49913–2134; tel. 906/337–6500; Jesse G. Tischer, Interim Presidnet

ASPIRUS LANGLADE HOSPITAL, 112 East Fifth Avenue, Antigo, WI, Zip 54409–2796; tel. 715/623–2331; Andrew J. Barth, Executive Director

ASPIRUS MEDFORD HOSPITAL & CLINICS, INC., 135 South Gibson Street, Medford, WI, Zip 54451; tel. 715/748–8100; Dale Hustedt, Chief Executive Officer

ASPIRUS ONTONAGON HOSPITAL, INC., 601 South Seventh Street, Ontonagon, MI, Zip 49953–1459; tel. 906/884–8000; Jesse G. Tischer, Interim President

ASPIRUS RIVERVIEW HOSPITAL AND CLINICS, INC., 410 Dewey Street, Wisconsin Rapids, WI, Zip 54494–4715, Mailing Address: P.O. Box 8080, Zip 54495–8080, tel. 715/423–6060; Todd Burch, Chief Executive Officer

ASPIRUS WAUSAU HOSPITAL, INC., 333 Pine Ridge Boulevard, Wausau, WI, Zip 54401–4187; tel. 715/847–2121; Darrell Lentz, President

COLUMBIA ST. MARY'S
 2025 East Newport Avenue, Milwaukee, WI, Zip 53211–2906; tel. 414/961–3300; Travis Andersen, President and Chief Executive Officer

COLUMBIA ST. MARY'S HOSPITAL MILWAUKEE, 2301 North Lake Drive, Milwaukee, WI, Zip 53211–4508; tel. 414/291–1000; Travis Andersen, Chief Executive Officer

COLUMBIA ST. MARY'S HOSPITAL OZAUKEE, 13111 North Port Washington Road, Mequon, WI, Zip 53097–2416; tel. 262/243–7300; Travis Andersen, President and Chief Executive Officer

COLUMBIA ST. MARY'S MILWAUKEE HOSPITAL, 2323 North Lake Drive, Milwaukee, WI, Zip 53211–4508, Mailing Address: 2301 North Lake Drive, Zip 53211–4508, tel. 414/585–1000; Kelly Elkins, President and Chief Executive Officer

COMMUNITY HEALTH NETWORK, INC.
 225 Memorial Drive, Berlin, WI, Zip 54923–1243; tel. 920/361–5580

THEDA CARE MEDICAL CENTER - WILD ROSE, 601 Grove Avenue, Wild Rose, WI, Zip 54984–6903, Mailing Address: P.O. Box 243, Zip 54984–0243, tel. 920/622–3257; Craig A. Kantos, Chief Executive Officer

THEDACARE MEDICAL CENTER-BERLIN, 225 Memorial Drive, Berlin, WI, Zip 54923–1295; tel. 920/361–1313; Tammy Bending, Vice President, Critical Access Hospital

GUNDERSEN HEALTH SYSTEM
 1900 South Avenue, La Crosse, WI, Zip 54601–5467; tel. 608/782–7300; Scott W. Rathgaber, M.D., Chief Executive Officer

GUNDERSEN BOSCOBEL AREA HOSPITAL AND CLINICS, 205 Parker Street, Boscobel, WI, Zip 53805–1698; tel. 608/375–4112; David Hartberg, Chief Executive Officer

GUNDERSEN LUTHERAN MEDICAL CENTER, 1900 South Avenue, La Crosse, WI, Zip 54601–5467; tel. 608/782–7300; Scott W. Rathgaber, M.D., Chief Executive Officer

GUNDERSEN MOUNDVIEW MEMORIAL HOSPITAL & CLINICS, 402 West Lake Street, Friendship, WI, Zip 53934–9699, Mailing Address: P.O. Box 40, Zip 53934–0040, tel. 608/339–3331; Francisco Perez-Guerra, Chief Executive Officer

GUNDERSEN PALMER LUTHERAN HOSPITAL AND CLINICS, 112 Jefferson Street, West Union, IA, Zip 52175–1022; tel. 563/422–3811; Tanya Tysland, Chief Executive Officer

GUNDERSEN ST. JOSEPH'S HOSPITAL AND CLINICS, 400 Water Avenue, Hillsboro, WI, Zip 54634–9054, Mailing Address: P.O. Box 527, Zip 54634–0527, tel. 608/489–8000; Danielle Gearhart, Chief Executive Officer

GUNDERSEN TRI-COUNTY HOSPITAL AND CLINICS, 18601 Lincoln Street, Whitehall, WI, Zip 54773–8605; tel. 715/538–4361; Joni Olson, Chief Executive Officer

Section B

Alliances

ALLIANCE OF INDEPENDENT ACADEMIC MEDICAL CENTERS

233 East Erie Street, Ste 306, Chicago, IL, Zip 60611; tel. 312/836–3712; Kimberly Pierce–Boggs, Executive Director

ARIZONA
Scottsdale
Alliance
  HonorHealth

CALIFORNIA
Colton
Alliance
  Arrowhead Regional Medical Center

Los Angeles
Alliance
  Cedars-Sinai Medical Center

Oakland
Alliance
  Kaiser Permanente Oakland Medical Center

COLORADO
Aurora
Alliance
  Medical Center of Aurora

Denver
Alliance
  Presbyterian-St. Luke's Medical Center
  Rose Medical Center
  Saint Joseph Hospital

Englewood
Alliance
  Swedish Medical Center

Lone Tree
Alliance
  Sky Ridge Medical Center

Thornton
Alliance
  North Suburban Medical Center

CONNECTICUT
Hartford
Alliance
  Saint Francis Hospital and Medical Center

DELAWARE
Newark
Alliance
  Christiana Care Health System

FLORIDA
Hollywood
Alliance
  Memorial Healthcare System

Orange Park
Alliance
  Orange Park Medical Center

Orlando
Alliance
  Florida Hospital
  Orlando Regional Medical Center

GEORGIA
Macon
Alliance
  Coliseum Medical Centers

ILLINOIS
Chicago
Alliance
  Advocate Illinois Masonic Medical Center

Oak Lawn
Alliance
  Advocate Christ Medical Center

Park Ridge
Alliance
  Advocate Lutheran General Hospital

Peoria
Alliance
  OSF Saint Francis Medical Center

INDIANA
Indianapolis
Alliance
  Community Health Network

IOWA
West Des Moines
Alliance
  UnityPoint Health

LOUISIANA
Baton Rouge
Alliance
  Our Lady of the Lake Regional Medical Center

New Orleans
Alliance
  Ochsner Health System

MAINE
Portland
Alliance
  Maine Medical Center

MARYLAND
Baltimore
Alliance
  Sinai Hospital of Baltimore

MASSACHUSETTS
Burlington
Alliance
  Lahey Hospital & Medical Center, Burlington

Springfield
Alliance
  Baystate Medical Center

MICHIGAN
Grand Rapids
Alliance
  Mercy Health Saint Mary's

Lansing
Alliance
  Sparrow Hospital

Rochester
Alliance
  Ascension Crittenton Hospital Medical Center

MINNESOTA
Bloomington
Alliance
  HealthPartners

MONTANA
Billings
Alliance
  Billings Clinic

NEW JERSEY
Brick Township
Alliance
  Hackensack Meridian Health Ocean Medical Center

Holmdel
Alliance
  Hackensack Meridian Health Bayshore Community Hospital

Livingston
Alliance
  Saint Barnabas Medical Center

Long Branch
Alliance
  Monmouth Medical Center, Long Branch Campus

Manahawkin
Alliance
  Hackensack Meridian Health Southern Ocean Medical Center

Neptune
Alliance
  Hackensack Meridian Health Jersey Shore University Medical Center

Newark
Alliance
  Newark Beth Israel Medical Center

Perth Amboy
Alliance
  Hackensack Meridian Health Raritan Bay Medical Center

Phillipsburg
Alliance
  St. Luke's Hospital - Warren Campus

Red Bank
Alliance
  Hackensack Meridian Health Riverview Medical Center

NEW YORK
Brooklyn
Alliance
  Maimonides Medical Center

Cooperstown
Alliance
  Bassett Medical Center

Mineola
Alliance
  NYU Winthrop Hospital

NORTH CAROLINA
Charlotte
Alliance
  Carolinas Medical Center

OHIO
Akron
Alliance
  Cleveland Clinic Akron General

Cincinnati
Alliance
  Christ Hospital
  TriHealth Evendale Hospital

Cleveland
Alliance
  Cleveland Clinic

Columbus
Alliance
  OhioHealth Grant Medical Center
  OhioHealth Riverside Methodist Hospital

OREGON
Hood River
Alliance
  Providence Hood River Memorial Hospital

Milwaukie
Alliance
  Providence Milwaukie Hospital

Portland
Alliance
  Providence Portland Medical Center
  Providence St. Vincent Medical Center

PENNSYLVANIA
Bethlehem
Alliance
  St. Luke's University Hospital - Bethlehem Campus

Philadelphia
Alliance
  Einstein Medical Center Philadelphia

Sayre
Alliance
  Guthrie Robert Packer Hospital

Wynnewood
Alliance
  Lankenau Medical Center

York
Alliance
  WellSpan York Hospital

SOUTH CAROLINA

Charleston
Alliance
Trident Medical Center

Myrtle Beach
Alliance
Grand Strand Regional Medical Center

TEXAS

Dallas
Alliance
Baylor Scott & White Health

Fort Worth
Alliance
JPS Health Network

Lubbock
Alliance
Covenant Children's Hospital

Covenant Medical Center

WASHINGTON

Seattle
Alliance
Kaiser Permanente Capitol Hill Campus

Swedish Medical Center-Cherry Hill Campus

Swedish Medical Center-First Hill

Virginia Mason Medical Center

WEST VIRGINIA

Charleston
Alliance
Charleston Area Medical Center

WISCONSIN

Marshfield
Alliance
Marshfield Medical Center

CAPSTONE HEALTH ALLIANCE
1200 Ridgefield Boulevard, Suite 200, Asheville, NC, Zip 28806; tel. 828/418–5050; Tim Bugg, President and Chief Executive Officer

ALABAMA

Butler
Alliance
Choctaw General Hospital

Dothan
Alliance
Southeast Alabama Medical Center

Eufaula
Alliance
Medical Center Barbour

Opelika
Alliance
East Alabama Medical Center

Wedowee
Alliance
Tanner Medical Center/East Alabama

ARKANSAS

Batesville
Alliance
White River Medical Center

Calico Rock
Alliance
Izard County Medical Center

Fordyce
Alliance
Dallas County Medical Center

Harrison
Alliance
North Arkansas Regional Medical Center

Mountain View
Alliance
Stone County Medical Center

Pine Bluff
Alliance
Jefferson Regional Medical Center

DELAWARE

Lewes
Alliance
Beebe Healthcare

GEORGIA

Bremen
Alliance
Higgins General Hospital

Carrollton
Alliance
Tanner Medical Center-Carrollton

Jesup
Alliance
Wayne Memorial Hospital

Lagrange
Alliance
Wellstar West Georgia Medical Center

Savannah
Alliance
Candler Hospital

St. Joseph's Hospital

Villa Rica
Alliance
Tanner Medical Center-Villa Rica

ILLINOIS

Centreville
Alliance
Touchette Regional Hospital

Chicago
Alliance
Loretto Hospital

Norwegian American Hospital

Thorek Memorial Hospital

Dixon
Alliance
Katherine Shaw Bethea Hospital

Elmhurst
Alliance
Elmhurst Hospital

Hoopeston
Alliance
Carle Hoopeston Regional Health Center

Kankakee
Alliance
Riverside Medical Center

Naperville
Alliance
Edward Hospital

Linden Oaks Hospital

Urbana
Alliance
Carle Foundation Hospital

INDIANA

Greenfield
Alliance
Hancock Regional Hospital

Rushville
Alliance
Rush Memorial Hospital

KANSAS

Manhattan
Alliance
Manhattan Surgical

KENTUCKY

Albany
Alliance
The Medical Center Albany

Bowling Green
Alliance
Commonwealth Regional Specialty Hospital

Medical Center at Bowling Green

Danville
Alliance
Ephraim McDowell Regional Medical Center

Edgewood
Alliance
St. Elizabeth Edgewood

Florence
Alliance
St. Elizabeth Florence

Fort Thomas
Alliance
St. Elizabeth Fort Thomas

Franklin
Alliance
Medical Center at Franklin

Glasgow
Alliance
T. J. Samson Community Hospital

Henderson
Alliance
Methodist Hospital

Horse Cave
Alliance
The Medical Center at Caverna

Morganfield
Alliance
Methodist Hospital Union County

Murray
Alliance
Murray-Calloway County Hospital

Scottsville
Alliance
Medical Center at Scottsville

Stanford
Alliance
Ephraim McDowell Fort Logan Hospital

Williamstown
Alliance
St. Elizabeth Grant

LOUISIANA

Abbeville
Alliance
Abbeville General Hospital

Baton Rouge
Alliance
Baton Rouge General Medical Center

Baton Rouge Rehabilitation Hospital

Spine Hospital of Louisiana (formally the NeuroMedical Center Surgical Hospital)

The NeuroMedical Center Rehabilitation Hospital

Woman's Hospital

Breaux Bridge
Alliance
St. Martin Hospital

Bunkie
Alliance
Bunkie General Hospital

Church Point
Alliance
Acadia-St. Landry Hospital

Columbia
Alliance
Citizens Medical Center

Crowley
Alliance
Acadia General Hospital

Delhi
Alliance
Richland Parish Hospital

Hammond
Alliance
North Oaks Medical Center

North Oaks Rehabilitation Hospital

Houma
Alliance
Terrebonne General Medical Center

Jennings
Alliance
Jennings American Legion Hospital

Kaplan
Alliance
Abrom Kaplan Memorial Hospital

Section B

Kenner
Alliance
   Extended Care Hospital
Kinder
Alliance
   Allen Parish Hospital
Lafayette
Alliance
   Lafayette General Medical Center
   Lafayette General Surgical Hospital
   Louisiana Extended Care Hospital of Lafayette
   University Hospital and Clinics
Marrero
Alliance
   Bridgepoint Continuing Care Hospital
Monroe
Alliance
   Specialty Hospital
Natchitoches
Alliance
   Louisiana Extended Care Hospital of Natchitoches
New Iberia
Alliance
   Iberia Medical Center
Opelousas
Alliance
   St. Landry Extended Care Hospital
Rayville
Alliance
   Richardson Medical Center
West Monroe
Alliance
   Louisiana Extended Care Hospital West Monroe
Winnsboro
Alliance
   Franklin Medical Center

MARYLAND
Annapolis
Alliance
   Anne Arundel Medical Center
Baltimore
Alliance
   Greater Baltimore Medical Center
   Levindale Hebrew Geriatric Center and Hospital
   Mercy Medical Center
   Sinai Hospital of Baltimore
Berlin
Alliance
   Atlantic General Hospital
Cumberland
Alliance
   Western Maryland Regional Medical Center
Elkton
Alliance
   Union Hospital
Frederick
Alliance
   Frederick Regional Health System
Lanham
Alliance
   Doctors Community Hospital
Randallstown
Alliance
   Northwest Hospital
Salisbury
Alliance
   Peninsula Regional Medical Center
Westminster
Alliance
   Carroll Hospital Center

MICHIGAN
Ypsilanti
Alliance
   Forest Health Medical Center

MINNESOTA
Blue Earth

Alliance
   United Hospital District

MISSISSIPPI
Bay Springs
Alliance
   Jasper General Hospital
Carthage
Alliance
   Baptist Medical Center Leake
Charleston
Alliance
   Tallahatchie General Hospital
De Kalb
Alliance
   John C. Stennis Memorial Hospital
Jackson
Alliance
   Mississippi Baptist Medical Center
Kosciusko
Alliance
   Baptist Medical Center Attala
Laurel
Alliance
   South Central Regional Medical Center
Louisville
Alliance
   Winston Medical Center
Magee
Alliance
   Magee General Hospital
Mendenhall
Alliance
   Simpson General Hospital
Meridian
Alliance
   Rush Foundation Hospital
Morton
Alliance
   Scott Regional Hospital
Quitman
Alliance
   H. C. Watkins Memorial Hospital
Ruleville
Alliance
   North Sunflower Medical Center
Union
Alliance
   Laird Hospital
Water Valley
Alliance
   Yalobusha General Hospital
Yazoo City
Alliance
   Baptist Medical Center Yazoo

NEBRASKA
Kearney
Alliance
   Kearney Regional Medical Center

NORTH CAROLINA
Asheville
Alliance
   Asheville Specialty Hospital
   CarePartners Health Services
   Mission Hospital
Boone
Alliance
   Watauga Medical Center
Brevard
Alliance
   Transylvania Regional Hospital
Bryson City
Alliance
   Swain Community Hospital
Cherokee
Alliance
   Cherokee Indian Hospital
Clyde

Alliance
   Haywood Regional Medical Center
Columbus
Alliance
   St. Luke's Hospital
Dunn
Alliance
   Harnett Health System
Elizabeth City
Alliance
   Sentara Albemarle Medical Center
Elizabethtown
Alliance
   Cape Fear Valley - Bladen County Hospital
Fayetteville
Alliance
   Cape Fear Valley Medical Center
   Highsmith-Rainey Specialty Hospital
Franklin
Alliance
   Angel Medical Center
Gastonia
Alliance
   CaroMont Regional Medical Center
Goldsboro
Alliance
   Wayne UNC Health Care
Hendersonville
Alliance
   Margaret R. Pardee Memorial Hospital
   Park Ridge Health
Hickory
Alliance
   Catawba Valley Medical Center
Highlands
Alliance
   Highlands-Cashiers Hospital
Marion
Alliance
   McDowell Hospital
Morehead City
Alliance
   Carteret Health Care
Newland
Alliance
   Charles A. Cannon Memorial Hospital
Oxford
Alliance
   Granville Health System
Pinehurst
Alliance
   FirstHealth Moore Regional Hospital
Raeford
Alliance
   Hoke Hospital
Roanoke Rapids
Alliance
   Halifax Regional Medical Center
Spruce Pine
Alliance
   Blue Ridge Regional Hospital
Statesville
Alliance
   Iredell Health System
Troy
Alliance
   FirstHealth Montgomery Memorial Hospital

NORTH DAKOTA
Cavalier
Alliance
   Pembina County Memorial Hospital and Wedgewood Manor

OHIO
Amherst
Alliance
   Specialty Hospital of Lorain
Bowling Green

Alliance
  Wood County Hospital

Cleveland
Alliance
  Grace Hospital

Cuyahoga Falls
Alliance
  Western Reserve Hospital

Salem
Alliance
  Salem Regional Medical Center

Steubenville
Alliance
  Life Line Hospital

PENNSYLVANIA
Corry
Alliance
  Corry Memorial Hospital

Erie
Alliance
  LECOM Health Millcreek Community Hospital

Kittanning
Alliance
  ACMH Hospital

Langhorne
Alliance
  Barix Clinics of Pennsylvania

Meadville
Alliance
  Meadville Medical Center

State College
Alliance
  Mount Nittany Medical Center

Titusville
Alliance
  Titusville Area Hospital

Tyrone
Alliance
  Tyrone Hospital

Windber
Alliance
  Chan Soon-Shiong Medical Center

SOUTH CAROLINA
Conway
Alliance
  Conway Medical Center

West Columbia
Alliance
  Lexington Medical Center

Winnsboro
Alliance
  Fairfield Memorial Hospital

TENNESSEE
Crossville
Alliance
  Cumberland Medical Center

Elizabethton
Alliance
  Sycamore Shoals Hospital

Erwin
Alliance
  Unicoi County Memorial Hospital

Greeneville
Alliance
  Laughlin Memorial Hospital

Johnson City
Alliance
  Franklin Woods Community Hospital

  Johnson City Medical Center

  Quillen Rehabilitation Hospital

Kingsport
Alliance
  Indian Path Medical Center

Knoxville
Alliance
  University of Tennessee Medical Center

Maryville
Alliance
  Blount Memorial Hospital

Mountain City
Alliance
  Johnson County Community Hospital

TEXAS
The Woodlands
Alliance
  Woodlands Specialty Hospital

VIRGINIA
Abingdon
Alliance
  Johnston Memorial Hospital

Chesapeake
Alliance
  Chesapeake Regional Medical Center

Christiansburg
Alliance
  Carilion New River Valley Medical Center

Clintwood
Alliance
  Dickenson Community Hospital

Front Royal
Alliance
  Warren Memorial Hospital

Gloucester
Alliance
  Riverside Walter Reed Hospital

Grundy
Alliance
  Buchanan General Hospital

Lebanon
Alliance
  Russell County Medical Center

Lexington
Alliance
  Carilion Stonewall Jackson Hospital

Luray
Alliance
  Page Memorial Hospital

Marion
Alliance
  Smyth County Community Hospital

Newport News
Alliance
  Riverside Regional Medical Center

Norton
Alliance
  Norton Community Hospital

Onancoke
Alliance
  Riverside Shore Memorial Hospital

Pearisburg
Alliance
  Carilion Giles Community Hospital

Roanoke
Alliance
  Carilion Roanoke Memorial Hospital

Rocky Mount
Alliance
  Carilion Franklin Memorial Hospital

South Hill
Alliance
  VCU Health Community Memorial Hospital

Tappahannock
Alliance
  Riverside Tappahannock Hospital

Tazewell
Alliance
  Carilion Tazewell Community Hospital

Williamsburg
Alliance
  Riverside Doctors' Hospital Williamsburg

Winchester
Alliance
  Winchester Medical Center

Woodstock
Alliance
  Valley Health Shenandoah Memorial Hospital

WEST VIRGINIA
Berkeley Springs
Alliance
  War Memorial Hospital

Charleston
Alliance
  Saint Francis Hospital

Elkins
Alliance
  Davis Medical Center

Huntington
Alliance
  Cabell Huntington Hospital

  St. Mary's Medical Center

Kingwood
Alliance
  Preston Memorial Hospital

Morgantown
Alliance
  Mon Health Medical Center

Point Pleasant
Alliance
  Pleasant Valley Hospital

Romney
Alliance
  Hampshire Memorial Hospital

South Charleston
Alliance
  Thomas Memorial Hospital

CATHOLIC CEO HEALTHCARE CONNECTION
  50 South Main Street, Suite 200,
  Naperville, IL, Zip 60540–5484;
  tel. 630/352–2220; Roger N. Butler,
  Executive Director

CALIFORNIA
San Francisco
Alliance
  Dignity Health

COLORADO
Broomfield
Alliance
  SCL Health

Englewood
Alliance
  Catholic Health Initiatives

ILLINOIS
Peoria
Alliance
  OSF Healthcare

Springfield
Alliance
  HSHS Hospital Sisters Health System

LOUISIANA
Baton Rouge
Alliance
  Franciscan Missionaries of Our Lady Health System, Inc.

MARYLAND
Marriottsville
Alliance
  Bon Secours Health System, Inc.

MISSOURI
Chesterfield
Alliance
  Mercy

Saint Louis
Alliance
  Ascension Healthcare

  SSM Health

OHIO
Cincinnati

Alliances

Alliance
Mercy Health
SOUTH DAKOTA
Sioux Falls
Alliance
Avera Health

TEXAS
Irving
Alliance
CHRISTUS Health

WASHINGTON
Renton
Alliance
Providence St. Joseph Health
Vancouver
Alliance
PeaceHealth

WISCONSIN
Manitowoc
Alliance
Franciscan Sisters of Christian Charity Sponsored Ministries, Inc.

HEALTH ENTERPRISES COOPERATIVE
5825 Dry Creek Lane NE, Cedar Rapids, IA, Zip 52402–1225; tel. 319/368–3619; Judy L. Sadler, President and Chief Executive Officer

IOWA
Ames
Alliance
Mary Greeley Medical Center
Chariton
Alliance
Lucas County Health Center
Charles City
Alliance
Floyd County Medical Center
Cherokee
Alliance
Cherokee Regional Medical Center
Davenport
Alliance
Genesis Health System
Denison
Alliance
Crawford County Memorial Hospital
Des Moines
Alliance
Broadlawns Medical Center
Fairfield
Alliance
Jefferson County Health Center
Grinnell
Alliance
UnityPoint Health - Grinnell Regional Medical Center
Guthrie Center
Alliance
Guthrie County Hospital
Humboldt
Alliance
Humboldt County Memorial Hospital
Ida Grove
Alliance
Horn Memorial Hospital
Independence
Alliance
Buchanan County Health Center
Iowa City
Alliance
Mercy Iowa City
Manchester
Alliance
Regional Medical Center
Maquoketa
Alliance
Jackson County Regional Health Center

Marshalltown
Alliance
UnityPoint Health - Marshalltown
Mount Pleasant
Alliance
Henry County Health Center
Newton
Alliance
Skiff Medical Center
Oskaloosa
Alliance
Mahaska Health Partnership
Pella
Alliance
Pella Regional Health Center
Pocahontas
Alliance
Pocahontas Community Hospital
Sac City
Alliance
Loring Hospital
Waukon
Alliance
Veterans Memorial Hospital
Waverly
Alliance
Waverly Health Center
West Burlington
Alliance
Great River Medical Center

MISSOURI
Bethany
Alliance
Harrison County Community Hospital
Fairfax
Alliance
Community Hospital-Fairfax

HOSPITAL NETWORK VENTURES, LLC
6212 American Avenue, Portage, MI, Zip 49002; tel. 269/329–3200; Gregory L. Hedegore, President and Chief Executive Officer

MICHIGAN
Allegan
Alliance
Allegan General Hospital
Kalamazoo
Alliance
Bronson Healthcare Group
Bronson Methodist Hospital
Marshall
Alliance
Oaklawn Hospital
Sturgis
Alliance
Sturgis Hospital

HOSPITAL SHARED SERVICES ASSOCIATION
P.O. Box 19741, Seattle, WA, Zip 98109–6741; tel. 206/399–0865; Joe McNamee, Executive Director

OREGON
Salem
Alliance
Oregon State Hospital

WASHINGTON
Bellevue
Alliance
Overlake Medical Center
Chelan
Alliance
Lake Chelan Community Hospital and Clinics
Clarkston
Alliance
Tri-State Memorial Hospital

Davenport
Alliance
Lincoln Hospital
Edmonds
Alliance
Swedish/Edmonds
Ephrata
Alliance
Columbia Basin Hospital
Grand Coulee
Alliance
Coulee Medical Center
Kirkland
Alliance
EvergreenHealth
Medical Lake
Alliance
Eastern State Hospital
Moses Lake
Alliance
Samaritan Healthcare
Mount Vernon
Alliance
Skagit Regional Health
Newport
Alliance
Newport Hospital and Health Services
Odessa
Alliance
Odessa Memorial Healthcare Center
Othello
Alliance
Othello Community Hospital
Prosser
Alliance
PMH Medical Center
Pullman
Alliance
Pullman Regional Hospital
Quincy
Alliance
Quincy Valley Medical Center
Republic
Alliance
Ferry County Memorial Hospital
Ritzville
Alliance
East Adams Rural Healthcare
Tacoma
Alliance
Western State Hospital
Tonasket
Alliance
North Valley Hospital

KENTUCKY HEALTH COLLABORATIVE
651 Perimeter Drive, Suite 650, Lexington, KY, Zip 40517–4134; tel. 859/286–3107; David Zimba, Managing Director

KENTUCKY
Bowling Green
Alliance
Medical Center at Bowling Green
Danville
Alliance
Ephraim McDowell Health
Edgewood
Alliance
St. Elizabeth Healthcare
Lexington
Alliance
Appalachian Regional Healthcare, Inc.
University of Kentucky Albert B. Chandler Hospital
Louisville
Alliance
Baptist Health

Norton Healthcare

Morehead
Alliance
St. Claire HealthCare

Owensboro
Alliance
Owensboro Health

TENNESSEE

Brentwood
Alliance
LifePoint Health

MEDI-SOTA, INC.
1280 Locust Street Suite 16, Dawson, MN, Zip 56232–2375; tel. 320/769–2269; Deb Ranallo, Executive Director

MINNESOTA

Appleton
Alliance
Appleton Area Health Services

Arlington
Alliance
Ridgeview Sibley Medical Center

Benson
Alliance
Swift County - Benson Health Services

Blue Earth
Alliance
United Hospital District

Canby
Alliance
Sanford Canby Medical Center

Dawson
Alliance
Johnson Memorial Health Services

Elbow Lake
Alliance
Prairie Ridge Hospital and Health Services

Glencoe
Alliance
Glencoe Regional Health Services

Glenwood
Alliance
Glacial Ridge Health System

Graceville
Alliance
Essentia Health-Graceville

Granite Falls
Alliance
Granite Falls Health

Hendricks
Alliance
Hendricks Community Hospital Association

Litchfield
Alliance
Meeker Memorial Hospital

Madelia
Alliance
Madelia Community Hospital

Madison
Alliance
Madison Healthcare Services

Mahnomen
Alliance
Mahnomen Health Center

Marshall
Alliance
Avera Marshall Regional Medical Center

Montevideo
Alliance
Chippewa County-Montevideo Hospital

Olivia
Alliance
RC Hospital and Clinics

Ortonville
Alliance
Ortonville Area Health Services

Paynesville
Alliance
CentraCare Health-Paynesville

Perham
Alliance
Perham Health

Pipestone
Alliance
Pipestone County Medical Center Avera

Redwood Falls
Alliance
Redwood Area Hospital

Saint Peter
Alliance
River's Edge Hospital and Clinic

Slayton
Alliance
Murray County Medical Center

Sleepy Eye
Alliance
Sleepy Eye Medical Center

Staples
Alliance
Lakewood Health System

Tracy
Alliance
Sanford Tracy Medical Center

Tyler
Alliance
Avera Tyler Hospital

Wadena
Alliance
Tri-County Hospital

Willmar
Alliance
Rice Memorial Hospital

Windom
Alliance
Windom Area Hospital

NORTHWEST KANSAS HEALTH ALLIANCE
2220 Canterbury Drive, Hays, KS, Zip 67601–2370; tel. 785/623–2300; Edward Herrman, R.N., FACHE, President and Chief Executive Officer

KANSAS

Ashland
Alliance
Ashland Health Center

Atwood
Alliance
Rawlins County Health Center

Beloit
Alliance
Mitchell County Hospital Health Systems

Colby
Alliance
Citizens Medical Center

Dighton
Alliance
Lane County Hospital

Dodge City
Alliance
Western Plains Medical Complex

Ellsworth
Alliance
Ellsworth County Medical Center

Garden City
Alliance
St. Catherine Hospital

Goodland
Alliance
Goodland Regional Medical Center

Great Bend
Alliance
University of Kansas Health System Great Bend Campus

Greensburg
Alliance
Kiowa County Memorial Hospital

Hill City
Alliance
Graham County Hospital

Hoisington
Alliance
Clara Barton Hospital

Hoxie
Alliance
Sheridan County Health Complex

Hutchinson
Alliance
Hutchinson Regional Medical Center

Jetmore
Alliance
Hodgeman County Health Center

Kinsley
Alliance
Edwards County Medical Center

La Crosse
Alliance
Rush County Memorial Hospital

Larned
Alliance
Pawnee Valley Community Hospital

Lawrence
Alliance
Lawrence Memorial Hospital

Leoti
Alliance
Wichita County Health Center

Lincoln
Alliance
Lincoln County Hospital

Lyons
Alliance
Hospital District No 1 of Rice County

Minneola
Alliance
Minneola District Hospital

Ness City
Alliance
Ness County Hospital District No 2

Norton
Alliance
Norton County Hospital

Oakley
Alliance
Logan County Hospital

Oberlin
Alliance
Decatur Health Systems

Osborne
Alliance
Osborne County Memorial Hospital

Ottawa
Alliance
Ransom Memorial Hospital

Phillipsburg
Alliance
Phillips County Hospital

Plainville
Alliance
Rooks County Health Center

Quinter
Alliance
Gove County Medical Center

Ransom
Alliance
Grisell Memorial Hospital District One

Russell
Alliance
Russell Regional Hospital

Saint Francis
Alliance
Cheyenne County Hospital

Salina
Alliance
  Salina Regional Health Center

Satanta
Alliance
  Satanta District Hospital and Long Term Care

Scott City
Alliance
  Scott County Hospital

Smith Center
Alliance
  Smith County Memorial Hospital

Stafford
Alliance
  Stafford County Hospital

Tribune
Alliance
  Greeley County Health Services

Wakeeney
Alliance
  Trego County-Lemke Memorial Hospital

OHSU PARTNERS
3303 SW Bond Avenue, Suite 6100,
Mail Code: CH6P, Portland, OR,
Zip 97239–4501; tel. 503/494–4036;
Peter F. Rapp, Chief Executive Officer

OREGON
Hillsboro
Alliance
  Tuality Healthcare

Salem
Alliance
  Salem Health

PANDION SOURCING & CONSULTING REGIONAL CORPORATION
3445 Winton Place, Suite 222,
Rochester, NY, Zip 14623–2950;
tel. 888/732–4282; Travis Heider,
President and Chief Executive Officer

GEORGIA
Fort Oglethorpe
Alliance
  CHI Memorial Hospital - Georgia

NEW JERSEY
Berkeley Heights
Alliance
  Runnells Center for Rehabilitation and Healthcare

Newark
Alliance
  Columbus Hospital LTACH

NEW YORK
Batavia
Alliance
  United Memorial Medical Center

Bath
Alliance
  Bath Veterans Affairs Medical Center
  Ira Davenport Memorial Hospital

Buffalo
Alliance
  Erie County Medical Center
  Roswell Park Cancer Institute
  Sisters of Charity Hospital of Buffalo

Canandaigua
Alliance
  F. F. Thompson Hospital

Clifton Springs
Alliance
  Clifton Springs Hospital and Clinic

Corning
Alliance
  Guthrie Corning Hospital

Dansville
Alliance
  Nicholas H. Noyes Memorial Hospital

Dunkirk
Alliance
  Brooks Memorial Hospital

Elmira
Alliance
  Arnot Ogden Medical Center
  St. Joseph's Hospital

Geneva
Alliance
  Finger Lakes Hospital

Hornell
Alliance
  St. James Mercy Hospital

Ithaca
Alliance
  Cayuga Medical Center at Ithaca

Jamestown
Alliance
  UPMC Chautauqua WCA

Kenmore
Alliance
  Kenmore Mercy Hospital

Lewiston
Alliance
  Mount St. Mary's Hospital and Health Center

Montour Falls
Alliance
  Schuyler Hospital

Newark
Alliance
  Newark-Wayne Community Hospital

Niagara Falls
Alliance
  Niagara Falls Memorial Medical Center

Olean
Alliance
  Olean General Hospital

Penn Yan
Alliance
  Soldiers and Sailors Memorial Hospital of Yates County

Rochester
Alliance
  Highland Hospital
  Rochester General Hospital
  Strong Memorial Hospital of the University of Rochester
  Unity Hospital

Springville
Alliance
  Bertrand Chaffee Hospital

Wellsville
Alliance
  Jones Memorial Hospital

PENNSYLVANIA
Bradford
Alliance
  Bradford Regional Medical Center

PANDION SOURCING NATIONAL LLC
3445 Winton Place, Suite 222,
Rochester, NY, Zip 14623–2950;
tel. 888/732–4282; Travis Heider,
President and Chief Executive Officer

GEORGIA
Fort Oglethorpe
Alliance
  CHI Memorial Hospital - Georgia

NEW JERSEY
Berkeley Heights
Alliance
  Runnells Center for Rehabilitation and Healthcare

Newark
Alliance
  Columbus Hospital LTACH

NEW YORK
Dansville

Alliance
  Nicholas H. Noyes Memorial Hospital

Geneva
Alliance
  Finger Lakes Hospital

Lockport
Alliance
  Eastern Niagara Hospital

Penn Yan
Alliance
  Soldiers and Sailors Memorial Hospital of Yates County

Springville
Alliance
  Bertrand Chaffee Hospital

Wellsville
Alliance
  Jones Memorial Hospital

PENNANT HEALTH ALLIANCE
2122 Health Drive SW Suite 100,
Wyoming, MI, Zip 49519–9698;
tel. 616/252–6800; Michael D. Faas,
Chief Executive Officer

MICHIGAN
Ann Arbor
Alliance
  University of Michigan Health System

Cadillac
Alliance
  Munson Healthcare Cadillac Hospital

Grand Rapids
Alliance
  Mary Free Bed Rehabilitation Hospital
  Mercy Health Saint Mary's

Grayling
Alliance
  Munson Healthcare Grayling Hospital

Wyoming
Alliance
  Metro Health - University of Michigan Health

PREMIER, INC.
13034 Ballantyne Corporate Place,
Charlotte, NC, Zip 28277–1498;
tel. 704/816–5353; Susan DeVore,
President and Chief Executive Officer

ALABAMA
Dothan
Alliance
  Southeast Alabama Medical Center

Opelika
Alliance
  East Alabama Medical Center

ARIZONA
Gilbert
Alliance
  Banner Health

Scottsdale
Alliance
  HonorHealth

ARKANSAS
Batesville
Alliance
  White River Medical Center

Pine Bluff
Alliance
  Jefferson Regional Medical Center

CALIFORNIA
Fresno
Alliance
  Community Medical Centers

Loma Linda
Alliance
  Loma Linda University Medical Center

Los Angeles
Alliance
  Verity Health System

Mountain View
Alliance
   El Camino Hospital

Rancho Mirage
Alliance
   Eisenhower Medical Center

Roseville
Alliance
   Adventist Health

San Francisco
Alliance
   Dignity Health

CONNECTICUT
Hartford
Alliance
   Saint Francis Hospital and Medical Center

Waterbury
Alliance
   Saint Mary's Hospital

DELAWARE
Dover
Alliance
   Bayhealth Medical Center

Lewes
Alliance
   Beebe Healthcare

FLORIDA
Altamonte Springs
Alliance
   Adventist Health System Sunbelt Health Care Corporation

Clearwater
Alliance
   BayCare Health System

Coral Gables
Alliance
   Baptist Health South Florida

Dunedin
Alliance
   BayCare Alliant Hospital

Jacksonville
Alliance
   Baptist Health

   Nemours

Miami Beach
Alliance
   Mount Sinai Medical Center

Tampa
Alliance
   H. Lee Moffitt Cancer Center and Research Institute

Vero Beach
Alliance
   Indian River Medical Center

Winter Haven
Alliance
   Winter Haven Hospital

GEORGIA
Carrollton
Alliance
   Tanner Medical Center-Carrollton

Lagrange
Alliance
   Wellstar West Georgia Medical Center

Savannah
Alliance
   Memorial Health

   St. Joseph's Hospital

HAWAII
Honolulu
Alliance
   Kuakini Medical Center

ILLINOIS
Chicago
Alliance
   Mount Sinai Hospital

Harvey
Alliance
   Ingalls Memorial Hospital

Naperville
Alliance
   Edward Hospital

Peoria
Alliance
   UnityPoint Health - Peoria

Urbana
Alliance
   Carle Foundation Hospital

INDIANA
Gary
Alliance
   Methodist Hospitals

KENTUCKY
Ashland
Alliance
   King's Daughters Medical Center

Bowling Green
Alliance
   Commonwealth Regional Specialty Hospital

Danville
Alliance
   Ephraim McDowell Regional Medical Center

Edgewood
Alliance
   St. Elizabeth Edgewood

Glasgow
Alliance
   T. J. Samson Community Hospital

Henderson
Alliance
   Methodist Hospital

Louisville
Alliance
   Alliant Management Services

   Baptist Health

   Norton Healthcare

Murray
Alliance
   Murray-Calloway County Hospital

LOUISIANA
Baton Rouge
Alliance
   Woman's Hospital

Hammond
Alliance
   North Oaks Health System

Houma
Alliance
   Terrebonne General Medical Center

Lafayette
Alliance
   Lafayette General Medical Center

Marrero
Alliance
   West Jefferson Medical Center

MAINE
Lewiston
Alliance
   Central Maine Medical Center

MARYLAND
Annapolis
Alliance
   Anne Arundel Medical Center

Baltimore
Alliance
   Greater Baltimore Medical Center

   Johns Hopkins Health System

   Mercy Medical Center

   Sinai Hospital of Baltimore

Cumberland
Alliance
   Western Maryland Regional Medical Center

Elkton
Alliance
   Union Hospital

Frederick
Alliance
   Frederick Regional Health System

Gaithersburg
Alliance
   Adventist HealthCare

Hagerstown
Alliance
   Meritus Medical Center

Lanham
Alliance
   Doctors Community Hospital

Marriottsville
Alliance
   Bon Secours Health System, Inc.

Randallstown
Alliance
   Northwest Hospital

Salisbury
Alliance
   Peninsula Regional Medical Center

Westminster
Alliance
   Carroll Hospital Center

MASSACHUSETTS
Boston
Alliance
   Tufts Medical Center

Fall River
Alliance
   Southcoast Hospitals Group

Springfield
Alliance
   Baystate Health, Inc.

MICHIGAN
Detroit
Alliance
   Henry Ford Health System

Grand Blanc
Alliance
   McLaren Health Care Corporation

Jackson
Alliance
   Henry Ford Allegiance Health

MINNESOTA
Minneapolis
Alliance
   Fairview Health Services

MISSISSIPPI
Laurel
Alliance
   South Central Regional Medical Center

Meridian
Alliance
   Rush Health Systems

MISSOURI
Saint Joseph
Alliance
   Mosaic Life Care

Saint Louis
Alliance
   SSM Health

MONTANA
Billings
Alliance
   Billings Clinic

NEW MEXICO
Albuquerque
Alliance
   Presbyterian Healthcare Services

NEW YORK
Rochester
Alliance
   Pandion Sourcing National LLC

   Rochester Regional Health

NORTH CAROLINA
Asheboro
Alliance
  Randolph Hospital
Asheville
Alliance
  Mission Health System
Boone
Alliance
  Watauga Medical Center
Charlotte
Alliance
  Atrium Health
Fayetteville
Alliance
  Cape Fear Valley Health System
Gastonia
Alliance
  CaroMont Regional Medical Center
Goldsboro
Alliance
  Wayne UNC Health Care
Greensboro
Alliance
  Moses H. Cone Memorial Hospital
Hendersonville
Alliance
  Margaret R. Pardee Memorial Hospital
Hickory
Alliance
  Catawba Valley Medical Center
Kinston
Alliance
  UNC Lenoir Healthcare
Lumberton
Alliance
  Southeastern Health
Morehead City
Alliance
  Carteret Health Care
Pinehurst
Alliance
  FirstHealth of the Carolinas
Roanoke Rapids
Alliance
  Halifax Regional Medical Center
Statesville
Alliance
  Iredell Health System

OHIO
Akron
Alliance
  Summa Health System
Cincinnati
Alliance
  Mercy Health
Cleveland
Alliance
  University Hospitals
Elyria
Alliance
  University Hospitals Elyria Medical Center
Kettering
Alliance
  Kettering Medical Center
Middleburg Heights
Alliance
  Southwest General Health Center
Parma
Alliance
  University Hospitals Parma Medical Center
Sandusky
Alliance
  Firelands Regional Health System

OKLAHOMA
Tulsa
Alliance
  Saint Francis Hospital

OREGON
Salem
Alliance
  Salem Hospital

PENNSYLVANIA
Beaver
Alliance
  Heritage Valley Health System
Bethlehem
Alliance
  St. Luke's University Health Network
Danville
Alliance
  Geisinger
King of Prussia
Alliance
  Universal Health Services, Inc.
Philadelphia
Alliance
  Einstein Healthcare Network
Washington
Alliance
  Washington Hospital

SOUTH CAROLINA
Anderson
Alliance
  AnMed Health Medical Center
Conway
Alliance
  Conway Medical Center
Greenwood
Alliance
  Self Regional Healthcare
West Columbia
Alliance
  Lexington Medical Center

SOUTH DAKOTA
Rapid City
Alliance
  Rapid City Regional Hospital
Sioux Falls
Alliance
  Avera Health

TENNESSEE
Crossville
Alliance
  Cumberland Medical Center
Greeneville
Alliance
  Laughlin Memorial Hospital
Johnson City
Alliance
  Mountain States Health Alliance
Knoxville
Alliance
  University of Tennessee Medical Center
Maryville
Alliance
  Blount Memorial Hospital

TEXAS
Arlington
Alliance
  Texas Health Resources
Dallas
Alliance
  Methodist Health System
  University of Texas Southwestern Medical Center
Galveston
Alliance
  University of Texas Medical Branch
Houston
Alliance
  Harris Health System
  University of Texas M.D. Anderson Cancer Center
Lubbock
Alliance
  University Medical Center

VIRGINIA
Abingdon
Alliance
  Johnston Memorial Hospital
Chesapeake
Alliance
  Chesapeake Regional Medical Center
Falls Church
Alliance
  Inova Health System
Marion
Alliance
  Smyth County Community Hospital
Newport News
Alliance
  Riverside Health System
Roanoke
Alliance
  Carilion Clinic
South Hill
Alliance
  VCU Health Community Memorial Hospital
Winchester
Alliance
  Valley Health System

WASHINGTON
Seattle
Alliance
  Kaiser Permanente Capitol Hill Campus
Vancouver
Alliance
  PeaceHealth

WEST VIRGINIA
Elkins
Alliance
  Davis Medical Center
Huntington
Alliance
  Cabell Huntington Hospital
  Pallottine Health Services
Morgantown
Alliance
  Mon Health Medical Center
Parkersburg
Alliance
  Camden Clark Medical Center
Point Pleasant
Alliance
  Pleasant Valley Hospital
South Charleston
Alliance
  Thomas Memorial Hospital
Weirton
Alliance
  Weirton Medical Center

THE NEW JERSEY COUNCIL OF TEACHING HOSPITALS
154 West State Street, Trenton, NJ, Zip 8608; tel. 609/656-9600; Deborah S. Briggs, President

NEW JERSEY
Camden
Alliance
  Cooper University Health Care
Hackensack
Alliance
  Hackensack Meridian Health Hackensack University Medical Center
Marlton
Alliance
  Weisman Children's Rehabilitation Hospital
Montclair
Alliance
  Hackensack Meridian Health Mountainside Medical Center

Morristown
Alliance
  Atlantic Health System
    Morristown Medical Center

New Brunswick
Alliance
  Children's Specialized Hospital

North Bergen
Alliance
  Hackensack Meridian Health Palisades Medical Center

Paterson
Alliance
  St. Joseph's University Medical Center

Summit
Alliance
  Overlook Medical Center

UNITED IROQUOIS SHARED SERVICES, INC.

15 Executive Park Drive, Clifton Park, NY, Zip 12065–5631; tel. 518/383–5060; Gary J. Fitzgerald, President

NEW YORK

Albany
Alliance
  Albany Memorial Hospital
  St. Peter's Hospital

Alexandria Bay
Alliance
  River Hospital

Amsterdam
Alliance
  St. Mary's Healthcare

Auburn
Alliance
  Auburn Community Hospital

Binghamton
Alliance
  Our Lady of Lourdes Memorial Hospital, Inc.
  United Health Services Hospitals-Binghamton

Buffalo
Alliance
  Roswell Park Cancer Institute

Carthage
Alliance
  Carthage Area Hospital

Cobleskill
Alliance
  Cobleskill Regional Hospital

Cooperstown
Alliance
  Bassett Medical Center

Cortland
Alliance
  Cortland Regional Medical Center

Cuba
Alliance
  Cuba Memorial Hospital

Delhi
Alliance
  O'Connor Hospital

Elizabethtown
Alliance
  The University of Vermont Health Network Elizabethtown Community Hospital

Glens Falls
Alliance
  Glens Falls Hospital

Glenville
Alliance
  Conifer Park

Gloversville
Alliance
  Nathan Littauer Hospital and Nursing Home

Hamilton
Alliance
  Community Memorial Hospital

Hudson
Alliance
  Columbia Memorial Hospital

Ithaca
Alliance
  Cayuga Medical Center at Ithaca

Little Falls
Alliance
  Little Falls Hospital

Lowville
Alliance
  Lewis County General Hospital

Malone
Alliance
  The University of Vermont Health Network - Alice Hyde Medical Center

Margaretville
Alliance
  Margaretville Hospital

Massena
Alliance
  Massena Memorial Hospital

Norwich
Alliance
  UHS Chenango Memorial Hospital

Ogdensburg
Alliance
  Claxton-Hepburn Medical Center

Olean
Alliance
  Olean General Hospital

Oneida
Alliance
  Oneida Healthcare

Oneonta
Alliance
  Aurelia Osborn Fox Memorial Hospital

Oswego
Alliance
  Oswego Hospital

Plattsburgh
Alliance
  The University of Vermont Health Network-Champlain Valley Physicians Hospital

Potsdam
Alliance
  Canton-Potsdam Hospital

Rome
Alliance
  Rome Memorial Hospital

Saranac Lake
Alliance
  Adirondack Health

Saratoga Springs
Alliance
  Saratoga Hospital

Schenectady
Alliance
  Ellis Hospital
  Sunnyview Rehabilitation Hospital

Springville
Alliance
  Bertrand Chaffee Hospital

Star Lake
Alliance
  Clifton-Fine Hospital

Syracuse
Alliance
  Crouse Health
  Upstate University Hospital

Troy
Alliance
  Samaritan Hospital
  Seton Health St. Mary's Hospital

Utica
Alliance
  Faxton St. Luke's Healthcare
  St. Elizabeth Medical Center

Walton
Alliance
  UHS Delaware Valley Hospital

Watertown
Alliance
  Samaritan Medical Center

UNIVERSITY OF IOWA HEALTH ALLIANCE

1755 59th Place, West Des Moines, IA, Zip 50266–7737; tel. 515/643–4000; Jennifer Vermeer, President and Chief Executive Officer

ILLINOIS

Aledo
Alliance
  Genesis Medical Center-Aledo

Silvis
Alliance
  Genesis Medical Center, Silvis

IOWA

Albia
Alliance
  Monroe County Hospital and Clinics

Algona
Alliance
  Kossuth Regional Health Center

Audubon
Alliance
  Audubon County Memorial Hospital

Belmond
Alliance
  Iowa Specialty Hospital-Belmond

Bloomfield
Alliance
  Davis County Hospital

Britt
Alliance
  Hancock County Health System

Cedar Falls
Alliance
  Sartori Memorial Hospital

Cedar Rapids
Alliance
  Mercy Medical Center

Centerville
Alliance
  Mercy Medical Center-Centerville

Clarinda
Alliance
  Clarinda Regional Health Center

Clarion
Alliance
  Iowa Specialty Hospital-Clarion

Clinton
Alliance
  Mercy Medical Center-Clinton

Corydon
Alliance
  Wayne County Hospital

Cresco
Alliance
  Regional Health Services of Howard County

Davenport
Alliance
  Genesis Medical Center, Davenport

De Witt
Alliance
  Genesis Medical Center, DeWitt

Des Moines
Alliance
  Mercy Medical Center-Des Moines

Dubuque
Alliance
  Mercy Medical Center-Dubuque

Dyersville
Alliance
  Mercy Medical Center-Dyersville

Section B

Elkader
Alliance
Central Community Hospital

Emmetsburg
Alliance
Palo Alto County Health System

Fairfield
Alliance
Jefferson County Health Center

Greenfield
Alliance
Adair County Health System

Grinnell
Alliance
UnityPoint Health - Grinnell Regional Medical Center

Hampton
Alliance
Franklin General Hospital

Hawarden
Alliance
Hawarden Regional Healthcare

Iowa City
Alliance
University of Iowa Hospitals and Clinics

Iowa Falls
Alliance
Hansen Family Hospital

Keosauqua
Alliance
Van Buren County Hospital

Knoxville
Alliance
Knoxville Hospital & Clinics

Leon
Alliance
Decatur County Hospital

Manning
Alliance
Manning Regional Healthcare Center

Maquoketa
Alliance
Jackson County Regional Health Center

Mason City
Alliance
Mercy Medical Center-North Iowa

Mount Ayr
Alliance
Ringgold County Hospital

Mount Pleasant
Alliance
Henry County Health Center

New Hampton
Alliance
Mercy Medical Center-New Hampton

Oelwein
Alliance
Mercy Hospital of Franciscan Sisters

Osage
Alliance
Mitchell County Regional Health Center

Pella
Alliance
Pella Regional Health Center

Perry
Alliance
Dallas County Hospital

Primghar
Alliance
Baum Harmon Mercy Hospital

Sigourney
Alliance
Keokuk County Health Center

Sioux City
Alliance
Mercy Medical Center-Sioux City

Vinton
Alliance
Virginia Gay Hospital

Washington
Alliance
Washington County Hospital and Clinics

Waterloo
Alliance
Covenant Medical Center

Waverly
Alliance
Waverly Health Center

Webster City
Alliance
Van Diest Medical Center

Winterset
Alliance
Madison County Health Care System

NEBRASKA
Oakland
Alliance
Oakland Mercy Hospital

Pender
Alliance
Pender Community Hospital

VANTAGE HEALTHCARE NETWORK, INC.
18282 Technology Drive, Suite 202, Meadville, PA, Zip 16335; tel. 814/337–0000; David Petrarca, Director Retail Operations

PENNSYLVANIA
Corry
Alliance
Corry Memorial Hospital

DuBois
Alliance
Penn Highlands DuBois

Ellwood City
Alliance
Ellwood City Medical Center

Erie
Alliance
LECOM Health Millcreek Community Hospital

Saint Vincent Hospital

Farrell
Alliance
UPMC Horizon

Kane
Alliance
UPMC Kane

Kittanning
Alliance
ACMH Hospital

Meadville
Alliance
Meadville Medical Center

Saint Marys
Alliance
Penn Highlands Elk

Seneca
Alliance
UPMC Northwest

Titusville
Alliance
Titusville Area Hospital

Warren
Alliance
Warren General Hospital

VIZIENT, INC.
290 East John Carpenter Freeway, Irving, TX, Zip 75062–2730; tel. 972/830–0000; Curtis W. Nonomaque, President and Chief Executive Officer

ALABAMA
Alexander City
Alliance
Russell Medical

Anniston
Alliance
RMC Anniston

Athens
Alliance
Athens-Limestone Hospital

Atmore
Alliance
Atmore Community Hospital

Bay Minette
Alliance
North Baldwin Infirmary

Bessemer
Alliance
Medical West

Birmingham
Alliance
University of Alabama Hospital

Boaz
Alliance
Marshall Medical Center South

Brewton
Alliance
D. W. McMillan Memorial Hospital

Carrollton
Alliance
Pickens County Medical Center

Decatur
Alliance
Decatur Morgan Hospital

Fairhope
Alliance
Thomas Hospital

Fayette
Alliance
Fayette Medical Center

Guntersville
Alliance
Marshall Health System

Marshall Medical Center North

Huntsville
Alliance
Huntsville Hospital

Mobile
Alliance
Mobile Infirmary Medical Center

USA Health University Hospital

University of South Alabama Children's and Women's Hospital

Montgomery
Alliance
Baptist Medical Center East

Baptist Medical Center South

Opp
Alliance
Mizell Memorial Hospital

Ozark
Alliance
Dale Medical Center

Prattville
Alliance
Prattville Baptist Hospital

Red Bay
Alliance
Red Bay Hospital

Scottsboro
Alliance
Highlands Medical Center

Sheffield
Alliance
Helen Keller Hospital

Tuscaloosa
Alliance
DCH Health System

DCH Regional Medical Center

Union Springs
Alliance
Bullock County Hospital

ALASKA

Anchorage
Alliance
  Providence Alaska Medical Center

  St. Elias Specialty Hospital

Cordova
Alliance
  Cordova Community Medical Center

Kodiak
Alliance
  Providence Kodiak Island Medical Center

Seward
Alliance
  Providence Seward Medical Center

Valdez
Alliance
  Providence Valdez Medical Center

Wrangell
Alliance
  Wrangell Medical Center

AMERICAN SAMOA

Pago Pago
Alliance
  Lyndon B. Johnson Tropical Medical Center

ARIZONA

Benson
Alliance
  Benson Hospital

Bisbee
Alliance
  Copper Queen Community Hospital

Flagstaff
Alliance
  Flagstaff Medical Center

Green Valley
Alliance
  Santa Cruz Valley Regional Hospital

Kingman
Alliance
  Kingman Regional Medical Center

Phoenix
Alliance
  Maricopa Integrated Health System

  Mayo Clinic Hospital

Safford
Alliance
  Mt. Graham Regional Medical Center

Tucson
Alliance
  Banner - University Medical Center South

  Banner - University Medical Center Tucson

  TMC HealthCare

Willcox
Alliance
  Northern Cochise Community Hospital

ARKANSAS

Arkadelphia
Alliance
  Baptist Health Medical Center-Arkadelphia

Booneville
Alliance
  Mercy Hospital Booneville

Clinton
Alliance
  Ozark Health Medical Center

Conway
Alliance
  Conway Regional Medical Center

Fayetteville
Alliance
  Washington Regional Medical Center

Heber Springs
Alliance
  Baptist Health Medical Center-Heber Springs

Hot Springs
Alliance
  CHI St. Vincent Hot Springs

Jonesboro
Alliance
  NEA Baptist Memorial Hospital

  St. Bernards Medical Center

Little Rock
Alliance
  Baptist Health Extended Care Hospital

  Baptist Health Medical Center-Little Rock

  Baptist Health

  CHI St. Vincent Infirmary Medical Center

Malvern
Alliance
  Baptist Health Medical Center-Hot Spring County

Morrilton
Alliance
  CHI St. Vincent Morrilton

North Little Rock
Alliance
  Baptist Health Medical Center - North Little Rock

Paragould
Alliance
  Arkansas Methodist Medical Center

Piggott
Alliance
  Piggott Community Hospital

Stuttgart
Alliance
  Baptist Health Medical Center-Stuttgart

Walnut Ridge
Alliance
  Lawrence Memorial Hospital

Wynne
Alliance
  CrossRidge Community Hospital

CALIFORNIA

Alameda
Alliance
  Alameda Hospital

Antioch
Alliance
  Kaiser Permanente Antioch Medical Center

Arcadia
Alliance
  Methodist Hospital of Southern California

Auburn
Alliance
  Sutter Auburn Faith Hospital

Bakersfield
Alliance
  Kern Medical Center

Berkeley
Alliance
  Alta Bates Medical Center-Herrick Campus

  Alta Bates Summit Medical Center

Burbank
Alliance
  Providence Saint Joseph Medical Center

Burlingame
Alliance
  Mills-Peninsula Health Services

Castro Valley
Alliance
  Eden Medical Center

Colton
Alliance
  Arrowhead Regional Medical Center

Concord
Alliance
  John Muir Medical Center, Concord

Covina
Alliance
  Citrus Valley Health Partners

  Citrus Valley Medical Center-Inter Community Campus

Crescent City
Alliance
  Sutter Coast Hospital

Davis
Alliance
  Sutter Davis Hospital

Downey
Alliance
  PIH Health Hospital - Downey

  Rancho Los Amigos National Rehabilitation Center

El Centro
Alliance
  El Centro Regional Medical Center

Escondido
Alliance
  Palomar Health

  Palomar Medical Center

Fairfield
Alliance
  NorthBay Medical Center

Fremont
Alliance
  Kaiser Permanente Fremont Medical Center

  Washington Hospital Healthcare System

French Camp
Alliance
  San Joaquin General Hospital

Fresno
Alliance
  Community Medical Centers

  Saint Agnes Medical Center

Glendora
Alliance
  Foothill Presbyterian Hospital

Jackson
Alliance
  Sutter Amador Hospital

King City
Alliance
  Mee Memorial Hospital

Lakeport
Alliance
  Sutter Lakeside Hospital

Lancaster
Alliance
  Antelope Valley Hospital

Los Angeles
Alliance
  Cedars-Sinai Medical Center

  LAC+USC Medical Center

  Martin Luther King, Jr. Community Hospital

  Ronald Reagan UCLA Medical Center

  Stewart & Lynda Resnick Neuropsychiatric Hospital at UCLA

  USC Norris Comprehensive Cancer Center

Los Banos
Alliance
  Memorial Hospital Los Banos

Manteca
Alliance
  Kaiser Permanente Manteca Medical Center

Marina Del Rey
Alliance
  Marina Del Rey Hospital

Mariposa
Alliance
  John C. Fremont Healthcare District

Martinez
Alliance
  Contra Costa Regional Medical Center

Menlo Park
Alliance
  Menlo Park Surgical Hospital

Mission Hills
Alliance
  Providence Holy Cross Medical Center

Modesto
Alliance
  Memorial Medical Center

Alliances

Monterey
Alliance
Community Hospital of the Monterey Peninsula

Moreno Valley
Alliance
Riverside University Health System-Medical Center

Mountain View
Alliance
El Camino Hospital

Novato
Alliance
Novato Community Hospital

Oakland
Alliance
Alta Bates Summit Medical Center - Summit Campus
Highland Hospital
Kaiser Permanente Oakland Medical Center

Oceanside
Alliance
Tri-City Medical Center

Ojai
Alliance
Ojai Valley Community Hospital

Orange
Alliance
UC Irvine Medical Center

Palo Alto
Alliance
Lucile Salter Packard Children's Hospital Stanford
Stanford Health Care

Pleasanton
Alliance
Stanford Health Care - ValleyCare

Pomona
Alliance
Pomona Valley Hospital Medical Center

Porterville
Alliance
Sierra View Medical Center

Portola
Alliance
Eastern Plumas Health Care

Poway
Alliance
Pomerado Hospital

Redlands
Alliance
Redlands Community Hospital

Redwood City
Alliance
Kaiser Permanente Redwood City Medical Center

Roseville
Alliance
Kaiser Permanente Roseville Medical Center
Sutter Roseville Medical Center

Sacramento
Alliance
Kaiser Permanente Sacramento Medical Center
Kaiser Permanente South Sacramento Medical Center
Shriners Hospitals for Children-Northern California
Sutter Center for Psychiatry
Sutter Health
Sutter Medical Center, Sacramento
University of California, Davis Medical Center

Salinas
Alliance
Natividad Medical Center

San Diego
Alliance
Scripps Health
UC San Diego Health

San Francisco
Alliance
California Pacific Medical Center-Davies Campus
California Pacific Medical Center-St. Luke's Campus

California Pacific Medical Center
Chinese Hospital
Kaiser Permanente San Francisco Medical Center
UCSF Medical Center
Zuckerberg San Francisco General Hospital and Trauma Center

San Jose
Alliance
Kaiser Permanente San Jose Medical Center
Santa Clara Valley Medical Center

San Leandro
Alliance
San Leandro Hospital

San Mateo
Alliance
San Mateo Medical Center

San Pedro
Alliance
Providence Little Company of Mary Medical Center San Pedro

San Rafael
Alliance
Kaiser Permanente San Rafael Medical Center

Santa Barbara
Alliance
Cottage Health
Goleta Valley Cottage Hospital
Santa Barbara Cottage Hospital

Santa Clara
Alliance
Kaiser Permanente Santa Clara Medical Center

Santa Cruz
Alliance
Sutter Maternity and Surgery Center of Santa Cruz

Santa Monica
Alliance
Providence Saint John's Health Center
UCLA Medical Center-Santa Monica

Santa Rosa
Alliance
Kaiser Permanente Santa Rosa Medical Center
Sutter Santa Rosa Regional Hospital

Solvang
Alliance
Santa Ynez Valley Cottage Hospital

South San Francisco
Alliance
Kaiser Permanente South San Francisco

Stockton
Alliance
Dameron Hospital

Sylmar
Alliance
LAC-Olive View-UCLA Medical Center

Tarzana
Alliance
Providence Tarzana Medical Center

Torrance
Alliance
Harbor-UCLA Medical Center
Providence Little Company of Mary Medical Center - Torrance
Torrance Memorial Medical Center

Tracy
Alliance
Sutter Tracy Community Hospital

Vacaville
Alliance
Kaiser Permanente Vacaville Medical Center

Vallejo
Alliance
Kaiser Permanente Vallejo Medical Center
Sutter Solano Medical Center

Ventura
Alliance
Community Memorial Hospital

Walnut Creek
Alliance
John Muir Health
John Muir Medical Center, Walnut Creek
Kaiser Permanente Walnut Creek Medical Center

Whittier
Alliance
PIH Health Hospital - Whittier

Yuba City
Alliance
Sutter Surgical Hospital - North Valley

COLORADO

Alamosa
Alliance
San Luis Valley Health

Aurora
Alliance
University of Colorado Hospital

Boulder
Alliance
Boulder Community Health

Canon City
Alliance
St. Thomas More Hospital

Colorado Springs
Alliance
Penrose-St. Francis Health Services
UCHealth Memorial Hospital

Denver
Alliance
Denver Health
National Jewish Health

Durango
Alliance
Mercy Regional Medical Center

Englewood
Alliance
Craig Hospital

Estes Park
Alliance
Estes Park Medical Center

Fort Collins
Alliance
UCHealth Poudre Valley Hospital

Grand Junction
Alliance
St. Mary's Hospital and Medical Center

Gunnison
Alliance
Gunnison Valley Hospital

La Jara
Alliance
San Luis Valley Health Conejos County Hospital

Lakewood
Alliance
St. Anthony Hospital

Loveland
Alliance
UCHealth Medical Center of the Rockies

Pueblo
Alliance
St. Mary-Corwin Medical Center

Steamboat Springs
Alliance
UCHealth Yampa Valley Medical Center

Westminster
Alliance
St. Anthony North Health Campus

Yuma
Alliance
Yuma District Hospital

CONNECTICUT

Bridgeport
Alliance
Bridgeport Hospital

Bristol
Alliance
Bristol Hospital

Danbury
Alliance
Danbury Hospital

Farmington
Alliance
UConn, John Dempsey Hospital

Greenwich
Alliance
Greenwich Hospital

Hartford
Alliance
Hartford Hospital
Saint Francis Hospital and Medical Center

Manchester
Alliance
Manchester Memorial Hospital

Middletown
Alliance
Connecticut Valley Hospital
Middlesex Hospital

Milford
Alliance
Milford Hospital

New Haven
Alliance
Connecticut Mental Health Center
Yale New Haven Health
Yale-New Haven Hospital

New London
Alliance
Lawrence + Memorial Hospital

Norwalk
Alliance
Norwalk Hospital

Putnam
Alliance
Day Kimball Hospital

Stamford
Alliance
Stamford Hospital

Torrington
Alliance
Charlotte Hungerford Hospital

Vernon
Alliance
Rockville General Hospital

DELAWARE
Wilmington
Alliance
St. Francis Hospital

DISTRICT OF COLUMBIA
Washington
Alliance
Howard University Hospital
MedStar Georgetown University Hospital
MedStar Washington Hospital Center
Sibley Memorial Hospital

FLORIDA
Apalachicola
Alliance
George E. Weems Memorial Hospital

Boca Raton
Alliance
Boca Raton Regional Hospital

Boynton Beach
Alliance
Bethesda Hospital East

Clermont
Alliance
South Lake Hospital

Cocoa Beach
Alliance
Health First Cape Canaveral Hospital

Coral Gables
Alliance
Baptist Health South Florida, Doctors Hospital

Daytona Beach
Alliance
Halifax Health Medical Center of Daytona Beach

Gainesville
Alliance
UF Health Shands Hospital

Gulf Breeze
Alliance
Gulf Breeze Hospital

Homestead
Alliance
Baptist Health South Florida, Homestead Hospital

Jacksonville
Alliance
Mayo Clinic Hospital in Florida

Jay
Alliance
Jay Hospital

Lakeland
Alliance
Lakeland Regional Health Medical Center

Leesburg
Alliance
Leesburg Regional Medical Center

Melbourne
Alliance
Health First Holmes Regional Medical Center

Miami
Alliance
Baptist Health South Florida, Baptist Hospital of Miami
Baptist Health South Florida, West Kendall Baptist Hospital
Jackson Health System

Milton
Alliance
West Florida Community Care Center

Naples
Alliance
NCH Baker Hospital

Ocoee
Alliance
Health Central Hospital

Orlando
Alliance
Orlando Health
Orlando Regional Medical Center

Palm Bay
Alliance
Health First Palm Bay Hospital

Panama City
Alliance
Bay Medical Sacred Heart

Pensacola
Alliance
Baptist Health Care Corporation
Baptist Hospital

Perry
Alliance
Doctor's Memorial Hospital

Rockledge
Alliance
Health First, Inc.

Starke
Alliance
Shands Starke Regional Medical Center

Stuart
Alliance
Martin Health System

Tallahassee
Alliance
Tallahassee Memorial HealthCare

Tampa
Alliance
H. Lee Moffitt Cancer Center and Research Institute
Shriners Hospitals for Children-Tampa
Tampa General Hospital

Tavernier
Alliance
Baptist Health South Florida, Mariners Hospital

The Villages
Alliance
The Villages Regional Hospital

Titusville
Alliance
Parrish Medical Center

Vero Beach
Alliance
Indian River Medical Center

Weston
Alliance
Cleveland Clinic Florida

GEORGIA
Adel
Alliance
Cook Medical Center-A Campus of Tift Regional Medical Center

Albany
Alliance
Phoebe Putney Health System
Phoebe Putney Memorial Hospital

Americus
Alliance
Phoebe Sumter Medical Center

Athens
Alliance
Piedmont Athens Regional Medical Center
St. Mary's Health Care System

Atlanta
Alliance
Emory Saint Joseph's Hospital of Atlanta
Emory University Hospital Midtown
Emory University Hospital
Grady Memorial Hospital
Northside Hospital
Wellstar Atlanta Medical Center

Augusta
Alliance
Augusta University Medical Center
Charlie Norwood Veterans Affairs Medical Center
University Hospital

Austell
Alliance
WellStar Cobb Hospital

Braselton
Alliance
Northeast Georgia Medical Center Braselton

Brunswick
Alliance
Southeast Georgia Health System Brunswick Campus
Southeast Georgia Health System

Bryon
Alliance
Medical Center of Peach County, Navicent Health

Cairo
Alliance
Grady General Hospital

Camilla
Alliance
Mitchell County Hospital

Canton
Alliance
Northside Hospital-Cherokee

Cedartown
Alliance
Polk Medical Center

Claxton
Alliance
Evans Memorial Hospital

Columbus
Alliance
Columbus Regional Healthcare System
Columbus Specialty Hospital

Alliances

Piedmont Columbus Regional Midtown

Piedmont Columbus Regional Northside

Cordele
Alliance
Crisp Regional Hospital

Cumming
Alliance
Northside Hospital-Forsyth

Cuthbert
Alliance
Southwest Georgia Regional Medical Center

Dalton
Alliance
Hamilton Medical Center

Decatur
Alliance
DeKalb Medical at Downtown Decatur

Douglas
Alliance
Coffee Regional Medical Center

Douglasville
Alliance
WellStar Douglas Hospital

Eatonton
Alliance
Putnam General Hospital

Fitzgerald
Alliance
Dorminy Medical Center

Gainesville
Alliance
Northeast Georgia Medical Center

Hiram
Alliance
WellStar Paulding Hospital

Homerville
Alliance
Clinch Memorial Hospital

Jackson
Alliance
Wellstar Sylvan Grove Hospital

Johns Creek
Alliance
Emory Johns Creek Hospital

Lakeland
Alliance
South Georgia Medical Center Lanier Campus

Lawrenceville
Alliance
Gwinnett Hospital System

Lithonia
Alliance
DeKalb Medical at Hillandale

Macon
Alliance
Medical Center, Navicent Health

Rehabilitation Hospital, Navicent Health

Marietta
Alliance
WellStar Health System

WellStar Kennestone Hospital

WellStar Windy Hill Hospital

Moultrie
Alliance
Colquitt Regional Medical Center

Nashville
Alliance
South Georgia Medical Center Berrien Campus

Newnan
Alliance
Southeastern Regional Medical Center

Perry
Alliance
Perry Hospital

Quitman
Alliance
Brooks County Hospital

Riverdale
Alliance
Southern Regional Medical Center

Rome
Alliance
Floyd Medical Center

Roswell
Alliance
Wellstar North Fulton Hospital

Saint Marys
Alliance
Southeast Georgia Health System Camden Campus

Sandersville
Alliance
Washington County Regional Medical Center

Savannah
Alliance
Memorial Health

Swainsboro
Alliance
Emanuel Medical Center

Sylvester
Alliance
Phoebe Worth Medical Center

Thomasville
Alliance
Archbold Medical Center

John D. Archbold Memorial Hospital

Thomson
Alliance
University Hospital McDuffie

Tifton
Alliance
Tift Regional Medical Center

Valdosta
Alliance
South Georgia Medical Center

Warm Springs
Alliance
Roosevelt Warm Springs Rehabilitation Hospital - Rehab

Roosevelt Warm Springs Rehabilitation and Specialty Hospitals - LTAC

Warner Robins
Alliance
Houston Medical Center

Waycross
Alliance
Memorial Satilla Health

GUAM
Dededo
Alliance
Guam Regional Medical City

HAWAII
Aiea
Alliance
Pali Momi Medical Center

Ewa Beach
Alliance
Sutter Health Kahi Mohala

Honolulu
Alliance
Kaiser Permanente Medical Center

Queen's Health Systems

Shriners Hospitals for Children-Honolulu

Straub Medical Center

The Queen's Medical Center

Kamuela
Alliance
North Hawaii Community Hospital

Kaunakakai
Alliance
Molokai General Hospital

Wahiawa
Alliance
Wahiawa General Hospital

IDAHO
American Falls
Alliance
Power County Hospital District

Blackfoot
Alliance
Bingham Memorial Hospital

Boise
Alliance
Saint Alphonsus Regional Medical Center

St. Luke's Health System

Bonners Ferry
Alliance
Boundary Community Hospital

Cascade
Alliance
Cascade Medical Center

Coeur D'Alene
Alliance
Kootenai Health

Cottonwood
Alliance
St. Mary's Hospital

Emmett
Alliance
Valor Health

Orofino
Alliance
Clearwater Valley Hospital and Clinics

Preston
Alliance
Franklin County Medical Center

Rupert
Alliance
Minidoka Memorial Hospital

Sandpoint
Alliance
Bonner General Hospital

Weiser
Alliance
Weiser Memorial Hospital

ILLINOIS
Alton
Alliance
Alton Memorial Hospital

Arlington Heights
Alliance
Northwest Community Hospital

Aurora
Alliance
Rush-Copley Medical Center

Barrington
Alliance
Advocate Good Shepherd Hospital

Belleville
Alliance
Memorial Hospital

Bloomington
Alliance
OSF St. Joseph Medical Center

Canton
Alliance
Graham Hospital Association

Carbondale
Alliance
Memorial Hospital of Carbondale

Southern Illinois Healthcare

Chester
Alliance
Memorial Hospital

Chicago
Alliance
Advocate Illinois Masonic Medical Center

Advocate Trinity Hospital

Ann & Robert H. Lurie Children's Hospital of Chicago

John H. Stroger Jr. Hospital of Cook County

La Rabida Children's Hospital

Louis A. Weiss Memorial Hospital
Mercy Hospital and Medical Center
Methodist Hospital of Chicago
Northwestern Memorial Hospital
Norwegian American Hospital
Presence Resurrection Medical Center
Provident Hospital of Cook County
Rush University Medical Center
Shriners Hospitals for Children-Chicago
Swedish Covenant Hospital
University of Chicago Medical Center
University of Illinois Hospital & Health Sciences System

Decatur
Alliance
Decatur Memorial Hospital

Downers Grove
Alliance
Advocate Good Samaritan Hospital

Eldorado
Alliance
Ferrell Hospital

Elgin
Alliance
Advocate Sherman Hospital

Elmhurst
Alliance
Elmhurst Hospital

Evanston
Alliance
NorthShore University Health System

Evergreen Park
Alliance
Little Company of Mary Hospital and Health Care Centers

Freeport
Alliance
FHN Memorial Hospital

Galesburg
Alliance
OSF St. Mary Medical Center

Geneva
Alliance
Northwestern Medicine Delnor Hospital

Greenville
Alliance
HSHS Holy Family Hospital in Greenville

Harvey
Alliance
Ingalls Memorial Hospital

Hazel Crest
Alliance
Advocate South Suburban Hospital

Herrin
Alliance
Herrin Hospital

Hinsdale
Alliance
AMITA Health Adventist Medical Center - Hinsdale
RML Specialty Hospital

Hoffman Estates
Alliance
Alexian Brothers Behavioral Health Hospital

Jacksonville
Alliance
Passavant Area Hospital

Jerseyville
Alliance
Jersey Community Hospital

Joliet
Alliance
Presence Saint Joseph Medical Center

Kewanee
Alliance
OSF Saint Luke Medical Center

Lake Forest
Alliance
Northwestern Medicine Lake Forest Hospital

Libertyville
Alliance
Advocate Condell Medical Center

Lincoln
Alliance
Abraham Lincoln Memorial Hospital

Macomb
Alliance
McDonough District Hospital

Maryville
Alliance
Anderson Hospital

Mattoon
Alliance
Sarah Bush Lincoln Health Center

Maywood
Alliance
Loyola University Medical Center

McHenry
Alliance
Centegra Hospital - McHenry

Monticello
Alliance
Kirby Medical Center

Murphysboro
Alliance
St. Joseph Memorial Hospital

New Lenox
Alliance
Silver Cross Hospital

Oak Lawn
Alliance
Advocate Christ Medical Center

Oak Park
Alliance
Rush Oak Park Hospital

Palos Heights
Alliance
Palos Health

Park Ridge
Alliance
Advocate Lutheran General Hospital

Peoria
Alliance
OSF Saint Francis Medical Center
UnityPoint Health - Peoria

Pittsfield
Alliance
Illini Community Hospital

Pontiac
Alliance
OSF Saint James - John W. Albrecht Medical Center

Quincy
Alliance
Blessing Hospital

Rock Island
Alliance
UnityPoint Health - Trinity Rock Island

Rockford
Alliance
OSF Saint Anthony Medical Center
SwedishAmerican - A Division of UW Health

Rushville
Alliance
Sarah D. Culbertson Memorial Hospital

Salem
Alliance
Salem Township Hospital

Shelbyville
Alliance
HSHS Good Shepherd Hospital

Shiloh
Alliance
Memorial Hospital East

Springfield
Alliance
Memorial Health System
Memorial Medical Center

Taylorville
Alliance
Taylorville Memorial Hospital

Urbana
Alliance
Carle Foundation Hospital

Winfield
Alliance
Northwestern Medicine Central DuPage Hospital

INDIANA
Anderson
Alliance
Community Hospital of Anderson & Madison County

Angola
Alliance
Cameron Memorial Community Hospital

Auburn
Alliance
DeKalb Health

Avon
Alliance
Indiana University Health West Hospital

Batesville
Alliance
Margaret Mary Health

Bedford
Alliance
Indiana University Health Bedford Hospital

Bloomington
Alliance
Indiana University Health Bloomington Hospital

Carmel
Alliance
Indiana University Health North Hospital

Clinton
Alliance
Union Hospital Clinton

Columbia City
Alliance
Parkview Whitley Hospital

Columbus
Alliance
Columbus Regional Hospital

Danville
Alliance
Hendricks Regional Health

Elkhart
Alliance
Elkhart General Hospital

Evansville
Alliance
Deaconess Health System
Deaconess Hospital

Fort Wayne
Alliance
Parkview Ortho Hospital
Parkview Health
Parkview Regional Medical Center

Franklin
Alliance
Johnson Memorial Hospital

Goshen
Alliance
Goshen Health

Hartford City
Alliance
Indiana University Health Blackford Hospital

Huntington
Alliance
Parkview Huntington Hospital

Indianapolis
Alliance
Community Health Network

Alliances

Community Hospital East
Community Hospital North
Community Hospital South
Eskenazi Health
Indiana University Health Methodist Hospital
Indiana University Health University Hospital

Jasper
Alliance
  Memorial Hospital and Health Care Center

Kendallville
Alliance
  Parkview Noble Hospital

Knox
Alliance
  Starke Hospital

Kokomo
Alliance
  Community Howard Regional Health

La Porte
Alliance
  La Porte Hospital

LaGrange
Alliance
  Parkview LaGrange Hospital

Lafayette
Alliance
  Indiana University Health Arnett Hospital

Logansport
Alliance
  Logansport Memorial Hospital

Madison
Alliance
  King's Daughters' Health

Marion
Alliance
  Marion General Hospital

Monticello
Alliance
  Indiana University Health White Memorial Hospital

Muncie
Alliance
  Indiana University Health Ball Memorial Hospital

New Albany
Alliance
  Baptist Health Floyd
  Southern Indiana Rehabilitation Hospital

New Castle
Alliance
  Henry Community Health

Newburgh
Alliance
  The Heart Hospital at Deaconess Gateway
  The Women's Hospital

Noblesville
Alliance
  Riverview Health

Paoli
Alliance
  Indiana University Health Paoli Hospital

Portland
Alliance
  Indiana University Health Jay Hospital

Richmond
Alliance
  Reid Health

Rochester
Alliance
  Woodlawn Hospital

Seymour
Alliance
  Schneck Medical Center

Shelbyville
Alliance
  Major Hospital

South Bend
Alliance
  Healthwin Hospital

Memorial Hospital of South Bend

Terre Haute
Alliance
  Union Hospital

Tipton
Alliance
  Indiana University Health Tipton Hospital

Vincennes
Alliance
  Good Samaritan Hospital

Wabash
Alliance
  Parkview Wabash County Hospital

IOWA
Anamosa
Alliance
  UnityPoint Health - Jones Regional Medical Center

Atlantic
Alliance
  Cass County Memorial Hospital

Bettendorf
Alliance
  UnityPoint Health - Trinity Bettendorf

Cedar Rapids
Alliance
  UnityPoint Health - St. Luke's Hospital

Centerville
Alliance
  Mercy Medical Center-Centerville

Clarinda
Alliance
  Clarinda Regional Health Center

Clinton
Alliance
  Mercy Medical Center-Clinton

Corning
Alliance
  CHI Health Mercy Corning

Council Bluffs
Alliance
  Methodist Jennie Edmundson Hospital

Decorah
Alliance
  Winneshiek Medical Center

Des Moines
Alliance
  Mercy Medical Center-Des Moines
  UnityPoint Health-Iowa Lutheran Hospital

Dubuque
Alliance
  Mercy Medical Center-Dubuque
  UnityPoint Health - Finley Hospital

Fort Dodge
Alliance
  UnityPoint Health - Trinity Regional Medical Center

Grundy Center
Alliance
  Grundy County Memorial Hospital

Guttenberg
Alliance
  Guttenberg Municipal Hospital

Hamburg
Alliance
  George C Grape Community Hospital

Hampton
Alliance
  Franklin General Hospital

Harlan
Alliance
  Myrtue Medical Center

Iowa City
Alliance
  University of Iowa Hospitals and Clinics

Iowa Falls
Alliance
  Hansen Family Hospital

Jefferson
Alliance
  Greene County Medical Center

Keokuk
Alliance
  UnityPoint Health-Keokuk

Keosauqua
Alliance
  Van Buren County Hospital

Lake City
Alliance
  Stewart Memorial Community Hospital

Le Mars
Alliance
  Floyd Valley Healthcare

Marengo
Alliance
  Compass Memorial Healthcare

Mason City
Alliance
  Mercy Medical Center-North Iowa

Missouri Valley
Alliance
  CHI Health Missouri Valley

Muscatine
Alliance
  UnityPoint Health - Trinity Muscatine

Nevada
Alliance
  Story County Medical Center

New Hampton
Alliance
  Mercy Medical Center-New Hampton

Orange City
Alliance
  Orange City Area Health System

Osceola
Alliance
  Clarke County Hospital

Pella
Alliance
  Pella Regional Health Center

Red Oak
Alliance
  Montgomery County Memorial Hospital

Rock Rapids
Alliance
  Sanford Rock Rapids Medical Center

Sheldon
Alliance
  Sanford Sheldon Medical Center

Shenandoah
Alliance
  Shenandoah Medical Center

Sigourney
Alliance
  Keokuk County Health Center

Sioux City
Alliance
  Mercy Medical Center-Sioux City
  UnityPoint Health - St. Lukes's Sioux City

Sumner
Alliance
  Community Memorial Hospital

Waverly
Alliance
  Waverly Health Center

West Des Moines
Alliance
  UnityPoint Health - Methodist West Hospital

West Union
Alliance
  Gundersen Palmer Lutheran Hospital and Clinics

KANSAS
Abilene
Alliance
  Memorial Health System

Ashland
Alliance
  Ashland Health Center

Atchison
Alliance
 Atchison Hospital

Atwood
Alliance
 Rawlins County Health Center

Belleville
Alliance
 Republic County Hospital

Beloit
Alliance
 Mitchell County Hospital Health Systems

Clay Center
Alliance
 Clay County Medical Center

Colby
Alliance
 Citizens Medical Center

Coldwater
Alliance
 Comanche County Hospital

Concordia
Alliance
 Cloud County Health Center

Dighton
Alliance
 Lane County Hospital

El Dorado
Alliance
 Susan B. Allen Memorial Hospital

Ellinwood
Alliance
 Ellinwood District Hospital

Ellsworth
Alliance
 Ellsworth County Medical Center

Emporia
Alliance
 Newman Regional Health

Fredonia
Alliance
 Fredonia Regional Hospital

Garden City
Alliance
 St. Catherine Hospital

Garnett
Alliance
 Anderson County Hospital

Girard
Alliance
 Girard Medical Center

Goodland
Alliance
 Goodland Regional Medical Center

Great Bend
Alliance
 University of Kansas Health System Great Bend
 Campus

Greensburg
Alliance
 Kiowa County Memorial Hospital

Hays
Alliance
 Hays Medical Center

Herington
Alliance
 Herington Municipal Hospital

Hiawatha
Alliance
 Hiawatha Community Hospital

Hill City
Alliance
 Graham County Hospital

Hoisington
Alliance
 Clara Barton Hospital

Hoxie
Alliance

 Sheridan County Health Complex

Junction City
Alliance
 Geary Community Hospital

Kansas City
Alliance
 The University of Kansas Hospital

La Crosse
Alliance
 Rush County Memorial Hospital

Larned
Alliance
 Pawnee Valley Community Hospital

Lawrence
Alliance
 Lawrence Memorial Hospital

Leavenworth
Alliance
 Saint Luke's Cushing Hospital

Lincoln
Alliance
 Lincoln County Hospital

Lindsborg
Alliance
 Lindsborg Community Hospital

Mankato
Alliance
 Jewell County Hospital

Medicine Lodge
Alliance
 Medicine Lodge Memorial Hospital

Minneapolis
Alliance
 Ottawa County Health Center

Minneola
Alliance
 Minneola District Hospital

Ness City
Alliance
 Ness County Hospital District No 2

Norton
Alliance
 Norton County Hospital

Oakley
Alliance
 Logan County Hospital

Overland Park
Alliance
 Menorah Medical Center
 Overland Park Regional Medical Center
 Saint Luke's South Hospital

Parsons
Alliance
 Labette Health

Phillipsburg
Alliance
 Phillips County Hospital

Plainville
Alliance
 Rooks County Health Center

Pratt
Alliance
 Pratt Regional Medical Center

Quinter
Alliance
 Gove County Medical Center

Ransom
Alliance
 Grisell Memorial Hospital District One

Russell
Alliance
 Russell Regional Hospital

Sabetha
Alliance
 Sabetha Community Hospital

Saint Francis
Alliance
 Cheyenne County Hospital

Salina
Alliance
 Salina Regional Health Center
 Salina Surgical Hospital

Satanta
Alliance
 Satanta District Hospital and Long Term Care

Scott City
Alliance
 Scott County Hospital

Smith Center
Alliance
 Smith County Memorial Hospital

Stafford
Alliance
 Stafford County Hospital

Topeka
Alliance
 Stormont Vail Health

Wakeeney
Alliance
 Trego County-Lemke Memorial Hospital

Wichita
Alliance
 Great Plains Health Alliance, Inc.
 Kansas Spine and Specialty Hospital

KENTUCKY
Bardstown
Alliance
 Flaget Memorial Hospital

Berea
Alliance
 Saint Joseph Berea

Cynthiana
Alliance
 Harrison Memorial Hospital

Florence
Alliance
 St. Elizabeth Florence

Lexington
Alliance
 Eastern State Hospital
 Saint Joseph East
 Saint Joseph Hospital
 University of Kentucky Albert B. Chandler
 Hospital

London
Alliance
 Saint Joseph London

Louisville
Alliance
 Jewish Hospital
 Our Lady of Peace
 University of Louisville Hospital

Martin
Alliance
 ARH Our Lady of the Way

Morehead
Alliance
 St. Claire HealthCare

Mount Sterling
Alliance
 Saint Joseph Mount Sterling

Mount Vernon
Alliance
 Rockcastle Regional Hospital and Respiratory Care
 Center

Owensboro
Alliance
 Owensboro Health Regional Hospital

Pikeville
Alliance
 Pikeville Medical Center

Shelbyville
Alliance
 Jewish Hospital-Shelbyville

LOUISIANA

Baton Rouge
Alliance
  Franciscan Missionaries of Our Lady Health System, Inc.

  Ochsner Medical Center - Baton Rouge

  Our Lady of the Lake Regional Medical Center

Bogalusa
Alliance
  Our Lady of the Angels Hospital

Church Point
Alliance
  Acadia-St. Landry Hospital

Covington
Alliance
  St. Tammany Parish Hospital

De Ridder
Alliance
  Beauregard Health System

Ferriday
Alliance
  Riverland Medical Center

Gonzales
Alliance
  St. Elizabeth Hospital

Jennings
Alliance
  Jennings American Legion Hospital

Kenner
Alliance
  Ochsner Medical Center - Kenner

Lafayette
Alliance
  Lafayette General Medical Center

  Our Lady of Lourdes Regional Medical Center

Lake Charles
Alliance
  Lake Charles Memorial Hospital

  Memorial Specialty Hospital

Mansfield
Alliance
  De Soto Regional Health System

Monroe
Alliance
  St. Francis Medical Center

  University Health Conway

Napoleonville
Alliance
  Assumption Community Hospital

Natchitoches
Alliance
  Natchitoches Regional Medical Center

New Iberia
Alliance
  Iberia Medical Center

New Orleans
Alliance
  Touro Infirmary

Raceland
Alliance
  Ochsner St. Anne General Hospital

Shreveport
Alliance
  Shriners Hospitals for Children-Shreveport

  University Health Shreveport

  Willis-Knighton Health System

  Willis-Knighton Medical Center

Slidell
Alliance
  Ochsner Medical Center - North Shore

Springhill
Alliance
  Springhill Medical Center

Sulphur
Alliance
  West Calcasieu Cameron Hospital

Vivian
Alliance
  North Caddo Medical Center

MAINE

Augusta
Alliance
  MaineGeneral Medical Center-Augusta Campus

  MaineGeneral Medical Center

Bangor
Alliance
  Eastern Maine Medical Center

  The Acadia Hospital

Bar Harbor
Alliance
  Mount Desert Island Hospital

Belfast
Alliance
  Waldo County General Hospital Maine Health

Biddeford
Alliance
  Southern Maine Health Care - Biddeford Medical Center

Blue Hill
Alliance
  Blue Hill Memorial Hospital

Brewer
Alliance
  Northern Light Health

Brunswick
Alliance
  Mid Coast Hospital

Damariscotta
Alliance
  LincolnHealth

Dover-Foxcroft
Alliance
  Mayo Regional Hospital

Ellsworth
Alliance
  Maine Coast Memorial Hospital

Farmington
Alliance
  Franklin Memorial Hospital

Fort Kent
Alliance
  Northern Maine Medical Center

Greenville
Alliance
  Charles A. Dean Memorial Hospital

Houlton
Alliance
  Houlton Regional Hospital

Machias
Alliance
  Down East Community Hospital

Millinocket
Alliance
  Millinocket Regional Hospital

Norway
Alliance
  Stephens Memorial Hospital

Pittsfield
Alliance
  Sebasticook Valley Health

Portland
Alliance
  Maine Medical Center

  Mercy Hospital of Portland

Presque Isle
Alliance
  The Aroostook Medical Center

Rockport
Alliance
  Pen Bay Medical Center

Skowhegan
Alliance
  Redington-Fairview General Hospital

Waterville
Alliance
  Inland Hospital

Westbrook
Alliance
  Spring Harbor Hospital

MARYLAND

Baltimore
Alliance
  Greater Baltimore Medical Center

  Johns Hopkins Bayview Medical Center

  Johns Hopkins Hospital

  MedStar Franklin Square Medical Center

  MedStar Good Samaritan Hospital

  MedStar Harbor Hospital

  MedStar Union Memorial Hospital

  Mercy Medical Center

  Mt. Washington Pediatric Hospital

  University of Maryland Medical Center Midtown Campus

  University of Maryland Medical Center

  University of Maryland Rehabilitation & Orthopaedic Institute

Bel Air
Alliance
  University of Maryland Upper Chesapeake Medical Center

Bethesda
Alliance
  Suburban Hospital

Cambridge
Alliance
  University of Maryland Shore Medical Center at Dorchester

Chestertown
Alliance
  University of Maryland Shore Medical Center at Chestertown

Cheverly
Alliance
  University of Maryland Capital Region Health Prince George's Hospital Center

Clinton
Alliance
  MedStar Southern Maryland Hospital Center

Columbia
Alliance
  Howard County General Hospital

  MedStar Health

Easton
Alliance
  University of Maryland Shore Medical Center at Easton

Elkton
Alliance
  Union Hospital

Glen Burnie
Alliance
  University of Maryland Baltimore Washington Medical Center

Hagerstown
Alliance
  Meritus Medical Center

Havre De Grace
Alliance
  University of Maryland Harford Memorial Hospital

La Plata
Alliance
  University of Maryland Charles Regional Medical Center

Laurel
Alliance
  University of Maryland Capital Region Health at Laurel Regional Hospital

Leonardtown
Alliance
  MedStar St. Mary's Hospital

Olney
Alliance
  MedStar Montgomery Medical Center

Prince Frederick
Alliance
  CalvertHealth Medical Center

Randallstown
Alliance
  Northwest Hospital

Rockville
Alliance
  Adventist Behavioral Health and Wellness Services
  Adventist Healthcare Shady Grove Medical Center

Silver Spring
Alliance
  Holy Cross Hospital

Takoma Park
Alliance
  Adventist Healthcare Washington Adventist Hospital

MASSACHUSETTS
Athol
Alliance
  Athol Hospital

Ayer
Alliance
  Nashoba Valley Medical Center

Belmont
Alliance
  McLean Hospital

Beverly
Alliance
  Beverly Hospital

Boston
Alliance
  Beth Israel Deaconess Medical Center
  Boston Medical Center
  Brigham and Women's Faulkner Hospital
  Brigham and Women's Hospital
  Carney Hospital
  Dana-Farber Cancer Institute
  Massachusetts Eye and Ear
  Massachusetts General Hospital
  Partners HealthCare System, Inc.
  Shriners Hospitals for Children-Boston
  Tufts Medical Center

Brighton
Alliance
  St. Elizabeth's Medical Center

Brockton
Alliance
  Good Samaritan Medical Center
  Signature Healthcare Brockton Hospital

Burlington
Alliance
  Lahey Hospital & Medical Center, Burlington

Cambridge
Alliance
  Cambridge Health Alliance
  Mount Auburn Hospital
  Spaulding Hospital for Continuing Medical Care Cambridge

Charlestown
Alliance
  Spaulding Rehabilitation Hospital

Concord
Alliance
  Emerson Hospital

East Sandwich
Alliance
  Spaulding Rehabilitation Hospital Cape Cod

Fall River
Alliance
  Saint Anne's Hospital

Gardner
Alliance
  Heywood Hospital

Greenfield
Alliance
  Baystate Franklin Medical Center

Holyoke
Alliance
  Holyoke Medical Center

Hyannis
Alliance
  Cape Cod Healthcare, Inc.

Leominster
Alliance
  UMass Memorial HealthAlliance-Clinton Hospital

Lowell
Alliance
  Lowell General Hospital

Marlborough
Alliance
  UMass Memorial-Marlborough Hospital

Melrose
Alliance
  Melrose-Wakefield Hospital

Methuen
Alliance
  Holy Family Hospital

Milton
Alliance
  Beth Israel Deaconess Hospital-Milton

Nantucket
Alliance
  Nantucket Cottage Hospital

Newton Lower Falls
Alliance
  Newton-Wellesley Hospital

Northampton
Alliance
  Cooley Dickinson Hospital

Norwood
Alliance
  Norwood Hospital

Oak Bluffs
Alliance
  Martha's Vineyard Hospital

Palmer
Alliance
  Baystate Wing Hospital

Plymouth
Alliance
  Beth Israel Deaconess Hospital Plymouth

Salem
Alliance
  North Shore Medical Center

South Weymouth
Alliance
  South Shore Hospital

Southbridge
Alliance
  Harrington Hospital

Springfield
Alliance
  Baystate Medical Center
  Shriners Hospitals for Children-Springfield

Taunton
Alliance
  Morton Hospital and Medical Center

Winchester
Alliance
  Winchester Hospital

Worcester
Alliance
  UMass Memorial Medical Center

MICHIGAN
Alma
Alliance
  MidMichigan Medical Center-Gratiot

Alpena
Alliance
  MidMichigan Medical Center - Alpena

Ann Arbor
Alliance
  University of Michigan Health System

Battle Creek
Alliance
  Bronson Battle Creek Hospital

Bay City
Alliance
  McLaren Bay Region
  McLaren Bay Special Care

Big Rapids
Alliance
  Spectrum Health Big Rapids Hospital

Cadillac
Alliance
  Munson Healthcare Cadillac Hospital

Carson City
Alliance
  Sparrow Carson Hospital

Cass City
Alliance
  Hills & Dales General Hospital

Chelsea
Alliance
  St. Joseph Mercy Chelsea

Coldwater
Alliance
  ProMedica Coldwater Regional Hospital

Dearborn
Alliance
  Beaumont Hospital - Dearborn

Detroit
Alliance
  Henry Ford Hospital

Farmington Hills
Alliance
  Beaumont Hospital - Farmington Hills

Flint
Alliance
  McLaren Flint

Fremont
Alliance
  Spectrum Health Gerber Memorial

Grand Haven
Alliance
  North Ottawa Community Hospital

Grand Rapids
Alliance
  Mary Free Bed Rehabilitation Hospital
  Pine Rest Christian Mental Health Services
  Spectrum Health - Butterworth Hospital
  Spectrum Health

Grayling
Alliance
  Munson Healthcare Grayling Hospital

Greenville
Alliance
  Spectrum Health United Hospital

Grosse Pointe
Alliance
  Beaumont Hospital - Grosse Pointe

Hastings
Alliance
  Spectrum Health Pennock

Holland
Alliance
  Holland Hospital

Ionia
Alliance
  Sparrow Ionia Hospital

Iron River
Alliance
  Aspirus Iron River Hospitals & Clinics, Inc.

Ironwood
Alliance
  Aspirus Ironwood Hospitals & Clinics, Inc.

Alliances

Kalamazoo
Alliance
Bronson Healthcare Group
Bronson Methodist Hospital

Lansing
Alliance
Sparrow Hospital
Sparrow Specialty Hospital

Laurium
Alliance
Aspirus Keweenaw Hospital, Inc.

Ludington
Alliance
Spectrum Health Ludington Hospital

Marlette
Alliance
Marlette Regional Hospital

Marshall
Alliance
Oaklawn Hospital

Midland
Alliance
MidMichigan Medical Center-Midland

Monroe
Alliance
ProMedica Monroe Regional Hospital

Mount Clemens
Alliance
McLaren Macomb

Mount Pleasant
Alliance
McLaren Central Michigan

Muskegon
Alliance
Mercy Health Hackley Campus

Ontonagon
Alliance
Aspirus Ontonagon Hospital, Inc.

Paw Paw
Alliance
Bronson LakeView Hospital

Petoskey
Alliance
McLaren Northern Michigan

Pontiac
Alliance
McLaren Oakland
St. Joseph Mercy Oakland

Port Huron
Alliance
McLaren Port Huron

Reed City
Alliance
Spectrum Health Reed City Hospital

Royal Oak
Alliance
Beaumont Hospital - Royal Oak

Saginaw
Alliance
Covenant Healthcare

Saint Johns
Alliance
Sparrow Clinton Hospital

Saint Joseph
Alliance
Lakeland Health
Lakeland Medical Center, St. Joseph

Sheridan
Alliance
Sheridan Community Hospital

South Haven
Alliance
Bronson South Haven Hospital

Taylor
Alliance
Beaumont Hospital - Taylor

Tecumseh

Alliance
ProMedica Herrick Hospital

Trenton
Alliance
Beaumont Hospital - Trenton

Troy
Alliance
Beaumont Hospital - Troy

Vicksburg
Alliance
Bronson Vicksburg Hospital

Watervliet
Alliance
Lakeland Hospital, Watervliet

Wayne
Alliance
Beaumont Hospital, Wayne

West Branch
Alliance
MidMichigan Medical Center - West Branch

Wyoming
Alliance
Metro Health - University of Michigan Health

Zeeland
Alliance
Spectrum Health Zeeland Community Hospital

MINNESOTA

Ada
Alliance
Essentia Health Ada

Albert Lea
Alliance
Mayo Clinic Health System - Albert Lea and Austin

Arlington
Alliance
Ridgeview Sibley Medical Center

Aurora
Alliance
Essentia Health Northern Pines Medical Center

Bagley
Alliance
Sanford Bagley Medical Center

Baudette
Alliance
CHI LakeWood Health

Bemidji
Alliance
Sanford Bemidji Medical Center

Benson
Alliance
Swift County - Benson Health Services

Blue Earth
Alliance
United Hospital District

Brainerd
Alliance
Essentia Health St. Joseph's Medical Center

Buffalo
Alliance
Buffalo Hospital

Burnsville
Alliance
Fairview Ridges Hospital

Cambridge
Alliance
Cambridge Medical Center

Canby
Alliance
Sanford Canby Medical Center

Cannon Falls
Alliance
Mayo Clinic Health System in Cannon Falls

Coon Rapids
Alliance
Mercy Hospital

Crookston
Alliance
RiverView Health

Deer River
Alliance
Essentia Health-Deer River

Detroit Lakes
Alliance
Essentia Health St. Mary's - Detroit Lakes

Duluth
Alliance
Essentia Health Duluth
Essentia Health St. Mary's Medical Center
Essentia Health
St. Luke's Hospital

Fairmont
Alliance
Mayo Clinic Health System in Fairmont

Faribault
Alliance
District One Hospital

Fergus Falls
Alliance
Lake Region Healthcare

Fosston
Alliance
Essentia Health Fosston

Glencoe
Alliance
Glencoe Regional Health Services

Graceville
Alliance
Essentia Health-Graceville

Grand Rapids
Alliance
Grand Itasca Clinic and Hospital

Granite Falls
Alliance
Granite Falls Health

Hallock
Alliance
Kittson Memorial Healthcare Center

Hastings
Alliance
Regina Hospital

Hutchinson
Alliance
Hutchinson Health

Jackson
Alliance
Sanford Jackson Medical Center

Lake City
Alliance
Mayo Clinic Health System in Lake City

Little Falls
Alliance
CHI St. Gabriel's Health

Long Prairie
Alliance
CentraCare Health-Long Prairie

Luverne
Alliance
Sanford Luverne Medical Center

Madelia
Alliance
Madelia Community Hospital

Mahnomen
Alliance
Mahnomen Health Center

Mankato
Alliance
Mayo Clinic Health System in Mankato

Maple Grove
Alliance
Maple Grove Hospital

Melrose
Alliance
CentraCare Health-Melrose

Minneapolis
Alliance
Abbott Northwestern Hospital

Allina Health

Hennepin Healthcare

Phillips Eye Institute

Shriners Hospitals for Children-Twin Cities

Monticello
Alliance
CentraCare Health-Monticello

New Prague
Alliance
Mayo Clinic Health System in New Prague

New Ulm
Alliance
New Ulm Medical Center

Ortonville
Alliance
Ortonville Area Health Services

Owatonna
Alliance
Owatonna Hospital

Park Rapids
Alliance
CHI St. Joseph's Health

Paynesville
Alliance
CentraCare Health-Paynesville

Perham
Alliance
Perham Health

Princeton
Alliance
Fairview Northland Medical Center

Red Wing
Alliance
Mayo Clinic Health System in Red Wing

Redwood Falls
Alliance
Redwood Area Hospital

Robbinsdale
Alliance
North Memorial Health Hospital

Rochester
Alliance
Mayo Clinic Hospital - Rochester

Mayo Clinic

Roseau
Alliance
LifeCare Medical Center

Saint Cloud
Alliance
CentraCare Health

St. Cloud Hospital

Saint James
Alliance
Mayo Clinic Health System in Saint James

Saint Paul
Alliance
Regions Hospital

United Hospital

Sandstone
Alliance
Essentia Health Sandstone

Sauk Centre
Alliance
CentraCare Health-Sauk Centre

Shakopee
Alliance
St. Francis Regional Medical Center

Slayton
Alliance
Murray County Medical Center

Springfield
Alliance
Mayo Clinic Health System in Springfield

Stillwater
Alliance
Lakeview Hospital

Thief River Falls
Alliance
Sanford Medical Center Thief River Falls

Sanford Thief River Falls Behavioral Health Center

Tracy
Alliance
Sanford Tracy Medical Center

Two Harbors
Alliance
Lake View Hospital

Virginia
Alliance
Essentia Health-Virginia

Waconia
Alliance
Ridgeview Medical Center

Warren
Alliance
North Valley Health Center

Waseca
Alliance
Mayo Clinic Health System in Waseca

Westbrook
Alliance
Sanford Westbrook Medical Center

Wheaton
Alliance
Sanford Wheaton Medical Center

Willmar
Alliance
Rice Memorial Hospital

Windom
Alliance
Windom Area Hospital

Worthington
Alliance
Sanford Worthington Medical Center

Wyoming
Alliance
Fairview Lakes Health Services

MISSISSIPPI
Booneville
Alliance
Baptist Memorial Hospital-Booneville

Columbia
Alliance
Marion General Hospital

Columbus
Alliance
Baptist Memorial Hospital-Golden Triangle

Corinth
Alliance
Magnolia Regional Health Center

Greenville
Alliance
Delta Regional Medical Center

Greenwood
Alliance
Greenwood Leflore Hospital

Grenada
Alliance
University of Mississippi Medical Center Grenada

Gulfport
Alliance
Memorial Hospital at Gulfport

Hattiesburg
Alliance
Forrest General Hospital

Indianola
Alliance
South Sunflower County Hospital

Jackson
Alliance
St. Dominic-Jackson Memorial Hospital

University of Mississippi Medical Center

Leakesville
Alliance
Greene County Hospital

Lexington
Alliance
University of Mississippi Medical Center Holmes County

Lucedale
Alliance
George Regional Hospital

Magnolia
Alliance
Beacham Memorial Hospital

McComb
Alliance
Southwest Mississippi Regional Medical Center

Meridian
Alliance
Anderson Regional Health System South

Anderson Regional Health System

Monticello
Alliance
Lawrence County Hospital

New Albany
Alliance
Baptist Memorial Hospital-Union County

Olive Branch
Alliance
Methodist Healthcare Olive Branch Hospital

Oxford
Alliance
Baptist Memorial Hospital-North Mississippi

Pascagoula
Alliance
Singing River Health System

Philadelphia
Alliance
Neshoba County General Hospital

Picayune
Alliance
Highland Community Hospital

Prentiss
Alliance
Jefferson Davis Community Hospital

Southaven
Alliance
Baptist Memorial Hospital-Desoto

Starkville
Alliance
OCH Regional Medical Center

Tupelo
Alliance
North Mississippi Health Services, Inc.

Tylertown
Alliance
Walthall County General Hospital

MISSOURI
Appleton City
Alliance
Ellett Memorial Hospital

Belton
Alliance
Belton Regional Medical Center

Bolivar
Alliance
Citizens Memorial Hospital

Bonne Terre
Alliance
Parkland Health Center-Bonne Terre

Branson
Alliance
Cox Medical Center Branson

Brookfield
Alliance
Pershing Memorial Hospital

Cameron
Alliance
Cameron Regional Medical Center

Cape Girardeau
Alliance
Saint Francis Medical Center

Alliances

Chillicothe
Alliance
Hedrick Medical Center

Clinton
Alliance
Golden Valley Memorial Healthcare

Columbia
Alliance
Boone Hospital Center

University of Missouri Health Care

Farmington
Alliance
Parkland Health Center - Farmington Community

Independence
Alliance
Centerpoint Medical Center

Jefferson City
Alliance
Capital Region Medical Center

Joplin
Alliance
Freeman Health System

Freeman Hospital East

Kansas City
Alliance
Children's Mercy Hospital Kansas City

Research Medical Center

Saint Luke's Health System

Saint Luke's Hospital of Kansas City

Saint Luke's North Hospital - Barry Road

Truman Medical Center-Hospital Hill

Truman Medical Center-Lakewood

Lamar
Alliance
Cox Barton County Memorial Hospital

Lee's Summit
Alliance
Lee's Summit Medical Center

Saint Luke's East Hospital

Lexington
Alliance
Lafayette Regional Health Center

Liberty
Alliance
Liberty Hospital

Macon
Alliance
Samaritan Hospital

Marshall
Alliance
Fitzgibbon Hospital

Milan
Alliance
Sullivan County Memorial Hospital

Monett
Alliance
Cox Monett Hospital

Neosho
Alliance
Freeman Neosho Hospital

O'Fallon
Alliance
Progress West Hospital

Osage Beach
Alliance
Lake Regional Health System

Poplar Bluff
Alliance
Black River Medical Center

Potosi
Alliance
Washington County Memorial Hospital

Saint Louis
Alliance
BJC HealthCare

Barnes-Jewish Hospital

Barnes-Jewish West County Hospital

Christian Hospital

Missouri Baptist Medical Center

Shriners Hospitals for Children-St. Louis

St. Louis Children's Hospital

Saint Peters
Alliance
Barnes-Jewish St. Peters Hospital

Salem
Alliance
Salem Memorial District Hospital

Sikeston
Alliance
Missouri Delta Medical Center

Springfield
Alliance
Cox Medical Center North

Cox Medical Centers

CoxHealth

Ste Genevieve
Alliance
Ste. Genevieve County Memorial Hospital

Sullivan
Alliance
Missouri Baptist Sullivan Hospital

Trenton
Alliance
Wright Memorial Hospital

Warrensburg
Alliance
Western Missouri Medical Center

MONTANA

Anaconda
Alliance
Community Hospital of Anaconda

Bozeman
Alliance
Bozeman Health Deaconess Hospital

Columbus
Alliance
Stillwater Billings Clinic

Conrad
Alliance
Pondera Medical Center

Deer Lodge
Alliance
Deer Lodge Medical Center

Ennis
Alliance
Madison Valley Medical Center

Hamilton
Alliance
Marcus Daly Memorial Hospital

Helena
Alliance
St. Peter's Hospital

Kalispell
Alliance
Kalispell Regional Healthcare

The HealthCenter

Libby
Alliance
Cabinet Peaks Medical Center

Missoula
Alliance
St. Patrick Hospital

Philipsburg
Alliance
Granite County Medical Center

Plains
Alliance
Clark Fork Valley Hospital

Polson
Alliance
Providence St. Joseph Medical Center

Ronan
Alliance
St. Luke Community Healthcare

Sidney
Alliance
Sidney Health Center

Townsend
Alliance
Broadwater Health Center

White Sulphur Springs
Alliance
Mountainview Medical Center

NEBRASKA

Alliance
Alliance
Box Butte General Hospital

Alma
Alliance
Harlan County Health System

Atkinson
Alliance
West Holt Medical Services

Beatrice
Alliance
Beatrice Community Hospital and Health Center

Bellevue
Alliance
Madonna Rehabilitation Specialty Hospital

Nebraska Medicine - Bellevue

Blair
Alliance
Memorial Community Hospital and Health System

Bridgeport
Alliance
Morrill County Community Hospital

Broken Bow
Alliance
Jennie M. Melham Memorial Medical Center

Columbus
Alliance
Columbus Community Hospital

Crete
Alliance
Crete Area Medical Center

Falls City
Alliance
Community Medical Center, Inc.

Franklin
Alliance
Franklin County Memorial Hospital

Gordon
Alliance
Gordon Memorial Health Services

Grand Island
Alliance
CHI Health Saint Francis

Hastings
Alliance
Mary Lanning Healthcare

Kearney
Alliance
CHI Health Good Samaritan

Lexington
Alliance
Lexington Regional Health Center

Lincoln
Alliance
Bryan Health

Bryan Medical Center

CHI Health Nebraska Heart

CHI Health St Elizabeth

Madonna Rehabilitation Hospital

Lynch
Alliance
Niobrara Valley Hospital

Minden
Alliance
Kearney County Health Services

Nebraska City
Alliance
   CHI Health St. Mary's

Neligh
Alliance
   Antelope Memorial Hospital

Norfolk
Alliance
   Faith Regional Health Services

O'Neill
Alliance
   Avera St. Anthony's Hospital

Omaha
Alliance
   CHI Health Creighton University Medical Center - Bergan Mercy
   CHI Health Immanuel
   CHI Health Lakeside
   Nebraska Medicine - Nebraska Medical Center
   Nebraska Methodist Health System, Inc.
   Nebraska Methodist Hospital
   OrthoNebraska Hospital

Ord
Alliance
   Valley County Health System

Oshkosh
Alliance
   Regional West Garden County

Osmond
Alliance
   Osmond General Hospital

Papillion
Alliance
   CHI Health Midlands

Plainview
Alliance
   CHI Health Plainview

Schuyler
Alliance
   CHI Health Schuyler

Scottsbluff
Alliance
   Regional West Medical Center

York
Alliance
   York General

NEVADA

Las Vegas
Alliance
   Sunrise Hospital and Medical Center
   University Medical Center

NEW HAMPSHIRE

Claremont
Alliance
   Valley Regional Hospital

Colebrook
Alliance
   Upper Connecticut Valley Hospital

Dover
Alliance
   Wentworth-Douglass Hospital

Keene
Alliance
   Cheshire Medical Center

Lancaster
Alliance
   Weeks Medical Center

Lebanon
Alliance
   Alice Peck Day Memorial Hospital
   Dartmouth-Hitchcock Medical Center

Nashua
Alliance
   Southern New Hampshire Medical Center

New London
Alliance
   New London Hospital

North Conway
Alliance
   Memorial Hospital

Peterborough
Alliance
   Monadnock Community Hospital

Plymouth
Alliance
   Speare Memorial Hospital

Woodsville
Alliance
   Cottage Hospital

NEW JERSEY

Atlantic City
Alliance
   AtlantiCare Regional Medical Center

Camden
Alliance
   Cooper University Health Care

Cape May Court House
Alliance
   Cape Regional Health System

Denville
Alliance
   Saint Clare's Denville Hospital

Edison
Alliance
   Hackensack Meridian Health JFK Medical Center
   JFK Health

Elmer
Alliance
   Inspira Medical Center-Elmer

Flemington
Alliance
   Hunterdon Medical Center

Hamilton
Alliance
   Robert Wood Johnson University Hospital at Hamilton

Marlton
Alliance
   Virtua Marlton

Morristown
Alliance
   Morristown Medical Center

Mount Holly
Alliance
   Virtua Memorial

Mullica Hill
Alliance
   Inspira Health Network

New Brunswick
Alliance
   Robert Wood Johnson University Hospital

Newark
Alliance
   University Hospital

Newton
Alliance
   Newton Medical Center

Pomona
Alliance
   Bacharach Institute for Rehabilitation

Pompton Plains
Alliance
   Chilton Medical Center

Rahway
Alliance
   Robert Wood Johnson University Hospital Rahway

Ridgewood
Alliance
   Valley Hospital

Somers Point
Alliance
   Shore Medical Center

Summit
Alliance
   Overlook Medical Center

Trenton
Alliance
   Capital Health

Vineland
Alliance
   Inspira Medical Center-Vineland

Voorhees
Alliance
   Virtua Voorhees

Woodbury
Alliance
   Inspira Medical Center-Woodbury

NEW MEXICO

Albuquerque
Alliance
   University of New Mexico Hospitals

Farmington
Alliance
   San Juan Regional Medical Center

Gallup
Alliance
   Rehoboth McKinley Christian Health Care Services

Rio Rancho
Alliance
   UNM Sandoval Regional Medical Center, Inc.

Santa Fe
Alliance
   CHRISTUS St. Vincent Regional Medical Center

NEW YORK

Albany
Alliance
   Albany Medical Center
   St. Peter's Hospital

Alexandria Bay
Alliance
   River Hospital

Binghamton
Alliance
   United Health Services Hospitals-Binghamton

Bronx
Alliance
   Montefiore Medical Center
   NYC Health + Hospitals / Jacobi
   NYC Health + Hospitals / North Central Bronx

Brooklyn
Alliance
   Brooklyn Hospital Center
   NYC Health + Hospitals / Coney Island
   NYC Health + Hospitals / Woodhull
   New York Community Hospital
   NewYork-Presbyterian Brooklyn Methodist Hospital
   SUNY Downstate Medical Center University Hospital

Buffalo
Alliance
   Erie County Medical Center
   Roswell Park Cancer Institute

Canandaigua
Alliance
   F. F. Thompson Hospital

Cooperstown
Alliance
   Bassett Medical Center

Corning
Alliance
   Guthrie Corning Hospital

Cortlandt Manor
Alliance
   New York-Presbyterian/Hudson Valley Hospital

Elizabethtown
Alliance
   The University of Vermont Health Network Elizabethtown Community Hospital

Elmhurst
Alliance
   NYC Health + Hospitals / Elmhurst

Flushing
Alliance
New York-Presbyterian Queens

Geneva
Alliance
Finger Lakes Health

Greenport
Alliance
Eastern Long Island Hospital

Hamilton
Alliance
Community Memorial Hospital

Ithaca
Alliance
Cayuga Medical Center at Ithaca

Jamaica
Alliance
NYC Health + Hospitals / Queens

Jamestown
Alliance
UPMC Chautauqua WCA

Malone
Alliance
The University of Vermont Health Network - Alice Hyde Medical Center

Mineola
Alliance
NYU Winthrop Hospital

Montour Falls
Alliance
Schuyler Hospital

Mount Vernon
Alliance
Montefiore Mount Vernon

New Rochelle
Alliance
Montefiore New Rochelle

New York
Alliance
Gracie Square Hospital

Lenox Hill Hospital

Mount Sinai Hospital

NYC Health + Hospitals / Bellevue

NYC Health + Hospitals / Harlem

NYC Health + Hospitals / Henry J Carter Specialty Hospital and Medical Center

NYU Langone Hospitals

New York-Presbyterian Hospital

New York-Presbyterian/Columbia University Medical Center

Rockefeller University Hospital

Norwich
Alliance
UHS Chenango Memorial Hospital

Nyack
Alliance
Nyack Hospital

Ogdensburg
Alliance
Claxton-Hepburn Medical Center

Plattsburgh
Alliance
The University of Vermont Health Network-Champlain Valley Physicians Hospital

Riverhead
Alliance
Peconic Bay Medical Center

Rochester
Alliance
Highland Hospital

Strong Memorial Hospital of the University of Rochester

University of Rochester Medical Center

Sleepy Hollow
Alliance
Phelps Memorial Hospital Center

Staten Island
Alliance
Staten Island University Hospital

Stony Brook
Alliance
Stony Brook University Hospital

Syracuse
Alliance
Crouse Health

Upstate University Hospital

Valhalla
Alliance
Westchester Medical Center

Walton
Alliance
UHS Delaware Valley Hospital

NORTH CAROLINA
Ahoskie
Alliance
Vidant Roanoke-Chowan Hospital

Bermuda Run
Alliance
Wake Forest Baptist Health-Davie Medical Center

Bolivia
Alliance
Novant Health Brunswick Medical Center

Cary
Alliance
WakeMed Cary Hospital

Chapel Hill
Alliance
University of North Carolina Hospitals

Charlotte
Alliance
Atrium Health

Novant Health Charlotte Orthopaedic Hospital

Novant Health Presbyterian Medical Center

Clinton
Alliance
Sampson Regional Medical Center

Dunn
Alliance
Harnett Health System

Durham
Alliance
Duke Regional Hospital

Duke University Hospital

Eden
Alliance
UNC Rockingham Health Care

Edenton
Alliance
Vidant Chowan Hospital

Elizabeth City
Alliance
Sentara Albemarle Medical Center

Elkin
Alliance
Hugh Chatham Memorial Hospital

Greenville
Alliance
Vidant Medical Center

Huntersville
Alliance
Novant Health Huntersville Medical Center

Jefferson
Alliance
Ashe Memorial Hospital

Kenansville
Alliance
Vidant Duplin Hospital

Lexington
Alliance
Wake Forest Baptist Health-Lexington Medical Center

Matthews
Alliance
Novant Health Matthews Medical Center

Morehead City
Alliance
Carteret Health Care

Nags Head
Alliance
The Outer Banks Hospital

New Bern
Alliance
CarolinaEast Health System

Raleigh
Alliance
Duke Raleigh Hospital

UNC REX Health Care

WakeMed Health & Hospitals

WakeMed Raleigh Campus

Roanoke Rapids
Alliance
Halifax Regional Medical Center

Rocky Mount
Alliance
Nash Health Care Systems

Salisbury
Alliance
Novant Health Rowan Medical Center

Siler City
Alliance
Chatham Hospital

Sparta
Alliance
Alleghany Memorial Hospital

Tarboro
Alliance
Vidant Edgecombe Hospital

Thomasville
Alliance
Novant Health Thomasville Medical Center

Washington
Alliance
Vidant Beaufort Hospital

Wilson
Alliance
Wilson Medical Center

Windsor
Alliance
Vidant Bertie Hospital

Winston Salem
Alliance
Novant Health

Winston-Salem
Alliance
Novant Health Forsyth Medical Center

Novant Health Medical Park Hospital

Wake Forest Baptist Medical Center

NORTH DAKOTA
Bismarck
Alliance
Sanford Bismarck

Devils Lake
Alliance
CHI St. Alexius Health Devils Lake Hospital

Dickinson
Alliance
CHI St. Alexius Health - Dickinson Medical Center

Fargo
Alliance
Sanford Medical Center Fargo

Grand Forks
Alliance
Altru Health System

Hillsboro
Alliance
Sanford Hillsboro Medical Center

Jamestown
Alliance
Jamestown Regional Medical Center

Kenmare
Alliance
Kenmare Community Hospital

Lisbon
Alliance
CHI Lisbon Health

Mayville
Alliance
Sanford Mayville Medical Center

Mcville
Alliance
Nelson County Health System

Minot
Alliance
Trinity Health

Northwood
Alliance
Northwood Deaconess Health Center

Oakes
Alliance
CHI Oakes Hospital

Valley City
Alliance
CHI Mercy Health

OHIO

Akron
Alliance
Akron Children's Hospital

Cleveland Clinic Akron General

Alliance
Alliance
Alliance Community Hospital

Ashland
Alliance
University Hospitals Samaritan Medical Center

Ashtabula
Alliance
Ashtabula County Medical Center

Athens
Alliance
O'Bleness Memorial Hospital

Barnesville
Alliance
Barnesville Hospital

Bellaire
Alliance
Belmont Community Hospital

Bellefontaine
Alliance
Mary Rutan Hospital

Bluffton
Alliance
Bluffton Hospital

Bucyrus
Alliance
Bucyrus Hospital

Cadiz
Alliance
Harrison Community Hospital

Cambridge
Alliance
Southeastern Ohio Regional Medical Center

Canton
Alliance
Aultman Hospital

Chardon
Alliance
University Hospitals Geauga Medical Center

Cincinnati
Alliance
Christ Hospital

Cincinnati Children's Hospital Medical Center

Good Samaritan Hospital

Shriners Hospitals for Children - Cincinnati

The Jewish Hospital - Mercy Health

UC Health

University of Cincinnati Medical Center

Circleville
Alliance
Berger Health System

Cleveland
Alliance
Cleveland Clinic Fairview Hospital

Cleveland Clinic

Lutheran Hospital

MetroHealth Medical Center

University Hospitals Cleveland Medical Center

Coldwater
Alliance
Mercer Health

Columbus
Alliance
Ohio State University Wexner Medical Center

OhioHealth Doctors Hospital

OhioHealth Grant Medical Center

OhioHealth Riverside Methodist Hospital

OhioHealth

Conneaut
Alliance
University Hospitals Conneaut Medical Center

Coshocton
Alliance
Coshocton Regional Medical Center

Cuyahoga Falls
Alliance
Edwin Shaw Rehab

Dayton
Alliance
Miami Valley Hospital

Defiance
Alliance
ProMedica Defiance Regional Hospital

Delaware
Alliance
OhioHealth Grady Memorial Hospital

Dover
Alliance
Cleveland Clinic Union Hospital

Dublin
Alliance
OhioHealth Dublin Methodist Hospital

Euclid
Alliance
Euclid Hospital

Findlay
Alliance
Blanchard Valley Hospital

Fostoria
Alliance
ProMedica Fostoria Community Hospital

Fremont
Alliance
ProMedica Memorial Hospital

Galion
Alliance
Galion Hospital

Garfield Heights
Alliance
Marymount Hospital

Geneva
Alliance
University Hospitals Geneva Medical Center

Greenville
Alliance
Wayne HealthCare

Hamilton
Alliance
Fort Hamilton Hospital

Kenton
Alliance
OhioHealth Hardin Memorial Hospital

Lima
Alliance
Lima Memorial Health System

Lodi
Alliance
Cleveland Clinic Akron General Lodi Hospital

Logan
Alliance
Hocking Valley Community Hospital

London
Alliance
Madison Health

Mansfield
Alliance
OhioHealth MedCentral Mansfield Hospital

Marion
Alliance
OhioHealth Marion General Hospital

Martins Ferry
Alliance
East Ohio Regional Hospital

Marysville
Alliance
Memorial Health

Mason
Alliance
Lindner Center of HOPE

Maumee
Alliance
St. Luke's Hospital

Medina
Alliance
Cleveland Clinic, Medina Hospital

Middleburg Heights
Alliance
Southwest General Health Center

Millersburg
Alliance
Pomerene Hospital

Mount Gilead
Alliance
Morrow County Hospital

New Albany
Alliance
Mount Carmel New Albany Surgical Hospital

Newark
Alliance
Licking Memorial Hospital

Norwalk
Alliance
Fisher-Titus Medical Center

Orrville
Alliance
Aultman Orrville Hospital

Paulding
Alliance
Paulding County Hospital

Portsmouth
Alliance
Southern Ohio Medical Center

Rock Creek
Alliance
Glenbeigh Hospital and Outpatient Centers

Shelby
Alliance
OhioHealth MedCentral Shelby Hospital

Sidney
Alliance
Wilson Memorial Hospital

Sylvania
Alliance
ProMedica Flower Hospital

Toledo
Alliance
ProMedica Health System

ProMedica Toledo Hospital

The University of Toledo Medical Center

Troy
Alliance
Upper Valley Medical Center

Upper Sandusky
Alliance
Wyandot Memorial Hospital

Alliances

Van Wert
Alliance
  Van Wert County Hospital

Warrensville Heights
Alliance
  South Pointe Hospital

Washington Court House
Alliance
  Fayette County Memorial Hospital

Westerville
Alliance
  Mount Carmel St. Ann's

Westlake
Alliance
  St. John Medical Center

Zanesville
Alliance
  Genesis HealthCare System

OKLAHOMA

Altus
Alliance
  Jackson County Memorial Hospital

Antlers
Alliance
  Pushmataha Hospital

Atoka
Alliance
  Atoka County Medical Center

Bethany
Alliance
  The Children's Center Rehabilitation Hospital

Carnegie
Alliance
  Carnegie Tri-County Municipal Hospital

Chickasha
Alliance
  Grady Memorial Hospital

Duncan
Alliance
  Duncan Regional Hospital

Edmond
Alliance
  INTEGRIS Health Edmond

Elk City
Alliance
  Great Plains Regional Medical Center

Enid
Alliance
  Integris Bass Baptist Health Center
  Integris Bass Pavilion

Grove
Alliance
  INTEGRIS Grove Hospital

Hobart
Alliance
  Elkview General Hospital

Hugo
Alliance
  Choctaw Memorial Hospital

Lawton
Alliance
  Comanche County Memorial Hospital

McAlester
Alliance
  McAlester Regional Health Center

Miami
Alliance
  INTEGRIS Miami Hospital

Norman
Alliance
  Norman Regional Health System

Oklahoma City
Alliance
  INTEGRIS Baptist Medical Center
  INTEGRIS Health
  INTEGRIS Southwest Medical Center
  Lakeside Women's Hospital

Stillwater
Alliance
  Stillwater Medical Center

Tahlequah
Alliance
  Northeastern Health System

Waurika
Alliance
  Jefferson County Hospital

Yukon
Alliance
  INTEGRIS Canadian Valley Hospital

OREGON

Forest Grove
Alliance
  Tuality Forest Grove Hospital

Grants Pass
Alliance
  Asante Three Rivers Medical Center

Hillsboro
Alliance
  Tuality Healthcare

Hood River
Alliance
  Providence Hood River Memorial Hospital

Medford
Alliance
  Asante Rogue Regional Medical Center
  Providence Medford Medical Center

Milwaukie
Alliance
  Providence Milwaukie Hospital

Newberg
Alliance
  Providence Newberg Medical Center

Ontario
Alliance
  Saint Alphonsus Medical Center - Ontario

Oregon City
Alliance
  Providence Willamette Falls Medical Center

Pendleton
Alliance
  CHI St. Anthony Hospital

Portland
Alliance
  OHSU Hospital
  Providence Portland Medical Center
  Providence St. Vincent Medical Center
  Shriners Hospitals for Children-Portland

Roseburg
Alliance
  Mercy Medical Center

Salem
Alliance
  Salem Hospital

Seaside
Alliance
  Providence Seaside Hospital

Silverton
Alliance
  Legacy Silverton Medical Center

The Dalles
Alliance
  Mid-Columbia Medical Center

PENNSYLVANIA

Abington
Alliance
  Abington Hospital

Allentown
Alliance
  Lehigh Valley Hospital

Bethlehem
Alliance
  Lehigh Valley Hospital-Muhlenberg

Brookville
Alliance
  Penn Highlands Brookville

Bryn Mawr
Alliance
  Bryn Mawr Hospital

Butler
Alliance
  Butler Health System

Chambersburg
Alliance
  Chambersburg Hospital
  Summit Health

Clearfield
Alliance
  Penn Highlands Clearfield

Darby
Alliance
  Mercy Fitzgerald Hospital

Drexel Hill
Alliance
  Delaware County Memorial Hospital

DuBois
Alliance
  Penn Highlands DuBois

East Norriton
Alliance
  Einstein Medical Center Montgomery

East Stroudsburg
Alliance
  Lehigh Valley Hospital - Pocono

Ephrata
Alliance
  WellSpan Ephrata Community Hospital

Gettysburg
Alliance
  WellSpan Gettysburg Hospital

Greensburg
Alliance
  Excela Health Westmoreland Hospital

Hanover
Alliance
  UPMC Pinnacle Hanover

Harrisburg
Alliance
  PinnacleHealth at Community General Osteopathic Hospital
  UPMC Pinnacle Harrisburg

Hazleton
Alliance
  Lehigh Valley Hospital - Hazleton

Hershey
Alliance
  Penn State Milton S. Hershey Medical Center

Huntingdon
Alliance
  J. C. Blair Memorial Hospital

Indiana
Alliance
  Indiana Regional Medical Center

Jefferson Hills
Alliance
  Jefferson Hospital

Lancaster
Alliance
  Penn Medicine Lancaster General Hospital

Langhorne
Alliance
  St. Mary Medical Center

Lansdale
Alliance
  Abington-Lansdale Hospital Jefferson Health

Latrobe
Alliance
  Excela Latrobe Area Hospital

Lebanon
Alliance
  WellSpan Good Samaritan Hospital

Lehighton
Alliance
  St. Luke's - Gnaden Huetten Campus

Malvern
Alliance
   Bryn Mawr Rehabilitation Hospital

Meadowbrook
Alliance
   Holy Redeemer Hospital

Media
Alliance
   Riddle Hospital

Monongahela
Alliance
   Monongahela Valley Hospital

Mount Pleasant
Alliance
   Excela Frick Hospital

Muncy
Alliance
   UPMC Susquehanna Muncy

New Castle
Alliance
   UPMC Jameson

Paoli
Alliance
   Paoli Hospital

Philadelphia
Alliance
   Children's Hospital of Philadelphia
   Einstein Medical Center Philadelphia
   Fox Chase Cancer Center-American Oncologic Hospital
   Hospital of the University of Pennsylvania
   Jeanes Hospital
   Jefferson Health Northeast
   Magee Rehabilitation Hospital
   Penn Presbyterian Medical Center
   Pennsylvania Hospital
   Temple University Hospital
   University of Pennsylvania Health System

Pittsburgh
Alliance
   St. Clair Hospital
   UPMC Presbyterian

Pottsville
Alliance
   Lehigh Valley Hospital - Schuylkill East Norwegian Street
   Lehigh Valley Hospital - Schuylkill

Reading
Alliance
   Penn State Health St. Joseph

Saint Marys
Alliance
   Penn Highlands Elk

Sayre
Alliance
   Guthrie Clinic
   Guthrie Robert Packer Hospital

Sellersville
Alliance
   Grand View Health

Towanda
Alliance
   Guthrie Towanda Memorial Hospital

Troy
Alliance
   Troy Community Hospital

Uniontown
Alliance
   Uniontown Hospital

Upland
Alliance
   Crozer-Chester Medical Center

Waynesboro
Alliance
   Waynesboro Hospital

Wellsboro
Alliance
   UPMC Susquehanna Soldiers + Sailors

West Chester
Alliance
   Chester County Hospital

West Reading
Alliance
   Reading Hospital

Williamsport
Alliance
   Divine Providence Hospital
   UPMC Susquehanna
   UPMC Susquehanna Williamsport Regional Medical Center

Wynnewood
Alliance
   Lankenau Medical Center

York
Alliance
   WellSpan Health
   WellSpan York Hospital

RHODE ISLAND
Newport
Alliance
   Newport Hospital

Providence
Alliance
   Butler Hospital
   Care New England Health System
   Lifespan Corporation
   Miriam Hospital
   Rhode Island Hospital
   Women & Infants Hospital of Rhode Island

Warwick
Alliance
   Kent County Memorial Hospital

Westerly
Alliance
   Westerly Hospital

SOUTH CAROLINA
Charleston
Alliance
   MUSC Health of Medical University of South Carolina

Cheraw
Alliance
   McLeod Health Cheraw

Clinton
Alliance
   Greenville Health System - Laurens County Memorial Hospital

Columbia
Alliance
   ContinueCARE Hospital at Palmetto Health Baptist
   Palmetto Health Baptist Parkridge
   Palmetto Health Baptist
   Palmetto Health Richland
   Providence Hospital

Darlington
Alliance
   McLeod Medical Center Darlington

Dillon
Alliance
   McLeod Medical Center Dillon

Easley
Alliance
   Baptist Easley Hospital

Florence
Alliance
   McLeod Regional Medical Center

Georgetown
Alliance
   Tidelands Georgetown Memorial Hospital

Greenville
Alliance
   GHS Greenville Memorial Hospital

   Patewood Memorial Hospital
   Shriners Hospitals for Children-Greenville

Greenwood
Alliance
   Self Regional Healthcare

Greer
Alliance
   GHS Greer Memorial Hospital

Loris
Alliance
   McLeod Loris Seacoast Hospital

Murrells Inlet
Alliance
   Tidelands Waccamaw Community Hospital

Seneca
Alliance
   Oconee Memorial Hospital

Simpsonville
Alliance
   GHS Hillcrest Memorial Hospital

Sumter
Alliance
   Palmetto Health Tuomey

Travelers Rest
Alliance
   North Greenville Hospital

SOUTH DAKOTA
Aberdeen
Alliance
   Sanford Aberdeen Medical Center

Armour
Alliance
   Douglas County Memorial Hospital

Burke
Alliance
   Community Memorial Hospital

Canton
Alliance
   Sanford Canton-Inwood Medical Center

Chamberlain
Alliance
   Sanford Chamberlain Medical Center

Clear Lake
Alliance
   Sanford Clear Lake Medical Center

Sioux Falls
Alliance
   Sanford Health
   Sanford USD Medical Center

Vermillion
Alliance
   Sanford Vermillion Medical Center

Viborg
Alliance
   Pioneer Memorial Hospital and Health Services

Watertown
Alliance
   Prairie Lakes Healthcare System

Webster
Alliance
   Sanford Webster Medical Center

Winner
Alliance
   Winner Regional Healthcare Center

TENNESSEE
Chattanooga
Alliance
   Erlanger Health System
   Erlanger North Hospital

Collierville
Alliance
   Baptist Memorial Hospital-Collierville

Columbia
Alliance
   Maury Regional Hospital

Covington
Alliance
   Baptist Memorial Hospital-Tipton

Franklin
Alliance
Williamson Medical Center

Harriman
Alliance
Roane Medical Center

Huntingdon
Alliance
Baptist Memorial Hospital-Huntingdon

Knoxville
Alliance
Covenant Health
Fort Sanders Regional Medical Center
Parkwest Medical Center
University of Tennessee Medical Center

Lenoir City
Alliance
Fort Loudoun Medical Center

Lewisburg
Alliance
Marshall Medical Center

Memphis
Alliance
Baptist Memorial Health Care Corporation
Baptist Memorial Hospital - Memphis
Baptist Memorial Hospital for Women
Methodist Healthcare Memphis Hospitals
Regional One Health
St. Jude Children's Research Hospital

Morristown
Alliance
Morristown-Hamblen Healthcare System

Nashville
Alliance
Vanderbilt University Medical Center

Oak Ridge
Alliance
Methodist Medical Center of Oak Ridge

Sevierville
Alliance
LeConte Medical Center

Tazewell
Alliance
Claiborne Medical Center

Union City
Alliance
Baptist Memorial Hospital-Union City

Waynesboro
Alliance
Wayne Medical Center

TEXAS
Andrews
Alliance
Permian Regional Medical Center

Baytown
Alliance
Houston Methodist Baytown Hospital

Bellville
Alliance
CHI St. Joseph Health Bellville Hospital

Dallas
Alliance
Baylor Scott & White Health
Children's Medical Center Dallas
Methodist Health System
Parkland Health & Hospital System
William P. Clements, Jr. University Hospital

El Paso
Alliance
University Medical Center of El Paso

Fort Worth
Alliance
JPS Health Network

Galveston
Alliance
Shriners Hospitals for Children-Galveston
University of Texas Medical Branch

Houston
Alliance
Baylor St. Luke's Medical Center
CHI St. Luke's Hospital - The Vintage Hospital
Harris Health System
Houston Methodist Hospital
Houston Methodist West Hospital
Houston Methodist Willowbrook Hospital
Memorial Hermann - Texas Medical Center
Memorial Hermann Greater Heights Hospital
Memorial Hermann Health System
Memorial Hermann Memorial City Medical Center
Shriners Hospitals for Children-Houston
TIRR Memorial Hermann

Humble
Alliance
Memorial Hermann Northeast

Katy
Alliance
Houston Methodist Continuing Care Hospital
Memorial Hermann Katy Hospital

Livingston
Alliance
CHI St. Luke's Health Memorial Livingston

Lubbock
Alliance
Covenant Health System
Covenant Medical Center-Lakeside

Lufkin
Alliance
CHI St. Luke's Health Memorial Lufkin

Midland
Alliance
Midland Memorial Hospital

Pasadena
Alliance
CHI St. Luke's Health - Patients Medical Center

Pearsall
Alliance
Frio Regional Hospital

Plano
Alliance
Community Hospital Corporation

San Antonio
Alliance
University Health System

San Augustine
Alliance
CHI St. Luke's Health Memorial San Augustine

Sugar Land
Alliance
Houston Methodist Sugar Land Hospital
Memorial Hermann Sugar Land Hospital

Sweeny
Alliance
Sweeny Community Hospital

The Woodlands
Alliance
CHI St. Luke's Health-Lakeside Hospital
CHI St. Luke's Health-The Woodlands Hospital

Tyler
Alliance
CHRISTUS Mother Frances Hospital - Tyler
UT Health North Campus Tyler

UTAH
Gunnison
Alliance
Gunnison Valley Hospital

Provo
Alliance
Utah State Hospital

Salt Lake City
Alliance
Shriners Hospitals for Children-Salt Lake City

University of Utah Health
University of Utah Neuropsychiatric Institute

VERMONT
Bennington
Alliance
Southwestern Vermont Medical Center

Berlin
Alliance
The University of Vermont Health Network Central Vermont Medical Center

Brattleboro
Alliance
Brattleboro Memorial Hospital
Brattleboro Retreat

Burlington
Alliance
University of Vermont Medical Center

Morrisville
Alliance
Copley Hospital

Newport
Alliance
North Country Hospital and Health Center

Rutland
Alliance
Rutland Regional Medical Center

Saint Johnsbury
Alliance
Northeastern Vermont Regional Hospital

Springfield
Alliance
Springfield Hospital

Townshend
Alliance
Grace Cottage Hospital

Windsor
Alliance
Mt. Ascutney Hospital and Health Center

VIRGIN ISLANDS
Saint Thomas
Alliance
Schneider Regional Medical Center

VIRGINIA
Bedford
Alliance
Centra Bedford Memorial Hospital

Charlottesville
Alliance
Sentara Martha Jefferson Hospital
UVA-HEALTHSOUTH Rehabilitation Hospital
University of Virginia Medical Center

Culpeper
Alliance
Novant Health UVA Health System Culpeper Medical Center

Farmville
Alliance
Centra Southside Community Hospital

Fishersville
Alliance
Augusta Health

Fredericksburg
Alliance
Mary Washington Hospital

Hampton
Alliance
Sentara CarePlex Hospital

Harrisonburg
Alliance
Sentara RMH Medical Center

Lynchburg
Alliance
Centra Lynchburg General Hospital

Manassas
Alliance
Novant Health UVA Health System Prince William Medical Center

Norfolk
Alliance
   Hospital for Extended Recovery
   Sentara Healthcare
   Sentara Leigh Hospital
   Sentara Norfolk General Hospital

Richmond
Alliance
   Children's Hospital of Richmond at VCU-Brook Road Campus
   VCU Medical Center

South Boston
Alliance
   Sentara Halifax Regional Hospital

Stafford
Alliance
   Stafford Hospital

Suffolk
Alliance
   Sentara Obici Hospital

Virginia Beach
Alliance
   Sentara Princess Anne Hospital
   Sentara Virginia Beach General Hospital

Williamsburg
Alliance
   Sentara Williamsburg Regional Medical Center

Woodbridge
Alliance
   Sentara Northern Virginia Medical Center

WASHINGTON
Aberdeen
Alliance
   Grays Harbor Community Hospital

Auburn
Alliance
   MultiCare Auburn Medical Center

Bellingham
Alliance
   PeaceHealth St. Joseph Medical Center

Bremerton
Alliance
   Harrison Medical Center

Burien
Alliance
   Highline Medical Center

Centralia
Alliance
   Providence Centralia Hospital

Chewelah
Alliance
   Providence St. Joseph's Hospital

Colfax
Alliance
   Whitman Hospital and Medical Center

Colville
Alliance
   Providence Mount Carmel Hospital

Dayton
Alliance
   Columbia County Health System

Edmonds
Alliance
   Swedish/Edmonds

Enumclaw
Alliance
   St. Elizabeth Hospital

Everett
Alliance
   Providence Regional Medical Center Everett

Gig Harbor
Alliance
   St. Anthony Hospital

Ilwaco
Alliance
   Ocean Beach Hospital

Issaquah
Alliance
   Swedish/Issaquah

Lakewood
Alliance
   St. Clare Hospital

Morton
Alliance
   Morton General Hospital

Olympia
Alliance
   Providence St. Peter Hospital

Pomeroy
Alliance
   Garfield County Public Hospital District

Port Angeles
Alliance
   Olympic Medical Center

Prosser
Alliance
   PMH Medical Center

Puyallup
Alliance
   MultiCare Good Samaritan Hospital

Renton
Alliance
   UW Medicine/Valley Medical Center

Richland
Alliance
   Kadlec Regional Medical Center

Seattle
Alliance
   Swedish Medical Center-Cherry Hill Campus
   Swedish Medical Center-First Hill
   UW Medicine/Harborview Medical Center
   UW Medicine/Northwest Hospital & Medical Center
   University of Washington Medical Center

Spokane
Alliance
   Providence Holy Family Hospital
   Providence Sacred Heart Medical Center & Children's Hospital
   Shriners Hospitals for Children-Spokane
   St. Luke's Rehabilitation Institute

Tacoma
Alliance
   MultiCare Health System
   MultiCare Tacoma General Hospital
   St. Joseph Medical Center

Walla Walla
Alliance
   Providence St. Mary Medical Center

WEST VIRGINIA
Charleston
Alliance
   CAMC Women and Children's Hospital
   Charleston Area Medical Center

Gassaway
Alliance
   Braxton County Memorial Hospital

Madison
Alliance
   Boone Memorial Hospital

Martinsburg
Alliance
   Berkeley Medical Center

Montgomery
Alliance
   Montgomery General Hospital

Morgantown
Alliance
   West Virginia University Hospitals

Princeton
Alliance
   Princeton Community Hospital

Ranson
Alliance
   Jefferson Medical Center

Ripley
Alliance
   Jackson General Hospital

Spencer
Alliance
   Roane General Hospital

Wheeling
Alliance
   Ohio Valley Medical Center
   Wheeling Hospital

WISCONSIN
Antigo
Alliance
   Aspirus Langlade Hospital

Appleton
Alliance
   ThedaCare, Inc.

Barron
Alliance
   Mayo Clinic Health System - Northland in Barron

Beaver Dam
Alliance
   Beaver Dam Community Hospitals

Beloit
Alliance
   Beloit Health System

Bloomer
Alliance
   Mayo Clinic Health System - Chippewa Valley in Bloomer

Boscobel
Alliance
   Gundersen Boscobel Area Hospital and Clinics

Eau Claire
Alliance
   Mayo Clinic Health System in Eau Claire

Friendship
Alliance
   Gundersen Moundview Memorial Hospital & Clinics

Green Bay
Alliance
   Bellin Memorial Hospital
   Bellin Psychiatric Center

Hillsboro
Alliance
   Gundersen St. Joseph's Hospital and Clinics

Hudson
Alliance
   Hudson Hospital and Clinic

La Crosse
Alliance
   Gundersen Lutheran Medical Center
   Mayo Clinic Health System - Franciscan Healthcare in La Crosse

Madison
Alliance
   UnityPoint Health Meriter
   University Hospital

Marinette
Alliance
   Bay Area Medical Center

Medford
Alliance
   Aspirus Medford Hospital & Clinics, Inc.

Menomonee Falls
Alliance
   Community Memorial Hospital

Menomonie
Alliance
   Mayo Clinic Health System - Red Cedar in Menomonie

Milwaukee
Alliance
   Froedtert and the Medical College of Wisconsin
   Froedtert Hospital

Neenah
Alliance
   ThedaCare Regional Medical Center-Neenah

Neillsville
Alliance
   Memorial Medical Center - Neillsville

New Richmond
Alliance
   Westfields Hospital and Clinic

Oconomowoc
Alliance
   Oconomowoc Memorial Hospital

Oconto
Alliance
   Bellin Health Oconto Hospital

Osseo
Alliance
   Mayo Clinic Health System - Oakridge in Osseo

Portage
Alliance
   Divine Savior Healthcare

River Falls
Alliance
   River Falls Area Hospital

Sparta
Alliance
   Mayo Clinic Health System - Franciscan Healthcare in Sparta

Superior
Alliance
   Essentia Health St. Mary's Hospital of Superior

Waukesha
Alliance
   ProHealth Care, Inc.
   Waukesha Memorial Hospital

Waupaca
Alliance
   ThedaCare Medical Center-Waupaca

Wausau
Alliance
   Aspirus Wausau Hospital, Inc.
   North Central Health Care

West Bend
Alliance
   St. Joseph's Hospital

Whitehall
Alliance
   Gundersen Tri-County Hospital and Clinics

Wild Rose
Alliance
   ThedaCare Medical Center - Wild Rose

Wisconsin Rapids
Alliance
   Aspirus Riverview Hospital and Clinics, Inc.

WYOMING
Buffalo
Alliance
   Johnson County Healthcare Center

Casper
Alliance
   Wyoming Medical Center

Cheyenne
Alliance
   Cheyenne Regional Medical Center

Douglas
Alliance
   Memorial Hospital of Converse County

Laramie
Alliance
   Ivinson Memorial Hospital

Lusk
Alliance
   Niobrara Health and Life Center

Sheridan
Alliance
   Sheridan Memorial Hospital

YANKEE ALLIANCE
138 River Road, Andover, MA, Zip 01810–1083; tel. 978/470–2000; James W. Oliver, President and Chief Executive Officer

CALIFORNIA
Long Beach
Alliance
   College Medical Center

Oceanside
Alliance
   Tri-City Medical Center

CONNECTICUT
Derby
Alliance
   Griffin Hospital

Hartford
Alliance
   Saint Francis Hospital and Medical Center

New London
Alliance
   Lawrence + Memorial Hospital

Stafford Springs
Alliance
   Johnson Memorial Medical Center

FLORIDA
Boca Raton
Alliance
   Promise Healthcare

Coral Gables
Alliance
   Baptist Health South Florida, Doctors Hospital

Homestead
Alliance
   Baptist Health South Florida, Homestead Hospital

Miami Beach
Alliance
   Mount Sinai Medical Center

Miami
Alliance
   Baptist Health South Florida, Baptist Hospital of Miami
   Baptist Health South Florida, South Miami Hospital
   Baptist Health South Florida, West Kendall Baptist Hospital

Miramar
Alliance
   Memorial Hospital Miramar

Pembroke Pines
Alliance
   Memorial Hospital Pembroke
   Memorial Hospital West

South Miami
Alliance
   Larkin Community Hospital

Tavernier
Alliance
   Baptist Health South Florida, Mariners Hospital

ILLINOIS
Geneva
Alliance
   Northwestern Medicine Delnor Hospital

Winfield
Alliance
   Northwestern Medicine Central DuPage Hospital

INDIANA
Gary
Alliance
   Methodist Hospitals

Mishawaka
Alliance
   Unity Medical & Surgical Hospital

KENTUCKY
Ashland
Alliance
   King's Daughters Medical Center

Benton
Alliance
   Marshall County Hospital

Corbin
Alliance
   Baptist Health Corbin

Elizabethtown
Alliance
   Hardin Memorial Health

La Grange
Alliance
   Baptist Health La Grange

Lexington
Alliance
   Baptist Health Lexington

Louisville
Alliance
   Baptist Health Louisville

Madisonville
Alliance
   Baptist Health Madisonville

Paducah
Alliance
   Baptist Health Paducah

Prestonsburg
Alliance
   Highlands Regional Medical Center

Richmond
Alliance
   Baptist Health Richmond

MAINE
Bangor
Alliance
   St. Joseph Hospital

Lewiston
Alliance
   St. Mary's Regional Medical Center

MASSACHUSETTS
Attleboro
Alliance
   Sturdy Memorial Hospital

Boston
Alliance
   Boston Medical Center
   New England Baptist Hospital
   Tufts Medical Center

Brockton
Alliance
   Signature Healthcare Brockton Hospital

Burlington
Alliance
   Lahey Hospital & Medical Center, Burlington

Fall River
Alliance
   Southcoast Hospitals Group

Great Barrington
Alliance
   Fairview Hospital

Lowell
Alliance
   Lowell General Hospital

Milford
Alliance
   Milford Regional Medical Center

Newburyport
Alliance
   Anna Jaques Hospital

Oak Bluffs
Alliance
   Martha's Vineyard Hospital

Pittsfield
Alliance
   Berkshire Medical Center

Westfield
Alliance
   Baystate Noble Hospital

Winchester
Alliance
  Winchester Hospital

NEW HAMPSHIRE

Concord
Alliance
  Concord Hospital

Exeter
Alliance
  Exeter Hospital

Franklin
Alliance
  Franklin Regional Hospital

Laconia
Alliance
  Lakes Region General Hospital

Manchester
Alliance
  Catholic Medical Center
  Elliot Hospital

Nashua
Alliance
  St. Joseph Hospital

North Conway
Alliance
  Memorial Hospital

Rochester
Alliance
  Frisbie Memorial Hospital

Salem
Alliance
  Northeast Rehabilitation Hospital

NEW YORK

Batavia
Alliance
  United Memorial Medical Center

Bath
Alliance
  Ira Davenport Memorial Hospital

Elizabethtown
Alliance
  The University of Vermont Health Network
  Elizabethtown Community Hospital

Elmira
Alliance
  Arnot Ogden Medical Center
  St. Joseph's Hospital

Glens Falls
Alliance
  Glens Falls Hospital

Gloversville
Alliance
  Nathan Littauer Hospital and Nursing Home

Plattsburgh
Alliance
  The University of Vermont Health Network-Champlain
  Valley Physicians Hospital

Warsaw
Alliance
  Wyoming County Community Hospital

OHIO

Logan
Alliance
  Hocking Valley Community Hospital

Montpelier
Alliance
  Community Hospitals and Wellness Centers-Montpelier

Salem
Alliance
  Salem Regional Medical Center

Seaman
Alliance
  Adams County Regional Medical Center

Sidney
Alliance
  Wilson Memorial Hospital

Steubenville
Alliance
  Life Line Hospital

PENNSYLVANIA

Honesdale
Alliance
  Wayne Memorial Hospital

Langhorne
Alliance
  Barix Clinics of Pennsylvania

Washington
Alliance
  Advanced Surgical Hospital

RHODE ISLAND

Providence
Alliance
  Roger Williams Medical Center

Wakefield
Alliance
  South County Hospital

Westerly
Alliance
  Westerly Hospital

SOUTH CAROLINA

Columbia
Alliance
  Providence Hospital

Fairfax
Alliance
  Allendale County Hospital

TEXAS

Austin
Alliance
  Arise Austin Medical Center

Houston
Alliance
  Healthbridge Children's Hospital of Houston

New Braunfels
Alliance
  Post Acute/Warm Springs Specialty Hospital of New
  Braunfels

Plainview
Alliance
  Covenant Hospital Plainview

WEST VIRGINIA

New Martinsville
Alliance
  Wetzel County Hospital

Abbreviations Used in the AHA Guide

AB, Army Base
ACSW, Academy of Certified Social Workers
AEC, Atomic Energy Commission
AFB, Air Force Base
AHA, American Hospital Association
AK, Alaska
AL, Alabama
AODA, Alcohol and Other Drug Abuse
APO, Army Post Office
AR, Arkansas
A.R.T., Accredited Record Technician
A.S.C., Ambulatory Surgical Center
A.T.C., Alcoholism Treatment Center
Ave., Avenue
AZ, Arizona

B.A., Bachelor of Arts
B.B.A., Bachelor of Business Administration
B.C., British Columbia
Blvd., Boulevard
B.S., Bachelor of Science
B.S.Ed., Bachelor of Science in Education
B.S.H.S., Bachelor of Science in Health Studies
B.S.N., Bachelor of Science in Nursing
B.S.W., Bachelor of Science and Social Worker

CA, California; Controller of Accounts
C.A.A.D.A.C., Certified Alcohol and Drug Abuse Counselor
CAC, Certified Alcoholism Counselor
CAE, Certified Association Executive
CAP, College of American Pathologists
CAPA, Certified Ambulatory Post Anesthesia
C.A.S., Certificate of Advanced Study
CCDC, Certified Chemical Dependency Counselor
C.D., Commander of the Order of Distinction
CDR, Commander
CDS, Chemical Dependency Specialist
CFACHE, Certified Fellow American College of Healthcare Executives
CFRE, Certified Fund Raising Executive
C.G., Certified Gastroenterology
CHC, Certified Health Consultant
CHE, Certified Healthcare Executive
C.L.D., Clinical Laboratory Director
CLU, Certified Life Underwriter, Chartered Life Underwriter
CMA, Certified Medical Assistant
C.M.H.A., Certified Mental Health Administrator
CNHA, Certified Nursing Home Administrator
CNM, Certified Nurse Midwife
CNOR, Certified Operating Room Nurse
C.N.S., Clinical Nurse Specialist
CO, Colorado; Commanding Officer
COA, Certified Ophthalmic Assistant
COMT, Commandant
C.O.M.T., Certified Ophthalmic Medical Technician
Conv., Conventions
Corp., Corporation; Corporate
C.O.T., Certified Ophthalmic Technician
CPA, Certified Public Accountant
C.P.H.Q., Certified Professional in Health Care Quality
CPM, Certified Public Manager
CRNA, Certified Registered Nurse Anesthetist
CRNH, Certified Registered Nurse Hospice
C.S.J.B., Catholic Saint John the Baptist
CSW, Certified Social Worker
CT, Connecticut
CWO, Chief Warrant Officer

D.B.A., Doctor of Business Administration
DC, District of Columbia
D.D., Doctor of Divinity
D.D.S., Doctor of Dental Surgery
DE, Delaware
Diet, Dietitian; Dietary; Dietetics
D.M.D., Doctor of Dental Medicine
D.MIN., Doctor of Ministry
D.O., Doctor of Osteopathic Medicine and Surgery, Doctor of Osteopathy
DPA, Doctorate Public Administration
D.P.M., Doctor of Podiatric Medicine
Dr., Drive
Dr.P.h., Doctor of Public Health
D.Sc., Doctor of Science
D.S.W., Doctor of Social Welfare
D.V.M., Doctor of Veterinary Medicine

E., East
Ed.D., Doctor of Education
Ed.S., Specialist in Education
ENS, Ensign
Esq., Esquire
Expwy., Expressway
ext., extension

FAAN, Fellow of the American Academy of Nursing
FACATA, Fellow of the American College of Addiction Treatment Administrators
FACHE, Fellow of the American College of Healthcare Executives
FACMGA, Fellow of the American College of Medical Group Administrators
FACP, Fellow of the American College of Physicians
FACS, Fellow of the American College of Surgeons
FAX, Facsimile
FL, Florida
FPO, Fleet Post Office
FRCPSC, Fellow of the Royal College of Physicians and Surgeons of Canada
FT, Full-time

GA, Georgia
Govt., Government; Governmental

HHS, Department of Health and Human Services
HI, Hawaii
HM, Helmsman
HMO, Health Maintenance Organization
Hon., Honorable; Honorary
H.S.A., Health System Administrator
Hts., Heights
Hwy., Highway

IA, Iowa
ID, Idaho
IL, Illinois
IN, Indiana
Inc., Incorporated

J.D., Doctor of Law
J.P., Justice of the Peace
Jr., Junior

KS, Kansas
KY, Kentucky

LA, Louisiana
LCDR, Lieutenant Commander
LCSW, Licensed Certified Social Worker
L.H.D., Doctor of Humanities

L.I.S.W., Licensed Independent Social Worker
LL.D., Doctor of Laws
L.L.P., Limited Licensed Practitioner
L.M.H.C., Licensed Master of Health Care
L.M.S.W., Licensed Master of Social Work
L.N.H.A., Licensed Nursing Home Administrator
L.P.C., Licensed Professional Counselor
LPN, Licensed Practical Nurse
L.P.N., Licensed Practical Nurse
L.S.W., Licensed Social Worker
Lt., Lieutenant
LTC, Lieutenant Colonel
Ltd., Limited
LT.GEN., Lieutenant General
LTJG, Lieutenant (junior grade)

MA, Massachusetts
M.A., Master of Arts
Maj., Major
M.B., Bachelor of Medicine
M.B.A., Masters of Business Administration
MC, Medical Corps; Marine Corps
M.C., Member of Congress
MD, Maryland
M.D., Doctor of Medicine
ME, Maine
M.Ed., Master of Education
MFCC, Marriage/Family/Child Counselor
MHA, Mental Health Association
M.H.S., Masters in Health Science; Masters in Human Service
MI, Michigan
MM, Masters of Management
MN, Minnesota
M.N., Master of Nursing
MO, Missouri
M.P.A., Master of Public Administration; Master Public Affairs
M.P.H., Master of Public Health
M.P.S., Master of Professional Studies; Master of Public Science
MS, Mississippi
M.S., Master of Science
MSC, Medical Service Corps
M.S.D., Doctor of Medical Science
MSHSA, Master of Science Health Service Administration
M.S.N., Master of Science in Nursing
M.S.P.H., Master of Science in Public Health
M.S.S.W., Master of Science in Social Work
M.S.W., Master of Social Work
MT, Montana
Mt., Mount

N., North
NC, North Carolina
N.C.A.D.C., National Certification of Alcohol and Drug Counselors
ND, North Dakota
NE, Nebraska
NH, New Hampshire
NHA, National Hearing Association; Nursing Home Administrator
NJ, New Jersey
NM, New Mexico
NPA, National Perinatal Association
NV, Nevada
NY, New York

OCN, Oncology Certified Nurse
O.D., Doctor of Optometry
O.F.M., Order Franciscan Monks, Order of Friars Minor
OH, Ohio
OK, Oklahoma
OR, Oregon

O.R., Operating Room
O.R.S., Operating Room Supervisor
OSF, Order of St. Francis

PA, Pennsylvania
P.A., Professional Association
P.C., Professional Corporation
Pharm.D., Doctor of Pharmacy
Ph.B., Bachelor of Philosophy
Ph.D., Doctor of Philosophy
PHS, Public Health Service
Pkwy., Parkway
Pl., Place
PR, Puerto Rico
PS, Professional Services
PSRO, Professional Standards Review Organization

RADM, Rear Admiral
RD, Rural Delivery
Rd., Road
R.F.D., Rural Free Delivery
RI, Rhode Island
R.M., Risk Manager
R.N., Registered Nurse
RNC, Republican National Committee; Registered Nurse or Board Certified
R.Ph., Registered Pharmacist
RRA, Registered Record Administrator
R.S.M., Religious Sisters of Mercy
Rte., Route

S., South
SC, South Carolina
S.C., Surgery Center
SCAC, Senior Certified Addiction Counselor
Sc.D., Doctor of Science
Sci., Science, Scientific
SD, South Dakota
SHCC, Statewide Health Coordinating Council

Sgt., Sergeant
SNA, Surgical Nursing Assistant
SNF, Skilled Nursing Facility
Sq., Square
Sr., Senior, Sister
St., Saint, Street
Sta., Station
Ste., Saint; Suite

Tel., Telephone
Terr., Terrace
TN, Tennessee
Tpke, Turnpike
Twp., Township
TX, Texas

USA, United States Army
USAF, United States Air Force
USMC, United States Marine Corps
USN, United States Navy
USPHS, United States Public Health Service
UT, Utah

VA, Virginia
VADM, Vice Admiral
VI, Virgin Islands
Vlg., Village
VT, Vermont
W., West

WA, Washington
WI, Wisconsin
WV, West Virginia
WY, Wyoming

Index

Subject Index

Notes

Notes

Notes

Notes

Notes

Notes